Fire Protection Handbook

Fire Protection Handbook™

Seventeenth Edition

Arthur E. Cote, P.E.
Editor-in-Chief

Jim L. Linville
Managing Editor

NFPA
National Fire Protection Association
Quincy, Massachusetts

Editor-in-Chief: Arthur E. Cote
Managing Editor: Jim L. Linville
Associate Editors: Kathleen Robinson
Deborah Shaw
Editorial Staff: Gene A. Moulton
Indexing: Hagerty and Holloway
Copy Editors: Hilary Davis
Clif Garboden
Carla Thompson
Art Editors: Deborah Shaw
John Petraglia
Artwork: George Nichols
Text Processing: Louise Grant
Muriel McArdle
Lynn Lupo
Elizabeth Turner
Composition: Cathy Ray
Claire McRudin
Nancy Maria
William Byrd Press
Cover Design: Cameron, Inc.
Production Coordinator: Donald McGonagle
Printed by: R.R. Donnelly & Sons

Second Printing, November 1992

Previous Editions

First	1896
Second	1901
Third	1904
Fourth	1909
Fifth	1914
Sixth	1921
Seventh	1924
Eighth	1935
Ninth	1941
Tenth	1948
Eleventh	1954
Twelfth	1962
Thirteenth	1969
Fourteenth	1976
Fifteenth	1981
Sixteenth	1986

Library of Congress Card Number: 62-12655
NFPA Number FPH1791 (J2-2140017)
ISBN: 0-87765-378-X
National Fire Protection Association
One Batterymarch Park, Quincy, MA 02269-9101

Printed in the United States of America

Dedication

To the professional men and women of the fire protection community whose untiring devotion to the task of protecting life and property from the ravages of fire has made this world a better place.

CONTENTS

INTRODUCTION

Since its first edition nearly a century ago, the *Fire Protection Handbook* has endeavored to fulfill the needs of the fire protection community for a single-source handbook on the state of the art in fire protection and fire prevention practices.

It was originally known as the Crosby-Fiske *Handbook of the Underwriter's Bureau of New England* and was first published in 1896, the same year that the National Fire Protection Association was founded. The original authors were Everett U. Crosby and Henry A. Fiske, who were joined by H. Walter Forster in 1918. In 1935, Crosby, Fiske, and Forster donated all rights to their handbook to the NFPA, and NFPA has published all successive editions since that 8th edition.

The *Fire Protection Handbook* has changed significantly in the last 95 years. While the body of knowledge in the field of fire protection has proliferated, the *Handbook* has kept pace, expanding from fewer than 200 pages in the first edition to over 2000 pages in this 17th edition. As the most pressing concerns of fire protection have evolved, from city-wide conflagrations in the late 1800s, through group fires and single building fires and more recently to room fires, the number of subjects covered by the *Handbook* has increased greatly. This is evidenced by the expansion of the text from the short, running commentary that made up the first edition to material organized into 189 chapters in this volume. Today, there are more chapters than there were pages in 1896!

This 17th edition of the *Handbook* has been completely reorganized to underscore the systems approach to fire protection that has become increasingly important as the amount of fire protection knowledge has grown. This edition is organized around the six major strategies that are the building blocks of a systems approach to firesafety through balanced fire protection:

- prevention of ignition,
- design to slow early fire growth,
- detection and alarm,
- suppression,
- confinement of fire, and
- evacuation of occupants.

Production of the *Fire Protection Handbook* through 17 editions has involved literally thousands of fire protection experts from within and outside NFPA. However, in addition to its founders, over the last half-century four individuals were especially responsible for establishing the *Handbook* as the "bible" of fire protection practitioners.

- Robert S. Moulton, late NFPA Technical Secretary who, during his 40 years of service, edited the 9th, 10th, and 11th editions;
- George H. (Hitch) Tryon, late NFPA Assistant Vice President who edited the 12th and 13th editions;
- Richard E. Stevens, retired NFPA Vice President and Chief Engineer, who, during his 35 years with the Association, contributed to five editions of the *Handbook* and served as chief technical consultant for the 14th and 15th editions; and
- Gordon P. (Mac) McKinnon, retired NFPA Editor-in-Chief, who was directly involved in the preparation of five editions of the *Handbook* over a quarter century. He served as Editorial Coordinator of the 12th edition, Managing Editor of the 13th edition, Editor of the 14th and 15th editions, and Consulting Editor for the 16th edition.

In offering this Edition of the *Fire Protection Handbook*, the editors solicit suggestions for improvements in the interest of making future editions increasingly useful to all concerned. Every effort has been made to ensure that the text is consistent with the best available information on current fire protection practices. However, the National Fire Protection Association, as a body, is not responsible for the contents, as there has been no opportunity for the membership to review the *Handbook* before to its publication. If readers discover errors or omissions, the editors would appreciate those shortcomings being called to their attention.

Arthur E. Cote, P.E.
Editor-in-Chief

PREFACE

Without a doubt, supervising the editing of the oldest, the largest, and the most comprehensive reference book on fire protection in the world has been one of the most challenging and complicated tasks I've had the pleasure of attempting during my 25 (plus) years in the field of technical book publishing. When compared to the 16th edition, the 17th edition has grown from 173 chapters and 2 appendices to 189 chapters with 5 appendices; from 1750 pages with more than 2000 illustrations to about 2000 pages with more than 2100 illustrations. The number of authors involved—all of whom are experts in their specialties—has increased from 191 to 204.

Each existing chapter has been thoroughly updated by the addition of new code and standards provisions, new techniques, and the latest fire experience statistics. But that's only part of the story.

For the first time in decades, the organizational structure of the book has been changed. We've switched the *Handbook* from the old, traditional subject-oriented outline to a new systems approach, that we believe more readily reflects the way fire protection professionals actually think about solving fire protection problems. The sequence of the sections and chapters is calculated to help the reader view fire protection problems and solutions in a logical, systems-oriented way.

The changes made in this edition are too numerous to list individually, but in general:

1. The organizational structure of the *Handbook* has been changed to reinforce the systems characteristics of fire protection.
2. Every chapter has been thoroughly updated, and there are 16 totally new chapters.
3. Dozens of "new" authors have contributed to the *Handbook* for the first time.
4. The chapter Bibliographies have been expanded and updated.The result is a professional reference book with more than 650 pages of "new" material and a grand total of more than 2000 pages, all of which have been revised and updated.

ACKNOWLEDGMENTS

It may be that only another editor can fully understand the complexity of a project like the *Fire Protection Handbook*, but the statistics are mind-boggling: 189 chapters by 204 authors; hundreds of reviewers to keep track of; more than 2100 illustrations to be rendered, captioned, cropped, and proofed; 3 or 4 million words to edit, keyboard, proof, typeset, and proof again; hundreds of tables and equations; 2000+ pages to lay out, review, correct, and lay out again; a readership that ranges from volunteer fire fighters and fire protection engineers to university professors and research scientists; a breakneck schedule with a small but dauntless staff augmented by freelancers; and an end-product with more pages than most major magazines publish in an entire year. But most important of all is the haunting knowledge that this book is different because, to tens of thousands of fire protection professionals—professionals on whom hundreds of millions of people depend for life safety, and protection of property from fire—it's THE HANDBOOK. There are times when you simply have to strive for excellence, and editing the *Fire Protection Handbook* is one of these times.

Each edition of any book as massive and as important is the *Fire Protection Handbook* is an enormous undertaking requiring the cooperation of hundreds of people, and this 17th edition is no exception. In one way or another, virtually every NFPA staff member has been involved—many made generous personal sacrifices of their time and talents. One member of our team, however, deserves special mention. Dr. John R. Hall, Jr., not only served as author or co-author of three of the chapters, he reviewed the vast majority of the statistical information, wrote the introductions to each section, and was almost single-handedly responsible for the new systems approach organizational scheme. If the 17th edition significantly differs from the 16th, it owes most of that difference to John.

Obviously, no single person can know everything about a subject as enormous and complex as fire protection. While every word in this edition was reviewed by the Editor-in-Chief and other appropriate NFPA staff members, selected chapters were also reviewed by qualified outside experts from all over the world. Therefore, the editors wish to acknowledge and thank all of these experts who contributed their time and energy to improving the *Handbook*. Special thanks are due to Joseph M. Redden, John M. Watts, J. Gordon Routley, and Wayne

G. Carson who served as the principle reviewers of many chapters. Additionally, the editors wish to thank Dr. Richard N. Wright, Director, National Institute of Standards and Technology; Mr. Paul M. Fitzgerald, Chief Operating Officer, Factory Mutual System; Mr. Stanley J. Cubillon, Vice-President Engineering, Industrial Risk Insurers; and Mr. Tom Castino, President, Underwriters Laboratories Inc. Their willingness to allow their respective staffs to devote the time required to participate as both reviewers and authors of many of the chapters in this *Handbook* is gratefully acknowledged. Without their help the book would have suffered. Recognition is also due Milosh Puchovsky, of Worcester Polytechnic Institute, who spent the summer of 1990 revising and updating many of the expanded bibliographies; Kay Villa, who helped out when we needed help; and Captains Peter Brennen and Walter Donnelly, of the Brookline Fire Department, who also read and critiqued every word.

This editor would like to personally thank Hilary Davis, who spent more sleepless nights and worked harder to ensure the success of the 17th edition than most; Deborah Shaw, who pitched in to help when needed most; Jane Lataille, Cathy Ray, Rolf Jensen, Muriel McArdle, Martha Curtis, Carl Peterson, Casey Grant, Ron Coté, Claire McRudin, Jim Lathrop, and Robert Solomon who were always there when they were needed; and Cathryn Place who helped smooth things out when they needed smoothing. Finally, thanks to Louise Grant: Louise, three editions are not enough, so please get well and please hurry back—the FPH needs you.

Over the five-year period between this and the previous edition, many conscientious readers have called errors and inconsistencies to our attention. We wish we had time and space to mention them all. Nothing is perfect, and so we continue to solicit your comments. We do try, we do care, and we will respond to each and every letter.

Jim L. Linville
Managing Editor

BASICS OF FIRE AND FIRE SCIENCE

Section 1 of the newly reorganized *Fire Protection Handbook* contains all the chapters you should read before you read anything else in the book. As the name says, it presents the basics—about the fire problem, fire protection, firesafety, fire science, and everything else that makes a systematic approach to fire possible.

Chapter 1 says, "This edition of the *Fire Protection Handbook* is more than an order of magnitude larger than the original edition." Chapter 2 says, "A little over one hundred years ago, structural steel was unknown, reinforced concrete had not been used in structural framing applications, and the first 'high-rise' building had just been built in the United States." It can be hard to realize just how much the fire problem in the United States has changed since the first handbook appeared and how much our knowledge of fire has grown.

Section 1 provides statistical information on the long-term trends in fire and on short-term trends and patterns that help to show the relative status and importance of various strategies to reduce that fire problem. Section 1 also provides a number of basic organizing principles to help provide unity and understandability to the large, sprawling subject of firesafety and fire protection. These principles and themes are then repeated and used throughout the *Handbook* to help show the connections between subjects. Finally, Section 1 presents the most basic and general systems concepts and physical-science concepts related to fire protection engineering.

As Chapter 1 explains, Sections 2 through 7 of the *Handbook* have been defined in terms of major types of strategies to prevent or mitigate fire. The section sequence roughly corresponds to the order in which these strategies become relevant in the timeline of fire development. Section 8 continues this strategy-type approach but organizes its chapters by specific property classes. Each chapter addresses the different strategies of firesafety with respect to its property class. Section 9 then addresses the organizations that provide fire protection, set up by statistical information on the U.S. fire service in Chapter 1.

Chapter 1 says of the post-ignition strategies, which are collectively known as fire protection, "It is important to remember that fire protection requires the development of an integrated system of balanced protection which uses many different design features and systems to reinforce one another and to cover for one another in case of the failure of any one. Success is measured by the extent of usage of effectively designed integrated fire protection systems."

The need to emphasize systems design and systems thinking is developed further in Chapters 2 and 3. Chapter 2 presents a systems approach to fire prevention and fire protection within the context of the critical *building design* phase of a property's life. Chapter 3 presents a brief overview of systems thinking and systems analysis in general, then shows how these general concepts can be applied to fire protection through the *firesafety concepts tree.* The firesafety concepts tree is a very general model and is particularly appropriate for Section 1 because it can be used simply as a conceptual or logical model or as a framework for detailed quantitative analysis, such as hazard analysis. As Chapter 3 says, "In the broadest sense, systems analysis is simply the methodical study of an entity as a whole."

Chapters 4 through 6 address the physical-science knowledge that underpins modern fire protection engineering. An understanding of these basic definitions and laws is essential to fire protection in the 1990s, when it is increasingly important to know not only *what* the codes, standards, and other rules of good practice say but *why* they say it.

Chapter 4 addresses "basic definitions of some of the physical properties and chemical terms applicable to the chemistry and physics of fire" to the extent of "basic background reference material applicable to this and other sections of this handbook." Chapters 5 and 6 extend this discussion to the particular subject of explosions and to physical relationships that can form the basis for interruption or reversal of the development of fire or explosion—that is, suppression, prevention, confinement, or other mitigation.

Also look for these: The first chapters of Sections 3 and 7 also present basic scientific material but material specific to one type of strategy and hence to those sections only. Chapter 1 of Section 3 addresses the biochemistry of combustion-product effects on people, and Chapter 1 of Section 7 addresses the human behavior patterns that affect evacuation. The whole of Section 10 may be seen as an elaboration of the brief introduction to modeling provided by the discussion of the firesafety concepts tree, as Section 10 addresses other modeling approaches and associated data sources and measurement methods. Finally, those interested in more on the science of fire should read *The SFPE Handbook of Fire Protection Engineering,* also published by NFPA.

AMERICA'S FIRE PROBLEM AND FIRE PROTECTION

John R. Hall, Jr. and Arthur E. Cote

When the first *Fire Protection Handbook* was published in 1896, it contained no information on the size, trends, or patterns of the U.S. fire problem. Like most scientific and engineering handbooks, especially in years gone by, the first *Fire Protection Handbook* merely compiled a series of rules, tables, and formulas, which the knowledgeable firesafety professional of that time would find useful. One had to read between the lines to realize that the information provided in that handbook said nothing about hazards to life and limb and little about fire prevention as a strategy to reduce fire loss. (One also saw very little about hazards related to fires and explosions, such as electrical shock, hazardous materials, and environmental risks, topics which later editions have steadily expanded.)

In nearly a century since that first edition appeared, the field of fire protection has grown tremendously. This edition of the *Fire Protection Handbook* is more than an order of magnitude larger than the original edition. With that growth of information has come an increasing need for context, perspective, and systematic approaches to organizing knowledge.

This chapter has two goals. One is to provide a perspective on the size, trends, and patterns of America's fire problem. The other is to provide a basic structure for the elements of fire protection—a structure which can be tied to particular measures of the fire problem and which is carried forward in the first-level organization of this handbook. There are ten major sections in this handbook. The first six correspond to the six principal types of strategies for fire protection. The seventh contains information on systems approaches to fire protection for particular property classes. The eighth addresses organizational considerations for fire protection organizations, such as fire departments. And the last major section addresses general sources of information and methods of analysis.

To understand the sequencing of the first six major sections, think of fire protection as a series of opportunities to intervene against a hostile fire, arrayed along a timeline of potential growth in fire severity. First, there are the opportunities to prevent the fire entirely. Second, there are opportunities to slow the initial growth and spread of fire or to reduce the severity of fires through the design, selection, and handling of materials and products. Third, there are opportunities to detect fire early, permitting effective intervention before damage becomes too severe. Fourth, there are opportunities for automatic or manual suppression. Fifth, there are opportunities to confine the fire in space through compartmentation and other passive fire protection methods. Sixth, there are opportunities to move occupants to safe locations, taking advantage of the extra time provided by the earlier steps to move people from hazardous locations to safety, or to defend them where they are.

Before examining each of these fire protection strategies, it is useful to assess the size of the fire problem that faces us and the success achieved in reducing it over the past decades.

U.S. FIRE LOSS TRENDS

Table 1-1A and Figures 1-1A through 1-1D show that the number of fires and associated losses leveled off—or reached a plateau—around 1982. Reported fires have been within 6 percent of 2.4 million every year from 1982 through 1988. Civilian fire deaths have been within 4 percent of 6,000 every year from 1982 through 1988, except 1984. Civilian fire injuries have been within 7 percent of 30,000 every year from 1977 through 1988, except 1986. And after adjustment for inflation, direct property damage has fallen within 9 percent of $5.5 billion in 1980 dollars every year from 1982 through 1988.

Table 1-1B and Figure 1-1E provide a longer perspective on U.S. fire deaths by switching to trends in the death-certificate data base. (NFPA uses this data base only for long-term trend analysis, where there is no alternative data base with as much consistency in methodology. Fires involving post-crash vehicle fires or arson are often excluded or missed from the fire totals in the death-certificate data base.)

Dr. John R. Hall, Jr., is NFPA's assistant vice president for Fire Analysis and Research. Arthur E. Cote, P. E., is assistant vice president and NFPA's chief engineer.

TABLE 1-1A. *The U.S. Fire Problem (1977–1988) Fires Reported to U.S. Fire Departments*

Year	Fires	Civilian Deaths	Civilian Injuries	Direct Property Damage[a]
1977	3,264,000	7,395	31,190	$4,709,000,000
1978	2,817,500	7,710	29,825	$4,498,000,000
1979	2,845,500	7,575	31,325	$5,750,000,000
1980	2,988,000	6,505	30,200	$6,254,000,000
1981	2,893,500	6,700	30,450	$6,676,000,000
1982	2,538,000	6,020	30,525	$6,432,000,000
1983	2,326,500	5,920	31,275	$6,598,000,000
1984	2,343,000	5,240	28,125	$6,707,000,000
1985	2,371,000	6,185	28,425	$7,324,000,000
1986	2,271,500	5,850	26,825	$6,709,000,000
1987	2,330,000	5,810	28,215	$7,159,000,000
1988	2,436,500	6,215	30,800	$8,352,000,000

[a] Direct property damage figures do not include indirect losses, such as business interruption, and have not been adjusted for inflation.
Source: NFPA National Fire Experience Survey.

TABLE 1-1B. *History of U.S Fire Fatalities*

Year	Fire Deaths[a]	Fire Deaths per 100,000 Population
1913	8,900	9.1
1920	9,300	8.7
1930	8,100	6.6
1940	7,500	5.7
1950	6,400	4.2
1960	7,600	4.3
1970	6,700	3.3
1980	5,800	2.6
1988	5,000	2.0

[a] Fire deaths are calculated on the basis of death certificates and are given to the nearest hundred. Fire deaths involving arson or post-collision vehicle fires may be omitted. Classification changes in 1968, 1958, and especially 1948 limit comparability of figures.
Source: National Safety Council, *Accident Facts*, National Safety Council, Chicago, 1989, pp. 19-21.

It can be seen that the plateau that began in 1982 came after a period of steady decline that lasted nearly two decades. Those in the fire protection field have seen progress every year for most of their professional lives. But that steady decline in the death toll has not existed for many years, and it will take a significant effort for that decline to resume.

Fire deaths have fallen by roughly 50 percent in the 70 years since their peak levels around World War I. Fire death *rates* have fallen by three-fourths. The decline in fire deaths was fairly irregular until the mid-1960s, because individual incidents with death tolls in the hundreds used to occur with some regularity. A few such incidents could significantly affect the total U.S. fire death toll in a given year. From 1955 to the present, there has been only one U.S. incident with a death toll of 100 or more—the Beverly Hills Supper Club fire in 1977. By contrast, the previous 55 years (1900 through 1954) produced 44 incidents involving death tolls of 100 or more. That's a decline from nearly one fire per year of that severity to less than one every three decades.

"America Burning",[1] the report of the National Commission on Fire Prevention and Control (NCFPC), set a goal in 1973 of reducing America's fire death toll by one-half in a generation, which is usually understood to mean 25 years. With two-thirds of that generation now gone, fire deaths measured by death certificates have fallen by only about one-fourth, nearly all of that before 1982. If current trends continue, this objective will not be met.

Fire is second only to falls as a cause of accidental death in the home, and it is the number one cause for children and young adults.

Fire death rates in the U.S. and Canada also are twice as high as those in western Europe and Japan. Further analysis has shown that the U.S. does well in holding down the average severity of fire (i.e., deaths per fire) but fares very poorly in holding down the fire incident rate, i.e., preventing fires.

Table 1-1C provides a longer perspective on property damage in fire, using estimates from the Insurance Services Office (ISO). (NFPA uses this data base only for long-term trend analysis, where there is no alternative data base with as much consistency in methodology. The data base has

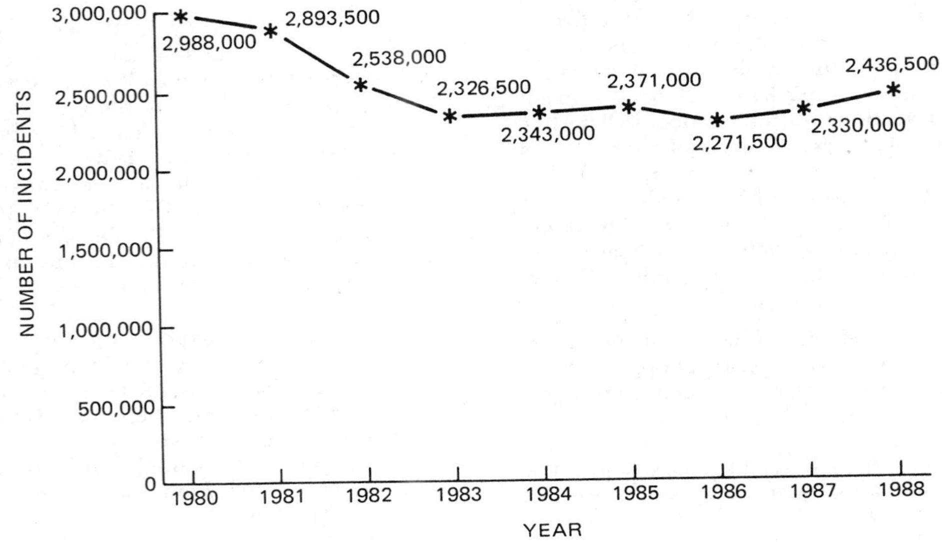

FIG. 1-1A. U.S. fire in ident trend (1980-1988). (Source: 1980-1988 NFPA survey)

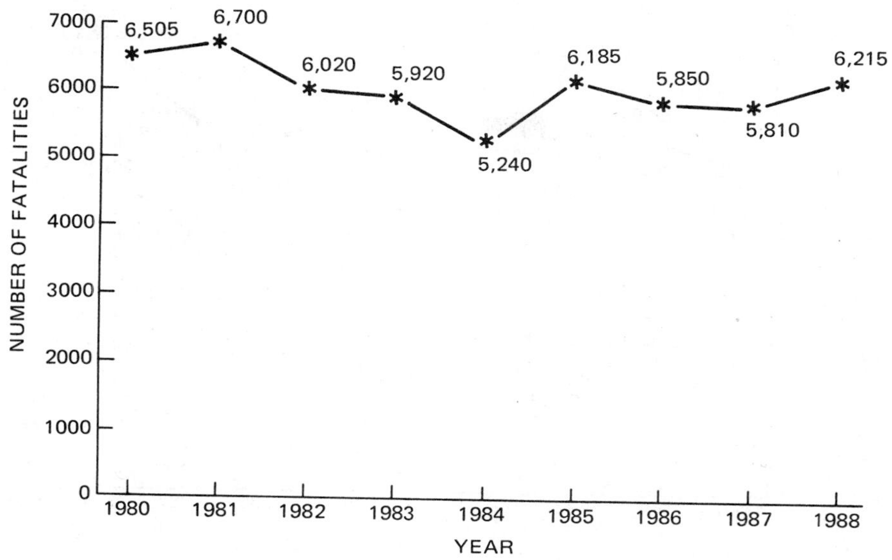

FIG. 1-1B. U.S. civilian fire death trend (1980-1988). (Source: 1980-1988 NFPA survey)

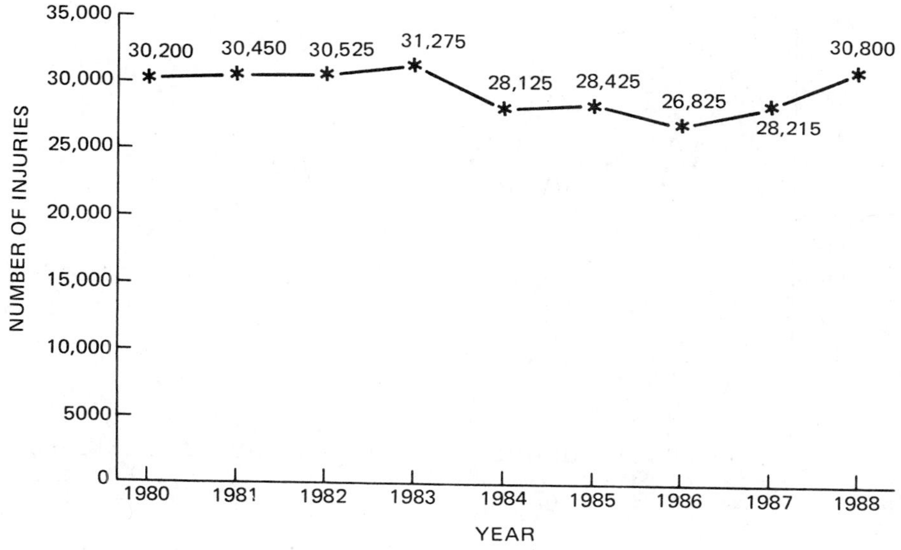

FIG. 1-1C. U.S. civilian fire injury trend (1980-1988). (Source: 1980-1988 NFPA survey)

considerable uncertainty due to its adjustments for uninsured and unreported losses.) Fire losses have grown roughly a hundred-fold in the past century, but this reflects a roughly 12-fold decline in the purchasing power of the dollar and a roughly 30-fold increase in the nation's economy [measured by gross national product (GNP)] after adjustment for those changes in purchasing power. As a fraction of GNP, fire loss has declined by roughly three-fourths since the turn of the century, a decline very similar to the decline in the fire death rate relative to population. America's fire losses, relative to the size of its economy, are quite comparable to the loss rates in western Europe and Japan. As a nation, the U.S. appears to do a better job protecting property than protecting its citizens, at least compared to the other fully industrialized democracies.

To put the total in another perspective, the property damage caused by fire in one year is more than the cost of building a hundred new homes of average cost (which was between $100,000 and $120,000 in 1987) each day for one year.

FIRE PATTERNS BY PROPERTY CLASS

The patterns of fire by property class can be examined at several different levels. The last edition of the *Fire Protection Handbook* introduced a property classification procedure first used in NFPA's long-range planning exercises. That classification is used here in a somewhat stripped-down form, as follows:

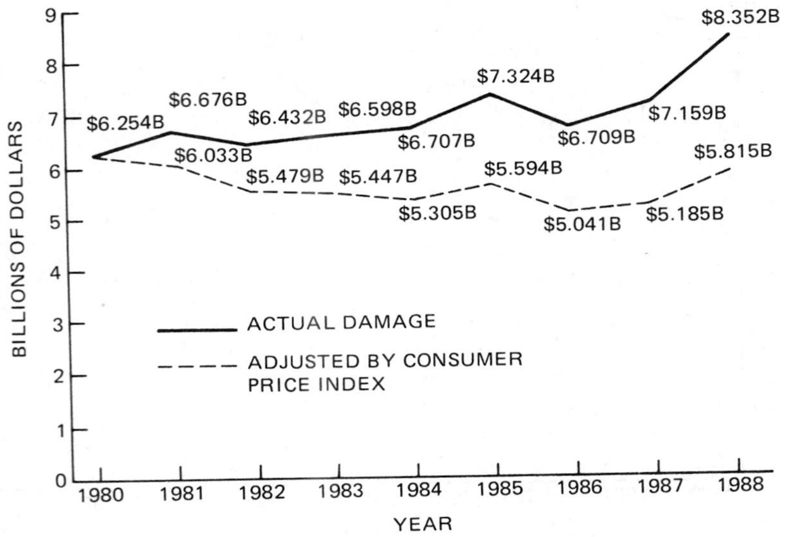

FIG. 1-1D. U.S. direct property damage trend (1980-1988). (Source: 1980-1988 survey)

FIG. 1-1E. U.S. fire deaths (1913-1988). (Source: National Center for Health Statistics, National Safety Council)

Homes and garages: This includes dwellings, duplexes, mobile homes, apartments, townhouses, condominiums, and detached dwelling garages.

American community: This includes all public assembly properties; all educational, health care, or correctional facilities; and stores and offices. It also includes any residential properties that do not qualify as homes, such as hotels and motels, rooming or boarding houses, dormitories, fraternity or sorority houses, and barracks. This revised definition of the American Community also incorporates what had been called the American Heritage property class in the last edition. The American Heritage consists of historically important places and objects. Its direct fire loss is quite small, but it deserves and receives special attention because losses in this property class may be quite literally irreplaceable.

Industrial environment: This includes all industrial, manufacturing, defense, and utility properties, and all storage facilities other than dwelling garages.

Other structures: This includes all buildings or structures that are vacant or under construction, demolition, or renovation. It also includes all structures that are not buildings, such as bridges and tunnels.

Mobile environment: This includes all vehicles.

Outdoor: This includes all wildlands, forests, brush, grass, timber, and crops. It also includes outdoor trash, such as dumpsters or litter. Note that the statistics used here capture only fires reported to local fire departments; therefore national, state, and private forests and parks may be significantly underrepresented. This corresponds to the Forests and Wildlands category used in the last edition and

TABLE 1-1C. *History of U.S Property Damage in Fire*

Year	Property Damage (in Millions)[a]	Property Damage (in Millions of 1987 Dollars)[b]	Property Damage per Capita)[c]	Property Damage per Capita (in 1987 Dollars)	Property Damage as Percentage of GNP[d]
1880	$ 75	$ 875	$ 1.49	$17.45	0.67
1890	$ 109	$1,373	$ 1.73	$21.81	0.83
1900	$ 161	$2,189	$ 2.12	$28.81	0.86
1910	$ 214	$2,600	$ 2.33	$28.26	0.61
1920	$ 448	$2,544	$ 4.24	$24.07	0.49
1930	$ 502	$3,415	$ 4.09	$27.81	0.56
1940	$ 286	$2,325	$ 2.18	$17.66	0.29
1950	$ 649	$3,059	$ 4.29	$20.21	0.23
1960	$1,108	$4,252	$ 6.18	$23.71	0.21
1970	$2,238	$6,552	$10.97	$32.12	0.22
1980	$5,579	$7,691	$24.55	$33.84	0.20
1987	$8,504	$8,504	$34.94	$34.94	0.19

[a] Insurance Services Office Estimates, including adjustments for estimated uninsured and unreported losses, as reported by Insurance Information Institute, *Insurance Facts*, 1988-89 ed., Insurance Information Institute, New York, 1989, p. 69.
[b] Based on Consumer Price Index, as calculated by U.S. Bureau of Labor Statistics, including estimates for historical times by U.S. Bureau of the Census.
[c] Based on U.S. residential population.
[d] Based on GNP estimates by U.S. Bureau of Economic Analysis, including estimates for historical times by U.S. Bureau of the Census.

probably also captures most of the vaguely defined Recreational Environment. Last edition's Agricultural (Rural) America category is scattered across this and the other categories, particularly the Outdoor category (cropland), the Industrial Environment (barns and silos), and the Homes and Garages category (farmhouses and rural homes, generally).

Other: This includes all other and unclassified properties. It is needed for completeness but is a factor only for fire incidents, not for human or property losses.

Figures 1-1F through 1-1I summarize the patterns of fire loss in these seven property categories in recent years. The Outdoor category accounts for the largest share of fire incidents.

Fire deaths, and to a lesser degree fire injuries, are overwhelmingly concentrated in Homes and Garages. The three other building and structure categories combined (i.e., American Community, Industrial Environment, and Other Structures) account for a fire death toll only half the size of the death toll in the Mobile Environment, which is itself only one-sixth the death toll in Homes and Garages. The majority of these vehicle fire deaths are due to fires following survivable crashes in people's personal cars or trucks. The U.S. fire death problem therefore is not a matter of large death tolls in large buildings, although these incidents dominate the news. Most people who die in fire die in ones or twos in the very places where they feel safest—their own homes and vehicles. Home and garage fires also lead the dollar loss due to fire, although here the share for other buildings is much larger.

Most of the visibility of America's fire problem and a large share of the public's fear and concern centers around very large fires. Here, the relative importance of the different property classes can be very different, as is shown in Tables 1-1D through 1-1G. Tables 1-1D and 1-1E list the ten deadliest U.S. fires and explosions of all time and of the 1980s, respectively, while Tables 1-1F and 1-1G list the ten costliest U.S. fires and explosions of all time and of the 1980s, respectively.

The ten deadliest fires and explosions of all time include five from the Mobile Environment, two that began in the Outdoor environment, and one from the Industrial Environment. Only two, the Iroquois Theater and the Cocoanut Grove nightclub, involved the American Community, which people tend to think of as the area of greatest risk of multiple-death fires. In a recent NFPA study of the 98 fires and explosions from 1900 to the present that killed at least 50 people, similar results, which may surprise the fire community, were found.[2] The leading category was the Industrial Environment with 68 incidents, 59 of them being mine fires or explosions. The American Community had twenty, the Mobile Environment had seven, the Outdoor environment had two, and the San Francisco earthquake and fire is hard to tie to any single

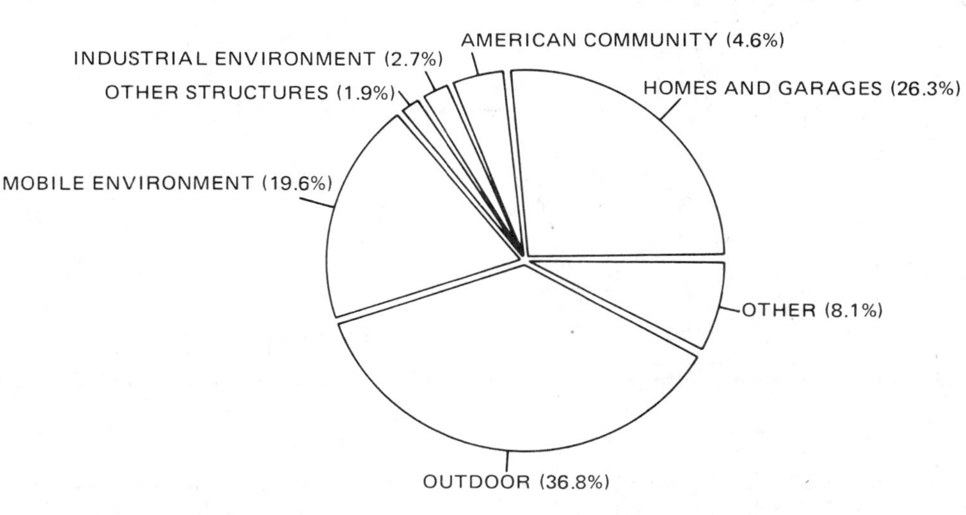

FIG. 1-1F. ***Reported fire incidents by major property class (1983-1987). (Source: 1983-1987 NFIRS and NFPA Survey)***

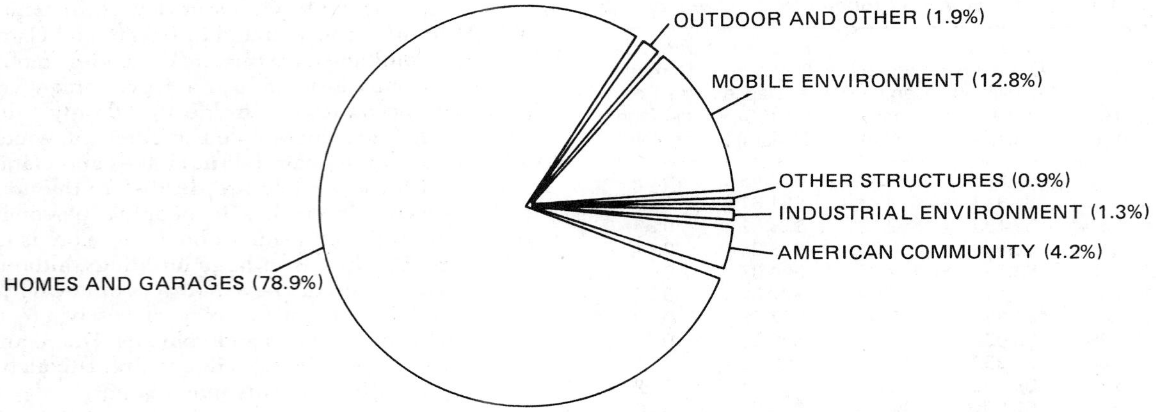

FIG. 1-1G. Civilian fire deaths by property use (1983-1987). (Source: 1983-1987 NFIRS and NFPA survey)

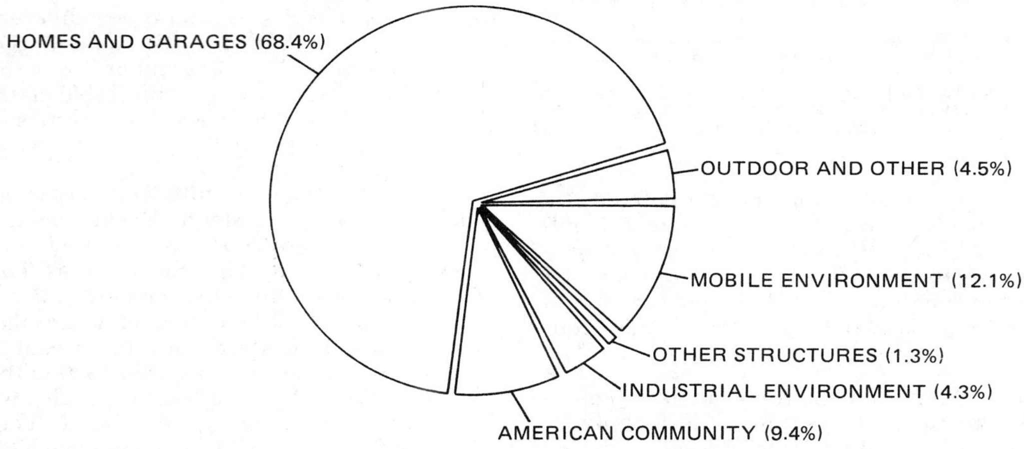

FIG. 1-1H. Civilian fire injuries by property use (1983-1987). (Source: 1983-1987 NFIRS and NFPA survey)

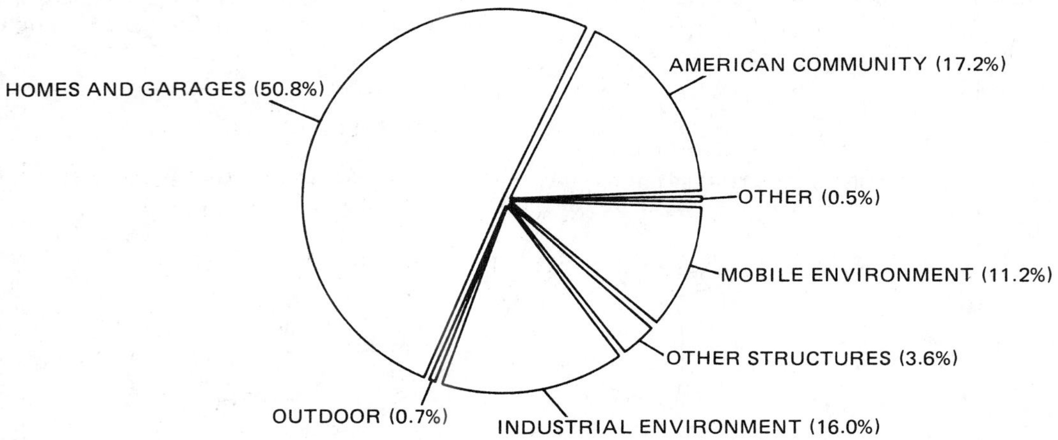

FIG. 1-1I. Direct property damage by major property use (1983-1987). (Source: 1983-1987 NFIRS and NFPA survey)

environment. Even in the 1980s, the ten deadliest fires include three from the Mobile Environment and one from the Industrial Environment (a mine incident), in contrast with six from the American Community.

Figure 1-1J gives still another perspective. Except for the Great Depression in the 1930s and World War II—periods which presented unique problems for code enforcement and compliance—the record shows considerable progress

TABLE 1-1D. ***The Ten Deadliest U.S. Fires and Explosions in History***

	Number of Deaths
1. S.S. Sultana steamship boiler explosion and fire Mississippi River, April 27, 1865	1,547
2. Forest fire Peshtigo, WI, and environs, October 8, 1871	1,152
3. General Slocum excursion steamship fire New York, NY, June 15, 1904	1,030
4. Iroquois Theater Chicago, IL, December 30, 1903	602
5. Forest fire Northern MN, October 12, 1918	559
6. Cocoanut Grove nightclub Boston, MA, November 28, 1942	492
7. S.S. Grandcamp and Monsanto Chemical Company plant Texas City, TX, April 16, 1947	468
8. Monongha Mine coal mine explosion Monogha, WV, December 6, 1907	361
9. North German Lloyd steamship Hoboken, NJ, June 30, 1900	326
10. Explosion of two ammunition ships at depot Port Chicago, CA, July 18, 1944	322

Source: *1984 Fire Almanac* and National Safety Council's *Accident Facts*.

TABLE 1-1E. ***The Ten Deadliest U.S. Fires and Explosions (1980-1989)***

1.	MGM Grand Hotel Las Vegas, NV, November 21, 1980	85
2.	Galaxy Airlines #203 Reno, NV, January 21, 1985	42
3.	United Air Lines #232 Sioux City, IA, July 19, 1989	35*
4.	Keansburg Rest Home board and care facility Morganville, NJ, January 9, 1981	31
5.	Harrison County Jail Biloxi, MS, November 8, 1982	29
6A.	Wilberg Coal Mine Orangeville, UT, December 19, 1984	27
6B.	Church school bus Carroliton, KY, May 14, 1988	27
8.	Stouffer's Inn conference facility Harrison, NY, December 4, 1980	26
9A.	Brinley Inn board and care facility Bradley Beach, NJ, July 26, 1980	24
9B.	Dorothy Mae Hotel home hotel Los Angeles, CA, September 4, 1982	24

* Based on preliminary separation of 111 deaths into fire and non-fire deaths, from news accounts.

Source: NFPA's Fire Incident Data Organization.

TABLE 1-1F. ***The Ten Largest U.S. Fire Losses in History****

		Loss (in Millions of 1989 Dollars)
1.	San Francisco earthquake and fire April 18, 1906 (Loss in year of occurrence—$350 million)	$4,814
2.	Great Chicago Fire October 8, 1871 (Loss in year of occurrence—$168 million)	$1,733
3.	Great Boston Fire November 9, 1872 (Loss in year of occurrence—$75 million)	$ 774
4.	Phillips Petroleum plastics manufacturing and storage plant, Pasadena, TX October 23, 1989 (Loss in year of occurrence—$750 million	$ 750
5.	Baltimore conflagration February 7, 1904 (Loss in year of occurrence—$50 million)	$ 688
6.	S.S. Normandie ocean liner, New York, NY February 9, 1942 (Loss in year of occurrence—$53 million)	$ 403
7.	S.S. Grandcamp and Monsanto Chemical Company plant, Texas City, TX April 16, 1987 (Loss in year of occurrence—$67 million)	$ 372
8.	Shell Oil Company petroleum refinery May 5, 1988 (Loss in year of occurrence—$330 million)	$ 346
9.	Great New York Fire of 1835 December 16, 1835 (Loss in year of occurrence—$26 million)	$ 311
10.	Forest fires in northern Minnesota October 12, 1918 (Loss in year of occurrence—$35 million)	$ 288

* The list is limited to fires for which some reliable dollar-loss estimate exists, is limited to fires occurring in or over the U.S., and includes direct property damage only.

Source: *1984 Fire Almanac*, NFPA Fire Incident Data Organization, and Consumer Price Index, including the U.S. Bureau of the Census's estimates of the index for historical times.

during this century against major loss-of-life building fires. This progress is particularly impressive considering that during the 80 years covered by Figure 1-1J, the U.S. population nearly tripled and great numbers of buildings addressed by the fire codes were constructed. These buildings include facilities that concentrate very large numbers of people.

From World War II through 1989, only four building fires in the U.S. resulted in 80 or more deaths—the Winecoff Hotel fire (119), the Our Lady of the Angels School fire (95), the Beverly Hills Supper Club fire (165), and the MGM Grand Hotel fire (85). (A fifth fire, the Happy Land Social Club, the Bronx, NY, occurred in early 1990.) That's four building fires in 45 years (1945-1989), compared to 14 building fires and explosions of comparable severity in the previous 45 years (1900-1944). As previous comparisons in this chapter also have shown, any threshold of severity chosen demonstrates the tremendous progress made in the first half-century in reducing the rate of loss of life in fire, both in general and especially in major life-loss fires. Figure 1-1J also shows that the most recent five-year period (1985-1989) is the first one in this century not to have even one building fire with a death toll of at least 25.

Another statistic may help to further explain this pattern. During 1983 to 1987 in structure fires outside of homes, 60 percent of all persons killed had been familiar with the building they died in for more than a year. More than 80 percent had been familiar with the building for more than a week. This suggests a fire fatality problem that affects employees (and possibly some long-term patients) far more than customers. (Long-term guests or tenants are not the answer because the percentage of fatal victims with long-term familiarity goes up if all residential properties are excluded.) In other words, the number one fear of Americans—a fatal fire in strange surroundings—has been reduced to a minority share of a shrinking problem, even if homes are excluded.

TABLE 1-1G. ***The 10 Largest U.S. Fire Losses (1980-1989)****

		Loss (in Millions of 1988 Dollars)
1.	Phillips Petroleum plastics manufacturing and storage plant, Pasadena, TX October 23, 1989 (Loss in year of occurrence—$750 million)	$750
2.	Shell Oil Company petroleum refinery Norco, LA, May 5, 1988 (Loss in year of occurrence—$330 million)	$330
3.	Hoechst Celanese chemical manufacturing plant Pampa, TX, November 14, 1987 (Loss in year of occurrence—$154 million)	$160
4.	Tinker Air Force Base jet engine repair facility Oklahoma City, OK, November 12, 1984 (Loss in year of occurrence—$138 million)	$157
5.	Multiple-tenant warehouse Elizabeth, NJ, February 21, 1985 (Loss in year of occurrence—$123 million)	$135
6.	K-Mart warehouse Fallsington, PA, June 21, 1982 (Loss in year of occurrence—$100 million)	$123
7.	Union Oil Company refinery Romeoville, IL, July 23, 1984 (Loss in year of occurrence—$100 million)	$114
8.	Northwestern National Bank building Minneapolis, NM, November 25, 1982 (Loss in year of occurrence—$92.8 million)	$114
9.	Pacific Engineering & Production Company rocket fuel manufacturing facility Henderson, NV, May 4, 1988 (Loss in year of occurrence—$103 million)	$103
10.	Group fire Lynn, MA, November 28, 1981 (Loss in year of occurrence—$70 million)	$97

* Reported losses are taken from best sources known to NFPA and cover only direct property damage.
Source: NFPA Fire Incident Data Organization and Consumer Price Index.

All these patterns underline the fact that lifesafety is a major issue everywhere—in homes and vehicles where most deaths occur, in the American Community where public concerns are highest, and in America's workplaces where the significant risk of fire death still exists. Conversely, Figure 1-1I shows that the Industrial Environment, which is typically considered the focus of potential property loss, actually contributes a smaller share of property damage than the American Community. In short, the dangers of fire to people and property are everywhere, and so strategies of design, fire protection, and other programs must also reach everywhere.

Tables 1-1D and 1-1E also deliver a very encouraging message, and that is the progress made in reducing gigantic deadly fires. In this century, there have been 55 fires and explosions with higher death tolls than the death toll at the MGM Grand Hotel, which was the deadliest U.S. fire of the 1980s. Tables 1-1F and 1-1G tell a similar tale for property damage, but note that the two costliest fires of the 1980s were also two of the ten costliest fires of all time.

Tables 1-1F and 1-1G also show how much the character of large costly fires has changed. Five of the ten costliest fires of all time were fires that engulfed whole cities, while only one of the ten costliest fires of the 1980s could even be called a group fire. The risk of conflagration has declined significantly from the pattern of a century ago.

"Conflagration," "group fire," and "city fire" (the last term used in Japan) lack fully standardized definitions. The definitions used to code death certificates use the term conflagration to mean any building fire. More often, conflagration is used colloquially to mean any large fire with significant flame showing outside. NFPA generally uses the term conflagration to describe a fire with major building-to-building flame spread over some distance. Significant building-to-building fire spread within a complex or among adjacent buildings is typically called a group fire.

Table 1-1H describes four different types of conflagrations, or group fires, and gives recent examples of each. The first type listed is also the most common conflagration scenario in recent years, which is the forest fire or brush fire that spreads to nearby buildings in what is called the urban/wildland interface. The classic conflagration scenario of the last century, involving narrow streets and closely packed buildings, is now comparatively rare. The 1973 Chelsea, MA, conflagration is the only major example in recent decades. The construction and density conditions for such fires are largely confined to the old manufacturing areas of some old cities, particularly in the Northeast. A more common problem, particularly in the Southwest, is the phenomenon of conflagrations driven by strong, hot, dry winds and untreated wood shingles. This problem has been around for as long as NFPA has been collecting information on major fires. Finally, the group fire scenario, in which fire extends to most or all of the buildings of the complex, also continues to occur. The conditions for these fires also are most common in the old manufacturing areas of old cities.

FIRE PREVENTION

Every hostile fire requires an initial heat source, an initial fuel source, and something to bring them together. That something nearly always has a human component, usually an immediate act or omission that brings heat and fuel together or sometimes the delayed effects of an error in design or installation. Fire also requires oxygen and sustainable chemical chain reactions, both of which can be useful points of attack for some suppression systems. Nevertheless, the three components of heat, fuel, and human error are central to nearly all fires and can be used as a framework for thinking about fire prevention, without much fear of oversimplification.

It is important to remember that prevention can occur through successful action on the heat source, the fuel source, or the behavior that brings them together. No one line of attack is clearly preferable to the other, and success is most likely to come if all three components are treated as real options at all times.

Product redesign is the means by which a heat source or a fuel source is changed. Such a change can come about in several ways: (1) regulation, (2) design to a set of voluntary, consensus codes and standards, (3) a voluntary industry-wide program to change product designs, not driven by laws or codes, and (4) product redesign in response to consumer demand.

Changing behavior means education, which also may be done by targeting a variety of audiences. School children are a group that can be reached when they are ready and able to learn substantial quantities of information.

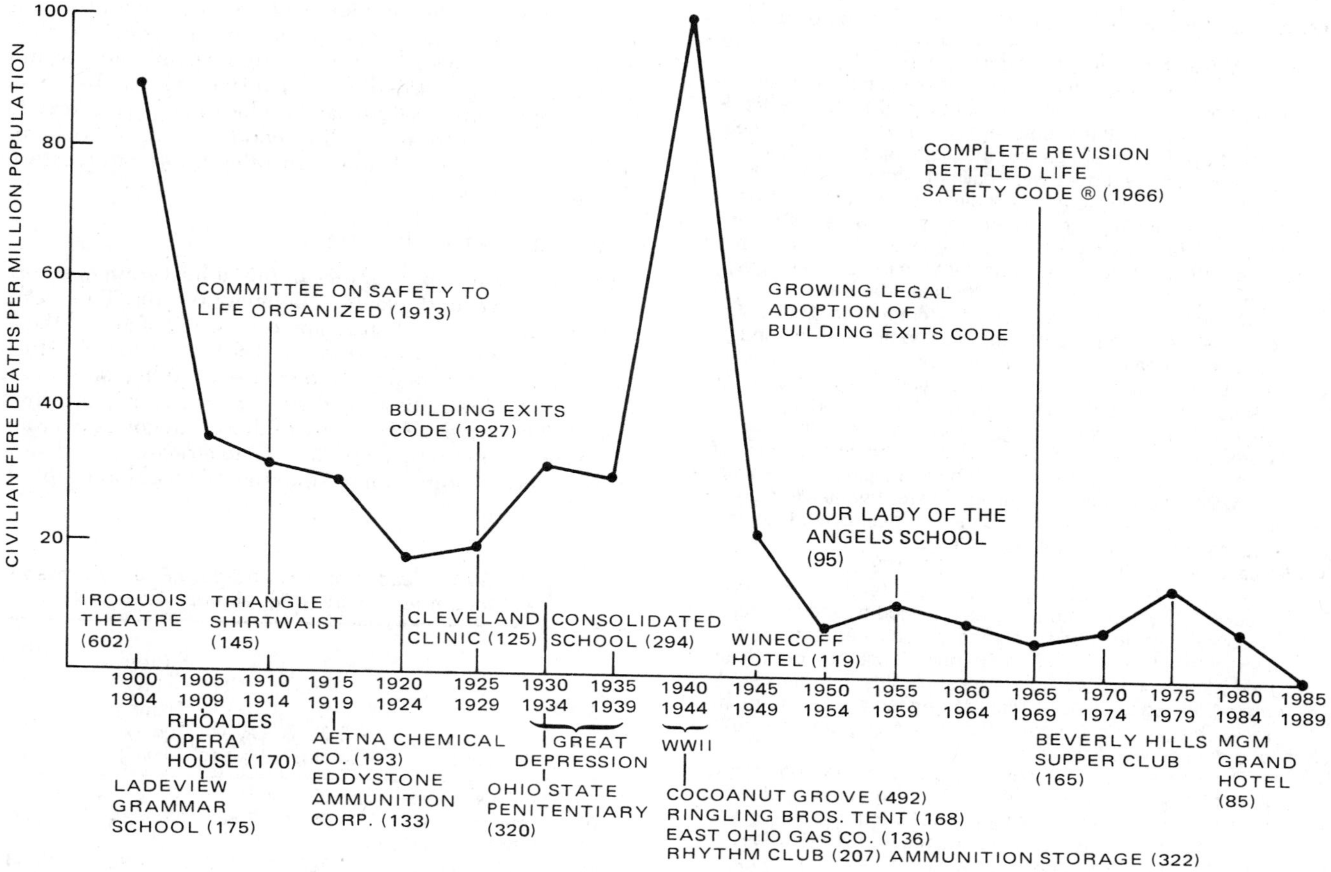

FIG. 1-1J. ***Major loss of life in 20th century U.S. building fires taking at least 25 lives.***

NFPA's *Learn Not to Burn*®[3] curriculum is designed for this audience. Manufacturers' labels and instructions reach consumers when they may be most disposed to learn rules for the firesafe use of products. Product advertisements and public service announcements (PSAs), such as the NFPA *Learn Not to Burn*[3] PSAs, have the potential to reach large audiences. Brochures, educational kits, community meetings, and the like can reach small, motivated audiences which may act as change agents. And Fire Prevention Week, of which NFPA is the originator and a sponsor, provides heightened attention to firesafety each October.

"America Burning,"[1] the report of the U.S. National Commission on Fire Prevention and Control, stated in 1973:

> Indifferent to fire as a national problem, Americans are similarly careless about fire as a personal threat. It takes the careless or unwise action of a human being, in most cases, to begin a destructive fire. In their home environments, Americans live their daily lives amid flammable materials, close to potential sources of ignition. Though Americans are aroused to issues of safety in consumer products, firesafety is not one of their prime concerns.

This is an understandable perception for people who work for firesafety full-time and give it the very highest priority. But a decade and a half later, it can be seen that this view is at least overstated. Many people do tend to believe that fire "only happens to the other guy," and that view ironically is strongest in populations with above-average fire risk. But many people probably come to these views out of a lack of understanding of the risks of what they do and, even more, a lack of perspective on how they can achieve greater safety without unacceptably high costs or other sacrifices of things that also matter to them.

People can be educated and motivated if approached in the right way. Addressing people effectively may involve nothing more than emphasizing what to do rather than what not to do. This is why an important milestone of the late 1970s was the introduction into the nation's schoolrooms of firesafety education based upon sound behavioral principles and good learning techniques. NFPA's *Learn Not to Burn*[3] campaign, which includes both a curriculum and a public information program, is a good example of thoughtfully prepared educational campaigns with specific, far-reaching goals. The *Learn Not to Burn*[3] curriculum, in particular, seeks to teach school children key firesafety behaviors that can be retained for a lifetime.

Product design strategies need to be carefully examined and not treated as simple technological "quick fixes." Many design improvements can be undone by product users if the users have not also been educated to the importance of firesafe product usage. Some product design proposals have high costs relative to the problem they address, and some involve the loss of other significant product performance features, even non-firesafety features. And with any product design strategy, except one driven by con-

TABLE 1-1H. ***Illustrative Recent Conflagrations and Group Fires***

1. Urban/Wildland Interface, Malibu, CA, 1987.
   A fire of incendiary origin with multiple points of origin was driven by Santa Ana winds gusting over 60 mph. The fire moved 12 mi. in 10 hrs, entering Malibu, where it damaged or destroyed 74 dwellings and mobile homes and 54,000 acres of property. Loses were estimated at nearly $9 million.
   Other major conflagrations originating as brush or forest fires and spreading to populated areas include a 1985 San Diego fire (also nearly $9 million in damages) and a 1987 Pebble Beach, CA, fire (also nearly $9 million in damages).
2. Congested, Combustible District, Chelsea, MA, 1973.
   The fire began in a yard area of a congested district of combustible buildings, including multi-family housing and storage properties. The heavy fuel load inside and outside the buildings, and the narrow separations between buildings created an ideal environment for rapid multi-building fire growth. The wind was strong, gusting up to 48 mph. The water supply was inadequate to support master streams, and some sprinklered properties had broken piping that depleted the water supply without fighting the fire. Eventually, hundreds of buildings over 17 blocks were destroyed. Damage was estimated at $4 million.
3. Untreated Wood Shingles, Anahelm, CA, 1982.
   A fire initially reported as a tree fire spread over several blocks. Untreated wood shingles provided a ready source of secondary ignitions and firebrands, which were transported by high winds, gusting up to 60 mph. These hot, dry Santa Ana winds spread damage to 53 structures, for total estimated damages of $50 million. More than any other fire in recent history, this illustrates the devastating potential hazard of untreated wood shingles.
   Other recent major fires involving untreated wood shingles as significant factors include a 1983 apartment complex fire in Dallas ($5.4 million damage), a 1985 brush fire in and near Los Angeles ($11.2 million damage), a 1985 office building fire in San Antonio ($4.2 million damage), and a 1988 home hotel fire in Lihue, HI ($5.5 million damage).
4. Group Fire—Commercial or Industrial Complex, Fall River, MA, 1987.
   A boiler flue pipe ignited wood components in a ceiling/floor space of a manufacturing plant. Multiple penetrations of the fire wall helped the fire spread into the main area of the plant, where it overwhelmed the plant's complete-coverage sprinkler system. Once the first building was fully involved, high winds (35 mph) helped spread fire to the other five buildings in the complex. Total damages were estimated at $50 million.
   Other recent group fires include a 1987 Lowell, MA, fire ($30 million damage), exacerbated by a shut-off sprinkler system and oil-soaked wood floors, and a $70 million fire that damaged or destroyed 20 buildings in Lynn, MA, in 1981.

Source: NFPA Fire Incident Data Organization.

sumer demand, there should be concern over the loss of freedom of choice.

Educational programs have concerns, too. NFPA's *Learn Not to Burn*[3] curriculum is in use in only 4 percent of U.S. schools. While many more schools have some firesafety education, there is a danger that brief exposure to firesafety slogans will be considered an adequate means of teaching firesafe behavior. This is not the case.

Also, in any fire prevention program, the highest-risk groups tend to be the hardest to reach. The poor may not be able to afford safer products. Small rural communities are too scattered to be reached efficiently by targeted means of communications. Pre-school children are harder to reach with curriculum programs. Elderly people may resist changes in products and practices. This means that a program with less-than-national coverage is likely to miss a disproportionate number of those most in need. The challenge to fire prevention is to recognize this danger and design programs that will reach everyone. It can be done. For example, universal firesafety education, particularly in the schools but also in neighborhoods, seems to be a crucial factor in the much lower fire death rates in western Europe and Japan.

Leading Causes of Fire

As noted, hostile fire requires an initial heat source, an initial fuel source, and usually a behavioral error. Therefore, causes can be defined and ranked in terms of any of these three components, as is done in Table 1-1I for structure fires. The cause categories shown are those that accounted for at least 300 civilian deaths per year in structure fires from 1983 through 1987. Many of these categories overlap. For example, more than one-fifth of all structure fire deaths involve the combination of smoking materials and upholstered furniture.

TABLE 1-1I. ***Major Causes of U.S. Structure Fires Reported to Fire Departments (1983-1987 Annual Average)***

Cause	Civilian Deaths	Civilian Injuries	Direct Property Damage (in Millions)	Fires
Defined by Heat Source				
Smoking material (i.e., lighted tobacco product)	1,560	3,830	$ 384	64,300
Heating equipment	820	3,110	$ 832	191,700
Electrical distribution system	450	1,780	$ 841	76,600
Cooking equipment	400	5,000	$ 389	132,100
Defined by First Ignited Item				
Upholstered furniture	1,070	2,450	$ 249	27,300
Mattress or bedding	800	3,500	$ 288	52,700
Combustible or flammable liquid or gas	640	5,110	$ 821	73,100
Structural member or framing	370	1,030	$ 984	68,200
Wall covering	330	870	$ 409	32,800
Defined by Behavior				
Arson or suspected arson	760	2,850	$1,747	137,600
Child fire play	390	2,190	$ 201	37,500

Source: NFIRS and NFPA Survey.

Homes and Garages: Table 1-1J provides a ranking of major fire causes for Homes and Garages.

Smoking materials are the number one cause of civilian fire deaths, accounting for three of every ten deaths, and most begin with ignition of *upholstered furniture, mattresses,* or *bedding*. The ignitability of these items by lighted tobacco products has been declining for some time, due to a federal law restricting mattress construction and a voluntary program by the upholstered furniture industry.

Arson and suspected arson are the number one cause of property damage for home and garage fires, accounting for more than one of every five dollars lost. Two of every five persons arrested for arson are juveniles.

TABLE 1-1J. ***Major Fire Causes for Homes and Garages (1983-1987)****

Major Cause	Fires	Civilian Deaths	Civilian Injuries	Direct Property Damage (in Millions)
	Annual Loss per Year			
Heating equipment	163,300 (26.6%)	770 (16.7%)	2,540 (13.0%)	$ 603.2 (17.2%)
Cooking equipment	105,000 (17.1%)	350 (7.7%)	4,300 (22.0%)	$ 285.5 (8.1%)
Incendiary or suspicious causes	73,600 (12.0%)	620 (13.6%)	1,990 (10.2%)	$ 738.4 (21.1%)
Electrical distribution system	47,000 (7.7%)	440 (9.6%)	1,280 (6.5%)	$ 457.7 (13.1%)
Other equipment	45,000 (7.3%)	240 (5.3%)	1,420 (7.3%)	$ 259.0 (7.4%)
Smoking materials	40,300 (6.6%)	1,320 (28.9%)	3,050 (15.6%)	$ 252.8 (7.2%)
Appliance, tool, or air conditioning	36,600 (6.0%)	130 (2.7%)	1,010 (5.1%)	$ 193.7 (5.5%)
Child playing	30,000 (4.9%)	370 (8.1%)	2,090 (10.1%)	$ 171.9 (4.9%)
Open flame	29,500 (4.8%)	130 (2.9%)	810 (4.2%)	$ 219.9 (6.3%)
Exposure (to other hostile fire)	20,300 (3.3%)	30 (0.7%)	160 (0.8%)	$ 152.2 (4.3%)
Other heat source	12,600 (2.1%)	160 (3.5%)	740 (3.8%)	$ 88.5 (2.5%)
Natural causes	9,800 (1.6%)	10 (0.2%)	160 (0.8%)	$ 83.5 (2.4%)
Total	613,200 (100.0%)	4,580 (100.0%)	19,550 (100.0%)	$3,506.4 (100.0%)

* This ranking uses a hierarchical sorting procedure developed by analysts at the U.S. Fire Administration, which focuses on heat sources and behavioral causes. Results will be affected by the sorting rules used and the sequence in which unknown-cause fires are proportionally allocated to known causes and results by the property-use class are aggregated. Fires are expressed to the nearest hundred, and deaths and injuries to the nearest ten.
Source: 1983-87 NFIRS and NFPA Survey.

Heating equipment is the leading cause of home fire incidents. Most involve portable or space heaters, and the current size of the heating fire problem reflects the growth in use of such devices in the late 1970s and early 1980s. *Cooking equipment* is the leading cause of home fire injuries and is involved in the majority of unreported home fires. Unattended cooking is the principal behavioral factor.

Child fire play, typically involving matches or lighters, accounts for only one of every 12 fire deaths, but it is the leading cause of preschooler fire deaths, accounting for three of every ten. *Electrical distribution system equipment* accounts for a much smaller share of the home fire problem than most people realize, ranking no higher than third among the twelve major cause categories for any measure of loss. The widespread use and enforcement of NFPA's *National Electrical Code®* is probably the primary reason why electrical systems are not among the leading causes of fire. Moreover, even a fire cause such as this, which seems so totally an equipment problem, usually involves human error. One benchmark study found the majority of home electrical fires involved code violations, particularly the general workmanship provisions. Exposed elements, such as cords, are even more subject to abuse by occupants.

American community: Arson and smoking dominate the ignition scenarios of fatal fires in the American Community, as Table 1-1K shows. Together, they accounted for nearly two-thirds of all fire deaths in these property classes from 1983 to 1987. Incendiary and suspicious fires (i.e., arson and suspected arson) are the leading cause for all four measures of fire loss specified in the table. Electrical distribution components are also significant contributors to fire problems in these properties. Cooking fires are a major problem in all properties where food or drink are served. They account for two out of every five fires in eating and drinking establishments, but even there, incendiary and suspicious fires account for the largest share of life and property loss.

Hotels, motels, and rooming or boarding houses accounted for half the 1983-1987 fire fatalities in the American Community. Other property classes with significant shares of fire deaths in the American Community were, in order, eating and drinking facilities, care-of-aged facilities, service stations and related road vehicle sales and service facilities, care-of-sick facilities, and offices. Eating and drinking facilities also accounted for the largest share of fire incidents and direct property damage and ranked second to hotels and motels in fire injuries.

Industrial environment: The many types of specialized equipment used in industry collectively accounted for the largest share of 1983 through 1987 structure fires and associated civilian deaths and injuries in the Industrial Environment, as Table 1-1L indicates. Incendiary and suspicious fires ranked second in fires and first in direct property damage. It is important to note, however, that these properties also had significant problems with open-flame fires (e.g., torches), electrical distribution systems, and heating equipment. Exclusive concentration on the more exotic hazards of any one industrial setting would be a mistake. Effective prevention requires a broad view encompassing all potential ignition scenarios.

Other properties: Post-collision fires and arson or suspected arson are the leading causes of fires and associated losses in vehicles, particularly for deaths, where they collectively account for more than half the total. Electrical system fires also are significant, as are overheated objects, such as tires, brakes, or exhaust pipes. Fires begun by smoking materials or associated lighting implements also account for tens of thousands of vehicle fires per year and tens of millions of dollars in losses per year.

Arson and suspected arson also is far and away the leading cause of outdoor fires in general and wildland fires in particular. Debris burning, careless handling of smoking materials, lightning, and children playing are other leading causes of wildland fires.

TABLE 1-1K. ***Major Fire Causes in the American Community (1983-1987)****

Major Cause	Average Loss per Year: Fires	Civilian Deaths	Civilian Injuries	Direct Property Damage (in Millions)
Incendiary or suspicious causes	27,800 (25.8%)	89 (36.2%)	680 (25.0%)	$ 490.8 (41.2%)
Dlectrical distribution system	14,500 (13.5%)	11 (4.4%)	290 (10.7%)	$ 167.9 (14.1%)
Cooking equipment	13,500 (12.5%)	10 (4.1%)	330 (12.2%)	$ 47.5 (4.0%)
Smoking materials	11,200 (10.4%)	68 (27.6%)	400 (14.6%)	$ 43.9 (3.7%)
Appliance, tool, or air conditioning	9,300 (8.6%)	6 (2.3%)	160 (5.9%)	$ 55.3 (4.6%)
Heating equipment	8,500 (7.9%)	17 (7.1%)	190 (6.8%)	$ 86.8 (7.3%)
Other equipment	8,300 (7.7%)	10 (4.3%)	230 (8.5%)	$ 91.6 (7.7%)
Open flame	6,700 (6.2%)	15 (6.3%)	270 (9.9%)	$ 56.6 (4.8%)
Exposure (to other hostile fire)	3,200 (3.0%)	4 (1.5%)	20 (0.9%)	$ 92.7 (7.8%)
Natural causes	1,800 (1.6%)	2 (1.0%)	40 (1.6%)	$ 34.7 (2.9%)
Other heat source	1,700 (1.6%)	7 (2.8%)	70 (2.7%)	$ 16.6 (1.4%)
Child playing	1,300 (1.2%)	6 (2.3%)	30 (1.1%)	$ 5.6 (0.5%)
	107,800 (100.0%)	245 (100.0%)	2,710 (100.0%)	$1,190.1 (100.0%)

* This ranking uses a hierachical sorting procedure developed by analysts at the U.S. Fire Administration, which focuses on heat sources and behavioral causes. Results will be affected by the sorting rules used and the sequence in which unknown-cause fires are proportionally allocated to known causes and results by property-use class are aggregated. Fires are expressed to the nearest hundred and injuries to the nearest ten.
Source: 1983-1987 NFIRS and NFPA Survey.

TABLE 1-1L. ***Major Fire Causes in the Industrial Environment (1983-1987)****

Major Cause	Average Loss per Year: Fires	Civilian Deaths	Civilian Injuries	Direct Property Damage (in Millions)
Other equipment	13,100 (21.0%)	20 (25.0%)	460 (36.9%)	$ 222.3 (20.2%)
Incendiary or suspicious causes	10,800 (17.3%)	10 (12.4%)	60 (4.5%)	$ 283.1 (25.7%)
Open flame	9,100 (14.6%)	10 (13.1%)	190 (15.5%)	$ 123.7 (11.2%)
Electrical distribution system	6,500 (10.5%)	5 (6.1%)	120 (9.7%)	$ 143.2 (13.0%)
Natural causes	4,500 (7.3%)	5 (5.8%)	110 (8.7%)	$ 68.0 (6.2%)
Exposure (to other hostile fire)	4,500 (7.2%)	1 (1.7%)	10 (1.1%)	$ 46.0 (4.2%)
Heating equipment	4,400 (7.1%)	8 (10.3%)	120 (10.0%)	$ 72.6 (6.6%)
Appliance, tool, or air conditioning	2,200 (3.5%)	2 (1.9%)	50 (4.1%)	$ 74.4 (6.8%)
Child playing	2,100 (3.4%)	4 (5.5%)	30 (2.4%)	$ 8.9 (0.8%)
Smoking materials	2,100 (3.3%)	5 (6.0%)	30 (2.3%)	$ 18.2 (1.7%)
Other heat source	1,700 (2.8%)	8 (10.2%)	40 (3.0%)	$ 19.4 (1.8%)
Cooking equipment	1,200 (1.9%)	2 (2.0%)	20 (1.8%)	$ 21.0 (1.9%)
Total	62,100 (100.0%)	78 (100.0%)	1,240 (100.0%)	$1,100.8 (100.0%)

* This ranking uses a hierarchical sorting procedure developed by analysts at the U.S. Fire Administration, which focuses on heat sources and behavioral causes. Results will be affected by the sorting rules used and the sequence in which unknown-cause fires are proportionally allocated to known causes and results by property-use class are aggregated. Fires are expressed to the nearest hundred and injuries to the nearest ten.
Source: 1983-87 NFIRS and NFPA Survey.

FIRE PROTECTION

Recognizing that prevention will never be 100 percent successful, it is necessary to plan and design so as to mitigate damages when fire occurs. The various strategies to do this constitute what is usually called fire protection. It is important to remember that fire protection requires the development of an integrated system of balanced protection which uses many different design features and systems to reinforce one another and to cover for one another in case of the failure of any one. Defense in depth and engineered redundancy are concepts that also are relevant here. The process of achieving that integration, balance, and redundancy to attain firesafety objectives is the essence of fire protection engineering, including codes and standards.

This means that success is not measured by the extent of use of any one technology or system or code. Success is measured by the extent of usage of effectively designed, integrated fire protection systems. No one system should be considered disposable, and no one system should be considered a panacea.

TABLE 1-1M. ***Sizes of Structure Fires (1983-1987)***

Extent of Flame Damage	Fires	Civilian Deaths	Civilian Injuries	Property Damage
Confined to room of origin	73.0%	20.4%	57.3%	18.7%
Confined to floor, but not room of origin	4.4%	11.4%	10.9%	8.1%
Beyond floor of origin	22.6%	68.1%	31.8%	73.3%
Other known	0.2%	0.0%	0.0%	0.0%

Source: NFIRS and NFPA Survey.

Once fire has started, the first opportunity to reduce its impact comes in the design of burnable items, i.e., the choice of materials and products and their environments. Both the growth of the fire from small to large and its spread along vertical or horizontal surfaces may be slowed through such design.

Active fire protection systems provide the next opportunity. Automatic detection systems will tend to activate first, followed by automatic sprinklers or other automatic suppression systems, although this will vary depending on the design of the detection and suppression systems.

TABLE 1-1N. ***Sizes of Home Fires (1983-1987)***

Extent of Flame Damage	Fires	Civilian Deaths	Civilian Injuries	Property Damge
Confined to room of origin	75.5%	20.1%	55.4%	19.3%
Confined to floor, but not room or origin	4.9%	11.7%	11.9%	10.1%
Beyond floor of origin	19.5%	68.2%	32.6%	70.7%
Other known	0.2%	0.0%	0.0%	0.0%

Source: NFIRS and NFPA Survey.

Passive fire protection provides the final opportunity to stop the fire and smoke but also plays an essential role in providing automatic systems with a manageable fire to act on. Passive protection is designed to confine fire and smoke in zones, a concept called compartmentation. Special attention is given to protection of the building's structural integrity and the spaces through which occupants will move to safety.

Occupant evacuation depends on effective detection and a system to alert occupants, along with a total firesafety design that will defend the occupants where they are or provide protected routes to safe refuges, inside or outside of the building. Evacuation also depends on the knowledge of the occupants.

MATERIALS, PRODUCTS, AND ENVIRONMENTS

If prevention fails, the first opportunity to reduce fire damage comes in the design of materials, products (including assemblies), and environments so as to slow down the growth and spread of fire. Tables 1-1M through 1-1O show that most structure fires never grow beyond the first involved room, but most deaths and property damage occur in the one-fourth of fires that do. This pattern holds for homes and for structures other than homes. Clearly, then, a fire that can be slowed in its growth so that it can be discovered and controlled before fire leaves the first room is likely to result in far less damage to people and property.

TABLE 1-1O. ***Sizes of Fire in Structures Other Than Homes (1983-1987)***

Extent of Flame Damage	Fires	Civilian Deaths	Civilian Injuries	Property Damage
Confined to room of origin	66.6%	20.1%	65.1%	19.3%
Confined to floor, but not room of origin	3.0%	11.7%	6.5%	10.1%
Beyond floor of origin	30.4%	68.2%	28.4%	70.7%
Other known	0.1%	0.0%	0.0%	0.0%

Source: NFIRS and NFPA Survey.

(Injuries are something of an exception, as they are almost as likely to occur in small fires as in large ones.)

The following are some of the fire protection approaches that may be taken under this overall strategy:

1. *Restrict materials used in contents and furnishings*
   - Reduce heat release rate
   - Reduce smoke generation rate
   - Prevent unusual toxic hazard relative to quantity of smoke generated
2. *Add fire retardant to materials*
   - Slow growth of heat release rate
3. *Use fire-resistive barriers*
   - Slow spread of fire to large secondary items
4. *Restrict total fuel load*
   - Limit contents based on total fuel potential
5. *Restrict linings of rooms to prevent rapid flame spread*
   - Restrict wall coverings
   - Restrict ceiling coverings
   - Restrict floor coverings
6. *Restrict materials in concealed spaces*
   - Restrict concealed combustibles
   - Restrict concealed space linings
7. *Require safe handling of large quantities of potential fuel*

With regard to the last point, large quantities of combustible or flammable liquids or gases are the most obvious examples of materials that could make a small fire huge very quickly.

It is important to handle and store these materials safely, following procedures such as those in NFPA 54, *National Fuel Gas Code*; NFPA 58, *Storage and Handling of Liquefied Petroleum Gases;* and NFPA 30, *Flammable and Combustible Liquids Code*. Unusually hazardous environments, such as oxygen-enriched atmospheres, also receive special attention.

DETECTION AND ALARM

The impact of automatic detection and alarm systems has been particularly great in the Homes and Garages environment. From less than 5 percent of homes having smoke detectors in 1972, the United States has risen to a position where 81 percent of homes had at least one smoke detector in 1988.[4] (See Figure 1-1K.) Detectors cut the risk of dying in a home fire roughly in half, and they do this despite the fact that one-third of detectors are non-operational (primarily because of dead or missing batteries) and many homes with detectors do not have all the detectors they need for code-compliant, every-level protection. Nevertheless, thousands of lives have been saved through the widespread use of home smoke detectors.

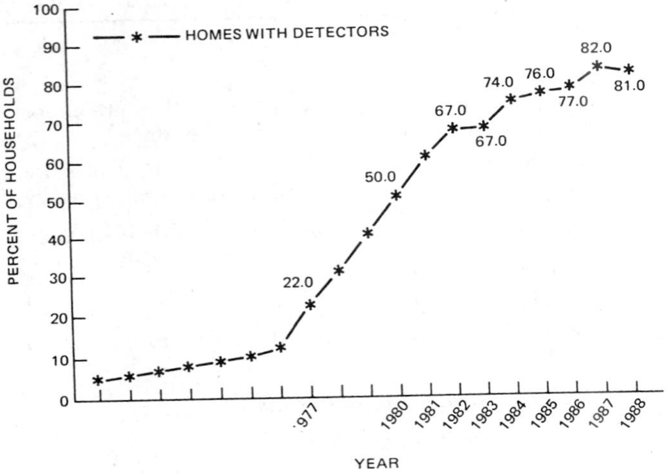

FIG. 1-1K. ***Growth in detector coverage (1970-1988). (Sources for homes with detectors: 1977, 1980, and 1982 estimates from sample surveys by the U.S. Fire Administration; 1983-1988 estimates from "The Prevention Index," a Louis Harris survey for Prevention Magazine.)***

This success has been achieved in several stages. The initial surge in detector usage was driven primarily by manufacturer advertising of an attractive, affordable product and secondarily by public service announcements promoting home smoke detectors. Since then, state and local laws have come along to help complete the process of equipping America's homes with smoke detectors, which is important, because the majority of reported home fires still occur in homes without smoke detectors. In 1977, most states had no home smoke detector requirements of any kind. By 1983, most states had a home smoke detector law, but most states still did not cover existing single-family homes, by far the largest segment of the population. By 1988, most states had laws that extended to all homes, new or existing, but most still did not mandate code-compliant, every-level coverage. The trend in state laws is clear—more complete and more thorough laws—but the process is still far from complete.

As noted, non-operational detectors typically are that way because of dead or missing batteries. Frustration over nuisance alarms, which typically outnumber real fire alarms by an order of magnitude, may be a factor in battery removal. Sensitivity drift, which is a gradual shift in the range of fire effects that will activate the detector, is an example of the problems that can affect older detectors. Tens of millions of homes bought their first detectors more than a decade ago and may need to replace their detectors.

The success of smoke detectors in the home—and the importance of completing the job of providing complete coverage by operational detectors in all homes—should not obscure the fact that automatic detection and alarm systems are an important part of an integrated system of fire protection in *any* property class. Major life-loss fires frequently cite problems with detection or alarm as significant contributing factors. Among the frequently cited problems in major fires with large loss of life are: (1) the absence of needed systems, (2) misapplication, i.e., using equipment or systems that were not appropriate for the property, (3) lack of maintenance, and (4) improper response by occupants to notification of the fire.

In too many property classes, the majority of fires occur in facilities with no detectors. This is true of just over half the fires in schools and other educational properties, for example, and also is true for three-fourths of fires in public assembly properties.

SUPPRESSION

Automatic sprinklers are highly effective elements of fire protection systems design for buildings. When sprinklers are present, the chances of dying in a fire are cut by one-third to one-half and property loss per fire is cut by one-half, compared to fires reported to fire departments where sprinklers are not present.[5] Furthermore, this simple comparison understates the potential value of sprinklers, because it lumps together all sprinklers, regardless of type, coverage, or operational status. If unreported fires could be included and complete, well-maintained, properly installed and designed systems could be isolated, sprinkler effectiveness would be seen as even more impressive.

When sprinklers do not produce satisfactory results, the reasons usually involve one or more of the following: (1) partial, antiquated, poorly maintained, or inappropriate systems; (2) explosions or flash fires that overpower the system before it can react; or (3) fires very close to people or to sensitive, valuable property that can be killed or expensively damaged, respectively, before a system can react.

Except for health care facilities, hotels and motels, and dormitories and barracks, sprinkler usage is rare in properties with large potential for life loss. Sprinkler usage is growing in these properties, but most fires still occur in properies without sprinklers. Most reported fires in storage properties—even in general-purpose warehouses—also occur in properties where sprinklers were reported as absent. There is considerable potential for expanded use of sprinklers to reduce the loss of life and property to fire.

In recent years, particular attention has gone to quick-response residential sprinklers for the home. The evidence of their potential for substantial reductions in loss of life and property is clear, but usage is still quite limited. Several communities have adopted requirements for these new sprinklers in new housing developments, and their experience provides the principal real-world proof to date of the tremendous fire protection value such systems deliver.

The suppression strategy for fire protection involves much more than home sprinklers or even sprinklers in general. Portable fire extinguishers are in use in roughly half of all homes and in many other properties, as well. Specialized, non-water-based suppression systems, using alternative suppression agents or other design characteristics adapted to the special needs of a particular property class, also exist. In the second half of the 1980s, the world became aware of and concerned about the potentially adverse environmental impacts of suppression systems using halogenated agents (the so-called halon/ozone problem). This development has led to research on alternative

TABLE 1-1P. ***Locations of Fatal Victims of Structure Fires (1983-1987)***

Victim Location	All Structures	Homes	Structures Other Than Homes
Intimate with ignition (i.e., very close to fire from its inception)	18.5%	17.7%	28.6%
Not intimate but in room of origin	21.6%	21.8%	19.2%
Not in room or origin, but on floor of origin	30.3%	31.2%	20.2%
Not on floor of origin, but in building of origin	27.3%	27.6%	23.9%
Outside building of origin	0.9%	0.7%	2.9%
Unclassified and other known	1.3%	1.1%	5.3%

Source: NFIRS and NFPA Survey.

fire protection technologies and new agents for critical electronic facilities. It also serves to underline the importance of considering major non-fire factors in any fire protection design.

CONFINING FIRES

The design of building features to contain fires effectively and their effects, is one of the most technically complex aspects of fire protection and is certainly the most difficult to evaluate statistically. In all the other phases—prevention, detection, suppression, evacuation—systems thinking also is essential, but it is at least possible to focus attention on one set of products or systems or occupants. But in fire confinement, systems thinking is both essential and unavoidable, because one must deal with every facet of building design and operation. One must consider not only the direct effects of wall assemblies, ceiling/floor assemblies, door assemblies, and the like on fire confinement but also their effectiveness in creating the design conditions assumed by every other part of the overall fire protection system.

The effectiveness of detectors and sprinklers can be demonstrated to some degree by comparisons of fire experience in buildings that have these systems to buildings that do not. Unfortunately, however, every building has walls, floors, ceilings, and doors, and the various types of assemblies have proved too diverse to be routinely documented in the national fire data bases. Therefore, no analogous simple measures of effectiveness are possible.

Problems in this area tend to be more subtle, too. For detectors and sprinklers, the leading problem is turning off or disabling the equipment—a clear-cut, yes/no change that is easy to document. For fire confinement features, the problems tend to be more a matter of degree, i.e., barriers partially breached for utility networks, some but not all doors blocked open, etc.

Setting the context for this important strategy therefore must be approached in other ways. One is to point out the strong correlation between fire damage, i.e., to life and property, and fire spread, as was done in Tables 1-1M through 1-1O. Table 1-1P provides more evidence on this point, as it shows that the majority of fatal fire victims, including roughly half the victims of fatal fires in structures other than homes, are located away from the room of fire origin. More than one-fourth of the victims are on another floor from the point of fire origin. What these figures indicate is that there are still many fatal victims of fire who might be saved by strategies that block or delay the passage of fire and smoke between rooms and floors. That's where fire protection design for fire confinement comes in.

Some of the options available for fire confinement are the following:

1. *Use construction barriers to block fire spread between zones*
   - Wall assemblies
   - Ceiling/floor assemblies
   - Barriers between occupied and concealed spaces
   - Firestopping in concealed spaces
   - Exterior barriers to vertical spread between floors
2. *Design doors and windows to block fire spread between zones*
   - Fire door assemblies
   - Window restrictions to block spread between buildings
3. *Separate buildings enough to prevent fire spread between buildings*
4. *Regulate design and operations of ducts to permit shut- off of air movement in fires*
5. *Regulate design and operation of systems for heating, venting, and air conditioning to prevent their serving as mechanisms to transfer smoke and gases into uncontaminated, occupied areas.*

Barriers around concealed spaces are of importance for two reasons. First, fires in concealed spaces cannot hurt people until smoke or flames break out into occupied spaces. Second, fires in occupied spaces may spread faster if they break into concealed spaces, because many interior barriers do not extend into concealed spaces. For example, fire may spread vertically through concealed wall spaces if they are not firestopped at each floor or horizontally through concealed floor/ceiling spaces if the walls do not extend past the suspended ceilings that many buildings have below their main ceilings.

Exterior flame spread can occur in several ways, all of which must be addressed. Flying brands or heat from other fires can ignite exterior materials. Flames from one floor can "lap" up the exterior walls to ignite combustible materials on other floors by radiation from flame fronts.

Large losses of life or property are virtually unknown in buildings that comply with the fire protection requirements of modern codes. This is clear evidence of their effectiveness. Nevertheless, large losses continue to occur because so many buildings are not in compliance with modern codes. A major reason is the frequent exclusion of existing buildings from many requirements by "grandfathering" or a lack of retroactive application of codes. Even where good codes are on the books, enforcement may be hurt by a scarcity of resources in overburdened building and fire departments. And some communities do not routinely update their codes, which can create areas of vulnerability.

Sustained, consistent attention to firesafety is key to the long-term success of an integrated system design for fire protection. Furthermore, universal application is essential to make a substantial impact on the fire problem.

Balanced fire protection really works, but there are no simple, one-time "quick fixes." The installed system must be maintained every day. If this is done, however, such systems will virtually eliminate large losses of life or property. In fact, very large fires usually involve multiple major failures of fire protection design, but sometimes one or two deficiencies can be enough to produce disaster in a building with many excellent features. Remember that fire protection succeeds or fails as a system and is therefore only as sound as its weakest link.

Universality means, in simple terms, that any successful program must go where the fires are, including poor neighborhoods, rural communities, big-city neighborhoods, pre-schoolers, the elderly, and existing buildings. These are among the hardest groups to reach and the most frequently overlooked in the design of programs. But the fight for American firesafety will largely be won or lost in these areas.

EVACUATION OF OCCUPANTS

Most fire protection strategies are designed to slow or divert the movement of smoke and fire, not stop it, so key questions are whether, where, and how to move the occupants. The occupant evacuation strategy, which includes defending in place and safe interior refuges as possibilities, involves both building design principles and behavioral/educational elements. The building design principles include the following:

1. *Two ways out from any location*
2. *Adequate numbers, sizes, and spacing of exits*
3. *Adequate capacity of all escape route parts*
4. *Protection for escape paths*
   - Mark exit paths clearly and light them
   - Restrict fuel loads and finishes in exit paths
   - Enclose stairways
   - Use construction barriers to keep fire out
   - Use smoke control methods to protect atmosphere in exit paths
5. *Escape to outside or to protected places, or adequate defense of places where occupants should remain*
6. *Avoidance of complex or makeshift security systems*

Protection of the exit paths begins with construction barriers to separate hallways from other rooms where fire may begin. Stairways need to be enclosed to separate them from all other spaces.

Exits from any room or area must be adequate for the number of people those exits will serve. This dictates minimum numbers and sizes of exits. Multiple exits from a room must be sufficiently separate to provide two distinct paths from the room to the outside so that escape will still be possible if one escape route is blocked. The paths themselves must not involve long distances, which dictates maximum distances from any occupied room to a stairway access or to the access to some other protected area. Restrictions on the fuel loads and finishes in areas that serve as parts of exit paths also are needed to prevent rapid spread of fire into and through these paths.

Once the building is designed for safe evacuation, the occupants have to be educated to the principles of escape behavior:

1. *Know whether to escape and where to go (e.g., stay in place, go to safe refuge, go outside)*
2. *Know two ways out*
3. *Get out fast*
4. *Practice escape*
5. *Check paths for safety before proceeding*
   - Feel the door
6. *Crawl low under smoke*

It is worth emphasizing the need for practice. Learning the rules of safe escape as slogans is not enough. (That is why it is a matter of concern that three out of every four American households have not developed and rehearsed an escape plan.) If fire occurs, one doesn't have time to make the mistakes that typically occur during learning. To use an analogy, suppose one has read about driving a car and even passed the state's written test. One doesn't want the first time behind the wheel to be a drive to the hospital emergency room. The lack of learned confidence in the key behavior could cost time when it can be least afforded.

Most people have not seen a real hostile fire. They have no idea how fast fire can grow or how bad it can get. They are not familiar with the phenomenon of flashover. Therefore, they spend time they can't afford confirming that there is a fire or gathering up valuables. They also tend to try to leave by their customary route, even in the face of serious fire hazard. Rehearsing safe behaviors is the only way to be sure that they will be used when necessary.

Special mention should be made of the problems posed by unusually vulnerable groups. Small children will need help to escape and are likely, on their own, to think hiding makes them safe. People who are elderly, handicapped, or impaired by substance abuse are likely to have physical or mental limitations that may present a need for help in escaping. Patients in health care facilities and inmates of confinement facilities present the largest problem, as they are large groups that cannot evacuate on their own. Specific plans need to be developed and rehearsed to address these situations.

SYSTEMS APPROACHES FOR PROPERTY CLASSES

In applying the general principles of fire protection, it usually becomes clear that particular property classes have special considerations that must be understood for an effective systems approach. Some of these special considerations are briefly summarized here.

Homes and Garages

Fire death rates in the biggest cities are nearly 50 percent higher than in the small cities, but fire death rates in rural communities of less than 5,000 population are more than 100 percent higher. The unusually high fire risk in rural communities is one of the hidden parts of America's fire problem. The peak rates in very small and very large communities are explained by the fact that poverty rates are highest in these two sizes of communities.

The American South has by far the highest fire death rates in the country (32 percent above the national average in 1984 through 1988). This is in large part because that region has proportionally more rural poverty than any other U.S. region.

Fire death rates are highest for pre-school children and older citizens. Pre-school children have twice the fire death rate of the population as a whole. At the other end, fire death rates begin climbing at age 50 and climb higher and higher as people age. People age 75 and over have fire death rates three times the national average. People age 85 and over have fire death rates four times the national average.

Since fire deaths occur primarily in Homes and Garages, patterns like these are true for those fire deaths and for all fire deaths, as well.

American Community

Community activities often concentrate large numbers of people, creating the risk of large loss of life should a fire occur in the properties that make up the American Community. For this reason, properties in the American Community are generally subject to legally binding fire codes, such as NFPA 101®, *Life Safety Code®*.

Historically, fires resulting in a major loss of life have resulted in important changes in building and fire codes and in standard fire protection or prevention practices. In the early 1900s, four building fires—the Iroquois Theatre in Chicago (1903), the Rhoades Opera House in Boyertown, PA (1908), the Lakeview Grammar School in Collinwood, OH (1908), and the Triangle Shirtwaist Factory in New York City (1911)—were largely responsible for the appointment in 1913 of the NFPA Committee on Safety to Life. The opening summary of the "Origin and Development of *101*" in the current NFPA 101, *Life Safety Code*, states:

> For the first few years of its existence, the Committee devoted its attention to a study of the notable fires involving loss of life and in analyzing the causes of this loss of life. This work led to the preparation of standards for the construction of stairways, fire escapes, etc., for fire drills in various occupancies, and for the construction and arrangement of exit facilities for factories, schools, etc., which form the basis of the present *Code*.

The 1937 fire at the Consolidated School in New London, TX, tragically pointed out the need for state laws to protect public buildings not subject to municipal ordinance and inspection. Then, in the 1940s, a series of multiple-death fires—including those at The Rhythm Club, The Cocoanut Grove, and the La Salle, Canfield, and Winecoff Hotels—focused national attention upon the need for adequate exits and other firesafety features in hotels and public buildings. These fires resulted in major changes to the "Building Exits Code" (as NFPA 101, *Life Safety Code*, was then known) over a period of almost two decades. NFPA 102, *Assembly Seating, Tents, and Membrane Structures*, was the result of still another multiple-death fire of the 1940s—the 1944 Hartford, CT, circus tent fire in which 168 people were killed.

Three hospital fires—St. Anthony's in Effingham, IL, in 1949 (74 killed); Mercy Hospital in Davenport, IA, in 1950 (41 killed); and Hartford Hospital, Hartford, CT, in 1961 (16 killed)—moved hospital administrators and fire prevention officials across the nation to assess the quality of construction and fire protection systems in hospitals.

The Our Lady of the Angels School fire in Chicago on Dec. 1, 1958 probably resulted in the swiftest action in the wake of any major fire since World War II. Within days of the fire, state and local officials throughout the nation ordered fire inspections of schools, and within one year, it was reported that major improvements in life safety had been made in 16,500 schools across the country. Improvements in the frequency and quality of exit drills and inspections, in the storage of combustible supplies, and in the disposal of waste materials were also reported in almost every community where schools were surveyed. This fire and the 1961 Hartford Hospital fire, which killed 16 people, also focused attention on the hazards of combustible ceiling finishes.

The effects of the two largest life-loss fires of recent decades—the Beverly Hills Supper Club fire (165 killed) and the MGM Grand Hotel fire (85 killed)—are still being felt in the fire protection community.

TABLE 1-1Q. ***Care-of-Aged Facility* Fires with at Least Ten Deaths (1970-1989)***

Date	Community	Death Toll
January 9, 1970	Marietta, OH	31
January 14, 1971	Buechel, KY	10
October 19, 1971	Honesdalek, PA	15
January 26, 1972	Cincinnati, OH	10
April 4, 1972	Denmark, WI	10
May 5, 1972	Springfield, IL	10
September 13, 1973	Philadelphia, PA	11
December 4, 1973	Wayne, PA	15
January 30, 1976	Chicago, IL	24
July 23, 1985	Sweet Valley, PA	10
October 5 1989	Norfolk, Va	12

* All were nursing homes except for the convalescent home in Marietta, OH, and the Denmark, WI, and Sweet Valley, PA, facilities, which did not have nursing staff.

Source: NFPA Fire Incident Data Organization.

TABLE 1-1R. ***Boarding Home Fires with at Least Ten Deaths (1979-1989)***

Date	Community	Death Toll
April 1, 1979	Connellsville, PA	10
April 2, 1979	Farmington, MO	25
April 11, 1979	Washington, DC	10
November 11, 1979	Pioneer, OH	14
July 26, 1980	Bradley Beach, NJ	24
January 9, 1981	Keansburg, NJ	31
July 4, 1984	Beverly, MA	15

Source: NFPA Fire Incident Data Organization.

Two recent examples of patterns of major fires drawing focused attention to new problems in the American Community are shown in Tables 1-1Q and 1-1R. During a four-year period from 1970 to 1973, there were eight care-of-aged facility fires, each killing at least ten people and collectively killing 112 people. This rapid succession of catastrophic fatal fires stimulated action in a way that the deadliest nursing-home fire of all time, which occurred in isolation in Ohio on the day after President Kennedy was assassinated, could not. A pattern was found of insufficient fire protection and sprawling, undivided construction based on adding extensions to aging, converted farmhouses. Codes were reexamined, and the new Medicare progam provided clout by tying reimbursement eligibility to code-compliance with NFPA 101, *Life Safety Code*. After one more major incident in 1976, nearly a decade passed before another incident of comparable severity occurred. More recently, a serious 1989 incident in a facility with nursing staff has re-intensified interest in these facilities.

During the period from 1976 through 1985, however, attention shifted to boarding homes, spurred by a rash of major fatal fires in those facilities in 1979 through 1981. Six severe fires, causing 114 deaths in all, with the first three fires all occurring in the same month, commanded attention. During the period from 1979 to 1984, boarding home residents had a risk of dying in a multiple-death fire that was five times the risk for residents of other residential properties. Analysis of these incidents and other smaller fatal fires showed that many of the residents had characteristics of age or chronic mental illness that should have received ongoing medical attention that the facilities were not licensed or equipped to provide. This gap between the fire protection and other features of the facilities and the needs of their occupants was a more difficult problem than the one posed by the nursing home fires because there were fewer mechanisms to enforce codes.

The factors in what came to be called the "board-and-care" home fire problem were all too familiar and can be summarized as an overall lack of basic fire protection provisions. Contributory factors include inadequate means of egress, combustible interior finishes, unenclosed stairways, lack of automatic detection or sprinkler systems, and lack of emergency training for the staff and residents. Many of the facilities were either licensed as something other than a boarding home (such as a hotel) or were unlicensed, "underground" boarding homes. None of the facilities were provided with automatic sprinkler protection.

There is no particular mystery about how to reduce these risks, either. Enclosed stairs, providing two ways out, avoiding the use of combustible interior finishes, compartmentation, providing automatic detection and sprinkler systems, and training staff and residents in emergency procedures all would greatly reduce the risk of multiple deaths if fire occurs.

These analyses and others (such as an NFPA study of two decades of hotel fires causing ten or more deaths, done for Congressional testimony) consistently point to the difficulty of delivering fire protection to and enforcing codes and standards on the facilities that cater to the poorest and most vulnerable populations. Simply creating and adopting good codes and standards is not enough. State and local authorities must adopt them and enforce them, being sure to pay attention to existing buildings, or this knowledge will lack practical impact where it is most needed.

Our American Heritage: Special mention also should be made of the small part of the American Community referred to as our American Heritage. Our American Heritage includes historic buildings, museums, art galleries, and memorial structures. Such structures often attract large numbers of visitors. Since many of these structures are owned and operated by nonprofit charitable organizations, funds for fire protection are often limited. In addition, many historic structures are located in remote areas where public protection is minimal at best. Museums and art galleries incorporate the special hazards of workrooms for restoration and storage. Also, many properties that are not wholly devoted to historical preservation contain major areas of historical importance. The large-loss fire in the Los Angeles Central Library in 1986 was a recent reminder of this point, as a number of unique collections were destroyed, damaged, or endangered.

There is a tendency to forget the vulnerability to fire of these vestiges of the American heritage that were so important to our ancestors and will be important to future generations. The small share of total dollar loss they typically represent does not begin to capture the real loss fires in such facilities can mean to American culture. The actual loss sustained when artifacts and ancient structures burn cannot be measured in dollars alone.

During the 1980s, fires have damaged or destroyed a long list of historic buildings. Included are the Paul Revere house in Boston, MA; the Wayside Inn in Sudbury, MA; Sutter's Mill in Sacramento, CA; the Daniel Boone dwelling in Defiance, MO; the Franklin Roosevelt home in Hyde Park, NY; the Legislative Office Building in Concord, NH; and the John C. Calhoun mansion in Clemson, SC.

Mobile Environment

One development of the past two decades has been an increased use of recreational vehicles, such as campers and trailers for travel, and tents for lodging. This increased usage creates a potential for increased fire hazard in these recreational-type properties, but so far the actual fire experience has been small by comparison to other road vehicles. For example, of the 410,000 road vehicle fires per year that occurred during 1982 to 1986, 5,240 involved all types of all-terrain vehicles (including motorcycles, golf carts, dune buggies, and snowmobiles), 3,460 involved motor homes (not mobile homes, which typically stay in one place), and 1,610 involved travel or camping trailers. Collectively, they represented roughly one out of every 40 road vehicle fires. (Tents and other similar outdoor sleeping quarters contributed less than 400 fires to the structure fire total.)

Another concern that is so far based more on changing activity patterns than on confirmed fire problems is the increasing use of automobile fuels other than gasoline and diesel (e.g., LP-Gas, LNG, and CNG). These new fuels introduce hazards with which the public and authorities are not totally familiar.

Changes in transportation preference, such as the growing use of public transportation, have opened up new problems for fire protection. The fire problems of public transportation center around equipment design and materials, as well as growing dependency on automation.

Transportation of raw materials and finished goods throughout the nation and in U.S. coastal waters by common carriers represents the potential for substantial economic loss if fire destroys the materials transported or the vehicles in which they are being moved. This type of transportation at the interstate level is subject to federal regulation.

Another key area is hazardous materials. This problem not only poses the potential for costly loss, but, more important, carries with it substantial risk to public safety. Hazardous materials often are transported over land, even through highly congested urban communities. The fire record shows an abundance of examples of disastrous accidents involving hazardous materials transportation.

Air transportation is also regulated by the federal government, with regard to the level of firesafety in aircraft design and fire potential following ground impact. Other fire protection concerns associated with air transportation include fuel servicing, aircraft maintenance, design of airport facilities, and aircraft rescue and fire fighting techniques.

Outdoor Environment

A significant part of the great American heritage is that created by nature. Forests and wildlands represent resources which have been recognized nationally in legislation as a part of the American heritage only since the days of Theodore Roosevelt's presidency (1901-1909). Forests and open lands provide raw materials, recreational facilities, and scenic breaks from the urban sprawl.

Great portions of the American landscape, including wildlands, forests, and deserts, are under the control of the U.S. Department of Agriculture. Departments of this federal agency have their own regulations which include fire prevention and suppression programs.

Wildland fires were much in the news in the second half of the 1980s. Environmental trends have produced a succession of years that are among the hottest and dryest on record in the United States. These weather conditions have combined with the expanded scale of activity in the wildland/urban interface to produce a number of very large property-loss fires, as demonstrated in Table 1-1S. Also, during 1979 to 1988, 152 fire fighters lost their lives to brush and forest fires—112 on the fireground and 40 during response or return. That is roughly one out of every eight line-of-duty fire fighter deaths during this period. Together, these figures point to a devastating toll of life and property that deserves the increased level of attention it has recently received through federal/private cooperative efforts, such as the Wildland/Urban Interface Program.

TABLE 1-1S. ***Ten Largest-Loss Brush and Forest Fires (1980-1988)***

Date	Location	Loss in Millions of Current Dollars	Loss in Millions of 1988 Dollars*
July 1, 1985	Camarillo, CA	$75.4	$82.9
November 24, 1980	San Bernardino, CA	$38.0	$54.6
June 22, 1981	Saint Helena, CA	$35.7	$49.2
September 30, 1988	Redding, CA	$45.0	$45.0
May 17, 1985	Bunnell, FL	$40.8	$44.9
November 16, 1980	Los Angeles, CA	$25.0	$35.9
September 12, 1988	Portland, OR	$30.0	$30.0
July 6, 1985	Holliston, CA	$26.2	$28.8
August 30, 1987	Salem, OR	$26.8	$27.9
July 1, 1985	San Luis Obispo, CA	$24.2	$26.6

*Adjusted using the Consumer Price Index.
Source: NFPA Incident Data Organization.

ORGANIZING FOR FIRE PROTECTION

Fire department organization is a critically important element of fire protection. The effectiveness of the organization and management of U.S. fire departments determines whether the more than $10 billion (1987 dollars) in annual expenditures for local fire protection are spent well or badly. More important, it also determines whether the more than one million U.S. fire fighters will be used effectively and safely. Protecting the community and protecting themselves are dual responsibilities of a fire department, and both are more likely when planning and preparation are fully used.

Table 1-1T gives a brief overview of the resource base of local fire departments. Only 10 percent of local fire departments are composed entirely or mostly of career fire fighters, but they protect 58 percent of the population, and 23 percent of all local fire fighters are career fire fighters. The majority of volunteer fire fighters serve in small, rural communities of less than 2,500 population.

Figure 1-1L shows that the workload for fire departments has been climbing in the 1980s, up 23 percent from 1980 to 1988, led by a 42 percent increase in emergency medical calls, which constitute more than half of all fire department calls. (See Figure 1-1M.) Since many communities still do not offer emergency medical service, those that do may find medical calls running at 80 to 90 percent of their calls.

TABLE 1-1T. ***Selected U.S. Local Fire Department Resources***

- 243,200 career fire fighters
- 816,800 volunteer fire fighters
- $10.9 billion in total public expenditures
- 29,700 fire departments
- 50,125 fire stations
- 74,200 pumper trucks (at least 500 gpm)
- 6,630 aerial apparatus

Source: 1987 NFPA Fire Experience Survey and Fire Service Inventory.

Fires constitute roughly one-fifth of all fire department calls, depending on how mutual-aid calls are categorized. (See Figure 1-1M.) But fire calls demand the majority of fire department resource utilization, including stress on people and equipment. The potential to overload a department's total resources still comes primarily from fires.

Hazardous materials calls are a small fraction of the total but a growing one, and they also can involve a lot of resources per incident. False alarms today are more often non-emergency activations of automatic detection systems and less often the malicious box-alarm activations that were of so much concern in the 1960s and 1970s.

The increasingly diverse responsibilities of the modern fire department are both an opportunity and a challenge. On the one hand, more duties mean more value delivered to the community. On the other hand, more duties mean a greater chance of overloading the system with simultaneous major calls. Since the rapid rise in calls for service has occurred during a period of generally declining or level staffing, the risk of overload is real.

A more subtle challenge comes from the need to design an emergency response system to cope with different types of emergencies having very different patterns. Emergency medical calls require swift response with a minimum of equipment and personnel. Fire calls require swift response with a large complement of equipment and personnel and may tend to occur in different parts of the community than those where emergency medical calls are concentrated. These competing bases for decision-making require sophisticated planning.

Organizing Before Fire Occurs

Preparing for fire begins with the promotion of fire prevention and built-in fire protection, which fire departments can do in a variety of ways.

First, fire departments typically are involved as inspectors and sometimes as certifiers for a wide range of fire-related regulations. Sometimes fire departments support building inspectors in their reviews of building code requirements for new and remodeled buildings. More often, fire departments handle ongoing fire code requirements for commercial buildings. Various permit requirements, from the general ones, such as occupancy permits and business licenses, to specific permits for hazardous materials and processes, also may be handled by fire departments. Smoke detector laws are among the few examples where existing homes may be covered by these activities. These code and permit inspections not only empower fire departments to control fixed hazards, they also provide

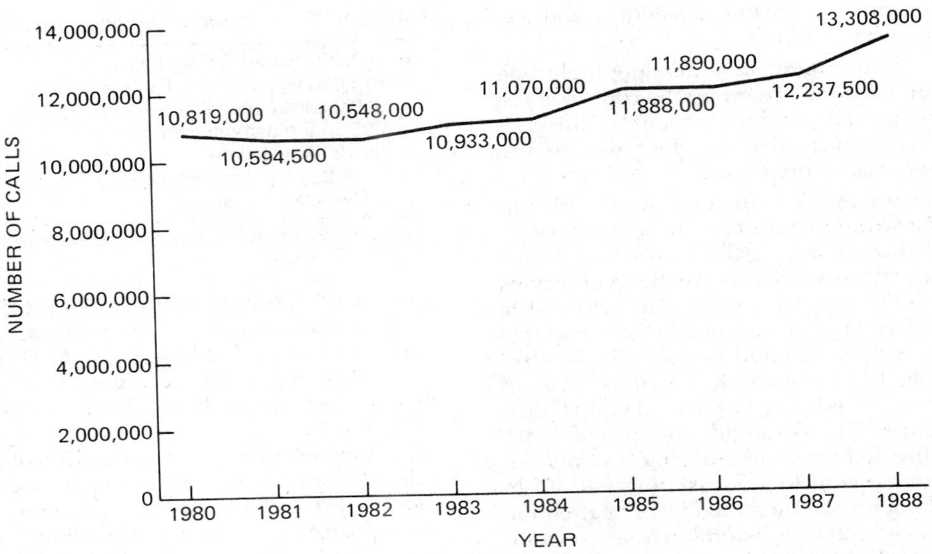

FIG. 1-1L. Fire department emergency calls (1980-1988). (Source: 1980-1988 NFPA Survey)

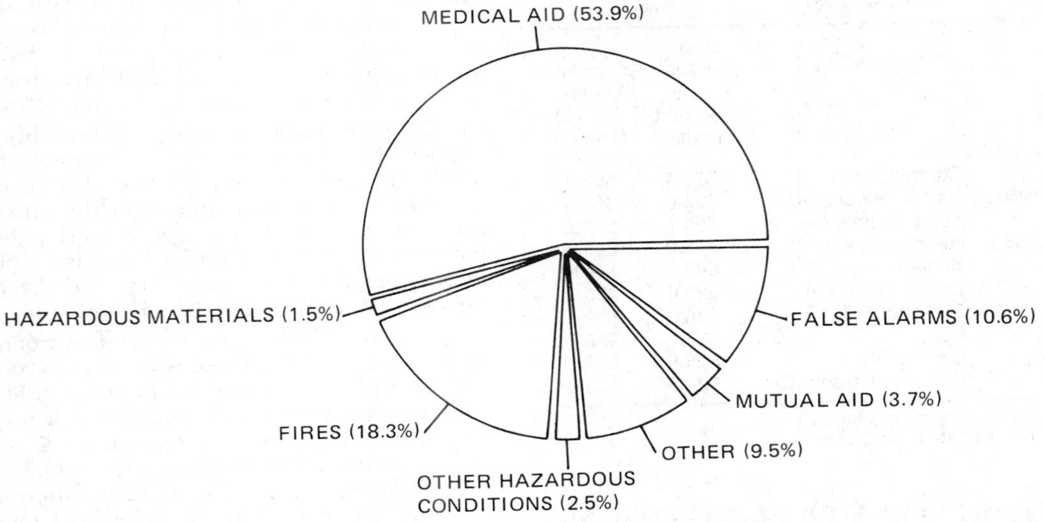

FIG. 1-1M. Fire department calls (1988). (Source: 1988 NFPA Survey)

an excellent opportunity to educate and motivate occupants on general rules of firesafety. Research has shown this educational effect can reduce the frequency of fire significantly. Second, fire departments investigate the causes of fires and pass on what they learn to a community whose attention is focused by the immediacy of a recent tragedy. Support for prosecution of arson cases is the most obvious example of the effect investigations can have. Changes in codes and standards can result from these findings, too.

The fire department also is the one constant in local programs to educate the public about firesafety, even though other groups may have primary authority for some programs. Fire departments can serve as catalysts for, and participants in, programs to counsel juvenile firesetters or to teach firesafety to school children. Fire departments often arrange for extensive programs of firesafety speeches to community groups, increasing community attention to the special programs of Fire Prevention Week in October. Fire departments can circulate firesafety messages by promoting local media use of firesafety public service announcements and by pointing out lessons from news coverage of local fires. Some fire departments are able to pursue even more ambitious programs, such as home fire inspections, using their own resources or acting as change agents to enlist a group of volunteers to do the job.

In summary, the fire department is central to local fire prevention and protection, and fire prevention and protection is central to the duties of the modern fire department.

With regard to preparing for non-fire emergencies, fire departments are increasingly called upon to serve as the local agents for enforcement of federal and state laws to achieve "cradle-to-grave" control of hazardous materials. This may involve regulations on storage, use, and transportation. In many communities, the fire department resources for gathering, processing, and acting on information in this new area are severely lacking. This is one of the areas where local fire departments are most in need of help to do the new jobs that are now expected of them.

Organizing Effectively at Fires

Effective fire suppression requires clear policies and objectives, with tactics that follow logically from those policies. A suppression policy or objective is a concise description of priorities for the use of resources available at a fire. Particularly in properties with large numbers of people, containment of the fire and protection of the large numbers of people outside the fire-involved zone may need first priority, ahead of any efforts to save people and property in areas already involved in fire. Some losses, such as injury or even death of occupants in the room of fire origin, occur so early in a fire that they cannot be consistently prevented by any suppression strategy of the fire department alone.

Objectives imply tasks, such as, forcible entry, rescue, application of water, ventilation, and salvage. And each task implies needs for staffing, equipment, the water delivery system, and response time. These needs are also affected by the level of on-site prevention and protection the community or the particular building has adopted.

For example, suppose a building has a certain size and a set of on-site hazards associated with the kind of business or use at the property. These imply a potential fire size for planning purposes. The potential fire size implies a required number of gallons per minute of water that would be needed to control and suppress that fire. The gallons-per-minute requirement, in turn, implies needs for water pressure and pipe sizes serving the nearest hydrants and for hose sizes and pumping capacity in the fire department apparatus that respond. All these requirements also imply a certain staffing level to handle all the needed fireground activity, including: (1) forcing entry if necessary, (2) finding and evacuate or protect any occupants in certain zones of the building, (3) ventilating as necessary, (4) carrying the needed hoses to the potentially distant fire location, and (5) applying water there until the fire is controlled and extinguished. This process is a task analysis of suppression resources and their use. Implicitly or explicitly, such an analysis should underlie all resource decisions.

It should be clear from this example that on-site sprinkler protection or limitations on quantities of burnable materials on-site can change the potential fire size, which might permit longer response times or smaller personnel complements. However, if anything and everything is permitted on-site, the fire department must plan for the worst, and if they lack the resources to do so, then disaster is there, just waiting to happen.

Pre-incident planning can range from the review and rehearsal of strategy and tactics for a single facility to the elaborate planning required to prepare for natural disasters or civil-defense emergencies. Large-scale planning of the latter type may involve the development and maintenance of multi-agency coordination systems and large-scale incident command and control systems.

Protecting Fire Fighters

Fire fighter deaths in the line of duty have been within 10 percent of 123 every year so far in this decade, except 1980. (See Figure 1-1N.) The highest death tolls occurred during 1980 to 1981 and in the last two years shown, 1987 to 1988, which had the highest death tolls since 1981. The high death tolls of the early part of the decade were led by career fire fighters, but the recent high death tolls have been dominated by volunteers. These totals reflect both immediate and delayed effects of acute injuries or illnesses but do not reflect deaths due to long-term chronic illnesses, such as cancer.

Each year, nearly half of all fire fighter deaths in the line of duty involve heart attacks. These deaths are limited to older fire fighters, at least 38 years of age, and are particularly prevalent in volunteer fire departments, where older fire fighters are more likely to serve. A large fraction of these heart attack deaths involve fire fighters with serious pre-existing health conditions, including arteriosclerosis, hypertension, and previous heart attacks. Since nearly half of all fire fighter deaths involve heart attacks, physical fitness is one of the most important elements of an occupational health and safety program.

Roughly one-fourth of all line-of-duty fire fighter deaths occur during response to, or return from, an emergency call. Vehicle accidents and heart attacks while operating vehicles are both major causes. This scenario affects volunteers more than career fire fighters. Driver training is needed to prevent vehicle accidents. Safe passenger practices must be emphasized because falls from vehicles are also a major cause of fire fighter deaths. Careful attention to the safety of the vehicles themselves, including inspection, maintenance, and repair, is needed, too.

Fire fighter safety on the fireground depends on good equipment. Protective clothing for fire fighters is sometimes referred to as the "protective envelope." Many of the advances in this equipment in recent years have come about as a result of a program of research sponsored by the U.S. Fire Administration. NFPA maintains and regularly updates standards for each type of protective clothing and equipment, including those needed for special environments, such as hazardous material incidents or airplane crash fire rescue.

Fire fighter injuries in the line of duty have been within 4 percent of 100,000 every year this decade, with no particular trend. Injuries at the scene of a fire emergency have declined from 72 percent of the total in 1980 to 60 percent in 1988. One reason the total remained so high was that injuries at the scene of a non-fire emergency have been increasing, from 9 percent of the total in 1981 to 12 percent in 1988.

INFORMATION AND ANALYSIS

Fire protection is becoming increasingly scientific. The advent of sophisticated new data bases, measurement techniques, and computer-based models in just the 1980s has produced a pace of change unlike anything seen before. The *Fire Protection Handbook* has reflected this acceleration of knowledge, as dozens of whole chapters simply did not exist as recently as two editions ago.

There is an increasing demand for hard evidence of the effectiveness and the cost-effectiveness of fire protection features, systems, codes, and standards. New technologies judged by old standards may be admitted too slowly or too quickly to the marketplace. The old "build and burn" approach to gathering information on the fire performance of materials, products, assemblies, buildings, systems, and features is very expensive and is increasingly seen as wasteful when valid alternatives exist.

Validity is the key, however. Fire protection engineers will find themselves having to deal with and control change in the content of their discipline at an ever-increasing rate. Use of unvalidated tests or models can bring dire conse-

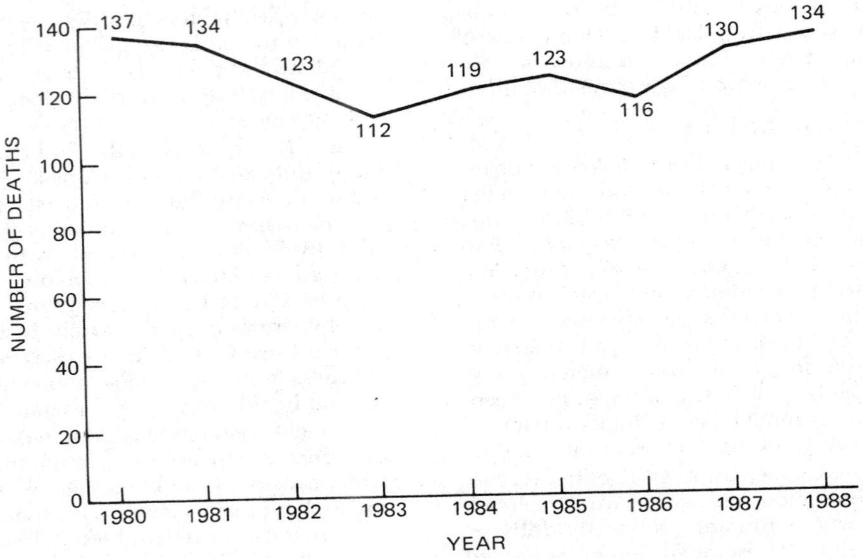

FIG. 1-1N. U.S. fire fighter death trend (1980-1988). (Source: 1980-1988 NFPA FIDO)

quences, but so can a failure to adapt to new techniques. Since the last edition of the *Fire Protection Handbook*, the first edition of the *SFPE Handbook of Fire Protection Engineering*[6] has appeared, published jointly by NFPA and the Society of Fire Protection Engineers. Much of the material within this section receives more elaborate treatment in the *SFPE Handbook*[6], as do the scientific fundamentals that underline these new methods.

If anything demonstrates why this is an exciting and challenging time to be a fire protection engineer, it is the last section of this handbook—a look at the future in real, practical terms.

BIBLIOGRAPHY

References Cited

1. NCFPC, "America Burning," report of the U.S. National Commission on Fire Prevention and Control, 1973, U.S. Government Printing Office, Washington, DC.
2. Fire Analysis Division, "The Deadliest Fires and Explosions of the 1900s," *Fire Journal*, Vol. 82, No. 3 (May/June 1988), pp. 48-54.
3. *Learn Not to Burn* (curriculum and public service announcements), National Fire Protection Association, Quincy, MA, 1987.
4. Hall, J. R., Jr., "U.S. Experience with Smoke Detectors," National Fire Protection Association Fire Analysis and Research Division, Oct. 1989, Quincy, MA.
5. Hall, J. R., Jr., "U.S. Experience with Sprinklers," National Fire Protection Association Fire Analysis and Research Division, Nov. 1989, Quincy, MA.
6. Society of Fire Protection Engineers and National Fire Protection Association, *The SFPE Handbook of Fire Protection Engineering*, 1st ed., SFPE and NFPA, Quincy, MA, 1988.

NFPA Codes, Standards, and Recommended Practices

Reference to the following NFPA codes, standards, and recommended practices will provide further information on the elements of fire protection discussed in this chapter. (See the latest *NFPA Catalog* for availability of current editions of the following documents.)

NFPA 30, *Flammable and Combustible Liquids Code.*

NFPA 54, *National Fuel Gas Code.*

NFPA 58, *Storage and Handling of Liquefied Petroleum Gases.*

NFPA 70, *National Electrical Code.*

NFPA *101, Life Safety Code.*

NFPA 102, *Assembly Seating, Tents, and Membrane Structures.*

Additional Readings

The NFPA Fire Analysis and Research Division, through its "One-Stop Data Shop" program, offers more than a hundred reports and packages that elaborate on the points in this chapter. Most are update annually.

Fahy, R. F., Tremblay, K. J., and Barry, J. J., "Catastrophic Fires of 1989," *Fire Journal*, Vol. 84, No. 4, (July/Aug. 1990), pp. 60-79.

Fahy, R. F. and Barry, J. J., "Why Were the Catastrophic Fires of 1987 So Deadly," *Fire Journal*, Vol. 82, No. 4, (July/August 1988), p. 5.

"FPA Large Fire Analysis for 1986," *Fire Prevention*, No. 212, Sept. 1988, pp. 24-31.

"FPA Large Fire Analysis for 1987," *Fire Prevention*, No. 223, Oct. 1989, pp. 21-28.

Garrison, W. G., "Major Fires and Explosions Analyzed for 30-Year Period," *Hydrocarbon Processing*, Vol. 67, No. 9, 1988, p.4.

Hall, J. R., Jr., "Calculating the Total Cost of Fire in the United States," *Fire Journal*, Vol. 83, No. 2, March 1989, p. 69.

Karter, M. J., Jr., "Fire Loss in the United States in 1988," *Fire Journal*, Sept. 1989.

Taylor, K. T., and Tremblay, K., "Large-Loss Fires in the United States During 1988," *Fire Journal*, Nov. 1989.

"The Deadliest Fires and Explosions of the 1900's," *Fire Journal*, Vol. 82, No. 3, 1988 (May/June), p. 48.

The 1984 Fire Almanac, National Fire Protection Association, Quincy, MA, 1983.

Tudhope, H., "International Fire Losses 1985-1987," *Fire Prevention*, No. 219, May 1989, pp. 34-38.

Wilmot, T., "Fire Statistics—the Way Ahead," *Proceedings* of the Conference on New Technology to Reduce Fire Losses and Costs, Elsevier, New York, 1986, pp. 28-33.

Wilmot, T., "National Fire Costs —A Wasteful Past but a Better Future," *Proceedings* of the First International Symposium on Fire Safety Science, Hemisphere, 1986, pp. 1009-1017.

Woodward, C.D., "Counting the Costs of Fire," *Fire Prevention*, No. 224, Nov.1989, pp. 18-19.

FUNDAMENTALS OF FIRESAFE BUILDING DESIGN

Revised by Dr. Robert W. Fitzgerald

Building design and construction practices have changed significantly during the past century. A little over one hundred years ago, structural steel was unknown, reinforced concrete had not been used in structural framing applications, and the first "high-rise" building had just been built in the United States.

The design professions have also advanced significantly during the past century. The practice of architecture has changed markedly, and techniques of analysis and design that were unknown a century or even a generation ago are available to engineers today. Building design has become a very complex process, with many skills, products, and technologies integrated into its system.

Fire protection has made developmental strides in the building industry similar to those of other professional disciplines. At the turn of the century, conflagrations were a common occurrence in cities. In later years, increased knowledge of fire behavior and building design enabled buildings to be constructed in such a manner that a hostile fire could be confined to the building of origin rather than to the block or larger areas. Progress has continued in the field of fire protection so that, at the present time, knowledge is available that enables a hostile fire to be confined to the room of origin or even to smaller spatial subdivisions in a structure.

DESIGN AND FIRESAFETY

Much activity is taking place today regarding firesafe building design. The general thrust of some developments appears to be directed toward quantification procedures and identification of a rational design methodology to parallel or supplement the traditional "go or no go" specifications approach. Knowledge in the field of fire protection is undergoing development and reorganization that will enable buildings to be designed for firesafety more rationally and efficiently. This section of the handbook identifies the components of a field that is changing dynamically in its analysis and design capabilities.

The material in this chapter identifies the components of a complete firesafety system. Consequently, this organizational structure may be used to analyze the relative safety of both new designs and also of existing buildings.

"America Burning," the report of the National Commission on Fire Prevention and Control,[1] identifies several areas in which building designers create unnecessary hazards, often unwittingly, for the building occupants. In some cases, these unnecessary hazards are the result of oversight or insufficient understanding of the interpretations of test results. In other cases, they are due to a lack of knowledge of firesafety standards.

The Commission's report cites that conscious incorporation of firesafety into buildings too frequently is given minimal attention by the designer and, further, that building designers, and their clients, are often content to meet the minimum safety standards of the local building code. Frequently, both assume incorrectly that the codes provide completely adequate measures, rather than minimal ones, as is the case. In other instances, building owners and occupants see fire as something that will never happen to them, as a risk that they will tolerate because firesafety measures can be costly, or as a risk adequately balanced by the provisions of fire insurance or the availability of public fire protection.

Fortunately, conditions arising from these attitudes need not exist, much less continue. Information is available for design professionals to incorporate a greater measure of fire protection into their designs. Use of fire protection information requires that the various members of the building design team recognize that fire conditions are a legitimate element of their design responsibilities. This requires a greater understanding of the special loadings that fire causes on building features and of the countermeasures that can be incorporated into designs.

Design for building firesafety represents a systematic approach to the six principal types of firesafety strategies identified in Section 1, Chapter 1, "Assessing the Magnitude of the Fire Problem," i.e., prevention, slowing of initial growth and spread, detection, suppression, compartmentation, and evacuation, in the context of the choices that can be built into or installed in a building. This

Robert W. Fitzgerald, P.E., is professor of fire protection engineering and civil engineering at Worcester Polytechnic Institute, Worcester, MA.

section of the handbook describes in general terms the processes required to create such a design. More specific guidance requires joining the general processes described here with the more detailed guidance in later chapters on the specific firesafety strategies. Also, this chapter addresses a seventh building strategy; designing the building to facilitate fire department operations, if and when these are necessary.

Objectives of Firesafe Design

The conscious, integrated process of design for building firesafety, if it is to be effective and economical, must be integrated into the architectural process. All members of the traditional building design team should include, as an integral part of their work, design for emergency fire conditions. The earlier in the design process that firesafety objectives are established, alternative methods of accomplishing those objectives are identified, and engineering design decisions are made, the more effective and economical the final results.

As the first step in the process, setting objectives is part of clearly identifying the specific needs of the client with regard to the function of the building. After the building functions and client needs are understood, the designer must consciously ascertain both the general and the unique conditions that influence the level of fire risk that can be tolerated in the building. The acceptable levels of risk and the focus of the firesafety analysis and design process are concentrated in the following three areas:

1. Life safety.
2. Property protection.
3. Continuity of building operations.

It is difficult to ascertain the level of risk that will be tolerated by the owner, occupants, and community. Often, it is necessary to make a conscious effort to recognize the sensitivity of the occupants, contents, and mission of the building as to the products of combustion. Consequently, firesafety criteria often are not identified in a clear, concise manner that enables the designer to provide appropriate protection for the realization of the design objectives. Unfortunately, it is impossible to provide more than general guidelines that must be considered in building design to assist in the identification of the firesafety objectives in this handbook. Specific objectives must be developed for each individual building.

Life safety: Adequate life safety design for a building is often related only to compliance with the requirements of local building regulations. This may or may not provide sufficient occupant protection, depending upon the particular building function and occupant activities.

The first step of life safety design is to identify the occupant characteristics of the building. What are the physical and mental capabilities of the occupants? What are the range of their activities and locations during the 24-hour, seven-day-a-week periods? Are special considerations needed for certain periods of the day or week? In short, the designer must anticipate the special life safety needs of occupants during the entire period in which they inhabit the building.

The identification of life safety objectives usually is not difficult, but it does require a conscious effort. In addition, it requires an appreciation of the time and extent to which the products of combustion can move through the building. The interaction of the building response to the fire and the actions of its occupants during the fire emergency determines the level of risk that the building design poses.

Property protection: Specific items of property that have a high monetary or other value must be identified in order to protect them adequately in case of fire. In some cases, specially protected areas are needed. In other cases, a duplicate set of vital records in another location may be adequate. The establishment of the firesafety objectives should ascertain if the user of the building has property that requires special fire protection.

Continuity of building operations: The maintenance of operational continuity after a fire is the third major design concern. The amount of "downtime" that can be tolerated before revenues begin to be seriously affected must be identified. Frequently, certain functions or locations are more essential to the continued operation of the building than others. It is important to recognize those areas particularly sensitive to building operations, so that adequate protection is provided for the vital business operations conducted in them. Often, these areas need special attention that is not required throughout the building.

In modern buildings, the value of the contents of a single room may be extremely high. This value may be due to the cost of equipment or records, or to the high cost of business interruption. The sensitivity of equipment and data to the effects of heat, smoke, gases, and water must be addressed. In any event, the designer should protect the specially sensitive rooms from products of a fire originating either inside or outside of the room.

ELEMENTS OF BUILDING FIRESAFETY

Fire Prevention

As noted earlier, the first opportunity to achieve firesafety in a building is through fire (ignition) prevention, which involves separating potential heat sources from potential first fuels. Table 1-2A lists major factors in fire prevention, consisting of major candidate heat sources and ignitable materials, major factors that bring them together, and building practices that can affect the success of prevention.

Most building fires are started by heat sources and ignitable materials that are brought into the building, not built into it. This means the design of the building, from the architect's and builder's standpoint, provides limited potential leverage on the building's future fire experience. The building's owners, managers, and occupants, however, will have numerous opportunities to reduce fire risks through prevention, and they should be urged to do so.

For design purposes, fire prevention will be enhanced by careful observance of codes and standards in the design and installation of the electrical and lighting system, the heating system, and any other major built-in equipment, such as cooking, refrigeration, air conditioning, and clothes washing and drying. Venting systems need to be designed carefully to carry carbon monoxide and potential fuels (e.g., lint) along protected paths. These venting systems will need to be inspected and cleaned regularly.

Protection from lightning and exposure fires will affect the external design of the building, particularly in certain parts of the country, such as areas near wildlands. A fire in one building creates an external fire hazard to neighboring structures by exposing them to heat by radiation,

TABLE 1-2A. *Fire Prevention Factors*

1. Heat Source
   a. Fixed equipment
   b. Portable equipment
   c. Torches and other tools
   d. Smoking materials and associated lighting implements
   e. Explosives
   f. Natural causes
   g. Exposure to other fires
2. Forms and Types of Ignitable Materials
   a. Building materials
   b. Interior and exterior finishes
   c. Contents and furnishings
   d. Stored materials and supplies
   e. Trash, lint, and dust
   f. Combustible or flammable gases or liquids
   g. Volatile solids
3. Factors that Bring Heat and Ignitable Material Together
   a. Arson
   b. Misuse of heat source
   c. Misuse of ignitable material
   d. Mechanical or electrical failure
   e. Design, construction, or installation deficiency
   f. Error in operating equipment
   g. Natural causes
   h. Exposure
4. Practices that Can Affect Prevention Success
   a. Housekeeping
   b. Security
   c. Education of occupants
   d. Control of fuel type, quantity, and distribution

and possibly by convective currents, as well as to the danger of flying brands of the fire. Any or all of these sources of heat transfer may be sufficient to ignite the exposed structure or its contents.

When considering protection from exposure fires, there are two basic types of conditions: (1) exposure to horizontal radiation, and (2) exposure to flames issuing from the roof or top of a burning building in cases where the exposed building is higher than the burning building. Radiation exposure can result from an interior fire where the radiation passes through windows and other openings of the exterior wall. It can also result from the flames issuing from the windows of the burning building or from flames of the burning facade itself. A source for guidelines and data on exposure protection is given in NFPA 80A, *Protection from Exposure Fires.*

Inside the building, design features may make arson or other human-caused fires more or less likely by making security and housekeeping easier or harder to perform. The interaction of the design with these critical support activities should be thought through and planned into the design from the outset.

Preventing Rapid Initial Growth or Spread

The concern here is with slowing the fire to provide other firesafety measures with sufficient time to be effective. A systematic design for this purpose must address all the possible ways that hazard can grow rapidly, e.g., flame spread, rapid growth in rate of heat release or rate of mass release (feeding smoke and toxic gases), unusually toxic gases, unusual corrosivity, quantity of fuel available to feed the fire, and so forth. Each of these can be evaluated separately in terms of the threat to exposed people, property, and mission of the building. The building design should provide effective countermeasures.

Experience has shown that, in a building fire, the most common hazard to humans is from smoke and toxic gases. Roughly two-thirds of all building-related fire deaths are directly related to these products of combustion. Death often results from oxygen deprivation in the bloodstream, caused by the replacement of oxygen in the blood hemoglobin by carbon monoxide. In addition to the danger of carbon monoxide, many other toxic gases that are present in building fires cause a wide range of symptoms, such as headaches, nausea, fatigue, difficult respiration, confusion, and impaired mental functioning.

Smoke, in addition to accompanying toxic and irritant gases, contributes indirectly to a number of deaths. Dense smoke obscures visibility, irritates the eyes, and can cause fear and emotional shock to building occupants. Consequently, the occupant may not be able to identify escape routes and utilize them. (For more information, see Section 3, Chapter 1, "Combustion Products and Their Effects on Life Safety.")

Although heat injuries do not compare in quantity to those caused by inhalation of smoke and toxic gases, they are painful, serious, and cause shock to victims. Statistically, this thermal product of combustion accounts for roughly one-third of fire deaths. In addition to these deaths, the pain and disfigurement caused by non-fatal burns can result in serious, long-term complications.

Property also is affected by the thermal and nonthermal products of combustion, as well as by extinguishing agents. Smoke may damage goods located long distances from the effects of the heat and flames. Fires that are not extinguished quickly often result in considerable water damage to the contents and the structure, unless special measures are incorporated to prevent that damage. It should be noted, however, that the water damage caused in extinguishing a fire rarely exceeds the fire damage resulting from a fire that is not suppressed.

Fast flame spread over finish materials or building contents and vertical propagation of fire are serious concerns. The ability of the fire service to contain or extinguish a fire is diminished significantly if the fire spreads vertically to two or more floors. With a given potential for fire growth, the prevention of vertical fire spread is influenced principally by architectural and structural decisions involving details of compartmentation, which are discussed later.

Designing Countermeasures to Fire Growth

The building firesafety system can be organized around the fire growth and its resulting products of combustion, i.e., flame/heat and smoke/gas. The ease of generation and movement of these products is influenced by the countermeasures provided by the building. The effectiveness of the building firesafety systems determines the speed, quantity, and paths of movement of these products of combustion.

The speed and certainty of fire growth and development in rooms can vary greatly. The contents and interior finish in some rooms are quite safe, and, for this type of situation, it is unlikely that, once ignited, a fire can grow to full involvement of the room. On the other hand, the interior design of other rooms poses a high hazard which, if an ignition were to occur, could lead to an almost certain full room involvement.

The traditional method of describing the fire growth hazard has been through fire loads reflected in use and occupancy classifications. Building types, rather than rooms within buildings, have been grouped with regard to their relative hazard. For example, residential and educational occupancies are considered low hazard, because they normally contain relatively low fuel loads in the rooms. Mercantile buildings are normally a moderate hazard, while certain industrial and storage buildings may be considered highly hazardous because they contain a high fuel load.

This type of classification is a basis for building code requirements, and, historically, it has been quite useful. However, a more detailed look at the fire growth potential within the rooms of a building can be a valuable part of a detailed firesafety design. The fire growth hazard, which identifies the speed and relative likelihood of a fire reaching full room involvement, is a useful base from which to design suppression interventions and to evaluate life safety problems. For example, situations where fast, severe fires will occur may call for automatic sprinkler protection, even though it may not be required by a building code.

The basis for a fire growth hazard analysis is the combustion characteristics in a room. The main factors that influence the likelihood and speed with which full room involvement occurs are: (1) fuel load (i.e., type of materials and their distribution); (2) interior finish of the room; (3) air supply; and (4) size, shape, and construction of the room.

Fire development in a room is neither uniform nor a guaranteed progression from ignition to full room involvement. Fires develop through several stages, called realms. Table 1-2B provides guidance on the technical definition of the realms. Within any realm a fire may continue to grow, or it may be unable to sustain continued development and die down. Table 1-2B includes a rough guide to the approximate flame sizes that may be used to describe the fire size of the realms. It also describes the major factors that influence growth within a realm. Absence of a significant number of the factors would indicate that the fire would self-terminate, rather than continue to develop.

Different rooms pose different levels of risk regarding the likelihood of reaching full room involvement and the time in which fire development takes place. The factors in Table 1-2B provide a general guide to the important types of factors.

If one were to focus on a single event that might be used to represent the relative level of risk posed by the contents and interior finish in a room, it would be the ability of flames to reach the ceiling. The arrangement of contents and types of fuels where it would be difficult for a fire to grow to touch the ceiling pose a relatively low fire growth hazard potential. On the other hand, where furniture combustibility and density will allow a fire to develop to ceiling height, or when combustible interior finish is present, the fire growth hazard potential usually is comparatively high.

Detection and Alarm

Fire detection provisions are needed so that automatic or manual fire suppression will be initiated, any other active fire protection systems will be activated (e.g., automatic fire doors for compartmentation and protection of escape routes), and occupants will have time to move to safe locations, typically outside the building.

TABLE 1-2B. ***Major Factors Influencing Fire Growth***

Realm	Approximate Ranges of Fire Sizes	Major Factors that Influence Growth
1 (Preburning)	Overheat to ignition.	Amount and duration of heat flux. Surface area receiving heat from material ignitability.
2 (Initial Burning)	Ignition to radiation point (10 in. [254 mm] high flame).	Fuel continuity. Material ignitability. Thickness. Surface roughness. Thermal inertia of the fuel.
3 (Vigorous Burning)	Radiation point to enclosure point (10 in. to 5 ft high flame [254 mm to 1.5 m]).	Interior finish. Fuel continuity. Feedback. Material ignitability. Thermal inertia of the fuel. Proximity of flames to walls.
4 (Interactive Burning)	Enclosure point to ceiling point (5 ft. [1.5 m] high flame to flame touching ceiling).	Interior finish. Fuel arrangement. Feedback. Tallness of fuels. Proximity of flames to walls. Ceiling height. Room insulation. Size and location of openings. HVAC operation.
5 (Remote Burning)	Ceiling point to full room involvement.	Fuel arrangement. Ceiling height. Length/width ratio. Room insulation. Size and location of openings. HVAC operations.

One reason for concern over any rapid initial fire growth is that it can shrink the time available after detection for these life— and property—saving responses. Therefore, detection provisions must be designed systematically to reflect the building's other features, its occupants, and its other firesafety features.

For example, smoke is often the first indicator of fire, so a system of automatic detection based on smoke detectors often makes sense. In certain properties or areas, however, detectors based on heat or rate of increase in heat may be more appropriate, because of the types of fires likely to occur in those areas or because of the potential for nonfire activations in those areas. Whatever is chosen, it is important that, for each area of the building, a realistic assessment be made of the implications for response time after the fire is detected and before a lethal or other high-hazard condition develops.

Alarm provisions need not be linked to the detection sensor locations but should be designed systematically to tell occupants what they need to do, based on where they are and on their ability to respond. This would include the possible use of central annunciator panels and monitors to inform responsible staff, voice messages to provide instructions on occupant movements, and direct remote alarms to supervised stations or fire departments. All of these options will have an impact on the time available for some type of response and possibly on the efficiency of that response. Therefore, the timeline provides a quantitative base for analysis and design of this and related building firesafety features.

Automatic Suppression

For more than a century, automatic sprinklers have been the most important single system for automatic control of hostile fires in buildings. Many desirable aesthetic and functional features of buildings that might offer some concern for firesafety because of the fire growth hazard potential can be protected by the installation of a properly designed sprinkler system.

Among the advantages of automatic sprinklers is the fact that they operate directly over a fire and are not affected by smoke, toxic gases, and reduced visibility. In addition, much less water is used because only those sprinklers fused by the heat of the fire operate, particularly if the building is compartmented.

Other automatic extinguishing systems, e.g., carbon dioxide, dry chemical, halon agents, and high-expansion foam, may be used to provide protection for certain portions of buildings or types of occupancies for which they are particularly suited.

An automatic sprinkler system has been the most widely used method of automatically controlling a fire. The major elements for determining the effectiveness of an automatic sprinkler system are: (1) its presence or absence, (2) if present, its reliability (i.e., will water issue from the sprinkler), and (3) if reliable, its design and extinguishing effectiveness.

Although automatic sprinkler systems have a remarkable record of success, it is possible for the system to fail. Often, failure is due to a problem that could have been avoided if appropriate attention had been given at the time of the system's design, installation, or inspection. Table 1-2C describes common failure modes and their causes. During the design stages, these factors should be addressed to increase the probability of successful extinguishment by the sprinkler system.

Compartmentation

Barriers, such as walls, partitions, and floors, separate building spaces. These barriers also delay or prevent fire from propagating from one space to another. In addition, barriers are important features in any fire fighting operation.

The effectiveness of a barrier is dependent upon its inherent fire resistance, the details of construction, and the penetrations, such as doors, windows, ducts, pipe chases, electrical raceways, and grilles. Although the hourly ratings of fire endurance do not represent the time that the barrier can withstand a building fire, unpenetrated rated barriers seem to perform rather well. This may be due to the rather large factor of safety inherent in the codes. On the other hand, it is quite common for rated barriers to fail because of inattention to penetrations. For example, the fire resistance of a rated floor-ceiling assembly can be voided because of large and numerous poke-throughs. The fire resistance of a rated partition is lost when a door is left open.

Fire resistance requirements imposed by the regulatory system often have comparatively little meaning because of inattention to the functional and construction details. To predict field performance of barriers, the penetrations and details of construction must be considered, in addition to the fire endurance of the base construction.

The major function of barriers is to prevent an ignition in an adjacent room or floor. It is useful to classify ignitions in two categories. One is a massive barrier failure, which would occur when a part of the barrier collapses or when a large penetration, such as a door or a large window, is open. When a massive failure occurs, the adjacent room can become fully involved in a short period of time. The second type of failure is a localized penetration failure; this occurs when flames or heat penetrate small poke-throughs or small windows. A localized penetration causes a hot spot to occur. If ignition occurs, this could lead to a full room involvement by the normal fire development progression.

Smoke and gases will move through a building much faster and more easily than flames and heat. The time duration from ignition until a building space is untenable is an important aspect of firesafety, as noted, and the loss of tenability may be due to smoke and gases more often than flames and heat. Therefore, barriers need to be designed and considered as barriers to smoke and gases, too.

In addition to their value as means of containing the fire generally, compartmentation and containment address specific needs for protection, such as structural integrity of the building and escape routes.

The collapse of structural building elements can be a serious life safety hazard. Although statistically it has not resulted in many deaths or injuries to building occupants, structural collapse is a particular hazard to fire fighters. A number of deaths and serious injuries to fire fighters occur each year because of structural failure. While some of these failures result from inherent structural weaknesses, many are the result of renovations to existing buildings that materially, though not obviously, affect the structural integrity of the support elements. A building should not contain surprises of this type for fire fighters.

The potential for structural collapse must be determined. Building codes address this aspect through construction classification requirements. The relationship between

TABLE 1-2C. *Common Automatic Sprinkler Failure Modes*

FAILURE MODE	POTENTIAL CAUSES
Water supply valves are closed when sprinkler fuses.	Inadequate valve supervision. Owner attitude. Maintenance policies.
Water does not reach sprinkler.	Dry pipe accelerator or exhauster malfunctions. Pre-action system malfunctions. Maintenance and inspection inadequate.
Nozzle fails to open when expected.	Fire rate of growth too fast. Temperature of link inappropriate for the area protected. Sprinkler link protected from heat. Sprinkler link painted, taped, bagged, or corroded. Sprinkler skipping.
Water cannot contact fuel (Note: The intent of this failure mode is to ensure that discharge is not interrupted in a manner that will prevent fire control by a sprinkler).	Fuel is protected. High-piled storage is present. New construction (walls, ductwork, ceilings) obstructs water spray.
Water discharge density is not sufficient.	Discharge needs are insufficient for the type of fire and the rate of heat release. Change in combustible contents occurred. Number of sprinklers open is too great for the water supply. Water pressure too low. Water droplet size is inappropriate for the fire size.
Enough water does not continue to flow.	Water supply is inadequate because of original deficiencies, changes in water supply, or changes in the combustible contents. Pumps are inadequate or unreliable. Power supply malfunctions. System is disrupted.

fire severity and fire resistance to collapse are the principal factors.

Collapse can occur when the fire severity exceeds the fire endurance of the structural frame. However, this is comparatively rare. Structural collapse is more commonly associated with deficiencies in construction. These deficiencies are not evident under normal, everyday use of the building. They become a problem when the fire weakens supporting members, triggering a progressive collapse.

Design for Evacuation and Occupant Movement

The design for life safety may involve one or a combination of the following three alternatives: (1) evacuation of the occupants, (2) defending the occupants in place, or (3) providing an effective area of refuge. These alternatives can be evaluated by the likelihood that the building spaces will be tenable for the period of time necessary to achieve the expected level of safety. The criteria for tenability therefore becomes an important part of the design.

Evacuation: The design for building evacuation involves two major components: (1) the availability of an acceptable path or paths for escape, and (2) the effective alerting of the occupants in sufficient time to allow egress before segments of the path of egress become untenable.

Alerting occupants to the existence of a fire is a vital part of the life safety design. A useful performance objective could be to identify that occupants should have at least x minutes to escape from the time they *know* of a fire until the escape route is blocked. To accomplish this, the designer either must ensure that the fire and the movement of its products of combustion will be slow enough to provide that time, or incorporate special provisions into the building to achieve that objective.

Defending in place: The second life safety design alternative is to defend the individual in place. This may be appropriate for occupancies such as hospitals, nursing homes, prisons, and other institutions. It may be an appropriate alternative for other buildings when the size or design may show that evacuation has an unacceptably low likelihood of success. Defend-in-place design also uses a performance criteria of time and tenability levels.

The performance criteria for time might state that the building space should be tenable for y minutes after the start of the fire. The duration for y could be identified as a period much longer than the duration of any possible fire. The definition of tenability may be quite different from that acceptable for evacuation because of the influence of both time and the products of combustion.

Refuge: The third alternative is to design for an area of refuge. This involves occupant movement through the building to specially designed refuge spaces. This type of design is more difficult than either of the other two alternatives because it involves the major design aspects of each. In certain types of buildings this may be a reasonable alternative. However, an evaluation of the effectiveness of the design and its likelihood of success are extremely important.

Life safety design for a building is difficult. It involves more than a provision for emergency egress. It requires attention to who will be using the building and what they will be doing most of the time. Consideration must then be given to communication, the protection of escape routes, and temporary or permanent areas of refuge for a reasonable period of time for the building occupants to achieve safety.

Even occupants familiar with their surroundings often experience difficulty in locating means of egress. The problem is compounded for transients and occasional visitors to the building. Architectural layout and normal circulation patterns are important elements in emergency evacuation. For example, many large office buildings are a maze of offices, storage areas, and meeting rooms. Clearly marked emergency travel routes can enhance life safety features in all buildings.

Design to Help Fire Departments

The protection offered by a community fire department has an important influence on building fire design. Some buildings are designed in a manner that helps the fire department extinguish fires while they are small; others are designed in a manner that hinders a fire department. Rarely does the designer consciously design the building to enable emergency forces to be able to handle the emergency. The following discussion provides some guidelines for building design to enhance the building's ability to allow the fire department to extinguish a fire with minimal threat to life and property.

Ideally, a building is designed so that, should a fire occur, it can be attacked before it extends beyond the room of origin. If that is not possible, the building design and construction features should retard fire spread so that the fire department will encounter a relatively small, easily controllable fire. The major aspects of this part of building design include: (1) fire department notification, (2) agent application, (3) fire extinguishment, (4) ventilation, (5) water supply and use, and (6) water removal. These aspects are discussed briefly to provide guidance for incorporating features into the building that enable departments to be more effective and less harmful to the building.

Fire department notification: The complete chain of events, i.e., (1) detection of the fire, (2) decision to inform the fire department, (3) sending of the message, and (4) correct receipt of the information by the fire department, should be a part of every building firesafety design. It should be designed consciously, rather than left to chance. The time durations for completing the events through agent application are dependent upon the speed of the fire spread. Buildings have been lost because of insufficient attention to the method of notifying the local fire department.

Agent application: The next critical event is fire department application of agent to the fire. This involves three distinct events for its success: (1) arrival at the site, (2) nozzle entrance into the room, and (3) water discharge from the nozzle. Each of these events can be affected by site access considerations in the design.

Ideal exterior accessibility occurs where a building can be approached from all sides by fire department apparatus. This is not always possible. In congested areas, only the sides of buildings facing streets may be accessible. In other areas, topography or constructed obstacles can prevent effective use of apparatus in combating the fire.

Some buildings located some distance from the street make the approach of apparatus difficult. If obstructions or topography prevent apparatus from being located close enough to the building for effective use, such equipment as aerial ladders, elevating platforms, and water tower apparatus are rendered useless. Valuable labor must be expended to carry ground ladders or hand carry hose lines long distances.

The matter of access to buildings has become far more complicated in recent years. The building designer must consider this important aspect in the planning stage. Inadequate attention to site details can place the building in an unnecessarily vulnerable position. If its fire defenses are compromised by preventing adequate fire department access, the building must compensate with more complete internal building protection.

The arrival at the site is only a part of the agent application evaluation. The fire fighters then must be able to enter the building, reach the floor of the fire, and find the involved room or rooms. This is often a time-consuming, difficult task. Considerable attention must be given to the problem of getting fire fighters and equipment to the fire.

Access to the interior of a building can be greatly hampered where large areas exist and where buildings have blank walls, false facades, solar screens, or signs covering a high percentage of exterior walls. Obstacles that prevent ventilation allow smoke to accumulate and obscure fire fighters' vision. Lack of adequate interior access can also delay or prevent fire department rescue of trapped occupants.

Windowless buildings and basement areas present unique fire fighting problems. The lack of natural ventilation facilities, such as windows, contributes to the buildup of dense smoke and intense heat, which hamper fire fighting operations. Fire fighters must attack fires in these spaces despite heat and smoke. This can result in lengthy times for fire extinguishment and greater damage by the products of combustion.

Manual extinguishment: After the time-consuming and sequential events of notification and agent application have transpired, the fire department is ready to fight the fire. The size of fire that is present at the time of agent application determines the fire fighting strategy and likelihood of success of the operation.

Broadly speaking, three categories of fire conditions that may be expected. (1) Comparatively small fires may be extinguished by direct application of water. (2) When the fire is larger than these smaller sizes that can be directly extinguished, the fire is pushed out of the building; i.e., the building is opened (ventilated), and the hose streams drive the fire, heat, and smoke out of the building. (3) Fires that are too large for this operation must be surrounded. All available techniques of ventilation and heat absorption by water evaporation are used; however, the fire area is lost, and the main purpose of this strategy is to protect exposures, both external and internal.

Ventilation: Ventilation is an important fire fighting operation. It involves the removal of smoke, gases, and heat from building spaces. Ventilation of building spaces performs the following important functions:

1. Protection of life by removing or diverting toxic gases and smoke from locations where building occupants must find temporary refuge.
2. Improvement of the environment in the vicinity of the fire by removal of smoke and heat. This enables fire fighters to advance close to the fire to extinguish it with a minimum of time, water, and damage.

3. Control of the spread or direction of fire by setting up air currents that cause the fire to move in a desired direction. In this way, occupants or valuable property can be more readily protected.
4. Provision of release for unburned, combustible gases before they develop a flammable mixture, thus avoiding a backdraft or smoke explosion.

The building designer should be conscious of these important functions of fire ventilation and provide effective means of facilitating venting practices whenever possible. This may involve access panels, movable windows, skylights, or other means of readily opened spaces in case of a fire emergency. Emergency controls on the mechanical equipment may also be an effective means of accomplishing the functions of fire ventilation. Each building has unique features, and, consequently, a unique solution should be incorporated into the design.

Water supply and use: Water is the principal agent used to extinguish building fires. Although other agents may be employed occasionally (e.g., carbon dioxide, dry chemical, foams and surfactants, and halons), water remains the primary extinguishing agent of the fire service. Consequently, the building designer should anticipate the needs of both the fire department and automatic extinguishing systems and provide an adequate supply of water at adequate residual pressure.

Water normally is supplied to the building site by mains that are part of the water distribution system. Few cities can supply a sufficient amount of water at required pressures to every part of the city. Consequently, water supplied to hydrants, standpipes, or sprinklers must be boosted by pumps located on fire department apparatus or in the buildings themselves.

Careful attention must be given to water supply, distribution, and pressure for emergency fire conditions. High-rise buildings are particularly sensitive in this respect because the water pressures that are required depend upon building height. The water-supply needs of large buildings must be given more careful attention.

Fire conditions that require operation of a large number of sprinklers or use of a large number of hose streams can reduce pressure in standpipe and sprinkler systems to the point where residual pressures in the distribution system are affected adversely. Fire department connections for sprinkler and standpipe systems are important components of building fire defenses. The building designer must carefully consider installation details of fire department connections to make sure they will be easily located, readily accessible, and properly marked. Locations should be approved by the local fire department.

Water removal: Watertight floors are important in this respect. Salvage efforts can be greatly affected by the integrity of the floors. Of greater importance is the number and location of floor drains. If interior drains and scuppers are available, salvage teams can effectively remove water with a minimum of damage to the structure.

BIBLIOGRAPHY

References Cited

1. NCFPC, "America Burning," the report of the National Commission on Fire Prevention and Control, 1973, Superintendent of Documents, U.S. Government Printing Office, Washington, DC.

NFPA Codes, Standards, and Recommended Practices

Reference to the following NFPA codes, standards, and recommended practices will provide further information on the fundamentals of firesafe building design discussed in this chapter. (See the latest *NFPA Catalog* for availability of current editions of the following documents.)

NFPA 13, *Installation of Sprinkler Systems.*

NFPA 80A, *Protection from Exposure Fires.*

Additional Reading

Allen, W., "Fire and the Architect—the Communication Problem," *Fire Safety Journal*, Vol. 14, No. 4, 1989, pp. 205-220.

Anchor, R. D., Malhotra, H. L., and Purkiss, J. A., eds., *Proceedings* of the International Conference on Design of Structures Against Fire, Elsevier, New York, 1986.00

Barker, J. A., "Training: The Key to Fire Safety," *Fire Prevention*, No. 224, Nov. 1989, pp. 28-30.

Beck, V. R. and Poon, S. L., "Results from a Cost-Effective Decision-Making Model for Building Fire Safety and Protection," *Fire Safety Journal*, Vol. 13, Nos. 2 & 3, 1988, pp. 197-210.

Cooper, L. Y., "Methods of Designing and Evaluating Facilities for Fire Safety," *NBSIR 85-3118*, 1985, National Bureau of Standards, Gaithersberg, MD.

Coppa & Avery Consultants, *Fire Safety in Building Design: Architectural Design in High-Rise Fire Safety, Fire Transmission, and Fire Protection Systems*, Vance Bibliographies, Monticello, IL, 1980.

Cox, D., "Pre-Fire Planning," *Fire Engineering*, Vol. 138, No. 5, 1985, pp. 51-54.

"Design Guide: Structural Fire Safety—CIBW14 Workshop Report," *Fire Safety Journal*, Vol. 10, No. 2, 1986, pp. 75-138.

Designing Buildings for Fire Safety, National Fire Protection Association, Quincy, MA, 1975.

"Design of Buildings for Fire Safety," *ASTM Special Technical Pub. 685*, American Society for Testing and Materials, Philadelphia, PA, 1979.

"Designing Effective Fire Protection," *Civil Engineering*, Jul.-Aug., 1988, p. 2.

Dunning, G., *Fireproof, Fire-Resistant or Semi-Combustible Designing for Fire Safety in High-Rise Buildings: A Partially Annotated Bibliography*, Vance Bibliographies, Monticello, IL, 1989.

Egan, M. D., *Concepts in Building Firesafety*, R. Krieger, Malabar, FL, 1986.

Fahy, R. F., "Building Fire Simulation Model: An Overview," *Fire Safety Journal*, Vol. 9, No. 2, 1985, pp. 189-203.

Featherstone, J. J., "Use of Computer Technology in Large-Scale Building Fire Protection," *Fire Journal*, Vol. 79, No. 1 (Jan. 1985).

Fire Test Standards, 2nd ed., American Society for Testing and Materials, Philadelphia, PA, 1988.

Gilardi, S. A., "Planning for Fire Safety," *Construction Specifier*, Vol. 41, No. 4 (Apr. 1988), pp. 33-34.

Glon, P. L., "Building Safety—A New Educational Approach," *Building Standards*, Vol. 56, No. 2, 1987, pp. 20-21.

Harmathy, T. Z., "Properties of Building Materials," *SFPE Handbook of Fire Protection Engineering*, National Fire Protection Association, Quincy, MA, 1988.

The Institution of Engineers, *Fire Safety Engineering for Building Structure and Safety*, E. A. Books, Crows Nest, Australia, 1989.

Iwankiw, N., "Design Aids for Fire Protection," *Proceedings—*Solutions in Steel, The National Engineering Conference, AISC, 1986, 23.

Koyamatsu, T. J., "Automatic Fire-Extinguishing Systems," *Building Standards*, Vol. 56, No. 3, 1987, pp. 5-8.

Lerup, C., and Chiang, L., *Learning from Fire: A Fire Protection Primer for Architects*, College of Environmental Design, Berkely, CA, 1977.

Ley, M., *Grading Methods of Building Fire Safety*, M. S. Thesis, Worcester Polytechnic Institute, Worcester, MA 1987.

Luck, H., *et al.*, "New Technologies in Automatic Detection and Supression," *Proceedings* of the Conference on New Technologies to Reduce Fire Losses and Costs, Elsevier, 1986, pp. 211-218.

Malhotra, H. L., *Fire Safety in Buildings*, Building Research Establishment, Borehamwood, England, 1987.

Morikawa, T., Yanai, E., and Nishina, T., "Evaluation of Toxic Gases from Experimental Fires in an Existing Building," 9th Joint Panel Meeting of the UJNR Panel on Fire Research and Safety, *NBSIR 88-3753*, Apr. 1988, National Bureau of Standards, Gaithersburg, MD, pp. 443-454.

Morris, J., "Life Safety and Sprinkler Protection," *Fire Prevention*, No. 209, May 1988, pp.18-21.

Nakamura, H., "Investment Model of Fire Protection Equipment for Office Buildings," *Proceedings* of the First International Symposium on Fire Safety Science, Hemisphere, Washington, DC, 1986, pp. 1019-1028.

Nelson, H. E., "An Engineering Fire Protection Design Assessment System," 9th Joint Panel Meeting of the UJNR Panel on Fire Research and Safety, *NBSIR 88-3753*, Apr. 1988, National Bureau of Standards, Gaithersburg, MD, pp. 157-171.

Nelson, H. E., "Room Fires as a Design Determinate—Revisited," *Fire Technology*, Vol. 26, No. 2 (May 1990), pp. 99-105.

Nelson, H. E., and Walton, W. D., "Basic Structure of the Fire Protection Design Assessment System," *NBSIR 85-3298*, Feb. 1986, National Bureau of Standards, Gaithersburg, MD.

Ow, C. S., and Thin, C. C., "Upgrading Fire Protection in Existing Buildings," *Fire International*, Vol. 12, No. 112 (Aug.-Sept. 1988), pp. 39-40.

Quintiere, J., "Analytical Methods for Firesafety Design," *Fire Technology*, Vol. 24, No. 4, 1988, pp. 333-352.

Rogowski, B. F. W., "Investigating the Contribution to Fire Growth of Combustible Materials Used in Building Components," *Proceedings* of the Conference on New Technology to Reduce Fire Losses and Costs, Elsevier, New York, 1986, pp. 88-105.

Shields, T. J., *Buildings and Fire*, Wiley, New York, 1987.

Singh, J., and Thomas, P. M., "Calculating the Overall Fire Risk in New Building Designs," *Fire Prevention*, No. 224, Nov. 1989, pp. 32-36.

Twilt, L. and Witteveen, J., "Trends in Fire Safety Design of Buildings," *Heron*, Vol. 32, No. 4, 1987, pp. 95-114.

Vance, M., *Fireproof Building: A Bibliography*, Vance Bibliographies, Monticello, IL, 1988.

Volkmann, P., "Three Leading Factors to Save Life and Property," *Fire International*, Vol. 12, No. 109 (Feb.-Mar. 1988), pp. 39-40.

White, A. G., *Fire Safety Workplace Security: A Selected Bibliography*, Vance Bibliographies, Monticello, IL, 1986.

Yurkonis, P. R., "Evaluating the Fire Safety of an Existing Building," *Facilities Management, Operation, and Engineering*, Vol. 16, No. 2, 1989, p. 16.

SYSTEMS CONCEPTS FOR BUILDING FIRESAFETY

Revised by John M. Watts, Jr.

The problem of building firesafety is overwhelming both in the number of variables and in the subsequent difficulty of obtaining detailed data. The established approach of building codes has limitations for many modern structures and for older buildings of historic significance. An alternative approach to dealing with this kind of situation is systems analysis. In the broadest sense, systems analysis is simply the methodical study of an entity as a whole. The objective is a credible process for making the best decision from among the alternatives.

This chapter introduces the concepts of systems and systems thinking. It then briefly describes principles of, and a generalized procedure for, systems analysis. Systems approaches to fire problems are discussed, and the structure and uses of the NFPA firesafety concepts tree are described.

Systems analysis is a way of identifying and using interrelationships of the factors and principles presented in Section 1, Chapter 2, "Fundamentals of Firesafe Building Design." It also encompasses many of the ideas and procedures discussed in Section 10, Chapter 6, "Fire Hazard Assessment," and Section 10, Chapter 7, "Fire Risk Analysis."

SYSTEMS

Russell Ackoff, in his book *Redesigning the Future*,[1] says we are living in the "systems age," an emerging intellectual era which is producing the "post-industrial revolution." Attention has expanded from elements to wholes with interrelated parts, i.e., to systems. Phenomena are now thought of as parts of a larger system rather than in terms of their components. It is recognized that optimizing the components does not optimize the system, in the same way that an all-star team does not play as well as the league champion.

John M. Watts, Jr., Ph.D., is director of the Fire Safety Institute, a not-for-profit information, research, and educational corporation, located in Middlebury, VT. He also serves as editor of NFPA's quarterly technical journal, *Fire Technology*.

The concept of a system has many common examples, such as automobile exhaust system, digestive system, democratic system of government, sewer system, ecosystem, fire suppression system, etc.

By definition a system is a set of components that work together for an overall objective. Sprinklers, piping, alarm valve, and water supply are components of an automatic sprinkler system, with an overall objective of fire control. Similarly, fire resistance, fire detection, and automatic sprinklers may be thought of as components of a system, the objective of which is to provide an acceptable level of building firesafety.

In a systems analysis, it is important that the system being studied is rigorously defined, i.e., in systematic fashion. This enables one to apply the concept of a system to many activities that are not ordinarily thought of as systems, e.g., a ship at sea, supermarket checkout, a warehouse, bidding for a contract, a family, the world,* etc.

Characteristics of Systems

A system can be highly complex. This often makes a rigorous definition difficult. All systems, however, have certain common characteristics that, if properly identified, will usually define the system adequately. These characteristics are:

1. Boundary,
2. Input and output,
3. Variables, and
4. Structure.

The interrelationships among these characteristics are illustrated in Figure 1-3A.

Boundary: The difference between systems analysis and a more generalized systems approach is the difference between "closed" and "open" systems.[2] In systems analysis, a system is considered to be bounded in such a manner that the system behavior of interest is generated entirely within the boundary; thus, it is a closed system.

*Indeed, the world has been systematically analyzed. See *World Dynamics,* by J. W. Forrester, Wright-Allen, Cambridge, MA, 1973.

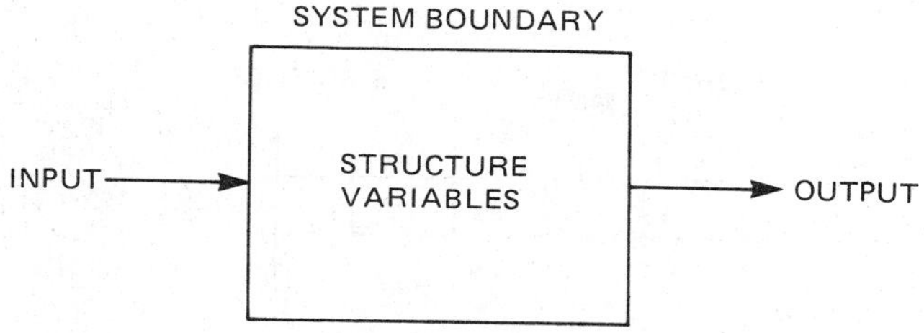

FIG. 1-3A. Characteristics of systems.

This does not mean the system does not interact with its environment, but outside events do not themselves govern the behavior of the system; i.e., there is no feedback mechanism between the system and external elements. For example, power failure is an event that may affect a firesafety system, but electrical generation and distribution may not be included within the system boundary. In building firesafety, the boundary consists of the structure and its contents. When fire service personnel enter the building, they become part of the system.

Input and output: A system that has input and output is a dynamic system. The system must act in some manner to convert the input to output. The conversion mechanism is the essence of the system. Building firesafety is a dynamic system, with time varying interactions between the fire and structure. The input is an ignition scenario and the output in some measure of success of the system, e.g., limitation of fire spread.

Variables: Certain components of the system may be under control of the designer or decisionmaker. These are the variables of the system. A system usually consists of a very large number of variables, many of which defy quantification. And the complexity of the system is a rapidly increasing function of the number of variables. There is very large number of decision variables in building firesafety design, e.g., physical and chemical properties of the materials of the building and its contents, geometrical features, attributes of detection and suppression systems, etc. The objective of a systems analysis is to arrive at the most desirable values of these variables.

Structure: System structure is the overall framework relating the variables within the system boundary. There are many basic structural forms that systems may take. Networks are a common structure of many systems. Among the various types of network structures are series-parallel, source-sink, decision, hierarchical, time sequence, logic, information flow, open-loop-closed-loop, and signal flow.

This list is not exhaustive, nor are the items mutually exclusive. Most systems are a combination of several such basic structures. Later in this chapter, of a hierarchical logic network approach to building firesafety—the firesafety concepts tree—is discussed.

SYSTEMS ANALYSIS

Systems analysis evolved in the 1950s as a popular spinoff of space and defense research. It is not a well-defined discipline in that it combines elements of many principles of scientific study with less formalized craftsmanship. The term "systems analysis" is used to describe a careful, methodical, comprehensive, and well-documented step-by-step approach to solving a problem about a system.

Systems analysis is both systemic and systematic. These two important terms are derived from the concept of a system. Systemic refers to the wholeness of things in an inclusive sense. For example, a systemic disease is one that afflicts the whole body. A systemic approach to firesafety is one that considers every part of the system. The alternative to a systemic approach is to look at only one piece of a problem at a time, ignoring the mechanisms by which the pieces are interrelated. This is sometimes referred to as disjoint incrementalism and is an all-too-frequent approach to firesafety.

Systematic refers to being methodical or acting according to a plan and not casually or at random. Repeatable methodology is the key characteristic of science, and science is the most acceptable way of increasing knowledge. A systematic approach establishes a basis for widespread acceptance, as opposed to a visceral approach. Systems analysis is therefore methodical or systematic, and inclusive or systemic. Thus, a systems analysis is a methodology applied to the whole system. (See Figure 1-3B.) This is also referred to as a systems approach.

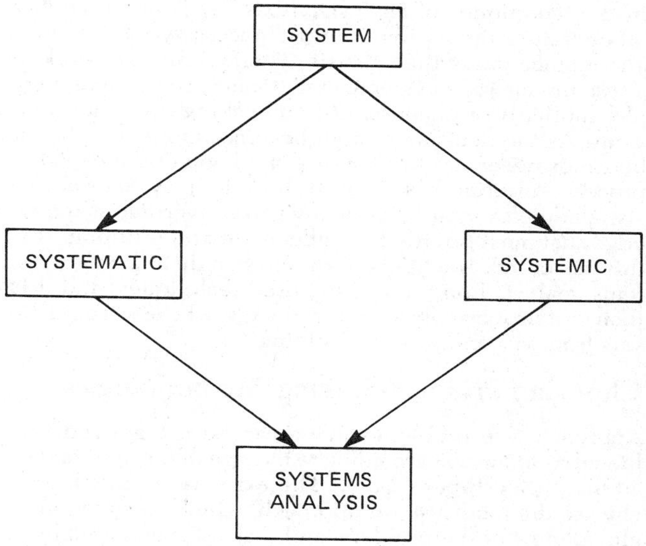

FIG. 1-3B. Systems analysis.

Systems Analysis and Scientific Method

Scientific method may be thought of as a systems concept. However, it is generally applied to "hard" rather than "soft" systems. Hard systems have components whose interrelationships are well defined and easily quantified, while soft systems contain inexact expressions. It is the need to resolve problems relating to soft systems that has given prominence to systems analysis.

Intellectual activities, such as science and systems analysis, may be represented on a scale of reproducibility. This scale is defined by its endpoints. At one end of the scale is pure science, which is characterized by its 100 percent reproducibility. At the other end of the scale is pure art, which has a reproducibility of zero (e.g., the Mona Lisa). In between these points lie the problem-solving activities of engineering and systems analysis, with engineering being closer to science and systems analysis closer to art. (See Figure 1-3C.)

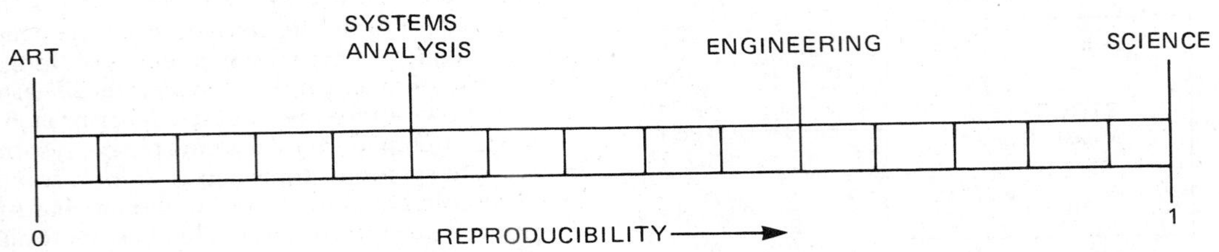

FIG. 1-3C. Problem-solving methodologies.

The Craft of Systems Analysis

Systems analysis may be defined as the systematic application of knowledge, skills, logic, and intuition to solve a problem about a system. Knowledge of the system undergoing analysis is required, as well as knowledge of techniques appropriate to the analysis. A systems analysis is often a multidisciplinary team project so that the knowledge of several individuals can be brought together. Skills in the techniques of analysis are as necessary as in any other craft or profession. Logic is necessary for the overall organization of the analysis. The logical framework of a systems analysis is essentially the same used by most people implicitly or unconsciously in making everyday decisions. As the decision system becomes more complex, it becomes necessary to formalize the logic of the decision process. Intuition has a significant role in systems analysis. A complex system has many gaps in verifiable knowledge that must be filled by judgement and intuition. It is this use of judgement and intuition that distinguishes systems analysis from more structured techniques, and it is their systematic application that distinguishes systems analysis from visceral problem-solving.

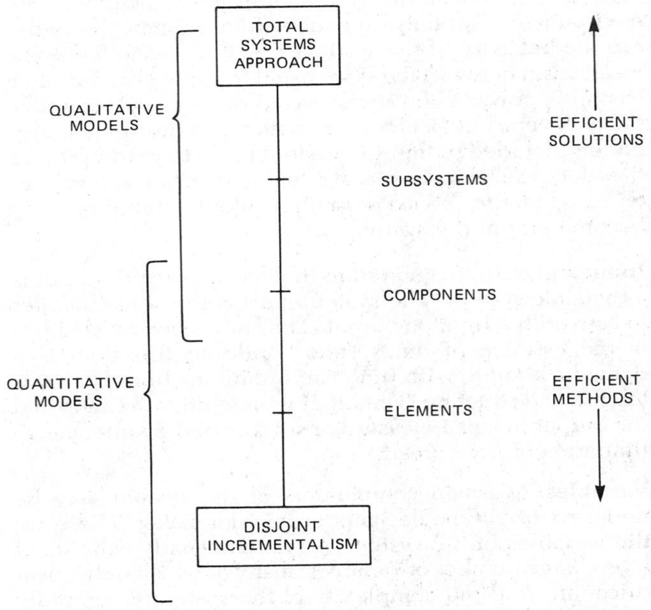

FIG. 1-3D. Problem-solving hierarchy.

Choosing Problem-Solving Methodologies

Approaches to problem-solving can be categorized in a hierarchical fashion according to the size of the system they address. (See Figure 1-3D.) The extremes of this hierarchy are the total systems approach, which takes the most global view of the problem, and disjoint incrementalism, which addresses only the smallest pieces, individually, without consideration of their interrelationships. Most present-day firesafety practices fall between these end points.

The systemic approach yields the most efficient solution, but requires a great deal of time-consuming analysis. It is desirable to move as far up this scale as is feasible. Where deterministic physical modeling can take one only so far toward a total systems approach, it is necessary to consider alternative mathematical models, such as probability theory, decision analysis, utility theory, etc., and, beyond their limits, to consider more qualitative models, such as heuristics, delphi, expert systems, etc.

Systems Analysis—A Procedure

Most descriptions of systems analysis outline a sequence of tasks to be performed in a more or less iterative fashion. Many of these schemes are quite varied and complex, yet may include similar components. Systems analyses tend to take their character from the analyst and from the problem addressed; hence, they may bear little resemblance to each other in detail. Specific techniques differ from study to study, and there may be only a thread of similarity that ties these studies together. The most elementary representation of this thread comprises three basic steps: (1) definition, (2) modeling, and (3) evaluation. This generalized three-part procedure begins with an analysis not of the problem but of the system within which the problem occurs. The second step is the synthesis of system activity into a conceptual model, and the third step is a comparison and questioning of the responsiveness of the model.

Definition: Problem definition is the first and most important step in a systems analysis. It is difficult to get a right answer from the wrong problem. Concise definition of the problem is the output of this initial step.

The problem definition process should provide a basis for understanding, communication, and verification. Real-world problems (as opposed to textbook theory) evolve in an amorphous form. It is necessary to reformulate the problem into a form amenable to analysis, and this requires a detailed understanding of the system. Thus, problem definition has two parts: (1) rigorous study of the system, and (2) development of a well-defined statement of the problem.

Problem definition usually includes identification of the scope, objectives, measures of effectiveness, variables, and interrelationships. The scope limits the commitment to the problem within the system and includes assumptions and constraints. Objectives are the desirable output of the system, while measures of effectiveness identify the degree to which objectives are achieved. The variables are those factors that can be manipulated to achieve objectives, and the interrelationships identify the known interactions of the variables within the system structure. Thorough documentation of the problem definition is essential to communication and validation of the analysis.

Modeling: Modeling is the formal representation of the understanding gained of the system in the problem definition step. This representation takes the form of a symbolic model of the system. It may be diagrammatic, mathematical, computerized, or, often, some combination of all three. The behavior of the system may be conveniently studied by manipulating the model rather than manipulating the system itself. For such a study to have validity, the model must closely represent the system's behavior of interest. However, the more the model is like the system, the more difficult it is to manipulate (like the system itself); therefore, approximations and simplifying assumptions are required to make the model tractable. Thus, an acceptable model must be sufficiently analogous to the real problem to evaluate alternatives with the accuracy to permit sound decisions, yet simple enough to be amenable to analysis.

Evaluation: The evaluation step selects, analyzes, and compares alternative courses of action. This is accomplished by manipulating the system model to maximize achievement of objectives. The analyst needs to maintain the perspective that it is the problem, not the model, that is important. The primary purpose of the evaluation step is to provide relatively simple rules that the decisionmaker can use to eliminate inferior alternatives. In a comprehensive study, evaluation also includes implementation of the best alternative and monitoring to ensure that expected results are actually realized.

Any scientific investigation is essentially an iterative process, and these steps are not always followed sequentially but, more often, cyclically. The modeling process may suggest refinements to the problem definition, while evaluation may suggest revisions to the model or additions to the problem definition. (See Figure 1-3E.)

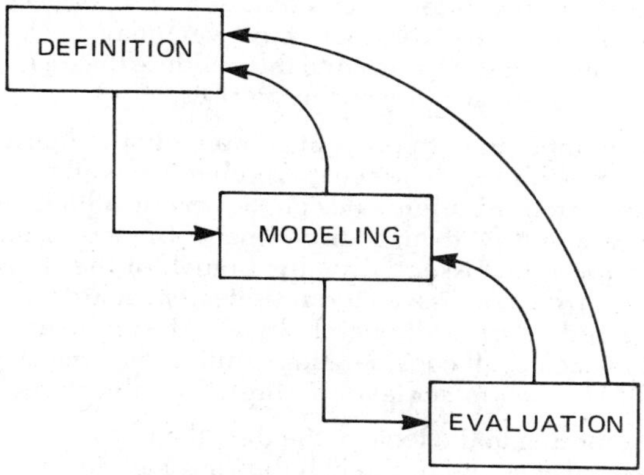

FIG. 1-3E. Basic steps and Cycles of a systems analysis.

Documentation

A professional systems analysis requires that, as the study proceeds, a record be made of assumptions, data, and parameter estimates, and why they were chosen; model structure and details; steps in the analysis; relevant constraints; results; sensitivity tests; validation; etc. This documentation is invaluable to the analyst, as well as to those who may be considering use of the results.

Clear and complete documentation enhances confidence in the analysis; its absence inevitably carries with it the opposite effect. No approach to building firesafety should be taken seriously, unless its development has left an adequate "paper trail."

SYSTEMS APPROACHES APPLIED TO THE FIRE PROBLEM

Firesafety can be incorporated into building design by three different methods:

1. Require design and construction to conform to requirements in specification-oriented building codes and standards. The requirements are based on fire experiences and are generally strict.
2. Use performance codes to overcome the inflexibility of specification codes. A major drawback to this approach is that building components are considered on an *ad hoc* basis. The definition of firesafety performance of the separate components and the measurement of that performance are difficult to obtain. Also, when considering the entire building as a system, the satisfactory physical performance of individual components does not ensure the desired level of safety for the building as a whole, as some components have a higher probability of successful performance than others.
3. Use systems analysis that incorporates an integrated method, including the aesthetic, functional, structural, electrical, and mechanical subsystems. Buildings can be designed for firesafety through the use of systems analysis rather than by strict compliance with codes. This approach to firesafety requires a higher degree of professional technology; however, it can achieve greater level of cost effectiveness than strict enforcement of codes, and most often allows greater flexibility.

Evaluation of current levels of building firesafety, and the recommendations for upgrading, can only be accomplished properly if the impact of a change in a structure can be evaluated in context. For example, if a building is to be rehabilitated, which requires bringing it up to code level, does this mean strict compliance, or are there alternative means to achieve the same level of firesafety? It is also desirable to consider all other factors bearing on the "firesafety system" when evaluating the impace of a code or standard change on the level of firesafety. In addition, *before* catastrophic fires occur, it is highly desirable to determine the impact of new processes and materials on the level of firesafety provided through compliance with a given code or standard.

FIRESAFETY CONCEPTS TREE

The firesafety concepts tree is the graphic form of the consensus of the NFPA Committee on Systems Concepts for Fire Protection in Structures. It represents the deliberations and professional judgements of this committee over many years. It is not, and is not represented as, the only manner in which the factors involved in firesafety can be organized.

A Qualitative Approach

During the 1960s there was a growing awareness that modern high-rise buildings designed to building codes and standards contained potential firesafety weaknesses. Various researchers and organizations, principally the U.S.General Services Administration (GSA) and the National Research Council of Canada (NRCC), identified aspects of weakness. Studies identifying the time of evacuation of high-rise buildings were published, and the problems relating to air movement in tall buildings were identified. Careful analysis of two fires in New York City, at One New York Plaza[3] and 919 Third Avenue,[4] focused attention even more clearly on the problem areas.

About the same time, NFPA formed a committee on high-rise structures. After initial meetings, this committee determined that its contribution should not be in developing standards for high-rise construction, but rather in identifying a system of firesafety for all buildings. After many modifications, the firesafety concepts tree, shown in Figures 1-3F through 1-3J, evolved.

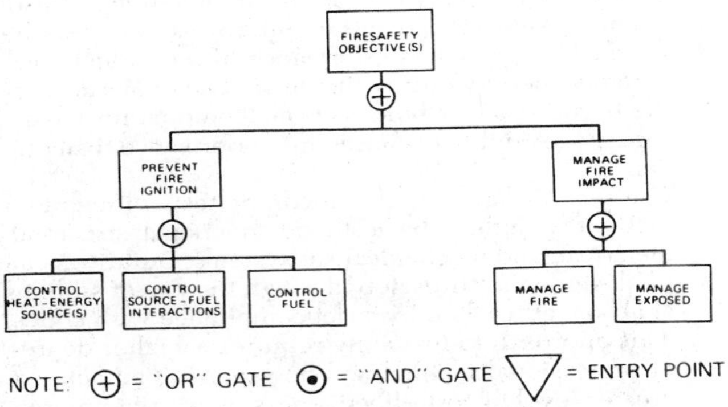

FIG. 1-3F. The principal branches of the firesafety concepts tree, as developed by the NFPA Committee on System Concepts for Fire Protection in Structures. Note the symbols at the bottom of the illustration. They apply equally to the tree branches shown in Figures 1-3G through 1-3J.

Structure of the Tree

The firesafety concepts tree, as presented in Figures 1-3F through 1-3J, shows the elements that must be considered in building firesafety and the interrelationship among those elements. It enables a building to be analyzed or designed by progressively moving through the various concepts in a logical manner. Its degree of success depends upon how completely each level is satisfied. Lower levels on the tree, however, do not represent a lower level of importance or performance; they represent a means for achieving the next higher level. In addition to the material in this chapter, see NFPA 550, *Firesafety Concepts Tree*, for detailed guidance in the use of the tree.

Firesafety Objective(s)

Use of the firesafety concepts tree requires that the firesafety objectives (goals) be clearly identified. These objectives describe the degree to which the building should protect its occupants, property and contents, continuity of operations, and neighbors. The objectives should be quantified wherever possible, rather than stated in broad or general terms.

The life safety objective, for example, might state that all occupants be safeguarded against the intolerable or untenable effects of the fire. It may be further stated that emergency personnel, such as fire fighters, who may be expected to stay in areas considered too dangerous for the occupants, should be protected against possible collapse of the building or entrapment. A range of specific life safety objectives may be appropriate for different types of occupancies. Nursing home requirements, for example, are vastly different from those for offices, and both differ from industrial occupancies or storage facilities.

To identify the property protection objectives, the building designer must ask a number of questions. For example, does a portion of the property have a significantly higher value than the rest of the property? If destroyed, which property cannot be replaced and which would significantly affect continued operations? Are there specific functions at the site that are vital to continuity of operations? Further, are there functions that can be performed at other sites on an emergency basis? Proper identification of factors such as these enable the designer to tailor the design to reflect the client's needs.

"Prevent Fire Ignition" or "Manage Fire Impact"

The firesafety concepts tree provides the logic required to achieve firesafety; i.e., it provides conditions whereby the firesafety objectives can be satisfied, but it does not provide the minimum condition required to achieve those objectives. Thus, according to the tree, the firesafety objectives can be met if fire ignition can be prevented or if, given ignition, the fire can be managed. This logical "OR" function is represented by the symbol (+) under Firesafety Objectives in Figure 1-3F.

The "prevent fire ignition" branch of Figure 1-3G (and associated performance standards) essentially forms a fire prevention code. Most of the concepts described in this branch require continuous monitoring for success. Consequently, the responsibility for satisfactorily achieving the goal of fire prevention is essentially an owner/occupant responsibility. The designer, however, may be able to incorporate certain features into the building that may assist the owner/occupant in preventing fires.

It is impossible to prevent completely the ignition of fires in a building. Therefore, to reach the overall firesafety objective, from a building design viewpoint, a high degree of success in the "manage fire impact" branch assumes a significant role. Essentially, this branch of the firesafety concepts tree (and associated firesafety standards) may be considered as a building code by the design team. After ignition occurs, all considerations shift to the "manage fire impact" branch to achieve the firesafety objectives.

According to the logic of the tree, the impact of the fire can be managed either through the "manage fire" or "manage exposed" branches. (See Figure 1-3F.) The "OR" (+) gate indicates that the objectives may be reached through

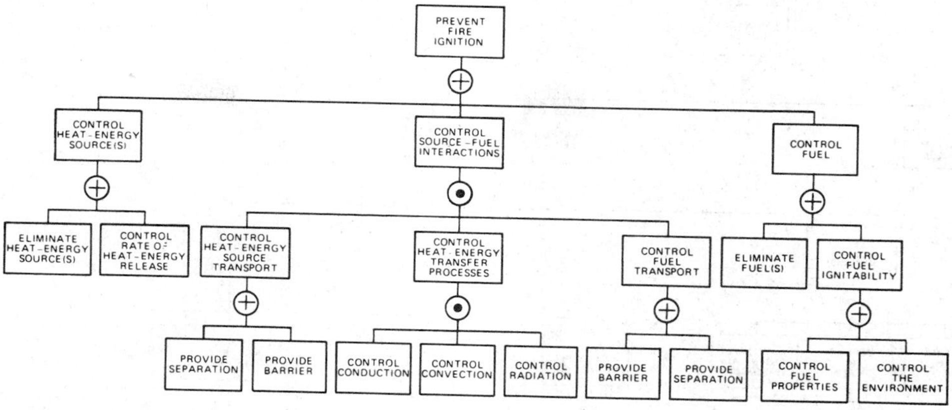

FIG. 1-3G. ***Components of the "prevent fire ignition" branch of the concepts tree.***

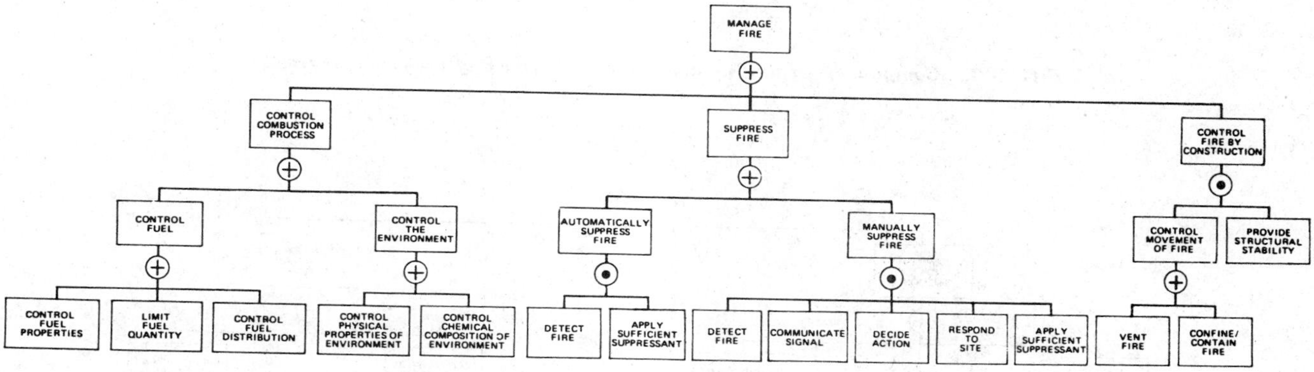

FIG.1-3H. ***Components of the "manage fire" branch of the concepts tree.***

either or both design branches, as long as the avenue selected completely satisfies the firesafety objective. Naturally, it is acceptable to do both, which will increase the probability of success over using one branch only.

Through the "manage fire" branch, the firesafety objectives can be achieved by managing the fire itself. Figure 1-3H shows that this can be accomplished by: (1) controlling the combustion process, (2) suppressing the fire, or (3) controlling the fire by construction. Here, again, any one of these branches of the tree will satisfy the "manage fire" concept. For example, in some fires, success is achieved where the building construction controlled the fire. In other fires, success is achieved by controlling the combustion process, either through control of the fuel or the environment.

The "suppress fire" event and its branches are also shown in Figure 1-3H. In this figure, the symbol (·) represents a logical "AND" gate, and signifies that all of the elements in the level immediately below the gate are necessary to achieve the concept above the gate. To accomplish the automatic suppression concept, for example, both concepts, i.e., detecting the fire and applying sufficient suppressant, are necessary. Similarly, to manually suppress the fire, five concepts must occur. The omission of any single concept is sufficient to break the chain and cause the failure of the suppression concept.

In considering the "control fire by construction" concept, structural integrity must be provided, and the movement of the fire itself must be controlled. As shown in Figure 1-3H, this can be accomplished either by venting, confining, or containing the fire.

As shown in Figure 1-3I, the fire impact can be lessened by managing the "exposed," i.e., people, property, or functions, depending upon the design aspects being considered. In considering the "manage exposed" branch, it can be successful either by limiting the amount exposed or by safeguarding the exposed. For example, the number of people as well as the amount or type of property in a space may be restricted. Often, this is impractical. If this is the case, the objectives can still be met by incorporating design features to safeguard the exposed.

The exposed people or property may be safeguarded either by moving them to a safe area of refuge or by defending them in place. For example, people in institutionalized occupancies, such as hospitals, nursing homes, or prisons, must generally be defended in place. To do this, the "defend exposed in place" branch shown in Figure 1-3I would be considered. On the other hand, alert, mobile individuals, such as those expected in offices or schools, could be moved to safeguard them from fire exposure on either a short-term or long-range basis, depending upon other key design elements. Figure 1-3I illustrates the concepts that must be achieved if firesafety objectives are to be met when managing the exposed property and people.

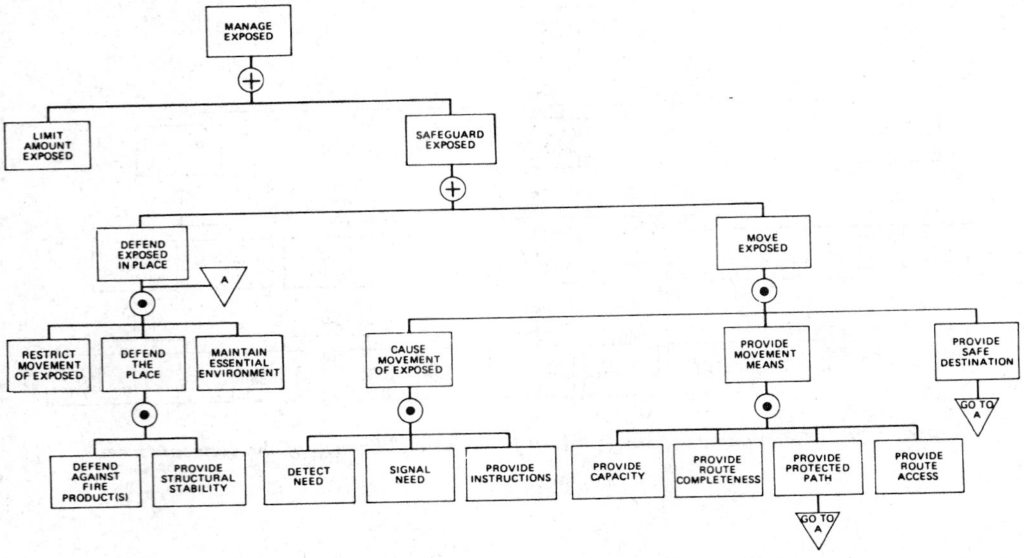

FIG. 1-3I. Components of the "manage exposed" branch of the concepts tree.

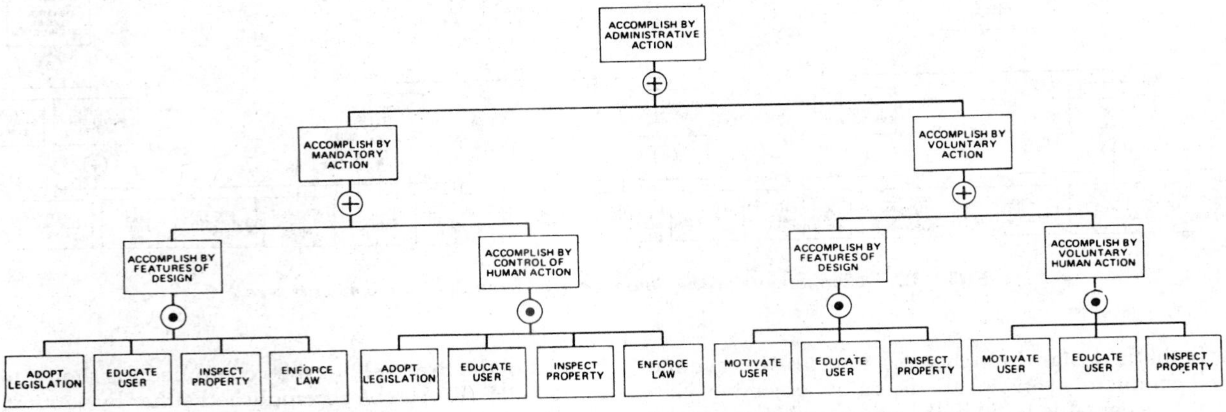

FIG. 1-3J. Components of the "administrative action guide"—a third dimension to the concepts tree.

Administration Action Guide

The administration action guide (see Figure 1-3J) organizes into a logical structure those actions that might be taken to carry out the elements of the basic firesafety concepts tree shown in Figures 1-3F through 1-3I. It can be thought of as the third dimension of the tree and, as such, a checklist of actions that might be taken. For example, "provide safe destination" (see Figure 1-3I) could be accomplished through code enforcement ("mandatory action") or public firesafety education ("voluntary action").

USE OF THE FIRESAFETY CONCEPTS TREE

The firesafety concepts tree can be adapted for a number of different functions. A particularly useful aspect of the tree is the descriptive feature of important code requirements.

Fire Prevention/Building Codes

The "prevent fire ignition" branch is essentially a fire prevention code. (See Figure 1-3G.) It describes and shows the interrelationships among the essential features of such a code.

The "manage fire impact" branch is essentially a building code. (See Figures 1-3F, 1-3H, and 1-3I.) It enables the code writer to organize the important elements of the building code and to identify their interrelationships. An important feature for building codes, for example, is the subject of alternatives, or "tradeoffs." The only legitimate areas in which alternatives can be established is among those factors below an "OR" (+) gate in the decision tree. The factors below an "AND" (·) gate are necessary and thus cannot be considered as alternatives. It is up to the authority having jurisdiction to decide what levels of protection are adequate to be allowed as tradeoffs for code or tree-mandated items.

Building Analysis

The firesafety concepts tree provides a framework to support firesafety analyses. It is a fundamental necessity that objectives be identified and agreed upon before they can be addressed. Once the fundamental firesafety objectives for a particular building are identified, the designer/architect can analyze the building's design by progressing successively through the various levels of concepts. Redundancies and deficiencies can be identified specifically and evaluated. Often, the weaknesses become so apparent that specific and effective solutions can be devised economically.

The building analysis, supported by the framework of the tree, has among its advantages the capacity to consider separately fire prevention considerations and the requirements involved in managing the fire impact in the event an ignition occurs. This definite separation of events can enable the owner/occupant to take immediate, corrective action for fire prevention, using thoughtful and effective methods.

Building Design

The firesafety concepts tree can be employed effectively in building design. If the architect incorporates the tree during the preliminary planning phase of design, many important decisions and alternatives can be defined more effectively. For example, decisions can be made regarding evacuation *versus* temporary refuge, including their implications on the functions of the building. Specific needs with regard to the decision are then recognized.

The tree also provides for the separation of the functions of fire prevention and building design. In this way, the responsibilities of the owner/occupant can be differentiated from those of the building design team. Those concepts that are eventually incorporated into the design can be identified with a specific member of the building design team.

Building codes and NFPA standards are important factors in building design, and the firesafety concepts tree should not supersede them. Rather, the tree enables those documents to be interrelated and, consequently, used more effectively. It also aids in design decisionmaking with regard to firesafety.

Specific minimum design guidelines and standards are still the appropriate domain of the building codes and the standards writers, because the concepts tree does not, in its present form, provide a firesafety score for a building. Other techniques have been developed to provide such scores. The major systems, some of which provide static measures, while others provide dynamic measures, are described elsewhere in this handbook.

BIBLIOGRAPHY

References Cited

1. Ackoff, R., *Redesigning the Future*, John Wiley, New York, 1974.
2. Checkland, P. B., "Toward a Systems-Based Methodology for Real-World Problem Solving," *Journal of Systems Engineering*, Vol. 3, No. 2, 1972, pp. 87-116.
3. Powers, R. W., "New York Office Building Fire," *Fire Journal*, Vol. 65, No. 1 (January/1971), pp. 18-23, 87.
4. Powers, R. W., "Office Building Fire, 919 Third Avenue, New York City," *Fire Journal*, Vol. 65, No. 2 (March/1971), pp. 5-7, 13.

NFPA Codes, Standards, and Recommended Practices

Reference to the following NFPA codes, standards, and recommended practices will provide further information on systems concepts for building firesafety discussed in this chapter. (See the latest *NFPA Catalog* for availability of the current edition of the following document.)

NFPA 550, *Firesafety Concepts Tree*.

Additional Reading

Beard, A., "Some Ideas on A systemic Approach," *Fire Safety Journal*, Vol. 14, 1986, pp. 943-952.

Churchman, C. W., *The Systems Approach*, Dell, New York, 1979.

Miser, H. J., and Quade, E. S., eds., *Handbook of Systems Analysis*, North-Holland, New York, 1985.

Watts, J. M., "A Theoretical Relationization of a Goal-Oriented Systems Approach to Building Fire Safety, " *NBS-GCR-79-163*, National Bureau of Standards, Washington, DC, February 1979.

Watts, J. M., "Why Systems Concepts?" *Proceedings* Systems Methodologies and Some Applications Symposium, Society of Fire Protection Engineers, Boston, MA, February 1980

Weinberg, G. M., *An Introduction to General Systems Thinking*, John Wiley, New York, NY, 1975.

CHEMISTRY AND PHYSICS OF FIRE

Revised by D. D. Drysdale

This chapter presents basic definitions of some of the physical properties and chemical terms applicable to the chemistry and physics of fire; it also discusses combustion, the principles of fire, heat measurement, heat transfer, and heat energy sources (i.e., sources of ignition).

The material contained in this chapter does not attempt to offer a comprehensive course of instruction on the subject, but is intended to present basic background reference material applicable to this and other sections of this handbook.

BASIC DEFINITIONS AND PROPERTIES

Atoms: The basic particles of chemical composition are called atoms. Atoms are extremely minute. Substances composed of only one type of atom are called elements. An atom has a compact core or nucleus around which electrons (negatively charged units of matter) travel in orbit. The nucleus is comprised of protons (positively charged) and neutrons (no charge). Substances that have loosely bound electrons generally are good electrical and thermal conductors. Those with rigidly bound electrons (so that no easy transfer of electrons is possible) are good insulators.

Molecules: Combined groups of atoms are called molecules. Substances composed of molecules that contain two or more different kinds of atoms are called compounds.

Chemical formula: The chemical formula shows the number of atoms of the various elements in the molecule, and indicates their arrangement. For example, the chemical formula for propane is C_3H_8, where C stands for carbon and H for hydrogen. (See Table 1-4A for symbols of other elements.)

Atomic number of an element: The number of protons in the nucleus of a particular atom determines the atomic number of that element, and its place in the periodic table.

Atomic weight of an element: The atomic weight of an element is proportional to the weight of its atom. The atomic weight of carbon (isotope C-12) is arbitrarily assigned the value of 12.00. Table 1-4A gives the atomic weights of elements.

Molecular weight of a compound: The molecular weight of a compound is the sum of the atomic weights of all atoms in its molecule. (In a chemical formula, the subscripts following an element's symbol indicate the number of atoms of that element present in the compound.)

Gram molecular weight: The gram molecular weight of a substance (in grams) is equal to its molecular weight.

Specific gravity: Specific gravity is the ratio of the weight of a solid or liquid substance to the weight of an equal volume of water. The scales of the most commonly used hydrometers are based on a specific gravity of 1 for water at 39.2°F (4°C) [0.06 cu in. (1 cc) of water at 39.2°F (4°C) weighs 0.0353 oz. (1 g)].

Gas specific gravity: Gas specific gravity is the ratio of the weight of a gas to the weight of an equal volume of dry air at the same temperature and pressure. It may be evaluated by the following: gas specific gravity equals its molecular weight divided by 29, where 29 is the composite molecular weight of dry air.

Buoyancy: Buoyancy is the upward force exerted on a body or volume of fluid by the ambient fluid surrounding it. If a volume of a gas has positive buoyancy, then it is lighter than the surrounding gas and will tend to rise. If it has negative buoyancy, it is heavier and will tend to sink. The buoyancy of a gas depends upon both its molecular weight (e.g., gas specific gravity) and its temperature.

If a flammable gas with a gas specific gravity greater than 1 escapes from its container, it will typically sink to a low level and can travel considerable distances to potential sources of ignition. Carbon dioxide (CO_2), which has a molecular weight of 44, is heavier than air and, when discharged from an extinguisher, will tend to accumulate near the ground. Generally, the higher the temperature of a gas, the lighter or less dense it is. Thus, hot products of combustion tend to rise.

D. D. Drysdale, Ph.D., is a reader in the Unit of Fire Safety Engineering at the University of Edinburgh, Scotland.

TABLE 1-4A. ***The Chemical Elements***

Based on the assigned relative atomic mass of the Carbon-12 isotope equal to 12.00. Most elements consist of isotope mixtures. Elements with atomic weights in parentheses are unstable isotopes.

Element	Symbol	Atomic No.	Atomic Weight
Actinium	Ac	89	(227)
Aluminum	Al	13	26.9815
Americium	Am	95	(243)
Antimony, stibium	Sb	51	121.75
Argon	Ar	18	39.948
Arsenic	As	33	74.9216
Astatine	At	85	(210)
Barium	Ba	56	137.34
Berkelium	Bk	97	(247)
Beryllium	Be	4	9.0122
Bismuth	Bi	83	208.980
Boron	B	5	10.81
Bromine	Br	35	79.904
Cadmium	Cd	48	112.40
Calcium	Ca	20	40.08
Californium	Cf	98	(251)
Carbon	C	6	12.011
Cerium	Ce	58	140.13
Cesium	Cs	55	132.9055
Chlorine	Cl	17	35.453
Chromium	Cr	24	51.996
Cobalt	Co	27	58.9332
Columbium, see niobium			
Copper	Cu	29	63.546
Curium	Cm	96	(247)
Dysprosium	Dy	66	162.50
Einsteinium	E	99	(254)
Erbium	Er	68	167.26
Europium	Eu	63	151.96
Fermium	Fm	100	(257)
Fluorine	F	9	18.9984
Francium	Fr	87	(223)
Gadolinium	Gd	64	157.2
Gallium	Ga	31	69.72
Germanium	Ge	32	72.59
Gold, aurum	Au	79	196.9665

Element	Symbol	Atomic No.	Atomic Weight
Hafnium	Hf	72	178.49
Helium	He	2	4.0026
Holmium	Ho	67	164.9303
Hydrogen	H	1	1.0080
Indium	In	49	114.82
Iodine	I	53	126.9045
Iridium	Ir	77	192.2
Iron, ferrum	Fe	26	55.85
Krypton	Kr	36	83.8
Lanthanum	La	57	138.905
Lawrencium	Lr	103	(257)
Lead, plumbum	Pb	82	207.2
Lithium	Li	3	6.941
Lutetium	Lu	71	174.97
Magnesium	Mg	12	24.305
Manganese	Mn	25	54.9380
Mendelevium	Md	101	(256)
Mercury, hydrargyrum	Hg	80	200.59
Molybdenum	Mo	42	95.94
Neodymium	Nd	60	144.2
Neon	Ne	10	20.179
Neptunium	Np	93	237.0482
Nickel	Ni	28	58.71
Niobium, columbium	Nb	41	92.9064
Nitrogen	N	7	14.0067
Nobelium	No	102	(254)
Osmium	Os	76	190.2
Oxygen	O	8	15.9994
Palladium	Pd	46	106.4
Phosphorus	P	15	30.9738
Platinum	Pt	78	195.09
Plutonium	Pu	94	(244)
Polonium	Po	84	(210)
Potassium, kalium	K	19	39.10

Element	Symbol	Atomic No.	Atomic Weight
Praseodymium	Pr	59	140.9077
Promethium	Pm	61	(145)
Protoactinium	Pa	91	231.0359
Radium	Ra	88	226.0254
Radon	Rn	86	(222)
Rhenium	Re	75	186.2
Rhodium	Rh	45	102.9055
Rubidium	Rb	37	85.4678
Ruthenium	Ru	44	101.07
Samarium	Sm	62	150.4
Scandium	Sc	21	44.9559
Selenium	Se	34	78.96
Silicon	Si	14	28.086
Silver, argentum	Ag	47	107.868
Sodium, natrium	Na	11	22.9898
Strontium	Sr	38	87.62
Sulfur	S	16	32.06
Tantalum	Ta	73	180.9479
Technetium	Tc	43	98.9062
Tellurium	Te	52	127.60
Terbium	Tb	65	158.9254
Thallium	Tl	81	204.37
Thorium	Th	90	232.0381
Thulium	Tm	69	168.9342
Tin, stannum	Sn	50	118.69
Titanium	Ti	22	47.90
Tungsten	W	74	183.8
Uranium	U	92	238.029
Vanadium	V	23	50.9414
Xenon	Xe	54	131.30
Ytterbium	Yb	70	173.04
Yttrium	Y	39	88.9059
Zinc	Zn	30	65.38
Zirconium	Zr	40	91.22

In the case of a spill of liquefied natural gas (LNG), the vapors are heavier than air because of their extremely low temperature—despite the fact that the gas specific gravity of methane (CH_4), the principal component, is less than 1 (its molecular weight is 16). LNG spills can be dangerous because the vapors can spread over a wide area with little dilution.

Vapor Pressure and Boiling Point

Because molecules of a liquid are always in motion (the amount of motion depends upon the temperature of the liquid), molecules are continually escaping from the free surface of the liquid to the space above. Some molecules remain in this space while others, due to random motion, collide with the liquid and are "recaptured."

If the liquid is in an open container, molecules (collectively called vapor) continuously escape from the surface, and the liquid evaporates. If, on the other hand, the liquid is in a closed container, the escaping molecules are confined to the vapor space, and a point of equilibrium eventually is reached where the rate of escape of molecules from the liquid equals the rate of their return to the liquid. The pressure exerted by the vapor at the point of equilibrium is called vapor pressure. It is measured in kilopascals (kPa) or pounds per square inch absolute (psia).*

*Absolute pressure equals the total force exerted against a unit of area. It is measured in Pascals (Newtons per square meter) or in pounds per square inch (psi). It often is expressed in fractions or multiples of atmospheric pressure, or in terms of the height of a column of liquid (usually mercury) which will balance the absolute pressure. In situations where pressure gages are used, absolute pressure is determined by adding gage pressure to atmospheric pressure. Atmospheric, or ambient, pressure equals 101.3 kPa, 14.7 psia, or 30 in. of mercury. A kilopascal equals 1000 Pascals.

As the temperature of a liquid increases, its vapor pressure approaches and ultimately exceeds atmospheric pressure. In the open air, the liquid will boil when its vapor pressure equals atmospheric pressure; the corresponding liquid temperature is known as the boiling point.

Although the vapor pressure of a liquid varies with its temperature, a great many variables affect the rate at which it actually evaporates when exposed to air. These variables include atmospheric temperature and pressure, and air movement.

Vapor-air specific gravity (vasg): Vapor-air specific gravity is the ratio of the weight of a vapor-air mixture (resulting from the vaporization of a liquid at equilibrium temperature and pressure) to the weight of an equal volume of air under the same conditions. The specific gravity (density) of a vapor-air mixture thus depends upon the ambient temperature, the vapor pressure of the liquid at the temperature, and the molecular weight of the liquid. At temperatures well below the boiling point of a liquid, the vapor pressure of the liquid may be so low that the vapor-air mixture, consisting mostly of air, has a density which approximates that of pure air, i.e., a vapor-air specific gravity near 1. As the temperature of the liquid increases to the boiling point, the rate of vaporization increases, the vapor displaces the surrounding air, and the vapor-air mixture specific gravity approaches that of the pure vapor specific gravity.

A vapor-air mixture with a density significantly above that of air at the ambient temperature will seek lower levels. On the other hand, diffusion and mixing by convection will limit the distance of travel of mixtures having densities near or less than 1.

The vapor-air specific gravity of a substance at ambient temperature may be calculated as follows:

Let P equal the ambient pressure, p the vapor pressure of the liquid at ambient temperature, and s its pure vapor specific gravity. Then,

$$\text{vasg} = \frac{ps}{P} + \frac{P - p}{P}$$

The first term, $\frac{ps}{P}$, is the contribution of the vapor to the specific gravity of the mixture; the second term, $\frac{P-p}{P}$, is the contribution of air.

EXAMPLE: Find the vapor-air specific gravity at 100°F (38°C) and atmospheric pressure for a flammable liquid whose vapor specific gravity is 2, and whose vapor pressure at 100°F (38°C) is 3.0 in. of mercury (10.1 kPa), or one-tenth of atmospheric pressure.

$$\text{vsag} = \frac{(10.1)(2)}{101} + \frac{101 - 10.1}{101} = 0.2 + 0.9 = 1.1$$

Endothermic and Exothermic Chemical Reactions

Heat of reaction is the energy that is absorbed or released when a given reaction takes place. In endothermic reactions, the new substances formed contain more energy than the reacting materials, so energy must be absorbed by the reaction. Exothermic reactions produce substances with less energy than that of the reacting materials, so energy is released by the reaction. While the energy may be in different forms, it is usually in the form of heat, added to or released from a chemical reaction.

COMBUSTION

Combustion is an exothermic, self-sustaining reaction involving a solid, liquid, and/or gas-phase fuel. The process is usually (but not necessarily) associated with the oxidation of a fuel by atmospheric oxygen. Some solids can burn directly by glowing combustion or smoldering, but in flaming combustion of solids and liquid fuels, vaporization takes place before burning. It is necessary to distinguish between two types of flaming: (1) pre-mixed, in which gaseous fuel is mixed intimately with air before ignition, and (2) diffusive, in which combustion takes place in the regions where the fuel and oxygen are mixing. If premixed burning takes place in a confined space, a rapid pressure rise will occur, giving rise to an explosion.

Oxidation Reactions

Fire involves oxidation reactions that are exothermic, i.e., heat is generated. The reactions are complex and are not understood in their entirety, although certain generalizations can be made.

For an oxidation reaction to take place, a combustible material (fuel) and an oxidizing agent must both be present. Fuels include innumerable materials which, due to their chemistry, can be oxidized to yield relatively stable species, such as carbon dioxide and water; thus, for example:

$$C_3H_8 + 5O_2 = 3CO_2 + 4H_2O$$

Hydrocarbons, such as propane (C_3H_8), consist entirely of carbon and hydrogen and may be regarded as "prototype fuels." Virtually all common fuels, whether solid, liquid, or gaseous, contain significant proportions of carbon and hydrogen.

In the present context, the most common oxidizing agent is molecular oxygen (O_2) in the air, which consists approximately of one-fifth oxygen and four-fifths nitrogen. However, there are certain chemicals that are powerful oxidizing agents, such as sodium nitrate ($NaNO_3$) and potassium chlorate ($KClO_3$), which if intimately mixed with a solid or liquid fuel a highly reactive mixture is obtained. Thus, gunpowder is a physical mixture of carbon and sulphur (the fuel) with sodium nitrate as the oxidizer. If reactive groups, such as the nitrate group, are incorporated chemically into a fuel, such as in cellulose nitrate or trinitrotoluene (TNT), the resulting species can be highly unstable and will decompose violently under appropriate conditions.

There are circumstances involving reactive species in which combustion may take place without oxygen being involved. Thus, hydrocarbons may "burn" in an atmosphere of chlorine, or zirconium dust can be ignited in pure carbon dioxide.

Ignition (piloted ignition and autoignition): Ignition is the process by which self-sustaining combustion is initiated. Considering first a flammable gas- or vapor-air mixture (see below), piloted ignition can be achieved by the introduction of an ignition source, such as a flame or spark. However, if the temperature is raised sufficiently, the mixture will undergo autoignition, in which the onset of combustion is spontaneous.

In general, both fuel and oxygen molecules must be first excited to some activated state before they can interact chemically to produce heat. This excitation can be induced by a pilot flame or spark, or by raising the general temperature of the mixture. After interacting chemically, the fuel and oxygen produce other excited molecules, as well as heat. If there is sufficient fuel and oxygen as well, as a sufficient number of excited species, ignition will occur as a chain reaction wherein the rate of production of activated molecules exceeds their natural rate of decay. Once ignition has occurred, combustion will continue until all the available fuel or oxidant has been consumed, or until the flame is extinguished. In general, a self-sustained ignition can occur only in those situations which are capable of supporting self-sustained combustion. For example, if the ambient pressure (or ambient oxidant concentration) is insufficient for sustaining combustion, it also will be insufficient for ignition.

For combustible liquids and solids, the initiation of flame occurs in the gas phase. Thermal energy (heat) must first be supplied to convert a sufficient part of the fuel to vapor, thus creating a flammable vapor-air mixture in the vicinity of the surface. For liquid fuels, this is principally a process of evaporation, but almost all solid fuels must undergo chemical decomposition before vapor is released. One can usually identify a minimum liquid or solid temperature which is capable of generating a flammable mixture close to the fuel surface. For liquid fuels, this is defined in terms of the bulk liquid temperature, and is called the flash point. The same phenomenon can be recorded for combustible solids, but must be defined as a surface temperature. Note that these are piloted ignition temperatures, because an external pilot is needed to ignite the mixture and only the flammable vapor-air mixture will burn. A slightly higher temperature—the fire point—must be achieved if the liquid (or solid) fuel is to continue burning after the flammable mixture has been consumed.

In practice, the piloted ignition temperatures of solids and liquids can be influenced by the rate of air flow (oxidant), the rate of heating, and the size and shape of the solid or liquid. As a result, reported piloted ignition temperatures, particularly for solids, depend somewhat upon the specific test methods.

In general, piloted ignition of a gas- or vapor-air mixture is affected by composition, ambient pressure, and the dimensions of the containing vessel, as well as the nature and energy of the pilot. For a given fuel-air mixture, there is a minimum pressure below which ignition does not occur. As the temperature increases, less and less pilot energy is required to ignite the mixture until, at a sufficiently high temperature, the mixture will ignite spontaneously. This temperature is referred to as the autoignition (or spontaneous ignition) temperature (AIT).

The autoignition temperature of a gaseous fuel also depends on composition and pressure, but it is particularly sensitive to the size and shape of the vessel in which the measurement is made. Differences in test apparatus can lead to significant differences in the results; for example, different values of AIT have been reported in the literature for the same vapor. (See Tables 1-4B and 1-4C.) (The same comments are relevant to the measurement of AIT for solid fuels.)

Explosions

Explosions generally occur in situations where the fuel and oxidant have been allowed to mix intimately before ignition. As a result, the combustion reaction proceeds very rapidly without being delayed by the need for first mixing fuel and oxidant. If premixed gases are confined, their tendency to expand on burning can cause a rapid pressure rise or explosion. This is in contrast to fires in which fuel and oxidant are initially separate and the combustion rate is controlled by the rate at which they are able to mix. As a result, the burning rate per unit volume is much lower for fires, and the very rapid increase in pressure characteristic of explosions is not encountered.

TABLE 1-4B. ***Variation of Autoignition Temperature with Mixture Composition.***

% Propane in air	Autoignition °C	Temperature °F
1.5	548	1018
3.75	502	936
7.65	476	889

TABLE 1-4C. ***Variation of Autoignition Temperature for Carbon Disulphide (CS_2) with Vessel Size***

Volume cm^3	in^3	Autoignition °C	Temperature °F
200	12	120	248
1000	61	110	230
10000	610	96	205

For ignition of a fuel that has been premixed with air, the fuel concentration must lie within the limits of flammability. Once ignition has occurred, flame will propagate through the unburnt mixture until all the flammable mixture has been consumed. The fuel may be in the form of gas or vapor, or a suspension of droplets (e.g., a mist) of a combustible liquid, or solid particles of an explosible dust.

The Limits of Flammability

The limits of flammability are the extreme concentration limits of a combustible in an oxidant through which a flame, once initiated, will continue to propagate at the specified temperature and pressure. For example, hydrogen-air mixtures will propagate flame for concentrations between 4 and 74 percent by volume of hydrogen at 70°F (21°C) and atmospheric pressure. The smaller value is the lower (lean) limit, and the larger value is the upper (rich) limit of flammability. When the mixture temperature is increased, the flammability range widens; when the temperature is decreased, the range narrows. (See Figure 1-4A.) A decrease in temperature can cause a flammable mixture to become nonflammable by placing it either above or below the limits of flammability for the specific environmental conditions.

Note in Figure 1-4A that for liquid fuels in equilibrium with their vapors in air, a maximum temperature exists for each fuel below which there is insufficient vapor to form a flammable vapor-air mixture: This is the flash point. There is also a maximum temperature above which the fuel vapor concentration is too high to propagate flame; gasoline in a partially full gasoline tank is an example of this. These may be referred to as the lower and upper flash

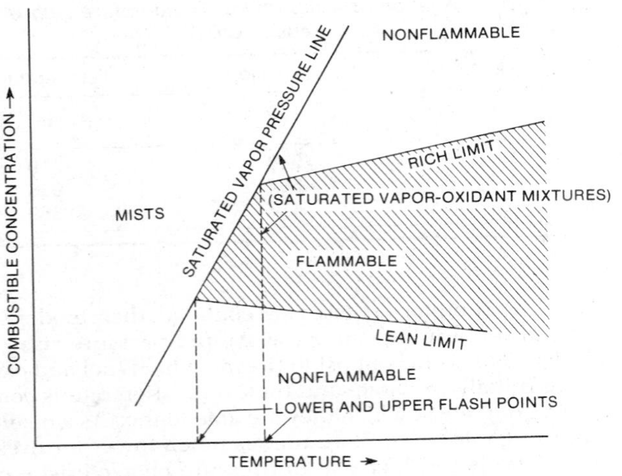

FIG. 1-4A. Saturated vapor-oxidant mixtures should be associated with the sloping vapor pressure line rather than just the upper flash point vertical line.

points in air, respectively, although the term "flash point" on its own invariably signifies the former. The flash point temperatures for a combustible liquid increase with environmental pressure.

Fire Point

Fire point may be defined as the lowest temperature of a liquid in an open container at which vapors evolve fast enough to support continuous combustion. The fire point is usually a few degrees above the flash point. For typical fuels, the minimum rate of vaporization required to support combustion is of the order of 2 g/m^2 sec.

It should be emphasized that, if a source of ignition has been established, fires can spread over liquids whose temperatures are considerably below their lower flash points. In such situations, the ignition source or fire itself heats the liquid surface locally so that its temperature rises above the fire point.

Catalysts and Inhibitors

Catalyst: A catalyst is a substance that greatly affects the rate of a chemical reaction but is not permanently changed by the reaction itself. For example, platinum in a car's catalytic converter causes residual fuel to burn without permanently consuming the platinum catalyst.

Inhibitors: Inhibitors, also called stabilizers, are chemicals that may be added in small quantities to an unstable material to prevent a vigorous reaction. For example, premature polymerization of styrene monomer is inhibited by the addition of at least 10 ppm (parts per million) of tertiary-butyl-catechol (TBC). Fire-retardant chemicals usually act as inhibitors. For example, small quantities of chlorine or bromine-related compounds, when added to plastics, can reduce plastics ignitability and ability to support the spread of small flames. Fire-retardant chemicals are generally less effective in large fires.

Stable and Unstable Materials

Stable materials: Stable materials are materials that have the capacity to resist changes in normal environmental exposure to air, water, heat, shock, or pressure. Most combustible materials can be classified as stable, although, of course, they can be made to burn.

Unstable materials: Unstable materials polymerize, decompose, condense, or become self-reactive when exposed to air, water, heat, shock, or pressure. For example, decomposition of pure gaseous acetylene, hydrazine, or ethylene oxide can result in violent explosions.

PRINCIPLES OF FIRE

Considerable technical knowledge exists concerning the ignition, burning, and fire spread characteristics of combustible materials (solids, liquids, and gases). However, most of this knowledge is for very simple geometric arrangements and thus is inadequate for predicting ignition and resultant burning in realistic situations. Nevertheless, insight can be gained from an understanding of these simplified situations.

Perhaps the simplest combustion situation is the burning of premixed, fuel-air gas mixtures involved in explosions. Much is known about premixed flames, as they have been the subject of much experimental research. The flammability limits and associated burning rates have been catalogued for most common vapor and gas mixtures.[1] In addition, scientists now can accurately calculate the burning rates for simple hydrocarbon fuel-air mixtures in terms of their multiple individual chemical reactions.[2]

Other simple situations involve the steady burning of fuel droplets or small samples of simple plastics. In such situations, the burning takes place in gas-phase laminar diffusion flames where the rate of combustion is controlled by the rate of fuel and air supply.

In contrast to explosions, fires occur in situations where fuel and oxidant are initially unmixed. Their burning rates are restricted primarily by the supply of fuel and oxidant (air) to the flames rather than the basic chemical reaction rates within the flames. In fires, the basic gas-phase combustion process usually occurs along thin flame sheets, called "diffusion flames," which separate regions rich in fuel vapor from regions rich in oxidant. Fuel vapor and oxidant diffuse toward each other from opposite sides of the flame sheet where they combine to produce combustion products and heat, which in turn diffuse away from the flame sheet.

When diffusion flames are small—e.g., from a burning match or candle—they typically appear quite smooth and steady. They are called "laminar" diffusion flames. If the fire is allowed to grow, the flames become unstable and wiggle around in search of more fuel or oxidant. Eventually, as the fire grows, the flame motion becomes truly random, in which case the flames are called "turbulent" diffusion flames.

Scientists have obtained a relatively clear understanding of small fires involving laminar diffusion flames. For example, they can calculate the rate of flame spread over solid surfaces,[3] and steady burning rates[4] in terms of basic combustion properties for a variety of simple geometries (e.g., smooth flat surfaces, cylinders, etc.). In these situations, the burning rates are controlled by the convective heat transfer from the flame to the solid fuel which, in response, gasifies and supplies fuel vapors to the flames. The oxidant (air) is supplied to the flames by the upward flow induced by the buoyant hot combustion products. The buoyant flow also may enhance the convective heat transfer from the flames to the solid fuel. In the case of a spreading flame, the spread rate is governed by the forward heat transfer from the flames to the as yet uninvolved fuel, which must be preheated before it can provide fuel vapors to the flames. (An analysis of many different fire spread situations which shows how one might predict their spread rates is contained in Williams, 1977.[3])

Larger fires involving turbulent diffusion flames are less well understood because of difficulties in describing the turbulent gas motion, and the flame radiation which is usually the dominant form of heat transfer for larger fires [fuel bed diameters greater than 12 to 20 in. (30 to 50 cm)]. Experience and measurements have shown that this enhanced role of flame radiation in larger fires often alters the relative flammability ranking of fuels in comparison to their small-scale flammability rankings.

The study of these larger (hazardous) scale fires is at the forefront of current fire research. In recent years, scientists have developed new laboratory tests that are capable of providing data relevant to full-scale fire behavior.[5] Furthermore, they have prepared complex computer models capable of predicting fire development from ignition through various stages of growth, to full room involvement (flashover), propagation to adjacent rooms, and possibly even to other buildings.

Ignition and Combustion

To illustrate the many physical and chemical processes involved in fires, it is necessary to first discuss the ignition, burning, and eventual extinction of a wood slab in a typical situation, such as a fireplace.[6]

1. Suppose the wood slab is initially heated by thermal radiation. As its surface temperature approaches the boiling point of water, gases (principally steam) slowly evolve from the wood. These initial gases have little, if any, combustible content. As the slab temperature increases above the boiling point of water, the "drying" process penetrates deeper into the wood.
2. With continued heating, the wood surface begins to discolor when the surface temperature approaches 572°F (300°C). This discoloring is visible evidence of pyrolysis, the chemical decomposition of matter through the action of heat. When wood pyrolyzes, it releases combustible gases while leaving behind a black, carbonaceous residue called char. This pyrolysis process penetrates deeper into the wood slab as the heating continues.
3. Soon after active pyrolysis begins, combustible gases typically evolve rapidly enough to support gas-phase combustion. However, combustion will occur only if there is a pilot flame or some other source of chemically activated molecules sufficient to support a piloted ignition. If no such pilot is present, the wood surface often must be heated to a much higher temperature before autoignition occurs.
4. Once ignition occurs, a diffusion flame rapidly covers the pyrolyzing surface. The diffusion flame shields the pyrolyzing surface from direct contact with oxygen. Meanwhile, the flame heats the fuel surface and causes an increase in the rate of pyrolysis. If the original radiant heat source is withdrawn at ignition, the burning will continue provided the wood slab is thin enough [less than 3/4 in. (2 cm)]. Otherwise, the flames will go out, because the slab surface loses too much heat by thermal radiation and thermal conduction into its interior. If there is an adjacent, parallel wood surface (or insulating material) facing the ignited slab, much of the surface radiation loss can be recaptured and returned, so the ignited slab can continue burning even after the withdrawal of the initial heat source. This explains why one cannot burn a single large log in a fireplace, but must use several logs to recapture the radiant heat losses.
5. As the burning continues, a char layer builds up. This char layer, which is a good thermal insulator, restricts the flow of heat to the wood interior, and consequently tends to reduce the rate of pyrolysis. The pyrolysis rate also will decrease when the supply of unpyrolyzed wood runs out. When the pyrolysis rate decreases to the point of not being able to sustain gas-phase combustion, oxygen from the air will come into direct contact with the char, permitting it to undergo direct glowing combustion, provided the radiant heat losses are not too large.
6. This scenario presumes an ample (but not excessive) supply of air (oxidant) for combustion. If there were insufficient oxidant to burn the available fuel vapor, the excess vapors would travel with the flow and possibly burn where they eventually would find sufficient oxidant. For example, this happens when fuel vapors emerge and burn outside a window of a fully involved but under-ventilated room fire. Generally, under-ventilated fires produce large amounts of smoke and toxic products (e.g., carbon monoxide).

If, on the other hand, one was to impose a forced draft onto the pyrolyzing surface, the oxidant supply may exceed that required for complete combustion of the fuel vapors. In this case, the excess oxidant can cool the flames sufficiently to suppress their chemical reaction and extinguish them, as happens, for example, when one blows out a match. In the case of larger fires with ample supply of fuel vapors, imposing a forced draft on them simply increases their rate of burning by increasing the flame-to-fuel-surface heat transfer which in turn enhances the fuel supply rate.

7. Following the ignition of a certain portion of our wood slab, the flames are likely to spread over the entire fuel array. Flame spread can be thought of as a continuous succession of piloted ignitions where the flames themselves provide the heat source. One commonly observes that upward flame spread is much more rapid than downward or horizontal flame spread. This is because hot flames generally travel upward and contribute their heat over a greater area in an upward direction. Thus, each successive "upward ignition" adds a much greater burning area to the fire than a corresponding "downward" or "horizontal" ignition.

Generally, materials which ignite easily (rapidly) also propagate flames rapidly. The ignitability of a material is controlled by its resistance to heating (thermal inertia) and by the temperature rise required for it to begin to pyrolyze. Materials with low thermal inertia, such as foamed plastics or balsa wood, heat rapidly when subjected to a given heat flux. These materials are often easy to ignite and can cause very rapid flame spread. On the other hand, dense materials, such as ebony wood, tend to have relatively high thermal inertias and are difficult to ignite.

8. The burning rates of larger, more hazardous fires are principally governed by the radiant heat transfer from the flames to the pyrolyzing fuel surface.[7] This flame

radiation comes primarily from the luminous soot particles in the flames. Combustibles that tend to produce copious amounts of soot or smoke, such as polystyrene, also tend to support more intense fires, despite the fact that their fuel vapors burn less completely, as evidenced by their higher smoke output.

Well-ventilated fires generally release less smoke than poorly ventilated ones. In well-ventilated fires, the surrounding air can gain speedy access to the unburned fuel vapors and soot before the fuel vapors cool down by radiation. Poorly ventilated fires can release copious amounts of smoke and incomplete products of combustion, such as carbon monoxide. In poorly ventilated fires, fuel vapors have insufficient air to burn completely before cooling off and leaving the fire area.

Fires occurring in oxygen-enriched atmospheres have higher flame temperatures, increased fractions of heat release by radiation, and increased burning rates per unit fuel area. These higher flame temperatures generally cause a much greater conversion of fuel vapors into soot, resulting in significantly increased smoke release rates. For example, a well-ventilated methanol fire typically burns with a blue (i.e., soot-free) flame in normal air. However, a similarly well-ventilated methanol fire can burn with a brightly luminous smoky flame in an oxygen-enriched atmosphere. This sensitivity to ambient oxygen concentration significantly increases the flame radiation, burning rates, and resultant fire hazard.

Flammability Properties of Solid and High Fire Point Liquid Combustibles

The above discussion can be summarized by describing the combustible properties that contribute to fire hazards in typical fire situations.

Heat of combustion: This is a measure of the maximum amount of heat that can be released by the complete combustion of unit mass of combustible material.

Stoichiometric oxidant: The mass of oxidant required for complete combustion of a unit mass of combustible is called the stoichiometric oxidant requirement. Combustibles with large stoichiometric oxidant requirements often produce large flame heights which in turn present greater fire spread hazards. The stoichiometric oxidant requirements for typical (organic) combustibles is approximately proportional to their heat of combustion, so that organic combustibles all release approximately the same amount of heat per unit mass of consumed oxidant.

Heat of gasification: The heat required to vaporize a unit mass of combustible material that is initially at ambient temperature is called the heat of gasification. This quantity is very important because it determines the amount of combustible vapor supplied to a fire in response to a given supply of heat to the pyrolyzing surface. The fire hazard of some plastics can be reduced by adding inert fillers, such as alumina trihydrate, which increase their effective heats of gasification.

Ignitability (piloted): Ignitability is inversely proportional to the time it takes for a given applied heat flux to raise the surface temperature of a material to its piloted ignition (fire point) temperature. This property is important both for ignition and fire spread.

Char formation: Char is a black, carbonaceous residue. Materials, such as wood and some thermosetting polymers, develop a char layer during pyrolysis. The insulating properties of such a layer can be very effective in reducing burning rates by restricting the flow of heat to the unpyrolyzed material. Intumescent paints simulate formation of char by swelling and forming an insulating protective layer when heated. Note that thermoplastics, such as polyethylene, tend not to char, but soften, melt, and flow instead.

Soot formation: Soot is comprised of minute solid carbonaceous particles formed as a result of incomplete combustion and pyrolysis, particularly in the fuel-rich regions of diffusion flames. Combustibles whose flames produce significant amounts of soot are generally more hazardous because the soot increases flame radiation which in turn increases the burning rate. The soot is also the source of smoke that is released from the flame and can result in significant smoke spread to points remote from the fire.

Inhibitors: The addition of small quantities of chemical inhibitors to the fuel or oxidant can impede gas-phase reactions. Such flame inhibitors can be quite effective in retarding ignition and flame spread involved in small fires. Flames also can be inhibited by introducing additives to solid combustibles which either promote char formation or produce higher concentrations of water vapor in the pyrolysis gases (or both).

Melting: Combustibles that tend to melt are often more hazardous, because the molten combustible can increase the pyrolyzing surface area. The molten material itself also can be a hazard.

Toxicity: Carbon monoxide usually is the principal toxicant produced by a fire. It is typically present in pyrolysis gases and combustion products that have not been completely oxidized. Some materials, especially those containing elements other than C, H, and O (e.g., polyvinylchloride or polyurethane), can produce additional toxicants (such as hydrogen chloride or hydrogen cyanide, respectively). (See Section 3, Chapter 1, "Combustion Products and Their Effects on Life Safety.")

Geometry: Last, but not least, the geometry of a material strongly influences its flammability. Thin materials usually ignite more readily and spread flames more rapidly. Upward flame spread is more rapid than downward or horizontal flame spread. Finally, geometric arrangements that provide ample air (oxidant) access while providing shielding to prevent radiant losses are usually the most hazardous.

Flammability Principles

The science of fire protection rests upon the following principles:

1. An oxidizing agent, a combustible material, and an ignition source are essential for combustion.
2. The combustible material must be heated to its piloted ignition temperature before it can be ignited or support flame spread.
3. Subsequent burning of a combustible is governed by the heat feedback from the flames to the pyrolyzing or vaporizing combustible.
4. The burning will continue until:
   a. The combustible material is consumed; or
   b. The oxidizing agent concentration is lowered to below the concentration necessary to support combustion; or
   c. Sufficient heat is removed or prevented from reaching the combustible material to prevent further fuel pyrolysis; or

d. The flames are chemically inhibited or sufficiently cooled to prevent further reaction.

All the material presented in this handbook for the prevention, control, or extinguishment of fire is based upon these principles.

HEAT MEASUREMENT

The temperature of a material is the condition that determines whether it will transfer heat to or from other materials. Heat always flows from higher to lower temperatures. Temperature is measured in degrees.

Temperature Units

Celsius: A Celsius (or centigrade) degree (°C) is 1/100 the difference between the temperature of melting ice and boiling water at 1 atmosphere pressure. On the Celsius scale, zero is the melting point of ice; 100 is the boiling point of water. This unit is approved by the International System of Units (SI).

Kelvin: A Kelvin degree or Kelvin (K) is the same size as the Celsius degree. However, the zero on the Kelvin scale (sometimes called Celsius Absolute) is –459.67°F (–273.15°C). Zero on the Kelvin scale is the absolute lowest achievable temperature; hence, the Kelvin scale provides us with so-called absolute temperatures. The Kelvin also is an approved SI unit.

Fahrenheit: A Fahrenheit degree (°F) is 1/180 the difference between the temperature of melting ice and boiling water at 1 atmosphere pressure. On the Fahrenheit scale, 32 is the melting point of ice (0°C); 212 is the boiling point of water (100°C).

Rankine: A Rankine degree (°R) is the same size as the Fahrenheit degree. On the Rankine scale, zero is –459.67°F (–273.15°C), so that the Rankine scale also provides an absolute temperature.

Fahrenheit and Rankine degrees are not approved SI units, and their use is greatly discouraged.

Heat Units

Joule (J): Conventionally, the Joule is defined as the energy (or work) expended when unit force (1 Newton) moves a body through unit distance (1 m). It is the most convenient unit of energy to use and can be related to the calorie (q.v.), which is defined in terms of the heat energy required to raise the temperature of unit mass of water by 1°. The Joule is an approved SI unit.

Watt (W): This is a measure of power, or the rate of energy flow. One Watt is equal to one Joule flowing per second (1W = 1J/s). The rate of heat release from a fire can be expressed in kilowatts (kW) or megawatts (MW)—units that are familiar to the electrical engineer.

Calorie: The amount of heat required to raise the temperature of one gram of water one degree Celsius [measured at 59°F (15°C)] is called a calorie. One calorie equals 4.183 Joules.

British thermal unit (Btu): The amount of heat required to raise the temperature of 1 pound of water one degree Fahrenheit [measured at 60°F (15.5°C)] is called the British thermal unit. One Btu equals 1,054 Joules (252 calories); therefore, it can be inferred that 1.054 kilowatts would heat 1 pound of water one degree Fahrenheit in 1 second.

Btu and calories are not approved SI units.

Heat energy has quantity, as well as potential (intensity). For example, consider the following analogy:

Two water tanks stand side by side. If the first tank holds twice as many gallons as the second, then the first tank can hold twice the quantity of water as the second. But if the level of water in the two tanks is equal, then their pressures or potentials are equal. If the bottoms of the two tanks are connected by a pipe, water will not flow from one to the other because both tanks have the same equilibrium pressure. In a similar manner, one body may hold twice the quantity of heat energy (measured in Joules or Btu) as a second body. But if the potentials or temperatures of the energies of the bodies are equal, no heat energy will flow from one body to the other when they are brought into contact, since the bodies are at equilibrium. If a third body at a lower temperature were brought into contact with the first body, heat would flow from the first to the third until both body temperatures became equal. The amount or quantity of heat flowing until this equilibrium is reached depends upon the heat retention capacities of each body involved.

[Note that, essentially, ignition involves the addition of sufficient heat (by heat transfer, q.v.) to raise the temperature to the appropriate value. On the other hand, extinction may be accomplished by the removal of heat. "Chemical" extinguishment works by another mechanism, i.e., by interrupting chemical reactions that are important in the combustion process.[2]]

Temperature Measurement

Devices that measure temperature depend upon physical change (expansion of a solid, liquid, or gas), change of state (solid to liquid), energy change (changes in electrical potential energy, i.e., voltage), or changes in thermal radiant emission and/or spectral distribution. The principles of operation of the more common temperature measuring devices are discussed here.

Liquid expansion thermometers: These thermometers consist of a tube partially filled with a liquid, which measures expansion and contraction of the liquid with changes in temperature. The tube is calibrated to permit reading of the level of the liquid in degrees of a temperature scale.

Bimetallic thermometers: Bimetallic thermometers contain strips of two metals, which are laminated, with different coefficients of expansion. As the temperature changes, the two metals expand or contract to different extents, causing the strip to deflect. The amount of deflection is measured on a scale that is calibrated in degrees of temperature.

Solid fusion: Solid fusion makes use of the melting or fusion point of a solid (metal, chemical, or chemical mixture) to indicate whether or not a hot object is above or below the melting point of the solid. For example, the eutectic metal in a sprinkler link melts in a fire environment, which activates the sprinkler.

Thermocouples: Thermocouples consist of a pair of wires of different metals connected to each other at one end (the sensing end). The other ends are connected to a voltmeter. When the sensing end is at a different temperature from the voltmeter, a voltage is set up, and the magnitude depends in part upon the temperature difference between the two ends. The voltmeter can be calibrated to give readings in degrees of temperature.

Pyrometers: Pyrometers measure the intensity of radiation from a hot object. Since intensity of radiation depends upon temperature, pyrometers can be calibrated to give readings in degrees of temperature. Optical pyrometers measure the intensity of a particular wavelength of radiation.

Specific Heat

The specific heat of a substance defines the amount of heat it absorbs as its temperature increases. It is expressed as the amount of thermal energy required to raise the unit mass of a substance one temperature degree and is measured in J/g(°C) or cal/g(°C) or Btu/lb(°F). Water has a specific heat of 4.2 J/g(°C), or 1 Btu/lb°F.

The specific heats of various substances vary over a considerable range; for most common substances, except water, they are less than 4.2 J/g(°C). Specific heat figures are significant in fire protection because they indicate the relative quantity of heat needed to raise the temperature to a point of danger, or the quantity of heat that must be removed to cool a hot substance to a safe temperature.

One reason for the effectiveness of water as an extinguishing agent is that its specific heat is higher than that of most other substances.

Latent Heat

Heat is absorbed by a substance when it is converted from a solid to a liquid, or from a liquid to a gas. This thermal energy is called latent heat. Conversely, heat is released during conversion of a gas to a liquid or a liquid to a solid.

Latent heat is the quantity of heat absorbed by a substance in passing between liquid and gaseous phases (latent heat of vaporization), or between solid and liquid phases (latent heat of fusion). It is measured in Joules per unit mass. The latent heat of fusion of water (normal atmospheric pressure) at the freezing or melting point of ice [32°F (0°C)] is 333.4 J/g; the latent heat of vaporization of water at its boiling point [212°F (100°C)] is 2257 J/g (or 970.3 Btu/lb or 539.5 cal/g). The larger heat of vaporization of water is another reason for the effectiveness of water as an extinguishing agent. It requires 3 million Joules to convert 1 kilogram of ice at 32°F (O°C) to steam at 212°F (100°C). The latent heats of most other common substances are substantially less than that of water. Thus, the heat absorbed by water is subtracted from the burning system so it cannot be used to propagate the flame further by vaporizing more liquid, or by pyrolyzing more solid.

HEAT TRANSFER

Transfer of heat governs the ignition, burning, and extinguishment of most fires. Heat is transferred by one or more of three methods: (1) conduction, (2) convection, or (3) radiation.

Conduction

Heat transferred by direct contact from one body to another is a process called conduction. Thus, a steam pipe in contact with wood transfers its heat to the wood by actual contact; in this example, the pipe is the conductor.

The quantity of heat energy transferred by conduction through a body or in a given time is a function of the temperature difference and the conductance of the path involved. Conductance depends on thermal conductivities, cross-sectional areas normal to the flow path, and length of flow path. The rate of heat transfer, then, is simply the quantity of heat per unit time, while the heat "flux" is the quantity of heat per unit cross-sectional area per unit time. The thermal conductivity of a material is the heat energy flux resulting from a unit temperature gradient (falloff of one degree per unit of distance). A typical unit of thermal conductivity is J/(cm · sec · °C), i.e. W/cm °C.

The conduction of heat through air or other gases is independent of pressure in the usual range of pressures. It approaches zero only at very low pressures. No heat is conducted in a perfect vacuum. Solids are better heat conductors than gases; the best commercial insulators consist of fine particles or fibers, with the spaces between the particles filled with air.

Heat conduction cannot be completely stopped by any "heat-insulating" material. Thus, the flow of heat is unlike the flow of water, which can be stopped by a solid barrier. Heat-insulating materials have a low heat conductivity. No matter how thick the insulation, solidly insulating the space between the source of heat and the combustible material may be insufficient to prevent ignition. If the rate of heat conduction through the insulating material is greater than the rate of dissipation from the combustible material, the temperature of the combustible material may increase to the point of ignition. For this reason, there should always be an air space or some manner of carrying the heat away by convection, rather than relying solely upon the heat-insulating material for protection. By the transmission of heat over a long period, fires have occurred through as much as a 2-ft (0.6 m) thickness of solid concrete.

For heat conduction, the most important physical properties of a material are thermal conductivity (k), density (ρ), and specific heat (c). Unfortunately, the last two quantities are usually listed separately, although it is their product (ρc) that is of interest in the field of heat conduction. The product ρc is a measure of the amount of heat necessary to raise the unit volume of the material by unit temperature. A typical unit might be Joules per cubic centimeter per degree Celsius [J/(cm^3 · °C)], and a possible name for the quantity is thermal capacity per unit volume.

Thermal conductivity and thermal capacity per unit volume are rarely of much importance individually. In fact, the solution to heat conduction problems is so complex that it cannot be adequately presented here. However, one or two interesting features can be appropriately mentioned. Probably the most useful feature is concerned with the time constant of a thickness (x) of a material. Thus, if the surface of a material is suddenly exposed to a temperature rise, then the temperature at a depth (x) within the material will begin to change substantially at a certain time.

$$t = \frac{x^2 \rho C}{k}$$

The dimensions of the time expression are given as:

$$\frac{\text{cm}^2 \cdot (\text{J/cm}^3 \cdot {}^\circ\text{C})}{\text{J/(cm} \cdot \text{sec} \cdot {}^\circ\text{C)}} = \text{sec}$$

Centimeters, Joules, and degrees Celsius cancel out, leaving the result of the dimension in seconds, i.e., time. This is a time constant; thus, the higher the number, the slower the transfer. It can be seen that the time required for a thermal wave to penetrate a body increases with the square of its thickness.

Convection

Convection involves the transfer of heat by a circulating medium—either a gas or a liquid. Thus, heat generated in a stove is distributed throughout a room by initially heating the air in contact with the stove by conduction; the circulation of heated air through the room to distant objects is heat transfer by convection. Finally, heat is transferred from the air to the objects by conduction. Heated air expands and rises, and, for this reason, heat transfer by convection often occurs in an upward direction, although air currents can be made to carry heat by convection in any direction, e.g., by use of a fan or blower.

Note that the term "convective heat transfer" is also used to describe the mode by which heat is transferred between a fluid and a solid surface. Indeed, the convective heat transfer coefficient (h) is defined by the expression

$$q = h\,\Delta T$$

where q is the rate of heat transfer per unit surface area (W/m^2) and ΔT is the temperature difference (°C) between the fluid and the surface.

Radiation

Radiation is a form of energy traveling across a space or through materials as electromagnetic waves, such as light, radio waves, or X-rays. In a vacuum, all the radiant energy waves travel at the same speed as light. On arrival at a body, they are absorbed, reflected, or transmitted. Visible light consists of wavelengths between 0.4×10^{-6} to 0.7×10^{-6} m (violet to red). Emission from combustion processes occurs principally in the infrared region (wavelengths longer than the red wavelength). Our eyes see only the tiny fraction that is emitted within the visible region.

A candle flame gives a common example of radiation. Air heated by the flame rises upward while cooler air moves in toward the candle to supply the flame with more oxygen, thus sustaining the burning process. If a hand is held to the side of the flame, it would experience a sensation of warmth. This energy is called radiant heat or radiation.

In the case of small fires, such as one involving a candle, most of the heat leaves the combustion zone by vertical convection, e.g., a hand held over the flame instead of beside it will sense more heat. However, larger, more hazardous fires release about equal amounts of radiative and convective energy. Radiated energy is potentially more dangerous because a stationary surface near the fire will absorb essentially all the radiation incident upon it, while most of the convected energy flows past the surface as it moves away with the gas stream.

Radiated energy travels in straight lines. Obviously, the heat received from a small source would be less than that received from a large radiating surface, provided the sources emit comparable energies per unit area. (See Figure 1-4B.)

Radiant heat passes freely through gases consisting of symmetrical diatomic molecules, such as hydrogen (H_2), oxygen (O_2), and nitrogen (N_2), but is absorbed by suspended particles, such as smoke, and in narrow wavelength bands by unsymmetrical molecules, such as water vapor (H_2O), carbon monoxide (CO), carbon dioxide (CO_2), and sulphur dioxide (SO_2). Although the concentration of these gases in the atmosphere is low, the presence of carbon dioxide and water vapor prevents radiation in the vicinity of 2.8 microns and 4.4 microns (in particular) from reaching the surface of the earth. Advantage is taken of this fact in the development of infrared flame detectors, which are blind to solar radiation and respond only to 2.8 microns or 4.4 microns. These wavelengths are emitted strongly by hot water vapor and carbon dioxide in flames. Note also that water vapor and carbon dioxide in the atmosphere can absorb appreciable amounts of radiation at distances from large fires. This helps to explain why forest fires or large LNG fires are less hazardous on days when humidity is high. Also, since water droplets absorb almost all of the incident infrared radiation, mists or water sprays are effective attenuators of radiation.

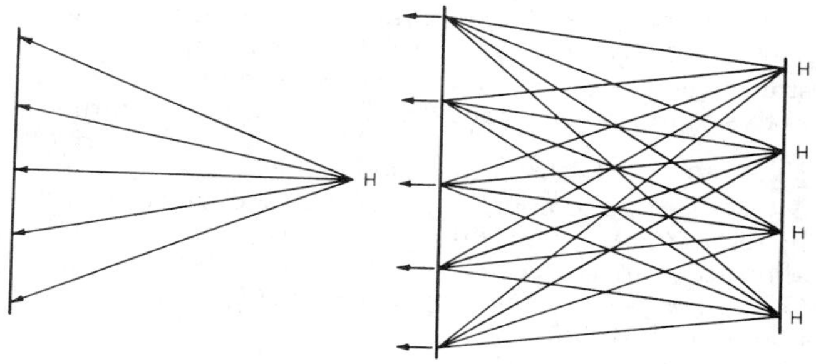

FIG. 1-4B. A comparison of heat absorption by surfaces of similar area from a pinpoint source (left) and a large radiating surface (right).

When two bodies face each other and one body is hotter than the other, radiant energy will flow from the hotter body to the cooler body until they both have the same temperature (i.e., thermal equilibrium). The ability to absorb this radiated heat is a function of the kind of surface of the cooler body and the area of the radiating surface of the hotter body. If the receiving surface is shiny or polished, it will reflect most of the radiant heat away; if it is black or dark in color, it will absorb most of the heat. Most nonmetallic materials are effectively "black" to infrared radiation, despite the fact that they may appear light or colored to visible radiation. Some substances, such as water or glass, are transparent to visible radiation and will allow it to pass through them with minimal absorption; however, both liquid water and glass are opaque to most infrared wavelengths. Glass greenhouses and solar panels operate on the principle of being transparent to the sun's visible radiation, while at the same time being opaque to the infrared radiation attempting to escape from the greenhouse or solar panel.

Shiny metallic materials are excellent reflectors of radiant energy. For example, aluminum foil often is used together with fiberglass in building insulation. Sheet metal is often used beneath stoves or on heat-exposed walls.

The Stefan-Boltzmann law states that the radiant emission per unit area from a black surface is proportional to the fourth power of its absolute temperature. The law can be expressed by the formula:

$$q = \epsilon\sigma T^4$$

where q is the radiant emission per unit surface area, ε is the surface emissivity correction factor (which is 1.0 for an ideal black surface and typically close to 1 for most nonmetallic materials in the infrared wavelength region), σ is the Stefan-Boltzmann proportionality constant [equal to 5.67×10^{-12} W/(cm$^2 \cdot$ K^4)], and T is the absolute temperature expressed in Kelvin. To appreciate the importance of this fourth power, consider the following situation.

EXAMPLE: A heater is designed to operate safely with an outside surface temperature of 500°F (260°C). What is the increase in radiation if this outside surface temperature is allowed to increase, say by 212°F (100°C) up to 680°F (360°C), or even increase by 464°F (258°C) to a total maximum to 932°F (500°C)?

First, it is necessary to convert the temperatures from degrees Celsius to their absolute values in Kelvin by adding 273 to them. Next, make the usual assumption that the surface is black, and then evaluate the radiant emission per unit area for safe operation [500°F (260°C)] as:

$$q = \sigma\,(260 + 273)^4 = 5.67 \times 10^{-12} \times (533)^4 = 0.46 \text{ Watts/cm}^2$$

The corresponding radiant emission per unit area at the higher temperatures are:

$$q = \sigma\,(360 + 273)^4 = 0.91 \text{ Watts/cm}^2$$

$$q = \sigma\,(500 + 273)^4 = 2.0 \text{ Watts/cm}^2$$

Thus, it can be seen that, by increasing the stove temperature by only 212°F (100°C), one approximately doubles its emission from 0.46 to 0.91 W/cm^2. This is the dramatic effect of the fourth power. If heat radiation was merely a function of the first power of the absolute temperature, then it would increase by only about 20 percent as the absolute temperature increased from 533 to 633 K. Finally, if one were so careless as to allow the stove to reach 932°F (500°C), it would emit 2.0 W/cm^2, which is sufficiently high to ignite many typical home furnishings.

Because residential coal or wood stoves can sometimes undergo a temperature "runaway" if given too much air, it is important to limit the maximum received radiant heat transfer by keeping all nearby furnishings away from the stove. The radiant energy transmitted from a point-like source to a receiving surface will vary inversely, as the square of their separation distance. If a stove is small relative to its distance from nearby objects, then it behaves like a point source; doubling its separation distance will decrease the incident radiant heat (per unit area) by a factor of four. However, if the nearby object is close to the stove, the stove appears like a large surface, and small changes in separation will have little or no effect on the severity of the radiative heat transfer (e.g., a large oven within a few centimeters from a combustible wall). In this case, one must protect the wall by some other means, e.g., a shiny, metal-coated. noncombustible board.

Generally, scientists and engineers have a good understanding of radiation between solid surfaces. They also can reliably estimate radiant heat transfer absorbed or emitted by gases of a known composition and temperature. However, they have difficulty in estimating the radiation from flames, because most of this radiation comes from the soot in the flames and there have been very few measurements of soot in flames. This lack of soot data often prevents the estimate of fire burning rates. There is, however, one useful rule of thumb: The total radiant output from flames [higher than about 8 in. (20 cm)] is usually about 30 to 40 percent of the maximum heat output, assuming complete combustion.[7] A comparable amount of energy leaves by convection, with the remaining fraction leaving in the form of incomplete combustion.

HEAT ENERGY SOURCES OR SOURCES OF IGNITION

Since fire prevention and extinguishment depend upon the control of heat, it is important to be familiar with the more common ways in which heat energy can be produced. Four sources of heat energy are: (1) chemical, (2) electrical, (3) mechanical, and (4) nuclear.

Chemical Heat Energy

Oxidation reactions usually produce heat. They are the source of the heat that is of primary concern to fire protection engineers.

Heat of combustion: The heat of combustion is the amount of heat released during a substance's complete oxidation (combustion, i.e., conversion to carbon dioxide and water). Heat of combustion, commonly referred to as calorific or fuel value, depends upon the kinds and numbers of atoms in the molecule, as well as their arrangement in the molecule. Calorific values are commonly expressed in Joules per gram, but are sometimes reported in Btu/lb or calories/g (1 Btu/lb = 2.32 J/g; and 1 cal/g = 4.18 J/g). In the case of fuel gases, calorific values are commonly reported in Btu/cu ft. Calorific values are used in calculating fire loading, but do not necessarily indicate relative fire hazard, since the fire hazard depends upon rate of burning, which is determined by the distribution of fuel, as well as upon the total amount of heat produced.

Also, heat is produced in incomplete or partial oxidations, which occur at some stage in almost all accidental fires and in spontaneous heating by oxidation. For almost all compounds of carbon and hydrogen, or of carbon, hydrogen, and oxygen (which include substances of vegetable or petroleum origin), the heat of oxidation, whether complete or partial, depends upon the amount of oxygen consumed. For these common substances, (e.g., coal, natural gas, common plastics, oils, wood, cotton, sugar, and vegetable and mineral oils) the heat of oxidation is approximately 3 kJ/g (3700 kJ/m^3, or 100 Btu/cu ft) of air consumed, regardless of the completeness of combustion. For this reason, the heat produced in a fire or in a spontaneous heating oxidation often is limited by the air (oxygen) supply.

Spontaneous heating: Spontaneous heating is the process whereby a material increases in temperature without drawing heat from its surroundings. If this results in a material reaching its ignition temperature, spontaneous ignition or spontaneous combustion can be said to have taken place. The fundamental causes of spontaneous heating are few, but the conditions are many and varied under which these fundamental factors may operate to create a dangerous condition. Three conditions that have much to do with whether an oxidation reaction will cause dangerous heating are: (1) rate of heat generation, (2) air supply, and (3) insulation properties of the immediate surroundings.

If exposed to the atmosphere, most all-organic substances capable of combination with oxygen will oxidize, with evolution of heat. The rate of oxidation at normal temperatures is usually so slow that it is usually imperceptible (e.g., the perishing of rubber); under these circumstances, the released heat is transferred to surroundings as rapidly as it is formed, with the result that there is no appreciable temperature increase in the combustible material being oxidized. This, however, is not true of all combustible materials, since certain oxidation reactions at normal temperatures (e.g., oxidation of powdered zirconium in air) generate heat more rapidly than it can be dissipated, with spontaneous ignition being the result.

In order for spontaneous ignition to occur, sufficient air must be available to permit oxidation, yet not so much air that the heat is carried away by convection as rapidly as it is formed. An oil-soaked (e.g., vegetable oil) rag which might heat spontaneously in the bottom of a wastebasket would not be expected to do so if hung on a clothesline where air movement would remove heat; nor would it be likely to heat up if it were sealed in a tightly packed bale of rags. On the other hand, because of more air and the insulating effect of the bale, a loosely packed bale might provide ideal conditions for heating. Because of the many possible combinations of the interrelated factors of air supply and insulation, it is impossible to predict with certainty whether a material will heat spontaneously.

In the presence of air, substances subject to oxidation will first form products of partial oxidation, which may act as catalysts to further oxidation. For example, olive oil which has turned rancid from exposure to the air will oxidize at a higher rate than fresh, pure oil.

Additional heat can initiate spontaneous heating in some combustible materials not subject to this phenomenon at ordinary temperatures. In these instances, preheating increases the rate of oxidation sufficiently so that more heat is produced than can be lost. Many fires have been caused by the spontaneous heating of foam rubber following preheating in a dryer.

A common cause of heating of agricultural produce is due to microbiological activity that generates heat. Since most bacteria cannot live at temperatures much above the range of 160 to 175°F (70 to 80°C), continued heating of such materials to their ignition temperatures is thought to be due to oxidation processes that become significant at these elevated temperatures.

The moisture content of agricultural products has a definite influence on the spontaneous heating by bacteria. Wet or improperly cured hay is very likely to heat in barn lofts. Experience has indicated that such heating may result in ignition within a period of two to six weeks after storage. Alfalfa meal that has been exposed to rain and then stored in bins or piles is very susceptible to spontaneous heating. Soybeans stored in bins have been known to sustain what is called "bin burn," i.e., the beans next to the bin walls are charred due to the moisture condensation on the inside surfaces of the wall and the self-heating of the beans. Other agricultural products susceptible to spontaneous heating are those with a high content of oxidizable oils, such as cornmeal feed, linseed, rice bran, and pecan meal.

Heat of decomposition: The heat of decomposition is the heat released by the decomposition of compounds which have been formed from their elements by endothermic reactions. Such compounds are intrinsically unstable, and when decomposition is started, such as by heating the substance above a critical temperature, decomposition continues with the liberation of heat. Acetylene and cellulose nitrate are well known for their tendency to decompose, with the liberation of dangerous quantities of heat. The chemical action responsible for this effect in many commercial and military explosives is the rapid decomposition of an unstable compound.

Heat of solution: The heat of solution is the heat released when a substance is dissolved in a liquid. Most materials release heat when dissolved, although the amount of heat is usually not sufficient to have any significant effect on fire protection. In the case of some chemicals, e.g., concentrated sulfuric acid, the heat evolved may be sufficient to be dangerous. The chemicals that react with water in this manner are not themselves combustible, but the liberated heat may be sufficient to ignite nearby combustible materials.

In contrast to most materials, ammonium nitrate absorbs heat when dissolved in water. (It is said to have a negative heat of solution.) Some first-aid products, for use where cold is recommended, consist of dry ammonium nitrate in watertight packages. These packages become cold when water is added.

Electrical Heat Energy

When current flows through a conductor, electrons pass from atom to atom within the conductor. The better conductors, such as copper and silver, have the most easily removed outer electrons, so that the force or voltage required to establish or maintain any unit electric current (or electron flow) through the conductor is less than for substances composed of more tightly bound electrons. Thus, the electrical resistance of any substance depends upon atomic and molecular characteristics; the electrical resistance is proportional to the energy required to move a unit quantity of electrons through the substance against the forces of electron capture and collision. This energy expenditure appears in the form of heat.

Resistance heating: Resistance heating is characterized by a rate of heat generation proportional to the resistance and the square of the current. Since the temperature of the conductor resulting from resistance heating depends upon dissipation of heat to the surroundings, bare wires can carry more current than insulated wires, without heating dangerously, and single wires can carry more current than closely grouped wires, or wires bundled into a cable of equivalent cross-sectional area.

The heat generated by incandescent and infrared bulbs is due to the resistance of the filaments in the bulbs. Material of very high melting point is used for the "white-hot" filaments of incandescent lamps, and destruction of the filament by oxidation is prevented by partial evacuation of the bulb and by removal of oxygen. The filaments of infrared lamps operate at a much lower temperature (a "red" heat); the most efficient infrared lamp reflectors are gold, because gold is one of the best reflectors of infrared radiation.

Dielectric heating: Whenever atoms are subjected to electric potential gradients from external sources, the arrangement of the atom (or of a molecule of several atoms) is distorted. A tendency exists for electrons to move in the direction of the positive potential and for protons to move in the opposite direction. This is true whether the externally applied potential is due to a battery or a generator, or is the result of a magnetic field. Even though the external potential is insufficient to break away any electrons, the distortion of the normal atomic or molecular arrangement represents an energy expenditure. This is of practically no consequence if the external force is unidirectional, but can be substantial if the potential is pulsating or alternating. For example, the heating of a dielectric (a good insulator) may be considerable if the frequency of alternation of external potential becomes high.

Induction heating: Whenever a conductor is subject to the influence of a fluctuating or alternating magnetic field, or whenever a conductor is in motion across the lines of force of a magnetic field, potential differences appear in the conductor. These potential differences result in the flow of current, with attendant resistance heating in the conductor. For rapidly changing or alternating potentials, additional energy is expended, and, as the polarity changes, this energy appears as heat energy due to the mechanical and electrical distortion of the molecular structure. This latter type of heating increases with the frequency of alternation. Food in a microwave oven, for example, is heated by the molecular friction induced by absorbed microwave energy.

A useful form of induction heating is created by passing a high-frequency alternating current through a coil surrounding the material to be heated.

An alternating current passing through a wire can induce a current in another wire parallel to it. If the wire in which a current is induced does not have adequate current-carrying capacity for the size of the induced current, resistance heating will occur. In this example, the heating is due primarily to resistance to flow, and only in a small degree to molecular friction.

Leakage current heating: Since all available insulating materials are imperfect insulators, there is always some current flow when the insulators are subjected to substantial voltages. This flow is commonly referred to as a leakage current and is usually not important from the standpoint of heat generation. However, if the insulating material is not suited for the service, or the material is too thin (for reasons of economy, space saving, or attempts to attain the maximum capacity in a condenser), leakage currents may exceed safe limits, resulting in heating of the insulator with consequent deterioration of the material and ultimate breakdown.

Heat from arcing: Arcing occurs when an electric circuit that is carrying current is interrupted either intentionally, as by a knife switch, or accidentally, as when a contact or terminal becomes loosened. Arcing is especially severe when motor or other inductive circuits are involved. The temperatures of arcs are very high, and the heat released may be sufficient to ignite combustible or flammable material in the vicinity. In some instances, the arc may melt the conductor and scatter molten metal. One requirement of an intrinsically safe electrical circuit is that arcing, due to accidental current interruption, will not release sufficient energy to ignite the hazardous atmosphere in which the circuit is located.

Static electricity heating: Static electricity (sometimes called frictional electricity) is an electrical charge that accumulates on the surfaces of two materials that have been brought together and then separated. One surface becomes charged positively, the other negatively. If the substances are not bonded or grounded, they will eventually accumulate sufficient electrical charge so that a spark may occur. Static arcs are ordinarily of very short duration and do not produce sufficient heat to ignite ordinary combustibles, such as paper. Some static arcs, however, are capable of igniting flammable vapors and gases, and clouds of explosible dust. Hydrocarbon fuel (e.g., gasoline) flowing in a pipe can generate enough static electricity of sufficient energy to ignite a flammable vapor.

Heat generated by lightning: Lightning is the discharge of an electrical charge from a cloud to an opposite charge on another cloud or on the ground. Lightning passing between a cloud and the ground can develop very high temperatures in any material of high resistance in its path, such as wood or masonry.

Mechanical Heat Energy

Mechanical heat energy is responsible for a significant number of fires each year. Frictional heat is responsible for most of these fires, although there are a few notable examples of ignition by the mechanical heat energy released by compression.

Frictional heat: The mechanical energy used in overcoming the resistance to motion when two solids are rubbed together is known as frictional heat. Any friction generates heat. The danger depends upon the available mechanical energy, the rate at which the heat is generated, and its rate of dissipation. An example of frictional heat is the heat caused by friction of a slipping belt against a pulley.

Friction sparks: Friction sparks include the sparks that result from the impact of two hard surfaces, at least one of which is usually metal. Some examples of friction sparks often reported as responsible for fires are sparks from dropping steel tools on a concrete floor, from falling tools striking machinery or piping, from tramp metal in grinding mills, and from shoe nails on concrete floors.

Friction sparks are formed in the following manner: heat, generated by impact or friction, initially heats the particle. The maximum temperature is usually determined by the lowest melting point of the materials involved, but with some metals, the freshly exposed surface of the particle may oxidize at the elevated temperature, with the heat of oxidation increasing the temperature until the particle is incandescent.

Although the temperatures necessary for incandescence vary with different metals, in most cases they are well above the ignition temperatures of flammable materials [e.g., the temperature of a spark from a steel tool approaches 2500°F (1400°C); sparks from copper-nickel alloys with small amounts of iron may be well above 500°F (300°C)]. However, the ignition potential of a spark depends upon its total heat content; thus, the particle size has a pronounced effect on spark ignition. The practical danger from mechanical sparks is limited by the fact that usually they are very small and have a low total heat content, even though each spark may have a temperature of 2000°F (1100°C) or higher. Mechanical sparks cool quickly and start fires only under favorable conditions, such as when they fall into loose dry cotton, combustible dust, or explosive materials. Larger particles of metal, able to retain their heat longer, usually are not heated to dangerous temperatures. Although the hazard of ignition of flammable vapors or gases by friction sparks is often overemphasized, it is best to avoid the use of grinding wheels and other sources of mechanical sparks in areas where any flammable liquids, gases, or vapors are, or may be, present. The possibility of ignition due to some unusual condition should not be overlooked.

Nickel, Monel metal™, and bronze have a very slight spark hazard; stainless steel has a much lower spark hazard than ordinary tool steel. Special tools of copper-beryllium and other alloys are designed to minimize the danger of sparks in hazardous locations. Such tools cannot, however, completely eliminate the danger of sparks because a spark may be produced under several conditions. Little or no benefit is gained by using nonsparking hand tools in place of steel to prevent explosions of hydrocarbons.[8] Leather, plastic, and wood tools are, however, free from the friction spark hazard.

Heat of compression: The heat of compression is the heat released when a gas is compressed. This is also known as the diesel effect. The temperature of a gas increases when compressed, and this has found practical application in diesel engines in which heat of compression eliminates the need for a spark ignition system. Air is first compressed in a diesel engine cylinder, after which an oil spray is injected into the compressed air. The heat released when the air is compressed is sufficient to ignite the oil spray.

Nuclear Heat Energy

Nuclear heat energy is energy released from the nucleus of an atom. The nucleus is composed of matter held together by tremendous forces which can be released when the nucleus is bombarded by energized particles. Nuclear energy is released in the form of heat, pressure, and nuclear radiation. In nuclear fission, energy is released by splitting the nucleus; in nuclear fusion, energy is released by the joining of two nuclei.

The energy released by bombardment of the nucleus is commonly a million times greater than that released by ordinary chemical reaction. Instantaneous release of large quantities of nuclear heat energy results in an atomic explosion. Controlled release of nuclear energy is a source of heat for everyday use (i.e., steam generation for electric generating stations).

BIBLIOGRAPHY

References Cited

1. Zabetakis, M. G., "Flammability Characteristics of Combustible Gases and Vapors," Bulletin 627, 1965, Bureau of Mines, U.S. Dept. of Interior.
2. Westbrook, C. K., and Dryer, F. L., "Chemical Kinetics and Modeling of Combustion Processes," Eighteenth Symposium (International) on Combustion, The Combustion Institute, Pittsburgh, PA, 1981.
3. Williams, F. A., "Mechanisms of Fire Spread," Sixteenth Symposium (International) on Combustion, The Combustion Institute, Pittsburgh, PA, 1977, pp. 1281-1294.
4. Kim, J. S., de Ris, J., and Kroesser, F. W., "Laminar Free-Convective Burning of Fuel Surfaces," Thirteenth Symposium (International) on Combustion, The Combustion Institute, Pittsburgh, PA, 1971, pp. 949-961.
5. Babrauskas, V., *New Technology to Reduce Fire Losses and Costs*, S. J. Grayson and D. A. Smith, eds., Elsevier, London, 1986, pp. 78-87.
6. Browne, F. L., "Theories of the Combustion of Wood and Its Control," Report No. 2136, 1958, Forest Products Laboratory, U.S. Dept. of Agriculture, Madison, WI.
7. deRis, J., "Fire Radiation—A Review," Seventeenth Symposium (International) on Combustion, The Combustion Institute, Pittsburgh, PA, 1979, pp. 1003-1016.1.
8. NFPA, "Friction Spark Ignition of Flammable Vapors," *NFPA Quarterly*, Vol. 53, No. 2 (Oct. 1959), pp. 155-157.

Additional Reading

Babrauskas, V., "Will the Second Item Ignite?" NBSIR 81-2271, National Bureau of Standards, Washington, DC, 1981.

Bowes, P. C., *Self-Heating: Evaluating and Controlling the Hazard*, HMSO, London, 1984.

Butcher, E. G., and Parnell, A. C., "Analysis of Fire Behavior," *Fire Surv.*, Vol. 14, No. 3 (1985), pp. 27-32.

Butcher, G., "Nature of Fire Size, Fire Spread and Fire Growth," *Fire Engineers Journal*, Vol. 47, No. 144 (1987), pp. 11-14.

Carslaw, H. S., and Jaeger, J. C., *Conduction of Heat in Solids*, 2nd ed., Oxford Univ. Press, London, England, 1959. [Reprinted 1986.]

Caydon, A. G., and Wolfhard, H. G., *Flames: Their Structure, Radiation and Temperature*, 4th ed., Chapman and Hall, London, England, 1979.

Drysdale, D. D., "Aspects of Smoldering Combustion," *Fire Prevention Science and Technology*, No. 23, 1980, p. 18.

Drysdale, D. D., *Introduction to Fire Dynamics*, John Wiley & Sons, New York, NY, 1985.

Friedman, R., "Ignition and Burning of Solids," ASTM STP 614 (1977), p. 91.

Friedman, R., *Principles of Fire Protection Chemistry*, 2nd ed., National Fire Protection Association, Quincy, MA, 1989.

Friedman, R., "Some Unresolved Fire Chemistry Problems," *Proceedings* of the First International Symposium on Fire Safety Science, Hemisphere, 1986, pp. 349-359.

Fristrom, R. M., and Westenberg, A. A., *Flame Structure*, NY, McGraw-Hill Inc., 1965.

Glassman, I., *Combustion*, 2nd ed., Academic Press, Orlando, FL., 1987.

Harmathy, T. Z., ed., *Fire Safety: Science and Engineering*, STP 882, American Society for Testing and Materials, Philadelphia, PA, 1985.

Heskestad, G., "Engineering Relations for Fire Plumes," TR 82-8, Society of Fire Protection Engineers, Boston, MA, 1982.

Huggett, C., "Rate of Heat Release—Implications for Engineering Decisions," *Proceedings*, Engineering Applications of Fire Technology Workshop, Society of Fire Protection Engineers, Boston, MA, 1980, pp. 233-145.

Kanury, A. M., *Introduction to Combustion Phenomena*, Gordon and Breach, New York, NY, 1977. [Reprinted 1984.]

Kelley, C., and Frickel, R., "Graybody Radiation from Conical Flames," *Fire Technology*, Vol. 8, No. 1 (Feb. 1972), pp. 24-32.

Kennedy, L. A., and Cooper, L. Y., "Before the Smoke Clears—Heat and Mass Transfer in Fires and Controlled Combustion," *Mechanical Engineering*, Vol. 109, No. 4 (1987), pp. 62-67.

Law, M., "Behavior of a Fire," *Proceedings* of the International Conference on the Design of Structures Against Fires, Elsevier, NY, 1986, pp. 15-20.

Levine, R. S., and Pagni, P. G., eds., *Fire Science for Fire Safety*, Gordon and Breach, NY.

Lyons, J. W., *Fire*, Scientific American Books, NY, 1986.

Palmer, K. N., *Dust Explosions and Fires*, Chapman and Hall, London, 1973.

Quintiere, J. G., *Fire Growth and Development*, Center for Fire Research, Gaithersburg, MD, 1989.

Quintiere, J. G., "Significant Parameters for Predicting Flame Spread," NBSIR 85-3109, Feb.1985, National Bureau of Standards, Gaithersberg, MD.

Rasbash, D. J., and Drysdale, D. D., "Fundamentals of Smoke Production," *Fire Safety Journal*, Vol. 5 (1982), p. 77.

Rasbash, D. J., and Drysdale, D. D., "Theory of Fire and Fire Processes," *Fire and Materials*, 7,2,79, 1983.

Schultz, N., *Fire and Flammability Handbook*, Van Nostrand Reinhold, NY, 1985.

SFPE Handbook of Fire Protection Engineering, "Section 1," National Fire Protection Association, Quincy, MA, 1988.

Spalding, D. B., *Some Fundamentals of Combustion, Butterworths*, London, England, 1955.

Strehlow, R. A., *Combustion Fundamentals*, McGraw-Hill Book Co., NY, 1984.

Weast, R. C., ed., *Handbook of Chemistry and Physics* 69th ed., CRC Press, Boca Raton, FL, 1988.

Zdanowski, M., Teadorczyk, A., and Wojcicki, S., "A Simple Mathematical Model of Flashover in Compartment Fires," *Fire and Materials*, Vol. 10 (1986), p. 145.

EXPLOSIONS

William J. Cruice

The term "explosion," in its most widely accepted sense, means a bursting associated with a loud, sharp noise and an expanding pressure front, varying from a supersonic shock wave to a relatively mild wind. Unfortunately, the term also has been extended to signify chemical or physical/chemical events that produce explosions. In addition, terms denoting specific chemical reactions are used as synonyms for "explosion." This blurring of meanings has caused confusion. Nevertheless, certain terms incorporating the word "explosion" that actually signify causative events must be used, since many such terms have relatively wide acceptance and reasonably specific meanings.

This chapter discusses explosions by detailing fundamental concepts, classifications by sources, blast effects and damage potential, physical explosions, gases and vapors, dusts and mists, thermal explosions and runaway reactions, deflagration/detonation, assessment of explosion potential, and countermeasures.

For related topics, see the following: Section 1, Chapter 4, "Chemistry and Physics of Fire;" Section 1, Chapter 6, "Theory of Fire and Explosion Control;" Section 3, Chapter 7, "Gases;" and Section 3, Chapter 12, "Dusts."

FUNDAMENTAL CONCEPTS OF AN EXPLOSION

An explosion is defined as a rapid release of high-pressure gas into the environment. The primary key word is "rapid"; the release must be sufficiently fast so that energy contained in the high-pressure gas is dissipated in a shock wave. The second key term is "high pressure," which signifies that, at the instant of release, the gas pressure is above the pressure of the surroundings.

Note that the basic definition is independent of the source or mechanism by which the high-pressure gas is produced. An explosion may result from the overpressurization of a containing vessel or structure by physical means (e.g., bursting of a balloon), physical/chemical means (e.g., boiler explosion), or a chemical reaction (e.g., combustion of a gas mixture). Certain explosions result from chemical reactions that proceed so quickly that the high-pressure gas is generated instantaneously, even though no confining vessel or structure exists (e.g., detonation of high explosives). The classification of explosions by their source of high-pressure gas is extremely useful. The fundamental concept of an explosion, then, is that of a sudden release of high-pressure gas and its dissipation of energy in the form of a shock wave.

The released high-pressure gas comes to equilibrium with the surroundings, creating certain effects while doing so. The characteristics of the effects of the gas on the surroundings depend upon: (1) the rate of release, (2) the pressure at release, (3) the quantity of gas released, (4) directional factors governing the release, (5) mechanical effects coincident with release, and (6) the temperature of the released gas. The latter two considerations are relatively straightforward in basic concepts. The striking of surrounding elements by high-temperature gases can cause severe heat damage, including direct damage to surfaces, thermal distortion, and fires in combustibles. Projectiles launched in the release process can impinge and cause crushing, piercing, and/or other structural failures. However, some explosions do not involve high-temperature gases and projectiles; the characteristics of the pressure wave are determined by the first four considerations.

Pressure equilibrates at the velocity of sound; in ambient air, the velocity of sound is approximately 1,100 ft per sec (300 m/s). For energy to be dissipated as a shock wave, the velocity of release must be sonic or supersonic. The initial shock wave spreads radially from the point of release. Its form near the point of release is of very short duration (milliseconds or microseconds) and includes a high-intensity impulse. As the distance from the point of release increases, the intensity (amplitude) decreases and the duration (period) increases until, far in the field, the impulse has a form similar to a mild breeze. (See Tables 1-5A and 1-5B, and Figure 1-5A.)

The initial intensity (amplitude) of the shock wave is determined by the pressure of the gas at the instant of release. The overall energy of the shock wave is related to the total quantity of gas released and the pressure and temperature at the instant of release. An estimate of the

William J. Cruice is vice president of Hazards Research Corporation, Mt. Arlington, NJ.

TABLE 1-5A. *Effect of Shock Waves (Physiological)*

Physiological Effect	Peak Overpressure, psi	(kPa)
Knock personnel down	1	(7)
Eardrum rupture	5	(34)
Lung damage	15	(100)
Threshold for fatalities	35	(240)
50% Fatalities	50	(345)
99% Fatalities	65	(450)

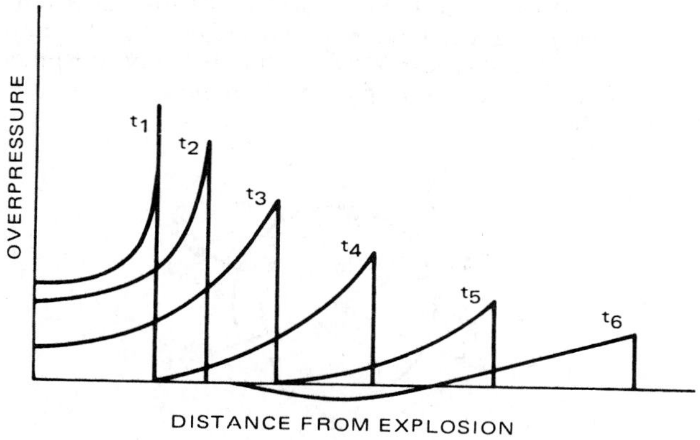

FIG. 1-5A. Decay of shock wave with distance. (Wave form at various times.)

overall energy available in a compressed gas is obtained by multiplying the pressure by the volume. In the event that high-pressure gas is generated following the initial release, the total energy released increases, but the shock wave intensity does not; the duration (period) of the impulse is longer.

If the gas is uniformly released simultaneously in all directions, the shock wave travels in an expanding sphere. However, the velocity of release must be at least sonic, and only certain types of events can bring about a uniform release at sonic or supersonic velocities. The vast majority of explosions involve some form of mechanical confinement (vessel or other structure) in which gas accumulates to high pressure. When its pressure exceeds the strength of the confining vessel, the vessel fails at its weakest point, and the shock wave travels in the direction of the failure. Thus, vessel failure explosions create a pressure wave that is generally not uniform in all directions.

Since the form of the initial shock wave impulse is dependent upon the total energy of release and is usually highly directional, the terms "near field" and "far field" are not numerically definable. "Near field" refers to the radial distance in which shock effects (shattering) predominate, whereas "far field" refers to the area beyond that, where observed damage corresponds to wind loading effects.

CLASSIFICATION OF EXPLOSIONS BY SOURCE

Physical *versus* Chemical

The basic division among explosions caused by a high-pressure gas is between physical and/or physical/chemical sources and chemical reaction sources. In certain cases, all of the high-pressure gas is produced by mechanical means or by events that do not involve a basic change of the chemical substance. Gas may be raised to high pressure mechanically; by external heating of gases, liquids, or solids; or a superheated liquid may be suddenly released by mechanical means and create high pressure by flash vaporization. None of these events involve changes in the basic chemical nature of the substances involved; the entire process of generating high pressure, and releasing and creating the effects of explosions, can be understood in terms of basic physics. These events are commonly called "physical explosions." (See Figure 1-5B.)

In other cases, generation of the high-pressure gas is the result of chemical reactions where the fundamental nature of the product(s) differs substantially from the material(s) previously present (reactant). The most common chemical reaction involved in explosions is combustion, in which a fuel (such as methane) mixed with air is ignited and burns to produce carbon dioxide, water vapor, and other products. Many other chemical reactions also give

TABLE 1-5B. *Effect of Shock Waves (Structural)*

Structural Element	Failure	Peak Overpressure, psi	(kPa)
Glass windows, large and small	Shattering usually, occasional frame failure	0.5–1	(3.5–7)
Corrugated asbestos siding	Shattering	1–2	(7–14)
Corrugated steel or aluminum paneling	Connection failure followed by buckling	1–2	(7–14)
Wood siding panels, standard house construction	Usually failure occurs in main connections allowing a whole panel to be blown in	1–2	(7–14)
Concrete or cinder block wall panels 8 or 12 in. (200 or 300 mm) thick (not reinforced)	Shattering of the wall	2–3	(14–21)
Self-framing steel panel building	Collapse	3–4	(21–28)
Oil storage tanks	Rupture	3–4	(21–28)
Wooden utility poles	Snapping failure	5	(34)
Loaded rail cars	Overturning	7	(48)
Brick wall panel, 8 or 12 in. (200 or 300 mm) thick (not reinforced)	Shearing and flexure failures	7–8	(48–55)

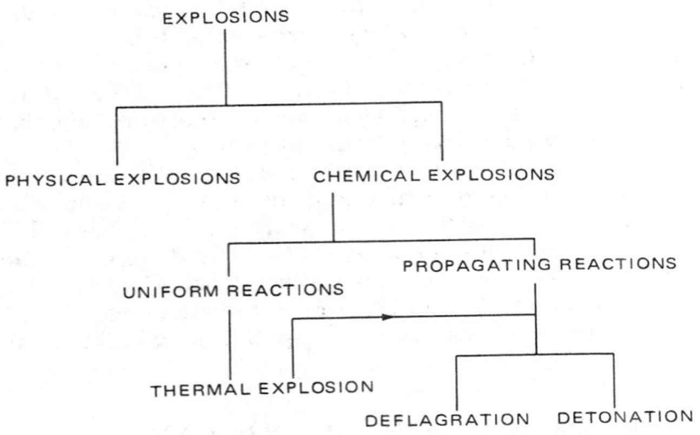

FIG. 1-5B. Classification of hazardous reactions.

rise to high-pressure gases. Explosions result from decomposition of pure substances, detonation, combustion, hydration, corrosion, and various interactions of two or more chemical substances in greater or lesser degrees of mixture. Any chemical reaction can cause an explosion if gaseous products are produced by the reaction, if substances not otherwise involved are vaporized by heat released by the reaction, or if gases already present are raised to higher temperatures by heat released by the reaction.

Chemical reactions are classified thermodynamically as either exothermic (heat releasing) or endothermic (heat absorbing). Whether heat is released or absorbed depends upon the conditions under which the substance(s) reacts. However, since a chemical reaction proceeds faster at higher temperatures and slower at lower temperatures, a chemical reaction that absorbs heat will cool and self-extinguish if external heat is not continually supplied. Thus, endothermic reactions can result in explosions only in special circumstances, where the reactant is brought into contact with a copious supply of external heat, and the reaction itself produces gaseous products. Examples of such reactions include certain decarboxylations, pyrolyses, and other forced decompositions.

Exothermic reactions, on the contrary, produce a temperature increase in the reaction mass, causing the reaction to proceed more rapidly. If heat is produced in the reaction mass faster than it can be lost to the surroundings, exothermic reactions easily become self-sustaining and self-accelerating. Such reactions can quickly become uncontrollable, even under carefully designed conditions, as well as under accidental conditions where few or no control mechanisms exist. Since heat is released, high-pressure gas can be created by vaporizing reactants, products, or surroundings, or by heating gases already present, even if no gases are directly produced by the reaction. Accordingly, nearly all chemical explosions result from exothermic reactions.

Uniform *versus* Propagating Reactions

Chemical reactions can be classified as *uniform* reactions, in which the chemical transformations occur essentially throughout the entire reaction mass, and *propagating* reactions, in which there is a clearly defined reaction zone separating the unreacted materials from the products of reaction, which moves through the reaction mass.

Uniform reactions: The rate of a uniform reaction depends only upon the temperature and the concentration(s) of the reacting agent(s) and is the same throughout the reaction mass.

As the temperature of the mass is raised, the energy-releasing reaction proceeds more rapidly and eventually leads to observable self-heating, in which the heat generated within the reaction mass exceeds that lost to the surroundings (in most cases, the walls of a vessel). Since heat is generated throughout the reaction mass, but lost more slowly from the center than from the outside surface, the center becomes hotter and its reaction rate increases. This rapidly increasing reaction rate in the center continues until the reactant(s) in the hot zone are either entirely consumed or the center erupts to dissipate the high temperature. (See Figure 1-5C.)

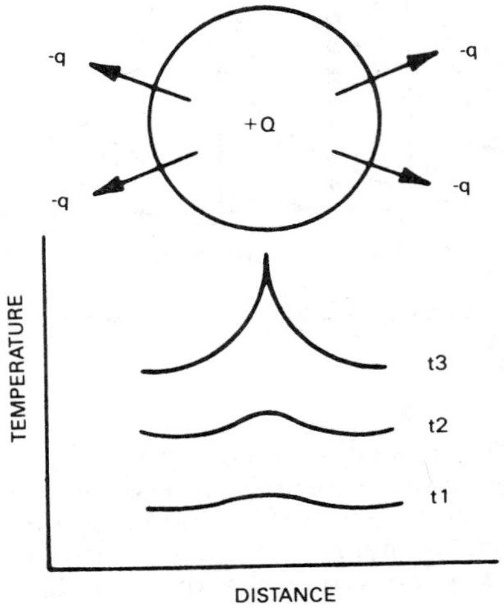

FIG. 1-5C. Growth of thermal explosion (+Q = heat generated, −q = heat lost, t = time).

Uniform reactions occur in solids, liquids, and gases. Gases undergo convection and diffusion quite readily; hot material can be transferred quickly from the center to the periphery, where heat can be lost more easily to the surroundings. Liquids also undergo convection and diffusion, although the effective rate of transfer is lower than with gases. Solids transfer heat exclusively by conduction and have the same higher heat production per unit volume as liquids. In general, solids present the greatest heat transfer problem. However, since mixtures of solids can react only at contact points between the reacting agents, most uniform reactions of solids occur with compounds that decompose, rather than with mixtures.

Pure liquids and true solutions can react rapidly and continuously. Liquid mixtures that form two separate phases, and liquids that react with undissolved solids, react only at the interface; the bulk rate of the reaction depends upon the surface area of globules or particles of the reacting phases where contact occurs. Stirring improves heat transfer from the center, which reduces the reaction rate of the system. However, stirring can also increase the reaction rate by bringing fresh, unreacted materials together (especially in multi-phase systems, such as slurries and immiscible liquids). The exact effect of agitation depends upon the specific system and the conditions existing within it.

Usually, uniform reactions generate gas too slowly to produce high pressure in the absence of a confining structure. A confined reaction can generate high-pressure gas by producing gaseous products, by vaporizing reactants or other materials, or by raising the temperature of gases present in the vessel. If a reaction produces a sufficiently high pressure, the confining vessel will rupture and an explosion will occur.

In practice, most chemical systems capable of uniform reaction can undergo alternative reaction paths, whether to the same or different products. The rates of reaction are quite different—largely determined by temperature, as shown in Figure 1-5D. Most uniform reactions, if not quenched by early release and/or dissipation of the high-temperature center, undergo a transformation to propagating reactions.

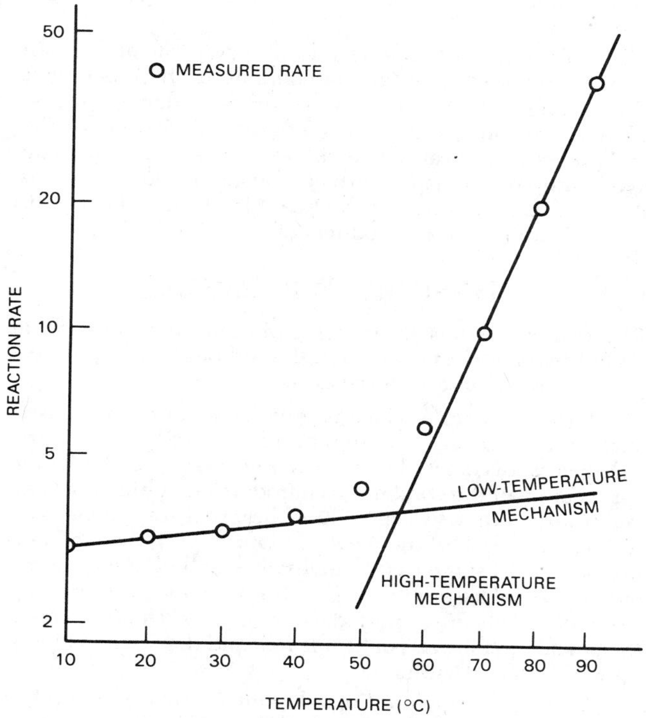

FIG. 1-5D. Change in dominant reaction path with temperature.

Propagating reactions: A mixture of hydrogen and oxygen can be stored at normal room temperatures for extensive periods with no sign of chemical reaction. However, most mixtures of hydrogen with oxygen react violently if an igniter is applied. The reaction begins at the igniter and travels through the mixture. Three distinct zones can be observed: (1) the reaction zone (flame), (2) the product zone (behind the flame), and (3) the unreacted zone (in front of the flame). This is a classic illustration of a propagating reaction. (See Figure 1-5E.)

A propagating reaction is always exothermic. The reaction is started by the creation of a relatively small high-temperature zone, whether by an external igniter (e.g., match, spark, or shock) or by heat buildup in the core of a uniform reaction system. For the reaction to propagate,

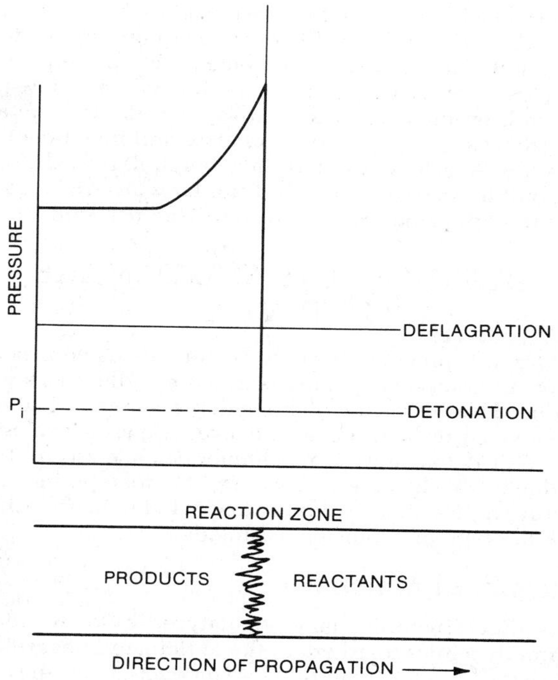

FIG. 1-5E. Instantaneous pressure profiles of propagating reactions.

the reaction core, which is activated by the igniter, must sufficiently raise the temperature of the surrounding material so that it reacts in like manner. The higher the initial temperature of the system, the easier it is to ignite, and the more likely it is to support a propagating reaction, since relatively less energy transfer is required to initiate the surrounding unreacted material.

Heat not transferred to the unreacted material is retained in the products of reaction or lost to the surroundings. The temperature of the products is determined by dividing the total heat retained by the heat capacity. Any pressure increase is determined by the vapor pressure of the system and conventional pressure-temperature-volume (PTV) relationships for any gases present or produced (directly or indirectly) by the reaction.

Since a propagating reaction begins at some specific point and travels through the reaction mass, the rate of energy release is related to the propagation velocity or rate of travel of the reaction zone. Propagation velocities vary from nearly zero to several times the speed of sound, depending upon composition, temperature, pressure, degree of confinement, and other considerations. Since pressure equilibrates at the speed of sound in the unreacted materials, a critical difference exists between subsonic reactions (deflagrations) and supersonic reactions (detonations).

Deflagrations and detonations propagate in gases, liquids, solids, pure compounds, and single-phase and multiphase mixtures. In many cases, a propagating reaction occurs only under some form of external confinement, as the reaction otherwise dissipates energy too rapidly to be self-sustaining. Confinement required for propagation varies widely with the rate of reaction and the physical state of the materials. It is necessary only that the reactants be kept in place long enough to react, and that the reaction zone retain energy for sufficient time to ignite unreacted material. Relatively weak confinement can be adequate for these purposes when the reaction time is only a few milliseconds or microseconds. Detonations and deflagrations can propagate in paper, plastic, glass and metal containers, pipes, reactors, tanks, drums, boreholes, wells, open pits, buildings, caves, tunnels, etc. Many materials sustain violent propagating reactions with no external confinement.

BLAST EFFECTS AND DAMAGE POTENTIAL

The primary procedures for estimating the damage potential of an explosion relate to the intensity of the shock wave produced by the release of the high-pressure gas. The most common means of estimating involve comparing explosions with TNT detonations, as much information exists on TNT-produced shock waves. However, the specific means of relating a potential explosion to TNT detonation differs with the type of explosion assumed.

Unconfined Materials

Unconfined materials may be analyzed by conventional thermodynamics to ascertain the anticipated heat release from a total reaction to most stable products. Once the available energy is determined, an assumption is made that the material can detonate, and the energy potential is considered to be released from an energy-equivalent mass of TNT. The intensity of the assumed shock wave then is obtained as a function of distance, using standard references.

It is essential to realize that this only provides an *estimate* of the possible damage potential *if the material can* detonate. Many materials will not support a detonation when unconfined. Whether or not a material can support a detonation must be determined by experimentation, using appropriately scaled samples. If the material cannot detonate, a very conservative estimate of deflagration pressure can be obtained by assuming that the thermal energy is released, and that the gases are formed at thermodynamic pressures within the geometry of the subject charge. A comparison then can be made using an energy equivalent mass of TNT.

Confined Materials

Confined materials must be analyzed in three ways. First, the charge should be evaluated in the same manner as for unconfined materials. The effective pressure front must be sufficient to rupture the confinement, or external damage will not occur due to an expanding shock front. Damage, however, may result from physical displacement of the confining structure due to unequal loading of internal shock waves.

Second, an analysis should be performed based upon thermodynamic pressure. The thermodynamic pressure must be sufficient to rupture the confining structure, or external damage from an expanding shock front will not be experienced. Conventional constructions (buildings, rooms, etc.) generally fail at quite low pressures; vessels generally fail at approximately four times the allowed working pressure. In all cases, the ultimate failure pressure of the confinement should be obtained from a competent structural engineer, with appropriate allowances for temperature, corrosion, and other weakening factors.

The third method of estimation is based upon equating the failure of the confinement to a shock front from a TNT charge. Vessel failure should be assumed and the amount of TNT required to produce a shock wave of intensity equal to the ultimate failure pressure of the vessel at the vessel wall should be determined, assuming the charge to be at the geometric center of the vapor space of the vessel. The shock wave then can be projected radially.

In all cases of confined materials, the pressure/shock wave estimates must be followed by an intelligent evaluation of the projectile effects, as ruptured vessels or building elements invariably produce some projectiles.

The initial estimation of the damage potential is frequently based upon the worst possible conditions of energy release, reaction velocity, etc. Using experimental data, the estimates can be refined. However, the confidence that can be placed in any estimate must be inversely proportional to the cost of being incorrect; conservative estimates of damage potentials are preferred, unless very strong evidence is cited to demonstrate that the worst case cannot occur.

Most combustions and explosions generate and release high-temperature gases and/or condensed-phase materials. These hot products can cause severe heat damage to personnel, structures, and adjacent equipment. Secondary fires and process upsets also are common. In assessing the damage potential associated with combustions and explosions, it is essential to consider the heat effects associated with the high-temperature products of reaction.

PHYSICAL EXPLOSIONS

Physical explosions are releases of high-pressure gas that do not involve chemical reactions, although most physical explosions involve vaporization.

Most physical explosions involve a confining vessel, such as a boiler, gas cylinder, or other tank. High pressure in the vessel is created by a mechanical compression of the gas, heating of the contents, or introduction of high-pressure gas from another vessel. When the pressure reaches the ultimate strength of the weakest portion of the vessel, failure occurs. In some cases, relatively small elements of the overall vessel assembly may be the weakest portions, and these elements are expelled as projectiles. In other cases, the actual vessel walls or seams fail, and the vessel is flung open with great violence.

Damage to surroundings depends primarily upon the failure mode. If small elements fail but the vessel remains essentially intact, the expelled projectiles are as dangerous as bullets or cannonballs; gas release, however, is highly directional and is controlled by the diameter(s) of the hole(s) created when the small elements are expelled. Under these conditions, the damage to the surroundings may be limited to projectile penetration, scorching or other harmful effects of hot gases, and/or minor displacement of weak structural elements. If the expulsion of small parts and the release of gases is unbalanced, the vessel will be thrust in the direction opposite to the gas expulsion, and may be toppled, hurled, or otherwise moved. Such an event can produce damage by crushing objects in the vessel's path, and/or can lead to the collapse of buildings or other structures if load-bearing elements are displaced or destroyed.

The failure of vessel walls or seams generally releases major projectiles and causes severe thrust of the vessel body in the direction opposite to the gas release. However, the gas release is extremely rapid under such circumstances, and a generally severe and broad shock wave is produced. The damage potential may be crudely estimated by multiplying the volume of gas in the vessel by the actual pressure at the moment of failure, although the accuracy of the estimate may vary considerably with the compressibility and the condensibility of the gas (which cools on expansion from the original vessel volume). The pressure wave from the rupture of the vessel is highly directional, traveling largely in the direction of release and creating equivalent pressure effects at much greater distances in that direction than in others, but substantial pressure effects are created in essentially all directions.

If the vessel contains a superheated liquid (i.e., a liquid at a temperature above its normal boiling point, or a liquefied gas, such as ammonia or carbon dioxide), flash vaporization of the liquid occurs when the vessel ruptures. A sufficient amount of liquid vaporizes to cool the discharged material to its normal boiling temperature, and the vaporized material adds significantly to severe pressure effects, depending upon the total amount of vaporizing per unit of time. This phenomenon is called a boiling liquid expanding vapor explosion (BLEVE).

An analogous phenomenon is the flash vaporization of a liquid (or, rarely, a solid) suddenly brought into contact with another substance at a temperature far above the ordinary boiling point of the liquid. Such events include spillage of cryogenic liquids or cold liquefied gases into the normal environment, or flash vaporization of liquids by hot metals or minerals. In such cases, the liquid receives heat from the hotter surface at a sufficient rate that a high-pressure gas is created instantly at the hot surface. If the interface between the cold liquid and the hot surface is large, vaporization can occur quickly enough to create a shock wave, spreading in all directions. Actually, the vaporization rate is usually significantly lower, but the rapid generation of gas frequently creates pressures high enough to destroy buildings or vessels. Sudden introduction of water into high-temperature boiler tubes, heat exchangers, or heat-transfer fluid tanks can produce severe explosions.

In the event that the discharged material can burn in air or otherwise chemically react with the environment into which it is discharged, a severe danger of secondary explosion exists.

GASES AND VAPORS

The most common form of chemical reaction that produces high-pressure gases from other gases or vapors is the combustion of gaseous fuels in air. However, other oxidizing gases (such as oxygen, chlorine, fluorine, and a variety of gaseous compounds and mixtures) may be substituted for normal air, frequently producing more severe combustion processes. Certain gases (such as acetylene, ethylene, ethylene oxide, butadiene, nitrous oxide, and others) can propagate a decomposition flame under proper conditions of temperature and pressure in the absence of any other gas. This latter phenomenon is generally called disproportionation.

For the general case of combustion involving a fuel gas and an oxidizing gas (such as air), mixtures are flammable only within a certain range of compositions. A minimum fuel proportion is required to sustain combustion; there is also a maximum fuel proportion above which combustion cannot be self-sustaining. Near these limiting fuel proportions, flames propagate through the mixture rather slowly, but in the middle of the flammable range, combustion velocities can be faster than the speed of sound. (See Figures 1-5F and 1-5G.)

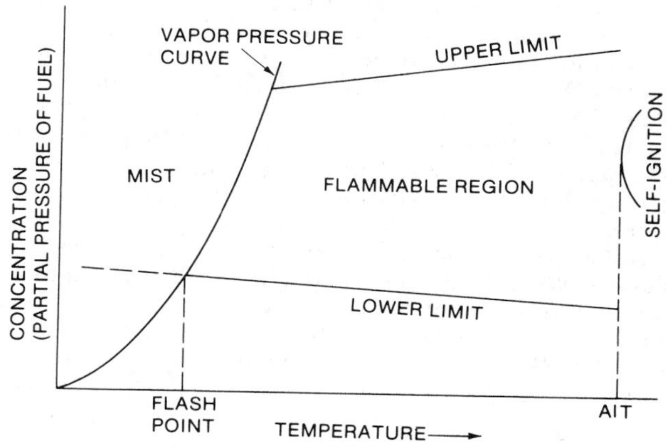

FIG. 1-5F. Flammability limits as a function of temperature.

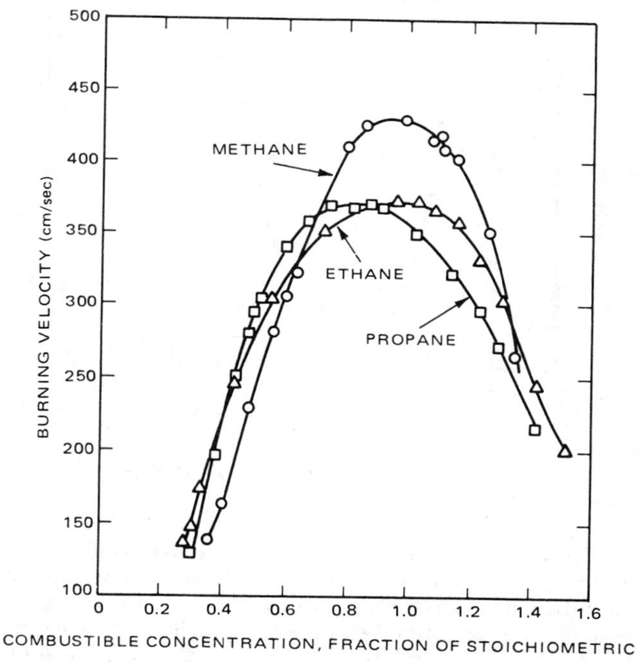

FIG. 1-5G. Combustion velocity vs. *concentration.*

In general, increasing the temperature and/or pressure of the mixture widens the flammable range and increases the combustion velocity throughout the flammable range. Generally, limits must be determined experimentally for the specific mixture, temperature, and pressure of interest.

The great majority of combustible gas mixtures are stable at ordinary temperatures and pressures. The combustion reaction must be initiated by some means. Once ignition occurs, the combustion reaction is self-sustaining by transferring heat and activated agents from the burned gas (products) to the unburned gas (reactants) at the flame front (reaction zone), and the reaction propagates from the ignition point to the physical limits of the combustible mixture.

Gas mixtures are generally more difficult to ignite near the flammable limits and most easily ignited somewhat above the precisely balanced (stoichiometric) mixture. In general, however, gas mixtures are very easily ignited anywhere in the flammable range. The concept of minimum energy requirement for ignition is very difficult to apply in practical situations, particularly since the minimum energy input required varies with the type of ignition source. The minimum electrical discharge energy required to initiate combustion is very different from the minimum shock energy, for example, and neither relates well to the energy requirements for hot surface ignition. Some mixtures (e.g., chlorine/fuel) can be ignited by radiant energy (e.g., visible light, ultraviolet light, etc.) of the correct frequency. (See Figure 1-5H.)

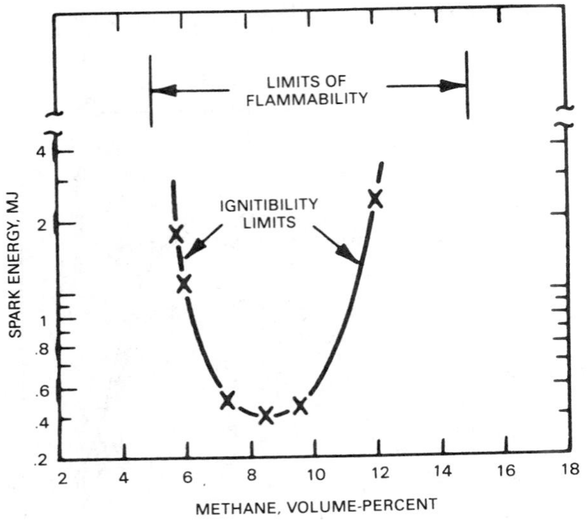

FIG. 1-5H. Ignition energy vs. *concentration.*

Most reactive gas mixtures are capable of self-ignition under specific conditions of temperature and pressure. At any given temperature, certain molecules are energetic enough to react when they meet; ordinarily such reactions and the heat liberated by them are not detectable. At some temperature, the intermolecular reactions are frequent enough so the gas mixture begins to self-heat and eventually reaches its kindling temperature. Propagating combustion then is initiated if the overall mixture is flammable at the temperature and pressure conditions attained.

Autoignition depends upon the specific mixtures of gases, the volume and geometry of the vessel, the materials of construction, and the initial temperature and pressure of the mixture and the surroundings. Published autoignition temperatures are specific to the method of determination and cannot be used indiscriminately. The existence of thermal and catalytic wall effects makes application of published autoignition temperatures to practical situations a delicate and potentially very dangerous activity. (See Figure 1-5I.)

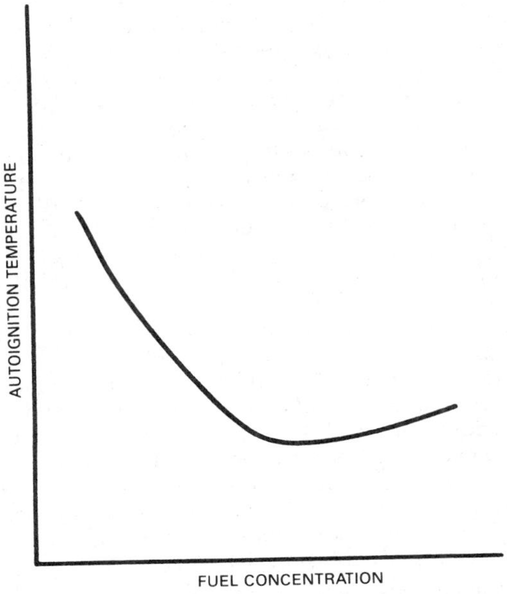

FIG. 1-5I. Autoignition temperature vs. *concentration.*

Pressure generated by the combustion of gas mixtures results primarily from the heat liberated and the consequent high temperature of the product gases. In most gas combustions, heat is lost to the surroundings by radiation from the flame, convection currents, etc. Generally, the highest pressures are attained when combustion occurs rapidly. For most confined subsonic combustions, the maximum pressure produced is approximately ten times the initial pressure, since the flame temperature is limited by dissociation reactions. This ratio may differ if the starting mixture is composed of compressible gases or if the fuel, oxidizer, or an otherwise inert component of the mixture can decompose and/or yield a significant change in the number of moles of gas in the system.

However, if the gas mixture is unconfined or if confinement is breached, the burning gas expands as a fireball at normal atmospheric pressure, and the maximum fireball volume is approximately ten times the initial volume of the mixture. As in the case of pressure generation, expansion of the mixture is least near the limiting concentrations and greatest near the middle of the range.

Gases that propagate decomposition flames generally exhibit minimum absolute concentrations (i.e., minimum reactive gas pressure and minimum ratio of gas to other gases in a mixture) below which the flame does not propagate. However, most such gases do not have upper limits, but are flammable from the lean limit to 100 percent. The characteristics of pressure generation, combustion velocity, fireball size, etc., are specific to each gas and do not relate readily to principles applicable to conventional fuel/oxidizer mixtures.

Certain gases and mixtures are inherently capable of supersonic, shock wave driven reaction (detonation) under appropriate conditions of temperature and pressure. For flammable gas/oxidizer mixtures, the detonable range is largely dependent upon the source of ignition, but always includes the stoichiometric and the fastest-burning ratios for the normal (subsonic) combustion reaction. Gases capable of sustaining a detonation ordinarily do not reach actual supersonic conditions unless initiated by a high-intensity shock wave. However, in certain confinement geometries, such as pipes, where the length exceeds the diameter by a factor of ten or more, a conventional combustion reaction can self-accelerate to the point where a transition from deflagration to detonation occurs if the mixture is in the detonable range of compositions. The final pressure generated in detonation is the same as the final pressure from deflagration, but the transient pressures created by the shock wave in the detonation process can be more than double the final pressure, and the effects on objects in the path of the shock wave can characteristically be more than four times the final pressure. Accordingly, vessels capable of containing deflagration maximum pressures can sustain partial or total destruction if the gas mixture detonates rather than deflagrates.

DUSTS AND MISTS

Dusts and mists (i.e., finely divided liquids) can generate high-pressure gas by combustion in air or another reactive gaseous environment. However, since the necessary chemical reactions can occur only at the interface of the dispersed particles or droplets with the surrounding gas, the rates of pressure generation are limited by the available surface area of the dispersed material. For any given mass of dust or mist, the surface area increases as the particle or droplet diameter decreases, so the violence of combustion for any given substance increases as the particles or droplets become finer. These dispersed condensed phases are quite similar in combustion behavior.

Combustion can occur with virtually any particle or droplet, but, in practice, most explosion hazards with dispersed materials are encountered with 20-mesh (840 micron) sizes or smaller. As the particle or drop size decreases, dispersion is more easily created and is relatively more stable and enduring. Accordingly, finer particles or droplets constitute graver hazards by making dispersions more likely, by remaining dispersed for a longer time, and by burning more rapidly than coarser particles. For most combustible agents, however, any ignition of a dispersion in air or other reactive gas can create pressures sufficient to destroy process equipment and structures.

There is a minimum uniform concentration for a propagating combustion to occur. There is no reliable upper concentration limit for dusts or mists, however, since the reaction is surface-area controlled. Most upper limits actually represent that concentration of dust or mist that renders some experimental igniter ineffective, rather than a true thermodynamic limiting concentration.

As a first step, the combustion process involves vaporization of volatile combustibles from the surface of the particle. Accordingly, coal with less than approximately 20 percent by weight volatiles (excluding moisture) does not propagate a dust combustion, but clay particles coated with volatile organics can produce dust explosions. In this context, "volatiles" include materials (e.g., soaps, flowing agents, silicones, etc.) that can be pyrolized or otherwise vaporized at high temperatures, as well as low-boiling solvents, etc.

The rate of pressure rise and the maximum pressure attained in dust combustions and mist combustions increase as the concentration of dispersed particles increases, generally passing through a maximum at a concentration that depends upon particle size, then slowly decrease as the concentration increases further. A substantial amount of data has been published for a wide variety of dusts, based on specific apparatus configurations. However, while useful for comparison with other dusts under the same conditions, the numerical values can be very misleading if improperly used. In particular, combustions of dispersed particulates are highly subject to turbulence, which greatly increases the rate of pressure rise actually experienced. Maximum pressures are about ten times the starting pressure, but are seldom attained. (See Figure 1-5J.)

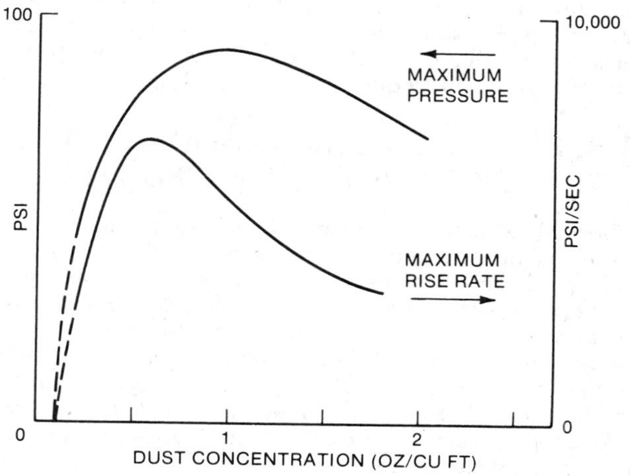

FIG. 1-5J. Severity of dust explosion vs. concentration.

Since dusts and mists frequently occur as dispersions in lightly constructed equipment, and since, in practice, there is usually a large supply of quiescent material that can be hurled into the air by the initial combustion, dust combustions and many mist combustions can self-propagate for large distances into areas where no flammable mixture previously existed. Dust explosions are frequently described as rolling explosions, characterized as sounding like distant thunder. Rolling explosions generally are initiated by a primary dust explosion that creates and ignites secondary dust dispersions, which in turn create and ignite further dust dispersions.

Ignition of dust and/or mist dispersions in air commonly is achieved by an electric discharge, open flame, or hot surface. The energy required for ignition is generally higher than that needed to ignite vapor/air mixtures, but is low compared to the energy sources available in the environment. Dusts and mists frequently cause abrasion and binding, with consequent generation of high-temperature surfaces or flames in mechanical equipment, which can, in turn, ignite the dispersion. Moving dust or mist particles frequently create electrostatic accumulations that eventually discharge and ignite the dispersion. Most insidious in dusty environments is the layering of particles on surfaces that become hot and initiate a combustion in the layer. A small puff of wind from the combustion in the layer creates adjacent airborne dispersions that are ignited by hot products from the original combustion. The resulting cloud formation can travel throughout an entire dusty area, creating widespread and massive destruction.

The presence of flammable vapors in dust dispersions, even far below the normal lower limit for the vapors, recently has been found to greatly enhance the ignitability and velocity of dust combustions. This synergistic effect emphasizes the uniqueness of many chemical systems and operating environments. Assumptions of behavior not experimentally or experientially confirmed or supported can be disastrous.

Effects of dust and mist explosions on the surroundings are analyzed in essentially the same manner as gas explosions. The same principles of vessel failure, structural failure, pressure generation, fireball generation, and secondary effects apply. However, unlike gaseous combustions, dust and mist combustions tend to create substantial amounts of condensed-phase products at very high temperatures, e.g., hot solids, tars, gums, oils, etc. These hot products tend to adhere to surfaces they contact, creating severe heat damage and frequently causing additional fires.

THERMAL EXPLOSIONS AND RUNAWAY REACTIONS IN CONDENSED PHASES

Thermal explosions and runaway reactions begin as uniform reactions, whether in reaction vessels, storage vessels, pools, or piles of material. All follow essentially the same pattern of heat accumulation and reaction rate acceleration. At some environmental and system temperatures, depending upon the size of the reaction mass, nonuniformities in temperature and the reaction rate lead to a change in the favored reaction mechanism so that it becomes a propagating reaction. If high-pressure gases are released, explosive effects are created in the environment, their form being determined by the rate at which the gas is released. In some cases, the change in mechanism may result in a detonation, with disastrous effects.

The general thermal runaway is frequently accelerated by either, or both, of two other chemical phenomena:

1. Autocatalytic reactions are those in which the reaction products chemically accelerate the initial reaction in which they were formed. The chemical acceleration often is more important than the self-heating effect. (See Figure 1-5K.)
2. The critical concentration effect can take two basic forms. In both cases, the initial reaction creates a metastable condition in the mass by slowly generating reactive products. In one form, these reactive products are capable of rapid exothermic decomposition, with the reaction rate being highly dependent upon the temperature. In the other form, the reactive products are capable of further exothermic reaction with the unreacted portion of the original chemical(s) present, and this form also is highly dependent upon temperature. In either event, the reactive products may accumulate in the overall mass until a slight increase in overall temperature produces an immense surge of reaction, rapid liberation of enormous quantities of heat and/or gaseous products, and usually a disastrous explosion.

Thermal explosions and runaway reactions differ from combustions of gases, mists, and dusts in several ways; these differences create significantly greater explosion potentials. First, the amount of material physically present in a unit volume is much greater in a condensed-phase system, and the total heat available within the reacting mass is many times greater than that for dispersions in air. Second, the attainable pressure is generally much higher for condensed phases, because the higher temperature reaction mechanisms usually produce large amounts of gaseous products in a limited vapor space. Third, the reaction mass generally swells and forms gas bubbles, with thermal expansion of the condensed phase. In some cases the thermal expansion alone can hydraulically fail a vessel that theoretically could contain the gases produced. This produces a BLEVE effect when the confinement is ruptured. Fourth, whether because of vessel rupture or boilover, large quantities of hot chemicals often are discharged into the environment. Under such circumstances, as the chemicals are usually combustible in air, catastrophic secondary explosions and fires occur.

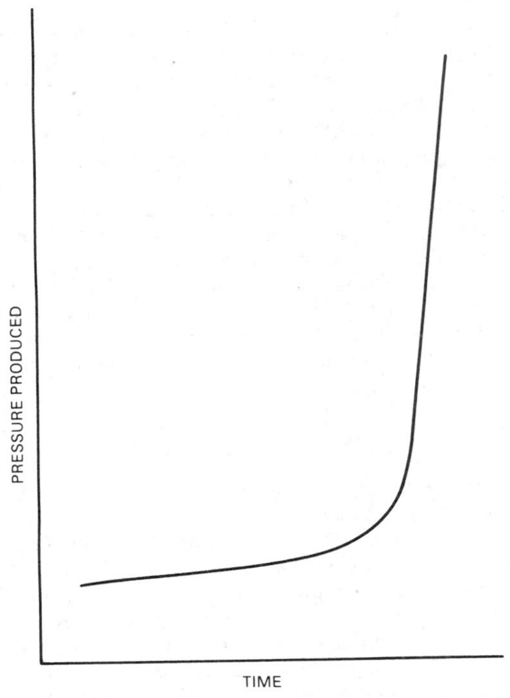

FIG. 1-5K. Autoacceleration of thermal decomposition.

Estimating the potential effects of thermal explosions and runaway reactions may be approached through the criteria just described; however, this method has limitations. It often is assumed that the ultimate pressure of a confining vessel is that at which it ruptures under any circumstances. In fact, the physical rupturing of a vessel requires a certain amount of time. If the reaction taking place in the vessel creates high pressure faster than the rate at which the vessel expands, the actual gas pressure upon release may be much higher than the pressure at which the vessel will fail under sustained load. Specific instances have occurred in which the effects of environmental damage clearly indicate that the actual gas pressure at release was two to ten times the maximum pressure the vessel would be expected to hold. Accordingly, if thermodynamic estimations of the damage potential predict significantly worse effects than would be anticipated from a rupturing vessel, it may be foolhardy to rely on the simple rupture model.

It is unwise to predict reaction paths in the absence of complete experimental information. Various evaluation methods are available to assess the actual severity and sensitivity of chemical systems under thermal explosion conditions; all the methods have limitations. Nevertheless, experimental assessments are essential for properly evaluating potential hazards of runaways. Furthermore, it is unrealistic to assess only the theoretical or desired compositions; process upsets in composition also must be anticipated and evaluated.

Thermal explosions and runaway reactions usually are associated with nitration, polymerization, and diazotization processes, and with chemical structures involving unsaturation or N-N, N-O, Cl-O, O-O, N-Cl bonds, among others. Generally, any reaction that is self-sustaining under existing environmental conditions theoretically can give rise to a thermal explosion. In chemical processing, this includes any reaction that does not require a continuous application of heat to proceed to completion. All such reactions must be assessed for thermal explosion/runaway reaction potential, with due regard for the fact that process equipment, controls, and personnel are subject to various failures and errors.

DEFLAGRATION/DETONATION IN CONDENSED PHASES

Theoretically, any exothermic reaction can be the basis for a deflagration or a detonation, provided the heat of reaction is directed in sufficient quantity into the unreacted materials. Accordingly, these features of the chemical system and its environment that promote such energy transfer favor propagation, whereas those that promote loss of the energy do not.

Propagating reactions deliver energy to the unreacted materials or to the surroundings. The amount of energy delivered is determined by the distance that the energy must travel and the ability of the energy to be transferred to the next reacting element. Consider a column of material, such as a full pipe, initiated at one end. The reaction zone may be represented as a cross-sectional element, with the radius being the distance the energy must travel to reach the surroundings. When the energy reaches the outer edge of the reaction zone, its loss to the surroundings is determined by the confinement characteristics (e.g., strength, heat capacity, etc.) of the containment vessel. Thus, propagation is generally favored when charges with larger diameters and stronger confinement vessels are used. There is a minimum diameter of charge below which a reaction will not propagate. This characteristic—the critical diameter—is specific to each chemical system and the effective characteristics of confinement. The principle of critical diameter applies equally to unconfined materials (e.g., solids, gels, etc.), although the critical diameter for an unconfined material is generally greater.

Propagating reactions that initiate in condensed phases are commonly associated with moving equipment, such as pumps and fast-acting valves, but they also begin from thermal decomposition in localized elements. Localized high-temperature conditions, whether arising from cavitation, friction, adiabatic compression, self-heating, external sources such as welding, electrical phenomena, mechanical impingement, fire, etc., can give rise to a propagating reaction if the chemical system and surroundings favor it. The effects of the reaction depend upon the velocity of propagation.

Deflagration of condensed phases produces higher pressures than deflagration of gases, mists, or dusts in air, as there is more energy released per unit of volume. The propagation proceeds by mass transfer (i.e., movement of heat and activated agents into the unreacted materials) at velocities ranging from millimeters per hour to hundreds of meters per second. The reaction zone is very hot and composed of gassified matter, much of which loses heat to confining pipes and vessels. In high-energy, low-velocity systems, the confinement frequently weakens due to excessive heating, and causes localized failures. Deflagrations are extremely pressure sensitive, since loss of confinement permits products and reactants to vaporize, and thus permits energy from the reaction zone to be lost as heat of vaporization. Accordingly, many deflagrations can be extinguished by releasing the pressure through venting mechanisms or by failure of confinement. The concept of critical diameter applied to deflagration relates more to heat capacity and thermal conductivity of the confinement vessel than to strength or rigidity. Since the reaction proceeds at mass transfer rates, heat losses to the walls are important, but the heat may travel through the walls to the unreacted material, sensitizing the system. Use of critical diameter principles in precluding deflagration is not widespread, since other, more reliable methods are available. (See Figure 1-5L.)

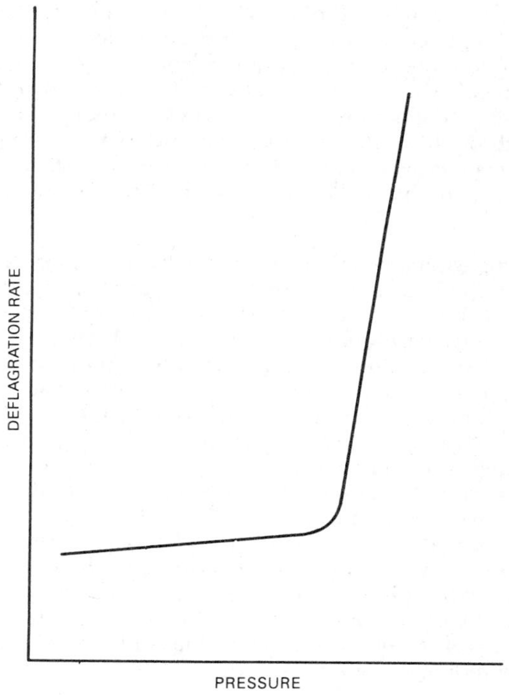

FIG. 1-5L. Effect of initial pressure on deflagration rate.

The detonation of condensed phases invariably produces extremely high pressures in the confinement vessel. The reaction proceeds in the unreacted material by shock compression at velocities ranging from slightly supersonic to several times the velocity of sound. There is a large impulse in the direction of propagation. The classic testing method for detonability of liquids involves placing a mild steel plate 0.375 in. (9.5 mm) thick above the 1.7-oz. (50 mL) sample and using a high-explosive charge to initiate the sample. If the sample propagates a detonation, a hole of the same diameter as the sample charge is produced in the unrestrained plate. (The test is usually done in a bunker, because in the open the plate may stay airborne for over 10 sec.)

Lateral pressures (at right angles to the direction of propagation) frequently are millions of pounds per square inch (PSI) (1 million PSI equals 6895 MPa), enduring at such levels for millionths of a second at any given point. Such tremendous impulses cause shattering of the confinement vessel, which flies apart, propelled by the still-high pressure of the products. Usually, the shock wave in the chemical system passes the fragmenting confinement vessel faster than the parts of the vessel can physically move. Detonations cannot be quenched by conventional venting methods. Propagation can be interrupted only by reducing the diameter of the unreacted material below the critical diameter in the specific confinement vessel, or by breaking the continuity of the chemical system creating the shock wave. Since the shock wave is traveling thousands of meters per second, the latter option is rarely feasible. The use of critical diameter traps with certain chemicals is well established, however.

Detonations obviously are more dangerous than deflagrations. Theoretically, however, any material that is exothermic can sustain a detonation under some set of circumstances. In keeping with theory, it is frequently found that condensed-phase deflagrations can self-accelerate under confinement to a point where a deflagration becomes a detonation. The transition is attributed to the preheating of unreacted materials by energy transmissions through confinement vessels and by pressure-piling and precursor wave effects in the unreacted material itself, as well as to physical changes, such as bubble formation, etc.

Propagating reactions in condensed-phase systems are particularly hazardous, in that large masses of liquids, solids, and slurries frequently are connected to operating equipment by pipelines, conveyors, etc. Accordingly, it is possible for a minor malfunction (e.g., pump cavitation, auger friction, valve compression) to initiate a reaction that can deflagrate or detonate through the mass transfer system to storage vessels or transportation tanks, with catastrophic results. The most insidious condition occurs when a deflagration reaction propagates in piping that is small enough to prevent transition to detonation. If the deflagration enters a vessel, it may easily become a detonation, because the vessel diameter is no longer the controlling factor. Under this condition, the entire volume of material in the vessel will probably detonate, because the shock wave travels through the material faster than the material can be moved by the pressure.

ASSESSMENT OF EXPLOSION POTENTIAL

All explosions involve materials that release energy to the surroundings. All accidental explosions result from abnormal conditions or "upsets" in a system at equilibrium. Assessing the explosion potential involves two distinct sets of information. The first involves the fundamental nature of the substances being processed, stored, handled, used, or transported. The second includes the characteristics of the specific equipment in which the substances are present. While the data sets are distinct, it is necessary to consider the effects of each on the other, so the actual assessment process involves a high degree of iteration. Consideration must also be given to the environment in which the system is located, including both abnormal energy inputs and the effects of system abnormalities.

Properties of Materials

This information may best be understood in terms of two basic concepts corresponding to two basic questions: (1) *Severity*—type and power of reactions, i.e., "What can it do?," and (2) *Sensitivity*—initiation modes, i.e., "What can cause it?" The distinction appears obvious, but confusion and error in explosion assessment results if the distinction is not made.

Severity: The various types of reactions have been discussed with particular characteristics highlighted. For assessment, however, it is inadequate to qualitatively describe reactions. It becomes essential to determine the maximum pressures and temperatures of reactions, rates of increase of pressure and temperature, heat of reaction, etc., and the conditions under which such reactions can occur. These determinations should be independent of the conditions under which handling, etc., is expected to occur, but maximum attention is often given to those conditions that are expected. Such practice can be risky, because all such characteristics and conditions are not predictable. Preferred practice includes a determination of the material properties under extreme conditions, at least initially.

Severity is a more critical element in assessing subject materials for several reasons. First, if the materials cannot undergo an explosion-generating reaction, questions regarding sensitivity do not apply. Second, if the material can react to produce explosive forces, it is reasonable to anticipate that input energy can somehow concentrate to initiate the reaction. Third, since severity experiments employ strong rather than marginal initiators, severity experiments are more reliable than sensitivity experiments.

Usually the first step in assessing severity involves comparing the material structures with those of materials having known properties. The thermodynamic potential is evaluated by manual or computerized calculations. [The manual process is arduous; use of the ASTM Chemical Thermodynamic and Energy Release Evaluation Program (CHETAH) is far superior.] In the final analysis, however, the results of such efforts must be tested by experimentation.

Sensitivity: All initiation mechanisms involve an input of energy into the subject materials. If a specific form of potential initiation energy is chosen, the minimum amount of such energy required to produce a reaction can be determined. However, it is essential to realize that the minimum energy requirement varies widely with the type of initiation energy chosen. There is no reliable quantitative relationship between sensitivity to electrical sparks and sensitivity to mechanical impact, for example. Relationships between different types of energy inputs are complicated in that any source delivers energy in multiple forms, and only those forms that can be absorbed by molecular bonds are effective in initiating chemical reactions. Even under carefully controlled conditions, sensitivity determinations are apparatus-dependent. Applying minimum energy values to real situations presumes that the same general phenomenon (e.g., electric arc) will exhibit the same distribution of energy forms in the laboratory and in the field. Such an assumption is never 100 percent reliable, and can be disastrous.

In practice, energy inputs that create localized high temperatures are those most likely to initiate a chemical reaction. The most commonly evaluated forms of energy input are flames, electrical discharges, hot surfaces, mechanical compression, and shock-wave compression. Other commonly recognized sources of initiation energy are special cases of the above, e.g., friction that creates hot surfaces and/or mechanical compression. Such initiation sources often are evaluated separately, but the measurements thus obtained are so highly apparatus-dependent that applying them to real situations is possible only by analogy.

Assessing thermal sensitivity is actually a severity procedure (i.e., responds to "What can it do?") rather than a sensitivity procedure. Although materials are ranked as more or less thermally sensitive according to the temperature at which self-accelerating decomposition appears, any determined threshold temperature for self-acceleration is highly apparatus-dependent. Further, thermal decomposition is dependent only upon the mass temperature and how it is attained. Thus, there is no way of measuring a discrete energy input that initiates uniform thermal decomposition. Essentially all sensitivity evaluations refer to propagating reactions of one form or another.

Thermal stability evaluations are, however, the most comprehensive and reliable assessments that can be performed, primarily since the reactivity is independent of the mode of energy input. The thermal stability of a chemical system, properly evaluated, provides more widely applicable information than any other evaluation procedure. Generally, if the subject materials can release energy, the phenomenon will appear in a proper thermal stability evaluation.

Assessing severity and sensitivity characteristics depends heavily upon selecting materials for evaluation. The potentials of the system must be probed, or the exercise can yield a false sense of security. Consideration must be given not only to those materials and ratios that are planned, but also to those that may arise from malfunctions, human errors, and normal variations in the operating system.

Properties of the System

The "system" used here refers to the operating equipment in which the materials are or can be found. Any system includes *active* or operating elements, and *passive* or nonoperating elements.

Active elements: This term refers to units that use moving parts, such as pumps, blowers, grinders, valves, stirrers, classifiers, etc. These represent paths by which external energy is supplied to the materials under normal operating conditions. Further, most such equipment has a built-in capacity that is greater than required for normal use, and, in the event of malfunction, can usually input energy at levels far above normal and can input energy in form(s) quite different from normal. (A blower or fan, for example, normally supplies energy for transporting gas; the energy is moderate and supplied discretely through the motion of the blades. If a blade is distorted, however, energy is concentrated in the form of molten particles from the fan blade or housing, which are highly efficient ignition sources.)

Assessing the explosion potential requires determining the type and intensity of energy transmitted to the materials and comparing it with the sensitivity characteristics of the materials. First, the analysis is performed with respect to the normal operation of active elements over the range of materials that could be affected. All active elements should be found safe in the normal mode by substantial margins. The types and intensities of energy input possible under various failure modes are then assessed, and the results compared again with the sensitivity of the materials. This analysis must indicate further safety margins, or action must be taken to prevent any failure mode from supplying excessive energy inputs, or, ultimately, action must be taken to protect personnel from the effects of the reaction(s) that may be produced.

Assessment of active element failure must be succeeded by the opposite consideration, i.e., the results expected when the active elements fail to function. Pump or valve failure may prevent the transfer of hot materials and consequently result in excessive high-temperature exposure. Filter failure may produce dangerous material concentrations downstream. Fan failure may permit accumulation of flammable vapors. Assessing this phase requires a good working knowledge of the system and all its elements, so that an elemental failure can be understood in terms of effects on other parts of the system. The ultimate objective is to ensure that the system is so designed that all such failures cannot lead to an explosion, or to ensure that proper design features are incorporated to control explosive effects and protect personnel and surroundings.

Passive elements: The nonoperating elements of the system do not supply energy to the materials. Instead, these elements confine materials and the energy that the materials carry or release. Passive elements thereby affect the type of reaction that can occur as well as the magnitude and form of pressure that is released. Passive elements also can create conditions under which energy in the materials can be concentrated and/or transformed, creating potential ignition conditions. Examples of such phenomena include generation of electrostatic charges in flowing materials, adiabatic compression of vapors in dead-ended pipes, and catalytic effects of container surfaces. Passive elements frequently can be corroded and/or dissolved by the contents, altering the composition of the materials that subsequently reach other points in the system. The geometry of passive elements can produce collection points for highly sensitive materials that tend to separate from the normal flow, thereby creating localized concentration gradients that may cause a disaster. The passive elements of the system cannot be ignored while assessing the explosion potential. Examining the passive elements of the system must be guided by a consideration of the characteristics of the materials to be contained and of the active elements. The passive elements must be appropriate in strength, geometry, and chemical properties for the contents under the conditions of energy inputs that can prevail during normal and malfunctioning conditions.

The Environment

Here "environment" refers to the immediate surroundings of the system that can interact with materials in the system. The immediate environment often is treated as an extension of the operating system, because environmental features also can be active or passive. Since all interactions are by definition abnormal, the evaluation procedures are often judgmental.

The environment can contribute energy to the system by lightning, welding or tapping, external fire or explosion, impingement of moving machinery or vehicles, and many other means. Some such inputs can be precluded by design, others by protective structures, and still others by administrative controls. For all practical purposes, any environmental energy input to the system that can be credibly anticipated must be considered, as much harm can be produced.

Environmental effects, such as loss of water, power, gas, etc., must be considered, and frequently present more severe problems than environmental energy sources. While utility losses frequently will be anticipated when considering the functional failure of active elements, it is desirable to separately assess the effects of losing utilities. This separate assessment requires evaluating the simultaneous failure of multiple functioning units, a condition often overlooked or considered unlikely, but an obvious result of utility losses.

Finally, the environment, e.g., a building, should be considered in regard to the escape of materials from the system, both by leakage and by explosive breaches of containment. In assessing the effects of leaks, concern should be given to the risk of fire/explosion within the escaped materials alone or as they are mixed with air. Explosive containment breaches create severe potentials for secondary explosions of the expelled materials in air; however, they also create failures in adjacent structures and systems, including the loss of utilities in otherwise unrelated areas. Assessing the explosion potential must address such secondary effects that can change a minor system upset into a disaster.

COUNTERMEASURES

Despite the best efforts of design and operating personnel, human errors occur, equipment breaks, and instruments fail, frequently producing potentially explosive conditions. However, by properly assessing explosion potential, the character and severity of such upsets and resultant explosive reactions can be determined, and countermeasures can be designed into the operating system. In this context, countermeasures mean system elements or operations designed to cope with explosive or potentially explosive reactions, rather than preventive measures.

Countermeasures can be grouped into five general types: (1) containment, (2) quenching, (3) dumping, (4) venting, and (5) isolation.

Containment

In many cases it is feasible to design the operating system to contain the maximum credible pressures and/or other forces that can be produced by the anticipated explosive reaction. Because of the design, there is no sudden release of pressure to the environment, there is no explosion, properly speaking.

The prime benefits of containment design are that it is *passive* (i.e., no operating function is involved), and it is clean (i.e., no dissipation of materials occurs). The primary disadvantage is that, since the energy released in the shock wave is closely related to the failure pressure, containment places a very high premium on accuracy of forecasted intensity. If the reaction should be intense enough to breach containment design, the resulting explosion will be far worse than would result from a normal operating design.

Containment is most easily practiced in cases involving gas-phase combustions, where maximum pressures of up to ten or twenty times the initial pressure are the rule. Containment can also be practiced in many cases involving dust and mist combustions, and in certain low-intensity condensed-phase runaway or thermal decomposition reactions.

Containment of normally intense thermal runaway/decomposition reactions is extremely difficult because of the overall volume of the reactants and the maximum pressures that can be attained to render containment design impractical from both engineering and economic viewpoints. Practical containment for normally intense thermal reactions is limited to relatively low-volume systems in bench-scale, pilot-scale, or custom processing operations. The same considerations apply to deflagration in condensed phases.

Containment of condensed-phase detonations is practical only in very limited cases, as the pressure and impulse characteristics are such that extremely heavy equipment is needed, and the lifetime of such equipment is usually very brief.

Quenching

Quenching of potentially or actually explosive conditions involves either heat removal or chemical inhibition. Heat removal may be performed by external means (e.g., emergency additional heat-sinking capacity of equipment) or by introduction of a new material to absorb heat of reaction. Chemical inhibition procedures involve introduction of new material(s) into the chemical system to abate reaction by dilution or by removing active chemical species. Quenching is attractive in many cases because no release to the environment is involved, but is practical only when the function (i.e., heat removal, dilution, etc.) requires a short time relative to the time to explosion.

The most common quenching application is the use of flame arrestors to prevent propagation of vapor/air combustions, wherein heat from the flame front is lost to the flame arrestor, the reaction zone is cooled, and the reaction rate drops sharply. To be effective, these passive units must have a high heat-sinking capacity relative to the heat output of the flame, must have a high surface area in contact with the flame, and must be large enough to cool the gas mixture below the temperature at which reignition can occur. Flame arrestors are generally designed to cope with a specific range of flames. It is essential in selection of flame arrestors that the designer be confident that the chosen unit will, in fact, cope with the potential flame.

Gas, dust, and mist combustions can also frequently be combated by dilution with carbon dioxide, water, mist, steam, certain dry powders, etc., to create enough internal heat-sinking capacity to abate or extinguish the flame front. Use of halogenated hydrocarbon suppressants for extinguishment of gas, dust, and mist combustions involves chemical interference with the flame propagation mechanism, as well as heat-sinking and dilution effects. In all cases, operation of an injection system is needed to introduce the quenchant. This system must operate fast enough to catch the flame front, an operation involving a detection subsystem and a discharge subsystem. Reliability of these subsystems must be considered in the assessment of explosion potential. Further, it must be considered in design whether the introduction of the quenchant will independently create sufficient pressure and/or other forces to cause damage, possibly equivalent in severity to the potential damage from the "prevented explosion." This latter consideration applies particularly to many applications in powder-handling equipment, storage vessels, and building-type structures.

Quenching by introduction of heat-absorbing, diluting, or chemically interfering reagents into condensed-phase systems is invariably a more time-consuming process, generally applicable only to uniform reactions caught early in the self-accelerating stage. In most condensed-phase systems, the mass of reagents is large, and a correspondingly large mass of quenchant must be introduced and thoroughly mixed to be effective. In certain cases, chemical inhibitors can be effective in relatively small concentrations, but the required extent of mixing is also very high. Selection of quenchants is a highly technical matter, but certain generally desirable characteristics may be mentioned. The quenchant should have a high effective heat capacity, fluidity, and miscibility with the reagent mixture, but should also have a low vapor pressure even at high temperatures. It is worth restating that, in all cases, the quenching process requires operation of subsystems for detection and injection; the reliability of these subsystems must be considered in a reassessment of explosion potential after the quenchant system has been designed.

Quenching is generally inapplicable in coping with propagating reactions in condensed phases, with the exception of critical-diameter traps for reaction in pipelines. Introduction and proper mixing of quenchants are generally too slow to be valuable for deflagration or detonation processes, especially in pipelines or other confinement of similar geometry.

Dumping

Dumping essentially means the release of the reaction mixture itself (as opposed to venting, which usually means release of gas). Dumping is ordinarily a relatively slow process applicable to the early stages of a self-accelerating uniform reaction, and, as ordinarily understood, implies the transfer of the reaction mixture to an alternate containment of some kind. The term is more commonly applied to condensed phases, but, in actuality, the procedure is often used with gas-phase systems that may be "blown down" in the event of an upset condition.

Dumping does not stop the reaction, of course, but merely transfers the problem to a (presumably) more favorable location for other treatment. Most commonly, condensed phases are dumped to a cold quenchant-filled vessel; this vessel must itself be capable of withstanding or coping with a potentially explosive condition in the event that the quench process does not proceed properly. Gas mixtures may be dumped through scrubbers, into catch tanks, and/or to the environment, depending on the gases involved. Again, receivers must be examined relative to the consequences of continued reaction after dumping. Further, dumping is again an active process requiring operation of subsystems whose reliability must be factored into the overall assessment of explosion potential.

Venting

Venting refers specifically to the release of gas from a vessel or confining structure in a controlled manner. The venting may be performed by manually operated elements; automated elements; preloaded elements; or fully passive elements, such as burst discs, rupture panels, or blowout walls. This countermeasure is useful for coping with gas, mist, and dust combustions, uniform or propagating condensed-phase reactions, and most conditions leading to physical explosions. The essential requirements are that the vent system be sufficiently fast acting to become fully operational in a timely manner, and that the vent be capable of releasing gas from the confining structure at the maximum rate at which gas is being formed by the potentially explosive situation.

Venting of all-gas systems is, in general, fairly well understood in practical terms. The rate of gas generation is reasonably easy to establish, and the equations describing the fluid dynamics are common currency in engineering. The situation changes markedly when the confining structure contains a liquid near or above its normal boiling point or a liquid with substantial amounts of gas dissolved under pressure. The sudden release of pressure almost invariably results in sudden boiling, swelling, and foaming of the liquid, and the vented matter is commonly a mixture of gas and liquid that obeys a radically different fluid dynamic.* In many cases, essentially all of the liquid is expelled from the tank in the venting process. Accordingly, even when the gas phase can safely be vented to atmosphere, provision must be made for effluent liquid as part of the overall design of the vent system.

In addition to the engineering design of the venting process elements, there are two other critical aspects of vent system design that must be considered:

1. The venting process releases material from the original location to another location. Venting frequently includes discharge of hot gases, liquids, and/or solids, which may burn or otherwise react with materials in the receiving location. Venting frequently includes discharge of flammables, and improper selection of a receiving location can produce a hazardous condition, possibly of greater severity than the original. Venting of "harmless" gases into occupied areas can reduce oxygen levels and cause personnel injuries. In general, venting should discharge to the outside or to locations designed specifically to cope with the vented materials.
2. The venting process produces dynamic effects on the equipment from which material is discharged and on equipment elements in the receiving area. Since the discharge is generally not uniform in all directions, the discharging element must be capable of withstanding the thrust effect, which is equal and opposite in direction to the discharge. The discharging element must also be capable of withstanding other dynamic effects of venting, such as vibration, internal materials flows, and sustained flowing pressure, during the venting process. In the receiving location, equipment and structural elements are subjected to shock and/or pressure effects from the venting process, and load-bearing elements must bear the mass of discharged material and (in cases of rupture or blowout elements) potential projectile effects. Accordingly, the overall design of the venting system extends beyond speed and capacity of the vent element to inherently include consideration of the effects of venting on the relieved location and on the receiving location, although different aspects of the overall design are frequently handled by different specialists.

*Venting of process vessels involving such two-phase flow has been extensively investigated by a consortium of commercial firms acting as the Design Institute for Emergency Relief Systems (DIERS), under the auspices of the American Institute of Chemical Engineers (AIChE). A number of papers based on this activity have been published in *Chemical Engineering Progress*. A DIERS project manual was published in the late 1980s.

Isolation

Isolation encompasses separation of an element from surroundings that may be adversely affected by an explosion. Separation may be achieved by remote location of the potentially hazardous element, or by blast-resistant structures designed to deflect, abate, or contain blast waves, missiles, and/or expelled materials.

Isolation simply by remote location is practical for facilities that routinely perform potentially hazardous work, such as explosives facilities, etc. Site selection must consider the magnitude of the potential explosion, blast range, and missile range relative to presently and foreseeably occupied areas, as well as those other considerations generally applicable to site selection activities. The same considerations apply to isolation by distance of a unit process from the balance of a plant. It is important to realize that distance is of primary benefit for the primary explosion only. Expelled materials may travel well beyond the pertinent blast range, and consideration of possible secondary effects is critical. Evaluation of secondary explosion potentials is especially important where expelled materials include, for example, flammable gas or atomized liquids, but assessment of effects on the overall environment is important even when no secondary explosion potential exists.

Isolation by blast-resistant structures requires a complex design process. The magnitude of the explosion must be assessed, as well as the form of the blast wave and the missiles and product materials produced. The structure must then be designed to withstand the shock or impulse load of the explosion, the static pressure created by gas released within the structure, the range and depth of penetration of missiles, and any secondary effects of expelled materials on the blast-resistant structure itself (combustion of expelled flammable vapors, for example).

Blast-resistant structures are seldom designed to fully contain effects of an explosion, but are employed to deflect or abate effects of the blast wave and missiles. Full containment of all explosion effects is practical only when the potentially explosive element is quite small. Certain bench-scale operations can be performed using full containment by blast-resistant structures, and certain flow reactors are small enough that full containment is feasible, but, generally, potentially explosive elements are too large to permit practical full-containment design. Accordingly, secondary effects of deflected blast waves, missiles, and expelled materials must be anticipated in the design of facilities incorporating blast-resistant structures.

Blast-resistant structures may be constructed of reinforced concrete, steel, timber, earth, sand, or a wide variety of other materials. Many designs utilize multiple elements of different materials to achieve specific effects under specific circumstances. Timber, earth, and sand are frequently used in construction of simple deflecting walls or revetments, often employed for relatively short-duration conditions and/or for separation of elements in remotely sited facilities. Construction of steel or reinforced concrete blast-resistant structures is more common in industrial process operations. A substantial body of information on blast-resistant structures has been compiled for military purposes[1] and is available to non-military designers for general application. An excellent short treatment has been published in *Chemical Engineering Progress*.[2]

In certain cases, where the potentially explosive condition is large and the environmental elements requiring protection are small, blast-resistant structures may be used to enclose key environmental elements rather than to confine the effects of explosion. Typical of such strategy is the use of blast-resistant control rooms in refineries and other large process plants. In such cases, the overall design must also consider personnel safety as regards oxygen supply, thermal loads, and toxic effects of expelled materials.

It is essential to understand that a blast-resistant structure is ordinarily rated in terms of a specific charge loading at a specific location. Use of a blast-resistant structure for purposes other than that for which it was originally designed requires reassessment of blast effects to be sustained. Any alteration of the system within the blast-resistant structure that involves movement of potentially explosive elements may render the structural design inadequate for continued protection. In particular, alterations that move elements closer to walls and/or corners increase resultant stresses of explosion on the structure, and failure of the structure may occur in the event of an explosion.

CONCLUSION

The foregoing is a necessarily brief summation of countermeasures technology. Generally speaking, countermeasures design incorporates more than one form of countermeasure in a single operating system, to provide intermediate levels of response. A reaction vessel may well be equipped with a pressure-relief valve, a dump valve, and a rupture disc, and yet may also be placed in a blast-resistant structure if the severity of the maximum credible reaction so warrants.

The most important single criterion in the selection of countermeasures is the ability of the system design to reliably perform the necessary functions in the available time. In general, it is preferred to buttress use of active countermeasures with passive countermeasures so that, in the event of failure of the active countermeasure, a second line of protection exists. Obviously, any system of countermeasures must be properly inspected, exercised, and maintained on a regular basis. Countermeasures can be frustrated by inadvertence. Circumstances change in the environment, and new technology continually becomes available. Finally, installation of countermeasures does not mean the system is "safe." Safety is maintained only by constant vigilance.

BIBLIOGRAPHY

References Cited

1. U.S. Army, "Structures to Resist the Effects of Accidental Explosions," U.S. Army Technical Manual, No. 5-1300, 1969, Department of Defense, Washington, DC.
2. Tunkel, Steven J., "Barricade Design Criteria," *Chemical Engineering Progress*, Vol. 79, No. 9, Sept. 1983, pp. 50-55.

NFPA Codes, Standards, and Recommended Practices

Reference to the following NFPA codes, standards, and recommended practices will provide further information on explosions discussed in this chapter. (See the latest *NFPA Catalog* for availability of current editions of the following documents.)

NFPA 61A, *Prevention of Fire and Dust Explosions in Facilities Manufacturing and Handling Starch.*

NFPA 61B, *Prevention of Fires and Explosions in Grain Elevators and Facilities Handling Bulk Raw Agricultural Commodities.*

NFPA 61C, *Prevention of Fire and Dust Explosions in Feed Mills.*

NFPA 61D, *Prevention of Fire and Dust Explosions in the Milling of Agricultural Commodities for Human Consumption.*

NFPA 65, *Processing and Finishing of Aluminum.*

NFPA 68, *Explosion Venting.*

NFPA 69, *Explosion Prevention Systems.*

Additional Reading

Baker, W. E., et al., *Explosion Hazards and Evaluation*, Elsevier Scientific Publishing Co., New York, 1983.

Baker, W. E., *Explosions in Air*, University of Texas Press, Austin, TX, 1973.

Bartknecht, W., *Explosions—Course Prevention Protection*, Springer-Verlag, New York, 1981.

Beausoleil, Robert W., et al., "Field Investigation of Natural Gas Pipeline Accident, Canterbury Woods, Annandale, Virginia," *Fire Journal*, Vol. 68, No. 3, May 1974, pp. 77-84.

Cashdollar, K. L., and Hertzberg, M., *Industrial Dust Explosions*, American Society For Testing and Materials, Philadelphia, PA, 1987.

Cook, M. A., *The Science of High Explosives*, R. E. Krieger Pub. Co., Malabar, FL, 1985. [Reprint of 1958 edition]

Cooper, M. G., Fairweather, M., and Tite, J. P., "On the Mechanisms of Pressure Generation in Vented Explosions," *Combustion and Flame*, Vol. 65, 1986, pp. 1-14.

Cross, J., and Farrer, D., *Dust Explosions*, Plenum Press, NY, 1982.

Davenport, J. A., "A Study of Vapor Cloud Incidents" *Loss Prevention*, Vol. 11, American Institute of Chemical Engineers, New York, NY, 1977.

Decker, D. A., "An Analytical Method for Estimating Overpressure from Theoretical Atmospheric Explosions," NFPA Annual Meeting, May 1974.

DiMeo, Michael, "Explosion in Fremont," *Fire Journal*, Vol. 70, No. 4, July 1976, pp. 15-19, 22.

Field, P., *Dust Explosions*, Elsevier, NY, 1982.

Fire and Explosion Index: Hazard Classification Guide, 6th ed., American Institute of Chemical Engineers, NY, 1987.

Garrison, W. G., "Major Fires and Explosions Analyzed for 30-Year Period," *Hydrocarbon Processing*, Sept. 1988.

Gray, P., and Lee, P. R., "Thermal Explosion Theory," *Oxidation and Combustion Reviews*, Vol. 2, 1967.

Johannsson, O., "The Disaster of San Juanico," *Fire Journal*, Jan. 1986, p. 32.

Kaufman, C. W., Srinath, S. R., & Tai, C. S., *Proceedings* of the International Symposium on the Explosion Hazard Classification of Vapors, Gases and Dusts, Nat. Acad. Press, Washington, DC, 1987, pp. 41-46.

Kletz, T. A., "Unconfined Vapor Cloud Explosions," *Loss Prevention*, Vol. 11, 1977.

Kuchta, J. M., *Investigation of Fire and Explosion Accidents in the Chemical, Mining, and Fuel Related Industries*, U.S. Department of the Interior, Bureau of Mines, 1985.

"Lessons from a L. P. Gas Utility Plant Explosion and Fire," *Fire Command*, Apr. 1972.

Lewis, B., and Von Elbe, G., *Combustion, Flame, and Explosions of Gases*, 3rd ed., Academic Press, Orlando, 1987.

McDaniel, J. T., "Explosion of a Benfield Solution Storage Tank," *Plant/Operations Progress*, Vol. 5, No. 1, 1986, pp. 45-48.

Nagy, J., and Verakis, H. C., *Development and Control of Dust Explosions*, Marcel Dekker, NY, 1983.

Palmer, K. N., *Dust Explosions and Fires*, Chapman & Hall, London, Distributed by Halsted Press—John Wiley & Sons, NY, 1973.

Pineau, J., *Gas and Dust Explosions in Closed and Vented Vessels: A Practical Guide to Gas and Dust Explosion Venting*, Europex, 1985.

Proceedings of the Symposium on Industrial Dust Explosions, STP 958, American Society for Testing and Materials, Pittsburgh, PA, 1987.

Rasbash, D. J., "Quantification of Explosion Parameters for Combustible Fuel-Air Mixtures," *Fire Safety Journal*, Vol. 11, Nos. 1 & 2, 1986, pp. 113-125.

Sharry, J. A., and Walls, W. L., "L. P. Gas Distribution Plant Fire," *Fire Journal*, Jan. 1974.

Stull, D. R., "Fundamentals of Fire and Explosions," *AICHE Monograph Series No. 10*, Vol. 73, American Institute of Chemical Engineers, NY, 1977.

Urbanski, T., *Chemistry and Technology of Explosives*, Vol. 1, Pergamon Press, NY, 1964, Vol. 2, 1967, Vol. 3, 1967. [Reprinted with corrections 1983]

Walls, W. L., "Just What is a BLEVE?" *Fire Journal*, Nov. 1978.

Zabetakis, M. G., "Flammability Characteristics of Combustible Gases and Vapors," *Bulletin 627*, U.S. Bureau of Mines, Pittsburgh, PA, 1965. [Reproduced by National Technical Information Service 1980]

Zalosh, R., "Explosion Protection," *SFPE Handbook of Fire Protection Engineering*, National Fire Protection Association, Quincy, MA, 1988.

THEORY OF FIRE EXTINGUISHMENT

Raymond Friedman

There are basically four ways a fire can be extinguished:

1. Physically separating the combustible substance from the flame.
2. Removing or diluting the oxygen supply.
3. Reducing the temperature of the combustible or of the flame.
4. Introducing chemicals that modify the combustion chemistry.

Any specific extinguishment technique may involve one of these mechanisms, or, more often, several of them simultaneously.For example, when water is applied to a fire of a solid combustible burning in air, several extinguishing mechanisms are involved simultaneously. The solid is cooled by contact with water, causing its rate of pyrolysis, or gasification, to decrease. The gaseous flame is cooled, causing a reduction in heat feedback to the combustible solid, and a corresponding reduction in the endothermic pyrolysis rate. Steam is generated, which, under some confined conditions, may prevent oxygen from reaching the fire. Water in the form of fog may block radiative heat transfer.

As another example, consider the application of a blanket of aqueous foam to a burning pool of flammable liquid. Several mechanisms may be operative. The foam prevents the fire's radiant heat from reaching the surface and supplying the needed heat of vaporization. If the fire point of the flammable liquid is higher than the temperature of the foam, the liquid is cooled and its vapor pressure decreases. If the flammable liquid is water-soluble, such as alcohol, then, by a third mechanism, it will become diluted by water from the foam, and the vapor pressure of the combustible will be reduced.

As yet another example, when dry chemical is applied to a fire, the following extinguishing mechanisms may be involved: (1) chemical interaction with the flame; (2) coating of the combustible surface; (3) cooling of the flame; and (4) blockage of radiative energy transfer.

Ideally, any fully successful theory of fire extinguishment should be able to predict the quantity and rate of application of extinguishing agent needed for a given fire. Such a theory would be better than empirical measurements that yield the same information because the empirical data would be fully reliable only in circumstances identical to those employed in the empirical testing. Furthermore, the theory would provide guidance toward improvement of extinguishment performance.

Unfortunately, the agents mentioned above—water, foam, dry chemical—each work by a combination of several mechanisms, and the relative importance of the various contributions will vary with the circumstances. The degree of complexity resulting from this situation, as well as other problems, has up to now prevented completion of a quantitative fundamental theory of extinguishment action. However, much is known about the various extinguishment modes, and this knowledge will be outlined below. A more detailed treatment can be found in Friedman.[1]

THE COMBUSTION PROCESS

Much scientific information has been developed about the combustion process, the understanding of which is central to the understanding of fire extinguishment. For details, one may refer to the texts by Friedman,[1] which is rather elementary; Drysdale,[2] Glassman,[3] which are more advanced; or Strehlow,[4] which is the most advanced. Only some simple, basic concepts of combustion which are especially relevant to fire extinguishment will be presented here.

The term combustion usually refers to an exothermic, or heat-producing, chemical reaction between some substance and oxygen. Chemical analysis of the combustion products would show the presence of certain molecules involving combinations of oxygen atoms with other types of atoms, such as CO_2, H_20, SO_2, NO_2, Al_20_3, or SiO_2.

A slow reaction is a reaction between some substance and oxygen that requires weeks or months to complete. Such a reaction, which is *not* combustion, releases heat so

Dr. Raymond Friedman was vice president in charge of fire research for Factory Mutual Research Corporation from 1969 to 1987. Now semi-retired, he is a consultant, as well as an adjunct professor at Worcester Polytechnic Insitute.

slowly that the temperature never increases more than a degree or so above the temperature of the surroundings. One example of this process is the rusting of metal.

The difference between a slow oxidative reaction and a combustion reaction is that the latter occurs so rapidly that heat is generated faster than it is dissipated, causing a substantial temperature rise of at least hundreds of degrees, and often several thousand degrees. Very often, the temperature is so high that visible light is emitted from the combustion reaction zone.

The concern in fire protection is generally with combustion reactions between various materials and the oxygen of the air.

A flame is a gaseous oxidation reaction, which occurs in a region of space much hotter than its surroundings and which generally emits light. Familiar examples include the yellow flame of a candle and the blue flame of a gas burner.

The flame has been referred to as gaseous. When a solid such as a match or a candle burns, a portion of the heat of the gaseous flame is transferred to the solid, causing the solid to vaporize. (See Figure 1-6A.) This vaporization can occur with or without chemical decomposition of the molecules. If chemical decomposition occurs, it is called pyrolysis.

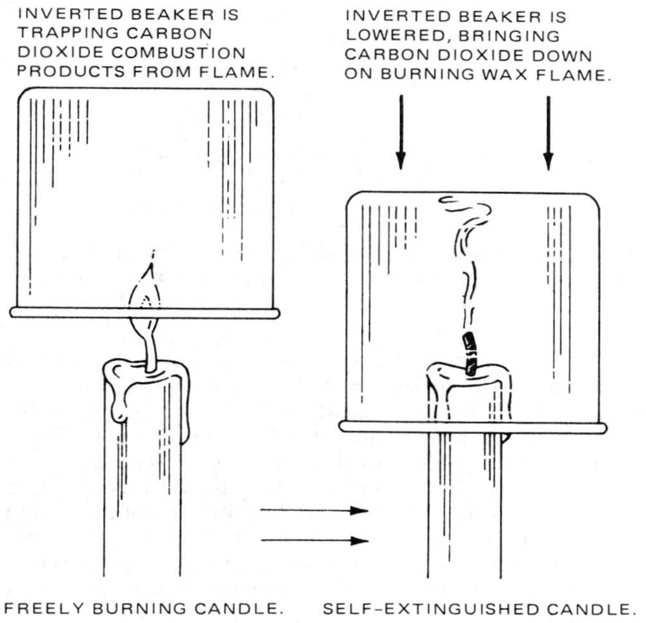

FIG. 1-6A. Flaming combustion (left) and extinguishment (right) by its own combustion products of a wax candle.

There is another mode of combustion that does not involve any flame. It is called smoldering, glowing, or nonflaming combustion. A cigarette burns in this way. Upholstered furniture containing cotton batting or polyurethane foam can also smolder. A large pile of wood chips, sawdust, or coal can smolder for weeks or even months.

Smoldering generally is limited to porous materials that can form a carbonaceous char when heated. The oxygen in the air slowly diffuses into the pores of the material, and there is a glowing reaction zone within the material, even though the glow might not be visible from outside. These porous materials are poor conductors of heat, so even though the combustion reaction occurs slowly, enough heat is retained in the reaction zone to maintain the elevated temperature needed to sustain the reaction.

It is not uncommon for a piece of upholstered furniture, once ignited, to smolder for several hours. During this time, the reaction zone spreads only 2 or 4 in. (5 or 10 cm) from the ignition point, and then suddenly, the furniture can burst into flames. The rate of burning during flaming combustion is many times greater than the rate of burning during smoldering combustion.

Combustion requires a high temperature, and the reactions must proceed fast enough at this high temperature to generate heat as fast as it is dissipated, so that the reaction zone will not cool down. If anything is done to upset this heat balance, such as introducing a coolant, it is possible that the combustion will be extinguished. It is not necessary for the coolant to remove heat as fast as it is being generated because the combustion zone in a fire is already losing some heat to the cooler surroundings. In some cases, only a modest additional loss of heat is needed to tip the balance toward extinguishment.

Extinguishment can be accomplished by cooling either the gaseous combustion zone or the solid or liquid combustible. In the latter case, the cooling prevents the production of combustible vapors. This is probably the primary mode of action when a wood fire is extinguished by applying water.

As an alternative to removing heat from the combustion zone to slow the reactions, it is also possible to reduce the temperature of the flame by modifying of the air which supplies the oxygen. Air contains 21 percent by volume of oxygen, the remainder being almost entirely the inert gas nitrogen. The nitrogen, which is drawn into the flame along with the oxygen, absorbs heat, with the result that the flame temperature is much lower than it would be in a fire burning in pure oxygen. If additional nitrogen or some other chemically unreactive gas, such as steam, carbon dioxide, or a mixture of combustion products, were to be added to the air entering the flame, the heat absorbed by these inert molecules would cause the flame temperature to be even lower.

The flame temperature is so important because the rate of a key combustion reaction ($H + O_2 \rightarrow OH + O$) is very sensitive to temperature. A small decrease in temperature causes a disproportionately large decrease in the rate of this reaction, according to Arrhenius' law.

The symbol H denotes a free hydrogen atom, as contrasted with the ordinary stable form of hydrogen, H_2. Combustion consists of rapid *chain reactions* involving these hydrogen atoms and other active species, hydroxyl free radicals OH and free oxygen atoms O. Figure 1-6C shows a sequence of reactions occurring in the hydrogen-oxygen flame. It is seen that a single H atom, when introduced into an H_2—O_2 mixture at an elevated temperature, will be transformed by a sequence of rapid reactions, requiring a fraction of a millisecond, to form two molecules of H_2O and three new H atoms. Each of these new H atoms can immediately initiate the same sequence, and a branching chain reaction is produced, which continues until the reactants are consumed. Then, the remaining H, O, and OH species recombine according to the reactions

$$H + O \rightarrow OH$$

and

$$H + OH \rightarrow H_2O.$$

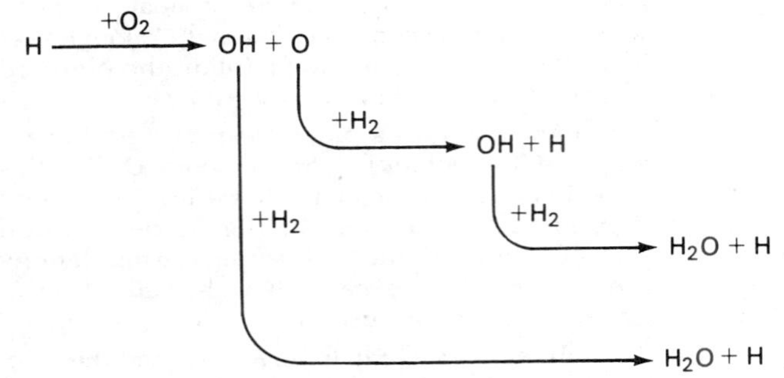

NET RESULT: $H + 3H_2 + O_2 \longrightarrow 2H_2O + 3H$

FIG. 1-6B. ***Chain reaction mechanism in the hydrogen-oxygen flame.***

Similar chain reactions occur in flames of any hydrogen-containing species. Hydrogen is present in the vast majority of combustibles, except for metals and pure carbon.

The ability of the hydrogen atoms to multiply rapidly in a flame depends, then, on the prevailing temperature in the flame, which is modified by heat loss or by inert gases, thus leading to extinguishment.It is also possible to remove hydrogen atoms or other active species from the flame by purely chemical means—that is, by introducing a species capable of chemical inhibition. This process will be discussed later.

Accordingly, there are two fundamental ways of reducing combustion intensity in a flame and ultimately causing extinguishment: reducing the flame temperature or adding a chemical inhibitor to interfere with the chain reaction.

Consider the effect of adding additional nitrogen to a fuel vapor-air mixture. Suppose the fuel vapor is methane, CH_4. Figure 1-6C shows that if more than about 35 percent additional nitrogen is added to a 9.5 percent methane-air mixture at 25°C, the resulting mixture is nonflammable. That is, the maximum flame temperature is reduced from about 1900°C to about 1200°C by the added nitrogen, and the rate of heat generation is then too low to sustain the flame against the heat losses from the flame to the surroundings.

Notice also from Figure 1-6C that a 9.5 percent methane-air mixture can be made nonflammable not only by adding nitrogen but, alternately, by adding additional air or additional methane. Such additions would produce an excess of one of the reactants and therefore a dilution and reduction of flame temperature.

The foregoing discussion of flammability limits applies to premixed combustion, or combustion of a uniform mixture of fuel and air and possibly a third component. This is often the case for explosions, but fires are generally diffusion flames rather than premixed flames. That is, a solid or liquid combustible is vaporizing, and air approaches the vapor cloud from the sides. The flame burns at the interface of the interdiffusing combustible vapors and air. The hot combustion products then rise because of buoyancy.

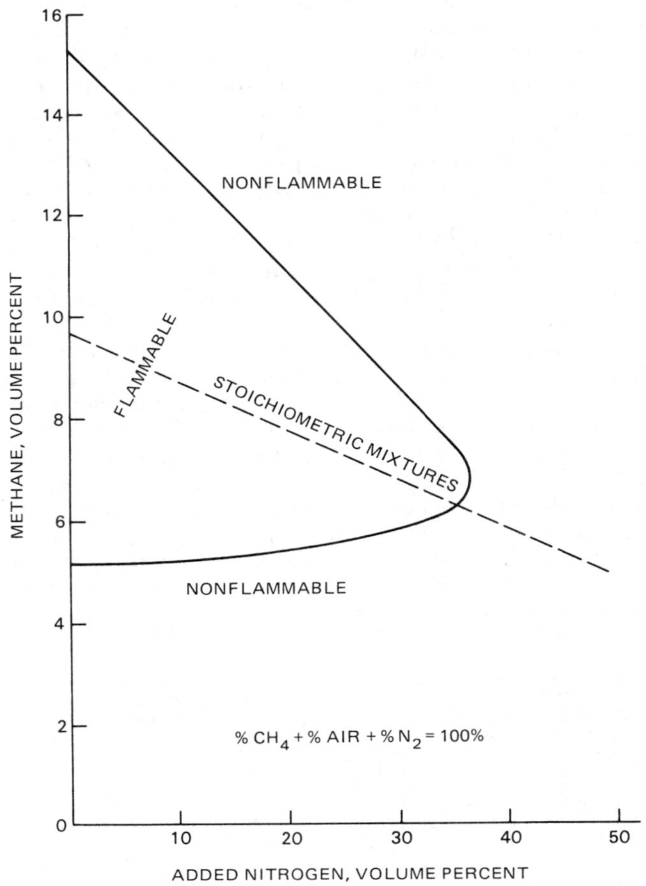

FIG. 1-6C. ***Limits of flammability of various methane-air-nitrogen mixtures at 25°C and 1 atmosphere. From Zabetakis.***[5]

Such a flame is clearly more complex than a premixed flame, but much the same principles apply to its extinguishment. If more inert gas is added to the air feeding a diffusion flame, extinguishment will occur when the flame temperature is reduced to about 1200 or 1300°C. However, another important way of extinguishing a diffusion flame over a solid or liquid is to cool the solid or liquid enough to interrupt the gasification process. If the gasification rate can be reduced to less than a few grams per square meter per second, the flame becomes unstable and can no longer sustain itself.

EXTINGUISHMENT WITH WATER

One might suppose that water is the most widely used extinguishing agent because of its low cost and ready availability, relative to other conceivable liquids. However, it turns out that, quite aside from cost and availability, water is superior to any other known liquid for fighting the majority of fires.

Water has a very high heat of vaporization per unit mass, at least four times as high as that of any other nonflammable liquid. It is also outstandingly nontoxic; even a chemically inert liquid such as liquid nitrogen can cause asphyxiation. Water can be stored at atmospheric pressure and normal temperatures. Its boiling point (100°C) is well below the 250 to 450°C range of pyrolysis temperatures for most solid combustibles, so evaporative cooling of the pyrolyzing surface is efficient. No other liquid, regardless of cost, can match these properties.

However, water is not an absolutely perfect extinguishing agent. It does freeze below 0°C. It does conduct electricity. It can irreversibly damage some items, although, in many cases, it is practical to salvage water-damaged items. Water may not be effective for flammable liquid fires, especially flammable liquids that are insoluble in water and float on water, such as hydrocarbons. Water is not compatible with certain hot metals or certain chemicals. With fires in these materials, other agents, such as aqueous foam, inert gases, halons, and dry chemical will be preferred.

Water may extinguish a fire by a combination of mechanisms: cooling the solid or liquid combustible, cooling the flame itself, generating steam that prevents oxygen access, and, as fog, blocking radiative transfer. While all these mechanisms may contribute to extinguishment, probably the most important is cooling a gasifying combustible.

In order for a solid to burn, a portion of it must be at a high enough temperature so that pyrolysis occurs at a sufficient rate to maintain the flame. For most solids, this temperature is 300 to 400°C, and the pyrolysis rate must be a few grams per square meter per second. If even a small amount of liquid water, with its high heat of vaporization, can reach this region, the solid can be cooled sufficiently to reduce or stop the pyrolysis, and the flame will be extinguished. Even deep-seated fires can be suppressed in this way. Accordingly, water is the obvious agent of choice for burning solids.

The two most common means of applying water are by a solid stream or spray from a hose and by spray from automatic sprinklers. The practical aspects of manual fire fighting and the use of sprinklers are discussed elsewhere in this handbook. From a scientific viewpoint, studies reviewed by Heskestad[6] and Rasbash[7] have investigated the minimum rate of water application to a burning solid surface that will cause extinguishment.

In an important paper by Magee and Reitz,[8] burning slabs of various plastics, horizontal and vertical, were simultaneously heated with radiant heaters and cooled with controlled water sprays. Extinguishment conditions were then determined. Figure 1-6D shows a linear relationship between the radiative heating rate and the water application rate required for extinguishment. The reciprocal of the slope of the line is found to be approximately the heat of vaporization of water, as theory would predict.

To extinguish burning polymethylmethacrylate (Lucite, Plexiglas, Perspex), enough water must be applied to reduce the burning rate to less than about 4 grams per square meter per second. Depending on the intensity of the externally imposed radiative flux—up to 18 kilowatts per square meter—a water application rate of from 1.5 to 8 grams per square meter per second was required. This is a very small application rate of water. For extinguishment with no external radiative flux, it was only necessary to spray enough water so that the heat absorbed by its vaporization was 3 percent of the heat of combustion.

Experiments with other plastics and with wood cribs have given similar results; only a few grams of water per square meter per second must be applied to the burning surface to cause extinguishment, and the rate of heat absorption by the water is only a few percent of the rate of heat generation by the fire before water application.

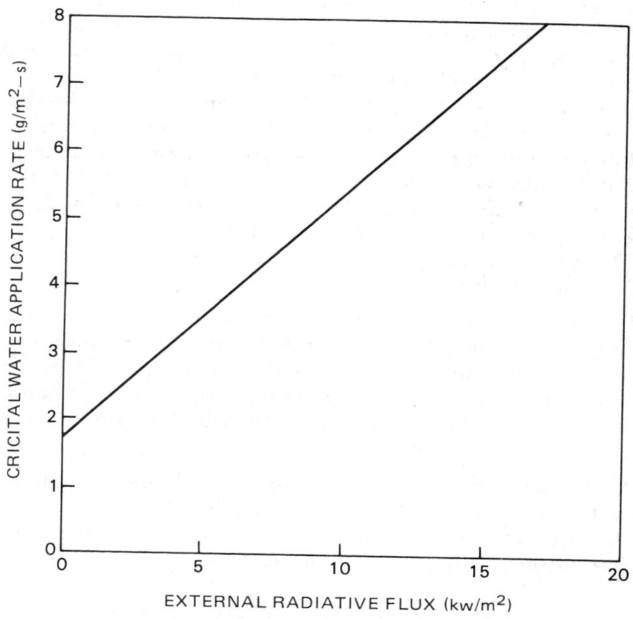

FIG. 1-6D. Water application rate needed to extinguish a fire on a vertical polymethyl methacrylate sheet.

The reason for this high efficiency is now well understood. Consider a horizontal slab of polymethyl methacrylate, 0.3 × 0.3 meters square, which is burning steadily on its top surface. Measurements[1] have shown that only about 12 percent of the energy released by combustion is transferred back to the surface. Of this energy arriving at the surface, primarily by radiation from the flame above, about 40 percent is reradiated from the hot surface to the surroundings, and only 60 percent of 12 percent, or 7 percent of the available combustion energy, is used to decompose and gasify the plastic. It is only necessary to apply enough water to the surface to drain off a substantial portion of this 7 percent of the combustion energy, and the rate of burning is then reduced to a point at which the flame can no longer sustain itself.

Of course, the evaporation of the water produces steam that dilutes the flame and reduces the flame temperature, causing some reduction in the rate of burning, but this effect is generally small and need not be considered in a first-approximation model of the extinguishment process.

It is interesting to note that, in ignition experiments, a solid surface is progressively heated, with a gradual increase in the rate of pyrolysis, or gaseous decomposition, but it is not possible to ignite the vapors to obtain a self-sustaining flame until the pyrolysis rate reaches a certain minimum value. This is roughly the same value to which the pyrolysis rate must be reduced when water is applied to a burning surface to accomplish extinguishment.

In practical fire fighting, water must be applied at 10 to 100 times the rates used in the research described above because of the difficulty of delivering the water directly to the burning surface.

In the case of fire suppression by use of sprinklers at the ceiling, it is possible to calculate the fraction of the water droplets able to penetrate the fire plume and arrive at the burning surface beneath. Such a calculation is complex and requires a powerful computer.[9] It is necessary to know the heat release rate of the fire, the location of the fire relative to the nearby ceiling sprinklers, and the distribution of drop sizes of the water. The calculation takes into account the aerodynamic drag on the downward-moving droplets encountering the upward-moving fire gases, and calculates the change in motion of the fire gases because of the downward momentum of the water spray. Droplet evaporation and cooling of the fire gases are included in the calculation.

The drop-size distribution of the water depends not only on the sprinkler design, but also on the pressure drop across the sprinkler. The mean drop size varies inversely with the cube root of the pressure drop. It also depends on the surface tension of the water, which could be modified with additives.

In some cases—for example, a purely gaseous fire—water may extinguish the fire by cooling the flame rather than the source of the fuel vapor. The theory of this action was discussed in the previous section.

EXTINGUISHMENT WITH AQUEOUS FOAMS

The principal application of aqueous foam agents is for fighting flammable liquid fires. If the flammable liquid is lighter than water and is insoluble in water, then application of water would simply result in the liquid floating on it and continuing to burn. If the flammable liquid is an oil or fat, the temperature of which is substantially above the boiling point of water, then the water will penetrate the hot oil, turn into steam below the surface, and cause an eruption of oil that will accelerate the burning rate and might spread the fire.

Foams are the primary tools for fighting fires that involve substantial quantities of petroleum products, such as those found at refineries, tankers, storage areas, and so on.

If the flammable liquid is water-soluble, like alcohols, then the addition of sufficient water will dilute the liquid to the point where it is no longer flammable. If there is a deep pool of alcohol rather than a shallow spill, however, the time required to obtain sufficient dilution might be so great that an aqueous foam would be a better extinguishing agent. If the nature of a liquid is unknown, an aqueous foam might be chosen instead of direct application of water.

Another important application of aqueous foam agents is on liquids or solids that are burning in difficult-to-access spaces, such as a room in a basement or the hold of a ship. The foam is used to flood the compartment completely.

Fire fighting foam is a mass of bubbles formed by various methods from aqueous solutions of specially formulated foaming agents. Because foam is much lighter than any flammable liquid, it floats on the liquid, producing an air-excluding, cooling, continuous layer of vapor-sealing, water-bearing material that can halt or prevent combustion.

Fire fighting foams are formulated in several ways for fire extinguishing action. Some foams are thick and viscous, forming tough heat-resistant blankets over burning liquid surfaces and vertical areas. Other foams are thinner and spread more rapidly. Some are capable of producing a vapor-sealing film of surface-active water solution on a liquid surface, and some are meant to be used as large volumes of wet gas cells for inundating surfaces and filling cavities. There are various methods for applying foams.

The use of foam for fire protection requires attention to its general characteristics. Foam breaks down and vaporizes its water content under attack by heat and flame. Therefore, it must be applied to a burning surface in sufficient volume and rate to compensate for this loss and to provide an additional amount to guarantee a residual foam layer over the extinguished portion of the burning liquid. Before starting to apply foam to a large fire, one must accumulate a sufficient number of barrels of foam concentrate to do the job. Nothing will be accomplished by putting out only part of a fire and then running out of foam because the fire will build back to its original intensity.

Foam is an unstable air-water emulsion and can be broken down easily by physical or mechanical forces. Certain chemical vapors or fluids can destroy foam quickly. When certain other extinguishing agents are used in conjunction with foam, severe breakdown of the foam can occur. Turbulent air or violently uprising combustion gases can divert light foam from the burning area.

There is no theoretical basis available to serve as a guide to the needed rates of application of the various types of foams in different situations. The guidelines come from experience or from empirical tests.

One useful laboratory measure of foam effectiveness is to fill a graduated cylinder with the foam and observe the time required for a certain fraction of the water in it to drain to the bottom. The more stable the foam, the slower it will drain. Clearly, the time for collapse of a foam layer should be greater than the time required to coat the entire surface of a large spill with foam. Thus, a basis is available for calculating the necessary rate of application. Of course, fire causes foam to break down at a greater rate than indicated by the drain test in a cylinder, so empirical information is still needed.

Another laboratory tool, useful for formulating film-forming foams, is the measurement of surface tension of the foam solution F and of the flammable liquid L, and the interfacial tension between the two liquids FL. The film will spread over the surface only if F plus L is greater than FL.

EXTINGUISHMENT WITH INERT GASES

Water acts to extinguish fires primarily by cooling, although the formation of steam helps to dilute the concentration of oxygen. On the other hand, inert gases act to extinguish a fire primarily by dilution. Carbon dioxide is the most commonly used inert gas, although nitrogen or steam could be used. Theoretically, helium, neon, or argon could be used, but they are expensive, and there is no reason to use them except in certain special cases, such as magnesium fires.

Table 1-6A presents the minimum proportions of carbon dioxide or nitrogen gas which, if added to air, will form an atmosphere in which various vapors will not burn. On a volume basis, carbon dioxide is substantially more effective than nitrogen. Note, however, that a given volume of carbon dioxide is 1.57 times as heavy as nitrogen (44 to 28 molecular weight ratio), so the two gases have more nearly equal effectiveness on a weight basis. Either gas, in sufficient quantity, will prevent the combustion of anything except certain metals or unstable chemicals such as pyrotechnics, solid rocket propellants, hydrazine, and so on.

If available, steam also can be used as an inert extinguishing agent. The percentage by volume required is intermediate between that required for carbon dioxide and for nitrogen.

TABLE 1-6A. ***Minimum Required Volume Ratios of Carbon Dioxide or Nitrogen to Air that will Prevent Burning of Various Vapors at 25°C.***

Vapor	Carbon dioxide (CO_2/air)	Carbon dioxide (% O_2)	Nitrogen (extra N_2/air)	Nitrogen (% O_2)
Carbon disulfide	1.59	8.1	3.0	5.2
Hydrogen	1.54	8.2	3.1	5.1
Ethylene	0.68	12.5	1.00	10.5
Ethyl ether	0.51	13.9	0.97	10.6
Ethanol	0.48	14.2	0.86	11.3
Propane	0.41	14.9	0.78	11.8
Acetone	0.41	14.9	0.75	12.0
n-Hexane	0.40	15.0	0.72	12.2
Benzene	0.40	15.0	0.82	11.5
Methane	0.33	15.7	0.63	12.9

See Friedman[1].

Table 1-6A shows that the required addition of either carbon dioxide or nitrogen reduces the oxygen level to a point at which exposed humans will suffer undesirable effects. In the case of carbon dioxide, an additional serious physiological effect will occur at the concentrations required to extinguish a fire.

Table 1-6A refers only to vapors, but the data are relevant to liquids or solids because they burn only by vaporizing or pyrolyzing. Accordingly, application of an inert gas can extinguish the flame over a liquid or solid. However, if the inert gas dissipates after several minutes, because, for example, the enclosure is not air-tight, it is possible that a glowing ember or hot metal could re-ignite the fire. Reignition is common for a deep-seated fire, such as might occur in upholstered furniture or in a carton of documents.

Some explanation of the physical forms of carbon dioxide is appropriate. Carbon dioxide is unusual in that it can exist only as a gas or solid at normal atmospheric pressure, but not as a liquid. Figure 1-6E shows the phase diagram of carbon dioxide.

The solid form of carbon dioxide, commonly known as "dry ice," at atmospheric pressure, exists only below –79°C (–110°F), at which temperature it undergoes sublimation directly to vapor, without melting. However, carbon dioxide liquid can exist at elevated pressures, as long as the temperature is above –57°C (–79°F) and the pressure is above 5.2 atmospheres. This temperature and pressure condition is known as the triple point of carbon dioxide because it is the only condition at which solid, liquid, and vapor can co-exist.

Liquid carbon dioxide can be kept in a pressure vessel at any temperature between +57°C and +31°C (the critical temperature). Above the critical temperature, there will no longer be a liquid-gas interface in the pressure vessel, so the fluid in the vessel would be a gas. A pressure vessel at 21°C (70°F) containing liquid carbon dioxide would be at a pressure of 58 atmospheres, which is the vapor pressure of carbon dioxide at that temperature. This pressure is used to expel liquid carbon dioxide from a cylinder in fire fighting. The cylinder normally would contain an internal dip tube reaching to the bottom so that liquid rather than vapor would be discharged. As the liquid droplets emerge from a nozzle into the lower-pressure environment, instantaneous evaporation occurs, with evaporative cooling of the residual liquid in each drop. This process causes solidification of the residual portion into "dry ice" particles at –79°C. If the liquid was originally at 21°C, about 75 percent of the discharged liquid would have evaporated and about 25 percent would have been converted to "dry ice" particles.

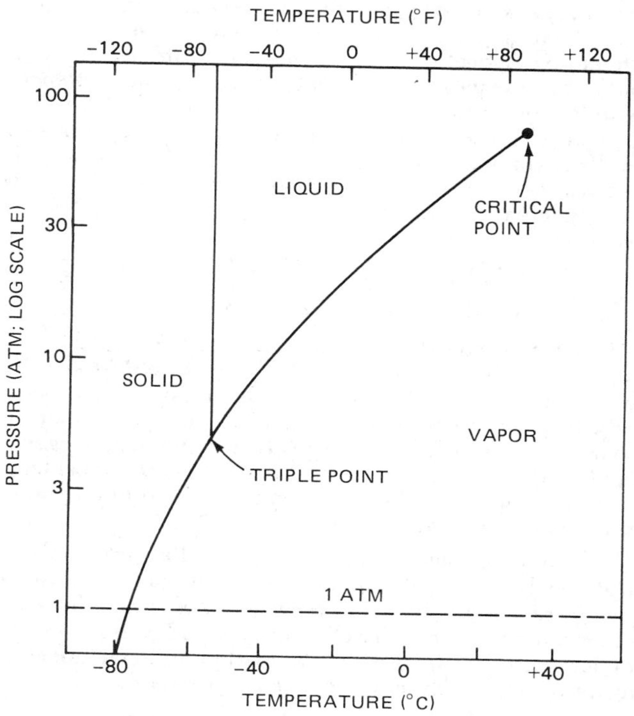

FIG. 1-6E. Phase diagram of carbon dioxide.

Some of the "dry ice" particles might impinge on a combustible surface and have a cooling effect. However, because the heat of sublimation of carbon dioxide is only about one-fourth the heat of vaporization of water and because only about one-fourth of the carbon dioxide discharged is converted to "dry ice," the cooling effect on a hot surface is only about one-sixteenth that produced by water discharged at an equal rate (on a mass basis).

In comparing carbon dioxide and nitrogen, carbon dioxide has the advantage that it can be stored in a cylinder as a liquid at a relatively moderate pressure of 58 atmospheres (21°C), while nitrogen at the same temperature must be stored as a gas, usually at about 140 atmospheres. A given size of cylinder at 21°C and these pressures could hold about 3 times as large a volume of carbon dioxide as nitrogen (measured after expansion, at atmospheric conditions). Nitrogen also could be stored for short periods more compactly as a cryogenic liquid at –196°C and 1 atmosphere. However, long-term storage would result in continuous loss of nitrogen. As a result of these factors, carbon dioxide is used more commonly than nitrogen as an inerting gas.

Semi-permeable membranes are being developed that can inexpensively separate the oxygen and nitrogen of the air. When and if such systems become cost-effective, it might be practical to provide permanent nitrogen-inerting of hazardous spaces that do not require human presence. A reduction of the oxygen percentage in the air from 21 percent to 10 percent by volume would make fires and explosions impossible, except for a few special gases such as hydrogen, acetylene, or carbon disulfide, which would require greater dilution.

EXTINGUISHMENT WITH HALOGENATED AGENTS

The halogenated extinguishing agents, or halons, are chemical derivatives of methane (CH_4) or ethane (CH_3—CH_3) in which some or all of the hydrogen atoms have been replaced with fluorine, chlorine, or bromine atoms, or by some combination of these halogen elements. These agents are liquids when stored in pressurized tanks at normal temperatures, but most of them are gases at atmospheric pressure and normal temperatures.

The halogenated agents can be used for fire applications such as those discussed previously for carbon dioxide. For example, they can be used on electrical fires, in cases where water or dry chemicals would cause damage, or for inert-gas flooding of compartments. Halogenated agents have two principal advantages over carbon dioxide:

1. Certain halogenated agents are effective in such low volumetric concentrations that sufficient oxygen remains in the air after compartment-flooding for comfortable breathing.
2. For several halogenated agents, only partial vaporization occurs initially during projection from a nozzle, and the liquid can be projected farther than carbon dioxide.

The drawbacks of using halogenated agents have to do with the toxicity and corrosivity of their decomposition products, and with the recently discovered detrimental effect halogenated compounds have on Earth's ozone layer.

Of the various halons, Halon 1301 (bromotrifluoromethane) is by far the most commonly used in fire protection because it has the lowest toxicity, as well as the highest effectiveness on a weight basis. Among the highly effective halons, it has the highest volatility, which is desirable for flooding applications. If a halon liquid is needed for direct application to a burning surface to accomplish cooling as well as inerting of the nearby region, however, a less volatile halon, such as Halon 1211 (bromochlorodifluoromethane) or Halon 2402 (dibromotetrafluoroethane), would be preferred.

Table 1-6B gives the physical properties of these three halons. They are all liquids at normal temperatures when stored in pressurized tanks. They can be stored under high-pressure nitrogen if the liquid must be expelled from the tank more rapidly than under the vapor pressure of the halon alone. The use of nitrogen for pressurization is especially important for outdoor storage in the winter.

The inerting capabilities of Halon 1301 and Halon 1211 are shown in Table 1.6C. If methane in any proportion is combined with a mixture containing 5.4 volumes of Halon 1301 and 100 volumes of air, at 25°C, then no combustion can result. By contrast, a mixture containing 33 volumes of carbon dioxide and 100 volumes of air is required to obtain the same result. This suggests that a molecule of Halon 1301 is $^{33}/_{5.46} = 6.1$ times as effective as a molecule of carbon dioxide.

TABLE 1-6B. ***Physical Properties and Chemical Formulas of Three Halon Extinguishing Agents***

	Halon 1301 CF_3Br	Halon 1211 CF_2ClBr	Halon 2402 $C_2F_4Br_2$
Boiling point (°C)	–58	–4	+47
Liquid density at 20°C (g/cc)	1.57	1.83	2.17
Latent heat of vaporization (J/g)	117	134	105
Vapor pressure at 20°C (atm)	14.5	2.5	0.46

Note, however, that the molecular weight of Halon 1301 is 149, while that of carbon dioxide is 44, so the ratio of molecular weights is $^{149}/_{44} = 3.39$. Accordingly, on a weight basis, Halon 1301 is only $^{6.1}/_{3.39} = 1.8$ times as effective as carbon dioxide for methane fires.

Table 1-6C shows that the inerting proportion of halon needed varies somewhat depending on the nature of the combustible, and substantially more halon is needed for hydrogen, carbon disulfide, or ethylene fires than for most other combustibles. Table 1.6C also shows that Halon 1301 and Halon 1211 have similar effectiveness on a volume basis for most combustibles. On the basis of molecular weights, a molecule of Halon 1211 is $^{165.5}/_{149} = 1.11$ times as heavy as a molecule of Halon 1301.

Table 1-6C is based on experiments in which a strong ignition source is applied to a uniform combustible-air-halon mixture and the occurrence or nonoccurrence of a propagating flame is noted. A somewhat smaller quantity of halon would be needed to cause an existing flame on a burner to become unstable and then extinguish itself; the quantity of halon needed will depend on the details of the burner. A flame burning on a solid is even more easily extinguished. Grant[10] found that the flames on most solids could be extinguished with 4 to 6 percent by volume of Halon 1301 in the surrounding atmosphere.

Still, the discussion in the previous section about problems with extinguishment of deep-seated fires by carbon dioxide or nitrogen is equally valid when a halon agent is used. Unless a sufficient quantity of the halon in liquid form can reach the seat of the fire and cool all the solid sufficiently, re-ignition can occur after the agent has dissipated. If the halon reaches the combustible as a gas via compartment-flooding, then no such cooling can occur, and the effect of the halon is to extinguish the gaseous flame without affecting the pyrolysis or smoldering.

Table 1-6C also shows that the addition of Halon 1301 or 1211 needed in the air will only reduce the oxygen percentage from 21 percent to about 19 percent for most combustibles, while the required amount of carbon dioxide would have reduced the oxygen level to 14 percent or 15 percent. Furthermore, the physiological effects of carbon dioxide on humans at the concentrations needed for inerting are greater than those of Halon 1301.

Recently, it has been found that halons and other chemicals work their way into Earth's upper atmosphere, where they appear to act as catalysts for the conversion of ozone, O_3, to normal oxygen, O_2. The ozone in the upper atmosphere plays a valuable role in filtering out the far-ultraviolet radiation of the sun, which would otherwise damage plant and animal life on Earth's surface. Destruction of the ozone layer also might affect the world's

TABLE 1-6C. ***Minimum Required Volume Ratios of Halons to Air at 25°C that will Prevent Burning of Various Vapors***

Vapor	Halon 1301 (1301/air)	(% O_2)	Halon 1211 (1211/air)	(% O_2)
Hydrogen	0.29	16.2	0.43	14.7
Carbon disulfide	0.15	18.2	—	—
Ethylene	0.13	18.5	0.114	18.8
Propane	0.073	19.5	0.065	19.7
n-Hexane	—	—	0.064	19.7
Ethyl ether	0.070	19.6	—	—
Acetone	0.059	19.8	0.054	19.9
Methane	0.054	19.9	0.062	19.7
Benzene	0.046	20.0	0.052	19.9
Ethanol	0.045	20.0	—	—

Calculated from tabulations by Kuchta[10].

weather. Accordingly, there has been international activity directed toward reducing or eliminating the production of halons and/or the release of halons into the atmosphere.

The halons used in fire protection make up only a small fraction of the total current halogenated hydrocarbon use, which includes refrigerants, blowing agents for foamed plastics, solvents, and propellants for aerosol products in cans, such as hair sprays or deodorants. For these nonfire uses, substitute fluids are available, and a changeover is occurring in various countries. But there are no known inerting agents for fighting fire other than the halons that permit a space to be flooded while retaining breathability. The long-term future of halons as extinguishing agents is uncertain.

It would, of course, be highly desirable if chemists discovered a substitute for Halon 1301 or Halon 1211 that provided both inerting and breathability qualities and did not attack the ozone layer. In considering this possibility, a review follows of what is known about why the CF_3Br and CF_2ClBr molecules are so much more effective than the carbon dioxide molecule.

Figure 1-6F shows a methane-air flammability limit diagram as modified by various volumetric proportions of bromotrifluoromethane or carbon dioxide. The enormous difference is obvious.

It has been established that carbon dioxide acts by absorbing heat and reducing the flame temperature from about 1900°C for a stoichiometric fuel-air mixture to about 1200 to 1300°C. Below these temperatures, most flames can no longer burn.

If nitrogen were added to a stoichiometric fuel-air mixture instead of carbon dioxide, a somewhat larger volume of inert agent would be needed because the heat capacity of the nitrogen molecule is less than that of the carbon dioxide molecule. Similarly, if argon were added—argon has an even lower heat capacity per molecule—an even larger volume of argon would be needed for inerting. In each case, the flame would go out when the temperature dropped below 1200 to 1300°C.

However, if a small volume of bromotrifluoromethane were added to a flame, so that the temperature dropped to only about 1500°C, the flame would be extinguished. Clearly, the mechanism is different.

The important chemical reactions in flames involve the free atoms H and O and the free radical OH, which undergo chain reactions with the fuel and oxygen. In particular, the branching chain reaction $H + O_2 \rightarrow OH + O$ is very important. It is believed that the CF_3Br molecule decomposes in the flame to form HBr, and the HBr then acts to remove H atoms and OH radicals, by the following two combustion reactions:

$$HBr + H \rightarrow H_2 + Br$$

and

$$HBr + OH \rightarrow H_2O + Br$$

It happens that the molecules HF and HCl cannot react as rapidly with H or OH as can HBr, so bromine appears to be essential to the inerting molecule. It has been found that hydrogen iodide, HI, is about as effective as HBr, but iodine is more expensive and heavier than bromine, as well as quite toxic, so iodine offers no advantage over bromine for flame extinguishment.

In addition to the destruction of chain carriers, it has been speculated that a secondary contribution of halons to flame extinguishment comes from the extreme sootiness of halogen-containing flames. The more sooty or luminous the flame, the greater the radiative heat loss and the lower the temperature.

The role of the fluorine in halogenated agents is twofold. First, the fluorine atoms replace hydrogen atoms in the methane or ethane, thereby reducing the flammability of the inerting agent itself. Second, the toxicity of the agent is reduced. For example, CH_3Br is much more toxic than CF_3Br, and, again, CH_2ClBr is much more toxic than CF_2ClBr.

This current degree of understanding about why CF_3Br is such a good inerting agent for flames does not provide clear guidance as to how other equally effective gaseous agents might be found. The vast majority of known molecules are liquids or solids, not gases, at room temperature and 1 atmosphere. The known gaseous molecules have all been considered for inerting effectiveness, but no practical substitute as effective as CF_3Br has yet emerged.

EXTINGUISHMENT WITH DRY CHEMICAL AGENTS

Dry chemical powders provide an alternative to carbon dioxide or the halons for extinguishing a fire without the use of water. These powders, which are 10 to 75 micrometers in size, are projected by an inert gas. Of the seven types of dry chemicals in use, only one, monoammonium phosphate, is effective against deep-seated fires because of a glassy phosphoric acid coating that forms over the combustible surface. All forms of dry chemical act to suppress the flame of a fire.

One reason that dry chemical agents other than monoammonium phosphate are popular has to do with corrosion. Any chemical powder can produce some degree of corrosion or other damage, but monoammonium phosphate is acidic and corrodes more readily than other dry chemicals, which are neutral or mildly alkaline. Furthermore, corrosion by the other dry chemicals is stopped by a moderately dry atmosphere, while phosphoric acid has such a strong affinity for water than an exceedingly dry atmosphere would be needed to stop corrosion.

Application of any dry chemical agent on electrical fires is safe, from the viewpoint of electric shock, for fire fighters. However, these agents, especially monoammonium phosphate, can damage delicate electrical equipment.

Because of the reasons given above, the most common application of dry chemical agents is for relatively small flammable liquid fires. For the special case of kitchen fires

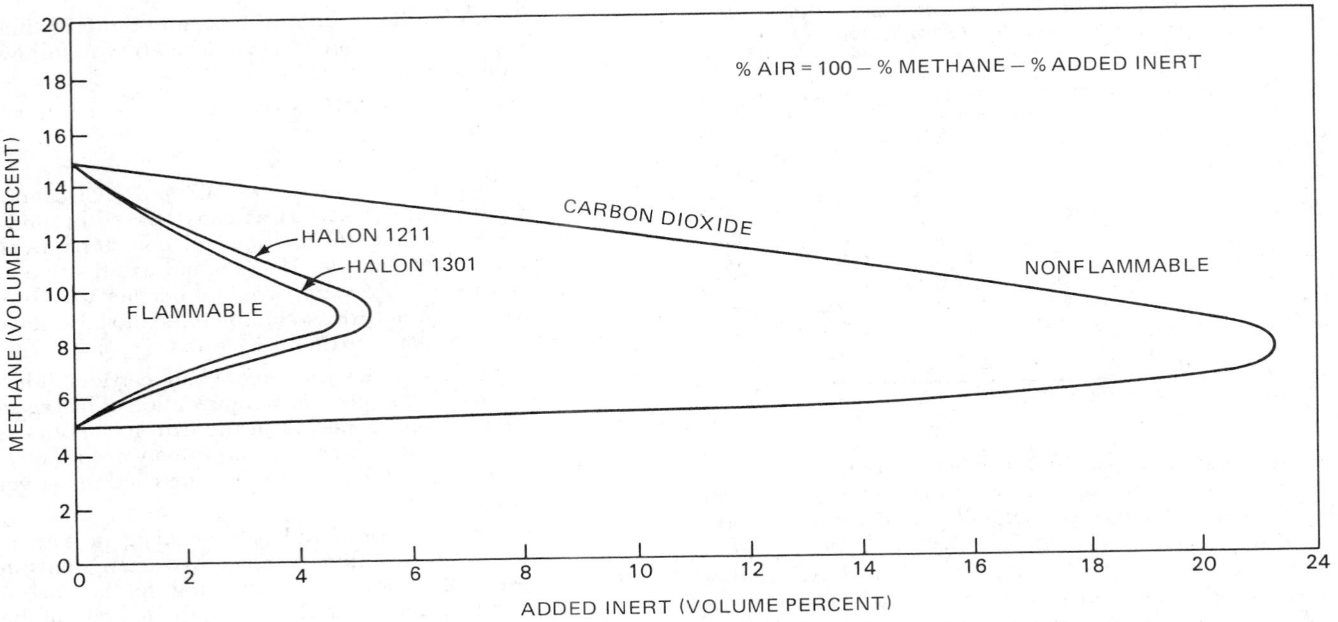

FIG. 1-6F. Flammability limits for methane-air mixtures with added inerting agents.[12]

involving hot fat, monoammonium phosphate is not recommended because of its acidic nature. An alkaline dry chemical, such as potassium bicarbonate, is preferred.

Table 1-6D lists the chemical names, formulas, and popular or commercial names of the various dry chemical agents. In each case, the particles of powder are coated with an agent, such as zinc stearate or a silicone, to prevent caking and to promote free flowing. The effectiveness of any of these agents depends on the particle size. The smaller the particles, the less agent is needed, as long as particles are larger than a critical size.[13] The reason for this is believed to be that the agent must vaporize rapidly in the flame to be effective.[14] However, if *extremely* fine agent were used, it would be difficult to disperse and apply to the fire.

It is difficult to compare precisely the effectiveness of one dry chemical with another because a comparison to reveal chemical differences would require each that agent have identical particle size, which is difficult to achieve. Furthermore, gaseous agents can be compared by studying the flammability limits of uniform mixtures at rest. If particles were present, however, they would settle out unless the mixture were agitated, thus modifying the combustion behavior.

TABLE 1-6D. ***Dry Chemical Agents***

Chemical name	Formula	Popular name(s)
Sodium bicarbonate	$NaHCO_3$	Baking soda
Sodium chloride	$NaCl$	Common salt
Potassium bicarbonate	$NHCO_3$	"Purple K"
Potassium chloride	KCl	"Super K"
Potassium sulfide	K_2SO_4	"Karate Massiv"
Monoammonium phosphate	$(NH_4)H_2PO_4$	"ABC" or Multipurpose
Urea + potassium bicarbonate	$NH_2CONH_2 + KHCO_3$	"Monnex"

It seems clear that the effective powders act on a flame by some chemical mechanism, presumably forming volatile species that react with hydrogen atoms or hydroxyl radicals. However, the precise reactions have not been established firmly. Although the primary action is probably removal of active species, the powders also discourage combustion by absorbing heat, by blocking radiative energy transfer, and, in the case of monoammonium phosphate, by forming a surface coating.

DEEP-SEATED FIRES

As was previously mentioned, combustion may occur in a smoldering, rather than a flaming, mode. Extinguishment of such fires is usually quite difficult.

Application of water or foam to the surface of a smoldering fire is not always effective, because the water cannot penetrate the hot interior where the combustion is occurring. Surrounding the smoldering material with an inert gas or a halon gas will only be effective if such an atmosphere can be maintained for the extensive time required for the interior to cool.

If the smoldering object can be sealed for a long time to prevent access of oxygen, the combustion will eventually cease. However, the pyrolysis and combustion product gases being generated in the interior of the porous material will generate pressure, which will tend to break through any sealant applied.

One practical approach is to remove the smoldering object from the building and either let it burn outside or submerge it in water for a long time. If the smoldering is occurring in a large outdoor pile, extinguishment will generally require digging into the pile and extinguishing the hot material with water as it is exposed.

Much research has been done on the theory of the smoldering process, but this has not yet led to new practical techniques for extinguishment.

SPECIAL CASES OF EXTINGUISHMENT

Extinguishment of a fire involving a *continuously flowing* combustible gas often is very difficult. The best tactic is to shut off the flow of gas. If extinguishment is accomplished while the gas is still flowing inside a building, then the danger of filling the building with an explosive gas mixture is introduced. In some cases, it might be preferable to let the flame continue to burn if the flow of combustible gas cannot be stopped.

If it is not possible to shut off the gas supply, fire fighting by any of several techniques is possible. One approach is to attack the *base* of the flame with a dry chemical nozzle, or carbon dioxide, or steam, or a halon. Whichever agent is used, it should be projected in the same general direction as the burning jet or plume.

When this tactic is used, it is advisable to cool any hot metal in the vicinity and to remove or de-energize any other ignition sources *before* attacking the fire itself. Otherwise, re-ignition is likely to occur after temporary extinguishment, and the supply of agent could be depleted by that time.

Water is usually the wrong agent for fires involving metals because a number of metals can react exothermically with water to form hydrogen, which, of course, burns rapidly. Furthermore, violent steam explosions can result if water enters molten metal.[15] As an exception, extinguishment has been accomplished when large quantities of water were applied to small quantities of burning magnesium, in the absence of pools of molten magnesium.

Table 1-6E is a list of extinguishing agents used for various metal fires. In general, metal fires are difficult to extinguish because of the very high temperatures involved and the correspondingly long cooling times required. Note that certain metals react exothermically with nitrogen, so the only acceptable inert gases for these metals are helium and argon. Halons should not be used on metal fires.

In addition to metals, certain inorganic chemicals are not compatible with water. For example, alkali and alkaline earth carbides, of which the best known is calcium carbide, react with water to form acetylene, which is highly flammable. Lithium hydride, sodium hydride, or lithium aluminum hydride react with water to produce hydrogen. The peroxides of sodium, potassium, barium, and strontium react exothermically with water. Cyanide salts react with acidified water to form a highly toxic gas, hydrogen cyanide. Even if these chemicals are not combustible themselves, they could be packed in combustible cartons and thus become involved in a fire. Or they could be stored in racks above combustible items.

Certain organic peroxides, used as polymerization catalysts in plastics manufacturing, are so unstable that they are stored under refrigeration to avoid exothermic heating. If water at normal room temperature were to be applied, it would provide heat to the peroxide and promote its exothermic decomposition.

A problem in applying water to fires involving toxic chemicals, such as pesticides, is associated with the runoff of contaminated water, which could cause groundwater pollution. If no other agent but water is available or practical, in such cases the only alternatives might be to use the minimum quantity of water possible or to allow a building to burn, thus producing downwind air pollution if the fire does not completely destroy the toxic chemicals.

TABLE 1-6E. ***Extinguishing Agents for Metal Fires***

Agent	Main ingredients	Used on
Powders		
"Pyrene" G–1 or "MetalGuard"	Graphitized coke + organic phosphate	Mg, Al, U, Na, K
"Met–L–X"	NaCl + $Ca_3(PO_4)_2$	Na
Foundry flux	Mixed chlorides + fluorides	Mg
"Lith–X"	Graphite + additives	Li, Mg, Zr, Na
"Pyromet"	$(NH_4)_2H(PO_4)$ + NaCl	Na, Ca, Zr, Ti, Mg, Al
"T.E.C."	KCl + NaCl + $BaCl_2$	Mg, Na, K
Dry sand	SiO_2	Various
Sodium chloride	NaCl	Na, K
Soda ash	Na_2CO_3	Na, K
Lithium chloride	LiCl	Li
Zirconium silicate	$ZrSiO_4$	Li
Liquids		
"TMB"	Trimethoxyboroxine	Mg, Zr, Ti
Gases		
Boron trifluoride	BF_3	Mg
Boron trichloride	BCl_3	Mg
Helium	He	Any metal
Argon	Ar	Any metal
Nitrogen	N_2	Na, K

From Prokopovitsh[15].

BIBLIOGRAPHY

References Cited

1. Friedman, R., *Principles of Fire Protection Chemistry,* 2nd ed., National Fire Protection Association, Quincy, MA, 1989.
2. Drysdale, D., *An Introduction to Fire Dynamics,* J. Wiley, NY, 1985.
3. Glassman, I., *Combustion,* 2nd ed., Academic Press, NY, 1987.
4. Strehlow, R. A., *Combustion Fundamentals,* McGraw-Hill, NY, 1984.
5. Zabetakis, M. G., *Flammability Characteristics of Combustible Gases and Vapors,* Bulletin 627, U. S. Bureau of Mines, 1965.
6. Heskestad, G., "The Role of Water in Suppression of Fire," *Fire and Flammability,* Vol. 11, 1980, pp. 254-259.
7. Rasbash, D. J., "The Extinction of Fire with Plain Water: A Review," *Fire Safety Science: Proceedings of the First International Symposium,* Hemisphere, NY, 1986, pp. 1145-1163.
8. Magee, R. S. and Reitz, R. D., "Extinguishment of Radiation-Augmented Plastic Fires by Water Sprays," *Fifteenth Symposium (International) on Combustion,* The Combustion Institute, Pittsburgh, PA, 1975, pp. 337-347.
9. Alpert, R. L., "Numerical Modeling of the Interaction between Automatic Sprinklers Sprays and Fire Plumes". *Fire Safety Journal,* Vol. 9, Nos. 1-2, 1985, pp. 157-163.
10. Grant, C., "Halon Design Calculations," *SFPE Handbook of Fire Protection Engineering,* National Fire Protection Association, Quincy, MA, 1988, Section 3, pp. 59-80.
11. Cogan, D. G., *Stones in a Glass House: CFC's and Ozone Depletion,* Investor Responsibility Research Center, Inc., Washington, D.C., 1988.
12. Kuchta, J. M., *Investigation of Fire and Explosion Accidents in the Chemical, Mining, and Fuel-Related Industries—A Manual,* Bulletin 680, U. S. Bureau of Mines, 1985.
13. Ewing, C. T., Faith, F. R., Hughes, J. T., and Carhart, H. W., "Flame Extinguishment Properties of Dry Chemicals," *Fire Technology,* Vol. 25, 1989, pp. 134-149.
14. Iya, K. S., Wollowitz, S., and Kaskan, W. E., "The Mechanism of Flame Inhibition by Sodium Salts," *Fifteenth Symposium (International) on Combustion,* The Combustion Institute, Pittsburgh, PA, 1975, pp. 329-336.

15. Prokopovitsh, A. S., "Combustible Metal Agents and Application Techniques," *Fire Protection Handbook*, 16th ed., National Fire Protection Association, Quincy, MA, 1986, pp. 49-54.

Additional Reading

Almgren, L. E., "Designing for Fire and Explosion Safety," *Proceedings* of the National Meeting of the American Institute of Chemical Engineers, American Institute of Chemical Engineers, NY, 1988, p. 10.

Application Guide for Explosion Suppression Systems, Fenwa Inc., Ashland, MA, Nov. 1979.

Bodurtha, F. T., *Industrial Explosion Prevention and Protection*, McGraw-Hill, NY, 1980.

Bruderer, R. E., "Design Example:Explosion Protection Selected for a Sray Drying Installation," *Plant/Operation Progress*, Vol. 8, No. 3 (July 1988), pp. 141-146.

Capraro, M. A. and Strickland, J. H., "Preventing Fires and Explosions in Pilot Plants," *Plant/Operation Progress*, Vol. 8, No. 4, 1989, pp. 189-194.

Dow's Fire and Explosion Index: Hazard Classification Guide, 6th ed., American Institute for Chemical Engineers, NY, 1987.

Fire Prevention and Control Master Planning: Introductory Summary, National Fire Prevention Control Administration, Fire Safety and Research Office, Washington, DC, 1978.

Groothuizen, T. M. and H. J. Pasman, "Explosions in Liquids and Solids," *Loss Prevention*, No. 9, 1975, pp. 91-96.

Hirst, R., Savage, N., and Booth, K., "Measurement of Inerting Concentrations," *Fire Safety Journal*, Vol. 4, No. 3, 1981/82, p. 147.

International Progress in Fire Safety, Fire Retardant Chemicals Association, Technomic, Lancaster, PA., 1987.

Klueg, E. P., "Liquid Nitrogen as a Powerplant Fire Extinguishant," *Fire Technology*, Vol. 5, No. 3 (Aug. 1969), pp. 197-202.

Najario, F. N., "Preventing or Surviving Explosions," *Chemical Engineering*, August 15, 1988.

Stull, D. R., *Fundamentals of Fire and Explosion*, Monograph Series No. 10, Vol. 73, American Institute of Chemical Engineers, NY, 1977.

Swift, I., "Design of Deflagration Protection Systems," *Journal of Loss Prevention in the Process Industries*, Vol. 1, 1988, pp. 5-15.

Swift, I., "Developments in Explosion Protection," *Plant/Operation Progress*, Vol.7, No.3 (July 1988), pp. 159-167.

Tucker, D. M., Drysdale, D. D., and Rasbash, D. J., "The Extinction of Diffusion Flames Burning in Various Oxygen Concentrations by Inert Gases and Bromotrifluoromethane," *Combustion and Flame*, 1981.

Tuhtar, D., *Fire and Explosion Protection: A Systems Approach*, Halsted Press, NY, 1989.

Wagner, H. G., "Gas Explosions, Their Origin and Effects," (Translated from *Chemie Ing. Tech.*, 1975, Vol. 47, No. 6, pp. 236-241.) United Kingdom Atomic Energy Authority, Risley Translation 2861, Risley, England, 1975.

Weldon, G. E., "Damage-Limiting Construction," *Fire Technology*, Vol. 9, No. 4 (Nov. 1973), pp. 263-270.

Wrenn, C., "Inerting for Fire Safety," *Plant/Operations Progress*, Vol.5, No.4 (Oct. 1986), pp.225-227.

Zalosh, R. G., "Explosion Protection," *SFPE Handbook of Fire Protection Engineering*, National Fire Protection Association, Quincy, MA, 1988.

Fire Prevention

Prevention is the first, and potentially the most powerful, of the six types of strategies for reducing fire losses. A fire that never happens causes no loss. Prevention can be achieved by changing the source of the initial heat, the initial fuel, or the behavior or mechanical/electrical circumstances that bring heat and fuel together. Section 2 of the *Fire Protection Handbook* addresses many different forms of fire prevention, but all involve one of these three approaches.

Changing behavior means firesafety education, which is the subject of Chapter 1. As Chapter 1 says, firesafety education "encompasses a wide spectrum of programs and activities presented to audiences as diverse as school children, older adults, homeowners, preschoolers, apartment dwellers, disabled people, employees, hospital and nursing home staffs, and church, service, and civic organizations." It's a mistake to think of firesafety education strictly in terms of self-contained programs that address only education, because the human element in fire is pervasive. Therefore, the discussion in Chapter 1 of the planning aspects of firesafety education is relevant to human-factors design in every area of firesafety a reader of the *Handbook* may need to address.

Chapter 2 addresses systems aspects and the need for comprehensive management and oversight of prevention in commercial and industrial properties, but the lessons and themes addressed here have analogues in all other areas of firesafety. Chapter 34, on housekeeping practices, also covers a very wide range of subjects and property classes in a systems context.

The other chapters of Section 2 address particular heat or fuel sources. All discuss the objects that can be sources of heat or fuel for fire, but many also discuss objects that are part of processes taking place in particular areas of activity in a building. In this larger context, it is possible to identify suppression, detection, confinement, and other fire protection approaches that are useful for the specific hazards posed by these processes, and, for that reason, some of the chapters in Section 2 will cover elements that might be expected to fall in other sections.

The leading heat source for *property damage* in U.S. building fires is the electrical distribution system, which is discussed in Chapter 3. Chapter 4 addresses heating devices, which are the leading heat source for fire *incidents* in U.S. buildings.

Most of the other chapters address more specific heat sources that pose hazards primarily or exclusively in industrial environments. Chapters 5 through 24, 31, 33, and 35 are of this type. A few of these chapters address heat sources that may be worth special attention because they account for large shares of fire loss in industrial and manufacturing properties. For property damage, these would include torch operations (Chapter 14), furnaces (Chapter 5), and working or shaping machines (Chapters 20 and 21). For deaths and injuries, chemical processing equipment (Chapter 15) might be included. On the other hand, Chapter 19 (lasers) is an example of a chapter of special interest because of the newness of the technology and hazards discussed.

The leading natural causes of fire in industrial and manufacturing properties are spontaneous ignitions, addressed in part through the discussion of housekeeping practices in Chapter 34, and lightning, addressed in Chapter 32.

Turning to potential fuel sources, the leading cause of injuries in fire and one of the leading causes for all measures of fire loss is combustible and flammable liquids and gases, covered in terms of storage practices in Chapters 25 and 26. Other sources of initial fuel posing special technical complexities in terms of storage are addressed in Chapters 27 through 30.

Also look for these: Most potential initial fuels are also important as potential fuel sources feeding rapid early growth of fire and so are discussed in Section 3. Of the other causes of fire, arson is discussed in terms of investigation techniques in Chapter 8 of Section 9 in the context of the investigative role of fire protection organizations. Many major fire causes, such as smoking, cooking, arson, and child fireplay, are addressed only briefly in the *Handbook* but are discussed in detail in NFPA's extensive *Learn Not to Burn* materials. The *Firesafety Educator's Handbook* is an excellent place to start, even if it is intended for use in employee training. Readers with a significant interest in particular hazards covered in this section are likely to need the more detailed guidance found in NFPA's specialized handbooks, such as the *Industrial Fire Hazards Handbook*, the *National Electrical Code* and *Handbook*, the *Flammable and Combustible Liquids Code Handbook*, the *National Fuel Gas Code Handbook*, and the *Liquefied Petroleum Gases Handbook*. In addition, some specialized prevention rules that tend to arise only in one class of properties may be found in the appropriate chapters of Section 8.

FIRESAFETY EDUCATION

Revised by Jan Gratton

Firesafety education is designed to increase knowledge and to develop or change the attitudes and behaviors of men, women, and children toward fire. It encompasses a wide spectrum of programs and activities presented to audiences as diverse as school children, older adults, homeowners, preschoolers, apartment dwellers, disabled people, employees, hospital and nursing home staffs, and church, service, and civic organizations. Firesafety education topics may include home fire escape planning, babysitting firesafety, cooking fires, clothing fires, juvenile fire setters, first aid for burns, home fire hazard inspections, scald prevention, smoke detectors, fire extinguishers, and home sprinkler systems, to name a few.

Whether a firesafety education program is large or small, it takes planning to be effective. From a short 30-second public service announcement to an extensive year-long program, firesafety education efforts must be well-planned, i.e., targeted, continual, and measurable.

This chapter discusses the planning and implementation processes that can be used for any program. The information provides the foundation for beginning or expanding successful firesafety education efforts in the community.

Effective firesafety education programs do not just happen. They are well thought out. They have measurable goals and objectives. And they are targeted at real problems.

The suggested process for firesafety education program development includes the following steps:

1. Initial planning phase.
   a. Establish responsibility and support.
   b. Form a planning team.
   c. Identify local fire problems.
   d. Define goals and objectives.
2. Design and implementation phase.
   a. Conduct audience/market research.
   b. Develop program strategies.
   c. Develop action plans for program objectives.
   d. Make a program proposal.
   e. Prepare teaching aids and train instructors.
   f. Conduct pilot tests.
3. Evaluation phase.
   a. Provide for program documentation.
   b. Determine effectiveness.
   c. Revise action plans and objectives.

INITIAL PLANNING PHASE

Establish Responsibility and Support

Before beginning to design an individual program or a program for an entire community, fire departments should clarify who will be responsible for firesafety education. The fire chief normally makes the assignment, thus demonstrating strong support for such efforts. One person, a small group, or an entire division might be responsible for developing programs. While a different person or group might be appointed to implement them, the same people may do both jobs. It is important that those with the responsibilities also have sufficient authority, time, and resources to get the job done.

Firesafety education responsibilities and tasks are assigned in various ways. In some fire departments, programs are conducted by career and volunteer fire fighters as part of their regular shift duties. Some fire chiefs assign personnel from the prevention bureau, or hire a specialist in education to develop and implement programs. Others enlist civilians, such as community volunteers, teachers, nurses, or senior citizens. Some fire departments use a combination of all of these people for their educational work. Whoever is responsible, it is important that the entire fire department, and eventually the community, supports them.

Originally written by Diane C. Roche, a fire education expert, this chapter was revised by Jan Gratton for the 17th edition. Ms. Gratton is a member of the NFPA Board of Directors who operates a private consulting business in Covina, CA. She is vice chairperson of the NFPA Education Section and serves as the NFPA Firesafety Education Representative for California, Nevada, Oregon, and Hawaii.

For fire personnel to actively support and encourage firesafety education, they need a working knowledge of the process involved. Fire departments should include firesafety education in rookie fire schools and in ongoing training programs for fire fighters. All fire personnel should also be encouraged to take a course in firesafety education at the National Fire Academy in Emmitsburg, MD, or at state and local fire schools and workshops offered by professional fire service organizations.

Form a Planning Team

After responsibilities are clarified, a planning team should be formed. This group should be responsible for the initial planning of community firesafety education efforts and can later serve in an advisory capacity. Planning teams have several advantages: (1) they divide the work load, (2) contribute creative ideas and objective opinions, (3) supply the expertise needed from outside the fire service, and (4) provide general support. Members of the team should include appropriate fire personnel, educators, community leaders, and others who can provide knowledge, expertise, influence, and resources. The ideal size for this group is ten persons, but if a larger group is needed to include everyone, smaller sub-groups or committees can be formed to expedite work.

An example of a local firesafety education planning team might be: fire chief, fire fighters, fire prevention personnel, a teacher, a doctor, a burn nurse, a lawyer, a city council representative, a representative of service organizations, a media representative, a social worker, a member of the crime prevention team, a chamber of commerce representative, an arson investigator, and a representative of the building industry.

Identify Local Fire Problems

Since effective firesafety education programs are aimed at correcting or reducing specific fire problems, one of the first tasks of the planning team is to identify the local fire problem. How lifesaving information is presented to the public depends on the types of fire problems occurring in the community. Develop a profile of the types and frequency of fires, causes of ignition, places of origin, types and behavior of victims, and fire patterns by neighborhood. Before people can be taught to stop starting fires, the behavior or misbehavior must be identified. In addition, the types of people causing fires need to be determined so that the program can be designed for a target audience. For example, messages on how to prevent hot liquid burns in children often target the parents or adults who care for them. Younger adults can also be educated to protect their aging parents and grandparents from fire and burns. Where the fires are starting also needs to be identified. Is the biggest problem house fires, car fires, industrial fires, fires in nursing homes or in schools?

To identify the fire problems, the planning team will need fire department records as well as records of hospitals, insurance companies, and state agencies. During this phase of development, the value of an organized reporting system is appreciated. In particular, a city that participates in the National Fire Incident Reporting System (NFIRS) will be able to analyze its fire experience by many factors useful in planning firesafety education.* (See Section 1, Chapter 1 entitled "America's Fire Problem and Fire Protection" for examples using national data.)

Once the statistical information is obtained, it becomes the baseline data and must be analyzed to determine problem areas or trends. In analyzing the data, it may appear that no particular fire or burn problem emerges. The lack of an obvious trend may cause departments to conclude that they really have "no fire problem." It is important to examine further the profile of the community. For example, in an area consisting of large numbers of elderly, even though there is no data to indicate fires caused by failure to install, check, and maintain smoke detectors, a survey may show that this potential risk does exist and a firesafety program is needed. The National Fire Protection Association's *Firesafety Educator's Handbook*[1] includes, in the "Message" section, instructions and examples for determining local fire problems. It is recommended that the planning team study this information.

Define Goals and Objectives

Once the planning team has identified the specific local fire problems, it can set goals and objectives and, eventually, develop action plans based on those goals and objectives. This goal setting is similar to deciding where one wants to go on a road map, then determining the fastest, most economical route with the fewest obstacles along the way. Although the final goal is always in mind, the route (i.e., objectives) requires most of one's attention and energy. To do so successfully, one must focus attention on finishing each portion of the trip that brings the final destination nearer.

Before goals and objectives are set, be certain the team distinguishes between them. (See Table 2-1A.)

Goals are achieved through completion of specific objectives, and objectives are completed through individual steps in an action plan. Goals are what should be ultimately achieved; objectives are the programs needed to achieve the goal. Action plans are the detailed steps to be completed to accomplish the objectives. Some objectives consist of on-going programs, while others are one-time efforts. Goals, objectives, and action plans form a pyramid, with development beginning at the top and achievement beginning at the bottom. (See Figure 2-1A.)

The need for goals and objectives appears at various levels and planning stages in the program design. First, discuss the overall goals and program objectives. Then take a look at the behavioral objectives involved in the program content.

The planning team should develop a major goal for its overall firesafety education efforts and should continually work toward it. Program objectives should be designed to bring the goal closer. In the design and implementation stage of this planning process, the team will need to work specificity and detail into the action plans. The following is an example of an overall goal for firesafety education:

*NFIRS—The National Fire Incident Reporting System—is a computer-based system that builds a data base at a local level, which also supports state and national data bases. The national data base is maintained by the U.S. Fire Administration, Federal Emergency Management Agency. Because the same definitions are used by fire departments of all sizes in all parts of the country, the computerized information forms a reliable base from which to draw local comparisons and determine local problem areas.

TABLE 2-1A. *Goals and Objectives.*

	Goal	Objective	Action Plan
	Utlimate End	Interim End	Means to the End
Time frame	Future	1–2 Years	Less than 1 year
Responsibility for completion	Entire department's organization	Program manager regional leader	Individual staff
Emphasis	Ultimate benefits to community. Future direction of the department	Your program's measurable results that constitute progress toward your goal	Your resources—how you will allocate time, money, and staff to achieve your objectives
Specifics	Not specific. Does not include target completion dates and measurement of success	Specific results, including target completion dates and measurement of success	Specific results, including responsibility for carrying out the plan

Figure 2-1A. Development pyramid.

to reduce the number of fires and the resulting deaths, injuries, and property damage by educating the public in the subjects of hazards of fire, methods of fire and burn prevention, and reactions necessary for a successful escape from fire.

The planning team should choose realistic objectives based on the scenarios of typical fire problems in their community. Keep in mind that, even when fire departments target their programs, they still receive many requests for programs dealing with general firesafety information and skills. These programs are also important and should be presented because they help reduce the risk of future fire problems by providing prevention and survival information.

The following are sample objectives for a community which determined that its major fire problems included a high rate of cooking fires in homes, home fire deaths due to improper reactions (especially by children), and a disregard for fire prevention at local nursing homes.

Objective—reduce cooking fires:

1. To present a lesson on cooking firesafety to each of the 20 cooking classes held in the four high schools. Do this by the end of April.
2. To produce, with the local radio and television stations, public service announcements telling how to prevent cooking fires and how to deal with one if it happens, and to get stations to air these messages twice a day, at breakfast and dinner times, for a two-month period.
3. To write a newspaper article on cooking firesafety to appear in the food section of the local newspaper within one week.

Objective—reduce house fire deaths, especially of children:

1. To provide firesafety lessons during October/November and April/May for all children enrolled in local preschools and daycare centers.
2. To provide four firesafety lessons to all fifth-grade students (approximately 2000) in public schools beginning in September and ending in June.
3. To provide annual firesafety assembly programs for grades K through 4 in the 22 public elementary schools during January, February, and March.
4. To include firesafety messages for children in on-going programs conducted by the Parks and Recreation Department and the public libraries.

Objective—reduce nursing home fires:

1. To conduct lessons in fire prevention and fire survival for all shifts at local nursing homes at regular intervals.

DESIGN AND IMPLEMENTATION PHASE

After the program goals and objectives have been defined, the design of the program(s) can begin. During this critical "drawing board" stage, basic decisions are made that will influence the program's effectiveness and public acceptance. Firesafety education should be designed to be functional (i.e., to reduce the fire problem), as well as appealing and motivational to the public.

Firesafety educators should give their target audiences a reason to listen to them and should motivate their audiences to respond to lifesaving suggestions. Since programs should convey the message in an efficient and effective manner, both audiences and the product should be well known to firesafety educators. Firesafety educators need to "sell" firesafety information to the public. They are the fire department "sales force" and programs should be designed with that in mind.

Conduct Audience/Market Research

One of the first steps in designing firesafety education programs is to research the attitudes, characteristics, learning abilities, and preferences of the audience. Too often, firesafety education programs are designed without regard for the audience's willingness or ability to listen and learn. Know the target audience. To do this, speak to audience members, to those who already know or work with them, and to researchers who study them. In the *Firesafety Educator's Handbook*[1] is a section titled "Market," which describes people and their ability to learn during different stages of their development. After referring to this section, determine the following.

Learning abilities: Determine at what level and rate the audience usually accepts information. In what form is the information usually presented, i.e., written, spoken, or pictorially? Do audience members learn best in small or large groups? Maturity levels should also be considered. It is not wise, for instance, to present a lesson on the proper use of portable fire extinguishers to a class of primary school children, who are not mature enough to decide when it is safe to use one.

Attitudes and behaviors: How does the group usually behave? Are they apathetic, friendly, hostile, hospitable, conservative, liberal? Do they usually respond well to people from outside their own group? Do they have any preferences that may affect their willingness to listen? Realize that some religious or social groups prefer a particular demeanor and/or dress code. Some school teachers prefer that guest speakers maintain a particular level of discipline during firesafety lessons in their classrooms. Unfortunately, some groups may even enjoy "testing" the guest speaker. Don't cater to the whims of any one group, but be aware of their particular attitudes and behaviors before appearing before them.

Accessibility: How easy is it to reach the audience? How does one gain access to their attention and time? Research their interests and/or occupations and find out where and when they meet as a group. Determine who will be the best contact person in setting up arrangements with this audience. The frequency with which the audience meets in a group will affect their accessibility. Generally, children are more accessible in school than in a social club which may meet only once a week or month. Find out also how accessible the audience can be through the media. Do they watch television, listen to the radio, read the newspaper?

Group size: Before planning any programs, determine the potential size of the audience. How many people are involved in the group or in similar or associated groups? Make sure that sufficient resources and personnel are available to handle the anticipated demand. For example, once a program is presented to a particular group and there are ten more such groups in the area, there may well be ten requests for similar programs. Conversely, if a program is planned for a particular group, involving many hours and some money for the design and preparation, and it turns out there are only a few such groups in the area, there would not be much demand for repeat performances. Do homework. Determine potential group size in advance.

Current knowledge of firesafety: Determine how much information the audience already may have received on the subject. If the majority has a mutual level of knowledge due to past lessons or due to individual occupations, adjust the program to avoid repetition. Never take for granted that the audience has attained a given level of understanding of firesafety. Check the records for previous program contact.

How can all of this audience/market research be obtained? The following are some suggestions:

1. Talk with members of the group before making a formal presentation.
2. Get in touch with caretakers or providers of the audience, e.g., teachers of preschool and school-age children, nurses in nursing homes, recreation specialists working with older adults, parents or relatives of disabled people, adult education specialists, social workers or psychologists who may work with juvenile firesetters, and special education teachers.
3. Get in touch with groups providing services for the audience, e.g., for a group of older adults, contact the American Association of Retired Persons, the mayor's council on aging, or the administration of a retirees' drop-in center.
4. Coordinate with other governmental or community leaders who visit these groups with other messages, e.g., the crime prevention officer, substance abuse specialists, or department of parks and recreation. What were their experiences with the audience?

It is important to gear the program content and approach to the audience's needs, while at the same time maintaining the integrity of the firesafety message. Find out in advance where the communication opportunities or barriers exist. Conduct a pre-survey to determine knowledge level, attitudes, and behaviors regarding firesafety. If a negative attitude exists, it will be necessary to modify that before the educational program can be truly effective. For example, if the older adults in the community resent the intrusion of government which requires them to install smoke detectors, their attitude may inhibit learning the importance of having an early warning device in their homes. A post-survey will indicate the success of a program designed to change attitudes, as well as knowledge and behavior. Anticipation and preparation are preferable to learning by mistakes or "playing it by ear."

Develop Program Strategies

Now that the audience has been evaluated, it's time to develop a strategy to reach them with firesafety messages. What will the approach be? Where, when, and how often will the audience receive the messages? What format will be used? These questions can be answered by learning about the following items.

Existing networks: There is usually a communication network of some kind already in use by any target audience. There are places where they meet or publications from which they already obtain information. Some of these meeting places, such as schools, may require attendance, while others, such as social groups, are totally voluntary. Utilizing existing networks will usually be easier and more effective than attempting to arrange special networks for firesafety education. Examples of some existing networks are school classrooms, civic leagues, service organizations, social clubs, safety committees in industry, fairs, exhibits, and neighborhood watch groups.

When a network does exist, integrating a firesafety program within that network as much as possible is important. For example, NFPA's *Learn Not to Burn*®[2] (*LNTB*) curriculum has been integrated into existing school subjects; this makes firesafety information attractive to the teachers because of the dual benefits. It is also true that many times the existing networks are looking for interesting and informative programs to fill their needs; e.g., many television and radio talk shows need as many as 30 interesting guests every week for 52 weeks of the year. Utilize such existing networks when possible and when appropriate.

Point of contact: Contact the target audience when and where they will be most likely to accept the firesafety message, i.e., when they will be most receptive. For example, avoid visiting a civic league on the night they are debating a heated local issue. Instead, visit them on the night of their banquet, when many people who might not otherwise attend are present and the general mood is hospitable. Avoid visiting community centers when card games, bingo, or other activities have been scheduled. Avoid scheduling school programs within two weeks of major holidays or vacations. School programs scheduled from January through March are much more acceptable, as are those during September and October, with Fire Prevention Week in the spotlight. Communicate with teachers and administrators so as not to conflict with programmed activities.

A place of business or industry is another good point of contact, especially if a safety committee is functioning and management encourages such participation.

Schedule programs and firesafety messages as conveniently as possible for the target audience, and determine where the best location will be, e.g., at home, work, school, or a recreation site. Where is the audience most likely to learn and retain a firesafety message?

Appropriate format: Determine how to convey the firesafety message to the target audience. There are as many formats as there are firesafety educators, but some of the more common formats are: lectures, demonstrations, printed materials, television, radio, public service announcements, press releases, newsletters, mobile vans, puppet shows, seminars, films, slide programs, videotape programs, posters, speeches, displays, and newspaper articles. The choice of format(s) will depend on such factors as:

- Size of the audience
- Available resources and cost of materials
- Preparation time
- Length of program
- Level of audience attention and involvement
- Age of the audience
- Nature of the firesafety message

For a listing of the advantages and disadvantages of available formats, see the *Firesafety Educator's Handbook*,[1] "Methods" section.

Decision to adopt, adapt, or create a program: It is important that firesafety educators do not isolate themselves or their programs from outside influences. It is not always necessary to create entirely new programs. Other fire departments or other communities have dealt with some of the same audiences and messages, and it often is possible to adopt or adapt an existing program. Nationally recognized programs, such as NFPA's *Learn Not to Burn*[2] curriculum, have been carefully designed to allow local community adaptation to fit local problems and circumstances.

A listing of some recent programs appears in the "Materials" section of the *Firesafety Educator's Handbook*.[1] In addition, most fire departments will share their materials at little or no cost. Avoid the "re-invent-the-wheel" syndrome. Tapping into existing networks and sharing programs is more cost-effective than developing programs from scratch. Educators need to set aside the pride of ownership and recognize the time-saving opportunities a well-established successful program offers. National and regional firesafety education conferences provide outstanding opportunities for exchange of program information and networking.

Develop Action Plans for Program Objectives

The initial planning phase was for development of networking program goals and objectives. Now that further information has been developed and implementation nears, it is time to develop action plans to meet the objectives. Action plans are the steps necessary to achieve the objective(s), e.g., to provide four firesafety lessons to every fifth-grade student (approximately 2000) in public schools, beginning in September and ending in June. Table 2-1B is an example of an action plan for this particular objective. The plans should be very specific and assigned to appropriate personnel. The plans can then serve as a reminder of what needs to be accomplished.

TABLE 2-1B. *Action Plan*

Steps	Target Date	Responsible Person
Revise program format.	7/01	Bob and Nancy
Develop and order handout materials.	11/15	Bill, Bob and Nancy
Schedule schools.	6/01	Bill
Provide the schedule to the school board for approval and distribution.	7/15	Bill
Contact each principal to verify the schedule four weeks prior to program.	as stated	Bob and Nancy
Present the assembly program	per schedule	Bob and Nancy
Ask the nearest fire company to arrange for a fire fighter to assist with the program.	two weeks prior to the program	Bob and Nancy
Develop an evaluation tool for this program.	11/04	Bill

Make a Program Proposal

Before proceeding with design and implementation, it is necessary to receive permission from the decisionmaker regarding the target audience or group. Before printing booklets, ordering audiovisual materials, and training instructors, be sure the audience is willing and ready for the program. It may also be necessary to receive permission from the fire department or planning team before going any further.

Contact the decisionmaker for the audience, e.g., superintendent of schools, curriculum director or advisor, teacher, club president, television or radio news or program director, or newspaper editor, and present a program proposal to this key person. Program proposals will vary in length and detail according to the audience and program. School systems, for instance, may want detailed lesson plans, including a list of audiovisual materials and handouts. Clubs and service organizations, on the other hand, will probably want only a general description of the program content. Television and radio stations may want to see script ideas.

If possible, do not mail program proposals. Make an appointment to see the decisionmaker for the audience and make the proposal in person. When doing so, (1) be prepared, (2) be confident, i.e., never approach the decisionmaker with "I think we would like to do something with you," and (3) have precise information on exactly what is to be achieved and the plan to accomplish it.

In general, proposals should include:

1. A statement of the need for the program and how the audience would benefit, i.e., explain the fire problem in local terms.
2. Behavioral objectives.
3. A format description including:
   a. proposed number and length of lessons.
   b. topics to be covered.
   c. audiovisual materials to be used.
   d. sample printed handouts, or a rough design and text for folders and booklets.
4. A cost estimate if the audience will be sharing any program expenses.
5. A description of evaluation tools used in the program.

Once there is a decision to proceed with the program, begin to prepare for the pilot test phase. If the decision is not favorable, find out what the objections were and attempt to reconcile them.

Prepare Teaching Aids and Train Instructors

After receiving permission from the intended audience to present the program(s), prepare for program implementation. It is strongly recommended that a pilot phase be included in the implementation process. Whether preparation is for a pilot phase or a full program, it will be necessary to prepare teaching aids and train program instructors/presenters.

Preparing teaching aids: Steps in preparing teaching aids should include the following.

Develop program outlines. Decide what the program content should be. Apply to the content what has been learned about the audience, strategy, and objectives. Develop a topical outline and a narrative outline. These can be used to train the presenters and as reference notes during the program. Narrative outlines indicate how the topics should be taught and provide a detailed description of the program content, including audiovisual aids. Program outlines help ensure that all presenters will be teaching from the same materials and delivering consistent messages.

Produce/order the written materials and audiovisual programs. Since the first phase of implementation will include a pilot test, materials should be produced and ordered with this in mind. If 10,000 brochures are printed and the pilot test indicates that they are not effective, valuable resources have been wasted. Once they have passed the pilot test, all print and audiovisual materials should be ordered well in advance of scheduled program dates.

Obtain audiovisual equipment. Buy, borrow, or lease enough film projectors, slide projectors, screens, video players, etc., to operate all programs. Make sure that all equipment is in good working condition; keep extra projector bulbs on hand.

Prepare a teaching aid checklist for each type of program. For example, include in a checklist for a home escape plan lesson these items:

Program outline.

Film.

Film projector, including take-up reel.

Extra projector bulbs.

Screen.

Extension cord with three-prong adapter.

Brochures.

Smoke detector with fresh batteries.

Folding escape ladder.

Sample evacuation on floor plan.

Training instructors: The program instructor/presenter may or may not be the program designer. In many fire departments, they are one and the same person. Some fire departments provide formal training in firesafety education for prevention and suppression forces alike.

Although firesafety educators need not be certified teachers, they should have some general training requirements in instructional techniques and communication skills, because conditions can vary from area to area. Many fire departments and state training offices give such courses.

Knowledge of subject matter and initial training may be obtained in several ways. The National Fire Academy at the National Emergency Training Center in Emmitsburg, MD, offers a residential course in Public Fire Education. The International Fire Service Training Association (IFSTA) publishes a manual, *Public Fire Education,*[3] which is used by many fire departments for this initial training. The *Firesafety Educator's Handbook*[1] is another valuable resource. Several states offer certification in public fire education.

Many fire departments utilize civilians in their firesafety education efforts. If these presenters do not have a knowledge of the fire service, they should be provided with information and training to familiarize them with the basics of fire suppression and the operation of a fire department.

After the initial training takes place, continual professional development should occur. This will keep the firesafety educator current with the state of the art. There are numerous conferences, seminars, and workshops on local, state, and national levels that can supply this training. Membership in national, state, and regional organizations concerned with firesafety education will keep the firesafety educator informed about training opportunities, as well as current literature in the field. The national organizations include the NFPA Education Section and the International Society of Fire Service Instructors.

Sometimes, scheduling a firesafety program involves no more than a telephone call and a follow-up letter of confirmation. At other times, scheduling can be a complicated and extensive task, depending on the number and nature of the programs and the accessibility of the audience. All programs should be as convenient as possible for the audience. The following information should be obtained at the time of scheduling:

1. Name and type of audience.
2. Program location, time, and length of presentation.
3. Kind of firesafety program requested (ask for a copy of the printed program if available in advance).
4. Name and telephone number of the contact person.
5. Size of group, age range.
6. Kind of room in which presentation will be made, including:

a. Type of seating arrangement.
b. Availability of electrical outlets.
c. Availability of projector screen.

Conduct Pilot Tests

Pilot tests are necessary to validate the program elements and teaching aids before full implementation of a program takes place. This ensures the effectiveness, accuracy, and appeal of the program before large amounts of time and resources are committed to the project.

Pilot tests vary in depth and duration. They may involve presenting a program to a sample audience a few times to see how members react to the materials and to the approach; or they may last as long as a year and involve many sample audiences and a great deal of evaluation. Whatever type of pilot test is appropriate, be sure that the sample audiences are representative of the total target audience and that all conditions are as realistic as possible. The pilot audience can supply feedback regarding:

1. Relevance and clarity of the program message.
2. Readability and appeal of the printed materials.
3. Effectiveness and impact of the audiovisual aids.
4. Ability of the instructor/presenter.
5. Appropriateness of the format and the point of contact.
6. Ability of the program to achieve the objectives.

EVALUATION PHASE

Provide for Program Documentation

After pilot testing and full implementation, it will be necessary to evaluate the program's effectiveness. If the program was aimed at reducing the high rate of cooking fires, did it succeed?

Before such questions can be answered, two tools are needed. First, refer to the information gathered in the identification phase. This information is the baseline data with which to make comparisons. Next is needed documentation that indicates how many programs were conducted, how many people were reached, and how many personnel it took to do the job. Also needed is information from any pre- and post-testing or any pre- and post-surveys or questionnaires completed by the target audience. To evaluate a media program, collect information concerning the number of viewers, listeners, or readers exposed to the message. Most television and radio stations and newspapers are willing to supply these figures. Also, keep clippings of articles and copies of public service announcements as a part of the media support documentation.

A sample firesafety education report is shown in Table 2-1C.

TABLE 2-1C. *Firesafety Education Program Report*

Type of Program	Approx. Length of Program	Number of Programs Completed: Reg.*	Number of Programs Completed: OT†	Number of People in Audience
School:				
5th grade	50–60 minutes	64		419
Assembly (K–4)	60 minutes	none		
Private schools	60 minutes	none		
Preschools/day care	60 minutes	1		55
Babysitting	50 minutes	6		124
General:				
Service clubs	1 hour		1	25
Dormitory firesafety	1 hour	2		230
Senior citizen	1 hour		1	40
Juvenile firesetters	1 hour	1		3
Fire extinguishers	1 hour		3	65
Displays	7 hours 6 hours 25 hours		3	(est.) 3,400
	TOTALS	74	8	4,361

Total Mileage: 1747

*Number of programs completed during regular working hours.
†Number of programs completed during overtime hours.

Determine Effectiveness

Ultimately, the planning team will need to report to the fire chief or others concerning the effectiveness of the firesafety education programs. It is extremely important for the ultimate success of any program to have ALL fire personnel aware of the educational content and messages being conveyed. Any fire department representative may be called upon to deliver a program, respond to inquiries, or demonstrate a firesafety education procedure. Training and program updates will help ensure consistent messages and department support at all levels. If the programs are not achieving the objectives, then revisions or alternate plans and programs will be needed. Reports using baseline data and documentation should be prepared for presentation. In addition, testimonials or letters of support from the target audience can be used to illustrate the program's effectiveness. Not all programs will result in a reduction of fires; it is very difficult to count how many fires the program may have prevented. What can be shown, however, is a gain in knowledge or awareness, which will lead to fewer fires in the future, and a change in behavior or attitude, which will affect the fire incidence rate. All such information should be analyzed.

Revise Action Plans and Objectives

Action plans and program objectives provide the basis for well-organized and effective programs. Once revised and approved, the plans and objectives should be used as management tools. However, they are never static and should be revised periodically to reflect changes in the local fire problem, goals, program content, or resources (e.g., financial, technological, material).

The information contained in this chapter about planning and implementing firesafety education programs can be utilized by fire personnel, whether they are career, volunteer, full-time, or part-time. The process can be very lengthy for extensive programs, or accomplished in a relatively short time for more limited programs.

What is important is that the fire service plans for firesafety education programs. It is essential that this planning include members of the community beyond the fire service. Well-targeted, organized, effective, measurable programs supported by the fire department and involving the community are those most successful at saving lives, preventing injuries, and reducing property damage. Firesafety education works when it is well-planned and supported.

LEARN NOT TO BURN®

Since the mid-1970s, the National Fire Protection Association has spearheaded a number of national projects in public firesafety education for people of all ages. Under the umbrella slogan "Learn Not to Burn," NFPA has developed programs and activities ranging from public service announcements on television to the *Learn Not to Burn*[2] curriculum for children from kindergarten through the eighth grade. *Learn Not to Burn*[2] activities are coordinated through the NFPA Public Education division.

In 1986, NFPA established the tax-exempt *Learn Not to Burn Foundation* to seek outside sources of funding for firesafety education projects aimed specifically at high-risk populations. Support from the Continental Corporation Foundation enabled the LNTB Foundation to release the *Learn Not to Burn Preschool Program* in 1991. In addition to a written guide for teaching focusing on seven firesafety behaviors for children aged three to six years old the preschool program features a cassette tape of original music by folksinger Jim Post to reinforce the lessons.

Twenty-two key firesafety behaviors are the core of the *Learn Not to Burn* [2] curriculum, and three behaviors are designated for local options, such as earthquake safety or pool safety. In some jurisdictions, use of the *LNTB* [2] curriculum has been mandated at the state or county level, as well as in local school systems. The National Education Association recommends the *LNTB* [2] curriculum for use by its members.

The most comprehensive firesafety program available nationally for school children, the *Learn Not to Burn*[2] curriculum organizes life-saving material to be taught year-round. Lessons in the *LNTB*[2] curriculum manual are arranged in three levels, for grades kindergarten through two; three through five; and six through eight.

The 22 specific behaviors of the *Learn Not to Burn*[2] curriculum, which can be integrated into the on-going subject areas of the classroom, are intended to teach children to prevent fires; to protect themselves, their families, and friends from fire; and to persuade others to be mindful of the need for firesafe behavior at all times. Each behavior is outlined for the teacher in terms of three objectives—attitude, knowledge, and behavior—and suggests participatory affirming activities that are within the subjects normally taught at that grade level (e.g., arithmetic, science, English, social studies, art, and music). Each *LNTB*[2] curriculum manual contains firesafety background information, evaluation instruments and an extensive reference guide to supporting materials.

Recognizing that firesafety education must compete with many other safety issues for time and resources in the school curriculum, NFPA introduced a new tool in 1991 to make teaching Learn Not to Burn easier and more affordable than ever. The *Learn Not to Burn Resource Books* are a set of teacher guides designed to introduce a few firesafety behaviors each year in a four-step sequence, kindergarten through grade three. Each step includes simple lesson plans with reproducible activity sheets to reinforce each behavioral objective, group activities for the classroom firesafety information to be shared with the student's family, and evaluation instruments. The resource books may be used to supplement a comprehensive LNTB program in primary grades or to introduce firesafety education to schools that have never had it before.

Implementation of the *Learn Not to Burn Curriculum* is facilitated by a network of twelve firesafety education representatives throughout North America, each an expert in teaching firesafety. These representatives conduct regional and state workshops to train interested individuals in establishing effective firesafety educaton programs at the local level. These representatives are also available to consult with fire departments, fire marshals, parent-teacher organizations, and other groups toward adoption of the LNTB curriculum for classroom teaching.

The following is an example of one method to integrate the *Learn Not to Burn*[2] curriculum into the school system.

THE SCHOOL FIRE DRILL—A LIFE-SAVING LESSON

Exit drills are required in schools so that occupants will know how to make an efficient and orderly escape according to NFPA *101®*, *Life Safety Code®*[4]. These drills give public fire educators countless opportunities over a child's school career to teach building escape. Fire drills can be used as a teaching opportunity if they are approached as an educational exercise and a learning experience. Fire drills as organized and understandable lessons allow administrators to incorporate firesafety education into the school's educational environment.

What is learned in a school fire drill can also be used in home escapes and escapes from public buildings, thereby teaching children proper evacuation procedures and allowing them opportunities to practice their newly learned behavior.

As in any escape plan, school drills should include the following steps:

1. Have a plan that includes a primary and secondary exit.
2. Have a meeting place outside the building.
3. Establish a method of determining the presence or absence of students.
4. Assign the people who will have the responsibility of calling the fire department.
5. Know the alarm sound.
6. When the alarm sounds, stop everything, and exit safely, quickly, and quietly.
7. Students should be taught to respond as if every fire drill were the "real thing," even if they were planned and announced in advance.
8. Once out, stay out until notified it is safe to go back inside.
9. Have an alternate plan in case you cannot follow your original plan.
10. If possible, incorporate the fire department in the school fire drill and have a fire fighter discuss fire behavior with the students.
11. Evaluate your drill performance, and alter your plans, if necessary.

Before and/or after a school fire drill is an opportunity for teachers and firesafety educators to discuss with the students the following *Learn Not to Burn*[2] *behaviors:*

- Responds correctly during fire and smoke drills.
- Uses home escape plan.

- Identifies exit signs and knows two ways out in public places.
- Performs the crawl-low-under-smoke procedure.
- Reports fire and smoke immediately.
- Performs the stop, drop, and roll procedure.
- Initiates first-aid practices for burns.
- Installs and maintains smoke detectors.
- Recognizes the fire department as a partner in community services.
- Recognizes the dangers of false alarms.

By starting now to educate youngsters in school, it is foreseen that, as today's students grow up, they will carry with them throughout their lives a healthy respect for fire, along with factual information on how to prevent fire and what to do if one occurs. As present-day students pass along good firesafety behaviors to their own children, successive generations of Americans should experience far fewer preventable fires and should be in a better position to save themselves and others in case of fire.

The best measure of success of the *Learn Not to Burn*[2] effort is in the number of people saved from burn injury and even from death because of what they learned from the program's fire prevention messages and classroom lessons. NFPA has documented hundreds of instances in which children and adults used their Learn Not to Burn knowledge to respond correctly in life-threatening situations.

Learn Not to Burn activities are coordinated through the NFPA Public Education Division.

BIBLIOGRAPHY

References Cited

1. *Firesafety Educator's Handbook: A Comprehensive Guide to Planning, Designing, and Implementing Firesafety Programs*, (FSP-61), National Fire Protection Association, Quincy, MA, 1983.
2. *Learn Not to Burn* curriculum resource books, pre-school program, and public service announcements, National Fire Protection Association, Quincy, MA, 1987.
3. Osterhout, C., ed., *Public Fire Education*, (IFSTA No. 606), International Fire Service Training Association, Stillwater, OK, 1990.
4. NFPA *101, Life Safety Code*, National Fire Protection Association, Quincy, MA.

NFPA Codes, Standards, and Recommended Practices

Reference to the following NFPA codes, standards, and recommended practices will provide further information about firesafety education. (See the latest *NFPA Catalog* for availability of the current edition of the following document.)

NFPA 1035, *Professional Qualifications for Public Fire Educator.*

Additional Materials and Resources

NFPA catalog of firesafety education materials. Contact 1-800-344-3555.

NFPA's *One-Stop Data Shop*, National Fire Protection Association, Quincy, MA. This publication includes fire data and statistics, reports, and services from the NFPA Fire Analysis and Research division.

U.S. Fire Administration/Federal Emergency Management Agency, (USFA/FEMA) P. O. Box 70274, Washington, DC, 20024. The following are free public fire education materials available through USFA/FEMA:

"Curious Kids Set Fires"

"It's a Real Protector, It's a Smoke Detector"

"Partnerships Against Fire"

"Public Fire Education Today: Fire Service Programs from Across America"

"Blueprint for Firesafety"

"Check Your Hot Spots!"

"Juvenile Firesetter Counseling Guides"

"Overcoming Barriers to Public Fire Education: Final Report of Symposium"

"*Sesame Street* Materials"

"Public Fire Education Resource Directory"

Additional Readings

Barker, J. A., "Training: The Key to Fire Safety," *Fire Prevention*, No. 224, Nov. 1989, pp. 28-30.

McKinney, C.D. and Corral, E.A., "Classifying Juvenile Arsonists," *Fire Command*, Vol. 52, No. 10 (Oct. 1985).

Coleman, R. J., *Firesense: A Manual for Firesafety Education and Emergency Assistance for the Deaf and Hearing Impaired*, Phenix Technology, San Clemente, CA, 1987.

Collins, L. A., and Roberts, D. L., "Are Parents Learning Fire Safety from Their Children?" *Fire Safety Journal*, Vol. 14, 1989, p. 143.

Crawford, J., "Firesafety Education: Not Just Kid Stuff," *Fire Command*, Vol.56, No.9 (Sept. 1989), pp. 14-17.

Fire Administration and Supervision, National Learning Corporation, Syosset, NY, 1987.

Fire Education and the News, U.S. Fire Administration, Federal Emergency Management Agency, Washington, DC, Apr. 1982.

Fire Service Directory of Training and Information Sources, Specialized Publication Services, NY, 1987.

Gaynor, J., *The Psychology of Child Firesetting: Detection and Intervention*, Brunner/Mazel, NY, 1987.

Introduction to Fire Safety Education, National Fire Academy, Emmitsburg, MD, 1985.

Kennedy, P. M., "The Crisis in Fire Protection Engineering," *Fire Journal*, Vol. 83, No. 6 (Nov./Dec. 1989), p. 13.

Lucht, D. A., "Fire Protection Engineering: Facing the Challenge," *Fire Journal*, Vol. 83, No. 2 (Mar./Apr. 1989), p.73.

Lucht, D. A., "Coming of Age," *Journal of Fire Protection Engineering*, Vol. 1, No. 2, 1989, pp. 35-48.

Master Planning for Public Fire Education, The Children's Museum, Boston, MA, and Whitewood Stamps Inc., Newton, MA, prepared for the National Fire Prevention and Control Administration, Washington, DC, (undated).

Nelson, H. E., *DuPont Plaza Hotel Fire San Juan, Puerto Rico, Dec. 31, 1986*, National Emergency Training Center, Learning Resource Center, Emmitsburg, MD, 1987.

Public Fire Education Planning: A Five-Step Process, United States Fire Administration, Washington, DC, 1980.

"Reaching the Public," Column appearing in most issues of *Fire Journal*, 1965 to 1986.

Robertson, J. C., "Programs for Public Fire Education," *Introduction to Fire Prevention*, 3rd ed., Macmillan, NY, 1989, pp.249-274.

The Fire Educator, Institute for Fire and Burn Education, Washington, DC, monthly publication.

Ward, M. L., "Educating the Fire Protection Engineer," *Fire Journal*, Vol. 83, No. 5 (Sept./Oct. 1989), p. 33.

FIRE PREVENTION PRACTICES IN COMMERCE AND INDUSTRY

Philip Blye and Paul Bacon

Large or even small fires at an industrial facility can severely interrupt production, disrupt the lives of those who depend upon the facility for a livelihood, and weaken the economy of the community in which the facility is located. Although the primary purpose of any fire prevention strategy is to protect lives, corporations have special responsibilities to their own viability and that of the community with respect to loss prevention. A fire occurring in an industrial setting can threaten the community and can be costly to extinguish, because of the materials and chemicals used in manufacturing processes. In addition to this immediate threat, ripple effects may follow in the wake of a serious industrial fire. Among these indirect consequences may be the following:

1. Suspension of production can force customers to seek alternate suppliers with whom they remain even after the damage from the fire has been corrected and production has been resumed.
2. Business records may be destroyed, requiring a costly, time-consuming process of reconstructing accounts, mailing lists, sales records, inventories, etc.
3. While repairs are in progress, employees who are laid off may find permanent employment elsewhere.
4. Insurance may be insufficient to cover property reconstruction and equipment replacement, thus forcing the corporation to draw from its assets to cover these costs.
5. If the fire spreads to neighboring properties, the owners may sue to recover damages.
6. Large claims paid by insurance companies are often the stimuli for increasing insurance premiums.
7. In some cases, the cumulative effect of these possibilities may leave no alternative but declaring bankruptcy and permanently closing the facility.

The community also may directly suffer from an industrial fire, from the initial cost of extinguishment to other, more long-lasting results, such as environmental damage, lost corporate taxes, personal income removed from the local economy, and unemployment compensation payments. Sound fire prevention practices help to protect a company and the community from the many difficulties that can result from an industrial or commercial fire.

Philip Blye is chairperson of the Department of Fire Science Technology at Massasoit Community College, Brockton, MA. He is also a captain in the Easton, MA, fire department. Paul Bacon is a senior training specialist with Metcalf & Eddy, based in Wakefield, MA, and a member of the Northboro, MA, fire department.

OBJECTIVES OF A FIRE PREVENTION PROGRAM

The primary goal of a fire prevention program is to reduce or eliminate fire in the workplace by heightening the firesafety awareness of all employees. While it usually is the specific responsibility of one person in the plant to institute, teach, and monitor sound fire prevention practices, a fire prevention program should provide all employees with the information necessary to recognize hazardous conditions and take appropriate action before such conditions result in a fire emergency.

There are several objectives that collectively help the facility manager attain the overall goal of firesafety. These objectives are discussed individually below.

Role of the Facility Firesafety Officer

Regardless of the size of a manufacturing facility, a specific individual should be responsible for the development and implementation of the fire prevention program. In large facilities, a firesafety officer administers a firesafety committee comprised of representatives from the various divisions of the company. The committee helps the firesafety officer devise and present fire prevention programs. The firesafety officer should also be in charge of coordinating code compliance with the local fire department, establishing and rehearsing evacuation plans, properly handling and storing flammable materials, and ensuring that fire suppression and alarm systems are properly installed, inspected, and maintained. Sometimes the firesafety officer is also the plant fire chief, in charge of the industrial fire brigade.

The firesafety officer must be knowledgeable about the fire hazards inherent in the type of industry in which the company is engaged. Specific manufacturing processes are associated with identifiable fire and explosion hazards. The duty of the firesafety officer is to become aware of these hazards and to protect employees and property from them. Additionally, the officer must be familiar with those behaviors of employees that may create fire hazards. Failure to act, as well as overt action, can be identified and corrected. The officer must also be cognizant of what periods of the day, month, and year a facility is more vulnerable to fire, and establish procedures to protect against this risk. It may be that large shipments of highly combustible materials enter the facility at predictable times; if so, these are the periods for heightened vigilance. Close communication with local, county, and state fire officials will also keep the firesafety officer informed about current fire prevention strategies. One of the best sources of firesafety training for employees is the local fire department.

Facility management should encourage periodic visits by municipal fire departments for the purpose of code compliance inspections and fire company pre-fire planning activities. The term "pre-fire planning" relates to site inspections that are made by fire companies to familiarize fire fighters with the physical complexities of facilities in their response district. Pre-fire planning tours are a chance for facility and fire personnel to exchange information and coordinate actions to be taken in the event of a fire or other emergency. Areas that should be covered by management during a pre-fire planning tour include:

1. Topography of the land on which the facility is located, as well as the surrounding area.
2. Site and building access.
3. Any plot plans or maps drawn by insurance carriers or facility engineers.
4. Construction (existing, new, or remodeled) of all buildings on the property.
5. Locations of fire-limiting construction features, such as fire walls and partitions, draft curtains, or heat and smoke vents.
6. Occupancy and contents of the buildings.
7. Types and locations of any hazardous material or hazardous waste kept on site, best routes of access to it, and correct extinguishing medium to use.
8. Review of fire protection systems at the site, including locations of any fire department connections for automatic sprinklers or standpipes, yard hydrants, sprinkler control valves, fire pumps, private water supply control valves, fire alarm system panel and components, and any special fire protection systems and equipment.
9. Management's policy for impairment to, or prevention of tampering with, any component of the fire protection systems.
10. Activities of the facility's firesafety officer and emergency organization during a fire.
11. Site security's role during a fire.

Once a fire prevention plan has been adopted at a facility, the firesafety officer must regularly monitor the plan's effectiveness in preventing fires. The only sure way to monitor such a plan is by frequent observations of the physical site and the behavior of the employees during work and nonwork periods. The firesafety officer must conduct regular inspections, covering important basic aspects of facility operations. Features to be inspected include:

1. Smoking habits of employees, in the facility as well as in the administrative offices.
2. Electrical equipment, wiring, and controls.
3. Fire alarm systems.
4. Fire extinguishing equipment.
5. Integrity of plant construction.
6. Heating, ventilating, and air conditioning (HVAC) systems.
7. Storage of combustible material.
8. Housekeeping practices.
9. Use of flammable and combustible liquids and gases.
10. Security.
11. Industrial processes, such as painting, cutting, welding, and creating flammable dust.
12. Removal of wastes from industrial processes.

Other important functions of the firesafety officer are recordkeeping and filing incident reports. The reports can be used to document the need for improvements in operating procedures, employee behavior, and equipment. In general, the company should establish a mechanism for regular review of the inspection logs and fire incident reports by management-level personnel with sufficient authority to take quick corrective action.

Essentials of a Fire Prevention Training Program

The person who should coordinate a facility fire prevention training program is the firesafety officer, who may also have the title of facility fire chief. This individual is the most familiar with the firesafety precautions and the vulnerable aspects of the facility. It takes a special talent, however, to operate successful fire prevention training programs because the focus of attention is on the intangible aspects of human beings as workers. The aim is to create an attitude of safety in the workplace and recognition on the part of employees that protecting the plant from fire also protects their lives and livelihood.

The human factor, whether an individual acts deliberately or indirectly through ignorance or negligence, is the major cause of fires. Therefore, a concerted effort to educate workers in fire prevention will go a long way in protecting lives and property. Employees must realize that a fire at their workplace may not only cause them physical harm but may mean loss of income until repairs from the fire are completed and production resumed. In some cases, the option of returning to the same job may never present itself because a serious fire at an industrial site forces the company to go out of business

Usually, training programs based on what workers might perceive as a remote threat to job security are less effective than a clear commitment on the part of the company to become more safety conscious. Fire prevention training programs can be included in the facility's right-to-know program. Concerned supervisors, workshops on fire prevention, helpful suggestions made during inspections by the firesafety officer, and awards presented to employees who help spot or correct a fire hazard all help create the desired fire-conscious attitude in employees.

The success of a fire prevention program can be measured by factors such as the reduction of fire incidents, the number and quality of suggestions made by employees to reduce fire hazards, and the results of surveys that compare the level of employee firesafety awareness prior to and after the initiation of a training program.

The test of a successful fire prevention program can best be demonstrated in the inspection logs of the firesafety officer. Through accurate and regularly kept inspection records, the firesafety officer will be able to see the long-term results of fire prevention efforts and how they might be improved further.

It is important to realize that the fire prevention program of an industrial facility cannot be limited to those locations most often identified with industrial fires, i.e., the production and storage areas. Because facilities also house offices where serious fires can originate, office personnel must be included in any employee fire prevention training program. The general office staff's awareness of firesafety can be heightened by comparing office fire hazards with those at home involving ordinary combustibles. The elements of a fire prevention program for office personnel should include advice about:

1. Use and disposal of smoking materials.
2. Checking for frayed electrical cords and faulty appliances.
3. Proper use of electrical equipment and appliances.
4. Unplugging coffee pots and other heat-producing equipment when not in use, and portable heaters at the end of each work day.
5. Correct storage of flammable and combustible materials.

All employees should be instructed on the location and proper use of fire extinguishers in their work areas. They should also know how to activate the facility's fire alarm system, and be familiar with evacuation plans and routes. Failure to give this instruction is an indication that the fire prevention program is deficient in some respect.

Operators of mechanical equipment have a special responsibility to themselves and others with respect to firesafety. A fire prevention program should alert them to:

1. Variations in the operating pressure and temperature of equipment from levels recommended by the manufacturers.
2. Potential sources of ignition from cutting, welding, faulty wiring, friction due to such factors as belts operating at the wrong tension or poorly lubricated bearings, and mechanical sparks caused by the moving metallic parts of a faulty or poorly maintained machine.
3. Corrosion of motor parts, or buildup of dust or lint around machinery.
4. Leakage of lubricants from motors or drip pans onto floors and walls.

Employees should be urged to report any of these and other hazardous conditions to their supervisor. Preventing such conditions requires adherence to a schedule of regular periodic equipment inspection, maintenance, and testing.

The type of maintenance inspection will depend upon the equipment, machinery, or materials being processed. Maintenance should be planned and based on:

1. Prior mechanical inspections.
2. Failure history of the equipment.
3. Length of time the equipment has been in service.
4. Significance of the equipment to the entire operation and any possible problems associated with its failure.
5. Conditions under which the equipment operates.
6. Any regulations or laws of the authority having jurisdiction.
7. Recommendations by insurance carriers.

Facility supervisors, firesafety officers, and factory workers must also be prepared to prevent fires in the general facility setting. The fundamental point to remember in all fire prevention activities is that all flammable and combustible materials must be separated from all sources of ignition. Materials and/or situations especially susceptible to ignition include undetected gas leaks, high concentrations of dust or flammable vapors, flammable liquid spills, oil-soaked rags, and improperly stored trash. Ignition sources often are faulty electrical wiring, equipment, or controls.

Another common source of ignition, however, is not associated with the facility or its equipment but with the habits of the workers. Failure to observe smoking restrictions in the workplace and careless disposal of ashes, cigarette butts, and matches cause deaths, injuries, and the destruction of property worth millions of dollars each year. A sound fire prevention program limits smoking to places designated as safe for this activity and ensures that there is an abundant supply of properly designed ashtrays and other noncombustible receptacles that are emptied frequently. Many facilities are now adopting strict no-smoking policies.

Many fires in the workplace can be prevented through good housekeeping practices. These practices are relatively inexpensive and uncomplicated. While a well-trained custodial staff is the key to safe housekeeping methods, all employees can make significant contributions to fire prevention where housekeeping is involved. General precautions include the following:

1. Trash and other waste should be stored in covered metal containers.
2. Work areas should be kept clean and free of flammable debris.
3. Hazardous materials should only be stored in designated locations and in properly capped or ventilated containers, depending upon the material.
4. Most flammable liquids should be kept tightly covered and must be in grounded and bonded containers if transferred from one container to another; gasoline requires vented containers.
5. Gas cylinder valves should be closed and cylinders secured when not in use.
6. Trash should be prevented from collecting in corners, under machinery, in stairwells, and in other out-of-the-way locations.
7. Oily or greasy deposits and condensates should be wiped up.

An indirect, yet contributing, factor involved with industrial fires is the abuse of controlled substances by some employees. Alcoholism and other drug abuse can cause the employee to be careless about fire hazards or can prevent the employee from properly reacting in an emergency. Part of any fire prevention program should be an awareness of how the intoxicated or drug-impaired employee can be a threat to the safety of other workers in the facility. Companies should refer employees with these problems to programs for appropriate treatment.

Fire Prevention Through Safe Plant Operations

Efficiency and economy, as well as fire prevention, are enhanced through the regular maintenance and repair of equipment used in the manufacturing process and in other facets of facility operation. As part of the normal operating procedures of a factory, a team of safety inspectors should check for properly operating valves; electrical wiring and motors; and ventilating, heating, and air conditioning equipment. Flues and vents must be kept free of dirt and combustibles. A strict maintenance schedule should be observed for such items as motors, switches, wiring, fans, bearings, chains, and conveyor belts. Loose fittings and supports should be tightened. The atmosphere of a facility with a potential for release of flammable vapors should be monitored regularly with a flammable-vapor indicator to detect any potentially dangerous conditions. As part of the Superfund Amendment and Reauthorization Act (SARA) Title III requirements, having the fire department and the safety inspection team review the hazardous materials at the facility will help give the fire department an awareness of the hazards. The fire department, in return, can offer fire prevention suggestions to the safety inspectors. Fire doors should be checked so they move freely and can close fully. Combustible wastes should be removed from the building every day and more frequently if necessary. Hazardous wastes should be removed from the work area and stored until they can be disposed properly. Safe shutdown procedures must be followed at the end of a work day or in an emergency.

Security Measures that Enhance Fire Prevention

During a regular work day, a facility is susceptible to fire hazards associated with production and with the expenditure of high levels of electrical or mechanical energy. However, it is wrong to assume that a facility is less at risk from fire at off periods, such as evenings, weekends, and vacations; this is why the facility maintenance crew and security force need to be totally integrated into the fire prevention plan. The custodians and security guards must be trained to notice and correct hazards or sound the alarm. Often it is their diligence that leads to the discovery of an overheated motor, faulty wiring, or a smoldering cigarette.

The security force especially must protect the facility from intruders and potential arsonists. Security personnel making their rounds throughout the facility should pay special attention to places where a person might hide or where combustibles are generally stored. Every point of possible entry by an intruder should be checked, including doors, windows, gates, and loading docks.

BIBLIOGRAPHY

NFPA Codes, Standards, and Recommended Practices

Reference to the following NFPA codes, standards, and recommended practices will provide further information on fire prevention practices in commerce and industry discussed in this chapter. (See the latest *NFPA Catalog* for availability of current editions of the following documents.)

NFPA 1, *Fire Prevention Code.*

NFPA 10, *Portable Fire Extinguishers.*

NFPA 600, *Private Fire Brigades.*

Additional Reading

Adolphs, W., "Fire Protection Covering the Risks Occuring in Industrial Plants," *Proceedings* of the Conference on New Technology to Reduce Fire Losses and Costs, Elsevier, 1986, pp. 329-331.

Almgren, L. E., "Designing for Fire and Explosion Safety," *Proceedings* of the National Meeting of the American Institute of Chemical Engineers, American Institute of Chemical Engineers, New York, 1988, p. 10.

Berl, W. G., "Protecting the Public from Fires," *Johns Hopkins APL Technical Digest*, Vol. 8, No. 1, 1987, pp. 148-151.

Bluebond, D. M., ed, *et al.*, "Workshop on Fire Protection Technology," *NBSIR 86-3360.*, Apr. 1986, National Bureau of Standards, Gaithersburg, MD.

Butcher, E. G., *Designing for Fire Safety*, Wiley, New York, 1983.

Conducting Fire Inspections: A Guidebook for Field Use, National Fire Protection Association, Quincy, MA, 1989.

Cote, A., ed., *Principles of Fire Protection*, National Fire Protection Association, Quincy, MA, 1988.

Cote, A. E. and Linville, J. L., eds., *Industrial Fire Hazards Handbook,* National Fire Protection Association, 3rd ed., 1990.

Davis, L., *Industrial Fire Control Concepts: People, Equipment, Procedures*, International Society for Fire Service Instructors, Ashland, MA, 1988.

"Designing Effective Fire Protection," *Civil Engineering*, Jul./Aug. 1988, p. 2.

Employee Evacuation Action for Survival, (Film and Videotape), National Fire Protection Association, Quincy, MA, 1984.

Fire Inspectors Guide to NFPA 1031, National Fire Protection Association, Quincy, MA, 1983.

Fire/Emergency Services Sourcebook, Specialized Publication Services, New York, 1989.

Grayson, S. J. and Smith, D. A., eds., *New Technology to Reduce Fire Losses and Costs*, Elsevier, New York, 1986.

Harron, J. G., "Loss Prevention Challenge: How One Refinery Meets It," *Hydrocarbon Processing*, Vol. 65, No. 9 (Sept. 1986), pp. 167-169, 171-172, 175.

James, D., *Fire Prevention Handbook*, Butterworths, Cambridge, U.K., 1986.

Larsen, O. H., "Passive Fire Protection in Hydrocarbon Industry," *Proceedings* of the Conference on Offshore Passive Fire Protection, Plastics and Rubber Institute, 1987, p. 15.

Lauriski, D. D. and Guymon, R. M., "Safety Management: What It Means to Us," *Mining Engineering*, Vol. 41 No. 10 (Oct. 1989), pp. 1032-1035.

Lees, F. P., *Loss Prevention in the Process Industries*, Butterworths, Boston, 1980.

Marchant, E., "Fire Safety Engineering—A Qualified Analysis," *Fire Prevention*, No. 210, June 1988, pp. 34-38.

Mourareau, R., "Fire Protection: The European Dimension," *Fire Prevention*, No. 197, Mar. 1987, pp. 32-34.

Nelson, H. E., "Concepts for Life Safety Analysis," *Fire Safety Journal*, Vol. 12, 1987, p. 167.

NFPA Inspection Manual: A Guide to Property Inspection for Fire Protection and Life Safety, 6th ed., National Fire Protection Association, Quincy, MA, 1989.

Pessemier, R., *Up in Smoke: A Business Guide to Fire and Life Safety*, Phoenix Publications, Redmond, WA, 1987.

Robertson, J. C., *Introduction to Fire Prevention*, MacMillan, New York, 1989.

Twilt, L. and Witteveen, J., "Trends in Fire Safety Design of Buildings," *Heron*, Vol. 32, No. 4, 1987, pp. 95-114.

Vance, M., *Fire Prevention: Monographs*, Vance Bibliographies, Monticello, IL, 1984.

Volkmann, P., "Three Leading Factors to Save Life and Property," *Fire International*, Vol. 12, No. 109 (Feb./Mar. 1988), pp. 39-40.

Wilmot, T., "Japan—The Success Story of Fire Prevention," *Fire Prevention*, No. 223, Oct. 1989, pp. 36-38.

ELECTRICAL SYSTEMS AND APPLIANCES

Revised by Mark W. Earley

This chapter discusses electrical systems and appliances. Specific topics include origins of electrical fires; codes and standards; building wiring, design, and protection; electrical household appliances; industrial and commercial equipment; electrical equipment for outdoor use; locations exposed to moisture and dust; communications systems; and special occupancy electrical problems.

Other chapters in this handbook detail the related components of fire hazards of building services, most notably Section 2, Chapter 4, "Heating Systems and Appliances;" and Section 6, Chapter 16, "Air Conditioning and Ventilating Systems."

Special considerations for the installation of electrical systems can be found elsewhere in this handbook. See Section 7, Chapter 2, "Concepts of Egress Design;" Section 2, Chapter 10, "Industrial and Commercial Heat Utilization Equipment;" Section 3, Chapter 6, "Medical Gases;" and Section 2, Chapter 32, "Lightning Protection Systems."

If properly designed, installed, and maintained, electrical systems are both convenient and safe; otherwise they may be a source of both fire and personal injury. Electricity may cause a fire if it arcs or overheats electrical equipment and can cause injury or death through shocks and burns.

When an electric circuit carrying a current is interrupted either intentionally, as by a switch, or unintentionally, as when a contact at a terminal becomes loosened, arcing at the switch contacts or heating from the high-resistance connection at the terminal is produced. The intensity of the arc and degree of heat depend largely upon the current and voltage of the circuit and the resistance of the contact at the terminal. The temperature may easily be high enough to ignite any combustible material in the vicinity.

An electric arc may not only ignite combustible material in its vicinity, e.g., the insulation and covering of the conductor, but it may also fuse the metal of the conductor. Hot sparks from burning combustible material and hot metal may be thrown about or fall, setting fire to other combustible material.

When an electrical conductor carries a current, heat is generated in direct proportion to the resistance (ohms) of the conductor and to the square of the current (amperage). The resistance of conductors used to convey current to the location in which it is used, or to convey it through the windings of a piece of apparatus (except resistance devices and heaters), should be as low as practical. Metals, such as copper and aluminum, are used for this purpose. In other instances, such as in electric heaters, electric cooking equipment, and soldering irons, the heat from the current serves a useful purpose.

The heating of electrical conductors is almost never a fire hazard under design conditions. NFPA 70, *National Electrical Code®* (*NEC*), specifies the maximum safe current a conductor may carry without overheating. (See Tables 2-3A through 2-3D.) This depends upon the size of conductor, the conditions of the installation, and the type of insulation. Where these specified currents are exceeded, or where a conductor is overloaded, the generation of heat becomes a hazard through (1) deterioration of the electrical insulation of the conductor, and (2) the excess heat generated. Apparatus or appliances that use electric conductors as heating elements or use an electric arc to generate heat (e.g., arc welders) can be fire hazards if improperly installed and used.

One common method of reducing the degree of hazard is to provide sufficient air circulation to prevent unsafe temperatures and premature breakdown of electrical insulation.

All standards governing electric equipment include requirements intended to prevent fires caused by arcing and overheating, and to prevent accidental contact, which may cause an electric shock. These primary sources of electrical hazards should be kept in mind whenever any work is being done on electric equipment.

Mark W. Earley, P.E., is chief electrical engineer on the staff of NFPA.

TABLE 2-3A ***Ampacities of Insulated Conductors Rated 0 Through 2000 Volts, 60° to 90°C (140° to 194°F) Not More than Three Conductors in Raceway or Cable or Earth (Directly Buried), Based on Ambient Tempertures of 30°C (86°F)***

Size	Temperature Rating of Conductor, See *NEC* Table 310-13								Size
	60°C (140°F)	75°C (167°F)	85°C (185°F)	90°C (194°F)	60°C (140°F)	75°C (167°F)	85°C (185°F)	90°C (194°F)	
AWG kcmil	TYPES †TW, †UF	TYPES †FEPW, †RH, †RHW, †THHW, †THW, †THWN, †XHHW, †USE, †ZW	TYPE V	TYPES TA, TBS, SA, SIS, †FEP, †FEPB, †RHH, †THHN, †THHW, †XXHW	TYPES †TW, †UF	TYPES †RH, †RHW, †THHW, †THW, †THWN, †XHHW, †USE	TYPE V	TYPES TA, TBS, SA, SIS, †RHH, †THHW, †THHN, †XHHW	AWG kcmil
	Copper				Aluminum or Copper-Clad Aluminum				
18	....	....	....	14	....	....	....	....	....
16	....	....	18	18	....	....	....	....	....
14	20†	20†	25	25†	....	....	....	....	....
12	25†	25†	30	30†	20†	20†	25	25†	12
10	30	35†	40	40†	25	30†	30	35†	10
8	40	50	55	55	30	40	40	45	8
6	55	65	70	75	40	50	55	60	6
4	70	85	95	95	55	65	75	75	4
3	85	100	110	110	65	75	85	85	3
2	95	115	125	130	75	90	100	100	2
1	110	130	145	150	85	100	110	115	1
1/0	125	150	165	170	100	120	130	135	1/0
2/0	145	175	190	195	115	135	145	150	2/0
3/0	165	200	215	225	130	155	170	175	3/0
4/0	195	230	250	260	150	180	195	205	4/0
250	215	255	275	290	170	205	220	230	250
300	240	285	310	320	190	230	250	255	300
350	260	310	340	350	210	250	270	280	350
400	280	335	365	380	225	270	295	305	400
500	320	380	415	430	260	310	335	350	500
600	355	420	460	475	285	340	370	385	600
700	385	460	500	520	310	375	405	420	700
750	400	475	515	535	320	385	420	435	750
800	410	490	535	555	330	395	430	450	800
900	435	520	565	585	355	425	465	480	900
1000	455	545	590	615	375	445	485	500	1000
1250	495	590	640	665	405	485	525	545	1250
1500	520	625	680	705	435	520	565	585	1500
1750	545	650	705	735	455	545	595	615	1750
2000	560	665	725	750	470	560	610	630	2000

Ampacity Correction Factors

Ambient Temp. °C	For ambient temperatures other than 30°C, multiply the ampacities shown above by the appropriate factor shown below.								Ambient Temp. °F
21–25	1.08	1.05	1.04	1.04	1.08	1.05	1.04	1.04	70–77
26–30	1.00	1.00	1.00	1.00	1.00	1.00	1.00	1.00	79–86
31–35	.91	.94	.95	.96	.91	.94	.95	.96	88–95
36–40	.82	.88	.90	.91	.82	.88	.90	.91	97–104
41–45	.71	.82	.85	.87	.71	.82	.85	.87	106–113
46–50	.58	.75	.80	.82	.58	.75	.75	.80	115–122
51–55	.41	.67	.74	.76	.41	.67	.74	.76	124–131
56–60	....	.58	.67	.71	....	.58	.67	.71	133–140
61–70	....	.33	.52	.58	....	.33	.52	.58	142–158
71–80	....	....	.30	.41	....	....	.30	.41	160–176

† Unless otherwise specifically permitted elsewhere in the *NEC*, the overcurrent protection for conductor types marked with an obelisk (†) must not exceed 15 amperes for 14 AWG, 20 amperes for 12 AWG, and 30 amperes for 10 AWG copper; or 15 amperes for 12 AWG and 25 amperes for 10 AWG aluminum and copper-clad aluminum after any correction factors for ambient temperature and number of conductors have been applied.

Source: NFPA 70-1990, *National Electrical Code.*

TABLE 2-3B. ***Ampacities of Single Insulated Conductors, Rated 0 Through 2000 Volts, in Free Air Based on Ambient Air Temperature of 30°C (86°F)***

Size	Temperature Rating of Conductor, See *NEC* Table 310-13								Size
	60°C (140°F)	75°C (167°F)	85°C (185°F)	90°C (194°F)	60°C (140°F)	75°C (167°F)	85°C (185°F)	90°C (194°F)	
AWG kcmil	TYPE †TW, †UF	TYPES †FEPW, †RH, †RHW, †THHW, †THW, †THWN, †XHHW, †ZW	TYPE V	TYPES TA, TBS, SA, SIS, †FEP, †FEPB, †RHH, †THHN, †THHW, †XXHW	TYPE †TW, †UF	TYPES †RH, †RHW, †THHW, †THW, †THWN, †XHHW,	TYPE V	TYPES TA, TBS, SA, SIS, †RHH, †THHN, †THHW, †XHHW, MI	AWG kcmil
	Copper				Aluminum or Copper-Clad Aluminum				
18	....	....	....	18	....	....	....	....	....
16	....	....	23	24	....	....	....	....	....
14	25†	30†	30	35†	....	....	....	....	....
12	30†	35†	40	40†	25†	30†	30	35†	12
10	40†	50†	55	55†	35†	40†	40	40†	10
8	60	70	75	80	45	55	60	60	8
6	80	95	100	105	60	75	80	80	6
4	105	125	135	140	80	100	105	110	4
3	120	145	160	165	95	115	125	130	3
2	140	170	185	190	110	135	145	150	2
1	165	195	215	220	130	155	165	175	1
1/0	195	230	250	260	150	180	195	205	1/0
2/0	225	265	290	300	175	210	225	235	2/0
3/0	260	310	335	350	200	240	265	275	3/0
4/0	300	360	390	405	235	280	305	315	4/0
250	340	405	440	455	265	315	345	355	250
300	375	445	485	505	290	350	380	395	300
350	420	505	550	570	330	395	430	445	350
400	455	545	595	615	355	425	465	480	400
500	515	620	675	700	405	485	525	545	500
600	575	690	750	780	455	540	595	615	600
700	630	755	825	855	500	595	650	675	700
750	655	785	855	885	515	620	675	700	750
800	680	815	885	920	535	645	700	725	800
900	730	870	950	985	580	700	760	785	900
1000	780	935	1020	1055	625	750	815	845	1000
1250	890	1065	1160	1200	710	855	930	960	1250
1500	980	1175	1275	1325	795	950	1035	1075	1500
1750	1070	1280	1395	1445	875	1050	1145	1185	1750
2000	1155	1385	1505	1560	960	1150	1250	1335	2000
	Ampacity Correction Factors								
Ambient Temp. °C	For ambient temperatures other than 30°C, multiply the ampacities shown above by the appropriate factor shown below.								Ambient Temp. °F
21–25	1.08	1.05	1.04	1.04	1.08	1.05	1.04	1.04	70–77
26–30	1.00	1.00	1.00	1.00	1.00	1.00	1.00	1.00	79–86
31–35	.91	.94	.95	.96	.91	.94	.95	.96	88–95
36–40	.82	.88	.90	.91	.82	.88	.90	.91	97–104
41–45	.71	.82	.85	.87	.71	.82	.85	.87	106–113
46–50	.58	.75	.80	.82	.58	.75	.80	.82	115–122
51–55	.41	.67	.74	.76	.41	.67	.74	.76	124–131
56–60	....	.58	.67	.71	....	.58	.67	.71	133–140
61–70	....	.33	.52	.58	....	.33	.52	.58	142–158
71–80	....	....	.30	.41	....	....	.30	.41	160–176

† Unless otherwise specifically permitted elsewhere in the *NEC*, the overcurrent protection for conductor types marked with an obelisk (†) must not exceed 15 amperes for 14 AWG, 20 amperes for 12 AWG, and 30 amperes for 10 AWG copper; or 15 amperes for 12 AWG and 25 amperes for 10 AWG aluminum and copper-clad aluminum.

Source: NFPA 70-1990, *National Electrical Code.*

TABLE 2-3C ***Ampacities of Three Single Insulated Conductors Rated 0 Through 2000 Volts, 150° to 250°C (302° to 482°F), in Raceway or Cable Based on Ambient Air Temperature of 40°C (104°F)***

Size	Temperature Rating of Conductors. See *NEC* Table 310-13				Size
	150°C (302°F)	200°C (392°F)	250°C (482°F)	150°C (302°F)	
AWG kcmil	TYPE Z	TYPES FEP, FEPB, PFA	TYPES PFAH, TFE	TYPE Z	AWG kcmil
	Copper		Nickel or Nickel-Coated Copper	Aluminium or Copper-Clad Aluminium	
14	34	36	39	...	14
12	43	45	54	30	12
10	55	60	73	44	10
8	76	83	93	57	8
6	96	110	117	75	6
4	120	125	148	94	4
3	143	152	166	109	3
2	160	171	191	124	2
1	186	197	215	145	1
1/0	215	229	244	169	1/0
2/0	251	260	273	198	2/0
3/0	288	297	308	227	3/0
4/0	332	346	361	260	4/0
250	...	...	...	...	250
300	...	...	...	...	300
350	...	...	...	...	350
400	...	...	...	...	400
500	...	...	...	...	500
600	...	...	...	...	600
700	...	...	...	...	700
750	...	...	...	...	750
800	...	...	...	...	800
1000	...	...	...	...	1000
1500	...	...	...	...	1500
2000	...	...	...	...	2000

Ampacity Correction Factors

Ambient Temp. °C	For ambient temperatures other than 40°C (104°F), multiply the ampacities shown above by the appropriate factor shown below.				Ambient Temp. °F
41-50	.95	.97	.98	.95	106-122
51-60	.90	.94	.95	.90	124-140
61-70	.85	.90	.93	.85	142-158
71-80	.80	.87	.90	.80	160-176
81-90	.74	.83	.87	.74	177-194
91-100	.67	.79	.85	.67	195-212
101-120	.52	.71	.79	.52	213-248
121-140	.30	.61	.72	.30	249-284
141-160	...	.50	.65	...	285-320
161-180	...	.35	.58	...	321-356
181-200	...	...	.49	...	357-392
201-225	...	...	.35	...	393-437

Source: NFPA 70-1990, *National Electrical Code.*

TABLE 2-3D. ***Ampacities for Single Insulated Conductors Rated 0 Through 2000 Volts, 150° to 250°C (302° to 482°F), in Free Air Based on Ambient Air Temperature of 40°C (104°F)***

Size	Temperature Rating of Conductor. See *NEC* Table 310-13						Size
	150°C (302°F)	200°C (392°F)		250°C (482°F)	150°C (302°F)		
AWG kcmil	TYPE Z	TYPES FEP, FEPB, PFA	Bare or covered conductors	TYPES PFAM, TPE	TYPE Z	Bare or covered conductors	AWG kcmil
	Copper			Nickel or Nickel-Coated Copper	Aluminum or Copper-Clad Aluminum		
14	46	54	30	59	....	25	14
12	60	68	35	78	47	30	12
10	80	90	50	107	63	35	10
8	106	124	70	142	83	55	8
6	155	165	95	205	112	75	6
4	190	220	125	278	148	100	4
3	214	252	150	327	170	120	3
2	255	293	175	381	198	135	2
1	293	344	200	440	228	160	1
1/0	339	399	235	532	263	185	1/0
2/0	390	467	275	591	305	215	2/0
3/0	451	546	320	708	351	250	3/0
4/0	529	629	370	830	411	285	4/0
250	....	....	415	....	....	325	250
300	....	....	460	....	....	360	300
400	....	....	520	....	....	405	350
400	....	....	560	....	....	435	400
500	....	....	635	....	....	495	500
600	....	....	710	....	....	560	600
700	....	....	780	....	....	615	700
750	....	....	805	....	....	635	750
800	....	....	835	....	....	660	800
900	....	....	865	....	....	715	900
1000	....	....	895	....	....	770	1000
1500	....	....	1205	....	....	980	1500
2000	....	....	1420	....	....	1215	2000

Ampacity Correction Factors

Ambient Temp. °C	For ambient temperatures other than 30°C, multiply the ampacities shown above by the appropriate factor shown below.						Ambient Temp. °F
41–50	.95	.97	....	.98	.95	....	106–122
51–60	.90	.94	....	.95	.90	....	124–140
61–70	.85	.90	....	.93	.85	....	142–158
71–80	.80	.87	....	.90	.80	....	160–176
81–90	.74	.83	....	.87	.74	....	177–194
91–100	.67	.79	....	.85	.67	....	195–212
101–120	.52	.71	....	.79	.52	....	213–248
121–140	.30	.61	....	.72	....	....	249–284
141–160	....	.50	....	.65	....	....	285–320
161–180	....	.35	....	.58	....	....	321–356
181–200	....	....	....	.49	....	....	357–392
201–225	....	....	....	.35	....	....	393–437

ORIGINS OF ELECTRICAL FIRES IN BUILDINGS

Table 2-3E provides an overview of 1983 through 1987 structure fires reported to U.S. fire departments that were coded as caused by electrical failure. This table will miss some relevant incidents because it is limited to fires coded as involving a short circuit, ground fault, or other electrical failure. Other causes, some of which may include a mix of electrical failures and other fires, are not included. Also, these statistics reflect cause determinations by fire officers on the scene, so some errors of inclusion or exclusion may occur.

TABLE 2-3E ***Structure Fires Due to Electrical Failure (Annual Average of 1983-87 Fires Reported to U.S. Fire Departments)***

Equipment Involved in Ignition	Average Number of Fires per Year	
HEATING EQUIPMENT	6,090	
Central heating unit		2,390
Water heater		930
Fixed area heating device		1,270
Indoor fireplace		30
Portable heating device		900
Chimney or flue		60
Chimney connector		20
Heat transfer system		110
Unclassified type		330
Unknown type		70
COOKING EQUIPMENT	5,870	
Stove		2,930
Oven or rotisserie		980
Fixed area cooking or warming device		230
Deep fat fryer		170
Portable cooking or warming device		750
Open-fired grill		20
Grease hood or duct		540
Unclassified type		200
Unknown type		40
AIR CONDITIONING OR REFRIGERATION EQUIPMENT	4,300	
Central air conditioning or refrigeration unit		990
Water cooling device or tower		220
Fixed area refrigeration unit		1,580
Fixed area air conditioning unit		750
Portable air conditioning or refrigeration unit		490
Unclassified type		200
Unknown type		40
ELECTRICAL DISTRIBUTION EQUIPMENT	44,840	
Fixed wiring		18,200
Transformer		910
Meter or meter box		700
Overcurrent protection device (e.g., fuse, circuit breaker		3,530
Switch, receptacle, or outlet		4,890
Lighting fixture, lampholder, ballast, or sign		5,950
Cord or plug		7,720
Lamp or light bulb		680
Unclassified type		1,280
Unknown type		990
APPLIANCE OR TOOL	13,120	
Television, radio, or phonograph		3,060
Dryer		2,410
Washing machine		1,340
Floor-care equipment (e.g., vacuum cleaner)		160
Separate motor or generator		960
Hand tool (e.g., drill, soldering iron)		90
Portable appliance to produce controlled heat (e.g., iron, electric blanket		2,020
Portable appliance not to produce controlled heat (e.g., can opener, electric razor)		850
Unclassified type		1,950
Unknown type		320
SPECIAL EQUIPMENT	1,550	
Electronic equipment (e.g., telephone, computer, x-ray)		460
Vending machine or drinking fountain		60
Office machine		140
Biomedical equipment		30
Separate pump or compressor		300
Internal combustion engine		40
Conveyor		40
Printing press		30
Unclassified type		400
Unknown type		50
PROCESSING EQUIPMENT	450	
Furnace, oven, or kiln		110
Casting, molding, or forging equipment		20
Heat treating equipment		30
Working or shaping machine		80
Coating machine		20
Printing equipment		60
Chemical process equipment		20
Waste recovery equipment		20
Unclassified type		70
Unknown type		10
SERVICE OR MAINTENANCE EQUIPMENT	460	
Incinerator		10
Bearing or brake		10
Rectifier or charger		160
Elevator		160
Torch		20
Unclassified type		90
Unknown type		10
OTHER	9,280	
Vehicle		510
No equipment involved		8,470
Unclassified type		260
Unknown type		40
UNKNOWN TYPE	4,420	
TOTAL	90,370	

Source: NFPA analysis of 1983-87 NFIRS and NFPA survey data.
Notes: "Electrical failure" defined as Ignition Factor 54 (short circuit or ground fault) or 55 (other electrical failure). Numbers rounded to nearest ten. Sums may not equal totals because of rounding error.

The 90,430 fires represented 11 percent of all structure fires in the same period. Electrically powered equipment is involved in several times this number of fires each year but in non-electrical failure scenarios, such as installation or use of equipment with hot surfaces too close to combustibles. In fact, nearly all fires involving electrically powered equipment stem from foreseeable or avoidable human error, such as:

Improper installation: Failure to observe all provisions of the *NEC*, including the workmanship provisions, can result in installation of equipment in ways that will lead to overloading, damage to equipment, or excessive heat exposure to nearby combustibles.

Lack of maintenance: Equipment wears out in service, e.g., through the deterioration of electrical insulation. Deterioration can be accelerated through improper installation, such as laying cords across heavy traffic areas, but it will occur naturally as a result of age even when installation is done properly in all respects.

Improper use: Listed equipment that is not used in accordance with the conditions of the listing can cause fires. Mismatching of wire gage size with equipment wattage is an example.

Carelessness or oversight: Even momentary lapses of caution in the use of equipment can cause fires. Failure to turn off devices (e.g., space heaters) not in use, dropping combustibles into equipment, and draping combustibles over operating equipment (e.g., clothes on a lamp) are all examples.

Some special studies have been done that provide additional insights going beyond the level of detail in Table 2-3E, although no other sources of representative national fire statistics exist. These studies include the annual tabulations by the International Association of Electrical Inspectors (IAEI) of fire and shock incidents that come to their attention and the several field studies done by the U.S. Consumer Product Safety Commission. These studies appear to support a few qualitative observations:

1. Cord fires every year include many fires involving extension cords, as opposed to lamp or other appliance cords. Extension cords are probably overused as semipermanent extensions of wiring systems.
2. Overcurrent protection device fires appear to involve circuit breakers more often than fuses, both overall and relative to the degree of use of each type of device. This is even more notable given that fuses are used primarily in much older homes, where deterioration due to age or damage due to system alterations would be more likely, and that fuses are more susceptible to tampering.
3. Color televisions account for far more fires than black-and-white televisions. This difference appears to be much larger than the ratio in usage of color vs. black-and-white televisions would explain and is not surprising, given the energy usage of the two types.

CODES AND STANDARDS

All electrical installations in the United States should be made, used, and maintained in accordance with the *NEC*, the *National Electrical Safety Code*, and other standards which apply in special situations, e.g., NFPA 70E, *Electrical Safety Requirements for Employee Workplaces*; NFPA 79, *Electrical Standard for Industrial Machinery* (hereinafter referred to as NFPA 79); NFPA 75, *Protection of Electronic Computer/Data Processing Equipment*; and NFPA 99, *Health Care Facilities* (hereinafter referred to as NFPA 99). There are also special standards for electrical installations on shipboard, aircraft, in hazardous (classified) locations, and other locations.

National Electrical Code (ANSI/NFPA 70)

NFPA 70, *National Electrical Code*, provides for the practical safeguarding of persons and property from hazards arising from the use of electricity. The *NEC* was first issued under its present name in 1897. It is revised every three years by the National Electrical Code Committee.

National Electrical Safety Code (ANSI C2)

As interest increased in electrical safety in the U.S., a need arose for a code to cover the practices of public utilities and others when installing and maintaining overhead and underground electric supply and communications lines. Accordingly, the first edition of the *National Electrical Safety Code* was completed in 1916. Currently this code is updated and published by the Institute of Electrical and Electronics Engineers (IEEE).

Canadian Electrical Code

The Canadian Standards Association sponsors and publishes the *Canadian Electrical Code*. This code establishes essential requirements and minimum standards for the installation and maintenance of electrical equipment. This code can be adopted and enforced by electrical inspection departments throughout Canada and was prepared with due regard for the *NEC* and the *National Electrical Safety Code*. Its several parts are the Canadian equivalent of the *NEC*, the *National Electrical Safety Code*, and the standards of Underwriters Laboratories Inc. (UL) in the U.S.

The National Electrical Code Handbook

While not in itself a code or standard that can have the force of law, the *National Electrical Code Handbook* is a valuable resource in implementing provisions of the *NEC*. The *NEC Handbook* contains the entire text of the *NEC* supplemented by comments, diagrams, and illustrations that are intended to clarify some of the intricate requirements of the *NEC*. The *NEC Handbook* is published by the NFPA; a new edition is published with each new edition of the *NEC*.

Listed and Labeled Electrical Equipment Manufacturers

Three publications are available that list the names of companies making electric appliances and materials that have been listed or labeled by UL. Devices and materials in the product categories listed have been tested for actual field use in accordance with the *NEC* and against UL safety standards. The lists are published so that the names of manufacturers of devices that meet test criteria may be readily obtained. The three publications are the *Hazardous Location Equipment Directory*, *Electrical Appliance and Utilization Equipment Directory*, and *Electrical Construction Materials Directory*. They are published annually by UL with six-month supplements. Certain types of electrical equipment are covered in other UL directories, such as the *Marine Products Directory*.

There are sections of the *NEC* that influence the design and construction of electric equipment. UL has complete published standards for most electric fittings, materials, and equipment, including specifications for performance under tests and in service, and further details of design and construction. Other testing laboratories in the U. S. and Canada that test electric equipment include Factory Mutual Research Corporation (FM); ETL Testing Laboratories, Inc. (ETL); U.S. Testing, Applied Research Laboratories; Dash, Straus, and Goodhue; and the Canadian Standards Association (CSA). Some laboratories stipulate compliance with the *NEC* in testing equipment. (Where no published standards are available for special equipment, arrangements usually can be made with testing laboratories for testing on an individual basis.)

BUILDING WIRING, DESIGN, AND PROTECTION

This section contains information on various types of building wiring and equipment, including panelboards and overcurrent protection; types of electric conductors;

identification of conductors, terminals, etc.; how to calculate loads; and similar subjects.

Service Entrance

Good practice requires that service entrance conductors comply in all respects with the detailed requirements of the *NEC*. Figure 2-3A provides typical arrangements of service entrance conductors.

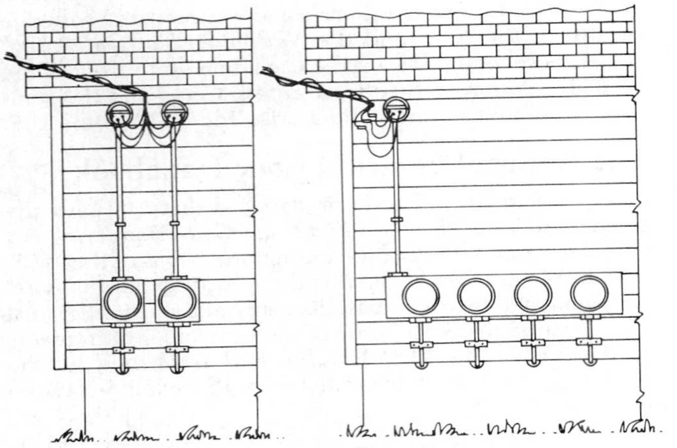

***FIG. 2-3A.** The diagram at left shows an installation in which two sets of service entrance conductors are tapped from one service drop, with meters mounted on the outside of the building. In the diagram at right, a set of main service entrance conductors is connected to the service drop and is carried through a trough and then through four sets of subservice entrance conductors to each service equipment. Here again, the meters are on the exterior wall.*

Means are provided for disconnecting all conductors in the building from the service entrance conductors. The principle is to permit disconnection of all conductors of the service at that location with no more than six operations of the hand. (See Figure 2-3B.) The limitation is applicable to all of the service disconnecting means located, or grouped, in one place. It does not include the services for fire pumps, emergency electrical systems, etc., which the *NEC* recognizes as being separate services for specific purposes.

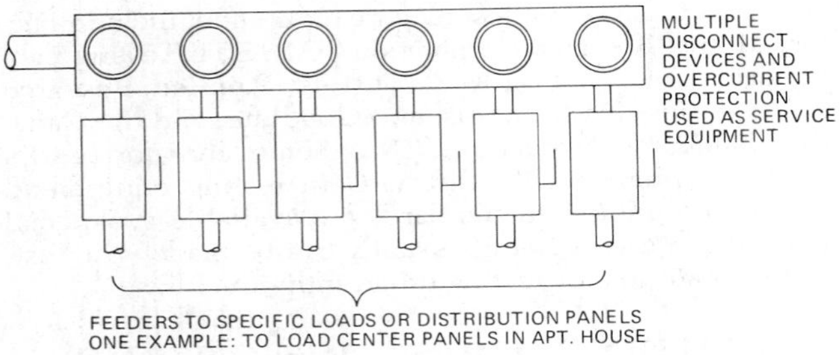

***FIG. 2-3B.** Typical layout for multiple disconnecting means. The maximum number of switches is six at any one location and the principle is to permit disconnecting all conductors of the service at that location with no more than six operations of the hand.*

The disconnecting means is either an outside or inside installation, at a readily accessible location nearest the point of entrance of the service entrance conductors. Service entrance conductors must be of sufficient size to carry the calculated load. In general, a building or other structure served should be supplied by only one service drop (see Figure 2-3A) or service (underground) lateral, but additional services are permitted for fire pumps, emergency electrical systems, multiple occupancies, large capacities, large areas, and different classes of use.

Underground service conductors must be protected against physical damage. (See Figure 2-3C.) Tables 2-3F and 2-3G give minimum cover requirements for underground installations. ("Cover" is defined as the distance between the top surface of direct buried cable, conduit, or other approved raceways and the finished grade.)

For circuits over 600 volts, there are variations in burial depths shown in Table 2-3G under certain circumstances. For example, the burial depth beneath areas subject to vehicular traffic is 24 in. (0.60 m). Under airport runways and adjacent areas, the burial depth must be a minimum of 18 in. (0.45 m). Lesser burial depths are permitted where access is necessary, or where termination or splicing points are located.

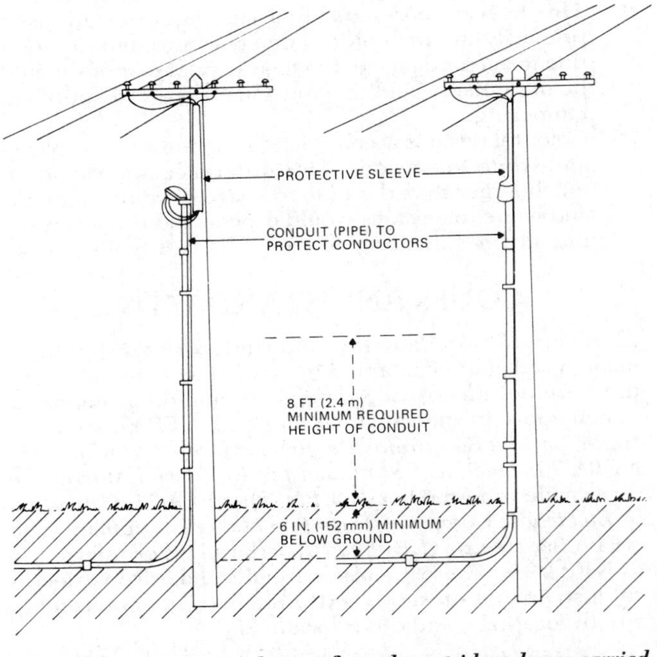

***FIG. 2-3C.** Service conductors from the outside pole are carried underground from the overhead supply line. Note the service head to protect the conductors against the entrance of water and that the point of connection of the service entrance conductors is below the level of the service head.*

Lightning (Surge) Arresters—Building Wiring

Lightning and surge arresters are not required but may be used, particularly where buildings are supplied by an overhead service and where thunderstorms are prevalent in the area. NFPA 78, *Lightning Protection Code* (hereinafter referred to as NFPA 78), requires the provision of lightning arresters on electrical service entrance conductors

TABLE 2-3F. ***Minimum cover requirements, 0 to 600 Volts, Nominal, Burial in inches (Cover is defined as the shortest distance measured between a point on the top surface of any direct buried conductor, cable, conduit or other raceway and the top surface of finished grade, concrete, or similar cover.)***

	Type of Wiring Method or Circuit				
Location of Wiring Method or Circuit	Direct Burial Cables or Conductors	Rigid Metal Conduit or Intermediate Metal Conduit	Rigid Nonmetalic Conduit Approved for Direct Burial Without Concrete Encasement or Other Approved Raceways	Residential Branch Circuit Rated 120 Volts or Less with GFCI Protection and Maximum Overcurrent Protection of 20 Amperes	Circuit for Control of Irrigation and Landscape Lighting Limited to Not More than 30 Volts and Installed with Type UF or in Other Identified Cable or Raceway
All locations not specified below	24	6	18	12	6
In trench below 2-inch-thick concrete or equivalent	18	6	12	6	6
Under a building	0 (in raceway only)	0	0	0 (in raceway only)	0 (in raceway only)
Under minimum of 4-inch-thick concrete exterior slab with no vehicular traffic and the slab extending not less than 6 inches beyond the underground installation	18	4	4	6 (direct burial) 4 (in raceway)	6 (direct burial) 4 (in raceway)
Under streets, highways, roads, alleys, driveways, and parking lots	24	24	24	24	24
One- and two-family dwelling driveways and parking areas, and used for no other purpose	18	18	18	12	1
In or under airport runways including adjacent areas where trespassing prohibited	18	18	18	18	18
In solid rock where covered by minimum of 2 inches concrete extending down to rock	2 (in raceway only)	2	2	2 (in raceway only)	2 (in raceway only)

Note 1. For SI Units: one inch = 25.4 millimeters
Note 2. Raceways approved for burial only where concrete encased shall require concrete envelope not less than 2 inches thick.
Note 3. Lesser depth shall be permitted where cables and conductors rise for terminations or splices or where access is otherwise required.
Note 4. Where one of the conduits listed in columns 1-3 is combined with one of the circuit types in column 4 and 5, the shallower depth of burial shall be permitted.
Source: NFPA 70-1990, *National Electrical Code.*

where the structure is provided with a lightning protection system. Surge arresters are also very useful where electronic equipment is used, because equipment using solid-state electronic components is very sensitive to line voltage surges.

Each lead-in from an outdoor antenna to a radio or television set or to an amateur radio transmitting station needs protection from lightning. Antenna discharge units should be installed to provide lightning protection for the equipment. Additional protection from power line surges or from connected communications equipment may also be desirable.

Grounding Requirements—Building Wiring

Dangerous voltages, which may be a fire hazard and a personal injury (shock) hazard, may be imposed on electric distribution systems and equipment. These voltages may be caused by lightning, inadvertent contact with a high-voltage

TABLE 2-3G ***Minimum Cover Requirements (Cover is defined as the shortest distance in inches measured between a point on the top surface of any direct buried conductor, cable, conduit or other raceway and the finished grade.)***

Circuit Voltage	Direct Buried Cables	Rigid Nonmetalic Conduit Approved for Direct Burial*	Rigid Metal Conduit and Intermediate Metal Conduit
Over 600-22kV	30	18	6
Over 22kV-40kV	36	24	6
Over 40kV	42	30	6

For SI units: one inch = 25.4 millimeters.
*Listed by a qualified testing agency as suitable for direct burial without encasement. All other nonmetallic systems shall require 2 inches (50.8mm) of concrete or equivalent above conduit in addition to above depth.
Source: NFPA 70-1990, *National Electrical Code.*

primary system, breakdown of insulation, surface leakage due to dirt or moisture, or by a wire coming loose from its connection.

By grounding one conductor of the electric circuit and then grounding all exposed metal that may come in contact with a live conductor, a fault to ground occurs if the ungrounded circuit conductor should become accidentally grounded. The fault current finds a path through the equipment grounding conductor and can cause the operation of an overcurrent device (fuse or circuit breaker) in the ungrounded circuit conductor and eliminate the dangerous condition. The impedance of the fault path must be low enough to permit sufficient current flow to cause the overcurrent device to operate quickly.

The metal enclosures of conductors (metal armor of cables, metal raceways, boxes, cabinets, and fittings) must be grounded. (Article 250 of the *NEC* contains general requirements for grounding electrical installations.)

The *NEC* also requires grounding of exposed noncurrent-carrying metal parts of cord- and plug-connected equipment likely to become energized in hazardous (classified) locations, where operated by persons standing on the ground or metal surfaces, or where operated at more than 150 V to ground, except for guarded motors. In some isolated cases, the metal frames of electrically heated appliances should also be grounded. The *NEC* also specifies grounding of particular cord- and plug-connected appliances in residential occupancies. These appliances include refrigerators, freezers, air conditioners, clothes washers and dryers, dishwashers, sump pumps, electric aquarium equipment, portable hand-held motor-operated tools, and some appliances, e.g., hedge clippers, lawn mowers, snow blowers, and wet scrubbers. Appliances may be excepted from grounding if equivalent protection via double insulation is provided.

A metallic underground water piping system must be used as the grounding electrode, where available, and where the buried portion of the pipe is more than 10 ft (3 m) in length. A metal underground water pipe grounding electrode, however, must be supplemented by an additional electrode so the integrity of the grounding electrode system is maintained. In addition, the following grounding electrodes must be used as part of the grounding electrode system, if available on the premises: (1) the metal frame of the building where effectively grounded, (2) a concrete-encased electrode, and (3) a ground ring. All grounding electrodes must be bonded together. (Article 250 of the *NEC* lists various methods of providing grounding electrode systems.) An example of a grounding electrode is shown in Figure 2-3D. Piping should be inspected to see if there are any insulating joints and nonconducting materials. Effective bonding must be provided around insulated joints and sections, and around any equipment that is likely to be disconnected for repairs or replacement.

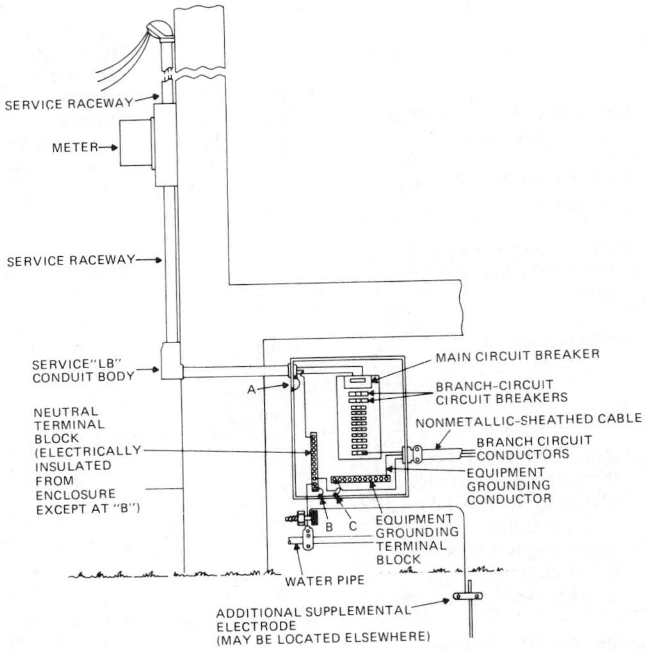

FIG. 2-3D. ***Grounding at a typical small service [ac, single phase, three wire (120/240 V)]. The service raceway is grounded through the metal of the box; this electrical connection is indicated at "A." The jumper shown is one of the methods employed to ensure electrical continuity at service equipment. The service enclosure is itself bonded to the grounded neutral conductor at point "B." This connection is often a removable strap or screw. The meter box and the upper portion of the service raceway or cable are grounded through threaded connectors making threaded connections to the meter box if metal conduit or electrical metallic tubing is used. The meter box on the line side of the service equipment is usually grounded by connection to the grounded neutral, and such ground would be required in case of service-entrance cable. The branch circuit equipment grounding conductor is connected to ground through the equipment grounding terminal block which is grounded at point "C." This connection is commonly the mounting screw for this terminal block. The grounding connection shown is to be an underground cold-water piping system. The connection should be as required by the NEC.***

Panelboards and Overcurrent Protection—Building Wiring and Equipment

Panelboards: A panelboard has buses (with or without switches) and automatic overcurrent devices for the control and protection of light, heat, or power circuits. The buses are mounted in a cabinet or cutout box which is placed in or on a wall and is accessible only from the front.

No more than 42 overcurrent devices of a lighting and appliance branch circuit panelboard are permitted by the *NEC* to be installed in any one cabinet or cutout box. Generally, not more than two main circuit breakers or two main sets of fuses are permitted to protect a branch-circuit panelboard. (See Figures 2-3E and 2-3F.) Figures 2-3G and

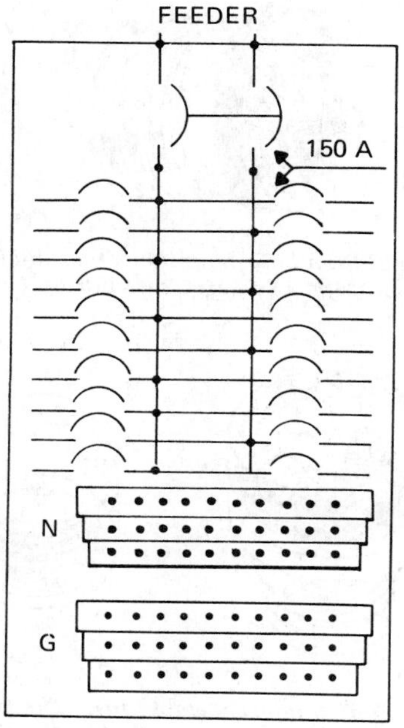

FIG. 2-3E. One main provided (two are permitted). Grounding terminal block may not be required, depending upon wiring system used.

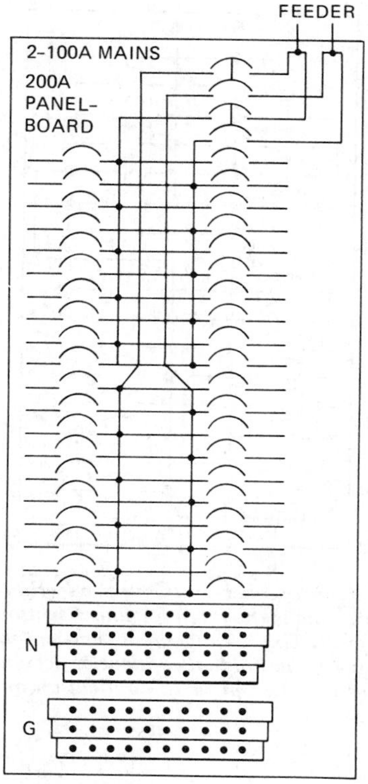

FIG. 2-3F. Two mains required. Grounding terminal block may not be required, depending upon wiring system used.

2-3H show exceptions to the general rule for individual protection of panelboards.

Panelboards installed in wet locations need weatherproof cabinets and must be mounted so that there is at least ¼ in. (6 mm) of air space between the cabinet and the wall or other supporting surface. Special requirements of Chapter 5 of the *NEC* govern installation of panelboards in hazardous (classified) locations.

Overcurrent protection: Conductors and equipment are provided with overcurrent protection to open a circuit if the current reaches a value that will cause an excessive or dangerous temperature in the conductor or conductor insulation. No feature of an electrical installation deserves more careful attention and supervision. In general, an overcurrent device rated or set in accordance with the ampacity, or current carrying capacity, of the *NEC* should be installed in each ungrounded conductor of each circuit and for each feeder at the point where the conductor to be protected receives its supply. (See Tables 2-3A through 2-3D.) Exceptions for fixture wires, cords, taps, motor circuits, remote-control circuits, and fire protective signaling circuits are covered in Articles 240, 430, 725, and 760 of the *NEC*.

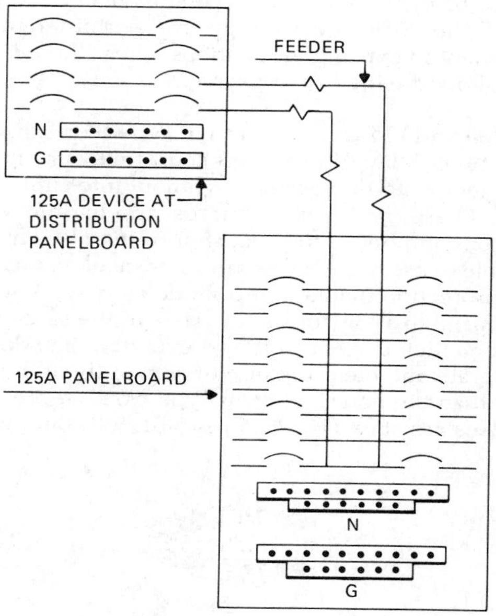

FIG. 2-3G. No mains required. Grounding terminal block may not be required, depending upon wiring system used.

Overcurrent Protective Devices

The most commonly used overcurrent protective devices for feeders, circuits, and equipment are fuses, circuit breakers, and thermal overload units. (Overcurrent and undervoltage relays, etc., are used on high-voltage, high-current systems.)

Plug fuses: There are two basic types of plug fuses: (1) the ordinary Edison-base type, and (2) Type S. Either of these may or may not be of the time-delay type.

The Type S fuse is designed to prevent tampering or bridging, or at least not without extreme difficulty. Adapters are available that fit the Edison-base fuseholders. After an adapter has been properly installed, it cannot be removed without damaging the fuseholder. The adapters

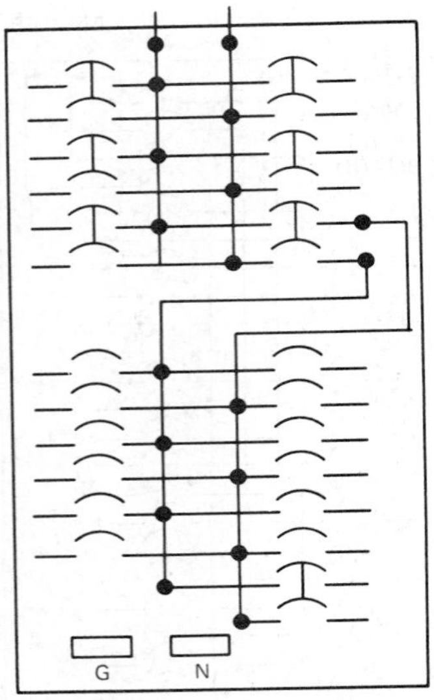

FIG. 2-3H. Circuit breakers in the upper section are the service circuit breakers. One is the main for lower section buses supplying branch circuits. This arrangement is acceptable only for the service to an existing individual residential occupancy where the panelboard was installed prior to application of the 1981 NEC requirements.

FIG. 2-3J. An Edison-base nonrenewable, dual-element fuse. (Source: Bussman Mfg. Div., McGraw-Edison Co.)

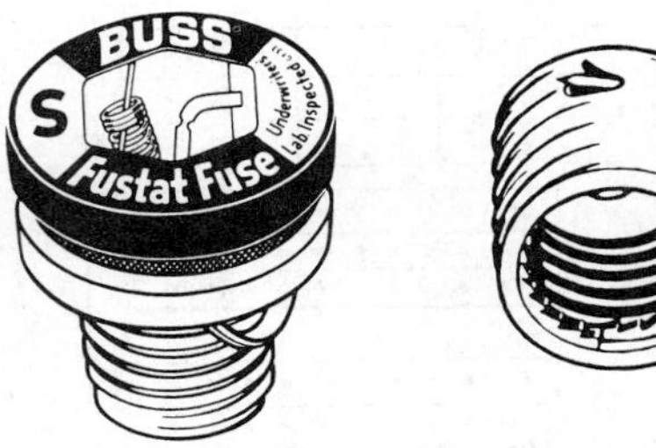

FIG. 2-3K. A Type S nonrenewable fuse. The time-lag type of fuse shown is acceptable but not required by the NEC. These fuses have been designed so that tampering or bridging can be done only with difficulty. The NEC specifies that fuseholders for plug fuses of 30 amp or less must not be used unless they are designed to use this Type S fuse or are made to accept a Type S fuse through use of an adapter. (Source: Bussman Mfg. Div., McGraw-Edison Co.)

are designed to prevent using Edison-base fuses in the fuseholder and to prevent using larger (higher rated) Type S fuses in an adapter designed for a lower rating. They also prevent the use of pennies and other common bridging schemes. An Edison-base fuseholder will take an Edison-base fuse of any size up to a maximum 30 amp rating. Plug fuses of the Edison-base type are permitted only for replacement in existing installations where there is no evidence of overfusing or tampering.

Time-delay plug fuses: Whether Type S or Edison-base design, time-delay fuses permit short-time current surges, such as motor starting currents, without interruption of the circuit. These momentary surges are harmless unless repeated a number of times at short intervals. This makes it possible to use Type S fuses in sizes small enough to give better protection than a non-time-delay type, which must be oversized to allow for such surges. In the case of a short circuit or a high-current fault, however, the time-delay type will operate and clear the circuit as rapidly or even more rapidly than the non-time-delay type. Some representative plug fuses are shown in Figures 2-3I, 2-3J, and 2-3K.

FIG. 2-3I. A typical Edison-base nonrenewable, single-element fuse. (Source: Bussman Mfg. Div., McGraw-Edison Co.)

Cartridge fuses: These are of both the time-delay and the non-time-delay types. They are also of the one-time and the renewable link types. When a one-time fuse opens, the entire fuse must be replaced. But when a renewable link fuse opens, the fuse link can be replaced inside the same cartridge unless the cartridge has also been damaged.

Renewable link fuses have two disadvantages: (1) the links can be doubled or tripled, etc., thereby defeating their purpose and usefulness, and (2) the links, upon replacement, can be left with loose connections. Several representative cartridge fuses are shown in Figures 2-3L and 2-3M.

Circuit breakers: There are two basic types of breakers: (1) adjustable trip and (2) nonadjustable trip. The adjustable-trip type may be of either the air-or oil-immersed type. The setting of the trip point is adjustable between a minimum and a maximum range and is usually used only on large installations having qualified operators and maintenance personnel. They are designed to trip when the current reaches that of the setting. The nonadjustable-trip type comes in a molded case, making it extremely difficult or impossible to change its rating. A molded-case breaker can be of the inverse-time thermal-magnetic type, or of the magnetic-only inverse-time type. Molded-case circuit breakers are designed so that the current has to exceed the rating (as is also true with all types of fuses) before it will trip. Unless it is the thermally compensated type, high ambient temperatures can reduce the current required to trip the circuit breaker (or fuse). A representative nonadjustable circuit breaker is shown in Figure 2-3N.

Thermal devices: These are not intended for protection against short circuits, but only for the protection of overload currents of a comparatively lower magnitude unless

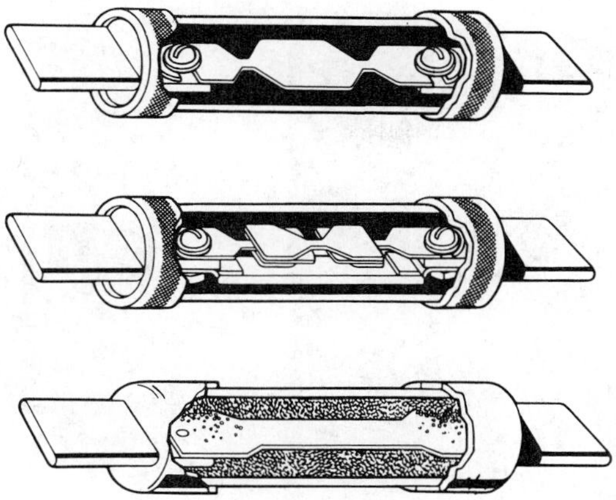

FIG. 2-3L. Three types of cartridge fuses: at top, an ordinary dropout link renewable fuse; at center, a super-lag renewable fuse; and at bottom, a one-time fuse. (Source: Bussman Mfg. Div., McGraw-Edison Co.)

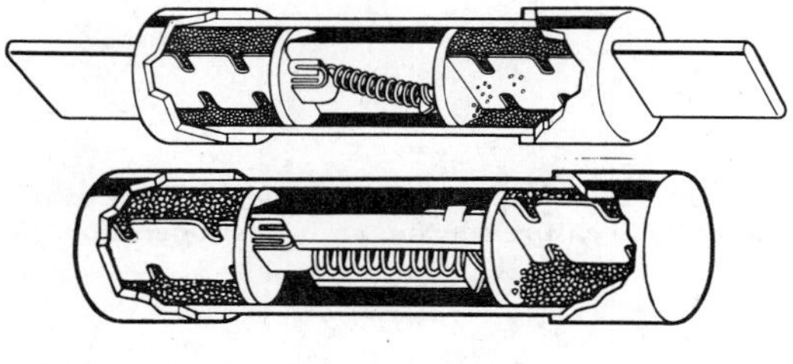

FIG. 2-3M. A dual-element cartridge fuse, blade and ferrule type. (Source: Bussman Mfg. Div., McGraw-Edison Co.)

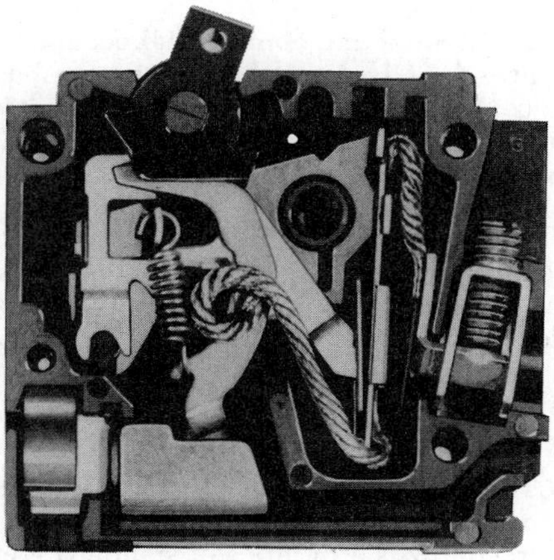

FIG. 2-3N. A 15-amp, single-pole, 120-V branch-circuit breaker. (Source: Westinghouse Electric Corp.)

otherwise designed. An example is overload protection for a motor where short-circuit and ground-fault protection is provided by the branch-circuit fuses or circuit breakers. For detailed requirements for motors and other equipment, see the applicable provisions of the *NEC*.

Current-limiting overcurrent protective devices:

These devices are provided in some installations where high current (more than 10,000 amps) is available under short-circuit conditions. They are designed so that when interrupting a specified current, the devices will consistently limit the short-circuit current in that circuit to a magnitude substantially less than that obtainable in the same circuit if the device were replaced with a solid conductor having comparable impedance. (See Figure 2-3O.) Fuseholders for current-limiting fuses are designed to make it difficult to install a noncurrent-limiting fuse.

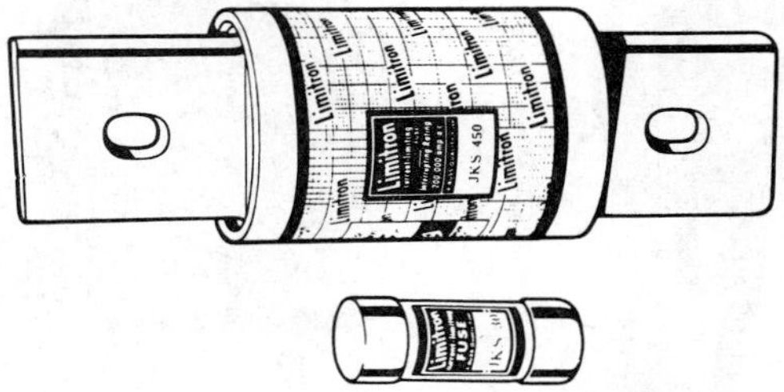

FIG. 2-3O. A current-limiting overcurrent protection device (rated 0 to 600 amps). (Source: Bussman Mfg. Div., McGraw-Edison Co.)

Ground-Fault Circuit-Interrupters

Circuit breakers and fuses open a circuit and stop the flow of electricity when the flow exceeds the ratings of the circuit breaker or fuse. Lighting and receptacle circuits are usually rated 15 or 20 amps. At times as little as 60 mA (milliamperes) can kill a normal healthy adult; thus the rating of lighting and receptacle circuits is high, relative to the amount of current that could kill a person.

Ground-fault circuit-interrupters (GFCI) are devices that sense when even a small amount of current passes to ground through any path other than the proper conductor. When this condition exists, the GFCI trips almost instantly, stopping all current flow in the circuit and through the person receiving the ground-fault shock.

Simplicity of design is one reason for the reliability of the GFCI. Figure 2-3P shows a typical circuit arrangement of a GFCI for personnel protection. Figure 2-3Q shows types of GFCI units and a GFCI tester.

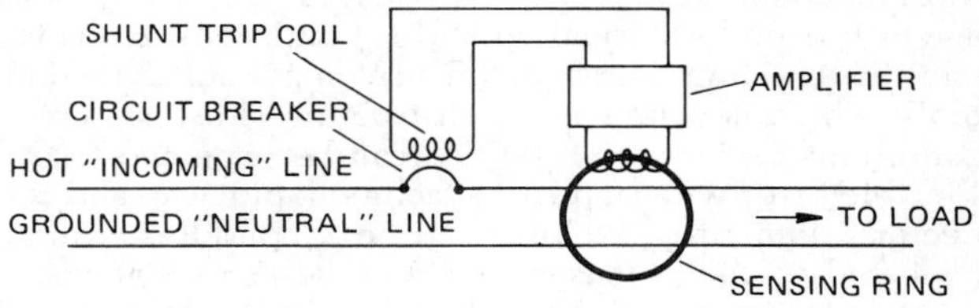

FIG. 2-3P. Circuit arrangement for a typical ground-fault circuit-interrupter for personnel protection. (Source: I-T-E Imperial)

Present GFCIs are set to operate when line-to-ground currents exceed 5 mA. Evaluation standards permit a differential of 4 to 6 mA. Even at trips of 5 mA, it should be clearly understood that the instantaneous current will be higher, and any shock during the time the fault is being cleared will be uncomfortable. A shock at 5 mA is unpleasant. The key to the ground-fault circuit-interrupter is the

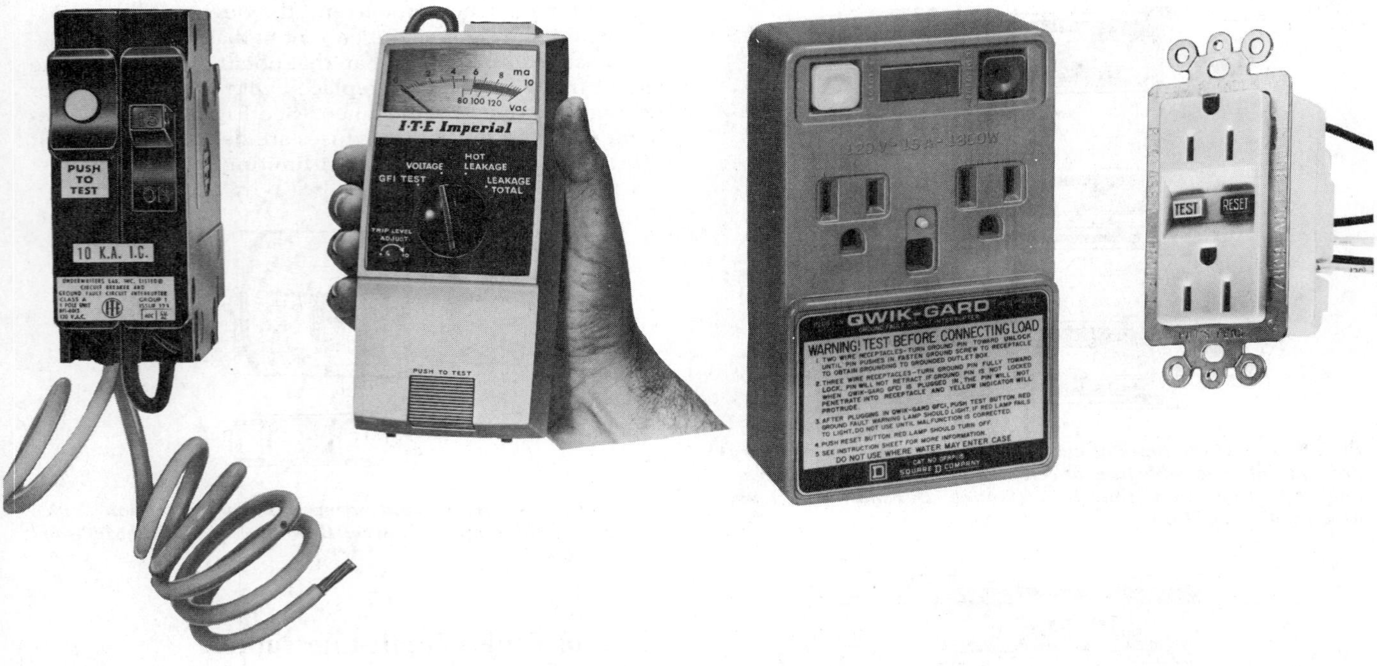

FIG. 2-3Q. ***A variety of GFCIs are available, including plug-in-circuit-breaker types and duplex-receptacle types. These also come in portable units and each has a test switch so that the unit can be checked periodically to ensure continuous proper operation. (Sources: I-T-E Imperial, Square D Co.)***

time-current characteristic. Trip-out time is about 1/40 of a sec (25 milliseconds) when the fault reaches or exceeds 6 mA. There are two classes of GFCIs—Class A and Class B. The Class A GFCI trips at not more than 6 mA. The Class B GFCI trips when the current exceeds 20 mA, and is for use only with swimming pool underwater lighting fixtures that were installed prior to local adoption of the 1965 edition of the *NEC*. The Class A GFCI is used where personnel protection against ground fault is required or desired.

GFCIs at construction sites: Precautions must be taken to aid the efficient operation of GFCIs on construction sites. Most laboratory-tested 120-V appliances have 0.5 mA leakage or less under normal operating conditions. However, moisture and improper maintenance on portable hand held tools, which is common at construction sites, can create conditions under which GFCIs can be expected to trip. Flexible cords with standard attachment plug cap and connector when dropped in water, e.g., puddles, can be expected to cause leakage currents (100 to 300 mA or greater) far in excess of GFCI trip currents. Motors with dirty brushes, carbon tracking on commutators, or moisture in the windings contribute to leakage current. A common-sense approach to installing, using, and maintaining GFCI circuits goes a long way toward eliminating nuisance tripping at construction sites. (Actually, tripping under any of the conditions mentioned is not nuisance tripping, but merely a device performing its intended function.)

Moisture is the major culprit in current leakage on wiring and equipment. Panelboards, receptacles, and cord caps and connectors intended for dry locations must not be subjected to wet conditions. Construction receptacles must be centrally located to enable cords 150 ft (46 m) or less in length to be used. There should be sufficient circuits available to minimize the number of tools necessary on each circuit. Receptacles must not be on the same circuit as lighting.

GFCIs in residential and commercial occupancies: The *NEC* requires GFCIs on all 125-V, single-phase 15- and 20-amp receptacle outlets in dwelling units installed outdoors with grade-level access, within 6 ft (1.8 m) of a kitchen sink to serve countertop surfaces, in unfinished basements, in garages (with some exceptions), and in bathrooms of both dwelling units and hotels and motels. Receptacles located within 20 ft (6 m) of the inside walls of swimming pools must be protected by GFCIs—as must receptacles and lighting fixtures near spas, hot tubs, hydromassage bathtubs, and electric equipment serving storable pools and fountains.

Types of Wiring Methods and Materials

The *NEC* recognizes a number of standard wiring methods, some of which are suitable for general use while others are suitable only for special purposes. In some localities, regulations restrict the use of some of the wiring methods recognized by the *NEC*. The most widely used wiring methods are rigid metal conduit; rigid nonmetallic conduit; intermediate metal conduit (IMC); electrical metallic tubing (EMT); metal-clad cable (MC); armored cable (AC; trade name: "BX"); nonmetallic sheathed cable (NM, NMC; trade name "Romex"), surface metal and nonmetallic raceways; wireways; busways; underfloor raceways; and cellular metal floor raceways. (See Figures 2-3R through 2-3U.) In some areas of the country, flexible metal conduit (trade name: "Greenfield") is used for complete wiring systems. None of these wiring methods should be used for either

FIG. 2-3R. A Type UF sheathed cable. The insulated conductors are jacketed in parallel and the overall covering must be flame retardant, moisture resistant, fungus resistant, corrosion resistant, and suitable for direct burial in the earth. (Source: Plastic Wire & Cable Corporation)

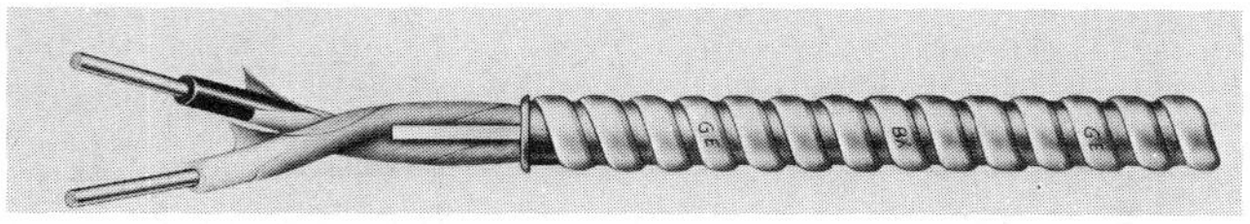

FIG. 2-3S. A typical armored cable (Type AC) that is frequently referred to as "BX." Another type (ACL) has lead-covered conductors and is often referred to as "BXL." (Both "BX" and "BXL" are trade names.) (Source: General Electric Company)

temporary or permanent work where they do not fully conform to *NEC* safety requirements.

Identification of Conductors, Terminals, Circuits, and Branch Circuits

With few exceptions, all interior wiring systems have a grounded circuit conductor that is continuously identified throughout. The identification for conductors of No. 6 or smaller (except for Type MI cable) should consist of an outer white or natural gray color. Insulated conductors larger than No. 6 should have similar identification or be identified by distinctive white markings at their terminations during installation. The grounded conductors of Type MI cable are also identified by distinctive markings at their terminations during installation.

In general, the terminals of electrical devices to which a grounded conductor is to be connected are identified by being made of metal substantially white in color, have a metallic plating substantially white in color, or the word "white" located adjacent to the terminal. If the terminal is not visible, the conductor entrance hole may be colored white. In the case of screw-shell-type lampholders, the (white) terminal is the one that is connected to the screw shell.

The equipment grounding conductor of a branch circuit is identified by a continuous green color or a continuous green color with one or more yellow stripes, unless it is bare. Ungrounded conductors of different voltages are permitted to be of any color other than green, white, or gray. In some special applications, such as isolated (ungrounded) circuits in hospital operating rooms, specific colors are required.

Lighting and Appliance Branch Circuits

A branch circuit is that portion of a wiring system extending between the final overcurrent device protecting the circuit and the outlets on the circuit. Branch circuits are further defined as: (1) a small appliance branch circuit supplying one or more outlets to which appliances are to be connected and which has no permanently connected lighting fixtures other than those that are part of an appliance, (2) a general-purpose branch circuit supplying two or more outlets for lighting and appliances, and (3) an individual branch circuit supplying only one piece of equipment.

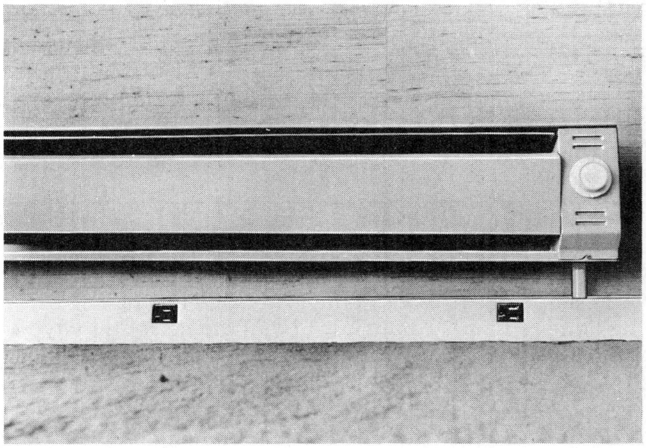

FIG. 2-3T. Installation of a typical metal raceway system showing an all-steel baseboard and a multioutlet system. (Source: The Wiremold Company)

FIG. 2-3U. The use of a surface metal raceway in a domestic kitchen installation. Frequent spacing of outlets eliminates interference from cords and reduces risk of injury. (Source: The Wiremold Company)

Receptacles rated at 15 amp connected to 15 or 20 amp branch circuits serving two or more outlets must not supply a total load in excess of 12 amp for portable appliances. Receptacles rated at 20 amp and connected to 20 amp branch circuits serving two or more outlets should not supply a total load in excess of 16 amp (80 percent of circuit capacity) for cord- and plug-connected appliances.

The total load must not exceed 80 percent of the branch circuit rating if motor-operated appliances are supplied by the circuit or, if in normal operation, the load will continue for three hours or more, as in store lighting and similar loads. Where the current drawn by resistance loads exceeds the motor current rating, as in clothes dryers and similar appliances, branch circuit conductors and overcurrent devices for individual branch circuits supplying such appliances must have a capacity of 125 percent of appliance nameplate ratings.

TABLE 2-3H ***Maximum Cord- and Plug-Connected Load to Receptacle***

Circuit Rating Amperes	Receptacle Rating Amperes	Maximum Load Amperes
15 or 20	15	12
20	20	16
30	30	24

Source: NFPA 70-1990, *National Electrical Code.*

TABLE 2-3I ***Receptacle Ratings for Various Size Circuits***

Circuit Rating Amperes	Receptable Rating Amperes
15	Not over 15
20	15 or 20
30	30
40	40 or 50
50	50

Source: NFPA 70-1990, *National Electrical Code.*

Lampholders, when connected to circuits having a rating of more than 20 amp, must be of the heavy-duty type.

Receptacles, when connected to circuits having two or more outlets, must conform to the ratings in Tables 2-3H and 2-3I. Where larger than 50 amp, the receptacle rating is not permitted to be less than the branch circuit rating.

Individual branch circuits may supply any loads. Branch circuits having two or more outlets may supply only loads as follows.

Branch circuits are for lighting units or appliances rated at 15 and 20 amp. The rating of any one cord- and plug-connected appliance must not exceed 80 percent of the branch circuit ampere rating. The total rating of fixed appliances must not exceed 50 percent of the branch circuit ampere rating when lighting units or other appliances are also supplied.

Branch circuits rated at 40 and 50 amp are permitted to supply fixed lighting units with heavy-duty lampholders or infrared heating units in other-than-dwelling occupancies, or fixed cooking appliances in any occupancy. Branch circuits rated larger than 50 amp may supply only nonlighting loads.

Receptacle outlets in dwelling occupancies, including guest rooms in hotels and motels, must be installed in every kitchen, family room, dining room, living room, parlor, library, den, sun room, bedroom, recreation room, or similar rooms. Insofar as practical, the outlets should be spaced equal distances apart. (See Figure 2-3V.) Most appliances and portable lamps are provided with flexible cords at least 6 ft (1.8 m) in length. Countertop appliances for use in the kitchen are usually supplied with shorter cords. Therefore, the *NEC* requires receptacles to be installed so that no point along the wall line is more than 24 in. (0.60 m), measured horizontally, from a receptacle. (See Figure 2-3W.)

Receptacles installed on 15 and 20 amp branch circuits must be of the grounding type and must be effectively grounded. This does not mean that all cord- and plug-connected equipment must be of the grounded type. (See the current *NEC* for specific details on grounding.)

Calculation of Loads

The methods specified in the *NEC* provide a basis for calculating the expected branch circuit and feeder loads and for determining the number of branch circuits required. Where in normal operation the maximum load of a branch circuit will continue for three hours or more (such as store lighting), the minimum unit loads specified should be increased by 25 percent.

The minimum unit lighting loads in volt-amperes per square foot for various types of occupancies are given in the *NEC*. In determining the load, open porches and garages in connection with dwelling occupancies are not

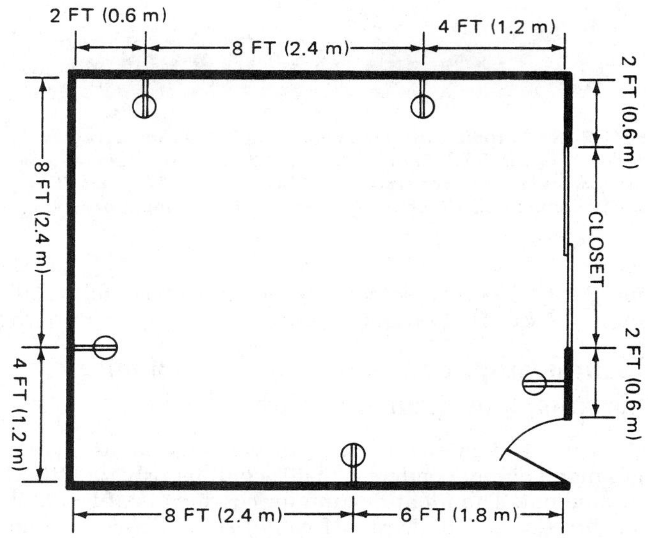

FIG. 2-3V. Illustration of the requirements in the NEC on the placement of receptacles in dwelling occupancies. Receptacles should be installed so that no point along the floor line is more than 6 ft (1.8 m), measured horizontally, from an outlet so as to permit a lamp or appliance, equipped with 6-ft (1.8 m) cords, to be located anywhere in the room.

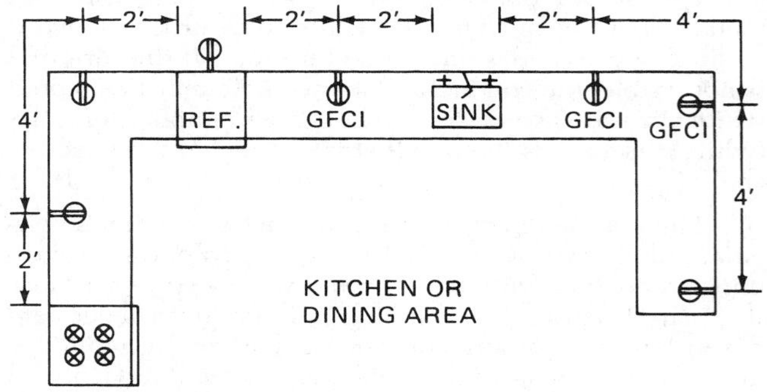

FIG. 2-3W. Illustration of the requirements in the NEC on the placement of receptacles at countertops in kitchens and dining areas of dwelling units.

included. Unfinished and unused spaces in dwellings need not be included unless adaptable for future use.

For other than general illumination lighting, general-use receptacles, appliances, and loads other than motor loads, the following minimum unit load should be included for each outlet:

1. Outlets supplying specific appliances and other loads—ampere rating of appliance or load served.
2. Outlets supplying heavy-duty lampholders—600 VA.
3. Other outlets—180 VA.*

Feeder Loads

Feeder conductors must have sufficient ampacity to supply the load served. The computed load of a feeder must not be less than the sum of all branch-circuit loads supplied by the feeder subject to the demand factor provisions of the *NEC*. Tables of demand factors for general illumination, electric ranges and other cooking appliances, and for clothes dryers are found in the *NEC*. Table 2-3J shows how the demand factors may be applied to that portion of the total branch circuit load computed for general illumination.

An optional method of calculating the load for a one-family residence served by a 120/240 V, three-wire, 100 amp or larger service where the total load is supplied by one feeder or one service is to use the percentages in Table 2-3K.

Examples of branch circuit and feeder calculations for other buildings and occupancies are given in the *NEC*.

Flexible Cords and Cables

Flexible cords are made in many types for various kinds of service ranging from wiring for portable lamps to elevator cables. Article 400 of the *NEC* gives a description, the ampacities, and the intended use of the various flexible cords now available. The ampacity of flexible cords is limited by type and gage of wire used. They must not be overloaded nor the size reduced where the gage is intended for mechanical strength.

Flexible cords are frequently subject to physical damage and rapid wear. Grounds or short circuits may occur if the insulation is damaged, and the resulting arc may ignite the insulation or nearby combustible material. Replacement of flexible cords as soon as they show damage or appreciable wear is of utmost importance.

Under present UL labeling practices, only replacement nondetachable power supply cords, range and dryer power supply cords, and cord sets, such as extension cords, carry the UL label on the product itself. Formerly, the original cords and power supply cords were labeled, and many consumers thought a label on the cord of an electrical appliance signified the appliance itself was investigated for safety. Nondetachable cords on new appliances do not now carry the UL label so the consumer cannot be misled into

TABLE 2-3J ***Lighting Load Feeder Demand Factors***

Type of Occupancy	Portion of Lighting Load to which Demand Factor Applies (volt-amperes)	Demand Factor Percent
Dwelling units	First 3,000 or less at	100
	From 3,001 to 120,000 at	35
	Remainder over 120,000 at	25
*Hospitals	First 50,000 or less at	40
	Remainder over 50,000 at	50
*Hotels and motels—including apartment houses without provision for cooking by tenants	First 20,000 or less at	50
	From 20,001to 100,000 at	40
	Remainder over 100,000 at	30
Warehouses (storage)	First 12,500 or less at	100
	Remainder over 12,500 at	50
All others	Total Volt-amperes	100

* The demand factors of this table shall not apply to the computed load of feeders to areas in hospitals, hotels, and motels where the entire lighting is likely to be used at one time; as in operating rooms, ballrooms, or dining rooms.Source: NFPA 70-1990, *National Electrical Code*.

TABLE 2-3K ***Optional Calculation for One-Family Dwelling Unit***

Largest of the following five selections.
(1) 100 percent of the nameplate rating(s) of the air conditioning and cooling, including heat pump compressors.
(2) 100 percent of the nameplate ratings of electrical thermal storage and other heating systems where the usual load is expected to be continuous at the full nameplate value. Systems qualifying under this selection must not be figured under any other selection in this table.
(3) 65 percent of the nameplate rating(s) of the central electric space heating including integral supplemental heating in heat pumps.
(4) 65 percent of the nameplate rating(s) of electric space heating if less than four separately controlled units.
(5) 40 percent of the nameplate rating(s) of electric space heating of four or more separately controlled units.
Plus: 100 percent of the first 10 kVA of all other load. 40 percent of the remainder of all other load.

Source: NFPA 70-1990, *National Electrical Code.*

---

* This provision is not applicable to receptacle outlets as required by the *NEC* for dwelling units. The 20 amp small-appliance branch circuits and laundry branch circuits in dwelling units are calculated at 1,500 VA per circuit. Other receptacle outlets rated 20 amp or less in dwelling units are considered part of the general lighting load calculated at 3 VA per sq ft. For receptacle outlets in other than dwelling units, each single or multiple receptacle on a single yoke or strap is considered at not less than 180 VA.

An example from the *NEC* of how to calculate the load in a single-family dwelling is presented to illustrate the principles involved:

For a dwelling that has a floor area of 1,500 sq ft (139 m2) (exclusive of a unoccupied cellar, unfinished attic, and open porches) and a 12 kW range, the load may be computed as follows:

General Lighting Load: 1,500 ft^2 (139 m^2) at 3 volt-amperes per ft^2 (0.09 m^2 = 4,500 volt-amperes.

Number of Branch Circuits Required

General Lighting Load:

4,500 ÷ 120 = 37.5 amp; or three 15 amp, 2-wire circuits; or two 20 amp 2-wire circuits

Small Appliance Load: Two 2-wire 20 amp circuits

Laundry Load: One 2-wire, 20 amp circuit

Minimum Size Feeders Required

Computed Load

General Lighting	4,500 volt-amperes
Small Appliance Load	3,000 volt-amperes
Laundry	1,500 volt-amperes
Total (without range	9,000 volt-amperes
3,000 volt-amperes at 100 percent	3,000 volt-amperes
9,000 – 3,000 = 6,000 volt-amperes at 35 percent =	2,100 volt-amperes
Net Computed (without range)	5,100 volt-amperes
Range Load	8,000 volt-amperes
Net Computed (with range)	13,100 volt-amperes

For 120/240 V system feeders 13,100 ÷ 240 = 55 amp.

Therefore, feeder size for total load may be selected on basis of 55 amp load.

Net computed load exceeds 10 kVA so service conductors shall be 100 amperes.

assuming the appliance itself has been UL tested, which may not be the case.

Flexible cords are not considered by the ***NEC*** as a wiring method. They are covered in the *NEC* chapter on equipment for general use. Flexible cords, including extension cords, are not acceptable as a substitute for the fixed wiring of a structure, but they are acceptable for use in extending the length of a cord on a portable lamp or on cord- and plug-connected appliances. They should be used in accordance with any instructions included with the listing or labeling, and the flexible cord itself should be used in accordance with Article 400 of the *NEC*. Flexible cords are not limited solely to "temporary wiring."

Switches

Switches are required for the control of lights and appliances, and as the disconnecting means for motors and their controllers. Switches may be of either the air-break or the oil-break type. In the oil-break type the interrupting device is immersed in oil.

A chief fire hazard in switches is the arcing produced when the switch is opened. This hazard is somewhat greater with oil-break switches. If operated much beyond their rated capacity, or if the condition of the oil is poor or its level is not properly maintained, the arc may vaporize the oil, rupture the case, and cause a fire. However, the amount of oil is comparatively small (except in high-voltage equipment) and these switches present no hazard if properly used and maintained.

ELECTRICAL HOUSEHOLD APPLIANCES

Electric Heating Equipment

Electric heating equipment is used widely, and it is important that all such devices be tested and listed by qualified electrical testing laboratories. Some fixed heating equipment covered in the *NEC* is acceptable for installation in direct contact with combustible material. Baseboard heaters listed by UL, for example, have been tested and found to incorporate suitable safeguards against fire hazards that might result from contact with draperies, furniture, carpeting, bedding, etc., although discoloration or scorching (but no glowing embers or flaming) may result on adjacent materials. Other electric air heaters, however, may present fire hazards if they come in contact with combustible materials or if they are covered or blocked in any manner. Space heating systems must not be installed where exposed to severe physical damage unless adequately protected, nor in damp or wet locations unless approved for such locations.

A heater installed in an air duct or plenum must be of a type suitable for that purpose. The *NEC* covers installation of heaters for ducts and plenums and such items as airflow reliability, problems of condensation, fan circuit interlock, limit controls, and location of disconnecting means. NFPA 90B, *Installation of Warm Air Heating and Air Conditioning Systems*, also contains details on central systems.

Electric Ranges, Wall-Mounted Ovens, and Counter-Mounted Cooking Units

Each of these devices needs a means for disconnection from all ungrounded conductors of the supply circuit, except that a separable connector or a plug and receptacle may serve as the disconnecting means for free-standing household ranges. A plug and receptacle connection at the rear base of the range, if accessible from the front by removal of a drawer, is considered satisfactory. Grounding requirements for ranges are covered in Article 250 of the *NEC*. The *NEC* gives the methods for calculating feeder loads for household electric ranges and other cooking appliances.

Refrigerators

Fire problems with refrigerators include deterioration in service of the fractional horsepower motors used and the possibility of overheating. Refrigerant coils and motors are susceptible to accumulations of lint and oily deposits, so cleanliness is a primary consideration in fire prevention. New devices have sealed motors not requiring oiling or maintenance, but overheating can result from improper use or inefficient cooling of the refrigerant due to coil dirt or damage. Ordinary household or commercial refrigerators must not be used to store flammable liquids. [Refrigerators for use in Class I hazardous (classified) locations and refrigerators for flammable materials storage in laboratories in health-related institutions in accordance with Chapter 7 of NFPA 99 are listed by UL.] Exposed noncurrent-carrying metal parts of refrigerators and freezers, which are likely to become energized, need to be grounded under provisions of the *NEC*.

Room Air Conditioning Units

These have the same fire hazards as other motor-operated appliances. The exposed noncurrent-carrying metal parts must be grounded as required by Article 250 of the *NEC*.

Incandescent Lamps

Because incandescent lamps produce considerable heat, they inherently possess the hazard of heating and igniting combustible material in contact with them. Under normal conditions, with incandescent lamps in approved lampholders and fixtures where properly guarded, the heating hazard is negligible, but ignition of combustible material may result if lamps are surrounded by or laid on such combustible material. Table 2-3L presents information on surface and base temperatures of standard lamps in open sockets. The temperature measurements are all taken at an ambient temperature of 77°F (25°C). In most instances where lamps are incorporated in various kinds of lighting equipment, the ambient temperature at which the lamps operate is higher; thus the surface temperatures of the bulbs are also higher. The bulb temperatures may be further increased if the lamp is in other than a vertical, base-up position. Figure 2-3X shows surface temperatures of 100W A-19 and 500W PS-35 lamps in various positions, but, again, these temperatures were measured in an ambient temperature of 77°F (25°C), so where enclosed in fixtures, the temperatures will be higher. Conventional Christmas tree lamps of U.S. manufacture have approximate average bulb surface temperatures at the hottest spot of approximately 260°F (127°C) for the blue and green colors, and somewhat lower for the white, red, and yellow colors.

The data in Table 2-3L was extracted from the *IES Handbook*, 5th ed., of the Illuminating Engineering Society and is used here with the permission of the Society. The reader is asked to keep in mind the above comments in the text regarding use of data in Table 2-3L and Figure 2-3X.

TABLE 2-3L. ***General Service Lamps for 115-, 120-, and 125-Volt Circuits***
(Will Operate in Any Position but Lumen Maintenance is Best for 40 to 1500 Watts When Burned Vertically Base-Up)

Watts	Bulb and Other Description	Base	Filament	Rated Average Life (hours)	Maximum Over-All Length in Inches (mm)	Average Light Center Length in Inches (mm)	Approximate Initial Filament Temp. (K)	Max. Bare Bulb Temp. °F (°C)	Base Temp. °F (°C)	Approximate Initial Lumens	Rated Initial Lumens Per Watt‡	Lamp Lumen Depreciation** (percent)
10	S-14 inside frosted or clear	Med.	C-9	1500	$3\frac{1}{2}$ (89)	$2\frac{1}{2}$ (63)	2420	106 (41)	106 (41)	80	8.0	89
15	A-15 inside frosted	Med.	C-9	2500	$3\frac{1}{2}$ (89)	$2\frac{3}{8}$ (60)	—	—	—	126	8.4	83
25	A-19 inside frosted	Med.	C-9	2500	$3\frac{7}{8}$ (98)	$2\frac{1}{2}$ (63)	2550	110 (43)	108 (42)	230	9.2	79
40	A-19 inside frosted and white¶	Med.	C-9	1500	$4\frac{1}{4}$ (108)	$2\frac{15}{16}$ (75)	2650	260 (127)	221 (105)	455	11.4	87.5
40	S-11 clear	Inter-med.	CC-2V or C-7A	350 500	$3\frac{5}{16}$ (59)	$1\frac{5}{8}$ (41)	2800 —	570 (299)	390 (199)	477 —	11.9 —	— —
50	A-19 inside frosted	Med.	CC-6	1000	$4\frac{7}{16}$ (113)	$3\frac{1}{8}$ (79)	—	—	—	680	13.6	—
60	A-19 inside frosted and white¶	Med.	CC-6	1000	$4\frac{7}{16}$ (113)	$3\frac{1}{8}$ (79)	2790	255 (124)	200 (93)	860	14.3	93
75	A-19inside frosted and white¶	Med.	CC-6	750	$4\frac{7}{16}$ (113)	$3\frac{1}{8}$ (79)	2840	275 (135)	205 (96)	1180	15.7	92
100	A-19 inside frosted and white¶	Med.	CC-8	750	$4\frac{7}{16}$ (113)	$3\frac{1}{8}$ (79)	2905	300 (149)	208 (98)	1740	17.4	90.5
100§	A-19 inside frosted and white	Med.	CC-8	1000	$4\frac{7}{16}$ (113)	$3\frac{1}{8}$ (79)	—	—	—	1680	16.8	—
100	A-21 inside frosted	Med.	CC-6	750	$5\frac{1}{4}$ (133)	$3\frac{7}{8}$ (98)	2880	260 (143)	194 (90)	1640	16.9	90
100§	A-23 inside frosted or clear	Med.	C-9	1000	$5\frac{15}{16}$ (151)	$4\frac{7}{16}$ (113)	—	—	—	1480	14.8	—
150	A-21 inside frosted	Med.	CC-8	750	$5\frac{1}{2}$ (140)	4 (102)	2960	—	—	2880	19.2	89
150	A-21 white	Med.	CC-8	750	$5\frac{1}{2}$ (140)	4 (102)	2930	—	—	2790	18.6	89
150	A-23 inside frosted or clear or white	Med.	CC-6	750	$6\frac{3}{16}$ (157)	$4\frac{5}{8}$ (117)	2925	280 (138)	210 (99)	2780	18.5	89
150	PS-25 clear or inside frosted	Med.	C-9	750	$6\frac{15}{16}$ (176)	$5\frac{1}{4}$ (133)	2910	290 (143)	210 (99)	2660	21.2	87.5
200	A-23 inside frosted or white or clear	Med.	CC-8	750	$6\frac{5}{16}$ (160)	$4\frac{5}{8}$ (117)	2980	345 (174)	225 (107)	4000	20.0	89.5
200	PS-25 clear or inside frosted	Med.	CC-6	750	$6\frac{15}{16}$ (176)	$5\frac{1}{4}$ (133)	—	—	—	3800	19.0	—
200	PS-30 clear or inside frosted	Med.	C-9	750	$8\frac{1}{16}$ (205)	6 (152)	2925	305 (152)	210 (99)	3700	18.5	85
300	PS-25 clear of inside frosted	Med.	CC-8	750	$6\frac{15}{16}$ (110)	$5\frac{3}{16}$ (132)	3015	401 (205)	234 (112)	6360	21.2	87.5
300	PS-30 clear or inside frosted	Med.	C-9	750	$8\frac{1}{16}$ (205)	6 (152)	3000	275 (135)	175 (79)	6100	20.3	82.5
300	PS-30 clear or inside frosted	Mog.	CC-8	1000	$8\frac{5}{8}$ (219)	7 (178)	—	—	—	5960	19.8	—

TABLE 2-3L. (CONTINUED) ***General Service Lamps for 115-, 120-, and 125-Volt Circuits (Will Operate in Any Position but Lumen Maintenance is Best for 40 to 1500 Watts When Burned Vertically Base-Up)***

Watts	Bulb and Other Description	Base	Filament	Rated Average Life (hours)	Maximum Over-All Length in Inches (mm)	Average Light Center Length in Inches (mm)	Approximate Initial Filament Temp. (K)	Max. Bare Bulb Temp. °F (°C)	Base Temp. °F (°C)	Approximate Initial Lumens	Rated Initial Lumens Per Watt‡	Lamp Lumen Depreciation** (percent)
300	PS-35 clear or inside frosted	Mog.	C-9	1000	$9\frac{3}{8}$ (238)	7 (178)	2980	330 (166)	215 (102)	5860	19.6	86
500	PS-35 clear or inside frosted	Mog.	CC-8	1000	$9\frac{3}{8}$ (238)	7 (178)	3050	415 (213)	175 (79)	10600	21.2	89
500	PS-40 clear or inside frosted	Mog.	C-9	1000	$9\frac{3}{4}$ (248)	7 (178)	2945	390 (199)	215 (102)	10140	20.3	—
750	PS-52 clear or inside frosted	Mog.	C-7A	1000	$13\frac{1}{16}$ (332)	$9\frac{1}{2}$ (241)	2990	—	—	15660	20.9	—
750	PS-52 clear or inside frosted	Mog.	CC-8 or 2CC-8	1000	$13\frac{1}{16}$ (332)	$9\frac{1}{2}$ (241)	3090	—	—	17000	22.6	89
1000	PS-52 clear or inside frosted	Mog.	C-7A	1000	$13\frac{1}{16}$ (332)	$9\frac{1}{2}$ (241)	2995	480 (249)	235 (113)	21800	21.8	—
1000	PS-52 clear or inside frosted	Mog.	CC-8 or 2CC-8	1000	$13\frac{1}{16}$ (332)	$9\frac{1}{2}$ (241)	3110	—	—	23600	23.6	89
1500	PS-52 clear or inside frosted	Mog.	C-7A	1000	$13\frac{1}{16}$ (332)	$9\frac{1}{2}$ (241)	3095	510 (265)	265 (129)	34000	22.6	78

* Lamp burning base up in ambient temperature of 77°F.
† At junction of base and bulb.
‡ For 120-volt lamps.
§ Used mainly in Canada.
¶ Lumen and lumen per watt values of white lamps are generally lower than for inside frosted.
** Percent initial light output at 70 percent of rated life.

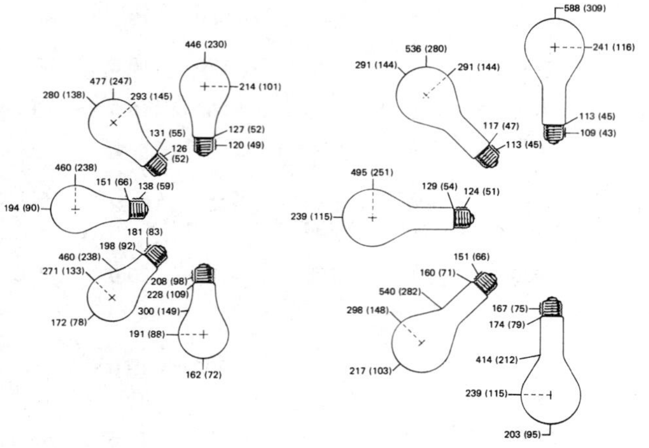

FIG. 2-3X. ***Surface temperatures of lamps in various positions. At left is a 100W, A-19 lamp, and at right a 500W, PS-35 lamp.***

In locations where there are flammable vapors or gases, combustible dusts, or readily ignitable fibers or flyings, etc., lamps in fixtures specially approved for the location must be used.

Electric Discharge (Fluorescent) Lamps

The operating temperature of a fluorescent tube is lower than that of the glass envelope of the incandescent lamp, but high voltage is often used to start the lamp. This requires the use of transformers, reactors, capacitors, and switches; the heat produced by this equipment must be taken into account and the equipment properly safeguarded.

Bulb temperatures on the surface of fluorescent lamps average between 100 and 110°F (38 and 43°C) over most of their length, since this is a requirement for efficient light production. There is a small area of higher bulb temperature directly above the cathode at each end of a fluorescent lamp which ranges from 120 to 250°F (49 to 121°C), depending upon the type involved.

Where fluorescent lamps having an open circuit voltage of more than 300 V are installed in dwelling occupancies, they ideally have no exposed live parts when lamps are being inserted, are in place, or are being removed.

Extreme care is required in mounting fluorescent lamp fixtures containing a ballast on combustible, low-density, cellulose fiberboard. Fixtures containing ballasts should not be mounted in contact with low-density, cellulose fiberboard unless they are specifically listed by a qualified electrical testing laboratory for mounting in that manner. If not specifically listed for this use, they should be spaced not less than $1\frac{1}{2}$ in. (38 mm) from the surface of the combustible material. A principal hazard is ignition of the low-density cellulose fiberboard, which under some conditions can ignite at relatively low temperatures. Integral thermal ballast protection is now provided for fluorescent fixtures installed indoors to protect against ballast overheating as a result of failure of capacitors, lamps, ballast winding shorts, etc.

Electric (High-Intensity) Discharge Lamps

The operating temperature of a high-intensity discharge lamp, such as a mercury vapor lamp, is usually much higher than the operating temperature of either Edison-base incandescent or fluorescent lamps, exceeding 550°F (288°C) in some sizes. Extreme care is therefore necessary where such lamps are encountered to prevent their contacting combustible material. Although such lamps were at one time used primarily for street lighting and other outdoor lighting applications, their higher lighting efficiency and new designs providing good color correction and lower wattages have resulted in increased use indoors. Such lamps usually require ballasts (transformers), sometimes capacitors, and are designed to fit into Edison-base lampholders. There are, however, self-ballasted lamps that can be substituted directly for incandescent lamps. High-intensity discharge lamps should be used only in fixtures listed by a qualified electrical testing laboratory for their use, as indicated on the fixture.

Portable Hand Lamps

Metal-shell, paper-lined lampholders are not designed to be used as portable lamps. A fire hazard may result from a defective or worn cord or from the breaking of a lamp. A personnel hazard may result from personal contact with bare spots on the cord or by contact with a live metal lamp socket. Portable hand lamps ideally have a handle and, where subject to physical damage or where the lamp may come in contact with combustible material, they have a substantial guard.

Portable hand lamps used in hazardous (classified) locations must be suitable for the purpose. (See Figure 2-3Y.) Portables used on grounded surfaces or in damp or wet locations must be grounded unless supplied through an isolating transformer with an ungrounded secondary of not more than 50 V.

Television and Radio Equipment

Outdoor antennas and lead-in conductors must be of corrosion-resistant material and securely supported. (See Figure 2-3Z.) They must not be attached to poles or similar structures carrying electric light or power wires or trolley wires, nor should they cross over or be near electric light or power circuits (to avoid accidental contact). Lead-in conductors also must be kept at least 6 ft (1.8 m) from any conductor forming a part of a lightning rod system. The metal sheath of the coaxial cable used for cable television systems must be grounded in accordance with Article 820 of the *NEC* to avoid electric shock and fire hazards. The sheath must be electrically bonded to the electrical system power ground. Use of a separate ground rod for the cable television ground without such bonding should not be permitted.

Masts and metal structures supporting antennas must be well grounded and each conductor of a lead-in from an outdoor antenna must be protected by an approved antenna discharge unit. Metal masts on buildings are required by NFPA 78 to be bonded to the nearest lightning conductor (where available). This is normally done with standard lightning conductors.

FIG. 2-3Y. A representative portable hand lamp of a type suitable for use in Class I, Group C and D locations in accordance with Article 501 of the NEC. It has an aluminum guard and globe holder. (Source: Stewart R. Browne Mfg. Co., Inc.)

Radio interference eliminators and noise suppressors connected to power supply leads and devices, intended to permit an electric supply circuit to be used in lieu of an antenna, should be listed for the purpose by a qualified electrical testing laboratory.

Operating television sets, even the new solid-state sets, can develop considerable heat, so most cabinets housing such equipment are provided with ventilation openings at the rear and bottom. It is important not to install television receivers so the desired ventilation is cut off or significantly

FIG. 2-3Z. A dangerous arrangement of a lightly supported television antenna in the proximity of power lines.

reduced (e.g., by recessing the set in a wall, bookcase, etc.) unless the receiver is designed for such use.

Washers and Dryers

These devices need a means for disconnecting from all ungrounded conductors of the supply circuit. A separable cord connector or an attachment plug and receptacle may serve as the disconnecting means.

Electric clothes washers and dryers and similar appliances are usually installed within reach of a person who can make contact with a grounded surface or object. Consequently, the exposed, noncurrent-carrying metal parts of these machines are grounded to remove the danger of electric shock.

Accumulations of lint in dryers and in lint traps also present a potential fire hazard if not periodically cleaned.

Smoothing Irons

These appliances intended for use in residences are required by the *NEC* to be equipped with approved means to limit the temperature. Even since the widespread use of automatic irons, some hazard still remains because satisfactory ironing of many fabrics requires a degree of heat sufficient to cause ignition if the iron is left in contact with some combustible materials for a considerable period of time.

Electrically Heated Pads and Bedding

The user must be warned by means of a marking on the appliance and by instructions packed with it against the common possible abuses which would increase the fire or shock hazard.

Because many fabrics readily absorb moisture, pads listed by UL (unless of the waterproof type) are provided with moisture-resistant envelopes. This envelope should be examined frequently for signs of deterioration. Blankets are normally designed so that they may be laundered; some cannot be dry cleaned (as with Stoddard Solvent or perchloroethylene) and are normally labeled "Do Not Dry Clean."

INDUSTRIAL AND COMMERCIAL EQUIPMENT

Furnaces

Industrial furnaces generally employ transformers, which may be either the dry type, askarel insulated type, oil-insulated type, or less flammable fluid type, e.g., dimethyl silicone. Although new transformers are no longer made with askarel (a material containing polychlorinated biphenyl, or PCB), there are many such transformers still in use. The *NEC* requires oil-insulated transformers of a total rating exceeding 75 kVA to be located in a fire-resistive vault.

Oil-filled circuit breakers that control arc furnaces are subjected to unusually severe duty and, unless frequently inspected and properly maintained, may fail with disastrous results. Circuit breakers on circuits operated at more than 600 V and which are used to control oil-filled transformers must be located outside the transformer vaults. Vents on high-voltage circuit breakers must be piped outdoors. Electric arc furnace circuits, due to the nature of the operation, are also subject to high surge voltages which can cause failure of the arc circuit breakers used. In these cases, shunt capacitors are installed in the circuit to prevent these high-voltage surges.

Inductive and dielectric heat-generating equipment employing high-frequency alternating currents is used in many heat-treating processes. To eliminate both the personnel hazards and fire hazards of such equipment, construction and installation should comply with the special requirements of the *NEC*.

Other hazards of electric furnaces are similar to those of furnaces employing other means of heating.

Motors

Ignition of the motor insulation or nearby combustible material may be caused by sparks or arcs when the motor winding short circuits or grounds, or when brushes operate improperly. Bearings may overheat because of improper lubrication, and sometimes excessive bearing wear allows the rotor to rub on the stator. The individual drives of machines of many different types sometimes makes it necessary to install motors in locations and under conditions that are injurious to motor insulation. Dust that can conduct electricity may be deposited on the insulation, or deposits of textile fibers, etc., may prevent the normal dissipation of heat. Motors should be cleaned and lubricated regularly. All motor installations should comply with the requirements of the *NEC*, which includes special rules for motors in hazardous (classified) locations.

Machine Tools

The electrical equipment of a modern machine tool or plastics processing machine may vary from a simple single-motor drill press or extruder to a large complicated multimotor automatic machine involving highly complex control systems and equipment. This latter type is generally custom designed and factory wired. Machine tools incorporate many devices and safeguards to provide safety to life, safety from fire, reduction of machine lost time due to replacement of parts, safety to the machine itself, and safety to the work in process.

NFPA 79, *Electrical Standard for Industrial Machinery*, covers the specific electrical equipment, apparatus, and wiring furnished as a part of an industrial machine, starting at the electrical supply connection, provided that the voltage is 600 V or less. The *NEC* contains requirements for general application, particularly for protection of several motors on one branch circuit.

Electrical equipment is subject to damage by oil, metal chips, coolants, and moving parts. The fixed wiring to the machines specified in the *NEC* generally should be conductors in conduit, tubing, or Type MI cable. Exceptions are connections to continuously moving parts, which must be extra-flexible, multi-conductor cable. For flexible connections where small or infrequent movement is involved, as at motor terminals, flexible metal conduit or liquidtight flexible metal conduit may be used.

Motor Control Center Rooms

Automation in industrial plants has led to the development of what is sometimes called "motor control center rooms." Automation of production machinery has greatly increased the use of motors and their related control circuits. This has resulted in grouping the motor control equipment in relatively large, compartmented, metal enclosures. These are specially designed, factory-built equipment, commonly referred to as "motor control centers." They are usually located in large rooms, and electrical failures or fires in the motor control center have often resulted in the destruction of the equipment in many compartments of the control center due to rapid temperature rise.

A factor in some large losses has been that multiconductor circuits have been installed stacked one above the other in cable trays. Heat from arcing or a fire in the control center could raise the temperature in the control center room to a point where normally slow-burning cables become readily combustible. A fire in such cables can shut down a process or an entire plant for weeks or months. The *NEC* covers the use and construction of cable trays, and should be strictly followed where this type of support is used.

The number of motor control centers in one room should be limited or so arranged that exposure of a large number of circuits or equipment to any one fire is avoided. Motor control center rooms should be of noncombustible construction, with a roof or ceiling not readily weakened by a major electrical disturbance or fire. In addition to normal ventilation, the room should be provided with emergency ventilation for removal of heat and smoke in event of a severe fire.

Suggested fire protection for motor control center rooms may consist of preaction sprinkler systems, fixed water spray protection to cover exposed cables, fire detectors to initiate an alarm at a central point in the event of abnormally high temperatures or smoke conditions, a carbon dioxide or halon flooding system, portable extinguishers for Class C fires located at each entrance to the control room, and small hose connections with suitable hose and adjustable spray nozzles readily available near the control room.

Switchboards

Ideally, switchboards are installed in clean, dry locations. They should be under competent supervision and accessible only to qualified persons. Where it is necessary to install a switchboard in a wet location or outside a building, it must be in a weatherproof enclosure. Ample space must be provided for maintenance operations, as stipulated in the *NEC*.

Insulated conductors grouped within switchboards, as well as the instrument and control wiring, should have a flame-retardant outer covering.

Circuit breakers and switches must have ample ratings for the maximum loads and ample interrupting capacity for the maximum short-circuit currents. Contacts of switches and circuit breakers should be kept in good condition, and the oil in oil circuit breakers renewed periodically and kept at the proper level.

Capacitors

Capacitors may be insulated with a combustible or a nonflammable liquid. Capacitors containing more than 3 gal (11 L) of flammable liquid must be enclosed in vaults or outdoor fenced enclosures. These safeguards prevent persons from coming into accidental contact or bringing conducting materials into accidental contact with exposed energized parts, terminals, or buses associated with them.

Capacitors must have a means of draining the stored charge. If no means were provided for draining off the charge stored in a capacitor after it is disconnected from the line, a severe shock might be received by a person servicing the equipment, or the equipment might be damaged by a short circuit.

Resistors and Reactors

Except when installed in connection with switchboards or control panels whose locations are suitably guarded from physical damage and accidental contact with live parts, resistors should always be completely enclosed in properly ventilated metal boxes. A resistor is always a source of heat, and, when mounted on a combustible wall, a thermal barrier should be required if the space between resistors and reactors and any combustible material is less than 12 in. (305 mm).

Large reactors are commonly connected in series, with the main leads of large generators or the supply conductors from high-capacity network systems assisting in limiting the current delivered on short circuit. Small reactors are used with lightning arresters to offer a high impedance to the passage of a high-frequency lightning discharge and aid in directing the discharge to ground. Another type of reactor, having an iron core and closely resembling a transformer, is used as a remote-control dimmer for stage lighting. Reactors are sources of heat and therefore should be mounted in the same manner as resistors.

Motion Picture Projectors and Studios

Motion picture projectors of the professional type [i.e., employing 35 or 70 mm film having 5.4 perforations per in. (25.4 mm) on each edge] must be located in approved enclosures. Motor-driven projector units consist of a listed projector and lamp with motors designed or guarded to prevent ignition of film by sparks or arcs. All professional projectors should be operated by qualified personnel.

Motor-generator sets, transformers, rectifiers, rheostats, and similar equipment for the supply or control of current to projection or spotlight equipment should, if practical, be located in a separate room. If placed in the projection room, the equipment must be so located or guarded that arcs or sparks cannot come in contact with film. Switches, overcurrent devices, or other equipment not normally required or used for projectors, sound reproduction, flood or other special-effect lamps, or other equipment (except remote-control switches for the auditorium lights, or a switch for the motor operating the curtain and masking of the motion picture screen) must not be installed in projection rooms.

In projection rooms suitable for use with cellulose acetate (safety) film only, a sign reading "SAFETY FILM ONLY PERMITTED IN THIS ROOM" must be posted on the outside of each projection room door and within the projection room itself in a conspicuous location.

Approved projectors of the nonprofessional or miniature type, when employing cellulose acetate (safety) film, may be operated without a projection room.

Special rules are also given in the *NEC* to cover electrical installations in motion picture studios, factories, laboratories, stages, or areas of buildings in which work is done on cellulose nitrate film. Provisions include wiring on stages, sets, dressing rooms, viewing, cutting, and patching tables, and film storage vaults.

Cranes and Hoists

Wiring methods and installation of electrical equipment for cranes and hoists are covered in Article 610 of the *NEC*. Where bare contact conductors are objectionable because of the presence of easily ignitable material, current may be conducted to a crane or hoist via a multiple cable on a cable reel or suitable takeup devices.

Where a crane operates over combustible material, the resistors must either be placed in (1) a well-ventilated cabinet of noncombustible material that will not emit flames or molten metal, or (2) a cage or cab constructed of noncombustible material that encloses the sides of the cage or cab from the floor to a point at least 6 in. (152 mm) above the top of the resistors.

Collectors must be designed to reduce sparking between them and the contact conductors to a minimum. When operated in rooms where easily ignitable fibers or materials producing combustible flyings are handled, manufactured, used, or stored, the installation must comply with the special requirements of Article 503 of the *NEC*.

All exposed metal parts of cranes, monorail hoists, hoists, and accessories (including pendant controls) should be metallically joined together into a continuous electrical conductor so the entire crane or hoist will be grounded.

Elevators, Dumbwaiters, Escalators, and Moving Walks

Installation of electric equipment and wiring for elevators, dumbwaiters, escalators, and moving walks are covered in Article 620 of the *NEC*.

All live parts of electrical apparatus in the hoistways, at landings, in or on cars of elevators and dumbwaiters, or in the wellways or landings of escalators or moving walks must be enclosed to prevent accidental contact. All wiring on panels, in raceways, and in or on cars, including the traveling cables, must have flame-retardant, moisture-resistant insulation, with the exception of conductors to main circuit resistors. These should be flame retardant and suitable for a temperature of not less than 194°F (90°C).

Traveling cables for operating, control, and signal circuits must be suspended at the car and hoistway in a manner that reduces strain on individual copper conductors to a minimum. Supports for the traveling cables must also be arranged to prevent damage to cables coming in contact with the hoistway or equipment. Where necessary, suitable guards can protect the cables.

To reduce the danger of electric shock, the following equipment must be effectively grounded in accordance with the grounding requirements of the *NEC*: (1) metal conduit, Type MC cable, or Type AC cable attached to elevator cars, (2) the frames of all motors, elevator machines, and controllers, (3) the metal enclosures for all electric devices in or on the car or hoistway, and (4) the frames of nonelectric elevators if accessible to persons and if any electric conductors are attached to the car.

Equipment mounted on members of the structural metal frame of a building is considered to be grounded. Metal car frames supported by metal hoisting cables attached to or running over sheaves or drums of elevator machines are deemed to be grounded when the machines are properly grounded.

Heating Cable

UL has listed a number of heating cables for use within buildings. These devices are primarily designed to be used around water pipes to prevent freezing and facilitate the flow of viscous liquids. The cable is secured to the pipe with straps, and the pipe and heating cable are then encased with thermal insulation. Where the pipe passes vertically through flooring or where the pipelines run along the floor level, the installation is best protected by sheet steel not less than No. 10 USS gage with the protection extending at least 4 ft (1.22 m) above the floor.

Some units incorporate a thermostat that automatically turns on the heating cable when the temperature drops below a predetermined value. The pipe heating cables are intended to be connected to a permanent supply wiring system. Unless specifically indicated otherwise by marking on the heating cables or in the installation instructions, the heating cables are intended for use only on metallic pipes. Electrical heating cables for outdoor ice- and snow-melting systems are covered in the *NEC*.

ELECTRICAL EQUIPMENT FOR OUTDOOR USE

Electric equipment that is installed outside of buildings must be weatherproof in design, i.e., constructed so exposure to the weather will not interfere with its successful operation; otherwise it must be enclosed in weatherproof cabinets. These enclosures are designed to prevent moisture or water from entering and accumulating within them. If mounted on a wall or other supporting surface, there should be at least 1/4 in. (6 mm) air space between the box or cabinet and the supporting surface.

Description of Devices

Electric equipment suitable for outdoor use is tested by qualified electrical testing laboratories. The tests encompass: (1) suitability of the materials used and the protective coatings for exposure to sunlight, rain, and snow, (2) effects of heat and cold, and (3) provisions for grounding, etc. The term "raintight," as used in the *NEC*, is applied to equipment that on exposure to a beating rain will not let water enter. The term "weatherproof," as used in the *NEC*, is applied to equipment that on exposure to the weather will still operate successfully.

Rainproof, raintight, or watertight equipment can fulfill the requirements for weatherproof equipment where varying weather conditions other than wetness, e.g., snow, ice, dust, or temperature extremes are not a factor.

Electric Signs and Outline Lighting

Except for portable indoor signs, signs and outline lighting equipment are usually constructed of metal or other noncombustible material. Wood may be used for external decoration only if placed not less than 2 in. (50 mm) from the nearest lampholder or current-carrying part. Enclosures for outside use should be weatherproof. All steel parts of enclosures must be galvanized or otherwise protected from corrosion. Signs, troughs, tube terminal boxes, and other metal frames must be grounded in the manner specified in the *NEC* unless they are insulated from ground and from other conducting surfaces and are inaccessible to unauthorized persons.

Each electric sign (other than the portable type) and each outline lighting installation must be controlled by an external operable switch or circuit breaker (handle on outside of switch enclosure), which will open all ungrounded conductors. The switch or breaker should be within sight of the sign or outline lighting installation unless it is capable of being locked in the open position.

Portable outdoor electric signs must be equipped with a GFCI, suitable for use on portable outdoor signs, in the sign, or in the attachment plug cap on the supply cord.

Electric Fences

Wire fences with electrical connections to produce a shock when animals come in contact with them are widely used on farms. To avoid hazard to persons and to livestock, the current and the time interval during which the current is on and off must be limited to values which will not cause fatalities or injuries to persons or animals, while still causing an unpleasant sensation of shock. Fatalities and fires have resulted from homemade equipment supplied from ordinary lighting circuits. The open circuit voltage need not be limited if the current is properly limited. UL Research Bulletin No. 14 and UL 69-1980, "Standard for Electric Fence Controllers," give detailed information on these installations.

The output characteristics of some controllers are such that combustible material may be readily ignited when a grounded object occupies a position respective to the energized fence to produce an electric arc. To protect against fire from such a cause, users should determine that the controller has been designed and tested with respect to this hazard. Electric fence controllers listed in accordance with the requirements of UL 69 have been so tested.

Marina and Boatyard Wiring

Marina and boatyard wiring presents special outdoor electric equipment wiring problems that are covered in Article 555 of the *NEC*. Metal raceways and metal boxes must not be depended upon for grounding; a continuous insulated copper conductor, not smaller than No. 12 AWG, must be provided for a grounding conductor from outlet boxes and receptacles to the service ground. Wiring over and under navigable water should be subject to approval by the authority having jurisdiction.

LOCATIONS EXPOSED TO MOISTURE AND NONCOMBUSTIBLE DUSTS

Special electric equipment is required for use where moisture and noncombustible dusts may be present. For years, the *NEC* referred to such equipment as "vaportight," but this term was dropped from the *NEC* because of confusion in the field between equipment so designated and "explosionproof" equipment. Many users assumed that "vaportight" equipment was safe to use in atmospheres containing flammable gases or vapors (Class I locations), combustible dusts (Class II locations), or easily ignitable fibers or flyings (Class III locations). To avoid this type of misunderstanding, the term "enclosed and gasketed" was developed by UL for this type of equipment. Some inspection authorities permit enclosed and gasketed lighting fixtures in Class I, Division 2; Class II, Division 2; and in Class III, Divisions 1 and 2 locations when marked to show the operating temperature and maximum wattage of permissible lamps. The *NEC* requires lighting fixtures to be marked for use in wet and damp locations when so used.

COMMUNICATIONS SYSTEMS

Communications systems, including telephone, telegraph, fire and burglar alarms, and watchman and sprinkler supervisory systems, usually operate with low voltages and currents, and if kept free from accidental contacts with higher voltage systems, they present no unusual hazards. There are, however, *NEC* requirements for the wiring of these systems if the wiring is in a duct, plenum, or other space for environmental air, because of the hazard of spreading products of combustion from one location to another. There are also *NEC* requirements for separation from other systems and for prevention of the spread of fire in shafts and where fire walls, etc., are penetrated. If the power supply is from storage batteries of appreciable current rating, e.g., from the lighting system of a building, or from transformers (other than approved signaling transformers), special precautions should be taken with the wiring and equipment. Because of the importance of these systems, they should be properly designed and installed to give reliable service.

Signaling systems and communications systems must be installed in accordance with the requirements of the *NEC* and NFPA Standards 71, 72A, 72B, 72C, 72D, 72E, and 74, which cover the proper electrical wiring and equipment for fire alarm services. (See bibliography for titles.) These standards also cross reference to the *NEC*. NFPA 72H, *Testing Procedures for Local, Auxiliary, Remote Station, and Proprietary Protective Signaling Systems*, is a guide for testing such systems upon installation and during service. Telephone communications circuits may be used for completing the fire-protective circuits between the protected premises and fire alarm headquarters.

EMERGENCY SYSTEMS

Requirements for the installation, operation, and maintenance of emergency system circuits and equipment are given in Article 700 of the *NEC*. The systems are intended to supply light and power when the normal supply fails. They are generally installed in places of assembly where artificial lighting is required, such as auditoriums, theaters, sports arenas, etc., occupied by large numbers of persons. (See Figures 2-3AA and 2-3BB.)

Legally required standby systems installed to serve loads, such as heating and refrigeration systems, communications systems, ventilation and smoke removal systems,

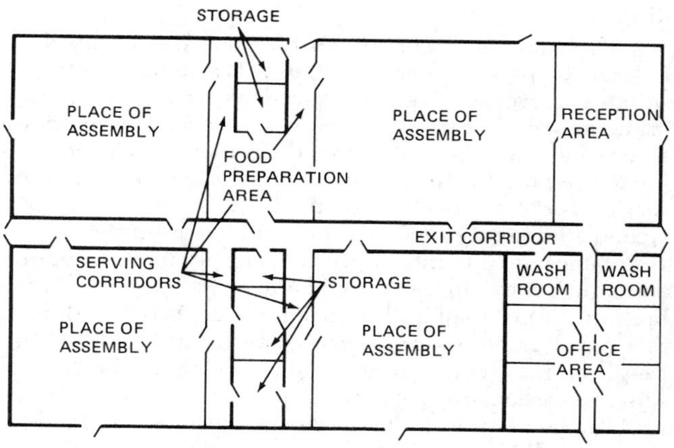

***FIG. 2-3AA.** The heavy lines represent walls required by typical local building codes to be of fire-rated construction. The light lines represent walls not required by typical local building codes to be of fire-rated construction.*

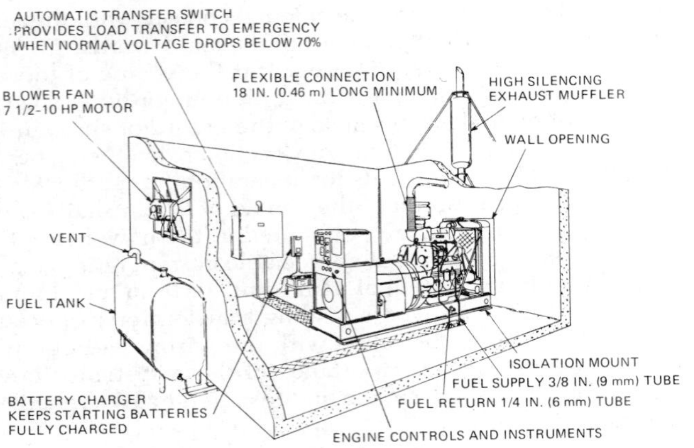

FIG. 2-3BB. Typical installation of a diesel-powered standby generator such as might be used for emergency light and power systems. (Source: P & H Harnischfleger Corp.)

sewerage disposal, lighting systems, and industrial processes, that, when stopped during any interruption of the normal electrical supply, could create hazards or hamper rescue or fire fighting operations are covered in Article 701 of the *NEC*. NFPA 110, *Emergency and Standby Power Systems*, covers the performance requirements for such systems.

NFPA *101*®, *Life Safety Code,*® specifies where emergency lighting is considered essential for life safety. NFPA 99, *Health Care Facilities*, Chapter 8, gives minimum factors governing the design, operation, and maintenance of those portions of health care facility electrical systems where any degree of interruption would jeopardize the effective and safe care of hospitalized patients. The provisions in NFPA 99 do not supercede the recommendations in NFPA 101 or the *NEC*, which both limit the type of alternate source of electrical power allowable for use to ensure electric power continuity in health care facilities. NFPA 99 recognizes the progressively greater dependence being placed upon electrical apparatus for the preservation of life of hospitalized patients, and is a guide in the selection of the electrical services for emergency supply to all lighting and power equipment considered essential, and for their design and maintenance in health care facilities.

The sources of electric current that can be used for emergency lighting equipment are: (1) a storage battery of suitable capacity, (2) a generator driven by some form of prime mover, (3) a second electric service widely separated electrically and physically from the regular service to minimize the possibility of simultaneous interruption of both services, or (4) connections on the line side of the main service, if sufficiently separated from the main service to prevent simultaneous interruption of supply to both regular and emergency circuits through an occurrence within the building or group of buildings served. NFPA 99 stipulates that the alternate source of power for health care facilities be prime mover driven generators or, where the normal source is an on-site generator, an external utility service may be the alternate source. Means must be provided for automatically energizing emergency lights upon failure of the regular lighting system supply. For hospitals, the transition time from the instant of failure of the normal power source to an emergency generator source must not exceed 10 sec.

Audible and visual signal devices are provided, where practical, to (1) warn of derangement of the emergency source, (2) indicate that the battery or generator is carrying load, (3) indicate when a battery charger is functioning properly, and (4) indicate a ground fault on large 480Y/277-V systems.

No appliances or lamps, other than those required for emergency use, are to be supplied by the emergency lighting circuits. A good emergency lighting system is designed so that the failure of any individual lighting element, such as the burning out of a light bulb, cannot leave any space in total darkness.

The emergency lighting circuit wiring is independent of all other wiring and equipment and must not enter the same raceway, cable, box, or cabinet with other wiring except at transfer switches and exit lighting fixtures supplied from both the normal and the emergency sources.

It is good practice to test the complete system upon installation and periodically thereafter to ensure it is maintained in proper operating condition. A written record should be kept of such tests and maintenance.

SPECIAL OCCUPANCY ELECTRICAL PROBLEMS

This section discusses hazardous (classified) locations and other special problems requiring individual attention for which the *NEC* has specific recommendations.

Hazardous (Classified) Locations—General

Electric lights, motors, and instrumentation are necessary or desirable in many hazardous locations because of the presence of flammable liquids, gases, combustible dusts, or readily ignitable fibers or flyings. In these areas, special electrical equipment is necessary for safety. In Article 500 of the *NEC*, hazardous (classified) locations are divided into three classes depending upon the kind of hazardous material involved; each class is further divided into two divisions according to the likelihood of the potential hazard existing. For the purposes of testing for approval and area classification, various air mixtures (not oxygen enriched) have been grouped on the basis of their characteristics. The groups are given in Tables 2-3M through 2-3P [statistics from Section 500-3 of the *NEC* and tables from NFPA 497M, *Classification of Gases, Vapors and Dusts for Electrical Equipment in Hazardous (Classified) Locations* (hereinafter referred to as NFPA 497M)]. For Group A, B, C, and D materials with flash points of 100°F (38°C) and higher, see NFPA 497M. For a more complete table of Group G dusts and information on Group E dusts, see the following and NFPA 497M.

Group G includes combustible dusts having a resistivity of 10^2 Ω-cm or greater. This group includes grain and food dusts, chemical dusts, plastics, and dust. Coal, coke, and carbonaceous dusts are classified in Group F. Group E includes combustible metal dusts regardless of resistivity, and other dusts of similarly hazardous characteristics having a resistivity of less than 10^2 Ω-cm.

Listed equipment is marked to show the class, group, and operating temperature, or temperature range, referenced to a 104°F (40°C) ambient. The temperature range, if provided, is indicated by identification numbers, as shown in Table 2-3Q. The identification numbers are marked on equipment nameplates.

TABLE 2-3M. ***Group Classification and Autoignition Temperature (AIT) of Selected Flammable Gases and Vapors of Liquids having Flash Points below 100°F (37.8°C)***

Material	Group	AIT	
		°F	°C
Acetaldehyde	C*	347	175
Acetone	D*	869	465
Acetonitrile	D	975	524
Acetylene	A*	581	305
Acrolein (inhibited)[a]	B(C)*	455	235
Acrylonitrile	D*	898	481
Allyl alcohol	C*	713	378
Allyl chloride	D	905	485
Ammonia	D*[b]	928	498
n-Amyl acetate	D	680	360
sec-Amyl acetate	D	—	—
Benzene	D*	1040	560
1,3-Butadiene[a]	B(D)*	788	420
Butane	D*	550	288
1-Butanol	D*	650	343
2-Butanol	D*	761	405
n-Butyl acetate	D*	790	421
iso-Butyl acetate	D*	790	421
sec-Butyl acetate	D	—	—
Butylamine	D	594	312
Butylene	D	725	385
Butyl mercaptan	C	—	—
n-Butyraldehyde	C*	425	218
Carbon disulfide[c]	—*	194	90
Carbon monoxide	C*	1128	609
Chlorobenzene	D	1099	593
Chloroprene	D	—	—
Crotonaldehyde	C*	450	232
Cyclohexane	D	473	245
Cyclohexene	D	471	244
Cyclopropane	D*	938	503
1,1-Dichloroethane	D	820	438
1,2-Dichloroethylene	D	860	460
1,3-Dichloropropene	D	—	—
Dicyclopentadiene	C	937	503
Diethyl ether	C*	320	160
Diethylamine	C*	594	312
Di-isobutylene	D*	736	391
Di-isopropylamine	C	600	316
Dimethylamine	C	752	400
1,4-Dioxane	C	356	180
Di-n-propylamine	C	570	299
Epichlorohydrin	C*	772	411
Ethane	D*	882	472
Ethanol	D*	685	363
Ethyl acetate	D*	800	427
Ethyl acrylate (inhibited)	D*	702	372
Ethylamine	D*	725	385
Ethyl benzene	D	810	432
Ethyl chloride	D	966	519
Ethylene	C*	842	450
Ethylenediamine	D*	725	385
Ethylene dichloride	D*	775	413
Ethylenimine	C*	608	320
Ethylene oxide[a]	B(C)*	804	429
Ethyl formate	D	851	455
Ethyl mercaptan	C*	572	300
n-Ethyl morpholine	C	—	—
Formaldehyde (gas)	B	795	429
Gasoline	D*	536–880	280–471
Heptane	D*	399	204
Heptene	D	500	260
Hexane	D*	437	225

TABLE 2-3M. (CONTINUED) ***Group Classification and Autoignition Temperature (AIT) of Selected Flammable Gases and Vapors of Liquids having Flash Points below 100°F (37.8°C)***

Material	Group	AIT	
		°F	°C
2-Hexanone	D	795	424
Hexenes	D	473	245
Hydrogen	B*	752	400
Hydrogen cyanide	C*	1000	538
Hydrogen selenide	C	—	—
Hydrogen sulfide	C*	500	260
Isoamyl acetate	D	680	360
Isoamyl alcohol	D	662	350
Isobutyl acrylate	D	800	427
Isobutyraldehyde	C	385	196
Isoprene	D*	743	395
Isopropyl acetate	D	860	460
Isopropylamine	D	756	402
Isopropyl ether	D*	830	443
Isopropyl glycidyl ether	C	—	—
Liquefied petroleum gas	D	761–842	405–450
Manufactured gas (containing more than 30% H_2 by volume)	B*	—	—
Mesityl oxide	D*	652	344
Methane	D*	999	537
Methanol	D*	725	385
Methyl acetate	D	850	454
Methylacetylene	C*	—	—
Methylacetylene-propadiene (stabilized)	C	—	—
Methyl acrylate	D	875	468
Methylamine	D	806	430
Methylcyclohexane	D	482	250
Methyl ether	C*	662	350
Methyl ethyl Ketone	D*	759	404
Methyl eormal	C*	460	238
Methyl eormate	D	840	449
Methyl isobutyl ketone	D*	840	440
Methyl isocyanate	D	994	534
Methyl mercaptan	C	—	—
Methyl methacrylate	D	792	422
2-Methyl-1-propanol	D*	780	416
2-Methyl-2-propanol	D*	892	478
Monomethyl hydrazine	C	382	194
Naphtha (petroleum)[d]	D*	550	288
Nitroethane	C	778	414
Nitromethane	C	785	418
Nonane	D	401	205
Nonene	D	—	—
Octane	D*	403	206
Octene	D	446	230
Pentane	D*	470	243
1-Pentanol	D*	572	300
2-Pentanone	D	846	452
1-Pentene	D	527	275
Propane	D*	842	450
1-Propanol	D*	775	413
2-Propanol	D*	750	399
Propionaldehyde	C	405	207
n-Propyl acetate	D	842	450
Propylene	D*	851	455
Propylene dichloride	D	1035	557
Propylene oxide[a]	B(C)*	840	449
n-Propyl ether	C*	419	215
Propyl nitrate	B*	347	175
Pyridine	D*	900	482
Styrene	D*	914	490
Tetrahydrofuran	C*	610	321

TABLE 2-3M. (CONTINUED) ***Group Classification and Autoignition Temperature (AIT) of Selected Flammable Gases and Vapors of Liquids having Flash Points below 100°F (37.8°C)***

Material	Group	AIT °F	AIT °C
Toluene	D*	896	480
Triethylamine	C*	—	—
Tripropylamine	D	—	—
Turpentine	D	488	253
Unsymmetrical dimethyl hydrazine (UDMH)	C*	480	249
Valeraldehyde	C	432	222
Vinyl acetate	D*	756	402
Vinyl chloride	D*	882	472
Vinylidene chloride	D	1058	570
Xylenes	D*	867–984	464–529

* Material has been classified by test.

[a] If equipment is isolated by sealing all conduit 1/2in. or larger, in accordance with Section 501-5(a) of the *NEC*, equipment for the group classification shown in parentheses is permitted.

[b] For classification of areas involving Ammonia, see "Safety Code for Mechanical Refrigeration," ANSI/ASHRAE 15, and "Safety Requirements for the Storage and Handling of Anhydrous Ammonia," ANSI/CGA G2.1.

[c] Certain chemicals may have characteristics that require safeguards beyond those required for any of the above groups. Carbon disulfide is one of these chemicals because of its low autoignition temperature and the small joint clearance to arrest its flame propagation.

[d] Petroleum naphtha is a saturated hydrocarbon mixture whose boiling range is 68 to 274°F (20° to 135°C). It is also known as benzine, ligroin, petroleum ether, and naphtha.

Sources: NFPA 497M, *Classification of Gases, Vapors, and Dusts for Electrical Equipment in Hazardous (Classified) Locations*, Autoignition temperatures listed above are the lowest value for each material as listed in NFPA 325M, *Fire Hazard Properties of Flammable Liquids, Gases, and Volatile Solids*, or as reported in an article by Hilado, C. J. and Clark, S. W., in *Chemical Engineering*, Sept. 4, 1972.

Since there is no consistent relationship among explosion properties, explosion pressure, maximum experimental safe gap, minimum ignition energy, and ignition temperature, testing requirements for groups and classes are independent of each other.

The operating temperature markings specified in Table 2-3Q are not to exceed the ignition temperature of the specific gas or vapor to be encountered.

For information regarding ignition temperatures of gases and vapors, see Table 2-3M, NFPA 497M, and NFPA 325M, *Fire Hazard Properties of Flammable Liquids, Gases, and Volatile Solids*.

Complete definitions of the several classes and divisions of hazardous (classified) locations and the methods of wiring and types of electrical equipment to be used in each are covered in detail in the *NEC*. Rules applying specifically to commercial garages, aircraft hangars, gasoline dispensing facilities and service stations, bulk storage plants, finishing processes, and areas in health care facilities containing flammable anesthetics are also covered in the *NEC*.

Class I, Division 1: Locations in which: (1) ignitable concentrations of flammable gases or vapors can exist under normal operating conditions, or (2) ignitable concentrations of such gases or vapors may exist frequently because of repair or maintenance operations or leakage, or (3) breakdown or faulty operation of equipment or processes might release ignitable concentrations of gases or vapors, and might also cause simultaneous electrical equipment failure. Motors and other rotating electrical machinery, lighting fixtures, most switches, circuit breakers, and similar electrical equipment in these locations must be of the explosionproof type or purged type approved for Class I locations of the proper group. (See NFPA 496, *Purged and Pressurized Enclosures for Electrical Equipment*.) (See Figures 2-3CC, 2-3DD, and 2-3EE.) Approved intrinsically safe equipment and circuits may also be used. These are usually limited to low-energy control, signal, and instrumentation systems.

TABLE 2-3N. ***Selected Nonconductive Dusts Classified as Group G—Ignition Sensitivity Equal to or Greater than 0.2; Explosion Severity Equal to or Greater than 0.5***

Material	Minimum Cloud or Layer Ignition Temp.[a] °F		Minimum Cloud or Layer Ignition Temp.[a] °C
AGRICULTURAL DUSTS			
Alfalfa meal	392		200
Cellulose	500		260
Cinnamon	446		230
Cocoa, natural, 19% fat	464		240
Corn	482		250
Corncob Grit	464		240
Corn dextrine	698		370
Cornstarch, commercial	626		330
Cork	410		210
Cottonseed meal	392		200
Garlic, dehydrated	680	NL	360
Malt barley	482		250
Milk, skimmed	392		200
Potato starch, dextrinated	824	NL	440
Rice	428		220
Rice bran	914	NL	490
Rice hull	428		220
Safflower meal	410		210
Soy flour	374		190
Soy protein	500		260
Sucrose	662	CI	350
Sugar, powdered	698	CI	370
Wheat 428			220
Wheat flour	680		360
Wheat starch	716	NL	380
Wheat straw	428		220
Woodbark, ground	482		250
Wood flour	500		260
Yeast, torula	500		260
CHEMICALS			
Acetoacetanilide	824	M	440
Adipic acid	1022	M	550
Anthranilic acid	1076	M	580
Azelaic acid	1130	M	610
2,2-Azo-bis-butyronitrile	662		350
Benzoic acid	824		440
Benzotriazole	824	M	440
Bisphenol-A	1058	M	570
Chloroacetoacetanilide	1184	M	640
Diallyl Phthalate	896	M	480
Dihydroacetic acid	806	NL	430
Dimethyl isophthalate	1076	M	580
Dimethyl terephthalate	1058	M	570
3,5-Dinitrobenzoic acid	860	NL	460
Diphenyl	1166	M	630
Ethyl Hydroxyethyl cellulose	734	NL	390
Fumaric acid	968	M	520
Hexamethylene tetramine	770	S	410
Hydroxyethyl cellulose	770	NL	410
Isotoic anhydride	1292	NL	700
Paraphenylene diamine	1148	M	620
Paratertiary butyl benzoic acid	1040	M	560
Pentaerythritol	752	M	400

TABLE 2-3N. (CONTINUED) ***Selected Nonconductive Dusts Classified as Group G—Ignition Sensitivity Equal to or Greater than 0.2; Explosion Severity Equal to or Greater than 0.5***

Material	Minimum Cloud or Layer Ignition Temp.[a] °F		°C
Phthalic anhydride	1202	M	650
Salicylanilide	1130	M	610
Sorbic acid	860		460
Stearic acid, aluminum salt	572		300
Stearic acid, zinc salt	950	M	510
Sulfur	428		220
Terephthalic acid	1256	NL	680
DRUGS			
Aspirin	1220	M	660
Gulasonic acid, diacetone	788	NL	420
Mannitol	860	M	460
l-Sorbose	698	M	370
Vitamin B1, mononitrate	680	NL	360
Vitamin C (ascorbic acid)	536		280
DYES, PIGMENTS, INTERMEDIATES			
Green base harmon dye	347		175
Red dye intermediate	347		175
Violet 200 dye	347		175
PESTICIDES			
Crag No. 974	590	CI	310
Dieldrin (20%)	1022	NL	550
Dithane	356		180
Ferban	302		150
Manganese vancide	248		120
Sevin	284		140
THERMOPLASTIC RESINS AND MOLDING COMPOUNDS			
Acetal resins			
Acetal, linear (polyformaldehyde)	824	NL	440
Acrylic resins			
Acrylamide polymer	464		240
Acrylonitrile polymer	860		460
Acrylonitrile-vinyl chloride-vinylidene chloride copolymer (70-20-10)	410		210
Methyl methacrylate polymer	824	NL	440
Methyl methacrylate-ethyl acrylate copolymer	896	NL	480
Methyl methacrylate-ethyl acrylate-styrene copolymer	824	NL	440
Methyl methacrylate-styrene-butadiene- acrylonitrile copolymer	896	NL	480
Methacrylic acid polymer	554		290
Cellulosic resins			
Cellulose acetate	644		340
Cellulose triacetate	806	NL	430
Cellulose acetate butyrate	698	NL	370
Nylon (polyamide) resins			
Nylon polymer (polyhexa-methylene adipamide)	806		430
Polycarbonate resins			
Polycarbonate	1310	NL	710
Polyethylene resins			
Polyethylene, high-pressure process	716		380
Polyethylene, low-pressure process	788	NL	420
Polyethylene wax	752	NL	400
Polymethylene resins			
Carboxypolymethylene	968	NL	520

TABLE 2-3N. (CONTINUED) ***Selected Nonconductive Dusts Classified as Group G—Ignition Sensitivity Equal to or Greater than 0.2; Explosion Severity Equal to or Greater than 0.5***

Material	Minimum Cloud or Layer Ignition Temp.[a] °F		°C
Polypropylene resins			
Polypropylene (no antioxidant)	788	NL	420
Rayon resins			
Rayon (viscose) flock	482		250
Styrene resins			
Polystyrene molding cmpd.	1040	NL	560
Polystyrene latex	932		500
Styrene-acrylonitrile (70-30)	932	NL	500
Styrene-butadiene latex (>75% styrene; alum coagulated)	824	NL	440
Vinyl resins			
Polyvinyl acetate	1022	NL	550
Polyvinyl acetate/alcohol	824		440
Vinyl chloride-acrylonitrile copolymer	878		470
Vinyl toluene-acrylonitrile butadiene copolymer	936	NL	530
THERMOSETTING RESINS AND MOLDING COMPOUNDS			
Allyl resins			
Allyl alcohol derivative (CR-39)	932	NL	500
Amino resins			
Urea formaldehyde molding compound	860	NL	460
Urea formaldehyde-phenol formaldehyde Molding compound (wood flour filler)	464		240
Epoxy resins			
Epoxy	1004	NL	540
Epoxy-bisphenol A	950	NL	510
Phenolic resins			
Phenol formaldehyde	1076	NL	580
Phenol formaldehyde molding cmpd. (wood flour filler)	932	NL	500
Polyester resins			
Polyethylene terephthalate	932	NL	500
Styrene modified polyester-glass fiber mixture	680		360
Polyurethane resins			
Polyurethane foam, no fire retardant	824		440
SPECIAL RESINS AND MOLDING COMPOUNDS			
Ethylene oxide polymer	662	NL	350
Ethylene-maleic anhydride copolymer	1004	NL	540
Petroleum resin (blown asphalt)	932		500
Rubber, crude, hard	662	NL	350
Rubber, synthetic, hard (33% S)	608	NL	320

[a] Normally, the minimum ignition temperature of a layer of a specific dust is lower than the minimum ignition temperature of a cloud of that dust. Since this is not universally true, the lower of the two minimum ignition temperatures is listed. If no symbol appears between the two temperature columns, then the layer ignition temperature is shown. "CI|| means the cloud ignition temperature is shown. "NL|| means that no layer ignition temperature is available and the cloud ignition temperature is shown. "M|| signifies that the dust layer melts before it ignites; the cloud ignition temperature is shown. "S|| signifies that the dust layer sublimes before it ignites; the cloud ignition temperature is shown.

TABLE 2-3O ***Selected Carbonaceous Dusts Classified as Group E - Ignition Sensitivity Equal to or Greater than 0.2; Explosion Severity Equal to or Greater than 0.5***

Material[b]	°F	Minimum Cloud or Layer Ignition Temp.[a]	°C
Aluminum, atomized collector fines	1022	CI	550
Aluminum, A422 flake	608		320
Aluminum - cobalt alloy (60-40)	1058		570
Aluminum - copper alloy (50-50)	1526		830
Aluminum - lithium alloy (15% Li)	752		400
Aluminum - magnesium alloy (downmetal)	806	CI	430
Aluminum - nickel alloy (58-42)	1004		540
Aluminum - silicon alloy (12% Si)	1238	NL	670
Boron, commercial-amorphous (85% B)	752		400
Calcium silicide	1004		540
Chromium, (975) electrolytic, milled	752		400
Ferromanganese, medium carbon	554		290
Ferrisilicon (885, 9% Fe)	1472		800
Ferrotitanium (19% Ti, 74.1% Fe, 0.06% C)	698	CI	370
Iron 98% H_2 reduced	554		290
Iron 99% carbonyl	590		310
Magnesium, Grade B, milled	806		430
Manganese	464		240
Tantalum	572		300
Thorium, 1.2% O_2	518	CI	270
Tin, 96%, atomized (2% Pb)	806		430
Titanium, 99%	626	CI	330
Titanium hydride (95% Ti, 3.8% H_2	896	CI	480
Vanadium, 86.4%	914		490
Zirconium hydride (93.6% Zr, 2.1% H_2)	518		270

[a] Normally, the minimum ignition temperature of a layer of a specific dust is lower than the minimum ignition temperature of a cloud of that dust. Since this is not universally true, the lower of the two minimum ignition temperatures is listed. If no symbol appears between the two temperature columns, then the layer ignition temperature is shown. "CI" means the cloud ignition temperature is shown. "NL" means that no layer ignition temperature is available and the cloud ignition temperature is shown.

[b] Certain metal dusts may have characteristics that require safeguards beyond those required for atmospheres containing the dusts of aluminum, magnesium, and their commercial alloys. For example, zirconium, thorium, and uranium dusts have extremely low ignition temperatures (as low as 20°C) and minimum ignition energies lower than any material classified in any of the Class I or Class II groups.

Source: NFPA 497M, *Classification of Gases, Vapors, and Dusts for Electrical Equipment in Hazardous (Classified) Locations.*

Class I, Division 2: Locations: (1) in which volatile flammable liquids or flammable gases are handled, processed, or used, but in which the liquids, vapors, or gases will normally be confined within closed containers or closed systems from which they can escape only in case of accidental rupture or breakdown of such containers or systems, or in case of abnormal operation of equipment, or (2) in which

TABLE 2-3P ***Selected Carbonaceous Dusts Classified as Group F - Ignition Sensitivity Equal to or Greater than 0.2; Explosion Severity Equal to or Greater than 0.5***

Material	°F	Minimum Cloud or Layer Ignition Temp.[a]	°C
Asphalt, (blown petroleum resin)	950	CI	510
Charcoal	356		180
Coal, Kentucky bituminous	356		180
Coal, Pittsburgh experimental	338		170
Coal, Wyoming	—		—
Gilsonite	932		500
Lignite, California	356		180
Pitch, coal tar	1310	NL	710
Pitch, petroleum	1166	NL	630
Shale, oil	—		—

[a]Normally, the minimum ignition temperature of a layer of a specific dust is lower than the minimum ignition temperature of a cloud of that dust. Since this is not universally true, the lower of the two minimum ignition temperatures is listed. If no symbol appears between the two temperature columns, then the layer ignition temperature is shown. "CI" means the cloud ignition temperature is shown. "NL" means that no layer ignition temperature is available and the cloud ignition temperature is shown.

Source: NFPA 497M, *Classification of Gases, Vapors, and Dusts for Electrical Equipment in Hazardous (Classified) Locations.*

ignitable concentrations of gases or vapors are normally prevented by positive mechanical ventilation, and which might become hazardous through failure or abnormal operation of the ventilating equipment, or (3) that are adjacent to Class I, Division 1 locations, and to which ignitable concentrations of gases or vapors might occasionally be communicated unless such communication is prevented by adequate, positive pressure ventilation from a clean air source, and effective safeguards against ventilation failure are provided. In general, ordinary types of motors that do not have brushes, switching mechanisms, etc., may be installed in these locations, but motors that do have sliding contacts, switches, etc., must have the switches in explosionproof or other type enclosure approved for Class

TABLE 2-3Q ***Temperature Identification Numbers***

Maximum Temperature °F	Maximum Temperature °C	Identification Number
842	450	T1
572	300	T2
536	280	T2A
500	260	T2B
446	230	T2C
419	215	T2D
392	200	T3
356	180	T3A
329	165	T3B
320	160	T3C
275	135	T4
248	120	T4A
212	100	T5
185	85	T6

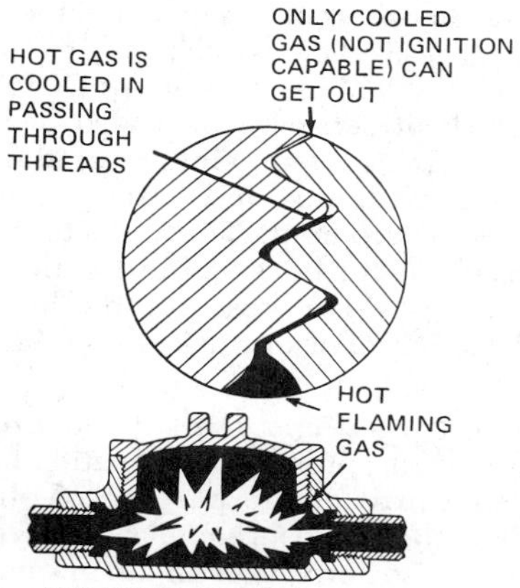

FIG. 2-3CC. Explanation of the principle of "explosionproof" equipment, indicating containment of hot gases within the enclosure. (Source: Crouse-Hinds Company)

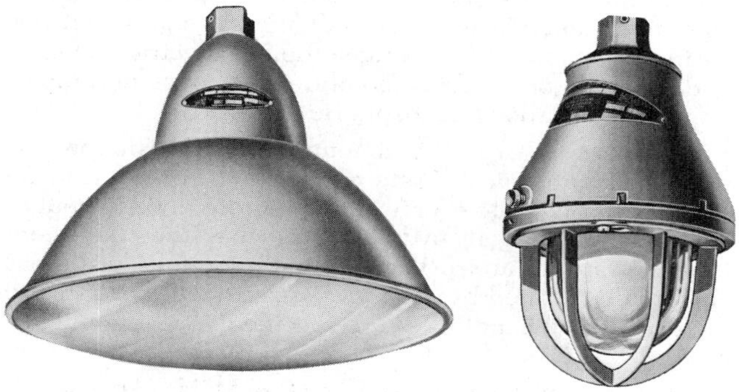

FIG. 2-3DD. Representative lighting fixtures for use in various hazardous locations. (Left) A lighting fixture for use in Class I hazardous locations (60-300 W). (Right) A dust-ignitionproof light fixture for use in Class II hazardous locations. (Source: Crouse-Hinds Company)

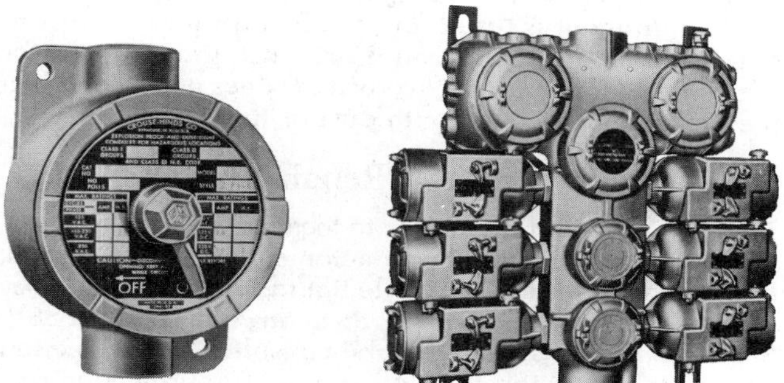

FIG. 2-3EE. Representative switching and panelboard equipment for use in various hazardous locations. (Left) An example of a panelboard for use in Class I hazardous locations. (Right) Tumbler switch for use in Class I and Class II hazardous locations. (Source: Crouse-Hinds Company)

I, Division 2 locations. Lamps that operate at temperatures above the ignition temperature of the gas or vapor involved must have approved explosionproof or purged enclosures. Units located where falling sparks or hot metal from broken lamps might ignite localized concentrations of flammable gases below the Division 2 location must also have suitable enclosures. Switches, circuit breakers, controllers, and other devices that create arcs or sparks and that are intended to interrupt ignition-capable energy in normal operation must either be explosionproof, have their contacts in hermetically sealed chambers, or have contacts immersed in oil. Enclosures for electrical equipment that does not interrupt ignition-capable energy or otherwise represent an ignition source under normal conditions may be of the general-purpose type. Portable lamps must be of the type satisfactory for use in a Class I, Division 1 location.

Class II, Division 1: Locations: (1) in which combustible dust is in the air under normal operating conditions in sufficient quantities to produce explosive or ignitable mixtures, or (2) where mechanical failure or abnormal operation of machinery or equipment might cause such explosive or ignitable mixtures to be produced, and might also provide a source of ignition through simultaneous failure of electric equipment, operation of protective devices, or from other causes, or (3) in which combustible dusts of an electrically conductive nature may be present in hazardous quantities. Motors must be of an enclosed type approved as dust-ignitionproof for the proper Class II locations. Lighting fixtures, switches, circuit breakers, controllers, and fuses that are intended to interrupt current in normal operation must be provided with dust-ignitionproof enclosures approved for the proper Class II locations. Maximum surface temperatures on equipment in Class II locations under actual operating conditions must not exceed the ignition temperature of the dust. See Tables 2-3N and 2-3P for information regarding ignition temperatures of dusts. For additional information, see NFPA 497M.

Class II, Division 2: Locations: (1) in which combustible dust is not normally in the air in quantities sufficient to produce explosive or ignitable mixtures, and (2) where dust accumulations are normally insufficient to interfere with normal operation of electrical equipment or other apparatus, but combustible dust may be in suspension in the air as a result of infrequent malfunctioning of handling or processing equipment, or (3) where combustible dust accumulations on, in, or near the electrical equipment may be sufficient to interfere with the safe dissipation of heat from the electrical equipment or may be ignitable by abnormal operation or failure of electrical equipment. In general, totally enclosed motors are suitable. Under certain conditions, standard, open-type motors without sliding contacts, switches, etc., may be used in many of these locations. Fixed lamps and lampholders must have enclosures designed to minimize the deposit of dust and prevent the escape of sparks, burning material, or hot metal. Switches, circuit breakers, controllers, and fuses should be provided with dust-tight enclosures. Division 1 temperature limits also apply to Division 2 locations.

Class III, Division 1: Locations in which easily ignitable fibers or materials producing combustible flyings are handled, manufactured, or used. In general, motors in these locations must be of the enclosed type except that, where only moderate accumulations of lint are present and cleaning and maintenance are satisfactory, self-cleaning, squirrel-cage, textile motors or standard, open-type motors without sliding contacts, switches, etc., may be installed. Lamps and lampholders, switches, circuit breakers, controllers, and fuses must be dust-tight. Maximum surface temperatures under actual operating conditions must not exceed 329°F (165°C) for equipment that is not subject to overloading and 248°F (120°C) for equipment such as motors, power transformers, etc., which may be overloaded.

Class III, Division 2: Locations in which easily ignitable fibers are stored or handled (except in manufacture). Motors must be of the enclosed type. Lamps, lampholders, switches, circuit breakers, controllers, and fuses must have enclosures similar to those specified for Class III, Division 1 locations. Division 1 temperature limits apply to Division 2 locations.

Equipment for Use in Hazardous Locations

Equipment for use in Class I, Division 1 hazardous (classified) locations as defined in the *NEC* is sometimes referred to as "explosionproof" equipment. The two basic design criteria for explosionproof apparatus for Class I locations are: (1) that it withstand internal explosions of flammable gas or vapor-air mixtures and (2) that it prevent propagation of the internal explosion to the surrounding flammable atmosphere. In other words, it is recognized that surrounding flammable gas or vapor-air mixtures will enter the enclosure of this equipment and the possibility exists of their ignition within the enclosure. To prevent the propagation of flame to the outside surrounding atmosphere, which may likewise contain flammable vapor-air mixtures, the enclosures of this equipment must: (1) arrest flame at joints or other openings to the outside, (2) be of sufficient strength to resist (without rupture or serious distortion) the internal pressure, and (3) ensure that the external surface temperature of the enclosure is not high enough to ignite the surrounding gas or vapor. The various gas or vapor-air mixtures vary considerably with respect to: (1) the propagation of flames through joints of such assemblies, (2) the pressure developed within the enclosure following ignition, and (3) the ignition temperature of the gas or vapor-air mixture. Thus, equipment should be tested and listed for use, and the various groups listed in Table 2-3M should be addressed, as necessary.

Equipment for use in Class I hazardous (classified) locations must also be designed to operate under full load and, in the case of equipment such as motors likely to be overloaded, must operate under overload conditions without developing surface temperatures above the ignition temperature of the flammable gas or vapor with which it is intended to be used.

As an alternative to "explosionproof" motors and generator equipment approved for use in Class I locations, it is permissible to use either of the following two designs:

1. Totally enclosed equipment supplied with positive pressure ventilation from a source of clean air with discharge to a safe area. Controls are arranged to prevent energizing the machine until ventilation has been established and the enclosure purged with at least ten volumes of air, and to automatically de-energize the equipment when the air supply fails.
2. Totally enclosed inert gas-filled equipment supplied with a suitably reliable source of inert gas for pressurizing the enclosure. Devices are provided to ensure a positive pressure in the enclosure as well as to automatically de-energize the equipment when the gas supply fails.

When either of these two designs is used, no external surface of the motors, generators, or other rotating electrical machinery can have an operating temperature (in degrees Celsius) in excess of 80 percent of the ignition temperature (in degrees Celsius) of the gas or vapor involved, as determined by ASTM test procedure D2155-69. Appropriate devices (heat sensors) must also be provided to detect any increase in temperature of the equipment beyond its design limits and then to automatically de-energize the equipment. The detectors and control equipment used are to be suitable for the atmosphere involved without positive pressure; in other words, they must be explosionproof or intrinsically safe if the location is Class I, Division 1.

NFPA 496, *Purged and Pressurized Enclosures for Electrical Equipment*, provides information for the design of purged enclosures for the purpose of eliminating or reducing within the enclosure a Class I hazardous (classified) location (gases or vapors in air in quantities sufficient to produce explosive or ignitable mixtures). Protective measures include supplying an enclosure with clean air or an inert gas at sufficient flow and positive pressure to achieve and maintain an acceptable safe level of the atmosphere.

Another alternative is the use of "intrinsically safe" equipment and wiring which is defined as equipment and wiring incapable of releasing sufficient electrical energy under normal or abnormal conditions to cause ignition of a specific hazardous atmospheric mixture.

In many cases, the amount of "explosionproof," purged, or intrinsically safe equipment required can be reduced through the exercise of ingenuity in the layout of electrical installations by locating much of the equipment in nonhazardous areas. The extent of the hazardous areas is normally defined by the codes and standards relating to the storage and handling of the specific flammable liquids, gases, or solids.

Equipment for use in Class II and Class III hazardous (classified) locations presents a somewhat different problem because the equipment is designed to be dust-ignitionproof for Class II, Division 1 and for some Class II, Division 2 locations, and to be dust-tight or totally enclosed with telescoping covers for some Class II, Division 2 locations and for Class III locations. It is thus not intended to resist internal explosions of dust-air mixtures. Such equipment is tested in specific dust-air mixtures to determine that the enclosures are dust-ignitionproof for Class II locations and that overheating does not occur when the device is blanketed with dust or lint and flyings.

Garages, Commercial (Repair and Storage)

The *NEC* requirements apply to locations used for the servicing and repair of passenger automobiles, buses, tractors, trucks, etc., in which flammable liquids or flammable gases are used. NFPA 88A, *Parking Structures*, and NFPA 88B, *Repair Garages*, should also be consulted in connection with further classifications of, and the fire protection recommendations applying to, garages. The specific hazardous (classified) areas in these garages are defined in the *NEC*.

Aircraft Hangars

Where aircraft containing gasoline, jet fuels, or other flammable liquids are stored or serviced, the specific (classified) hazardous areas are as defined in the *NEC*. Reference should also be made to NFPA 409, *Aircraft Hangars*, for guidance on the construction and protection of these structures.

Service Stations

This occupancy group includes locations where gasoline or other volatile flammable liquids or liquefied petroleum gases are transferred to the fuel tanks or auxiliary fuel tanks of self-propelled vehicles. Reference should be made to NFPA 30, *Flammable and Combustible Liquids Code*, and NFPA 30A, *Automotive and Marine Service Station Code*, as well as the *NEC* for information on the hazardous (classified) areas and other guidance on firesafety in service stations.

Bulk Storage Plants (Flammable Liquid)

Where gasoline or other volatile flammable liquids are stored in tanks having an aggregate capacity of one carload or more and from which such products are distributed, the hazardous (classified) areas are defined in NFPA 30, *Flammable and Combustible Liquids Code*, and the *NEC*. NFPA 30 also contains many requirements for the safe construction and utilization of bulk storage plants.

Paint Spray Booths and Areas

The *NEC* hazardous (classified) locations requirements apply to areas where paints, lacquers, or other flammable finishes are regularly or frequently applied by spraying or dipping, or by other means and where volatile flammable solvents or thinners are used, or where readily ignitable deposits or residues from such paints, lacquers, or finishes may occur. Further information regarding safeguards for finishing processes are contained in NFPA 33, *Spray Application Using Flammable and Combustible Materials*, and NFPA 34, *Dipping and Coating Processes Using Flammable or Combustible Liquids*. Hazardous (classified) areas with respect to flammable vapors are defined in the *NEC*.

Chemical Plants

In chemical plants where flammable liquids or gases are processed or handled, NFPA 497A, *Classification of Class I Hazardous Locations for Electrical Installations in Chemical Plants*, provides information on the extent of the hazardous (classified) location.

Flammable Anesthetics

Special rules apply in hospital operating rooms and other locations where flammable anesthetics are or may be administered to patients. The *NEC* defines the anesthetizing (hazardous) area as any area in which any flammable inhalation agent will be administered. The areas include operating rooms, delivery rooms, emergency rooms, and anesthetizing rooms, and other areas when used for induction of anesthesia with flammable anesthetizing agents. In a flammable anesthetizing location the entire area is considered to be a Class I, Division 1 location extending upward to a level 5 ft (1.5 m) above the floor. For further information on the subject of flammable anesthetics, reference should be made to Chapter 3 of NFPA 99.

Places of Assembly, Theaters, and Similar Locations

In places of assembly, theaters, and similar locations where numbers of people congregate, it is important that the electrical equipment be properly designed and installed. The general rules of the *NEC* as well as its special requirements for these occupancies should be followed in installing the equipment. NFPA *101, Life Safety Code*, should be consulted for further information on use of emergency lighting.

BIBLIOGRAPHY

NFPA Codes, Standards, and Recommended Practices

Reference to the following NFPA codes, standards, and recommended practices will provide further information on the safeguards for electrical systems and appliances discussed in this chapter. (See the latest *NFPA Catalog* for availability of current editions of the following documents.)

NFPA 12, *Carbon Dioxide Extinguishing Systems*.

NFPA 30, *Flammable and Combustible Liquids Code*.

NFPA 30A, *Automotive and Marine Service Station Code*.

NFPA 33, *Spray Application Using Flammable and Combustible Materials*.

NFPA 34, *Dipping and Coating Processes Using Flammable or Combustible Liquids*.

NFPA 70, *National Electrical Code®*.

NFPA 70B, *Electrical Equipment Maintenance*.

NFPA 70E, *Electrical Safety Requirements for Employee Workplaces*.

NFPA 71, *Installation, Maintenance, and Use of Signaling Systems for Central Station Service*.

NFPA 72D, *Installation, Maintenance, and Use of Proprietary Protective Signaling Systems*.

NFPA 72E, *Automatic Fire Detectors*.

NFPA 72H, *Testing Procedures for Local, Auxiliary, Remote Station, and Proprietary Protective Signaling Systems*.

NFPA 74, *Household Fire Warning Equipment*.

NFPA 75, *Protection of Electronic Computer/Data Processing Equipment*.

NFPA 77, *Static Electricity*.

NFPA 78, *Lightning Protection Code*.

NFPA 79, *Electrical Standard for Industrial Machinery*.

NFPA 88A, *Parking Structures*.

NFPA 88B, *Repair Garages*.

NFPA 90B, *Installation of Warm Air Heating and Air Conditioning Systems*.

NFPA 99, *Health Care Facilities*.

NFPA *101®, Life Safety Code®*.

NFPA 110, *Emergency and Standby Power Systems*.

NFPA 325M, *Fire Hazard Properties of Flammable Liquids, Gases, and Volatile Solids*.

NFPA 409, *Aircraft Hangars*.

NFPA 496, *Purged and Pressurized Enclosures for Electrical Equipment*.

NFPA 497A, *Classification of Class I Hazardous Locations for Electrical Installations in Chemical Plants*.

NFPA 497M, *Classification of Gases, Vapors and Dusts for Electrical Equipment in Hazardous (Classified) Locations*.

NFPA 501A, *Manufactured Home Installations*.

NFPA 501C, *Recreational Vehicles*.

NFPA 501D, *Recreational Vehicle Parks and Campgrounds*.

NFPA 513, *Motor Freight Terminals*.

Additional Reading

Alvares, N. J., *et al.*, "Thermal Degradation of Cable and Wire Insulations," in ASTM, "Behavior of Polymeric Materials in Fire," *ASTM STP 816*, (E. L. Schaffer, ed.), American Society for Testing and Materials, Philadelphia, PA, 1982.

An Illustrated Guide to Electrical Safety, U.S. Department of Commerce, Occupational, Safety and Health Administration, Washington, DC, 1983.

Beland, B., "Electricity as a Cause of Fires," *SFPE TR 84-5*, Society of Fire Protection Engineers, Boston, MA, 1984

Bernstein, T., "Investigation of Alleged Appliance Electrocutions and Fires Caused by Internally Generated Voltages," *IEEE Transactions on Industry Applications*, Vol. 25, No. 4 (Jul.-Aug. 1989), pp. 664-668.

Braun, E., Shields, J. R., and Harris R. H., "Flammabilty Characteristics of Electrical Cables Using the Cone Calorimeter," *NISTIR 88-4003*, Jan. 1989, Center for Fire Research, Gaithersburg, MD.

Crouse-Hinds ECM Code Digest 1984, Crouse-Hinds Electrical Construction Materials, Division of Cooper Industries, 1984.

Earley, M. W., Murray, R. H. and Caloggero J. M. eds., *National Electrical Code Handbook*, 5th ed., National Fire Protection Association, Quincy, MA, 1990.

Electrical Appliance and Utilization Equipment Directory, Underwriters Laboratories Incorporated, Northbrook, IL.

Electrical Construction on Materials Directory, Underwriters Laboratories Incorporated, Northbrook, IL.

Electrical Inspection Illustrated, 2nd ed, National Safety Council, Chicago, IL, 1984.

"Electricity in Emergencies," *Industrial Fire World*, Vol. 2, No. 4 (Aug. 1987), pp. 24-27.

Freund, A., "Fire-Testing Cast-Coil Transformers," EC&M, NY, 1986.

Gibbons, J. A. M. and Stevens, G. C. "Limiting the Corrosion Hazard from Electrical Cables Involved in Fires," *Fire Safety Journal*, Vol. 15, No. 2, 1989, pp. 183-190.

Gomberg, A. and Hall, J. R., "Analysis of Electrical Fire Investigations in Ten Cities," *NBSIR 83-2677*, National Bureau of Standards, Gaithersburg, MD, Mar. 1983.

Goto, K., *et al.*, "Flame Retardance and Flammability Test of Insulating Components of Electrical Apparatus," *Proceedings* of the Symposium on Electrical Insulating Materials, Institute of Electrical Engineers of Japan, 1986, pp. 293-296.

Harvey, C. S., "Fire in a Code-Complying Electrical Installation," *Fire Journal*, Vol. 73, No. 2 (Mar. 1979), pp. 73-78, 90.

Hazardous Location Equipment Directory, Underwriters Laboratories Incorporated, Northbrook, IL.

Hilado, C. J., *Flammability of Electrical and Electronic Materials*, Technomic Publishing Co., Lancaster, PA, 1985.

Lazar, I., "System and Equipment Grounding for Industrial Plants," *Consulting-Specifying Engineer*, Vol. 3, No. 3, 1988, pp. 86-89.

Magison, E. C., *Electrical Instruments in Hazardous Locations*, 3rd ed., Instrument Society of America, Pittsburgh, PA, 1978.

McGuinnes, W. J., *Mechanical and Electrical Equipment for Buildings*, 7th ed, Wiley, New York, 1986.

Northrup, S. D., "Evaluation of Less Flammable Transformer Liquids," *Proceedings* of the 5th BEAMA International Electrical Insulation Conference, Cavanagh Associates, Leatherhead, England, 1986, pp. 101-106.

National Electrical Safety Code, Institute of Electrical and Electronics Engineers, NY, 1989.

Orbeck, T., "Development of Guides for Fire Hazards Assessments for Electrical Insulating Materials and Systems," *Conference Record* of the 1986 IEEE International Symposium on Electrical Insulation, IEEE, 1986, pp. 265-269.

Palko, E., "1990 National Electrical Code: What the Changes Mean to Plant Engineers," *Plant Engineering*, Vol. 44, No. 7 (Apr. 12, 1990), p. 79.

Schram, P. J. and Earley, M. W., *Electrical Installations in Hazardous Locations*, National Fire Protection Association, Quincy, MA, 1988.

Smith, L. E. and McCoskrie, D., "What Causes Wiring Fires in Residences?," *Fire Journal*, Vol. 84, No. 1 (Jan./Feb. 1990), p. 18.

Snell, J. E., "Measuring Hazards of Products of Combustion from Electrical Systems," *Fire Journal*, Vol. 81, No. 5 (Sept./Oct. 1987), pp. 108-109.

"Standard for Television Receivers and Video Products," *UL 1410*, Underwriters Laboratories Incorporated, Northbrook, IL.

Sundin, D. W. and Northrup, S. D., "Relationship Between Liquid Flammability Tests and Transformer Fire Situations," *Conference Record*—Industrial and Commercial Power Systems Technical Conference 1987, IEEE, 1987, pp. 117-121.

Swingler, S. G., Stevens, G. C., and Gibbons, J. A. M., "Small-scale Assessment of Flame Propagation and Heat Release Rate of Electric Cable Materials," *Proceedings* of the Fifth International Conference on Dielectric Materials, Measurements and Applications, IEE Conference Publication No. 289, IEE, London, 1988, pp. 45-50.

"Tests for Flammability of Plastic Materials for Parts in Devices and Appliances," *UL 94*, Underwriters Laboratories Incorporated, Northbrook, IL.

Whittington, B. W., "Electrical Installations in Industrial Locations," *Industrial Fire Hazards Handbook*, 3rd ed., National Fire Protection Association, Quincy, MA, 1990, pp. 863-883.

Yereance, R. A., *Electrical Fire Analysis*, Charles C. Thomas, Springfield, IL, 1987.

HEATING SYSTEMS AND APPLIANCES

Revised by J. J. Drechsler and Richard Peacock

Heat-producing appliances and associated equipment are among the most prevalent causes of fire because they operate at temperatures above the ignition temperature of many common materials. In addition, combustion-type appliances may involve the hazards of an accumulated combustible mixture, the discharge of unburned fuel, and possible exposure of fuel to ignition sources.

Additional information about heating systems and appliances can be found in: Section 1, Chapter 4, "Chemistry and Physics of Fire"; Section 2, Chapter 3, "Electrical Systems and Appliances"; Section 2, Chapter 5, "Boiler Furnaces"; Section 2, Chapter 10, "Industrial and Commercial Heat Utilization Equipment"; Section 2, Chapter 25, "Storage of Flammable and Combustible Liquids"; Section 2, Chapter 26, "Storage of Gases"; Section 3, Chapter 7, "Gases"; and Section 6, Chapter 16, "Air Conditioning and Ventilating Systems."

FUELS AND METHODS OF FIRING

Combustion may be defined as a chemical reaction between a fuel and oxygen, with evolution of heat and light. In a fuel-burning, heat-producing device, this reaction needs to be continuous so a balance will be established between the rate at which oxygen, or air, and fuel is supplied and the rate at which heat and the products of combustion are removed. Complete combustion takes place when all of the fuel is oxidized by the air supplied to it. Air left over after complete oxidation is called excess air. If only enough air is supplied for complete combustion, perfect combustion results under suitable conditions. This is impractical in most heat-producing appliances; thus, the appliances operate with some excess air.

J. J. Drechsler is retired from Baltimore Gas and Electric Co. He has been a long-term member of the National Fuel Gas Code Committee, and currently serves as its chairman.Richard Peacock is a chemical engineer in the Hazard Analysis Group, Building and Fire Research Laboratory, National Institute of Standards and Technology, Gaithersburg, MD. He has been involved in many research studies on solid fuel safety and has served as a member of the NFPA committee on Chimneys, Fireplaces, Vents, and Solid Fuel Burning Appliances since 1978.

Air for combustion is supplied in two ways: (1) primary air is introduced through or with the fuels, and (2) secondary air is supplied to the combustion zone. In some cases, all of the air supplied is primary air, while in others only part is primary air and the balance is secondary air.

Incomplete combustion in a fuel-burning device can produce hazardous carbon monoxide. This condition indicates poor efficiency, since the fuel is not completely oxidized, and its total heating value is not obtained. Incomplete combustion usually results from inadequate air supply, insufficient mixing of air and gases, or a temperature too low to produce or sustain combustion.

Solid Fuel—Coal

Coal is one of the principal solid fuels used in heat-producing appliances. There are a number of types of coal, each having widely different characteristics. In many cases, there is no distinct line of demarcation between them, and the qualities of one type can overlap those of another. Pulverized coal systems, however, require the use of coals having characteristics within the specific range of the coal-handling and coal-burning equipment.

The seven principal types of coal used in heat-producing appliances are:

Anthracite: A clean, dense, hard coal. It burns with a minimum of smoke and has a minimum dust hazard during handling.

Semianthracite: A coal having a higher volatile content than anthracite but not as hard.

Bituminous: This includes many types of coal with different properties, depending upon where they are mined. It gives off considerable smoke and soot if improperly fired. Bituminous coal may be subject to spontaneous ignition under some storage conditions and has a dust hazard during handling.

Semibituminous: A dusty soft coal that tends to break up. It may be subject to spontaneous ignition under some storage conditions. It normally produces less smoke than bituminous coal.

Subbituminous: A coal subject to spontaneous ignition under some storage conditions. It burns with very little smoke and soot.

Lignite: A coal having a woody structure and normally a high moisture content. It is subject to spontaneous ignition under some storage conditions. It burns with little smoke and soot.

Coke: A product of the destructive distillation of coal. The type of coke produced is determined by the coal used and the temperatures and time of distillation. Petroleum coke is produced from the destructive distillation of oil.

Combustion of Coal

When coal is burned in a firebox, oxygen in the air passing through the grate (primary air) unites with the carbon in the lower portion of the fuel bed, called the oxidation zone, to form carbon dioxide. Some of this carbon dioxide is then reduced to carbon monoxide in the upper part of the fuel bed, called the reduction zone. Gases liberated from the fuel bed are carbon monoxide, carbon dioxide, nitrogen, and some oxygen. Oxygen from the air admitted over the fuel bed (secondary air) combines with some of the carbon monoxide to form carbon dioxide. When fresh coal is applied to the fire, moisture is driven off as steam and the hydrocarbon gases are distilled, combined with oxygen, and burned above the grate in what is called the distillation zone.

Methods of Firing Coal

Coal is fired either manually or automatically by stokers or pulverized coal burners.

Hand firing: There are many acceptable hand firing methods. With highly volatile coals, the objective is to leave a suitable bed of glowing fuel to ignite the gases as they are driven off from the fresh coal charge; otherwise the gas may accumulate and explode. Draft regulation is the only automatic feature of a hand fired furnace. Draft can be controlled by a room thermostat, steam pressure, or water temperature. But, as with any hand fired solid fuel, the fire is continuous and overtemperature conditions are difficult to control unless the fire is continually attended.

Mechanical stokers: These are classified according to their coal burning capacities, and range from those that handle 10 lb (4.5 kg) per hr to those handling over 1200 lb (540 kg) per hr. A stoker feeds fuel to the combustion chamber and usually supplies air for combustion under automatic control. There are four basic types of stokers: (1) underfed, (2) overfed, (3) traveling and chain grate, and (4) spreader, with fired grate or continuous ash discharge.

Underfed stokers move the coal by screw conveyor or rams. (See Figure 2-4A.) Overfed stokers feed the coal pneumatically or by rotors. Spreader stokers similarly feed coal by rotors or paddles and discharge onto stationary or traveling grates. Stokers may feed from hoppers or directly from bins. They are equipped with fueling controls that either change the firing rate or stop the fuel altogether. Some stokers are equipped with a control that will stop the feeding of fuel if the fire goes out.

Pulverized coal systems: These are of two general types: (1) the direct fired, or unit, system, and (2) the storage, or bin, system. In the direct fired system, raw coal is fed directly to a pulverizer where it is pulverized, mixed with

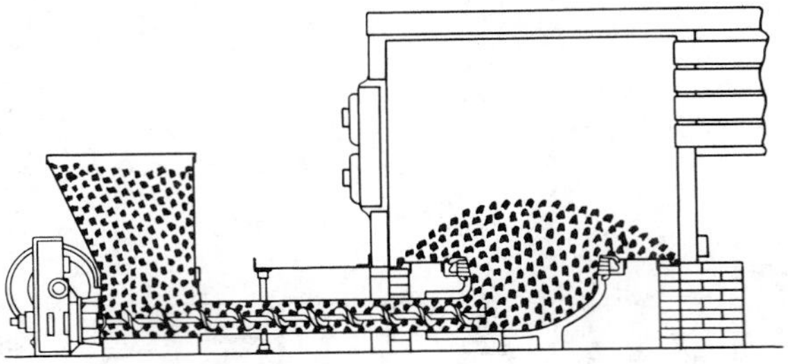

FIG. 2-4A. One type of underfed coal stoker.

air, and blown to the burners. In the storage system, coal is delivered to a raw fuel bin and then passed to a pulverizer where it is reduced to a powder and dried for storage in a pulverized fuel bin before delivery to the furnace.

Solid Fuels—Miscellaneous

Miscellaneous solid fuels include: wood, logs, scrap lumber, and wood waste from lumber and paper mills (sawdust, shavings, bark); hogged fuel (sawmill refuse run through a disintegrator or "hog" to form uniform chips or shreds); charcoal; briquets; peat; bagasse; sugar cane; and a host of other combustibles such as tanbark, wet bark, straw, city refuse, paper, etc. The methods of firing these fuels vary considerably with the type of device and the nature of the particular fuel.

Combustion of wood takes place in two stages. The first is destructive distillation such as that which occurs in a charcoal kiln, where the heat drives off combustible gases from the wood and leaves charcoal. The second stage involves burning of the gases in the air above the wood and burning of the charcoal combined with oxygen, forming an intensely hot and luminous bed of coals. The heat from both burning gases and charcoal distills more volatiles from the wood and increases the temperature and rate of combustion. The acceleration of combustion is limited only by the rate at which air can be brought into contact with the burning wood.

Liquid Fuel—Fuel Oils

This section discusses fuel oil used in heat-producing appliances and equipment.

Fuel oil, like other petroleum products, is composed of varying compounds of hydrocarbons. Even the same grade of fuel oil will vary as to its chemical composition, depending upon such factors as the type of crude oil used and the refining process employed.

Types of fuel oil: Fuel oils obtained from present-day refining processes are known as "cracked" oils, and practically all petroleum products on the market today are obtained by the cracking process. No. 1 and No. 2 fuel oils, as well as those fuels commonly known as kerosene, range oil, furnace oil, star oil, and diesel oil, may still be broadly classed as distillates, and No. 4, No. 5, and No. 6 oils (as well as Bunker C) as residuals.

Oil burners are constructed (and subsequently tested and listed by testing laboratories) for a specific grade or grades of fuel oil. For example, burners listed by Underwriters Laboratories Inc. (UL) have the grade or grades of fuel oil that may be used in each inscribed on the UL listing mark applied to the unit. (See Figures 2-4B and 2-4C.)

It is important that only the proper grade or grades of oil be used in each burner for safety as well as efficiency. Specifications for fuel oil are outlined by the American Society for Testing and Materials (ASTM) in ASTM D-396, *Specifications for Fuel Oils*, and in Canadian Government Specification 3-GP-28. (See Table 2-4A.)

FIG. 2-4B. Listing mark used on an oil burner listed by Underwriters Laboratories Inc. Note that the grade of oil satisfactory for use in the device appears at the bottom of the marker.

FIG. 2-4C. Listing mark used on an oil-fired boiler assembly listed by Underwriters Laboratories Inc. Note the grade of oil satisfactory for use in the device appears at the bottom of the marker.

Methods of Firing Fuel Oil

Two methods, i.e., vaporization and atomization, are used to prepare fuel oil for combustion. Air for combustion is supplied by natural or mechanical draft. Ignition is by an electric ignition system, a gas pilot, an oil pilot, or manual means. Operation may be continuous, modulating with high-low flame, or intermittent. While most burners operate from automatic temperature- or pressure-sensing controls, some simpler types are operated manually.

Oil burners may be classified in several different ways, i.e., by application, by type of vaporizer or atomizer, by firing rates, etc. They are divided into two major groups: (1) residential, and (2) commercial-industrial. Vaporizing burners and atomizing burners having capacities of not more than 7 gal/hr (25 L/hr) are considered residential types and are intended to be used with oil fuels not heavier than No. 2. The major portion of residential-type burners produced is the pressure atomizing type, commonly referred to as the gun type.

Vaporizing burners: These burners include the sleeve type, the pot type, and the vertical rotary wall flame type. Sleeve-type burners (see Figure 2-4D) are used in residential heating and cooking stoves. Natural draft pot burners (see Figure 2-4E) have applications similar to sleeve-type burners, while forced-draft pot burners may be used in central heating furnaces. Vertical rotary wall flame vaporizing burners are used in residential boilers and furnaces for central heating. While the gun-type burner is the most common, many of the burners listed above are still in service.

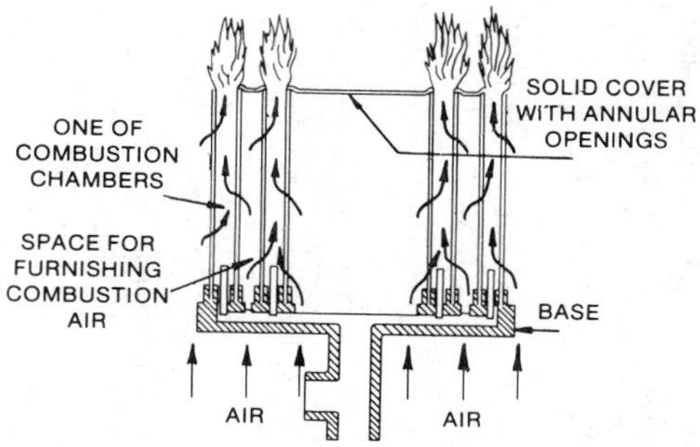

FIG. 2-4D. A sleeve-type burner that consists essentially of a flat, cast-iron or pressed steel base having two or more interconnecting grooves. Perforated metal cylindrical sleeves are placed in the grooves so that the space between the inner two sleeves and the outer two sleeves becomes a combustion chamber. The space between the second and third sleeves is for the purpose of furnishing combustion air. Covers with annular openings are usually placed on top of the sleeves. Sleeve burners may or may not employ wicks in the annular spaces in the base, depending upon the make and type of burner.

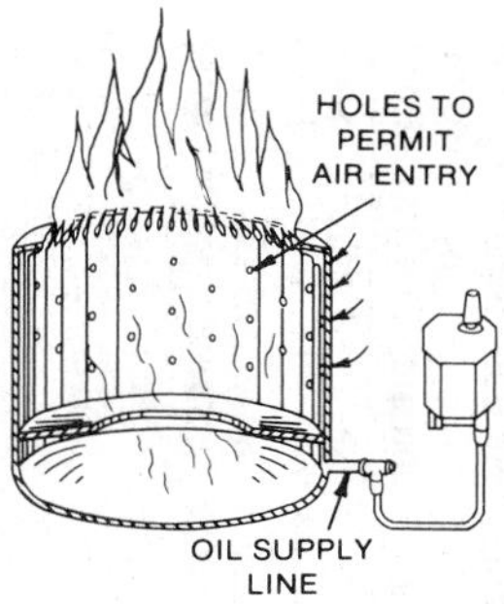

FIG. 2-4E. A vaporizing pot-type burner. The oil is introduced into the bottom of the burner and is continually vaporized by the heat of the fire. The holes on the side permit primary and secondary air to enter the burner where they mix with the oil vapors for proper combustion. The primary air is mixed with oil vapors before combustion takes place, and the secondary air is supplied to complete the combustion process. At full fire, the velocity of the vapors and the amount of air required result in the flame burning only at the top of the burner.

Atomizing: These burners include high- and low-pressure types, horizontal rotary cup types, and air and steam atomizing types, the latter used primarily for commercial and industrial applications. High-pressure, gun-type burners consist of a motor, oil pump (with integral or separate pressure-regulating and shutoff valve), strainer, fan, ignition transformer, nozzle, and electrode assembly. (See Figure 2-4F.) The motor-driven pump draws oil from the supply tank and delivers it to the nozzle at pressures of

TABLE 2-4A. *Detailed Requirements for Fuel Oils*††*

Grade of Fuel Oil	Flash Point, deg F (deg C)	Pour Point, deg F (deg C)	Water and Sediment, percent by volume	Carbon Residue on 10 percent Bottoms, percent	Ash, percent by weight	Distillation Temperatures, deg. F (deg C): 10 percent Point	Distillation Temperatures, deg. F (deg C): 90 percent Point		Saybolt Viscosity, sec: Universal at 100°F (38°C)		Saybolt Viscosity, sec: Furol at 122°F (50°C)		Kinematic Viscosity, centistokes: At 100°F (38°C)		Kinematic Viscosity, centistokes: At 122°F (50°C)		Gravity, deg. API	Copper Strip Corrosion	Sulfur, percent
	Min	Max	Max	Max	Max	Max	Min	Max	Min	Max	Min	Max	Min	Max	Min	Max	Min	Max	Max
No. 1: A distillate oil intended for vaporizing pot-type burners and other burners requiring this grade of fuel	100 or legal (38)	0§	trace	0.15	—	420 (215)	—	550 (288)	—	—	—	—	1.4	2.2	—	—	35	No. 3	0.5 or legal
No. 2: A distillate oil for general purpose domestic heating for use inburners not requiring No. 1 fuel oil	100 or legal (38)	20§ (—7)	0.05	0.35	—	—	540§ (282)	640 (338)	(32.6)#	(37.93)	—	—	2.0§	3.6	—	—	30	—	0.5§ or legal
No. 4: Preheating not usually required for handling or burning	130 or legal (55)	30 (—7)	0.50	—	0.10	—	—	—	45	125	—	—	(5.8)	(26.4)	—	—	—	—	‖
No. 5 (Heavy): Preheating may be required for burning and in cold climates, may be required for handling	130 or legal (55)	—	1.00	—	0.10	—	—	—	150	300	—	—	(32)	(65)	—	—	—	—	‖
No. 5 (Heavy): Preheating may be required for burning and, in cold climates, may be required for handling	130 or legal (55)	—	1.00	—	0.10	—	—	—	350	750	(23)	(40)	(75)	(162)	(42)	(81)	—	—	‖
No. 6: Preheating required for burning and handling	150 (65)	—	2.00**	—	—	—	—	—	(900)	(9000)	45	300	—	—	(92)	(638)	—	—	‖

* It is the intent of these classifications that failure to meet any requirement of a given grade does not automatically place an oil in the next lower grade unless in fact it meets all requirements of the lower grade.

† Outside U.S. the sulfur limit for No. 2 must be 1.0 percent.

‡ Legal requirements to be met.

§ Lower or higher pour points may be specified whenever required by conditions of storage or use. When pour point less than 0°F is specified, the minimum viscosity must be 1.8cSt (32.0 sec, Saybolt Universal) and the minimum 90 percent point must be waived.

‖ The 10 percent distillation temperature point may be specified at 440°F (226°C) maximum for use in other-than-atomizing burners.

Viscosity values in parentheses are for information only and not necessarily limiting.

** The amount of water by distillation plus the sediment by extraction must not exceed 2.00 percent. The amount of sediment by extraction must not exceed 0.50 percent. A deduction in quantity shall be made for all water and sediment in excess of 1.0 percent.

†† This table reprinted from ASTM D-396-69. See complete specification ASTM D-396-69.

from 100 to 300 psi (690 to 2068 kPa). The nozzle atomizes the oil into fine particles and swirls it into the combustion chamber as a cone-shaped spray where it mixes with air and is ignited. They are generally designed to burn No. 2 oil, although some of the larger sizes are made for No. 4 oil.

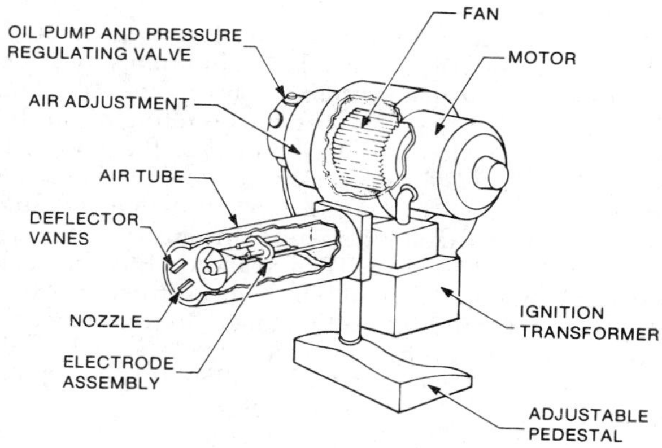

FIG. 2-4F. ***A high-pressure atomizing oil burner.*** *(Source: National Oil Fuel Institute, Inc.)*

The industrial version of the high-pressure burner, known as the mechanical atomizing burner, is a high-capacity burner for use with large boilers and industrial furnaces. Figure 2-4G shows a typical piping arrangement for one or more burners supplied by separate pump sets.

The low-pressure gun burner is similar to, but differs from, the high-pressure gun burner in two ways. First, the burner includes an air pump to supply compressed air for atomization, and second, the oil and air are delivered to the nozzle at pressures of 15 psi (100 kPa) or less. The size ranges, ignition, and fuel used are as described for the high-pressure gun burner.

The horizontal rotary-cup oil burner atomizes the oil by spinning it in a thin film from a horizontal rotating cup and injecting high-velocity primary air into the oil film through an annular nozzle that surrounds the rim of the cup. Secondary air for combustion is supplied from a separate fan that forces air through the burner wind box. The introduction of secondary air by means of natural draft is not recommended. These burners are used for firing boilers and furnaces and may be used singly or as multiple units on a single appliance. No. 2 fuel may be used with some of the smaller sizes, but Nos. 4, 5, or 6 are generally used with the larger sizes. (See Figure 2-4H.)

In the steam atomizing burner, atomization is accomplished by the impact and expansion of steam. Oil and steam flow in separate channels through the burner gun to the nozzle where the steam and oil mix before being discharged through an orifice into the combustion space. This type of burner is used mainly on large boilers generating steam at 100 psi (690 kPa) and higher and having capacities above 12,000,000 Btu per hr (3.5 MW) input.

Air atomizing burners are designed to use compressed air at either high or low pressure for atomization. The high-pressure burner is nearly identical with the steam atomizing burner in design and application. Some burners operate well with either medium.

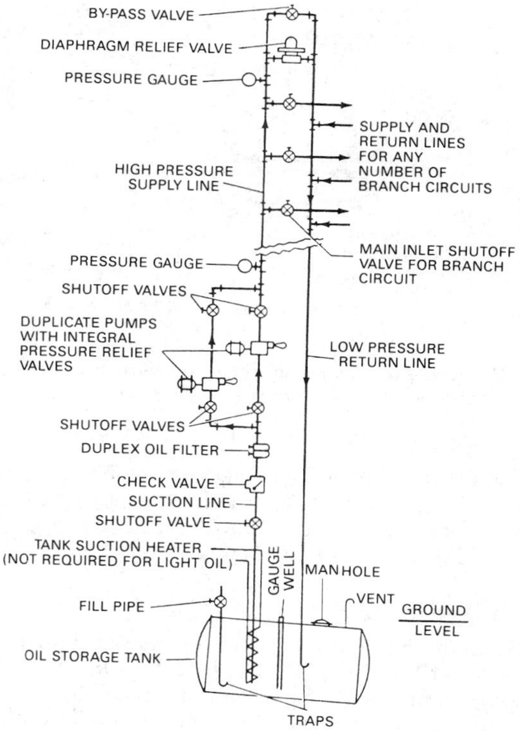

FIG. 2-4G. ***Typical piping arrangements for burners supplied by separate pump sets.*** *(Source:* **Combustion Handbook, *North American Mfg. Co.)***

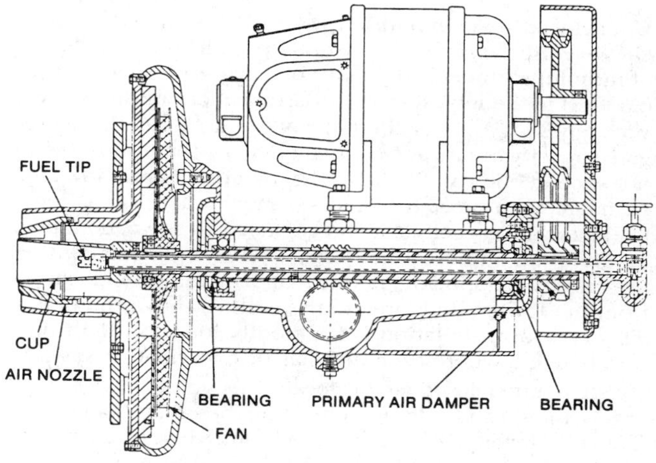

FIG. 2-4H. ***Horizontal rotary-cup oil burner.*** ***(Source: National Oil Fuel Institute, Inc.)***

The low-pressure air atomizing burner uses comparatively large volumes of air at low pressure of 5 psi (35 kPa) or less. Air from the blower passes through the burner body and is discharged through annular slots between the body and the nozzle tip, where it meets the film of oil at an angle as it issues from the tip. The impact of the air stream upon the oil film produces a fine mist that is projected into the combustion space. These burners may be fired with light or heavy oil and are most often used to fire industrial heating and processing furnaces. (See Figure 2-4I.)

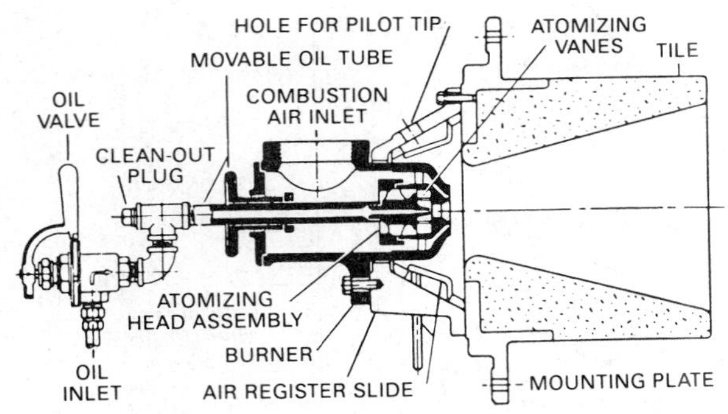

FIG. 2-41. ***Low-pressure air atomizing oil burner.*** **(*Source:* Combustion Handbook, *North American Mfg. Co.*)**

Combination oil and gas burners, which combine the features of certain oil burners with provisions for burning gas, have been developed. These permit the operator to choose either fuel as circumstances may dictate.

Fuel Oil Storage

Details on the installation of fuel oil tanks and related piping are described in NFPA 31, *Installation of Oil Burning Equipment*. NFPA 31 covers the installation of tanks underground, unenclosed and enclosed inside buildings, and outside aboveground. The installation requirements in NFPA 31 differ slightly from the requirements for tanks in NFPA 30, *Flammable and Combustible Liquids Code*, which covers liquids with a wider range of flash points which are used in a variety of locations.

Unenclosed tanks in buildings: NFPA 31, *Installation of Oil Burning Equipment,* currently permits the installation of individual unenclosed tanks of capacities up to 660 gal (2500 L) in the lowest story or basement of buildings. Two such tanks may be installed in any one area, but the aggregate capacity of tankage connected to any one burner may not exceed 660 gal (2500 L). If separation is provided for each tank with capacities of less than 660 gal (2500 L) each, the aggregate capacity may be greater. The separation must be either an unpierced masonry wall or a partition with a fire-resistance rating of not less than 2 hr and should extend from the lowest floor area to the ceiling above the tanks. This type of installation is frequently found in multiple-unit housing where each unit has its own heating system.

If an unenclosed tank is located above the lowest story or basement of a building, it must not be larger than 60 gal (230 L) capacity. All unenclosed tanks inside buildings must be located not less than 5 ft (1.5 m) from any fire or flame, either in or external to any fuel-burning appliance. Furthermore, such tanks must not obstruct quick and safe access to any utility service meter, switch panel, or shut-off valve.

Corrosion of tanks: Internal corrosion of unenclosed fuel oil tanks, caused by the electrolytic action of water on steel, has been a major problem. Corrosion and subsequent tank leakage have actually been more of a nuisance than a fire hazard. Fire can occur, however, when a burner is located in a pit in the basement and oil from a leaking tank enters the pit. Two generally accepted procedures are recommended to correct the cause of corrosion. One method is to slope the tank to one end and take the burner oil supply line from the bottom of that end. In this way, water is not permitted to accumulate in the bottom of the tank. The quantity of water that comes from condensation inside the tank is so small that it does not present a problem in the safe operation of the burner. The second method is to add a small amount of an alkaline solution to the oil itself or to add a small amount of the solution directly into the tank at periodic intervals.

Enclosed tanks in buildings: Tanks larger than 660-gal (2500 L) capacity may be installed in buildings, provided the tanks are within an enclosure constructed of walls, floor, and ceiling which has a fire-resistance rating of not less than 3 hr. The walls must be bonded to the floor. Any opening into the enclosure is required to have a noncombustible sill or ramp at least 6 in. (152 mm) high and, since it is a Class A (horizontal) opening, it must be provided with a self-closing fire door. The top and walls of the enclosure must be independent of building construction, except that an exterior building wall having a fire resistance rating of not less than 3 hr may also serve as a wall for the tank enclosure. This method of installation is found only in commercial and industrial buildings.

Outside aboveground tanks: Tankage not in excess of 1320 gal (5000 L) may be installed outside aboveground in built-up areas. The tanks may be adjacent to buildings, but must be kept away from the line of adjacent property. Not more than one or two tanks having an aggregate capacity of not more than 660 gal (2500 L) are permitted to be connected to one oil-burning appliance. Tankage in excess of 1320 gal (5000 L) may be installed. However, such installations must meet all of the relevant requirements of NFPA 30, *Flammable and Combustible Liquids Code.*

Underground tanks: These are tanks built to conform to NFPA 31, *Installation of Oil Burning Equipment,* which also gives special precautions regarding building foundations, property line setbacks, protection against traffic (e.g., vehicle movement over the buried tanks), and areas subject to flooding. (See NFPA 30, *Flammable and Combustible Liquids Code,* for additional information on protecting tanks containing flammable liquids in locations that may be flooded.)

Centralized oil distribution systems: A system of piping that supplies oil from a central tank or tanks to a number of buildings, mobile homes, recreational vehicles, etc., may be used under certain conditions. For details covering such systems see NFPA 31, *Installation of Oil Burning Equipment*.

Fill and vent pipes: Underground tanks and tanks larger than 10-gal (38 L) capacity inside buildings must have fill and vent pipes terminating outside of buildings. Vent openings and vent pipes must be large enough to prevent abnormal pressure during filling, and must not be smaller than 1¼ in. (30 mm) nominal pipe size for 550-gal (2082 L) capacity, and correspondingly larger for tanks having greater capacity. In addition, outside aboveground tanks must have some form of construction or device to relieve excessive internal pressure that may be caused by an exposure fire.

Gaging devices are required, but on inside tanks they must not allow oil or vapor to be discharged into the building. Test wells are not allowed on inside tanks. Piping to the burner(s) and the required accessories are covered in NFPA 31, *Installation of Oil Burning Equipment*.

Small-capacity tanks: There are several types of small tanks used with cooking appliances and room heaters. An auxiliary tank of not over 60-gal (227 L) capacity may be provided between the burner and the main fuel supply tank. An unenclosed supply tank of not more than 10-gal (38 L) capacity for an individual appliance is permitted, provided it is placed not less than 2 ft (0.6 m) from a source of heat either inside or outside the appliance being served, and provided that the temperature of the oil in the tank will not exceed 25°F (–4°C) above room temperature at the maximum firing rate.

Integral tanks are furnished by manufacturers as a component part of some oil-burning appliances, e.g., kerosene and oil stoves. Stoves with integral tanks [not over 5-gal (20 L) capacity] operate on the gravity or barometric feed principle. The tank reservoir oil and the burner oil are at the same level. As the oil level drops due to burning, oil runs into the reservoir from the tank, either because a float drops and opens a valve (gravity feed), or because air enters the tank through the cap and allows oil to enter the reservoir until it covers the air opening (barometric feed).

NFPA 31, *Installation of Oil Burning Equipment,* contains specific provisions on supply tanks for kerosene and oil stoves, portable kerosene heaters, and conversion range oil burners.

Liquid Fuels—Miscellaneous

Alcohol and gasoline are used for some heat-producing appliances and equipment to a limited extent. Alcohol stoves and torches, and gasoline torches are examples. NFPA 30, *Flammable and Combustible Liquids Code,* gives additional basic data on the safe storage practices for these liquids.

Gas Fuels

Generally, gas-fired, heat-producing devices and equipment use natural gas, LP-Gas (liquefied petroleum gas), an LP-Gas/air mixture, or mixtures of these gases. Natural gas is the most commonly used gas fuel in the United States, because gas transmission pipeline systems supply most areas of the country. LP-Gas-fired heating devices also are popular, particularly in sparsely settled areas and in recreational vehicles. A number of other flammable gases are used as fuel in many industrial processes for special purposes.

Natural gas consists principally of methane and some ethane, propane, butane, and small amounts of carbon dioxide and nitrogen. Fuel gases can be made in a variety of ways from coal, or by the cracking of oils. Liquefied petroleum gases are largely propane, propylene, butane, and butylene, or mixtures of these gases.

Typical calorific values of various gases as fuel are given in Section 3, Chapter 7, "Gases." Various procedures for sampling, analyzing, measuring, and testing gaseous fuels are outlined in thirteen ASTM standards, which have been compiled in the publication, *ASTM Standards on Gaseous Fuels*.

Methods of Firing Fuel Gases

Air is either mixed with gas at the burner of a gas-fired appliance or premixed with gas. A wide variety of types and sizes of burners are used to mix the gases effectively under different conditions. Every burner is designed to transform the potential energy of the fuel gas into useful heat which can be absorbed in the most effective manner.

Injection (bunsen) burners: Practically all residential and commercial gas appliances and some industrial gas-fired appliances use injection-type gas burners. A jet of gas injects primary air for combustion into the burner and mixes it with the gas. This mixing occurs before the gas reaches the burner ports or point of ignition. Figure 2-4J shows a typical injection-type gas burner.

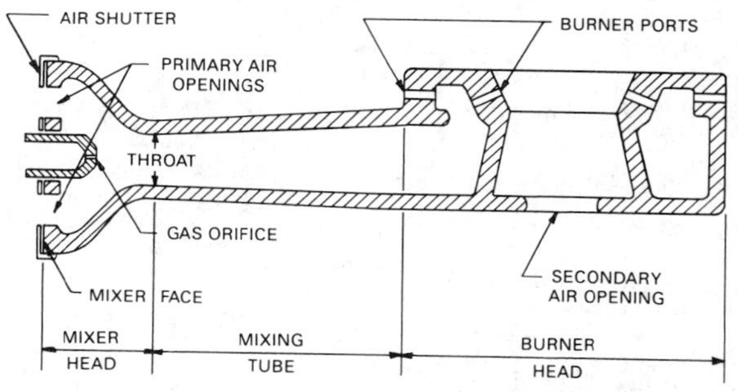

FIG. 2-4J. A schematic view of a typical injection-type burner.

Luminous or yellow-flame burner: In the luminous or yellow-flame burner, only air externally supplied at the point of combustion is used for burning the gas. The flame is produced without premixing air with the gas.

Catalytic burners: Another type of burner is the catalytic burner that permits combustion of the gas at temperatures well below the normal ignition temperature of fuel gas/air mixtures.

Power burners: In a power burner, either gas or air or both are supplied at pressures exceeding the line pressure of the gas and atmospheric pressure of the air. The added pressure is applied at the burner. When air for combustion is supplied by a fan ahead of the appliance, the appliance is known as a forced-draft burner. A premixing burner is a power burner in which all or nearly all of the air for combustion is mixed with the gas as primary air (air that mixes with the gas before it reaches the burner port or ports). A pressure burner is supplied with an air/gas mixture under pressure [usually from 0.5 to 14 in. of water (0.1 to 3.5 kPa) and occasionally higher].

Figure 2-4K illustrates some of the types of industrial appliance gas burners.

Interchanging gases: Changing from one kind of gas to another may cause serious problems unless the appliance is designed to accept the change. Appliance designs certified by the American Gas Association (AGA) laboratories are tested for satisfactory performance with one or more gases as requested by the manufacturer. These include natural and mixed gases, as well as LP-Gas and LP-Gas/air mixtures. The specific gas or gases that may be used in an appliance are marked on the appliance. Although such appliances may be converted in the field to any one of the marked gases, the conversion may require some interchange of parts and may involve some element of hazard unless carefully performed by experienced, qualified personnel.

Appliance and Piping Installation

Installation, alteration, and repair of gas appliances and gas piping should be done only by qualified agencies fully experienced in this work. Provisions outlined in NFPA 54,

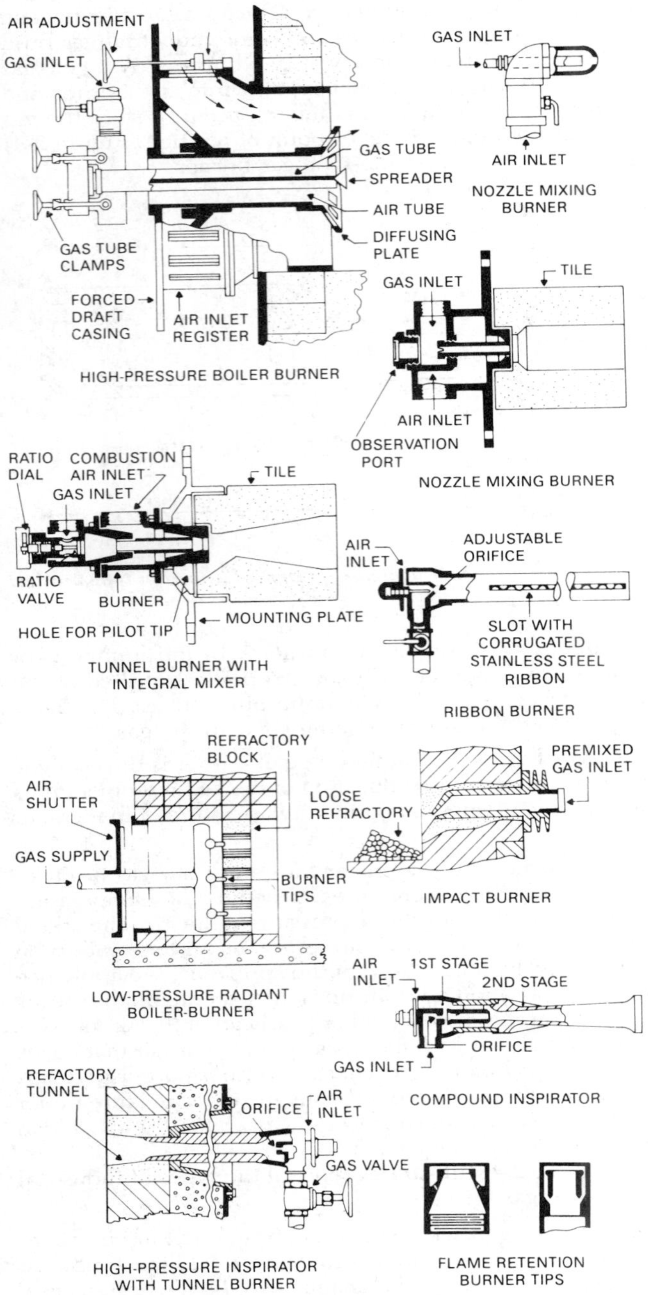

FIG. 2-4K. Types of industrial appliance gas burners.

National Fuel Gas Code, provide the necessary guidance. Gas must be turned on *only after* the system has been thoroughly tested to be certain there is no leakage. All air in piping must be purged, as a remaining slug of air will extinguish the flame. When gas flows again, unburned gas will escape, resulting in a potentially hazardous condition.

The uncontrolled flow of unburned gas into any gas appliance could form an explosive gas/air mixture. Safeguards to prevent this are extremely important, particularly in industrial and other large gas-burning devices. Without such safeguards, unburned gas may accumulate in combustion chambers or ovens at the time of lighting or when the gas pressure fluctuates. If the pressure is reduced below a certain point, the flame may be extinguished. With a subsequent return of normal pressure, unburned gas might continue to flow. An increase in pressure may increase the velocity of flow through the burner in excess of the flame propagation rate. This will force the flame away from the burner. A number of automatic devices are available to safeguard against this hazard, and are commonly found on the larger installations.

Electricity

Heating by electricity involves two basic electrical properties: (1) resistance, and (2) induction.

Units of electrical heat: Heating calculations for electrical heating are expressed in kilowatt hour (kWh) requirements. One kWh equals 3412 Btu.

Controls: Automatic regulation of the electrical input (usually through proportional-type step controllers) allows heaters to be energized and deenergized in increments small enough to prevent excessive total operation of all heaters during temperature drops.

Method of installation: Electric heating systems should be installed in accordance with NFPA 70, *National Electrical Code®*.

Types of electrical heating appliances: Most electrical heating appliances for heating small rooms and for other small heating jobs involve resistor heating elements which are usually one or more metal alloy wires, nonmetallic carbon rods, or printed circuits. Resistor heating is used in radiators, unit heaters, convectors, central hot water systems, central warm air heating systems, and panel-type radiant heat installations for walls, floors, and ceilings. Resistor heating is also used for household electrical appliances, such as stoves, irons, toasters, etc.

CONTROLS FOR FUEL BURNERS

The uncontrolled flow of unburned fuel into appliances and burners can lead to serious consequences. When fired with pulverized coal, gas, or oil, a combustible mixture could accumulate within the confines of the appliance or equipment. If ignited, it could result in an explosion. To guard against the discharge of unburned fuel or improper mixtures of fuel and air, certain controls are required for all fuel burners.

Primary Safety Controls

These required controls cause the fuel to shut off in the event of ignition failure or flame failure. Except for pot-and-sleeve-type vaporizing burners, shutoff is usually accomplished via a primary safety control. For gas appliances, an automatic gas ignition system is used. Both types of controls sense the presence or absence of flame. Upon ignition or flame failure, they cause the fuel to be shut off in the prescribed period of time. All fuel to the burner should be shut off. Primary safety controls usually provide for starting and stopping the burner in response to changes in demand (room thermostat, process controller, etc.). Controls for commercial and industrial burners may provide a purge period for air to flow through the appliance prior to starting fuel flow. The control also prohibits main burner fuel from being admitted until the control has proved the existence of the ignition flame.

The discharge of unburned oil from pot-and-sleeve-type vaporizing burners should be prevented by a constant level valve or by barometric feed. Each of these provisions maintains a predetermined level of oil in the burner below any point of overflow.

Air/Fuel Interlocks

If the safe operation of a burner depends upon a forced or induced draft fan or air compressor to supply combustion air, an interlock is needed to shut off fuel in case the air supply is interrupted.

Atomizer/Fuel Interlocks

In an oil-burning system, where air, steam, or other means for atomization can be interrupted without stopping oil delivery to the burner, an interlock must be provided to immediately shut off the oil if atomization fails.

Pressure Regulation and Interlocks

Gas burners and pressure-type oil burners require uniform fuel pressure so fuel burns safely and efficiently. Pressure regulators are used to maintain uniform fuel pressures. In situations where fuel pressure fluctuations may be expected, pressure interlocks are provided which shut off the fuel to the main burners when the pressure is too low or too high for safe operation.

Oil Temperature Interlocks

Oil burners requiring heated oil for satisfactory operation are equipped with a low oil temperature switch to prevent the burner from starting or to shut it down if the oil temperature falls below the required minimum.

Manual Restart

If a burner is not equipped to provide safe automatic restarting after shutdown, its control system must be arranged to require manual restarting after any control operates to extinguish the burner flame.

Remote Shutoff

It is good practice to provide a remote control for manually stopping the flow of fuel to the burner. An identified switch in the burner supply circuit, placed near the entrance to the room where the burner is located, can be used with electrically powered equipment. A valve in the fuel supply line, operable from a location reached without passing near the burner, may also be used.

Safety Shutoff Valves

Safety shutoff valves prevent the abnormal discharge of fuel. They should be constructed so they cannot be readily restrained or blocked in the open position. Such valves should automatically close when deenergized, regardless of the position of any damper-operating lever or reset handle. Electrically operated valves should not need to be energized to close. Pressure-operated valves should close upon failure of the operating pressure.

Safety Control Circuits

Safety control ac circuits are of the two-wire type with one side grounded. They must not exceed a nominal 120 V and must be protected with suitable fuses or circuit breakers. All switches should be in the hot ungrounded line. The accidental grounding of such a circuit will not cause a required safety control to be bypassed.

Appliances and equipment fired with fuel burners require some additional controls to avoid excessive pressure, temperature, or other abnormal conditions. These controls are covered later in this chapter.

Appliances listed by testing agencies are equipped with all the required safety controls. The application of controls to fuel-burning systems assembled in the field or intended for specific applications should be entrusted only to people specializing in this work. The standards pertaining to fuel-burning equipment referenced in the bibliography include specific information on controls essential to safe operation of fuel-burning equipment.

Safety controls are generally preset by the manufacturer or the installer. Any alteration of these settings or bypassing any safety control could lead to serious consequences. When a faulty control is replaced, a similar model and setting should be used. Figures 2-4L and 2-4M illustrate typical arrangements of safety valves and interlocks for industrial gas and oil burners, respectively.

HEATING APPLIANCES AND THEIR APPLICATIONS

Central heating appliances, room heating and cooking appliances, and miscellaneous heat-producing devices, which are fired by the various fuels and methods discussed, are described here.

Central Heating Appliances

Central heating appliances are divided into four broad categories: (1) boilers, (2) central furnaces, (3) floor furnaces, and (4) wall furnaces.

Boilers: These are either of the steam or hot water type and are constructed of cast iron or steel. (See Figure 2-4N.) The *ASME Boiler and Pressure Vessel Code* defines low-pressure boilers (for low-pressure steam heating, hot water heating, and hot water supply) as those steam boilers that operate at pressures not exceeding 15 psi (100 kPa), and hot water boilers as those that operate at pressures not exceeding 160 psi (1100 kPa) and at temperatures not exceeding 250°F (120°C). The *ASME Boiler and Pressure Vessel Code* also covers the construction of power boilers and locomotive boilers.

Boilers are equipped with safety devices to prevent overpressure conditions. Automatically fired boilers also have controls that will shut off the burner or electric heating elements under low water conditions or when a predetermined pressure or temperature has been reached.

The fire problems of boilers involve their mountings and clearances to combustibles. Explosions resulting from unburned fuel accumulations in the combustion chamber or due to overpressure conditions could rupture fuel lines, thus contributing to the potential for subsequent fire or explosion damage.

Central warm air furnaces: The residential types currently installed in the U.S. are usually equipped with circulating fans, filters, and other features that make them, in effect, air-conditioning systems.

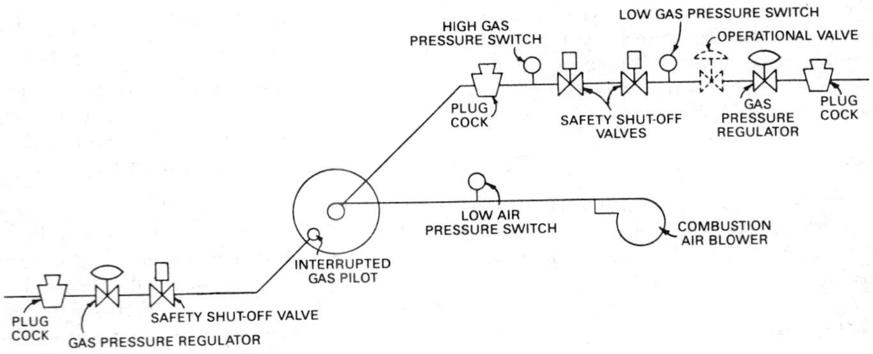

FIG. 2-4L. Typical safety valves and interlock arrangement for industrial gas burner.

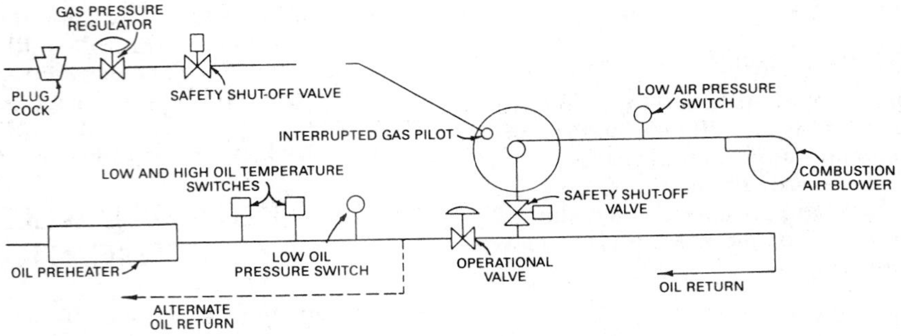

FIG. 2-4M. Typical safety valves and interlock arrangement for industrial oil burner.

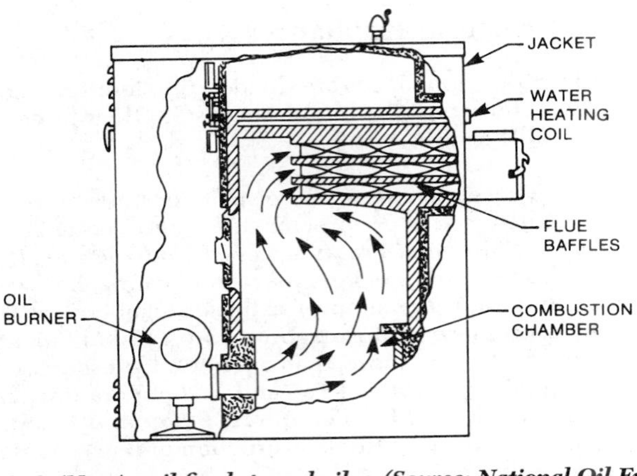

***FIG. 2-4N.** An oil-fired steam boiler. (Source: National Oil Fuel Institute, Inc.)*

Central warm air furnaces are of the following types:

1. Gravity—depends primarily upon the circulation of air by gravity.
2. Gravity with integral fan—fan is an integral part of the furnace construction and is used to overcome internal resistance to airflow.
3. Gravity with booster fan—fan does not restrict flow of air by gravity when fan is not operating.
4. Forced air—equipped with fan that provides the primary means of circulating air. (See Figure 2-4O.)

Forced-air central warm-air furnaces may be classified according to the direction of airflow through them, i.e., as horizontal, upflow, or downflow.

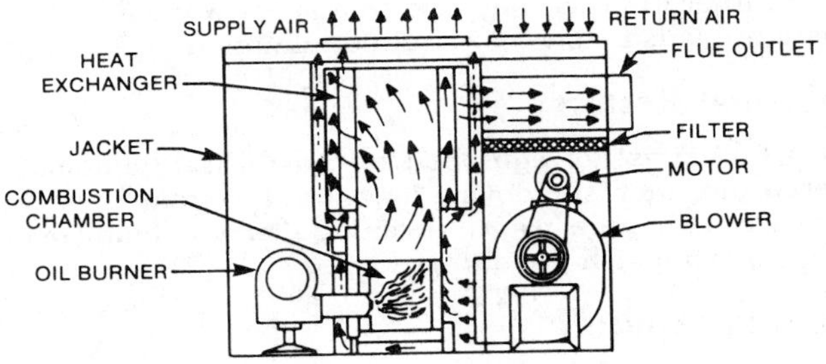

***FIG. 2-4O.** An oil-fired forced-air furnace. (Source: National Oil Fuel Institute, Inc.)*

Gravity furnaces are floor mounted and can heat only spaces above them. Forced-air furnaces may be floor mounted or suspended and may be found on most any floor of a building, including the attic and roof.

Under some conditions of operation, plenums of warm-air heating furnaces may become hot enough to ignite adjacent unprotected woodwork. Clearances or insulation are necessary in these instances. (Complete requirements for installation of systems in residences can be found in NFPA 90B, *Installation of Warm Air Heating and Air Conditioning Systems*.)

Automatic controls, also called high-limit controls, can shut off the fuel or electric supply whenever the air in the furnace warm air plenum or at the beginning of the main supply duct—at a point not affected by radiated heat—reaches 250°F (120°C) or less, depending upon the type of furnace and its installation. (See Figure 2-4P.) Automatic controls cannot be set above prescribed temperature lim-

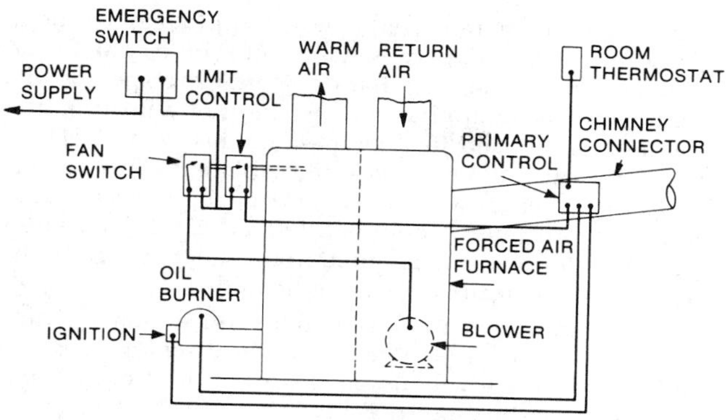

FIG. 2-4P. Control wiring schematic, oil-fired forced warm air furnace. (Certain primary controls are mounted on the burner assembly.) (Source: National Oil Fuel Institute, Inc.)

its. Some furnaces used only with special duct systems are factory equipped to permit temperatures above 250°F (120°C) at the inlet of the supply ducts.

Central warm air furnaces also cause fires due to inadequate clearances to combustible construction, lack of proper limit controls, heat exchanger burnouts, and other causes associated with lack of proper installation, servicing, and maintenance.

Pipeless furnaces: These are essentially gravity warm air furnaces that are not connected to ducts. The furnace is mounted directly under the space to be heated. All the air heated in its outer jacket is discharged through a register above the heat exchanger. They are used for heating small homes and other small one-story properties.

Pipeless furnaces may produce dangerously high temperatures, particularly if the air circulation is restricted. For example, if the register in the floor of a small hallway heats adjoining rooms by air circulating through opened doors, the temperature of the entire hall may be raised to a dangerous degree if the doors are closed tightly at a time when the furnace is in full operation. Fires also have occurred when clothing left to dry above a central floor register was ignited. It is good practice to equip automatically fired pipeless furnaces with limit controls.

Floor furnaces: Most oil- and gas-fired floor furnaces are designed so they may be installed in combustible floors (see Figure 2-4Q); however, they should not be installed in combustible floors if they have not been listed by a testing laboratory for such use. Clearances should be sufficient not only for protection of combustible floors and walls, but also to keep the furnace casing and the piping connected to it out of contact with earth or damp materials.

Temperature limit controls are provided on floor furnaces to shut off the fuel supply when the temperature of the discharged air reaches a predetermined level.

In auditoriums, public halls, or assembly rooms, floor furnaces should not be installed in the floor of any aisle, passageway, or exitway. Floor furnace registers may become hot enough to cause burns under some conditions; therefore, registers in dwellings should not be located in passageways to bathrooms, where persons would be likely to step with bare feet. Users should be warned against covering registers or placing clothing on them to dry. Older types of floor furnaces do not have a temperature limit control, and may become dangerously hot if the air passages are blocked with dust and lint. Inspection and vacuum

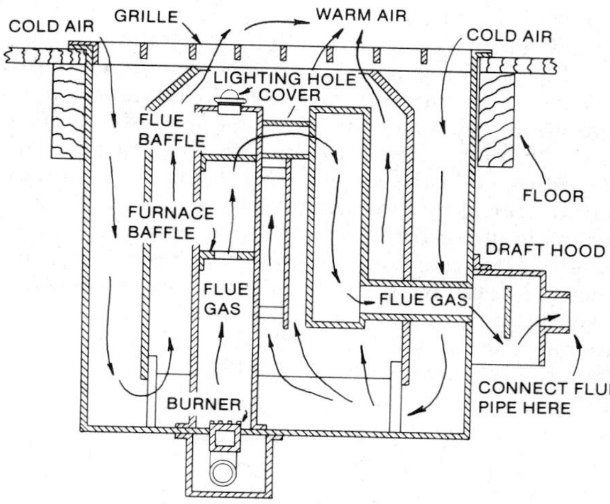

FIG. 2-4Q. A typical floor furnace.

cleaning or hand removal of this blockage is essential for continued safe operation.

Wall furnaces: These are self-contained indirect-fired gas or oil heaters installed in or on a wall. They supply heated air directly to the space to be heated, either by gravity or a fan through grills on openings or boots in the casing supplied by the manufacturer. The furnaces may be of the direct-vent type or are vent- or chimney-connected, depending upon the fuel. Limit controls limit outlet air temperature. The fire problems with recessed wall furnaces are similar to those encountered with most warm air furnaces. A wall furnace installation is shown in Figure 2-4R.

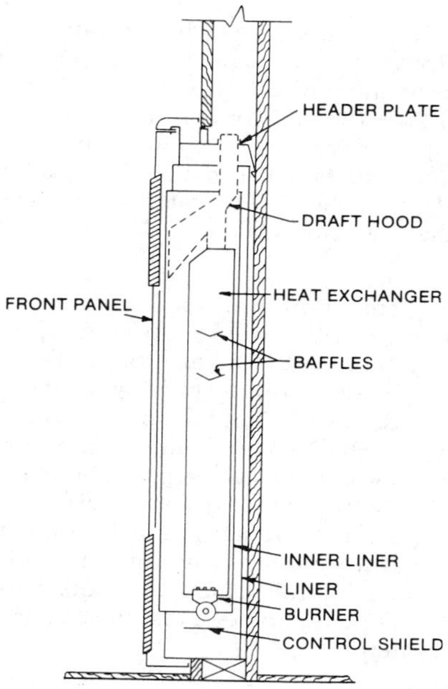

FIG. 2-4R. Typical gas-fired wall furnace.

Duct furnaces: These furnaces are installed directly in ducts of some warm air and air-conditioning systems and depend upon air circulation from a blower not furnished as a part of the furnace. They may be oil or gas fired or electrical, and are equipped with a limit control to shut off the fuel supply or electricity at excessive temperatures.

When duct furnaces are used in conjunction with refrigeration coils in a combined heating and cooling system, the furnace should be located upstream from the refrigeration coil or parallel with it to prevent condensation from corroding the furnace. There are, however, furnaces made of corrosion-resistant material which may be installed downstream from the refrigeration coil. When the furnace is located upstream from the refrigeration coil, the coil should be designed so that excessive pressures and temperatures will not develop in the coil. A duct furnace installation is shown in Figure 2-4S.

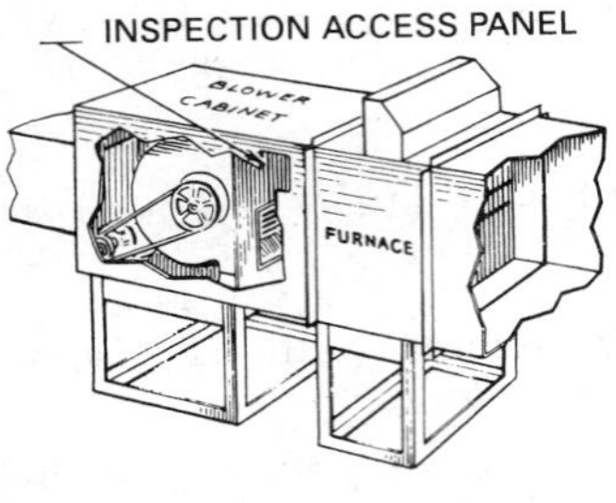

FIG. 2-4S. A duct furnace installation.

Warm air heating panels: These are used in low-temperature, forced-air systems to circulate warm air through plenums or chambers that have one or more surfaces exposed to the space to be heated. NFPA 90B, *Installation of Warm Air Heating and Air Conditioning Systems,* gives recommendations for the use, construction, and installation of these panels.

Radiant heating: This type of heating utilizes panels of hot water piping or electric heating elements which usually operate at moderate temperatures. The panels are embedded in plaster walls or ceilings or in cement floors. Hot water pipes or electrical equipment in radiant systems should conform to standard installation practices. NFPA 70, *National Electrical Code,* contains specific recommendations on the installation of electrical space heating equipment.

Heat pump: This term is applied to a type of forced-air heating system in which refrigeration equipment is used in such a way that heat is taken from a heat source and given up to the conditioned space when heat service is wanted and is removed from the space and discharged to a heat sink when cooling and dehumidification are desired. These systems frequently have supplemental heating units. In such cases, the units are equipped with an interlock to prevent the unit from operating, unless the indoor air circulating fan on the system is running. The units also have temperature limit controls. Hazards are those presented by power, refrigeration equipment, and heat units, if these are part of the system.

Unit Heaters

These are classed as self-contained, automatically controlled, chimney- or vent-connected air heating appliances with an integral means for air circulation. They may be floor mounted or suspended and are equipped with temperature limit controls. The term unit heater as used in NFPA standards is intended to cover appliances for heating nonresidential properties. Thus, it excludes room heaters, floor furnaces, and similar devices. More specifically, a unit heater is an appliance consisting of a heating element and fan housed in a common enclosure and placed within or adjacent to the space to be heated. Unit heaters should not be confused with heat exchangers, which are equipped with fans to circulate heated air. In the latter type, hot water or steam is piped from a heating unit to the heat exchanger in the area to be heated.

Unit heaters that are designed for connection to a duct system may be considered as central heating furnaces and should be provided with the same safeguards. A typical unit heater is shown in Figure 2-4T.

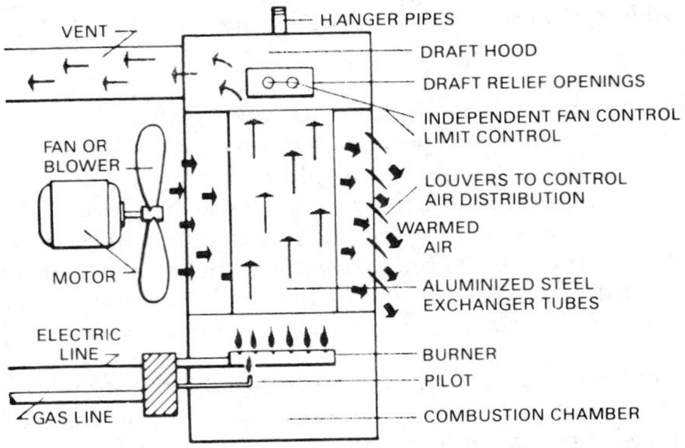

FIG. 2-4T. Typical gas-fired unit heater.

Room Heaters and Cooking Appliances

A room heater differs from a central heating furnace in that it is a self-contained air heating appliance designed for the direct heating of the space around it. External pipes or ducts are not used to distribute the heat. Room heaters fall into two general types: (1) circulating, and (2) radiant. A fuel-burning circulating heater has an outer jacket surrounding the combustion chamber. It is arranged with openings at the top and bottom so that air circulates between the inner and outer shell. It does not have openings in the sides of the outer jacket in order to permit direct radiation. From a safety point of view, room heaters other than those specifically designed as circulating type are classified as being of the radiant type. They include such appliances as wood and coal stoves, electric and gas logs, open-front heaters, wall heaters, gas coal baskets, and fireplace inserts. Care must be taken, especially with heaters that can be moved easily, to place the radiant type so that radiating elements and surfaces are not directed toward walls, drapes, or furniture in close proximity to the heater.

Fuel-burning heaters and residential cooking appliances should be connected to a chimney or vent, where appropriate. The exceptions are gas room heaters and gas cooking appliances listed for unvented use.

Fuel-burning room heaters are not to be installed in sleeping quarters for use of transients, as in hotels and motels, nor in institutions such as homes for the aged, sanitariums, convalescent homes, orphanages, etc. It is good practice to install direct-vent-type heating appliances in sleeping quarters where heaters are permitted and in rooms generally kept closed.

Solid Fuel Room Heaters

Fires involving coal and wood stoves or room heaters have dropped dramatically over the last few years. (See Figure 2-4U.) Much of the improvement can be attributed to increased vigilence in the correct installation and operation of the appliances. Fires in solid-fuel room heaters are due to two underlying conditions: (1) inadequate clearances to combustible materials, and (2) improper or inadequate maintenance. Many wood stoves need frequent charging, often involving much regulating of draft controls to prevent overheating. Sometimes, too, weather conditions can affect the chimney draft, causing improper combustion.

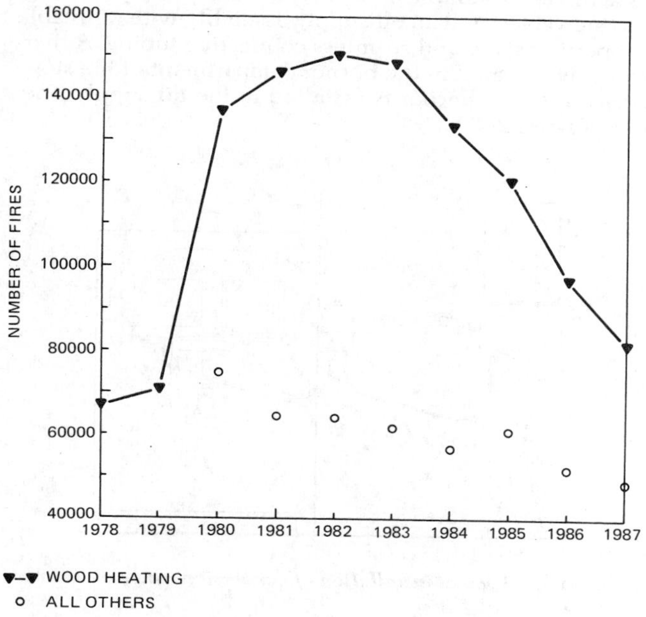

FIG. 2-4U. ***Room heater fire incidences from 1978 through 1987.***

A solid-fuel heater essentially is a fire chamber surrounded by a decorative enclosure. The chamber may be equipped with manual draft controls or a thermostatic control and provided with a chimney connector and other parts that may be required for installation. Instructions that come with heaters that have been listed by testing laboratories are quite precise on the type of heat shielding and the clearances from combustibles that are required.

The vast majority of solid-fuel room heaters are designed to burn only wood, which is easily burned on the bottom of the fire chamber, resting on a bed of firebrick, ashes, or sand. For coal, a grate or other provision to supply air below the fuel bed is needed.

Unless a special chimney is called for by the listing or installation instructions (as in the case of room heaters for use in mobile homes), the typical solid-fuel heater can be connected to either a standard masonry chimney or any listed factory-built chimney. Laboratory tests for listing heaters establish the dimensions required for adequate clearances. Because clearances from large heaters may exceed 36 in. (0.9 m), the tests may be performed with supplemental heat protection or shielding for walls. For proper clearances and floor protection, see the section of this chapter on installation.

Hazards with Solid-Fuel Room Heaters

1. Overfiring. If an appliance is overheated deliberately or through neglect, there is a severe and immediate hazard if the unit or its connector glows even a very dull red. Control is to simply close doors and air dampers until things cool down.
2. Careless handling of ashes containing live coals. Ashes should never be collected in combustible containers, nor should the containers ever be placed on a combustible floor.
3. Inadequate connector clearance. This includes violations of the required 18-in. (457 mm) clearance or lack of adequate protection where a single wall connector must penetrate a combustible wall to join a masonry chimney. Reduced connector clearances are permissible in some instances, such as the entry of single wall connectors into listed supports for factory-built chimneys. The reduced clearances have been validated by tests and are described in the installation instructions for listed heaters. (See Figure 2-4V.)

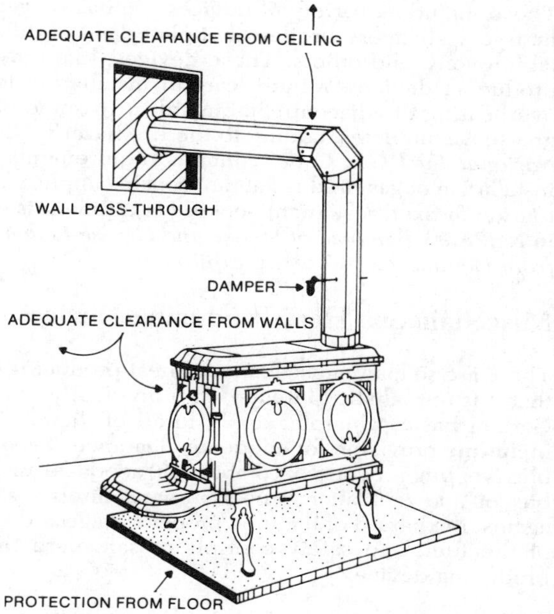

FIG. 2-4V. ***Adequate clearances should be maintained in order to ensure safe operation of coal and wood stoves.***

4. Creosote accumulation and fires. Low-temperature operation of any wood-burning heater for long periods will produce creosote which can deposit in the heater and in its connector and chimney. Airtight wood-burning stoves, because of the relatively low temperatures at which they can be fired, can produce an increased rate of creosote deposits in chimneys and connectors. Therefore, frequent inspection, and, when required, cleaning of the chimney system is in order when these appliances are used. Creosote deposits will build up even when burning dry seasoned wood of any kind, and enough creosote can accumulate in several

days to support a chimney fire. Thin accumulations of creosote can be ignited and burned when the surface temperature reaches the ignition temperature of creosote, which is roughly 900 to 1000°F (480 to 540°C). However, this could be a dangerous practice because there is no way to guarantee that the thickness of the deposit will be uniform over the entire inner surface of the chimney system. Therefore, ignition of the creosote deposit could produce temperatures that could result in damage to the chimney system or ignite nearby combustibles. A daily hot fire with a fresh charge of wood may control creosote deposits indefinitely; however, the operator must pay attention and not allow overheating to take place.

If creosote is building up excessively, symptoms include drips out of the joints, a dull sound if the connector is tapped, and blockage of the chimney and loss of draft, evidenced by smoking. Large accumulations should be removed mechanically, because the excessive amount of fuel deposited in the chimney could be damaging even if the fire is carefully controlled.

Restaurant Cooking Appliances

These include a variety of devices such as ranges, deep fat fryers, steamers, broilers, hot plates and griddles, portable ovens, and others. These devices, like other heat-producing devices, require careful installation to avoid overheating of adjacent combustibles. In some of them, grease accumulates, adding to the fire hazard. NFPA 54, *National Fuel Gas Code,* contains requirements for the installation of gas-fired restaurant cooking appliances. Ventilation of fixed restaurant cooking equipment is covered in NFPA 96, *Removal of Smoke and Grease-Laden Vapors from Commercial Cooking Equipment.*

Miscellaneous Heat-Producing Devices

There are so many miscellaneous heat-producing devices that it is unrealistic to treat each individually in this text. Certain basic principles apply to all of them, however, including provision for adequate clearances to combustibles, venting products of combustion, adequate air for combustion and ventilation, proper burner controls to safeguard against the hazard of the fuel, proper storage and handling of the fuel, and safety controls to safeguard the heat-producing device.

Testing laboratories test and list many miscellaneous types of heat-producing appliances, such as direct-fired heaters, incubators, lanterns, forges, torches, etc.

Kerosene stoves: These may be defined as self-contained, self-supporting, kerosene-burning ranges, room heaters, or water heaters that are not connected to chimneys but are equipped with integral fuel supply tanks not exceeding 2-gal-(7.6 L) capacity. Terms often applied to kerosene room heaters are cabinet heaters and space heaters. Since they are not connected to chimneys, they can be moved rather easily although they are not considered portable. This feature of kerosene stoves has frequently resulted in creation of severe fire and life hazards due to improper placement of the stoves in relation to nearby combustibles and paths of exitways. Kerosene stoves listed by testing laboratories incorporate fire protection features that may be missing from those not listed. Among the more important features of listed stoves are the types of construction materials, primary control valves, and drip pans used in them.

Portable kerosene heaters: These are similar in hazard to kerosene stoves because they are not connected to a chimney. The hazard in their use, however, is increased by their even greater portability and subsequent misuse and misplacement. The safest heaters incorporate firesafety features not included in others, such as special types of latching devices and integral sheet-metal trays under the burners to catch oil drips. They usually employ wick-type burners integral with the oil reservoir.

Conversion range oil burners: These consist essentially of a single- or double-sleeve-type burner assembly, regulating valves, and an oil supply assembly with a suitable supporting stand and seamless connecting tubing. A thermal valve located in the burner compartment of the stove adjacent to the burner is installed in the oil supply line. (See Figure 2-4W.)

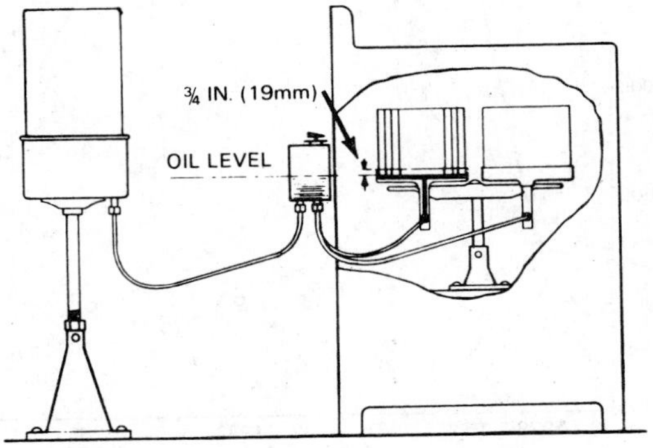

FIG. 2-4W. Typical installation of conversion range oil burner.

Range oil burners, which are found most frequently in the northeastern section of the U.S., are designed to burn kerosene, range oil, or similar fuel. They are primarily installed only in stoves or ranges originally designed to use solid fuel. Range oil burners should not be mistaken for conversion oil burners of the vaporizing-pot type designed for conversion of central heating appliances.

Salamanders: These are typical miscellaneous portable heating devices. They are used at construction sites and in unheated buildings. Too frequently, a salamander consists of only a metal drum with some holes punched in it for draft, and wood scrap and other construction waste materials for fuel. These devices present an acute spark hazard, and the hazard of carbon monoxide poisoning because they are not chimney connected. Crude salamanders of this type, and gas- and oil-fired salamanders that have not been tested and listed by a laboratory, should not be used.

UL and American Gas Association (AGA) laboratories test and list portable gas- and oil-fired heaters, such as salamanders. One way to use salamanders is to carry heated air indoors through flexible ducts from a heating unit located outdoors. NFPA 58, *Storage and Handling of Liquefied Petroleum Gases,* has extensive material on the use of LP-Gas-fired portable heaters.

DISTRIBUTION OF HEAT BY DUCTS AND PIPES

Warm Air Distribution Systems

Central warm air heating systems consist basically of a heat exchanger with an outer casing or jacket that is connected to a system of ducts, air passages, or plenums that carry heated air (the supply side) to the spaces to be heated and return air (the return side) from the heated spaces to the heat exchanger.

NFPA 90B, *Installation of Warm Air Heating and Air Conditioning Systems,* contains specific requirements for systems that are installed in one- and two-family dwellings and other occupancies not exceeding 25,000 cu ft (700 m^3) in volume. Systems that are installed in spaces exceeding 25,000 cu ft (700 m^3) are covered in NFPA 90A, *Installation of Air Conditioning and Ventilating Systems*. The text of this portion of the handbook is confined to a discussion of ducts for warm air heating systems installed in dwellings and other relatively small spaces.

Warm air supply ducts: Warm air ducts must be installed with clearances as given in Table 2-4B. They are substantially constructed of metal or of Class 0 or Class 1 duct materials* and are properly supported and protected against injury.

Supply air plenums: It is common practice in some localities to use the crawl space as the supply plenum for warm air heating systems when a one-story single-family house does not have a basement. These systems utilize a downflow furnace that discharges warm air through directional ducts into the crawl space. An opening cut in the floor of each room of the house and covered with a grill serves as the supply register. The hazards of these systems include: use of combustible construction as a plenum, use of the crawl space for storage, presence of a large enclosed combustible area with no limitations on fire spread and with direct openings to every room of the house, and the possibility of reverse flow in the downflow furnace (the cold air return then becomes the supply duct). NFPA 90B, *Installation of Warm Air Heating and Air Conditioning Systems,* gives specific recommendations and limitations applicable to the use of under-floor space as supply plenums, and it should be consulted for detailed guidance.

Horizontal supply ducts and vertical ducts, risers, boots, and register boxes within certain limits of the warm air furnace can reach temperatures that can become hazardous; therefore, safe clearances to combustibles must be maintained. The clearances required for the many possible configurations of warm air ductwork are specifically provided in NFPA 90B, *Installation of Warm Air Heating and Air Conditioning Systems,* which should be consulted.

Registers: To prevent excessive heat from developing in the duct system, one register or grill must be installed without a shutter and without a damper in the duct to it. The exceptions are automatic oil- or gas-fired systems that have approved temperature limit controls or systems with dampers and shutters designed so that they cannot shut off more than 80 percent of the duct area.

Where registers are installed in the floor over the furnace, as in pipeless furnaces or floor furnaces, the register box should consist of a double wall with an air space of not less than 4 in. (102 mm) between walls. Furnaces with a cold air passage around the warm air passage comply with this requirement.

Return air ducts and plenums: The best way to conduct return air to the furnaces and duct heaters is through continuous ducts. Return ducts do not need to be made of the same materials as supply ducts except for those portions directly over the heating surface or within 2 ft (0.6 m) of the outer casing or jacket of the furnace or duct heater. They should not, however, be made of materials more combustible than 1-in. (25.4 mm) nominal wood boards. Underfloor spaces may be used for return ducts from rooms directly above, but such spaces are used only if they are not more than 2 ft (0.6 m) in depth from the bottom of floor joists, are clean of all combustible material, and are tightly and substantially enclosed. No vertical stack for return air is connected to registers on more than one floor.

The interior of combustible ducts must be lined with metal at points where there is danger from smoldering or burning incandescent particles dropped through a register, such as directly under floor registers and at the bottom of vertical ducts.

Air filters: Air filters should be the kind that will not burn freely or emit large volumes of smoke or other objectionable products of combustion. Filters qualifying as Class 1

*NOTE: Duct materials are tested and listed by UL in accordance with UL Standard 181, *Air Ducts*, and are classified as follows: Class 0—Air duct materials having a fire hazard classification of zero (flame spread and smoke developed). Class 1—Air ducts that have a flame spread rating of not more than 25 without evidence of continued progressive combustion and a smoke developed rating of not more than 50.

TABLE 2-4B. ***Installation Clearances for Horizontal Warm Air Ducts***

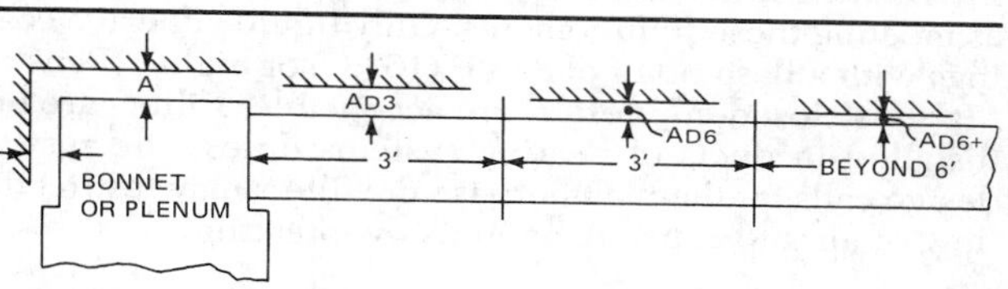

A—Clearance above top of casing, bonnet, plenum, or appliance determined by Table 8-3G.
A_{D3}—Clearance from horizontal warm air duct within 3 ft (0.9 m) of plenum.
A_{D6}—Clearance from horizontal warm air duct between 3 and 6 ft (0.9 and 1.8 m) of plenum.
A_{D6+}—Clearance from horizontal warm air duct beyond 6 ft (1.8 m) of plenum.
E_P—*Clearance from any side of bonnet or plenum.*

If A Equals	A_{D3} Equals	A_{D6} Equals	A_{D6+} Equals	E_P Equals	Method of Firing
1	1	0	0	1	Automatic oil, comb. gas-oil, or gas
2	2	0	0	2	Automatic oil, comb. gas-oil, or gas
6	6	6	0	6	Automatic oil, comb. gas-oil, or gas
6	6	6	1*	6	Automatic stoker fired†
18	18	6	1	18	Any fuel or control.

* Clearance A_{D6+} to be maintained to a point where there is a change in direction equivalent to 90 degrees or more.

† Furnace must be equipped with limit control that cannot be set higher than 250°F (120°C) and must also have a barometric draft control operated by draft intensity and permanently set to limit draft to a maximum intensity of 0.13 in. water gage (32 kPa) otherwise clearances should be as indicated for any fuel.

and Class 2 as defined in NFPA 90B, *Installation of Warm Air Heating and Air Conditioning Systems,* are accepted as meeting these requirements. Only liquid adhesive coatings with a flash point of 325°F (163°C) or higher (Pensky-Martens closed-cup tester) are acceptable. Filters are not installed in ducts of heating systems unless the system design calls for them. Otherwise the filters may restrict the flow of air and cause dangerous overheating.

Heating panels:

NFPA 90B, *Installation of Warm Air Heating and Air Conditioning Systems,* recommends that heating panels be used only with automatically fired gas- or oil-burning or electric forced warm air systems that will limit furnace outlet air temperature to 200°F (93°C) or systems equipped with steam or hot-water heat exchangers utilizing steam that cannot exceed 15 psig (100 kPa) or hot water that cannot exceed 250°F (120°C).

Panels used with automatically fired forced warm air systems must be of noncombustible material or at least of material with a flame spread rating of not more than 25, as determined in accordance with NFPA 255, *Method of Test of Surface Burning Characteristics of Building Materials*.

Where the warm air supply is from a steam or hot-water heat exchanger, the panels may be made of material not more flammable than 1-in. (25.4 mm) nominal wood boards. No single vertical heating panel should serve more than one story of any building.

Steam and Hot-Water Pipes

The temperature of saturated steam varies with the pressure. For example, at atmospheric pressure the temperature of steam is 212°F (100°C), while at 25 psig (172 kPa) its temperature is 266.7°F (130.4°C). Other values of temperature of saturated steam at various pressures are given in Table 2-4C.

TABLE 2-4C. ***Temperature of Saturated Steam***

Gage Pressure		Temperature		Gage Pressure		Temperature	
psi	kPa	°F	°C	psi	kPa	°F	°C
0*		212.0	100.0	35	241	280.6	138.1
1	6.895	215.4	101.8	40	275	286.7	141.5
2	13.79	218.5	103.3	45	310	292.3	144.6
3	20.69	221.5	105.3	50	345	297.7	147.6
4	27.58	224.4	106.9	75	517	320.0	160.0
5	34.48	227.1	108.4	100	690	337.8	169.9
6	41.37	229.6	109.8	125	862	352.9	178.3
7	48.26	232.3	111.3	150	1034	365.9	185.5
8	55.16	234.7	112.6	200	1379	387.9	197.7
9	62.06	237.0	113.9	300	2068	421.7	216.5
10	68.9	239.4	115.2	400	2758	448.2	231.2
11	75.84	241.5	116.4	500	3448	470.1	243.4
12	82.74	243.7	117.6	600	4137	488.8	253.8
13	89.64	245.8	118.8	700	4826	505.6	263.1
14	96.53	247.8	119.9	800	5516	520.3	271.3
15	103.4	249.8	121.0	900	6205	534.0	278.9
20	137.9	258.8	126.0	1000	6895	546.4	285.8
25	172.4	266.7	130.4	1500	10,342	597.6	314.2
30	206.8	274.1	134.5	2000	13,790	636.8	336.0
				3211	22,139	706.1†	374.5

* Zero gage pressure corresponds to an absolute pressure of 14.696 psi (101.329 kPa).
† Critical point, from Keenan's Tables.
Note: Superheated steam has a higher temperature than saturated steam at the same pressure, depending upon the degree of superheat.

Water at high temperature and pressure is also used for heating. The system pressure must always exceed the pressure at the saturation temperature to prevent the water from flashing to steam. This means that the pressure in high-temperature hot-water systems must exceed the values shown in Table 2-4C at the specific temperature at which the system operates. Most systems operate at temperatures between 250 and 430°F (120 and 220°C).

Recommended clearances for steam and hot-water pipes and radiators are given in Table 2-4D.

TABLE 2-4D. ***Installation Clearances for Steamand Hot-Water Pipes and Radiators***

Description	Clearances in.	mm
A. Hot-water pipes and radiators supplied by automatically fired gas, gas-oil or oil burning boilers equipped with limit control that cannot be set to permit a watertemperature above 150°F (66°C).	None	
B. Hot-water and steam pipes and radiators supplied with hot water at not more than 250°F (121°C) except as permitted in A above, and with steam at not over 15 psig (103 kPa).	1*	25*
C. Steam pipes carrying steam at pressures above 15psig (103 kPa) but not over 500 psig (3450 kPa)	6	15

* At points where pipes emerge from a floor, wall or ceiling,the clearance of the opening through the finish floor boards or wall orceiling boards may not be less than ½ in. (13 mm). Each suchopening shall be covered with a plate of noncombustible material.

Radiators and pipes should not be used as racks for drying purposes. Where radiators are placed in window recesses or concealed spaces, such spaces should be lined with noncombustible material, have ample air circulation, and be kept clean.

INSTALLATION OF HEATING APPLIANCES

Any source of heat is a potential fire hazard unless it is arranged to prevent the possibility of dangerous temperatures developing on adjacent combustible materials. It is possible for wood and certain other combustible materials to ignite at temperatures far below their usual ignition temperatures if they are continually exposed to relatively moderate heat over long periods of time. To safeguard against this possibility, heat-producing appliances must be installed with adequate clearance between the appliance and combustibles. Then, under conditions of maximum heat (long and continued exposure), the temperature of exposed combustibles will not exceed dangerous limits. Minimum clearances for various types of heat-producing devices, which should prevent the temperature from exceeding the maximum in exposed combustibles, have been determined by testing laboratories and through field experience. Table 2-4E gives the required standard clearances around and above gas- and oil-fired and electrical residential, commercial, and industrial heat-producing appliances. Table 2-4F gives clearances for solid-fuel burning appliances. The term "listed appliance," which appears in the subheads of Tables 2-4E and 2-4F, refers to appliances that have been tested by testing laboratories. The proper clearances for these appliances, as determined by tests, are published in a listing. The recommended clearances are also indicated either on the appliance or in the manufacturer's installation manual included with the appliance.

TABLE 2-4E. ***Standard Installation Clearances for Heat-Producing Appliances (See Note 1.)***

These clearances apply unless otherwise shown on listed appliances. Appliances should not be installed in alcoves or closets unless so listed. For installation on combustible floors, see Note 2.

Residential Type Appliances For Installation in Rooms Which Are Large (See Note 3)		Appliance: Above Top of Casing or Appliance		From Top and Sides of Warm-Air Bonnet or Plenum		From Front (See Note 4)		From Back		From Sides	
		in.	mm	in.	mm	in.	mm	in.	mm	in.	mm
Boilers and Water Heaters											
Steam Boilers–15 psi (103 kPa) Water Boilers—250°F (120°C) Water Heaters—200°F (93°C) All Water Walled or Jacketed	Automatic Oil or Comb. Gas-Oil	6	152	—		24	610	6	152	6	152
	Automatic Gas	6	152	—		18	457	6	152	6	152
	Electric	6	152	—		18	457	6	152	6	152
Furnaces—Central											
Gravity, Upflow, Downflow, Horizontal and Duct. Warm-Air—250°F (120°C) Max.	Automatic Oil or Comb. Gas-Oil	6[5]	152	6[5]	152	24	610	6	152	6	152
	Automatic Gas	6[5]	152	6[5]	152	18	457	6	152	6	152
	Electric	6[5]	152	6[5]	152	18	457	6	152	6	152
Furnaces—Floor											
For Mounting in Combustile Floors	Automatic Oil or Comb. Gas-Oil	36	914	—		12	305	12	305	12	305
	Automatic Gas	36	914	—		12	305	12	305	12	305
	Electric	36	914	—		12	305	12	305	12	305
Heat Exchanger											
Steam—15 psi (103 kPa) Max Hot Water—250°F (120°C) Max.	—	1	25	1	25	1	25	1	25	1	25
Room Heaters											
Circulating Type Vented or Unvented	Oil	36	914	—		24	610	12	305	12	305
	Gas	36	914	—		24	610	12	305	12	305
Radiant or Other Type Vented or Unvented	Oil	36	914	—		36	914	36	914	36	914
	Gas	36	914	—				18	457	18	457
	Gas with double metal or ceramic back	36	914	—		36	914	12	305	18	457
Radiators											
Steam or Hot Water	Gas	36	914	—		6	152	6		6	
								Firing Side		Opp. Side	
Ranges—Cooking Stoves		See Note 7									
Vented or Unvented	Oil	30	762	—		—		9	229 24″*	10	457 18″*
	Gas	30	762	—		—		6	152 6″	6	152 6″
	Electric	30	762	—		—		6	152	6	152
Clothes Dryers											
Listed Types	Gas	6	152	—		24	610	6	152	6	152
	Electric	6	152	—		24	610	0		0	
Incinerators	See Note 10										
Domestic Types	—	36	914	—		48	1219	36	914	36	914

TABLE 2-4E. ***(Continued)***

Low-Heat Appliances Any and All Physical Sizes Except as Noted		Appliance: Above Top of Casing or Appliance (See Note 8) in.	mm	From Top and Sides of Warm-Air Bonnet or Plenum in.	mm	From Front in.	mm	From Back (See Note 8) in.	mm	From Sides (See Note 8) in.	mm
Boilers and Water Heaters											
100 ft^3 (2.8 m^3) or less Any psi Steam	All Fuels	18	457	—		48	1219	18	457	18	457
50 psi (345 kPa) or Less Any Size	All Fuels	18	457	—		48	1219	18	457	18	457
Unit Heaters											
Floor Mounted or Suspended—Any size	Steam or Hot Water	1	25	—		—		1	25.4	1	25.4
Suspended—100 ft^3(2.8 m^3) or less	Oil or Comb, Gas-Oil	6	152	—		24	610	18	18	457	
Suspended—100 ft^3 (2.8 m^3) or less	Gas	6	152	—		18	457	18	457	18	457
Suspended—Over 100 ft^3 (2.8 m^3)	All Fuels	18	457	—		48	1219	18	457	18	457
Floor Mounted Any Size	All Fuels	18	457	—		48	1219	18	457	18	457
Ranges—Restaurant Type Floor Mounted	All Fuels	48	1219	—		48	1219	18	457	18	457
Other Low-Heat Industrial Appliances Floor Mounted or Suspended	All Fuels	18	457	18	457	48	1219	18	457	18	457

Commercial-Industrial Type Medium-Heat Appliances		Appliance: Above Top of Casing or Appliance (See Note 9) in.	mm	From Top and Sides of Warm-Air Bonnet or Plenum in.	mm	From Front in.	mm	From Back (See Note 9) in.	mm	From Sides (See Note 9) in.	mm
Boilers and Water Heaters Over 50 Psi Over 100 cu ft	} All Fuels	48	1.22	—		96	2.44	36	0.91	36	0.91
Other Medium-Heat Industrial Appliances All Sizes	All Fuels	48	1.22	36	0.91	99	2.44	36	0.91	36	0.91
Incinerators All Sizes	—	48	1.22	—		96	2.44	36	0.91	36	0.91
High-Heat Industrial Appliances All Sizes	All Fuels	180	4.57	—		360	9.14	120	0.91	120	0.91

1. Standard clearances may be reduced by affording protection to combustible material in accordance with Table 2-4G.
2. An appliance may be mounted on a combustible floor if the applianceis listed for installation on a combustible floor, or if the floor is protected in an approved manner. For details of protection reference may be made to the Code for the Installation of Heat-Producing Appliances, obtainable from the American Insurance Service, 85 John Street, New York, N.Y. 10038, or Part 6 of the National Building Code of Canada publishedby the National Research Council, Ottawa, Canada.
3. Rooms which are large in comparison to the size of the appliance arethose having a volume equal to at least 12 times the total volume of a furnace and at least 16 times the total volume of a boiler. If the actualceiling height of a room is greater than 8 ft (2.4 m), the volume of a roomshall be figures on the basis of a ceiling height of 8 ft (2.4 m).
4. The minimum dimension should be that necessary for servicing the appliance including access for normal maintenance, care, tube removal, etc.
5. for a listed oil, combination gas-oil, gas, or electric furnace thisdimension may be 2 in. (51 mm) if the furnace limit control cannot be sethigher than 250°F (120°C) or this dimension may be 1 in. (25 mm) if thelimit control cannot be set higher than 200°F (93°C).
6. The dimension may be 6 in. (152 mm) for an automatically stoker-fired forced warm-air furnace equipped with 250°F (120°C) limit control andwith barometric draft control operated by draft intensity and permanently set to limit draft to a maximum intensity of 0.13 in. (32 Pa) water gage.
7. To combustible material or metal cabinets. If the underside of such combustible material or metal cabinet is protected with asbestos millboardat least 1/4 in. (6.4 mm) thick covered with sheet metal of not less than 24 in. (610 mm).
8. If the appliance is encased in brick, the 18 in. (459 mm) clearance above and at sides and rear may be reduced to not less than 12 in. (305 mm).
9. If the appliance is encased in brick the clearance above may be not less than 36 in. (914 mm) and at sides and rear may be not less than 18 in. (457 mm).
10. Clearance above the charging door should be not less than 48 in. (1.2 m).

*1 in. = 25.4 mm

TABLE 2-4F. *Standard Clearances for Solid Fuel Burning Appliances*
(For Reduced Clearances, see Table 2-4G)
These clearances apply to listed appliances installed in rooms which arelarge in comparison with the size of the appliances.
Source: NFPA 211, *Chimneys, Firep laces, Vents, and Solid Fuel Burning Appliances.*

Kind of Appliance	Above Top of Casing or Appliance Above Top and Sides of Furnace Planum or Bonnet in.	mm	From Front in.	mm	From Back[3] in.	mm	From Sides[3] in.	mm
Residential Appliances Steam Boilers—15 psi (103 kPa) max. Water Boilers—250°F (121°C) max. Water Boilers—200°F (93°C) max. All Water Walled or Jacketed	6	152	48	1219	6	1522[2]	6	1522[2]
Furnaces Gravity and Forced Air[4]	18	457	48	1219	18	457	18	457
Room Heaters, Fireplace Stoves, Combinations	36	914	36	914	36	914	36	914
					Firing Side		Opp. Side	
Ranges Line Firechamber	30	762[1]	36	914	24	610	18	457
Unlined Firechamber	30	762[1]	36	914	36	914	18	457

[1] To combustible material or metal cabinets.If the underside of such combustible material or or metal cabinet is protected with sheet metal of not less than 0.024 in. (0.61 mm) (24 gage) spaced out 1 in. (25.4 mm) the distance may be reduced to not less than 24 in. (610 mm).
[2] Adequate clearance for cleaning and maintenance shall be provided.
[3] Provisions for fuel storage shall be located atleast 36 in. (914 mm) from any side of the appliance.
[4] For clearances from air ducts, see NFPA 90B.
[5] Exceptions: Appliances listed for installation with clearances less than specified may be installed in accordance with the terms of their listing and manufacturer's instructions. Heating furnaces and boilers, and water heaters specifically listed for installation in spaces such as alcoves may be installed in accordance with the terms of their listing provided the specified clearance is maintained regardless of whether the enclosure is of combustible or noncombustible material.

Examples of laboratories that test and list appliances are the Factory Mutual Research Corporation, Underwriters Laboratories Inc., Underwriters Laboratories of Canada, and American Gas Association Laboratories.

Modifications of Clearances

Listings of heat-producing appliances and methods for setting clearances between appliances and combustible surfaces are based upon criteria in Underwriters Laboratories Inc. test standards:[1]

- Maximum temperature rise of 150°F (65°C) above room temperature on exposed surfaces; and
- Maximum temperature rise of 121°F (50°C) above room temperature on unexposed surfaces, such as beneath the appliance, floor protector, or wall-mounted protective device.

These requirements are based upon the fact that, while the ignition temperature of wood products is generally quoted to be on the order of 392°F (200°C),[2] wood that is exposed to constant heating over a period of time may undergo chemical change, resulting in a much-lowered ignition temperature and increased potential for self-ignition.

Mitchell[3] presents data on wood fiberboard exposed to temperatures as low as 229°F (109°C) that resulted in ignition after prolonged exposure. MacLean[4,5] reports charring of wood samples at temperatures as low as 200°F (93°C). He concludes that wood should not be exposed to temperatures appreciably higher than 151°F (66°C) for long periods. McGuire[6] suggests that the maximum safe temperatures on the surface of a combustible material adjacent to a constant heat source should be no more than 212°F (100°C).

Clearly, the ignition of wood at moderately elevated temperatures is a complex phenomenon; the length of exposure is indeed an important parameter.[7,8] While exact limits recommended in the literature vary due to exposure time and details of the tests conducted, the numerous documented fires involving the ignition of wood members near low-pressure steam pipes[9] suggest an upper temperature limit for combustible materials exposed to long-term, low-level heating should not be appreciably higher than 212°F (100°C).

The clearances given in Tables 2-4E and 2-4F will provide reasonable protection for exposed surfaces, including those of considerable area, against assumed conditions of continuous operation of heat-producing appliances at maximum temperatures. However, where the appliance is very large, increased clearances to combustible materials may be required. This is a good reason why all appliances should be tested and installed in accordance with the terms of their listing. On the other hand, there are many installations that have not had fires where the clearances are less than that specified. Careful operation of the devices in many such cases has limited temperatures to below the maximum. Yet, every year there are thousands of heating-plant fires when cold weather forces long operation at maximum temperatures. Therefore, where the appliance is used more frequently and for longer periods of time in very cold weather, more frequent checks should be made of the temperature of exposed combustibles and the chimney system.

Installing heating appliances, which under normal operation will not expose adjacent combustible materials to dangerous temperatures, is not sufficient. Clearances and protection also must be designed for reasonable protection when the heating device is operated at its maximum temperature. However, under any conditions of operation the temperature of the exposed combustible materials should not exceed 180°F (82°C). Some provision for ventilation, air circulation, or other method of cooling is necessary to dissipate heat.

In large rooms, a suitable clearance between a heating appliance and combustible material is all that is necessary to prevent ignition. In small rooms or poorly ventilated spaces, particularly where the size of the heating device is large in proportion to the room, dangerous temperatures may be built up no matter how great the clearance unless some provision is made for cooling by air circulation. Only appliances designed and tested for installation in confined spaces, such as alcoves or closets, are to be installed in such spaces. The clearances specified for them are observed whether the enclosing walls are combustible or noncombustible.

Table 2-4G and Figures 2-4X through 2-4CC show how clearances can be reduced by installing protection between the heat-producing device and the combustible material. This information is especially helpful in situations of inadequate clearance where it would be impractical to move the heat-producing appliance.

Clearance reduction systems: If the air space between heating appliances and combustible material is small, a barrier of metal, metal and insulating material, or masonry heat-resistive material should be installed. Metal and masonry shields, or clearance reduction systems, tend also to distribute the heat, preventing in some measure its building up at one location. An air space must be left between the shields and the heat-radiating surface on one side and between the barrier and the combustible material on the other. (See Table 2-4G.) The air currents set up by this procedure will prevent the combustible material from attaining a dangerous temperature, even with the smaller clearance.

Limitations of Insulation

To make certain that insulating material will provide adequate protection, one needs to understand its limitations. The insulation may be used on the heating appliance or in combination with sheet metal and air spaces (Table 2-4G) if its value under such circumstances has been verified by tests. Many heat-producing appliances have built-in insulation, which makes it safer to reduce the required clearances to combustible material.

Insulation alone, however, is not sufficient. Regardless of the thickness of insulation, long continued heat may eventually penetrate it. However, if some method is used to conduct the heat away before it reaches the combustible material, the insulation will provide adequate protection.

Continued high temperatures over long periods of time have caused many fires under apparently safe conditions. Figure 2-4DD shows fires caused under conditions that the layperson would consider safe. Solid masses of brick or concrete or plaster finish may not provide any fire protection under some circumstances, especially where masonry coverings are attached directly to the surface of the combustible material. Heat transfer to the combustible material is usually more efficient as the density of the covering material increases. Therefore, without an air space between the masonry and the combustibles, the heat transfer can actually increase, resulting in the ignition of the combustibles. However, since the masonry products do have a relatively large mass, it will take some time of operation of the appliance to transfer sufficient energy to ignite combustibles. This, however, is entirely dependent upon the weight and dimensions of the masonry and the rate of heat transfer from the appliance. The same rationale would also apply to products other than masonry attached directly to the surface of combustibles.

Mountings

The limitations of masonry, concrete, metal, and other materials as insulating mediums apply particularly to the underside of stoves, heaters, boilers, furnaces, and other similar heat-producing appliances. Tables 2-4H and 2-4I give a list of mountings for various classes of heat-producing appliances.

The testing laboratories indicate in their listings whether the appliances tested may be installed on combustible or noncombustible floors. In some cases, there is a statement on the appliance itself to the effect that it may be installed on a combustible floor. If no such indication appears, however, it is advisable to check the listing for the particular appliance.

Air for Combustion and Ventilation

In many locations, combustion-type heat-producing appliances have ample sources of air for efficient combustion in addition to the ventilation required to prevent undue temperature rises. In basements of dwellings, for example, sufficient air comes in through the cracks around doors and windows.

In relatively tight rooms, such as furnace and boiler rooms, a means to supply air for combustion and ventilation must be provided. Because there are so many variables involved, there is no universally accepted formula for calculating the size of openings necessary to provide adequate air for combustion and ventilation. For example, the tightness and size of the furnace or boiler room, and the operation of exhaust fans and other equipment, would affect the static air pressure in the building. Both NFPA 31, *Installation of Oil Burning Equipment,* and NFPA 54, *National Fuel Gas Code,* as well as other standards pertaining to heat-producing appliances, include specific recommendations on how to supply the air for combustion and ventilation.

For certain laboratory-tested appliances, notably gas- and oil-burning appliances for installation in closets, the minimum size necessary to provide enough air for the operation of the unit and ventilation of the room or space is specified for an opening to the heater room or space.

Clearances for Servicing

Clearances must also be provided for servicing and maintenance of equipment. Lack of proper servicing and good maintenance can result in fires. If lack of space around an appliance makes accessibility difficult, the appliance, or at least some parts of it, will be neglected. This same reasoning applies to appliances located in out-of-the-way places and places difficult to reach. Suspended furnaces and furnaces in attics and underfloor crawl spaces are typical examples of such installations.

CHIMNEY AND VENT CONNECTORS

Chimney and vent connectors are specifically the pipe or breeching used to connect fuel-burning appliances with the required chimney or vent, unless the chimney or vent

TABLE 2-4G. ***Reduction of Appliance Clearance with Specified Forms of Protection***
Source: NFPA 211, *Chimneys, Fireplaces, Vents, and Solid FuelBurning Appliances*

Clearance reduction system applied to and covering all combustible surfaces within the distance specified as required clearance with no protection (see Table 2-4F).	Maximum allowable reduction in clearance (percent)		When the required clearance with no protection is 36 in. (0.9 m), the clearances below are the minimum allowable clearance. For other required clearances with no protection, calculated minimum allowable clearance from maximum allowable reduction. (See Notes 9 and 10)			
			As Wall Protector		As Ceiling Protector	
	As Wall Protector	As Ceiling Protector	in.	mm	in.	mm
(a) 3½ in. (90 mm) thick masonry wall without ventilated air space.	33%	—	24	610		—
(b) ½ in. (13 mm) thick noncombustible insulation board over 1 in. (25 mm) glass fiber or mineral wool batts without ventilated air space.	50%	33%	18	457	24	610
(c) 0.024 in./0.61 mm (24 gage) sheet metal over 1 in. (25 mm) glass fiber or mineral wool batts reinforced with wire, or equivalent, on rear face with ventilated air space.	66%	50%	12	305	18	457
(d) 3½ in. (90 mm) thick masonry wall with ventilated air space.	66%	—	12	305	—	
(e) 0.024 in./0.61 mm (24 gage) sheet metal with ventilated air space.	66%	50%	12	305	18	457
(f) ½ in. (13 mm) thick noncombustibel insulation board with ventilated air space.	66%	50%	12	305	18	457
(g) 0.024 in./0.61 mm (24 gage) sheet metal with ventilated air space over 0.024 in./0.61 mm (24 gage) sheet metal with ventilated air space.	66%	50%	12	305	18	457
(h) 1 in. (25 mm) glass fiber or mineral wool batts sandwiched between two sheets 0.024 in./0.61 mm (24 gage) sheet metal with ventilated air space.	66%	50%	12	305	18	457

Notes to Table 2-4G.
[1] Spacers and ties shall be of noncombustible material. No spacers or ties shall be used directly behind appliance or conductor.
[2] With all clearance reduction systems using a ventilated air space, adequate air circulation shall be provided as described in Fig. 2-4Z. There shall be at least 1 in. (25 mm) between the clearance reduction system and combustible walls and ceilings for clearance reduction systems using a ventilated air space.
[3] Mineral wool batts (blanket or board) shall have a minimum density of 8 lb per ft^3 (128.7 kg/m^3) and have a minimum melting point of 1,500°F (816°C).
[4] Insulation material used as part of clearance reduction system shall have a thermal conductivity of 1.0 (BTU-In.)/(Sq ft-Hr-°F) [(1.730 w/m.K)] or less. Insulation board shall be formed of noncombustible material.
[5] If a single wall connector passes through a masonry wall used as a wall shield, there shall be at least ½ in. (13 mm) or open, ventilated air space between the connector and the masonry.
[6] There shall be at least 1 in. (25 mm) between the appliance and the protector. In no case shall the clearance between the appliance and the wall surface be reduced below that allowed in the table.
[7] Clearances in front of the loading door and/or ash removal door of the appliance shall not be reduced from those in Section 8-6 of NFPA 211.
[8] All clearances and thicknesses are minimums; larger clearances and thicknesses are acceptable. Clearances are not to be less than 12 in. (305 mm) from appliances.
[9] To calculate the minimum allowable clearance, the following formula may be used: $C_{pr} = C_{un} \times (1 - R/100)$. C_{pr} is the minimum allowable clearance, C_{un} is the required clearance with no protection, and R is the maximum allowable reduction in clearance.
[10] Refer to Figures 2-4AA and 2-4BB for other reduced clearances using materials (a) through (h) above.

is attached directly to the appliance. NFPA 211, *Chimneys, Fireplaces, Vents, and Solid Fuel Burning Appliances*, includes requirements for chimney and vent connectors, and should be consulted for information on materials to be used and the sizing and installation of connectors.

Chimney and vent connectors must be installed with adequate clearances to combustibles. Table 2-4J provides guidance for appropriate clearances. Table 2-4K shows how clearances can be reduced by installing protection between the connector and combustible material.

Connectors for residential-type appliances may pass through walls or partitions constructed of combustible material if the connector is either listed for wall pass-through or is routed through a device listed for wall pass-through. Connectors for residential-type appliances with inside diameters less than or equal to 10 in. (254 mm) may pass through walls or partitions constructed of combustible material to a masonry chimney if the connector system selected or fabricated is installed as illustrated in Table 2-4L. Figures 2-4EE and 2-4FF illustrate two example installations in detail.

Appliances to Be Chimney or Vent Connected

All oil-fired appliances are chimney connected, except direct-fired heaters, listed kerosene stoves, and portable kerosene heaters. All solid-fueled appliances are chimney connected.

NFPA 54, *National Fuel Gas Code,* is quite specific on the type of gas appliances that are required to be vented through vents or chimneys, and those not requiring vents.

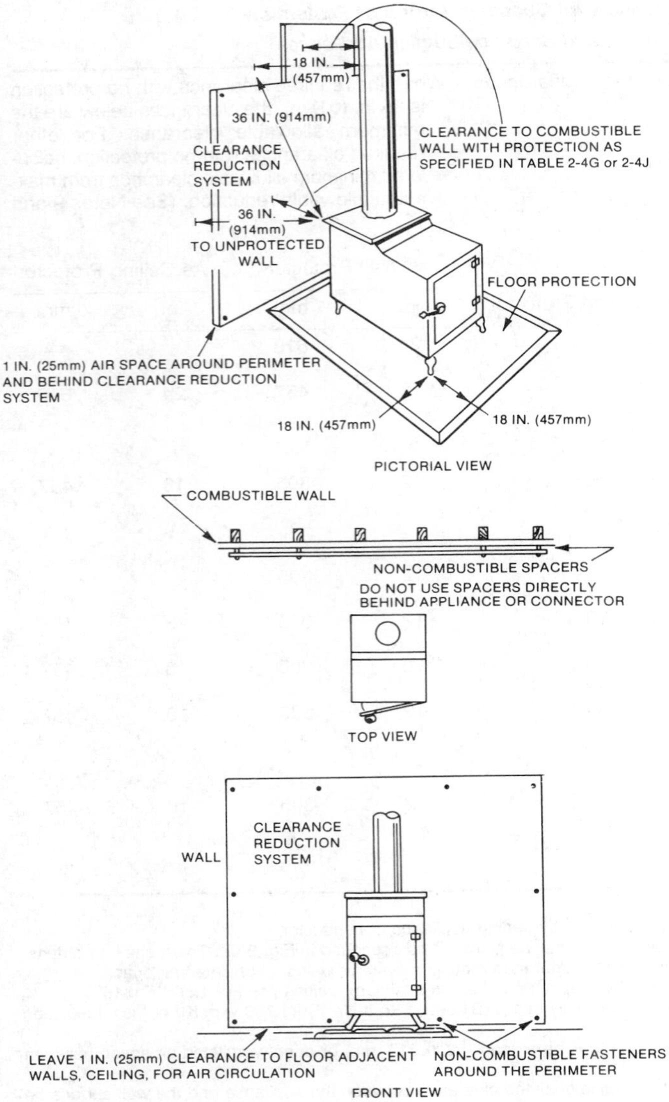

FIG. 2-4X. A clearance reduction system for a heat-producing appliance. The system is a barrier of metal, metal and insulating material, or masonry heat-resistive material with an air space between the barrier and a combustible surface.

Generally, it is the larger type of heating appliances, e.g., boilers and furnaces, that require venting, while smaller appliances, such as listed cooking stoves and hot plates, do not. However, if several smaller appliances that normally do not require venting are located within the same space or room, some may require venting if the aggregate input for all the appliances exceeds 20 Btu per hr per cu ft (0.2 kW/m^3) of the space in which they are installed. NFPA 54 should be consulted for the specifics on the type of appliances requiring venting, the conditions under which vents may be omitted or required, and the type of chimney, gas vent, or venting system that can be used and their installation.

Listed unvented room heaters may be used, but care should be taken to follow the manufacturer's instructions. Such heaters are equipped with an oxygen depletion safety

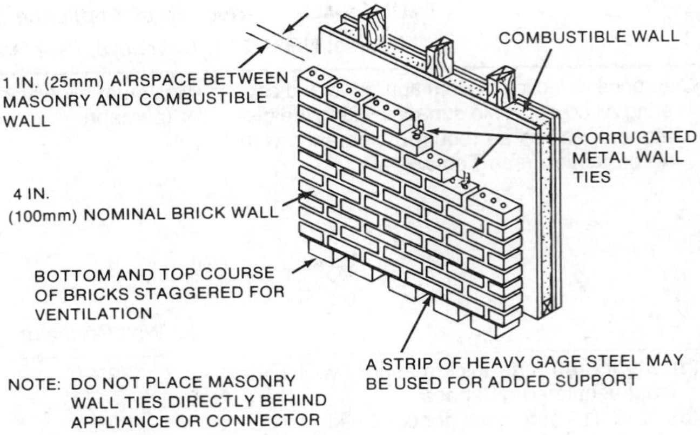

FIG. 2-4Y. Details of a masonry clearance reduction system.

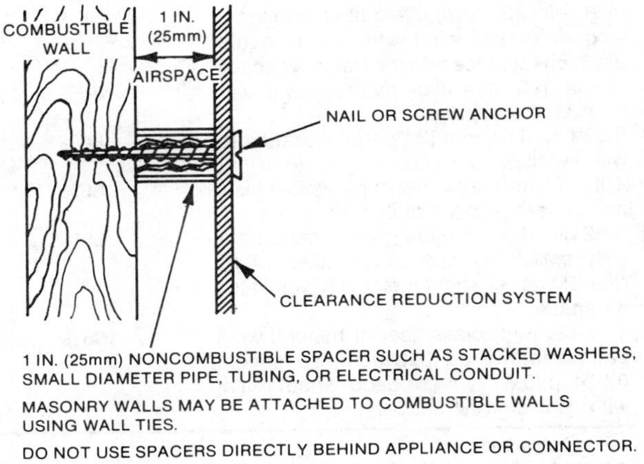

FIG. 2-4Z. Details of anchoring a clearance reduction system to a combustible wall.

shutoff system designed to shut off the gas supply to the heater if the oxygen in the surrounding atmosphere is reduced below a safe level. Unvented room heaters are not to be used in sleeping quarters or bathrooms or in institutions, convalescent homes, orphanages, etc.

Ventilating hoods and exhaust systems may be used to vent gas utilization equipment installed in commercial applications. They may also be used to vent industrial equipment, particularly when the process itself requires fume disposal. If industrial gas utilization equipment is located in a large and well-ventilated space, it may be operated by discharging the products of combustion directly into the atmosphere.

VENTS

Vents are laboratory-tested, factory-built units used to vent fuel-burning heat-producing appliances. Specific types of vents have specific uses. (See Table 2-4M.)

Types of Vents

Type B gas vents: These vents are used to vent listed gas appliances with draft hoods or which are specifically listed to be used with Type B gas vents.

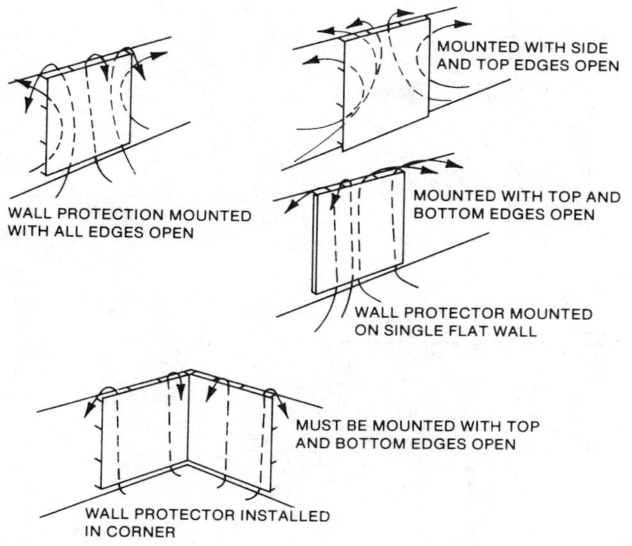

FIG. 2-4AA. Airflow patterns for various configurations of clearance reduction systems having an air space between the barrier and the combustible surface it protects.

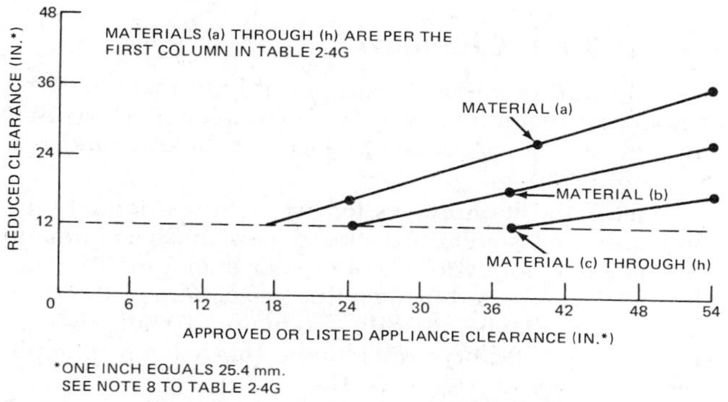

FIG. 2-4BB. Wall protection using materials specified in Table 2-4G.

Type BW gas vents: These vents are used with listed gas wall furnaces having capacities not greater than that of Type BW gas vents. (See Figure 2-4GG.)

Type L vents: These vents are used to vent oil-burning appliances listed for use with Type L vents and gas appliances listed for use with Type B vents.

Single-wall metal pipe: Single-wall metal pipe, constructed of galvanized sheet steel not lighter than No. 20 galvanized sheet gage [0.020 in. (0.61 mm)] or other noncombustible corrosion-resistant material, may be used to vent residential-type and low-heat gas appliances equipped with draft hoods. They may also be used to vent incinerators used outdoors, such as in open sheds, breezeways, or carports. (See Table 2-4M.) Single-wall metal pipe is not used with solid-fuel appliances that require either masonry or factory-built chimneys.

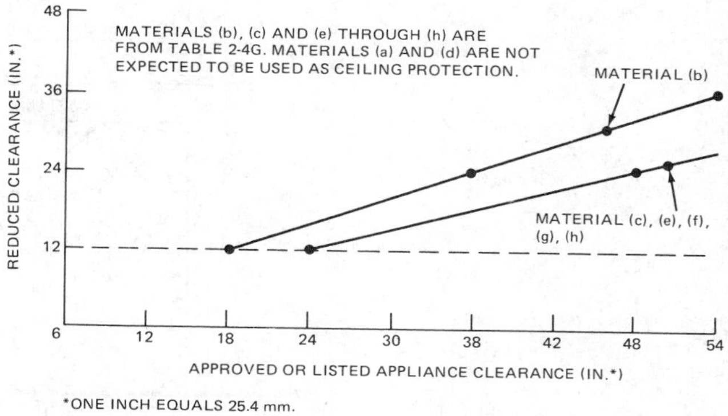

FIG. 2-4CC. Ceiling protection using materials specified in Table 2-4G.

Venting High-Efficiency Heating Appliances

Manufacturers have developed more efficient heating appliances to conserve energy. To obtain efficiencies approaching 90 percent or better, the flue gases from these appliances have been reduced to temperatures as low as 100°F (38°C). Because these temperatures are too low to allow atmospheric venting, mechanical venting is required to exhaust the flue gases under positive pressure. Furthermore, the temperature of the flue gases is low enough to cause condensation of the water vapor in flue gases. Thus, special treatment is needed to provide a venting system that will retain and dispose of the condensate and, in cases of mechanical venting, to prevent leakage of flue gases from the venting system. High-efficiency appliances, if used, should be listed, installed, and vented in compliance with the instructions furnished by the manufacturer with the appliance.

Installation of Vents

Types B, BW, and L vents: Installations must be made in compliance with the terms of their laboratory listings and the manufacturers' instructions, making certain that the required clearances are maintained.

Single-wall metal pipe: The use of single-wall metal pipe is restricted to runs directly from the space in which the gas appliance is located through the roof or exterior wall to the outside. The pipe is not to originate in any attic or concealed space and is not to pass through any attic or inside space, nor through any floor or ceiling. The minimum clearances from combustible material for single-wall metal pipe are as given for connectors in Table 2-4J. (See Figure 2-4HH.) These clearances may be reduced if appropriate protection is provided for combustible materials. (See Table 2-4K.) Where a single-wall metal pipe passes through an exterior wall constructed of combustible material, or the pipe passes through a roof constructed of combustible material, it is protected at the point of passage as specified for connectors in Table 2-4L. If the appliance the pipe serves is a gas appliance for use with a Type B gas vent, protection is by a noncombustible, nonventilating thimble not less than 4 in. (102 mm) larger in diameter than the pipe and extending not less than 18 in. (457 mm) above and 6 in. (152 mm) below the roof, with annular space open at the bottom and closed at the top.

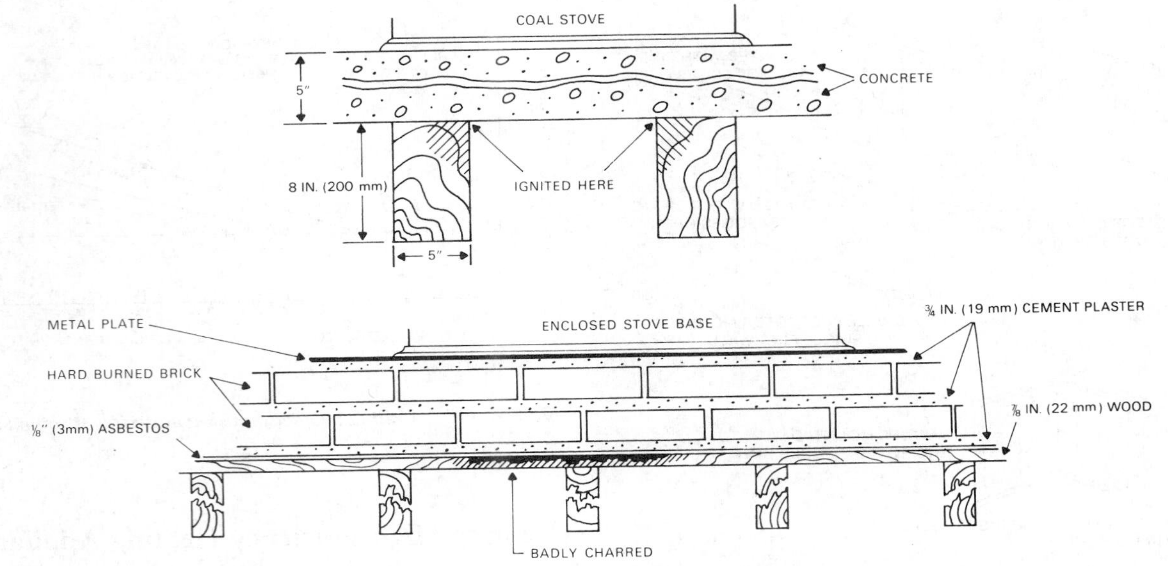

FIG. 2-4DD. Typical fires due to improperly installed heating appliances.

Venting capacities: The venting capacities of various sizes of Type B gas vents, chimneys, and single-wall metal pipe used for venting gas appliances are given in tables in NFPA 54, *National Fuel Gas Code*. NFPA 54 also contains data that may be used to calculate the size of vents required under various circumstances and to establish configurations of venting arrangements. Approved engineering methods may also be used.

Firestopping: Vents that pass through floors of buildings requiring the protection of vertical openings are enclosed within walls having a fire-resistance rating of not less than 1 hr if the vents are in a building less than four stories in height, and not less than 2 hr if the vents are located in a building four stories or more in height.

Draft Hoods

A draft hood is a device built into an appliance, or made a part of the vent connector from an appliance. It is designed to: (1) ensure the ready escape of the flue gases in the event of no draft, backdraft, or stoppage beyond the draft hood; (2) prevent a backdraft from entering the appliance; and (3) neutralize the effect of stack action of the chimney or gas vent upon the appliance operation.

Draft hoods are an important safety feature of gas appliances and are generally required on all vented appliances, except incinerators, dual-oven-type combination ranges, direct-vent appliances, and units designed for power burners or for forced venting by mechanical means.

CHIMNEYS AND FIREPLACES

Chimneys are classified into three major types: (1) factory built, (2) masonry, and (3) metal (smokestacks). In addition to the major chimney classes, there are subclasses that involve type of building and surroundings. For example, small, well-insulated, factory-built chimneys may be installed at close clearances in residential frame construction, while larger chimneys for the same type of appliances are suitable mainly for noncombustible surroundings or in well-ventilated open-room use at much greater clearance to combustibles. Details of installation for chimneys, fireplaces, and vents are provided in NFPA 211, *Chimneys, Fireplaces, Vents, and Solid Fuel Burning Appliances*.

Factory-Built Chimneys

A factory-built chimney is an assembly of manufactured components that form a completed chimney. Factory-built chimneys are tested for compliance with safety standards. (See bibliography.)

Factory-built chimneys for use with residential-type appliances are tested fully enclosed to establish a minimum clearance to combustibles not greater than 2 in. (51 mm). The test is conducted using a flue gas generator that simulates an appliance steadily producing 1000°F (540°C) gases. A typical factory-built chimney for residential appliances is shown in Figure 2-4II.

For building heating equipment [gases to 1000°F (540°C)], commercial ovens and furnaces [gases to 1400°F (760°C)], and medium-heat appliances [gases to 1800°F (980°C)], factory-built chimneys are available in sizes from 10 in. (250 mm) to several feet (one foot equals 0.3 m) in diameter. These chimneys are tested for the appropriate temperature and are used mainly in noncombustible surroundings, although tested thimbles are available for penetration of combustible roofs. None of these are suitable for close clearance to combustible enclosures; however, this is seldom a problem in the usual large building of masonry or metal construction. A typical unenclosed type of large factory-built chimney for serving building boilers is shown in Figure 2-4JJ.

Current information on types, usage, and installation limitations of all UL-listed factory-built chimneys is given in the UL *Gas and Oil Equipment Directory*, published annually with a supplement.

Masonry Chimneys

Field construction requirements for masonry chimneys are detailed in NFPA 211, *Chimneys, Fireplaces, Vents, and Solid Fuel Burning Appliances,* as well as in building codes. Field-erected masonry chimneys, which are subject

TABLE 2-4H. ***Floor Mountings for Heat-Producing Appliances***

Type of Mounting	Required for the Following Types of Heaters and Furnaces
No Floor Protection: Combustible floors.*	Residential-type central furnaces so arranged that the fan chamber occupies the entire area beneath the firing chamber and forms a well-ventilated air space of not less than 18 in. (457 mm) in height between the firing chamber and the floor, with at least one metal baffle between the firing chamber and the floor. Low heat appliances (see Table 7-3E for examples) in which flame and hot gases do not come in contact with the base, on legs which provide not less than 18 in. (457 mm) open space under the base of the appliance, with at least one sheet metal baffle between any burners and the floor. Other appliances for which there is evidence that they are designed for safe operation when installed on combustible floors.
Metal: A sheet of metal not less than No. 24 U.S. Gage (0.024 in./0.61 mm) or other approved noncombustible material, laid over a combustible wood floor.*	Heating and cooking appliances set on legs or simulated legs which provide not less than 4 in. (100 mm) open space under the base. Ordinary residential stoves with legs. Residential ranges with legs. Residential room heaters with legs. Water heaters with legs. Laundry stoves with legs. Room heaters with legs.†
Hollow Masonry: Hollow masonry not less than 4 in. (100 mm) in thickness laid with ends unsealed and joints matched in such a way as to provide free circulation of air through the masonry.	Downflow furnaces.
Hollow Masonry and Metal: Hollow masonry not less than 4 in. (100 mm) in thickness covered with a sheet of metal not less than No. 24 U.S. Gage (0.024 in./0.61 mm), laid over a combustible floor. The masonry will be laid with ends unsealed and joints matched in such a way as to provide a free circulation of air from side to side through the masonry.	Heating furnaces and boilers in which flame and hot gases do not come in contact with the base: Floor mounted heating and cooking appliances. Residential stoves without legs. Residential ranges without legs. Room heaters without legs. Water heaters without legs. Laundry stoves without legs. Residential type incinerators. Restaurant ranges on 4 in. (100 mm) legs. Other low heat appliances on 4 in. (100 mm) legs. Medium heat appliances on legs which provide not less than 24 in. (610 mm) open space under the base.
Two Courses Masonry and Plate: Two courses of 4-in. (100 mm) hollow clay tile covered with steel plate not less than 3/16 in. (4.76 mm) in thickness, laid over a combustible floor. The courses of tile will be laid at right angles with ends unsealed and joints matched in such a way as to provide a free circulation of air through the masonry courses.	Heating furnaces and boilers in which flame and hot gases come in contact with the base. Restaurant ranges. Other low heat appliances.
Fire Resistive Floors Extending 6 in. (152 mm): Floors of fire-resistive construction with noncombustible flooring and surface finish and with no combustible material against the underside thereof, or on fire-resistive slabs or arches having no combustible material against the underside thereof. Such construction will extend not less than 6 in. (152 mm) beyond the appliance on all sides, and where solid fuel is used, it will extend not less than 18 in. (457 mm) at the front or side where ashes are removed.	Floor mounted heating and cooking appliances. Residential type room heaters. Residential type water heaters.
Fire Resistive Floors Extending 12 in. (305 mm): Floors of fire-resistive construction with noncombustible flooring and surface finish and with no combustible material against the underside thereof, or on fire-resistive slabs or arches having no combustible material against the underside thereof. Such construction will extend not less than 12 in. (305 mm) beyond the appliance on all sides, and where solid fuel is used, it will extend not less than 18 in. (457 mm) at the front or side where ashes are removed.	Heating furnaces or boilers. Restaurant-type cooking appliances. Residential-type incinerators. Other low heat appliances.

TABLE 2-4H. *Floor Mountings for Heat-Producing Appliances (Continued)*

Type of Mounting	Required for the Following Types of Heaters and Furnaces
Fire Resistive Floors Extending 3 ft (0.9 m): Floors of fire-resistive construction with noncombustible flooring and surface finish and with no combustible material against the underside thereof, or on fire-resistive slabs or arches having no combustible material against the underside thereof. Such construction will extend not less than 3 ft (0.9 m) beyond the appliance on all sides, and where solid fuel is used, it will extend not less than 8 ft (2.4 m) at the front or side where ashes are removed.	Medium heat appliances and furnaces. (See Table 2-4G for examples.)
Fire Resistive Floors Extending 10 ft (3.1 m): Floors of fire-resistive construction with noncombustible flooring and surface finish and with no combustible material against the underside thereof. Such construction will extend not less than 10 ft (3.1 m) beyond the appliance on all sides, and where solid fuel is used, it will extend not less than 30 ft (9.1 m) at the front or side where hot products are removed.	High heat appliances and furnaces. (See Table 2-4G for examples.)

* Where an appliance is mounted on a combustible floor, and solid fuel is used or the appliance is a domestic type incinerator, a sheet of 1/4-in. (25 mm) asbestos covered by a sheet of metal not less than No. 24 U.S. Gage (0.024 in./0.61 mm) will be required extending at least 18 in. (457 mm) from the appliance on the front or side where ashes are removed. (The sheet of asbestos may be omitted where the protection required under the appliance is a sheet of metal only.) For residential type incinerators the protection must also extend at least 12 in. (305 mm) beyond all other sides. If the appliance is installed with clearance less than 6 in. (152 mm) the protection for the floor should be carried to the wall.

† Floor protection for radiating type gas burning room heaters which make use of metal, asbestos or ceramic material to direct radiation to the front of the device should extend at least 36 in. (914 mm) in front when the heater is not of a type approved for installation on a combustible floor.

to the know-how and ability of available labor, are not tested, except perhaps for a smoke test. A minimum residential masonry chimney consists of a refractory fire clay tile liner and an air space of roughly ½ in. (13 mm) between the liner and brick, with all liner joints grouted both to prevent leakage and to center and support the tile liners. (See Figure 2-4KK.) One course of common brick around the liner suffices for usual residential chimneys. For higher temperature classifications, firebrick is used as the liner, with additional courses of brick for larger size or greater strength and security. All chimneys should, of course, be supported by footings suitable for the chimney size and weight and be provided with cleanouts between the points of entry and the lowest chimney level.

For residential and low-heat chimneys, a minimum of 2 in. (5 cm) of air space is required between the chimney and surrounding combustibles. For higher heat chimneys, larger clearances are appropriate.

As a general rule, the best and safest chimney operation and appliance control is obtained with only one appliance attached to a chimney flue. Two or three gas appliances, however, may be connected into a masonry chimney flue at one level of a building, provided that the connector size, its vertical rise, and chimney size and height are in accordance with tabulated capacity data in NFPA 54, *National Fuel Gas Code*. The construction of masonry chimneys for open-front fireplaces is the same as for other residential appliances and is specified in NFPA 211, *Chimneys, Fireplaces, Vents, and Solid Fuel Burning Appliances*.

Metal Chimneys

Metal chimneys are suitable for all the classes of appliances, but are not subjected to safety testing of any kind. The major hazard with these chimneys is inadequate clearance to combustibles where they penetrate ceilings and roofs. (See Figure 2-4LL.)

Metal chimneys may be of single-wall metal for low-temperature use, such as with gas appliances, or metal lined with firebrick or refractory mortar for medium- and high-heat service. They may be located inside or outside of buildings, but not inside one- and two-family dwellings or buildings of wood-frame construction. The conditions under which metal chimneys may be used are quite limited and are spelled out in detail in NFPA 211, *Chimneys, Fireplaces, Vents, and Solid Fuel Burning Appliances*. The standard is also quite specific on acceptable materials of construction.

Regardless of permitted clearances, metal chimneys should not be enclosed with combustible construction. It is particularly important that the metal used be resistant to corrosion if the gases are 350°F (177°C) or below, because exposed outdoor portions of the chimney walls may be below the dew point. The resulting continuous condensation can lead to rapid corrosion and very short chimney life.

Chimney Functions

The purpose of a chimney is to create draft or negative pressure to provide combustion air for the fuel or fuel bed and to remove products of combustion from the appliance and building. For open fireplaces or for gas appliances having draft hoods, chimney draft has very little influence on the combustion process; the chimney serves only as a conduit for carrying away the products of combustion. For forced-draft or packaged boilers, the chimney may be under slight positive pressure and, again, serves only as a duct to carry away combustion products. The advantage of the slight positive pressure, commonly from 0.5 to 1.5 in. of water column (120 to 370 Pa), is that it permits use of much smaller chimneys and eliminates some concerns about the draft-producing ability or height of the chimney.

The technology of matching the size, height, and configuration of a chimney to the temperature, type, and quantity of fuel for its correct capacity is covered in the *ASHRAE Handbook and Product Directory 1988 Equipment*. (See bibliography.)

Height of Chimneys

A variety of factors determine the height of any chimney, including the type of appliance, need for draft, roof con-

TABLE 2-4I. ***Floor Mountings for Solid Fuel Burning Appliances***

Kind of Appliance	Allowed Mounting
(1) All forced air & gravity furnaces, steam and water boilers. (2) Residential type ranges, stoves, room heaters, and combination fireplace stove/room heaters, having less than 2 in. (51 mm) of ventilated open space beneath the fire chamber or base of the unit.	Floors of fire resistive construction with noncombustible water heaters, fireplace flooring and surface finish, or fire resistive arches or slabs. These constructions shall have no combustible material against the underside thereof. Such construction shall extend not less than 18 in. (457 mm) beyond the appliance on all sides. These appliances shall not be placed on combustible floors.
(3) Residential-type ranges, water heaters, fireplace stoves, room heaters and combination stove/room heaters having legs or pedestals providing 2 to 6 in. (51 to 152 mm) of ventilated open space beneath the fire chamber or base of the heater.	On combustible floors when such floors are protected by 4 in. (102 mm) of hollow masonry, laid to provide air circulation through the masonry layer. Such masonry shall be covered with 24 U.S. Gage (0.024 in./0.61 mm) sheet metal. The required floor protection shall extend not less than 18 in. (457 mm) on all sides of the appliance. On noncombustible floors, such floors shall extend not less than 18 in. (457 mm) on all sides of the appliance.
(4) Residential-type ranges, water heaters, fireplace stoves, room heaters and combination fireplace stove/room heaters having legs or pedestals providing over 6 in. (152 mm) of ventilated open space beneath the fire chamber or base of the covered heater.	On combustible floors when such floors are protected by closely spaced masonry units of brick, concrete or stone, which provide a thickness of not less than 2 in. (51 mm). Such masonry shall be covered by or placed over a sheet of 24 U.S. Gage (0.024 in./0.61 mm) steel. The required floor protection shall extend not less than 18 in. (457 mm) on all sides of the appliance. On noncombustible floors, such floors shall extend not less than 18 in. (457 mm) on all sides of the appliance.

struction, and building height. The minimum height of a chimney (or gas vent) for gas appliances having draft hoods is based on the height specified in the applicable test standard for that appliance. For example, gas furnaces, water heaters, boilers, and room heaters must pass draft hood spillage tests with 5 ft (1.5 m) of chimney height measured from the draft hood to chimney outlet, while wall furnaces require a vent outlet at least 12 ft (3.7 m) above the floor.

In contrast to these low heights for draft hood appliances, some older types of solid fuel boilers require up to 50 or 70 ft (15 to 20 m) of chimney to produce the draft needed to overcome fuel bed and internal flow resistance and to develop rated heat output.

Residential oil furnaces and boilers with pressure atomizing burners are designed to function with negative outlet draft settings in the range of 0.04 to 0.06 in. of water column (10 to 15 Pa). Manufacturers of factory-built resi-

TABLE 2-4J. ***Chimney Connector and Vent Connector Clearance from Combustible Materials***

Description of Appliance	Minimum Clearance in.	mm (*See Note 1*)
RESIDENTIAL-TYPE APPLIANCES		
Single-Wall Metal Pipe Connectors		
Gas Appliances without Draft Hoods	18	(457)
Electric, Gas, and Oil Incinerators	18	(457)
Oil and Solid-Fuel Appliances	18	(457)
Unlisted Gas Appliances with Draft Hoods	9	(229)
Boilers and Furnaces Equipped with Listed Gas Burners and with Draft Hoods	9	(229)
Oil Appliances Listed at Suitable for use with Type L Vents	9	(229)
Listed Gas Appliances with Draft Hoods (*See Note 3*)	6	(152)
Type L Vent Piping Connectors		
Gas Appliances without Draft Hoods	9	(229)
Electric, Gas, and Oil Incinerators	9	(229)
Oil and Solid-Fuel Appliances	9	(229)
Unlisted Gas Appliances with Draft Hoods	6	(152)
Boilers and Furnaces Equipped with Listed Gas Burners and with Draft Hoods	6	(152)
Oil Appliances Listed as Suitable for Use with Type L Vents	(*See Note 2*)	
Listed Gas Appliances with Draft Hoods	(*See Note 3*)	
Listed Gas Appliances with Draft Hoods	(*See Note 3*)	
LOW HEAT APPLIANCES		
Single-Wall Metal Pipe Connectors		
Gas, Oil, and Solid-Fuel Boilers, Furnaces, and Water Heaters	18	(457)
Ranges, Restaurant-Type	18	(457)
Oil Unit Heaters	18	(457)
Unlisted Gas Unit Heaters	18	(457)
Listed Gas Unit Heaters with Draft Hoods	6	(152)
Other Low Heat Industrial Appliances	14	(457)
MEDIUM HEAT APPLIANCES		
Single-Wall Metal Pipe Connectors		
HIGH HEAT APPLIANCES		
Massonry or Metal Connectors		
All Gas, Oil, and Solid fuel Appliances	(*See Note 4*)	

Notes to Table 2-4J

Note 1: These clearances apply except if the listing of an appliancespecifies different clearance, in which case the listed clearances takesprecedence.

Note 2: If listed Type L vent piping is used, the clearance may be in accordance with the vent listing.

Note 3: If listed Type B or Type L vent piping is used, the clearancemay be in accordance with the vent listing.

Note 4: Clearances must be based on good engineering practice and acceptable to the authority having jurisdiction.

The clearance from connectors to combustible materials may be reducedif the combustible material is protected in accordance with 2-4K.

Source: NFPA 211, *Chimneys, Fireplaces, Vents, and Solid Fuel Burning Appliances.*

TABLE 2-4K. *Reduction of Connector Clearance with Specified Formsof Protection*[a,b,c,d,e,f,g,h]

Clearance reduction applied to and covering all combustible surfaceswithin the distance specified as required clearance with no protection (seeTable 2-4J).	Maximum allowable reduction in clearance (percent)		When the required clearance with not protection is 18 in., the clearances below are the minimum allowable clearances. For other required clearances, calculate minimum allowable clearance from maximumallowable reduction.[h]	
	As Wall Protector	As Ceiling Protector	As Wall Protector	As Ceiling Protector
(a) $3\frac{1}{2}$ in. (90 mm) thick masonry wall without ventilated air space.	33%	—	12/305	—
(b) $\frac{1}{2}$ in. (13 mm) thick noncombustible insulation board over 1 in. (25 mm) glass fiber or mineral wool batts without ventilated air space.	50%	33%	9/229	12/305
(c) 0.024 in./0.61 mm (24 gage) sheet metal over 1 in. (25 mm) glassfiber or mineral wood batts reinforced with wire, or equivalent, on rear facewith ventilated air space.	66%	50%	6/152	9/229
(d) $3\frac{1}{2}$ in. (90 mm) thick masonry wall with ventilated air space.	66%	—	6/152	—
(e) 0.024 in. 0.61 mm (24 gage) sheet metal with ventilated air space.	66%	50%	6/152	9/229
(f) $\frac{1}{2}$ in. (13 mm) thick noncombustible insulation board with ventilated air space.	66%	50%	6/152	9/229
(g) 0.024 in./0.61 mm (24 gage) sheet metal with ventilated air spaceover 0.024 in./0.61 mm (24 gage) sheet metal with ventilated air space.	66%	50%	6/152	9/229
(h) 1 in. (25 mm) glass fiber or mineral wood batts sandwiched betweentwo sheets 0.024 in./0.61 mm (24 gage) sheet metal with ventilated air space.	66%	50%	6/152	9/229

[a] Spaces and ties must be of noncombustible material. No spaces or ties can be used directly behind appliance or connector.

[b] With all clearance reduction systems using a ventilated air space, adequate air circulation must be provided. There must be at least 1 in. (25 mm) between the clearance reduction system and combustible walls and ceilings for clearance reduction systems using a ventilated air space.

[c] Mineral wood batts (blanket or board) must have a minimum density of 8 lb per ft^3 (128.7 kg/m^3) and have a minimum melting point of1500°F (816°C).

[d] Insulation material used as part of clearnace reduction system must have a thermal conductivity of 1.0 (Btu-in.)/sq ft-hr-°F orless. Insulation board must be formed of noncombustible material.

[e] If a single wall connector passes through a masonry wall used as a wall shield, there must be at least $\frac{1}{2}$ in. (13 mm) of open, ventilatedair space between the connector and the masonry.

[f] There must be at least 1 in. (25 mm) between the connector and the protector. In no case can the clearance between the appliancesand the wall surface be reduced below that allowed in the table.

[g] All Clearance and thickness are minimum; larger clearances and thickness are acceptable.

[h] To calculate the minimum allowable clearance, the following formula may be used:

$C_{pr} = C_{un} \times (1 - R/100)$.

C_{pr} is the minimum allowable clearance, C_{un} is the required clearance with no protection, and R is the maximum allowance reduction in clearance.

Source: NFPA 211, *Chimneys, Fireplaces, Vents and Solid Fuel Burning Appliances.*

dential chimneys have prepared draft chimney height tables that allow for such factors as the number of connector elbows, fuel input rating, and outlet size, so that an adequate height can be selected.

Building or dwelling height and configuration also govern chimney height. The generally cited rule for minimum height of the chimney outlet is illustrated in Figure 2-4MM. The chimney height selected must be adequate for proper appliance operation and for adequate chimney flow, as well as for proper height above the roof. Owing to the aerodynamic complexity of buildings, roofs, and chimneys, the dimensions suggested in Figure 2-4LL sometimes are not adequate for efficient operation, which is attested to by the proliferation of special vent caps, chimney extensions, and other devices used in attempting to cure fireplace or draft problems.

Airflow over the roof must be visualized to analyze a structure for the correct chimney top location and to minimize backdrafts due to wind. Only the pressure or windward side of pitched roofs needs to be considered, because the flow moving up a building wall or toward the ridge separates from the downward side at the ridge or building edge and creates a zone of negative pressure, which circulates and eddies in this protected or cavity zone as shown

TABLE 2-4L. ***Connector Systems and Clearances from Combustible Walls for Residential Heating Appliances***

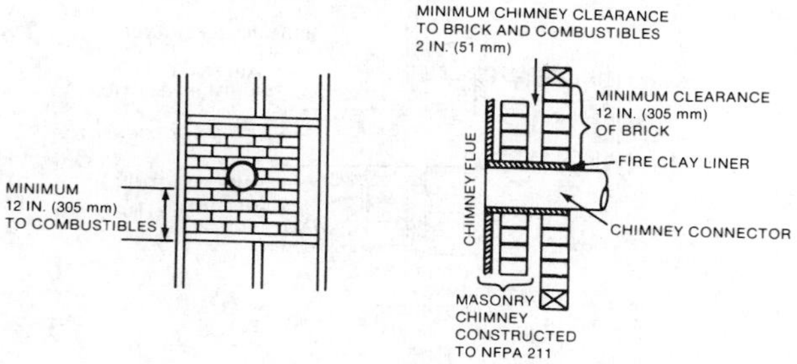

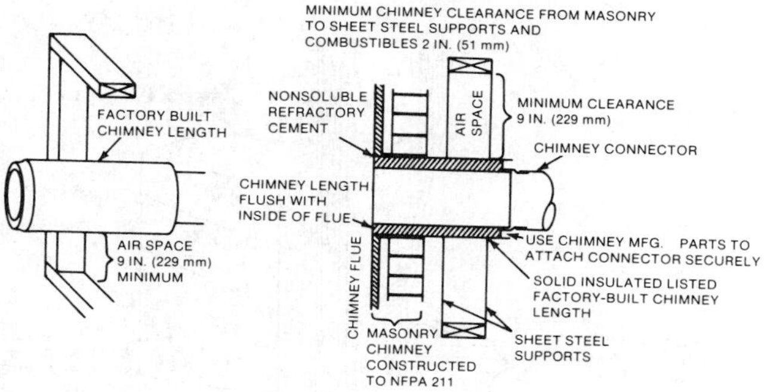

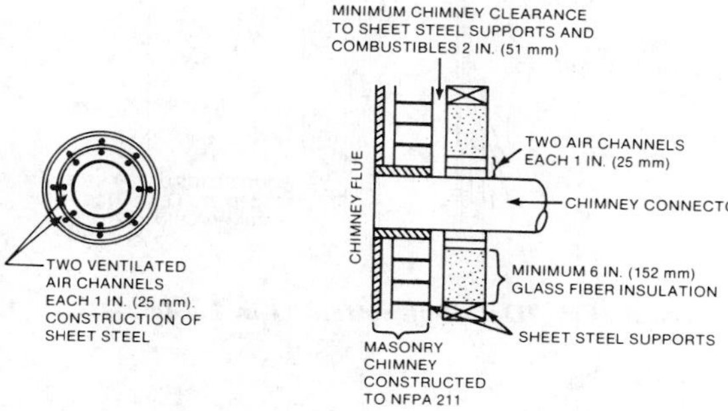

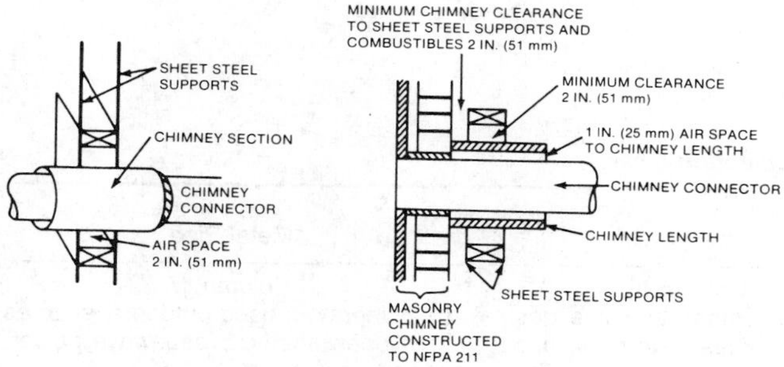

System		Clearance in mm
A	Minimum 3.5-in. (90-mm) thick brick masonary wall framed intocombustible wall with a minimum of 12 in. (305 mm) brick separation from clay liner to combustibles. Fire clay liner (ASTM C315 or equivalent), minimum $^5/_8$-in. (16-mm) wall thickness, shall runfrom outer surface of brick wall to, but not beyond, the inner surfaceof chimney flue liner and must be firmly cemented in place.	12/305
B	Solid insulated listed factory-built chimney length of the same inside diameter as the chimney connector and having 1 in. (25 mm) or more of insulation with a minimum 9-in. (229-mm) air space between the outer wall of the chimney length and combustibles. The inner end of the chimney length must be flush with the inside of the masonry chimney flue and must be sealed to the flue and to the brick masonry penetration with nonwater-soluble refractory cement. Supports must be securely fastened to wall surfaces on all sides. Fasteners between supports and the chimney length must not penetrate the chimney liner.	9/229
C.	Sheet steel chimney connector, minimum 24 gage [0.024 in.) 0.61 mm)] in thickness, with a ventilated thimble, minimum 124 gage [0.024 in. (0.61 mm)] in thickness, having two 1-in. (25-mm) air channels, separated from combustibles by a minimum of 6 in. (152 mm) of glass fiber insulation. Opening must be covered and thimble supported with a sheet steel support, minimum 24 gage [0.024 in. (0.61 mm)] in thickness. Support must be securely fastened to wall surfaces on all sides and shall be sized to fit and hold chimney section. Fasteners used to secure chimney sections must not penetrate chimney flue liner.	6/152
D.	Solid insulated listed factory-built chimney length with an inside diameter 2 in. (51 mm) larger than the chimney connector and having 1 in. (25 mm) or more of insulation, serving as a pass-through for a single wall sheet steel chimney connector of minimum 24 gage [0.024 in. (0.61 mm)] thickness, with a minimum 2-in. (51-mm) air space between the outer wall of chimney section and combustibles. Minimum length of chimney section must be 12 in. (305 mm). Chimney section concentric with and spaced 1 in. (25 mm) away from connector by means of sheet steel support plates on both ends of chimney section. Opening must be covered and chimney section supported on both sides with sheet steel supports of minimum 24 gage [0.024 in. (0.61 mm)] thickness. Supports must be securely fastened to wall surfaces on all sides and must be sized to fit and hold chimney section. Fasteners used to secure chimney sections must not penetrate chimney flue liner.	2/51

Additional Requirements:

1. Insulation material used as part of wall pass-through system must be of noncombustible material and must have a thermal conductivity of 1.0 Btu•in./ft^2•°F (3.88 kg•cal/hr•°C) or less.
2. All clearances and thicknesses are minimums; larger clearances and thicknesses are acceptable.
3. hAny material used to close up an opening for the connector must be of noncombustible material.
4. A connector to a masonry chimney, except for System B, must extend to on piece through the wall pass-through system and the chimney wall to the inner face of the flue liner, but not beyond.

Source: NFPA 211, *Chimneys, Fireplaces, Vents and Solid Fuel Burning Appliances.*

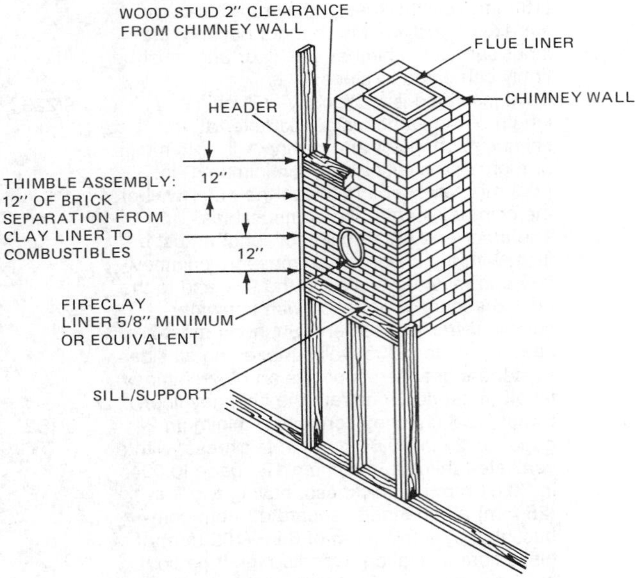

FIG. 2-4EE. Detail of System A in Table 2-4L.

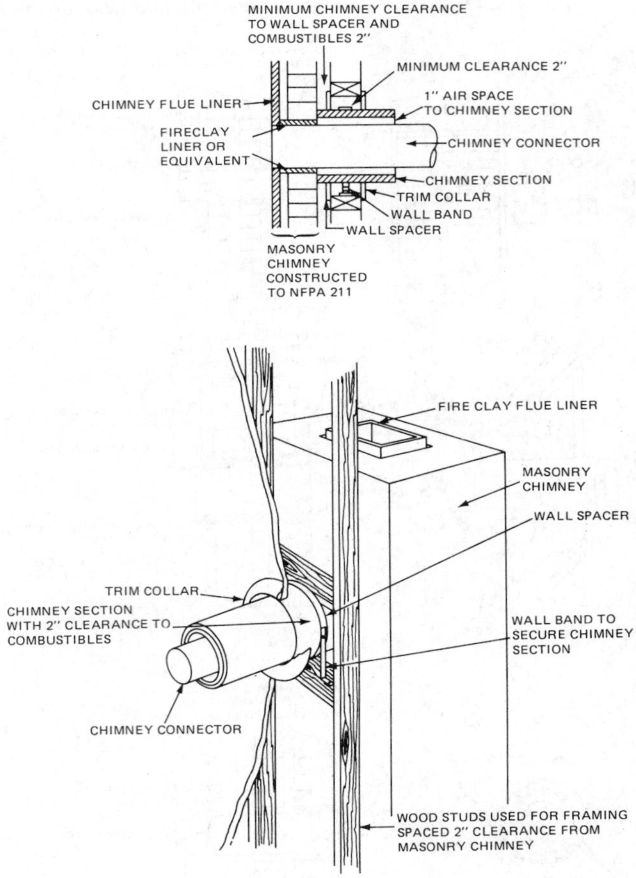

FIG. 2-4FF. Detail of System D in Table 2-4L.

TABLE 2-4M. *Vent Selection Chart*

Type of Vent			
Type B—Gas	Type BW—Gas	Type L—Oil	Metal Pipe
Column I	Column II	Column III	Column IV
All listed gas appliances with draft hoods such as: 1. Central furnaces 2. Duct furnaces 3. Floor furnaces 4. Heating boilers 5. Ranges 6. Built-in ovens 7. Vented wall furnaces listed for use with Type B vents 8. Room heaters 9. Water heaters 10. Horizontal furnaces 11. Unit heaters	1. Vented wall furnaces listed for use with Type BW vents only	1. Low temperature flue gas appliances listed for use with Type L vents 2. Gas appliances shown in Column I	1. Incinerators used outdoors, such as in open sheds, breezeways or car-ports. 2. Gas appliances shown in Column I 3. Listed residential and low heat gas appliances without draft hoods and unlisted residential and low heat gas appliances with or without draft hoods

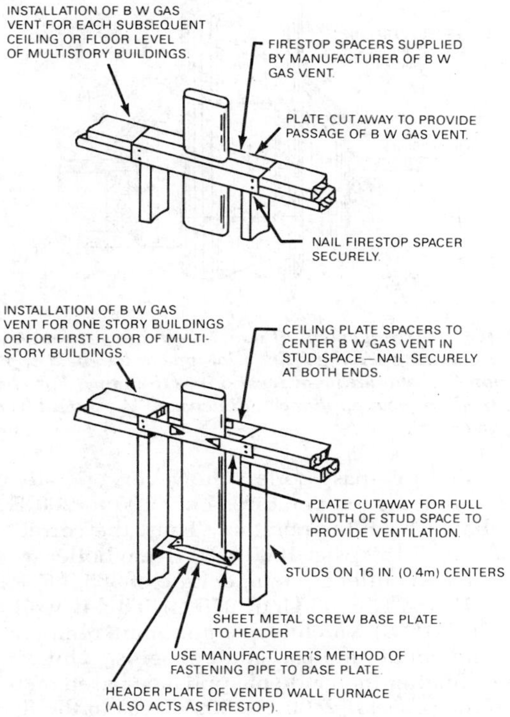

FIG. 2-4GG. Installation of Type BW gas vents for vented wall furnaces.

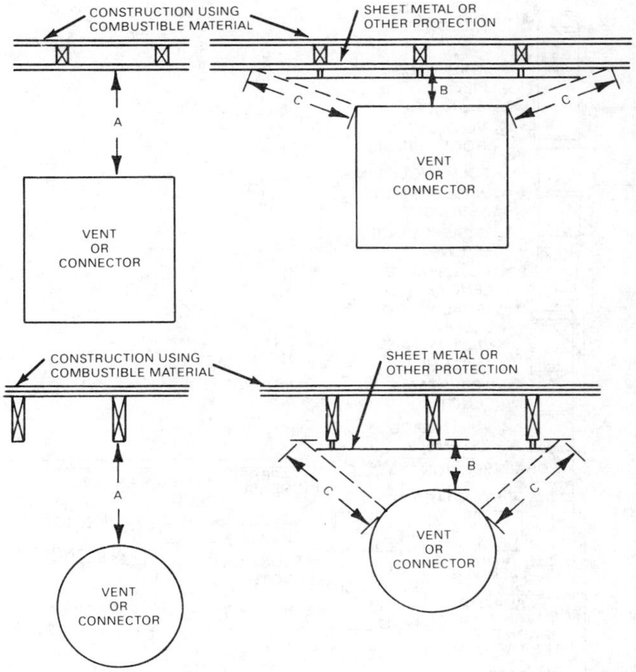

FIG. 2-4HH. Extent of protection required to reduce clearances from combustibles for vents and connectors. "A" equals the required clearance with no protections as specified in Table 2-4J; "B" equals the reduced clearance permitted by the types of protection specified in Table 2-4K. The protection applied to construction using combustible material should extend far enough in each direction to make "C" equal to "A."

in Figure 2-4NN. The building thus may aid or impede chimney flow by using the wind to create a zone of negative or positive pressure at the chimney outlet.

Spark Arresters on Chimneys

Spark arresters are required on refuse burners or incinerators, but are desirable for all solid fuels. If sparks are expected from a fireplace or solid-fuel appliance, a chimney of any kind should have a spark screen and/or the roof surface material should be noncombustible. The usual recommendation for an arrester is for a wire mesh cloth or expanded metal having approximately ½-in. (13 mm) square openings. Smaller openings clog rapidly, while larger ones could allow passage of some sparks. Stainless-steel material is recommended, with galvanized steel hardware cloth a poor second choice because the coating soon burns off and frequent replacement is necessary. Factory-built chimney manufacturers offer a variety of chimney cap options with integral and accessory spark-arrester screens.

Selection of Chimneys

As an aid to selecting chimneys, heat-producing appliances have been graded by temperatures developed in the heating media or material being heated, and also by size. The grades of low-, medium-, and high-heat appliances can then be used to choose the chimney. (See Table 2-4N.) This selection method provides help if the appliance outlet gas temperature is consistent with its grade; however, a study of several hundred types of process appliances, ovens, and furnaces has indicated the precepts of the grading system do not always hold true. With the availability of modern temperature instrumentation and controls and the need to conserve energy, the outlet flue gas temperature and other conditions can and should be known more precisely than heretofore for the vast majority of fuel-burning equipment.

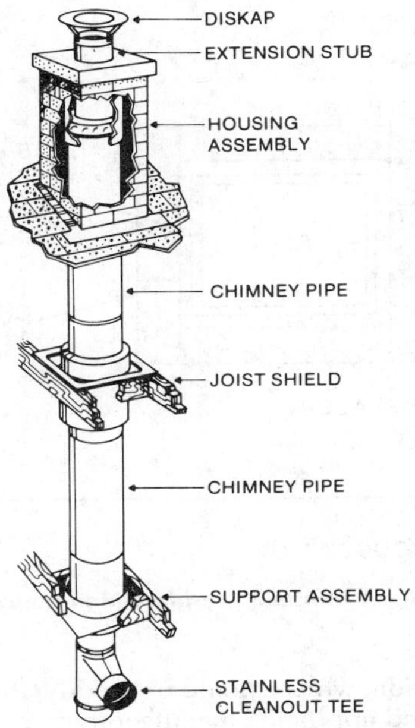

FIG. 2-4II. A typical factory-built chimney. (Source: Metalbestos Div., Wallace-Murray Corp.)

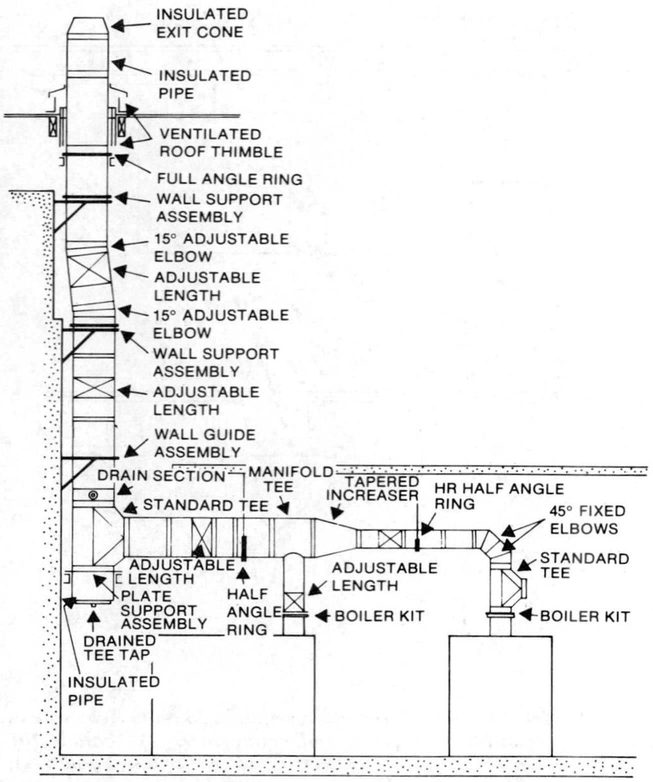

FIG. 2-4JJ. A typical unenclosed factory-built chimney for serving building boilers.

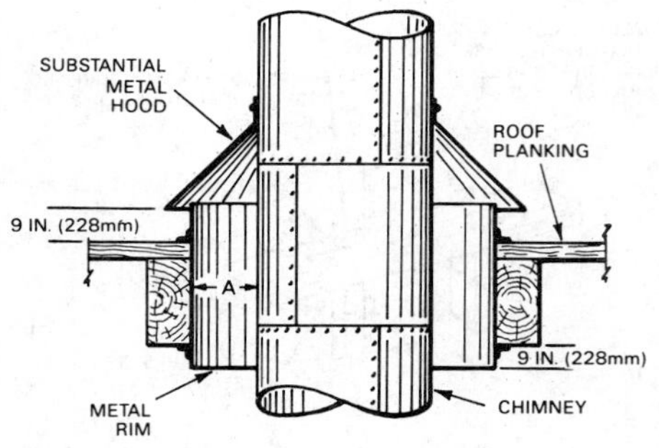

FIG. 2-4LL. Arrangement of a metal chimney through a wood roof. For chimneys serving residential-type or low-heat appliances, dimension "A" should be at least 6 in. (152 mm). For chimneys serving medium-heat appliances, dimension "A" should be at least 18 in. (457 mm).

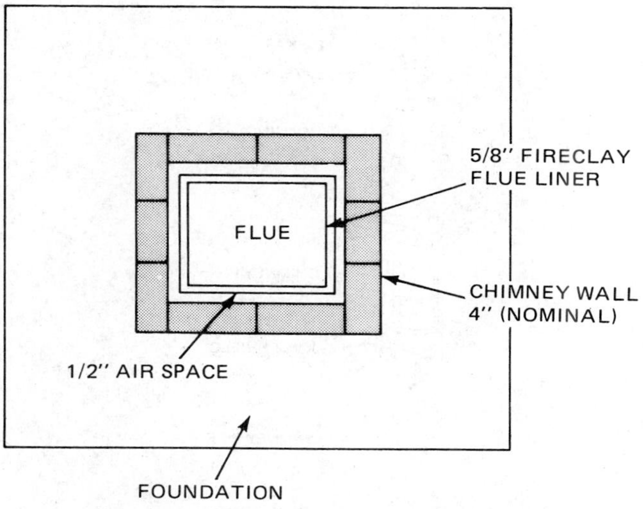

FIG. 2-4KK. A minimum residential masonry chimney.

This information, which should be readily obtainable from equipment and appliance manufacturers, can offer a logical basis for chimney selection and for determining safe conditions of installation and use.

As an example of a grading inconsistency, a steam boiler operating at more than 50 psig (350 kPa) is classified in some codes as a medium-heat appliance. In selecting a chimney, it could be assumed that the outlet temperature was as high as 1500 to 1800°F (815 to 980°C).

Modern multiple-pass boilers, however, operate at controlled outlet gas temperatures only 100 to 200°F (38 to 93°C) above steam temperature. Thus, the correct chimney for even a 150 psig (1000 kPa) steam boiler would be selected for an outlet gas temperature of 365.9°F + 200°F, or 565.9°F (185°C + 93°C, or 278°C). This is well below the 600°F (316°C) which is one minimum temperature at which the medium heat grade begins. Thus, in this instance, neither the grade of appliance based on temperature of the process [2400°F (1300°C) gas in the flame] or material [365.9°F (185°C) steam] provides a conclusive basis for selecting the boiler's chimney.

Chimney Selection Checklist

Selection of the correct chimney may be aided by the following two checklists. (In those areas with adopted building codes, the code requirements take precedence over the generalities in the checklists; however, if special engineering is needed for a particular application, this approach should generally also meet the intent of any modern performance code.)

Code factors

Applicable building code
Type or grade of appliance
Appliance manufacturers' instructions
Chimney manufacturers' instructions
Listed, certified appliance
Unlisted appliance
Earthquake zone—for masonry types
Air quality and external discharge factors
Type, occupancy, and use of building
Availability of fire protection service

Engineering factors

Temperature of gases from appliance
Characteristics of fuel and combustion gases
Corrosives, particulates, deposits, dew point
Quantity of combustion products
Operating needs and cycle of appliance
Method of draft control
Location of chimney in or outside of structure
Materials adjacent to chimney
Space available for chimney
Length and insulating ability of chimney

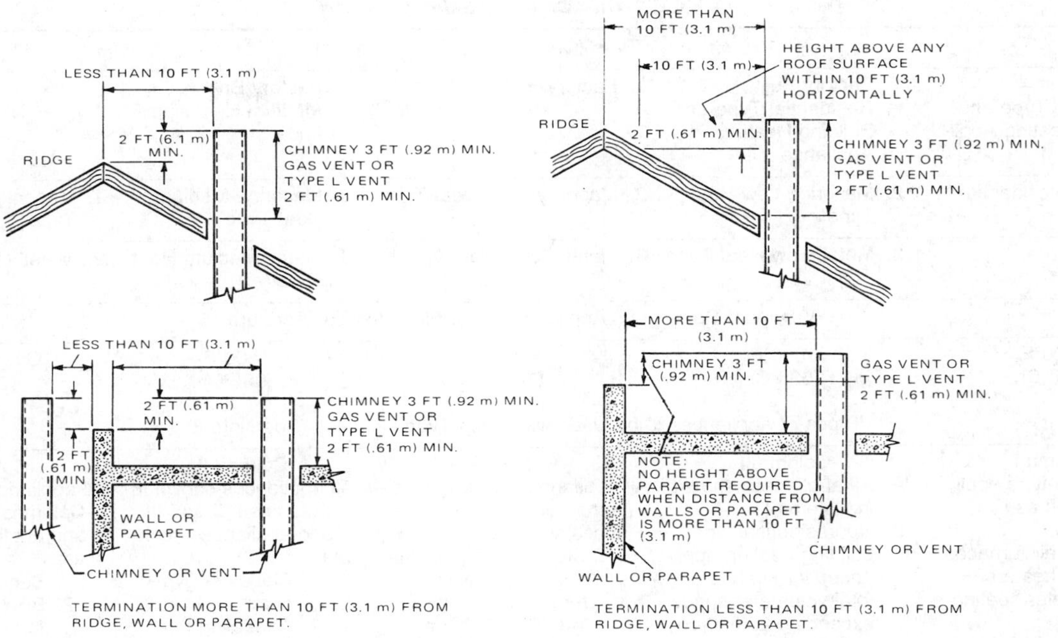

FIG. 2-4MM. Termination of vents and chimneys above buildings.

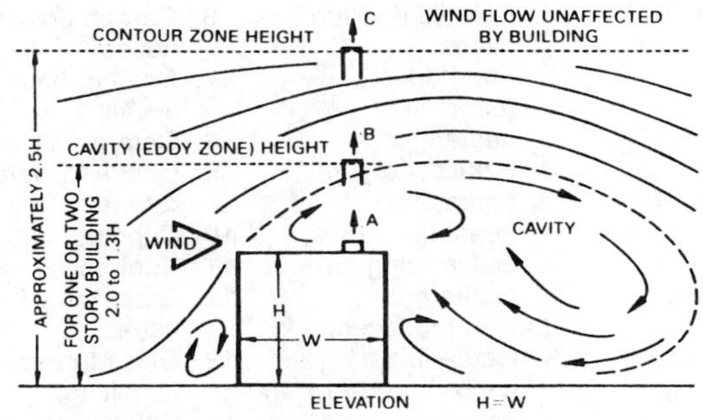

FIG. 2-4NN. Eddy and contour zones due to airflow for one- or two-story buildings and their effect on chimney gas discharge.

Hazards of Chimneys

For chimneys serving oil, wood, or coal appliances the possibility of fire involves one or more of the following elements: (1) operator error or ignorance, (2) control failure, (3) improper installation, (4) use of a defective or unlisted appliance, (5) ignition of combustible soot or creosote deposits in the chimney, (6) serious cracks or internal collapse of the masonry, (7) defective construction, and (8) failure to secure joints of factory-built products.

Even masonry chimneys for gas appliances operating at very low temperatures have their problems. Condensation of flue product moisture may eventually disintegrate the mortar, leaving the chimney weak and easily toppled—a hazard to passersby.

In masonry chimneys, the following conditions may cause a fire in adjacent combustible materials:

1. Filling the space between the chimney and wood framing with combustible insulation, or placing framing into or against the chimney wall.
2. Using a restrictive chimney cap in combination with cracks or failed mortar in a chimney, which may cause excessive leakage of hot gas at roof level, thus endangering rafters and roofing.
3. Prolonged overfiring, which may cause excessive heating on adjacent walls. At temperatures of 500°F (260°C) on the brick exterior surface, 2-in. (51 mm) clearance to nearby combustibles is of little protective value, particularly if there is little ventilation airflow.
4. Creosote or soot fires, insofar as masonry chimneys are susceptible to collecting creosote deposits. When thick or heavy enough, these deposits can burn long enough to cause outer chimney surface temperatures that can ignite the structure around them. Further, upward gas flow velocity may be sufficient to carry sparks up from the fire or burning creosote and to drop them on the roof. After a severe chimney fire, both the tile liner and bricks may have serious cracks due to thermal expansion.

Factory-built chimneys provide many opportunities for installation errors and shortcuts, which can lead to fire hazards. Among these are:

1. Installation of the chimney ceiling support above the ceiling framing. This necessitates passing the single-wall connector through ceiling framing at what could be dangerously close clearance; thus, the hazard might more properly be blamed on the connector.
2. Failure to secure joints or align gas-carrying parts. Many designs of factory-built chimneys allow very little tolerance for misalignment. Failure to make sure that the inner pipes of a multi-wall chimney are aligned and connected can allow flames to enter external passages reserved for cooling airflow.
3. Use of mismatched chimney parts. A given design or brand of chimney is intended to be assembled only

TABLE 2-4N. *Chimney Selection Chart*

Chimney Type (Construction Requirements)				
1. Factory Built—Residential Type and Building Heating Appliance	1. Factory Built—Residential Type and Building Heating Appliance	1. Factory Built—1,400°F (760°C)	1. Factory Built—Medium Heat Appliance	
2. Masonry, Residential Type	2. Masonry, Low Heat Type	2. Masonry, Low Heat Type	2. Masonry, Medium Heat Type	1. Masonry, High Heat Type
	3. Metal, Low Heat Type	3. Metal, Low Heat Type	3. Metal, Medium Heat Type	2. Metal, High Heat Type
Maximum Continuous Appliance Outlet Flue Gas Temperature				
1000°F (538°C)	1000°F (538°C)	1400°F (760°C)	1800°F (982°C)	Over 1800°F (982°C)
Types of Appliances to be Used with Each Type Chimney (See Note 2)				
Column I	Column II	Column III	Column IV	Column V
A. Residential-type appliances, such as: 1. Ranges 2. Warm air furnaces 3. Water heaters 4. Hot water heating boilers 5. Low pressure steam heating boilers 6. Incinerators 7. Floor furnaces 8. Wall furnaces 9. Room heaters 10. Fireplace stoves 11. Fireplace stoveroom heater B. Fireplaces: 1. Factory built 2. Masonry 3. Freestanding (see Fireplace stove)	A. All appliances shown in Column I. B. Nonresidential type building heating appliances for heating a total volume of space exceeding 25,000 cu ft (708 m^3) C. Steam boilers operating at not over 1000°F (538°C) flue gas temperature; pressing machine boilers	All appliances shown in Columns I and II, and appliances such as: 1. Class A ovens or furnaces operating at temperatures below 1400°F (760°C) as defined in NFPA 86 (Note 3) 2. Annealing baths for hard glass (fats, paraffine, salts, or metals) 3. Bake ovens (in bakeries) 4. Candy furnaces 5. Core ovens 6. Feed drying ovens 7. Forge furnaces (solid fuel) 8. Gypsum kilns 9. Hardening furnaces (below dark red) 10. Lead melting furnaces 11. Nickel plate (drying) furnaces 12. Paraffine furnaces 13. Restaurant type cooking appliances using solid or liquid fuel 14. Sulphur furnaces 15. Tripoli kilns (clay, coke and gypsum) 16. Wood drying furnaces 17. Zinc amalgamating furnaces	All appliances shown in Columns I, II and III, and appliances such as: 1. Alabaster gypsum 2. Annealing furnaces (glass or metal) 3. Charcoal furnaces 4. Cold stirring furnaces 5. Feed driers (direct fire heated) 6. Fertilizer dryers (direct fire heated) 7. Galvanizing furnaces 8. Gas producers 9. Hardening furnaces (cherry to pale red) 10. Incinerators, commercial and industrial 11. Lehrs and glory 12. Lime kilns 13. Linseed oil boiling 14. Porcelain biscuit kilns 15. Pulp driers (direct fire heated) 16. Steam boilers operating at over 1000°F (538°C) flue gas temperature 17. Water-glass kilns 18. Wood-distilling furnaces 19. Wood-gas retorts	All appliances shown in Columns I, II, III, and IV and appliances such as: 1. Bessemer retorts 2. Billet and bloom furnaces 3. Blast furnaces 4. Bone calcining furnaces 5. Brass furnaces 6. Carbon point furnaces 7. Cement brick and tile kilns 8. Ceramic kilns 9. Coal and water gas retorts 10. Cupolas 11. Earthenware kilns 12. Glass blow furnaces 13. Glass furnaces (smelting) 14. Glass kilns 15. Open hearth furnaces 16. Ore roasting furnaces 17. Porcelain baking and glazing kilns 18. Pot-arches 19. Puddling furnaces 20. Regenerative furnaces 21. Reverberatory furnaces 22. Vitreous enameling ovens (ferrous metals)

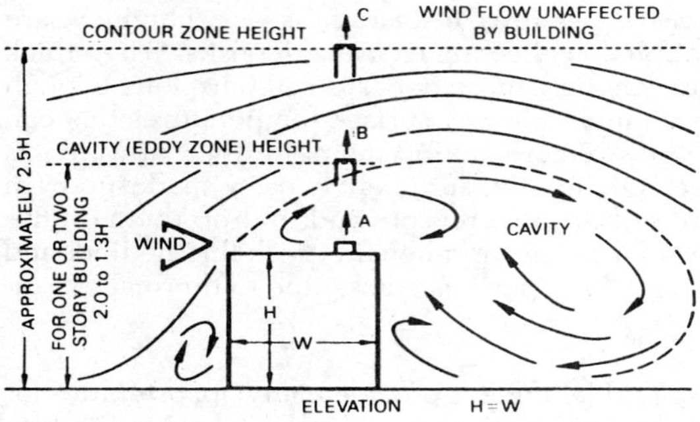

Notes to Table 2-4N.
1. Single wall metal chimneys or unlisted metal chimneys shall not be used inside one and two family dwellings.
2. For appliance types not listed in Column I through V, the appropriate chimney shall be selected on the basis of the appliance outlet flue gas temperature when appliance is fired at its normal maximum input, and type of surroundings.
3. NFPA 86, *Ovens and Furnaces.*

with identical parts. There is no interchangeability and it is extremely bad practice to mix multi-wall and insulation-filled chimney sections.

The foregoing installation errors may cause fires at relatively low flue gas temperature; however, even a correctly assembled and installed chimney lacks the capability of repeatedly acting as a combustion chamber.

Chimney or Creosote Fires

The term creosote as applied to chimney systems refers to the tarry brown or hard black internal deposits produced by burning wood. Combustion of wood produces varying amounts of complex hydrocarbons that can condense and accumulate inside connector and chimney surfaces. These combustible deposits ignite when temperature is sufficiently high and will burn at temperatures in the range of 1200 to 2000°F (650 to 1100°C). The temperature and duration of the fire both depend upon the accumulated thickness of creosote, availability of oxygen, type of heating appliance, type of chimney, etc.

In masonry chimneys, intense fires can cause cracking of tiles and brick masonry, as well as excessive heat transfer through chimney walls and hazardous overheated external surface temperatures. In factory-built chimneys, as with masonry, the effect of chimney fires varies depending upon attained temperature. Gas temperatures up to 1700°F (930°C) for periods not in excess of 10 min can be endured repeatedly. If it is suspected that an extreme chimney fire has occurred, the liner should be visually inspected. Slight buckling inward [¼ to ½ in. (6 to 13 mm)] is not cause for concern but indicates that temperatures may have reached the 2000°F (1100°C) level. This should not be allowed to recur. If serious damage of the chimney inner liner is seen, the affected chimney sections should be replaced. In general, if the outer chimney is not discolored and remains shiny, it is unlikely that any building structural damage has occurred, since shiny surfaces are unlikely to radiate damaging amounts of heat if the chimney is installed at correct clearance.

Control of chimney fires: In wood-burning stoves and heaters having air dampers and doors, reducing the air supply by closing them is the best option; then the combustion rate in the chimney depends upon its air supply. When other appliances are connected to the chimney or a barometric damper is used for draft control, these can supply air and must also be closed to control a chimney fire. Open-front fireplaces or fireplace stoves without doors may not accumulate creosote rapidly, but under fire conditions air control is difficult. The best policy with fireplaces is routine chimney inspection and mechanical cleaning (brushes and scraping).

FIREPLACES AND FIREPLACE STOVES

Fireplaces of masonry or factory-built construction are primarily open fire-chamber appliances with no controls on the air supply to the fire. These require a properly sized chimney to carry out the smoke and combustion gases. Fireplace stoves are free standing, factory-built appliances operating with an open front, but, if these have doors, they may also operate as stoves or heaters with controlled combustion air. The addition of glass doors to a masonry fireplace, or the installation of a closed-front fireplace insert, will transform its combustion characteristics to that of a heater.

Masonry Fireplaces

Field-constructed masonry fireplaces must conform to local building codes or provisions of applicable standards (e.g., NFPA 211, *Chimneys, Fireplaces, Vents, and Solid Fuel Burning Appliances*) to ensure safe operation. They may be served by a masonry residential chimney or may use a factory-built chimney with a suitable factory-furnished transition between smoke chamber and chimney. Prefabricated designs of masonry fireplaces and masonry fireplace chimney combinations are available in some localities. When a lining of low-duty firebreak (ASTM C64, Type 6) is provided, masonry fireplaces require at least 8 in. (203 mm) of brick thickness or equivalent for the back and sides, with 2-in. (51 mm) clearance to combustibles at the sides and 4-in. (102 mm) minimum clearance from the back. When the lining described above is not used, the thickness of the masonry at the back and sides should not be less than 12 in. (305 mm). The entire fireplace must be supported on a noncombustible footing, with structural floor framing well away from direct heat conduction from the fire zone or external hearth. (See Figure 2-4OO.)

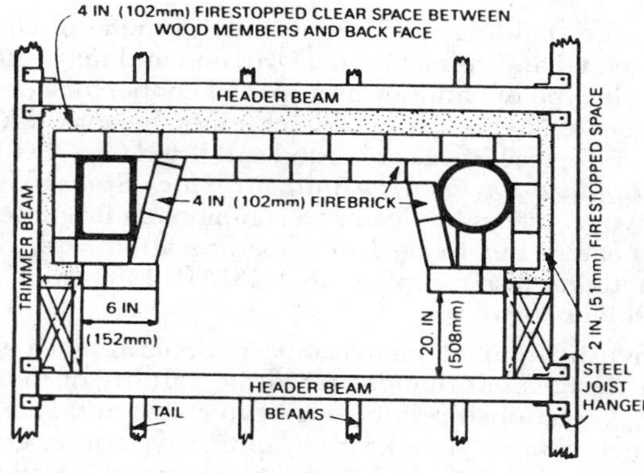

FIG. 2-4OO. Floor framing around a fireplace, when the fireplace opening is 6 sq ft (10.56 m²) or larger.

Hearth extensions of approved noncombustible material must be provided for all fireplaces. The hearths must extend at least 16 in. (406 mm) in front and 8 in. (203 mm) beyond the sides of fireplaces with an opening of less than 6 sq ft (0.56 m²). If the opening is 6 sq ft (0.56 m²) or larger, the hearth must extend at least 20 in. (508 mm) to the sides.

Steel fireplace units or heat circulators incorporating an air chamber may be installed in masonry fireplaces. A total thickness at back and sides of not less than 8 in. (203 mm) must be provided, of which not less than 4 in. (102 mm) is solid masonry. The same clearances to surrounding combustibles apply to fireplaces with circulators.

Factory-Built Fireplaces

Factory-built fireplaces are mainly of metal construction using multiple air spaces, refractory hearths and liners, and insulation to obtain the required level of safety. Factory-built fireplaces are tested and listed to ANSI/UL 127, *Standard for Factory-Built Fireplaces*. Each fireplace must be installed with the specific chimney and other parts called for by the manufacturer's instructions and the terms of its listing.

Chimney Sizes for Fireplaces

For masonry fireplaces, the correct size and height of chimney will ensure that all smoke, fire, and gas goes up the chimney. The typical masonry fireplace requires a true chimney flue area of one-eighth of the frontal opening for a minimum-height chimney. The nominal size of tile liner must be carefully checked to ensure that the internal cross-section area is adequate. In addition, the area of opening through the damper throat must be approximately twice the required flue area or greater, or it may reduce flow and possibly cause smoking.

Charts are available for factory-built and masonry chimneys in the *ASHRAE Handbook and Product Directory 1988 Equipment*, and in manufacturers' literature, that indicate the correct chimney size and height in relation to frontal opening, based on an average room air velocity of not less than 0.8 ft per sec (0.24 m/s) into the opening. This minimum velocity rule is valid for a wide variety of open fire chamber combustion systems, including masonry fireplaces as well as combination room heaters and fireplace stoves.

Factory-Built Fireplace Stoves

These free-standing units are usually of metal or combination metal and refractory construction and may require a specific type of chimney and special connectors, or may be connected to any acceptable chimney by conventional means. Fireplace stoves are tested and listed (see ANSI/UL 737, *Standard for Factory-Built Fireplace Stoves*), but if the stove has doors it becomes a combination fireplace and room heater, and to be listed for operation with doors closed it must also comply with ANSI/UL 1482, *Solid Fuel Type Room Heaters*.

Investigation of many combination fireplace stove heater designs has demonstrated the validity of the geometrical relationship between heater size and required clearance. Simply stated, larger units may require greater than standard clearance. To be sure of correct installation, the manufacturer's installation instructions for listed stoves and heaters should be scrupulously observed. These instructions have been reviewed for consistency with test results and are as essential to the safety of an installation as are the design features of the stove.

While untested fireplace stoves and related heaters can be installed and operated safely, they are seldom accompanied by carefully written instructions. Many imitations of listed designs can be found which are sold through retail outlets having little interest in the final installation. The lack of clear instructions and warnings poses many hazards to the consumer.

Hazards of Fireplaces and Their Chimneys

Open fireplaces, transferring heat primarily by radiation from the fire, can create several kinds of hazards:

1. Ignition by radiation of furnishings or walls located too close to the fire.
2. Ignition of furnishings or carpeting by sparks or from logs rolling out of the fire. For large, high fireplaces having a high fuel capacity, the 20-in. (508 mm) hearth width requirement may be grossly inadequate.
3. Ignition of combustible structural materials by excessive heat conducted through hearth or fireplace walls which can make prolonged overfiring of a masonry fireplace dangerous.
4. Escape of gases from the opening into a construction gap between the fireplace shell and the front facing wall. This is a common installation fault with factory-built fireplaces, since a smoking unit—one with insufficient chimney flow—allows very hot gas to escape into this area.
5. Sparks and embers falling onto a combustible floor between the fireplace and its hearth extension. This can be prevented by placing the masonry orfactory-furnished hearth extension flush against the front of the fireplace, or by using a sheet of metal at the floor surface under the joint between the fireplace and its hearth.
6. Burning highly combustible solid materials, such as a dried Christmas tree and wrappings. The high gas temperatures resulting may ignite creosote deposits, or cause damage to the masonry. The high rate of burning may cause the flames, heat, and smoke to billow out of the fireplace opening, possibly igniting nearby combustibles. Regardless of how flammable these materials are, burning them a little at a time obviously will cause no problem.
7. Use of any flammable liquid to start or rekindle a fire, or in any room with or near an open fire.
8. Failure to clean the chimney whenever creosote deposits build up to dangerous thickness. A layer of creosote 1/16 in. (1.6 mm) thick in an 8-in. (200 mm) size chimney 15 ft (4.6 m) high contains as much as 122,000 Btu (128 MJ) of fuel. If this burns off in 15 min, the resulting temperature may reach 1700°F (930°C) at a heat release rate as high as 488,000 Btu per hr (140 kW).
9. Use of an incorrect or mismatched chimney. For safe operation, many types of factory-built fireplaces require a chimney that interconnects with its air passages. Failure to connect the fireplace to this specific chimney could be extremely dangerous, and clearly violates installation requirements and the listing.
10. Failure to install firestopping around chimneys, which might be termed an indirect installation hazard. This will not start a fire, but, if one starts elsewhere, the lack of firestopping may cause severe losses. Because of the numerous possibilities for operator or construction errors in the vicinity of the fireplace itself, every precaution should be taken to prevent rapid involvement of the entire structure in case of fire. Many modern single and multiple residences of frame construction utilize a chase or vertical enclosure, inside or external to the dwelling, containing one or more fireplace chimneys. The absence of floors or other internal framing makes it easy to install all the chimneys, but also provides an ideal passage for rapid vertical spread of flame to upper levels and the roof. The shape and size of firestopping for this sort of installation cannot readily be anticipated by the fireplace manufacturer, but carefully fitted sheet metal or lath and plaster may limit the spread and allow time for effective fire fighting.

BIBLIOGRAPHY

References Cited

1. UL 1482, *Standard for Room Heaters, Solid Fuel Type*, Underwriters Laboratories Inc., Northbrook, IL, 1979.
2. Schaffer, E. L., "Smoldering Initiation in Cellulosics Under Prolonged Heating," *Fire Technology*, Vol. 16, No. 1, Feb. 1980, pp. 22-28.

3. Mitchell, N. D., "New Light on Self-Ignition," *NFPA Quarterly*, Vol. 45, No. 2, Oct. 1951, pp. 165-172.

4. MacLean, J. D., "*Effect of Heat on Properties and Serviceability of Wood: Experiments on Thin Wood Specimens*," Report No. R1471, 1945, Forest Products Laboratory, Madison, WI.

5. MacLean, J. D., *Rate of Disintegration of Wood Under Different Heating Conditions*, American Wood-Preservers Association, 1951.

6. McGuire, J. H., "Limiting Safe Temperature of Combustible Materials," *Fire Technology*, Vol. 5, No. 3, Aug. 1969.

7. "Ignition and Charring Temperatures of Wood", Report No. 1464, 1958, Forest Products Laboratory, Madison, WI.

8. Shelton, J. W., *Wood Heat Safety*, Garden Way Publishing, Charlotte, VT, 1979.

9. Matson, A. F., Dufori, R. E., and Breen, J. F., *Performance of Type B Gas Vents for Gas-Fired Appliances, Part II, Survey of Available Information on Ignition of Wood Exposed to Moderately Elevated Temperatures,* UL Bulletin of Research No. 51, May 1959, Underwriters Laboratories Inc., Northbrook, IL.

References

ANSI/UL 103, *Standard for Factory-Built Chimneys,* Underwriters Laboratories Inc., Northbrook, IL, 1988.

ANSI/UL 127, *Standard for Factory-Built Fireplaces*, Underwriters Laboratories Inc., Northbrook, IL., 1988.

ANSI/UL 737, *Standard for Factory-Built Fireplace Stoves,* Underwriters Laboratories Inc., Northbrook, IL, 1988.

ANSI/UL 959, *Chimney for Medium-Heat Appliances,* Underwriters Laboratories Inc., Northbrook, IL, 1986.

ANSI/UL 1482, *Solid Fuel Type Room Heaters,* Underwriters Laboratories Inc., Northbrook, IL, 1988.

ASME Boiler and Pressure Vessel Code, American Society of Mechanical Engineers, New York, 1989.

ASTM Standards on Gaseous Fuels, (Parts 23, 24, 25, and 26), American Society for Testing and Materials, Philadelphia, PA, 1988.

ASTM D-396, *Specifications for Fuel Oils,* American Society for Testing and Materials, Philadelphia, PA.

ASHRAE Handbook and Product Directory 1988 Equipment, Chapter 26, American Society of Heating, Refrigerating, and Air Conditioning Engineers, Inc., Atlanta, GA, 1988.

Combustion Handbook, North American Mfg. Co., Cleveland, OH, 1978.

UL Standard 181, *Air Ducts,* Underwriters Laboratories Inc., Northbrook, IL.

UL *Gas and Oil Equipment Directory,* Underwriters Laboratories Inc., Northbrook, IL.

NFPA Codes, Standards, and Recommended Practices

Reference to the following NFPA codes, standards, and recommended practices will provide further information on the heating systems and appliances discussed in this chapter. (See the latest *NFPA Catalog* for availability of current editions of the following documents.)

NFPA 30, *Flammable and Combustible Liquids Code.*

NFPA 31, *Installation of Oil Burning Equipment.*

NFPA 54, *National Fuel Gas Code.*

NFPA 58, *Storage and Handling of Liquefied Petroleum Gases.*

NFPA 70, *National Electrical Code.*

NFPA 85A, *Prevention of Furnace Explosions in Fuel-Oil and Natural Gas-Fired Single Burner Boiler-Furnaces.*

NFPA 85B, *Prevention of Furnace Explosions in Natural Gas-Fired Multiple Burner Boiler-Furnaces.*

NFPA 85D, *Prevention of Furnace Explosions in Fuel Oil-Fired Multiple Burner Boiler-Furnaces.*

NFPA 85E, *Prevention of Furnace Explosions in Pulverized Coal-Fired Multiple Burner Boiler-Furnaces.*

NFPA 86, *Ovens and Furnaces.*

NFPA 86C, *Industrial Furnaces Using a Special Processing Atmosphere.*

NFPA 90A, *Installation of Air Conditioning and Ventilating Systems.*

NFPA 90B, *Installation of Warm Air Heating and Air Conditioning Systems.*

NFPA 96, *Removal of Smoke and Grease-Laden Vapors from Commercial Cooking Equipment.*

NFPA 97M, *Standard Glossary of Terms Relating to Chimneys, Vents, and Heat-Producing Appliances.*

NFPA 211, *Chimneys, Fireplaces, Vents, and Solid Fuel Burning Appliances.*

NFPA 255, *Method of Test of Surface Burning Characteristics of Building Materials.*

Additional Reading

AGA Directory of Certified Appliances and Accessories, American Gas Association, Cleveland, OH, 1979.

Alternative Heater Fires: A Critical Review of Safety Issues, Federal Emergency and Management Agency, Emmitsburg, MD, 1988.

ANSI Z83.3, *American National Standard for Gas Utilization Equipment in Large Boilers*, American Gas Association Laboratories, Cleveland, OH, 1971.

"Are Kerosene Heaters Safe?," *Consumer Reports*, Oct. 1982, pp. 499-507.

ASME Boiler and Pressure Vessel Code, Section 4: Rules for Construction of Heating Boilers, American Society of Mechanical Engineers, NY, 1989.

Code for the Installation of Heat-Producing Appliances, American Insurance Association, NY.

Dyer, D., et al, *Residential Consumers Handbook for Wood-Fired Appliances*, Auburn University, AL, 1981.

Hall, J. R., "Update on the Auxiliary Heating Fire Problem," *Fire Journal*, Vol. 80, No. 2, 1986, p. 52.

Harris, R. J., *The Investigation and Control of Gas Explosions in Buildings and Heating Plants*, E. and F. N. Spon, London, England, 1983.

Harwood, B., and Kale, D., *Fires Involving Fireplaces, Chimneys, and Related Appliances*, U.S. Consumer Product Safety Commission, 1982.

Harwood, B., and Kluge, P., *Hazards Associated with the Use of Wood or Coal-Burning Stoves or Free-Standing Fireplaces*, U.S. Consumer Product Safety Commisssion, 1980.

Havens, D., *The Woodburner's Handbook*, Media House, Portland, ME, 1973.

Kale, D., "Fires in Woodburning Appliances," Dec. 1982, U.S. Consumer Product Safety Commission, Washington, DC.

Lawson, D. I., Fox, L. L., and Webster, C. T., "The Heating of Panels by Flue Pipes," Fire Research Special Report No. 1, Mar. 1952, Fire Protection Association, London, England.

Lawson, D. I., and Simms, D. L., "The Ignition of Wood by Radiation," *British Journal of Applied Physics*, Vol. 3, Sept. 1952, pp. 288-292.

Lee, B. T., and Walton, W. D., "Fire Experiments and Flash Point Criteria for Solar Heat Transfer Liquids," NBSIR 79-1931, Nov. 1979, National Bureau of Standards, Gaithersburg, MD.

Lentini, J. J., "Gasoline and Kerosene Don't Mix—At Least Not in Kerosene Heaters," *Fire Journal*, Vol. 83, No. 4, 1989, p. 13.

Loftus, J. J., "Evaluation of Wall Protection Systems for Wood Heating Appliances," NBSIR 82-2506, May 1982, National Bureau of Standards, Gaithersburg, MD.

Loftus, J. J., "An Evaluation of Wall Protection Systems for Wood Heating Appliances," *Fire Journal*, Vol. 77, No. 5, Sept. 1983, pp. 23-25, 30, 39.

Loftus, J. J., and Peacock, R. D., "Clearances and Methods of Protection for Wall and Ceiling Surfaces Exposed to Radiant Heating Appliances," NBSIR 1205, Dec. 1984, National Bureau of Standards, Gaithersburg, MD.

Loftus, J. J., and Peacock, R. D., "Evaluation of Thimble—Chimney Connector Wall-Pass Through Systems for Solid Fuel Burning Appliances," NBSIR 84-2969, Nov. 1984, National Bureau of Standards, Gaithersburg, MD.

Loftus, J. J., and Peacock, R. D., "Wall and Ceiling Protection for Heating Appliances," *Fire Technology*, Vol. 24, No. 3, 1985, pp. 213-229.

Maxwell, T. T., et al, *Design Handbook for Residential Wood-Burning Equipment*, Department of Mechanical Engineering, Auburn University, AL, 1979.

Maxwell, T. T., et al, "An Investigation of Creosoting and Fireplace Inserts," NBS-GCR-81-365, Dec. 1981, National Bureau of Standards, Gaithersburg, MD.

Neale, J. A., Clearances and Insulation of Heating Appliances, UL Bulletin of Research No. 27, Feb. 1943, Underwriters Laboratories Inc., Northbrook, IL.

Ohlemiller, T., and Sharb, W., "Products of Wood Smolder and Their Relation to Wood Burning Stoves," NBSIR 88-3767, May 1988, National Bureau of Standards, Gaithersberg, MD.

Parsons, R. A., *ASHRAE Handbook—Fundamentals*, American Society of Heating, Refrigerating and Air Conditioning Engineers, Atlanta, GA, 1989.

Peacock, R. D., "A Review of Fire Incidents, Model Building Codes and Standards Related to Wood-Burning Appliances," NBSIR 79-1731, May 1979, National Bureau of Standards, Gaithersburg, MD.

Peacock, R. D., "Chimney Fires: Intensity and Duration," *Fire Technology*, Vol. 22, No. 3, 1986, pp. 234-252.

Peacock, R. D., "Intensity and Duration of Chimney Fires in Several Chimneys," NBSIR 83-2771, Dec. 1983, National Bureau of Standards, Gaithersburg, MD.

Peacock, R. D., "Wood Heating Safety Research: An Update," *Fire Technology*, Vol. 23, No. 4, 1987, pp. 292-312.

Peacock, R. D., and Ruiz, E., "Fire Safety of Wood-Burning Appliances, Part I: State of the Art Review and Fire Tests, Vols. I and II," NBSIR 80-2140, Nov. 1980, National Bureau of Standards, Gaithersburg, MD.

"Recommended Rules for Care and Operation of Heating Boilers," Section VI, *ASME Boiler and Pressure Vessel Code*, American Society of Mechanical Engineers, NY, 1989.

"Recommended Requirements to Code Officials for Solar Heating, Cooling and Hot Water Systems," DOE/CS/34281-01, June 1980, U.S. Department of Energy, Washington, DC.

Shelton, J., *The Woodburners Encyclopedia*, Vermont Crossroads Press, Waitsfield, VT, 1978.

Shoub, H., *Survey of Literature on the Safety of Residential Chimneys and Fireplaces*, NBS Misc. Pub. 252, Dec. 1963, National Bureau of Standards, Gaithersburg, MD.

Soderstron, N., "Heating Your Home with Wood," *Popular Science*, 1978.

Stone, R. L., "Fireplace Operation Depends Upon Good Chimney Design," *ASHRAE Journal*, Feb. 1969, pp. 63-69.

Thulman, R. K., Temperatures Developed in Chimneys for Low Cost Houses, Technical News Bulletin 328, Aug. 1944, National Bureau of Standards, Gaithersburg, MD.

Thulman, R. K., Performance of Masonry Chimneys for Houses, Housing Research Paper No. 13, Nov. 1952, U.S. Housing and Home Finance Agency.

Toy, D. A., "Take Those Hazards out of Your Gas Supply System," *Semiconductor International*, Vol. 12, No. 8, July 1989, pp. 66-70.

UL 103, *Standard for Chimneys, Factory-Built Residential Type and Building Appliance*, Underwriters Laboratories Inc., Northbrook, IL.

UL 372, *Primary Safety Controls for Gas and Oil-Fired Appliances*, 4th ed., Underwriters Laboratories Inc., Northbrook, IL, 1985.

UL 1482, *Standard for Room Heaters, Solid Fuel Type*, Underwriters Laboratories Inc., Northbrook, IL.

Using Coal and Wood Stoves Safely, A Hazard Study, National Fire Protection Association, Quincy, MA, 1974.

Vickers, A. K., "Kitchen Ranges in Fabric Fires," NBS Tech Note—817, Apr. 1974, National Bureau of Standards, Gaithersburg, MD.

Voigt, G. Q., Fire Hazard of Domestic Heating Installations, NBS Research Paper RP596, Sept. 1933, National Bureau of Standards, Gaithersburg, MD.

Walton, W. D., "Fire Testing of Roof Mounted Solar Collectors by ASTM E-108," NBSIR 81-2344, Aug., 1981, National Bureau of Standards, Gaithersburg, MD.

Walton, W. D., "Solar Collector Fire Incident Investigation," NBSIR 81-2326, Aug. 1981, National Bureau of Standards, Gaithersburg, MD.

Wood Heating Seminar Proceedings, Documents 1-1977, 2-1977, 3-1978, 4-1979, 5-1979, Wood Energy Institute, Camden, ME.

BOILER-FURNACES

O. W. Durrant

Boiler-furnaces use controlled combustion to generate steam to power machinery or provide heat required by industrial processes. Basically, there are two types of boilers—watertube and firetube. In watertube units, water passes through tubes surrounded by hot combustion gases and is converted to steam. In firetube units, however, the hot combustion gases pass through tubes that are immersed in circulating water, which is converted to steam. Though this chapter discusses watertube boilers, the safety principles outlined are also applicable to firetube boilers. Fuel burning systems and related control equipment for single- and multiple-burner industrial and public utility boiler-furnaces for fuels burned in suspension and on fluidized beds are discussed here. Solid fuel burning units, such as stokers, are not.

THE COMBUSTION PROCESS

Combustion can be defined as the rapid chemical combination of oxygen with the combustible elements of a fuel. There are three combustible elements of significance to this chapter—carbon, hydrogen, and sulfur. Sulfur is usually of minor importance as a source of heat, but can be of major significance in corrosion and pollution problems.

Carbon and hydrogen, when burned to completion with oxygen, unite according to the following:

$C + O_2 = CO_2$ + 14,100 Btu/lb (or 32 797 kJ/kg) of carbon

$2H_2 + O_2 = 2H_2O$ + 61,100 Btu/lb (or 142 119 kJ/kg) of hydrogen

Air is the usual source of oxygen for boiler-furnaces. These combustion reactions are exothermic, and the heat released is about 14,100 Btu/lb (32 797 kJ/kg) of carbon burned and 61,100 Btu/lb (142 119 kJ/kg) of hydrogen burned. The objective of efficient combustion is the release of all available heat while minimizing losses from combustion imperfections and superfluous air.

The combination of combustible elements and compounds of a fuel with all the oxygen requires a *temperature* high enough to ignite the constituents, *turbulence* or mixing, and sufficient *time* for complete combustion. These factors are often referred to as the "three Ts" of combustion.

The combustion process in a boiler-furnace results from a continual introduction of fuel and air in a flammable mixture. It is necessary to maintain control not only of the flow rates of both fuel and air, but also of the fuel-air ratio, at both the point of ignition and for the entire burner, as well as the source of ignition. If any one of the inputs is interrupted or becomes irregular, ignition can be lost and the controlled flammable mixture can become an uncontrolled explosive mixture.

Figure 2-5A shows schematically how fuel and air are introduced and burned in a furnace through a modern high-capacity burner. The fuel and air are injected in separate impinging streams. Normally the total burner air is limited by some means at the point of fuel introduction to provide a flammable mixture zone, often fuel rich, and to ensure stable ignition, assuming there is sufficient ignition energy. The mixing and burning of the remaining fuel and air takes place in the furnace. With a turbulent, inherently stable burner, ignition always occurs at the burner and can be designed to be as stable with a fuel-rich ratio as with an air-rich ratio. With ignition established at the burner, combustion continues as the air and fuel continue to mix in the furnace and become flammable until all of the oxygen is consumed (fuel-rich ratio) or until all the fuel is consumed (oxygen-rich ratio). The combustion process, therefore, proceeds toward completion through a wide range of air-fuel ratios, with the final result dependent on the total ratio of air to fuel over the entire path of the flame.

FUELS

Natural gas, oil, and pulverized coal are the most commonly used fuels to fire boiler-furnaces. However, there are also alternative fuels, such as crushed coal, methanol, or liquefied petroleum gas; and supplementary fuels, such as waste gases or flammable liquids in chemical plants and refineries, which may demand special precautions in addition to those required by the more common fuels. Sometimes more than one fuel is used; Figure 2-5B shows

O. W. Durrant, retired from Babcock & Wilcox, Barberton, OH, is now a consultant.

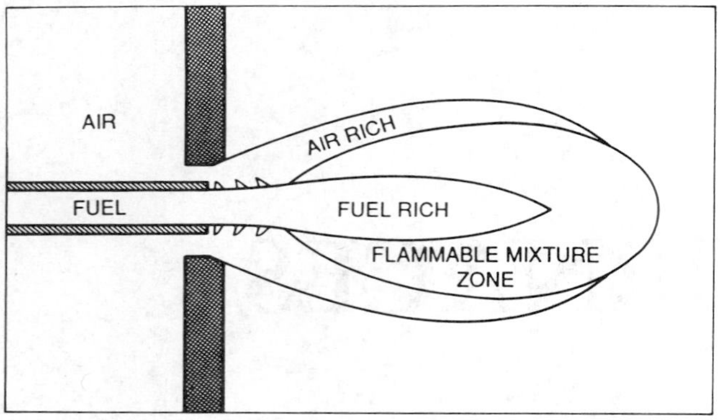

FIG. 2-5A. Schematic of burner flame conditions. (Source: Babcock & Wilcox)

FIG. 2-5B. Installation for combination oil and gas firing in a large electric utility boiler. (Source: Babcock & Wilcox)

combination oil and gas burners on a larger public utility boiler-furnace.

OIL- AND GAS-BURNING SYSTEMS

The burner is the principal component of oil and gas firing equipment. Its purpose is to introduce fuel and air into the furnace in the proper proportion to sustain the exothermic chemical reactions (combustion) for the most effective release of heat. The feed rates of fuel and air should be able to satisfy the load demand on a boiler over a predetermined operating range. The efficiency of a burner should be as high as possible to minimize both the amount of unburned fuel and excess air in the combustion products. The design of the burner and materials used in its construction should be capable of providing reliable operation under specified service conditions. Safety should be a prime concern under all operating conditions.

Normal use of a steam generator requires operation at different outputs to meet varying load conditions. The specified operating range or load range for a burner is the ratio of full load on the burner to the minimum load at which the burner must be capable of stable ignition and reliable operation. For example, with a boiler of 100,000 lb/hr (45 359 kg/hr) capacity (steam delivered), a load range of four-to-one on the burners means that the unit can produce stable ignition and complete combustion at any load from 100,000 lb/hr (45 359 kg/hr) down to 25,000 lb/hr (11 340 kg/hr) without necessitating a change in the number of burners in operation.

It is necessary to supply more than the theoretical air quantity to ensure complete combustion of the fuel in the combustion chamber. The amount of excess air provided should be just enough to burn the fuel completely in order to minimize the heat loss in stack gases. The excess air normally required with oil and gas, expressed as a percent of theoretical air, is given in Table 2-5A.

TABLE 2-5A. ***Usual Amount of Excess Air Supplied to Fuel-burning Equipment***

Fuel	Type of Furnace or Burners	Excess Air (% by weight)
Pulverized coal	Completely water-cooled furnace for slag-tap or dry-ash removal	15–20
	Partially water-cooled furnace for dry-ash removal	15–40
Crushed coal	Cyclone furnace, pressure or suction	10–15
Fuel oil	Oil burners, register-type	5–10
	Multifuel burners and flat-flame	10–20
Acid sludge	Cone- and flat-flame-type burners, steam-atomized	10–15
Natural, coke-oven, and refinery gas	Register-type burners	5–10
	Multifuel burners	7–12
Blast-furnace gas	Intertube nozzle-type burners	15–18

Continuity of service is enhanced by designing the furnace and arranging the burners to minimize slagging and fouling of heat-absorbing surfaces for the normal range of fuels burned.

The most frequently used burner for gas and oil is the circular burner shown in Figure 2-5C. Normally, the capability of an individual circular burner is limited to 190-200 million Btu/hr (55 689 to 58 620 kW). The tangentially displaced doors built into the air register provide the turbulence necessary to mix the fuel and air and to produce stable flames. While the fuel is introduced to the burner in a fuel-rich mixture in the center, the direction and velocity of the air and the fuel dispersion pattern thoroughly mix the fuel with the combustion air. The circular burner may be modified with an inner register to limit air in the primary ignition zone to limit formation of oxides of nitrogen (NO_x). The principle and performance are similar to those shown for the dual-register coal burner. (See Figure 2-5I.)

Oil Burners

To burn fuel oil at the high rates demanded of modern boiler units, it is necessary that the oil be atomized; that is, introduced into the furnace as a fine mist. This increases the ratio of fuel particle surface to air, which ensures prompt ignition and rapid combustion. There are several types of oil atomizers or vaporizers, but the discussion here is limited to the two most popular types—steam or air atomizers, and mechanical atomizers.

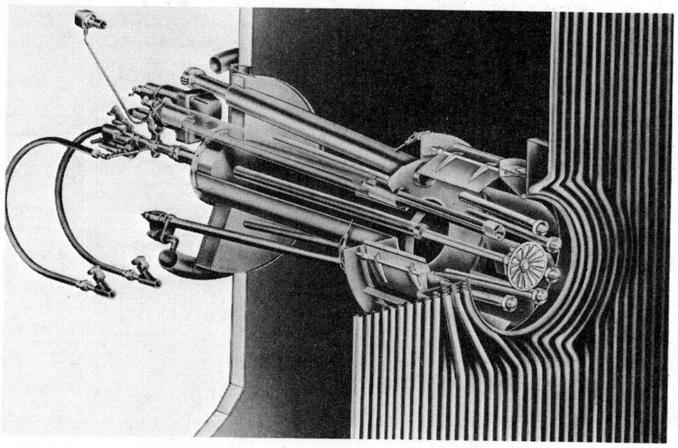

FIG. 2-5C. Circular register for gas and oil firing. (Source: Babcock & Wilcox)

For proper atomization, oil of grades heavier than No. 2 must be heated to reduce their viscosities to between 135 and 150 SUS.* Steam or electric heaters are used to raise the oil temperature to the required level—approximately 135°F (57.2°C) for No. 4 oil, 185°F (85°C) for No. 5, and 200 to 220°F (104.4°C) for No. 6. With certain oils, better combustion is obtained at somewhat higher temperatures than are required for atomization. However, oil temperature must not be raised to the point where vapor binding occurs in the pump that is supplying the oil, since this could cause flow interruptions followed by loss of ignition.

It is also important that oil be free of acid, grit, and other foreign matter that might clog or damage burners or their control valves.

Steam or air atomizers: The steam or air-oil atomizer is the most widely used. (See Figure 2-5D.) In general, it operates by producing a steam-fuel (or air-fuel) emulsion that atomizes the oil through the rapid expansion of the steam when released into the furnace. The atomizing steam must be dry because moisture causes pulsations, which can lead to loss of ignition. Where steam is not available, moisture-free compressed air can be substituted.

The steam atomizer performs more efficently over a wider load range than other types of atomizers. It normally atomizes the fuel properly down to 20 percent of rated capacity; in some instances, steam atomizers have been successfully operated at 5 percent of capacity. Frequently these extremes in range cannot be fully utilized, because the temperature of the combustion space falls to a level insufficient to complete the combustion process adequately despite the excellent quality of atomization.

Mechanical atomizers: In the mechanical atomizer, the pressure of the fuel itself is used as the means for atomization. Many forms have been developed. Those with rotating mechanical parts that are close to the furnace have lost favor, especially for multiburner boilers, because of the excessive maintenance required to keep them operational.

*Abbreviation for Saybolt Universal Seconds. This is the efflux time in seconds of 60 ml (approx. 2 oz) of sample flowing through a calibrated universal orifice ina Saybolt viscometer under specified conditions.

Return-flow atomizers are used for many marine installations and some stationary units where the use of steam is inappropriate, impractical, or uneconomic. (See Figure 2-5E.) Oil pressure required at these atomizers for maximum capacity ranges from 600 to 1000 psi (4137 to 6895 kPa), depending on capacity, load range, and fuel.

Mechanical atomizers are available in sizes up to 180 million Btu/hr (52 758 kW) input, which can consume about 10,000 lbs (4536 kg) of oil per hr. The acceptable operating range may be as much as ten to one or as little as three to one, depending on the maximum oil pressure used for the system, the furnace configuration, air temperature, and burner throat velocity. Return-flow atomizers are ideally suited for standard grades of fuel oil where it is desired to meet load variations without changing sprayer plates, or cutting burners in and out of service.

Natural Gas Burners

Natural gas is an ideal fuel for a burner, since it requires no preparation to be suitable for rapid and intimate mixing with combustion air. Basically, gas burners mix fuel and air in either of two ways—premix or external mix.

In premix burners, fuel and a portion of the air are mixed before they are introduced to the burner nozzle input. A common method involves mixing gas and air in the suction side of a mechanical blower. Another method uses the venturi effect, wherein a gas jet creates a negative pressure at the air input orifice and draws air into the mixer. The third method also uses the venturi effect, but, in this case, an air jet draws fuel gas into the mixer, thus requiring a gas regulator to reduce fuel gas pressure to atmospheric before gas and air are mixed.

In external-mix gas burners, the fuel and air are mixed external to the nozzle. In external-mix gas burners having individual elements or spuds (see Figure 2-5C), part or all of the gas discharges in front of the impeller, which provides a local fuel-rich zone and thus serves as an ignition stabilizer at high loads. Each burner comprises several spuds, each of which is a gas pipe with multiple holes at the end to discharge gas for ignition at the burner throat. Each spud is fitted with a larger diameter flame holder to provide a local fuel-rich zone to stabilize ignition at low inputs. Fuel ports are relatively large to minimize plugging in service. Gas spuds are located so that oil will not impinge on them when provision is made for firing multiple fuels. Because of its unusually good ignition stability, even under severe variations in airflow, the multiple spud-type burner is expected to replace most natural gas element designs now used on circular-type burners.

With the proper selection of control equipment, a multifuel-fired furnace with a multiple spud-type burner is capable of changing from one fuel to another without a drop in load or boiler pressure. It is also capable of simultaneous firing of natural gas and oil in the same burner. The control system's primary function is to balance fuels, in the proper relationship with burner air flow, to achieve complete and efficient combustion. This type of element is designed for use with natural gas or other gaseous fuels containing at least either 70 percent methane, 70 percent propane, or 25 percent hydrogen by volume. The element is also designed for a maximum input of 173 million Btu per hr (50.7 mW) per burner.

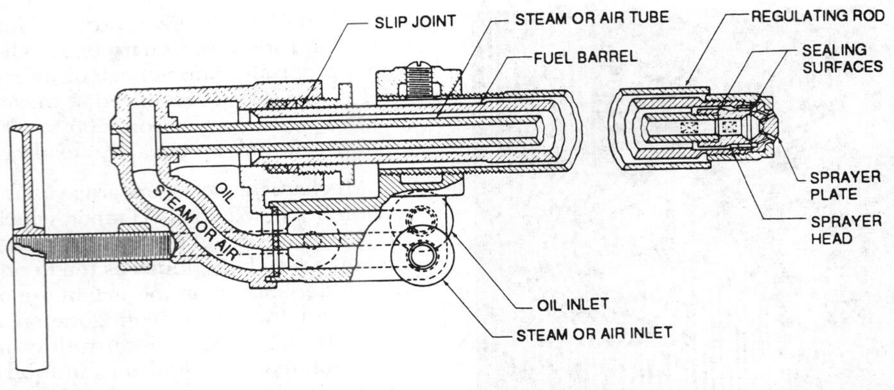

FIG. 2-5D. Steam (or air) oil atomizer assembly. (Source: Babcock & Wilcox)

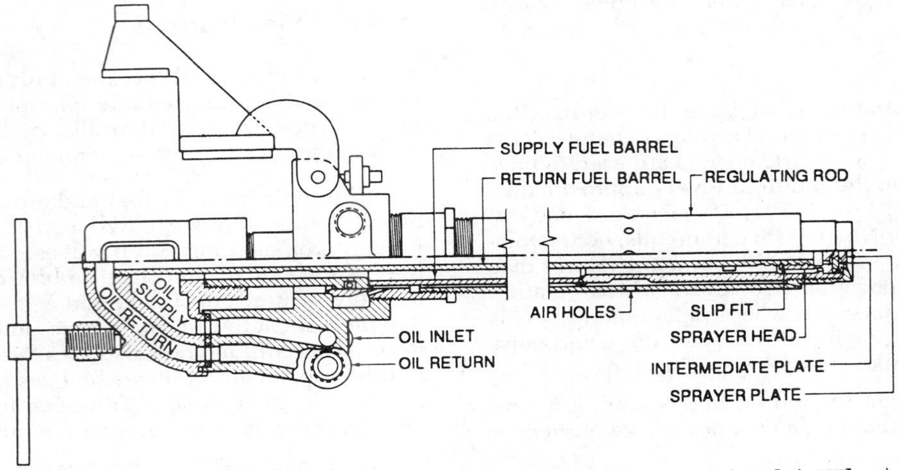

FIG. 2-5E. Mechanical return-flow oil atomizer assembly. (Source: Babcock & Wilcox)

To provide safe operation, ignition of a gas burner should remain close to the burner impeller(s) throughout the full range of allowable gas pressures, not only with normal airflows, but also with abnormally high airflows. Ideally, it should be possible, at the minimum load, to pass full-load airflow through the burner and as much as 25 percent in excess of theoretical air at full load, without loss of ignition. With this range of airflow, it is not likely that ignition can be lost, even momentarily, during some upset in airflow due to improper operation or error.

PIPING AND CONTROL DEVICES

It is essential that boiler-furnace fuels be as free as possible from contamination and be under control to ensure combustion safety. The design and reliability of fuel-handling systems are, therefore, important factors in minimizing the risk of explosion and hostile fire.

Oil-Fired Systems

Fuel supply equipment should be designed and sized to ensure a continuous, steady flow of fuel that will meet all the operating requirements of the unit. This includes coordinating the pressure regulator, shutoff valves, and associated piping volume to prevent fuel pressure transients that might exceed stable flame burner limits as a result of cutting burners in or out of service. (See Figure 2-5F.)

Fill and recirculation lines should be connected to storage tanks below the liquid level to avoid excessive evaporation and the generation of static electrical charges in free-falling fuel.

Fuels oils may contain abrasive, corrosive, or waxy contaminants, which may clog filters, produce wear, or otherwise damage oil-burning equipment. Strainers, fillers, traps, and sumps are some of the devices that may be used to remove harmful contaminants from oil-burning systems.

It is good practice to route piping and locate valves to minimize their exposure to physical damage and temperature extremes that may alter fuel viscosity or pressure.

Burner shutoff valves should be located as close to the burner as possible to minimize the volume of oil that may remain in the burner line downstream of the valve or that may drain into the furnace following an emergency trip or burner shutdown. Positive means must be provided to prevent oil from leaking into an idle burner.

Fuel oil must be delivered to the burners at a specific temperature and pressure to ensure proper atomization. Adequate recirculation provisions must be made for controlling the viscosity of the oil at the burners for initial light-off and subsequent operation. It is important that these systems prevent excessively hot oil from entering the pumps; otherwise, the pumps may become vapor-bound and interrupt the supply of fuel to the burners.

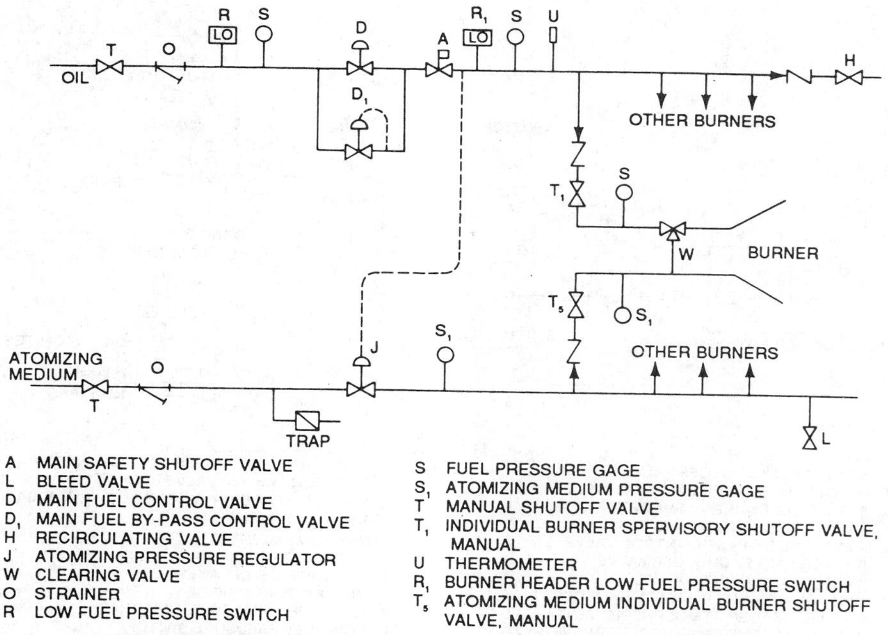

FIG. 2-5F. Schematic of typical main oil burner—steam atomizing.

Positive means are needed to prevent fuel oil from entering the burner header system through the recirculating valve, particularly from the fuel supply system of another boiler. Check valves have proved unreliable for this function in heavy oil service.

Provisions should also be required for clearing or scavenging the passages of an atomizer into the furnace when the burner is taken out of service.

Gas-Fired Systems

Natural gas fuel-supply systems must be able to provide a continuous, steady flow of fuel that is adequate for all operating requirements of the unit and within specified fuel header pressure limits for the burners. The system includes a pressure regulating valve and a fuel bypass (minimum pressure regulating) valve. The bypass valve comes into use automatically for startup and low-flow operation to avoid operating with a header pressure below the minimum pressure prescribed for burner stability.

The portion of the fuel supply system shown in Figure 2-5G located outside the boiler room is arranged to prevent excessive fuel gas pressure in the burner supply system, even in the event of failure of the main supply constant gas pressure regulators. Usually this is accomplished by providing full relieving capacity vented to a safe location. Where full relieving capacity is not installed, a high supply gas pressure trip may be provided.

The system should have positive means to prevent gas from leaking into an idle furnace. Piping should be vented upstream of the last shutoff valve in any line to a burner or igniter. Provision should also be made in the gas piping to permit testing for leaks and for their subsequent repair. These provisions should include means for making tightness tests of the main gas supply safety shutoff valves and the main burner gas safety shutoff valves.

Vents should be located so that there is no possibility of vented gases entering the boiler room, adjacent buildings, or air intakes to ventilating systems. The vents should be placed high enough that escaping gas will not be a fire hazard. Header vent lines should be run independently, and the igniter vent subsystem should be run independent of the burner vent subsystem. There must be no cross-connection between venting systems of different boilers.

PULVERIZED COAL SYSTEMS

There are several possible arrangements for pulverized-coal-fired systems. One of the variables is the location of the primary air fan in relation to the air heater and pulverizer. The combination shown in Figure 2-5H is known as a "hot" system, and includes individual primary air fans for each pulverizer located downstream of the air heaters. Often the blowers are located ahead of the pulverizer, as shown in the figure. Sometimes, the air fans are exhausters located after the pulverizer.

Pulverized-coal-fired systems capable of burning a wide range of coal fuels have several necessary functions. Stored coal must be transferred to the pulverizer in measured and controlled quantities. Hot air mixed with tempering cooler air is blown into the pulverizer to dry the coal. The temperature of the air-coal stream at the outlet of the pulverizer is maintained between specific limits determined by the type of coal being burned. Temperature that is too low will impair the efficiency of the pulverization process, while temperature that is too high may cause coking and increase the risk of fire occurring within the pulverizer and piping. Coal is pulverized to a fineness such that it can be volatized and burned in suspension without delayed ignition or unburned combustibles as indicated by sparklers in the furnace, or carbon in the flyash.

The coal and its primary air are transported from each pulverizer to its associated burners in measured, controlled amounts, well distributed among the burners. The coal-air mixture is combined with a measured and controlled amount of secondary air at the burner to serve several purposes:

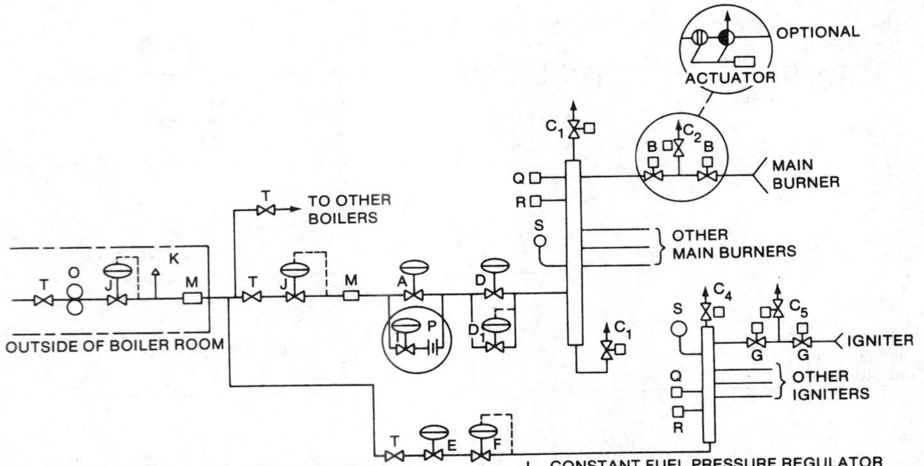

A MAIN SAFETY SHUTOFF VALVE
B INDIVIDUAL BURNER SAFETY SHUTOFF VALVE
C_2 INDIVIDUAL BURNER ATMOSPHERIC VENT VALVE
D MAIN FUEL CONTROL VALVE
D_1 MAIN FUEL BY-PASS CONTROL VALVE
E IGNITER SAFETY SHUTOFF VALVE
F IGNITER FUEL CONTROL VALVE
G INDIVIDUAL IGNITER SAFETY SHUTOFF VALVE
C_1 BURNER HEADER ATMOSPHERIC VENT VALVE
C_5 INDIVIDUAL IGNITER ATMOSPHERIC VENT VALVE
I CHARGING VALVE (OPTIONAL—MUST BE SELF CLOSING)

J CONSTANT FUEL PRESSURE REGULATOR
K PRESSURE RELIEF VALVE
C_4 IGNITER HEADER ATMOSPHERIC VENT VALVE
T MANUAL SHUTOFF VALVE

OTHER EQUIPMENT:
M FLOW METER
O STRAINER OR CLEANER
P RESTRICTING ORIFICE
Q HIGH FUEL PRESSURE SWITCH
R LOW FUEL PRESSURE SWITCH
S FUEL PRESSURE GAGE

FIG. 2-5G. Typical fuel supply system for natural gas-fired multiple-burner boiler-furnace.

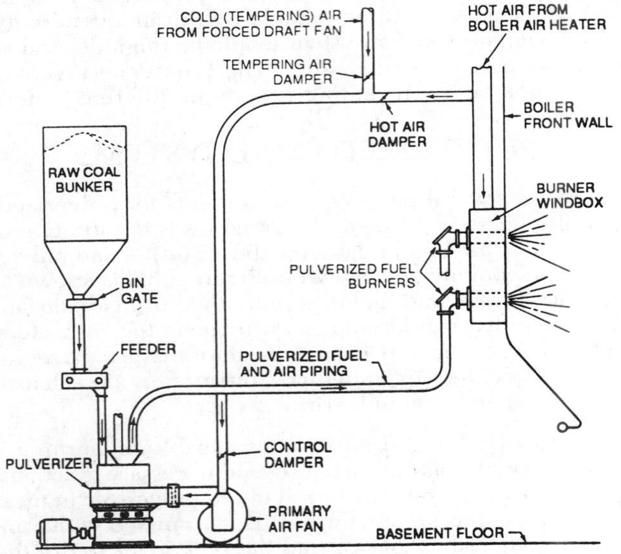

FIG. 2-5H. Direct-firing system for pulverized coal. (Source: Babcock & Wilcox)

1. The fuel must be volatized and completely consumed in a continuous process starting with an initial zone of stable ignition at the burner and continuing through the combustion process with no more than a trace of unburned combustibles in the stack gas and ash hoppers.
2. The amount of oxygen in the initial combustion zone is limited in order to control stack emissions, especially oxides of nitrogen.
3. The total air to each burner and to the burner zone of the furnace must contain a low level of excess air in order to maintain a low level of NO_x, and to limit stack losses.
4. The limited air should surround the combustion process at each burner to minimize reducing atmosphere in contact with tube surfaces.
5. Stable ignition is necessary at each burner to ensure continuous combustion and a means of flame detection at each burner.

Sufficient furnace-water wall surface between burners is necessary both to minimize the generation of thermal NO_x by cooling the combustion zone, and to cool ash particles below the temperature that causes slag deposits on furnace or superheater surfaces.

Products of combustion are transported from the furnace through platen and pendant superheater and reheater surfaces, through the convection pass including the economizer surface, and through the air heater to accomplish the necessary heat transfer before being transported to the air pollution control system(s) by the induced draft (ID).

Achieving the environmental limitation on NO_x levels requires a low-turbulence burner with the air and fuel well distributed to minimize the available oxygen in the initial ignition zone and excess air in the furnace. To achieve the conditions discussed in the preceding paragraphs, burner designs similar to that shown in Figure 2-5I, and a compartmented burner system, such as that shown in Figure 2-5J were developed.

Figure 2-5I shows the operating principles of a dual-register pulverized coal burner to achieve low levels of oxides of nitrogen emissions. The burner, as its name implies, has two registers to proportion the air between the fuel-rich, initial ignition zone and the secondary combustion air zone. A third means of adjustment is the position of the swirler vanes to control the turbulence and, thus, the stability of the initial ignition zone. The turbulence and quantity of secondary air to the initial ignition zone is limited to that required for initial ignition and for continuous combustion of the fuel. The remainder of the secondary combustion air is mixed with the fuel within the furnace

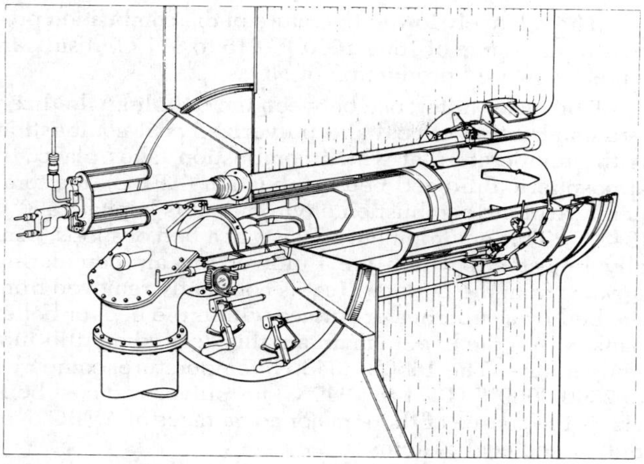

FIG. 2-5I. Dual-register burner for NOx control pulverized coal firing.

to provide slow but efficient and continuous combustion until the fuel is completely consumed. A flow-distribution device is located in the coal nozzle to ensure a uniform mix of the primary air and coal just prior to emission from the nozzle.

The compartmented burner system shown in Figure 2-5J provides each burner group served by its pulverizer with a separate windbox with secondary air measured and controlled at each end. Thus, combustion control has been modified from a total boiler basis to a per-pulverizer basis to achieve more precise and more flexible control of the combustion process.

Figure 2-5J shows another fan-to-pulverizer combination of a pulverized coal system known as a "cold air" or "common primary" fan system. Here, the primary air fans blow (cold) air through (air) heaters to supply the common duct for hot primary air, and the common duct for cold primary air that bypasses the airheaters.

The large steam-generating capacity of modern boilers coupled with poorer fuel quality have created the need for high-capacity pulverizers capable of processing 50 tons (45.36 metric tons) or more of coal per hr. The pulverizer shown in Figure 2-5K is a roll-and-race type that utilizes three large-diameter rolls spaced equally around the mill. The rolls are mounted on axles; and, in turn, the roll assemblies are attached by a pivoted connection to a stationary overhead frame that keeps them in their roll path while permitting limited radial freedom of movement. Grinding pressure is supplied by springs that apply force to the axles of the rolls. The grinding ring rotates at low speed and is shaped to form a race in which the rolls run.

Circulation of coal is similar to that shown in Figure 2-5K. Raw coal is fed into the mill either inside or outside of the grinding race. It immediately mixes with the partially ground coal that is circulated within the grinding zone by the airflow through the pulverizer. As the coal is

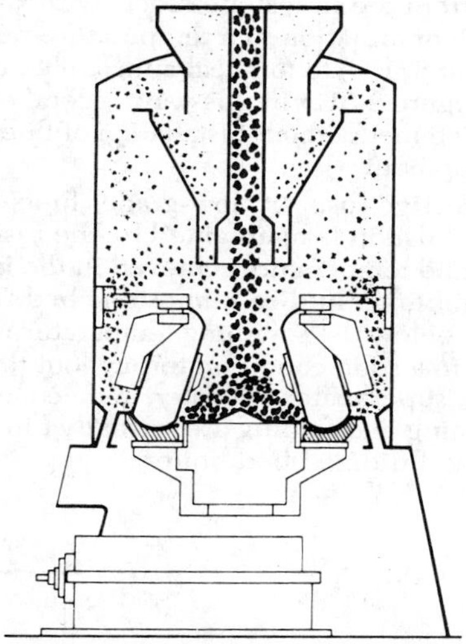

FIG. 2-5K. MPS pulverized coal recirculation. (Source: Babcock & Wilcox)

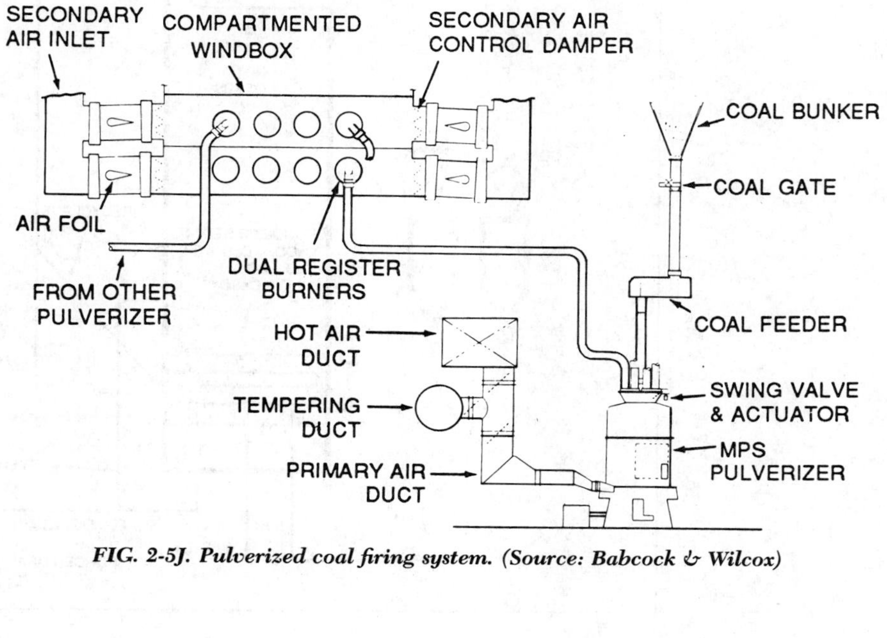

FIG. 2-5J. Pulverized coal firing system. (Source: Babcock & Wilcox)

reduced in size, the air carries it to the classifier. Fine coal, along with air, leaves the pulverizer through the outlet pipes. The oversize coal is returned to the grinding zone through a seal at the bottom of the classifier.

FLUIDIZED BED COAL SYSTEMS

The rising cost of fuel, and the requirements of air pollution laws to meet sulfur, NO_x, and particulate emission regulations have caused the utility and industrial power industry to develop more economical and efficient boiler systems. A recent technology developed to meet these challenges is the fluidized bed boiler. It is designed to meet federal sulfur and NO_x emissions regulations; it uses low-grade, lower-cost energy sources.

Fuel combustion is carried out in a fluidized bed in the presence of a bubbling bed of calcined limestone. Calcium oxide from the limestone reacts with sulfur dioxide produced in combination in a temperature range of 1500-1600°F (815 to 871°C) to form calcium sulfate in a dry solid state. (See Figure 2-5L.) In this way, federal emission regulations can be met without installation of flue gas desulfurization equipment.

Cost-effective use of low-grade fuels is possible because combustion is maintained by the residence time, turbulence, and temperature achieved in the immense, hot mass of a bubbling, fluidized limestone bed. Temperature of the bed is below the softening temperature of ash so the ash remains in a solid condition throughout the boiler convection pass, superheater, reheater, and economizer. Problems of slagging and fouling are virtually eliminated from the bubbling, fluidized bed boiler.

The relatively low temperature of the combustion process in the range of 1500-1600°F (815 to 871°C) results in a much lowered production of NO_x.

The major difference between the bubbling, fluidized bed combustion of coal and pulverized coal combustion is the temperature at which combustion takes place. In atmospheric fluidized bed combustion (AFBC), the temperature of the combustion environment is kept at 1550°F (843°C). This environment consists of a bed of solids (usually limestone) which are fluidized by air perculating upward from the bottom. Heat is constantly removed from the bed by a superheater surface within the bed, or boiler bank within the bed, to maintain this desired equilibrium temperature. The 1550°F (843°C) temperature, compared to 2500-3000°F (1371 to 1649°C) for pulverized coal boilers, is the source of three major advantages of AFBC over pulverized coal systems:

1. Sulfur dioxide (SO_2) absorption by a limestone bed is near optimum at this temperature, eliminating the need for a flue gas scrubber.
2. Nitrogen oxides (NO_x) emissions are kept well below federal emissions standards.
3. Slagging and fouling by the coal ash is prevented by being well below the fusion temperature of the ash.

Bubbles of the flue gas are formed in the combustion process which rise through the bed, causing highly turbulent mixing. Smaller limestone particles become entrained in the gas stream and are carried over through the convection pass. These smaller limestone particles are collected in multiclone dust collectors for recycling to the fluidized bed. Recyling of the unreacted limestone and unburned

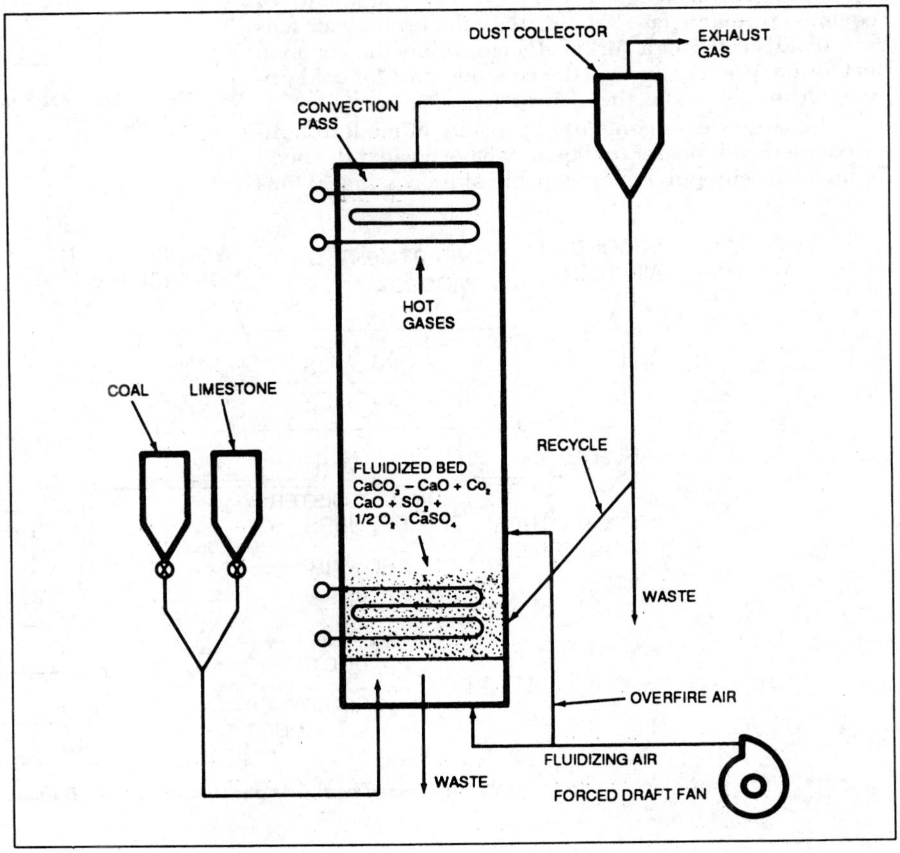

FIG. 2-5L. Fluidized bed system.

carbon for reinjection into the fluidized bed greatly increases efficiency of both sulfur capture and carbon burnup.

The integration of the fluidized-bed combustion process with a boiler includes the boiler surface within the bed, superheater surface within the bed, waterwall enclosure to contain the bed, and a water-cooled air distributor plate to support the bed.

A second generation of fluid bed systems is the circulating fluid bed system shown in Figure 2-5M.

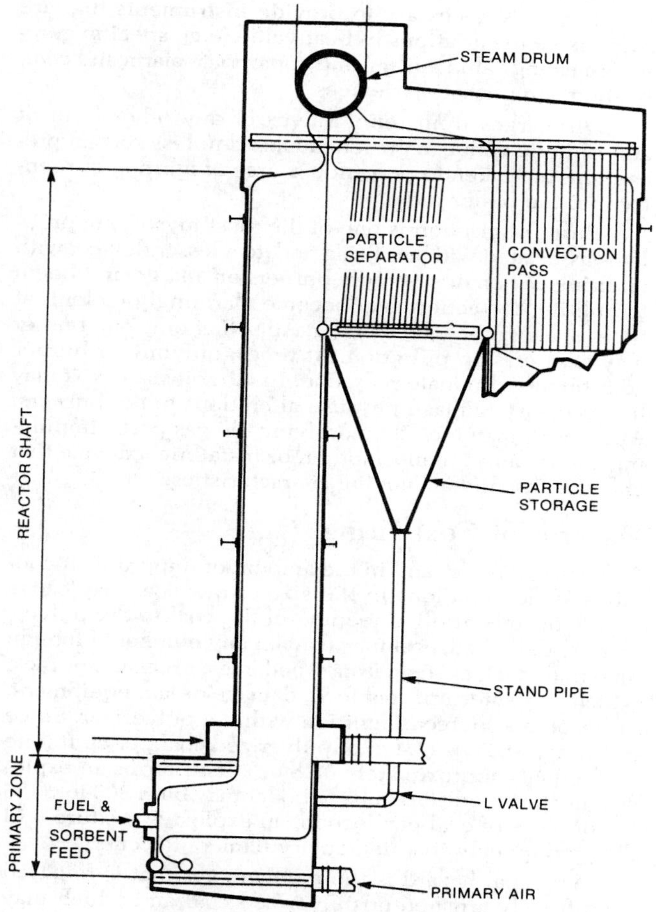

FIG. 2-5M. Circulating fluid bed system.

The circulating fluid bed system consists of a circulating bed of fine particles superimposed on a bubbling, dense-phase, fluid bed. Crushed coal or other fuel and limestone are fed into the lower, primary combustor section where the fuel is partially burned and much of the SO_2 is captured. Fluidizing velocities are 3.0 to 6.5 ft/sec (1 to 2 m/s) in this area.

Secondary air is added at the throat of the circulating bed section for completing combustion and providing gas velocities on the order of 10 to 25 ft/sec (3 to 7.6 m/s). Solids loading in the circulating bed zone is 1 to 5 lb/ft^3 (16 to 80 kg/m^3). The flue gas, with the entrained bed material, flows from the reactor to the particle separator where the entrained bed material is removed. The cleaned gases then flow across a convective heat transfer surface, through an air heater and bag house, and exit to a stack. The bed material captured by the particle separator flows to a hopper and is circulated back into the reactor through an L-valve, thus maintaining a stable circulating bed inventory.

Particulate removed from the gas stream drops into storage hoppers below the separators. Standpipes from the hoppers feed L-valves which recirculate the material back to the primary section of the reactor. By regulating the rate at which the material is recirculated, the reactor bed temperature can be controlled.

The recirculation flow rate is controlled by a small amount of fluidizing air added at the control nozzle on each L-valve. As the volume of this fluidizing air is increased, the amount of recirculated solids increases. The resulting increase in particle density leads to higher heat transfer to the reactor walls. When combined with increased fuel feed the extra heat of combustion is balanced by the increased heat transfer. This allows fast response to load changes, without bed temperature upsets. This arrangement effectively eliminates the need for an external heat exchanger and allows continuous control of bed temperature to the optimum level for SO_2 and NO_x control.

Because of high particle residence times in the furnace, the circulating fluid bed system offers excellent combustion efficiencies on all types of fuels. Hard-to-burn fuels, e.g., oil shale, petroleum coke, and anthracite culm, and problem fuels, such as high-sulfur coal, can all be effectively utilized, usually at significant cost savings over conventional fuels.

A third-generation system is now being installed for initial testing based on pressurized fluid bed combustion (PFBC). Such systems will include gas turbine generators for combined cycle operation.

BOILER-FURNACE HAZARDS

Explosion and fire are the principal hazards of boiler-furnaces and their associated fuel supplies, pipes, ducts, and fans. Explosions are the result of the ignition of combustible mixtures of fuel and air that have accumulated in the confined spaces of the equipment. Generally, such accumulations are the result of a malfunction or operator error associated with an inadequate or improper purge or incorrect operation of the burner equipment.

A temporary loss of flame caused by an interruption in fuel or air delivery or in ignition energy may allow a combustible fuel-air mixture to accumulate in the furnace before ignition is re-established. Leaking fuel may collect in an idle furnace and ignite explosively when the burner is lighted. In multiburner units, the loss of flame at one or more burners may allow an explosive mixture to accumulate, only to be ignited by other burners, either while operating normally or while being lighted. A classic example of operator error is the failure to purge the furnace of combustible mixtures between repeatedly unsuccessful attempts to light off the burner.

Hazards of Oil Firing

Like other petroleum products, fuel oil is a complex blend of hydrocarbons having a wide variety of molecular weights, and boiling, freezing, and flash points. When subjected to sufficiently high temperatures, fuel oils will partially decompose or volatize, or both, thereby creating new and unpredictable liquid, gaseous, and solid fuels. While the refining process controls the properties of fuel oils within standard limits, the properties of crude oils can vary considerably. For example, crude oils contain volatile light ends, such as propane, butane, and pentane; fuel oils do not.

Historically, there were two grades of fuel oils—distillates and residuals. Residual fuel oils were the residues left after the distillation of crude oils to obtain distillate fuel oils. Modern refining practices involving the cracking process permit more and different types of finished products to be obtained from a single barrel of crude; thus, a wide range of fuel oils is now available. No. 1 and No. 2 fuel oil, and fuels commonly known as kerosenes, range oil, furnace oil, and diesel oil, may still be broadly classified as distillates, while No. 5 and No. 6 fuel oil may be referred to as residuals. Most power boiler fuel systems are designed for the heavier Nos. 5 or 6 oils, although distillate fuels may be used for boilers designed with natural gas as the primary fuel. The use of crude oils, even those that have been given some treatment to remove the gassy light ends, is no longer a common practice. It is necessary to preheat the heavier oils (Nos. 4, 5, and 6) to hold the viscosity of the oil flowing to the burners within acceptable limits that will ensure proper atomization.

If sludge is allowed to accumulate in storage tanks, it may be drawn into the burners and plug strainers or burner tips, causing a flameout. Water in the oil may also cause flameout.

If two shipments of fuel having widely different viscosities or specific gravities are stored in the same tank, a significant change in fuel input rate without a corresponding change in airflow may occur and impair the efficiency of combustion.

Combustion efficiency of mechanical atomizing burners may also be affected by a change in orifice size caused by wear. In burners operating with very little excess air, combustibles may collect in the furnace. Periodic flow testing and/or replacement of sprayer plates may be necessary. Unsafe operating conditions can also be created by the failure of installation or maintenance personnel to install a nozzle or sprayer plate in the burner assembly.

Very rapid transients in oil flow through operating burners can be caused by rapid operation of an oil supply valve, individual burner shutoff valves, or the regulating valve in the return oil line from the burner header. These uncontrolled changes in the fuel input to the furnace can introduce very hazardous conditions.

Oil flow to individual oil guns can be adversely affected by such conditions as variations in burner elevation, distance from the regulating valve, and pipe size, all of which can be hazardous on low-pressure burners.

Hazards of Gas Firing

The primary hazards in gas-fired systems are gas leaks and the development of fuel-rich mixtures within the furnace or structural enclosures. Potentially hazardous accumulations are most likely to develop within buildings, particularly where gas piping is routed through confined areas that are not adequately ventilated.

Within the furnace it is possible for air-fuel ratios to be altered severely without producing any visible evidence at the burners, furnace, or stack, thus allowing the condition to progressively deteriorate. Combustion systems that respond to reduced boiler steam pressure or steam flow with an increase in their demand for fuel are potentially dangerous unless protected or interlocked to prevent the creation of a fuel-rich mixture and a loss of ignition.

Natural gas may be either wet or dry. A wet gas implies the presence of distillate, which, if carried into the burners, can result in momentary increases in fuel input and/or a flameout followed by possible reignition and explosion. For this reason, systems using wet gas require special attention.

Gases supplied from one or more sources can introduce unacceptable hazards if they have significant differences in volumetric heating value. With such variable supplies, it is necessary to provide instruments that are responsive to variations in heat value (e.g., specific gravity or heating value meters) and appropriate alarm and combustion compensation devices.

Discharges from relief valves or any other form of atmospheric vent can present a hazard unless special precautions are taken to prevent a source of ignition or reentry into the boiler room.

Burner pulsation is one of the most mystifying problems associated with gas firing and, to a lesser degree, with oil firing. When one or more burners on a large unit begin to pulsate, the action may become alarmingly violent, at times shaking the whole boiler. Adjusting only one burner may start or stop pulsation. At times, only minor burner adjustments eliminate pulsation. In other instances, it may be necessary to make physical alterations to the burners. Alterations may include modifying the gas ports, impinging gas streams on one another, or installing a device that changes the fuel-air mixing characteristics.

Hazards of Coal Firing

Coal varies in size and in the amount of impurities it contains. Wide variations in the size of raw coal may cause erratic or uncontrolled feeding of the coal to the pulverizer. As delivered, coal may contain any number of foreign materials, such as scrap iron, wood, rags, excelsior, or rock, which may interrupt coal feed, damage or jam equipment, or become a source of ignition within a pulverizer. Since as little as 0.05 oz (1.4 g) of pulverized coal per cu ft (one cu ft equals approximately 0.28 m^3) of air forms an explosive mixture, and since a large boiler may burn 300 lbs (136 kg) or more of coal per second, an explosive mixture will develop quickly if a momentary flameout occurs.

A special hazard is the methane gas that is released from freshly crushed or pulverized coal and which may accumulate in enclosed spaces, such as storage bins, and within pulverizers and burner piping.

Fuel (finely divided coal) is conveyed through pipes from the pulverizer to the burners entrained in an air stream. To prevent the settling out of coal particles in the burner pipes, and potential preignition, it is necessary to maintain an air velocity that is sufficient to keep the pulverized coal in suspension.

Provisions should be made for cooling down and emptying the pulverizer and/or burner lines when the burners they supply are shut down. This is to prevent spontaneous combustion and a possible explosion in the pulverizer or burner lines.

Pulverizer fires and explosions are serious hazards. A sudden and considerable increase in the temperature of the fuel-air mixture leaving the pulverizer or in the temperature of the outer casing are indications that a pulverizer fire has started. Such a fire may be caused by feeding burning fuel from the raw fuel bin into the pulverizer or by spontaneous combustion of fuel in the pulverizer or piping. If a fire occurs in any part of a pulverized fuel system, it should be looked upon as serious and should be dealt with promptly. The necessary steps for extinguishing the fire are the following:

1. Remove the pulverizer from service without emptying it to avoid creating an air-rich condition.
2. Isolate the pulverizer against air infiltration by closing all burner line valves and inlet air dampers, and sealing the air valve.
3. Admit steam or inert gas into the pulverizer through the connection provided for that purpose to smother the fire and to maintain an inert atomsphere until the coal has been removed and the housing has cooled.
4. Dump the coal stored in the pulverizer through the pyrite gates and into the sluice system.
5. Rotate the pulverizer without operating the primary air fan to complete the swirling and cleaning procedure.

A similar procedure should be followed for pulverizers that have been tripped full of subbituminous B, C, or lignite coal without immediate restart to avoid pulverizer explosions while out of service or when started up. Recommended emergency procedures should be reviewed with pulverizer manufacturers to include requirements peculiar to each design.

Meters that detect combustibles are not infallible when used with pulverized coal, as they measure only gaseous combustibles. Since the generation of combustibles requires both high temperature for volatilization and limited oxygen in the combustion zone, the lack of a meter indication of combustibles does not rule out the presence of unburned coal particles.

The limited operating experience of fluidized bed boilers has not yet identified any unique, hazardous condition. It is expected that the incidence of furnace explosions will be less than for pulverized coal primarily because of the larger size of crushed coal as compared to pulverized coal.

The furnace safety and burner interlock systems for pulverized coal are currently being applied to experimental and pilot plant installations of fluidized bed boilers. This practice will be continued with special emphasis on the requirements for continuous purge procedures and on interlocks for igniters and auxiliary burners. Compartment alarms and trips may be initiated by both high and low bed temperatures. For any installation, the interlock requirements should be reviewed with the manufacturer and the consulting engineer for the project.

It is not the intent of this chapter to include startup, shutdown, or operating procedures or a detailed description of interlock and trip systems. This information is contained in the applicable NFPA standards listed at the end of this chapter.

Open Register Light-off or Continuous Purge Procedure

One important consideration is the use of the open register light-off or continuous purge procedure for all fuels. This procedure maintains airflows at or above the prescribed minimum of 25 percent of full load volumetric airflow during all operations of the boiler. Volumetric airflow is specified to recognize that weight flow rate must be increased at low air temperature to maintain air and gas velocities.

The open register purge rate or continuous purge procedure is based upon the concept that three basic operating conditions will significantly improve the margin of operating safety, particularly during startup. Those conditions are:

1. Minimum number of required equipment manipulations, thereby minimizing exposure to operating errors or equipment malfunction;
2. Means for establishing the desired fuel-rich condition at individual burners during light-off; and
3. An air-rich furnace atmosphere during light-off and warm-up by maintaining total furnace airflow at the same rate as that required for the furnace purge.

In its simplest form, the basic procedure that satisfies these three operating objectives is as follows:

- Place all or most of the burner air registers in a predetermined open position.
- Purge the furnace and boiler settings with the burner air registers in that same predetermined position. The total airflow for purge must not be less than 25 percent of full load volumetric airflow.
- Light the first burner or group of burners without any change in airflow setting or in burner air register position.

Each boiler should be tested to determine whether any modifications are required to obtain satisfactory ignition or to satisfy other design limitations during light-off and warm-up. For example, some boilers will be purged with the registers in the normal operating position. In this event, it may be necessary to momentarily close the registers of the burner being lighted to establish ignition. However, unnecessary modifications in basic procedure should be avoided, thereby satisfying to the greatest degree possible the three basic objectives set forth earlier, particularly that of keeping the number of equipment manipulations to a minimum.

FIRE AND EXPLOSION PROTECTION

The foundation of fire and explosion protection is prevention. Reliable equipment, good facility design, system monitoring and malfunction alarm instrumentation, operator training, and maintenance are key elements in preventing fires and explosions in boiler-furnace systems.

The entire system—boiler, furnace, fuel supply, air supply, vents, piping, and ducts—should be designed to specific parameters and for specific operating limits. At no time should these limits be exceeded.

Good facility design requires the boiler to be installed in a separate room or structure, preferably of noncombustible construction. Boiler-furnaces should be set on concrete floors or platforms that extend beyond the equipment for a distance of at least 4 ft (1.2 m) in each direction. If they must be set on combustible floors, there should be sufficient air circulation beneath the furnace to keep the temperature of the combustible floor below 160°F (71°C).

Metal chimneys or smokestacks should not extend through combustible floors, ceilings, or walls. If such chimneys must be passed through combustible roofs, sufficient clearance and/or insulation should be provided to keep the temperature of the combustible materials below 160°F (71°C). Generally, minimum clearance is considered to be 18 in. (0.46 m).

A system of interlocks should be provided to prevent improper sequencing by operating personnel and to shut down operations if certain critical malfunctions occur. Audible and visual alarms serve to warn operators to take certain corrective steps; others may indicate what automatic functions have been performed to reduce a hazard. New boilers should not be fired until adequate safeguards have been installed and tested.

Safe operation cannot be ensured solely by equipment design and adherence to a manufacturer's operating instructions. Knowledgeable and competent operators who understand the processes involved are also needed. Technical competence should be maintained by a continuing program of retraining so that increasing familiarity with the system does not tempt operating personnel to take "short cuts" in operating procedures or to bypass safety devices.

A program of preventive maintenance is needed to maintain the reliability of the equipment and its control devices. Poor preventive maintenance can lead to frequent corrective maintenance. Cleanliness and good housekeeping, especially where pulverized coal is the fuel, will also contribute to the prevention of fire and explosion.

Automatic sprinkler or water spray systems are practical forms of fire protection in combustible boiler rooms. In noncombustible boiler rooms where the potential for sustained fire may be slight, portable fire extinguishers or small hose lines may be adequate. Additional guidance on fire protection for fuel supply systems can be found in the following chapters: Section 2, Chapter 25, "Storage of Flammable and Combustible Liquids" and Section 3, Chapter 7, "Gases."

BIBLIOGRAPHY

References

Babcock & Wilcox, "B & W/Studsvik Circulating Fluid Bed," 9-1795, March 1986, Babcock & Wilcox, Barberton, OH.

Cote, A. E., ed., *Industrial Fire Hazards Handbook*, 3rd ed., National Fire Protection Association, Quincy, MA, 1990.

Factory Mutual Research Corporation, "Elements of Combustion, Controls, and Safeguards in Industrial Heating Equipment," *Loss Prevention Data 6-0*, Factory Mutual Research Corp., Norwood, MA.

Factory Mutual Research Corporation, "Boiler-Furnaces Oil- or Gas-Fired Single Burner," *Loss Prevention Data 6-4*, Factory Mutual Research Corp., Norwood, MA.

Factory Mutual Research Corporation, "Boiler-Furnaces Oil- or Gas-Fired Multiple Burner," *Loss Prevention Data 6-5*, Factory Mutual Research Corp., Norwood, MA.

NFPA Codes, Standards, and Recommended Practices

Reference to the following NFPA codes, standards, and recommended practices will provide further information on the safeguards for boiler-furnaces discussed in this chapter. (See the latest *NFPA Catalog* for availability of current editions of the following documents.)

NFPA 30, *Flammable and Combustible Liquids Code.*

NFPA 68, *Explosion Venting.*

NFPA 85A, *Prevention of Furnace Explosions in Fuel Oil- and Natural Gas-Fired Single Burner Boiler-Furnaces.*

NFPA 85B, *Prevention of Furnace Explosions in Natural Gas-Fired Multiple Burner Boiler-Furnaces.*

NFPA 85D, *Prevention of Furnace Explosions in Fuel Oil-Fired Multiple Burner Boiler-Furnaces.*

NFPA 85E, *Prevention of Furnace Explosions in Pulverized Coal-Fired Multiple Burner Boiler-Furnaces.*

NFPA 85F, *Installation and Operation of Pulverized Fuel Systems.*

NFPA 85G, *Prevention of Furnace Implosions in Multiple Burner Boiler-Furnaces.*

Additional Reading

ANSI/ASME, *Boiler and Pressure Vessel Code*, American Society of Mechanical Engineering, NY, 1989.

Davis, G. D., "Investigation and Repair of an Auxiliary Boiler Explosion," *Plant/Operation Progress*, Vol. 6, No. 1, Jan. 1987, pp. 42-45.

Durrant, O. W., "Design, Operation, Control and Modeling of Pulverized Coal Fired Boilers," paper presented to Boiler-Turbine Modeling and Control Seminar, University of New South Wales, Sydney, Australia, 1977.

Durrant, O. W., and Krippene, G. C., "Combustion Principles and Processes for NO_x Control Natural Gas-Fired Utility Boilers," presented to the American Gas Association, Atlanta, GA, 1972.

Durrant, O. W., and Zadiraka, A. J., "Control of Pulverized Coal-fired Utility Drum Boilers During Load Changes, Presented to American Power Conference, Chicago, IL, 1981.

El-Wakil, M. M., "Fosil-Fuel Steam Generations," *Powerplant Technology*, McGrow Hill, NY, 1984, pp. 79-121.

Factory Mutual Engineering Corporation, "Elements of Combustion, Controls, and Safeguards in Industrial Heating Equipment," Loss Prevention Data 6-0, Factory Mutual System, Norwood, MA, 1977.

FMEC, "Boiler-Furnaces Oil- or Gas-Fired Single Burner," Loss Prevention Data, 6-4, 1976.

FMEC, "Boiler-Furnaces Oil- or Gas-Fired Multiple Burner," Loss Prevention Data, 6-5, 1978.

Graham and Trotman, Ltd, eds., Boiler Operator's Handbook, 2nd ed., State Mutual Book and Periodical Service, Ltd., New York, NY, 1989.

Heil, T. C., and Durrant, O. W., "Designing Boilers for Western Coal," presented to Joint Power Generation Conference, Dallas, TX, 1978.

Katzel, J., "Focus on Boilers," *Plant Engineering*, May 24, 1990, Vol. 44, No. 10, p. 67.

Resource Systems International, *Boiler: Repair and Maintenance*, Reston Publishing Co., Reston, VA, 1982.

Resource Systems International, *Boiler Systems and Components I and II*, Reston Publishing Co., Reston, VA, 1982.

Sheehan, E., "Heat Transfer Oil Boilers," *Plant/Operation Progress*, Vol. 5, No. 4, Oct. 1986, pp. 193-195.

Shields, C., Boilers, McGraw-Hill, New York, NY, 1982.

Spring, H. M., and Kohan, A. L., Boiler Operator's Guide, 2nd ed., McGraw-Hill, New York, NY, 1981.

Trinks, W., Industrial Furnaces, (Vols. 1 and 2), John Wiley and Sons, New York, NY, 1967.

Walker, R. R., and Zadiraka, A. J., "Integrated Fuel and Air Control System for PC Firing," presented to the American Power Conference, Chicago, 1975.

Whitney, S. A., and Smith, J. W., "Industrial Fluidized Bed Design and Operation of the TVA Test Facility," presented to 6th International Coal and Lignite Utilization Exhibition and Conference, Houston, TX, 1983.

STATIONARY COMBUSTION ENGINES

Revised by Vincent J. Hession

Reciprocating engines and gas turbine engines, the two types of combustion engines in general stationary use, are frequently used as prime movers to drive alternators, pumps, and compressors. Increasingly, these engines are being used to drive alternators in emergency situations.

Engine-driven pumps and compressors handle a variety of fluids, including flammable liquids and gases. This chapter discusses the potential fire hazards associated with such engines. It provides recommendations for the safe location, storage of fuel, and installation of the engines.

For a more in-depth discussion of the fire hazards associated with the use and storage of flammable liquids and gases, see Section 3, Chapter 5, "Flammable and Combustible Liquids;" Section 3, Chapter 7, "Gases;" Section 2, Chapter 25, "Storage of Flammable and Combustible Liquids;" and Section 2, Chapter 26, "Storage of Gases." Protective devices are covered in Section 5, Chapter 23, "Selection, Operation, Distribution, and Maintenance of Fire Extinguishers" and Section 5, Chapter 24, "The Role of Extinguishers in Fire Protection," which provide detailed information about the use of fire extinguishers.

POTENTIAL HAZARDS

Potential fire hazards associated with combustion engines are: (1) their fuels, lubricants, and in some cases the material being pumped or compressed; (2) the temperature of exposed engine parts, particularly exhaust manifolds and pipes, which can be hot enough to ignite flammable or combustible liquids or other materials; (3) the presence of arcing electrical components, such as starters, generators, distributors, and magnetos, which can ignite flammable liquids and gases; and (4) engine disintegration.

LOCATION

Engines may be located outdoors, inside structures, or on roofs of structures. However, depending on the site, consideration should be given to locating the engine with respect to exterior wall openings, distance to combustible walls and ceilings, and availability of sufficient air for combustion and ventilation. Engine room compartmentation should comply with applicable standards and local codes which specify minimum fire resistance ratings.

Because of the presence of hot surfaces, engines should be isolated from locations where combustible dust or airborne flyings can be produced, and from liquids and gases having unusually low ignition temperatures. Exhaust manifolds and piping can reach temperatures over 1000°F (538°C) but, in order for ignition to occur, conditions must be favorable for reasonably prolonged contact between the combustible and the hot surface. For this reason, these surfaces seldom ignite flammable liquid vapors or flammable gases. However, dust and flyings can be deposited on these surfaces, and proper precautions should be observed.

FUEL SUPPLY

Many engine applications require on-site fuel supplies for reliability. The fuel may be stored outdoors or within a building. Codes and standards restrict fuel tank size and location. (See bibliography.)

Gasoline, due to its low flash point, presents a greater potential fire hazard than some other fuels. Because of this, gasoline storage in buildings is limited to the capacity of the integral tank on the engine. When larger quantities of liquid fuel are required in buildings, diesel fuel is used.

When gas-fueled engines are used, they should be installed in accordance with applicable codes and standards. LP-Gas in the liquid phase should not be stored within a building. Gaseous vapors, e.g., gasoline and propane, are heavier than air and have a tendency to collect in low-lying areas. Special precaution should be taken to ensure proper ventilation when using these fuels.

INSTALLATION SAFEGUARDS

Codes and standards provide minimum requirements for safe installation of engines and include specifications for engine room compartmentation, fuel supply piping, room ventilation, engine exhaust piping, protective devices, and alarms. (See Figure 2-6A.)

Vincent J. Hession, P.E., is manager of standards and codes firesafety for Bell Communications Research, Piscataway, NJ.

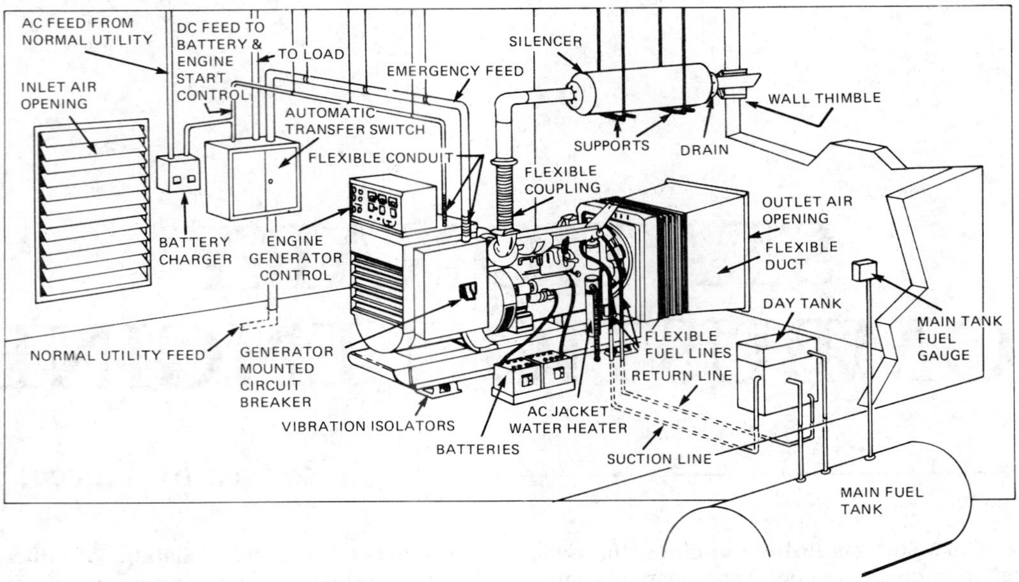

FIG. 2-6A. A typical generator installation used to supply emergency power. (Source: Caterpillar)

Escaping fuels and lubricants can present hazards regardless of the degree of fuel flammability. Liquid fuel supply systems should be installed to minimize the accidental discharge of fuel into the engine room. Methods or devices, e.g., dikes around fuel storage tanks, drains, float-controlled valves, and adequate alarms, can be used. Larger installations should have provision for a remote emergency shutdown of the engine. Most installations also have a remote means of shutting down fuel and lubricating oil pumps not directly driven by the engine. Liquid fuel is supplied to engines by pumps; however, gravity feed is permitted from an integral tank on an engine. The fuel supply to tanks above the lowest level of a building should be pumped in a manner acceptable to the authority having jurisdiction.

Backfires through gas-air mixers and carburetor air intakes occur as a result of engine malfunction. These can ignite grease and oil deposits on and around the engine. Flame-arresting equipment should be provided at these points if flammable liquids or gases are being pumped or compressed.

A lubricating oil mist is often present in the crankcases of large reciprocating engines which, upon ignition, can result in a combustion explosion in the crankcase. Such engines are often equipped with crankcase explosion vents and, sometimes, the crankcase is maintained under a nonflammable atmosphere.

Arcing electrical engine components are safeguarded by flashover shielding, flame arresters, purging, or ventilation if flammable liquids or gases are being pumped or compressed.

Engine exhaust systems, e.g., manifolds, mufflers, exhaust piping, etc., can reach temperatures in excess of 1,000°F (538°C), and special precautions are needed when these items penetrate combustible construction. Many fires have been caused by failure to allow sufficient clearance between exhaust piping and combustible walls, ceilings, or roofs. The exhaust system should terminate outside the structure at a point where the hot gases or sparks will be discharged harmlessly and not come in contact with combustible material.

Engine disintegration is rare. Gas turbines are somewhat more subject to this phenomenon than reciprocating engines because of the turbine's very high rotational speeds. Furthermore, the design of gas turbines for stationary installations usually incorporates construction features to contain the compressor, turbine blades, and rotor parts. The hazard is controlled by providing automatic engine speed governors. An overspeed shutdown device is provided on large engines of both types.

Instructions for normal starting, stopping, operation, and routine maintenance procedures should be posted near the equipment. Appreciable quantities of combustible materials should not be stored in the engine room. Finally, fire extinguishers should be provided in accordance with applicable standards and codes.

BIBLIOGRAPHY

NFPA Codes, Standards, and Recommended Practices

Reference to the following NFPA codes, standards, and recommended practices will provide further information on the safeguards for stationary combustion engines discussed in this chapter. (See the latest *NFPA Catalog* for availability of current editions of the following documents.)

NFPA 10, *Portable Fire Extinguishers.*

NFPA 20, *Installation of Centrifugal Fire Pumps.*

NFPA 30, *Flammable and Combustible Liquids Code.*

NFPA 37, *Stationary Combustion Engines and Gas Turbines.*

NFPA 54, *National Fuel Gas Code.*

NFPA 58, *Storage and Handling of Liquefied Petroleum Gases.*

NFPA 68, *Explosion Venting.*

NFPA 70, *National Electrical Code®.*

NFPA 99, *Health Care Facilities.*

NFPA 211, *Chimneys, Fireplaces, Vents, and Solid Fuel Burning Appliances.*

NFPA 220, *Standard Types of Building Construction.*

Additional Reading

"Procurement Standard for Gas Turbine Ratings and Performance," ANSI, B133.6, American Society of Mechanical Engineers, NY, 1978.

"Welded Steel Tanks for Oil Storage," API 650, American Petroleum Institute, Washington, DC, 1980.

"Engine Power Test Code—Spark Ignition and Diesel," SAE J1349, Society of Automotive Engineers, Warrendale, PA, 1980.

EMERGENCY AND STANDBY POWER SUPPLIES

Manuel J. DeLerno

The Northeast blackout of 1965 dramatically demonstrated the need for a source of electric power independent of electric public utilities. The San Francisco earthquake of 1989 is a recent example of the need for localized electric power in an emergency. Power interruptions occur due to natural or man-made causes. Natural causes are storms, floods, earthquakes, and the like; man-made causes are many, such as vehicles striking transformers or utility poles, equipment failure from one or more causes, and human operational error.

NFPA 70, *National Electrical Code*® (*NEC*), recognizes two types of private power supply systems: (1) emergency, and (2) standby. Emergency power systems are systems supplying power for illumination; critical heating, ventilation, and air conditioning (HVAC); fire pumps and alarms; public address systems; and other loads essential to the safety of life and property when public utility power is unavailable and where required by local, state, or federal codes. (See Figure 2-7A.) Standby power systems are subdivided into two categories: (1) legally required, and (2) optional. Standby power systems provide an alternate power source (to the public utility source) for subsystems that may cause damage to the overall process if deenergized or discomfort to people if stopped abruptly. For specifics, see Articles 701 and 702 of the *NEC*.

The loads to be served by the emergency or standby power system can be classified as critical and non-critical. Critical loads are loads that must be served within a relatively short time period after the power is needed in order to preserve life or property. Non-critical loads are all other loads that are permitted to be connected to the system.

There exists today a number of terms that overlap each other, such as alternate power systems, standby power systems, legally required standby systems, alternate power sources, etc. NFPA 110, *Emergency and Standby Power Systems,* and NFPA 110A, *Stored Emergency Systems*, place all such systems into categories defined in terms of type, class, and level, rather than using such aforementioned terms. Type defines the maximum allowable time that the load is without acceptable electrical power. Class defines the minimum allowable time that the alternate source has the capability of providing its rated load without being refueled. Level defines the equipment performance stringency requirements.

This chapter provides information on the components that alone, or in combination, form emergency and standby power systems.

ENERGY SOURCES

Energy sources for emergency and standby power supplies are generally one of the following: liquid petroleum products, liquefied petroleum gas, natural or synthetic combustible gas, or batteries. Other sources, such as steam, rotating mass (flywheel), and compressed noncombustible gas, have limitations that restrict their use for these purposes.

On-site storage of the energy source to supply power for the duration of the need for emergency and standby power is an important consideration, especially in areas subject to severe environmental disturbances, such as storms, earthquakes, flooding, etc. Section 2, Chapter 6, "Stationary Combustion Engines" provides details on safe storage of on-site fuels.

Batteries

Batteries, in general, are the most dependable energy source for emergency and standby power and are primarily used for emergency lighting, either as a central battery system or as a self-contained lighting assembly. They are also used with uninterruptible power supplies (UPS), a system that automatically provides power, without delay or transients, during a period when the normal power source is incapable of performing acceptably. A single battery or a group of batteries is limited in the amount of usable energy it is capable of delivering before becoming discharged; hence, backup to the battery source is often supplied in the form of other on-site emergency or standby power supplies.

Batteries used for this service are usually either lead-acid or nickel-cadmium type. The lead-acid battery is less costly and requires less space for the same capacity, but

---

Manuel J. DeLerno is president of S-P-D Industries, located in Berwyn, IL. He is secretary of the NFPA Emergency Power Supplies Committee, and a member of NFPA's Fire Pumps Committee.

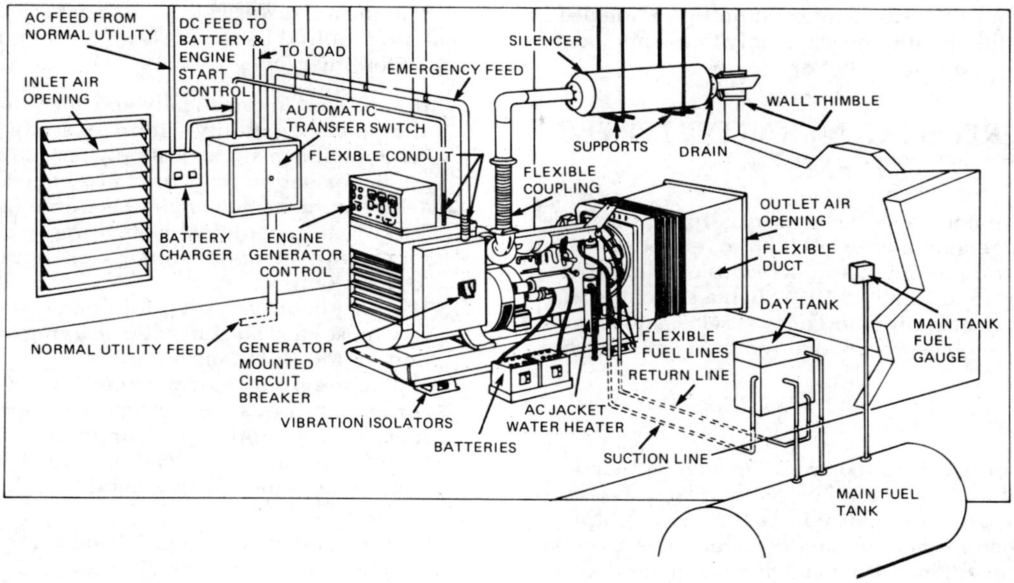

FIG. 2-7A. A typical generator installation used to supply emergency power. (Source: Caterpillar)

the nickel-cadmium type has a longer life, more rugged construction, and requires less maintenance. Sealed batteries (those not requiring periodic replacement of water) are favored for use with self-contained lighting assemblies.

After use, batteries must be recharged so as to have power available again when needed. A self-contained lighting assembly normally is provided with an automatic recharger and a sensing relay for determining normal power supply loss to the normal illuminating means. Consideration should be given to having the battery recharger connected to the emergency or standby power source (when such a source is installed) upon loss of normal power where evacuation of the installation is not expected during a normal power outage or where a large number of people could be stranded in a high-rise building for a duration longer than the expected usuable discharge time of the battery without recharging. Central battery systems and UPS systems are normally provided with more complex battery rechargers, such as dual-rate, regulated, etc., to maximize battery life and minimize gassing.

Proper location of batteries with adequate ventilation is an important environmental consideration. The gaseous products of electrolysis (hydrogen and oxygen) can be a fire hazard.

UNINTERRUPTIBLE POWER SUPPLIES AND OTHER STORED ENERGY POWER SUPPLIES

A true UPS system providing continuous and transient-free single-phase or polyphase ac power is used to supply such critical load applications as sensitive electronic and computer equipment for data processing, life support, communications, and control equipment. Such a system, upon loss of normal power, continues to supply power without waveform distortion, and the load is totally unaware of normal power loss.

There are applications where such purity is not required, and either waveform distortion (transient or phase displacement of waveform) or a brief lapse of power to the load, or both, is acceptable. Economic considerations will bear upon the type of stored energy power supply used.

Batteries, combined with rectifiers and solid-state inverters (converters of dc power to ac power), provide power to the majority of UPS systems in use. Such systems are known as static UPS systems. This system rectifies the incoming ac power to dc power, then inverts the dc power back to ac power for delivery to the load. A battery is permanently connected between the rectifier and inverter (on the dc bus) and takes over as the power source immediately upon loss of the incoming ac power. Upon return of the incoming ac power, this power serves to power the load as well as to recharge the battery. The inverter serves to determine the characteristics of the ac power to the load, so that any voltage or frequency variations or transients on the incoming power are absent from the load. The rectifier is continuously sized to the capacity of the load plus that required for battery recharging, while the inverter is continuously sized to the capacity of the load.

Other UPS systems are variations of a rotating generator driven by various drivers (engines, ac and dc motors), with or without a flywheel.

A stored energy power supply system similar to the UPS system, but economically more attractive, is one in which the normal ac power is fed through to the load with a static transfer switch transferring the load to an inverter supplied by a battery upon loss of the normal ac power. The inverter receives a continuous synchronizing signal from the normal ac power, so that, upon loss of this power, the inverter is still approximately in phase with the power just lost. This, coupled with a transfer time of a few milliseconds, permits the load to be without power for only a brief period and without serious transients occurring upon application of inverter power. Note, however, that the inverter need only be sized intermittently for the load power and that the rectifier be sized only to accommodate the recharging power of the battery.

ENGINE-DRIVEN GENERATOR POWER SYSTEMS

An engine generator power system usually consists of a prime mover, a generator coupled thereto (either direct or geared), transfer equipment, and distribution and protective equipment. (See Figure 2-7B.) Such a system is supplied for either standby or emergency service, and is most common where such power is required for a considerable period of time.

Prime Mover

The prime mover may be a reciprocating engine fueled by gasoline, diesel fuel, or natural or synthetic gas. Gas turbines are also used, particularly in larger power outputs. Gasoline and natural and synthetic gas engines are less costly than diesel engines, but have disadvantages that are considerable, such as the gasoline engine and fuel storage therein are more susceptible to fire and explosion, and the natural gas engine usually obtains its energy supply from an off-site gas utility, a supply that may not be available at the same time of unavailability of the normal power supply (for this reason, an on-site fuel supply might be required by the authority having jurisdiction).

Gas turbines are much smaller than reciprocating engines of the same output, and operate at much higher speeds. They require no cooling-water connection and burn natural gas, kerosene, diesel fuel, or fuel oil. They are, however, quite inefficient and are slow in coming up to full speed (more than 10 sec).

The prime mover and its associated auxiliary equipment are required by the *NEC* to have the following conditions for emergency service:

1. It must start automatically and come up to full speed and power capability within 10 sec of demand.
2. A minimum on-site fuel supply permitting full engine-generator output for 2 hrs must be available.
3. Where water-cooled engines are used (generally above 50 kW), the municipal water supply cannot be used for cooling (i.e., municipal water supply input, waste to drain output).
4. Where a battery is used for engine starting, the battery must have an automatic charging means independent of the prime mover.
5. Where the prime mover requires more than 10 sec to come up to full speed and power capability, an auxiliary power supply may supply the required power (within 10 sec) to the load, provided it can continue to do so until the load is assumed by the prime mover.

A prime mover driving a legally required standby power system must meet conditions 2, 3, and 4 above, and condition 1 within 60 sec.

A governor maintains the speed of the prime mover approximately constant throughout the full power output range by varying the fuel input to the prime mover. Governors may be mechanical, electrical, hydraulic, or a combination thereof.

The Generator

Generators convert the mechanical shaft output of the prime mover into the electrical power for use by the loads connected thereto. The performance of the generator and its voltage regulator under varying load conditions must

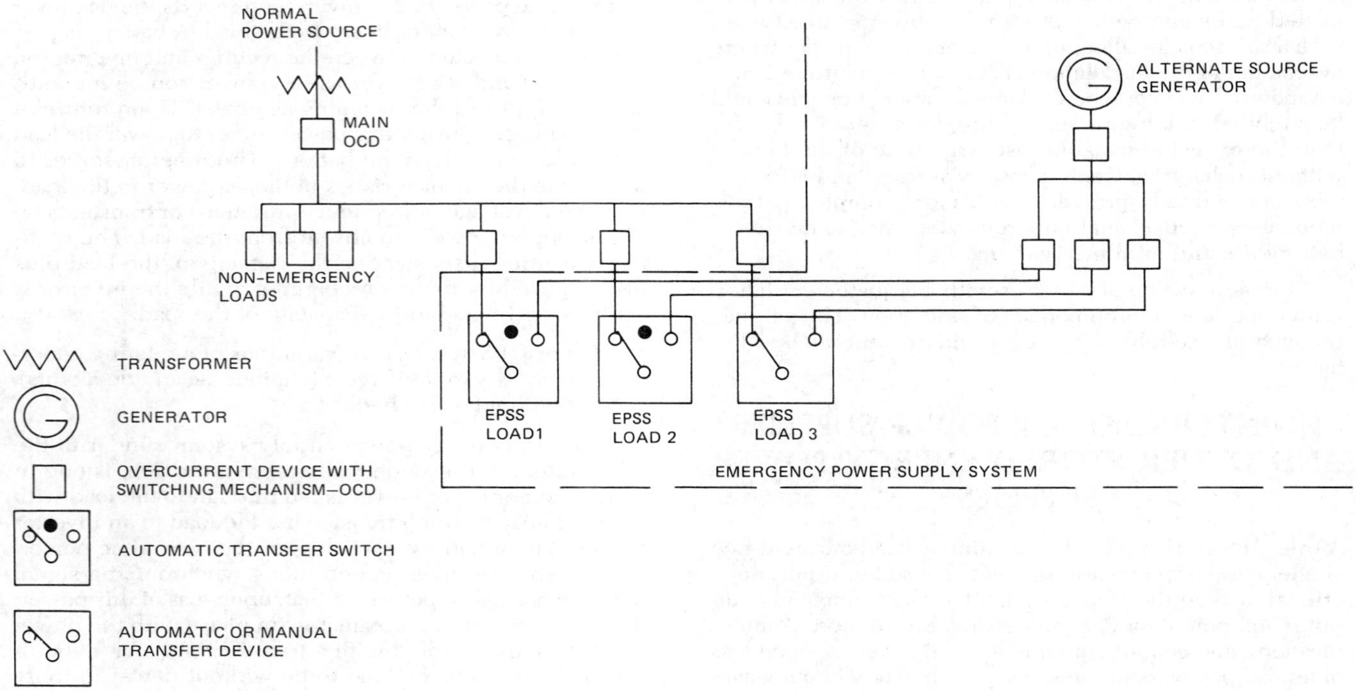

FIG. 2-7B. Typical rotating emergency power supply system.

be considered in determining its suitability. The output voltage of a generator drops suddenly when a load is applied, and rises suddenly when a load is removed. At present, generators larger than a few kilowatts in size have automatic voltage regulators that quickly bring the voltage back to the specified value. The initial voltage drop is important because if the drop is excessive, even for a few cycles, electromagnetic components, e.g., relays, motor starters, etc., may drop out and may or may not, depending upon circuitry, reclose when the voltage is restored, or they may cycle open and close repeatedly, causing equipment damage. Voltage rise (overshoot) upon load removal may cause damage to equipment remaining connected. The initial voltage drop is not usually of concern when the loads being connected are within the ratings of the generator. However, it is customary to exceed the rated current of the generator by two to three times during motor starting only. The initial voltage dip during these current overloads is, therefore, one of the limiting factors in sizing the generator. The performance of the generator when subjected to a short-circuit or heavy overload condition is also a matter of consideration. Under this condition, the generator current output decays with time, a characteristic inherent in the generator, so that in a relatively short time the current lessens to a magnitude of only several times its rating. If the decay rate is too rapid, it may not be possible to have selective tripping of overcurrent devices in the current loop.

Transfer Equipment

Electromechanical automatic transfer switches are normally used to transfer selected loads to the engine generator power supply when the normal source fails. The transfer switch senses normal power, usually all phases, and upon loss of normal power automatically signals the prime mover to start. A brief time delay is generally built into the transfer switch logic to delay the signal so that a momentary normal power interruption or flicker does not activate the prime mover. The transfer switch also senses the voltage and frequency of the generator output and, when these reach acceptable levels, either immediately thereafter or after a time delay (for selective load pickup), the switch transfers the load to the engine generator output. Upon restoration of the normal power supply to acceptable levels, the transfer switch may transfer the load automatically (usually after a time delay to allow for permanent normal power restoration) back to the normal source, or manual transfer of the load may be required, the choice having been originally made by the characteristics of the load. Transfer switches, in general, immediately retransfer the load back to the normal source (if available and at an acceptable level), should the emergency source fail. Maintenance of a transfer switch may require deactivation of loads connected to the switch while the maintenance is being performed. Some loads are so critical that such deactivation is unacceptable. In such cases, the transfer switch is furnished with an isolation by-pass switch, making it possible for the load to be served by the normal or emergency source while the automatic transfer switch is being serviced.

Distribution

Distribution of the available auxiliary power (emergency or standby) concerns itself with the loads served, the order of priority, and the total loading of the engine generator set. Protection concerns itself primarily with equipment protection and with continued availability of power to unfaulted loads upon a system electrical fault.

Engine generator set loading prioritizes the need for power and the magnitude of the various loads. Critical loads must be served first, followed by non-critical large motor loads. A motor load produces a heavy power and kVa load upon first starting, which influences momentary voltage and frequency output of the generator, causing a decrease in each. Step loading of the engine generator set is accomplished by using multiple transfer switches, timed to operate in sequence in the order of priority. Other more complex arrangements with programmable controllers or computers are sometimes used.

Permissible loading of the engine generator set during periods of loss of normal power is governed by codes and standards. Generally, during such periods, it is permissible to use available power not being used for critical loads to power non-critical loads and to resort to load-shedding techniques to pick up the critical loads when needed.

Protection, while generally in accordance with established procedures for the normal power supply, must take into account the usual situation of limited power availability of the engine generator set *versus* the larger power availability of the normal source. As indicated earlier, generators, under short-circuit or heavy overload conditions, have collapsing outputs such that the sustained total current output of the generator drops to a magnitude comparable to its full-load value. Rapid clearing of the fault is essential (prior to the drop in current to its sustained value), otherwise the protective device will not see the short-circuit condition. Rapid fault clearing is also important to enable the generator to reestablish itself (voltage restoration) and continue to serve the loads still connected to it.

MISCELLANEOUS CONSIDERATIONS

Multiple-engine generator sets are sometimes used to supply emergency and standby power. Such sets are usually operated in parallel, with load-shedding provisions incorporated should one of the sets fail. Because of the sizable monetary investment in an emergency or standby power system, some installations use the engine generator set in conjunction with the normal power supply for peak-shaving purposes. Peak shaving is the transfer of some loads from the normal power source to the auxiliary power source during periods of maximum loading of the normal power source. The economic benefit of peak shaving is a result of the utility rate structure. If a user can keep the ratio of maximum (or peak) power usage to average power usage low, then the utility charge is lessened. By transferring selected loads to the engine generator set during periods of peak power usage, the aforementioned ratio is lowered.

Motor-starting methods for large motors is another significant consideration. Two matters of concern are: (1) the power required from the prime mover, and (2) the kVa required from the generator. Selection of the proper type of reduced voltage starting is equally important. Open-transition reduced voltage starting is not a recommended method, nor is primary resistance reduced voltage starting. Auto-transformer starting and closed transition wye-delta starting are generally preferred to other methods.

BIBLIOGRAPHY

References

"IEEE Recommended Practice for Emergency and Standby Power Systems for Industrial and Commercial Applications," *ANSI/IEEE 446-1987*, The Institute of Electrical and Electronics Engineers, Piscataway, NJ.

"Kohler Engineer's Guidebook to Power Systems," *Consulting Engineer*, Vol. 64, No. 2, Part 2 of 2, Feb. 1985.

Battery Service Manual, 10th ed., Battery Council International, Chicago, IL.

NFPA Codes, Standards, and Recommended Practices

Reference to the following NFPA codes, standards, and recommended practices will provide further information on emergency and standby power supplies discussed in this chapter. (See the latest *NFPA Catalog* for availability of current editions of the following documents.)

NFPA 37, *Stationary Combustion Engines and Gas Turbines*.

NFPA 70, *National Electrical Code®*.

NFPA 99, *Health Care Facilities*.

NFPA 110, *Emergency and Standby Power Systems*.

NFPA 110A, *Stored Energy Systems*.

HEAT TRANSFER SYSTEMS (NONWATER MEDIA)

Revised by Peter J. Gore Willse

The term "heat transfer fluid" refers to the broad spectrum of either liquid or vapor media used to transfer heat energy at a controlled rate from one place to another. While practically all industrial processes involve the exchange of heat in one form or another, the use of heat transfer fluids is common in the chemical, paint, textile, plastics, food, petroleum, and paper industries. The fluids are used to heat or cool reaction vessels, heat stills, heat rollers for drying paper, calender plastics, and for many other forms of processing.

For additional information relevant to heat transfer systems, see Section 2, Chapter 10, "Industrial and Commercial Heat Utilization Equipment"; Section 2, Chapter 15, "Chemical Processing Equipment"; Section 2, Chapter 17, "Molten Salt Baths"; Section 2, Chapter 25, "Storage of Flammable and Combustible Liquids"; and Section 3, Chapter 5, "Flammable and Combustible Liquids."

TYPES OF TRANSFER FLUIDS

Approximately 95 percent of all heat transfer fluids used are either steam or water. If the temperature of the process is above the freezing point of water and below about 350°F (177°C), the choice is usually between these two media. On the other hand, if the temperature of the process is above or below these two points, it is desirable, if not necessary, to consider other fluids. For temperatures below the freezing point of water, the most common heat transfer fluids are air; refrigerants, such as halogenated hydrocarbons; ammonia; brines; or solutions of ethylene glycol and water.

When temperatures increase above 350°F (177°C), the vapor pressure of water increases rapidly, requiring expensive high-pressure processing equipment. Therefore, a more practical and inexpensive means of heating or temperature control at higher temperatures is to use a fluid or vaporizing fluid with a high boiling temperature. Care should be taken to use high flash point, thermally stable, and noncorrosive fluids designed for this purpose. The high boiling point liquids that are commonly used can be generally categorized as either heat transfer oils, molten salts, or specially formulated heat transfer media.

There are two types of heat transfer systems: (1) liquid, and (2) vapor phase. With liquid-phase systems, the temperature of the fluid changes as heat is transferred, resulting in nonuniform temperatures even if large circulation rates are employed. (See Figure 2-8A.) With vapor-phase systems, heat is transferred at the saturation temperature of the vapor which affords controlled temperatures. Combinations of these systems may be used. (See Figures 2-8B and 2-8C.)

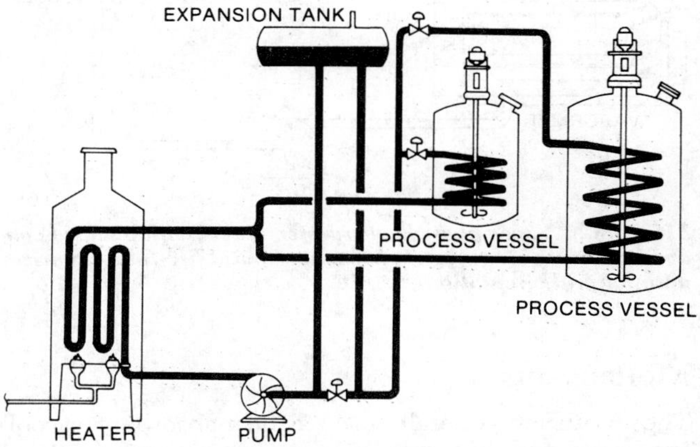

FIG. 2-8A. Liquid-phase heat transfer system with forced circulation-type heater.

Heat Transfer Oils

These are specially refined petroleum oils for use at temperatures up to approximately 600°F (315°C). At higher temperatures, the oils undergo thermal cracking to produce light hydrocarbons and polymers. Petroleum oils are also subject to oxidation at temperatures above 392°F (200°C) and in contact with air. These oils will provide a long service life and good heat transfer when the manufacturers recommended guidelines are followed.

Peter J. Gore Willse is research consultant, Industrial Risk Insurers (IRI), Hartford, CT.

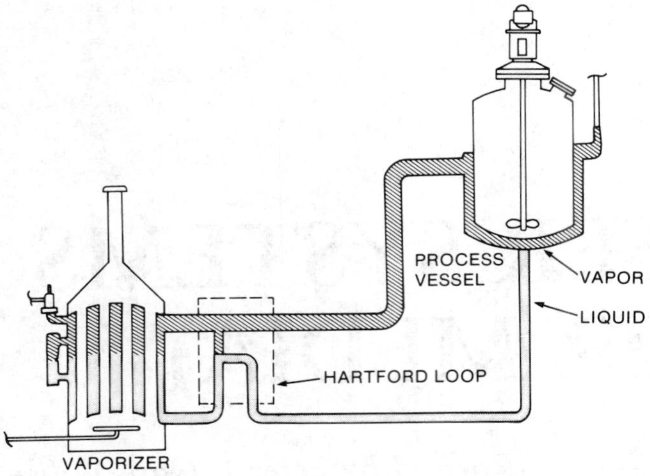

FIG. 2-8B. Vapor-phase gravity condensate return heat transfer system. This sytem has a vertical fire-tube-type vaporizer with natural circulation.

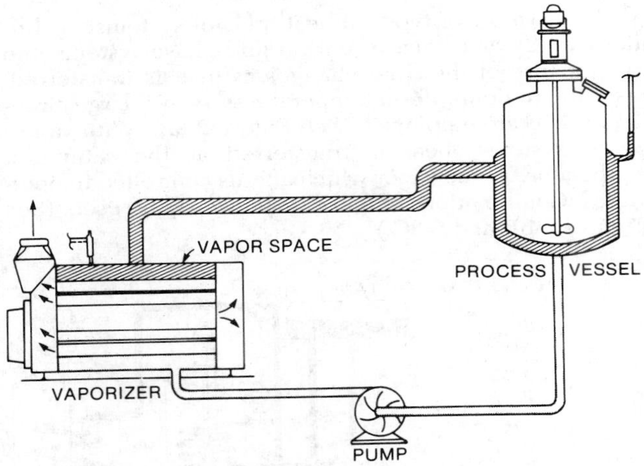

FIG. 2-8C. Vapor-phase heat transfer system with pumped condensate return. This system has a horizontal fire-tube vaporizer with natural circulation.

Molten Salts

These salts are generally used as heat absorbers or cooling media, and thus serve to control exothermic reactions which occur in the manufacture of certain chemicals. The most frequently used salt is a mixture of sodium and potassium salts having a relatively low melting point. Since these salts are solid at room temperature, it is obvious that care must be exercised to keep the temperature of the salt above its melting point to prevent salt solidification in the system. Also, care must be taken during startup to control the heat input so the mixture will melt slowly. Many molten salts are strong oxidizers, and this should also be considered where these salts are used.

Synthetic Fluids

A variety of specially formulated synthetic fluids are very widely used as a heat transfer fluid. Synthetic fluids are subject to thermal cracking and oxidation; however, they are safe, noncorrosive, essentially nontoxic, and thermally stable when used under the manufacturer's recommended guidelines. The synthetics create a fire hazard if released into the firebox of a fuel-fired heater. Table 2-8A gives the physical properties of some common heat transfer fluids and oils.

When these fluids are used in the liquid state, the unit is referred to as a heater, and when the fluid is vaporized the unit is called a vaporizer. Two types of equipment are manufactured: (1) fuel-fired heaters which are generally designed for heat duty use in excess of 1 million Btu per hr (29,280 kW), and (2) electric heaters which are usually designed for heat duty use of less than 1 million Btu per hr (29,280 kW). Capacities of vaporizers and heaters range from a few thousand to over 175 million Btu per hr (524,694 kW).

HAZARDS OF ORGANIC HEAT TRANSFER FLUIDS

The basic hazards of organic heat transfer liquids are those associated with the heating and transfer of a combustible liquid near or above its fire point in a closed system.

The type of vaporizer shown in Figure 2-8D is designed for relatively low heat release. The lower drum provides a space for the collection of any sludge or foreign substances within the system, preventing such materials from fouling the heating surface. Precautions must be taken to prevent the liquid level from falling below the tops of the tubes and impairing circulation. In direct-fired units, impingement of heater burner flames on empty tubes might produce excessive local temperatures, resulting in deposits and ultimate failure of the tubes.

Some organic heat transfer media have very low surface tension and viscosity. To prevent leakage, special care is necessary in the fabrication and erection of equipment. Construction in accordance with the *ASME Boiler and Pressure Vessel Code* is mandatory in nearly all U.S. and Canadian jurisdictions. The wide range in temperature requires provision for expansion of piping. High temperatures may make ordinary relief valve springs unreliable.

Because of the cost of organic fluids, it is common practice to set the blowoff points of safety valves so high that there is very little likelihood of blowing. To allow for this, the *ASME Boiler and Pressure Vessel Code* requires that reservoirs be designed for a working pressure of at least 40 psi (276 kPa) above the normal operating pressure, but the reservoirs should not be intentionally fired at rates above rated capacity and temperature.

Most corrosive problems result from contamination of the system by foreign chemicals. Contamination by leakage from the process side can lead to attack in the heat transfer loop. The severity and nature of attack in these instances depends on the degree and specific type of contamination. For example, chloride contamination can cause failure in the 300 series of stainless steels because of embrittlement or stress corrosion cracking.

SAFEGUARDS FOR FLAMMABLE HEAT TRANSFER SYSTEMS

Where a flammable heat transfer system having a flash point below 300°F (149°C) is heated above its atmospheric boiling point, the vaporizer or heater and the user facility should be located in a detached area or in a cutoff room of damage-limiting construction.

TABLE 2-8A. ***Physical Properties of Typical Heat Transfer Fluids***

Compound	Freezing Point		Boiling Point		Flash Point		Fire Point	
	°F	°C	°F	°C	°F (C.O.C.)	°C	°F (C.O.C.)	°C
1,2,4-trichlorobenzene	63	17	417	213	210	99	*	*
Tetrachlorobenzene (isomer mixture)	170	77	480	249	None	—	*	*
Diphenyl ether—diphenyl eutectic	54	12	495	257	255	124	275	135
Biphenylyl phenyl ether (isomer mixture)	99	37	680	360	370	188	410	210
O-biphenylyl phenyl ether	122	50	670	354	370	188	410	210
Di- and triaryl ethers	<0	−17	572	300	305	152	315	157
Dimethyl-diphenyl ether (isomer mixture)	−40**	−40	554	290	—	—	—	—
Tetramethyl diphenyl ether (isomer mixture)	—	—	590	310	—	—	—	—
Di-sec-butyl diphenyl ether (isomer mixture)	—	—	705	374	380	193	400	204
Dicyclohexyldiphenyl ether (isomer mixture)	—	—	785	418	—	—	—	—
Dodecyldiphenyl ether (isomer mixture)	45**	7	>800	>427	410	210	440	227
Ethyldiphenyl (isomer mixture)	<−60**	<−51**	536	280	—	—	—	—
Partially hydrogenated terphenyl	−15**	−26**	690	366	335	168	375	191
Aliphatic oil	15	−9	720–950	382–510	425	218	475	246
Alkylaromatic oil	20	−6	~650	342	350	177	390	199

*None to boiling point
**Pour point

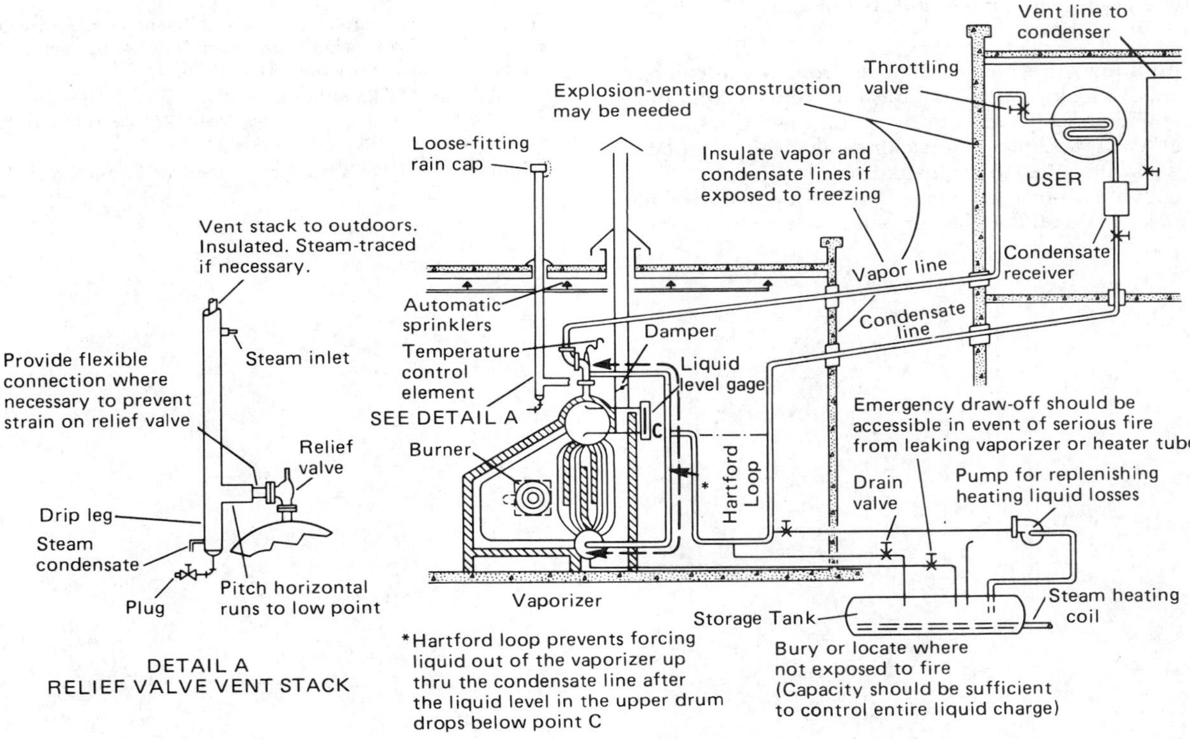

FIG. 2-8D. ***Gravity return vaporizer arrangement. (Source: Factory Mutual Research Corp.)***

If located in a processing building, the vaporizer and heater room should have the following features:

1. Automatic sprinkler protection.
2. Cutoff from other important facilities by construction with a minimum one-hour fire-resistance rating.
3. Piping securely supported and otherwise protected against mechanical injury, with adequate clearance from combustible materials.
4. Floors curbed and drained to protect nearby facilities.

Equipment should always be operated within the temperature and pressure limits specified by the supplier or manufacturer of the heat transfer medium and by the manufacturer of the equipment. Good maintenance is a key factor to any accident-free operating system and should include periodic testing of the heat transfer medium, heater fire surfaces, safety valves, and control devices.

System vaporizers and heaters should be under automatic control and regulated by temperature and pressure switches in the outlet. On vapor systems, separate safety limit switches should be provided to shut down the heater automatically and sound an alarm either when the vaporizer level becomes dangerously low, or when the vapor pressure or temperature is excessive. On circulating liquid systems, limit switches in addition to the low liquid level cutoff should be provided to shut off the heater automatically if liquid temperature is excessive or if circulation rate is low.

A manually controlled steam or inert gas smothering system for the firebox is advisable where a supply of steam or inert gas is available. If fire occurs in the vaporizer, follow these steps:

1. Shut off the heating units.
2. Open steam or inert gas smothering systems or use portable Class B extinguishers at openings to the firebox.
3. Unless a leak is near the bottom of the vaporizer, do not drain the liquid until after the fire has been extinguished and the unit is cooled down—otherwise, vaporizer drums and tubing may become overheated.
4. If necessary, drain liquid in the vaporizer back to the storage tank. If a storage tank is not available, drain to a safe location.

To minimize the hazard of fires from organic heat transfer media leaking and soaking into pipe insulation, heating spontaneously, and igniting, eliminate the source of leakage when it occurs by repacking valve stems, replacing leaky gaskets, etc. Cover insulation in areas of potential leakage with oil-resistant cement or use a nonabsorbent insulation, such as cellular glass or reflective aluminum foil.

BIBLIOGRAPHY

Reference

ASME Boiler and Pressure Vessel Code, American Society of Mechanical Engineers, NY, 1989.

NFPA Codes, Standards, and Recommended Practices

Reference to the following NFPA codes, standards, and recommended practices will provide further information on heat transfer systems discussed in this chapter. (See the latest *NFPA Catalog* for availability of current editions of the following documents.)

NFPA 10, *Portable Fire Extinguishers*.

NFPA 12, *Carbon Dioxide Extinguishing Systems*.

NFPA 13, *Installation of Sprinkler Systems*.

NFPA 86, *Ovens and Furnaces*.

Additional Reading

Albrecht, A. R., and Seifert, W. F., "Accident Prevention in High Temperature Heat Transfer Systems," Paper presented at AIChE Loss Prevention Symposium, Atlanta, GA, 1970.

Bownan, J. W., and Perkins, R. P., "Preventing Fires with High Temperature Vaporizers," *Plant/Operations Progress*, Vol. 9, No. 1, 1990, pp. 39-43.

Factory Mutual Research Corporation, "Heat Transfer by Organic Fluids," *Loss Prevention Data Sheet 7-99/12-19*, Factory Mutual Research Corp., Norwood, MA, 1975.

"Heat Transfer Media Other than Water," *Kirk-Othmer Encyclopedia of Chemical Technology*, Vol. 12, Interscience Publishers, New York, 1984, pp. 171-190.

"Molten Salt for Heat Transfer," *Chemical Engineering*, Vol. 70, 1963, p. 129.

FLUID POWER SYSTEMS

Revised by Paul K. Schacht

Fluid power systems are used for transmitting power or motion to various parts of equipment and machines. The function of the fluid may be power multiplication as in a hydraulic press, actuation of automatic equipment as in die casting, or remote actuation or pressure control of machines or instruments. (See Figure 2-9A.)

Hydraulic fluids are generally petroleum-based and present fire hazards. For additional information on allied topics, consult the following chapters: Section 3, Chapter 5, "Flammable and Combustible Liquids;" and Section 2, Chapter 25, "Storage of Flammable and Combustible Liquids."

Early fluid power systems used water as the hydraulic medium. Because of its corrosive effect on the metallic parts of the machine and lack of lubricity, it was replaced by petroleum-based oil. Except for its fire hazard, oil is an ideal hydraulic fluid. It is noncorrosive, is compatible with a wide variety of seals, has good lubricating properties, is readily available, and is relatively inexpensive. Flashpoints range from 300 to 600°F (148 to 316°C) and autoignition temperatures from 500 to 750°F (260 to 399°C).

FLUIDS UNDER PRESSURE

Pressurized oil in fluid power systems presents a considerable fire hazard, particularly where ignition sources are constantly present as in die casting, plastic molding, automatic welding, heat treating of metals, and the engines of mobile equipment.

High-pressure pipe with welded and screwed joints, steel tubing, and metal-reinforced rubber hose are used to conduct oil at pressures ranging up to 10,000 psi (68 950 kPa). Failure of piping, particularly at threaded sections, failure of valves and gaskets or fittings, pulling out of tubing from fittings, and rupture of flexible hose have been the principal causes of oil being released from a fluid power system. Lack of adequate supports or anchorage to prevent vibration or movement of piping has often been a factor in these failures. Repeated flexing and abrasion of rubber hose against other hose or parts of machines have created weak spots which eventually failed. Tubing under pressure has failed due to being accidentally cut by torches or stepped on during maintenance procedures.

Guidelines to be followed when selecting hydraulic tubing can be found in the National Fluid Power Association and Society of Automotive Engineers (SAE) standards listed in the bibliography.

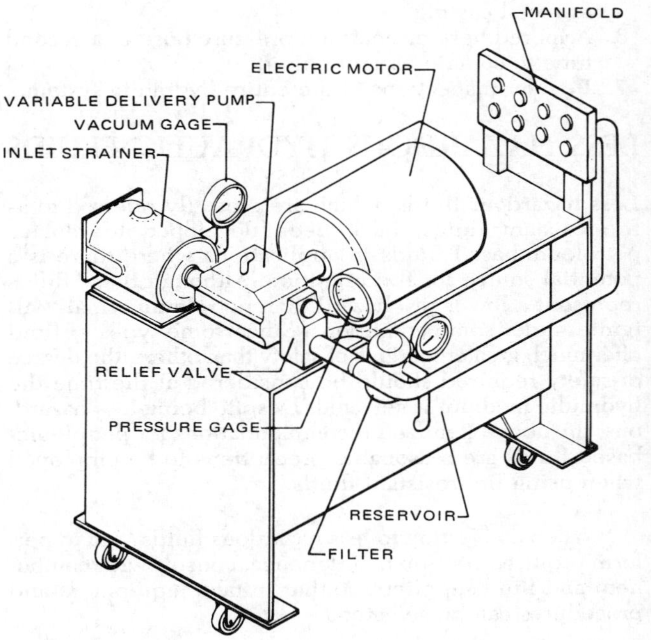

FIG. 2-9A. A nonspecific power unit that might be used to run any of a variety of machines, e.g., a drill or press. (Source: National Fluid Power Association)

Paul K. Schacht is manager of research and development, Racine Fluid Power, Inc., Division, Robert Bosch Corporation, Racine, WI, and chairman of the fluids coordinating committee for the National Fluid Power Association.

FIRE CHARACTERISTICS

When oil under pressure is released by failure of equipment, the usual result is an atomized spray of mist or oil droplets which, depending on pressure, may encompass large areas. The oil spray is readily ignited and the resulting fire is usually torchlike with a very high rate of heat release.

If systems contain oil, the following recommendations should be met in addition to those recommended for less hazardous fluids:

1. Automatic sprinklers provided in the area.
2. Automatic or remote manual switches to shut off the hydraulic pumps in the event of fire, if over 100 gal (378 L) of fluid are involved.
3. Fire extinguishers provided suitable for Class B fires.
4. Threaded pipe connections avoided wherever possible.
5. Machines isolated from positive ignition sources, such as metal casting.
6. Armored hose or enclosed pressure hose in a second tube to contain escaping fluid.
7. Regular inspections of the entire hydraulic system.

LESS HAZARDOUS HYDRAULIC FLUIDS

Less hazardous fluids, which are typically referred to as fire-resistant fluids, have been developed to replace petroleum-based fluids in applications where there is a potential source for fluid ignition. Although these fluids represent a lower fire hazard than petroleum oil, all will ignite under some conditions. Since some types of fluid offer much greater margins of safety than others, the degree of safety required should be considered at the time the hydraulic medium is selected. Despite being less hazardous, the above itemized recommendations for petroleum-based fluids are reasonable precautions to be employed when using fire-resistant fluids.

When converting to less hazardous fluids, and to perform required routine maintenance, consult with component and fluid suppliers, so that suitable equipment and procedures can be selected.

Precautions and recommendations to be used in changing from one type of hydraulic fluid to any other are published by the National Fluid Power Association.

Water-Glycol Fluids

Water-glycol fluids normally consist of 35 to 50 percent water, and ethylene or propylene-glycol, thickeners, and additives. Recommended temperature limits are 0 to 150°F (-18 to 66°C), with normal operating temperatures of 120 to 130°F (49 to 54°C). At higher temperatures, the rate of water evaporation is such that addition of makeup water is frequently required. As the water evaporates, the viscosity increases, and the fire resistance decreases.

Water-glycol fluids are compatible with most types of seals, gaskets, and hoses made from nitrile, fluorocarbon, butyl, or ethylene-propylene, but are incompatible with certain types of leather, cork, and paper. These fluids generally have a solvent action on most petroleum-compatible paints and coatings.

Synthetic Fluids

Synthetic fluids are nonwater-containing man-made materials, such as phosphate esters, blends of phosphate esters with petroleum oil, and polyol esters. Recommended temperature limits are 20 to 150°F (-7 to 66°C), with normal operating temperatures of 120 to 130°F (49 to 54°C).

Phosphate esters and phosphate ester blends are not compatible with seals, gaskets, or hoses made from nitrile, neoprene, or natural rubber, and these elements must be replaced with fluorocarbon or other compatible materials.

Polyol esters are compatible with seals, gaskets, or hoses made from nitrile or fluorocarbon.

All synthetics typically attack paints, coatings, and electrical insulation.

Water-in-Oil Emulsions

Water-in-oil emulsions consist of 35 to 40 percent water, petroleum oil, emulsifiers, and additives. The water is dispersed in fine droplets in the oil phase. Recommended temperature limits for the emulsion are 50 to 150°F (10 to 66°C), with normal operating temperatures of 120 to 130°F (49 to 54°C). At higher temperatures, frequent addition of water is required. Loss of water tends to reduce viscosity and increase flammability. Water-in-oil emulsions are compatible with most seals and gaskets, and with hoses made from nitrile, fluorocarbon, or neoprene. Seals or gaskets made from cork, paper, leather, or butyl are unacceptable. These fluids generally have a solvent action on most petroleum-compatible paints and coatings.

BIBLIOGRAPHY

NFPA Codes, Standards, and Recommended Practices

Reference to the following NFPA codes, standards, and recommended practices will provide further information on the safeguards for fluid power systems discussed in this chapter. (See the latest *NFPA Catalog* for availability of current editions of the following documents.)

NFPA 10, *Portable Fire Extinguishers.*

NFPA 13, *Installation of Sprinkler Systems.*

NFPA 30, *Flammable and Combustible Liquids Code.*

Additional Reading

American Institute of Physics, *Hydraulic Devices*, McGraw-Hill, New York, NY, 1975.

Anders, J. E., *Industrial Hydraulics Troubleshooting*, McGraw-Hill, New York, NY, 1983.

Corbin, E. and Sale, J. W., "Fire Protection at the Grand Coulee Hydro Project," *Proceedings* of the International Conference on Hydropower: Waterpower '87, ASCE, NY, 1988, pp. 2091-2099.

"Development of Nonflammable Hydraulic Fluids and Lubricants," Olin Corporation, Cryogenics Division (U.S. Department of Commerce, Office of Technical Services) Stamford, CT, June 1964.

"Fluid Systems 1978: Looking Ahead Ten Years," *Machine Design*, Vol. 50, No. 22 (Sept. 28, 1978), pp. 2-5.

"Fluids," *Machine Design*, Vol. 50, No. 22 (Sept. 28, 1978), pp. 112, 115-116.

Foitl, R. J., and Kycera, W. J., "Formation and Evaluation of Fire-Resistant Hydraulic Fluids," *Iron and Steel Engineer*, Vol. 41, No. 7, July 1964, pp. 117-120.

Friedman, R., *Principles of Fire Protection Chemistry*, 2nd Edition, National Fire Protection Association, Boston, MA, 1989.

Hathaway, L. R., "Turbine-Generator Fire Prevention Programs Cut Costs," *Fire Journal*, Vol. 84, No. 3 (May/June 1990), p. 47.

Henrikson, K. H., "Fire Resistant Fluids in Mobile Equipment," 650671, Sept. 1965, Society of Automotive Engineers, New York, NY.

Holmstedt, G., and Persson, H., "Spray Fire Tests with Hydraulic Fluids," *Proceedings* of the First International Symposuim on Fire Saftey Science, Hemisphere, NY, 1986, pp. 869-879.

"Hydraulic Fluids," *Data Sheet 7-98*, Factory Mutual System, Norwood, MA, 1974.

"Hydraulic Fluid Power-Fire Resistant Fluids-Information Report on Company Trade Names," T2.13.2R2-1980. National Fluid Power Association, Milwaukee, WI.

Johnson, O. A., *Fluid Power for Industrial Use: Hydraulics*, 2 Vols., Krieger Publishing Co., Melbourne, FL, 1984.

Millett, W. H., "Fire Resistant Hydraulic Fluids," Sept. 1973, E.F. Houghton & Co., Philadelphia, PA. (Paper presented at the Twenty-Ninth National Conference on Fluid Power.)

Pingree, D., "Looking at Fire Hazards: Hydraulic Fluids," *Fire Journal*, Vol. 59, No. 6 (Nov. 1965), p. 23.

Pippenger, J., and Hicks, T., *Industrial Hydraulics*, 3rd Edition, McGraw-Hill, New York, NY, 1979.

Polack, S. P., "Bureau of Mines Evaluates Fire Resistance of Hydraulic Fluids," *Iron and Steel Engineer*, Vol. 41, No. 8 (Aug. 1964), pp. 105-110.

"Pressure Ratings for Hydraulic Tubing and Fittings," SAE J1065, Society of Automotive Engineers, Warrendale, PA.

Protheroe, A. R., "Fire Resistant Hydraulic Fluids: New Capabilities Expand Applications," *Hydraulics and Pneumatics*, Vol. 31, No. 5 (1978), pp. 73-75.

Roberts, A. F., and Brookes, F. R., "Hydraulic Fluids: An Approach to High Pressure Spray Flammability Testing Based on Measurement of Heat Output," *Fire and Materials*, Vol. 5, No. 3 (1981), pp. 87-92.

Snyder, C. E., Krawetz, A. A., and Tovrog, T., "Determination of the Flammability Characteristics of Aerospace Hydraulic Fluids," *Lubrication Engineering*, Vol. 37, No. 12 (Dec. 1981), pp. 704-714.

"Standard Practice for the Use of Fire Resistant Fluids in Industrial Hydraulic Fluid Power Systems," ANSI/B93.5M-1979, National Fluid Power Association, Milwaukee, WI.

Stewart, H. L., *Hydraulic and Pneumatic Power for Production*, 4th Edition, Industrial Press Inc., New York, NY, 1977.

"Synthetic Fire-Resistant Hydraulic Fluids for General Industrial Use," *Hydraulic, Pneumatic and Mechanical Power*, April 1979, pp. 145-148.

INDUSTRIAL AND COMMERCIAL HEAT UTILIZATION EQUIPMENT

Revised by James M. Simmons

Heat utilization equipment has potential hazards involving both heat generation and the process materials. Fuel-fired systems, electrically heated systems, and heat transfer systems all have their individual hazards. The hazards of exposure of adjacent materials and overheating may be common to any type of heating system. The hazards and control methods are discussed in subsequent paragraphs of this chapter.

The process hazards within the equipment may involve combustible materials, flammable liquids, or flammable gases; such hazards would occur in the curing of solvent-based coating materials, roasting or drying of combustible agricultural products, or heat treating in a flammable special atmosphere. The principal method of fire or explosion prevention is to prevent overheating or an accumulation of a gas or vapor-air mixture in the explosive range. Subsequent paragraphs in this chapter describe the various classes of ovens, furnaces, and dryers, and present general process hazards. The prevention and protection methods which usually are applied to those processes and devices also are described.

Guidelines, rules, and methods applicable to the safe operation of such equipment are covered by NFPA standards and those of other organizations. These should be referred to for details that could not be included in this text. Additional information is available in this handbook in the following chapters: Section 3, Chapter 5, "Flammable and Combustible Liquids;" and Section 3, Chapter 7, "Gases." The grading of heat-producing appliances is discussed in these chapters: Section 2, Chapter 4, "Heating Systems and Appliances;" Section 2, Chapter 5, "Boiler Furnaces;" and Section 2, Chapter 8, "Heat Transfer Systems (Nonwater Media)."

Heat utilization equipment is so varied in size, complexity, location, and use that it has been difficult to develop rules that would apply to every type of oven, furnace, or dryer. Users and designers must use engineering and supervisory skills to bring together the proper combination of controls, protective devices, and operator training necessary for proper equipment operation.

James M. Simmons, P.E., is engineering specialist, Factory Mutual Research Corp., Norwood, MA.

Practically all heat utilization equipment failures are caused by people, usually because someone either ignored safety procedures and designs or was unaware they existed. Failures have resulted from inadequate training of operators and maintenance technicians, faulty equipment design, complacency on the part of users, and improper selection of combustion safeguards.

This chapter is not a guide to solving all of these problems. However, if the guidelines and principles it presents are used, a number of problems either will be mitigated or solved.

INDUSTRIAL HEAT UTILIZATION EQUIPMENT

Industrial heat utilization equipment includes a variety of forges, furnaces, kettles, kilns, ovens, and retorts which are heated by gas, oil, solid fuels, or electricity. They may be fired directly, with the products of combustion entering the process space, or indirectly, with radiant tubes or other heat exchanger methods. Heat transfer media, such as organic fluids, also are used where steam or hot water do not provide the temperature or thermal efficiencies desired for the equipment. Figures 2-10A and 2-10B illustrate typical industrial heat utilization equipment.

Industrial ovens and furnaces, special atmosphere furnaces, vacuum furnaces, after-burners and catalytic combustion systems, dehydrators, dryers, and lumber kilns are discussed in this chapter.

Fire and Explosion Problems

When heat utilization equipment is installed, the following factors need to be considered: (1) the proximity and combustibility of the contents of the building where the equipment is located; (2) construction of the building; (3) setting; (4) ventilation; (5) location within the building; (6) heat, gas, and smoke disposal; (7) maximum temperature required; and (8) handling of heated materials in connection with equipment. Fire in combustibles can be prevented by insulation or by separating them from the source of heat. Overheating can be prevented by temperature controls.

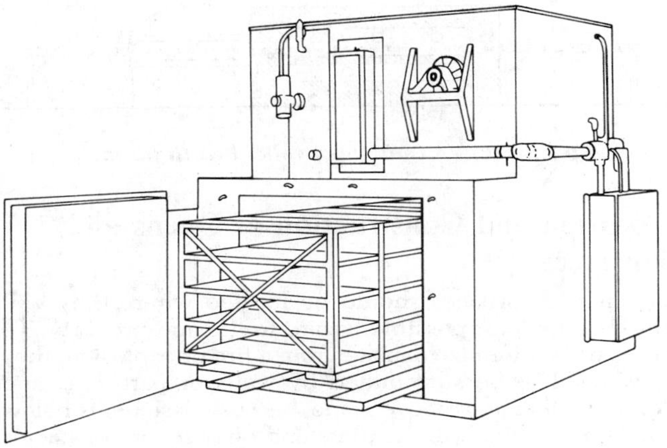

FIG. 2-10A. A typical industrial oven. (Source: Electronics Corp. of America)

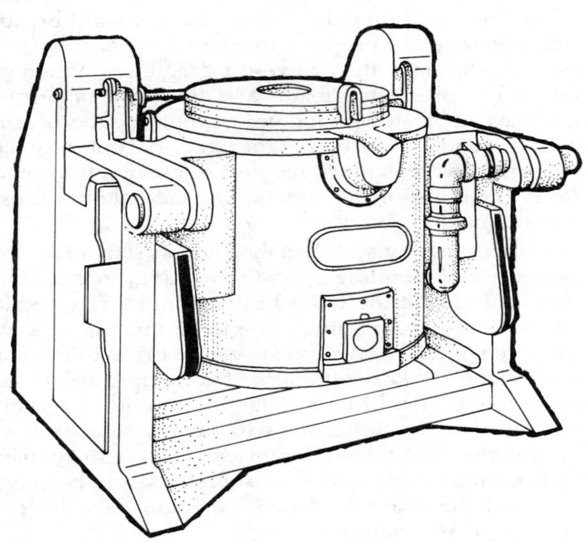

FIG. 2-10B. A fuel fire melting furnace. (Source: Electronics Corp. of America)

Explosion hazards exist where there are flammable vapor-air mixtures from gas or oil fuel or from the volatiles released from the material being dried. Explosions or fires may be prevented by ventilation and controls that keep the flammable vapor content below 25 percent of the lower flammable limit (LFL) of the vapor-air mixture.

Some special process ovens and furnaces contain hydrogen or other flammable gases for such purposes as annealing copper and heat treating other metal shapes. To operate these devices safely, it is necessary to prevent air from entering the processing enclosure under normal operating conditions. Both normal and unscheduled starts and stops of these devices require special safety procedures that depend heavily upon a skilled operator and adequate control equipment.

OVENS AND FURNACES

This discussion covers the location, design, construction, operation, protection, and maintenance of the industrial heating enclosures known as ovens or furnaces. It does not cover small-cabinet or stove-type ovens for domestic use. The source of heat for industrial heating may be gas burners, oil burners, electric heaters, infrared lamps, induction heaters, or steam radiation systems. In practically all cases, there are fire or explosion hazards from either the fuel used, volatiles produced by material in the oven, or by a combination of both.

There is no clear distinction between an oven and a furnace. The dictionary definition of an oven is "a compartment or receptacle for heating, baking, or drying by means of heat" and a furnace is "an enclosed chamber or structure in which heat is produced for heating a building, reducing ores and metals, baking pottery, etc." It has been an industry rule of thumb to classify heating devices that do not "indicate color" [i.e., operate at temperatures of less than approximately 1000°F (540°C)] as ovens. This rule does not always apply, e.g., coke ovens operate at temperatures in excess of 2000°F (1098°C), and some furnaces operate at temperatures below 1000°F (540°C).

NFPA Classification of Ovens and Furnaces

The classification system for heat processing equipment as set forth in NFPA 86, *Ovens and Furnaces*, is as follows:

Class A ovens or furnaces are heat utilization equipment operating at approximately atmospheric pressure wherein there is a potential explosion and/or fire hazard which may be occasioned by the presence of flammable volatiles or combustible material processed or heated in the oven. Such flammable volatiles and/or combustible material may, for instance, originate from paints, powder, or finishing processes including dipped, coated, or sprayed-on impregnated materials, or wood, paper and plastic pallets, or spacers or packaging materials. Polymerization or similar molecular rearrangements and resin curing are processes which may produce flammable residues and/or volatiles. Potentially flammable materials, such as quench oil, waterborne finishes, cooling oil, etc., in sufficient quantities to present a hazard, are ventilated according to Class A standards. Ovens may also utilize a low-oxygen atmosphere to evaporate solvent.

Class B ovens or furnaces are heat utilization equipment operating at approximately atmospheric pressure wherein there are no flammable volatiles or combustible material being heated.

Class C furnaces are those in which there is a potential hazard due to a flammable or other special atmosphere being used for treatment of material in process. This type of furnace may use any type of heating system and includes the special atmosphere supply system(s). Also included in the Class C standards are integral quench and molten salt bath furnaces. (See NFPA 86C, *Industrial Furnaces Using a Special Processing Atmosphere*.)

Class D furnaces are vacuum furnaces which operate at temperatures above ambient to over 5000°F (2760°C) and at pressures below atmospheric using any type of heating system. These furnaces may include the use of special processing atmospheres. (See NFPA 86D, *Industrial Furnaces Using Vacuum as an Atmosphere*.)

Classification by Type of Handling System

Ovens and furnaces may be further classified according to the way a material is handled. The two principal types are: (1) the batch oven or furnace, sometimes referred to as "in and out," "intermittent," or "periodic" types; and (2) the continuous oven or furnace.

Batch type: In the batch oven or furnace the temperature is practically constant throughout the interior. The material to be heated is placed in a predetermined position and remains there until the process is complete. Material is then removed, generally through the opening by which it entered. Figures 2-10C and 2-10D are examples of a batch-type furnace and oven, respectively.

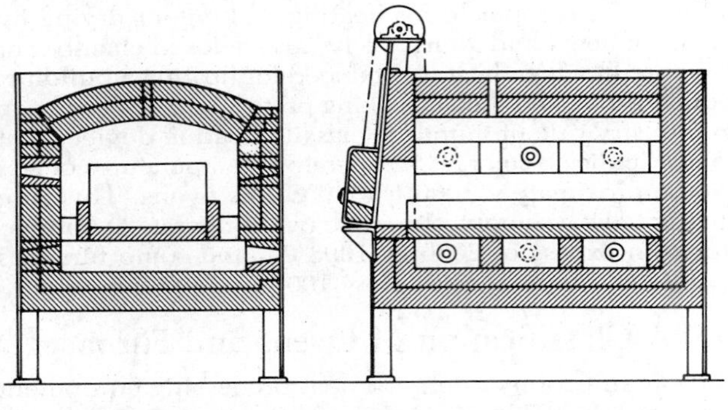

FIG. 2-10C. A large batch-type, under- and over-fired, semi-muffle, heat treating furnace.

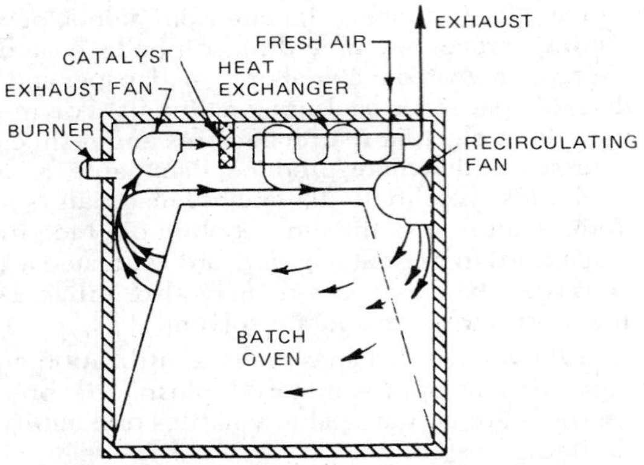

FIG. 2-10D. Batch oven with a catalytic heater for air pollution control.

Continuous type: In the continuous furnace or oven, the material moves through the furnace while being heated. The straight-line furnace is probably the most common of this type. The material passes through a continuous oven or furnace on a conveyor or on rollers. The oven or furnace may operate at a constant temperature throughout, or it may be divided into zones maintained at different temperatures. Figure 2-10E is an example of a continuous-type furnace.

A common variation of the continuous-type furnace or oven is one known as a rotating hearth or rotating table furnace. In it, the material is placed on the hearth and is removed after the hearth has completed one revolution. Another design feeds the material being processed through the revolving hearth furnace or tube by means of a stationary internal screw thread.

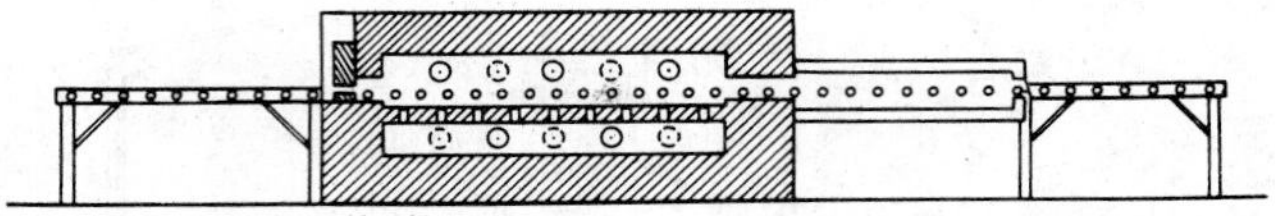

FIG. 2-10E. A continuous roller hearth furnace.

Location and Construction of Ovens and Furnaces

Ovens and furnaces should be located where they will present the least possible hazard to life and property. To prevent or minimize damage from a fire or explosion, they may need to be surrounded by walls or partitions and located either at or above grade, because basements below grade are difficult to ventilate and offer severe obstacles to proper explosion release.

The oven or furnace and the building which houses it need to be of noncombustible construction, and explosion relief venting should be provided where required. Combustibles in the vicinity of the oven should be adequately separated or properly insulated and each oven or furnace should have its own venting facilities. When gas or oil fuel is used, the heater and the oven or furnace should have separate venting unless the products of combustion discharge directly into the oven. Except in special cases, separate mechanical means are needed to provide air for the combustion and ventilation; natural draft is usually inadequate.

Furnaces that exhaust directly outdoors sometimes may be necessary, depending upon the heating process, type of combustion, and the hazard to personnel. If a furnace exhausts directly into a room, the room must have a balanced mechanical ventilation system to bring in fresh air and carry the exhaust outdoors. The supply inlets and exhaust outlets should be arranged to provide a uniform flow of air throughout the area without any dead-air pockets. The system should also remove any toxic contaminants at their maximum anticipated rate of release and keep concentrations below the established maximum allowable concentration (MAC) values.

Some furnaces are made of metal with a brick or masonry covering, some are made of metal with metal supports but no covering, and others have an inner lining of ceramic fibers or fire clay products. Occasionally furnaces have air spaces or noncombustible fillers between the outer and inner walls.

Ovens and furnaces should be well separated from valuable stock, important power equipment, machinery, and automatic sprinkler risers, so there will be minimum interruption to production and protection if there are accidents to the oven or furnace. They should be readily accessible with adequate space above them for automatic sprinklers, the proper use of hose streams, the proper functioning of explosion vents, and routine inspection and maintenance. Roofs and floors of ovens should be insulated. The space above and below the ovens should be ventilated to keep temperatures at combustible ceilings and floors below 160°F (71°C).

Oven and Furnace Heating Systems

The three most common methods of transferring heat to materials in ovens or furnaces are: (1) direct contact with the products of combustion, (2) convection and direct radiation from the hot gases, and (3) reradiation from the hot walls of the furnace. In muffle furnaces, the products of combustion are separated from the material being heated by a metal or refractory muffle, and heat transfer occurs by radiation. (See Figure 2-10C.) In liquid bath furnaces, i.e., salt baths or molten metal used for tempering, hardening, galvanizing, tinning, etc., a metal pot containing a liquid is heated and the heat is transferred through the liquid to the material placed in the pot.

Oven heaters: The two general types of oven heaters are direct fired and indirect fired. In direct-fired heaters, the products of combustion enter the work chamber and contact the work in process; this is not the case in indirect-fired oven heaters. Instead, heating comes from radiation from tubes or from air passing over tubes and into the oven. Dangerous fuel-air mixtures cannot readily fill the work space of an indirect-fired oven. Nevertheless, explosions may still occur from vapors given off by a flammable liquid drying process.

There are several arrangements of these two types of oven heaters—direct-fired internal, direct-fired external, indirect-fired internal, and indirect-fired external heaters. Figure 2-10F shows three variations of direct-fired external heaters, two of indirect-fired internal heaters, and three of indirect-fired external heaters, with the advantages and disadvantages for each type. The exhaust ventilation arrangements in these designs provide for air movement through the oven with no recirculation through the exhaust fan. The direct-fired external-type oven may have a single or relatively small number of burners which simplifies the completing of automatic safety controls.

Furnace heaters: Furnace heaters are usually arranged like ovens—direct-fired internal, indirect-fired external, etc., though sometimes the terms are different. If products of combustion are under a hearth and then carried up and into the heating chamber, the furnace is said to be underfired. When the same thing occurs in a chamber at one side of the furnace and passes over a bridge wall into the heating chamber, the furnace is referred to as side-fired. A furnace in which the products of combustion are produced in a space above the heating chamber and pass through a perforated arch into the heating chamber is called an over-fired furnace. If combustion occurs at some distance above the heating chamber and hearth, and the products of combustion are deflected onto the hearth by an arched roof, the furnace is called a reverberatory furnace. A radiant-tube-heated furnace is an arrangement for indirect firing. (See Figure 2-10G.)

Sources of Heat

Heat for an oven or furnace may be provided by gas burners, oil burners, electric heaters, steam radiation, or heat transfer medium systems. It is important that flames, heating surfaces, or other possible sources of ignition be located where drippings or dust cannot fall or accumulate on them.

Gas fired: Gas fuel is any type of gas in common industrial use. It is important that the burner, its adjustment, and the means of combustion be suitable for the type of gas to be burned. The burner may have a single nozzle, with burners located singly or in groups, or it may have multiple nozzles in perforated-pipe, ribbon, or slot burners. Burners must light easily, have a stable flame at all ports, and not have the tendency to flash back or blow off over the entire range of turndown under all draft conditions in the oven. A supply of air adequate for complete combustion may be premixed with the gas, nozzle-mixed at the burner, or otherwise provided.

Oil fired: Oven heating systems may be fired with fuel oil. Oil must be vaporized before it can be burned. Most oven and furnace burners atomize and then vaporize oil while mixing it with combustion air. Heat for vaporization is generated by the flame. Atomization may be caused by pressure, mechanical spraying into fine droplets, sonic vibration, low-pressure air, high-pressure air, or steam.

Combination gas- and fuel-oil fired systems use either separate gas and oil burners, or configurations where an oil atomizing nozzle is centered on a gas burner and arranged to use a common combustion air source.

Electric heating systems: There are five types of electric heating systems for ovens and furnaces: (1) resistance, (2) infrared, (3) induction, (4) arc, and (5) dielectric.

Resistance heat is produced by current flow through a resistive conductor. Resistance heaters may be "open," with bare heating conductors, or "insulated sheath," with heater conductors covered by a protective sheath that may be filled with electrical insulating material. (See Figure 2-10H.)

Infrared heat is transmitted as electromagnetic waves from incandescent lamps with filaments that operate at temperatures lower than the filament temperature of ordinary incandescent lamps, so that most of the radiation occurs in the infrared part of the spectrum. These waves pass through air and transparent substances but not opaque objects, and release their heat energy to these objects.

Induction heat is developed by electric currents induced in the charge by an externally applied alternating magnetic field. Induction heaters have an electric coil surrounding the oven space, and heating is by electric currents induced in the work being processed.

Arc heat is caused by an electric current that passes between either a pair of electrodes or between electrodes and the work, causing an arc that releases energy in the form of heat.

Dielectric heat occurs when dielectric materials are exposed to an alternate electric field. The frequencies are generally 3MHz or more—higher than those in induction heating. This type of heater is useful for heating materials that are commonly considered nonconductive.

Electric systems can be arranged so that processing does not require an oven enclosure. "Ovenless," i.e., unenclosed heating systems, can employ lamps, resistance-type electric elements, or infrared heaters to vaporize flammable, toxic, or corrosive liquids and their residues. Enclosures around ovenless systems are advisable to prevent flammable, toxic, or corrosive vapors from escaping into the general area, and to help provide better ventilation and safeguards for personnel. However, heating systems with energy input of under 100 kW may be excluded if adequate area ventilation is provided. (NFPA 70, *National Electrical Code®*, gives guidance for electrical installations in hazardous locations.)

All parts of heaters that operate at elevated temperatures within an oven or furnace and all other energized parts must be protected to prevent contact by persons, and to prevent accidental contact with materials being processed and with drippage from the materials.

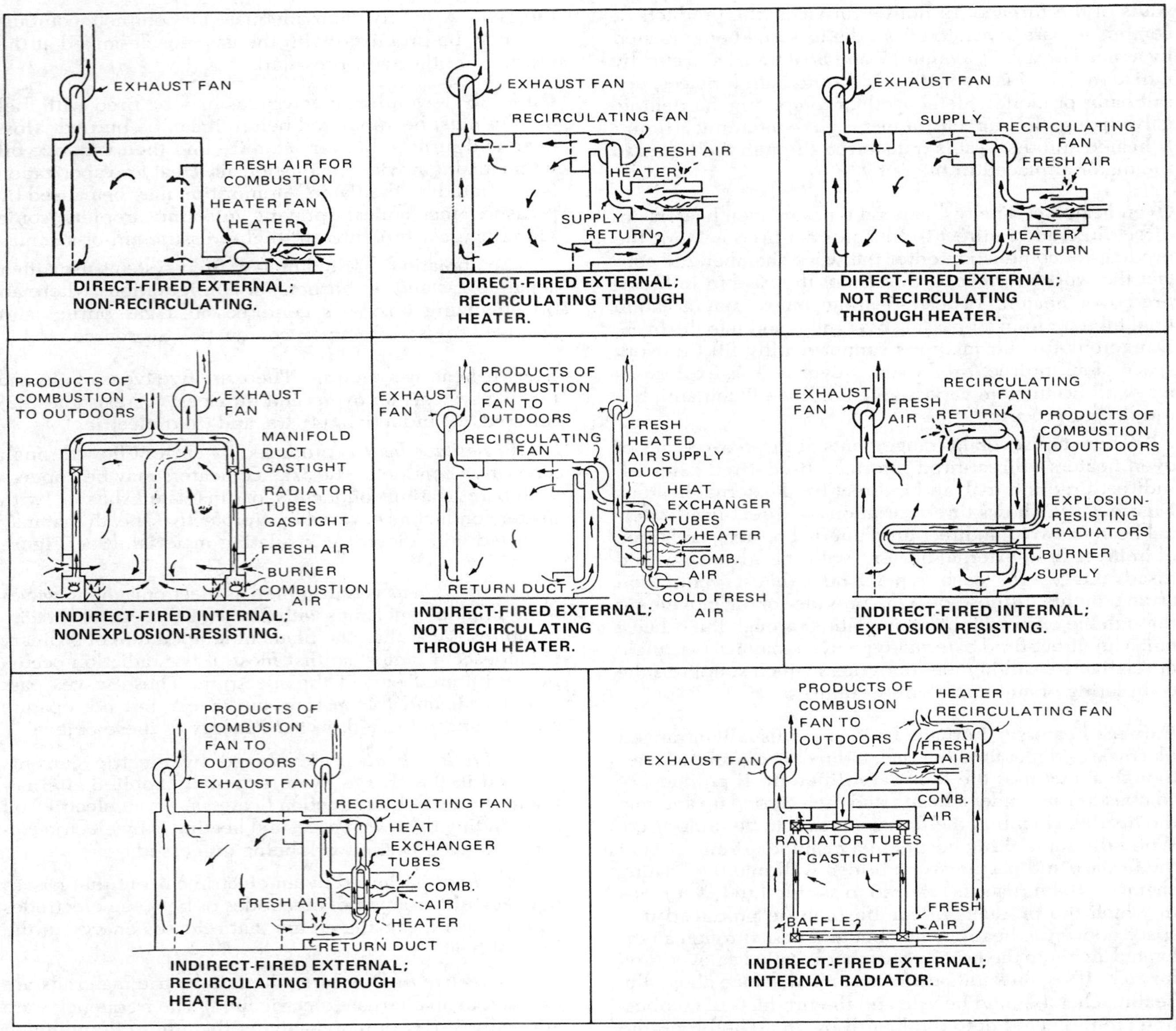

FIG. 2-10F. Types of oven heating systems.

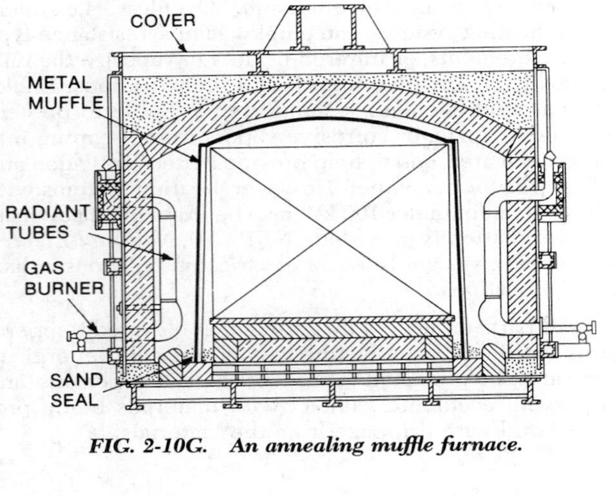

FIG. 2-10G. An annealing muffle furnace.

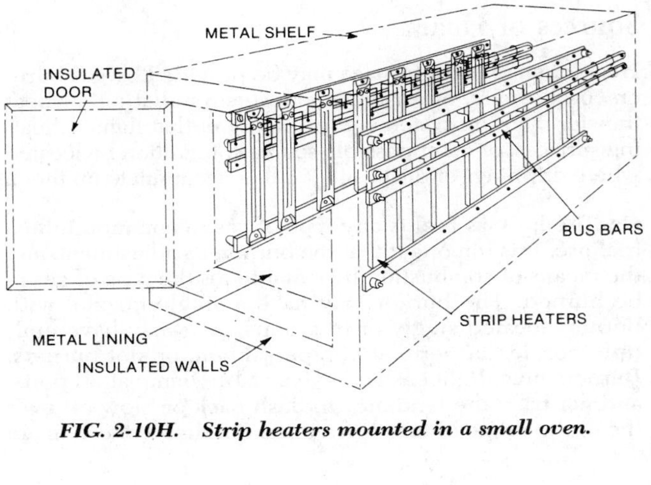

FIG. 2-10H. Strip heaters mounted in a small oven.

Steam heating systems: In steam heating systems, the steam pressure in heat exchanger coils must be regulated at the minimum required to provide the proper drying temperatures. This avoids unnecessarily high temperatures at coil surfaces. The coils must not be located on the floor of the oven or anywhere that paint drippings or other combustibles, such as recirculated lint, may accumulate on them.

Thermal heat transfer fluid systems: As with steam heating systems, the heat exchanger should be kept free of combustibles, such as lint. The heat exchanger may be located external of the work chamber and a recirculating heated air system used.

Fuel Hazards

Gas or vapors from unburned or incompletely burned fuel may, when mixed with air, be within the explosive range. These hazards develop during lighting off, firing, and shutting down the oven or furnace; therefore, it is necessary to treat each operation as a separate condition requiring certain specific operating procedures to avoid mishaps.

Lighting off: Before torches, sparks, or other ignition sources are introduced, and until all burners are properly lighted, the operator must take every precaution, using all practical automatic safety controls, to avoid producing dangerous unburned fuel accumulations. The following precautions should be followed:

1. Purge possible accumulations of unburned fuel.
2. Ignite burners promptly with substantial igniters.
3. If another ignition attempt is necessary, purge before introducing the ignition source and fuel again.

Firing: In the firing phase, safety requires continuous ignition and complete burning of the fuel before it passes beyond its normal combustion zone. To maintain this, the mixer and burner assembly must proportion fuel and air properly throughout the combustion zone, and the mixture velocity in the combustion zone must be neither too high, causing extinguishment by blowoff, nor too low, causing the flame to flashback or "go out." Thus good burner mixer design will be one of the main factors in safety during firing.

Air for combustion is obtained from the primary and secondary air supplied at the burner. Partial or total failure of the combustion air supply can cause an unstable flame which in turn may lead to flame failure, and the introduction of unburned fuel into the combustion chamber. When too little air is supplied, the result is an over-rich mixture and incomplete combustion. The flammable incomplete products of combustion that leave the burner at concentrations too high for prompt ignition may later, within the oven or ductwork, become diluted by air into the flammable range and ignite, causing an explosion. Over-rich combustion also may produce rapid smothering and extinguishment of the burner flame. The flammable products of incomplete combustion followed by raw fuel likewise may become explosive when later diluted by air in another part of the system. Therefore, precautions must be taken to shut off the fuel and to require manual reset in the event that the air supply for combustion fails.

Liquid fuel, like fuel oil, must be atomized so that it will ignite easily and burn quickly. This can be accomplished by ejecting the liquid fuel at high pressure, or by directing steam or air jet into the oil stream. Improper oil temperature or high viscosity can prevent proper flow, and can create partial obstructions in burner tips and loss of oil or atomizing medium pressures, causing improper atomization. Failure to atomize properly will usually result in an unstable flame which in turn can lead to flame failure. Other conditions which may cause flame failure are stoppage of fuel supply by an improperly closed fuel valve or other pipe obstruction, and the presence of water in a fuel oil line.

Shutting down: Following a shutdown, a dangerous accumulation of unburned fuel may occur in an oven and heating system if any manual fuel valves are left open or are leaking, and/or safety shutoff valves are not tight-closing. If the leaking fuel subsequently is ignited by hot refractory material or by another ignition source when starting up, an explosion may occur.

Supervisory Controls for Ovens and Furnaces

It is essential that all ovens and furnaces processing flammable materials, involving flammable vapors, or heated with combustible fuels be provided with adequate supervisory devices that ensure sufficient pre-ventilation, adequate ventilation during operation, and proper operating conditions that will not permit fires or explosions to develop. These devices should be "fail safe." While it is true that a competent operator is essential, it is also true that assistance is needed because the operator cannot continually supervise everything. The operator is, however, responsible for the proper maintenance and testing of the oven's operating and control equipment.

The type of supervisory control equipment used with oven or furnace assemblies depends upon the requirements of the particular operation. A list of the principal types of supervisory controls is given in Table 2-10A. Figure 2-10I shows a typical arrangement of the devices for a gas-fired unit. Most of these units are tested by testing laboratories and listed according to the appropriateness of the devices for varying situations. Equipment for Ovens and Furnaces

Full supervisory control of a gas- or oil-fired oven, especially one that is direct fired, may require the following: (1) determining that all fuel valves are closed and not leaking, (2) establishing and maintaining required ventilation, (3) turning on and igniting the gas pilot only at the conclusion of a required pre-ventilation period, and (4) opening the fuel valves (including the safety shutoff valve) that supply the burner only after the combustion safeguard shows that the pilot flame has been ignited, and that fuel and air (or other atomizing agent) pressures are correct. If the burner flame is not promptly established, the safety shutoff valve will close and the entire cycle must be repeated, starting from the beginning. Once started, operation continues only as long as the supervisory controls indicate normal conditions; failure in any respect shuts down the entire system and the full cycle must begin again.

NFPA 86, *Ovens and Furnaces*, NFPA 86C, *Industrial Furnaces Using a Special Processing Atmosphere*, and NFPA 86D, *Industrial Furnaces Using Vacuum as an Atmosphere*, specify in considerable detail the safeguards needed for different types of ovens and furnaces.

When installations contain a large number of burners, the usual supervisory controls for each pilot and each burner may not be considered practical; in such cases, special devices and arrangements may have to be employed.

TABLE 2-10A. ***Supervisory Control Equipment for Ovens and Furnaces***

Ventilation controls:
- Air flow switches
- Pressure switches
- Fan shaft rotation detectors
- Dampers
- Position limit switches
- Electrical interlocks
- Preventilation time-delay relays

Fuel supervisory controls:
- Safety shutoff valves
- Supervising cock (FM cock)
- Flame detection units (combustion safeguards)
- Flowmeters
- Firechecks
- Reliable ignition sources
- Pressure switches
- Program relays

Temperature controllers
Temperature limit controls
Continuous vapor concentration indicators and controls
Conveyor interlocks (with steam and electirc-resistance heating equipment)
Electrical overload protection (with resistance and induction heating equipment)
Low oil-temperature limit controls (on oil-burner equipment using heavy residual fuel oil, such as No. 5 and No. 6, which require preheating)

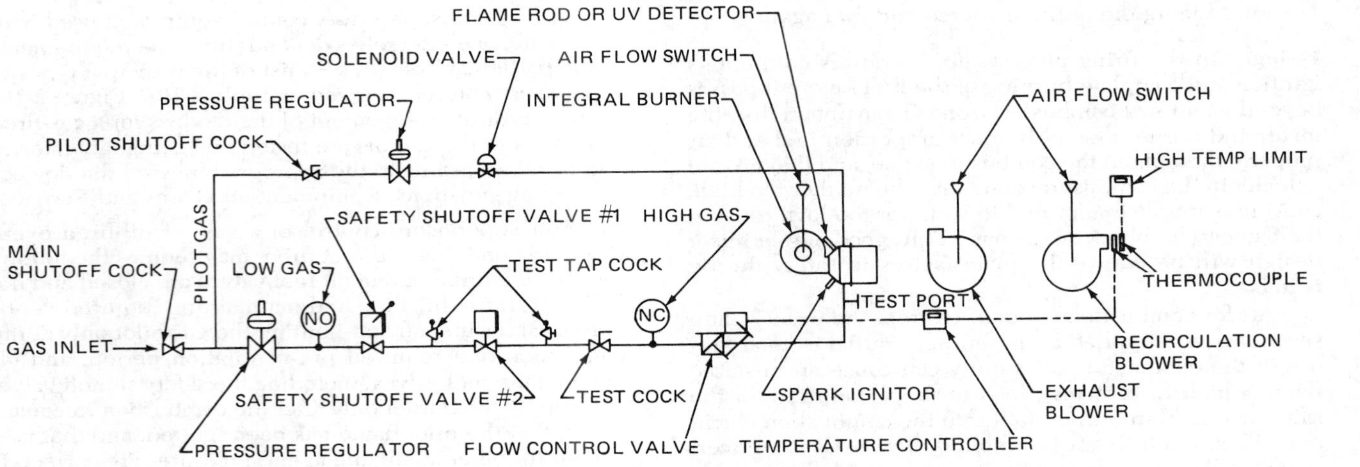

FIG. 2-10I. Example of a gas piping diagram.

A special continuous line pilot for multiple burners is illustrated in Figure 2-10J.

Controls for a large number of cup burners with flame propagation between individual burners may be provided as shown in Figure 2-10K.

When burners are so numerous that it is not practical to provide combustion safeguards for each, a system for supervising cocks and gas supervisory controls may be provided. This makes it possible to determine that all fuel valves are closed and that none are leaking. When interlocking devices indicate that all individual burner valves are closed, the safety shutoff valve may be opened and each burner valve then opened manually and the burner lighted. The supervising cock and two typical layouts are shown in Figures 2-10L and 2-10M, respectively.

Multiburner combustion safeguards are now available, making it possible to install flame supervision for each burner, where previously the supervisory cock system was the only safeguard available.

When the capacity of a gas-fired burner system exceeds 400,000 Btu per hr (117 kW), two safety shutoff valves are required. A manually operated plug cock and test tap must be provided downstream of the safety valves. This arrangement ensures positive fuel shutoff when testing the valves for leakage.

Safety ventilation is not needed in an oven which never contains flammable or noxious vapors, and it is unnecessary to guard against flammable fuel-air mixtures in an electric or steam-heated oven.

Operator Training

Alert and competent operators are essential to safe operations. New operators should be thoroughly trained and tested in the use of the equipment. Regular operators should be retrained at intervals to maintain proficiency and effectiveness. Operators must have access to operating instructions at all times.

Operating instructions should be provided by the equipment manufacturer. These instructions should include schematic piping and wiring diagrams, as well as: (1) light-up procedures, (2) shutdown procedures, (3) emergency procedures, and (4) maintenance procedures.

Operator training should include information on: (1) combustion of air-fuel mixtures, (2) explosion hazards, (3) sources of ignition and ignition temperature, (4) atmosphere analysis, (5) handling of flammable atmosphere gases, (6) handling of toxic atmosphere gases, (7) functions of control and safety devices, and (8) purpose and basic principles of the gas atmosphere generators.

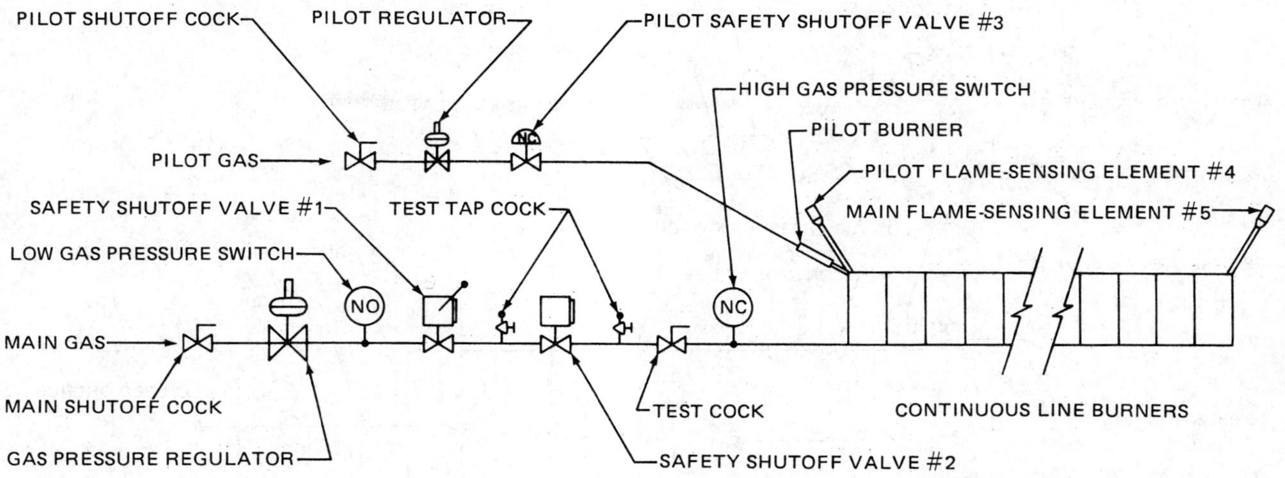

FIG. 2-10J. ***Example of an approved combustion safeguard supervising a pilot for a continuous line burner during lighting-off and the main flame alone during firing.***

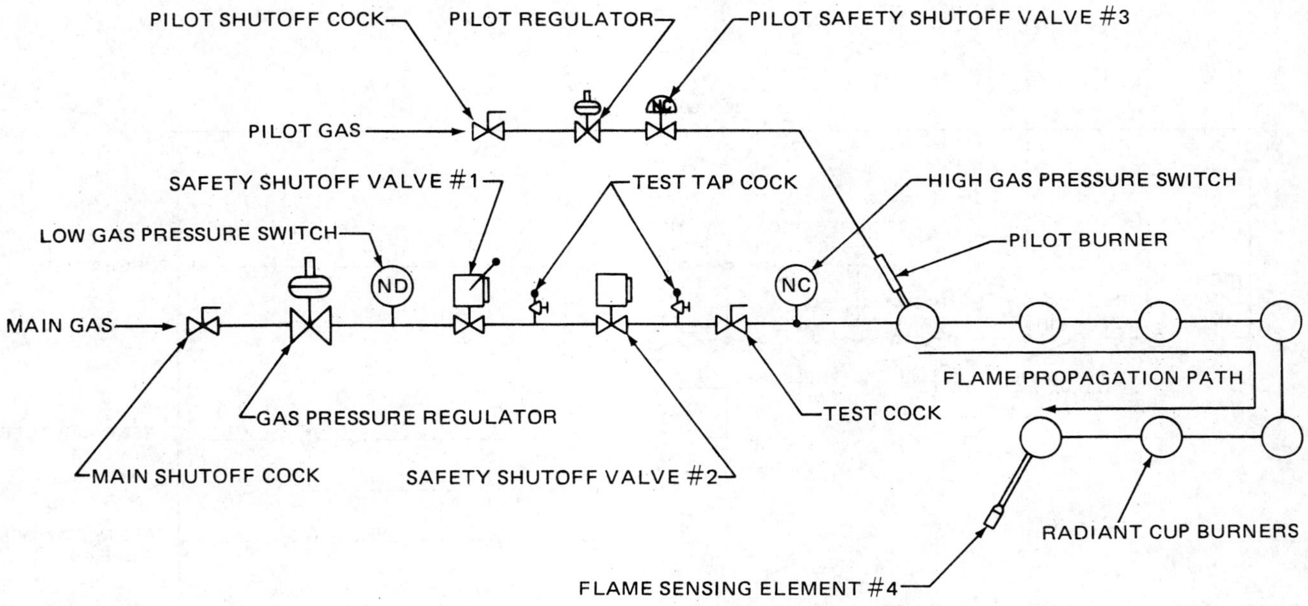

FIG. 2-10K. ***Example of an approved combustion safeguard supervising a group of radiant-cup burners having reliable flame-propagation characteristics from one to the other by means of flame-propagation devices.***

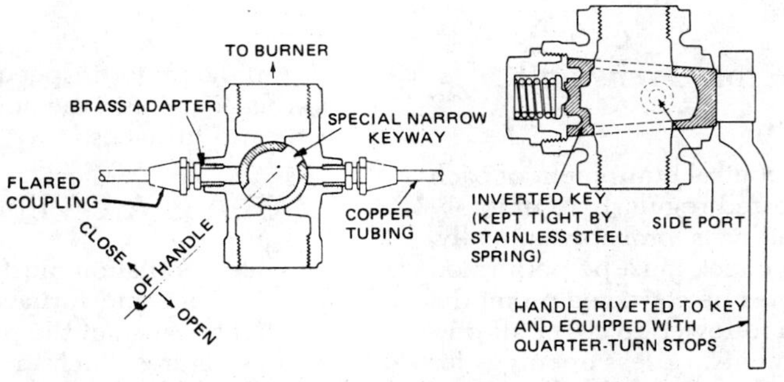

FIG. 2-10L. ***Details of a supervising cock (FM cock).***

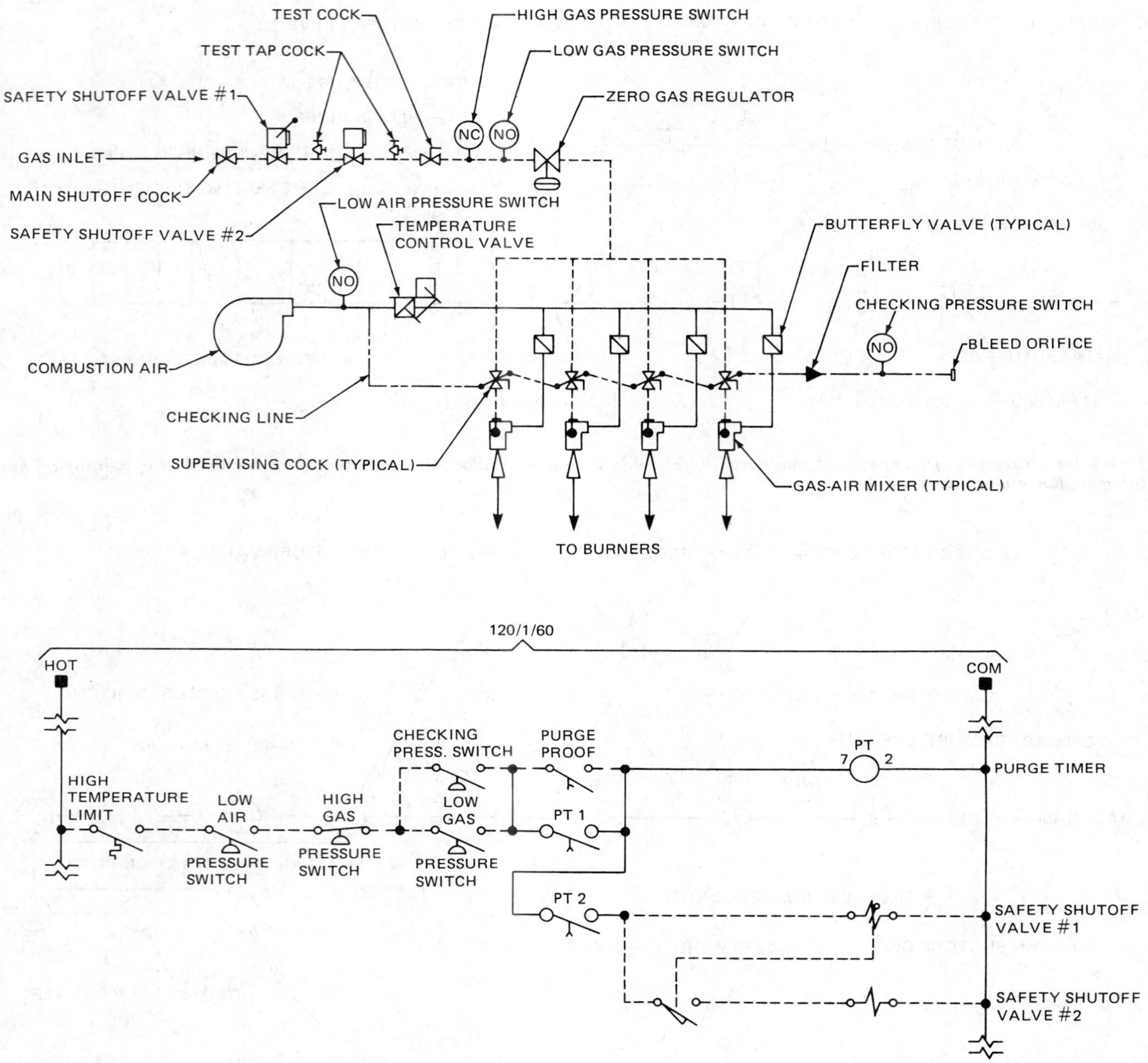

***FIG. 2-10M.** Example of a supervising cock and fuel gas safety control system—pneumatic type. At top, piping; at bottom, electrical.*

Testing and Maintenance for Ovens and Furnaces

The operating and supervisory control equipment of each oven should be checked and tested regularly, preferably once a week. At less frequent intervals, probably annually, a more comprehensive test and check must be performed by an expert. All deficiencies must be corrected promptly, and a regular cleaning program followed to cover all portions of the oven and its attachments. Access openings for cleaning the oven enclosure and the connecting ducts must be provided.

A program for inspecting and maintaining oven safety controls is given in the appendices of NFPA standards for ovens and furnaces.

CLASS A OVENS AND FURNACES

Adequate ventilation must be provided in the operation of Class A ovens and furnaces where there is an explosion potential because of the presence of flammable vapors or fuel-air mixtures. Such fires or explosions may, in general, be prevented by good ventilation and supervisory controls that keep the flammable vapor content well below the LFL.

Ventilation

Ventilation is required while an oven is in operation and flammable vapors are given off. Control devices ensure that the ventilating and pre-ventilating systems are operating. Failure of the ventilating fan causes shutdown of the heating system and the conveyor which carries material into a continuous oven. The following discussion refers only to that ventilation required for safe operation, and not that required for combustion and recirculation. It also does not apply to ovens operating in conjunction with solvent recovery systems which may use a low-oxygen atmosphere.

Proper ventilation includes a sufficient supply of fresh air, proper exhaust to outdoors, and properly distributed air circulation sufficient to ensure that the flammable vapor concentration throughout the oven is safely below the LFL at all times. The quantity of fresh air required for safe ventilation is determined by the amount of vapor released during the process.

In general, mechanical ventilation to outdoors is required on all ovens in which flammable or toxic vapors are liberated, as well as for ovens heated by direct-fired gas or oil heaters.

Ovens in which flammable or toxic vapors are never released do not require ventilation for safety, if heated by steam or electric energy, or by gas- or oil-fired indirect heating equipment. On new ovens of every size, ventilation provided by a separate exhauster is advisable whenever appreciable amounts of flammable vapors are given off by the work.

Continuous conveyor ovens: The general rule for ventilating continuous conveyor-type ovens is to provide not less than 10,000 cfm (283 m^3/min) of fresh air at 70°F (21°C) for each 1 gal (3.79 L) of common solvent introduced into the oven. The basis for this rule is that 1 gal (3.79 L) of common solvent produces a quantity of flammable vapor which will diffuse in air to form roughly 2500 cu ft (71 m^3) of the leanest explosive mixture. Because a considerable portion of the ventilating air may pass through the oven without completely traversing the zone in which vapors are given off, the ventilation air may be distributed unevenly. To provide a margin of safety, four times this amount of air, or 10,000 cu ft (283 m^3) [referred to 70°F (21°C)], is required for each 1 gal (3.79 L) of solvent evaporated. In certain solvents, however, the volume of air rendered barely explosive exceeds 2500 cu ft (71 m^3), and the safety factor decreases proportionately.

When a continuous-type oven is designed to operate with a particular solvent and the ventilating air can be accurately controlled, the required ventilation can be determined by calculation. [See NFPA 86, *Ovens and Furnaces*, for information on how to calculate the volume of vapor produced by 1 gal (3.79 L) of solvent and the volume of air required to provide sufficient dilution to prevent an ignitable mixture.] As with the general rule for oven ventilation, the calculated rate of air change includes a factor of safety four times the volume of air required to prevent an ignitable mixture.

Batch process (Box) ovens: The nature of the work being processed is the basis for determining the ventilation rate in batch process ovens. Because of the wide variations in the materials, rate of evaporation, and coating thickness, it is preferable to make tests and calculations to figure the proper ventilation rate. However, years of testing and experience have shown that approximately 380 cfm (10.7 m^3/min) [referred to 70°F (21°C)] of ventilation for each 1 gal (3.79 L) of flammable volatiles released from a batch of sheet metal or metal parts being baked after dip coating is a reasonably safe rate of air change.

For other types of work, the figure of 380 cfm (10.7 m^3/min) [referred to 70°F (21°C)] is also used, unless the required ventilation rates can be calculated from reliable previous experience, or the maximum evaporation rate is determined by tests run under actual operating conditions. In the latter case, a safety margin requires a rate of air change equaling four times the volume of air needed to produce an ignitable mixture. In any event, caution is needed when applying this estimating method to work of low mass, e.g., paper, textiles, etc., which will heat quickly, or work coated with materials containing highly volatile solvents. Either condition may give too high a peak evaporation rate for the estimating method.

Temperature correction: Temperature corrections must be made when using the above rules, since the volume of a gas varies in direct proportion to its absolute temperature (0°F is equivalent to approximately 460° abs and 0°C is equivalent to approximately 273°K).

For example, to supply 10,000 cu ft of fresh air referred to 70°F (530° abs) to an oven operating at 300°F (760° abs), it is necessary to exhaust:

$$\frac{760}{530} \times 10{,}000 = 14{,}320 \text{ cu ft of } 300°\text{F air.}$$

The metric equivalent is:

To supply 283 m^3 of fresh air referred to 21°C (294°K) to an oven operating at 149°C (422°K), it is necessary to exhaust:

$$\frac{422}{294} \times 283 = 406 \text{ m}^3 \text{ of } 149°\text{C air.}$$

In some cases, process requirements call for more ventilation than needed to maintain safe conditions in an oven. When this is true, an approximate method of figuring ventilation may be adequate for checking safety requirements. Except in these cases, all factors, including solvent characteristics, type of oven, material being processed, oven temperatures, effect of temperature on the LFL, must be carefully considered so that an adequate safety factor is ensured.

Low-oxygen ovens: Low-oxygen ovens are used for evaporation of solvent in an atmosphere where the oxygen concentration is below the flammability level of the solvent. For some solvents this operating value would be approximately 8 percent oxygen, which includes a safety factor of approximately 3 percent. There is a need for oxygen analysis to verify the low oxygen concentrations. Inert gas is used to displace the oxygen (air) during startup, and combustibles during shutdown. These systems are used for solvent recovery from the coating cure process in the oven as shown in Figure 2-10N. The treated product passes into and out of the oven enclosure through the oven openings. The oven atmosphere consists of an inert carrier gas which is continuously recirculated through the oven enclosure (line 1). Solvents evolve from the treated product and build up to an equilibrium vapor level which is much higher than the allowable levels in an air atmosphere. A bleed stream (line 2), which is typically 1 percent of the recirculation flow, is processed by a solvent recovery system. A liquid (line 3), which provides cooling through vaporization, acts to condense the solvents which are pumped to storage (line 4). After solvents are stripped from the inert gas stream, it is returned directly to the oven enclosure (line 5) to resume its role as a solvent vapor carrier.

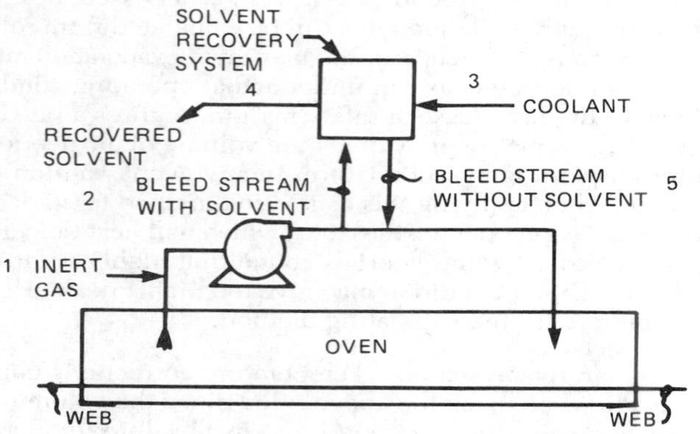

FIG. 2-10N. An example of a low-oxygen oven with a solvent recovery system.

Fire and Explosion Protection

Automatic sprinklers and water spray systems should be considered for heat processing equipment that contains or processes sufficient combustible materials to sustain a fire. The amount of protection required depends upon the construction and arrangement of the oven and the materials handled in it. If combustible material is processed, or if trucks or racks are combustible (or subject to loading with excess finishing material), fixed protection must extend as far as necessary into the enclosure and exhaust ducts. It also should be present where an appreciable amount of flammable drippings from finishing materials accumulates within the oven. If desired, supplementary carbon dioxide, foam, dry chemical, or halon protection may be permanently installed, but such protection is not a substitute for automatic sprinklers.

The use of steam for fire protection in ovens and dryers generally is not recommended. However, when there is no alternative, steam smothering systems may be allowed when oven temperatures exceed 225°F (107°C) and large supplies of steam are available at all times. Complete standards have not been developed for the use of steam as an extinguishing agent. Steam is not as dependable as water, carbon dioxide, dry chemical, halon, or foam. It should be noted that the future of halon extinguishing systems is in considerable doubt due to its ozone-depleting qualities.

Portable extinguishers are needed near the oven, oven heater, and related equipment, including dip tanks or other finishing processes operated in conjunction with the oven. Small-hose stations with combination nozzles also should be provided so all parts of the oven structure can be reached.

Ovens that may contain flammable gas or vapor mixtures must be equipped with unobstructed relief vents to release internal explosion pressures. These vents, panels, or doors may be secured with explosion-relieving hardware or gravity-retained panels that provide adequate insulation and possess the necessary structural strength. The weight of the panel should be minimal to permit movement at the lowest practical pressures. Explosion-relief panels must be proportioned according to the ratio of area to the explosion-containing volume of the oven, with due allowance made for openings or access doors equipped with approved explosion-relieving hardware. The preferred ratio is 1 sq ft (0.09 m^2) of relief panel area to every 15 cu ft (0.42 m^3) of oven volume.

CLASS B INDUSTRIAL FURNACES

In many ways, Class B furnaces are similar to Class A ovens and furnaces. But, because no flammable volatiles or residues are present, there is nothing combustible in the construction or contents of the Class B furnace.

In many Class B furnaces, little or no effective explosion-relief venting can be provided because of the weight and strength of the walls. Pre-ventilation is important before a source of ignition is introduced into the furnace. In some cases, completely automatic purging may be practical; in others, purging may be partly manual. In either case, supervisory controls are needed to interlock the ventilation, fuel supply, combustion air, safety shutoff valve, and flame failure devices.

In multiburner installations, combustion safeguards with flame supervision should be applied where possible and practical. In some of these installations, furnace design, burner design, and the rigors of the service may preclude the application of flame supervision, and a supervisory cock and gas safety control system may be provided. (See Figures 2-10L and 2-10M.) When furnaces have zones operating at different temperatures, the zones may have to be treated as separate units.

Changes in the usual safety requirements may be permitted in some ovens or furnaces, but if there is any possibility of explosion from unburned fuel, adequate safeguards should be provided. An audible alarm may be installed to indicate unsafe conditions.

CLASS C INDUSTRIAL FURNACES USING A SPECIAL PROCESSING ATMOSPHERE

Special atmosphere furnaces are used to improve the quality of metals and metal alloys by heating them in an atmosphere in which air has been replaced by other gases, some of which are combustible. In most cases, the atmosphere gas is used to prevent oxidation of the metal during heating, but it also may prevent the removal or addition of carbon. Some processes that use atmospheric gases are bright annealing of copper and steel, scale-free hardening and annealing of castings, brazing, and sintering. Examples of protective gases used in these processes are hydrogen, charcoal gas, and dissociated ammonia. Also used are various hydrocarbon gases produced by equipment that processes the gas used for firing, generally in the presence of a catalyst. During the past few years, synthetic atmospheres which include methanol and other stored gas components have been used.

Some heat-treating furnaces contain an inert atmosphere (carbon dioxide, helium, argon, nitrogen) so they present no special fire hazard; however, these gases could present a health hazard. Other gases produce a flammable atmosphere (hydrogen, dissociated ammonia, incompletely burned hydrocarbon gas, carbon monoxide, and methane) which presents an explosion hazard; therefore their use requires special safeguards. Atmosphere furnaces are not limited to flammable gases but also may contain acid gases, such as chlorine and anhydrous hydrochloric. When the latter are used in a special atmosphere, extreme care must be taken to keep air from entering the furnace. Regardless of the type of special atmosphere, Class C furnaces have fuel hazards similar to those of the Class A and B ovens and furnaces discussed earlier (although most Class C units are indirectly fired or electrically heated). The hazards in Class C furnaces exist chiefly at three times: (1) before the process starts and the flammable atmosphere is replacing air in the furnace; (2) when the process is finished and air is being readmitted; and (3) when, for some reason, the special atmosphere supply is interrupted and air is permitted to enter. If at each of these times sufficient inert gas can be introduced into the furnace to prevent a combustible mixture, there is no danger of an explosion. Automatic introduction of inert gas upon failure of the special atmosphere supply is desirable; at the least, an audible alarm should notify the oven operator of atmosphere supply failure or other upset conditions.

Inert Gas Purge Procedure

Begin by verifying the adequacy of the inert gas supply. After all doors (if any) are closed, make sure that the flammable atmosphere gas, flame curtain, and other valves are closed. The furnace may then be heated to operating temperature. If so, introduce the inert gas at a rate capable of maintaining a positive pressure in the furnace. Sample the furnace atmosphere until two consecutive readings indicate the oxygen content is below 1 percent. With at least one furnace zone above 1400°F (760°C), ignite the pilots at the outer doors and effluent vents. The flammable special atmosphere then may be introduced. When the flammable atmosphere is flowing, the inert gas should be turned off immediately. When flames appear at the vestibule effluent ports, the atmosphere introduction has been completed. The curtain burners then may be ignited.

To remove the flammable atmosphere with the furnace at operating temperature, the doors (if any) should remain closed, the inert gas purge actuated, and a positive furnace pressure maintained. Shut off the special atmosphere, flame curtain, and other valves; and sample the atmosphere until two consecutive analyses indicate the atmosphere is below 50 percent of its lower explosive limit (LEL). The furnace is then purged, and the doors may be opened, and the inert gas turned off.

The normal procedure for startup or shutdown of most Class C furnaces when the temperature is above 1400°F (760°C) is to burn out the air at the start of the process and the flammable atmosphere at the finish. In furnaces with an operating temperature above 1400°F (760°C), burning may be performed at the start by bringing the temperature up to 1400°F (760°C) before the special atmosphere is introduced. Automatic means are required to prevent the introduction of flammable fluids into a furnace before the furnace temperature has risen to 1400°F (760°C). At this temperature the flammable gas will burn in the oven until the oxygen is used up and the hazard removed, allowing the operation to be started. At the end of the process, the heating should be continued so the temperature stays above 1400°F (760°C); then the flammable gas supply is shut off and air gradually admitted. When burning stops, the flammable gas has been consumed. When an alarm indicates failure of the flammable gas supply or of the heating system, the oven operator must immediately initiate an inert gas purge, or start the admission of air to burn the flammable gas in the furnace. This must be done before the furnace cools to below 1400°F (760°C). Where operators are not present and flammable gas flow is interrupted because of insufficient temperature inside the furnace, a flow control unit should automatically admit a flow of inert gas that will restore positive pressure without delay.

Special Atmosphere Generators

Special atmosphere generators are a source for the atmospheric gases used in some Class C furnaces. One type of generator (i.e., exothermic) produces the atmospheric gas by completely or partially burning fuel gas at a controlled ratio, usually at 60 to 100 percent aeration, while another type (i.e., endothermic) produces the atmosphere at a controlled ratio of less than 50 percent. Atmospheres from an exothermic generator may be either inert or flammable, depending upon the generator design and operating range, while those from endothermic generators are always flammable.

Another type of generator is an ammonia dissociator, which, by temperature reaction with a catalyst in an externally heated vessel, produces dissociated ammonia (25 percent nitrogen and 75 percent hydrogen) from ammonia.

The special atmosphere generator must be provided with adequate supervisory controls. These would normally include interlocking of raw gas, air (if needed), burners for heating or processing, feed and discharge pressures, etc. Safety shutoff valves are usually provided in feed and discharge piping, and devices also are provided to indicate the pressure or rate of flow of processed gas to the furnace, and its analysis. This can vary. The operator is thus assisted in his/her efforts to supply the furnace with the desired special atmosphere.

The best location for the generator and its auxiliary equipment, such as surge tank, compressor, aftercooler, storage tank, etc., is in a separate, detached building of light, noncombustible construction.

CLASS D VACUUM FURNACES

Vacuum furnaces are used for heat treating metals; they are not, however, limited to this industry. In a vacuum furnace a vacuum pump is used to displace oxygen, and, in most cases, to reduce the water vapor content or dew point, as well.

Vacuum furnaces are usually batch furnaces. Batch furnaces are further classified into hot-wall and cold-wall furnaces; the latter are in greater use at the present time. Examples of hot-wall and cold-wall vacuum furnaces are shown in Figures 2-10O and 2-10P, respectively. In the hot-wall furnace, the entire vacuum vessel is heated, though usually not above 1800°F (982°C) because of the reduction in the strength of materials at elevated temperatures. However, installation of a second vacuum vessel outside the vacuum retort (within which a roughing vacuum is maintained during the heating cycle) permits construction of larger hot-wall furnaces with higher operating temperatures.

Cold-wall furnaces consist of a water-cooled vacuum vessel. Usually the heating elements are inside the vacuum vessel. The walls can be maintained at near ambient temperature during high temperature operations; thus large units operating at high temperatures [4000 to 5000°F (2206 to 2760°C)] may be constructed. The two most common methods of heating cold-wall furnaces are by resistance and induction, with the heating elements located

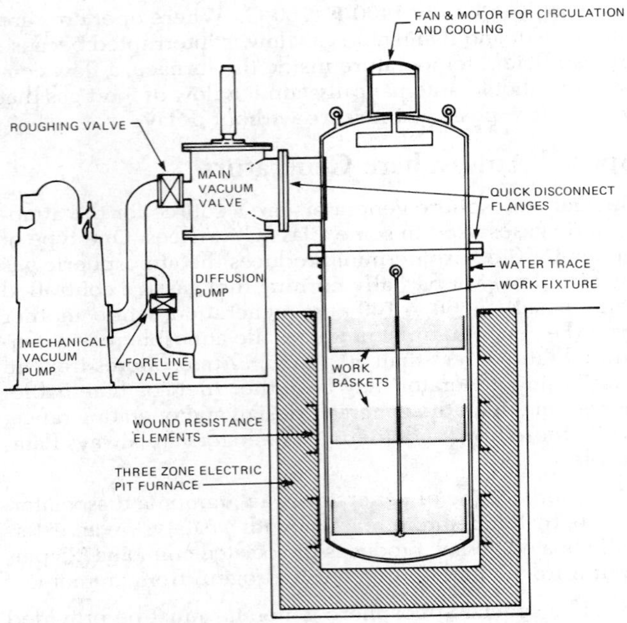

FIG. 2-10O. Example of a hot-wall, single-pump retort vacuum furnace.

within the vacuum vessel. The heating elements are usually water-cooled, though occasionally they may be air-cooled. Insulation may be effected by radiation shields constructed of low-emissivity, oxidation-resistant metals with proper vapor-pressure characteristics. Refractory insulation can be used in some instances; but this is difficult due to out-gassing of entrapped air in the refractory.

Mechanical-type pumps may achieve vacuum pressures of 10^{-3} to 10^{-2} torr. (Torr is a unit of pressure equal to 1/760 of an atmosphere.) For greater vacuum, booster oil-diffusion pumps are used to achieve pressures in the range of 10^{-5} to 10^{-7} torr; they must be "backed" by a supplementary pump.

Fractionating oil-diffusion pumps also are used and are always backed by a rotary pump, or rotary and mechanical booster combination. They produce pressures from below 10^{-3} torr down to about 5×10^{-7} torr. The accidental admission of air into a heated diffusion pump has resulted in an explosion of the pump fluid. The explosion forces damaged both the pump and the furnace hot zone.

Vacuum furnaces have the same hazards as most Class C furnaces. Besides those hazards associated with the heat sources, the additional hazards of vacuum furnaces are:

1. Water leaks in either heating elements or vessel jackets can cause explosions. If water enters the furnace at operating temperatures, it will cause more than just a steam explosion.
2. Collapse of the furnace wall if a relief valve on the water jacket fails.
3. Collapse of the vacuum retort in a hot-wall furnace, if the vessel uses materials that have inadequate strength at high temperatures. If this occurs in a gas-fired unit, the flame can be pulled into the vacuum pump and ignite the oil in the pumps.
4. Vacuum pumps which pull fluids (water or oil) from hydraulic seal pots.
5. The condensed metallic vapors on electrical insulators which can cause short circuiting, because this kind of furnace operates at pressures which can vaporize metals.
6. Short circuiting, if improperly supported heat shields sag at high temperatures and contact heating elements.
7. Hot spots on furnace walls that can weaken the furnace wall, if heat shields sag.

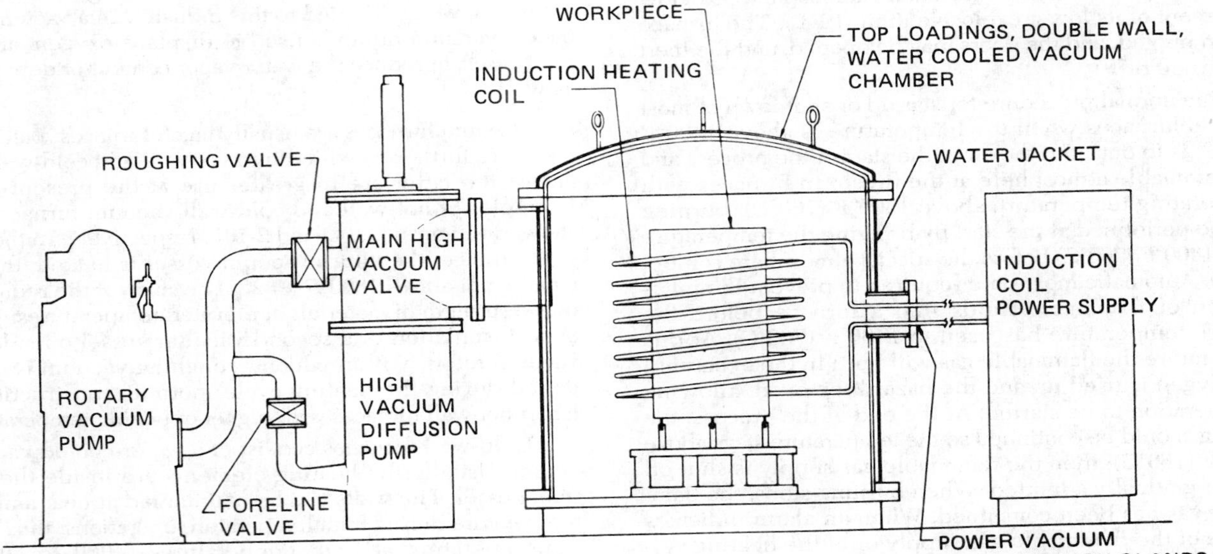

FIG. 2-10P. Example of a cold-wall, induction-heated vacuum furnace.

8. Temperature control problems not present in other types of furnaces and ovens. Optical pyrometers must have a line of sight to the work and their accuracy may be seriously impaired by gases, smoke, or discoloration of the sight glass.
9. Heat transfer—unless the thermocouple is actually attached to the part being measured, the heat transfer is based wholly on radiation. In air, a thermocouple receives heat by conduction and convection; therefore, with no air (or gas) in the furnace, the thermocouple response is slower. A gap of as little as 0.001 in. (0.025 mm) between the thermocouple and part or surface being measured can change significantly the response time of the thermocouple. A thermocouple on the heating element could mean that the parts would not reach the desired temperatures because the heating elements would of necessity have a temperature higher than the part (center of furnace), at least until equilibrium has been reached.
10. Induction heating—keeping piping conduits, building columns, beams, etc., out of the induction field, if the furnace is heated by induction. Any one of these items near an improperly shielded furnace can be heated by the induction coil inside the furnace. For instance, a steel bar placed so that it touches the furnace and a metal floor will be visibly hot in a matter of minutes. Of course, this also can happen on a Class B induction furnace.

AFTERBURNER AND CATALYTIC COMBUSTION SYSTEMS

Fume incinerators are combustion oxidation chambers designed to destroy process exhaust vapors or fumes by heat. Both direct flame and catalytic oxidation are used to reduce fumes, odors, vapors, and gases to acceptable exhaust products, such as carbon dioxide and water vapor. Exhaust that contains something besides plain hydrocarbons and oxygenated species may require additional special treatment, scrubbing, and filtration to remove particulate matter as well as halogens, hydroxides, sulfur oxides, and nitrogen oxides.

The advantages of fume incinerators can include reduced cleaning costs, reduced equipment downtime, reduced fire and explosion hazards, compliance with federal, state, and local pollution regulations, and savings in plant heating costs. Process fuel consumption can be reduced by the heat recovery of the burned exhaust fumes.

Installations have been damaged by fires in ducts between the process units and the incinerator, explosions of accumulated vapors in the ducts before or during startup, improper operation of gas-fired incinerators, and overheating of the catalytic element or combustion chambers. The causes of these fires have been inadequate duct cleaning; inadequate duct design; incomplete prepurging of the ducts, process unit, and incinerator; failure by the operator to follow proper operating procedures; and malfunction of burner and temperature controls.

Afterburner (Direct-Flame) Incineration

Direct-flame fume incinerators can be used for a wide range of organic solvent vapors, organic dusts, and combustible gases. In order to burn, the fumes must be heated to their autoignition temperatures with sufficient oxygen present to complete the chemical reaction. Quenching the burner flame may occur if the burner capacity is insufficient or the flame pattern and mixing are inadequate. The fumes must reach the autoignition temperature and remain there long enough (dwell time) for the chemical reaction to occur (the dwell time is usually 0.4 to 0.8 sec). Ample oxygen, more than 16 percent, is necessary for complete combustion. The step sequence for successful incineration is shown in Figure 2-10Q.

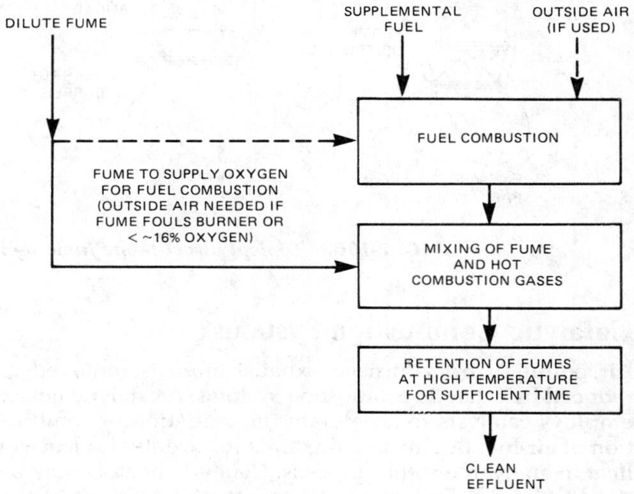

FIG. 2-10Q. Steps required for successful incineration of dilute fumes.

Operating temperatures in the combustion chamber are usually 1200 to 1500°F (650 to 816°C). Tests on some units have reported approximately 92 percent conversion efficiency to CO_2 at 1300°F (704°C) and 96 percent conversion efficiency at 1450°F (788°C). These conversion percentages of fumes to CO_2 are frequently required by air pollution codes. In any case, complete combustion requires that the fumes have sufficient air, proper mixing with the air, adequate dwell time, and adequate combustion chamber temperature.

Direct-flame combustion chambers are usually heavy refractory lined with external burners, such as tunnel burners, or light refractory with sectional line burners or line burners with mixing plates. (See Figure 2-10R.)

When metal construction is used, the design must take into account high thermal stresses and possible overheating of the metals. The combustion chambers, kiln, and boiler burner flames sometimes are used as fume incinerators.

Contaminated process waste streams might be inert gases with a low combustible hydrocarbon content. This mixture may be mixed with sufficient air to ensure combustion, then oxidized in a direct-flame or catalytic incinerator.

Special precautions must be taken where concentrated fumes are exhausted from the process. For safety, they are usually diluted with air to below 50 percent LEL for transfer to the incinerator.

Concentrated combustible fumes above the LEL are normally burned in flare stacks or as fuel in various types of heating equipment. The latter requires special burner design and combustion control supervision.

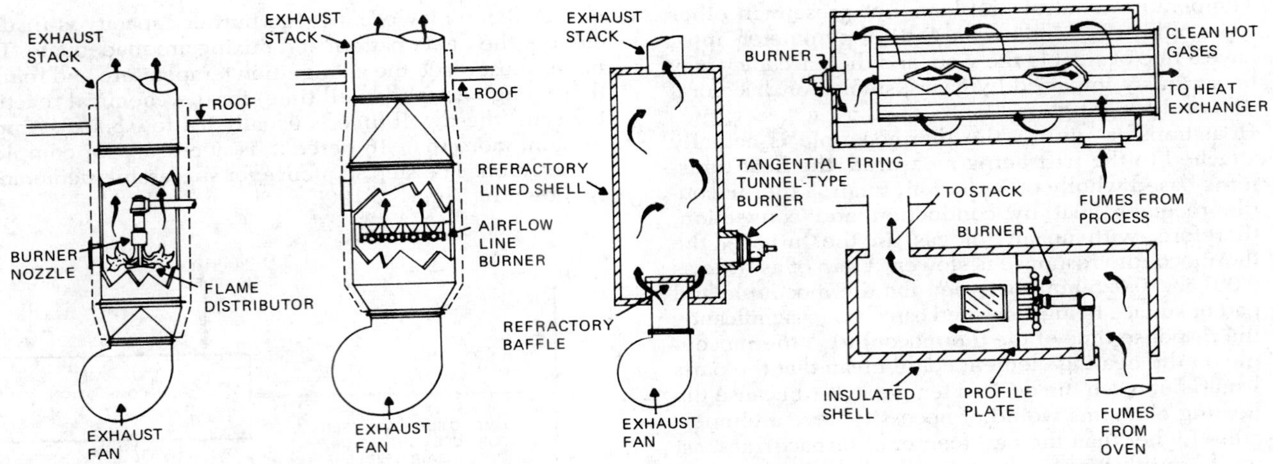

FIG. 2-10R. Typical direct-flame fume incinerators. (Source: Maxon Premix Burner Co., Inc.)

Catalytic Combustion Systems

Air pollution from furnace exhaust often is removed or reduced by catalytic combustion systems. A catalytic heater employs catalysts to accelerate the oxidation or combustion of air-fuel or air-fume mixtures for eventual release of heat to an oven or other process. Catalytic heaters may be used to burn a fuel gas, with substantial portions of the energy released as radiation to the processing zone. Alternately, catalytic heaters may be installed in the oven exhaust stream to release heat from evaporated oven byproducts, with available energy returned by a heat exchanger for recirculation through the oven processing zone.

Three types of catalytic combustion elements are available. The first is an all-metal mat used either as a fuel-fired radiant heater or alternately to oxidize combustible materials in air-fume mixtures. The second type is of ceramic or porcelain construction arranged in various configurations for gas fuel or fume oxidation with catalyst media, including a variety of "rare earth" elements, e.g., platinum, or metallic salts. Both types of these elements are classified as "fixed-bed" catalysts since they are normally held rigidly in place by clamps, cement, or other means. A third type of element consists of a bed, pellets, or granules supported or retained between screens in a fixed position, but with the individual members free to migrate within the bed.

Heating systems that employ catalysts are widely used to conserve oven fuel and control air pollution emissions. (See Figures 2-10S and 2-10T.) Catalytic heaters cannot, however, oxidize or consume silicones, chlorine compounds, and metallic vapors as from tin, mercury, and zinc; these elements and various inorganic dusts may retard or paralyze the catalysts.

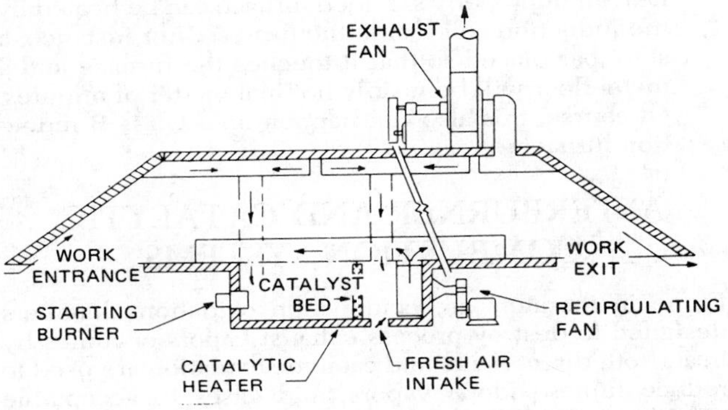

FIG. 2-10S. A direct-type catalytic oven heater for partial air pollution control.

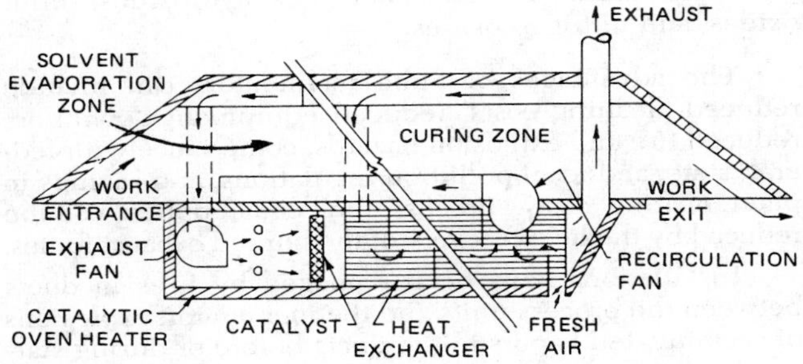

FIG. 2-10T. An indirect-type catalytic oven heater for full air pollution control.

Installation

All components of the afterburners and catalytic combustion system, related process equipment, and interconnecting ducts must be provided with controls and safeguards to supervise conditions during startup, operation, and shutdown. In some installations, many different concentrations of fumes may develop. The fume collection and delivery to the incinerator is an important part of the system. A careful investigation must be made for the incinerator and the associated equipment, including the appropriateness of the design and operating procedures.

HEAT RECOVERY

Heat exchangers and direct recirculation methods of heat recovery are often used to make process and fume incineration more economical. Some plants have calculated that if heat recovery methods are applied to heat generating processes, including fume incineration, the recovered heat can supply a substantial portion of the entire plant's heat or process demands. (See Figure 2-10U.)

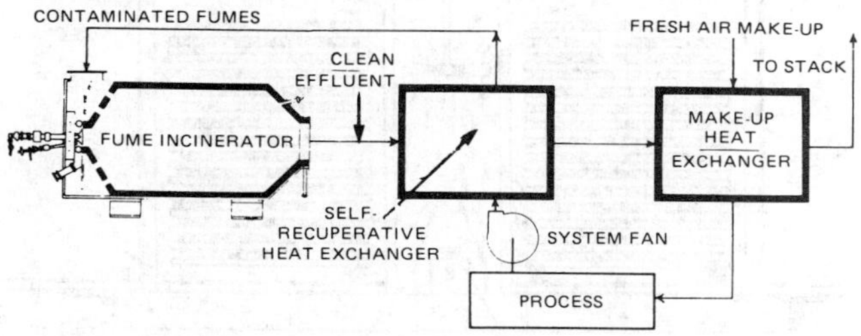

FIG. 2-10U. Typical incineration system incorporating waste heat recovery with fume and process air preheating.

Recovered heat may be used for: (1) the process as either a sole or supplementary heat source, (2) the process for some zones in a multizone unit, (3) other nearby processes, (4) preheating fumes to incinerators, (5) heating plant makeup air, and (6) a waste heat boiler serving multiple plant services. However, dirty stream deposits in the heat exchanger may make it inoperable. Combustible deposits and flammable liquids heated to high temperatures within the heat exchanger could cause a fire or explosion.

LUMBER KILNS

Drying lumber to a predetermined moisture content is accomplished in a variety of structures called kilns. Kilns make it possible to turn freshly cut, green wood into dry, accurately dimensioned lumber in a much shorter time than seasoning wood in open air. Because large quantities of combustible material are exposed to temperatures that can approximate ignition temperatures, kilns present a high degree of fire hazard.

Although called dry kilns, wood dryers usually employ moisture to maintain a uniform content within the wood during the drying, thus eliminating warping, checking, and splitting. The amount of moisture will vary with the species, and significant variations may be found within trees of the same species. The length of time required to bring the moisture content down to an optimum of about 2 percent depends upon the species, its original moisture content, the dimensions of the pieces being seasoned, the type of kiln, and the volume of material.

Types of Kilns

A dry kiln is basically an oven with controlled heat and humidity. It may operate as a batch dryer or as a progressive dryer. The wood being dried in a batch or compartment kiln remains stationary throughout the process. Temperature and humidity in all parts of the kiln are maintained as uniformly as possible and are adjusted as the wood dries.

Progressive kilns permit green lumber to be introduced in one end while dried lumber is being removed from the other end. Such kilns are designed so that somewhat higher temperatures are maintained at the dry, or discharge, end rather than at the loading end.

In natural circulation kilns, heated air rises up through the stacked lumber by convection. (See Figure 2-10V.) Losing its heat, air travels down to the heating device and is reheated. During the first part of the drying cycle, the air flows up along the sides, over the stacked lumber, and down through air passages in the stack. When the moisture content has been reduced to somewhere between 20 and 10 percent, heated air is directed up through the center of the stack to equalize the drying. Vents in the walls or roof of the kiln exhaust the hot, moisture-laden air.

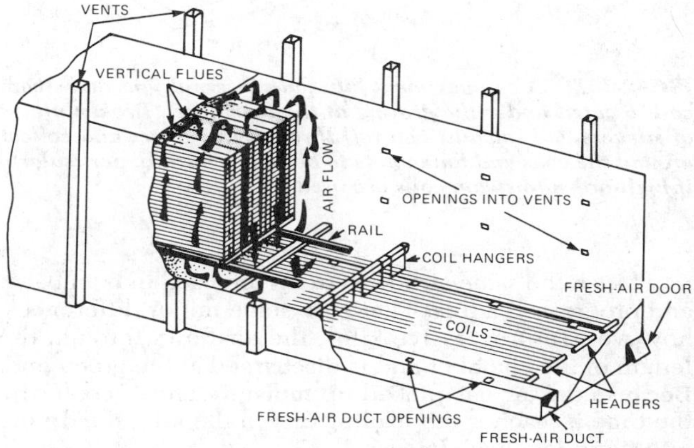

FIG. 2-10V. A natural circulation, steam-heated compartment kiln. Arrows indicate air movement during the early stages of the drying cycle.

Forced circulation kilns move air through the stacked lumber by either internal or external blowers. (See Figure 2-10W.) Figure 2-10X shows an internal fan kiln with fans located beneath the floor. Internal fans are reversible, changing the airflow for optimum drying. Internal fan kilns normally require cloth or metal baffles to eliminate turbulence and keep the air flowing in the desired direction.

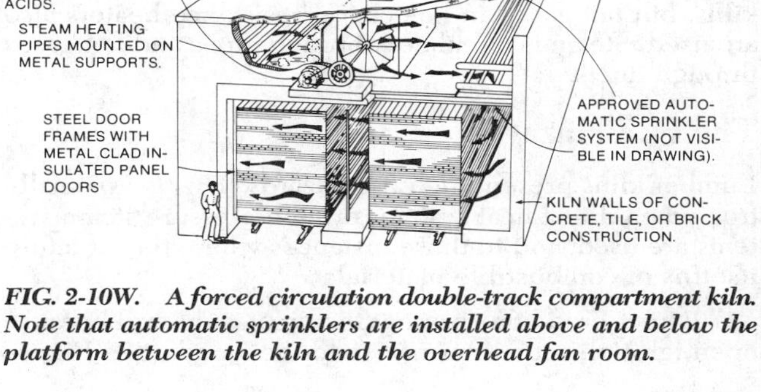

FIG. 2-10W. A forced circulation double-track compartment kiln. Note that automatic sprinklers are installed above and below the platform between the kiln and the overhead fan room.

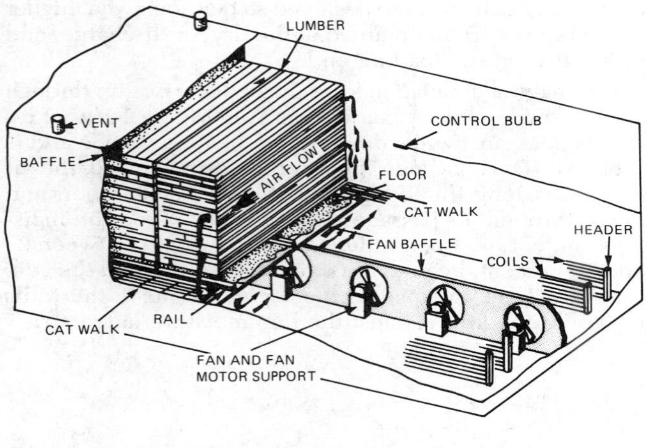

FIG. 2-10X. A compartment kiln with internal fans and steam coils located under the grating at the floor level. Broken pieces of stickers and sawdust can fall through the grates and collect around the coils and fan motors to become a hazard, particularly if high-pressure steam coils are used.

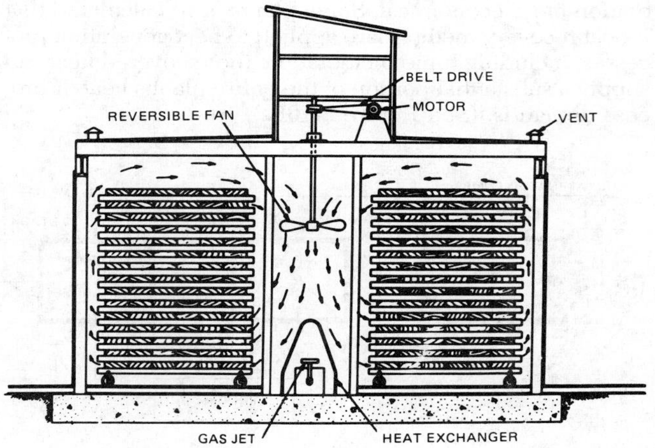

FIG. 2-10Y. A double-track, internal fan compartment kiln that is heated directly by a gas burner.

Much the same airflow systems are used in both batch and progressive kilns. There are some minor differences, however. In progressive kilns, the air flows through the length of the chamber and is discharged at the green end. Because the air has picked up moisture and is cooler by the time it reaches the loading end of the kiln, the drying rate there is much slower.

Kiln Construction

Unlike most other buildings, kilns are subjected to extreme variations in internal temperature and humidity. Such variations cause unusual expansion and contraction that reduce structural integrity of the kiln and increase heat loss. Untended structural defects also can lead to premature failure of the structure. To reduce the fire hazard, kilns should be of fire-resistive or heavy-timber construction.

Heat Sources

Dry kilns require a constant source of heat, provided either directly or indirectly, to vaporize the water content of the wood. Direct heating is accomplished by circulating hot gases (produced by burning gas, oil, sawdust, or other fuels) through the stacked lumber. It also can be done by heating large metal surfaces with an open gas or oil flame as in Figure 2-10Y. Air circulated by internal fans passes over the metal which acts as a heat exchanger, then flows over the lumber, carrying off moisture vapor.

Steam is a common source of heat for indirectly heated kilns, but hot gases and electrical resistance heaters also are used. Steam is circulated through pipes and hot gases through ducts.

The Fire Hazards

Lumber kilns present high fire hazards. This is especially true when direct heat systems or high-pressure steam systems are used, and in those instances where the structure itself is of combustible materials.

Direct-fired kilns present the greatest hazard because open ignition sources are close to the wood. (See Figure 2-10Y.) The kilns should be considered analagous to Class A ovens in that they should be equipped with all the combustion controls normally required for drying ovens where the heating fuel is introduced into the heating enclosure itself. Indirectly heated kilns utilizing steam coils as heat exchangers and having controlled humidity are usually considered to be of low hazard.

The Safeguards

The important requirements for firesafety are automatic sprinkler protection, sound construction, good housekeeping, automatic humidity control, good air circulation, and proper ventilation. Kilns should be situated at safe distances from storage yards, sheds, and mill buildings. Ideally, they should be of fire-resistive construction and equipped with a complete automatic sprinkler system connected to an adequate water supply. The sprinkler protection should extend to fan houses and control rooms. Hydrants or hose connections should be located on the exterior for manual fire fighting.

DEHYDRATORS AND DRYERS

Dehydrators and dryers for agricultural products, commonly referred to as dryers, use heat to reduce the moisture content of products. The hazards of dryers are: (1) the possibility of igniting combustible materials near them, (2) the use of fuel or electricity as a heat source, and (3) the ignition of stock being dried.

Types of Dehydrators and Dryers

The three types of agricultural product dryers are: (1) continuous, (2) batch, and (3) bulk. They differ in the arrangement and operation of the drying chamber.

Continuous dryers include:

1. Drum dryers for milk, puree, and sludges.
2. Spray dryers for milk, eggs, and soup.
3. Flash dryers for chopped forage crops.
4. Gravity dryers (may also be batch type) for small grains, beans, and seeds. (See Figure 2-10Z.)

5. Tunnel dryers (may also be batch type, and may be further classified according to airflow and whether or not intermediate heating is used) for fruits, vegetables, grains, seeds, nuts, fibers, and forage crops. (See Figure 2-10AA.)
6. Rotary dryers for milk, puree, and sludges. (See Figure 2-10BB.)

Batch dryers may be either fixed or portable and include pan dryers for sugar, puree, sludges, and other products. (See Figure 2-10CC.)

Bulk dryers dry the product in a bin, crib, or compartment in which it is to be stored. They are used to dry seeds, grains, nuts, tobacco, hay, and forage. (See Figure 2-10DD.)

Dryer Controls

Some suggested controls for dryers, except those on the heating equipment, include:

1. A method for automatically shutting down the dryer in the event of fire or excessive temperature.
2. A thermostat in the exhaust air when the product is fed automatically from the dryer to a storage building. In the event of excessive temperature, the thermostat (a) shuts off heat to the dryer and stops airflow (except when the product being dried is in suspension), (b) stops the flow of the product, and (c) sounds an audible alarm.

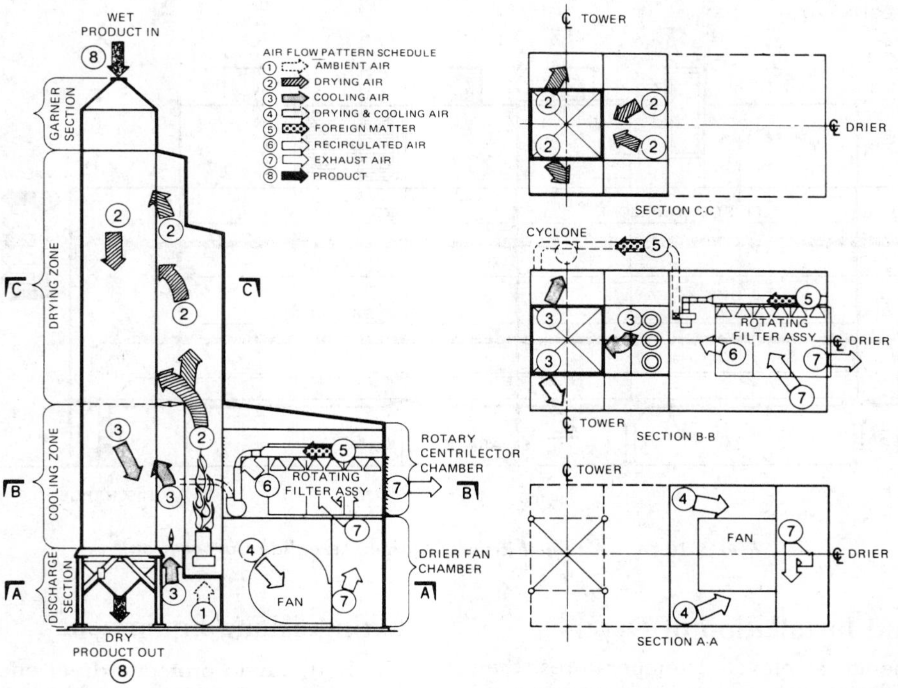

FIG. 2-10Z. A tower-type gravity dryer. (Source: Aeroglide Corporation)

Methods of Heating

Dryers for agricultural products may be direct fired (where products of combustion contact the material being dried) or indirect fired. The heaters may be oil fired, gas fired, solid-fuel fired, electrical, or heated by a heat transfer medium, such as steam. In general, the requirements for burner installation and fuel storage are the same as those for other heat-producing devices.

If gas-fired infrared heaters or lamps are used, their focal length should be ample so the surface of the drying product does not reach unsafe temperatures. If electrical infrared lamps are used in dryers, the lamps should be located where they cannot collect combustible dust.

Solid-fuel furnaces (other than those burning coke and anthracite coal) should not be used where the products of combustion can enter the drying chamber. Indirect solid-fuel dryers need temperature-controlled heat relief openings to the outside.

3. A thermostat in combustible dryers which, when the temperature of the combustible reaches 165°F (74°C), shuts off heat to the dryer but permits unheated air to pass through, and activates an audible alarm.
4. A device to shut off heat to the dryer if air movement through the dryer stops.
5. A high-limit thermostat located between the heat-producing device and the dryer.

Burner Controls

In general, the burner controls for dryers are the same as those for other automatically fired devices. A manual, quick-closing shutoff valve should be installed in the supply line of gas- and oil-fired burners, and controls should be arranged so that following automatic shutdown, manual restart will be necessary. Other control safeguards include flame failure protection, and pre-ventilation of the combustion chamber. All supervisory controls should be arranged to "fail safe."

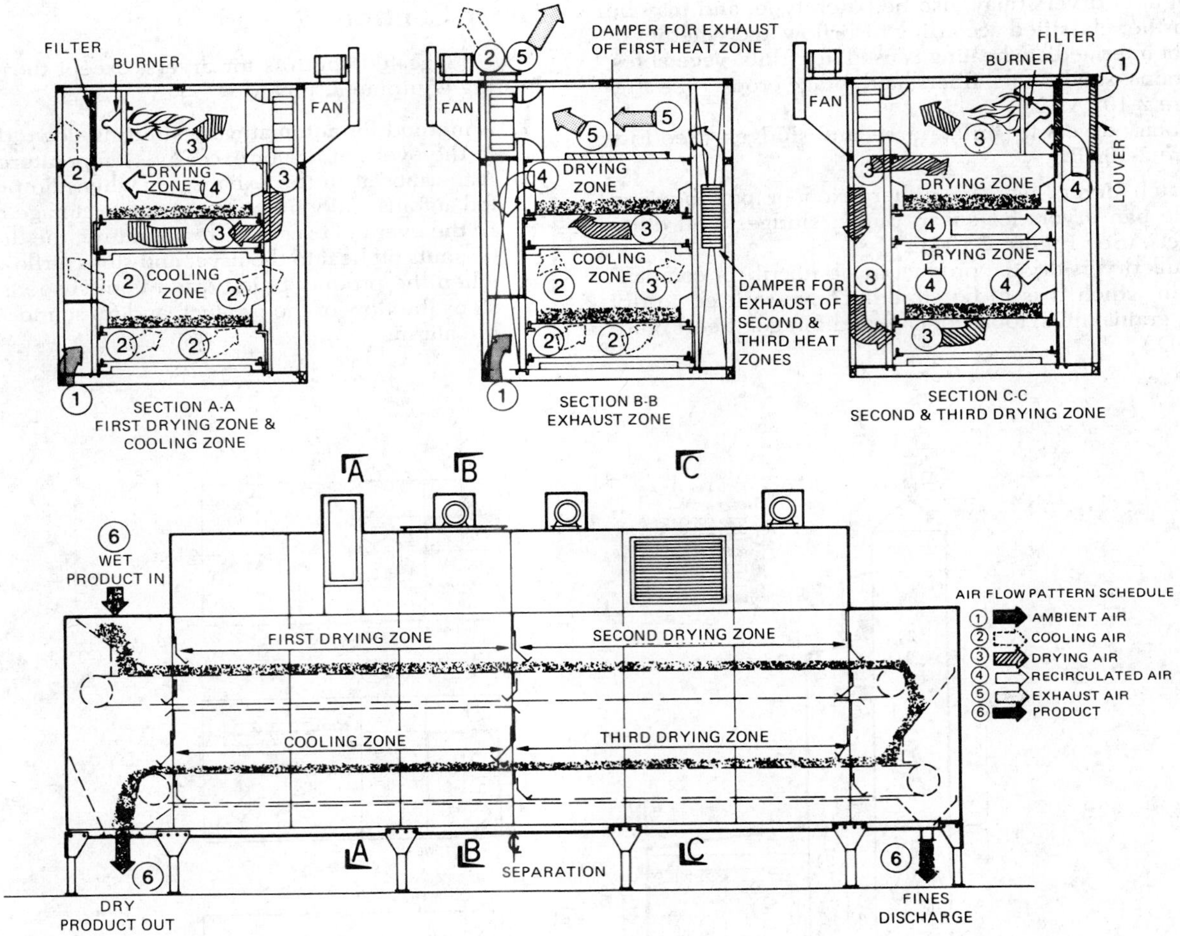

FIG. 2-10AA. A tunnel dryer. (Source: Aeroglide Corporation)

Construction and Installation of Dryers

Because dryers operate at elevated temperatures, they should be made of fire-resistive or noncombustible materials. If combustible materials must be used, dryers must not be subjected to sustained temperatures in excess of approximately 165°F (74°C). Expansion joints should be provided to prevent damage from expansion and contraction.

Secondary air openings for direct-fired dryers are screened with ½-in. (12.5 mm) mesh screen so materials cannot enter the combustion chamber. Primary air openings require screens with mesh ¼ in. (6.3 mm) or smaller. An ample supply of easily opened access panels is necessary for inspection, cleaning, and fire fighting.

When stock is moved through the dryers so that it generates static electricity, all conductive parts of the dryers should be electrically bonded and grounded.

Like any heat-producing device, a dryer must have adequate clearance from nearby combustibles to prevent overheating. If there is a combustible dust hazard in the same building as the dryer, the heating device and blowers are installed in a dust-free room or area separated from the rest of the building. Ducts to convey heated air to the dryer and exhaust air from the dryer to the outside should be noncombustible.

Extinguishing Equipment

The best way to protect a dryer enclosure is to install a water spray or automatic sprinkler system within the enclosure where possible. An exception to this is the direct-fired rotary dryer, which may be damaged by the internal application of water. A carbon dioxide system is satisfactory protection for this type dryer.

Fire protection may be needed in the product and exhaust dust collecting system, bins, chutes, ducts, cyclone collectors, and dust collectors. In addition to automatic sprinkler or deluge systems, high-speed infrared detectors with water spray may be needed to extinguish ignition sources, sparks, or embers in the ducts and to prevent propagation to the bins or dust collectors.

To extinguish small fires in and around most dryers, standpipe hoses are most useful, though water-type portable fire extinguishers also may be used.

Cooling of Dehydrated Products

A product being dried requires adequate cooling before it is packaged or stored. The amount of cooling required to prevent subsequent ignition will depend upon the properties of each material and how it is to be packaged or stored.

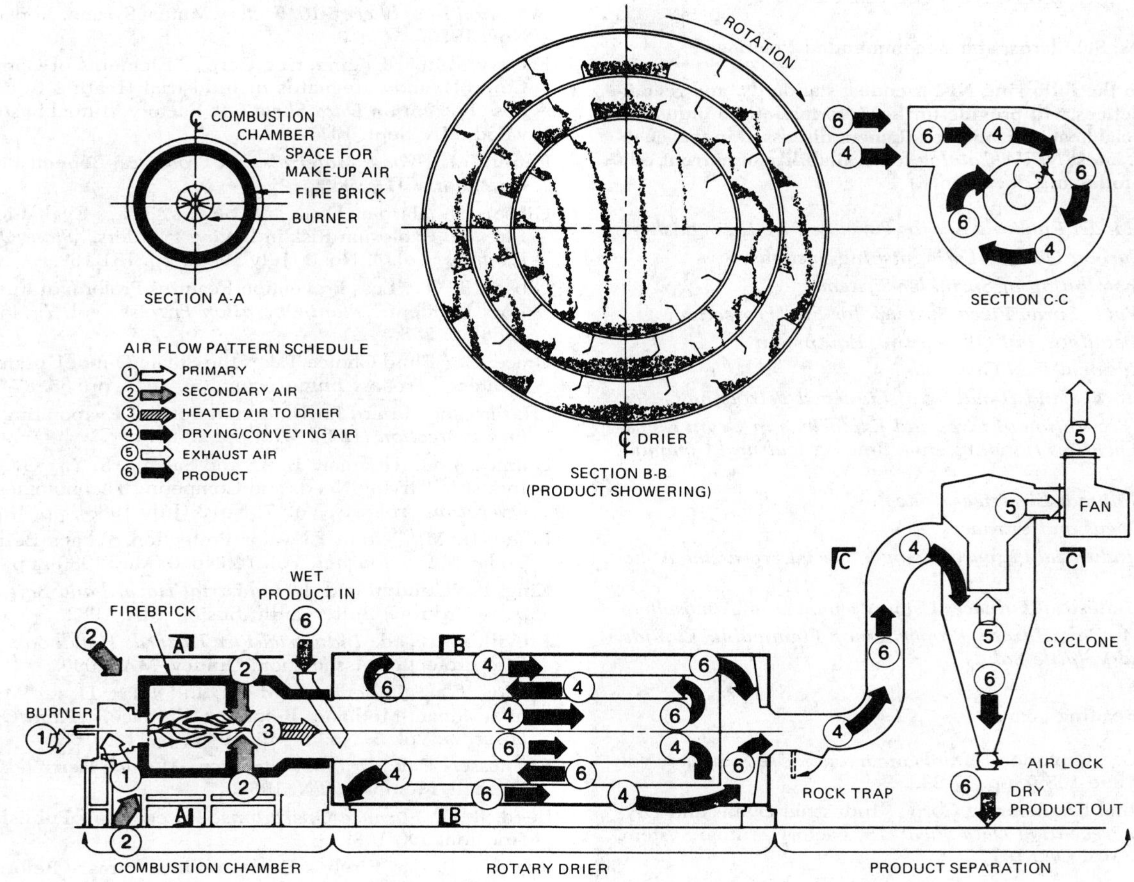

FIG. 2-10BB. A rotary dryer. (Source: Aeroglide Corporation)

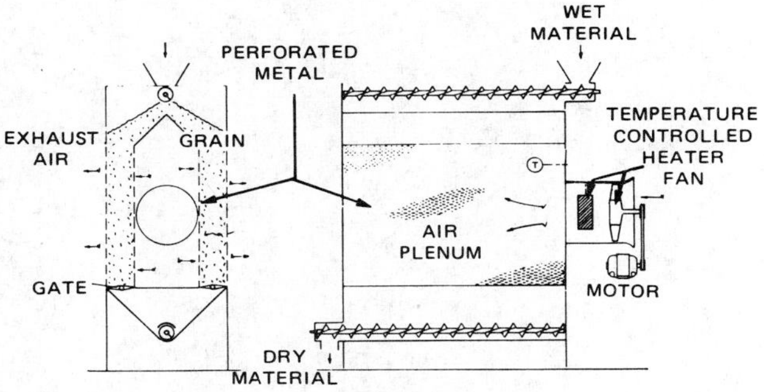

FIG. 2-10CC. A batch-type grain dryer.

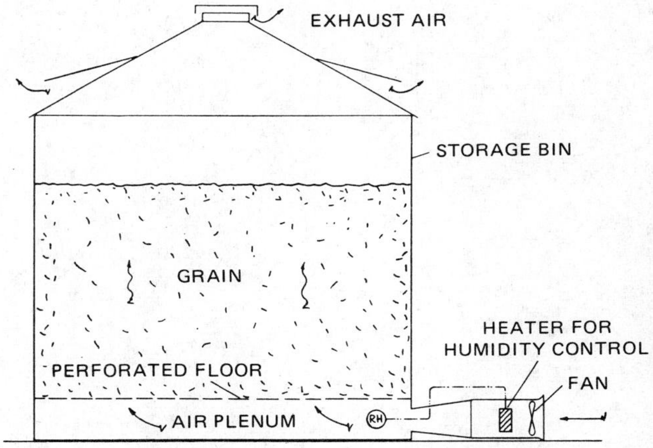

FIG. 2-10DD. A bulk-type grain dryer.

BIBLIOGRAPHY

NFPA Codes, Standards, and Recommended Practices

Reference to the following NFPA codes, standards, and recommended practices will provide further information on industrial and commercial heat utilization equipment discussed in this chapter. (See the latest *NFPA Catalog* for availability of current editions of the following documents.)

NFPA 10L, *Model Enabling Act for Portable Fire Extinguishers.*

NFPA 12, *Carbon Dioxide Extinguishing Systems.*

NFPA 13, *Installation of Sprinkler Systems.*

NFPA 15, *Water Spray Fixed Systems for Fire Protection.*

NFPA 31, *Installation of Oil Burning Equipment.*

NFPA 54, *National Fuel Gas Code.*

NFPA 58, *Storage and Handling of Liquefied Petroleum Gases.*

NFPA 61B, *Prevention of Fires and Explosions in Grain Elevators and Facilities Handling Bulk Raw Agricultural Commodities.*

NFPA 70, *National Electrical Code®.*

NFPA 86, *Ovens and Furnaces.*

NFPA 86C, *Industrial Furnaces Using a Special Processing Atmosphere.*

NFPA 86D, *Industrial Furnaces Using Vacuum as an Atmosphere.*

NFPA 325M, *Fire Hazard Properties of Flammable Liquids, Gases, and Volatile Solids.*

Additional Reading

Crowhurst, D., "Explosion Hazards in Dryers," *Fire Surveyor*, Vol. 8, No. 3 (June 1989), pp. 17-23.

Factory Mutual Engineering Corp., "Industrial Ovens and Dryers," *Loss Prevention Data Sheet 6-9*, Factory Mutual System, Norwood, MA, Oct. 1977.

Factory Mutual Engineering Corp., "Process Furnaces," *Loss Prevention Data Sheet 6-10*, Factory Mutual System, Norwood, MA, Nov. 1976.

Factory Mutual Engineering Corp., "Elements of Combustion, Controls, and Safeguards in Industrial Heating Equipment," *Loss Prevention Data Sheet 6-0*, Factory Mutual System, Norwood, MA, Sept. 1977.

Feirer, J. L., *Wood: Materials and Processes*, Bennett Publishing Co., Peoria, IL, 1980.

Gibson, N., Harper, D. J., and Rogers, R. l., "Evaluation of the Fire and Explosion Risk in Drying Powders," *Plant/Operation Progress*, Vol. 4, No. 3 (July 1985), pp. 181-189.

Gibson, T. O., "Loss Prevention Features Preform in Fuel Heater Loss Incident," *Plant/Operation Prgress*, Vol. 7, No. 4 (Oct. 1988), p. 258.

Grace, C., "Fluid Choice Takes the Steam Out of Unsafe Process Heaters," *Process Engineering*, (5), 1977, pp. 85, 87-88.

"Hazard and Hazard Prevention in Solvent Evaporating Ovens," *Fire Protection (127)*, 1978, pp. 22-25.

Holmes, J. G., Hedman, B. A., and Salama, S. Y., "Overview of Industrial Drying Needs and Competing Technologies," *Plant/Operation Progress*, Vol. 7, No. 3 (July 1988), pp. 199-203.

Jaffee, H. M., "Grain Elevator Protection, What's Being Done Today?" *Fire Journal*, Vol. 74, No. 3 (May 1980), pp. 131-132.

King, P. W. and Magid, J., *Industrial Hazard and Safety Handbook*, 3rd rev., Butterworth, Boston, MA, 1982.

Linville, J. L., ed., *Industrial Fire Hazards Handbook*, National Fire Protection Association, Quincy, MA, 1990.

McCoy, C. S., Dillenback, M. D., and Triax, D. J., "Major Fire in a Steam-Methane Reformer Furnace," *Plant/Operation Progress*, Vol. 5, No. 3 (July 1986), pp. 165-168.

Rasmussen, E. F., *Dry Kiln Operator's Manual*, Harwood Research Council, Memphis, TN, 1988.

Reed, R. D., *Furnace Operations*, 3rd ed., Gulf Publishing Co., Houston, TX, 198l.

Sparrow, R. E., "Firebox Explosion in a Primary Reformer Furnace," *Plant/Operation Progress*, Vol. 5, No. 2 (April 1986), pp. 122-128.

OIL QUENCHING

Revised by Raymond Ostrowski

One process in the heat treatment of metals is a controlled cooling or quenching of heated materials by immersion in a liquid quenching medium. This process hardens and tempers the metal by imparting metallurgical changes in its surface. Due to the combustible nature of quench oils, the process presents serious fire hazard potentials.

Additional hazard and protection information relevant to oil quenching can be found in the chapter entitled Section 2, Chapter 9, "Fluid Power Systems." Fire suppression information can be found in the "Suppression" section.

Contributing to the hazards of oil quenching are:

1. Special atmosphere requirements (a flammable gas blanketing the surface of the oil).
2. Temperature requirements of the quench medium.
3. Physical properties of the quench medium.
4. Volume limitations of the quench medium.
5. Size and configuration of process materials.
6. Locations of furnaces and quench tanks.
7. Mutual exposure between quenching and other processing or storage facilities.

Whether the quenching is an automatic and continuous, semiautomatic, or batch operation, it will involve elevators, conveyors, hoists, and cranes, either individually or in combination, to immerse the work in, move it through, and remove it from the oil bath. (See Figure 2-11A.) Although all three steps are important to the process, the one that is critical to safety is the entrance of the work into the quench.

QUENCHING OILS

In most cases, mineral oils are used for quenching, but specific metallurgical requirements may dictate the use of mixtures with animal or vegetable oils. In addition, wetting agents may be blended with certain oils or oil mixtures. In any case, it is important to use a quenching oil with a low viscosity.

Raymond Ostrowski is sales manager with Protection Controls, Inc., Skokie, Illinois.

Essential quench oil properties include the ability to remain stable over periods of extended usage and to retain fluidity. For unheated quenching, operating temperatures between 100 and 200°F (38 and 93°C) are considered normal. Standard quench oils for use in this temperature range usually have flash points somewhat above 300°F (149°C). For heated quenching, operating temperatures between 200 and 400°F (93 and 204°C) are common. Quench oils used at these temperatures generally have a flash point above 500°F (260°C).

POLYMER QUENCHING

A rather recent development is the use of polymer quenchant in integral quench furnaces. A furnace designed for oil is not designed for a quick change to polymer quenching. Caution should be observed and the original furnace manufacturer should be contacted prior to changing from oil to polymer quenchant.

QUENCH TANKS

A quench tank should allow proper quenching under normal conditions, and provide for minor variations in equipment control functions and operator error. The design of the tank freeboard, overflow drains, and liquid level control are all critical. A fire that is confined to the liquid surface within a tank is much more readily controlled and extinguished than a fire involving quench oil that has overflowed the tank.

The distance from the quench surface to the top of the tank, with the tank loaded to capacity, is known as the freeboard. Freeboard design should take into account the splashing to be expected when the maximum workload is immersed with maximum speed. The distance between the liquid level with the workload submerged and any openings in the tank wall should be not less than 6 in. (152 mm) below the door or any opening into the furnace.

Adequately sized, fully trapped overflow drains are important safety features for all oil quench tanks. They should direct the overflow to a safe location outside of buildings or into special tanks. As a practical matter, small quench tanks frequently may be installed without overflow drains. However, quench tanks with a liquid capacity of

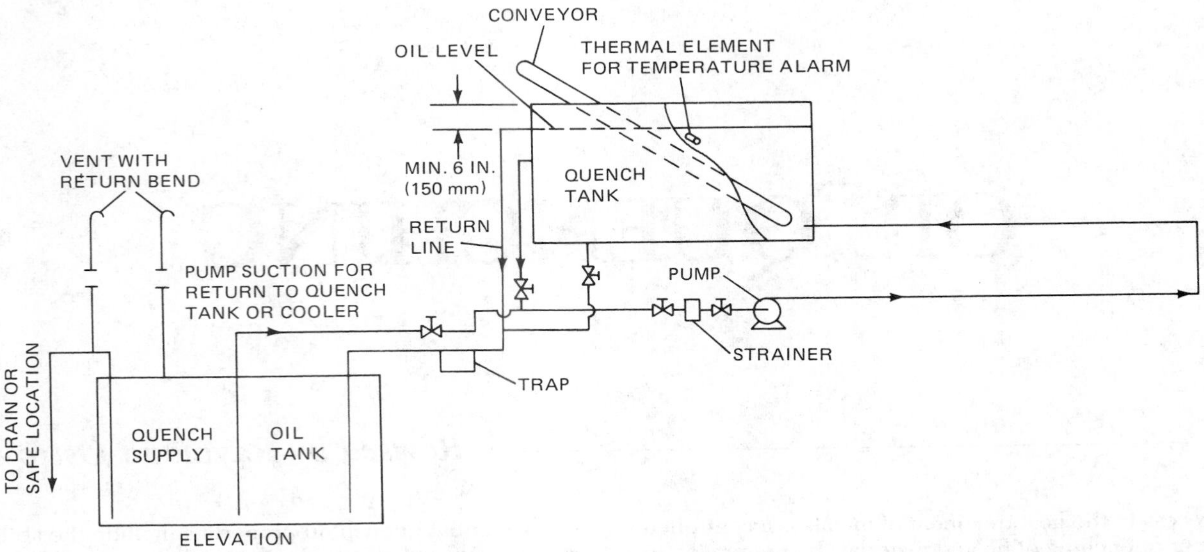

FIG. 2-11A. A schematic of a typical continuous-type oil quench tank. (Source: Factory Mutual Research Corp.)

150 gal (0.57 m^3) or a liquid surface area of 10 sq ft (0.9 m^2) or larger should be provided with overflow drains.

While overflow drains should be specifically designed for each tank, certain minimum sizes have been established and accepted. (See Table 2-11A.) For large quench tanks, multiple overflow pipes are preferable to a single large pipe, provided the aggregate cross-sectional area is equivalent to that of a single pipe. Piping connections on drains and overflow lines must be designed to permit ready access for inspection and cleaning.

TABLE 2-11A. ***Quench Tank Overflow Drains, Minimum Pipe Sizes***

Liquid Surface Area		Minimum Pipe Diameter (I.D.)	
sq ft	m^2	in.	mm
10–75	0.92–6.7	3	76
75–150	6.7–14	4	101
150–225	14–21	5	127
225–325	21–30.2	6	152
325+	30.2+	8	203

Emergency Drains

Under serious fire conditions, it may be necessary to empty a quench tank in order to reduce the amount of quench fluid available. This can be performed readily through adequately sized, fully trapped, and valved bottom drains directed to safe locations. Where gravity drainage is not possible, special pumps may be provided for oil removal. Drains and pumps should be sized so that the quench oil can be removed within 5 min. Gravity drains should be sized according to the tank capacities and drain diameters given in Table 2-11B.

Emergency drains must be used only under the guidance and control of well-trained and experienced personnel, as improper usage can result in greater hazards. Whenever a flammable gas processing atmosphere is maintained above the quench oil, removal of the oil can create a negative pressure that can result in explosion, an increase in fire severity, or both.

TABLE 2-11B. ***Gravity Drain Pipe Diameters, I.D.***

Tank Capacity		Pipe Diameter (I.D.)	
gal.	m^3	in.	mm
500–750	1.9–2.8	3	76
750–1000	2.8–3.8	4	101
1000–2500	3.8–9.5	5	127
2500–4000	9.5–15	6	152
Over 4000	Over 15	8	203

Tank Location

Heat-treating operations involving combustible quench oils should be housed in fire-resistive buildings and should be well separated from exit areas, combustible materials, valuable stock, power equipment, and important process equipment.

The safest location for quench tanks is at grade level. Boilover from tanks above grade can be expected to spread fire to floors below, thereby making fire control more difficult and significantly increasing the potential fire loss. Fires in below-grade locations will make manual fire fighting difficult and result in a significant increase in fire loss.

MATERIAL TRANSFER

Rapid and complete immersion of the work in process is essential to safe and proper heat-treating metallurgical processes. The method of immersion must result in minimal splashing and no overflow of the quench oil outside of the tank. It is also essential that the possibilities for partial immersion be eliminated or minimized. Partial immersion of the work is the most common cause of quench oil fires.

Chutes

Many furnaces are designed so that the work in process drops off the end of a conveyor, through a chute, and into the quench oil. The chute design and construction must allow the work to fall freely under all normal furnace feed conditions. This will involve proper chute sizing to accommodate the work, proper pitch to ensure continued stock motion, and smooth surfaces to prevent the work from being stuck in the chute. (See Figure 2-11B.)

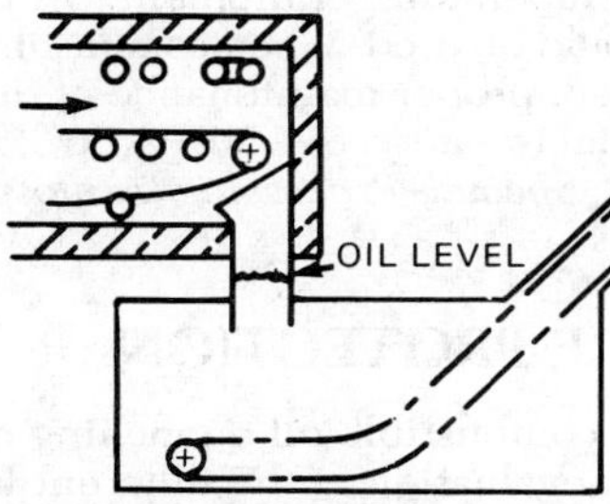

FIG. 2-11B. Bottom chute-type quench.

Elevators

When stock in process is handled on trays or in baskets, elevators are commonly used to immerse the work in the quench oil. (See Figures 2-11C and 2-11D.) Partial immersions are caused more by trays or baskets and elevators than by any other method. The following are three critical concerns:

1. The elevating mechanism must be adequately supported by structural members to prevent its falling unevenly.
2. Adequate guides must be provided to ensure uniform movement within the quench tank and to prevent an elevator from being wedged, as this could result in partial immersion.
3. Suitable guides and stops must be provided to prevent shifting of the workload, as this can cause elevator jamming and partial immersion.

Hoists and Cranes

A hoist or crane is usually required for moving large, specialized workloads into and out of the quench tank. Proper positioning of this equipment can be accomplished by stops and/or limit switches. Mechanical guides may be required to ensure that the work is properly positioned as it enters the quench tank.

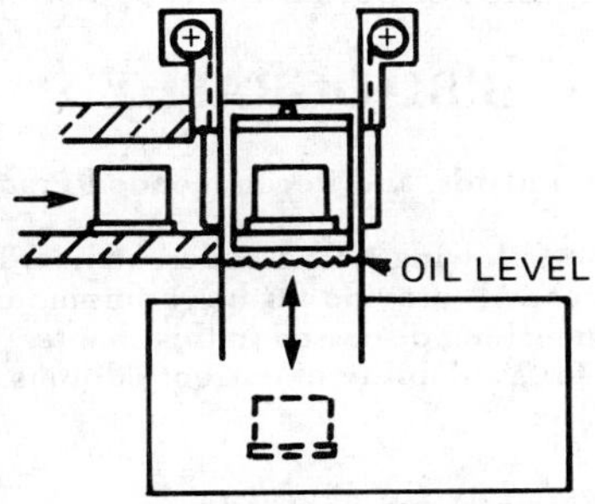

FIG. 2-11C. Dunk-type elevator quench.

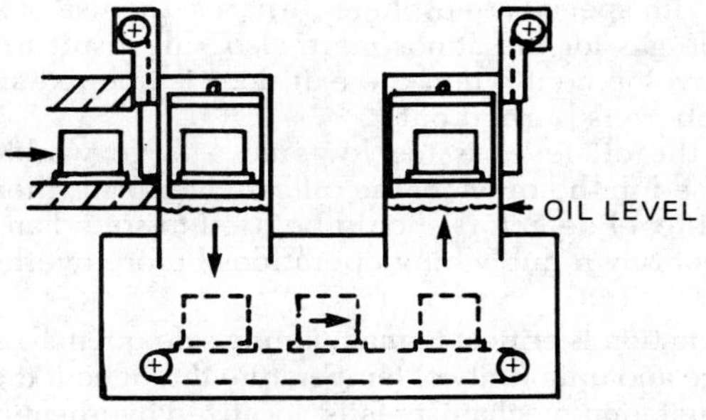

FIG. 2-11D. Transfer-type elevator quench.

Unless the oil drains off the work at the end of the quench period, an excessive amount of oil will be lost. Usually the work will still be warm at this time and some oil may vaporize. Any ignition source can produce a fire at this point in the process. Oil vapors will condense on cool surfaces above the drain area and thus contribute significantly to the potential fire loss.

OIL TEMPERATURE CONTROL

The control of quench oil temperature within specified design limits is essential to the heat-treating process as well as for safety. Failure of a cooling system can cause the oil to overheat. What is more hazardous, however, is a cooling system failure that allows water to enter the quenching oil. An excessive amount of water can produce a boilover when a hot workload is immersed in the quench. The exact critical water volume varies somewhat with the specific oil or oil mixtures being used, but if the water content reaches 0.50 percent by volume, the oil is no longer considered safe to use.

Quench oil can be cooled by water circulating through coils in the quench tank, by external heat exchangers, or by water jackets for the quench tank. Water jackets and internal water coils *should not* be used with combustible quenching oils. In these designs, any mechanical failure of the coil or the quench tank shell will result in water entering the quench medium. Such failures are not readily detectable; the first indication may be a boilover or a steam explosion when a hot workload is immersed in the quench.

If an external heat exchanger is used, quench oil must be circulated through the exchanger at a higher pressure than the exchange medium (water). If a leak should develop, oil will enter the water and be wasted. If the water pressure is higher than the oil pressure, such a leak would result in water entering the oil, creating a potential for boilover or steam explosion.

The continuous flow of cooling water is essential for temperature control. This can be properly supervised by observing the discharge from an open drain on the water side of the heat exchanger. Waterflow indicators are needed where a completely closed system must be used.

An oil quench tank is built as an integral part of many special atmosphere furnaces. In these cases, the vestibule above the quench tank is water-cooled, usually by water jackets. Many failures of the interior jacket walls have released cooling water into the quench tank below. As a result, safety considerations have dictated the use of special materials for vestibule jackets or the use of external coils. With special atmosphere furnaces, the use of a combustible gas for the atmosphere also will result in moisture development when the exit door is opened and the atmosphere is burned out.

If the oil level is too low and a large workload is immersed in the quench, the oil can overheat. Therefore, low-oil-level detectors should be used to sound an alarm and shut down quenching operations before overheating occurs.

Agitation is critical to maintaining safe quench oil temperature and uniformity of temperature throughout the bath. If the agitation mechanism fails, localized overheating will occur, which may cause a fire at the surface. Agitation failure and subsequent overheating can cause excessive vaporization, which can raise the pressure inside an enclosed special atmosphere furnace. Gas and oil vapor may then be forced out of the chamber around doors and through vents. Frequently, these escaping gases ignite, damaging the facilities. Agitation systems should be supervised automatically and their failure should result in the safe shutdown of operations.

Where the process requires that the quench be heated, i.e., fuel fired, electrically heated, or steam heated, immersion units are used as the heat source. All three methods of heating will create excessive temperatures at the interface of the heating unit and the quenching oil. A quench heating system should be prevented from operating if the oil level is too low, the agitation equipment is not functioning, or the oil temperature is too high. Where combustible oils are used, a separate excess high-limit temperature controller should be interlocked in the system to prevent quenching and to shut off the oil heating system when the oil temperature exceeds a specified maximum limit.

CENTRAL OIL SYSTEM

Many heat-treating plants utilize a quenching oil that is common to several operations. Properly designed central oil systems can contribute to the maintenance of reasonably dependable and problem-free oil quenching operations. A proper design includes filtering to remove particulate contamination, water removal for safety of operations and prevention of boilover, and cooling to deliver the quenching medium at an acceptable temperature.

Water separation can be accomplished by settling and the use of centrifuges. However, these systems are not dependable enough to eliminate the need for the oil in quench tanks to be tested periodically.

Since central systems involve a constant removal and replacement of oil from the quench tanks, it is essential for safety that oil flow be supervised. To avoid foaming and boilover, replenishment oil should not be added while the quench temperature is 212°F (100°C) or higher. Regardless of the oil being used, the temperature must never be permitted to rise to a value that is less than 50°F (28°C) below its flash point.

THE SAFEGUARDS

All automatic shutdowns of quenching operations should result in the workload being completely immersed in, or removed from, the quench. Partial immersion always must be considered hazardous.

Whenever movement of the workload into, or out of, the quench has been stopped by a malfunction, qualified operating personnel must be permitted to override the safety interlocks so that manual attempts can be made to complete immersion or remove the workload. If exit doors must be opened, a fire condition should be anticipated. Extinguishing facilities adequate to protect the operator and prevent property damage should be available.

All safety controls and their interlocking functions should be tested on a regular schedule. The time interval between tests should be adequate for each installation but should not exceed six months. Refer to manufacturers' guidelines.

Hydraulic control systems add to the fire hazard in the vicinity of high-temperature equipment. Fire-resistant hydraulic fluids should be used. When combustible hydraulic oils must be used, proper maintenance of the hydraulic equipment is vital to safety. See NFPA 86C, *Industrial Furnaces Using a Special Processing Atmosphere*, for detailed safeguards.

FIRE PROTECTION

Fire protection for combustible oil quenching operations requires a detailed evaluation of the inherent fire potentials. One of the most effective forms of area protection is the automatic water spray system. Experience has shown that these ceiling-mounted sprinkler systems will limit building and equipment damage from quench oil fires whether they are confined to the quench tank surface or spread over a large area by a quench oil boilover.

Specific protection for open quench tank surfaces and oil drainage areas is also important. Most oil fires can be extinguished by fixed carbon dioxide or dry chemical systems. In some operations, various foam systems can also be effective. However, the suitability of foam will be determined by the quenching oil used and the temperatures involved. These systems are designed to operate automatically, well in advance of any potential sprinkler system discharge.

Those situations that may require operating personnel to manually release jammed workloads and close furnace doors will dictate the provision of fire control and/or extinguishing facilities for the protection of the operator. In these instances, carbon dioxide or fixed water spray systems are the most effective. The most important fire protection features in every heat-treatment shop are the manual fire extinguishing and control equipment and plant personnel properly trained in its use. In addition to an adequate supply of portable, hand-carried fire extinguishers, the larger, wheeled extinguishers should also be available.

Appropriately spaced hose connections with water fog or water spray nozzles should be considered an essential part of all heat-treating area fire protection. These can provide prolonged periods of fire control and life safety beyond the limited supplies of portable extinguishers.

BIBLIOGRAPHY

NFPA Codes, Standards, and Recommended Practices

Reference to the following NFPA codes, standards, and recommended practices will provide further information on the safeguards for oil quenching discussed in this chapter. (See the latest *NFPA Catalog* for availability of current editions of the following documents.)

NFPA 10, *Portable Fire Extinguishers.*

NFPA 11, *Low Expansion Foam and Combined Agent Systems.*

NFPA 12, *Carbon Dioxide Extinguishing Systems.*

NFPA 13, *Installation of Sprinkler Systems.*

NFPA 14, *Standpipe and Hose Systems.*

NFPA 15, *Water Spray Fixed Systems for Fire Protection.*

NFPA 17, *Dry Chemical Extinguishing Systems.*

NFPA 34, *Dipping and Coating Processes Using Flammable or Combustible Liquids.*

NFPA 70, *National Electrical Code®.*

NFPA 86, *Ovens and Furnaces.*

NFPA 86C, *Industrial Furnaces Using a Special Processing Atmosphere.*

NFPA *101®*, *Life Safety Code®.*

Additional Reading

Benedetti, R. P., *Flammable and Combustible Liquids Code Handbook*, 3rd, National Fire Protection Association, Quincy, MA, 1987.

Factory Mutual System, "Oil Quenching of Metals," *Handbook of Industrial Loss Prevention* 2nd ed., McGraw-Hill, NY, 1967.

Flash Point Index of Trade Name Liquids, 9th ed., National Fire Protection Association, Quincy, MA, 1978.

Linville, J. L., ed., "Oil Quenching," *Industrial Fire Hazards Handbook*, 3rd ed., National Fire Protection Association, Quincy, MA, 1990.

SPRAY FINISHING AND POWDER COATING

Don R. Scarbrough

Spray application of coatings is a process basic to the manufacture of a broad variety of fabricated products, and a high percentage of factories operate at least one paint spray booth. Regardless of the purpose for which the coating is applied, flammable or combustible materials are commonly used in the process. Fires in paint operation areas develop very quickly, have high heat release rates, and produce large volumes of toxic smoke. Preventive and protective measures for control of these hazards must be undertaken with special attention to the peculiar hazards of each process.

TYPES OF COATINGS

Fluid Coatings

The most familiar atomizing device for fluid coatings is the air spray gun, which uses jets of high-pressure air to break up fluid into a fine mist. Another device commonly seen in high-volume production processing is the airless atomizer, which generates a spray of fluid by hydraulic means without using compressed air. Fluid pressures used with this type of atomizer range from 300 psi (2068 kPa) to approximately 3,000 psi (20 685 kPa).

Air and airless atomizers are also used in electrostatic spray operations. For this process, the appropriate atomizer is built into a spray gun that has a high-voltage electrical input. Voltages applied to the gun range from approximately 35,000 to somewhat over 100,000 V. There is less overspray with the electrostatic method than with the air or airless spray methods because the charged atomized particles are attracted to the grounded workpiece.

A third type of atomizer depends upon electrostatic forces for its operation. In its most common configuration, a sharp-edged disc with a diameter of 6 to 12 in. (152 to 305 mm) is mounted with its axis oriented vertically and is then charged electrically to about 100 kV. The disc is spun about its axis while the coating fluid is poured slowly onto the surface. Centrifugal force spreads the fluid into a thin film and carries it to the sharp edge of the disc, where the film is disrupted by electrostatic forces and sprayed in a 360-degree pattern. Workpieces are carried to the process zone by a conveyor and collect coating as they pass through. A form of this device that has gained popularity has the disc developed into the form of a cup or bell 2 or 3 in. (15 or 76 mm) in diameter that rotates at a high speed—sometimes approaching 60,000 rpm. Bell atomizers are frequently seen mounted in banks of 6 to 12 units at a single spray station.

Powder Coatings

A coating process that has gained broad acceptance is the application of organic coatings in the form of dry powder. In this process, the powder is first suspended in air and then charged electrostatically from a dc power supply operating between 60 and 120 kV. The powder is then directed toward the workpiece and held in place by electrostatic forces. The powder is formed into a continuous coating as it melts during passage through a process oven. The powder coating process differs substantially from the fluid coating processes because no organic solvents are used.

Electrostatic application of powder is most commonly accomplished with spray guns. These spray guns are simple devices to which a mixture of powder and air is fed through a single tube. A separate cable connected to the gun provides the high voltage necessary for operation of "corona-type" guns, while those that operate by frictional charging (referred to as "tribo-charging" guns) require no external source of high voltage.

Workpieces having dimensions less than approximately 4 in. (102 mm) can be powder coated with a device known as an electrostatic fluidized bed. In this process, powder is held in a container having an open top and a porous bottom through which an upward flow of air causes the powder mass to levitate or "fluidize." Charging electrodes near the surface impart an electrical charge to the powder. Electrically grounded workpieces pass over the surface of the bed and collect a coating of powder. The coating is then cured in a baking oven.

Don R. Scarbrough is product safety staff consultant for the Nordson Corporation, Westlake, Ohio.

Athough they are not widely used, there are techniques for applying dry powder coatings without the use of electrostatics. These processes typically involve preheating the workpiece to a temperature substantially above the melting point of the powder and then applying the powder, either by dipping the workpiece into a fluidized bed or by spraying air-suspended powder directly onto the hot surface of the workpiece. The powder melts immediately upon contact and flows to form a film, which is subsequently cured in a bake oven.

SPRAY PROCESS EQUIPMENT AND COMPONENTS

Fluid Supply

Air spray guns draw their coating fluid from either small cups mounted on the guns, or through hoses connected to larger pressurized containers called paint tanks or pressure pots that have capacities varying from 10 to 60 gal (38 to 227 L). In very high production arrangements, the coating may be fed by a pump from a bulk tank.

To ensure satisfactory results, industrial coating mixtures are usually modified shortly before spraying by the addition of solvents to adjust viscosity. A safety tank or container is used to reduce the possibility of a flammable liquid spill while handling or transporting this blended material.

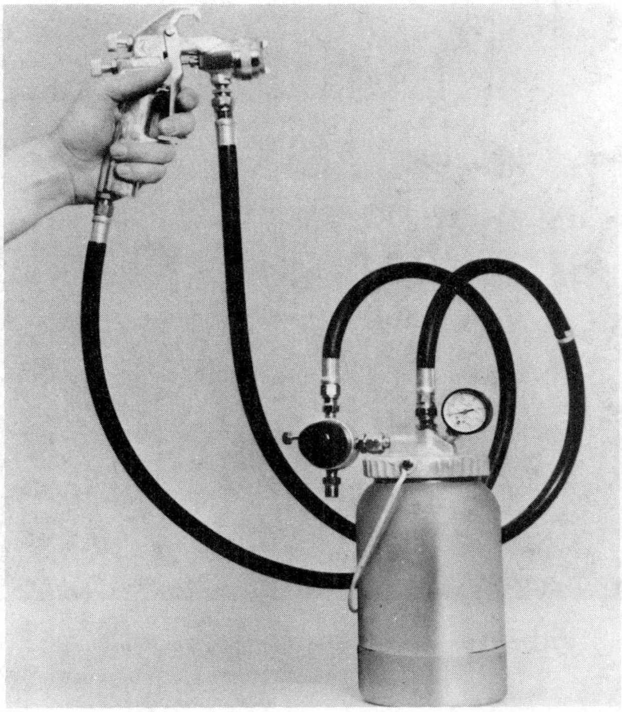

FIG. 2-12A. Hand air spray gun with fluid supplied from 2-qt (1.9 L) pressure pot. (Source: DeVilbiss)

Spray Guns and Devices

Among the various forms of industrial air spray guns, the two most commonly used are the pistol grip hand spray gun and the machine-mounted automatic air spray gun. Air is supplied to the hand spray gun through one hose, while fluid is either hose fed or drawn from a gun-mounted container. (See Figure 2-12A.)

Electrical grounding of airless spray guns to drain off static electricity generated during spraying is provided through a wire or conductive layer built into the fluid hose. A manual safety lock is usually provided on hand units to secure the trigger and prevent accidental actuation.

Hand-held and automatic electrostatic spray guns have electrically nonconducting extensions at the front end to insulate the energized components from the grounded parts. In addition to being connected to coating fluid and air supplies, these guns are also connected to high-voltage power supplies. Voltage at the atomizer is in the 30 to 75 kV range for hand-held units and in the 30 to 120 kV range for automatic units. In hand spray guns of this type, the cable carrying the high-voltage power to the gun also supplies an electrical ground for the pistol grip and trigger. To prevent electrical sparking from accidental contact of the charged elements of the gun with a grounded object, the cable is usually terminated at the gun in an electrical resistance on the order of 75 to 250 MΩ (megohm). Some automatic electrostatic spray guns are not equipped with a high-impedance termination, but rely on the process control approach of maintaining separation between gun and workpiece to prevent electrical sparking.

Figure 2-12B shows an electrostatic disc surrounded by chairs hanging from a conveyor loop. Immediately above the disc is its motor drive. Partially obscured, at the top of the illustration, is a device that moves the disc up and down, enabling it to coat workpieces over the entire height of the carriers. Separate electrical and fluid inputs are remotely controlled. Discs commonly are equipped with variable voltage power supplies that can be adjusted over a range of approximately 50 to 120 kV. Since considerable electrical energy is stored on the disc, adequate distance must be maintained between it and the workpiece to prevent sparking.

Spray Booths

A spray booth is a power-ventilated structure used to enclose a spraying operation. While in most cases the booth structure physically surrounds the spray operation, some configurations leave the spray operation unenclosed and surround the operation with a controlled stream of air drawn into the booth.

The most popular type of spray booth is the "open face" or "open front" arrangement. It is a boxlike structure that has one open side. The ventilation system associated with the booth may provide an airflow horizontal to the floor (cross draft) or vertical to the floor (down draft) as demanded by process requirements.

For some operations, such as production finishing of automotive bodies, a tunnel spray booth is used. (See Figure 2-12C.) This structure is virtually always arranged with vertical down draft ventilation and a horizontal floor-mounted conveyor running the length of the tunnel. Makeup air is introduced through special ductwork and air diffusers in the ceiling.

FIG. 2-12B. Electrostatic disc. (Source: Ransburg)

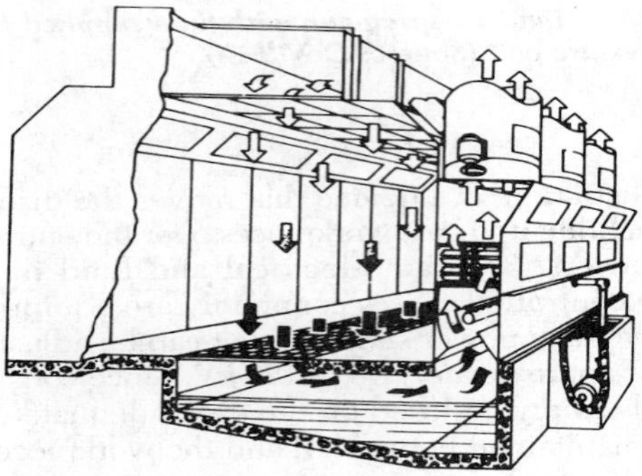

FIG. 2-12C. Tunnel booth. (Source: Binks)

Special-Purpose Enclosures

Continuous coaters: These enclosures are individually engineered for a specific coating process. Within the coater enclosure is an array of spray guns which apply coatings to workpieces that pass through the coater at conveyor speeds between 100 and 600 fpm (30 and 183 m/min). The entry and exit vestibules are equipped with exhaust shrouds to capture any vapors or minor amounts of overspray that drift out from the main enclosure. Most of the overspray is collected in a sump and drawn off through a pumping system, which recycles the coating into the coating process.

Decorating machines: These machines are used in conjunction with masking devices to paint stripes or other patterns on workpieces, such as automobile side moldings. The mask is mounted in the opening beneath the row of cylinders at the front of the machine, and the workpiece is placed face down on the mask. When the operating cycle is started, air-driven pistons in the row of cylinders clamp the work to the machine. Spray guns inside the cabinet automatically tilt in one direction and travel the length of the workpiece. At the end of the workpiece, the spray guns tilt in the opposite direction and travel back to the starting point. The air-driven clamps automatically release the work at the end of the operation.

An exhaust system draws fresh air in through the grill at the front of the machine, and internal filters remove overspray from the air vapor stream before it is exhausted. Since the process is totally enclosed, the risk of escaping vapors or overspray and subsequent ignition is significantly diminished.

Spray Rooms

The size, shape, and weight of some workpieces may make the use of spray booths impractical. When this is the case, an entire room dedicated to the spray process is a legitimate alternative. Such rooms, called spray rooms, are classified as hazardous areas. Power ventilation removes the combustible vapors that are released during the process, but velocities are not high enough to capture particulate matter. Therefore, overspray is permitted to settle to the floor where it accumulates as a combustible residue until it is removed by a mechanical cleaning process. Vapor removal systems are most effective when the exhaust intake is located along one wall within 1 ft (0.3 m) of the floor and the makeup air is introduced along the opposite wall.

Open-Floor Spraying

A spray operation conducted without a spray booth and in an area not separated by a partition from general factory operations is called open-floor spraying. Depending upon the quantity of volatiles to be released in the operation and existing ventilation within the building, forced ventilation may or may not be provided. Whether forced or not, adequate ventilation must be provided to prevent accumulation of flammable concentrations of vapor. Particulate overspray materials are allowed to settle to the floor and their residues are removed by mechanical means. Ignition sources incidental to other factory operations are a great concern whenever open-floor spray techniques are used, and it is common to establish a buffer zone surrounding the spray area for about a 20-ft (6 m) radius to separate processes.

Overspray Collectors

Vapor and overspray removal systems associated with spray booths or enclosures typically include a fan to create an airflow, and a collection system which separates and collects particulate matter from the airstream and exhausts vapors to the exterior of the building. Overspray collectors can generally be placed into one of four categories, as follows.

Baffle maze: The baffle maze consists of a series of flat panels arranged in a staggered pattern through which the airstream is directed. A substantial portion of its particulate burden is removed by direct impaction and collection upon the surface of the dry baffle panels where it remains until removed by mechanical cleaning. Such systems are of limited efficiency and permit appreciable amounts of fine particulates to pass through.

Dry filter: Collectors using paper or fiberglass filter elements are called dry filters and are popular for low-to-intermediate volume spray operations. The typical filter used in this type of collector is a replaceable element approximately 20 in. (508 mm) square and perhaps 2 in. (51 mm) thick. Particulate residues are permitted to accumulate on the filter until a significant obstruction of the airflow through the filter is noted, then the fouled filters are discarded and replaced.

Waterfall and cascade scrubbers: Where high-volume spray coating operations are conducted for several hours a day, waterfall or cascade scrubbers are commonly used. The exhaust airstream is either scrubbed directly by sprays of water coming from nozzles or it follows a path that takes it through several stages of waterfall. Figure 2-12D is an example of one variation of this type of scrubber. Particulate matter is accumulated in a water tank from which it is removed either manually or automatically by a sludge removal device.

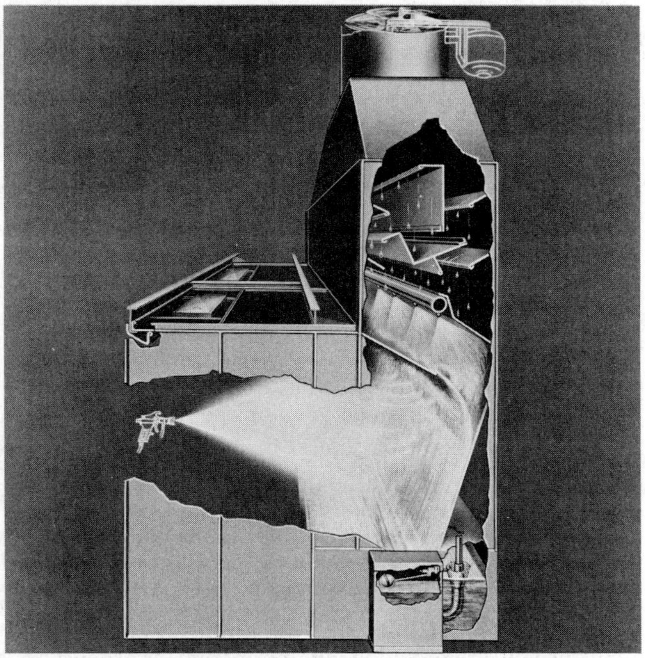

FIG. 2-12D. Water wash booth. (Source: DeVilbiss)

Chemical compounds must be added to the water to prevent paint residues from adhering to the walls or piping thereby creating open channels through the water curtain. Air passing through these open channels will not be adequately cleansed and will carry particulate matter into the exhaust system; the particulate matter may be deposited on the lining of the exhaust stack, on exhaust fan blades, or on the roof of the building.

Venturi scrubbers: Perhaps the most efficient overspray collector is the venturi scrubber. This device directs the exhaust airflow through a narrow throat (venturi) through which a high-velocity spray of water is also directed. Virtually all particulate matter is extracted from the airstream and trapped in the water. The water is processed through a tank where residues are removed by settling and skimming. The same chemical compounds mentioned in the discussion of the waterfall-type scrubber must be added to the water used in this system to prevent plugging and blocking of nozzles. Figure 2-12E is a schematic of a venturi scrubber.

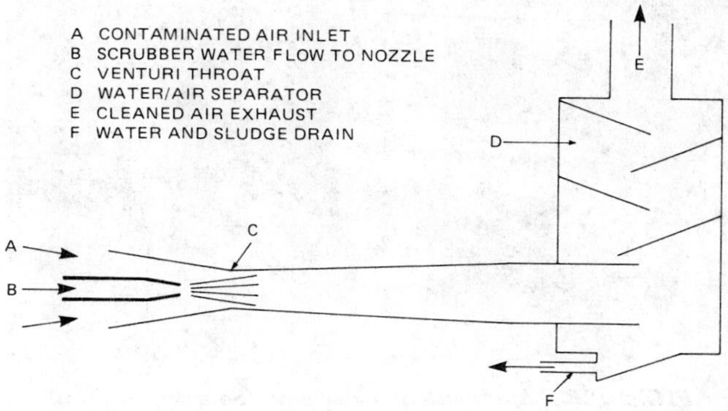

FIG. 2-12E. Venturi scrubber. (Source: Nordson)

POWDER COATING PROCESS EQUIPMENT AND COMPONENTS

Spray Process

The powder coating spray process utilizes a device called a feeder that mixes powder with air and supplies the mixture to the spray guns. The powder may be contained in a fluidized bed or in a hopper having an inverted cone-shaped bottom. Feeders may supply a single gun or several guns with a separate ejector for each gun.

The most common coating powder is epoxy powder, but others include acrylic, polyester, vinyl, nylon, butyrate, polyolefin, and alkyd. These powders are shipped from the manufacturer to the user in containers of 25 to 100 lb (11.34 to 45.36 kg) capacity. They may be classified as ordinary combustibles and, as such, may be stored without requirements for extra-hazard protection.

Spray guns used for the electrostatic application of dry powders do not differ greatly in appearance from guns used for the electrostatic application of fluids. (See Figure 2-12F.) Since no atomization is required, the functions of the spray gun are simply to control the shape of the spray pattern and to impress a high-voltage charge upon the powder cloud. Powder and electrostatic power input connections may be made at the rear of the barrel or from below to the base of the grip and the forward portion of the barrel. Connections to automatic guns typically are made at the rear.

Electrostatic power supplies rectify stepped-up common ac line voltage inputs, either 115 or 230 V, to produce dc output ranging from 30 to 100 kV. Several automatic guns may be connected to a single power supply. For hand-gun applications, however, a separate power supply is provided for each gun, and each supply has a control circuit that prevents the pack from being energized unless the trigger is actuated.

The interconnection between power supply and spray gun is usually made through a high-voltage coaxial cable. At the termination of the cable within the spray gun, the

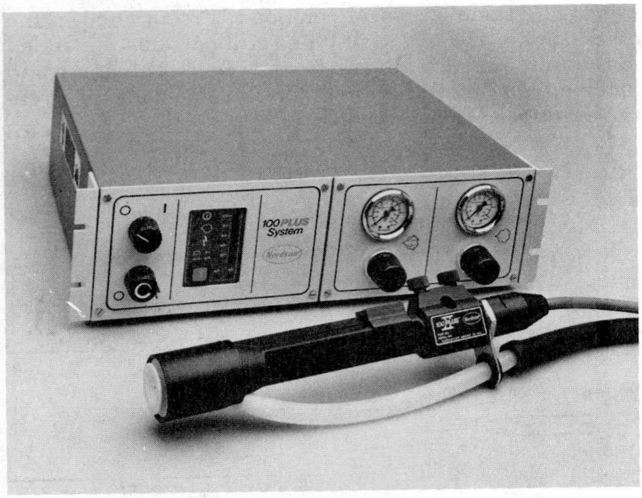

FIG. 2-12F. Automatic powder gun. (Source: Nordson)

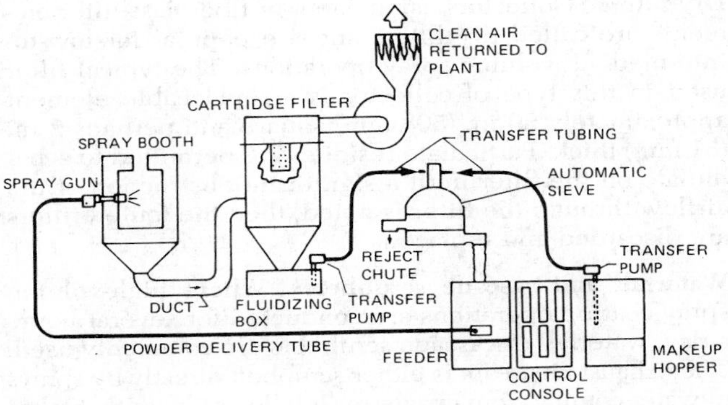

FIG. 2-12G. Diagram of automatic recycle of a single-color powder-coating system showing the booth, collector, fan, and filter. (Source: Nordson)

charging circuit is connected to the gun electrode through a 75 to 250 megohm resistor. In operation, a faint blue glow, called a corona, is developed around the end of the electrode which projects through the front of the gun. Individual powder particles are charged as they pass through the corona.

In a class of equipment commonly referred to as "tribo-charging guns," no external power supply or cable is used. These devices generate static charge directly upon the surface of the powder granules through frictional contact between the high-velocity airborne granules and internal surfaces of the apparatus.

A common facility in which electrostatic powder spray operations are conducted is a spray booth with a hopper bottom through which exhaust air is drawn into a ductwork that leads to a powder collector. A cloth or fabric filter within the collector separates the powder from the airstream. Powder separated within the collector falls to the bottom of the hopper from which it is extracted and is subsequently reintroduced to the feeder for the spray guns. A basic outline of this arrangement is shown in Figure 2-12G.

A more recent development is the integration of the spray booth and powder recovery system into a single structure. (See Figure 2-12H.) In this equipment, cartridge-type filters and the exhaust fan are built into the structure of the spray booth. The ductwork, which conventionally would separate the booth from the powder collector, is eliminated. Collected powder is pneumatically pumped from the hoppers immediately beneath the recovery filters directly back to the spray gun feeders. Within the last 10 years this arrangement has gained dominance in new installations. A further development that has gained broad acceptance is the use of flame-retardant plastics for the spray enclosure.

Electrostatic powder coating can also be conducted within an enclosure commonly referred to as a pipe coater. The device consists of a steel enclosure, a ring of automatic electrostatic powder spray guns, and a conveyor. The workpiece enters at one end, passes through a cloud of coating powder, and leaves the coater at the opposite end. The workpiece is preheated to a temperature above the melting point of the powder, so the powder will fuse upon contact. The coater is provided with an exhaust system and powder recovery filter system similar to that used with the booth arrangement described in connection with Figure 2-12G.

Fluidized Bed

Fluidized beds may be constructed in a wide variety of sizes. They have vertical walls (typically steel) and a porous floor (textile or plastic). Air flows upward through the floor and through the powder. When the airstream is adjusted properly, the powder will behave as a liquid, flowing readily around, and contacting all surfaces of any object that is dipped into it. It will immediately fuse to a workpiece that has been preheated above the melting point of the powder. After the workpiece has been removed from the bed, it is placed in an oven to complete the curing of the coating.

An electrostatic fluidized bed has a series of high-voltage electrodes near the surface of the fluidized powder mass. Grounded workpieces, which may or may not be preheated, pass over the electrodes and are coated electrostatically, then cured in a bake oven.

Both regular and electrostatic fluidized bed arrangements usually are provided with peripheral air exhaust systems that collect any powder grains escaping the bed and prevent their distribution into the general factory area.

FLUID SPRAY PROCESS HAZARDS AND CONTROL

Materials and supplies used in organic spray finishing processes are usually flammable or combustible, are often toxic, and, in some cases, may be highly reactive or unstable. For these reasons, spray finishing operations are considered hazardous, and suitable preventive and protective measures should be taken to minimize the hazards.

Fire Prevention

Hazard identification: Materials' hazards should be identified and marked upon containers as soon as they arrive in the facility. A detailed method of identification is con-

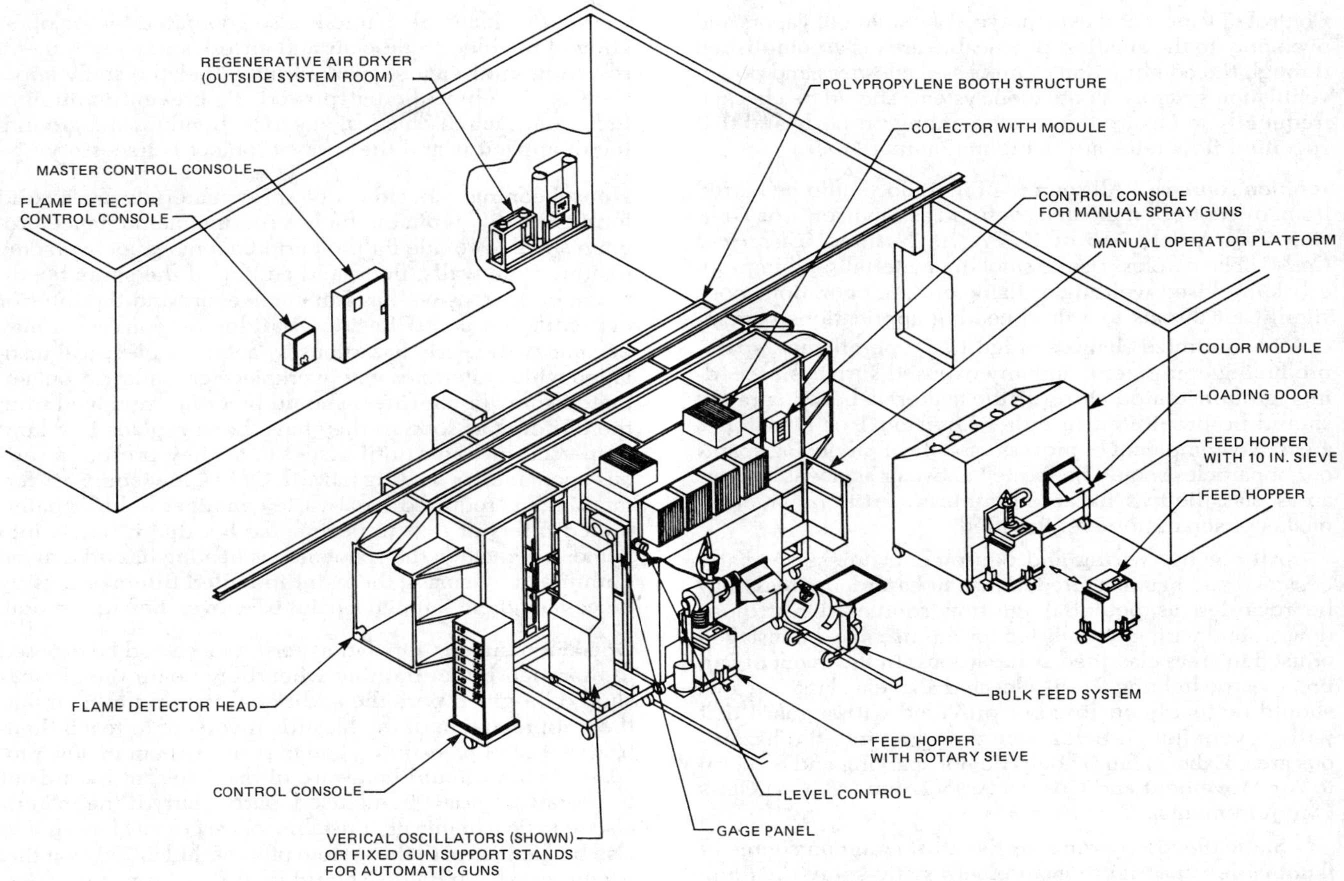

FIG. 2-12H. Integrated powder spray booth/recovery system. (Source: Nordson)

tained in NFPA 704, *Identification of the Fire Hazards of Materials*. The NFPA 704 system provides for the identification of five degrees of health, flammability, and reactivity hazards.

Storage and handling: Bulk supplies of flammable liquids should be stored outdoors, away from buildings. Smaller quantities are then brought indoors to a mixing room where they are prepared for use. The mixing room should be located adjacent to an outside wall provided with explosion-relief vents, and should be isolated from the rest of the building by fire-resistive construction. The room should have sufficient mechanical ventilation to prevent the development of flammable vapor concentrations in the explosive range. All flammable liquid containers of greater than 5-gal (19 L) capacity that are kept indoors should be equipped with a special plug that incorporates a pressure-relief valve, a vacuum-relief valve, and a flame arrester.

Prepared coating materials are transported from the mix room to the spray area in containers or through piping. Containers should be equipped with tightly clamped lids that will retain vapors and liquids in the event the container is upset. Piping should be identified as process pipe containing flammable materials, and a shutoff valve should be installed at each point where a hose is connected to the system. Emergency stop controls and fire alarm interlocks are very important to keep runaway pumps from continuing to feed a fire after hoses have been burned off. All piping, pumps, and supply and receiving vessels must be electrically grounded and bonded to prevent accumulation of dangerous static electrical charges during transfer of fluids.

Quantities of flammable or combustible liquids kept in or near process areas should be limited to the amount needed for one working shift at a time. The materials should be put in closed containers equipped with appropriate pressure-relief devices and flame arresters at all openings.

Flammable or combustible liquids should never be transferred from one container to another by the application of air pressure to the original shipping container. Pressurizing such containers may cause them to rupture, creating a serious flammable liquid spill. Any pressure vessels used should be designed specifically for such use and be manufactured in conformance with the American Society of Mechanical Engineers' (ASME) *Code for Unfired Pressure Vessels*.

Fluid hoses connected to some electrostatic equipment must have a special structure to resist both fluid and high-voltage electrical stresses that result from use of electrically conductive paint. If ordinary hose or tube is substituted for this use, electrical failure of the hose wall will lead to pinhole failures and ignition of fires.

Control of vapors and overspray: Limitation of vapors and overspray to the smallest practicable area is accomplished through the combination of process enclosures and power ventilation systems. Ventilation systems should be checked frequently to ensure they are operating properly and that specified flow rates are being maintained.

Ignition sources: All sources of ignition should be barred from, or controlled in, areas defined as Division 1 or Division 2 in Article 516 of NFPA 70, *National Electrical Code®*. The careless use of smoking materials and improperly supervised welding or flame cutting operations pose significant threats to a fluid coating applications system.

To minimize chances of ignition, open flames, spark-producing equipment, and any exposed surfaces exceeding ignition temperature of the material being sprayed should be prohibited in either Division 1 or Division 2 areas. No equipment or process capable of producing sparks or hot particles should be located above or adjacent to those areas classified as hazardous unless partitions or other means of separation are provided.

All electric wiring and equipment, unless specially designed and manufactured for use in hazardous areas, may be regarded as potential ignition sources. Only those devices and wiring types listed for this use may be installed or used in areas classified as hazardous. In the event of failure, electric lighting fixtures located above a classified area should be totally enclosed or provided with a guard that will prevent hot particles from dropping into the hazardous area. Exhaust fans should be nonsparking and conform to Air Movement and Control Association (AMCA) Class C requirements.

Static electricity remains the most common source of flammable vapor ignition in electrostatic spray finishing operations. Energized electrodes send generous amounts of electrical charge into the air, and it then collects upon surrounding surfaces. Accumulation of this charge may raise a surface to a high voltage. Electrostatic spray systems should be equipped with electrical interlocks to de-energize the electrostatic power supply any time the spray guns are not actually in use. Most modern electrostatic spray guns that are listed for use with flammables include a charging circuit that limits the energy of a discharge arc to a value below that which is sufficient to cause ignition.

Electrostatic ignition can be prevented by electrically bonding together all the elements of a fluid transfer or spray system along with the workpiece and all other electrically conductive objects located within 10 ft (3 m) of the charged elements, and then grounding the bond. Additional information on bonding and grounding can be found in NFPA 77, *Static Electricity*.

Human beings are also conductors of electricity; thus, the spray operator cannot be overlooked in the grounding process. Gripping the grounded spray gun with the bare hand or wearing shoes with electrically conductive soles, provided the floor is grounded, are two workable methods for grounding the operator. Even in the absence of electrostatic equipment, dangerous static electrical charges can be generated by the simple act of walking across a spray area floor that is covered with sticky paint residue. The charging mechanism is identical to that seen in the more familiar act of walking across a wool or nylon carpet on a dry day: a spark and shock results when a doorknob or switchplate is touched. That spark is quite capable of igniting flammable vapors.

Static electrical charge is also generated by the operation of nonelectrostatic air and airless spray equipment, resulting in discharge sparks from either the spray apparatus or the object being sprayed. To prevent ignition of fires from such discharges, electrical bonding and grounding of apparatus and the sprayed object is necessary.

Housekeeping: Residues of spray materials are a solid form of readily ignitable fuel. A routine maintenance program should provide for the periodic removal of overspray residue from walls, floor, and ceiling of the spray booth, room, or area, as well as from conveyors and the interior of ventilation ducts. Residue buildup on conveyors may become particularly hazardous by acting as electrical insulation which interferes with workpiece grounding. Contaminated spray booth filters should be either removed from the building as soon as they have been replaced, or kept immersed in water until disposal, as they present a serious spontaneous heating hazard. Only a few hours of "fermenting" is required for a waste container holding paint-fouled filters or rags to become so hot that it bursts into flame. Alternately, the spontaneous heating hazard may be eliminated by curing the paint in fouled filters or rags by processing them through a paint bake oven before disposal.

Operator training: Operating personnel should be exposed to thorough initial training when they begin the job and should be given periodic additional training to maintain their appreciation of the hazards involved, to teach them hazard control procedures, and to educate them in new processes. They should be aware of the inherent hazards of the spray materials being used, particularly if the materials are toxic, chemically unstable, or reactive. They should also be familiar with the system of hazard identification that is employed. Operators should be drilled in proper operating, bonding and grounding, emergency, and maintenance procedures.

Fire Protection

Areas in which fluid spray processes are conducted and areas where coatings and solvents are mixed or stored should be separated from other plant operations by appropriate distance or partitions. Automatic sprinklers inside spray booths, ventilation ducts, and at the ceiling contribute considerably to the control of fire. In open areas, draft curtains extending down from the ceiling around spraying operations, along with smoke and heat vents, will slow the "mushrooming" of hot combustion gases along the ceiling and thus limit the number of sprinklers that will activate. This will concentrate sprinkler discharge into the area where it is most needed and will minimize smoke and heat interference with fire fighting efforts.

Any fluid transfer or supply system for flammables, whether driven by pump or by pressure vessel, should be arranged with emergency shutdown provisions to interrupt flow in the event of fire or accidental spill, thereby limiting available fuel.

Portable fire extinguishers and standpipe hoses are useful against fires involving small spray operations. The rate of fire development across residue accumulations is very high, however. It must be recognized that in only a few seconds a fire can grow to a size that will be beyond portable extinguisher control, particularly in spray booths of the baffle- or the dry-filter type or in operations where paint residues are permitted to accumulate on the floor. For enclosed or semi-enclosed coating processes, such as in continuous coaters or automatic decorating machines, automatic fire extinguishing systems may be used to flood the interior of the machines.

A spray booth and its exhaust ductwork should maintain structural integrity (i.e., not collapse) during a fire of nominal proportions so that the major portion of flame, heat, and fire gases produced will vent from the building through the exhaust ductwork, thereby diminishing the chances of fire spread in the building. Spray booths and their exhaust ductwork are required by various codes and standards to be constructed of steel, masonry, or other material of equivalent fire resistance. Survivability of booth structure is considerably enhanced by the cooling effect of water from sprinklers inside the stack and booth. The probability that heat from a fire within a booth and stack will ignite nearby combustible materials can be reduced to an acceptable level by reasonable clearances between any combustible structure or stored materials and the surfaces of the booth or stack. (For recommended clearances, see NFPA 33, *Spray Application Using Flammable and Combustible Materials*.) Spray rooms are usually required to be separated from other occupancies within the same building by walls, floors, and ceiling structures with a minimum two-hour fire-resistance rating.

POWDER COATING PROCESS HAZARDS AND CONTROL

Powder coating operations using combustible organic powders are classified as hazardous processes because the powders can burn vigorously when suspended as airborne dusts and can explode when confined. There are no flammable vapors in the powder coating process, and the energy required to ignite a cloud of air-suspended coating powder is from 100 to 1000 times higher than that required to ignite flammable vapors.

Fire Prevention

Storage and handling: Coating powders that are kept in shipping containers are not customarily classified as hazardous materials and are commonly stored under conditions appropriate for ordinary combustible materials. Reasonable care is required in the handling and movement of the powder containers because a fire hazard could be created should the containers be broken and the powder distributed as an air-suspended cloud of dust.

Waste powder is commonly packaged into fiber drums or cardboard cartons lined with plastic bags and shipped to a landfill for disposal in accordance with Environmental Protection Agency (EPA) regulations. If the waste container has been processed through a baking cycle, the waste powder will have fused into a solid block of plastic that is no longer vulnerable to scattering if the container is broken.

Coating operations: Virtually all spray powder coating processes are conducted in spray booths that are more tightly enclosed and permit considerably less overspray to escape than those booths used for fluid coating processes. All connections in the hoses and piping associated with pneumatic transfer equipment should be routinely checked to confirm that they are secure and that ground connections are in place. Breakage of any such connection during operation could create a substantial hazard by blowing powder into the workspace air outside the process enclosure.

To prevent the escape of powder, the spray booth must have adequate ventilation that provides effective capture velocity at all its openings. Minimum average velocities are considered to be in the vicinity of 60 fpm (18 m/min). Interlocks should be installed to permit operation of the powder application equipment only while the ventilation equipment is in operation and, similarly, to permit operation of the electrostatic power supply only during the time the powder is actually being applied.

Ignition sources: The control methods for ignition sources for powder coating are similar to those for spray finishing.

Static accumulations on electrically isolated conductive objects are the major cause of fires in electrostatic powder coating installations. Metal workpieces suspended from conveyor hangers that do not provide an effective electrical circuit between the workpiece and ground pass through the coating process zone while discharging hot electrical sparks. This sparking can ignite the powder cloud, and flaming will be sustained by the continuing flow of powder and air. In an electrostatic fluidized bed, the entire volume of the bed can become involved in fire.

Some application equipment will discharge incendiary sparks when approached too closely by a grounded object. Proper use of this type of equipment requires safeguards to prevent any grounded object from approaching the electrically charged high-voltage elements closer than twice the sparking distance. Discharge sparks that do occur during use of this type of equipment are usually traceable to improper racking of parts on a conveyor or swinging of the conveyor racks. To reduce the probability of a small fallen part being drawn into a duct and producing mechanical sparking, grillwork at the intake of any exhaust duct is highly recommended, and magnetic devices can be added to catch tramp metal.

Fire Protection

Protective measures for powder coating installations are: (1) keep the powder collector from becoming involved in a fire that has originated in the spray operation, (2) equip the collector with pressure-relief vents and ductwork in order to prevent its rupture in an explosion, and (3) protect the building from heat and pressure effects that would be generated by an explosion.

To prevent a fire in a powder spray booth from spreading through connecting ductwork, the ventilation system is usually arranged to keep powder concentrations in the ductwork below one-half the minimum explosible concentration (MEC). In those cases where fire has persisted in the spray booth for periods ranging beyond approximately 15 sec, however, the powder collector is threatened by glowing embers that have formed in the spray fire. These glowing embers are independent of powder concentration and are capable of igniting the powder collector.

Powder collectors can be protected by a fast-acting flame detector within the spray booth, interlocks to shut down equipment, and a fast-acting damper to interrupt airflow in the duct between the spray booth and the powder collector. In operation, this apparatus will recognize any flame that has ignited in the spray booth and respond quickly (within ½ sec) to the flame by shutting down all process equipment energy supplies (including electricity and compressed air) and by closing the ductwork damper. This same equipment can be arranged to extend the response sequence by discharging an inerting gas into the dust collector.

For those application systems that require operation with combustible concentrations of powder in the ductwork between the application area and the powder collector, a potential exists for almost instantaneous involvement of the collector whenever a fire occurs in the application area. Such systems should either be equipped with appropriately engineered suppression systems or designed in such a manner that the powder application and collection equipment will be fire and explosion resistant.

Airborne clouds of powder in a confined space will burn at far higher rates than in unconfined space. Since the interior of a conventional dust collector is a confined space, steps must be taken to accommodate the sudden pressurization and volumes of smoke and fire gases that will evolve in the event of ignition. The usual protective technique used is to install automatic pressure-relief vents in the collector housing. These vents will open should an ignition occur and allow the combustion products to escape, thereby limiting pressure development. When the collector is located within a building, ductwork is usually required to direct the vented combustion products to the exterior of the building or to a safe location. Vent ductwork must be kept short. Lengths in excess of 10 ft (3 m) are of questionable value.

If powder escapes, it will collect on horizontal surfaces and create a potential for a secondary explosion. The primary explosion may throw loose powder into the air in suspension where it could be ignited by flames or embers that persist from the initial combustion. If a substantial quantity of powder is thrown into suspension by the primary explosion, the secondary explosion could be considerably more serious than the primary. Protection is achieved primarily through: (1) maintenance of process equipment, (2) procedures, and (3) through scrupulous housekeeping to collect any powder that does escape.

The dust explosion hazard is virtually eliminated (through elimination of the confined space necessary to form an explosion) in an integrated spray booth/collector of the type shown in Figure 2-12H and in other apparatus incorporating the same design principles. This class of equipment, since it operates without explosion risk, needs no explosion vent or ductwork. However, flame detectors are still needed—when automatic spray guns are used—to quickly interrupt powder feed in the event of fire and thereby limit heat damage and formation of toxic smoke.

After ignition of a spray gun powder cloud or a fluidized bed, the flame can usually be extinguished almost instantly by simply turning off the spray gun feeder or the air supply to the fluidized bed. The normal velocity of the feed systems exceeds typical flame-front propagation velocities and flame therefore does not backstream in hoses from guns to feeders, even though powder concentrations in hoses may exceed MEC.

Automatic sprinkler systems are commonly required in factory areas where powder coating operations take place. Because sprinklers have rather long operating delays relative to the duration of a powder fire (in a system equipped with automatic flame detectors), it is common for powder fires to be extinguished by shutting down the equipment before sprinklers can activate. In those cases where small fires have persisted in spray booth residues, portable water fire extinguishers or sprinklers arranged to protect the filter cartridges or bags have been found to be adequate.

BIBLIOGRAPHY

NFPA Codes, Standards, and Recommended Practices

Reference to the following NFPA codes, standards, and recommended practices will provide further information on the safeguards for spray finishing and powder coating discussed in this chapter. (See the latest *NFPA Catalog* for availability of current editions of the following documents.)

NFPA 10, *Portable Fire Extinguishers.*

NFPA 13, *Installation of Sprinkler Systems.*

NFPA 30, *Flammable and Combustible Liquids Code.*

NFPA 33, *Spray Application Using Flammable and Combustible Materials.*

NFPA 68, *Explosion Venting.*

NFPA 69, *Explosion Prevention Systems.*

NFPA 70, *National Electrical Code.*

NFPA 77, *Static Electricity.*

NFPA 704, *Identification of the Fire Hazards of Materials.*

Additional Reading

Benedetti, R. P., ed., *Flammable and Combustible Liquids Code Handbook*, 3rd ed., National Fire Protection Association, Quincy, MA, 1987.

Bright, A. W., "Electrostatic Hazards in Liquids and Powders," *Journal of Electrostatics*, Vol. 4, No. 2 (1977-78), pp. 131-147.

Factory Mutual Engineering Corporation, "Spray Applications of Flammable and Combustible Materials," Loss Prevention Data 7-27, Factory Mutual System, Norwood, MA.

"Fire Hazards of Electrostatic Paint Spraying," *Fire Prevention*, (124), 1978, pp. 19-20.

Flash Point Index, 9th ed., National Fire Protection Association, Quincy, MA, 1978.

Gillies, M. T., ed., Powder Coatings: Recent Developments, Noyes Data Corp., Park Ridge, NJ, 1981.

"Instantaneous Fire Detection/Suppression System for Jaguar Paint Spray Electrostatic Plant" *Product Fininshing* Vol. 40, No. 7, 1987, pp. 14-15.

Meidl, J. H., *Flammable Hazardous Materials*, 2nd ed., Macmillan Publishing Co., Inc., New York, NY, 1978.

Scarbrough, D. R., Chap. 25, "Spray Finishing and Powder Coating," *Industrial Fire Hazards Handbook*, J. L. Linville, ed. 3rd ed., National Fire Protection Association, Quincy, MA, 1990.

Talbot, G., "Static Electricity," *Fire*, 70(871), 1978, pp. 397-398.

DIPPING AND COATING PROCESSES

Nicholas L. Talbot and Paul H. Dobson

This chapter discusses the processes, equipment, hazards, and fire protection of dipping and coating operations that use flammable and combustible liquids. Such processes often involve liquids having tremendous heat energy and heat release capabilities, which can cause rapid property destruction when involved in a fire if not properly protected. The heat of combustion of flammable liquids is approximately two and one-half times that of an equivalent weight of wood.[1] In addition, heavy concentrations of smoke and toxic products of combustion often develop and make fire fighting extremely difficult as well as dangerous.

THE PROCESSES

Applications

Dipping and coating processes include, but are not limited to, finishing, impregnating, priming, cleaning, quenching, and other similar operations during which materials are immersed in, passed through, or coated by flammable or combustible liquids.

Processes vary widely and range from the cleaning of small parts in small quantities to an automated part-finishing process that uses a tank containing several thousand gallons (1000 gallons equals 3780 L) of a flammable or combustible liquid. As is the case with any potentially hazardous operation, a complete evaluation of the process and an understanding of the properties of the liquid(s) in use are essential.

Equipment

Dip tanks, roll coaters, curtain coaters, and flow coaters—the basic process equipment—present similar hazards. Related process equipment often used in conjunction with dipping and coating operations includes conveyors, pumps, piping systems, flammable or combustible liquid storage tanks, ovens, liquid heaters or heat exchangers, agitators, detearing equipment, and ventilation and exhaust systems, including energy recovery and pollution control devices. Support equipment must be selected and installed with full consideration of the inherent process hazards involved.

Dip tanks: Dip tanks are simply liquid containers of various sizes and shapes designed for the process involved. Tank sizes vary from a few gallons with small sq ft exposed surface area to several thousand gallons with a hundred or more sq ft of surface area. (One gallon equals 3.78 L; one sq ft equals 0.093 m^2). Figure 2-13A is an example of a typical dip tank process system. Dip tanks, their drainboards, and their covers should be constructed of noncombustible material, such as heavy metal, reinforced concrete, or masonry. They should be designed for the process and liquid involved, with consideration given to static head of the liquid, corrosion, mechanical damage, and ease of maintenance and repair. Spill or exposure fires could weaken tank supports, possibly causing tank collapse. Therefore, supports for large tanks should be made of reinforced concrete or protected steel.

Flow coaters: In flow coaters, the coating material is applied from nozzles or slots in an unatomized state onto the material being coated. (See Figure 2-13B.) The excess is collected in a trough or sump below the workpiece, returned to the reservoir, and recirculated to the nozzles by a pump. The nozzles may be fixed or oscillating, but the use of oscillating nozzles reduces the number required. The more nozzles used, the larger the reservoir and pump capacities required, and the greater the solvent loss will be. The workpiece usually enters and leaves through conveyor openings, and a drip tunnel is used in place of the drainboards that are used with dip tanks. The tunnel is enclosed on all sides, except for the conveyor opening, and is sloped toward the trough or sump. Airborne solvent concentration in the tunnel is sometimes used to keep the coating from drying before it gets to the oven.

Curtain coaters: Curtain coaters are used to apply coating material to flat or slightly curved workpieces. (See Figure 2-13C.) Coating material is pumped from a reservoir to a coating head, which has a small reservoir with a dam or weir forming one side. Coating material pumped to the head overflows the dam and forms a continuous vertical

Nicholas L. Talbot is senior loss control specialist, IRM Services, Inc., Pompano Beach, FL. Paul H. Dobson is senior engineer with the Factory Mutual Research Corporation, Norwood, Massachusetts.

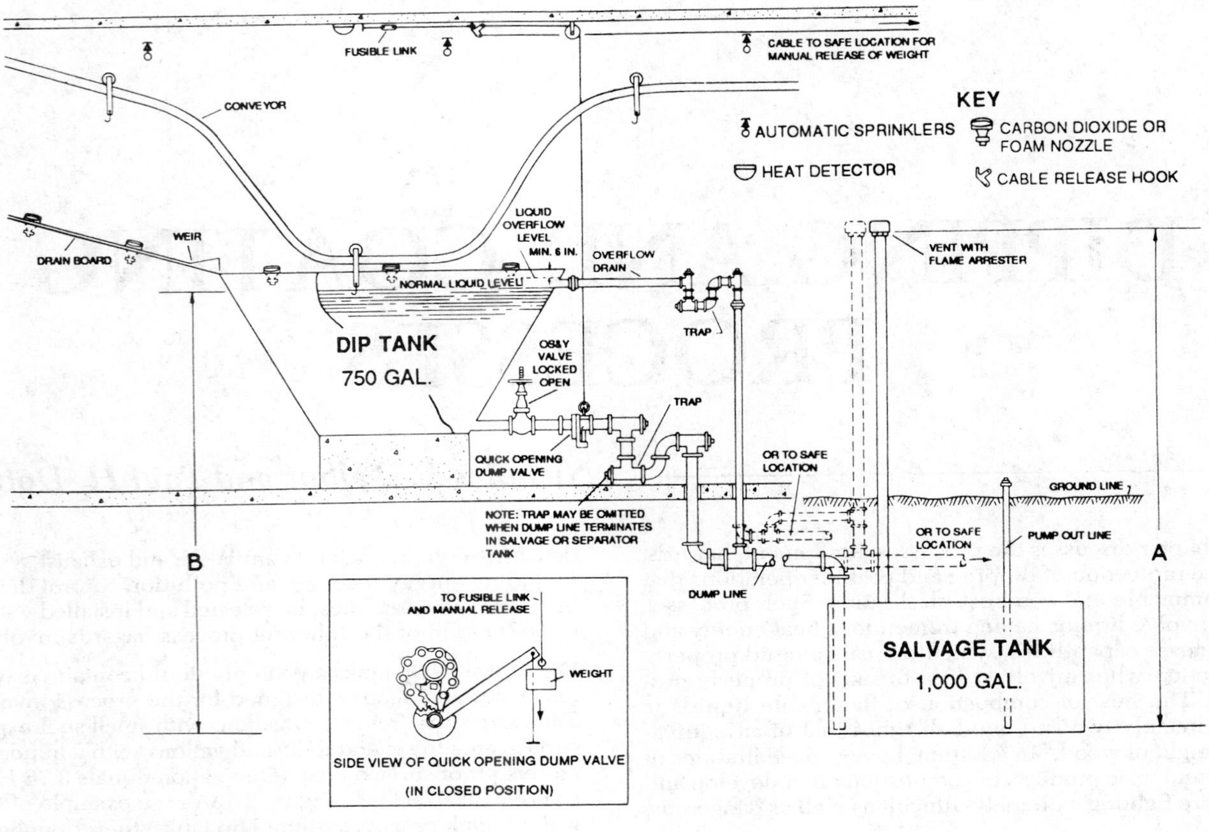

FIG. 2-13A. Dip tank, drainboard, and conveyor system.

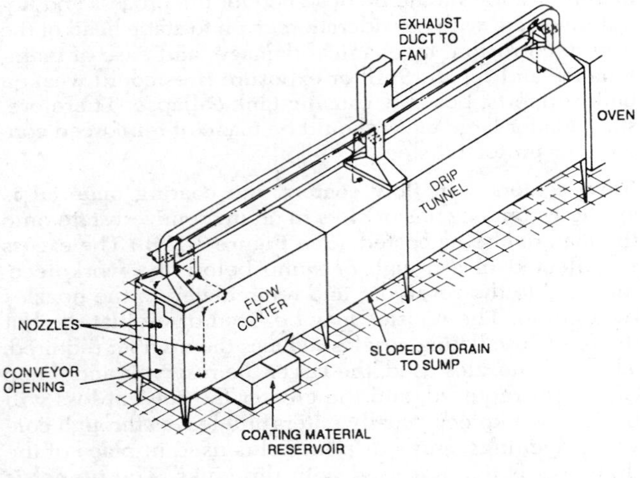

FIG. 2-13B. Flow coater. (Source: Factory Mutual Research Corp.)

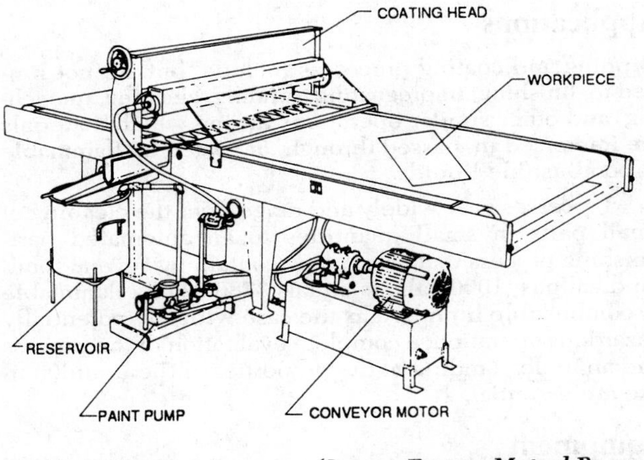

FIG. 2-13C. Curtain coater. (Source: Factory Mutual Research Corp.)

stream, which drops down onto the workpiece. Excess coating material drops into a trough and returns to the reservoir to be recirculated.

Roll coaters: In a roll coater, coating material is applied by bringing the workpiece into contact with one or more liquid-coated rollers. (See Figure 2-13D.) The coating material may come from an open pan or a nip formed by two rollers. Coating material is supplied from a reservoir by a pump and piping system.

THE PROCESS HAZARDS

Dipping and coating articles or materials by passing them through flammable and combustible liquids involves the danger of fire and explosion of vapor-air mixtures. Generally, the severity of the hazard depends on the character and flammability of the liquids used, the quantities present, and the rate of vapor generation. (Characteristics of flammable and combustible liquids are discussed in detail in Section 2, Chapter 25, "Storage of Flammable and Combustible Liquids.")

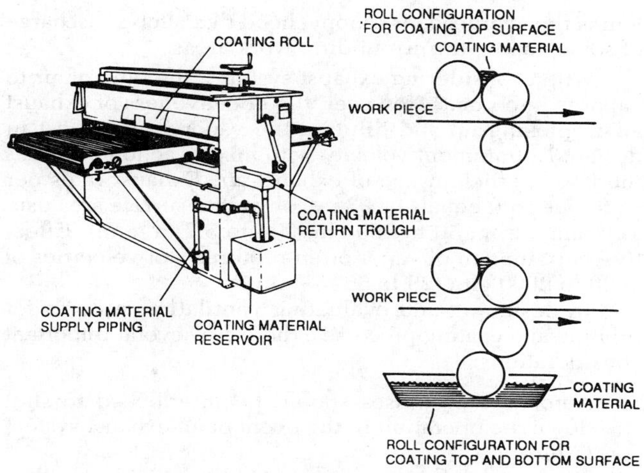

FIG. 2-13D. Roll coater. (Source: Factory Mutual Research Corp.)

Ease of ignition and the rate of flammable vapor generation from the liquid surface and from surfaces of freshly coated articles, floors, drain or drip boards, and other related equipment define the extent of the hazard. The intensity, persistence, and burning characteristics of the flammable vapor evolved and the probability of fire spread from radiated heat or from the flow of burning liquids because of a container rupture, boilover, or overflow complete the total hazard picture.

Flammable liquid vapors are usually heavier than air and, therefore, flow to low points. They may travel great distances before being exposed to ignition sources that can cause flashback to the process area.

Flammable liquids are often lighter than, and immiscible in, water. During fire fighting operations, water applied to such liquids may cause overflow and float the burning liquid away from the process to other areas.

HAZARD REDUCTION

Hazards inherent in dipping and coating operations can be reduced by properly locating the processes, installing ventilation and exhaust systems, eliminating ignition sources, and providing proper maintenance and periodic inspections. Special equipment design, employee training, and proper fire protection will also help to reduce process hazards.

Process Location

The principle of segregating hazards to confine fires and limit damage is fundamental in the selection of locations for dipping and coating operations. The personal safety of workers and other building occupants as well as the potential exposure of large values must also be considered.

A preferable location for dipping and/or coating operations would be in a detached or cutoff one-story sprinklered building of fire-resistive construction. When operations are located on upper stories, floors should be made waterproof and equipped with drains. Dipping and coating operations should not be located below grade, directly over basements, or near pits or trenches, because liquid drainage and vapor removal will be difficult to achieve. Curbs and trapped drains should be provided to control liquid flow where necessary.

When, due to its nature, the process cannot be cut off, it should be located in an area that is clear of combustibles, paths of egress, and other important processes. Combustible floors, ceilings, and surrounding walls should be protected; noncombustible curtainboards should be installed around the perimeter of the process or protected construction area and extended downward as far as is practical.

As flammable and combustible liquid fires generally develop rapidly and release large amounts of heat, automatic roof vents are extremely desirable, especially in unsprinklered buildings where heat buildup would quickly involve the entire building. Roof vents allow heat and smoke to escape, improving the chances of fire control by automatic sprinklers or the fire department.

When processes are located in confined areas, and highly flammable or unstable liquids are used, explosion relief venting may be provided to lessen potential losses. Venting can be in the form of lightweight walls and roofs or explosion-relieving wall panels, roof latches, and windows. Explosion relief is discussed in detail in NFPA 68, *Venting of Deflagrations*.

Careful evaluation of the process is necessary in developing location requirements for dipping and coating operations. Unfortunately, small dipping and coating operations generally are not considered in the same light as the larger operations, and, therefore, little consideration is given to their locations. However, it is often the small operation that produces a major fire loss.

Figure 2-13E, parts a, b, and c, shows common location features of dipping and coating operations.

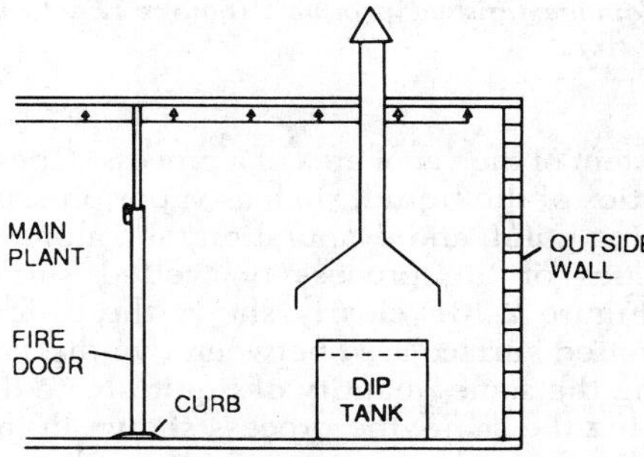

FIG. 2-13E(a). Most satisfactory arrangement for location of processes. Tank located near an outside wall, cut off from main plant areas by fire-resistive construction. (Source: Factory Mutual Research Corp.)

Ventilation and Exhaust Systems

When processes involve liquids that produce vapors, ventilation is necessary to limit the vapor area to the smallest practical space possible. The vapor area created by dipping and coating processes is defined as "any area containing vapor at or above 25 percent of the lower flammable limit (LFL) in the vicinity of dipping and coating processes, their drainboards or associated drying, conveying, or other equipment during operation or shutdown periods."[2]

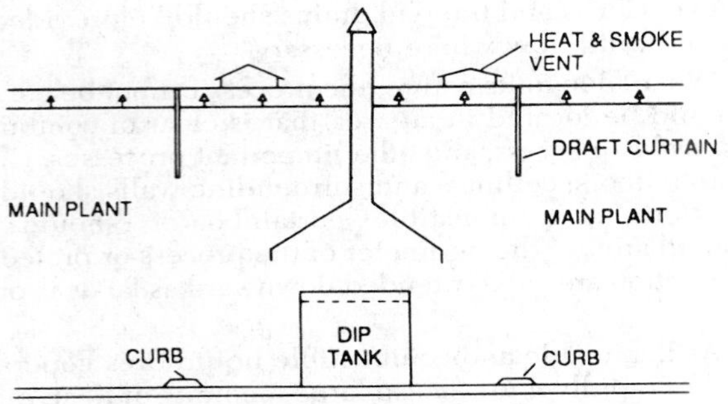

FIG. 2-13E(b). Satisfactory arrangement. Tank located in main plant area cut off by draft curtains and curbing. Heat and smoke vents should limit opened sprinklers to those near the fire and reduce smoke damage. (Source: Factory Mutual Research Corp.)

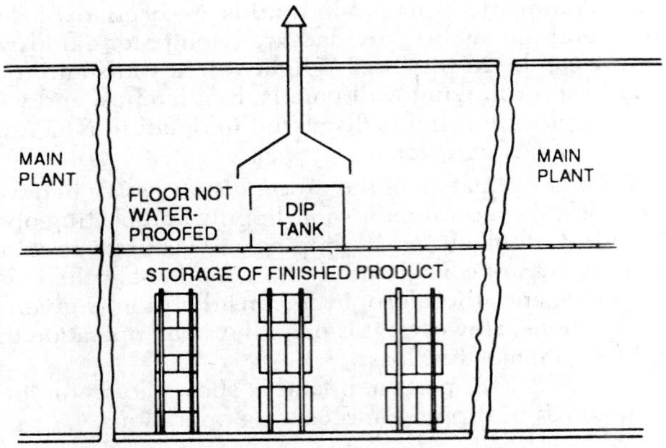

FIG. 2-13E(c). Unsatisfactory arrangement. Tank not cut off from main plant area. Water from hose streams will leak down through floor and damage finished product. (Source: Factory Mutual Research Corp.)

The extent of the vapor area of a process depends upon the properties of the liquid, such as vapor pressure, flash point, boiling point, and evaporation rate, along with the characteristics of the process or wetted surface area exposed. Figure 2-13F clearly shows the difference in exposed wetted surface area between two dip tank operations using the same quantity of liquid. Note that, with all else being the same, the process shown in the upper part of the figure would generate a greater volume of vapor and have a higher rate of heat release than that in the lower part; thus it would offer a greater fire hazard.

Vapor areas for each process should be kept as small as is practical but should not extend more than 5 ft (1.5 m) from the vapor source. The extent of a vapor area can be determined with a combustible gas analyzer. A theoretical ventilation rate can be determined when the liquid usage rate is known.[3] Since vapor concentrations vary widely from one process to another, a single safety exhaust ventilation system cannot be designed for all operations. The prime objective is to limit the vapor area to the smallest space possible and to prevent dead air spaces or pockets where vapors can accumulate.

Because flammable liquid vapors are heavier than air, low-point peripheral ventilation systems are usually more desirable than overhead hood arrangements. Two types of design are shown in Figure 2-13G. The least efficient system is the overhead, or canopy, hood that allows discharge of some vapors to surrounding work areas.

When considering exhaust systems, the ratio of air to vapor is important. However, the effectiveness of exhaust air in picking up and diluting the vapor is often lost in design. Entrainment velocity with mixing action becomes the key to efficient use of exhaust air. Exhaust rates per sq ft (one sq ft equals 0.093 m^2) of wetted surface area usually range from 50 to 200 cfm (1.4 to 5.7 m^3/min). Effective entrainment of vapor often requires slot velocities of 1000 to 2000 cfm (28 to 56 m^3/min).[4]

In designing and evaluating ventilation systems for dipping and coating processes, there are several important considerations:

1. Automatic processes should be interlocked to shut down the operation in the event of an exhaust system failure.
2. The supply of makeup air should be sufficient to allow efficient operation of the exhaust fans and to minimize dead air spaces.
3. Ideally, each exhaust system should discharge directly outdoors. When exhaust gases must be treated to satisfy environmental protection requirements or when energy conservation measures are used, individual, direct discharge of each system may not be practical. Manifold systems increase the hazard; therefore, all such systems should be specifically approved and strict preventive maintenance measures taken. Reactive materials and coatings should not be used when ducts are connected to a manifold.
4. Exhaust air should not be used for makeup air in occupied spaces. It can be used in unoccupied areas, but only if it has been decontaminated to safe levels.
5. Exhaust ducts should not discharge near air intakes, nor should they discharge less than 6 ft (1.8 m) from a combustible wall or roof or 25 ft (7.6 m) from combustible construction or an unprotected opening in a noncombustible exterior wall.
6. Exhaust ducts should be equipped with ample access doors to facilitate cleaning.
7. Ducts should be constructed of fire-resistive material, such as steel or masonry, and should be substantially supported. They should be installed with adequate clearance from combustibles. Dampers should not restrict exhaust ventilation to below minimum safe levels.

Ignition Sources

The key to minimizing the hazard of fire or explosion from vapor-air mixtures in dipping and coating processes is maintaining concentrations well below the lower flammable limit (LFL) through properly designed safety exhaust ventilation systems. Without vapor (fuel) and air (oxygen), properly mixed, ignition cannot take place even though sources of ignition are available. As it is almost impossible to keep processes free of flammable vapor-air mixtures in the explosive range, sources of ignition must be eliminated or equipment must be designed for use in hazardous areas containing flammable vapors and/or combustible residue.

Electrical equipment: Where flammable liquids are used or where combustible liquids are used at or above their flash point temperatures, electrical equipment should conform to the requirements for hazardous locations as outlined in NFPA 70, *National Electrical Code®* (*NEC*). The *NEC* classifies areas in which special types of electrical

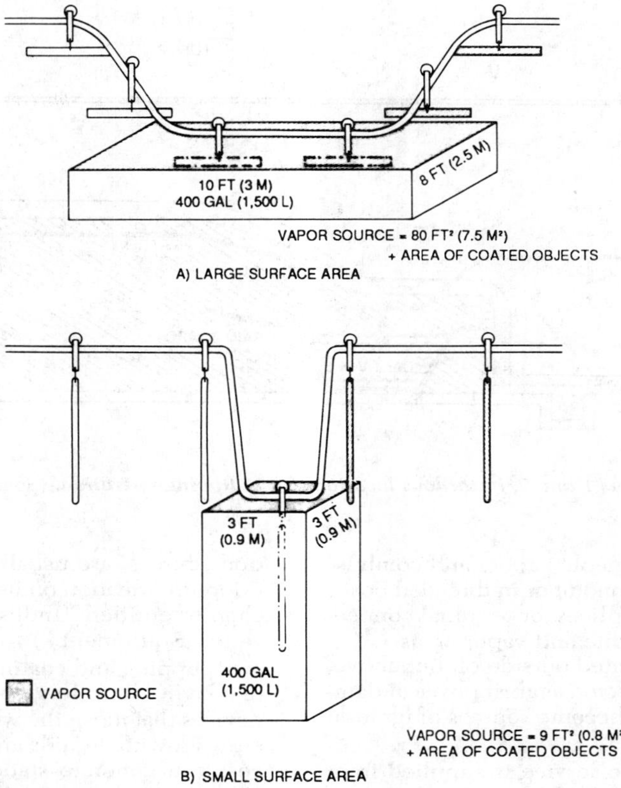

FIG. 2-13F. The difference in vapor source area between two dip tanks with the same coating volume. (Source: Factory Mutual Research Corp.)

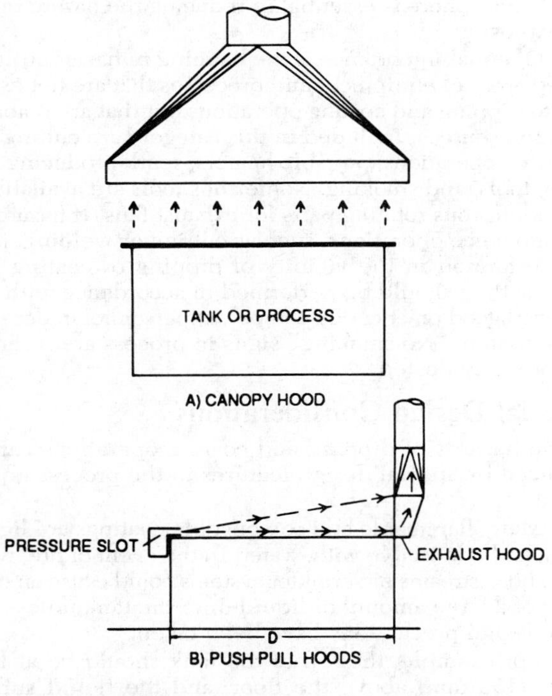

FIG. 2-13G. Ventilation systems used for open process tanks. (Source: Factory Mutual Research Corp.)

equipment must be used. In the case of dipping and coating processes, the classified areas are measured from the vapor source, which may be the liquid surface (open tanks) or wetted surfaces (freshly coated workpieces, drain boards, floors). The space containing hazardous vapor concentrations normally extends laterally and upward a short distance from the vapor source and, since the vapors are usually heavier than air, downward to the floor.

Classified areas are shown in Figure 2-13H. Class I, Division 1 electrical equipment is required within a radial distance of 5 ft (1.5 m) from the vapor source and within a horizontal distance of 25 ft (7.6 m) from the vapor source when the equipment is in pits. If a pit is not vapor-stopped at a point 25 ft (7.6 m) from the vapor source, the entire pit is considered a classified area. Class I, Division 2 electrical equipment is required 3 ft (0.91 m) beyond Division 1 in all areas down to 3 ft (0.91 m) above the floor. In the space between the floor and 3 ft (0.91 m) above the floor, the Division 2 area extends 20 ft (6.1 m) beyond the Division 1 area. An exception to the electrical requirements above is tanks containing 5 gal (19 L) or less and having 5 sq ft (0.46 m^2) or less of exposed surface area. These installations generally present less of a hazard and ordinary electrical equipment may be accepted more than 8 ft (2.4 m) from the vapor source.

It is usually undesirable to install electrical equipment in the vicinity of dipping and coating operations. In such locations, the equipment would be subject to deposits of combustible residue, which would complicate maintenance and cleaning procedures. However, if electrical equipment must be installed in such locations, it should be a type that

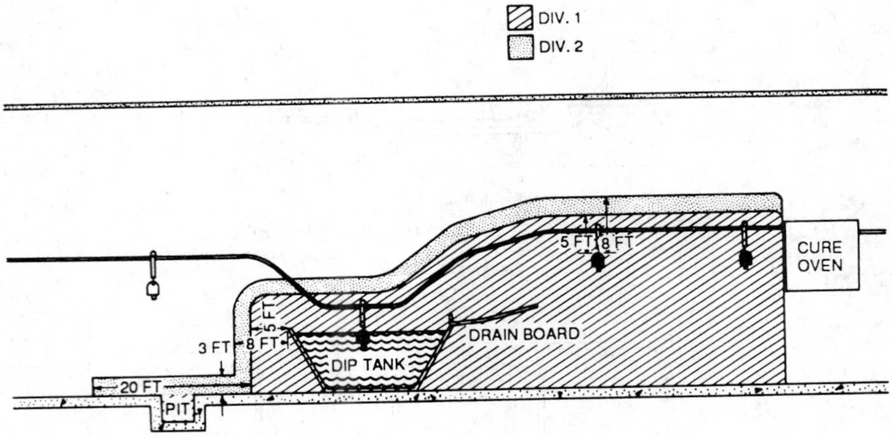

FIG. 2-13H. The Class I, Divisions 1 and 2, hazardous locations for a dipping operation. (Source: Factory Mutual Research Corp.)

can be exposed safely to flammable vapors and combustible residues. Wiring in rigid conduit or in threaded boxes or fittings containing no taps, splices, or terminal connections is permitted in both residue and vapor areas.

Fixed lighting fixtures located outside of, but above, classified areas should be protected against physical damage, which may allow them to become sources of ignition of flammable vapors.

In areas where the electric service is supplied from overhead wires and lightning is a fairly common occurrence, protection against lightning-induced surge voltages should be provided. In the absence of lightning protection, high surge voltages could enter vapor areas and create high-energy ignition sources. Suitable protection includes lightning arresters, interconnection of all grounds, and surge protection capacitors.

Under abnormal conditions, overheating and arcing can occur in electrical circuits and equipment. Therefore, it is important that electrical circuits and equipment servicing dipping and coating processes have the proper overcurrent protection, are grounded, and receive regular maintenance.

Dipping and coating processes are frequently changed when new coating materials are introduced, production demand is increased, and new equipment is installed. Quite often, unsafe electrical installations and poor maintenance habits creep into the production process. It is common to find extensions connected to additional fans and lighting that are not suitable for use in classified hazardous areas.

Other ignition sources: The presence of open flames, spark-producing processes or devices, and heated surfaces having temperatures high enough to ignite flammable vapors should be prohibited in flammable vapor areas.

Ovens located directly above or adjacent to dipping and coating operations have been the ignition source for many fires. This equipment should be located as far as practical from dipping and coating operations, with noncombustible partitions provided when reasonable distances cannot be maintained. Ventilation exhaust systems of ovens and dryers located directly above, or adjacent to, dipping and coating processes should be interlocked with process ventilation systems, so that heating and process equipment cannot function unless all ventilation equipment is in operation. Indirect heating systems, which do not present ignition sources, are usually preferred in drying operations. (More information on heating systems can be found in the chapter entitled "Industrial and Commercial Heat Utilization Equipment.")

Dipping and coating processes often involve the use of conveyors, rollers, collectors, festoon dryers, and other devices that move the workpiece or liquid through the process. Flowing liquids and materials moving through a process can generate static electricity. A static charge can accumulate on process equipment and develop a difference in electrical potential sufficient to cause a spark containing enough energy to ignite flammable vapor-air concentrations. Static elimination by bonding and grounding process equipment or by humidification or ionization of the local atmosphere is essential in reducing the hazard of fire or explosion.

Of equal importance is the banning in hazardous classified areas of equipment and processes that are not essential to dipping and coating operations but that are potential ignition sources. Included in this category are cutting and welding operations, portable heaters, spark-producing (ferrous) tools, and smoking. Nonferrous tools are available as are nonferrous rotating parts for exhaust fans. If hazardous maintenance operations, such as cutting or welding, must be performed in the vicinity of dipping or coating processes, they should be performed in accordance with recognized good practices by competent personnel under strict supervision. "No smoking" signs in process areas should be properly posted.

Special Design Considerations

Some hazards of dipping and coating operations can be reduced by special design features in the process equipment.

Many flammable and combustible coatings are lighter than, and immiscible with, water. In the event of fire, water from hose streams or sprinkler systems could cause an overflow of a large amount of liquid from the tank unless certain design precautions have been taken.

For example, the top of the tank should be at least 6 in. (152 mm) above the floor, and the liquid surface should be at least 6 in. (152 mm) below the top of the tank. Tanks having a capacity of more than 150 gal (568 L) or a liquid surface area of 10 sq ft (0.93 m^2) or more should be equipped with trapped overflow pipes that discharge to a safe location. Overflow pipes should be capable of handling the maximum delivery of the tank's fill pipes or of the automatic sprinkler discharge. In any case, overflow pipes should never be less than 3 in. (76.2 mm) in diameter.

Larger tanks—those having a capacity of 500 gal (1.9 m^3) or more—should be equipped with a bottom drain of sufficient size to empty the tank in 5 min. The flammable liquid should be drained to a vented salvage tank or other safe location. If gravity flow is not practical, pumps may be used to empty the tank. The drain may be operated manually or automatically. However, if a manual drain release is used, it should be accessible and at a safe location. If, due to increased hazard or by nature of the operation, bottom drains cannot be provided, the process should be cut off or fully diked, and both an automatic special extinguishing system and sprinklers should be installed.

Conveyor systems used in dipping and coating processes should be arranged to stop automatically in the event of a fire or failure of the exhaust ventilation system.

In processes where there is a possibility of flammable liquids being heated above their boiling points or to within 100°F (37.8°C) of their autoignition temperatures, suitable excess temperature limit controls are needed to prevent rapid vapor buildup and possible autoignition.

Controls should limit the surface temperatures of heated workpieces to at least 100°F (37.8°C) below the autoignition temperature of the coating material used. This limitation does not apply to quenching tanks, which are discussed in Section 2, Chapter 11, "Oil Quenching."

Limit controls, such as liquid level devices, meters, and timers, should be used to prevent overfilling of tanks where automatic filling is designed into the process. If pumps are used, they should be interlocked to shut down in the event of fire.

Maintenance, Training, and Inspection

While location, ventilation, equipment design, and the elimination of ignition sources go a long way toward reducing the hazards in dipping and coating processes using flammable and combustible liquids, maintenance, training, and regular inspection of equipment are essential to safe operations. Unfortunately, due to production schedules, changes in processes, and turnover of personnel, these essentials may be neglected, resulting in unsafe operating conditions.

Areas in the vicinity of dipping and coating processes should be kept free of accumulations of combustible residues and unnecessary combustible materials. Spontaneous ignition, due to oxidation or exothermic reaction between various coating components, often occurs when excess residue accumulates in work areas, ducts, duct discharge points, or other adjacent areas. When excess residues accumulate in such locations, operations should be discontinued until conditions are corrected.

Combustible coverings (e.g., thin paper or plastic) and strippable coatings are often used to facilitate cleanup of drippings and residues. The increased amount of combustibles introduced by the use of these materials is offset by the improved housekeeping and ease of cleaning that they provide. Suitable containers should be provided for the disposal of waste and rags used for cleaning.

The size and complexity of dipping and coating operations may vary widely but, in all operations, the personnel involved should be instructed in the potential safetyand health hazards inherent in the particular process employed. The nature of the process and operational, maintenance, protection, and emergency procedures should be included. It is desirable to record such training and provide refresher instruction from time to time to ensure continuity and proper action in the event of an emergency.

Depending upon the size and nature of the process, periodic (usually at least monthly) inspection should be made of dipping and coating processes. Inspections should include noting the condition of equipment covers, overflow pipe inlets and outlets, discharge, bottom drains and valves, electrical wiring and equipment, grounding and bonding connections, ventilation equipment, and extinguishing equipment. Inspections and protection equipment tests should be documented and conducted using a checklist. Defective equipment and unsafe conditions should be corrected promptly.

FIRE PROTECTION

In spite of the considerable care taken in the operation of dipping and coating processes that use flammable and combustible liquids, fires and explosions do occur, and fire protection and suppression equipment are necessary.

Fire loss experience has shown that damage in small processes is often as severe as in large operations. Less consideration is usually given to the location of small processes, and they may be in areas that expose high values or combustible construction. Some form of protection is usually required for all dipping and coating processes.

By far the simplest device for extinguishing a fire in a process tank is a self-closing cover, which cuts off the fire's air supply. Normally the cover is held open by a cable and fusible link. When exposed to the heat of a fire, the solder in the fusible link melts, releasing the cover and allowing it to drop tightly in place over the tank. (See Figure 2-131.)

Automatic sprinklers are often provided at ceiling level and can provide adequate protection for small processes and where combustible coatings are used with limited liquid surface area exposure. Sprinklers are intended to help control the fire, prevent damage to the building, and allow effective manual fire fighting. Automatic sprinklers are often required as backup to special extinguishing systems.

Where processes involve considerable volumes, large liquid surface areas, or large wetted areas of low flash point materials, special extinguishing systems should be provided. In the case of dip tanks, special systems should be provided for tanks having capacities in excess of 150 gal (569 L) or surface areas greater than 10 sq ft (0.93 m^2). Suitable protection systems use foam, carbon dioxide, dry chemical, or a halogenated agent as the extinguishing medium. For liquids having flash points above 140°F (60°C), water spray systems may be used. All systems should operate automatically and conform to fire protection standards. The complexity and value of some processes and the absence of sprinklers as backup often make it desirable to provide redundancy in protection systems.

Dipping and coating process areas should be equipped with portable fire extinguishers suitable for use on flammable and combustible liquids fires.

Due to the flash fire conditions that usually prevail in flammable liquids fires, emergency personnel or fire brigades should be trained to act immediately to bring all protection elements to bear on the fire in hopes of achieving rapid control and limiting possible injury and damage.

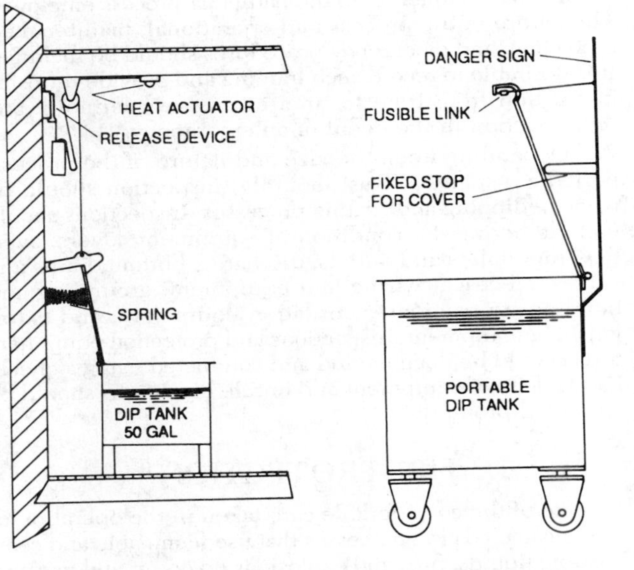

FIG. 2-131. Automatic closing covers for small fixed and portable dip tanks. (Source: Factory Mutual Research Corp.)

BIBLIOGRAPHY

References Cited

1. Factory Mutual Research Corporation, "Flammable Liquids—General Safeguards," *Loss Prevention Data 7-35*, Jan. 1977, Factory Mutual Research Corp., Norwood, MA, p. 1.
2. NFPA 34, *Dipping and Coating Processes Using Flammable or Combustible Liquids*, National Fire Protection Association, Quincy, MA, 1989.
3. NFPA 86, *Ovens and Furnaces*, National Fire Protection Association, Quincy, MA, 1985, p. 36.
4. *Industrial Ventilation—A Manual of Recommended Practice*, 14th ed., Committee on Industrial Ventilation, Lansing, MI, pp. 5-57 to 5-60.

NFPA Codes, Standards, and Recommended Practices

Reference to the following NFPA codes, standards, and recommended practices will provide further information on the safeguards for dipping and coating processes discussed in this chapter. (See the latest *NFPA Catalog* for availability of current editions of the following documents.)

NFPA 10, *Portable Fire Extinguishers.*
NFPA 11, *Low Expansion Foam and Combined Agent Systems.*
NFPA 12, *Carbon Dioxide Extinguishing Systems.*
NFPA 12A, *Halon 1301 Fire Extinguishing Systems.*
NFPA 12B, *Halon 1211 Fire Extinguishing Systems.*
NFPA 13, *Installation of Sprinkler Systems.*
NFPA 13A, *Inspection, Testing, and Maintenance of Sprinkler Systems.*
NFPA 15, *Water Spray Fixed Systems for Fire Protection.*
NFPA 34, *Dipping and Coating Processes Using Flammable or Combustible Liquids.*
NFPA 35, *Manufacture of Organic Coatings.*
NFPA 68, *Explosion Venting.*
NFPA 69, *Explosion Prevention Systems.*
NFPA 70, *National Electrical Code.*
NFPA 77, *Static Electricity.*
NFPA 86, *Ovens and Furnaces.*
NFPA 91, *Blower and Exhaust Systems for Dust, Stock, and Vapor Removal or Conveying.*
NFPA 327, *Cleaning or Safeguarding Small Tanks and Containers.*
NFPA 497M, *Classification of Gases, Vapors and Dusts for Electrical Equipment in Hazardous (Classified) Locations.*

Additional Reading

Meidl, J. H., *Flammable Hazardous Materials*, 2nd ed., Macmillan Publishing Co., Inc., New York, 1978.
Tabar, D. C., "Coatings Industry Responsibility in Safety and Loss Prevention," *Coatings*, Vol. 41, No. 2, Washington D.C., 1989.
Talbot, G., "Static Electricity," *Fire*, 70 (871), 1978, pp. 397-398.
Weiby, P., and Dickinson, K. R., "Monitoring Work Areas for Explosive and Toxic Hazards," *Chemical Engineering*, Vol. 83, No. 22, 1976, pp. 139-145.

WELDING AND CUTTING

Revised by A. F. Manz

In its largest sense, welding includes any materials joining process. As used in this chapter, welding means only fusion welding, i.e., melting together. The American Welding Society (AWS) defines welding as "a joining process that produces coalescence* of materials by heating them to the welding temperature, with or without the application of pressure or by the application of pressure alone, and with or without the use of filler metal." Similarly, melting is the significant feature in reference to thermal cutting. The AWS defines thermal cutting as "a group of cutting processes that severs or removes metal by localized melting, burning, or vaporizing of the workpiece." Both welding and thermal cutting require high-intensity energy sources—usually electricity or the heat of combustion of a fuel gas. In this text it is not possible to cover all welding and cutting processes; therefore only basic information about the more common processes is discussed. AWS terms will be used, where possible, in the remainder of this chapter.

For additional information, consult Section 2, Chapter 20, "Metalworking Processes;" and Section 2, Chapter 26, "Storage of Gases;" and Section 3, Chapter 7, "Gases."

Torch fires account for about 4 percent of fires each year in non-residential structures and 8 percent in industrial and manufacturing properties.[1,2] Typically, three-fourths of torch fires are due to cutting or welding torches, which amounts to thousands of fires a year. However, education, training, and on-the-job practice can significantly reduce the potential for welding and cutting fires. There are four factors that must be kept in mind:

1. Two sides of the fire triangle are always present, i.e., a source(s) of ignition and air to support combustion. The other controllable element is the combustible material.
2. Familiarity with cutting or welding as an activity. A shop that performs welding or cutting operations on a routine basis in a fixed location can develop confidence and reinforce safe habits more than a shop that performs welding or cutting only occasionally and in a variety of different temporary locations.
3. The kind of process and equipment used and their potential fire effect. Cutting, as well as certain arc welding operations, produces literally thousands of ignition sources in the form of sparks and hot slag. Other types of torches, such as arcs and oxy-fuel gas flames, have only themselves as ignition sources.
4. The supervision and training of the welder. Is the welder trained in the proper use of the equipment and mindful of the exposure? Who has knowledge of and has assessed the risks involved in bringing a torch into the work area and has authorized its use there?

PROCESSES USING ELECTRICITY

Arc Welding (AW)

This term applies to a number of processes that use an electric arc as the heat source for melting and joining metals. The arc is a useful tool because its heat can be concentrated and controlled quite effectively. Frequently, but not always, a filler metal must be used to obtain a good joint. The arc is struck between the metals to be welded and an electrode, which is maneuvered along the joint or which may remain stationary while the work is moved beneath it. The electrode may be consumable or nonconsumable. If the latter, a separate rod or wire may be used as the filler metal. Consumable electrodes supply their own filler metal by melting. The molten metal and weld zone may be protected from atmospheric contamination by use of a supplementary shielding gas, or a shielding atmosphere produced by decomposition of a flux which is used with certain types of electrodes and wires.

Shielded metal arc welding (**SMAW**): This simple well-known process is widely used with ferrous-based metals. (See Figure 2-14A.) It produces coalescence of metals by heating them with an arc between a covered metal electrode and the workpiece. The process requires an alternat-

August Manz is president of A.F. Manz Associates, welding technology and safety consultants, Union, NJ.

*This is the preferred American Welding Society term used to describe the flowing together into one body of the materials being welded.

ing or direct current power supply, power cables, and an electrode holder. Shielded metal arc welding can be performed readily in remote, unusual, or confined locations. Consequently, this process is widely used in such industrial applications as construction, shipbuilding, and pipeline erection. Fairly simple, portable units are frequently used in maintenance and field construction work.

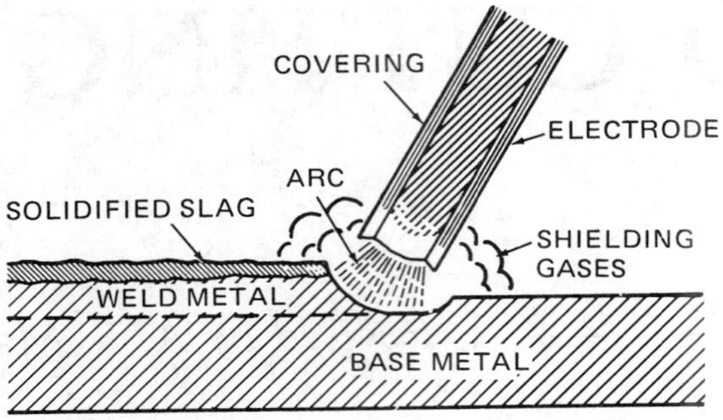

FIG. 2-14A. Schematic diagram of a typical shielded metal arc welding operation. (Source: Lincoln Electric Company)

Gas metal arc welding (GMAW): This process uses a continuous, solid-wire filler metal, which functions as one terminal of the arc, and a gas to shield the arc and the weld metal. The shielding gas depends on the base metal and process variations. It may be an inert gas, such as argon or helium; an active gas, such as carbon dioxide (oxidizing or oxidizing and carburizing); or mixtures involving these gases with additions of hydrogen, nitrogen, or oxygen. Overall, this process can be used to join just about any metal in any configuration of joint.

Flux cored arc welding (FCAW): Although this process is similar to gas metal arc welding in equipment used and types of applications, it uses cored rather than solid electrodes. Minerals and alloys in the core assist in weld protection, and many such electrodes are intended for use with shielding gases. Other kinds of cored electrodes are self-shielding and produce their own protective envelope without an auxiliary shielding gas.

Gas tungsten arc welding (GTAW): This process is similar to gas metal arc welding and flux cored arc welding, but it uses a nonconsumable tungsten electrode for one pole of an inert gas-shielded arc. Filler metal may be used. The most common shielding gases are argon and helium. Equipment required comprises a power supply, welding torch, source of inert gas, suitable pressure regulators and flow meters, and connecting hoses.

Plasma arc welding (PAW): This is characterized by the plasma state, wherein the temperature of a gas is raised until the gas becomes at least partly ionized, enabling it to conduct an electric current. A plasma arc torch incorporates an electrode and an orifice through which a small flow of gas forms the arc plasma. Secondary gas, which flows through an outer nozzle cup arrangement that encircles the arc plasma orifice, shields the arc and the weld. Typical shielding gas may be argon, helium, or mixtures of argon with hydrogen or helium. Filler metal may or may not be used. Equipment required is not unlike that for gas tungsten arc welding, with necessary differences in power supply and control, torch design, and gas supply and control.

Submerged arc welding (SAW): In this process the arc and molten metal are shielded by molten flux and a layer of unmelted flux granules. A continuously fed electrode is submerged in the flux. The arc is submerged below the flux. Radiation and fumes are minimal, and fire hazard potential is likewise relatively minor compared to other processes.

Resistance Welding (RW)

Welding heat for these processes is created by resistance to flow of current through the parts being joined. Resistance welding is generally used to join two metal pieces that may have different thicknesses and composition. Electrodes conduct current through the pieces, which are clamped or rigidly held together to provide good contact and pressure for holding molten metal at the joint.

Flash Welding (FW)

Although defined by the AWS as resistance welding, flash welding is considered a process unto itself. Heat is created by both resistance to current flow and by arcs at the interface. Force is applied after heating, resulting in the expulsion of metal, formation of a flash, and usually a significant shower of sparks. Applications usually involve butt welding rods or bars end to end or edge to edge. The process is almost always automatic. Flash welding machines vary significantly in size, some being large enough to weld sheets in a steel mill.

Electroslag Welding (ESW)

Electroslag welding is a process used primarily for vertical position welding. This process uses a slag, which is conductive while molten, to protect the weld and melt base-metal edges and filler metal. An arc is needed to start the process by melting the slag and preheating the work because the unfused, solid slag is nonconductive. Once the process is started, the arc is no longer necessary, and resistance to current flow through the molten slag produces the heat to sustain the process.

Arc Cutting (AC)

This term applies to a group of thermal cutting processes that, like the kindred welding processes, melt the metals to be cut by heating with an arc struck between an electrode and the base metal.

Air carbon arc cutting (CAC-A): This process uses electrodes comprising a mixture of graphite and carbon, and coated with a copper layer to improve current-carrying capacity. Metal melted by the arc is blown away by a jet of compressed air supplied by conventional compressors, usually at about 80 psi (550 kPa). Current is provided by standard electric welding power supply units rated for CAC-A duty, or special power units.

Plasma arc cutting (PAC): This cutting process achieves cutting action with an extremely hot jet at high velocity. The hot jet is produced by forcing an arc and gas through a small orifice. Arc energy confined to a small area melts the metal, and the jet of highly heated, expanding gases forces the molten metal from the cutting area. High arc voltages, special power supplies, and water-cooled torches are required. Air, nitrogen, argon-hydrogen, argon-nitrogen, and argon-helium gases are commonly used.

OXY-FUEL GAS PROCESSES

Oxy-Fuel Gas Welding (OFW)

This process uses the heat of combustion of a fuel gas and oxygen flame at high temperatures to melt the workpiece base metal and filler metal, if these are used. The flame (except for oxygen-hydrogen) is readily adjusted to provide a "neutral," oxidizing (excess oxygen) or carburizing* (excess fuel gas) environment. The type of flame used depends on the materials being welded.

Acetylene remains the pre-eminent welding fuel because it has the highest flame temperature of all the fuel gases. Other fuel gases or mixtures, such as methyl acetylene-propadiene (stabilized), have found some acceptance. Other hydrocarbons (propane, propylene, butane, natural gas-methane) are not suitable for welding ferrous metals. Hydrogen has a low flame temperature and heat content, and its flame, which is colorless, is difficiult to adjust for oxygen-fuel gas ratio. Oxy-hydrogen welding does have application for welding lead, which is frequently but erroneously called lead burning. Table 2-14A shows neutral flame temperatures of some fuel gases.

TABLE 2-14A. ***Flame Temperatures of Fuel Gases with Oxygen***

Gas	Neutral Flame Temperature °F	°C
Acetylene	5589	3087
Methyl acetylene-propadiene (stabilized)	5301	2927
Propylene	5250	2900
Propane	4579	2526
Natural gas-methane	4600	2538
Hydrogen	4820	2660

With the exception of acetylene, neutral flame temperatures are significantly lower than the maximums, so it is not possible to melt and control the weld, except perhaps for thin sheet metal. At maximum temperatures, the flames are strongly oxidizing and not usable because of deleterious metal oxide formation in the weld metal. Limited use of methyl acetylene-propadiene (stabilized) requires special procedures.

Brazing and Braze Welding

Brazing (B): This is broadly defined by the AWS as a welding process in which the base metal is heated but not fused and the joining is accomplished with a filler metal having a liquidus temperature above 840°F (450°C) and below the solidus temperature of the base metal. Moreover, brazing is characterized by the filler metal being distributed through a closely fitted joint by capillary action.

Braze welding: Braze welding is of more significance as it relates to fire prevention because of its frequent use in repair and maintenance activities. It differs from brazing in that capillary action in the joint is not a factor; the filler metal is laid down in a groove or fillet at the point of application. The edges of the joint are heated to a dull red color, flux is used, and filler metal is supplied by a bronze rod. However, the base metal is not melted, only the filler metal melts. The process is widely used on ferrous metals, as well as on copper and nickel alloys. Sometimes it provides a solution to the problem of joining dissimilar metals.

Hard soldering: This common but incorrect term is used to describe brazing with a silver-base filler metal. The operation is often performed with an oxy-fuel gas torch, as in assembling copper pipe joints with silver brazing alloy. Many times, however, the oxygen is not pure gas but is supplied as air, as in the air-acetylene torch. Thus, only one small gas supply cylinder may be needed, enhancing portability.*

Surfacing

The oxy-fuel gas flame (usually oxy-acetylene) is used not in a true welding sense but rather to deposit a layer of filler metal on a base metal to obtain certain surface properties or dimensions. Bronze may be used, but more frequently the process is one of hard facing, where the deposited layer is a special alloy that will greatly prolong the life of parts subject to extreme wear or abrasion. Surfacing can also be accomplished by use of arc welding and thermal spraying processes.

Oxy-Fuel Gas Heating Operations

There are numerous industrial and commercial operations that regularly employ an oxy-fuel or air-fuel flame but do not involve a joining or severing operation. The flame and the nature and location of these operations nonetheless may represent an appreciable fire potential. Some such operations are:

Forming: Heating (ironwork, piping, etc.) to facilitate bending, shaping, or straightening.

Annealing, flame hardening, flame softening: Use of the flame in a controlled manner to obtain specific properties.

Flame priming: Heating to remove scale and rust in preparing metal surfaces for painting.

Flame descaling: Heating (generally a steel mill application) to remove scale from bars, billets, slabs, etc., to facilitate machining or inspection.

Other applications: Paint burning, glass finishing, leather edging, babbitting, or antiquing of wood.

Oxy-Fuel Gas Cutting

This term describes a process or group of processes named by the specific fuel gas used (e.g., oxy-acetylene cutting, oxy-natural gas cutting) for severing metals by the reaction of high-purity oxygen with the metal at elevated temperatures.

*Sometimes carburizing flames are called reducing flames.

*The air-fuel gas flame, particularly air-acetylene, also finds significant use in soldering, commonly called "soft soldering," which by definition involves a filler metal that melts below 840°F (450°C). Plumbing jointwork, refrigeration piping, and heating and ventilating duct assemblies are applications where the air-fuel gas flame is used. Equipment portability is an advantage—but it may also signify access to places where fire prevention is not easily accomplished and is easily overlooked because a singlejoint operation can be done in a matter of minutes.

Burning iron in oxygen produces iron oxide, normally a solid, but the oxide melts at a temperature below the melting point of iron or steel and runs off as slag. A variation in the process is oxy-fuel gas gouging, wherein a relatively low-velocity oxygen jet permits gouging or grooving of a metal surface in a reasonably smooth, well-defined manner.

Oxy-Fuel Gas Welding and Cutting Equipment

Basic elements are fuel gas and oxygen supplies, pressure regulators, conduits (hoses or piping) to convey the gases, and a torch to mix and burn the gases in controlled fashion and provide the jet used in cutting operations.

In its simplest form, the equipment comprises a cylinder each of fuel gas and oxygen, a pressure regulator on each cylinder, hoses, and a torch. (See Figure 2-14B.) A steel mill, however, might have a major installation for cutting and welding operations. (See Figure 2-14C.) Fuel gas might be supplied from large multicylinder manifolds (possibly truck mounted and replaceable), from storage tanks for liquefied fuel, or from a public utility natural gas main. Oxygen may be supplied from the mill's own on-site oxygen-generating plant, from storage tanks for liquid oxygen or high-pressure gas or both, or from multicylinder manifolds. A major installation may also have an extensive fixed-piping distribution network and consuming devices running the gamut from simple hand torches to sophisticated steel-conditioning machines.

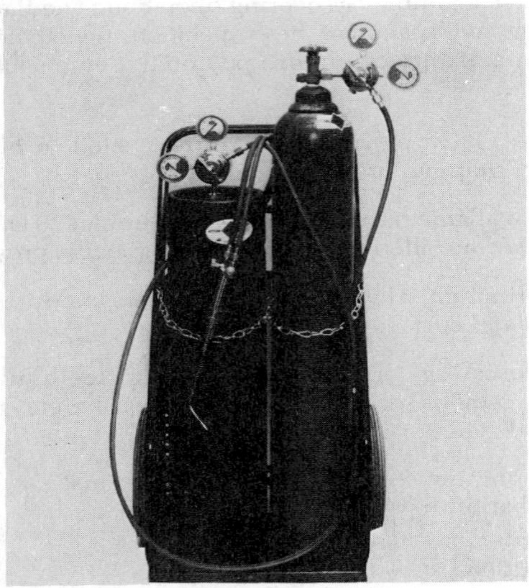

FIG. 2-14B. A portable welding outfit with oxygen and acetylene outfits chained to an easy-rolling cylinder truck (cutting attachments not shown). (Source: Linde Div., Union Carbide Corporation)

Auxiliary—but necessary—equipment includes standardized[3] fuel gas and oxygen hose connections, standardized hose,[4] protective equipment for service piping systems, and shutoff valves at points (station outlets) where gas is withdrawn from the piping system. Protective equipment for piping, which may be installed at one or more locations, should prevent the backflow of oxygen into the fuel gas supply system, the passage of flame flashback into the fuel gas supply system, and the development of pressures in excess of system components ratings. In some systems, backflow prevention devices also may be required at station outlets. (See NFPA 51, *Oxygen-Fuel Gas Systems for Welding, Cutting, and Allied Processes*.)

FIG. 2-14C. A large stationary oxy-fuel gas cutting machine in operation. (Source: Linde Div., Union Carbide Corporation)

Welding torches have inlet connections and valves for each gas at the rear of the handle. (See Figure 2-14D.) The gases are controlled by inlet valves and thoroughly mixed before issuing from the torch tip. Cutting torches are similar but provide passageways and separate valving for supplying and controlling the cutting oxygen jet at the center of the tip.

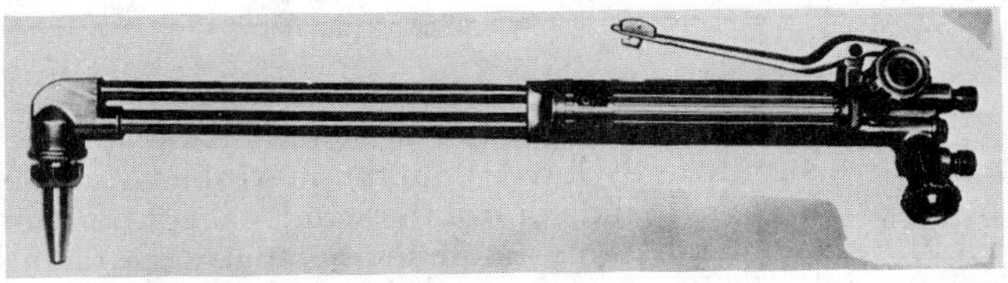

FIG. 2-14D. A typical cutting torch. All control valves are located at the rear of the body. (Source: Linde Div., Union Carbide Corporation)

Mechanized cutting is common. Equipment varies from relatively simple, portable machines, used for straight-line work and perhaps circles and some irregular shapes, to highly sophisticated multi-torch machines that can trace (by photocell or other electronic means) intricate shapes and accurately and simultaneously produce a number of parts of the same shape.

THERMAL SPRAYING (THSP)

Closely allied to welding are several processes, known collectively as thermal spraying,* in which finely divided metallic or nonmetallic materials are deposited in molten or near-molten condition to form coatings. Special "guns"

*American Welding Society preferred terminology for "metal spraying" or "metallizing."

are used. (See Figure 2-14E.) In flame spraying, an oxy-fuel gas flame is used to melt the coating material, and an auxiliary compressed gas may be used to assist in atomizing and propelling coating material to the workpiece.

Electric arc spraying employs an arc between two consumable electrodes of coating material, plus auxiliary compressed gas to atomize and propel the coating particles. Plasma spraying uses a plasma arc as the heat source and for propelling the coating material. In detonation flame spraying, the coating material is melted and propelled by the controlled explosion of fuel gas and oxygen.

FIG. 2-14E. Thermal spray gun. (Source: American Welding Society)

THE SAFEGUARDS

Equipment Preparation and Condition

Although it is beyond the scope of this chapter to describe all the fire prevention considerations that are tied into proper equipment design, installation, and maintenance, some significant items have been selected for specific attention.

Oxy-Fuel Gas Equipment

Equipment meeting recognized standards (e.g., torches, cylinder manifolds, pressure regulators, pipeline protective devices, etc.) should be used.

Since oxygen is a far more powerful oxidizer than air, oxygen equipment must be kept clean (i.e., free of oil, grease, and other combustible contaminants). According to NFPA 51B, *Cutting and Welding Processes*, "Materials that burn in air will burn violently in pure oxygen at normal pressure and explosively in pressurized oxygen. Also, many materials that do not burn in air will do so in pure oxygen, particularly under pressure." Consequently, it is widely recognized good practice to reserve equipment for oxygen service only.

Proper storage of gas cylinders is important. Details can be found in NFPA 51, *Oxygen-Fuel Gas Systems for Welding, Cutting and Allied Processes*.

Cylinders should be moved and handled in accordance with recognized practices, e.g., those of the American National Standards Institute (ANSI) and the Compressed Gas Association (CGA). (See bibliography.) There are many such recognized practices, and their importance may vary with working locations and conditions. However, cylinders should always be supported or located in such a way that they cannot be knocked over. Ruptured cylinders can explode.

Oxy-fuel gas cutting and welding equipment should be tested periodically for leaks. (See Figure 2-14F.) Testing frequency depends upon the specific kind of equipment involved and how often it is used. Hose connections are known possible trouble spots. Also, experience has shown that fires occur at fuel gas cylinder-to-regulator connections simply because someone failed to tighten the joint properly. The ignition of leaking gas at this point may in turn cause the release of cylinder safety devices, especially with acetylene cylinders fitted with fusible plugs, thereby releasing more gas and increasing the size of the fire.

FIG. 2-14F. Before operating an oxy-fuel gas outfit, the equipment should be checked for leaks. After pressurizing both hose lines (with torch valves tightly closed), test for leakage at the following points, using an approved leak-test solution: (1,2) acetylene cylinder connection and acetylene cylinder valve spindle, (3) acetylene regulator-to-hose connection, (4) oxygen valve spindle, (5) oxygen cylinder connection, (6) oxygen regulator-to-hose connection, (7,8) hose connections at the torch, and (9) torch tip (for leakage past the torch valves). Later, after lighting the torch, check for leakage at the throttle valve stems (A,B) and at the welding head-to-torch handle connection (C). (Source: Linde Div., Union Carbide Corporation)

Only standard welding hose should be used.[4] It should be frequently inspected for burns, cuts, worn places, abrasions, and similar defects. Taped repairs are unacceptable. Replace the damaged hose, or, if feasible, cut out the affected area and insert a proper splice.

When repairs to equipment, e.g., torches and regulators, are required, they should be carried out by trained, skilled mechanics.

Arc Welding Equipment

When using arc welding equipment, the following should be addressed:

1. Use equipment meeting recognized American National Standards Institute, National Electrical Manufacturers Association, and Underwriters Laboratories Inc. (UL) criteria. Installation, including incoming power lines

and grounding of the machine frame or case, should comply with NFPA 70, *National Electrical Code®*, with particular attention to its Article 630, "Electric Welders," and with ANSI/ASC Z49.1, *Standard for Safety in Welding and Cutting.*
2. Proper storage and handling procedures for cylinders of shielding gases should be observed.
3. At each work location, cylinders should be supported or located in such a way that they cannot be knocked over accidentally. Precautions must be taken that the cylinders are not grounded.
4. Cable sizes should be adequate for current and anticipated duty cycles. Sustained overloading of inadequate cables may burn away insulation. Cables should be inspected frequently for wear and damage, and properly repaired or replaced when necessary.

Precautions for the Work Area

Hazardous sparks, e.g., globules of molten, burning metal or hot slag, are produced by both welding and cutting operations. Sparks from cutting, particularly oxy-fuel gas cutting, are generally more hazardous than those from welding because the sparks are more numerous and travel greater distances. In a sense, they are jet propelled by the oxygen or airstreams used in cutting processes. Oxy-fuel gas flames and electric arcs are inherent and obvious ignition sources, as are hot workpieces or sections cut from the base workpiece.

Either isolation or protection of combustibles is essential, for they may be exposed to sparks that fall through cracks or other openings in floors and partitions. If those sparks are of sufficient mass to retain heat for a time, they may ignite combustibles. The minimum requirements for combustible control in the cutting or welding work area are:

1. Move all combustibles a safe distance away—at least 35 ft (10.6 m) horizontally—and be sure that there are no openings in walls or floors within 35 ft (10.6 m); or
2. Move the work to a safe location; or
3. If neither of the foregoing steps is possible, protect the exposed combustibles with suitable fire-resistant guards and provide a trained fire watcher with extinguishing equipment readily available.

These steps are only a partial solution to the problem of preventing cutting and welding fires. There are other important factors to consider. Are there any inconspicuous combustibles in an area proposed for cutting and welding operations? What conditions must be met before cutting and welding operations can take place? Who has the responsibility for authorizing the work to proceed? Are cutters, welders, and their supervisors properly trained in the use of their equipment and in emergency procedures should a fire occur? If an outside firm is engaged to do cutting and welding work, chances are that its employees will be unfamiliar with the premises and its contents. Have they been briefed on the conditions in the areas where they will work?

Based on the fundamental but necessary understanding that welders, their supervisors, and facility management share the responsibility for firesafety, the following abridged version of NFPA 51B, *Cutting and Welding Processes,* should be helpful:

1. Management should establish areas designed and authorized for cutting and welding and/or designate a knowledgeable person to authorize welding or cutting in areas not specifically designed for such processes. This management designee should require trained fire watchers where the potential exists for a significant fire to develop. Fire watchers should also be required where appreciable quantities of shielded combustibles are less than 35 ft (10.6 m) away; where wall or floor openings within 35 ft (10.6 m) expose combustibles in adjacent areas; or where combustibles adjacent to opposite sides of partitions, ceiling, or roofs are likely to be ignited by heat from the work. Management should select contractors with a view to their awareness of risks and the quality of their personnel. Management should also advise contractors of the presence of flammable materials or other hazardous conditions on the property work site.
2. The supervisor of welding and cutting operations, e.g., the plant manager, plant maintenance foreman, contractor, or contractor's foreman, in areas not designed for such processes should be assigned the following responsibilities:
   a. Determine what combustible materials are present at the work site.
   b. If necessary, have the work or the combustibles moved, or have the combustibles shielded.
   c. Secure authorization from management, preferably in the form of a written permit.
   d. See that the welder is aware of the authorization and conditions.
   e. See that fire watchers are available when required.
   f. Make a final check for fires one-half hour after completion of welding or cutting operations in cases where a fire watcher was not required.
3. Welders should have their supervisor's approval before starting to cut or weld, should handle their equipment safely, and should continue to work only so long as approval conditions do not change.
4. There are a number of precautions to be observed during welding and cutting operations:
   a. Welding and cutting must not be permitted in flammable (explosive) atmospheres; near large quantities of exposed, readily ignitable materials; in areas not authorized by management; or on metal partitions, walls, or roofs with combustible covering or with combustible sandwich-type panel construction.
   b. Floors should be free of combustibles, such as wood shavings. If the floor is of combustible material, it should be kept wet or otherwise protected.
   c. If combustibles are closer to the welding or cutting process than 35 ft (10.6 m) and the work cannot be moved or the combustibles relocated at least 35 ft (10.6 m) away, they should be protected with flameproofed covers or metal guards or curtains. This also applies to walls, partitions, ceilings, or roofs of combustible construction.
   d. Openings in walls, floors, or ducts should be covered if within 35 ft (10.6 m) of the work.
   e. Cutting or welding on pipes or other metal in contact with combustible walls, partitions, ceilings, or roofs should not be performed if close enough to cause ignition by heat conduction.

f. Charged and operable fire extinguishers should be readily available. Trained fire watchers should be posted. In the absence of fire watchers, an important minimum step would be to check the work area and adjacent areas carefully for at least one-half hour after completion of welding or cutting to detect possible smoldering fires.

SPECIAL SITUATIONS AND ADDITIONAL PRECAUTIONS

Containers that Have Held Combustibles

Welding or cutting on containers that contain or have contained combustibles can cause—and has caused—explosions or fires with potential for deaths or serious injuries. Therefore it is essential that flammable liquids, solids, or vapors be removed from containers by some type of adequate cleaning procedure before welding or cutting.

Depending upon the application, it may be necessary or desirable to supplement the cleaning with inerting, water flooding, or periodic testing (for flammables) of the atmosphere within the container. With some materials, water washing or flushing may be sufficient; others may respond to steam cleaning; some may require alkaline cleaners (trisodium phosphate or caustic soda); some may call for more specialized cleaning methods. Heavy, viscous liquids and solids can be especially difficult to remove completely. Residues are especially dangerous because they may be volatilized or decomposed into flammable products by the heat of the torch or arc. For details concerning these hazards, see UL *Safety Standard for Transformer-Type Arc Welding Machines* and AWS F4.1, "Recommended Safe Practices for the Preparation for Welding and Cutting of Containers that Have Held Hazardous Substances."

Jacketed Containers and Hollow Parts

There are some similarities between the hazards of cutting or welding jacketed containers or other hollow workpieces, and hazards of cutting or welding containers that have held combustible materials. Air confined inside an unvented hollow part will expand when heated, and pressure will increase. Since hot metal rapidly loses its strength, the container or hollow piece may burst with explosive force at the focus of the cutting or welding work. It is well to be suspicious of closed metal parts that seem unusually light. Drilling a vent hole before heating the part may be necessary.

Hot Tapping

Occasionally, there are situations where emergency repair or the complete impracticality of emptying and cleaning demand welding or cutting on a container while it holds flammable gas or liquid (for example, a natural gas transmission pipeline or utility distribution system). Schemes to accomplish such hot tapping with relative safety have been developed. (See ANSI B31.8, "Gas Transmission and Distribution Piping Systems," and API PSD-2201, "Welding or Hot Tapping on Equipment Containing Flammables.") Needless to say, any such work should be performed only by specially trained and qualified staff, using recognized and authorized methods.

Public Exhibitions and Demonstrations

Special and enhanced fire safeguarding is necessary when welding or cutting is performed at trade shows and exhibitions. Characteristically, places of public assembly, such as auditoriums and hotel exhibit halls, and concentrations of people are involved. When welding or cutting work is planned in such exposures, the fire department should have prior notification, operations should be under the control of a qualified person, gas cylinders should be charged to only one-half their maximum permissible content, storage sites for gas cylinders should have special restrictions, and fire extinguishing equipment should be appropriate to the situation.

Personnel Protection and Ventilation

One aspect of welding and cutting fire protection that is sometimes overlooked or inadequately considered is the safety of the operator, helpers, or nearby workers. Flame-resistant gloves, wool clothing, aprons of leather or other durable flame-resistant material, cape sleeves or shoulder covers with skull caps under helmets or with goggles for overhead work, leggings for heavy work, and high-top safety shoes are generally recommended. Trousers should not be turned up or cuffed on the outside, front pockets on clothing should be eliminated, and sleeves and collars kept buttoned to prevent sparks from entering and lodging in such places. Outer clothing should be free of oil and grease. Cotton instead of wool clothing may be worn if the cotton is chemically treated to reduce its combustibility.

Adequate ventilation must be provided wherever welding and cutting are performed to protect the operator from inhaling noxious gases and fumes. Potentially hazardous materials may exist in certain fluxes, coatings, and filler metals. In some cases, general natural draft ventilation may be adequate. Other operations may require forced-draft ventilation, local exhaust hoods or booths, or personal respirators or air-supplied masks.

Oxygen, since it accelerates combustion, must never be used to cool the welder, ventilate a confined space, or dust off clothing. Tests and experience have shown that oxygen-saturated clothing or clothing in an oxygen-enriched atmosphere will literally burn in a flash, with extremely serious and sometimes fatal results.

Manufacturers' Recommendations

Procedures given in manufacturers' instructions for setting up, connecting, lighting or starting, adjusting, and maintaining equipment have specific, safety-oriented purposes. These procedures should be followed. In addition, precautions and safe practices publications with valuable information about fire and personnel safety are available from equipment suppliers.

BIBLIOGRAPHY

References Cited

1. Manz, A. F., "Who Needs Fire Watches for Welding and Cutting? You Do!," *Fire Journal*, Vol. 83, No. 1 (Jan./Feb. 1989), pp. 58-60 .

2. Hall, John R., Jr., "The U.S. Fire Problem Overview Report Through 1988," NFPA Fire Analysis and Research Division, Quincy, MA, Nov. 1989.

3. "Standard Connections for Regulators, Torches, and Fitted Hose for Welding and Cutting Equipment," *CGA Pamphlet E-1*, Compressed Gas Association, Arlington, VA, 1980.

4. *Specifications for Rubber Welding Hose*, 4th ed., Rubber Manufacturers Association, Washington, DC, and Compressed Gas Association, Arlington, VA, 1976.

References

ANSI B31.8, *Gas Transmission and Distribution Piping Systems*, Paragraph 841.27, American National Standards Institute, New York, 1975.

ANSI Z49.1, *Standard for Safety in Welding and Cutting*, American National Standards Institute, New York, 1988.

"Electric Arc Welding Apparatus," *NEMA EW-1*, 1983, National Electrical Manufacturers Association, Washington, DC.

"Procedures for Welding or Hot Tapping on Equipment Containing Flammables," *API PSD-2201*, American Petroleum Institute, Washington, DC, 1985.

"Recommended Safe Practices for the Preparation for Welding and Cutting of Containers that Have Held Hazardous Substances," *AWS F4.1*, American Welding Society, Miami, FL, 1988.

"Safe Handling of Compressed Gases in Containers," *CGA Pamphlet P-1*, Compressed Gas Association, Arlington, VA, 1984.

UL 551, *Safety Standard for Transformer-Type Arc Welding Machines*, Underwriters Laboratories Inc., Chicago, IL.

NFPA Codes, Standards, and Recommended Practices

Reference to the following NFPA codes, standards, and recommended practices will provide further information on the safeguards for welding and cutting operations discussed in this chapter. (See the latest *NFPA Catalog* for availability of current editions of the following documents.)

NFPA 10, *Portable Fire Extinguishers.*

NFPA 50, *Bulk Oxygen Systems at Consumer Sites.*

NFPA 51, *Oxygen-Fuel Gas Systems for Welding, Cutting, and Allied Processes.*

NFPA 51B, *Cutting and Welding Processes.*

NFPA 70, *National Electrical Code®.*

NFPA 306, *Control of Gas Hazards on Vessels.*

NFPA 327, *Cleaning or Safeguarding Small Tanks and Containers.*

Additional Reading

"Acetylene Cylinders—Hazards and Procedures," *Fire Prevention*, No. 202 (Sept. 1987), pp. 31-32.

ANSI, Z117.1, *Safety Requirements for Working in Tanks and Other Confined Spaces*, American National Standards Institute, NY, 1977.

"Safe Practices in Gas and Electric Cutting and Welding," *Publication 2009*, 4th ed., American Petroleum Institute, Washington, DC, 1976.

"Cleaning Tank Vehicles Used for Transportation of Flammable Liquids," *Publication 2013*, 1st ed., American Petroleum Institute, Washington, DC, 1975.

"Cleaning Petroleum Storage Tanks," *Publication 2015*, 3rd ed., American Petroleum Institute, Washington, DC, 1985.

Ashmore, F. and McNally, M., "Dealing with Acetylene," *Fire Prevention*, No. 204 (Nov. 1987), pp.37-38.

C5.2-83, *Recommended Practices for Plasma Arc Cutting*, American Welding Society, Miami, FL, 1983.

Safe Practices, American Welding Society, Miami, FL, 1988.

Safety and Health Fact Sheets, American Welding Society, Miami, FL, 1990.

Bartknecht, W., "Ignition Capabilities of Hot Surfaces and Mechanically Generated Sparks in Flammable Gas and Dust/Air Mixtures," *Plant/Operation Progress*, Vol. 7, No. 2, 1988, pp. 114-121.

Buehrer, P., "Check List for the Prevention of Fires Arising from Welding and Allied Processes," *Welding in the World*, Vol. 14, No. 5-6, 1976, pp. 122-125.

Compressed Gas Association, *Handbook of Compressed Gases*, 3rd ed., Van Nostrand Reinhold, NY, 1990.

Connor, L. P., *Welding Handbook*, 8th ed., American Welding Society, Miami, FL, 1987.

"Handling Acetylene Cylinders in Fire Situations," *Bulletin SB-4*, Compressed Gas Association, Arlington, VA, 1972 (Reaffirmed 1980).

"Hose Line Check Valve Standards for Welding and Cutting," *Pamphlet E-2*, 2nd ed., Compressed Gas Association, Arlington, VA, 1983.

"Industrial Practices for Gaseous Oxygen Transmission and Distribution Piping Systems," 2nd ed., *Pamphlet G-4.4*, Compressed Gas Association, Arlington, VA, 1980.

"Oxygen," 8th ed., *Pamphlet G-4*, Compressed Gas Association, Arlington, VA. 1987.

"Pipeline Regulator Inlet Connection Standards," 2nd ed., *Pamphlet E-3*, Compressed Gas Association, Arlington, VA, 1981.

"Standard for Gas Regulators for Welding and Cutting," 2nd ed., *Pamphlet E-4*, Compressed Gas Association, Arlington, VA, 1980.

"Torch Standard for Welding and Cutting," *Pamphlet E-5*, Compressed Gas Association, Arlington, VA, 1977.

CGA-G-1, "Acetylene," *Pamphlet*, 7th ed., Compressed Gas Association, Arlington, VA. 1980.

CGA-V-1, *Compressed Gas Cylinder Valve Outlet and Inlet Connections*, 6th ed., Compressed Gas Association, Arlington, VA, 1987.

CGA-C4, *Method of Marking Portable Compressed Gas Containers to Identify the Material Contained*, 3rd ed., Compressed Gas Association, Arlington, VA, 1978.

Hoelemann, H. and Worpenberg, R., "Investigations on Fires Caused by Welding, Cutting, and Related Procedures—Damage Evaluation," *Schweissen und Schneiden*, Vol. 38, No.4, 1986, pp. E60-E63.

Kennebeck, M. E., "Eight Points to Ponder for Safe Welding and Cutting," *Welding Journal*, Vol. 67, No. 9, 1988, pp. 67-69.

Koellhoffer, L., Manz, A. F., and Hornberger, E. G., *Welding Processes and Practices*, Wiley, NY, 1988.

Manz, A. F., *The Welding Power Handbook*, Union Carbide Corporation, Tarrytown, NY, 1973.

Manz, A. F., "Who Needs Fire Watches for Welding and Cutting? You Do!," *Fire Journal*, Vol. 83, No. 1 (Jan./Feb. 1989), pp. 58-60.

Nightingale, P. J., "Investigation into an Explosion that Occured During a Welding Operation," *Plant/Operation Progress*, Vol. 8, No. 1 (Jan. 1989), pp. 29-32.

NSC, *Accident Prevention Manual for Industrial Operations*, 9th ed., National Safety Council, Chicago, IL, 1988.

OSHA, 29 CFR 1910. 252, Subpart Q, *Welding and Cutting*, Government Printing Office, Washington, DC.

"Prevent Cutting/Welding Fires," The Minnesota Fire Chief, Vol. 16, No. 5 (May/June 1980), pp. 16, 48, 54.

Safety in Welding and Cutting, American Welding Society, Miami, FL, 1988.

UL-123, *Standard for Oxy-Fuel Gas Torches*, 5th ed., Underwriters Laboratories, Inc. Chicago, IL, 1975.

UL-252, *Standard for Gas Pressure Regulators*, 4th ed., Underwriters Laboratories Inc., Chicago, IL, 1973.

UL-407, *Standard for High-Pressure Gas Manifolds*, 3rd ed., Underwriters Laboratories Inc., Chicago, IL, 1972.

CHEMICAL PROCESSING EQUIPMENT

Revised by W. J. Bradford

This chapter discusses the chemical reactions, the means of reaction control, and the equipment used to produce chemicals and synthetics, such as fibers, plastics, and some drugs. Operations to chemically change the properties of materials, as in the chemical pulping of wood or the tanning of leather, are also covered. However, in discussing fire and explosion prevention and loss control, the hazards inherent in each system must be considered as a whole when appropriate separation distances and other means of minimizing damage are examined.

Additional relevant information can be found in the following chapters: Section 1, Chapter 5, "Explosions;" Section 1, Chapter 6, "Theory of Fire and Explosion Control;" Section 2, Chapter 8, "Heat Transfer Systems (Nonwater Media);" Section 2, Chapter 14, "Welding and Cutting;" Section 2, Chapter 33, "Waste Handling Systems and Equipment;"and Section 9, Chapter 17, "Hazardous Waste Control."

PLANT SITING

Loss Prevention in the Process Industries[1] notes that safety is a prime consideration in plant siting. The most important feature is distance between the site and areas of high population density. Distance tends to reduce casualties; i.e., if a toxic release occurs, the effect of distance reduces the concentration of the gas and buys time to permit evacuation. The chemical disaster at Bhopal, India, in December 1984 was undoubtedly exacerbated by the very high population density immediately adjacent to the plant. If the hazard is fire or explosion, distance will reduce the intensity of radiant heat or blast overpressure as well as damage done by missiles. The density of population adjacent to the liquefied petroleum gas tanks that exploded in Mexico City in September 1984 led to very high loss of life. These two fairly recent incidents resulted in over 3000 fatalities, and rank among the worst industrial incidents in history.

A plant with serious toxic gas release potential or major fire or explosion hazards must be designed to high standards of safety and loss prevention. Distance and plant siting cannot be relied upon to prevent disasters but must be considered as key features in limiting the potential magnitude of an incident.[2]

Separation Distances

Single or allied processes are usually located on individual blocks of land surrounded by access roads. The theory behind the block approach is that fires or unignited spills then can be attacked from all directions. This approach provides maximum latitude to take advantage of both wind direction and the shelter afforded by peripheral structures in the block. If the right of way for these roads is 50 ft (15.25 m) wide, a minimum distance of 50 ft (15.25 m) between structures on adjacent blocks is ensured. This distance has proved adequate to prevent the spread of fire through highly protected properties.

Chemical manufacturing plants pose a special danger of explosion, especially in a large-loss incident. During 1971 to 1988, for example, there were 15 chemical plant fires each involving $5 million in damage reported to NFPA. These 15 incidents collectively caused 20 deaths and $418.9 million in direct property damage. Nine of the 15 incidents (62 percent of dollar loss, 90 percent of deaths) began with explosions, another two incidents (26 percent of dollar loss, 10 percent of deaths) had explosions after fire began, a twelfth had explosions that may have preceded or followed the fire (5 percent of dollar loss), and two had reports that did not indicate whether explosions occurred (4 percent of dollar loss). Only one of the 15 (3 percent of dollar loss) definitely did not involve an explosion.

Where an explosion is possible, the 50-ft (15.25 m) distance does not provide sufficient protection. One solution has been to place any unit involving an explosion hazard at least 50 ft (15.25 m) away from the block perimeter. This gives a minimum distance (in the adjacent blocks) of 100 ft (30.5 m) from an explosion hazard to a fire hazard, or 150 ft (45.72 m) between explosion hazards. In the case of equipment explosions resulting from an increase in internal pressure, the shock wave would probably be adequately

W. J. Bradford, P.E., is a loss prevention consultant. He is a registered professional engineer in Connecticut and Rhode Island, and is a member of AIChE and SFPE. He serves on several NFPA technical committees.

attenuated by that distance. This is true whether the explosion is of the thermal type, represented by an ordinary runaway reaction and failure of the container, or of the shock type, where the pressure increase is caused by a reaction at supersonic speed. In the latter case, the rapid pressure increase could produce shrapnel, so a containment barricade would be needed. If the material that might cause the explosion is a true explosive, whether formed intentionally or accidentally, and whether inside or outside of equipment, the spacing then should be in accordance with the American Table of Distances for Storage of Explosives. (See also NFPA 495, *Manufacture, Transportation, Storage, and Use of Explosive Materials.*)

Conservative views on spacing are taken by the American Oil Company. Its *Engineering for Safe Operations* states: "Generally, a distance of 250 ft (76.2 m) between units or between units and tankage has been used as a desirable spacing."[3] Also, Table 2-15A gives the recommendations of the Industrial Risk Insurers (IRI) with respect to petrochemical plants. Their booklet also suggests distances for separation of units in refineries, gasoline plants, terminals, oil pump stations, and offshore property.[4]

The greater distances suggested by the American Oil Company and IRI are justified by the large amounts of flammables usually present in equipment and piping in oil refineries and petrochemical plants. They are probably adequate for controlling even large flammable liquid fires.

Another method for plant spacing was presented using the Mond Fire, Explosion, and Toxicity Index.[5] This resulted from an official inquiry into the Flixborough disaster in 1974. It requires a ranking of hazards of various units at an early stage of the design. The rankings are then used to lay out a plant to minimize loss potential. The method has undergone further study and a revision was suggested in 1989.[6]

For another type of explosion hazard, no spacing standards exist. This is the explosion which results when a flammable gas or super-heated flammable liquid is released into the atmosphere and mixes with air to form a cloud with a volume in the explosive range. Such a cloud can release some 2 to 10 percent of its heat of combustion in the form of explosive energy. In estimating potential losses from vapor clouds, IRI uses the 2 percent figure. This decision was reached after studying the results of 79 cases of vapor cloud formation.[7] In 7 cases there was no ignition; in 17 there was ignition but no pressure was generated. The remaining 55 cases formed the data base.

If a hydrocarbon releases 20,000 Btu per lb (46.5 mJ/kg) when burned and 2 percent of that, or 400 Btu per lb (930 kJ/kg) were released explosively by ignition of its mixture with air, then 5 lb (23 kg) of hydrocarbon would release 2000 Btu per lb (4.65 mJ/kg) explosively—the same as 1 lb (0.45 kg) of TNT. Where such releases are possible, spacing is not a reliable defense against damage, since no one can predict where the cloud will drift before it is ignited.

Procedures used to estimate damage from explosion pressure resulting from ignition of a vapor cloud are:

1. Estimate the volume of vapor produced by the release.
2. Assume that a percentage of the heat of combustion of this volume will be released as explosion energy.
3. Equate this energy to an equivalent amount of TNT.
4. Estimate damage, based on the explosion of that amount of TNT.

This is discussed briefly by Davenport.[7] More extensive comments, with a table of pressure ranges at which different units of equipment may be expected to fail, have been made by Nelson.[8]

Experimental work has been performed to develop an improved method to predict the blast effect from vapor clouds.[9] The method recognizes the importance of partial confinement, with regard to the strength of vapor cloud explosions. The experiments were made to quantify the influence of obstacles and partial confinement.

Other Means of Loss Control

As chemical plants process larger quantities of materials, it becomes impractical to provide ever-increasing separation of units. Where toxic, flammable, reactive, or otherwise hazardous materials may be spilled, the logical approach is to:

1. Minimize the possibility of uncontrolled spills.
2. Minimize the size of a possible spill (if spills do occur, design features should keep them small).
3. Minimize the spread of a possible spill (if spills are large in volume, design features should keep them confined).
4. Prepare alarm and evacuation plans if toxic releases can occur.
5. Control sources of ignition.
6. Provide protection for exposed property if ignition does occur.

In 1988, the AIChE published *Guidelines for Vapor Release Mitigation,*[10] to reduce the risk of accidental releases of toxic or flammable vapors. This book should be of considerable assistance in reducing situations that have caused major fire, health, and environmental problems.

EXPOSURE PROTECTION

Automatic fire control and extinguishing systems are the first line of defense against fire and explosion emergencies. However, if an explosion hazard exists, system designs would require barricades for protection of important components, such as deluge valves and dry pipe valves.[11] If they might be exposed to explosion pressure, however improbably, process control houses, including areas where people congregate (e.g., change houses), should be of explosion-resistant design.[12–15] The procedure suggested by Bradford and Culbertson[12] is based on resistance to static pressure; that in the Chemical Manufacturers Association's Safety Guide[13] is based on elastic response to a timed pressure impulse. Lawrence and Johnson[15] give a concise exposition of the design theory. Reliably available water at pressure and volume adequate to supply the maximum foreseeable fire fighting and exposure protection demand for a minimum of four hours is desirable. Of course, built-in or added fire resistance can give excellent exposure protection.

Protection for a chemical plant generally requires a specialized fire department where each fire fighter is equipped with full protective clothing, including self-contained breathing apparatus (SCBA), and where acid-resistant hose and special extinguishing equipment are available. NFPA 49, *Hazardous Chemicals Data,* is an excellent source for information on personal protection

TABLE 2-15A. ***General Recommendations for Spacing in Petrochemical Plants***

Minimum Distance in Feet*	Process Unit—HH	Process Unit—LH	Tank Farms—HH	Tank Farms—LH	Product Whses—LH	Ship'g. & Rec'g.—HH	Ship'g. & Rec'g.—LH	Service Buildings	Boiler Area	Fire Pumps	Emergency Controls	Water Spray Controls	Turret Nozzles	Emergency Flares	Pilot Plants	Large Cooling Towers	Fire Hydrants	Fired Process Heaters
Process unit—(high hazard)[B]	200[A]									250	100	50[5]	50–100 to center of target	For 100' flare that is 25' above surrounding equipment, use 300'	200	150	50 to 250	50 to 100
Process unit—(low hazard)	100[A]	50[A]								150	50	100[5]			200	100		50
Tank farms—(high hazard)[C]	250[1]	250[1]	1 1/2 dia. larger							250		100[5]			250	250		200
Tank farms—(low hazard)	200[2]	100[3]	1 dia. larger	1/2 dia. larger						200					200	200		200
Product warehouse (low hazard)[D]	150	50[4]	250[1]	100[3]	50[4]					200					200	150		100
Shipping & receiving (high hazard)[E]	200	200	150[2]	100[3]	150	50				150	100	50[5]			200	200		200
Shipping & receiving (low hazard)	150	100	100	50	20	50	—			100	50				150	150		100
Service buildings[F]	200	100	200	100	100	150	100	See bldg. chart		100					200	100		100
Boiler area	200	150	200	150	100	200	100	100	—	—					200	100		100

Recommended Spacing Within Process Units

	React.	Comp.	Tanks	Fract. Equip.	Cont. Rooms
Reactor	25[6]				
Small compressor house or pump house	40[6]				
Intermediate storage tanks high Hazard rundown-feed	100 to 200	100 to 200	17 dia.		
Fractionation equipment	50	30	100		
Control rooms[G]	50[6] to 100	50 to 100	100	50 to 100	10

Notes:

(A) Distance between process units is measured from battery limits.

(B) A high hazard process unit includes those with high or extreme explosion hazards.

A process with high explosion hazard is one where there is considerable explosion potential or probability with susceptibility to considerable damage or serious delays in restoration. Examples are: acetylene purification; acrylonitrile formation from hydrogen cyanide and ethylene oxide; acrylonitrile formation from hydrogen cyanide and acetylene; alkylation (using acetylene); partial oxidation of low flash point (below 110°F) (43°C) liquids, such as oxidation of acetaldehyde to acetic acid; vinyl acetate formation from acetylene and acetic acid; vinyl chloride formation from acetylene and hydrogen chloride; and ethylene oxide production, recovery and purification.

A process with an extreme explosion hazard is one employing extreme pressures or is one that is unpredictable and not susceptible to design that will limit the extent of the damage or interruption to minor proportions. These processes, while not susceptible to exact description, can generally be recognized by engineering analysis. A process that uses very high pressures in equipment properly designed for the purpose and in connection with processes of predictable hazard (a synthetic ammonia plant is an example) does not of itself require classification as an extreme explosion hazard. Examples of processes with extreme explosion hazards are: acetylene compression when the partial pressure is 20 psia (139kPa) or higher; storage of organic coated ammonium nitrate or ammonium nitrate with an additive; acrolein drum storage; acrolein recovery and purification and acrolein barreling.

(C) High hazard tanks are those that contain liquids having a flash point below 110°F (43°C) or are tanks or gas holders containing flammable gases other than anhydrous ammonia (for hazard rating purposes, anhydrous ammonia is classified as a liquid having a flash point above 200°F (93°C). Tanks containing unstable liquids or gases, such as acrolein, acrylonitrile, ethylene oxide, hydrogen cyanide, styrene, vinyl acetate and vinylidene chloride require special consideration unless the materials contain stabilizing inhibitors known to be effective.

(D) High hazard product warehouses contain unstable materials, low-flash flammable liquids, or high combustible solids. These require special consideration.

(E) High hazard shipping and receiving denotes stable materials with flash point below 110°F (43°C). High hazard shipping and receiving of unstable materials requires special consideration.

(F) Service buildings include offices, gate houses, change houses, laboratories, shops, garages, maintenance warehouses, cafeterias, hospitals, etc. Experimental laboratories classify as process units.

(G) Control houses serving unusually large or hazardous units and central control houses for multiple units or housing computer equipment, require greater spacing and may require blast-resistant construction.

(1) For specific vertical tank, use 5 diameters.

(2) For specific vertical tank, use 4 diameters.

(3) For specific vertical tank, use 3 diameters.

(4) Standard firewall and sprinklered warehouse acceptable. Limit warehouse to maximum 25,000 sq ft (2322.5 m^2) floor area.

(5) Two stations desirable.

(6) Barricades desirable for hazardous reactors.

(7) Over 100,000 gal (378.5 m^3) requires special consideration.

General Notes:

Keep open flames 100 feet (30.5 m) from vapor hazard area.

Deviation from the distances in this table requires superior construction or special protective installations such as fixed foam systems, water spray systems,

automatic sprinklers of a water spray from hose lines capable of supplying about 2500 gpm (9.5 m^3) to the points of need and a trained brigade adequately manned to use the water spray.

In borderline cases, high value requires high hazard classification.

Vertical storage tanks should be individually diked. If not, capacity in a single dike should not exceed 25,000 barrels. For horizontal storage tanks, maximum is 400,000 gal (1514 m^3) per group, with 100 feet (30.4 m) between groups, or other suitable arrangement.

*one ft equals 0.304 m

measures needed to fight fires involving different chemicals, as well as the tactics that should be used in emergencies. Appropriate symbols from NFPA 704, *Identification of the Fire Hazards of Materials,* posted at locations on the property where chemicals are present, can give helpful guidance on inherent hazards of materials present and on planning effective fire fighting operations.

IGNITION SOURCES

The general notes in Table 2-15A recommend that open flames be kept at least 100 ft (30.5 m) from any hazardous area. These notes contemplate fixed equipment; however, they could also apply to maintenance work. A better approach is to prohibit open flames or other hotwork in all but predetermined specified areas, except where the hotwork to be done has been examined and found safe, and the work is done under a permit that limits scope and duration. It must be remembered that piping for high-pressure steam, heat-transfer media, and hot process streams may need insulation to keep it from becoming a source of ignition. When piping operating at high temperatures is insulated, it may be necessary to leave flanges uninsulated. If the bolts joining flanges get too hot, their thermal expansion will relax the compression on the joints and may lead to leakage.

CONTROL OF SPILLS

Large flammable liquid spills should be confined where they may occur. Although retaining dikes are often used, they may not prevent liquid around the spill source from burning. Equipment may be damaged further or the spill aggravated unless efficient, prompt, and preferably automatic fire control measures are taken. A better approach is to provide drainage to an impounding basin located where a fire, if not extinguished, can burn out harmlessly or a nonburning toxic material can be appropriately neutralized. A spill is often ignited at some time during the drainage process, so care must be taken to avoid damage during drainage. If the sewerage system is underground and is not provided with liquid seals at all entrance points, explosions in the system could result. Fire in open drainage ditches could damage anything without adequate protection that is located alongside the ditches or that crosses them, such as utility or piping systems. Problems associated with such drainage can be avoided by using the trench system described in NFPA 15, *Water Spray Fixed Systems for Fire Protection.*

Total confinement of a large flammable gas or vapor spill is not possible, due to the gaseous nature of the spill. Hose lines or monitors with spray nozzles can be used, because of the air entrained by the spray, to dilute the gas cloud and to move it in a desired direction until it dissipates. Fixed water spray nozzles may be used to set up water curtains which prevent a cloud from drifting to a furnace or other ignition source. Units that have been effective in experiments with small, low-level vapor releases were discussed in a number of articles in *Loss Prevention.*[14,16] The use of steam nozzles to dilute and direct vapors upward at an installation in England has been reported.[17] There are problems with this approach. Large steam capacity must always be available; and there is the need for meticulous grounding of all metallic material that might be charged by steam passing over it or condensing on it, in order to avoid static sparks that might ignite material being dispersed.

Keeping Spills Small

Hazardous spills can be kept small by keeping the amount of hazardous material used in the process small. Where this is impractical, valves to isolate all large quantities of material should be provided. These valves should be installed at each outlet of any large container through which material might escape (except at relief devices). They can also be used to subdivide long runs of large-diameter pipe. The valves should be firesafe, i.e., they should not leak appreciably when exposed to fire after being closed, and they should be arranged to operate both remotely and at the valve. If operated by electric motor, both the power wiring to the motor and the signal wiring to the starting switch should be arranged to remain functional during any fire or other emergency requiring valve operation, for at least as long as it would take to discover the emergency, transmit the alarm, and operate the valve. A minimum of 15-min fire protection for wiring is suggested. If valves are held open by instrument air pressure and closed by spring or gravity when air pressure is lost, plastic tubing can be used in the air line, at least near the valve. The plastic will melt quickly in a fire, and the valve will close before it is damaged. Since it is necessary to detect spills before ignition, flammable vapor detectors of the diffusion-head type may be used for that purpose.[18]

The distinction between a small spill and a large one must be fixed individually for each plant. A small spill is one that can be easily handled by the exposure protection and confinement means. All others are large spills. In the case of jets of liquefied flammable gas[19,20] or hot flammable liquid[21] where spacing is not a reliable defense against explosion damage, various quantities have been proposed as limits that must not be exceeded. One organization suggests 10,000 lb (4536 kg) of gas or vapor as a maximum permissible spill. Another suggests a maximum permissible leakage rate as one that would permit formation of no more than 1,000 lb per min (454 kg/min) of flammable gas or vapor.

Preventing Spills

Because many chemicals cause unusual corrosion or abrasion problems, or their processing requires unusually high or low temperatures, chemical plants should be constructed of appropriate materials and should follow good maintenance practices. Assuming that there are no problems in these areas, the reaction systems themselves may cause trouble.

In general, reactions are used to produce desired commodities that differ chemically from the raw materials from which they are made. The differences are produced by controlled chemical changes. Uncontrolled changes tend to produce both unwanted materials and more or less violent system failures that result in spills. The common denominator in these failures is overheating, i.e., overheating of a container so that it softens and fails, or overheating of the contents so that the container bursts from too much pressure. Accidents of these types result from a failure to move heat adequately from a heat source to a heat-absorbing system or to a coolant from a heat-releasing system. Heat is usually produced when materials dissolve, crystallize, condense, or are adsorbed. Heat is also produced mechanically by crushing, grinding, milling, compressing, and pumping, and by exothermic chemical reactions. Heat transfer is also required when heat is needed for evaporation, melting, decreasing viscosity, drying, desorbing, distillation, warming expanding gas, initiating exothermic chemical reactions, and driving endothermic reactions. In any case, loss prevention requires an understanding of heat transfer.

HAZARDS OF HEAT TRANSFER

When a hot fluid, gas, or liquid transfers heat to a cooler fluid through a barrier such as the metal wall of a vessel, the resistance to heat flow, as shown by a temperature drop, is mainly in fluid films on the metal surfaces rather than in the metal. (See Figure 2-15A.) Flow in the heating and heated fluids is usually turbulent, with invisible swirls and eddies; but in the films, it is laminar with thin layers of molecules sliding slowly over each other. The film layer nearest the metal moves slowest and its temperature is nearest that of the metal. This is important because high temperature causes decomposition of most organic and some inorganic fluids. Although a large temperature differential between the fluids moves heat faster than a small one, the hottest part of the heated film must be kept cool enough so that it does not decompose and form a solid film. When a solid film builds up, the temperature of the metal on the heated side may go so high, trying to force the heat through, that the metal is damaged and a "burnout" occurs.

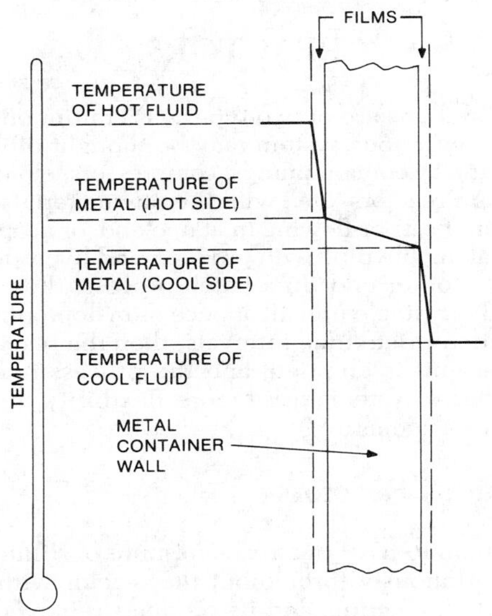

FIG. 2-15A. The effect of fluid films on temperatures at the surfaces of the metal wall of a vessel.

Precautions consist of methods to detect the fluid breakdown, such as checking the fluid for tar, solids, or significant change in viscosity or volatility. Where the heater is of a single tube design, an internal buildup will cause an easily observable increased pressure drop as the fluid flows through the tube. For this reason, single-pass tube heaters are to be preferred over those of multiple fluid path design.

When the breakdown of the fluid is intentional, as in the case of cracking a petroleum fraction, the internal deposits are removed on a scheduled basis before they reach dangerous thickness. This is usually done by burning them out with air or a mixture of air and steam.[22] Requirements for safety involve:

1. Purging the unit of flammables, usually with steam, before introducing the oxidizing atmosphere.
2. Purging after burning out the deposits.
3. Safe disposal of the materials purged.
4. A system of valving, usually involving double valves with a purged or vented space between, to ensure against mixing air and combustibles.

If the heated fluid is a liquid and starts to boil, heat transfer improves as the film is thinned by the action of bubbles of vapor forming on the metal, growing, and breaking away. This formation of bubbles on the heated surface is called "nucleate boiling." If the temperature of the heat source is then raised in an attempt to increase the rate of boiling, the temperature may become too high. Vapor bubbles then coalesce into a vapor film, instead of breaking away individually. This is called "film boiling." Vapor films offer more resistance to heat flow, so, again, "burnout" may occur.

Endothermic Reactions

Endothermic reactions are most commonly supplied with heat by combustion processes. This energy may be truly direct, i.e., cracking natural gas to acetylene by burning part of it with oxygen and quenching suddenly, concentrating a liquid by submerged combustion (burning a premixed gaseous fuel beneath the surface of a liquid), or roasting ore or cementitious material in a kiln. It may also be first degree indirect (usually and hereinafter called direct since the container, tube, or kettle is directly exposed to the flames); or second degree indirect (usually and hereinafter called indirect) where the flames heat a heat transfer fluid. In this process, the use of tempered flue gas constitutes indirect heating.

The same general hazards exist whether the material being heated is a reacting system or one being decomposed or heated. All cases require consideration of the metallurgical and construction characteristics of the equipment. These problems are accentuated in the case of direct-fired equipment. The heater must resist corrosion, pitting, and scaling from the materials being heated as well as from combustion on the firebox side, and must often do so at temperatures much higher than is the case with conventional heat transfer media. Construction must be such that heated and cooled portions can expand and contract freely. This is particularly important if the alloys used enter or pass through a brittle phase at any stage of heating or cooling.

Two more important, but sometimes overlooked, points are:

1. The metal of the heater and heat transfer system and the fluids with which they are in contact must be compatible. The common molten salt heat transfer medium, a mixture of sodium nitrate and sodium nitrite used in indirect-fired heaters, will support the combustion of steel if the temperature is high enough and ignition occurs[23]; steel and copper in thin sections, as on the fins of heat transfer tubes, can ignite easily in hot chlorine.
2. The heat transfer medium should not create a hazard if it leaks into the material being heated or *vice versa.* Where leakage one way but not another can be temporarily tolerated (sulfuric acid into water as opposed to water into sulfuric acid, for example), pressures of the coolant and the cooled material must be suitably different. Alternatively, annular tubes with the annulus separating the two fluids may be used with means

to detect leakage into the annulus from either direction. To promote heat transfer, the annulus may be filled with a conducting liquid inert to both fluids or, as in "still" tubes, intermittently bridged with heat conducting metal wires or perforated discs.

The preceding discussion applies equally well when the heat transfer is from an exothermic reaction to a fluid used for cooling.

It is impossible to be all inclusive about the hazards of heat transfer. Two examples, however, may indicate the scope of the problem. In the first example, electric induction heat was being used on a cast-iron vessel with thermostatic controls. Cast-iron growth (caused by precipitation of carbon from the heated cast iron) caused intercrystalline cracking. The cracks interrupted the flow of the induced electric currents throughout the vessel, the thermostats called for more heat, and the vessel eventually failed from localized overheating. In another instance, sodium silicate was condensed on a stainless-steel pipe where it acted as a flux to remove one of the alloying elements so that the pipe lost its corrosion resistance and failed.

Exothermic Reactions

Proper application of heat transfer principles is essential to the control of exothermic reactions. Such use requires knowledge of the reaction system. First, it is necessary to know the thermal stability and shock sensitivity of the system and each of its components, raw materials, intermediates, products, and byproducts. Second, the reaction kinetics must be known, i.e., the total amount of heat released and how fast it is released. For completely safe process design, it is necessary to have all of this data under conditions that would exist if the reactants were supplied in grossly wrong proportions, in the wrong order, without mixing (both with and without a subsequent late start of the mixing system), at the wrong temperatures, if power failed, if a coolant line broke, or if any other upset condition imaginable should occur.

STABILITY AND SHOCK SENSITIVITY

Most chemicals are reasonably stable and insensitive. Where this is not true, data usually is available from the supplier or in the literature. NFPA 49, *Hazardous Chemicals Data,* discusses specific chemicals, and NFPA 491M, *Manual of Hazardous Chemical Reactions,* covers hazardous systems. Both of the standards provide lists of references. Where data are not available, thermodynamic calculations and laboratory-scale stability testing should be used.[24-29] Part 41 of the 1979 ASTM Standards contains test procedures developed by Committee E-27 (ASTM annually). Where explosive materials are involved, the hazard may be reduced to an acceptable level by diluting the explosive material in an inert chemical or by providing barricades around the explosive materials.

If the instability hazard is less than explosive, there are various ways to reduce it. Chemical reactions progress faster as the temperature rises, so the methods used involve keeping the material from being heated to an unsafe level. For example, the boiling point of a liquid is lowered by vacuum. Vacuum or freeze drying can help avoid overheating. A high boiling material that becomes unstable at or near its boiling point may have steam bubbled through it at a temperature below the boiling point. Vapor from the material goes along with the steam, and separation can be made after condensing the steam-vapor mixture. Viscous materials can be concentrated by running them down the heated interior walls of a wiped film evaporator. Mechanically operated blades keep wiping the interior surface and the film cannot thicken, so the film layer nearest the hot wall will not overheat. (See Figure 2-15A.) Liquid nitrogen or dry ice may be added to material going to a grinder. This not only takes care of the heat produced mechanically but also tends to inert the atmosphere and reduce chances of a dust explosion.

In some cases, pressure may affect stability. Liquids, such as propargyl bromide and nitromethane, will boil away when heated at atmospheric pressure. If heated under pressure, so the boiling point is raised, they sometimes explode. Pure gases, such as acetylene, ethylene, and nitrous oxide, can be exploded under sufficient pressure. The testing described earlier should be thorough enough to detect such a possibility. Also, when considering systems, one should keep in mind that pressure may cause a phase change. For example, chlorine gas liquefies fairly easily, and a system easy to control when using the gas may be hard to control if the liquid is accidentally formed.

REACTORS

Reaction systems are of two types: (1) continuous, and (2) batch. A continuous system may be thought of as a pipe, although it may contain pumps, compressors, elongater vessels that are reactors, etc., with the raw materials and possibly an inert carrier flowing in at one end, or at appropriate intervals along the pipe with products and byproducts flowing out the other end. In a batch process, the chemicals are added to a single unit all at once or in appropriate quantities at appropriate time intervals; then the reaction takes place, the unit is emptied, and the process is repeated. Batch process systems have more flexibility in use than continuous systems.

Continuous Reactors

It is common to have one reactant, pure or diluted, circulating continuously throughout the reactor with another being added, reacting, and its products removed by condensation, washing, filtering, or similar appropriate means. In normal operation, the major safety control is automatically cutting off the appropriate feed stream if the heat transfer system fails. Arrangements are often made for alternate means of supplying the heat transfer fluids. Reliability of the shutoff system may be enhanced by using two valves in series with a vent between them. (This is known as the double block and bleed system.) Depending on the complexity of the system, this same shutoff may be actuated by changes in other process conditions. An example of a process condition change might be too low a temperature, which would indicate that the reaction was not going properly. This signals that concentrations of unreacted materials may be building up to the point where they could suddenly all react with explosive violence and overpower the means of heat removal, or react in a part of the system designed to recover product rather than control the reaction. Also, when starting up or shutting down, the continuous reactor may go through situations that are more hazardous than its normal operation.

Batch Reactors

The essential parts of a batch reactor are:

1. A vessel to contain the reaction at its maximum pressure.
2. A heat transfer system to control the temperature of the reacting mixture.
3. A stirrer or agitator to keep the temperature and composition of the reacting mixture uniform.
4. A relief system to protect the vessel against overpressure.

The vessel: This may range from an open wood or rubber-lined steel tank in which bauxite ore reacts with sulfuric acid to produce a solution of alum to a glass-lined or stainless-steel pressure vessel. Regardless of size or configuration, the vessel used as a batch reactor will probably have to be entered for cleaning, while the continuous reactor can often be cleaned automatically with a cleaning fluid. Cleaning or entering vessels will require special precautions if flammable cleaning agents are used or if vapors or residues make entry hazardous.

Heat transfer methods: Common methods of heat transfer use jackets or coils on the exterior of the vessel or coils in the interior. Others circulate the reacting mixture from the vessel through an external heat exchanger and back to the vessel. A third method allows the reacting mixture to boil. The heat of vaporization then is removed by condensing the vapor externally, which allows the condensed liquid to run back and continue the cycle. This last method does not provide means to heat the material in the vessel, heat that may be needed to start the reaction even though cooling is needed as the reaction progresses.

Mixing: This is usually performed with an agitator mounted on a shaft driven by an external motor. If an external heat exchanger is used, the mixture leaving it may be jetted back into the vessel to accomplish mixing. Where heat-sensitive materials are involved and it is necessary to avoid moving parts because they might rise to a dangerous temperature due to friction, mixing can be done by bubbling in air or inert gas.

Pressure relief of batch reactors: Batch reactors in which an explosive atmosphere might sometimes exist are usually designed to contain the pressure that might result from ignition, or they are purged or inerted to eliminate the hazard. If vessels are constructed according to the *Pressure Vessel Code* of the American Society of Mechanical Engineers (ASME), they are required to have a relief device adequate to keep the vessel from being overpressured because of overheating from an external source, including an exposure fire, normal heating, or the introduction of fluids at pressures higher than those for which the vessel is designed. The *Code* gives no guidance for the relief of pressure caused by heat of reaction.

Most chemical reactions double in speed with each rise in temperature of 18°F (10°C). This means that a heat removal system would have to remove twice as much heat at 140°F (60°C) as at 122°F (50°C), four times as much at 158°F (70°C), etc. For this reason, it is unsafe to run a batch reaction at a temperature more than 32°F (14°C) above that of the cooling medium.[30] If the cooling system is overpowered, the reaction keeps increasing in speed, the retained heat builds up pressure, and the pressure must be relieved or the vessel will explode. Austin has given a good explanation of this problem.[31] The Dow Chemical Company's "*Guidelines for Process Scale-up*" asks the following questions about runaway reactions:[32]

Can you prevent runaway reactions?	Yes	No
By adequate heat transfer	___	___
By quenching the reaction	___	___
By stopping feed streams	___	___
By dilution of the reactor contents	___	___

Score: Two or more methods—You're in good shape. Only one method—Better find a second line of defense. None of the above—You'd better stop right now and reconsider your design for safety.

However, since even multiple safeguards may fail, emergency venting is supplied as last ditch protection for the vessel. For example, loss of mixing could make all the suggested preventive measures inoperative or dangerously inefficient. Materials that have leaked into the hollow shaft of an agitator have created pressure and spewed materials into the main reaction system, which speeds up the main reaction so that it overpowers the cooling system. Other problems were discussed earlier in this chapter in the section "Exothermic Reactions."

The problem of adequate sizing for emergency venting was recognized by AIChE, and a committee was organized to study the problem. This was known as the Design Institute for Emergency Relief Systems (DIERS). Twenty-nine companies sponsored the work and spent $1.6 million. The project was successfully completed in 1985. The key contributions developed to provide the chemical process industry with the tools necessary to evaluate emergency vent requirements are:

1. Emphasizing the importance of proper determination of the source term (i.e., energy release rate and gas generation rate for vapor and gassy systems, respectively) under upset conditions, and development of a new bench-scale apparatus in which such determination can be obtained and extrapolated directly to full-scale application.
2. Emphasizing the importance of two-phase flow in the emergency relief discharge process, and development of vent sizing techniques that are valid for multi-phase behavior.

The DIERS methodology can be complex and time consuming and may be beyond the capability of many small plants. As a result, some inexpensive and easily employed techniques have been developed. These commercially available tools should make it possible for all facilities to design adequate emergency venting for processing plants. A number of articles have appeared in AIChE publications, *Chemical Engineering Progress,* and *Plant/Operations Progress* on the DIERS program and ways to use the information obtained.[33–42]

Safety Instrumentation

Safety instrumentation will vary from process to process and plant to plant. There are, however, a few general rules:[43]

1. Measure, as directly as possible, the variables of interest. For example, if an agitator is driven by an electric motor, a relay can be used to show that the switch to the motor is closed. An ammeter would be better because that would show current is flowing; a wattmeter would be best because it would show that work is being done and that the impeller has not fallen off the agitator shaft.

2. Reliability and maintenance must be of high quality, e.g., if an external fire could upset the reaction, the warning instrument should not be disabled by the fire. Since safety instruments will not have to operate often, frequent checks must be made to ensure they are in operating condition.
3. Provide redundancy or diversity in the system. If temperature is critical, provision of two thermocouples may lead to two opposite readings. It is best to provide three and trust the majority of the readings. However, since a temperature increase is usually accompanied by a pressure increase, one pressure sensor and one thermocouple may be used, with credence given to the more pessimistic report.

CHEMICAL PLANT OPERATIONS AND EQUIPMENT

The generally accepted unit physical operations require equipment to carry out the following functions:

1. Heat transfer
2. Fluid flow
3. Crushing and grinding
4. Mixing
5. Mechanical separation
6. Distillation.
7. Evaporation
8. Crystallization
9. Filtration
10. Absorption
11. Adsorption
12. Drying

Descriptions of individual pieces of equipment can be found in most engineering handbooks.

Heaters and Coolers (Heat Transfer)

These devices are either: (1) direct (flue gas, kilns, spray cooling, vaporization), or (2) indirect (coils and jackets). Heat transfer media usually work by boiling to absorb heat or condensing to give it up, but also may work just by becoming hotter or cooler without phase change. Hazards of heat transfer have been discussed previously in this chapter.

Fluid Flow

This is accomplished by: (1) fans and compressors, (2) pumps, or (3) vacuum jets. Fans, compressors, and pumps heat the materials they move because of mechanical work. Compressors require good aftercoolers. The liquid in pumps can boil, and the pump bearings fail from overheating, if a pump operates against a closed discharge valve. If a centrifugal pump suction is inadequate, cavitation may cause the pump to chew up itself. Failure of vacuum devices may permit unwanted air to enter the equipment and cause the temperature in the equipment to rise.

Crushing and Grinding

Equipment for these operations include: (1) mills (impact, ball, hammer, roller, disk), and (2) crushers (cone, gyratory, jaw). All of these devices produce heat and may produce fine material capable of dust explosion. Ball mills may become overpressured as liquid portions of their contents are heated. If gaskets fail and the liquids are flammable, a dangerous situation will result.

Mixing

Devices used in the mixing process include: (1) tumblers; (2) venturi mixers; (3) kneaders, rolls, and mullers; and (4) propellers, blades, and turbines. These devices also produce heat in varying degrees. When it is necessary to produce a hazardous mixture, e.g., a blend of starch and an oxidizer for use as a flour ager, the mixer is open to avoid an equipment explosion. Any dust collector should be of the water-wash type.

Mechanical Separation

These include: (1) cyclones, (2) bag filters (shake or blow back), (3) ore tables, (4) screens, (5) electrostatic precipitators, (6) flotation separators, and (7) centrifuges. The first five are usually dry type and the latter two wet, although there are liquid cyclones and wet screening processes. Devices used in dry service for combustible dusts should have explosion venting or an explosion suppression system. If collectors have internal combustible bags, an internal sprinkler system is desirable. It may not save the bags, but it will save the housing and mechanical devices. When materials wet with flammable liquids are centrifuged, the operation should be conducted under inert gas or with an explosion suppression system.

Distillation

The types of stills are: (1) batch, (2) continuous, (3) pressure, (4) vacuum, and (5) steam. All distillations involve heat transfer. The major hazard of this operation is that a flammable vapor may be released to the atmosphere.[44] The direct use of steam is discussed in the "Stability and Shock Sensitivity" section of this chapter.

Evaporation

The three types of evaporators are: (1) multiple effect, (2) vacuum, and (3) wiped film. All three use heat transfer. The multiple-effect system condenses vapor from the first unit to heat the second, etc. The initial heat transfer medium is used in the first, where the material is most concentrated and boils at the highest temperature. Vacuums and wiped films have been discussed previously in this chapter.

Crystallization

The two types of crystallizers are: (1) vacuum, and (2) pan. Both involve cooling to remove the heat of crystallization.

Filtration and Agglomeration

Filtration and agglomeration involve: (1) plate and frame filters, (2) Nutsche filters (vacuum), (3) drum type, (4) rotary cell type, (5) agglomerating tables, and (6) pelletizers. No unusual hazards are involved other than possible exposure of flammable liquids to the air.

Adsorption

The two types of adsorbers are: (1) activated carbon, and (2) zeolites (molecular sieves). Adsorption produces heat just as absorption does. However, when the material being adsorbed is a flammable vapor or gas, the heat is retained in the small pores of the adsorbent. Heat may build up enough to cause fire in the activated carbon or exothermic polymerization of adsorbed reactive materials, such as ethylene. This hazard can be minimized by wetting the adsorbent prior to each use.

Drying

The six general types of dryers are: (1) spray and fluid bed, (2) vacuum, (3) tray, (4) belt, (5) drum, and (6) azeotropic. All these involve heat transfer. In the case of azeotropic dryers, where heat is removed by boiling, condensation, and return of the cool liquid, the unwanted component, usually water, can be discarded if the condensate forms a two-phase system. All other types of dryers may present problems of mixing flammable vapors with air. Spray and fluid-bed dryers may expose thermally unstable dry materials to hot heat-transfer surfaces.

CONCLUSION

A summary of necessary knowledge and procedures to ensure safe chemical processing has been suggested as follows:[45]

1. Know the total reaction energy in the system.
2. Know the rate of energy release.
3. Evaluate thermal and shock sensitivity data.
4. Design the process to control the rate of energy release, and in doing so:
   a. Be alert for trace compounds or catalytic impurities which may accelerate reaction rates.
   b. Prevent buildup or concentration of high-energy materials in the system. Calculate a material balance.
   c. Design into the process the ability to safely accommodate inadvertent releases.

BIBLIOGRAPHY

References Cited

1. Lees, F. P., *Loss Prevention in the Process Industries*, Vol. 1, Butterworth & Co., Ltd., London, 1980, pp. 210-230.

2. Melancon, C. L., "Improving Emergency Control and Response Systems," *Loss Prevention,* Vol. 13, AIChE, New York, 1980 pp. 43-49.

3. *Engineering for Safe Operations*, No. 8, American Oil Company (now Standard Oil of Indiana), Chicago, IL, 1964.

4. *General Recommendations for Spacing*, Industrial Risk Insurers, Hartford, CT.

5. Lewis, D. W., "The Mond Fire, Explosion, and Toxicity Index Applied to Plant Layout and Spacing," *Loss Prevention,* Vol. 13, AIChE, New York, 1980, pp. 20-26.

6. Lewis, D. J., "Plant Layout and Storage Area Spacing," *Proceedings* of 6th International Symposium on Loss Prevention and Safety Promotion in the Process Industries, Vol. 1, European Federation of Chemical Engineers, Oslo, Norway, 1989, pp. 7-1, 7-16.

7. Davenport, J. A., "A Survey of Vapor Cloud Incidents," *Loss Prevention*, Vol. 11, AIChE, New York, 1977, pp. 39-49.

8. Nelson, R. W., "Know Your Insurers' Expectations," *Hydrocarbon Processor,* 1977, pp. 103-108.

9. van Wingerden, C. J. M., "Experimental Investigation into the Strength of Blast Waves Generated by Vapour Cloud Explosions in Congested Areas," *Proceedings* of 6th International Symposium on Loss Prevention and Safety Promotion in the Process Industries, Vol. 1, European Federation of Chemical Engineers, Oslo, Norway, 1989, pp. 26-1—26-16.

10. Prugh, R. W., *Guidelines for Vapor Release Mitigation*, American Institute for Chemical Engineers, 1988.

11. Rinder, R. M., and Wachtell, S., "Establishment of Design Criteria for Safe Processing of Hazardous Materials," *Loss Prevention*, Vol. 7, AIChE, New York, 1967, pp. 28-30.

12. Bradford, W. J., and Culbertson, T. L., "Design of Control Houses to Withstand Explosive Forces," *Loss Prevention*, Vol. 1, AIChE, New York, 1967, pp. 28-30.

13. "Siting and Construction of New Control Houses for Chemical Manufacturing Plants," *Safety Guide SG22*, Chemical Manufacturers Association, Washington, DC.

14. Eggleston, L. A., Herrera, W. R., and Pish, M. D., "Water Spray to Reduce Vapor Cloud Spray," *Loss Prevention*, Vol. 10, AIChE, New York, 1976, pp. 31-42.

15. Lawrence, W. E. and Johnson, E. E., "Design for Limiting Explosion Damage," *Chemical Engineering*, Vol. 81, No. 1, 1974, pp. 96-104.

16. Watts, J. W., Jr., "Effects of Water Spray on Unconfined Flammable Gas," *Loss Prevention*, Vol. 10, AIChE, New York, 1976.

17. *The Safe Dispersal of Large Clouds of Flammable Heavy Vapors,* Imperial Chemical Industries Ltd., Heavy Organic Chemicals Division, Billingham, England, 1971.

18. Johanson, K. A., "Gas Detectors by the Acre," *Instrumentation Technology,* Vol. 21, No. 8, 1974, pp. 33-37.

19. Burgess, D. S. and Zabetakis, M. G., "Detonation of a Flammable Cloud Following a Propane Pipeline Break," *RI 7752*, USDI Bureau of Mines, Pittsburgh, PA.

20. Goforth, C. P., "Functions of a Loss Control Program," *Loss Prevention*, Vol. 4, AIChE, New York, 1970, pp. 1-5.

21. Kletz, T., "Lessons to Be Learned from Flixborough," *Loss Prevention*, Vol. 9, AIChE, New York, 1975.

22. Armistead, G., Jr., *Safety in Petroleum Refining and Related Industries*, 1st ed., John G. Simmonds & Co., Inc., New York, 1950, pp. 118-119.

23. "Potential Hazards in Molten Salt Baths for Heat Treatment of Metals," *NBFU Research Report RR-2*, American Insurance Association, New York, 1954.

24. Coffee, R. D., "Hazard Evaluation Testing," *Loss Prevention*, Vol. 3, AIChE, New York, 1969, pp. 18-21.

25. Coffee, R. D., "Hazard Evaluation: The Basis for Chemical Plant Design;" *Loss Prevention*, Vol. 7, AIChE, New York, 1973, pp. 58-60.

26. Davis, E. J. and Ake, J. A., "Equilibrium Thermochemistry Computer Programs as Predictors of Energy Hazard Potential," *Loss Prevention*, Vol. 7, AIChE, New York, 1973, pp. 67-73.

27. Stull, D. R., "Linking Thermodynamics and Kinetics to Predict Real Chemical Hazards," *Loss Prevention*, Vol. 7, AIChE, New York, 1973, pp. 67-73.

28. Trewick, D. N., Claydon, C. R., and Seaton, W. H, "Appraising Energy Hazard Potentials," *Loss Prevention*, Vol. 7, AIChE, New York, 1973, pp. 21-27.

29. Way, D., "Fire Protection Engineering," *Loss Prevention*, Vol. 3, AIChE, New York, 1969, pp. 23-25.

30. Boynton, E. D., Nichols, W. B., and Spurlin, H. M., "Control of Exothermic Reactions," *Industrial & Engineering Chemistry*, Vol. 51, No. 4, 1959, pp. 489-494.

31. Austin, G. T., "Hazards of Commercial Chemical Reactions," *Safety and Accident Prevention in Chemical Operations*, (edited by H. H. Fawcett and W. S. Wood), John Wiley & Sons, New York, 1965.

32. Kline, P. E., *et al.*, "Guidelines for Process Scale-Up," *Chemical Engineering Progress*, Vol. 70, No. 10, 1974, pp. 67-70.

33. Fauske, H. K., "A Quick Approach to Reactor Vent Sizing," *Plant/Operations Progress*, Vol. 3, No. 3, 1984, pp. 145-146.

34. Fauske, H. K. and Leung, J. C., "New Experimental Technique for Characterizing Runaway Chemical Reactions," *Chemical Engineering Progress*, Vol. 81, No. 8, 1985, pp. 39-45.

35. Fauske, H. K., "Emergency Relief Systems (ERS) Design," *Chemical Engineering Progress*, Vol. 81, No. 8, 1985, pp. 53-58.

36. Fauske, H. K., "Emergency Relief System Design for Reactive and Non-Reactive Systems: Extension of the DIERS Methodology," *Plant/Operations Progress,* Vol. 7, No. 3, 1988, pp. 153-158.

37. Fauske, H. K., Grolmes, M. A., and Clare, G. H., "Process Safety Evaluation Applying DIERS Methodology to Existing Plant Operations," *Plant/Operations Progress*, Vol. 8, No. 1, 1989, pp. 19-24.

38. Fauske, H. K., *et al.*, "An Easy and Inexpensive Approach to DIERS Methodology," presented at AIChE Loss Prevention Symposium, Houston, TX, Apr. 1989.

39. Fisher, H. G., "DIERS Research Program on Emergency Relief Systems," *Chemical Engineering Progress*, Vol. 81, No. 8, 1985, pp. 33-36.

40. Grolmes, M. A., Leung, J. C., and Fauske, H. K., "Large-Scale Experiments of Emergency Relief Systems," *Chemical Engineering Progress*, Vol. 81, No. 8, 1985, pp. 57-62.

41. Grolmes, M. A. and Leung, J. C., "Code Method for Evaluating Integrated Relief Phenomena," *Chemical Engineering Progress*, Vol. 81, No. 8, 1985, pp. 47-52.

42. Leung, J. C. and Stepaniuk, N. J., "Emergency Relief Considerations Under Severe Segregation Scenarios," presented at AIChE Loss Prevention Symposium, New Orleans, LA, Mar. 1988.

43. Doyle, W. H., "Instrument Connected Losses in the CPI," *Instrumentation Technology*, 1972, pp. 38-42.

44. Doyle, W. H., "Minimizing Serious Fires and Explosions in the Distillation Process," *Technology Report 74-2*, Society of Fire Protection Engineers, Boston, MA, 1974.

45. *The ABCs of Reactive Chemical Processing*, Dow Chemical Company, Midland, MI.

References

Pressure Vessel Code, American Society of Mechanical Engineers, New York, (Continuously updated.)

Annual Book of Standards, American Society for Testing and Materials, Philadelphia, PA, (Updated annually).

NFPA Codes, Standards, and Recommended Practices

Reference to the following NFPA codes, standards, and recommended practices will provide further information on the safeguards for chemical processing equipment discussed in this chapter. (See the latest *NFPA Catalog* for availability of current editions of the following documents.)

NFPA 15, *Water Spray Fixed Systems for Fire Protection.*

NFPA 49, *Hazardous Chemicals Data.*

NFPA 68, *Explosion Venting.*

NFPA 306, *Control of Gas Hazards on Vessels.*

NFPA 491M, *Manual of Hazardous Chemical Reactions.*

NFPA 495, *Manufacture, Transportation, Storage, and Use of Explosive Materials.*

NFPA 704, *Identification of the Fire Hazards of Materials.*

Additional Reading

Atallah, S. and Allan, D. S., "Safe Separation Distances from Liquid Fuel Fires," *Fire Technology*, Vol. 7, No. 1 (Feb. 1971), pp. 47-55.

Bahme, C. W., *Fire Officer's Guide to Dangerous Chemicals*, 2nd ed, National Fire Protection Association, Inc., Boston, MA, 1978.

Bartknecht, W., *Explosions*, Springer-Verlag, Berlin, Heidelberg, NY, 1981.

Chappell, W. G., "Calculating a Pressure-Time Diagram for an Explosion Vented Space," *Loss Prevention*, Vol. 11, American Institute of Chemical Engineers, NY, 1977.

Chohan, R. K. and Upadhyaya, B. R., "Safety and Fault Detection in Process Control Systems and Sensors," *Fire Safety Journal*, Vol. 14, No. 3, 1989, pp. 167-178.

Cocks, R. E. and Rogerson, J. E., "Organizing a Process Safety Program," *Chemical Engineering*, Vol. 85, No. 23, 1978, pp. 138-146.

Coffee, R. D., "Dust Explosions: An Approach to Protection Design," *Fire Technology*, Vol. 4, No. 2 (May 1968), pp. 81-87.

Coffee, R. D., "Evaluation of Chemical Stability," *Fire Technology*, Vol. 7, No. 1 (Feb. 1971), pp. 37-45.

Creech, M. D., "Combustion Explosions in Pressure Vessels Protected with Rupture Discs," *Transactions*, Vol. 63, No. 7, American Society of Mechanical Engineers, NY.

Crowl, D. A. and Louvar, J. F., "Instructional Videotape on Chemical Process Safety," *Plant/Operation Progress* Vol. 8, No. 4, 1989, pp. 221-227.

Cubbage, P. A. and Marshall, M. R., "Explosion Relief Protection for Industrial Plants of Intermediate Strength," Institution of Chemical Engineers Symposium Series 39, London, England, Apr. 1974.

Davenport, J. A., "Explosion Losses in Industry," *Fire Journal*, Vol. 75, No. 1 (Jan. 1981), pp. 52-56, 71-73.

Doran, P. and Greig, R., "Mond Index Assesses Hazard Potential of Chemical Plant," *Process Engineering*, Vol. 70, No. 2, 1989, pp. 67-68.

"Explosion and Fire Hazards in the Storage and Handling of Organic Peroxides in Plastic Fabricating Plants," *SPI-FPC 19*, The Society of the Plastics Industry, NY, June 1964.

Fawcett, H. H. and Wood, W. S., eds., *Safety and Accident Prevention in Chemical Operations,* 2nd ed., Wiley—Interscience, NY, 1982.

Fire Inspectors Guide to NFPA 1031, National Fire Protection Association, Quincy, MA, 1983.

Grace, C., "Fluid Choice Takes the Steam Out of Unsafe Process Heaters," *Process Engineering*, (5), 1977, pp. 85, 87, 88.

Halpaap, W., "Special Appliance for the Chemical Industry," *Fire International*, 5(56), 1977, pp. 44-50.

Howard, H. A., "Chemical Plant Fire," *Fire Engineering*, Vol. 142, No. 2, 1989, pp. 28-34, 37-43.

Howard, W. B., "Efficient Time Use to Achieve Safety of Processes," *Paper* presented at EFCE 4th International Symposium on Loss Prevention, Harrogate, England, Sept. 1983.

Joschek, H. I., "Risk Assessment in the Chemical Industries," *Plant/Operations Progress*, Vol. 2, No. 1 (Jan. 1983), pp. 1-5.

King, R., "Plant Hazards," *Engineering*, Vol. 216, No. 4, London, England, 1976, pp. 277-279.

Kirk, R. E. and Othmor, D. F., *Encyclopedia of Chemical Technology*, 3rd ed., Interscience Encyclopedia, Inc., New York, 1983.

Kletz, T. A., "Fires and Explosions of Hydrocarbon Oxidation Plants," *Plant/Operation Progress*, Vol. 7, No. 4, Oct. 1988, pp. 226-230.

Kuchta, J. M., *Investigation of Fire and Explosion Accidents in the Chemical, Mining, and Fuel Related Industries: A Manual*, U.S. Department of Interior, Bureau of Mines, Pittsburg, PA, 1986.

Lewis, B. and Von Elbe, G., *Combustion, Flames, and Explosions of Gases*, 3rd ed., Academic Press, NY, 1987.

MacDarmid, J. A. and North, G. J. T., "Lessons Learned From a Hydrogen Explosion in a Process Unit," *Plant/Operation Progress*, Vol. 8, No. 2 (Apr. 1989), pp. 96-99.

McDaniel, "Explosion of a Benfield Solution Storage Tank," *Plant/Operation Progress*, Vol. 5, No. 1, 1986, pp. 45-48.

McElroy, Frank E., ed., *Accident Prevention Manual for Industrial Operations*, 9th ed., National Safety Council, Chicago, IL, 1988.

Nostrom, Gail P. II, "Fire/Explosion Losses in the CPI," *Chemical Engineering Progress*, Vol. 78, No. 8 (Aug. 1982), pp. 80-87.

Pajgit, O., ed., *Processing of Polyester Fibres*, Elsevier Science Publishing Co., Inc., NY, 1980.

Perry, R. H. and Green, D. W., eds., *Chemical Engineers' Handbook*, 6th ed., McGraw-Hill, NY, 1984.

Pilborough, L., *Inspection of Chemical Plants*, Gulf Publishing Co., Houston, TX, 1982.

"Protection Against Ignitions Arising Out of Static, Lightning, and Stray Currents," *RP-2003*, American Petroleum Institute, Washington, DC, 1967.

"Safe and Efficient Plant Operation and Maintenance," *Chemical Engineering*, McGraw-Hill, NY, 1980.

Sax, N. I., *Dangerous Properties of Industrial Materials*, 7th ed., Van Nostrand Reinhold Company, NY, 1989.

Sommer, E. C., "Preventing Electrostatic Ignitions," *Paper* presented at a meeting of the American Petroleum Institute Central Committee on Safety and Fire Protection, Tulsa, OK, Apr. 1967.

Verralin, C. H., ed., *Fire Protection Manual for Hydrocarbon Processing Plants*, 3rd ed., Gulf Publishing Company, Houston, TX, 1985.

Weiby, P., and Dickinson, K. R., "Monitoring Work Areas for Explosive and Toxic Hazards," *Chemical Engineering*, Vol. 83, No. 22, 1976, pp. 139-145.

Zabetakis, M. D., "Flammability Characteristics of Combustible Gases and Vapor, " *Bulletin 627,* U. S. Bureau of Mines, Pittsburgh, PA, 1965.

EXTRUSION AND MOLDING PROCESSES

Revised by Richard Gottwald

The multi-billion dollar plastics industry is the fourth largest industry in the United States. Plastics are a basic material of use—on a par with metals, glass, wood, and paper. They have become increasingly important to advanced concepts in architecture, aerospace, communications, transportation—even medicine and the arts. The plastics industry originated in the U.S. in 1868 when John Wesley Hyatt developed celluloid—the first American plastic.

Currently the United States leads the world in the production of plastics, supplying more than half the total output. At least 6000 companies in the U.S. make plastics; i.e., they produce basic material, process or fabricate plastics into products or parts, or finish their goods. Companies that use plastics or these materials and services number well into the tens of thousands.

Plastic is any one of a large and varied number of materials consisting wholly or in part of combinations of carbon with oxygen, hydrogen, nitrogen, and other organic and inorganic elements. While it is solid in the finished state, at some stage in its manufacture it is molten or softened, and thus capable of being formed into various shapes, most through the application, either singly or together, of heat and pressure. Whatever their properties or form, however, plastics fall into one of two groups: thermoplastics or thermosets. (See Table 2-16A.)

Thermoplastic resins can be repeatedly softened and hardened by heating and cooling, without a chemical change taking place.

Thermoset resins, when heat treated, undergo a chemical reaction and cannot be softened by further heating without causing a chemical change that would forever alter the material.

There are approximately 30 major classes of plastics or polymer groupings, with numerous variations of individual plastic products. This diversity has made plastics applicable to an extremely broad range of end-uses and products. Yet, paradoxically, this diversity has also made it difficult to grasp the concept of a single family of materials encompassing such a far-reaching span of physical and chemical properties and fire hazard characteristics.

Relevant material can also be found in Section 2, Chapter 34, "Housekeeping Practices" and Section 3, chapter 5, "Flammable and Combustible Liquids."

PLASTICS PROCESSING

The plastics industry as a whole has three broad areas of processing: manufacturing, conversion, and fabricating. Although each is basically distinct, they may be conducted in the same or at different locations.

Manufacturing, or synthesizing, of the basic plastic or feedstock sometimes includes compounding with colorants or other additives. The hazards of the synthesis plant are basically those of a chemical plant. (See Section 3, Chapter 8, "Chemicals.")

Conversion of the plastics materials into useful articles by molding, extrusion, or casting usually involves heating the plastic so it will flow into a shape that is retained when the plastic is cooled. Although chemical reactions are not often a significant part of these operations, the plastic industry refers to them as "processing" or "converting."

Fabricating encompasses the largely mechanical operations of bending, machining, cementing, decorating, and polishing plastics.

These three areas, i.e., manufacturing, conversion, and fabricating, accurately categorize the fire hazards that may be encountered in the plastics industry. It is important to recognize, though, that the synthesis, or manufacturing, of a given plastic may be much more hazardous than its molding or extrusion. It's also important to recognize that some plants nominally doing only converting and/or fabricating may also be conducting chemical operations with flammable or reactive materials. One example is the overlapping of molding and synthesis operations in a plant that impregnates liquid polyester resins into reinforcing glass fibers for molding boat hulls or containers.

Alfred J. Hogan, P.E., a fire protection engineer and consultant based in Cypress Gardens, FL, originally wrote this chapter. Richard Gottwald, coordinator of technical affairs for The Society of the Plastics Industry, Inc., Washington, DC, revised it for this edition.

TABLE 2-16A. *Examples of Plastics Materials*

Thermoplastic		Thermoset	
ABS (acrylonitrile-butadiene-styrene)	Polyethylene	Epoxy	Silicones
A combination of three different monomers—acrylonitrile, butadiene, and styrene—suitable for tough products; has good electrical insulating qualities; used to make automobile front grills; household appliance components, business machine and telephone components.	Tough; excellent chemical resistance and electrical insulating quality; near zero moisture absorption; used for packaging, molded housewares, and toys.	Excellent for chemical resistance, electrical properties, and dimensional stability; will bond metals, glass, hard rubber, etc.; used for aircraft components, tanks, and electrical and electronic assemblies.	Long-term heat resistant, water repellent, electrical insulator, and mineral acid resistant; used in the electrical and electronics industry; insulation in meters and generators and induction heating apparatus.

This chapter discusses the processing, or converting, phase of the plastics which includes recognizing, of course, that in some instances hazards associated with all three phases of the industry are carried on in one location.

The Basic Hazards

Most plastics are combustible organic compounds that can burn under certain conditions. But aside from the inherent combustibility of plastic formulations influenced by the basic polymers used, the nature of plastic additives, the form the final product takes, and the conversion of feedstock plastics into finished articles involves the hazards associated with combustible dusts, flammable solvents, electrical faults, hydraulic fluids, and the storage and handling of large quantities of combustible raw materials and finished products. (See the chapters in this handbook that specifically discuss these hazards.)

Terminology

Before discussing the converting of plastic feedstocks into finished products, and the associated hazards, certain process terms and definitions are provided.

Additive: Any material added in a minor amount to basic resins or compounds to alter properties. Additives may be dyes, pigments, powdered fillers for stiffening, plasticizers for flexibility, fibers to reinforce, antioxidants, lubricants to aid flow into or release from a mold, or fire retardants.

Binders: The resins in a plastic mixture that hold together all of the other ingredients.

Blowing agent: Any substance that alone or in combination with other substances is capable of producing a cellular structure in a plastic.

Blown tubing: A thin film made by extruding a tube and simultaneously inflating it with air while hot; distention may be 20 times the diameter of the extruded tube.

Casting: Flowing liquid material into a mold or against a substrate with little or no pressure, followed by solidification and removal of the formed object.

Extrusion: The process of passing molten plastic under pressure through a die to form a continuous profile; the equipment is called an extruder.

Fabrication: The making of articles by machining, cementing, heat-sealing or thermoforming of preformed sheets, rods, or tubes. The term is used in contrast to "processing."

Fillers: Materials added to plastics to modify physical properties and/or reduce its cost. For example, they may be used to increase heat resistance and alter the dielectric strength. A wide variety of products are used, including wood flour, cotton, sisal, glass, and clay.

Film: A general term for sheets of plastic not more than 0.01 in. (0.25 mm) thick, regardless of the process used to make it.

Finishing: The removal of burrs, flash, gates, and defects from plastic articles, and also the development of a desired surface texture.

Flash: Unwanted projections from molded articles resulting from flow of plastic into space between matching parts of a mold. (The term has no fire connotation.)

Foam (cellular plastic): A plastic with numerous cells dispersed throughout its mass. Rigid foams have rapidly reached large-volume production as thermal insulation boards for construction, cups for hot and cold drinks, trays for prepackaged meats, and shock-resistant packaging; flexible foams are used for furniture padding and insulation of outer garments.

Foaming agent: See "blowing agent."

Forming: The process in which the shape of plastic pieces, such as sheets, rods, or tubes, are changed into a desired configuration.

Laminate: A composition of several layers of material(s) firmly held together by heat and pressure, bonding, or impregnation.

Lubricant: Material added to improve feeding of powder or granules into molding or extrusion machines, to improve flow of molten plastic through machines and into molds, or to prevent adhesion of plastic to molds; the last of these uses is called "mold-release." Typical lubricants are zinc stearate, carnauba wax, and silicone oil.

Molding: The process of forcing plastic into a cavity to achieve a desired shape.

Monomers: A simple compound usually containing carbon and of low molecular weight, which can react to form a polymer by combination with itself or with other similar molecules or compounds.

Plasticizers: Materials added to plastics to make the finished product more flexible or to facilitate compounding. Some plasticizers increase the combustibility of the plastic while others serve as flame retardants.

Plastics: Materials that contain as an essential ingredient an organic substance of large molecular weight, are solid in their finished state, and at some stage in their manufacture or processing into finished articles can be shaped by flow.

Polymerization: The process by which molecules of a monomer are made to respectively combine with other monomers. The result is a much longer chain-like molecule.

Processing: The converting of polymers into useful articles by molding or extrusion from granules, depositing film from solvent, or laminating resin and reinforcement. Most often the molding operation uses heat, but it is largely or entirely a physical rather than a chemical process.

Reinforced plastic: A plastic with a fibrous filler which significantly increases flexural, impact, or tensile strength. Additives are usually glass, cotton, or nylon fibers. Reinforced plastics may be thermoplastic granules for injection molding, or may be materials using large areas of reinforcement as in layup molding or pulp molding.

Resin: A solid, semisolid, or pseudosolid organic material which often has high molecular weight, and which exhibits a tendency to flow when subjected to stress and usually has a softening or melting range. However, common usage of the term in the plastics industry does not always conform to the definition. The term is often used for uncured fluid thermosetting materials, some chemically modified material resins, and is often used synonymously with the terms "plastic" and "polymer."

RAW MATERIALS

Many plastic feedstocks are derivatives of petroleum or gas recovered during the refining process; e.g., ethylene monomer (a widely used feedstock) is derived in gaseous form from petroleum refinery gas, liquefied petroleum gases, or liquid hydrocarbons.

The monomer is subjected to a chemical reaction, known as polymerization, that causes the small molecules to link together into increasingly longer molecules. Chemically, the polymerization reaction has turned the monomer into a polymer (the reason names of so many plastics materials begin with the prefix "poly"). The polymer, or plastic resin, must next be prepared for use by the processor, who will turn it into a finished product. In some instances, it is possible to use the plastic resin or feedstock as it comes out of the polymerization reaction. More often, however, it is transformed into a form that can be more easily handled by the processor and more easily handled in processing equipment. The most common solid forms for the plastic resin are pellets, granules, flakes, and powder. Some feedstocks are also available as semisolids, e.g., pastes, or as liquids (for casting).

THE PRODUCTION PROCESS

The ways in which plastics can be processed into useful end-products are as varied as the plastics themselves.

Though the processes differ, there are common elements. In the majority of cases, thermoplastic compounds in the forms of pellets, granules, flakes, and powder must be melted by heat so they can flow. Pressure is usually involved in forcing the molten plastic into a mold cavity or through a die, and cooling must be provided to allow the molten plastic to harden. With thermosets, heat and pressure also are most often used. In their case, however, heat serves to trigger a chemical reaction and causes the thermosetting resin to cure (set) in the mold under pressure. When thermoplastic or thermoset resins are in liquid form, heat and/or pressure need not necessarily be used, although in many casting techniques intended for high-speed production, they do play a role.

The following descriptions of processes cover the basics of the major manufacturing systems. It should be recognized, however, that there are variations in virtually every process.

Blow molding: This process is generally used only with thermoplastics. It is applicable to the production of hollow plastics products, such as bottles and gas tanks. Blow molding involves the melting of the thermoplastics resin and then forming it into a tube-like shape (known as a par-

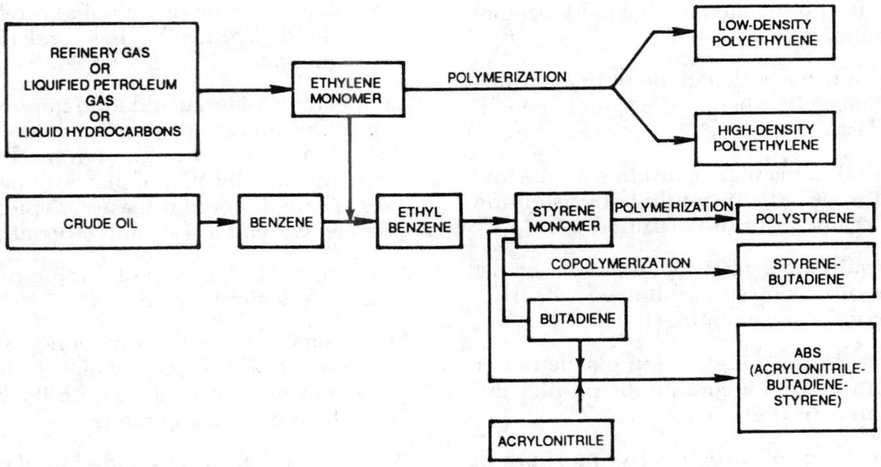

FIG. 2-16A. Flow chart shows ethylene's role in the manufacture of polyethylene, polystyrene, and styrene copolymers. (Source: Society of the Plastics Industry)

ison). The ends of the tube are then sealed and air is injected into the tube. The tube, in a softened state, is inflated inside the mold and forced against the walls of the mold. (See Figure 2-16B.)

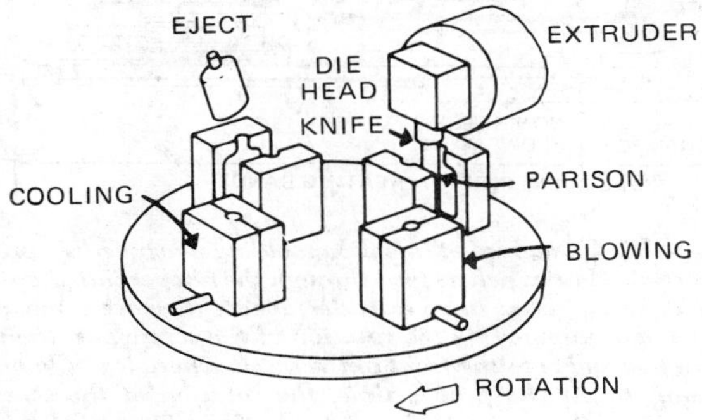

FIG. 2-16B. Diagram of continuous extrusion blow-molding setup, using a rotating horizontal table. Plastic parison (in cylindrical shape) is extruded from die into mold which closes on the parison (knife cuts the parison off from the extrudate). Mold then rotates to second station where air is injected into the parison (still hot and therefore formable) to blow it out to the shape of the inside mold cavity. At third station, the blown part is allowed to cool and set. Mold finally rotates to last station where finished part (in this case, a bottle) is ejected from mold. (Source: Society of the Plastics Industry)

Calendering: This process can be used to convert thermoplastics into film and sheeting, and to apply a plastic coating to textiles or other supporting materials. In calendering film and sheeting, the plastic compound is passed between a series of three or four large heated revolving rollers which squeeze the material between them into a sheet or film.

Casting: This process may be used both with thermoplastics and thermosets to make products, shapes, rods, and tubes, by pouring a liquid monomer-polymer solution into an open mold or a closed mold where it finishes polymerizing into a solid. Pressure need not be used with the casting process, unlike the molding process. The starting material in the casting process is usually in liquid form rather than solid form.

Coating: Coating may be accomplished by using either thermoplastic or thermosetting materials. The coating may be applied to metal, wood, paper, glass, fabric, leather, or ceramics. (See Figure 2-16C.)

Compounding: Mixing additives into previously formed resin, using kneading mixers, screw extruders of varied design, masticating rolls, or calenders, is called compounding. Rolls and kneaders are heated by high-pressure steam or heat transfer fluids.

Screw extruders have largely displaced rolls and kneaders for compounding, because they provide better control, continuous output, and less exposure of hot plastic to air.

Compression molding: This is the most common method of forming thermosetting materials. Compression molding is simply the squeezing of material into a desired shape by applying heat and pressure to the material in a mold. (See Figure 2-16D.)

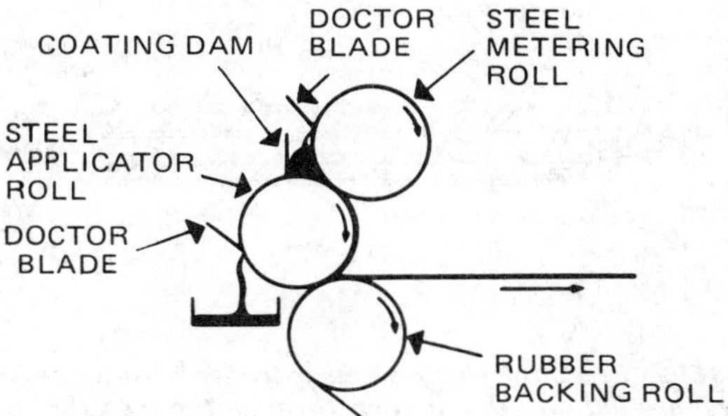

FIG. 2-16C. A typical coating setup, known as a 3-roll nip-fed reverse roll coater. Plastic feeds from dam through nip between steel metering and applicator rolls, rotating in the same directions. At bottom of the applicator roll, plastic is laid on top of the substrate (e.g., fabric, paper, etc.) as it comes in contact with the substrate at nip between applicator roll and backing roll (which carries the substrate up from the bottom of setup). Doctor blade is used to scrape off excess plastic from applicator roll. (Source: Society of the Plastics Industry)

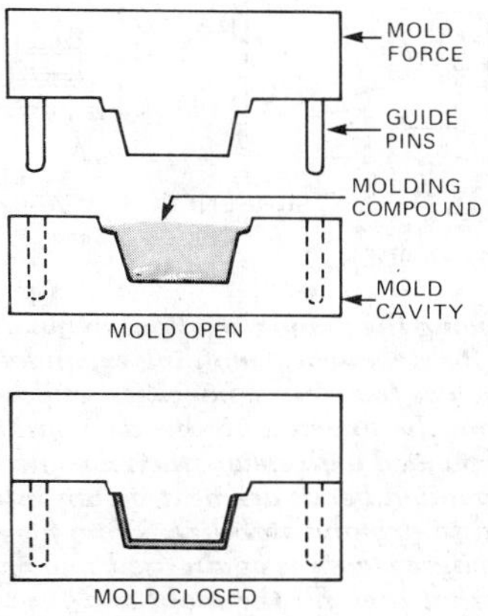

FIG. 2-16D. Basics of a simple two-piece compression mold. Plastic molding material is loaded into lower half (cavity) of the heated mold (shown at top). Top half of the mold (mold force) is then lowered and the two halves are brought together under pressure (shown below). The softened molding material is thus formed into the shape of the cavity and allowed to harden with further heating. Mold is then opened and part is removed. (Source: Society of Plastics Industry)

Extrusion: This method is employed to form thermoplastic materials into continuous sheeting, film, tubes, rods, profile shapes, or filaments and to coat wire, cable, and cord. (See Figure 2-16E.)

Foam plastics molding: This is the manufacturing process where foams can be used in casting, calendering, coating, rotational molding, flow molding, and even injection molding and extrusion. (See Figure 2-16F.) The manufacturing of foamed products is discussed in more detail later in this chapter in the subsection "Flammable Solvents."

High-pressure laminating: A process that uses thermosetting plastics to hold together reinforcing materials, such as cloth, paper, wood, or glass fibers. Heat and pressures of at least 1000 psi (6894 Pa) are used to produce the laminated product.

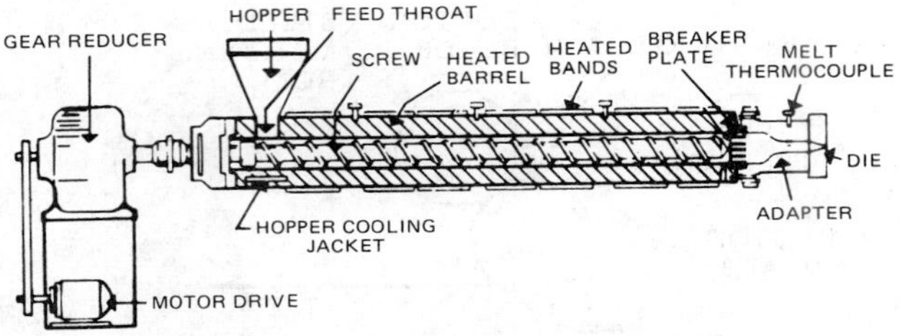

FIG. 2-16E. In a basic single-screw extruder, plastics pellets (or powders) are fed into the hopper, through the feed throat, and into a screw that rotates in a heated barrel. The rotation of the screw (which is powered by the drive motor) conveys the plastic forward for melting and delivery through the breaker plate (reduces the rotary motion of the melt), through the adapter, and into the die which dictates the shape and size of the final extrudate. (Source: Society of the Plastics Industry)

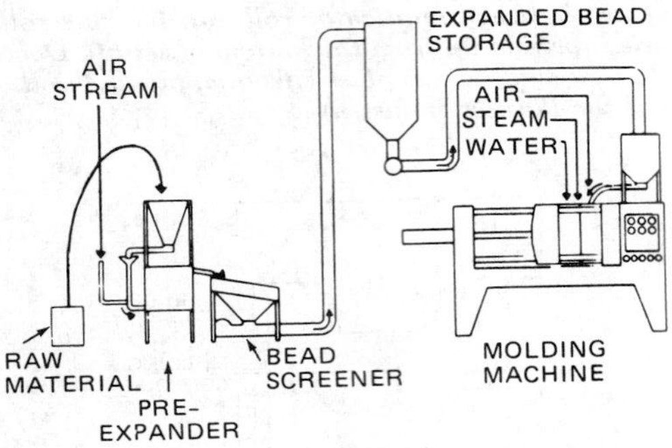

FIG. 2-16F. Among the many variations in molding foamed plastics is this setup for steam-chest molding expandable styrene beads into products such as foam cups, novelties, building products, etc. In this operation, the expandable beads, containing a blowing agent, are pre-expanded with steam, then screened to remove large clumps. The expanded beads are next blown into a storage hopper and allowed to dry and stabilize. From here, they feed into the final mold where steam is again used to complete expansion of the beads so that they fill the mold and fuse together. Water is used for cooling, prior to opening the mold and removing the finished foamed styrene part. (Source: Society of the Plastics Industry)

Injection molding: The method of forming objects from granular or powdered plastics, most often of the thermoplastic type, in which the material is fed from a hopper to a heated chamber in which it is softened, after which a ram or screw forces the material into a mold. Pressure is maintained until the mass is hardened sufficiently for removal from the mold. (See Figure 2-16G.)

Reaction injection molding (RIM): This is a technique used primarily for molding polyurethane elastomers of foams into end-products with solid integral skins and cellular cores. Basically, two or more pressurized reactive streams are impinged together under high pressure in a mixing chamber. The resulting mixture is then injected, under low pressure, into the mold. There, the reaction begins and continues until the liquid mixture has set up into a solid or cellular finished product.

Reinforced plastics processing: In this process, resins (acting as binder material) are combined with reinforcing materials (usually in fibrous form) to produce composite products having exceptional strength-to-weight ratios and outstanding physical properties. The resins may be either thermosets or thermoplastics. (See Figure 2-16H.)

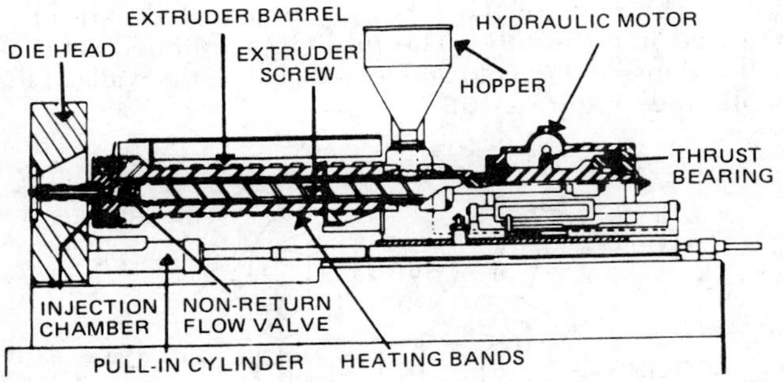

FIG. 2-16G. Diagram of injection molding machine (reciprocating screw). Plastics pellets feed through the hopper into the screw (much like the screw in an extruder) where they are compacted, melted, and pumped by the rotation of the screw past the non-return flow valve to the front of the screw where it is allowed to accumulate. At the proper time, the rotation of the screw is stopped and the amount of molten plastic in front of the screw is injected into the mold, using the screw as a plunger activated by the hydraulic injection cylinders. In the mold, the molten plastic flows throughout the cavity, completely filling it. The plastic is then allowed to cool and harden, the mold is opened, and the finished part removed. The back end of the machine shown above contains the motors and drives needed to power the machine. (Source: Society of the Plastics Industry)

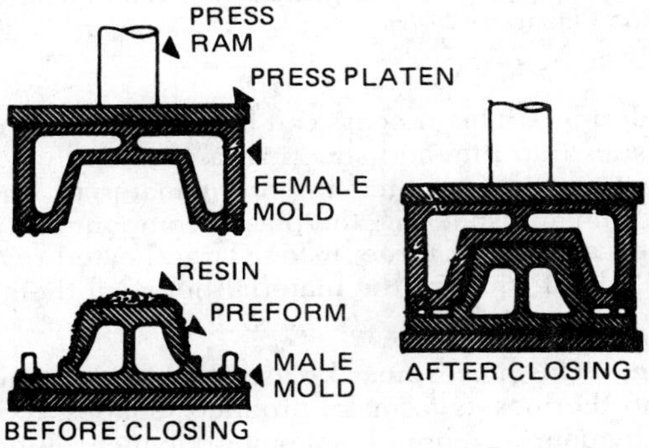

FIG. 2-16H. Matched-die molding is one technique for producing reinforced plastic parts. Basically, it is a compression molding process in which resin and glass fibers are shaped into the finished product under heat and pressure between the two halves of a mold (male and female halves). The glass-fiber reinforcements are laid over the male mold in the form of a "preform," a combination of glass and resin preformed before molding to the basic shape of the part to be molded. Additional liquid resin mix is added before mold is closed. (Source: Society of the Plastics Industry)

Rotational molding: A process used to make hollow, one-piece parts. Finely powdered plastic or molding granules are placed in a cavity that is rotated about two axes to distribute the plastic. While rotating, the mold is heated to melt the plastic and then cooled to solidify the part.

Thermoforming: Thermoplastic sheeting is heated to its softening temperature and forced against the contours of a mold by mechanical means, e.g., tools, plugs, solid molds, etc., or by pneumatic means, e.g., differentials in air pressure created by pulling a vacuum between sheet and mold (vacuum forming) or by using the pressures of compressed air to force the sheet against the mold (pressure forming). (See Figure 2-16I.)

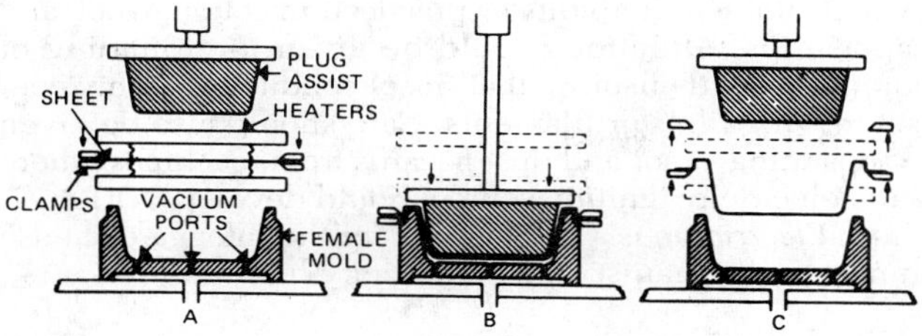

FIG. 2-16I. This variation on the thermoforming of plastic sheet is known as plug-assist vacuum forming. In operation, the plastic sheet is clamped in place and heaters move in to heat the sheet top and bottom to soften it (A). Heaters are then withdrawn, and the frame holding the sheet is lowered down to contact the mold. At this point, the plug-assist is lowered into the softened sheet, stretching it down to the bottom of the mold cavity (B). After the plug-assist has reached its closed position, a vacuum is drawn through the ports to pull the stretched sheet completely into the cavity and finish the forming. Next, the plug-assist is withdrawn, the formed sheet is cooled, and the clamps are opened to remove the formed part from the frame (C). (Source: Society of the Plastics Industry)

Transfer molding: Most generally used for thermosetting plastics, this is a process similar to compression molding. The molding material is placed in a pot at the top of a closed mold and a plunger is used to force the material into the gates, runners, and cavities of the mold. Heat is used to cure the material and the part is then removed.

THE FIRE HAZARDS

Plants converting feedstocks into finished products are subject to a variety of hazards that can result in explosions and fire. The broad area of hazard involves the presence of combustible dusts, flammable and combustible liquids, high-heat elements, hydraulic and heat transfer fluids, static electricity, and failure to observe good storage and housekeeping practices.

Dusts

Although when in solid massive form many plastics can be difficult to ignite and will not continue to burn on removal of exterior fuel, nearly all will burn rapidly in the form of dust, and if dispersed in air can be explosively ignited by a spark, flame, or metal surface above 700°F (371°C). Dust explosions should be considered possible when operations use pulverized plastic, convey larger granules through pneumatic conveying systems, or produce dust by machining or sanding in finishing work. Additives, such as wood flour or finely ground dye stuffs, also require safeguarding when being added to plastics.

Plastic pellets for injection or extrusion molding are commonly known as molding powder. In reality they are not pulverized material but cubes or cylindrical pellets. They are usually screened to remove finer particles to permit more uniform feeding to machines, and they are free from hazard of dust explosion. However, dust can be generated by abrasion of these particles when conveyed in a long pneumatic system.

Trimmings from injection molding are cut to small size for reuse alone or by blending with fresh (virgin) molding pellets. This cutting is called "regrinding," although it is a shearing and impacting action deliberately intended to avoid making dust and fine particles. Regrinding usually generates some fine powder, and dust hazards should be considered when much regrinding is done.

Compounding of resins with such additives as dyes, pigments, fillers, mold-release or flow-improving lubricants, plasticizers for flexibility, ultraviolet or heat stabilizers, or modifying resins is also a source of dust hazards. For rapid mixing, most of these are charged to mixing equipment as fine powders, and dust explosions are possible with any of these ingredients. Some compounding, especially for reclaiming of once-processed materials, is done at molding machines in plastics plants of all types.

Incorporation of wood flour, cotton flock, or other combustible fillers usually increases the explosibility of dust. Incorporation of low percentages of fire retardants has but little effect on explosibility of dusts.

It is important that the escape and dispersion of dust into the atmosphere of a converting plant be kept to a minimum. Equally important is that provisions are made to reduce the possibility of ignition, relieve explosion pressure, and confine and control fire. Guidance in controlling dust explosion hazards in plastics plants is found in NFPA 654, *Prevention of Fire and Dust Explosions in the Chemical, Dye, Pharmaceutical, and Plastics Industries*. Other applicable standards are NFPA 68, *Venting of Deflagrations*; NFPA 69, *Explosion Prevention Systems;* and NFPA 650, *Pneumatic Conveying Systems for Handling Combustible Materials.* NFPA 650 is useful as a guide for evaluating pneumatic conveying systems.

Flammable Solvents

Flammable organic solvents are found in nearly every plastics plant. They may be used in very small quantities to apply adhesives, lacquers, or paints to molded or fabricated items; in large amounts to coat plastic on cloth, paper, leather, or metal; or on metal belts from which a dried film will be stripped. There may be increased hazard when solvents are applied to plastics, particularly when printing or coating on fast-moving films, because plastics usually have high electrical resistivity; they generate and retain static charges more readily than paper or cotton fabric.

Small plants are increasing their use of solvents for the preparation of both rigid and flexible foam plastic. The plastic is moistened with solvent and heated above the boiling point of the solvent in a closed mold or extruder. Upon release of pressure, the boiling solvent expands the resin and produces a bubbled structure. Another type of foaming process heats a resin containing a chemical additive which evolves gas, usually nitrogen, carbon dioxide, or steam. Either the solvent or the chemical agent is called a blowing agent. The most common rigid foam is made from beads of polystyrene moistened with about 10 percent pentane or a similar hydrocarbon. The pentane does not soften and expand the resin at room temperature, but does so at the low-pressure steam temperature used in molding to shape, or in extruding as sheet. It is imperative that sources of electric spark or flame be avoided. Resin is usually shipped from the manufacturer with the hydrocarbon blowing agent already mixed with it. Containers will have free vapor of pentane, and should be opened outdoors or with good exhaust ventilation. Expanded articles should be aged under forced hot air to remove nearly all flammable blowing agent before shipping.

Flexible urethane foams for upholstery and garments, or rigid foams for pour-in-place construction or refrigeration insulation, are blown by steam and carbon dioxide generation which are by-products of the formation of the urethane resin from basic ingredients. Urethane foams of lower density may be made with a low-boiling hydrocarbon in the resin mixture to increase the expansion.

Foams of polyvinyl chloride are used in garments and upholstery. These are usually called "expanded vinyl," because the extent of foaming is limited to provide an essentially continuous outer surface. These are usually made with the chemical blowing agent azodicarbonamide, also called azobisformamide. Above 300°F (149°C) it provides nitrogen gas at a controlled rate, is essentially nonhazardous in the proportions used, and does not give off flammable vapors. Drums of the reagent should be cooled with water when exposed to fire.

Improper handling of flammable liquids has caused serious fires in plastics plants. Failure to recognize the importance of static spark prevention, explosionproof electrical equipment, and vapor removal systems has been the most frequent cause of flammable liquid fires. NFPA Standards 30, 33, 35, 70, 77, and 91 (see bibliography for titles) contain further information on safeguards to observe in the handling and use of flammable liquids as they apply, or may apply, to the plastics industry.

Heating Elements

Molding and extrusion operations, for both shaping and compounding, have hazards associated with local overheating of electrical components. Operating temperatures normally range from 300° to 650°F (149° to 343°C), depending on the plastic being processed. The upper temperature range is beyond that practical for heat transfer fluids, so electric resistance heating is almost universally employed. Heater bands are required to fuse the resin in the feed section at the upstream end of the extruder barrel. It is not uncommon for controllers to stick, permitting resistance heaters to exceed the temperature set for the thermocouple controller. In most cases, the character of extrudate will markedly change—and thus warn the operator—well before heater bands get hot enough to be a source of ignition.

Some areas within equipment may not be regularly purged by flow of the plastic feedstock. Material remaining in such areas can be subject to exclusively high temperature or be kept too long at a normally acceptable temperature. Decomposition may then take place, resulting in the release of gases that may be combustible. It is good practice to start heating such equipment first at the downstream end to ensure fluidity of material and hence relief of pressure.

Cleanliness in molding and extruding areas is vital to reduce the hazard of ignition from overheated bands where flammable vapors may be generated.

Electrical wiring in heat processing equipment on plastics machines should be installed in accordance with applicable provisions of NFPA 70, *National Electrical Code®*.

Static Electricity

Many operations in plastics plants generate static electricity. Because plastics are such good electrical insulators, static electricity on them can rapidly build up to spark discharge—a hazardous condition if dust or flammable vapors are present. Operations that can generate static are stripping of films from production or printing equipment, or rapid passage of films across rolls or guides. Belts for power transmission also are a significant source of static discharge. Because of their low water-absorption and high resistivity, plastics cannot have their static charge dissipated by high ambient humidity as practiced in cotton, wool, and paper mills. Attention should be given to grounding of equipment and ensuring that tinsel conductors firmly contact moving films or filaments. Care should also be given to separating vapor and dust hazards from machines where static electricity ignition sources could develop. NFPA 77, *Static Electricity*, is a good source for the safeguards to use in protecting against static electricity hazards.

Hydraulic Pressure Systems

Hydraulic systems are used to clamp molds and to provide pressure to rams or screws which force molten plastic into molds by compression, transfer, or injection molding. The molten plastic may be at pressures up to 20,000 psi (138,000 kPa), but the hydraulic systems are normally less than 2000 psi (13,800 kPa). Petroleum fluids have been used in plastics operations where heating elements are generally below 600°F (315°C). (The same fluids have a poor record in die-casting metals parts because molten metal is at a much higher temperature.)

Fire-resistant water-glycol or water-oil emulsions or "synthetic" fluids are available for hydraulic systems. Substituting fire-resistant fluids for petroleum fluids should follow the recommendations of the manufacturers of hydraulic system components.

Storage Arrangements

The fire hazards of plastics in storage, whether as feedstocks for the conversion process or as finished articles, are determined by their chemical composition, physical form, and storage arrangement. The physical form may be foam, solid sheet, pellets, flakes, random-packed small objects, bags, or cartons. The storage of plastics generally should not exceed a maximum height of approximately 20 ft (6.1 m). The hazard of a particular plastic in any form of storage arrangement is the same whether it is encapsulated or nonencapsulated. If fire occurs, large quantities of smoke are usually generated, making manual fire fighting difficult and venting desirable in building construction consideration.

Plastics, such as fluorocarbons, unplasticized polyvinyl chloride, and phenolics, can be protected the same way as any Class III commodity (wood, paper, and natural fiber cloth), regardless of their physical form or storage arrangement. Pellets and small objects can be protected the same as Class IV commodities. (Commodity classifications are based on NFPA 231, *General Storage*.)

Thermoplastics that present a fire hazard include polystyrene and acrylonitrile-butadiene-styrene (ABS), as well as polyurethane, polyethylene, plasticized polyvinyl chloride, and thermosets such as polyesters, although all of these to a lesser extent. These plastic materials will melt and break down (depolymerize) into their monomers, acting and burning like flammable liquids. High sprinkler discharge densities over relatively large areas are necessary to protect these types of plastics. In the form of foamed material, these plastics present the most severe fire hazard.

One-story buildings without basements are preferable for storage of plastics materials because of greater efficiency for fire fighting, ventilation, and salvage operations. Plastics should be stored, handled, and piled according to their fire characteristics.

Housekeeping Practices

Housekeeping is basic to good firesafety. Good housekeeping practices reduce the danger of fire simply because they are time-proven methods of controlling the presence of unwanted fuels, obstructions, and sources of ignition. Approved containers should be provided and properly maintained for the disposal of refuse and rubbish. Spills of flammable liquids or combustible materials should be promptly cleaned up and properly disposed. Removal of combustible dust and lint accumulations from walls, ceilings, and exposed structural members is necessary. Smoking control, in addition to sensible regulations, also requires receptacles for spent smoking materials. Areas containing flammable liquids, vapors, or combustible plastics materials, as well as areas used for processing, manufacturing, or storage, must be clearly identified to prohibit smoking or the use of open-flame devices.

THE SAFEGUARDS

Good fire protection starts with the firesafe design of the plant or warehouse, or inspection and modification of the existing facilities. Sprinkler-protected, noncombustible construction is appropriate for buildings occupied for storage, processing, and manufacturing of combustibles such as those involved in the plastics industry. Automatic sprinklers, standpipe and hose systems, and water-type portable extinguishers should be supplemented by fire extinguishers and special automatic systems suitable for flammable liquid fires and electrical fires, where these hazards exist.

Consideration should be given to the provision of roof vents, particularly in large one-story warehouses of manufacturing plants.

Building Construction

Long, narrow buildings provide greater ease in protection and fire fighting than large, square buildings. One-story buildings without basements are preferable to multistory buildings which may be subject to the spread of fire from lower to upper floors.

Large properties are best subdivided into fire areas to limit the spread of fire. Storage and manufacturing areas particularly need to be separated from each other by walls with sufficient fire rating to protect each area and occupancy from the other in case of fire. Preferably, fire walls should be without openings, but if openings are necessary, protection can be provided by self-closing or automatic fire doors suitable for openings in fire walls. Generally, a single fire area should not exceed 50,000 sq ft (4645 m^2).

Fire Control Systems

An alarm system that alerts building occupants, notifies fire suppression departments, and activates automatic suppression equipment is a necessary protection feature. Rapid extinguishment may be achieved by providing plastics processing equipment, conveyors, and manufacturing machinery subject to ignition or explosion with automatic fire-, smoke-, or explosion-detecting devices to initiate an alarm and to activate automatic suppressing systems (water spray, foam, dry chemical, carbon dioxide, or halogenated extinguishing agents).

Sprinklers are the most important single system for automatic control of fires in plastics plants. Among the advantages of automatic sprinklers is the fact that they operate directly over a fire and that smoke, toxic gases, and reduced visibility do not affect their operation. Automatic sprinklers, standpipes, and fire hose connections depend upon an adequate water supply delivered with the necessary pressure to control fires.

BIBLIOGRAPHY

References

Cote, A. E., ed., *Industrial Fire Hazards Handbook*, 3rd ed., National Fire Protection Association, Quincy, MA, 1990.

1988 Facts and Figures of the Plastics Industry, Society of the Plastics Industry, Washington, DC, 1988.

The Story of the Plastics Industry, 13th ed., Society of the Plastics Industry, New York, 1971.

NFPA Codes, Standards, and Recommended Practices

Reference to the following NFPA codes, standards, and recommended practices will provide further information on the safeguards for extrusion and molding processes discussed in this chapter. (See the latest *NFPA Catalog* for availability of current editions of the following documents.)

NFPA 10, *Portable Fire Extinguishers.*

NFPA 11, *Low-Expansion Foam and Combined Agent Systems.*

NFPA 11A, *Medium and High Expansion Foam Systems.*

NFPA 12, *Carbon Dioxide Extinguishing Systems.*

NFPA 12A, *Halon 1301 Fire Extinguishing Systems.*

NFPA 13, *Installation of Sprinkler Systems.*

NFPA 14, *Standpipe and Hose Systems.*

NFPA 15, *Water Spray Fixed Systems for Fire Protection.*

NFPA 16, *Deluge Foam-Water Sprinkler and Spray Systems.*

NFPA 17, *Dry Chemical Extinguishing Systems.*

NFPA 30, *Flammable and Combustible Liquids Code.*

NFPA 33, *Spray Application Using Flammable and Combustible Materials.*

NFPA 35, *Manufacture of Organic Coatings.*

NFPA 40E, *Safe Storage of Pyroxylin Plastics.*

NFPA 68, *Venting of Deflagrations.*

NFPA 69, *Explosion Prevention Systems.*

NFPA 70, *National Electrical Code.®*

NFPA 77, *Static Electricity.*

NFPA 91, *Blower and Exhaust Systems for Dust, Stock, and Vapor Removal or Conveying.*

NFPA *101®*, *Life Safety Code®.*

NFPA 231, *General Storage.*

NFPA 650, *Pneumatic Conveying Systems for Handling Combustible Materials.*

NFPA 654, *Prevention of Fire and Dust Explosions in the Chemical, Dye, Pharmaceutical, and Plastics Industries.*

Additional Reading

Beck, R. D., *Plastic Product Design*, 2nd ed., Van Nostrand Reinhold Co., NY, 1980.

Bresle, A., "The Hazards of PVC—A Second View," *Fire Prevention*, No. 217, Mar. 1989, pp. 19-23.

Bulletin No. 3, *Fire Hazards of Hydraulic Fluids Used in Processing Plastics*, Society of the Plastics Industry, NY.

Bulletin No. 6, *Fire and Explosion Due to Electrostatic Charges in the Plastics Industry*, Society of the Plastics Industry, NY.

Bulletin No. 9, *Planning Good Fire Protection for Plastics Plants*, Society of the Plastics Industry, NY.

Bulletin No. 10, *Portable Fire Extinguishers for Use in the Plastics Industry*, Society of the Plastics Industry, NY.

Bulletin No. 12, *Fire Safe Electrical Installations for Hazardous Locations in the Plastics Industry*, Society of the Plastics Industry, NY.

Bulletin No. 13, *Flammable and Combustible Waste Disposal in the Plastics Industry*, Society of the Plastics Industry, NY.

Bulletin No. 14, *A Plastics Plant Fire Squad*, Society of the Plastics Industry, NY.

Bulletin No. 16, *A Basic Fundamental of Fire Protection for Small Plastics Plants*, Society of the Plastics Industry, NY.

Bulletin No. 21, *Fire Safety in the Storage of Materials in Plastics Plants*, Society of the Plastics Industry, NY.

Crawford, R. J., *Plastics Engineering*, 2nd ed., Pergamon Press, NY, 1987.

Dubois, J. H., ed., *Plastics*, 6th ed., Van Nostrand Reinhold, NY, 1981.

Pajgit, O., ed., *Processing of Polyester Fibres*, Textile Science and Technology Series, Elsevier, NY, 1980.

Schwartz, S. and Goodman, S., *Plastics Materials and Processes*, Van Nostrand Reinhold Co., NY, 1982.

MOLTEN SALT BATHS

Revised by Q. D. Mehrkam

Molten salt baths have become increasingly popular for the heat treatment of metals, ceramics (e.g., glass), or polymers (e.g., Teflon®) because they provide rapid and precise heat transfer and the required equipment is relatively inexpensive. A molten salt bath is defined as any heated container that holds a melt or fusion of one or more chemical salts in a fluid state. The work to be treated is immersed in the bath. There are many kinds of salt baths that use various salts and salt mixtures and that operate at various temperatures, depending on the results required.

Additional information can be found in Section 2, Chapter 10, "Industrial and Commercial Heat Utilization Equipment" and Section 2, Chapter 27, "Storage and Handling of Chemicals."

As work is immersed fully into a salt bath, the salt serves as a protective environment. Heat is transferred more rapidly than by any other type of furnace heating. Moreover, because of the constant convection currents in the heated liquid medium, uniform temperature distribution is more easily attained.

TYPES OF SALT BATHS

The various types of salt baths available today can be classified by the heating method, application, or the particular salt mixture utilized.

Salt baths may be electrically heated or fuel-fired. Electrically heated baths may have electrodes introduced through the top surface of molten salt or through the sides of the furnace below the salt surface. (See Figures 2-17A and 2-17B.) In some instances, ribbon-type resistance elements are used around a metal pot or container. (See Figure 2-17C.)

There are two types of fuel-fired salt baths. In one, the burners are fired directly outside a retort containing the salt. In some instances the burners are fired in metal tubes, known as radiant tubes, and the tubes are immersed in the molten salt. (See Figure 2-17D.)

Q. D. Mehrkam is president of the Ajax Electric Company, manufacturer of industrial furnaces, based in Huntingdon Valley, PA.

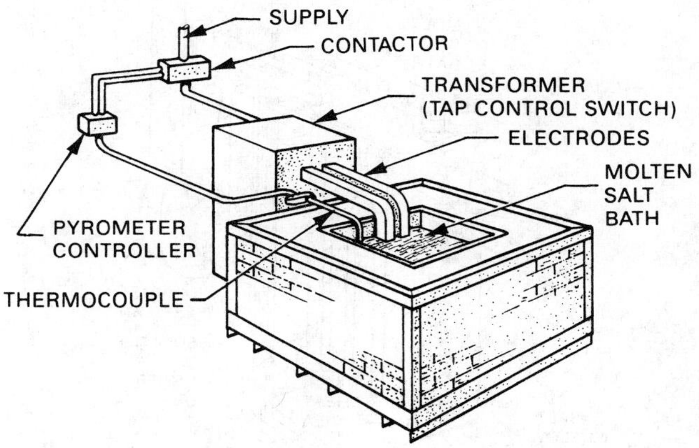

FIG. 2-17A. Typical electrode immersion-type electrical heating arrangement.

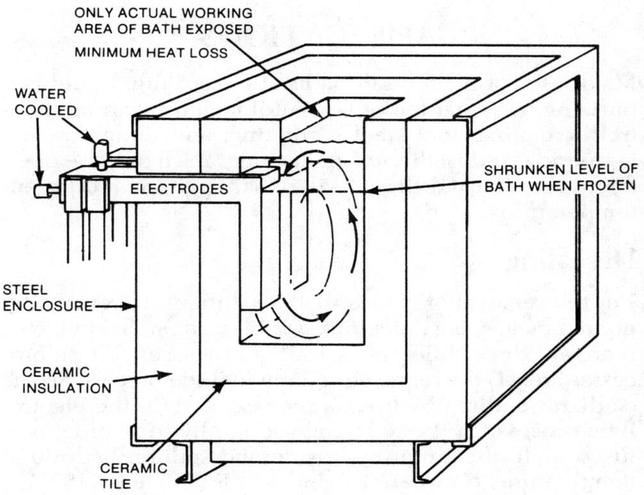

FIG. 2-17B. Submerged electrode-type salt bath. (Source: Ajax Electric Co.)

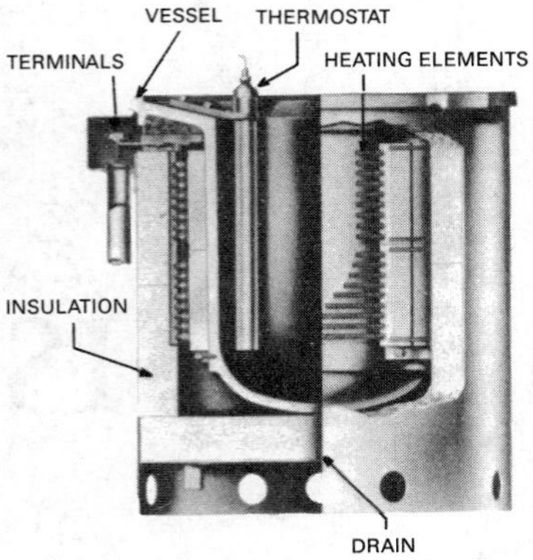

FIG. 2-17C. ***Resistance heated salt bath with pot. (Source: Sunbeam Equipment Co.)***

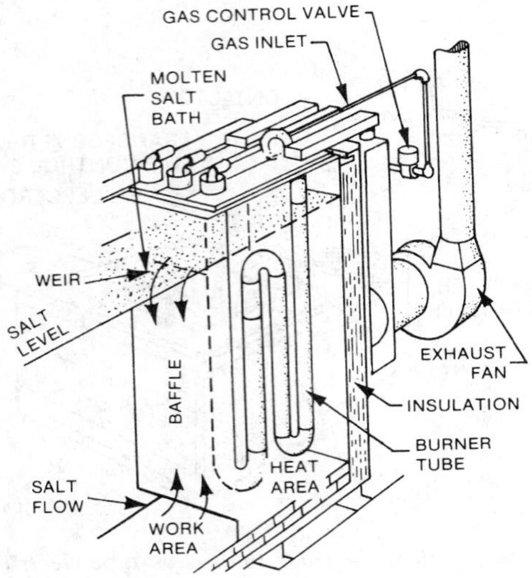

FIG. 2-17D. ***Gas-fired radiant tube salt bath heating section.***

APPLICATIONS

Major uses of molten salt baths are descaling, liquid carburizing (case hardening), cyaniding and nitriding, neutral hardening, tool steel hardening, annealing, brazing tempering, and isothermal quenching. Each of these operations requires a different salt or salt mixture at different temperatures.

Descaling

For the removal of oxides that are difficult to remove by normal means, e.g., pickling, grit blasting, polishing, etc., there are three different descaling processes. These processes are: (1) the reducing sodium hydride process, (2) the oxidizing sodium hydroxide process, and (3) the electrolytic process. In the reducing sodium hydride process, a fused melt of sodium hydroxide and sodium hydride at temperatures between 650 and 780°F (343 and 415°C) is used. For oxidizing, a melt of sodium carbonate, sodium chloride, and sodium hydroxide is used at temperatures from 700 to 950°F (371 to 510°C). In the electrolytic process, a fused melt of sodium carbonate, sodium chloride, and sodium hydroxide is used at about 900°F (402°C). Electrolytic oxidation reduction is accomplished by passing direct current through the work. A reversing switch changes the polarity of the work from positive to negative which effectively cleans the surfaces.

Liquid Carburizing

Case hardening is accomplished by diffusing carbon and small amounts of nitrogen into steel surfaces. The salts used are molten mixtures of sodium cyanide, sodium chloride, and barium chloride at temperatures between 1450 and 1750°F (788 and 955°C), depending upon the depth of case required. (See Figure 2-17E.)

FIG. 2-17E. ***Liquid carburizing and isothermal heat treating line. (Source: Ajax Electric Co.)***

Cyaniding and Nitriding

These two operations are also performed with either sodium or potassium cyanides as the chief ingredient. Usually the operating temperatures are lower, usually 950 to 1050°F (371 to 565°C), for nitriding.

Neutral Hardening

The hardening of ferrous alloys without harmful surface effects is performed in mixtures of sodium, potassium, and barium chlorides. Operating temperatures may range between 1400 to 2350°F (760 to 1288°C).

Hardening of High-Speed Tool Steels

High-speed tool steels are hardened in a series of molten salt baths at various temperatures. A preheat bath at approximately 1400°F (760°C) may be followed by a high-heat bath at 2350°F (1288°C), which in turn is followed by a quench bath at 1100°F (593°C). All of these baths are mixtures of barium, sodium, and potassium chlorides. (See Figure 2-17F.)

Isothermal Quenching

To achieve various levels of physical properties in the heat treatment of steels, isothermal quenching rapidly cools metal parts in a molten salt bath. The three major types of isothermal quench are austempering, martempering, and cyclic annealing. Each produces different hardness properties in metal alloys. Bath temperatures vary from 400 to 1300°F (205 to 705°C). The salts used are nitrate/nitrite salts for the lower temperatures and neutral chloride types for the higher temperatures.

FIG. 2-17F. Salt bath for hardening of high-speed tool steel. (Source: Ajax Electric Co.)

Annealing

Process annealing of carbon steels is usually carried out in carbonate and chloride salts at a temperature of 1,250 to 1,300°F (677 to 704°C). For stress relief of carbon steels, the melt is usually a nitrate salt at approximately 1,000°F (538°C). Chloride salts are used to anneal stainless steel products as well as nickel-chrome alloys at temperatures of 1,550 to 2,150°F (844 to 1177°C).

Brazing

Salt bath brazing of ferrous and nonferrous alloys with silver and aluminum alloys, brass, and copper is another popular application for molten salt baths. Depending on the alloy and type of brazing, temperatures and salt mixtures vary considerably. For aluminum dip brazing, the salt is a mixture of chlorides with smaller percentages of sodium and/or aluminum fluorides, which act as fluxes. In copper brazing, barium chloride mixtures are used. Chlorides of sodium and potassium are used for silver alloy and brass brazing applications. Carburizing salts are used for a combination of brass brazing and carburizing.

THE HAZARDS

The hazards common to salt bath furnaces can be divided into the following three types:

1. Fire caused by contact of molten salt with combustibles.
2. Explosion of the salt mixture due to physical or chemical reaction.
3. The danger to operating personnel.

Since salts are used at temperatures from 300 to 2,400°F (149 to 1315°C), the ejection of salt by popping, spattering, or spilling will create a fire hazard if it comes in contact with anything combustible, including wood floors. Since molten salts have relatively little surface tension and low viscosities, any minor physical disturbance or chemical reaction can result in salt being ejected. When liquids (water, oil, etc.) or materials reactive to the particular salt utilized penetrate the surface of the salt bath, a violent ejection can result. Table 2-17A lists common salts and their melting points. Table 2-17B lists common salt mixtures and their melting points. Proprietary mixtures of these salts are formulated for specific applications and temperatures. Intermixing of certain salts is hazardous, e.g., nitrates and cyanide. Consult supplier for recommendations. (See Table 2-17B.)

TABLE 2-17A. *Melting Points of Common Chemical Salts*

Salt	Melting point °F	Melting point °C
*Barium chloride	1764	963
Barium fluoride	2336	1280
Boric oxide (Anhydride)	1071	578
*Calcium chloride	1422	773
Calcium fluoride	2480	1360
Calcium oxide	4662	2575
*Lithium chloride	1135	613
Lithium nitrate	491	255
Magnesium fluoride	2545	1397
Magnesium oxide	5072	2802
*Potassium carbonate	1636	892
*Potassium chloride	1429	777
*Potassium cyanide	1174	635
Potassium fluoride	1616	880
*Potassium hydroxide	716	380
*Potassium nitrate	631	333
*Potassium nitrite	567	297
*Sodium carbonate	1564	852
*Sodium chloride	1479	805
*Sodium cyanide	1047	564
*Sodium fluoride	1796	980
*Sodium hydroxide	605	319
Sodium metaborate	1771	967
*Sodium nitrate	586	308
*Sodium nitrite	520	271
Sodium tetraborate	1366	742
Strontium chloride	1603	873

* Most Common Salts.

Nitrates are particularly hazardous due to their ability to start and support combustion. When nitrates are overheated to temperatures in excess of 1100°F (593°C), rapid dissociation with the release of nitrous oxide fumes occurs. These fumes are injurious to operating personnel and are corrosive to the adjacent equipment. Explosions may occur if nitrate salt leaks from an externally heated container (pot) into a superheated combustion chamber. The overheating of nitrates can be caused by temperature controls that malfunction, an accumulation of sludge in the bath, or by operator errors.

If the operating temperature of a nitrate or nitrite bath exceeds the maximum limit, the following emergency action should be taken:

1. Shut off the heat supply.
2. Remove all work from the bath.
3. Move employees to a safe location.

Heated nitrate salts will react strongly with carbonaceous materials, such as oil, soot, tar, graphite, and cyanides—all of which may be utilized in some other metal-treating process. Accidental mixing of cyanides with molten nitrates can cause explosions of considerable magnitude.

TABLE 10-17B. ***Melting Points of Common Salt Mixtures****

Mixture and proportion	Melting points °F	°C
Lithium nitrate 23.3, sodium nitrate 16.3, potassium nitrate 60.4	250	121
Potassium hydroxide 80, potassium nitrate 15, potassium carbonate 5	280	138
†Potassium nitrate 53, sodium nitrate 7, sodium nitrite 40	285	141
Potassium nitrate 56, nitrite 44	295	146
Potassium nitrate 51.3, sodium nitrate 48.7	426	219
†Sodium nitrate 50, sodium nitrite 50	430	221
Sodium hydroxide 90, sodium nitrate 8, sodium carbonate 2	560	294
Lithium chloride 45, potassium chloride 55	666	353
†Barium chloride 31, calcium chloride 48, sodium chloride 21	806	430
†Calcium chloride 66.5, potassium chloride 5.2, sodium chloride 28.3	939	504
Calcium chloride 67, sodium chloride 33	941	505
†Potassium chloride 35, sodium chloride 35, lithium chloride 25, sodium fluoride 5	960	516
†Potassium chloride 40, sodium chloride 35, lithium chloride 20, sodium fluoride 5	990	533
†Barium chloride 48.1, potassium chloride 30.7, sodium chloride 21.2	1026	555
Sodium chloride 27, strontium chloride 73	1049	565
†Potassium chloride 50, sodium carbonate 50	1086	585
Barium chloride 35.7, calcium chloride 50.7, strontium chloride 13.6	1110	599
Barium chloride 50.3, calcium chloride 49.7	1112	600
Potassium chloride 61, potassium fluoride 39	1121	605
†Sodium carbonate 56.3, sodium chloride 43.7	1177	637
Calcium chloride 81, potassium chloride 19	1184	640
†Barium chloride 70.3, sodium chloride 29.7	1209	654
†Potassium chloride 56, sodium chloride 44	1220	660
Sodium chloride 72.6, sodium fluoride 27.4	1247	675
Barium fluoride 70, calcium fluoride 15, magnesium fluoride 15	1454	790
Barium chloride 83, barium fluoride 17	1551	845
Calcium fluoride 48, magnesium fluoride 52	1738	949

* Lowest constant melting points given; proportions are percentages by weight.
† Most common salt mixtures.

The introduction of aluminum parts into a nitrate bath approaching or exceeding the melting points of these metals can cause fire and explosion. Magnesium alloys should never be immersed in a nitrate salt.

The storage of salts can cause serious problems. Chemicals, such as nitrates and cyanides, may mix and interact. Many salts are hydroscopic and, when stored in damp areas, will absorb moisture. When these salts are subsequently heated, moisture will be released below the surface and an explosion will ensue.

Intensive external reheating and remelting of a solidified salt bath may result in sufficiently rapid expansion to bulge or rupture the container. Such reheating can generate enough pressure to fracture the surface crust of the salt and scatter hot salts over a wide area.

When exposed to air having even a slight moisture content, the fumes from many salt baths become corrosive because chlorides, fluorides, and other salts will form acids by hydrolysis. These fumes are highly corrosive to adjacent building structures, wiring, and equipment and are, of course, detrimental to the bath operator.

THE SAFEGUARDS

While there appear to be many hazards connected with the operation of molten salt bath furnaces, fire, explosion, and injury can be prevented by the constant observance of ordinary precautions.

Clean dry sand may be used for diking purposes to confine and prevent the spread of the escaped melt. Carbon dioxide or dry chemical extinguishers may be used to extinguish burning carbonaceous material in the immediate vicinity of the salt bath.

The preferred location for a salt bath is a noncombustible area. The bath may be housed in a cement-lined pit or curbed area large enough to contain the contents in case of leakage or spill. It should be protected against leakage of liquids from other sources and be provided with baffles to prevent splashover from one tank to another. Salt bath furnaces provided with steel enclosures greatly reduce risks of leakage.

All salts should be shipped and stored in tightly covered containers designed to prevent the absorption of liquids or moisture. Nitrate salts should be stored in a fire-resistive, damp-free room and separated a reasonable distance from heat, liquids, and reactive chemicals. Nitrate and/or nitrite salts should never be stored in the vicinity of cyanide salts. Only the actual amount required to recharge the bath should be removed from the storage area, and this amount should be melted immediately. Salts should be transported from the storage area to the furnace in suitable containers to prevent loss during transport.

The safety precautions that apply to the heating systems of salt baths are identical to those for the heating systems of other industrial furnaces. Some additional safety measures are necessary. Flame should be tangential to the wall of a salt pot or container when a gas- or oil-fired heating system is used. The products of combustion should be vented. Radiant tubes and electrodes should be of materials resistant to the corrosive action of the salts used.

The buildup of sludge in any type of salt bath should be avoided, and the sludge periodically removed. Sludge is caused by the deterioration of salt, the introduction of foreign material into the bath, the dropping of small parts into the bath, or the freezing of salt due to a cold furnace bottom. Several methods of removing sludge and foreign objects are available. Some equipment has been designed to alleviate the buildup problem. Properly applied mechanical agitation greatly aids in the elimination and/or removal of the contaminants. Agitation prevents temperature stratification and freezing on the furnace bottom. Agitation also suspends and directs the contaminating particles into a settling pan or through a filter basket. (See Figures 2-17G and 2-17H.)

Two thermocouples properly located in the bath will provide safe control and protection from overheating. An overtemperature control should be arranged to automatically shut off the heat source and actuate visual and audible alarms in the event of a malfunction of the normal operating controls. All sensing couples must be protected from the corrosive effects of the particular salt used.

For the removal and control of any toxic, corrosive, or heated fumes, all salt bath furnaces should be equipped with hoods made of material that will not be affected by the corrosive nature of such fumes. In many cases, chemical scrubbers or suitable filters should be installed to remove the particulates. (See Figure 2-17I.) Removal or neutralization of fumes may require special equipment.

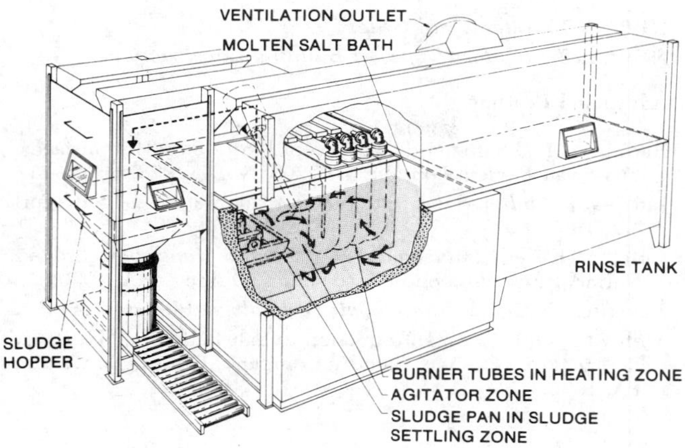

FIG. 2-17G. Descaling salt bath showing sludge pan construction. (Source: Kolene Co.)

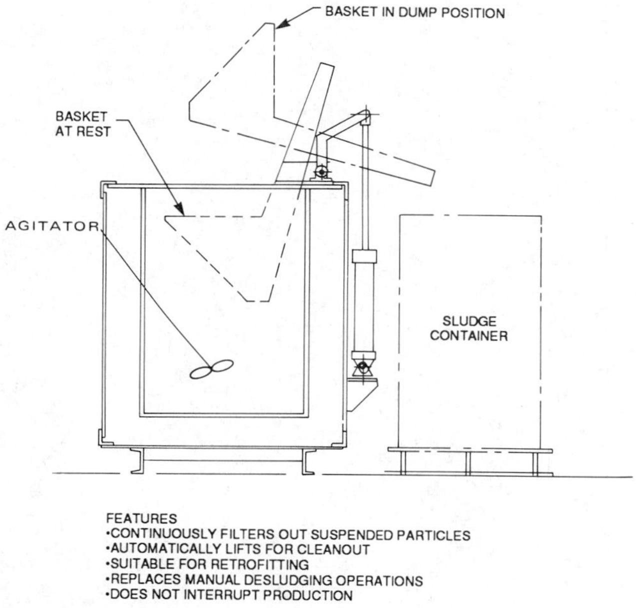

FIG. 2-17H. Automatic basket dumper. (Source: Ajax Electric Co.)

All fixtures used for dipping parts in baths, such as hooks, ladles, or baskets, should be of a solid, closed design without corners which could retain water. Parts such as closed piping or other hollow metallic articles in which air or moisture may be trapped should not be inserted into a molten bath without making provisions for venting the heated, expanded air or moisture. Immersion of hollow parts in salt baths should be very gradual. Any fixture used in one salt bath should be thoroughly cleaned and dried before it is immersed in another bath.

When electrodes are water cooled, an instrument should be provided to detect failure of the water cooling system.

If a salt bath is used as an internal quench in a furnace with a combustible atmosphere, measures should be provided to prevent carbon precipitation onto the salt surface.

FIG. 2-17I. Typical hooded enclosure, overhead hoist, and work platform greatly improve safety together with improved productivity and ease of maintainence.

In addition, adequate salt circulation should be provided to prevent localized hot spots whenever the salt is exposed to furnace temperatures.

A cold salt bath that has frozen over should be remelted or liquefied by applying initial heat as near to the top as possible. The application of heat to the external bottom surfaces will cause melting near the bottom and leave the top solidified. Expanding volume, causing excessive pressure and failure of the container with the subsequent ejection of hot salts. Breaking the surface crust will result in an explosive ejection of the salt. This hazard can be avoided by inserting a tapered solid bar in the molten salt adjacent to the immersed electrodes. After the salt has frozen, the bar is removed. The cavity created by the removal of the bar will serve as a vent duct for the escape of the gases formed. Gas burners that heat the top layers and gradually heat downward may be used if they are used carefully. For the submerged type of electrodes, a resistance heating coil set in between electrodes is recommended. Pumps are available to remove salt while it is in the molten state. Considerable care should be exercised in removing any molten salt; it should be pumped directly into steel drums where it can freeze over immediately. Salt and drums may then be properly discarded. For all types of heating, a "soft start" with reduced power input is recommended until melting is established from top to bottom.

All operators and workers in the vicinity of molten salt baths should be provided with corrosion-resistant and heat-resistant shoes, gloves, aprons, hard hats, and face shields. Solutions for cleansing eyes and supplies for treating minor burns should be available at all times. Breathing apparatus should also be provided for emergency use against oxides of nitrogen or corrosive fumes, such as chlorides and fluorides.

Constant vigilance with safety in mind and good housekeeping by intelligent and well-trained personnel can keep a salt bath operation as safe as any other metallurgical process conducted in an industrial furnace.

BIBLIOGRAPHY

NFPA Codes, Standards, and Recommended Practices

Reference to the following NFPA codes, standards, and recommended practices will provide further information on the safeguards for molten salt baths discussed in this chapter. (See the latest *NFPA Catalog* for availability of current editions of the following documents.)

NFPA 10, *Portable Fire Extinguishers.*

NFPA 70, *National Electrical Code®.*

NFPA 86, *Ovens and Furnaces.*

NFPA 86C, *Industrial Furnaces Using a Special Processing Atmosphere.*

NFPA *101®*, *Life Safety Code.®*

NFPA 220, *Standard Types of Building Construction.*

Additional Reading

Bartels, A. L., "Safeguards to Prevent Ignition by Hot Surfaces," *Electrical Review London*, Vol. 203, No. 4, 1978, pp. 29-31.

Janz, G. J., *Molten Salts Handbook*, Academic Press, New York, NY, 1967.

Cote, A. E., ed. *Industrial Fire Hazards Handbook*, 3rd ed., National Fire Protection Association, Quincy, MA, 1990.

Lovering, D. G., ed., *Molten Salt Technology*, Plenum, NY, 1982.

Mehrkam, Q. D., "An Introduction to Salt Bath Heat Treating," *Reprint No. 182*, Ajax Electric Company, Huntingdon Valley, PA, 1972.

REFRIGERATION SYSTEMS

Emil E. Roy and John R. Anderson

Industrial refrigeration systems usually are designed to provide a means for cooling specific locations to temperatures below ambient. Although there are many types of refrigeration systems, they are all heat exchangers differing only in mechanical and thermal design, employing different fluids for refrigerants.

This chapter identifies some of the more common types of refrigeration systems and hazards associated therewith, but excludes systems designed exclusively for air cooling building occupants.

Industrial refrigeration systems perform four major functions. They provide: (1) low-temperature storage for food and other products that deteriorate at normal ambient temperatures; (2) cooled air for the comfort of building occupants; (3) low-temperature air or gas-air mixtures for critical processes, such as the grinding of spices, rubber, and resins and the fast freezing of foods; and (4) they convert cryogenic gases to liquids for more efficient storage and transport.

HOW THE SYSTEM WORKS

Basically, all refrigeration systems take heat from one space or medium and transfer it to another. To accomplish the transfer, fluids are used that will readily absorb, transport, and release heat under controlled conditions. These fluids used as refrigerants perform in both the liquid and gaseous states. When a refrigerant in a liquid state changes to a gas, it absorbs heat from its surroundings. Conversely, when a refrigerant in a gaseous state condenses back to a liquid, it releases heat to its surroundings. The most effective refrigerant is a material that can vaporize and condense at the desired temperatures and pressures.

A refrigeration system consists of a receiver, a refrigerant, a control device, an evaporator, a compressor or heat absorber, and a condenser. At the start of a cycle the refrigerant passes from the receiver at high pressure to the control device, which is an expansion valve where the high-pressure gas is allowed to expand (thus reducing its pressure), and then to the evaporator which consists of many coils or tubes distributed in the area to be cooled. At the lower pressure, the gas evaporates and absorbs heat. The compressor, where an outside energy source is used for operation, takes the low-pressure gas, increases its pressure, and then discharges the high-pressure gas into a condenser. Here the gas gives up the heat obtained in the evaporator and condenses into a liquid, passing then to the receiver where it is stored for use as needed.

Refrigeration systems require two pressure levels—low pressure in the evaporator and high pressure in the condenser. Pressure differentials are obtained either by mechanical compression or by heat absorption.

Figure 2-18A illustrates the relationship of a mechanical compressor to the evaporator and condenser coils. Mechanical compressors can be of the reciprocating type with horizontal, vertical, or "V" design, or of the centrifugal type. (See Figures 2-18B and 2-18C). Regardless of the type, compressors should be made of materials that are compatible with the refrigerant used and equipped with the proper safeguards against overpressure and leakage. Typical safeguards include relief valves, purge valves, liquid separators, and oil separators.

Heat Absorption System

The compression stage of a heat absorption system occupies the same relative position in the refrigeration system as does the mechanical compressor. In heat absorption systems, heat supplied by steam, hot water, or a gas flame raises the pressure of the refrigerant so that it will flow through the expansion valve to the evaporator. The refrigerant, lithium bromide for air conditioning applications or ammonia for low-temperature process applications, is vaporized and goes into solution with an absorbent, usually water. After it has passed through a heat exchanger, the solution enters a generator in which heat drives the refrigerant from the absorbent. The refrigerant is then purified and returned to the condenser for reuse. (See Figure 2-18D.)

Emil E. Roy, vice president, Loss Prevention Services, for Frank B. Hall & Company, originally wrote this chapter. John R. Anderson, P.E., a consulting engineer in Marshfield, MA, significantly revised it for this edition.

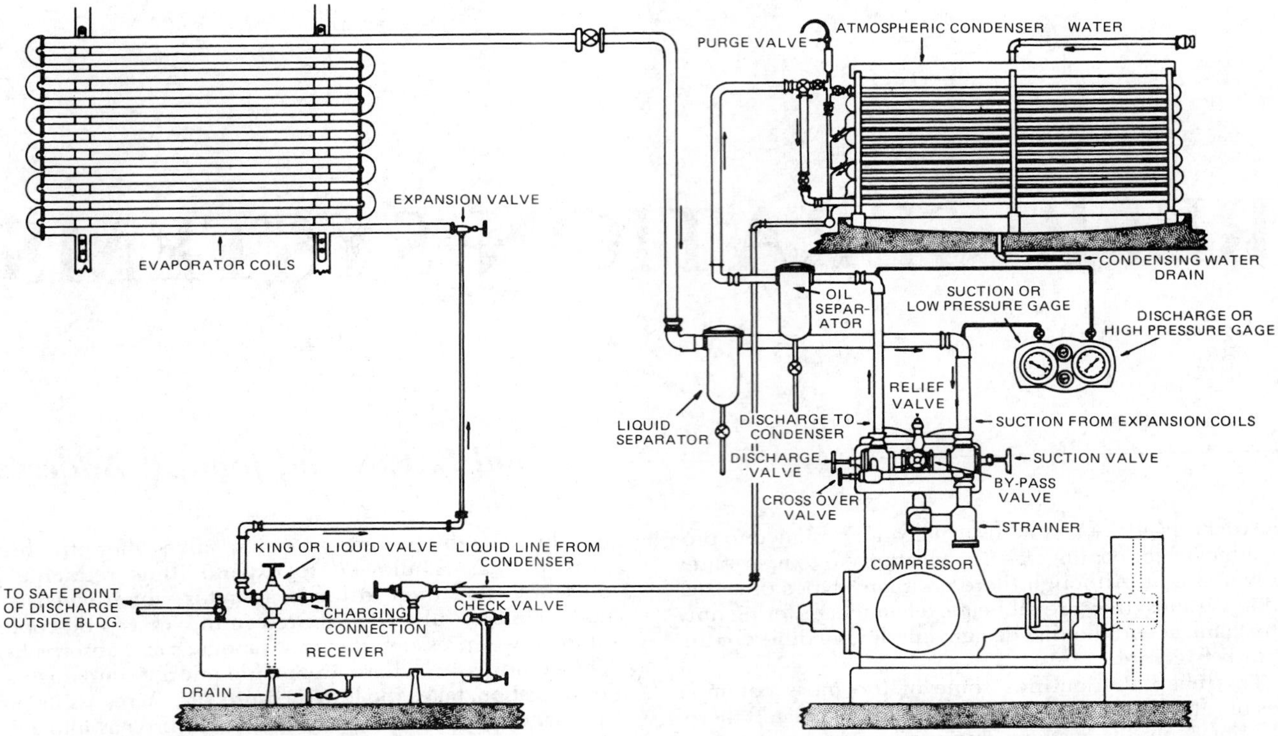

FIG. 2-18A. Typical ammonia refrigeration plant. (Source: Factory Mutual Research Corp.)

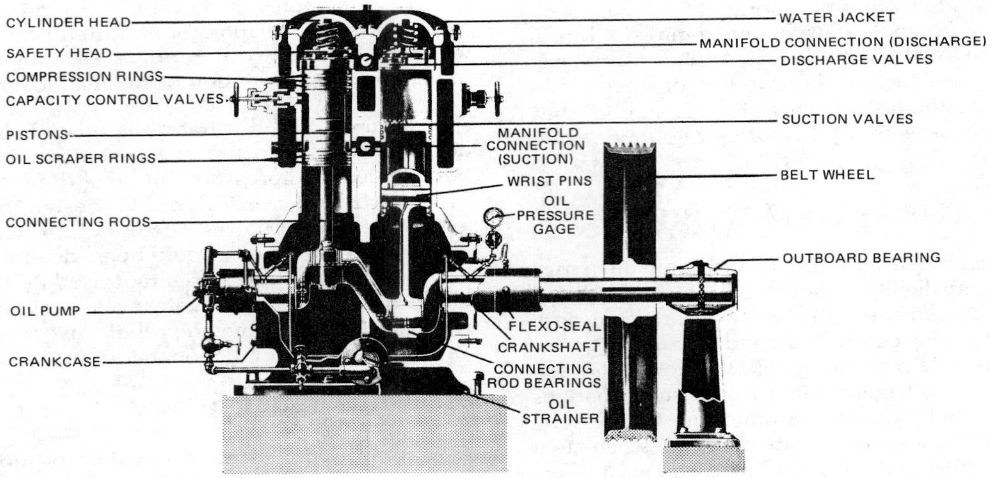

FIG. 2-18B. Reciprocating compressor, vertical single acting. (Source: Factory Mutual Research Corp.)

Compression Systems

Most of the commercial and industrial refrigeration systems in use today are of the mechanical compressor type. This type permits a wider selection of refrigerants to be used than does the absorbent type.

Compression Stages

Refrigeration systems may be single-stage, or multi-stage with compound compression, depending upon the desired extent of cooling needed. For example, two-stage compound systems provide cooling usually from –10°F (–23°C) to –70°F (–57°C).

Direct Systems

In addition to being classified according to the type of compression stage employed, refrigeration systems are further differentiated as direct or indirect. In the direct type, the evaporator is in direct contact with the product or space

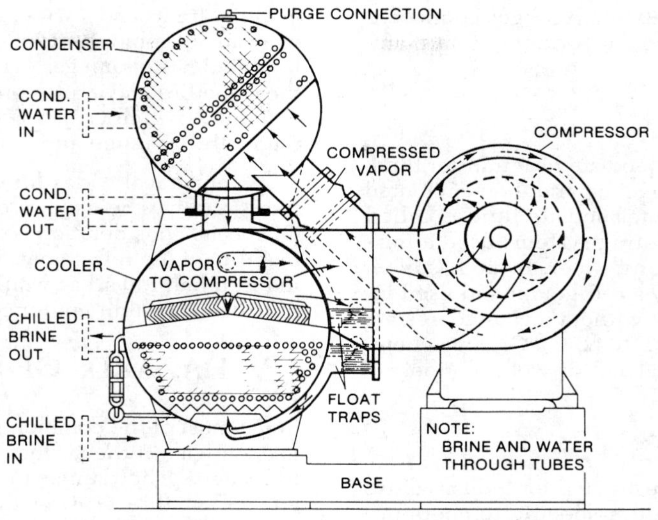

FIG. 2-18C. Cross-section of centrifugal refrigeration system showing refrigeration cycle. (Source: Factory Mutual Research Corp.)

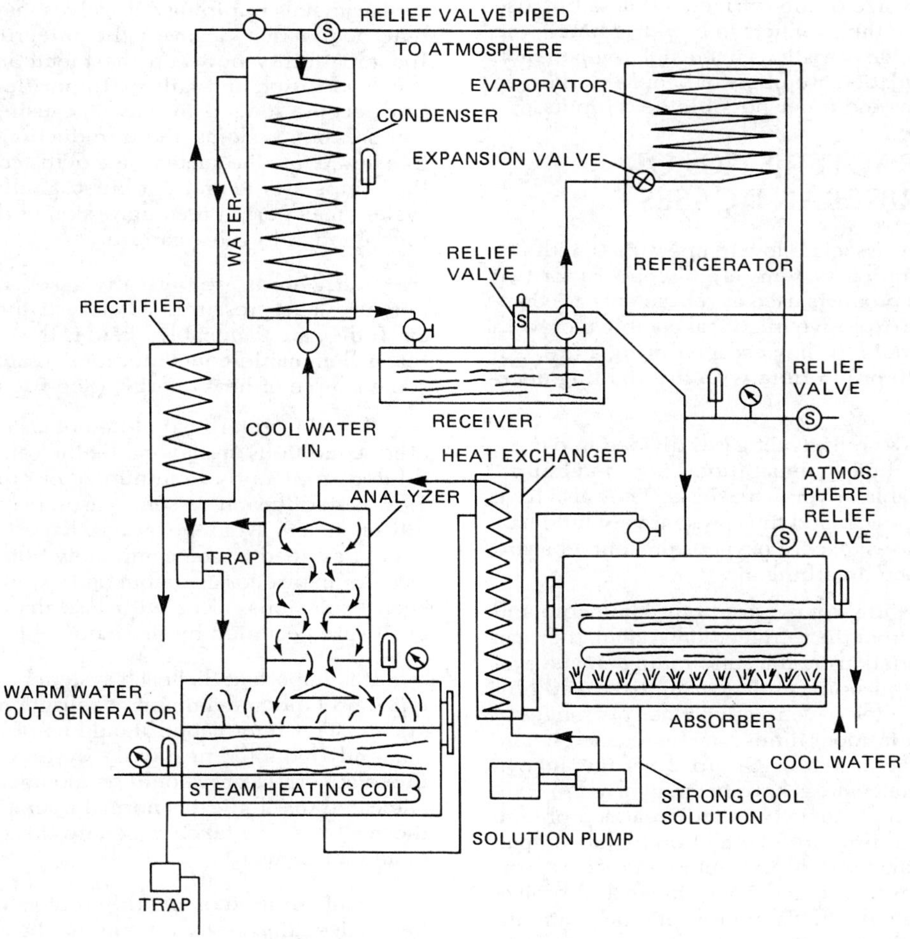

FIG. 2-18D. Heat absorption-type refrigeration system. (Source: National Safety Council)

to be cooled, or it is in air-circulating passages connected to the area or product. A household refrigerator is an example of a direct system.

Indirect Systems

An indirect system uses an intermediate heat transfer fluid, which is first cooled by the refrigerant and then circulated to the material or space. The intermediate fluid is called "brine," because early refrigerating systems used a mixture of sodium or calcium salt and water. Brine has been defined as any liquid cooled by a refrigerant and used for the transmission of heat energy without a change in state having a flash point above 150°F (65.6°C). Organic chemical solutions, such as ethylene glycol, as well as brine, are employed in indirect systems.

Refrigeration Capacity

Today, refrigeration systems constructed for industrial use are usually designed to provide a specific temperature range under varying relative humidities depending upon the nature of the products to be cooled. Some food products, e.g., meat, would require high humidity, while others, e.g., candy, would require low humidity.

The capacity of a refrigeration system depends upon not only the desired size of the refrigerated area but also upon the heat load of the products to be refrigerated, the length of time in storage, variations in outside temperature, the efficiency of insulation, numbers of people working in the refrigerated area, and other possible heat inputs.

CHARACTERISTICS OF REFRIGERANT GASES

One does not usually associate low temperatures with fire hazards, but refrigeration systems are of concern for two reasons. Some of the products used as refrigerants are flammable, and some are explosive in critical combination with air. Others are toxic and, if they escape during a fire, can cause injury or death or interfere with fire fighting operations.

Table 2-18A shows refrigerant gases divided into three classes according to their flammability. Those in Group 1 are either nonflammable or very weakly so. They also have rather low levels of toxicity and thus present very little hazard. However, all gases (except oxygen) present a hazard to life if they displace breathing air.

The refrigerants in Group 2 are both flammable and toxic. If they escape from the refrigeration system, they can reach critical concentrations in the surrounding air and produce combustion explosions, endangering lives and hindering fire fighting. They have relatively narrow ranges of flammability, and their upper limits may be reached before combustion is initiated. While Group 2 refrigerants in tightly closed refrigerated areas have been involved in combustion explosions, their toxicity is the greater problem. Ammonia systems require careful attention to the compatibility of the materials used. Moist ammonia reacts vigorously with copper and zinc and many brass and bronze alloys, rapidly eroding them. Therefore, ammonia systems require iron or steel pipe systems.

Though the refrigerants in Group 3 do not present the same toxicity hazards as those in Group 2, they present much greater fire hazards. They generally have lower flammability limits and a wider range. Butane, ethane, and propane are all components of liquefied natural gas (LNG) and liquefied petroleum gas (LPG), and they present relatively the same fire and explosion hazards as do LNG and LPG. Ethylene, which is also a component of LPG, has a wide flammability range and a high burning velocity.

Mechanical codes limit the type of refrigeration systems that may be used in different types of occupancies. Of special consideration is the quantity, toxicity, and flammability of the refrigerant. For example, the use of ammonia in inhabited areas would be undesirable in the event of leaks or system malfunction.

HAZARDS OF REFRIGERATION

Since most of the common refrigerants are at least slightly toxic, a leak in the system will be a hazard to health and life safety. The danger to people and products is much greater in a direct system than in an indirect system. However, the degree of hazard is dependent upon how completely the direct portion of the system is isolated from the space or product being cooled.

Leaks can occur for many different reasons. Pipe joints may weaken and fail because of excessive vibration. Dissimilar metals in piping and valves may set up an electrolytic action that destroys the integrity of the junction. Incompatibility between the metal and refrigerant may cause corrosion and failure. Impurities in the refrigerant can become lodged in valves, causing malfunctions. In compression systems, the introduction of a noncompressible liquid into the suction side of the compressor can cause the compressor to crack or burst. Faulty valves within the system may permit recompression of the gas to pressures high enough to cause failure.

Refrigerants are normally gases at atmospheric temperatures and pressures. Therefore, they mix readily with air. If they are flammable, there is the danger that they will reach flammable concentrations, ready to be ignited by some source of heat energy. (See Figure 2-18E.)

If the surrounding volume of air is large enough and other conditions are favorable, the refrigerant gas may be diluted sufficiently to minimize or eliminate the hazard. However, diffusion, in some cases, may not take place rapidly enough to avoid the hazard. Experience has shown that structures need not be completely filled with a flammable gas-air mixture for a combustion explosion to occur. Most such explosions occur with less than 25 percent of the enclosure occupied by the flammable mixture.

It is important that each system be identified as to the type and kind and amount of refrigerant contained in the system. This information should be printed on a plate permanently mounted next to the system. Also, an easily visible plate or placard should be mounted where the system is located that indicates normal operating procedures and those steps to be taken to secure the system in the event of an emergency.

A substitution of any different refrigerant in an existing refrigeration system should not be allowed without the written approval of the system designer, the equipment manufacturer, and the operator. Introducing a different refrigerant may result in system failure, including explosion.

TABLE 2-18A. *Basic Hazard Data for Some Common Refrigerants*

Classification of Refrigerants	Formula	Boiling Point °F	Boiling Point °C	Calculated Density Gas (air = 1)	Autoignition Temperature °F	Autoignition Temperature °C	Flammable Limits, Percent by Volume in Air Lower	Flammable Limits, Percent by Volume in Air Upper	Toxicity
Group 1 (nonflammable, except as noted):									
Carbon dioxide (R-74)	CO_2	−109.0	−78.3	1.52					Slightly toxic
Monochlorodifluoromethane (R-22)	$CHClF_2$	−42.0	−41.1	2.98	1170	632	Very weakly flammable		Slightly toxic
Dichlorodifluoromethane (R-12)	CCl_2F_2	−22.0	−30.0	4.17					Nontoxic for ordinary exposure
Dichlorofluoromethane (R-21)	$CHCl_2F$	48.0	8.9	3.55	1026	552	Very weakly flammable		Slightly toxic
Dichlorotetrafluoroethane (R-14)	$C_2Cl_2F_4$	38.4	3.5	5.89					Nontoxic
Trichlorofluoromethane (R-11)	CCl_3F	74.8	23.8	4.79					Slightly toxic
Methylene chloride (R-30)	CH_2Cl_2	105.2	40.7	2.93	1139	615	Very weakly flammable		Slightly toxic
Trichlorotrifluoroethane (R-113)	$C_2Cl_3F_3$	117.6	47.5	6.46	1256	680	Very weakly flammable		Slightly toxic
Group 2 (flammable):									
Ammonia (R-717)	NH_3	−28.0	−33.3	0.59	1204	651	16	25.0	Toxic
Dichloroethylene (R-1130)	$C_2H_2Cl_2$	99–141	37–61	3.35	856	458	9.7	12.8	Moderately toxic
Ethyl chloride (R-160)	C_2H_3Cl	54.0	12.2	2.22	966	519	3.8	15.4	Moderately toxic
Methyl formate R-611)	$C_2H_4O_2$	90.0	32.2	2.07	869	465	5.0	23.0	Toxic
Group 3 (highly flammable):									
Butane (R-600)	C_4H_{10}	31.0	−0.5	2.01	900–1000	482–538	1.55	8.6	Slightly toxic
Ethane (R-170)	C_2H_6	−128.0	−88.8	1.04	959	515	3.0	12.5	Slightly toxic
Propane (R-240)	C_3H_8	−44.0	−42.2	1.52	920–1120	493–604	2.2	9.6	Slightly toxic
Ethylene (R-1150)	C_2H_4	−154.8	−103.8	0.98	914	490	2.7	36.0	Slightly toxic

FIG. 2-18E. Result of an anhydrous ammonia explosion in Houston, TX, on December 11, 1983. (Source: Houston Fire Department)

Various substances have been developed through the years that have been used as refrigerants. The use of halogenated hydrocarbons for refrigerant fluids has proved to be very effective and cost-saving. However, the use of some halons has been linked to the depletion of the ozone layer in the Earth'satmosphere. Therefore, governmental agencies are limiting the production of these materials, and at some point will terminate their production completely. Newer fluids will be developed, but care should be taken by authorities having jurisdiction and others that characteristics of these new materials will not introduce a greater degree of hazard in terms of fire, explosion, and toxicity.

EMERGENCY CONTROLS AND PROCEDURES

Refrigerant gases present three basic hazards—toxicity, flammability, and explosion hazard—which can either create nonfire or fire emergencies.

Control of the nonfire emergency is accomplished by directing, diluting, and dispersing the gas to prevent it from coming in contact with people. Simultaneously, steps should be taken to stop the flow of gas. Air, water, and steam are practical media for accomplishing dilution and dispersion. Water in the form of a spray from hoses or fixed nozzles is most commonly used for this purpose.

Control of fire emergencies generally consists of reducing the heat of the fire with water and, if possible, shutting off the gas supply. Water should be applied as a spray from hoses or fixed nozzles. Carbon dioxide, dry chemical, and halogenated extinguishing agents are useful in most instances. Ammonia is easily controlled with water, but suitable breathing apparatus and protective clothing should be worn.

With the exception of carbon dioxide, the refrigerants in Group 1 are halogenated hydrocarbons, commonly known as halons. (See Table 2-18A.) Related halons, most of which are bromine compounds, are used as fire extinguishing agents. Halon refrigerants are usually referred to by numbers (R-11, etc.) as is shown in Table 2-18A. They have varying characteristics and, therefore, have varying applications.

R-11 and R-114 are low-pressure refrigerants. This means that the pressure in the evaporator is below atmospheric pressure; thus, the pressure in the condenser is relatively low. For cooling water for air conditioning and industrial processing, R-11 is commonly used. For cooling brines to temperatures between 20°F and –20°F (–6 and –28°C), R-114 is usually employed. R-12 is used for very low temperatures down to –120°F (–84°C). Though classified as nonflammable (except as noted), halon refrigerants can present some hazards. R-12, for example, can react vigorously with aluminum at elevated temperatures of about 1,200°F (–684°C).

These halogenated refrigerants are commonly used in centrifugal refrigeration systems. In such systems, the brine is cooled by passing it through tubes immersed in the refrigerant. The vaporized refrigerant is forced by the compressor into the condenser, where it is liquefied. At this point, an economizer partially cools the compressed refrigerant by partial evaporation, and the vapor goes to the second stage of the compressor. A purge recovery unit takes air or other noncondensable gas out of the refrigerant and discharges it to the atmosphere.

Refrigeration equipment should be installed with careful regard to the many variables that affect life safety and fire hazards. The occupancy should determine whether a direct or indirect system should be installed. Limitations should be imposed upon the quantity of refrigerant available, based upon the concentration that would be attained if the entire quantity were discharged into the area. The quantity, of course, should be determined by the toxicity, flammability, and explosion hazard of the refrigerant. Materials used in the system should be compatible with the type of refrigerant used, and the system should include the proper safety devices and relief valves. Electrical equipment and wiring should be properly grounded, shielded, and installed in conformance with NFPA 70, *National Electrical Code®*, and all other possible ignition sources eliminated.

BIBLIOGRAPHY

References

Factory Mutual Research Corporation, "Refrigeration," *Loss Prevention Data 7-13* (with revisions), Factory Mutual Research Corp., Norwood, MA.

NFPA Codes, Standards, and Recommended Practices

Reference to the following NFPA codes, standards, and recommended practices will provide further information on the safeguards for refrigeration equipment discussed in this chapter. (See the latest *NFPA Catalog* for availability of current editions of the following documents.)

NFPA 10, *Portable Fire Extinguishers.*

NFPA 12, *Carbon Dioxide Extinguishing Systems.*

NFPA 12A, *Halon 1301 Fire Extinguishing Systems.*

NFPA 12B, *Halon 1211 Fire Extinguishing Systems.*

NFPA 17, *Dry Chemical Extinguishing Systems.*

NFPA 30, *Flammable and Combustible Liquids Code.*

NFPA 70, *National Electrical Code®.*

NFPA 325M, *Fire Hazard Properties of Flammable Liquids, Gases, and Volatile Solids.*

Additional Readings

Benedetti, R. P., *Flammable and Combustible Liquids Code Handbook,* 3rd ed., National Fire Protection Association, Quincy, MA, 1987.

Factory Mutual Engineering Corp., "Refrigeration," *Loss Prevention Data 7-13*, Factory Mutual System, Norwood, MA, Oct., 1975.

Factory Mutual Engineering Corp., "Refrigerated Warehouses," *Loss Prevention Data* 8-29, May 1976.

"Fire and Explosion Hazards of Compressors," *Fire Prevention*, (122), 1977, pp. 19-21.

Loader, K., "Fire Protection of Cold Storage Warehouses," *Fire Prevention*, Feb. 1981, pp. 11-15.

McRae, H., "Ammonia Explosion Destroys Ice Cream Plant, "*Fire Command*, Apr. 1984, pp. 36-37.

Meacock, M. H., *Refrigeration Processes: A Practical Handbook on the Physical Properties of Refrigerants and their Applications*, Pergamon Press, Inc., NY, 1979.

Miller, R., *Refrigeration and Air Conditioning Technology*, Bennett Publishing Co., Peoria, IL, 1983.

"Number Designation of Refrigerants," *ASHRAE 34*, American Society of Heating, Refrigeration, and Air Conditioning Engineers, Atlanta, GA, 1978.

Safety Code for Mechanical Refrigeration, ANSI B9.1-1971, American Society of Mechanical Engineering, New York

"Safety Code for Mechanical Refrigeration," ASHRAE 15, American Society of Heating, Refrigeration, and Air Conditioning Engineers, Atlanta, GA, 1978.

"Sprinkler Protection of Small Cold Stores," *Fire Prevention,* Vol. 143, No. 17 (Aug. 1981).

Weiby, P. and Dickinson, K. R., "Monitoring Work Areas for Explosive and Toxic Hazards," *Chemical Engineering*, Vol. 83, No. 22, 1976, pp. 139-145.

LASERS

John A. Sharry

Lasering applications have expanded rapidly during the past decade. Lasers in some form are in use in almost all fields. In construction, lasers are used for measuring distances, projecting straight lines for tunneling and pipelines, and projecting a plane of light for the alignment of ceilings and floors. In the manufacturing area, lasers are used to cut, weld, and drill. Lasers are used in the entertainment field for public displays, music shows, and demonstrations. Most of us have by now come in contact with lasers in the checkout lanes in supermarkets and other high-volume merchandizing establishments where they are used to scan the product code on merchandise. Many of us are also accustomed to using lasers in business in the form of laser printers. Other common laser applications include extensive use in the medical fields of gynecology, neurosurgery, general surgery, dermatology, urology, ophthalmology, and podiatry, to name just a few. Not as common, but nevertheless important, is the use of lasers in research facilities and military applications.

LASER PROPERTIES

The term laser is actually an acronym for "light amplification by stimulated emission of radiation." The radiation referred to in the acronym laser should not be confused with ionizing radiation associated with radioactive materials, but rather it refers to the broad spectrum of electromagnetic radiation which includes visible light, ultraviolet light, and infrared light.

Visible light is one form of electromagnetic radiation. Electromagnetic radiation consists of electrical and magnetic energy traveling together in wave form. Other forms of electromagnetic radiation are not visible to the human eye, such as radio waves, ultraviolet light, and microwaves.

All forms of electromagnetic radiation taken together produce the electromagnetic spectrum. Different portions of this spectrum describe the frequency and wavelength of the various electromagnetic wave forms. (See Figure 2-19A.)

John A. Sharry is the fire chief at Lawrence Livermore National Laboratory, Livermore, CA.

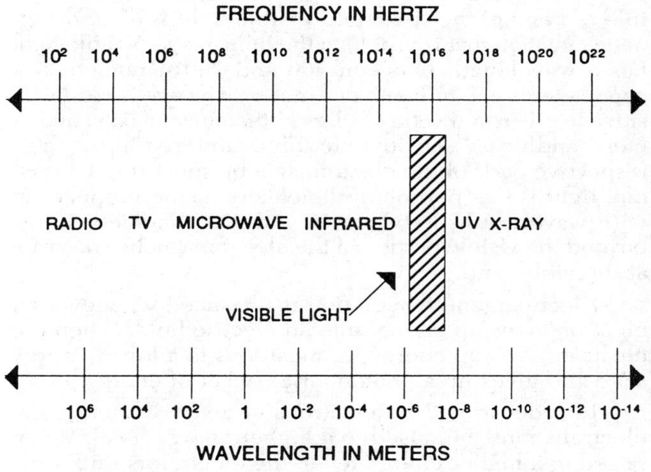

FIG. 2-19A. Electromagnetic spectrum.

Wavelength refers to the distance between peaks on a wave or the distance for the wave to complete one cycle. Wavelength is measured in meters. Frequency refers to the number of cycles the wave completes in one second. A "hertz" is one cycle per second, and is the normal term of expression for frequency.

Figure 2-19A shows that low-frequency, long wavelength radiation is found at the low end of the spectrum, while high-frequency, short wavelength radiation is found at the high end of the spectrum. Examples of low-frequency, long wavelength radiation are radio waves, television waves, and microwaves. Examples of high-frequency, short wavelength radiation are ultraviolet light and X rays. Radiation visible to the human eye in the form of light makes up a small portion of the entire spectrum. Figure 2-19B illustrates the visible light range within the electromagnetic spectrum.

The study of laser light is generally concentrated in the optical spectrum, or that portion of the electromagnetic spectrum from infrared to ultraviolet light, which includes visible light.

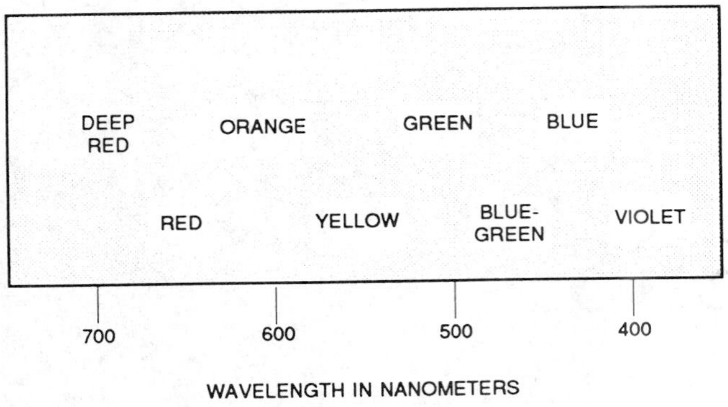

FIG. 2-19B. Visible light spectrum.

Infrared radiation is radiation with wavelengths ranging between 10^{-4} and 10^{-6} meters. The name infrared comes from the fact that the wavelengths are longer than the visible red end of the spectrum. Visible light is electromagnetic radiation that is visible to the human eye. Visible light has a wavelength between 400 and 700 nanometers (a nanometer is one billionth of a meter). The eye is most sensitive to green and yellow colors in the range of 555 nanometers and least sensitive to blue and red near their respective ends of the electromagnetic spectrum. Ultraviolet light is that portion of the electromagnetic spectrum with wavelengths between 10 and 400 nanometers, just beyond the visible portion of the electromagnetic spectrum at the violet end.

Electromagnetic radiation is produced whenever an electron gives up energy into an electric field. When the electron gives up energy, it transitions to a lower energy state and gives up a photon, or a packet of energy.

In order to get the electrons to give up energy, the electrons must be raised to a higher energy level. When raised to a higher energy level, the electron is said to be excited, or in an excited state. When electrons randomly give up photons by transitioning to a lower energy state, the light or electromagnetic radiation is diffuse. However, if the atoms can be excited and then influenced to produce the emission of a photon of a certain wavelength and in a certain direction, then the resulting light can be utilized in unique ways. Obviously, to make the light emitted useful, a great many photons of the proper type must be produced.

Laser light has several unique properties. One of those properties is that laser light consists of only a single color. In addition, the wavelengths of this single color are within a very narrow range. This property is called monochromaticity. A second property is that of directionality. Normal light is radiated in all directions in a random fashion. Laser light, however, is radiated in a narrow beam in a single direction. The third unique property of laser light is that of coherence. Laser light is radiated in an orderly pattern known as being "in phase." When all the separate waves are in phase the resultant combination wave is much stronger. Thus, laser light is a very intense light of a single color, being radiated in a single direction, with little divergence. It is these properties that give laser light its diverse applications and its hazards.

A laser, then, must be constructed of components that can produce the necessary photons in sufficient quantities to produce a useful light beam. Lasers consist of generally three components: (1) a lasing medium, (2) an energy source (or pumping system), and (3) a feedback mechanism. (See Figure 2-19C.) Other accessories, such as lenses, mirrors, and shutters may be added to the system to produce special effects, but only the basic three are needed for lasing action.

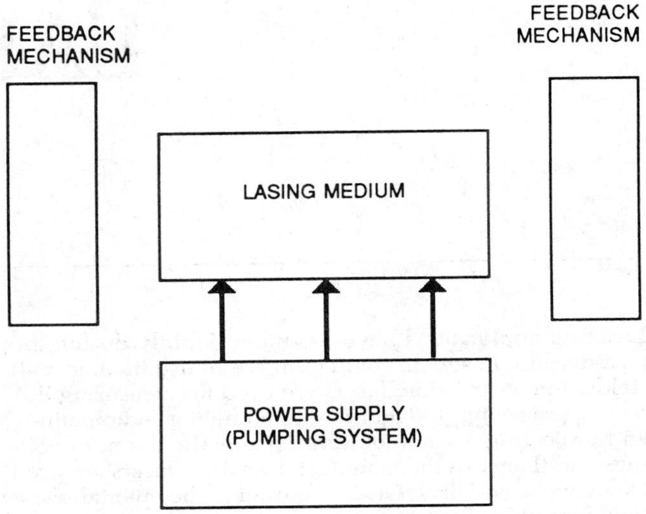

FIG. 2-19C. Laser components.

Lasing Medium

The lasing medium is a collection of atoms that can be excited to a state to produce a stimulated emission of photons. The active medium may be a solid, liquid, or gas, or semiconductor material.

Energy Source

The pumping system is a source of energy that can be used to raise the electrons in the lasing medium to their excited state. The pumping system may take one of several forms: (1) optical pumping systems use strong sources of light, such as xenon flashtubes or flashlamps, or a continuous arc lamp; (2) electron collision pumping is created when an electric current is passed through the laser material; or (3) chemical pumping is created by the making or breaking of chemical bonds. All three forms of pumping are commonly in use.

Feedback Mechanism

The feedback mechanism is an apparatus that returns a portion of the laser light created in the lasing medium back to the lasing medium. This feedback creates a situation where the photons created in the lasing medium are passed back through the lasing medium creating more photons. If sufficient feedback is created, the creation of laser light can be made continuously and at high levels. The normal feedback mechanism is a pair of mirrors aligned to reflect the laser light back and forth. One of the mirrors is only partially reflective, permitting some light to leave the laser. The portion of the light that is not emitted continues to be reflected, creating more photons. (See Figure 2-19D.)

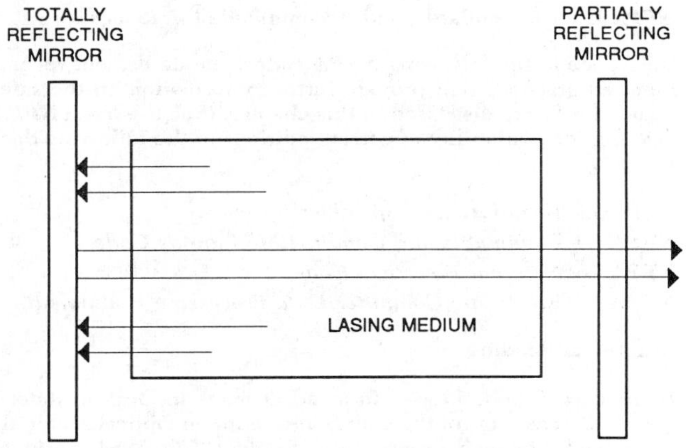

FIG. 2-19D. Schematic of feedback mechanism.

LASER OPERATION

Laser operation can best be described in three steps:

1. Energy is supplied to the laser material by the pumping system. This energy is stored by the laser material in the form of electrons in their excited state. The pumping system must continue until a population inversion (i.e., more electrons in the excited state than in their normal state) takes place for laser light to be produced.
2. Once the population inversion is achieved, the decay of a few electrons to a lower energy level will start a chain reaction. Photons released will strike electrons, creating more photons of the same wavelength, phase, and direction.
3. When the photons reach one of the mirrors, they will be reflected back into the laser material, supporting continued chain reaction and the production of even more photons. Some photons will strike the partially reflective mirrors; when that occurs, some of them will be reflected back into the laser material and some will be emitted as laser light.

Modes of Operation

The modes of laser operation are differentiated by the rate at which energy is delivered. Some lasers produce a steady flow of light. These lasers are known as continuous wave lasers, or CW lasers. Pulsed lasers are lasers operated to create repetitive laser pulses. A special type of pulsed laser is a Q-switched laser. In the Q-switched laser, a shutter-like device is placed between the mirrors of a laser to interrupt the lasing action. The shutter can act as a mirror in itself, allowing the continued reflection of photons and buildup of excited electrons, but not allowing any photons to escape through the partially reflective mirror. When the shutter opens, a very intense pulse is released.

THE HAZARDS

The American National Standards Institute (ANSI) has adopted a classification system for lasers, based on the ability of the primary laser beam or reflected primary laser beam to cause biological damage to the eye or skin during intended use:

Class I: A low-powered laser device that cannot, under normal circumstances, emit laser radiation that creates an optical hazard. These are sometimes called exempt lasers.

Class II: Low-powered laser devices operating in the visible spectrum that cannot injure a person accidentally, but which may injure the eye when viewed directly for an extended period of time.

Class III: Medium-powered laser devices that are capable of causing eye damage with short-duration exposures to the direct or specularly reflected beam.

Class IV: Lasers that can injure if viewed directly or if reflections are viewed. These lasers can also cause severe skin damage and are to be considered a fire hazard.

In addition to the biological hazards classified by the ANSI system, lasers produce several other hazards which must be considered.

The most common hazard associated with lasers of all types is the electrical hazard. Almost all lasers contain high-energy power supplies. These power supplies can produce both electrical shock hazards and, as in all electrical pieces of equipment, fire hazards. Normal electrical safety devices, such as fuses, circuit breakers, insulation, grounding devices, and interlocks, can effectively control these hazards.

Many lasers use capacitors. Capacitors store electrical charges, with the intent to release these high electrical charges in a very short period of time. Accidental discharge of capacitors is, therefore, extremely dangerous. Shorting or internal electrical faults can cause capacitor rupture, fires, or explosions. Because of all these possible hazards, capacitors require certain safety precautions. Capacitors should be isolated within screens, shields, barriers, or uninhabited rooms designed to protect against shock, burns, and fire, and to contain fragments from an explosive capacitor failure. Covers or doors to capacitors should be interlocked to prevent charging (when open) by dumping and grounding the capacitors.

Special fire hazards are created in the target area of Class IV lasers. The beam from these powerful lasers can ignite materials surrounding the target area. Good housekeeping in the target area, with removal of combustibles, is a must. In some cases, lasers use an alcohol-based dye. Normal flammable liquids control measures are effective in controlling these hazards.

Experimental lasers can produce special hazards. These hazards can be effectively controlled by careful planning and conducting a laser hazard evaluation. Because many experimental lasers are "home-built," they may not be built with listed or labeled components that have been tested for that special use. Electrical components may be unique and not tested for hazardous (classified) locations. Because of the experimental nature of these installations, other special precautions may be necessary to control the fire hazards.

Lasers can produce hazardous material byproducts. Special consideration must be given to the proper containment and disposal of these hazardous materials.

FIRE PROTECTION EQUIPMENT

Although lasers are still thought of as unique pieces of equipment, the fire protection methods used to protect other high-value pieces of electrical equipment are applicable to protecting lasers. The use of automatic sprinklers is considered the baseline requirement for high-value protection. The installation of fire detection systems and other automatic extinguishment systems as a supplement should be considered for large laser systems of particular value. As a guide, the fire protection methods used for computer centers are generally applicable, with special consideration for flammable liquid hazards.

BIBLIOGRAPHY

References

"Standard for the Safe Use of Lasers," *ANSI Z136.1-1986*, American National Standards Institute, Washington, DC.

"Standard for the Safe Use of Lasers in Health Care Facilities," *ANSI Z136.3-1988*, American National Standards Institute, Washington, DC.

"Control of Hazards to Health from Laser Radiation," *Technical Bulletin TB MED 279*, Department of the Army, Washington, DC, 1975.

NFPA Codes, Standards, and Recommended Practices

Reference to the following NFPA codes, standards, and recommended practices will provide further information on the safeguards for lasers discussed in this chapter. (See the latest *NFPA Catalog* for availability of current editions of the following documents.)

NFPA 13, *Installation of Sprinkler Systems.*

NFPA 30, *Flammable and Combustible Liquids Code.*

NFPA 70, *National Electrical Code®.*

NFPA 75, *Electronic Computer/Data Processing Equipment.*

Additional Reading

Bennet, H. E., ed., "Laser Induced Damage in Optical Materials," *Proceedings* of the 16th Symposium on Optical Materials for High Powered Lasers, 1984, Boulder, CO, 1984, National Institute for Standards and Technology, Gaithersburg, MD, 1986.

Zilcer, P., *Laser Technology: A Survey*, National Aeronautics and Space Administration, Washington, DC, 1973.

METALWORKING PROCESSES

Paul Dobbs

This chapter describes the various methods used to shape, dimension, and finish metals. These include tool, electrical discharge, and electromechanical machining. The fire and explosion hazards of the various processes, metals, and fluids are indicated and the proper safeguards discussed.

Additional information on the characteristics of metals is included in Section 3, Chapter 13, "Metals." Extinguishing agents for metals are discussed in Section 5, Chapter 21, "Combustible Metal Agents and Application Techniques." For more information, the Bureau of Mines publishes a bulletin on the explosibility of metal dusts.[1]

THE METALWORKING PROCESS

The metalworking process includes shaping, dimensioning, or surface finishing of a wide variety of metals. The operations include turning, planing, shaping, slotting, milling, sawing, boring, drilling, grinding, abrasive cutting, filing, threading, reaming, broaching, deburring, lapping, chamfering, spinning, etc. Some of these same operations and equipment are also used to work on other-than-metal materials, such as plastics or wood. These other materials likely would increase the hazard of the operation; however, the extent of that increase, or the additional protection that may be necessary, is not covered in this chapter.

Upon cursory observation of a machining operation, it would appear there are few, if any, fire hazards about which to be concerned. This is deceptive for there are aspects of machining that require careful and constant attention. The fire record is full of experiences that point to the need for considerable pre-planning and preventive action. The principal hazards involve the coolants/lubricants used for the lubrication of the cutting tools and the possible combustion of the cuttings (chips) and fine particles (fines) that are produced as the workpiece is shaped and cut. The three principal sources of ignition are: (1) the heat generated by the work being done, (2) the friction created by the cutting tool, and (3) spontaneous oxidation of materials used. It is important to remember that nearly all metals will burn in air under certain conditions, depending on size, shape, and quantity.

The machining operation can be broken down into five components for the purpose of analyzing the hazards present: (1) machine tool; (2) cutting tool; (3) raw materials; (4) oils, including cutting oils, lubricating oils, and hydraulic oils; and (5) machine cuttings and their collection systems.

The Machine Tool

The modern industrial machine tool may be a single-motor machine, such as a drill press, or it may be a very large multi-motored automatic machine with a highly complex electronics control system. Stock can be brought as needed to an individual machine where a worker then mounts it to the machine and initiates the operation manually. More likely there is some degree of automation in these operations, and, in many cases, several machines can be located in close proximity to facilitate the easy movement of stock from one machining operation to the next. Almost all machines are electric-motor operated and likely contain some lubricating oils and grease. Electrical supply to this equipment is generally 480 V or less; however, some larger equipment will operate at higher voltages.

In almost all cases, the lubricating oil for the machine is self-contained, i.e., in the unit. Although the amount may become significant [50 to 100 gal (189 to 378 L)], it is not an inherently significant hazard. The containment structures for these oils are usually substantial, and leaks are rare.

The electric motors and the lubricating oils systems on the machines do not alone constitute a hazard sufficient to warrant any automatic protection. However, portable Class BC extinguishers should be available in the area.

Traditionally, the machine tool is a stand-alone piece of equipment, usually operated manually by a trained operator, who sets up the stock, then controls the cutting operation. In the modern industrial setting, this arrangement has gradually given way to numerically and digitally controlled equipment, leading to more sophisticated electronic equipment in the vicinity of these operations. While this

Paul Dobbs is district engineering manager for American Risk Management, based in Plymouth, MI.

equipment does not inherently present significant fire hazards, it may create additional revenue loss due to fire exposure. It can also be a factor in the damage and downtime of a piece of equipment involved in a fire. In addition, modern electronic equipment is more susceptible to damage from exposure fires. This potential for increased loss due to exposure fires should be included in the evaluation of automatic protection in occupancies that include such equipment.

Cutting Tool

The cutting tool can either be fixed in place while the stock is moved past it, such as on a lathe, or the tool itself can be moving, such as in a mill, surface grinder, or boring machine. The tools may be pointed or bladed and may be of hardened high-carbon steel, high-speed steel, hard ceramics, or steel tipped with hard metal carbides of tungsten, cobalt, tantalum, or other hard metallic elements. Grinding abrasives are usually alundum or silicon carbide grains bonded with resin or ceramics and pressed into the shape of wheels. These cutting tools shape the raw materials into the finished part. They can also represent a point of ignition, as they can develop significant heat from the friction of the work they are performing. Dull tools not only increase the requirement for power and influence the quality and tolerance of the work being done, but also are often the ignition source of fires in machines. Dull tools tend to produce finer particles that are more readily combustible or explosive than the larger chips, which are generally produced by sharp tools. Cutting tools normally do not require any special protection. Of course if they are transported on wood pallets or in cardboard cartons or other combustible containers, those materials may necessitate the provision of sprinkler protection.

Raw Materials

The raw materials arriving at a machining plant may be in the form of clean castings, forgings, rough-cut plate, rolled or drawn bar or merchant mill stock, fabrications, tubes, or rolled or extruded shapes. In general, these raw materials have significant mass and so can be considered as noncombustible unless exposed to massive fire. This applies even to the light metals which are known to be more readily combustible when they have a large surface-to-mass ratio. In most cases, though, the raw materials do not present any significant combustible loading. However, the packaging materials used in the transport of these materials must be considered, and, if sufficient combustibles are present, automatic sprinkler protection should be provided as necessary.

Other raw materials include cutting, lubricating, and hydraulic oils; cutting tools; etc. Bulk shipments and storage of combustible oils should be handled in accordance with accepted standards. Further discussion of these hazards can be found in Section 2, Chapter 25, "Storage of Flammable and Combustible Liquids."

Hazard potentials can change significantly once the raw materials are subjected to the metalworking processes. The type of operation the stock is subject to determines the size of pieces of that material that will be removed in the form of chips or fines. Chips and fines significantly increase the surface-to-mass ratio of the material, and, in some cases, they may become subject to spontaneous ignition or to ignition from outside sources. Table 2-20A shows the combustibility of fine powders of various metals, and the amount of energy needed to initiate combustion. Almost all metals have some degree of combustibility, and, in the case of such materials as aluminum, magnesium, and titanium, they can represent a very significant hazard. As mentioned, some chips in cuttings may be subject to spontaneous ignition. Zirconium and uranium powders tend to ignite spontaneously. However, spontaneous ignition in such apparently noncombustible materials as iron and steel borings and turnings has been recorded in scrapyards and in the holds of ships carrying scrap. In these cases, fires have occurred where the heat of oxidation cannot be dissipated sufficiently to the surrounding atmosphere to prevent the development of ignition temperatures in these materials.

Metals, e.g., magnesium and titanium, resist the normal extinguishing methods, such as automatic sprinklers, fire hoses, or regular portable extinguishers. When these materials are being used, special dry-powder extinguishers rated for Class D fires should be available nearby for use, if needed.

Oils

Oil is used during metalworking operations. On the machines, lubricating oils and/or greases may be used to facilitate the operation of the equipment. Coolant/lubricants are often used to cool and lubricate the tool and stock at the point of operation, and to facilitate removal of chips and cutting fines; these oils vary from alkaline aqueous solutions to light petroleum distillates and compounded oils. They are usually liberally applied to the point of operation for the mentioned purposes and then collected, separated from the chips, filtered, and reused. The cleaning and filtering equipment can either be self-contained to the machine itself, or part of the larger central system that interconnects many machines. Essentially all of the oil-based and compounded cutting fluids are combustible to some degree.

Compounded oils that are acidic or contain organic additives that may oxidize and then become acidic with use should not be used for the machining of magnesium and certain other metals, because the acid can react with the metal to release hydrogen. In these cases, only uncompleted mineral oils should be used. Water-oil emulsions are sometimes used as cutting fluids, especially where only light machining operations are taking place. In the emulsion state these oils are nearly noncombustible. Before being mixed with water or if they come out of emulsion, as might happen if the water evaporates from the emulsion, the hazard becomes that of the oil itself. Nevertheless, water-oil emulsions or other noncombustible oils should be used wherever possible to reduce hazards. Where regular cutting oils are used, the quantity and extent of use should be evaluated and automatic sprinkler protection considered.

In some cases where additional cooling is required, mineral oil, kerosene, or other materials having lower flash points are sometimes used. If these fluids are utilized within close proximity of their flash point [50°F (10°C)], special extinguishing systems, such as local applications of CO_2 or dry chemical systems, should be considered.

Cutting oils have a tendency to form fine mists around the cutting operations that can drift from the equipment and can condense on other machines, floors, and building structural members. Housekeeping in the surrounding areas

TABLE 2-20A. *Ignition and Explosibility of Metal Powders*[1]

	Ignition temp. cloud layer		Min. Explosive concentration		Min. ignition energy dust cloud milli-	Maximum pressure		Maximum rate of pressure rise		Explosibility†
	°F	°C	oz/ft³	g/m3	joules	psig	kPa	psi/sec	Pa/sec	Index
Aluminum	650	343	0.045	45	50	73	503	20000	508	>10
Magnesium	620	327	0.040	40	40	90	620	9000	228	>10
Zirconium	20	7	0.045	45	15*	55	379	6500	146	>10
Titanium	330	165	0.045	45	25	70	482	5500	140	>10
Uranium	20	7	0.060	60	45*	53	365	3400	86	>10
Iron	440	227	0.200	200	72–305	45	310	600	15	0.1
Zinc	680	360	0.500	500	960	48	331	1800	45	<0.1
Bronze	370	188	1.000	1000	—	44	303	1300	33	—
Copper	700	371	—	—	—	—	—	—	—	<0.1

* In this test, 1 gram of powder was used. Larger quantities ignited spontaneously.
† Index of Explosibility: None 0, Weak 0.1, Moderate 0.1–1.0, Strong 1.0–10, Severe 10.

is important in these instances, as severe fires can develop and spread over wide areas utilizing these oils. This is most significant where oil deposits have accumulated on vertical surfaces, such as the sides of equipment and building columns. Where such accumulations occur, periodic cleaning of these areas is important. Adequate enclosures and exhaust ventilation to remove this oil spray and mist should be provided.

Where central oil collection and cleaning systems are provided, the dirty oil is often collected in floor trenches that can interconnect numerous machines. If these systems are used, they should be tightly covered, or, preferably, fixed piping systems should be utilized. Where floor trenches are utilized, the possibility of spreading fire from one piece of equipment to the next is greatly enhanced, and, therefore, some form of automatic protection, such as sprinklers or carbon dioxide systems, should be considered. The central cleaning system will generally have quantities of oil present sufficient to warrant at least automatic sprinkler protection in the area. Provisions for overflow of the oil tanks in these areas caused by water from sprinklers or fire hose should be provided, channeling to a safe area.

As one of the purposes of the cutting fluid is to remove heat from the work area, the temperature of the return oil to the work station should be checked regularly to ensure that it does not approach its flash point. Where oil from a central system is pumped back to individual work stations, provisions should be made for manual or, preferably, automatic shutoff of the oil supply. Automatic shutoff can be actuated by sprinkler waterflow detection, or other automatic fire detection systems.

Automatic ceiling sprinkler protection should be provided where combustible cutting oils are used on a general basis. This protection should be installed on an ordinary-hazard basis, with adequate water supplies provided.

Many machine tools employ hydraulic devices for various control actuators. Oil pressures used can vary from 400 to several thousand psi (400 psi equals approximately 42 kPa). The reservoirs and pumps for the hydraulic oil can either be self-contained, i.e., within the machine itself, or part of a larger central system.

Nearly all hydraulic oils are combustible to some extent, even though there are some less-hazardous hydraulic fluids that significantly reduce the fire hazard. These less hazardous fluids will burn when released at high pressure and then brought into contact with a source of ignition. However, they do not sustain combustion when that ignition source is eliminated.

The resulting fire from a high-pressure hydraulic oil leak is usually a very intense torch-like flame that characteristically has a very high rate of heat release. Causes of hydraulic oil release can be deteriorated flexible hoses; failure of pipe joints, especially if threaded connections are utilized; or failure of valve packing or gaskets.

One of the easiest ways to extinguish hydraulic oil leak fires is simply shutting off the oil supply. However, experience has shown that if there is a failure in a pressurized oil system, especially one that results in an intense fire, personnel in the area are likely to run for safety without shutting down the pump. For this reason, remotely located emergency shutoff switches should be provided, or, as a more positive step, automatic shutoff should be provided. Automatic shutdown can be provided by low-level switches in the main oil reservoir; an excess flow switch; a fixed-temperature release, such as a fusible link or thermostat provided in the vicinity of the equipment; or through interconnection to a sprinkler waterflow switch. In most cases where significant hydraulic oil systems are utilized, automatic sprinkler protection should be provided. If the building is not sprinklered completely, the system should extend for at least 20 ft (6 m) beyond all areas of hydraulic usage. Suitable Class BC portable extinguishers are also necessary throughout these areas.

Welded connections should be used wherever possible to eliminate the possibility of leaks from threaded joints. Tubing should be used in preference to pipe. Piping or tubing should be securely fastened in place, and flexible hoses should be kept clear of all objects and not allowed to bend in excessively tight turns. Routine maintenance checks of all hydraulic system components should be made, and necessary repairs or corrective action taken on a timely basis. Leaks should not be allowed to continue, and good housekeeping should be maintained around all equipment.

Most petroleum-based hydraulic oils have a flash point between 350 and 600°F (177 and 315°C). Less hazardous hydraulic fluids also have flash points in a similar range, however they do not sustain combustion when the ignition source is removed. These fluids are generally of the oil-water emulsion type, water and glycol type, or purely synthetic fluids. Each type has characteristics that cover nearly the entire range of operating temperatures and gasket and seal materials used in conjunction with petroleum-based oils. (See Section 2, Chapter 9, "Fluid Power

Systems," for further information on the hazards and safeguards associated with hydraulic pressure systems.) It is important to ensure that the fluid being used is compatible with the seals, gaskets, and packing in the system. If a less hazardous fluid is being retrofilled to an existing system, this compatibility factor becomes especially important.

Machine Cuttings

All machining operations result in the creation of chips, which will vary widely in character, size, and configuration, depending on the operation being performed, the feed and speed of cutting, and the intrinsic characteristics of the metal being cut. Frequently, cuttings and chips appear to be quite large and heavy, and, for this reason, it is often an erroneous assumption that they do not constitute a fire hazard or an explosion hazard. However, a significant amount of fines may be obscured by the more obvious heavy chips.

Combustibility depends upon the combustible character of the metal and upon the ratio of the exposed surface of the cutting or chip to its mass. The thinner the cutting and the smaller the particles, the greater the likelihood of fire. Table 2-20A indicates that relatively small amounts of energy are needed to initiate combustion in some fine metal powders.

The accumulation of chips, cuttings, or fine particles should never be permitted at the machine. They should be removed and placed in a noncombustible container and suitably stored. In small, single-machine operations, the removal of chips is often done manually. In the larger integrated and automated operations, central collection systems are often used.

Where heavy chips and cuttings are generated, they are often mechanically separated from the cutting fluids and stored in some suitable container until disposed. Heavy chips represent the hazard attributable to the particular metal involved. In addition, there is the likelihood that cutting oil residue remains on these chips, and that hazard must also be considered in determining protection for the storage and handling of these materials.

Where high-speed operations, harder metals, or grinding and more precise finishing operations are used, much smaller chips and finer particles of the metal are often generated. The removal and collection of these particles is often accomplished with a pneumatic transport system. These systems usually consist of hoods over the work area, connected by ductwork to a central material/air separator. These separators can be in the form of cyclone collectors, bag collectors, wet collectors, and electrostatic precipitators.

Because of the flow of a significant amount of fine particles in the system, it should be designed with explosion hazards in mind, especially when dealing with the more combustible metals. The system should be designed so that at no time will the fine dust concentration approach the lower explosion limit (LEL) of the dust. The ductwork should be designed and constructed so that it can contain the pressure buildup from an explosion without failing. Bag-type collectors are usually not utilized for collection of fine metal dust, because they inherently provide the optimum condition for rapid and complete combustion. Any combustible filter medium would tend to catch the particles of combustible or explosive metals and hold them in an envelope of oxygen; therefore, all that would be necessary to initiate a fire or explosion would be a very small amount of energy, such as a static discharge.

Wet collectors for fine metal dusts should be used only after careful consideration. Many light-metal dusts react with water to produce highly explosive hydrogen gas. Wetted sludge of these metals is also highly explosive, unless it is kept submerged in the water. Figure 2-20A is a schematic diagram of a water-precipitation-type collector. Further discussions of this aspect of metalworking operations can be found in the following chapters: Section 3, Chapter 12, "Dusts," and Section 6, Chapter 19, "Air-Moving Equipment."

ALTERNATE MEANS OF MACHINING

There are other processes used for the shaping and finishing of metals that require no cutting edge as such.

Electric Discharge Machining

Most important and widely used of the alternate processes is the electric discharge machine (EDM). Electric discharge machining is a process for metal removal by electric arc discharge. In this machine, an electrode is placed in close proximity of the workpiece and is bathed in a continuous flow of dielectric fluid. A direct current of up to 400 amps at 400 V is pulsed from the control unit, and a current flows from the electrode through the dielectric fluid to the workpiece. Each pulse partially ionizes the dielectric fluid and causes a submerged spark that melts into and dislodges a small metal particle. Thus, the required shape is created by this eroding process. A continuous flow of the dielectric fluid is maintained to remove the metal particles. This fluid is filtered before being recirculated to the work area. This filtration system can either be proprietary to an individual machine or a part of a larger central system. The principal hazard associated with this operation is the dielectric fluid, which almost always is combustible. Flash points can be as low as 200°F (93°C). Under normal work conditions, there is a sufficient level of oil above the electrode to quench the spark and prevent the ignition of the oil. However, if the oil level is allowed to become too low, the electrode arc can become a ready source of ignition.

Several large losses have occurred in recent years that have been associated with EDM operations. These losses highlight the importance of maintaining proper fluid levels in the machine and the need for proper precautions when central oil filtration systems are utilized. Because fires within the individual machine work areas are generally confined to a particular piece of equipment, it is important to keep some separation between these machines. At least 5 ft (1.5 m) is considered the minimum clearance to prevent fire spread from one machine to the next. Due to the quantities and combustible nature of the dielectric fluid, automatic sprinkler protection on an ordinary-hazard basis should be provided throughout areas of this occupancy. Suitable Class BC portable extinguishers are also necessary and should be provided within close proximity of these machines.

In order to prevent operation of the machine when there is insufficient fluid to cover the electrode, a low-level interlock should be provided within the work tank. If gravity flow of fluid to the work tank is provided, then automatic-closing fusible-link-operated shutoff valves should be provided to close off the flow of oil in the event of fire.

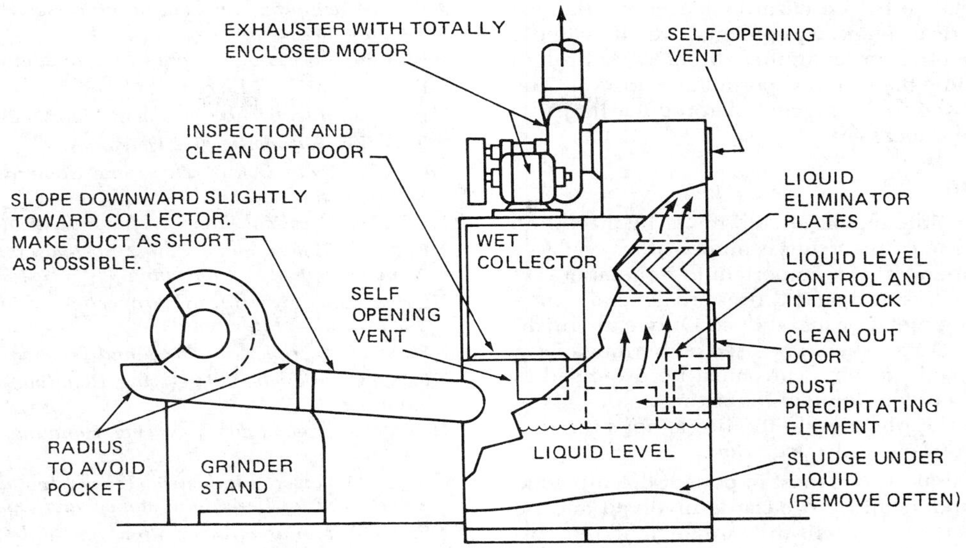

FIG. 2-20A. A schematic diagram of a water-precipitation-type collector for use in collecting dry combustible metal dust without creating explosive dust clouds or dangerous deposits in ducts or collection chambers. The diagram is intended only to show some of the features that should be incorporated in the collector design. The collector may be used for all combustible metal dusts.

Significantly greater hazard is created in EDM operations where there is a central oil filtration system. Where these systems are used, at least a 1-hr fire-rated cutoff should be provided to separate these operations from the remaining occupancy. A manual emergency shutoff switch controlling the central oil system should also be provided and located in an area that would be easily accessible during a fire at either the central oil system or the EDM work station. Oil flow between the filtration system and EDM should only be within rigid or flexible metal piping. No plastic or rubber hoses should be utilized, unless specifically listed for such application.

Electromechanical Machining

Electromechanical machining (ECM) is a process in limited specialized use. It operates by anodic dissolution in an electric cell in which the workpiece is the anode and the tool is the cathode. A direct current of 50 to 2,000 amps at 4 to 30 V is imposed. At 1000 amp, the rate of metal removal is approximately 1 cu in. per min (16.4 mm^3/min). Current densities of 100 to 2000 amps per sq in. (one square inch equals 64.5 mm^2) are employed.

FIRE HAZARDS

The principal hazards encountered in a machining operation are:

1. Chip fires at the machine, where ignition is caused by the heat of metalworking, friction of the chip against the tool, or both;
2. Spontaneous combustion of cuttings;
3. Combustion of coolant/lubricants;
4. Fine particles that are either combustible or explosible;
5. Reaction of certain metals with water or other agents;
6. Combustion of pressurized hydraulic fluids used for the actuation of machine tools and/or their accessories;
7. Combustion of oil vapors deposited on building structures;
8. Combustion of oil-saturated floors; and
9. Combustion of dielectric fluid in EDM equipment.

The principal sources of ignition are:

1. Smoking materials;
2. Heat of cutting;
3. Spontaneous oxidation;
4. Hot particles from grinding, dressing of grinding wheels, and welding and cutting;
5. Hot surfaces, such as furnaces, torches, etc.;
6. Electrical sparking or arcing; and
7. Impact ignition of certain pyrophoric surface compounds, which sometimes form during the earlier stages of fabrication. (An example of this is magnesium nitride, which sometimes appears on the surface of castings and can explode under the impulse of a very minor impact.)

SAFEGUARDS

Building Construction and Protection

Buildings that house metalworking processes should be of fire-resistive construction with a noncombustible roof deck. If the building is large, fire walls should be installed in the roof support structure, where possible, to limit the spread of fire.

The need for sprinkler protection should be carefully considered. It will depend largely upon the combustible characteristics of the building structure, especially the floors and roof deck, and the extent of the hazard posed by the metalworking machine or raw material as previously discussed. Small fires at machines can be best controlled with portable extinguishers of the correct classification. If proper housekeeping is practiced, the fire hazard from cuttings and turnings is minimal.

Buildings where machining operations are performed should be regularly inspected for the accumulation of oily deposits and/or fine combustible metal particles. Cleaning should be undertaken before hazardous accummulations develop. All electrical control equipment, particularly those for numerical control or computer-directed control of machines, should be housed in vaportight enclosures. The equipment itself should be inspected at regular intervals and cleaned when necessary.

Fire Protection

The more combustible metals should never be machined unless a suitable fire extinguisher is immediately available to the machine operator. It is important to remember that extinguishers for Class A, B, and C fires are generally ineffective for burning metal or metal dust. Only extinguishers rated for Class D fires should be used on burning metal. When they are used, extreme care must be exercised to ensure that the emergent force of the extinguishing agent or the action of its application to the fire is not sufficient to create an explosive metal dust cloud.

For their own safety, it is most important that all workers thoroughly understand the hazards involved and be properly instructed so they will fully understand the possible consequences of unconsidered or improper action under stress. In many instances, it is highly desirable that local fire fighters, who would normally respond to an alarm, be similarly instructed.

BIBLIOGRAPHY

References Cited

1. U.S. Bureau of Mines, "Explosibility of Metal Dusts," *Bulletin RI-6516*, 1964, U.S. Bureau of Mines, Washington, DC.

NFPA Codes, Standards, and Recommended Practices

Reference to the following NFPA codes, standards, and recommended practices will provide further information on metalworking processes discussed in this chapter. (See the latest *NFPA Catalog* for availability of current editions of the following documents.)

NFPA 10, *Portable Fire Extinguishers*.

NFPA 13, *Installation of Sprinkler Systems*.

NFPA 30, *Flammable and Combustible Liquids Code*.

NFPA 34, *Dipping and Coating Processes Using Flammable or Combustible Liquids*.

NFPA 65, *Processing and Finishing of Aluminum*.

NFPA 70, *National Electrical Code®*.

NFPA 70B, *Electrical Equipment Maintenance*.

NFPA 72E, *Automatic Fire Detectors*.

NFPA 75, *Protection of Electronic Computer/Data Processing Equipment*.

NFPA 79, *Electrical Standard for Industrial Machinery*.

NFPA 91, *Blower and Exhaust Systems for Dust, Stock, and Vapor Removal or Conveying*.

NFPA 325M, *Fire Hazard Properties of Flammable Liquids, Gases, and Volatile Solids*.

NFPA 480, *Storage, Handling, and Processing of Magnesium*.

NFPA 481, *Production, Processing, Handling, and Storage of Titanium*.

NFPA 482, *Production, Processing, Handling, and Storage of Zirconium*.

NFPA 505, *Powered Industrial Trucks, Including Type Designations, Areas of Use, Maintenance, and Operation*.

NFPA 651, *Manufacture of Aluminum and Magnesium Powder*.

NFPA 801, *Facilities Handling Radioactive Materials*.

Additional Reading

Avitzur, B., *Handbook of Metal-Forming Processes*, John Wiley & Sons, New York, 1983.

Bartels, A. L., "Safeguards to Prevent Ignition by Hot Surfaces," *Electrical Review London*, Vol. 203, No. 4, 1978, pp. 29-31.

Bellows, G., *Machining: A Process Checklist*, 3rd ed., Metcut Research Associates, Cincinnati, OH, 1982.

Follette, D., *Machining Fundamentals*, ed. by R. Williams and E. J. Weller, Society of Manufacturing Engineers, Dearborn, MI, 1980.

Jacobsen, M., Cooper, A., and Nagy, J., "Explosibility of Metal Powders," *RI-6516*, U.S. Bureau of Mines, Washington, DC, 1964.

King, P. W. and Magid, J., *Industrial Hazard and Safety Handbook*, Butterworths Publishers, Inc., Woburn, MA, 1979.

Marks, L. S., *Mechanical Engineers Handbook*, 9th ed., McGraw-Hill, NY, 1988.

Walker, J. R., *Machining Fundamentals*, Goodheart-Willcox Co., Inc., South Holland, IL, 1989.

WOODWORKING PROCESSES

Revised by Benjamin B. Aycock

Woodworking plants, except for the newest facilities, have characteristics that make fire control by sprinkler systems and other preventive measures difficult. In general, woodworking facilities are highly combustible structures filled with wood and/or fabric-covered finished and semifinished goods, as well as other raw materials. Finishing room exhaust systems, plus sawdust and shaving removal systems, create high draft conditions throughout most plants.

The two principal problem areas in woodworking facilities are spray finishing and dust collection. (See Figure 2-21A.) Most finishing room fires start from maintenance workers' torches, saw or grinder sparks, or overheated motors. Other contributing factors to fire are the dirty rags used in finishing operations, accumulation of overspray, and poor ventilation, which leads to a dangerous accumulation of solvent vapors.

Even with the best dust removal systems, the threat of fire and explosion is always present. Primarily, dust fires start at the wood hog, a grinder that turns scrap wood into splinters and chips, where an accumulation of "tramp" metal in the hog trap can become red hot. From the wood hog, fire can spread to cyclones, to the dust house, and often out onto the building roof. Dust fires are hard to control because fires in dust can burrow and smolder even when wetted by sprinkler spray.

FIG. 2-21A. A sanding machine for applying a smooth finish to furniture legs prior to finishing. The sanding operation is particularly hazardous because of the fineness of the dust created.

THE PRODUCTION PROCESS

After lumber has been dried and conditioned to approximately 7 percent moisture content, it is rough milled into long planks and converted to rough blanks which are later converted to finished parts. By the time parts have progressed through rough milling and finish machining, approximately 50 percent of the original material has been discarded. Approximately 35 percent of this discarded material is conveyed to the wood hog to be converted to wood splinters and chips for use as fuel in generating process steam and heat or for manufacturing particleboard, hardboard, or paper. (See Section 3, Chapter 3, "Wood and Wood-Based Products.")

Most furniture manufacturers use hardwood veneers attached to softer woods or particleboard for some furniture parts. In some cases, formica or high-density laminated plastic sheets are adhered to particleboard or plywood. Generally, hot-melt glues are used to adhere hardwood veneers to particleboard. These adhesives are applied by machine and are not particularly hazardous.

The process for spray finishing and hot-air curing of wood products is much the same as in other industries that involve coating and curing operations. Nitrocellulose coatings, wash coats, and top coats continue to be industry favorites because these materials allow easy refinishing.

This chapter was originally written by the late Edwin P. Bounous. It has been reviewed and updated by Benjamin B. Aycock, P.E., plans examiner with Charlotte-Mecklenburg Building Standards Dept., Charlotte, NC, and a member of the NFPA Member Advisory Council and Committee on Protective Signaling Systems.

The principal flammable solvents used in wood finishing and their approximate flash points are acetone, –4°F (–20°C); methyl ethyl ketone, 16°F (–9°C); naphtha VM&P, 50°F (10°C); xylene, 81°F (27°C); and toluene, 40°F (4.4°C).

In many modern woodworking plants, the finishing process can employ as many as 20 spray booths in a conveyorized operation using 20,000 to 40,000 sq ft (1858 to 3716 m^2) of floor space.

Ovens for curing the finished pieces operate at approximately 250°F (121°C), but even with high temperature, high air velocity [4,000 fpm (1220 m/min) maximum], and conveyor movement through the curing ovens, most multicoat finishes require overnight storage to ensure that all the solvents have been released.

THE FIRE HAZARDS

Insofar as fire origin is concerned, spray finishing and dust collecting are the most hazardous places in most woodworking plants. The most costly fires, other than total burnout fires, are those occurring in the finishing, rubbing, and finished goods storage areas. Fires in lumberyards are also costly and hard to control. Despite the fire hazards presented by the materials and the processes, the worst fires are likely to result from poor maintenance and repair practices involving welding and similar activities.

In the lumberyard, boards are individually inspected and built into hacks for drying and handling. Lumber hacks are about 14 ft (4.3 m) long, 6 to 8 ft (1.8 to 2.4 m) wide, and vary in height from 4 to 6 ft (1.2 to 1.8 m). Each layer of boards in the hack is separated by spacers known as kiln sticks. Hacks are stacked by forklift trucks back to back and as high as 16 ft (4.9 m). The honeycomb construction and the related easy access to oxygen make it almost impossible to extinguish a fire once it is underway in a lumber hack. Aisle widths should allow fire fighting equipment to maneuver effectively.

Among the main fire hazards around lumber storage areas, which usually have only hydrant protection, are lightning, discarded cigarettes, and boiler room sparks. Portable heaters and bonfires or barrel fires lit for warmth also pose hazards during the winter.

Waste material that ranges from small edgings to fine dust is removed by conveyors, hand trucks, and pneumatic systems. The larger parts, such as slivers, larger edgings, and blocks are conveyed to the wood hog by belt conveyor for reduction into particles small and light enough to be moved to boiler room fuel silos or storage bins. Magnetized pulleys for conveyor systems that carry wood refuse to hogs reduce the danger of fire caused by tramp metal. Trucks take waste material to the hog chute from machines not serviced by the conveyor. Sweepings are a great source of trouble, because metal dropped into the chute can become a source of friction sparks in the pulverizer.

Smaller chips, shavings, and wood dust are carried by air-moving equipment connected to cyclones, bag filter systems, or equivalent equipment. In many installations, about 80 percent of the air is returned to the plant. Reinjection of air into the plant atmosphere can cut down on the air make-up requirement and reduce plant heating fuel needs. However, this practice may introduce fire and explosion hazards. NFPA 664, *Prevention of Fires and Explosions in Wood Processing and Woodworking Facilities,* and NFPA 91, *Blower and Exhaust Systems for Dust, Stock, and Vapor Removal or Conveying,* contain guidance for the installation and protection of air-moving systems for wood waste.

The principal hazard of the spray application of finishers involves flammable and combustible liquids and their vapors or mist, and combustible residues in spray booths. Properly constructed booths with adequate mechanical ventilation are the ideal way to discharge vapor to a safe location in order to reduce the possibility of explosion. Minimizing all sources of ignition in the spraying area and constantly supervising the overall finishing process are essential to a safely conducted operation. NFPA 33, *Spray Application Using Flammable and Combustible Materials,* outlines good practices to be followed in operations involving flammable coatings.

Mechanical ventilation of the spraying area should remove solvent vapors and control overspray. Generally, ventilation provides an average velocity of not less than 100 fpm (30 m/min) over the open face of the booth, sufficient to confine overspray to the booth interior. In a good installation, each spray booth exhausts approximately 25,000 cfm (708 m^3/min). The make-up air moves at a significant velocity throughout the plant. These conditions can help a fire to spread and become more intense.

The curing ovens associated with the finishing process are essentially continuous-type Class A ovens as identified by NFPA 86, *Ovens and Furnaces.* These are enclosures that operate at approximately atmospheric pressure and in which there is an explosion or fire hazard from flammable volatiles and combustible residues. The oven exhaust system may lead directly to the outdoors for removal of the vapors, or it may be permitted to exhaust directly into the immediate area. In the latter instance, the area needs balanced ventilation to bring fresh make-up air from outside in order to exhaust the vapor-laden air. Vapors should be removed before recirculating air into the area.

THE SAFEGUARDS

Automatic sprinkler coverage is the best protection for woodworking facilities. However, in some older buildings, it may be difficult to achieve full protection. NFPA 13, *Installation of Sprinkler Systems,* requires design of sprinkler systems to be based on ordinary hazard Group 3 for the machine room. Other areas, such as spray-paint rooms and upholstery rooms, may need heavier designs that involve larger pipe sizes and closer spacing of sprinklers. Whenever possible, these processes should be located in separate buildings or separated from each other by fire-rated construction with openings protected by automatic fire doors.

The degree of protection needed can vary from facility to facility, but a basic recommendation is that a yard system of mains and hydrants should be capable of supplying at least 1000 gpm (3.78 m^3/min), enough to sustain four 2½-in. (64 mm) hose streams simultaneously. If conditions warrant, expanded supplies and larger fire stream appliances may be needed for effective fire control. Good unobstructed fire lanes are needed in the yards so that fire equipment can approach the lumber piles. NFPA 46, *Storage of Forest Products,* and NFPA 24, *Installation of Private Fire Service Mains,* provide guidance on protection for lumber in storage and on supplying sprinklers, hydrants, monitor nozzles, etc., for yard systems

BIBLIOGRAPHY

NFPA Codes, Standards, and Recommended Practices

Reference to the following NFPA codes, standards, and recommended practices will provide further information on the safeguards for woodworking processes discussed in this chapter. (See the latest *NFPA Catalog* for availability of current editions of the following documents.)

NFPA 10, *Portable Fire Extinguishers.*

NFPA 13, *Installation of Sprinkler Systems.*

NFPA 24, *Installation of Private Fire Service Mains.*

NFPA 30, *Flammable and Combustible Liquids Code.*

NFPA 33, *Spray Application Using Flammable and Combustible Materials.*

NFPA 46, *Storage of Forest Products.*

NFPA 51B, *Cutting and Welding Processes.*

NFPA 68, *Explosion Venting.*

NFPA 70, *National Electrical Code®.*

NFPA 86, *Ovens and Furnaces.*

NFPA 91, *Blower and Exhaust Systems for Dust, Stock, and Vapor Removal or Conveying.*

NFPA *101®*, *Life Safety Code®.*

NFPA 231, *General Storage.*

NFPA 600, *Private Fire Brigades.*

NFPA 664, *Prevention of Fires and Explosions in Wood Processing and Woodworking Facilities.*

Additional Readings

Aycock, B. B., "Furniture Manufacturing," *Industrial Fire Hazards Handbook*, 3rd ed., National Fire Protection Association, Quincy, MA, 1990.

Deacon, F. C., "Designing Fire Protection to Limit Monetary Loss," *SFPE Technology Report No. 80-2*, Society of Fire Protection Engineers, Boston, MA, 1980.

"Fires in Furniture Factories," *Fire Protection*, Mar. 1980, pp. 34-35.

"Moving Fire: Fire Hazards of Belt Conveyors," *Record*, Vol. 54, No. 6, 1977, pp. 18-21.

"Prevent Cutting/Welding Fires," *Minnesota Fire Chief*, Vol. 16, No. 5 (May/June 1980), pp. 16, 48, 54.

Richards, D., "Fire Risks in the Furniture Industry," *Fire Engineers Journal*, Vol. 38, No. 10, 1978, pp. 23-24.

AUTOMATED PROCESSING EQUIPMENT

John F. Bloodgood

Like many other facets of industry, automation has benefitted greatly from the technological developments of the last few decades. Thirty years ago, automation was accomplished by use of large relay control panels. In 1969, programmable controllers (PCs) began to replace relays in the automotive industry. By 1971, other industries were using PCs. In 1977, microprocessor-based PCs were controlling automated processes. Today, automation has become very complex and sophisticated. A great deal of care is needed to design safe automated systems.

Programmable controllers have introduced new fire protection problems into the processes that they automate. This is because the PC has been given control over such things as flammable liquids flow, the position of combustible materials, the initiation of sparks and flames, the motion of friction-causing parts, and other potential sources of fuel and ignition. As a result, any kind of failure in the PC can cause a fire or explosion. This chapter addresses how to analyze and deal with the increased potential for fire or explosion with automated equipment. The chapter does not cover the hazards and protection of individual pieces of equipment that are included in other chapters of this handbook. Many of the issues raised also are germane to independently operated machines.

Modern automated machinery usually consists of many pieces of equipment acting in a coordinated manner without operating personnel control. These systems are commonly referred to as manufacturing cells or flexible manufacturing systems. Common examples include numerically controlled machine tools (NC), computerized numerically controlled machine tools (CNC), industrial robots, work-handling machines or systems, material/workpiece transfer equipment, and associated control and information-handling equipment. (See Figure 2-22A.) Automated systems also control many other types of processes.

Each application of automation must be reviewed for any hazardous situations it may introduce. This is done by reviewing both the PC and the process being controlled.

John F. Bloodgood, P.E., is president of JFB Enterprises, Consulting Engineers, Fond du Lac, WI.

FIG. 2-22A. ***Industrial robots are increasing productivity, lowering manufacturing costs, and improving the product quality. The robots pictured here are spot-welding automobile frames. (Source: Robotic Industries Association)***

GENERAL CONSIDERATIONS

Automated processing systems consist of two or more machines grouped together to perform a series of operations on materials or parts. Typically, these machines run automatically without an operator, or sometimes one person may run more than one machine. A supervisory controller (usually a computer) directs the interrelations between these machines, transmits information to the individual machine controllers, and monitors the process. The individual machine units (machine and controller) may be supplied by different vendors, thus requiring compatibility between the individual units and the supervisory controller. The issue of compatibility places additional responsibility on the manufacturer for proper installation, maintenance, and training of the end user. In addition, the machine controllers and the supervisory controllers utilize sophisticated computer equipment, operating in a real-time mode, that transmits large amounts of information at low levels and high speeds—conditions that require greater attention to the design, installation, operation, and maintenance of these systems.

AUTOMATED PROCESSING EQUIPMENT

Analysis of the Controller

Microprocessor-based PCs introduce failures never before dealt with in relay-controlled automation. The most common of these failures are described in Table 2-22A.

TABLE 2-22A. ***Programmable Computer Failures***

CPU STALL —	Processor ceases to execute the program.
INPUT/OUTPUT SCAN FAILURE —	Processor fails to scan input/output signals for change in status.
INPUT FAILURE —	Input module locks in "on" position and does not respond to further input changes.
ADDRESSING FAILURE —	Processor fails to correctly consult input/output intelligence.
OUTPUT FAILURE —	Output module locks in "on" position and does not respond to the controller.
MEMORY FAILURE —	Incorrect bit in memory causes an improper instruction to be given.
WATCHDOG TIMER FAILURE —	Timer controlling execution of instructions fails.
PROGRAM CARD FAILURE —	Any problem with the program card.
MOMENTARY POWER OUTAGE —	Temporary loss of power to controller.

The effect these failure modes will have on the process being controlled will then determine the degree of hazard introduced.

Problems of personnel safety, power networks and distribution, grounding, electrical noise interference, software application and maintenance, and failsafe requirements are more evident in these integrated manufacturing systems. Another way PCs introduce fire or explosion potential is by their introduction into areas where relay control panels didn't fit, but which may contain flammable vapors. When this is done, the controller should be intrinsically safe as described in NFPA 493, *Intrinsically Safe Apparatus in Division I Hazardous Locations.*

Safety

The operation of integrated manufacturing systems is more automated than individual machines, in terms of starting motions and the transferring of material or parts, without operator intervention. Integrated systems can also cover more complex operations on larger areas of a factory floor. It is therefore necessary to provide additional safety measures beyond those for conventional single-machine work stations. Typical measures include barriers and gates, presence-sensing devices, and visual or audible warning devices to announce pending machine and/or material movement.

Movement of a machine or workpiece and/or a material-handling device that occurs at unannounced times could catch personnel in a "pinch point" and result in a serious injury. Thus, the primary safety consideration is to keep personnel out of the work area while the system is operating. Enclosing the system in a cage or fence is one solution to the problem, but it is not always practical, since many systems require personnel in the work area during operation. Often, it is not possible to determine if anyone is in the work area when the equipment is operating. One alternate solution in particularly hazardous work areas is to provide barriers and/or guards, interlocked with the individual controllers or the supervisory controller. All hazardous motions should be automatically stopped if the interlock is interrupted.

Another alternative is to provide presence-sensing devices, such as floormats or light-beam curtains, that will either stop all dangerous motions immediately or stop the automatic cycle once the motions in progress have been completed. Visual or audible annunciators that warn of pending axis motions or the cycling of auxiliary equipment also can be used if personnel must be in the work area during automatic operation.

Failsafe travel limits, such as mechanical stops or hardwired travel switches, always should be used in systems where software controllers for individual machines or system monitoring are utilized. The failsafe travel limits ensure that, if the controller should fail or a runaway condition should exist in either an axis motion or an auxiliary cycle, the motion would be physically restrained or the power would be removed from that motion.

ANALYSIS OF THE PROCESS

For some processes, failure of a PC will merely result in inconvenience. Usually, however, more serious problems are introduced. For example, PC-controlled robot welders may destroy parts if the arc is not turned off at the right time. They could also ignite combustible materials that mistakenly end up in the area.

PCs controlling hazardous processes, such as spray painting, solvent drying, and fuel firing, also present many potential fire and explosion hazards. A PC failure could create hazardous conditions by not stopping paint guns, solvent introduction, or fuel flow.

Another complication of automated processing is the potential for interruption of production. In automated processes that cannot be run manually, PC failures will stop production. The length of time needed to repair or replace controllers must be considered. Off-the-shelf controllers are easier to replace than custom-made ones. Since off-the-shelf controllers would require reprogramming, software backup should be maintained in a safe location.

Power Networks and Distribution

Careful consideration must be given to the design of the automatic factory power network when large systems are installed. Busbars, which supply electrical power to machines or equipment that are highly inductive or utilize power converters, should be isolated from those that supply power to sensitive electronic equipment. Electrical noise on common power distribution lines can cause malfunctions or permanent damage to electronic equipment. Separate power buses, isolation transformers, and filtering devices are some of the techniques used to minimize the problems associated with power distribution. In some cases, it is necessary to monitor bus loading and automatically schedule the sequencing of particularly heavy electrical loads on the network.

Grounding: The grounding of electrical equipment has always been a consideration for the safety of personnel to guard them from electrical shock. In systems using sensitive electronic equipment, grounding is a primary concern to protect the controller and its input/output connections from the effects of electrical noise. The grounding of control equipment in industrial environments should be integrated by the equipment user into a coordinated ground system. When control equipment is grounded, it is interconnected into the system ground by building columns or ground rods.

In electrical/electronic controllers, there are usually subsystems that are tied to the ground system. It is essential that the noncurrent-carrying metallic enclosures be grounded, including all internal frames and equipment support structures. A specific ground point is provided within the enclosure for the equipment ground to make connection to the ground system. A separate tie point is provided to connect the control common (the zero potential reference point for the electrical and electronic equipment) to the ground system. Having two separate ground reference points separates the two ground systems within the controller, eliminating ground loop problems. Providing two separate ground reference points within the enclosure allows the equipment ground to be connected to the building, while the control ground is connected to a separate ground rod independent of the building structure.

DESIGN SOLUTIONS

For dependability in PC-run processes, important controller functions should be supervised. Input circuits, input/output addressing, and input/output scanning are verified with a dynamic safety check on the order of several times each second. Output status is monitored. The central processing unit (CPU) is checked by the watchdog timer, which itself is provided with a dynamic safety check. Sum and parity checks are used on memories.

Above all else, the entire process control system must be designed to fail safely. The response to detection of PC abnormalities can be an alarm, the shutdown of chosen process functions, or both. However, if a PC failure can result in unsafe process conditions, the process should be safely shut down upon this failure. In other words, the system should be failsafe.

Process control devices that may fail in a shorted condition (e.g., rectifiers) can be arranged to be disabled manually. Critical controller functions can be independently hard-wired to ensure the ability to operate properly in the event of failure.

Electrical Noise Interferences

Because entire books have been written on this complicated subject, only the most important considerations are covered here. The effects of coupling electrical noise into control equipment become more pronounced as the operating speed and equipment complexity increase, while the immunity to disturbances decreases. This is certainly the case with controllers applied to industrial automation equipment. The microelectronic circuits operate above 1 MHz, with harmonics in the range of 2100 MHz to 1 GHz. Signal levels are typically below 15 volts. Noise coupling from disturbing sources, such as power inverters, motors, contactors, and relays, and associated wiring runs can be detrimental to the operating system, unless proper techniques are used to reduce the disturbances or minimize coupling into the sensitive circuits. Commonly used methods of reducing the disturbing effects of electrical noise are: (1) employing transformers or filters to isolate power wiring from signal and control wiring, or (2) shielding sensitive control and signal wiring by using shielded conductors or coaxial cable. Proper grounding of the shield (usually at only one end) is a must. For extremely sensitive circuits, the use of double shielding (one shield tied to the equipment ground and the other tied to the control common) may be required. Some circuits or subsystems may have to be entirely enclosed in a grounded shield.

Sensitive signal conductors should be separated to the greatest degree practical from noise sources. One example of this problem involves power leads that are run in the same cable or raceway as digital transmission or analog signal lines. Wherever possible, these lines should be in separate cables or raceways. When this is not possible, it is necessary to use shielding or additional conductors that are tied to the ground. Remember that all unused conductors should be grounded at one end to minimize coupling.

The effect of electrostatic discharge is another potentially serious problem that is often overlooked. Microelectronic devices (memory and logic chips) must be handled by personnel who are grounded by either a wrist strap or conductive plates located on the soles of their shoes. However, nonconductive materials (clothing, paper, etc.) in close proximity to the chips also carry an electrostatic charge which can be neutralized by ionized air. The precautions taken for handling microelectronic parts are typically discontinued once the chips are inserted into a printed circuit assembly. Although a completed printed circuit assembly will dissipate some of the charge, the chips are still subject to damage from electrostatic discharge. The grounding or discharging of personnel who are required to work with integrated circuits, including those who assemble, inspect, test, ship, or maintain the equipment, is important to ensure reliable operation of the electronic equipment. An electric charge of thousands of volts can be developed by simply getting up from a chair or paging through a set of schematic drawings. With the present technology, as little as 50 volts of electric charge can permanently damage, degrade the performance of, or shorten the life of these components. In industrial systems employing thousands or tens of thousands of these devices, the potential for a malfunction or failure due to electrostatic discharge is very high and should be considered as serious a problem as shock hazard.

Software Application and Maintenance

The use of programmable electronic controllers and software programming has introduced a new series of problems that were not present with hardware systems. Failure modes and malfunctions are harder to detect and correct since the controllers must first verify the proper operation of the hardware and then test with application software. Since the software tends to be unique for each controller (one of the major advantages of programmable electronic controllers), elaborate testing and verification methods must be devised to ensure that the software functions properly under all dynamic conditions. This problem is compounded when the controllers must interact in a manufacturing system. Even if the software is properly certified before shipment to the end user, it is often modified in the field to correct for unexpected conditions of actual use. Many times, the corrected software is put into operation without a complete recertification, or, even worse, it is corrected at the job site without being retested. In a large, complex system, the results of this "on-the-fly" modification method can be disastrous.

The typical failure mode being "fail unsafe" is another problem created by the introduction of electronic circuitry. Silicone-controlled rectifiers, triacs, and electronic switching devices usually fail in a shorted condition, resulting in such hazards as axis or auxiliary cycle runaway. Short of removing power to the portion of the system that has failed, the condition cannot be corrected. Typical methods of overcoming this problem are redundant circuits, hardwired contacts which can break the connection to the drives or motors that control motions or auxiliary cycles, or control circuits that monitor and automatically disable equipment that can create hazardous conditions.

The transmission of large amounts of digital information between system elements presents the potential of system malfunctions if the data are not properly received. Wrong axis commands, machine conditions, or even entirely incorrect part programs may be sent or received. Since there is no operator intervention before machine or controller action is initiated, injury can result to personnel or damage can occur to the machine or the work in progress. Redundant transmission or error checking and correction are means of reducing the effects of this problem. Proper shielding and protection of these transmission lines is mandatory if these problems are to be kept to a minimum.

STANDARDS RELATED TO AUTOMATED PROCESSING EQUIPMENT

A number of standards have been or are in the process of being developed that relate to factory automation and address subjects previously covered in this chapter. ANSI B11, *Construction, Care, and Use of Machine Tools*, correlates the hazards to persons created by various types of machine tools and the measures to be used to ensure minimum exposure to these hazards. Currently, a standard on safety issues related to manufacturing systems/cells (B11.20) is being developed. This proposed standard deals with hazards created from the interaction of a number of machines working in a coordinated manner to produce discrete parts or assemblies. There is also a safety standard for robots that has been developed by a committee sponsored by the Robotics Industries Association (RIA). All of these standards reference the work of NFPA 79, *Electrical Standard for Industrial Machinery*.

Internationally, work is being done on safety standards related to manufacturing systems/cells and robots, as well as electrical equipment of industrial machines. The International Electrotechnical Commission (IEC) electrical standard IEC 204-1 is used widely in Europe and will be one of a series of standards that will become part of the European Economic Community law when the trade barriers are removed at the end of 1992. The European Community is also developing standards for individual industrial machines (e.g., machine tools, and plastics and rubber machinery), and it is anticipated that work at the international level on safety standards for various types of industrial machines will be introduced shortly.

Standards related to programmable controllers are being developed by a technical committee of the International Electrotechnical Commission. The programmable controller standards cover a diverse range of topics, including operating conditions, interfacing to various input/output devices, and programming languages. There is also a project on safety aspects of programmable electronic systems. There are no corresponding U.S. standards on programmable controllers. All effort in the U.S. in this area has been focused on the work of the IEC.

The Institute of Electrical and Electronics Engineers (IEEE) has produced a standard on electrical interferences: IEEE 518, *Electrical Guide on Electrical Noise*, which covers various types of noise that can affect the operation of electrical equipment (e.g., common mode, electromagnetic, and electrostatic) and aims to reduce the effects of these interferences. Similar work is underway in the IEC, covering immunity testing methods, as well as sources and reduction methods.

Considerable effort both in the U.S. and internationally has been expended on the encoding and transmission of digital information over industrial networks. The most prominent of these projects is the manufacturing automation protocol (MAP) specification, which is based on the international open system interconnection (OSI) model. Coupled with this work is the standard on manufacturing message specification (MMS), which is both a U.S. and an international standard. An essential element of these standards is the guarantee of proper transmission of information.

BIBLIOGRAPHY

References

ANSI B11.20, *Safety of Manufacturing Systems/Cells*, American National Standards Institute, New York, (To be published).

IEC 204-1, *Electrical Equipment of Industrial Machines*, International Electrotechnical Commission, Geneva, 1984.

IEEE 518, *Electrical Guide on Electrical Noise*, Institute of Electrical and Electronics Engineers, Piscataway, NJ, 1982.

NFPA Codes, Standards, and Recommended Practices

Reference to the following NFPA codes, standards, and recommended practices will provide further information on automated processing equipment discussed in this chapter. (See the latest *NFPA Catalog* for availability of current editions of the following documents.)

NFPA 79, *Electrical Standard for Industrial Machinery.*

NFPA 493, *Intrinsically Safe Apparatus in Division I Hazardous Locations.*

Additional Reading

"Digital Systems Offer Flexible, Reliable Process Control Operations," *Pulp & Paper*, Feb. 1982.

"Guidelines Help You Interface Field Sensors With Computers," *Power*, Sept. 1983.

Merrick, D., "Fire Protection for Robotics—A Systems Approach," *Industrial Fire World*, Vol. 2, No. 4 (Aug. 1987), pp. 18-21.

"Modern Boiler Control and Why Digital Systems Are Better," *Hydrocarbon Processing*, Aug. 1982.

"Programmable Controller Update," *Plant Engineering*, Mar. 28, 1985.

"Reference File: Programmable Controllers," *Plant Engineering*, Nov. 23, 1983.

"Refinery Changeover to Microprocessor Control," *EC&M*, Aug. 1983.
"Significant Process Automation Changes Expected in Next Decade," *Pulp & Paper*, Feb. 1982.
"Troubleshooting Programmable Controllers," *Plant Engineering*, Oct. 14, 1982.
"Understanding Fiber Optics for Automated Control," *Plant Engineering*, June 23, 1983 and July 21, 1983.
"Understanding Programmable Controllers," *Plant Engineering*, Apr. 17, 1980.

AEROSOL CHARGING OPERATIONS

Henry C. Scuoteguazza

Aerosol products play a large part in the nation's economy. It would be an unusual household or business that did not possess at least one aerosol product at any time. Products so packaged include food (such as whipped toppings), release agents for cooking and industrial processes, deodorants, hair sprays, carburetor cleaners, paints, pesticides, window cleaners, de-icers, and engine cleaners, as well as many others.

Due to the nature of the propellants and the pressures under which they are used, aerosol products present some very real fire prevention and protection problems. This chapter is concerned with these problems. Requirements for the storage and handling of the liquefied petroleum gases used as propellants are covered in Section 2, Chapter 26, "Storage of Gases."

CONTAINERS AND PROPELLANTS

The typical aerosol container is a small, welded-joint, high-strength metal can with a capacity of up to 1 quart containing up to 16 oz. (473 mL) of liquid. The top and base of the container are domed to withstand the pressure which is normally 240 to 400 psi (1655 to 2758 kPa). A spring-loaded plunger nozzle cap is pressed to release the pressurized product or mixture of liquefied gas and product. (See Figure 2-23A.)

The propellants normally used are hydrocarbons such as propane, butane, and isobutane, either alone or in various mixtures, depending upon the product and its uses. They are gaseous at ambient temperatures and pressures and will condense to liquids at moderate pressures or low temperatures. They maintain a relatively constant pressure at a given temperature until all the liquid propellant has been converted to gas. Other less common propellants are nitrogen, carbon dioxide, and nitrous oxide. The hydrocarbons are highly flammable, and, although nitrous oxide is nonflammable, it is an oxidizer and can contribute to the fire hazards of aerosols.

Henry C. Scuoteguazza, P.E., is the former standards coordinator for Factory Mutual Research Corp., Norwood, MA. He is now located at the Allendale Insurance Co., Norwalk, CT.

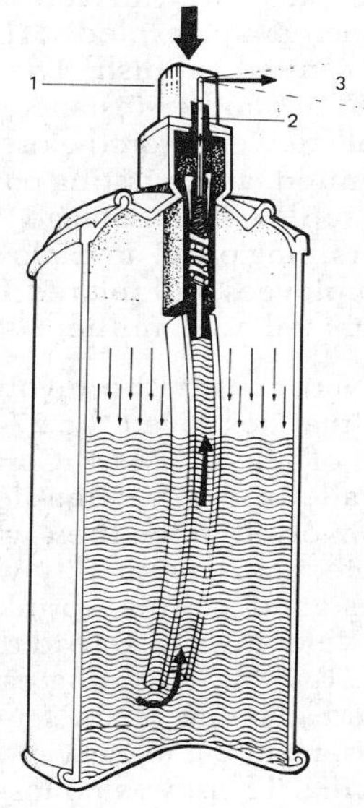

***FIG. 2-23A.** An aerosol can. When the plunger (1) is pressed, a hole in the valve (2) allows a pressurized mixture of product and propellant (3) to flow through the plunger's exit orifice.*

The quantity of propellant in an aerosol product ranges from 0.5 to 90 percent of the total weight of the contents. There is some feeling that the flammability of the base product is a major concern and that the propellant adds little to the overall hazard unless the propellant accounts for most of the can's contents.[1] Despite this, hydrocarbons are extremely flammable and require careful storage and handling.

The vapor pressure of these materials and the large quantities of gas they produce when vaporized makes them suitable propellants. The vapor pressure at 70°F (21°C) is 108 ± 6 psig (745 ± 41 kPa) for propane; 31 ± 2 psig (214 ± 13.8 kPa) for isobutane; and 17 ± 2 psig (117 ± 13.8 kPa) for n-butane. They can be mixed to deliver any vapor pressure between the two extremes and, thus, are suitable for use in a wide variety of products.

The basic fire hazard properties of these hydrocarbon propellants are listed in Table 2-23A.

TABLE 2-23A. ***Fire Hazard Properties of Hydrocarbon Propellants***

	Flammable Limits*		Flash Point		Autoignition Temperature	
	Lower	Upper	°F	°C	°F	°C
Propane	2.1	9.5	−156	−104	940	504
Isobutane	1.8	8.4	−117	−83	890	477
n-Butane	1.8	8.4	−101	−74	860	460

* Percent in air by volume.

FIRE HAZARDS

Aerosol products have been directly involved in and sometimes responsible for extensive, costly, and occasionally fatal fires. In one instance, an aerosol can which was thrown into an incinerator exploded, blew off the incinerator door, and ignited rubbish. The damage was estimated at $35,000. In another instance, aerosol cans with flammable propellant were stored close to a heater. Leaking propellant ignited, and bursting containers made fire fighting efforts futile. The damage was estimated at $800,000. At a can filling plant, an explosion involving isobutane killed 4 employees and injured 18 others. Property damage was estimated at $1 million.

Perhaps the most costly fire involving aerosol products was the fire that destroyed the 27-acre (10.9 ha) distribution center of the K Mart Corporation in Falls Township, PA. Palletized petroleum-liquid-based aerosol containers were involved in the fires, which overwhelmed the sprinkler protection. The facility was protected with hydraulically designed ceiling sprinkler systems. The extremely fast-developing fire spread through the aerosol storage on June 21, 1982; rocketing cans spread the fire throughout this and adjoining areas. The fire overtaxed fire protection systems, resulting in early roof collapse and broken sprinkler piping. There was no loss of life. However, the loss of property was in excess of $100 million.[2] (See Figure 2-23B.)

FIG. 2-23B. These aerosol cans were located in the area of fire origin of the K Mart fire.

Classification of Aerosols

Aerosol products are classified by NFPA 30B, *Aerosol Products,* into one of three hazard categories, based on the percentage of flammable material in the base product, the miscibilty of the flammable material with water, and the percentage of flammable propellant compared to total container contents. The three hazard categories are described below.

Level 1 aerosol products are those whose base products contain up to 25 percent by weight of materials, with flash points of 500°F (260°C) or less.

Level 2 aerosol products are those whose base products contain more than 25 percent by weight of water-miscible materials, with flash points of 500°F (260°C) or less, or whose base products contain more than 25 percent, but not more than 55 percent, by weight of water-immiscible materials with flash points of 500°F (260°C) or less.

Level 3 aerosol products are those whose base products contain more than 55 percent by weight of water-immiscible materials, with flash points of 500°F (260°C) or less, or whose flammable propellant equals or exceeds 80 percent of the net weight of the container contents.

Factory Mutual Research Corporation (FMRC) developed an aerosol flammability test in 1988.[3] This test procedure was instrumental in the development of the above classification system and can be used to determine the proper classification of a specific product in cases where actual test data are desired. The aerosol flammability test is described in FMRC's Loss Prevention Data Sheet 7-29S.

Table 2-23B shows the classification table used by NFPA 30B, *Aerosol Products*. A simplified decision tree is shown in Figure 2-23C.

Fire Behavior of Aerosols

The behavior of filled aerosol cans in fire tests confirms what has often been reported about actual fires. Level 2 aerosols produce fires so intense that ruptured containers rocketed through the test area, occasionally trailing burning liquid. Sometimes flaming packaging material or plastic caps were propelled beyond the test area.

Level 3 aerosols burned more intensely and rocketed with trailing burning liquid more frequently than Level 2 aerosols. In addition, they produced dense black smoke that completely obscured visibility in 4 to 5 minutes.

In rack storage tests, the ruptures of both Level 2 and Level 3 aerosols spanned the aisle, but ignition of the target rack occurred only in Level 3 tests. In both rack and pallet storage, rupturing cans dislodged surrounding containers and exposed others inside the load, increasing the fire severity.

As indicated by the fires cited previously, there are three phases in the production and distribution of aerosol products:

1. Transport, transfer, and storage of bulk propellants.
2. Filling or "gassing" the aerosol containers.
3. Storage of charged containers in warehouses.

TABLE 2-23B ***Classification of Aerosol Products***

If Percentage of Flammable Material in Base Product Is:	And Percentage of Flammable Propellant Is:	Then Level Is:
≤25%	0%*	1
≤25%	<50%	1
≤25%	≥ 50% but < 80%	2
<85% and water-miscible	0%*	1
>25% and water-miscible	<50%	2
>25% and water-miscible	≥50%	3
>25% but ≤55% and water-immiscible	0%	2
>25% but ≤55% and water-immiscible	<50%	2
>25% but ≤55% and water-immiscible	≥50%	3
>55% and water-immiscible	0% to 100%	3
any %	≥80%	3

Propellant is nonflammable.

NOTE 1: The base product is defined as the contents, excluding the propellant. A base product component is considered flammable if its flash point is below 500°F (260°C). The percentage of flammable material in the base product is calculated as follows:

$$\%\ \text{flammable material} = \frac{\text{weight of flammable base components}}{(\text{wt. of contents} - \text{wt. of propellant})} \times 100$$

NOTE 2: The percentage of flammable propellant is its proportion of the total contents, by weight. Any nonflammable portion of a propellant blend is not included in the calculation. The percentage is calculated as follows:

$$\%\ \text{flammable propellant} = \frac{\text{weight of flammable propellant components}}{\text{weight of contents}} \times 100$$

Aerosol Filling Plants

Because the hydrocarbon aerosol propellants are highly flammable, container filling plants require special design considerations and operating procedures. Gases present hazards both when they are confined and when they escape. Compressed gases and liquefied gases are affected somewhat differently when heated. When heated, compressed gas simply attempts to expand according to the gas laws, whereas a liquefied gas experiences the simultaneous combination of three effects.

First, the gas phase is subject to the same effect as a compressed gas. Second, the liquid attempts to expand and compresses the vapor. Third, the vapor pressure of the liquid increases as the temperature increases. The combined result is a rapid pressure increase when the container is heated. Containers of liquefied gases can release this energy rapidly and violently, resulting in a BLEVE (boiling liquid expanding vapor explosion). If some of the propellant is still liquid at the time of rupture, it will expand immediately and help disperse the base product, especially if the propellant is soluble in the base product.

THE SAFEGUARDS

In late 1987, the aerosol products industry proposed the formation of an NFPA technical project directed at the development of a fire protection standard for aerosol products manufacturing and warehousing. This project was approved, and the NFPA Technical Committee on Aerosol Products began an accelerated effort, beginning in February 1988, to develop a suitable code. NFPA 30B, *Aerosol Products,* was finally adopted in May 1990. The purpose of NFPA 30B is to provide a minimum set of fire protection and fire prevention requirements for facilities that manufacture or store aerosol products.

Chapter 3 of NFPA 30B, *Aerosol Products*, concentrates its efforts on the aerosol charging operation. Because a release of hydrocarbon propellants within the charging (gassing) room can create an explosive atmosphere, the room should be located and constructed to reflect a combustion explosion hazard. Often, the room is a separate building apart from the main production building. The separation should be a minimum of 5 ft (1.5 m), with conveyor openings as small and few as possible. The rooms may be located within the main building, but if so, they should be constructed and vented in accordance with the provisions of NFPA 58, *Storage and Handling of Liquefied Petroleum Gases*, and NFPA 68, *Venting of Deflagrations,* and separated from the rest of the building by noncommunicating walls.

If separate from the main building, the filling room should be at least 10 to 25 ft (3 to 7.6 m) from the bulk storage facilities (depending upon building construction), 25 ft (7.6 m) from a property line which can be built upon, and at least 25 ft (7.6 m) from ignition sources. The wall facing the main building should have a minimum pressure rating of 100 lbs/sq ft (488 kg/m^2).[2] The venting area should be at least 1 sq ft per 30 cu ft (0.1 m^2/m^3) of enclosed volume. Explosion venting areas should be designed to vent at a minimum static pressure of 20 lbs/sq ft (97.6 kg/m^2).

Even in a well-maintained and efficiently operated charging room, enough flammable vapor is released to create a locally explosive atmosphere unless there is a ventilation system which maintains a concentration below the

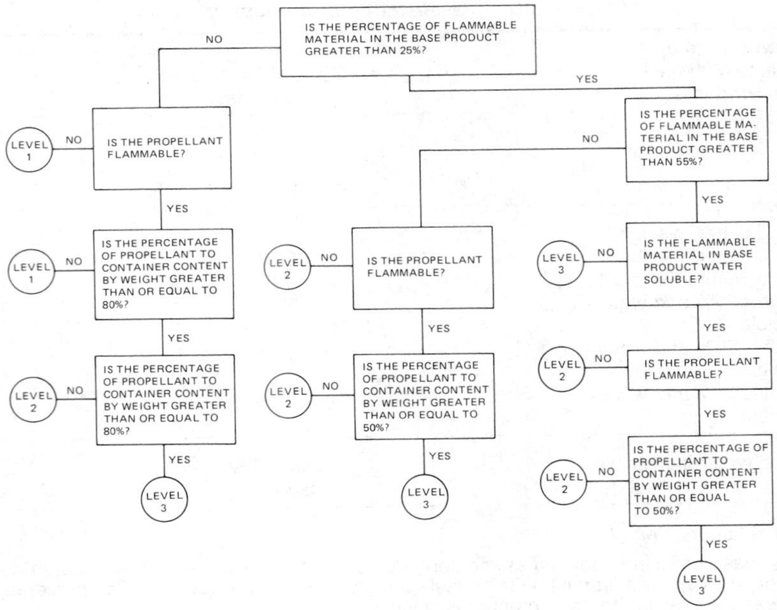

FIG. 2-23C. Decision tree for determining level classification of aerosol products.

lower flammable limit (LFL). As noted in Table 2-23A, the LFL is about 2 percent by volume in air for hydrocarbon propellants.

Because hydrocarbon propellant vapors are heavier than air, the ventilation system should be designed to let uncontaminated intake air flow over the floor to pick up vapors and discharge them through and out an exhaust stack. It is wise to maintain a slight negative pressure within the charging room to prevent migration of the vapors to other areas.

Further, NFPA 30B, *Aerosol Products*, establishes the required ventilation rate based on 1.2 times the estimated propellant loss under normal operating conditions and a "design level," which is defined as the maximum desired concentration of flammable vapor. This maximum concentration is expressed as a fraction of the lower flammable limit. Usually, sufficient ventilation is provided to ensure that the vapor concentration does not exceed 10 percent of the LFL, under normal operating conditions. The formula used is described below, but NFPA 30B should be consulted for details of its application.

$$\text{CFM} = \frac{(100 - \text{LEL})(\text{V})(\text{R})}{(\text{DL})(\text{LEL})}$$

where

CFM = required ventilation flow rate, cu ft per min;

LEL = lower explosive limit of propellant, percent by volume;

V = volume of vapor produced by 1 gallon of liquid propellant, cu ft;

R = estimate of the propellant lost during the normal filling operation, plus an additional 20 percent for occasional leaks, gal per min;

DL = LEL design level. This is the maximum allowable vapor concentration, expressed as a percentage of the lower explosive limit, normally not more than 10 percent.

Equipment failures or other accidents may release quantities of vapor greater than can be handled by the general ventilation. The system, therefore, should be designed to automatically provide a high ventilation level when the monitoring system indicates a vapor concentration of 25 percent of the LFL.

The charging room should be equipped with gas detection devices as part of a system that will shut off the propellant supply, purge the atmosphere, and isolate ignition sources. Such systems are generally electric or electronic. As such, they have the potential of providing an ignition source, unless properly selected and installed. Refer to NFPA 70, *National Electrical Code®*; NFPA 496, *Purged and Pressurized Enclosures for Electrical Equipment*; and UL 913, *Intrinsically Safe Apparatus and Associated Apparatus for Use in Class I, II, and III, Division 1, Hazardous (Classified) Locations.*

Despite the extent and efficiency of fire and explosion preventive measures, a fire or explosion is still possible. As added safety measures, then, fire detection and extinguishing equipment should be installed.

For a charging room, such equipment may be any of the usual systems, e.g., automatic sprinkler, carbon dioxide, foam, dry chemicals, and explosion suppression. The most common extinguishing system is the open-head deluge system with rate-of-rise heat detection.[4] This system reacts quickly and allows a water application of at least 0.35 gpm per sq ft [14 (L/min)/m^2]. It reacts quickly, is effective regardless of the condition of the room, and involves no physical danger to personnel.

While special fire extinguishing systems (carbon dioxide, foam, dry chemical, and halon) are fast-acting and effective, they do not replace the need for sprinklers for the following reasons: (1) application must be delayed until personnel can be evacuated; (2) a gas fire that is extinguished before the escape of gas has stopped can lead to an explosion; (3) foam is of value only for fires in flammable products; and (4) such systems have a limited amount of extinguishing material.

TABLE 2-23C ***Arrangement and Protection of Palletized and Solid-Pile Level 2 Aerosol Storage****

Max. ceiling ht (ft)	30	30	25	25
Maximum pile ht (ft)	5	15	18	20
Sprinkler	1/2 in. or 17/32 in.	ESFR	large drop 0.64 in.	ESFR
Temp. rating**	high	ordinary	ordinary	ordinary
Sprinkler spacing (ft^2)	100 max.	80-100	80-100	80-100
Sprinkler demand	0.30 gpm/ft^2 over 2500 ft^2	12 sprinklers at 50 psi	15 sprinklers at 50 psi	12 sprinklers at 50 psi
Hose stream demand (gpm)	See 2-6.4	See 2-6.4	See 2-6.4	See 2-6.4
Duration (hr)	2	1	2	1

* All fire tests on which this table is based were conducted with standard spray, large-drop, or ESFR sprinklers. This does not include large-drop sprinklers equipped with quick response links. The Response Time Index (RTI) of standard spray and large-drop sprinklers must not be less than 181 $(ft/sec)^{1/2}$ [100 $(meter/sec)^{1/2}$].
** When use of higher temperature rated sprinklers is necessary, such as near unit heaters, refer to NFPA 13, *Installation of Sprinkler Systems.*

TABLE 2-23D ***Arrangement and Protection of Palletized and Solid-Pile Level 3 Aerosols****

Max. ceiling ht (ft)	30	30	25	20
Maximum pile ht (ft)	5	15	15	10
Sprinkler	1/2 in. or 17/32 in.	ESFR	ESFR	large-drop 0.64 in.
Temp. rating**	high	ordinary	ordinary	ordinary
Sprinkler spacing (ft^2)	100 max.	80-100	80-100	80-100
Sprinkler demand	0.60 gpm/ft^2 over 2500 ft^2	12 sprinklers at 75 psi	12 sprinklers at 50 psi	15 sprinklers at 75 psi
Hose stream demand (gpm)	See 2-6.4	See 2-6.4	See 2-6.4	See 2-6.4
Duration (hr)	2	1	1	2

* All fire tests on which this table is based were conducted with standard spray, large-drop, or ESFR sprinklers. This does not include large-drop sprinklers equipped with quick response links. The Response Time Index (RTI) of standard spray and large-drop sprinklers shall not be less than 181 $(ft/sec)^{1/2}$ [100 $(meter/sec)^{1/2}$].
** When use of higher temperature rated sprinklers is necessary, such as near unit heaters, refer to NFPA 13, *Standard for the Installation of Sprinkler Systems.*

TABLE 2-23E ***ESFR Arrangement and Protection of Level 2 Rack Storage****

Max. ceiling ht (ft)	30	25
Max. storage ht (ft)	15	20
Temp. rating**	ordinary	ordinary
Sprinkler spacing (ft^2)	80-100	80-100
Sprinkler demand	12 sprinklers at 50 psi	12 sprinklers at 50 psi
Hose stream demand (gpm)	250	250
Duration (hr)	1	1

* Single- and double-row racks only.
** When use of higher temperature rated sprinklers is necessary, such as near unit heaters, refer to NFPA 13, *Installation of Sprinkler Systems.*

TABLE 2-23F ***ESFR Arrangement and Protection of Level 3 Rack Storage****

Max. ceiling ht (ft)	30	25
Max. storage ht (ft)	15	15
Temp. rating**	ordinary	ordinary
Sprinkler spacing (ft^2)	80-100	80-100
Sprinkler demand	12 sprinklers at 75 psi	12 sprinklers at 50 psi
Hose stream demand (gpm)	250	250
Duration (hr)	1	1

* Single- and double-row racks only.
** When use of higher temperature rated sprinklers is necessary, such as near unit heaters, refer to NFPA 13, *Installation of Sprinkler Systems.*

Explosion suppression systems have been employed effectively in charging rooms. Such systems provide protection by extinguishing flame before damage occurs. Ultraviolet sensors react in milliseconds, releasing a halon agent or water which traps the spark or flame before explosive pressures can develop. Halon 1301 is approximately twice as effective as water in an explosion suppression system.

Disposal of defective cans is an essential part of aerosol product manufacture. After filling, containers are passed through a warm water bath to detect leaks. Leaking containers are removed and crushed in a separate facility. Safety precautions in this area should be on the same order as those in the filling room.

Product development and quality control laboratories associated with aerosol product plants also present fire and explosion hazards. They should be built, equipped, and operated in accordance with the various safety standards; among these are the NFPA standards listed at the end of this chapter.

TABLE 2-23G ***Protection of Rack Storage of Level 2 Aerosols with Standard Spray Sprinkler***

Level	Ceiling Sprinkler Arrangement	In-Rack Sprinkler Arrangement	Clearances: Storage to Sprinklers	Ceiling Demand	In-Rack Sprinkler Demand	Duration: Sprinklers and Hose Stream
2	286°F (141°C) rated; 100 ft² max. spacing 1/2 in. or 17/32 in. orifice	165°F (74°C) or less Sprinklers 8 ft apart max. One line at each tier except top. Locate in longitudinal flue spaces double-row racks. For multiple-row rack storage, refer to NFPA 30B, *Aerosol Products.*	15 ft max. Need barrier with sprinklers beneath if clearance exceeds 15 ft (*See note*)	0.30 gpm/ft² over 2500 ft²)	30 psi per sprinkler minimum. Base on operation of hydraulically most remote: (1) 8 sprinklers if one level. (2) 6 sprinklers each of 2 levels if only 2 levels. (3) 6 sprinklers on top 3 levels if 3 or more levels.	2 hr

NOTE: Provide approved rack storage sprinklers with built-in water shields. Locate longitudinal flue in-rack sprinklers at least 2 ft (0.6 m) from rack uprights. Provide at least 6 in. (150 mm) between sprinkler deflectors and top of storage in tier.

TABLE 2-23H ***Protection of Rack Storage of Level 3 Aerosols with Standard Spray Sprinklers***

Level	Ceiling Sprinkler Arrangement	In-Rack Sprinkler Arrangement	Clearance: Storage to Sprinklers	Ceiling Demand	In-Rack Sprinkler Demand	Duration Sprinklers and Hose Stream
3	286°F (141°C) rated 17/32 in. orifice 100 ft² max. spacing.	165°F (74°C) or less sprinklers 8 ft apart max. Install in longitudinal flue and on face of each tier.	5 ft or less	0.30 gpm/ft² over 2500 ft²	30 gpm per sprinkler minimum. Base on operation of hydraulically most remote: (1) 8 sprinklers if one level (2) 6 sprinklers each of 2 levels if only 2 levels. (3) 6 sprinklers on top 3 levels if 3 or more levels.	2 hr
			More than 5 ft to 15 ft	0.60 gpm/ft² over 1500 ft² to 2500 ft² Interpolate for clearances between 5 ft and 15 ft	30 gpm per sprinkler minimum. Base on operation of hydraulically most remote: (1) 8 sprinklers if one level. (2) 6 sprinklers each of 2 levels if only 2 levels. (3) 6 sprinklers on top 3 levels if 3 or more levels.	2 hr
			More than 15 ft	0.60 gpm/ft² over 2500 ft² plus a barrier above top tier with face sprinklers below	30 gpm per sprinkler minimum. Base on operation of hydraulically most remote: (1) 8 sprinklers if one level. (2) 6 sprinklers each of 2 level if only 2 levels. (3) 6 sprinklers on top 3 levels if 3 or more levels.	2 hr
		165°F (74°C) or less sprinklers 8 ft (2.4m) apart max. One line at each except top. Locate in longitudinal flue. For multiple row rack, see NFPA 30B, *Aerosol Products.*	Up to 15 ft	0.60 gpm over 2500 ft²	30 gpm per sprinkler minimum. Base on operation of hydraulically most remote: (1) 8 sprinklers if one level. (2) 6 sprinklers each of 2 levels if only 2 levels. (3) 6 sprinklers on top 3 levels if 3 or more levels.	2 hr
			More than 15 ft	0.6 gpm over 2500 ft² plus a barrier above top tier with face sprinklers below	30 gpm per sprinkler minimum. Base on operation of hydraulically most remote: (1) 8 sprinklers if one level. (2) 6 sprinklers each of 2 levels if only 2 levels. (3) 6 sprinklers on top 3 levels if 3 or more levels.	2 hr

NOTE: Single and double row racks only.

Product Warehousing

Wet-pipe sprinkler systems are recommended for aerosol storage. Sprinkler spacing, size, and temperature rating will depend upon the classification of the aerosol product and the storage method. Level 2 aerosols in palletized or solid-pile storage should have one sprinkler per 100 sq ft (9.3 m^2) delivering 0.30 gpm per sq ft [12.2 (L/min)/m^2] over 2500 sq ft (232 m^2) as a minimum. Values for Level 2 and Level 3 are shown in Tables 2-23C through 2-23H as set forth in NFPA 30B, *Aerosol Products*.

Level 1 aerosols should be protected as Class 3 commodities in both palletized and rack storage. Any aerosol products that cannot be identified also should be protected as Level 3 aerosols.

Whether in-rack or palletized storage, Level 3 aerosols should be in a cut-off area with walls or ceiling-high partitions having a 1 hr fire resistance rating. Wet-pipe sprinkler protection should be in accordance with the figures in Tables 2-23D, 2-23F, and 2-23H.

Rack storage of Level 2 aerosols also should be in a dedicated area with sprinkler protection as shown in the tables. It is important to have in-rack sprinklers in every tier to prevent the fire from spreading throughout the rack. For small quantities and picking areas, Level 2 aerosols may be stored on the first tier with in-rack sprinklers provided specifically for that level and the one above.

BIBLIOGRAPHY

References Cited

1. Factory Mutual Research Corporation, "Storage of Aerosol Products," *Loss Prevention Data Sheet 7-29S*, 1983, Factory Mutual Research Corp., Norwood, MA.
2. Best, R., "$100 Million Fire in K Mart Distribution Center," *Fire Journal*, Vol. 77, No. 2 (Mar. 1983), pp. 36-42.
3. Factory Mutual Research Corporation, "Aerosol Flammability Test," *Technical Advisory Bulletin*, filed with *Loss Prevention Data Sheet 7-29S*, Factory Mutual Research Corp., Norwood, MA.
4. *Hydrocarbon Propellants: Considerations for Effective Handling in the Aerosol Plant and Laboratory*, Chemical Specialties Manufacturers Association, Washington, DC, 1979.

References

UL 913, *Intrinsically Safe Apparatus and Associated Apparatus for Use in Class I, II, and III, Division 1, Hazardous (Classified) Locations*, Underwriters Laboratories Inc., Northfield, IL.

Factory Mutual Research Corporation, "Storage of Aerosol Products—ESFR Protection," Technical Advisory Bulletin, Filed with LPDS 7-29S, Factory Mutual Research Corp., Norwood, MA.

NFPA Codes, Standards, and Recommended Practices

Reference to the following NFPA codes, standards, and recommended practices will provide further information on aerosol charging operations discussed in this chapter. (See the latest *NFPA Catalog* for availability of current editions of the following documents.)

NFPA 11A, *Medium- and High-Expansion Foam Systems.*

NFPA 12, *Carbon Dioxide Extinguishing Systems.*

NFPA 12A, *Halon 1301 Fire Extinguishing Agent Systems.*

NFPA 13, *Installation of Sprinkler Systems.*

NFPA 15, *Water-Spray Fixed Systems for Fire Protection.*

NFPA 17, *Dry Chemical Extinguishing Systems.*

NFPA 18, *Wetting Agents.*

NFPA 30, *Flammable and Combustible Liquids Code.*

NFPA 30B, *Aerosol Products.*

NFPA 33, *Spray Application Using Flammable and Combustible Materials.*

NFPA 45, *Fire Protection for Laboratories Using Chemicals.*

NFPA 58, *Storage and Handling of Liquefied Petroleum Gases.*

NFPA 68, *Venting of Deflagrations.*

NFPA 69, *Explosion Prevention Systems.*

NFPA 70, *National Electrical Code®.*

NFPA 77, *Static Electricity.*

NFPA 91, *Blower and Exhaust Systems for Dust, Stock and Vapor Removal or Conveying.*

NFPA 231C, *Rack Storage of Materials.*

NFPA 493, *Intrinsically Safe Apparatus for Use in Hazardous Locations.*

NFPA 704, *Identification of the Fire Hazards of Materials.*

Additional Reading

A Guide to Safety in the Aerosol Industry, British Aerosol Manufacturers Association, London, 1985.

"Aerosol Storage: The Problems and Solutions," P8207, Factory Mutual Research Corporation, Norwood, MA.

"Assessing the Flammability of Aerosols in Warehouses," *Fire Prevention*, No. 201 (July-Aug. 1987), pp. 24-28.

Benedetti, R., *Flammable and Combustible Liquids Code Handbook*, 3rd ed., National Fire Protection Association, Quincy, MA, 1990.

"Concern Over Warehouse Fires Leads to Tests on Aerosols," *Fire*, Jan. 1981, pp. 410-412.

Davenport, J. A., "Explosion Losses in Industry," *Fire Journal*, Vol. 75, No. 1 (Jan. 1981), pp. 52-56, 71-73.

Deacon, F. L., "Designing Fire Protection to Limit Monetary Loss," *SFPE Technology Report No. 80-2*, Society of Fire Protection Engineers, Boston, MA, 1980.

Dennis, R., ed., *Handbook on Aerosols*, ERDA Technical Information Center, 1976.

"Fire and Explosion Hazards with Aerosols," *Fire Prevention*, Dec. 1980, pp. 22-24.

Hinds, W. C., *Aerosol Technology: Properties, Behavior, and Measurement of Airborne Particles*, John Wiley and Sons, Inc., New York, 1982.

Johnsen, M. A., *Aerosol Handbook*, 2nd ed., Dorland Publishing Co., Mendham, NJ, 1982.

Magison, E. C., *Electrical Instruments in Hazardous Locations*, 3rd ed., Instrument Society of America, Pittsburgh, PA, 1978.

Marple, V. A., and Liu, B. Y. H., eds., *Aerosols in the Mining and Industrial Work Environments*, Vols. 1-3, Ann Arbor Science Publications, Woburn, MA, 1983.

Rizzo, J. J., "The Development of the duPont Aerosol Flammability Test," *Fire Journal*, Vol. 81, No. 2, 1987, p. 32.

Roberts, D. J., "Aerosols and Fire Prevention," *Fire Prevention*, No. 217, Mar. 1989, pp. 24-27.

"Safe and Efficient Plant Operation and Maintenance," *Chemical Engineering Magazine*, McGraw-Hill, New York, 1980.

"$10 Million Spent for Aerosol Plant Fire Safety," *Fire Engineering*, Vol. 134, No. 12 (Dec. 1981), p. 42.

SEMICONDUCTOR MANUFACTURING

Lawrence A. McKenna, Jr.

Semiconductor devices, such as computer chips, are commonplace in the modern world. Applications range from the digital wristwatch to the most advanced supercomputers under development. In between, uses include televisions, VCRs, electronic controls on appliances, and the control module in many newer automobiles.

Semiconductors are made from a variety of basic materials. The most common is silicon. Other types include gallium arsenide, germanium, gallium phosphide, and gallium arsenide phosphide. A single manufacturing plant may use any combination of these materials as the base crystal. All are prepared in a similar manner.

Semiconductor devices have extremely small circuit patterns. A single particle of microscopic dust can ruin a chip. Because of this, the devices are fabricated, or manufactured, in a cleanroom. A room can be considered to be a cleanroom if it can maintain a particle level of less than 100,000 particles per cu ft (0.028 m^3) of air. Such a room would be a Class 100,000 cleanroom. The most advanced semiconductors today require cleanrooms of Class 10 or Class 1 design. That is, the rooms have no more than 10, or 1, particles larger than 0.5 micrometers (0.0000196 in.) in size in each cu ft (0.028 m^3) of air. In contrast to this, normal urban air has particle counts in the range of 5,000,000 particles per cu ft (0.028 m^3), while rural air averages 1,000,000 particles per cu ft (0.028 m^3). (The human body can release up to 2,000,000 particles per minute into the atmosphere.)

The finished devices are extremely safe and generally present no unique hazard to users or to fire fighters. In contrast to this, the manufacturing process presents several unique hazards to production workers and fire fighters alike. Acids, alkalis, flammable liquids, flammable gases, pyrophoric gases, and toxic gases are common in semiconductor manufacturing facilities.

The loss potential in a semiconductor manufacturing plant can be enormous. Typical plants cost more than $100 million to construct and equip. Add to this the value of completed chips and in-process chips, which are very susceptible to damage from fire and smoke, and potential disruption in production schedules and product distribution, and the potential loss can be staggering.

Most materials either conduct electricity (conductors) or do not conduct electricity (insulators). Semiconductor materials do not fall into either of these classifications, since they are neither good conductors nor good insulators. Their electrical conductivity can be altered by minute changes in their chemical makeup or by creating changes in electrical fields inside the device. Many different ways exist to create such changes, and much of the research in the field has been directed toward improving present methods and developing new ones. This capability to change the electrical properties of a material, or of selected regions of the material, is what makes semiconducting materials so valuable in modern electronics.

In the manufacturing process, selected portions or areas of the semiconductor material (generally silicon) are made to be either conductors or insulators, thus creating electrical circuits, transistors, capacitors, etc. Highly sophisticated manufacturing techniques allow circuit patterns as narrow as 5 millionths of an inch (1/8 micron) in width. The circuit patterns are applied in sequential layers, one upon the other. Forty or more layers of circuit patterns may be combined on a single chip, depending on chip design. A modern 4 MB (4 million bits of information) memory chip typically contains over 8 million individual transistors and capacitors.

THE PRODUCTION PROCESS

Numerous steps go into the manufacture of an integrated circuit, or chip. In general, these can be broken down into pre-production and wafer fabrication. The pre-production steps include circuit design, crystal growth and preparation, and mask production. The wafer fabrication process includes a number of different operations which are used to create the intricate pattern of the circuit in successive layers. Figure 2-24A shows the general process.

Lawrence A. McKenna, Jr., is senior fire protection engineer, for AT&T, Basking Ridge, NJ.

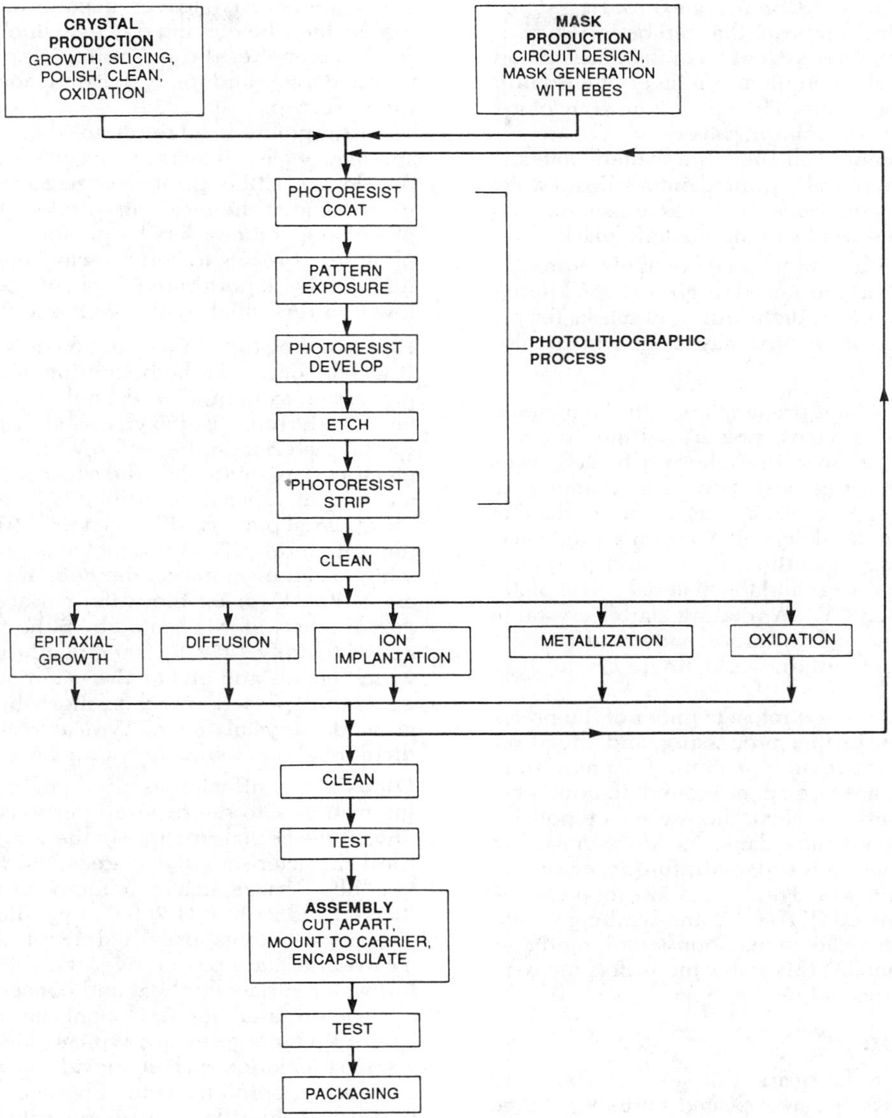

FIG. 2-24A. Flow chart for semiconductor manufacturing.

Pre-Production

The pre-production processes center on the preparation of materials needed in the fabrication stage of chip manufacture. These materials include the base crystal or wafer, and the masks necessary to develop the various circuits.

A chip is constructed of millions of individual transistors, capacitors, and the paths (wires) connecting them. These components are constructed on the chip in layers. Each layer must align perfectly with the layers below it. Failure to attain this perfect alignment results in chips that do not function.

Photolithography is the process currently used to define the circuit components and paths. This process, which is similar to common photography, uses "masks"—the same way that photographic film negatives are used—to project an image onto the coated chip. These masks are extremely critical in defining the circuit and achieving perfect alignment of the layers, and must be very carefully made. The ability to make the masks and to use them is one of the main limiting factors in developing chips that have many components on them.

Chip design: Once the design objectives for a particular device have been formulated, sophisticated computers are used in the design of the chip. Computer simulation assists designers in optimizing the performance of the chip being developed and in meeting strict reliability requirements. Layout is the process of locating the components on the surface of the chip. Computer-aided layout permits precise, error-free positioning of the hundreds of thousands of geometric elements required to form a single chip design.

The basic task of layout is to position components so that they can be assembled, and then to design the masks needed to manufacture the integrated circuit. Once the design is completed, the manufacturing data is fed to the electron beam exposure system (EBES) which makes the masks used to fabricate the wafers.

Mask production: The electron beam exposure system is a process using an electron beam that can be focused very accurately to etch a surface. It is used in the mask-making operation to selectively etch off a thin layer of chromium deposited on a flat glass plate. The result is an array of geometric openings in the chromium layer.

The design geometry on these imprinted plates, or masks, is photolithographically printed onto (silicon) wafers during wafer fabrication. Since the chips are small, many identical patterns can be placed on a single mask.

Since most chips are made of layers of electronic circuits, multiple masks are required. A typical 256 kilobyte (Kb) memory chip requires eight different masks for production. More complicated chips may require many more masks.

Crystal growth, slicing, and preparation: In the manufacture of silicon-based devices, polycrystalline silicon is placed into the crystal grower, an electrically heated, water-cooled furnace. Impurities, also known as dopants, are added to the grower in precise amounts to control the electrical resistivity of the final crystal. To form a single crystal, the charge of polycrystalline silicon and dopants is heated in the crystal grower until the material is completely molten at 2,552°F (1,400°C). A rotating starter crystal, or seed, is dipped into the molten silicon, and withdrawn very slowly. As the seed is withdrawn, a single crystal ingot grows around it.

The final ingot is ground into a cylinder of the precise diameter required for further processing, and sliced into very thin wafers, approximately 0.03 in. (0.76 mm) thick. The resulting wafers are lapped, or ground, to obtain perfectly flat, parallel surfaces. Next, the wafers are polished to remove any residual surface damage, using abrasives or chemical etchants such as nitric, hydrofluoric, or sulfuric acid, or sodium hydroxide. The wafers are then cleaned by rinsing with deionized (DI) water and washing with an organic solvent, such as acetone, isopropanol, methanol, or 1,1,1-trichloroethane. At this stage, the wafers are ready for the fabrication process.

Wafer Fabrication

The steps used in the fabrication of specific chips vary widely. Generally, the steps are repeated a number of times during the fabrication process, in differing orders, to define each successive layer of the circuit. Most of the steps are pattern-creating steps which first define a pattern on the chip and then create portions of the circuit in the pattern defined. The major processes usually include photolithography, epitaxial growth, diffusion, oxidation, ion implantation, metallization, etching, and cleaning. As noted in Figure 2-24A, the process steps can be repeated many times before the chip is completed. Each process is discussed in more detail below.

Photolithography: Photolithography is, in many respects, the most critical process in wafer fabrication, and is very similar to the photography processes used to make common snapshots. It is used to define the patterns where portions of the circuit will be created in operations, such as etching, diffusion, ion implanting, etc.

A typical photolithographic sequence includes application of the photoresist (a light-sensitive emulsion) on the wafer, alignment of the mask over the wafer, exposure of the uncovered portions of photoresist through the mask using ultraviolet light, and development of the photoresist to remove the unexposed photoresist. Removal of this unexposed photoresist leaves a patterned area of the chip exposed for the etching process which follows. After etching is complete, the remaining (exposed) photoresist is stripped away and the wafer is cleaned in preparation for the next step.

Equipment used in photolithography includes wafer spinners, wafer aligners, ovens, masks, steppers, and wafer developers. Either positive or negative photoresist may be used. Various chemicals are used in the development and processing of the wafers for photolithography. Because the photoresist reacts to certain wavelengths of light, photolithography is performed in cleanrooms with special yellow lighting which will not expose the photoresist.

Epitaxial growth: Epitaxial growth is not a patterned step. It usually occurs at the beginning of the wafer fabrication process or, as in bipolar technology, after an initial buried layer patterning. Epitaxy is used to grow a thin layer of crystal material on the wafer, which may have a different electrical resistivity than the substrate material. Generally, a chemical vapor deposition (CVD) technique is used in the epitaxial process, although metal organic chemical vapor deposition (MOCVD) and molecular beam epitaxy (MBE), which is an evaporation method, are also used to grow a crystalline layer on the wafer surface. In CVD epitaxial growth, the wafer is heated by radio frequency heating to approximately 1472°F (800°C) and exposed to hydrogen, which cleans and etches the wafer surface. The reactant gas is then passed over the wafer where it decomposes to grow the crystal layer. Typical reactant gases include dichlorosilane, tetrachlorosilane, and arsine.

Diffusion: Diffusion is used to introduce dopants, or impurities, into the exposed portions (see photolithographhy) of the crystal structure of the wafer to change the electrical characteristics of that area. Diffusion is normally done in a tube furnace, heated to temperatures between 1652°F (900°C) and 2192°F (1,200°C) by radio frequency heating. The dopant atoms, usually drawn through the furnace in a carrier gas, are passed over the wafers, and driven into the wafer surface by heat and concentration gradients to a predetermined depth. Dopants are always single atoms. The following gases are typical dopant sources: arsine, arsenic trichloride, arsenic trioxide, boron tribromide, boron trichloride, boron trioxide, diborane, boron nitride, phosphorus oxychloride, phosphorus tribromide, phosphorous pentoxide, or phosphine.

Oxidation: Oxidation is used to grow a layer of oxide on the surface of the wafer. Oxidation is frequently performed in a tube furnace, as is diffusion, at temperatures between 1472°F (800°C) and 1832°F (1,000°C) (lower temperatures than diffusion). In this process, steam and either wet oxygen or dry oxygen are introduced into the furnace to cause growth of the layer. Alternate techniques for growing an oxide layer utilize the decomposition of silane, or other silicon-containing gases, in either a high- or low-pressure environment, and the use of an oxygen-containing plasma. The thickness of the oxide layer is controlled by the time and temperature in the furnace and the rate of gas flow.

Ion implantation: Ion implantation is used to place atoms of a particular dopant into the crystal structure of the wafer. The wafer is loaded into the ion implanter, and a controlled high-energy beam of ions of the selected dopant gas is directed at the wafer. The beam may be directed at the entire wafer, implanting ions into all exposed regions (see photolithography), or it may be narrowly focused onto a small region. Common ion implant gases are arsine, boron trifluoride, diborane, hydrogen, and phosphine.

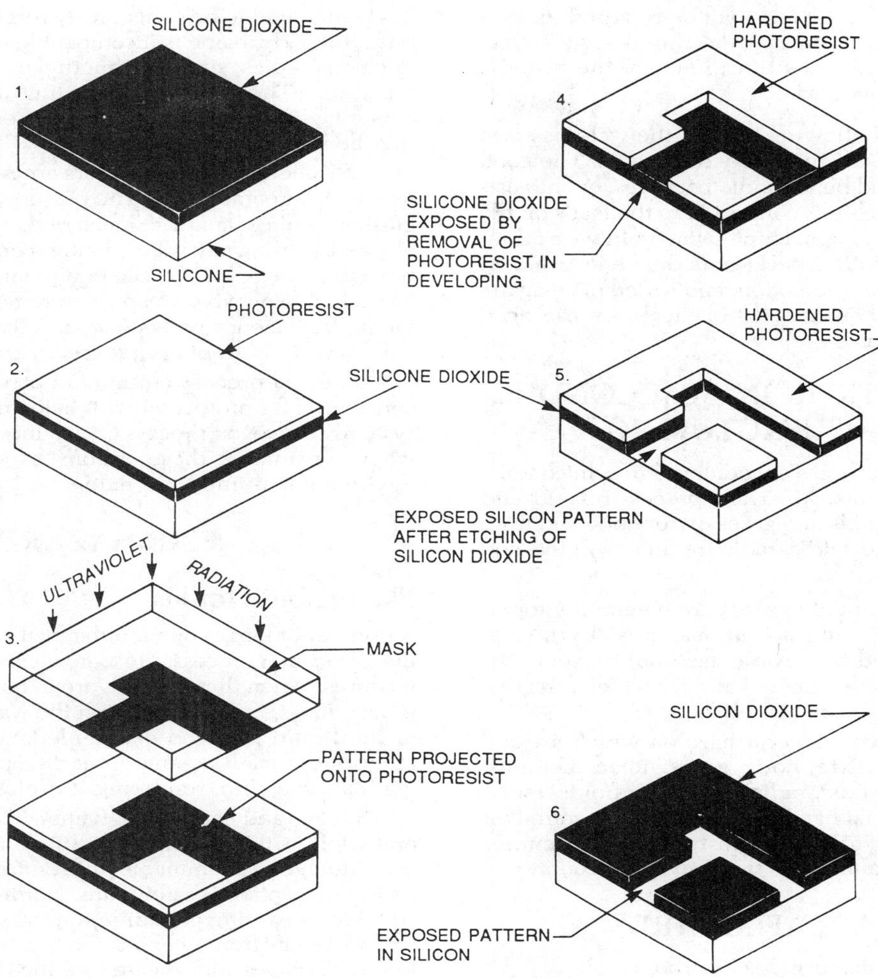

FIG. 2-24B. Photolithography. A pattern is etched onto a silicon dioxide layer that has been (1) grown on to the surface of the wafer. (2) The wafer is coated with photoresist. (3) The coated wafer is exposed to ultraviolet light through the patterned mask. (4) Exposure renders the exposed photoresist insoluble. The unexposed photoresist is removed in the developing process, leaving a patterned area of silicon dioxide exposed. (5) The exposed silicon dioxide is removed by etching. The remaining hardened photoresist protects the unexposed silicon dioxide from the etchant. (6) Remaining photoresist is stripped away in a chemical bath leaving a pattern on the surface of the wafer.

Metallization: Metallization is used to interconnect the various elements to form a completed circuit. In metallization, the exposed (see photolithography) regions of the wafer are coated with the metal to create circuit paths. Typical metallization processes include flash evaporation and sputtering. The process is conducted in a vacuum where the metal is evaporated by an electron beam or radio frequency (RF) induction. The evaporated metal condenses on the wafer in the desired film thickness. Among the materials used are the metals aluminum, gold, silver, nickel, chromium, and titanium, and metal silicides.

Etching: Most wafers go through the etching process several times at different stages of the fabrication. Etching is used to remove selected portions (see photolithography) of the chip pattern in preparation for further process steps. Two etching processes are used: wet etching and dry etching.

Wet etching is frequently performed in an open bath, commonly called a wet bench, in the cleanroom, although automated enclosed units are available. Ammonium fluoride and hydrofluoric acid are used as oxide etches; acetic, nitric, and phosphoric acids are used as metal etches. Wet benches also typically contain baths for neutralizing the etchant remaining on the wafer and for cleaning the wafer.

Dry etching is performed in an evacuated bell jar where an etchant gas is passed over the wafer. Boron trichloride, chlorine, nitrogen trifluoride, oxygen, trifluoromethane, and tetrafluoromethane are common etchant gases.

Cleaning: Wafer cleaning is necessary at many stages in the fabrication process to ensure proper preparation for critical operations that follow. Most cleaning is performed in open baths in the wet benches, using sulfuric acid, hydrogen peroxide, 1,1,1-trichloroethane, and isopropanol.

Test and repair: Once the wafer fabrication is completed, the wafer is cleaned and ready for testing. Each of the chips on the wafer (as many as 300 chips may be on a single wafer) is tested for proper operation by a computerized test apparatus. Chips failing the test may be repaired using a laser repair system, depending on the chip design. Defective chips are marked for identification, and the wafer is sent on to the assembly area.

Assembly and test: Following testing, the wafer is sawn apart with a diamond saw into individual chips. The good chips are sorted out and bonded into packages, or chip carriers. Circuitry on the chip is connected to the leads on the carrier by a computerized machine using gold wires thinner than a human hair. The package is then encapsulated in an epoxy material for protection, and tested once again. Chips passing the final quality control checks are packaged for shipment to the customer.

HAZARD CONTROL IN SEMICONDUCTOR MANUFACTURING

Several classes of hazards are encountered in semiconductor manufacturing plants. Most are process-related and include flammable liquids and gases, pyrophoric and toxic gases, toxic liquids and solids, radio frequency fields, and ionizing radiation.

Most of these potential hazards are commonly found in other industries. Plating operations, crystal growing, flammable liquids, and flammable gases all present hazards which are widely recognized and for which effective loss prevention controls are established.

There are, however, several hazards which are not widely encountered. Pyrophoric gases, toxic materials (gases, liquids, and solids), radio frequency fields, ionizing radiation, and special handling techniques required for certain chemicals due to purity constraints are examples of uncommon potential hazards that may be encountered.

GENERAL SAFEGUARDS

Semiconductor manufacturing cleanrooms should be located in fire-resistive construction and equipped with a full automatic sprinkler system. The cleanroom should be cut off from other areas of the plant by fire-rated construction having a minimum rating of one hour. Because of the high values present, additional compartmentation is highly desirable. Ventilation systems, including recirculating and exhaust systems, should be independent of ventilation systems in adjoining compartments.

Recirculating air systems should be designed to shut down in the event of a fire or chemical spill. Exhaust systems serving processes using toxic materials should continue running during such incidents. This will allow continued removal and treatment of potentially dangerous fumes and vapors from the cleanroom. [Most of these exhaust systems contain treatment processes to remove or neutralize the chemical(s) in the exhaust stream.] Caution should be used in placing automatic sprinklers inside plastic ducts used for fume exhaust, because tests have demonstrated that sprinklers can significantly reduce the flow through the duct when operating. This may be undesirable in exhausts handling toxic fumes or vapors.

Fire extinguishers and hose stations should be provided. The minimum extinguisher capability should be 2A:40B:C, distributed on an extra-hazard schedule in fabrication areas. (See NFPA 10, *Portable Fire Extinguishers*.)

Halon *must not* be used in cleanrooms. In particular, halon is dangerous in areas where inorganic hydrides, such as silane, diborane, dichlorosilane, *et al*, are in use. Halon has been found to be dangerously reactive with these materials. Similarly, halon is incompatible with metal alkyls and organometallics, such as trimethylaluminum and trimethylgallium. The concerns regarding the depletion of the ozone layer should also be considered when contemplating the use of halon extinguishers.

Dry chemical extinguishers are *not recommended* for use in cleanrooms either. The powders used in these extinguishers will contaminate much of the cleanroom when discharged, causing any wafers in the room to be contaminated beyond salvage. Most of the equipment will require meticulous and expensive cleaning to remove the powder, and the high-efficiency particulate air (HEPA) filters will probably have to be replaced at great expense.

Selected process equipment or wet benches may be considered for protection with halon or CO_2 extinguishing systems. However, process constraints should be evaluated when considering these options, as well as the potential environmental impact of halon.

FIRE HAZARDS

Flammable Liquids

A number of fairly common flammable liquids are used in the fabrication process. Most are alcohols, or alcohol-based mixtures. When these liquids are to be used in direct wafer processing, i.e., in contact with the wafers, absolute purity of the liquid must be maintained. As in the cleanroom atmosphere itself, a single microscopic particle can contaminate the chip, rendering it useless.

Storage and handling of flammable liquids should generally follow the principles outlined in Section 2, Chapter 25, "Storage of Flammable and Combustible Liquids." A notable exception is safety cans. Normal safety cans are not suitable for storing certain high-purity flammable liquids. The materials from which these cans are constructed tend to shed particles and contaminate the liquid. Stainless steel, Teflon®-coated stainless steel, and plastic safety cans are available, but even these are not acceptable in certain instances. The simple act of transferring the liquid from the glass containers provided by the supplier to safety cans can introduce contaminant. In these cases, it is generally necessary to store and dispense the flammable liquid in the glass containers in which the supplier packages them.

Special precautions are necessary to handle flammable materials safely. These include carts designed specifically to transport the glass containers safely from the flammable liquid storage room to the cleanroom. These carts hold the containers firmly upright and can even contain the contents in the event of breakage. Regardless of container construction, flammable liquids not being used should be stored in listed flammable liquid storage cabinets. Personnel training and restricted travel routes for the carts between storeroom and cleanroom should be provided.

In some cases, the flammable liquid is piped into the process equipment. The bulk supply will vary in size and location according to process requirements. Appropriate safeguards must be taken to ensure stability of the pipe system.

Flammable and Pyrophoric Gases

Many of the gases used in semiconductor manufacturing are either flammable or pyrophoric (i.e., ignite spontaneously upon contact with air). The gases may be pure, or they may be found as mixtures, with a carrier gas such as hydrogen or nitrogen.

These gases are used in process equipment, or "tools," which are highly automated. Safety devices are included in the design of these tools, and include a variety of pressure and temperature sensors, gas detectors, overpressure relief devices, and shutoff valves.

Gas cylinders containing ordinary gases, e.g., non-pyrophoric, non-corrosive, and non-toxic gases, are generally found in racks or cabinets in the vicinity of the cleanroom. (Ion implanters usually have a small cylinder, commonly called a "lecture bottle," of gas within their enclosure.) The ordinary gas is then piped into the cleanroom and to the tool.

Pyrophoric and toxic gases should be placed outside the plant, in special ventilated gas cabinets, or in vaults or bunkers. The gas is piped to the cleanroom in a fashion similar to the ordinary gases, but in welded, double-walled, stainless steel tubing. The gas travels in the inner tube(s), while the annular space between the outer tube and the inner tube(s) is used to confine any leak from the inner tube(s). This annular space is usually inerted or evacuated, and monitored by pressure sensors and gas detectors to automatically shut off the flow of gas in the event of a leak.

Process equipment using high concentrations of pyrophoric gases, such as silane, should be equipped with "burn boxes" in the exhaust system. The burn boxes are essentially reactors where any unreacted gas is mixed with air to complete the oxidation reaction. Since this reaction (fire and/or detonation) is exothermic and may generate overpressures in the reactor, the burn boxes are generally constructed of heavy-gage stainless steel, with overpressure relief.

The burning characteristics of pyrophoric gases, such as silane, dichlorosilane,diborane, and phosphine, are not fully understood. This is mostly because the engineering controls provided for these processes have been so successful in eliminating uncontrolled releases. Experience has shown that when a leak occurs in an unconfined area (e.g., outdoors), the pyrophoric gases usually ignite upon release, and subsequently burn in a manner similar to other flammable gases. When released into a confined area, such as a gas cabinet, silane has been known to detonate.

Cleanroom Furnishings

Work stations, wet benches, and other equipment used in fabrication areas are specially designed to reduce dust accumulation and release of particulates (from the finish treatment) into the room, and for compatibility with the chemicals used in or around the equipment. Plastic ducts, for exhaust of corrosive fumes and other combustible materials, are usually present.

HEALTH HAZARDS

Health hazards are also present in semiconductor manufacturing, but are beyond the scope of this handbook. They are mentioned briefly only to acknowledge their existence. For additional information concerning any particular hazard, consult an industrial hygienist or safety engineer. Semiconductor plants should have persons on staff trained in these disciplines.

Several of the gases used, such as arsine, phosphine, and diborane, are highly toxic. The toxicity hazards are controlled in the same fashion as the pyrophoric gases. In addition to the piping and control systems, the exhaust systems from the process tools should include treatment processes for these materials to avoid release into the atmosphere.

Many of the liquid and solid chemicals used in semiconductor manufacturing are also toxic. Examples include arsenic, various acids, and solvents. Safety considerations include ventilation and employee training.

In addition to chemical hazards present in the fabrication area, ion implant machines contain sources of ionizing radiation. The machine should have the appropriate safety devices and controls incorporated into it.

BIBLIOGRAPHY

NFPA Codes, Standards, and Recommended Practices

Reference to the following codes, standards, and recommended practices will provide further information on the processes and protective systems for semiconductor manufacturing discussed in this chapter. (See the latest *NFPA Catalog* for availability of current editions of the following documents.)

NFPA 10, *Portable Fire Extinguishers.*

NFPA 12A, *Halon 1301 Fire Extinguishing Systems.*

NFPA 13, *Installation of Sprinkler Systems.*

NFPA 13A, *Inspection, Testing and Maintenance of Sprinkler Systems.*

NFPA 24, *Installation of Private Fire Service Mains.*

NFPA 30, *Flammable and Combustible Liquids Code.*

NFPA 70, *National Electrical Code®.*

NFPA 75, *Protection of Electronic Computer/Data Processing Equipment.*

NFPA 86, *Ovens and Furnaces, Design, Location, and Equipment.*

NFPA 90A, *Installation of Air Conditioning and Ventilating Systems.*

NFPA 91, *Blower and Exhaust Systems for Dust, Stock and Vapor Removal or Conveying.*

NFPA 231, *General Storage.*

NFPA 231C, *Rack Storage of Materials.*

NFPA 255, *Method of Test of Surface Burning Characteristics of Building Materials.*

Additional Reading

Anderson, M., "Fire Protection Problems—Electronics and Semiconductor Industries," *Papers* Presented at the Summer National Meeting of the American Institute of Chemical Engineers, AIChE, 1987, 13 p.

Bartels, A. L., "Safeguards to Prevent Ignition of Hot Surfaces," *Electrical Review*, London, England, Vol. 203, No. 4, 1978, pp. 29-31.

Bolmen, R. A., "Designing For Fire Safety," *Semiconductor International*, Vol. 9, No. 11 (Nov. 1986), pp. 112-114.

Davis, R. H., "Fire Protection Systems (for Computers)," *Data Management*, Vol. 14, No. 11, 1976, pp. 11-14.

Deacon, F. L., "Designing Fire Protection to Limit Monetary Loss," *SFPE Technology Report No. 80-2*, Society of Fire Protection Engineers, Boston, MA, 1980.

Fisher, F. L., et al., "Fire Protection of Flammable Work Stations in the Clean Room Environment of a Microelectronic Fabrication Facility," *Fire Technology*, Vol. 22, No. 2, 1986, pp. 148-166.

King, P. W. and Magid, J., *Industrial Hazard and Safety Handbook*, 3rd rev. Butterworths, Woburn, MA, 1982.

Nailen, R. C., "Toxic, Flammable Chemicals, Gases, Breed Trouble in Electronic Plants," *Fire Engineering*, Vol. 133, No. 10 (Oct. 1980), pp. 54-57.

Perkins, C. and Berenblut, B. J., "Electronic Equipment: What Protection Is Required?" *Fire Surveyor*, Vol. 9, No. 5 (Oct. 1980), pp. 28-33.

Singer, P. H., "Wet Bench Fire Suppression," *Semiconductor International*, Vol. 10, No. 10, 1987, pp. 154-157.

Toy, D. A., "Take Those Hazards out of Your Gas Supply System," *Semiconductor International*, Vol. 12, No. 8 (July 1989), pp. 66-70.

Yang, E. J., *Fundamentals of Semiconductor Devices*, McGraw-Hill, NY, 1978.

STORAGE OF FLAMMABLE AND COMBUSTIBLE LIQUIDS

Revised by Orville M. Sly, Jr.

The first requirement for the storage of flammable and combustible liquids is properly designed containers that are liquid-tight and from which release of vapors, if required, is carefully controlled. The containers range from large, upright, outdoor storage tanks of millions of gallons (100,000 gals equals 378 m^3) capacity down through drums to small cans containing ounces of liquid.

This chapter discusses the various types of containers used in the storage and transportation of flammable and combustible liquids and the precautions that should be observed in handling the liquids as they are loaded, unloaded, or dispensed.

Additional information relevant to the storage of flammable and combustible liquids can be found in Section 1, Chapter 5, "Explosions;" Appendix A, "Tables and Charts;" Section 9, Chapter 14, "Identification of the Hazards of Materials;" Section 2, Chapter 31, "Control of Electrostatic Ignition Sources;" Section 4, Chapter 6, "Gas and Vapor Testing;" and Section 5, "Suppression."

TANK STORAGE

Tanks may be installed aboveground, underground, or, under certain conditions, inside buildings. Openings and connections to tanks, for venting, gaging, filling, and withdrawing, can present hazards if they are not properly safeguarded.

Given substantially constructed, properly installed, and well-maintained tanks, storage of flammable and combustible liquids is less dangerous than transferring these liquids. The severity of the storage hazard might seem to depend upon the quantity stored. As a practical matter, however, the size of the tank or the number of tanks is less important than such factors as the characteristics of the liquid stored, the design of the tank and its foundation and supports, the size and location of vents, and the piping and its connections.

Flammable liquids expand when heated. Gasolines expand about 0.07 percent in volume for each 10°F (5.5°C) increase in temperature within ordinary atmospheric temperature ranges. The effect of temperature increase on the volume of acetone, ethyl ether, and certain other flammable liquids with higher coefficients of expansion is greater than in the case of gasolines. To avoid danger of overflow, tanks should not be filled completely, particularly where cool liquid is placed in a tank in a warm atmosphere—for example, when filling an automobile tank from an underground gasoline tank on a warm day.

Several methods are used to prevent storage evaporation loss and loss of vapors as the tank is filled. Underground tanks reduce evaporation losses, since there is less fluctuation of temperature. Aboveground tanks often are painted with aluminum or white paint to reflect heat, thus decreasing the temperature rise of liquid contents and slowing evaporation of tank contents. Floating roof tanks minimize vapor loss and tend to reduce the fire hazard. Storage of gasoline in pressurized tanks reduces the loss of vapor. In some cases, vapors are conserved by the use of lifter roof or vapor dome tanks, or the vents from several cone roofed tanks may be connected through manifolds to a vapor dome or pressure-type tank.

The vapor space in tanks storing flammable liquids with vapor pressures above 4 psia (28 kPa), such as gasoline, is normally too rich to burn. The ratio of vapor to air is above the upper flammable (explosive) limit (UFL). However, if the temperature of the liquid gasoline is in the range of –10 to –50°F (–23 to –46°C), the vapor space may be within the flammable range. When a tank is being offloaded, or when there is a sudden cooling rainstorm on a hot day, a portion of the tank vapor spaceway may be within flammable limits, resulting from introduction of air. This condition may remain for several hours or even days, due to stratification of the vapors.

The vapor space in tanks storing low vapor pressure liquids (below approximately 2 psia or 14 kPa), such as kerosene, is normally too lean to burn. The ratio of vapor to air is below the lower flammable (explosive) limit (LFL). However, if the entire body of liquid is heated to its flash point, as may happen during refining processes or by exposure to fire, the vapor space may enter the flammable range. It should be noted that it is the temperature of the liquid and not the temperature of the vapor space that determines the presence of a flammable vapor-air mixture. The oil

Orville M. Sly, Jr., P.E., is president of Loss Control Associates, Inc., a consulting firm located in Langhorne, PA.

vapors driven off by the heated air in the vapor space are condensed back to liquid by the cooler body of oil. Therefore, the vapors are only flammable for a very short distance above the liquid surface despite the fact that the air within the tank may be considerably above the flash point temperature.

Tank storage of ethyl and methyl alcohol, JP-4 or Jet B turbine fuel, and other liquids of similar vapor pressure (approximately 2 to 4 psia at 100°F or 14 to 28 kPa at 38°C) presents an unusual hazard, since the vapors are normally in the flammable range. Storage in floating roof or similar tanks or the addition of inert gas in the vapor space is desirable to reduce the possibility of an explosion in the vapor-air mixture in the tank. Floating roof tanks, cone roof tanks with internal floating roofs, lifter roof tanks, and vapor dome tanks are also used for vapor conservation purposes for Class I liquids.

Aboveground Storage Tanks

Storage tanks come in a variety of designs. However, they may be divided into three general categories of pressure design: (1) atmospheric tanks, for pressures of 0 to 0.5 psig (0 to 4 kPa); (2) low-pressure storage tanks, for pressures from 0.5 to 15 psig (4 to 103 kPa); and (3) pressure vessels, for pressures above 15 psig (103 kPa). Some of the more common types of aboveground storage tanks are shown in Figures 2-25A and 2-25B. Pressure tanks and pressure vessels normally are used for vapor conservation purposes, particularly for liquids with high vapor pressures.

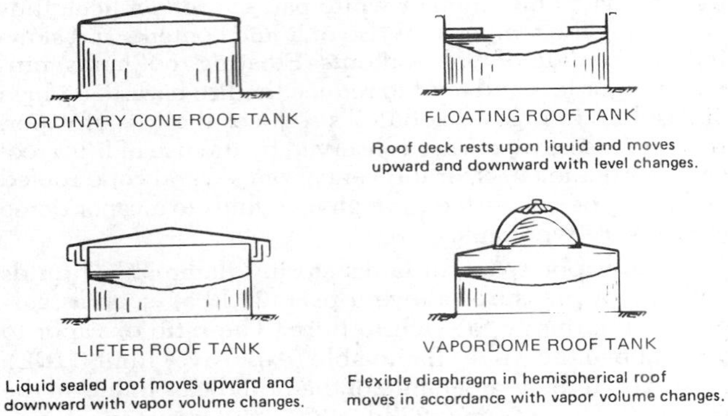

FIG. 2-25A. Common types of atmospheric storage tanks.

Construction: The thickness of the metal used in tank construction is based not only on the strength required to hold the weight of the liquid, but also on an added allowance for corrosion. When intended for storing corrosive liquids, the specifications for the thickness of the tank shell are increased to provide additional metal and allow for the expected service life of the tank. In some cases, special tank linings are used to reduce corrosion. Periodic inspection should be made to ascertain metal thickness of the tank, establish safe operating limits, and avoid overstressing the tank. The inspection of tanks for corrosion may be performed visually, or by drilling, calipering, or using sonic devices; provision of weep holes; or experience gained by the storage of similar materials. Sonic devices operate on a principle of the length of time it takes for sound waves

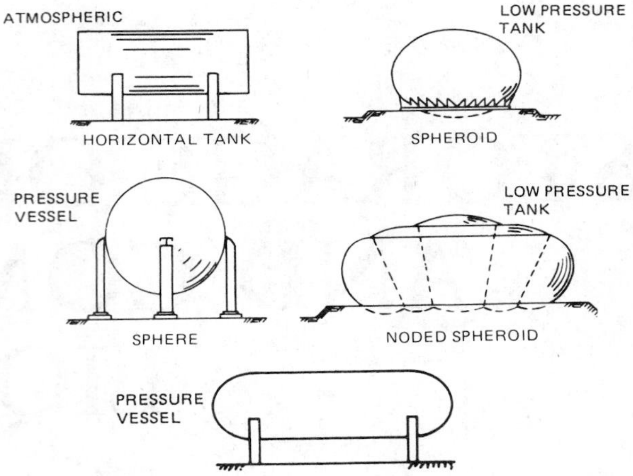

FIG. 2-25B. Common types of low-pressure tanks or pressure vessels.

to reflect from a surface. Any difference in metal thickness is quickly disclosed by these instruments, which are particularly effective when large areas with many potential corrosion spots are involved.

All aboveground storage tanks should be built of steel or concrete, unless the character of the liquid necessitates the use of other materials. Both steel and concrete tanks resist heat from exposure fires. Tanks built of materials less resistant to heat (e.g., low melting point materials) might result in tank failure and fire spread.

Tanks with the label of Underwriters Laboratories Inc. (UL) or those built in accordance with American Petroleum Institute (API) standards meet exacting specifications. For atmospheric, vertical, cylindrical, and aboveground welded tanks, API Standard 650, *Welded Steel Tanks for Oil Storage*,[1] may be used in calculating the minimum thickness of shell plate.

The nominal thicknesses of shell plates, including shell extensions for floating roofs, must be no less than those values given in Table 2-25A. The maximum nominal thickness of tank shell plates is 1/2 in. (18 mm).

TABLE 2-25A. ***Shell Plate Thickness***

Nominal Tank Diameter in Feet*	Nominal Thickness in Inches†
Smaller than 50	3/16
50 to, but not including, 120	1/4
120 to 200, inclusive	5/16
Over 200	3/8

* 1 ft = 0.304 m
† 1 in. = 25.4 mm

Concrete tanks require special engineering, and unlined concrete tanks should be used only for the storage of liquids with a specific gravity of 40° API or heavier. Tanks built of material other than steel should be designed to specifications embodying equivalent steel safety factors.

Installation: Aboveground tanks should be installed in accordance with NFPA 30, *Flammable and Combustible Liquids Code*. NFPA 30 specifies distances from tanks to

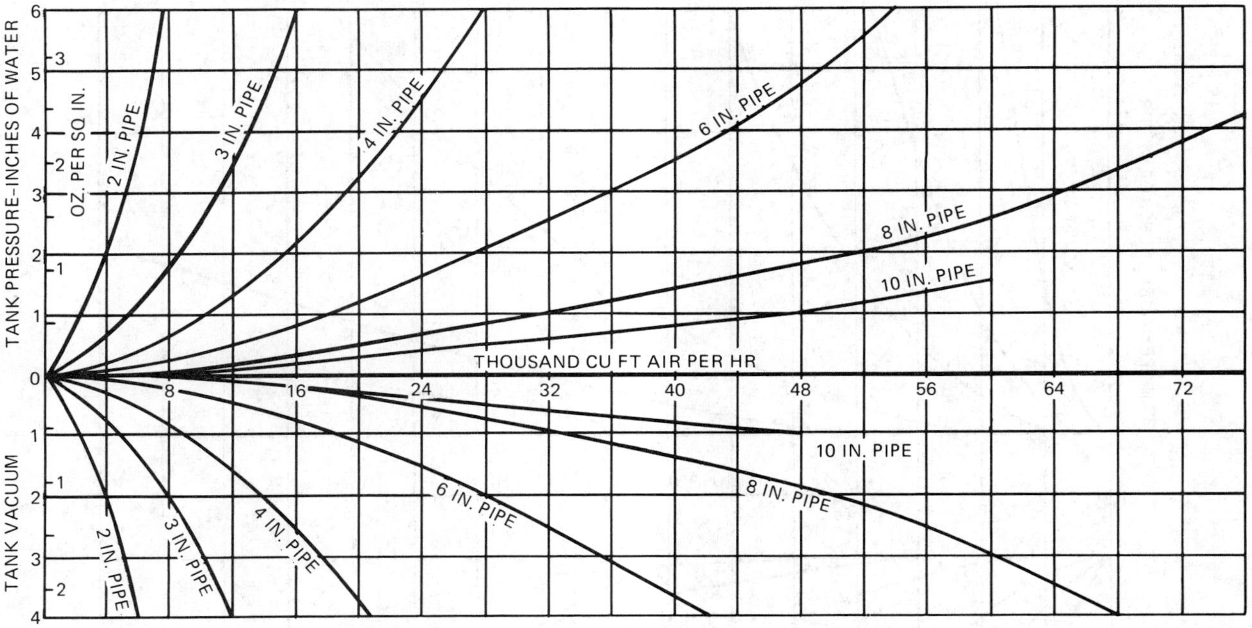

FIG. 2-25C. Average flow capacity of listed flame arresters for oil storage tanks in thousands of cubic feet of air for positive and negative pressures (1 in. = 25.4 mm; 1 in. of water = 249 kPa; 1,000 cu ft = 28.3 m^3; 1 oz. per sq in. = 3 kPa/mm).

property lines that can be built upon, and to public ways or important buildings. These distances will vary depending upon whether the pressures in the tanks, including those attained during fire exposure, can be under or over 2.5 psig (17 kPa), as well as whether the contents are stable or unstable liquids, or liquids having boil-over characteristics. Other factors affecting distances are the design of the tank, protection for exposures, fire extinguishing or control systems provided, and other protection features. The spacing between tanks is also specified in NFPA 30.

Municipal ordinances usually prohibit aboveground storage of flammable and combustible liquids in congested business districts, and zoning restrictions commonly exclude them from residential areas and from the vicinity of schools and hospitals. When a tank is located in an area that may be subjected to flooding, applicable provisions in NFPA 30 should be followed.

Venting and flame arresters: An appropriate vent must be provided for normal operation of any tank to permit filling and emptying and for the maximum expansion or contraction of the tank contents with changes in temperature. API Standard 2000, *Venting Atmospheric and Low-Pressure Storage Tanks*,[2] provides information on sizing vents for product movement and breathing. Clogged or inadequately sized vents may result in the rupture of tanks from internal pressure, or collapse due to internal vacuum. During the filling operation, the vents discharge flammable vapors. If the mixture is sufficiently rich or if the vent location is such that the released vapor is a hazard, the vapors should be piped to a place where they can dissipate safely. The vapor release should not occur close to doors, windows, or possible sources of ignition.

Venting devices are normally closed when the tank is not under pressure or vacuum. Devices installed on vent pipes can be approved pressure-vacuum conservation vent valves or flame arresters to prevent flashback into tanks. These devices are required when a flammable mixture is present, and for the storage of all Class I liquids. Arresters constructed of banks of parallel metal plates or tubes having a large surface of metal to dissipate heat are more effective than screens for larger openings and are less subject to clogging and corrosion. Heat is absorbed by the metal plates or tubes, which lower the temperature of the vapor below its self-ignition point. However, if the flame arrester is exposed to long burning periods, the metal plates can become sufficiently hot on the bottom side to ignite any flammable vapor-air mixtures in the tank. Figure 2-25C shows average capacities of laboratory-tested arresters; Figure 2-25D shows average capacities of flame arrester vent combinations. Similar data is also available for conservation vent valves. Vent design should be suitable for venting tank vapor space in accordance with API 2000[2], and NFPA 30 and not restrict vapor relief under design conditions.

Where the liquids stored have flash points in the range of normal summer temperatures, the vapor space above the liquid in the tank will normally contain vapors in the flammable range. Flame arresters have their most important application on such tanks. However, condensation and crystallization of certain liquids and freezing of moisture in winter may make conservation vents and flame arresters impractical. Steam tracing (steam heating) is provided in some cases to prevent freezing or crystallization of contents.

Although a wire screen of 40 mesh* ordinarily will prevent the passage of flame through small openings, it can-

*A woven wire fabric in which there are 40 wires per in. (25.4 mm) in each direction, and 1,600 interstices per sq in. (645 mm^2). The size of the openings depends upon the diameter of the wires and upon the mesh of the screens, but the size of wire is approximately uniform for any given mesh, and specifying a screen in terms of its mesh determines the size of the openings with sufficient accuracy for practical purposes. The individual opening in a 40-mesh screen has an area of about 0.00022 sq in. (0.14 mm^2).

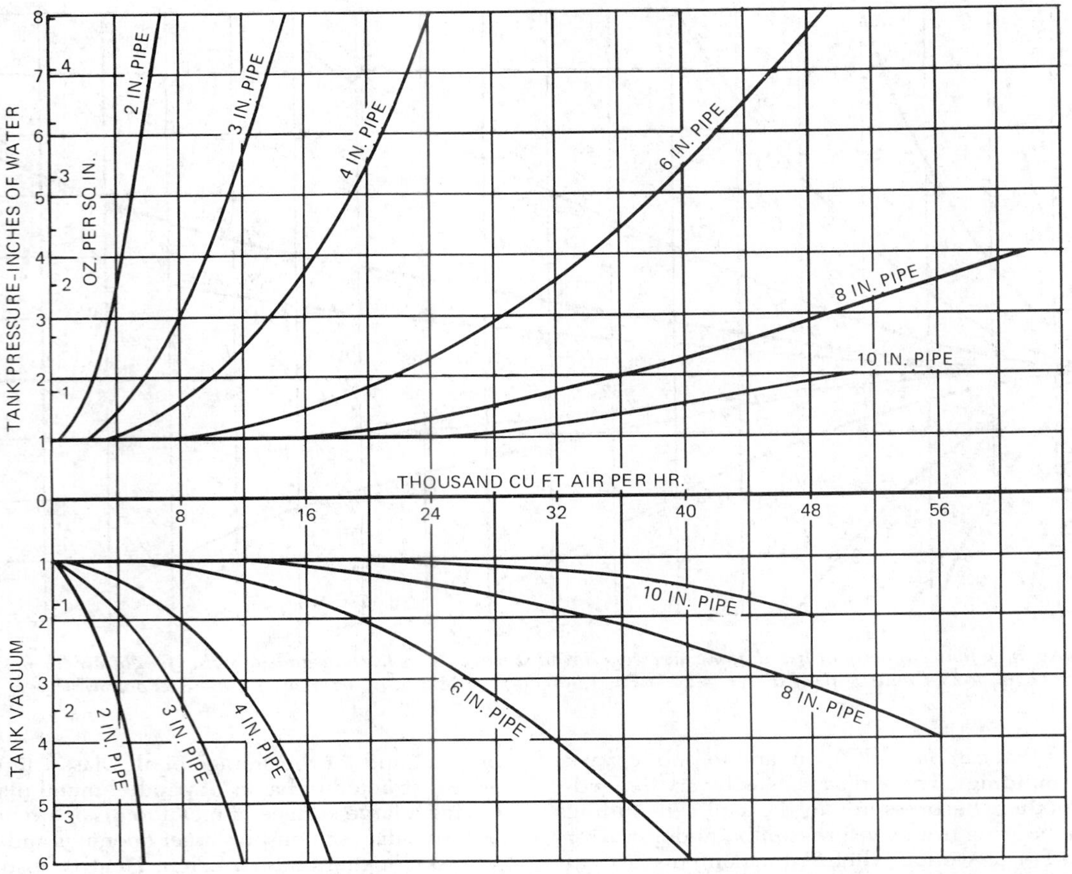

FIG. 2-25D. Average flow capacity of listed flame arrester vent valve combinations for oil storage tanks in thousands of cubic feet of air for positive and negative pressures (1 in. = 25.4 mm; 1 in. of water = 249 kPa; 1,000 cu ft = 28.3 m³; 1 oz. per sq in. = 3 kPa/mm).

not be relied upon as an effective flame arrester because of possible physical damage to the wires or clogging of the mesh by dirt or other residues.

Emergency venting: In addition to the normal operating vents, emergency relief of internal pressure is required for most aboveground tanks in the event a fire occurs under or around the tank. In the absence of proper provision for such relief, high pressures may be generated when the tank is exposed to external fire, resulting in a boiling liquid expanding vapor explosion (BLEVE). Such explosions are infrequent, but when they do occur, the results may be disastrous to life and property. BLEVEs can be avoided by providing adequate pressure relief, which permits the vapors to escape and burn at the vents and prevents the tank from rupturing. Emergency relief venting may take the form of loose manhole covers that lift under pressure, weak roof-to-shell seams, floating roofs, rupture disks, remotely actuated vapor depressuring, or commonly used emergency relief vents designed for the purpose.

Unless they are adequately vented, horizontal cylindrical tanks under excessive internal pressure commonly fail at the ends. For vertical cone roofed tanks designed with weakened seams at the roof-to-shell joint, the lifting of the roof or top of the roof-to-shell seam affords adequate emergency pressure relief. Vertical cone roofed tanks are required to have the roof-to-shell seam of weaker construction than the bottom-to-shell seam to prevent failure at the bottom of the tank which would release a wave of liquid. (See Figure 2-25E.)

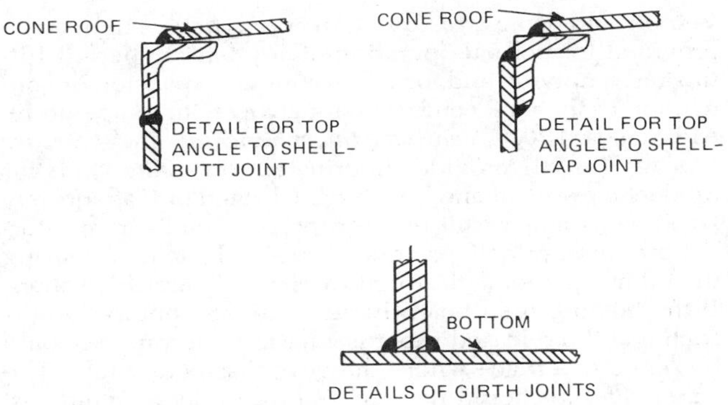

FIG. 2-25E. In cone roofed tanks, the roof-to-shell seams are required to be weaker than the bottom-to-shell seams (compare top drawings to bottom drawing). Although designed as emergency vents, weakened roof seams, as illustrated, have actually served as explosion relief in some instances as the entire roof has been blown off by an internal explosion.

On small cone roofed tanks, under 20 ft (6 m) in diameter, supplemental venting may be needed to prevent preferential failure of the shell-to-bottom seam. Dome roofed designs should meet API 650, *Welded Steel Tanks for Oil Storage*,[1] construction and vent requirements for this type of roof, and should not be mistaken for cone roofed designs.

The danger of tank failure from internal pressure when exposed to fire depends to a considerable extent upon the characteristics of the liquid, the size and type of the tank, and the intensity and duration of the fire. The smaller the tank or the smaller the volume of the liquid in the tank, the shorter the time under fire exposure before a BLEVE occurs.

Table 2-25B is based upon the required discharge from both normal and emergency vents, derived from a consideration of the probable maximum rate of heat transfer per unit area; the size of tank and the percentage of total area likely to be exposed; the time required to bring tank contents to boil; the time required to heat unwet portions of the tank shell or roof to a temperature where the metal will lose strength; and the effect of drainage, insulation, and the application of water in reducing fire exposure and heat transfer. Due to the wide variance in flow characteristics of manufactured vents, each vent design under 8 in. (203 mm) should be flow tested rather than relying upon vent size. The flow capacity of larger vents may be flow tested or calculated in accordance with the formula in NFPA 30.

The wetted area referred to in Table 2-25C is the internal portion of the tank in contact with the liquid (assuming a full tank) that is expected to be exposed to the flame of an external ground fire. The requirements for emergency venting are based on the heating of the liquid in the tank. Therefore, the wetted area (exposed to an external ground fire, such as a spill) varies with different tank designs: 55 percent of the total exposed area of a sphere or spheroid, 75 percent of the total exposed area of a horizontal tank, and the first 30 ft (9 m) abovegrade of the exposed shell area of a vertical tank.

For tanks and storage vessels designed for pressures over 1 psig (7 kPa), the total rate of venting is given in Table 2-25C. When the exposed wetted area or the surface is greater than 2800 sq ft (260 m²), the total rate of venting is as given in Table 2-25C, or it can be calculated by the following formula:

$$CFH = 1{,}17A^{0.82} \text{ where}$$

CHF = venting requirement, in cu ft or m³ of free air per hour

A = exposed wetted surface, in sq ft of m²

For SI Units:

$$\text{m}^3/\text{hr} = 220\ A^{0.82}$$

The foregoing formula is based on $Q = 21{,}000A^{0.82}$.

The total emergency relief venting capacity for any specific liquid may be determined by the following formula:

$$\text{Cu ft of free air per hour} = V\,\frac{1{,}337}{L\sqrt{M}}$$

For SI Units:

$$\text{m}^3/\text{hr} = \frac{3{,}107}{L\sqrt{M}}$$

where

V = cu ft or m³of free air per hour from Table 2-25B

L = latent heat of vaporization of specific liquid in Btu per lb or kJkg

M = molecular weight of specific liquids

TABLE 2-25B. *Wetted Area Versus Amount of Free Air per Hour Required for Relief Venting for Aboveground Tanks*
(For purposes of calculating the capacity of venting devices, "free air" is defined as air at 14.7 psia and 60°F or 101 kPa and 15.5°C)

ft²	m²	ft³/hr	m³/hr
20	1.86	21,100	597
30	2.78	31,600	895
40	3.71	42,100	1 192
50	4.64	52,700	1 492
60	5.57	63,200	1 790
70	6.50	73,700	2 037
80	7.43	84,200	2 384
90	8.36	94,800	2 675
100	9.29	105,000	2 973
120	11.15	126,000	3 568
140	13.00	147,000	4 163
160	14.86	168,000	4 757
180	16.72	190,000	5 380
200	18.58	211,000	5 975
250	23.23	239,000	6 768
300	27.87	265,000	7 504
350	32.51	288,000	8 155
400	37.16	312,000	8 834
500	46.45	354,000	10 024
600	55.74	392,000	11 100
700	65.03	428,000	12 120
800	74.32	462,000	13 082
900	83.61	493,000	13 960
1000	92.90	524,000	14 838
1200	111.48	557,000	15 772
1400	130.06	587,000	16 622
1600	148.64	614,000	17 387
1800	167.22	639,000	18 095
2000	185.80	662,000	18 746
2400	222.96	704,000	19 935
2800	260.12	742,000	21 011

Note: Interpolate for intermediate values.

TABLE 2-25C. *Rate of Venting for Tanks with an Exposed Wetted Area Larger than 2800 Sq Ft*

ft²	m²	ft³/hr	m³/hr
2,800	260	742,000	21 011
3,000	279	786,000	22 257
3,500	325	892,000	25 258
4,000	372	995,000	28 175
4,500	418	1,100,000	31 149
5,000	464	1,250,000	35 396
6,000	557	1,390,000	39 360
7,000	650	1,570,000	44 457
8,000	743	1,760,000	49 838
9,000	836	1,930,000	54 652
10,000	929	2,110,000	59 749
15,000	1393	2,940,000	83 252
20,000	1858	3,720,000	105 339
25,000	2322	4,470,000	126 577
30,000	2787	5,190,000	146 965
35,000	3251	5,900,000	167 070
40,000	3716	6,570,000	186 043

The required flow rate may be multipled by the appropriate factor listed in the following schedule when protection is provided as indicated (only one factor may be used for any one tank):

- 0.5 for approved drainage for tanks over 200 sq ft (18.6 m²) of wetted area.

- 0.3 for approved water spray
- 0.3 for approved insulation
- 0.15 for approved water spray with approved insulation

When pressure tanks or vessels are exposed to fire, a violent BLEVE may result if the steel in the vapor space is softened by heat. Localized overheating of the tank shell has been caused by vent fires impinging on tank surfaces. When an exposure fire builds up pressure within the tank, a BLEVE will take place. The outlets of all vents and vent drains on aboveground tanks designed for 2.5 psi (17 kPa) or greater should be arranged to prevent localized overheating of any part of the tank from a vent fire.

Foundations and supports: Tanks should be set on firm foundations and adequately supported. Vertical tanks are normally set on a slightly elevated pad to provide a sound base, and normally above the adjacent ground level to protect the bottom of the tank from any water in the area. Any exposed piling or steel supports under any flammable liquid tank are to be protected by fire-resistive materials to provide a fire-resistance rating of not less than two hours.

Drainage and dikes: Where waterways or properties would be endangered by release of liquids stored in tanks, it is necessary to provide a means to control any spillage. The most desirable method is to locate the tanks on sloping ground. Directional dikes or drainage ditches could then divert spillage away from all tanks and into an impounding basin where the liquid could burn safely without exposing other tanks, property, or waterways. Where impounding basins cannot be used, dikes built around the tanks can prevent the spread of liquid. Dikes may be constructed of earth, concrete, or steel built to withstand the lateral pressure of a full liquid head. When several large tanks are in a single diked enclosure, it may be desirable to place "spill dikes" between tanks. While only a minimum of 18 in. (457 mm) high, these intermediate dikes will prevent any small spills from exposing other tanks in the enclosure. Such spills may result from a leaking valve or connection, or from overfilling the tank.

Diked enclosures are designed to contain the greatest amount of liquid that can be released from the largest tank within the enclosure, assuming a full tank. When calculating the volumetric capacity of the diked enclosure, the volume of tanks within the diked area to the height of the dikes must be considered as unavailable space for the liquid to flow.

Where needed, diked areas are provided with trapped drains to remove rain water or water used for fire fighting. The best practice is to keep drain valves normally closed, and open them at intervals as needed, since permanently opened drains would discharge liquids in case of leakage from the tank. The drain valves should also be accessible under fire conditions, i.e., they should be located outside the dike. Oil separators are effective in skimming off oil flowing on the surface of water, but separators normally will not control oil discharge when the entire flow through the drain is oil.

Dikes higher than 6 ft (1.8 m) are not desirable without additional safety measures. Where circumstances require high, close dike walls, means should be provided for access to tanks, valves, and other equipment, and for safe egress from the diked enclosure. Where Class I liquids are stored, normal operation of valves and access to tank roofs must be available without requiring entry below the top of the dike. These provisions reflect a concern for the accumulation of Class I liquid vapors reaching harmful levels when confined in the narrow space between the high dike wall and the tank.

Fire effects on aboveground tanks: Actually, the probability of fire in a modern, properly constructed and installed tank is much less than in an ordinary building. Where tanks and buildings are adjacent, building fires expose the tanks more often than tank fires expose the buildings. However, experience indicates that if a tank fire occurs, the possibility of fire spread is increased materially when the tank is not built and installed in compliance with NFPA standards.

A commonly encountered type of aboveground tank installation includes tanks on unprotected steel supports. Tank truck loading can be accomplished by gravity when done immediately adjacent to the tanks. The typical fire at such installations originates at the tank vehicle, and, in short order, the unprotected steel supports fail and drop the tanks to the ground. The tanks may break the piping or rupture on hitting the ground, releasing the entire contents. To prevent tank collapse, steel supports should be protected by two-hour fire-resistive coverings. The loading rack should be at least 25 ft (7.6 m) from the tanks if Class I flammable liquids are handled, and 15 ft (4.6 m) with Class II and Class III liquids.

Improper and inadequate emergency venting have been major factors in tank failures during exposure to fire. Since inadequate and improperly designed vents have been the cause of severe BLEVEs and have resulted in deaths and injuries to fire fighters and spectators, it is of vital importance that the standards on venting be followed. In fighting tank fires, it is essential to cool the shell above the liquid level to keep the steel from overheating. Failure to do so could cause the tank to bulge and rupture, regardless of the adequacy of the venting.

A major factor in fires involving storage tanks has been the failure of piping and valves. Such failures have resulted in the addition of the contents of the tanks to the ground fire. Pipe systems may be located either aboveground or underground. Piping from aboveground tanks is normally placed aboveground to avoid corrosion problems and to aid in detecting pipe leaks. If piping is in open trenches, suitable fire barriers should be placed at certain intervals to prevent the flow of liquid from one section of the facility to another. Underground piping is not subject to fire exposure. All piping must be protected against physical damage and excessive stresses that arise from expansion, contraction, vibration, and settlement. Materials that are subject to failure due to thermal shock, such as cast iron, should not be used. Steel or nodular iron pipe and valves should be used for external tank connections through which liquid would normally flow, unless the chemical characteristics of the liquid stored are incompatible with steel. Welded pipe connections or flanged joints are preferred for aboveground piping, particularly for large-size pipe. Screwed pipe connections larger than 3 in. (76 mm) are subject to disengagement in a long-exposure fire unless the connections are back-welded. Pipe joints dependent upon the friction characteristics of combustible materials for mechanical continuity of piping are subject to failure under fire exposure conditions.

Most storage tank fires originate with an internal explosion or by a spill fire exposing the tanks. In a typical prolonged tank fire, the shell of a large vertical tank will fold into the tank above the burning liquid level, without splitting the tank shell.

Internal explosions of storage tanks can occur when the vapor space above the liquid reaches the flammable range. Liquids with flash points near the stored temperature are most susceptible to ignition. Liquids with low flash points will have a flammable vapor-air mixture in the vapor space if the temperature is markedly reduced, and high-flash-point liquids will form a flammable vapor-air mixture when heated. During fire exposures, internal explosions have occurred in tanks containing liquids with flash points above the stored liquid temperature. Such explosions occur because the liquid is heated by the exposure fire and the vapor passes into the flammable range when a part of the tank shell in the vapor space is hot enough to ignite the vapors.

Floating roof tanks provide greater firesafety for aboveground installations and, as a result, are permitted to be located closer to a property line than are other types of tanks. Explosions may occur, however, when floating roof tanks are virtually empty of liquid or the roof has been allowed to rest on the low-level supports, which may create a flammable vapor space. When fires occur in floating roof tanks, they are normally restricted to the seal space between the roof and the shell and often can be extinguished by portable extinguishers or hand-held foam lines. There have been a few cases, however, where a floating roof tank has been overfilled or the roof has sunk.

Fire protection equipment should be installed on tanks where needed. (See NFPA 11, *Low Expansion Foam and Combined Agent Systems*.)

Underground Storage Tanks

Underground tanks are designed to withstand safely the service to which they are subjected, including the pressure of the earth, pavement, or possible aboveground vehicle traffic.

Construction: Rigid specifications established by UL ensure reasonable safety for those tanks bearing its label. Underground tanks also may be of unlined concrete for the storage of liquids having a specific gravity of 40° API or heavier. Lined concrete tanks may be used for liquids having a lighter specific gravity, provided the lining is suitable for the liquid being stored and has satisfactory adherence to the concrete.

Installation: Underground tanks are generally considered the safest form of storage. However, recent concern about groundwater contamination has increased concern about use of underground storage tanks. Environmental safety regulations should be reviewed when planning installation of underground storage tanks. Such tanks may be buried outside or under buildings. Tanks that are buried underneath buildings should have fill and vent connections outside the building walls. Tanks should be set on firm foundations and surrounded with soft earth or sand that is well tamped into place.

Underground tanks must be protected against damaging loads imposed by the cover over the tanks and such factors as building foundations and vehicular traffic. Normally, no special protection is needed if the tanks are well supported underneath and buried sufficiently deep. However, if tanks are located in areas where higher-than-normal loads may be imposed, paving or additional earth coverage may be necessary. Piping subject to possibly damaging loads or vibrations is frequently protected by sleeves, casings, or flexible connectors to ensure the integrity of the line.

The normal life expectancy of properly installed underground steel tanks is 15 to 20 years. If improperly installed and in a corrosive soil, they may leak in less than three years. Environmental regulations or a hazard analysis may require the use of double-containment tank design and/or the use of groundwater monitoring for tank and piping leaks. The soil in which the tank is buried is very important, since some soils may be highly corrosive because of their chemical composition or moisture content. This is particularly true if construction debris, cinders, shale, or other foreign matter is mixed, even in very small quantities, with otherwise "clean" backfill. The use of homogeneous, clean backfill and protective coatings prolongs the life of steel tanks and piping. Cathodic protection of buried tanks and piping is often necessary. NFPA 30 requires that tanks and their piping be protected either by using corrosion-resistant materials of construction, or by using a properly engineered, installed, and maintained cathodic protection system in accordance with recognized standards of design.

Electrolytic corrosion in an electrically conductive tank and piping system may occur at points where metals having different electromotive qualities, such as steel and brass, are connected. Connections of two dissimilar metals should be avoided to prevent galvanic corrosion.

Stray electrical currents may set up corrosive action, but their presence may be difficult to determine until after the action has progressed to the point where damage has been done to the tank or piping. Cathodic protection or insulation is sometimes used to protect underground tanks from stray currents.

Fiberglass-reinforced plastic (FRP) tanks for underground installation eliminate the corrosion problem encountered with steel tanks. However, it is vitally important that the manufacturer's instructions for proper installation of these tanks be followed closely. Care should be taken in the use of FRP tanks to ensure that liquids stored in the tanks are not destructive to the plastic tank construction.

Tanks should be anchored or weighted to prevent floating in locations where the groundwater level is high or may rise in case of flood. Details of installation and protection are covered in NFPA 30. Typical sizes for underground tanks are shown in Table 2-25D.

The proximity of underground tanks to a building foundation is not a direct measure of the potential danger to the building if a leak should develop in the tanks. Leaking contents from underground tanks have been known to travel several miles underground (1 mile equals 1.6 km) or to penetrate 24 in. (610 mm) of waterproofed concrete before appearing in a building. Tanks suspected of leaking should be tested hydrostatically with the same liquid stored in the tank. (See Figure 2-25F.) Air tests or testing with liquids other than that stored in the tank have proved to be dangerous and inconclusive for detecting suspected leaks in underground tanks. Additional details about the causes of corrosion, locating leaking tanks, and removal of liquids in the ground are covered in NFPA 329, *Underground Leakage of Flammable and Combustible Liquids*.

TABLE 2-25D. *Typical Sizes of Underground Flammable Liquid Tanks*

Capacity		Diameter			Length		
Gal	L	Ft	In.	m	Ft.	In.	m
300	1136	3	0	0.91	6	0	1.83
560	2120	4	0	1.22	6	0	1.83
1000	3785	4	0	1.22	11	0	3.35
1000	3785	5	4	1.62	6	0	1.83
1000	3785	4	0	1.22	11	0	3.35
1000	3875	5	4	1.62	6	0	1.83
1500	5678	5	4	1.62	9	0	2.74
2000	7571	5	4	1.62	12	0	3.66
2500	9463	5	4	1.62	15	0	4.57
3000	11,356	5	4	1.62	18	0	5.49
3000	11,356	6	0	1.83	14	0	4.27
4000	15,142	5	4	1.62	24	0	7.32
4000	15,142	6	0	1.83	19	0	5.79
5000	18,927	6	0	1.83	24	0	7.32
6000	22,712	6	0	1.83	29	0	8.84
6000	22,712	8	0	2.44	16	0	4.88
7500	28,390	8	0	2.44	20	0	6.10
10,000	37,854	8	0	2.44	27	0	8.23
10,000	37,854	9	0	2.74	21	0	6.40
10,000	37,854	10	0	3.05	17	0	5.18
10,000	37,854	10	6	3.20	15	7	4.75

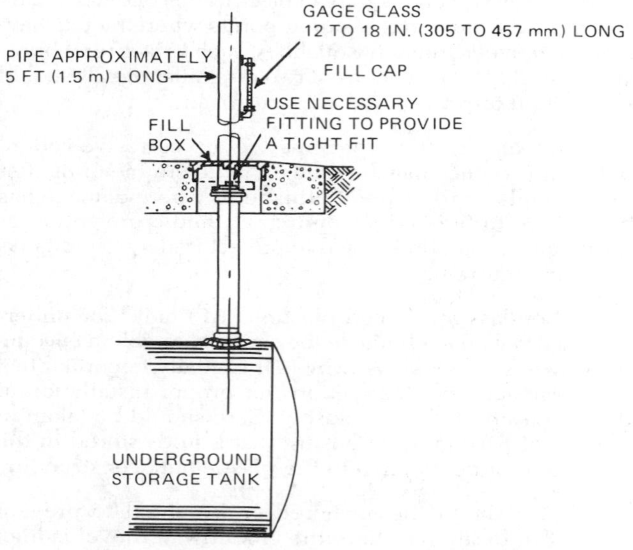

FIG. 2-25F. Simple leak test equipment in a typical underground tank installation.

Tanks Inside Buildings

Design: Tanks designed for installation in fire-resistive enclosures within buildings have the same metal thicknesses and design features as required for all tanks. Fuel-oil tanks designed for use inside buildings without being enclosed in a fire-resistive cutoff room are normally restricted to less than 660 gal (2500 L) capacity. Although the metal thicknesses for the tanks designed for differing situations are approximately the same, the locations of the pipe connection openings differ. Pipe connections for underground tanks and enclosed fuel-oil tanks inside buildings are in the top of the tank only, whereas unenclosed tanks are provided with bottom outlets for gravity-feed piping to such installations as oil-burning equipment. In certain specialized processing operations, large tanks are required and are designed as low-pressure storage tanks or pressure vessels as specified for aboveground storage tanks.

Installation: Storage tanks inside buildings will vary, depending upon the class of liquid and the occupancy of the building. For specific requirements for the installation of tanks inside buildings, see NFPA 30.

Where it is impractical to install a gasoline tank underground, a special liquid-tight and vapor-tight enclosure without backfill may be used. Such an enclosure is constructed of 6 in. (152 mm) of reinforced concrete with access through the top of the enclosure. Means are also provided for using portable ventilating equipment to discharge flammable vapors outside the building.

Fuel-oil tanks over 660 gal (2500 L) capacity may be placed inside buildings in enclosures with a fire-resistance rating of not less than three hours. Such tank enclosures may have an opening protected by a self-closing fire door designed for Class A openings and a raised, noncombustible, liquid-tight sill or ramp. If the sill or ramp is more than 6 in. (152 mm) high, the enclosure walls, up to a height corresponding to the calculated liquid level from a possible leaking tank, should be built to withstand the lateral pressure caused by the liquid head. Provision also should be made for ventilating the enclosure before inspection or repair of the tank. Additional storage may be permitted if the fuel-oil tank enclosure is located in a room cut off from the rest of the building by walls, floor, and ceiling of two-hour fire-resistive materials. The installation of fuel-oil tanks connected to oil burners is covered in NFPA 31, *Installation of Oil Burning Equipment.*

Where the nature of certain types of processing operations calls for tanks to be located inside buildings, particular attention should be given to the desirability of providing automatic sprinkler systems or water spray systems, thermally actuated valves adjacent to the tanks in pipelines, and steel valves and pipe. Vents and fill pipes from tanks inside buildings should terminate on the outside of the building.

Gaging Tanks

Tank openings for gaging or measuring the quantity of liquid may permit the escape of vapors during the gaging operation. Such openings are particularly undesirable in tanks located in buildings or buried under basements, and are prohibited by NFPA standards unless protected by a spring-loaded check valve or other approved device. Substitutes for manual gaging include heavy-duty flat-gage glasses; magnetic, hydraulic, or hydrostatic remote reading devices; and sealed float gages. These devices, however, must be maintained in reliable operating condition. Ordinary gage glasses should not be used, since their breakage may permit the escape of liquid.

Cleaning Tanks

Cleaning tanks for the purpose of making repairs requires great care. Precautions must be taken to avoid igniting flammable vapors and to protect personnel against toxic vapors.[3,4]

Work on empty tanks must be performed only under the supervision of persons well versed in the fire and explosion hazard, and in the procedures required to properly safeguard the operation. Unless the work can be done with the tank and all connected piping and fittings completely filled with water, all vapors should be removed by cleaning with steam or chemical solutions, or by displacement with water, air, or inert gas. In some instances, the tank vapor space may be filled with inert gas by specially qualified personnel to provide a safe atmosphere. The selection of the method of rendering a tank safe will depend upon several factors, such as the character of the liquid, the size of the tank, the flammability and reactivity of residues, and the type of work to be performed. With many reactive materials, it will be necessary to obtain information from the manufacturer regarding recommended practices for safe cleaning.

Removal of flammable vapors by displacement: This is sometimes referred to as "purging," and may be accomplished by one of several methods.

1. Displacement with water: Where the flammable liquid previously contained is known to be readily displaced by, or soluble in, water, it can be removed completely by using water to alternate or fill and drain the tank. The operation should be repeated several times until tests with a combustible gas indicator show that the vapors are no longer present. Acetone and ethyl alcohol are examples of water-soluble liquids.

2. Displacement with air: Frequently, flammable vapors may be removed by purging with air through the use of venturi-type air movers or low-pressure blowers, and a safe atmosphere is sustained by continuous ventilation. Air movers should be restricted to those operated by steam, by air, or by electric motors approved for use in the atmosphere involved. When steam operates the air mover, the air mover should be bonded or in electrical contact with the tank. When small tank openings cannot accommodate an air mover, the contents can sometimes be purged with compressed air connected to a metallic pipe bonded to the tank. Care should be exercised to prevent overpressuring a small tank if compressed air is used. Irregularly shaped tanks may not be thoroughly purged by this method if the air stream leaves pockets that cannot be reached effectively with the uncontaminated air. In air purging, the concentration of flammable vapors in air in the tank may go through the flammable range before safe atmospheres are obtained. Therefore, all precautions must be taken to minimize the hazards of ignition by static electricity. Air movers should be clamped or bolted, and thereby inherently bonded, to the vessel being ventilated. (See Figure 2-25G.)

3. Displacement with inert gas: When nitrogen in cylinders, or carbon dioxide in low-pressure containers or in solid form (dry ice) is available in sufficient quantity, it may be used to purge the flammable vapors from tanks without the hazards incident to having the vapor-air mixture in the tank vapor space pass through the flammable range. This procedure should be followed by air ventilation of the tank. High-pressure carbon dioxide, such as that from a fire extinguisher, should not be used because static electricity is generated. Several explosions or fires have occurred when CO_2 extinguishers were used to inert tanks or vessels.

Inerting the vapor space: Inerting is a means of safeguarding a tank by reducing the oxygen content to the point where combustion cannot take place in the vapor space. However, individuals in direct charge of the work must be thoroughly familiar with the limitations and characteristics of the inert gas being used. Attempting such work without proper knowledge or equipment can be hazardous because a false sense of security is engendered. The oxygen content should be maintained at substantially zero during the entire period work is in progress. Inerting gases include carbon dioxide and nitrogen. Both may be obtained in tanks, and carbon dioxide may also be obtained in solid form.

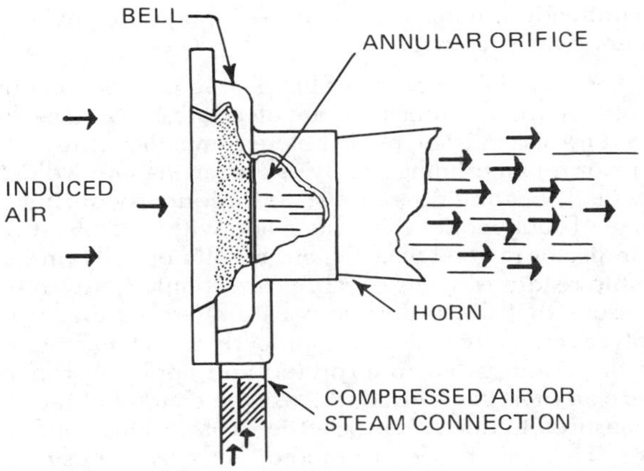

FIG. 2-25G. Schematic drawing of the operation of an air remover. Compressed air or steam is admitted to the bell of the air remover and enters the horn through the annular orifice around the base. As the steam or compressed air passes through the horn, its expansion induces a rapid flow of air, equal to approximately ten times the volume of the steam or compressed air.

Removal of residues: Liquid or solid residues might release flammable vapors during "hot work." The residues must be removed, and this can be accomplished by steam or chemical cleaning or by other recognized methods. In steam cleaning, the rate of steam supply should be sufficient to exceed the rate of condensation, and the steam nozzle should be electrically bonded to the container shell. During the steam cleaning process, the entire container is, of course, heated close to the boiling point of water [212°F (100°C)]. Chemical cleaning may be necessary to remove some residues, but this may present personnel health hazards that should be guarded against.

Large tanks are continuously ventilated by air movers at the roof manholes. After the atmosphere is sufficiently free for safe entry, more vapor may be released from the residue while it is being removed from the tank. By continuous ventilation during work, the vapor concentration can be kept at a safe limit. Continuous monitoring of the tank vapor space is necessary to prevent fire or explosion.

Special care must be taken to eliminate any source of ignition in the vicinity of the container or in the path of vapors being displaced. Bonding, either with special bond wires or by metal-to-metal contact with clamped or bolted connections providing inherent bonding, must be used where static-producing devices are used. All electrical equipment, such as inspection lights and motors, used in connection with the cleaning operations must be designed for such use.

Tests for the presence of flammable vapors constitute the most important phase of the cleaning or safeguarding procedure and must be made before commencing any alterations or repairs; immediately after starting any welding, cutting, or heating operations; and frequently during the course of such work. The tests made with a combustible-gas indicator in good working order will normally produce reliable readings. Considerable care should be exercised to ensure that the indicator is calibrated for the vapors involved, correctly scaled, and properly used and read, and that the readings are interpreted and applied properly. Where an inert gas is used, the oxygen content of the tank is measured to determine whether a hazardous condition exists. This may be determined directly by the use of an oxygen indicator, or indirectly by the use of an indicator showing the concentration of the inert gas being used. All testing must be conducted by persons experienced in the operation and in the limitations of the indicators used.

When hot work is to be done on small tanks or containers that cannot be entered, the combustible gas indicator should show no appreciable indication of the presence of flammable vapors. Extra precautions are necessary if the container last contained a high-flash-point liquid, because no vapor reading will show on the indicator. If welding or cutting is done, the heat may vaporize some of the liquid, create a flammable vapor-air mixture in the drum, and explode it. Such containers require special precautions.

Hot work may be performed safely, under qualified supervision, in tank cars, tank trucks, and tanks that can be entered when the flammable vapors are under 20 percent of the lower flammable limit. Additional precautions, such as protective clothing and self-contained breathing apparatus, are necessary to protect the health of persons entering tanks that have contained leaded gasoline or other highly toxic residues.

Where toxic materials have been stored in a tank, additional tests may be required to determine if the atmosphere is safe from the standpoint of health. For example, leaded gasoline tanks need to be lead-free before they can be entered without breathing equipment and specialized protective clothing.

More complete instructions for cleaning tanks or containers are covered in NFPA 327, *Cleaning or Safeguarding Small Tanks and Containers*; NFPA 306, *Control of Gas Hazards on Vessels*; API RP 2013, *Cleaning Mobile Tanks in Flammable or Combustible Liquid Service*[3]; and API RP 2015, *Cleaning Petroleum Storage Tanks*.[4]

OTHER STORAGE OF FLAMMABLE LIQUIDS

The principal hazard of closed container storage is the possibility of overpressure failure of the container when exposed to fire. This release of liquid adds to the intensity of a fire and may cause the rupture of other containers, resulting in a rapidly spreading fire. Fire tests prove that ordinary automatic sprinkler systems may be inadequate to control a fire involving drums of flammable liquids, or to prevent overpressuring of drums if flammable liquid containers are piled too high. See Table 2-25E for storage limitations for inside storage rooms.

TABLE 2-25E. ***Storage Limitations for Inside Storage Rooms***

Automatic Fire Protection Provided	Fire Resistance	Maximum Size		Allowable Loading of Floor Area	
		ft^2	m^2	Gal/sq ft	L/m^2
yes	2 hr	500	46.45	10	407
no	2 hr	500	46.45	4	163
yes	1 hr	150	13.94	5	204
no	1 hr	150	13.94	2	82

Container Storage in Buildings

Special storage buildings or rooms and other rooms or portions of buildings where containers may be stored should be designed to protect the containers from exposure to fires in other portions of the building. The life hazard to the occupants of buildings, exposure to other buildings, building construction, and the degree of fire protection provided are factors to be considered when evaluating the amount of container storage in buildings. Details and limitations on closed container storage are given in NFPA 30.

Specially designed metal storage cabinets are available for storing up to a total of 60 gal (227 L) in small containers. (See Figure 2-25H.) Specifications for wooden storage cabinets are given in NFPA 30.

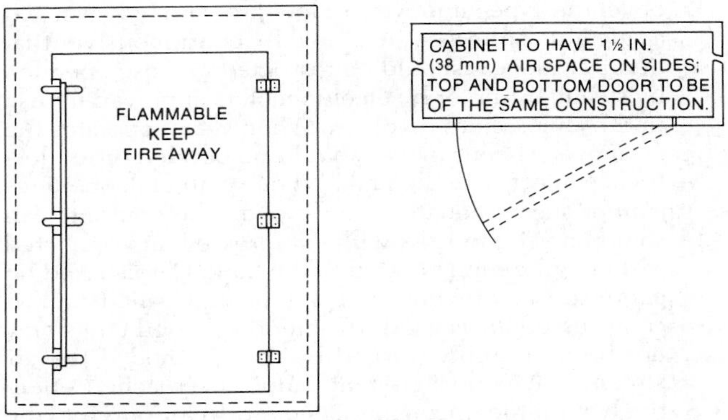

FIG. 2-25H. Typical metal storage cabinet recommended by NFPA Committee on Flammable and Combustible Liquids for quantities less than 60 gal (227 L). Material is 18 US gage sheet iron, tight joints. Door has three-point lock with sill raised to at least 2 in. (51 mm) above the bottom of the cabinet.

Drum Storage Outdoors

Outdoor drum storage should be located in such a manner as to reduce the spread of fire to other materials in storage or to other property. (See Table 2-25F.) Areas used for drum storage should be kept free of combustibles and open flames, and smoking should be prohibited.

HANDLING OF FLAMMABLE AND COMBUSTIBLE LIQUIDS

Loading and Unloading

Spills may occur at loading and unloading stations for tank cars and tank vehicles. Tank vehicle and tank car stations for Class I liquids should be located a minimum of 25 ft

TABLE 2-25F. ***Outdoor Liquid Storage in Containers and Portable Tanks***

	1				2				3		4		5	
Class	Container Storage Max. per Pile*§				Portable Tank Storage Max. per Pile Gallons*				Distance Between Piles or Racks		Distance to Property Line That Can Be Built Upon†‡		Distance to Street, Alley, or Public Way‡	
			Height							Height				
	Gal	m3	ft	m	Gal	m³	ft	m	ft	ft	m	m	ft	m
IA	1,100	4.16	10	3.05	2,200	8.32	7	2.1	5	1.5	50	15.2	10	3.0
IB	2,200	8.32	12	3.66	4,400	16.65	14	4.3	5	1.5	50	15.2	10	3.0
IC	4,400	16.65	12	3.66	8,800	33.30	14	4.3	5	1.5	50	15.2	10	3.0
II	8,800	33.30	12	3.66	17,600	66.62	14	4.3	5	1.5	25	7.6	5	1.5
III	27,000	88.28	18	5.49	44,000	166.56	14	4.3	5	1.5	10	3.0	5	1.5

* See 4-8.1.1 of NFPA 30 regarding mixed class storage.
† See 4-8.1.3 of NFPA 30 regarding protection for exposures.
‡ See 4-8.1.4 of NFPA 30 for smaller pile sizes.
§ For storage in racks, the quantity limits per pile do not apply, but the rack arrangement must be limited to a maximum of 50 ft (15.2 m) in length and two rows of 9 ft (2.7 m) in depth.

(8 m) from storage tanks, other plant buildings, and the nearest line of property that can be developed. Level ground is desirable, and drains, diversionary curbs, or natural ground slope can be utilized to prevent spills from spreading to other parts of the plant or to other property.

Bonding provisions for protection against static sparks must be provided at all loading stations when Class I liquids are loaded. The bonding must be provided between the fill pipe or piping and the tank vehicle. Bonding connections are made before the dome covers are opened. Closed metal piping systems (eliminating exposure to air) for loading and unloading may eliminate the need for special bonding provisions, since the piping system is inherently bonded to the vehicle.

Stray electrical current protection is necessary for ship and tank car loading and unloading in those areas where stray currents may be present.

Tank ships and barges are loaded and unloaded at oil piers that may or may not be used exclusively for this purpose. The location of the oil piers is governed by direction and velocity of the waterway, the range of tides, and the direction and frequency of prevailing high-velocity winds. Hazards related to the loading and unloading of vessels are comparable to those for tank vehicles and tank cars, except the quantities of liquid involved are generally larger.

Many liquids, including gasoline, jet fuels, toluene, and light fuel oil, can build up dangerous static electrical charges on the surface of the liquid. If a flammable vapor-air mixture is present at the surface of the liquid when high static electrical discharges occur, an explosion or fire can result. Excessive turbulence, pumping two dissimilar materials, the free fall of liquid through the vapor space, and the use of filters capable of removing micron-sized particles are the most common causes of explosions or fires originating from static electricity in aboveground tanks, tank vehicles, tank barges, and tank ships. Where flammable vapors may exist, and to reduce static-caused ignitions, it is recommended that the delivery rate be slowed until the fill pipe is covered. A minimum 30-sec relaxation time should be provided downstream of a filter. For further details on control of static, refer to NFPA 77, *Static Electricity*, and API Standard 2003, *Protection Against Ignitions Arising Out of Static, Lightning, and Stray Currents*.

Piping and Valves

Substantial piping systems protected against physical damage are preferable to portable containers for conveying quantities of liquids throughout buildings. All piping systems should be designed so that, in case of pipe breaks, liquid will not continue to flow by gravity or by siphoning. Valves should be provided at accessible points to control or stop the flow. Emergency remote controls are frequently provided for valves or pumps, particularly at dispensing locations. Other remotely controlled valves installed for normal operating procedures can frequently be used during fire emergency procedures to control or stop the flow of liquids. Valves are available that close automatically if subjected to fire conditions. Dispensing outlets for systems under gas pressure or gravity head should be equipped with self-closing valves.

Pipe materials should be used that: (1) are resistant to the corrosive properties of the liquid handled; (2) have adequate design strength to withstand the maximum service pressure (including shock and surge pressures that may be expected) and temperature; and (3) when possible, are resistant to physical damage and thermal shock. Where low melting point materials, such as aluminum and brass; materials that soften on fire exposure, such as plastics; or nonductile material, such as cast iron, are necessary, special consideration should be given to their behavior on exposure to fire. After installation, piping systems should be tested at 150 percent of the maximum anticipated pressure of the system, or pneumatically tested to 110 percent of the maximum anticipated pressure of the system, but not less than 5 psig (35 kPa) at the highest point of the system.

Since some valves are used infrequently, it is necessary to make periodic maintenance inspections to ensure that the valves will operate during emergency conditions. All aboveground piping and connections should be inspected periodically to detect and prevent leakage. Internal corrosion in pipes is a particular problem when liquids are corrosive, or where piping is used for the continuous flow of liquid under high-pressure operations common at refineries or chemical plants. Maintenance inspections of the thickness of pipe walls can be performed in several ways similar to the inspection of tanks. Underground piping is also subject to external corrosion and should be protected against such corrosion by suitable coatings and cathodic protection. Tests for possible leaks in underground piping can be performed hydrostatically, using the liquid normally handled in the piping system.

Dispensing and Handling Methods

Large quantities of flammable or combustible liquids are best transferred through piping by pumps. Gravity flow is not desirable, except as required in process equipment. If positive displacement pumps are used, they should be provided with a pressure relief that discharges back to the tank or to the pump section. The transfer of Class I or Class II liquids by means of air pressure is not good practice. Although inert gas may be used for transferring all classes of liquids, and air pressure may be used for transferring Class III liquids, they are acceptable only if the pressure is controlled, as by use of pressure-relief devices, to limit the pressure so it cannot exceed the design pressure of the vessel, tank, or container.

The safest method for handling flammable or combustible liquids is to pump the liquid from buried storage tanks, through an adequately designed piping system protected from physical damage, to the dispensing equipment located outdoors or in specially designed inside storage rooms. Such a room should have at least one exterior wall for explosion relief and accessibility for fire fighting, interior walls with two-hour fire-resistance ratings, and adequate ventilation and drainage, and be free of sources of ignition.

Where solvents are pumped from storage tanks to the point of use in an industrial building, emergency switches should be located in the dispensing area, at the normal exit door or at other safe locations outside the fire area, and at the pumps to shut down all pumps in case of fire.

Where dispensing is by gravity flow, such as in the filling of containers in an industrial operation, a shut-off valve should be installed as close as practical to the vessel being unloaded. A control valve should be located near the end of the discharge pipe. Additionally, in some filling operations, a heat-actuated valve is desirable to shut off the flow of liquid.

The preferred method of dispensing flammable and combustible liquids from a drum is by use of an approved hand-operated pump drawing through the top. In certain cases, an approved drum faucet may be used for dispensing from a drum. However, hand-operated pumps are safer than faucets, because the hazard of leakage is reduced.

For handling small quantities of flammable and combustible liquids, safety cans are preferred. Safety cans are substantially constructed to avoid the danger of leakage and are designed to minimize the likelihood of spillage or vapor release and of container rupture under fire conditions. (See Figure 2-25I.) Liquids can also be dispensed from the original shipping containers. Open pails or open buckets are never used for storage.

Flammable liquids should always be handled and dispensed in a well-ventilated area free of sources of ignition, and bonding should be provided between the dispensing equipment and the container being filled. (See Figure 2-25J.)

FIG. 2-25I. Typical safety cans having pouring outlets with tight-fitting caps or valves normally closed by springs, except when held open by hand, so that contents will not be spilled if a can is tipped over. The caps also provide an emergency vent when the cans are exposed to fire.

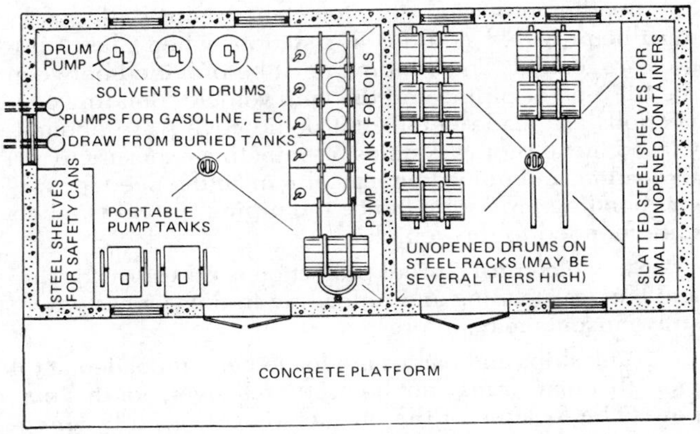

FIG. 2-25J. Layout of a storage and dispensing house.

TRANSPORTATION OF FLAMMABLE AND COMBUSTIBLE LIQUIDS

Tank Vehicles

NFPA 385, *Tank Vehicles for Flammable and Combustible Liquids*, provides for substantially constructed vehicles and tanks that present relatively little danger of fire when involved in minor traffic accidents. Under these recommendations, tanks are constructed to withstand all but the most violent impact without rupturing and releasing liquid. Vents are provided so that, if a tank is subjected to fire, vapor will burn at the vent, avoiding the danger of rupture from excessive internal pressure.

For all but viscous liquids, a shut-off valve located inside the shell of the cargo tank is required. It is kept closed, except during loading or unloading operations. A

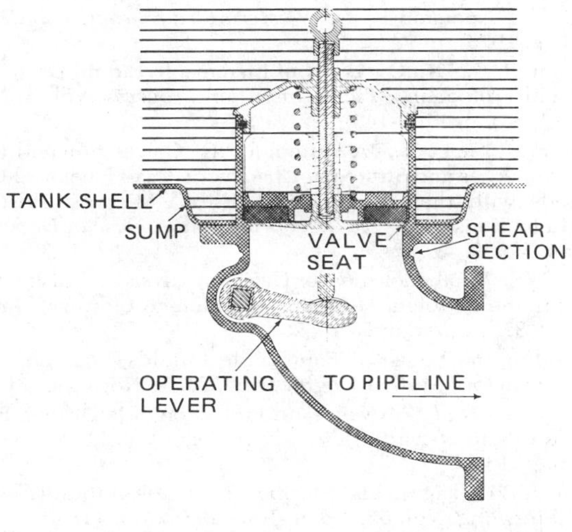

FIG. 2-25K. Shut-off valve located inside tank shell, with shear section to leave valve seat if discharge faucet breaks.

shear section is provided in the piping connected to the internal valve. Therefore, in an accident that could damage the piping, the piping breaks at the shear section, leaving the internal valve undamaged and closed.

The operating mechanism for the valve is also required to have a secondary control, remotely located, that can be used to shut off the valve in case of fire or severe spillage during unloading. In addition, a fusible section is required in the control mechanism for the valve to permit the valve to close automatically in case of fire. (See Figures 2-25K and 2-25L.) Other important fire protection features are detailed in NFPA 385, *Tank Vehicles for Flammable and Combustible Liquids*.

In the past, many cities have attempted to minimize fire problems by specifying the maximum sizes of cargo tanks on trucks. The wisdom of this sort of provision is dubious. Assume, for example, that it is necessary to transport 4000 gal (15000 L) of gasoline over city streets to make local deliveries. A legal restriction as to the maximum size of the tank might require the use of four 1000-gal (3800 L) tank trucks in place of one 4000-gal (15000 L) tank. This quadruples the tank-truck traffic, with four times the accident potential. The danger from a gasoline fire is not directly proportionate to the quantity of gasoline involved. For this reason, NFPA standards have not recommended any limitation on the maximum size of tank trucks.

Tank-truck traffic through congested districts of cities should be avoided as much as possible, since any fire is likely to have more serious consequences in congested districts than in sparsely settled areas. Bypass routes, such as those commonly specified for all kinds of through truck traffic, are the obvious solution to this particular problem.

Parking of loaded tank vehicles is another feature that can be appropriately regulated by municipalities. Such parking can be prohibited on city streets. Similarly, tank vehicles should not be parked in public garages. Permissible parking locations for tank vehicles may be specified, if necessary. Any property zoned for aboveground oil storage, e.g., the ordinary bulk oil plant, should be a location where tank vehicles can be parked without any undue increase in hazard to the public.

Transportation of flammable liquids in tank vehicles in interstate commerce is governed by regulations of the U.S. Department of Transportation (DOT), as contained in the *Code of Federal Regulations,* Title 49, "Transportation."[5] There are comprehensive specifications and labeling requirements for shipping containers for various types of products. (Absence of a label does not necessarily mean that the material is nonhazardous, however.)

Rail, Ship, and Pipeline

The transportation of flammable liquids by railroad tank cars is under the jurisdiction of the DOT.[5] The design of tank cars is rigidly controlled and is governed by the nature of the contents being carried. Emergency venting requirements are included in DOT regulations.

The transportation of flammable and combustible liquids in bulk on board vessels in the United States is under the jurisdiction of the Commandant of the U.S. Coast Guard. These transportation requirements include the design of the vessel, whether it be a tank ship or tank barge, as well as requirements for extinguishing systems or portable extinguishers. Further requirements include limitations on container storage of drums or portable tanks,

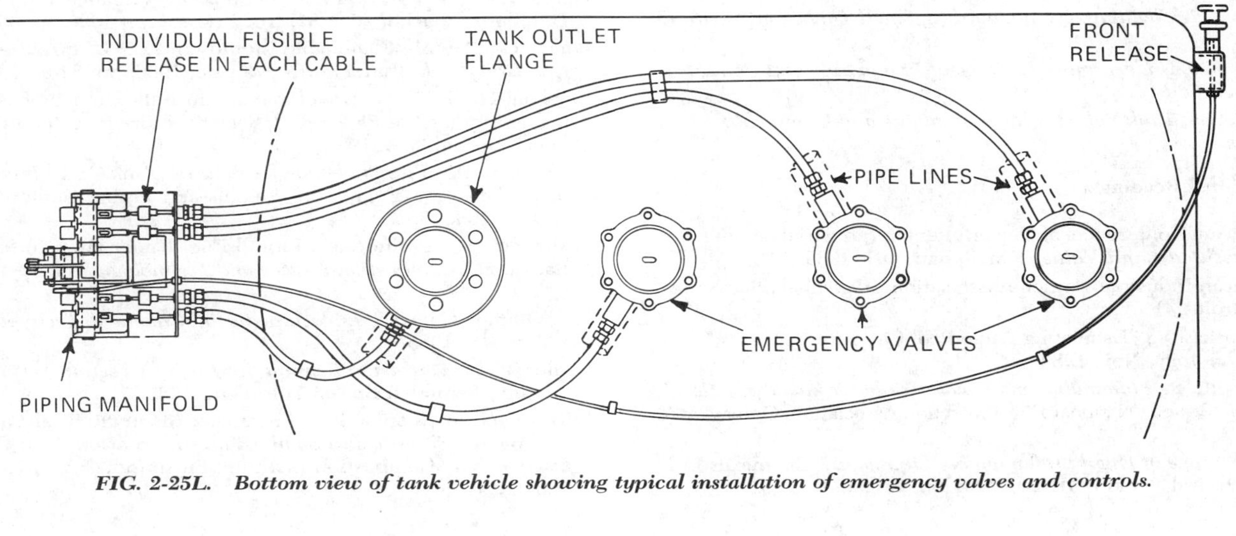

FIG. 2-25L. Bottom view of tank vehicle showing typical installation of emergency valves and controls.

restrictions for passenger-carrying vessels, and many other requirements for the safe transportation of flammable and combustible liquids by water. Details of these requirements can be secured at the nearest U.S. Coast Guard Merchant Marine Inspection Office.

Standards for pipelines transporting liquids are published by the American Society of Mechanical Engineers (ASME). These standards include piping requirements and installation recommendations.

BIBLIOGRAPHY

References Cited

1. API Standard 650, *Welded Steel Tanks for Oil Storage*, American Petroleum Institute, Washington, DC, 1986.
2. API Standard 2000, *Venting Atmospheric and Low-Pressure Storage Tanks*, American Petroleum Institute, Washington, DC.
3. API RP 2013, *Cleaning Mobile Tanks in Flammable or Combustible Liquid Service*, 5th ed., American Petroleum Institute, Washington, DC, 1975.
4. API RP 2015, *Cleaning Petroleum Storage Tanks*, American Petroleum Institute, Washington, DC, 1975.
5. *Code of Federal Regulations*, Title 49, "Transportation," U.S. Government Printing Office, Washington, DC.

Reference

API Standard 2003, *Protection Against Ignitions Arising Out of Static, Lightning, and Stray Currents*, American Petroleum Institute, Washington, DC.

NFPA Codes, Standards, and Recommended Practices

Reference to the following NFPA codes, standards, and recommended practices will provide further information on storage of flammable and combustible liquids discussed in this chapter. (See the latest *NFPA Catalog* for availability of current editions of the following documents.)

NFPA 11, *Low Expansion Foam and Combined Agent Systems*.

NFPA 30, *Flammable and Combustible Liquids Code*.

NFPA 30A, *Automotive and Marine Service Station Code*.

NFPA 31, *Installation of Oil Burning Equipment*.

NFPA 77, *Static Electricity*.

NFPA 306, *Control of Gas Hazards on Vessels*.

NFPA 325M, *Fire Hazard Properties of Flammable Liquids, Gases, and Volatile Solids*.

NFPA 327, *Cleaning or Safeguarding Small Tanks and Containers*.

NFPA 329, *Underground Leakage of Flammable and Combustible Liquids*.

NFPA 385, *Tank Vehicles for Flammable and Combustible Liquids*.

Additional Reading

American Conference of Governmental Industrial Hygienists, *Threshold Limit Values*, Cincinnati, OH, 1989.

American Industrial Hygiene Association, *Hygienic Guide Series*, Detroit, MI.

Babrauskas, V., "Estimating Large Pool Fire Burning Rates," *Fire Technology*, Nov. 1983.

Benedetti, R., *Flammable and Combustible Liquids Code Handbook*, 3rd ed., National Fire Protection Association, Quincy, MA, 1987.

Bulk Storage of Highly Inflammable Liquids, BP Chemicals Ltd., Technical Booklet SB 122, London, England, 1978.

Campbell, J. A., "Combustible Liquids Ignite Below Flash Points in Cloth Dispersion Tests," *Western Fire Journal*, Vol. 27, No. 10 (Oct. 1975), p. 9.

Capizzani, R. E., "An Overview of Flammable Liquid Drum Storage and Protection," *Plant/Operation Progress*, Vol. 4, No. 3 (July 1985), pp. 139-143.

Carpenter, R. A., *et al.*, "A System for the Correlation and Physical Properties and Structural Characteristics of Chemical Compounds with their Commerical Uses," Midwest Research Institute, Kansas City, MO. (reprint from *American Documentation*, Vol. X, No. 2).

CONCAWE: "Methodologies for Hazard Analysis and Risk Assessment in the Petroleum Refining and Storage Industry," *Report No. 10182*, Netherlands, 1982.

"Controlling the Power of Flammable Liquids," *Pamphlet No. P7045*, Factory Mutual Engineering Corp., Norwood, MA.

DiMaio, L. R., *et al.*, "Advances in Protection of Polar-type Flammable Liquid Hazards," *Fire Technology*, Vol. 11, No. 3 (Aug. 1975), p. 164.

Dunbar, J., "Packaging and Storing Flammable Liquids," *Products Finishing*, Vol. 52, No. 9 (June 1988), pp. 118-121.

Factory Mutual Engineering Corporation, *Handbook of Industrial Loss Prevention*, 2nd ed., McGraw-Hill Inc., NY, 1967.

Flick, E. W., ed., *Industrial Solvents Handbook*, 4th ed., Noyes Data Corp., Park Ridge, NJ, 1990.

Fox, R. B., "Tank Fires: A Case Study History," *Industrial Fire World*, Vol. 1, No. 9, 1986.

Fullam, B. W., "Fire Protection of LPG Vessels," *Proceedings* of the Gastech 86 LNG/LPG Conference, Gastech, 1986, pp. 152-156.

Gibson, R. B., "Control Flammable Liquid Fires by Premixing," *Fire Engineering*, Vol. 138, No. 2, 1985, p. 50.

Hadjisophocleous, G. V., Sousa, A. C. M., and Venart, J. E. S., "Fire Engulfment of Horizontal Cylinder Tanks," *Proceedings* of the 1989 National Heat Transfer Conference: Heat Transfer Phenomena in Radiation, Combustion, and Fires, American Society of Mechanical Engineers: Heat Transfer Division, NY, 1989, pp. 339-347.

Hawley, G. G., ed., *The Condensed Chemical Dictionary*, 11th ed., Van Nostrand Reinhold, NY, 1984.

Hawthorne, E., *Petroleum Liquids—Fire and Emergency Control*, Prentice-Hall, Englewood Cliffs, NJ., 1987.

Hughes, J. R., *Storage and Handling of Petroleum Liquids*, 3rd ed., Chas. Wiley, NY, 1987.

Hunt, D. L. M. and Ramskill, P. K., "A Description of ENGULF—A Computer Code to Model the Thermal Responce of a Tank Engulfed in Fire," *Report No. SRD/HSE/R 354*, March 1987, United Kingdom Atomic Energy Authority, Warrington, UK.

Isner, M. S., "$49 Million Loss in Sherwin-Williams Warehouse Fire," *Fire Journal*, Vol. 82, No. 2 (Mar./Apr. 1988), p. 65.

James, D., "Highly Flammable Liquids and LPG," *Fire Prevention Handbook*, Butterworths, Boston, 1986, pp. 84-95.

Johnson, D. M., "New Developments in Bulk Storage of Flammable Liquids," *SFPE TR 81-1*, Society of Fire Protection Engineers, Boston, MA, 1981.

Johnson, M. R., "Fire Protection for Railroad Tank Cars," *Proceedings* of the ASME Pressure Vessels and Piping Conference, ASME, 1986, 8p.

Kashiwagi, T., "Ignition of a Liquid Fuel Under High Intensity Radiation," *Combustion Science and Technology*, Vol. 21, 1980, p. 131.

Kirk-Othmer Concise, *Encyclopedia of Chemical Technology*, Wiley, NY, 1985.

Leffler, W. L., *Petroleum Refining for the Non-Technical Person*, 2nd ed., Pennwell Books, Tulsa, OK, 1985.

Lois, E. and Swithenbank, J., "Fire Hazards in Oil Tank Arrays in a Wind," *Seventeenth Symposium (International) on Combustion*, The Combustion Institute, Pittsburgh, PA, 1978, pp. 1087-1098.

Marks, A., *Petroleum Storage Principles*, Pennwell Books, Tulsa, OK, 1983.

Martinsen, W. E., Johnson, D. W., and Millsap, S. B., "Determining Spacing by Radiant Heat Limits," *Plant/Operation Progress*, Vol. 8, No. 2 (Jan. 1989), pp. 25-28.

Masters, R. W., "Large-Area Hydrocarbon Firefighting," *Industrial Fire World*, Vol. 2, No. 4 (Aug. 1987), pp. 7-12.

National Safety Council, *Accident Prevention Manual for Industrial Operations*, 9th ed., Chicago, IL, 1988.

Perry, J. H. and Green, D. W., eds., *Chemical Engineers' Handbook*, 6th ed., McGraw-Hill, NY, 1984.

Phillips, H. and Pritchard, D. K., "Performance Requirements of Flame Arresters in Practicle Applications," *Proceedings* of the Conference on Hazards in the Process Industries, Institution of Chemical Engineers, 1986, pp. 47-61.

Potapov, A. Y., "Calculation of the Allowable Probability of Failure of an Acetylene Flame Arrestor," *Chemical and Petroleum Engineering*, (English Translation), Vol. 23, Nos. 11-12, 1988, pp. 569-571.

Presdee, B., "Computerized Oil Rig Fires Could Save Lives," *Fire International*, Vol. 12, No. 113 (Oct.-Nov. 1988), p. 49, 52-53.

Przybyla, L., and Gandhi, P., "The Results Are in on Flammable Liquids in Plastic Containers," *Fire Journal*, Vol. 84, No. 3 (May/June 1990), p.38.

"Safe Storage and Handling of Flammable and Combustible Liquids," *Professional Safety*, Vol. 20, No. 12 (Dec. 1975), pp. 24-27.

Safety Digest of Lessons Learned, Vols. 3, 6, 7, 8, 9, American Petroleum Institute, NY, 1986.

Sax, N. I., *Dangerous Properties of Industrial Materials*, 7th ed., Van Nostrand Reinhold, NY, 1989.

Schoen, W. and Droste, B., "Investigations of Water Spraying Systems for LPG Storage Tanks by Full-Scale Fire Tests," *Journal of Hazardous Materials*, Vol. 20, Dec. 1988, pp. 73-82.

Schwab, R. F., "Consequences of Solvent Ignition During a Drum Filling Operation," *Plant/Operation Progress*, Vol. 7, No. 4 (Oct. 1988), p. 242.

"Shipping," Title 46, Parts 146 to 149; Title 49, "Transportation," Parts 171 to 178, *Code of Federal Regulations*, U.S. Government Printing Office, Washington, DC.

Siddle, J. F., "Fire Hazards of Flammable Liquids in Small Containers," *Proceedings* of the Conference on Hazards in the Process Industries, Institute of Chemical Engineers, 1986, pp. 111-120.

Steinbrecher, L., "Analysis of a Tank Fire 'Classic'," *Fire Engineers Journal*, Vol. 47, No. 144, 1987, pp. 15-17.

Stevens, A., "Flammable Liquids—Why the Hazard?" *Journal of Chemical Education*, Vol. 56, No. 3 (Mar. 1979), pp. 119A-124A.

Stevens, A. M., "Handling Flammable Liquids," *Plant Facilities*, Vol. 11, No. 2 (Feb. 1979), pp. 30-33.

Swirn, B. P., "New Fire Regulations to Affect Packaging and Storage of Flammable Liquids," *Industrial Fire World*, Vol. 3, No. 4 (Aug. 1987), pp. 8-11.

Tabor, D. C., "Foam-Water Sprinkler Protection for Flammable Liquids," *Plant/Operation Progress*, Vol. 8, No. 1, 1989, pp. 218-224.

Van Dolah, R. W., *et al.*, "Flame Propagation, Extinguishment and Environmental Effects on Combustion," *Fire Technology*, Vol. 1, No. 2 (May 1965), pp. 138-145.

Vervalin, C. H., ed., *Fire Protection Manual for Hydrocarbon Processing Plants*, 3rd ed., Gulf Publishing Co., Houston, TX, 1985.

Walls, W. L., "Just What Is a BLEVE?," *Fire Journal*, Vol. 72, No. 6 (Nov. 1978), pp. 46-47.

Welker, J. R. and Sliepcevich, C. M., "Burning Rates and Heat Transfer from Wind-Blown Flames," *Fire Technology*, Vol. 2, No. 3 (Aug. 1966), pp. 211-218.

Welker, J. R., *et al.*, "The Effect of Wind on Flames," *Fire Technology*, Vol. 1, No. 2 (May 1965), pp. 122-129.

"Which of the Following Presents the Greatest Challenge to Sprinklers? Flammable Liquids in: (a) aerosol cans, (b) metal containers, (c) glass containers, (d) plastic containers," *Record*, Jan./Feb. 1987, pp. 4-9.

Williams, D., "Extinguishing Flammable Liquid Fires," *Fire International*, Vol. 11, No. 107 (Oct./Nov.1987), pp. 126-127.

STORAGE OF GASES

Revised by Theodore C. Lemoff

This chapter describes essential firesafety characteristics of containers in which gases are stored, as well as some fundamental precepts for storage arrangements.

A gas must be stored in a container that is gastight for: (1) the range of temperature and pressure conditions present at the storage location, and (2) the conditions represented by the transportation environment prior to arrival at a storage site. Thus, it is preferable that the storage container contains the source of energy needed to remove the gas from storage and convey it to the point of use. This energy is represented by the pressure of the gas in the container.

In the case of containers in which the gas is entirely in the gaseous phase (compressed gases), the pressure is applied at the charging plant or, in the case of pipelines, by compressors spaced along the pipeline. In the case of containers of gas in which the gas is partly in the gaseous phase and partly in the liquid phase (i.e., liquefied gases, including cryogenic liquefied gases), the pressure is obtained as a result of heat stored in the liquid, which is directly related to how much the temperature of the liquid is above its normal boiling point.

Therefore, gas containers, whether shaped as tanks or as pipelines, are closed pressure vessels containing considerable energy per unit of volume, and requiring careful design, fabrication, and maintenance. Furthermore, because the containers are closed and excessive pressures can develop when they are exposed to rather nominal heat sources and fire (or by overfilling, in the case of liquefied gas containers), overpressure protection is usually needed.

GAS CONTAINERS

Most countries have regulations for the design, fabrication, and maintenance of gas containers. Although basically similar, the regulations differ in detail. This chapter concentrates on North American practices.

In North America, there are two types of gas containers: (1) cylinders, and (2) tanks. Originally, the distinction between cylinders and tanks was based upon size. Cylinders, being the smaller, were considered portable; the tanks, being the larger, were essentially used in stationary service. There was also a distinction that reflected the pressures in the containers. Cylinders were thought of as being used for high pressures and tanks for low or moderate pressures. Over the years, these distinctions have lessened so that, today, the only real distinction lies in the regulations or codes under which the container is built.

Practically all gases must be transported from the manufacturer to the user, making the safety of the container in transportation a matter of primary concern. As a result, criteria for many gas containers reflect transportation safety conditions. Because it could be hazardous as well as uneconomical to require gases to be transferred from a shipping container to a separate container for other use, every effort has been made to utilize the same container whenever feasible. This is generally the procedure used for the smaller containers.

Gas Cylinders

Gas cylinders are fabricated in accordance with regulations and specifications of the U.S. Department of Transportation (DOT) in the United States and the Canadian Transport Commission (CTC) in Canada. The requirements are the same in both countries. Prior to April 1, 1967, DOT regulations were promulgated by the Interstate Commerce Commission (ICC), and many cylinders are still in service with ICC markings. Cylinders are generally limited to a maximum water capacity (i.e., the capacity when completely filled with water) of 1000 lb (454 kg), or approximately 120 gal (450 L) of water.

The regulations cover the service pressure the cylinder must be designed for, the gas or group of gases that it can contain, safety devices, and requirements for in-service (transportation) testing and requalification. The specifications cover such criteria as metal composition and physical testing, wall thickness, joining methods, nature of openings in the container, heat treatments, proof testing, and marking.

Theodore C. Lemoff, P.E., is the gases engineer on the staff of NFPA.

Gas Tanks

Customarily, gas tanks are fabricated in accordance with Section VIII, "Unfired Pressure Vessels", of the *Boiler and Pressure Vessel Code* , published by the American Society of Mechanical Engineers (ASME), or tank fabrication standards of the American Petroleum Institute (API). ASME tanks are usually smaller tanks under moderate pressure, and API tanks are usually very large tanks under low pressure.

Cylinders or tanks that are part of transportation units, such as cargo vehicles or railcars, are subject to additional criteria in the regulations, primarily to reflect the fact that the containers are on wheels. Tanks for cargo vehicles are basically ASME code tanks, while tanks for railcars are covered by specific DOT and CTC specifications.

In the late 1960s and early 1970s, a series of serious railcar derailments occurred in the U.S., reflecting the deterioration of tracks and track beds due to inadequate maintenance. These incidents were characterized by both impact and fire-caused boiling liquid expanding vapor explosions (BLEVEs) of tank cars containing liquefied flammable gases. As a result, DOT regulations were revised in 1977 to require that these tank cars be protected thermally and equipped with a type of coupler that prevents vertical disengagement. Unless the insulation is contained in a steel outer jacket, the car also must be equipped with heavy steel-plate head shields for impact protection. Existing cars were required to be retrofitted by the end of 1980. In the few derailments involving tank cars outfitted in this fashion, these safeguards have proved effective—a BLEVE either has not occurred at all, or has been delayed for several hours.

A number of such containers are exempted by the regulations. These include certain very small containers and containers with nonflammable cryogenic gases, including oxygen, where the pressure in the container as shipped is below 40 psia (276 kPa).

There is usually a lag in time between the need to ship a gas that is new to commerce and the promulgation of specifications for a transportation container. In such cases, DOT or CTC exemptions, which spell out safety criteria agreed upon by the authorities, are issued.

In themselves, the DOT and CTC regulations apply only to cylinders and tanks in transportation in interstate or interprovincial commerce. However, many consensus codes and standards extend these regulations to transportation in intrastate commerce, and also extend applicable criteria to use and storage at consumer sites.

The aforementioned requirements for "in-service" reinspection and requalification of DOT specification containers are also extended to use and storage at consumer sites by the consensus standards and codes. However, the ASME *Boiler and Pressure Vessel Code* and API standards do not contain such provisions. If not covered by consensus standards and codes, in-service inspection and requalification become a matter of owner judgment, and of such state or local regulations as may apply, or conditions set forth in an insurance contract.

Regardless of the degree of structural integrity incorporated into gas containers, abuse of the container must be avoided. This is especially true of portable cylinders, which are subject to mishandling. General handling of safety precautions for gas cylinders is contained in the Compressed Gas Association's "Safe Handling of Compressed Gases in Containers."

Pipelines

Gases used in large volumes are often transported by pipelines. Natural gas is customarily transported by pipeline, as is much LP-Gas and some industrial gases, such as anhydrous ammonia, oxygen, hydrogen, and ethylene.

Since 1968, most of the transmission and distribution of flammable gases by pipeline has been regulated in the U.S. by the DOT Office of Pipeline Safety and is covered by federal regulations. These regulations cover such items as pipe materials; design for pressure and other stresses (which, among other criteria, require stronger piping as population density increases); piping components, including valves (emergency flow control valve spacing in the pipeline system is also affected by population density); joining methods; installation of meters, service regulators, and service lines; corrosion control; test requirements; certain operating requirements; and maintenance, including leakage surveys.

Normally, DOT regulations do not apply to piping on consumer premises. Such piping for the more common gases is covered by consensus codes and standards, notably NFPA 54 (ANSI Z223.1), *National Fuel Gas Code*, and ANSI B31, *Code for Pressure Piping*.

STORAGE SAFETY CONSIDERATIONS*

Fire protection safeguards for gas storage reflect: (1) the hazards of the container/gas combination, and (2) the hazards of the gas when it escapes from the container. Discussions of the basic hazards of gases, gas emergency control, and specific gases are especially pertinent.

During at least some period, any fire incident can manifest both of these hazards at the same time. However, the container/gas combination hazard always exists. The fire hazard of escaping gas, on the other hand, may be negligible if the gas is nonflammable.

Container/Gas Hazard Safeguards

The major container/gas hazard is the BLEVE. The BLEVE hazard is restricted to containers of liquefied gases, and the major cause of such BLEVEs in storage is fire exposure. BLEVEs resulting from corrosion of a container are far less frequent, and impact-caused BLEVEs even more so for containers in storage.

Container insulation: The BLEVE hazard is greatly affected by container features that restrict the opportunity for the container metal to be overheated. Especially notable in this respect is the presence of insulation between an exposing fire and the portion of the container subject to internal pressure. All cryogenic liquefied gas containers are insulated as a matter of functional necessity. The BLEVE hazard can essentially be eliminated by also considering insulation system behavior under fire exposure. North American standards for such systems on storage containers reflect this situation. For example, insulation for flammable cryogenic gas containers is required to be noncombustible and (if in a form such that loss of an enclosing jacket could cause a serious loss in insulating capacity, e.g., powder or granules), the container jacket is required to be steel or concrete rather than aluminum.

*The philosophy of this analytical approach is developed in Section 3, Chapter 7, "Gases"; it would be worthwhile to study that chapter before proceeding further in this chapter.

Containers of noncryogenic gases are not required to be insulated for operational reasons, and are seldom insulated for firesafety reasons. However, insulation of larger liquefied flammable gas tanks is becoming more frequent in specific installations where other BLEVE prevention measures, e.g., water cooling, are deficient.

A basic BLEVE safeguard is to reduce the chances of fire exposure to the container. This philosophy is also applicable to containers of nonliquefied gases (compressed gases) because, although by definition they are not subject to a BLEVE, they can still fail explosively from fire exposure.

Limiting combustibles in the area: Essential to this safeguard is limiting the quantity of combustibles in the vicinity of gas containers. This is valid whether the storage is indoors or outdoors. Except where small quantities of gas are involved, e.g., one or two cylinders of compressed gas, it is highly desirable that storage rooms or docks be of noncombustible or limited combustible construction. (See NFPA 220, *Standard Types of Building Construction*, for these definitions.) If the building that houses the storage room presents a substantial fire load, the storage room walls should have a suitable fire-resistance rating.

Preferably, containers of flammable gases should not be stored with containers of nonflammable gases. This is especially true with respect to gases that, if released, could intensify combustion of the flammable gases. Notable in this respect are oxidizing gases, such as oxygen or nitrous oxide. However, it is best also to avoid storage of inert gases near flammable gases because the container hazard reflects only pressure. Storage of nonflammable and oxidizing gases in the same area is safe.

Separation: As a general rule applicable to cylinders and small liquefied gas tanks, separation of flammable gases from nonflammable gases by 20 ft (6 m) is appropriate. Provision of a noncombustible barrier as high as the containers [usually 5 ft (1.5 m)] and having a fire-resistance rating of at least ½ hr is an acceptable substitute for this distance where cylinders or small tanks [less than 1000 lb (454 kg) water capacity] are involved.

The use of barriers around larger containers of flammable gases is questionable unless they permit application of cooling water, prevent pocketing of escaping gas, and allow unrestricted egress of personnel from the area in an emergency.

For restrictions over the proximity of combustibles to oxidizing gases, it must be recognized that the degree of combustibility has little practical significance in the presence of these gases. For example, asphalt paving is not normally considered to be combustible. However, in contact with oxygen, especially liquid oxygen, it is not only combustible, but can be explosive.

Application of water: During a fire exposure, the application of water is a basic safeguard to prevent a BLEVE or a compressed gas container failure. In indoor locations, automatic sprinkler protection can greatly limit pressure rise from heat and high metal temperatures from fire exposure. However, for maximum effectiveness, the system should be capable of furnishing a discharge density of at least 0.25 gpm per sq ft [10 (L/min)/m^2] over an area of at least 3000 sq ft (279 m^2), and the sprinklers should be located not more than 20 ft (6 m) above the floor where the containers are stored. Further characterization of sprinkler protection may be needed if the storage is in racks or in high piles.

A water spray fixed system of similar capacity is also effective and can be installed outdoors. For the protection of larger containers of liquefied flammable gases (chemically not self-reactive), a density in excess of 0.25 gpm of water per sq ft [10 (L/min)/m^2] of container surface is needed to prevent failure, although a 0.25 gpm density [10 (L/min)/m^2] may prevent a crack from proceeding to the point of container rupture.

Water application may not always be appropriate for tanks containing cryogenic liquids. Keep in mind that these containers are usually not pressure vessels, and the cold liquid is at its normal atmospheric boiling point. Thus, the container cannot BLEVE. Application of water could result in water entering the pressure-relief device and freezing, rendering it inoperative and resulting in pressure vessel failure. Also, water is at a temperature well above the temperature of the liquid, and is a heat source that may promote vaporization of the liquid.

Overpressure limiting devices: The satisfactory operation of container overpressure limiting devices is vital to controlling the BLEVE or compressed gas container failure hazard. Even though these devices cannot by themselves always prevent container failure, they do extend the prefailure time in all cases and often can prevent failure under many fire exposure conditions. It is essential that the device not be blocked closed by corrosion, paint deposits, etc., and not be damaged mechanically. Portable containers should be checked for this every time they are taken into the facility and whenever they are connected to consuming equipment or are filled.

Spring-loaded pressure-relief valves on the larger stationary storage containers should be tested at five- to ten-year intervals (more often if in corrosive or reactive gas service).

Relief devices on liquefied gas containers should always directly contact and monitor the vapor space, because their relieving capacity is determined under vapor discharge conditions and is severely restricted if liquid is discharged. With the exception of some LP-Gas containers used in mobile engine fuel systems and 1-ton (907 kg) chlorine containers, portable liquefied gas containers should be stored in an upright position to attain this effect.

Care in handling: Also reflecting the container/gas hazard, it is important that the containers not be subjected to physical abuse. Although quite sturdy as a result of their design as pressure vessels, any dent or gouge can reduce safety factors and, at the least, shorten failure times from fire exposure or lead to impact failures upon subsequent movement. If the valve is broken off on some smaller portable compressed gas containers, the nozzle reaction from escaping gas can be sufficient to propel the cylinder violently. Where the container is designed for a valve-protecting cap or collar, these always should be in place during storage or movement.

DOT requalification: DOT containers must be requalified at intervals specified in the federal regulations. These intervals vary with the kind of gas and type of container. In most cases, this interval is five years, but can be as long as twelve years, depending on the retest method used. A requalified DOT container must be marked with the date of requalification. If such a marking is not present on a compressed gas DOT specification container and the manufacture date marking is more than five years old, it should be brought to the attention of whoever last charged the container.

The container owner is responsible for requalification. In many instances, the user/storer of portable gas containers is not the owner. In others, however, the user/storer is the owner, such as for LP-Gas containers used in industrial truck service and filled on site. Those responsible for such containers should be aware of this and of the fact that the requalification procedures are rigorous and require considerable technical expertise.

Safeguards for Escaping Gas

The major escaping gas hazard is combustion of flammable gas and is, in turn, manifest as either a fire or a combustion explosion. Fire, of course, can also lead to the previously discussed explosive container failures. Again, the reader is referred to Section 3, Chapter 7, "Gases," for a discussion of the elements of this hazard.

Gases in storage do not present many sources of escaping gas beyond those already discussed under container/gas hazard safeguards. The container itself, its valves, and overpressure protection devices are the only sources of escaping gas, provided that the gas is not being transferred into and out of storage.

Inspection for leakage: All storage containers should be inspected periodically for leakage from container appurtenances or from the container itself. Portable containers should not be placed into storage if they are leaking. To prevent this, incoming shipments should always be inspected upon arrival.

The senses of sight, sound, and smell are invaluable leak detectors. Although most gases are invisible, some do have color, e.g., chlorine. Liquefied gases escaping as liquids can lead to the formation of a visible cloud of condensed water vapor. Because they are stored under pressure, a leak can be accompanied by a hissing sound. Although many gases are odorless, some do possess strong odors, e.g., chlorine and anhydrous ammonia. Natural gas and LP-Gas have an odorant added to them. Many gas detection instruments are manufactured. Leak detection solutions are available that, when applied to small leaks, show bubbles.

One of the more common sources of escaping gas in storage locations is the operation of overpressure protection devices. Because the pressure in a gas container is directly related to the gas temperature, and the gas temperature in uninsulated containers reflects the temperature of the surroundings, room temperature and solar radiation will affect the pressure. In general, this pressure will result in the operation of overpressure devices on fully charged containers if the temperature reaches 130 to 140°F (54 to 60°C). Therefore, storage areas should not be allowed to reach such temperatures, and reflective paint should be maintained on outdoor containers subject to solar radiation.

Leakage from containers themselves is rare and develops slowly, so detection is facilitated prior to the development of a hazardous situation. Leakage from the inner container of an insulated container for a cryogenic gas is indicated by the formation of water condensate or frost on the outside container due to contact with air on the cold surface. While this often only indicates a void in the insulation rather than leakage, this appearance should be investigated.

Overpressure protection: Overfilled liquefied gas containers can lead to overpressure device operation at much lower temperatures. (See discussion of Charles' Law in Section 3, Chapter 7, "Gases.") Portable liquefied gas containers should be checked for proper quantities before being placed into storage. Many such containers may be checked by weighing them. The weight of the empty container (tare weight) must be marked on the container in accordance with DOT regulations. The weight of gas must be determined by the use of data that include the specific gravity of the gas and its temperature when placed into the container. In other cases, the quantity is checked by the use of a gage that measures the liquid level. The most accurate gage requires that a small amount of gas be released. This should be done outside under carefully controlled conditions. These gages are known as fixed-tube gages or try-cocks. They will release gas only if the level is safe and will release liquid if there is too much in the container.

Ventilation of spaces: Indoor storage areas should be ventilated, regardless of the chemical hazard of the gas. In areas used solely for storage (no filling of containers), the amount of ventilation need not be great—one-half to one air change per hour or so. However, even inert gases, because they are often odorless and colorless, can present asphyxiation hazards in unventilated areas.

Controlling ignition sources: Ignition sources should be controlled in flammable gas storage areas. The vapor density of the gas, in part, determines the extent of the area in which ignition sources should be eliminated or controlled. Many gases are heavier than air at all times. Others will be temporarily heavier than air when they are released in liquid form and vaporize. In general, flammable gas storage areas with no container filling are classified as Division 2 locations for purposes of installing electrical equipment because of the ventilation provided and the nominal leakage potential.

Most flammable gases are Group C or D materials, in the context of NFPA 70, *National Electrical Code®*. Acetylene (Group A) and hydrogen (Group B) are common exceptions. Because of the limited variety of Group A and B electrical equipment available, electrical equipment may have to be avoided; be purged and ventilated in accordance with NFPA 496, *Purged and Pressurized Enclosures for Electrical Equipment;* or be intrinsically safe.

Fire protection and control of gas fires is discussed in Section 3, Chapter 7, "Gases." Sprinkler and water spray protection have been discussed in this chapter. An essential aspect is that the extinguishment of gas fires by the application of extinguishing agents should be restricted to small leaks where the consequences of reignition can be tolerated.

BIBLIOGRAPHY

References

ASME *Boiler and Pressure Vessel Code*, American Society of Mechanical Engineers, Philadelphia, PA.

ANSI B31, *Code for Pressure Piping*, American National Standards Institute, Washington, DC.

CGA, "Safe Handling of Compressed Gases in Containers," *Pamphlet P-1*, Compressed Gas Association, Arlington, VA.

NFPA Codes, Standards, and Recommended Practices

Reference to the following NFPA codes, standards, and recommended practices will provide further information on storage of gases discussed in this chapter. (See the latest *NFPA Catalog* for availability of current editions of the following documents.)

NFPA 50, *Bulk Oxygen Systems at Consumer Sites.*

NFPA 50B, *Liquefied Hydrogen Systems at Consumer Sites.*

NFPA 51, *Oxygen-Fuel Gas Systems for Welding, Cutting and Allied Processes.*

NFPA 51B, *Cutting and Welding Processes.*

NFPA 54, *National Fuel Gas Code.*

NFPA 58, *Storage and Handling of Liquefied Petroleum Gases.*

NFPA 59, *Storage and Handling of Liquefied Petroleum Gases at Utility Gas Plants.*

NFPA 59A, *Production, Storage, and Handling of Liquefied Natural Gas (LNG).*

NFPA 70, *National Electrical Code®.*

NFPA 99, *Health Care Facilities.*

NFPA 220, *Standard Types of Building Construction.*

NFPA 496, *Purged and Pressurized Enclosures for Electrical Equipment.*

Additional Reading

Bettis, R. J., Makhviladze, G. M. and Nolan, P. F., "Behavior of Heavy Gas and Particulate Clouds," *Proceedings* of the First International Symposium on Fire Safety Science, Hemisphere, 1986, pp. 919-930.

Colton, W. and Mayer, P. E., "Fire Detection and Suppression in Natural Gas Pipeline Compressor Stations," *Papers* Presented at the ASME Gas Turbine Conference and Exhibition, American Society of Mechanical Engineers, 87-GT-103, 1987, 7 p.

Compressed Gas Association, *Handbook of Compressed Gases*, 3rd ed., Van Nostrand Reinhold, NY, 1990.

Coward, H. F. and Jones, G. W., "Limits of Flammability of Gases and Vapors," *Bulletin No. 503*, U.S. Bureau of Mines, Washington, DC, 1965.

Davenport, J. A., "Insurer's View of Gas Plant and Fuel Handling Facilities," *Proceedings* of the American Institute of Chemical Engineers 1986 Annual Meeting, AIChE, 1986, 19 p.

DeNeuers, N., "Propane Over-Filling Fires," *Fire Journal*, Vol. 81, No. 5 (1987), p. 80.

Fullam, B. W., "Fire Protection of LPG Vessels," *Proceedings* of the Gastech 86 LNG/LPG Conference, Gastech, 1986, pp. 152-156.

Lewis, B. and Von Elbe, G., *Combustion, Flames and Explosions of Gases*, 3rd ed., Academic Press, Troy, MI, 1987.

LP-Gas Safety Handbook, National LP-Gas Association, Oak Brook, IL, 1981.

"LPG: Storage of Liquified Petroleum Gas," (P7717), Factory Mutual Engineering Corp., Norwood, MA.

Nettleton, M. A., *Gaseous Detonations: Their Nature, Effects, and Control*, Chapman and Hall, New York, 1987.

Schoen, W. and Droste, B., "Investigations of Water Spraying Systems for LPG Storage Tanks by Full Scale Fire Tests," *Journal of Hazardous Materials*, Vol. 20, Dec. 1988, pp. 73-82.

Senesky, J., "Safe Storage and Handling of Compressed Gases," Plant Engineering, Vol. 33, No. 10 (Oct. 1979), pp. 143-148.

"The Design and Construction of Liquified Petroleum Installations at Marine and Pipeline Terminals, Natural Gas Processing Plants, Refineries, Petrochemical Plants and Tank Farms," *API Standard 2510*, American Petroleum Institute, Washington, DC.

Wesson, H. R., *et al.*, "Fire Extinguishment of High Evaporation Rate LNG Spills," *Operating Section Proceedings D-1974*, American Gas Association, 1974.

Zabetakis, M. D., "Flammability Characteristics of Combustible Gases and Vapors," *Bulletin No. 627*, U.S. Bureau of Mines, Washington, DC, 1965.

Zuber, K., "LNG Facilities—Engineered Fire Protection Systems," *Fire Technology*, Vol. 12, No. 1 (Feb. 1976), pp. 41-48.

STORAGE AND HANDLING OF CHEMICALS

William J. Bradford

Safe storage of chemicals requires a knowledge of all of the hazardous properties of the chemicals. Many materials exhibit more than one potential for fire and explosion, and detailed knowledge of hazard potential is best obtained from the manufacturer's detailed literature on the chemical. All manufacturers are required by law to prepare and distribute material safety data sheets (MSDS) for all products they make. The MSDS gives information on toxicity, flammability, reactivity, and stability, as well as safe handling and storage practices.

The quantity, size, and nature of the container, as well as its storage arrangement, affects the safety of storage. In addition to knowledge of the hazard potential, it is also necessary for safe handling to have details on the process in which the chemical is to be used. The temperature, pressure, and concentration of all chemicals involved in the process must be known. Other factors to be considered include potentially hazardous byproducts due to normal operating conditions, and byproducts that could be formed by contamination or operation outside the normal parameters. Only with complete information can safe storage and handling of chemicals be achieved.

PRINCIPLES OF GOOD STORAGE

Segregation

The first principle of good storage practice for chemicals is segregation, including separation from other materials in storage, from processing and handling operations, and from incompatible materials. Segregation can take the form of isolation in a separate detached structure, or isolation in the same building (by means of fire walls). Segregation can also be achieved by separating chemicals within the same building by an intervening empty area or by intervening storage of inert or nonhazardous materials. The extent of segregation depends upon the quantity of materials being stored, the physical state of the chemicals, and their degree of incompatibility. In addition, the known behavior of materials under fire conditions will affect the extent and type of segregation needed. Rupture of vessels and possible mixing of incompatible materials under fire conditions must be considered.

Protection Against Physical Damage

Containers for chemicals are designed to be compatible with the materials they contain. However, when containers are subjected to physical abuse, containers may be damaged by the release of chemicals, which can considerably increase fire and explosion hazards. For this reason, protection of the containers against physical damage in shipment, transfer, and storage is very important. In addition, the container may represent a potential hazard under fire conditions. For example, storage of oxidizers in fiber packs or even plastic containers may be safe under normal conditions, but if a fire occurs, the oxidizers and the combustible packages can magnify fire intensity.

Hazard Identification

All storage areas should conspicuously display signs to identify the material stored in the area. The hazard identification system described in NFPA 704, *Identification of the Fire Hazards of Materials*, should be used. When materials having different hazard identifications are stored in the same area, the area should be marked to indicate the most severe health, flammability, and reactivity hazard present. Hazard identifications for many materials can be found in NFPA 49, *Hazardous Chemicals Data*, and in NFPA 325M, *Fire Hazard Properties of Flammable Liquids, Gases, and Volatile Solids*.

Fire Control

The selection of extinguishing agents is determined by the reactivity of the chemical, the physical state of the chemical (i.e., solid, liquid, or gas), the toxicity of the chemical, and its expected products of combustion. Water is normally used as the extinguishing agent, except on chemicals that may be dangerously water-reactive. However, the toxicity of the material in water must be considered as an additional factor. The contamination of potable water supplies

William J. Bradford, P.E., is a loss prevention consultant. He is a registered professional engineer in Connecticut and Rhode Island, a member of AIChE and SFPE, and serves on several NFPA technical committees.

by toxic runoff from fire fighting could create a major health hazard.

Automatic protection for storage should be employed wherever possible. The protection must be specifically designed based upon the extent of fire hazard, the arrangement of material, and the maximum quantity that can be stored.

Manual fire fighting to supplement the automatic protection may be severely limited by the toxicity of the material, obscuration due to smoke, the nature of the products of combustion, or the possibility that fires may lead to explosions in storage areas for reactive chemicals. Fire fighters should wear self-contained breathing apparatus (SCBA) to avoid the hazard of toxic materials. Where explosion is a possibility, manual fire fighting should be conducted from a remote location. In some cases, the hazard will be sufficiently high so that fire fighters should not approach the area to attempt any type of manual fire fighting.

OXIDIZING CHEMICALS

In considering storage facilities for oxidizing chemicals, remember that oxidizing chemicals usually are not themselves combustible, but may provide oxygen to accelerate the burning of other combustible materials. Combustible materials and flammable liquids, therefore, should not be stored in the same storage areas with oxidizing chemicals. Storage buildings should be of noncombustible or fire-resistive construction. Combustible packaging and wood pallets may represent a severe hazard and should be eliminated. Because certain oxidizing materials undergo dangerous reactions with specific noncombustible materials, the possibility of dangerous reactions should be considered when deciding on acceptable storage facilities. Chlorates, for example, should not be stored with acids or combustible materials. Inorganic peroxides also react with acids, yielding hydrogen peroxide. A suitable storage facility for inorganic peroxides would be a dry, fire-resistive storage room in which there are no combustible contents or acids. When classifying chemicals for storage purposes, one should keep in mind that the label on the container required for interstate shipment classifies the chemical by hazard for transportation purposes only; a knowledge of the fire, health, and reactivity hazards of the chemical should be the guide when arranging storage.

Because of the probability that spilled material will become mixed with combustible refuse, it is important to clean up all spills immediately and thoroughly. Combustible linings of barrels should be removed from the storage area and destroyed as soon as the barrels are empty.

Two NFPA standards are directed specifically toward storage of oxidizing chemicals: NFPA 43A, *Storage of Liquid and Solid Oxidizing Materials*, and NFPA 43C, *Storage of Gaseous Oxidizing Materials*.

Ammonium Nitrate

Because of its characteristics and widespread use, ammonium nitrate deserves special mention. Proper storage methods for bagged ammonium nitrate were intensively investigated following the catastrophic Texas City, TX, explosion in 1947 which involved cargoes of ammonium nitrate aboard vessels.[1] Storage recommendations for bagged and bulk ammonium nitrate published in NFPA 490, *Storage of Ammonium Nitrate*, cover building construction, pile sizes and spacing, separation of ammonium nitrate from contaminating materials that could increase its sensitivity during a fire, elimination of floor drains into which molten nitrate might flow, cleanliness of the storage area, and precautions against ignition sources.

Fire Control Methods

With one or two exceptions, water appears to be the only suitable extinguishing agent for fires involving inorganic oxidizing agents. Water in large quantities should be used to control fires involving nitrates, nitrites, and chlorates. Carbon dioxide and other smothering agents are of little or no extinguishing value because the oxidizing material furnishes its own oxygen for combustion. Although inorganic peroxides decompose when moist and liberate oxygen, water should still be used on fires in combustible materials that are located in the vicinity of the peroxide.

It may be possible to extinguish a fire involving a peroxide spill with a dry chemical extinguisher or by smothering with dry sand or soda ash. If these methods fail, the area should be flooded with water from hose streams.

Self-contained breathing apparatus should be worn by fire fighters. During a fire involving nitrates, one of many dangers is inhalation of oxides of nitrogen. As much ventilation as possible should be provided to permit rapid dissipation of the products of combustion and heat. When water in solid streams strikes molten nitrate, steam explosions may cause a violent eruption of the molten material.

COMBUSTIBLE CHEMICALS

Essentially, all organic chemicals are combustible. Storage practices for such chemicals closely follow those for the more common solid combustible materials discussed in other chapters. Sulfur and sulfides of sodium, potassium, and phosphorus may be considered principally as combustible chemicals. They do have some properties that warrant special mention. Combustion of these materials produces sulfur dioxide, an irritating gas. Storage should be away from oxidizing materials and, in the case of sulfides, should be separated from strong acids.

Water should be used for fighting sulfur and sulfide fires. For fighting fires of sulfur dust, water spray is recommended, principally to avoid stirring up dust clouds and causing a dust explosion. Fires in closed spaces, e.g., tanks of molten sulfur, can best be fought by closing the container and allowing the heavy sulfur dioxide produced by combustion to smother the fire.

UNSTABLE CHEMICALS

Special precautions must be taken for storage of chemicals that are subject to spontaneous decomposition or other dangerous reactions. The precautions should be planned to minimize the possibility of a dangerous reaction and to prevent injuries and extensive property damage if one should occur. Steps to be taken to protect against the hazard will depend upon the conditions that affect the stability of the chemical being stored. Points peculiar to unstable chemicals to be considered are: (1) the catalytic effect of containers, (2) materials in the same storage area that could initiate a dangerous reaction, (3) the presence of inhibitors, and (4) the effect of direct sunlight or temperature changes. There is a need for pressure-relief vents for containers and explosion venting for the storage area in addition to the usual considerations, such as automatic sprinkler or water spray protection, and elimination of all combustible material from the storage area. Whenever possible, unstable chemicals should be stored in a detached outside location.

Fire fighters should be thoroughly briefed on the proper procedures to be followed if called upon to fight a fire involving or exposing a storage area containing unstable chemicals.

Organic Peroxides

This widely used group of unstable chemicals deserves special mention. Many organic peroxides are diluted to the point where hazardous reactions are impossible; others require special precautions. The manufacturer of the peroxide should be consulted for specific recommendations.

NFPA 43B, *Storage of Organic Peroxide Formulations*, gives quantity and arrangement specifications for various formulations.

Fire Control Methods

Water is the recommended extinguishing agent for fires involving unstable chemicals, including organic peroxides. Automatic sprinklers are the best protection because fires involving such materials can lead to explosions. Manual fire fighting must be conducted from a distance where the fire fighters will be protected from an explosion.

WATER- AND AIR-REACTIVE CHEMICALS

Water-Reactive Chemicals

Anhydrides, carbides, hydrides, alkali metals (lithium, sodium, potassium), and similar chemicals should be stored in dry areas in waterproof and airtight containers that are kept off the floor on skids. The storage area should not contain combustible material and/or incompatible chemicals.

Air-Reactive Chemicals

Aluminum hydride, aluminum alkyls, yellow phosphorous, and similar chemicals must be stored to avoid contact with air. Yellow phosphorous, for example, is stored under water. Other materials, such as aluminum alkyls, which react with both water and air, must be stored under inert liquids or inert gas. Storage areas should contain no incompatible materials.

Fire Control Methods

The value of automatic sprinklers depends upon the type of chemical reaction that will occur when the chemical comes in contact with water. Fires involving hydrides, for example, can be smothered with a special graphite-base powder or with inert material, such as dry, finely divided calcium magnesium carbonate (dolomite). Hydride fires in an enclosed space should not be put out because the continued evolution of hydrogen after extinguishment will create an explosion hazard. For the fires involving air-reactive white (or yellow) phosphorus, water will solidify the phosphorus melted by the heat of the fire, after which it can be covered with dry sand or dirt. All of the chemical must be disposed of before it can dry out and reignite.

Several of these chemicals are both air- and water-reactive and the water reaction can be particularly violent, e.g., aluminum alkyls. Fires of such materials can be contained by dry chemical while the material burns out under control. Metallic sodium, which is both water- and air-reactive, can be extinguished by the use of dry chemical. The residual sodium should then be submerged in oil.

CORROSIVE CHEMICALS

Inorganic Acids, Alkalis

These materials, including sulfuric, nitric, and hydrochloric acids, as well as sodium hydroxide, should be stored in cool, well-ventilated places away from incompatable chemicals or combustibles. Acids and alkalis should not be stored in the same area. Spilled acids or alkalis should be diluted at once with large quantities of water. Combustible materials contaminated with nitric, sulfuric, or perchloric acid should be washed thoroughly or removed to a safe location before spontaneous ignition can occur.

Chlorine and Fluorine Cylinders

Preferably, these are stored outside under a noncombustible sun shield. If stored inside, these cylinders should be in a noncombustible, well-ventilated, segregated room. Both these gases present a serious inhalation hazard.[2] Areas of suspected gas leakage should not be entered without self-contained breathing apparatus. Fluorine causes severe flesh burns and is also highly toxic by inhalation. Special protective clothing is necessary, in addition to self-contained breathing apparatus.

Fire Control Methods

Water in spray form is recommended for fighting fires in acid and alkali storage areas. Water from straight streams mixing with concentrated acid or a caustic agent will heat and spatter the corrosive chemicals. A fire involving perchloric acid can cause an explosion if the acid becomes mixed with organic material. Ample precautions should be taken to protect fire fighters from possible explosions. Fire fighters should avoid contact with spilled acids and inhalation of their toxic fumes by the use of self-contained breathing apparatus.

Chlorine and fluorine do not represent fire hazards, but the release of dangerous toxic gases should be expected if cylinders are present in a fire. It is mandatory that self-contained breathing apparatus be used when fighting a fire where chlorine or fluorine cylinders are located.

RADIOACTIVE MATERIAL

The direct fire and explosion characteristics of a material are not affected by the radioactivity of its constituents. For example, neither radioactive nor nonradioactive cobalt is a fire hazard, and the frequency or the extent of fires will not be affected. However, because of the radiation hazards during and after a fire, it is extremely important that all practical steps be taken to prevent a fire from involving these materials. Radioactivity is not detectable by any of the human senses; special instruments and measuring techniques are required to identify and evaluate the hazard. Radioactivity can cause injuries, loss of life, and damage to and extended loss of the use of materials, equipment, and buildings. A major problem is the need for decontamination of buildings, equipment, and materials after a fire.

Radioactive materials should be stored with a shielding equivalent to that used in shipping. Storage should be in fire-resistant cabinets, safes, or equivalent enclosures, or in wells or pits below the lowest floor level of a building.

Automatic protection is of the greatest importance in areas where radioactive materials are stored, because manual fire fighting exposes fire fighters to radioactivity. There will also be a delay in salvage work and in resumption of normal operations in a location where fire or explosion causes loss of control over radioactive substances. Smoke and products of combustion from these fires especially must be controlled. Fire fighters need protective clothing and respiratory protection equipment. Fire control must be thoroughly planned. Special emphasis must also be placed upon the disposal of water from sprinklers and hose streams to avoid contamination of buildings and equipment.

MATERIAL SUBJECT TO SELF-HEATING

Charcoal

Spontaneous heating hazards with charcoal can be controlled by thorough cooling and ventilation before bagging and storage. It is important to keep the charcoal dry, to prevent contamination with foreign combustibles, and to avoid contact with heat sources. Small quantities of charcoal are normally stored in heavy paper bags. The spontaneous heating hazard of individual small bags, as may be found in a dwelling, is not serious.

When fire occurs in charcoal, water should be used, but directed only on the fire, without wetting nonburning material. The damaged and wet materials should be removed from the storage building at once, because wet charcoal is even more susceptible to self-heating than when dry.

Agricultural Products

Spontaneous heating in agricultural products can be prevented by control of moisture. Proper curing (as for hay) and adequate aeration will prevent heat buildup. Where the moisture content cannot be controlled, or where any suspicion of spontaneous heating exists, thermocouples may be used in stacks or bales. Pointed, hollow metal rods or pipes with holes drilled in the lower ends often are used to permit insertion of temperature-recording instruments into the subsurface areas of the stored material. Regular checks can then be made for the development of any hazardous temperature conditions. Where evidence of dangerous spontaneous heating is noted, the material should be removed quickly from storage.

When spontaneous heating occurs in agricultural products, it is important to have ample fire fighting facilities available. Water hoses are needed to combat a fire that may occur spontaneously on exposure of the hot spots to air. Hay, in and around hot spots, should be wetted thoroughly before complete uncovering or attempted removal.

HANDLING CHEMICALS

Safe handling of hazardous chemicals includes attention to all of the precautions used for their storage. In addition, however, it is necessary to consider other potential problems and employ additional safeguards. Normal handling of the chemicals includes removing them from the manufacturer's shipping container and mixing them with other materials. Therefore, complete details are needed on the process in which the chemical is to be employed. Consideration must be given to the control techniques available to limit potentially hazardous runaway reactions, which can result in fires or explosions, and to limit the release of flammable and toxic materials from processing.

A hazard analysis should be performed on all processes, using one or more of the techniques outlined in *Guidelines for Hazard Evaluation Procedures*, from AIChE Center for Chemical Process Safety. A brief, but useful, outline is given in *Process Safety Management*, from Chemical Manufacturers Association. (See bibliography.)

Reactive and Unstable Chemicals

Particular attention must be given to the handling of reactive or unstable chemicals that can cause fires or explosions. It is necessary to handle all air-reactive chemicals in a closed system, which is best kept under an inert gas atmosphere. Use of a vacuum atmosphere is much less desirable because any breach of the integrity of the system will automatically admit air. Dissolving water-reactive chemicals in an organic solvent or covering them with a layer of oil will keep moisture from attacking the chemical. For unstable chemicals, an inhibiting catalyst may be employed, unless processing of the chemical will be adversely affected. Refrigeration can be used to slow the speed of the chemical reaction. These and other methods should be used to prevent dangerous exothermic reactions involving reactive and unstable chemicals; however, these methods must be supplemented by emergency means, such as the use of rupture discs or emergency relief valves for relieving dangerous pressures. In some cases, reactions can be controlled by the introduction of a "short stop" to actually kill the reaction. In other cases, a runaway reacting mass may be dumped into a tank containing a material that will stop the reaction by dilution. Fire fighting personnel should be made aware of the fire and explosion potential in areas where reactive or unstable chemicals are handled.

Toxic Chemicals

Protection against the toxic effects of chemicals during handling can be accomplished in two ways. The first is by using the most practical of the available methods of controlling and confining the chemical so that the toxic material cannot be contacted, ingested, or inhaled during normal operations. The second is by educating all personnel, who may be in areas where toxic chemicals are handled, about the hazards, danger signals, precautionary procedures to be followed, and proper steps to be taken in case of an emergency.

Toxic chemicals will normally be handled in closed systems. However, leaks can develop in any closed system, thereby subjecting people to a severe health hazard. If the release of a toxic material cannot be seen or smelled, toxic-gas indicators will have to be used to alert personnel of the danger. The use of personal protective equipment is always a valuable adjunct to safety in areas where toxic materials are present.

TRANSPORTATION OF CHEMICALS

The safe transportation of chemicals depends upon a knowledge of the hazardous properties of the chemicals, the normal and abnormal conditions to which the chemicals may be exposed during shipment, and the conditions of packing and shipping that will minimize the possibility of accidental release or reaction of chemicals.

In the U.S., shipments of hazardous chemicals in interstate or foreign commerce by land, water, or air must comply with U.S. Department of Transportation (DOT) regulations. Among items covered by these regulations are: (1) construction of containers; (2) methods of packing; (3) weight of chemical per package; (4) marking and labeling; (5) loading, placarding, and movement of railroad cars; and (6) regulations for motor vehicle equipment and motor vehicle operation on the highway.

State regulations for intrastate transportation usually agree with DOT interstate commerce regulations. In Canada, shipment of explosives and other dangerous chemicals are regulated by the Canadian Transport Commission (CTC). Chemicals shipped in accordance with Canadian regulations may be shipped to a destination in the U.S. or through the U.S. *en route* to a point in Canada.

Principles governing the safe transportation of chemicals include:

1. Constructing the container of material that will not react with or be decomposed by the chemical.
2. Excluding chemicals that can react dangerously with each other from the same outside container.
3. Packaging toxic and radioactive chemicals so they will not present a health hazard during normal transportation conditions and will not be released in an accident or under other abnormal conditions.
4. Providing sufficient outage for maximum expansion of liquids under conditions to be expected during transportation.
5. Limiting the amount of chemical that can be released through container breakage or leakage by limiting maximum size of individual containers.
6. Cushioning containers to minimize the possibility of breakage.

WASTE CHEMICAL DISPOSAL

The safe disposal of hazardous chemical waste is controlled by a 1976 federal law—the Resource Conservation and Recovery Act (RCRA PL 94-590, Subtitle C, Hazardous Waste Management). This act provides for cradle-to-grave regulation of potentially dangerous byproducts spawned by industrial technology. Specifically, the law covers any solid, liquid, or gaseous waste that exceeds federal criteria established for the following characteristics:

1. Toxicity,
2. Persistence and degradability in nature,
3. Potential for accumulation in tissue (bioaccumulation),
4. Reactivity,
5. Flammability,
6. Corrosivity, and
7. Radioactivity.

Standards have been published that regulate generators of hazardous waste in several different areas, i.e., recordkeeping practices, labeling and containerization, disclosure of waste composition to haulers and disposers, use of a manifest to monitor the life cycle of a waste stream, and reporting requirements to applicable local, state, and federal agencies. Additionally, standards have been developed to control the storage, transportation, and final disposition to ensure that these compounds are handled in properly designed facilities. For example, secured chemical landfills must have a sufficiently impervious base to prevent contaminated leachate from entering adjacent groundwater, and incinerators must achieve a 99.9 percent destruction efficiency. Recognizing the hazards involved, it is advisable to verify the capabilities of any firm utilized for disposal of hazardous wastes. At the very minimum, operating permits should be reviewed to confirm that a particular waste can be legally processed by any company under consideration for this service.

BIBLIOGRAPHY

References Cited

1. National Fire Protection Association, "Texas City Disaster," *NFPA Quarterly*, Vol. 41, No. 1, 1947, pp. 24-57.
2. Chlorine Institute, *Chlorine Manual*, 5th ed., The Chlorine Institute, Washington, D.C., 1986.

References

AIChE, *Guidelines for Hazard Evaluation Procedures*, AIChE Center for Chemical Process Safety, New York, 1985.

CMA, *Process Safety Management*, Chemical Manufacturers Association, Washington, DC, 1985.

NFPA Codes, Standards, and Recommended Practices

Reference to the following NFPA codes, standards, and recommended practices will provide further information on the safeguards for storage and handling of chemicals discussed in this chapter. (See the latest *NFPA Catalog* for availability of current editions of the following documents.)

NFPA 43A, *Storage of Liquid and Solid Oxidizing Materials.*

NFPA 43B, *Storage of Organic Peroxide Formulations.*

NFPA 43C, *Storage of Gaseous Oxidizing Materials.*

NFPA 49, *Hazardous Chemicals Data.*

NFPA 325M, *Fire Hazard Properties of Flammable Liquids, Gases, and Volatile Solids.*

NFPA 490, *Storage of Ammonium Nitrate.*

NFPA 491M, *Manual of Hazardous Chemical Reactions.*

NFPA 655, *Prevention of Sulfur Fires and Explosions.*

NFPA 704, *Identification of the Fire Hazards of Materials.*

NFPA 801, *Facilities Handling Radioactive Materials.*

Additional Reading

Bahme, C. W., *Fire Officer's Guide to Dangerous Chemicals*, 2nd ed., National Fire Protection Association, Quincy, MA, 1978.

Barron, M. J., "Railroads and Transportation Safety," *Loss Prevention*, Vol. 5, American Institute of Chemical Engineers (AIChE), NY, 1971, pp. 7-12.

Bigelow, C. R., "Chemical Industry Transportation Emergency Information System," *Loss Prevention*, Vol. 5, AIChE, NY, 1971, pp. 21-25.

Botkin, L. A., "Chemical Transport Over the Highway: Equipment Design and Regulations," *Loss Prevention*, Vol. 14, AIChE, NY, 1981, pp. 44-53.

Brasie, W. C., "The Hazard Potential of Chemicals," *Loss Prevention*, Vol. 10, AIChE, NY, 1976, pp. 135-140.

Condensed Chemical Dictionary, 11th ed., Van Nostrand Reinhold Co., NY, 1984.

DeHaven, E. S., "Using Kinetics to Evaluate Reactivity Hazards," *Loss Prevention*, Vol. 12, AIChE, NY, 1979, pp. 41-44.

Doyle, W. H., "Protection in Depth for Increased Chemical Hazards," *Fire Journal*, Vol. 59, No. 5 (Sept. 1965), pp. 5-7.

Drake, E. M. and Croce, P. A., "Guidelines for Safe Storage and Handling of High Toxic Hazard Materials: A New CCPS Publication," *Plant/Operation Progress*, Vol. 7, No. 4 (Oct. 1988), pp. 257-264.

Duch, M. W., *et al.*, "Thermal Stability Evaluation Using Differential Scanning Calorimetry and Accelerative Rate Calorimetry," *Plant/Operations Progress*, Vol. 1, No. 1, 1982, pp. 19-26.

Fauske, H. K., "Preventing Explosions During Chemicals and Materials Storage," *Plant/Operation Progress*, Vol. 8, No. 4, 1989, pp. 181-184.

Fawcett, H. H. and Wood, W. S., eds., *Safety and Accident Prevention in Chemical Operations*, 2nd ed., Wiley, NY, 1982.

Fenlon, W. J., "A Comparison of ARC and Other Thermal Stability Test Methods" *Plant/Operations Progress*, Vol. 3, No. 4, 1984, pp. 197-202.

Fire and Explosion Index Hazard Classification Guide, 6th ed., American Institute of Chemical Engineers, NY, 1987.

Fox, P., "Tank Fires: A Case Study History," *Industrial Fire World*, Vol. 1, No. 9, 1986.

Gillespie, P., "Protecting Petrochemical Tanks With Firefighting Foam," *Fire Journal*, Vol. 83, No. 3 (May/June 1989), p. 44.

Green, D. W. and Perry, J. H., eds., *Chemical Engineers' Handbook*, 6th ed., McGraw-Hill Inc., NY, 1984.

Handbook of Chemistry and Physics, 69th ed., CRC Press, Boca Raton, FL, 1988.

Kirk-Othmer Concise, *Encyclopedia of Chemical Technology*, Wiley, NY, 1985.

Linville, J. L., ed., *Industrial Fire Hazards Handbook*, 3rd ed., National Fire Protection Association, Quincy, MA, 1990.

Nitromethane: Storage and Handling, NP Series TDS No. 2, 3rd ed., IMC Chemical Group, Inc., Terre Haute, IN.

Novak, R. G., "Hazardous Chemicals Disposal in a Large Chemical Complex," *Loss Prevention*, Vol. 6, AIChE, NY, 1971.

"The Handling of Explosives," Explosives Division, Department of Energy, Mines and Resources, Ottawa, Canada.

Sax, N. I., *Dangerous Properties of Industrial Materials*, 7th ed., Van Nostrand Reinhold, NY, 1989.

"Storage and Handling of Organic Peroxides in Reinforced Polyester Fabricating Plant," *Safety and Loss Prevention Bulletin No. 19*, Society of the Plastics Industry, Inc., NY, 1978.

Stull, D. P., *Fundamentals of Fire and Explosion*, M-10, AIChE, NY, 1976.

Stull, D. P., "Linking Thermodynamics and Kinetics to Predict Real Chemical Hazards," *Loss Prevention*, Vol. 7, AIChE, NY, 1973, pp. 67-73.

"Suggested Code of Regulations for the Manufacture, Transportation, Storage, Sale, Possession, and Use of Explosive Materials," *Safety Library Publication No. 3*, Institute of Makers of Explosives, Washington, DC.

Thorp, R. J., "Protecting BASF's Chemicals Site," *Fire Prevention*, No.221 (Jul./Aug. 1989), pp. 28-30.

Waeckerlig, H. U., "Lessons from a Major Chemical Storage Fire," *Chemsa*, Vol. 14, No. 5, 1988, p. 7.

STORAGE AND HANDLING OF GRAIN MILL PRODUCTS

Max R. Spencer

The grain industry encompasses the movement, storage, and processing of grains, such as wheat, corn, oats, and sorghums, and oilseeds, such as soybeans and sunflower seeds. It can be separated into two broad categories—grain elevator operations, and millers or processors. Grain elevators primarily accumulate, store, and ship whole grains and oilseeds. Their end product is virtually identical to their raw material, with only minimal drying, cleaning, and fumigation to preserve and meet product quality standards. Grain millers and processors, on the other hand, take whole grains as their raw material and process these into products, such as: animal feeds, cereals, flour, starch, vegetable oils, corn sugars, brewery products, etc. The discussion which follows is primarily aimed at the grain elevator segment of the industry and that portion of grain milling and processing which handles and stores whole grains on a bulk commodity basis.

The growth of the grain industry in the United States has paralleled the phenomenal growth in production, consumption, and export of grains and oilseed products. This growth has been the result of many factors—the most important of which is the ideal temperate climate of the U.S. to produce these agricultural commodities, combined with the mechanization of farming, the development of high-yielding hybrids, the free market system, and uniquely efficient storage and transportation systems. Table 2-28A shows dramatically the rate of growth in harvested grain and oilseed crops.[1]

TABLE 2-28A. ***Production of U.S. Grains and Oilseeds in Bushels****

	Corn	Wheat	Soybeans	Others	Total (1,000 bu)
1950	3,131,009	1,026,755	287,010	2,105,195	6,549,969
1955	3,184,836	938,159	371,276	2,548,501	7.042,772
1960	4,352,668	1,363,443	558,778	2,317,196	8,592,085
1965	4,084,342	1,315,613	845,608	2,227,321	8,472,884
1970	4,151,938	1,351,588	1,127,100	2,272,590	8,903,216
1975	5,828,961	2,122,459	1,547,383	2,092,432	11,591,235
1980	6,644,841	2,374,306	1,792,062	1,767,121	12,578,330

Source: *Statistical Reporting Service*, U.S. Dept. of Agriculture.[1]
*1 bushel = 0.3523 m^3

RAW MATERIALS

Grain and oilseeds consist primarily of starch or carbohydrates, protein, fiber, and various vegetable oils, all capable of burning under very specific conditions. In their raw, whole-kernel states, these commodities are stable and not readily subject to combustion if protected from moisture, insects, and fungi. So-called spontaneous combustion is a product of microbiological spoilage created by fungi combined with certain levels of moisture and temperature.[2] The incidence of this source of ignition of fires and explosions in grain elevators is rare, although it has been known to occur. Good grain industry practice is to store grains at moistures and temperature levels which will not only prevent spontaneous combustion, but will keep the grain from deteriorating in quality. Where grain is stored for long duration in large storage vessels, temperature can be monitored by installation of temperature detection systems.

As size reduction of the grain kernel proceeds, the susceptibility to fires and explosions increases dramatically.[3] The frequent handling of grain from farm to consumer progressively creates more broken kernels, hence more dust. This reduction in size also occurs as an integral part of the milling and processing segment of the industry.

Grain is essentially handled as a bulk commodity. The economies of scale have dictated larger and more automated handling units. Only a small fraction of the total harvest is bagged, consisting primarily of seed stocks and small amounts for export to a few emerging nations which are not equipped to discharge bulk vessels.

STORAGE

Bulk storage facilities can consist of upright concrete silos, wood bins, steel silos, steel tanks, conventional warehouse structures referred to as flat storage, or even outdoor temporary piles during harvest periods. The function of the

Max R. Spencer was vice president of operations, Continental Grain Company, New York, NY.

specific elevator, i.e., whether it is for long-term storage, short-term holding, or an adjunct to a processing or milling plant, determines the configuration and type of storage the designer may choose. These facilities are often categorized as country elevators, inland terminals, transfer stations, truck-to-rail terminals, river stations, or export terminals. Many have a multipurpose function and can be included in more than one definition.

Size of storage structure is determined by the nature of an individual facility's operation. Individual bins may range from 1,000 bushels (35.4 m^3) or smaller to 500,000 bushels (17 700 m^3) or larger.

HANDLING

The primary process of a grain handler, other than storage and quality preservation, is that of conveying grain horizontally and vertically into and out of the storage facility. Conveyors common to most bulk handling industries are used in this process. The discussion below shows how these conveyors are used in the grain industry and highlights modified designs tailored to grain industry needs.

Belt Conveyors

The most common conveyor employed to move grain horizontally from point to point is the troughed-belt conveyor. By virtue of the wide choices of speeds and belt widths available, any desired volume can be accommodated in this manner. The fire hazards associated with these conveyors are the combustible rubber construction material of the belting and the tendency of dust to be liberated from the grain moving on open belts. The fire hazard can be minimized by the use of flame-resistant belting[4] and good hot-work permit procedures. The dust hazard can be mitigated by enclosures, aspiration, belt speed control, or a combination of these.

Chain Conveyors

Alternatives to the belt conveyor include the *en masse*, drag, or chain conveyors, which are totally encased in a housing that prevents the escape of dust. These are usually of more limited capacity and convey at reduced linear speeds with much deeper grain depths. Normally, only the loading point or discharge point needs to be aspirated. Higher energy use than belt conveyors and installation costs must be considered.

Screw Conveyors

The helical screw conveyor is a standard for low-volume conveying for short distances. The grain industry generally uses screw conveyors only for specialized purposes because of the damage they cause to whole grain.

Pneumatic Conveyors

The milling end of the industry uses pneumatic conveying systems extensively. These are especially effective for confinement and movement of finely ground commodities in a complex processing operation requiring multipoint pickup or distribution. There is some concern about static electricity buildup and discharge in ungrounded systems.

Bucket Elevators

The common principle used in grain elevator design is that of elevating the commodity to the highest optimum point, then permitting the material to flow by gravitational force down through the various garners, weighing scales, cleaners, and finally through spouts into the storage compartment. (See Figure 2-28A.) This not only makes efficient use of the energy required to move the mass, but eliminates re-elevating and rehandling with all the inherent physical damage to the kernel. Each subsequent rehandling contributes to reducing the quality of the grain, and generation of additional quantities of fine particles and dust. The bucket elevator (or "leg," as it is referred to in the industry) is the primary equipment used to gain these elevations. Inclined belts have been used in several large export terminals, but they are impractical for most applications.

The bucket elevator is not only the workhorse of the industry, but is also the single most hazardous piece of equipment from an explosion standpoint. The dust concentration within a bucket elevator is likely to be above the lower explosive limit (LEL) during normal operations. This, combined with the pumping action of the buckets moving in a confined space and the high amount of mechanical energy inherent to its operation, have led to its identification as the principal ignition source in explosions.[5,6]

Spouting and Lining

Grain and oilseeds are very abrasive commodities that can rapidly erode steel conveying spouts used to channel the flow through elevators. This creates an almost constant demand for maintenance to eliminate leaks and dust emissions. While patching and repair are adequate temporary measures, they seldom fully restore a spout. An alternative has been the wide use of abrasion-resistant liners which can be totally replaced without disruption of the outer spout. Materials most commonly used are abrasion-resistant alloy steel plates, high-density synthetic plastics, and certain vitreous ceramics. These can usually be formed or molded to the contour of the spouts and bolted into place without the need for welding or other heating devices. Although the high-density plastics are not easily ignited, they can burn and must be removed or protected whenever welding or cutting is conducted on the spout.

Receiving and Shipping

The first and last adjuncts to a grain storage elevator are the machinery and structures needed to unload or load the grain from and into a carrier. Whether a railroad, truck, or barge shipping/receiving system is used, these operations are at ground level, partly or completely in the open, and usually connected to the main storage structure with an underground tunnel beneath the discharge receiving hopper, or with an overhead bridge.

The free-fall of grain through open spaces into receiving hoppers presents a unique dust control problem influenced by surface winds and the lack of sufficient enclosures to contain the dust emission. The problem is less of an explosion or fire hazard than a nuisance, as the dust can fly about since the operation is essentially an open-air one. Environmental laws and regulations have required the same attention to these ground-level emissions as to elevated sources of emissions which have a much more distant scatter and settlement pattern.

Grain Drying

The principal processing operation at most grain elevators is that of drying the grain to moisture levels low enough to preserve quality during storage or to meet grain standards.

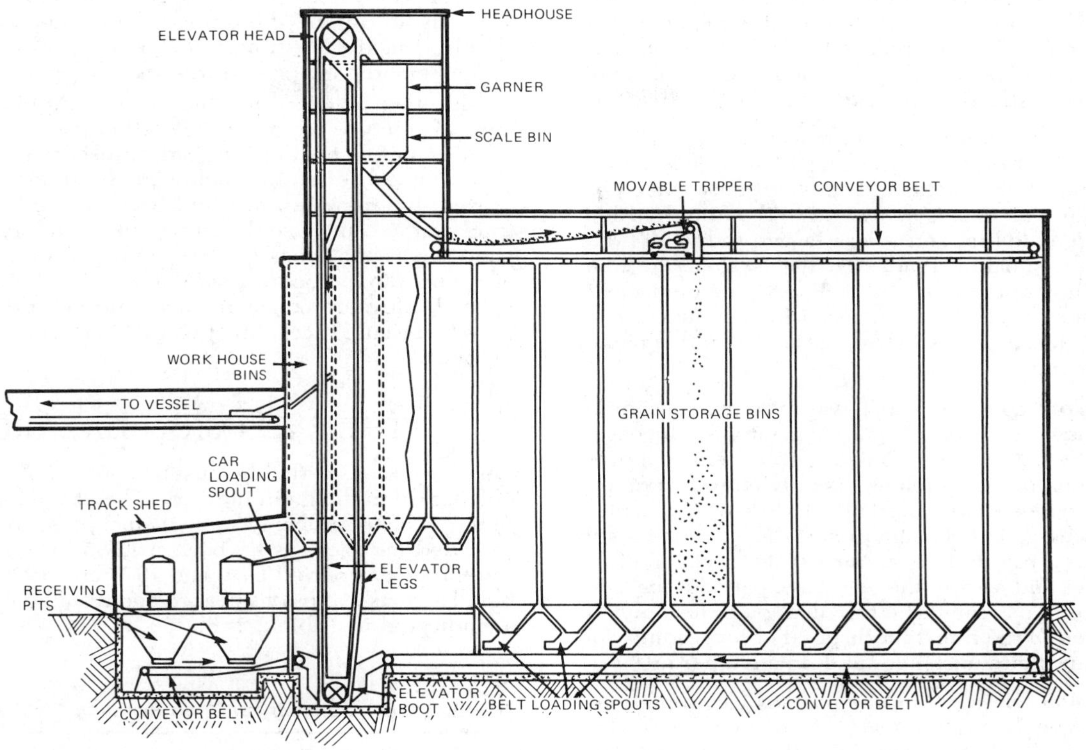

FIG. 2-28A. Diagrammatic section view of a terminal-type grain elevator.

The typical modern grain dryer is direct-fired, i.e., the heat of the burned fuel is directed into a stream of air that is passed directly through the moist grain. The fuels are principally natural gas, fuel oil, or vaporized liquid propane. Although dryers are designed to minimize their fire hazards, inadequate maintenance can result in ignition of the grain being dried. The most frequent initiator of these fires is improper cleaning of dryer screens, racks, or columns. The resulting "hang ups" and overdried extraneous material readily ignites when burner temperature gets too hot or small embers are entrained in the plenum air.

Ideally, a dryer should be housed in a structure completely removed from the storage facility. The grain is fed to the dryer from an elevated source, and returned from the dryer to storage in a second separate conveyance for distribution into silos. Locating a direct-fired dryer away from the storage unit itself and good operating procedures minimize the risk of more serious fires or explosions within the silo structure. In cases where a dryer serves solely to heat grain without cooling, the hot grain is often cooled in the storage silos by high-pressure fans forcing ambient air up through the grain mass until air-temperature equilibrium is reached.

The grain temperature seldom exceeds 150°F (65.5°C) in a drying operation, thus avoiding heat damage to the kernels.[2] As the wet grain is heated, the evaporating water at the surface of the kernels has a cooling effect that prevents the kernels from overheating. The heated air leaving the dryer is in a near-saturated state, and some coarse dust and fine particles escape with it.

Grain Cleaning

The second most important processing activity in a grain-handling facility is usually a screening, cleaning, or scalping system that removes extraneous material from the grain, such as bits of stalks, stems, seed pods, husks, corn cobs, weed seeds, or fine broken grain particles. These materials not only affect the quality of the grain, but are also more prone to ignition than the grain itself by virtue of their extremely dry state and high fiber content. The grain is cleaned by passing it over vibrating or gyratory motion screening devices or stationary gravity screens for simple size separation. A positive air aspiration system is used to remove dust generated by the grain movement within the device.

Grinding and Cracking

Some grain facilities serve specialty industries that require grain to be cracked or ground. This entails the use of hammermills or grinders to accomplish the size reduction. These are common sources of dust explosions, particularly in feed milling operations. The hammermill is frequently used to grind corn and other feed grains for use in rations. Care must be taken to exclude foreign objects, especially stones and metallic objects, from entering the grinding mechanisms.

Dust Control

Supplementing the conveying, elevating, drying, screening, and storage activity is the dust control process. Each point of grain handling can produce suspended dust nearby. A complete dust control system at an elevator consists of a combination of passive dust control methods such as the use of enclosures and reduced grain handling speeds. Active dust control provided by mechanical dust collection systems is most effective in reducing fugitive emissions.

The dust collector most commonly employed is the "baghouse" or fabric filter wherein the dust-laden air is passed through filter media and exits virtually 99.95 percent dust-free. The dust is recovered in the filter housing, stored in a remote bin, and sold as a by-product of grain for use by the animal feed industry. Such systems are complex processing operations with self-cleaning devices for the bags, automatic discharge mechanisms, continuous conveying to disposal points or storage tanks, and separate load-out systems.

The cyclone collector, which was in common use prior to clean-air laws, served as a quasi-separator for dust aspirating systems, but was only 75 to 80 percent efficient overall. For fine particles, efficiency is only 50 to 60 percent and merely concentrates the collected dust at a central point for discharge into the atmosphere. The cyclone is still often used as a preskimmer in dust systems ahead of filters to remove and recover the very large particles for reentry into the grain stream. The fine dust particles only are then collected in the filters for disposal or for readmission into the grain if circumstances and practice permit.

Dust collection systems themselves can sometimes increase the fire hazard because they concentrate the dust in specific pieces of equipment. For this reason, dust filters should be located outside and should be equipped with deflagration vents to minimize possible damage should an explosion occur.

THE FIRE HAZARD

Although dust explosions are the overriding hazard in the grain industry, there are several other fire hazards unique to the grain industry. These are primarily the grain dryer, the grain itself, and the use of propane.

The grain dryer's most significant fire hazard is that of igniting the grain or extraneous material. The large amount of heat needed—in some dryers, more than 20,000,000 Btu/hr (21.12 million kJ/hr)—combined with the large size—up to 80 ft high (24.4 m)—requires that control of this hazard be focused on good operating procedures and mechanical/electronic safeties such as temperature sensors, UV flame detectors, and fuel train safety devices.

In addition to the preventive measures used to reduce the possibility of a grain dryer fire, each elevator must consider an emergency plan for dealing with a fire. The size and unique design of a grain dryer makes fighting the fire with hose streams difficult. Probably the most effective consideration in fighting a dryer fire is moving the burning grain to a safe area away from the elevator where water can be selectively applied.

The hazard of grain itself igniting must also be addressed from a preventive, as well as a fire fighting, standpoint. Preventive measures are basically to keep open flame (welding, torch cutting, cigarettes) away from the grain. Once grain ignites, it becomes quite difficult to extinguish, and, if the extinguishing method creates a dust cloud, an explosion is likely. Application of large amounts of water in a storage bin will not only deteriorate the grain, but, in the case of soybeans, could cause enough swelling of the soybeans to rupture the bin itself. Elevator management should consider meeting with local fire departments to review emergency procedures should a grain fire occur.

Another potential fire hazard in grain elevator operations is the use of propane. Whether used for grain drying or comfort heating, propane presents a serious fire hazard because of the below-grade tunnels normally present in grain elevators and because the heavy rail or truck traffic can cause deterioration in underground propane pipes. If a break occurs, the liquid propane vapors can seep into the below-grade tunnels until discovered or ignited. Elevator management should insist that propane lines be installed according to NFPA codes and maintained regularly.

THE EXPLOSION HAZARD

Dust explosions certainly must be considered the number one hazard in the grain industry. They have been present in the industry probably since its inception, and there are recorded instances as far back as 1785.[3] For instance, in the three-year period between 1976 and 1978, the number of serious explosions peaked and resulted in 94 deaths, as indicated in Table 2-28B.

TABLE 2-28B. ***Summary of Grain Handling Facility Explosions***

Year	# of Grain Handling Facility Explosions	# of Deaths	# of Injuries
1977	20	65	84
1978	19	8	36
1979	19	2	18
1980	44	10	47
1981	21	13	62
1982	14	6	34
1983	13	0	14
1984	21	9	30
1985	22	4	20
1986	21	2	14
1987	15	0	18
1988	12	8	10
1989	13	2	7
1990	15	0	7

Source: Robert W. Schoeff, Dept. of Grain Science and Industry, Kansas State University in cooperation with Ralph Regan FGIS-USDA.

As a result of that increase in grain dust explosion incidents and fatalities, the National Grain and Feed Association established a Research Council to increase the industry's understanding of known causes of explosions and to conduct research into the basic factors contributing to grain dust explosions. Their research is an ongoing effort which promises to result in an improved understanding of the causes and development of preventive measures necessary to reduce the incidents of dust explosions.

Elements of a Dust Explosion

The elements of a grain dust fire or explosion are almost axiomatic; namely, that to be initiated and sustained there must be fuel, oxygen, and an ignition source. To have an explosion, a fourth element, confinement, which confines the rapidly expanding heated gases of combustion within a constraining enclosure until the pressures exceed the ultimate strength of the enclosure, is necessary.

The precise circumstance under which an explosion of a grain dust will occur is a complex combination of dust particle size, concentration in the air (gram/cubic meter), the energy of the ignition source, and less easily determined factors such as the moisture content of the dust (or percent relative humidity of the air) and the actual composition of the dust. Dust from each agricultural commodity has its own explosion characteristics. While researchers have not agreed precisely on the limits of the various characteristics of a particular dust, their conclusions are generally within an acceptably narrow range. Table 2-28C is generally accepted as being a good approximation of lower explosive limits. Others have reported lower explosive limits as low as 20 g/m^3 and as high as 100 g/m^3.

TABLE 2-28C. ***Lower Explosive Limits of Grain Dusts***[3]

Dusts	g/m^3
Corn cob	45
Corn starch	40
Alfalfa	100
Malt barley	55
Peanut hull	45
Rice	50
Soybean flour	60
Sugar	45
Wheat, flour	50
Wheat, starch	45
Cottonseed meal	55

The fuel: Dust particles emanating from various emission points within a grain elevator are of varying composition and of a wide range of sizes. It is generally agreed by researchers that particle sizes below the 100 (micron) range constitute the greatest hazard.[7] As indicated in Table 2-28D, a considerable portion of dust within the elevator environment is smaller than 100 . Larger particles not only tend to settle out rapidly (see Table 2-28E), but have a lower ratio of surface area to mass available for combustion. Approximations indicate a concentration of 20 g/m^3 (near the lowest required for an explosion) would be nearly impossible to see through at a path length of one meter.[5]

While it seems improbable that such a dense cloud would exist within the ambient space of an elevator structure where personnel are present, such concentrations have been measured within the confines of bucket elevators and may also occur in conveyor housings, bins being loaded, silos, dust collecting systems, and connecting spout work.

The mechanism of an explosion depends upon the immediate heat release of a burning particle to ignite and support the burning of adjacent particles.[3] As this rapid spread of flame proceeds from particle to particle, pressure waves and thermal expansion of the air can create an intense shock sufficiently strong to rupture the typical reinforced concrete structure. In studies performed by the U.S. Bureau of Mines,[8] the maximum pressures for corn dust are greater than 100 psig (690 kPa). Concrete structures found in elevators can usually withstand no more than 25 psig (172 kPa).

Suspended dust is not the only fuel with which to be concerned. Dust accumulation on floors, walls, rafters, and equipment may become suspended if disturbed by vibration, fires, or small explosions. If this accumulated dust is suspended in sufficient concentration, the resulting explosive dust concentration can become ignited and progress into an explosion. This resuspended dust can encompass large volumes and propagate minor explosions through an entire elevator.

Oxygen: The oxygen concentration required for a dust explosion is that found in the atmosphere. Using inert gases in equipment to reduce the oxygen concentration enough to prevent explosions has been suggested, but has limited application due to the large size and volume of grain handling equipment. Processing equipment, such as hammermills, may be more likely candidates for inerting.

Ignition sources: The second most important element of a grain dust explosion is ignition of the suspended dust cloud by a source of energy of sufficient intensity and duration. One ignition source that has been identified in a large percentage of known instances is improper use of welding and cutting equipment. (See Tables 2-28F and 2-28G.)

Other identified ignition sources include heat caused by the frictional energy of mechanical equipment such as bucket elevators, bearings and belt drives. Heat or arcing caused by the failure of electrical equipment, such as lighting, motors, and wiring, has also been identified as an ignition source. Miscellaneous ignition sources include open flames from matches or smoking, space heaters, lightning, and internal combustion engines on vehicles such as industrial trucks.

Welding and cutting is a particular concern in the grain industry because many elevators do not have full-time maintenance personnel. This results in unsupervised contractors performing welding operations within the grain elevators. These contractors may be unfamiliar with the fire and explosion potential of grain dust and need to be monitored by elevator management.

Inasmuch as the majority of known locations of explosions in grain elevators stems from the bucket elevator, it would follow that this single piece of operational equipment presents the most serious ignition hazard to the grain handler.[5,6] This conveyance produces ignition energy in a number of ways. Overloading or stalling of the belt generates intense frictional heat on the revolving drive pulley. This has been known to burn the belting to the point of failure, allowing the severed and flaming pieces to drop within its housing. Failure of belt splices could lead to the same results.

Misalignment of belts can cause the leg casing to become hot enough to ignite combustible materials, such as dust or lubricants. The misaligned belt itself probably does not get hot enough to ignite while it is moving, since it has a chance to cool as it moves, but may ignite after the equipment is turned off and the belt is stationary next to the hot casing.

Another potential ignition source associated with bucket elevators is that of overheating bearings. Some older conveyor designs have tail or head pulley bearings located inside of the casings. If these bearings overheat, they can provide sufficient heat for ignition of static or suspended dust. Even bearings located outside of casings can ignite layered dust which in turn can be drawn into the leg casing by the dust collection aspiration or the "air pumping" action of the leg itself.[5]

TABLE 2-28D. *Size Distribution*[9]

Dust size (μ)	Dump pit (mostly beeswings) Retained on %	Dump pit % cum	Belt loading (mostly starch dust) Retained on %	Belt loading % cum	Main elevator (60:40 mixture beeswings: starch) Retained on %	Main elevator % cum	Beans dust Retained on %	Beans dust % cum	Mesh	Inches	mm
+150	94.8	94.8	—	—	56.0	56.0	16.0	16.0	+100	—	—
150–100	3.7	98.5	—	—	11.3	67.3	12.1	28.1	100	0.0059	0.150
100–74	1.1	99.6	—	—	7.0	74.0	13.4	41.5	150	0.0041	0.104
74–38	0.4	100.0	—	—	6.0	80.0	9.2	50.7	200	0.0029	0.074
38–21	—	—	31	31	6.0	86.0	16.3	67.0	450	0.0017	0.043
21–16	—	—	28	59	5.0	91.0	16.0	83.0	630	—	—
16–8	—	—	22	81	4.0	95.0	11.0	94.0	937	—	—
8–6	—	—	10	91	3.0	98.0	4.0	98.0	1875	—	—
6–4	—	—	3	94	2.0	100.0	2.0	100.0	2300	—	—
4–2	—	—	2	96	—	—	—	—	4500	—	—
2–1	—	—	3	99	—	—	—	—	6250	—	—
−1	—	—	1	100	—	—	—	—	12500	—	—
Total	100.0	—	100.0	—	100.0	—	100.0	—	—	—	—

TABLE 2-28E. *Settling Rates for Various Sized Particles*[9]

Size (μ)	Rate of Fall in./min	in./hr	m/min	m/hr
100	320.0	—	8.128	
50	160.0	—	4.064	
10	7.0	—	0.178	
5	1.8	—	0.045	
1	—	5.0	—	0.127
0.5	—	1.4	—	0.035
0.1	—	0.05	—	0.001
smaller	—	~0	—	~0
—		Browian motion		

Note: Specific gravity = 1.0

TABLE 2-28F. *Probable Location of Primary Explosion (1958-1978)*[10]

Location	No. of Facilities	Percent of Facilities
Unknown	107	42.8
Bucket elevator	58	23.2
Hammer mills, roller mills or other grinding equipment	17	6.8
Storage bins or tanks	13	5.2
Headhouse	9	3.6
Adjacent or attached feed mill	8	3.2
Basement	4	1.6
Processing equipment	3	1.2
Dust collector	3	1.2
Tunnel	2	0.8
Distributor heads	2	0.8
Passenger elevator or manlift shaft	2	0.8
Grain drier	2	0.8
Outside and adjacent to facility	2	0.8
Pellet collector	2	0.8
Conveyor system	2	0.8
Receiving pit	2	0.8
Other handling equipment	2	0.8
Processing plant	1	0.4
Down spout	1	0.4
Corn tester	1	0.4
Feed room	1	0.4
Sampler	1	0.4
Storage room	1	0.4
Boiler or feed mill	1	0.4
Electrical switch	1	0.4
Auger conveyor	1	0.4
Electric panel	1	0.4
Sample size	250	100.0

Extraneous foreign material, such as scrap metal, tools, wood, stones, or pieces of concrete, are also a concern within a bucket elevator. They may or may not produce sparks with sufficient energy to ignite dust, but certainly can result in plugged spouts, damage to the belting, or deformation of the elevating cups. When this occurs, the chances of belts stalling or continuous frictional rubbing is increased.

Nonconductive belting moving over the pulleys in bucket elevators can create significant static electricity on the buckets. Research indicates that sufficient energy to initiate a dust explosion is not released from this static discharge, but prudent practice is to reduce this static accumulation by using electrostatically conductive belting and good grounding practices.[11]

The energy inherent in electrical systems is extremely high, but can be minimized as an ignition source by strict adherence to the provisions of NFPA 70, *National Electrical Code®*, for Class II, Group G atmospheres. This applies with equal importance to portable electrical devices, lighting, low-voltage control circuitry, extension drop-lights, and communications equipment.

Confinement: As with all dust explosions (except detonations), the pressures generated after ignition of a grain dust explosion increase until the fuel or oxygen is consumed or until the explosion is vented. If there is no confinement (i.e., unlimited venting), explosion pressures are

TABLE 2-28G. *Probable Ignition Sources (1958-1978)*[5]

Source	No. of Facilities	Percent of Facilities
Unknown	103	41.2
Welding	43	17.2
Electrical failure	10	4.0
Tramp metal	10	4.0
Fire other than welding or cutting	10	4.0
Unidentified foreign objects	9	3.6
Friction from choked leg	8	3.2
Overheated bearings	7	2.8
Other spark	7	2.8
Friction sparks	7	2.8
Lightning	6	2.4
Extension cords in legs	4	1.6
Faulty motors	4	1.6
Static electricity	3	1.2
Fire from friction of slipping belt in leg	3	1.2
Flammable vapor	3	1.2
Smoldering grain	2	0.8
Smoking material	2	0.8
Firecracker	1	0.4
Volatile chemical escaped from soybean processing	1	0.4
External cob pile fire	1	0.4
Heating system	1	0.4
Gas in bin ignited	1	0.4
Extinguishing fire	1	0.4
Leak in gas pipe ignited	1	0.4
Electric control panel explosion	1	0.4
Slipping conveyor belt	1	0.4
Sample size	250	100.0

minimal, and the incident should more properly be called a flash fire. On the other hand, as confinement increases, the explosion pressures can build up to experimentally observed levels over 100 psig (690 kPa). Grain elevator structures and equipment cannot withstand pressures anywhere near these levels, so considerable damage will occur, unless these pressures can be vented. Due to structural considerations, most existing grain elevators would be nearly impossible to retrofit with adequate venting, but newly designed elevators are adaptable to increased venting and the resulting reduction in explosion confinement.

THE SAFEGUARDS

Building Design

NFPA 61B, *Prevention of Fires and Explosions in Grain Elevators and Facilities Handling Bulk Raw Agricultural Commodities*, has been prepared as a standard to assist designers of grain handling facilities, devoting considerable attention to the physical structure. NFPA 61B is not intended to apply to existing facilities, which may have been constructed prior to its publication (1989); however, major modification or expansion made to an existing facility should enhance safety to life and property. The following discussion summarizes the current industry thinking concerning the design of new facilities and does not necessarily reflect the view of the author.

The modern design approach is to construct upright storage silos of reinforced concrete or steel, with a high contiguous structure known as a headhouse to elevate the grain high enough to pass through necessary scales, samplers, garners, cleaners, and distributors by gravity into the storage bins. Structures should be of noncombustible materials. Enclosures, such as silos, tanks, bucket elevator housings, and ancillary structures, should be designed to relieve explosion pressure waves as much as possible if such an incident happens. This is not always physically possible because of the very nature of the configuration of the enclosure.

According to NFPA 68, *Explosion Venting*, numerous methods have been proposed for calculating the vent area for an enclosure. Some venting models have used the surface area of the enclosure as a basis for determining vent area. Analysis of available data shows that such methods overcome certain deficiencies of previous methods of calculating vent area. The recommended venting equation is as follows:

$$A_p = \frac{CA_s}{(P_{red})^{1/2}}$$

where A_p = vent area (ft^2 or m^2)
C = venting equation constant (see Table 2-33H) A_s = internal surface area of enclosure (ft^2 or m^2)
P_{red} = maximum internal overpressure that can be withstood by the weakest structural element (psi or kPa)

TABLE 2-28H. *Fuel Characteristic Constant for Venting Equation*

Fuel	C(psi)$^{1/2}$	C(kPa)^1
Anhydrous ammonia	0.05	0.13
Methane	0.14	0.37
Gases with fundamental burning velocity less than 1.3 times that of propane	0.17	0.45
St-1 dusts	0.10	0.26
St-2 dusts	0.12	0.30
St-3 dusts	0.20	0.51

The use of doors, windows, multiple explosion-relief panels, and light-gage structural coverings on steel structures is a practical approach to an acceptable design. Stairwells and elevator shafts, where they are enclosed, should be protected with approved fire doors. Fire walls of approved design can be provided to separate the grain handling function from adjoining grain processing operations, such as flour milling, preparation for oil extraction, feed milling, or grinding. Where tunnels, basements, or other underground structures can be avoided, the alternate use of ground-level or aboveground structures can give opportunity for maximum openings to the atmosphere. Where sufficient land area is available, the placement of structures for weighing, cleaning, and other operational functions can be remote from silo storage and interconnected with inclined belt systems.

All surfaces, bin bottoms, and spout inclinations should be designed to be self-cleaning when the grain or grain products flow. Structural ledges, beams, or other horizontal surfaces should be designed, where practicable, with an inclination of a minimum of 60 degrees from the horizontal to prevent gradual buildup of static dust. Where possible, design should accommodate the flushing down of accumulated dust on vertical walls and overhead structures with water.

No direct interconnecting openings should be constructed between silos or storage bins. Other methods of controlling the displaced air of filling and emptying should be provided. Where possible, the placement of bucket elevators, in open air, apart from the structure should be considered. Additionally, office buildings, employee break rooms, maintenance shops, inspection labs, and control rooms should be located remote from concrete structures when constructing new elevators.

Mechanical Design

Many devices are available to detect, warn, and control faulty operation of mechanical equipment or their components. Many of these systems were neither available nor sufficiently developed to be applicable in Class II, Group G dust atmospheres until recent years. Among them are hot-bearing sensors, speed indicators, alignment devices, level-sensing gages, slowdown detectors, overflow alarms, and pressure gages, all of which can serve to indicate or react to malfunctioning units. Particularly important among these are the speed indicator and alignment devices for monitoring bucket elevators. If properly designed, installed, and monitored, these devices can prevent ignition from stalled and rubbing belting.

A combination of mesh screens, grating, scalpers, or magnets will prevent large extraneous material and metal from entering into the grain handling machinery. Depending on individual elevators, permanent or electro-magnets, large-mesh screening, grizzlies, and specific gravity separators may be appropriate. Their use is particularly important just prior to the point where the grain enters hammermills or other types of grinders.

Dust Control

The need for adequate dust control has been established. Dust control in elevators, however, should not be limited to installation of dust collection systems, but should be a systematic approach to dust control. This systematic approach should include designs which limit the amount of dust liberated from the grain, mechanical dust collection at grain transfer points where dust occurs, containment of dust to selected points where mechanical dust collection can be effective, reduction of dust concentrations within equipment, maintenance of dust collection equipment, and manual housekeeping to complement mechanical dust control.

The design of dust collection systems must provide sufficient capture velocity at the point of emission, particularly at conveyor loading and discharge points. Design must also provide sufficient air velocity within the ducts to prevent settlement of the particles and subsequent plugging. Blast gates and fresh-air inlet dampers are necessary to balance the air flow to all points served by the system so that starving of some remote emission points is avoided. Operators must understand the dust collection systems, so that they can monitor and maintain their effectiveness on a daily basis.

If a baghouse or fabric filter is used, the porosity of the filter media must be maintained to avoid diminishing the air flow. High humidity and fine dust particles often form a cake on the bags and reduce the air passage. In such instances, replacement or laundering of the bags is necessary. (See NFPA 91, *Blower and Exhaust Systems for Dust, Stock and Vapor Removal or Conveying*, and NFPA 650, *Pneumatic Conveying Systems for Handling Combustible Materials*, for further information on the application and design of air-moving systems.)

Containment of dust to selected points not only makes the mechanical dust collection system more effective, but also limits the amount of manual housekeeping effort needed to maintain the lowest feasible level of accumulated dust.

Typical methods to reduce dust liberation from grain include reducing the distance and velocity grain is allowed to free fall onto conveyors or from spouting. (Choke feeding, where possible, is the best approach to limit grain velocity.) Reduction of conveyor belt speeds and adequate belt tension can both be effective dust control methods where horizontal belt conveyors are used. Well-designed transition points that do not have abrupt changes in direction can also limit the amount of dust liberated from the grain. Additives, such as water, soybean oil, and mineral oil, have been proposed as an additional method to control dust. Research is being conducted to determine whether these additives deteriorate grain quality for the end-user and whether grain so treated can meet the grading standards of the USDA.

Regardless of the facility design or amount of mechanical dust collection, manual housekeeping efforts are important in grain elevator facilities. Although safe levels of accumulated dust are impossible to determine, housekeeping programs at each facility should be designed to keep the dust accumulation at the lowest feasible level. This housekeeping program should focus on not only grain dust but also any type of combustibles to reduce the possibility of their providing an ignition source for a dust explosion.

Electrical Design

Electrical wiring and equipment in grain dust environments should be installed in accordance with Articles 500 and 502 and, where applicable, Article 504 of NFPA 70, *National Electrical Code* (*NEC*). These articles need to be thoroughly understood by those installing or maintaining electrical equipment in a grain elevator facility. Individual paragraphs in these articles cover equipment requirements for maximum surface temperature, transformers and capacitors, surge protection, wiring methods, switches/breakers, etc.; motors; ventilating piping; utilization equipment; lighting equipment; flexible cords; receptacles and plugs; signal and communication systems; live parts; and grounding. No attempt is made here to paraphrase these articles. The reader is encouraged to review the most current edition of NFPA 70, *National Electrical Code*.

Away from the technical requirements of NFPA 70, *National Electrical Code*, the development of economical and miniaturized electronic components for use in Class II, Group G atmospheres has made the operation and control of grain elevators more sophisticated and less labor intensive. Remote control of the entire facility from a centralized control center is now a reality in new installations. This technological advance has dictated the need for redundant detection of malfunctions, since people are no longer in an operating area to observe the minute by minute activity.

The more common safeguards include electrical interlocking to simultaneously shut down all activities in a sequenced fashion when one unit of a sequentially connected operation fails. Annunciator panels can display the exact cause of shutdown to the operator. Ammeters and load indicators can depict the exact weight being carried by conveying equipment. Spring-return pneumatic devices can activate shutdown conditions even in a total power failure. Fully electronic scales now safely transmit millivolt differentials, detected by a load cell or strain gage, to a remote amplifier for direct conversion into information on weight.

Maintenance

A preventive maintenance program is essential not only to ensure trouble-free operation and to minimize breakdowns, but, in grain elevator facilities, it is also a critical safeguard for eliminating ignition sources. This preventive maintenance program should include lubrication of bearings, checking of belt splices, replacement of bent or missing bucket elevator cups, and the early remedy of leaking, worn-out spouting.

Dust filters should be checked frequently for plugging, excessive pressure drop, and worn or poorly sealed rotary airlocks. Ductwork in the aspiration system should be free of plug-ups and bent ducts, and blast gates should be opened or closed consistent with system balancing. Grain traps should be emptied frequently and floor-sweep openings kept closed except when in use.

Electrical junction boxes should be kept closed and lighting fixture protective globes kept in place. Whenever maintenance work on the electrical systems is performed, qualified personnel should ensure that the power is disconnected or that hazardous dust concentrations are not present.

Welding and any other hotwork should be rigidly controlled by facility management. The use of a written "hotwork permit" is generally the best system to ensure that hotwork is not performed in the presence of explosive dust concentrations. This is particularly important with contractors whose employees may not be aware of the dust explosion hazard.

Improved maintenance diagnostic equipment can also be effective in monitoring equipment that could become an ignition source for an explosion. This diagnostic equipment includes bearing temperature monitors, bearing vibration monitors, and infrared analysis of electrical and mechanical equipment.

Pesticides

Pesticides and fumigants present minimal hazard from a fire standpoint if properly used. The only two concerns are the flash point of the pesticide being used and the toxic products of combustion to which fire fighters could be exposed.

Liquid fumigants and pesticides as applied to grain normally have flash points well in excess of 100°F (37.8°C). However, some undiluted, residual-type pesticides have flash points near this 100°F (37.8°C) level. Whenever possible, these concentrates should be stored away from the elevator, and only the dilute mixtures utilized within the elevator.

Solid phosphine-based fumigants also have a potential fire hazard. Self-ignition of phosphine gas can take place at 1.79 percent volumetric concentration. This concentration is more than 10 times the level that manufacturers recommend for effectiveness. However, phosphine fumigant storage canisters and poorly distributed fumigants can achieve these ignition concentrations. Fumigant storage canisters should always be opened away from other flammables and dust hazard environments, and only qualified or certified personnel should be allowed to apply phosphine.

Fire Control Systems

Grain elevators have few applications where traditional automatic sprinkler systems would provide much protection. The nature of the explosion hazard is such that, even if sprinklers are installed, the lines would likely be ruptured by the shock waves. Additionally, explosions are normally initiated so rapidly that fusible links would have insufficient time to react. Combine this ineffectiveness with the lack of combustibles present and the catastrophic damage which could result from water leaks seeping into grain storage bins and it becomes clear that general-purpose automatic sprinkler systems would do little to mitigate damage from an explosion hazard. There are, however, several specific applications where sprinklers, fixed water spray nozzles, and explosion suppression systems can be effective.

Wood elevators, which have a significant fire hazard potential, as well as the explosion hazard, are the major exception where automatic sprinkler installation can be justified. Additional specific applications where sprinklers or fixed water spray nozzles can have some benefit are within the drive pulley enclosure of bucket elevators; at remote, elevated belt gallery structures where manual fire fighting would be impossible; and within some grain dryers in which, because of design, it would be impossible to use hose streams effectively.

Explosion suppression offers the grain industry a possible tool to reduce the number of explosions. Explosion suppression technology (rapid detection of incipient explosion and immediate introduction of suppressing agent) has been used effectively in other industries for some time. Recent research efforts directed at applying the technology to the grain industry have resulted in the development of self-contained explosion suppression devices that are suitable for installation on bucket elevators.[12] Although a number of bucket elevators have had these suppressors installed, it is too soon to evaluate their long-range effectiveness and ability to survive in the elevator environment.

One additional fire control method which needs consideration is that of manual fire fighting. A number of explosions have been reported to occur after hose streams were used to fight fires within an elevator.[13] Application of hose streams within an elevator where the possibility of a dust explosion exists must be a well-considered endeavor. Any application of high-pressure water or use of fire extinguishers that disperse accumulated dust must be avoided to prevent an airborne dust concentration which could be ignited.

SUMMARY

Much of the above discussion is a reiteration of concepts and principles that have been known by the grain handling industry for a number of years or recently learned through its research efforts. The devices, systems, and machinery now available are much more extensive than in earlier years. There are an estimated 10,000 grain elevators in the United States ranging from crossroad country stations to newly constructed export facilities. Many of these newer facilities have incorporated the devices mentioned above.

In spite of this, grain dust explosions still occur, and, in the majority of instances, the exact location of the primary explosion and ignition source are not precisely known. (See Figure 2-28B.) However, this much is known: the initial explosion has the characteristic of transmitting pressure waves, vibration, and air movement throughout the facility which could result in other deposited dust being thrown into suspension. This additional dust might have been lodged on the ledges, beams, walls, floors, and inaccessible places and is exposed to the progressing flame front. The result is a series of additional explosions known as secondary explosions.[14]

FIG. 2-28B. Elevator explosion scene.

In summarizing the potential hazards associated with the handling and storage of grain, one must remember that its dust is a powerful fuel. Prudent consideration of its inherent dangers requires respect, care, and adherence to building codes and regulations in the design and construction of each facility. Once the facility is built, each day requires positive management appreciation of the inherent dangers, and action to ensure that all those working in the facility understand the basics of proper operations, maintenance, safety, housekeeping, and training.

Investigations are continuing into the causes of grain dust explosions in hope of more clearly defining the practices and methods needed to reduce the hazard. It would appear that the most fruitful field for concentration is the reduction in the potential of bucket elevators as ignition sources. This will require a better understanding of the methods to reduce dust concentration within the enclosure and better methods for detecting the impending mechanical failures that could lead to ignition.

If it is assumed that some dust will aways be present within the grain elevator facility, the elimination of the explosion hazard can only be accomplished by controlling the dust and removing its ignition sources.

BIBLIOGRAPHY

References Cited

1. Source: Verbal Communications, Statistical Reporting Service, U.S. Department of Agriculture, Washington, DC, 1989.
2. Christensen, C. M., ed., *Storage of Cereal Grains and Their Products*, American Association of Cereal Chemists, St. Paul, MN, 1982.
3. Palmer, K. N., *Dust Explosions and Fires*, Chapman and Hall, London, 1973.
4. "Mineral Resources," 30 CFR 18.65, U.S. Government Prining Office, Washington, DC.
5. "Prevention of Grain Elevator and Mill Explosions," Publication #NMAB 367-2, 1982, National Materials Advisory Board, National Academy of Science, National Academy Press, Washington, DC.
6. Anderson, Robert, *Proceedings of International Symposium on Grain Dust Explosions*, Session III, Grain Elevator and Processing Society, Minneapolis, MN, 1977.
7. Lilienfeld, Pedro, "Special Report on Dust Explosibility," GCA-TR-78-17-6, EPA Contract No. 68-01-4143 Technical Service Area 1, Task Order No. 24, March 1978, GCA Technology Division, Environmental Protection Agency, Washington, DC.
8. Jacobsen, M., *et al*, "Explosibility of Agricultural Dust," R1 5753, 1961, U.S. Bureau of Mines, Washington, DC.
9. Matkovic, Dr. Ing. Mijo, "Dust Composition, Concentration, and Its Effects," *Proceedings of International Symposium on Grain Dust Explosions*, Grain Elevator and Processing Society, Minneapolis, MN, 1977.
10. "Prevention of Grain Elevator Explosions—An Achievable Goal," U.S. Department of Agriculture, Washington, DC, 1979.
11. Dahn, J., *Electrostatic Grounding Characteristics of Grain Facilities*, National Grain and Feed Association, Fire and Explosion Research Council, Washington, DC, 1982.
12. Gilles, J., *Explosion Venting and Suppression of Bucket Elevators*, National Grain and Feed Association, Fire and Explosion Research Council, Washington, DC, 1980.
13. "Guidelines for Investigation of Grain Dust Explosion," Publication #NMAB 367-4, 1983, National Materials Advisory Board, National Academy of Science, Washington, DC.
14. Tamanini, F., *Dust Explosion Progagation in Simulated Grain Conveyor Galleries*, National Grain and Feed Association, Fire and Explosion Research Council, Washington, DC, 1983.

NFPA Codes, Standards, and Recommended Practices

Reference to the following NFPA codes, standards, and recommended practices will provide further information on the safeguards for grain and grain milling discussed in this chapter. (See the latest *NFPA Catalog* for availability of current editions of the following documents.)

NFPA 10, *Portable Fire Extinguishers.*

NFPA 13, *Installation of Sprinkler Systems.*

NFPA 14, *Standpipe and Hose Systems.*

NFPA 15, *Water Spray Fixed Systems for Fire Protection.*

NFPA 61B, *Prevention of Fires and Explosions in Grain Elevators and Facilities Handling Bulk Raw Agricultural Commodities.*

NFPA 61C, *Prevention of Fire and Dust Explosion in Feed Mills.*

NFPA 61D, *Prevention of Fire and Dust Explosions in the Milling of Agricultural Commodities for Human Consumption.*

NFPA 68, *Explosion Venting.*

NFPA 69, *Explosion Prevention Systems.*

NFPA 70, *National Electrical Code.*

NFPA 77, *Static Electricity.*

NFPA 78, *Lightning Protection Code.*

NFPA 91, *Blower and Exhaust Systems for Dust, Stock, and Vapor Removal or Conveying.*

NFPA 493, *Intrinsically Safe Apparatus in Division I Hazardous Locations.*

NFPA 650, *Pneumatic Conveying Systems for Handling Combustible Materials.*

Additional Reading

Allen, J., and Calcote, H. F., "Grain Dust Ignition by Friction Sparks," SMS-81-049, 1981, National Grain and Feed Association, Washington, DC.

Bartknecht, W., "Effectiveness of Explosion Venting as a Protective Measure for Silos," *Plant/Operation Progress*, Vol. 4, No. 1 (1985), pp. 4-13.

Bartknecht, W., "Dust Explosions Course Prevention Protection," Springer Verlog, Berlin Herdelberg, NY, 1989.

Britton, L. G., "Systems for Electrostatic Evaluation in Industrial Silos," *Plant/Operation Progress*, Vol. 7, Jan. 1988, pp. 45-50.

Britton, L. G. and Kuby, D. C., "Analysis of a Dust Deflagration," *Plant/Operation Progress*, Vol. 8, No. 3 (July 1989), pp. 177-180.

Christensen, C. M., ed., *Storage of Cereal Grains and Their Products*, American Association of Cereal Chemists, St. Paul, MN, 1982.

Corbett, G. P., "Dust Explosion Destroys New Jersy Flour Mill," *Fire Engineering*, Vol. 138, No. 2 (1985), p. 22.

"Dust Collectors," *Loss Prevention Data Sheet 7-73*, Factory Mutual Engineering Corp., Norwood, MA.

Dust Control for Grain Elevators, National Grain and Feed Association, Washington, DC, 1981.

Eckhoff, R. K., Fuhre, K., and Pedersen, G. H., "Vented Maize Starch Explosions in a 236 Cubic Meter Experimental Silo," Fire and Explosion Research Report No. ESV-86-070, 1986, National Grain and Feed Association, Washington, DC.

Factory Mutual Engineering Corporation, "Grain Storage and Grain Milling," *Loss Prevention Data Sheet 7-15*, Factory Mutual System, Norwood, MA.

Frank, T. E., "Fire and Explosion Control in Bag Filter Dust Collection Systems," *Fire Journal*, Vol. 75, No. 2 (Mar. 1981), pp. 73-80, 94.

Gillis, J. P., "Rapid Fire Detection in Dust Process Equipment Utilizing High Air Flows," *Proceedings* of the American Institute of Chemical Engineers National Meeting, AIChE, 1988, p. 25.

Hertzberg, M., *A Critique of the Dust Explosibility Index*, U.S. Department of the Interior, Bureau of Mines, Pittsburg, PA, 1987.

Hoenig, S. A., "Reducing the Hazards of Dust Explosions," *Plant/Operation Progress*, Vol. 8, No. 3 (July 1989), pp. 119-128.

Joffe, H. M., "Grain Elevator Protection, What's Being Done Today," *Fire Journal*, Vol.74, No. 3 (May 1980), pp. 131-133.

Lunn, G. A., "Note on the Lower Explosibility Limit of Organic Dusts," *Journal of Hazardous Materials*, Vol. 17, No. 2 (Feb. 1988), pp. 207-213.

Moore, P. E., "Industrial Dust Explosions," K. L. Cashdollar and M. Hertzberg, eds., ASTM Special Publication 958, American Society for Testing Materials, Philadelphia, PA., 1987.

"Moving Fire: Fire Hazards of Belt Conveyors," *Record*, Vol. 54, No. 6 (1977), pp. 18-21.

National Materials Advisory Board, *Prevention of Grain Elevator and Mill Explosions*, Publication NMAB-2, National Academy Press, Washington DC, 1982.

NFGA, Fire and Explosion Research Council Research Reports (series), National Grain and Feed Association, Washington, DC.

"Risks in Handling Combustibile Dusts," *Fire Prevention*, No. 213 (Oct. 1988), pp.32-33.

Shutske, J. M., and Field, W. E., "Early Detection and Suppression of Farm Machinary Fires," *Proceedings* of the Agri-Mation 2 Conference and Exposition, ASAE, 1986, pp. 174-183.

Shutske, J. M., and Field, W. E., "Nature and Magnitude of Fires Involving Agricultural Equipment," *Papers* Presented at the 1986 Summer Meeting of the American Society of Mechanical Engineers, ASME, 1986, 11 p.

Spencer, M. R., "Bulk Grain Handling," *Industrial Fire Hazards Handbook*, 3rd Edition, National Fire Protection Association, Quincy, MA, 1990.

Williams, G. M., "Quantitative Method for the Analysis of Electrostatic Hazards and Risks," *Industry Applications Society*, Annual Meeting, Oct. 2-6, 1977, pp. 1058-1064.

STORAGE AND HANDLING OF SOLID FUELS

Revised by John E. O'Green

This chapter discusses the practices and fire hazards associated with the storage and handling of the two principal solid fuels—coal and wood—particularly as they apply to electric generation and industrial and commercial environments. The hazards associated with the actual use of these fuels in firing boilers and furnaces are covered in Section 2, Chapter 5, "Boiler Furnaces." This chapter confines itself to the hazards associated with the storage and handling of the fuels to the point of delivery into the firing system.

The following chapters may be of interest to readers of this chapter: Section 8, Chapter 7, "Outdoor Storage Practices," which contains information about the outdoor storage of wood products; Section 8, Chapter 31, "Materials Handling Equipment" and Section 6, Chapter 19, "Air Moving Equipment," which both offer information about conveying systems; Section 6, Chapter 18, "Special Systems for Explosion Damage Control," which discusses explosion venting; and Section 8, Chapter 34, "Motor Vehicles," which contains information about the use of motor vehicles in storage facilities.

COAL AS A FUEL

Coal presents hazards between the time it is mined and its eventual consumption in boilers and furnaces. These hazards are associated with its transportation, storage, and bunkering. They can be classified as: (1) spontaneous heating, (2) dust explosions, and (3) gas generation and explosions.

Oxidation

ASTM D 388, *Specifications for Classification of Coals by Rank*, ranks coal by its tendency to absorb oxygen. The lower the rank, the greater the tendency for coal to absorb oxygen (i.e., oxidize).

The simple downward classification of coals is: (1) anthracite, (2) bituminous, (3) subbituminous, and (4) lignite. Some coals oxidize far more readily than others. Anthracite, the highest ranked coal, has very low spontaneous heating tendencies.

Generally, the following statements are true of coal:

1. The higher the inherent (equilibrium) moisture, the higher the oxidizing tendency.
2. The lower the moisture and ash-free Btu, the higher the oxidizing tendency. The higher the oxygen in the coal, the higher the heating tendency.
3. Sulphur, once considered a major factor, is now thought to be a minor factor in the spontaneous heating of coal. There are many very-low-sulphur western subbituminous and lignite coals that have very high oxidizing characteristics, and there are high-sulphur coals that exhibit relatively low oxidizing characteristics.
4. Spontaneous oxidation is a solid-to-gas reaction, which happens initially when air (a gas) scrubs past a coal surface (a solid). Oxygen from the air is absorbed by the coal, raising the temperature of the coal. As the reaction proceeds, the moisture in the coal is liberated as a vapor, and then some of the volatile matter that normally has a distinct odor is released. The amount of surface area of the coal that is exposed is a direct factor in its heating tendency. The finer the size of the coal, the more surface is exposed per unit of weight and the greater the oxidizing potential, all other factors being disregarded.
5. Many times, segregation of the coal particle sizes is the major cause of heating. The coarse sizes allow the air to enter the pile at one location and react with high surface area fires at another location. Coals with a large top size, e.g., ≥4 in. (100 mm), will segregate more in handling than those ≤2 in. (50 mm) in size.
6. It is generally believed that the rate of reaction doubles for every 15 to 20°F (8 to 11°C) increase in temperature.
7. Freshly mined coal has the greatest oxidizing characteristic, but a hot spot in a pile may not appear before one or two months. As the initial oxidation takes place, the temperature gradually increases and the rate of oxidation accelerates.

John E. O'Green is safety and health director for American Electric Power Service Corp., Lancaster, OH.

8. There is a critical amount of airflow through a portion of a coal pile that maximizes the oxidizing or heating tendencies of coal. If there is no airflow through a pile, there is no oxygen from the air to stimulate oxidation. If there is a plentiful supply of air, any heat generated from oxidation will be carried off, and the pile temperature will reach equilibrium with the air temperature; this is considered a ventilated pile.
9. When there is just sufficient airflow for the coal to absorb most of the oxygen from the air and an insufficient airflow to dissipate the heat generated, the reaction rate increases, and the temperatures may eventually exceed desirable limits.

The general ranges of densities of coal are given in Table 2-29A to illustrate the significance of the density of the coal at various stages in its utilization.

TABLE 2-29A. ***General Ranges of Densities of Coal***

Physical Description of Coal	Range of Density lbs/cu ft (kg/m^3)	Approximate Percentage of Coal Pile Occupied by Air
Coal in the seam before mining	80–85 (12.8–13.6)	0%
Coal size 2″ × 0 normal shipping size as loaded in RR car, truck, etc., *No* Compaction	50–55 (8–8.8)	36%
Coal size 2″ × 0 compacted with track-mounted dozers	60–65 (9.6–10.4)	24%
Coal size 2″ × 0 compacted with rubber-tired carryall or sheepsfoot roller	70–75 (11.2–12)	12%

STORAGE PRACTICES FOR COAL

The methods used to build outside storage piles and to fill silos, bins, and bunkers are significant in controlling the oxidation hazard of coal. Coal is usually stored either in an uncompacted [50 to 55 lbs/cu ft (801 to 881 kg/m^3)] or compacted [70 to 75 lbs/cu ft (1121 to 1201 kg/m^3)] form. When coal is not compacted, air occupies approximately 35 percent of the volume of the pile, so it is relatively easy for air to move through the pile. Coal is at this density when it is handled on conveyors or placed in trucks, railroad cars, bunkers, or silos, or in any form of "live" pile. Coal is uncompacted whenever it is moved and falls on itself.

Compacted Coal Storage

Generally, when coal is compacted, it is placed in relatively thin layers from 6 to 12 in. (15 to 25 mm) thick. Each layer is then rolled over with a device that has a relatively high loading in lbs/sq ft (kg/m^2) of surface area (1 lb/sq ft equals 4.9 kg/m^2). Rubber-tired carryalls are normally used for this purpose, since they compact the coal while they convey the coal to the desired location.

A coal pile should be compacted on all sides to eliminate any low-density areas. When coal is compacted, it has a density of 70 to 75 lbs/cu ft (1121 to 1201 kg/m^3), and air occupies only 12 percent of the pile. This makes it far less likely that there would be appreciable air movement through the pile. Virtually all types of coal have been stored successfully in this manner, including piles exceeding 1 million tons (1 ton equals 1016 kg) and at depths approaching 100 ft (30.5 m).

Large users of coal, e.g., utilities and large industries, will generally have compacted permanent storage piles and uncompacted "live" storage piles, while the smaller users, e.g., small industry, commercial, and residential, normally have uncompacted storage. All coal users have some form of uncompacted storage, and this form of storage may require special fire protection considerations.

Uncompacted Coal Storage

Ideally, all uncompacted coal is stored in properly designed bunkers, silos, bins, and even outside piles so all of the coal moves through the storage system with no dead or unmoving portion of the coal pile. Although the coal is still subject to the slow oxidation, it will move through the system before any appreciable heating can occur. Many new bunkers, silos, and bins are designed for mass flow of coal, and heating problems have been virtually eliminated. Coal piles may be worked in such a manner that the piles are rotated and the first coal in is the first coal out. This achieves the same results as the mass flow conditions in bins where none of the coal remains for prolonged periods of time.

When bunkers, silos, or bins have not been, or cannot be, designed to achieve mass flow, heating of the coal may occur and create problems. As much as practical, sealing off the bottom of the storage system can minimize the airflow through the coal; however, space above the coal in the storage system should not be sealed. This will prevent the accumulation of gases that may become liberated from freshly mined or crushed coal. In these cases, the area above the coal should be ventilated to carry off any accumulation of gases. Some storage systems, particularly ones where pulverized coal is stored, are designed to prevent the formation of a hazardous mixture of gases and coal dust with air.

It may be necessary to routinely draw down the storage system and clean the static deposits of coal from the bunker to minimize problems. Because cleaning bunkers, silos, or bins can be hazardous, special safety precautions should be taken.

If heating occurs in a bunker, silo, or bin, it is generally in an area where static deposits of coal have remained for a period of time. Normally, this condition is resolved by drawing down the bin and removing the heated, or static, deposits. A controlled amount of water, wisely applied, may provide sufficient cooling to allow the user to remove the heated coal and burn it in a normal manner; however, it is very difficult to apply water into stored coal and successfully eliminate further heating. Extreme caution should be practiced when using water on large areas of hot coal in a confined volume to prevent the accumulation of hazardous amounts of water gas that contain varying amounts of hydrogen and carbon monoxide. Generally, moving hot coal in an outside environment will cool the coal substantially.

Care should be exercised whenever using water so that puffs of steam that could impair visibility are not formed. Excessive amounts of water should be avoided because handling and utilization problems may be created.

Selecting an outside storage site: Many plants have uncompacted storage piles on the ground, and some precautions must be taken in selecting and preparing a storage site. First, it should be determined that the proposed site is not over open sewers or other devices that may bring air into the base of the pile. Neither should the site contain any steam lines or systems that could raise the temperature of a portion of the pile beyond normal ambient temperatures.

Once selected, the site should be cleaned of all vegetation and foreign materials, particularly materials that may have heating tendencies. Then it should be graded smoothly and contoured so that water will not drain into the base of the pile. The periphery of a pile should be given special attention in the grading process to make sure that all of the water draining from the pile will be carried away.

Recognizing that uncompacted piles may tend to heat, a good practice is to size and/or shape a pile for easy access to areas that have heat so that they can then be handled appropriately. It is also good practice to limit the height of an uncompacted pile to approximately 15 ft (4.6 m) if the coal is known to have high heating tendencies. Greater pile heights can be tolerated if the coal has low heating characteristics and if the pile can be rotated with ease.

Weatherproofing of Coal Piles

In very special cases, e.g., when coal piles are to be retained for long periods or coking properties are of special importance, the exclusion of air can be further improved by covering the completed pile with road tar in the same manner as the same dressing is applied to roads. Experience has shown that road tar is an efficient and economical method and, in addition, can be used on heated heaps which, in the complete absence of air, would then stop oxidizing and cool off. The sealing of a coal pile has some added advantages, such as protection against wind loss and reduction of channeling due to heavy rain. A secondary effect, therefore, is reduction of atmospheric and river pollution.

Special Storage Precautions

It is beneficial to handle coal going to storage in a manner that prevents segregation of coarse coal from the fines. Segregation occurs when coal is placed in a conical pile; the coarse coal runs to the edge and outside of the pile, and the fines collect in the center. The air can then move readily through the coarse coal to the fines containing the large surface area, greatly encouraging heating of the pile.

Placing coal in storage near a vertical wall presents special problems, because coal tends to be less compacted when it is placed near these vertical surfaces unless special precautions are taken. Preferably, coal should not be stored around supporting beams or similar members. Less dense coal provides a natural flue for air ventilation. When vertical walls or surfaces of any kind cannot be avoided, the coal should be stored along the wall or parallel to the wall, as opposed to pushing the coal up to the vertical surface.

Selecting Coal for Storage

Commercial and domestic users select the size of coal best suited for their burning equipment, and, in most cases, it is usually a double-screened coal with a 1¼-in. (32 mm) top size, a ¼-in. (6 mm) bottom size, and a relatively small percentage of fines. This size coal, if handled reasonably well, will not segregate, and a pile can be considered fully ventilated. There will be a minimum tendency of heating because of fewer fines and because any heat generated will be readily removed from the pile.

Industries and utilities normally use a coal with a larger percentage of fines, and it is advantageous to use a coal that can be handled and stored with ease. Normally, a good shipping size is 2-in. (50 mm) top size or less, but if a larger size is used, extra care should be exercised to minimize segregation and oxidizing in storage.

Detection of Heating

Heating in a coal storage pile is usually detectable by smelling or seeing the vapor. Vapor will travel through the path of least resistance in a storage pile and may emerge from the pile at a location remote from the hot spot. This vapor should not be confused with a moisture vapor that may be noticeable on cool mornings.

When heating occurs in coal, the vapor generally emitted has a distinct odor. It is part of the volatile matter of the coal and may contain some sulphur compounds that are particularly noticeable. As stated, in many cases this vapor is visible, and it should alert the operator to start planning a procedure to eliminate a potential hazard. Depending on the materials of construction, and whether the heating has occurred in bunkers, bins, or silos, the operator has several choices. One alternative is to select a convenient time to empty the storage vessel to the point where the hot material can be removed, or cooled and removed. In some cases the vessel can be sealed and inerted with an inert gas; this will minimize further heating. Care may still need to be taken in ultimate utilization of the coal.

Sometimes small-diameter pipes of approximately 1 in. (25 mm) in diameter are placed into a pile to record temperatures at several elevations; however, it is easy to be misled, because temperatures within a pile can vary, even within a few feet of each other. Normally, if the pile is less than the temperature the human body can tolerate, e.g., 125°F (51.6°C), it is reasonable to leave the pile as is, but to continue monitoring. If the temperature is over 125°F (51.6°C), plans should be made to remove the hot area. A hot area usually can be dug out and spread out to cool on the surface of the pile if the heated area is not too large and hot. At other times, the coal can be dug out and sprayed with water and mixed with cooler coal and then consumed as soon as possible. When hot coal is fed to pulverized fuel-fired equipment, the operator should use extreme caution and be familiar with the potential hazards.

DUST EXPLOSIONS WITH COAL

The conditions that create dust explosions usually occur when dry coal is being transferred from place to place or when an air current disturbs dust that has accumulated on surfaces. An ignition source must also be present at the location of the coal dust/air mixture to create the explosion.

Although these types of explosions are rare, when they do occur, injury and loss of life and damage to equipment can be substantial.

There are several precautions that can be taken to help eliminate this problem. Commercial and domestic coals, for example, can be double-screened to minimize the number of fines, and they may also be treated with oil. Providing sufficient surface moisture to the coal to get the fine dust to stick to the larger sizes can be very effective in many installations.

Wetting agents sometimes are used with water to improve dust control. Many industrial and utility plants use vacuum hoods or other sophisticated systems to minimize the dust problem. Eliminating ignition sources is desirable, but is not always possible; therefore, it is more effective to eliminate coal dust/air mixtures that may explode. Some of the ignition sources that can be controlled are smoking, cutting, and welding. Some of the causes that are much more difficult to eliminate are static electricity and occasional electrical sparks.

GAS GENERATION AND EXPLOSIONS WITH COAL

Methane and other gases can be liberated from freshly mined and freshly crushed coal. An accumulation of a dangerous proportion of gas from this source is rare, but when explosions do occur, severe and fatal losses may result.

Dangerous accumulations of gas can occur over the tops of bins, silos, and bunkers, and in underground coal reclaiming facilities. Adequate ventilation is the best solution to prevent dangerous accumulation. The ventilation system should sweep airflow across the tops of bins, silos, and bunkers, and through the conveyor gallery of underground reclaiming systems. Care should be taken in the design and operation of the storage system to minimize any airflow through the stored coal, thus preventing spontaneous heating. In addition, any airflow through the pile should be in a direction that will minimize any dangerous accumulations of gas.

If there is any suspicion of gas accumulations, a methane monitor can be permanently installed, and portable detectors can be used by personnel working in these areas.

WOOD AS A FUEL

Wood is becoming widely used because of the cost and occasional shortage of crude oil and because of improved technology for whole tree chipping on site. States, e.g., Maine, New Hampshire, Vermont, and other northern tier states, that have reasonably abundant supplies of wood are continuing to research how wood can be converted into usable form to produce energy for heat and power generation. In Maine alone, more than 20 wood-to-energy projects have been proposed that would have a total capacity of 479 megawatts.

The increasing use of wood as an energy source competes with the use of wood as raw material for pulp, paper, and building products. Consequently, much of the research into wood use today is concentrated upon the less commercially useful wood species and upon wood waste from the forest products industry. The emphasis is upon total use of the tree, either in the production of the product or of the waste as fuel.

Hazards of Wood Fuels

Given a source of ignition, wood in all its forms will burn. As the tree is cut and processed into its eventual use, the hazard of fire increases from two directions: (1) reduction of moisture content from air drying, and (2) reduction of the wood particle size from the standing tree to finished lumber, to chips for fuel and chemical pulp, to waste wood particles the size of finely divided dust and flour. As the drying and reduction process proceeds from the relatively large particles down to the dust/flour stage, the hazard changes from that of a Class A combustible material subject to typical burning characteristics to one of such rapid combustion that it is termed an explosion. In considering the storage of wood as a fuel, the hazards encountered will range from those for solid wood to those for wood dust/flour.

Solid wood: The hazard for solid wood is Class A combustible material not readily ignited but capable of generating a large amount of heat if allowed to burn unimpeded. The rapidity with which fire will spread depends upon pile configuration; moisture of the wood and surrounding atmosphere; physical characteristics of the wood, i.e., size of individual pieces; whether wood is peeled or with bark; and species of wood. Pile size and configuration will determine the amount of radiant heat released.

Chips: This form of wood is being used on an ever-increasing scale as fuel for heat and power generation because it can be mechanized on the scale needed. The hazard is again one of a Class A combustible, and because of its small size [$^5/_8$ to $1^1/_4$ in. (16 to 32 mm)], fires in piles tend to be surface type with no more than a few inches (mm) of fire penetration into the pile itself. Internal fires do occur from spontaneous heating as a result of excessive internal heat buildup. These fires are usually from fines that cause too much compaction or humus material within the pile, which is subject to more rapid oxidation than clean wood chips.

The chip fines can present a flash fire or explosion hazard if handled inside and dispersed in a manner which allows the wood dust to collect on structural members or to be suspended in air at concentrations above the lower explosive limit (LEL).

Sawdust and shavings: Sawdust and shavings, a byproduct of the lumber mill and wood processing plants, are generally used as a fuel on site. If strategically located, the usable material, along with other waste wood, may be shipped to other locations for use in manufacturing pulp, particleboard, or pellet fuel. The hazards are Class A combustible material and possible explosion in storage and handling from wood dust buildup.

Other wood waste: Wood scrap and edgings are another waste byproduct, particularly of lumber mills and furniture manufacturing plants. This material is generally put through a hog to reduce the size for conveying or blowing to storage bins and boiler rooms for fuel. If the larger pieces of scrap are recoverable for use as chips in pulp manufacturing, they are conveyed to a chipper and pneumatically blown to a loading station for transfer into rail cars or tractor trailers for shipment. The hazards are similar to those for chips and sawdust. The larger wood particles are readily ignited, while the fines generated by the sawing, planing, and chipping processes may contain particles small enough to be an explosion hazard.

Pellets: This form of solid wood is in the developmental stage and is in commercial production only to a limited extent. The process uses pulverized wood waste from the forest products industry which is formed under high temperature and pressure into pellets approximately 1/4 by 3/4 in. (6 by 19 mm). The finished pellets are stored in bulk form inside to keep them dry; the raw stock of wood waste is stored outside. The finished pellet storage presents little dust hazard but will burn as a Class A combustible material.

Bark: Bark is generated at pulp mills, sawmills, and chip plants as a waste material and used to a limited extent as a soil conditioner and as fuel for limited-size boilers (when mixed with other wood scrap from the process), or it is simply disposed of by burning in teepee-type bark burners. Until recent years, bark was basically a disposal problem. Some pulp mills, however, generated too much bark over the years to be disposed of by the above means, and it was simply piled at a detached site convenient to the plant. Over many years of operation, these piles have grown into miniature mountains. The sheer height and bulk of the piles has created a fire hazard from internal heating leading to spontaneous ignition, and from external sparks from heavy equipment used to build the pile, particularly during dry periods.

A method has been outlined for eliminating fires in wood bark piles by controlling the flow of air (oxygen) horizontally into the pile.[1] Oxygen control is achieved by sloping the pile at a 30- to 40-degree angle from the horizontal. In Figure 2-29A, dimension "A" is the depth at which pressure and moisture allow the chemical reaction to generate enough heat and volatile material to provide two sides of the fire triangle, i.e., heat and fuel. Dimension "B" is the distance air (oxygen) must travel to complete the fire triangle and is approximately three times greater, with a 30-degree slope than with a 60-degree slope. The upward flow of heated gases within the pile prevents oxygen from reaching the point of combustion except from the nearly horizontal direction, which means the resistance to oxygen flow increases as dimension "B" increases. Where increasing the slope is not practical, sealing the slope to air penetration is an alternative.

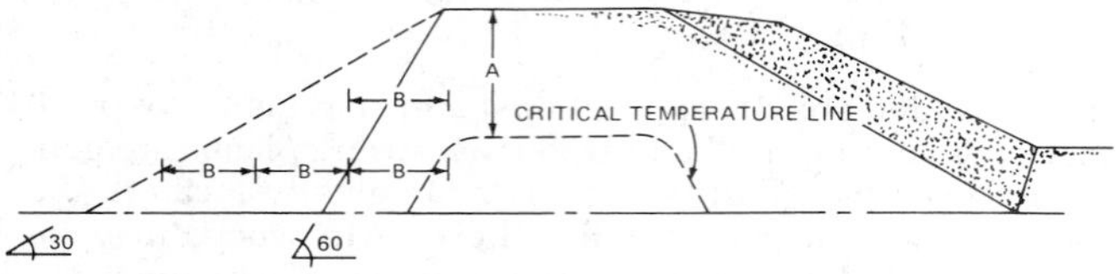

FIG. 2-29A. A method for eliminating fires in wood bark piles by controlling the flow of oxygen horizontally into the pile.

What was formerly a waste disposal problem has become a valuable commodity as the price of fuel oil has gone up and the technology for burning bark on a large scale has improved. For those with such piles, they can be reclaimed as fuel for relatively large bark boilers. The reclaimed bark is mixed with the bark generated daily in the pulp manufacturing process.

STORAGE PRACTICES FOR WOOD FUELS

Logs that are to be brought to the use site for industrial and commercial conversion to chips for fuel should be stored in ranked piles (i.e., piled in parallel form), because such piles are lower in height with less volume and less radiant heat exposure than stacked piles (i.e., large circular "matchstick" piles). The use of long logs, which is likely, will dictate the ranking method of storage. The piles should be 100 ft (30.5 m), and preferably more, from the nearest important building. The length and width of piles and pile height should be kept as small as practical to make fire fighting easier and to limit the amount of wood subject to a fire. The storage area should be clean and on solid ground, with good access for fire fighting purposes.

Residential use of cordwood and long logs is generally in the five to fifteen cord range and presents a relatively light hazard. Common sense dictates maintaining as much clear space as possible between the rough storage and dwelling. After cutting and splitting for use, the wood often is moved into the basement or garage for seasoning where there can be a fire potential from heating appliances, electrical wiring, and smoking. Care should be taken to store the wood away from the furnace it is to be burned in, electrical switchboxes, and wiring. A better method is to store the wood in a pile detached from the residence and bring in a week's supply as needed.

The use of wood chips for a residential fuel is still in the developmental stage. Furnaces and the means of automatically stoking them with the chips as well as chip storage are being developed and marketed. Wood chips for fuel, often mixed with other biomass, has forged ahead in industrial and independent energy projects as illustrated by the numerous wood-to-energy projects proposed in the State of Maine.

Where chips for fuel are used on a large scale, it likely will be in a relatively isolated area close to the wood source and unfortunately away from municipal fire protection facilities and water supplies. Only the larger operations under these conditions can economically justify an independent water supply distribution system, and it will be doubly important to limit outdoor chip pile size and height to dimensions even less than those recommended in NFPA 46, *Storage of Forest Products*. The plant should be located, if possible, near a pond or stream so water is available for hose streams. Any outside storage should be well isolated from processing buildings and surrounding forests.

Storage of chips, sawdust, shavings, and sander wood waste, in silos, bins, and buildings, may present fire and explosion hazards. Therefore, storage should be arranged to minimize these hazards by proper location, preferably outside the buildings, and by physical construction of the bin or silo and associated ducts with explosion-relief venting and explosion-isolating chokes.

Large-scale bark-burning boilers require a continuous supply of fuel to avoid fluctuations in steam output or the need to fire oil burners to take up the slack. Consequently, it is common practice to provide an enclosed surge storage area capable of providing a one- or two-day supply of fuel. One design used for such a storage building is the "A" frame style with storage capacities up to 2000 short tons (1814 metric tons) at 50 to 60 percent moisture. These storage buildings should be designed to minimize the possibility of wood dust buildup on structural building members by minimizing surface areas on which the wood dust can collect. If possible, the walls should be sloped at angles approaching 60 degrees. Structural members that cannot be sloped should be covered with sheet metal designed to eliminate flat surfaces upon which the dust can settle.

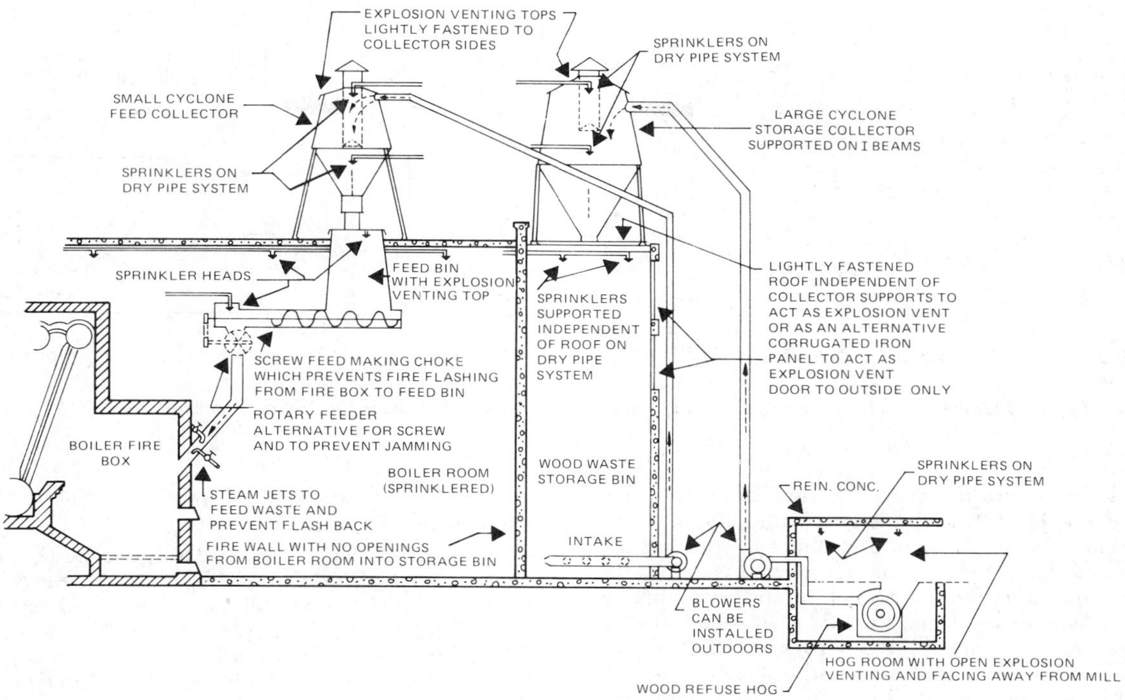

FIG. 2-29B. ***Suggested arrangement for wood waste firing of boiler to minimize explosion and fire hazard.***

HANDLING WOOD FUELS

Logs, either tree length or cordwood, are loaded and piled using mechanical equipment mounted either on the log truck or on a separate vehicle. Logs present minimal fire hazard exposure to the wood-handling operation.

Wood chips and wood waste material are generally transferred either pneumatically or by belt conveyor from one place to another. The fans, ducts, cyclones, and collectors associated with air movement of wood fuel constitute a fire and explosion hazard to the process of which they are a part; therefore, they should be located so as to minimize this exposure, preferably outside the buildings whenever possible. (See Figure 2-29B.)

Magnetic separators should be provided to reduce the possibility of a spark igniting the dust. The fans should be downstream of the collectors, if possible, to prevent passage of the wood fuel through the fan.

Belt conveyors present a fire hazard from the belt material as well as from the wood material being conveyed. Sources of ignition are frictional heat from belt slippage, cutting and welding, smoking, and overheated bearings. Belt conveyor fires are sometimes complicated by the need to run the belts overhead, particularly in large bark-burning boilers. Overhead conveyors present an access problem for hose stream use.

Screw conveyors and rotary airlocks should be utilized to provide chokes for fire and explosion isolation where the wood material being handled is fine enough to present an explosion hazard. It is necessary to remove a revolution (helix) of the screw in order to provide the choke. Backdraft dampers can also be used in high-velocity systems. (See Figure 2-29C.)

FIRE PREVENTION FOR WOOD FUELS

Where there is outside bulk storage of wood for fuel in any form, the first line of defense should be to limit the pile size to the absolute minimum required for economical operation. The homeowner and small commercial stick wood consumer will likely limit inventory to one or possibly two years' supply, whereas the larger commercial and industrial users who consume wood fuel to generate heat and power will likely restrict inventory to one day or even hours since, in many cases, they are consuming the wood waste as it is generated in the process.

Logs should be ranked rather than stacked and otherwise arranged in accordance with NFPA 46, *Storage of Forest Products.* If large chip piles are necessary, they should be arranged as outlined in NFPA 46. Two or more smaller piles are better than one large pile.

There is indication that foreign material in piles of chips or bark accelerates the buildup of heat, possibly from chemical reaction or simply the increased porosity that allows freer movement of air through the pile. Keeping the piles free of contamination is effective fire prevention.

Pile site selection, whether for chips or bark, should take into consideration the topography of the ground, which should be clean and free of combustibles. Clearance from surrounding forest, brush, or grass should be adequate to prevent an exposure fire from reaching the storage pile. Piles should be detached from buildings and located sufficiently apart from each other to allow fire fighting efforts to control an exposing fire.

Bark piles stored outside, whether rough or hogged bark, create heat which can lead to spontaneous ignition under certain conditions. The piles should be limited in

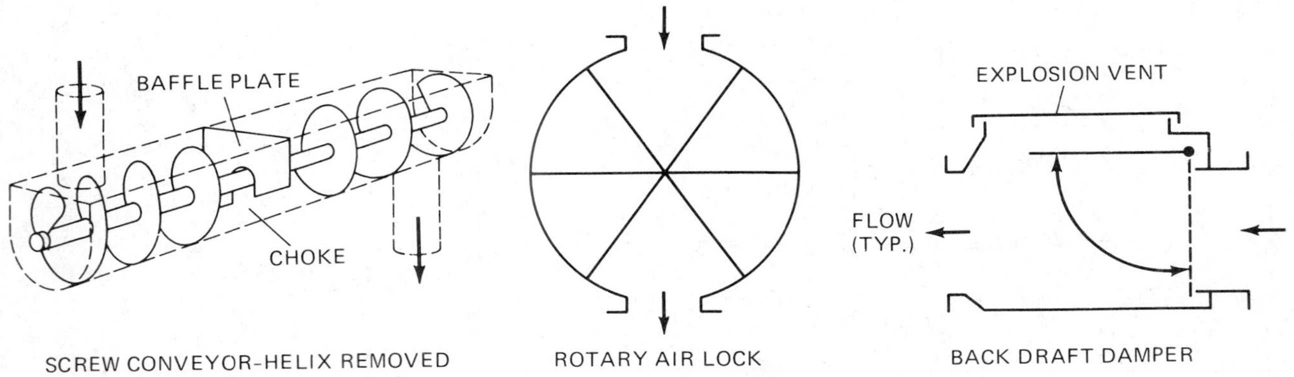

FIG. 2-29C. Types of chokes used to isolate fire and explosion when wood material is fine enough to explode.

height and contoured to restrict the flow of air (oxygen) through the pile. Heat that is generated within the pile rises to the surface and is dissipated to the surrounding air, which tends to keep the internal temperature below the spontaneous ignition point. However, in northern climates a blanket of ice and snow can impede heat release to the extent that combustion does occur. Thus, restricting the pile height to limit heat from pressure and restricting airflow through the side of the pile become doubly important under these conditions. (See Figure 2-29A.)

Storage bins, silos, and vaults for waste wood fine enough to be an explosion hazard should be outside plant buildings, if possible, or, if inside, should be arranged to vent explosions to the outside. For further details, see NFPA 664, *Prevention of Fires and Explosions in Wood Processing and Woodworking Facilities.*

The need to control moisture content of wood waste fuel for more efficient combustion may require use of lightly constructed metal buildings on a concrete slab to protect the fuel from the weather. Such buildings should be designed to minimize dust buildup on structural members. Lighting, if required, should conform to applicable provisions of NFPA 70, *National Electrical Code®*.

If the wood waste being stored contains a considerable amount of fines in the wood/flour range (such as sander fines), it may be necessary to incorporate explosion relief in the building design. A partially open structure may be a feasible design.

FIRE PROTECTION FOR WOOD FUELS

The bins, silos, or vaults in which chips or other wood waste are collected should be constructed of metal and located outside the boiler building, where possible. Collector and storage units handling fines that present an explosion hazard should be constructed with explosion-relief venting arranged to operate well below the design strength of the equipment. If bulk storage must be in or adjacent to the boiler building, it should be cut off with a fire-rated masonry wall.

Ranked log piles, arranged as previously described, should be protected with a yard hydrant system suitable for the storage arrangement and size, as defined in NFPA 46, *Storage of Forest Products*. Where the plant location and size preclude having an adequate water supply and a plant fire brigade, smaller, more segregated piles will be necessary, with greater clear space between the wood storage and plant.

Chip and bark piles also require large amounts of water to control and extinguish fires. While it is likely that storage piles of chips and bark to be used as fuel would not be the same size as piles of these materials at pulp mills, conscious effort should be made to keep the piles limited in size in order to reduce the volume of water and the fire fighting effort needed to combat a fire. (See NFPA 46, *Storage of Forest Products*, for details of yard fire protection.)

Automatic sprinkler protection (on a dry-pipe system, where necessary) should be provided in the collecting and storage areas. Where fuel storage buildings are utilized in the system, they should be provided with automatic sprinkler protection in accordance with NFPA 13, *Installation of Sprinkler Systems*, and NFPA 15, *Water Spray Fixed Systems for Fire Protection*.

Where bark or chips are transported from the outside storage pile or silo to an inside bin for feeding to the boiler by enclosed conveyors, the structure should be noncombustible and arranged to meet applicable safety codes. The conveyor housing should not exceed 10 ft (3 m) in width to limit the required sprinkler system to one line. The day storage bin should have sprinkler protection inside and, depending upon design, automatic sprinkler protection over it and the conveyor.

Automatic sprinkler protection on a wet pipe system should be provided in the enclosed conveyors and should be hydraulically designed to provide minimum operating pressure on the end sprinklers. Where temperatures in winter will not allow use of wet systems, dry-pipe or pre-action systems should be used. Regardless of the system type used, the conveyor should be interlocked to shut down upon actuation of the sprinkler or detection system.

BIBLIOGRAPHY

Reference Cited

1. Halsey, Ken, "Controlling Bark Pile Fires," *Pulp and Paper Magazine*, Dec. 1980.

Reference

ASTM D 388, *Specifications for Classification of Coals by Rank*, American Society for Testing and Materials, Philadelphia, PA.

NFPA Codes, Standards, and Recommended Practices

Reference to the following NFPA codes, standards, and recommended practices will provide further information on the storage and handling of solid fuels discussed in this chapter. (See the latest *NFPA Catalog* for availability of current editions of the following documents.)

NFPA 13, *Installation of Sprinkler Systems.*

NFPA 15, *Water Spray Fixed Systems for Fire Protection.*

NFPA 46, *Storage of Forest Products.*

NFPA 68, *Explosion Venting.*

NFPA 70, *National Electrical Code®.*

NFPA 91, *Blower and Exhaust Systems for Dust, Stock and Vapor Removal or Conveying.*

NFPA 664, *Prevention of Fires and Explosions in Wood Processing and Woodworking Facilities.*

Additional Reading

Bowes, P. C., *Self-Heating: Evaluating and Controlling the Hazards*, Elsevier, NY, 1984.

Braun, E., "Self Heating Properties of Coal," *NBSIR 87-3554*, Aug. 1987, Center for Fire Research, Gaithersburg, MD.

Castleberry, J. C. and Smith, P. A., "Pulp and Paper Processing," *Industrial Fire Hazards Handbook*, 3rd ed., National Fire Protection Association, Quincy, MA, 1990.

"Coal and Coal Storage," *Loss Prevention Data Sheet 8-10*, Factory Mutual Engineering Corporation, Norwood, MA, Aug. 1975.

Collins, P. K., et al., "Flammability Characteristics of Treated Coals," *Proceedings* of the Fossil Fuels Combustion Symposium 1989, Twelfth Annual Energy-Sources Technology Conference and Exhibition, American Society of Mechanical Engineers, Petrolium Division, v.25, NY, pp. 19-24.

"Combustible Dusts," *Loss Prevention Data Sheet 7-76*, Factory Mutual Engineering Corporation, Norwood, MA, Aug. 1976.

Eisfeld, D., "Activation Process in the Spontaneous Ignition of Coal," *Glueckauf-Forschungshefte*, Vol. 49, No. 6 (Dec. 1988), pp. 298-308.

Essenhigh, R. H., *et al.*, "Ignition of Coal Particles—A Review," *Combustion and Flame*, Vol. 77, No. 1 (Jul. 1989), pp. 3-30.

Factory Mutual Engineering Corporation, *Handbook of Industrial Loss Prevention*, Chapters 66 and 70, Norwood, MA.

Hall, K. F., "Wood Pulp," *Scientific American*, Vol. 230, No. 4 (April 1974), pp. 52-62.

Industrial Risk Insurers, *The Sentinel*, Jan.-Feb. 1979.

Mutanen, K., Nissinen, K., and Linna, V., "Improvement of Safety in Peat Handling," *Proceedings* of the Symposium on Low-Grade Fuels, Part 2, Technical Research Center of Finland, 1989, pp. 31-42.

Naujokas, A. A., "Spontaneous Combustion of Carbon Beds," *Plant/Operation Progress*, Vol.4, No. 2 (April 1985), pp. 120-126.

NFPA Industrial Fire Protection Section, Pulp & Paper—Wood Products Industry Committee, "Wood Products," *Industrial Fire Hazards Handbook*, 3rd ed., National Fire Protection Association, Quincy, MA, 1990.

"Outdoor Storage of Wood Chips," *Loss Prevention Data Sheet 8-27*, Factory Mutual Engineering Corporation, Norwood, MA, Dec. 1980.

"Prevention, Detection, and Control of Coal Pulverizer Fires and Explosions," Electric Power Research Institute, *Report EPRI CS No. 5069*, 1987, Palo Alto, CA, 280 p. 1987.

Reineke, L. H., "Wood Fuel Preparation," *U.S. Forest Service Research Note EPL-090*, Forest Products Laboratory, Madison, WI, Jan. 1969.

Robertson, J. W. and Woolbert, G. D., "Improved Coal Mill Monitoring for Fire and Explosion Prevention," *Proceedings* of the 7th International Coal and Lignite Utilization Conference: Coal Technology '84, Vol.III, Industrial Publications, 1984, pp. 53-62.

Smith, A. C, Miron, Y., and Lazzara, C. P., "Inhibition of Spontaneous Combustion of Coal," *Report of Investigations No. 9196*, 1988, U.S. Bureau of Mines, Pittsburgh, PA.

Thompson, C., "Fire Safety in Bulk Sulphur Handling Locations," *Fire Prevention*, No. 208, 1988, pp. 28-31.

Tuominen, J. and Ihatsu, R., "Handling of Solid Fuels in Multi-Fuel Power Plants," *Bulk Solids Handling*, Vol. 6, No. 5, 1986, pp. 855-858.

STORAGE AND HANDLING OF RECORDS

Revised by Thomas Goonan

The information explosion brought about by such modern technology as telecommunications and computers has created a massive increase in the total volume of records that are generated. This massive increase has intensified the problems involved in protecting records from fire. Traditional fire-resistive containers, such as insulated file cabinets, safes, and vaults, have not lost any of their capabilities to protect paper records. In fact, recent advances have introduced devices that can safeguard magnetic or photographic records. In many cases, however, the volume of records material has become so great that it is impractical to invest in either the devices or the space that would be required to safeguard all the records to the level of protection which is justified. New methods of records storage have been developed that use the maximum cubic capacity of the area assigned to records storage. Some of these storage arrangements not only place the records at risk, but also contain sufficient fire potential to be a danger to the structure and all other operations housed in it.

This chapter discusses ways of identifying and classifying valuable records to determine the amount of protection, justified by their value, against fire and its associated perils. The relative susceptibility of various records to flame, heat, smoke, and water exposure is discussed. Because water damage is a serious byproduct of fire containment efforts, information on salvaging water-soaked documents is provided. The different ways in which the risk of extensive loss of valuable records can be mitigated are considered. Protection against perils not associated with fire is not discussed.

Detailed discussions of the best ways to provide maximum reasonable protection for records are contained in NFPA 232, *Protection of Records*, and NFPA 232AM, *Fire Protection for Archives and Records Centers*. Further information can be found in the report "Protecting Federal Records Centers and Archives from Fire,"[1] and the reference book *Protecting the Library and Its Resources*.[2]

Adequate provisions must be maintained for the safety of persons in records storage facilities. This can be a particularly difficult task when the facility is designed to provide maximum security of its contents against illegal entry. However, emergency exits are often necessary to ensure life safety for persons in the records area in case of fire, even at some sacrifice in security. Alternate egress from catwalks in records centers often requires a common-sense design approach. General good practice recommendations for means of egress should be followed.

Thomas Goonan, P.E., F.S.F.P.E., is a principal of Tom Goonan Associates, Springfield, VA.

STORAGE OPTIONS

Bulk Storage

Bulk storage of records creates a fire hazard in itself. Bulk storage describes any sizeable collection of records not contained in vaults, safes, or insulated cabinets. This includes collections of records ranging from small file rooms to the largest archives or records centers. Storage methods include, but are not limited to, file cabinets; various types of shelving, including open shelves and mobile shelves; palletized cardboard boxes; transport cases; miscellaneous cardboard boxes; and devices for unusually shaped records, such as blueprints, magnetic tapes, photographic film, and other media. Locations may range from an area within a general office complex to specially built records facilities. It is not uncommon to house record collections in basements or attics of public buildings, in office buildings, in converted factory or warehouse buildings of various constructions and levels of quality, in public warehouses, underground, or in facilities protected against war-time disasters.

Open-Shelf Storage

The trend toward making the maximum use of available space in buildings has sometimes resulted in using open-shelf storage methods, normally with the records held in either file folders or various kinds of cardboard boxes. Typically, the racks of records face each other across 25- to 30-in. (0.6 to 0.75 m) aisles. The aisle exposure presents a wall of paper made up of the sides of boxes or loose ends of paper sticking out of file folders. They can be easily ignited accidentally by any ignition source, such as a match, a cigarette, a portable heater, faulty fluorescent ballast, or by an exposed incandescent light bulb. Paper ignites at a relatively low temperature. Ignition of a few pieces of paper, on a filing cart, for instance, can readily transmit ignition to the boxes.

Attempts have been made to develop economical methods for increasing the flame resistance of the typical records center cardboard boxes. The most frequently attempted method is coating the box with an intumescent type of fire-retardant paint. Tests of records boxes protected by such paint, properly applied, show that the coating will substantially delay actual ignition of the cardboard box material. However, since intumescent paint does not effectively react to heat under about 400°F (204°C), the temperature of any modest exposure fire (such as might occur on a file cart) will weaken the paper in the box to the point where the box will break open under the weight of the paper it contains and expose the ordinary combustible contents of the box to ignition. In a small-scale test, in the 1960s, conducted as a joint effort by the NFPA Committee on Records Protection and the U.S. General Services Administration (GSA), a fire-retardant paint coating on boxes only briefly delayed ignition and the spread of fire up and across the face of the records in storage.

Full-scale fire tests were conducted in December 1974 in boxes of paper records stored on open steel shelves 13 ft (4 m) high.[1] Properly designed sprinklers were adequate to control the fire, but the fire developed very rapidly anyway. From a small ignition source, flames reached the top of the rack in 4½ minutes. Eight seconds later, the facing array of boxes across the 30-in. (0.75 m) aisle flashed into flame from top to bottom. The first sprinkler had a 286°F (141°C) rating and activated in a little more than 5 minutes. By then, the ceiling temperature directly over the fire had reached 1,900°F (1038°C). The direct cause of the intense fire was rupture of the walls of the cardboard cartons and the release of the contents. Paper records exfoliated into the aisle and many burned while falling. A test was conducted with an identical arrangement, except that open files were oriented perpendicular to the aisle, which exposed the edges of paper to easy ignition. In this test, fire spread at a leisurely pace and did not develop into an intense fire. The basic difference in the rate of fire growth between these two fire tests was attributed to whether or not paper records exfoliated into the aisles. The progress of the fire can also be dramatically changed by changing sprinkler temperature ratings and sprinkler drop size characteristics.[3]

In other tests of high-piled storage conducted by Underwriters Laboratories Inc. (UL)[4] and tests of 6-ft (1.5 m) high archival shelving arrangements conducted by the GSA, the fire, at the end of an early and relatively short development stage, preheated a sufficient amount of the exposed boxes so that fire development characteristics changed suddenly, temperatures rose quickly, and the flame enveloped large areas. Neither of the tests involved exposed loose paper typical of systems with open-shelf filing.

In open-shelf storage, the close proximity of the opposing sides of the aisle can result in increased radiant heat feedback and flaming ignition of evolved gases across the narrow aisle. The severity and rapidity of fire development is accelerated by increased stack height and slowed by increased aisle width.

Properly designed automatic sprinklers will control the fire, but factors that speed fire development and penetration increase the amount of information loss and the amount of irrecoverable damage.

Mobile Shelving

A class of storage devices known variously as mobile shelving, track files, compaction files, moveable files, etc., consists of open-shelf units mounted on tracks. In use, all of the shelves are pushed together except that one aisle is left open for access to two units. To access another unit, all of the shelf units are moved on the tracks until access to the desired unit is gained. Units may be moved electrically or manually. The shelves that are pushed together form continuous horizontal tunnels. Mobile shelving containing combustibles should be protected by overhead sprinklers.

A fire in the open aisle of mobile shelving is similar to a fire in open-shelf storage and is readily controllable by overhead sprinklers. Because a fire elsewhere in the mobile shelving array is a burrowing fire, it is sheltered from sprinkler application. Full-scale fire tests conducted in 1978 indicate that a fire will develop and spread very slowly. When shielded from direct sprinkler discharge, fire is likely to continue spreading through the entire array unless each shelf unit has internal metal dividers.[5] Although protection by sprinklers alone may permit fire involvement of the entire array, overhead sprinklers provide adequate protection for a building containing mobile shelving, and prevents fire from jumping to other arrays. In addition to sprinkler protection, a smoke detection system is suggested in mobile shelving areas not continuously occupied to provide a fire warning well in advance of sprinkler operation. Early-warning smoke detectors may help limit the extent of fire damage in mobile shelving if skilled forces are quickly available during nonoperating hours.

Plastic Media

The flammability of magnetic media and its containers is a prime concern when such media are stored in bulk quantities. Generally, acetate and polyester-based tapes do not present a hazard any more severe than paper. Polystyrene cases and reels, however, present a severe fire hazard condition because they have a high fuel value, a high heat release rate, and shed water. UL tests conducted in the 1960s have shown that storage systems designed to safeguard materials of cardboard or paper composition would not adequately protect materials involving polystyrene. If the containers are made of another plastic, the condition may vary, although most thermosplastics exhibit similar properties. In any case, it is necessary to limit the height and extent of the storage of reels encased in plastic or to design special protection systems for them.

DAMAGEABILITY AND SALVAGE

Ordinary paper records survive reasonably well when exposed to most of the effects of fire, except direct exposure to flaming. With rare exceptions, the burned paper record represents a total loss, while a high recovery rate is practical where the records have been exposed only to water, high humidity, smoke, and moderately high temperatures of about 350°F (177°C). Nonpaper records media tend to be more susceptible to damage than paper.

Photographic Records

Photographic records, whether they are on traditional acetate, glass base, or any special base, consist of an image held in place by an emulsion. The image can be distorted or destroyed under any condition that loosens the emulsion. Tests have demonstrated that these emulsions will not withstand high temperature and humidity conditions, and that they are particularly susceptible to steam.[6,7] The traditional insulated safe or insulated filing device depends upon the water of crystallization in the insulation material to limit the internal temperature, and is usually vented into the interior of the device. Therefore, it must be expected that a steam atmosphere at 212°F (100°C) or higher will exist within the records protection equipment under severe fire exposure. The tests demonstrated that such exposure would damage or destroy the information on photographic media. A high degree of safety, however, may be achieved by placing the photographic media inside a steel can and sealing it with a moisture-resistant tape before storage within a record container.

The fire problem with photographic records that are stored in bulk facilities is similar to that encountered with paper records, except that in salvage efforts it is important to give priority to the photographic records. While the cold water used in extinguishing the fire will not immediately attack the photographic emulsion as would steam, it will tend to cause some softening. If salvage efforts are not undertaken immediately, there is a tendency for the emulsion to stick to adjacent material and damage the image.

Magnetic Media

The more common magnetic records consist of magnetic impulses retained in an iron oxide or similar deposit held to an acetate, polyester, or similar plastic-based material. The tapes are usually wound on polystyrene or similar plastic reels and contained in polystyrene cases. This is particularly true of many tapes used with electronic computer systems. The security of the record is primarily related, as with photographic records, to the stability of the emulsion. Even minor distortion is severe in the case of magnetic records, since machines cannot make subjective judgments regarding distortion. If the emulsion is softened by the heat from fire, for example, there is a tendency for the layers of tape to stick to each other on the reel and to be destroyed in efforts to unreel. A tape can be considered safeguarded only up to temperatures in the range of 125°F (52°C) and in a relative humidity not exceeding 85 percent.

Salvage

The problem of recovering wet records is the same whether they are damaged by a fire, or some other source, such as flood, hurricane, heavy rainstorm, roof leakage, spillage from operations located above, or a breakdown of any of the numerous water or steam systems in the building. It is generally recognized that virtually any wet paper records can be recovered, provided prompt and proper action is taken.

Good sources for further information on salvaging records are contained in NFPA 910, *Protection of Libraries and Library Collections*, "Salvaging and Restoring Records Damaged by Fire and Water,"[8] *Managing the Library Fire Risk*,[9] "After the Water Comes,"[10] and *Procedures for Salvage of Water-Damaged Library Materials*.[11]

RECORDS STORAGE

Factory-Built Devices

Small quantities of valuable records may be stored in factory-built records protection equipment, such as insulated records containers, fire-resistant safes, insulated filing devices, and insulated file drawers. These devices are available in varying degrees of resistance to fire, heat, and impact, and the degree of protection to be specified for a particular application will depend upon the severity of the exposure and the items to be stored. The test procedure applicable to this equipment and the ratings employed are as follows.[12]

Records protection equipment is classified in terms of two elements: (1) an interior temperature limit and (2) a time in hours. Three temperature limits are employed: 350°F (177°C), regarded as a suitable limit for paper records; 150°F (66°C), regarded as a limiting temperature for photographic records; and 125°F (52°C), regarded as suitable for most magnetic media. The time limits employed are ½, 1,2,3, or 4 hrs. The complete rating, consisting of the two elements, indicates that the specified interior temperature limit is not exceeded when the record container, safe, or filing device is exposed to a standard test fire as described in UL 72,[12] for the length of time specified.

Ratings are assigned to the various categories as follows:

Insulated Records Containers

Class 125—4 hr
Class 125—3 hr
Class 125—2 hr
Class 125—1 hr
Class 150—4 hr
Class 150—3 hr
Class 150—2 hr
Class 150—1 hr
Class 350—4 hr
Class 350—3 hr
Class 350—2 hr
Class 350—1 hr

Fire-Resistant Safes

Class 125—4 hr
Class 125—3 hr
Class 125—2 hr
Class 125—1 hr
Class 150—4 hr
Class 150—3 hr
Class 150—2 hr
Class 150—1 hr
Class 350—4 hr
Class 350—3 hr
Class 350—2 hr
Class 350—1 hr

Insulated Filing Devices

Class 125—1 hr
Class 125—½ hr
Class 150—1 hr
Class 150—½ hr
Class 350—1 hr
Class 350—½ hr

Insulated File Drawers

Class 125—1 hr
Class 150—1 hr
Class 350—1 hr

Insulated records containers and fire-resistant safes must protect contents from heat to an extent described in the requirements, before and after a fall from 30 ft (9 m). Insulated filing devices, which are not drop-tested, are not required to have the strength to endure such an impact.

Insulated records containers, fire-resistant safes, insulated filing devices, and insulated file drawers must sustain sudden exposure to high temperatures to an extent described in the requirements without the unit exploding as a result of such exposure.

Ordinary, uninsulated steel files and cabinets provide only a limited measure of protection from an exposure fire, as heat sufficient to char contents is quickly transmitted to the interior. However, they can be very useful where the major fire exposure is from the records themselves. They are commonly used for records having no extraordinary value. They are also used for the organized storage of valuable records in protected facilities, including vaults, file rooms, and document buildings. A records vault or file room in which all records are kept in metal file cabinets is much safer than one in which the records are kept in cardboard boxes or on open shelves. If an ignition occurred in an open file drawer, fire development would likely be very slow. An ignition in open-shelf files, however, could be beyond manual control within a few minutes.

Files and cabinets made of wood, fiberboard, or other combustible materials can release their contents in a fire, adding to the fire hazard. They should not be used where they will expose valuable records storage.

Vaults and File Rooms

Standards for the construction of fire-resistive vaults and file rooms are contained in NFPA 232, *Protection of Records*. The term "vault" refers to a completely fire-resistive enclosure up to 5000 cu ft (142 m^3) in volume, used exclusively for records storage, with no work to be carried on inside. It is equipped, maintained, and supervised to minimize the possibility of a fire starting within, and to prevent a severe fire of long duration on the outside from entering, provided the vault door is closed. Vaults are designed to fire resistance classifications of 2,4, and 6 hrs, indicating that, under standard test conditions, heat will not rise above a specified temperature inside and the construction will withstand both the exposure fire and the application of fire hose streams during that period. Vaults are constructed in the field and do not carry a testing laboratory label. Vault doors, however, are laboratory tested and carry ratings conforming to the vault construction in which they are to be used. (See NFPA 232, *Protection of Records*.) Unlike some other fire doors, vault doors limit the temperature on the interior face to 350°F (177°C) during fire exposure, so that paper could be stored in contact with the door without danger of ignition. Provisions in NFPA 232, *Protection of Records*, require sprinklers for oversize vaults up to 25,000 cu ft (708 m^3) in volume.

Vaults usually contain a substantial fuel load, and by their nature contain only vital and important records. The internal contents of some vaults are more of a fire hazard than any external exposure. In recognition of this situation, vault standards were revised in 1986 to permit sprinkler systems, lighting, and low-energy circuits, with suitable safeguards. This change permits installation of smoke detectors and/or sprinklers to detect and extinguish a vault fire with a minor increase in ignition sources. A fire within an unprotected vault can be disastrous unless it is immediately discovered and extinguished with portable fire fighting devices. Fire extinguishers of the water type or fire hose, or both, should be outside the vault in an accessible location near the door.

A standard fire-resistive file room is defined as an enclosure not exceeding 50,000 cu ft (1416 m^3) in volume and 12 ft (3.66 m) in height and designed to a fire resistance classification of 1,2,4, or 6 hrs. The volume and height limitations restrict the quantity of records exposed to destruction by fire in a single enclosure and reduce the possibility of fire originating within the enclosure.

File room doors are labeled as to their fire resistance following a laboratory test under the procedures of UL 155, "Tests for Fire Resistance of Vault and File Room Doors,"[13] but the ratings are only for ½ or 1 hr. These ratings anticipate that paper and other combustibles will not be stored nearer than 3 ft (0.9 m) from the unexposed face of the door, nor 6 in. (152 mm) to the side from the door jambs.

Lighting, heating, ventilation, etc., are permitted inside file rooms, as are filing cabinets and furniture, provided they are noncombustible. Although it is not to be used as a working space for other than filing purposes, the file room is more susceptible to a fire start than a vault. Due to this vulnerability, installation of automatic fire detection and fire control systems should be considered in relation to the values involved. Automatic sprinklers are required in file rooms having open-shelf filing.

Records Centers and Archives

Bulk storage of records in buildings set aside for the specific purpose or in major portions of other buildings [in rooms exceeding the 50,000 cu ft (1416 m^3) fire-resistive file room limitation] should comply with the recommendations set forth in NFPA 232AM, *Fire Protection for Archives and Records Centers*. For facilities of this size, where the most severe hazard may not be from a fire exterior to the facility but from a fire starting and spreading entirely within the records storage area, the level of fire-resistive construction and protection must be individually determined. Within such a facility, secondary operations may have to be segregated from the actual storage by fire-resistive construction. Full-scale fire tests of 14-ft (4.3 m) high open-shelf records storage in a sprinklered facility indicated the likelihood of ceiling temperatures in excess of 1200°F (649°C) for periods of up to 8 minutes when using standard 286°F (141°C) sprinklers.[1] Lightweight bar joist roofs often present in records centers are vulnerable to early collapse unless additional precautions are taken, such as might be provided by developments in large-drop sprinklers, quick-response sprinklers, or fireproof coatings for the steel. A thorough fire risk analysis by qualified personnel should be conducted due to the high risk of fire from the concentration of combustibles and the probability of total loss of large volumes of valuable documents.

FIRE RISK ANALYSIS

Maximum possible protection is not desirable for the bulk of what comprises records storage. Most records can be reconstructed, and duplicates are often available in other locations, and their loss may not create any substantial hardship. The value of certain, irreplaceable documents war rants especially sophisticated protective measures to preserve a single sheet of paper. The great majority of records in a particular collection, however, may dictate consideration of less-than-optimum methods of records protection and anticipation of small fire losses, yet still provide a high degree of assurance against a significant loss.

Records protection programs should be based on an inventory that determines type, volume, rate of acquisition, duplication of data, rate of disposal, and class of importance of the records. Records can be generally classified in one of two ways to assess their value:

1. Vital Records: These records are irreplaceable; records where reproduction does not have the same value as an original; records that give direct evidence of legal status, or ownership; records needed to sustain a business or avoid delay in restoration of production, sales, or service; or records of accounts receivable.
2. Important Records: These are records that can be reproduced from original sources only at considerable expense or loss of time.

Other records may be useful, but should be kept well separated from vital and important records because they may constitute a fire exposure in and of themselves.

Fire Risk Evaluation Factors

In considering the protection of valuable records, four basic items must be evaluated. They are:

1. The probability that the building containing the records, as well as neighboring operations, will have a fire outside the records storage activity that will spread to the records. Determining the probability of such fire hazards will involve consideration of building construction, contents, possible fire causes, and general features of fire protection that might stop a fire originating elsewhere before it reaches the records. (See Section 6, Chapter 5, "Structural Integrity During Fire.")
2. The probability of a fire starting within the records storage activity. This includes assessing the nearby heat sources, including vulnerability to arson, and the susceptibility of the records, or their containers, to ignition.
3. The quantity of fuel the records represent, particularly as it relates to available or proposed capability for fire extinguishment and the structural stability of the storage arrangement and the building enclosure.
4. The susceptibility of the records to damage from fire, fire effects (heat, smoke, vapors, etc.), and fire extinguishing efforts (principally water damage and impact damage from hose streams and other extinguishing devices, and physical disruption from manual fire fighting).

When records must be housed in a building that may burn around them, properly rated vaults and containers can give reasonable protection against the external fire exposure. The hazard of the records themselves, such as those stored within a vault, file room, segregated floor or section of a fire-resistive building, or records center, can be substantial. For example, a fire involving military records of 19 million U.S. servicemen occurred in an unsprinklered, six-story, fire-resistive building. The top floor, where the fire started, was completely destroyed. Fire fighting efforts prevented the fire from spreading downward. Had the fire started on a lower floor, it is likely that the entire building would have been lost.[1]

The protection methods described in this chapter yield protection guidelines commensurate with the hazard and the sophistication of the protection systems. The degree of fire risk and the potential for loss in collections not suitable for cabinet or vault storage may require evaluation by a person knowledgeable in this type of analysis.

FIRE RISK REDUCTION

Since records media are almost always combustible, 100 percent effective protection is not feasible and efforts should be directed to reducing the risk of fire and its associated effects. One of the most effective means for limiting the disastrous effects of a fire in a records storage facility is to prepare duplicates and store them away from the originals where they will not be subject to the same incident. Often the duplicate copy is on microfilm, which is inexpensive, easily transported, and easily stored at a remote facility. Once such a duplicate has been prepared, the value of the original is reduced considerably, unless the original document is required for legal purposes or is of intrinsic or historic value. If the duplication is complete, up-to-date, and easily accessible, and the degree of protection is extremely high, then reduced protective measures may be justified for both the original and the duplicate collection.

If the prior generation of computer records is stored at a remote location, the effect of loss of the present generation of records in use at the computer center would be minimized. Although they are not exact duplicates, the earlier records still greatly simplify the task of reconstructing current records.

Protective Containers

Heavily insulated, massive vaults, safes, and filing cabinets are the traditional way to safeguard valuable records against the effects of fire. The practice of encapsulating the records so that they are fully protected against the greatest potential fire exposure is still viable. Containers are available that will keep the internal temperature and humidity as low as necessary to retain the data on magnetic tape and other temperature-sensitive media.

Vaults are usually used where the volume of valuable records is large. They are often the only practical method of protection in nonfire-resistive buildings where the probable fire severity exceeds the rated endurance of 4-hr safes. Safes are used for smaller volumes of records where it is necessary to have records near their point of use, where the cost of vault construction would be prohibitive, or where the building does not lend itself to vault construction.

Protective containers for records are rated by tests under standard fire conditions. They are rated according to the time elapsed before the interior of the container reaches 350°F (177°C). This time factor provides a measure of safety, since the ignition temperature of most paper is somewhat higher.

Records containers are also rated for interior temperatures that do not exceed 150°F (66°C) and relative humidity that does not exceed 85 percent at temperatures above 120°F (49°C). Containers rated with these more stringent requirements are intended to provide protection for films, magnetic tapes, disc packs, and similar materials. The development of new and different records materials, however, requires a careful evaluation of their characteristics to ensure proper protection. An important limitation on this type of container is that it is not subjected to the traditional drop test while containing magnetic or similar media records. The device should not be considered capable of safeguarding magnetic and similar records in any building that could collapse in a fire and cause debris to fall on the container, nor should the container itself be allowed to fall several floors.

Table 2-30A indicates the approximate fire resistance that can be safely expected from various types of records containers. The protection provided varies considerably depending upon design and materials. Thickness of insulation alone does not give a reliable indication of fire resistance, which can be determined accurately only by tests.

TABLE 2-30A. ***Fire Resistance of Record Containers***

Insulated record vault doors	2, 4, and 6 hrs
Insulated file room doors	1/2 and 1 hr
Steel-plate vault doors with inner doors	about 15 min
Steel-plate door without inner doors	less than 10 min
Modern safes	1, 2, and 4 hrs
"Old Line," "Iron," or "Cast Iron" safes, 2 to 6 in. wall thickness	Uncertain
Insulated record containers (files and cabinets, etc.)	1/2, 1, and 2 hrs
Containers with air space or with cellular or solid insulation less than 1 in. thick	10 to 20 min
Uninsulated steel files, cabinets—wooden files—wooden or steel desks	about 5 min

Statistical information on patterns of records container performance in real fires has not been collected since a special five-year study done by NFPA nearly four decades ago.[14] While the statistics from that study can no longer be considered representative, the leading factors of contents destruction are probably the same ones one would find today. They are listed below in order of frequency from the old study.

- Container exposed to fire beyond its capacity to withstand (mostly unlabeled containers, some 1-hr containers, a few 2-hr containers, no 4-hr containers)
- Obsolete design or construction of unlabeled container
- Container submerged in water
- Container door left open

The first two of these were cited much more often than the second two, which underlines the importance of selecting the right containers for the fire hazard in the first place. As one might expect, the longer the time rating, the more likely the container was to preserve the contents, ranging from only a 61 percent success rate for unlabeled containers to success rates of 87 to 89 percent for 1-hr and 2-hr containers, to a 97 percent success rate for 4-hr containers, whose only failure involved a door left open.

The Concept of Early Warning

Records administrators usually consider the sprinkler system as an option when they plan records protection. A smoke detection system coupled with manual response, once highly favored by archivists and librarians as a substitute for sprinkler protection, is now generally accepted as a useful supplement to sprinklers under favorable conditions. In a slowly developing fire, a well-designed smoke detection system can give an advance warning before heat-responsive devices, such as automatic sprinklers, operate. If manual fire extinguishment is mobilized by a manned emergency center, it may be able to attack the fire before it gains headway. Whether manual extinguishment causes more or less damage than sprinklers depends upon the skill of the responding force and how the fire progresses while the responding force is mobilizing. In any case, although automatic detection and manual extinguishment can be valuable adjuncts to automatic sprinklers, they would not constitute an acceptable alternative to automatic sprinkler protection under most conditions found in records storage.

Contrary to popular belief, a smoke detection system will not outperform alert occupants, except under the most unusual circumstances. Smoke detectors in records storage are only useful when the area is unoccupied, when rapid mobilization of occupants with hand extinguishers is most unlikely. Detectors on ceilings are unlikely to be activated until smoke from a smoldering fire completely permeates the air, or flaming fire gains sufficient headway to drive a column of smoke and heat to the ceiling.

Smoke detection systems are of little value in open-shelf records storage, where fire development is likely to be very rapid. They may provide supplementary protection in high-value collections, particularly if measures have been taken to slow down development of a fire (such as storage in totally closed metal containers), or burning material is prevented from falling off shelves. Smoke detection equipment can be useful in unoccupied areas of mobile shelving or other arrangements in which combustible contents are sheltered from sprinklers.

Smoke detection systems are also used to activate extinguishing systems, such as carbon dioxide, halon, or high-expansion foam. They are used to activate preaction sprinkler systems, which are installed to prevent accidental water damage. In this application, failure of the detection system for any reason (e.g., loss of power, loose connection) will prevent operation of the sprinklers, so system reliability is reduced. The reliability of sprinkler systems is much greater than the reliability of smoke detectors because of the design simplicity of sprinkler systems.

Duct detectors are used to shut down fans, activate dampers, or initiate smoke control measures. Detectors are also used to cause held-open doors to close and to stop conveyors, in a variety of single-purpose actions.

Heat detectors can perform most of the same duties as smoke detectors, usually with a much longer time lag. An extended time lag is sometimes desirable, such as in the opening of a sprinkler, or the release of halon gas.

Hand Extinguishing Appliances

Even if the facility is equipped with an automatic extinguishing system, manual fire control devices should be provided for staff use. Fire extinguishers are most often encountered. The preferred types are those containing clear water as the extinguishing agent. Although carbon dioxide extinguishers do not leave a residue or dampen documents, they are not effective on the deep-seated fires likely to occur in records storage. Halon extinguishers have the same limited extinguishing ability as carbon dioxide, in that they are ineffective on deep-seated fires. The user of halons should also be aware of the toxicity of the agent and not be exposed to high concentrations of the agent. Although national standards rightly limit human exposure to the various halons, there is no mechanism, except the knowledge and alertness of the extinguisher operator, to manage the extent of exposure to halon. Most extinguisher users, however, are unaware of this hazard and are at risk of overdose. Multipurpose dry chemical extinguishers may be provided, but they leave considerable residue and have only limited effectiveness on deep-seated fires.

Water hose lines may supplement, or be used instead of, fire extinguishers. To minimize water damage, rubber-lined hose with an adjustable water spray, straight stream, and shutoff nozzle is preferable in records storage areas. Its use greatly expands the fire fighting capabilities of the staff. Hose lines connected to carbon dioxide or halon storage tanks or cylinders have been used. However, these systems should not be undertaken without extensive training and appropriate protective equipment because the danger to the fire brigade is much greater than with the use of hand extinguishers containing the same agent.

AUTOMATIC EXTINGUISHING SYSTEMS

A variety of automatic fire extinguishing systems are suitable for records storage protection; the choice depends upon the economics of a particular situation and the degree of sophistication desired. All of the extinguishing systems described are loss initiated; the system does not detect and begin extinguishment until a fire is established and a fire loss has occurred. Systems that are more sensitive and reactive are available for highly specialized requirements. A large increase in cost and rate of false operation should be expected. Increased maintenance is usually required in more sophisticated systems to attain the reliability inherent in standard sprinkler systems.

Automatic Sprinklers

Automatic sprinkler systems are the most common type of automatic protection. They have proved effective in records storage fire incidents in limiting both fire and water damage. Water is discharged only in the immediate vicinity of the fire, and salvage techniques have been perfected to the point where recovery of wetted items is no longer unusual. Accidental opening of a sprinkler is rare. The probability of water damage from an accidental discharge can be further reduced using a preaction sprinkler system where water does not enter the piping until a fire detector operates. Preaction systems introduce additional failure modes, which may be unacceptable. A more sophisticated variation is a system where the control valve cycles on and off, depending upon the actual presence of fire as sensed by a detector in the fire area. Also available are sprinklers that cycle on and off individually, but the piping remains filled with water. However, the increased cost of these systems must be weighed against the value of the records being stored.

Foam Systems

Tests have shown high-expansion foam to be an effective fire control system for records, though few high-expansion foam systems are known to have been installed in records centers.[15] Rapid fire control comparable to, or possibly even faster than, that achieved by automatic sprinkler protection may be expected. Water damage to any single item will be low, but all items within the room or fire area involved will be affected. (A side effect unrelated to fire was observed in a large-scale test, which may be a disaster in itself: The records box labels exposed to foam loosened and slid off.)

Carbon Dioxide Systems

A few automatic total flooding carbon dioxide systems having a high rate of discharge have been installed in records storage or library areas. A properly designed system should promptly control fire with limited damage. To be successful, a high concentration of gas must be maintained for an extended period. The concentration must be maintained until a deep-seated fire cools below its ignition temperature. The operation of such systems, however, involves a hazard to life and must be delayed until the area to be flooded is cleared of people.

Halon Systems

Automatic total flooding halon systems utilize flame-inhibiting liquefied gas under pressure. Halon 1301 (bromotrifluoromethane) is being marketed to use in specially engineered systems for the protection of valuable records. Primary advantages are that the gaseous agent leaves no residue and is only mildly toxic in the concentrations in which it is used. Occupants, however, should not be unnecessarily exposed to Halon 1301. Deep-seated smoldering fires will not be extinguished by halon, as it inhibits flaming only.

The halons, particularly Halon 1301, are proposed for limitations on manufacture and use because of their effect on the Earth's ozone layer.

System Reliability

All fire control systems are subject to failure when various conditions are exceeded or not met. In Australia, where sprinklers are closely supervised, the success rate is more than 98 percent. Other systems, where statistics are very selective or nonexistant, are often assumed to have similar success rates, but this is far from the truth.

A long list of things that could go wrong is not sufficient evidence of an unusually high failure rate in practice. Gaseous systems are particularly vulnerable to failure. An independent detection system must work and must be correctly linked to the gas release. Usually, electric power is required for the detection system, linkage, and release to operate. The gas containers must be filled and connected to distribution piping. If the room has been enlarged since the system was installed, the gas volume applied may be inadequate. If any of the doors fail to close properly, a critical amount of gas may escape. If the ventilating system continues to operate, critical duct dampers fail to close, a window remains open or gets broken, or walls are breached for construction, a critical amount of gas may escape. If fire fighters open doors to assist in extinguishment, a critical amount of gas may escape. If deep-seated fires are not extinguished prior to gas dissipation, rekindling of the fire may be beyond the control of manual forces if no connected reserve gas supply is available for reapplication.

High-expansion foam systems have similar detection and activation vulnerabilities. They are especially vulnerable to loss of power because substantial power is required to operate the large fans used to generate the foam. Foam is also subject to blockage by doors, walls of stock, and fabric curtains. It is also somewhat vulnerable to loss of containment, although not nearly to the extent of gaseous systems.

Fire Prevention and Emergency Planning

Although detection and extinguishing systems are important, particularly for the bulk storage of valuable records, the first line of defense remains a good fire prevention and risk reduction program. Good housekeeping, orderliness, maintenance of equipment, and prohibition of smoking in records storage and handling areas are fundamental principles of good records management.

An emergency action plan that is kept current and practiced is essential to limit damage in case a fire occurs. Staff personnel cannot be expected to approach a fire and use extinguishers or hose lines effectively without adequate training. Fire-resistive containers and vaults are of much greater value if there has been training in procedures for fire emergencies. The following suggestions apply:

1. Records should be returned to their places of safety accurately, quickly, and without confusion or oversight. If there is no standard records protection, the best plan is to have the most important records carried out of the building. Drills are valuable to train employees to meet emergencies.
2. Records belonging in vaults or safes should never be left out overnight.
3. Important materials that belong under protection should not be allowed to accumulate on desks.
4. Because records normally safeguarded are often unprotected while temporarily on loan, copies instead of the originals should be loaned, and the originals retained in safe storage.

BIBLIOGRAPHY

References Cited

1. General Services Administration, "Protecting Federal Records Centers and Archives from Fire," General Services Administration, Washington, DC, 1977.
2. Gage-Babcock & Associates, *Protecting the Library and Its Resources*, American Library Association, Chicago, IL, 1963.
3. Chicarello, P. J. and Troup, J. M., *Fire Tests of Records Storage in a Fixed Storage Module Under the Protection of Large-Drop Sprinklers*, Factory Mutual Research Corp. (sponsored by U.S. General Services Administration), West Glocester, RI, 1980.
4. Jensen, R. H., *Report on Fire Tests in High-Piled Combustible Stock*, Underwriters Laboratories Inc., (sponsored by FIA and NBFU), Chicago, IL, 1963.
5. Chicarello, P. J., *et al.*, *Fire Tests in Mobile Storage Systems for Archival Storage*, Factory Mutual Research Corp. (sponsored by U.S. General Services Administration), West Glocester, RI, 1978.
6. McCrea, J. L., *et al.*, "Report to the Committee on Protection of Records of the National Fire Protection Association on Fire Tests on Microfilms Stored in Insulated Records Containers," Eastman Kodak Co., Rochester, NY, 1956.
7. McCrea, J. L. and Adelstein, P. Z., "Fire Tests on Microfilm in Insulated Records Containers," Second Report to the Committee on Protection of Records of the National Fire Protection Association, Eastman Kodak Co., Rochester, NY, 1958.
8. Fire Council, "Salvaging and Restoring Records Damaged by Fire and Water," *Federal Fire Council Recommended Practice No. 2*, Federal Fire Council, Washington, DC, 1963.
9. Morris, J., *Managing the Library Fire Risk*, University of California, Office of Insurance and Risk Management, Berkeley, CA, 1975.
10. Spawn, W., "After the Water Comes," *Bulletin of the Pennsylvania Library Association*, Vol. 28, No. 6, 1973, pp. 242-251.
11. Waters, P., *Procedures for Salvage of Water-Damaged Library Materials*, Library of Congress, Washington, DC, 1975.
12. Underwriters Laboratories Inc., "Tests for Fire Resistance of Records Protection Equipment," UL 72, Underwriters Laboratories Inc., Northbrook, IL, 1985.
13. Underwriters Laboratories Inc., "Tests for Fire Resistance of Vault and File Room Doors," UL 155, Underwriters Laboratories Inc., Northbrook, IL, 1979.
14. National Fire Protection Association, "Records Container Performance," *NFPA Quarterly*, Vol. 47, No. 2, 1953, pp. 159-170.
15. Atomic Energy Commission, "High-Expansion Foam Fire Control for Records Storage Centers," *Atomic Energy Commission Report IDO-12050*, Idaho Falls, ID, 1966.

NFPA Codes, Standards, and Recommended Practices

Reference to the following NFPA codes, standards, and recommended practices will provide further information on the safeguards for records storage discussed in this chapter. (See the latest *NFPA Catalog* for availability of current editions of the following documents.)

NFPA 10, *Portable Fire Extinguishers*.

NFPA 11, *Low-Expansion Foam and Combined Agent Systems*.

NFPA 12, *Carbon Dioxide Extinguishing Systems*.

NFPA 12A, *Halon 1301 Fire Extinguishing Systems*.

NFPA 13, *Installation of Sprinkler Systems*.

NFPA 14, *Standpipe and Hose Systems*.

NFPA 72E, *Automatic Fire Detectors*.

NFPA 232, *Protection of Records*.

NFPA 232AM, *Fire Protection for Archives and Records Centers*.

NFPA 910, *Protection of Libraries and Library Collections*.

Additional Reading

Bibliography of Micrographics, National Micrographics Association, Silver Springs, MD, 1977.

Bibliography on Records Management, Association of Records Managers and Administrators, Bradford, RI, 1980.

Cutler, H. R., *Engineering Analysis of Compact Storage Fire Tests*, Firepro, Inc., Wellesley Hills, MA, 1979.

Waegemann, C. P., *Handbook of Record Storage and Space Management*, Quorum, Westport, CT, 1983.

CONTROL OF ELECTROSTATIC IGNITION SOURCES

Revised by Don R. Scarbrough

Static electricity as a source of ignition is a hazard common to a wide variety of industries and processes. This chapter explains the nature of static electricity and means and methods of eliminating or minimizing it as an ignition source. Information on the hazards of static electricity in specific circumstances and processes can be found in the following chapters: Section 1, Chapter 5, "Explosions;" Section 2, Chapter 25, "Storage of Flammable and Combustible Liquids;" Section 3, Chapter 7, "Gases;" Section 3, Chapter 12, "Dusts;" Section 2, Chapter 3, "Electrical Systems and Appliances;" Section 6, Chapter 18, "Special Systems for Explosion Damage Control;" and Section 2, Chapter 12, "Spray Finishing and Powder Coating."

The term "static electricity" is used in this chapter to mean the electrification of materials through the physical processes described below, and the effects of the positive and negative charges so formed, particularly where sparks may result which constitute a fire or explosion hazard.

The development of electrical charges in itself may not be a potential fire or explosion hazard. There must be a discharge or sudden recombination of separated positive and negative charges. In order for static to be a source of ignition, four conditions must be fulfilled:

1. There must be an effective means of static generation.
2. There must be a means of accumulating the separate charges and maintaining a suitable difference of electrical potential.
3. There must be a spark discharge of adequate energy.
4. The spark must occur in an ignitible mixture.

Static electricity may appear as the result of motions that involve the separation or pulling apart of contacting surfaces, usually of dissimilar substances, either liquid or solid, one or both of which usually must be a poor conductor of electricity. Charge generated by this mechanism is usually referred to as the result of "separation" or "frictional" or "tribo" charging. Examples of such motion that are commonly found in industry are:

1. Motions of all sorts that involve friction between contacting surfaces, usually of dissimilar liquids or solids.
2. Steam, air, or gas flowing from any opening in a pipe or hose, when the steam is wet or the air or gas stream contains particulate matter.
3. The separation of a stream of liquid from contact with a hose, faucet, or pouring spout.
4. Pulverized materials passing through chutes or pneumatic conveyors.
5. Nonconductive power or conveyor belts in motion.
6. Moving vehicles.

Charge may appear upon the surface of an object when that object is simply brought near another object that bears a static charge. This charge mechanism is known as "induction" and results fundamentally from manipulation (through repulsion and attraction) of the inherently balanced charges within an uncharged object to produce separated regions upon its surface which bear balanced, but opposite charges.

An initially uncharged surface may become charged through "contact" with another object or surface that is charged. For example, a pail placed to collect a falling stream of liquid or pulverized material poured from a faucet or other container (the stream therefore being charged by "separation") will become charged by contact with the charged stream of material.

Yet another mechanism for placing charge upon a surface involves "bombardment" of the surface with charged molecules (ions) of air which themselves have become charged by bombardment with electrons within a corona near a high-voltage electrode. In this process the target surface becomes charged through attachment of the impacting ions, some of which may remain attached, and some of which may surrender their charge to the surface and then float away.

Other processes through which charge may be imparted to an object or fluid involve exposure to an electron beam or flow around a high-voltage electrode. These techniques are commonly referred to as "charge injection."

Around 1890, electricity was described as a "subtle agent, without weight or form, that appears to be diffused through all nature, existing in all substances, which gives

Don R. Scarbrough is the staff consultant for product safety for the Nordson Corporation, Westlake, OH.

no indication of its presence in the latent state, but is capable of producing sudden and destructive effects in its active state." With the discovery of the electron, this definition now seems prophetic, and the adjective "static" more meaningful. Electricity can move freely through some substances, such as metals, that are called "conductors," but can flow with difficulty or not at all through or over the surface of a class of substances called "nonconductors" or "insulators." This latter group includes gases, glass, amber, resin, sulfur, paraffin, most synthetic plastics, and dry petroleum oils.

When electricity is present on the surface of a nonconductive body, where it is trapped or prevented from escaping, it is termed static electricity. Electricity on a conducting body which is in contact only with nonconductors is also prevented from escaping and is therefore nonmobile or "static." In either case, the body on which this electricity is evident is said to be "charged."

The generation of static electricity cannot be prevented absolutely, because its intrinsic origins are present at every interface. The object of most static-corrective measures is to provide a means whereby charges separated by whatever cause may recombine harmlessly before sparking potentials are attained. If hazardous static conditions cannot be avoided in certain operations, means must be taken to ensure that there are no ignitible mixtures at points where sparks may occur.

Some electrical terms used in this chapter are defined as follows:

Capacitance: Electrons received by an electrically neutral body of material, such as a person, a car, or an aircraft, raise the voltage at a rate determined by the surface area and shape of the body. The voltage is determined by the surface characteristics (capacitance) of the body and the number of electrons on this surface. The larger the body, the more electrons are needed to raise the voltage a specific amount; hence, the higher the capacitance of this body.

Capacitance is measured in terms of "farads" or millionths of a farad, i.e., "microfarads." Millionths of one millionth of a farad are called "picofarads."

Charge: Measured in coulombs or fractions thereof, the static charge on a body is the number of separated electrons on the body (negative charge) or the number of separated electrons not on the body (positive charge). Electrons cannot be destroyed; so when an electron is removed from one body, it must go to another body. Thus there are always equal and opposite charges produced [leaving behind a positive (+) void]. Since it would be awkward to say there are 6,240,000,000,000,000,000 electrons on a body, instead it is said that the body has a charge of one "coulomb." A coulomb is simply a name for this specific quantity of electrons. In electrostatics an even more practical unit is a microcoulomb, representing a charge of 6.24×10^{12} electrons.

Current: Just as water flow is measured in terms of the amount of water that passes a certain point in a specific period of time (gallons or liters per minute), so too is the flow of electrons past a certain point measured by time. The flow of electrons is called current. Current is measured in terms of electrons per second, coulombs per second, or amperes. When dealing with static electricity, current is commonly limited to the microampere range.

Energy: Energy is measured in joules or fractions thereof. A spark is energy being expended. Energy is required to do work. The measure of energy takes several forms. Often it is physical energy, which is measured in foot-pounds or joules or watts. If it is heat energy, it is measured in British thermal units (Btu) or Pascals (P); and if it is electrical energy it is measured in watt-seconds or in joules. A joule is the energy expended in 1 sec by an electric current of one ampere in a resistance of one ohm (approximately 0.738 foot-pound). Static spark energy is usually measured in thousandths of a joule (millijoules or mJ). A static spark needs a minimum amount of energy to cause problems.

Incendive: A spark that has enough energy to ignite an ignitible mixture is said to be incendive. Thus an incendive spark can ignite an ignitible mixture and cause a fire or explosion. A nonincendive spark does not possess the energy required to cause ignition even if it occurs within an ignitible mixture.

Incendivity: The ability of a spark to ignite an ignitible mixture is called incendivity. The energy level required for incendivity varies as described in the text and can be calculated.

Potential: Stored energy is able to do work. In electricity, this ability is expressed in terms of the potential of doing work. Potential in electricity is measured in terms of "volt," "kilovolts," or "millivolts." Potential, or voltage, is measured from a base point. This point can be any voltage but is usually "ground" which is theoretically zero voltage. When one point with a potential of "x" volts to ground is compared with another point with a potential of "y" volts to ground, then we say that a potential difference of "x-y" volts exists between the two. Then, when a point with a potential of 2500 (+) volts to ground is compared with a point with a potential of 1500 (–) volts to ground, the potential difference is 4,000 volts.

Resistance: Electrical current encounters difficulty in passing through an electrical circuit or conductor. This difficulty can be measured and is called resistance. Resistance can be measured in terms of voltage drop over a part of the circuit but is usually measured in terms of "ohms" or "megohms." The resistance of a circuit in ohms is equal to the ratio of voltage in volts to current in amperes, i.e.,

$$\frac{10\text{ V}}{1\text{ amp}} = \text{ohms}, \quad \frac{1\text{ V}}{1\mu\text{ amp}} = \text{megohm}.$$

STATIC GENERATION

When two bodies composed of dissimilar materials are in close physical contact, there is likely to be a transfer of free electrons between them, one giving up electrons to the other, and an attractive force is established. When the bodies are separated, work must be done in opposition to these attractive forces. The expended energy reappears as an increase in electrical tension or voltage between the two surfaces. If the bodies are insulated from their surroundings, both are said to be "charged;" the one having the excess of electrons is said to have a negative charge, while the other is said to have an equal positive charge. If a conductive path is available between them, the charges thus separated will reunite immediately. If no such path is available, as is the case with insulators, the potential increase with separation may easily reach values of several thousand volts.

In many cases, one of the objects has a deliberate or inherently conductive path to the earth, and its charge is immediately lost to the earth, which is considered to have an infinite capacity to absorb or give up electrons. The other (insulated) object now retains its "charge" (often called potential or voltage) with respect to its surroundings. It would hold this charge indefinitely, except for the fact that it must somehow be supported and no supporting insulator (even air) is a perfect nonconductor.

If one of the bodies is itself a nonconductor, the flow of electrons across its surface is inhibited, and the charge tends to remain at the points where electron transfer originally occurred. A highly charged insulating surface can be discharged with the appearance of a spark by bringing an "earthed" conductor close to it, but only a limited area will be so discharged, and sparks so produced seldom release enough energy to cause ignition. Thus, nonconductors, the bodies most directly involved in charge separation, are usually not directly responsible for fires and explosions. (An exception is flammable liquids, which are discussed later in this chapter.) However, such charges can in some cases be the agency for building up or accumulating a charge on a conductive body, which can release all of its stored energy in an incendive spark.

On a conductive body the charge is free to move. Because like charges repel each other, the charge will distribute itself over the surface. If no other body is in close proximity, the concentration will favor the surface having the least radius of curvature; for a point, if the voltage is high enough, the voltage gradient may exceed the breakdown potential of air (about 30,000 volts per centimeter) and the air can be ionized, and a brush discharge may occur.

Like charges repel each other and unlike charges attract, because of forces resident in the electrical fields that surround them. These forces have a strong influence on nearby objects. If the neighboring object is a conductor it will experience a separation of charges by induction. Its repelled charge is free to give or receive electrons as the case may be; if another conductor is brought near, the transfer may occur through the agency of a spark, very often an energetic spark. When the inducing charge is moved away from the insulated conductor, there follows a reversed sequence of events, and sparks may result. Thus, in many situations, induced charges are far more dangerous than the initially separated ones upon which they are dependent.

If the object close to the highly charged nonconductor is itself a nonconductor, it will be polarized, i.e., its constituent molecules will be oriented to some degree in the direction of the lines of force, since the electrons have no true migratory freedom. Because of their polarizable nature, insulators and nonconductors are often called dielectrics. Their presence as separating media enhances the accumulation of charge.

Capacitance

Two conductive bodies separated by an insulator constitute a capacitor or condenser, and where a potential difference is applied between these bodies, electricity can be stored. One body receives a positive and the other an equal negative charge. In many instances involving accumulation of static electricity, one of the bodies is the earth, the insulating medium is the air, and the insulated body is some object to or from which a charge (electrons) has been transferred by one of the mechanisms previously described.

When a conducting path is made available, the stored energy is released, or the condenser is "discharged," possibly producing a spark. The energy so stored and released by the spark is related to the capacitance of the condenser (*C*) and the voltage (*V*) in accordance with the following:

$$\text{Energy} = \frac{C}{2} \times V^2$$

Energy (millijoules = C/2 (picofarads) × V^2 (volts × 10^{-9}).

Spark Discharge

The ability of a spark to produce ignition of a flammable mixture is governed largely by the energy transferred to the mixture, which will be some fraction of the total stored energy available because some energy is expended in heating the electrodes. Experiments at atmospheric pressure with plane electrodes have shown that the spark breakdown voltage has a minimum value at a critical short gap distance—about 350 volts for the shortest measurable gap (e.g., 0.01 mm). Increased gaps require proportionately higher voltages. At close spacing the heat loss or flame quenching effect virtually precludes ignition of the electrodes.

At most favorable electrode spacing, tests have shown that optimum mixtures of saturated hydrocarbon vapors and gases in air require about 0.25 millijoules of discharge energy to produce ignition. Examples of the capacitance necessary to store the required 0.25 millijoules at various voltages are listed in Table 2-31A.

TABLE 2-31A. ***Examples of Conditions Required to Produce Ignition***

	Potential volts	Capacitance pf	Gap Length	
A.	350	4,000	Minimum voltage to jump shortest measurable gap. Quenching effect precludes ignition.	
B.	1500	222	Gap about 0.5 mm, just exceeding quenching distance. Incendiary sparks.	
C.	5000	20		1.5 mm
D.	10,000	5	Object the size of a baseball.	3+ mm
E.	20,000	1¼	Object the size of a large marble.	7 mm

For gaps of 1.5 mm or more, substantially longer than the quenching distance, the total energy required to produce ignition is increased somewhat in proportion to the excess of spark length over the diameter of the necessary critical flame volume. This, in turn, may require somewhat greater capacitance than indicated above. This explains why corona discharge from a sharp point at very high voltage may not be incendive.

Ignitible Mixtures

Elimination of ignitible mixtures in the areas where sparks of static electricity can occur is the surest method of preventing static-caused fires. This is practical in certain areas, and is better discussed later in connection with the specific process involved.

Summary

In summary, static electricity will be manifest only where highly insulated bodies or surfaces are found. If a body is "charged" with static electricity, there will always be an equal and opposite charge produced. If a hazard is suspected, the situation should be analyzed to determine the location of both charges and to see what conductive paths are available between them. Tests of the high-resistance paths should be made with an applied potential of 500 volts or more, in order that a minor interruption (e.g., paint or grease film or air gap) will be broken down and a correct reading of the instrument obtained. Resistances as high as 10,000 megohms will provide an adequate leakage path in many cases; when charges are generated rapidly, however, a resistance as low as 1 megohm might be required. Where bonds are applied, they should connect the bodies on which the two opposite charges are expected to be found.

DISSIPATION OF STATIC ELECTRICITY

A static charge which already exists can be removed or allowed to dissipate itself. The acts or conditions which can accomplish this are the same as those acts or conditions which permit the separation of charges to occur in the first place. Thus, dissipation of static and prevention of its generation are opposite approaches to the same objective.

Humidification

A static charge cannot persist except on a body insulated from its surroundings. Most commonly encountered materials which are not usually thought of as conductors, such as fabrics, paper, wood, concrete or masonry foundations, etc., contain a certain amount of moisture in equilibrium with that in the surrounding atmosphere. This moisture content varies, depending on weather (and to a large measure controls the conductivity of the material), and hence its ability to prevent the escape of static electricity. In an analogous manner, under some conditions water vapor may condense on the surface of some nominally insulating materials, notably glass and porcelain, to render the surface conductive.

The conductivity of the materials under discussion—wood, paper, etc.—is not controlled by the absolute water content of the air but by its relative humidity. This figure, as ordinarily recorded in weather reports and comfort charts, is the ratio of the partial pressure of the moisture in the atmosphere to the partial pressure of water at the prevailing atmospheric temperature. Under conditions of high relative humidity (50 percent or higher) the materials in question will reach equilibrium conditions containing enough moisture to make the conductivity adequate to prevent static accumulations. The generating mechanism may be present, but the generated charge leaks away so fast that no observable accumulation results.

At the opposite extreme, with relative humidities of 30 percent or less, these same materials may dry out, become good insulators, and static manifestations become noticeable. There is no definite boundary line between these two conditions.

It should be emphasized that the conductivity of these materials is a function of relative humidity. At any constant moisture content, the relative humidity of an atmosphere decreases as the temperature is raised. In cold weather, the absolute humidity of the outdoor atmosphere may be low, even though the relative humidity may be high. When this same air is brought indoors and heated, the relative humidity becomes very low. As an example, a saturated atmosphere at an outdoor temperature of 30°F (–1°C) would have a relative humidity of only a little over 20 percent if heated up to a room temperature of 70°F (21°C). This phenomenon is responsible for the common belief that static generation is always more intense during winter months. The static problem is usually more severe during this period because static charges on a material have less ability to dissipate when relative humidities are low.

Where static electricity has introduced operational problems, such as the adhesion or repulsion of sheets of paper, layers of cloth, fibers, and the like, humidifying the atmosphere has proved to be a solution. It is usually stated that a relative humidity of about 50 percent or higher will avoid such difficulties.

Unfortunately, it is not practical to humidify all occupancies in which static might be a hazard. It is necessary to conduct some operations in an atmosphere having a low relative humidity to avoid deleterious effects on the materials handled. High humidity can also cause intolerable comfort conditions in operations where the dry bulb temperature is high. On the other hand, a high humidity may advantageously affect the handling properties of some materials, thus providing an additional advantage. In some cases, localized humidification produced by directing a steam jet onto critical areas may provide satisfactory results without the need for increasing the humidity in the whole room. However, it must be remembered that steam which contains droplets of water may itself generate static. Local static can be reduced by providing a low-velocity jet of humidified air.

It does not follow that humidification is a cure for all static problems. In particular, it must be remembered that the conductivity of the air is not appreciably increased by the presence in it of water in the form of a gas. If static electricity accumulates on some surface which is heated above normal atmospheric temperature, e.g., cloth passing over heated rollers, alterations in the relative humidity in the surrounding air may do no good whatsoever.

Another situation where the control of atmospheric humidity appears to accomplish little is in controlling the charge of static electricity that appears on the surface of oils under some circumstances. Such a surface does not absorb water vapor in the same way as paper or wood does, so it can remain an insulating surface capable of accumulating static charges even though the atmosphere above it may have a relative humidity up to 100 percent.

In summary, humidification of the atmosphere to a relative humidity of 50 percent or higher may be a cure for static problems where the surfaces on which the static electricity accumulates are those materials that reach equilibrium with the atmosphere, such as paper or wood, and that are not abnormally heated. For heated surfaces and for static on the surface of oils and some other liquid and solid insulating materials, high humidity will not provide a means for draining off static charges, and some other solution must be sought.

Bonding and Grounding

Where natural conditions, including humidity, do not ensure a conductive path to prevent static accumulation, artificial conducting paths may be necessary.

"Bonding" is the process of connecting two or more conductive objects together by means of a conductor. "Grounding" (earthing) is the process of connecting one or more conductive objects to the ground, and is a specific form of bonding. A conductive object may also be grounded by bonding it to another conductive object that is already connected to the ground. Some objects are inherently bonded or inherently grounded by their contact with the ground. Examples are underground piping or large storage tanks resting on the ground. Bonding minimizes potential differences between conductive objects. Grounding minimizes potential differences between objects and the ground.

Bond wires and ground wires should have adequate capacity to carry the largest currents that may be anticipated for any particular installation. When currents to be handled are small, the minimum size of wire is dictated by required mechanical strength rather than current carrying capacity. The currents encountered in the bond connections used in the protection against accumulations of static electricity are in the order of microamperes (one millionth of an ampere).

The acceptable resistance in a ground connection depends upon the type of hazard for which it is intended to give protection. To prevent the accumulation of static electricity, the resistance need not be less than 1 megohm and in most cases may be even higher. To protect electrical power circuits, the resistance must be low enough to ensure operation of the fuse or circuit breaker under fault conditions. Any ground that is adequate for power circuits or lightning protection is more than adequate for protection against static electricity.

A bond or ground is composed of suitable conductive materials having adequate mechanical strength, corrosion resistance, and flexibility for the service intended. Since the bond or ground does not need to have low resistance, nearly any conductor size will be satisfactory from an electrical standpoint. Solid conductors are satisfactory for fixed connections. Flexible conductors are used for bonds that are to be connected and disconnected frequently. Conductors may be insulated or uninsulated. Some prefer uninsulated conductors so that defects can be easily spotted by visual inspections. If insulated for mechanical protection, the concealed conductor is checked for continuity at regular intervals, depending on the inspector's experience. Connections may be made with pressure-type ground clamps, brazing, or welding. Battery clamps, or magnetic or other special clamps, provide metal-to-metal contact.

A special situation requiring substantial conductors may arise if there is a possibility that a ground wire may be called upon to carry current from power circuits or lightning protection systems. Obviously, any ground that is adequate for power circuits is more than adequate for protection against accumulations of static electricity.

Ionization

Under certain circumstances air may become sufficiently conductive to bleed off static charges.

Static comb: A static charge on a conducting body is free to flow, and on a spherical body in space it will distribute itself uniformly over the surface. If the body is not spherical, the self-repulsion of the charge will make it concentrate on the surfaces having the least radius of curvature.

If the body is surrounded by air (or other gas) and the radius of curvature is reduced to almost zero, as with a sharp needle point, the charge concentration on the point can produce ionization of the air, rendering it conductive. As a result, whereas a surface of large diameter can receive and hold a high voltage, the same surface equipped with a sharp needle point can reach only a small voltage before the leakage rate equals the rate of generation.

A "static comb" is a metal bar equipped with a series of needle points. Another variation is a metal wire surrounded with metallic tinsel. If a grounded static comb is brought close to an insulated charged body (or a charged insulating surface), ionization of the air at the points will provide enough conductivity to make the charge speedily leak away or be "neutralized." This principle is sometimes employed to remove the charge from fabrics, power belts, and paper.

Electrical neutralization: The electrical neutralizer is a line-powered high-voltage device which is an effective means for removing static charges from materials, such as cotton, wool, or silk, or paper in process, manufacturing, or printing. It produces a conducting ionized atmosphere in the vicinity of the charged surfaces. The charges thereby leak away to some adjacent grounded conducting body. Electrical neutralizers should not be used where flammable vapors, gases, or dust may be present, unless approved specifically for such locations.

Radioactive neutralizer: Another method for dissipating static electricity involves the ionization of the air by radioactive material. Such installations require no redesign of existing equipment. However, engineering problems are involved, such as elimination of health hazards, dust accumulations, determination of radiation required, and proper positioning in relation to the stock, machine parts, and personnel. These considerations are best worked out in consultation with radiation specialists.

Open flame: Ionization of the air can also be obtained by an open flame. This method is frequently used in the printing industry to remove static from paper sheets as they come off the press, thus avoiding the mechanical problems involving one sheet of paper adhering to another, but obviously not avoiding an ignition source.

CONTROL OF IGNITIBLE MIXTURES

Despite efforts to prevent accumulation of static charges, which should be the primary aim of good design, there are many operations involving the handling of nonconductive materials or nonconductive equipment which do not lend themselves to this built-in solution. It may then be desirable, or essential, depending on the hazardous nature of the materials involved, to provide other measures to supplement or supplant static dissipation facilities. For example, where a normally ignitible mixture is contained within a small enclosure, such as a processing tank, an inert gas may be used to bring the mixture well below its flammable range. When operations are normally conducted in an atmosphere above the upper flammable limit, it may be practicable to apply the inert gas only during the periods when the mixture passes through its flammable range.

Mechanical ventilation may be applied in many instances to dilute an ignitible mixture to well below its normal flammable range. Also by directing the air movement, it may be practical to prevent the flammable liquids or dusts from approaching an operation where an otherwise uncontrollable static hazard may exist. To be considered reliable, the mechanical ventilation should be interlocked with the equipment to ensure its proper operation.

Where a static-accumulating piece of equipment is unnecessarily located in a hazardous area, it is preferable to relocate the equipment to a safe location rather than to rely upon prevention of static accumulation.

FLAMMABLE LIQUIDS

Static is generated when liquids move in contact with other materials. This occurs commonly in such operations as flowing through pipes, and in mixing, pouring, pumping, filtering, or agitating. Under certain conditions, particularly with liquid hydrocarbons, with high-velocity flow, and with filtration through insulative, resin-bonded media, static may accumulate. If the accumulation is sufficient, a static spark may occur. If the spark occurs in the presence of a flammable vapor-air mixture, an ignition may result. Therefore, steps must be taken to prevent the simultaneous occurence of the two conditions.

Standard control measures are designed to prevent incendive sparks, or the formation of ignitible vapor-air mixtures. In many cases, air which may form an ignitible mixture with the vapor can be eliminated or reduced in concentration to render the mixture nonflammable.

Before a container is filled, contact is made between the filling nozzle and the container and the contact should be maintained throughout the filling operation. By this procedure, any difference in potential between the container and nozzle will be dissipated before the filling operation is started, and differences in potential between the nozzle and container are prevented from forming during the filling operation. See Figure 2-31A for methods of bonding containers and nozzles during container filling.

The relative static-accumulating tendencies of a number of petroleum products have been measured in laboratory tests. In general, aliphatic solvents and lower boiling hydrocarbons exhibited lower charging tendencies than higher boiling products. However, the charging tendency of any given product was found to vary widely from one sample to the next.

The conductivity of a liquid is a measure of its ability to hold a charge. The lower the conductivity, the greater the ability of the liquid to hold a charge. If the conductivity of a liquid is greater than 50 pS/m (picoseimens per meter), any charges that are generated will dissipate without accumulating to a hazardous potential.

Free Charges on Surface of Liquid

If an electrically charged liquid is poured, pumped, or otherwise transferred into a tank or container, the unit charges of similar sign (i.e., + or –) within the liquid will be repelled from each other toward the outer surfaces of the liquid, including not only the surfaces in contact with the container walls but also the top surface adjacent to the air space, if any. It is this latter charge, often called the "surface charge," that is of most concern in many situations.

In most cases the container is of metal, and hence conducting. Two situations can occur, somewhat different with respect to protective measures, depending on whether the container is in contact with the earth or is insulated from it. These two situations are: (1) an ordinary storage tank

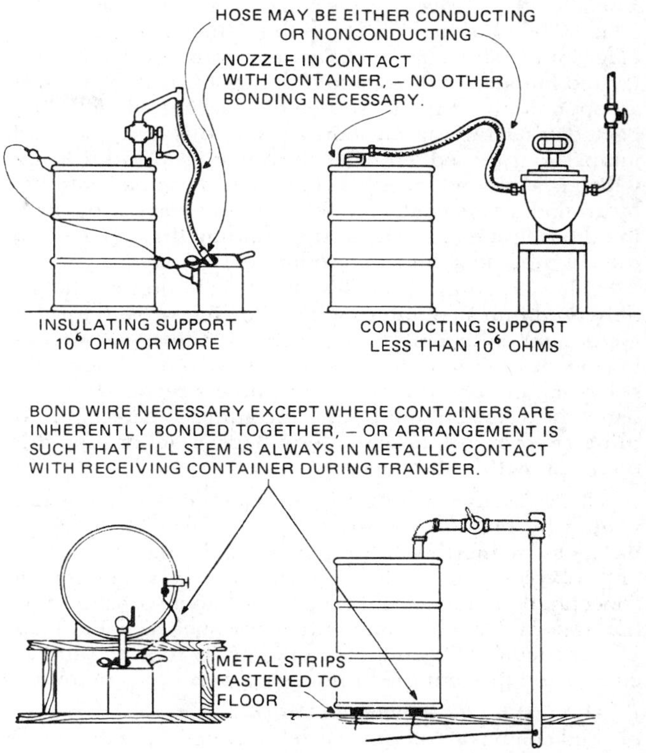

*FIG. 2-31A. **Recommended methods of bonding flammable liquid containers during container filling.***

resting on earth or concrete or other slightly conducting foundation, and (2) a tank truck on dry rubber tires.

In the first situation, the metal container is connected to ground. The charges that reach the surfaces in contact with the vessel will reunite with charges of opposite sign which have been attracted there. During this process, the tank and its contents, considered as a unit, are electrically neutral, i.e., the total charge in the liquid and on its surface is exactly equal and opposite to the charge on the tank shell. This charge on the tank shell is "bound" there, but gradually disappears as it reunites with the charge migrating through the liquid. The time required for this to occur is called "relaxation time." The relaxation time depends primarily on the conductivity of the liquid. It may be a fraction of a second or several minutes.

During this process, the tank shell is at ground potential. Externally, as already mentioned, the container is electrically neutral. But internally, there may be differences of potential between the container wall and the fluid, lasting until charges on the fluid have gradually leaked off and reunited with the unlike charges on the tank walls.

If the potential difference between any part of the liquid surface and the metal tank shell should become high enough to cause ionization of the air, electrical breakdown may occur and a spark may jump to the shell. A spark across the liquid surface is an ignition hazard where flammable vapor-air mixtures are present. No bonding or grounding of the tank or container can remove this internal surface charge.

In the second situation, when the tank shell is highly insulated from the earth, the charge on the liquid surface attracts an equal and opposite charge to the inside of the container. This leaves a "free" charge on the outside of the tank, of the same sign as that in the liquid, and of the same magnitude. This charge can escape from the tank to the ground in the form of a spark. In filling a tank truck through an open dome, it is this source of sparking which is suspected of having caused some fires; in this case, the spark jumps from the edge of the fill opening to the fill pipe which is at ground potential. This hazard can be controlled by grounding the container before filling starts or by bonding the fill pipe to the tank. If grounding the tank is used, the fill pipe must also be grounded.

The foregoing discusses the distribution of charges delivered into a container with a flowing stream. Further generation or separation may occur within the container in several ways to produce a surface charge: (1) flow with splashing or spraying of the incoming stream, (2) disturbance of water bottom by the incoming stream, (3) bubbling of air or gas through a liquid, or (4) jet or propeller blending within the tank.

These charges on the surface of a liquid cannot be prevented by bonding or grounding, but can be rendered harmless by inerting the vapor space, by displacing part of the oxygen with a suitable inert gas, or by increasing the concentration of flammable gas in the vapor space to above the upper flammable limit with a gas, such as natural gas. Use of conductivity additives will rapidly relax the surface charge and prevent the buildup of a hazardous potential.

It must be recognized that mists and foams of flammable and combustible liquids can be ignited by static sparks in much the same way dusts can be ignited. Ignition is possible even though the liquid in the mist is below its flash point.

GASES

Gases not contaminated with solid or liquid particles have been found to generate little, if any, electrification in their flow. When the flowing gas is contaminated with dust, metallic oxides, scale particles, etc., or with liquid particles or spray, electrification may result. A stream of such particle-containing gas directed against a conductive body will charge the latter unless it is grounded or bonded to the discharge pipe.

When any gas is in a closed system of piping and equipment, the system need not be electrically conductive or electrically bonded. Compressed air or steam-containing particles of condensed water vapor often manifests strong electrification when escaping.

Carbon dioxide, discharged as a liquid from orifices under high pressure (where it immediately changes to a gas and "snow"), can result in static accumulations on the discharge device and the receiving container. This condition is not unlike the effect from contaminated compressed air or from steam flow where the contact effects at the orifice play a part in the static accumulation. High-pressure carbon dioxide should not be discharged into flammable atmospheres because it presents a high risk of ignition due to static spark.

Hydrogen-air and acetylene-air mixtures may be ignited by a spark energy of as little as 0.017 millijoule. In the pure state, no static charges are generated by the flow of hydrogen. However, as gaseous hydrogen is commercially handled in industry, such as flowing through pipelines, discharging through valves at filling racks into pressure containers, or flowing out of containers through nozzles, the hydrogen may be found to contain particles of oxide carried off from the inside of pipes or containers. In this contaminated state, hydrogen may generate static.

The liquefied petroleum gases (LP-Gases) behave in a manner similar to uncontaminated gases in the gas phase and to contaminated gases in the mixed phase. Bonding is not required when LP-Gas vehicles are loaded or unloaded through closed connections so that there is no release of vapor at a point where a spark could occur, irrespective of whether the hose or pipe used is conducting or nonconducting. (A closed connection is one where contact is made before flow starts and is broken after flow has ended.)

DUSTS AND FIBERS

As previously pointed out, the flow of a stream of gas containing small particles can result in a separation of electrons and the accumulation of a static charge on any insulated conductive body with which it comes in contact. Also, dust displaced from a surface on which it rests may develop a considerable charge. The ultimate charge depends on the inherent properties of the substance, size of particle, amount of surface contact, surface conductivity, gaseous breakdown, external field, and leakage resistance in a system. Greater charges develop from smooth rather than from rough surfaces, probably because of greater initial surface contact. Electrification develops during the first phase of separation. Subsequent impact of airborne particles on obstructions may affect their charge slightly, but if the impact surface becomes coated with the dust, this effect is slight.

Charge generation seldom occurs if both materials are good electrical conductors, but it is likely to occur with a conductor and a nonconductor or two nonconductors. When like materials are separated, as in dispersing quartz dust from a quartz surface, positive and negative charges are developed in the dispersed dust in about equal amounts to give a net zero charge. With materials differing in composition, a charge of one polarity may predominate in the dust. Each of the materials becomes equally charged but with opposite polarity. With a metallic and an insulating material, the former usually assumes a positive and the latter a negative polarity.

Electrostatic charge generation in moving dust normally cannot be prevented. High humidity or grounding of the surface from which dust is dispersed will not eliminate the charge generation. The method of dispersion of the dust, the amount of energy expended in dispersal, the degree of turbulence, and the composition of the atmosphere usually do not affect the magnitude or distribution of the charges.

Not only can dust participate in the generation of static, it may also be the material ignited by static sparks. A suspension of finely divided combustible particles in air has much the same properties as a flammable gas-air mixture, except for a generally higher ignition energy. (With some metallic dust, ignition energy is comparable to gas-air mixtures.) It can burn to produce explosive effects. It has a lower flammable limit, but no strictly definable upper limit.

Ignition of Dust by Static Discharge

Dust clouds and layers of many combustible materials (with or without a volatile constituent) have been ignited experimentally by static discharge. In some instances, the charge was generated by movement of dust, in others by a static generator (Wimshurst machine), or by electronic equipment. With dust clouds, it has been shown that a minimum dust concentration exists below which ignition cannot take place regardless of the energy of the spark. At the minimum dust concentration a relatively high energy is required for ignition. At higher dust concentrations (5 to 10 times the minimum), the energy required for ignition is at a minimum.

The energy stored in a capacitative circuit has been previously discussed, where it was tacitly assumed that all of this energy was released in the spark (zero circuit resistance). For the ignition of dusts it has been shown that a circuit resistance of 10,000 to 100,000 ohms may be required for optimum igniting power, indicating that some of the energy is dissipated in the circuit instead of being released in the spark, with a corresponding increase in the total energy required.

A layer of combustible dust can be ignited by static discharge and will burn with a bright flash, glow, or, for some metallic dusts, with flame. Apparently, there is little correlation in the minimum energy required for ignition of dust layers and clouds. Layers of some metallic dusts, such as aluminum, magnesium, titanium, and zirconium, require less energy for ignition than carbonaceous materials.

Primary explosives, e.g., mercury fulminate and tetryl, are readily detonated by static spark discharge. Steps necessary to prevent accidents caused by static electricity in explosives manufacturing operations and storage areas vary considerably with the static sensitiveness of the material being handled. In all instances in which static electricity was authentically established as the cause of ignition, the spark occurred between an insulated conductor and ground. It has not been verified experimentally that a dust cloud can be ignited by static discharge within itself.

STATIC DETECTORS

The following devices have an application in the measurement and determination of static electricity within the limitations of each device as described.

Electroscopes

The leaf electroscope is a simple but sensitive device that demonstrates the presence or absence of electrical charges by the repulsion of its leaves when the device is charged. Only units intended as portable dosimeters for ionizing, radiation, and one or two classroom demonstration models are available.

Neon Lamps

A small neon lamp or fluorescent tube will light up feebly when one terminal is grounded (or held in the hand) and the other makes contact with any sizeable conductor that carries a charge potential of 70 volts or more. Like the electroscope, it gives but little quantitative information; however, when it passes current, it may give a rough idea of the rate at which charges are being produced in certain operations. Adjustable series-parallel groupings of such lamps and small capacitors can be arranged to give a semblance of quantitative information.

Electrostatic Voltmeters

These meters operate by electrostatic attraction between movable and stationary metal vanes. No current is passed to maintain deflection because one set of vanes (usually the stationary one) is very highly insulated. Small portable, accurately calibrated instruments are available in several ranges from 100 to 10,000 volts. This type of meter may be used for quantitative electrostatic analysis.

Electrometers

Electrometers are frequently used for laboratory and field investigations of static electricity. These instruments employ special input stages designed for high input resistance and low grid current and may be used in several ways. With a small antenna mounted on the grid terminal, they are very suitable for detecting transient electrostatic charge effects; in the presence of a constant field, the charge induced on the grid will leak off and the meter pointer will return to zero. However, as the rate of leakage is not high, the electrometer finds considerable use for "on-the-spot" static checks. Often electrometers are equipped with high-resistance terminal shunts to convert them to current meters in the nanoampere range. They can thus be used in many applications to indicate the rate of charge development. A simple adaptation converts the instrument into a megohm meter, as explained in the manufacturer's instruction manual.

Field Mills

A "field mill" is a device that overcomes the serious limitation of the electrometer in that it provides a continuous indication of charge by providing its own transients in the form of continuous grid modulation. It can therefore "look" at a distant charge and determine its potential. The electrical field extending from the charge is chopped by a motor-driven variable condenser or window. The resulting pulsations are transformed, amplified, and rectified to give a dc meter deflection proportional to the strength of the field. A similar instrument of suitable design can be immersed in a liquid, as in a pipeline, to measure charge density.

BIBLIOGRAPHY

NFPA Codes, Standards, and Recommended Practices

Reference to the following NFPA codes, standards, and recommended practices will provide further information on electrostatic ignition sources discussed in this chapter. (See the latest *NFPA Catalog* for availability of current editions of the following documents.)

NFPA 30, *Flammable and Combustible Liquids Code.*

NFPA 33, *Spray Application Using Flammable and Combustible Materials.*

NFPA 45, *Fire Protection for Laboratories Using Chemicals.*

NFPA 61A, *Prevention of Fire and Dust Explosions in Facilities Manufacturing and Handling Starch.*

NFPA 61B, *Prevention of Fires and Explosions in Grain Elevators and Facilities Handling Bulk Raw Agricultural Commodities.*

NFPA 61C, *Prevention of Fire and Dust Explosion in Feed Mills.*

NFPA 61D, *Prevention of Fire and Dust Explosions in the Milling of Agricultural Commodities for Human Consumption.*

NFPA 65, *Processing and Finishing of Aluminum.*

NFPA 70, *National Electrical Code®*.

NFPA 77, *Static Electricity*.

NFPA 385, *Tank Vehicles for Flammable and Combustible Liquids*.

NFPA 407, *Aircraft Fuel Servicing*.

NFPA 480, *Storage, Handling, and Processing of Magnesium*.

NFPA 481, *Production, Processing, Handling, and Storage of Titanium*.

NFPA 482, *Production, Processing, Handling, and Storage of Zirconium*.

NFPA 650, *Pneumatic Conveying Systems for Handling Combustible Materials*.

NFPA 651, *Manufacture of Aluminum and Magnesium Powder*.

NFPA 654, *Prevention of Fire and Dust Explosions in the Chemical, Dye, Pharmaceutical, and Plastics Industries*.

NFPA 655, *Prevention of Sulfur Fires and Explosions*.

NFPA 664, *Prevention of Fires and Explosions in Wood Processing and Woodworking Facilities*.

NFPA 850, *Fire Protection for Fossil Fueled Steam Electric Generating Plants*.

NFPA 1124, *Manufacture, Transportation, and Storage of Fireworks*.

NFPA 1125, *Manufacturing of Model Rocket Engines*.

Additional Reading

American Petroleum Institute, *Recommended Practice for Protection Against Ignitions Arising Out of Static, Lightning, and Stray Currents*. (RP 20003), 3rd ed., American Petroleum Institute, Washington, DC, 1974.

Beach, R., "Preventing Static Electricity Fires," *Chemical Engineer*, Vol. 88 (Feb. 1, 1965), pp. 85-88.

Berkey, B. D., Pratt, T. H., and Williams, G. M., "Review of Literature Related to Human Spark Scenarios," *Plant/Operations Progress*, Vol. 7, No. 1 (Jan. 1988), pp. 32-36.

Britton, L. G., "Systems for Electrostatic Evaluation in Industrial Silos," *Plant/Operation Progress*, Vol. 7, No. 1 (Jan. 1988), pp. 45-50.

Britton, L. G. and Smith, J. A., "Static Hazards of Drum Filling, Parts 1 & 2," *Plant/Operations Technology*, Vol. 7, No. 1 (Jan. 1988), p. 53.

Bustin, W. M. and Dudek, W. G., *Electrostatic Hazards in the Petroleum Industry*, Research Studies Press, Ltd. England, 1983.

Bustin, W. M., Koszman, I., Tobye, I. T., "New Theory for Static Relaxation From High Resistivity Fuel." Presented to a Special Joint Meeting of the Operating Practices Committee, Division of Refining, and the Central Committee on Safety and Fire Protection, Division of Science and Technology, Esso Research and Engineering Co., Houston, TX, Oct. 1964.

Davis, K., "Electrostatic Discharges—Stopping the Sparks Flying," *Fire Prevention*, No. 228, Apr. 1990, pp. 21-24.

Eichel, F. G., "Electrostatics," *Chemical Engineering*, Mar. 1967, pp. 153-167.

Electrostatic Properties of Materials, (Std. No. 101B—Method 4046), General Services Administration, Washington, DC, Jan. 1969.

Expert Commission for Safety in the Swiss Chemical Industry, "Static Electricity: Rules for Plant Safety," *Plant Operations Progress*, Vol. 7, No. 1 (Jan. 1988), pp. 1-22.

"Fire and Explosion Due to Electrostatic Charges in the Plastics Industry," *Bulletin No. 6*, Society of the Plastics Industry, NY.

Glor, M., "Hazards Due to Electrostatic Charging of Powders," *Journal of Electrostatics*, Vol. 16, No. 2 (May 1985).

Guest, P. G., Sikora, V. W., and Lewis, B., *Static Electricity in Hospital Operating Suites: Direct and Related Hazards and Pertinent Remedies*, Bulletin 520, Bureau of Mines, Washington, DC, 1953 (reprinted 1962).

Harper, W. R., *Contact and Frictional Electrification*, Oxford Press, 1967.

Haase, H., *Electrostatic Hazards; Their Evaluation and Control*, 2nd ed., (translated by Michael Wald), Verlay Chemical International, NY, 1977.

Heidelberg, E., "The Ignition of Explosives Mixtures by Static Electricity," *Proceedings* of the International Conference on the Safe Use of Electrical Energy in Spaces Where the Danger of an Explosion Exists, Gottwaldov, West Germany, Oct. 1968.

"Instantaneous Fire Detection/Suppression System for Jaguar Paint Spray Electrostatic Plant" *Product Fininshing* Vol. 40, No. 7, 1987, pp. 14-15.

Johnson, O. W., "The Hazard from Static Electricity on Moving Rubber-Tired Vehicles," *Fire Journal*, Vol. 61, No. 1 (Jan. 1967), pp. 25-27.

"Let Static Flow," *Record*, Factory Mutual Engineering Corp., May-June 1966.

Leonard, J. T. and Carhart, H. W., "Static Electricity Measurements During Refueler Loading," *NRL Report 7203*, (AD717-347), Naval Research Laboratory, Washington, DC, 1971.

Leonard, J. T. and Clark, R. C., "Electrostatic Hazards Produced by Carbon Dioxide in Inerting and Fire-Extinguishing Systems," *NRL Report No. 7928*, (AD A015 003), Naval Research Laboratory, Washington, DC, 1975.

Luo, H., "Experimental Investigation of Electrostatic Fire Accidents After Aircraft Landing and Preventive Measures," *Journal of Aircraft*, Vol. 26, No. 5, 1989, pp. 405-409.

Luttgens, G., "Collection of Accidents Caused by Static Electricity," *Journal of Electrostatics*, Vol. 16, 1985, pp. 247-255.

Martel, C. R., "An Evaluation of the Static Charge Reducer for Reducing Electrostatic Hazards in the Handling of Hydrocarbon Fuels," *Technical Report AFAPLTR-70-22*, Air Force Aero Propulsion Laboratory, Wright-Patterson Air Force Base, OH, July 1970.

Mancini, R. A., "The Use (and Misuse) of Bonding for Control of Static Ignition Hazards," *Proceedings* of the 21st Annual Loss Prevention Symposium, AICHE, August 1987..

Meal, L., "Static Electricity," *Fire Engineering*, Vol. 142, No. 5, 1989, p. 61.

Owens, J. E., "Spark Ignition Hazards Caused by Charge Induction," *Plant/Operations Progress*, Vol. 7, No. 1 (Jan. 1988), pp. 37-39.

Purcer, P. R., "Ignition by Electrostatic Sparks in Hyperbaric Oxygen," *The Lancet*, Dec. 24, 1966.

Rogers, G. J. and Evans, D. D., "Characterizations of Electrical Ignition Sources within Television Receivers," *NBS Technical Note 1109*, National Bureau of Standards, Gaithersburg, MD, 1979.

Rosenthal, L. A., "Static Electricity and Plastic Drums," *Plant Operations/Progress*, Vol. 7, No. 1 (Jan. 1988), pp. 51-52.

Sommer, E. C., "Preventing Electrostatic Ignitions," Paper presented at API Central Committee on Safety and Fire Protection, Tulsa, OK, Apr. 1967.

Schram, P. J. and Earley, M. W., *Electrical Installations in Hazarddous Locations*, National Fire Protection Association, Quincy, MA, 1989.

Talbot, G., "Static Electricity," *Fire*, Vol. 70, 1979, pp. 397-398.

LIGHTNING PROTECTION SYSTEMS

Revised by Norman H. Davis III

Lightning is a frequent fire cause, and, in some areas, it is the leading fire cause, bringing loss to life and personal injury due to its instantaneous and seemingly unpredictable nature. Each year, the National Center for Health Statistics estimates that 240 Americans will die (about one per every million) and another 1500 will be injured from lightning. Nearly 90 percent of these accidents will occur in rural, golf course, and beach areas. Lightning is responsible for more deaths and property loss than tornadoes, hurricanes, and floods combined.

Unlike many other causes of death and injury that one can run away from, lightning strikes before the warning thunder. The principles of protection and personal safety are well known and are spelled out in NFPA 78, *Lightning Protection Code*. It must be remembered, nevertheless, that lightning involves many uncertainties and that, while a given pattern of lightning behavior may be probable, there is no guarantee that a lightning discharge will not deviate from that pattern.

Frequency and severity of thunderstorms: The frequency of thunderstorms varies throughout the world. The severity of thunderstorms, as distinguished from their frequency of occurrence, is much greater in some locations than in others. Hence, the need for protection varies geographically, although not necessarily in direct proportion to thunderstorm frequency. A few severe thunderstorms a season may make the need for protection greater than a relatively large number of storms of lighter intensity. (See Figures 2-32A and 2-32B for statistical data on the frequency of thunderstorms in the United States and Canada, and Figure 2-32C for world data.)

Earth resistivity: Figure 2-32D illustrates the estimated average earth resistivity in the United States in ohm-meters. The highest earth resistivity is located in the northeast segment of the country, with 2000 ohm-meters in Long Island, NY, northern New Hampshire, and Vermont. Structures in these areas will generally sustain more damage due to lightning when there is no lightning protection system.

Value and nature of building and contents: Buildings often have a historical or sentimental value which is uninsurable. The type of building construction will also influence the degree of protection to be considered. Some buildings do not require supplemental lightning protection due to their construction. The real or intangible value of the contents of the building must also be considered, and, in some cases, attention must be given to the nature of and the susceptibility of the contents to damage by induced lightning currents, e.g., storage of explosives.

Appendix I of NFPA 78, *Lightning Protection Code*, contains a risk assessment guide, which provides guidelines on the need for lightning protection. That appendix, which is not part of the requirements of NFPA 78, was included for information purposes only.

Personal hazards: The lightning hazard to human beings in a building is a major consideration. Since a stroke of lightning may lead to a considerable degree of discomfort, if not injury or death, lightning protection may be necessary to eliminate possible personal hazards in buildings of any type (other than those constructed of structural steel framing). In places of public assembly, the potential of panic should be considered, because a lightning discharge over a structure, even if not accompanied by fire, can have visual and audible effects which may induce panic.

Relative exposure: In closely built-up towns and cities, the hazard is not as great as in the open country. In the latter, farm barns are most frequently hit. In hilly or mountainous areas, a building located upon high ground is usually subject to greater hazard than one in a valley or otherwise sheltered area.

Indirect losses: In addition to direct losses, e.g., due to damage of buildings or their contents by lightning, fire resulting from lightning, killing of livestock, etc., there may be indirect losses. Interruption of business, computer oper-

Norman H. Davis III, P. E., Technical Advisor USNC/IEC/TC 81, former Secretary for NFPA 78, CMP 5 NEC, and IEEE, IAEI, ASQC, is a senior staff engineer, Underwriters Laboratories Inc., Northbrook, IL.

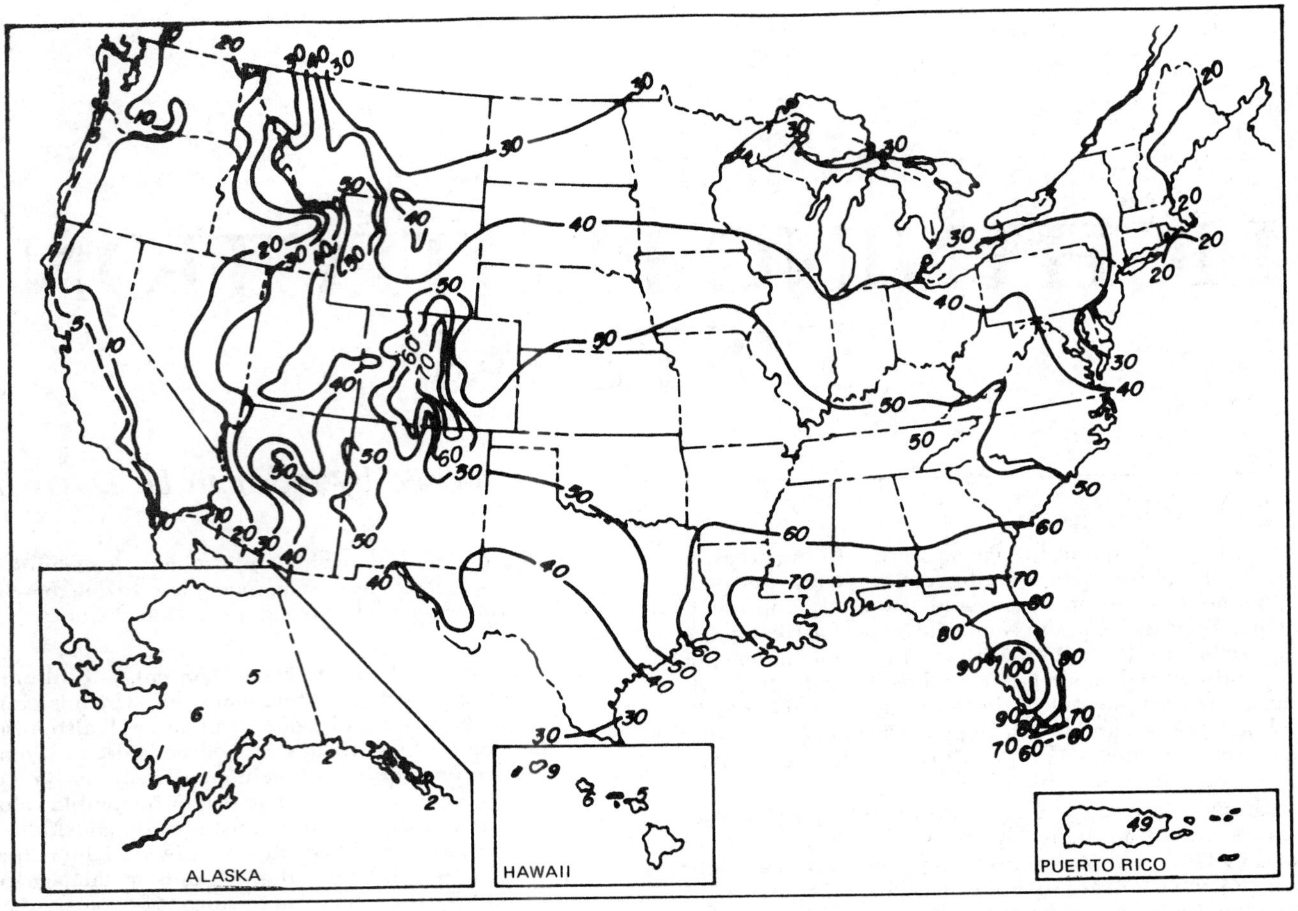

FIG. 2-32A. Statistics for continental United States showing mean annual number of days with thunderstorms. The highest frequency is encountered in south-central Florida. Since 1894, the recording of thunderstorms has been defined as the local calendar day during which thunder was heard. A day with thunderstorms is so recorded regardless of the number occurring on that day. The occurrence of lightning without thunder is not recorded as a thunderstorm. (Data supplied by Environmental Science Service Administration, U.S. Department of Commerce)

ations, or farming operations, especially at certain times of the year, may involve losses quite distinct from and in addition to those arising from direct property damage. There are also cases where whole communities depend on the integrity of a single structure for a measure of safety and comfort, e.g., the brick chimney of a water pumping plant. A stroke of lightning to the unprotected chimney of a plant of that sort might have serious consequences, resulting in lack of sanitary drinking water, irrigating water, water for fire protection, or some similar effect.

Nature of Lightning

There are four types of lightning strokes: (1) the negative downward stroke, (2) the positive downward stroke, (3) the positive upward stroke, and (4) the negative upward stroke.

Lightning strokes may occur within a cloud, between clouds, or between a cloud and earth. Most experts believe that different kinds of ice interact in a cloud to cause the charges. Updrafts in the cloud separate charges so that positive charges end up at the top of the cloud while the negative charges flow to the bottom. When lightning strokes occur between a cloud and earth, charges of opposite polarity are generated in the cloud while the charge in the ground below the cloud is induced by the lower cloud charge. In effect, the result is a giant capacitor and, when the charge builds up sufficiently, a discharge occurs.

It is generally agreed that a lightning stroke is initiated by a downward leader, which originates in the charged cloud and progresses toward the earth in discrete steps. It is also generally agreed that the major part of the lightning discharge current is carried in the return stroke, which flows from the earth to the charged cloud along the ionized path created by the stepped leader. However, the path of the lightning stroke and the point struck are determined by the leader.

The development of a stepped leader is diagrammed in Figure 2-32E. When sufficient charge has built up on a cloud, a "pilot streamer" will develop in a generally downward direction. This streamer ionizes a path in the air. The current associated with it is small, on the order of only a few amperes. The streamer initially extends on the order of 150 ft (45.7 m) below the cloud. After a pause of about 50 microseconds, the streamer will proceed for a second step, again generally downward but usually in a somewhat different direction from the initial step. Subsequent steps occur at intervals of about 50 microseconds.

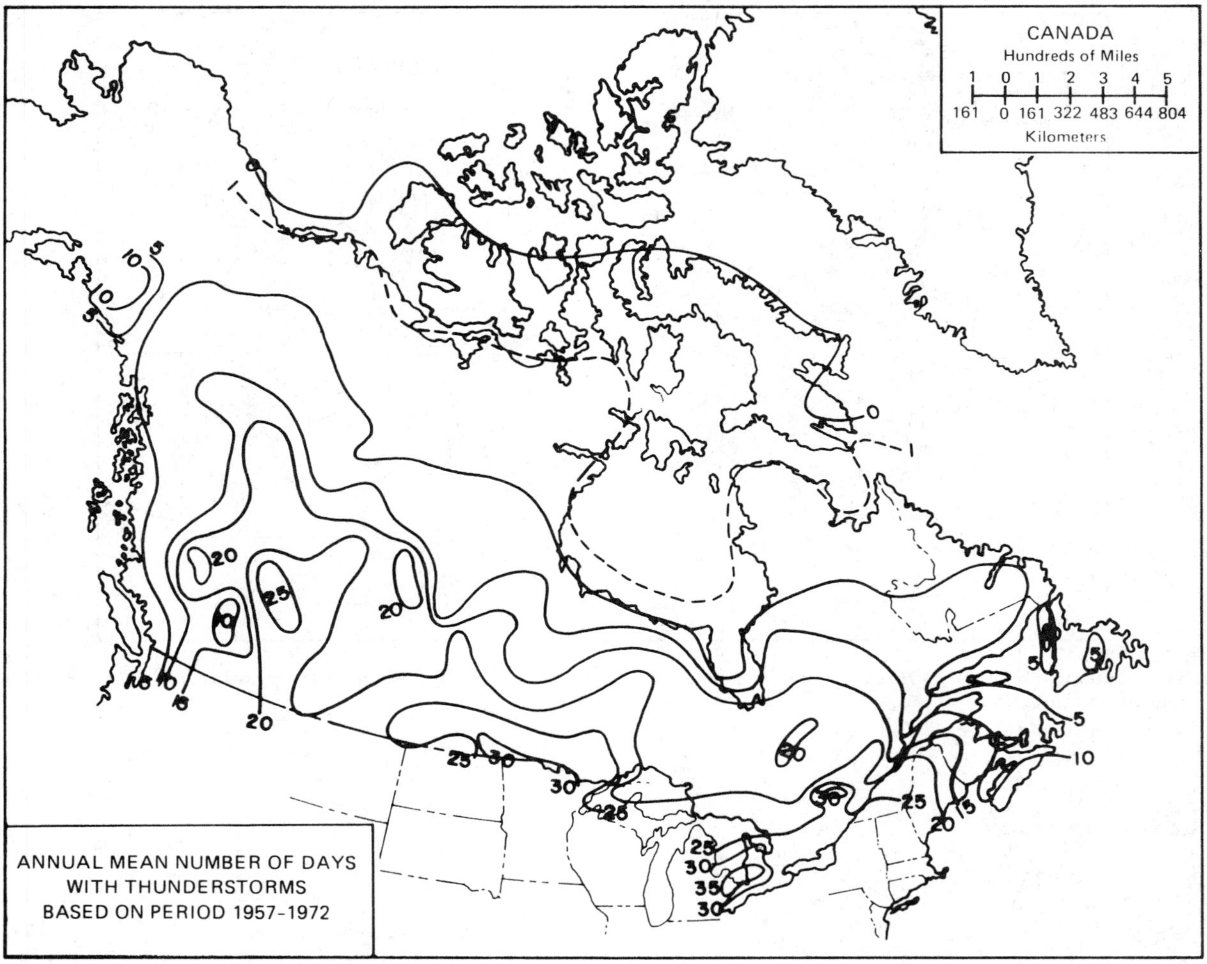

FIG. 2-32B. Canadian statistics showing annual average of days with thunderstorms. Data based on the period 1957-1972. (Source: Meteorological Division, Department of Transportation, Canada)

The path of each step is essentially straight, but each new step generally takes a different direction. The change in direction at each junction results in the zigzag path characteristic of lightning. Branches may (and usually do) occur but, for simplification, these are not shown in Figure 2-32E.

As the leader progresses downward, it creates an ionized path of high conductivity in the air. Thus, the tip of the leader essentially remains at cloud potential, and the voltage gradient between the tip and the earth increases as the tip progresses downward. At some critical point (point 6 in Figure 2-32E), the voltage gradient becomes high enough to break down the remaining air gap, and the initial stroke to ground is completed. The point from which the final breakdown occurs is called the point of discrimination, and the distance over which this breakdown occurs is defined as the striking distance.

As many as 40 component strokes have been observed in a single flash. Speeds range from 100 miles per second (161 km/sec) for the first pilot leader stroke to 20,000 miles per second (32,190 km/sec) for the main stroke. Currents average about 24,000 amperes but range up to 270,000 amperes in extreme cases, lasting for a few millionths of a second, but lesser currents are present for a longer period. Potentials have been estimated as high as 15 million volts.

Because of the high voltage and rapid changes in current flow, induced charges are important. Thus, NFPA 78, *Lightning Protection Code*, requires the interconnection of metallic masses as a part of any lightning protection system.

Lightning causes fire only where sufficient heat is produced to ignite combustible materials. Substantial damage, however, can be produced without resulting in fire. Dry wood beams in houses struck by lightning are often severely splintered and windows are blown outward. Such damage primarily results from pressure generated by the expanding lightning channel. Since some of the effects of lightning can be indirect, it is not necessary for lightning to strike a building to damage it. Because lightning striking overhead wires may be conducted to buildings over the wires, lightning arresters (surge arresters) should be provided to minimize such damage. Although there are several types of surge arresters, all permit the free flow of lightning charges to ground, while preventing the flow of ordinary electric current over the same path. The surge arrester should be backed up with a transient voltage surge suppressor on branch circuits that serve computers and electronic appliances.

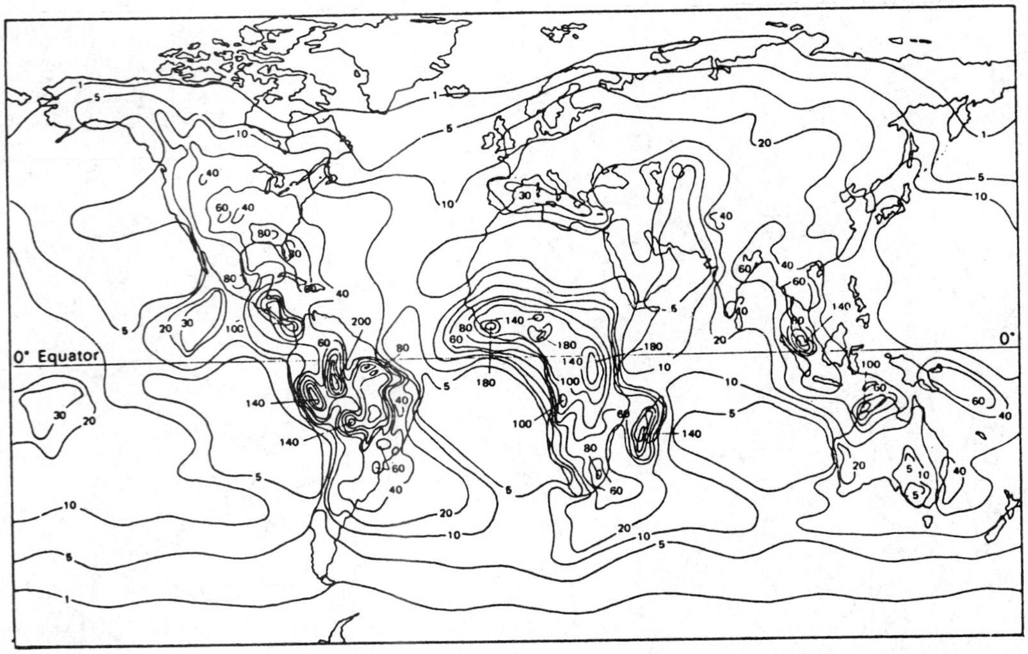

FIG. 2-32C. Annual frequency of thunderstorm days as compiled by the World Meteorological Organization, 1956. (Source: World Meteorological Organization)

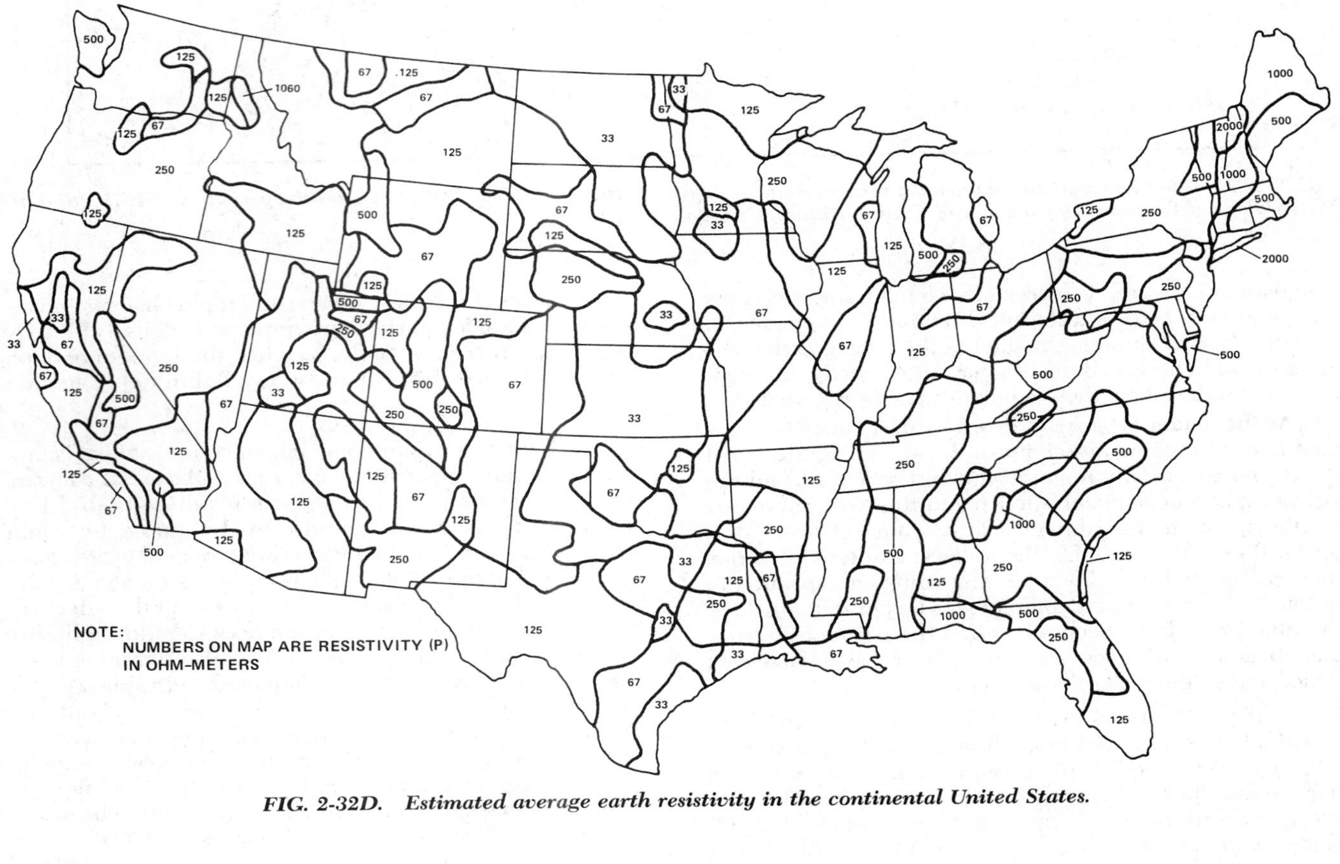

FIG. 2-32D. Estimated average earth resistivity in the continental United States.

FIG. 2-32E. Development of a stepped leader.

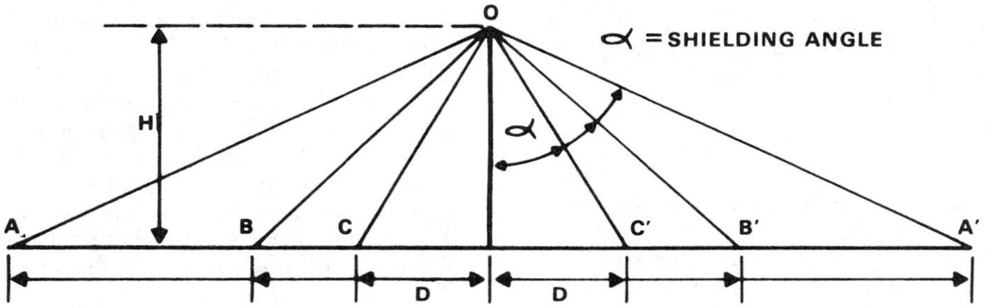

ZONE	D/H	α	AUTHORITY	RECOMMENDED FOR
AOA′	2/1	63°	NFPA	ORDINARY CASES
BOB′	1/1	45°	NFPA	IMPORTANT CASES
			BRITISH CODE	ORDINARY STRUCTURES
COC′	0.58/1	30°	BRITISH CODE	DANGER STRUCTURES

FIG. 2-32F. Conventional concept of protected zones.

TRADITIONAL THEORY OF LIGHTNING PROTECTION

The theory of lightning protection is simple—to provide means by which a lightning discharge may enter or leave the earth without damaging the property protected. There is no evidence that any form of protection can prevent the occurrence of a lightning discharge. A lightning protection system has two functions: (1) to intercept a lightning discharge before it can strike the object protected, and (2) to discharge the lightning current harmlessly to earth.

Conventional Concept

The zone protected by a grounded rod or mast is conventionally taken as the space enclosed by a cone which has its apex at the top of the mast. Similarly, the zone protected by a grounded horizontal overhead wire is conventionally taken as a triangular prism, with the upper edge along the wire. In either case, the degree of protection is generally assumed to be a function of the shielding angle, i.e., the angle between an element of the cone and a vertical line through the apex, or between the side of the prism and the vertical plane through the horizontal wire. This is sometimes expressed as the ratio of the horizontal distance protected to the height of the mast or wire.

Figure 2-32F illustrates this concept and tabulates some generally accepted zones of protection. Previous NFPA lightning protection codes stated that a distance equal to the height of a rod or mast in important cases, or up to twice the height of a rod or mast in less important cases, has been found to be substantially immune to direct strokes. The *British Standard Code of Practice* stated that a shielding angle of 45 degrees provides an acceptable level of protection for ordinary structures, but that for structures with explosives or highly flammable contents, the shielding angle should not exceed 30 degrees. Both codes indicated that complete protection cannot be guaranteed in any case. It is assumed, however, that the criteria presented reduces the probability of lightning strikes to a practical minimum. While these criteria provide essentially complete protection in most cases, theoretical consideration indicates that even the 30-degree shielding angle is not always adequate. Experience with electric power transmission lines corroborates this.

Geometric Concept of Lightning Protection

The geometry of lightning protection is illustrated in Figure 2-32G which shows a hypothetical cross section of an area protected by two vertical masts (or horizontal overhead wires). Consider first a downward leader descend-

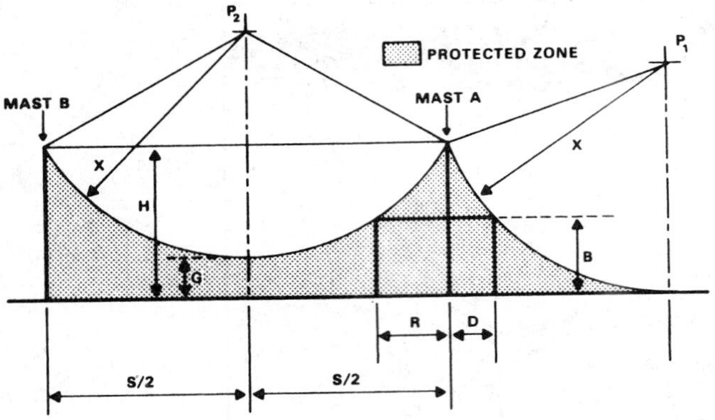

P_1, P_2 = POINT OF DISCRIMINATION
X = STRIKING DISTANCE
R, D = HORIZONTAL DISTANCES FOR PROTECTED HEIGHT B
G = MINIMUM ELEVATION COMPLETELY PROTECTED

$$D = H\sqrt{\frac{2X}{H}-1} - B\sqrt{\frac{2X}{B}-1} \qquad (H \leq X)$$

$$R = (H-G)\sqrt{\frac{2X}{(H-G)}-1} - (B-G)\sqrt{\frac{2X}{(B-G)}-1}$$

$$G = H - X + \sqrt{X^2 - \left(\frac{S}{2}\right)^2} \qquad (S \leq 2X)$$

FOR H>X,

$$D = X - B\sqrt{\frac{2X}{B}-1}$$

FIG. 2-32G. Geometric concept of lightning protection.

ing to the right of Mast A. Final breakdown will occur when the leader tip approaches within a distance X (the striking distance) of any grounded object or surface. If the point of discrimination, P (the point at which final breakdown will occur), is equidistant from the tip of the mast and the ground, either the mast or the ground may be struck. If P is close to the mast, it will intercept the stroke, and if P is farther from the mast, the ground will be struck. If any structure to the right of the mast extends above ground to within a distance less than X of Point P, the structure will be struck.

It can be seen that the zone protected by a single mast (or by an outside mast of a multi-mast system, in a direction away from the other masts) is bounded by the arc of a circle of radius X, passing through the tip of the mast and tangent to the ground. Geometrically, it can be shown that the protected distance D at an elevation B above ground is given by the expression shown where H is the height of the mast above ground and X is the striking distance.

Similarly, for a leader extending downward between the two masts, the protected zone is bounded by the arc of a circle of radius X passing through the tips of the two masts. If the masts are close enough together, the space between them is completely protected for an elevation above ground which is a function of mast height H and spacing S. In this case, the protected distance R at elevation B and the minimum elevation G, which is completely in the protected zone, are given by the two expressions shown.

These equations hold only if H is less than or equal to X, and S is less than or equal to $2X$. Further, G must be positive. If G is negative, complete protection does not exist between the two masts, and the equation for D holds.

The geometric concept shows that the protected zone is not a cone or prism, but is bounded by surfaces generated by concave arcs. This fact is not generally appreciated, although it is at least partially recognized in transmission line shielding. Further, the protected distance is seen to be a function of:

1. Striking distance.
2. Height of mast or overhead wire above ground.
3. The distance between two or more masts or overhead wires.

Figure 2-32G shows why the protected zone between two masts is greater than the total of the zones of the two masts considered individually. Previous NFPA lightning protection codes recognized this qualitatively but not quantitatively. The figure also shows why the shielding angle required on transmission lines decreases as tower (and overhead ground wire) height increases.

Striking Distance

The striking distance is related to the potential of the lightning stroke, which is directly related to the charge on the cloud. Since the peak stroke current is also related to the charge on the cloud, it can be shown that the striking distance is directly related to the peak stroke current. For a given mast or ground wire height, the protected distance increases with increasing striking distance. Thus, an adequately designed lightning protection system provides maximum protection against what could be the most damaging strokes. Since minimum protection exists for a minimum striking distance (and minimum stroke current), the lightning protection system should be designed to protect against minimum anticipated striking distances.

A review of lightning stroke current data indicates that the peak stroke current is usually at least 10,000 amp. This corresponds to a striking distance of slightly over 100 ft (30.5 m). It is therefore believed that a protective system based on a minimum striking distance of 100 ft (30.5 m) will provide essentially complete protection. This is considered to be a reasonable design basis.

Design Curves

Using the derived equations and an assumed striking distance, the protection provided by a single mast (or horizontal overhead wire) may be readily calculated. Similarly, the configuration of masts or overhead wires required to protect a given structure may be investigated. However, the calculations are tedious, and it is not convenient to determine directly by simple algebra the mast or overhead wire height required to protect a structure of given dimensions. Hence, curves showing the relationship between protected zones and various mast or horizontal overhead wire configurations are useful. Such curves can be readily constructed graphically. (See Figures 2-32H and 2-32I.) These curves are based on a striking distance of 100 ft (30.5 m).

PROPERTY PROTECTION

Components

Air terminals: According to current United States practice, as indicated in NFPA 78, *Lightning Protection Code*, conditions required for protection of ordinary buildings are met by placing metal air terminals on the uppermost parts of the building or its projections, with conductors connecting the air terminals with each other and to the ground. By this means, a relatively small amount of metal, properly proportioned and distributed, affords a satisfactory degree of protection, and it can be installed in a way that

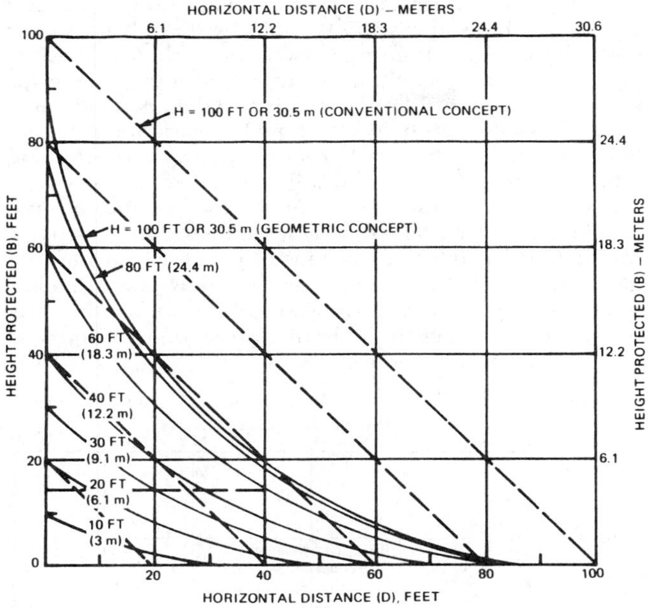

FIG. 2-32H. Zone protected by a single mast, horizontal wire, or air terminal. Solid curves are the geometric concept, with a striking distance of 100 ft (30.5 m). Dashed lines are the conventional concept, with a shielding angle of 45 degrees. "H" equals height of mast or horizontal wire. (One foot equals 0.305 m.)

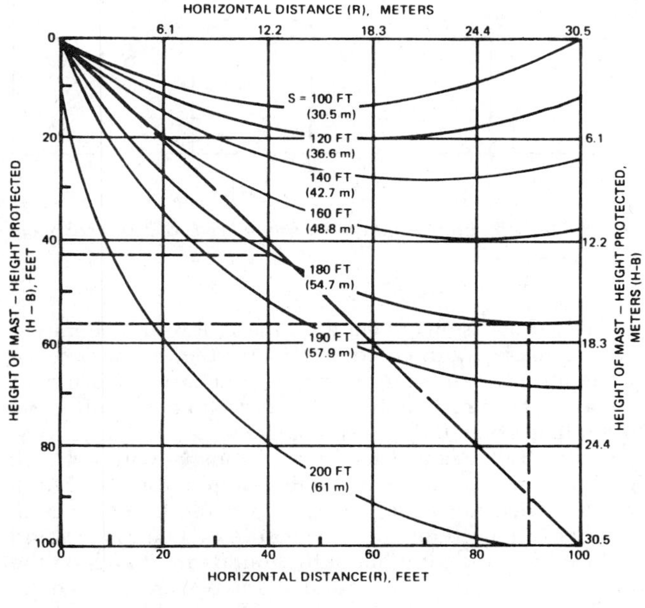

FIG. 2-32I. A zone protected by two masts, two horizontal wires, or two air terminals; the striking distance is 100 ft (30.5 m). "H" equals the height of the horizontal wire, "S" is the spacing between masts or wires, and "B" is the height protected above ground. (One foot equals 0.305 m.)

interferes only minimally with the contour and appearance of the building. In the current *British Standard Code of Practice*, "The Protection of Structures Against Lightning,"[1] the use of pointed air terminals (vertical finials) is not considered essential except where dictated by practical considerations.

One theory states that a protective system based on a minimum striking distance of 100 ft (30.5 m) for structures containing flammable liquids and gases will provide 99.9 percent protection, and a minimum striking distance of 150 ft (45.7 m) will provide 99.5 percent protection for ordinary structures which are generally capable of withstanding minor direct strokes.[2,3,4] This theory supports the use of 10-in. (254 mm) minimum height air terminals above the object to be protected at 20-ft (6.1 m) maximum intervals. A convenient geometric equation:

$$Y = \sqrt{R^2 - (R - h)^2}$$

where:

Y = radius of horizontal protected zone

R = striking distance

h = height of air terminal illustrates that a striking distance of 100 ft (30.5 m) will provide a 12.9-ft (3.9 m) radius of horizontal protected zone or 25.8 ft (7.9 m) horizontal protected zone between air terminals, and a striking distance of 150 ft (45.7 m) will provide a 15.8-ft (4.8 m) radius of horizontal protected zone or 31.6 ft (9.6 m) horizontal protected zone between air terminals.

The subject of sharply pointed *versus* blunt air terminals is under study by the NFPA Lightning Protection Committee. According to one researcher,[5] pointed air terminals have a built-in defense against lightning strikes. The strength of the electric field around the tip of an air terminal is limited by a phenomenon called "point discharge." When the electric field reaches a certain strength, but before lightning strikes, the stepped leader current flows from the air through the air terminal to the ground. The effect is called point discharge because the point is letting the surrounding air lose charge, or discharge electricity. A pointed air terminal will presumably discharge sooner than a blunt one. Accordingly, Moore[5] concludes that a blunt air terminal is more likely to intercept a lightning strike and complete a circuit.

Conductors: NFPA 78, *Lightning Protection Code*, specifies the use of copper or aluminum metals for lightning conductors. Where copper and aluminum are used together, special precautions must be taken against electrolytic corrosion. Conductors are coursed along ridges of sloping roofs, around the edges of flat roofs, and vertically from these and from the air terminals to ground. Vertical runs are designated as "down conductors" and there are never fewer than two on any kind of structure, except for flagpoles, masts, spires, and similar structures. The down conductors are normally placed at diagonally opposite corners of square or rectangular structures, but other factors, such as direct coursing, security against displacement, location of metallic elements in the structure, location of water pipes, and favorable ground conditions, need to be considered in determining optimum placement. For detailed instructions about the installation of conductors, their form and size, and about the installation of air terminals, refer to the latest edition of NFPA 78, *Lightning Protection Code*.

The down conductors to ground must be substantial and must provide a reasonably direct path. The blocking effect (choke) of electrical induction must be avoided. For example, a lightning conductor that is run through a piece of iron pipe for protection, unless bonded to the pipe at the top and bottom, largely cancels the value of the conductor.[6]

Grounding: Ground connections are essential to the effectiveness of a lightning protection system, and every effort should be made to provide ample contact with the earth. (See Figure 2-32J.) Resistance of the protective system to ground is not critical. However, resistance and surge impedance must be low enough to prevent side flashes between the down conductor and other grounded objects. Also, the resistance must be low enough to prevent excessive voltage gradients in the soil surrounding the ground electrode. Excessive voltage gradients can be dangerous or fatal to people or animals that may be standing or walking in the vicinity when a lightning stroke occurs. If the down conductor is remote from other grounded objects, and people or animals are not likely to be near the ground electrode during a lightning storm, a relatively high ground resistance can be tolerated. Otherwise, an extensive wire network will need to be laid on the surface.

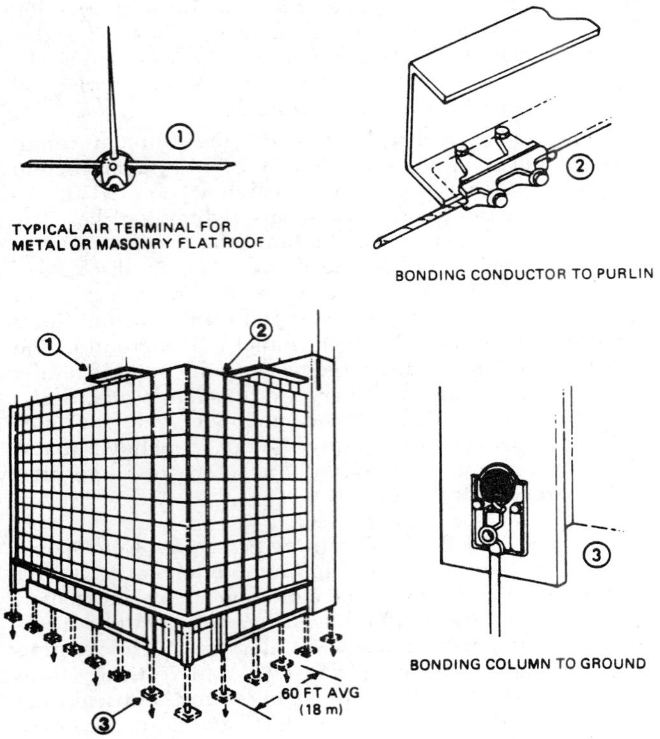

FIG. 2-32J. Grounding and bonding of lightning down conductors. Water pipe grounds (if pipes are metallic) can be made at 1, 2, or 3.

NFPA 78, *Lightning Protection Code*, does not specify any maximum recommended ground resistance. The *British Standard Code of Practice*[1] recommends a maximum resistance of ten ohms for a lightning protection system which will normally include two or more ground electrodes. Also ten ohms is generally considered a reasonably good ground resistance for transmission towers. In this case, a high ground resistance may result in flashover to the line conductors even though the overhead ground wire intercepts the direct lightning stroke. A United States Department of Agriculture bulletin states that a ground resistance as high as 50 ohms is acceptable for protection of farm structures.

The ground resistance of a ground electrode is directly proportional to soil resistivity. Soil resistivity varies over wide limits (see Figure 2-32D); nevertheless, 10,000 ohm/cm is a reasonable order of magnitude average for many areas. Figure 2-32K, which is based on derived equations,[7] has been prepared to show the variation in resistance to earth of vertical rods or pipes as a function of length in 10,000 ohm/cm soil. For other soil resistivities, the resistance to ground may be obtained by multiplying the indicated resistance by the known soil resistivity divided by 10,000. Vertical rods or pipes driven into the ground are commonly used as ground electrodes. In addition, where buried metallic water pipes are nearby, it is required to connect the lightning protection ground system to the piping system.

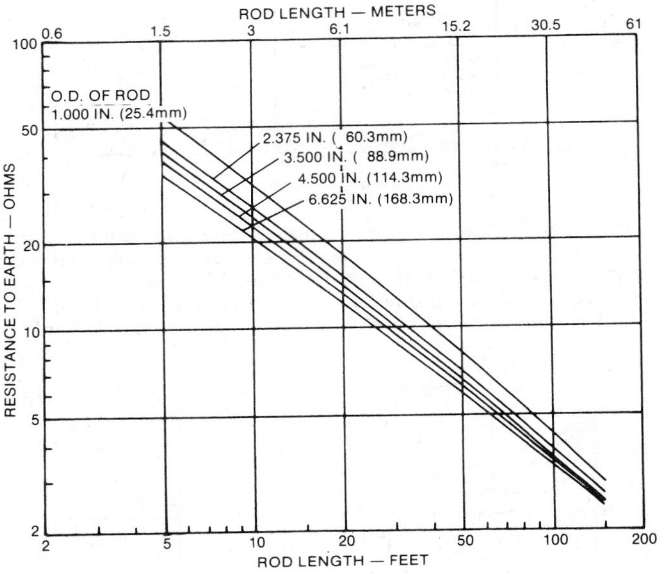

FIG. 2-32K. Resistance of vertical ground rods in 10,000 ohm/cm soil.

If bedrock is on or near the surface, it would be impossible to make a ground connection in the ordinary sense of the term because most kinds of rock are insulating, or at least of high resistivity, and in order to obtain effective grounding, other and more elaborate means are necessary. One effective means is to use an extensive wire network (grid) laid on the surface of the rock surrounding the building, to which the down conductors could be connected. Another is to use ground ring conductors. One ring should be installed at the bottom of the foundation to which the down conductors or structural steelwork are connected, with a second ring conductor provided by blasting a circular trench around the periphery and placing in it a strip conductor. The blasted area should be thoroughly compacted with backfill, and the two ring conductors electrically interconnected. Using one of these methods would make the distribution of the electrical potential around the protected building substantially the same as if it were resting on conducting soil, and the resulting protective effect would be equal.

For sandy soil, or any dirt covering the foundation, a concrete-encased electrode (commonly called a "Ufer" ground, after the inventer Herb Ufer) should be installed for new construction. This electrode consists of tying in the steel reinforcing bars or rods in the footing of the foundation that is in direct contact with the earth.

In general, the extent of the grounding arrangements will depend upon the character of the soil, ranging from simple extension of the conductor into the ground where the soil is deep and of high conductivity, to an elaborate buried network where the soil is very dry or of very poor conductivity. Where a network is required, it should be buried if there is soil enough to permit it, as this adds to its effectiveness. Its extent will be determined largely by the judgment of the person planning the installation, following the minimum requirements of NFPA 78, *Lightning Protection Code*, and keeping in mind that, as a rule, the more extensive the underground metal available, the more effective the protection.

Protection of Structures (Traditional Systems)

Underwriters Laboratories Inc. "Master Label Service" for lightning protection systems: UL has had a "Master Label Service" for lightning protection systems since 1923. It provides for both factory inspection and labeling of lightning protection materials (components), as well as field inspections of a substantial number of installations for which Master Labels have been issued. The service covers the installation of labeled lightning protection materials (components) on all types of structures, with the exception of those used for the production, handling, or storage of ammunition, explosives, flammable liquids or gases, and explosive ingredients. Protection of electrical transmission lines and equipment is not within the scope of the "Master Label Service."

Structural steel buildings: Buildings constructed of structural steel framing may be protected by the installation of air terminals at the high parts of the building, connecting such air terminals to the metal framing, and grounding the framing at the bottom end. This assumes that the structural steel framework is electrically continuous, or is made electrically continuous by bonding. Grounding is required from approximately every other steel column around the perimeter, and is arranged so that grounds average not more than 60 ft (18.3 m) apart except as noted below.

Air terminals are not required if the steel columns extend at least 10 in. (254 mm) above the object to be protected. Air terminals are not required on metal roofs where the metal is not less than $3/16$ in. (4.8 mm) thick.

Additional grounding is not required if the steel column extends 10 ft (3.05 m) or more into the earth or is connected to a concrete-encased electrode.

Reinforced concrete structures: Reinforced concrete buildings, in which the reinforcing rods are electrically bonded together and grounded, are similar to structural steel buildings in regard to lightning protection. In usual building practice, as successive reinforcing bars are fitted, they are made to overlap lengthwise with bars already installed and are then tied together with metal binding wire. With thousands of such connections in a completed framework, the electrical resistance is fully acceptable for the purpose of lightning protection. However, if the reinforcing rods are electrically discontinuous, the building should be treated the same as a building of nonconducting materials. Lightning strokes to reinforced concrete buildings where there are insulating gaps between reinforcing rods are likely to cause cracks at places where beams and floor slabs are connected to their supports. Prestressed concrete buildings are a particular problem. If the wires in precast units are not interconnected (as they frequently are not), individual units are isolated and when a lightning charge is induced, serious damage can result.

Metal-roofed and metal-clad buildings: Metal roofing and siding must not be substituted for the main conductors and air terminals of a lightning protection system, unless constructed of $3/16$ in. (4.8 mm) minimum sheet metal which has been made electrically continuous by bonding or an approved interlocking contact. This is because there is a likelihood that lightning will puncture thinner sheet metals and ignite wood framing, etc. Acceptable constructions will require ground terminals (ground rods, rings, etc.).

Tanks containing flammable and combustible liquids and gases: Tanks containing flammable and combustible liquids or flammable gases stored at atmospheric pressures have been set on fire by lightning. Fires may be started by direct hits which ignite vapors escaping from the tank, or may be started on the roofs of wood-roofed tanks. A lightning stroke in the vicinity may, by induction, produce sparks which may ignite such vapors. If there are openings in the roof, either intentional or accidental, externally ignited vapors may carry flame inside the tank, possibly resulting in an explosion or fire if there is a flammable or combustible vapor-air mixture inside.

Aboveground tanks storing flammable or combustible liquids or flammable gases at atmospheric pressures are considered to be reasonably well protected against lightning if constructed entirely of steel, and if: (1) all joints between steel plates are riveted, bolted, or welded; (2) all pipes entering the tanks are metallically connected to the tank at point of entrance; (3) all vapor openings are closed or are provided with flame arresters (Class I or II liquids, as defined in NFPA 321, *Classification of Flammable and Combustible Liquids*); (4) the tank and roof are constructed of $3/16$ in. (4.8 mm) minimum thick sheet metal so holes will not be burned through by lightning strokes; and (5) the roof is continuously welded, bolted, or riveted and caulked to the shell to provide a vaportight seam and electrical continuity. Where additional protection is desired, the internal supporting members of the roof may be bonded to the roof at 10-ft (3.05 m) intervals, or an overhead ground-wire system or mast protection may be installed in accordance with NFPA 78, *Lightning Protection Code*. (See Figure 2-32L.)

Steel tanks in direct contact with the ground or aboveground steel tanks connected to extensive properly grounded metallic piping systems are considered to be inherently grounded.

Steel tanks with wood or other nonmetallic roofs are not considered self-protecting, even if the roofs are essentially vaportight or sheathed with thin metal. Such tanks should be protected by an overhead ground-wire system or mast protection. (See Figure 2-32L.)

Floating roof tanks with hangers located within a vapor space may be protected by bonding the roof to the shoes of the seal at 10-ft (3.05 m) intervals around the circumference of the tank and by providing insulated joints or installing jumper bonds around each pinned joint of the hanger mechanism. Based upon experience, floating roof

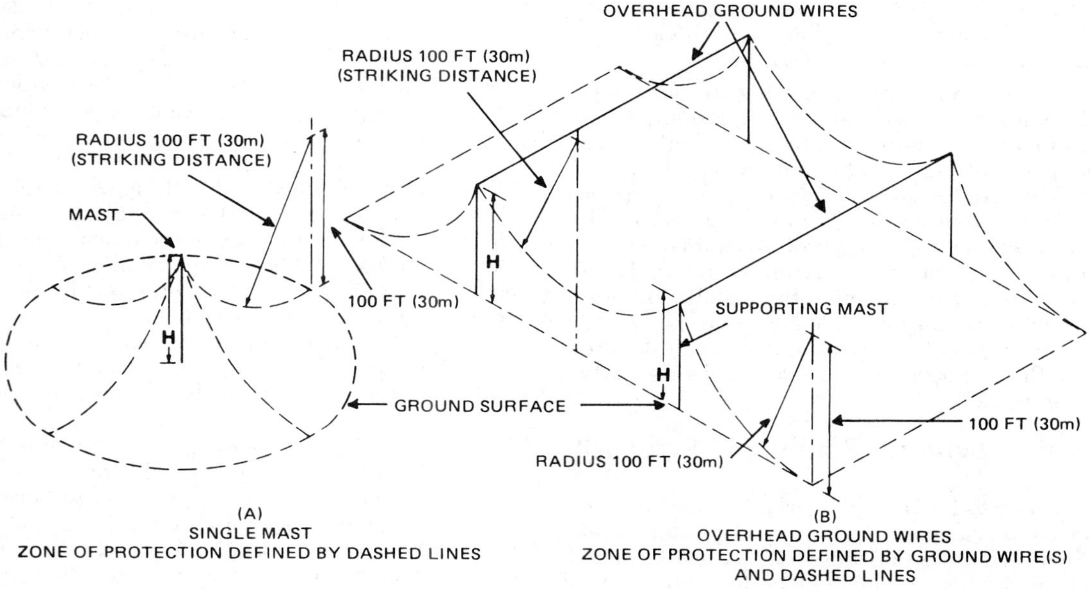

FIG. 2-32L. Zone of protection for mast height "H."

tanks without vapor spaces would not appear to need lightning protective measures.

Aboveground storage tanks or containers of flammable liquids or liquefied petroleum gas under pressure are considered to be safe from lightning-caused explosions since the vapor-air mixture is "too rich" to burn, and the vapor is contained within the tank.

Tall structures: Spires, masts, and flagpoles of materials other than metal and other slender structures require one air terminal extending 10 in. (254 mm) or more above the uppermost point, a down conductor, and a ground terminal in compliance with NFPA 78, *Lightning Protection Code*. Church steeples will require one air terminal with a two-way path to ground at the extremities and additional air terminals on the lower-level portion that is outside of the steeple zone of protection.

In Great Britain, brick chimneys, church spires, etc., are protected by using two down conductors connected at the top to an existing metal cap, or to a circular conductor with no air terminals. (See Figure 2-32M.) Metal smokestacks need no protection against lightning other than that provided by their construction if they are grounded.

Trees, other specialized structures, and facilities: Trees are sometimes provided with lightning protection where they are especially valuable, are of historical significance, overhang buildings, or provide a shelter for livestock. Guidance on the installation of lightning protection is given in Appendix G of NFPA 78, *Lightning Protection Code*. Other appendices of NFPA 78, *Lightning Protection Code*, cover: (1) sailboats, power boats, small boats, and ships; (2) parked aircraft; (3) livestock in fields; and (4) picnic grounds, playgrounds, ball parks, and other open places. (See Figure 2-32N.)

Grounding metal masses (bonding): Extensive masses of metal which form part of a building or its appurtenances, such as metal ventilators and television or radio antennas, must be bonded to the lightning protection system.

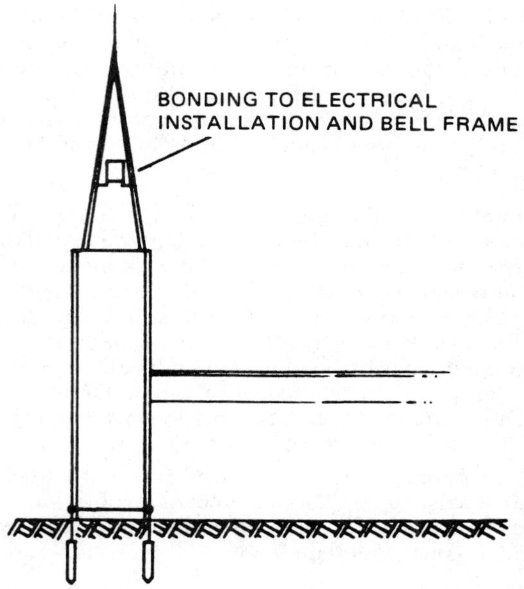

FIG. 2-32M. An installation of a lightning protection system in a church steeple according to* British Standard Code of Practice[1] *requirements. (Note absence of air terminals on lower-level portion; protection is provided by an elevated conductor above the ridge.)

Nevertheless, the grounding of metal windowsills could be a hazard to human life in the event of a direct lightning strike. Details are given in NFPA 78, *Lightning Protection Code*, under "Metal Bodies," "Potential Equalization," and "Bonding of Metal Bodies," which determine the need for bonding and require loop conductors around a structure at various levels to be bonded to all down conductors. This will equalize the down currents and diminish possible induced currents which affect computers and other electronic equipment.

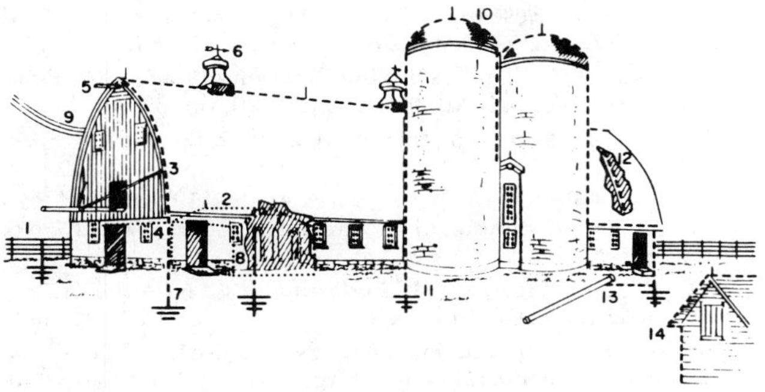

FIG. 2-32N. Lightning protection system on a typical large barn. The numbers indicate the following features: (1) ground-attached wire fence; (2) extend protection to any addition; (3), (4), and (5) show bonding conductors to litter, metal door, and hay tracks; (6) shows air terminal on cupolas, ventilators, etc.; (7) indicates ground connection (there should be at least two grounds); (8) illustrates tie-in of metal stanchions; (9) power lines to building need lightning arresters; (10) at least one air terminal should be on each domed silo (at least two on each flat roof or unroofed silo); (11) shows special ground for silo, if required; (12) illustrates connections to vents and (13) connections to water pipes; and (14) illustrates desirability of protecting adjacent buildings.

Maintenance

Proper maintenance of lightning protection systems is essential to effective protection. Particular attention should be given to ground connections, as rods may be broken or corroded at ground level or just below, where the damage is not apparent. Materials (components) may be missing because of storm damage, or stolen because of their value. Details are given in Appendix B of NFPA 78, *Lightning Protection Code*.

Surge Arresters and Suppressors on Electrical Apparatus and Circuits

The installation of surge arresters on power and communications lines where they enter structures and at power utility plants is covered in Article 280 of NFPA 70, *National Electrical Code*®. More information on the protection of electrical apparatus and circuits against damage due to lightning can be found in the "Additional Reading" section of the bibliography, under "Surge Arresters." The use of secondary service arresters on electric services is required for buildings equipped with a UL Master-Labeled Lightning Protection System. Such arresters may be installed at the yard pole, at the outside electric service entrance, or at the interior service entrance equipment, depending on local regulations. Home lightning protectors are available that are designed for installation at the dwelling weatherhead or indoors at the service entrance equipment. These protectors (arresters) drain lightning surge-induced charges harmlessly to ground, and then open to restore electrical service to normal. Before installing a secondary service arrester, it should be determined that the neutral wire is grounded.

The surge arrester should be coupled with a transient voltage surge suppressor on branch circuits that serve computers and electronic appliances. These devices are constructed as portable (plug-in) or permanently wired.

In the United States, except on the Pacific Slope where lightning storms are infrequent, most electric utilities install lightning arresters on the primaries of important transformers on systems of 44,000 volts or less.

PROTECTION OF PERSONS

The lightning hazard is greatest among persons whose occupations keep them outdoors. The probability of injury to the individual from lightning is, in general, very small, except under certain circumstances of exposure out of doors. Within buildings of considerable size and residential buildings of modern construction, cases of injury from lightning are relatively rare. They are more frequent within small unprotected buildings of the older type. Isolated small schoolhouses and small churches where people may congregate during thunderstorms present a considerable lightning hazard if unprotected.

Guide for Personal Safety During Thunderstorms

Do not go out of doors or remain out during thunderstorms unless it is necessary. Seek shelter inside buildings, vehicles, or other structures or locations that offer protection from lightning.

Seek shelter in the following places which may protect persons from lightning:

1. Dwellings or other buildings that are protected against lightning.
2. Underground shelters, such as subways, tunnels, and caves.
3. Large metal or metal-framed buildings.
4. Large unprotected buildings.
5. Enclosed automobiles, buses, and other vehicles with metal tops and bodies.
6. Enclosed trains and streetcars.
7. Enclosed metal boats or ships.
8. Boats that are protected against lightning.
9. City streets that are shielded by nearby buildings.

If possible, avoid the following places which offer little or no protection from lightning:

1. Small unprotected buildings, barns, sheds, etc.
2. Tents and temporary shelters (not lightning protected).
3. Automobiles (nonmetal top or open).
4. Recreational vehicles (nonmetal or open).
5. Also, avoid use of or contact with electrical appliances, telephones, and plumbing fixtures.

Certain locations are extremely hazardous during thunderstorms and should be avoided if at all possible. Approaching thunderstorms should be anticipated and the following locations avoided when storms are in the immediate vicinity:

1. Open fields, athletic fields, and golf courses.
2. Parking lots and tennis courts.
3. Swimming pools, lakes, and seashores.
4. Near wire fences, clotheslines, overhead wires, and railroad tracks.
5. Under isolated trees.

In the above locations, it is especially hazardous to be riding in or on any of the following during lightning storms:

1. Open tractors and other farm machinery operated in open fields.
2. Golf carts, scooters, bicycles, and motorcycles.
3. Open boats (without masts) and hovercraft.
4. Automobiles (nonmetal top or open).

It may not always be possible to choose an outdoor location that offers good protection from lightning. Follow these rules when there is a choice in selecting locations:

1. Seek depressed areas—avoid hilltops and high places.
2. Seek dense woods—avoid isolated trees.
3. Seek buildings, tents, and shelters in low areas—avoid unprotected buildings and shelters in high areas.
4. If you are hopelessly isolated in an exposed area and you feel your hair stand on end, indicating that lightning is about to strike, drop to your knees and bend forward putting your hands on your knees. Do not lie flat on the ground or place your hands on the ground.

BIBLIOGRAPHY

References Cited

1. "The Protection of Structures Against Lightning," *British Standard Code of Practice*, BS 6651, 1985, British Standards Institute.
2. Offerman, Paul F., "Lightning Protection of Structures," IEEE Conference Record of 1969 Fourth Annual Meeting of the IEEE Industry and General Applications Group, 69 C5-IGA, 1969.
3. Lee, Ralph H., "Protection Zone for Buildings Against Lightning Strokes Using Transmission Line Protection Practice," IEEE *Transactions* on Industry Applications, Vol. 1A-14, No. 6, Nov./Dec. 1978.
4. Davis, Norman H., "The Rolling Sphere Interception Concept," *Proceedings* of the 19th International Conference on Lightning Protection, Graz, Austria, Vol. I, Apr. 25-29, 1988.
5. Moore, Brook, and Krider, "A Study of Lightning Protection Systems," The Atmospheric Science Program of the Office of Naval Research, (under Contract No. 00014-78M-0090).
6. Kaufmann, Richard H., "Some Fundamentals of Equipment – Grounding Circuit Design," AIEE *Transactions*, 54-244, Nov. 1954.
7. Sunde, E. D., *Earth Conduction Effects in Transmission Systems*, D. Van Nostrand Co., Inc., 1949, pp. 75-80.

NFPA Codes, Standards, and Recommended Practices

Reference to the following NFPA codes, standards, and recommended practices will provide further information on lightning protection systems discussed in this chapter. (See the latest *NFPA Catalog* for availability of current editions of the following documents.)

NFPA 70, *National Electrical Code*.

NFPA 78, *Lightning Protection Code*.

NFPA 302, *Pleasure and Commercial Motor Craft*.

NFPA 321, *Classification of Flammable and Combustible Liquids*.

Additional Reading

Electrical Construction Materials Directory, published annually in May with November Supplements, Underwriters Laboratories Inc., Northbrook, IL.

Factory Mutual Research Corp., "Lightning Arresters and Grounds", *Loss Prevention Data Sheets*, 5-11/14-19.

Frydenlund, M. G., "Understanding Lightning Protection," *Plant Engineering*, Vol. 44, No. 9, May 10, 1990, pp. 62-66.

Golde, R. H., *Lightning Protection*, Academic Press, New York, 1977.

Golde, R. H., "Protection of Structures Against Lightning," *Proceedings*, The Institution of Electrical Engineers, Vol. 115, No. 10, Oct. 1968.

Hart, C. W., and Edgar, W. M., *Lightning and Lightning Protection*, Interference Control Technologies, Gainesville, VA, 1988.

Hedlund, C. F., "Lightning Protection for Buildings," IEEE *Transactions* on Industry and General Applications, Vol. IGA-3, No. 1, Jan./Feb. 1967, Institute of Electrical and Electronics Engineers, New York.

IEEE Standard 142-1982 (ANSI/IEEE), Chapter 3, "Static and Lightning Protection Grounding."

Journal of the Franklin Institute, Philadelphia, Vol. 283, No. 6, June 1967, (special issue on lightning research).

"The Lightning Flash," published bi-monthly by Lightning Technologies, Inc., 10 Downing Parkway, Pittsfield, MA.

"Lightning Protection System, General with Regard to Installation," German Standard DIN 57185, Part 1/VDE 0185, Part 1/11.820000 (Engl.), English Translation, 1983.

Plumer, J. A., "We Need Better Lightning Protection," *Fire Journal*, Vol. 81, No. 1, 1987, p. 41.

Proceedings of the International Conference on Lightning Protection, Published Bi-annually by different publishers, 20th ed. by Swiss Electromechanical Assn., Interlocken, Switzerland.

Towne, H. M., *Lightning—Its Behavior and What To Do About It*, United Lightning Protection Association, Inc., Webster, NY, 1956.

Uman, M.A., *Lightning*, Dover Publication, Inc., Mineola, NY, 1983.

Uman, M.A., *All About Lightning*, Dover Publication, Inc., Mineola, NY, 1986.

Underwriters Laboratories Inc., UL 96, *Standard for Lightning Protection Components*, 2nd ed., Dec. 1986, Northbrook, IL.

Underwriters Laboratories Inc., UL 96A, Standard for Installation Requirements for Lightning Protection Systems, Revised June 1987, Northbrook, IL.

Viemeister, P.E., *The Lightning Book*, MIT Press, Cambridge, MA, 1975.

Surge Arresters, ANSI Standards

ANSI/IEEE C62.32-1981, *Air Gap Surge-Protective Devices (Excluding Valve and Expulsion Type Devices)*, Test Specifications for the Low Voltage.

ANSI/IEEE C62.31-1987, *Gas Tube Surge-Protective Devices*, Test Specifications for.

ANSI/IEEE C62.1-1984, *Surge Arresters for Alternating-Current Power Circuits*.

ANSI/IEEE C26.11-1987, *Standard for Metal-Oxide Surge Arrestor for AC Power Circuits*

WASTE HANDLING SYSTEMS AND EQUIPMENT

Lawrence G. Doucet

The term "industrial waste" generally describes waste emanating from manufacturing facilities, processing plants, factories, and the like. However, it essentially has no meaning without further definition, because it encompasses an almost infinite variety of materials.

It has been estimated that more than 350 million tons of industrial waste are generated in the United States every year. A large portion of this waste is considered hazardous. A 1981 survey by the U.S. Environmental Protection Agency (EPA) determined that about 150 million tons of hazardous industrial waste were generated, and that the largest 150 generators alone produced about 35 billion gallons of hazardous waste. According to a 1987 study by the Office of Technology Assessment, about 250 million metric tons of hazardous waste are generated each year. These quantities are projected to increase steadily at an annual rate of 5 to 10 percent. The typical, average waste generation rates of a few major industries are given in Table 2-33A. The approximate distribution of hazardous wastes generated by some major industries is shown in Figure 2-33A.

Disposal of such tremendous waste quantities is a matter of great public concern in light of recent revelations of improper or indiscriminate dumping practices at numerous locations. It has been estimated that there are more than 30,000 hazardous waste dumpsites throughout the United States, of which more than 2000 present significant health and environmental problems. The EPA has documented hundreds of cases whereby indiscriminate or improper hazardous waste disposal has severely damaged the environment and endangered life.

To protect against further hazardous waste mismanagement, the Congress enacted the Resource Conservation and Recovery Act of 1976 (RCRA). Under this Act, the EPA has instituted a complex set of regulations for controlling hazardous waste from generation through final disposal. This is known as "cradle-to-grave" control. To deal with dumpsite cleanup costs and liabilities not covered by RCRA, the EPA enacted legislation known as the "Superfund" bill. The Toxic Substances Control Act (TSCA) of 1976 was established to regulate chemicals not controlled under other regulations. This Act, for example, specifies disposal requirements for polychlorinated biphenyl compounds (PCBs).

TABLE 2-33A. ***Industrial Solid-Waste Production Rates***[1]

SIC* Code	Industry	Waste Production Rate (tons/employee/year)
201	Meat processing	6.2
2033	Cannery	55.6
2037	Frozen foods	18.3
Other 203	Preserved foods	12.9
Other 20	Food processing	5.8
22	Textile-mill products	0.26
23	Apparel	0.31
2421	Sawmills and planning mills	162.0
Other 24	Wood products	10.3
25	Furniture	0.52
26	Paper and allied products	2.00
27	Printing and publishing	0.49
281	Basic chemicals	10.00
Other 28	Chemical and allied products	0.63
29	Petroleum	14.8
30	Leather and plastic	2.6
31	Leather	0.17
32	Stone, clay	2.4
33	Primary metals	24
34	Fabricated metals	1.7
35	Nonelectrical machinery	2.6
36	Electrical machinery	1.7
37	Transportation equipment	1.3
38	Professional and scientific instruments	0.12
39	Miscellaneous manufacturing	0.14

*Standard Industries Classification

For most industries, particularly those generating hazardous waste, the evaluation and selection of waste management and disposal systems is difficult and complex. First of all, there are numerous options and alternate technol-

Lawrence G. Doucet is a principal of Doucet & Mainka, P.C., consulting engineers, Peekskill, NY.

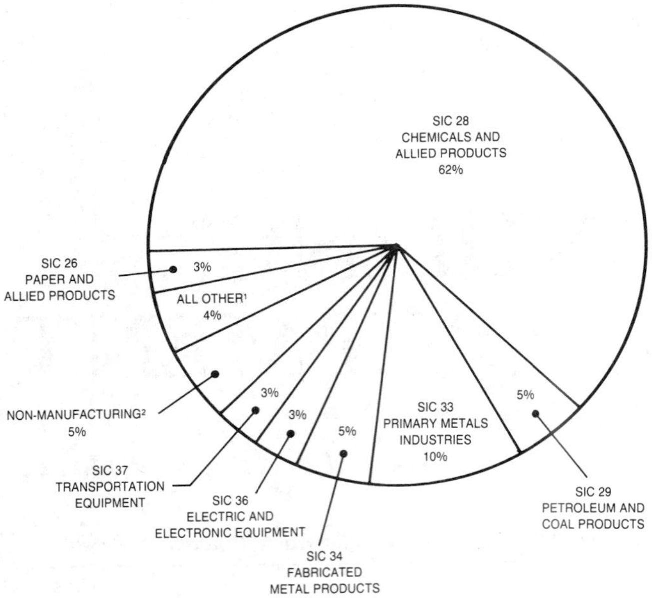

[1] ALL OTHER

SIC 22 TEXTILE MILL PRODUCTS
SIC 24 LUMBER AND WOOD PRODUCTS
SIC 25 FURNITURE AND FIXTURES
SIC 27 PRINTING AND PUBLISHING
SIC 30 RUBBER AND MISCELLANEOUS PLASTIC PRODUCTS
SIC 31 LEATHER AND LEATHER TANNING
SIC 32 STONE, CLAY AND GLASS PRODUCTS
SIC 35 MACHINERY EXCEPT ELECTRICAL
SIC 38 INSTRUMENTS AND RELATED PRODUCTS
SIC 39 MISCELLANEOUS MANUFACTURING INDUSTRIES

[2] NON-MANUFACTURING CATEGORIES:

SIC 5085 DRUM RECONDITIONERS
SIC 07 AGRICULTURAL SERVICES
SIC 5161 CHEMICAL WAREHOUSES
SIC 40 RAILROAD TRANSPORTATION
SIC 55 AUTOMOTIVE DEALERS AND GASOLINE SERVICE STATIONS
SIC 72 PERSONAL SERVICES
SIC 73 BUSINESS SERVICES
SIC 76 MISC. REPAIR SERVICES
SIC 80 HEALTH SERVICES
SIC 82 EDUCATIONAL SERVICES

FIG. 2-33A. Pie chart showing the distribution of hazardous waste generation by Standard Industrial Classification (SIC) code in 1980.2

ogies available, each with differing benefits, risk factors, and costs. Secondly, the forms and properties of waste materials vary widely and greatly impact the feasibilities and cost-effectiveness of the alternate technologies. Thirdly, regulatory requirements and restrictions may limit the suitability of various technologies. These complexities and multiplicities are also site specific, making it necessary to evaluate each facility on an individual, case-by-case, basis.

WASTE MATERIALS

Industrial waste is as varied as the raw materials used in production operations. However, the nature of the industry generally determines the nature of the waste. A furniture plant, for example, discards wood scraps, sawdust and shavings, fabric scraps, glues, stains, and varnishes. Within any specific industry there may be many different types of waste materials, ranging from plant trash to spent chemicals and objectionable fumes. Other items may include production residues and byproducts, packaging scraps, reject products, returned goods, and even animal carcasses from research activities. Such waste can be in the form of solids, sludges, liquids, or gases. The waste can be hazardous or nonhazardous, and it can be combustible or noncombustible. Obviously, the combinations are virtually endless.

Hazardous Waste

Hazardous waste is generally defined as any waste or combination of wastes that poses a substantial danger, now or in the future, to human, plant, or animal life, and which, therefore, cannot be handled or disposed of without special precautions. Hazardous waste categories include toxic chemical, flammable, corrosive, reactive, explosive, radioactive, and biological. If improperly handled or disposed, such waste can contaminate surface and ground waters as well as the ambient atmosphere. They can poison, burn, maim, blind, and kill people and other living organisms. Some are nondegradable and persist in nature indefinitely. Some may accumulate in living things, and some may work their way into the food chain. Also, some may catch fire or explode at normal temperatures and pressures when exposed to air or water, or by being jarred or dropped.

The EPA, under RCRA, defines and regulates wastes that are hazardous because of either ignitibility, corrosivity, reactivity, or toxicity. The regulations not only identify specific hazardous criteria, but also list specific waste types, constituents, and sources generating wastes with these hazardous characteristics. Radioactive waste is regulated by the Nuclear Regulatory Commission (NRC). Biological, or infectious, waste is usually regulated by state and local environmental agencies and health departments.

The Medical Waste Tracking Act of 1988 was promulgated by Congress to regulate the management and disposal of various potentially infectious waste items through a complex manifest system. These regulations were included as a section under RCRA (Subtitle J), and they carry severe criminal and civil fines for violators. However, this Act is legislated to be in force for only two years, although the time period may be extended. Only five states are included under this Act. Several states, however, have independently enacted comprehensive legislation.

Hazardous Characteristics

Ignitibility: Liquid wastes are considered ignitibly, or flammably, hazardous if their flash point is less than 140°F (60°C). These mainly consist of contaminated organic solvents, but they may include oils, plasticizers, complex organic sludges, and off-specification chemicals.

Nonliquid wastes are considered ignitibly hazardous if they are capable, under standard temperatures and pressures, of causing fires through friction, absorption of moisture, or through spontaneous chemical changes. These include pyrophoric materials, such as phosphorous and aluminum alkyls, which ignite when exposed to air.

Organic vapors and fumes may be flammably hazardous if released in combustible concentrations. These may travel considerable distances, reach an ignition source, and ignite. NFPA 86, *Ovens and Furnaces*, identifies specific requirements for the safe venting of such gases.

Corrosivity: Corrosive wastes can severely damage skin and other living tissues, as well as construction materials, such as metals and finished surfaces. Wastes are defined as corrosively hazardous if their pH values are 2 or less, 12 or more, or if they corrode steel at a rate greater than 1/4 in. (6.35 mm) per year. These wastes generally comprise strong acids and alkalis.

Reactivity: Hazardous wastes characterized as reactive are normally unstable and readily undergo violent changes without detonation. Some reactive wastes are capable of detonation or explosive decomposition at standard temperatures and pressures. Also, some reactive wastes react vio lently with water, and some form potentially explosive mixtures or toxic vapors if mixed with water. Reactive materials, such as sodium, potassium, and aluminum alkyls, react violently with water and burn fiercely. Strong oxidizers in contact with organic materials may cause rapid combustion or explosion.

Toxicity: Toxic wastes poison, or produce injury, upon contact with or through accumulation in or on the body of a living organism. This may occur by inhalation or through contaminated food or water. It is both a short-term and long-term problem. Most toxic wastes contain either metals, such as arsenic, barium, cadmium, chromium, and lead, or synthetic organics, such as various pesticides. RCRA specifies extraction procedure (EP) testing to determine whether such materials are present in significant concentrations to be a toxic hazard.

Explosives: These mainly consist of obsolete ordnance and manufacturing wastes from commercial explosives industries. They may also consist of wastes from the manufacturing of various propellants and pyrotechnics. However, some wastes, such as carbon and organic dusts, may be potentially explosive in various air concentrations when exposed to ignition sources, such as open flames or sparks.

Radioactivity: Most radioactive wastes consist of conventional, nonradioactive materials contaminated with radionuclides in concentrations ranging from parts per billion to as much as 50 percent. Biological hazards from radioactive materials are due to the effects of penetrating and ionizing radiation rather than chemical toxicity. The long-term hazards associated with specific radioactive waste are not necessarily proportional to the nominal level of radioactivity, but rather to the specific toxicity and decay rate of each radionuclide. Radioactive industrial wastes are primarily generated from biomedical research activities. These generally comprise items such as animal carcasses and liquid scintillation counting (LSC) vials with tracer level, or low-level, concentrations of radioactivity.

Biohazard: Wastes characterized as biohazards contain pathogens capable of producing infection. A pathogen is any disease-producing microorganism or material, and includes bacteria, fungi, viruses, viroids, rickettsiae and protozoa. Industrial wastes which are biohazards are almost exclusively generated from biomedical research activities.

Waste Characterization

Waste stream characterization provides the starting point for designing waste handling and disposal systems. This involves identification of average, or representative, waste composition and properties, deviations from these averages, and the forecasting of likely changes.

A characterization program usually begins with a detailed inventory and classification of all waste stream sources, components, and constituents. These are then organized into various groupings, or categories, to facilitate further evaluations. Typical groupings include form, such as solids, sludges and liquids, combustible vs. noncombustible, and hazardous vs. nonhazardous. The waste classification system shown in Table 2-33B has proved particularly useful to the author.

The next step in a characterization program usually involves determination of the physical and chemical properties of the waste materials, or groups of waste materials. Physical properties of concern typically include physical state, size, shape, weight, volume, temperature, viscosity, and pressure. Chemical properties typically include elemental constituents, toxicity, corrosivity, explosivity, flash point, heat of combustion, and products of combustion. Table 2-33C is a comprehensive checklist of parameters that may be significant in a waste characterization program.

Depending on the specific waste, sufficient characterization data may be readily available in published literature or engineering handbooks. When such data is not available or inadequate, laboratory testing and analytical work may be required. Waste testing methodologies are typically in accordance with American Society for Testing and Materials (ASTM) procedures. Hazardous waste sampling and analysis procedures are usually in accordance with "Test Methods for Evaluating Solid Waste—Physical/Chemical Methods," SW-846, as issued by the EPA.

WASTE MANAGEMENT SYSTEMS

Waste management generally comprises the collection, internal transport, interim storage, treatment, and final disposal of waste materials. A great variety of alternate processes and equipment are available for providing these functions as part of a total waste management system. Depending upon the specific types, forms, quantities, and hazardous characteristics of the waste materials, management systems can range from a few simple processes to a complex combination of many processes.

Waste handling generally refers to those functions associated with the movement of wastes after creation, excluding storage, processing, treatment, and final disposal. It includes collection of wastes at points of generation, transport of the materials, and unloading from the transport system. Waste handling systems and equipment include conveyors, chutes, carts, and transport vehicles, elevators and lifts, as well as pumps and piping for liquids, and ducts and blowers for gases. These systems can range in sophistication from fully manual to fully automatic operation.

Waste storage includes the interim containment of accumulated materials prior to subsequent handling, processing, treatment, or disposal. Waste storage, depending on the waste type and form, can be loose, compacted, or other processed form. It can also be stored in bulk or individual containers, such as drums or cartons.

Waste processing includes those functions which prepare or alter the waste by changing its shape, size, uniformity, or consistency. Such processes are usually provided to facilitate handling, storage, treatment, or disposal processes. Waste processing systems and equipment include compactors, shredders, crushers, pulpers, pulverizers, baggers and encapsulators, extruders, and dewatering devices.

Systems for storing and handling liquid chemical wastes often require special designs and safety provisions. Problems of concern typically include viscosity, freeze protection, abrasion, corrosion, slagging, and adverse chemical reactions, such as spontaneous ignition, rapid heat release, foaming, precipitation, solidification, and vaporization of low-boiling-point compounds. Safety provisions include spill and runoff containment, static electricity prevention, flame arresters, and systems for handling the vapors or fumes vented from the storage tanks. In addition, special precautions are usually provided to ensure that incompatible wastes are segregated to prevent undesirable reactions.

TABLE 2-33B. ***Waste Classification System3***

Class	Remarks	Example
I. Solid wastes		
A. Putrescibles		
Household garbage		
Vegetable and fruit processing wastes		
Animal manure		
Dead animals		
Meat, poultry and seafood processing wastes		
Others, not elsewhere classified[1]		
B. Bulky containers	Bulky is defined to mean a material of a size to present problems by jamming in a compaction truck hopper, an incinerator feed chute, or other such problems in handling or disposal. Its dimensions may not be defined, except by the size and nature of handling or disposal equipment.	
Wood		Timbers, pallets, cross-ties
Paper and paper products		Large cardboard packing boxes, box-car linings
Cloth		Filter cloths, mattresses
Plastics		Styrofoam logs, polystyrene sheets, garden hose
Rubber		Belting, tires
Leather		Conveyor belting
Yard and street wastes		Tree limbs
C. Bulky noncombustibles		
Metal		Drums, bedsprings
Mineral		Carboys, bathroom fixtures
D. Small combustibles	Small is defined to mean a piece of waste material of a small enough size to give no danger of jamming equipment, or otherwise causing problems because of its size. It refers to the size of a piece of the material, not the size of the delivered load.	
Wood		
Paper and paper products		
Cloth		Gloves
Leather		Shoes
Plastics		Milk cartons
Rubber		Galoshes, butyl rubber crumb
Yard and street wastes		Street sweeping, leaves
E. Small noncombustibles		
Metal		Cans
Mineral		Bottles
Ashes		Furnace ashes
F. Non-empty cans, bottles, and drums	This functional class will require precise definition of the contents by one of the other classes. If must be considered to establish the quantity of material delivered in this manner instead of in bulk form.	Bottles of wastes from laboratories
G. Gas cylinders		Oxygen, acetylene
H. Powders and dusts		
Organic		Pesticides, grain dusts, chemical powders, coal dusts
Metallic inorganic		
Non-metallic inorganic		
Explosive		
I. Pathological wastes		
Cloth, paper and plastic		
Animal and human wastes		
Instruments and utensils		
J. Sludges	Materials which are solid in appearance, but are wet, either from water or liquid organics. The solids portion is classified.	
Chlorinated		
Brominated		
Fluorinated		
Acid		
Alkaline		
Water-reactive (unhydrolyzed)		
Air-reactive	May represent a material highly reactive with the moisture in the air, or with the oxygen in the air.	

TABLE 2-33B. ***Waste Classification System[3] (continued)***

Class	Remarks	Example
Putrescible	May represent the wet form of any of the materials listed under the Functional Class of the same name, but also includes such materials as waste-water treatment plant sludges.	
Miscellaneous organic		
Metallic inorganic	Refers to metals in the uncombined form.	Particles of metal in oil.
Non-metallic inorganic	Inorganic compounds.	Filter cakes, $CaCO_3$ precipitate
K. Demolition an construction	This functional class will be subdivided into the analytical classes shown for bulky and small, combustibles and non-combustibles. It is included as a separate class to quantify materials from this source, and to recognize that a delivery may contain a wide mixture of large and small combustibles and non-combustibles.	
L. Abandoned vehicles		
M. Radiological wastes	This functional class will require further definition by one of the other classes. It must be considered to define this type of contamination to refuse, and to consider the special measures involved.	
II. Liquid wastes		
A. Wastewaters	Waste liquids composed almost entirely of water, but containing contaminants in low enough concentration (usually much less than 1.0 percent) to be handled through a sewer system to a waste-water treatment plant. This definition is proposed for exclusion purposes, since these wastes are not normally considered as refuse.	
B. Contaminated waters	Waters containing contaminants in a concentration too high, or of a nature, that handling through a wastewater treatment plan is too practical.	
Chlorinated		
Brominated		
Fluoridated		
Acid		
Alkaline		Blood, grease
Putrescibles		
Insoluble oils		
Soluble oils		
Toxic organics		
Toxic inorganics		
Soluble metals		
Others, (not elsewhere classified)†		
C. Liquid organics	Liquid at all ambient temperatures.	
Chlorinated		Many solvents
Brominated		
Fluoridated		
Sulfurated		
Acid		
Alkaline		
Water reactive (unhydrolyzed)		
Shock reactive		
Toxic and hazardous		Pesticides
Soluble metals		
Others (not elsewhere classified)†		
D. Tars	Stiff materials which are semi-solid at low ambient temperatures.	
Chlorinated		Chlorinated-substituted hydrocarbons
Brominated		Brominine-substituted hydrocarbons
Fluorinated		Fluorine-substituted hydrocarbons
Sulfurated		Sulfur-substituted hydrocarbons
Acid		Low pH, corrosive solvents
Alkaline		
Water-reactive		Unhydrolyzed materials which react violently

TABLE 2-33B. *Waste Classification System*[3] *(continued)*

Class	Remarks	Example
Chemically reactive		
Self-reactive (monomers)		Sodium, calcium
Toxic and hazardous		
Soluble metals		
Others (not elsewhere classified)†		
E. Slurries	Liquid materials which contain solids, but which readily flow or pump. The liquid and solid materials both are classified.	
Organic in water		
Inorganic in water		Lime slurry
Organic in liquid organic		
Inorganic in a liquid organic		Metallic sodium in oil
III. Gaseous wastes	This classification is restricted to those gaseous materials which have been or might become the responsibility of a disposal group or department to treat, burn, or otherwise alter before discharge to the atmosphere.	
A. Odorous		Mercaptans, H_2S
B. Combustible particulate		
Solids		
Mists		
C. Organic vapors		Volatile solvents
D. Acid gases		SO_2,HCl

†Other (not elsewhere classified)—represents the "cleanest" of material and is not intended as a catch-all grouping.

For safely handling fumes or vapors from industrial ovens and furnaces, dilution air is required such that the combustible concentrations are below 50 percent, and usually less than 25 percent, of lower explosive limits (LEL). Potentially explosive dusts require controls to prevent combustible air mixtures from forming and being ignited.

Waste handling systems also comprise equipment and devices for loading or charging waste into treatment systems and processes. For example, mechanical loading devices may be part of a system for charging solid waste into an incinerator. Such devices not only provide for a regulated loading rate, but they also provide a continual seal between the incinerator furnace and ambient surroundings during loading to prevent flame and smoke exfiltrations. Table 2-33D gives the applicability of various waste management and disposal methods for different waste classes.

TREATMENT AND DISPOSAL SYSTEMS

Because of the high costs and liabilities typically associated with waste treatment and disposal, initial efforts are usually directed to reducing waste quantities. Techniques include reuse and recycling of materials which would otherwise be waste, changes in manufacturing and production operations, and substitutions of raw materials to others generating less waste. Also, substitutions and reductions in the usage of hazardous chemicals may result in reduced hazardous waste disposal requirements.

One study for the EPA reported 43 potentially feasible waste treatment processes. These processes include physical treatment, chemical treatment, biological treatment, and thermal treatment. They provide such functions as volume reduction, separations of waste stream components, and destruction and detoxification of hazardous constituents. Often several treatment processes are linked in series to provide a required degree of treatment. Residues from these processes usually require disposal, such as land burial or deep well injection.

Selection of treatment processes depends on the type, form, and quantities of waste, required performance to satisfy environmental requirements, and overall system economics. Table 2-33E summarizes the currently available hazardous waste treatment and disposal processes discussed below.

Physical Treatment

Physical treatment processes generally provide for separation of waste stream components or phases. These are particularly useful for concentrating specific hazardous constituents within dilute waste mixtures, thus reducing the overall quantities requiring disposal as a hazardous waste. These also provide for the recovery of specific materials in resource recovery operations.

The following physical treatment processes are potentially feasible for wastes:

- Adsorption
- Centrifugation
- Dialysis
- Electrodialysis
- Electrolysis
- Electrophoresis
- Filtration
- Flocculation
- Flotation
- Freeze crystallation
- Freeze drying
- Freezing
- High-gradient magnetic separation
- Reserve osmosis

TABLE 2-33C. ***General, Physical, and Chemical Parameters of Possible Significance in the Characterization of Solid Wastes***[4]

General Parameters

Compositional weight fractions
- A. Domestic, commercial and institutional
  - Paper (broken into subcategories
  - Food wastes
  - Textiles
  - Glass and other ceramics
  - Plastics
  - Rubber
  - Leather
  - Metals
  - Wood (limbs, sawdust)
  - Bricks, stones,dirt, ashes
- B. Other municipal
  - Dead animals
  - Street sweepings
  - Catch-basin cleanings
- C. Agricultural
  - Field
  - Processing
- D. Industrial
- E. Mining/metallurgical
- F. Special
  - Radioactive
  - Munitions, etc.
  - Pathogenic
  - Moisture

Process weight fractions
- Combustible
- Compostable
- Processable by landfill
- Salvegeable
- Having instrinsic value

Physical parameters

Total wastes
- Size
- Shape
- Volume
- Weight
- Density
- Density stratification
- Surface area
- Compaction
- Compactability
- Temperature
- Color
- Odor
- Age
- Radioactivity
- Physical state
  - Total solids
  - Liquids
  - Gas

Solid wastes
- Soluble (%)
- Suspendable (%)
- Combustible (%)
- Volatile (%)
- Ash (%)
  - Soluble (%)
  - Suspendable (%)
- Hardness

Particle characteristics
- Shape distribution
  - "Shape"
  - "Surface"
  - "Porosity"
  - "Sorption"
  - "Density"
  - "Aggregation"

Liquid wastes
- Turbidity
- Color
- Taste
- Odor
- Temperature
- Viscosity data
  - Specific gravity
  - Stratification
- Total solids (%)
  - Soluble (%)
  - Suspended (%)
  - Settlable (%)
- Dissolved oxygen
- Vapor pressure
- Effect of shear rate
- Effect of temperature
- Gel formation

Gaseous wastes
- Temperature
- Pressure
- Volume
- Density
- Particulate (%)
- Liquid (%)

Chemical Parameters

General
- pH
- Alkalinity
- Hardness ($CaCO_3$)
- MBAS (methylene-blue active substances)
- BOD (biochemical oxygendemand)
- COD (chemical oxygen demand)
- Rate of availability of nitrogen
- Rate of availability of phosphorus
- Crude fiber
- Organic (%)
- Combustion parameters
  - Heat content
  - Oxygen requirement
  - Flame temperature
  - Combustion products (including ash)
  - Flash point
  - Ash-fusion characterization
  - Toxicity
  - Corrosivity
  - Explosivity
  - Other safety factors
  - Biologicalstability
  - Attractiveness to vermin

Inorganic and elemental
- Moisture content
- Carbon
- Hydrogen
- (P_2O_5 and phosphate)
- Sulfur content
- Alkali metals
- Alkaline-earth metals
- Precious metals
- Heavy metals
  - Especially Mercury
  - Lead
  - Cadmium
  - Copper
  - Nickel
- Toxic materials
  - Chromium
  - Especially Arsenic
  - Selenium
  - Beryllium
  - Asbestos
- Eutrophic materials
  - Nitrogen
  - Potassium
  - Phosphorus

Organic
- Soluble (%)
- Proteinnitrogen
- Phosphorus
- Lipids
- Starches
- Sugars
- Hemicelluloses
- Lignins
- Phenols
- Benzene oil
- ASB (alkyl benzene sulfonate)
- CCE (carbon chloroform extract)
- PCB (Polychlorinated biphenyls)
- PNH (Polynuclear hydrocarbons)
- Vitamins (e.g., B-12)
- Insecticides (e.g., Heptochlor, DDT, Dieldrin, etc.)

- Stripping
- Ultrafiltration
- Zone refining

Chemical Treatment

Chemical treatment processes are particularly useful for the detoxification of hazardous wastes. They also provide for the separation of specific waste stream components. However, they are generally limited to liquid forms of waste materials.

The following chemical treatment processes are potentially feasible for wastes:

- Chemical oxidation
- Chemical reduction
- Hydrolysis
- Liquid-liquid solvent extraction
- Neutralization
- Ozonation
- Photolysis

TABLE 2-33D. *Waste Management and Disposal Methods for Different Waste Classes*

	Potential Hazards				Management Methods															
Waste Classification Utilization Chart	Toxicity	Explosiveness/ Flammability	Pathogenicity	Radioactivity	Std. Storage	Spec. Storage	Std. Coll. Vehicle	Spec. Coll. Vehicle	Std. Pipeline	Spec. Pipeline	Compaction	Grinding	Pulping (w/H_2O)	Composting	Incineration	Incineration (Liquid)	Incineration (Spec.)	Chemical Treat. or Alteration	Sanitary Landfill	Ocean Disposal‡
Solid wastes																				
Putrescible			X		X		X					X	X	X	X				X	
Bulky combustible						X		X			X	X			X		X		X	
Bulky non-combustible						X		X			X	X							X	
Small combusible					X		X				X	X	X	X	X				X	
Small non-combustible*					X		X				X	X							X	
Non-empty cans, bottles, drums*	X	X	X	X	X	X	X	X									X		X	
Gas cylinders		X				X		X									X		X	
Powders and dusts		X				X		X									X		X	
Pathological wastes	X		X	X		X		X							X		X	X	X	
Sludges	X					X		X							X		X	X	X	X
Demolition and construction						X		X				X					X		X	
Abandoned vehicles						X		X			X	X					X		X	
Radiological waste				X		X		X									X		X	X
Liquids wastes§																				
Waste waters									X							X		X		
Contaminated waters†	X			X		X		X	X	X					X		X			
Liquid organics†	X		X			X		X	X	X						X		X		X
Tars	X	X				X		X	X	X						X	X	X		
Slurries	X					X		X	X	X						X		X		X
Gaseous wastes§																				
Odorous	X	X				X		X									X	X		
Combustible particulate		X				X		X									X	X		
Organic vapors	X	X				X		X									X	X		
Acid gases	X	X				X		X									X	X		

* For contents treatment see proper classification; this class for container only.
† Pipeline selection dependent upon specific contaminant.
‡ Ocean disposal as locally permitted or approved—not recommended procedure.
§ Final disposal of these wastes requires an initial transformation to the solid class (except as noted).

Thermal Treatment

Thermal treatment processes include pyrolysis and incineration. Incineration is high-temperature oxidation, or combustion, while pyrolysis is thermal decomposition in the absence of oxygen. Thermal treatment processes can be designed to dispose of virtually all types and forms of waste materials, but only their organic constituents can be actually destroyed by thermal treatment.

Depending on waste type and composition, thermal treatment processes can provide the greatest weight and volume reduction. In addition, they can destroy or detoxify hazardous organics, sterilize infectious materials, and provide for waste heat recovery. Some industries utilize thermal treatment processes in conjunction with their production operations for the conversion, reclamation, and reuse, or recovery, of residues and byproducts. Examples include thermal distillation for spent solvent reclamation and hydrochloric acid recovery from the incineration of chlorinated hydrocarbons in conjunction with a quench/neutralization system.

Specific types of thermal treatment processes are as follows:

Pyrolysis: As indicated, pyrolysis is a thermal treatment process similar to incineration except that decomposition occurs in the absence of oxygen. Heat usually is added externally, and temperatures typically are maintained much lower than incineration temperatures.

The pyrolysis process basically distills the volatile fraction from the waste, leaving inorganics, or ash, and fixed carbons, or char, behind. The volatiles can be combusted as fuel in a boiler or furnace. If the inorganics have non-slagging characteristics and comprise only a small percentage of the solid residues, the char can also be burned as fuel. Pyrolysis is a potentially useful process for treating wastes containing salts, metals, and other contaminants which would slag conventional incineration systems. However, several types of incinerators, including rotary kilns, multiple hearth incinerators, and special designs, can be operated in a pyrolytic mode.

TABLE 2-33E. ***Hazardous Waste Treatment and Disposal Processes***[5]

Processes	Functions Performed†	Types of Waste‡	Forms of Waste§	Resource Recovery Capacity
Physical treatment:				
Carbon sorption	VR, Se	1, 3, 4, 5	L, G	Yes
Dialysis	VR, Se	1, 2, 3, 4	L	Yes
Electrodialysis	VR, Se	1, 2, 3, 4, 6	L	Yes
Evaportaion	VR, Se	1, 2, 5	L	Yes
Filtration	VR, Se	1, 2, 3, 4, 5	L, G	Yes
Flocculation/setting	VR, Se	1, 2, 3, 4, 5	L	Yes
Reverse osmosis	VR, Se	1, 2, 4, 6	L	Yes
Ammonia stripping	VR, Se	1, 2, 3, 4	L	Yes
Chemical treatment:				
Calcination	VR	1, 2, 5	L	
Ion exchange	VR, Se, De	1, 2, 3, 4, 5	L	Yes
Neutralization	De	1, 2, 3, 4	L	Yes
Oxidation	De	1, 2, 3, 4	L	
Precipitation	VR, Se	1, 2, 3, 4, 5	L	Yes
Reduction	De	1,2	L	
Thermal treatment:				
Pyrolysis	VR, De	3, 4, 6	S, L, G	Yes
Incineration	De, Di	3, 5, 6, 7, 8	S, L, G	Yes
Biological treatment:				
Activated sludges	De	#	L	No
Aerated lagoons	De	3	L	No
Waste stabilization ponds	De	3	L	No
Trickling filters	De	3	L	No
Disposal/storage:				
Deep-well injection	Di	1,2, 3, 4, 6, 7	L	No
Detonation	Di	6, 8	S, L, G	No
Engineered storage	St	1, 2, 3, 4, 5, 6, 7, 8	S, L, G	No
Land burial	Di	1, 2, 3, 4, 5, 6, 7, 8	S, L	No
Ocean dumping	Di	1, 2, 3, 4, 7, 8	S, L, G	No

† Functions: VR, volume reduction; Se, separation; De, detoxification; Di, disposal; and St, storage.

‡ Waste types: 1, inorganic chemical without heavy metals; 2, inorganic chemical with heavy metals; 3, organic chemical without heavy metals; 4, organic chemical with heavy metals; 5, radiological; 6, biological; 7, flammable; and 8, explosive.

§ Waste forms: S, solid; L, liquid; and G, gas.

Incineration: Incineration is an engineered process using high-temperature combustion. Variables most affecting incineration system design, construction, and operations include waste combustibility and heating values, operating temperatures, retention times for both waste and products of combustion, turbulence within the combustion zone, and emission requirements. There are many basic types of industrial incinerators. Each is generally suitable for specific waste types, forms, and quantities; and each has limitations, advantages, and disadvantages.

The standard, basic types of industrial incinerators include:

Open burning: Basically limited to the detonation of explosive waste in remote, open areas on a flat, gravel base. Open burning for other waste is prohibited in most of the country.

Open-pit or air curtain destructor:/mSingle chamber, above or below ground, with an open top for burning explosive or reactive materials, such as nitrocellulose. A high-velocity air stream across the open top provides a "curtain" of air to promote combustion turbulence within the pit.

Multiple-chamber incinerator: Consists of a primary and one or more secondary chambers, and operates with high-excess combustion air—typically 200 to 300 percent. Wastes are loaded into the primary chamber for combustion, and most combustibles entrained in the flue gases are burned in the secondary chambers. Usually limited to solid wastes, but hearth designs can accommodate sludges. Liquid wastes can be burned in suspension.

Controlled-air incinerator: A two-stage combustion process: waste in the primary chamber, or first stage, is burned under starved air, or oxygen-deficient conditions; smoke and volatiles from the first stage are combusted in the secondary chamber under excess air conditions—typically 100 to 200 percent. Usually limited to solid wastes and limited quantities of sludges. Liquid wastes can be burned in suspension.

Rotary kiln incinerator: Comprises a cylindrical combustion chamber, or kiln, oriented at a slight incline to horizontal, which rotates slowly on its axis. Waste is loaded at one end, and kiln rotation provides turbulence for thorough waste destruction as well as for the discharge of ash residues from the opposite end. Combustibles entrained in the flue gases from the kiln are burned in a secondary chamber. Rotary kilns are highly versatile systems suitable for most organic wastes, including solids and sludges. Liquid wastes can be burned in suspension or loaded in drums or containers.

Multiple-hearth incinerator: Wastes move slowly downward through vertically stacked refractory hearths within a vertically oriented, cylindrical chamber. Rotating rabble arms with plow blades move wastes across and downward through each hearth level. Usually limited to organic sludges, but can accommodate granulated solid wastes. Liquids and gases can be injected between various hearths.

Rotary hearth incinerator: Comprises a flat, horizontally oriented, doughnut-shaped hearth which rotates around its central axis within a combustion chamber. Sludges are fed onto the hearth at one location, they are combusted as the hearth rotates, and resultant ash residues are scraped off at a discharge point just prior to a full rotation. System is basically limited to sludges, and it operates predominantly in a pyrolytic mode.

Fluidized-bed incinerator: Wastes injected into hot agitated bed of granular particles which are suspended within cylindrical chamber by a high-pressure blower. Rapid combustion and heat transfer between wastes and bed. Usually limited to organic sludges, but can accommodate granulated solid wastes. Liquids and gases can be injected into the bed.

Infrared incinerator: Wastes are loaded onto a slowly moving conveyor belt which passes below a series of infrared heaters within a combustion chamber. Ash residues are discharged at the end of the belt. System is limited to sludges, granulated solids, and contaminated soils.

Liquid injection incinerators: Refers generically to those systems designed to burn liquid wastes in suspension within a combustion chamber. Depending on heating value, wastes can be injected through nozzles or combusted through a burner system.

TABLE 2-33F. *Summary of Waste Incinerators*[6]

Type	Process Principle	Application	Combustion Temp.	Residence Time
Rotary kiln	Slowly rotating cylinder mounted at slight incline to horizontal. Tumbling action improves efficiency of combustion.	Most organic wastes; well suited for solids and sludges; liquids and gases.	810–1650°C (1500–3000°F)	Several seconds to several hours
Multiple hearth	Solid feed slowly moves through vertically stacked hearths; gases and liquids fed through side ports and nozzles.	Most organic wastes, largely in sewage sludge; well suited for solids and sludges; also handles liquids and gases.	750–980°C (1400–1800°F)	Up to several hours
Liquid injection	Vertical or horizontal vessels; wastes atomized through nozzles to increase rate of vaporization.	Limited to pumpable liquids and slurries (750 SSU or less for proper atomization).	650–1650°C (1200–3000°F)	0.1 to 1 sec
Fluidized bed	Wastes are injected into a hot agitaged bed of inert granular particles; heat is transferred between the bed material and the waste during combustion.	Most organic wastes; ideal for liquids, also handles solids and gases.	750–870°C (1400–1600°F)	Seconds for gases and liquids; longer for solids
Pyrolysis	Thermal decomposition in the absence of oxygen; transforms organic materials into solids, liquids and gaseous organic materials of simpler structure.	Primary as fuel; useful with solids and sludges; potential for resource recovery of breakdown products.	480–810°C (900–1500°F)	Normally 12–15 min

Gaseous waste incinerators: Refers to those systems designed for the combustion of fumes, vapors, odors, and the like. Three basic types include:

1. Flares: Open burning of combustible gases that are either near or above their lower explosive limits (LEL) of concentration or above their upper explosive limits (UEL) of concentration.
2. Thermal burners: Combustion of dilute, or low-combustible, gases in the presence of a burner flame within a chamber.
3. Catalytic burners: Combustion of dilute gases which are preheated, exposed to a catalyst material, and oxidized at relatively lower temperatures. Catalyst materials are subject to damage or deactivation from gas stream contaminants.

Other types of industrial incinerators which are either highly specialized, unique, or still under development include:

- Molten-salt incineration
- Wet air oxidation or zimmerman process
- Plasma destruction
- High-temperature fluid-wall reactor (HTFW) or thagard process
- Supercritical fluid technology or MODAR process
- Critical fluid system (CFS)

Biological Treatment

Biological treatment processes utilize microorganisms for the decomposition of organic compounds in the waste. These are applicable to aqueous waste streams with solid or solvent organics. Composting is a biological treatment process used for solid wastes.

The following biological treatment processes are potentially feasible for wastes:

- Activated sludge
- Aerated lagoons
- Anaerobic digestion
- Composting
- Enzyme treatment
- Trickling filters
- Stabilization ponds

Other Technologies

Other thermal treatment technologies and variations to conventional incineration used for waste combustion include:

- Burning in conventional boilers
- Cement kilns
- Other industrial furnaces or ovens
- At-sea incineration
- Mobile incineration

Steam sterilization, or autoclaving, is a thermal treatment process for infectious waste. Autoclave equipment is designed to kill pathogens in waste by exposing them to relatively high temperatures—between 240 and 280°F (116 to 138°C)—for periods ranging from about 15 minutes to several hours. Retention times are dependent on steam temperatures and pressures, types and forms of the waste, quantities of waste, and specific type and design of the autoclave system.

TABLE 2-33G. ***Matrix for Matching Waste Type with Incineration Process***[7]

Waste Type	Rotary Kiln*	Multiple Hearth*	Fluidized Bed*	Liquid Incinerator	Multiple-Chamber Incinerator
Solids					
Granular homogeneous	X	X	X		X
Irregular bulky (Pallets, etc.)	X				X
Low melting point (Tars, etc.)	X		X	If material can be melted and pumped	
Organic compounds with fusible ash constituents	X	X			
Gases					
Organic vapor laden			X		
Liquids					
HIgh organic strength aqueous wastes, often toxic	If equipped with auxiliary liquid injection nozzles		X		
Organic liquids	If equipped with auxiliary liquid injection nozzles		X	X	
Solids/liquids					
Waste contains halogenated aromatic compounds (2,200°F minimum)	X	X	If liquid		
Aqueous organic sludges	Provided waste does not become sticky upon drying	X	X		

* Suitable for pyrolysis operation

Table 2-33F summarizes the major incineration technologies, and Table 2-33G shows the applicability of various incineration technologies to different waste types.

ULTIMATE DISPOSAL

Ultimate disposal is basically the final treatment or disposition of treated and untreated waste materials and residues. For example, with solid-waste incineration, a substantial percentage of residues typically remain as ash and/or sludges from the air pollution control system, and need disposal. If the waste being incinerated is regulated as hazardous, the ash residues must be analyzed to determine whether they require disposal as a hazardous waste in a permitted facility. Likewise, the ash residues from incinerating radioactive waste may also require disposal in a permitted site if radionuclide concentrations exceed NRC levels. In some states, even ash residues from infectious and non-hazardous wastes must be analyzed to determine whether their heavy metal concentrations will not exceed safe toxicity concentration levels when placed in landfills. Alternate disposal processes include land burial, deep-well injection, and ocean dumping.

Land Burial

Two types of land burial are: (1) sanitary landfills and (2) secure, or industrial, landfills. These are engineered systems as opposed to indiscriminate dumping. Sanitary landfills are used for the disposal of nonhazardous solid wastes. Wastes are covered daily with earth to minimize health vector problems, blowing of debris, and open burning. However, unless specially designed, sanitary landfills have the potential for surface and groundwater pollution from leaching, as well as air pollution from gas venting.

Secure landfills for hazardous wastes are regulated under RCRA. These require special liner materials to prevent leaching, special caps to prevent surface exposures, venting systems for handling gases, and monitoring and test wells for verifying the integrity of the liner structure.

Deep-Well Injection

Deep-well injection involves the pumping of liquid wastes into underground cavities or reservoirs that have been identified as geologically secure. Since a prime concern is to protect all usable underground water, the reservoirs must be located far below potable water aquifers and isolated by thick, nearly impermeable strata, such as shale, limestone, or dolomite. Average well depths are about 5,000 ft (1524 m), with some as deep as 10,000 ft (3048 m). Most are located in the southwest where the geology favors this disposal technology.

Ocean Dumping

Sewage sludges, industrial wastes, and explosives have been dumped at sea for years in designated and approved

TABLE 2-33H. *Comparison of Some Hazard Reduction Technologies*[8]

	Disposal		Treatment		
	Landfills and Impoundments	Injection Wells	Incineration and Other Thermal Destruction	Emerging High-Temperature Decomposition†	Chemical Stabilization
Effectiveness: how well it contains or destroys hazardous characteristics	Low for volatiles, questionable for liquids; based on lab and field tests	High, based on theory, but limited field data available	High, based on field tests, except little data on specific constituents	Very high, commercial-scale tests	High for many metals, based on lab tests
Reliability issues:	Siting, construction, and operation Uncertainties: long-term integrity of cells and cover, liner life less than life of toxic waste	Site history and geology; well depth, construction and operation	Monitoring uncertainties with respect to high degree of DRE; surrogate mea sures, PICs incinerability§	Limited experience Mobile units; onsite treatment avoids hauling risks Operational simplicity	Some inorganics still soluble Uncertain leachate test, surrogate for weathering
Environmental media most affected	Surface and ground-water	Surface and ground-water	Air	Air	Ground-water
Least compatible wastes‡	Linear reactive; highly toxic, mobile, persistent, and bioaccumulative	reactive; corrosive; highly toxic, mobile, and persistent	Highly toxic and refractory organics, highly heavy metals concentration	Some inorganics	Organics
Costs: low, mod, high	L–M	L	M–H (Coincin.=L)	M–H	M
Resource recovery: potential	None	None	Energy and some Acids	Energy and some metals	Possible building material

† Molten salt, high-temperature fluid wall, and plasma arc treatments.
‡ Wastes for which this method may be less effective for reducing exposure, relative to other technologies. Wastes listed do not necessarily denote common usage.
§ DRE = destruction and removal efficiency. PIC = product of incomplete combustion.

locations. The U.S. Army Corps of Engineers and the U. S. Coast Guard are basically responsible for the sea transportation and disposal areas for industrial wastes. Of course, the primary concern with this type of disposal is the threat to marine life and coastal areas from improperly sealed containers of hazardous wastes. Because of recent washups of sewage sludge and medical waste on beaches in the northeast, national legislative measures have been taken to outlaw ocean dumping of all waste.

Table 2-33H compares some of the hazardous waste treatment and disposal technologies.

CODES, REGULATIONS, AND STANDARDS

The proper and safe management and disposal of industrial waste require in-depth knowledge of the material properties, alternate treatment technologies, and applicable regulations. There are also various codes and standards dealing with waste handling and disposal. The more significant of these are listed below.

Federal Codes and Regulations Applicable to Waste Management and Disposal

1. Resource Conservation and Recovery Act of 1976 (RCRA), Subtitle C, Hazardous Waste Regulations, 40 CFR, parts 260-265 and 122-124.
2. Nuclear Regulatory Commission (NRC), Standards for Protection Against Radiation, 10 CFR, part 20.
3. Toxic Substances Control Act of 1976 (TSCA).
4. Clean Air Act of 1963 (CAA), including:
   - National Ambient Air Quality Standards (NAAQS),
   - National Emission Standards for Hazardous Air Pollution (NESHAP),
   - Prevention of Significant of Deterioration (PSD), and
   - Nonattainment Regulations (NA).
5. Federal Pesticide Control Act of 1972; also known as Federal Insecticide, Fungicide, and Rodenticide Act (FIFRA).
6. Oil Pollution Act of 1961.
7. Federal·Water Pollution Control Act of 1948 (FWPCA).
8. Occupational Safety and Health Act of 1970 (OSHA), including National Institute of Occupational Safety and Health (NIOSH).
9. Hazardous Substances and Hazardous Waste Response, Liability and Compensation Act; also known as "Superfund."
10. Medical Waste Tracking Act of 1988, Subtitle J of RCRA, 40 CFR, parts 22 and 259.

General Standards Dealing with Waste Materials and Their Management

NFPA 43A, *Liquid and Solid Oxidizing Materials*.

NFPA 480, *Storage, Handling, and Processing of Magnesium*.

NFPA 49, *Hazardous Chemicals Data*.

NFPA 69, *Explosion Prevention Systems.*

NFPA 321, *Basic Classification of Flammable and Combustible Liquids.*

NFPA 325M, *Fire Hazard Properties of Flammable Liquids, Gases, and Volatile Solids.*

NFPA 481, *Production, Processing, Handling, and Storage of Titanium.*

NFPA 482, *Production, Processing, Handling, and Storage of Zirconium.*

NFPA 491M, *Hazardous Chemical Reactions.*

NFPA 654, *Prevention of Fire and Dust Explosions in the Chemical, Dye, Pharmaceutical, and Plastics Industries.*

"Guide for Infectious Waste Management," *NTIS Pub. No. 86-199130,* Industrial Environmental Research Laboratory, U.S. Environmental Protection Agency, Washington, DC, May 1987.

"Sampling and Analysis Methods for Hazardous Waste Incineration," 1st ed., *Contract 68-02-3111,* Industrial Environmental Research Laboratory, U.S. Environmental Protection Agency, Washington, DC, Feb. 1982.

"Test Methods for Evaluating Solid Waste—Physical/Chemical Methods," *SW-846, Revision B,* Industrial Environmental Research Laboratory, U.S. Environmental Protection Agency, Washington, DC, July 1981.

"Biosafety in Microbiological and Biomedical Laboratories," Draft, U.S. Department of Health and Human Services—Public Health Service: Center for Disease Control and National Institutes of Health, Atlanta, GA, March 1983.

General Standards Dealing with Waste Treatment and Disposal Systems

NFPA 30, *Flammable and Combustible Liquids Code.*

NFPA 82, *Incinerators, Waste and Linen Handling Systems and Equipment.*

NFPA 86, *Ovens and Furnaces.*

NFPA 801, *Facilities Handling Radioactive Materials.*

"Draft Manual for Infectious Waste Management," *SW-957,* Office of Solid Waste, U.S. Environmental Protection Agency, Washington, DC, Sept. 1982.

General Standards Dealing with Burners and Equipment

NFPA 31, *Installation of Oil Burning Equipment.*

NFPA 54, *National Fuel Gas Code.*

UL 296, *Oil Burners.*

UL 372, *Primary Safety Controls for Gas- and Oil-Fired Appliances.*

UL 795, *Commercial—Industrial Gas—Heating Equipment.*

NFPA 850, *Fossil Fueled Steam and Combination Turbine Electric Generating.*

The above codes and standards are not all-inclusive. Other agencies, such as Industrial Risk Insurers (IRI), American National Standards Institute (ANSI), and American Society for Testing and Materials (ASTM), may have standards applicable to specific waste management and disposal operations. In addition, state and local regulations and requirements may be more stringent than federal regulations or standards.

BIBLIOGRAPHY

References Cited

1. Wilson, D. G., *Handbook of Solid Waste Management,* Van Nostrand Reinhold Co., New York, 1977.
2. "Hazardous Waste Generation and Commercial Hazardous Waste Management," *SW-894,* U.S. Environmental Protection Agency, Washington, DC, p. III-3, Dec. 1980.
3. *State-Wide Comprehensive Solid-Waste Management Study,* New York State Department of Health, Albany, NY, 1970.
4. Ulmer, N. S., "Physical and Chemical Parameters and Methods for Solid-Waste Classification," *Open-File Progress Report RS-03-68-17,* U.S. Environmental Protection Agency, Washington, DC, 1970.
5. "Report to Congress—Disposal of Hazardous Wastes," *SW-115,* U.S. Environmental Protection Agency, Washington, DC, 1974.
6. Shen, T. T., Chen, M., and Lauber, J., "Incineration of Toxic Chemical Wastes," *Pollution Engineering,* Oct. 1978, pp. 45-50.
7. Hitchcock, D., "Solid Waste Disposal: Incineration," *Chemical Engineering,* May 21, 1979, pp. 185-194.
8. "Technologies and Management Strategies for Hazardous Waste Control," *OTA-M-197,* Congressional Office of Technology Assessment, Washington, DC, March 1983.

References

"Serious Reduction of Hazardous Waste," OTA-ITE-318, Congressional Office of Technological Assessment, Washington, DC, Sept. 1986.

NFPA Codes, Standards, and Recommended Practices

Reference to the following NFPA codes, standards, and recommended practices will provide further information on the control of hazardous waste discussed in this chapter. (See the latest *NFPA Catalog* for availability of current editions of the following documents.)

NFPA 30, *Flammable and Combustible Liquids Code.*

NFPA 31, *Installation of Oil Burning Equipment.*

NFPA 43A, *Liquid and Solid Oxidizing Materials.*

NFPA 49, *Hazardous Chemicals Data.*

NFPA 54, *National Fuel Gas Code.*

NFPA 82, *Incinerators, Waste and Linen Handling Systems and Equipment.*

NFPA 86, *Ovens and Furnaces.*

NFPA 321, *Basic Classification of Flammable and Combustible Liquids.*

NFPA 325M, *Fire Hazard Properties of Flammable Liquids, Gases, and Volatile Solids.*

NFPA 480, *Storage, Handling, and Processing of Magnesium.*

NFPA 481, *Production, Processing, Handling, and Storage of Titanium.*

NFPA 482, *Production, Processing, Handling, and Storage of Zirconium.*

NFPA 491M, *Manual of Hazardous Chemical Reactions.*

NFPA 801, *Facilities Handling Radioactive Materials.*

Additional Reading

Conway, R. A. and Ross, R. D., *Handbook of Industrial Waste Disposal,* Van Nostrand Reinhold, NY, 1980.

Doucet, L. G., *Incineration: State-of-the-Art Design,* Procurement and Operations, *Paper* presented at 71st Annual Meeting of the Association of Physical Plant Administrators of Colleges and Universities, Columbus, OH, June 18, 1984.

Doucet, L. G. and Knoll, W. G., Jr., "The Craft of Specifying Solid Waste Systems," *Actual Specifying Engineer*, May 1974, pp. 107-113.

"Engineering Handbook for Hazardous Waste Incineration," *EPA SW-889*, Environmental Protection Agency, Washington, DC, Sept. 1981.

"Fire Protection for Belt Conveyors," *FMRC Loss Prevention Data Sheet 7-11*, Factory Mutual Engineering Corp., Norwood, MA.

"Flammable and Combustible Waste Disposal in the Plastics Industry," *Bulletin No. 13*, Society of the Plastics Industry, NY.

Hitchcock, D., "Solid Waste Disposal: Incineration," *Chemical Engineering*, May 21, 1979, pp. 185-194.

Inemeration Standards (microform), Enviromental Protection Agency, Washington DC, 1981.

McColgan, I. J., "Air Pollution Emmission and Control Technology: Packaged Incinerators—Economic and Technical Review," *EPS 3-AP-77-3*, Canadian Environmental Protection Service, 1977.

Nollet, A. R., "How to Prevent Shredding Plant Explasions," *World Wastes*, Vol. 32, No. 7, 1989, pp. 56-60.

Pavoni, J. L., Heer, J. E., Jr, and Hagerty, D. J., *Handbook of Solid Waste Disposal*, Van Nostrand Reinhold Co., NY, 1975.

Shulz, J. F., "Standards for Refuse-Handling in Apartment Houses," *Fire Journal*, Vol. 68, No. 2 (Mar. 1974), pp. 82-86.

Solid Waste Handling and Disposal in Multistory Buildings and Hospitals, Volumes I and II, SW-34, Environmental Protection Agency, 1972.

Vance, M., *Industrial Waste Disposal: A Bibliography*, Vance Bibliographies, Monticello, IL, 1982.

Wilson, D. G., *Handbook of Solid Waste Management*, Van Nostrand Reinhold, NY, 1977.

HOUSEKEEPING PRACTICES

John T. Higgins

The Occupational Safety and Health Act (OSHA) requires that every employer maintain a safe and healthful place of employment. This means the care and maintenance of the property. This is the definition of good housekeeping. It is basic to firesafety and should be a major concern in every type of occupancy, from the simplest dwelling to the most complex industrial facility.

This chapter covers the fundamentals of good housekeeping practices. It discusses in some detail the specifics of practices to be observed in providing firesafe and effective housekeeping in connection with the care and maintenance of buildings.

Proper layout of equipment and good storage and handling practices are important and complementary to success in maintaining cleanliness and order. This program also requires a good preventive maintenance program to limit or eliminate potential sources of ignition.

Good storage practices for various materials and the different storage configurations used for them can be found in the following chapters: Section 2, Chapter 25, "Storage of Flammable and Combustible Liquids;" Section 2, Chapter 26, "Storage of Gases;" Section 2, Chapter 27, "Storage and Handling of Chemicals;" Section 2, Chapter 28, "Storage and Handling of Grain Mill Products;" Section 2, Chapter 29, "Storage and Handling of Solid Fuels;" Section 2, Chapter 30, "Storage and Handling of Records;" and Section 9, Chapter 17, "Hazardous Waste Control."

GOOD HOUSEKEEPING THEORY

A good housekeeping program concerns itself with the less complex aspects of tidiness and order, waste control, and the regulation of such personal practices as smoking, which, without reasonable controls, could lead to hazardous conditions.

Poor housekeeping contributes to loss potential by increasing fire and explosion hazards in several ways:

1. It provides more places for a fire to start.
2. It creates a greater continuity of combustibles, which makes it easier for fire to spread.
3. It provides a greater combustible loading for the initial fire to feed upon.
4. It creates the potential for flash fires or dust explosions when layers of lint or dust are allowed to accumulate.
5. It allows spills or drips of flammable or combustible liquids to accumulate, which could catch fire.
6. When not properly addressed, friction, static, or electrical connections can be sources of ignition.
7. Poorly controlled smoking policies can lead to a source of ignition.
8. It increases the potential for spontaneous ignition.

In addition to the increased hazard, poor housekeeping can have a negative effect on production. Quality is hard to maintain when the workspace is crowded and messy. Efficiency suffers because people normally tend to work faster and more accurately if their surroundings are clean. Thus, good housekeeping will not only prevent fires but can improve production and employee morale as well.

The Essentials of Good Housekeeping

The degree of effort and attention needed for proper housekeeping is influenced, of course, by the type of building and the overall size of the facility involved. But most significant are the specific occupancies of the facility. Some processes produce more waste, leakage, and vapors than others, thus contributing to the extent of housekeeping problems. In addition, the acceptable level of cleanliness varies from occupancy to occupancy. What is satisfactory in a foundry would probably not be tolerable in an office building. And the cleanliness of the average office would hardly be satisfactory for an electronic "clean room."

In order to have good housekeeping, the program must start at the top. The facility manager or top-level facility supervisors must set the tone. This is not to say that the individual supervisor at a department level cannot go it alone, but his/her success will be much improved if the top management is behind the program. To begin, supervisors (at all levels) must define what is meant by good

John T. Higgins, P.E., is a senior safety specialist in the corporate safety and loss prevention department of Dow Corning Corporation, Midland, MI.

housekeeping. To do this, each level of management should review the plant and then determine:

1. Is the present level of housekeeping acceptable?
2. Are the appropriate tools provided for general plant cleanup? For emergency cleanup?
3. Are adequate storage areas provided for both incoming raw materials and outgoing product?
4. Are management's offices reflective of the good housekeeping required of the facility areas?
5. Are adequate waste receptacles provided?

Proper housekeeping does not just happen. It requires the leadership and wholehearted support of management and the cooperation of all employees. Management cannot merely decree that good housekeeping is a desired goal. Good housekeeping requires effort from everyone. First, management must set the tone, i.e., the level of acceptable housekeeping. Next, management must enlist the aid of everyone to help. Employee ideas should be solicited on how to maintain good housekeeping. Management must either act on the employee ideas or explain why it cannot.

It is important that all employees accept the responsibility for housekeeping in their respective area. The facility will probably either hire a contract janitorial service or create a janitorial department, or have a combination of both. However, janitors will only do the general cleaning. Ensuring that materials, tools, wastes, etc., are placed in their proper locations is the job of each employee who handles them.

Safety inspections are important. When doing so, management must demonstrate with their actions and words the level of housekeeping they will accept.

Where proper housekeeping does not exist, it is usually because inadequate attention is paid to, or inadequate action taken in, one or more of the following areas.

Communication: Management must publicize its commitment to good housekeeping. This publicity must be reinforced periodically, and recognition given whenever notable improvement or outstanding performance takes place. Supervisors must provide feedback to management on how the program is working and on what they need to meet the program goals. This can be done through safety inspection reports prepared by supervisors and periodic inspections by management. In addition, supervisors must be able to meet with management periodically to review performance, to revise goals, and to offer and substantiate recommendations. These supervisors should also encourage feedback from employees, in the form of suggestions and constructive criticism. More efficient housekeeping methods can often be more readily identified by the worker who uses the area than by management.

Equipment: Housekeeping efforts should not founder from lack of necessary tools or equipment. This includes the tools normally used by the housekeeping department. The simple step of placing a sufficient number of easily accessible wastebaskets or trash receptacles at points of need can reduce the amount of waste deposited on the floor or in the product.

In some production and handling areas, dust, lint, and other waste may be produced constantly. In these cases, vacuum pick-up stations tied into an exhaust and collection system may be needed at specific points of waste generation. For area cleaning, powered floor sweepers or rail-mounted traveling cleaners may be necessary. Areas in which large quantities of scrap or discarded packing materials continuously accumulate may need not only large trash containers, but also motorized equipment that can be emptied or replaced frequently. In areas where grease or oil may accumulate, a high-pressure steam floor-washing system may be required.

A well-planned preventive maintenance program on all equipment will find and eliminate leaks of liquid, electrical hazards, static buildup, and friction caused by lack of lubrication.

Layout and storage: Overcrowding is a major impediment to proper housekeeping. Blocked or restricted aisles limit access and, in so doing, hamper efficient cleaning and trash pickup. Lack of sufficient workspace and storage capacity results in inefficient operations, an inability to maintain order, and worker frustration. The creative use of racks, shelving, and bins, or marking aisles and storage areas by painting lines on the floor can provide solutions.

With its negative influence on good housekeeping, disorganized and haphazard storage is usually a detriment to effective fire protection, as well. Fire extinguishers, small hose stations, and sprinkler system control valves can become blocked and inaccessible, while other fire equipment, such as fire doors, may be made inoperable.

Environment: Equally as important as the natural environment is the artificial environment created in the workplace. The control of process fumes, vapors, dusts, and flyings required today for the well-being of the worker has also had a beneficial impact on overall cleanliness in many work areas. Consideration should be given to totally enclosed dust- and/or vapor-tight process equipment in addition to the ventilation equipment.

Personnel: Employees must be informed on the necessity of keeping their respective areas clean. This is a critical part of the program. To do this, management must constantly communicate to the employees what is acceptable and unacceptable about the way the facility is being maintained, from a housekeeping standpoint.

BUILDING CARE AND MAINTENANCE

The three basic requirements for good housekeeping are: (1) proper layout and equipment; (2) correct materials handling and storage; and (3) cleanliness and order. Any facility that implements these basics has laid the foundation for good housekeeping. Using them, the facility can develop special housekeeping practices to deal with its own specific problems.

In pursuing cleanliness and order, effective care and maintenance of buildings require special housekeeping practices to reduce the fire danger to buildings.

Floors

The general care, treatment, cleaning, and refinishing of floors may present a fire hazard if flammable solvents or finishes are used or if combustible residues are produced in quantity. For example, many fires have resulted from the use of a flammable liquid, such as gasoline, to clean a greasy spot on the floor. In general, cleaning solvents with flash points below room temperature are too dangerous to use to clean floors. When selecting a cleaning agent, care should be taken about its toxicity to employees and to the environment if it is eliminated through the sewer system.

Safe materials are available for most of the following purposes.

Sweeping compounds: Many excellent compounds exist on the market for sweeping floors and absorbing oily materials. Noncombustible materials should be used for this purpose. Sawdust and similar combustible materials should be avoided or, if used, should be disposed of in covered metal containers.

Floor oils: Compounds containing oils and low-flash-point solvents are a hazard, particularly when freshly applied. In addition, component oils may be subject to spontaneous heating. To reduce the fire hazard, suitable attention must be given to the safe storage of oily mops, sponges, and wiping rags in metal or other noncombustible containers. Any combustible oil used to excess increases the combustibility of the floor. Oil-soaked floors, the product of years of use, also show increased combustibility.

Floor waxes: Low-flash-point solvents are hazardous, especially when used with electric polishers. In such instances, ignition might result from friction and sparking. Water-emulsion waxes are preferable.

Furniture polishes: Furniture polishes containing oils subject to spontaneous heating become hazardous when rags that are saturated with these polishes are not disposed of properly. Such oil-soaked rags should be placed in metal or other noncombustible containers.

Nonhazardous cleaning agents: Flammable cleaning solvents need not be used since a number of nonhazardous cleaning agents are available. These relatively safe materials are stable and have high flash points and low toxicity. There are several commercial stable solvents available that have flash points ranging from 140 to 190°F (60 to 88°C) and have a comparatively low degree of toxicity. Safe materials are available for most of the preceding purposes.

Dust and Lint

A necessary procedure in many occupancies is the removal of combustible dust and lint accumulations from walls, ceilings, and exposed structural members. Unless this procedure is performed safely, as by vacuum cleaners or air-moving (blower and exhaust) systems, this procedure may present a fire or explosion hazard. In some cases, vacuum cleaning equipment must be equipped with dust ignition-proof motors to ensure safe operation in dust-ladened atmospheres.

Care should be taken not to dislodge into the atmosphere any appreciable quantities of combustible dust or lint which might ignite or form an explosive mixture with air. A lot of work can be eliminated by applying suction at locations where dust may escape from processing machinery, and conveying the aspirated dust to safely located collectors. Blowing down dust with compressed air may create dangerous dust clouds, and such cleaning should be done only when other methods cannot be used and after all possible sources of ignition have been eliminated. In most localities, it is possible to obtain the services of reliable professional industrial cleaning specialists to remove dust accumulations safely.

Exhaust Ducts and Related Equipment

The exhaust ducts from the hoods over cooking ranges, such as those found in facility cafeterias, present troublesome problems because grease condenses inside the ducts and on exhaust equipment. Grease accumulations can be ignited by sparks from the range or, more often, by small fires in overheated cooking oil or fat. Without these grease accumulations in the hood and duct, stovetop fires can often be extinguished or allowed to burn out without causing appreciable damage. Fires occur frequently in frying because cooking oils and fats are heated to their flash points and may reach their self-ignition temperatures when accidentally overheated or spilled on the hot stovetop.

Grease removal devices: All exhaust systems for kitchen cooking equipment must be equipped with grease removal devices. These include such items as grease extractors, grease filters, or special fans designed to remove grease vapors effectively and provide a fire barrier. Grease filters, including frames, and other grease removal devices should be made of noncombustible materials.

Ducts: There is no practical method for preventing all kitchen duct fires, but the danger can be minimized through a combination of precautions as outlined in NFPA 96, *Removal of Smoke and Grease-Laden Vapors from Commercial Cooking Equipment*. It is good practice to clean hoods, grease removal devices, fans, ducts, and associated equipment frequently. The exhaust system should be inspected daily or weekly, depending on its use, to determine if grease or other residues are accumulating in it.

Clean ducts are essential to firesafety, but they often remain dirty because cleaning them is a difficult and unpleasant job. One source of help is a commercial firm that specializes in this sort of work. In any case, never try burning the grease out; it is a dangerous practice, even though duct systems installed according to NFPA standards are designed to withstand burnout.

In cleaning the exhaust system, avoid using flammable solvents or other flammable cleaning aids. Do not start the cleaning process until all electrical switches, detection devices, and extinguishing system supply cylinders have been turned off or locked in a "shut" position. This will prevent both the exhaust fan and the fire extinguishing system (if the exhaust duct is equipped with one) from actuating accidentally. Once the cleaning process is completed, the switches and other controls should be returned to normal operating positions.

Satisfactory cleaning results have been obtained with a powder compound consisting of one part calcium hydroxide and two parts calcium carbonate. This compound saponifies the grease or oily sludge (i.e., converts it to soap), thus making it easier to remove and clean. The process requires proper ventilation. Another cleaning method is to loosen the grease with steam and then scrape the residue out of the duct. This has proved to be quite effective.

Spraying duct interiors with hydrated lime after cleaning is a fire prevention method used commercially. This procedure tends to saponify the grease and may facilitate subsequent cleaning, but it does not provide permanent fire retardency.

Other duct systems: All duct systems can accumulate dirt and whatever other material is dispersed in the facility. Frequent cleaning of these systems is necessary for good housekeeping. Filters that are changed frequently can help. Particular attention should be given to building ventilation systems, including fire cutoff devices. In today's tight building design, it has been shown that microorganisms can build up and cause problems in these systems, or illness. Dirty outlets on ceilings and walls are evidence of the effects of neglect.

The use of a professional cleaning company or specially trained employees should be considered to ensure proper handling of the dust and dirt from ducts. This is especially true if the dust is combustible or explosive, since special equipment is needed to clean this type of system.

OCCUPANCY AND PROCESS HOUSEKEEPING

Housekeeping programs must give special consideration to disposal of rubbish, control of smoking habits, and other housekeeping hazards.

Disposal of Rubbish

The proper handling and disposal of rubbish is an integral part of the housekeeping process, and its success depends primarily upon having and observing a satisfactory routine. The proper and regular disposal of combustible waste products is of the utmost importance.

In both industrial and commercial properties, the removal of combustible waste products at the end of each workday or at the end of each work shift is a common practice. In some properties, more frequent waste disposal is necessary. In others, the collection, storage, and disposal routine vary with the nature of the property use. In all cases, however, an adequate program for dealing with this problem is a firesafety essential. Keeping a place tidy also depends on providing enough wastebaskets, bins, cans and other proper containers so that building users will find tidiness convenient.

Receptacles: Noncombustible containers should be used for the disposal of waste and rubbish. This is true even of such small receptacles as ashtrays and wastebaskets and applies, of course, to the larger units found in commercial and industrial properties. Industrial waste barrels should be made of metal and equipped with fitted covers. Care should be taken to avoid mixing waste materials where such mixing introduces hazards of its own. (See Figure 2-34A.)

Plastic wastebaskets of varying sizes are readily available and are popular because they are quiet, attractive, and scratch and dent resistant; however, not all plastic baskets have the same burning characteristics. Some melt and burn readily, adding fuel to a fire and creating a comparatively serious fire exposure problem by collapsing and spilling their burning contents. This is also true of many plastic liners used for wastebaskets and receptacles. Other baskets may contribute relatively little fuel to the fire while maintaining their shape fairly well.

Segregation of waste: It is not good housekeeping practice to dump all manner of dry waste down refuse chutes or to place it in a common bin or storage receptacle. For example, combustible metal dusts and metal powders dumped into chutes may explode if ignited. Mercury batteries and pressurized containers, such as the ubiquitous aerosol can, may also explode when incinerated or mixed with rubbish that is subsequently burned. Precautions should be taken to keep combustible items separate from each other and from noncombustible items.

Requirements of the U.S. Environmental Protection Agency (EPA) and the state waste control departments must also be considered. Most chemicals must be handled in a specific prescribed manner. These rules are contained in the Resource Conservation and Recovery Act (RCRA) and the Hazardous Waste Amendment to that act (HSWA). Contact the EPA for further information.

*FIG. 2-34A. **Waste containers designed to snuff out accidental fires in their contents and to limit external surface temperatures to no more than 175°F (80°C) above room temperature. (Source: Justrite Mfg. Co.)***

Control of smoking: Smoking may be a difficult problem to handle, particularly because of the personal factors involved. It is a habit that is hard to break, even though it may put the smoker in direct conflict with the firesafety regulations and production standards in effect in various areas. When these areas contain flammable liquids or dusty and linty atmospheres, self-preservation alone makes smoking control relatively easy. However, control of smoking is also required in less obvious places, such as shipping and receiving areas, with their large quantities of loose packing materials, and storage areas, which may have high-piled concentrations of combustible materials. In these areas, carefully planned smoking regulations are necessary.

Smoking regulations should be specific as to location and, preferably, time. Areas in which smoking is permissible, as well as those in which it is limited or prohibited entirely, must be clearly marked by appropriate signs that leave no question as to what is allowed where. (See Figure 2-34B.)

In addition to sensible regulations, smoking control also requires adequate receptacles for spent smoking materials. Properly designed ashtrays are essential to safe smoking. They should be made of noncombustible materials, with grooves or snuffers that hold cigarettes securely. Their sides should be steep enough to force smokers to place cigarettes entirely within the ashtray. (See Figure 2-34C.) In industrial buildings, large containers of sand are often used to conveniently and safely extinguish and dispose of spent smoking materials.

Improperly designed ashtrays may constitute a hazard, particularly if they allow a lit cigarette or cigar to fall or roll away. A lighted butt also may easily come in contact with combustible materials and start a fire under certain circumstances.

The contents of ashtrays must be disposed of carefully because a live butt may well be mixed in with apparently innocuous ashes. If lighted smoking materials were to be

FIG. 2-34B. Examples of signs permitting or forbidding smoking in designated areas. (Source: Factory Mutual Research Corp.)

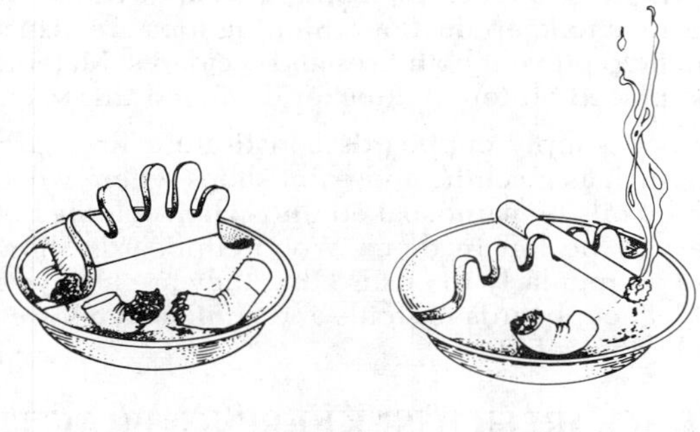

FIG. 2-34C. Two types of well-designed ash trays.

dumped into an ordinary wastebasket, they could set paper or some other piece of combustible rubbish on fire. To prevent this from happening, reserve special covered metal containers for discarded smoking materials only.

Industrial Housekeeping Hazards

Some industrial occupancies have special housekeeping problems inherent to the nature of their operations. For these particular problems, specific planning and arrangements are necessary.

Clean waste and rags: Clean cotton waste or wiping rags are generally considered to be mildly hazardous, chiefly because they are readily flammable when not baled, and there is always the likelihood that dirty waste may become mixed with them. The presence of dirty waste or small amounts of certain oils may lead to spontaneous heating. Reclaimed waste is considered somewhat more hazardous than new waste. It is common practice to handle clean waste in the same manner as dirty waste, although the fire hazard is relatively small.

Large supplies of clean waste are best kept in bins made entirely of metal, or of wood lined with metal and provided with covers that are normally kept closed. Several bins may be provided where the supplies are large or where different kinds of waste are kept. The covers on such bins should be counterweighted so that they may be readily raised and lowered. The counterweight ropes can have fusible links to ensure that the covers are closed automatically in the event of fire.

Local supplies of clean waste are usually kept in small, properly marked waste cans. Providing local supply points for clean waste can help eliminate the practice of keeping waste in clothes lockers, drawers, benches, and similar locations. If clean waste is put in such places, workers may mistakenly believe that other, more oily waste is also allowed there when, in fact, the combination of the two may result in fire. These same policies should apply to reused (clean) cotton gloves and may also apply to cotton coveralls and uniforms.

Coatings and lubricants: Paints, greases, and similar combustibles are widely used at industrial occupancies, and a good housekeeping program will make sure that their combustible residues are collected and disposed of safely. The discharge of vapors from spray booths should be so arranged that the vapors are conducted directly to the outside and the residues accumulate safely. Use of wash-water spray booths for painting should also be considered.

Drip pans: Drip pans are essential at many locations, notably under motors, machines using cutting oils, and bearings. They are also used with borings and turnings that may contain oil. Drip pans should also be used wherever flammable and combustible liquids are dispensed. Drip pans should be made of noncombustible material and contain an oil-absorbing compound. At many industrial occupancies, commercial oil-absorbing compounds consisting largely of diatomaceous earth are used instead of sawdust or sand. The regular removal of oil-soaked material is recommended.

Flammable liquid spills: Flammable liquid spills may be anticipated wherever such products are handled or used, and some means of coping with these spills must be kept on hand. These include a supply of suitable absorptive material and special tools to help limit the spill. Workers should understand and promptly take the steps needed to cut off sources of ignition, ventilate the area, and safely dissipate any flammable vapors.

Flammable and corrosive liquids waste disposal: The disposal of combustible liquid waste often presents a troublesome problem. Any waste material that is a corrosive liquid (pH <2 or >12.5), or is a liquid with a flash point of 140°F (60°C) or less, is considered a hazardous waste under the Federal Resource Conservation and Recovery Act (RCRA). Drums of this waste must be labeled in accordance with this act. This includes labeling the liquid as hazardous waste and including the proper EPA codes. These waste products must be disposed of in a facility that is licensed to handle this waste. Care should be taken to ensure that the facility taking the waste will properly dispose of it.

Oily waste: Oily wiping rags, sawdust, lint, clothing, and other items are highly dangerous, particularly if they contain oils subject to spontaneous heating. To dispose of all such materials in ordinary quantities, a standard waste can that has been listed and labeled by testing organizations is best. For large amounts, heavy metal barrels with covers are ideal. Good practice calls for cans containing oily waste to be emptied daily and for wiping rags to be kept in covered metal containers until they can be laundered. (See Figure 2-34D.)

Oil puddling: Accumulations of oil can present a housekeeping problem at industrial locations where a considerable amount of oil is used. Poor maintenance of industrial hydraulic elevator installations may result in oil leaks which

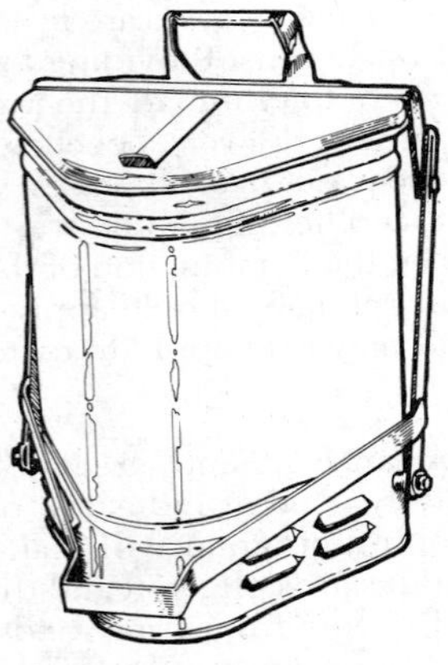

FIG. 2-34D. A portable waste can that is equipped with a self-closing cover. This type of container can be used to store oily waste materials, particularly if they are subject to spontaneous heating. (Source: The Protectoseal Co.)

eventually form puddles on the elevator machine room floors and in the bottoms of hoistway pits. Although most oils used in hydraulic elevator systems have high flash points, any combustible oil can be a source of fire, particularly when it is found in puddles that contain accumulations of debris. Puddled oil and materials used to absorb oil spills should be disposed of in metal barrels.

Packing materials: Almost all packing materials used today are combustible and, consequently, hazardous. Plastic pellets and rigid forms, excelsior, shredded paper, sawdust, burlap and other such materials should be treated as clean waste. However, large quantities may have to be kept in special vaults or storerooms. Automatic sprinklers are the best protection for areas where considerable quantities of packing materials are stored or handled.

Used or waste packing materials and the crating materials from receiving and shipping rooms must be removed and disposed of as promptly as possible in order to minimize the danger of fire. Ideally, the packing and unpacking processes should be conducted in an orderly manner so that excessive quantities of packing materials do not become strewn about the premises. A specially marked (or identified) area should be provided to accumulate this material. This area should be cleaned frequently and the debris removed to an outside storage receptacle.

Lockers and Cupboards

Many industrial facilities provide their employees with lockers in which to put their personal belongings. These lockers may present a fire hazard if they are untidy or are used as general storerooms for such waste material as oily rags and cloths or paint-smeared clothing. These items may ignite spontaneously or they may be accidentally ignited by matches and imperfectly extinguished pipes and cigars that employees inadvertently leave in their lockers.

Wood lockers can ignite and spread fire. Metal ones are preferred, but they should be inspected regularly. Metal lockers may contain a fire if they are of solid construction, including fronts and bottoms, partitions, and backs. Backs and partitions made of expanded metal or wire screen may allow fire to spread unchecked and should not be used.

Lockers that are arranged in two tiers, i.e., one upon the other, are generally unsatisfactory. They do not hold clothes without mussing them and it often becomes the habit of those using such lockers to keep their clothes outside the locker or to throw them haphazardly into the locker, thus increasing the danger of spontaneous heating when such clothing is spotted with oil or paint.

Some lockers are provided with mechanical exhaust ventilation. Where this is true, NFPA 91, *Blower and Exhaust Systems for Dust, Stock and Vapor Removal or Conveying*, should be followed to avoid spreading a fire that originates in a locker.

Industrial plants that furnish and wash their employees' protective clothing may use a system of wire baskets, one per employee, suspended from the ceiling by a small chain running over a pulley, instead of lockers. This method has proved successful in maintaining cleanliness and thereby reducing the fire hazard.

Where automatic sprinklers are installed, lockers must have expanded metal or screen tops to enable water from the sprinklers to reach the contents. Paper can be pasted on the tops to keep dust out. Sloping tops are also advisable to help prevent both fires and accidents. Material cannot be placed on top of a locker designed this way.

Wood supply cupboards constitute a fire hazard in places such as machine and paint shops where woodwork becomes oil- or paint-soaked and where clothes or oily waste may be left in them. Wood cupboards should be inspected regularly to ensure that they are always clean. The ideal cupboards for tools and similar items are made entirely of steel.

OUTDOOR HOUSEKEEPING PRACTICES

Good housekeeping practices are as essential out-of-doors as they are indoors. Failure to comply with good housekeeping practices out-of-doors may threaten the security of exposed structures and goods stored outside. The accumulation of rubbish and waste and the growth of tall grass and weeds adjacent to buildings or stored goods are probably the most common hazards. A regular program for policing the grounds is essential.

Grass and Weed Control

Tall grass, dry weeds, and bushes around buildings, along highways, on railroad properties, and along the streets of large industrial and commercial complexes present a definite fire hazard. To reduce this hazard, those responsible for maintaining these properties have tried to control or destroy such vegetation.

One way to get rid of unwanted vegetation is to apply a chemical solution which poisons the weeds. Among the chemicals used are chlorate compounds, particularly sodium chlorate. Unfortunately, those who use chlorate compounds do not always realize that they are oxidizing agents. When these compounds come in contact with combustible materials, they virtually prime those materials for a fire or explosion. During hot periods in the summer, large numbers of fires have resulted from the use of sodium chlorate solutions on dry grass and weeds. Fires have also been reported in buildings and other structures in which such solutions have been spilled. Chlorate compounds spilled on clothing may present a danger to personnel, too.

There are weed killers that are not toxic and do not pose a fire hazard. Calcium chloride and agricultural borax, applied dry or in solution, are effective nonhazardous weed killers, as are various proprietary solutions. A number of commercial chemical weed killers, such as ammonium sulfamate, have little or no fire hazard and only a slight toxic hazard. Sodium arsenite and other compounds containing arsenic are efficient herbicides, but they are poisonous and not generally recommended.

The amounts of various chemicals needed to effectively kill weeds and the duration of their effect vary, depending on the weed-killing agent used, the character of the vegetation, the climate, and the soil. Manufacturers' directions indicate the proper amounts to be used under various conditions.

Another way to remove vegetation is to burn it. This may be done only where environmental regulations permit outdoor burning and must be carefully controlled. Adequate fire extinguishing equipment must be readily available at all times. Using this method, grass and weeds are usually cut down, collected in piles, and ignited. When the grass is too damp to propagate fire easily, flame-throwing torches may be used on the piles. However, these torches introduce a hazard if not carefully operated.

All burning introduces a hazard. Grass fires frequently spread out of control and ignite nearby buildings. To avoid this hazard, controlled burning should only be done at certain times of the year and then under the direct supervision of the fire department.

Fire authorities issue fire permits, where permissible, to help them control burning. These permits provide the authorities with an opportunity to educate the public in safe burning. They also help the fire department limit burning to nonhazardous periods of the year and better manage burning done during the hazardous periods.

Outdoor Storage

Goods stored outdoors should be properly separated from buildings of combustible construction and from other combustible storage that might constitute an exposure hazard. These separations should be maintained by the housekeeping staff, who must see to it that they are never blocked, even temporarily, by such things as contractors' shacks, discarded crates, pallets, or other combustibles. Obstructed aisles could hamper fire fighting operations if the need for them ever arises. Passageways between storage piles should also be unobstructed and clear of combustibles.

Proper housekeeping also requires that smoking in outdoor storage areas be controlled. Suitable signs should be posted and large noncombustible receptacles should be provided for the disposal of smoking materials before entering a "no smoking" area.

Outdoor Rubbish Disposal

Combustible waste materials stored outdoors to await subsequent disposal as rubbish should be placed not less than 20 ft (6 m), and preferably 50 ft (15 m), from buildings, and at least 50 ft (15 m) from public roadways and sources of ignition, such as incinerators. They should also be enclosed with a secure noncombustible fence of adequate height.

The most satisfactory solution to the rubbish disposal problem is regular collection and removal from the premises. Burning rubbish is generally unsafe and is not permitted in built-up urban areas.

If rubbish must be burned outdoors, it should be done in the early morning or at night, because the night moisture reduces the chance that sparks will ignite combustibles in the surrounding area. This is the reasoning behind certain fire department and forest service regulations that limit outdoor burning to certain days or times of day. Of course, there are some times when outdoor burning is strictly prohibited. Most parts of the United States and Canada experience days when things are so dry that any burning is dangerous.

Even when rubbish is not burned outdoors, it can present a fire hazard. All rubbish dumps, even landfills, are susceptible to fire. And sparks and flying brands from dump fires can carry the fire long distances. This is also true of sparks and brands produced by bonfires and incinerators that lack adequate spark arresters.

INSPECTION

Housekeeping inspections are an important part of an overall housekeeping program. This type of program should be combined with a complete safety inspection program. This type of inspection has four main objectives:

1. Maintain a safe work environment.
2. Control unsafe actions of employees.
3. Maintain operations profitability (and product quality).
4. Maintain operations to meet or exceed acceptable safety and government standards.

Although the word "housekeeping" is never mentioned, it does not take much imagination to see good housekeeping is involved in each objective. Good housekeeping is an essential part of any successful safety program, and that includes the firesafety program.

There are several types of inspections. Some involve preventive maintenance of equipment, such as lubrication of equipment or static grounding continuity. Others involve fire equipment inspections. But most important is a regular inspection by the supervisor and top management.

These inspections must be well defined. The program should include what areas are to be inspected, how often the inspections should be made, what is acceptable performance, and who will conduct the inspections.

When inspections are conducted, a checklist may be valuable, such as is shown in Figure 2-34E.

In order to prevent inspections from taking considerable time, the inspector should:

1. Have a definite schedule.
2. Inspect only one part of the department at a time.
3. Rotate inspection responsibilities among department members.
4. Make a point of looking for housekeeping problems as part of a daily routine.

Trading inspections between departments can help increase inspection effectiveness; monotony can distort evaluation of real problem areas.

SUMMARY

A well-planned housekeeping program will yield the following benefits:

- Reduced operating costs
- Increased production
- Improved production control
- Conservation of material and parts
- Reduced production time

FIRE PREVENTION CHECKLIST

Electrical Equipment

NO MAKESHIFT WIRING
EXTENSION CORDS SERVICEABLE
MOTORS AND TOOLS FREE OF DIRT AND GREASE
LIGHTS CLEAR OF COM

CIRCUITS PROPERLY FUSED OR OTHERWISE PROTECTED
EQUIPMENT APPROVED FOR USE IN HAZARDOUS AREAS (IF REQUIRED)
GROUND CONNECTIONS CLEAN AND TIGHT AND HAVE ELECTRICAL CONTINUITY

Friction

MACHINERY PROPERLY LUBRICATED

MACHINERY PROPERLY ADJUSTED AND/OR ALIGNED

Special Fire-Hazard Materials

STORAGE OF SPECIAL FLAMMABLES ISOLATED

NONMETAL STOCK FREE OF TRAMP METAL

Welding and CUTTING

AREA SURVEYED FOR FIRE SAFETY

COMBUSTIBLES REMOVED OR COVERED
PERMIT ISSUED

Open Flames

KEPT AWAY FROM SPRAY ROOMS AND BOOTHS
NO GAS LEAKS

PORTABLE TORCHES CLEAR OF FLAMMABLE SURFACES

Portable Heaters

SET UP WITH AMPLE HORIZONTAL AND OVERHEAD CLEARANCES
SECURED AGAINST TIPPING OR UPSET
COMBUSTIBLES REMOVED OR COVERED

SAFELY MOUNTED ON NONCOMBUSTIBLE SURFACE
NOT USED AS RUBBISH BURNERS
USE OF STEEL DRUMS PROHIBITED

Hot Surfaces

HOT PIPES CLEAR OF COMBUSTIBLE MATERIALS
AMPLE CLEARANCE AROUND BOILERS AND FURNANCES

SOLDERING IRONS KEPT OFF COMBUSTIBLE SURFACES
ASHES IN METAL CONTAINERS

Smoking and Matches

"NO SMOKING" AND "SMOKING" AREAS CLEARLY MARKED
BUTT CONTAINERS AVAILABLE AND SERVICEABLE

NO DISCARDED SMOKING MATERIALS IN PROHIBITED AREAS

Spontaneous Ignition

FLAMMABLE WASTE MATERIAL IN CLOSED, METAL CONTAINERS
FLAMMABLE WASTE MATERIAL CONTAINERS EMPTIED FREQUENTLY

PILED MATERIAL, COOL, DRY, AND WELL VENTILATED
TRASH RECEPTACLES EMPTIED DAILY

Static Electricity

FLAMMABLE LIQUID DISPENSING VESSELS GROUNDED OR BONDED
MOVING MACHINERY GROUNDED

PROPER HUMIDITY MAINTAINED

Housekeeping

NO ACCUMULATIONS OF RUBBISH
SAFE STORAGE OF FLAMMABLES
PASSAGEWAYS CLEAR OF OBSTACLES
AUTOMATIC SPRINKLERS UNOBSTRUCTED

PREMISES FREE OF UNNECESSARY COMBUSTIBLE MATERIALS
NO LEAKS OR DRIPPING OF FLAMMABLES AND FLOOR FREE OF SPILLS
FIRE DOORS UNBLOCKED AND OPERATING FREELY WITH FUSIBLE LINKS INTACT

Extinguishing Equipment

PROPER TYPE
IN PROPER LOCATION
ACCESS UNOBSTRUCTED
CLEARLY MARKED

IN WORKING ORDER
SERVICE DATE CURRENT
PERSONNEL TRAINED IN USE OF EQUIPMENT

FIG. 2-34E. A sample checklist can serve as a guide for the supervisor in drawing up an inspection list. It should be reviewed regularly to keep it up to date.

- Better use of space
- Improved traffic flow (i.e., permits faster travel)
- Reduced accident rate
- Reduced fire hazards
- Compliance with OSHA Act

BIBLIOGRAPHY

NFPA Codes, Standards, and Recommended Practices

Reference to the following NFPA codes, standards, and recommended practices will provide further information on housekeeping practices discussed in this chapter. (See the latest *NFPA Catalog* for availability of current editions of the following documents.)

NFPA 13A, *Inspection, Testing, and Maintenance of Sprinkler Systems*.

NFPA 82, *Incinerators, Waste and Linen Handling Systems and Equipment*.

NFPA 91, *Blower and Exhaust Systems for Dust, Stock and Vapor Removal or Conveying*.

NFPA 96, *Removal of Smoke and Grease-Laden Vapors from Commercial Cooking Equipment*.

Additional Reading

Cote, A. E., ed., "Industrial Housekeeping Practices," *Industrial Fire Protection Handbook*, 3rd ed., National Fire Protection Association, Quincy, MA, 1990, pp. 1049-1063.

Feldman, E. B., *Housekeeping Handbook for Institutions, Business and Industry*, Frederick Fell, NY, 1979.

Garside, R., "Maintaining Maintenance in Hazardous Areas," *Control and Instrumentation*, Vol. 18, No. 11, 1986, pp. 35, 37.

"Good Housekeeping," *National Safety and Health News*, Vol. 134, No. 3, Sept. 1986, pp. 28-32.

Higgins, L., R., and Morrow, L. C., eds, "Sanitation and Housekeeping," *Maintenance Engineering Handbook*, 4th ed., McGraw-Hill, NY, 1988.

Higgins, L. R., *Maintenance Engineering Handbook*, 44th ed., McGraw Hill, New York, Ny

"How to Apply Good Housekeeping," *The Handbook of Property Conservation*, Ch. 23, Factory Mutual System, Norwood, MA, 1983, pp. 189-193.

Lee, R., *Building Maintenance Management*, 3rd ed., Collins, London, 1987.

Phillips, C., *Plant Engineer's Desk Handbook*, Prentice-Hall, Englewood Cliffs, NJ, 1980, pp. 161-173.

Rosaler, R. C., Rice, J. O., and Hicks, T. G., eds, *Industrial Maintenance Reference Guide*, McGrow-Hill, NY, 1987.

Schultz, J. F., "Standards for Refuse-Handling in Apartment Houses," *Fire Journal*, Vol. 68, No. 2, Mar. 1974, pp. 82-86.

GRINDING PROCESSES

Revised by Delwyn D. Bluhm

This chapter discusses the fire hazards of grinding processes. Grinding (or pulverizing) is an industrial process in which materials are reduced to very small particles. Sometimes the grinding process of combustible and some normally noncombustible materials produces a highly explosive dust that is hazardous when dispersed in critical concentrations in air. A serious dust fire or explosion can begin either in the grinding equipment itself or in the environment surrounding the equipment. Examples of materials having combustible dust hazards are wheat flour, wood flour, sulfur, starch, coal, some plastics, aluminum, and magnesium.

According to experts[1] in coal mining, electric power generation, grain handling, plastics, chemicals, wood products, and metal powders industries, dust explosions and fires have been a continuing problem. Various preventive and protective measures must be taken to ensure safety, utilizing both existing technologies and new data for practical designs of safe new industrial equipment.

It is important to distinguish the processes used to reduce the size of materials by grinding from those processes which employ abrasive wheels, disks, or drums to prepare surfaces or shape articles of wood, metal, or plastic. The latter processes could produce explosive dusts under certain conditions. However, those operations normally are conducted in environments where there is little likelihood that dust concentrations will reach the lower explosive limit (LEL). This chapter, therefore, is concerned only with the hazards of milling or grinding operations involving large quantities of potentially explosive materials.

Section 1, Chapter 5, "Explosions" and Section 1, Chapter 6, "Theory of Fire and Explosion Control" present guidelines for grinding hazards control. Section 8, Chapter 3, "Food Processing" and Section 2, Chapter 21, "Woodworking Processes" offer additional insight into the hazards of organic dusts. See also Section 2, Chapter 28, "Storage and Handling of Grain Mill Products."

Delwyn D. Bluhm, Ph.D., P.E., is senior engineer and manager of engineering for Ames Laboratory and Institute for Physical Research and Technology, operated by Iowa State University, Ames, IA.

GENERAL

Processes

Grinding operations are performed either wet or dry. Water is an excellent medium for wet grinding, though other liquids are sometimes used. Kerosene, for example, is used for the wet milling of magnesium. Because dust fires or explosions are the major hazards of grinding processes, dry grinding is emphasized in this chapter.

Materials

Agricultural products, such as wheat, corn, and other grains, present explosion hazards both during storage and processing into flour or starch. Wood flour, finely divided sawdust, sulfur, coal, and some plastics present the same hazards as magnesium and aluminum. An explosion or fire can originate in the process equipment itself or in the ambient environment into which dust may escape and accumulate.

Actual occurrences, reinforced by laboratory tests, have demonstrated that finely divided particles of almost any readily oxidized material suspended in proper concentration in air will ignite and explode or burn. Table 2-35A classifies 59 different materials into three groups according to the range of explosibility. The table includes nine different plastic dusts, but does not cover the entire range of explosive plastic dusts. Table 2-35B gives the explosion characteristics of a variety of agricultural and industrial dusts. Materials other than those mentioned also may be explosive under proper conditions of particle size and oxygen availability.

Table 2-35A also cites low, moderate, and high maximum rates of pressure rise for selected explosive materials.

The maximum rate of pressure rise is calculated from the steepest part of the pressure versus time curve. As with the maximum explosion pressure, appropriate adjustments need to be made if the dispersing air effectively increases the ambient pressure. The average rate of pressure rise is also calculated from the pressure versus time curve. An

TABLE 2-35A. ***Classification of Explosive Material According to Rates of Pressure Rise***

Class A Materials (Low maximum rates of pressure rise†)	
Metal Dusts	**Miscellaneous Dusts**
Antimony	Anthracite
Cadmium	Carbon Black
Chromium	Coffee
Copper	Coke, low volatile
Iron (impure)	Graphite
Lead	Leather
Tungsten	Tea
Class B Materials (Moderate maximum rates of pressure rise†)	
Metal dusts, or Powders	Polyethylene
Iron (carbonyl, electrolytic or H_2,reduced)	Polystyrene
Manganese	Urea—Melamine
Tin	Vinyl butryal
Zinc	
	Miscellaneous Dusts
Grains, Spices, etc.—Dusts	Bituminous Coal
Alfalfa	Cork
Cocoa	Calcium Lignosulfonic Acid
Grain Dust and Flour	Coumarone Indene
Mixed Grains	Dextrin
Rice	Lignin
Soy Bean	Lignite
Spices	Peat
Starch	Powdered Drugs
Yeast	Pyrethrum
	Shellac
Plastic Dusts	Silicon
Cellulose Acetate	Sulfur
Methyl Metharylate	Tung
Phenolformaldehyde	Wood Flour
Phthalic anhydride and its resins	
Class C Materials (High maximum rates of pressure rise§)	
Metal Dusts	*Sorbic Acid
Aluminum	*Titanium
*Stamped Aluminum	*Zirconium
Magnesium	Some Metal Hydrides
Magnesium—aluminum alloys	

*These are exceptionally fast.
†≤7300 psi/sec (500,000 kPa/sec) measured via the Hartman apparatus.
±7300 to 22000 psi/sec (500,000 to 151,000 kPa/sec) measured via the Hartman apparatus.
§>22,000 psi/sec (151,000 kPa/sec) measured via the Hartman apparatus.

approximate correlation often exists between the average and maximum rates of pressure rise, but the latter is preferred when assessing practical needs. The average rate of pressure rise can be affected by slow development of the explosion and is usually one-half to one-third the value for the maximum rate of pressure rise.

The United States Bureau of Mines has developed three additional measures of the relative explosion hazard: the ignition sensitivity (IS), the explosion severity (ES), and the explosibility index (EI). Each of these is a dimensionless value derived by comparing the measured explosibility parameters for a given dust, as described above, with those of Pittsburgh coal dust. The relative explosion hazards may be derived using the following formulas:

$$IS = \frac{\min T_i' \times \min E_i' \times \min C_c'}{\min T_i \times \min E_i \times \min C_c}$$

$$ES = \frac{\max T_c' \times \max p'}{\max T_c \times \max p}$$

$$ES = IS \times ES$$

where

IS = Ignition sensitivity
ES = Explosion severity
EI = Explosibility index
T_i = Ignition temperature
E_i = Ignition energy
C_c = Explosive concentration
P_c = Explosive pressure
p = Rate of pressure rise

(Prime parameters represent Pittsburgh coal dust; unprimed paramaters represent dust samples.)

Known values for these quantities are included in Table 2-35B. In the absence of a sound theoretical basis for predicting explosion hazards of dusts, the explosibility index provides a useful evaluation of relative explosibility. An empirical correlation between the U.S. Bureau of Mines indices and a descriptive categorization, the explosion hazard rating, is shown in Table 2-35C.

TABLE 2-35C. ***Correlation Between Descriptive Categories for Dust Explosions and U.S. Bureau of Mines Indices****

Type of Explosion	Ignition Sensitivity	Explosion Severity	Explosibility Index
Weak	<0.2	<0.5	<0.1
Moderate	0.2–1.0	0.5–1.0	0.1–1.0
Strong	1.0–5.0	1.0–2.0	1.0–10
Severe	>5.0	>2.0	>10

* (From: Jacobson *et al.*, U.S. Bureau of Mines, RI5753, "The Explosibility of Agricultural Dusts.")

Materials are ground either in batches or continuously. Continuous processes may be either open or closed circuit. (See Figures 2-35A and 2-35B.) In air-swept mills, air is blown in at one end and the ground material is removed at the other end in air suspension. Batch mills are generally used only where small quantities are processed, due to the high labor costs for charging and discharging the mill.

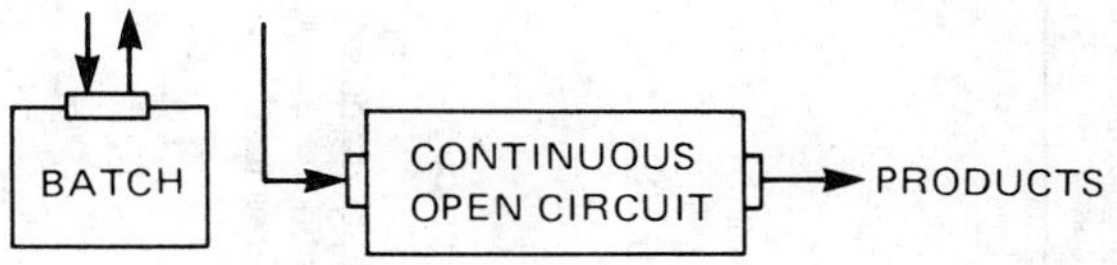

FIG. 2-35A. ***Batch and continuous grinding systems.***

Grinding equipment is classified according to the manner in which force is applied to the material. The material may be ground: (1) between two solid surfaces, (2) by being forced against one solid surface (jet mill method), (3) by the action of the surrounding medium, or (4) by the

TABLE 2-35B. ***Explosion Characteristics of Various Dusts***

(Compiled from the following reports of the U.S Department of Interior, Bureau of Mines; RI 5753, The Explosibility of Agricultural Dusts; RI 6516, Explosibility of Metal Powders; RI 5971, Explosibility of Dusts Used in the Plastics Industry; RI 6597, Explosibility of Carbonaceous Dusts; RI 7132, Dust Explosibility of Chemicals, Drugs, Dyes and Pesticides, and RI 1200, Explosibility of Miscellaneous Dusts.)

Type of Dust	E_i Explosibility Index	I_s Ignition Sensitivity	E_s Explosion Severity	P_e Maximum Explosion Pressure Rise		p Max Rate of Pressure Rise		T_c Ignition Temperature: Cloud		Layer		E_i Min. Cloud Ignition Energy	C_e Min. Explosion Conc.		Limiting Oxygen Percentage* (Spark Ignition)
				psig	kPa	psi/sec	kPa/sec	°C	°F	°C	°F	joules	oz/cu ft	g/m3	
Agricultural Dusts															
Alfalfa Meal	0.1	1.2	66	455	1,100	7585	530	986	—	—	0.320	0.105	105	—	
Cocoa bean shell	13.7	3.6	3.8	77	531	3,300	22754	470	878	370	698	0.030	0.040	40	—
Coffee, raw bean	<0.1	0.1	0.1	33	228	150	1034	650	1202	280	536	0.320	0.150	150	C17
Cornstarch, commercial product	9.5	2.8	3.4	106	731	7,500	51713	400	752	—	—	0.040	0.045	45	—
Cork dust	>10.0	3.6	3.3	96	662	7,500	51713	460	860	860	210	0.035	0.035	35	—
Grain dust, winter wheat, corn, oats	9.2	2.8	3.3	131	903	7,000	48265	430	806	230	446	0.030	0.055	55	—
Peat, sphagnum, sun dried	2.0	2.0	1.0	104	717	2,200	15169	460	860	240	464	0.050	0.045	45	—
Pyrethrum, ground flower leaves	0.4	0.6	0.6	95	655	1,500	10344	460	860	210	410	0.080	0.100	100	—
Rice	0.3	0.5	0.5	47	324	700	4827	510	950	450	842	0.100	0.085	85	—
Soy flour	0.7	0.6	1.1	94	648	800	5116	550	1022	340	644	0.100	0.060	60	C15
Wheat flour	4.1	1.5	2.7	97	669	2,800	19306	440	824	440	824	0.060	0.050	50	—
Yeast, torula	2,2	1.6	1.4	123	848	3,500	24133	520	968	260	500	0.050	0.050	50	—
Carbonaceous Dusts															
Charcoal, hardwood mixture	1.3	1.4	0.9	83	572	1,300	8964	530	986	180	356	0.020	0.140	140	—
Coke, petroleum	0.1†	0.1†	—	—	—	200	1379	670	1238	—	—	‡	1.000	1005	—
Graphite	0.1§	0.1§	—	—	—	—	—	§	—	580	1076	—	—	—	—
Lignite, California	>10	5.0	3.8	94	648	8,000	55160	450	842	200	392	0.030	0.030	30	—
Metals															
Cadmium, atomized (98% Cd)	—	—	—	7	48	100	690	570	1058	250	482	4,000	—	—	—
Iron, Carbonyl (99% Fe)	1.6	3.0	0.5	43	296	2,400	16548	320	608	310	590	0.020	0.105	105	C10
Lead, atomized (99% Pb)	—	—	—	—	—	—	—	710	1310	270	518	—	—	—	—
Magnesium, milled, Grade B	>10	3.0	7.4	116	800	15,000	103425	560	1040	430	806	0.040	0.030	30	—
Manganese	0.1	0.1	0.7	53	365	4,900	33786	460	860	240	464	0.305	0.125	125	—
Tantalum	0.1	0.1	0.7	55	379	4,400	30338	630	1166	300	572	0.120	<0.200	<200	—
Thermoplastic Resins and Molding Compounds															
Cellulose acetate	>10	8.0	1.6	85	586	3,600	24822	420	788	—	—	0.015	0.040	40	C14
Methyl methacrylate polymer	6.3	7.0	0.9	84	579	2,000	13790	480	896	—	—	0.020	0.030	30	C11
Polyethylene, low-pressure process	>10.0	22.4	2.3	80	552	7,500	51713	450	842	—	—	0.010	0.020	20	—
Polystyrene molding compound	>10.0	6.0	2.0	77	531	5,000	34475	560	1040	—	—	0.040	0.015	15	C14
Thermosetting Resins and Molding Compounds															
Phenolformaldehyde	>10.0	9.3	1.4	77	531	3,500	24133	580	1076	—	—	0.015	0.025	25	C17
Urea formaldehyde molding compound, Grade II, fine	1.0	0.6	1.7	89	614	3,600	24822	460	860	—	—	0.080	0.085	85	C17
Special Resins and Molding Compounds															
Lignin, hydrolized-wood-type, fines	>10.0	5.6	2.7	102	703	5,000	34475	450	842	—	—	0.020	0.040	40	C17
Rubber, synthetic, hard, contains 33% sulfur	>10.0	7.0	1.5	93	641	3,100	21375	320	608	—	—	0.030	0.030	30	C15
Shellac	>10.0	25.2	1.4	73	503	3,600	24822	400	752	—	—	0.010	0.020	20	C14

* Numbers in this column indicate oxygen percentage while the prefix indicates the diluent gas. For example, the entry "C17" means dilution to an oxygen content of 17 percent with carbon as the diluent gas.
† 0.1 designates materials presenting primarily a fire hazard as ignition of the dust cloud is not obtained by the spark or flame source but only by the intense heated surface source.
‡ Guncotton ignition source. § No ignition.

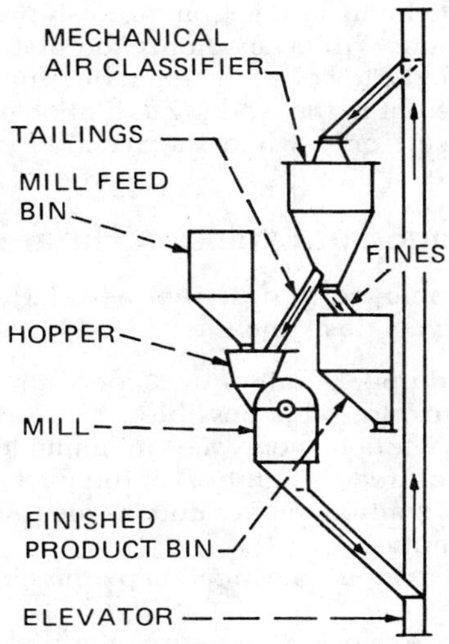

FIG. 2-35B. A hammer mill in a closed circuit with air classifier.

nonmechanical introduction of energy, such as thermal shock, explosive shattering, or electrohydraulic processes. This chapter is concerned mainly with the first two methods. Also associated with grinding equipment are classifiers which separate out the fine product and return the coarse mill for regrinding.

Fire and Explosion Safety

All mills that produce combustible dusts should be isolated. If possible, they should be in separate, detached, one-story, noncombustible buildings entirely above grade. Adequate explosion venting is essential. The surfaces of interior walls and equipment should be smooth to minimize dust accumulations and facilitate cleaning. If a milling operation must be located in a multi-purpose building, it should be in a room with at least one exterior wall that can be arranged to relieve explosion pressures, and the interior walls around the mill area should be of explosion-resistant construction.

Although the mill is the source of combustible dust and may also provide an ignition source, explosions generally develop somewhere in the system downstream of the mill. Also, mills are generally constructed substantially enough to withstand explosion pressures. Explosion venting is needed where this is not the case.

As much as practical, nonsparking construction materials should be used to minimize sparks. Magnetic separators should be installed in front of mills to remove foreign ferrous metal, and screens should be used to remove rock and other nonferrous foreign material. Mills should be grounded to minimize the possibility of ignition by static sparks. Open flames and smoking should not be permitted, and welding and cutting equipment should be used only when the mill is shut down and the area has been made entirely dust free.

Good housekeeping is essential. Although well-designed grinding mills minimize dust leakage and reduce necessary cleaning, it is not always possible to maintain absolutely tight systems. Vacuum cleaning is the best way to remove any dust which escapes into the room, as it prevents the dust from forming explosive clouds.

For grinding operations where ignition sources are difficult to control, the equipment may be protected by introducing a continuous flow of inert gas, such as carbon dioxide, nitrogen, or flue gas. This will keep the normal oxygen content within the equipment sufficiently low to prevent an explosion.

GRINDING HAZARDS

The hazards of grinding operations lie in the fact that the process produces very fine particles of readily oxidized materials that may be mixed with process or environmental air in flammable or explosive concentrations. To separate the properly sized material from the coarser particles being fed into the mill, a system of classifiers is used. For the most part, classifiers are based on the force of gravity and the principles of air drag and particle inertia. A continuous flow of air passes through the mill, regulated so that particles of the desired fineness are carried through to a collecting bin or compartment, while coarser particles fall out and return to the mill for further grinding. This principle is illustrated in Figure 2-35B.

There are several different types of air classifiers, some of which may be external to the mill as in Figure 2-35B. Others may be internal as in the ring-roller mill illustrated in Figure 2-35C. Here the whizzers are rotating blades whose centrifugal action throws the coarser particles outward, permitting them to drop back onto the grinding surfaces. The finished product is carried through an outlet by the airstream.

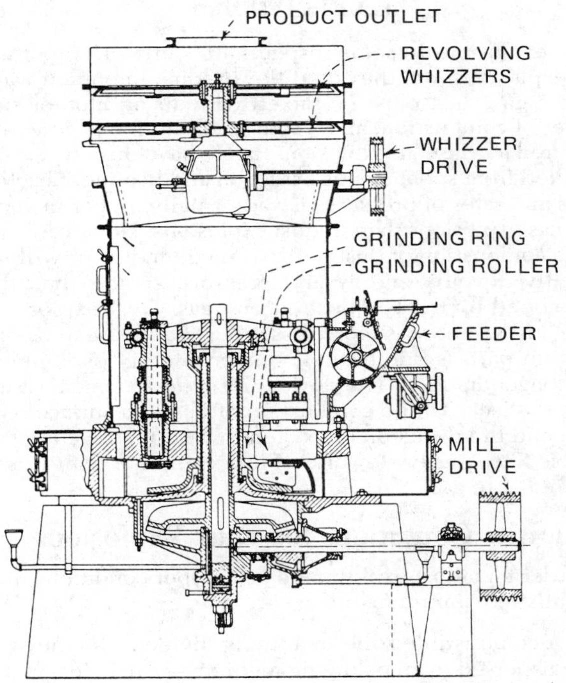

FIG. 2-35C. A Raymond high-side mill with internal whizzer classifier.

Theoretically, the process airstream should be fully and tightly enclosed so that it does not carry the finished product or unwanted dust into the atmosphere surrounding the mill. In practice, this is rather difficult to accomplish, and dust builds up in the structure housing the mill. There are, then, two distinct hazards. One is that an explosion may occur within the milling system, and the other is that an explosion may occur in the structure. All that is required is a critical concentration of the material in air and an ignition source.

The lower limit of flammability will vary from one material to another. For some, such as phthalic anhydride, shellac, aluminum stearate, and phenothiazine, it may be as low as 0.015 oz/cu ft (15 g/m^3). For zinc, it may be as much as 0.5 oz/cu ft (500 g/m^3). Upper flammability limits for dusts, i.e., the concentration above which an explosion will not occur, are poorly defined, not usually reproducible, and not yet determined for many dusts. Therefore, any concentration above the lower limit should be considered potentially explosive. The minimum electric spark energy required for ignition of a dust cloud can vary from as little as 10 mJ (millijoule) to as much as 4000 J (Joules).

Ignition sources, too, can vary widely. Since a bit of metal accidentally entering the mill may cause a spark as it strikes against one of the grinding surfaces, mills should be equipped with magnetic or mechanical separators to remove any tramp metal from the feed system. Sparking may also be caused by tools made of ferrous metals. Other possible ignition sources are static electricity, hot surfaces, friction, open flames, welding arcs, and personnel smoking in the area.

CHARACTERISTICS OF DUST EXPLOSIONS

Dust explosions in some respects are similar to vapor and gas explosions, but they do differ in some important ways. Like a gas, dust must be mixed with air or another supporter of combustion, and a source of ignition is generally required to cause an explosion. Rarely have dust explosions resulted from spontaneous oxidation and heating. Reaction rates and rates of pressure rise are usually higher in vapor and gas explosions than in dust explosions. However, complete combustion of dust in a given volume of air will frequently develop energy and pressure greater than that developed by the combustion of a gas. Dust explosions, then, are sometimes more disastrous than gas explosions. This, in part, is due to their slower rate of development and longer duration. The slower rate of development results from the fact that the combustion of dust is a surface reaction, and the diffusion of oxygen toward the reacting surface is necessarily slower and less complete than it is in a flammable gas.

Requisite Conditions for Dust Explosions

In order for a dust explosion to occur, four conditions must be satisfied simultaneously:

1. A combustible solid in a finely divided state must be dispersed in an oxidizing medium—usually oxygen in air.
2. The concentration of the dust in air must be within the explosible range.
3. An external source of ignition of sufficient energy and duration to initiate the explosive chain reaction for that particular dust must be present.
4. The chemical reaction must occur in a confined volume.

The rapid chemical reaction, or flash fire, characteristic of explosions will occur if only the first three conditions are satisfied. However, the rapid buildup of excessive pressures, inherent in the working definition of dust explosions, will result only when the reaction occurs in an enclosed space.

Characterization of Explosion Hazards of Dusts

Parameters employed to describe the relative explosion hazards of various dusts include:

1. Lower and upper limit of dust concentrations within which an explosion is possible.
2. Minimum ignition energy, i.e., minimum electric spark energy required for ignition of the dust cloud.
3. Minimum ignition temperature as measured by a furnace apparatus.
4. Maximum oxygen concentration permissible to prevent ignition.
5. Maximum explosion pressure attained during the course of the explosion.
6. Maximum rate of pressure rise (sometimes also the average rate of pressure rise).

Values for these parameters are not fixed but depend on various factors—namely, particle size and shape, ambient temperature and pressure, moisture content of the dust, degree of turbulence in the suspension, and size of the ignition source. (See Table 2-35B.) Experimental work has made possible some qualitative observations of the effects of these factors, but quantitative relations are not available.

Definitions of dust in terms of particle size vary, but normally dust is defined as particles with diameters of 0.1 to 1000 microns (1 micron equals 10^{-6} m).

The minimum explosible concentration and the minimum ignition energy generally tend to decrease with a decrease in average particle size (i.e., the explosion hazard increases with a decrease in particle size). For average particle sizes less than 50 microns, the effect is much less pronounced. According to Palmer,[2] uniform dispersion of the dust in laboratory test equipment may become more difficult as particles become very small. Due to the greater cohesiveness of very fine particles, some may exist as agglomerates rather than as individual particles, leading to an apparent reduction in explosibility. A different method of dispersion or a more vigorous ignition source may break up the agglomerations, resulting in an increased explosion hazard. Tests performed in large-scale coal mines are said to confirm this.

Little experimental evidence is available concerning the effect of particle shape on explosibility. Particles may resemble fibers, needles, or flakes, as well as spheres. Studies employing atomized spherical particles and flaked aluminum particles indicate that a significant difference in explosibility can occur with changes in particle shape. Size and shape, which are generally measured before ignition, may be altered during preignition stages, and subsequently affect propagation of the explosion. Changes may occur as a result of melting, vaporization, expansion to form hollow spheres, and fragmentation.

The effect of ambient temperature on explosibility would be particularly applicable to industrial situations, such as dryers, but no information is available on measurements in plant-scale units. Theoretically, it would be expected that the minimum ignition energy would decrease as the ambient temperature increased, other factors remaining constant. If the final temperature reached by the combustion products is limited by the molecular dissociation of product gases, then the maximum explosion pressure would be expected to decrease as the ambient temperature increases, and the rate of pressure rise would increase as the ambient temperature increased. Laboratory tests employing coal dust revealed that the minimum ignition energy decreased with increasing ambient temperature as expected, but only over a limited temperature range; thereafter, it increased. Palmer[2] also notes that the minimum ignition energy would depend on previous exposures to high temperatures.

If the pressure in the reaction vessel is atmospheric when the explosion is initiated, rises in pressure during the course of the explosion are not considered to be changes in ambient pressure. Laboratory tests employing methane/air mixtures resulted in proportional increases in maximum explosion pressures with increased initial pressure, but smaller increases were obtained for coal dust/air mixtures. The maximum explosible concentration decreased with increasing ambient pressure, while the minimum explosible concentration remained relatively unchanged. Explanations for these effects have not yet been explored.

An increase in moisture content of dust tends to increase the minimum explosible concentration, the minimum ignition energy, and the minimum ignition temperature when measured in small-scale apparatus. These effects are apparently due to the absorption of heat in vaporizing water and to the decrease in dispersibility of the dust. Nineteen percent water content (on a weight basis) was found to prevent ignition of starch dust.

Tests with coal dust air suspensions have indicated that explosions tend to increase in severity (i.e., maximum explosion pressure and/or maximum rate of pressure rise increases) with increases in the size of the ignition source. The nature of the ignition source also affects the explosibility of dusts. Organic dusts tend to be ignited more readily by heated coils, but metal dusts react more readily to spark ignition.

Experiments indicate that some dusts produce stronger explosions than others. Metallic dusts, such as stamped aluminum powder, milled and stamped magnesium, and atomized aluminum, produce the most violent dust explosions. Phenolformaldehyde resin, cornstarch, soybean protein, wood flour, and coal dust, respectively, followed the metallic dusts in explosive intensity.

The character and severity of any dust explosion will be affected by several factors. One of these is particle size. For any given material, the finer the particle size, the more violent the explosion. Less energy will be required to ignite the dust, and it will remain in suspension for a longer time, increasing the total force exerted. Figure 2-35D shows the relationship of particle size to the explosibility index.

Turbulence is another factor that contributes to the severity of a dust explosion. Turbulence speeds up the diffusion of oxygen to the reacting surfaces and promotes stronger explosions. The smaller the particle size and the greater the turbulence, the more the dust resembles a gas or vapor in its explosive characteristics.

Relatively little investigation has been undertaken with regard to the effects of turbulence on explosibility. Tests with coal dust/air suspensions revealed an increase in maximum explosion pressure and maximum rate of pressure rise with increased turbulence. Both parameters passed through maxima and then decreased, although more slowly in the case of the maximum explosion pressure. Sources of turbulence can include the presence of obstacles and rapid volume expansion due to flame.

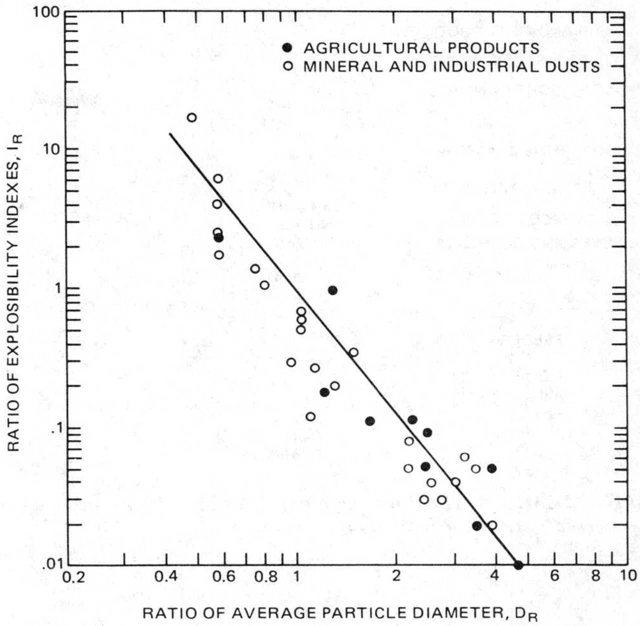

FIG. 2-35D. ***Effect of particle diameter on relative explosibility index. Relative average particle diameter is the ratio of the mean particle size of the dust to the mean size of the through No. 220 sieve sample. Relative explosibility index is the ratio of the index computed for the dust to that computed for a through No. 200 sieve sample. (Source: U.S. Bureau of Mines RI 5753)***

Particle Size Classifiers

Classifiers separate out the fine product and return the coarse material (circulating load) to the mill for regrinding, along with new material being fed to the mill. If the fines are continuously removed, a mill performs much more efficiently. Closed circuit grinding with size classifiers provides even more uniform size distribution and is also more economical.

Wet classifiers are generally used for large-scale wet milling operations, as in cement and ore processing plants. The simplest type of wet classifier is a settling basin arranged so that the fines do not have time to settle out and are drawn off, while the coarse material is raked to a central discharge. Wet classifiers of this type do not present an explosion hazard.

Dry classifiers may be installed external to the mill in a closed circuit (see Figure 2-35B), or they may be internal as an integral part of the mill (see Figure 2-35C).

Air classifiers are used for most dry milling operations. There are a number of different types, but all these classifiers are based upon the principles of air drag and particle inertia. One type directs an airstream across a stream of the particles to be classified. Another has adjustable flow baffles, and still another changes the direction of air flow. (See Figure 2-35E.) The double-cone classifier uses centrifugal action, induced by flow through vanes, which cause coarse particles to move outward and down the wall of the

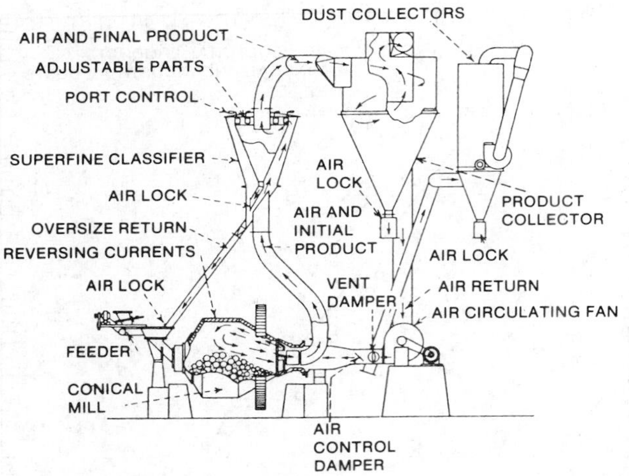

FIG. 2-35E. ***A Hardinge conical (tumbler type) mill with reversed current air classifier.***

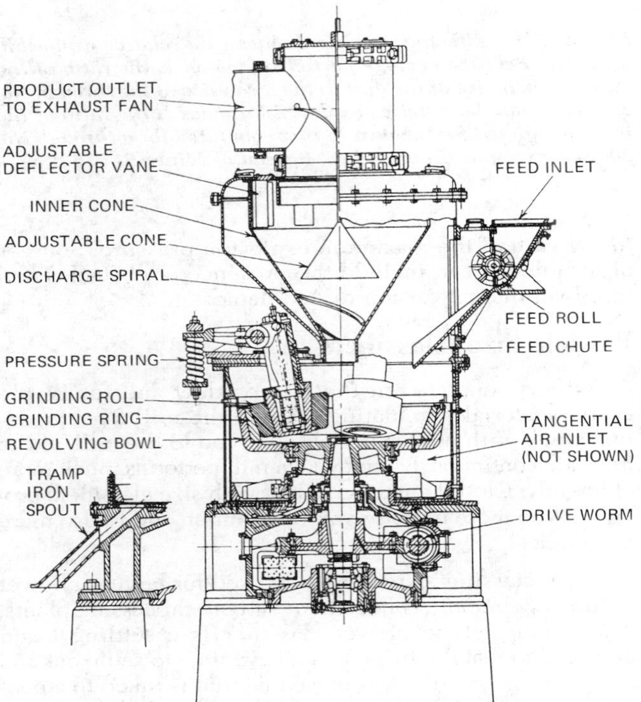

FIG. 2-35F. ***A bowl mill (variation of a ring roller mill). (Source: C.E. Raymond, Combustion Engineering, Inc.)***

inner cone and thus return to the grinding zone, while the upward-moving air stream entrains the fines. (See Figure 2-35F.)

Rotating blades are the main elements of several types of classifiers. The centrifugal motion established by the rotating blades tends to throw the coarser particles outward and returns them to the grinding zone, while the fines are carried off in the airstream. (See Figure 2-35C.)

GRINDING EQUIPMENT

Equipment for reducing particle size of a given material can be classified into four groups, according to the method of grinding used: (1) a material can be reduced between two solid surfaces; (2) it can be reduced by impact on one solid surface; (3) it can be reduced by action of the surrounding medium; or (4) it can be reduced by nonmechanical means, such as thermal shock, explosive shattering, or electrohydraulic processes.

Most grinding is performed by machines that pass the material between two solid surfaces. Such machines can be classified into tumbling mills, ring roller mills, roller mills, hammer mills, attrition mills, and jet mills.

Tumbling Mills

Tumbling mills consist of a cylindrical or conical shell charged with balls of steel, flint, or porcelain, or with steel rods. As the shell revolves about its horizontal axis, the balls or rods tumble about, grinding the material to be reduced against the wall of the shell or between themselves. (See Figure 2-35E.) The size of the balls or rods and the duration of the operation determine particle size. Some tumbling mills are compartmented by perforated partitions that allow material to pass from one compartment to another for finer grinding.

Ring Roller Mills

A second type of grinding machine is known as a ring roller mill. Mills of this type consist of a grinding ring or plate which moves between rollers. (See Figure 2-35C.) The ring may be either horizontal or vertical, and either it or the roller may rotate, grinding the product between the two surfaces. A variation of the ring roller mill is the bowl mill, in which a bowl and ring revolve around stationary rollers to grind the product. (See Figure 2-35F.) There is no metal-to-metal contact, and the space between the bowl and rollers can be preset to produce the required particle size.

Roller Mills

Roller mills differ from ring roller mills in that the material to be ground passes between two or more rollers revolving in opposite directions at different speeds. (See Figure 2-35G.) A scraper blade at the discharge end removes the finely ground material. Most dry materials are ground between rollers having corrugations which determine the final particle size. Corrugations may be either sharp or dull, and they may be used in various combinations to achieve the desired results.

Hammer Mills

Hammer mills have hammers, or beaters, attached to a rotating shaft. (See Figure 2-35H.) The hammers may be of almost any shape and hinged or fixed to the shaft. The fineness of the finished product is determined by the speed of the rotating shaft, the clearance between the hammers and grinding plates, the number and size of the hammers, the feed rate, and the size of the discharge openings. Two variations of the hammer mill are the disintegrator and the pin mill.

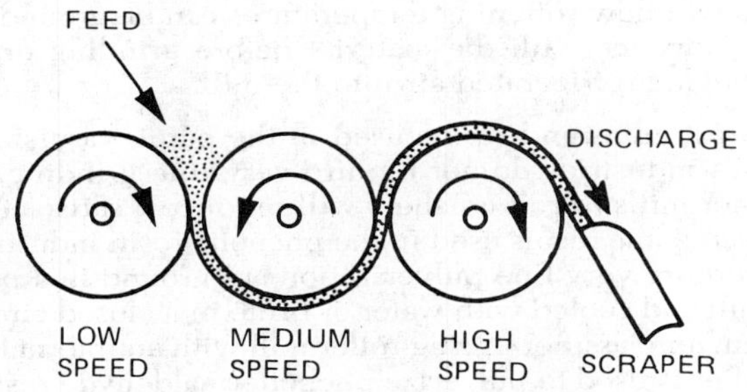

FIG. 2-35G. A roller mill for paint grinding.

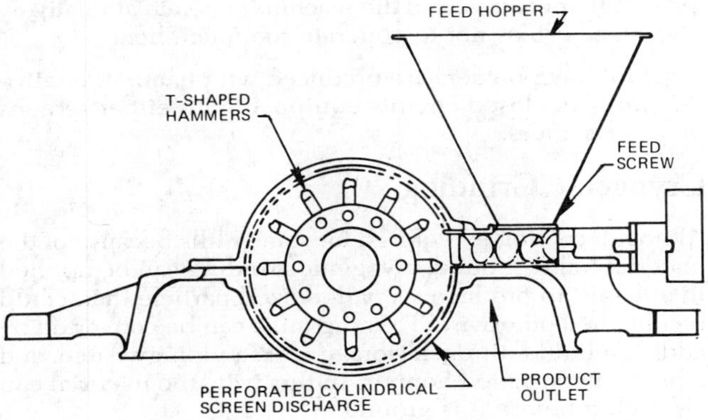

FIG. 2-35H. A Milro-Pulverizer hammer mill. (Source: Pulverizing Machinery Co.)

The disintegrator has a vertical rotating shaft with hammers that run at close tolerances to a cylindrical screen. (See Figure 2-35I.) Material is fed parallel to the rotating shaft, and the centrifugal action of the hammers discharges the ground material into a primary chute.

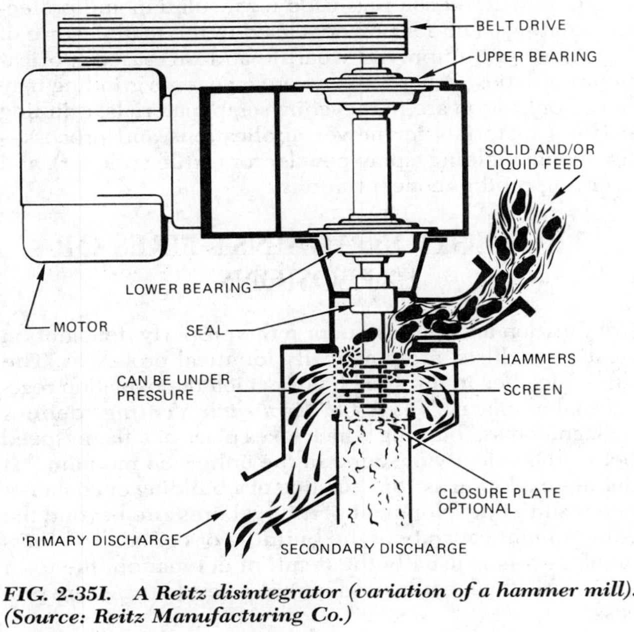

FIG. 2-35I. A Reitz disintegrator (variation of a hammer mill). (Source: Reitz Manufacturing Co.)

The pin mill is a high-speed mill with two disks in which pins are set in alternating circular rows. Either one or both of the disks may rotate. If both rotate, they do so in opposite directions. The material to be ground is broken up between the pins. (See Figure 2-35J.)

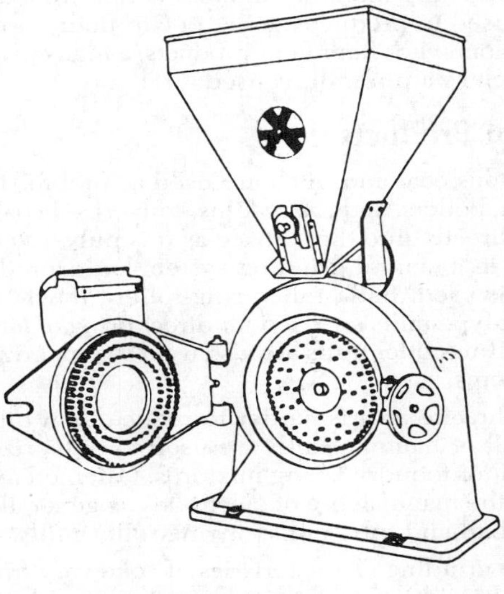

FIG. 2-35J. An Alpine-Kolloplex pin mill (variation of a hammer mill). (Source: Alpine-American Corp.)

Attrition Mills

Attrition mills use metallic or abrasive grinding plates that rotate at high speed on either a horizontal or vertical plane. One disk may be stationary, or the two may rotate in opposite directions. The material enters at the axis and is discharged at the periphery of the grinding plates. One type of attrition mill, known as the Buhrstone mill, uses two circular stones instead of metal or abrasive disks between which the material is ground.

Jet Mills

Another type of mill, the jet mill, differs from the others in that the material is not ground against a hard surface. Instead, a gaseous medium is introduced. The gas may convey the feed material at high velocity in opposing streams, or it may move the material around the periphery of the grinding and classifying chamber. The high turbulence causes the particles of feed material to collide and grind upon themselves.

APPLICATION OF GRINDING EQUIPMENT

Agricultural Products

The roller mill is the traditional machine for grinding wheat and rye into high-grade flour. Generally, rollers with dull corrugation are used. For very tough wheat, however, a sharp roller is used against a sharp roller, and for other grades, combinations of dull and sharp rollers are used. Rollers with sharp corrugations are used for grinding corn and feed. High-speed hammer mills or pin mills are used to produce flour with controlled protein content. Disk attrition mills are also used for grinding wheat.

After the oil has been extracted, soybeans or soybean cake is ground in attrition mills or flour rollers, depending upon whether the product is to be a feed meal or flour. In some cases, a hammer mill may be used as a preliminary disintegrator for pressed cakes, including linseed and cottonseed cake.

Where only medium fineness is required, a hammer mill is used to produce starch, potato flour, tapioca, and similar flours. For finer flour products, a high-speed impact mill, such as a pin mill, is used.

Carbon Products

Bituminous coal and pitch are used as fuel for industrial furnaces, boilers, and rotary kilns. Pulverized coal is either blown directly into the furnace as it is pulverized, or pulverized in a central grinding system and stored in a bin until it is used. Ball-, tube-, ring-roller-, bowl-, and ball-and-ring-type mills are used for direct firing of large installations. Ring-roller mills are also used to pulverize coal for bin systems.

Anthracite coal is harder to reduce than bituminous coal. Ball or hammer mills are used to pulverize anthracite coal for foundry facing mixtures. Calcined anthracite, used in the manufacture of electrodes, is generally pulverized in ball-and-tube mills, or ring-roller mills.

The grinding characteristics of coke vary from petroleum coke, which is relatively easy to grind, to certain foundry and retort coke, which is difficult to grind. Where uniform size of particles with a minimum of fines is required, rod or ball mills are used in a closed circuit with screens.

Natural graphite is classified in three grades: (1) flake, (2) crystalline, and (3) amorphous. Flake is the most difficult to grind to a fine powder, and crystalline is the most abrasive. Ball, tube, ring-roller, and jet mills with or without air classification are used for grinding graphite. For handling large capacities, ball and tube mills are used, especially for the flake and crystalline grades. Graphite for pencils is ground in a jet pulverizer. Ball mills in a closed circuit with air classifiers have been used for grinding artificial graphite. Charcoal and Gilsonite™ are ground in hammer mills with air classifiers.

Chemicals

Hammer mills are generally used to pulverize dry colors and dyestuffs, with pebble mills used for small lots. Hammer or jet mills with air classifiers for size limitation are used for dyes that are coarsely crystalline. A ring-roller mill is used for fine grinding of sulfur, with inert gas injected into the mill.

Pulverizing of metallic soaps, such as stearates, requires certain provisions to keep the material cool and in rapid motion. Since these materials tend to cake, batch grinding is not practicable. Stearates are pulverized in multi-cage mills, screen mills, and hammer mills with air classification.

Organic Polymers

The grinding characteristics of various resins, gums, waxes, hard rubbers, and molding powders are such that when a finely ground product is required, it may be necessary to use a water-jacketed mill or a pulverizer with an air classifier in which cooled air is introduced into the system. Hammer mills are generally used for this purpose. Some resins with low softening temperatures can be ground by mixing dry ice with the material before grinding or by introducing refrigerated air into the mill.

Most gums and resins used in the paint, varnish, or plastics industries do not require very fine grinding, so hammer mills or roll crushers will produce a satisfactory product. Some resins used in the phenolic resin industries that require very fine pulverization are ground in a pebble mill and cooled with water or brine in a closed circuit with an air classifier. A ring-roller mill with an internal air classifier is used to pulverize phenolformaldehyde resins.

Hard rubber is ground on heavy steam-heated rollers. The materials pass through a series of rollers in a closed circuit with screens and air classifiers. Usually the rollers are of different sizes, and the machines operate at relatively low speeds so as not to generate too much heat.

Molding powders are produced with hammer or attrition mills in closed circuits equipped with either screens or air classifiers.

Cryogenic Grinding

Although cooling is required for some mills because of the material being ground, cryogenic grinding can be applied in any mill to produce a smaller-sized particle than could be obtained otherwise. Existing mills can be converted by adding a liquid nitrogen storage tank, a piping system, and a properly designed hopper. In this way, the material can be cooled before it is ground.

The material can be precooled in the hopper by immersing it in a nitrogen bath, it can be cooled in the grinding chamber by spraying it with liquid nitrogen, or both methods can be used simultaneously. Gaseous nitrogen has been used for years to provide an inert atmosphere in mills, particularly in jet mills. Cryogenic grinding can be designed to provide a protective inert atmosphere within the mill. In spice grinding, freezing the spice before grinding gives it a superior appearance and it retains the aroma and flavor usually lost when it is not precooled.

Cryogenic grinding has been applied to the production of powdered coatings used for insulation and protective coatings, and for powders used in the manufacture of bearings, with improved wearlife and increased lubrication properties. Other areas where cryogenic grinding may have application are in recycling scrap materials, grinding existing materials for newer applications and processes (rotational molding, spray powder for textile stiffener), and grinding protein concentrations.

PROTECTION AGAINST FIRES OR EXPLOSIONS

Combustion and explosion, or more properly deflagration relative to dusts, are practically identical processes. The difference lies in the speed with which the oxidation reaction takes place. NFPA 68, *Explosion Venting*, defines deflagration as "burning which takes place at a flame speed below the velocity of sound in the unburned medium." It defines explosion as "the bursting of a building or container as a result of development of internal pressure beyond the confinement capacity of the building or container." Inasmuch as this is usually the result of detonation, the term explosion, as generally used herein, refers to the entire process.

Because an explosion takes place almost instantaneously, it cannot be brought under control by containment as can many fires. The effects, however, can be minimized by certain protective measures; these are prevention, venting, inerting, and suppression.

Prevention

The simplest means of preventing an explosion is to keep a critical concentration of dust from developing and to eliminate any potential sources of ignition.

In grinding operations, there are two types of locations where dust accumulation may become critical. One is within the milling or grinding equipment itself. The other is in the surrounding environment, i.e., the structure in which the equipment is housed.

The design and construction of the structure may vary considerably, depending upon the product being ground. It is impractical to construct a building that will withstand the pressure generated by a dust explosion. An ordinary 12-in. (0.3 m) thick brick wall can be destroyed by an internal pressure of less than 1 psi (6.9 kPa). Most dust explosions produce much higher pressures. Typical pressures range from 13 psi (90 kPa) for zinc to 89 psi (614 kPa) for stamped aluminum, with most being above 30 psi (207 kPa).

If a dust explosion hazard exists, the structure should be designed with panels, vents, windows, or other closures that will open at the lowest practical pressures and minimize structural damage.

Materials used should be noncombustible or fire resistive. Any interior walls intended to serve as fire walls should be capable of providing at least three hours of fire resistance under standard fire test methods. Interior stairs, lifts, or elevators should be enclosed in shafts of noncombustible materials and have fire-resistive ratings of at least one hour. Such enclosures should be protected by automatically closing fire doors, and any openings in fire walls should be similarly protected.

The number of horizontal surfaces that might collect dust and are difficult to reach or are inaccessible for cleaning should be minimized. Wherever practical, such surfaces should be built up to an angle of at least 60 degrees from the horizontal so that dust will tend to slide off rather than accumulate. Good housekeeping is a necessary part of explosion prevention. It means both equipment and structure must be kept clean so dust cannot accumulate. Dust should be removed by vacuum systems. Brushing or sweeping will disperse the dust and increase turbulence, which in turn increases the possibility of an explosion occurring and increases its potential severity. In grain elevators, recently developed grain dust probes may be used to alarm when dust levels exceed explosive limits.[1]

Equipment should be made of metal and be as dust-tight as possible. It should be designed so that there is continuous suction at openings during grinding, dumping, transfer, and similar operations. The collected dust should be conveyed through tightly constructed ducts or chutes to well-designed dust collectors located in a safe place, preferably outside the structure.

Since many dusts can be ignited by low-energy sparks, potential ignition sources should be eliminated from or adequately shielded in the area. Welding, cutting, or any other operation that uses an open flame or arc should not be permitted unless the work area is dust free. Smoking should be prohibited. Torque-limiting or fluid-drive couplings should be designed to dissipate heat readily. Moving equipment, elevators, belts, and conveyors should be grounded or of nonconductive material to eliminate the possibility of static sparks. All electrical wiring should conform to the requirements of NFPA 70, *National Electrical Code®*, for hazardous locations containing combustible dusts.

Extinguishing

Adequate fire extinguishing equipment, both fixed and portable, should be provided. Hose nozzles should be of the spray type, since solid streams can cause turbulence and dispersion of dust into the air and increase the explosion hazard. Automatic sprinklers should be provided to protect the buildings.

Venting

Vents are openings in the equipment or structure that allow heated explosion gases to escape more readily. Venting does not prevent explosions, but it does serve to limit the maximum pressure resulting from a deflagration. The most effective vents are free and unrestricted openings; however, these are not always practical.

Vents should be closed in such a manner that they will open under the lowest practical pressure. Typical venting arrangements include rupture diaphragms, hinged or blow-out windows and panels, and weakly constructed walls and roofs.

The venting area required, as calculated from empirical formulas, depends upon the expected pressure and its rate of rise, the type of closure, and the volume and strength of the enclosure. Determination of vent area for an enclosure is mostly empirical. Vents should be located where minimum damage will result from the shattering or blowing out of the vent closure.

Inerting

One method of preventing a dust explosion is inerting, i.e., the replacement of oxygen in the grinding process with an inert gas, such as nitrogen or carbon dioxide. Such equipment as grinders, pulverizers, mixers, dryers, conveyors, dust collectors, and filling machines can be protected by this method.

The amount of oxygen that must be replaced to provide a safe concentration depends upon the type of dust, particle size, concentration, turbulence, diluent gas, and intensity of the ignition source. To prevent ignition of carbonaceous dusts by a spark, for example, oxygen should be reduced to 8 percent by nitrogen or to 11 percent by carbon dioxide. However, if a stronger ignition source is present, the oxygen should be reduced to 3 and 4 percent, respectively.

Many factors will affect the use of inerting to prevent explosion. Among them are protection of personnel, the hazard to be protected, the required reduction in oxygen concentration, the availability and cost of the inert gas supply, and the necessary control equipment.

Suppression

Explosion suppression is a technique of stopping an explosion before it develops destructive pressures. The factors involved here are much the same as those used in the extinguishment of fire, namely cooling, limiting the supply of oxygen, and inhibiting flame spread.

Despite the rapidity with which combustion proceeds in an explosion, there is a short period of time before which the destructive force is evolved. During this time, the initial pressure rise can be detected by suitable sensing devices, which automatically trigger the release of the suppressing agent, normally an inert gas or liquid, that inhibits the combustion process.

Explosion suppression systems can be used in confined spaces, such as reactors, mixers, pulverizers, mills, dryers, storage bins, ovens, bucket elevator transport systems, and pneumatic transport systems. The effective application of such systems requires careful consideration of many factors. Among them are characteristics of the dust, rate of pressure rise, ignition sources, and characteristics of the suppressant. Though the principles of explosion suppression apply to all installations, each suppression system must be individually designed to cover the wide range of variables that will be encountered.

BIBLIOGRAPHY

References Cited

1. Cashdollar, K. L., and Hertzberg, M., eds., "Industrial Dust Explosions," ASTM Special Technical Publication 958, 1986, American Society for Testing and Materials, Philadelphia, PA.
2. Palmer, K. N., *Dust Explosions and Fires*, Chapman and Hill, London, 1973.

References

Johnson, *et al*, "Explosibility of Agricultural Dusts," U.S. Bureau of Mines RI 5753, 1961, U.S. Bureau of Mines, Washington, DC.

NFPA Codes, Standards, and Recommended Practices

Reference to the following NFPA codes, standards, and recommended practices will provide further information on grinding processes discussed in this chapter. (See the latest *NFPA Catalog* for availability of current editions of the following documents.)

NFPA 61A, *Prevention of Fire and Dust Explosions in Facilities Manufacturing and Handling Starch*.

NFPA 61B, *Prevention of Fires and Explosions in Grain Elevators and Facilities Handling Bulk Raw Agricultural Commodities*.

NFPA 61C, *Prevention of Fire and Dust Explosion in Feed Mills*.

NFPA 68, *Explosion Venting*.

NFPA 69, *Explosion Prevention Systems*.

NFPA 70, *National Electrical Code*.

NFPA 651, *Manufacture of Aluminum and Magnesium Powder*.

NFPA 654, *Prevention of Fire and Dust Explosions in the Chemical, Dye, Pharmaceutical, and Plastics Industries*.

NFPA 655, *Prevention of Sulfur Fires and Explosions*.

NFPA 664, *Prevention of Fires and Explosions in Wood Processing and Woodworking Facilities*.

Additional Reading

Bartencht, W., *Explosions: Course, Prevention, Protection*, Springer-Verlag, New York, NY, 1981.

Bartknecht, W., "Ignition Capabilities of Hot Surfaces and Mechanically Generated Sparks in Flammable Gas and Dust/Air Mixtures," *Plant/Operation Progress*, Vol. 7, No. 2, 1988, pp. 114-121.

Bluhm, D. D., "Grinding and Milling Operations," *Industrial Fire Hazards Handbooks*, 3rd ed, NFPA, Quincy, MA, 1990.

Britton, L. G., and Kuby, D. C., "Analysis of a Dust Deflagation," *Plant/Operation Progress*, Vol. 8, No. 3, July 1989, pp. 177-180.

Bruderer, R. E., "Ignition Properties of Mechanical Sparks and Hot Surfaces in Dust/Air Mixtures," *Plant/Operation Progress*, Vol. 8, No. 3, July 1989, pp. 152-164.

Davenport, J. A., "Explosion Losses in Industry," *Fire Journal*, Vol. 75, No. 1, pp. 52-56, 71-73.

Eckhoff, R. K., "A Study of Selected Problems Related to the Assessment of Ignitability and Explosibility of Dust Clouds," *CHR*, Michelsons Institute, Bergen, 1976.

Explosion Hazards and Evaluation, Elsevier, New York, NY, 1983.

Factory Mutual Engineering Corporation, "Grain Storage and Milling," *Loss Prevention Data*, 7-75, Norwood, MA, Aug. 1976.

Factory Mutual Engineering Corporation, "Combustible Dusts," *Loss Prevention Data*, 7-76, Norwood, MA, Aug. 1976.

Friedman, R., *Principles of Fire Protection Chemistry*, 2nd ed., National Fire Protection Association, Quincy, MA, 1989.

"Grain Elevator and Processing Society," *Proceedings*: International Symposium on Grain Dust Explosions, Kansas City, MO, 1977.

Grobel, E., "Cryogenic Grinding Gives Process Flexibility," *Cryogenics and Industrial Gases*, Vol. 9, No. 4, July/Aug. 1974, pp. 27-30.

Milling: Methods and Machines, Society of Manufacturing Engineers, Dearborn, MI, 1982.

Milling One and Milling Two, State Mutual Book and Periodical Service, Ltd., NY, 1983.

Moore, P. E., "Industrial Dust Explosions," K. L. Cashdollar and M. Hertzberg eds, *ASTM Special Publication 958*, American Society for Testing and Materials, Philidelphia, PA, 1987.

Palmer, K. N., "Dust Explosions: Initiation, Characteristics, and Protection," *Chemical Engineering Progress*, Vol. 86, No. 3, March 1990, pp. 33-36.

Perry, R. H., and Green D. W., *Chemical Engineers Handbook*, 6th ed., McGraw-Hill, NY, 1984.

Plaster, C., et al, eds., *Milling*, Vol. 1, 2nd ed., International Ideas, Inc., Philadelphia, PA, 1977.

"Prevention, Detection, and Control of Coal Pulverizer Fires and Explosions," Electric Power Research Institute, *Report* EPRI CS No. 5069, 1987, Palo Alto, CA, 280p. 1987.

Spencer, A. G., *Milling*, Vol. 2, International Ideas, Inc., Philadelphia, PA, 1969.

Verkade, M., and Chiotti, P., *Literature Survey of Dust Explosions in Grain-Handling Facilities: Cause and Prevention*, Energy and Mineral Resources Research Institute, Iowa State University, Ames, IA, 1976.

Weiby, P., and Dickinson, K. R., "Monitoring Work Areas for Explosive and Toxic Hazards," *Chemical Engineering*, Vol. 83, No. 22, 1976, pp. 139-145.

Wrenn, C., "Inerting for Safety," *Plant/Operation Progress*, Vol. 5, No. 4, Oct. 1986, pp. 225-227.

Zalosh, R. G., "Review of Coal Pulverizer Fire and Explosion Incidents," *Symposium* on Industrial Dust Explosions, STP 958, 1987, American Society of Testing Materials.

MATERIALS, PRODUCTS, AND ENVIRONMENTS

If prevention fails, the next opportunity to reduce fire losses comes in the selection and arrangement of everything that can burn in the space where the fire started. A small fire in a trash can, for example, will pose no serious threat if the trash can is set out as the only object on an enormous concrete floor in the middle of some vast storage room. However, that same small trash-can fire could start a devastating fire if it were located instead against the side of an upholstered chair in a densely furnished room in an occupied residential property or against a wall paneled with untreated plywood in the lobby of an old hotel.

The differences among these scenarios lie in the burning properties of the materials near the point of initial ignition, the way those materials are used in products or assemblies, and other features of the environment of the point of ignition. The first item ignited in an unwanted fire, if it is small enough, might be considered merely the "fuse" to the first large fuel package, which is the real key to creating a serious fire hazard. Section 3 addresses the burning properties of materials and products in environments, paying special attention to those materials, products, and environments which may promote such rapid and severe early fire growth that the effectiveness of later-acting fire-protection strategies will be seriously impaired.

Chapters 1 and 2 of Section 3 are about the basic science of this part of fire protection. Chapter 1 focuses on the range of combustion products—toxic gases and other dangerous effects—that can become components in the smoke and gas produced by fire. Chapter 2 addresses burning properties more generally, with special attention to thermal properties, such as fast or slow development and high or low rates of heat release. Chapters 1 and 2 help to place the other chapters of Section 3 in context.

Chapters 3 and 4 address the types of materials most frequently found in large fuel packages of ordinary combustibles—wood and fibers or textiles, respectively. Chapter 11 addresses the most common *forms* of materials (i.e., types of products) in large fuel packages initially involved in fires, namely, upholstered furniture and mattresses.

Chapters 5 through 9, 12, and 13 address certain types of materials or products that are of special concern, typically because of their potential for extremely rapid fire development, including explosions. Chapter 16 addresses pesticides, which are another product of special concern, though more because of their unusual toxic properties, even in non-fire incidents. Chapter 10 addresses plastics and rubber, the other major types of materials involved in large fuel packages of ordinary combustibles.

Chapters 14 and 15 address certain specialized environments—those created by energy conservation programs and oxygen-enriched atmospheres, respectively—that may affect the burning properties of many different products and materials. For example, energy conservation may lead to fewer air changes per unit time and thus affect the oxygen flow to a fire, while an oxygen-enriched atmosphere obviously affects oxygen availability, as well. Finally, Chapter 17 addresses modification of the burning properties of some classes of products through fire retardancy or flame resistance.

Also look for these: Chapters 25 through 30 and 34 of Section 2 discuss potential fuel sources in the context of prevention, but that discussion will be of interest here as well because the role of first fuel and the role of first *major* fuel are so closely linked. Section 6 addresses the impact of materials, products, and environments on fire confinement, which includes the burning property of flame spread. See Chapters 2 through 4 in particular. Finally, as Chapter 2 of this section says, "It is becoming possible to predict how a material, burning in a given scenario, will influence the hazard to life from that fire. This emerging field of fire protection, known as fire hazard analysis, requires information on the burning properties of a material, and its conditions of use, as well as smoke obscuration and smoke toxicity data." Systematic, state-of-the-art consideration of materials, products, and environments and their impact on early fire development increasingly requires the kind of measurement and modeling described in Section 10, especially in Chapters 6 through 14.

COMBUSTION PRODUCTS AND THEIR EFFECTS ON LIFE SAFETY

Gordon E. Hartzell

This chapter discusses fire gases, heat, visible smoke, and the development of toxic hazard.For detailed discussions of allied topics, consult the following chapters: Section 7, Chapter 1, "Human Behavior and Fire"; Section 3, Chapter 2, "Fire Hazards of Materials: An Overview"; and Section 8, Chapter 10, "Assessing Life Safety in Buildings."

Exposure to the products of combustion presents numerous hazards to humans. Predominant among these hazards are effects from heat, impaired vision due to smoke density or eye irritation, narcosis from inhalation of asphyxiants, and irritation of the upper and/or lower respiratory tracts.

These effects, often occurring simultaneously in a fire, contribute to physical incapacitation, loss of motor coordination, faulty judgment, disorientation, restricted vision, and panic. The resulting delay or prevention of escape may lead to subsequent injury or death from further inhalation of toxic gases and/or the suffering of thermal burns. Survivors from a fire also may experience post-exposure pulmonary (lung) complications and burn injuries which can lead to delayed death.

Assessment of the overall physiological and behavioral effects of human exposure to fire and its combustion products is an extremely difficult and complex task. Fundamental to such assessment is the concept of "dose." Physiological responses are usually dose-related, i.e., the magnitude of the effect increases with increasing dose or accumulated body burden of a physiologically active agent. Since the real dose of toxicants from smoke inhalation cannot be measured directly, the assumption is made that the dose is a function of smoke (or toxicant) concentration and exposure time.[1] This dose is really an expression of the insult to which a subject is exposed. The term "exposure dose" probably is more accurate and has become the preferred term in combustion toxicology.

Concentrations of common fire gas toxicants, such as carbon monoxide (CO) and hydrogen cyanide (HCN), usually are expressed as parts per million (ppm) by volume. Therefore, the exposure dose can be expressed as the product of the concentration and time, i.e., ppm-min. In the case of a changing concentration of a gaseous toxicant, the exposure dose is actually the integrated area under a concentration *vs* time curve.

One can also deal with the concept of exposure dose as it applies to smoke. Since smoke concentration cannot be quantified, an approximation is made that the smoke concentration is proportional to the mass loss during a fire. The integrated area under a mass loss per unit volume *vs* time curve thus becomes a measure of smoke exposure dose, e.g., mg-min/L, lb-min/ft^3, etc.[2,3] Smoke exposure dose at any moment in time can be calculated from data obtained from a laboratory combustion device, instrumented experimental fires, data generated from mathematically modeled fires, and even data estimated from real fires. In the case of real-fire scenarios, smoke transport models and dilution calculations can provide for estimation of smoke exposure doses even in areas remote from a fire. It is an important concept that "toxicological exposure doses" can be visualized as quantified entities that are generated from a fire, transported, and then administered to exposed subjects.

In general, several important factors are integral to complete understanding of the effects of products of combustion on life safety, as follows.

Acute Exposure Assessment

Most available toxicological data relevant to humans has been developed specifically for assessment of long-term exposures in the workplace. These data generally are not applicable for evaluation of the acute effects from brief exposure to the relatively high concentrations of combustion products which may be present in a fire.

Development of Toxicological Data

Development of the desired toxicological data from scientific experiments under controlled laboratory conditions usually cannot be accomplished with human subjects, since the experiments themselves would be hazardous to humans. Research in this field normally must be limited to the exposure of experimental animals, usually rodents, or, in some cases, nonhuman primates.

Gordon E. Hartzell, Ph.D., a consultant on toxic hazards in fires, is based in San Antonio, Texas.

Extrapolation

Reasonably reliable extrapolation to human exposures may be made, providing that both qualitative and quantitative differences in toxicological effects between laboratory animals and humans are understood. Sometimes this is not the case. Consequently, assessment of the toxicological effects of the exposure of humans to combustion products often involves considerable speculation and a variety of opinions, even among the experts.[4]

FIRE GASES

Smoke most often is defined as the airborne solid and liquid particulates and fire gases evolved when a material undergoes pyrolysis or combustion.[5] The fire gases have received the most attention, while knowledge of the effects of inhalation of particulates and aerosols from smoke is still quite limited.

Although a wide variety of fire gases may be generated, the toxicant gases are usually separated into three basic classes: (1) the asphyxiants or narcosis-producing toxicants; (2) the irritants, which may be sensory or pulmonary; and (3) those toxicants exhibiting other or unusual specific toxicities.

In pharmacologic terminology, a "narcotic" is a drug that induces unconsciousness (narcosis), with loss of pain. In combustion toxicology, the term refers primarily to asphyxiant toxicants that are capable of resulting in central nervous system depression, with loss of consciousness and ultimate death. Effects of the asphyxiant or narcosis-producing toxicants depend upon the accumulated doses, i.e., both concentration and time of exposure. The severity of the effects increases with increasing doses. Although many asphyxiants may be produced by combustion of materials, only carbon monoxide and hydrogen cyanide have been measured in sufficient concentrations in fire gases to cause significant acute toxic effects.

Irritant effects, produced by essentially all fire atmospheres, are normally considered by combustion toxicologists as being of two types: (1) sensory irritation, including irritation of the eyes and the upper respiratory tract; and (2) pulmonary irritation, which affects the lungs. Most irritants produce signs and symptoms characteristic of both sensory and pulmonary irritation.

Eye irritation, an immediate effect which depends only upon the concentration of an irritant, may be under estimated in its ability to impair escape of a victim from a fire situation. Nerve endings in the cornea are stimulated, causing pain, reflex blinking, and tearing. Severe irritation also may lead to subsequent eye damage. Victims may shut their eyes, which can partially alleviate these effects but also may impair their escape from a fire.

Airborne irritants enter the upper respiratory tract, where nerve receptors are stimulated, causing burning sensations in the nose, mouth, and throat, along with the secretion of mucus. Sensory effects are primarily related to the concentration of the irritant and do not normally increase in severity as the exposure time is increased.

Following signs of initial sensory irritance in primates, significant amounts of inhaled irritants are quickly taken into the lungs, with the symptoms of pulmonary or lung irritation being exhibited. Lung irritation often is characterized by coughing, bronchoconstriction, and increased pulmonary flow resistance. Tissue inflammation and damage, pulmonary edema, and subsequent death often follow exposure to high concentrations, usually after 6 to 48 hrs. Furthermore, exposure to pulmonary irritants appears to increase susceptibility to bacterial infection. Unlike sensory irritation, the effects of pulmonary irritation are related both to the concentration of the irritant and to the duration of the exposure.

Carbon Monoxide

Although carbon monoxide (CO) is not the most toxic of gases in terms of the effects of a particular concentration, it is always one of the most abundant and, therefore, is the major threat in most fire atmospheres. Under controlled burning conditions, the carbon of most organic materials can be oxidized completely by supplying excess oxygen. In the uncontrolled burning of an accidental fire, the availability of oxygen is never ideal and some of the carbon is incompletely oxidized to carbon monoxide. In a confined smoldering fire, the ratio of carbon monoxide (CO) to carbon dioxide (CO_2) is usually greater than in a well-ventilated, free-burning fire.

The toxicity of CO is primarily due to its affinity for the hemoglobin in blood, resulting in formation of carboxyhemoglobin (COHb) and a decreased capacity of the blood to transport oxygen to body tissues (hypoxia). The carbon monoxide content of blood can readily be measured and is expressed as percent COHb saturation.

There exists no minimum blood COHb saturation associated with death, below which it can be certain that a victim died from other causes or toxicants. The actual blood COHb saturation levels associated with both incapacitation and death vary quite widely over the general population and depend upon many factors. With some persons having pre-existing functional impairments, even quite low COHb saturations are likely to be dangerous. The very young, the elderly, the physically disabled, those under the influence of alcohol, drugs, or medication, and those with heart disease are particularly susceptible. The two high-risk age groups—children age 5 and under and adults age 65 and over—account for 45 percent of home fire deaths.[6]

From studies involving both rats and nonhuman primates, along with a reasonable amount of human exposure data, it is felt that any COHb saturation above approximately 30 percent would be potentially hazardous to most humans. A saturation of about 50 percent is likely to be lethal to many individuals.[7] Analysis of data from victims of improperly operated gas heaters showed a mean COHb saturation of 49.5 percent, with a standard deviation of 14.0 percent.[8] Some of the victims died at COHb levels as low as about 35 percent, while others survived at saturations as high as 64 percent.

In terms of CO concentrations required to reach hazardous COHb levels, a simple rule of thumb may be used. Any exposure in which the product of concentration (ppm) × time (minutes) exceeds approximately 35,000 ppm-min is likely to be dangerous.[7] Thus, a 10-min exposure to 3500 ppm of carbon monoxide would be expected to be hazardous and possibly incapacitating to many people. The concentration × time rule of thumb must be applied with caution at high concentrations, since progressively lower doses can be tolerated as the concentration is increased. It is, however, reasonably applicable for the range of CO concentrations normally generated in fires.

Extensive investigations examining human fire fatalities with respect to exposure to toxic atmospheres have shown carbon monoxide to be the primary toxicant.[9,10] In approximately half of the fire fatality cases studied, blood COHb levels resulting from inhalation of carbon monoxide were found sufficiently high as to be lethal. In an additional 30 percent of the victims, combinations of carbon monoxide with preexisting heart disease and/or alcohol intoxication were considered to be the cause of death. Of the fire fatalities in which alcohol was a factor, data showed that 88 percent of the victims had sufficient blood alcohol levels to be classified as legally intoxicated.

Hydrogen Cyanide

Hydrogen cyanide (HCN) is produced from the burning of materials that contain nitrogen. Natural and synthetic materials, such as wool, silk, acrylonitrile polymers, nylons, polyurethanes, and urea-containing resins, are included.

Hydrogen cyanide is a very rapidly acting toxicant which is approximately 20 times more toxic than carbon monoxide. It does not combine appreciably with hemoglobin, but the toxicant inhibits the use of oxygen by cells (histotoxic hypoxia). There is no evidence for synergism between hydrogen cyanide and carbon monoxide, and so these two toxicants are generally agreed to be additive in their effects.[11,12]

Data relating symptoms in humans to various concentrations of HCN are very limited. One widely used descriptive account of hydrogen cyanide intoxication of humans reports that 50 ppm may be tolerated for 30 to 60 min without difficulty, 100 ppm for that same period is likely to be fatal, 135 ppm may be fatal after 30 min, and 181 ppm may be fatal after 10 min.[13] Since incapacitation normally occurs at one-third to one-half the lethal dose, the data suggest that doses for incapacitation by HCN range from approximately 2500 ppm-min at 100 ppm to 750 ppm-min at 200 ppm. Using a rule of thumb analogous to that for carbon monoxide, it would appear that a product of hydrogen cyanide concentration (ppm) × time (minutes) in the range of about 1500 ppm-min would likely be hazardous to humans.[7] With hydrogen cyanide, in particular, progressively lower doses can be tolerated as the concentration is increased and the rule of thumb must be applied with caution.

The role of hydrogen cyanide as a causative agent in human fire fatalities is considerably less clear than that of carbon monoxide. Documented cases are rare in which hydrogen cyanide alone can be shown to be the primary toxicant. Blood can be analyzed in the laboratory for cyanide, but the procedure is more complex than that for carbon monoxide. Analyses must be interpreted with caution, due both to uncertainties in the accuracy of the data and also because cyanide is normally present in blood as a result of destruction of body tissue. It is generally regarded that blood cyanide concentrations greater than 1.0 microgram per milliliter are indicative of possibly significant toxicological effects due to hydrogen cyanide.[9,14] Blood cyanide levels greater than 3.0 micrograms per milliliter are generally lethal. In one study, cyanide was found at elevated levels in the blood of 70 percent of the fire victims, with possible toxic levels of blood cyanide found in 13 percent of the victims.[9] However, significant levels of blood cyanide also were normally found associated with high levels of carboxyhemoglobin saturation.[9,10] Thus, the contribution of each to death could not be determined with confidence.

Carbon Dioxide

Carbon dioxide (CO_2) usually is evolved in large quantities from fires. While not particularly toxic at observed levels, moderate concentrations of carbon dioxide increase both the rate and depth of breathing, thereby increasing the respiratory minute volume (RMV). This condition contributes to the overall hazard of a fire gas environment by causing accelerated inhalation of toxicants and irritants. The rate and depth of breathing are increased about 50 percent by 2 percent carbon dioxide. If 4 percent carbon dioxide is breathed, the RMV is approximately doubled, but the effect may be scarcely noticed by an individual. Any further increase in carbon dioxide from 4 percent up to 10 percent produces a correspondingly greater RMV, and at 10 percent, the RMV may be 8 to 10 times the resting level. The subject also may have symptoms of dizziness, faintness, and headache.[15]

Insufficient Oxygen

Oxygen (O_2) is consumed from the atmosphere during combustion. When oxygen drops from its usual level of 21 percent in air to approximately 17 percent, a person's motor coordination is impaired. When oxygen drops into the range of 14 to 10 percent, a person is still conscious but may exercise faulty judgment and will be quickly fatigued. In the range of 10 to 6 percent oxygen, a person loses consciousness and must be revived with fresh air or oxygen within a few minutes to prevent death.[16] During periods of exertion, increased oxygen demands may result in oxygen deficiency symptoms at higher oxygen levels.

Acrolein

Acrolein is a particularly potent irritant, both sensory and pulmonary, which has been demonstrated to be present in many fire atmospheres.[17] It is formed from the smoldering of all cellulosic materials and also from pyrolysis of polyethylene.[18] Acrolein is extremely irritating, with concentrations as low as a few parts per million being irritating to the eyes and possibly psychologically incapacitating. Surprisingly, studies with nonhuman primates have shown that concentrations up to 2780 ppm for 5 min were not physically incapacitating during exposure.[19] However, pulmonary complications caused by even lower concentrations did result in death within hours after the exposure.

Hydrogen Chloride

Hydrogen chloride (HCl) is formed from the combustion of chlorine-containing materials, the most notable of which is polyvinyl chloride (PVC). It is both a potent sensory irritant and also a strong pulmonary irritant. Concentrations as low as 75 ppm are extremely irritating to the eyes and the upper respiratory tract, and impairment from a behavioral standpoint also has been suggested. However, hydrogen chloride gas has been found not to be physically incapacitating to nonhuman primates subjected to concentrations up to 17,000 ppm for 5 min.[19] The toxicant was reported to cause post-exposure death at doses that did not appear to incapacitate. Comparable studies have not been conducted using actual PVC smoke, however, and it is claimed that other irritants also may be present from PVC in a real fire atmosphere.[20] Furthermore, the question remains as to the extent of respiratory dysfunction and susceptibility to infection caused by exposure to hydrogen chloride and PVC smoke. One study, using baboons exposed to PVC smoke containing up to 4000 ppm HCl, did not, however, indicate any significant residual effects on pulmonary function when tested at three days and again at three months postexposure.[21]

Considerable controversy exists as to what concentration of HCl is hazardous to humans. Although numerous studies of the acute effects of HCl have been conducted with rodents, it is questionable whether lethality data from rodents can be directly extrapolated to humans because of anatomical differences in the respiratory tract of the rodent and the primate. Interestingly, exposure doses (concentration × time) of HCl that cause post-exposure lethality in rats are in the same range as those that have resulted in post-exposure deaths of baboons, although the data for baboons are very limited and the comparison made is rather subjective.[22] The lethal toxic potency of HCl with rats is actually only somewhat greater than that of carbon monoxide.[23] Consideration of the exposure dose of carbon monoxide thought to be *hazardous* to humans would lead one, based simply on relative lethal toxic potencies, to suspect that exposure to humans to the range of 700 ppm or more of HCl for 30 min would be highly dangerous. It is prudent to realize that HCl is dangerous to humans at concentrations well below those indicated by its lethal toxic potency.[24,25]

Nitrogen Oxides

Nitrogen dioxide (NO_2) and nitric oxide (NO) comprise a mixture usually referred to as NO_x. The nitrogen oxides result from oxidation of nitrogen-containing materials, with HCN also being a source of NO_x from its combustion at high temperatures. Nitrogen "fixation" from air also is a possibility. Studies on rats exposed to NO_2 under the conditions of smoke toxicity test methods indicate NO_2 to have a lethal toxic potency comparable to HCN.[26] Nitric oxide is only about one-fifth as potent as NO_2.[27] In contrast to HCN, the toxicity of NO_x is primarily due to its properties as a pulmonary irritant, with lethality of rats being postexposure, usually within one day.

Although one study reported NO_x production from nitrogen-containing fuel to be far less than that for HCN (and therefore of less importance toxicologically than HCN), there are conflicting data in the literature.[27] Further studies are needed to examine the role of nitrogen oxides in combustion toxicology.

Other Irritants

Other irritants formed in a fire depend upon many variables. The principal variables are:

1. Chemical composition of the burning material,
2. Amount of oxygen available for combustion, and
3. Temperature.

Sulfur dioxide, ammonia, hydrogen fluoride, hydrogen bromide, isocyanates, phosphorous compounds, and a wide variety of volatile hydrocarbons have been identified in smoke.[28] In general, effects of acute exposure to these toxicants have not been sufficiently characterized and quantified to enable assessment of their hazards when present in fire atmospheres. However, a mass loss of material during burning of 10 g for each cubic meter of volume has been suggested as likely to present highly dangerous concentrations of irritants.[29]

Mixed Fire Gases

Although individual fire gas toxicants may exert quite different physiological effects through different mechanisms, when present in a mixture each may result in a certain degree of compromise experienced by an exposed subject. It should not be unexpected that varying degrees of a partially compromised condition may be roughly additive in contributing to incapacitation or death. This has been demonstrated in a number of studies using rodents and is a key element in the assessment of toxic hazard.

For example, it is fairly well agreed that carbon monoxide and hydrogen cyanide appear to be additive when expressed as fractional doses required to cause an effect.[11,12] Thus, as a reasonable approximation, the fraction of an effective dose of CO can be added to that of HCN in estimating the presence of a hazardous condition.

In the case of mixtures of hydrogen chloride and carbon monoxide, empirical analysis of toxicological data shows that exposure doses leading to lethality of rats also may be additive.[23] These studies imply that hydrogen chloride may be much more dangerous than previously thought when in the presence of carbon monoxide or, conversely, carbon monoxide intoxication may be much more serious in the presence of an irritant. A rapid respiratory acidosis was seen in the blood of rats exposed to HCl which, when coupled with the metabolic acidosis produced by CO, resulted in severely compromised animals. The effect may have significance with human exposure, such as prolonged hypoxemic conditions following rescue or escape. There also is some suggestion that the incapacitating effects of carbon monoxide may be enhanced in primates upon simultaneous exposure to HCl, the presence of which causes the partial pressure of oxygen in arterial blood to be decreased.[30] This is probably the case with other irritants as well.

It has been observed from studies using rats that there also may be additivity of fractional effective doses between HCl and HCN.[31] Particularly striking was the incidence of post-exposure deaths from concentrations of the toxicants, each of which alone would not be expected to result in any post-exposure lethality. Deaths often were several days after the exposure.

Carbon dioxide is quite low in its own toxicological potency and is not, by itself, normally considered to be a significant factor in combustion toxicology. However, it does stimulate respiration, leading to an increased rate of loading of blood COHb from inhalation of CO. The same equilibrium COHb saturation is reached as in the absence of CO_2. However, increased incidence of lethality (particularly postexposure) has been observed with certain combinations of CO and CO_2,[32] perhaps analogous to that seen with mixtures of CO and HCl. The effect may be associated with the combined insult of respiratory acidosis (caused by CO_2) and metabolic acidosis (caused by CO), a condition from which the rodent has difficulty recovering postexposure. Whether or not these effects of CO_2 occur with primates has not been determined.

Testing for Toxicity of Combustion Products

Typically, tests for the toxicity of smoke produced by a burning material involve some quantitative measurement in the laboratory of the toxic potency. A concentration/response relationship is determined by measuring the response of animals, usually rodents, exposed over a fixed time to different concentrations of a combustion atmosphere. This is accomplished by conducting a series of experiments in which the quantity of combusted material or the flow rate of diluting air is varied in order to produce the different concentrations. The number of animals showing a response, such as lethality or incapacitation, will increase as the exposure concentration is increased. In combustion toxicology, concentration traditionally has been expressed either as the mass of test material used per chamber unit volume (the material charge), or the material mass loss per chamber unit volume (the combustion product concentration). When the percent of animals responding within a specified time is plotted as a function of the logarithm of the concentration, a straight line is typically approximated. From these data, the concentration that will produce a response or effect in 50 percent of the animals within the specified time is obtained by statistical methods. This concentration, commonly termed the EC_{50}, is a measure of the toxic potency of the smoke. The EC_{50} is a general term and may be used for any observed response of the animal. When lethality is the observed response, the term LC_{50} is used to denote the concentration that produces death in 50 percent of the animals. Similarly, the IC_{50} designates the concentration necessary to incapacitate 50 percent of the animals.

Some test methods measure the rapidity of action of the combustion atmosphere rather than its toxic potency in causing either lethality or incapacitation. In these methods, the times are recorded at which animals die or are incapacitated when exposed to a fixed concentration of material or combustion atmosphere. From these data, a mean time-to-death or time-to-incapacitation is determined to characterize the toxicity of the smoke. If time to the effect (either death or incapacitation) is measured for different exposure concentrations, a time/concentration relationship can be determined.

The major test methods for assessing materials with regard to the toxic potency of combustion products can be summarized as follows.

DIN method: The DIN 53436 method (Federal Republic of Germany-Deutches Institut fuer Normung) is characterized by the use of a moving annular tube furnace operated at a constant temperature, with fire effluents being diluted with air.[33] Fire effluents are generated dynamically, i.e., continuously, over the exposure time of the animals. Concentration-response relationships are easily obtainable, with concentration being varied by dilution of the fire effluents before the rats are exposed. The test, primarily used under nonflaming conditions with rat lethality as the bioassay, is required in West Germany for certain "noncombustible" construction materials.

NBS method: The NBS test (U.S.—National Institute of Standards and Technology) is a static (closed) system using a cup-type furnace as the combustion device, operated just below and just above the autoignition temperature of the specimen.[34] Concentration-response (lethality) relationships for 30-min exposures (14-day post-exposure observation) are determined using rats held in tubular restrainers for head-only exposure. Six rats are used per test. Concentration is controlled by varying the sample weight charged to the cup. Data for both nonflaming and flaming combustion are obtained.

UPITT method: The UPITT test (U.S.—University of Pittsburgh) exposes four mice per test to fire effluents produced in a dynamic (flow-through) system from the 20°C per minute ramped heating of a specimen in a box or muffle furnace.[35,36] Exposures are for 30 min (plus 10 min postexposure), starting when 1 percent of the sample weight has been lost. Bioassays include concentration-response and time-to-death for lethality. Respiratory rate depression for assessment of irritants also was included in early versions of the test. In the UPITT test, the concentration term in the LC_{50} refers only to the weight of test specimen charged to the furnace. Thus, LC_{50} values for this test are not directly comparable to those from the NBS method. This test currently is required in the United States by the State of New York for certain construction materials. No acceptance levels have been set.

Japanese Building Law method: The Standard Fire Test of Japanese Building Law (Ministry of Construction—Code No. 1231) provided in 1976 for a gas toxicity test. This test employs a radiant heat furnace and exposes mice to smoke produced in a dynamic system from the ramped heating of a specimen.[37] Incapacitation times of eight mice placed in rotary cages are determined and compared with those for red lauan wood as a reference material. The test is required in Japan for "semi-noncombustible" and "fire-retardant materials" used as internal linings in certain types of buildings. Two new types of test apparatus using radiant heat cone-type heaters also are being used in research studies in Japan. Both expose mice in rotary cages for determination of the time to incapacitation.

Radiant Furnace method: The combustion device used in this method consists of a horizontally mounted cylindrical quartz combustion cell connected to an animal exposure chamber through a rectangular stainless steel chimney. The chimney is divided into three channels, creating a heat pump action by inducing smoke to flow up the center channel, while air from the exposure chamber circulates down the outer channels. External to the combustion cell are four tungsten-quartz radiant heatlamps focused onto the plane of the specimen. A platform accommodating test specimens is connected to a load cell located underneath the combustion chamber in order to monitor continuously the specimen weight. A high-energy spark plug is used as an ignition source.

Unique to this method is a proposal that the test method be used to develop an "index of potential toxic hazard" for screening of test materials by procedurally combining time to ignition, rate of decomposition, and toxic potency.* Alternatively, it has been proposed that these separate parameters be extracted from the test for use in toxic hazard engineering calculations. In this latter approach, a test specimen is subjected to ignition while exposed to radiant heat, with the smoke produced being collected for 30 min in a chamber communicating with the combustion assembly. Concentrations of the major gaseous toxicants are monitored over the 30-min period, with exposure doses for each being determined from integration of the areas under the respective concentration-time plots. These data, along with the mass loss of the test specimen during the test, are then used in calculations to estimate the 30-min LC_{50} of the test specimen. The estimated LC_{50} is then validated by exposure of rats. Validation assures that the monitored toxicants account for the observed toxic effects and that there is no unusual toxicity.

Toxicity data for materials and/or products are best obtained from laboratory tests which utilize a combination of analytical data along with exposure of rodents. The tests yield two useful types of information: 1) the principal type(s) of intoxication, i.e., asphyxiaton, sensory or pulmonary irritation, etc. and 2) the lethal toxic potency (LC_{50})

* This use of the test method is commonly referred to as the National Institute of Building Sciences (NIBS) test.

of the smoke. Toxic potency data obtained from laboratory tests are, however, subject to the following limitations and/or considerations:

1. No single laboratory combustion device is appropriate for all materials and products under the conditions of all fire types and stages. Therefore, there can be no universal "smoke toxicity test." The laboratory combustion device used in a test must be chosen and operated so as to replicate the conditions of the type of fire being examined. (Laboratory-scale combustion furnaces may, under certain conditions, produce less CO per unit mass of sample burned than would occur in a real fire. Thus, laboratory LC_{50} values may need to be "adjusted" for use in hazard calculations.)
2. All LC_{50} values have an associated level of statistical confidence. Furthermore, interlaboratory comparisons suggest LC_{50} determinations can vary by a factor of about 2.5.
3. Although calculated from data based on exposure of rodents, lethal toxic potency values can be extrapolated to human exposure with reasonable confidence for asphyxiants and for pulmonary irritation. Sensory irritation is not addressed with current laboratory smoke toxicity tests. (Hazard assessments currently tend to set threshold tenability levels for acid gases and other combustion products known to have irritant properties.)
4. Currently employed laboratory smoke toxicity tests do not directly measure the incapacitating effects of smoke inhalation. Incapacitation must be inferred from lethal toxic potency values.

TOXIC HAZARD ASSESSMENT

With the realization that data from laboratory smoke toxic potency tests are not at all indicative, in themselves, of toxic hazard, considerable effort in recent years has gone into the development of engineering calculations to provide for a better approach to the problem. These calculations range from that of a simple "hazard index" to more sophisticated models based on mass loss rates and either smoke toxic potency or toxicant yield data.

For example, in order to provide for a toxic hazard parameter having at least some integration of toxicity and combustibility factors, a "Quick Toxic Hazard Index" has been proposed.[38] For a specific material, it involves the mass loss rate per unit area divided by the product of the time to ignition and the LC_{50} (as determined by any of the common test methods). The hazard index is not intended to be a substitute for a comprehensive assessment, but it does reflect the dependence of toxic hazard on fire growth. The method has been criticized as assuming an arbitrary, oversimplified, and perhaps even unrealistic relationship between mass loss rate, time to ignition, and toxic potency.

Toxic hazard is being investigated increasingly by using mathematical modeling methodology. The most widely used approach to hazard models involves incremental exposure doses ($C \times dt$) of a toxic species which are calculated and related to the specific Ct exposure dose required to produce a given toxicological effect. Thus, a Fractional Effective Dose (FED) is calculated for each small time interval.[39] Continuous summation or integration of these fractional effective doses is carried out in order to calculate the accumulated exposure dose of a toxic species.

Mathematically, the FED of an individual toxic component "i" can be expressed as:

$$\text{FED} = \int_{o}^{t} \frac{C_i}{(Ct)_i}\, dt \qquad (1)$$

where C_i is the concentration of the toxic component "i" and $(Ct)_i$ is the specific exposure dose required to produce the toxicological effect, usually lethality. Concentrations may be in units of percent or ppm for toxicant gases or $g{\cdot}m^{-3}$ (mass loss per unit volume) for smoke produced from the burning of a material.

Since fractional effective doses for individual toxicants have, to a first approximation, been shown to be additive, the total FED for a system can be represent by:

$$\text{Total FED} = \sum_{i=1}^{n} \int_{o}^{t} \frac{C_i}{(Ct)_i}\, dt \qquad (2)$$

where, again, concentration values may be in percent or ppm for toxicant gases or in mass loss per unit volume for smoke from materials.

Most toxicological modeling methodologies make use of these concepts in one form or another. Individual toxicant concentration data are useful in estimating LC_{50} values for the smoke produced from the burning of a material and also for predicting the time to hazardous conditions in a real fire, provided that the appropriate data are available. Mass loss data are useful for predicting hazardous conditions in a real fire if LC_{50} values for individual materials are known. Even if these values are not known, simplifying assumptions can often be made to enable one to obtain useful information.

A variation of the FED is the N-Gas model[40]. This model is based upon studies of the lethal interactions in rats of four gases (CO, CO_2, HCN, and low O_2). Although it is really a form of the FED model, in that gas concentrations are expressed as fractions of lethal concentrations, it does not allow for the integration of changing concentrations with time. It is used largely for 30-min exposures to *constant* concentrations. However, other exposure times may be used. The method is mainly useful for small-scale materials tests or smoke samples taken from large-scale tests to determine the extent to which rat lethality can be explained in terms of the four common gases, or whether some other agent is important in causing the toxic effects.

The following equation has been derived experimentally to predict the death of 50 percent of exposed rats within either a 30-min exposure or a 24-hr postexposure period for the four gases:

$$\frac{m\,(Co)}{(CO_2) - b} + \frac{(HCN)}{LC_{50}\,HCN} + \frac{21 - (O_2)}{21 - LC_{50}O_2} = 1 \qquad (3)$$

The brackets indicate actual concentrations of the gases. The LC_{50} value of CO is based on 30-min exposures and is 6600 ppm. The LC_{50} value of HCN is 160 ppm for deaths occurring within the 30-min exposure or 110 ppm for deaths occurring during exposure or in the subsequent 24-hr postexposure observation period. And 5.4 is the percent O_2 that cause 50 percent of the animals to die in 30 min. The terms m and b are the slope and intercept of the interactive curve of CO and CO_2 which depicts the increasing toxicity of CO as CO_2 increases up to 5 percent. These terms equal –18 and 122,000, respectively, if the CO_2 concentrations are 5 percent or less; and 23 and –39,000, respectively, if the CO_2 concentrations are above 5 percent. The period under consideration here is restricted to 24 hrs. A more recent version of the N-Gas model also includes a term for incorporating the postexposure lethality of rats due to the pulmonary irritant effects of HCl.

Another model, also based on FED concepts, is applied to actual physiological uptake functions and to effects of the major toxic fire gases.[29] It is designed to predict toxic hazard in terms of exposure dose and time to incapacitation for humans in fires, and is intended for use in fire engineering calculations of modeled fire scenarios, full-scale fire tests, and data related to real fire victims. Like all the multiple toxicant models, it relies on measured or calculated concentration-time data for the important toxic fire gases. Potentially, it may be the most sophisticated of models, making use of known physiological reactions of humans to CO, CO_2, HCN, oxygen vitiation, irritants and even heat and smoke obscuration. The FED equations developed for the model are derived primarily from experimental data obtained with humans and primates.

Many of the basic concepts of toxicological modeling just described are employed in the tenability (TENAB) routine used in Hazard I program developed at the Center for Fire Research of the National Institute of Standards and Technology.[41] Hazard I combines expert judgment and calculations to estimate the consequences of a specified fire. The heart of the model is a sequence of computer software procedures that calculate the development of hazardous conditions over time and, the time needed by building occupants to escape under those conditions, and an estimate of the resulting loss of life based on tenability criteria and assumed occupant behavior.

The tenability routine in Hazard I calculates the impact of the fire on occupants, predicting whether or not escape is made. Toxicity is appraised in two ways: (1) using a concentration-time product parameter (Ct) for smoke; and (2) by an FED method which considers exposure to hydrogen cyanide and carbon monoxide, as well as accounts for the impact of the simultaneous exposure to carbon dioxide and reduced oxygen.

Overall, the best strategy currently available for evaluating the potential toxic hazards in the event of fire involving materials and/or products involves the following elements:

1. Identify each product/occupancy/fire scenario.
2. Using fire performance data for candidate materials obtained from relevant laboratory tests, engineering calculations appropriate to each fire scenario should be carried out to determine the sensitivity of the predicted toxic hazard to toxic potency. This is done using a range of arbitrary toxic potency values in the calculations.
3. If the predicted toxic hazard of a scenario is found to be relatively insensitive to toxic potency, there should be no need to determine actual values. Attention should be concentrated on other parameters.
4. Should the predicted toxic hazard of a scenario be deemed significantly sensitive to toxic potency, laboratory smoke toxicity testing should then be conducted to identify the principal toxic effects and to establish the actual LC_{50} values for use in the engineering calculations.
5. Experimentally determined toxic potency data for candidate materials and/or products should then be used in the hazard engineering calculations in order to characterize their relative firesafety implications.

Since considerable judgment is required in conducting hazard assessment, the various models should be selected and used under the guidance of an expert professional skilled in the various techniques.

HEAT

The burning of most materials is an exothermic chemical oxidation process. Energy from the process is evolved as heat, which possesses both convective (hot gases) and radiative components. The radiative component represents energy released in the visible and infrared portions of the spectrum and is seen as flame or luminosity of a fire.

Heat poses a significant physical danger to humans. If the total heat energy reacting with the body surpasses the capability of the physiological defense processes to compensate, a series of events will occur, ranging from minor injury to death. The effects of exposure to heated air are greatly augmented by the presence of moisture in the fire atmosphere. With higher moisture content, transfer of heat energy is more efficient and the body is less able to rid itself of the heat burden. Moisture can be present in a fire environment as the result of natural humidity, from the combustion itself, and from the application of water for extinguishment.

If excessive heat is conducted rapidly to the lungs, a serious decline in blood pressure may result, along with capillary blood vessel collapse, leading to circulatory failure. Severe heat also may cause fluid buildup in the lungs. In fire tests conducted by the National Research Council of Canada (NRCC), 300°F (140°C) was taken as the maximum survivable breathing air temperature.[42] A temperature this high can be endured for only a short period and not at all in the presence of moisture. It has been suggested that fire fighters should not enter any hostile atmosphere without full protective clothing and masks.

In school fire tests conducted in Los Angeles in 1959, a temperature of 150°F (65°C) at the 5-ft (1.5 m) level was selected as the temperature beyond which teachers and children could not be expected to enter a corridor from a relatively cool room.[43] This selection assumed exposure to dry air, and only for the brief period of time necessary to reach exits.

Skin tissue burns commonly are classified as first-, second-, or third-degree burns. First-degree burns involve only the outer layer of the skin and are characterized by abnormal redness, pain, and sometimes a small accumulation of fluid underneath the skin. Second-degree burns penetrate more deeply into the skin. The burned area is moist and pink, the skin blisters, and there is usually a considerable amount of subcutaneous fluid accumulation. Third-degree burns usually are dry, charred, or pearly white. If a large percentage of the body skin tissue has suffered third-degree burns, post-exposure consequences may be extremely critical.

Studies have shown that a skin surface temperature as low as 160°F (71°C) will result in second-degree burns if contact is maintained for 60 sec.[44] If the surface temperature is increased, the time to produce second-degree burns decreases. For example, burns result in 30 sec at 180°F (82°C), and in 15 sec at 212°F (100°C). A tolerance limit for radiant heat of 0.25 W/cm^2 has been suggested.[45]

Before human skin can absorb sufficient heat to raise its surface temperature, the body's heat-dissipating capabilities must be defeated. The body dissipates heat by evaporative cooling (perspiration) and by circulation of blood. The cooling effect of evaporation of skin moisture may compensate for the effect of heat on skin up to 140°F (60°C) or more in dry air. This limit is lower in moist air. The time for the skin temperature to increase depends upon the exposure temperature, which, in most fires, increases very rapidly. Under these conditions, the skin temperature may increase faster than the defense mechanisms can function. Thermal tolerance data for unprotected skin of humans at rest would suggest a limit of about 248°F (121°C), above which considerable pain would quickly be incurred.[29] Exposure to convective heat below this temperature may still result in hyperthermia, without the production of actual burns.

Hyperthermia occurs if the body absorbs heat faster than it can be dissipated by evaporation of surface moisture and outward radiation. The entire body temperature is thereby elevated sufficiently above normal to cause damage to the central nervous system and, possibly, death.

VISIBLE SMOKE

In addition to fire gases, smoke also consists of finely divided particulate matter and suspended liquid droplets known as aerosols. These are formed from the burning of most materials under the conditions of incomplete combustion normally present in fires. Since the average size of the particulates and aerosols is about the same as the wavelength of visible light, the light is scattered and vision through smoke is obscured. Petroleum-derived materials, especially those from aromatic hydrocarbons, are particularly prone to the formation of dark, sooty smoke. There is, however, no relationship between the color of visible smoke and the toxicity of fire gases that may be present.

Since smoke obscures the passage of light, visibility to exits may be blocked, thus impairing escape of victims from a fire. The development of quantities of smoke sufficient to impair egress can be very rapid and usually is the first hazard to occur in a fire. As evidenced in nearly every one of the Los Angeles school fire tests, smoke in the corridors arising from fires in the basement reached untenable levels before temperatures attained hazardous conditions.[43] In the tests, smoke, as it pertained to visibility, was the principal hazard. Although smoke frequently provides an early warning of fire, it also contributes to creation of panic because of its blinding and irritating effects.

Smoke obscuration normally is expressed either as the optical density per meter (OD/m) or as the extinction coefficient, K ($K = OD/m \times 2.3$). Tenability limits for the extinction coefficient of from 1.2/m[45] down to 0.15/m[46] have been suggested, the latter value being appropriate for subjects unfamiliar with a route of escape.

Smoke particulates and aerosols also can be harmful when inhaled, and long exposure may cause damage to the respiratory system. Smoke particulates often are of a sufficiently small size that enable them to be inhaled deeply into the lungs, where absorbed toxicants may produce damage to the respiratory system. These effects have not been sufficiently studied as to enable a full understanding of their consequences.

DEVELOPMENT OF TOXIC HAZARDS

Full-scale fire tests are useful for placing the development of toxic hazard in perspective. Four such tests were reported by Southwest Research Institute (SWRI) in which fires were set in a fully furnished simulated hotel room with attached corridor and remote room.[47] (See Figure 3-1A.) During the tests, the door from the fire room to the corridor was fully open. The door between the corridor and the remote room was open approximately 1 in. (25 mm) until about 3 min after flashover, when it was closed to prevent the development of excessive concentrations of toxicants.

The sequence of events that occurred in the burn room is shown as a composite illustration in Figure 3-1B. The tests were initiated with a smoldering fire in the chair closest to the sofa. During the smoldering phase of approximately 19 min, no conditions were attained which would be considered hazardous to life. Following flaming ignition of the chair, the fire progressed rapidly to flashover within about 8 min, accompanied by life-threatening conditions of temperature, carbon monoxide, hydrogen cyanide, and oxygen depletion in the room of origin. After flashover in the burn room, tenability in the remote room also quickly deteriorated, as shown in Figure 3-1C, first with visual obscuration by smoke, followed by rapidly increasing concentrations of toxic gases. Test animals (rats) in the remote room became incapacitated within about 2 min, with death occurring from carbon monoxide asphyxiation approximately 11 min after flashover. From present knowledge of carbon monoxide intoxication, it is likely that humans in the remote room would have been incapacitated and killed in approximately the same time intervals.

It was considered significant in these tests that the toxic hazard did not develop until flashover was approached in the burn room. After that point, smoke obscuration and life-threatening conditions increased very rapidly in the burn room, corridor, and the remote room. The smoke detectors employed in these tests provided adequate warning (5 min) prior to the development of acutely toxic concentrations of combustion products. The sprinkler activation times demonstrated that a properly installed and working sprinkler system, by controlling the fire at an early stage, would have prevented any significant toxic threat from developing.

Combustion products produced in a fire are always toxic and extremely hazardous to life safety. Calculations have shown that exposure to smoke for 30 min from the consumption by burning of only about 300 g of fuel load in a 3 × 4 × 2.5-m room would be likely hazardous to an occupant.[48] It was further calculated that the burning of only about 12 kg of a material, testing as "typical" in a smoke toxicity test, would produce sufficient smoke as to be hazardous in 20 such rooms upon only 15 min of exposure. Smoke, even of "average" toxicity, is still *very* toxic.

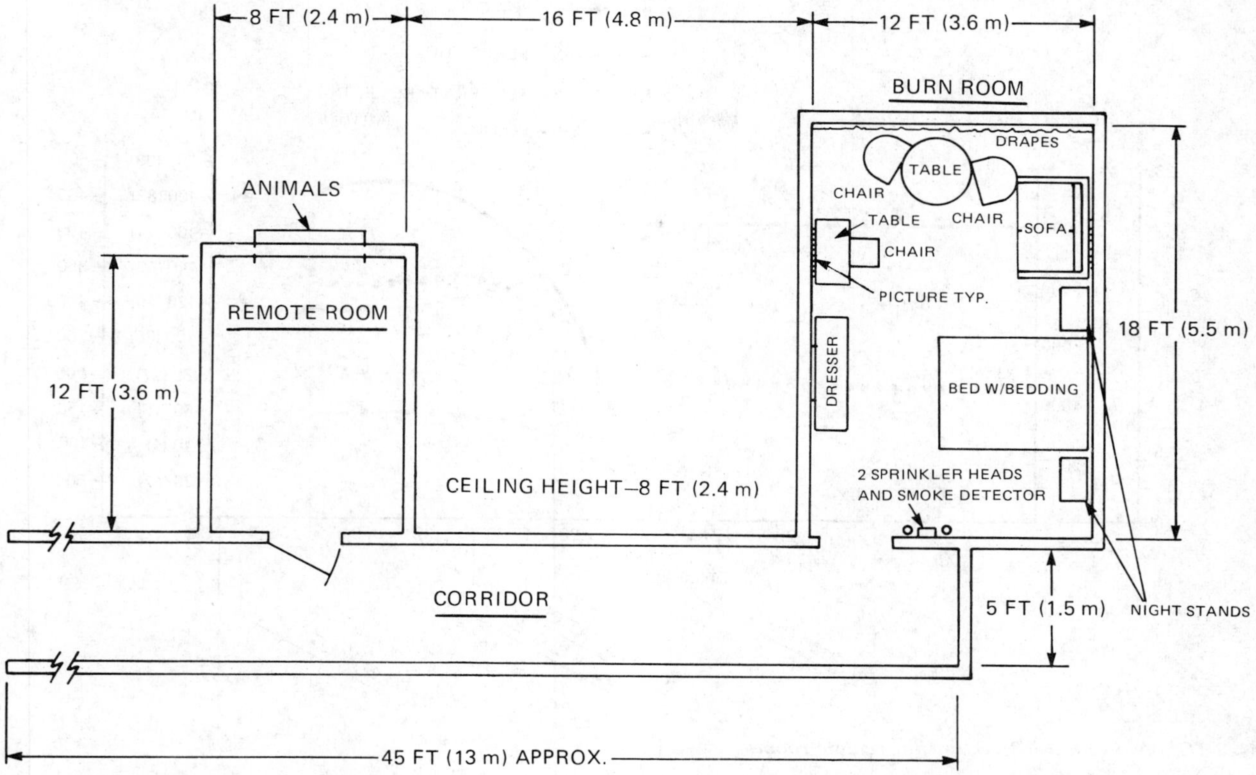

FIG. 3-1A. Burn room, corridor, and remote room full-scale test facility at Southwest Research Institute.

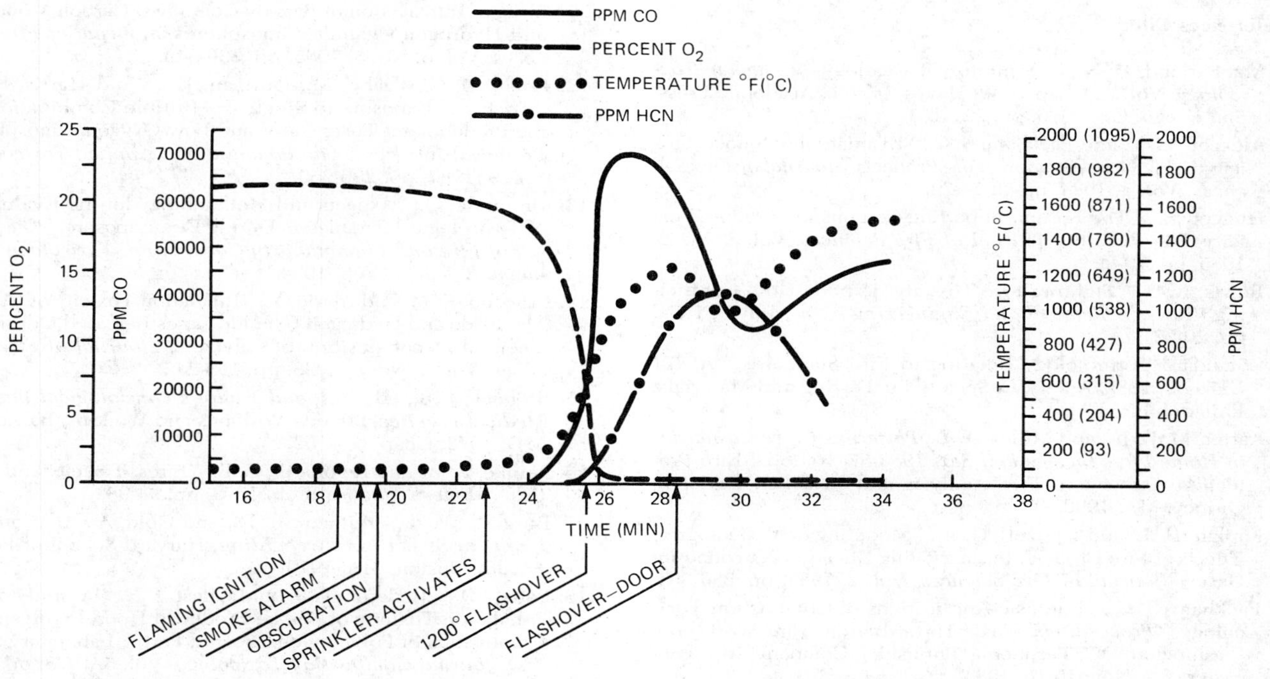

FIG. 3-1B. Composite illustration of events and development of hazardous conditions at 5½-ft (1.7 m) level in the burn room during fully furnished room fires conducted at SWRI.

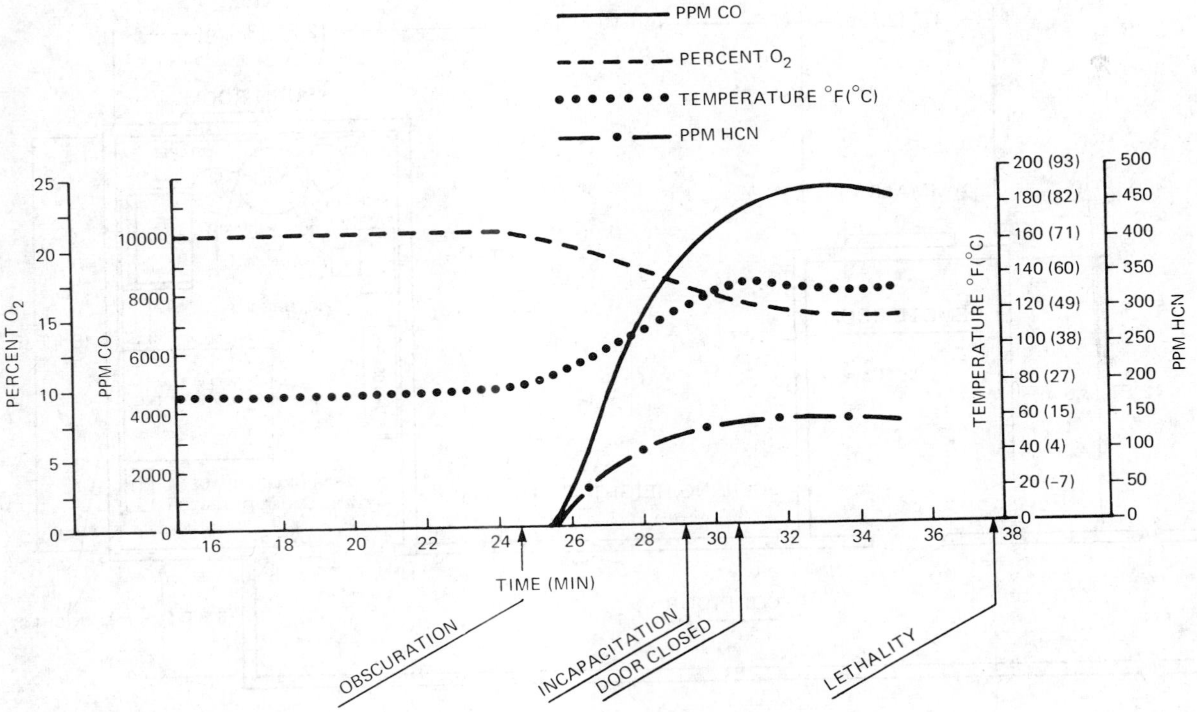

***FIG. 3-1C.** As in Figure 3-1B, but for remote room.*

BIBLIOGRAPHY

References Cited

1. MacFarland, H. N., "Respiratory Toxicology," *Essays in Toxicology*, Vol. 7., Chap. 5, W. Hayes, Jr., ed., Academic Press, San Diego, CA, 1976, pp. 121-154.
2. Alexeeff, G. V. and Packham, S. C., "Evaluation of Smoke Toxicity Using Concentration-Time Products," *Journal of Fire Sciences*, Vol. 2, 1984, pp. 362-379.
3. Huggett, C., "The Forum: Reporting Combustion Product Toxicity Test Results," *Journal of Fire Sciences*, Vol. 3, No. 2, 1985, pp. 79-82.
4. Rawls, R. L., "Fighting Fire Toxicity: Experts Hold Conflicting Views," *Chemical and Engineering News*, July 9, 1984, pp. 20-22.
5. "Standard Terminology Relating to Fire Standards," *ASTM E176-82*, 1982, American Society for Testing and Materials, Philadelphia, PA.
6. Karter, M. J., Jr., and Miller, A. L., *Patterns of Fire Casualties in Home Fires by Age and Sex, 1983-87*, National Fire Protection Association Fire Analysis and Research Division, Quincy, MA, 1990.
7. Kaplan, H. L. and Hartzell, G. E., "Modeling of Toxicological Effects of Fire Gases: I. Incapacitating Effects of Narcotic Fire Gases," *Journal of Fire Sciences*, Vol. 2, 1984, pp. 286-305.
8. Packham, S. C., "Forensic Applications of Combustion Toxicology," *Proceedings*, Toxic Hazards from Fire Workshop, Washington, DC, Technomic Publishing Company, Inc., Lancaster, PA, Nov. 15-16, 1984.
9. Halpin, B. M. and Berl, W. G., "Human Fatalities from Unwanted Fires," Report NBS-GCR-79-168, U.S. National Bureau of Standards, Washington, DC, 1978.
10. Harland, W. A. and Woolley, W. E., "Fire Fatality Study," *Building Research Establishment Information Paper*, University of Glasgow, IP 18/79, Glasgow, Scotland.
11. Hartzell, G. E., Switzer, W. G., and Priest, D. N., "Modeling of Toxicological Effects of Fire Gases: V. Mathematical Modeling of Intoxication of Rats by Combined Carbon Monoxide and Hydrogen Cyanide Atmospheres," *Journal of Fire Sciences*, Vol. 3, No. 5, 1985, pp. 330-342.
12. Levin, B. C., Paabo, M., Gurman, J. L., and Harris, S. E., "Effects of Exposure to Single or Multiple Combinations of the Predominant Toxic Gases and Low-Oxygen Atmospheres Produced in Fires," *Fundamental and Applied Toxicology*, Vol. 9, 1987, pp. 236-250.
13. Kimmerle, G., "Aspects and Methodology for the Evaluation of Toxicological Parameters During Fire Exposure," *The Journal of Fire and Flammability Combustion Toxicology Supplement*, Vol. 1, Feb. 1974.
14. Esposito, F. M. and Alarie, Y., "Inhalation Toxicity of Carbon Monoxide and Hydrogen Cyanide Gases Released During the Thermal Decomposition of Polymers," *Journal of Fire Sciences*, Vol. 6, No. 3, 1988, pp. 195-242.
15. Brobeck, J. R., ed., *Best and Taylor's Physiological Basis of Medical Practice*, 9th ed., Williams and Wolkins, Baltimore, MD, 1973, Chap. 6, p. 52.
16. Reinke, R. W. and Reinhardt, C. F., "Fires, Toxicity and Plastics," *Modern Plastics*, Feb. 1973, pp. 94-98.
17. Burgess, W. A., Treitman, R. D., and Gold, A., *Air Contaminants in Structural Firefighting*, Harvard School of Public Health, Boston, MA, 1979.
18. Potts, J. W., Lederer, T. S., and Quast, J. F., "A Study of the Inhalation Toxicity of Smoke Produced Upon Pyrolysis and Combustion of Polyethylene Foams, Part I: Laboratory Studies," *Journal Combustion Toxicology*, Vol. 5, 1978, pp. 408-433.
19. Kaplan, H. L., *et al.*, "A Research Study of the Assessment of Escape Impairment by Irritant Combustion Gases in Postcrash Aircraft Fires," Southwest Research Institute, *Final Report, DOT/FAA/CT-84/16*, U.S. Department of Transportation, Federal Aviation Administration, Atlantic City, NJ, 1984.

20. Barrow, C. S., Alarie, Y., and Stock, M. F., "Sensory Irritation Evoked by the Thermal Decomposition Products of Plasticized Poly-Vinyl Chloride," *Journal of Fire and Materials*, Vol. 1, 1976, pp. 147-153.

21. Kaplan, H. L., Anzueto, A., Switzer, W. G., and Hinderer, R. K., "Acute Respiratory Effects of Inhaled Polyvinyl Chloride (PVC) Smoke in Nonhuman Primates," *The Toxicologist*, Abstracts of Papers, Society of Toxicology, Inc., 26th Annual Meeting, Vol. 1, No. 1, 1987, p. 202.

22. Hartzell, G. E., Packham, S. C., Grand, A. F., and Switzer, W. G., "Modeling of Toxicological Effects of Fire Gases: III. Quantification of Postexposure Lethality of Rats from Exposure to HCl Atmospheres," *Journal of Fire Sciences*, Vol. 3, No. 3, 1985, pp. 195-207.

23. Hartzell, G. E., Grand, A. F., and Switzer, W. G., "Modeling of Toxicological Effects of Fire Gases: VI. Further Studies on the Toxicity of Smoke Containing Hydrogen Chloride," *Journal of Fire Sciences*, Vol. 5, No. 6, 1987, pp. 368-391.

24. Henderson, Y. and Haggard, N., "Noxious Gases and the Principles of Respiration Influencing Their Action," *Chemical Catalog Co.*, New York, 1927, pp. 126-127.

25. *Chlorine and Hydrogen Chloride*, National Academy of Sciences, National Research Council, Washington, DC, 1976, p. 142.

26. Hartzell, *et al.* Unpublished data.

27. Tsuchiya, Y., "Relative Significance of NO_x and HCN in Fire Gas Toxicity," Second International Symposium on Fire Safety Science, Tokyo, Japan, 1988.

28. Kaplan, H. L., Grand, A. F., and Hartzell, G. E., *Combustion Toxicology: Principles and Test Methods*, Technomic Publishing Co., Inc., Lancaster, PA, 1983.

29. Purser, D. A., "Toxicity Assessment of Combustion Products," *The SFPE Handbook of Fire Protection Engineering*, National Fire Protection Association, Quincy, MA, Sect. 1, Chap. 14, 1988, pp. 200-245.

30. Kaplan, H. L., Southwest Research Institute, personal communication, 1987.

31. Hartzell, G. E., Grand, A. F., and Switzer, W. G., "Studies on the Toxicity of Smoke Containing Hydrogen Chloride," Symposium on Fire and Polymers, American Chemical Society Meeting, Dallas, TX, 1989.

32. Levin, B. C., Paabo, M., Gurman, J. L., Harris, S. E., and Braun, E., "Toxicological Interactions Between Carbon Monoxide and Carbon Dioxide," *Proceedings* of 16th Conference on Toxicology, Air Force Medical Research Laboratory, Dayton, OH, October 1986; *Toxicology*, Vol. 47, pp. 135-164.

33. German Standards Institution, DIN 53436, 1981.

34. Levin, B. C., Fowell, A. J., Birky, M. M., Paabo, M., Stolte, A., and Malek, D., "Further Development of a Test Method for Assessment of the Acute Inhalation Toxicity of Combustion Products," *NBSIR 82-2532*, National Institute of Standards and Technology, Gaithersburg, MD, 1982.

35. Kaplan, H. L., Grand, A. F., and Hartzell, G. E., *Combustion Toxicology: Principles and Test Methods*, Technomic Publishing Company, Inc., Lancaster, PA, 1983, pp. 83-108.

36. "New York State Uniform Fire Prevention and Building Code," Article 15, Part 1120, *Combustion Toxicity Testing*, Office of Fire Prevention and Control, Department of State, New York State, Albany, NY, 1986.

37. Tsuchiya, Y., "New Japanese Standard Test for Combustion Gas Toxicity," *Journal of Combustion Toxicology*, Vol. 4, 1977, pp. 5-7.

38. Babrauskas, V., Ph.D., "Toxic Hazard from Fires: A Simple Assessment Method," *Fire: Control the Heat...Reduce the Hazard*, QMC Fire and Materials Centre, London, 1988, pp. 16.1-16.10.

39. Hartzell, G. E. and Emmons, H. W., "The Fractional Effective Dose Model for Assessment of Hazards Due to Smoke from Materials," *Journal of Fire Sciences*, Vol. 6, No. 5, 1988, pp. 356-362.

40. Levin, B. C., Paabo, M., Gurman, J. J., and Harris, S. E., "Effects of Exposure to Single or Multiple Combinations of the Predominant Toxic Gases and Low Oxygen Atmospheres Produced in Fires," *Fundamental and Applied Toxicology*, Vol. 9, pp. 236-250, 1987.

41. Bukowski, R. W., Peakcock, R. D. Jones, W. W., and Forney C. L., "HAZARD I Fire Hazard Assessment Method," *NIST Handbook 146*, National Institute of Standards and Technology, Gaithersburg, MD, 1989.

42. Shorter, G. W., *et al.*, "The St. Lawrence Burns," *NFPA Quarterly*, Vol. 53, No. 4 (Apr. 1960) pp. 300-316.

43. *Operation School Burning*, National Fire Protection Association, Quincy, MA, 1959, p. 25.

44. Woodson, W. E., *Human Factors Design Handbook*, McGraw-Hill, Inc., New York, 1981, p. 812.

45. Babrauskas, V., Ph.D., "Full-Scale Burning Behavior of Upholstered Chairs," *Technical Note 1103*, National Institute of Standards and Technology, Gaithersburg, MD, 1979.

46. Jin, T., *Journal of Fire and Flammability*, Vol. 12, 1981, p. 130. (No longer published.)

47. Grand, A. F., *et al.*, "An Evaluation of Toxic Hazards from Full-Scale Furnished Room Fire Studies," ASTM Symposium on Application of Fire Science to Fire Engineering, Denver, CO, June 26-27, 1984, *ASTM Special Technical Publication* (STP), Philadelphia, PA, 1985.

48. Hartzell, G. E., "Understanding of Hazards to Humans," *Advances in Combustion Toxicology*, Vol. 1, G. E. Hartzell, ed., Technomic Publishing Company, Inc., Lancaster, PA, 1988, pp. 33-34.

Additional Reading

Alarie, Y. and Anderson, R., "Toxicologic Classification of Thermal Decomposition Products of Synthetic and Natural Polymers," *Toxicology and Applied Pharmacology*, Vol. 57, 1981, pp. 181-188.

Babrauskas, V., "Fire Hazard Comparison of Fire Retarded and Non-Fire Retarded Products," *NBS SP 749*, National Bureau of Standards, Gaithersburg, MD, July 1988.

Babrauskas, V., Levine, B. C., and Gann, R. G., "A New Approach to Fire Toxicity Data for Hazard Evaluation," *Fire Journal*, Vol. 81, No. 2 (Mar./Apr. 1987) p. 22.

Birky, M. M., "Toxicity and Incapacitation Due to Hydrogen Chloride," *Fire and Materials*, Vol. 10, 1986, p. 125.

Braun, E., *et al.*, "Large-Scale Compartment Fire Toxicity Study: Comparison with Small-Scale Toxicity Test Results," *NBSIR 88-3764*, National Bureau of Standards, Gaithersburg, MD, July 1988.

Bukowski, R. W., Peacock, R. D., Jones, W. W., and Forney, C. L., "HAZARD I Fire Hazard Assessment Method," *NIST Handbook 146*, National Institute of Standards and Technology, Gaithersburg, MD, 1989.

Cooper, L. Y., "Compartment Fire-Generated Environment and Smoke Filling," *SFPE Handbook of Fire Protection Engineering*, National Fire Protection Association, Quincy, MA, 1988.

Emmons, H. W., "Why Fire Model? The MGM Fire and Toxicity Testing," *Fire Safety Journal*, Vol. 13, 1988, p. 77.

Fowell, A. J., "Assessing Toxic Hazard as It Relates to Overall Fire Hazard," *Fire Technology*, Vol. 21, No. 3, 1985, pp. 199-212.

Hartzell, G. E., ed., *Advances in Combustion Toxicology*, Vols. 1 and 2, Technomic Publishing Company, Inc., Lancaster, PA, 1988.

Hartzell, G. E., Priest, D. N., and Switzer, W. G., "Mathematical Modeling of Toxicological Effects of Fire Gases," *First International Symposium on Fire Safety Science*, Hemisphere Publishing Co., 1986, p. 1059.

Harwood, B., and Hall, J. R., "What Kills in Fires: Smoke Inhalation or Burns?" *Fire Journal*, Vol. 83, No. 3 (May/June 1989) p. 28.

Jin, T. Y., "Irritating Effect of Fire Smoke on Visibility," *Fire Science and Technology*, Vol. 5, 1985, p. 79.

Jones, G. R. N., "Cyanide and Fire Victims: A Hazard in Focus," *Fire Technology*, Vol. 26, No. 2, 1990, pp. 141-148.

Kaplan, H. L., Grand, A. F., and Hartzell, G. E., *Combustion Toxicology: Principles and Test Methods*, Technomic Publishing Company, Inc., Lancaster, PA, 1983.

Levin, B., *et al.*, "Further Development of a Test Method for the Assessment of the Acute Inhalation Toxicity of Combustion Products," *NBSIR 82-2532*, National Bureau of Standards, Washington, DC, June 1982.

Levin, B. C., "An Exploration of Combustion Limitations and Alternatives to the NBS Toxicity Test Method," *NBSIR 85-3274*, National Bureau of Standards, Washington, DC, 1985.

Levin, B. C., *Toxicological Effects of the Interactions of Fire Gases*, Center for Fire Research, Gaithersburg, MD, 1986.

Levin, B. C., Paabo, M. P., Gurman, J. L., and Harris, S. E., "Effects of Exposure to Single or Multiple Combinations of the Predominant Toxic Gases and Low Oxygen Atmospheres Produced in Fires," *Fundamental and Applied Toxicology*, Vol. 9, 1987, p. 236.

Mulholland, G., "Smoke Production and Properties," *SFPE Handbook of Fire Protection Engineering*, National Fire Protection Association, Quincy, MA, 1988.

Purser, D. A., "The Effects of Fire Products on Escape Capability in Primates and Human Fire Victims," *Proceedings* of the First International Symposium on Fire Safety Science, Hemisphere Publishing Corp., New York, 1986, pp. 1101-1110.

Purser, D. A., "Toxicity Assessment of Combustion Products and Modeling Toxic and Thermal Hazards of Fire," *SFPE Handbook of Fire Protection Engineering*, National Fire Protection Association, Quincy, MA, 1988.

Teague, P. E., "The Analysis of the Toxicity Problem Continues," *Fire Journal*, Vol. 83, No. 3 (May/June 1989) p. 62.

Tewarson, A., "Generation of Heat and Chemical Compounds in Fires," *SFPE Handbook of Fire Protection Engineering*, National Fire Protection Association, Quincy, MA, 1988.

Woolley W. D. and Fardell, P. J., "Basic Aspects of Combustion Toxicology," *Fire Safety Journal*, Vol. 5, 1982, pp. 29-48.

Zikria, B., *et al.*, "Smoke and Carbon Monoxide Poisoning in Fire Victims," *Journal of Trauma*, Vol. 12, No. 6, 1972.

FIRE HAZARDS OF MATERIALS: AN OVERVIEW

Frederic B. Clarke

This section of the handbook is devoted to the specific fire problems posed by various kinds of materials. Solving such problems involves preventing ignition or, if ignition occurs, minimizing the size of the fire. In addition, increased attention must be paid to understanding and controlling the effects of smoke. Such effects include smoke's toxic and chemical characteristics, as well as its ability to hamper vision.

This chapter addresses the various kinds of fire hazards, ways of characterizing those hazards, and some of the methods used to reduce them. The most commonly encountered classes of materials, and their special fire problems, are dealt with in detail in the succeeding chapters of this section.

Ordinary burning means oxidation, i.e., the chemical reaction of a material with oxygen to form relatively simple compounds called oxides. A material will burn if the reaction with oxygen results in the release of energy, which usually appears as heat and light. The first descriptor of the hazard of a material might be the amount of heat it produces when it burns, i.e., the heat of combustion. The greater the heat of combustion, the greater its potential as a fuel, and the hotter it burns.

The amount of heat produced on burning is determined almost entirely by the chemical composition of the material. The speed with which the heat is produced, on the other hand, is determined by the physical form of the material. For example, excelsior burns more quickly than a solid block of wood, although equal weights of the two will produce essentially the same amount of heat.

BURNING OF MATERIALS

Organic Materials

Any discussion of the fire hazards of materials must center upon those materials that are organically derived, i.e., those that are based on carbon. This is simply because organic materials as a class are ubiquitous. The simplest organic compounds, such as methane and propane, are common commercial fuels. They are also building blocks for more complex materials. Organic liquids are fuels, solvents, and chemical intermediates, but the richest variety of materials are organic solids. They include everything from specific compounds, such as aspirin, to common but complex everyday materials, such as wood, paper, textiles, and common plastics. These materials have carbon as their principal constituent; almost all contain hydrogen; and many contain oxygen, nitrogen, and other elements in varying amounts. Most organic materials burn readily. The common products of combustion of organic materials are water, which is the oxide of hydrogen, and carbon dioxide.

A tabulation of the heats of combustion of organic materials is contained in Appendix A. The heats of combustion outlined in that appendix are based on complete burning. In practice, there may be insufficient oxygen available to convert all of the carbon to carbon dioxide; some carbon monoxide or soot may be formed. Thus, as a practical matter, the heats are upper limits of the actual amount of heat to be expected for the combustion of materials under normal conditions.

Examination of the heat of combustion tables in Appendix A will show that, while the heat of combustion is quite different for different organic materials, the heat produced per equivalent of oxygen consumed is the same within about 10 percent. This fact, sometimes called Thornton's Rule,[1] allows one to use oxygen consumption as a reasonable measure of the heat produced by a burning organic material.

Solid organic materials fall into two broad classes: (1) hydrocarbon based, and (2) cellulose based. The former are derivatives of the unoxidized hydrocarbon building blocks: $-CH_2-$, or $-CH-$. The latter are based on a partly oxidized carbon unit: $-CH(OH)-$. In a sense, cellulose-based material is already partly burned in its natural state, so that when the two classes are combusted to carbon dioxide and water, cellulose consumes less oxygen and produces less heat.

For equivalent amounts of oxide formed, the hydrocarbon-based materials consume 50 percent more oxygen and thus produce about 50 percent more heat. On a

Frederic B. Clarke, Ph.D., is president of Benjamin/Clarke Associates, Inc., of Kensington, MD, a firm specializing in fire hazard analysis.

weight basis, the difference is greater; hydrocarbons produce over twice the heat, pound for pound, as do cellulosics.

Until the middle 1950s, this fact was of limited significance to life safety. Naturally occurring hydrocarbon materials were almost entirely industrial chemicals or commercial fuels, and the civilian population exposed to such fires was relatively small. However, the development of modern plastics changed all that. Most plastics are made from hydrocarbon, not cellulosic, materials. Their wide use in building materials and consumer goods, such as furniture, has meant increasingly that the burning properties of hydrocarbons are of consequence to the firesafety of the general population.

Polymers

The linking of small molecules into long chains is called polymerization. The products are called polymers. Most of the simplest polymers are manmade and are what are commonly referred to as "plastics." Polyethylene, a long, relatively unbranched hydrocarbon chain, is produced by the end-to-end linkage of ethylene molecules, C_2H_2. A typical "molecule" of polyethylene will consist of several thousand ethylene units joined together. The repeating units used to make up the polymer are called monomers.

$$+CH_2 - CH_2+CH_2 - CH_2+CH_2 - CH_2+$$

$$\nwarrow \qquad \uparrow \qquad \nearrow$$

Original Ethylene Units

Naturally occurring polymers are drawn from a smaller class of monomers than are manmade materials. However, they have a wide variety of structural variations, and these, more than chemical differences, account for the differing properties of such natural materials as wood, paper, and cotton. All of these are cellulosic materials; they have a polymeric backbone based on the glucose molecule, $C_6H_{12}O_6$. There are other natural polymer families as well, e.g., protein-based materials, but the cellulosics are particularly widespread.

Rate of Burning

The rate at which the fire products are produced is always an important component of fire hazard, whether the concern is for heat, smoke, or toxic gases. Later sections of this chapter address the measurement of this factor, but it is instructive to examine some of the general physical factors that contribute to the burning rate.

The burning material may be gaseous, liquid, or solid, but the oxygen (normally free oxygen in the air) is usually in a gaseous state. For the necessary chemical actions to occur, the fuel and oxygen must be brought into contact at a molecular level, and this, in turn, means that burning is generally a vapor-phase phenomenon.

The rate of burning is a function of how fast the chemical reaction of oxidation occurs, as well as the speed at which the vaporized fuel and the oxygen are delivered to the combustion zone. In premixed flames, i.e., those in which mixing has occurred before the combustion is initiated, the burning rate is controlled only by the inherent rate at which the substances combine. This is generally quite fast; flames propagate under premixed conditions at several feet per second (one ft per sec equals 0.3 m/sec). It is for this reason that the contact of air and combustible vapors is so dangerous; the process, once started, is virtually impossible to interrupt, except in closed spaces specifically equipped for that purpose.

A more common mode of burning is the diffusion flame, shown schematically in Figure 3-2A. In this case, vaporized fuel mixes with oxygen in the combustion zone. The rate of burning is essentially controlled by the rate at which the two components arrive in the heated combustion zone. Once they arrive, combustion is, by comparison, instantaneous.

Since gases mix with one another readily, the burning of a gaseous fuel, such as hydrogen or methane in air, is a rapid process. However, the burning of a liquid or solid requires first that the fuel be converted to the gaseous state (volatilization). This process requires the input of an appreciable amount of heat energy, often from the fire itself, and is almost always slow when compared to the rate of oxidation. As a practical matter, therefore, the rate of volatilization of a material strongly affects its rate of burning. Unlike smaller molecules, polymer molecules are too large to be transported "as is" into the vapor phase. Actual chemical bonds must first be broken, and this consumes energy. This fact provides an extra opportunity to measure and to control the hazard components of polymeric materials. Liquids and solids are more concentrated fuels than are gases. Propane, for example, burns completely according to the following expression:

$$C_3H_8 + 5O_2 \rightarrow 3CCO_2 + 4H_2O$$

At any given pressure, one volume of propane gas consumes five volumes of oxygen, or about 25 volumes of air. By contrast, liquefied propane is some 300 times denser than propane gas under normal conditions. This means that one volume of the liquid will produce 300 times as much heat, but it will also require 300 times as much air. Thus, the burning of highly volatile liquids and solids may also be affected by the rate of delivery of oxygen to the combustion zone, especially under poorly ventilated conditions.

Except for hypergolic combinations of materials (i.e., those that ambient temperatures are sufficient to ignite), the initiation of the combustion reaction requires some added heat. This heat must be sufficient to vaporize enough of the fuel to initiate reaction and to accelerate the chemical combustion reaction to a rate where it can sustain itself. The heat required for ignition is greatly dependent upon the physical state of the materials and the heat transfer properties of its environment. Thus, combustible materials present in a dust, i.e., with a large surface-to-volume ratio, may burn very readily or explode, while the same material in a solid block may be very difficult to ignite at all.

EXTREMES OF BURNING BEHAVIOR

The extremes of burning behavior differ principally from normal burning in the time scale over which burning occurs. At the fast end of the spectrum are explosions, while at the slow end are the phenomena of auto-oxidation and smoldering. Explosions are a source of substantial hazard and are discussed in detail in several chapters in this handbook. The slow processes, however, are less well known. Auto-oxidation is the combination of a material with oxygen at a rate too slow to produce the heat and light normally associated with fire. Metals are particularly prone to auto-oxidation, demonstrated by the rusting of iron, the anodization of aluminum, and the tarnishing of silver. Many organic materials are also prone to auto-oxidation. The deterioration of rubber and plastics over time is often the result of slow oxidative processes. Antioxidants can be added to such materials in order to increase their durability and

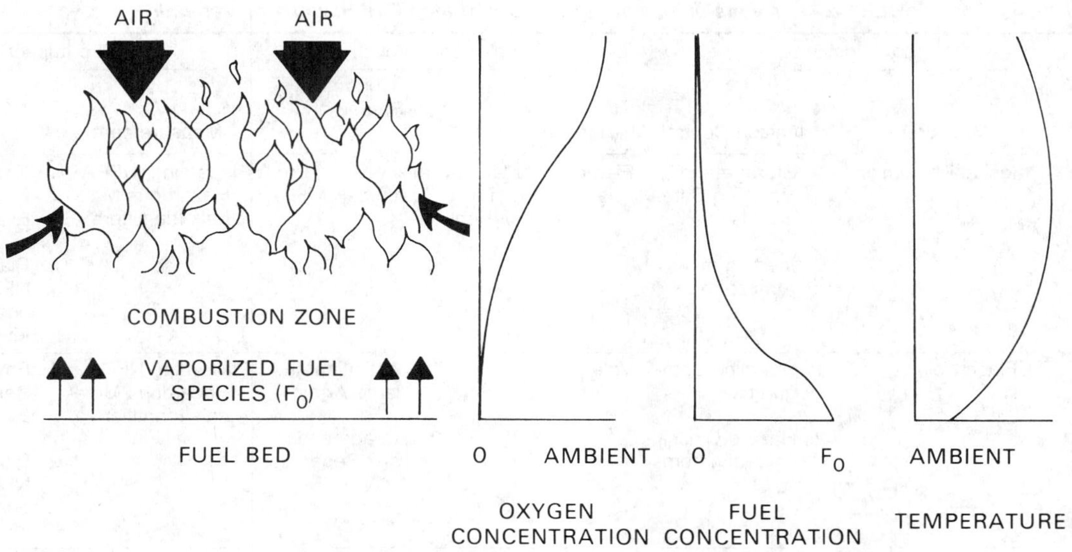

FIG. 3-2A. A schematic view of a burning surface, showing profiles of oxygen, fuel, and temperature as a function of distance above surface.

working life. Such additives operate either by being themselves oxidized in preference to the organic material, or by chemically inhibiting the oxidation reaction.

Self-heating, and eventual spontaneous ignition, can occur if the heat produced by the auto-oxidation is not removed. This is especially true in porous solids, such as coal, where air can diffuse into the interior of the material, and yet the heat produced is effectively contained by the insulating properties of the material.

Smoldering is a distinct burning process, quite different from flaming. Only a small fraction of combustible materials will smolder, including those that do appear to be able to produce a porous char during the course of combustion. This char allows air to reach the smoldering region, which is on or below the surface of the fuel. Compared to flaming, smoldering is a slow process. Temperatures in the smolder zone are typically 900 to 1600°F (483 to 871°C)[2]; temperatures in a flame typically reach 2700°F (1482°C). When materials smolder, the degree of combustion is usually less complete than when the same materials burn under flame.

Most smolderers are organic; all are solids, and, with the exception of carbon itself, they tend to be complex natural or synthetic polymers, which can yield both volatile fuel species and a rigid, porous char structure.

MEASURING AND CONTROLLING HAZARDS

The vastly different burning characteristics of gases, liquids, and solids pose different types of hazards. The methods for measuring and controlling them are also different. Table 3-2A shows the different kinds of measurement techniques available for different components of hazard. It is most convenient to think of hazard control in terms of controlling first the likelihood of ignition, then the control or containment of the fire spread, and finally management of the fire impact if ignition and spread cannot be prevented.

Fire Hazards of Gases and Dusts

Gases and dusts burn rapidly once ignited, so avoidance of ignition is very desirable. The principal measurement tool for doing this is the determination of flammability limits, i.e., the concentration range of a particular gas or dust (usually in air) within which combustion will occur. It is possible to reduce the likelihood of ignition of a gas or dust by adding chemical inhibitors to raise the lower flammability limit. In practice, however, this is rarely done, either because of expense or because it alters otherwise desirable properties.

Ignition control is generally effected by stringent storage and handling safeguards; the bulk of the discussion in the chapters on flammable gases are concerned with these procedures. It is also possible in closed environments to reduce the amount of oxygen available and thereby to raise the effective flammability limit. Conversely, atmospheres that are enriched with oxygen beyond normal atmospheric concentrations offer special explosion hazards for vapors and dusts. The intensity of a fire resulting from gases, vapors, or dust is a function of the density of gas or the concentration and particle size of the dust. Very light gases, e.g., hydrogen, and very finely divided dust are rapidly dispersed and can lead to the onset of explosive conditions in a correspondingly shorter period of time than more dense materials. Fire and explosion control efforts concentrate on containing the products and, under specialized conditions, providing for automatic suppression of an incipient explosion. This is done by rapidly introducing a suppressant, such as water vapor or a chemical inhibitor, into the exploding cloud. To be effective, automatic suppression must occur in a time scale of a few hundredths of a second.

In recent years there has been a growing concern over the possibility of large flammable gas fires in populated areas. With vast quantities of gaseous fuels now being transported either in bulk or by pipeline, the likelihood of such occurrences increases. The principal means by which the impact of such accidents is minimized is the use of haz-

TABLE 3-2A. ***Means of Measuring and Controlling Fire Hazards of Materials***

	Ignition		Spread and Growth		Fire Impact	
Hazard Component Material	Measurement	Ignition Control	Measurement	Control of Spread and Growth	Measurement	Control of Fire Impact
Gases	Ignitability Limits	1. Storage and Handling Safeguards 2. Inerting of Atmospheres	Flammability Limits, Density, Diffusion Coefficient	Tank Venting Procedures	Placarding, NFPA Hazardous Materials Identifiers	1. Emergency Response and Evacuation 2. Placarding, NFPA Hazardous Materials Identifiers
Liquids	Flash Point	1. Handling Safeguards 2. Hazard Classification Systems	Volatility	1. Ventilation and Flame Arrest 2. Storage and Tank Separation	Placarding NFPA Hazardous Materials Identifiers	1. Emergency Response and Evacuation 2. Placarding, NFPA Hazardous Materials Identifiers
Solids 1. Textiles, Cushioning Materials	1. Ease of Ignition Tests and Small-Scale Flame Spread Tests	1. Flame resistive Materials and Treatments 2. Protective Layers	1. Supported Flame Spread 2. Rate-of-Heat Release	1. Material Selection and Assembly 2. Detection and Suppression	1. Toxicity of Combustion Products (under development) 2. Smoke Generation	1. Breathing Apparatus for Fire Fighters 2. Smoke Control Systems
2. Structural Materials, Building Components and Finishes	Same	Same	Flame Spread Rate-of-Heat Release	1. Fire Resistivity 2. Low Combustibility 3. Fire-resistive Coatings 4. Detection and Suppression	1. Fire Endurance (Stability, Integrity, Insulation 2. Smoke and Toxic Combustion Products	Same, Plus Construction Design: Compartmentation; Separation

ardous material identification systems, e.g., placarding and NFPA 704, *Identification of the Fire Hazards of Materials.* In the absence of a major breakthrough in the prevention or suppression of such fires, the most appropriate means of minimizing fire impact is the advanced planning, preparedness, and response of trained emergency personnel.

Fire Hazards of Liquids

Since burning actually occurs in the vapor phase, the most hazardous combustible liquids are those with a high vapor pressure, or volatility. An empirical measure that combines volatility with the heat-producing capabilities of the vapor is the flash point determination. The flash point is simply the temperature at which a liquid gives off vapors that can be ignited under specified laboratory conditions. Flash point determinations give rise to hazard classification systems, the most severe hazard being afforded by those liquids with the lowest flash points. As in the case of gases, however, the principal means of controlling the ignition of combustible liquids is in handling safeguards. Elaborate procedures exist to minimize the escape of flammable vapors in the handling of volatile liquids and to avoid sources of ignition.

If a fire involving such materials is initiated, means are also available to prevent the supply of additional combustible fuel to the fire. These include designs for the venting of storage tanks in order to minimize explosions, and flame arrestors to guard against the travel of the flame into the storage area itself. Storage and separation criteria for bulk storage of flammable liquids are also used to minimize the likelihood that additional supplies of flammable liquids will come in contact with the fire. The intensity of the fire once begun is a function both of the volatility and of the amount of heat released when the fuel burns. Thus, heavy oils or tars may be difficult to ignite, but can burn readily once underway. A portion of the heat produced in the flame radiates back to the fuel surface and vaporizes more fuel. For most common organic liquids, the heat required to vaporize a given amount of material is a small percentage of the heat of combustion.

Some fire fighting techniques interfere with the passage of fuel from the liquid to the vapor phase. These include cooling the liquid to slow vaporization and the use of foam to cover the liquid surface.

Solids

The part of Table 3-2A relating to solids concentrates on structural materials; it ignores the large group of chemicals that are solid but which are primarily found in industrial environments. Unless these materials are present as dusts, foams, or in other forms that present high surface areas, their fire hazards are similar to those of liquids.

In Table 3-2A, solid materials are divided into two major classes: (1) flexible materials, such as textiles and cushioning; and (2) structural materials, which can include everything from steel and concrete to wood and synthetic structural plastic foams. For both of these classes of materials there is a variety of tests to determine their susceptibility to ignition. However, since ignition requires the volatilization of some of the solid fuel, ignition behavior is strongly dependent upon the amount of heat applied to the surface. Therefore, different ignition tests often give different results, depending on the size of the ignition source. The same principle applies to tests that attempt to measure flame spread over small samples. In many such tests, a sample receives no radiant heat load except that available from its own burning. The larger the amount of sample burning, the greater the heat transferred to the unburned area ahead of the flame, and a large sample will appear to have a higher flame spread rate than a small one.

The fire hazards posed by inorganic structural materials are most likely to be passive. For example, steel can lose its strength, concrete can crack and spall, and glass can break and melt on exposure to high temperature. Such materials are therefore rated on their ability to withstand such high-temperature effects.

Flame-Resistant Treatments

Improvements in ignition control of materials have come about as a result of flame-resistant treatments developed for both natural and synthetic polymerics. It is also possible to design polymeric systems in which a substantial fraction of the material is unavailable as fuel. One example is the dilution of the polymer with a large amount of alumina trihydrate, a nonburning, heat-absorbing material. Another example is the inclusion of halogen atoms, such as chlorine or fluorine, in the monomers from which plastics are made. A third approach is the development of polymers based on materials other than carbon. These include silicone polymers, and phosphonitrilic whose composition is principally phosphorus and nitrogen.

Flame spread tests are probably the best known fire performance tests. The most widely used of these are the Steiner Tunnel Test, contained in NFPA 255, *Method of Test of Surface Burning Characteristics of Building Materials*; (ASTM E 84); and the radiant panel test, included in ASTM E 162. These tests attempt to simulate spread of fire across a plane surface and may include the imposition of a known external radiant flux.

The role of heat release rate in determining fire hazards has recently been recognized. Two standard test methods for heat release rate have recently been developed: (1) NFPA 263, *Method of Test for Heat and Visible Smoke Release Rates for Materials and Products* (ASTM E 906), and (2) ASTM E 1354. These tests measure the rate at which heat is produced, generally as a function of the imposed radiant energy. Because of the importance of an imposed flux in real fire hazard, these measurements promise to be of wide utility in predicting fire hazards. Ideally, fire-resistant treatments should be detectable as diminished heat release rate measurements.

It is important to recognize that claims for flame resistance are tied closely to the test method that is used to evaluate fire performance. Materials that resist ignition or behave acceptably in small-scale tests may be wholly inappropriate for use when more severe or substantially different fire conditions are encountered. Figure 3-2B, for example, shows that the burning rate depends heavily on imposed heat load (external flux). The relative performance of materials under a radiant heat load of 1 or 2 W/cm^2 may be different from their performance at 5 W, an external flux representative of what might be imposed on an exposed surface in a well-developed room fire. This makes it important that materials be tested under conditions that duplicate those expected in real fire scenarios whenever possible.

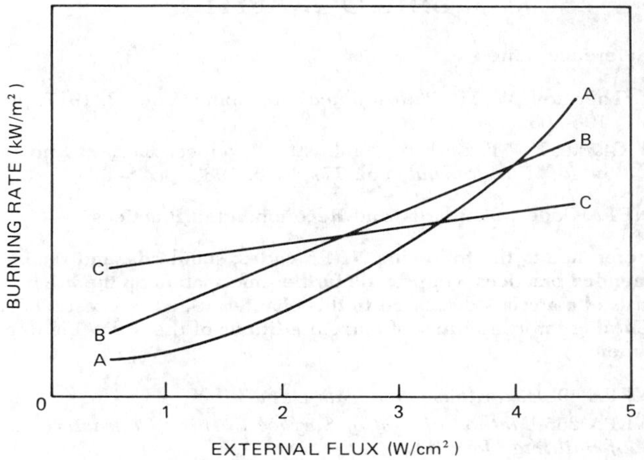

FIG. 3-2B. Burning behavior of various materials as a function of external flux (W/cm^2).

SMOKE

Because smoke* is usually the primary threat to life safety, it receives a great deal of attention. Traditionally, smoke has been characterized simply by its ability to obscure light. However, there has been increasing interest in the identity and effects of combustion products themselves, as synthetic materials have become common components of building construction and furnishings. Because of the variability of their chemical composition, smoke from synthetic materials is more likely to contain constituents not often encountered when natural materials were the rule. The real question, however, is not whether new materials produce toxic combustion products—they do—but whether these products represent a kind different from, or a more serious hazard than, those of traditional materials. There is no general answer to this question—it depends on the material in question and the use to which it is put. Moreover, the tests used to measure the toxicity of smoke often give results that are more dependent on test conditions than on the material tested.[2] The amount of smoke produced and the chemistry of the combustion products (i.e., the smoke's toxicity) are greatly influenced by the manner in which the smoke is generated. The heating rate or combustion temperature of the sample, the availability of oxygen, whether the sample smolders or flames—all of these are important factors. Therefore, using test conditions to predict full-scale smoke conditions must be done with considerable care.

*Smoke is defined here as the total airborne effluent from heating or burning a material. Thus, expressions such as "smoke and toxic gases" are, by this definition, redundant.

Although these measurement techniques are far from perfect, their development means that it is becoming possible to predict how a material, burning in a given scenario, will influence the hazard to life from that fire. This emerging field of fire protection, known as fire hazard analysis, requires information on the burning properties of a material, and its conditions of use, as well as smoke obscuration and smoke toxicity data. Fire hazard analysis is described in more detail in the Section 10, Chapter 7, "Fire Risk Analysis."

BIBLIOGRAPHY

References Cited

1. Thornton, W. M., *Philosophical Magazine*, Vol. 33, 1917, pp. 196-203.
2. Clarke, F., "Toxicity of Combustion Products: Current Knowledge," *Fire Journal*, Vol. 77, No. 5, 1983, pp. 84ff.

NFPA Codes, Standards, and Recommended Practices

Reference to the following NFPA codes, standards, and recommended practices will provide further information on the fire hazards of materials discussed in this chapter. (See the latest *NFPA Catalog* for availability of current editions of the following documents.)

NFPA 49, *Hazardous Chemicals Data.*

NFPA 255, *Method of Test of Surface Burning Characteristics of Building Materials.*

NFPA 258, *Standard Research Test Method for Determining Smoke Generation of Solid Materials.*

NFPA 259, *Standard Test Method for Potential Heat of Building Materials.*

NFPA 263, *Method of Test for Heat and Visible Smoke Release Rates for Materials and Products.*

NFPA 701, *Standard Methods of Fire Tests for Flame-Resistant Textiles and Films.*

NFPA 704, *Identification of the Fire Hazards of Materials.*

Additional Reading

Babrauskus, V., "Burning Rates," *SFPE Handbook of Fire Protection Engineering*, National Fire Protection Association, Quincy, MA, 1988.

Babrauskas, V., "Cone Calorimeter—A Versatile Bench-Scale Tool for the Evaluation Fire Properties," *Proceedings* from the Conference on New Technology to Reduce Fire Losses and Costs, Elsevier, NY, 1986, pp.78-87.

Becker, W., "Testing for Fire Safety—What Are the Limitations," *Proceedings* of the Conference on New Technology to Reduce Fire Losses and Costs, Elsevier, 1986, pp. 116-121.

Belles, D. W., "Reducing Fire Hazards with Fire Retardants," *Fire Journal*, Vol, 83, No. 2, May 1989, p. 52.

Bowes, P. C., *Self-Heating: Evaluating and Controling the Hazards*, Elsevier, NY, 1984.

Bryan, J., "Damageability of Buildings, Contents and Personnel from Exposure to Fire," *Fire Safety Journal*, Vol. 11, 1986, p. 15.

Drysdale, Dougal D., *Fire Dynamics*, Wiley, NY, 1985.

Emmons, H. W., "Analyzing Far Field Effects," *Fire Safety Journal*, Vol. 12, No. 3, 1987, p. 183.

Fire and Smoke: Understanding the Hazards, National Academy Press, Washington, DC, 1986.

Friedman, R., "Quantification of Threat From a Rapidly Growing Fire in Terms of Relative Material Properties," *Fire and Materials*, Vol. 2, 1978, pp. 27-33.

Govmark Flammability Standards Book, The Govmark Organization Inc., Bellmore, NY, 1987.

Harland, W. A., and Anderson, R. A., "Causes of Death in Fires," *Conference* of Smoke and Toxic Gases from Burning Plastics, Industrial Research Ltd., London.

Harwood, B., "Trends in Fire Deaths 1970-1985," 1988, U.S. Consumer Product Safety Commission, Washington, DC.

Huggett, C., "Estimation of Rate of Heat Release by Means of Oxygen Consumption," *Fire and Materials*, Vol. 4, 1980, pp. 61-65.

Kanury, A. M., *Introduction to Combustion Phenomena*, Gordon and Breach, NY, 1977. [Reprinted 1984]

Krause, R., and Gann, R., "Rate of Heat Release Measurements Using Oxygen Consumption," *Journal of Fire and Flammability*, Vol. 11, 1980, p. 117.

Lyons, J., *The Chemistry and Uses of Fire Retardants*, R. E. Krieger Pub. Co., Malabar, FL, 1987. [Reprint of 1970 edition]

Mulholland, G. W., "Smoke Production and Properties," *SFPE Handbook of Fire Protection Engineering*, National Fire Protection Association, Quincy, MA, 1988.

Quintiere, J. G., "Application of Flame Spread Theory to Predict Material Performance," *Journal of Research of the National Bureau of Standards*, Vol. 93, No. 1, Jan.-Feb. 1988, pp. 61-70.

Rashbash, D. J., and Drysdale, D. D., "Fundamentals of Smoke Production," *Fire Safety Journal*, Vol. 5, 1983, pp. 77-86.

Sax, N. I., and Lewis, R. J., *Dangerous Properties of Industrial Materials*, 7th ed., Van Nostrand Reinhold, NY, 1989.

Schultz, N., *Fire and Flammablility Handbook*, Van Nostrand Reinhold, NY, 1985.

Spalding, D. B., *Combustion and Mass Transfer*, Pergamon Press, London, 1979.

Tewarson, A., "Generation of Heat and Chemical Compounds in Fires," *SFPE Handbook of Fire Protection Engineering*, National Fire Protection Association, Quincy, MA., 1988.

Tewarson, A., "Scale Effects on Fire Properties of Materials," *NBS-GCR-85-488*, Feb. 1985, National Bureau of Standards, Gaithersburg, MD.

Thomas, D., "Self-Heating and Thermal Ignition—A Guide to its Theory and Applications," *Ignition, Heat Release and Noncombustibility of Fuels*, American Society of Testing and Materials, Philadelphia, 1972.

WOOD AND WOOD-BASED PRODUCTS

Revised by Harold O. Beals

Wood is one of the most useful materials of construction. It is employed for framing, sheathing, siding, shingles, underlayment, concrete formwork, and interior finish. Wood-based building products include fiberboard, insulation board, ceiling tile, plywood, flakeboard, strandboard, and particleboard. Wood-based materials are found in furniture, cabinets, and in manufactured housing.

Wood is the major raw material source for paper and paper-based products, such as cardboard, box board, and corrugated board used in containers. Paper, used alone or combined with metal foils and plastics, is employed in the manufacture of many hundreds of products, including writing and wrapping papers, magazines, books, bags, wall coverings, and labels. As the source material for most cellulose-based products, it is found in textiles, explosives, transparent films and coatings, plastics, and in many food products.

The products made from wood and wood-based material are legion. As their grades often overlap, it is sometimes difficult to separate those made from wood, paper, or cellulose.

Wood and its cellulose derivatives are frequently involved in fire, and an understanding of the behavior of this versatile material under fire exposure is important. The discussion of wood in this section will be limited to solid wood and wood-based products, including paper and paper products, and their ignition and burning characteristics. Those interested in a more detailed treatment on the subject should consult the list of references at the end of this chapter.

Wood-based cellulosic fiberous materials used in textiles, including acetates and various rayons, are discussed in Section 3, Chapter 4, "Fibers and Textiles." Other reconstituted cellulose materials used in explosives and propellents are discussed in Section 3, Chapter 9, "Explosives and Blasting Agents." Plastics and films made from cellulose are covered in Section 3, Chapter 10, "Plastics and Rubber." Fire hazards of finely divided wood particles, such as sander dust, are discussed in Section 3, Chapter 12, "Dusts." Cellulose-based lacquers and paints are covered in Section 2, Chapter 12, "Spray Finishing and Powder Coating." Manufacturing and process information on various wood products is found in Section 2, Chapter 21, "Woodworking Processes." Fire hazards of wood fuels are covered in Section 2, Chapter 29, "Storage and Handling of Solid Fuels." Biomass and standing timber hazards are discussed in Section 8, Chapter 32, "Wildland Fires." Products of combustion, their importance on the fire scene, their physiological effects on persons trapped in the fire environment, and the degree to which they affect rescue and fire fighting efforts are discussed in Section 3, Chapter 1, "Combustion Products and Their Effects on Life Safety." Fire-retardant treatments are discussed in Section 3, Chapter 17, "Fire-Retardant and Flame-Resistant Treatments of Cellulosic Materials."

THE NATURE OF WOOD AND WOOD-BASED PRODUCTS

Wood products made from solid wood include lumber, laminated beams, large timbers, mine timbers, railroad ties, poles, and pilings. Other solid wood products are cooperage (barrels), boxes, crates, and other containers. Hardwoods are used for firewood and in the manufacture of furniture. Wood products made from thin sheets of wood (veneer) bonded together with adhesives are plywood and laminated wood.

Wood-based products are those in which the wood has been mechanically reduced in size to form flakes, strands, splinters, fibers, or particles, and bonded with adhesives or other binders to make flat panels or shapes. These products include flakeboard, oriented strand board (OSB), medium-density fiberboard (MDF), other fiberboards and hardboards, cement excelsior boards, particleboard, and some insulation boards and ceiling tile.

Paper and paper-based products differ from wood-based products in that no adhesive is used to bond the paper fibers together. Most papers are made by a chemical process that removes the lignin and hemicellulose from the wood and leaves the cellulose fibers intact. An exception is newsprint, in which the fibers are separated by a

Harold O. Beals is associate professor of wood products, School of Forestry, Auburn University, AL.

mechanical or grinding process—no chemicals are used. Paper and paper-based products may be made without additives (absorbent papers), but most contain binders (wet-strength resins), fillers (clay), pigments (titanium dioxide), colorants (dyes), sizes (rosin, starch), or other materials to provide improved appearance or performance. Some papers are coated with wax (paraffin) or various plastic materials for use in container applications. Many paper products are printed with colored inks for use as containers or labels. Paper and paper-based products are often classified into such categories as kraft or sulfate (brown papers), used for wrapping and container applications; sulfite (white papers), used for writing, book, and magazine papers; and groundwood, used for tissue and newsprint. Paper products are generally available in the form of thin sheets or rolls. Paper-based products are thicker and, when graded, can overlap into wood-based materials, such as the fiberboards, and it is sometimes difficult to place such products into either category.

Cellulose-based products are made from purified wood cellulose obtained from certain special grades of paper pulp called dissolving pulp. Wood has been used for dissolving pulp since about 1920, replacing cotton linters which were formerly used for this purpose. Most cellulose-based products are not discernible as being made from wood or paper, but they often have the odor of burnt paper when combusted. Cellulose-based products include the nitrocellulose lacquers, films, and plastics; acetate films; textiles and plastics; rayon textiles; cellophane; and smokeless powder used in small-arms cartridges. An expanding market for purified wood cellulose fibers is in disposible sanitary applications, such as baby diapers and feminine protection products. Purified cellulose is a common ingredient of many food products where it is used to thicken liquids and to improve the texture of foods. It is commonly found in diet aids where it serves as a bulking agent.

Wood cellulose can be broken down to glucose, using appropriate chemical techniques, to make molasses suitable for cattle feed supplements, or fermented to make ethyl alcohol (grain alcohol) for use as a gasoline additive. The hemicellulose portion of wood (composed of five carbon sugars, such as xylose) can be fermented to make methyl-ethyl-ketone (MEK) or butyl alcohol (butanol), used as solvents. At present, hemicellulose cannot be fermented to make ethyl alcohol, but it is anticipated that new organisms will be developed through techniques, such as gene splicing or recombinant DNA, to accomplish this.

Destructive distillation of wood produces charcoal, methanol (wood alcohol), acetic acid, formic acid, and wood creosote, as well as a low heat-output fuel that can be used to power internal combustion engines.

Turpentine and rosin, known as naval stores, are produced from standing pine trees treated with paraquat, from old stumps, and as a byproduct in the manufacture of kraft paper by the sulfate process. Both turpentine and rosin are highly flammable and may cause spontaneous ignition under certain conditions.

Wood and wood-based products are combustible—they char, smolder, ignite, and burn when the thermal environment is conducive to such reactions. Rarely do they self-ignite except in certain forms and under certain conditions of storage and moisture content. Normally a spark, open flame, contact with hot surfaces, or exposure to thermal radiation is required for ignition. Even then, ignition will be a function of the intensity of the ignition source and the length of exposure, as well as other factors to be considered later in this chapter.

Dry wood burns with the characteristic odor of wood smoke. The smoke is bluish or dark when the wood is green or wet and low temperature or insufficient air is present; but, with high temperature and excess air, the smoke is often almost invisible. Burning wood produces smoke containing glowing particles and large amounts of a gray ash. Wood burned under conditions of incomplete combustion in which little or no air is present produces charcoal and a number of condensible vapors in a process known as destructive distillation. Burning wood in modern airtight stoves is considered destructive distillation. When the tars and creosote are condensed in the chimney, they are easily ignited and burn at very high temperatures, and may cause house fires. Charcoal burns with little smoke and uniform heat. Wood is considered to be a clean fuel because it contains no sulfur.

As woody materials are buried in water environments, they become the basis for the fossil fuels, such as peat, coal, and natural gas. Some woody materials contribute to the formation of petroleum, although their role in this process is not clear at this time. Decomposing woody materials may emit various amounts of flammable gases containing methane, and are known as swamp gas or blackdamp. Occasionally, these decomposing woody materials become phosphorescent or luminescent and produce a ghostly light. This phenomenon is caused by a fungus and is called "fox-fire."

Fire-retardant chemicals can be, and frequently are, added or applied to wood and wood-based products. When properly formulated and used, fire-retardant chemicals reduce the combustibility of these products. Depending on the formulations used, flame and glow can be reduced once the outside source of heat is removed. Some fire-retardant treatments (FRT) may adversely affect the strength properties of plywood sheathing and structural lumber, causing them to become brittle and fail prematurely. This is due to the high temperatures used to redry FRT plywood and lumber after treatment, or to the dryness in attic spaces after construction is completed. Use of fire-retardant treated lumber and plywood has greatly increased in recent years due to a greater awareness of fire-safety.

To resist rot and insect damage, railroad crossties, utility poles, and pilings are usually pressure treated with various toxic chemicals (wood preservatives) containing creosote (made from coal tar) and pentachlorophenol in solutions of oil similar to diesel or fuel oil, or with water-soluble salt solutions containing arsenic, chromium, copper, or phenol. Waterborne salts are usually used to treat lumber and plywood but are commonly used for treating utility poles. Wood products freshly treated with creosote or pentachlorophenol in oil solutions are easily ignited because of the oil; however, after the wood ages and the oil evaporates, ignition is more difficult.

Wood and wood-based products are often used in combination with other materials to provide a greater degree of fire protection. An insulated, plywood-faced wood stud wall, for instance, will provide a greater degree of fire resistance than one without insulation. Also, it is possible to construct fire-rated interior partitions using gypsum board and wood framing members. The relatively slow burning or char rate of heavier wood members provides a degree of protection because of the insulating effects of the char buildup. Finishes or additives used to improve the properties of many wood- and paper-based materials, such as binders, adhesives, fillers, sizes, etc., can often modify the fire performance of these materials as compared to bare wood. Coatings applied to wood or wood-based products may cause them to ignite more easily and to burn more rapidly than the unfinished wood.

During the 1970s there were pronounced changes in the types and use of wood and wood-based building products, due primarily to a desire for a more "natural" appearance in homes by more external use of wood materials (wood shingles or siding) and enactment of new legislation designed to encourage conservation and save energy. In many parts of the country, a return to wood as a primary fuel (burned in fireplaces and stoves) and to log homes with shingle roofs has created greater fire risks and air pollution problems. The 1980s saw increased usage of vinyl-clad fiberboards used for building sidings, and substitution of oriented strandboards (OSB) or flakeboards for plywood in construction. Use of wood shingles declined with a return to fiberglass and asphalt materials. There has also been a decline in log buildings, although many are still being built in certain parts of the country. As energy prices have stabilized and fallen, the use of wood for residential fuel burned in wood stoves has also declined but industrial use has increased. There has also been a marked increase in the manufacture and use of treated lumber and plywood in construction. More insulation products made from various organic and inorganic materials are now being used, but asbestos has been virtually eliminated in sidings and flooring materials. All of these factors have important bearings on the performance of wood and wood-based materials in building fires today.

CHEMICAL COMPOSITION OF WOOD

Wood consists primarily of carbon, hydrogen, and oxygen, with lesser percentages of nitrogen and other elements, but it contains no sulfur which is often present in other fuels. (See Table 3-3A.)

TABLE 3-3A. ***Chemical Composition of Dry Woods***

	Constituents, Percent by Weight				
Species	Carbon	Hydrogen	Oxygen	Nitrogen	Ash
Oak	50.16	6.02	43.26	.09	0.37
Ash	49.18	6.27	43.19	.07	0.57
Elm	48.99	6.20	44.25	.06	0.50
Beech	49.06	6.11	44.17	.09	0.57
Birch	48.88	6.06	44.67	.10	0.29
Pine	50.31	6.20	43.08	.04	0.37
Poplar	49.37	6.21	41.60	.96	1.86
Calif. redwood	53.50	5.90	40.30	.10	0.20
Western hemlock	50.40	5.80	41.40	.10	2.20
Douglas fir	52.30	6.30	40.50	.10	0.80

Although wood is a complex of many substances, cellulose $[(C_6H_{10}O_5)_x]$ represents its major component. Wood contains about 50 percent cellulose by weight, approximately 25 percent hemicellulose in the form of sugars, 24 percent lignin, and 1 percent extractives (in the form of minerals, gums, resins, and other materials). Some pieces of wood may contain flammable extractives in the form of resins, e.g., lighter wood southern pine, but most woods contain no extracts of any consequence. The ash formed from burning wood is high in mineral content, primarily potash. Wood also contains moisture, the amount present depending upon the degree of previous drying. Removal of moisture above the fiber saturation point has little effect on wood other than to reduce its weight, but removal of moisture below the fiber saturation point increases the strength properties of wood.

The major difference between various woods depends largely on density (specific gravity), which is related to cell wall thickness or strength properties, and on infiltrated materials or extracts that contribute to the color and other properties of wood. Some of these extracts consist of flammable resinous products that may cause spontaneous ignition in certain wood products, e.g., piled chips of southern pine used in making paper.

Bark is an important residue often used for fuel in many wood industries. Bark contains large amounts of tannin (used in tanning leather) and suberin (cork) which makes it resistant to penetration by water. Commercial cork, obtained from the bark of the cork oak, is resistant to high temperatures and ignition and burns with difficulty. Cork contains a natural adhesive that allows small particles to be bonded under heat and pressure to make composition cork. Bark and cork are generally drier than wood.

Wood-based products, paper, and paper-based products generally contain much less moisture than wood and are easier to ignite and burn than solid wood. Many fibrous cellulosic-based materials, such as bagasse (spent sugar cane stalks), jute, hemp, or sisal, have burning characteristics similar to wood-based materials. Often these and other similar products are impregnated, pressure treated, or coated with a variety of chemicals that may enhance or reduce the ignition and burning rate of such materials.

Wood-based and paper-based products are frequently bonded, coated, or combined with various plastic resins (including urea, melamine, phenolformaldehyde, nitrocellulose, vinyl chloride, urethane, isocyanates, latex, or acrylics) that may modify their burning characteristics and products of combustion.

VARIABLES INFLUENCING IGNITION AND BURNING CHARACTERISTICS

Physical Form

The influence of physical form on the ignition and burning characteristics of wood and wood-based products is illustrated by the fact that wood kindling will flame and burn from relatively small heat sources while heavier wood logs will resist ignition to a considerable degree. Paper is easier to ignite than small pieces of wood. The reason for this is that as the size of the particle diminishes, the ratio of surface area to volume (mass) increases. Thus there is both greater exposure of fuel to air and less mass to conduct heat away from the particle; consequently, heat does not readily dissipate within the material. It follows that small, thin forms of wood (such as excelsior), or other combustible solids (such as paper), will burn more readily than larger objects of the same material.

Although paper is considered to be easy to ignite, large, compact masses of paper, such as books or cut and packaged stacks of paper, do not burn readily due to charring and insufficient air in the interior of the mass, as well as the influence of additives, such as binders, colorants, sizes, etc., in the paper. However, contrary to the general opinion that compact paper in rolls will not burn, large rolls of paper or paper-based products stacked on end may unwind during a fire, exposing long, single sheets of paper which are easily ignited and burn readily.

Very finely divided wood particles, such as sander dust or wood flour (made from nut shells), are prone to explosion and flash fire as are other carbonaceous dusts. But sawdust, which has a much larger particle size, generally does not present such explosion and flash fire hazard under most conditions. Fires in dust control, dryer, or exhaust systems are a constant hazard in most wood manufacturing operations due to ignition of finely divided wood particles.

Thermal (Heat) Conductivity

Thermal conductivity (K factor—the inverse of insulating value, R factor) of a particular material greatly influences how a material will burn. Thermal conductivity is a measure of the rate at which absorbed heat will flow through the mass material. For instance, wood is a poor heat conductor, and thus has a high insulating value. Steel and aluminum are about 350 and 1,000 times more conductive, respectively. The low thermal conductivity of wood finds common illustration in the fact that a wood match burning at one end can be held between the fingers, while a steel needle of similar form, heated at one end, cannot be held with equal comfort.

The thermal conductivity of wood is dependent on the direction of heat flow with respect to the axis of grain orientation in wood, the moisture content of the wood, and the density (specific gravity) of the wood. Thermal conductivity is two to three times greater along the grain in the longitudinal direction than across the grain. Thermal conductivity of wood in any direction is about one-third greater for moisture content above 30 percent than for drier wood.

Thermal conductivity of wood is further illustrated by the fact that the structural framing of an unsprinklered building of heavy timber construction will withstand fire exposure for a considerably longer time than the unprotected framing of a light metal-framed building. This is explained, in part, by the insulating effect of the char that develops as wood burns. More importantly, unprotected steel will absorb heat from the fire much faster and will eventually reach its yield point.

Moisture Content

Wood and cellulose are hygroscopic materials, and they have an affinity for water in both the liquid and vapor form. Wood may contain moisture in the form of: (1) liquid water (free water) in the cell cavities above the fiber saturation point (FSP), which is usually considered to be 25 to 30 percent moisture content; (2) absorbed or bound water located in the cell walls below the fiber saturation point; and (3) water of constitution, which is the water contained in the various components that comprise wood. This water cannot be removed without destroying the physical structure of wood. Both the free water and the absorbed water have an important bearing on the physical and mechanical properties of wood as well as on the ignition and burning of wood. As wood comes from the living tree (green wood), it contains a great deal of moisture in the form of liquid water; but, as it dries, air replaces much of the water, and moisture remains in the form of vapor in the cell cavity or as absorbed water in the cell wall. Dry wood, however, always contains some moisture. Construction lumber is considered to be dry at 19 percent moisture content, but wood used for furniture is dried to 6 percent moisture content or less. Moisture content (MC) in wood is calculated as a percentage of the oven dry weight by the formula:

$$MC = \frac{\text{Original Weight} - \text{Oven Dry Weight}}{\text{Oven Dry Weight}} \times 100$$

Wood reaches an equilibrium moisture content (EMC) with its surroundings at a given temperature and relative humidity. In a heated building, the EMC of wood used in its construction is generally slightly less than 10 percent moisture content in the winter months and about 12 percent moisture content in the summer. Thus, a newly constructed building generally contains wetter wood than one that has been built for some time. Figure 3-3A illustrates conditions under which equilibrium will be established at three different temperatures.

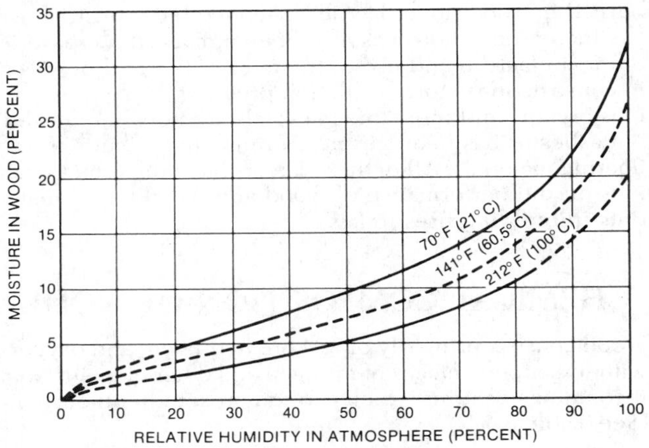

FIG. 3-3A. Equilibrium moisture content of wood.

Moisture content has an important bearing on the electrical properties of wood. Dry wood is a good insulator but wet wood is a conductor. The electrical resistance of wood increases in approximate proportion to the moisture content of wood, from 25 percent to about 6 percent moisture content where it becomes too high to measure with a resistance moisture meter. Within this range, the moisture content of wood can be determined with reasonably accurate instruments. The most accurate determination of moisture content in wood is generally performed by oven drying and weighing. However, the moisture in wood is not uniformly distributed, and wood is often drier or wetter at the surface than in its interior. Surface layers which control ignition and flame spread respond much faster to changes in atmospheric conditions than the interior; thus bulk moisture contents can sometimes be misleading.

The rate of moisture loss or gain depends a great deal upon the size and shape of the wood product. Some finely divided cellulosic materials absorb or lose moisture very rapidly and their combustibility can vary from low to high within just a few hours. Examples are shredded newspaper, tissues, and loose forest litter (duff). Dense and compact combustibles, such as books or large timbers, change moisture content much more slowly. Rate of moisture loss depends on the relative humidity, the temperature, and the air velocity. Moisture loss is quite slow in air drying where there is no control over air velocity, temperature, or relative humidity; lumber may require 30 days or more to dry in such an environment. But in a kiln, where humidity, temperature, and air velocity can be adjusted, lumber can be dried in less than 24 hours. As a general rule of thumb, the amount of time required to dry lumber varies with the square of the thickness. Thus, a 1-in. thick (25.4 mm) board can be air dried in a few weeks, but a railroad crosstie or large timber requires 24 to 30 months. If wood is dried below the EMC it will reach in service, it will regain moisture slowly until it reaches that EMC. (See Figure 3-3A.)

Ignition and burning tests in the laboratory show that the behavior of combustible solids of the same size, shape, and chemical composition varies markedly depending upon the moisture content. In research conducted by the British Department of Scientific and Industrial Research (now the Ministry of Technology), the influence of the moisture content of oak and western red cedar on the time necessary for these woods to ignite was studied; the results are shown in Figure 3-3B.[1] Radiation intensity in this figure is expressed in terms of the number of calories falling on one square centimeter of the exposed wood in one sec, using a test apparatus developed by the Ministry.

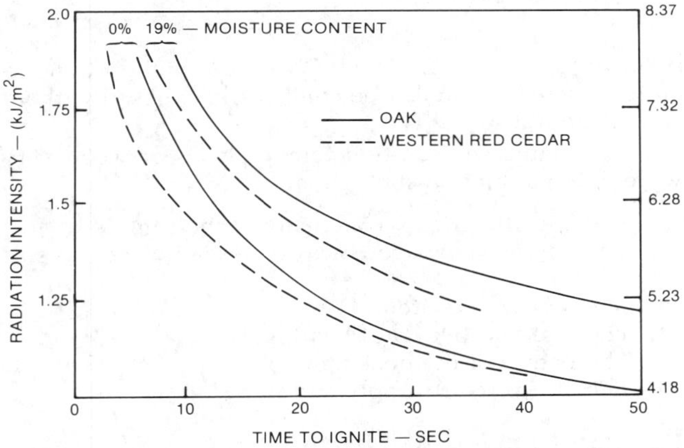

FIG. 3-3B. Effect of moisture content on the ignition of wood.

Once a fire is well under way, the significance of the moisture factor decreases, since the heat radiation and therefore the rate of pyrolysis increases. Under such conditions, wood with a moisture content of 50 percent or more will burn.

Conflagration experience in the United States illustrates the effect of moisture content on structural fire susceptibility. In many conflagrations, it has been noted that prolonged dry weather preceded the outbreak of fire. This dryness had a noticeable effect on the susceptibility of shingles, as well as other combustibles present, to ignition from flying brands and thermal radiation. The tragic Peshtigo, WI, forest fire on October 8, 1871 followed a prolonged period of extremely dry weather. It occurred the same weekend as the Great Chicago Fire and destroyed 17 towns and claimed 1,152 lives. (See Section 1, Chapter 1, "America's Fire Problem and Fire Protection.")

There is a time lag between changes in the fuel moisture content of cellulosic materials and changes in atmospheric humidity. Most solid cellulosic combustibles are not immediately absorptive of airborne water vapor; conversely, the moisture content of most solids will be retained for a longer period of time than air retains its moisture in suspension. Thus, the humidity in the ambient air is not always a reliable index of the moisture content of ordinary combustibles.

IGNITION OF WOOD AND WOOD PRODUCTS

The thermal degradation of wood is a complex process. Four stages of decomposition of wood on exposure to heat have been described:[2]

Temperature	Reaction
392°F (200°C)	Production of water vapor, carbon dioxide, formic and acetic acids—all noncombustible gases.
392-536°F (200-280°C)	Less water vapor, some carbon monoxide—still primary endothermic reaction.
536-932°F (280-500°C)	Exothermic reaction with flammable vapors and particulates. Some secondary reaction from charcoal formed.
Over 932°F (500°C)	Residue principally charcoal with notable catalytic action.

Ignition temperatures may vary, depending on the analytical method and test equipment used. With proper test equipment some exothermic reaction can be observed in the first stage just listed. In the third stage, ignitable gases are produced and the pilot ignition temperature is reached. When the decomposition has progressed to the point where the evolved gases no longer insulate the charcoal layer from oxygen, spontaneous ignition may result.

Specific ignition temperatures of wood are difficult to determine because of the many variables involved. Leading research groups have attempted to pinpoint the ignition temperature of wood, but the results vary greatly. In one series of tests using untreated, air-dried wood blocks 1¼ by 1¼ by 4 in. (32 × 32 × 102 mm), and of nine different species, the Forest Products Laboratory, Madison, WI, found that the specimens could be heated to temperatures varying from 315 to 385°F (157 to 196°C) for 40 min. in a stream of heated air (held at a constant temperature) without igniting. In another series of tests by the same laboratory, using the same test procedures but higher temperatures, 34 untreated softwood and hardwood species ignited in 4 to 6 min. at temperatures varying from 608 to 660°F (320 to 349°C) for the softwood, and from 595 to 740°F (313 to 393°C) for the hardwood. It was noted that a fairly close relationship existed between the specific gravity of the wood under test and the ignition temperature. In general, low-density species ignited at lower temperatures than high-density species.[3] The National Bureau of Standards [now the National Institute for Standards and Technology (NIST)] tested three conifers and two hardwoods and reported ignition temperatures from 378 to 428°F (192 to 220°C) in small samples varying from shavings to match size.

TABLE 3-3B. ***Time Required to Ignite Wood Specimens***[4]

Wood 1¼ by 1¼ by 4 in. (32 × 32 × 102 mm)	No Ignition in 40 min		Exposure Before Ignition, By Pilot Flame, Minutes						
	°F	°C	356°F (180°C)	392°F (200°C)	437°F (225°C)	482°F (250°C)	572°F (300°C)	662°F 350°C)	752°F (400°C)
Long leaf pine	315	157	14.3	11.8	8.7	6.0	2.3	1.4	0.5
Red oak	315	157	20.0	13.3	8.1	4.7	1.6	1.2	0.5
Tamarack	334	167	29.9	14.5	9.0	6.0	2.3	0.8	0.5
Western larch	315	157	30.8	25.0	17.0	9.5	3.5	1.5	0.5
Noble fir	369	187	—	—	15.8	9.3	2.3	1.2	0.3
Eastern hemlock	356	180	—	13.3	7.2	4.0	2.2	1.2	0.3
Redwood	315	157	28.5	18.5	10.4	6.0	1.9	0.8	0.3
Sitka spruce	315	157	40.0	19.6	8.3	5.3	2.1	1.0	0.3
Basswood	334	167	—	14.5	9.6	6.0	1.6	1.2	0.3

The ignition and charring temperatures of wood were recorded at the Forest Products Laboratory.[4] The findings, represented in Table 3-3B, show the length of time before wood specimens maintained at the specified constant temperatures evolved combustible gases in sufficient quantities to be ignited by a pilot flame located about ½ in. (12.7 mm) above the specimen. The specimens, 1¼ by 1¼ by 4 in. (32 × 32 × 102 mm) in size and oven-dry, were heated in a vertical quartz chamber 3 in. (76 mm) in diameter by 10 in. (254 mm) long which was maintained at constant temperature by an electric furnace.

C. R. Brown reported on ignition temperatures of some materials, as shown in Table 3-3C.[5] In his investigations, specimens about 2½ in. (63.5 mm) long and weighing 3 g (0.10 oz.) were suspended in a vertical glass container 2½ in. (63.5 mm) in diameter and 4¹³⁄₁₆ in. (122 mm) high. The container was heated by an electric furnace, the temperature being increased at a predetermined rate. Air preheated to the temperature of the furnace was passed through the container at measured rates of flow. The results were found to be affected by the size of the sample, the rate of heating, and the rate of air flow over the specimens.

TABLE 3-3C. ***Ignition Temperatures of Woods***[5]

Wood 2½ in. (63.5 mm) long and weighing 3 g (0.10 oz)	Self-Ignition Temperature °F	°C
Western red cedar	378	192
White pine	406	207
Long leaf pine	428	220
White oak	410	210
Paper birch	399	204

In 1947 the National Bureau of Standards (now NIST) reported ignition temperatures of wood as shown in Table 3-3D. In these tests, the specimens of wood in the form of shavings were heated in a glass test tube in the presence of a measured flow of heated air at optimum velocity. Ignition temperature was determined to be the lowest temperature at which the exothermic oxidation reaction culminated in an ignition, as indicated by flaming or glowing combustion.

Wood in contact with steampipes or a similar constant temperature source over a very long period of time may undergo a chemical change, resulting in the formation of charcoal which is capable of heating spontaneously. It has been suggested that 212°F (100°C) is the highest temperature to which wood can be continually exposed without risk of ignition.[6]

TABLE 3-3D. ***Ignition Temperatures of Woods Shavings****

Wood Shavings	Self-Ignition Temperature °F	°C
Short leaf pine	442	228
Long leaf pine	446	230
Douglas fir	500	260
Spruce	502	261
White pine	507	264

* Source: National Bureau of Standards [now the National Institute for Standards and Technology (NIST)].

To summarize, ignition temperatures of wood vary widely depending on such variables as:

1. The specific gravity or density of the sample.
2. The physical characteristics of the sample, i.e., its size and form.
3. The moisture content.
4. The rate and period of heating.
5. The nature of the heat source.
6. The air (oxygen) supply and its velocity.

Rate and Period of Heating

The rate and duration of heating influence the susceptibility of wood and wood products to ignition. Compared to flammable liquids or gases, combustible solids are usually less hazardous because they do not vaporize readily nor do they emit flammable vapors at normal ambient temperatures and atmospheric pressures. Thus, ignition of solid combustibles usually requires long enough contact between the heat source and the material to permit release of ignitable vapors. This contact can be either momentary or prolonged, with actual ignition depending on the variables just discussed. An exception is glowing combustion, which may occur without vaporization of some materials; an example of this is charcoal.

Ignition will occur when a material is heated above its autoignition temperature. Thus, if moderate heat is applied long enough to raise a combustible to its autoignition temperature, it may cause ignition. However, high heat applied momentarily to a combustible may not cause ignition. For example, a steampipe in contact with wood over a period of time may result in ignition, whereas a gas-fired blowtorch held momentarily on a painted wood surface may blister the paint but not ignite the wood, despite the fact that the torch flame temperature is much higher than the ignition temperature of the wood. However, because the precise reaction in both cases cannot be determined in advance, it is common practice to avoid direct contact between steampipes and adjacent combustibles and to condemn as unsafe the practice of burning paint off wood surfaces. The illustrations do, however, show the influence of the rate and period of heating on the ignition of the same type of combustible in roughly the same shape and form.

The shape and form of a sample of combustible material not only influence its susceptibility to ignition, as explained earlier in this chapter, they also affect the reaction of the combustible to any given rate and period of heating. Likewise, the moisture content of the combustible, the air space between the heat source and the material, and other variables affect the potential for ignition.

Fire experience further illustrates these factors. It is common experience for fire departments to arrive at a fire scene after a delayed alarm and find a wood structure seriously involved and threatening adjacent combustible structures. If water cannot be applied to adjacent structures in time, ignition of the adjacent exposed property may occur. This is a result of the direct relationship between ignition and the rate and period of heat exposure. In actual fires, accurate measurements of such rates and periods of heating are, of course, not practical. Laboratory fire tests, however, do confirm what takes place. (See the preceeding discussion on ignition temperatures of wood.)

Spontaneous Heating and Ignition

Spontaneous heating and ignition of wood and wood-based products usually result only from contamination or induced artificial heating. For example, cellulosic materials that are clean and dried will not heat spontaneously; on the other hand, those soaked with certain drying oils (e.g., linseed oil, tung oil, and turpentine) and stored in unventilated spaces can heat spontaneously. If spontaneous heating is allowed to continue, ignition results. Similarly, a measure of artificial heating can cause certain combustibles to self-heat to their ignition temperature. For example, if wood fiberboards are not subjected to a direct, artificial heat source either during manufacture or when installed in structures, they will not heat spontaneously. On the other hand, tests have shown that heating such fiberboards at relatively moderate temperatures can set up an exothermic reaction leading to their ignition.[7] In one such test, a 22-in. (559 mm) high stack of wood fiberboards 1/8 in. (3 mm) thick, subjected to a heat source of 228°F (109°C), was ignited in 96 hours.

Wood and wood-based products are not susceptible to the same type of spontaneous heating from microbiological action that is prevalent in certain agricultural products.

Air Volume and Velocity

An adequate amount of air (oxygen) is essential if combustion is to continue. Combustion engineers have suggested a formula for the minimum volume of air required for complete combustion of solid fuels with air at 62°F (17°C):

$$V_m = 147 \left[C + 3 \left(H - \frac{O}{8} \right) \right] \text{cu ft}$$

where

V_m = minimum volume of air in cu ft,
C = part by weight of carbon in 1 lb of fuel,
H = parts by weight of hydrogen in 1 lb of fuel, and
O = parts by weight of oxygen in 1 lb of fuel.

While this formula may have little direct application in fire protection engineering, smoldering fires which are starved of adequate air (oxygen) are frequently encountered by fire fighters, so that the significance of this factor must not be overlooked.

The effect of air on the ignition and combustion of wood and wood-based materials varies depending on the amount (volume) and velocity of air present, as well as the shape, size, density, and composition of the material to be burned. In addition, the products of combustion and the residues remaining after combustion also vary according to the volume and velocity of the air that is present. Unlike liquid and gaseous fuel appliances, whose rate of combustion is regulated by varying the amount of supplied fuel with a fixed air ratio, solid fuel combustion is regulated by varying the amount of air available to the fire through a series of adjustable vents. Coal-burning appliances differ, however, from wood-burning appliances in that air is required to be supplied under the fire, and the coal is burned on a grate. Wood-burning appliances have no grate and air is supplied over the fire. This is why a campfire of wood can be built directly on the ground. When excess air is supplied to a wood fire, the solid residue remaining after combustion is in the form of a gray ash.

As wood combustion progresses through the endothermic stage where heat must be supplied, it reaches a point where the combustion becomes exothermic. At this stage, the supply of air can be greatly reduced and almost completely shut off. The wood continues to carbonize in a process known as pyrolysis. As pyrolysis is completed, the solid residue is in the form of carbon or charcoal. The primary gaseous product of combustion is carbon monoxide. However, if excess air is admitted during the pyrolysis, the carbon is burned and ashes are formed.

Air velocity also contributes to the rate of ignition and combustion of wood and wood-based materials. By increasing the velocity of air supplied to a wood fire by means of a forced draft (e.g., by blowing on a glowing splinter), both ignition and combustion can be accelerated. However, if the air velocity becomes too great, both ignition and combustion may be retarded or extinguished; examples of this can be observed in fires on moving vehicles in which the fire remains small until the vehicle slows or stops.

High air velocity is used in high-temperature dry kilns used to dry softwood dimension lumber in 24 hours or less. The temperature used in the kiln is above that needed for charring wood, but the lumber does not ignite because of the air velocity and moisture in the wood. However, if the wood becomes too dry, the lumber may char or ignite when the fans are turned off at the end of the drying cycle. Kiln fires were common when high-temperature kilns were first introduced in the 1970s, but improved kiln designs and better controls have greatly reduced this problem.

Rate of Combustion

In most fires involving combustible solids, there is a time delay between ignition and rapid combustion. This statement might be challenged because of the exceptional speed of some fires, particularly some dwelling fires that result in fatalities. In most such cases, however, investigation shows that detection was delayed or that flammable liquids, gases, or similar materials were involved. The rate of combustion is significantly influenced by the physical form of the combustible, the air supply present, the moisture content, and allied factors; but there is the fundamental need for progressive vaporization of the solid by heat exposure for combustion to proceed.

Speed of Flame Propagation

Speed of flame propagation over the surface of a combustible critically affects the severity of a fire in many cases. The 1959 Los Angeles School Fire Tests[8] showed that under controlled test conditions, flames spread over combustible surfaces with such speed that observers had to flee the sudden release of heat and flame. In 1949 the British Department of Scientific and Industrial Research conducted full-scale dwelling fire tests on the influence of combustible wallboards *vs* the use of plaster finish.[9] The record of the British tests graphically illustrates the observed time-temperature curves in the living rooms of the two houses tested. Originating in an easy chair in the living room, the fires in their initial stages were identical in both dwellings. The loading of combustible materials was roughly proportional to the loadings observed in occupied dwellings in England. It should be noted that in the United States and Canada, earlier ignition and faster flame spread on the combustible surfaces could be expected, since winter heating in these countries results in lower relative humidities and thus lower moisture content of the combustibles. Mobile homes, because of their construction and design, are especially prone to high-speed flame propagation.

Compared with flammable vapors or gases, the speed of flame propagation across most combustible solids is slow; the presence of readily ignitable vapors with the former materials is the primary reason for this difference. Also, pyrolysis gases from combustible solids must be mixed in proper proportions with air; thus flame spread is frequently influenced by the need of these gases to find an adequate air supply to be progressively consumed.

Amount of Fuel Contributed

The amount of fuel contributed by a substance is normally measured by its heat of combustion. Table 3-3E shows some figures for the heats released by various wood products and also gives comparative figures for some other materials. It should be noted that the heat of combustion of most dry wood products is less per pound than that of the other fuels listed. This is of significance when comparing a measured quantity of combustibles to the fire exposure it creates. It is common practice in fire protection engineering to weigh or estimate the weight of combustibles in a fire area to determine, for instance, the needed fire resistance of structural elements or the optimum quantity of water required per square foot, or meter, of floor area for sprinkler discharge. Reasoned judgments are frequently necessary in applying this principle. Libraries, for example, would appear to have a phenomenal fire load, but due to the method of storage and the physical shape of library materials (i.e., books, magazines, etc.), the fire load is considered to be low. However, if the fire load is defined as pounds of combustibles/sq ft then the fire load is considered high but, because of the physical arrangement, the ignition potential is low. While there have been very serious fire losses in these properties, strict application of the calculated fire load to the sprinkler requirements would not be appropriate in most of these cases because of the physical arrangement of the combustibles. On the other hand, a relatively low loading is frequently misused by those seeking to depreciate the need and value of sound fire protection.

TABLE 5-3E. ***Heat of Combustion of Various Wood and Wood-Based Products and Comparative Substances***

Substance	Heating Value	
	Btu per lb	kJ/kg
Wood sawdust (oak)	8,493*	19 755
Wood sawdust (pine)	9,676*	22 506
Wood shavings	8,248*	19 185
Wood bark (fir)	9,496*	51 376
Corrugated fiber carton	5,970*	13 866
Newspaper	7,883*	18 336
Wrapping paper	7,106*	16 529
Petroleum coke	15,800	36 751
Asphalt	17,158	39 910
Oil (cottonseed)	17,100	39 775
Oil (paraffin)	17,640	41 031

* Dry

The amount of fuel contributed by one combustible *vs* another, or different forms of the same combustible, can also be used to evaluate the desirability of utilizing the material in a given situation. This is particularly true for measuring the fuel contributed by certain forms of building materials.

Heat Release Rate

The total heat release rate of the materials of construction and furnishings is an important factor in determining whether a room will reach flashover conditions. If the total heat release rate in megawatts exceeds $0.75\ A\sqrt{h}$, the room is likely to flashover.[10] Here, A and h are the area and height of the window or door opening. A better approximation takes the wall and ceiling and their thermal properties into account.[11] The heat release rate of wood depends on the incident radiant flux, moisture content, thickness, orientation, the boundary conditions at the rear face, and the oxygen concentration of the ambient air. It is also a function of time characterized by an early peak followed by a slow decay until flaming ceases. A second peak will also occur if the rear face of the specimen is insulated. For an oven-dry vertical pine board of nominal 1-in. thickness (one inch equals 25.4 mm) exposed to a thermal radiation level of 60 kW/m^2 in normal air with the rear face exposed to a water-cooled plate, a peak heat release rate of 250 kW/m^2 in 19 min. was reached when the flame went out.[12] A series of wood products with moisture contents of about 8 percent exhibited peak heat release rates between 90 and 170 kW/m^2 under the same conditions. The heat release rate of wood products increases linearly with the density.[13]

BIBLIOGRAPHY

References Cited

1. FOC, *Fire Research Report for the Year 1952*, Department of Scientific and Industrial Research and Fire Offices' Committee, Her Majesty's Stationery Office, London, 1952.
2. Beall, F. C., and Eichner, H. W., "Thermal Degradation of Wood Components: A Review of the Literature," Report No. 130, 1970, Forest Products Laboratory, Madison, WI.

3. Fleischer, H. O., "The Performance of Wood in Fire," Report No. 2202, 1960, Forest Products Laboratory, Madison, WI.
4. McNaughton, G. C., "Ignition and Charring Temperatures of Wood," Mimeo No. R1464, 1944, Forest Products Laboratory, Madison, WI.
5. Brown, C. R., "The Ignition Temperatures of Solid Materials," *NFPA Quarterly*, Vol. 28, No. 2, 1934, pp. 135-145.
6. McGuire, J. H., "Limited Safe Surface Temperatures for Combustible Materials," *Fire Technology*, Vol. 5, No. 3, 1969, pp. 237-241.
7. Mitchell, N. D., "New Light on Self-Ignition," *NFPA Quarterly*, Vol. 45, No. 2, 1951, pp. 165-172.
8. LAFD, *Operation School Burning No. 1*, Los Angeles Fire Department, National Fire Protection Association, Quincy, MA, 1959.
9. FOC, *Fire Research Report for the Year 1950*, Department of Scientific and Industrial Research and Fire Offices' Committee, Her Majesty's Stationery Office, London, 1950.
10. Babrauskas, V., "Estimating Room Flashover," *Fire Technology*, Vol. 16, No. 2, May 1980.
11. McCaffrey, B. J., Quintiere, J. G., and Harkelroad, M. F., "Estimating Room Temperatures and the Likelihood of Flashover Using Fire Data Correlations," *Fire Technology*, Vol. 17, No. 2, 1980.
12. Parker, W. J., and Long, M. E., "Development of a Heat Release Rate Calorimeter at NBS," *Ignition, Heat Release, and Noncombustibility of Materials*, (ASTM STP 502), American Society for Testing and Materials, Philadelphia, PA, 1972, pp. 135-151.
13. Chamberlain, D. L., "Heat Release Rate Properties of Wood-Based Materials," NBSIR 83-2597, 1983, National Bureau of Standards, Gaithersburg, MD.

References

Bierberdorf, F. W., and Yuill, C. H., "An Investigation of the Hazards of Combustion Products in Building Fires," U.S. Public Health Service Contract No. PH86-62-208, Final Report, 1963.

BOCA, *The BOCA Basic Building Code*, 5th ed., Sec. 922, Building Officials and Code Administrators International, Chicago, 1970.

Brenden, J. J., "Determining the Utility of a New Optical Test Procedure for Measuring Smoke from Various Wood Products," Research Paper 137, 1970, Forest Products Laboratory, Madison, WI.

Ferguson, G. E., "Fire Gases," *NFPA Quarterly*, Vol. 27, 1933.

ICBO, *Uniform Building Code*, Vol. 1, Sec. 4202b, International Conference of Building Officials, Whittier, CA, 1970.

Imaizumi, Katsuyoshi, "Stability in Fire of Protected and Unprotected Glued Laminated Beams," *Transactions*, No. 263, Chalmers University of Technology, Gotenburg, Sweden, 1963, pp. 46-71.

NFPA, "Fire Gas Research Report," *NFPA Quarterly*, Vol. 45, No. 3, 1952.

NSF, "Answers to Burning Questions—Reducing the Hazards of Fire," *Mosaic*, National Science Foundation, Washington, DC, 1973.

NFPA Codes, Standards, and Recommended Practices

Reference to the following NFPA codes, standards, and recommended practices will provide further information on wood and wood-based products discussed in this chapter. (See the latest *NFPA Catalog* for availability of current editions of the following documents.)

NFPA 255, *Method of Test of Surface Burning Characteristics of Building Materials*.

NFPA 258, *Standard Research Test Method for Determining Smoke Generation of Solid Materials*.

Additional Reading

Atreya, A., "Pyrolysis, Ignition, and Fire Spread on Horizontal Surfaces of Wood," Ph.D. Thesis, Harvard University, Cambridge, MA, May 1983.

Atreya, A., and Emmons, H. W., "Wood Ignition and Pyrolisis," *9th Joint Panel Meeting* of the UJNR Panel on Fire Research and Safety, NBSIR 88-3753, Apr. 1988, National Bureau of Standards, Gaithersburg, MD.

Beall, F. C., "Specific Heat of Wood—Further Research Required to Obtain Meaningful Data," *Research Note FPL-0184*, Forest Products Laboratory, Madison, WI, 1968.

Beyreis, J. R., Monsen, H. W., and Abbasi, A. F., "Properties of Wood Crib Flames," *Fire Technology*, Vol. 7, No. 2, May 1971, pp. 145-155.

Chamberlain, D. L, "Heat Release Rates of Lumber and Wood Products," *ASTM Special Technical Pub. 816*, American Society for Testing and Materials, Philadelphia, PA, 1982.

Chamberlain, D. L., "Heat Release Rate Properties of Wood-Based Materials," *NBSIR 82-2597*, National Bureau of Standards, Washington, DC, 1983.

Desch, H. E., *Timber, Its Structure, Properties, and Utilization, Timber Press*, Forest Grove, OR, 1981.

Egan, M. R., and Litton, C. D., "Wood Crib Fires in a Ventilated Tunnel," *No. 9045*, 1986, U.S. Department of the Interior, Bureau of Mines, Washington, DC.

Emmons, H. W., and Atreya, A., "The Science of Wood Combustion," *Indian Acad. Sci. Eng. Sci.*, Vol. 5, pp. 259-269.

Fire Retardent Chemicals Association, *Fire Safety Problems Leading to Current Needs and Future Opportunities*, Technomic, Lancaster, PA, 1989.

"Flammability of Cellulosic Materials," *Fire and Flammability Series*, Vol. 2, Technomic Publishing Company, Westport, CT, 1973.

Gardner, W. D., and Thomson, C. R., "Flame Spread Properties of Forest Products: Comparison and Validation of Prescribed Australian and North American Flame Spread Test Methods," *Fire and Materials*, Vol. 12, No. 2, June 1988, pp. 71-85.

Handbook of Wood and Wood-based Materials for Engineers, Architects, and Builders. Forest Products Laboratory, Hemisphere, NY, 1989.

Hurst, N. W., and Jones, T. A., "Review of Products Evolved from Heated Coal, Wood, and PVC," *Fire and Materials*, Vol. 9, 1985, pp. 1-8.

"Ignition, Heat Release, and Noncombustibility of Materials," *STP 502*, 1972, American Society for Testing and Materials, Philadelphia, PA.

Isner, M. S., "Untreated Wood Shingles Spread Apartment Fire," *Fire Journal*, Vol. 83, No. 2, Mar. 1989, pp. 77.

Kanury, A. M., "Ignition of Cellulosic Solids—A Review," *Fire Research Abstracts and Review*, Vol. 14, No. 1, 1972, pp. 24-52.

Kashiwagi, T., Werner, K., and Ohlemiller, T. J., "Products of Wood Gasification," NBSIR 85-3127, Apr. 1985, National Bureau of Standards, Gaithersburg, MD.

Knudson, R. M., and Schniewind, A. P., "Performance of Structual Wood Members Exposed to Fire," *Forest Products Journal*, Vol. 25, No. 2, 1975, pp. 23-32.

Koch, P., "Energy, Fuels, and Chemicals" (Chapter 26), *Utilization of Hardwoods Growing on Southern Pine Sites*, Vol. 3, 1st ed., USDA Forest Service Handbook No. 605, Government Printing Office, Washington, DC, 1985.

Koch, P., "Burning" (Chapter 26) *Utilization of the Southern Pines*, Vol. 2, 1st ed., USDA Forest Service Handbook No. 420, Government Printing Office, Washington, DC, 1972.

Koohyar, A. N., Welker, J. R., and Sliepcevich, C. M., "The Irradiation and Igniton of Wood by Flame," *Fire Technology*, Vol. 4, No. 4, Nov. 1968, pp. 284-291.

Kotoyori, T., "Critical Ignition Temperatures of Wood Sawdusts," *Proceedings* of the First International Symposium on Fire Safety Science, Hemisphere, NY, 1986, pp. 463-471.

Odeen, K., "Fire Resistance of Wood Structures," *Fire Technology*, Vol. 21, No. 1, Feb. 1985, p. 35.

Ohlemiller, T., and Sharb, W., "Products of Wood Smolder and Their Relation to Wood Burning Stoves," *NBSIR 88-3767*, May 1988, National Bureau of Standards, Gaithersburg, MD.

Ohlemiller, T. J., Kashawagi, T., and Werner, K., "Wood Gasification at Fire Level Heat Fluxes," *Combustion and Flame*, Vol. 69, 1987, pp. 155-170.

Panshin, A. J., and DeZeew, C., *Textbook of Wood Technology*, 4th ed., McGraw-Hill, NY, 1980.

Parker, W. J., "Development of a Model for the Heat Release Rate of Wood—A Status Report," NBSIR 85-3163, May 1985, National Bureau of Standards, Gaithersburg, MD.

Parker, W. J., "Prediction of the Heat Release Rate of Wood," *Proceedings* of the First International Symposium on Fire Safety Science, Hemisphere, NY, 1986, pp. 207-216.

R. R. McNeil, "Fire Impact on Wood: The Next Five Years," *Wood and Fiber*, Vol. 9. No. 1, pp. 2-12.

Schaffer, E. L., "How Well Do Wood Trusses Really Perform During a Fire?," *Fire Journal*, Vol. 82, No. 2, Mar. 1988, p. 57.

Schaffer, E. L., "Smoldering Initiation in Cellulosics Under Prolonged Low-level Heating," *Fire Technology*, Vol. 16, No. 1, 1980, pp. 22-28.

Schaffer, E. L., "Charring Rate of Selected Woods—Transverse to Grain," *Research Paper FPL 69*, Forest Products Laboratory, Madison, WI, 1967.

Schaffer E. L., "Review of Information Related to the Charring Rate of Wood," *Research Note FPL-0145*, Forest Products Laboratory, Madison, WI, 1980.

Schaffer E. L., "On the Pilot Ignition of Wood by Radiation," *Combustion and Flame*, Sept. 1963.

Smith, P., and Thomas, P. H., "The Rate of Burning of Wood Cribs," *Fire Technology*, Vol. 6, No. 1, Feb. 1970, pp. 29-38.

Springer, G. S., *Degradation of Mechanical Properties of Wood During Fire*, NTIS, Springfield, VA, 1983.

Steinhagen, P. A., "Thermal Conductive Properties of Wood: A Literature Review," *Research Note FPL-0184*, Forest Products Laboratory, Madison, WI, 1977.

White, Robert H., and Schaffer, E. L., "Application of CMA Program to Wood Charring," *Fire Technology*, Vol. 14, No. 4, Nov. 1978, p. 279.

"Wood Handbook: Wood as an Engineering Material," *USDA Forest Service Handbook*, No. 72, Government Printing Office, Washington, DC, 1987.

"Wood and Wood Products," *Fire Safety Aspects of Polymeric Materials*, National Materials Advisory Board, National Academy of Sciences, Technomic Publishing, Westport, CT, 1977.

Wood Fire Behavior and Fire Retardant Treatment, (A Review of the Literature), Canadian Wood Council, Ottawa, Nov. 1966.

White, R. H., "Analytical Methods for Determining the Fire Resistance of Timber Members," *SFPE Handbook of Fire Protection Engineering*, National Fire Protection Association, Quincy, MA, 1988.

Yates, J. M., "Firefighters Push for Mandatory Flammability Testing," *Wood and Wood Products*, Vol. 92, No. 11, Oct. 1987, p. 38.

FIBERS AND TEXTILES

Revised by John F. Krasny

This chapter discusses commonly used fibers and textiles, as well as their flammability, their end use, and the fire-retardant treatments used on them. Also detailed in this chapter are special environments where textiles are used, and the testing methods employed in evaluating and creating standards for the use of fibers and textiles.

Much allied information with more specific discussion can be found elsewhere in this handbook, especially in the following chapters: Section 3, Chapter 6, "Medical Gases"; Section 3, Chapter 11, "Upholstered Furniture and Mattresses; "Section 3, Chapter 15, "Oxygen-Enriched Atmospheres"; Section 6, Chapter 4, "Interior Finish"; and Section 10, Chapter 3, "Use of Fire Loss Information."

Textiles are an important part of daily life. Clothing, furniture, carpets, and curtains are examples of the ways textiles are used. Almost all textiles are combustible. This fact, combined with the prevalence of textile products in human activities, explains the frequency of textile-related fires and the many deaths and injuries that result.

Studies of fatal fires continue to show that textiles provide the initial fuel for the largest share of fatal structure fires. From 1984 through 1988, for example, 42.5 percent of fatalities in structure fires came in fires that began with the ignition of a textile product. These fires also accounted for 15.3 percent of 1984 through 1988 structure fire incidents and 13.8 percent of direct property damage from 1984 through 1988 structure fires.

Table 3-4A shows the leading fabric products, ranked by their share of textile fires, and the number of fires and civilian deaths and dollars of direct property damage occurring in fires where the first fuel was textile in that product. Table 3-4B provides a similar display by type of textile.

TEXTILES—GENERAL

Fibers are the basic components of all textiles. These are usually spun into yarns and then woven or knitted into a variety of fabrics, e.g., plain or patterned fabrics or pile, such as flannels, towels, artificial furs, and carpets. Fibers also can be processed directly into useful structures, such as nonwoven fabrics or battings. Fabrics are usually scoured, bleached, and dyed and/or finished with chemicals which give them a stiffer or softer hand, durable press characteristics, luster, or flame or weather resistance.

Nonwoven fabrics are made from various fibers by gluing them together, either before they are fully hardened in the spinning process, or by means of latex adhesives. They are widely used in hazmat protective clothing, disposables, and other areas; some are treated with flame retardant.

The ignitability, rate of flame spread and heat release, total heat produced, heat shrinkage, and ease of fire extinction in textiles depends on their fiber content, weight, and construction. The finish generally does not affect these properties significantly, unless it is flame retardant.

Common textile fibers are listed in Table 3-4C, along with some of their burn hazard properties, major trade names, and end uses. The data have been collected from a variety of sources.[1,2,3] The descriptions of burning behavior in this table and the discussions throughout this chapter are based on small-scale tests and may be misleading when large fires or strong radiation are encountered. In such cases, even fabrics that are considered flame retardant may burn readily.

Natural fibers include cellulosic and protein fibers. Man-made fibers are produced by processing liquids through small holes and allowing the emerging filaments to harden (coagulate). The resulting products can be used as "filament yarns," or can be cut into shorter lengths and spun into "staple yarns." The staple yarns can contain more than one type of fiber, e.g., blends of polyester and cotton. Many different textile properties can be attained by blending various fibers.

All common natural fibers, except glass, contain organic compounds and the elements carbon and hydrogen, and often also oxygen and nitrogen. Chlorine is found in vinyl-coated fabrics.

Natural Fibers

The most important cellulosic fiber is cotton. Cotton consists of more than 90 percent cellulose $(C_6H_{10}O_5)_x$. Other

John F. Krasny, retired from the Center for Fire Research, National Institute of Standards and Technology, is a textile flammability consultant, based in Kensington, MD.

TABLE 3-4A. ***Structure Fires Involving Textiles as the Initial Fuel, by Fabric Product****

Fabric Product	Fires	Civilian Deaths	Direct Property Damage (in Millions)
Mattress, bedding, or pillow	44,000 (35.8%)	753 (34.5%)	$264.8 (30.4%)
Upholstered furniture	20,400 (16.6%)	876 (41.3%)	$200.4 (23.0%)
Clothing on or off a person	18,100 (14.7%)	251 (11.8%)	$117.7 (13.5%)
Curtain, drape, or tapestry	6,000 (4.9%)	33 (1.6%)	$ 38.4 (4.4%)
Linen, other than bedding	5,600 (4.6%)	15 (0.7%)	$ 21.0 (2.4%)
Carpet or rug	5,600 (4.5%)	69 (3.3%)	$ 45.7 (5.2%)
Fiber or lint	4,800 (3.9%)	3 (0.1%)	$ 9.1 (1.0%)
Other known	17,200 (14.0%)	107 (5.0%)	$166.2 (19.1%)
Unknown	1,200 (1.0%)	13 (0.6%)	$ 8.4 (1.0%)
Total	122,900 (100.0%)	2,121 (100.0%)	$871.6 (100.0%)

* Annual average of U.S. fire experience reported to fire departments, 1985–1988.
Source: NFIRS and NFPA Survey.

TABLE 3-4B. ***Structure Fires Involving Textiles as the Initial Fuel, by Textile Type****

Textile Type	Fires	Civilian Deaths	Direct Property Damage (in Millions)
Cotton, rayon, or cotton-polyester blend	67,600 (55.1%)	1,000 (47.2%)	$4384.8 (44.1%)
Man-made fabric	39,400 (31.1%)	768 (36.2%)	$ 323.8 (37.1%)
Wool or wool mixture	2,200 (1.8%)	19 (0.9%)	$ 15.0 (1.7%)
Fur, silk or other fabric	500 (0.4%)	11 (0.5%)	$ 3.3 (0.4%)
Other or unclassified	4,400 (3.6%)	56 (2.7%)	$ 66.0 (7.6%)
Unknown	8.800 (7.1%)	266 (12.5%)	$ 78.7 (9.0%)
Total	122,900 (100.0%)	2,121 (100.0%)	$ 871.6 (100.0%)
	15.3%	42.5%	13.8%

* Annual average of U.S. fire experience reported to fire departments, 1984–1988.
Source: NFIRS and NFPA Survey.

plant fibers, such as jute, flax (linen), hemp, and sisal also are basically cellulose in composition. Cotton and the other plant fibers are combustible; the ignition temperature of cotton fiber is 752°F (400°C). When ignited they produce heat, smoke, carbon dioxide, carbon monoxide, water, and numerous other compounds. The plant fibers char but do not melt.

Protein fibers, such as silk, wool, and other hair fibers derived from animals, are chemically different from cotton because they consist of complex protein molecules containing high percentages of nitrogen as well as carbon, hydrogen, oxygen, and small amounts of sulfur. Wool supports combustion with difficulty, and, other factors being equal, is more difficult to ignite, burns more slowly, and is easier to extinguish than cotton. This is seen in wool's very small share of the fire problem, as evidenced in Table 3-4B.

Man-Made Fibers

Man-made fibers can be divided into two groups: (1) "regenerated" or "reconstituted" fibers, and (2) fully synthetic fibers. The major regenerated fiber in use today is viscose rayon. Rayon is made from dissolved cellulose and is similar to cotton in its charring and burning properties. Acetate is made by the reaction of cellulose and acetic acid; it melts before burning. It is more similar in its burning characteristics to the thermoplastic fibers (nylon, olefin, and polyester) than to cellulose.

The major fully synthetic fibers are acrylics (which char, intumesce, and burn when exposed to heat) and the thermoplastic fibers, such as nylon, olefin (including polypropylene and the less popular polyethylene fibers), and polyester. Acrylics and nylon contain nitrogen atoms and, like wool, produce hydrogen cyanide when burned. The thermoplastics do not char but shrink away from heat sources and melt, form holes near the heat source, and/or ablate. If such fabrics burn at all, the upward flame spread tends to be slow. Molten polymer runs downward, moving the flames sideward and downward, or forms drops which may or may not flame. Compared to fabrics containing cellulose, thermoplastics are generally more difficult to ignite, and the flames tend to cover smaller areas, travel more slowly, or self-extinguish.

There are, however, many situations in which thermoplastics can burn readily. This occurs when they are stiffened by finishes or heavy dye application, causing them to lose their ability to evade flames and ablate. It also occurs in blends of thermoplastic and char-forming fibers (even when the latter are flame retardant), e.g., in the popular polyester/cotton blends which burn more like 100 percent cotton than 100 percent polyester. A thermoplastic-fiber fabric in contact with a char-forming fabric, e.g., a polyester/cotton skirt in contact with a nylon slip,[4] or a polyester curtain in contact with a foam lining, can burn readily. If a burning outer garment is not in contact with a nylon or polyester undergarment, the latter may not ignite but become limp, shrink, make close contact with, and possibly stick to, the skin, causing injury even without burning. Finally, if an ablated thermoplastic fabric still flames when it falls, it can ignite garments or furnishings below it.

However, with such exceptions, thermoplastics can be considered relatively safe with respect to small-flame ignition, as compared to cellulosics and if used as single-layer

TABLE 3-4C. ***Fire Hazard Properties of Common Textile Fibers***

Fiber Designation	Temperatures, °F (°C) Decomp.	Melting	Ignition	Burning	Burning Behavior	Typical Trade Names	End Uses
A. Natural Fibers							
Cellulosic: cotton, hemp, jute, linen, sisal, etc.	580–610 (305–320)	—	490–750 (255–400)	1560 (850)	char, burn, sometimes afterglow	—	apparel, furnishings, towels, cordage
Protein: wool, mohair cashmere, camel hair, etc.	450 (230)	—	1060–1110 (570–600)	1720 (940)	char, intumesce, burn less readily than cellulosics	—	apparel, blankets, carpets, furniture covers
B. Man-made Fibers							
Acetate	570 (300)	500 (260)	820–1000 (440–525)	1720 (960)	melts and burns	Ariloft, Celanese, Chromspun, Estron	apparel, lingerie, furnishings
Acrylic	540–590 (285–310)	— —	860–1050 (460–560)	1560 (850)	chars, intumesces, burns	Acrilan, Creslan, Orlon, Zefran	apparel, furnishings, carpets, blankets, pile fabrics
Nylon	600–790 (315–420)	420–490 (215–255)	840–1060 (450–570)	1600 (875)	melts, ablates, burns	ACE, Anso, Antron, Blue "C", Caprolan, Celanese, Cordura, Courtaulds, Cumnloft, Ultron	apparel, lingerie, furnishings, carpets, cordage, industrial uses
Olefin (polypropylene)	750 (400)	330 (165)	930–1060 (500–570)	1540 (840)	melts, ablates, burns	Herculon, Marquesa, Marvess, Patlon	knitted sportwear, carpets, cordage, furniture covers, industrial uses
Polyester	680–750 (360–400)	480–570 (250–300)	840–1040 (450–560)	1290–1330 (700–725)	melts, ablates, burns	A.C.E., Avlin, Dacron, Fortrel, Holofil, Kodel, Trevira	apparel, lingerie, furnishings, carpets, blankets, fiberfill, cordage, industrial uses
Rayon (viscose)	550 (290)	—	790 (420)	1560 (850)	chars, burns	Avril, Coloray, Fibro, Zantrel	apparel, lingerie, furnishings
Spandex	581–671 (305–355)	446–482 (230–250)	780 (415)	NA	melts, burns	Lycra	in apparel and lingerie where stretch is desired

Furnishings: upholstery, bedding, curtains and drapes
NA—not available

apparel. Thus, accidents in which children's nightwear was the first item to ignite have been essentially eliminated since the introduction of the children's nightwear standard,[5] and the subsequent change from cotton to primarily thermoplastic nightwear,[6,7] at no additional cost of the garments.[8] On the other hand, thermoplastics, even if they are hard to ignite, should not be used in garments which are intended to protect against heat, such as fire fighter or industrial uniforms, because of their tendency to shrink, melt, and stick when exposed to heat.

In addition to the burn behavior, Table 3-4C lists temperatures that have been cited for onset of decomposition, melting, ignition, and the burning temperature of the flames. The ranges are often quite wide for any one fiber because of the differences in methods for measuring such temperatures as well as the variety of polymer compositions used in each fiber group for various end uses. In the case of nylon, there are two major types—Nylon 6 and Nylon 66—which vary in the structure of the base molecule. For the ignition temperature of cotton, one finds two values in the literature, 490 and 750°F (255 and 400°C); it is possible that the lower value was obtained with aged cotton. (It is well known that the ignition temperature of wood decreases with aging, and that may hold for cotton as well.) The ignition temperature of blends tends to be similar to that of the component with the lower ignition temperature. Thus, measured by one method, the ignition temperature for 14 different fiber types ranged from 750°F (400°C) for cotton to 1110°F (600°C) for wool; 50/50 blends of cotton and another fiber ranged from 770 to 860°F (410 to 460°C).[2]

Noncombustible Textiles

Noncombustible fabrics include those made entirely from inorganic materials. Table 3-4D lists noncombustible fibers. Glass fabrics listed by testing laboratories for use as draperies are woven from uncoated glass yarns which do not burn or propagate flame. If a sufficient quantity of combustible coating or decorative material is applied to glass fabrics or to other noncombustible fabrics, however, the fabrics will support continued flaming. The inherent brittleness of glass and the other fibers listed in Table 3-4D eliminates them from use in clothing fabrics. They are used as reinforcement for plastics, and, in the case of the relatively low-priced glass fibers, for curtains and draperies.

High-Temperature and Flame-Retardant Textiles

Several of the fibers that resist high temperatures and are used in textiles are listed in Table 3-4E[9,10] and in Table 3-4F, along with their ignition temperatures, limiting oxygen index (LOI), and some other physical properties.

TABLE 3-4D. ***Noncombustible Fibers***

Beta fiber	Stainless steel
E-glass	Super alloy
Quartz	Refractory-whiskers
Carbonaceous residue	Alumina
Carbon	Zirconia
Graphite	Boron

TABLE 3-4E. ***High-Temperature, Flame-, and Chemical-Resistant Fibers***

	Ryton	*Ultratec*	*Nomex*[d,f]	*Kevlar*[d,f]	PBI[f]	T-84 Polyimide	Kynol[e,f] Phenolic
Softening point							
°C	285	>315					
°F	545	>600		Decompose[b]			NA
Upper Use Temp. (50% tenacity)							
°C	200	260	230	260	>315	>230	
°F	400	500	450	500	>600	>550	NA
Strength (g/denier)	2–4	4–6	3–5	18–20	3–5	3–4	1.5
Elongation (%)	20–40	20–40	20–40	3–4	25–40	30–40	35
Chemical resistance							
hot acid	VG	G	P	P	VG	VG	P
hot base	VG	VG	P	F	G	P	P
hydrolysis	VG	VG	F	F–P	VG	VG	NA
solvents	VG	VG	G	VG	VG	VG	VG
Dry heat resistance	G	VG	G	G	VG	VG	VG
Flammability (LOI)[c]	34	26	30	29	38–49	37	29–31
Smoke density [a]	NA	NA	5	5	3	7	low

[a] Smoke density is a relative scale where, for example, wool = 46 and cotton = 26.
[b] Decomposes rather than melts.
[c] LOI—Limiting Oxygen Index, i.e., the percent oxygen in an oxygen/nitrogen volume mixture that just sustains combustion. Wool = 28; cotton = 19.
[d] Generic name: aramid
[e] Novoloid
[f] Presently used in structural firefighter's protective gear.
VG = very good; G = good; F = fair; P = poor; NA = not available

Table, with minor additions, reproduced by courtesy of Albany International Research Co. Mansfield, MA.

TABLE 3-4F. ***Flame-Retardant (FR) Fibers***

Fiber Type	LOI	Ignit. Temp. °F/°C	Burning Behavior	Trade Names
PVC	37	930/500	chars, shrinks at low temps.	*Rhovyl, Leavyl, Teviron*
FR rayon	31	—	chars	*PFR*
Matrix	29–32	930–1000/ 500–600	chars at 220/430, shrinks	Kohjin, Cordelan
Modacrylic	27–30	600/315	chars, shrinks at .140–180/ 280–360	*SCF*
FR polyester	28		melts at 250/480	*Trevira* 271, *Heim*
FR wool	32–34	1060–1100/ 570–600	chars, intumesces	—
FR cotton	28–32	450/290	chars	—

The limiting oxygen index is a way to measure the tendency of a fabric, once ignited, to continue burning after the ignition source is removed. LOI is defined as the minimum volume concentration of oxygen in a mixture of oxygen and nitrogen that will just support sustained combustion of the material when ignited in a vertical position at its uppermost edge.[11] Cotton fabrics, for example, have a LOI of 19 percent, which means that if the oxygen is reduced below 19 percent the cotton will not continue to burn after the ignition source is removed. The higher the LOI of a fabric, the greater the probability that it will cease to burn once the ignition source is removed. Fabrics with high ignition temperatures and high LOIs can be expected to be safe for clothing and furnishings, since they will not ignite readily and will not continue to burn after an accidental ignition source is removed. However, it should be noted that the use of the LOI test for textiles has abated in recent years; full-scale tests of the various items are considered more reliable.

As previously discussed, many synthetic fabrics shrink when exposed to temperatures approaching their melting or decomposition temperatures. When shrinkage brings the fabric into contact with the skin, the insulating layer of air is eliminated and the amount of heat transferred to the skin is increased significantly. Thermal shrinkage is a particularly important property to consider when selecting fabric for use in protective clothing. Another important property of fabrics used in protective clothing is the ability to maintain integrity during a fire. Fabrics that weaken by charring may split apart and fall away, leaving the skin directly exposed to heat.

FLAME-RETARDANT TREATMENTS

The flame-retardant treatment of theater scenery, curtains, and draperies in places of public assembly is commonly required by local fire authorities. Treated fabrics are used in hotels, hospitals, and other occupancies in the interest of preservation of lives and property.

Many businesses specialize in the flame-retardant treatment of theater scenery, draperies, and other fabrics, using standard chemicals. However, some of these businesses may not treat fabrics properly or may use relatively ineffective or nonpermanent chemicals. It is therefore advisable to deal only with businesses of known reliability, or, if dealing with an unknown concern, to have treated fabrics tested for adequacy of treatment.

The resistance of such treatments to aging, laundering, and drycleaning must be ensured. Also, it must be emphasized that such treatments are only expected to make fabrics resistant to ignition by small flames, and that they may burn readily in larger fires.

The effects of chemical treatments in reducing the flammability of combustible fabrics are varied and complex, and all phases are not fully understood. There are five different ways in which chemicals or mixtures retard spread of flame and afterglow: (1) they generate noncombustible gases that tend to exclude oxygen from the burning surface, (2) radicals or molecules from degradation of the flame-retardant chemical react endothermically and interfere with chain reactions in the flame, (3) the flame-retardant chemical decomposes endothermically, (4) a nonvolatile char or liquid is formed by the chemical, which reduces the amount of oxygen and heat that can reach the fabric, and (5) finely divided particles are formed that change the combustion reactions. Usually a flame-retardant chemical or mixture affects flammability in more than one of these ways. A review of flame-retardant treatments for textiles can be found in *Fire Safety Journal*.[12] Flame-retardant treatments can increase the LOI of cotton from 19 to 27 or 32, and of wool from 25 to 34.

Hundreds of different chemicals have been suggested as flame retardants for textiles. It must be emphasized that no one system works for all fibers, as can be seen from Table 3-4G. In addition, some chemical systems change textile properties, e.g., resistance to sunlight, absorption, color, and flexibility, or lose some of their effectiveness when exposed to high temperatures or repeated launderings. Much progress has been made in overcoming most of these undesirable effects. Loss of strength, for example, has become a minor problem in correctly treated flame-retardant cotton fabrics. However, concern that some flame retardants may be skin irritants, carcinogens, or too expensive can deter wider use.

TABLE 3-4G. ***Flame-Retardant Chemicals for Textiles***

Fiber	Typical Flame-Retardant Chemicals
Cotton	Tetrakis (hydroxy methyl) phosphonium salt insolubilized with ammonia gas
Cotton-rayon (disposable, nondurable finish)	Diammonium phosphate Ammonium sulfamate Boron compounds
Rayon (modified fiber)	Hexapropoxy phosphazene
Polyester (modified fiber)	Oligomeric phosphonate
Polyester, acetate, nylon	decabromo-diphenyl ether (DBDPO) and antimony oxide
Nylon (nondurable finish)	Thiourea
Wool	Ti, Zr compounds Dibromo-terephthalic acid
Modacrylics (modified fibers)	Vinylchloride, vinylidene chloride, vinylbromide as co-monomer

It must be emphasized that treatments which protect against ignition of textiles by small flames do not necessarily impart resistance to smoldering ignition by cigarettes. For example, flame-retardant treatment of cotton generally lowers the charring temperature of cotton, but often decreases the cigarette ignition resistance.

RELATIONSHIP OF FLAMMABILITY AND END USE OF TEXTILES

So far this discussion of textile flammability has been confined primarily to the textiles themselves. The end use of the textile, e.g., ordinary or heat-protective clothing, curtains, carpets, etc., is very important when evaluating the flammability of a textile.

Clothing

Congress passed the *Flammable Fabrics Act of 1953*,[13] after a rash of serious fire accidents in which rayon-pile fabrics made into children's cowboy chaps or sweaters were involved. All wearing apparel sold since 1953 has to pass a test described in the Consumer Product Safety Commission's (CPSC) "Standard for the Flammability of Clothing Textiles."[14] The test, however, excluded the rayon-pile fabrics and other extremely flammable fabrics, such as very-high-pile cotton flannels, stiffened nylon nets, and very light fabrics. However, all normal apparel fabrics must pass this test.

Several studies indicated that additional protection of young and old populations would be desirable. For example, in a study of 463 fire fatalities that occurred from 1972 through 1977 in the State of Maryland,[15] deaths from clothing ignitions comprised 5.5 percent of the fatalities. Of those victims, 21.6 percent were 9 years old or younger, and 20.5 percent were 60 years old or older. Persons aged 50 years and older were more likely to become fire casualties. The number of fire deaths in this age group was approximately twice the predicted number, based on 1970 census data for Maryland. Factors that contributed to the increased proportion of fire fatalities at both ends of the age spectrum were inability to rapidly and successfully cope with the fire situation and lowered tolerance to toxic combustion products. This applied especially to the older population, where increased cardiopulmonary weakness contributed to lower tolerance to toxic exposures. In addition, it was shown that many victims of garment fires wore nightwear at the time of the incident.

Consequently, a children's nightwear standard was promulgated for sizes 0 to 6x in 1971, followed by a standard for sizes 7 to 14 three years later.[5] At the time of promulgation, this standard strained the state of the art, but thermoplastic and flame-retardant garments were soon produced, which passed this rather severe test. The results have been unexpectedly beneficial.

Since the introduction of the children's sleepwear standard, the number of burn deaths among children under age 15 due to ignitions of any type of clothing have dropped to five or fewer a year. However, a serious problem still exists for older adults. From 1983 through 1985, for example, clothing-ignition burn deaths accounted for roughly one fire death of every 20 fire deaths overall, but for one of every eight fire deaths for people age 65 and over. Since people age 65 and over also have twice the fire death rate of the whole population, this means they have five times the rate of death due to burns from clothing ignition fires.[16]

The style or type of garment is an important factor in evaluating its fire hazard. For example, a full-length gown containing several yards of flammable fabric could be a death trap, whereas a tightly fitting blouse or shirt made of the same material might be far less dangerous. Not only would the gown present much more fuel for burning, but its size and loose shape would make it far more vulnerable to contact with typical ignition sources. Flared skirts, large bows, and full-sleeved kimonos are other examples of easily ignitable garments. The availability of oxygen on both sides of loosely fitting garments accelerates flame spread.

Curtains, Draperies, and Wall Coverings

Curtains, draperies, and wall coverings can ignite from such ignition sources as electrical malfunction or wastepaper-basket fires. Flames rapidly spread to walls and ceilings. It has been shown that large differences exist between the potential of various domestic curtain materials to ignite wall-covering materials and the production of heat and smoke this creates.[17] Curtains in public occupancies are regulated by local authorities, and conforming materials do not seem to present major problems during the initial stages of a fire. The test most prescribed by regulatory authorities for curtains and draperies is NFPA 701, *Standard Methods of Fire Tests for Flame-Resistant Textiles and Films.* NFPA 701 recently addressed that, even if single layers of curtain fabrics pass the requirements of the standard, the combination of two or three layers, often found in motels, etc., may burn vigorously. This was illustrated in a full-scale test.[18] Attempts are presently being made to develop a test method for multiple layers.

Carpets

Until 1960 there was very little fire experience to indicate that carpets were a significant factor in fires. Consequently, floor coverings were customarily exempted from coverage in building codes regulating life safety from fire. Since 1960, although there was a small number of fires reported in which carpets spread fire, those that have been reported indicate that carpets can be the prime material involved in the development or spread of a fire. In 1970 a fire in a California dwelling was first seen by an occupant when it was a few feet in diameter on carpeting in front of the fireplace.[19,20] As the occupant applied water with a garden hose to the burning carpet, the fire spread rapidly on the carpet and enveloped the entire room within ten minutes after discovery, including furniture and wood paneling. Because of such experiences, carpet flammability is currently being regulated at the federal, state, and municipal levels. The persistence of fatal carpet and rug fires noted in Table 3-4A primarily occurs in the much less regulated home environment.

Among the many factors in carpet construction that may affect ease of ignition and ability to spread fire are: fiber type, area unit weight density (or, loops per square inch), pile height, backing material, padding, type of adhesive, single versus double back, and type of dye. (Carpet flammability tests for residential and special occupancies are discussed later in this chapter.)

Heat-Protective Clothing

Heat-protective clothing should not burn, melt, or disintegrate on exposure to heat or flame. It should be an effective thermal barrier (consistent with the ability of the wearer to tolerate the weight, heat load, bulkiness, and stiffness of highly insulative garments, such as fire fighters' coats and pants), should not shrink excessively when heated, and should be durable. Detailed reviews of research and development on heat protective garments and methods to measure their properties can be found in other publications.[21,22] Abbott and Schulman have made an analysis of exposure conditions encountered by fire fighters, and protective materials for routine and emergency conditions.[23]

For structural fire fighting, turnout coats are generally worn in the U.S. These coats consist of a water- and abrasion-resistant outer shell, a vapor barrier to prevent penetration of water and chemicals, and an inner liner to provide further insulation against heat and cold. The common materials for the outer shell are Nomex®, blends of PBI and Kevlar®, and flame-retardant cotton. Among the vapor barriers used are neoprene-coated polyester/cotton fabrics or Goretex® fabrics, which are water vapor permeable but do not permit liquid water permeation. Nomex® needled or batting materials, flame-retardant cotton or wool fabrics, etc., are popular inner liners. Similar materials are used in bunker pants, gloves, and hoods used to protect the ears and neck. European fire departments frequently use wool outer shells in their turnout coats; wool tends to char at relatively low temperatures.

TEXTILE FLAMMABILITY TESTS

The severity of the hazard of a fabric in a particular type of product, such as a dress, curtain, or carpet, depends greatly upon the ease of ignition of the product, the speed with which flame spreads, the amount of heat generated and the rate at which it is released, susceptibility to melting, and the quantity and composition of the smoke and gaseous products of combustion. No individual test method gives a complete evaluation of the hazard, and there are no nationally recognized test methods to measure some of the hazards. Many of the more important test methods for textile products have been summarized.[24,25,26] With the exception of the test methods for mattresses and upholstered furniture, those in common use in the United States are described below.

Clothing

The federal *Flammable Fabrics Act of 1953* was signed into law in 1953 and amended in 1967.[13] The Act prohibits the sale of all wearing apparel and fabrics subject to the Act that are classified "highly flammable" when tested according to Part 1610, which was formerly designated Commercial Standard CS 191-53.[14] The specified test is designed to measure ease of ignition and rate of flame spread. It does this by impinging a 5-in. (127 mm) long gas flame for 1 sec against the lower end of the upper face of a 2 by 6 in. (51 by 152 mm) specimen that is suspended at a 45-degree angle from the horizontal in a test chamber. If the fabric is ignited by the 1-sec exposure, the time required for the flame to spread 5 in. (127 mm) on the fabric is used to classify the fabric. This test has been successful in excluding inordinately flammable garments from interstate commerce. It does not discriminate among other apparel fabrics, even though large differences may exist between them. For example, pile fabrics, such as cotton/polyester terry fabrics and cotton flannels cut into gowns, robes, and pajamas, gave considerably higher burn injury estimates (percentage of body surface burned weighted by depth of burn) than estimates obtained with almost 60 other common apparel fabrics when burned on an instrumented mannequin.[27,28] The same fabrics ranked high on the flammability scale when tested in 12 laboratory fabric flammability tests, but easily passed the Part 1610 requirements. One-hundred percent nylon and polyester fabrics also passed the test, as well as some blends containing wool or modacrylic fibers, which produced very low injury estimates on the mannequin and low flammability results in the other laboratory tests.

The test method in NFPA 702, *Classification of the Flammability of Wearing Apparel*, is the same as that in Part 1610,[14] with two important exceptions. The committee that drafted the NFPA wearing apparel standard noted that many fabrics, particularly those without raised fiber surfaces, were not ignited when the top surface was touched by a small test flame for 1 sec. Those fabrics could not be evaluated for rate of flame spread. Furthermore, the committee concluded that the lower edge of a fabric should be easier to ignite than the surface. Consequently, the test flame in NFPA 702 is brought in contact with the lower edge of all samples and, in the case of those without raised fiber surface, is held there until ignition occurs. Many fabrics that do not ignite in Part 1610[14] ignite in the NFPA 702 test.[29]

More stringent standards were introduced for children's sleepwear in the early 1970s; Parts 1615 and 1616[5] are much more restrictive than Part 1610.[14] Fabric samples 10 by 3 in. (254 by 89 mm) are suspended vertically in a cabinet and subjected to a test flame along the bottom edge. A fabric passes the test if the average char length of five specimens does not exceed 7 in. (178 mm), and no specimen has a char length of 10 in. (254 mm). The barrel of the test flame burner is 3/4 in. (19 mm) below the lower edge of the sample and the test flame is adjusted to extend 1 1/2 in. (38 mm). The sample is exposed for 3 sec. Char length is the distance from the fabric's lower edge to the end of the void or tear in the charred, burned, or damaged area. The tear is made by lifting the sample by one of the corners near the lower edge after weights had been attached to the opposite corner near the lower edge. The small-scale test method in NFPA 701, *Standard Methods of Fire Tests for Flame-Resistant Textiles and Films*, and *Federal Test Method Standard No. 191*, "Flame Resistance of Cloth; Vertical Method 5903.2,"[30] are similar to the childrens sleepwear test.[5]

The U.S. thus has two apparel flammability standards: (1) the children's sleepwear standard, which has greatly reduced the incidence of accidents but restricted the choice of fabrics, and (2) the general apparel standard, which has eliminated inordinately flammable, limited-use fabrics, but does not significantly affect fabric choice. However, it permits many highly flammable fabrics to be used without regard to garment configuration. Attempts to further categorize fabric flammability hazards have been made; some have based such categorization on flame-spread rate measurements.[29,31] Flame-spread rate measured on remainders of garments involved in fire accidents, however, did not correlate with the size of the victim's burn injury.[32] Researchers have developed methods for measuring the rate of heat release from burning fabrics.[33,34,35] Braun *et al* [35] suggested that fabrics with a low rate of heat release could be used in all garments; those with short ignition times and higher rate of heat release could be used only in tightly fitting garments; and finally suggested the elimination of fabrics with short ignition time (1/2 sec or less) and high heat release rate. The International Standards Organization (ISO) is also proposing a standard based on garment fit.

Heat-Protective Clothing

NFPA 1971, *Protective Clothing for Structural Fire Fighting*, employs three methods to evaluate the firesafety of turnout coats:

1. An ignition test: "Flame Resistance of Cloth: Vertical Test Method 5903.2"[30] which is quite similar to the children's sleepwear test, except that it uses a different gas, with a flame temperature of 1550°F (843°C), and a 12-sec ignition time. Maximum char length is 4 in. (102 mm), afterflame time 2 sec.
2. A heat stability test: The fabrics used in the ensemble must not char, separate, or melt when exposed in a forced-air oven at 482°F (250°C) for 5 min.
3. A heat protection test: The thermal protection performance (TPP) test, which is described below.[36]

The third method measures actual heat transfer through the ensemble and relates it to burn injury potential, rather than relying on the ensemble thickness. A horizontal specimen cut from the ensemble is placed over a heat source delivering 2 cal/cm^2 per sec (84 kW/m^2 per sec or 7.4 Btu/sq ft per sec). The heat source consists of two gas flames and nine quartz heaters adjusted to obtain a 50:50 ratio of convective and radiative heat. The time until an incipient second-degree burn to skin would occur in contact with the inner layer is measured; this is based on work correlating the rate of heat and the total heat delivered to skin with burn injury severity.[37] This time measure, multiplied by two because of the exposure to 2 cal/cm^2 per sec, is called the thermal protection performance. A minimum TPP rating of 35, well within the state of the art, has been proposed as the acceptance criterion.

The Health and Safety Division of the International Association of Fire Fighters has written guidelines for procurement of fire fighter protective clothing, citing, among other items of interest, Occupational Safety and Health Administration (OSHA) standards and military procurement specifications as of 1983.[38,39] NFPA also has standards for station/work uniforms, helmets, gloves, and protective footwear for structural fire fighters.

The protection in real fires provided by turnout coats varying widely in construction and ranging in TPP from 33 to 53 was investigated. It was concluded that the TPP is predictive of protection afforded if the coats are exposed to rapidly increasing heat. A coat with a TPP of 35 will provide protection for only a few seconds in a flashover situation.[40,41]

A TPP test like the one described above, but using a 84 kW/m^2 per sec gas flame rather than a combination of flame and radiant heat, is listed by the American Society for Testing and Materials (ASTM).[42] Fabrics exposed to other heat sources on one side and in contact with artificial skin or other thermosensors can be ranked according to protective value.[42,43,44] Tests for the tendency of molten metals to adhere to protective clothing, for thermal protective performance of materials when in contact with hot surfaces, and for resistance to penetration by chemicals have been developed or are under development.

Blankets

In an ASTM blanket flammability test,[45] a small flame is brought down on the center of a specimen for 1 sec. The specimen is covered with a paper monitor with a 2-in. (5 cm) circular cutout. If the paper monitor does not char or become discolored, the material is Class 1, and is considered acceptable.

Carpets and Rugs

Carpets and rugs are currently regulated in the U.S. by federal regulations.[46] Separate parts of the regulations apply to particular sizes. In testing these carpets and rugs, a 9 by 9 in. (229 by 229 mm) sample is placed on the floor of a test chamber, and a flat steel plate with a 8-in. (203 mm) diameter hole in the center is placed on the sample. A methanamine tablet is placed in the center of the hole and ignited. The sample passes the test if the charred portion does not extend beyond 1 in. (25.4 mm) of the edge of the hole at any point. Seven of eight specimens of other-than-small carpets and rugs must pass if carpets made of the tested material are to be sold. In the case of small carpets and rugs, those that do not pass the test may be sold if they carry a permanent label stating that they failed to pass and should not be used near an ignition source. This requirement eliminated only a small percentage (usually low quality) of the carpets on the market at the time the standard was introduced.

Hospitals and other institutions receiving federal financial aid are required to comply with flammability limits for carpets and other floor coverings used on patient-occupied areas and exit ways. The flame spread rating of floor coverings must not exceed 75, as determined by ASTM E84-70, "Test for Surface Burning Characteristics of Building Materials."[47] This test is similar to NFPA 255, *Method of Test of Surface Burning Characteristics of Building Materials*, and is commonly referred to as the Steiner Tunnel Test.

The Appendix of NFPA *101*®, *Life Safety Code*®, suggests that where limitations are to be placed on the flammability of floor coverings, the test method in NFPA 255, *Method of Test of Surface Burning Characteristics of Building Materials*, is to be used. Objections have been raised regarding its use to evaluate floor coverings, because positioning the test specimen on top of the tunnel bears no resemblance to its position when in place in a building. The method is also criticized because it may result in delamination, melting, and dripping of test specimens, which removes combustible material from the reach of the burner. The Canadian carpet test places the specimen on the floor of a tunnel.[48]

In an effort to more correctly assess the flame spread hazard of flooring materials, the concept of critical radiant flux was developed. In their work on model corridor fire tests, the National Bureau of Standards (now NIST) found that the radiant energy impacting on a floor covering had a significant influence on the propagation of flame across the floor covering. This work led to the development of the flooring radiant panel test (FRPT).

The flooring radiant panel test as embodied in NFPA 253, *Standard Method of Test for Critical Radiant Flux of Floor Covering Systems Using a Radiant Heat Energy Source*, subjects a horizontal floor-covering specimen to a radiant energy flux from a gas-fired panel at a 30-degree angle. The radiant energy flux decreases along the length of the specimen according to a standard energy flux *vs* distance profile. A pilot flame ignites the specimen at the end with the higher radiant energy flux. The flame front is allowed to travel until it is no longer reinforced by the radiant energy flux and extinguishes. The heat flux at this point of the specimen is called the "critical radiant flux." For corridors and exitways in such occupancies as hospitals and nursing homes, a minimum of 0.45 W/cm^2 is recommended, except for corridors and exitways in other occupancies (except one- and two-family houses—where the recommendation is 0.22 W/cm^2).[49] The critical heat flux of carpets then is believed to have aggravated the initial fire conditions, e.g., the Baptist Tower fire was found to be 0.1 W/cm^2.[50] However, the above requirements are well within the state of the art of carpet manufacture.

Textiles in Aircraft

The flammability of textiles in the crew and passenger compartments of aircraft is regulated by the Federal Aviation Administration (FAA). The vertical test method 5903.2 is used[30]; average char length for three specimens must not exceed 8 in. (203 mm), afterburn time must be less than 15 sec, and the time that drippings may continue to flame must be less than 5 sec. In addition, the FAA has specified a new test for passenger seats.[51] For the purpose of this test, a unique oil burner that has the following specifications is used: (1) kerosene consumption, 2 gal per hr (7.57 L/h); (2) nozzle diameter, 6 in. (152 mm); (3) distance of nozzle from side of seat to be tested, 4 in. (102 mm);

(4) heat delivery to seat specimen, 10 Btu per sq ft per sec (115 kW/m^2 per sec); and (5) temperature at specimen, 1850°F (1010°C). At least three seats must be tested. For at least half of the number tested, the flame spread must not reach the side of the cushion opposite the burner, the average weight loss must not exceed 10 percent, and there must be no flaming melt drip below the cushion. Among the seat assemblies that pass this test are: (1) those that contain the widely used wool/nylon fabric; (2) interlayers consisting of aluminized or ordinary Nomex® or PBI fabrics which prevents pyrolysis gases from venting toward the flames; and (3) polyurethane foam. An interliner made from Vonar® neoprene-type foam sheet also makes it possible to pass this test, but the lighter fabrics are more cost effective in this application. Other interliner materials are under development, and the use of interliners has spread to institutional furniture, as well.

Textiles in Motor Vehicles

Materials used in the occupant compartments of passenger cars, multi-purpose passenger vehicles, trucks, and buses in the U.S. must not burn or transmit a flame front across the surface at a rate of more than 4 in. (102 mm) per min when tested according to the motor vehicle safety standard of the Department of Transportation (DOT).[52] In that standard, a specimen is suspended in a horizontal position in a test chamber, and one end is ignited by a Bunsen burner flame. The specimen is held in a U-shaped clamp and the assembly is suspended so that the top of the barrel of the burner is 3/4 in. (17 mm) below the exposed edge of the specimen. The burner flame is adjusted to 1 1/2 in. (38 mm) high and the flame temperature to that of a natural gas flame. The specimen is exposed to the test flame for 15 sec. Timing begins when the flame from the burning specimen reaches a point 1 1/2 in. (38 mm) from the open end of the specimen and timing ends when the flame has progressed to 10 in. (254 mm) or self-extinguishes. As previously mentioned, burn rate must not exceed 4 in. (102 mm) per min. This test can be considered to provide only minimum protection, and work is in progress to develop a more realistic test, especially for school buses.

Tents, Tarpaulins, Air-Supported Structures

NFPA 102, *Assembly Seating, Tents, and Membrane Structures*, requires that the textiles used in these structures meet the appropriate flame-resistance requirements when tested in accordance with NFPA 701, *Standard Methods of Fire Tests for Flame-Resistant Textiles and Films*. Covered by NFPA 102 are: (1) tents and air-supported structures used for assembly; (2) tents and air-supported structures in which animals are stabled; (3) tents and air-supported structures located in a portion of the premises used by the public; (4) tents and air-supported structures in places of assembly in or about which fuel-burning devices are located; and (5) all tarpaulins used in connection with (1) through (4).

The small-scale test in NFPA 701, *Standard Methods of Fire Tests for Flame-Resistant Textiles and Films*, was mentioned earlier. The large-scale test in NFPA 701 uses specimens 7 ft (2.135 m) long and 5 or 25 in. (0.127 or 0.645 m) wide, depending upon whether the specimen is to be tested as a flat sheet or is to be hung in folds. The flat specimen is suspended vertically in an open-ended metal stack and its lower edge is exposed to a 11-in. (280 mm) high flame from a Bunsen burner, the top of whose barrel is 4 in. (102 mm) below the bottom of the specimen. A folded specimen is tested with its folds 1/2 in. (12.7 mm) apart in the same metal stack and with the same burner arrangement. For both single-sheet and folded specimen, the test flame is applied for 2 min, then withdrawn, and the duration of flaming combustion recorded. Length of char, i.e., the distance from the top of the test flame to the top of the charred area resulting from spread of flame or afterglow, is also recorded. To pass the test, afterflame time cannot exceed 2 sec, and the char length cannot exceed 10 in. (254 mm). For specimens in folds, maximum afterflame time cannot exceed 2 sec, and maximum char length cannot exceed 35 in. (840 mm), but afterglow may spread in the folds.

In addition, the Canvas Products Association International (CPAI) has developed CPAI-84, *A Specification for Flame-Resistant Materials Used in Camping Tentage*.[53] The test for wall and top material is essentially the same as the 5903.2 test[30]; and for flooring, the methanamine tablet carpet test is prescribed. Maximum char length for walls and tops varies from 4.5 in. (114 mm) for light fabrics to 9 in. (228 mm) for heavy fabrics. For floors, the Part 1630 criteria apply.[46] Provisions for leaching, weathering, and simulated sunlight exposure are part of this voluntary standard. Conforming tents carry the CPAI label.

Curtains, Draperies, and Wall Coverings

Curtains and draperies for public occupancies are generally regulated by local or state fire authorities, and the most widely used test is described in NFPA 701, *Standard Methods of Fire Tests for Flame-Resistant Textiles and Films*. The small-scale part of this method excludes certain thermoplastic fabrics that develop unacceptable char length, because in the specimen frames they cannot shrink freely away from the flames and ablate as they can in real-life situations. The American Society for Testing and Materials' ASTM D3659, "Standard Test Method for Flammability of Apparel Fabrics by Semi-Restraint Method,"[54] has been suggested to replace the small-scale NFPA 701 test. In this test, the 15 by 6 in. (381 by 152 mm) specimens are attached to a bar on top of the test apparatus, and are somewhat restrained from movement by chains that loosely connect the bottom corners of the specimens to fixed points. With the specimen frames removed, more thermoplastic materials pass the test. According to the present version of NFPA 701, materials that fail the small-scale test can still be qualified if they pass the large-scale test.

Curtain fabrics that can pass NFPA 701, *Standard Methods of Fire Tests for Flame-Resistant Textiles and Films*, as single layers can burn vigorously in combination with other curtain fabric layers.[18] Such multi-layer curtain types are often found in motels.

Many jurisdictions require that wall coverings including fabrics, be tested by ASTM E84-70[47] or NFPA 255, *Method of Test of Surface Burning Characteristics of Building Materials*. A study was undertaken to compare the burning characteristics of a number of textile wall coverings in full-scale tests, yielding results of two bench-scale tests—the cone calorimeter and the lateral ignition flame-spread test (LIFT).[55] In this test, specimens approximately 32 × 6 in. (80 by 15 cm) are mounted on an inert insulating material, with the longer dimension horizontal. A radiant panel is mounted at an angle to the specimen so that the heat flux over the specimen is varied. Flame spread and heat flux at which ignition occurs are measured. Use of such tests may eventually obviate the use of the more complex tunnel tests in which the materials—unrealistically for wallcoverings—are mounted horizontally in a tunnel.

TEXTILES IN SPECIAL ENVIRONMENTS

Certain ambient atmospheric conditions influence the behavior of treated textiles in fire situations. They are: (1) oxygen-enriched atmospheres, (2) compressed-air atmospheres, (3) atmospheres where flammable inhalation anesthetizing agents may be present, and (4) exposure to weather.

Action of Treated Textiles in Oxygen-Enriched Air

Some industrial processes require work in atmospheres enriched above the normal oxygen content. Such atmospheres present a high fire hazard, particularly to the clothing worn by the workers. The effect of flame-retardant treatments on the combustibility of the fabrics has been studied.[56]

An indication of the resistance to burning of flame-retardant textiles in oxygen-enriched atmospheres can be inferred from the limiting oxygen indices in Table 3-4F.

The textile fibers department of the Du Pont Company has conducted research on their Nomex® high-temperature-resistant nylon fiber in both high-pressure air environments and oxygen-enriched atmospheres at greater-than-normal pressures. Nomex®-based fabric was found to retain its flame-retardant qualities under air pressure of four atmospheres (59 psig or 405 kPa). At this pressure and in higher oxygen concentrations (40 percent and greater), Nomex® did support combustion, but at a substantially slower rate than did untreated, readily combustible fabrics. NASA has further improved the state of the art in this area, and uses materials such as PBI, flame-retardant cotton, etc., in the oxygen-rich atmospheres.

Fabrics used for hospital operating room garments, or in other atmospheres with flammable gas contamination, should be electrically conductive to prevent accumulation of static electricity. Such accumulations, if discharged to ground, could provide a spark of sufficient energy to ignite the gas.

Weather-Exposed Textiles

Flame-retardant treatments for tents, awnings, tarpaulins, and other fabrics exposed to the weather must not leach out over a period of time. If water-soluble chemicals are used, the treatments must be renewed at frequent intervals. Both the NFPA 701, *Standard Methods of Fire Tests for Flame-Resistant Textiles and Films*, and CPAI[53] tests for tentage specify methods for determination of the effects of weathering.

A wide variety of chemicals can be used for treating fabrics exposed to the weather. Many of the formulas used include chlorinated paraffin, chlorinated synthetic resins, or chlorinated rubber, in combination with various water-insoluble metallic salts, plasticizers, stabilizers, synthetic resins, pigments, binders, mildew inhibitors, etc. Such mixtures are not water soluble and are used with hydrocarbon solvents, or are suspended in aqueous emulsions. The effective application of such treatments calls for techniques and equipment ordinarily available only for factory processing or to businesses specializing in flame-retardant applications. Application of paint to these treated fabrics may lessen their flame resistance.

BIBLIOGRAPHY

References Cited

1. MMFPA, *Man-Made Fibers Fact Book*, Man-Made Fibers Producers Association, Inc., Washington, DC, 1988.
2. Gottlieb, I. M., and Beck, L. R., Jr., "Thermal Stability, Flammability, and Melting Characteristics of Textile Substrates," *Annals NY Academy of Science*, Vol. 82, 1959, pp. 724-743.
3. Einsele, U., "Uber das Brennverhalten und den Brennmechanismus von Synthesefasern," *Melliand Textilberichte*, Vol. 53, 1972, pp. 1395-1402.
4. McCullough, E. A., and Noel, C. J., "Flammability Characteristics of Layered Fabric Assemblies", *Proceedings* Information Council on Fabric Flammability, 1978, pp. 175-184.
5. CPSC, *Code of Federal Regulations*, Part 1615, "Standard for the Flammability of Children's Sleepwear: Size 0 Through 6x (FF 3-71)"; Part 1616, "Sizes 7 Through 14 (FF5-74)." U.S. Consumer Product Safety Commission, Washington, DC, 1974.
6. Bolieu, S., "Children's Sleepwear Flammability Standards: Have They Worked?," *Proceedings* Information Council on Fabric Flammability, 1977, pp. 1-5.
7. Crikelair, G. F., "A Win for the Team," *Proceedings* Information Council on Fabric Flammability, 1975, pp. 218-233.
8. Beckwith, O. P., "Current Status of Children's Sleepwear Manufacturing and Marketing," *Proceedings* Information Council on Fabric Flammability, 1979, pp. 114-122.
9. AIRC, *Chemical, High-Temperature, and Fire-Resistant Fibers*, Albany International Research Co. (formerly FRL), Newsletter 11/1, 1988, Mansfield, MA.
10. Carborundum, *Kynol Flame-Resistant Fibers*, The Carborundum Co., Sanborn, NY, 1975.
11. ASTM, "Method for Measuring the Minimum Oxygen Concentration to Support Candle-Like Combustion of Plastics (Oxygen Index)," ASTM D2863, 1977, American Society for Testing and Materials, Philadelphia, PA.
12. Gordon, B. F., "Flame Retardants and Textile Materials," *Fire Safety Journal*, Vol. 4, 1981, pp. 109-123.
13. CPSC, *Flammable Fabrics Act of 1953* (as amended and revised 1967), U.S. Consumer Product Safety Commission, Washington, DC, 1967.
14. CPSC, *Code of Federal Regulations*, Part 1610, "Standard for the Flammability of Clothing Textiles (formerly CS 191-53)," and Part 1611, "Standard for the Flammability of Vinyl Plastic Film (formerly CS 192-53)," U.S. Consumer Product Safety Commission, Washington, DC, 1988.
15. Berl, W. G., and Halpin, B. M., "Human Fatalities from Unwanted Fires," *Fire Journal*, Vol. 73, No. 5, Sept. 1979, pp. 105-123.
16. Harwood, B., and Hall, J. R., Jr., "What Kills in Fires: Smoke Inhalation or Burns," *Fire Journal*, May/June 1989, pp. 28-34.
17. Moore, L. D., "Full-Scale Burning Behavior of Curtains and Draperies," NBSIR 78-1448, 1978, U.S. National Bureau of Standards, Washington, DC.
18. Belles, D. W., and Beitel, J. J., "Do Multi-Layer Draperies Pass the Single-Layer Fire Test?," *Fire Journal*, Sept./Oct. 1988.
19. "Burning Incense Fell on Carpet," *Fire Journal*, Vol. 64, No. 4, July 1970, p. 50.
20. "Polyester Carpet Fire, Suisun, CA," *Fire Journal*, Vol. 64, No. 5, pp. 88, 89.
21. Brewster, E. P., and Barker, R. L., "A Summary of Research on Heat-Resistant Fabrics for Protective Clothing," *American Industrial Hygiene Association Journal*, Vol. 44, 1983, pp. 123-130.
22. ASTM, "International ASTM Symposium on the Performance of Protective Clothing," *ASTM Special Technical Publication*, American Society for Testing and Materials, Philadelphia, PA, 1984.

23. Abbott, N. J., and Schulman, S., "Protection from Fire: Nonflammable Fabrics and Coatings," *Journal of Coated Fabrics*, Vol. 6, July 1976, pp. 48-64.

24. Hilado, C. J., *Flammability Test Methods Handbook*, Technomic Publishing Company, Inc., Westport, CT, 1973.

25. Krasny, J. F., "Flammability Evaluation Methods for Textiles," *Flame-Retardant Polymeric Materials*, Vol. 3, M. Lewin, S. M. Atlas, and E. M. Pearce, eds., Plenum, NY, 1982.

26. Troitzsch, J., *International Plastics Flammability Handbook: Principles—Regulations—Testing and Approval*, MacMillan, New York, 1983.

27. Bercaw, J. R., "Cooperative Program on General Apparel Flammability: Status Report," *Proceedings* Information Council on Fabric Flammability, 1977, pp. 175-190.

28. Krasny, J. F., "Apparel Flammability: Accident Simulation and Bench-Scale Tests," *Textile Research Journal*, Vol. 56, 1986, pp. 287-303.

29. Weaver, J. W., "Rate of Burning of Apparel Fabrics," *Journal of the American Association of Textile Chemists and Colorists*, Vol. 8, 1976, pp. 176-181.

30. GSA, "Flame Resistance of Cloth: Vertical Method 5903.2," Federal Test Method Standard No. 191, 1971, General Services Administration, Washington, DC.

31. Nielsen, E. B., and Richards, H. R., "A Proposed Method for Measuring Rate-of-Burn," *Journal of the American Association of Textile Chemists and Colorists*, Vol. 1, 1969, pp. 270-277.

32. Vickers, A., Krasny, J., and Tovey, H., "Some Apparel Fire Hazard Parameters," *Proceedings* Information Council on Fabric Flammability, 1973, pp. 205-226.

33. Miller, B., "A New Concept for Monitoring the Burning Behavior of Fabric," *Proceedings* Information Council on Fabric Flammability, 1976, pp. 198-208.

34. Miller, B., and Meiser, C. H., Jr., "Heat Emission from Burning Fabrics, Potential Harm Ranking," *Textile Research Journal*, Vol. 48, 1978, pp. 238-243.

35. Braun, E., *et al*, "Back-up Report for the Proposed Standard for the Flammability of General Wearing Apparel," NBSIR 76-1072, 1976, National Bureau of Standards, Washington, DC.

36. Behnke, W. P., "Predicting Flash Fire Protection of Clothing from Laboratory Tests Using Second-Degree Burn to Rate Performance," *Fire and Materials*, Vol. 8, No. 2, 1984, pp. 5763.

37. Stoll, A. M., and Chianta, M. A., "Method and Rating Systems for Evaluation of Thermal Protection," *Aerospace Medicine Journal*, Vol. 40, 1969, pp. 1232-1238.

38. Smith, M. J., *et al*, *Procuring Fire Fighter Protective Clothing*, Health and Safety Division, Department of Research, International Association of Fire Fighters, AFL-CIO-CLC, Washington, DC, 1983.

39. Veghte, J. H., *Firefighter's Protective Clothing*, Janesville, Dayton, OH, 1988.

40. Krasny, J., F., Rockett, J. A., and Dingyi, H., "Protecting Fire Fighters Exposed in Room Fires: Comparison of Results of Bench-Scale Tests for Thermal Protection and Conditions During Room Flashover," *Fire Technology*, Vol. 24, 1988, pp. 5-19.

41. Krasny, J. F., and Peacock, R. D., "Protecting Fire Fighters Exposed in Room Fires: Part 2. Performance of Turnout Coat Materials under Actual Fire Conditions," (unpublished, 1989).

42. ASTM, "TPP of Materials for Clothing by Open Flame Method," ASTM D4108, 1982, American Society for Testing and Materials, Philadelphia, PA.

43. Schoppe, M. M., Welsford, J. M., and Abbott, N. J., "Resistance of Navy Shipboard Work Clothing Materials to Extreme Heat," Tech. Rep. No. 148, 1982, Navy Clothing and Textile Research Facility, Natick, MA.

44. Braun, E., *et al*, "Measurement of the Protective Value of Apparel Fabrics in a Fire Environment," *Journal of Consumer Product Flammability*, Vol. 7, 1980, pp. 15-25.

45. ASTM, "Standard Test Method for the Flammability of Blankets," D 4151, 1986, American Society for Testing and Materials, Philadelphia, PA.

46. CPSC, *Code of Federal Regulations*, Part 1630: "Standard for the Surface Flammability of Carpets and Rugs (FFI-70)," Part 1631: "Standard for the Surface Flammability of Small Carpets and Rugs (FF2-70)," U.S. Consumer Product Safety Commission, Washington, DC, 1970.

47. ASTM, "Test for Suface Burning Characteristics of Building Materials," ASTM E84-70, 1970, American Society for Testing and Materials, Philadelphia, PA.

48. CGSB, "Standard Method of Test for Surface Burning Characteristics of Flooring and Floor Covering Materials," B.54.9-1972, 1972, Canadian Government Specification Board, Ottawa, Ontario.

49. Benjamin, I. A., and Davis, S., "Flammability Testing of Carpet," NBSIR 78-1436, 1978, National Bureau of Standards, Washington, DC.

50. Willey, A. E., "Fire, Baptist Towers Housing for the Elderly," *Fire Journal*, Vol. 67, No. 3, 1973, pp. 15-21, 103.

51. FAA, "Flammability Requirements for Aircraft Seat Cushions," 14 CFR, Parts 25, 29, and 1231, Oct. 11, 1983, Federal Aviation Administration, Washington, DC.

52. DOT, *Code of Federal Regulations*, Part 571, "Motor Vehicle Safety Standard No. 302, Flammability of Interior Materials—Passenger Cars, Multipurpose Passenger Vehicles, Trucks, and Buses," U.S. Department of Transportation, Washington, DC.

53. CPAI, *A Specification for Flame-Resistant Materials Used in Camping Tentage*, Canvas Products Association International, St. Paul, MN, 1984.

54. ASTM, "Standard Test Method for Flammability of Apparel Fabrics by Semi-Restraint Method," ASTM D3659, 1959, American Society for Testing and Materials, Philadelphia, PA.

55. Hackleroad, M. F., "Fire Properties Data Base for Textile Wallcoverings," NISTIR 89-4065, 1989, National Institute of Science and Technology, Washington, DC.

56. Turner, H. L., and Segal, L., "Fire Behavior and Protection in Hyperbaric Chambers," *Fire Technology*, Vol. 1, No. 4, 1965, pp. 269-277.

NFPA Codes, Standards, and Recommended Practices

Reference to the following NFPA codes, standards, and recommended practices will provide further information on fibers and textiles discussed in this chapter. (See the latest *NFPA Catalog* for availability of current editions of the following documents.)

NFPA *101*, *Life Safety Code*.

NFPA 102, *Assembly Seating, Tents, and Membrane Structures.*

NFPA 253, *Standard Method of Test for Critical Radiant Flux of Floor Covering Systems Using a Radiant Heat Energy Source.*

NFPA 255, *Method of Test of Surface Burning Characteristics of Building Materials.*

NFPA 701, *Standard Methods of Fire Tests for Flame-Resistant Textiles and Films.*

NFPA 702, *Classification of the Flammability of Wearing Apparel.*

NFPA 1971, *Protective Clothing for Structural Fire Fighting.*

NFPA 1972, *Helmets for Structural Fire Fighting.*

NFPA 1973, *Gloves for Structural Fire Fighters.*

NFPA 1974, *Protective Footwear for Structural Fire Fighting.*

NFPA 1975, *Station/Work Uniforms for Fire Fighters.*

Additional Reading

"Baled Fibers," *Loss Prevention Data Sheet 8-7*, Factory Mutual Research Corp., Norwood, MA.

Belshaw, R. L., and Jerram, D. L., "Garments Designed to Reduce Fire Hazard," *Fire Safety Journal*, Vol. 10, No. 1, 1986, pp. 19-28.

Beninate, John V., *et al*, "Wool: Its Effect on Flame Retardant Properties of Blend Fabrics," *Journal of Fire Sciences*, Vol. 1, No. 2, Mar./Apr. 1983, pp. 145-154.

Bhatnagar, V. M., ed., "Advances in Fire Retardant Textiles," and "Flammability of Apparel," Vols. 5 and 7, respectively, *Progress in Fire Retardancy Series*, Technomic, Westport, CT, 1975.

Carroll-Porczynski, C. Z., *Flammability of Composite Fabrics*, 1st American ed., Chemical Publishing Co., NY, 1984.

Corbman, Bernard P., *Textiles: Fiber to Fabric*, 6th ed., McGraw-Hill, New York, 1983.

Davis, S., Lawson, J. R., and Parker, W. J., "Examination of the Variability of the ASTM E 648 Standard with Respect to Carpets," NISTIR 89-4191, Oct. 1989, National Bureau of Standards, Gaithersburg, MD.

Fire Safety Progress in Regulations, Technology, and New Products, Technomic, Lancaster, PA, 1987.

Griggs, D., "Furniture Flammability—A Textile Specialist's Viewpoint," *Fire Prevention*, No. 210, June 1988, pp. 28-30.

Harkleroad, M. F., "Fire Properties Database for Textile Wall Coverings," NISTIR 89-4065, May 1989, National Bureau of Standards, Gaithersburg, MD.

"Hospitals and Flammable Fabrics: California Case History," *Fire Journal*, Vol. 66, No. 3, May 1972, pp. 18-24.

Johnson, Robert F., "Camping Tent Flammability—What the Record Shows," *Fire Journal*, Vol. 71, No. 4, July 1977, pp. 50-55.

Kalloren, R., *et al*, "The Toxicity of Fire Effluents from Textiles and Upholstery Materials," *Journal of Fire Science*, Vol. 3, 1985, p. 145.

Krasny, J. F., "Apparel Flammability: Accident Simulations and Bench-Scale Tests," *Textile Research Journal*, Vol. 56, No. 5, May 1986, pp. 287-303.

Krasny, J. F., Singleton, R. W., and Pettengill, J., "Performance Evaluation of Fabrics Used in Fire Fighter's Turnout Coats," *Fire Technology*, Vol. 18, No. 4, 1982, pp. 309-318.

Krasny, J. F., "Some Characteristics of Fabrics for Heat Protective Garments," *Performance of Protective Clothing*, American Society for Testing and Materials, Philadelphia, PA, 1986, pp. 463-474.

Martin, J. R., and Miller, B., "The Thermal and Flammability Behavior of Polyester-Wool Blends," *Textile Research Journal*, Vol. 48, 1978, pp. 97-103.

Morotz-Cecei, K., and Beda, L., "Comparative Testing of the Flammability of Upholstery Textiles," *Journal of Thermal Analysis*, Vol. 32, No. 3, 1987, pp. 901-908.

Needles, H. L., *et al*, "Assessment of Flame Retardant Coated Fabric Flammability by Small Scale Test Methods," *Journal of Coated Fabrics*, Vol. 17, Oct. 1987, pp. 129-134.

Peterson, Barbara A., and King, Rosalie R., "Laboratory Testing of Pile Fabrics—A Proposed Flammability Standard," *Fire Technology*, Vol. 16, No. 2, May 1980, pp. 142-149.

Price, D., and Tunc, M., "Textile Flammability," *Chem. Br.*, Vol. 23, No. 3, 1987, pp. 235-236.

Saville, N., "Overview of Fire Blocking Fabrics," *Proceedings* of the 32nd International SAMPE Symposium and Exhibition: Advanced Materials Technology '87, SAMPE, Covina, CA, 1987, pp. 1347-1359.

Sund, J. L., and King, R. R., "Longitudinal Wear Study of Four Work Shirts in Ferrous Metal Operations," *Fire Technology*, Vol. 19, No. 3, Aug. 1983, pp. 163-169.

Tinsworth, D. K., "Hazard Data Related to the Flammability of Wearing Apparel," Apr. 1985, U.S. Consumer Product Safety Commission, Washington, DC.

Uehara, Y., and Umezawa, M., "Evaluation of Garment Flammability Using Thermal Mannequins," *Proceedings* of the 1st International Symposium on Fire Safety Science, Hemisphere, Washington, DC, 1986, pp. 839-848.

Villa, K. M., and Krasny, J. F., "Flammability Tests for Industrial Fabrics—Relevance and Limitations," Industrial Fabrics Association International, *Textile Technology*, 1988, pp. 119-134.

Woolliscroft, D., "Flame and Fire Protection," *Textile Horizons*, Vol. 7, No. 11, 1987, pp. 42-43.

Yates, J. M., "Firefighters Push for Mandatory Flammability Testing," *Wood and Wood Products*, Vol. 92, No. 11, Oct. 1987, p. 38.

Yuill, C. H., "Floor Coverings: What is the Hazard?," *Fire Journal*, Vol. 61, No. 1, Jan. 1967, pp. 11-19.

"The Flammability of Floor Coverings," *Journal of Fire and Flammability*, Vol. 1, 1970, pp. 64-70.

FLAMMABLE AND COMBUSTIBLE LIQUIDS

Revised by Orville M. Sly, Jr.

The discussion of flammable and combustible liquids presented in this chapter focuses on the fire hazards of these materials. After these fire hazards are discussed, the NFPA classification system for flammable and combustible liquids is presented. The physical and fire characteristics of these materials is discussed next, including a special section on the burning characteristics of liquids. Methods to prevent fires while using flammable and combustible liquids completes the chapter.

For more information about flammable and combustible liquids not contained in this chapter, see the following chapters: Section 1, Chapter 4, "Chemistry and Physics of Fire," which includes information about the physical and fire characteristics of liquids and other materials; Section 2, Chapter 31, "Control of Electrostatic Ignition Sources," which discusses the control of static electricity as an ignition source; Section 6, Chapter 18, "Special Systems for Explosion Damage Control," which discusses explosion venting; and Section 6, Chapter 19, "Air Moving Equipment," which discusses blower and exhaust systems for flammable and combustible liquids.

Flammable and combustible liquids fires can be controlled and extinguished using foam, dry chemical agents, carbon dioxide, halogenated agents, or water. Section 5, Chapter 15, "Water Spray Protection," reviews use of water spray for cooling and extinguishment; Section 5, Chapter 17, "Carbon Dioxide and Application Systems," reviews use of carbon dioxide agents; Section 5, Chapter 18, "Halogenated Agents and Systems," discusses halon agents; Section 5, Chapter 19, "Dry Chemical Agents and Application Systems," discusses use of dry chemical agents; and Section 5, Chapter 20, "Foam Extinguishing Agents and Systems," contains information on use of foam agents for extinguishment of flammable and combustible liquids fires.

HAZARDS OF FLAMMABLE AND COMBUSTIBLE LIQUIDS

It is not the flammable and combustible liquids that burn or explode by themselves, but, rather, the flammable vapors resulting from the evaporation of liquids when elevated to temperatures above their flash points when exposed to an ignition source, such as a spark. Since, by definition, most flammable liquids are normally stored and handled above their flash points, they continually give off vapors when the vapor-air mixture is within the flammable range.

Ignitable mixtures occur when concentrations of vapors in air are within a definite percentage range, commonly referred to as the flammable (explosive) range. The lower limit of the range is known as the lower flammable limit (LFL). The upper limit of the range is known as the upper flammable limit (UFL). For example, the proportions (flammable range) for carbon disulfide are from about 1 to 44 percent carbon disulfide vapors in air by volume; for ethyl alcohol, from about 4 to 19 percent by volume; and for gasoline, from about 1.4 to 7.6 percent by volume. Therefore, storing flammable and combustible liquids in the proper closed containers and minimizing the exposure of the liquid to air while in use are fundamental safety measures.

Explosions of flammable vapor-air mixtures near the lower or upper limits of the flammable range are less intense than those occurring in intermediate concentrations of the same mixture. Flammable vapor-air explosions occur most frequently in confined spaces, such as containers, tanks, rooms, or buildings. The violence of flammable vapor explosions depends upon the nature of the vapors and enclosure containing the mixture, as well as on the quantity of vapor-air mixture.

Distinct from an explosion of a flammable vapor-air mixture inside a tank or container is the overpressuring of a tank which results in a rupture. As with vapor explosions, pressure ruptures vary in intensity. Any closed container may rupture violently when exposed to a severe fire.

Fire and explosion prevention measures are based on one or more of the following techniques or principles: (1) exclusion of sources of ignition, (2) exclusion of air (oxygen), (3) storage of liquids in closed containers or systems,

Orville M. Sly, Jr., P.E., is president of Loss Control Associates, Inc., Langhorne, PA.

(4) ventilation to prevent the accumulation of vapor within the flammable range, and (5) use of an atmosphere of inert gas instead of air. Extinguishing methods for flammable and combustible liquids fires involve shutting off the fuel supply, excluding air by various means, cooling the liquid to stop evaporation, or a combination thereof.

Gasoline is the most widely used flammable liquid. It is commonly known that gasoline generates flammable vapors at ambient temperatures. There are many other volatile flammable products. A comprehensive list of the more commonly used flammable or combustible liquids, including the characteristics of each, appears in NFPA 325M, *Fire Hazard Properties of Flammable Liquids, Gases, and Volatile Solids*.

Flash point, though commonly accepted as the most important criterion of the relative hazard of flammable and combustible liquids, is not the only factor used to evaluate the hazard. The ignition temperature, flammable range, rate of evaporation, reactivity when contaminated or exposed to heat, density, and rate of diffusion of the vapor also affect the hazard. The flash point and other factors that determine the relative susceptibility of a flammable or combustible liquid to ignition have comparatively little influence on the liquid's burning characteristics after fire has burned for a short time.

The use of flammable and combustible liquids produced by chemical and petrochemical companies is increasing rapidly. Although many of these products can be classed as normal or stable liquids, others introduce the problem of instability or reactivity.

The storage, handling, and use of unstable (reactive) flammable or combustible liquids require special attention. It may be necessary to increase the distances to property lines and between tanks or to provide extra fire protection. For example, it would be poor practice to locate heat-reactive and water-reactive flammable or combustible liquids tanks adjacent to each other. In the event of a ground fire, water applied to the heat-reactive tank for protection might penetrate the tank of water-reactive liquid and cause a violent reaction.

CLASSIFICATION OF FLAMMABLE AND COMBUSTIBLE LIQUIDS

For fire protection purposes, an arbitrary division between liquids and gases has been established, based upon the definition of a flammable liquid found in NFPA 321, *Basic Classification of Flammable and Combustible Liquids*. Liquids are defined as those fluids with a vapor pressure not exceeding 40 psia (275 kPa), which is approximately 25 psi gage pressure (172 kPa) at 100°F (38°C). Another arbitrary division also has been established between liquids and solids for the purposes of this classification system. A liquid is additionally defined as one which has a fluidity greater than that of 300 penetration asphalt.

The following classification system for flammable and combustible liquids (from NFPA 321, *Basic Classification of Flammable and Combustible Liquids*) is based on the division of flammable liquids into three categories. It is anticipated that in most areas the indoor temperature could reach 100°F (38°C) at some time during the year. Therefore, all liquids with flash points below 100°F (38°C) are called Class I liquids. In some areas, the ambient temperature could exceed 100°F (38°C), requiring only a moderate degree of heating to bring the liquid to its flash point. Based on this concept, an arbitrary division of 100 to 140°F (38 to 60°C) was established for liquids in this flash point range, to be known as Class II liquids. Since liquids with flash points higher than 140°F (60°C) would require considerable heating from a source other than ambient temperatures, they have been identified as Class III liquids.

Flammable Liquids

1. Flammable liquids have flash points below 100°F (38°C) and vapor pressures not exceeding 40 psia at 100°F (275 kPa at 38°C).
2. Class I liquids include those with flash points below 100°F (38°C) and may be subdivided as follows:
   (a) Class IA liquids includes those with flash points below 73°F (23°C) and with boiling points below 100°F (38°C).
   (b) Class IB liquids includes those with flash points below 73°F (23°C) and with boiling points at or above 100°F (38°C).
   (c) Class IC liquids includes those with flash points at or above 73°F (23°C) and below 100°F (38°C).

Combustible Liquids

Liquids with flash points at or above 100°F (38°C) are referred to as combustible liquids and may be subdivided as follows:

1. Class II liquids have flash points at or above 100°F (38°C) and below 140°F (60°C).
2. Class IIIA liquids have flash points at or above 140°F (60°C) and below 200°F (93°C).
3. Class IIIB liquids have flash points at or above 200°F (93°C).

Other Classification Systems

There are other classification systems for flammable and combustible liquids. In some, the break points between classes of liquids are different, or the open-cup flash-point tester is used to determine the flash point. In other classification systems, the solubility of the liquid with water is considered.

Solids with Flash Points

Many combustible chemicals that are solids at 100°F (38°C) or above are classified as solids. When heated, the solid becomes liquid and gives off flammable vapors; flash points can then be determined. In their liquid state, these solids should be treated as liquids with similar flash points. Some manufactured solids, such as paste waxes or polishes, may contain varying amounts of flammable liquids. The flash point and amount of liquid in such manufactured solid materials will indicate the degree of hazard.

PHYSICAL PROPERTIES OF LIQUIDS

In liquids, molecules move freely among themselves, but they do not tend to separate from one another in the way that molecules in gases do. Liquids, unlike gases, are only slightly compressible and are incapable of indefinite expansion. They differ from solids in the ease with which their molecules move against one another, causing them to adapt to the shape of the containing vessel. Some liquids are very viscous, however, and no sharp definition can be drawn between these liquids and solids. Neither is there a sharp line of demarcation between liquids and gases. Materials can exist in either state, depending upon temperature and pressure conditions. Liquids tend to become gases as their temperatures increase or their pressures decrease. On the other hand, gases tend to become liquids as their temperatures decrease or their pressures increase. However, a material can only exist as a gas, regardless of pressure, if its temperature is above the so-called *critical temperature.* (The critical temperature is an intrinsic property of a material and is the temperature above which the material can exist only in the gaseous state.) In all cases, the actual state of a liquid is determined by the combination of temperature and pressure.

PHYSICAL CHARACTERISTICS OF FLAMMABLE AND COMBUSTIBLE LIQUIDS

Specific Gravity

Since the specific gravity of water equals one, a liquid with a specific gravity of less than one will float on water (unless it is water soluble). A specific gravity greater than one indicates that water will float on the liquid. Because fire fighting foams are water-based extinguishing agents, this is an important consideration in fighting a flammable or combustible liquids fire.

Vapor Density Ratio

Vapor density is the weight per unit volume of a pure gas or vapor. For fire protection purposes, vapor density is reported in terms of the ratio of the relative weight of a volume of vapor to the weight of an equal volume of air, under the same conditions of temperature and pressure. In this respect, the vapor density ratio is similar to the specific gravity of a liquid, except that air is used as the standard in place of water. Air is taken as unity and the vapor density is reported as a ratio. A vapor density of 3 (i.e., 3:1) indicates that the vapor is three times as dense, or heavy, as air.

$$\text{Vapor density ratio} = \frac{\text{molecular weight (MW) of the material}}{\text{composite molecular weight of air}} = \frac{\text{MV}}{29}$$

Vapor density ratios are reported at equilibrium temperature and atmospheric pressure conditions. Unequal or changing conditions will appreciably change the density of any vapor.

Generally, pure vapors are seldom found, except when the liquid is normally stored above its boiling point. For those liquids that are stored or handled below their boiling points, the vapor located above the liquid will be a mixture of vapor and air.

For liquids with boiling points above the prevailing ambient temperature at atmospheric pressure, the vapor density may be a misleading figure. For example, the boiling point of ethyl acetate is 171°F (77°C). At 70°F (21°C) its vapor pressure is about 2.35 psi (16.2 kPa) or 0.16 atm (atmospheres). Thus, an equilibrium mixture of ethyl acetate vapor and air at 70°F (21°C), as might be found in a closed vessel, would have a composition of 16 percent ethyl acetate vapor and 84 percent air. The "theoretical" vapor density of ethyl acetate is 3.0. The "actual" density of the "vapor-air mixture" that is produced by ethyl acetate at 70°F (21°C) and at atmospheric pressure is:

$$0.16 \times 3.0 + 0.84 \times 1 = 1.32$$

Vapor densities are ordinarily used only as an indication of the settling or rising tendency of a vapor.

Vapor Pressure

Where a liquid is present in a closed container with an atmosphere of vapor-air mixture above the liquid surface, the percentage of vapor in the mixture may be determined from the vapor pressure. The percentage of vapor is directly proportional to the relationship between the vapor pressure of the liquid and the total pressure of the mixture. For example, acetone at a temperature of 100°F (38°C) has a vapor pressure of 7.6 psia (52 kPa). Assuming total pressure at 14.7 psia (101 kPa), the proportion of acetone vapor present will be 7.6 divided by 14.7, or 52 percent. Vapor pressures of petroleum liquids usually are determined by the Reid method, as recommended by the American Society for Testing and Materials (ASTM). This method gives the vapor pressure in psia (kPa) at 100°F (38°C), which differs slightly from the true vapor pressure. Vapor pressure figures for many substances can be found in chemical handbooks. If the closed-cup flash point of a liquid and the vapor pressure at the flash point temperature are known, the lower flammable limit for the vapor (at the flash point temperature), in percent by volume at normal atmospheric pressure, can be calculated as follows:

$$\text{LFL} = \frac{V}{0.147}$$

$$\text{in SI: LFL} = \frac{V}{1.01}$$

where LFL is percent vapor by volume at the lower flammable limit, and V is vapor pressure in psia (kPa) at flash point temperature. At other pressures,

$$\text{LFL} = \frac{100V}{P}$$

where P is the ambient pressure in psia (kPa).

In a mixture of volatile flammable liquids, the effects of the two vapor pressures, one upon the other, generally depend upon whether the two liquids are completely miscible, partly miscible, or completely immiscible. If the two liquids are completely miscible, they lower each other's vapor pressures; if they are nearly completely immiscible, the vapor pressure of the mixture is the sum of the partial pressure of each liquid layer (Dalton's Law of Partial Pressure); if both liquids are partially miscible, the relationships are more complex.

Evaporation Rate

Evaporation rate is the rate at which a liquid is converted to the vapor state at any given temperature and pressure. The differing rates of mixture evaporation is of primary concern in fire protection. In general, as the boiling point decreases, the vapor pressure and the evaporation rate increases.

Viscosity

The viscosity of a liquid is a measure of its resistance to flow resulting from the combined effects of adhesion and cohesion, i.e., a measure of internal friction in a fluid. Although there are several recognized devices for determining viscosity, the measurement principles are generally the same. These involve measuring the time required for a predetermined quantity of liquid at a specified temperature to flow into a receiving flask or through an orifice of a prescribed size.

Latent Heat of Vaporization

Latent heat of vaporization is the heat that is absorbed when one gram of liquid is transformed into vapor at the boiling point under one atmosphere pressure, and is expressed in calories per gram (Cal/g) or in Btu per pound.

Solubility in Water and Surface Tension

Solubility in water and surface tension are other characteristics of a liquid that concern the fire protection field. Fires in liquids that are water soluble can be extinguished by dilution of the liquid with water, or by use of "alcohol-type" foams for extinguishment. The use of wetting agents affects the surface tension of a liquid and, in some cases, aids in fire extinguishment.

FIRE CHARACTERISTICS OF LIQUIDS

Flash Point

A vapor mixed with air in proportions below the lower limit of flammability may burn at the source of ignition, i.e., in the zone immediately surrounding the source of ignition, without propagating (spreading) flame away from the ignition source. The flash point of a liquid corresponds roughly to the lowest temperature at which the vapor pressure of the liquid is just sufficient to produce a flammable mixture at the lower limit of flammability. (See Figure 3-5A.)

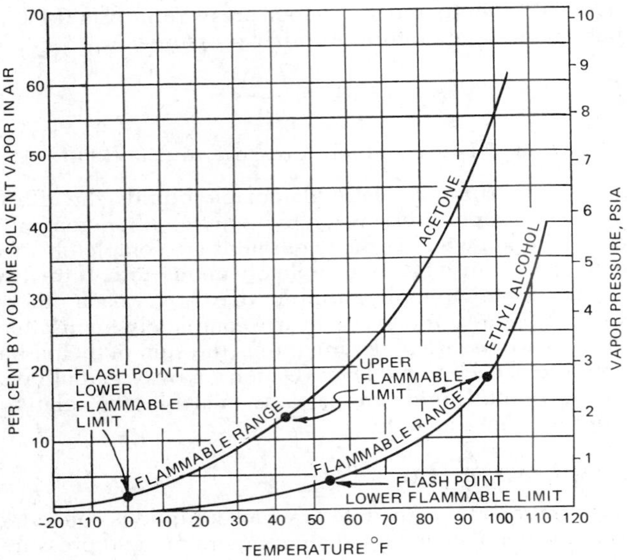

FIG. 3-5A. Relationship among flash point, flammable limits, temperature, and vapor pressure for acetone and ethyl alcohol. Liquid, vapor, and air in equilibrium in a closed container at normal atmospheric pressure. [One psia equals psi + 14.7 × 6.985; 5/9 (°F − 32) equals °C.]

There are several types of test apparatus used for determining flash point. (See Figure 3-5B.) NFPA 321, *Basic Classification of Flammable and Combustible Liquids*, specifies the Tagliabue (Tag) Closed Tester for testing liquids, except for certain viscous or film-forming materials, with a flash point at or below 200°F (93°C), as described in ASTM D 56, *Standard Method of Test for Flash Point by the Tag Closed Tester*. The Pensky-Martens Closed Tester, as described in ASTM D 93, *Standard Test Method for Flash Point by the Pensky-Martens Closed Tester*, is specified for testing liquids with flash points above 200°F (93°C) or for certain viscous or film-forming materials.

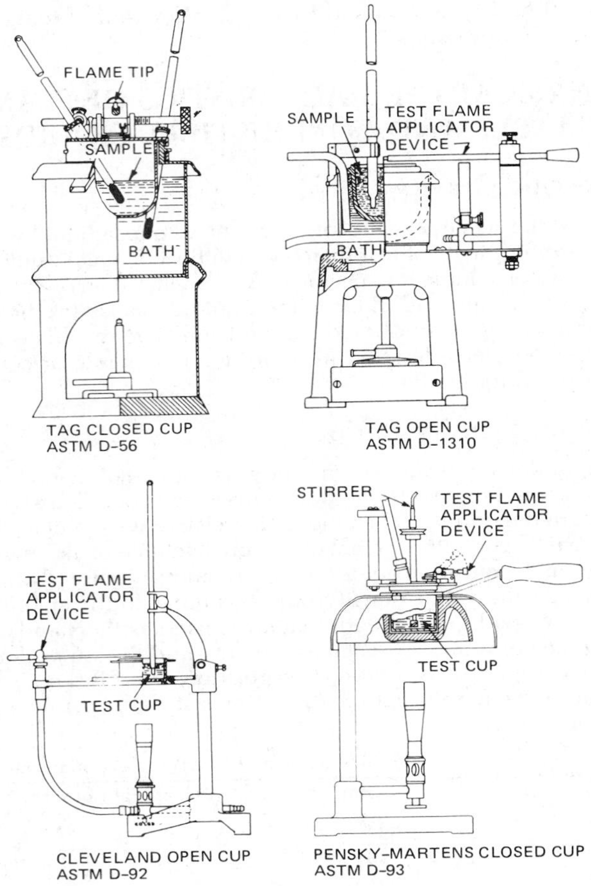

FIG. 3-5B. Four of the commonly used testers for determining flash points of flammable or combustible liquids. The material to be tested is slowly heated, and at periodic intervals a test flame is applied to the vapor space. Flash point is the temperature at which a flash of fire is seen when the test flame is applied. The full details of conducting tests for each type of testing apparatus are given in the applicable standards of the American Society for Testing and Materials, or by the manufacturer.

ASTM D 3278, *Standard Test Methods for Flash Point Liquids by Setaflash Closed-Cup Apparatus*, is used for testing paints, enamels, lacquers, varnishes, and related products and their components with flash points between 32 and 230°F (0 and 18°C).

Open-cup flash points are sometimes used in grading flammable liquids in transportation and are determined by the ASTM D 1310, *Tagliabue (Tag) Open-Cup Apparatus*, or the ASTM D 92, *Cleveland Open-Cup Apparatus*. Open-cup flash points represent conditions with the liquid in the open and are generally higher than the closed-cup flash point figures for the same substances. However, closed-cup flash-point figures are generally higher than the actual lower temperature limit of flammability (flash point) when tested in a vertical tube utilizing the principle of upward flame propagation.

It is essential to realize that flash point varies with pressure and with the oxygen content of the atmosphere, as well as with the purity of the product being tested, the method of test, and the skill of the operator conducting the test. It is quite possible to have a flammable mixture far below the stated flash point value if the pressure is considerably less than one atmosphere.

Ignition Temperature (Autoignition Temperature, Autogenous Ignition Temperature)

The autoignition temperature reported for a flammable liquid is generally the temperature to which a closed or nearly closed container must be heated in order that the liquid in question, when introduced into the container, will ignite spontaneously and burn. Time lags of a minute or more are frequently involved. The standard testing method for autoignition temperatures of petroleum products is described in ASTM D 2155, *Autoignition Temperature of Liquid Petroleum Products.*

Ignition Temperatures and Molecular Weights

Within a given hydrocarbon series, such as the straight chain series running from normal methane down through normal decane, ignition temperature decreases as molecular weight or carbon chain length increases, all other factors being equal. (See Figure 3-5C.) Thus, pentane [$CH_3(CH_2)_3CH_3$; molecular weight 72.1] has a higher ignition temperature than hexane [$(CH_3CH_2)_4CH_3$; molecular weight 86.2].

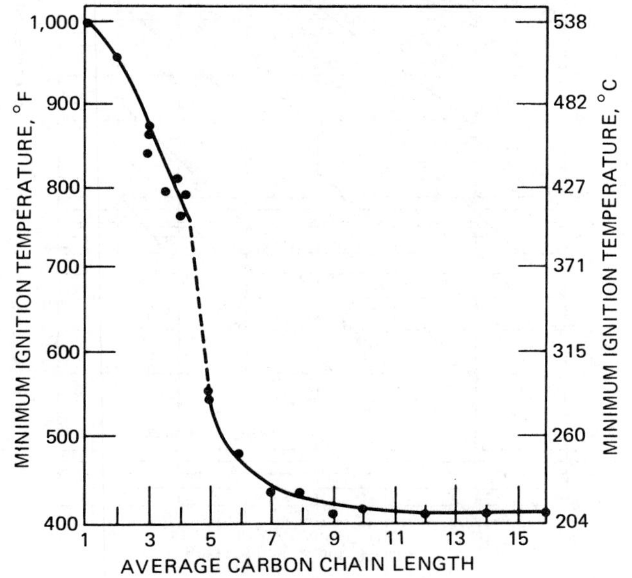

FIG. 3-5C. Minimum ignition temperatures of hydrocarbons of various carbon chain lengths.

Boiling Point

The temperature at which the equilibrium vapor pressure of a liquid equals the total pressure on the surface is known as the boiling point. The boiling point is entirely dependent on the total pressure. (Boiling point increases with an increase in pressure.) Theoretically, any liquid may be made to boil at any desired temperature by sufficiently altering the total pressure on its surface. Similarly, unless decomposition takes place, any liquid may be made to boil at any desired pressure by sufficiently changing its temperature.

The temperature at which a liquid boils when under a total pressure of one atmosphere (14.7 psia or 101 kPa) is termed the normal boiling point.

The above applies to pure materials or constant boiling mixtures. Most flammable liquids and gases on the market today are mixtures and do not follow the physical laws governing pure materials. The boiling points of mixtures are reported as distillation curves. The 10 percent point of a distillation performed in accordance with ASTM D 86, *Standard Method of Test for Distillation of Petroleum Products*, is used as the boiling point for most NFPA standards.

Flammable (Explosive) Limits

The term "lower flammable limit" (LFL) describes the minimum concentration of vapor to air below which propagation of a flame will not occur in the presence of an ignition source. The "upper flammable limit" (UFL) is the maximum vapor to air concentration above which propagation of flame will not occur. If a vapor-to-air mixture is below the lower flammable limit, it is described as being "too lean" to burn, and if it is above the upper flammable limit, it is "too rich" to burn.

When the vapor-to-air ratio is somewhere between the lower flammable limit and the upper flammable limit, fires and explosions can occur. The mixture is then said to be within its flammable or explosive range. When the mixture happens to be in the intermediate range between the LFL and UFL [synonymous with lower explosive limit (LEL) and upper explosive limit (UEL), respectively], the ignition is more intense and violent than if the mixture were closer to either the upper or lower limits.

Calculating Vapor Volume and Flammable Mixtures

It is frequently helpful to calculate the volume of air required to provide dilution sufficient to prevent the formation of an ignitible mixture as, for example, in the design of a ventilating system for a drying oven. This can be readily done when the quantity of solvent supplied is known or can be reasonably estimated.

For example, consider a process in which acetone vapor is released. The flammable range for acetone vapor in air is from 2.6 to 12.8 percent by volume. Any mixture containing more air than 100 minus 2.6, or 97.4 percent of air—equivalent to 97.4 divided by 2.6, or approximately 37 volumes of air to one volume of vapor—will be too lean to be ignitible. Hence, if the volume of vapor can be estimated, it is a simple matter to determine the required air volume.

The volume of vapor produced from 1 gal of solvent can be calculated from the specific gravity of the liquid and the vapor density as follows:

Cubic feet of vapor from 1 gal of liquid =

$$\frac{8.33 \times \text{specific gravity of liquid } (H_2O = 1)}{0.075 \times \text{vapor density of vaport (air = 1)}}$$

where 8.33 is the weight of 1 gal of water in pounds and 0.075 is the weight of 1 cu ft of air in pounds.

Stated more simply:

$$\text{Vapor equivalent of one gal is: } 111 \times \frac{\text{Sp. G.}}{\text{V.D.}}$$

If the vapor density is not known, it can readily be calculated from the molecular weight.

Again, taking acetone as an example [specific gravity (Sp.G.) = 0.792; vapor density (V.D.) = 2], yields:

$$\text{Vapor equivalent of one gal is: } 111 \times \frac{0.792}{2} = 44 \text{ cu ft.}$$

The volume of air required to dilute vapor from 1 gal of acetone to below the lower flammable limit is:

$$44 \times 37 = 1{,}628 \text{ cu ft}$$

If the rate of evaporation of acetone into a given space (oven, etc.) should be 1 gpm, it would require 1,628 cfm of uncontaminated ventilating air to keep the vapor concentration below the lower flammable limit.

For S.I. units, the volume of vapor (m^3) produced by 1 liter of solvent can also be calculated from the specific gravity of the liquid and the vapor density as follows:

The cubic meter vapor equivalent of 1 liter (L) of liquid is:

$$L = 0.83 \times \frac{\text{Sp. G.}}{\text{V.D.}}$$

For acetone, vapor equivalent of 1 liter (L) is:

$$L = \frac{0.83 \times 0.792}{2} = 0.33 \text{ m}^3$$

In S.I. units, the volume of air required to dilute 1 liter of acetone to below the lower flammability limit is:

$$0.33 \times 37 = 12.2 \text{ m}^3$$

For different evaporation rates, the air quantity would be proportional. In practice and as a safety factor, a substantial excess of air ventilation would be applied because of the inevitable nonuniformity of the atmosphere within the enclosure.

Where it is desirable to keep a space "too rich" to be ignitible, a similar procedure (using the upper flammable limit) may be used to determine the maximum air quantity that can be tolerated. This is not, however, a recommended procedure, since it is necessary to enter and pass through the flammable range.

Variation in Hazard with Temperature and Pressure

The temperature and pressure to which a particular liquid is subjected must often be considered in the practical application of the flammable limits of flammable liquids. It can be shown that these factors have a pronounced effect on the fire and explosion hazard and are as important in safe handling as are the flammable limits themselves. A liquid that has a flash point above room temperature and, therefore, is not expected to produce flammable vapors, will do so if its temperature is raised to its flash point or higher.

The extent of liquid vaporization varies as pressure in the vapor space over the liquid is increased or lowered. More vapor is released as pressure is lowered, and less vapor will result from increased pressure above the liquid. In the same manner, at a higher temperature the liquid will have a higher vapor pressure and will tend to vaporize in greater amounts. When at a given temperature and pressure the liquid has vaporized to the point where no further vaporization will occur unless conditions are changed, a state of equilibrium is said to have been reached. It is evident that equilibrium cannot exist in other than a closed system. In the open air, a vaporizing liquid would continue to vaporize until the supply was exhausted. The pressure-temperature effect, therefore, is applicable only in tanks, pipes, and processing equipment, in which the liquid and vapor-air mixture approach equilibrium.

Figures 3-5D and 3-5E show the effect of temperature and pressure on flammable limits, as determined by F. C. Mitchell and H. C. Vernon.[2] In using these charts, it should be noted that they represent equilibrium conditions, and that, prior to the establishment of equilibrium, values may be different.[2] For example, when a liquid is introduced into a pressure container with air at a temperature such that the resultant vapor-air mixture will be above the upper flammable limit (according to the chart), some time will elapse before sufficient evaporation has taken place to reach this condition; meanwhile, the mixture may be flammable or explosive.

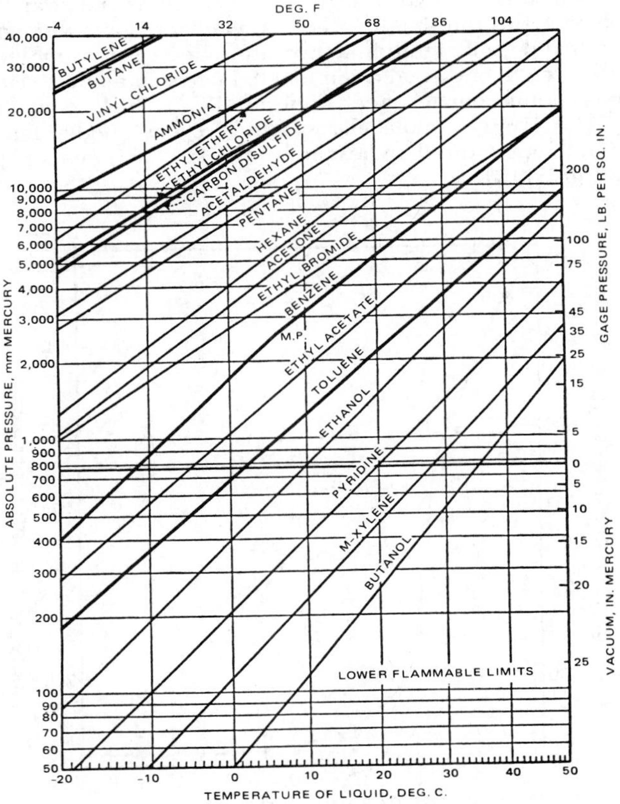

FIG. 3-5D. ***Variation of lower flammable limits with temperature and pressure. This chart is applicable only to flammable liquids or gases in equilibrium in a closed container. Mixtures of vapor and air will be too "lean" to burn at temperatures below and at pressures above the values shown by the line on the chart for any substance. Conditions represented by points to the left and above the respective lines are accordingly nonflammable. Points where the diagonal lines cross the zero gage pressure line (760 mm of mercury, absolute pressure) indicate flash-point temperatures at normal atmospheric pressure.***

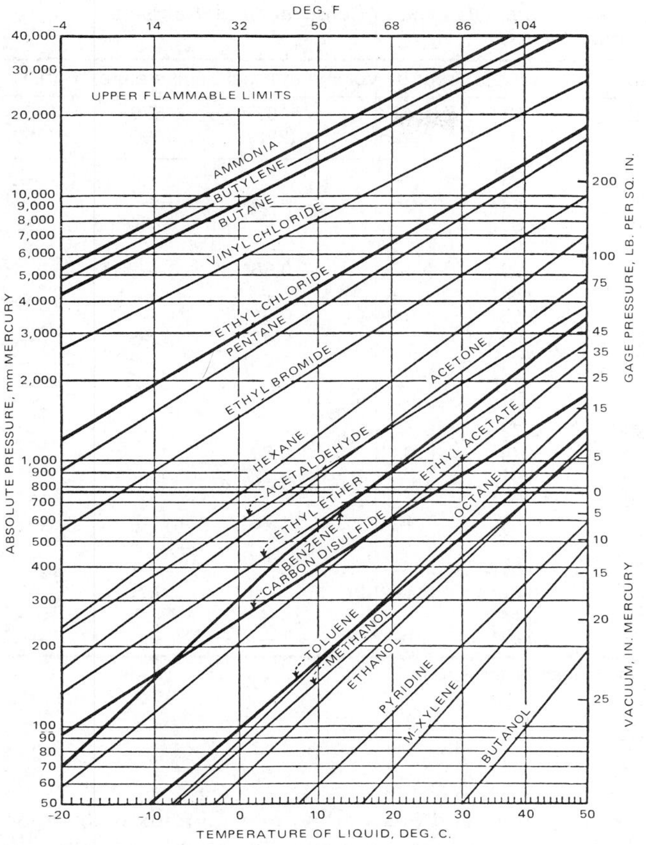

FIG. 3-5E. Variation of upper flammable limits with temperature and pressure. This chart is applicable only to flammable liquids or gases in equilibrium in a closed container. Mixtures of vapor and air will be too "rich" to be flammable at temperatures above and pressures below the values shown by the line on the chart for any substance. Conditions represented by points to the right of and below the respective lines are accordingly nonflammable.

It should also be noted that the pressures developed, or the intensity of an explosion, will vary with the initial pressure of the vapor-air mixture. With high initial pressures, the pressures are greater, as in the familiar example of the gasoline engine. With low initial pressures, the pressures are relatively lower.

The lower limits of flammability of solvent vapors are affected by the temperature. This is a safety factor in installations, such as industrial ovens, where pressure is not a factor but where temperature needs to be taken into account in hazard evaluation. In such industrial ovens, mechanical or forced ventilation is usually employed to dilute the concentration of the vapors below their lower flammable limits in air and to remove them from the oven. Information on the lower flammable limits of the vapors at elevated temperatures is needed in order to determine the amount of ventilation required for safe operation of an oven. (See Table 3-5A.)

Energy Required for Ignition of Vapors

The principal sources of ignition of flammable liquids include flames, hot surfaces, electrical or frictional sparks, and adiabatic compression.

Flames: Except for extremely small examples produced under laboratory conditions, flames are unfailing sources of ignition for flammable vapor-air mixtures that are within the flammable range. Flames must be capable of heating the vapor to its ignition temperature in the presence of air in order to be a source of ignition. For some liquids and solids, it will be necessary for the flame to be of sufficient duration and heat to volatilize the fuel and to ignite the released vapors. Once ignited, the radiated heat from the burning vapors perpetuates the burning process.

Electrical, static, and friction sparks: These must have sufficient energy to ignite flammable vapor-air mixtures. Electrical sparks from most commercial electrical supply installations are above flame temperatures and will usually ignite flammable mixtures. However, friction sparks may fail to ignite a flammable mixture because the spark may be of such short duration as to fail to heat the vapor to its ignition point. Also, not only must an electrical spark have sufficient intensity and length, but some variable conditions must also exist within certain limits before ignition will occur. The nature of the ignition points and surfaces, as well as the composition, temperature, and pressure of vapor-air mixtures, are the principal variables in calculating ignition. Most of these same factors and variables also apply to static electrical sparks and frictional sparks as a source of ignition because, in either case, the spark must be of sufficient duration, intensity, or both, to create sufficient heat to cause ignition.

Hot surfaces: These can be a source of ignition if they are large enough and hot enough. The smaller the heated surface, the hotter it must be to ignite a mixture. The larger the heated surface in relation to the mixture, the more rapidly ignition will take place and the lower the temperature necessary for ignition. A flammable liquid, however, must remain in contact with a hot surface for a sufficient length of time to form a vapor-air mixture within its flammable range. For example, a single drop of a low-viscosity, highly volatile flammable liquid that falls on the surface of an electric hotplate at 2,000°F (1093°C) may ignite. A hot exhaust pipe in the open seldom ignites a flammable mixture, even though the surface temperature may be considerably above the environmental ignition temperature test method.

Adiabatic compression: This has been the cause of several destructive explosions. When controlled, adiabatic compression is the basis of diesel engine operation. A rapidly compressed flammable mixture will be ignited when the heat generated by the compressing action is sufficient to raise the flammable vapor to its ignition temperature.

Behavior of Mixed Liquids

The behavior of mixed liquids varies considerably, depending upon physical characteristics of the liquid and environmental conditions. However, the vapor pressure or evaporation rate of mixed liquids is particularly important in the prevention of fires. These factors are significant when a mixture of liquids is listed as nonflammable or has a high flash point but becomes flammable under conditions of use. As a specific example, sufficient carbon tetrachloride can be added to gasoline so that the mixture has no flash point. However, while standing in an open container, the carbon tetrachloride will evaporate more rapidly than the gasoline. Over a period of time, therefore, the residual liquid will first show a high flash point, then a progressively lower

TABLE 3-5A. ***The Effect of Elevated Temperature on the Lower Flammable Limit of Combustible Solvents as Encountered in Industrial Ovens‡***

Solvent	Flash Pt Closed Cup	Lower Flammable Limit Percent Vapor by Volume at Initial Temperature, °F (°C)						
		Room Temp.	212 (100)	392 (200)	437 (225)	482 (250)	572 (300)	662 (350)
Acetone	3	2.67	2.40	2.00*	—	—	—	—
Amyl Acetate, Iso	77	—	1.00	0.82	—	0.76*	—	—
Benzene	−4	1.32	1.10	0.93	—	—	0.80*	—
Butyl Alcohol, Normal	100	—	1.56	1.27	1.22*	—	—	—
Cresol, Meta-Para	202	—	1.06†	0.93	—	0.88*	—	—
Cyclohexane	−4	1.12	1.01	0.83*	—	—	—	—
Cyclohexanone	111	—	1.11	0.96	0.94	0.91*	—	—
Ethyl Alcohol	54	3.48	3.01	2.64	—	2.47	2.29*	—
Ethyl Lactate	131	—	1.55	1.29	—	1.22*	—	—
Gasoline	−45	1.07	0.94	0.77*	—	—	—	—
Hexane, Normal	−15	1.08	0.90	0.72*	—	—	—	—
High-Solvency Petroleum Naphtha	36	1.00	0.89	0.74	0.72	0.69*	—	—
Methyl Alcohol	52	6.70	5.80	4.81	—	4.62	4.44*	—
Methyl Ethyl Ketone	21	1.83	1.70	1.33*	—	—	—	—
Methyl Lactate	121	—	2.21	1.86	1.80	1.75*	—	—
Mineral Spirits, No. 10	104	—	0.77	0.63*	—	—	—	—
Toluene	48	1.17	0.99	0.82	—	—	0.72*	—
Turpentine	95	—	0.69	0.54*	—	—	—	—
V. M. & P. Naptha	28	0.92	0.76	0.67*	—	—	—	—

* Rapid and extensive thermal decomposition and oxidation reactions in vapor-air mixture at this temperature.
† Lower limit determined at 302°F (150°C).
‡ From NFPA *Quarterly*, April 1950; UL Bulletin of Research, No. 43.

one, until the flash point of the final 10 percent of the original sample will approximate that of the higher boiling fractions of gasoline.

In order to evaluate the fire hazard of such liquid mixtures, fractional evaporation tests can be conducted at room temperature in open vessels. After evaporation of appropriate fractions, such as 10, 20, 40, 60, and 90 percent of the original sample, flash-point tests can be conducted on the residue. The results of such tests indicate the class into which the liquid should be placed if the conditions of use are such as to make it likely that appreciable evaporation will take place.

With other liquid mixtures, the flash point may increase as evaporation occurs.

Noncompatible Materials

Noncompatible materials of construction or equipment are those materials with which an unstable flammable liquid or its normal reaction products will combine, or whose products of corrosion are contaminants. For example, if mercury is a harmful contaminant, then mercury thermometers should not be used. If a chlorinated compound slowly releases hydrochloric acid, aluminum should not be used. The aluminum chloride formed by this acid may act as a catalyst. There are many materials that will chemically react with each other; when there is a question, reference should be made to NFPA 491M, *Manual of Hazardous Chemical Reactions*.

BURNING CHARACTERISTICS OF LIQUIDS

Since it is the vapors from flammable liquids which burn, the ease of ignition as well as the rate of burning can be related to such properties as the vapor pressure, flash point, boiling point, and evaporation rate. Liquids with vapors in the flammable range above the liquid surface at the stored temperature will have a rapid rate of flame propagation. Flammable and combustible liquids with flash points above temperatures at which they are stored have a slower rate of flame propagation, because it is necessary for the heat of the fire to sufficiently heat the liquid surface and form a flammable vapor-air mixture before the flame will spread through the vapor. There are many variables affecting the rate of flame propagation and burning, including environmental factors, wind velocity, temperature, heat of combustion, latent heat of vaporization, and barometric pressure.

Liquid hydrocarbons normally burn with an orange flame and emit dense clouds of black smoke. Alcohols normally burn with a clean blue flame and produce very little smoke. Certain terpenes and ethers burn with considerable ebullition (boiling) of the liquid surface, making it difficult to extinguish fires involving these substances.

Boilover, Slopover, and Frothover

Three specific conditions—boilover, slopover, and frothover—deserve special mention in regard to fires in open-topped tanks containing various types of oils.

Boilover: Boilover is a phenomenon that may occur spontaneously during a fire in an open-top tank containing certain types of crude oils. This may occur when the roof of a tank is blown off by an explosion, usually caused by lightning. After a long period of quiescent burning, there is a sudden overflow or ejection of some of the residual oil in the tank. It is caused by boiling water that forms a quickly expanding steam-oil froth. The frothing results from the existence of the following three conditions, the absence of any one of which will prevent the occurrence:

1. The tank must contain free water or water-oil emulsion at the tank bottom. This situation will normally prevail in tanks storing crude oil.
2. The oil must contain components having a wide range of boiling points, such that when the lighter components have been distilled off and burned at the surface, the residue, with a temperature of 300°F (149°C) or over, is more dense than the oil immediately below. This residue sinks below the surface and forms a layer of gradually increasing depth which advances downward at a rate substantially faster than the rate of regression of the burning surface. This sets up the so-called "heat wave," which is the result of localized settling of a part of the hot surface oil until it reaches the colder oil below. There is no heat conduction from the burning surface downward.
3. Sufficient content of heavier oils are present in the oil to produce a residue that can form a tough persistent froth of oil and steam.

What is believed to be the most serious loss-of-life tank fire in history occurred on December 19, 1982 in Tacoa, Venezuela. The storage tank, located a few miles northwest of Caracas in the small seaside village of Tacoa, supplied fuel to an electric generating plant. Two workers died upon ignition of the tank. After six hours of intense burning, the contents of the tank erupted into an extremely violent boilover. The final toll—more than 150 people dead, scores more injured, others still unaccounted for, and damage estimated at $50 million. Forty of those who died were fire fighters, which also makes the Tacoa incident the gravest of its kind in terms of loss of life of fire personnel. (See Figure 3-5F.)

***FIG. 3-5F.** Emergency personnel on the scene of the fuel-oil storage tank fire boilover in Tacoa, Venezuela, December 19, 1982. At this moment, the fire had been declared under control. Note the fire fighters on the top of the dike, and the other personnel along the roadway fence. The boilover occurred minutes after this photo was taken, and all of the people shown above were reportedly killed.*

Slopover: Slopover can result when a water stream is applied to the hot surface of a burning oil, provided the oil is viscous and its temperature exceeds the boiling point of water. Since only the surface oil is involved, a slopover is a relatively mild occurrence.

Frothover: Frothover refers to the overflowing of a container not on fire when water boils under the surface of a viscous hot oil. A typical example would be when hot asphalt is loaded into a tank car containing some water. The first asphalt is cooled by contact with the cold metal, and, at first, nothing may happen. But when the water becomes heated and starts to boil, the asphalt may overflow the tank car.

A similar situation can arise when a tank containing a water bottom or wet emulsion is used for storing oil slops or residium at temperatures below 200°F (93°C), and the tank receives a substantial addition of hot residium at a temperature of 300°F (149°C) or higher. After enough time has elapsed for the effect of the hot oil to reach the water in a tank, a prolonged boiling action can take place, which can remove a tank roof and spread froth over a wide area.

Burning Rates of Liquids

The burning rate of flammable liquids will vary somewhat similar to the rate of flame propagation. Gasoline, a compound of light and heavy fractions, will burn more rapidly at first while the lighter fractions are burning, while the heavier fractions will burn at a rate approaching that of kerosene. The burning rate for gasoline is 6 to 12 in. (150 to 300 mm) of depth per hr, and for kerosene the rate is 5 to 8 in. (130 to 200 mm) of depth per hr. For example, a pool of gasoline, 1/2 in. (12.7 mm) deep, could be expected to burn itself out in 2 1/2 to 5 min.

In a series of tests conducted at the U.S. Bureau of Mines,[3] the burning rates of several liquids and gases were determined and found to approach "a maximum and constant value with increasing pool diameter. This constant burning rate is proportional to the ratio of the net heat of combustion to the sensible heat of vaporization."[3]

Based upon these observed burning rates in petroleum tank fires, an estimate can be made of the extent of area that will be involved in fire from a petroleum spill. When a spill is burning, the fire area will first be small and then spread to a point of equilibrium where it will burn as fast as it is released. At a burning rate of 1 ft per hr (0.3 m/hr), 1 gal per min (3.8 L/min) of spillage will reach an equilibrium burning area of about 8 sq ft (0.74 m^2). Thus, a 10 gpm (38 L/min) spill rate will be in equilibrium with 80 sq ft (7.4 m^2) of burning area; 100 gpm at 800 sq ft (380 L/min at 74 m^2); etc. For liquids having higher burning rates, the area would be smaller; and for those liquids having lower burning rates, the area would be larger. Also, the terrain will have an influence on the shape of the burning area.

FIRE PREVENTION METHODS

Whenever flammable and combustible liquids are stored or handled, the liquid is usually exposed to the air at some stage in the operation, except where the storage is confined to sealed containers that are not filled or opened on the premises or where handling is in closed systems and vapor losses are recovered. Even when the storage or handling is in a closed system, there is always the possibility of breaks or leaks, which permit the liquid to escape. Therefore, ventilation is of primary importance to prevent the accumulation of flammable vapors. It is also good practice to eliminate sources of ignition in places where low-flash-point flammable liquids are stored, handled, or used, even though no vapor may ordinarily be present.

Whenever possible in manufacturing processes involving flammable or combustible liquids, equipment, such as compressors, stills, towers, and pumps, should be located in the open. This will lessen the fire potential created by the escape and accumulation of flammable vapors. Gasoline and almost all other flammable liquids produce heavier-than-air vapors, which tend to settle on the floor or in pits or depressions. Such vapors may flow along the floor or ground for long distances, be ignited at some remote point, and flash back. The removal of such vapors at the floor level (including pits) is usually the proper method of ventilation. Convection currents of heated air or normal vapor diffusion may carry even heavy vapors upward, and, in such instances, ceiling ventilation may also be desirable. Ventilation to eliminate flammable vapors may be either natural or artificial. Although natural ventilation; which depends upon temperature and wind conditions, has the advantage of not being dependent on manual starting or on power supply, it is not so easily controlled as is mechanical ventilation. Mechanical ventilation should be used wherever there are extensive indoor operations involving flammable and combustible liquids.

Explosion Venting

In rooms or buildings where possible explosions of flammable vapors may occur, it is recommended that relief through explosion venting be provided for at least Class 1A liquids and unstable liquids.

Substitution of Nonflammable Liquids

The hazard created by flammable liquids may be avoided or reduced by the substitution of relatively safe materials. Such materials should be stable, have a low toxicity, and be either nonflammable or have a high flash point. For example, trichloroethylene, though higher in price, is nonflammable at ordinary temperatures, and may for some uses be substituted for a more hazardous flammable solvent. Tetrachloroethylene (perchloroethylene) is another nonflammable liquid. However, even though these products are less toxic than carbon tetrachloride, they should be used only in well-ventilated areas, with full vapor recovery and controls to prevent release to the atmosphere.

There are several commercial-type stable solvents available that have flash points from 140 to 190°F (60 to 88°C) and that have a comparatively low degree of toxicity.

Specially refined petroleum products, first developed as "Stoddard Solvent" but now sold by different companies under a variety of trade names, have solvent properties approximating gasoline, but with fire hazard properties similar to those of kerosene. A danger in their use lies in the possibility that persons believing that they are using a safe solvent without fire hazard may neglect ordinary precautions that would be observed with a liquid such as kerosene. When heated to above their flash point [about 100°F (38°C)], these solvents produce vapors as flammable as those of gasoline at its flash-point temperature.

Several other types of commercial solvents which are mixtures of liquids with differing rates of evaporation are available. Some are mixtures of gasoline or one of the various naphthas and a chlorinated solvent having a different and often higher evaporation rate than the flammable solvent which, over a period of time, would leave the original low-flash-point solvent. These mixtures create a toxicity hazard, as well as a fire hazard, and their use in open containers should be discouraged.

Solvents and solvent vapors are toxic in varying degrees, and ventilation is almost always necessary to keep vapor concentration within safe limits.

BIBLIOGRAPHY

References Cited

1. ASTM D 323, *Standard Test Method for Vapor Pressure of Petroleum Products*, American Society for Testing and Materials, Philadelphia, PA.
2. Mitchell, F. C., and Vernon, H. C., "Effect of Pressure on Explosion Hazards," *NFPA Quarterly*, Vol. 31, No. 4, Apr. 1938, pp. 306-313.
3. Burgess, D. S., Strasser, A., and Grumer, J., "Diffusion Burning of Liquid Fuels in Open Trays," *Fire Research Abstracts and Reviews*, Vol. 3, 1961, pp. 177-192.

References

ASTM D 56, *Standard Method of Test for Flash Point by the Tag Closed Tester*, American Society for Testing and Materials, Philadelphia, PA.

ASTM D 86, *Standard Method of Test for Distillation of Petroleum Products*, American Society for Testing and Materials, Philadelphia, PA.

ASTM D 92, *Cleveland Open-Cup Apparatus*, American Society for Testing and Materials, Philadelphia, PA.

ASTM D 93, *Standard Test Method for Flash Point by the Pensky-Martens Closed Tester*, American Society for Testing and Materials, Philadelphia, PA.

ASTM D 1310, *Tagliabue (Tag) Open-Cup Apparatus*, American Society for Testing and Materials, Philadelphia, PA.

ASTM D 2155, *Autoignition Temperature of Liquid Petroleum Products*, American Society for Testing and Materials, Philadelphia, PA.

ASTM D 3278, *Standard Test Methods for Flash Point Liquids by Setaflash Closed-Cup Apparatus*, American Society for Testing and Materials, Philadelphia, PA.

"Bulletin of Research No. 43," Underwriters Laboratories Inc., Northbrook, IL.

NFPA Quarterly, Apr. 1950.

NFPA Codes, Standards, and Recommended Practices

Reference to the following NFPA codes, standards, and recommended practices will provide further information on flammable and combustible liquids discussed in this chapter. (See the latest *NFPA Catalog* for availability of current editions of the following documents.)

NFPA 30, *Flammable and Combustible Liquids Code*.

NFPA 30A, *Automotive and Marine Service Station Code*.

NFPA 30B, *Aerosol Products*.

NFPA 31, *Installation of Oil Burning Equipment*.

NFPA 68, *Explosion Venting*.

NFPA 69, *Explosion Prevention Systems*.

NFPA 321, *Basic Classification of Flammable and Combustible Liquids*.

NFPA 325M, *Fire Hazard Properties of Flammable Liquids, Gases, and Volatile Solids*.

NFPA 327, *Cleaning or Safeguarding Small Tanks and Containers*.

NFPA 385, *Tank Vehicles for Flammable and Combustible Liquids*.

NFPA 491M, *Manual of Hazardous Chemical Reactions*.

Additional Reading

Accident Prevention Manual for Industrial Operations, 9th ed., National Fire Safety Council, Chicago, 1988.

Atallah, Sami, and Allan, Donald S., "Safe Separation Distances from Liquid Fuel Fires," *Fire Technology*, Vol. 7, No. 1, Feb. 1971, pp. 47-56.

Babrauskas, V., "Pool Fires: Burning Rates and Heat Fluxes," *SFPE Handbook of Fire Protection Engineering*, National Fire Protection Association, Quincy, MA, 1988.

Benedetti, R. P., ed., *Flammable and Combustible Liquids Code Handbook*, 3rd ed., National Fire Protection Association, Quincy, MA, 1987.

Burgess, D. S., and Zabetakis, M. G., "Fire and Explosion Hazards Associated with LNG," Report 6099, U.S. Bureau of Mines, Washington, DC, 1962.

"Controlling the Power of Flammable Liquids," Pamphlet No. P7045, Factory Mutual Research Corp., Norwood, MA.

Donakowski, T. D., "Is Liquid Hydrogen Safer than Liquid Methane?," *Fire Technology*, Vol. 17, No. 3, Aug. 1981, pp. 183-188.

Dunbar, J., "Packaging and Storing Flammable Liquids," *Products Finishing*, Vol. 52, No. 9, June 1988, pp. 118-121.

"Evaluation of the Fire Hazard of Water-Borne Coatings," Scientific Circular 804, National Paint and Coatings Association, Washington, DC, 1977.

Factory Mutual Research Corporation, *Handbook of Industrial Loss Prevention*, 2nd ed., McGraw-Hill, New York, 1967.

Flash Point Index of Trade Name Liquids, 9th ed., National Fire Protection Association, Quincy, MA, 1978.

Gann, Richard G., and Manka, Michael J., "Ignitability of Decomposed Transformer Fluids," *Fire Technology*, Vol. 18, No. 3, Aug. 1982, pp. 251-258.

Glassman, I., and Dryer, F. L., "Flame Spreading Across Liquid Fuels," *Fire Safety Journal*, Vol. 3, Nos. 2-4, Jan.-Mar., 1981.

Goodall, D. G., and Ingle, R., "The Ignition of Flammable Liquids by Hot Surfaces," *Fire Technology*, Vol. 3, No. 2, May 1967, pp. 115-128.

Gugan, K., *Unconfined Vapor Cloud Explosions*, Gulf Publishing, Houston, 1979.

Handbook of Organic Industrial Solvents, 6th ed., Alliance of American Insurers, Schaumburg, IL, 1987.

"Hazardous Materials Identification System," *Raw Materials Rating Manual*, National Paint and Coatings Association, Washington, DC, 1984.

Hird, D., "Fire-Fighting Foams for Flammable Liquid Fires," *Fire Prevention*, No. 202, Sept. 1987, pp. 20-22, 24, 26.

Holmstedt, G., and Persson, H., "Spray Fire Tests with Hydraulic Fluids," *Proceedings* of the First International Symposium on Fire Safety Science, Hemisphere, NY, 1986, pp. 869-879.

Johnson, Donald M., "New Developments in Bulk Storage of Flammable Liquids," TR 81-1, Society of Fire Protection Engineers, Boston, MA, 1981.

Kanury, M. A., "Ignition of Liquid Fuels," *SFPE Handbook of Fire Protection Engineering*, National Fire Protection Association, Quincy, MA, 1988.

Kashwogi, T., "Ignition of a Liquid Fuel Under High-Intensity Radiation," *Combustion Science and Technology*, Vol. 21, 1980, p. 131.

Kokkala, M., Andsten, T., and Bjorkman, J., "Extinguishment of Liquid Fires with Sprinklers and Water Sprays: Description of Tests," *Valtion Teknillinen Tutkimuskeskus*, No. 593, 1989, Technical Research Institute of Finland, Espo, Finland.

Linville, J., ed., *Industrial Fire Hazards Handbook*, 3rd ed., National Fire Protection Association, Quincy, MA, 1990.

"LNG Safety Research Program," Report IS 3-1, 1974, American Gas Association.

Martinsen, W. E., Johnson, D. W., and Terrell, W. F., "BLEVES: Their Causes, Effects, and Prevention," *Hydrocarbon Processing*, Vol. 65, No. 11, 1986, pp. 141-148.

May, W. G., and McQueen, W., "Radiation from Large Liquified Natural Gas Fires," *Combustion Science and Technology*, Vol. 7, 1973, pp. 51-56.

Mellan, Ibert, *Industrial Solvents Handbook*, Noyes Data Corp., Park Ridge, NJ, 1977.

Modak, A. T., "Ignitability of High Fire-Point Liquid Spills," EPRI NP-1731, Mar. 1981, Electric Power Research Institute, Palo Alto, CA.

Mudan, K. S., and Croce, P. A., "Fire Hazard Calculations for Large Open Hydrocarbon Fires," *SFPE Handbook of Fire Protection Engineering*, National Fire Protection Association, Quincy, MA, 1988.

Mudan, Krishna S., "Thermal Radiation Hazards from Hydrocarbon Pool Fires," *Progress in Energy and Combustion Sciences*, Vol. 10, 1984, pp. 59-80.

Northrup, S. D., "Evaluation of Less Flammable Transformer Liquids," *Proceedings* of the 5th BEAMA International Electrical Insulation Conference, Cavanagh Associates, Leatherhead, England, 1986, pp. 101-106.

Perry, R. H., and Green, D. W., eds., *Chemical Engineers' Handbook*, 6th ed., McGraw-Hill, NY, 1984.

Pingree, Daniel, "Looking at Fire Hazards: Hydraulic Fluids," *Fire Journal*, Vol. 59, No. 6, Nov. 1965, p. 23.

"Procedures for Working with Substances that Pose Hazards Because of Flammability or Explosibility," *Prudent Practices for Handling Hazardous Chemicals in Laboratories*, National Academy Press, Washington, DC, 1981.

Sawyer, W., "Relationship of Flash Points of Solvents, Resin Solutions, and Paints," *Journal of Coatings Technology*, Vol. 49, 1977, pp. 52-55.

Sax, N. I., *Dangerous Properties of Industrial Materials*, 7th ed., Van Nostrand Reinhold Co., NY, 1989.

Shimy, A. A., "Calculating Flammability Characteristics of Hydrocarbons and Alcohols," *Fire Technology*, Vol. 6, No. 2, May 1970, pp. 135-139.

Stevens, A., "Flammable Liquids—Why the Hazard?," *Journal of Chemical Education*, Vol. 56, No. 3, Mar. 1979, pp. 119A-124A.

Sundin, D. W., and Northrup, S. D., "Relationship Between Liquid Flammability Tests and Transformer Fire Situations," *Conference Record*—Industrial and Commercial Power Systems Technical Conference 1987, IEEE, 1987, pp. 117-121.

"The Fearsome Fireballs of Flammable Liquids," *The Sentinel*, Vol. 35, No. 6, Nov.-Dec. 1979, pp. 3-9.

Thorne, P. F., "Flashpoints of Mixtures of Flammable and Non-Flammable Liquids," *Fire and Materials*, Vol. 1, 1976, pp. 134-140.

Threshold Limit Values, American Conference on Governmental Industrial Hygienists, Cincinnati, OH, 1989.

Vervalin, C. H., ed., *Fire Protection Manual for Hydrocarbon Processing Plants*, 3rd ed., Gulf Publishing Co., Houston, 1985.

Weast, R. C., ed., *Handbook of Chemistry and Physics*, 69th ed., CRC Press, Boca Raton, FL, 1988.

Williams, D., "Extinguishing Flammable Liquid Fires," *Fire International*, Vol. 11, No. 107, Oct.-Nov. 1987, pp. 126-127.

MEDICAL GASES

Revised by Burton Klein

The use of flammable, nonflammable, and oxidizing gases in a hospital represents a fire hazard which is different from that of any other type of occupancy. Many patients cannot be moved easily, even under ideal conditions, because of their dependency upon life-support equipment which is not readily portable. The combination of a flammable gas and an immobile patient can be lethal in an emergency, such as a fire.

The introduction of nonflammable anesthetic agents shortly after World War II has been offset, in part, by the increased use of oxygen (which enhances combustion), the proliferation of throwaway items made of paper and plastic (which increases combustible loading), and an ever-increasing reliance on electrical appliances (which increases fire and shock hazard). Thus, while practices have changed, the hospital still represents a firesafety problem that is unique in modern society. This chapter discusses those parts of the health care firesafety problem related to the storage and use of medical gases, both flammable and nonflammable.

It should be noted that the hazards and safe practices discussed in this chapter apply to all health care facilities that use medical gases, e.g., ambulatory health care centers, nursing homes, dental offices, etc.

Other information of interest to those concerned with the problems and hazards of medical gases and equipment can be found in the following chapters: Section 2, Chapter 25, "Storage of Flammable and Combustible Liquids;" Section 2, Chapter 26, "Storage of Gases;" Section 2, Chapter 31, "Control of Electrostatic Ignition Sources;" Section 3, Chapter 2, "Fire Hazards of Materials: An Overview;" Section 3, Chapter 5, "Flammable and Combustible Liquids;" Section 3, Chapter 7, "Gases;" Section 3, Chapter 15, "Oxygen-Enriched Atmospheres;" and Section 8, Chapter 29, "Fire Protection for Laboratories Using Chemicals."

ANESTHETIC AGENTS

The introduction of diethyl ether as an anesthetic in 1846 led to dramatic changes in surgical practice. Its benefits were so obvious that general anesthesia rapidly became a technique thoroughly accepted by all segments of the medical world. Yet, diethyl ether had many drawbacks (including flammability), and the search for better agents led to the development and introduction of others. Initially, these agents were volatile liquids, i.e., agents which were stored as liquids and converted to a gas in a liquid vaporizer. With the advent of more modern, practical methods for compressing, storing, and delivering gases in regulated amounts, the use of the so-called true gases (e.g., nitrous oxide, cyclopropane) became popular.

The enrichment of the anesthetic atmosphere with oxygen (a step nearly simultaneous with the introduction of nitrous oxide) allowed early anesthetists to give patients high concentrations of anesthetic agents while at the same time maintaining adequate levels of oxygenation. The practice of using oxygen as a component of inhalation anesthesia has persisted to this day.

The Flammability of Anesthetics

Initially, most of the anesthetic agents used were flammable. The careless use of these agents, through either ignorance or disregard of safety precautions, led to a number of fires, explosions, injuries, and fatalities during the early days of anesthesia. While ether mixed with air will only burn briskly, ether mixed with oxygen generally will explode violently. Cyclopropane-oxygen mixtures create even more violent explosions, since this mixture frequently attains stoichiometric proportions.

Practically all anesthesiologists and anesthetists have abandoned the use of flammable anesthetizing agents. Flammable agents are used in only very rare instances where the characteristics of nonflammable anesthetizing agents or the patient's condition dictate the use of a flammable agent.

Flammable agents include cyclopropane and ethylene (true gases) and diethyl ether, divinyl ether, and ethyl chloride (which are volatile liquids). Nonflammable anesthetic agents include nitrous oxide (a true gas) and chloroform, halothane, methoxyflurane, ethrane, forane, and trichloroethylene (all liquids).

Burton Klein, P.E., is chief health care fire protection engineer on the staff of NFPA.

One method of reducing the flammability of a hydrocarbon (diethyl ether, divinyl ether, and cyclopropane are hydrocarbons) is to substitute halogen atoms (usually fluorine or chlorine) for some of the hydrogen atoms. For example, chloroform is trichloromethane, a nonflammable but toxic agent, made by substituting chlorine atoms for three of the hydrogen atoms in methane.

The search for a safe, nonflammable agent intensified after World War II. Ultimately fluroxene was developed, the first of a number of fluorine-containing inhalation anesthetic agents. Fluroxene is minimally flammable because it is partially halogenated and will not burn when used in the usual concentrations of less than 4 percent. Yet, because of its potential hazard, it is still considered a flammable agent.

Following its introduction into clinical practice, fluroxene was joined by halothane, methoxyflurane, and then ethrane, all halogenated inhalation agents with minimal (or absent) flammability. If methoxyflurane, halothane, or trichloroethylene are heated, they will burn. Under the usual conditions of use and the absence of any active heating well above room temperature, however, these agents are considered to be nonflammable, and are so utilized in anesthetic situations.

Neither nitrous oxide nor oxygen will burn, although both support combustion readily. The oxygen in the nitrous oxide will be released under flame conditions, contributing to the oxidation-reduction reaction.

Safe Practices in Using Anesthetics

A consideration of safe practices in the field of anesthesia and ancillary hospital activities begins with an understanding of the basic chemistry and physics of oxygen and the anesthetic gases, as well as the vapors produced by the volatile liquid agents, such as diethyl ether.

A gas consists of molecules that move individually in a linear fashion at high velocities. The molecular movement increases with a rise in temperature, and decreases as the gas cools. This movement produces a parallel increase or decrease in the pressure exerted by that gas, depending upon its temperature. When a gas is compressed, its individual molecules will be forced closer together, thus increasing molecular movement and the temperature of the gas. Gases possess definite mass, but neither definite shape nor definite volume (i.e., they always assume the shape and volume of their containers, if any).

The relationship among pressure, volume, and temperature is given by the various gas laws. From all of these gas laws, one may establish what is known as the general gas law, i.e., the pressure of any given quantity of gas is proportional to its absolute temperature and inversely proportional to its volume. Algebraically, pressure times volume divided by temperature equals a constant. These gas laws assume the gas is ideal, while in actual practice no gas is ideal.

The gaseous anesthetic agents (cyclopropane, ethylene, nitrous oxide, and oxygen) are stored as compressed gases under high pressure or as liquids. They are dispensed as gases through needle valves and flowmeters. In contrast, liquid anesthetic agents (such as diethyl ether, chloroform, halothane) are stored and dispensed as liquids.

Liquids possess definite volume and mass but no definite shape. At any gas-liquid interface, molecules are continually escaping from the liquid state into the gaseous state. The pressure created by the molecules that have escaped into the gaseous state is called vapor pressure. As the temperature of a liquid is continually raised, the vapor pressure also is raised, approaching atmospheric pressure as the temperature of the liquid reaches its boiling point. When the temperature of the liquid reaches its boiling point, molecules will pass freely into the gaseous state and the liquid will boil.

In the operation of a volatile liquid vaporizer during anesthesia, the temperature of the liquid never reaches its boiling point. The carrier gases (nitrous oxide and oxygen), which are used to deliver the inhalation anesthetic agents to the patient, pass through the vaporizer in a steady flow. These gases carry away to the anesthesia circuit the vaporized molecules of the volatile liquid. In the absence of applied heat, the temperature of the volatile liquid remaining in the reservoir, and that of the reservoir itself, will fall as the volatile liquid vaporizes (the latent heat of vaporization). As the temperature of the remaining liquid falls, so does its volatility. Some anesthetic vaporizers are designed to maintain, by one of several methods, the temperature of the liquid at or near room temperature to promote even rates of vaporization.

Because of the fire and explosion hazards associated with the use of flammable anesthetizing agents, a number of measures were instituted to reduce the chance of sparks of sufficient energy from occurring. These included humidity control, antistatic measures, conductive flooring, and the use of isolated power systems.

Gas Anesthesia Apparatus

Anesthetic agents are administered by a gas anesthesia apparatus. (See Figures 3-6A and 3-6B.) This device consists of a number of components. First, there must be a device to supply a source of gas. This may either be a cylinder or a connection to a central piping system. Next, a regulator may be necessary to reduce any high-pressure gases to a lower working pressure. Gases are then fed to needle valves, which precisely control the flow of the gas to be delivered to the anesthesia circuit. To measure the flow of these gases, each gas is passed through a flowmeter.

The flowmeter most commonly encountered in modern gas anesthesia apparatus is the rotameter, or Thorpe tube. This is a tapered glass tube that contains a bobbin or rotor which floats in the gas stream. The space between the outside of the rotor and the inside of the glass tube consists of an annular orifice which increases as the rotor rises in the tube. When the gas passes across this orifice, a fall in pressure occurs. The difference between the upstream and downstream pressures is equal to the weight of the rotor or bobbin when the flowmeter is in equilibrium. Each flowmeter is calibrated by first passing that specific gas through a master flowmeter. Flows are indicated by noting the position of the top of the rotor as related to a card affixed beside the tapered tube.

From the flowmeters the gases enter a common mixing manifold. The mixture of gases then will enter the anesthesia circuit. The anesthetic circuit is the portion of the gas machine from which the patient draws the mixture of anesthetic vapors, gases, and oxygen, and into which the patient exhales. During exhalation, a small amount of carbon dioxide, a product of the body's metabolism, enters the anesthesia circuit. Some method must be utilized to remove this waste gas from the anesthetic atmosphere. The most common method is chemical absolution, employing an

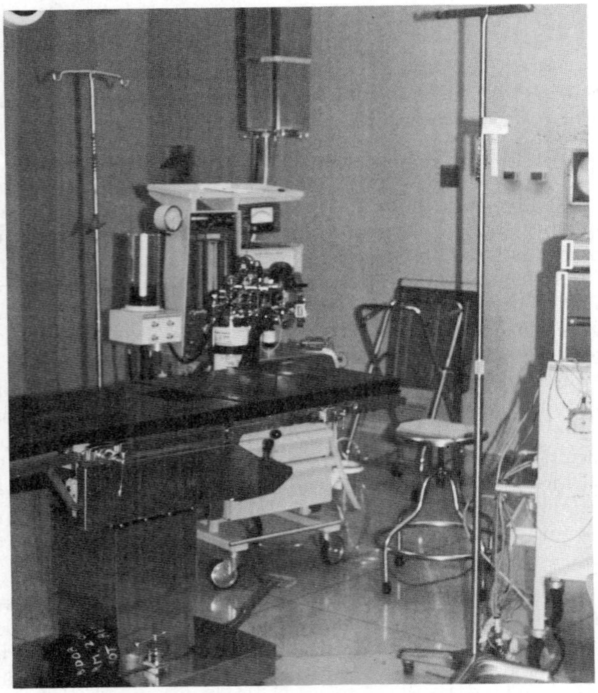

FIG. 3-6A. General view of modern anesthesia apparatus. Anethesia machine is in background; monitoring equipment is on right.

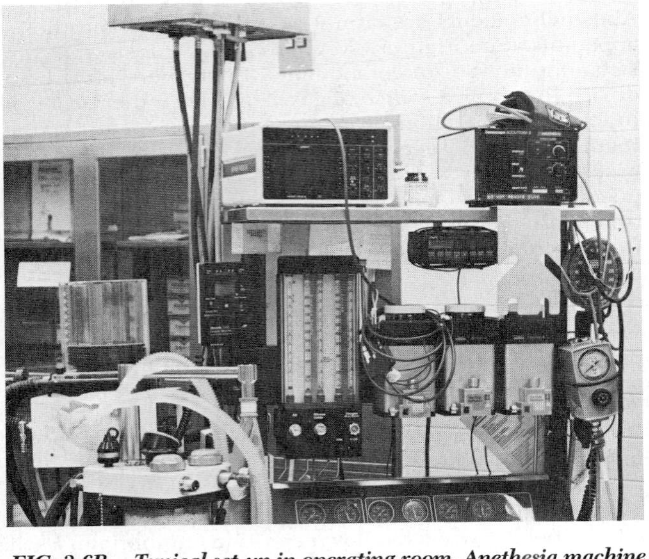

FIG. 3-6B. Typical set-up in operating room. Anethesia machine is in middle, with a small patient monitor on shelf. Overhead stanchion provides electricity, gases, and vacuum.

absorber which contains one-half to one liter of granular soda lime (soda lime is a mixture of sodium and calcium hydroxides, water, and a binder).

Valves in the anesthesia circuit allow the patient to breathe in a unidirectional fashion, i.e., from the lungs through the absorber to a rebreathing bag, and then back again to the lungs for inhalation. Sometimes the vaporizer is placed in a breathing circuit. At other times, it may be located somewhere between the gas delivery of the anesthesia machine and the breathing circuit.

Storage of Flammable and Nonflammable Anesthetizing Agents

In any operating suite in which flammable agents are utilized, provisions must be made for storage of the reserve supplies of gases and flammable liquids. Specifications for storage include a room with a conductive floor which is ventilated to the outside with a minimum of six to eight air changes per hour. (See Chapter 4 of NFPA 99, *Health Care Facilities*, for details.)

This room with its conductive floor must not communicate directly with a room utilized for the storage of nonflammable and/or oxidizing gases, such as nitrous oxide, oxygen, or compressed air. In addition, these gases must not be stored in the same location as the volatile liquid anesthetizing agents.

Waste ether should be stored in a safety can with a spring-closing lid and an internal screen to prevent propagation of flame into the can. Waste ether should be disposed off-premises by disposal specialists, or in accordance with the U.S. Environmental Protection Agency (EPA) requirements.

Open cans of ether must not be stored in a refrigerator unless it is of the type acceptable for the storage of flammable liquids, e.g., with a sealed thermostat to prevent accidental ignition of any vapors within the refrigerator cabinet. Such refrigerators usually carry the label of a testing laboratory which specifically indicates that the refrigerator is approved for the storage of flammable liquids.

In some flammable anesthetizing locations, ether is used to prep the skin. This is a dangerous practice and is not recommended. There are better nonflammable agents for preparing the skin, such as inhibited 1-1-1-trichloroethane or trifluorotrichloroethane. Neither of these solvents will burn, and both are good agents to degrease and prepare the patient's skin for plastic and similar draping.

OXYGEN

Oxygen as a Medical Agent

In the early days of inhalation anesthesia, diethyl ether was administered by the drop technique. Poured or dropped on a gauze-covered mask, the ether was volatilized in the air of the operating room atmosphere. No oxygen enrichment was utilized. Today the large majority of inhalation anesthetics are administered with oxygen. In the presence of an oxygen-enriched atmosphere, the lower limit of flammability and the ignition temperature of all flammable agents are reduced. Additionally, such a mixture may approach stoichiometric concentrations, i.e., the proportions of oxygen and fuel may be close to those which will allow complete combustion of the flammable substance with neither reactant being present in any significant amount after the oxidation-reduction reaction.

Yet, from a practical standpoint, one cannot eliminate oxygen. Oxygen-enriched atmospheres are commonly utilized in anesthesia apparatus to enhance the administration of the anesthetics and promote a wider margin of safety for the patient. Respiratory therapy also utilizes oxygen-enriched atmospheres to a significant degree. Hyperbaric chambers for various forms of hyperbaric medicine also utilize oxygen-enriched atmospheres, either in the form of compressed air or compressed oxygen. Thus, recognizing that oxygen-enriched atmospheres are present to varying degrees, fire or explosion prevention in health care facilities must take into account the control of these fuels and ignition sources.

Oxygen Supplies

The principal method of preparing oxygen for medical use is by the compression and liquefaction of air, followed by fractional distillation. Once it has been purified, the oxygen may be transported to, and stored at, the site of consumption as a compressed gas or liquid. Because of the economies in bulk oxygen use, practically all medium-size to large hospitals rely on a bulk oxygen storage unit on site. NFPA 50, *Bulk Oxygen Systems at Consumer Sites,* covers safety standards for the design and operation of such bulk oxygen storage units.

Distribution Systems for Medical Gases

Where bulk oxygen is used at a health care facility, a piping distribution system is required. A pipeline system also may be employed for nitrous oxide. Oxygen and nitrous oxide pipeline systems, as installed in health care facilities, require the use of copper or brass tubing or pipe with screwed, brazed, or otherwise high melting-point joints. The system must be pressure tested with oil-free dry air or nitrogen before it is put to use. (See NFPA 99, *Health Care Facilities,* for details.)

The piping system terminates with station outlets at each bedside or operating room. These outlets are equipped with a threaded or quick-connect terminal keyed to the specific gas in the pipe. Because it is extremely difficult to extinguish a fire being supplied by a continuous source of oxygen or nitrous oxide, all piping systems containing an oxidizing gas for use in health care facilities require a remote shutoff valve that can shut off the flow of gas to a station outlet or series of station outlets involved in a fire.

Whenever more than one medical piped-gas system is to be installed, care must be taken to check all station outlets for delivery of the correct gas before the systems are put in use. Cross connections have accidentally been made, resulting in injury or death of patients from anoxia.

All specifications for the design, installation, testing, and operation of nonflammable medical piped gas systems for health care facilities are covered in Chapter 4 of NFPA 99, *Health Care Facilities*. Certain Compressed Gas Association (CGA) publications cover requirements related to the installation of systems. (See bibliography for titles.)

Station outlets for medical gas supply systems must be equipped with noninterchangeable fittings, keyed to the specific supply. Station outlets also require a label with the name of the gas being supplied to the outlet. Medical gas cylinder outlets are also keyed as to the gas supplied. The Diameter Index Safety System is utilized for larger size gas cylinders and mating connectors. For small-size cylinders, the Pin Index System is employed. This system uses two holes drilled along a radius beneath the outlet orifice of the valve body, and keyed to that gas. The cylinder yokes are equipped with pins that mate with the holes in the valve body of the cylinder containing the correct gas. The holes and pins are located in such a manner that it is impossible to insert a cylinder in the yoke for a different gas.

Gas cylinders can be color coded. The American standard for color coding includes green for oxygen, blue for nitrous oxide, orange for cyclopropane, brown for helium, red for ethylene, and gray for carbon dioxide. Color combinations are available for gas mixtures of certain percentages. *However, color coding is secondary to labeling very clearly the contents of a cylinder*; for example, persons who are color blind would not be able to distinguish cylinder contents if cylinders were only identified by different colors.

Cylinder weights, sizes, pressures, and contents are shown in Table 3-6A from Appendix C-12.5 of NFPA 99, *Health Care Facilities*. Data for this appendix was supplied by the Compressed Gas Association.

In some health care facilities, oxygen may be supplied to the piping system by a manifold to which cylinders are connected and not by a bulk source as described above. Another arrangement still used is individual oxygen cylinders at each site of administration.

Cylinder handling requires certain safety precautions. Larger cylinders are heavy and mechanical damage to them, as well as injuries to personnel, may result if cylinders are dropped. Cylinders should be transported only by the use of an approved cylinder cart. When large cylinders are moved, the cylinder cap must be tightly affixed. Cylinders in use or in storage must be chained to a wall, affixed to a cylinder stand, or (in the case of smaller cylinders) securely attached to an item of therapy equipment. Valves on cylinders must not be damaged. If a valve breaks off, the cylinder may be propelled by the reactive release of the high-pressure contents; serious injury or even death of personnel may result.

Oxygen is also utilized in emergency vehicles. Generally, small cylinders are employed. The same precautions are to be exercised for this situation as in a facility.

Transfilling gas from large cylinders to small cylinders is a hazardous procedure, and should only be done by qualified personnel. It should always be done remote from patient areas, and in locations acceptable to the authority having jurisdiction. (See NFPA 99, *Health Care Facilities*, for details.) The Compressed Gas Association has published a safety guide to follow when such transfilling is accomplished. (See bibliography.)

RESPIRATORY THERAPY

Respiratory therapy began with the use of oxygen-enriched atmospheres inside oxygen tents. Subsequently, various other methods for application of oxygen in medical care were developed. These included oxygen hoods (especially useful for children), incubators for newborn infants, oronasal or nasal masks, and the nasal catheter. The most recent development has been devices to mechanically assist or control the patient's breathing while delivering medical gases. This equipment, which intermittently generates pressure, will deliver mixtures of oxygen and therapeutic agents, or air-oxygen mixtures. These devices may be powered by the pressurized oxygen supply or by an electrically operated motor and pump system. One type of respiration unit is shown in Figure 3-6C.

In any oxygen-enriched atmosphere, combustible substances possess a lower ignition temperature and burn much more rapidly than in air. Flame spread can be extremely rapid, especially if bedding or clothing are saturated with oxygen. The safe practices for the use of respiratory therapy equipment are detailed in Chapter 8 of NFPA 99, *Health Care Facilities*.

TABLE 3-6A. ***Typical Medical Gas Cylinders—Volume and Weight of Available Contents*‡***

All Volumes at 70°F.(21.1°C)

Cylinder Style & Dimensions	Nominal Volume Cu In./Liter	Contents	Air	Carbon Dioxide	Cyclo-Pro-pane	Helium	Nitrogen	Nitrous Oxide	Oxygen	Mixtures of Oxygen: Helium	Mixtures of Oxygen: CO_2
B	87/1.43	psig		838	75				1900		
3½″ od × 13″		Liters		370	375				200		
8.89 × 33 cm		Lbs.-Oz.		1-8	1-7¼				—		
		Kilograms		.68	0.66				—		
D	176/2.88	psig	1900	838	75	1600	1900	745	1900	**	**
4½″ od × 17″		Liters	375	940	870	300	370	940	400	300	400
10.8 × 43 cm		Lbs.-Oz.	—	3-13	3-5½	—	—	3-13	—	**	**
		Kilograms	—	1.73	1.51	—	—	1.73	—	**	**
E	293/4.80	psig	1900	898		1600	1900	745	1900	**	**
4¼″ od × 26″		Liters	625	1590		500	610	1590	660	500	660
10.8 × 66 cm		Lbs.-Oz	—	6-7		—	—	6-7	—	**	**
		Kilograms	—	2.92		—	—	2.92	—	**	**
M	1337/21.9	psig	1900	838		1600	2200	745	2200	**	**
7″ od × 43″		Liters	2850	7570		2260	3200	7570	3450	2260	3000
17.8 × 109 cm		Lbs.-Oz.	—	30-10		—	—	30-10	122 cu ft	**	**
		Kilograms	—	13.9		—	—	13.9	—	**	**
G	2370/38.8	psig	1900	838		1600		745		**	**
8½″ od × 51″		Liters	5050	12,300		4000		13,800		4000	5330
21.6 × 130 cm		Lbs.-Oz.	—	50-0		—		56-0		**	**
		Kilograms	—	22.7		—		25.4		**	**
H or **K**	2660/43.6	psig	2200			2200	2200	745	2200†		
9¼″ od × 51″		Liters	6550			6000	6400	15,800	6900		
23.5 × 130 cm		Lbs.-Oz.	—			—	—	64	244 cu ft		
		Kilograms	—			—	—	29.1	—		

* Computed contents based on nominal cylinder volumes and rounded to no greater variance than ±1 percent.
** Pressure and weight of mixed gases will vary according to the composition of the mixture.
† 275 cu ft (7800 L) cylinders at 2490 psig (19 237 kPa) are available upon request.
‡ Source: Compressed Gas Association.

Helium/oxygen mixtures are occasionally used in treating some forms of respiratory distress. This gas mixture should be treated like any other oxygen-enriched gas (i.e., the precautions noted above.)

COMPRESSED AIR

Atmospheric air compressed to greater than ambient pressure [i.e., greater than 14.7 psi (101 kPa)] constitutes an oxygen-enriched atmosphere. Although it is not as hazardous as one of pure oxygen, the ease of ignition of combustible substances is nevertheless increased, and flame spreads with much greater rapidity than in atmospheric air at ambient pressures. The fire hazards created by the compressed-air are significant. It is very difficult to extinguish such a fire unless a water-deluge system is employed. Fire blankets and dry chemical agents are ineffective. The burning material must be cooled by water.

If a fire occurs in an electrically powered item of equipment located in this atmosphere, it is first necessary to deenergize the equipment. Then, the fire can be fought with water.

Pressurized air has a wide variety of uses in modern medicine. It is used in hyperbaric chambers. If purified, it may be mixed with oxygen to allow ventilation of the patient's lungs without the necessity for giving the patient pure oxygen to breathe. It can also be used for laboratory apparatus. Chapter 4 of NFPA 99, *Health Care Facilities*, includes provisions for the installation of a central piping system for compressed air for medical purposes.

Compressed Air Supplies

If a health care facility elects to utilize a compressor as a source of air for a piped medical air system, it must be of a type that will not add impurities to the air stream, such as hydrocarbons, carbonaceous particulates, or carbon monoxide; in other words, it must not degrade the localized air. To meet these specifications, the air supply (at minimum) must not come from the building in which the compressor is located. Additionally, the air must be free of any lubricants or products resulting from the breakdown of lubricants. Under the pressures and temperatures generated in an air compressor, some lubricants may break down and release carbon monoxide which could be distributed in the compressed air system.

In a health care facility using a compressor to furnish air for essential health care facility services, including the operating room and as an adjunct to respiratory therapy, electric power to the compressor must be wired to the critical branch of the essential electrical system of the facility. The specifications for this electric system are set forth in Chapter 3 of NFPA 99, *Health Care Facilities*.

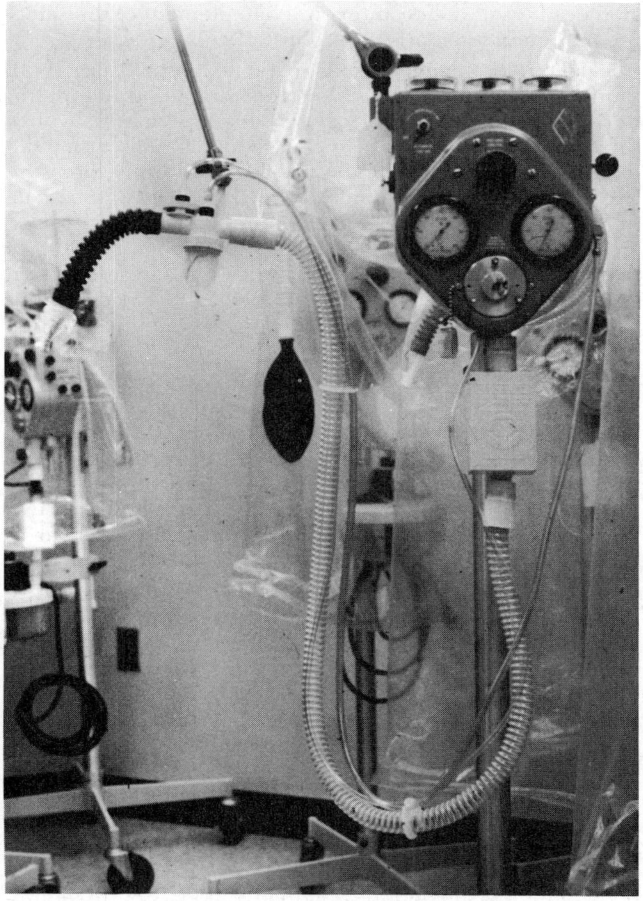

FIG. 3-6C. A respiration unit used for oxygen therapy. The control unit (upper right) is connected to the hospital compressed air and oxygen distribution system viaquick-connect couplers on hoses at rear. Desired air-oxygen mixture is fed to patient via bacteria filter (at bottom of control unit) and through the attached corrugated hose. Patient's oxygen mask is attached to black hose at left.

If a health care facility is located in an area in which the atmosphere is highly contaminated, it may be desirable to utilize compressed air in cylinders rather than compressing it on the site. Because even the supplier of these cylinders may not have a pure source of atmospheric air, an oxygen-nitrogen mixture may be utilized. This so-called "synthetic air" is much purer than the ambient air, because it is made up of pure oxygen and nitrogen in a one to four ratio. It contains no atmospheric pollutants of any kind.

Because of the problems of back firing, the medical compressed air system is not to be used for any non-patient purposes.

VACUUM SYSTEMS

In addition to central piped gas systems for compressed air, oxygen, and nitrous oxide, central vacuum systems have become a standard feature in most health care facilities. Station *inlets* for the vacuum system are now commonly installed in emergency rooms, operating rooms, recovery rooms, intensive care facilities, delivery rooms, nurseries, and patient rooms. While portable individual vacuum pump units have been commonly utilized in the past, the trend is to move away from them, including those for low-level suction used to remove fluids and air from the patient's thoracic cage.

A central vacuum system requires both collection bottles and trap bottles at the station inlets. The collection bottles collect the fluids. The trap bottles ensure that none of the material so collected will enter the suction line and clog it. Modern practice dictates retaining the suction material at the patient care site. This prevents the possibility of contamination and cross infection within the premises.

A central vacuum system requires adequate piping capacity and pump units of sufficient size to meet peak needs. Two pumps (at minimum) are required, sized so that, if one fails, the other(s) can meet the needs of the health care facility. The pumps are connected so that they will run alternately to provide even wear. Central vacuum systems are also required to be wired to the critical branch of the essential electrical system, since the system provides life support function in many situations.

A central vacuum system may also be used in the laboratory and other hospital facilities. If so, it should not be connected to the medical-surgical vacuum system piping; however, a common receiver tank is permitted.

In the operation of any central vacuum system, it is vitally important to avoid drawing any flammable gases or liquids into the system. At the opposite end, the discharge of this system to the outside of the building is to avoid contamination returning back into the facility. Requirements for vacuum systems in health care facilities are included in Chapter 4 of NFPA 99, *Health Care Facilities*.

Waste Anesthetic Gas Disposal (Scavenging)

Though not recommended, central vacuum systems of health care facilities are sometimes utilized for waste anesthetic gas disposal (WAGD). For several years it has been recognized that waste anesthetic gases (notably nitrous oxide and halothane) may create an occupational hazard for operating room personnel. Studies have suggested an increased incidence of carcinoma, spontaneous abortion, and minor birth defects in the offspring of such personnel. Anesthesia techniques employed for the use of these agents generally utilize high gas flows. A significant portion of the excess gases are vented to the operating room atmosphere, thus creating the alleged hazard.

If a central vacuum system is to be used for WAGD, it must have a capacity greater than that for conventional operating room requirements (i.e., suctioning only surgical patients). Additionally, a system of this type cannot be employed when flammable anesthetic agents are used unless special precautions are taken to keep the concentration of such agents below their flammable limits.

Workable alternative scavenging systems include a low vacuum-high volume blower system if the operating rooms are equipped with air-handling systems and exhaust ducts which afford no recirculation. The "scavenging" inlets from the anesthesia circuit (and ventilator if one is used) are connected to tubing which extends to the plenum of the air exhaust duct. A system of this type could be used in the flammable anesthetizing location to scavenge flammable anesthetic agents. In practice, the safe use of flammable anesthetic agents requires low flows and a closed anesthetic circuit. Thus, only small amounts of flammable agents would enter such a scavenging system, and then only at the termination of the anesthesia.

For more details on WAGD, ANSI Z79.11, *Standard for Anesthetic Equipment—Scavenging Systems for Excess Anesthetic Gases*, should be reviewed.

Housekeeping Vacuum Systems

In some health care facilities, a vacuum system for housekeeping purposes may be desired. It can be used in conjunction with vacuum equipment for cleaning corridors, drapes, and other related housekeeping chores. *This system must, of course, be separate from the central vacuum system used for medical purposes.*

HEALTH CARE FACILITY LABORATORIES

Health care facility laboratories may utilize a wide variety of gases and gaseous mixtures for chemical analysis, the generation of flames, and other purposes. Chapter 10, "Laboratories" of NFPA 99, *Health Care Facilities*, sets forth the design features and practices required for the safe operation of such a laboratory.

GAS STERILIZING

For many years, sterilization by either dry heat or steam heat was standard practice for the eradication of bacteria and other pathogens from reusable medical equipment. Recent years have seen the introduction of the ethylene oxide sterilizer. This sterilizer employs ethylene oxide, an extremely volatile liquid that vaporizes readily at normal room temperatures. It is also an effective bacteriocidal and virocidal agent.

To sterilize objects, the sterilizer chamber is first evacuated of air, and then filled with the ethylene oxide gas. The gas penetrates the material contained in the chamber and kills all bacteria, viruses, and other pathogenic organisms.

Ethylene oxide is highly flammable and chemically reactive, and proper operation of the equipment is required in order to avoid the danger of accidental ignition or explosive chemical reaction. The liquid is delivered to the facility in cylinders that must be stored properly, as is the case with any container of flammable liquid or gas. It also can be delivered mixed with other gases to reduce flammability. Ethylene oxide is toxic to humans, and proper venting of the ethylene oxide sterilizer to the outside of the building is mandatory.

Other chemical sterilizing and disinfecting agents have been used in the past. These have included chlorine, ozone, sulfur dioxide, and formaldehyde gas. Because of the problems in handling these agents, their corrosive nature, and the greater efficacy and safety associated with heat and ethylene oxide sterilization, ozone, formaldehyde, sulfur dioxide, and chlorine are no longer used for medical sterilization purposes.

FIRE PREVENTION AND FIRE RESPONSE

Fire and Explosion Prevention

Sources of ignition in flammable anesthetic atmospheres include adiabatic heating of gases, electric sparks, friction sparks, heated objects (including open flame), and static electricity. In view of the hazards involved, fire prevention methods generally strive for redundancy to establish built-in safeguards of a multifaceted nature so that an explosion or fire will not occur even if one element of the safety recommendations fails or is omitted.

To prevent dangerous adiabatic heating of gases (both flammable and oxidizing), it is recommended that cylinder valves be *opened very slowly* to allow gradual introduction of the high-pressure gas downstream from the cylinder valve. This will allow a slow buildup of pressure and hence temperature, thus allowing the mass of the metal of the regulator or other gas-containing component to dissipate the heat rapidly enough to prevent the buildup of dangerously high temperatures. Additionally, safety standards forbid the use of any hydrocarbon substance to lubricate any components containing any oxidizing gas at high pressures.

The elimination of electric sparks, other than static sparks, is directed toward the proper design, application, and maintenance of electrical equipment. Specifications for this electrical equipment, as well as for line cords and power supplies, are set forth in NFPA 99, *Health Care Facilities*. Recommendations for the proper use of this equipment by facility personnel are also spelled out in NFPA 99.

The elimination of static electricity from any area designated for the administration of flammable anesthetics, such as an operating room,* is another example of the multifaceted approach to hazard control. First, the humidity in such locations is maintained at 50 percent. Second, all floors in the area and immediately adjacent corridors are made conductive (conductive floors are designed to keep all items resting on or moving across the floor at the same potential). Third, personnel entering the area are required to wear either conductive shoes or conductive overshoes that maintain contact with the skin of their feet or legs to ensure an adequately conductive pathway between the body of the person and the conductive floor. Fourth, equipment for use in flammable anesthetizing locations has certain requirements, including specifications for conductive straps or conductive castors or feet. This applies to stools, kick basins, mayo stands, operating tables, and gas anesthesia apparatus. Finally, all outer clothing worn by operating room personnel and all patient gowns, drapes, belting, and other components and accessories are of conductive nature. All of these steps preclude the buildup of static electricity in the hospital operating room. The primary document controlling the use of anesthetic agents is NFPA 99, *Health Care Facilities*.

Because there exists the possibility of electrocution in such a conductive environment, both the shoes and the floor have built-in internal resistances which will prevent a direct, low-resistance pathway to ground. A conductive shoe tester is shown in Figure 3-6D.

Fire Fighting Problems

Oxygen-enriched atmospheres are encountered during practically every inhalation anesthetic administration and all respiratory therapy. When patients' bedding and clothing become saturated with oxygen, and a fire occurs, flame spread will be extremely rapid and large quantities of water are required for extinguishment. Dry chemical extinguishers and fire blankets are ineffective. If the fire involves electrical equipment, such equipment must first be deenergized. The fire then may be knocked down with water.

*It is recognized that flammable inhalation anesthetics are rarely used anymore in the U.S. However, their use is not banned.

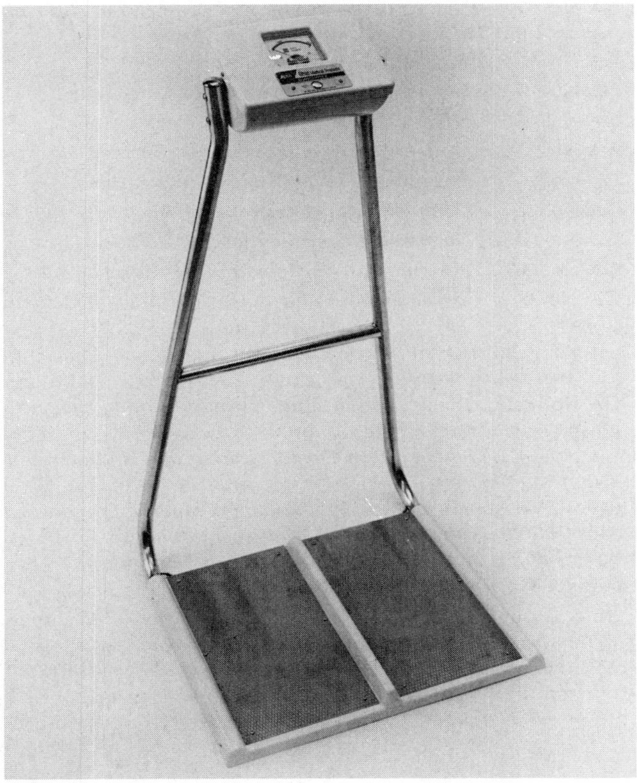

FIG. 3-6D. A conductive shoe tester. Located at entrance to sterile corridor of designated flammable anesthetizing locations, the tester indicates proper function of conductive shoes and "booties." The meter at the top of the frame indicates the resistance between ground and a person standing on the footplates of the pedestal. (Source: Ohio Medical Products—Airco Division)

Safe practices for the prevention of fires during the use of respiratory therapy are covered in Chapter 8, "Gas Equipment," of NFPA 99, *Health Care Facilities*. Included is a recommended response in the event of a fire involving respiratory therapy equipment.

Flammable solvents are present in most health care facilities: in pharmacy storage, hospital laboratories, and housekeeping and other areas. Special fire problems are created if any of these substances are allowed to enter drains, the central suction system, or ventilation ducts. Finally, mechanical hazards are created by the potential energy contained in compressed gas cylinders.

While high-voltage electrical (e.g., radiological) and electronic (e.g., medical monitoring and computer) equipment does not by itself usually create a fire hazard, combustibles stored in the vicinity may be involved in a fire. The free use of water would be inadvisable because of the electric shock hazard to the fire fighter or damage to the equipment. The presence of radioisotopes may also hamper fire suppression methods. Fire service personnel must be made aware of all special problems created by equipment or supplies in any health care area.

An aid to the identification of hazards associated with medical gases and agents is the NFPA hazards identification symbol system. (See NFPA 704, *Identification of the Fire Hazards of Materials*.) This identification scheme, based on the "704 diamond," can visually present information on flammability, health, and self-reactivity hazards, as well as special information associated with the hazards of the materials being identified. Chapter 10, "Laboratories," of NFPA 99, *Health Care Facilities*, requires application of the NFPA hazards identification symbols to laboratories. It is also a good prudent policy to apply the system throughout a facility in such areas as general stores, housekeeping, pharmacy, operating rooms, gas and flammable liquid storage rooms, and any other location where volumes of combustible or flammable materials are stored or used, or where certain special fire fighting problems exist. Fire fighting personnel are trained to recognize and decipher the meaning of the "704 diamond."

Adoption of the 704 symbol system affords not only enhanced fire protection, but also some measure of prevention and education of employees as well. Fire personnel are instantly apprised of the hazards they face. In addition, employees are educated about the hazardous nature of the materials that they employ daily. Also, it is possible that in deploying the system, personnel may discover hazardous materials no longer in use that should be removed from the hospital premises, thus eliminating potential problems.

HYPERBARIC CHAMBERS

One use of an oxygen-enriched atmosphere is in the operation of hyperbaric chambers. Some chambers may be small and accommodate only a single patient; others may be designed to allow the performance of an operation or other procedure, and are thus large enough to accommodate one or more patients and several attendants. But because the pressure of the air in the chamber is elevated, an increased partial pressure of oxygen will result (unless means are taken to limit the oxygen content). Sometimes the percent of oxygen is deliberately increased in the chamber (certain medical problems are treated in this manner). Safety standards for hyperbaric chambers and facilities are detailed in Chapter 19 of NFPA 99, *Health Care Facilities*.

AMBULATORY CARE FACILITIES

Many requirements for the safe use of inhalation anesthetics in the dentist's office and other ambulatory care facilities are identical to those for hospitals. Individual vacuum units are commonly utilized, rather than a central system, because of the relatively small amount of suction needed in the dentist's office, as compared to the hospital. However, in larger dental offices, or other ambulatory care facilities in which minor operations are performed under general anesthesia, it may be desirable to incorporate a central vacuum system for the operating rooms and the recovery rooms, as well as for the central piping of oxygen and nitrous oxide.

Requirements for inhalation anesthetics in such facilities are contained in Chapter 13, "Ambulatory Health Care Centers," Chapter 14, "Clinics," and Chapter 15 "Medical and Dental Offices," of NFPA 99, *Health Care Facilities*.

BIBLIOGRAPHY

NFPA Codes, Standards, and Recommended Practices

Reference to the following NFPA codes, standards, and recommended practices will provide further information on medical gases discussed in this chapter. (See the latest *NFPA Catalog* for availability of current editions of the following documents.)

NFPA 10, *Portable Fire Extinguishers.*

NFPA 30, *Flammable and Combustible Liquids Code.*

NFPA 49, *Hazardous Chemicals Data.*

NFPA 50, *Bulk Oxygen Systems at Consumer Sites.*

NFPA 53M, *Fire Hazards in Oxygen-Enriched Atmospheres.*

NFPA 77, *Static Electricity.*

NFPA 99, *Health Care Facilities.*

NFPA *101*®, *Life Safety Code*®.

NFPA 325M, *Fire Hazard Properties of Flammable Liquids, Gases, and Volatile Solids.*

NFPA 491M, *Manual of Hazardous Chemical Reactions.*

NFPA 704, *Identification of the Fire Hazards of Materials.*

NFPA 801, *Facilities Handling Radioactive Materials.*

Additional Reading

The following pamphlets are published by the Compressed Gas Association, 1235 Jefferson Davis Hwy, Arlington, VA 22202.

CGA No. C-4 (ANSI Z48), *Method of Marking Portable Compressed Gas Containers to Identify the Material Contained.*

CGA No. C-9, *Standard Color-Marking of Compressed Gas Cylinders Intended for Medical Use in the United States.*

CGA No. G-4, *Oxygen.*

CGA No. G-4.3, *Commodity Specification for Oxygen.*

CGA No. G-6, *Carbon Dioxide.*

CGA No. G-6.2, *Commodity Specification for Carbon Dioxide.*

CGA No. G-7, *Compressed Air for Human Respiration.*

CGA No. G-7.1, *Commodity Specification for Air.*

CGA No. G-9.1, *Commodity Specification for Helium.*

CGA No. G-10.1, *Commodity Specification for Nitrogen.*

CGA No. P-2, *Characteristics and Safe Handling of Medical Gases.*

CGA No. P-2.5, *Transfilling of High-Pressure Gaseous Ocygen to be Used for Respiration.*

CGA No. P-2.6, *Transfilling of Low-Pressure Liquid Ocygen to be Used for Respiration.*

CGA No. S-1.1, *Safety Relief Device Standards—Cylinders for Compressed Gases.*

CGA No. V-1, *American National-Canadian Standard Compressed Gas Cylinder Valve Outlet and Inlet Connections,* (ANSI-B57.1, CSA-B96)

CGA No. V-5, *Diameter Index Safety System.*

CGA No. V-6, *Standard Cryogenic Liquid Transfer Connections.*

The following document is available from the American National Standards Institute, 1430 Broadway, New York, NY 10018.

ANSI Z79.11, *Anesthetic Equipment—Scavenging Systems for Excess Anesthetic Gases.*

GASES

Revised by Theodore C. Lemoff

The term "gas" describes the physical state of a substance that has no shape or volume of its own but will take the shape and fill the entire volume of whatever container or other enclosure it occupies. This is in contrast to a liquid, which has no shape of its own but does have volume, and to a solid, which has both its own shape and volume. Gases are composed of extremely minute particles in constant motion. This motion affects the properties and behavior of gases; e.g., the higher the temperature, the more rapid the motion.

This chapter presents a definition of the substance known as gas and then outlines the various ways gases are classified. The hazards that gases present in storage differ from those presented when gases escape—both kinds of hazards are discussed along with the control measures to follow in an emergency. The chapter concludes with a summary of the properties and behavior of some common gases. For each gas, information is provided about its classification, chemical properties, physical properties, usage, hazards inside containers, hazards when released from containment, and emergency control.

Additional information about gases can be found in the following chapters: Section 1, Chapter 5, "Explosions;" Section 2, Chapter 26, "Storage of Gases;" Section 3, Chapter 15, "Oxygen-Enriched Atmospheres;" Section 6, Chapter 18, "Special Systems for Explosion Damage Control;" and Section 5, Chapter 20, "Foam Extinguishing Agents and Systems."

GASES DEFINED

Because all substances can exist as gases, depending upon the temperature and pressure applied to them, the term "gas" as used in this chapter is applied only to substances that exist in the gaseous state at so-called "normal" temperature and pressure (NTP) conditions—approximately 70°F (21°C) and 14.7 psia (101 kPa). However, even at normal or near normal temperatures and pressures, many substances can exist as either liquids or gases. The term "gas" is not precisely defined in NFPA standards. However, NFPA standards partially define a flammable liquid as a liquid having a vapor pressure not exceeding 40 psia at 100°F (275 kPa at 38°C). For comparative purposes, any substance, or mixture of substances, that in its liquid state exerts a vapor pressure greater than 40 psia at 100°F (275 kPa at 38°C) can be considered a gas.

CLASSIFICATION OF GASES

Effective handling of the great number and variety of gases in commerce and in the environment requires that gases be classified. These classifications are based on certain common denominators that reflect the chemical and physical properties of gases and the primary uses of gases.

Classification by Chemical Properties

The chemical properties of gases are of primary fire protection concern due to their ability to react chemically with other materials (or within themselves) to produce potentially hazardous quantities of heat or reaction products, or to produce physiological effects hazardous to humans.

Flammable gases: In NFPA usage, any gas that will burn in the normal concentrations of oxygen in the air is considered a flammable gas. Flammable gases will burn in air the same way flammable liquid vapors burn in air, i.e., each gas will burn only within a certain range of gas-air mixture compositions (the flammable or combustible range) and will ignite only at or above a certain temperature (the ignition temperature).

In a few instances, consideration of the width of the flammable range or the magnitude of the lower limit of flammability or both has resulted in classification of an ostensibly flammable gas as nonflammable because the chances of fire are low under certain conditions. Anhydrous ammonia is notable in this respect. While it is a flammable gas in the context of the previous paragraph, it is classified by the U.S. Department of Transportation (DOT) as a nonflammable gas for purposes of transportation in interstate commerce.

Although flammable liquid vapors and flammable gases exhibit similar combustion characteristics, the term "flash point," which describes a common and useful combustion

Theodore C. Lemoff, P.E., is the gases engineer on the staff of NFPA.

property of flammable liquids, has no practical significance for flammable gases. The flash point is basically a measure of the temperature at which a flammable liquid produces sufficient vapors for combustion, and this temperature is always below the normal boiling point. A flammable gas exists normally at a temperature exceeding its normal boiling point, even when the gas is in the liquid state (as it often is in shipment and storage). Thus, the gas exists at a temperature that not only exceeds its flash point, but which is usually well above it.

Nonflammable gases: Nonflammable gases are those that will not burn in any concentration of air or oxygen. A number of these gases, however, support combustion while others suppress combustion. Those gases that support combustion are often referred to as oxidizers or oxidizing gases. They are generally either oxygen or mixtures of oxygen and other gases, such as oxygen-helium or oxygen-nitrogen mixtures, or certain gaseous oxides, such as nitrous oxide. These mixtures contain considerably more oxygen than is present in the oxygen-nitrogen mixture that comprises air.

Gases that will not support combustion are generally known as inert gases. Among the most common are nitrogen, argon, helium, and other rare gases in the atmosphere, as well as carbon dioxide and sulfur dioxide. (There are some metals, however, that are combustible and can react vigorously in carbon dioxide or nitrogen atmospheres, e.g., magnesium.)

Reactive gases: Most gases can be made to react chemically with some other substance under some conditions. Therefore, the term "reactive gas" is used to distinguish gases that will either react with other materials or within themselves (producing potentially hazardous quantities of heat or reaction products) by a chemical reaction other than burning (combustion) and under reasonably anticipated initiating conditions of environmental heat, shock, etc.

Fluorine is an example of a highly reactive gas, because it reacts with practically all organic and inorganic substances at normal temperatures and pressures, often fast enough to result in flaming. Another example is the reaction between chlorine (a nonflammable gas) and hydrogen (a flammable gas), which can produce flames.

Several gases can rearrange themselves chemically when subjected to reasonably anticipated conditions of environmental heat and shock, including fire exposure to their containers, with the production of potentially hazardous quantities of heat or reaction products. Examples of these gases are acetylene, methyl acetylene, propadiene, and vinyl chloride. For transport or storage, these gases are usually mixed with other substances or placed in special containers to stabilize them against reasonably anticipated reaction initiators.

Toxic gases: Certain gases can present a serious life hazard if they are released into the atmosphere. These gases, which are poisonous or irritating when inhaled or contacted, include chlorine, hydrogen sulfide, sulfur dioxide, ammonia, and carbon monoxide, among others. The presence of these gases may complicate fire fighting efforts by exposing fire fighters to toxic hazard.

Classification by Physical Properties

These properties are of primary fire protection concern because they affect the physical behavior of gases while they are inside containers and after any accidental release from containers. Until they are used, gases must be completely confined in containers during transportation, transfer, and storage. In any situation, the quantity (weight) of gas is important, since gases are inherently lighter than liquids or solids. It is a matter of practical economic necessity and the ease of usage that gases be packaged in containers that contain as much gas as is practical. These requirements have resulted in transportation and storage of gases in the liquid as well as the gaseous state. Distinguishing between gases in a liquid or gaseous state is important for the application of sound fire prevention and protection practices.

Compressed gases: For purposes of this chapter, a compressed gas is one that exists solely in the gaseous state under pressure at all normal atmospheric temperatures inside its container. The pressure depends on the pressure to which the container was originally charged, and on how much gas remains in the container, although the gas temperature will have some effect. There are no universally defined lower or upper limits to the container pressure. In the United States, the lower limit is customarily considered to be 25 psig (273 kPa) at normal temperatures [70 to 100°F (21 to 38°C)]. The upper limit is restricted only by the economics of container construction and is usually in the range of 1,800 to 3,600 psig (12 512 to 24 923 kPa).

A container of compressed gas is still rather limited in the weight of gas it can hold. For example, the largest common portable cylinder of compressed oxygen contains only about 20 lb (9 kg) of oxygen, or about 245 cu ft (6.9 m^3) of oxygen measured at NTP of 70°F (21°C) and 14.7 psia (101 kPa).

Liquefied gases: A liquefied gas is one that, at 70°F (21°C) inside its closed container, exists partly in the liquid state and partly in the gaseous state, and under pressure as long as any liquid remains in the container. The pressure depends on the temperature of the liquid, although the quantity of liquid can affect this under some conditions.

A liquefied gas is much more concentrated than a compressed gas. For example, the aforementioned compressed oxygen cylinder could hold about 116 lb (53 kg) of liquefied oxygen, or about 1,400 cu ft (39.6 m^3) of oxygen measured at NTP, which is about six times greater. This comparison is valid only for illustrative purposes, because compressed oxygen and liquefied oxygen will not be found in the same type of container.

Cryogenic gases: A cryogenic gas is a liquefied gas that exists in its container at temperatures below –130°F (–90°C). A principal reason for this distinction with respect to a liquefied gas is that a cryogenic gas cannot be retained indefinitely in a container. Heat from the atmosphere, which can be slowed but not prevented from entering the container, tends to continually raise the container pressure. If the gas is confined, the resulting pressure could greatly exceed any feasible container strength.

Some pertinent physical properties of liquefied gases, including cryogenic gases, are given in Table 3-7A. It is emphasized that these descriptions of gas classifications by physical properties pertain only to usage in context of this chapter. Somewhat different descriptions of the terms compressed gas, liquefied gas, and cryogenic gas can be found in codes and regulations, particularly the DOT hazardous materials regulations applicable to interstate transportation. For example, many liquefied gases are classified as compressed gases by the DOT.

TABLE 3-7A. ***Physical Properties of Cryogenic Gases***

(Compiled from data in the *Handbook of Compressed Gases*, Compressed Gas Association)

	Normal Boiling Point								Normal Conditions 70°F, 14.7 psi (21°C, 101 kPa)			
	Temp		Liquid Density		Gas Density		Latent Heat		Gas Density		Cu Ft Gas from 1 cu ft Liquid	m^3 Gas from 1 m^3 Liquid
Name	°F	°C	lb/cu ft	kg/m³	lb/cu ft	kg/m³	Btu/lb	kJ/kg	lb/cu ft	kg/m³		
Air	−317.8	−194.3	54.6	87.5	—	—	88.2	205.1	0.075	0.120	728	726
Argon	−302.6	−158.9	86.98	139.3	0.356	0.570	70.2	163.3	0.103	0.165	842	842
Carbon monoxide	−312.7	−191.5	51.12	81.9	—	—	92.8	215.8	0.073	0.117	706	706
Ethylene	−154.8	−103.7	35.4	56.7	0.130	0.208	208.0	483.8	0.072	0.115	487	487
Fluorine	−306.6	−188.1	94.1	150.7	0.363	0.581	74.1	172.3	0.098	0.160	961	961
Helium	−452.1	−268.9	7.8	12.5	0.106	0.170	10.3	23.9	0.01	0.016	754	754
Hydrogen	−423.0	−252.8	4.43	7.1	0.084	0.134	192.7	448.2	0.005	0.008	850	850
Methane	−258.7	−161.5	26.5	42.4	0.111	0.178	219.2	509.8	0.042	0.067	636	636
Nitrogen	−320.4	−195.8	50.46	80.8	0.288	0.461	85.7	199.3	0.072	0.115	696	696
Oxygen	−297.4	−183.0	71.27	114.2	0.296	0.474	91.7	213.3	0.083	0.133	861	861

Classification by Usage

Standard- and code-making organizations and general industry often classify gases by their principal use. This classification scheme is not as precise as the preceding scheme, and there is much overlap in uses with the gases.

Fuel gases: These gases are flammable gases customarily used for burning with air to produce heat, which in turn is used as a source of heat (comfort and process), power, or light. By far the principal and most widely used fuel gases are natural gas and the liquefied petroleum gases (butane and propane).

Industrial gases: These include the entire range of gases classified by chemical properties customarily used in industrial processes, for welding and cutting, heat treating, chemical processing, refrigeration, water treatment, etc.

Medical gases: By far the most specialized usage classification, medical gases are used for medical purposes, such as anesthesia and respiratory therapy. Oxygen and nitrous oxide are common medical gases.

BASIC HAZARDS OF GASES

A systematic evaluation of gas hazards distinguishes between the hazards presented by a gas when it is confined in a container and the hazards presented when it escapes from a container—even though both of these hazards may be simultaneously present in a single incident.

Hazards within Containers

Gases expand when heated, producing an increase in pressure on a container, which can result in gas release and/or cause container failure. In addition, containers can lose their strength and fail during a fire. Compressed and liquefied gases are affected somewhat differently when heated.

A compressed gas (solely in the gaseous state) simply attempts to expand and follow the classic gas behavior laws. No actual gas follows these laws exactly, but the laws of Boyle and Charles are sufficiently accurate to predict the behavior of compressed gases under commonly encountered conditions. It is essential, however, that a consistent set of U.S. customary or SI units be used in calculations using the "absolute" values for temperature and pressure. In the formulas, T = absolute temperature (deg F + 459; or deg C + 273), P = absolute pressure (gage pressure in lb per sq in. + 14.7 psi; or kPa), and V = volume in cu ft or m^3 or any other suitable unit of volume.

Boyle's Law

Boyle's Law states that the volume occupied by a given mass of gas varies inversely with the absolute pressure if the temperature is not allowed to change, or

$$PV = \text{constant}$$

Charles' Law

Charles' Law states that the volume of a given mass of gas is directly proportional to the absolute temperature if the pressure is kept constant. Thus:

$$\frac{V}{T} = \text{constant}$$

Therefore, for most gases, within practical working limits, the relation among temperature, pressure, and volume may be closely approximated by the following formula:

$$\frac{T_1}{T_2} = \frac{P_1 \times V_1}{P_2 \times V_1}$$

T_1, P_1, and V_1 refer to initial conditions; T_2, P_2, and V_2 refer to changed conditions to be determined.

Example 1: Assume a 10 cu ft cylinder of compressed gas at 70°F has a gage pressure of 1000 psi. Assume that the temperature is increased to 150°F. What will be the pressure?

$T_1 = 70 + 459 = 529$
$P_1 = 1000 + 14.7 = 1014.7$
$V_1 = 10$
$T_2 = 150 + 459 = 609$
$P_2 =$ to be determined
$V_2 = 10$

Substituting in the formula:

$$\frac{529}{609} = \frac{1014.7 \times 10}{P_2 \times 10}$$

$$P_2 = 1014.7 \times \frac{609}{529} = 1170$$

Therefore, gage pressure will be 1170 – 14.7, or 1155.3 psi.

Example 2: Assume a 2.0 m^3 cylinder of compressed gas at 20°C has a gage pressure of 1200 kPa. Assume that the gas is further compressed into a 1.0 m^3 cylinder and maintained at 50°C. What will be the gage pressure?

$T_1 = 20 + 273 = 293$
$P_1 = 1200 + 101 = 1301$
$V_1 = 2.0$
$T_2 = 50 + 273 = 323$
$P_2 =$ to be determined
$V_2 = 1.0$

Substituting in the formula:

$$\frac{293}{323} = \frac{1301 \times 2.0}{P_2 \times 1.0}$$

$$P_2 = 2868$$

A liquefied gas, including a cryogenic gas (which is partly in the liquid state), exhibits a more complicated behavior because the net end result of heating is the combination of three effects. First, the gas phase is subject to the same effect as for a compressed gas. Second, the liquid attempts to expand, compressing the vapor. Third, the vapor pressure of the liquid increases as the temperature of the liquid increases. The combined result of these effects is an increase in pressure when the container is heated.

A most serious pressure rise can occur if the liquid expansion results in the container becoming full of liquid (the initial gas-phase condensing). If this happens, a small amount of additional heating results in a large increase in pressure. For this reason, it is *vital* never to place more liquefied gas in the liquid phase into a container than can be accommodated—leaving a vapor space—if the liquid temperature is raised to a level commensurate with the expected ambient temperatures. The proper quantity varies considerably with the liquefied gas and the factors that affect expected temperature rises, such as the temperature of the liquid when placed into the container, the size of the container, and whether the container is insulated or installed above or below ground. The quantities permitted are commonly expressed as "filling densities" or "loading densities" and are specified for specific gases (in some cases, groupings of similar gases) by codes, standards, and regulations. Filling densities expressed in terms of weight are absolute values, i.e., the designated weight of gas may always be placed into the container. Filling densities expressed in terms of volume, however, must always be qualified by specifying the liquid temperature.

Table 3-7B shows an example of how filling densities are expressed for liquefied gases—in this case, liquefied petroleum gases stored at normal temperatures in uninsulated containers. Note that larger quantities of higher specific gravity materials are permitted (reflecting the fact that these liquids tend to expand less) and that larger containers can be filled more than smaller ones can (reflecting the fact that it takes longer for them to absorb heat from atmospheric temperatures or solar radiation). Also, underground containers can be filled even more (reflecting the fact that their ambient temperatures are relatively constant and well below summer atmospheric temperatures).

Containers of compressed or liquefied gases can represent high levels of potential energy release due to the concentration of matter by compression or liquefaction. Container failure releases this energy—often extremely rapidly and violently—with a simultaneous release of gas to the surroundings and propulsion of the container or container pieces. Compressed gas container failures are distinguished more by the flying missile hazard than by the results of gas release, because these containers contain lesser quantities of gas. Liquefied gas container failures can release larger quantities of gas.

Overpressure Relief Devices

Spring-loaded pressure-relief valves or bursting discs, or sometimes both, are provided on most compressed and liquefied gas containers to limit container pressure to a level the container can safely withstand, although fusible plugs are sometimes used on smaller containers. The start-to-discharge pressure settings of these devices are related to the strength of the container. In most cases, the relieving capacity (in terms of gas flow rate through them) is based upon consideration of heat input rates resulting from fire exposure, because this is generally the largest anticipated source of heat. In some instances, such as underground or insulated containers, other sources of overpressure may be the dominant effect of fire exposure.

As noted, the relieving capacity of these devices is based upon discharge of gas. In the case of liquefied gas containers exposed to fire, it is possible to have conditions such that liquid will be discharged instead of gas, i.e., when the container is tipped over. Under such conditions, the relieving capacity will be reduced—in some cases as much as 60 to 70 percent. With the possible exception of the fire exposure condition, this reduction is of little practical significance. Even in the case of fire exposure, this situation is not as critical as it may appear, because prevention of container failure under fire exposure conditions requires other safeguards in addition to the overpressure relief device.

Instances of failure of overpressure devices are rather rare, even though inspection, maintenance, and replacement of these devices are essentially unregulated and they are subject to potentially harmful influences.

Containers of certain poisonous and highly toxic gases do not have overpressure relief devices, because the overall hazard of a prematurely operating or leaking relief device outweighs the hazard of container failure from overpressure. It is also the practice in some countries, especially in Asia and the Mediterranean area, not to provide overpressure protection on liquefied gas containers—a practice that reflects the widespread use and installation of such containers inside buildings, including homes, and commer-

TABLE 3-7B. ***Maximum Permitted Filling Density***

(LP Gas Stored at Normal Temperatures in Uninsulated Containers)

	Above ground Containers					
	0 to 1,200 gal.*		Over 1,200 gal.*		All Underground Containers	
Specific Gravity at 60°F (15.6°C)	% of WWC†	Vol. % at 60°F‡	% of WWC†	Vol. % at 60°F‡	% of WWC†	Vol. % at 60°F‡
0.496—0.503	41	82.0	44	88.0	45	90.0
0.504—0.510	42	82.6	45	88.5	46	90.5
0.511—0.519	43	83.5	46	89.4	47	91.3
0.520—0.527	44	84.3	47	90.0	48	91.8
0.528—0.536	45	84.7	48	90.3	49	92.2
0.537—0.544	46	85.2	49	90.7	50	92.5
0.545—0.552	47	85.6	50	91.2	51	93.0
0.553—0.560	48	86.4	51	91.8	52	93.6
0.561—0.568	49	87.0	52	92.3	53	94.1
0.569—0.576	50	87.5	53	92.7	54	94.4
0.577—0.584	51	87.9	54	93.1	55	94.8
0.585—0.592	52	88.3	55	93.5	56	95.1
0.593—0.600	53	88.9	56	94.0	57	95.6

* Total water capacity, U.S. gallons (1200 U.S. gallons equals 4.54 m3)
† WWC—water weight capacity
‡ 60°F = 15.6°C

cial and institutional buildings. In such cases, the hazard of gas release indoors due to operation of the relief device is felt to outweigh the hazard of container failure due to overpressure.

The Liquefied Gas BLEVE

Instances where containers of liquefied gases fail and break into two or more pieces are common enough to warrant treatment in some detail. This failure is termed "boiling liquid expanding vapor explosion" (BLEVE), a type of pressure-release explosion.

All liquefied gases are stored in containers at temperatures above their boiling points at NTP and remain under pressure only so long as the container remains closed to the atmosphere. This pressure ranges from less than 1 psi (6.895 kPa) for some cryogenic gas containers to several hundred psi (kPa) for noncryogenic liquefied gas containers at normal storage temperatures. If the pressure is reduced to atmospheric, such as through container failure, the substantial heat that is in effect "stored" in the liquid causes very rapid vaporization of a portion of the liquid, to a degree directly proportional to the temperature difference between that of the liquid at the instant of container failure and the normal boiling point of the liquid. For many liquefied flammable gases, this temperature difference at normal atmospheric temperatures can result in vaporization of about one third of the liquid in the container.

Because overpressure relief devices are set to discharge at pressures corresponding to liquid temperatures above normal atmospheric temperatures (to prevent premature operation), the liquid temperature is higher than this if container failure occurs when a relief device is functioning. Therefore, more liquid is vaporized under these conditions—often over one half of the liquid in the container. This is the usual situation when a container fails from fire exposure. The remaining liquid unvaporized is cooled by the "self-extraction" of heat when the pressure is reduced to atmospheric and is cooled to near its normal boiling point.

Liquid vaporization is accompanied by a large liquid-to-vapor expansion. (See Table 3-7A.) It is this expansion process which provides the energy for propagation of cracks in the container structure, propulsion of pieces of the container, rapid mixing of the vapor and air resulting in the characteristic fireball upon ignition by the fire which caused the BLEVE, and atomization of the remaining cold liquid. Many of the atomized droplets burn as they fly through the air. However, it is not uncommon for the cold liquid to be propelled from the fire zone too quickly for ignition to occur and fall to Earth still in liquid form. In one case, dissolved spots in asphalt paving were noted up to ½ mile (0.8 km) from the site of an LP-Gas BLEVE. In other BLEVEs, fire fighters have been cooled by cold liquid passing in their vicinity.

Reduction of internal pressure to atmospheric level in a container results from structural failure of the container. Failure is most often due to weakening of the container metal from flame contact; however, this will happen if the container is punctured or fails for any other reason.

As shown in Figure 3-7A, the strength of carbon steel steadily decreases with temperature increases above about 400°F (204°C). Figure 3-7A is based upon a typical low-carbon steel. The curves will vary quantitatively with other steels, but the loss of strength with increasing temperature is valid for all common metals, and the critical temperatures are well below those attainable in a fire.

Figure 3-7A also shows why entirely satisfactory performance of a spring-loaded relief valve to design parameters cannot prevent a BLEVE. By its nature, such a valve cannot reduce the pressure to atmospheric but only to a point somewhat below its start-to-discharge pressure. Therefore, the liquid will always be at a temperature above its normal boiling point, pressure will remain inside the container, and the container structure will be stressed in tension. This stressed area is shown as a shaded area in Figure 3-7A for a common type of LP-Gas container having a pressure-relief valve set for 250 psi (172 kPa). Again, while this area will vary for different steels or pressure vessel relief valve design characteristics, it is evident that if the metal is heated above this range (which is quite possible in the event of direct flame contact), the metal will not withstand the stress and the container will fail.

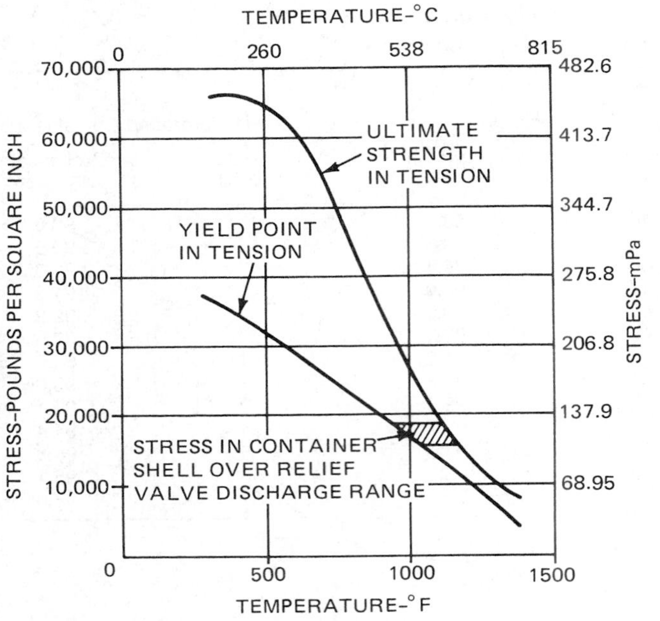

FIG. 3-7A. Behavior of liquefied gas container metal (carbon steel) when exposed to fire.

It is extremely difficult to significantly heat the container metal where it is in contact with liquid because the liquid conducts the heat away from the metal and acts as a heat absorber. For example, when the relief valve cited in this example is discharging, the propane liquid stays in the 120 to 140°F (49 to 60°C) range. As a result, the metal temperature is well within safe limits. This situation does not exist for the metal in the vapor space of the container, as vapor is relatively nonheat conductive and has little heat-absorbing capacity.

In most BLEVEs where the failure is due to metal overheating, it originates in the metal of the vapor space, and is characterized by both the metal stretching and thinning out and the appearance of a longitudinal tear which progressively gets larger until a critical length is reached. At this time, the failure becomes brittle in nature and propagates at sonic velocity through the metal in both longitudinal and circumferential directions. As a result, the container comes apart in two or more pieces.

Magnitude of a BLEVE: Although most liquefied gas BLEVEs that involve container failure result from fire exposure, a few BLEVEs have occurred due to container failures from other causes, such as corrosion or impact from an outside force. Impact failures are particularly noticeable in transportation accidents involving railcars and cargo vehicles. In these cases, the BLEVE generally occurs simultaneously with impact. In one instance, however, a 30,000-gal (113.5 m^3) tank car of LP-Gas was only severely weakened by impact during derailment and did not BLEVE until more than 40 hrs later. The tank car had been lifted and moved without incident in the interim. At the time of failure, however, the internal pressure was increasing as the ambient temperature was rising.

The size of a BLEVE depends basically upon the weight of the container pieces and upon how much liquid vaporizes when the container fails. This is analogous in many respects to the performance of rockets, as far as propulsion of container parts is concerned. Most liquefied gas BLEVEs occur when containers are from slightly less than ½ to about ¾ full of liquid. The liquid vaporization-expansion-energy to container-piece weight ratio is such that pieces are propelled for distances up to approximately ½ mile (0.8 km). Deaths from such missiles have occurred up to 800 ft (244 m) from larger containers. Fireballs several hundred feet in diameter are not uncommon, and deaths from burns have occurred to persons as much as 250 ft (76 m) from the larger containers.

A major LP-Gas disaster with multiple BLEVEs occurred on November 19, 1984, near Mexico City, Mexico. According to a Swedish investigator who cooperated with the NFPA, and contrary to earlier published reports, this incident occurred at about 5:00 a.m. on a Monday while the terminal was being filled by pipeline from a refinery in another part of the country. A failure in a component of the 12-in. (25.4 mm) fill line resulted in a line break and the development of a large LP-Gas cloud which ignited upon reaching a ground-level flare about 20 minutes later. The resulting explosion and fire is believed to have been the major factor in the 500 deaths reported. The flame issuing from the broken pipeline impinged on one of the four 10,000-barrel (1590 m^3) spheres which BLEVEd about 10 minutes later. In all, approximately 15 BLEVEs were noted on seismic charts among the four 10,000-barrel (1590 m^3) spheres and 48 horizontal tanks.

The two 15,000-barrel (2384 m^3) spheres remained on their foundations, but were severely damaged. (See Figure 3-7B.) The four 10,000-barrel (1590 m^3) spheres were found in pieces both on and off the terminal site. All 48 horizontal tanks were damaged in varying degrees, with major sections as far as 3,600 ft (1.1 km) from the site. Figure 3-7C illustrates the spectacular dimensions a BLEVE can reach.

FIG. 3-7B. Two of the 15,000-barrel (2384 m^3) spheres involved in the Mexico City LP-Gas disaster. Note how far out of vertical they are. This is due to partial failure of the container supports.

Time intervals for fire-caused BLEVEs: The time between initiation of flame contact and a BLEVE varies because it depends upon such widely varying factors as the size and nature of the fire as well as the container itself. Uninsulated containers located aboveground can BLEVE in the absence of water cooling in a matter of a very few

FIG. 3-7C. The fireball formed in a BLEVE involving LP-Gas railroad tank cars at Crescent City, IL, on June 21, 1970. The elevated water tank at center is a point of reference in visualizing the dimensions of the fireball.

minutes in the case of small containers to a few hours for very large containers. A study of such LP-Gas storage containers, ranging in size from 1,000 to 30,000 gal (3.8 to 113 m^3), showed a time range from 8 to 30 min, with 58 percent occurring in 15 min or less. Data on insulated containers is meager because only cryogenic containers and some reactive-gas containers are usually insulated. However, there is no doubt that insulation designed for fire-exposure conditions can delay BLEVE times significantly. In one case involving an insulated LP-Gas railroad tank car, the BLEVE did not occur until 20½ hr of fire exposure—undoubtedly an extreme example. In comparison, using fire tests on LP-Gas railroad tank cars, a BLEVE occurred in 93 min in the insulated case, as opposed to 25 min for the uninsulated tank.

Protection against a BLEVE: Protection for an uninsulated liquefied gas container that may be exposed to fire is provided by the application of water so that a film of water coats portions of the container not in internal contact with liquid. The methods used can range from hose streams to installation of water spray fixed systems.

The preceding data on BLEVE magnitude, time intervals, and protection is applicable only to unreactive liquefied flammable gases. The additional chemical energy in reactive gases introduces chemical factors not present in the purely physical and combustion phenomena just described, even though the outward appearance and general effects are similar. The hazard can be increased by evolution of internal heat of chemical reaction (which adds to the heat from the exposing fire) and the inability of externally applied cooling water to cool the liquid inside the container.

Combustion within Containers

A less frequent but significant hazard of gas stored in containers is the danger of container failure from overpressure, resulting from combustion of the gas while inside the container. Flammable gas-air or gas-oxygen mixtures are seldom intentionally provided in containers, but can be established accidentally. Most of these explosions have occurred in industrial and medical gas applications where oxygen or compressed air is often used in conjunction with flammable gases. Where such a possibility is inherent in a process, e.g., an oxygen-fuel gas metal cutting system, provisions are made to prevent the occurrence of such mixtures in containers. More generally, most explosions can be prevented by education and training in proper container filling procedures. Consumers of industrial and medical gases seldom have the expertise needed to fill containers safely.

Combustion when Released from Containers

When gases are released from their containers, the hazards vary according to the chemical and physical properties of the gas and the nature of the environment into which they are released. All gases, with the exception of oxygen and air, present a hazard to life if they displace the breathing air. Nitrogen, helium, argon, and other odorless and colorless gases are particularly hazardous, because they are not detectable by the human senses. The minimum oxygen concentration in air for survival is about 6 to 10 percent (compared with the normal 21 percent) by volume, but even at higher concentrations judgment and coordination are affected.

Toxic or poisonous gases: These gases present obvious life hazards. They are especially dangerous when released during a fire because they can impede fire fighting efforts by either preventing or delaying access to the site by fire fighters.

Oxygen and other oxidizing gases: Although these gases are nonflammable, they can make combustibles ignite at lower temperatures, accelerate combustion, and start fires by causing flames in fuel-burning appliances to extend beyond their combustion chambers.

Liquefied gases, including cryogenic gases: Because of their low temperatures, these gases present a hazard to persons and property when they escape as liquids. Contact with cold liquid can cause frostbite which can be severe if the exposure is prolonged. The properties of many structural materials, particularly carbon steel and plastics, are affected by low temperatures and embrittlement, which could lead to structural failure.

Flammable gases: Because of their prevalence, the behavior of flammable gases when released from their containers is of major interest. Released flammable gases present two basic hazards: (1) combustion explosions, and (2) fire. Failure to distinguish between the circumstances surrounding these two hazards can result in misapplication of protective measures.

Combustion Explosions

It is useful to consider a flammable gas combustion explosion as occurring in the following sequence:

1. A flammable gas or the liquid phase of a liquefied flammable gas is released from its container, piping, or equipment (including the normal operation of an overpressure relief device). If liquid escapes, it rapidly vaporizes and produces the potentially large quantities of vapor associated with this liquid-to-vapor transition.
2. The gas mixes with the air.

TABLE 3-7C. ***Combustion Properties of Common Flammable Gases***

Gas	Btu per Cu Ft (Gross)	MJ/m^3 (Gross)	Limits of Flammability Percent by Volume in Air		Specific Gravity (Air = 1.0)	Air Needed to Burn 1 Cu Ft of Gas Cu Ft	Air Needed to Burn 1 m^3 of Gas m^3	Ignition Temp	
			Lower	Upper				°F	°C
Natural gas									
High inert type *(Note 1)*	958–1051	35.7–39.2	4.5	14.0	.660–.708	9.2	9.2	—	—
High methane type *(Note 2)*	1008–1071	37.6–39.9	4.7	15.0	.590–.614	10.2	10.2	900–1170	482–632
High Btu type *(Note 3)(*	1071–1124	39.9–41.9	4.7	14.5	.620–.719	9.4	9.4	—	—
Blast furnace gas	81–111	3.0–4.1	33.2	71.3	1.04–1.00	0.8	0.8	—	—
Coke oven gas	575	21.4	4.4	34.0	.38	4.7	4.7	—	—
Propane (commercial)	2516	93.7	2.15	9.6	1.52	24.0	24.0	920–1120	493–604
Butane (commercial)	3300	122.9	1.9	8.5	2.0	31.0	31.0	900–1000	482–538
Sewage gas	670	24.9	6.0	17.0	0.79	6.5	6.5	—	—
Acetylene	1499	55.8	2.5	81.0	0.91	11.9	11.9	581	305
Hydrogen	325	12.1	4.0	75.0	0.07	2.4	2.4	932	500
Anhydrous ammonia	386	14.4	16.0	25.0	0.60	8.3	8.3	1204	651
Carbon monoxide	314	11.7	12.5	74.0	0.97	2.4	2.4	1128	609
Ethylene	1600	59.6	2.7	36.0	0.98	14.3	14.3	914	490
Methylacetylene, propadiene, stabilized *(Note 4)*	2450	91.3	3.4	10.8	1.48	—	—	850	454

Note 1: Typical composition CH_4 71.9–83.2%; N_2 6.3–16.20%
Note 2: Typical composition CH_4 87.6–95.7; N_2 0.1–2.39
Note 3: Typical composition CH_4 85.0–90.1; N_2 1.2–7.5
Note 4: MAPPd Gas

3. With certain proportions of gas and air (in the flammable or combustible range), the mixture is ignitable and will burn. (See Table 3-7C.)
4. When ignited, the flammable mixture burns rapidly and produces heat rapidly.
5. The heat is absorbed by everything in the vicinity of the flame and by the very hot gaseous combustion products.
6. Nearly all materials expand when they absorb heat. The one material in the vicinity of the flame or hot gaseous combustion products that expands most when it is heated is air. Referring to the "gas laws" cited earlier in this chapter, it will be noted that air expands to double its original volume for every 459°F (237°C) it is heated.
7. If the heated air is not free to expand because, for example, it is confined in a room, the result is a rise in pressure in the room.
8. If the room structure is not strong enough to withstand the pressure, some part of the room will suddenly and abruptly move and depart from its original position, and a bang, woosh, boom, or other noise will be heard. This activity, in part, describes an explosion. Because the source of pressure is combustion, this kind of explosion is called a combustion explosion. It is also called less accurately a room explosion or vapor-air explosion.

A combustion explosion requires that a quantity of flammable gas-air mixture accumulates in an enclosure. In addition, the quantity/strength-of-enclosure relationship must be such that the strength of some part of the enclosure must be exceeded by the pressure-building potential of the mixture. If the enclosure is strong enough to withstand the pressure, a combustion explosion could not occur, because it is the manner in which the enclosure performs that basically determines whether such an explosion occurs. However, few enclosures are strong enough to withstand such pressure.

If an enclosure was full of a flammable gas-air mixture at atmospheric pressure, the enclosure would have to withstand about 60 to 110 psi (400 to 750 kPa) in order to remain intact to prevent a combustion explosion. If a reactive flammable gas is involved or oxygen enrichment occurs, even higher pressures are possible. Conventional structures are capable of withstanding pressures only in the order of ½ to 1 psi (3.5 to 7 kPa). This wide pressure disparity shows clearly that conventional structural enclosures are vulnerable even if they are not full of a flammable gas-air mixture. Experience supports this conclusion, and it has been estimated that most combustion explosions of conventional structures occur with less than 25 percent of the enclosure occupied by the flammable mixture. This fact should not be overlooked—it is erroneous to assume that a flammable gas-air mixture needs to completely fill a room or building before an explosion can occur.

The mechanics of gas accumulation in a structure are affected by the rate of gas release, whether the gas is in the liquid or gas phase, the density of the gas, and the ventilation in the structure. Classic diffusion laws are of little significance under actual conditions, because the combination of extremely slow release rates and airtight structures seldom happens. For this reason, and the fact that most flammable gas-air mixtures are about 90 percent air and, thus, have about the same density as air, the density of the gas itself (i.e., whether it is lighter or heavier than air) is seldom a significant factor in gas combustion explosions involving structures.

Due to the large and rapid flammable gas-air mixture potential of liquefied gases, codes and standards impose severe limitations on the handling of such gases indoors. Considering the fireball aspect of the BLEVE, it is evident that an indoor fireball behaves similarly to an ignited gas-air mixture accumulation; the results of a BLEVE of a container located indoors can be very similar to a combustion explosion.

Combustion Explosion Safeguards

Basic combustion explosion prevention safeguards are designed to limit flammable gas-air mixture accumulation in a structure. Fundamental safeguards are the use of rugged containers and equipment that minimize the chance of leakage, the minimal quantity of gas released by emergency flow control devices, and the use of limiting orifices to minimize the quantity released. Burners are often equipped with flame failure devices that shut off the flow of gas if the flame is extinguished for any reason.

Many gases are colorless and odorless, and it is common to odorize the more widely used fuel gases to increase chances of leak detection. This is particularly true for the common fuel gases, e.g., natural gas and LP-Gas. Codes, standards, and regulations customarily require that these gases be odorized so that they are detectable by humans at gas concentrations in air not exceeding one fifth of the lower limit of flammability. The odorants are usually volatile organic liquids containing chemically combined sulfur and have a characteristic "gassy" odor.

While it is an effective safeguard, odorization has limitations. The functioning detector, i.e., a human's sense of smell, is not always present, such as when the premises are vacant or the occupants are asleep. In addition, all odors deaden the sense of smell if inhaled long enough, and senses of smell vary. Odorants can be scrubbed from the gas by some soils, a factor where leakage stems from underground piping. Mixture accumulations can also be limited by ventilation systems in structures. These systems, however, are usually in industrial operations, and even then only rather nominal release rates can be handled by practical ventilation systems because of the necessity to condition the makeup ventilation air for comfort purposes.

Ignition source control is also fundamental to combustion explosion prevention. However, this safeguard is also limited mainly to industrial operations where the many flammable gases burned in heat-producing equipment provide an inherent ignition source.

In addition to combustion explosion prevention safeguards, the severity of the explosion can be reduced by special structural design whereby some elements of the structure are designed to dislocate at lower pressures, and other elements are designed to stay in place at the lower pressures which result. This is known as "explosion venting" and is covered in some detail in NFPA 68, *Explosion Venting.* Such building design is not practical for most ordinary buildings, however, so this practice is essentially restricted to certain industrial structures.

Flammable gas fires: The flammable gas fire can be considered as an aborted combustion explosion wherein an explosive quantity of flammable gas-air mixture does not accumulate because the mixture is either ignited too quickly or a confining structure is not present. As would be expected when flammable gas escapes outdoors, fires usually occur. However, if a massive release occurs, it is possible for the air or surrounding buildings to comprise enough confinement to lead to a type of combustion explosion known as an open-air explosion or space explosion. Liquefied noncryogenic gases are subject to this phenomenon, as are hydrogen, ethylene, and some reactive gases that have an extremely rapid rate of flame propagation. An example of the intentional provision of prompt ignition to achieve a fire instead of a combustion explosion is the use of pilots in gas-burning equipment, such as range ovens, water heaters, boilers, and furnaces.

Gas fire prevention safeguards include many of the combustion explosion prevention safeguards. However, unlike the combustion explosion, the destructive effects of the gas fire can be minimized by control measures applied after the fact.

GAS EMERGENCY CONTROL

Controllable gas emergencies resulting from the escape of gas from containers present two basic forms of hazard: (1) toxic, inert, or oxidizing gases can present hazards to persons or property and unignited flammable gases can be ignited, possibly explosively ("no fire" emergencies); and (2) gas fires can present thermal hazards to persons or property ("fire" emergencies) and, if such fires expose gas containers, introduce the possibility of container failure and the BLEVE. A fire in any combustible material also presents the hazard of container failure from fire exposure.

Control of "No Fire" Emergencies

Control generally consists of directing, diluting, and dispersing the gas to prevent contact with persons, preventing it from infiltrating structures if release is outdoors, and avoiding its contact with ignition sources while, if possible, simultaneously stopping the flow of escaping gas. Gas direction, dilution, and dispersion require the use of a carrier fluid; air, steam, and water have proved to be practical. The use of air, for all practical purposes, is limited to indoor situations and is an extension of the ventilation safeguards against a combustion explosion. Steam has been distributed through systems of fixed nozzles around outdoor ethylene processing equipment and where the large quantities of needed steam are available.

Water in the form of a spray, applied from hoses or monitor nozzles or by fixed water spray systems, is the most common carrier fluid. The use of hose streams is largely a fire department operation because of the personnel requirements. Fixed water spray systems for this purpose are designed differently from the more conventional spray systems used to control fire. To date, such systems have been provided at a few outdoor ethylene and liquefied natural gas (LNG) facilities. When water is used on cryogenic liquid containers, care must be taken to ensure that water does not contact the pressure-relief valve, as it can easily freeze and defeat the operation of this important safety device.

The physical properties of the escaping gas affect control techniques. With compressed gases, the density of the gas is an important factor. When such gases are colorless and odorless, control tactics may be complicated because instruments may be needed to define the extent of the hazardous area.

Liquefied gases possess an inherent visible indicator of their location, because the refrigerating effect of their vaporization condenses water vapor from the air and produces a visible fog. The fog roughly defines the gas area, but invisible ignitible gas-air mixtures often extend for several feet (1 ft = 0.3 m) beyond the extremities of the visible fog.

Because noncryogenic liquefied gases contain considerable heat for vaporization, they will often vaporize so rapidly from contact with the air or ground that they will not exist in the liquid phase once they escape—at least not to the extent that a pool will form. The lower vapor pressure noncryogenic liquefied gases, such as butane and chlorine, and those with high latent heats of vaporization, such as anhydrous ammonia, are exceptions. Even the higher vapor pressure gases, such as propane, will pool when ambient temperatures are well below freezing.

The cryogenic liquefied gases, on the other hand, must obtain nearly all the heat for vaporization from ground or air contact and, therefore, will characteristically form a pool if the leak continues for a long enough time. In such cases, application of a carrier fluid will increase the vaporization rate if applied to the liquid—an often undesirable effect.

The gas produced near the source of vaporization of a liquefied gas is always heavier than air at normal temperatures because of the low temperature of the gas at that point. This, together with the associated water fog, tends to cause even normally lighter-than-air gases to hug the ground for some distance.

The use of foam, particularly high-expansion foam, to control the flow of gas produced by a vaporizing cryogenic gas which is lighter than air at ambient temperatures, has been investigated to some extent. A sufficiently thick blanket of foam can warm the gas to the point where it will rise above the blanket instead of flowing horizontally near the ground. However, this is applicable only to established pools of vaporizing liquid and not to the initial high vaporization rate escape phase.

Some gases will react chemically with the carrier fluid—particularly if the carrier is steam or water. Chlorine is a notable example—the reaction produces hydrochloric acid. However, the principal problem in this respect is enlargement of the leak as the metal container reacts with the acid.

A special type of "no fire" control for indoor application to flammable gases is the explosion suppression system. Actually, such systems do permit ignition to occur but arrest the combustion of the flammable gas-air mixture before the pressure needed for a combustion explosion is obtained.

Control of "Fire" Emergencies

Control of fire emergencies is generally the control of heat from the fire by the application of water while, if possible, stopping the flow of escaping gas. Many gas fires can be extinguished by conventional extinguishing agents, including carbon dioxide, dry chemical, and the halogenated agents. However, the potential conversion of a gas fire into a combustion explosion if gas continues to escape after extinguishment must be recognized. The generally accepted practice is to limit actual extinguishment by agent application to small leaks that will not present a hazard if they reignite. In addition, the use of halogenated agents is being phased out because of their detrimental effect on Earth's ozone layer.

Methods of water application are the same as described for the "no fire" emergencies, i.e., hose streams, monitor nozzle streams, and fixed water spray systems, as well as sprinkler systems. The selection of the particular application method, or combination of methods, requires a sound fire protection analysis of the existing conditions. This is particularly true where water is used to prevent a BLEVE because of the limited time available if uninsulated containers are involved. This, together with the specialized tactics needed for safety of emergency personnel, has been shown to severely tax the capabilities of hose stream application in many instances. Manual actuation of fixed systems (water spray or sprinkler) that have nozzles and dry piping in the fire area is questionable, because the immediate intensity of a gas fire can quickly damage the piping before the water is turned on.

Conventional automatic sprinkler protection is limited to indoor or roofed-over areas. However, sprinklers have been effective in greatly reducing the number of overpressure relief devices on cylinders that operate during a fire. In turn, the number of cylinders that may fail from contact with the burning relief device effluents is reduced; sprinkler spacing and water density must be tailored to this hazard.

Foam can control a fire in a pool or tank of cryogenic gas, but cannot extinguish it. The degree of control depends upon the extent to which the foam can cover the liquid and the length of time the foam application can be maintained.

SPECIFIC GASES

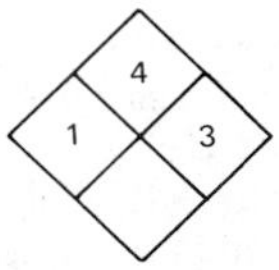

UN#1001

Acetylene

Classifications: Reactive, flammable, compressed, industrial.

Chemical properties: Acetylene is comprised of carbon and hydrogen joined by a triple chemical bond which is responsible for its reactivity. In the liquid or solid states, or in the gaseous state at moderate or high pressures, acetylene can decompose rapidly with the formation of carbon and hydrogen and evolution of heat. Decomposition can be initiated by heat. Decomposition of liquid or solid acetylene also can be initiated by mechanical impact. In a confined space, the heated decomposition gases can cause overpressure and container, piping, or equipment failure.

As an indication that a hazardous, heat-producing reaction can occur in the absence of air, an upper flammable limit of 100 percent is often found in the literature, rather than the 81 percent given in Table 3-7C. This technical misapplication of the flammable range concept has caused confusion.

Acetylene can react with certain metals to produce metallic acetylides, extremely shock-sensitive explosive compounds which, if detonated even in small quantities, can initiate acetylene decomposition. Copper and some copper alloys are notable in this respect, and their use must be avoided in most acetylene piping and equipment. However, these metals can be used in some components of acetylene systems under certain conditions that reflect the reaction kinetics involved. Torch tips, for example, fall into this category.

Acetylene is not toxic and has been used as an anesthetic. Pure acetylene is odorless, but acetylene in general use has a characteristic odor due to minor impurities inherent in its generation from calcium carbide or derivation from other hydrocarbons.

Physical properties: Although acetylene is considered a compressed gas, the usual acetylene container used in transportation and storage does not exclusively contain acetylene in the gaseous phase and is unique in this respect. To ensure stability under reasonably anticipated thermal and mechanical impact conditions, acetylene cylinders are filled with a porous-mass packing material containing very small pores or cellular spaces so that any volume of gas therein is correspondingly small. This limits the decomposition energy available and restricts communication between spaces. In addition, the mass is saturated with acetone—a flammable liquid in which acetylene is very soluble. In this manner, acetylene gas can be compressed in solution in a manner similar to that of carbon dioxide in water to produce carbonated water. When the pressure is reduced, e.g., by opening a cylinder valve, the gas escapes from solution and thus leaves the container in the gaseous state. Currently, a charging pressure maximum of 250 psig at 70°F (1724 kPa at 21°C) is recognized by DOT and the Canadian Transport Commission (CTC) regulations. There will be a variation of about 2.5 psig rise or fall per °F of temperature change (9 kPa per 1°C). For each atmosphere (14.7 psi or 101.3 kPa) of pressure, acetone will dissolve about 25 times its own volume of acetylene so that at 250 psig (1724 kPa) acetone will dissolve about 425 volumes of acetylene.

An acetylene cylinder is illustrated in Figure 3-7D.

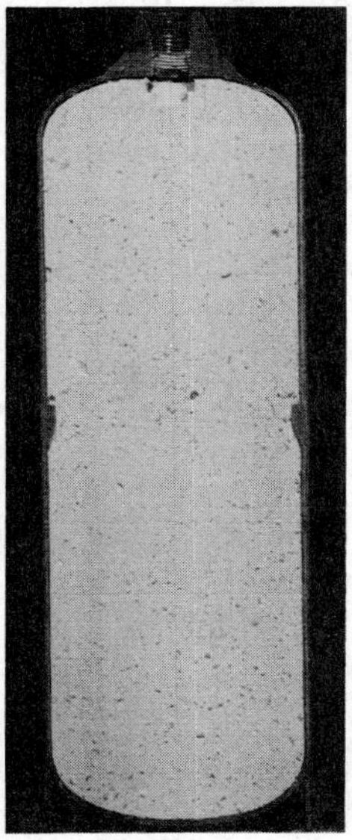

FIG. 3-7D. Cutaway of a typical acetylene cylinder showing porous filler material. Cylinder valve and packing for well at top of cylinder are not shown.

Usage: Acetylene is used primarily in chemical processing and as a fuel gas in oxygen-fuel gas cutting and welding operations. Occasionally it is manufactured at the consuming location by reacting calcium carbide (a solid) and water in acetylene generators and piped directly to gas holders or to the point of use.

Hazards inside containers: Acetylene is shipped in DOT and CTC cylinders as described previously and stored in these or in low-pressure gas holders. It is either handled in hoses or piping systems.

Acetylene cylinders are indirectly protected against overpressure by heat-actuated devices, usually fusible plugs of eutectic alloys which have low melting points similar to those alloys employed in automatic sprinklers. Unlike spring-loaded pressure relief valves, operation of fusible plugs results in complete reduction to atmospheric pressure, because both the compressed gas and acetone are released at the same time. Due to this mode of overpressure protection, acetylene cylinders are not subject to a BLEVE, which by definition cannot occur if the liquid contents are not above their boiling points at NTP. Under fire exposure conditions and during charging operations in acetylene cylinder charging plants, however, internal decomposition has occurred which has resulted in BLEVE effects, such as cylinder rupture and propulsion, accompanied by small fireballs.

Because susceptibility to decomposition is directly related to pressure, i.e., the higher the pressure, the easier it is to initiate decomposition and the more violent the effects, an acceptable degree of stability in most piping systems containing gaseous acetylene is achieved by limiting the pressure. In general, this pressure does not exceed 15 psi (103 kPa). In applications requiring higher pressures, particularly in acetylene cylinder charging plants, special piping design features can be employed to control this hazard.

The use of acetylene in either the liquid or solid phases is especially hazardous, and is prohibited by standards and codes covering conventional applications.

Hazards when released from containment: When acetylene is released from containment, it presents combustion explosion and fire hazards. Because of its reactivity, it is easier to ignite than most flammable gases and burns more rapidly. The latter effect increases the severity of combustion explosions and increases the difficulty of providing explosion venting. Acetylene is only slightly lighter than air. (See Table 3-7C.)

Because of acetylene's reactivity, the design of electrical equipment for use in acetylene atmospheres is unique to this material, and Group A electrical equipment (see Article 500, *National Electrical Code®*) is devoted exclusively to acetylene. In practice, electrical equipment is avoided in the more likely acetylene release areas or the release potentials are reduced to a level where Group C or D equipment can be used. As a result, available Group A equipment is extremely limited in variety.

Emergency control: Because of the limited quantities of acetylene in conventional shipping modes and storage practices, "no fire" emergencies seldom occur. Fire control measures are similar to those involved with any flammable, nontoxic gas—i.e., application of water to containers and stopping the flow of escaping gas if possible.

Hazards of acetylene cylinders exposed to fire: Special precautions are needed when acetylene cylinders are exposed to fire. If an acetylene cylinder is exposed to fire, the fusible-metal pressure-relief devices will function when the metal reaches about 212°F (100°C). The nature of acetylene presents hazards that may not be present with other gases. Acetylene will decompose into hydrogen and carbon at temperatures in excess of 570°F (300°C). This property can present a danger when cylinders are involved in fire and heated locally above 570°F (300°C). When this occurs, cylinders can become overpressured and can, in some cases, rupture violently. The decomposition of acetylene can be so rapid that the pressure-relief provided by a plug(s) cannot always prevent rupture. Rupture can occur in as soon as a few minutes, or up to several hours after exposure.

Acetylene cylinders in the U.S. and Canada have fusible-metal pressure-relief devices incorporated into the cylinder or cylinder valve. Small cylinders incorporate the fusible metal into the valve. Medium and large cylinders incorporate the fusible metal in a plug(s) in the top head or bottom head. Most acetylene cylinders in Europe and other parts of the world do not have pressure-relief devices and are more susceptible to overpressure and rupture. When part of an acetylene cylinder is exposed to fire and is heated over 570°F (300°C), the acetylene will begin to decompose, liberating heat. Cylinders exposed to fire should be sprayed with water from a protected location, and persons should not approach an acetylene cylinder that has been exposed to fire.

A more common hazard of acetylene cylinders happens when a small leak occurs and ignites, resulting in a small flame. This small flame can cause heating of the fusible metal, resulting in the release of a torch-like flame which can be as much as 12 ft (3.6 m) in length. This sudden flame can be a danger to people in the area and to other cylinders.

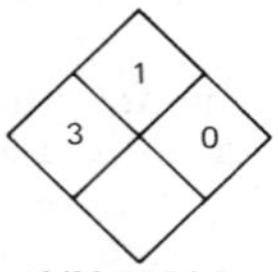

UN#1005

Anhydrous Ammonia

Classifications: Flammable, liquefied (including cryogenic), industrial.

Chemical properties: Anhydrous ammonia is comprised of nitrogen and hydrogen. While often referred to simply as "ammonia," this term is more appropriately used to describe a solution of anhydrous (which means "without water") ammonia in water. The nitrogen component is inert in the combustion reaction and accounts for the somewhat limited flammability of anhydrous ammonia as manifest by its high lower-flammability limit and low heat of combustion. (See Table 3-7C.)

Moist ammonia will vigorously attack copper and zinc and many of their brass or bronze alloys. This has caused some problems in agricultural areas where, because of their similar vapor pressures, anhydrous ammonia and propane are often handled in the same storage tanks, transport containers, and associated equipment at different times of the year. LP-Gas equipment customarily utilizes brass, bronze, copper, and zinc extensively for valves, gages, piping, regulators, etc. This equipment, if converted to anhydrous ammonia service, must be changed to steel. Subsequently, anhydrous ammonia must be carefully purged from a container when it is reconverted to LP-Gas service.

The characteristic pungent odor and irritant properties of anhydrous ammonia serve as warnings for this relatively toxic gas. However, the effectiveness of the warning depends upon the rate of release. Large clouds of ammonia gas have been rapidly produced from large liquid leaks, so that people have been trapped and killed before they could evacuate the area.

Physical properties: At its normal boiling point of –28°F (–33°C), anhydrous ammonia has a liquid density of 42.6 lb per cu ft (682.4 kg/m^3), a gas density of 0.055 lb per cu ft (0.88 kg/m^3), and a latent heat of vaporization of 589.3 Btu/lb (1371 kJ/kg). At NTP, the gas has a density of about 0.045 lb per cu ft (0.72 kg/m^3), and vaporization of 1 cu ft (0.3 m^3) of liquid will produce about 885 cu ft (25 m^3) of gas.

Usage: Anhydrous ammonia is used primarily as an agricultural fertilizer, as a refrigerant, and as a source of hydrogen for metal heat treating and semi-conductor manufacturing special atmospheres.

Hazards inside containers: Anhydrous ammonia is shipped in DOT and CTC cylinders, and DOT-specification cargo trucks, railroad tank cars, and barges. It is stored in cylinders, American Society of Mechanical Engineers (ASME) code tanks, and in cryogenic form in insulated American Petroleum Institute (API) tanks.

Anhydrous ammonia containers with a capacity of less than 165 lb (79 kg) are not required to be equipped with overpressure protection devices. This reflects the toxicity of the gas and is a safety tradeoff between the hazards of container rupture from overpressure and gas release due to operation of an overpressure protective device, especially indoors where the smaller containers are often found.

BLEVEs of uninsulated anhydrous ammonia containers are infrequent, reflecting the limited flammability of the gas which minimizes the probability of it supplying the exposing fire. What fires have occurred, have been in other combustibles.

Hazards when released from containment: Anhydrous ammonia presents combustion explosion and fire hazards (as well as a toxicity hazard) when released from containment. However, its high lower limit of flammability and low heat of combustion reduce these hazards substantially.

If anhydrous ammonia is released outdoors, it is difficult for it to reach the lower flammability limit concentration except for small zones in the immediate vicinity of the leak. Even where large quantities of liquid are released, ignitible concentrations tend to be in discontinuous pockets and this, together with the low heat of combustion, reduces the possibilities of sustained burning. Experience indicates that similar circumstances apply when the release occurs indoors in conventional and reasonably well-ventilated buildings. In unusually tight rooms, such as refrigerated process or storage areas, however, the release of liquid or large quantities of gas can result in the accumulation of hazardous quantities of a flammable mixture and result in a combustion explosion. In such cases, even though the low heat of combustion produces lower pressures than most flammable gases, the pressure is enough to do major structural damage. As a result of these factors, anhydrous ammonia fires are infrequent and, where ignition does occur, a combustion explosion is the likely result. In a NFPA fire record analysis of 36 incidents from 1929 through 1969 where released gas or liquid was ignited, 28 incidents, or about 78 percent, resulted in a combustion explosion. All occurred indoors.

Emergency control: At normal temperatures, anhydrous ammonia gas weighs about 0.6 times as much as air. Because of its pronounced solubility in water, the spread of escaping anhydrous ammonia gas can be readily controlled by water spray. If hose streams are used, the toxic and inerting properties of anhydrous ammonia require fire fighters to use protective breathing apparatus. Where liquid contact is likely, full protective clothing should be worn. If release of liquid in cryogenic form occurs, pooling is possible and application of water to pools should be avoided, unless the vapors can be controlled, in order to prevent increasing vaporization rate.

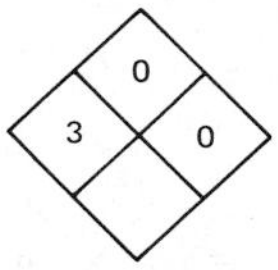

UN#2187
Cryogenic Liquid

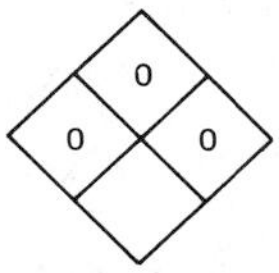

UN#1013
Compressed Gas

Carbon Dioxide

Classifications: Nonflammable (inert), liquefied, industrial.

Chemical properties: Carbon dioxide is composed of carbon and oxygen. The ability of carbon to chemically link with as much oxygen as possible prohibits its further oxidation (combustion), making it nonflammable. Although nontoxic, carbon dioxide can cause asphyxiation due to the displacement of air.

Physical properties: Carbon dioxide exhibits some unique physical properties. At a temperature of –69.9°F (–56.6°C) and a pressure of 60.4 psig (416.4 kPa), it can exist in a container simultaneously as a liquid, solid, and gas (the triple point). At temperatures and pressures above these and below 87.8°F (30.8°C), it exists as both liquid and gas. Above 87.8°F (30.8°C), it exists only in the gaseous phase. At normal temperatures, the gas is about 1½ times heavier than air.

Usage: Carbon dioxide is used primarily to carbonate beverages, to provide an inert atmosphere, and to extinguish fires.

Hazards inside containers: Carbon dioxide is shipped in DOT and CTC cylinders and insulated DOT-specification cargo trucks and railroad tank cars. It is stored in cylinders at a pressure of about 850 psi at 70°F (5861 kPa at 21°C) or in insulated ASME-code tanks at pressures of about 200 to 312 psi (1380 to 2150 kPa) and temperatures of –20 to +40°F (–28.8 to +4.4°C).

Cylinders are provided with overpressure protection in the form of frangible (bursting) discs. Insulated tanks are equipped with pressure-relief valves. Carbon dioxide cylinders have BLEVEd as a result of corrosion, with enough energy to nearly demolish small cargo vehicles. The NFPA has no reports of BLEVEs of other types of containers.

Hazards when released from containment: In addition to the hazard of asphyxiation, contact with cold vaporizing carbon dioxide can cause frostbite. For these reasons, actuation of automatic room-flooding extinguishing system applications should incorporate a time delay if personnel occupy the protected area.

Emergency control: Carbon dioxide emergencies are "no fire" emergencies involving potential asphyxiation hazards. Structure ventilation indoors and water spray control outdoors are applicable. Self-contained breathing apparatus should be used.

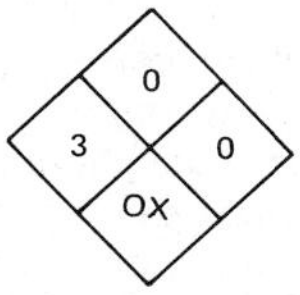

UN#1017
Chlorine

Chlorine

Classifications: Reactive, nonflammable, liquefied, toxic, industrial.

Chemical properties: Chlorine is a basic chemical element. Although it is nonflammable, it can react with many organic materials corrosively and, in some instances, explosively, particularly with acetylene, turpentine, ether, gaseous ammonia, hydrocarbons, most fuel gases, and finely divided metals.

The reactivity of chlorine necessitates special attention to the container, piping, and equipment materials of construction. Below 230°F (110°C), steel, copper, iron, and lead are widely used. In contact with water, chlorine forms hypochlorous and hypochloric acids which are corrosive to most metals.

Chlorine is toxic enough to be considered as a poison and has been used in warfare as a poison gas. Liquid chlorine can burn skin. Its sharp odor serves as a warning.

Physical properties: The normal boiling point of chlorine is about –30°F (–34.4°C). At 32°F (0°C), the liquid density is 91.7 lb per cu ft (1468 kg/m^3) and the gas density is 0.2 lb per cu ft (3.2 kg/m^3). The latent heat of vaporization at the normal boiling point is 123.7 Btu/lb (287.7 kJ/kg). At 32°F (0°C), the vaporization of 1 cu ft of liquid will produce about 458 cu ft of gas (1 m^3 of liquid will produce about 458 m^3 of gas). Chlorine has a greenish-yellow color.

Usage: Chlorine is used primarily in chemical processing, bleaching, purification of drinking water and swimming pools, and sanitation of industrial and sewage wastes.

Hazards inside containers: Chlorine is shipped in DOT and CTC cylinders, in DOT-specification portable tanks (so-called "one-ton containers"), and in insulated railroad tank cars.

Chlorine cylinders and 1-ton (1016 kg) containers are provided with overpressure protection by fusible plugs. Tank cars are protected by pressure-relief valves. Because the operation of fusible plugs results in complete depressurization, the probability of a BLEVE is low and has not occurred in practice. The NFPA has no record of a BLEVE of a tank car containing chlorine, even though such an occurrence is theoretically possible.

Steel is a suitable material for a chlorine container at normal temperatures; however, it is rapidly attacked at temperatures above approximately 230°F (110°C), and leaks can develop upon fire exposure. For this reason, as well as for BLEVE protection, water should be applied to fire-exposed containers. Insofar as possible, application of water directly upon a leak should be avoided, because it may enlarge the leak from acid corrosion.

Hazards when released from containment: Chlorine presents primarily toxicity and corrosion hazards when released from containment. Since chlorine gas is about 2½ times heavier than air, it will hug the ground.

Emergency control: The gas can be controlled by water spray. If hose streams are used, fire fighters should wear full protective clothing. Water applied to liquid chlorine will accelerate vaporization, cause significant corrosion, and can accelerate the leakage rate.

The chlorine industry has developed an extensive leak-control program that includes strategic siting of trained emergency personnel and special equipment kits for stopping the more common leaks in cylinders, ton containers, and tank cars. Information on this program is available from The Chlorine Institute, Inc., 2001 L Street, N.W., Suite 506, Washington, D.C., 20036.

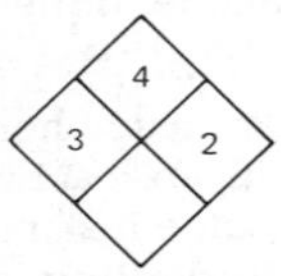

UN#1038
Cryogenic Liquid

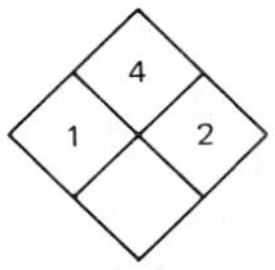

UN#1962
Compressed Gas

Ethylene

Classifications: Flammable, compressed, cryogenic, industrial.

Chemical properties: Ethylene is comprised of carbon and hydrogen and contains a double chemical bond that imparts a degree of reactivity. Except at very high pressures normally encountered only in chemical processing, it is a stable material. It has a wide flammable range (see Table 3-7C) and high burning velocity, reflecting its reactivity. Although it is nontoxic, ethylene is an anesthetic and asphyxiant.

Physical properties: See Table 3-7A.

Usage: Ethylene is principally used in chemical processing, e.g., manufacture of polyethylene plastic. It is also used to ripen fruit.

Hazards inside containers: Ethylene is shipped as a compressed gas in DOT and CTC cylinders and as a cryogenic gas in insulated cargo trucks and railroad tank cars in accordance with DOT specifications and regulations. It is stored in cylinders or in insulted ASME-code or API tanks.

Ethylene cylinders (except for medical cylinders which may have fusible plugs or combination safety devices) are protected against overpressure by frangible (bursting) discs. Insulated truck tanks and tank cars are protected by pressure-relief valves. Cylinders are subject to failure from fire exposure, but not to BLEVEs because they do not contain liquid. Insulated containers are subject to BLEVEs, but actual occurrence of this is rare. One such incident occurred in Spain; however, the cargo tank and insulation system did not comply with North American standards. A few instances of cryogenic truck container overpressure rupture have occurred due to freezing of relief valves that closed due to improper installation of the valves.

Hazards when released from containment: Ethylene presents combustion explosion and fire hazards when released from containment. A wide flammable range and high burning rate accentuate these hazards. In a number of instances involving rather large outdoor releases, open-air or open-space explosions have occurred.

Emergency control: Escaping ethylene presents both "no fire" and "fire" emergency situations. At normal atmospheric temperatures, ethylene gas is very slightly lighter than air. Ethylene gas vaporizing from the cryogenic liquid near its normal boiling point is heavier than air at 70°F (21°C) and can spread along the ground. Escaping liquid will also pool on the ground. Although the visible fog created is a rough indication of the extent of the hazardous area, the hazard can extend beyond the visible area.

Escaping gas can be controlled by water spray. Contact between water and pooled ethylene should be avoided to prevent increased vaporization, unless the vapors can be controlled. Water should be applied to fire-exposed containers and the flow of escaping gas should be stopped if possible.

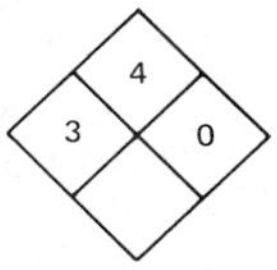

UN#1066
Cryogenic Liquid

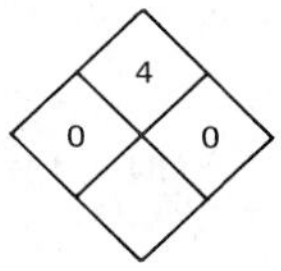

UN#1049
Compressed Gas

Hydrogen

Classifications: Flammable, compressed, cryogenic, industrial.

Chemical properties: Hydrogen is a basic chemical element. Hydrogen has an extremely wide flammable range and the highest burning velocity of any gas. Its ignition temperature is reasonably high, but its ignition energy is very low. Because hydrogen contains no carbon, it burns with a nonluminous flame which is often invisible in daylight. Hydrogen is nontoxic.

Physical properties: See Table 3-7A.

Usage: Hydrogen is principally used in chemical processing, for hydrogenation of edible oils, in welding and cutting, as a metal heat-treating special atmosphere, and as a coolant in large electrical generators.

Hazards inside containers: Hydrogen is shipped as a compressed gas in uninsulated DOT and CTC cylinders, as a cryogenic gas in insulated DOT and CTC cylinders, and in insulated cargo trucks and railroad tank cars according to DOT specifications and regulations. It is stored in cylinders or in ASME-code insulated tanks.

Compressed hydrogen cylinders are protected against overpressure by frangible (bursting) discs or such discs in combination with fusible plug devices. Insulated cylinders, trucks and railcar tanks, and storage tanks are protected by pressure-relief valves and frangible disks. Compressed gas cylinders are subject to failure, but not to BLEVEs because they do not contain liquid. Insulated cryogenic containers are theoretically subject to BLEVEs, but NFPA has no record of such an occurrence.

Hazards when released from containment: Hydrogen presents both combustion explosion and fire hazards when released from containment. Although its wide flammable range and high burning rate accentuate these hazards, its low ignition energy, low heat of combustion on a volume basis, and its nonluminous (low thermal radiation level) flame exert counteracting influences in many instances.

Because of its low ignition energy, when gaseous hydrogen is released at high pressure, nominally small heat-producing sources, e.g., friction and static generation, often result in prompt ignitions. Accordingly, hydrogen is frequently thought of as self-igniting under these circumstances. The record of releases in high-pressure applications reveals that fires rather than combustion explosions occur. When hydrogen is released at low pressures, however, self-ignition is unlikely. Rather, hydrogen combustion explosions occur that are characterized by very rapid pressure rises which are extremely difficult to vent effectively. Open-air or open-space explosions have occurred from large releases of gaseous hydrogen.

Because of its very low boiling point, contact between liquid hydrogen and air can result in condensation of air and its oxygen and nitrogen components. A mixture of hydrogen and liquid oxygen is potentially explosive, even though the quantities involved are likely to be small. Accidents from this source have been generally restricted to the interiors of liquefaction equipment and to small containers of liquid hydrogen that are handled in the open atmosphere.

At ordinary temperatures, hydrogen is very light, weighing only about 1/15 as much as air. The accordingly high diffusion rate makes it difficult for hydrogen to accumulate in conventional structures, unless the escape rate is high. This tends to reduce its combustion explosion hazard.

Emergency control: Escaping gaseous hydrogen seldom presents a "no fire" emergency situation, because it either ignites promptly or rises in the atmosphere rapidly. Hydrogen gas vaporizing from the cryogenic liquid near its normal boiling point is slightly heavier than air at 70°F (21°C); this fact, together with the visible fog of condensed water vapor created, causes it to spread along the ground for sizable distances (depending upon leak size and meteorological conditions). Because of the low gas density of vapors produced from vaporizing cryogenic hydrogen liquid, impounding or diked areas have not been required.

Ignitible mixtures can extend well beyond the visible cloud. Such escapes can be controlled by water spray. Contact between water and pooled hydrogen should be avoided to prevent increased vaporization, unless the vapor can be controlled.

Water should be applied to fire-exposed containers and the flow of gas stopped, if possible. Because hydrogen burns with a flame that is often invisible in daylight and because its flames produce low levels of thermal radiation, people have actually walked into its flames. When approaching hydrogen fires, a useful technique is to hold a broom out in front, while progressing slowly and at the same time throwing dirt ahead. The combustibles in the dirt will incandesce and locate the edge of the fire.

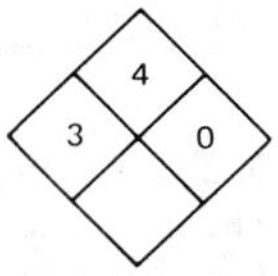

UN#1972

Liquefied Natural Gas (LNG)

Classifications: Flammable, cryogenic, fuel.

Chemical properties: LNG is a mixture of materials all comprised of carbon and hydrogen. The principal component is methane, with lesser amounts of ethane, propane, and butane. The composition will vary, depending principally upon whether the source of the natural gas (which has been liquefied) is a transmission pipeline or gas wells. In the former instance, more of the propane and butane is removed prior to introduction into the pipeline. (See Table 3-7D.)

LNG is nontoxic but is an asphyxiant.

TABLE 3-7D. ***Approximate Properties of LNG***

Composition	
Methane	83–99%
Ethane	1–13%
Propane	0.1–3%
Butane	0.2–1.0%
Physical Properties	
Normal boiling point (NBP)	–250° to –260°F (–160 to –164°C)
Density liquid at NBP	3½ to 4 lbs per gal (0.42 to 0.48 g/cm³)
Density vapor at NBP (compared with air at 70°F or 21°C)	1.47
Liquid to vapor expansion	600 to 1
Heat of vaporization	220–248 Btu/lb (512–577 kJ/kg) 770–990 Btu/gal (215–276 MJ/m³)
Combustion Properties	
Flammable range	5–14% (methane at normal temperatures) 6–13% (methane near –260°F or –127°C)
Heat of combustion	22,000 Btu/lb (51.2 MJ/kg)
Burn rate, steady-state pool	0.2–0.6 in. (5 to 15 mm) per minute

Physical properties: See Table 3-7D.

Usage: LNG is used as a source of natural gas to augment pipeline supplies during periods of extreme demand (peak shaving), to supply gas distribution systems in areas remote from central distribution systems, and as a basic supply of natural gas. To a small extent, it is used as a vehicle propulsion fuel.

Hazards inside containers: LNG is shipped as a cryogenic gas in insulated cargo trucks built to DOT specifications and regulations and in marine vessels under DOT authorization. It is stored in insulated ASME-code or API tanks. LNG containers are protected against overpressure by pressure-relief valves. Such containers are theoretically subject to BLEVEs, but NFPA has no record of such an occurrence.

Hazards when released from containment: LNG presents both combustion explosion and fire hazards when released from containment. At the present time, LNG is seldom used indoors and when so used the structure is designed for a combustion explosion hazard in accordance with national standards and regulations. Available test and experience data indicates that escaping LNG is not subject to open-air or open-space explosions.

Emergency control: Escaping LNG presents both "no fire" and "fire" emergency situations. LNG gas vaporizing from the cryogenic liquid near its normal boiling point is about 1½ times heavier than air is at 70°F (21°C) and will spread along the ground accompanied by the visible fog created by condensed water vapor. This distance will depend upon the leak size and meteorological conditions and upon the geometry of the required liquid-impounding area provided. Ignitible areas are roughly defined by the visible cloud, but can extend beyond the visible area. Such escape can be controlled by water spray. Contact between water and pooled LNG should be avoided to prevent increased vaporization, unless the vapor can be controlled. Water should be applied to fire-exposed containers and the flow of gas stopped, if possible.

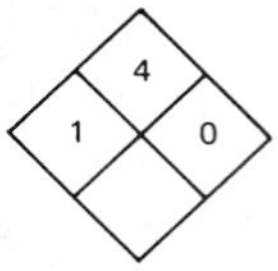

UN#1075

Liquefied Petroleum Gases (LP-Gas)

Classifications: Flammable, liquefied (including cryogenic), fuel.

Chemical properties: LP-Gas is a mixture of hydrocarbon materials. In commerce, LP-Gas is predominantly either propane or normal butane or mixtures of these with smaller amounts of ethane, ethylene, propylene, iso-butane, and butylene (including isomers). Principal variations in composition occur depending upon whether the source is gas wells or petroleum refineries. LP-Gas is nontoxic but is an asphyxiant.

Physical properties: See Table 3-7E.

Usage: LP-Gas is used principally as a domestic, commercial, agricultural, and industrial fuel gas, in chemical processing, and as an engine fuel. In domestic and recreational applications, it is sometimes known as bottled gas.

Hazards inside containers: LP-Gas is shipped as a liquefied gas in uninsulated DOT and CTC cylinders and in ASME tanks and in DOT-specification cargo trucks, railroad tank cars, and marine vessels. It is also shipped at low temperatures near its normal boiling point at atmospheric pressure in insulated marine vessels. It is stored in cylinders, ASME-code tanks, and insulated API tanks.

LP-Gas containers are generally protected against overpressure by pressure-relief valves, although some cylinders are protected by fusible plug devices and, occasionally, by a combination of these. Most containers are subject to BLEVEs.

Hazards when released from containment: LP-Gas presents both combustion explosion and fire hazards when released from containment. Because most uses of LP-Gas are indoors, the combustion-explosion experience dominates. This hazard is accentuated when LP-Gas is used indoors—reflecting the fact that 1 gal (3.78 L) of liquid propane or butane will produce about 245 to 275 gal (927 to 1041 L) of gas. For this reason, standards and codes severely restrict the uses of liquid-phase LP-Gas indoors. Large releases of LP-Gas outdoors have led to a few reported open-air detonations.

Emergency control: Escaping LP-Gas presents both "no fire" and "fire" emergency situations. LP-Gas vapor is normally 1½ to 2 times heavier than air, and the vapor produced as LP-Gas vaporizes from the liquid at its normal boiling point is even heavier. Therefore, it will tend to spread along the ground accompanied by the created visible fog of condensed water vapor. Ignitible mixtures extend beyond the visible area. Such escape can be controlled by water spray. When propane is stored and handled at atmospheric temperatures, it is unlikely to pool, except under very low ambient temperature conditions. Butane stored and handled at atmospheric temperatures and low-temperature LP-Gas are likely to pool. Contact between water and pooled LP-Gas should be avoided to prevent increased vaporization, unless the vapor can be controlled. Water should be applied to fire-exposed containers and the flow of gas stopped, if possible.

TABLE 3-7E. *Approximate Properties of LP-Gases*

	Commercial Propane NLPGA Av.	Commercial Butane NLPGA Av.
Vapor Pressure in psig at:		
70°F	127	17
100°F	196	37
105°F	210	41
130°F	287	69
Vapor Pressure in kPa at:		
20°C	895	103
40°C	1482	285
45°C	1672	345
55°C	1980	462
Specific Gravity Liquid at 60°F (15.5°C)	0.509	0.582
Initial Boiling Point at 14.7 psia	−44°F	15°F
Initial Boiling Point at 101 kPa	−42°C	−9°C
Weight per gal of liquid at 60°F, lb	4.20	4.81
Weight per m^3 of liquid at 15.5°C	504 kg	582 kg
Specific Heat of Liquid, Btu/lb at 60°F	0.630	0.549
Specific Heat of Liquid, kJ/kg at 15.5°C	1.46	1.28
Cu ft of Vapor per gal at 60°F	36.38	31.26
m^3 of Vapor per L at 15.5°C	0.271	0.235
Cu ft of Vapor per lb at 60°F	8.66	6.51
m^3 of Vapor per kg at 15.5°C	0.534	0.410
Specific Gravity of Vapor (Air = 1) at 60°F (15.5°C)	1.50	2.01
Ignition Temperature in Air,	920–1120°F (493–549°C)	900–1000°F (482–538°C)
Maximum Flame Temperature in Air,	3,595°F (1980°C)	3,615°F (1990°C)
Limits of Flammability in Air, Percent of Vapor in Air-Gas Mixture:		
(a) Lower	2.15	1.55
(b) Upper	9.60	8.60
Latent Heat of Vaporization at Boiling Point:		
(a) Btu per lb	184	167
(b) Btu per gal	773	808
(c) kJ/kg	428	388
(d) KJ/L	216	226
Total Heating Values after Vaporization:		
(a) Btu per cu ft	2,488	3,280
(b) Btu per lb	21,548	21,221
(c) Btu per gal	91,547	102,032
(d) KJ/m^3	92,430	121,280
(e) KJ/kg	49,920	49,140
(f) KJ/m^3	25,140	28,100

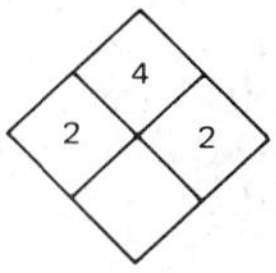

UN#1060

Methylacetylene-Propadiene, Stabilized (MPS)

Classifications: Flammable, liquefied, industrial.

Chemical properties: Methylacetylene-propadiene, stabilized, is a mixture of materials all comprised of carbon and hydrogen. In commerce, and in compliance with standards covering its use as a metal-cutting gas, MPS has composition per Table 3-7F.

TABLE 3-7F. ***MAPPS Composition***

1. Methylacetylene-propadiene (in combination with a maximum ratio of 3.0 moles of methylacetylene per mole of propadiene in the initial liquidphase in a storge container)	—68 mole percent *maximum*
2. Propane, butane, isobutane (in combination)	—24 mole percent *minimum,* of which at least one-third (8 mole percent of total mixture) shall be butane and/or isobutane
3. Propylene	—10 mole percent *maximum*
4. Butadiene	—2 mole percent *maximum*

Methylacetylene (also known as "propyne") and propadiene (also known as "allene") contain double and triple chemical bonds and are unstable, reactive materials presenting hazards similar to acetylene. The achievement of an adequate degree of stability for this product depends upon the existence of a sufficient quantity of the propane, butane, and iso-butane components of the mixture. MPS is marketed under various trade names, including "MAPP GAS" (Monsanto Chemical Co.), and "APACHE GAS" (Air Products and Chemicals, Inc.).

MPS has a degree of chemical reactivity with metals, similar to acetylene—especially as it pertains to the use of copper and copper alloys. (See "Acetylene" in this chapter.)

MPS is nontoxic but has some anesthetic and narcotic effects. It has a strong odor detectable at concentrations as low as 100 ppm in air. (See Tables 3-7C and 3-7G.)

Physical properties: See Table 3-7G.

Usage: MPS is principally used as a metal-cutting fuel gas with oxygen.

Hazards inside containers: MPS has physical properties very similar to propane and is shipped as a liquefied gas in uninsulated DOT and CTC cylinders and in DOT-specification cargo trucks and tank cars. It is stored in cylinders and ASME-code tanks. Its hazards inside containers are analogous to propane. The pressure of MPS in piping systems is not restricted.

TABLE 3-7G. ***Selected Properties of MPS****

Molecular Weight (Average-stabilized mixture)	42.3
Heat of Vaporization	227 Btu/lb (528 kJ/kg)
Gross Heat of Combustion	21,700 Btu/lb (50.5 MJ/kg)
Normal Boiling Range, 1 Atm.	−36 to −4°F (−37.8 to −20°C)
Flame Temperature in Oxygen	5301°F (2927°C)
Specific Heat, Liquid Cp—70°F, (21°C) 1 Atm.	0.362 Btu/lb°F [1.5 J/(kg/°K)]
Specific Heat, Liquid Cv—70°F, (21°C) 1 Atm.	0.277 Btu/lb°F [0.9 J/(kg/°K)]
Critical Temperature	245°C (118°C)
Critical Pressure	752 psi (5.2 MPa)
Burning Velocity	15.4 ft/sec (4.7 m/sec)
Explosive Limits in Oxygen	2.5 to 60%
Vapor Pressure at 70°F (21°C)	94 psi (648 kPa)
Specific Gravity of the Liquid (60/60°F)	0.576
Specific Volume of the Gas at 60°F (21°C), 1 Atm.	8.85 cu ft/lb (0.55 m^3/kg)
Heat of Formation	1075 Btu/lb (2.5 MJ)
Minimum Ignition Energy	0.2–0.25 MJ

* MAPP GAS (Dow Chemical Company).

Hazards when released from containment: MPS presents combustion explosion and fire hazards when released from containment. It is easier to ignite (due to a lower ignition energy) than propane and burns more rapidly; thus, it is similar to ethylene in these respects.

MPS is classified as a Group C material for purposes of suitability of electrical equipment installed in classified hazardous areas.

Emergency control: See "Liquefied Petroleum Gases" in this chapter.

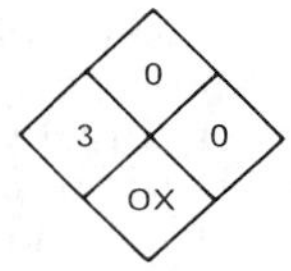

UN#1073
Cryogenic Liquid

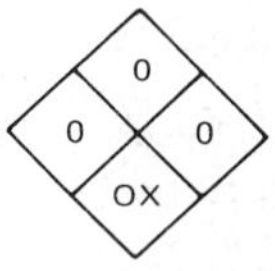

UN#1072
Compressed Gas

Oxygen

Classifications: Nonflammable (oxidizing), compressed, cryogenic, industrial, medical.

Chemical properties: Oxygen is a basic chemical element. It reacts with practically all materials and the general reaction is known as oxidation. Combustion is a particular type of oxidation reaction. In most combustion reactions, the oxygen is accompanied by nitrogen, in a mixture known as air. Nitrogen contributes nothing to the combustion reaction and actually inhibits it. Therefore, concentrations of oxygen in excess of its concentration in air increase most combustion hazards to a degree directly related to the concentration. This affects all basic combustion parameters, except for the heat of combustion. For example, ignition temperatures and energies are lowered, the flammable range is widened, and the burning rate is increased as the oxygen concentration increases—the ultimate effects occurring at an oxygen concentration of 100 percent. In consideration of these properties, the design of systems containing 100 percent oxygen requires particular attention to these factors from a compatibility standpoint.

Physical properties: See Table 3-7A.

Usage: Oxygen is primarily used in the production of steel, in metal welding and cutting, in medical applications, in life-support systems, in aeronautic and aerospace applications, and in chemical processing.

Hazards inside containers: Oxygen is shipped as a compressed or cryogenic gas in DOT and CTC cylinders and in tank cars and trucks in accordance with DOT specifications and regulations. It is stored in DOT-specification cylinders (insulated or uninsulated) or in ASME-code insulated tanks.

Compressed-oxygen cylinders are protected against overpressure by frangible (bursting) discs or a combination of these with fusible plugs. Insulated cryogenic containers are protected with pressure-relief valves. Metals for containers and piping must be carefully selected, depending on service conditions. The various steels are acceptable for many applications, but some service conditions may call for other materials (usually copper or its alloys) because of their greater resistance to ignition and lower rate of combustion.

Similarly, materials that can be ignited in air have lower ignition energies in oxygen. Many such materials may be ignited by friction at a valve seat or stem packing or by adiabatic compression produced when oxygen at high pressure is rapidly introduced into a system initially at low pressure.

Oxygen container failures from fire exposure are rare—probably reflecting standards that require separation of containers from flammable gases and other combustibles. Most oxygen system components have failed due to accumulations of grease, oil, etc., on the surfaces of these components in contact with oxygen, reflecting poor housekeeping practices. Since materials such as grease are rather easily ignited in air, they are especially ignitible in 100 percent oxygen. Their ignition often results in combustion of system components that are noncombustible in air, including metallic components. Such incidents usually involve only small portions of such components, but may occur in a spectacular way, causing property damage and personal injury. They are referred to conventionally as "flashes."

Hazards when released from containment: Release of compressed or liquefied oxygen is usually observed by acceleration of the fire in whatever is burning. Release of liquid oxygen in the absence of fire presents an increased possibility that an oxygen-fuel mixture may occur prior to ignition. If ignition delay occurs under these circumstances, an explosion may result. Almost any combination of liquid oxygen and a combustible material is potentially explosive due to the rapid combustion circumstances produced. Some commercial explosives have been derived in this manner.

Oxygen is slightly heavier than air at the same temperature.

Emergency control: Escaping oxygen presents basically a "no fire" situation, but can create a "fire" situation in the vicinity of fired equipment or arcing electrical equipment by causing these to get out of control. For example, metallic components of internal combustion engines have burned in the oxygen-rich atmospheres produced by escaping oxygen. Oxygen gas vaporizing from the cryogenic liquid near its normal boiling point is approximately four times heavier than air is at 70°F (21°C) and will spread along the ground accompanied by the visible fog of condensed water vapor that has been created. Such escape can be controlled by water spray. Contact between water and pooled liquid oxygen should be avoided to prevent increased vaporization, unless the vapor can be controlled. Water should be applied to fire-exposed containers and the flow of gas stopped, if possible.

Utility Gases

Classifications: Flammable, fuel.

Chemical properties: The term "utility gas" is applicable to any flammable gas distributed by gas utilities as a fuel gas. Natural gas dominates this field today. Some LP-Gas is distributed by gas utilities. Most utilities use LP-Gas to augment natural gas supplies during short periods of peak demand which occur in unusually cold weather.

The creation of natural gas is the result of decomposition of organic material by heat, pressure, and bacteriological action in the absence of air, usually below ground. As it is evolved underground, natural gas consists of both flammable and nonflammable gases. The flammable gases are comprised of carbon and hydrogen and are principally methane and ethane with some propane, butane, and pentane. The nonflammable gases are principally nitrogen and carbon dioxide. In commerce, most of the nonflammable gases are removed prior to distribution so that the natural gas consists of about 70 to 90 percent methane, with the remainder mostly ethane. (See Table 3-7C.)

Natural gas is nontoxic but is an asphyxiant. This is in marked contrast to the manufactured gas formerly widely distributed as utility gas and which contained quantities of poisonous carbon monoxide.

Utility natural gas has no odor of its own and is generally odorized as distributed.

Physical properties: With the exception of liquefied natural gas (LNG), utility natural gas is distributed in piping as a compressed gas at pressures ranging from approximately 0.25 to 1,000 psi (1.72 to 6895 kPa) and in cylinders at pressures up to 3,600 psi (24.8 MPa). The gas has a density of about ⅔ that of air.

Usage: Utility natural gas supplies about one third of the total fuel energy of the United States for domestic, commercial, and industrial heating and power. It is also being used as a motor fuel and is known as "compressed natural gas (CNG)." Natural gas (usually supplied from a gas utility distribution piping system) is compressed to 2,400 to 3,600 psi (16.5 to 24.8 MPa), stored in a fueling station, and dispensed into vehicle containers at the same pressure.

Hazards inside containers: Utility natural gas is distributed nearly exclusively by a network of more than 1 million miles (1 million miles equals 1.6 million km) of underground pipeline in the United States and Canada. It is transported from gas wells in producing areas in large-diameter transmission pipelines at pressures up to approximately 1,000 psi (6895 kPa). These pipelines are tapped by utility gas companies, and pressures are reduced for distribution—generally to around 0.25 to 60 psi (1.72 to 414 kPa). Regulators and safety relief devices are used to control pressures.

Steel and cast-iron pipe are used extensively. In recent years, thermoplastic and thermosetting plastic piping have been used extensively in distribution piping at pressures up to approximately 100 psi (689.5 kPa).

Because most gas piping is underground, fire exposure is not a significant problem. Most failures of utility natural gas piping are the result of mechanical damage due to excavation operations and corrosion.

In CNG applications, both the fueling station storage containers and the vehicle containers are either DOT- or CTC-specification or exemption cylinders, or ASME-code containers. DOT/CTC cylinders are protected against overpressure by combination frangible (bursting) disc/fusible plug devices. ASME-code containers are equipped with spring-loaded pressure-relief valves.

CNG containers are subject to failure, but not to BLEVEs because they do not contain liquid.

Hazards when released from containment: Natural gas presents both combustion explosion and fire hazards when released from containment. Because most uses of natural gas are indoors, the combustion explosion experience dominates. In approximately three fourths of the combustion explosions, the gas escapes from the underground distribution main in the street or the service connection between the street main and the building piping. In the remainder, the gas escapes from the building piping or gas-burning equipment.

Open-air or open-space explosions have resulted from failures of large-diameter, high-pressure transmission pipelines.

Combustion explosions of biologically produced natural gas are increasing as a result of the use of marshy land and former sanitary landfills for buildings.

The use of CNG in the United States has been limited. Fires in fueling stations have been limited to ignition of the discharge of overpressure-relief devices, with minor consequences. No vehicle fires have been reported in the U.S. Some fire tests indicate that fires in vehicles operating on their other fuels (gasoline/CNG dual-fueled vehicles are common) can be expected to produce short-lived flareups as the gas is released from the containers through their overpressure-relief devices, without container failure.

Emergency control: Escaping natural gas presents both "no fire" and "fire" emergency situations. Although utility gas is considerably lighter than air, most gas escapes underground and can travel underground—usually following underground water, sewer or water piping, or electrical conduits—for hundreds of feet (100 ft equals approximately 30.5 m) to enter below-grade building spaces or hollow wall spaces. Because of this escape mode, control consists of ventilation rather than use of hose streams.

Fire-exposed CNG containers should be kept cool with water.

Because of its lightness, unignited natural gas escaping outdoors is seldom a problem.

Natural-gas fires should normally be extinguished by stopping the flow of gas only.

BIBLIOGRAPHY

Reference Cited

1. Compressed Gas Association, *Handbook of Compressed Gases*, 3rd ed., Van Nostrand Reinhold Co., New York, 1989.

NFPA Codes, Standards, and Recommended Practices

Reference to the following NFPA codes, standards, and recommended practices will provide further information on gases discussed in this chapter. (See the latest *NFPA Catalog* for availability of current editions of the following documents.)

NFPA 12, *Carbon Dioxide Extinguishing Systems.*

NFPA 50, *Bulk Oxygen Systems at Consumer Sites.*

NFPA 50A, *Gaseous Hydrogen Systems at Consumer Sites.*

NFPA 50B, *Liquefied Hydrogen Systems at Consumer Sites.*

NFPA 51, *Oxygen-Fuel Gas Systems for Welding, Cutting, and Allied Processes.*

NFPA 51A, *Acetylene Cylinder Charging Plants.*

NFPA 51B, *Cutting and Welding Processes.*

NFPA 52, *Compressed Natural Gas (CNG) Vehicular Fuel Systems.*

NFPA 54, *National Fuel Gas Code.*

NFPA 58, *Storage and Handling of Liquefied Petroleum Gases.*

NFPA 59, *Storage and Handling of Liquefied Petroleum Gases at Utility Gas Plants.*

NFPA 59A, *Production, Storage and Handling of Liquefied Natural Gas (LNG).*

NFPA 68, *Explosion Venting.*

NFPA 70, *National Electrical Code.*

NFPA 99, *Health Care Facilities.*

NFPA 302, *Pleasure and Commercial Motor Craft.*

NFPA 328, *Flammable and Combustible Liquids and Gases in Manholes, Sewers, and Similar Underground Structures.*

Additional Reading

"Acetylene," Pamphlet G-1, Compressed Gas Association, Inc., NY.

Allan, D. S., "A Cryogenic Line Leak Detector," *Fire Technology*, Vol. 11, No. 4, Nov. 1975, pp. 270-273.

ANSI B31.8-1986, Gas Transmission and Distribution Piping, American Society of Mechanical Engineers, NY, 1987.

ANSI B138.1-1972, Design and Construction of LP-Gas Installations at Marine and Pipeline Terminals, Natural Gas Processing Plants, Refineries, and Tank Farms, American Society of Mechanical Engineers, NY.

ANSI K61.1-1972, Safety Requirements for the Storage and Handling of Anhydrous Ammonia, American Society of Mechanical Engineers, NY.

Atallah, Sami, "U.S. History's Worst LNG Disaster," *Firehouse*, Jan. 1979, p. 29.

Bahme, C. W., *Fire Officer's Guide to Dangerous Chemicals*, National Fire Protection Association, Quincy, MA, 1978.

Benedick, W. B., Kennedy, J. D., and Morosin, D., "Detonation Limits of Unconfined Hydrocarbon/Air Mixtures," *Combustion and Flame*, Vol. 5, 1970, pp. 83-84.

Braker, W., and Mossman, Al, *Matheson Gas Data Book*, The Matheson Company Inc., Lyndhurst, NJ, 1980.

Buckland, I. G., Butlin, R. N., and Annadale, D. J., Gas Explosions in Buildings; Part VI, Fire Research Station, Department of the Environment, Borehamwood, Herts, England, 1976.

Burgess, D. S., and Zabetakis, M. G., "Fire and Explosion Hazards Associated with LNG," Report 6099, U.S. Bureau of Mines, Washington, DC, 1962.

Cato, R. J., *et al.*, "Effect of Temperature on Upper Flammability Limits of Hydrocarbon Fuel Vapors in Air," *Fire Technology*, Vol. 3, No. 1, Feb. 1967, pp. 14-19.

Code of Federal Regulations, Title 49, Parts 171-190.

Compressed Gas Association, *Handbook of Compressed Gases*, 2nd ed., Van Nostrand Reinhold Co., NY, 1981.

Compressed Gas Association, *Handbook of Compressed Gases*, 3rd ed., Van Nostrand Reinhold, NY, 1990.

Danakowski, T. D., "Is Liquid Hydrogen Safer than Liquid Methane?" *Fire Technology*, Vol. 17, No. 3, Aug. 1981, pp. 183-188.

DeNevers, N., "Propane Over-Filling Fires," *Fire Journal*, Vol. 81, No. 5, 1987, p.80.

Ditzel, Paul C., "BLEVE—Boiling Liquid Expanding Vapor Explosions Can Be Fatal," *Firehouse*, June 1977, p. 28.

Dunn, V., "BLEVE: The Propane Cylinder," *Fire Engineering*, Vol. 141, No. 8, 1988, pp. 63-70.

Ellis, Donald L., "Propane Cloud and a Lot of Luck," *Fire Command*, Vol. 41, No. 2, Feb. 1974, p. 18.

Fire, F. L., "Ethylene," *Fire Engineering*, Vol. 140, No. 8, 1987, p. 53.

Fire, F. L., "Liquified Petrolium Gas," *Fire Engineering*, Vol. 142, No. 1, 1989, pp. 51-55.

Gubin, E. I., and Dik, I. G., "Flame Propagation in a Dusty Gas," *Combustion, Explosion and Shock Waves*, (English Translation), Vol. 23, No. 6, May 1988, pp. 685-690.

Gugan, K., *Unconfined Vapor Cloud Explosions*, Gulf Publishers, Houston, TX, 1979.

Harris, R. J., *Gas Explosions in Buildings and Heating Plants*, E. & F.N. Spon, London, 1983.

Hilado, Carlos J., and Cumming, Heather J., "The HC Value: A Method for Estimating the Flammability of Mixtures of Combustible Gases," *Fire Technology*, Vol. 13, No. 3, Aug. 1977, p. 195.

Hord, J., "Is Hydrogen Safe?" NBS Tech Note 690, National Bureau of Standards, Gaithersburg, MD, 1976.

Hustad, J. E., and Sonju, O.K., "Experimental Studies of Lower Flammability Limits of Gases and Mixtures of Gases at Elevated Temperatures," *Combustion and Flame*, Vol. 71, No. 3, March 1988, pp. 283-294.

"Hydrogen," Pamphlet G-5, Compressed Gas Association, NY.

Johannsson, O., "The Disaster of San Juanico," *Fire Journal*, Jan. 1986, p. 32.

Johnson, D. W., *et al.*, "Control and Extinguishment of LPG Fires," DOE/EV/06020-T3, U.S. Department of Energy, Washington, DC, 1980.

Kajino, Higeo, and Noso, Kiyoto, A Study of Possible Hazards by Leakage of Compressed Hydrogen Gas, Institution for Safety of High Pressure Gas Engineering, Tokyo, 1979.

Kilmartin, John, "Two Liquid Oxygen Explosions," *Fire Journal*, Vol. 65, No. 2, Mar. 1971, pp. 15-22.

Lewis, B., and Von Elbe, G., *Combustion, Flames and Explosions of Gases*, 3rd ed., Academic Press, Troy, MD, 1987.

Liquified Petrolium Gas, John Wiley & Sons, Chichester, 1987.

"LNG Importation and Terminal Safety," Proceedings of Conference of National Academy of Sciences, Boston, June 13-14, 1972.

"LPG: The Hazards and Precautions," Fire Protection, Apr. 1980.

LP-Gas Safety Handbook, National LP-Gas Association, Oak Brook, IL, 1981.

Lyons, P. R., "What Can We Do About Methane?" *Fire Command*, Feb. 1973, pp. 24-25.

Martinsen, W. E., *et al.*, "BLEVEs: Their Causes, Effects, and Prevention," *Hydrocarbon Processing*, Nov. 1986.

"Mapp Industrial Gas," Loss Prevention Data Sheet 7-94, Factory Mutual System, Norwood, MA.

McRae, M. H., "Anhydrous Ammonia Explosion in an Ice Cream Plant," *Plant/Operations Progress*, Vol. 6, No. 1, Jan. 1987, pp. 17-19.

Minzer, G. A., and Eyre, J. A., "Large Scale LNG and LPG Pool Fires," I. Chem. E. Symposium Series No. 71, 1982, pp. 147-163.

National Transportation Safety Board, several reports of investigations of utility natural gas explosions and fires, National Transportation Safety Board, Washington, DC.

Nettleton, M. A., *Gaseous Detonations: Their Nature, Effects, and Control*, Chapman and Hall, NY, 1987.

Powell, F., "Can Non-sparking Tools and Materials Prevent Gas Explosions ?," *Gaz-Eaux-Eaux Usees*, Vol. 66, No. 6, 1986, pp. 419-428.

"Properties and Essential Information for Safe Handling and Use of Ethylene," SD-100, 1973, Manufacturing Chemists' Association, Washington, DC.

Prugh, R. W., "Mitigation of Vapor Cloud Hazards," *Plant/Operations Progress*, Vol. 4, No. 2, April 1985, pp. 95-103.

Prugh, R. W., "Mitigation of Vapor Cloud Hazards," *Plant/Operations Progress*, Vol. 5, No. 3, July 1986, pp. 169-174.

Rasbash, D. J., "Review of Explosion and Fire Hazard of Liquified Petroleum Gas," *Fire Safety Journal*, Vol. 2, No. 4, July 1980, pp. 223-236.

Senesky, J., "Safe Storage and Handling of Compressed Gases," Plant Engineering, Vol. 33, No. 10, Oct. 1979, pp. 143-148.

U.S. Dept. of Energy Research Reports, Contract DE-AC06-76 RLO 1830, Pacific Northwest Laboratory, Battelle Memorial Institute (NTIS)

PNL-4401, LNG Annotated Bibliography

PNL-4398, LNG Fire and Vapor Control System Technologies

PNL-3991, Assessment of Research and Development

Needs in LPG Safety and Environmental Control.

"Just What is a BLEVE?" *Fire Journal*, Vol. 72, No. 6, Nov. 1978, p. 46.

Van den Berg, A. C., *et al.*, "Current Research at T.N.O. on Vapor Cloud Explosion Modeling," *Proceedings* of the International Conference on Vapor Cloud Modeling, Boston, 1987.

Van Wingerden, C. J. M., *et al.*, "Vapor Cloud Explosion Blast Prediction," *Plant/Operation Progress*, Vol. 8, No. 4, 1989, pp. 234-238.

Zabetakis, Michael D., "Flammability Characteristics of Combustible Gases and Vapors," *Bulletin 627*, U.S. Bureau of Mines, Washington, DC, 1965.

CHEMICALS

Revised by W. J. Bradford

Safe and effective fire control measures when chemicals are involved require a knowledge of the hazardous properties of chemicals. This chapter discusses chemicals that produce hazards due to properties other than, or in addition to, combustibility. It also contains fire hazard information on combustible chemicals that are not discussed elsewhere in this section.

For the purposes of this discussion, chemicals are classified according to the following hazardous properties: (1) ability to oxidize other materials, (2) combustibility, (3) instability, (4) reactivity with air or water, (5) corrosiveness, and (6) radioactivity. Although many chemicals possess more than one of these properties, it is customary to classify each by its predominant hazard. The danger of such a procedure is that an unmentioned hazardous property may be overlooked. For this reason, it is necessary to refer to chemical dictionaries; manufacturers' data sheets; NFPA 49, *Hazardous Chemicals Data*; NFPA 491M, *Manual of Hazardous Chemical Reactions*; NFPA 325M, *Fire Hazard Properties of Flammable Liquids, Gases, and Volatile Solids*; and similar sources of information when evaluating the hazards of a particular chemical. Benzoyl peroxide, for example, is not only combustible but also very reactive; the degree of reactivity depends on the concentration. Another example is a commercial blasting mixture composed of ammonium nitrate mixed with oxidizable substances. For the purposes of transportation, these mixtures have been classified as oxidizing materials; however, they are also explosives. Thus, NFPA recommendations for the storage and handling of blasting agents closely parallel those for commercial explosives. At the end of each hazard classification, there is a discussion of the properties of the most common chemicals in the class and recommendations for storage and fire fighting.

For information about chemicals not contained in this chapter, see Section 3, Chapter 9, "Explosives and Blasting Agents," and Section 3, Chapter 12, "Dusts." Section 2, Chapter 15, "Chemical Processing Equipment," gives information on chemical processing equipment and describes processing in terms of specific reactions. Section 8, Chapter 25, "Nuclear Facilities," provides information about the hazards of radioactive materials in processes. Section 2, Chapter 27, "Storage and Handling of Chemicals," details safe storage practices and fire suppression techniques used with the various classes of chemicals.

W. J. Bradford, P.E., is a loss prevention consultant. He is a registered professional engineer in Connecticut and Rhode Island, a member of AIChE and SFPE, and serves on several NFPA technical committees.

TOXICITY OF CHEMICALS

The toxicity of chemicals is particularly important from the point of view of fire protection, regardless of the toxic material's fire hazard. A fire or explosion may subject fire fighters to a severe life hazard if the toxic material is accidentally released while they are present. In situations where fire officers are aware of a real or potential toxicity hazard, the decision may be made to forgo effective manual fire fighting.

Before using a chemical, one should obtain and evaluate information about its toxicity. When the toxicity problem appears to be severe, an effort should be made to find a suitable less toxic substitute. If there is no practical way to eliminate the toxic material, protection should be provided for those subject to daily exposure and for fire department personnel. Those who may be exposed during a fire or other emergency should be informed of the potential hazard and advised of the proper protective clothing and breathing apparatus to wear. Automatic fire protection should always be provided when a fire hazard is present in conjunction with a toxicity hazard.

Information on the toxicity of chemicals can be obtained from various sources, including the manufacturers of the chemicals; NFPA 49, *Hazardous Chemicals Data*; Patty's *Industrial Hygiene and Toxicology*; and other references.

There are two ways to protect against the toxic effects of chemicals during handling. First, use the most practical of the available methods for controlling and confining the chemical so that the toxic material cannot be contacted, swallowed, or inhaled in dangerous quantities during normal operations. Second, in areas where toxic chemicals are handled, educate all persons about the hazards, precautionary procedures, danger signals, and emergency procedures to be followed.

Of the methods used to control and confine toxic chemicals, handling them in a closed system is absolutely necessary. However, a leak in the system is always possible and could subject persons to a severe health hazard. If the gas is not an irritant, personnel must be warned of the exposure by automatically operated toxic gas indicators or other alarm devices. In some installations, it may be possible to maintain a slight negative pressure on the closed system to prevent the escape of toxic materials in case of a minor leak. Generally, such systems are ducted to a scrubber where the toxic gas can be neutralized. Wherever possible, processes should be installed outdoors where natural air movement will dilute and dissipate toxic gases or vapors.

OXIDIZING CHEMICALS

Several important groups of chemicals known as oxidizing agents provide oxygen for combustion. Although most oxidizing chemicals are not combustible, they may increase the ease of ignition of combustible materials and they invariably increase the intensity of burning. A few oxidizing agents are susceptible to spontaneous decomposition (instability), and thus possess within themselves all the ingredients for a fire or explosion.

Nitrates

Awareness of the fire hazard properties of the inorganic nitrates is important because these materials are widely used in fertilizers, salt baths, and other industrial applications. Under fire conditions, inorganic nitrates may melt and release oxygen, causing the fire to intensify. Molten nitrates react with organic materials with considerable violence, usually releasing toxic oxides of nitrogen. When solid streams of water are used for fire fighting, they may produce steam explosions upon contact with molten material. Common nitrates are discussed in this section. Other nitrates have somewhat similar properties.

Sodium nitrate: Noncombustible sodium nitrate promotes combustion of other materials. It evolves oxygen when heated to about 700°F (370°C), thereby increasing the intensity of any fire in its vicinity. It is soluble in water and is hygroscopic. This water solubility (common to most nitrates) is indirectly responsible for many serious fires. Paper, burlap, or cloth bags of nitrates that become moist during shipment or storage retain an impregnation of nitrate after drying and are thus highly combustible. For this reason, nitrates should be transferred from bags or wood barrels to noncombustible bins for storage. The bags or barrels should be thoroughly washed. For the same reason, storage of bulk sodium nitrate on wood floors or against wood walls or posts is hazardous. An intimate mixture of sodium nitrate and organic material can be exploded by a flame.

Potassium nitrate: The properties and hazards of potassium nitrate are similar to those of sodium nitrate; however, potassium nitrate is less moisture absorbent.

Ammonium nitrate: Like other inorganic nitrates, ammonium nitrate is an oxidizing agent and will increase the intensity of a fire. The oxidizing gas it gives off is nitrous oxide rather than oxygen. Chemical- and fertilizer-grade ammonium nitrate must not be confused with certain ammonium nitrate combustible material mixtures used as explosives. All grades of ammonium nitrate can be detonated if they are in the proper crystalline form, if the initiating source is sufficiently large, or if heated under sufficient confinement (the purest material needing the greatest confinement).

As is evident from the shipboard explosions at Texas City, TX, and Brest, France (both in 1947), and the Red Sea in 1953; the explosion following a freight train wreck at Traskwood, AR, Dec. 1960; and the explosion in a bulk warehouse near Pryor, OK, Jan. 1973, certain conditions other than initiation by explosives can cause ammonium nitrate to detonate. An extensive series of tests to determine the explosion hazards of fertilizer-grade ammonium nitrate under fire exposure was conducted by the U.S. Bureau of Mines,[1] and from that study it would appear that the following conclusions can be reached:

1. Although detonation initiation in ammonium nitrate as a result of fire exposure cannot be ruled out completely, a direct burning-to-detonation transition in commercial fertilizer-grade ammonium nitrate (referred to, hereafter, as "AN") appears to be possible only in a pile of extremely large dimensions, with the ignition at the bottom or center of the pile. (The ammonium nitrate involved in the Texas City, Brest, and Red Sea explosions was organic coated, with substantially different burning characteristics from those of the AN manufactured today.)
2. Projectiles derived from nearby explosions can initiate reactions leading to detonations, particularly in hot AN. Ordinary sporting arms bullets are incapable of initiating detonations of AN under normal storage conditions.
3. When AN is intimately mixed with fuel oil, ground polyethylene, or ground paper, transition from burning to detonation is possible, although quite unlikely, in pile sizes that are typical of those found in storage and transportation. Such mixtures are properly classified as blasting agents and should be stored according to the requirements in NFPA 495, *Manufacture, Transportation, Storage, and Use of Explosive Materials*.
4. Gas detonations are incapable of initiating detonation of AN.
5. Hot AN can be detonated by projectile impact. (Initiation of detonation of AN in the Traskwood freight train wreck and fire may have been by projectiles derived from a gasoline-nitric acid detonation, because tank cars of gasoline and of nitric acid were also in the wreck. Nitric acid may have become mixed with the burning gasoline.)

Tests conducted by Underwriters Laboratories Inc. indicate that mixtures of ammonium nitrate and ammonium sulfate containing not more than 40 percent by weight of ammonium nitrate, and mixtures of ammonium nitrate and calcium carbonate (calcium ammonium nitrate) containing not more than 61 percent ammonium nitrate, are not explosive under conditions met in practice. When exposed to fire, calcium ammonium nitrate forms calcium nitrate and ammonium carbonate which absorbs heat while decomposing to ammonia, carbon dioxide, and water. However, the contamination problem has not been thoroughly investigated.

Ammonium nitrate in water solution is not hazardous unless spilled into combustible material and permitted to dry. Research, however, has shown that solutions containing up to 8 percent water can be detonated.[2]

Cellulose nitrate: For hazards and properties of cellulose nitrate, see Section 3, Chapter 10, "Plastics and Rubber."

Nitric Acid

(See the section "Corrosive Chemicals," in this chapter.)

Nitrites

Nitrites should not be confused with nitrates. Nitrites contain one less oxygen atom than nitrates but are more active oxidizing agents since they melt and release oxygen at lower temperatures. Because nitrites in mixtures with combustible substances are hazardous, such mixtures should not be subjected to heat or flame. Certain nitrites, notably ammonium nitrite, are by themselves explosive. Nitrites should be treated like nitrates with respect to storage, handling, and fire fighting.

Inorganic Peroxides

Sodium, potassium, and strontium peroxide: Although these chemicals are themselves noncombustible, they react vigorously with water and release oxygen as well as large amounts of heat. Large quantities of sodium and potassium peroxides may react explosively with water, and heat from reaction with just a little water may cause the contents of an entire container to decompose. If organic or other oxidizable material is present when this reaction takes place, fire is likely to occur.

Barium peroxide: Heat releases oxygen from barium peroxide. Intimate mixtures of barium peroxide and combustible or readily oxidizable materials are explosive and easily ignited by friction or by contact with a small amount of water.

Hydrogen peroxide: In contrast to the four above-mentioned peroxides, which are white powders, hydrogen peroxide is a syrupy liquid. In pure form, it is relatively stable. When heated to and kept at a temperature of 212°F (100°C), 99.2 percent hydrogen peroxide decomposes at the rate of 4 percent per year, and 50 to 90 percent hydrogen peroxide at a rate of something less than 2 percent a day. An increase in temperature increases the decomposition rate of hydrogen peroxide about 1½ times for each 10°F (–12°C). Near the boiling point, the rate of decomposition is very rapid, and, if adequate venting is not provided, the pressure in the container may cause it to rupture. In general, the dilute material is less stable than the concentrated.

Solutions at concentrations of between 86 and 90.7 percent hydrogen peroxide have been demonstrated to be detonatable.[3] At a concentration above about 92 percent, the liquid can be exploded by shock. Concentrated hydrogen peroxide vapors can be exploded by a spark. At atmospheric pressure, the boiling material must be 74 percent hydrogen peroxide or higher to produce explosive vapors.

Decomposition of hydrogen peroxide produces water, oxygen, and heat. At concentrations above 35 percent, the heat is sufficient to turn all the water into steam, assuming that the decomposition began at room temperature [72°F (22°C)]. This means that a steam explosion is possible with the sudden decomposition of concentrated material. Decomposition may be caused by contamination with iron, copper, chromium, and many other metals (except aluminum) or their salts. Decomposition can also be caused by combustible dust, or by contact with a rough surface, such as ground glass.

Hydrogen peroxide is a strong oxidizing agent and may cause ignition of combustible material with which it remains in contact. This possibility is remote, except in the case of concentrations greater than 35 percent.

Chlorates

An adequate understanding of the fire hazard properties of the chlorates can be gained from the best-known member of the group, potassium chlorate.

Potassium chlorate: This white crystalline substance is water soluble, noncombustible, and a strong oxidizing agent. When heated, it gives up oxygen even more readily than do nitrates. Mixture with combustible materials, e.g., floor sweepings, should be prevented because under such conditions potassium chlorate may ignite or explode spontaneously. Drums containing chlorates may explode when heated. Sodium chlorate has properties similar to potassium chlorate.

Chlorites

Sodium chlorite: This is a powerful oxidizing agent that forms explosive mixtures with combustible materials. In contact with strong acids, it releases explosive chlorine dioxide gas. At 347°F (175°C), sodium chlorite decomposes with the evolution of heat.

Dichromates

Among the dichromates, all of which are noncombustible, ammonium dichromate is most readily decomposed. It begins to decompose at 356°F (180°C); above 437°F (225°C) the decomposition becomes self-sustaining and is accompanied by swelling and the release of heat and nitrogen gas. Closed containers rupture at the decomposition temperature.

The other dichromates, such as potassium dichromate, react with readily oxidizable materials which, in some cases, may cause them to ignite. They release oxygen when heated.

Hypochlorites

Calcium hypochlorite at a concentration above 50 percent by weight may cause combustible or organic materials to ignite on contact. When heated, it gives off oxygen. With acids or moisture, it freely evolves chlorine, chlorine monoxide, and some oxygen at ordinary temperatures. It is sold as bleaching powder or, when concentrated, as a swimming pool disinfectant.

Perchlorates

Perchlorates contain one more oxygen atom than chlorates. They have roughly similar properties, but are more stable than chlorates. They are explosive under some conditions, such as when in contact with concentrated sulfuric acid.

Ammonium perchlorate: This chemical has great explosive sensitivity when contaminated with such impurities as sulfur, powdered metals, carbonaceous materials, and reducing agents. The pure material in finely divided form can detonate if involved in a fire. A mixture with a chlorate may form spontaneously explosive ammonium chlorate.

Potassium perchlorate, sodium perchlorate, and magnesium perchlorate: Each of these chemicals forms explosive mixtures with combustible, organic, or other easily oxidizable materials. Magnesium perchlorate is sometimes used in laboratories in place of calcium chloride as a dessicant. Such use requires vigilance to avoid dangerous contamination.

Permanganates

Mixtures of inorganic permanganates and combustible material are subject to ignition by friction or may ignite spontaneously if an inorganic acid is present. Explosions may occur whether the permanganate is in solution or is dry.

Potassium permanganate: This chemical reacts violently with finely divided oxidizable substances. On contact with sulfuric acid or hydrogen peroxide, it is explosive.

Persulfates

Persulfates, e.g., potassium persulfate, are strong oxidizing agents which may cause explosions during a fire. Oxygen released by the heat of a fire may cause an explosive rupture of the container, or the explosion may follow an accidental mixture of the persulfate with combustible material.

COMBUSTIBLE CHEMICALS

Carbon Black

Carbon black may be formed by the decomposition of acetylene, by incomplete combustion of natural gas, or a mixture of natural gas and a liquid hydrocarbon, or by cracking hydrocarbon vapor in the absence of air. It is most hazardous immediately following manufacture when bags of the finished product may contain red-hot carbon particles. While carbon black adsorbs oxygen, slow smoldering may develop. To prevent this hazard, carbon black is stored in an observation warehouse before shipment or final storage. It is well established that carbon black will not heat spontaneously after thorough cooling and airing, although it may generate heat in the presence of oxidizable oils.

Tests show that a dust explosion hazard does not exist. Red-hot metal, electric sparks, and burning magnesium ribbon will not cause carbon black dust clouds to ignite explosively, but ignition has been obtained by using 1 oz. (28 g) of gunpowder.

Carbon black comprises 98 percent of the world's production of powdered carbon.

Lamp Black

Lamp black is formed by burning low-grade heavy oils or similar carbonaceous materials with insufficient air. It adsorbs gases to a marked degree and often ignites spontaneously when freshly bagged. It has great affinity for liquids, and heats in contact with drying oils. The possibility of lamp black dust explosions is increased by the presence of unconsumed oil that adheres to the carbon. Bureau of Mines' tests indicate that a dust explosion hazard may exist if the oil content exceeds 13 percent. Lamp black should be thoroughly cooled before it is bagged and then stored in a cool, dry area away from oxidizing materials.

Lead Sulfocyanate

Lead sulfocyanate burns slowly. It decomposes when heated, yielding among its decomposition products highly toxic and flammable carbon disulfide and highly toxic but nonflammable sulfur dioxide.

Nitroaniline

This combustible solid melts at 295°F (146°C) and its flash point is 390°F (199°C). In the presence of moisture, it nitrates organic materials, which may result in their spontaneous ignition.

Nitrochlorobenzene

Nitrochlorobenzene is a solid material at ordinary temperatures and gives off flammable vapors when heated.

Sulfides

Antimony pentasulfide: This is readily ignited and hazardous in contact with oxidizing materials. On contact with strong acids, antimony pentasulfide yields hydrogen sulfide.

Phosphorus pentasulfide: This ignites readily, and in the presence of moisture may heat spontaneously to its ignition temperature [287°F (142°C)]. The products of combustion include highly toxic sulfur dioxide and phosphorus pentoxide. Reaction of phosphorus pentasulfide with water yields hydrogen sulfide.

Phosphorus sesquisulfide: With an ignition temperature of only 212°F (100°C), this chemical is easily ignited and is considered highly flammable. Toxic sulfur dioxide is a product of combustion.

Potassium sulfide and sodium sulfide: These are moderately flammable solids that form toxic sulfur dioxide when burning, and hydrogen sulfide on contact with acids.

Sulfur

Sulfur at ordinary temperatures is a yellow solid or powder consisting of rhombic crystals which melt in the vicinity of 234°F (112°C), depending on their purity. Sulfur boils at about 832°F (444°C). Except in small quantities, it is shipped and stored as a liquid at a temperature below 300°F (149°C). It is combustible, and its vapor forms explosive mixtures with air. [Its flash point is 405°F (207°C).] Finely divided sulfur dust likewise possesses an explosion hazard that requires control during storage and handling. Ignition temperatures of dust clouds vary upward from 374°F (190°C). Sulfur contains varying amounts of hydrocarbons, depending on the source. These hydrocarbons gradually react with the molten material to form combustible and highly toxic hydrogen sulfide. Storage tanks and pits for molten sulfur must be ventilated to prevent accumulation of this gas. Except in the presence of lamp black, carbon black, charcoal, and a few less common substances, spontaneous ignition of sulfur is practically nonexistent. It melts and flows when burning and evolves large quantities of toxic, irritating, and suffocating sulfur dioxide. This gas attacks the eyes and throat, and complicates fire fighting. Sulfur also forms highly explosive and easily detonated mixtures with chlorates and perchlorates, and forms gunpowder when mixed with potassium nitrate and charcoal.

Naphthalene

Naphthalene is combustible both in solid and in liquid form. Naphthalene vapors and dusts form explosive mixtures with air.

UNSTABLE CHEMICALS

Certain chemicals spontaneously polymerize, decompose, or otherwise react with themselves in the presence of a catalytic material or even when pure. Such reactions may become violent.

Acetaldehyde

Acetaldehyde is a highly reactive compound. Under suitable conditions, the oxygen or any hydrogen can be replaced. Acetaldehyde undergoes numerous condensation, addition, and polymerization reactions which may take place with explosive violence.

Ethyl acrylate, methyl acrylate, methyl methacrylate, and vinylidene chloride: These are flammable liquids that may polymerize at elevated temperatures, as in fire conditions. If the polymerization takes place in a closed container, the container may rupture violently. These liquids usually contain an inhibitor to prevent polymerization.

Ethylene Oxide

Ethylene oxide may polymerize violently when catalyzed by anhydrous chlorides of iron, tin, or aluminum; oxides of iron (i.e., iron rust) and aluminum; and alkali metal hydroxides. Violent polymerization of ethylene oxide may be initiated by heat or shock. Ethylene oxide reacts with alcohols, organic and inorganic acids, ammonia, and many other compounds. The heat liberated by these exothermic reactions may cause polymerization of the unreacted ethylene oxide. Ethylene oxide vapors may detonate if some initiating heat source is present. Ethylene oxide vapors in a tank exposed by fire may be rapidly heated to their ignition temperature unless the tank is kept wet with water spray. The flammable range of ethylene oxide in air is 3 to 80 percent. Although the upper limit is frequently reported to be 100 percent, explosions of mixtures containing greater than 80 percent ethylene oxide are the result of chemical decomposition.

Hydrogen Cyanide

Hydrogen cyanide is flammable and poisonous. In either liquid or vapor states, it has a tendency to polymerize. The reaction is catalyzed by alkaline materials, and since one of the products of the polymerization reaction is alkaline (ammonia), an explosive reaction will eventually take place. By adding sulfuric, phosphoric, or some other acid to neutralize the ammonia, the rate of polymerization in the liquid can be held down to a safe speed. Potassium cyanide and sodium cyanide on contact with acids release poisonous and flammable hydrogen cyanide vapor.

Nitromethane

Nitromethane is a combustible liquid. At 599°F (315°C) and 915 psig (6308 kPa), it decomposes explosively. Noteworthy detonations of nitromethane in railroad tank cars occurred at Niagara Falls, NY, and at Mt. Pulaski, IL, in 1958. Although undiluted nitromethane may detonate under certain conditions of heat, pressure, shock, and contamination, the causes of these two tank car explosions were not definitely determined. A possible explanation is contamination of the nitromethane by some material previously carried in the tanks. For a discussion of the hazards of nitromethane and other nitroparaffins, see AIA Research Report No. 12.[4]

Organic Peroxides

Organic peroxides are an important group of chemicals widely used in the plastics industry as polymerization reaction initiators, in the milling industry as flour bleaches, and in the chemical and drug industries as catalysts. All organic peroxides are combustible and, as in the case of inorganic peroxides, increase the intensity of a fire. Many organic peroxides can be decomposed by heat, shock, or friction. The rate of decomposition depends on the particular peroxide formulation and the temperature. Some, such as methyl ethyl ketone peroxide, are detonatable. Organic peroxides may be liquid (e.g., t-butyl perbenzoate) or solid (e.g., benzoyl peroxide) and are often dissolved in flammable or combustible solvents. The peroxides are often found wet with water or diluted with stable liquids. With solutions, sensitive crystals can be formed by freezing.

Benzoyl peroxide: In undiluted form, benzoyl peroxide ignites very readily and burns with great rapidity, similar to burning an equal amount of black powder. Decomposition by heat is rapid, and, if the benzoyl peroxide is confined when heated, explosive decomposition will occur. Decomposition can also be initiated by heavy shock or frictional heat. Most benzoyl peroxide is shipped diluted or water-wet to reduce the fire hazard.

Ether peroxides: During storage, practically all ethers form ether peroxides. When the ether peroxide mixture is heated or concentrated, the peroxide may detonate. With some ethers, the quantities of peroxide formed are too small to be of significance. Peroxide formation is a hazardous property of diethyl ether, ethyl tertiary butyl ether, ethyl tertiary amyl ether, and the isopropyl ethers. Isopropyl ether is said to be considerably more susceptible to peroxide formation than other ethers. When pure, dry ether is stored under laboratory conditions in a clear and colorless bottle, it will develop detectable amounts of peroxides in one month. Light seems to be a more important factor than heat, although peroxides have been known to form in amber bottles. Ether sealed in copper-plated cans or in otherwise inhibited cans is not likely to form peroxides. Although there is apparently no means yet available to completely eliminate peroxide formation, using any one of numerous patented inhibitors, or copper or iron along with storage in metal or opaque amber glass containers, provides sufficient stability for all practical purposes. Ether should not be dry-distilled unless peroxides have been proved absent.

Styrene

Styrene polymerizes slowly at ordinary temperatures, and the rate increases as the temperature increases. Since the polymerization reaction is exothermic, the reaction will eventually become violent as it is accelerated by its own heat. Inhibitors are added to styrene to prevent dangerous polymerization.

Vinyl Chloride

Vinyl chloride is a toxic and flammable gas that may polymerize at elevated temperatures, as in fire conditions, and cause violent rupture of the container. Vinyl chloride usually contains an inhibitor to prevent polymerization.

WATER- AND AIR-REACTIVE CHEMICALS

Water-reactive and air-reactive chemicals present significant fire hazards. Significant quantities of heat are liberated during the reactions. If the chemical is combustible, it is capable of self-ignition; if noncombustible, the heat of reaction may be sufficient to ignite nearby combustible materials.

Alkalies (Caustics)

Caustic soda (sodium hydroxide or lye) and caustic potash (potassium hydroxide) are the most common alkalies. Although caustics are noncombustible, they generate heat when mixed with water. In contact with water, dry solid caustics will react. The heat generated (heat of solution) may be sufficient to ignite combustible material. Caustic solutions may generate hydrogen on contact with zinc, galvanized metals, or aluminum.

Aluminum Trialkyls

Most of these organic metal compounds are pyrophoric, i.e., they ignite spontaneously on exposure to air, and react violently with water and certain other chemicals. Triethylaluminum, the most common member of this group, ignites spontaneously in air and on contact with water. When it is mixed with strong oxidizing agents or with halogenated hydrocarbons, violent reactions or detonations may occur.

Anhydrides

Acid anhydrides are compounds of acids from which water has been removed. They react with water, usually violently, to regenerate acids. Organic acid anhydrides are combustible and usually are more hazardous than their corresponding acids, since their flash points are lower. Acetic anhydride has a flash point of 129°F (54°C); propionic anhydride, 165°F (74°C), open cup; butyric anhydride, 190°F (88°C), open cup; and maleic anhydride, 218°F (103°C). Inorganic acid anhydrides, e.g., chromium anhydride and phosphorus anhydride, are not combustible.

Carbides

The carbides of some metals, such as sodium and potassium, may react explosively on contact with water. Many, such as calcium carbide, lithium carbide, potassium carbide, and barium carbide, decompose in water to form acetylene. In addition to the hazard of the formation of flammable gas, another fire hazard of certain carbides is the generation of heat in contact with water. When one-third its weight of water is added to a water-reactive carbide, the temperature may be raised sufficiently to ignite the gas generated. Sodium carbide becomes heated to incandescence when placed in chlorine, carbon dioxide, or sulfur dioxide. The carbides of silicon and tungsten are very stable.

Charcoal

Under certain conditions, charcoal reacts with air at a sufficient rate to cause the charcoal to heat spontaneously and ignite. Charcoal made from hard wood by the retort method appears to be particularly susceptible. Spontaneous heating occurs more readily in fresh charcoal than in old material; the more finely divided it is, the greater the hazard. The principal causes of spontaneous heating of charcoal appear to be: (1) lack of sufficient cooling and airing before shipment; (2) charcoal becoming wet; (3) friction in grinding of finer sizes, particularly of material insufficiently aired before grinding; and (4) carbonizing of wood at too low a temperature, leaving the charcoal in a chemically unstable condition.

Coal

Under some conditions, virtually all grades of coal (except high-grade anthracite) are subject to spontaneous heating and ignition. Although the basic causes for the spontaneous heating of coal are not well defined, it is believed that adsorption of oxygen or oxidation of finely divided particles is the main cause. While instances of spontaneous heating of coal are numerous, the number of fires from this cause is insignificant when the large number of coal storage piles is considered.

The principal conditions believed to affect the susceptibility of coal to spontaneous heating are: (1) the fineness of the particles, (2) the oxygen adsorptive abilities of the particles, (3) the trapped and confined moisture content of the coal, (4) air trapped in voids in coal piles, (5) the presence of sulfur in the form of pyrites or marcasites, (6) free gases in the pile, (7) foreign substances in the pile, (8) the method and depth of piling, (9) the temperature of the containing walls and floor or of surrounding or surrounded surfaces, and (10) the type and amount of ventilation.

Hydrides

Most hydrides are compounds of hydrogen and metals. Metal hydrides react with water to form hydrogen gas.

Sodium hydride: A gray-white crystalline, free-flowing powder, sodium hydride will ignite with explosive violence on contact with water. When exposed to air, absorption of moisture may cause ignition.

Lithium hydride: When this combustible solid reacts vigorously with water, hydrogen gas and heat are evolved. Lithium hydride dust is likely to explode in humid air. Static electricity may cause the dust to explode in dry air.

Lithium aluminum hydride: Like lithium hydride, this chemical is a combustible solid that reacts rapidly with water to form hydrogen gas and heat. The heat will probably cause the hydrogen to ignite. When lithium aluminum hydride is in a solution with ether, a fire involving the solution is essentially an ether fire. Small amounts of water cause the burning to intensify. Combustible materials on which the solution has spilled may ignite spontaneously or be ignited by light friction.

Oxides

Oxides of some metals and nonmetals react with water to form alkalies and acids, respectively. This reaction takes place violently with the infrequently used sodium oxide. Calcium oxide, more commonly known as quicklime or unslaked lime, also reacts vigorously with water (slaking) with the evolution of enough heat to ignite paper, wood, or other combustible material under some conditions.

Phosphorus

Two forms of phosphorus, i.e., white and red, are in common use.

White (or yellow) phosphorus: This type is the more dangerous because of its ready oxidation and spontaneous ignition in air. It is common practice to ship and store white phosphorus under water, usually with the mixture in a hermetically sealed metal container. Periodic checks should be made to ensure that containers do not leak. White phosphorus is very toxic and should not be permitted to come in contact with the skin. On ignition, dense white clouds of toxic fumes are evolved which attack the lungs.

Red phosphorus: This type is less hazardous than white, does not oxidize and burn spontaneously at ordinary temperatures, and can be shipped and stored without the protection of water, although it should be kept in closed containers away from oxidizing agents. It is formed by heating white phosphorus. The solid form is not toxic but, once vaporized, it takes on all the fire hazards of white phosphorus to which it reverts on condensation. Care should be taken in opening containers of red phosphorus because spontaneous ignition has been known to take place with exposure to air.

Sodium

(See Section 3, Chapter 13, "Metals.")

Sodium Hydrosulfite

Sodium hydrosulfite burns slowly and produces sulfur dioxide as a combustion product. On contact with moisture and air, sodium hydrosulfite heats spontaneously and may ignite nearby combustible materials.

CORROSIVE CHEMICALS

The term "corrosive" refers to those chemicals that have a destructive effect on living tissues. Although some corrosive chemicals are strong oxidizing agents, they are separately classified to emphasize their injurious effect upon contact or inhalation. It should not be inferred, however, that a chemical is not injurious because it is otherwise classified. For example, caustics, classified as water- and air-reactive chemicals, are also corrosive. *Care should be taken to prevent inhalation, ingestion, and contact with all chemicals unless they are known to be harmless.*

Inorganic Acids

Concentrated aqueous solutions of the inorganic acids are not in themselves combustible. Their chief hazard lies in the danger of leakage and possible mixture with other chemicals or combustible material stored in the vicinity, since fire or explosions could occur in some cases.

Hydrochloric acid: In concentrated solution, hydrochloric acid is hazardous because its reaction with certain metals (including tin, iron, zinc, aluminum, and magnesium) forms hydrogen gas. Strong oxidizing agents mixed with hydrochloric acid causes the release of chlorine gas. A mixture of nitric and hydrochloric acids generates chlorine and nitrous oxide.

Hydrofluoric acid: Either anhydrous or aqueous hydrofluoric acid is noncombustible and does not cause ignition of combustible materials with which it comes in contact. However, it is highly toxic, irritating to the eyes, and inflicts severe skin burns. When it comes in contact with metals, hydrogen is generated.

Nitric acid: Under certain conditions nitric acid nitrates cellulose material. Thus, wood that comes in contact with the acid or its vapor may ignite much more easily. Spontaneous heating follows if strong solutions of the acid mix with organic material. In general, concentrated nitric acid nitrates organic materials; dilute acid oxidizes them, giving off oxides of nitrogen during the process. These oxide fumes (colorless to brown) are usually present in fires in buildings where nitric acid is used. A concentration of this gas (actually a mixture of several gases) so small that it is not objectionable at the time of inhalation can result in serious illness or death to the victim, although no effects may be felt for some time. If white fuming nitric acid (more than 97.5 percent nitric acid) is spilled into burning gasoline, it will detonate.[1]

Perchloric acid: When misused or used in concentrations greater than 72 percent, perchloric acid can be extremely dangerous. At the normal commercial strength (72 percent), it is a strong oxidizing and dehydrating agent when heated, but a strong nonoxidizing acid at room temperature. Because of this and other advantageous properties, it is widely used in analytical laboratories. The rate of burning of organic substances is greatly increased by contact with perchloric acid. Explosions have occurred at wood and plastic laboratory hoods after long exposure of the hoods to perchloric acid vapors. Strong dehydrating agents, such as concentrated sulfuric acid or phosphorus pentoxide, convert perchloric acid solution to anhydrous perchloric acid, which decomposes even at room temperature and explodes with terrific violence. It also explodes on contact with many organic substances. For these reasons, dehydrating agents should never be mixed with perchloric acid.

Sulfuric acid: This chemical has the added hazardous property of absorbing water from organic material with which it may come in contact. Charring takes place and sufficient heat may be evolved to cause ignition. Particular care must be taken to avoid painful skin burns inflicted by bodily contact. Dilute sulfuric acid will dissolve metals with the evolution of hydrogen.

The Halogens

The members of the halogen (salt-producing) group are all chemically active and have similar chemical properties. The individual elements, i.e., fluorine, chlorine, bromine, and iodine, differ from each other in decreased chemical activity in the order named. Bromine and iodine have the least fire hazard. They are noncombustible, but will support combustion of certain substances. Turpentine, phosphorus, and finely divided metals ignite spontaneously in the presence of the halogens. The fumes are poisonous, as well as corrosive and irritating to the eyes and throat.

Bromine: This is a dark reddish-brown corrosive liquid which may cause fire when in contact with combustible materials.

Chlorine: This is a heavy, greenish-yellow, highly toxic gas given off in some manufacturing processes and by bleaching powder (chloride of lime), especially in the presence of strong acids. It is not flammable itself, but may cause fires or explosions, especially if it comes in contact with acetylene, ammonia, turpentine, hydrocarbons, or finely powdered metals. At 484°F (251°C), mild steel ignites and burns in chlorine. Adequate ventilation should be provided in any process where this gas is generated.

Fluorine: A greenish-yellow gas, fluorine is one of the most reactive elements known. It combines, in most cases spontaneously, with practically all known elements and compounds under suitable conditions. Fluorine reacts violently with hydrogen and many organic materials. It explodes in contact with metallic powders, attacks glass and most metals, and reacts explosively in contact with water vapor. It may be safely handled in nickel or Monel™ cylinders. Fluorine reacts with these two metals, but forms a protective nickel fluoride layer that prevents further action. However, moisture or other impurities within the cylinder may cause such violent reaction that the metal will melt and ignite in the fluorine. The tank will then burst and scatter molten metal.

Iodine: This chemical is usually in the form of purplish-black volatile crystals which are corrosive. Reports indicate that iodine is explosive when diffused with ammonia (it forms explosive nitrogen triiodide) and when mixed with turpentine or lead triethyl.

RADIOACTIVE MATERIALS

Radioactive elements and compounds have fire and explosion hazards identical to those of the same material when not radioactive. An additional hazard is introduced by the various types of radiation emitted, all of which are capable of causing damage to living tissue. Under fire conditions, vapors and dusts (smoke) may be formed that could contaminate not only the building of origin but neighboring buildings and outdoor areas. The fire protection engineer's main concern is to prevent the release or loss of control of these materials by fire during fire extinguishment.

Fire Protection for Radioactive Materials

The life hazard introduced by an escape of radioactive dusts and vapors during a fire makes it vitally important to take all practical steps to prevent a fire from involving these materials. Radioactivity is not detectable by any of the human senses. Special instruments and measuring techniques are required to identify and evaluate it. The hazard is affected by the form of the material, i.e., whether solid, liquid, or gas, and by the container in which it is kept or handled.

Radioactivity can cause loss of life, injuries, and damage to and extended loss of materials used, as well as damage to equipment and buildings. Manual fire fighting may be limited by the danger to fire fighters from exposure to radioactivity. Salvage work and resumption of normal operations at a property may be delayed where a fire or explosion causes loss of control over radioactive substances. The need to decontaminate buildings, equipment, and materials presents a serious and complicated problem.

Smoke and products of combustion from fires in places where there are radioactive materials must be controlled. The runoff of water used in fighting fires must also be controlled. Fire fighters require protective clothing and respiratory protection equipment. Fire control must be thoroughly preplanned. With radiation hazards, automatic sprinklers are preferable to measures requiring manual fire fighting. This lessens the amount of radioactive smoke or products of combustion and water runoff to be dealt with manually.

Handling Radioactive Materials

The possibility of accidental release of radioactive material because of a fire or explosion, with the resultant health hazard to fire fighters and others, is a strong argument for careful attention to methods of fire prevention and control in laboratories and other occupancies handling radioactive materials.

More information can be obtained from NFPA 801, *Facilities Handling Radioactive Materials.* This publication calls attention to basic information concerning radiation protection methods and provides some guidance on fire protection practices to those who design and operate such facilities. Most radioactive materials introduce little or no fire or explosion hazard, so the fire hazard of facilities handling radiation usually can be determined by a knowledge of the combustibility of the building and its furnishings, and the fire and explosion hazards of the nonradioactive chemicals.

The fire and explosion hazard can be substantially reduced by use of a fire-resistive building, noncombustible interior finish and furnishings wherever possible, and enforcement of strict controls to minimize the hazards of flammable liquids and other chemicals that may be necessary for laboratory work or for other occupancies. In any facility handling radioactive materials, one feature that can cause trouble unless the building has been properly designed is the duct system usually required for the safe disposal of contaminated vapors, gases, and dusts. Unless this system is properly arranged, it can spread radioactive contaminants to noninvolved parts of a facility during a fire.

Due to the need to immediately control any fire that might eventually release radioactive materials and the potential health hazard to those who could be exposed to radiation during manual fire control, there can be no question as to the desirability of automatic sprinkler protection for radiation laboratories and other areas where radioactive materials are handled. Special precautions to be followed by fire fighting personnel are described in *Handling Radiation Emergencies.*[5] The procedures stress steps that should be taken to protect fire fighters at all times, including the use of radiation monitoring devices, self-contained breathing apparatus, and regular fire department protective clothing.

MIXTURES OF CHEMICALS

This chapter has presented several examples of dangerous reactions that can occur when certain chemicals are mixed. Examples have been given of chemicals that can increase the ease of ignition or the intensity of burning of the combustible materials with which they are mixed. In order to recognize the innumerable combinations of so-called incompatible chemicals, it is necessary to have a knowledge of the potentially dangerous reactions of individual chemicals. NFPA 491M, *Manual of Hazardous Chemical Reactions*, contains more than 3,400 dangerous reactions that have been reported in chemical literature and elsewhere.

BIBLIOGRAPHY

References Cited

1. Van Dolah, R. W., *et al*, "Explosion Hazards of Ammonium Nitrate Under Fire Exposure," RI 6773, 1966, USDI Bureau of Mines, Pittsburgh, PA.
2. Fukuyama, I., "Sensitive Ammonium Nitrate," *Journal of Industrial Explosives Society*, (Kogyo Kayaku Kyohaishi), Vol. 18, No. 1, 1957, pp. 64-66.
3. U.S. Bureau of Mines, "Research and Technologic Work on Explosives, Explosions, and Flames: Fiscal Year 1967," IC 8387, Aug. 1968, USDI Bureau of Mines, Washington, DC.
4. AIA, "Nitroparaffins and Their Hazards," NBFU Research Report No. 12, 1959, American Insurance Association (formerly National Board of Fire Underwriters), New York.

5. Purington, Robert, and Patterson, Wade, *Handling Radiation Emergencies*, National Fire Protection Association, Quincy, MA, 1977.

NFPA Codes, Standards, and Recommended Practices

Reference to the following NFPA codes, standards, and recommended practices will provide further information on chemicals discussed in this chapter. (See the latest *NFPA Catalog* for availability of current editions of the following documents.)

NFPA 43A, *Storage of Liquid and Solid Oxidizing Materials.*

NFPA 43B, *Storage of Organic Peroxide Formulations.*

NFPA 43C, *Storage of Gaseous Oxidizing Materials.*

NFPA 49, *Hazardous Chemicals Data.*

NFPA 325M, *Fire Hazard Properties of Flammable Liquids, Gases, and Volatile Solids.*

NFPA 490, *Storage of Ammonium Nitrate.*

NFPA 491M, *Manual of Hazardous Chemical Reactions.*

NFPA 495, *Manufacture, Transportation, Storage, and Use of Explosive Materials.*

NFPA 655, *Prevention of Sulfur Fires and Explosions.*

NFPA 704, *Identification of the Fire Hazards of Materials.*

NFPA 801, *Facilities Handling Radioactive Materials.*

Additional Reading

Bahme, C. W., *Fire Officer's Guide to Dangerous Chemicals*, National Fire Protection Association, Quincy, MA, 1978.

Bowen, J. E., "Understanding Chemical Toxicity," *Fire Engineering*, Vol. 140, No. 8, 1987, p. 18.

Bowen, J. E., "Unforeseen Dangers of Chemical Mixtures," *Fire Engineering*, Vol. 143, No. 2, 1990, p. 33.

Brethrick, A. L., *Handbook of Reactive Chemical Hazards*, 4th ed, Butterworths, Boston, 1990.

Coffee, R. D., "Evaluation of Chemical Stability," *Fire Technology*, Vol. 7, No. 1, Feb. 1971, pp. 37-45.

Condensed Guide to Chemical Hazards, U.S. Coast Guard, Washington, DC, 1985.

Dean, J. A., ed., *Lange's Handbook of Chemistry*, 13th ed., McGraw-Hill, New York, 1985.

Fawcett, H. H., and Wood, W. S., eds., *Safety and Accident Prevention in Chemical Operations*, 2nd ed., Wiley, New York, 1982.

Fire and Explosion Index: Hazard Classification Guide, 6th ed., Dow Chemical Co., Midland, MI, 1987.

Gibson, J. R., *Handbook of Selected Properties of Air- and Water-Reactive Materials*, Library of Congress, Washington, DC, 1968.

Hawley, G. G., *The Condensed Chemical Dictionary*, Van Nostrand Reinhold, New York, 1984.

Howard, H. A., "Chemical Plant Fire," *Fire Engineering*, Vol. 142, No. 2, 1989, pp. 28-34, 37-43.

"Hygienic Guide Series" (reports on individual chemicals), American Industrial Hygiene Association, Westmont, NJ. (Published periodically.)

Kirk-Othmer Concise Encyclopedia of Chemical Technology, Wiley, New York, 1985.

Lees, F. P., *Loss Prevention in the Process Industries*, Butterworths & Co., London, England, 1980.

Marshall, V. C., *Major Chemical Hazards*, Ellis Harwood, Chichester, UK, 1987.

Norback, C. T., *Hazardous Chemicals on File*, Facts on File Publications, New York, 1989.

Sax, N. Irving, *Dangerous Properties of Industrial Materials*, 7th ed., Van Nostrand Reinhold, New York, 1989.

Sax, I., and Lewis, R. J., *Hazardous Chemical Desk Reference*, Van Nostrand Reinhold, New York, 1987.

Stull, D. R., "Linking Thermodynamics and Kinetics to Predict Real Chemical Hazards," *Loss Prevention*, Vol. 7, American Institute of Chemical Engineers, New York, 1973, pp. 67-73.

Van Dolah, R. W., Gibson, F. C., and Murphy, J. N., "Further Studies on Sympathetic Detonations," *RI 6903*, USDI Bureau of Mines, Pittsburgh, PA, 1966.

Van Dolah, R. W., Gibson, F. C., and Murphy, J. N., "Sympathetic Detonation of Ammonium Nitrate and Ammonium Nitrate-Fuel Oil," *RI 6746*, USDI Burau of Mines, Pittsburgh, PA, 1966.

Weast, R. C., ed., *Handbook of Chemistry and Physics*, 69th ed., CRC Press, Boca Raton, FL, 1988.

West, A. S., "Safety Evaluation of Chemicals: The Regulatory Framework," *Plant/Operations Progress*, Vol. 5, No. 1, Jan. 1986, pp. 11-16.

Windzholz, M., ed., *Merk Index*, 10th ed., Merk & Co., Inc., Rahway, NJ, 1983.

EXPLOSIVES AND BLASTING AGENTS

Revised by Samuel J. Porter

This chapter gives a short description of explosives and explosive materials, with emphasis on their fire and explosion hazards. Additional important data concerning the manufacture, transportation, storage and use of explosive materials can be found in NFPA 495, *Explosive Materials Code*, and in other referenced material. NFPA 495, *Explosive Materials Code*, is a current and comprehensive guide which should be studied by all who have anything to do with explosives.

NFPA 495, *Explosive Materials Code*, provides a rule that must be obeyed always: *Do not fight fires involving explosive materials.* Look for the explosive signs. Do not fight the fire. Evacuate the area. In 1988, six Kansas City, MO, fire fighters were killed fighting a fire in an ammonium nitrate-based blasting agent storage facility.

The hazardous nature of explosives has long been recognized, and the rapid increase in their production and use makes it necessary to point out those properties that contribute most to the inherent dangers of these very important industrial and military products. In the industrial field alone, approximately 3.7 billion pounds of explosives and blasting agents were used in 1983, compared with 2.7 billion pounds in 1972 and 0.7 billion pounds in 1950 (1 lb = 0.45 kg). Of these totals, approximately 90 percent were used in mining and the remainder principally in construction operations.

Black powder was the first explosive known, although fireworks and pyrotechnics were known and used many centuries earlier.[1] The preparation and properties of black powder were described by Roger Bacon in the 13th century, and it was first used for military purposes in the 14th century. Black powder was first used for mining operations in the latter part of the 17th century and it remained the dominant commercial explosive until the latter part of the 19th century. In 1846, the compound nitroglycerin was first prepared and its explosive properties studied. The extremely hazardous nature of this compound prevented wide use until 1867 when Alfred Nobel made the discovery that nitroglycerin absorbed in an inert material, such as diatomaceous earth, produced a mixture that was relatively safe to handle. This explosive mixture, with many modifications and improvements, remained the predominant commercial explosive until the introduction of modern blasting agents in the mid 1950s. Meanwhile, the use of black powder decreased to an insignificant quantity largely because of its great fire hazard. In less than 20 years, blasting agents based principally on the sensitization of ammonium nitrate have taken over approximately 90 percent of the market.[2] This change is based largely on economic considerations and the greatly improved safety of non-nitroglycerin explosive materials.

Samuel J. Porter is a consultant in explosives, based in Woodbridge, VA.

NATURE OF EXPLOSIVE MATERIALS

Terminology

An understanding of the nature of explosive materials is essential before one can understand the fire and explosion potential of these admittedly hazardous products. A few general terms are defined below to provide a background for future discussions.

Blasting agent: Any material designated for blasting which has been tested for blasting cap sensitivity, differential thermal analysis, thermal stability, and fire characteristics according to tests specified in Title 49 of the U.S. *Code of Federal Regulations* (49 CFR) Part 173,[3] and found to be so insensitive that there is very little probability of accidental initiation to explosion or of transition from deflagration to detonation.

Detonator: Any device containing a detonating charge that is used for initiating detonation in an explosive. The term includes, but is not limited to, electric blasting caps of instantaneous and delay types, blasting caps for use with a safety fuse, and detonating cord delay connectors.

Explosion: An explosion is an effect produced by the sudden violent production or expansion of gases. It may be accompanied by heat, shock waves, and the disruption or enclosing of nearby structures or materials.

Explosive: An explosive is a substance or a mixture of substances which, when subjected to the proper stimuli, undergoes an exceedingly rapid self-propagating reaction characterized by the formation of more stable products (usually gases), evolution of heat, and the development of a sudden pressure effect through the action of this heat on produced or adjacent gases. A somewhat simpler, but less accurate, definition states that an explosive is any chemical compound, mixture, or device whose primary or common use is to function by explosion. The term includes, but is not limited to, dynamite, black powder, initiating explosives, detonators, safety fuses, squibs, detonating cords, igniter cords, and igniters.

Explosive material: Includes explosives, blasting agents, water gels (slurries), and detonators.

Propellant: An explosive material which normally functions by deflagration (burning) and is used for propelling purposes.

An explosion may result from: (1) chemical changes, such as those which accompany the detonation of an explosive or the combustion of a flammable gas-air mixture; (2) physical or mechanical changes, such as the bursting of a steam boiler, or a high-pressure reaction vessel; and (3) atomic changes, such as those which occur in a nuclear explosion.

Fires and Explosions

A distinction must be made between controlled and unwanted fires and explosions. Controlled combustion reactions are basic to the production of power and necessary for an industrial economy. Likewise, detonation reactions are essential for use by the mining and construction industries. On the other hand, the loss of life and natural resources from unwanted fires and explosions is a matter of national concern. Since fire is a major hazard associated with the utilization of explosives and blasting agents, this chapter discusses the basic nature of these materials and methods for reducing the loss from uncontrolled reactions in these materials.

TYPES OF EXPLOSIVE MATERIALS

Although this chapter mainly addresses commercial explosives, some of the similarities and differences between commercial and military explosives should be considered. Most military explosives have high shattering power and relatively high detonation velocities. Military explosives are often kept in storage for relatively long periods of time and therefore must have good stability. It is essential that these explosives detonate reliably even after storage in a wide variety of conditions. While there are no truly military explosives equivalent to the blasting agents used in commercial operations, the military uses commercial-type explosives and blasting agents for operations such as road building, airstrip preparations, and a wide variety of similar operations.

As stated previously, commercial explosives have a wide range of properties. Explosives to be used in underground operations must have relatively good fume characteristics. This requires formulations which are nearly oxygen balanced and therefore produce a minimal amount of carbon monoxide and oxides of nitrogen. The most widely used military explosives, such as trinitrotoluene (TNT) and cyclonite (RDX), are quite oxygen deficient and therefore produce large quantities of toxic gases. Commercial dynamites normally have a fairly long storage life, but blasting agents are more often used soon after manufacture, so storage is not as important a factor. However, prolonged storage of dynamites, slurries, or ammonium nitrate with fuel oil (ANFO) at high or low temperature extremes or high humidity may result in serious changes in sensitivity or effectiveness or both.

Commercial Explosive Types

Explosive materials can be divided into a number of specific types according to their characteristic properties.[4] The following types are generally recognized in industry.

Primary or initiating high explosives: These are quite hazardous materials, but they play a very important role in the utilization of explosive materials. Typical explosives of this type are mercury fulminate, lead styphnate, and lead azide. Because of their hazardous nature they are seldom, if ever, used alone, and their principal function is to initiate detonation in less sensitive explosives. These primary explosives are readily detonated by the addition of heat or the application of a mild mechanical shock. They are used almost exclusively as the initiating agent in detonators, and are classified by the Department of Transportation (DOT) as Class A.

Secondary high explosives: These are materials that are relatively insensitive to mechanical shock and heat and yet are readily detonated by the shock from a primary explosive. They are much more powerful than the primary explosives. They are used for most military purposes and are often used in commercial blasting operations. Secondary high explosives include such products as dynamite, nitroglycerin, TNT, RDX, and pentaerythrital tetranitrate (PETN). Because of its sensitivity, nitroglycerin is never used alone. Secondary high explosives are generally cap sensitive, which distinguishes them from blasting agents, and are classified by DOT as Class A.

Low explosives or propellants: These are used primarily for propulsion purposes. They normally function by burning rather than detonation, although many propellants are susceptible to detonation. Black powder, smokeless powder, and solid rocket fuels fall into this category. Fire constitutes the greatest hazard in the handling and use of propellant explosives. Classes A, B, and C may be represented in this group.

Blasting agents: As stated previously, almost 90 percent of all blasting operations in the United States are carried out using non-nitroglycerin materials. The most commonly used blasting agent is a fuel oxidizer system which consists primarily of ammonium nitrate and a fuel, such as Number 2 diesel fuel. The formulation is termed ANFO and is sold under a variety of trade names. The addition of approximately 6 percent fuel oil to specially prepared ammonium nitrate prills (pellets) produces an amazingly successful blasting material. This combination has the advantage of low cost, satisfactory fume characteristics, and greatly increased safety over the nitroglycerin dynamites. While the combination does not burn readily, it still may change in a well-established fire to produce a detonation. ANFO does have a disadvantage in that it is difficult or impossible to use it under very wet conditions. Many variations of the basic ANFO formulation have been developed and successfully used. Powdered aluminum is now added in certain operations to increase the general strength of the material.

Water gels or slurries: Operations where a water-resistant explosive material is a necessity, and where higher densities than those which can be obtained with ANFO are desirable, have led to the development of water gels or slurries. These may be classed as either blasting agents or explosives, depending on their formulation and sensitivity. Ammonium nitrate is usually the basic oxidizer in this type of explosive, and it may be sensitized by a variety of materials, the most common of which is powdered or flaked aluminum. Other additives include paint-grade aluminum, monomethylamine nitrate, TNT, gilsonite, sodium nitrate, and various gelling agents. Approximately 10 percent of the market has been taken over by water gels.

Nuclear explosives: Nuclear explosives are used for military purposes only.

CLASSES OF EXPLOSIVES

The DOT[3] divides commercial explosive materials into separate classes for transportation purposes. Industry has generally accepted this classification system, since it corresponds roughly to the hazards in handling, storing, and transporting these materials. These explosive materials are discussed in the order of decreasing sensitivity.

Class A Explosives

Explosives of this class possess detonating or otherwise maximum hazard. They include dynamite, desensitized nitroglycerin, lead azide, mercury fulminate, black powder, blasting caps, detonators, detonating primers, and certain smokeless propellants.

Class B Explosives

Explosives of this class have a high flammable hazard and include most propellant materials.

Class C Explosives

Explosives of this class include manufactured articles which contain limited quantities of Class A or Class B explosives as one of their components. These explosives include such materials as detonating cord, explosive rivets, fireworks, etc. Class C explosives will not normally mass detonate under fire conditions.

Blasting Agents

Blasting agents are generally considered safer than Class A, B, or C explosives and yet, when properly initiated, they function in the same manner as Class A explosives. Not being cap sensitive, they require a strong primer.

Other Classification Systems

The Bureau of Alcohol, Tobacco, and Firearms (ATF), Department of the Treasury, has a classification system based on the type of explosive material involved. In their system, explosive materials are classified as high explosives, low explosives, and blasting agents. Since some low explosives are as hazardous as high explosives, this classification does not indicate relative hazard. While this system is not generally used industrially, it is working satisfactorily from a security standpoint for the control of explosive materials. This classification is employed in the enforcement of Title 11, Regulation of Explosives, of the *Organized Crime Control Act of 1970* (18 U.S.C., Chapter 40). At least annually the ATF director publishes a list of explosives determined to be within the coverage of the law.

Permissible Explosives

While the term "permissible explosive" is not exactly a classification, it does describe a type of explosive which has been tested and approved by the Department of Labor Mine Safety and Health Administration as meeting the minimum safety requirements for use in underground coal mines.[5] These materials are modified dynamites or water gels which exhibit reduced tendencies to ignite flammable gas-air or gas-air-coal dust mixtures.

Two-Component Explosives

Two-component explosives, also referred to as plosphoric or binary substances, consist of two or more unmixed, commercially manufactured, prepackaged chemicals, including oxidizing chemicals, flammable liquids, or solids that are not independently classified as explosives. When combined, however, the mixture is classified as an explosive and is stored, transported, and handled as an explosive.

MANUFACTURE OF EXPLOSIVE MATERIALS

With the possible exception of blasting agents, and some water gels or slurries, explosive materials are produced in plants under the close supervision of qualified personnel. While the potential for accidents is relatively high, the safety record is very good, largely because the hazards are well recognized. Fire is a principal cause of accidents, but a normal plant layout keeps this hazard within reasonable limits. Smoking is never allowed near the explosive operations, and the use of flame-producing equipment is allowed only in specific locations under strict safety regulations. The relative ease of mixing ANFO mixtures and slurries, in addition to their reduced fire and explosion potential, has led to the construction of many small manufacturing plants which are located in widely scattered areas. Manufacturing methods may include: (1) plant-mixed ANFO delivered to site by bulk truck; (2) ANFO mixed by bulk truck at site; (3) plant-mixed slurry delivered to site by bulk truck; and (4) slurry mixed by bulk truck at site. These changes in methods have resulted in major variations in safety practices from normal explosive plant safety procedures.

Bulk trucks present a new fire hazard. There have been several fires on the Mesabi Iron Range in Minnesota involving this type of equipment.

TRANSPORTATION OF EXPLOSIVE MATERIALS

The DOT regulates the transportation of all explosive materials in accordance with regulations set forth in U.S. *Code of Federal Regulations*, Title 49, Chapter I, Parts 100-199.[6] Copies of these regulations can be obtained from the U.S. Government Printing Office, or from the Bureau of Explosives of the Association of American Railroads.

Most commercial explosives are now transported over public highways by truck. Military explosives are transported both by rail and by truck. Fire is the most common cause of accidents in truck transportation, and the most probable point of initiation of fire is a truck's tires. Tire fires are quite common and represent a hazard which is difficult to control because the driver of a truck is often unaware of the fire until it has gained considerable headway. Detonators may be transported in limited quantities on the same vehicle with explosives and blasting agents, provided DOT regulations concerning quantity and type of container are observed. Truck transportation over public highways is of particular concern because there is maximum exposure of the public to fire and explosion hazards. Unfortunately, fires and other types of accident situations tend to draw spectators, which increases the danger of casualties. While rail transportation generally provides a lesser hazard to the public, there is an increased danger resulting from the mixing of different types of cargo in a given train load.

STORAGE OF EXPLOSIVE MATERIALS

A primary objective for the storage of most nonexplosive industrial materials is to provide protection for such materials from their surroundings. Because of the hazardous nature of explosive materials, additional factors must be considered. Safety to the industrial workers involved and to the general public in the vicinity of such storage is of primary importance. Since most explosive materials are utilized by the mining and construction industries, these industries have primary concern in training their employees to provide maximum attainable safety. Employees of the explosive manufacturing firms are well aware of the hazards of their occupation, and safety is an integral part of their work. However, employees in mining and construction industries are less likely to be aware of the precautions required to obtain a satisfactory degree of safety.

Another factor connected with storage is indirectly related to safety and involves the element of security. In recent years it has become increasingly important to protect the public from the illicit use of explosives which are often obtained by individuals through illegitimate means. The world-wide increase in terrorism has made security an important consideration in the storage of explosives. Most of the explosives used for illegal purposes are obtained from legitimate stores of the materials. To assist in preventing this misuse of explosives, federal law now provides that the Bureau of Alcohol, Tobacco, and Firearms, Department of the Treasury, must regulate the manufacture, distribution, and storage of explosive materials. Copies of these regulations can be obtained from that agency.

Storage Magazines

To provide proper storage for the wide variety of explosive materials now being produced, five different types of magazines are recognized. The requirements for these five types of magazines are given in the regulations developed by the Bureau of Alcohol, Tobacco, and Firearms. The specifications for these magazines and the types of materials to be put in them can be obtained from ATF or can be found in NFPA 495, *Explosive Materials Code*.

Magazine storage aside, it is a widespread practice in industry to transport relatively insensitive blasting agents to mining or construction sites in truck trailers. The manufacturer parks the trailer in a designated area, disconnects the cab, and picks up an empty trailer for the return trip. The blasting agents are then transported by small truck to the site of operations. This is considered as providing adequate safety from the fire hazard. When trucks transporting explosives or blasting agents must stop in transit, or the load must be transferred in transit, terminals are now provided in the vicinity of many large cities for motor vehicles carrying explosives. These terminals are well guarded and are operated under strict safety regulations. Requirements for these terminals are contained in NFPA 498, *Explosives in Motor Vehicle Terminals*.

While the probability of the accidental initiation of an explosive while in an approved storage location is slight, accidents still occur. To safeguard the general public, the American Table of Distances for Storage of Explosives has been prepared to indicate the isolation distances for stores of explosives from points of contact with the public. (See Table 3-9A.) This table is revised periodically by The Institute of Makers of Explosives. While blasting agents are appreciably less sensitive than Class A explosives, once they are initiated to detonation, the damage produced by such an accident is comparable to that for Class A explosives. Therefore, the Table of Recommended Separation Distances of Ammonium Nitrate and Blasting Agents from Explosives or Blasting Agents is used to determine the safe distances for stores of blasting agents from inhabited buildings, railroads, etc. (See Table 3-9B.) However, because of the lower sensitivity of blasting agents, the separation distances between magazines or stores of explosives and blasting agents need not be as great as that between stores of explosives, as shown in Table 3-9A. Table 3-9B shows these recommended separation distances and the thickness of artificial barricades recommended for these less sensitive materials. When no barricades separate stores, the distances must be increased as shown in Table 3-9B (Note b).

FIRE PROTECTION FOR EXPLOSIVE MATERIALS

Fire is a principal cause of accidents involving explosive materials. Although explosives and blasting agents vary in their sensitivity to fire conditions, they are liable to produce a disastrous explosion when subjected to fire. The only effective method for fire protection with explosive materials is to eliminate the sources of fire. This means meticulous housekeeping standards. It is often a small fire in oily rags or wastepaper that triggers a major catastrophe. Smoking or the use of any fire-producing equipment should not be permitted where explosive materials are produced, handled, stored, or used. Because of the relative insensitivity of blasting agents, there is always a danger that personnel will become careless around these materials. A fire and subsequent explosion in a blasting agent mixing house near Norton, VA, illustrates the potential hazard from the careless use of heat-producing equipment.[7] Another fire and explosion in a blasting agent storage facility killed six Kansas City, MO, fire fighters who were fighting the fire.[8]

Some of the materials used in making explosives and blasting agents may be as hazardous as the final product. Materials likely to be found include aluminum powder, paint-grade aluminum, ammonium nitrate, ammonium perchlorate, sodium nitrate, fuel oil, gilsonite, bagasse, and various types of finely divided gums. NFPA codes should be consulted for proper storage and protection of these materials.

For all explosive materials, whether in manufacture, storage, transportation, or use, housekeeping should be of the highest order.

TABLE 3-9A. ***American Table of Distances for Storage of Explosives***

As Revised and Approved by The Institute of Makers of Explosives February, 1986.

Distances in feet*

EXPLOSIVES(1,2,3,4)		Inhabited Buildings(9)		Public Highways(11) Class A to D		Passenger Railways—Public Highways with Traffic Volume of more than 3,000 Vehicles/Day(10,11)		Separation of Magazines(5,12)	
Pounds† Over	Pounds† Not Over	Barricaded (6,7,8)	Unbarricaded	Barricaded (6,7,8)	Unbarricaded	Barricaded (6,7,8)	Unbarricaded	Barricaded (6,7,8)	Unbarricaded
2	5	70	140	30	60	51	102	6	12
5	10	90	180	35	70	64	128	8	16
10	20	110	220	45	90	81	162	10	20
20	30	125	250	50	100	93	186	11	22
30	40	140	280	55	110	103	206	12	24
40	50	150	300	60	120	110	220	14	28
50	75	170	340	70	140	127	254	15	30
75	100	190	380	75	150	139	278	16	32
100	125	200	400	80	160	150	300	18	36
125	150	215	430	85	170	159	318	19	38
150	200	235	470	95	190	175	350	21	42
200	250	255	510	105	210	189	378	23	46
250	300	270	540	110	220	201	402	24	48
300	400	295	590	120	240	221	442	27	54
400	500	320	640	130	260	238	476	29	58
500	600	340	680	135	270	253	506	31	62
600	700	355	710	145	290	266	532	32	64
700	800	375	750	150	300	278	556	33	66
800	900	390	780	155	310	289	578	35	70
900	1,000	400	800	160	320	300	600	36	72
1,000	1,200	425	850	165	330	318	636	39	78
1,200	1,400	450	900	170	340	336	672	41	82
1,400	1,600	470	940	175	350	351	702	43	86
1,600	1,800	490	980	180	360	366	732	44	88
1,800	2,000	505	1,010	185	370	378	756	45	90
2,000	2,500	545	1,090	190	380	408	816	49	98
2,500	3,000	580	1,160	195	390	432	864	52	104
3,000	4,000	635	1,270	210	420	474	948	58	116
4,000	5,000	685	1,370	225	450	513	1,026	61	122
5,000	6,000	730	1,460	235	470	546	1,092	65	130
6,000	7,000	770	1,540	245	490	573	1,146	68	136
7,000	8,000	800	1,600	250	500	600	1,200	72	144
8,000	9,000	835	1,670	255	510	624	1,248	75	150
9,000	10,000	865	1,730	260	520	645	1,290	78	156
10,000	12,000	875	1,750	270	540	687	1,374	82	164
12,000	14,000	885	1,770	275	550	723	1,446	87	174
14,000	16,000	900	1,800	280	560	756	1,512	90	180
16,000	18,000	940	1,880	285	570	786	1,572	94	188
18,000	20,000	975	1,950	290	580	813	1,626	98	196
20,000	25,000	1,055	2,000	315	630	876	1,752	105	210
25,000	30,000	1,130	2,000	340	680	933	1,866	112	224
30,000	35,000	1,205	2,000	360	720	981	1,962	119	238
35,000	40,000	1,275	2,000	380	760	1,026	2,000	124	248
40,000	45,000	1,340	2,000	400	800	1,068	2,000	129	258
45,000	50,000	1,400	2,000	420	840	1,104	2,000	135	270
50,000	55,000	1,460	2,000	440	880	1,140	2,000	140	280
55,000	60,000	1,515	2,000	455	910	1,173	2,000	145	290
60,000	65,000	1,565	2,000	470	940	1,206	2,000	150	300
65,000	70,000	1,610	2,000	485	970	1,236	2,000	155	310
70,000	75,000	1,655	2,000	500	1,000	1,263	2,000	160	320

TABLE 3-9A. ***American Table of Distances for Storage of Explosives (Cont.)***
Distances in feet.

EXPLOSIVES(1,2,3,4)		Inhabited Buildings(9)		Public Highways(11) Class A to D		Passenger Railways— Public Highways with Traffic Volume of more than 3,000 Vehicles/ Day(10,11)		Separation of Magazines(5,12)	
Pounds† Over	Pounds† Not Over	Barri-caded (6,7,8)	Unbarri-caded	Barri-caded (6,7,8)	Unbarri-caded	Barri-caded (6,7,8)	Unbarri-caded	Barri-caded (6,7,8)	Unbarri-caded
75,000	80,000	1,695	2,000	510	1,020	1,293	2,000	165	330
80,000	85,000	1,730	2,000	520	1,040	1,317	2,000	170	340
85,000	90,000	1,760	2,000	530	1,060	1,344	2,000	175	350
90,000	95,000	1,790	2,000	540	1,080	1,368	2,000	180	360
95,000	100,000	1,815	2,000	545	1,090	1,392	2,000	185	370
100,000	110,000	1,835	2,000	550	1,100	1,437	2,000	195	390
110,000	120,000	1,855	2,000	555	1,110	1,479	2,000	205	410
120,000	130,000	1,875	2,000	560	1,120	1,521	2,000	215	430
130,000	140,000	1,890	2,000	565	1,130	1,557	2,000	225	450
140,000	150,000	1,900	2,000	570	1,140	1,593	2,000	235	470
150,000	160,000	1,935	2,000	580	1,160	1,629	2,000	245	490
160,000	170,000	1,965	2,000	590	1,180	1,662	2,000	255	510
170,000	180,000	1,990	2,000	600	1,200	1,695	2,000	265	530
180,000	190,000	2,010	2,010	605	1,210	1,725	2,000	275	550
190,000	200,000	2,030	2,030	610	1,220	1,755	2,000	285	570
200,000	210,000	2,055	2,055	620	1,240	1,782	2,000	295	590
210,000	230,000	2,100	2,100	635	1,270	1,836	2,000	315	630
230,000	250,000	2,155	2,155	650	1,300	1,890	2,000	335	670
250,000	275,000	2,215	2,215	670	1,340	1,950	2,000	360	720
275,000	300,000	2,275	2,275	690	1,380	2,000	2,000	385	770

Numbers in ( ) refer to explanatory notes.

Note 1: "Explosive materials" means explosives, blasting agents, and detonators.

Note 2: "Explosives" means any chemical compound, mixture or device, the primary or common purpose of which is to function by explosion. A list of explosives determined to be within the coverage of "18 U.S.C. Chapter 40, Importation, Manufacture, Distribution and Storage of Explosive Materials" is issued at least annually by the Director, Bureau of Alcohol, Tobacco, and Firearms, Department of U.S. Treasury. For quantity and distance purposes, detonating cord of 50 grains per foot should be calculated as equivalent to 8 lbs (3.7 kg) of high explosives per 1,000 feet (305 m). Heavier or lighter core loads should be rated proportionately.

Note 3: "Blasting Agents" means any material or mixture, consisting of fuel and oxidizer, intended for blasting, not otherwise defined as an explosive: provided that the finished product, as mixed for use or shipment, cannot be detonated by means of a number 8 test blasting cap when unconfined.

Note 4: "Detonator" means any device containing any initiating or primary explosive that is used for initiating detonation. A detonator may not contain more than 10 g of total explosives by weight, excluding ignition or delay charges. The term includes, but is not limited to, electric blasting caps of instantaneous and delay types, blasting caps for use with safety fuses, detonating cord delay connectors, and nonelectric instantaneous and delay blasting caps that use detonating cord, shock tube, or any other replacement for electric leg wires. All types of detonators in strengths through No. 8 cap should be rated at 1½ lb (0.7 kg) of explosives per 1,000 caps. For strengths higher than No. 8 cap, consult the manufacturer.

Note 5: "Magazine" means any building, structure, or container, other than an explosives manufacturing building, approved for the storage of explosive materials.

Note 6: "Natural Barricade" means natural features of the ground, such as hills, or timber of sufficient density that the surrounding exposures which require protection cannot be seen from the magazine when the trees are bare of leaves.

Note 7: "Artificial Barricade" means an artificial mound or revetted wall of earth of a minimum thickness of three feet (0.9 m).

Note 8: "Barricaded" means that a building containing explosives is effectually screened from a magazine, building, railway, or highway, either by a natural barricade, or by an artificial barricade of such height that a straight line from the top of any sidewall of the building containing explosives to the eave line of any magazine, or building, or to a point twelve feet (3.7 m) above the center of a railway or highway, will pass through such intervening natural or artificial barricade.

Note 9: "Inhabited Building" means a building regularly occupied in whole or in part as a habitation for human beings, or any chruch, schoolhouse, railroad station, store, or other structure where people are accustomed to assemble, except any building or structure occupied in connection with the manufacture, transportation, storage or use of explosive materials.

Note 10: "Railway" means any steam, electric, or other railroad or railway which carries passengers for hire.

Note 11: "Highway" means any public street, public alley or public road. "Public Highways Class A to D" are highways with average traffic volume of 3,000 or less vehicles per day as specified in "American Civil Engineering Practice" (Abbett, Vol. 1, Table 46, Sec. 3-74, 1956 Edition, John Wiley and Sons).

Note 12: When two or more storage magazines are located on the same property, each magazine must comply with the minimum distances specified from inhabited buildings, railways, and highways, and, in addition, they should be separated from each other by not less than the distances shown for "Separation of Magazines," except that the quantity of explosive materials contained in detonator magazines shall govern in regard to the spacing of said detonator magazines from magazines containing other explosive materials. If any two or more magazines are separated from each other by less than the specified "Separation of Magazines" distances, then such two or more magazines, as a group, must be considered as one magazine, and the total quantity of explosive materials stored in such group must be treated as if stored in a single magazine located on the site of any magazine of the group, and must comply with the minimum of distances specified from other magazines, inhabited buildings, railways, and highways.

Note 13: Storage in excess of 300,000 lbs. (136,200 kg) of explosive materials in one magazine is generally not required for commercial enterprises.

Note 14: This Table applies only to the manufacture and permanent storage of commercial explosive materials. It is not applicable to transportation of explosives or any handling or temporary storage necessary or incident thereto. It is not intended to apply to bombs, projectiles, or other heavily encased explosives.

* one foot equals 0.3048 m

† one pound equals 0.4536 kg

TABLE 3-9B. ***Table of Recommended Separation Distances of Ammonium Nitrate and Blasting Agents from Explosives or Blasting Agents[1,6]***

Donor Weight		Minimum Separation Distance of Receptor when Barricaded[2] (ft§)		Minimum Thickness of Artificial Barricades[5] (in.)#
Pounds‡ Over	Pounds‡ Not Over	Ammonium Nitrate[3]	Blasting Agent[4]	
	100	3	11	12
100	300	4	14	12
300	600	5	18	12
600	1,000	6	22	12
1,000	1,600	7	25	12
1,600	2,000	8	29	12
2,000	3,000	9	32	15
3,000	4,000	10	36	15
4,000	6,000	11	40	15
6,000	8,000	12	43	20
8,000	10,000	13	47	20
10,000	12,000	14	50	20
12,000	16,000	15	54	25
16,000	20,000	16	58	25
20,000	25,000	18	65	25
25,000	30,000	19	68	30
30,000	35,000	20	72	30
35,000	40,000	21	76	30
40,000	45,000	22	79	35
45,000	50,000	23	83	35
50,000	55,000	24	86	36
55,000	60,000	25	90	35
60,000	70,000	26	94	40
70,000	80,000	28	101	40
80,000	90,000	30	108	40
90,000	100,000	32	115	40
100,000	120,000	34	122	50
120,000	140,000	37	133	50
140,000	160,000	40	144	50
160,000	180,000	44	158	50
180,000	200,000	48	173	50
200,000	220,000	52	187	60
220,000	250,000	56	202	60
250,000	275,000	60	216	60
275,000	300,000	64	230	60

Note 1: Recommended separation distances to prevent explosion of ammonium nitrate and ammonium nitrate-based blasting agents by propagation from nearby stores of high explosives or blasting agents referred to in the Table as the "donor." Ammonium nitrate, by itself, is not considered to be a donor when applying this Table. Ammonium nitrate, ammonium nitrate-fuel oil or combinations thereof are acceptors. If stores of ammonium nitrate are located within the sympathetic detonation distance of explosives or blasting agents, one-half the mass of the ammonium nitrate should be included in the mass of the donor.

These distances apply to the separation of stores only.

Note 2: When the ammonium nitrate and/or blasting agent is not barricaded, the distances shown in the Table shall be multiplied by six. These distances allow for the possibility of high velocity metal fragments from mixers, hoppers, truck bodies, sheet metal structures, metal containers, and the like which may enclose the "donor." Where storage is in bullet-resistant magazines* recommended for explosives or where the storage is protected by a bullet-resistant wall, distances and barricade thicknesses in excess of those prescribed in the American Table of Distances are not required.

Note 3: The distances in the Table apply to ammonium nitrate that passes the insensitivity test prescribed in the definition of ammonium nitrate fertilizer promulgated by the National Plant Food Institute;† and ammonium nitrate failing to pass said test shall be stored at separation distances determined by competent persons and approved by the authority having jurisdiction.

Note 4: These distances apply to nitrocarbonitrates and blasting agents which pass the insensitivity test prescribed in the U.S. Department of Transportation (DOT) and the U.S. Department of the Treasury, Bureau of Alcohol, Tobacco, and Firearms.

Note 5: Earth, or sand dikes, or enclosures filled with the prescribed minimum thickness of earth or sand are acceptable artificial barricades. Natural barricades, such as hills or timber of sufficient density that the surrounding exposures which require protection cannot be seen from the "donor" when the trees are bare of leaves, are also acceptable.

Note 6: For determining the distances to be maintained from inhabited buildings, passenger railways, and public highways, use the Table of Distances for Storage of Explosives in Appendix A of *NFPA, 1973, Code for the Manufacture, Transportation, Storage, and Use of Explosive Materials.*

* For construction of bullet-resistant magazines see Chapter 6 of NFPA No. 495, *Explosives Materials Code.*

† Definition and Test Procedures for Ammonium Nitrate Fertilizer, National Plant Food Institute, November 1964.

‡ one pound equals 0.4536 kg

§ one ft equals 0.3048 m

\# one in equals 25.4 mm

FIGHTING FIRES INVOLVING EXPLOSIVES AND BLASTING AGENTS

No attempt should be made to fight a fire involving explosive materials. The area should be evacuated to a distance of at least 2000 ft (610 m).

The Norton, VA, fire mentioned previously is a good example of the necessity of retreating from an established fire involving blasting agents. The Luckenback Pier fire in Brooklyn, NY, in 1959 shows that even Class C explosives represent a potential hazard. Several tons (one short ton equals 0.91 metric ton) of detonating cord were stored on a pier that became involved in a serious fire. After considerable delay, the entire mass detonated with many lives lost and property damage in the millions of dollars.

Truck fires involving explosive materials pose the greatest threat to the public, because the number of trucks in transit is so large. Many of these incidents have resulted in explosions. Immediate evacuation in such incidents is imperative.

DESTRUCTION OF EXPLOSIVE MATERIALS

Surplus, abandoned, or damaged explosives unfit for further use should not be disposed of by burning, detonating, water leaching, chemical decomposing or any other means, except under the supervision of the manufacturer or the manufacturer's designated representative. This is especially true in the case of explosives that have been damaged during fire fighting operations. If the manufacturer is not known, The Institute of Makers of Explosives, 420 Lexington Avenue, New York, NY, 10017, should be contacted for assistance.

When bombs or other sabotage devices are suspected, disposal should be under the supervision of trained bomb-disposal experts.

BIBLIOGRAPHY

References Cited

1. Dixon, W. T., and Fisher, A. W., eds., *Chemical Engineering in Industry*, Chapter 12, American Institute of Chemical Engineers, New York, 1958.
2. U.S. Dept. of the Interior, "Apparent Consumption of Industrial Explosives and Blasting Agents in the United States," 1983, Mineral Industry Surveys, USDI Bureau of Mines, Pittsburgh, PA.
3. U.S. *Code of Federal Regulations*, Title 49, Chapter I, "Transportation," Parts 170-189, 1972, U.S. Government Printing Office, Washington, DC.
4. Cook, Melvin A., *The Science of High Explosives*, Reinhold Publishing Co., New York, 1958.
5. U.S. *Code of Federal Regulations*, Title 30, Chapter I, Subchapter C, Part 15, "Explosives and Related Articles," 1969, U.S. Government Printing Office, Washington, DC.
6. U.S. *Code of Federal Regulations*, Title 49, Chapter I, "Transportation," Parts 100-199, 1978, U.S. Government Printing Office, Washington, DC.
7. Van Dolah, R. W., and Malesky, J. S., "Fire and Explosion in a Blasting Agent Mix House Building, Norton, VA," RI 6015, 1962, USDI, Bureau of Mines, Pittsburgh, PA.
8. Isner, Michael S., *NFPA Fire Investigation Report*, "Blasting Agent Explosion—Six Fire Fighters Killed, Kansas City, MO, Nov. 29, 1988, National Fire Protection Association, Quincy, MA.

NFPA Codes, Standards, and Recommended Practices

Reference to the following NFPA codes, standards, and recommended practices will provide further information on explosives and blasting agents discussed in this chapter. (See the latest *NFPA Catalog* for availability of current editions of the following documents.)

NFPA 490, *Storage of Ammonium Nitrate*.

NFPA 495, *Explosive Materials Code*.

NFPA 498, *Explosives in Motor Vehicle Terminals*.

Additional Reading

"Another Bad Year For Fireworks Injuries," *Fire Journal*, Vol. 83, No. 4, 1989, p. 20.

"ATF Explosives Laws and Regulations," ATF Publication 5400.7; Bureau of Alcohol Tobacco and Firearms, Washington, DC, Nov., 1982.

Blasters Handbook, 175th Anniversary Edition, E. I. DuPont de Nemours and Co., Wilmington, DE, 1980.

Construction Guide for Storage Magazines, IME Safety Library Publication No. 1; Institute of Makers of Explosives, Washington, DC, Jan. 1983.

Damon, Glenn H., "Blasting Agents: History, Hazards and Protection," *Fire Journal*, Vol. 59, No. 2, Mar. 1965.

Department of Defense Explosive Hazard Classification Procedures, *DLAR 8220.1*, Defense Logistics Agency, Washington, DC, 1989.

Destruction of Commercial Explosives, IME Safety Library Publication No. 21, Institute of Makers of Explosives, Washington, DC, Dec. 1981.

Dick, R. A., Fletcher, L. R., and D'Andrea, D. V., Explosives and Blasting Procedures Manual, Information Circular 8925, U.S. Bureau of Mines, Washington, DC, 1983.

Dos and Don'ts, IME Safety Library Publication No. 4, Institute of Makers of Explosives, Washington, DC, June, 1982.

Explosion and Explosives: *Journal of the Industrial Explosives Society*, Japan, Industrial Explosives Society, Japan, publ. periodically.

"Fireworks: Spectacular but Dangerous," *Fire Command*, Vol. 56, No. 7, July 1989, pp. 11-14.

Fordham, S., *High Explosives and Propellants*, 2nd ed., Pergamon Press, NY, 1980.

Glossary of Industry Terms, IME Safety Library Publication No. 12, Institute of Makers of Explosives, Washington, DC, Jan. 1985.

IME Standard for the Safe Transportation of Class C Detonators in a Vehicle with Certain Other Explosives, IME Safety Library Publication No 22, Institute of Makers of Explosives, Washington, DC, Mar. 21, 1979.

Meidl, H. H., *Explosive and Toxic Hazardous Materials*, Glencoe Press, Beverly Hills, CA, 1970.

Safety in the Transportation, Storage, Handling, and Use of Explosives, IME Safety Library Publication No. 17, Institute of Makers of Explosives, Washington, DC, April 1974.

Safety Recommendations for Sensitized Ammonium Nitrate Blasting Agents, IC 8179, 1963, USDI, Bureau of Mines, Pittsburgh, PA.

Safety Requirement for the Transportation, Storage, Handling and Use of Commercial Explosives and Blasting Agents in the Construction Industry, ANSI A10.7, American National Standards Institute, NY 1970.

Urbanski, T., *Chemistry and Technology of Explosives*, 4 vols, Pergamon, NY, 1983.

Van Dolah, R. W., Gibson, F. C., and Murphy, J. N., "Sympathetic Detonation of Ammonium Nitrate and Ammonium Nitrate-Fuel Oil," *RI 6746*, USDI, Bureau of Mines, Pittsburgh, PA, 1966.

"Further Studies on Sympathetic Detonation of Ammonium Nitrate and Ammonium Nitrate-Fuel Oil," *RI 6903*, 1966, USDI, Bureau of Mines, Pittsburgh, PA.

Van Dolah, R. W., Mason, C. M., and Forshey, D. R., "Development of Slurry Explosives for Use in Potentially Flammable Gas Atmospheres," *RI 7195*, USDI, Bureau of Mines, Pittsburgh, PA, 1968.

Winning, C. H., "Detonation Characteristics of Prilled Ammonium Nitrate," *Fire Technology*, Vol. 1, No. 1, Feb. 1965, pp. 23-31.

PLASTICS AND RUBBER

Revised by Bert M. Cohn

The plastics industry is one of the most rapidly developing technologies today. Since World War II, the types, variations, and uses of plastics have proliferated at a tremendous rate, producing a family of materials that is extraordinarily complex and varied. Each of the variations can be considered combustible. Some burn very rapidly, and under certain conditions present extreme hazards to life and property. When such hazardous characteristics are identified, modifications can be made in manufacture and application that can reduce the hazard to acceptable levels. For example, cellulose nitrate motion picture film presents the hazard of flash burning. This hazard was controlled by phasing out the cellulose nitrate film and replacing it with slow-burning "safety" film. More recently, the hazards of cellular plastics, such as polyurethane and polystyrene, which are used for exposed interior finish in buildings, have been controlled by using flame-retardant additives during manufacture combined with thermal barriers installed in the field.

This chapter focuses on the fire behavior of plastics that are used as building materials and on the characteristics of polymers in general. The tests that are used to identify the relative hazards from fire and smoke of plastics used in building applications are also discussed. Plastics in fibers and textiles (including clothing, upholstery fabrics, and mattresses) are discussed in Section 3, Chapter 4, "Fibers and Textiles." The fire hazards associated with the manufacturing, processing, and warehousing of plastics and elastomers are discussed in Section 2, Chapter 16, "Extrusion and Molding Processes."

While being a part of the family of polymers, natural and synthetic rubbers, technically, are not plastics. Yet, because of the many similarities and the formulations that intermix the traditional characteristics of plastics and elastomers, rubbers are often included in discussions of plastics. In this chapter, the general term "plastic" is intended to include rubber, but it should be understood that rubber has a whole complex technology of its own—one that predates the modern plastics industry.

Bert M. Cohn, P.E., is president of Bert Cohn Associates, Inc., Chicago, IL.

PLASTICS TERMINOLOGY

The following terms are used in this chapter or are commonly encountered in the application, use, and storage of plastics products.

Additive: Any material mixed with a resin to modify its processing or end-use properties. The resulting mix usually is called a "plastic" to distinguish it from the "resin" or principal ingredient. Additives may be dyes, pigments, powdered fillers for stiffening, plasticizers for flexibility, fibers to reinforce, antioxidants, lubricants to aid flow into or release from a mold, or flame retardants.

Binders: The resins in a plastic mixture that hold together all of the other ingredients. They are usually a product of polymerization or a naturally occurring substance of high molecular weight.

Blowing agent: A material that releases gas upon heating so that the plastic in which it is mixed will expand into foam. The gas may result from boiling of a liquid or from decomposition of the blowing agent (foaming agent).

Copolymers: High molecular weight compounds produced when two or more monomers are involved in a polymerization process.

Crosslinking: The establishing of chemical bonds between adjacent molecules so as to make a network that will reduce solubility or resist flow on heating. The amount of crosslinking may be enough to render the plastic highly resistant to flow at temperatures up to thermal decomposition, in which case the plastic is said to be a thermoset.

Fillers: Materials that modify the strength and working properties of a plastic. They may be used to increase heat resistance or alter the dielectric strength. A wide variety of products are used, including wood flour, cotton, sisal, glass, and clay.

Film: A general term for plastic not more than 0.01-in. (0.25 mm) thick, regardless of the process used to make it. "Foil" is used today only to describe metal.

Foam: Plastic with many small gas bubbles; cellular plastic.

Foaming agent: The same as a blowing agent.

Inhibitor: A material added to prevent or retard an undesired chemical reaction.

Laminate: A composition of two or more layers of plastic firmly adhered either by partly melting one or more of the layers, by an adhesive, or by impregnation. High-pressure laminates are rigid stock made in presses at pressures above 400 psi (2760 kPa).

Monomers: The small starting molecules, usually gaseous or liquid, used to produce the polymer resins.

Plastic (ASTM definition): A material that contains as an essential ingredient one or more organic polymeric substances of large molecular weight, is solid in its finished state, and at some stage in its manufacture or processing into finished articles can be shaped by flow.

Plasticizers: Organic materials added to plastics to make the finished product more flexible or to facilitate compounding. Some plasticizers increase the combustibility of the plastic while others serve as flame retardants.

Polymerization: The process by which molecules of a monomer are made to add to themselves or to other monomers in a repetitive way, forming a much longer chainlike molecule.

Polymers: Large molecules made by combining smaller molecules by chemical reaction.

Reinforced plastic: A plastic with a filler which significantly increases flexural, impact, or tensile strength. Additives are usually glass, asbestos, cotton, or nylon fibers.

Resin (ASTM definition): A solid or pseudosolid organic material often of high molecular weight, which exhibits a tendency to flow when subjected to stress, usually has a softening or melting range, and usually fractures conchoidally. Note: In a broad sense, the term is used to designate any polymer that is a basic material for plastics.

Sheet: A general term for plastics 0.01 in. (0.25 mm) and thicker, regardless of the method of manufacture.

Stabilizer: A material added to prevent or retard an undesired chemical reaction. When used to prevent polymerization, the preferred term is "inhibitor." Stabilizers usually are present in less than one percent. They may be antioxidants, screening agents for ultraviolet radiation, or chemicals to neutralize decomposition products during hot processing.

Thermoforming: The process of stretching or bending a plastic sheet which has been softened by heating.

Thermoplastic (ASTM definition): A plastic that can be repeatedly softened by heating and hardened by cooling through a temperature range characteristic of the plastic, and that in the softened state can be shaped by flow into articles by molding or extrusion.

Thermoset (ASTM definition): A plastic that, after having been cured by heat or other means, is substantially infusible and insoluble.

THE FAMILY OF POLYMERS

In the classification of engineering materials, polymers are one division under the general category of nonmetals, which also includes ceramics, glasses, and materials, such as oils, greases, lubricants, papers, etc. Polymers are further subdivided into three classes—elastomers, thermosets, and thermoplastics—as shown in Figure 3-10A. Basically, all polymers are characterized by their very large molecules, formed in chemical "polymerization" reactions, which link two or more molecules into larger molecules. These larger molecules contain repeating structural units of the original molecules. If the linkages result in a rigid "cross-linked" molecular structure, a thermosetting plastic results. If the molecular structure is more flexible, including side chains not rigidly linked to the other molecules, the resulting material is a thermoplastic.

POLYMERS

THERMOSETS	THERMOPLASTICS	ELASTOMERS
Alkyds	ABS	Butadiene
Allyls	Acetals	Butyl
Epoxies	Acrylics	Fluoroelastomers
Melamine	Cellulosics	Hypalon
Phenolics	Fluoroplastics	Isoprene
Polyesters	Ionomers	Natural rubber
Polyurethane	Nylons	Neoprene
Silicones	Olefins	Nitrile
Urea	Polycarbonate	Polysulfide
and others	Polyester	Silicones
	Polyimide	Urethane
	Polystyrene	and others
	Vinyls	
	and others	

FIG. 3-10A. The family of polymers.

The products known as "plastics" include the common types of thermosetting and thermoplastic polymers included in Figure 3-10A, plus many more. In addition to the polymer constituent, most finished plastics contain plasticizers, colorants, fillers, stabilizers, reinforcing agents, lubricants, or other special additives. The variation of individual plastics-product formulations runs into the thousands. The ultimate form of each product, whether it appears in solid sections, films and sheets, foams, molded forms, synthetic fibers, pellets, or powders, has a significant effect on its fire properties. Additionally, the fire properties are influenced by the environment, and the resultant hazard by the quantity of the product and the conditions of its use. For these reasons, it is important to conduct fire tests of products in their end-use configuration and under conditions that simulate the end-use environment.

Elastomers

Elastomers are commonly referred to as "synthetic rubbers" and are characterized by their elastic or rubberlike properties. As a whole, this class of polymers is intended to reproduce or surpass the best properties of natural rubber for particular applications. The fire characteristics of elastomers are usually similar to those of natural rubber. A discussion of both natural and synthetic rubbers is included in this chapter.

Thermosetting Plastics

Thermosetting plastics, or thermosets, are hardened into a permanent shape in the manufacturing process. These materials cannot usually be softened by heating. For those that can be softened, the parts cannot be remelted or restored to their original state before curing. The components of thermosets can be purchased in liquid form as either monomer/polymer mixtures or as partially polymerized molding compounds. Thermosets are usually formed into their final shape with heat (sometimes under pressure), although some are cured at room temperature.

Thermoplastics

Thermoplastics do not cure or set into a permanent shape under the application of heat since heat will cause them to soften. They can be softened and rehardened repeatedly, although eventual thermal aging will cause a degradation of the material and limit the number of reheat cycles. When heated to a flowable state, thermoplastics can be transferred to a mold and cooled into the shape of the mold. Thermoplastics can be extruded through dies and solidified around other materials, such as insulation over electrical wiring. Generally, no chemical reaction takes place.

There is some overlap between thermosets and thermoplastics. Thermoplastics, after extrusion, can be crosslinked chemically or by irradiation to produce a thermoset product. The molding techniques typical of thermoplastics have been modified to permit injection molding of thermosets, such as phenolics.

USES OF PLASTICS

Plastics have wide ranging and continuously expanding applications. In building construction applications, plastics can be found in thermal and acoustical insulation, roofing materials, decorative trims and imitation wood parts, ceiling and wall panels, resilient flooring, light fixture diffusers, electrical conduits, insulation on wiring, water and gas piping, bathtubs and sinks, and heating ducts. Plastics are found in the housings and parts of equipment and appliances. Entire pieces of furniture, seat cushions, mattresses, carpeting, wall coverings, and draperies are often plastics, as are countertops, desktops, and tabletops. Textiles in clothing today often are partially or totally plastics products. Other uses of plastics include major parts, trim, and interiors of automobiles, buses, airplanes, and trains; packaging materials, including plastic wrap; housewares; sports equipment; toys; photographic films; magnetic tapes; phonograph records; and luggage.

Lack of stability under high temperatures and inherent combustibility so far have ruled out the use of plastics for applications where fire-resistance ratings are a requirement. One exception is the use of special silicone plastic foams for sealing openings in fire walls; the material retains its sealing and insulating properties while it slowly burns away during fire exposure.

ADDITIVES AND BLENDS

The physical properties of the basic types of polymers can be altered substantially during manufacturing by a variety of techniques. An extraordinary number of combinations of special properties are obtainable through the blending, or alloying, of one polymer with another. Additives, such as carbon black, glass fibers, flame retardants, and fillers ranging from cotton to clay, can alter not only the strength and other properties needed for the finished product but also the response to heat and flame.

Fiberglass and other threads added to plastics (usually, polyethylene) are used in the manufacture of fiber-reinforced plastic (FRP) products, such as boat hulls, automobile body parts, fishing rods, skis, motor homes, swimming pools, bathtubs, shower enclosures, building panels, and translucent roofing and siding. While flame retardants can be added to lower the ASTM E84 flamespread index to a range of 20 to 75, general-purpose FRP panels and other products are likely to have much higher surface flamespread ratings, in the range of 150 to 400.[1]

MAJOR GROUPS OF PLASTICS

The major groups of plastics are briefly described in the following paragraphs. Hundreds of variations are sold under thousands of individual trade names. More detailed information can be obtained from consulting the standard reference works of the industry. (See references at the end of this chapter.)

Positive identification of the plastic used in a product is often very difficult. Guidelines are available to assist in the identification of the more common types. Braun[2] sets forth simple laboratory tests using heat (pyrolysis), flame, and melting, compiled in a small, easy-to-read reference volume. Saechtling's plastics identification material is included. (See Figures 3-10B through 3-10E.) Figure 3-10F presents a number of simple tests that take advantage of the unique characteristics that many common plastics possess.

According to Saechtling,[3] plastics can be divided into four groups that reflect their derivation, method of synthesis, and historical development: (1) plastics from natural products, starting with vulcanized fiber in 1859, celluloid in about 1870, and artificial horn in 1897 as the oldest plastics (see Figure 3-10B); (2) "classical" condensation resins, including thermosets stemming from the discovery of Bakelite™ in about 1910 (see Figure 3-10C); (3) Staudinger polymerized plastics, deriving from foundations in 1922 for the polymerization of unsaturated monomers into long-chain macromolecules (see Figure 3-10D); and (4) plastics from multifunctional aliphatic and aromatic intermediate products, derived from work since the 1950s in combining various intermediates into a series of general-purpose and specially tailored engineering plastics (see Figure 3-10E.)

Commonly accepted abbreviations have been developed for many plastics materials and some of these have been standardized by the American Society for Testing and Materials (ASTM D1600).[5] Manufacturers are being urged to offer the abbreviation along with trademark names to aid in the rapid identification of the material. This is particularly important for plastics products used in building construction. For the purposes of this text, the abbreviation is noted either in parentheses in the heading or after the name of the plastic in the descriptions that follow.

ABS

Developed to offset some of the shortcomings of polystyrene, ABS plastics are copolymers of acrylonitrile, butadiene, and styrene monomers in varying proportions. They are balanced for mechanical toughness, good service temperature for other-than-high temperature applications, and

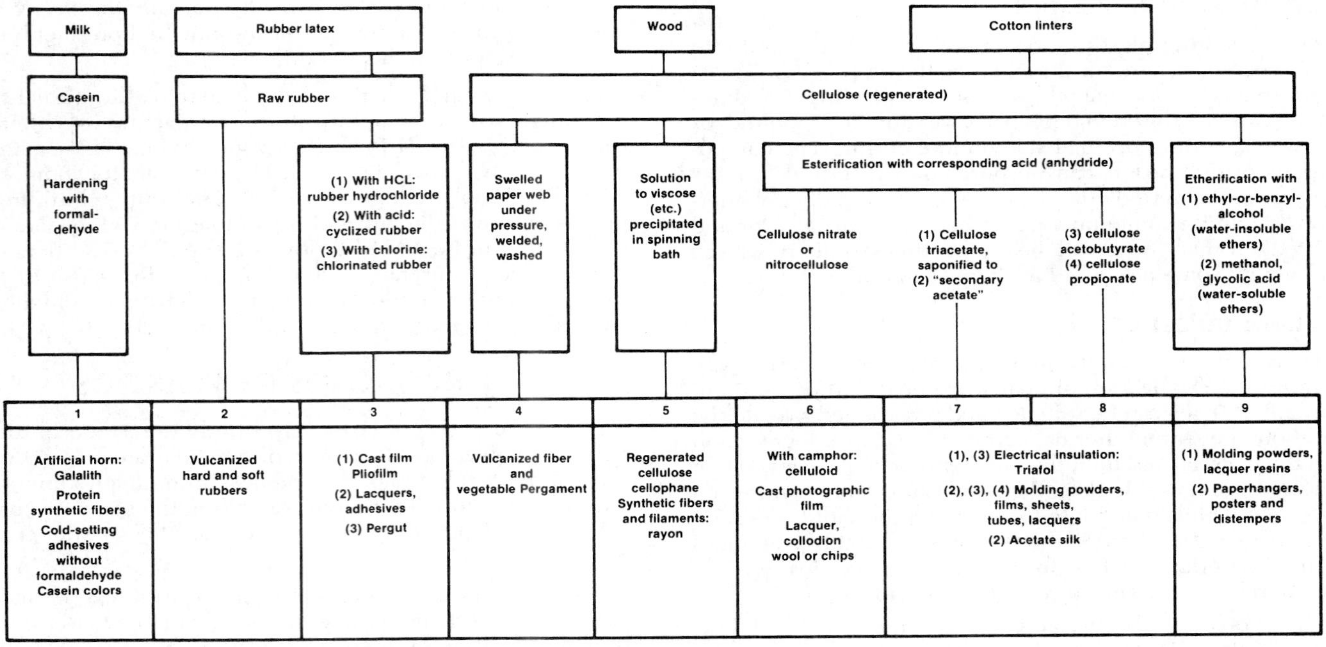

FIG. 3-10B. Plastics from natural products.[2,3]

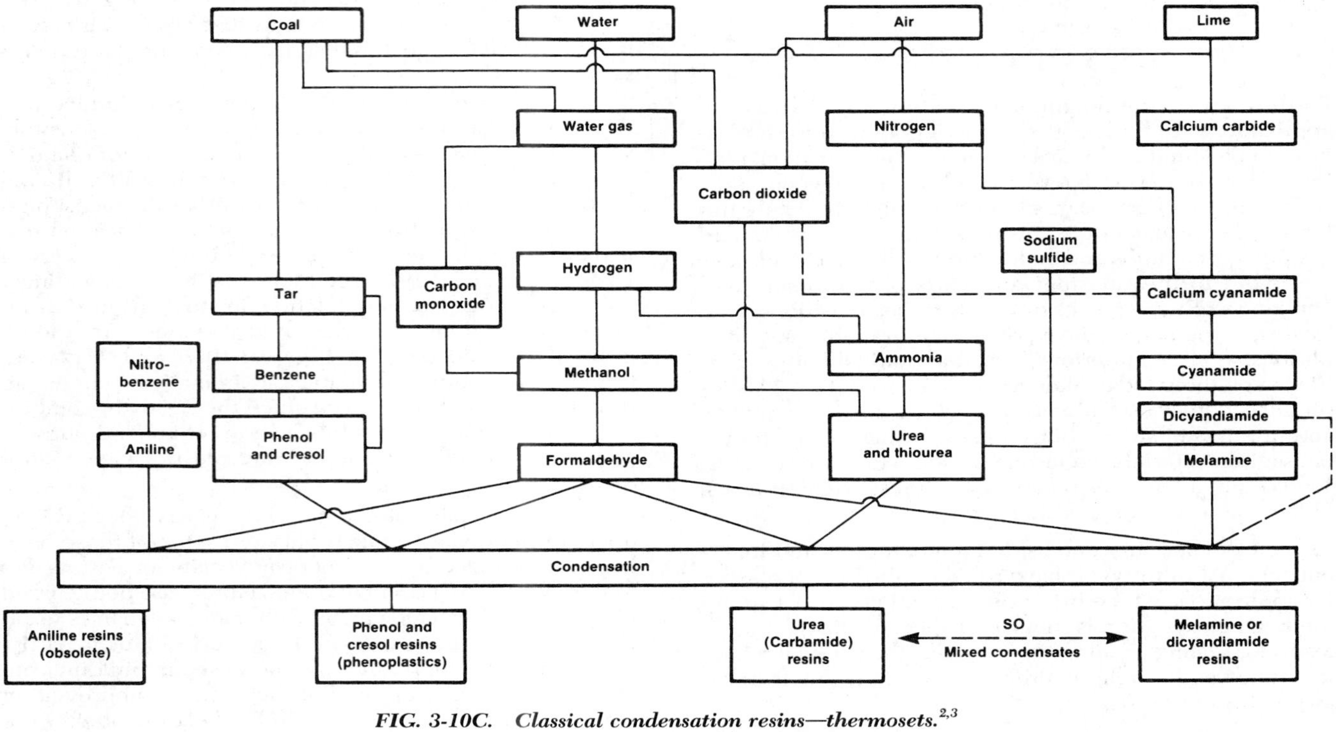

FIG. 3-10C. Classical condensation resins—thermosets.[2,3]

ease of fabrication. ABS materials have relatively good electrical insulating properties, good resistance to a wide range of chemicals, and good dimensional stability. Typical applications include automobile dashboards, pump impellers, refrigerator parts, appliance housings, luggage, protective helmets, battery cases, telephones, pipe and fittings, shoe heels, knobs, and tool handles. Typical trade names include Abson, Cycolac™, GravoFLEX™, Kralastic, Ravikral, Styrophane, and Terluran.

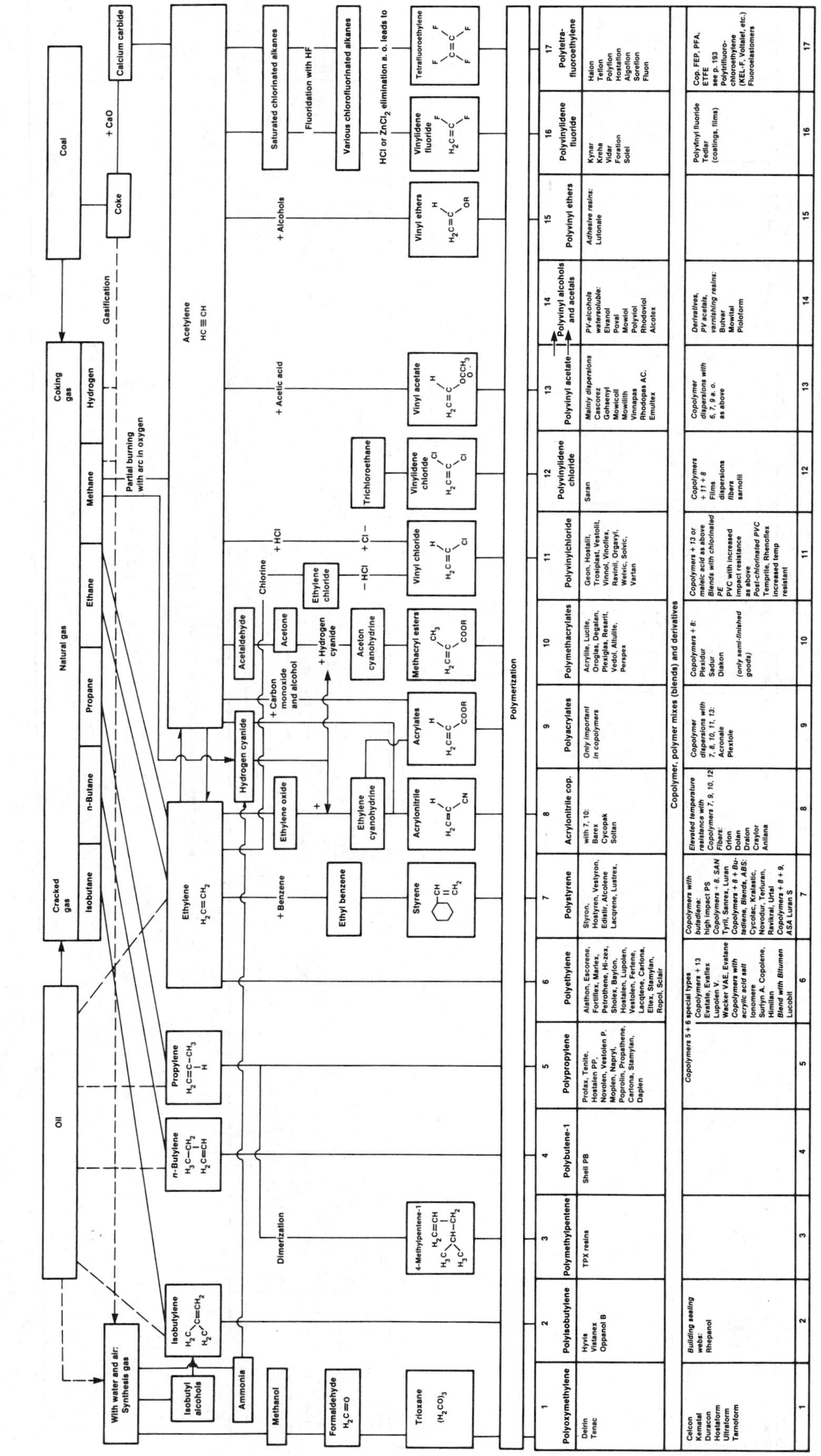

FIG. 3-10D. Double-bond polymerization thermoplastics.[2,3]

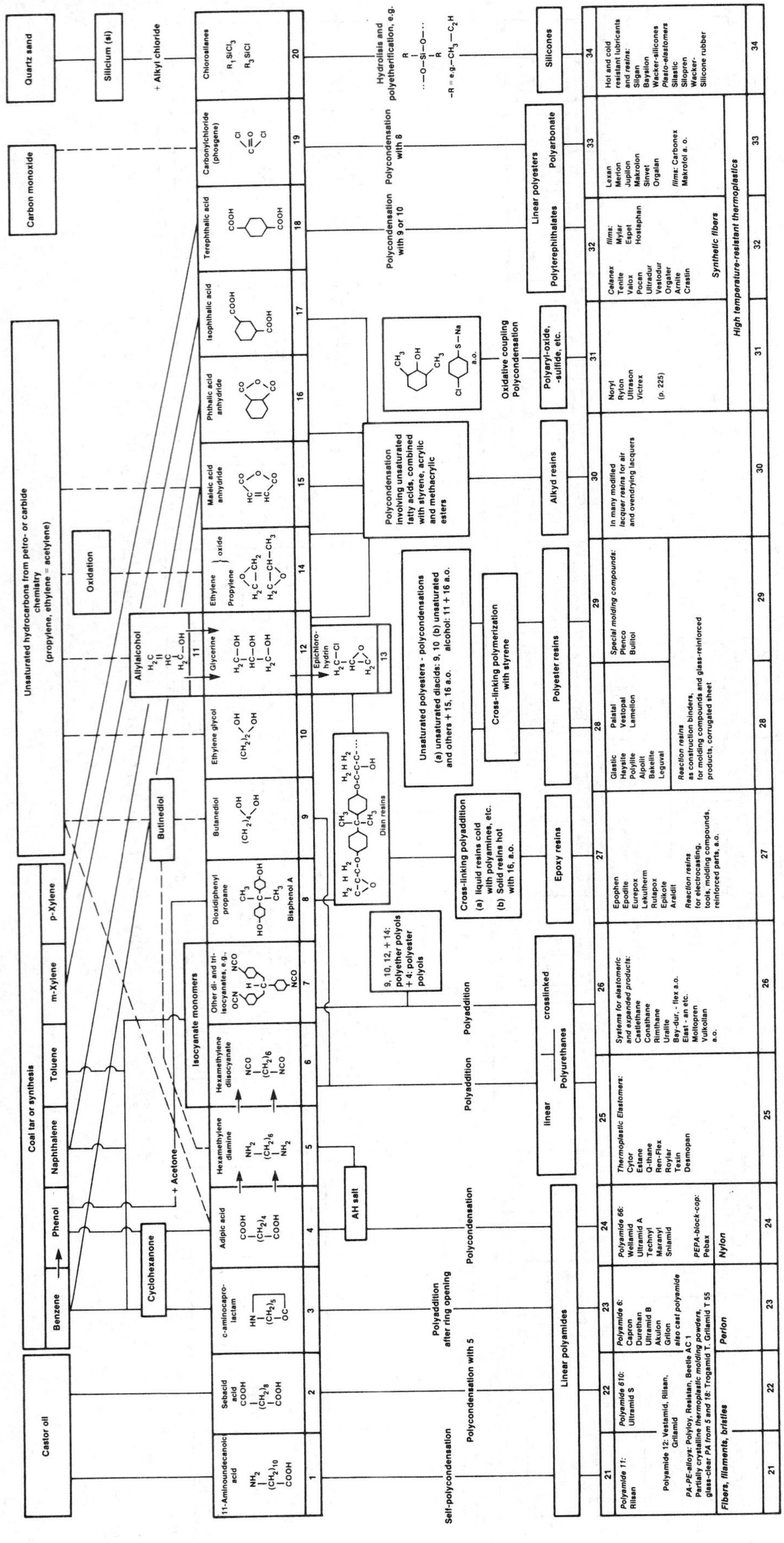

FIG. 3-10E. Plastics from multifunctional intermediate products.[2,3]

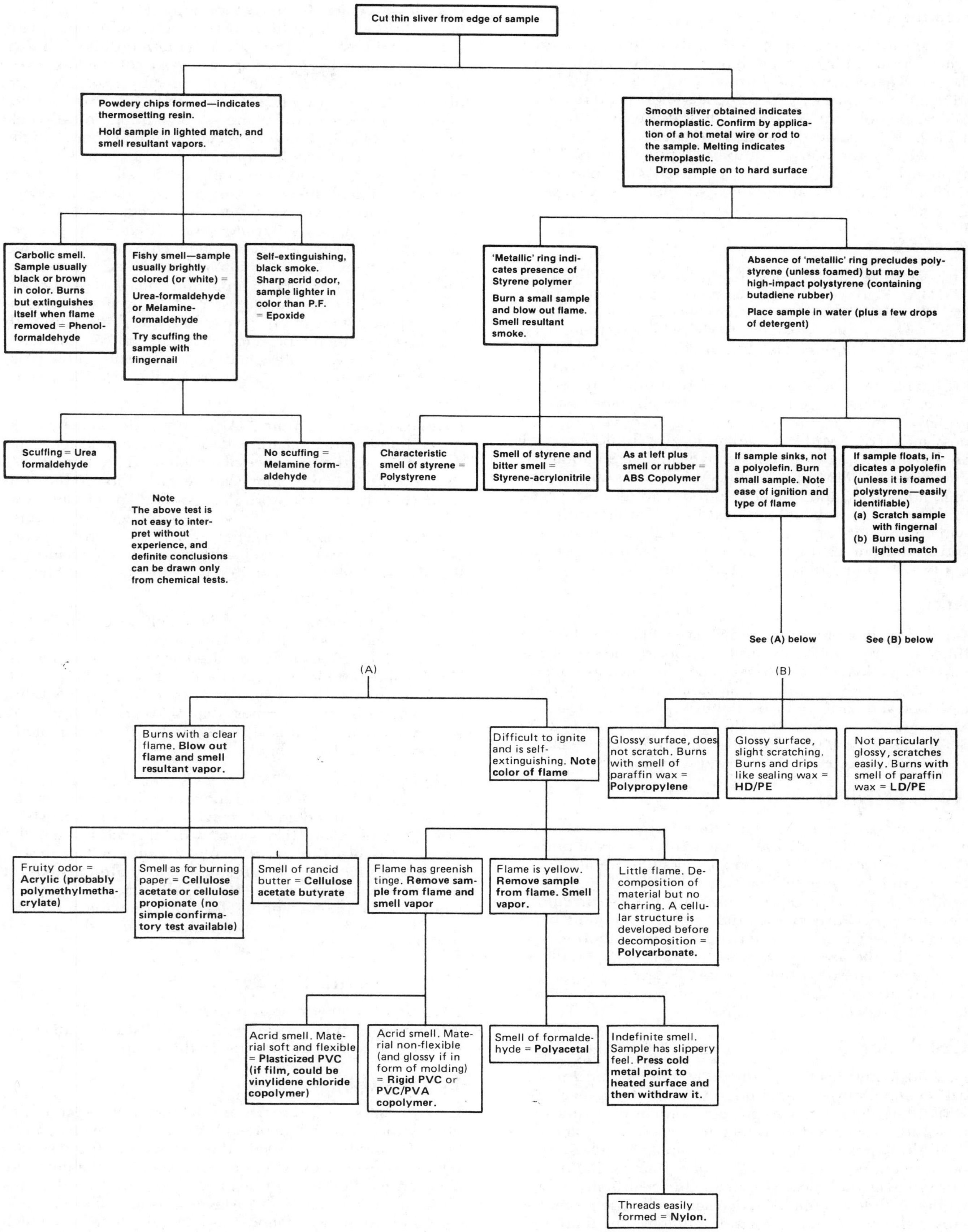

FIG. 3-10F. Simple tests for identifying the more common plastics. (Adapted from Briston, J. H., and Grosselin, C. C., Introduction to Plastics, *Newnes-Butterworth, London, 1968.*[4]*)*

Acetals (AR)

The acetal resins are made primarily by the polymerization of formaldehyde. Copolymers of acetal are also produced. These materials form one of the strongest and stiffest thermoplastics. The products show good resistance to organic solvents; however, they do react with strong acids or bases. These plastics are widely used for equipment gears, automotive equipment, plumbing parts, and appliances. Two basic types are: (1) a homopolymer (e.g., DuPont's Deltrin®), and (2) a copolymer (e.g., Celanese's Celcon®).

Acrylics

The acrylics are basically polymethyl methacrylate (PMMA). Marketed under the common tradenames Lucite and Plexiglas, PMMA is known for its excellent clarity, high transparency, good resistance to sharp blows, strength, and rigidity. It is odorless, tasteless, and nontoxic, but the surface scratches easily, and contact with grit and harsh scouring agents must be avoided. Because it is a thermoplastic, it loses its shape in boiling water, although some cast acrylics have higher heat resistance. In sheets of varying thickness and color, PMMA is used for glazing, building panels, advertising displays, and protective shields. Solutions and emulsions of PMMA are produced for use as surface coatings, adhesives, and finishes. In rods and tubes, it is used for electric lighting and medical illuminating equipment which utilize its capacity to transmit light along its length and around curves. In its molded form, it is used for lenses, dentures, toilet articles, and telephones.

Alkyds

Good insulating properties, excellent moldability, short cure time, and low cost are primary reasons for the use of thermosetting alkyds in electrical materials, such as housings and cases for switchgear, encapsulation of capacitors and resistors, and parts for fuses, light switches, and insulators. Maximum use temperature of the molded parts is 250 to 300°F (120 to 150°C). Liquid resins are used for enamels and lacquers for cars, stoves, and refrigerators.

Allyls (Allylics)

Allyl resins and monomers are thermosetting plastics that are commercially available as the diallyl esters of phthalic (DAP) and isophthalic (DAIP) acids. Other monomers in this grouping are diallyl maleate (DAM) and diallyl chlorendate (DAC). The latter is used for flame-resistant formulations because of the high chlorine content of the resins. They can be polymerized by raising their temperature or by the use of peroxide initiators. The molding and electrical properties of these materials are excellent. They are primarily used for electrical components, decorative laminates, sealants, and coatings.

Cellulosics

Cellulosic plastics are produced by the chemical modification of cellulose, a natural polymer that is a major constituent of plant life. The primary sources of cellulose for this purpose are cotton linters and wood pulp. The term "cellulosic plastics" applies only to plastics whose resinous content is an ester or ether of cellulose. Included in this group are cellulose acetate, cellulose acetate butyrate, methyl cellulose, cellulose triacetate, cellulose propionate, ethyl cellulose, cellulose nitrate, cellulose films, and fibers.

Cellulose acetate (CA): A thermoplastic made by treating cellulose with acetic acid and acetic anhydride, with sulfuric acid as a catalyst. It can be formed into molding powder, foamed by rapid evaporation of a solvent, dissolved for lacquers, cast into film, and spun from solution into fibers. It has replaced hazardous cellulose nitrate for photographic use under the name "safety" film. (See also cellulose triacetate.) Cellulose acetate molding compositions are tough and of good color and gloss; hardness is controlled by varying the ratio of plasticizer and ranges from rigid to flexible. Primary uses are in electronic components, insulation tapes, food packaging, toys, eyeglass frames, and sound recording and computer tapes. Rigid cellulose acetate foam is used as the core in sandwich panels and marine floats. Variations in composition include the degree of esterification of cellulose and amount and choice of plasticizer, which is usually a phthalate ester. Molding stocks for general purposes ignite easily, give off burning drips, burn with a dark yellow flame, produce moderate smoke, and have an odor of vinegar, unless masked by the odor of the plasticizer. Flame-resistant stocks are widely used for molding.

Cellulose acetate butyrate (CAB): A plastic made by treating cellulose with a mixture of acetic and butyric acids and anhydrides in the presence of a catalyst. The ratio of acetic and butyric components can be varied to produce the desired flexibility. It absorbs less water than cellulose acetate. Compositions with ultraviolet stabilizers are used for small outdoor and indoor signs. Major uses are for automobile steering wheels and taillights, telephone handsets, toothbrush handles, business machine keys, appliance housings, piping, and tubing.

Cellulose propionate (CP): A thermoplastic molding composition made from cellulose and propionic acid. Molding compositions are usually supplied as granules or pellets, and finished articles can be fabricated by injection molding or extrusion. It has similar uses to CA and CAB, but due to better surface hardness than CAB and less moisture sensitivity than CA, it is also used for mechanical pencils, telephones, and shoe heels.

Cellulose triacetate (CAT): A thermoplastic made by reacting cellulose with acetic anhydride. It differs from cellulose acetate in chemical structure in that it consists of three acetate groups (instead of two) attached to each glucose unit of the cellulose molecule. Because of its high softening temperature, it is not suitable as molding stock. It has lower water absorption than CA and is now the prevalent base for photographic safety film, drawing and printing film, magnetic tape, and transformer and capacitor dielectrics.

Cellulose Nitrate (CN)

Because of the extreme fire hazards associated with cellulose nitrate in its processing, use, and storage, this plastic is discussed in detail later in this chapter.

Epoxies (EP)

Epoxy resins are primarily produced by the reaction of epichlorohydrin and bisphenol-A in the presence of a catalyst. By varying the ratio of the ingredients, the resultant product may be a low-viscosity fluid or a high-melting solid. Two primary classes are available: (1) the liquid resins which are combined with curing agents for adhesives, potting, and tooling compounds, and (2) the solid resins which are modified with other resins to make coating materials. The epoxy resins also are used as "body solders" for automobile repair, as dies for forming sheet metal, as piping and tubing, and as foamed blocks for construction insulation.

Fluoroplastics

Fluoroplastics or fluorocarbons are commercially available in several major groups under the headings polyethylenetetrafluoroethylene (ETFE); polyethylenechlorotrifluoroethylene (ECTFE); polytetrafluoroethylene (TFE); polyfluoroethylene-propylene (FEP); polychlorotrifluoroethylene (CTFE); polyvinyl fluoride (PVF); and polyvinylidene fluoride (PVF_2). All of these resins are characterized by resistance to solvents and chemical attack and good-to-excellent weatherability. Six are described below.

Polytetrafluoroethylene (TFE): A representative of a group of completely fluorinated resins. It is handled as general-purpose molding powders, fine granules, and aqueous dispersions. The methods of processing include compression molding, extruding, dip coating, and film casting. TFE has a very extended range of serviceable temperatures, from –450 to 500°F (–265 to 260°C). It is used as chemical gasketing, high-frequency and high-temperature electrical insulation, lubricants, and on molded bearings and coated cookware.

Polyfluoroethylene-propylene (FEP): A copolymer of tetrafluoroethylene and hexafluoropropylene. FEP can be handled through the melt-flow processes involved in extrusion and injection molding. It is widely used in industrial applications, particularly as insulation for process industries involving heat and corrosive atmospheres. It is also used as a lining for vessels, pipes, valves, and fittings handling corrosive fluids.

Polyethylene-tetrafluoroethylene (ETFE): A copolymer of ethylene and tetrafluoroethylene. It is processed by the conventional method of extrusion and injection molding. Its applications include use as gears, pump components, automotive parts, labware, valve linings, electrical connectors, and wire coatings. ETFE can be reinforced with glass fiber.

Polychlorotrifluoroethylene (CTFE): A thermoplastic resin produced in various formulations of fluoroplastics. It differs from the usual fluoroplastic in that its molecular structure contains chlorine. It flows like FEP for injection molding or extrusion, but is less thermally stable. It is chemically resistant to many corrosive liquids. Its serviceable temperatures range from –400 to 390°F (–240 to 200°C). Its electrical and thermal properties make it valuable for insulation, cable assemblies, printed circuits, and electronic components. It also is used in the chemical process industries in valves, fittings, and gaskets.

Polyethylene-chlorotrifluoroethylene (ECTFE): A 1:1 copolymer of ethylene and chlorotrifluoroethylene. ECTFE is processed by extrusion, molding, rotocast, and powder coating techniques. Applications include chemically resistant linings, coatings, containers, labware, moldings, wire coatings, fibers, and films.

Polyvinyl fluoride (PVF): A plastic produced through the polymerization of vinyl fluoride. Films are cast from selected hot solvents, and the major use is as a weather-resistant surface on building siding made of aluminum, wood, composite boards, or polyester glass fiber laminates.

Ionomers

The term "ionomer" is used to describe the class of thermoplastic polymers in which ionized carboxyl groups create ionic crosslinks in the intermolecular structure. Ionomer resin formulations are available in a wide variety of compositions. They are outstanding plastics, with regard to toughness, transparency, and solvent resistance, and resist impact at temperatures as low as –160°F (–107°C). Articles made from these plastics include housewares, toys, containers, safety shields, tool handles, electrical insulation, and packaging. These plastics are also used in the lamination of various building construction materials.

Melamines (MF)

Melamine, one of the members of the amino family, is a thermosetting plastic noted for its extreme hardness, permanent colors, and good electrical insulating characteristics. Alpha-cellulose filled, general-purpose grades are used for dishes and kitchenware, where their lack of taste and odor and resistance to food stains make them particularly desirable. Mineral-filled grades are used in electrical applications. The resin may be bonded with fabrics, paper, wood veneers, etc., to produce laminates for building applications.

Nylon

See polyamides.

Olefins

See polybutylene, polyethylene, polyallomers, and polypropylene.

Phenolics (PF)

The discovery of phenol formaldehyde plastics (Bakelite™) in about 1910 marked the beginning of the plastics industry. Many varieties are now available, marked by low cost and good mechanical, electrical, and thermal properties. General-purpose, wood-filled grade phenolics are suitable for use up to about 300°F (150°C), but glass- or mineral-filled compounds have long-term retention of properties up to approximately 500°F (260°C). Some special, heat-resistant types are usable for up to 1 hr at temperatures as high as 1000°F (540°C).

Paper or fabric impregnated with phenolic resin in a water or organic solvent can be wound into tube form or pressed into flat sheets to make tough thermoset "laminates" with low water absorption and high service temperature capabilities. Laminates are used for electrical insulation and bearings for marine propellers and heavy rolling mills. Similar compositions are used as laminating adhesives for exterior-grade plywood and as impervious surfacing materials. Paper impregnated with phenolic resin and printed with wood grain is frequently the top surface for wall panels or furniture, with backing of other phenolic laminates or plywood. Phenolics are standard binders for brake shoes, sandpaper, grinding wheels, sand-casting foundry molds, and wood chip particle board.

Two types of phenolic foam—reaction foam and syntactic foam—are used in construction or for thermal insulation. Reaction foam is made by curing the phenolic resin with agitation so rapid that water is produced as a byproduct, and is vaporized and trapped to make the voids in the foam. Syntactic foam is made from hollow spheres of phenolic resin with a phenolic or other resin binder. Each type is used for cores in sandwich panels, and as buoyancy or a stiffening means in marine and aircraft structures. Cast phenolic resin is largely used for decorative applications.

Polyallomers

Polyallomers are made by polymerizing two monomers with catalysts so that blocks of each polymer are formed in the polymer chain. The most common polyallomer contains ethylene and propylene. Applications for polyallomers include films, bottles, appliance parts, automotive parts, toys, and closures.

Polyamides

Two aliphatic polyamides—nylon-6,6 and nylon-6—find their greatest uses in home furnishings, apparel, and tire cord, and account for most of the production in this family of polymers. The manufacture of nylon-6,6 started in 1938, and nylon-6 in 1939. The first major application was in the hosiery market. Nylon has become one of the leading polymers due to its high-impact strength, versatility, and east of processing. Other forms of nylons are also commercially available and find application in ropes, fishlines, cable jacketing, gears, slide fasteners, boat propellers, and appliance parts.

Aromatic polyamides are more heat resistant. Their commercial production started in 1961 with DuPont's Nomex™ and, more recently, Kevlar™ fiber. Nomex™ is found in items such as fire fighter's protective clothing, while Kevlar™ is ideally suited for tires and ballistic vests because of its strength. Kevlar™, together with graphite, is finding a use in superior composite materials, such as fiber-reinforced plastics (FRP). Polyamide imides and polyimides are other members of this grouping, typically used for heat-resistant electrical wire and cable insulation.

Polybutylene (PB)

Polybutylene is flexible, has excellent creep resistance at room and elevated temperatures, and has higher long-term temperature resistance than other polyolefins. Other advantages include good toughness, high tear strength, and good moisture barrier and electrical insulation characteristics. Applications include film and sheeting, hot-melt coatings and adhesives, flexible pipe and tubing, and shrink film.

Polycarbonates (PC)

Polycarbonates are thermoplastic polyesters of carbonic acid. The resin is available in several different forms, including pellets, powder, film, sheet, rod, plate, and tubing. High-impact strength, good electrical properties, clarity, and resistance to creep have caused this material to find many applications, such as in appliances, electrical and electronics equipment, food-handling systems, and sporting goods. Its transparency makes it useful for lenses, safety shields, and glazing.

Polyester, High-Temperature Aromatic

Important characteristics of this material are its dimensional stability at high temperatures [over 600°F (315°C)], self-lubricating properties, good stiffness, electrical insulating properties, and solvent resistance. It decomposes rapidly at approximately 1000°F (540°C). An unusual aspect of this thermoplastic is its very high thermal conductivity, which makes the material useful in applications, such as bearings and electrical insulation, where failure from localized hot spots is a problem with most plastics. Stick-free coatings for frying pans and encapsulation of electronic parts are among its other uses. Trade names include Ekonol™ and Ekcel™.

Polyesters, Thermoplastic

Unsaturated polyesters show good weathering resistance, light stability, and heat resistance. Their primary application is in the production of reinforced plastics. They are used to fabricate structures ranging in size from electrical components to large boat hulls.

Saturated polyesters do not have the double bond that would permit further polymerization by treatment with initiators, such as organic peroxides. Saturated polyesters of high molecular weight, such as ethylene glycol terephthalate, are used principally in fiber and film production, e.g., magnetic recording tapes, tough or boil-in-bag food packaging, and satellite balloons. They can be backplated with metals for decorative films and nameplates. The low molecular weight esters are used as plasticizers for vinyl and acrylic resins.

Thermoplastic polyester molding compositions are available. Besides poly (ethylene-terephthalate)—PET, there are poly (1,4-butylene-terephthalate)—PBT, poly (tetramethylene-terephthalate)—PTMT, and poly (cyclohexylenedimethylene-terephthalate-isophthalate)—PCDT. PBT and PTMT are the same chemically.

Thermoplastic polyesters have engineering applications, including automotive parts, appliance parts, business machine parts, electrical and electronic parts, gears, bearings, pulleys, and pump components. The polyester PET, discovered in Britain during World War II, can be spun into a fiber that is commonly used in textiles (e.g., Dacron™, etc.).

Polyethylene (PE)

Three major types of polyethylene are marketed: the low-, medium-, and high-density products. In addition, copolymers of ethylene-ethyl acrylate, ethylene-vinyl acetate, and ethylene-butylene are produced. The three density ranges are 56.8 to 57.7, 57.8 to 58.7, and 58.8 to 60.2 lb per cu ft (90.9 to 92.4 kg/m^3, 92.5 to 94.0 kg/m^3, and 94.1 to 96.4 kg/m^3).

Low-density stocks are waxy, relatively limp, and are the toughest of the polyethylenes, with an upper service temperature of approximately 160°F (70°C). As density increases, so does surface hardness, stiffness, resistance to permeation by oils and water, and softening temperature. For polyethylenes of the highest density, the upper service temperature is 240°F (115°C) under no-load conditions.

The outstanding properties of polyethylenes are: (1) good moldability, (2) good mechanical properties, (3) excellent electrical resistance, (4) low moisture vapor transmission, (5) resistance to solvents and chemicals, and (6) lightness in weight. Polyethylene is widely used for film, sheeting, plastic bottles, piping, tubing, dish pans, garbage containers, laundry baskets, electronic components, insulation, and textiles. Boat and motor vehicle fuel tanks are a recent application for high-density polyethylene. Polyethylene can be crosslinked chemically or by irradiation to form a thermoset with high heat resistance.

Polyphenylene Oxide (PPO)

Polyphenylene oxide is a thermoplastic resin formed by the catalyzed oxidation of 2,6-xylenol. It is a specialized, highly engineered plastic with a wide temperature range, good mechanical and electrical properties, and resistance to corrosive materials. It has many electrical and electronic applications, and is used for packaging frozen foods and as a replacement for glass and stainless steel in hospital utensils and medical instruments.

Polyphenylene Sulfide (PPS)

Excellent chemical resistance and high stiffness at elevated temperatures make this material useful as a coating for various metals, including aluminum, steel, cast iron, brass, etc., and in the petroleum and chemical processing industries. Other uses include cookware, pump impellers, pumps, conveyor rollers, and machine parts.

Polypropylene (PP)

Polypropylene possesses the lowest density of the commercially available thermoplastics. In addition, it exhibits good rigidity, high yield strength, good surface hardness, exceptional flexural properties, resistance to chemicals, and excellent dielectric properties. Like all olefins, it has excellent resistance to water solutions that are highly damaging to many metals.

Primary areas of use include the usual categories of molding, as well as in film and piping. It is used for luggage, housewares, automobile and aviation components, and appliance parts. Because of its superior insulating properties, it is also used to make electronic components. Carpeting made of polypropylene fibers also is available. Polypropylene filled with asbestos offers high-impact strength, stiffness [up to 250°F (120°C)], and low friction.

Polystyrene (PS)

A glassy, transparent thermoplastic, primary characteristics of polystyrene are hardness, rigidity, clarity, and heat and dimensional stability. By varying the polymerization reaction, polystyrenes have been developed with higher heat distortion temperatures. Styrene polymers are marketed in granular and powder form for extrusion or molding. Beads of polystyrene that contain the flammable gas pentane as a blowing agent are sold for the production of polystyrene foam.

General-purpose and impact grades of polystyrene are used for refrigerator liners, appliance housings, automotive applications, films for wrapping, sporting goods, toys, and novelties. Heat-resistant polystyrene is used for television sets, radios, and illuminated signs. Glass-filled polystyrene is used for business machines, electronic equipment, and military hardware. Polystyrene foam is used to make toys, insulation, displays, shipping containers, and molded furniture. Construction panels, consisting of cores of polystyrene foam between sheets of plywood, plastic, or aluminum, and foamed-in-place polystyrene insulation are used in the building industry.

Polysulfone (PSU)

Polysulfone is a thermoplastic resin that contains a diphenylene group. This group imparts certain desirable characteristics to the polymer, including thermal stability [over 300°F (150°C)], oxidation resistance, and rigidity. Glass fibers may be added for improved environmental stress crack resistance. Commercial applications include electronic units, electrical circuit breaker parts, automobile engine parts, aircraft interiors, kitchen range hardware, electroplating equipment, and appliance hardware.

Polyurethane (PUR)

The polyurethanes consist of a group of polymers that are produced in the following two general forms: (1) foams, e.g., flexible, semi-flexible, and rigid; and (2) elastomers, e.g., casting compounds and elastoplastic resins, adhesives, coatings, and spandex fiber. The basic reaction used to produce the urethane polymers involves isocyanates and reactive hydrogen-bearing materials, such as polyethers, castor oils, amines, carboxylic acid, and water. By varying the number of branchings, it is possible to make polyurethanes that are thermoplastic or thermosetting.

The polyurethane foams are widely used in the production of upholstered furniture, bedding, sponges, toys, wearing apparel, and medical dressings. Rigid urethane foams are used for insulation in building construction. Substantial quantities of the polyurethanes are used to produce coatings and adhesives. Its rubberlike qualities aid in the production of specialty fillers and elastomers. Gears, sprockets, and rolls are produced from urethanes. Very thin films are used to produce containers impermeable to gas and moisture.

Silicones (SI)

The silicone resins comprise a large group of polymers consisting of chains of alternating silicone and oxygen atoms with organic groups, e.g., methyl groups attached to the silicone atoms. They are stable at high and low temperatures, have good dielectric properties, resist weathering, do not react with most chemicals, and repel water.

Silicone emulsions are used as mold release agents, defoamers, and waterproofing materials. A compound of liquid silicone and finely divided filler produces a grease suitable for high-temperature lubrication applications. Silicone paints, varnishes, and enamels have many uses, including cloth and wire coating. With inorganic fillers, such as glass or asbestos, silicones are molded into such products as connector plugs, coil bobbins, insulators on induction furnaces, and heat barriers in jet engine afterburners. Silicone glass laminate applications include rigid hot air ducts for aircraft, terminal boards, and transformer spools and spacers. Rigid silicone foams can be preformed or foamed in place. High-temperature insulation is the principal use of rigid silicone foams.

Styrene Acrylonitrile (SAN)

Produced through the copolymerization of styrene and acrylonitrite, styrene acrylonitrile is a transparent thermoplastic with improved heat resistance, stiffness, and scratch and impact resistance. It finds application in decorative panels, food packages, "dishwasher-safe" housewares, battery cases, lenses, glasses, appliance parts, and automobile components.

Ureas (UF)

Urea formaldehyde, as a thermosetting plastic, is especially suitable for any application that must resist heat. The material has excellent resistance to oils and greases, but is not recommended for high humidity environments. Because urea formaldehyde is hard, strong, odorless, and tasteless, it has been frequently used in tableware, crockery, and decorative articles for the home. Other uses are for electrical parts, such as switches and outlet covers, bottle tops, toys, and as a laminate in building panels. Plaskon™ and Beetle™ are two well-known trade names.

Vinyls

The vinyl resins are thermoplastics that exist in a wide variety of polymers and copolymers. Commercial production of the vinyl chloride monomer starts with acetylene or ethylene. Most vinyl plants utilize an oxychlorination process with ethylene to produce vinyl chloride. Copolymers of vinyl chloride and vinyl acetate account for a large part of vinyl production.

The major applications for flexible and rigid vinyls include: automobile seat covers, floor mats, and moldings; shower curtains; window shades; wrappings; bottles; adhesives; flooring; siding; piping; wiring; swimming pools; records; and medical appliances.

Polyvinyl chloride (PVC): This type of plastic is made as a rigid product for a number of building components and as a flexible plasticized stock for upholstery and wearing apparel. It exists in hundreds of individual formulations. It has good abrasion resistance.

The unplasticized PVC softens as it burns, producing white smoke and acrid fumes, which can be corrosive. Most of the chlorine content of PVC is released as hydrogen chloride. The fire properties of plasticized PVC are determined to a large extent by the nature of the plasticizer. Building products should be tested individually.

Vinyl chloride—vinyl acetate copolymers (polyvinyl acetate) (PVAC): These contain from 5 to 20 percent vinyl acetate in the polymer. They are used for more flexible stocks than PVC and are more readily softened by plasticizers. Their properties are essentially those of PVC.

Polyvinyl dichloride (PVDC): Because this plastic is made by chlorinating PVC, its properties are essentially those of rigid PVC. It is used most where more toughness, stiffness, and heat resistance are needed than is offered by PVC.

Vinyl acetate polymer (VAC): A thermoplastic that is used in coatings, as a wood primer, and as an adhesive in a milky aqueous dispersion. It is not used as a molding or sheet plastic, as its upper service temperature is below 120°F (50°C).

Vinyl alcohol resins (PVA): Because they are made by hydrolysis of polyvinyl acetate, PVA products swell or dissolve completely in water. They are highly impervious to oils and many lacquer solvents. They are used in hoses for spray painting and as water-soluble film for dose-packaging detergents, etc.

Polyvinyl butyral (PVB): Polyvinyl butyral is produced by condensing butyraldehyde with polyvinyl alcohol. It has remarkable adhesive qualities and is primarily used as plasticized film for laminating automotive safety glass.

Polyvinyl formal (PVFM): This plastic is produced by condensing formaldehyde with polyvinyl alcohol to make a hard resin. Polyvinyl formal is then mixed with small amounts of phenolic resin to improve the bond and reduce creep. It is not to be confused with polyvinyl fluoride. (See Fluoroplastics.) Its principal use is as standard insulation enamel for magnet wire in small motors and electronic equipment.

Vinylidene chloride polymer: This is a thermoplastic that as a film has low permeability to water vapor. A principal use is as a coating on cellophane. Filaments are used for webbing on garden furniture and for window screening.

Vinylidene chloride-vinyl chloride copolymer: This plastic is less rigid than PVC and flows more readily in extrusion and molding. Its major use is as a coating for metals and molded electrical parts.

NATURAL AND SYNTHETIC RUBBER

Like plastics, rubber appears in many shapes and forms, from very soft and pliable products to hard rubber that looks and feels like a molded plastic. Many polymers can be manufactured in elastomeric grades and are classified in that form as synthetic rubbers. Crepe soles fall in that category.

Natural Rubber (NR)

Natural rubber is a constituent of latex, the white milky sap collected from the rubber tree. The processed rubber may be used in sheet form for items like shoe soles, extruded into products like inner tubes, or compression molded with heat to make items like tires and hot-water bottles. Liquid latex has a variety of applications. It is often coated on fabrics for waterproofing, mixed with cement for superior bonding qualities, included in water-based paints to produce a cohesive film after the paint dries, and expanded into the familiar foam latex, or foam rubber. The density of the foam is controlled by varying the ratio of foam to air and the size of the cavities.

Vulcanization is a curing process that changes the isoprene molecule to a polyisoprene and produces a thermoset polymer that cannot be reshaped or remolded when reheated. By prolonging the vulcanization process, the degree of hardness can be varied, eventually resulting in "hard rubber" (known as ebonite or vulcanite in England). Hard-rubber tubes and rods have been popular products, valued for their resiliency, electrical insulating quality, and chemical inertness. Other common products have included automobile battery cases, combs, telephone receivers, castors, wheels, and bushings. In many of these applications, synthetics have replaced natural rubber.

Synthetic Rubber (SR)

These materials are intended to imitate the elasticity of natural rubber, and they can be vulcanized. They have similar long-chain molecular structures, built up from copolymerized synthetic monomers, such as butadiene with styrene, or butadiene with acrylonitrile. The former method produces styrene-butadiene rubber (SBR), such as the early Buna™ and Buna-S™ rubbers; styrene-butadiene rubber is used extensively in automobile tires. Nitrile rubber (NBS) is the product of the butadiene-acrylonitrile reaction, while butyl rubber is produced from an isobutylene isoprene copolymer. Neoprene (GR) is a very strong and durable synthetic made from chloroprene.

Synthetic foam rubber usually means a soft flexible product of the polyurethane type and is either polyester (AU) or polyether (EU). However, new types are continually being developed, including ethylene-propylene rubber (EPR), polybutadiene (BR), and polyisoprene, the synthetic equivalent of natural rubber.

Silicone rubber (SI) incorporates the inorganic, inert element silicone, which gives it a number of unique properties. It is the only satisfactory soft material for human implants, and it is commonly used for breast implants and many other implants, including artificial ears, skull plates, and jawbones. In building applications, self-curing, water-repellant silicone rubber is used as a sealant, and it finds many applications where a nonstick surface is desired. Some formulations have been used successfully as firestops and to seal openings in fire walls, where its flexibility gives performance superior to grout or plaster.

Additional information sources on synthetic rubbers are: *Plastics: Design and Materials*,[6] *Introduction to Industrial Polymers*,[7] and *Rubber Technology Handbook*.[8]

CELLULOSE NITRATE (CN)

Cellulose nitrate (also referred to as nitrocellulose and pyroxylin) is made by the action of nitric and sulfuric acids on cellulose materials, such as cotton. Pyroxylin plastic comprises the lower nitrated products and contains from 11 to 12 percent nitrogen.

Cellulose nitrate plastics possess the most unusual and serious burning characteristics of all plastics. Cellulose nitrate material that has been subjected to heat, such as that salvaged from a fire, may be so altered in composition that it is subject to spontaneous ignition.

When cellulose nitrate products are heated to temperatures above 300°F (150°C), decomposition starts, which generates further heat and soon raises the material to its ignition temperature. Some researchers have reported decomposition after long-continued exposure to temperatures not much above that of boiling water. There are a number of cases on record of ignition from contact with steam pipes and electric light bulbs. Decomposition of cellulose nitrate generates heat and does not depend upon an external air supply.

Some of the gases produced by decomposition are highly toxic. The effect of carbon monoxide is well known. The toxic effect of the oxides of nitrogen is often delayed; persons exposed to these gases may show no immediate ill effects, but fatalities may follow some hours or days after exposure.

Cellulose nitrate, when in solution in acetone or any of the various solvents, has no greater hazard than that of the solvent. If the solvent is lost, the hazard reverts to that of cellulose nitrate.

Most articles formerly made of cellulose nitrate are now made from less hazardous plastics, but it is still used to some extent in industrial applications, for items such as shoe heels, some housewares, and as a pigment in lacquers.

Processing Cellulose Nitrate

Firesafety in plants processing cellulose nitrate plastic consists essentially of four parts: (1) segregation of hazards, (2) elimination of ignition sources, (3) good housekeeping, and (4) strong fire control facilities. In some plants, finished cellulose nitrate plastic parts may be assembled with other articles that do not involve any special fire hazard, e.g., toilet seats. In such cases, the hazard and necessary protection depend upon the quantity of cellulose nitrate used. If the quantities used are large, the same safeguards should be followed as for plants in which the product is made entirely from cellulose nitrate.

Cellulose Nitrate Storage

Storage of cellulose nitrate plastics requires special facilities. Depending on the quantity to be stored, these facilities may be cabinets, vaults, storage rooms, or isolated storage buildings. Storage facilities are described in detail in two NFPA standards: NFPA 40, *Cellulose Nitrate Motion Picture Film*, and NFPA 40E, *Safe Storage of Pyroxylin Plastics*.

Cellulose Nitrate Photographic Film

All photographic film made in the United States and Canada since 1952 is the safety-base type, usually cellulose acetate or triacetate or polyester. An engraving process used in some printing plants engraves on cellulose nitrate plates.

There is comparatively little storage of cellulose nitrate X-ray film, although some hospitals may still store X rays made on cellulose nitrate film many years ago. However, appreciable quantities of old nitrate motion picture and aero film still exist. Small amounts of portrait, industrial, and amateur nitrate film probably exist, but the usual storage of this material (in paper envelopes) poses no serious hazard. Nitrate-based film manufactured in the Soviet Union or Germany may occasionally be found.

The existence of old nitrate motion picture and aero film does present a hazard, since persons handling this material may not be familiar with its serious hazards and the elaborate precautions necessary to handle it safely. Although it is unlikely that nitrate film will be projected in a theater handling present-day motion pictures, it is quite possible that such material may be shown in small "art" or "film society" theaters. Unfortunately, projectionists may not be aware of the fact that a nitrate print is to be shown. For this reason, theater projection standards for nitrate film should still be kept in effect. Storage of nitrate film should be in accordance with NFPA 40, *Cellulose Nitrate Motion Picture Film*.

The amounts of scrap-nitrate motion picture film have greatly decreased, and most of the agencies that formerly handled this material are no longer in existence. This has given rise to the possibility that scrap could accumulate in dangerous quantities. Prior to environmental concern with air pollutants from outdoor burning, the best procedure for disposing of scrap nitrate film was to burn it at a remote location in the open, with all personnel at a safe distance upwind (because toxic oxides of nitrogen are among the products of combustion of this film). If accumulations of scrap-nitrate film are a problem, the best course to follow would be to check with environmental authorities to learn if such open burning is permitted locally.

Transportation of Cellulose Nitrate

The U.S. Department of Transportation (DOT) regulates the interstate transportation of cellulose nitrate plastic by rail, land, or water. These regulations permit dry shipment of cellulose nitrate (pyroxylin) scrap when specially packaged, but if there is evidence, or the possibility of decomposition, the cellulose nitrate must be packaged under water. Shipment of cellulose nitrate sheets, rolls, rods, and tubes is not subject to special DOT regulation, except when shipped by rail express or water.

Articles manufactured entirely of or containing cellulose nitrate plastic do not require special packaging when shipped by land, rail, or water. Special shipping regulations apply to cellulose nitrate wet with alcohol, solvent, or water.

Shipments of cellulose nitrate motion picture and X-ray films are permitted when certain packaging requirements are met, including inside containers made of light metal, cardboard, or fiberboard for individual reels of film. NFPA

40, *Cellulose Nitrate Motion Picture Film*, places restrictions on the transportation of nitrate film in public vehicles so as to protect the public against the consequences of a possible fire involving the film.

Air transportation of cellulose nitrate plastic scrap is not permitted by regulations of the International Air Transport Association. Cellulose nitrate plastic rods, sheets, rolls, tubes, manufactured articles, and motion picture and X-ray films are permitted only when specially packaged.

Extinguishing Cellulose Nitrate Fires

Large volumes of water are required to extinguish cellulose nitrate fires. Automatic sprinklers constitute the best general protection for areas where cellulose nitrate materials are stored or handled. Water supplies should be particularly strong. Closer sprinkler spacing than for ordinary occupancies is required in order to supply sufficient water to absorb the heat. The water from sprinklers, in addition to its extinguishing and cooling effects, tends to absorb the poisonous oxides of nitrogen fumes but has no effect on carbon monoxide.

If hose streams are required, the objective should be to get large quantities of water on the fire as soon as possible. Fire fighters should be located upwind or protected by self-contained breathing apparatus to prevent inhalation of the products of combustion.

FIRE BEHAVIOR OF PLASTICS

While there is no special fire hazard for most accepted usages of plastics, some exhibit burning characteristics that are considerably different from those encountered with the more traditional cellulosic building materials.

Special Fire Behavior Problems

Test methods, which in the past have been adequate to indicate the relative hazard of materials under actual use conditions, have failed to predict the fire behavior of some plastics. In addition, different fire conditions cause significantly different burning characteristics. Of principal concern has been fire behavior that poses unusual hazards to life and property, including the following.

Ignitability and rate of burning: Although plastics tend to have a higher ignition temperature than wood and other cellulosic products, some are easily ignited with a small flame and burn vigorously. Very high surface flame spread rates have been reported—up to approximately 2 ft per sec (0.6 m/sec), or 10 times the rate of flame spread across most wood surfaces.

Smoke produced: The burning of some plastics is characterized by the rapid generation of large amounts of very dense, sooty, black smoke. Chemicals added to inhibit flammability may increase smoke production.

Toxic gases: Any fire will generate lethal products of combustion, principally carbon monoxide. Depending on the plastic and the particular fire conditions, highly toxic gases, such as hydrogen cyanide, hydrogen chloride, and phosgene, may also evolve.

Flaming drips: Thermoplastic articles tend to melt and flow when heated. In a fire situation, this characteristic may cause the material to melt away from the flame front and inhibit further burning, or it may produce flaming and tar-like dripping which is difficult to extinguish and which may start secondary fires.

Deviation from test results: Small-scale "Bunsen burner" tests are used for product development and laboratory control purposes. In the past they were used to indicate that certain plastics were "self-extinguishing" or "nonburning" and, presumably, safe for use. Unfortunately, in real-life situations the same materials have shown flash burning characteristics. Somewhat larger-scale tests, such as the NFPA 255, *Method of Test of Surface Burning Characteristics of Building Materials*, "tunnel test" also fail to adequately predict flash burning characteristics under some end-use conditions.

Corrosion: Severe corrosion damage to sensitive electronic equipment and to metal surfaces has been reported following fires involving commonly used plastics, such as polyvinyl chloride.

The fire behavior problems summarized above can occur under every conceivable condition of burning, from complete to partial combustion or smoldering and destructive pyrolysis. When the plastics and their constituent modifying agents, including flame-retardant additives, burn, they can produce a wide variety of noxious and toxic byproducts in varying concentrations. In this respect, plastics are similar to most ordinary combustibles, such as wood, leather, wool, silk, etc., in that they are capable of thermal degradation into volatile and gaseous products of combustion able to cause harmful physiological effects when breathed. In general, carbon monoxide is generated more rapidly than other toxic gases and tends to be the principal factor in fire fatalities. Nevertheless, unusually high burning rates, unusually heavy smoke production, and a higher heat content per unit weight are responsible for a greater concern about the fire behavior of certain plastics.

Smoke Generation

Smoke generation from a given polymer may vary widely depending upon the nature of the polymer, the additives present, whether fire exposure was flaming or smoldering, and the type of ventilation which was present. Several comments from Gaskill's[9] comprehensive study on smoke density are especially pertinent:

1. Woods and most polymeric material pyrolytically degrade, yielding smokes that are dense to very dense. Ventilation tends to clear the smoke, but in most cases it does not reduce the intensity to the point of satisfactory visibility. With fire retardants incorporated into the polymer (at least in the case of solid materials), heat and flame generally produce very dense smokes, and this occurs rapidly.
2. Woods and those polymeric materials that burn cleanly will yield smokes, under conditions of heat and flame, of somewhat less density.
3. Urethane foams under flaming or nonflaming exposures generally yield dense smokes, and, with few exceptions, obscuration occurs in a fraction of a minute. Flaming exposure usually causes the smokes to be generated in less than 15 sec, and the intensities in this case are usually higher than in the nonflaming case.

Cellular Plastics

Cellular plastics (or foamed or expanded plastics) have been in widespread use since the 1960s. Without adequate flame retardants and without barriers to resist ignition, however, these plastics in flexible form, e.g., mattresses, seat cushions, carpet padding, etc., and in rigid form, e.g., building insulation, have created an unacceptable fire hazard. Many reports tell of fast-spreading, high-intensity fires and voluminous smoke production. The low resistance of cellular plastics to excessive heat and their ease of ignition contrast sharply with their most valuable property in building construction—their excellent resistance to heat transfer. In a 1969 study of the flammability of cellular plastics,[10] Underwriters Laboratories Inc. (UL) reported on an analysis of 34 fires where rigid cellular plastics had been used as building materials. The report indicated that:

1. The fire performance of cellular plastics can vary considerably depending upon whether they are exposed or protected and/or flame resistant, along with the degree of flame resistance. But the reduction in flammability through the use of inhibitors or protective coverings is not conclusively demonstrated by the study.
2. In 8 of 21 fires, a high rate of flame spread was reported and appeared to be especially typical of uninhibited, sprayed-on polyurethane and rigid, polyurethane boards. Flame spread ratings from NFPA 255, *Method of Test of Surface Burning Characteristics of Building Materials*, tunnel tests of some of the materials ranged from 5 to 1375 (red oak, 100).
3. The fire behavior of cellular plastics appears to be affected by the extent of foam application, i.e., whether the foam is applied to the walls and ceiling or only to the walls.
4. The fire behavior of the flexible foam plastics appears to be similar to that of the rigid plastic foams. (Peculiar to the flexible foams, though, is the pool of liquid product that can be generated in a fire in the bulk storage of the foam "buns." The liquefied plastic burns like a high flash-point flammable liquid.)

Whereas untreated rigid polyurethane burns rapidly and is readily ignited by common ignition sources found in the environment, fire-retardant grades have substantial resistance to localized, temporary ignition sources under most fire environments. Sustained application of heat and flame causes such foam to burn, but the burning rate tends to be retarded. Often, burning will cease entirely when the external flame source is removed. The production of dense smoke is a characteristic of both treated and untreated urethane.

Untreated rigid polystyrene foam, likewise, ignites easily and burns vigorously with the production of dense, black smoke and a very black, viscous melt product which can burn with the intensity of a flammable liquid. Fire-retardant treatments inhibit ignition; the plastic tends to shrink away from fixed heat sources without igniting. The heat of combustion of styrene is about 50 percent higher than that of urethane foam [18,000 Btu/lb *vs.* 12,000 Btu/lb (42 Mj/kg *vs.* 28 Mj/kg)].

At times, cellular plastics that exhibit good resistance to burning under most exposure conditions have shown a markedly different behavior when surfaces of the exposed plastic are arranged to cause a feedback of radiant heat between the surfaces.[11] The combination of low thermal conductivity, high rate of heat release, and rapid degradation under heat exposure appear to be responsible for a rapid upward propagation of the flame front occurring in a room corner configuration. When the ceiling is also insulated with the exposed foamed plastic, the corner configuration encourages rapid extension of the fire across the underside of the ceiling. This phenomenon has occurred with very small ignition sources, such as a wastebasket fire. The laboratories of Factory Mutual Research Corporation devised the "corner test" to simulate this exposure condition.

Witnesses to fire incidents in buildings that were insulated on the inside with exposed spray-on or board foam have reported extremely high flame-spread rates across the surface of the insulation immediately after the fire was first noticed. One theory for this phenomenon is that fire had been smoldering unnoticed inside or behind the insulation and generating large quantities of unburned, largely invisible products of combustion which collected under the roof. When the fire eventually broke out into the open, it ignited the accumulation of gases which accounted for the flash fire behavior. Rapid fire spread across the surface of exposed insulation has been reported for fire-retardant treated and untreated urethane and styrene.

Rubber

Burning rubber is notable for its smell and dense smoke. The material, as generally used, is not easily ignited and does not burn with unusual rapidity. In normal applications, the most severe hazard appears to be in the use of foam rubber mattresses, particularly in institutional occupancies, such as hospitals, nursing homes, and prisons. Accidental ignition by smoking materials or deliberate ignition with matches or other small sources has caused the rapid evolution of dense, toxic smoke which has resulted in multiple-fatality fires.

Foam rubber is subject to spontaneous heating when exposed to a heat source, such as an industrial dryer or a domestic clothes dryer. Cases have been reported of spontaneous ignition of foam rubber in shoes and clothing after the items were removed from clothes dryers. Foam rubber underlayment for carpeting has been reported to have contributed to the extension of fires in buildings; however, the U.S. Department of Commerce "pill test" for carpeting appears to weed out the worst offenders.

The bulk storage of rubber items, particularly rubber tires, is subject to hot, difficult-to-control, and very smoky fires. Surface application of water often is only marginally effective because the fire tends to burrow into the material. Special automatic sprinkler protection is required to help ensure control if the storage is more than 5 ft (1.52 m) high. (See NFPA 231D, *Storage of Rubber Tires*.)

Rubber or plastic jacketing on grouped electrical cables has provided the fuel for very expensive and potentially very dangerous fires in the electrical and communications industries. Considerable work has been done to raise the operating temperature limits and ignition temperatures of insulation for electric power and control cables. An applicable standard is IEEE 383. Butyl/neoprene and neoprene rubber insulation tend to burn readily and fail such small-scale tests, while Hypalon™, for instance, is a jacketing material with more resistance to heat and ignition.

No significant differences appear to exist in the ignition or combustion characteristics of natural rubber and the various synthetics. Silicone rubbers can be formulated to reduce combustibility to a minimum under ordinary conditions, but not all silicone rubbers have that quality: the material failed the requirement of no flashover in a quarter-scale room fire test conducted at the National Bureau of Standards.[12]

Test Results

The variation of the fire behavior of plastics when compared to other building materials was further demonstrated in tests conducted at Underwriters Laboratories Inc.[13] Thirty-one materials were subjected to the Steiner tunnel test (NFPA 255, ASTM E84, and UL 723) to establish flame spread and smoke-developed classifications. These materials were also subjected to a 20-lb (9.1 kg) wood crib exposure fire in a full-size corner configuration. Testing established that the 20-lb (9.1 kg) wood crib presented fire severity conditions about equal to the 5,000 Btu per min (88 kW) burner in the tunnel test, generating a heat flux of about 0.97 Btu per sec/ft^2 (1.1 W/cm^2). Four materials in the test series achieved an identical flame-spread classification of 18 (cement asbestos, 0; red oak, 100), but the smoke that developed and the extent of burning were markedly higher for the flame-retardant grade of plastic foam. (See Table 3-10A.)

TABLE 3-10A. ***Test Results (Cellular Plastics) for a 20-lb (9.1 kg) Wood Crib Fire Test***

Code Letter	Material	FSC*	SDC**	Affected Area†
E	3½ in. (89 mm) thick glass fiber blanket insulation, 6% resin by weight, unfaced, 0.65 pcf (10.4 kg/m^3) density	18	3	24%
I	½ in. (12.7 mm) thick wood fiberboard acoustic ceiling panels, integrally flame retardant treated, decorative finished, 18.8 pcf (301.2 kg/m^3) density	18	4	37%
T	½ in. (12.7 mm) thick wood particle board, integrally flame retardant treated	18	37	25%
Z	2 in. (51 mm) polyurethane spray cellular, plastic on ¼ in. (6 mm) asbestos cement board; 2.2 pcf (35.2 kg/m^3) density, flame retardant	18	935	85%

* Flame spread classification, tunnel test result.
** Smoke developed classification, tunnel test result.
† Percent of 192 sq ft (17.8 m^2) total wall and ceiling area affected in full-scale corner test (7% affected in control fires).

These four building materials were also subjected to exposures in the heat-release rate calorimeter test developed by the National Bureau of Standards.[14] As reported by UL[13] in the document on the 1973-74 test series, the first three specimens, code letters E, I, and T, yielded identical heat release rates of 0.26 Btu per sec/ft^2 (0.3 W/cm^2) at an exposure energy level of 2.6 Btu per sec/ft^2 (3 W/cm^2). However, a heat release rate 25 times higher [6.6 Btu per sec/ft^2 (7.5 W/cm^2)] was recorded for the flame-retardant plastic, code letter Z.

Another cellular plastic, 2-in. (51 mm) extruded polystyrene cellular plastic boardstock [1.8 lb per cu ft (0.03 g/cm^3) density, flame retardant], obtained a flame spread classification of 3 in the tunnel test, but its smoke developed classification was 785 (red oak, 100), and 146 sq ft (13.6 m^2), or 76 percent, of the wall-ceiling area of the corner test structure was adversely affected by the burning.

The fire problem associated with plastics was studied by the Products Research Committee (PRC), formed to administer a trust fund established by a number of companies engaged in the manufacture and sale of cellular plastics and their ingredients. The PRC issued its final report in 1980[15] after a five-year effort, which included sponsoring a number of research programs. Highlights of conclusions reached by the PRC included the following:

1. Provisions of current building codes, requiring a thermal barrier over cellular plastic insulation in wall cavities, should remain in force until further advances are realized in firesafety engineering.
2. Properly designed interlayers between furniture fabric and padding are an effective means of reducing the fire risk of upholstered furniture.
3. The use of results of many different small-scale fire tests to obtain an estimate of behavior of a material in fire is appropriate; however, the present state of the art does not allow regulatory decisions to be made without considerable expert judgment and, preferably, data from full-scale fire tests in which the most probable fire scenarios are simulated.

FIRE TESTS FOR PLASTICS

Combustibility characteristics and suitability for use should be determined for any material or assembly on the basis of tests that simulate the end-use condition as realistically as possible. The tests should be designed to show how the product will perform when it is subjected to the type of fire exposure that can be anticipated under the conditions of use. The most desirable tests, from the standpoint of fire protection, engineering, and codes, are those that are suitable for all products for a particular application and that treat all products equally. Separate tests for plastics, or any other group of materials, that do not allow comparison of the fire behavior under like test conditions are undesirable.

As explained previously, small-scale tests are now used mostly for product development and production control. Such tests are also suitable for determining the ignitability of such items as upholstery, where the ignition source is small and of low intensity, but are unsuitable for evaluating the fire characteristics of materials under room fire or other full-scale fire conditions.

Somewhat greater-intensity fire exposures are produced by standard fire tests, such as the Steiner tunnel test and the radiant panel test, both of which are used to determine the suitability of all kinds of materials as interior finish for walls and ceilings in buildings. As previously indicated, these tests have been proved inadequate to accurately predict the burning characteristics of some plastics under certain conditions. Higher-intensity exposures encountered under actual-use conditions may cause fire behavior substantially more hazardous than indicated by the results of these tests. The Factory Mutual Research Corporation corner test tends to reproduce these more severe exposure conditions. It is now common to require materials, such as plastics, to be qualified under more than one test in order to ensure their suitability in building construction. Factory Mutual has written about its corner test as follows:

> The characteristic of rapid flame spread across the exposed surface of polyurethane, even with automatic sprinkler protection, prompted the development of the Factory Mutual corner test. The test determines

the performance of various types of foamed plastic insulation, in combination with various surface treatments, under full-scale fire conditions. The test procedure is designed to simulate the exposure that would be expected in an essentially noncombustible occupancy (e.g., an isolated stack of pallets). When sprinklers are provided, the exposure is increased to simulate a fire in a combustible occupancy.[16]

The full-scale corner test is conducted in a 25-ft high (7.6 m) test building and the initiating fire is a 750-lb (340 kg) wood crib. A scaled-down version, 1/12 full scale, produces similar results at lower cost.

Other tests that may be required by the authority having jurisdiction are used to determine, separately, ignition temperature, surface flame spread index, and the rate of smoke production. Potential heat (caloric value) of the plastic material may have to be determined, but this parameter is of little significance in fire protection engineering; more important is the rate at which heat is liberated and contributes to the intensity of the fire. A multiplicity of tests to qualify plastics, or any other material, for end-use applications may not be required in the future. One standard test method (ASTM E906) uses the Ohio State University (OSU) release-rate apparatus and is capable of producing varying radiant heat fluxes corresponding to the severity of the fire exposure that can be anticipated for the product being tested. (See Figure 3-10G.) Measurements include heat and smoke particles released by the test specimen per unit time and total during the test, toxic gases given off, ease of ignition, and flame spread rate. Research is continuing on this and other heat and smoke release tests, including a "cone calorimeter" developed at the National Institute for Science and Technology (formerly NBS), which tests for heat and visible smoke release rates using an oxygen consumption calorimeter.

The flammability test methods that follow are presently included in the *Book of ASTM Standards* specifically for the testing of plastics, Underwriters Laboratories Inc. small-scale flammability tests for plastics, and tests for plastics of some federal agencies.

American Society for Testing and Materials

ASTM has standardized several small-scale test procedures intended for plastics research, product development, and manufacturing control purposes. Results of these tests are not valid for evaluating the fire hazard of plastics under room-fire conditions or most other end-use conditions. The following standard test methods are included in the *1988 Book of ASTM Standards:*

D229-86, *Rigid Sheet and Plate Materials Used for Electrical Insulation.* (One of the procedures included is for burning rate and flame resistance.)

D568-77, *Rate of Burning and/or Extent and Time of Burning of Flexible Plastics in a Vertical Position.*

D635-81, *Rate of Burning and/or Extent and Time of Burning of Self-Supporting Plastics in a Horizontal Position.*

D1929-77, *Ignition Properties of Plastics.* (This test uses a Setchkin furnace to heat the specimen prior to ignition by a pilot flame.)

D2843-77, *Density of Smoke from the Burning or Decomposition of Plastics.*

D2863-87, *Measuring the Minimum Oxygen Concentration to Support Candlelike Combustion of Plastics.* (Oxygen index.)

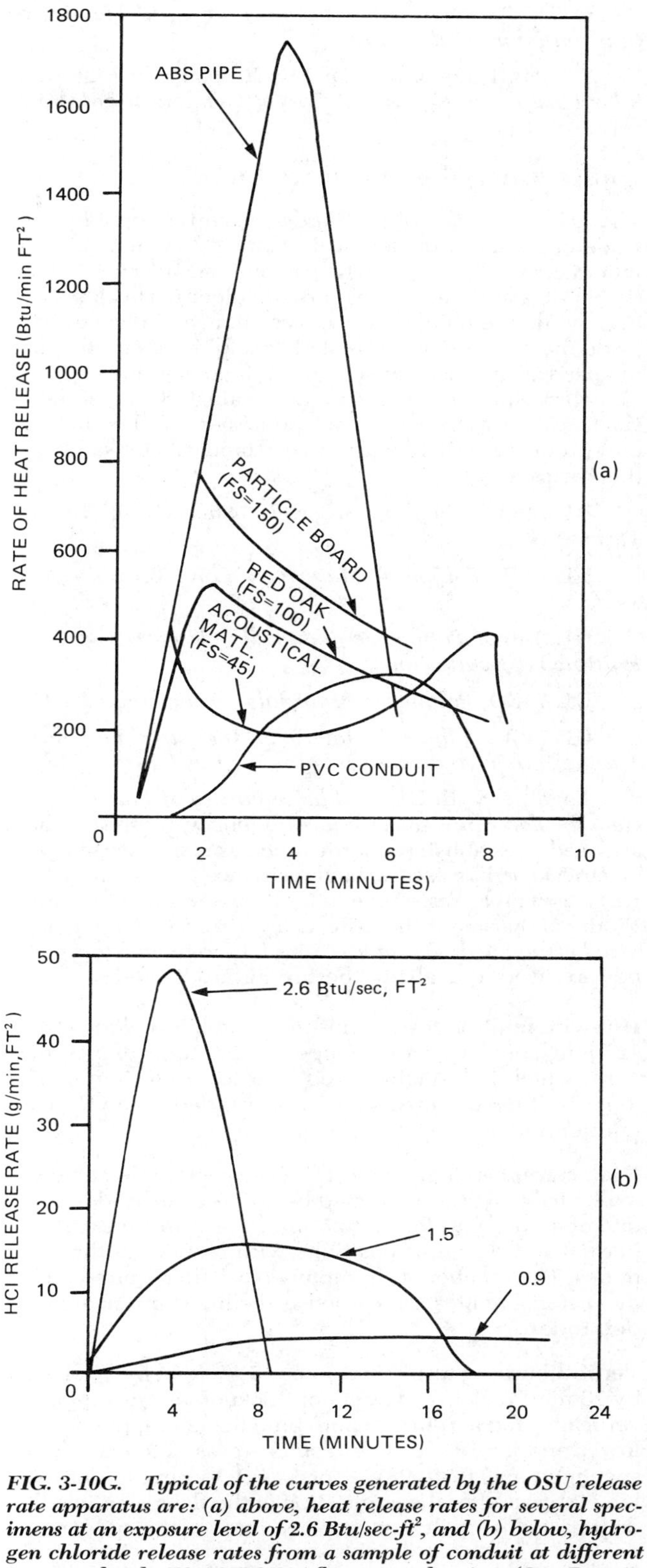

FIG. 3-10G. Typical of the curves generated by the OSU release rate apparatus are: (a) above, heat release rates for several specimens at an exposure level of 2.6 Btu/sec-ft², and (b) below, hydrogen chloride release rates from a sample of conduit at different exposure levels. FS ASTM E84 flamespread rating. (One Btu per sec/ft² equals 0.053 W/m².)

D3675-83, *Surface Flammability of Flexible Cellular Materials Using a Radiant Heat Energy Source.*

D3713-78, *Measuring Response of Solid Plastics to Ignition by a Small Flame.*

D3894-81, *Evaluation of Fire Response of Rigid Cellular Plastics Using a Small Corner Configuration.* (Mini-corner test.)

Underwriters Laboratories Inc.

The UL 746 series of standards recognize the advances made in the safety of electrical products due, in part, to the introduction of plastic materials in their manufacture.[17] Plastic handles and enclosures provide electric shock protection, while the moldability and resilience of plastics have made these materials particularly useful for guarding moving parts against accidental contact. Flammability and ignition characteristics of plastics are evaluated by a series of small-scale tests under the procedures established in these end-product standards. The five "standards for safety" in this series are:

UL 746A, *Polymeric Materials—Short-Term Property Tests.*

UL 746B, *Polymeric Materials—Long-Term Property Tests.*

UL 746C, *Polymeric Materials—Use in Electrical Equipment Evaluations.*

UL 746D, *Polymeric Materials—Fabricated Parts.*

UL 746E, *Polymeric Materials—Industrial Laminates, Tubing, Fiber, and Materials for Wiring Boards.*

Together with UL 94, *Flammability of Plastic Materials for Parts in Devices and Appliances,* these standards are used to establish properties such as resistance to aging, electrical spark resistance, and resistance to heat on molded parts, as well as resistance to ignition and rate of burning. Products that meet the criteria are listed in UL's *Recognized Component Directory.* Four UL-originated test methods are used to evaluate the fire hazard, as follows.

Hot-wire ignition test: Half-inch wide, 5-in. long (13 by 127 mm) specimens are wrapped with 5 turns of nichrome wire, which is brought to red heat for up to 5 min. The length of time to cause ignition is recorded as the hot wire ignition index.

High-current arc ignition test: The specimen is subjected to electrical sparks generated between 2 electrodes at the rate of 40 per min for up to 5 min. Tests are run with the plastic in 4 different positions with respect to the electrodes. The number of arc ruptures that are required before the material ignites is recorded as the high-current arc ignition index.

Vertical burning test: Specimens 5 in. long by 1/2 in. (127 by 13 mm) wide in a variety of thicknesses are supported vertically, and a 3/4-in. (19 mm) blue flame is applied to the lower end for 10 sec. The results are used to classify the specimen as 94V-0, 94V-1, or 94V-2, depending on how long it burns after the application of the flame and whether drip particles ignite cotton placed under the specimen.

Horizontal burning test: The same size specimen as in the vertical burning test is mounted horizontally, and a 1-in. (25.4 mm) blue flame is applied to the end for 30 sec. (See Figure 3-10H.) With limited burning, the material will be classified 94-HB. More severe testing may be used to establish a 94-5V classification, and classifications 94-HBF, 94-HF-1, and 94-HF-2 are used for foamed materials. The radiant panel test, ASTM E162, may be used for additional evaluations.

FIG. 3-10H. Specimen being tested under the horizontal burning test of UL 94, **Flammability of Plastic Materials for Parts in Devices and Appliances,** *for flammability of plastics. (Source: Underwriters Laboratories Inc.)*

Federal Agencies

Under MVSS-302, the DOT regulates interior materials for automobiles, using a test for burning rate in the horizontal mode. The U.S. Coast Guard, under Subchapter T, regulates materials used as resins for hulls in boats-for-hire carrying more than six passengers. The U.S. Coast Guard also uses a modified version of ASTM E136 to establish the "noncombustibility" of materials used in the interior of passenger-carrying ships. Guidelines for the flammability of carpets, rugs, children's sleepwear, mattresses, and mattress pads are issued by the U.S. Consumer Product Safety Commission, which is currently studying proposals for low-intensity, cigarette ignition tests for upholstered furniture. The U.S. Nuclear Regulatory Commission has issued guidelines for the ignitability and flammability of plastics used in the insulation of electrical cables requiring qualification under test procedures in IEEE 383.

INSTALLATION SAFEGUARDS

In the current state of the art, large areas of cellular plastics left exposed in interior building construction or decoration must be considered to be extremely hazardous. Exposed foam on ceilings or walls, in air-handling plenums, in shafts, in other flue-like vertical spaces inside walls, or above hung ceilings should be avoided. A low flame-spread classification (e.g., 25 or less) does not ensure that a product has limited combustibility under such conditions, nor can it be assumed that automatic sprinklers will control the hazard. Coating such surfaces with a fire-retardant paint, intumescent or otherwise, is not likely to produce satisfactory results.

Model building codes require that foamed plastic used as interior wall insulation be covered with a thermal barrier, such as 1/2-in. (12.7 mm) thick ordinary gypsum board, or other method that reduces the risk of ignition and the subsequent flash-fire propensity. The use of foamed plastics in the cavities of hollow masonry walls, such as perimeter insulation around the foundation of a building, insulation below concrete slabs on the ground, and for roof insulation under certain conditions, is generally accepted without thermal barrier protection. All such plastics in the thickness and density used must have a smoke-developed rating no greater than 450 and a flame-spread rating no greater than 75, under ASTM E84 (NFPA 255, *Method of Test of Surface Burning Characteristics of Building Materials*) tunnel test conditions.

In other-than-noncombustible or fire-resistive building types, foamed-plastic insulated steel, or aluminum exterior building panels are permitted by the model building codes, provided the foam core has a flame-spread classification of 25 or less and the space is protected by automatic sprinklers.

When used as interior wall and ceiling finish, plastic materials other than foamed plastic generally are not subject to any special requirements. As for any other materials, plastics are subject to limitations on surface flame spread and often on the smoke generated, as measured by standard test procedures, such as the Steiner tunnel test or radiant panel test. These or other special limitations may be applied to plastics used as diffusers in lighting fixtures, where it is often acceptable to have a plastic that deforms and drops out of the fixture at an elevated temperature still well below its ignition point. Special limitations may also be set forth by building codes for the use of plastic glazing instead of glass in exterior walls of buildings, where the normal requirement for conformance to the limitations for interior finish may be waived.

Plastic laminates for countertops, kitchen cabinets, tabletops, etc., are not usually included in the definition of interior finish, as regulated by building codes. Even when it is not regulated by local code, the flammability level should be limited to that encountered when natural products are used in these applications. Plastic laminates are commonly available with low-surface flame-spread classifications, in the range of 25 to 75.

Further guidelines for the installation of plastics in various applications can be found in publications of the Society of the Plastics Industry[18] and Factory Mutual Research Corporation.[19]

The packaging, storage, and shipping precautions that are customarily observed for ordinary combustible materials apply generally to most plastics. No special shipping requirements for plastics (other than cellulose nitrate) have been adopted by the DOT.

FIRE- AND FLAME-RETARDANT TREATMENTS

All organic and some inorganic materials burn under proper conditions. Fire and flame retardants can make a given material more difficult to ignite, and when ignited, cause it to burn more slowly. Retardants can be very effective in preventing ignition from low-level, short-duration flame and heat exposures. Even under moderate exposures, the burning characteristics can be greatly improved by fire retardants, depending upon the product and the additive used. For severe exposures, such as from a fully developed room fire, treated and untreated plastics typically show similar fire behavior.

Fire- and flame-retardant chemicals are added to plastics during the manufacturing process. Because of the widely varying properties of plastics, no single, universal additive is available, nor is there only one effective mechanism for imparting flame resistance. Fire- and flame-retardant additives may be blended into the polymer mix during processing, or they may be reactants that change the molecular structure of the polymer. The additives can be chemically reacted throughout the polymer substrate or on the surface of finished or semifinished products. Surface treatments added after the manufacturing process, such as fire-retardant paints or coatings, are unreliable without test data to prove the effectiveness of the combination.

Additives blended into the mix may be organic or inorganic materials. Organic additives typically are chlorinated and brominated hydrocarbons or halogenated and nonhalogenated organophosphorous compounds. Among the inorganic flame retardants are the salts of antimony, zinc, molybdenum, and aluminum. Those classed as reactants include brominated aromatics, brominated aliphatic polyols, and phosphorous-containing polyols.

Phosphorous additives appear to improve flame resistance by: (1) promoting formation of char to reduce concentration of carbon-containing gases; (2) forming a glassy, insulating layer; and (3) either entering into chemical reactions that remove heat from the combustion system, or chemically inhibiting the combustion process, or both. Compounds containing halogens, such as chlorine and bromine, tend to inhibit burning in the gas phase by interrupting chain reactions needed for continuous burning. Other flame retardants involve heat absorption reactions, e.g., by providing a heat sink through evaporation of water of hydration.[20]

A complicating aspect of treating plastics and other materials is that a fire-retardant chemical that works on one substrate system will not necessarily work on other substrates. Thus, fire-retardant chemicals for polystyrene will not necessarily work on polyethylene, nylon, wood, or cotton. Fire-retardant chemicals often impair some other material properties. For example, fire-retardant treatments for cotton fabrics generally reduce fabric strength and wear life. Fire retardants in plastics may reduce allowable processing temperatures and impair physical properties. Costs are generally increased.

Smoldering, rather than free-burning, combustion is likely to increase the amount of smoke produced, and there tends to be more smoke when fire retardants are added to polymers; but this is not true in all cases. Comparisons were made among five different types of products in fire-retardant and non-fire-retardant versions in a series of tests sponsored by the Fire Retardant Chemicals Association at the National Institute of Science and Technology.[21] Included were polystyrene TV cabinets, polyphenylene oxide business machine housings, polyurethane foam-padded chairs, electrical cable with polyethylene insulation and rubber jacketing, and polyester/glass electric circuit boards. Heat release, spread of flames, and the propensity for flashover were reduced when the fire-retardant products were tested. Smoke yields generally were similar, but fire-retardant TV cabinets produced twice the amount of smoke than the non-fire-retardant versions. None of the test specimens produced smoke of extreme toxicity. Potential escape times for occupants were reported to be 15 times greater when the fire-retardant products were used in the tests.

FIGHTING FIRES IN PLASTICS

Plastics other than cellulose nitrate are classified as ordinary combustibles. Consequently, extinguishing methods suitable for fires involving wood and other ordinary combustibles (Class A fires) should be used to extinguish a burning plastic. Some plastics, e.g., flexible polyurethane, may form a pool of burning liquid during a fire, similar to a high-flash-point combustible liquid (Class B) fire. Water from automatic sprinklers or spray nozzles on hoselines can be used for fire control, although the extent of a pool fire is likely to be overshadowed by the more generalized fire in the area.

Storage with a preponderance of plastic products or materials can develop into fires with extremely high temperatures that tremendously magnify the normal problem of radiant heat, structural damage, and exposure.[22] Rapid fire spread, high burning rates, and thick, dense smoke in heavy clouds can be anticipated. Factory Mutual Research Corporation recommends a two-fold attack: (1) properly designed sprinkler protection, and (2) appropriate manual fire fighting techniques. Large-orifice (17/32 in.) sprinklers have been found to be substantially better in controlling fires in plastics, and large-drop and early suppression fast response (ESFR) sprinklers were developed at Factory Mutual specifically to address the high-challenge plastics fire.

The physical form of plastics will greatly influence their fire behavior. Molding pellets, which are shipped in bags, drums, or large cartons, provide little surface for access to air. These same plastics in such shapes as flashlight cases will have much more access to air and may burn vigorously until heat causes the shapes to melt, thereby reducing the surface area exposed to air. Melting may be a hazard if it causes burning drips to carry flame to a lower floor or spreads fuel for later ignition.

While fire may develop more slowly in the more dense, unexpanded form than in foamed products, once established, the burning rate is comparable. For fires that have become well established in a large quantity of plastics products in a sprinklered warehouse, "buttoning up" the building to limit combustion air and letting the sprinklers do the work of fire control, for hours if necessary, before moving in for final mop-up by conventional means, is an approach recommended by Factory Mutual Research Corporation.[22] Shutting off sprinklers to allow the smoke to rise and vent the building is dangerous because the high combustibility of the storage can cause the blaze to rapidly flash out of control.

Toxicity: Possibly because of the long chemical names of some plastics, combustion and thermal decomposition products of plastics have been a cause for concern among fire fighters. For plastics now in commercial use, the hazard of carbon monoxide from partial combustion greatly outweighs the toxic effects of other fire gases, both as to nature and amount.

On burning, some plastics, e.g., polyvinyl chloride or ethylene sulfide rubbery caulking materials, generate hydrogen chloride or sulfur dioxide. Because these are strongly irritating, they ordinarily force evacuation long before their toxic effects become dangerous. These gases also are corrosive to metals and electrical equipment; therefore, such equipment should be ventilated, rinsed, or treated with dilute ammonia, and rinsed as soon as possible after exposure.

BIBLIOGRAPHY

References Cited

1. Gaylord, M. W., *Reinforced Plastics, Theory & Practice*, 2nd ed., Cahners, Boston, 1974.
2. Braun, Dietrich, *Identification of Plastics*, 2nd ed., Macmillan, New York, 1986.
3. Saechtling, Dr. H., *Plastics Handbook*, Hanser Press, Macmillan, New York, 1983.
4. Briston, J. H., and Grosselin, C. C., *Introduction to Plastics*, Newnes-Butterworth, London, 1968.
5. ASTM D1600, *Standard Abbreviations of Terms Relating to Plastics*, American Society for Testing and Materials, Philadelphia, PA.
6. Katz, Cassell, and Collier, *Plastics: Design and Materials*, Macmillan Publishers, London, 1978.
7. Ulrich, Henri, *Introduction to Industrial Polymers*, Oxford University Press, New York, 1982.
8. Hoffman, Werner, *Rubber Technology Handbook*, Macmillan, New York, 1988.
9. Gaskill, J. R., "Smoke Development in Polymers During Pyrolysis or Combustion," *Journal of Fire and Flammability*, Vol. 1 (July 1970), pp. 183-216.
10. UL, "Report on Flammability Study of Cellular Plastics," File NC 522, 1969, The Society of the Plastics Industry, Underwriters Laboratories Inc., Northbrook, IL.
11. Troup, W. W. J., *Cellular Plastics and the Building Fire Problem*, Factory Mutual Research Corp., Norwood, MA, 1969.
12. NBS, "Fire Hazard Evaluation of Shipboard Hull Insulation and Documentation of a Quarter-Scale Room Fire Test Protocol," NBSIR 83-2642, 1983, National Bureau of Standards, Washington, DC.
13. UL, "Flammability Studies of Cellular Plastics and Other Building Materials Used for Interior Finishes," Subject 723, 1975, Underwriters Laboratories Inc., Northbrook, IL.
14. Parker, W. J., and Long, M. E., "Development of a Heat Release Rate Calorimeter at NBS," ASTM Special Technical Publication 502, 1972, American Society for Testing and Materials, Philadelphia, PA.
15. PRC, "Fire Research on Plastics: The Final Report of the Products Research Committee," Products Research Committee, John W. Lyons, Chairman, National Bureau of Standards, Washington, DC, 1980.
16. FMRC, "Rigid Foamed Polyurethane and Polyisocyanurate for Construction," Loss Prevention Data 1-57, 1978, Factory Mutual Research Corp., Norwood, MA.
17. Bogue, R. J., "Spirit of 746," *UL Lab Data*, 1979, Underwriters Laboratories Inc., Northbrook, IL.
18. Society of the Plastics Industry, *Expanded Polystyrene Division*, Washington, DC, (various dates).
19. FMRC, Loss Prevention Data of the Factory Mutual Research Corporation, Norwood, MA:
    a. 1-57, "Rigid Foamed Polyurethane and Polyisocyanurate for Construction," 1978.
    b. 1-58, "Foamed Polystyrene for Construction," 1978.
    c. 1-59, "Reinforced Plastic Panels in Construction," 1978.
    d. 8-9, "Storage of Plastics and Elastomers," 1981.
20. *Modern Plastics Encyclopedia*, 1984-85, Vol. 56, No. 10A, McGraw-Hill, New York, 1985.
21. *Fire Safety Through Use of Flame-Retardant Polymers*, Fire Retardant Chemical Association Conference Series, 1985, Technomie Publishing, Lancaster, PA.
22. "Stored Plastics—The High-Challenge Risk," Pamphlet P7742, 1987, Factory Mutual Research Corp., Norwood, MA.

References

American Society for Testing and Materials, Philadelphia, PA:

ASTM E84, *Standard Test Method for Surface Burning Characteristics of Building Materials.*

ASTM E136, *Standard Test Method for Behavior of Materials in a Vertical Tube Furnace at 750°C.*

ASTM E906, *Test Method for Heat and Visible Smoke Release Rates for Materials and Products.*

1988 Book of ASTM Standards.

The Society of the Plastics Industry, Inc., Des Plaines, IL:

"Fire Safety Guidelines for Use of Expanded Polystyrene in Building Construction," EPS 301.

"Flammability of Expanded Polystyrene Insulation Used in Conjunction with Gypsum Wallboard."

"Flammability of Expanded Polystyrene Insulation when Used as Full-Scale Building Enclosure Ceiling Construction Material."

"Flammability of Expanded Polystyrene Insulation Used in Conjunction with Plywood Paneling."

"Flammability of Exposed Polystyrene Insulation (with and without Wooden Dividers)."

"Foamed Plastic, Full-Scale Corner Test, 7½-in. Thickness," EPS Polyurethane Division.

Literature Review of the Combustion Toxicity of Expanded Polystyrene.

Urethane Safety Group, Society of the Plastics Industry, Inc., New York:

U-100R2, "Fire Safety Guidelines for Use of Rigid Polyurethane Foam Insulation in Building Construction."

U-102R, "An Update Report on Findings of Fire Study of Rigid Cellular Plastic Materials for Wall and Roof Ceiling Insulation."

U-103, "Large-Scale Corner Wall Fire Tests of Spray-On Coatings over Rigid Polyurethane Foam Insulation."

U-105, "Evaluation of the Fire Performance of Carpet Underlayments."

U-106, "Fire Safety Guidelines on Flexible Polyurethane Foams Used in Upholstered Furniture and Bedding."

U-107, "Room-Scale Compartment Corner Tests of Spray-On Coatings over Rigid Polyurethane Foam Insulation."

U-110, "Flexible Polyurethane Foams and Combustibility."

U-111, "Using Flexible Polyurethane Foams Safely."

U-118, "Guide for Safe Handling and Use of Polyurethane and Polyisocyanurate Foam Systems."

Underwriters Laboratories Inc., Northbrook, IL:

UL 94, *Flammability of Plastic Material for Parts in Devices and Appliances.*

Recognized Component Directory.

NFPA Codes, Standards, and Recommended Practices

Reference to the following NFPA codes, standards, and recommended practices will provide further information on plastics and rubber discussed in this chapter. (See the latest *NFPA Catalog* for availability of current editions of the following documents.)

NFPA 40, *Cellulose Nitrate Motion Picture Film.*

NFPA 40E, *Safe Storage of Pyroxylin Plastics.*

NFPA 49, *Hazardous Chemicals Data.*

NFPA 231C, *Rack Storage of Materials.*

NFPA 231D, *Storage of Rubber Tires.*

NFPA 255, *Method of Test of Surface Burning Characteristics of Building Materials.*

NFPA 701, *Standard Methods of Fire Tests for Flame-Resistant Textiles and Films.*

Additional Reading

Alarie, Y. C., *Toxicity of Plastic Combustion Products*, National Bureau of Standards, Gaithersburg, MD, 1986.

Annamalai, K., and Sibulkin, M., "Ignition and Flame Spread Tests of Cellular Plastics," *Journal of Fire and Flammability*, Vol. 9, 1978, pp. 445-458.

ASTM, "Standard Method of Test for Density of Smoke from the Burning or Decomposition of Plastics," ANSI/ASTM D2843-77, 1977, American Society for Testing and Materials.

Barry, Thomas J., and Newman, Bernard, "Some Problems of Synthetic Polymers at Elevated Temperatures," *Fire Technology*, Vol. 12, No. 3 (Aug. 1976), pp. 186-192.

Beyler, C., "Thermal Decomposition of Polymers," *SFPE Handbook of Fire Protection Engineering*, National Fire Protection Association, Quincy, MA, 1988.

Boettner, E. A., Ball, G. L. and Weiss, B., "Combustion Products from the Incineration of Plastics," EPA Report 670/2-73-049, 1973, Environmental Protection Agency, Washington, DC.

Bowen, John E., "Hazards of Burning Plastics," *Fire Chief*, Dec. 1975.

Braun, Dietrich, *Identification of Plastics*, T-C Publications, CA, 1982.

Braun, E., and Levin, B. C., "Nylons: A Review of the Literature on Products of Combustion and Toxicity," NBSIR 85-3280, Feb. 1986, National Bureau of Standards, Gaithersburg, MD.

Cellular Plastics in Construction Applications and Fire Protection, Cellular Plastics Div., The Society of the Plastics Industry, Inc., NY, 1975.

"Combustion Toxicology of Polymers," NMAB 318-3, 1978, National Materials Advisory Board, Washington, DC.

Cox, G., and Steven, G., eds., *Fundamental Aspects of Polymer Flammability*, American Institute of Physics, 1987.

Cullis, C. F., and Hirschler, M. M., *The Combustion of Organic Polymers*, Clarendon Press, Oxford, England, 1981.

Damant, G. H., "Should Polyurethane Foam Be Banned?," *Fire Journal*, Vol. 82, No. 3, 1988, p. 68.

D'Souza, M. V., and McGuire, J. H., "ASTM E84 and the Flammability of Foamed Thermosetting Plastics," *Fire Technology*, Vol. 13, No. 2 (May 1977), pp. 85-94.

Dynamics of Current Developments in the Firesafety of Polymers, Technomic, Lancaster, PA, 1988.

Einhorn, I., "Physiological and Toxicological Aspects of Smoke Produced During the Combustion of Polymeric Materials," *Environmental Health Perspectives*, Vol. 11, 1975, p. 163.

Fire Safety Through Use of Flame Retardant Polymers (Fire Retardant Chemical Associations Conference Series), Technomic, 1985.

Frados, Joel, ed., *Plastics Engineering Handbook of the Society of the Plastics Industry, Inc.*, 4th ed., Van Nostrand Reinhold Co., New York, 1976.

Gurman, J. L., Baier, L., and Levine, B. C., "Polystyrenes: A Review of the Literature on the Products of Thermal Decomposition and Toxicity," NBSIR 85-3277, Mar. 1986, National Bureau of Standards, Gaithersburg, MD.

Hall, C., *Polymeric Materials: An Introduction for Technologists and Scientists*, Macmillan, London, England, 1981.

Harmathy, T. Z., "Properties of Building Materials," *SFPE Handbook of Fire Protection Engineering*, National Fire Protection Association, Quincy, MA, 1988.

Harper, Charles A., ed., *Handbook of Plastics and Elastomers*, McGraw-Hill, New York, 1975.

Hilado, C. J., ed., *Flammability of Solid Plastics*, Technomic, Lancaster, PA, 1985.

Hilado, Carlos, *Flammability Handbook for Plastics*, 3rd ed., Technomic Publishing Co., Westport, CT, 1982.

Hilado, Carlos J., "An Overview of the Fire Behavior of Polymers," *Fire Technology*, Vol. 9, No. 3 (Aug. 1973), pp. 198-208.

Hilado, C. J., Casey, C. J., and Schneider, J. E., "Effect of Pyrolysis Temperature on Relative Toxicity of Some Plastics," *Fire Technology*, Vol. 15, No. 2 (May 1979), pp. 122-129.

Ives, J. M., Hughes, E. E., and Taylor, J. K., "Toxic Atmospheres Associated with Real Fire Situations," Report 10, 807, Feb. 16, 1972, National Bureau of Standards, Washington, DC.

Juniper, R., ed., *Rapra New Trade Names 1983-1984*: In *the Rubber and Plastics Industries*, Pergamon, 1984.

Kanury, A. M., Alvares, N. J., and Martin, S. B., "Flammability Testing of Polymers," SRI Research Report, 1977, Chemical Manufacturers Association, Washington, DC.

Kidder, R. C., "Effect of Fire Safety Regulatory Activities on the Plastics Scene in the USA," *Flame Retardents '85*, Plastics and Rubber Institute, 1985, p. 16.

Landrock, Arthur H., *Handbook of Plastics Flammability and Combustion Technology*, 1983, Noyes.

Levin, B. C., "A Summary of the NBS Literature Reviews on the Chemical Nature and Toxicity of the Pyrolysis and Combustion Products from Seven Plastics," NBSIR 85-3267, 1986, National Bureau of Standards, Washington, DC.

Lyons, John W., *et al*, "Fire Research on Cellular Plastics: The Final Report of the Products Research Committee," Products Research Committee, 1980.

Madorsky, S. L., *Thermal Degradation of Organic Polymers*, John Wiley Interscience, New York, 1964.

Markstein, G. H., "Radiative Properties of Plastics Fires," 17th *Symposium* (International) on Combustion, The Combustion Institute, Pittsburgh, PA, 1979, pp. 1053-1062.

Maroni, W. F., "SLRP Analysis of Recommended Protection for Foamed Plastic Wall Ceiling Building Insulations," presentation at annual meeting of National Fire Protection Association, 1974.

Maroni, W. F., "Large-Scale Fire Tests of Rigid Cellular Plastic Wall and Roofing Insulations," *Fire Journal*, Vol. 67, No. 6 (Nov. 1973), pp. 24-29.

McCarter, R. J., "Smoldering of Flexible Polyurethane Foam," *Journal of Consumer Product Flammability*, Vol. 3, 1976, pp. 128-140.

Modak, A. T., and Croce, P. A., "Plastic Pool Fires," *Combustion and Flame*, Vol. 30, 1977, pp. 251-265.

Ohlemiller, T. J., and Rogers, F. E., "A Survey of Several Factors Influencing Smolder Combustion in Flexible and Rigid Polymer Foams," *Journal of Fire and Flammability*, Vol. 9, 1978, pp. 489-509.

O'Neill, T. J., "Assessing the Corrosion Risk of Plastics in Fires," *Fire Safety Journal*, Vol. 15, No. 1, 1989, pp. 45-56.

"Plastic Fire Hazard Classifications," Pamphlet P6221, Factory Mutual Research Corp., Norwood, MA.

Rawls, Rebecca L., "Fire Hazards of Plastics Spark Heated Debate," *Chemical and Engineering News*, Vol. 61 (Jan. 1983), pp. 9-16.

Reinke, R. E., and Reinhardt, C. F., "Fires, Toxicity, and Plastics," *Modern Plastics*, Vol. 50, No. 2, pp. 94-95, 97-98.

Roberts, A. F., "Polyurethane Foam: Some Studies Relating to Its Behavior in Fire," *Fire Technology*, Vol. 7, No. 3 (Aug. 1971).

Rubin, Irvin I., *Handbook of Plastic Materials and Technology*, Wiley, New York, 1988.

Saechtling, H., *International Plastics Handbook*, Macmillan, 1984.

Schaffer, E. L., ed., "Behavior of Polymeric Materials in Fire," STP 816, 1983, American Society for Testing and Materials, Philadelphia, PA.

Schafran, Eugene, "Development of Flammability Specifications for Furnishings," *Fire Journal*, Vol. 68, No. 2 (Mar. 1974), pp. 36-39.

Schwartz, Seymour, and Goodman, Sidney, *Plastics Materials and Processes*, Van Nostrand Reinhold Co., New York, 1982.

Smith, G. F., "Assessment of PVC Smoke," *Journal of Vinyl Technology*, Vol. 10, No. 2 (June 1988), pp. 84-89.

Smith, S. R., "Plastics—The Hidden Danger in Our Surroundings," *Fire Safety Journal*, Vol. 45, No.1, 1985, pp. 22-26.

Snyder, M., "Flammability Testing: Emergence of the Cone Calorimeter," *Plastics Compounding*, Vol. 10, No. 6, 1987, pp. 32-34.

Tewarson, A., and Pion, R. F., "Burning Intensity of Commercial Samples of Plastics," *Fire Technology*, Vol. 11, No. 4 (Nov. 1975), pp. 274-281.

Tewarson, A., "Heat Release Rates from Burning Plastics," *Journal of Fire and Flammability*, Vol. 8, 1977, p. 115.

Tewarson, A., and Pion, R. F., "Flammability of Plastics: I. Burning Intensity," *Combustion and Flame*, Vol. 26, 1976, pp. 85-103.

Thomson, H. E., and Drysdale, D. D., "Flammability of Plastics," *Fire and Materials*, Vol. 11, No. 4 (Dec. 1987), pp. 163-172.

UL 94, *Tests for Flammability of Plastic Materials for Parts in Devices and Appliances*, Underwriters Laboratories Inc., Northbrook, IL, 1982.

Whittington's Dictionary of Plastics, Technomic, 1978.

Zinn, B. T., *et al*, "Investigation of the Properties of the Combustion Products Generated by Fire-Retarded Polyurethanes," *Final Report* of the Products Research Committee Project No. RP-75-1-15-Revised, Sept. 1977.

UPHOLSTERED FURNITURE AND MATTRESSES

Vytenis Babrauskas and John F. Krasny

Upholstered items, e.g., upholstered furniture and mattresses, play a major part in residential fires. It is estimated that there were approximately 48,000 residential structure fires per year from 1984 to 1988 that were reported to U.S. fire departments as starting with the ignition of upholstered furniture or mattresses. These fires caused 1,390 civilian deaths, 3,910 civilian injuries, and $340.3 million in direct property damage. Approximately 48 percent of these fires were caused by cigarettes. Other major ignition sources were matches, fixed and portable space heaters, cords and plugs, and lamps and light bulbs. Lighted tobacco products led to approximately 31 percent of residential fire deaths in 1987 and are the single largest cause of such deaths each year. However, they accounted for only 8 percent of the 1987 residential fires, and 16 percent of the injuries. Mortality and morbidity in cigarette-initiated fires are thus inordinately high. Victims of cigarette fires are not always the careless smokers themselves, and 45 percent of those killed by such fires are not in the same room as the fire when it begins.

Upholstered furniture may be ignited by cigarettes, by flaming sources, or by other sources, such as electric blankets. The latter account for only a tiny fraction of fire incidents and will not be considered here.

The need for cigarette ignition resistance of upholstered items is unique—other furnishings, such as carpets and curtains, or apparel textile items are rarely, if ever, ignited by cigarettes. Unfortunately, cigarette ignition resistance and resistance to flames are not necessarily compatible. Among common upholstery fabrics, medium and heavyweight thermoplastic fabrics (e.g., nylon, olefin, and polyester) generally resist cigarette ignition but do not resist flame ignition. Similarly, cellulosic materials (e.g., cotton, hemp, jute, linen, rayon fabrics, and batting) have poor cigarette ignition resistance, but over polyurethane foam they burn at a slower rate than the common combination of thermoplastic fabric and polyurethane foam. Only more expensive fabric/padding combinations, e.g., wool fabric over neoprene padding, combine good cigarette ignition resistance with relatively high resistance to flames.

Many aspects of flammability are similar for upholstered furniture and mattresses. However, the following distinction must be made: mattresses have predominantly flat surfaces which are not as likely to ignite by cigarettes as furniture crevices, i.e., the juncture of seat cushion and armrests and back of upholstered furniture. Similarly, the horizontal flat furniture surfaces are not as easily ignited by flame ignition sources as the vertical surfaces.

On the other hand, cigarettes on mattresses may be inadvertently covered with sheets, blankets, and/or pillows. This increases the probability of ignition by cigarettes. Also, these intermediary materials may ignite from flames more readily than mattresses, and then expose the mattress to a much more severe fire. Consequently, it is more difficult to develop relevant ignition tests and standards for mattresses than for upholstered furniture.

Upholstered furniture can contain well over a dozen materials, e.g., cover fabrics and fabrics between the cover fabric and the padding (interliners); different padding materials in the seat, sides, and back; weltcords; another fabric and type of padding below the seat cushion (decking); and frames, springs, stiffening for the sides, etc. Mattresses are complex but contain fewer materials. In the ignition process, whether from a cigarette or small flame, the cover fabric and material immediately below it—one or two layers of padding—are important. As the fire progresses, other materials, including the frame and springs, become involved, which can affect the manner in which the burning item collapses.

Smoldering of upholstered items, which is the typical consequence of exposure to a burning cigarette, can produce enough smoke and toxic gases to incapacitate and kill persons not only in the room of origin but also in some cases those who are remote from the fire. Transition from smoldering to flaming does not occur in all cases; when it does, times from placement of the cigarette to flaming of 20 minutes to several hours have been reported.[1,2] In a closed room, flaming can revert to smoldering when the oxygen supply is exhausted. With sufficient oxygen, a single upholstered item of sufficient burning rate can lead to room flashover.

Vytenis Babrauskas, Ph.D., is head of Fire Toxicity Measurement, and John F. Krasny retired as a textile technologist, at the Center for Fire Research, National Institute of Science and Technology (formerly National Bureau of Standards), Gaithersburg, MD.

Another feature of upholstered item fires is the difficulty of ensuring extinction, since wetting out or even immersion of the item in water does not ensure extinguishment. Items should be removed from the premises, torn apart, and the pieces thoroughly wetted. Many fire victims have wetted down a smoldering area in an upholstered chair or sofa, retired for the night, only to be faced several hours later with impenetrable smoke or a full-scale fire.

A monograph on upholstered furniture flammability contains an in-depth discussion of cigarette and small flame ignition resistance and postignition behavior.[3]

UPHOLSTERED ITEM FLAMMABILITY TESTS

Some cigarette and flame ignition standards and tests for upholstered items are listed in Table 3-11A. They can be classified as: (1) voluntary standards and tests, (2) federally enforced standards, and (3) state-imposed standards. A more extensive discussion of these and other international tests was recently presented.[4]

Voluntary and Regulatory Standards

Voluntary standards are proposed by trade organizations, such as the Upholstered Furniture Action Council (UFAC) for residential furniture, and the Business and Institutional Furniture Manufacturers Association (BIFMA) for their products. These two standards have also been developed as NFPA 260A, *Standard Methods of Tests and Classification System for Cigarette Ignition Resistance of Components of Upholstered Furniture*, and NFPA 260B, *Standard Method of Test for Determining Resistance of Mock-Up Upholstered Furniture Material Assemblies to Ignition by Smoldering Cigarettes*. The BIFMA standard was originally developed by the National Bureau of Standards (NBS) for the Consumer Product Safety Commission (CPSC). CPSC decided to hold this standard pending success of the UFAC voluntary approach. It has been reported that UFAC has succeeded in improving the cigarette ignition resistance of furniture.[5]

Many tests developed by voluntary standards organizations, especially those described in Group C of Table 3-11A, are more severe than federal or state standards in that they employ larger ignition sources and/or heating with radiative sources before pilot ignition. These tests often prescribe flame spread and smoke measurements, and are frequently used for research, product development, and regulation of special occupancies by some state and local authorities.

On the other hand, the mattress cigarette ignition standard and regulations are enforced by CPSC on the federal level. The state of California has its own residential and special occupancy regulations; other states may also pass such regulations.

In recent years, the fire fighting community and others have expressed great concern about the rapid fire spread, high heat release rate, and copious smoke development from polyurethane foam, as compared to the materials used in older upholstered furniture and mattresses. In fact, many fire fighters say they now encounter considerably more severe residential fires than before the introduction of polyurethane foam. In England this concern has lead to passage of a regulation that basically banned nonflame-retardant polyurethane foam.[6] The regulation specifies a number of tests for foams, fabrics, and mock-ups, as well as rules for labeling, etc. Foams would have to pass the requirements of British Standard BS 5852, Part 2, i.e., withstand ignition from a 0.6-oz. (17 g) wood crib

TABLE 3-11A. ***Flammability Tests for Upholstered Furniture and Mattresses****

	Ignition Source		Status			Test specimen		Occupancy	
Sponsor	Cigarette	Flame	Voluntary	Regulatory	Proposed	Compon.	Mockup or Actual Item	Res.	Special
A. Upholstered furniture									
UFAC-NFPA 260A	X		X			X		X	
BIFMA-NFPA 260B	X	X†	X				X		X
CPSC	X				X		X	X	
California 116	X	X		X		X		X	
California 117		X	X	X		X		X	
British (ISO)	X	X‡		X			X	X	X
B. Mattresses									
CPSC	X			X			X	X	X
Canadian	X			X			X	X	X
California 121		X		X		X		X	
C. Upholstered furniture and mattresses (larger flames, radiation)									
ASTM E162, ASTM D3675, FTMS 191, Method 5903, NFPA 258		X		X§		X	X		X
NY, NJ Port Authority		X		X		X			X
MVSS No. 302 (motor vehicles)		X		X			X		X
ASTM E906		X§	X			X	X		X
Cone Cal. ASTM E1354, NFPA 204A		X#	X			X		X	
California 133		X		X			X		X

* Sources: UFAC 1984; BIFMA 1980; CPSC 1981; CPSC 1984; CBHF 1980, 1981, 1987, 1988; BSI 1982; CGSB 1977; ASTM 1988a, 1988b, 1988c; GSA 1971; Port Authority 1981; Federal Register 1975; Babrauskas 1982; FAA 1984) (See Bibliography for titles.)

† Small flame test of fabrics and padding.

‡ Seven flame ignition sources of increasing severity, with smallest intended for residential furniture, others for special occupancies (e.g., No. 5, a 17 g wood crib, is specified for special occupancies and children's furniture.

§ Some of these methods are used by state and local authorities for furniture components or assemblies of cover fabric and padding.

\# Ignitability and rate of heat release rate can be measured.

placed into the crevice of a mockup of polyester fabric and the foam to be tested. Melamine-treated polyurethane foam, reportedly in ample supply in England, is acceptable, and the price increase is modest. With the advent of the common European market in 1992, these regulations may well be adopted by most of Europe.

In the U.S., upon urging by the International Association of Fire Fighters, several states are considering adoption of the California test T.B. 133 regulation [ignition source: 3.2 oz. (90 g) of balled-up newspaper held in a wire cage placed into the crevice of a mockup or actual piece of furniture; criteria include temperature rise, CO concentration, and smoke density in several locations in the test room, and weight loss] for buildings with occupancies of more than 50 persons, as designated by the state fire marshal. In most cases, an interliner fabric, such as vinyl-coated glass fabric, or Nomex or PBI nonwoven or woven fabrics, would have to be used between the cover fabric and the padding. Among other possibilities is the use of flame-retardant fabrics and combustion-modified, high-resiliency (CMHR) foam.

Component or Mockup Tests

Some tests are performed on mockups of furniture or on the actual furniture. Other tests prescribe testing of the individual components, i.e., the cover fabric, padding, welt-cord, etc., separately. The component tests do not consider interaction between materials. Sometimes the tests are configured so as to employ "standard materials" for those components not being tested. If that standard material is not the worst-case selection, the test results may be difficult to interpret or apply; e.g., upholstered padding in the UFAC-NFPA tests (NFPA 260A, *Standard Methods of Tests and Classification System for Cigarette Ignition Resistance of Components of Upholstered Furniture*, and NFPA 260B, *Standard Method of Test for Determining Resistance of Mock-Up Upholstered Furniture Material Assemblies to Ignition by Smoldering Cigarettes)* is tested while covered with an approximately 14 oz. per sq yd (400 g/m^2) cotton fabric, but many fabrics with higher propensity to ignite from cigarettes are frequently used on furniture.

Cigarette tests specify placement of the cigarette in the most vulnerable configuration, which is the crevice formed by the horizontal and vertical upholstered surfaces except, of course, for mattress tests. The cigarette is covered with a piece of sheeting. This makes the test slightly more severe and more reproducible, presumably because of exclusion of air currents from the smoldering area.

For flame ignition component tests, ignition is often by a gas flame at the bottom of a vertical specimen, such as foam or fabrics.[6,7] Flaming ignition in furniture mockups is generally at the crevice location.

Two U.S. flammability tests for transportation seats present a wide range of severity. On the low end of the scale, the Motor Vehicle Safety Standard No. 302 requires a horizontal specimen, and has minimal flame-spread requirements.[8] A strengthening of this requirement is under consideration for school buses. On the other end, a newly adopted Federal Aviation Administration (FAA) test[9] specifies a 115 kW, 6-in. (150 mm) diameter kerosene burner directed for two minutes on the side of the seat. The flames must not spread across the seat, no flaming drip must fall, and a maximum weight loss is specified.

Pass/fail criteria in the tests in Groups A and B of Table 3-11A are most often expressed in terms of char length or obvious ignition (i.e., sustained, expanding smoldering) for cigarettes, and char length and afterflame and afterglow time for flame ignition. The tests in Group C of Table 3-11A give quantitative results or ratings: i.e., flame spread ratings, ASTM E162 and D3675; smoke density, ASTM E906 and NFPA 258, *Standard Research Test Method for Determining Smoke Generation of Solid Materials*; and heat release rate, ASTM E906 and the cone calorimeter. Like the FAA test,[9] the California institutional test T.B.133 specifies maximum permissible weight loss and temperature, as well as CO and smoke concentrations in the test room.

The cigarette used in all U.S. smoldering ignition tests is a filterless, 85-mm commercial cigarette (Pall Mall® brand). It is representative of many other cigarette brands in its propensity to ignite. In recent years, bills have been submitted to the U.S. Congress and about a dozen state legislatures of bills that would require cigarettes to conform to yet-to-be-developed ignitability standards. In 1984, Congress passed H.R. 1880, the "Cigarette Safety Act," which called for a study of the feasibility of making cigarettes with a low propensity to ignite, without increasing tar and nicotine. It was found that this propensity does not relate to the rate of burning or burning cone temperature of cigarettes, but to complex interactions among the tobacco column, the cigarette paper, and the surface on which the cigarette rests. This propensity can be greatly reduced by lowering tobacco packing density and cigarette diameter (both of which reduce fuel loading and tar and nicotine delivery), as well as by lowering cigarette paper porosity.[10]

CHARACTERISTICS OF IGNITION SOURCES

Table 3-11B shows the characteristics of some ignition sources that have been used in flammability experimentation with upholstered furniture items. The sources range over four orders of magnitude—5 to 50,000 W. The maximum heat fluxes for the sources, except the methenamine pill, range between 15 and 42 kW/m^2. What differs mainly when ignition source strength is increased is not the peak incident flux, but rather the area over which the flux is applied. In the case of the polyethylene wastebasket, the area over which fluxes exceed 20 kW/m^2 is about 2.36 by 27.55 in. (60 by 700 mm); for a match this would be approximately 0.39 by 1.18 in. (10 by 30 mm). Higher heat fluxes are required to raise small target areas to ignition temperature than large areas. In addition, one may consider ignition as occurring when the lower flammability limit of pyrolysate gases is reached. This is determined both by the pyrolysate mass flux rate from the surface and by the entrainment and mixing conditions. The latter have not been studied as a function of the heated area size.

It should be noted that the above data are all for "incidental" fire sources. Heat fluxes from specialized sources, such as oxy-acetylene torches, may be much higher, e.g., 140 kW/m^2.[11]

FLAME SPREAD

Flame spread has long been the basis of flammability evaluation of building materials; however, little quantitative work has been done on the flame spread over upholstered

TABLE 3-11B. ***Characteristics of Furniture Ignition Sources****

	Typical Heat Output (W)	Burn Time† (s)	Maximum Flame Height (mm)	Flame Width (mm)	Maximum Heat Flux kW/m2
Cigarette 1.1 g (not puffed, laid on solid surface)					
bone dry	5	1200	—	—	42
conditioned to 50% R.H.	5	1200	—	—	35
Methenamine pill, 0.15 g	45	90		4	
Match, wooden (laid on solid surface)	80	20–30	30	14	18–20
Wood cribs, BS 5852 Part 2					
No. 4 crib, 8.5 g	1000	190		15#	
No. 5 crib, 17 g	1900	200		17#	
No. 6 crib, 60 g	2600	190		20#	
No. 7 crib, 126 g	6400	350		25#	
Crumpled brown lunch bag, 6 g	1200	80			
Crumpled wax paper, 4.5 g (tight)	1800	25			
Crumpled wax paper, 4.5 g (loose)	5300	20			
Folded double-sheet newspaper, 22 g (bottom ignition)	4000	100			
Crumpled double-sheet newspaper, 22 g (top ignition)	7400	40			
Crumpled double-sheet newspaper, 22 g (bottom ignition)	17,000	20			
California T.B. 133, Crumpled newspaper, 95-105g	15,000	110	710	610	80**
Polyethylene wastebasket, 285 g, filled with 12 milk cartons (390 g)	50,000	200‡	550	200	35§

* Sources: Behnke 1969; Moulen and Grubits, undated; Tu and Davis 1976; Paul and Clevely 1983; Paul 1981; and unpublished NIST data. (See Bibliography for titles.)

† Time duration of significant flaming.

‡ Total burn time in excess of 1800 sec.

§ As measured on simulation burner.

\# Measured from 25 mm away.

** Wide scatter.

items. Cotton and rayon cover fabrics by themselves were shown to have flame spread rates inversely proportional to their weight[12]; however, when tested over polyurethane padding, the differences between flame spread rates were small. This is another case where component tests can give rise to misleading results, as mentioned earlier.

In another experimental series, the flame spread over seat cushions of chair mockups was measured by counting the number of 3.93-in. (100 mm) squares covered by flames as a function of time from ignition.[13] This flame-spread rate was found to correlate fairly well with bench-scale measurements on the same fabric/padding composites. There were major differences, however, in the behavior of charring and melting (thermoplastic) fabrics. Cotton and rayon, the cellulosic fabrics, charred ahead of the flame, and on the side of the chair opposite to the one which was burning. Eventually the char burst into flame. The thermoplastic fabrics initially shrank away from the ignition source, but being supported by the foam, the shrunken material bead burned and presented a relatively large ignition source for the foam padding. The fabric on the chair side opposite the burning side ablated, exposing the foam to the radiation. Thus, flames spread more rapidly over the thermoplastic fabric-covered mockups, even when the foam was neoprene and did not significantly flame during the test.

General flame-spread theory has not been much applied to upholstered items, primarily because of the variety of configurations and interaction between fabrics and padding. Dimensions in these items are sufficiently large so flame-spread and heat-release behavior are dominated by radiative, rather than convective, mechanisms. Some studies of flame spread in the predominant "against the wind" mode, i.e., in the opposite direction to the draft induced by the buoyancy of the flame, have been conducted.[14]

HEAT RELEASE RATE

In the last few years, the importance of the heat release rate for prediction of flashover potential has been realized. Several methods to measure it have been suggested. One early technique is to directly measure the sensible enthalpy of the fire gas outflow. However, this requires corrections be made for the heat losses to the room walls; these losses vary widely for various wall materials, and depend on the heat release rate of the specimen. A method based on this principle—the Ohio State University (OSU) calorimeter—has been used widely.[15]

Since the late 1970s, the oxygen consumption principle for measuring heat release rate has come to the forefront. The principle states that the combustion heat released for most combustible species is proportional to the amount of oxygen consumed to within about ± 5 percent. The proportionality constant is 13.1×10^3 kJ per kg of O_2 consumed. By contrast, the heat of combustion of a fuel can vary widely and is given as the heat released per kg of fuel. Furniture calorimeters, i.e., large-scale instruments in which furniture can be tested, have been built in a number of laboratories. A bench-scale instrument, i.e., the cone calorimeter (so-called because of the cone-shaped heater used to irradiate the specimen), has been developed. The OSU method can also be modified to use this principle of heat release measurement.

There are methods to translate, within limitations, small-scale heat release rate results on upholstery fabric/padding combinations to flashover potential of furniture in a room. For any one combination, the peak heat release rate measured in an upholstered furniture calorimeter was found to be proportional to cone calorimeter results, as follows.[3]

$\dot{q}_{fs} = 0.63\ (\dot{q}''_{bs})$ (mass factor) (frame factor) (style factor)

where

$\dot{q}_{fs}$ (kW) = the full-scale peak heat release result measured in the furniture calorimeter

$\dot{q}_{bs}$ (kW/m^2) = the bench-scale heat release rate measure in the cone calorimeter under 25 kW/m^2 irradiance and averaged over 180 sec after ignition occurs

mass factor = total combustible mass, kg

frame factor = { 1.7 for noncombustible frames; 0.6 for melting plastic frames; 0.3 for wood frames; 02 for charring plastic frames }

style factor = { 1.0 for plain, primarily rectilinear construction; 0.5 for ornate, convoluted shapes (with intermediate values for intermediate shapes) }

The style factor accounts for certain geometrical flame-spread effects on the heat-release rate. The frame factor reflects both combustibility and structural integrity effects on fire development.

This rule does not apply to constructions with a very low rate of heat release, e.g., heavy cotton fabrics over neoprene foam, since rapid, complete combustion does not occur, and the mass factor overestimates the output for the relatively dense neoprene. Also, the rule is not applicable to types of constructions that lack a conventional structural frame, due to lack of adequate test data. Recent cooperative research conducted at National Institute of Science and Technology (NIST) and at the California Bureau of Home Furnishings has clarified the behavior of the low-heat-release-rate constructions.[16] Correlations are indicated that, as expected, do not depend on specimen mass.

Furniture calorimeter results, obtained with unlimited air supply, have been validated against those obtained in room burns with various degrees of air supply limitations in some, but not all, experiments.[3,17] Figure 3-11A shows typical rate of heat-release time curves from such experiments, which indicate that no systematic influence of room ventilation conditions was seen. The ability to utilize furniture calorimeter data to represent heat-release rates in room fires extends only to the fuel-limited regime. Fires with such a small ratio of ventilation to heat-release rate as to have no excess oxygen in the combustion gas stream ("ventilation limited"), because of such a small ratio of ventilation to heat-release rate, cannot be so simply represented and, as yet, have not been quantified for upholstered furniture.

Prediction techniques for assessing the potential of room flashover occurring due to upholstered furniture have been addressed.[18]

In addition to those methods for estimating the potential for flashover caused by a single upholstered furniture item, a few studies have addressed the tendency of one item to ignite other furnishings.[19,20] Irradiances measured at 19 in. (0.5 m) from the edge of chair mockups ranged from 15 to 45 kW/m^2 for combinations of ordinary and flame-resistant polyurethane foam covered by four types of fabrics. The upper range is more than sufficient to ignite other upholstered furniture items and many other furnishings, such as wastepaper baskets and wood chairs, placed at that distance. Since distances between furnishings can-

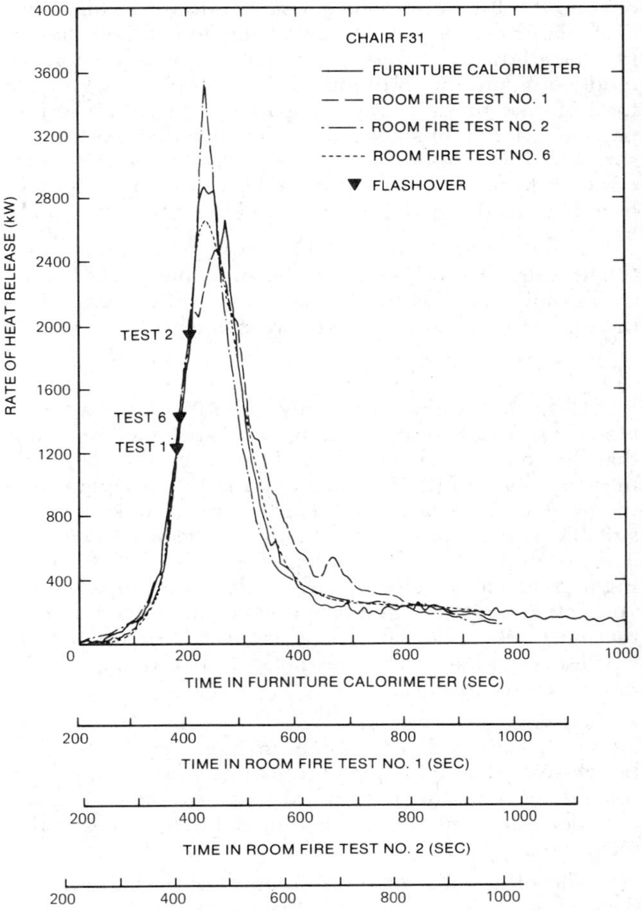

FIG. 3-11A. Comparison of furniture calorimeter and room fire results for a loveseat with Olefin cover fabric, flame-retardant polyurethane foam, and a wood frame (three room fires, with varying ventilation openings).

not be regulated, flame resistance of all furnishings in special occupancies, such as hospital rooms, is important.

Recently, NFPA has published a new standard, NFPA 264A, *Standard Method of Test for Heat Release Rates of Upholstered Furniture,* which addresses the details of measuring the heat release rates of upholstered furniture samples in the cone calorimeter. An appendix to the standard provides some preliminary help in interpreting the results and evaluating the performance of products.

SMOKE AND TOXIC GASES

Human incapacitation or fatalities in fires are more often due to smoke and toxic effects than to direct burn injuries. Thus, a logical way of characterizing fire hazard would be according to the time for incapacitation. This approach is natural for analyzing standardized room fires, given suitable measurements of toxic gases and a pertinent set of tenability criteria. Such an approach was taken for mattresses,[2,21] where tenability criteria for CO, CO_2, and O_2 depletion; heat flux; and smoke were established and applied. This approach remains appealing for cases where a fixed compartment scenario is to be involved. Transportation vehicles are a natural example; recent evaluations of aircraft cabin performance have been assessed in terms of available escape time. In the evaluation of movable furnishings, however, there is no unique possible compartment configuration. Although the California test T.B. 133 for high-risk, high-density occupancy furniture prescribes pass/fail criteria for smoke and CO concentrations as measured in a fixed room,[22] other current engineering methods have focused on measuring certain basic fire properties from hazards that could be predicted by computer models.

The most tractable model for toxic gas evolution postulates that a fixed fraction of the specimen mass is realized as any given gas species (or smoke particulates). Thus, the mass rate of production of species is:

$$\dot{m}(t) = \dot{m}(t)\,\Gamma x$$

Here the production of any quantity (x = soot, CO, etc.) is expressed as the fraction, Γx, of specimen mass loss that becomes the species x, multiplied by the specimen mass loss rate in (t). The concentration at any point in a room can then be calculated if airflow rates are known and suitable assumptions on mixing (or stratification) are made. The assumption that the fraction of specimen mass becoming a given gas species is reasonable where fires are not ventilation limited. When fires do become oxygen limited, the most noticeable effect is a rise in CO production, as oxygen is depleted. This has not yet been quantified for upholstered furniture.

Extensive experimental work was done recently in attempting to predict full-scale toxic gas evolution from bench-scale data.[17] Simple correlations were adequate for some gases. For others, specifically CO, simple scaling was not adequate. A more advanced model that would predict CO correctly is not yet available.

The effect of smoke obscuration on lethality is not direct; nonetheless, it is real in that escape can be hindered or precluded where visibility does not exist. The conversion of specimen mass into soot mass is, just as for toxic gas species, dependent upon ventilation and other effects. An examination of the limited available data, however, suggests that the assumption of a constant soot mass ratio is not a bad one. Bench-scale measurements of smoke have typically been made in the NBS smoke chamber, where an optical beam attenuation is measured. These optical measurements can be related to the soot particulate mass fraction, Γ s, by empirical relationships. Newer tests are being developed that allow dynamic measurements of beam attenuation, along with direct determination of Γs.

MATERIAL RANKING

Table 3-11C summarizes the results from a wide variety of studies on the cigarette ignition and small flame ignition resistance of upholstered items. The materials in the table are listed from top to bottom in the approximate order of decreasing resistance to ignition for cigarette ignition source (Part A) and in order of decreasing resistance to small flames and increasing fire growth after ignition (Part B). There is considerable overlap between these characteristics of materials listed near each other, depending upon such factors as density, amount of smolder-resistant or flame-retardant agent, fabric finish and backcoating, and other factors.

It should again be emphasized that some materials with good cigarette ignition resistance do not necessarily have good small flame ignition resistance, and *vice versa*, e.g., thermoplastic fabrics tend to resist cigarette ignition because some of the heat transferred to the fabric is consumed in melting the fibers. On the other hand, cigarettes induce smoldering in medium to heavyweight cellulosic fabrics, with consequent heat transfer to the padding. However, the thermoplastics shrink, melt, and curl away from an open flame and expose the padding, while cellulosic fabrics char and, until the char breaks, protect the padding. Similarly, some flame retardants for polyurethane foam reduce resistance to smoldering, while others enhance both flame and cigarette ignition resistance.

To prevent ignition by cigarettes, it is not necessary to use only the materials listed on top of each column in Table 3-11C; e.g., the combination of medium-weight thermoplastic with ordinary polyurethane foam, or the combination of light- to medium-weight cellulosic fabric with a layer of polyester batting over the polyurethane foam, each have a low probability of cigarette ignition. Many wool and medium to heavy PVC-coated fabrics can be used with flame-resistant or ordinary polyurethane foam or mixed batting. Material combinations that are, for all practical purposes, cigarette ignition resistant in a crevice configuration can be chosen on the basis of a few trials in a qualified laboratory. The number of such trials can be held small by using the information from the table.

Unfortunately, no such simple scheme can be recommended for ensuring the flame resistance of materials listed in Table 3-11C, Part B. Here, even the materials listed on top of each column will ignite if the flame is large enough or applied long enough, or both. However, Part B may be helpful in choosing material, e.g., combinations with a low probability of ignition from matches, or which may have lower rates of flame growth when ignited with a larger source.

As examples for use of Table 3-11C, Part B, medium- to heavy-weight wool and vinyl-coated cellulosic fabrics (vinyl-coated thermoplastics open up and expose the padding to the flame) have been shown to resist match ignition, regardless of padding material, but ignite with larger flame exposure. Heavy cotton fabric over neoprene padding burned and then smoldered, while the neoprene did not enter the combustion process except for smoldering in the crevice. (Smoldering of neoprene, like that of cotton batting, is hard to extinguish and is best done by immersing torn up pieces in water for prolonged periods.) Total rates of heat release and combustion product formation were negligible after the fabrics stopped burning. Aircraft seats constructed with wool/nylon fabric, an aluminized aramid fabric interliner, and polyurethane foam self-extinguished even after a severe flame exposure for two minutes. This type of interliner is used because it is gas impermeable and prevents pyrolysis gases formed in the urethane foam from reaching the flames (cushion venting is provided in areas not likely to be in the fire path). A polychloroprene-type foam sheet interliner (Vonar®) was also effective in making these seats self-extinguishing. Aluminized interliners are also effective in increasing cigarette ignition resistance, Vonar perhaps somewhat less so. For applications where weight is not important, vinyl-coated glass fabric is being used.

Some highly flame resistant treated polyurethane foams have almost as good flame resistance as neoprene but do not smolder. They can be considered for such occupancies

TABLE 3-11C. ***Upholstered Furniture Components Listed in Approximate Order of Descending Ignition Resistance***

Ignition Resistance	Cover Fabric	Padding	Interliner Fabric	Weltcords	Construction Parameters
A. CIGARETTE IGNITION RESISTANCE					
HIGH	Wool, PVC	Specialty foams†	Aluminized fabrics	Aluminized	Flat areas
	Heavy thermoplastics	Polyester batting	Neoprene sheets	PVC	Flat areas near
			Vinyl coated glass fab.	Thermoplastics	welt cord
	Cellulose/thermoplastics blends	SR PU	Novoloid felts	SR treated	Tufts
	(depending on thermoplastic	SR cellulosic batting	Thermoplastic fabrics	cellulosics	Crevices
	percentages)	Untreated PU	Cellulosic fabrics	Cellulosics	
	Light thermoplastics	Mixed fiber batting			
	Light cellulosics	Cellulosic batting			
LOW	Heavy cellulosics				
B. SMALL FLAME IGNITION RESISTANCE AND FIRE GROWTH					
HIGH	FR wool	Specialty foams‡	Aluminized, gas imperme-	Effect of weltcord has	Flat areas
	Wool, PVC coated cellulosics‡	FR cellulosic batting	able fabrics	not been investi-	Vertical areas
	Cellulosics‡	FR PU	Neoprene sheets‡	gated, believed	Corner areas
		Cellulosic batting	Novoloid fabrics§	minor	
	Thermoplastics	Polyester batting	Aramid fabrics‡§		
		Untreated PU	Vinyl coated glass fabrics‡		
		Latex foam	FR cellulosic fabrics‡§		
			Cellulosic fabrics†§		
LOW			Thermoplastic fabrics		

SR—smolder resistant; FR—flame resistant; PU—polyurethane foam.
* Data on the behavior of acrylic are sparse but it seems to act more like cellulosics (smolder) than thermoplastics.
† Neoprene; combustion modified, high resiliency PU.
‡ Heavier materials have higher flame ignition resistance and generally higher heat release and lower flame spread rate.
§ Fabrics here include woven, knitted and nonwoven structures.

as prisons, where cover fabrics and interliners can be expected to be cut open in arson attempts. Cotton batting treated with boric acid is widely used in prison mattresses.

For any combination of fabric and padding material, cigarette ignition resistance is better in flat areas than in crevices. Tufted areas also may have lower cigarette ignition resistance than flat areas, and are usually tested separately, as are areas near the welt edge outside the crevices.

Flames seem to start faster when ignition is on a vertical furniture surface, especially a corner, rather than on a horizontal surface. Some furniture item fires are started by children playing with matches on the underside of furniture items. Making the bottom from thermoplastic fabric (which ablates readily) has been suggested as a remedy. All visible furniture surfaces are usually covered by one fabric, but the padding frequently varies greatly in one furniture item: e.g., firm foam in the seat, less firm foam or batting in the back, and even less firmness on the sides. On the outside, there may be only light padding, or the fabric may not be in contact with the padding at all. For proper firesafety design, each of these material combinations then needs to be evaluated.

The ranking of materials during fully involved flaming is approximately the same as that given in Table 3-11C. There is little information on the effects of furniture configuration. However, observations suggest that flame spread over curved and convoluted surfaces can be slower initially, but may be appreciably accelerated when larger, radiatively driven flames come to dominate. Peak heat-release rate per unit mass was found to increase when simulated furniture geometry was changed from a single cushion to two, three, and four sides of a cube, with ignition in the enclosed space. When cushion thickness was varied, it was found that the peak rate of heat release was not quite proportional to specimen mass, but was somewhat higher, per unit mass, for thinner cushions.

A limited amount of work has been done on the effect of the furniture frames. Near the time of the peak burning rate, the manner in which the frame starts to collapse becomes important. A polyurethane frame produced the lowest burning rate, followed by a wood frame, while a polypropylene frame melted early in the fire.[23] Wood frames fail at the frame connections, and here metal connections seem to perform worse than glued ones.

Total fuel content of the furniture item can be used to roughly estimate the burning time. A method was developed based on this, where the heat-release rate curve is approximated as a triangular form.[3]

The amount of smoke data for upholstered furniture items is rather small. In one series of mattress tests, bench-scale smoke data were validated against full-scale measurements. Because of significant mass differences, these values tend to be determined largely by the padding and not the fabric. Latex foam constituted the worst case, with 20 percent of the specimen mass becoming smoke particulate. Polyurethane foams typically yield 10 to 15 percent smoke, although some specimens yield as low as 5 percent, and, with cotton ticking fabric, 0.5 percent. Neoprene smoke production also depends upon foam formulation; low smoke formulations are commercially available. Polyester and polyester/cotton battings show low values, similar to pure cotton batting. Flame-retarded foam generally released more smoke than ordinary polyurethane foam, but at a somewhat lower rate.

Among the fabrics, wool tended to release relatively little smoke at a low rate. Next in order were cellulosic fabrics, thermoplastic fabrics, and worst, PVC cover fabrics. Similarly, the order from best to worst padding was wool, cotton and other vegetable fibers, and polyurethane foams. Fire barrier interliners reduced and delayed smoke release. Modacrylic fabrics produced high smoke-release results; aramid fabrics yielded low smoke-release results. Acrylic/

cellulosic blends seemed to be worse than all-cellulose fabrics.

The major toxic products expected to be found in upholstered item fires are CO, CO_2, HCN, HCl, and NO_x. Depletion of oxygen also has a toxic effect. Perhaps more than in other fields, there is no agreement on relevant test conditions and evaluation of results. It is quite widely accepted that significant differences in toxic effects are expressed by differences in order of magnitude in LC_{50}. On that basis, the differences between most upholstery materials are not significant. However, materials may show a lower toxic effect behavior by showing a slower burning rate, not just lower per mass-burned toxicity. Based on such a fuller understanding of toxic effects, differences in furniture materials can be seen, even though the LC_{50}s do not differ by an order of magnitude.

CONCLUSIONS

The fire hazard due to upholstered furniture items has to be considered in the context of all relevant parameters. These parameters include:

1. Resistance to smoldering (cigarette) and flame ignitions (not necessarily the same for some typical upholstery materials).
2. Flame spread.
3. Heat-release rate (related primarily to flashover propensity in a room) and irradiance (related to ignition of nearby furnishings and walls).
4. Smoke development.
5. Toxic effects due to heat, oxygen depletion, and products such as CO, CO_2, HCl, HCN, NO_x, etc.

Many present test methods for these properties were designed before a total concept approach was seen to be necessary. They need to be reviewed and modified or replaced by more up-to-date ones where necessary. The present trend to more intensely look beyond the fire resistance of the building construction and toward that of contents and furnishings will provide major contributions to the overall reduction of fire losses.

BIBLIOGRAPHY

References Cited

1. Braun, E., *et al*, "Cigarette Ignition of Upholstered Chairs," *Journal of Consumer Product Flammability*, Vol. 9, 1982, pp. 167-183.
2. Hafer, C. A., and Yuill, C. H., *Characterization of Bedding and Upholstery Fires*, Southwest Research Institute, San Antonio, TX, 1970.
3. Babrauskas, V., and Krasny, J. F., "Fire Behavior of Upholstered Furniture," Monograph MN-173, 1985, National Bureau of Standards, Gaithersburg, MD.
4. Babrauskas, V., "Flammability of Upholstered Furniture with Flaming Sources," *Cellular Polymers*, Vol. 8, 1989, pp. 198-224.
5. Fairall, P., "Analysis of CPSC 40 Chair Test Program," 1984, U.S. Consumer Product Safety Commission, Washington, DC.
6. Secretary of State, "Consumer Protection, The Furniture and Furnishings (Fire) (Safety) Regulations 1988," No. 1324, 1988, Her Majesty's Stationery Office, London.
7. CBHF, *Flammability Information Package*, California Bureau of Home Furnishings, North Highlands, CA, 1987.
8. Federal Register, "Flammability of Interior Materials—Passenger Cars, Multipurpose Passenger Vehicles, Trucks, and Buses," Motor Vehicle Safety Standard No. 302, Vol. 35, 1975, Federal Register.
9. FAA, "Flammability Requirements for Aircraft Seat Cushions," *Code of Federal Regulations* 14 CFR, Parts 25, 29, 121, 1984, Federal Aviation Administration, Washington, DC.
10. Gann, R. G., Harris, R. H., Jr., Krasny, J. F., Levine, R. S., Mitler, H. E., Ohlemiller, T. O., "The Effect of Cigarette Characteristics on the Ignition of Soft Furnishings," NBS Technical Note 1241, 1988, National Bureau of Standards, Gaithersburg, MD.
11. Paul, K. T., and Christian, S. D., "Standard Flaming Ignition Sources for Upholstered Composites, Furniture, and Bed Assemblies," *Journal of Fire Sciences*, Vol. 5, 1987, pp. 178-211.
12. Lee, B. T., and Wiltshire, L. W., "Fire Spread Models of Upholstered Furniture," *Journal of Fire and Flammability*, Vol. 3, 1972, pp. 164-175.
13. Krasny, J. F., and Babrauskas, V., "Burning Behavior of Upholstered Furniture Mockups," *Journal of Fire Sciences*, Vol. 2, 1984, pp. 205-231.
14. Rockett, J. A., "Mathematical Modeling of Radiant Panel Test Methods," Fire Safety Research Journal (SP 411), 1974, National Bureau of Standards, Gaithersburg, MD.
15. ASTM, "Test for Surface Flammability of Flexible Cellular Materials Using a Radiant Heat Energy Source," ASTM D3675, 1988, American Society for Testing and Materials, Philadelphia, PA.
16. Parker, W. J., Tu, K. M., Nurbahksh, S., and Damant, G. H., "Furniture Flammability: An Investigation of the California Bulletin 133 Test, Part III: Full-Scale Chair Burns," NISTIR 4375, 1990, National Bureau of Standards, Gaithersburg, MD.
17. Babrauskas, V., Harris, R. H., Jr., Gann, R. G., Levin, B. C., Lee, B. T., Peacock, R. D., Paabo, M., Twilley, W., Yoklavich, M. F., and Clark, H.M., "Fire Hazard Comparison of Fire-Retarded and Non-Fire-Retarded Products," NBS Special Publication SP 749, 1988, National Bureau of Standards, Gaithersburg, MD.
18. Babrauskas, V., "Upholstered Furniture Room Fires—Measurements, Comparison with Furniture Calorimeter Data, and Flashover Predictions," *Journal of Fire Sciences*, 2, 1984, pp. 5-19.
19. Palmer, K. N., *et al*, "Fire Hazard of Plastics in Furniture and Furnishings; Fires in Furnished Rooms," 1976, Building Research Establishment, Boreham Wood, Hertfordshire, England.
20. Babrauskas, V., "Will the Second Item Ignite?," *Fire Safety Journal*, 1982, pp. 287-292.
21. Babrauskas, V., "Combustion of Mattresses Exposed to Flaming Ignition Sources, Part I: Full-Scale Tests and Hazard Analysis," NBSIR 77-1290, 1977, National Bureau of Standards, Gaithersburg, MD.
22. CBHF, "Flammability Test Procedure for Seating Furniture for Use in High Risk and Public Occupancies," Technical Bulletin No. 133, 1988, California Bureau of Home Furnishings, North Highlands, CA.
23. Babrauskas, V., "Upholstered Furniture Heat Release Rates; Measurements and Estimation," *Journal of Fire Sciences*, Vol. 1, 1983, pp. 9-32.

References

ASTM, "Test for Surface Flammability of Materials Using a Radiant Heat Energy Source," ASTM E162, 1988, American Society for Testing and Materials, Philadelphia, PA.

ASTM, "Standard Test Method for Heat and Visible Smoke Release Rates for Materials and Products," ASTM E906, 1988, American Society for Testing and Materials, Philadelphia, PA.

Babrauskas, V., "Development of the Cone Calorimeter—A Bench-Scale Heat Release Rate Apparatus Based on Oxygen Consumption," NBSIR 82-2611, 1982, National Bureau of Standards, Gaithersburg, MD.

Behnke, W., "Cigarette Study: Heat Flux and Ember Temperatures," document presented to ASTM Committee D-13, 1969.

BIFMA, *Standard and Institutional Furniture Manufacturer's Association First Generation Voluntary Upholstered Furniture Flammability Standard for Business and Institutional Markets*, Business and Institutional Furniture Manufacturer's Association, Grand Rapids, MI, 1980.

BSI, "Fire Tests for Furniture, Part 1: Methods of Test for the Ignitability by Smokers' Materials of Upholstered Composites for Seating," BS 5852, Part 1: 1979, British Standards Institution, London.

BSI, "Fire Tests for Furniture, Part 2: Methods of Test for the Ignitability of Upholstered Composites for Seating by Flaming Sources," BS 5852, Part 2: 1982, British Standards Institution, London.

CBHF, "Flammability Test Procedure for Mattresses for Use in High Risk Occupancies," Technical Bulletin 121, 1980, California Bureau of Home Furnishings, Sacramento, CA. (Contains Technical Bulletins 116, 117.)

CGSB, "Method of Test for the Combustion Resistance of Mattress; Cigarette Test," 1977, Canadian Government Specification Board, Ottawa, Ontario, Canada.

CPSC, "Standard for the Flammability of Mattresses (and Mattress Pads)," *Code of Federal Regulations*, Part 1632, Final Rule, Oct. 10, 1984, U.S. Consumer Product Safety Commission, Washington, DC.

CPSC, "Proposed Standards for the Flammability (Cigarette Ignition) of Upholstered Furniture," *Code of Federal Regulations*, Part 1633, U.S. Consumer Product Safety Commission, Washington, DC.

GSA, "Flame Resistance of Cloth; Vertical Methods 5903.2," Federal Test Standard No. 191, 1971, General Services Administration, Washington, DC.

Krasny, J. F., and Gann, R. G., "Relative Propensity of Selected Commercial Cigarettes to Ignite Soft Furnishings Mockups," NBSIR 86-3421, 1986, National Bureau of Standards, Gaithersburg, MD.

Krasny, J. F., *et al*, "Development of a Candidate Test Method for the Measurement of the Propensity of Cigarettes to Cause Smoldering Ignition of Upholstered Furniture and Mattresses," NBSIR 81-2363, 1986, National Bureau of Standards, Gaithersburg, MD.

Macaluso, C., "Cigarette Ignition Studies," Testimony before the Subcommittee on Health and the Environment, Committee on Energy and Commerce on March 21, 1983, U.S. House of Representatives.

Moulen, A. W., and Grubits, S. J., "Paper Ignition Sources Used to Examine the Fire Behavior of Seating and Bedding," Technical Record 474, (undated), Experimental Building Station, Department of Housing and Construction, Chatswood, N.S.W., Australia.

Port Authority, "Specifications Governing the Flammability of Upholstery Materials and Plastic Furniture," 1981, The Port Authority of New York and New Jersey, New York.

Tu, K. M., and Davis, S., "Flame Spread of Carpet Systems Involved in Room Fires," NBSIR 76-1013, 1976, National Bureau of Standards, Gaithersburg, MD.

UFAC, *Important Consumer Safety Information from UFAC*, Upholstered Furniture Action Council, High Point, NC, 1984.

NFPA Codes, Standards, and Recommended Practices

Reference to the following NFPA codes, standards, and recommended practices will provide further information on upholstered furniture and mattresses discussed in this chapter. (See the latest *NFPA Catalog* for availability of current editions of the following documents.)

NFPA 258, *Standard Research Test Method for Determining Smoke Generation of Solid Materials.*

NFPA 260A, *Standard Methods of Tests and Classification System for Cigarette Ignition Resistance of Components of Upholstered Furniture.*

NFPA 260B, *Standard Method of Test for Determining Resistance of Mock-Up Upholstered Furniture Material Assemblies to Ignition by Smoldering Cigarettes.*

NFPA 264A, *Standard Method of Test for Heat Release Rates for Upholstered Furniture*

Additional Reading

Alarie, Y., et al, "Toxicity of Smoke During Chair Smoldering Tests and Small Scale Tests Using the Same Materials," *Fundamental and Applied Toxicology*, Vol. 3, 1983, pp. 619-626.

Alarie, Y. C., and Anderson, R. C., "Toxicological and Acute Lethal Hazard Evaluation of Thermal Decomposition Products of Synthetic and Natural Polymers," *Tox. Appl. Pharm.*, 1979, pp. 341-362.

Ames, S. A., "Measuring Fire Growth in Furniture," *Fire Surveyor*, Vol. 17, No. 2, April 1988, pp. 4-10.

Anderson, B., and Magnusson, S. E., "Fire Behavior of Upholstered Furniture—An Experimental Study," *Report No. R80-4, TVBB-0055*, Lund Institute of Technology, Lund, Sweden, 1982.

Annual Flammable Fabrics Report, US Consumer Product Safety Commission, Washington, DC.

Babrauskas, V., *et al*, "Upholstered Furniture Heat Release Rates Measured With a Furniture Calorimeter," *NBSIR 82-2604*, National Bureau of Standards, Gaithersburg, MD, 1982.

Babrauskas, V., and Krasny, J. F., "Prediction of Upholstered Chair Heat Release Rates From Bench-Scale Measurements," (ASTM STP).

Babrauskas, V., "Upholstered Furniture Room Fires—Measurements, Comparison With Furniture Calorimeter Data, and Flashover Predictions," *Journal of Fire Sciences*, Vol. 2, 1984, pp. 5-19.

Babrauskas, V., "Performance of the Ohio State University Rate of Heat Release Apparatus Using Polymethylmethacrylate and Gaseous Fuels," *Fire Safety Journal*, Vol. 5, 1982, pp. 9-20.

Babrauskas, V., "Applications of Predictive Smoke Measurements," *Journal of Fire and Flammability*, Vol. 12, Jan. 1981, pp. 51-64.

Babrauskas, V., "Combustion of Mattresses Exposed to Flaming Ignition Sources, Part II, Bench-Scale Tests and Recommended Standard Test," *NBSIR 80-2186*, National Bureau of Standards, Gaithersburg, MD, 1980.

Babrauskas, V., "A Laboratory Flammability Test for Institutional Materials," *Fire Journal*, Vol. 75, No. 5, Nov. 1981, pp. 35-40.

Babrauskas, V., "Flammability of Upholstered Furniture with Flamming Sources," European Conference on Furniture Flammability, London, 1988.

Babrauskas, V., "Pillow Burning Rates," *Fire Safety Journal*, Vol. 8, No. 3, 1985, pp. 199-200.

Babrauskas, V., *et al.*, "Upholstered Furniture Heat Release Rates Measured with a Furniture Calorimeter," NBSIR 82-2604, 1982, National Bureau of Standards, Gaithersburg, MD.

Babrauskas, V., and Walton, W. D., "A Simplified Characterization of Upholstered Furniture Heat Release Rates," *Fire Safety Journal*, Vol. 11, 1986, pp. 181-192.

Birky, M., *et al.*, "Study of Biological Samples Obtained From Victims of MGM Grand Hotel Fire," *Journal of Anal. Toxicology*, Vol. 7, 1983, pp. 265-271.

Blankenbaker, S., "Cigarettes and Electric Heating Elements as Ignition Sources," *Proceedings of the Thirteenth Annual Meeting*, Information Council on Fabric Flammability, Atlanta, GA, Dec. 1979.

Clarke, F. II, and Ottoson, J., "Fire Death Scenario and Firesafety Planning," *Fire Journal*, Vol. 70, May 1976, pp. 20-22, 117, 118.

Colver, C. P., and Colver, J. C., "Review of Progress Towards the Development of an Upholstered Furniture Flammability Standard," *Journal of Fire Sciences*, Vol. 5, No. 5, 1987, pp.326-337.

D. C. 1983. Cigarette Safety Act, U.S. Government Printing Office, Washington.

Dietenberger, M., "Description and Results of Furniture Fire Models within FAST (HEMFAST)," NBS-GCR-87-527, March 1987, National Bureau of Standards, Gaithersburg, MD.

Dietenberger, M., "Mathematical Modeling of Furniture Fires," NBS-GCR-86-506, Feb. 1986, National Bureau of Standards, Gaithersburg, MD.

Dietenberger, M. A., "A Validated Furniture Fire Model with FAS-T(HEMFAST)," NIST-GCR-89-564, June 1984, National Bureau of Standards, Gaithersburg, MD.

Fang, J. B., "Fire Buildup in a Room and the Role of Interior Finish Materials,"Tech. Note 879, National Bureau of Standards, Washington, DC, 1975.

Fitzgerald, W. E., and Kanakia, M., "Calorimetric Evaluation of the Role of Fire Retardants in Selected Polymers," Fire Retardant Chemicals Association Conference Workshop, Mar. 12-15, 1978, Technomic, Westport, CT, pp. 21-30.

Fitzgerald, W. E., "Quantification of Fires: 1. Energy Kinetics of Burning in a Dynamic Room Size Calorimeter," *Journal of Fire and Flammability*, Vol. 9, Oct. 1978, pp. 510-527.

"Furniture and Furnishings Regulations," *Fire Surveyor*, Vol. 18, No. 1, Feb. 1989, pp. 5-13.

Griggs, D., "Furniture Flammability—A Textile Specialists Viewpoint," *Fire Prevention*, No. 210, June 1988, pp. 28-30.

Harwood, B., and Kale, D., *Fires in Upholstered Furniture*, US Consumer Product Safety Commission, Washington, DC, May 1980.

Heskestad, G., "A Fire Products Collector for Calorimetry into the MW Range," *FMRC J. I. OC2E1.RA*, Factory Mutual Research Corp., Norwood, MA, 1981.

Hill, R. G., *et al.*, "Aircraft Seat Fire Blocking Layers: Effectiveness and Benefits Under Various Scenarios," DOT/FAA/CT-83/43, Federal Aviation Administration, Atlantic City, NJ, 1984.

Hoebel, J. F., and Sharman, L. J., "National Estimates—1983 Fire Losses Associated with Upholstered Furniture and with Mattressess and Bedding," March 1985, U.S. Consumer Product Safety Commission, Washington, DC.

Holmstedt, G., and Kaiser, I., "Brand i Vordbaddar," SP-RAPP 1983:04 Statens Provningsanstalt, Boras, Sweden, 1983.

Huggett, C., "Estimation of Rate of Heat Release by Means of Oxygen Consumption Measurements," *Fire and Materials*, Vol. 4, 1980, pp. 61-65.

Jervis, R. L., "Missing Link: Fire-Resistant Furnishings," *Fire Journal*, Vol. 81, No. 6, 1987, p. 56.

Kaplan, H. L., *et al.*, *Combustion Toxicology: Principles and Methods*, Technomic Publishing Co., Lancaster, PA, 1983.

Krasny, F., and Huang, D., "Small Flame Ignitability and Flammability Behavior of Upholstered Furniture Materials," NBSIR 88-3771, June 1988, National Bureau of Standards, Gaithersburg, MD.

Krause, R. F., and Gann, R. G., "Rate of Heat Release Measurements Using Oxygen Consumption," *Journal of Fire and Flammability*, Vol. 11, Apr. 1980, pp. 117-130.

Levin, B. C., *et al.*, "Conditions Conducive to the Generation of Hydrogen Cyanide From Flexible Polyurethane Foam," *7th Joint Meeting*, U.S. Japan Panel on Fire Research and Safety, Washington, DC, Oct. 1983.

Levin, B. C., *et al.*, "An Acute Inhalation Toxicological Evaluation of Combustion Products From Fire Retarded and Non-Fire Retarded Flexible Polyurethane Foam and Polyester," NBSIR 83-2791, National Bureau of Standards, Gaithersburg, MD, Nov. 1983.

Levin, B. C., *et al.*, "Further Development of a Test Method for the Assessment of the Acute Inhalation Toxicity of Combustion Products," NBSIR 82-2532, National Bureau of Standards, Gaithersburg, MD, 1982.

Marchant, R., "Furniture Fire Hazards Coming Under Control," *Fire Prevention*, No.226, Jan./Feb. 1990, pp. 28-30.

Mischutin, V., "Flame-Retardant Home Furnishings," *American Dyestuff Reporter*, Vol. 76, No. 3, 1987, pp. 38-42, 49.

Morotz-Cecei, K., and Beda, L., "Comparative Testing of the Flammability of Upholstery Textiles," *Journal of Thermal Analysis*, Vol. 32, No. 3, 1987, pp. 901-908.

Parker, W. J., "Calculations of the Heat Release Rate by Oxygen Consumption for Various Applications," NBSIR 81-2427, National Bureau of Standards, Gaithersburg, MD, 1982.

Powell, D., "The Role of Combustion Modified Foams in Furniture: A Closer Look," *Fire Prevention*, No.216, Jan./Feb. 1989, pp. 27-30.

Prager, F. H., and Wood, J. F., *Full-Scale Investigation of the Fire Performance of Upholstered Furniture*, Part I, (RAPRA 4), International Isocyanate Institute, 1979.

Quintiere, J. G., "An Assessment of Correlations Between Laboratory and Fire-Scale Experiments for the FAA Aircraft Fire Safety Program, Part 1: Smoke," NBSIR 82-2508, National Bureau of Standards, Gaithersburg, MD, 1982.

Rogowski, B. F. W., "Investigating the Contribution to Fire Growth of Combustible Materials Used in Building Components," *Proceedings* of the Conference on New Technology to Reduce Fire Losses and Costs, Elsevier, NY, 1986, pp. 88-105.

Spears, A. W., "A Technical Analysis of the Problems Relating to Upholstered Furniture and Mattress Fires Relative to Proposed Cigarette Legislation Including a Review of Relevant Patents," Testimony, Subcommittee on Health and the Environment, Committee on Energy and Commerce, March 21, 1983, US House of Representatives.

Springer, G. S., "Behavior of Furniture Frames During Fire," NBS-GCR-86-512, April 1986, National Bureau of Standards, Gaithersburg, MD.

Tewarson, A., "Identification of Fire Properties Relevant to the Prediction of Fire Growth," *Paper RC83-TP-11*, Factory Mutual Research Corp., Norwood, presented at 7th UJNR Panel Meeting, Washington, DC, Oct. 1983.

Williams, S. S., *Flammability Regulations and Standards in the United States for Upholstered Furniture*, Technomic, Lancaster, PA, 1985.

Wooley, F. D., and Fardell, P. J., "The Prediction of Combustion Products," *Fire Research*, Vol. 1, 1977, pp. 11-21.

Yates, J. M., "Firefighters Push for Mandatory Flammability Testing," *Wood and Wood Products*, Vol. 92, No. 11, Oct. 1987, p. 38.

Yockers, J. R., and Segal, L., "Cigarette Fire Mechanisms," *NFPA Quarterly*, Vol. 49, No. 3, Jan. 1956, pp. 213-22.

Zicherman, J. B. and Allard, D. L., "Compartment Tests of Plyurethane Foam Seating Assemblies," *Fire Technology*, Vol. 24, No. 2, 1988, pp. 128-137.

DUSTS

Revised by Richard F. Schwab

Most finely divided combustible materials are hazardous. When suspended in air and ignited, they can cause severe explosions. This phenomenon has been known for over 200 years. The first recorded dust explosion occurred on Dec. 14, 1785: a flour dust explosion in a warehouse in Turin, Italy. The entire industrial spectrum, including agriculture, chemical, metallurigical, mining, plastics, and woodworking industries, continues to be plagued by this problem.[1]

Although the basic principles for controlling dust explosion hazards have been understood for many years, and knowledge is becoming increasingly sophisticated, serious incidents continue to occur.[2,3,4]

FACTORS INFLUENCING THE EXPLOSIBILITY OF DUSTS

The chance of a dust cloud igniting is governed by the size of its particles, dust concentration, impurities present, oxygen concentration, and the strength of the source of ignition.

Dust explosions usually occur as a series. Frequently, the initial deflagration is rather small in volume but intense enough to jar dust from beams, ledges, etc., or even rupture small pieces of equipment within buildings, such as dust collectors or bins. Subsequently, a much larger dust cloud develops, through which a secondary explosion can propagate. It is not unusual to have a series of explosions propagating from building to building.[4]

Hazards of Dusts

The hazard of any given dust is related to its ease of ignition and the severity of the ensuing explosion. The Bureau of Mines of the U.S. Department of the Interior has developed an arbitrary scale based on small-scale tests, which is quite useful for measuring the hazard. The ignition sensitivity (IS) is a function of the ignition temperature (of the dust cloud) and the minimum energy of ignition; the explosion severity (ES) is a function of the maximum explosion pressure and the maximum rate of pressure rise. To facilitate comparisons of explosibility data in Bureau of Mines tests, all test results[5] are related to a standard Pittsburgh coal dust taken at a concentration of 0.50 oz/cu ft (500 g/m^3), with the exception of some metal dusts.[6]

The ignition sensitivity and explosion severity of a dust are defined as:

$$\text{IS} = \frac{(T_i \times E_m \times C_m)\ \text{Pittsburgh coal dust}}{(T_i \times E_m \times C_m)\ \text{Sample dust}}$$

$$\text{ES} = \frac{(P_{max} \times R_{max})\ \text{Sample dust}}{(P_{max} \times R_{max})\ \text{Pittsburgh coal dust}}$$

where

T_i = ignition temperature of a dust cloud
E_m = minimum ignition energy of a dust cloud
C_m = minimum concentration for a combustible dust cloud
P_{max} = maximum explosion pressure
R_{max} = maximum rate of pressure rise in the test apparatus.

The explosibility index (EI) is the product of the ignition sensitivity and explosion severity. This method allows one to rate the relative hazard of the dusts, as follows:

Type of Explosion	Explosibility Index	Ignition Sensitivity	Explosion Severity
Weak	<0.1	<0.2	<0.5
Moderate	0.1 – 1.0	0.2 – 1.0	0.5 – 1.0
Strong	1.0 – 10	1.0 – 5.0	1.0 – 2.0
Severe	>10	>5.0	>2.0

Table 3-12A gives the explosibility index, ignition sensitivity, explosion severity, maximum explosion pressure, maximum rate of pressure rise [not necessarily at the concentration of 0.50 oz/cu ft (500 g/m^3)], ignition temperature of both the dust cloud and a layer, the minimum ignition energy of the dust cloud, minimum explosion concentration, and the limiting oxygen concentration in a spark-ignition chamber.

Richard F. Schwab, P.E., S.F.P.E., AIChE, is manager of process safety and loss prevention, Allied-Signal, Inc., Morristown, NJ.

TABLE 3-12A. *Explosion Characteristics of Various Dusts*

(Compiled from the following reports of the U.S. Department of Interior, Bureau of Mines: RI 5753, The Explosibility of Agricultural Dusts; RI 6516, Explosibility of Metal Powders; RI 5971, Explosibility of Dusts Used in the Plastics Industry; RI 6597, Explosibility of Carbonaceous Dusts; RI 7132, Dust Explosibility of Chemicals, Drugs, Dyes and Pesticides; and RI 7208, Explosibility of Miscellaneous Dusts.)

Type of Dust	Explosibility Index	Ignition Sensitivity	Explosion Severity	Maximum Explosion Pressure psig*	Max Rate of Pressure Rise psi/sec*	Ignition Temperature† Cloud °C	Ignition Temperature† Layer °C	Min Cloud Ignition Energy joules	Min Explosion Conc oz/cu ft‡	Limiting Oxygen Percentage§ (Spark Ignition)
Agricultural Dusts										
Cellulose, alpha	>10	2.7	4.0	117	8,000	410	300	0.040	0.045	—
Cornstarch commercial product	9.5	2.8	3.4	106	7,500	400	—	0.04	0.045	—
Lycopodium	16.4	4.2	3.9	75	3,100	480	310	0.04	0.025	C13
Wheat starch, edible	17.7	5.2	3.4	100	6,500	430	—	0.025	0.045	C12
Wood flour, white pine	9.9	3.1	3.2	113	5,500	470	260	0.040	0.035	—
Carbonaceous Dusts										
Charcoal, hardwood mixture	1.3	1.4	0.9	83	1,300	530	180	0.020	0.140	—
Coal, Pennsylvania, Pittsburg (Experimental Mine Coal)	1.0	1.0	1.0	90	2,300	610	170	0.060	0.055	—
Chemicals										
Adipic acid	1.9	1.7	1.1	84	2,700	550	—	0.060	0.035	—
Bis-phenol A	>10	11.8	2.8	89	8,500	570	—	0.015	0.020	C12
Phthalic anhydride	6.9	11.9	1.4	72	4,200	650	—	0.015	0.015	C14
Stearic acid, aluminum salt (aluminum tristearate)	>10	21.3	1.9	87	6,300	420	440	0.015	0.015	—
Sulfur	>10	20.4	1.2	78	4,700	190	220	0.015	0.035	C12
Drugs										
Aspirin (acetylsalicylic acid) o-$CH_3COOC_6H_4COOH$	>10	2.4	4.3	88	>10,000	660	Melts	0.025	0.050	—
Vitamin C, ascorbic acid, $C_6H_8O_6$	2.2	1.0	2.2	88	4,800	460	280	0.060	0.070	C15, N12
Metals										
Aluminum flake, A 422 extra fine lining, polished	>10	7.3	10.2	127	20,000+	610	326	0.010	0.045	—
Magnesium, milled, Grade B	>10	3.0	7.4	116	15,000	560	430	0.040	0.030	—
Alloys and Compounds										
Aluminum-cobalt alloy (60–40)	0.4	0.1	3.5	92	11,000	950	570	0.100	0.180	—
Thermoplastic Resins and Molding Compounds										
Acrylamide polymer	2.5	4.1	0.6	85	2,500	410	240	0.030	0.040	—
Methyl methacrylate polymer	6.3	7.0	0.9	84	2,000	480	—	0.020	0.030	C11
Cellulose acetate	>10	8.0	1.6	85	3,600	420	—	0.015	0.040	C14
Polycarbonate	8.6	4.5	1.9	96	4,700	710	—	0.025	0.025	C15
Phenol formaldehyde molding compound, wood flour filler	>10	8.9	4.7	94	9,500	500	—	0.015	0.030	C14

* 1 psi = 6.894 kPa.
† °F = 9/5 (°C + 32).
‡ 0.1 oz/cu ft = 100 g/m³.
§ Numbers in this column indicate percentage while the letter prefix indicates the diluent gas. For example, the entry "C13" means dilution to an oxygen content of 13 percent with carbon dioxide as the diluent gas. The letter prefixes are: C = carbon dioxide and N = nitrogen.

Particle Size

The smaller the size of the dust particle the easier it is to ignite the dust cloud, insofar as the exposed surface area of a unit weight of material increases as the particle size decreases. It is also true that particle size has an effect on the rate of pressure rise. For a given weight concentration of dust, a coarse dust will show a lower rate of pressure rise than a fine dust. The lower explosive limit (LEL) concentration, ignition temperature, and the energy necessary for ignition will decrease as dust particle size decreases. Numerous studies by various investigators show this effect for a variety of dusts.[7]

Decrease in particle size also increases the capacitance of dust clouds, i.e., the size of electrical charges that can accumulate on particles in the cloud.[8] Because capacitance of solids is a function of surface area, the possibility of developing electrostatic discharges of sufficient intensity to ignite a dust cloud increases as average particle size decreases. However, to produce such electrostatic discharges requires, among other things, large quantities of dust in large volumes, with relatively high dielectric dust strengths and consequent long relaxation times. Because of the high ignition energies required for dust clouds to ignite in comparison with ignition energies of gases, attributing the cause of dust explosions to static electricity should be held suspect, unless definite evidence exists to show that static electricity was a likely cause.[4]

Concentration

As with flammable gases and vapors, there is a specific range of dust concentration within which a dust explosion can occur. It is customary to express the concentration figures in terms of weight per unit volume, though, without knowledge of the particle size distribution of the sample, this expression is meaningless. The results presented in Table 3-12A were developed by the U.S. Bureau of Mines and were obtained with dusts small enough to pass through a 200 mesh screen (74 microns or smaller). More recent tabular data was published in West Germany,[9] based on the data shown in Table 3-12A. The median particle size is shown for every test. These more recent tables were condensed from far more extensive tables in the original reference,[9] which also included the particle size distribution for most of the reported tests.

Variations in minimum explosive concentrations will occur with changes in particle diameter, i.e., the minimum explosive concentration is lowered as the diameter of particles decreases. Sample purity, oxygen concentration, strength of ignition source, turbulence of dust cloud, and uniformity of dispersion also effect the lower explosive limit of dust clouds.

Upper explosive limits (UEL) for dust clouds have not been determined, mainly because of experimental difficulties. There is also a question of whether a clear-cut upper limit exists at all, and, from a practical point of view, whether this information is of questionable use. Curves formed by plotting explosion pressures and rates of pressure rise against concentration show that explosion pressures and rates of pressure rise are at a minimum at the lower explosive limit, then rise to maximum value at a given optimum concentration, then slowly decrease from this point. It is to be noted that the maximum pressure and the maximum rate of pressure rise do not always occur at precisely the same concentration. The destructive effect is determined primarily by the rate of pressure rise.

It appears that the most violent explosion occurs at a concentration slightly above that required for reaction with all of the oxygen in the atmosphere. At lower dust concentrations, less heat is generated and smaller peak pressures are developed. With dust concentrations greater than those causing the most violent explosions, absorption of heat by unburned dust is apparently the reason for less-than-maximum explosive pressures.

Moisture

Moisture in dust particles raises the ignition temperature of the dust because of the heat absorbed during heating and vaporization of the moisture. The moisture in the air surrounding a dust particle has no significant effect on the course of a deflagration once ignition has occurred. There is, however, a direct relationship between moisture content and minimum energy required for ignition, minimum explosive concentration, maximum pressure, and maximum rate of pressure rise. For example, the ignition temperature of cornstarch may increase as much as 122°F (50°C), with an increase of moisture content from 1.6 percent to 12.5 percent. As a practical matter, however, moisture cannot be considered an effective explosion preventive, since most ignition sources provide more than enough heat to vaporize the moisture and to ignite the dust. In order for moisture to prevent ignition of a dust by common sources, the dust would have to be so damp that a cloud could not be formed.

Inert Material

The presence of an inert solid powder reduces the combustibility of a dust because it absorbs heat, but the amount of inert powder necessary to prevent an explosion is usually higher than concentrations that would normally be found or could be tolerated as foreign material. The addition of inert material reduces the rate of pressure rise and increases the minimal dust concentration. Rock dusting of coal mines is a practical application of the use of inert dust to prevent explosion of a combustible dust. For general rock dusting of coal mine entries, enough rock dust usually is added to provide an inert dust concentration of at least 65 percent of the total dust.[4]

Inert gas is effective in preventing dust explosions because it dilutes the oxygen to a concentration too low to support combustion. In selecting a suitable inert gas, care must be taken to choose one that is not reactive with the dust. Certain metallic dusts, for example, react with carbon dioxide or nitrogen.[6] Helium and argon are suitable diluents in such instances.

Oxygen Concentration, Turbulence, and Effect of Flammable Gas

Variations in oxygen concentrations affect the ease of ignition of dust clouds and the explosion pressures. With a decrease in the partial pressure of oxygen, the energy required for ignition increases, ignition temperature increases, and maximum explosion pressures decrease. The type of inert gas used as the diluent for reduction of the oxygen concentration also has an effect apparently related to molar heat capacity.

The combustion of dust takes place at the surfaces of the dust particles. The rate of reaction therefore depends on intimate mixing of the dust and oxygen. It is for this reason that turbulent mixing of dust and air results in more violent explosions than those obtained by ignition in relatively quiescent mixtures.[10] The data presented in Table 3-12A were gathered by igniting the dust under violently turbulent conditions; thus, they cannot be compared to explosion data for flammable gases which were gathered under comparatively quiescent conditions.

Addition of a small amount of flammable gas to a dust cloud and igniting the resultant aerosol greatly increases the violence of the explosion, particularly at lower dust concentrations. The resultant rates of pressure rise are very much higher than usually anticipated. Without the dust, the remaining fraction of the total combustible in air, represented by the flammable vapor, would be in itself below the lower flammable limit (LFL). In certain drying operations, involving the evaporation of a flammable vapor from a combustible powder with entrainment of the combustible dust along with the flammable vapor, explosions occurred that were far more violent than anticipated when only the fraction represented by the flammable vapor alone was considered.[11] Indeed, explosions occurred in such flammable vapor-combustible dust-air mixtures when the flammable vapor-air portion was below the LFL. When encountered, these situations need special safeguards, such as inert gas dilution, explosion suppression, very large explosion vents, and careful static electricity elimination designs.

DUST CLOUD IGNITION SOURCES

Dust clouds have been ignited by open flames, lights, smoking materials, electric arcs, hot filaments of light bulbs, friction sparks, high-pressure steam pipes and other hot surfaces, static sparks, spontaneous heating, welding and cutting torches and sparks from these operations, and other common sources of heat for ignition. The dust cloud ignition temperatures given in Table 3-12A for the most part fall between 572 and 1,112°F (300 and 600°C), and a large majority of the reported minimum spark ignition energies were between 10 and 40 millijoules. This can be contrasted to flammable vapor ignition energies with a range for the most part between 0.2 and 10 millijoules. As a general rule, combustible dusts require 20 to 50 times the ignition energy of flammable vapors.

Because ignition temperatures and ignition energies required for dust explosions are much lower than the temperatures and energies of most common sources of ignition, it is not surprising that dust explosions have been caused by common sources of ignition. For this reason, the elimination of all possible sources of ignition is a basic principle of dust explosion prevention. Ignition sources in dust-handling operations are identified and recommendations for their elimination are described in various NFPA standards for the prevention of dust explosions. (See bibliography.)

DEFLAGRATION CHARACTERISTICS OF SELECTED COMBUSTIBLE DUSTS

Tables 3-12B through 3-12F are based on information obtained from *Forschungsbericht Staubexplosionen: Brenn und Explosions Kenngrossen von Stauben.*[9] For each dust, the tables show the median particle size of the material tested, as well as the following test results obtained in a 1 cu m vessel: minimum explosive concentration, maximum pressure developed by the explosion (P_{max}), and the maximum rate of pressure rise $(dP/dt)_{max}$. Also shown is the K_{St} value, which is the equivalent to $(dP/dt)_{max}$ because of the size of the test vessel.

TABLE 3-12B. *Agricultural Products*

Material	Median particle size, μ	Minimum explosive concentration g/m²	P_{max}, bar ga	$(dP/dt)_{max}$, bar/sec	K_{St} bar-m sec	Dust Hazard Class
Cellulose	33	60	9.7	229	229	2
Cellulose, pulp	42	30	9.9	62	62	1
Cork	42	30	9.6	202	202	2
Corn	28	60	9.4	75	75	1
Egg white	17	125	8.3	38	38	1
Milk, powdered	83	60	5.8	28	28	1
Milk, nonfat, dry	60	–	8.8	125	125	1
Soy flour	20	200	9.2	110	110	1
Starch, corn	7	–	10.3	202	202	2
Starch, rice	18	60	9.2	101	101	1
Starch, wheat	22	30	9.9	115	115	1
Sugar	30	200	8.5	138	138	1
Sugar, milk	27	60	8.5	82	82	1
Sugar, beet	29	60	8.2	59	59	1
Tapioca	22	125	9.4	62	62	1
Whey	41	125	9.8	140	140	1
Wood flour	29	–	10.5	205	205	2

TABLE 3-12C. *Carbonaceous Dusts*

Material	Median particle size, μ	Minimum explosive concentration g/m²	P_{max}, bar ga	$(dP/dt)_{max}$, bar/sec	K_{St} bar-m sec	Dust Hazard Class
Charcoal, activated	28	60	7.7	44	44	1
Charcoal, wood	14	60	9.0	10	10	1
Coal, bituminous	24	60	9.2	129	129	1
Coke, petroleum	15	125	7.6	47	47	1
Lampblack	<10	60	8.4	121	121	1
Lignite	32	60	10.9	151	151	1
Peat, 15% H_2O		58	10.9	60	157	1
Peat, 22% H_2O		46	8.4	25	69	1
Soot, pine	<10	–	7.9	26	26	1

TABLE 3-12D. *Chemical Dusts*

Material	Median particle size, μ	Minimum explosive concentration g/m²	P_{max}, bar ga	$(dP/dt)_{max}$, bar/sec	K_{St} bar-m sec	Dust Hazard Class
Adipic Acid	<10	60	8.0	97	97	1
Anthraquinone	<10	–	10.6	364	364	3
Ascorbic Acid	39	60	9.0	111	111	1
Calcium Acetate	92	500	5.2	9	9	1
Calcium Acetate	85	250	6.5	21	21	1
Calcium Stearate	12	30	9.1	132	132	1
Carboxymethylcellulose	24	125	9.2	136	136	1
Dextrin	41	60	8.8	106	106	1
Lactose	23	60	7.7	81	81	1
Lead Stearate	12	30	9.2	152	152	1
Methylcellulose	75	60	9.5	134	134	1
Paraformaldehyde	23	60	9.9	178	1782	1
Sodium Ascorbate	23	60	8.4	119	119	1
Sodium Stearate	22	30	8.8	123	123	1
Sulfur	20	30	6.8	151	151	1

FACTORS INFLUENCING THE DESTRUCTIVENESS OF DUST EXPLOSIONS

While the destructiveness of a dust explosion depends primarily upon the rate of pressure rise, other contributing factors are the maximum pressure developed, the duration of the excess pressure, the degree of confinement of the explosion (deflagration) volume, and the oxygen concentration.

TABLE 3-12E. *Metal Dusts*

Material	Median particle size, μ	Minimum explosive concentration g/m[2]	P_{max}, bar ga	$(dP/dt)_{max}$, bar/sec	K_{St} bar-m sec	Dust Hazard Class
Aluminum	29	30	12.4	415	415	3
Bronze	18	750	4.1	31	31	1
Iron Carbonyl	<10	125	6.1	111	111	1
Magnesium	28	30	17.5	508	508	3
Zinc	10	250	6.7	125	125	1
Zinc	<10	125	7.3	176	176	1

Effect of Rate of Pressure Rise

The rate of pressure rise can be defined as the ratio of the increase in explosion pressure to the time interval of that increase. It is the most important single factor in evaluating the hazard of a dust, and principally determines the destructiveness of a deflagration.

The rate of pressure rise is also an important consideration in the design of explosion (deflagration) vents since it largely determines the size of the vent. In many cases, an extremely rapid rate of pressure rise indicates that an explosion vent design is either impractical or, at best, extremely difficult. In those cases, alternate protective schemes, such as use of inert gases, explosion suppression, or containment, should be considered. (See NFPA 69, *Explosion Prevention Systems.*)

Effect of Maximum Explosion Pressure

The maximum explosion pressures reported by recognized test procedures are for the most part in excess of 50 psig (345 kPa) and, in some cases, in excess of 100 psig (690 kPa). These figures are valid only for test conditions and are subject to changes by variation in particle size, concentration, and other variables. Considering that an ordinary brick wall 12 in. (0.3 m) thick can be destroyed by less than 1 psi (6.89 kPa) pressure, it is evident that it is not practical to construct a building strong enough to resist the maximum pressures resulting from a dust deflagration.

One reason why the degree of destruction is not greater in many dust explosions is that the dust is not uniformly dispersed throughout the explosion volume. A dust cloud is rarely ignited under optimum concentration conditions, with respect to development of maximum explosion pressures.

Effect of Duration of Excess Pressure

Closely associated with maximum pressure and rate of pressure rise as indications of the destructiveness of dust explosions is the length of time the excess pressure is exerted on the surroundings. The area under the time-pressure curve determines the total impulse exerted. It is this total impulse rather than the force exerted at any one moment that will determine the amount of destruction. The relationship between destructiveness and total impulse explains why dust explosions, which generally have slower average rates of pressure rise than gas explosions, may be more destructive than gas explosions.

Effect of Confinement

When a dust explosion occurs, gaseous products are formed and heat is released, which raises the temperature of the

TABLE 3-12F. *Plastics*

Material	Median particle size, μ	Minimum explosive concentration g/m[2]	P_{max}, bar ga	$(dP/dt)_{max}$, bar/sec	K_{St} bar-m sec	Dust Hazard Class
(poly) Acrylamide	10	250	5.9	12	12	1
(poly) Acrylonitrile	25	—	8.5	121	121	1
(poly) Ethylene (Low Pressure Process)	>10	30	8.0	156	156	1
Epoxy Resin	26	30	7.9	129	129	1
Melamine Resin	18	125	10.2	110	110	1
Melamine, molded (Wood flour and Mineral-filled Phenol-Formaldehyde	15	60	7.5	41	41	1
Melamine, molded (Phenol-Cellulose)		60	10.0	127	127	1
(poly) Methyl Acrylate	21	30	9.4	269	269	2
(poly) Methyl Acrylate, Emulsion Polymer	18	30	10.1	202	202	2
Phenolic Resin	>10	15	9.3	129	129	1
(poly) Propylene	25	30	8.4	101	101	1
Terpene-Pheonol Resin	10	15	8.7	143	143	1
Urea-Formaldehyde Cellulose, Molded	13	60	10.2	136	136	1
(poly) Vinyl Acetate/ Ethylene Copolymer	32	30	8.6	119	119	1
(poly) Vinyl Alcohol	26	60	8.9	128	128	1
(poly) Vinyl Butyral	65	30	8.9	147	147	1
(poly) Vinyl Chloride	107	200	7.6	46	46	1
(poly) Vinyl Chloride/ Vinyl Acetylene Emulsion Copolymer	35	60	8.2	95	95	1
(poly) Vinyl Chloride/ Ethylene Vinyl Acetylene Suspension Copolymer	60	60	8.3	98	98	1

air in the enclosure. Since gases expand when heated, destructive pressures will be exerted on the surrounding enclosure, unless enough vent area is provided to release the gas pressure before dangerous pressures are reached.

Bartknecht,[1,12] Nagy and Verakis,[13] Field,[14] Palmer,[4] Cross and Farrer,[15] and Hartmann *et al*[7] have examined the effect in some detail. The work of Bartknecht[1,12] and his associates is generally considered to be the most comprehensive and lead to basic design methods for deflagration vents and is the basis for the procedures shown in NFPA 68, *Explosion Venting*. Generally his procedures relate to vessels or enclosures that are capable of withstanding 1.5 psig (10.4 kPa) or more. The work of Swift and Epstein[16] is the basis of the design procedures for low-strength structures [weaker than 1.5 psig (10.4 kPa)] in NFPA 68, *Explosion Venting*.

In some instances, it may be impractical to provide sufficient vent area to reduce pressures to a safe level. In these situations, the dust-producing operation can be conducted in the open, under an inert atmosphere, or protected by an explosion suppression system. The explosion suppression system consists of a flame or pressure detector and a flame-quenching agent which is expelled rapidly during the incipient stage of a deflagration.

Effect of Inerting on Explosion Pressures and Rates of Pressure Rise

Data published by the U.S. Bureau of Mines[17] and Bartknecht[12] show that reduction in the oxygen concentration in the atmosphere, and mixture of inert powder (Fuller's earth, or rock dust) or moisture with the combustible dust, reduces the maximum explosion pressure and rates of pressure rise. These data are shown in Figures 3-12A and 3-12B for explosions of 0.50 oz. per cu ft (500 g/m^3) of cornstarch. A slight reduction in the atmospheric oxygen concentration or slight additions of inert powder or moisture have little effect on the explosion pressure. The effect of the inerting on the dust explosion becomes marked only when limiting values are approached. The maximum rate of pressure rise developed by the explosion (deflagration) appears to decrease almost linearly with use of inerting.

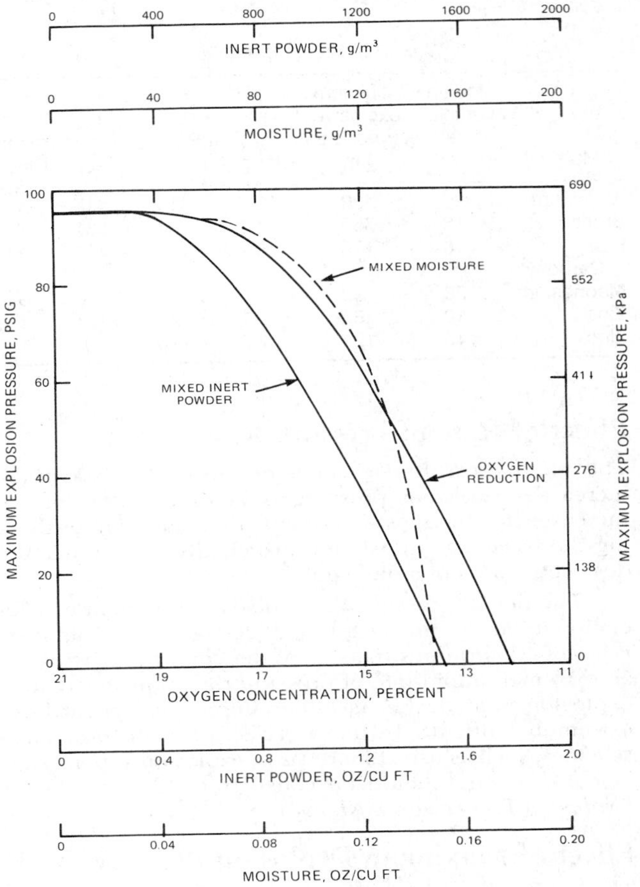

FIG. 3-12A. Effect of inerting on maximum pressure developed by explosion of 0.50 oz per cu ft (500 g/m^3) of cornstarch.

DUST EXPLOSION TEST APPARATUS AND PROCEDURES

There are a number of different types of dust explosion test chambers, and even more procedures for using them, each of which can profoundly affect the test results for any given dust sample. For example, the result of the dust explosion test in a closed chamber is affected by the geometry of the chamber, i.e., interior dimensions (cubical, spherical, cylindrical, etc.), and by the method of creating the dust cloud in the chamber (the method affects the turbulence of the cloud and uniformity of particle dispersion). This situation causes considerable difficulty in attempting to compare results obtained by various methods. In fact, unless several test results on the same dust sample are made in different chambers, and a consequent correlation is developed between the test methods, it can be said without reservation that any comparison of data obtained by different test methods is at best only qualitative. For example, attempts to correlate test results obtained in the Hartmann bomb with the 20-L spherical bomb developed by Bartknecht have been unsuccessful.

Lack of uniformity in test procedures also rules out any attempt to compare the pressures and rates of pressure rise resulting from tests on flammable vapors and dusts. By far, the largest amount of dust explosion test data has been obtained from tests conducted by the U.S. Bureau of Mines. The U.S. Bureau of Mines test equipment and procedures are described in RI 5624.[18] The test equipment used by the U.S. Bureau of Mines is a cylindrical vessel of about 75 cu in. (1.2 L), standing about 13 in. (0.33 m) high, referred to as the Hartmann apparatus. (See Figure 3-12C.) All of the data recorded in Table 3-12A has been collected in this type of test apparatus. This type of data, however, is not satisfactory for designing explosion (deflagration) relief vents.

Recent data, particularly that intended for use in obtaining test data for use in designing explosion (deflagration) vents, have been collected in spherical vessels. Bartknecht and his associates have developed a 20-L (about 5 gal) spherical bomb.[19,20] (See Figure 3-12D.) Data collected in these containers tend to give more consistent results and follow the "cubic law" (described below). Data collected in a spherical bomb, properly calibrated, have been shown to generally follow the "cubic law" over a range from 20 liters to 250 cubic meters. This is the basis for the nomographs contained in NFPA 68, *Explosion Venting*.

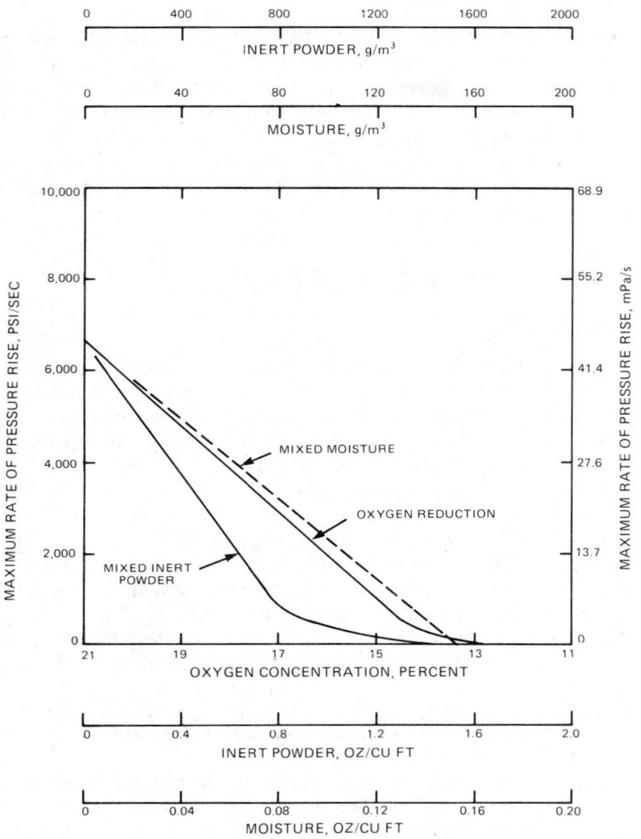

FIG. 3-12B. Effect of inerting on maximum rate of pressure rise developed by explosion of 0.50 oz per cu ft (500 g/m³) of cornstarch.

FIG. 3-12C. The Hartmann apparatus. (Source: U.S. Bureau of Mines)

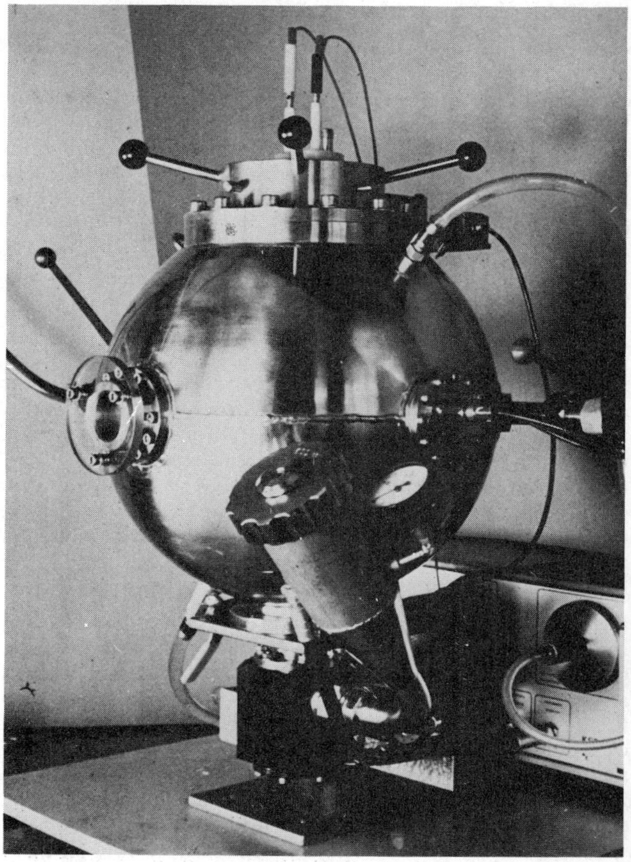

FIG. 3-12D. The Bartknecht apparatus. (Source: W. Bartknecht)

Interpretation and Application of Dust Explosion (Deflagration) Test Data

Dust explosion test data is gathered in a variety of chambers, from a highly turbulent dust cloud to a practically stagnant cloud. Most modern test data are gathered in calibrated spherical test vessels that follow the "cubic law," which is represented for dusts as follows:

$$(dP/dt)_{max} \times (V)^{1/3} = K_{st}$$

where
P = pressure (bar)
t = time (sec)
V = volume (cu m)
K_{st} = normalized index (bar m/s)

This can also be expressed by the following relationship:

$$R_1/R_s = \left(V_s/V_1\right)^{1/3} = A_1/A_s$$

where:
R_1 = rate of pressure rise in the large chamber
R_s = Rate of pressure rise in the small chamber
V_1 = volume of the large chamber
V_s = volume of the small chamber
A_1 = vent ratio of the large chamber
A_s = Vent ratio of the small chamber
(All variables must in consistent units.)

This law indicates that test data gathered in small chambers can be extrapolated to larger chambers with some degree of confidence, though care must be taken to keep the shape of small chambers and large chambers within reasonable limits. If the test is done in small spheres, the results cannot be expected to hold up in the design of explosion (deflagration) relief for a long narrow vessel.

Ignition Temperature

One piece of apparatus developed at the U.S. Bureau of Mines consists essentially of an electrically heated vertical cylindrical tube at the top of which is a small container holding a weighed amount of dust. The dust is projected down through the tube as a uniform cloud by a controlled blast of compressed air directed at the dust sample. The ignition temperature is considered to be the lowest temperature at which flame issues from the open bottom end of the tube. Differences in results are due to differences in the size and shape of test containers.[18] This test is used to determine the temperature of the dust cloud.

The furnace is also used to determine the ignition temperature of a dust layer sample, ½ in. (1.25 cm) deep, 1 in. (2.5 cm) diameter, in a container suspended in the furnace heated by a stream of hot air flowing at 30 cu in. per min (½ L/min) past the sample.[18] Other recognized testing agencies use hotplates with the dust layers ¾ in. (19 mm) deep.[9] Other researchers have reported test data using different test procedures[21] designed to investigate ignition sources encountered under industrial conditions.

Ignition in Inert Atmospheres

For the determination of the ignitibility of dust in various inert gas-air mixtures, the apparatus consists of a vertical cylindrical tube containing tungsten electrodes to produce a spark for ignition. The tube is designed so that it can be flushed with the inert gas-air mixture prior to the test. The dust sample in a container near the top of the tube is projected downward as a cloud by a controlled blast of the inert gas-air mixture. Flame issuing from the open bottom of the tube signifies ignition. Bruderer[21] has also investigated limiting oxygen concentrations for various ignition sources in his work.

Minimum Energies for Ignition

Apparatus developed at the U.S. Bureau of Mines used to determine minimum energies needed to cause ignition of dust clouds consists of a vertical cylindrical lucite tube. In this test, the dust is dispersed upward in the tube by controlled discharge of compressed air into the dust chamber at the bottom of the tube. A spark discharged by an electrical condenser is used as the ignition source, and by using condensers with different capacities, spark energy can be varied. Discharge of the condenser is synchronized with the formation of the dust cloud. Visible flame in the tube signifies ignition.

The data presented in Table 3-12A for cloud ignition energies has been gathered in this fashion. Recent work[22,23] has shown that, if the spark is generated in a different fashion with a high resistance in series with the capacitance discharge, it is possible to obtain ignition of the dust cloud considerably below that reported by the U.S. Bureau of Mines technique. Generally speaking, the data reported by the U.S. Bureau of Mines might be expected to be a factor of 3 to 5 times too high.[15]

Eckhoff[22] has managed to ignite some of the more sensitive dusts, such as aluminum (5-μm) and sulfur, at energies of 1 mJ or less. The U.S. Bureau of Mines quotes 15 mj for these materials. It is questionable whether a circuit that produces such a low-level spark of the nature required would occur naturally. Ignitability is not solely a function of spark energy but also a function of spark duration, with long-duration sparks igniting dusts more easily than short-duration sparks.[15]

Explosion Pressures

Apparatus described by the U.S. Bureau of Mines for determining maximum explosion pressures and rates of pressure rise consists of a vertical cylindrical steel bomb into which a weighed sample of dust can be dispersed upward by a jet of compressed air. Pressures are measured by a strain gage transducer mounted in the top of the bomb. A pressure-time record is obtained on an oscillograph using a light beam galvanometer system.

BIBLIOGRAPHY

References Cited

1. Bartknecht, Wolfgang, *Dust Explosions*, Springer Verlag, 1989.
2. van Laar, G.F.M., "Review of Incidents," European Information Centre for Explosion Protection, Antwerp, Belgium, 1989.
3. Best, R., "Two Grain Elevator Explosions Kill Five in Missouri," *Fire Journal*, Vol. 72, 1978, pp. 50-54.
4. Palmer, K. N., *Dust Explosions & Fires*, Chapman & Hall, London, England, 1973.
5. Jacobson, M., *et al*, "Explosibility of Agricultural Dusts," RI 5753, 1961, USDI Bureau of Mines, Pittsburgh, PA.
6. Jacobson, M., *et al*, "Explosibility of Metal Powders," RI 6516, 1964, USDI Bureau of Mines, Pittsburgh, PA.
7. Hartmann, I., *et al*, "Recent Studies on the Explosibility of Cornstarch," RI 4725, 1964, USDI Bureau of Mines, Pittsburgh, PA.
8. Kunkel, W. G., "The State of Electrification of Dust Particles on Dispersion into a Cloud," *Journal of Applied Physics*, Vol. 21, 1950, pp. 820-832.
9. *Forschungsbericht Staubexplosionen: Brenn und Explosions Kenngrossen von Stauben*, Hauptverband der gewerblichen Berufsgenossenschaften e. V., Bonn, West Germany, 1980.
10. FIA, *Dust Explosions Analysis and Control*, Factory Insurance Association (now Industrial Risk Insurers), Hartford, CT, 1966.
11. Cotton, P. E., "New Test Apparatus for Dust Explosions," *NFPA Quarterly*, Vol. 45, No. 2, 1951, pp. 157-164.
12. Bartknecht, W., *Explosions: Course, Prevention, Protection*, Springer Verlag, Berlin, Heidelberg, New York, 1981.
13. Nagy, John, and Verakis, Harry C., *Development and Control of Dust Explosions*, Marcel Dekker, Inc., New York, 1983.
14. Field, P., *Dust Explosions*, Elsevier, Amsterdam, 1982.
15. Cross, Jean, and Farrer, Donald, *Dust Explosions*, Plenum Press, New York, 1982.
16. Swift, I., and Epstein, M., "Performance of Low-Pressure Explosion Vents," *Plant/Operations Progress*, Apr. 1987, pp. 98-105.
17. Nagy, J., *et al*, "Pressure Development in Laboratory Dust Explosions," RI 6561, 1964, USDI Bureau of Mines, Pittsburgh, PA.
18. Dorsett, H. G., *et al*, "Laboratory Equipment and Test Procedures for Evaluating Explosibility of Dusts," RI 5624, 1960, USDI Bureau of Mines, Pittsburgh, PA.
19. Bartknecht, W., "Explosion Pressure Relief," AIChE Loss Prevention Symposium, Vol. 11, 1977, pp. 93-105.
20. Donat, C., "Pressure Relief as Used in Explosion Protection," AIChE Loss Prevention Symposium, Vol. 11, 1977, pp. 87-92.
21. Bruderer, R. E., "Ignition Properties of Mechanical Sparks and Hot Surfaces in Dust/Air Mixtures," *Plant/Operations Progress*, Vol. 8, No. 3, July 1989, pp. 152-164.
22. Eckhoff, R. K., "A Study of Selected Problems Related to the Assessment of Ignitability and Explosibility of Dust Clouds," *CHR*, Michelsens Institute for Vendenskapog Andsfrihet, Beretninger, XXXVIII, Bergen, Norway, 1976.
23. Mertzberg, M., *et al*, "The Flammability of Coal Dust-Air Mixtures, Lean Limits, Flame Temperatures, Ignition Energies and Particle Size Effects," RI 8360, 1979, USDI Bureau of Mines, Pittsburgh, PA.

References

ASTM E789-89, *Standard Test Method for Pressure and Rate of Pressure Rise for Dust Explosions in a 1.2-Liter Closed Cylindrical Vessel*, American Society for Testing and Materials, Philadelphia, PA.

ASTM E1226-88, *Standard Test Method for Pressure and Rate of Pressure Rise for Combustible Dusts (20-Liter Spherical Vessel)*, American Society for Testing and Materials, Philadelphia, PA.

Britton, L. G., and Kirby, D. C., "Analysis of a Dust Deflagration," *Plant/Operations Progress*, Vol. 8, No. 3, July 1989, pp. 177-180.

Bruderer, R. E., "Design Example: Explosion Selected for a Spray Drying Installation," *Plant/Operations Progress*, Vol. 8, No. 3, July 1989, pp. 141-146.

Cashdollar, K. L., and Hertzberg, Martin, "Industrial Dust Explosions," ASTM Special Publication 958, 1987, American Society for Testing and Materials, Philadelphia, PA.

Conti, R. S., Cashdollar, K. L., Hertzberg, M., Liebman, I., "Thermal and Electrical Ignitability of Dust Clouds," RI 8798, 1985, USDI Bureau of Mines, Pittsburgh, PA.

Dorsett, H. G., *et al*, "Laboratory Equipment and Test Procedures for Evaluating Explosibility of Dusts," RI 5624, 1960, USDI Bureau of Mines, Pittsburgh, PA.

Field, P., and Abrahamsen, A. R., *Dust Explosion—The Respective Roles of the Hartmann Bomb and the 20-Liter Sphere in Prescribing the Size of Explosion Relief Vents: A Preliminary Study*, Building Research Establishment, Hertfordshire, UK, June 1981.

Field, P., *Dust Explosion Protection—A Comparative Study of Methods for Sizing Explosion Relief Vents*, Building Research Establishment, Hertfordshire, UK, July 1982.

Hoenig, S. A., "Reducing the Hazard of Dust Explosions: Agglomerate the Fines, Cool Off the Hot Spots, Collect the Fines at the Point of Origin, Neutralize Local Electrostatic Charges," *Plant/Operations Progress*, Vol. 8. No. 3, July 1989, pp. 119-128.

Lathrop, J. K., "54 Killed in Two Grain Elevator Explosions," *Fire Journal*, Vol. 72, No. 1, 1978, pp. 29-35.

Lunn, G. A., *Venting Gas and Dust Explosions—A Review*, Institution of Chemical Engineers, Rugby, UK, 1984.

Lunn, G. A., *Guide to Dust Explosion Prevention and Protection*, Part 3-Venting of Weak Explosions and the Effect of Vent Ducts, Institution of Chemical Engineers, Rugby, UK, 1988.

Randant, S., "Dust Explosion Venting of Vessels and Silos," European Information Centre for Explosion Protection, Antwerp, Belgium, 1989.

Schofield, C., *Guide to Dust Explosion Prevention and Protection*, Part 1-Venting, Institution of Chemical Engineers, Rugby, UK, 1984.

Schofield, C., and Abbott, J. A., *Guide to Dust Explosion Prevention and Protection*, Part 2-Ignition Prevention, Containment, Inerting, Suppression, and Isolation, Institution of Chemical Engineers, Rugby, UK, 1988.

Senecal, J. A., "Deflagration Suppression of High K_{St} Dusts," *Plant/Operations Progress*, Vol. 8, No. 3, July 1989, pp. 147-151.

Siwek, Richard, "Dust Explosion Venting for Dusts Pneumatically Conveyed into Vessels," *Plant/Operations Progress*, Vol. 8, No. 3, July 1989, pp. 129-140.

Siwek, Richard, "New Knowledge about Rotary Air Locks in Preventing Dust Ignition Breakthrough," *Plant/Operations Progress*, Vol. 8, No. 3, July 1989, pp. 165-176.

Swift, I., "Designing Explosion Vents Easily and Accurately," *Chemical Engineering*, Apr. 1988, pp. 65-68.

Swift, I., "NFPA 68, *Explosion Venting*: What's New and How It Affects You," *Journal of Loss Prevention in Process Industries*, Vol. 2, Jan. 1989, pp. 5-15.

Tonkin, P. S., and Berlement, C. F. J., "Dust Explosions in a Large-Scale Cyclone Plant," Fire Research Note 942, July 1972, Dept. of the Environment and Fire Offices' Committee, Joint Fire Research Organization, London, UK.

NFPA Codes, Standards, and Recommended Practices

Reference to the following NFPA codes, standards, and recommended practices will provide further information on dusts discussed in this chapter. (See the latest *NFPA Catalog* for availability of current editions of the following documents.)

NFPA 49, *Hazardous Chemicals Data.*

NFPA 61A, *Prevention of Fire and Dust Explosions in Facilities Manufacturing and Handling Starch.*

NFPA 61B, *Prevention of Fires and Explosions in Grain Elevators and Facilities Handling Bulk Raw Agricultural Commodities.*

NFPA 61C, *Prevention of Fire and Dust Explosion in Feed Mills.*

NFPA 65, *Processing and Finishing of Aluminum.*

NFPA 68, *Explosion Venting.*

NFPA 69, *Explosion Prevention Systems.*

NFPA 480, *Storage, Handling, and Processing of Magnesium.*

NFPA 481, *Production, Processing, Handling, and Storage of Titanium.*

NFPA 482, *Production, Processing, Handling, and Storage of Zirconium.*

NFPA 651, *Manufacture of Aluminum and Magnesium Powder.*

NFPA 654, *Prevention of Fire and Dust Explosions in the Chemical, Dye, Pharmaceutical, and Plastics Industries.*

NFPA 655, *Prevention of Sulfur Fires and Explosions.*

NFPA 664, *Prevention of Fires and Explosions in Wood Processing and Woodworking Facilities.*

Additional Reading

Atallah, S., "Fumigants and Grain Dust Explosions," *Fire Technology*, Vol. 15, No. 1, Feb. 1979, p. 5.

Britain's Plastic Industry, Jordon and Sons, London, 1987.

Britton, L. G., and Kuby, D. C., "Analysis of a Dust Deflagation," *Plant/Operations Progress*, Vol. 8, No. 3, July 1989, pp. 177-180.

Bull, B., "Grain Elevator Explosions," *Firehouse*, Apr. 1978, pp. 40-41.

Cartwright, P., "Combating the Problem of Dust Explosions," *Process Engineering*, Vol. 70, No. 2, 1989, pp. 49-52.

Cassel, H. M., "Some Fundamental Aspects of Dust Flames," RI 6551, 1964, USDI Bureau of Mines, Pittsburgh, PA.

Cocks, R. E., "Dust Explosions: Prevention and Control," *Chemical Engineering*, Vol. 86, No. 24, Nov. 1979, pp. 94-101.

"Combustible Dusts," Loss Prevention Data Sheet 7-76, Factory Mutual Research Corp., Norwood, MA.

Conti, Ronald S., *et al*, *Thermal and Electrical Ignitability of Dust Clouds*, U.S. Bureau of Mines, Pittsburgh, PA, 1983.

Corbett, G. P., "Dust Explosions Destroy New Jersey Flour Mill," *Fire Engineering Journal*, Vol. 45, No. 138, 1985, pp. 22-24.

Dahm, C. J., Ashum, M., and Williams, K., "Contribution of Low-Level Flammable Vapor Concentration to Dust Explosion Output," *Plant/Operations Progress*, Vol. 5, No. 1, Jan. 1986, pp. 57-64.

Donat, C., "Selection and Dimensioning of Pressure Relief Devices for Dust Explosions," Staub-Reinhaltung der Luft (English transl.), Vol. 31, No. 4, Apr. 1971, pp. 17-29.

"Dust Explosions: An Often Unsuspected Potential for Disaster," *CUA Inspector*, Vol. 10, No. 3, 1973, pp. 1-3.

"Dust Explosion and Fires: A Manual," National Particle Board Association, Silver Spring, MD, 1977.

Eggleston, L. A., and Pryor, A. J., "The Limits of Dust Explosibility," *Fire Technology*, Vol. 3, No. 2, May 1967, pp. 77-89.

Essenhigh, R. H., Froberg, R., and Howard, J. B., "Combustion Behavior of Small Particles," *Industrial & Engineering Chemistry*, Vol. 57, No. 9, Sept. 1965, pp. 33-43.

Essenhigh, R. H., Goldberg, P. M., and Shull, H. E., "Suppression of Dust Explosions in Coal Mines: Use of a Stirred Reac tor to Test Mechanisms of Reaction of Coal Dust Flames," U.S. Bureau of Mines OFR-104-78, Combustion Laboratory, Pennsylvania State University, 1978.

Factory Mutual Engineering Division, "Dust Explosions," *Handbook of Industrial Loss Prevention*, 2nd ed., McGraw-Hill, New York, 1967, pp. 66-1-66-16.

Field, P., *Explosibility Assessment of Industrial Powders and Dusts*, Building Research Establishment, Her Majesty's Stationery Office, London, 1983.

Gubin, E. I., and Dik, I. G., "Flame Propagation in a Dusty Gas," *Combustion, Explosion and Shock Waves*, (English translation), Vol. 23, No. 6, May 1988, pp. 685-690.

Hertzberg, M., *A Critique of the Dust Explosibility Index*, USDI Bureau of Mines, Pittsburgh, PA, 1987.

Hertzberg, M., Cashdollar, K. L., and Opferman, J. J., *The Flammability of Coal Dust Air Mixtures: Lean Limits, Flame Temperatures, Ignition Energies and Particle Size Effects*, USDI Bureau of Mines, Pittsburgh, PA, 1979.

Hoenig, S. A., "Reducing the Hazard of Dust Explosions," *Plant/Operations Progress*, Vol.8, No. 3, July 1989, pp. 119-128.

Lunn, G. A., "Note on the Lower Explosibility Limit of Organic Dusts," *Journal of Hazardous Materials*, Vol. 17, No. 2, Feb. 1988, pp. 207-213.

"Metal Dust Ignites," *Fire Journal*, Vol. 90, No. 5, Sept. 1976, p. 47.

Nagy, J., Dorsett, H. G., and Cooper, A. R., "Explosibility of Carbonaceous Dusts," Rl 6597, 1965, USDI Bureau of Mines, Pittsburgh, PA.

Nagy, J., and Mitchell, D. W., "Experimental Coal-Dust and Gas Explosions," Rl 6344, 1963, USDI Bureau of Mines, Pittsburgh, PA.

Nagy, J., and Surincik, D. J., "Thermal Phenomena During Ignition of a Heated Dust Dispersion," RI 6811, 1966, USDI Bureau of Mines, Pittsburgh, PA.

Palmer, K. N., "Dust Explosion Hazards in the Bulk Handling of Polymers," *Symposium Series No. 73*, Institute of Chemical Engineers, 1982, pp. c39-c57.

Palmer, K. N., "Dust Explosions: Initiation, Characteristics, and Protection," *Chemical Engineering Progress*, Vol. 86, No. 3, March 1990, pp. 33-36.

Raftery, M. M., "Explosibility Tests for Industrial Dusts," Fire Research Technical Paper No. 21, 1968, Ministry of Technology and Fire Offices' Committee, Boreham Wood, Herts, Great Britain. (See also Raftery, M. M., Staub-Reinhaltung der Luft (English transl.), Vol. 31, No. 4, Apr. 1971, pp. 1-10.)

"Risks in Handling Combustibile Dusts," *Fire Prevention*, No. 213, Oct. 1988, pp. 32-33.

Rosenhan, A. K., "How Dust Causes Grain Elevator Explosions," *Firehouse*, Apr. 1978.

Skinner, S. J., "Case Histories of Dust Explosions," *Plant/Operations Progress*, Vol. 8, No. 4, 1989, pp. 211-217.

Verkade, M., and Bluhm, D., "Supplement and Index to Grain-Dust Fire and Explosion Bibliography, November 1976—May 1978," DHEW, NIOSH Publication No. 78-183, 1978, U.S. Department of Health, Education and Welfare, Robert A. Taft Laboratories, Cincinnati, OH.

Verkade, M., and Chiotti, P., *A Bibliography of Topics Related to the Study of Grain-Dust Fire and Explosion*, Iowa State University Energy and Mineral Resources Research Institute, Ames, IA, May 1978.

Verkade, M., and Chiotti, P., "Literature Survey of Dust Explosions in Grain Handling Facilities: Cause and Prevention," IS-EMRRI-2, 1976, Energy and Mineral Resources Research Institute, Iowa State University, Ames, IA.

V.D.I., Guideline 2263, "Dust Fires and Dust Explosions Hazards—Assessment-Protective Measures," Beuth Verlog Gmb., Berlin, 1986.

Zeeurven, J. P., "Dust Explosions—How to Assess the Risk," *Fire Prevention*, No. 228, Apr. 1990, pp. 26-28.

METALS

Revised by Robert O'Laughlin

This chapter covers the fire hazard properties of combustible metals and storage, handling, and transportation methods to prevent their ignition and to protect against other hazardous properties. Also discussed are the major fire problems that arise while combustible metals are processed in machine shops and foundries.

Nearly all metals will burn in air under certain conditions. Some oxidize rapidly in the presence of air or moisture, generating sufficient heat to reach their ignition temperatures. Others oxidize so slowly that heat generated during oxidation is dissipated before the metals become hot enough to ignite. Certain metals, notably calcium, hafnium, lithium, magnesium, plutonium, potassium, sodium, thorium, titanium, uranium, zinc, and zirconium, are referred to as combustible metals because of the ease of ignition of thin sections, fine particles, or molten metal. However, the same metals in massive solid form are comparatively difficult to ignite.

More information on the hazards of metal dusts is contained in Section 3, Chapter 12, "Dusts." Extinguishing agents suitable for use on combustible metal fires are discussed in Section 5, Chapter 21, "Combustible Metal Agents and Application Techniques."

Some metals, such as aluminum, iron, and steel, that are not normally thought of as combustible, may ignite and burn when in finely divided form. Clean, fine steel wool, for example, can be ignited. Particle size, shape, quantity, and alloy are important factors to be considered when evaluating metal combustibility. Dust clouds of most metals in air are explosive. Alloys, consisting of different metals or metallic compounds combined in varying proportions, may differ widely in combustibility from their constituent elements. Metals tend to be most reactive when in finely divided form, and some may require shipment and storage under inert gas or liquid to reduce fire risks.

Hot or burning metals may react violently upon contact with other materials, such as any of the extinguishants used on fires involving ordinary combustibles or flammable liquids. A few metals, such as thorium, uranium, and plutonium, emit ionizing radiations (e.g., gamma, beta, and alpha particles) that can complicate fire fighting and introduce a contamination problem.

Temperatures produced by burning metals are generally much higher than temperatures generated by burning flammable liquids. Some hot metals can continue burning in carbon dioxide, nitrogen, or steam atmospheres in which ordinary combustibles or flammable liquids would be incapable of burning.

Properties of hot burning metal fires cover a wide range. Burning titanium produces little smoke, while burning lithium smoke is dense and profuse. Some water-moistened metal powders, such as zirconium, burn with near-explosive violence, while the same powder wet with oil burns quiescently. Sodium melts and flows while burning; calcium does not. Some metals, e.g., uranium, acquire an increased tendency to burn after prolonged exposure to moist air, while prolonged exposure to dry air may make it more difficult to ignite the metal.

Inasmuch as the extinguishment of fires in combustible metals involves techniques not commonly encountered in conventional fire fighting operations, it is good practice for those responsible for controlling combustible metal fires to gain experience in this area prior to the actual fire emergency. Fire fighters should practice extinguishing fires in those metals in an isolated outdoor location.

Where metals other than those described in this chapter are in use, it is most important that fire fighters gain some experience in extinguishing test fires involving the specific combustible metals.

MAGNESIUM

Properties

The ignition temperature of massive magnesium is very close to its melting point of 1,202°F (650°C). (See Table 3-13A.) However, ignition of magnesium in certain forms may occur at temperatures well below 1,200°F (650°C); magnesium ribbons and shavings can be ignited under certain conditions at about 950°F (510°C), and finely divided magnesium powder can ignite below 900°F (482°C).

Robert O'Laughlin, P.E., C.S.P., is a fire protection consulting engineer in Knoxville, TN.

TABLE 3-13A. *Melting, Boiling, and Ignition Temperatures of Pure Metals in Solid Form*

	Temperature					
	Melting Point		Boiling Point		Solid Metal Ignition	
Pure Metal	°F	°C	°F	°C	°F	°C
Aluminum	1,220	660	4,445	2452	1832*‡	1000‡
Barium	1,337	725	2,084	1140	347*	175*
Calcium	1,548	842	2,625	1441	1,300	704
Hafnium	4,032	2222	9,750	5399	—	—
Iron	2,795	1535	5,432	3000	1,706*	930*
Lithium	367	186	2,437	1336	356	180
Magnesium	1,202	650	2,030	1110	1,153	623
Plutonium	1,184	640	6,000	3316	1,112	600
Potassium	144	62	1,400	760	156*†	69†*
Sodium	208	98	1,616	880	239‡	115‡
Strontium	1,425	774	2,102	1150	1,328*	720*
Thorium	3,353	1845	8,132	4500	932*	500*
Titanium	3,140	1727	5,900	3260	2,900	1593
Uranium	2,070	1132	6,900	3816	6900*§	3816*§
Zinc	786	419	1,665	907	1,652*	900*
Zirconium	3,326	1830	6,470	3577	2,552*	1400*

* Ignition in oxygen
† Spontaneous ignition in moist air
‡ Above indicated temperature
§ Below indicated temperature

Metal marketed under different trade names and commonly referred to as magnesium may be one of a large number of different alloys containing principally magnesium, but also significant percentages of aluminum, manganese, and zinc. Some of these alloys have ignition temperatures considerably lower than pure magnesium, and certain magnesium alloys will ignite at temperatures as low as 800°F (427°C). Flame temperatures can reach 2,500°F (1371°C), although flame height above burning metal is usually less than 12 in. (305 mm).

Thin, small pieces of magnesium, such as ribbons, chips, and shavings, may be ignited by a match flame, whereas castings and other large pieces are difficult to ignite even with a torch because of the high thermal conductivity of the metal. In order to ignite a large piece of magnesium, it is usually necessary to raise the entire piece to the ignition temperature. Magnesium melts as it burns and may form puddles of molten magnesium, which may present explosion hazards in the presence of sufficient water.

Scrap magnesium chips or other fines may burn as the result of ignition of waste rags or other contaminants. Chips wet with water, water-soluble oils, and oils containing more than 0.2 percent fatty acid may generate hydrogen gas. Chips wet with animal or vegetable oils may burn if the oils ignite spontaneously. Fines from grinding operations generate hydrogen when submerged in water, but they cannot be ignited in this condition. Grinding fines that are slightly wetted with water may generate sufficient heat to ignite spontaneously in air, burning violently as oxygen is extracted from the water with the release of hydrogen.

Storage and Handling (Including Transportation)

The more massive a piece of magnesium, the more difficult it is to ignite, but once ignited, magnesium burns intensely and is difficult to extinguish. The storage recommendations in NFPA 480, *Storage, Handling, and Processing of Magnesium*, take these properties into consideration. Recommended maximum quantities of various sizes and forms to be stored in specific locations are covered in this standard. The storage building preferably should be noncombustible, and the magnesium should be segregated from combustible material as a fire prevention measure.

With easily ignited lightweight castings, segregation from combustible materials is especially important. In the case of dry fines (fine magnesium scrap), storage in noncombustible covered containers in separate fire-resistive storage buildings or rooms with explosion venting facilities is preferable. For combustible buildings or buildings containing combustible contents, NFPA 480, *Storage, Handling, and Processing of Magnesium*, recommends automatic sprinkler protection to ensure prompt control of a fire before the magnesium becomes involved.

Because of the possibility of hydrogen generation and of spontaneous heating of fines wet with coolants (other than neutral mineral oil), it is preferable to store wet scrap fines outdoors. Covered noncombustible containers should be vented.

Magnesium in powder, pellet, or ribbon form is shipped as a flammable solid and must be appropriately labeled according to U.S. Department of Transportation (DOT) requirements. Massive pieces or castings do not require special shipping safeguards.

If dry magnesium scrap in the form of borings, shavings, and turnings is to be shipped in interstate commerce in less-than-carload lots, the shipper may use closed metal drums. In carload or truckload lots, four-ply paper bags may also be used.

Less-than-carload lots of scrap in the form of chips or sheets may be shipped in closed metal drums, wood barrels, or wood boxes. For bulk shipments, tight box cars, tightly closed steel-covered gondola cars, and closed or completely covered truck bodies may be used.

Process Hazards

In machining operations involving magnesium alloys, sufficient frictional heat to ignite the chips or shavings may be created if the tools are dull or deformed. If cutting fluids are used (machining of magnesium is normally performed dry), they should be of the mineral-oil type that has a high flash point. Water or water-oil emulsions are hazardous, since wet magnesium shavings and dust liberate hydrogen gas and burn more violently than dry material when ignited. Machines and the work area should be frequently cleaned and the waste magnesium kept in covered, clean, dry steel or other noncombustible drums which should be removed from the building at regular intervals. Magnesium dust clouds are explosive if an ignition source is present. Grinding equipment should be equipped with a water-spray-type dust precipitator. (See Figure 3-13A.) A good grinder installation is designed to operate only if the exhaust blower and water spray are functioning properly. The equipment should be restricted to magnesium processing only.

Molten magnesium in the foundry presents a serious fire problem if not properly handled. Sulfur dioxide or melting fluxes are commonly used to prevent oxidation or ignition of magnesium during foundry operations. The action of sulfur dioxide is to exclude air from the surface of the molten magnesium; it is not an extinguishing agent.

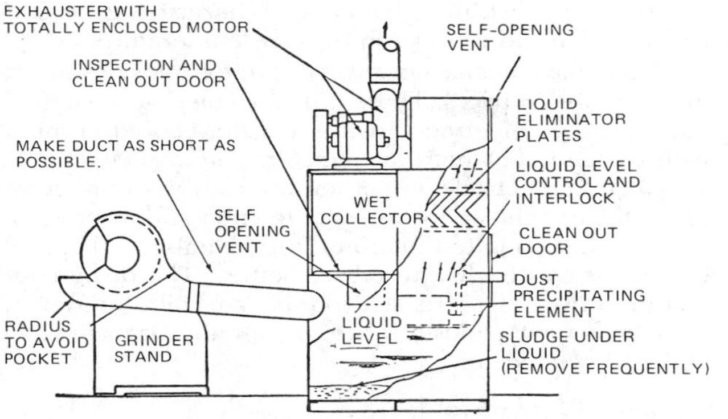

FIG. 3-13A. A schematic diagram of a water-precipitation-type collector for use in collecting dry combustible metal dust without creating explosive dust clouds or dangerous deposits in ducts or collection chambers. The diagram is intended only to show some of the features that should be incorporated in the design of a collector. It may be used for all combustible metal dusts.

Pots, crucibles, and ladles that may contact molten magnesium must be kept dry to prevent steam formation or a violent metal-water reaction. Containers should be checked regularly for any possibility of leakage or weak points. Steel-lined runoff pits or pits with tightly fitting steel pans should be provided, and the pans must be kept free of iron scale. Leaking metal contacting hot iron scale results in a violent thermite reaction. Use of stainless-steel pans or linings will eliminate this possibility.

Heat-treating ovens or furnaces, where magnesium alloy parts are subjected to high temperatures to modify their properties, present another special problem. Temperatures for heat treating needed to secure the desired physical properties are often close to the ignition temperatures of the alloys themselves, and careful control of temperatures in all parts of the oven is essential. Hot spots leading to local overheating are a common cause of these fires. Large castings do not ignite readily, but fine fins or projections on the castings, as well as chips or dust, are more readily subject to ignition. For this reason, castings should be thoroughly cleaned before heat-treating. Magnesium castings in contact with aluminum in a heat-treating oven will ignite at a lower temperature than when they are placed on a steel car or tray.

Magnesium should not be heat treated in nitrate salt baths. Certain commonly used molten mixtures of nitrates and nitrites can react explosively with magnesium alloys, particularly at temperatures over 1,000°F (538°C).

Fighting Magnesium Fires

Magnesium and its alloys present special problems in fire protection. Magnesium combines so readily with oxygen that under some conditions, water applied to extinguish magnesium fires may be decomposed into its constituent elements, i.e., oxygen and hydrogen. The oxygen combines with the magnesium, and the released hydrogen adds to the intensity of the fire. None of the commonly available inert gases are suitable for extinguishing magnesium fires. The affinity of magnesium for oxygen is so great that it will burn in an atmosphere of carbon dioxide. Magnesium may also burn in an atmosphere of nitrogen to form magnesium nitride. For these reasons, any of the common extinguishing methods that depend on water, water solutions, or inert gas are not effective on magnesium chip fires. Halogen-containing extinguishing agents (the halons) react violently with burning magnesium, the chlorine or other halogen combining with the magnesium. However, inerting with noble gases, e.g., helium or argon, will extinguish burning metal.

The method of extinguishing magnesium fires depends largely upon the form of the material. Burning chips, shavings, and small parts must be smothered and cooled with a suitable dry extinguishing agent, e.g., graphite and dry sodium chloride. Where magnesium dust is present, care must be taken to prevent a dust cloud from forming in the air during application of the agent because this may result in a dust explosion.

Fires in solid magnesium can be fought without difficulty if attacked in their early stages. Often, it may be possible to remove surrounding material, leaving the small quantity of magnesium to burn itself out harmlessly. Considering the importance of prompt attack on magnesium fires, automatic sprinklers are desirable because they provide automatic notification and control of fire. While the water from the sprinklers may have the immediate effect of intensifying magnesium combustion, it will serve to protect the structure and prevent ignition of surrounding combustible material. An excess of water applied to fires in solid magnesium (avoiding puddles of molten metal) cools the metal below the ignition temperature after some initial intensification, and the fire goes out rapidly.

Magnesium fires in heat-treating ovens can best be controlled with powders and gases developed for use on such fires. By using melting fluxes to exclude air from the burning metal, fires in heat-treating furnaces have been successfully extinguished. Boron trifluoride gas is an effective extinguishing agent for small fires in heat-treating furnaces. Cylinders of boron trifluoride can be permanently connected to the oven or mounted on a suitable cart for use as portable equipment. Boron trifluoride is allowed to flow into the oven until the fire is extinguished, or, where large quantities of magnesium are well involved before discovery or where the furnace is not tight, the boron trifluoride will control the fire until extinguishment can be completed by the application of flux.

TITANIUM

Properties

Titanium, like magnesium, is classified as a combustible metal, but here again the size and shape of the metal determine to a great extent the ease of ignition. Castings and other massive pieces of titanium are not combustible under ordinary conditions. Small chips, fine turnings, and dust ignite readily, and, once ignited, burn with the release of large quantities of heat. Tests have shown that very thin chips and fine turnings could be ignited by a match, and heavier chips and turnings by a Bunsen burner. Coarse chips and turnings $\frac{1}{32}$ by $\frac{3}{28}$ in. (0.79 by 2.7 mm) or larger may be considered as difficult to ignite, but, unless it is known that smaller particles are not mixed with the coarser material in significant amounts, it is wise to assume easy ignition is possible.

Dry titanium fines collected in cyclone separators have ignited spontaneously when allowed to drop freely through the air. Ignition temperatures of titanium dust clouds in air range from 630 to 1,090°F (332 to 588°C) and of titanium dust layers from 720 to 950°F (382 to 510°C). Titanium dust can be ignited in atmospheres of carbon dioxide or nitrogen. Titanium surfaces that have been treated with nitric acid, particularly with red fuming nitric acid containing 10 to 20 percent nitrogen tetroxide, become pyrophoric and may be explosive.

Fine titanium chips coated with water-soluble oil have spontaneously ignited. The unusual conditions under which massive titanium shapes will ignite spontaneously include contact with liquid oxygen, in which case it will detonate on impact. It has been found that under static conditions, spontaneous ignition will take place in pure oxygen at pressures of at least 350 psi (2413 kPa). If the oxygen was diluted, the required pressure increased, but in no instance did spontaneous heating occur in oxygen concentrations less than 35 percent. Another requirement for spontaneous heating was a fresh surface which oxidizes rapidly and exothermically in an oxygen atmosphere.[1]

Storage and Handling (Includes Transportation)

Titanium castings and ingots are so difficult to ignite and burn that special storage recommendations for large pieces are not included in NFPA 481, *Production, Processing, Handling, and Storage of Titanium*. Titanium sponge and scrap fines, on the other hand, do require special precautions, such as storage in covered metal containers and segregation of the containers from combustible materials. Because of the possibility of hydrogen generation in moist scrap and spontaneous heating of scrap wet with animal or vegetable oils, a yard storage area remote from buildings is recommended for scrap that is to be salvaged. Alternate recommended storage locations are detached scrap storage buildings and fire-resistive storage rooms. Buildings and rooms for storage of scrap fines should have explosion vents.

There are no special shipping requirements for titanium except when in powder form. When possible, titanium powder is shipped wet (not less than 20 percent water) in tightly closed metal shipping containers, which can be packed in outside wood boxes. The inside containers are limited to 10 lb (4.54 kg) net weight each, and the gross weight of the outside container cannot exceed 75 lb (34 kg). Cushioning of inside containers by noncombustible material, such as rock wool, is required. Single-trip metal barrels or drums with cushioned-inside metal drums are permitted by the DOT. Inside containers are flushed with inert gas before filling.

Process Hazards

Contact of molten metal with water is the principal hazard during titanium casting. To minimize this hazard, molds are usually thoroughly predried and vacuum or inert gas protection is provided to retain accidental spills.

The heat generated during machining, grinding, sawing, and drilling of titanium may be sufficient to ignite the small pieces formed by these operations or to ignite mineral-oil-based cutting lubricants. Consequently, water-based coolants should be used in ample quantity to remove heat, and cutting tools should be kept sharp. Fines should be removed regularly from work areas and stored in covered metal containers. To prevent titanium dust explosions, any operation that produces dust should be equipped with a dust collecting system discharging into a water-type dust collector. (See Figure 3-13A.)

Descaling baths of mineral acids and molten alkali salts may cause violent reactions with titanium at abnormally high temperatures. Titanium sheets have ignited upon removal from descaling baths. This hazard can be controlled by careful regulation of bath temperatures.

There have been several very severe explosions in titanium melting furnaces. These utilize an electric arc to melt a consumable electrode inside a water-cooled crucible maintained under a high vacuum. Stray arcing between the consumable electrode and crucible, resulting in penetration of the crucible, permits water to enter and react explosively with the molten titanium. Indications are that such explosions approach extreme velocities. The design and operation of these furnaces require special attention in order to prevent explosions and to minimize damage when explosions do occur.

Fighting Titanium Fires

Tests conducted by Industrial Risk Insurers (IRI) on titanium machinings in piles and in open drums showed that water in coarse spray was a safe and effective means of extinguishing fires in relatively small quantities of chips.

Carbon dioxide, foam, and dry chemical extinguishers are not effective on titanium fires, but good results have been obtained with extinguishing agents developed for use on magnesium fires.

The safest procedure to follow with a fire involving small quantities of titanium powder is to ring the fire with a special powder suitable for metal fires and to allow the fire to burn itself out. Care should be taken to prevent formation of a titanium dust cloud.

ALKALI METALS: SODIUM, POTASSIUM, NaK, AND LITHIUM

Properties

Sodium: At room temperature sodium oxidizes rapidly in moist air, but spontaneous ignitions have not been reported except when the sodium is in a finely divided form. When heated in dry air, sodium ignites in the vicinity of its boiling point [1,616°F (880°C)]. Sodium in normal room air and at a temperature only slightly above its melting point [208°F (98°C)] has been ignited by placing sodium oxide particles on its surface. This indicates the possibility of ignition at temperatures below the boiling point. Once ignited, hot sodium burns vigorously and forms dense white clouds of caustic sodium oxide fumes. During combustion, sodium generates about the same amount of heat as an equivalent weight of wood.

The principal fire hazard associated with sodium is its rapid reaction with water. It floats on water (density 0.97), reacting vigorously and melting. The hydrogen liberated by this reaction may be ignited by the heat of the reaction. Sodium (like other burning, reactive metals) reacts violently with halogenated hydrocarbons, with halogens, e.g., iodine, and with sulfuric acid.

Potassium: The fire hazard properties of potassium are very similar to those of sodium, with the difference being that potassium is usually more reactive. For example, the reaction between potassium and the halogens is more violent, and, in the case of bromine, a detonation can occur. There is an explosive reaction with sulfuric acid. Unlike sodium, potassium forms some peroxides during combustion. These peroxides may react violently with organic contaminants.

NaK (sodium-potassium alloys): NaK is the term used when referring to any of several sodium-potassium alloys. The various NaK alloys differ from each other in melting point, but all are liquids or melt near room temperature. NaK alloys possess the same fire hazard properties as those of the component metals, except that the reactions are more vigorous. Under pressure, NaK leaks have ignited spontaneously.

Lithium: Lithium, like sodium and potassium, is one of the so-called alkali metals. Lithium undergoes many of the same reactions as sodium. For example, both sodium and lithium react with water to form hydrogen, but whereas the sodium-water reaction can generate sufficient heat to ignite the hydrogen, the far-less violent lithium-water reaction does not. Lithium ignites and burns vigorously at a temperature of 356°F (180°C), which is near its melting point. Unlike sodium and potassium, it will burn in nitrogen. Noble gases, such as helium and argon, are used for inerting purposes in equipment and storage containers involving lithium. The caustic (oxide and nitride) fumes accompanying lithium combustion are more profuse and dense than those of other alkali metals burning under similar conditions. Lithium is the lightest of all metals. During combustion, it tends to melt and flow.

Storage and Handling (Includes Transportation)

Because of their reactivity with water, alkali metals require special precautions to prevent contact with moisture. Drums and cases preferably are stored in a dry, fire-resistive room or building used exclusively for alkali metal storage. Since sprinkler protection would be undesirable, no combustible materials should be stored in the same area. However, if exposure fires could jeopardize equipment containing alkali metals, sprinkler protection should be considered. It is good practice to store empty as well as filled alkali metal containers in the same area, and all containers should be on skids. There should be no water or steam pipes, but sufficient heat should be maintained to prevent moisture condensation due to atmospheric changes. Ventilation at a high spot in the room is desirable to vent any hydrogen that may be released by accidental contact of alkali metal with moisture.

Large quantities of alkali metal are often stored outdoors in aboveground tanks. In such installations weatherproof enclosures should cover tank manholes, and the free space within the tank should contain a nitrogen atmosphere. Argon or helium atmospheres should be substituted for nitrogen in the case of lithium.

Dry alkali metal is customarily shipped in watertight, steel barrels or drums. It is also shipped as a solid in tank car quantities. The DOT specifies the type of barrels, drums, and tank cars that are to be used in interstate transportation.

Transfer of an alkali metal to and from tank cars and storage tanks requires heating the metal to its melting point. This is accomplished by circulating hot oil through pipes within the tank. The alkali metal is transferred by a vacuum pump, and as the metal is removed from the tank it is replaced by nitrogen. An alkali metal-level indicator should be provided and a low-pressure warning device should be part of the nitrogen system.

An alkali metal covered with an organic solvent may be shipped in 1-qt (946 mL) metal cans, each can placed in another can and cushioned with soda ash. The cans are shipped in wood boxes of 100-lb (45.4 kg) maximum gross weight.

Liquid alkali metal alloys may be shipped in pressure-tested metal cans, cushioned with noncombustible material and packed in wood boxes. Carload and truckload lots are permitted if special steel barrels and drums are used.

For small-scale transfer of solid alkali metal from a storeroom to the use area, a metal container with a tight cover is recommended. Alkali metal should be removed from storage in as small quantities as practicable. When stored on workbenches, it should be kept under kerosene or oil in a closed container. Alkali metal, with its great affinity for moisture, may react at the time it is sealed in a container with any atmospheric moisture. Due to the possible presence of hydrogen, containers should not be opened by hammering on the lid.

Process Hazards

Liquid alkali metal is valuable as a high-temperature heat transfer medium. For example, it is used in hollow exhaust valve stems in some internal combustion engines and in the transfer of heat from one type of nuclear reactor to a steam generator. In the latter process or other large-scale use of molten alkali metal, any equipment leak may result in a fire. Where molten alkali metal is used in process equipment, steel pans are located underneath to prevent contact and violent reaction of burning sodium with concrete floors.

Processing of alkali metal is essentially remelting it to form sticks or bricks or to add as a liquid to closed transfer systems. During this handling, contact with moist air, water, halogens, halogenated hydrocarbons, and sulfuric acid must be avoided.

Fighting Fires in Sodium, Potassium, NaK, and Lithium

The common extinguishing agents, such as water, foam, and vaporizing liquids, should never be used because of the violent reactions of alkali metals with them. Special dry powders (essentially graphite) developed for metal fires, dry sand, dry sodium chloride, and dry soda ash are effective. These finely divided materials blanket the fire while the metal cools to below its ignition temperature. Alkali metal burning in an apparatus can usually be extinguished by closing all openings. Blanketing with nitrogen is also effective. In the case of lithium, argon or helium atmospheres should be used.

ZIRCONIUM AND HAFNIUM

Properties

Zirconium: The combustibility of zirconium appears to increase as the average particle size decreases, but other variables, such as moisture content, also affect its ease of ignition. In massive form, zirconium can withstand extremely high temperatures without igniting, whereas clouds of dust in which the average particle size is 3 microns have spontaneously ignited at room temperature. Dust clouds of larger particle size can be readily ignited if an ignition source is present, and such explosions can occur in atmospheres of carbon dioxide or nitrogen, as well as in air. Zirconium dust will ignite in carbon dioxide at approximately 1,150°F (621°C) and in nitrogen at approximately 1,450°F (788°C). Tests have also indicated that layers of 3-micron-diameter dust are susceptible to spontaneous ignition. The depth of the layer and its moisture content are important variables for ignition. A cloud of zirconium dust in air presents a serious flash-fire hazard, in addition to a potential explosion hazard. Spontaneous heating and ignition are also possibilities with scrap chips, borings, and turnings if fine dust is present. Layers of 6-micron-diameter dust have ignited when heated to 374°F (190°C). Combustion of zirconium dust in air is stimulated by the presence of limited amounts (5 to 10 percent) of water. When very finely divided zirconium powder is completely immersed in water, it is difficult to ignite, but once ignited it burns more violently than in air.

Massive pieces of zirconium do not ignite spontaneously under ordinary conditions, but ignition will occur when an oxide-free surface is exposed to sufficiently high oxygen concentrations and pressure. The explanation for this reaction is the same as that cited for a similar titanium reaction. Zirconium fires (like fires involving titanium and hafnium) attain very high temperatures, but generate very little smoke.

Explosions have occurred while zirconium was being dissolved in a mixture of sulfuric acid and potassium acid sulfate. Zirconium has exploded during and following pickling in nitric acid, and also during treatment with carbon tetrachloride or other halogen-containing materials. Spontaneous explosions have occurred during handling of moist, very finely divided, contaminated zirconium scrap.

Hafnium: Hafnium has similar fire properties to zirconium. Hafnium burns with very little flame, but it releases large quantities of heat. Unless inactivated, hafnium in sponge form may ignite spontaneously.

Hafnium is generally considered to be somewhat more reactive than titanium or zirconium of similar form. Damp hafnium powder reacts with water to form hydrogen gas, but at ordinary temperatures this reaction is not sufficiently vigorous to cause the hydrogen to ignite. Under some conditions, however, ignition of the hydrogen may be expected to proceed explosively.

Storage and Handling (Including Transportation)

Special storage precautions are not required for zirconium castings because of the very high temperatures massive pieces of the metal can withstand without igniting. Zirconium powder, on the other hand, is highly combustible; consequently, it is customarily stored and shipped in 1-gal (3.78 L) containers with at least 25 percent water by volume. For specific details, refer to NFPA 482, *Production, Processing, Handling, and Storage of Zirconium*.

Zirconium powder storerooms should be of fire-resistive construction equipped with explosion vents. Cans should be separated from each other to minimize the possibility of a fire at one can involving others and to permit checking of the cans periodically for corrosion. One plant handling zirconium has established the procedure of disposing cans containing powder that have been on the shelf for six months.

Dry zirconium powder or sponge is customarily shipped inside metal cans in wood or fiberboard boxes. The DOT does not require compliance with these shipping regulations if the particle size of the powder is greater than 20 mesh.

Wet zirconium powder and zirconium sludge may be shipped in glass or polyethylene containers within metal drums or wood boxes.

Hafnium transportation regulations and storage recommendations are the same as for zirconium.

Process Hazards

In general, processing recommendations for zirconium and hafnium are the same. Handling of zirconium powder, whenever possible, should be under an inert liquid or in an inert atmosphere. An inert atmosphere of argon or helium in equipment and storage containers is a method used to prevent flash fires and explosions. If zirconium or hafnium powder is handled in air, extreme care must be used because the small static charges generated may cause ignition.

To prevent dangerous heating during machining operations, a large flow of mineral oil or water-base coolant is required. In some machining operations, the cutting surface is completely immersed. Turnings should be collected frequently and stored under water in cans. Where zirconium dust is a byproduct, dust-collecting equipment that discharges into a water-precipitation-type collector is a necessity. (See Figure 3-13A.)

Fighting Fires in Zirconium and Hafnium

Zirconium and hafnium fires can be fought in the same way. Fires exposing massive pieces of zirconium, for example, can be fought with water. Limited tests conducted by Industrial Risk Insurers have indicated that the discharge of water in spray form would have no adverse effect on burning zirconium turnings. When a sprinkler opened directly above an open drum of burning zirconium scrap, there was a brief flareup, after which the fire continued to burn quietly in the drum. When a straight stream of water at a high rate of flow was discharged into the drum, water overflowed and the fire went out.

Where small quantities of zirconium powder or fines are burning, the fire can be ringed with a special extinguishing powder to prevent its spread, after which the fire can be allowed to burn out. Special extinguishing powders have been effective in extinguishing zirconium fires. When zirconium dust is present, the extinguishing agent should be applied so that a zirconium dust cloud will not form. If the fire is in an enclosed space, it can be smothered by introducing argon or helium.

CALCIUM AND ZINC

Properties

Calcium: The flammability of calcium depends considerably on the amount of moisture in the air. If ignited in moist air, it burns without flowing at a somewhat lower rate than sodium. It decomposes in water to yield calcium hydroxide and hydrogen, which may burn. Finely divided calcium will ignite spontaneously in air. It should be noted that barium and strontium are very similar to calcium in their fire properties.

Zinc: Zinc does not introduce a serious fire hazard in sheets, castings, or other massive forms because of the difficulty of ignition. Once ignited, however, large pieces burn vigorously. Moist zinc dust reacts slowly with the water to form hydrogen, and, if sufficient heat is released, ignition of the dust can occur. Zinc dust clouds in air ignite at 1,110°F (599°C). Burning zinc generates appreciable smoke.

Storage, Processing, and Fighting Fires in Calcium and Zinc

The storage, handling, and processing recommended for magnesium is generally applicable to calcium and zinc.

METALS NOT NORMALLY COMBUSTIBLE

Aluminum

The usual forms of aluminum have a sufficiently high ignition temperature so that its burning is not a factor in most fires. However, very fine chips and shavings are occasionally subject to somewhat the same type of combustion as described for magnesium. Powdered or flaked aluminum, however, can be explosive under certain conditions. (See Table 3-13A.)

When aluminum is substituted for iron, steel, or copper, the lower melting temperature is an important factor if resistance to fire temperatures is essential. Figure 3-13B shows the decrease in strength of an aluminum alloy (6061-T6) at elevated temperatures. Compare this with Figure 3-13C for steel.

The alloy 6061-T6 is typical of those used for architectural applications. Figure 3-13B also shows the strength of 6061-T6 alloy at various temperatures for five different heating times.[2]

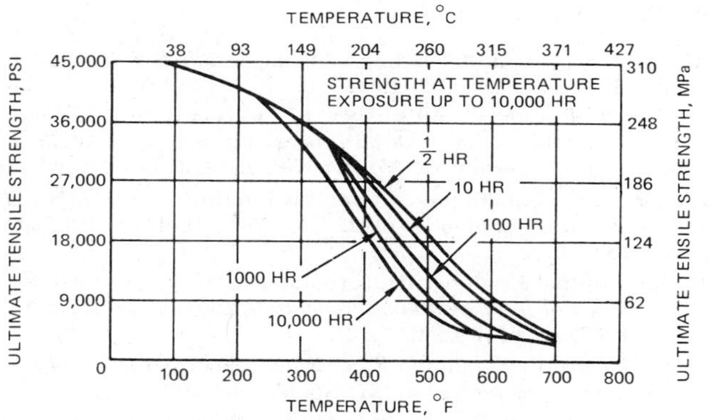

FIG. 3-13B. Effect of temperature on the strength of 6061-T6 wrought aluminum alloy.

Aluminum roofing laid directly on structural supports without a roof deck may be expected to melt through and vent a fire beneath it. For fire fighters working on such a roof, the hazard is greater than on a steel roof due to the strength loss under fire conditions.

Aluminum tubing is used in place of copper in many applications for flammable liquids and gases. While in many cases aluminum is suitable for tubing, it should be used with respect for its lower melting temperature. A number of aircraft fires have been charged to the failure of thin-walled aluminum alloy tubing used in hydraulic lines containing flammable liquids. Under pressure, short circuits caused arcs to the tubing, melting the aluminum, and releasing the flammable liquid.

Iron and Steel

Iron and steel are not usually considered combustible; in a massive form (as in structural steel, cast-iron parts, etc.), they do not burn in ordinary fires. Steel in the form of fine steel wool or dust may be ignited in the presence of heat from, for example, a torch, yielding a form of sparking rather than actual flaming in most instances. Fires have been reported in piles of steel turnings and other fines scrap which presumably contained some oil and were perhaps also contaminated by other materials that facilitated combustion. Spontaneous ignition of water-wetted borings and turnings in closed areas, such as ship hulls, has also been reported. The strength of structural steels (A7 and A36) when subjected to fire temperatures is shown in Figure 3-13C.

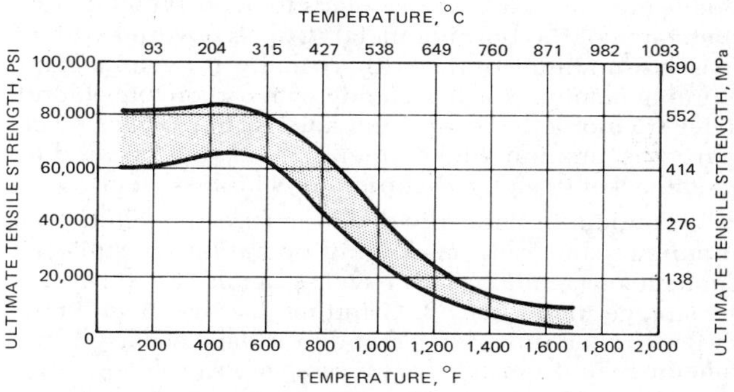

FIG. 3-13C. Strength of A7 and A36 structural steels at elevated temperature. The band indicates performance of a range of structural steels at elevated temperature. Actual performance will vary with the shape, size, and type of assembly exposed to fire conditions. (Data provided by the American Iron and Steel Institute.)

RADIOACTIVE METALS

For all practical purposes, radioactivity does not influence nor is it influenced by fire properties of a metal. Radioactive metals include those few that occur naturally, e.g., uranium and thorium, and those produced artificially, e.g., plutonium and cobalt-60. Any metal can be made radioactive. Since radioactivity cannot be altered by fire, radiation will continue wherever the radioactive metal may be spread during a fire. Smoke from fires involving radioactive materials frequently causes more property damage than the fire. The "damage," however, is not physical but results from radioactive contamination that must be cleaned up to avoid exposure.

Naturally occurring radioactive metals consist of a mixture of atoms having slightly different mass. These are called isotopes. For example, the radioactivity of each uranium isotope is different, and it follows that the radiation hazards from any given piece of uranium will change with its isotopic composition, which can be varied by special processing. Change of isotopic content of a piece of uranium alters the nature and magnitude of radiation hazards, but does not alter the chemical or fire properties of the metal. The same is equally true of thorium and plutonium. Pre-fire planning is particularly important where radioactive materials are involved. Automatic sprinkler protection is generally provided for facilities containing radioactive materials.

In nuclear reactors, uranium, plutonium, and thorium may build up considerably higher levels of radioactivity. A few nuclear reactors utilize molten metallic sodium as a coolant, so the sodium becomes radioactive. Fortunately, the requirements for fire protection are generally consistent with those independently necessitated for operational reasons.

Uranium

Normal uranium is a radioactive metal that is also combustible. Its radioactivity does not affect its combustibility, but can have a bearing on the amount of fire loss. Most metallic uranium is handled in massive forms that do not present a significant fire risk unless exposed to a severe and prolonged external fire. Once ignited, massive metal burns very slowly. A 1-in. (25.4 mm) diameter rod requires about one day to burn out after ignition. In the absence of strong drafts, uranium oxide smoke tends to deposit in the immediate area of the burning metal. Unless covered with oil, massive uranium burns with virtually no visible flame. Burning uranium reacts violently with carbon tetrachloride, 1,1,1 trichloroethane, and the halons. For power reactor purposes, uranium fuel elements are always encased in a metal jacket (usually zirconium or stainless steel).

Uranium in finely divided form is readily ignited, and uranium scrap from machining operations is subject to spontaneous ignition. This reaction can usually be avoided by storage under dry oil. Grinding dust has been known to ignite even under water, and fires have occurred spontaneously in drums of coarser scrap after prolonged exposure to moist air. Larger pieces generally have to be heated entirely to their ignition temperature before igniting. Moist dust, turnings, and chips react slowly with water to form hydrogen. Uranium surfaces treated with concentrated nitric acid are subject to explosion or spontaneous ignition in air.

Thorium

Thorium, like uranium, is a naturally occurring element. Both are known as "source materials," the basic materials from which nuclear reactor fuels are produced. The powdered form of thorium requires special handling techniques because of its low ignition temperature. It is handled dry in a helium or argon atmosphere. The dry metal powder should not be in air because the friction of the particles falling through the air or against the edge of a glass container may produce electrostatic ignition of the powder.

Powdered thorium is usually compacted into solid pellets weighing about 1 oz. (28 g) each. In this form it can be safely stored or converted into alloys with other metals. Improperly compacted thorium pellets have been known to slowly generate sufficient heat through absorption of oxygen and nitrogen from the air to raise a steel container to red heat.

Plutonium

Plutonium, like uranium, is radioactive as well as combustible. Plutonium is somewhat more susceptible to ignition than uranium and is normally handled by remote-control means in an inert gas or "bone dry" air atmosphere. In finely divided form, such as dust or chips, plutonium is subject to spontaneous ignition in moist air.

Plutonium metal is never intentionally exposed to water, in part because of fire considerations. The massive metal ignites at about 1,112°F (600°C) and burns in a manner quite similar to uranium, except that plutonium oxide smoke damage, i.e., airborne radioactive contamination, is more difficult to control and also more hazardous. Because of certain nonfire hazard considerations, it is necessary to limit the quantity of plutonium kept at one location, thus limiting the maximum size of a fire in this metal. Plutonium, which ignites spontaneously, is normally allowed to burn under conditions limiting both fire and radiological contamination spread.

BIBLIOGRAPHY

References Cited

1. CEN, "Titanium Does a Fast Burn," *Chemical and Engineering News*, Vol. 36, No. 31, Aug. 1958, pp. 36-37.
2. DOD, "Metallic Materials and Elements for Aerospace Vehicles," MIL-HDBK-5, (undated), U.S. Department of Defense, Washington, DC.

NFPA Codes, Standards, and Recommended Practices

Reference to the following NFPA codes, standards, and recommended practices will provide further information on metals discussed in this chapter. (See the latest *NFPA Catalog* for availability of current editions of the following documents.)

NFPA 65, *Processing and Finishing of Aluminum.*

NFPA 480, *Storage, Handling, and Processing of Magnesium.*

NFPA 481, *Production, Processing, Handling, and Storage of Titanium.*

NFPA 482, *Production, Processing, Handling, and Storage of Zirconium.*

NFPA 651, *Manufacture of Aluminum and Magnesium Powder.*

Additional Reading

American Society of Metals International, *Metals Handbook*, 10th ed., Materials Park, OH, 1990.

Duclos, P., Binder, S, and Riester, R., "Community Evacuation Following the Spencer Metal Processing Plant Fire," *Journal of Hazardous Materials*, Vol. 22, No. 1, Sept. 1989, pp. 1-11.

Eisner, H. S., "Aluminum and the Gas Ignition Risk," *The Engineer*, London, England, Vol. 223, No. 5795, Feb. 17, 1967, pp. 259-260.

Factory Mutual Engineering Corporation, "Metals and Alloys," *Handbook of Industrial Loss Prevention*, 2nd ed., McGraw-Hill, NY, 1967, pp. 62-1, 62-6.

"Fire Hazards in Aluminum Processing," *The Institution of Fire Engineers Quarterly*, Vol. 27, No. 65, Mar. 1967, pp. 94-97.

"Fire Protection for Combustible Metals," *National Safety News*, Vol. 119, No. 6, June 1979, pp. 75-82.

Jacobson, M., Cooper, A. R., and Nagy, J., *Explosibility of Metal Powders*, RI 6516, USDI, Bureau of Mines, Pittsburgh, PA, 1964.

McCormick, J. R., and Schmitt, C. R., "Extinguishment of Selected Metal Fires Using Carbon Microspheroids," *Fire Technology*, Vol. 10, No. 3, August 1974, pp. 196-200.

Metals and Ores, Volume 3 of Chemical Technology, *An Encyclopedic Treatment*, Barnes and Noble Books, Imports, Totowa, NJ, 1970.

Markstein, G. H., "Combustion of Metals," *Journal of the American Institute of Aeronautics & Astronautics*, Vol. 1, 1963, pp. 550-562.

Miller, G. S., "Use of Aluminum Wire in Homes Spurs Fears of Fires, Leads Suits," *Wall Street Journal*, Vol. 191, No. 7, Jan. 11, 1978, pp. 1, 25.

Peloubet, J. A., "Machining Magnesium—A Study of Ignition Factors," *Fire Technology*, Vol. 1, No. 1, Feb. 1965, pp. 5-14.

Peterson, W. S., ed, Guidelines for Handling Molton Aluminum, The Aluminum Association, Washington, DC, 1982.

Poster, A. R., *Handbook of Metal Powders*, Van Nostrand Reinhold, NY, 1966.

Rhein, R. A., Baldwin, J. C., and Beach, C. L., "Compositions for Extinguishing Titanium Fires," *Chemical Abstracts*, Vol. 103, 1985.

Riley, John F., "Na-X, A New Fire Extinguishing Agent for Metal Fires," *Fire Technology*, Vol. 10, No. 4, Nov. 1974, pp. 269-274.

Schmitt, C. R., "Pyrophoric Materials—A Literature Review," *Fire Prevention and Suppression*, ed by Hilado, Carlos J. (Vol. 10, Fire and Flammability Series), Technomic, Westport, CT, 1974, pp. 74-89.

Sharma, T. P., Lal, B. B., and Singh, J., "Metal Fire Extinguishment," *Fire Technology*, Vol. 23, No. 3, 1987, pp. 205-229.

Smithells, C. J., *Metals Reference Book*, 7th ed., Butterworths, Boston, 1991.

Twilt L., "Strength and Deformation Properties of Steel at Elevated Temperatures: Some Practicle Implications," *Fire Safety Journal*, Vol. 13, No. 1, 1988, pp. 1-8.

Van Horn, K. R., ed., *Aluminum*, American Society for Metals, Metals Park, OH, 1967.

ENERGY CONSERVATION IN BUILDINGS

T. T. Lie

In the wake of energy crises, worldwide efforts are being made to conserve energy. Energy conservation in buildings is an important objective in many countries, and various approaches have been taken to achieve it. Two well-known methods for conserving energy in buildings are: (1) to increase the amount of insulation used, and (2) to seal air leaks. Another method is replacement of energy from nonrenewable sources, such as oil and gas, by energy derived from renewable ones, such as the sun and wind.

Although these various measures have contributed to a more efficient use of energy, they have also created problems. Some fire problems, for example, are an increased number of types of ignition sources and materials that may contribute to spread of fire and the production of smoke and toxic gases. The fraction of air recycled in heated and air-conditioned buildings is often increased, which tends to increase the hazard of combustion products because of confinement of these products. Other examples are increases of rate of fire growth and fire temperature (with better insulation), and the reduction of fire resistance of structural elements in specific cases (due to insulation).

This chapter discusses the role of building energy conservation measures, particularly insulation, on the fire behavior of structures. Closely allied with the subject matter of this chapter are two other chapters: Section 6, Chapter 4, "Interior Finish," and Section 3, Chapter 1, "Combustion Products and Their Effects on Life Safety."

INSULATION

Most of the fire problems associated with energy conservation measures in buildings are related to increased use of thermal insulation in the buildings. Insulation affects a fire in all phases of its development from inception to decay. These phases will be discussed briefly because knowledge of the characteristics of the various phases of fire that will be considered in this chapter is important for understanding the influence of insulation on firesafety.

Phases of Fire

Normally, a room fire starts as a small fire caused by ignition of a material by a heat source, e.g., the flame of a match or the heat of a stove or hot electrical wire. Depending upon various factors, such as the nature of the material that is exposed to the ignition source or the size of the ignition source, the fire may self-extinguish or grow to full development. Usually the fully developed stage of a fire is preceded by flashover, which is characterized by instantaneous ignition of materials in all parts of the room.

The course of a fire is usually divided into three periods: (1) a growth period, (2) a fully developed period, and (3) a decay period. (See Figure 3-14A.) In the growth period, i.e., the period before flashover, the temperatures in the room are relatively low, even when close to the burning materials, and evacuation from the fire area presents no problems. During flashover, however, the temperature rises very sharply to such a level that survival of the fire by persons still in the room at that stage becomes unlikely. Thus, the time interval between the start of a fire and the occurrence of flashover is a major factor in the time that is available for safe evacuation of the fire area.

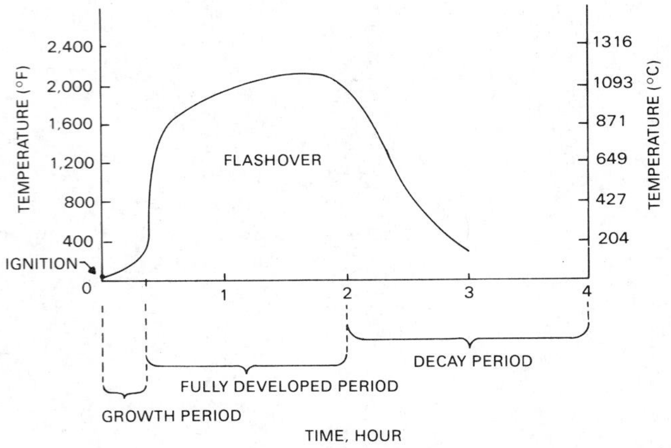

FIG. 3-14A. Temperature course of a typical fire.

T. T. Lie is research officer, Institute for Research in Construction, National Research Council of Canada.

There is negligible risk of structural failure in the growth period because of the low temperatures. Actual risk of failure of structural elements or of fire separations begins in the fully developed stage of the fire, after flashover. This risk also exists in the decay period, during which remnants of the combustible materials are consumed.

Influence on Ignition of Materials

If thermal insulation is installed to surround heat-producing objects, such as electrical wires and light fixtures, those objects may become ignition sources. The insulation will impede the dissipation of heat, which will result in heat buildup in the objects. They may become hot enough to ignite combustible materials in contact with them.

Insulation also plays a role in the ignition of a material when it is applied to the back of a thin lining; it reduces heat losses at the back of the lining. The increase of surface temperature at the front side of an insulated interior finish material exposed to an ignition source may be significantly more rapid than that of an uninsulated material. Therefore, the insulated interior finish material may ignite more rapidly than the uninsulated one. The influence of insulation is small for thicker materials, i.e., thicker than 1/4 in. (6.3 mm) for cellulosic linings, such as wood and board.[1]

In addition to the cases mentioned in which insulation indirectly contributes to the ignition of materials, the insulation itself may be a potential ignition hazard. The increased use of a wide variety of insulating materials, particularly foamed plastics, has created concern about this possibility. The plastics industry is now conducting extensive studies to investigate the fire performance of plastics to develop ways in which they can be used with reasonable safety.

Influence on Growth of Fire

During the growth of a fire, unburned material is successively ignited. The rate of growth of a fire depends upon many factors; one of the most important is the nature of the materials that contribute to fire growth. The faster the materials propagate fire and the more heat they develop, the faster the fire will grow. The heat developed by burning materials in the growth period is particularly important in enclosures of rather limited size, such as offices, living rooms, and classrooms. During the growth of the fire, the heat developed by the burning materials accumulates in the room. Because of this, other materials in the room may be heated so severely that after a short time they also ignite and, at this stage, flashover occurs.

Adding insulation may significantly affect the rate of growth of a fire. Because of the insulation, heat from fire will be conserved in the room in the same way as heat from heating systems is conserved. Consequently, the accumulation of heat in the room is accelerated, and the flashover stage may be reached much earlier than in a less-insulated room. According to estimates, the growth period reduces by a factor of about three by insulating a room of brick-plaster construction with a noncombustible lining of low thermal conductivity.[2]

In addition to accelerating fire growth by heat conservation, insulation may propagate flames itself, also affecting the growth of a fire.

Propagation of Flames

Once a material, e.g., interior finish in a room, is ignited, the flame may spread across the surface of the material. For flame to spread, heat transferred from the flame to the material must be sufficient to liberate flammable gases from the material near the flame front. Those gases will, in turn, be ignited. The gases are developed initially from the surface of the material; therefore, surface temperature is an important factor in determining the attainment of a condition favorable to flame spread. The faster the temperature rise of the surface, the faster the propagation of the flames.

The rate of temperature rise of the surface depends to a high degree upon the thermal properties of the material. In particular, the thermal conductivity (K) and the thermal capacity (rc) of the material are important. The lower the thermal conductivity, the less of the heat received at the surface is transferred to the inside of the material. If, in addition, the thermal capacity of the material is small and thus relatively little heat is required to raise the temperature of the material, the temperature rise of the surface may be substantial in a short time. It can be shown for an idealized case that the time to reach a specific critical surface temperature, e.g., the temperature at which the surface ignites, is proportional to a quantity, $K \rho c$, which is often termed the thermal inertia of the material.[3]

In actual practice, however, more factors play a role in the determination of the surface temperature rise. For the purpose of illustrating the role of thermal inertia in flame propagation, the idealized case will be assumed in the following discussion.[4]

In Table 3-14A, typical values are given for the thermal inertia of some materials. The table also gives the time it takes to raise the surface temperature of the material to a level at which wood and plastic produce a significant amount of combustible gases, here assumed to be 400°F (204°C). It is further assumed that heat is supplied at a rate of 1,050 Btu per sq ft per hr (3300 W/m^2). At this rate, wood would attain this critical surface temperature in 600 seconds, or 10 minutes. Under the same circumstances, fiber insulation board, which is known to propagate flames rapidly, would attain the critical surface temperature in 23 seconds; for a foamed plastic it would take only a few seconds before its surface temperature reached the critical value.

The very rapid temperature rise of the surfaces of foamed plastics is probably the reason why they may propagate flames with extreme speed; this applies particularly to nonmelting or thermosetting foamed plastics. Thermoplastic foam may melt before its temperature reaches a critical value. In that case, the rate of temperature rise of the surface of the molten plastic slows, because the thermal inertia of the plastic surface increases and because heat is used in melting the plastic. Extremely fast propagation of fire is less likely to occur on thermoplastic foams that melt at relatively low temperatures [such as polystyrene and polyvinyl chloride, which melt at temperatures on the order of 250°F (121°C)] than on those that melt at higher temperatures. There are many thermoplastics, however, that do not melt before their surface reaches the critical temperature.

Protected Foamed Plastic

Several building codes recognize a material with a flame spread rating of 25 or less (as ascertained by the tunnel test in NFPA 255, *Method of Test of Surface Burning Char*

TABLE 3-14A. *Thermal Inertia (Kρc) and Rate of Surface Temperature Rise of Various Materials*
[Rate of Heat Supply: 1050 Btu/(sq ft hr) (3300 w/m²]

Material	Density range lb/cu ft (kg/m³	Typical values of *Kρc* Btu²/(sq ft °F)² hr [w²/(m² °C)²s†]	Time to reach a surface temperature of 400°F (204°C) (sec)
Wood	30–40 (480–640)	1.7 (1.98 × 10⁵)	600
Asbestos board	40–50 (640–800)	1 (1.16 × 10⁵)	353
Gypsum board	40–50 (640–800)	0.6 (7.0 × 10⁴)	212
Fiber insulation board	10–20 (160–320)	0.13 (1.51 × 10⁴)	46
Cork board	5–10 (80–160)	0.06 (7.0 × 10³)	21
Foam plastics:	1–3 (16–48)	0.01 (1.16 × 10³)	4
Polyurethane			
Phenol-formaldehyde			
Polystyrene			
Cellular PVC			
Isocyanurate			
Fiber batts:	0.5–1.0 (8–16)	0.005 (5.81 × 10²)	2
Glass fiber			
Mineral wool			

acteristics of Building Materials) as a low fire hazard material. Tests carried out on urethane foam, however, suggest that foams may accelerate the growth of fire much faster than expected on the basis of tunnel test results.

Concern about this possibility and the occurrence of a number of large-loss fires involving foamed plastic has led to more stringent requirements regarding the use of foams. One of these requirements is that plastic foams should be protected by a thermal barrier capable of preventing excessive heat transfer from heat source to plastic during a specified time.

Methods exist for evaluating the performance of a material as a thermal barrier. One of them is the method described in NFPA 251, *Standard Methods of Fire Tests of Building Construction and Materials*, in which the area of the test specimen exposed to the test fire is at least 100 sq ft (9.3 m²). To pass the test, the protection must be capable of preventing excessive temperature rise at the unexposed side for 15 minutes or more when one side of the test specimen is exposed to standard heating. Because the temperatures during standard heating are of the same magnitude as those encountered in the post-flashover stage of a fire, the test method, which is intended to evaluate the performance of a protection in the pre-flashover stage of a fire, is a severe one. Temperatures in the pre-flashover stage of a house-burn test are shown in Figure 3-14B.[5] It can be seen that up to approximately 15 minutes, the fire temperatures are substantially lower than the NFPA 251 standard curve.

Another method, which is less severe but sufficient to evaluate the performance of a protection in the pre-flashover stage of a fire and which will reasonably ensure that the foamed plastic will not contribute to the growth of a fire for at least the time measured in the test, is described in ULC-S124.[6] In this test, the thermal barrier is also exposed on one side to heating of a severity equal to that in the NFPA 251, *Standard Methods of Fire Tests of Building Construction and Materials*, fire test. The area of the specimen, however, is smaller, about 10 sq ft (0.93 m²), and the test also classifies thermal barriers that provide protection for less than 15 minutes.

The times during which materials provide protection against a post-flashover fire are given in Table 3-14B. Protection time in this table may be regarded as the approximate time it takes the temperature at the interface of the protective cover and the plastic foam to rise 250°F (121°C) above ambient. The total time before the plastic starts contributing significantly to the fire is thus equal to the time for the fire to grow from ignition to flashover, added to the protection time given in the table. If a combination of protecting materials is used, the total protection time may be assumed to be at least equal to the sum of the protection times of the individual protecting materials.

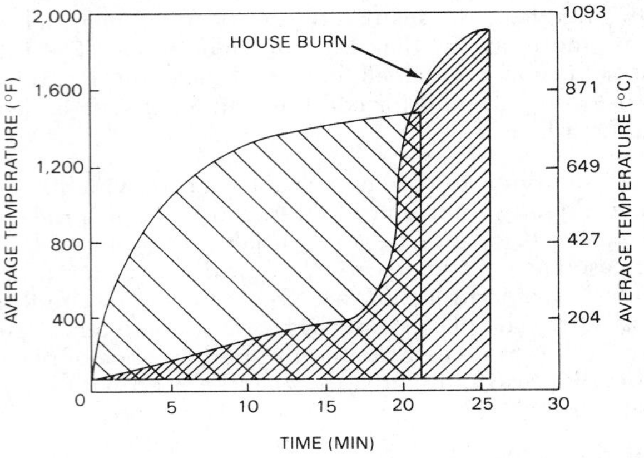

FIG. 3-14B. Temperature-time relationship according to NFPA 251, and for a house burn.[5]

Because propagation of flame is a process that is determined mainly by the surface characteristics of the exposed materials, provision of a cover will reduce or remove the influence of the foamed plastic on fire growth. In this case, the propagation of flame will be determined by the surface characteristics of the cover material. If it has a low flame spread rating and its behavior is not significantly affected by the foamed plastic insulation, fast growth of a fire due to plastic insulation can be prevented in a room. It is possible, however, for fire to propagate in the cavity behind the cover, e.g., if the cover has a high thermal conductivity or openings are formed in it. It is also possible for fire to originate inside the cavity, e.g., because of overheating of electrical wires due to thermal insulation.

TABLE 3-14B. ***Time of Protection Against Post-flashover Fire***

Material of Protection	Thickness of Protection in. (mm)	Protection Time (min)
Gypsum wallboard	3/8 (9.5)	11
Gypsum wallboard	1/2 (12.7)	15
Gypsum wallboard	5/8 (15.9)	20
Magnesium oxychloride	1/4–3/8 (6.4–9.5)	10–15
Magnesium oxychloride	1/2–5/8 (12.7–15.9)	20–25
Plywood	1/8 (4.9)	3
Plywood	1/4 (6.4)	5
Plywood	3/8 (9.5)	8
Plywood	1/2 (12.7)	11
Hardboard	1/8 (4.9)	3
Hardboard	1/4 (6.4)	5
Hardboard	3/8 (9.5)	8
Particleboard	1/4 (6.4)	4
Particleboard	3/8 (9.5)	6
Particleboard	1/2 (12.7)	8

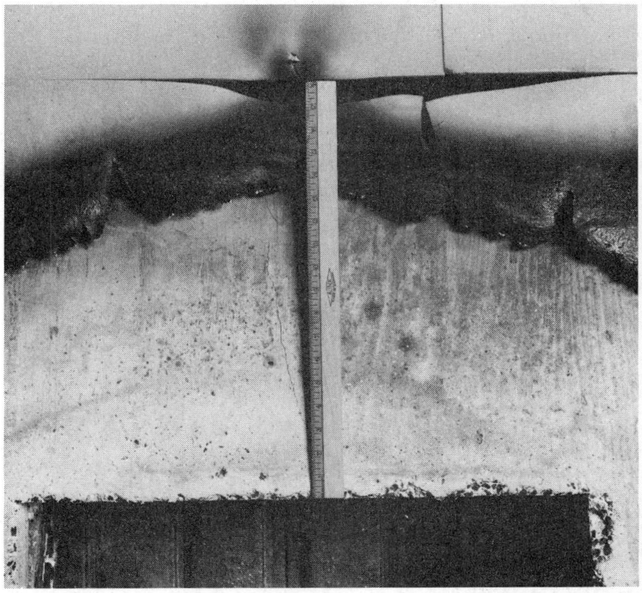

FIG. 3-14C. Test specimen after exposure to fire in a cavity wall (no air space, exposure time of 6 hrs). (Source: National Research Council of Canada)

Foamed Plastic in Cavity Walls

Foamed plastic in cavity walls is usually sandwiched between two layers of material forming the wall. Sometimes there is an air space between the plastic and the wall, and sometimes the wall material is in direct contact with the plastic on both sides of it.

Depending upon the presence of an air space and the type of construction, i.e., whether the building is of noncombustible construction, a number of North American codes require that the insulation must satisfy specific flame spread ratings determined by using the test method described in NFPA 255, *Method of Test of Surface Burning Characteristics of Materials*. Because of doubt whether the contribution of insulation to the propagation of a fire in a cavity is related to its flame spread rating, in particular in those cases where there is no air space, tests were carried out to obtain more insight into the behavior of materials in cavities.[7] In these cases, the speed of propagation of the fire in the cavity is not determined by the speed of propagation over the surface of the plastic foam, but by the speed with which the plastic at the underside burns away.

The test results indicate that for materials sandwiched between two layers of noncombustible materials without air space, the upward propagation of the fire is slow, even for materials with a high flame spread rating. In Figure 3-14C, a picture is shown of a burned part of a urethane foam test specimen with a high flame spread rating (333 according to NFPA 255, *Method of Test of Surface Burning Characteristics of Materials*) after it has been exposed at the bottom to a standard fire (NFPA 251, *Standard Methods of Fire Tests of Building Construction and Materials*) for 6 hours. In this time, the fire had propagated to about 14 in. (356 mm) above the part of the specimen that was exposed to the fire.[7]

The fire may spread rapidly upward if there is an air space between the wall and foamed plastic. The speed of propagation depends not only upon the properties of the foamed plastic but also on several other factors, such as the properties of the wall material, width of the air space, and flow of hot gases through the cavity (due to chimney effect). Research is now in progress to examine the influence of a number of important factors on the speed of propagation of fire in cavity walls.

Irrespective of the circumstances, however, spread of fire from story to story in a cavity wall can be prevented by the use of well-designed fire stops. The installation of fire stops is prescribed in many codes. The role of fire stops has become very important due to the increase in the use of insulation in cavity walls. Therefore, much can be gained by measures that promote the installation of effective fire stops in multistory buildings.

Another consequence of the increasing use of combustible insulation in cavity walls is an increase in the chance of outbreak of fire in the cavity. Strictly speaking, however, this is not true. The chances of death in any given fire are roughly the same.

Insulation in Attics

The greatest concern for concealed-space fires is in situations where a large, undivided or unfirestopped space provides a route for fire growth that circumvents a building's compartmentation. Such spread has been observed in the common attics of rowhouses, for example. The hazard of a large, undivided space is increased if the combustible load is great.

Increase of building insulation and introduction of new insulating materials may have aggravated this situation. There is concern that widespread installation of thermal insulation may have adverse consequences on the performance of electrical wires, cables, and other electrical devices.[8] Since such devices generate heat, they may become overheated during operation if they are covered by building insulation. Tests have shown that electrical equipment located in insulated cavities operated at higher temperatures than in uninsulated cavities. However, many electrical devices are now listed for use with insulation covering them. Others are listed with specific clearances to the fixture indicated. Another cause of overheating is the liberation of exothermic heat by insulating materials as they cure.

A type of insulation known as loose-fill insulation is frequently used in attics. There are noncombustible insulating materials, such as mineral wool, but often combustible insulation made of cellulosic material is used. These cellulosic insulations are generally made of pulverized or finely chopped paper, frequently waste paper.[8] In this condition, the material is highly flammable and flame-retardant compounds have to be added to reduce its flammability. If the materials are properly treated with flame retardants, which can be determined by testing, and fire stops are installed in large attic areas, cellulosic insulation can be utilized without excessive risk.

SMOKE AND TOXIC GASES

Fire statistics show that thermal decomposition products (smoke and toxic gases) are responsible for the majority of fire deaths. Many new materials release harmful decomposition products very rapidly, and some of them produce much more smoke or toxic gas than traditional building materials. With the increased use of these new materials, the problem of smoke and toxic products has attracted even more attention.

Regulations to exclude the use of materials with excessive smoke production and methods to determine smoke density are specified in several codes.[9,10,11] However, there are as yet no accepted standard methods for evaluating toxicity, although considerable effort is being made toward developing standard procedures for determining fire toxicity of materials. (See Section 3, Chapter 1, "Combustion Products and Their Effects on Life Safety.")

Smoke

A major hazard of smoke is that it reduces visibility. It may impede the escape of occupants from a burning building and prolong exposure to the harmful effects of fire, such as the smoke itself, toxic products, and heat.

One of the most important factors that determines the reduction in visibility in a given space is the concentration of the smoke generated in that space. A measure of this concentration is the optical density of the smoke, which is a quantity that is directly proportional to the smoke concentration. In Table 3-14C, the second column lists relative optical densities of smoke generated by various materials under similar conditions. The third column lists times required to obscure a given room under the same conditions, assuming that wood smoke would obscure the room in ten minutes. Although wood is considered here as a single material, there are differences in the smoke production among various species of wood. The figures, therefore, should be regarded as approximate and are intended to show the order of magnitude of the smoke production of various materials under one specific test condition.

It can be seen that some materials used as insulation, e.g., cork and some foamed plastics, produce significantly more smoke than wood. If the insulation surface area is large in comparison with that of the other combustible materials in the room, and they are unprotected, smoke production will be dominated by the insulation. In this case, the time of obscuration, which is a measure of the time available for safe evacuation of the fire area, may drop to levels substantially lower than that if the smoke had been produced solely by wood. If, however, the insulation surface area is a small fraction of the surface area of the combustible materials in the room (not more than 10 percent of the surface area of the fire load), smoke contribution of the insulation will not be excessive in comparison with the total smoke produced by all burning materials.

TABLE 3-14C. ***Smoke Production of Various Unprotected Materials***[12]

Material	Optical density	Time of obscuration (min)
Phenolformaldehyde foam	0.1	100
Wood	1	10
Boards	1-2	5-10
Cork	3	3.3
Polystyrene foam	5	2
Cellular PVC	10	1
Polyurethane foam	15	0.7

If the insulation is protected, its smoke production may drop to very low values. Table 3-14D shows the influence of protection consisting of 1/2-in. (12.7 mm) Type X gypsum wallboard on the smoke production of a number of materials.

TABLE 3-14D. ***Influence of Protection on Smoke Production***[12]

[Protection of 1/2-in. (12.7 mm) Type X gypsum wallboard]

Material	Optical density	Time of obscuration (min)
Wood (unprotected)	1	10
Cork:		
Unprotected	3	3.3
Protected	0.06	180
Polystyrene foam:		
Unprotected	5	2
Protected	0.8	13
Polyurethane foam:		
Unprotected	16	0.6
Protected	4	2.5

Toxic Gases

Toxic gases can be fatal if they are present for a sufficient time and in sufficient quantities. In recent years, various new materials, especially synthetic polymers, have found increasing use in buildings, and their introduction has heightened the concern of fire authorities over toxic combustion products. Part of this increased concern has arisen because of the lack of information on toxic combustion products and the problem of assessing their potential hazard.

Comprehensive chemical analysis is necessary to identify unusual toxicants that may be produced during fires. For most practical applications, however, this is not necessary, since testing for a few of the most important known toxicants often gives sufficient information. Some compounds, such as carbon monoxide (CO), hydrogen chloride (HCl), hydrogen cyanide (HCN), and oxides of nitrogen, are recognized as harmful products; others, such as water vapor and the hydrocarbons, contribute little or no toxic hazard. It is usually sufficient to decompose materials under specified conditions and determine the resulting concentrations of a few of the most important toxicants. From this information, a reasonable indication of the toxicity of the mixture of products can be obtained.

Table 3-14E shows the main harmful products of a number of materials and approximate values of the harmful concentrations for an exposure time of 30 minutes. According to the figures in this table, one of the most toxic products is HCN, which is harmful at concentrations of about $1/30$th of the harmful concentration of CO. If the materials that produce HCN are present in small quantities, however, their contribution to toxicity may be less than that of the CO normally produced during a fire. This is also the case if the materials that generate very toxic products are properly protected. According to measurements made during tests in rooms with walls insulated with isocyanurate foam and protected with $1/4$-in. (6.2 mm) Douglas fir plywood, no HCN was observed in the pre-flashover period, up to 21 minutes after the ignition.[5] The results indicate that, from the point of view of hampering safe evacuation of people by toxic combustion products, the materials in the room play a far greater role than the insulation in the walls if the insulation is adequately protected, for example, by boards or plywood of not less than $1/4$-in. (6.2 mm) thickness.

HEATING SYSTEMS

The price of oil and uncertainties in its supply have stimulated the use of heating systems that do not operate on oil. Such heating systems, for example, utilize solar energy, wood, coal, and natural gas. Coal and gas have been used as the main fuels for heating buildings for a long time in several countries. The use of solar energy is relatively new, and wood has enjoyed renewed interest as a household heating fuel; in some areas, their use for heating buildings has increased tremendously.

Most of the fire risk introduced by these systems is related to the high temperatures that they may attain. For example, 400°F (204°C) for solar collectors is not abnormal, whereas wood-stove encasements may reach temperatures of over 1,000°F (538°C). There is the risk that combustible materials may ignite spontaneously after prolonged exposure to these temperatures.

BUILDING STRUCTURE

Fire Severity

Actual risk of failure of structural elements or fire separations usually begins after flashover in the fully-developed stage of a fire. The temperature of the fire in this stage will be affected by thermal insulation in the boundaries, such as walls and roofs, of the rooms; the greater the amount of insulation, the higher the fire temperature. Less of the heat generated by the burning materials in the room will be absorbed by the boundaries, and, as a consequence, the fire gas temperature will increase. The higher temperature in turn will accelerate the rate of decomposition of the materials in the room, which may result in an increase in the heat released in the room. According to existing information, however, this rate is a very weak function of the temperature of the fire gases.[14] Therefore the only significant effect on fire severity caused by adding insulation is expected to be a rise of fire temperatures, whereas the duration of the fire will be practically unchanged.

In addition to causing higher fire temperatures, insulation in roofs and walls also directly influences the temperatures reached in them by altering the heat transfer through the roof or walls. These temperature changes may affect the fire performance of structural elements and fire separations in various ways.

Roofs

Roof constructions in which fire performance may be affected by the addition of insulation are those supported by steel members, such as joists and beams, and those supported by steel wires, such as reinforcing and prestressing steel. Steel loses strength when it is heated to high temperatures; the higher its temperature, the lower its strength. In general, a critical steel temperature can be indi-

TABLE 3-14E. ***Main Harmful Products of Materials and Harmful Concentrations***[13,14,15]

Material	Harmful Product	Harmful concentration in parts per million parts of air (30-min exposure)
Wood and Paper	Carbon Monoxide (CO)	4,000 ppm
Polystyrene	CO—also styrene, but present in smaller quantities	
Polyvinyl Chloride (PVC)	HCl—also corrosive CO	1,000–2,000 ppm
Plexiglas or perspex	CO—also methylmethacrylate, which is as toxic as CO but produced in smaller quantities	
Polyethylene Ureaformaldehyde Isocyanurate	CO	
Polyurethane Acrylic Fibres Wool Nylon	Hydrogen Cyanide (HCN) CO	120–150 ppm

cated at which the steel has lost so much strength that it can no longer support the load. Often a temperature of 1,100°F (593°C) is assumed as the critical temperature of structural steel members and reinforcing steel, and a temperature of 800°F (427°C) as the critical temperature of prestressing steel.

Typical roof constructions that are supported by steel members are assemblies consisting of a steel deck supported by steel beams or joists and covered with concrete. Often the steel is protected from attaining excessive temperatures during a fire by a fire-resistive ceiling. At present, more roof insulation is placed on top of the concrete than in the past, to conserve energy. Because the insulation reduces heat losses to the air above the roof, all temperatures inside the structure, including the temperatures of the supporting beams, will be higher with increased insulation. If the concrete is sufficiently thick, however, the increase in temperature will be small. According to tests, the addition of insulation on top of the concrete has no significant effect on the fire resistance of the roof assembly if the thickness of the concrete is 2 in. (51 mm) or more.[16] If there is no concrete cover, and the insulation is placed directly on the steel deck, the fire resistance of the roof assembly may be reduced substantially. The influence on the fire resistance of the assembly depends upon the thermal properties and thickness of the insulation. A maximum thickness can be found beyond which there will be no further reduction in the fire resistance of the assembly. The order of magnitude of this thickness is 1.5 in. (38 mm), which was found during tests with a commonly used noncombustible insulation.

Typical roof constructions that are supported by steel wires are those consisting of reinforced or prestressed concrete slabs. If insulation is added on top of the concrete, the temperature of the reinforcing or prestressing wires may rise more rapidly than if the concrete is uninsulated. The influence of insulation on the temperatures of the wires depends upon various factors, such as the properties of the insulation, position of the wires in the concrete, and the thickness of the concrete. If the concrete is not very thin, say not less than 3 in. (76 mm) for normal-weight concrete, the influence is small. For lightweight concrete, the influence of adding insulation is less than for normal-weight concrete.

Walls

If walls are lined on the room side with an insulating material, the fire temperatures will increase. On the other hand, the temperatures in the wall will be lower, and, as a result, the fire resistance of the wall will improve. It is likely that lining a wall will have a favorable effect on its structural fire performance, particularly if the lining is a good insulator.

If the insulation is installed in a cavity, however, the effect on the structural fire resistance of the wall may be unfavorable. This is particularly true for thin walls in which unequal expansion of the wall layers on each side of the cavity may produce large deflections and cause the wall to buckle.

Insulation may reduce the structural fire performance of fire barriers, such as roofs, floors, and walls, but it increases their thermal fire resistance, i.e., their ability to prevent excessive heat penetration through the fire barriers.

BIBLIOGRAPHY

References Cited

1. Lie, T. T., *Fire and Buildings*, Applied Science Publishers Ltd., London, 1972, pp. 26-27.
2. Thomas, P. H., and Bullen, M. L., "The Effects of Insulation in Fires," *Fire*, 1980, p. 434.
3. Carslaw, H. S., and Jaeger, J. C., *Conduction of Heat in Solids*, 2nd ed., Oxford University Press, London, 1959.
4. Thomas, P. H., and Bullen, M. L., "On the Role of *Krc* of Room Lining Materials in the Growth of Room Fires," *Fire and Materials*, No. 3, 1979, pp. 68-73.
5. Holmes, Carlton A., *et al*, "Fire Development and Wall Endurance in Sandwich and Wood-Frame Structures," Research Paper FPL 364, 1980, Forest Products Laboratory, U.S. Department of Agriculture.
6. ULC, "Standard Method of Test for the Evaluation of Protective Coverings for Foamed Plastic," ULC-S124, 1985, Underwriters Laboratories of Canada, Toronto, Ontario, Canada.
7. Lie, T. T., "Contribution of Insulation in Cavity Walls to Propagation of Fire," Fire Study No. 29, 1972, National Research Council of Canada, Ottawa, Ontario, Canada.
8. Degenkolb, J. H., "Energy Conservation and Its Effect on Buildings from the Fire Protection Viewpoint," *Fire Journal*, Vol. 72, No. 3, May 1978, pp. 86-90; and Vol. 72, No. 6, Nov. 1978, p. 8.
9. BOCA, *The BOCA Basic Building Code*, Building Officials Conference of America, Inc., Chicago, IL, 1984.
10. ICBO, *The Uniform Building Code*, International Conference of Building Officials, Pasadena, CA, 1982.
11. NRCC, *National Building Code of Canada*, National Research Council of Canada, Ottawa, Ontario, Canada, 1985.
12. Lie, T. T., "Smoke Contribution of Some Partition Components During a Fire Test," Technical Note 524, 1968, National Research Council of Canada, Ottawa, Ontario, Canada.
13. Sumi, K., and Tsuchiya, Y., "Evaluating the Toxic Hazard of Fires," *Canadian Building Digest*, 1978, National Research Council of Canada, Ottawa, Ontario, Canada.
14. Harmathy, T. Z., "Effect of the Nature of Fuel on Fully Developed Compartment Fires," *Fire and Materials*, No. 3, 1979, pp. 49-60.
15. Woolley, W. D., Ames, S. A., and Fardell, P. J., "Chemical Aspects of Combustion Toxicology of Fires," *Fire and Materials*, No. 3, 1979, pp. 110-120.
16. Stanzak, W. W., and Konicek, L., "Effect of Thermal Insulation and Heat Sink on the Structural Fire Endurance of Steel Roof Assemblies," *Canadian Journal of Civil Engineering*, No. 6, 1979, pp. 32-35.

Reference

Sumi, K., and Tsuchiya, Y., "Combustion Products of Polymeric Materials Containing Nitrogen in Their Chemical Structure," *Journal of Fire and Flammability*, 1973, pp. 15-22.

NFPA Codes, Standards, and Recommended Practices

Reference to the following NFPA codes, standards, and recommended practices will provide further information on energy conservation in buildings discussed in this chapter. (See the latest *NFPA Catalog* for availability of current editions of the following documents.)

NFPA 251, *Standard Methods of Fire Tests of Building Construction and Materials.*

NFPA 255, *Method of Test of Surface Burning Characteristics of Materials.*

Additional Reading

Belles, D. W., "Fire Hazard Analysis of Foam Plastic Insulation in Exterior Walls of Buildings," SFPE TR 82-1, Society of Fire Protection Engineers, Boston, MA, 1982.

"Building Insulation: Energy Conservation or Fire Hazard," *Factory Mutual Record*, Nov.-Dec., 1978.

Choi, K. K., "Combustion of Insulation in Cavity Walls," *Journal of Fire Sciences*, May/June 1984.

Choi, K. K., "Effects of Foamed Plastic Insulation on Severity of Room Fires," *Fire Technology*, Vol. 22, No. 1, 1986, pp. 5-13.

Eisner, H., "How Safe Are Foam Roof Linings," *Fire Prevention*, No. 226, Jan.-Feb. 1990, pp. 32-33.

Ellis, J. W., "Rigid Foam Plastic Insulation," *Fire Surveyor*, Vol. 19, No. 1, Feb. 1990, pp. 21-24.

"For Architects and Builders: Home Insulation," *Fire Journal*, May 1978.

Harmathy, T. Z., "Thermal Inertia or Thermal Absorbtivity," *Fire Technology*, Vol.21, No. 2, 1985, pp. 146-149.

Henderson, R. L., "Reflective Insulation," Costa Mesa Fire Department, Costa Mesa, CA, Apr. 15, 1980.

Hilado, C., *Flammability Handbook for Thermal Insulation*, Technomic Publishing Co., Lancaster, PA, 1983.

Lawson, J. R., "Environmental Cycling of Cellulosic Thermal Insulation and Its Influence on Fire Performance," NBSIR 84-2917, National Bureau of Standards, Gaithersburg, MD, Aug. 1984.

Mazzoni, S., "Safety Considerations of Energy Savings Materials and Devices," SFPE TR 78-6, Society of Fire Protection Engineers, Boston, MA, 1978.

McCarter, R. J., "Combustion Inhibition of Cellulose by Powders—Preliminary Data and Hypotheses," *Fire and Materials*, Vol. 5, No. 2, June 1981, pp. 66-72.

Mehaffey, J. R., "Fire Performance of Combustible Insulation in Buildings," *Journal of Thermal Insulation*, Vol. 10, Apr. 1987, pp. 256-269.

Melott, R. K., "Is Energy Conservation Firesafe?," SFPE TR 78-8, Society of Fire Protection Engineers, Boston, MA, 1978.

Ohlemiller, T. J., and Rogers, F. E., "Cellulosic Insulation Material—Effect of Additives on Some Smolder Characteristics," *Combustion Science and Technology*, Vol. 24, 1980, pp. 139-152.

Proceedings of the Conference on Energy Conservation and Firesafety in Buildings, National Research Council, National Academy of Sciences, Washington D.C., 1982.

Prusaczyk, J. E., "Fire Performance Characteristics in Rooms as the Result of Increased Insulation," SFPE TR 78-2, Society of Fire Protection Engineers, Boston, MA.

Raeber, J. A., "Foamed Plastic Insulations: Three Controversies," *Construction Specifier*, Vol. 41, No. 11, 1988, pp. 31-32.

Ripley, D., "Insulation—A Costly Item," *Naval Architect*, 1988, p. 131.

Schwartz, Kenneth J., "Effects of Thermal Insulation on Fire Resistive Assemblies," SFPE TR 81-7, Society of Fire Protection Engineers, Boston, MA, 1981.

Siddiqui, S. A., "Round Robin Fire Safety Tests on Cellulose Insulation," *Journal of Thermal Insulation*, Vol. 10, July 1986, pp. 11-21.

Stirling, C. M., and Southern, J. R., "Stabilizing External Insulation in Fires," *Insulation Journal*, Vol. 33, No. 1, 1989, pp. 10-12.

"Thermal Insulation and Fire Protection," *Insulation Journal*, Vol. 30, No. 8, 1986, pp. 13-14.

OXYGEN-ENRICHED ATMOSPHERES

Revised by George J. Frankel

This chapter discusses the fire hazards that may be associated with oxygen-enriched atmospheres and the methods that can be used to reduce them and to protect against them. Oxygen is a clear, colorless, odorless, and tasteless element commonly found in the gaseous state. It comprises about 21 percent of Earth's atmosphere and is by far the most common oxidizing material. An oxygen-enriched atmosphere (OEA) is defined as any atmosphere in which the concentration of oxygen exceeds 21 percent by volume, or the partial pressure of oxygen exceeds 160 torr (21.3 kPa), or both. (See Table 3-15A.)

The normal concentration of oxygen available in the atmosphere is generally sufficient for human needs, but oxygen-enriched atmospheres are often needed in medical practice, industry, underwater tunneling and caisson work, space and deep-sea exploration, and in commercial and military aviation. They also are inherent to oxygen processing, transport, and storage facilities. In addition, oxygen-enriched atmospheres can develop inadvertently when oxygen or compressed air is transported, stored, or utilized.

Further information of interest to those dealing with oxygen-enriched atmospheres can be found in the following chapters: Section 2, Chapter 9, "Fluid Power Systems;" Section 3, Chapter 2, "Fire Hazards of Materials: An Overview;" Section 3, Chapter 5, "Flammable and Combustible Liquids;" Section 3, Chapter 6, "Medical Gases;" Section 3, Chapter 7, "Gases;" Section 5, Chapter 22, "Special Systems and Extinguishing Techniques;" Section 8, Chapter 13, "Health Care Facilities;" and Section 8, Chapter 29, "Protection for Laboratories."

FIRE HAZARDS IN OXYGEN-ENRICHED ATMOSPHERES

Fire, as a chemical reaction between a fuel and oxygen, is affected by the concentration of the reactants. The commonly encountered fire involves the 21 percent concentration of oxygen available from the atmosphere.

The degree of fire hazard of an oxygen-enriched atmosphere varies with the concentration of oxygen present, the concentration of any nonflammable (diluent) gas present, and the total pressure. However, an oxygen-enriched atmosphere, as defined, does not necessarily result in an increased fire hazard. Certain oxygen-enriched atmospheres may exhibit combustion-supporting properties similar to ambient air; while others are incapable of supporting the combustion of normally flammable materials. For example, a 4 percent oxygen mixture in nitrogen or helium at a total pressure of 12 atmospheres (1216 kPa) will not support the combustion of paper, even though it is an oxygen-enriched atmosphere, because the partial pressure of oxygen is 365 torr (48.7 kPa). However, different concentrations and pressures may accelerate the combustion of these materials, facilitate ignition, and, in general, increase the fire hazard. Most commonly encountered oxygen-enriched atmospheres fall into this latter category.

Fires and explosions have occurred in many diverse circumstances involving both intentional and unintentional oxygen-enriched atmospheres. Among them are:

1. Oxygen production, transportation, and transfer. This may involve truck delivery of liquid oxygen, high-pressure oxygen cylinder recharging, oxygen columns, and compressors.
2. Medical. This may involve operating rooms and anesthesia machines, oxygen tents and infant incubators, or oxygen respirators, such as those used by ambulances, rescue squads, and fire and police, and near swimming pools.
3. Cutting and welding.
4. Industrial processing. This may involve the manufacture of gasoline, ammonia, methanol, acetylene, nitric acid, ethylene, etc.
5. Hospital and laboratory supply systems.
6. Space and deep-sea activities. This category may involve missile fueling/defueling, rocket engine testing, manned space environment simulation/spacecraft testing, and deep-sea diving decompression chambers.

George J. Frankel, a consultant based in Highland Park, NJ, is chairman of the NFPA Committee on Fire Hazards in Oxygen-Enriched Atmospheres.

TABLE 3-15A. ***Partial Pressures of Oxygen at Altitudes Above and Below Sea Level***

Total Absolute Pressure				Altitude Above or Depth Below Sea Level — Air or Sea Water		Partial Pressure of Oxygen if Atmosphere is Air	Concentration of Oxygen if Partial Pressure of Oxygen is 160 mm Hg or torr
Atmospheres	mm Hg or torr	kPa	psia	Feet	Meters	mm Hg or torr*	% by Volume
1/5	152	20.3	2.9	38,500	11,735	32	100.0†
1/3	253	33.8	4.9	27,500	8,382	53	62.7†
1/2	380	50.7	7.3	18,000	5,486	80	42.8†
2/3	506	67.6	9.8	11,000	3,353	106	31.3†
1	760	101.3	14.7	Sea Level	Sea Level	160	20.9
2	1,520	202.7	29.4	−33	−10	320†	10.5
3	2,280	304.0	44.1	−66	−20	480†	6.9
4	3,040	405.3	58.8	−99	−30	640†	5.2
5	3,800	506.6	73.5	−132	−40	800†	4.2

* This column shows the increased available oxygen in compressed- air atmospheres.
† Oxygen-enriched atmosphere.

7. Aircraft oxygen systems. Included here are commercial and military aircraft onboard oxygen breathing systems, and aircraft maintenance operations in the presence of oxygen.
8. Inadvertent substitution of oxygen for air or nitrogen.

IGNITION AND COMBUSTION OF MATERIALS IN OEAs

The minimum energy that molecules (including those of fuels and oxygen) must possess to permit chemical interaction is referred to as the activation energy. If the energy released by this chemical reaction is sufficient to impart activation energy to other molecules on a self-sustaining basis, ignition has occurred. The rate of combustion depends upon the chemical nature and physical characteristics of the fuel and oxidant, their relative concentrations, environmental pressure and temperature, and other physical parameters, such as geometry and ventilation.

The likelihood of ignition and the rate of flame propagation of a combustible are greatly influenced by the oxygen content of the environment. In general (although not in every case), the greater the oxygen concentration, the lower the minimum ignition energy required for ignition, and the faster the flame spread rate. This is shown graphically in Figures 3-15A and 3-15B.

Thus, in general, the fire hazard in an oxygen-enriched atmosphere is significantly greater than that in an ordinary atmosphere. Almost all materials are flammable in a pure oxygen environment; therefore, increased oxygen concentration may change the classification of a material from the nonflammable to the flammable category.

Figures 3-15C and 3-15D depict three combustion zones for vertical filter paper strips in mixtures of oxygen-nitrogen and oxygen-helium, respectively. Those combinations of oxygen concentrations and total pressure lying above the 0.21 atmosphere oxygen partial-pressure isobar (lower dashed line) are, by definition, oxygen-enriched atmospheres, but they may be located in any of three zones: (1) noncombustion, (2) incomplete combustion, or (3) complete combustion. Note that there are certain oxygen-enriched atmospheres that do not produce an increased fire hazard.

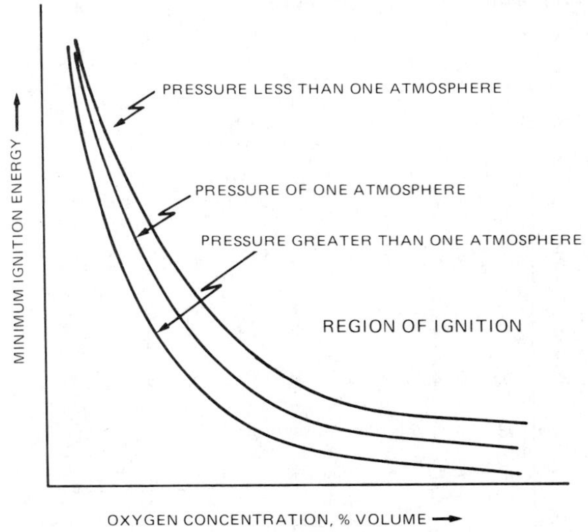

FIG. 3-15A. ***Minimum ignition energy behavior of combustibles in oxygen-diluent atmospheres at different pressures.***

Behavior of Materials in OEAs

Since combustible materials ignite more easily and burn more rapidly in an oxygen-enriched atmosphere than in a normal atmosphere, the careful selection of materials for use in association with an oxygen-enriched atmosphere can do much to reduce the fire hazard.

Combustible liquids and gases: For combustible liquids and gases, the potential fire or explosion hazard can be defined, in part, by the temperature required for the formation of flammable mixtures, the temperature and energy requirements for ignition of the mixture, and the critical fuel concentration (limits) for flame propagation. Such information is presented in Table 3-15B for various representative liquid and gas combustibles in oxygen or air atmospheres, or in both.

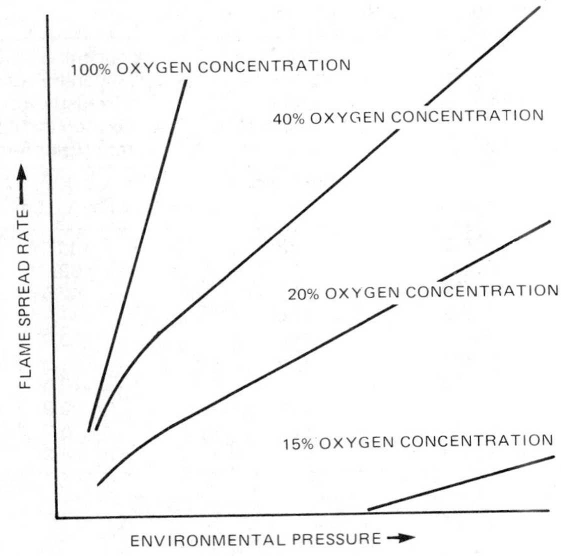

FIG. 3-15B. Effects of atmosphere oxygen content and environmental pressure on flame spread rate.

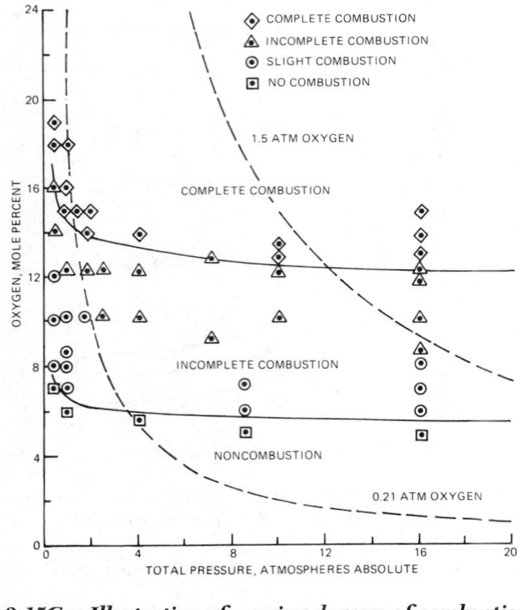

FIG. 3-15C. Illustration of varying degrees of combustion in an oxygen-nitrogen OEA.[1]

The minimum autoignition temperatures (AITs) of most hydrocarbon fuels, solvents, and anesthetic agents fall between 400 and 1,000°F (204 and 538°C) in air at 1 atmosphere pressure. (See Table 3-15B.) Although the autoignition temperature tends to be lower in oxygen than in air, the differences are not great for many hydrocarbons. In the case of lubricants and hydraulic fluids, however, the effect of oxygen concentration on the AIT tends to be greater than observed for the neat hydrocarbons in Table 3-15B. Figure 3-15E shows that the AITs for five of the hydraulic fluids decrease between 200 and 300°F (93 and 149°C) when the oxygen concentration is increased from 21 to 100 percent.

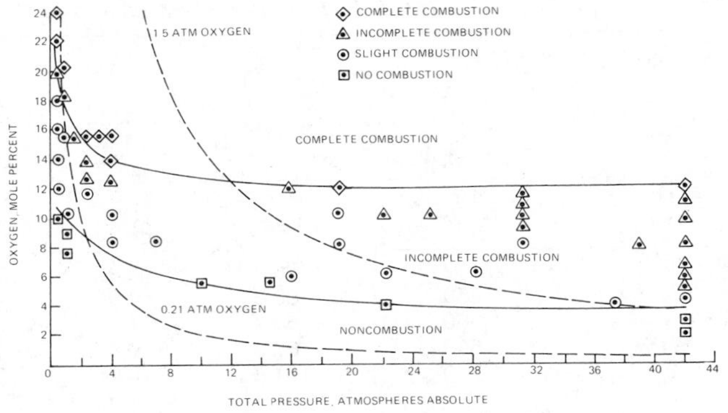

FIG. 3-15D. Illustration of varying degrees of combustion in an oxygen-helium OEA.[1]

A correlation of AIT with oxygen partial pressure is shown in Figure 3-15F for several combustible fluids at various pressures and oxygen concentrations.

The limits of flammability are of interest, also. Although most lower limits in oxygen do not differ greatly from those in air, the upper limits are usually much higher in oxygen, and tend to be above 50 percent for many materials. Furthermore, some materials, such as the halogenated materials bromochloromethane and dibromodifluoromethane, are flammable in oxygen over a wide range of mixture compositions; however, they are not reported as being flammable in air. Of the halogenated solvents, trichloroethylene displays the widest range of flammability in both air and oxygen, although elevated temperatures are necessary.

In general, most flammable liquids and gases can be expected to form flammable mixtures over a wide range of oxygen or oxygen-diluent concentrations. Nonflammable or inert gases are frequently used for explosion prevention. Nitrogen is more effective than helium, but not as effective as carbon dioxide or water vapor. Figures 3-15G and 3-15H show the complete range of flammable mixture compositions that may be expected with a hydrocarbon (cyclopropane) in air or oxygen, and various inert gases at atmospheric pressure.

The minimum oxygen percentage below which most hydrocarbon mixtures are not flammable is about 14 percent with carbon dioxide, and 10 to 12 percent with nitrogen. Corresponding values for hydrogen and carbon monoxide are 6 percent and 5 to 5.5 percent, respectively.

Combustible solids: For combustible solids, the ignition and flammability data for any given material are dependent on many variables, e.g., the specimen's physical characteristics, the ignition source, the orientation of the specimen, the environmental characteristics, ventilation characteristics, inerting diluents, etc. In general, however, ignition temperatures are lower and flame resistance is less in an oxygen-enriched atmosphere than in a normal atmosphere. (See Tables 3-15C and 3-15D.)

Additionally, the rate of flame spread increases with increase in the oxygen concentration at constant pressure or with increase in the total pressure at a constant percentage of oxygen (increased oxygen partial pressure). Various flame spread rate data are given in Tables 3-15E, 3-15F, and 3-15G.

TABLE 3-15B. ***Ignition and Flammability Properties of Combustible Liquids and Gases in Air and Oxygen at Atmospheric Pressure***

	Flash Point* Air		Min. Ign. Temperature†				Min. Ign. Energy‡		Flammabiltiy Limits§ Vol. %			
			Air		Oxygen				Air		Oxygen	
Combustible	°F	°C	°F	°C	°F	°C	Air mJ	Oxygen mJ	LFL**	UFL††	LFL**	UFL††
				Hydrocarbon Fuels								
Methane	Gas	Gas	1166	630	—	—	0.30	0.003	5.0	15	5.1	61
Ethane	Gas	Gas	959	515	943	506	0.25	0.002	3.0	12.4	3.0	66
n-Butane	−76	−60	550	288	532	278	0.25	0.009	1.8	8.4	1.8	49
n-Hexane	25	−3.8	437	225	424	218	0.288	0.006	1.2	7.4	1.2	52*
n-Octane	56	13.3	428	218	406	208	—	—	0.8	6.5	≤0.8	—
Ethylene	Gas	Gas	914	490	905	485	0.07	0.001	2.7	36	2.9	80
Propylene	Gas	Gas	856	458	793	423	0.28	—	2.4	11	2.1	53
Acetylene	Gas	Gas	581	305	565	296	0.017	0.0002	2.5	100	≤2.5	100
Gasoline (100/130)	−50	−45.5	824	440	600	316	—	—	1.3	7.1	≤1.3	—
Kerosene	100	37.8	440	227	420	216	—	—	0.7	5	0.7	—
				Anesthetic Agents								
Cyclopropane	Gas	Gas	932	500	849	454	0.18	0.001	2.4	10.4	2.5	60
Ethyl Ether	−20	−28.8	380	193	360	182	0.20	0.0013	1.9	36	2.0	82
Vinyl Ether	<−22	−30	680	300	331	166	—	—	1.7	27	1.8	85
Ethylene	Gas	Gas	914	490	905	485	0.07	0.001	2.7	36	2.9	80
Ethyl Chloride	−58	−50	961	516	874	468	—	—	4.0	14.8	4.0	67
Chloroform				Nonflammable								
Nitrous Oxide				Nonflammable								
				Solvents								
Methyl Alcohol	54	12.2	725	385	—	—	0.14	—	6.7	36	≤6.7	93
Ethyl Alcohol	55	12.8	689	365	—	—	—	—	3.3	19	≤3.3	—
n-Propyl Alcohol	59	15	824	440	622	328	—	—	2.2	14	≤2.2	—
Glycol	232	111.1	752	400	—	—	—	—	3.5*	—	≤3.5	—
Glycerol	320	160	698	370	608	320	—	—	—	—	—	—
Ethyl Acetate	24	−4.4	800	427	—	—	0.48	—	2.2	11	≤2.2	—
n-Amyl Acetate	76	24.4	680	360	453	234	—	—	1.0	7.1	≤1.0	
Acetone	0	−17.7	869	465	—	—	1.15	0.0024	2.6	13	≤2.6	60‖
Benzene	12	−11.1	1040	560	—	—	0.22	—	1.3	7.9	≤1.3	30
Naphtha (Stoddard)	~100	37.8	~450	232	~420	216	—	—	1.0	6	≤1.0	—
Toluene	40	4.4	896	480	—	—	2.5	—	1.2	7.1	≤1.2	—
Butyl Chloride	20	−6.6	464	240	455	235	0.332	0.007‖	1.8	10	1.7	52
Methylene Chloride	—	—	1139	615	1123	606	—	0.137	15.9‖	19.1‖	11.7*	68
Ethylene Chloride	56	13.3	889	476	878	470	2.37	0.011‖	6.2	16	4.0	67.5
Trichloroethane	—	—	856	458	784	418	—	0.092	6.3‖	13‖	5.5*	57‖
Trichloroethylene	90	32.2	788	420	745	396	—	18*	10.5*	41*	7.5	91‖
Carbon Tetrachloride				Nonflammable								
				Miscellaneous Combustibles								
Acetaldehyde	−17	−27.2	347	175	318	159	0.38	—	4.0	60	4.0	93
Acetic Acid	104	40	869	465	—	—	—	—	5.4‖	—	≤5.4	—
Ammonia	Gas	Gas	1204	651	—	—	>1000	—	15.0	28	15.0	79
Aniline	168	75.5	1139	615	—	—	—	—	1.2‖	8.3	≤1.2	—
Carbon Monoxide	Gas	Gas	1128	609	1090	588	—	—	12.5	74	≤12.5	94
Carbon Disulfide	−22	30	194	90	—	—	0.015	—	1.3	50	≤1.3	—
Ethylene Oxide	<0	<−17.8	804	429	—	—	0.062	—	3.6	100	≤3.6	100
Propylene Oxide	−35	−37.2	—	—	—	—	0.14	—	2.8	37	≤2.8	—
Hydrogen	Gas	Gas	968	520	752	400	0.017	0.0012	4.0	75	4.0	95
Hydrogen Sulfide	Gas	Gas	500	260	428	220	0.077	—	4.0	44	≤4.0	—
Bromochloromethane	—	—	842	450	694	368	—	—	NF‡‡	NF	10.0	85
Bromotrifluoromethane	Gas	Gas	>1100	>593	1215	657	—	—	NF	NF	NF	NF
Dibromodifluoromethane	Gas	Gas	930	499	847	453	—	—	NF	NF	29.0	80

* (NFPA 325M; Humphrey & Morris 1957); open-cup method.
† (Litchfield *et al* 1966; Perlee et al 1966; Scott *et al* 1948; Zabetakis 1965).
‡ (Lewis & Von Elbe 1961; NACA 1957; Blane *et al* 1947; Calcote *et al* 1952; Litchfield *et al* 1966).
§ (Fenn 1951; Litchfield *et al* 1966; Perlee *et al* 1966; Zabetakis 1965; NFPA 491M).
‖ Data at 200°F (93.3°C).
‡‡ NF—No flammable mixtures found in Perlee, 1966.
** LFL–Lower flammable limit.
†† UFL–Upper flammable limit.
Note: See bibliography for sources.

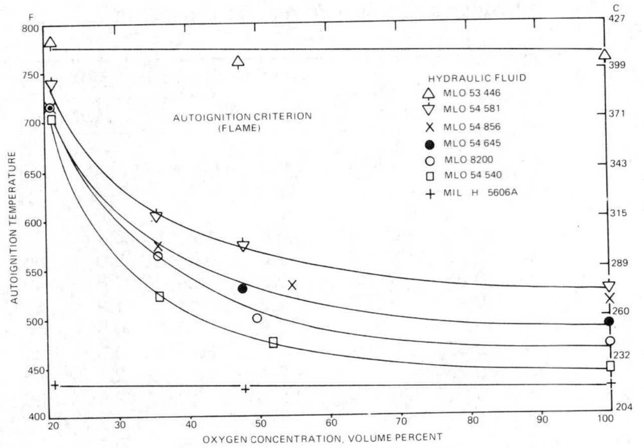

FIG. 3-15E. Minimum autoignition temperatures of seven hydraulic fluids at atmospheric pressure in various oxygen-nitrogen atmospheres (200-cc Pyrex vessel).[3]

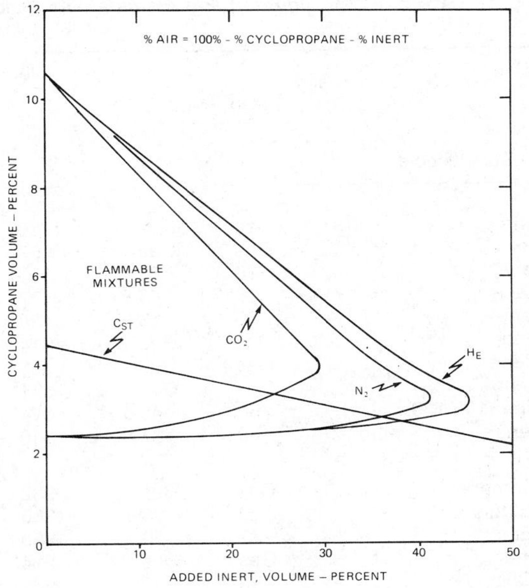

FIG. 3-15G. Limits of flammability of cyclopropane-carbon dioxide-air, cyclopropane-nitrogen-air, and cyclopropane-helium-air mixtures at 77°F (25°C) and atmospheric pressure.[4] *(C_{ST}=stoichiometric composition = line defining amount of combustible vapor required for complete combustion.)*

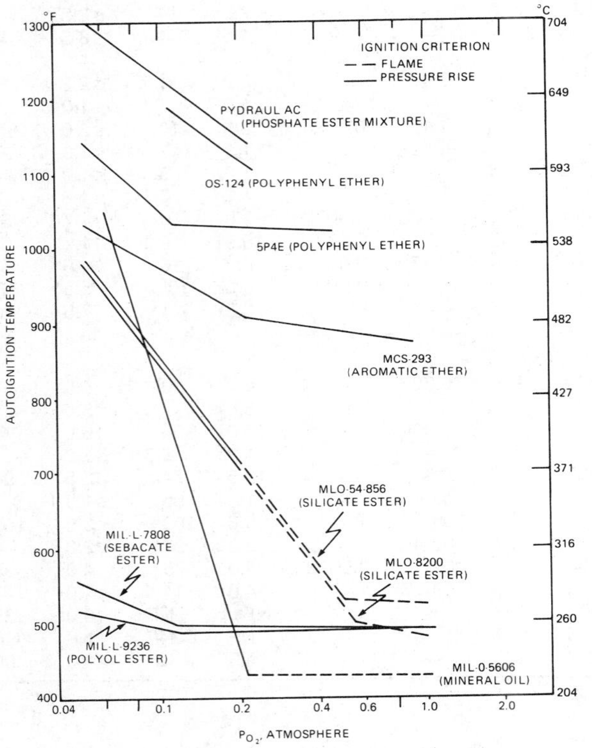

FIG. 3-15F. Variation of minimum autoignition temperature with oxygen partial pressure (PO_2) for various lubricants.[3]

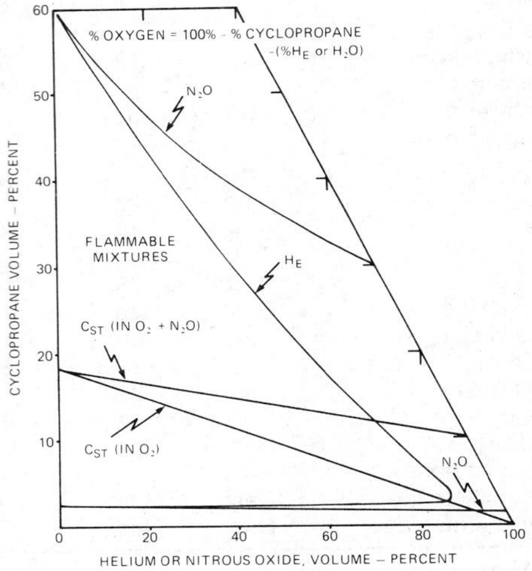

FIG. 3-15H. Limits of flammability of cyclopropane-helium-oxygen and cyclopropane-nitrous oxide-oxygen mixtures at 77°F (25°C) and atmospheric pressure.[4] *(C_{ST} = stoichiometric composition = line defining amount of combustible vapor required for complete combustion.)*

TABLE 3-15C. ***Minimum Hot Plate Ignition Temperatures of Six Combustible Materials in Oxygen-Nitrogen Mixtures at Various Total Pressures****

		Ignition Temperature, °C§			
		Total pressure			
Material	Oxidant	1 Atm	2 Atm	3 Atm	6 Atm
Cotton sheeting	Air	465	440(425)‡	385	365
	42% O2, 58% N_2	390	370	355	340
	100% O_2	360	345	340	325
Cotton sheeting treated†	Air	575	520(510)	485(350)	370(325)
	42% O_2, 58% N_2	390(350)	335	315	295
	100% O_2	310	—	300	285
Conductive rubber sheeting	Air	480	395	370	375
	42% O_2, 58% N_2	430	365	350	350
	100% O_2	360	—	345	345
Paper drapes	Air	470	455	425	405
	42% O_2, 58% N_2	430	—	400	370
	100% O_2	410	—	365	340
Nomex fabric	Air	>600	>600	>600	560
	42% O_2, 58% N_2	550	540	510	495
	100% O_2	520	505	490	470
Polyvinyl chloride sheet	Air	>600	—	495	490
	42% O_2, 58% N_2	575	—	370	350
	100% O_2	390	—	350	325

* (Kuchta *et al* 1967).
† Cotton sheeting treated with Du Pont X-12 fire retardant; amount of retardant equal to 12 percent of cotton specimen weight.
‡ Values in parentheses indicate temperature at which material glowed.
§ °F = 9/5 × °C + 32
Note: See bibliography for sources.

The rate at which flame spreads under a given set of circumstances in an OEA is the most important single property of a solid material from the fire hazard point of view. Several methods for determining flame spread rate characteristics of materials are in use, including NFPA 255, *Method of Test of Surface Burning Characteristics of Building Materials,* and the following American Society for Testing and Materials (ASTM) methods:

1. ASTM E162, *Test for Surface Flammability of Materials Using a Radiant Heat Source.*
2. ASTM D568, *Test for Flammability of Flexible Plastic.*
3. ASTM D1230, *Test for Flammability of Clothing Textiles.*
4. ASTM D2863, *Test for Flammability of Plastics Using the Oxygen Index Method.*

Selected materials are tested under conditions of intended use prior to utilization in oxygen-enriched atmospheres.

DESIGN OF SYSTEMS FOR OEAs

Fire hazard considerations in the design of systems associated with oxygen-enriched atmospheres, e.g., heating, ventilating, and air conditioning (HVAC); hydraulic services; gas and compressed air supplies; suction apparatus; both power and electronic electrical systems; etc.; include:

1. Characteristics of materials of construction (flame spread rate, ignition susceptibility).
2. Risk of fire initiation (expectancy).
3. Presence of potential energy, in the form of compressed gas, etc.
4. Personnel escape paths from occupied areas.

In addition to evaluating the firesafe characteristics of all materials involved in oxygen-enriched environments under end-use performance conditions, oxygen service durability is evaluated by accelerated time tests for deterioration, and by high-energy tests for degradation.

The acceptability of candidate materials for oxygen-enriched atmosphere systems applications is, in part, based on data developed by tests, such as: (1) flash and fire points; (2) upward/downward combustion propagation rates; (3) calorific fuel values (heat of combustion); (4) electrical wire insulation, coating, and accessory flammability tests; (5) electrical overload and hot-wire ignition tests; and (6) odor toxicity, off-gassing, etc.

Electrical equipment used in oxygen-enriched atmospheres is limited to that which is approved at the maximum anticipated oxygen pressure and concentrations. Since most metals burn freely in oxygen-enriched atmospheres, electrical contacts that do not burn in normal atmospheres could burn away and initiate insulation fires in an oxygen-enriched atmosphere.

Some "fire stopping" techniques that may be considered in the design of a system to minimize ignition potential and fire spread in an oxygen-enriched atmosphere are:

1. Avoidance of mass concentration of combustible materials near potential heat or ignition sources.
2. Spatial separation and configuration to minimize or eliminate flame propagation paths.
3. "Thermal damping" by judicious placement of fire-resistant heat-sink masses.
4. Flashover barriers.
5. Sealed packaging, e.g., inerted compartmentation, fire-resistant encapsulation, etc.
6. Automatic fire monitoring, e.g., infrared thermography, etc.

TABLE 3-15D. ***Flame Resistance of Materials Held Vertically at One Atmosphere Pressure in O^2/N_2 Mixtures****

NRL Sample Number	Material	Combustion in O_2/N_2 Mixtures		
		21% O_2	31% O_2	41% O_2
FM-1	Rosin-impregnated paper	Burned	—	—
FM-3	Cotton terry cloth	Burned	—	—
FM-28	Cotton cloth, white duck	Burned	—	—
FM-4	Cotton terry cloth, Roxel-treated	No	No	Burned
FM-5	Fleece-backed cotton cloth, Roxel-treated	Surface only	Burned	Burned
FM-14	Cotton, O.D. Sateen, Roxel-treated	No	Burned	—
FM-15	Cotton, green whipcord, Roxel-treated	No	Burned	—
FM-16	Cotton, white duck, Roxel-treated	No	Burned	—
FM-17	Cotton, King Kord, Roxel-treated	No	Burned	—
FM-29	Cotton white duck, treated with 30 boric acid-70% borax	No	Burned	Burned
FM-30	Cotton terry cloth, treated with 30 boric acid-70% borax	No	Burned	Burned
FM-6	Fire-resistant cotton ticking	No	Burned	—
FM-7	Fire-resistant foam rubber	No	No	Burned
FM-9	Nomex temperature-resistant Nylon	No	Burned	—
FM-10	Teflon fabric	No	No	No
FM-11	Teflon fabric	No	No	No
FM-12	Teflon fabric	No	No	No
FM-13	Teflon fabric	No	No	No
FM-19	Verel fabric	No	Burned	Burned
FM-22	Vinyl-backed fabric	No	Burned	Burned
FM-23	Omnicoated Du Pont high-temperature fabric	No	Burned*	Burned
FM-24	Omnicoated glass fabric	No	No	Burned†
FM-20	Glass fabric, fine weave	No	No	No
FM-21	Glass fabric, knit weave	No	No	No
FM-25	Glass fabric (coarse weave)	No	No	No
FM-26	Glass fabric (coarse weave)	No	No	No
FM-27	Aluminized asbestos fabric	No	No	Burned
FM-32	Rubber from aviator oxygen mask	Burned	Burned	Burned
FM-33	Fluorolube grade 362	No	No	No‡
FM-34	Belco no-flame grease	No	No	No‡

* (Johnson & Woods 1966).
†Burned only over igniter.
‡ White smoke only.
Note: See bibliography for source.

TABLE 3-15E. ***Effect of Oxygen and Storage in Oxygen on Flame Spread Rates over Various Materials (Edges Not Inhibited)****

Material†	Flame spread rate (in./sec‖)		
		In 258 mm Hg oxygen	
	In air	Before storage	After 30 day storage
Butyl rubber	0.006	0.40 ± 0.04	0.31 ± 0.04
Canvas duck	NP‡	0.25 ± 0.05	—
Cellulose acetate	0.012	0.28 ± 0.12	0.24 ± 0.12
Kel-F	NI§	NI	NI
Natural rubber	0.010	0.61 ± 0.05	0.61 ± 0.08
Neoprene rubber	NI	0.32 ± 0.04	0.25 ± 0.05
Nylon 101	NI	0.19 ± 0.05	0.15 ± 0.01
Plexiglas	0.005	0.35 ± 0.01	0.24 ± 0.01
Polyethylene	0.014	0.25 ± 0.05	0.36 ± 0.06
Polypropylene	0.010	0.35 ± 0.01	0.36 ± 0.12
Polystyrene	0.032	0.80 ± 0.20	0.51 ± 0.01
Polyvinyl chloride	NI	0.10 ± 0.01	0.06 ± 0.01
Silicone rubber	NI	0.14 ± 0.01	0.14 ± 0.01
Teflon	NI	NI	NI
Viton A	NI	0.003 ± 0.002	0.01 ± 0.005

* (Hugget *et al* 1965).
† All samples except canvas duck, 3 by 1/2 by 1/5 in (76.2 × 12.7 × 5 mm); canvas duck, 3 by 1/2 by 1/20 in. (76.2 × 12.7 × 1.3 mm).
‡ NP—No sustained propagation of flame.
§ NI—No ignition of material.
‖ 1 in./sec = 25.4 mm/sec.
Note: See bibliography for source.

FIRE EXTINGUISHMENT IN OEAs

Fire extinguishing systems for use in oxygen-enriched atmospheres face new requirements in addition to those imposed on conventional systems because of ignition susceptibility, increased flame spread rate, increased burning intensity, and flammability of normally nonflammable materials. In general, these new requirements cannot be satisfied by the simple extension of classic extinguishment techniques. In addition to special instruction and training of emergency personnel, extinguishing agents and systems must be specially selected.

In view of the increased burning rates of most common materials in oxygen-enriched atmospheres, fire extinguishants should act rapidly to be effective. To protect occupants of affected areas, they should be inherently nontoxic and should not produce significant amounts of toxic decomposition products.

Water has been shown to be an effective extinguishing agent in oxygen-enriched atmospheres when applied in sufficient quantities.[3,4] Water at a spray density of 1¼ gpm per sq ft [50 (L/min)/m^2] applied for 2 min will extinguish cloth burning in 100 percent oxygen at a pressure of 1 atmosphere (101.3 kPa).[3] The method of application of the water to the fire is all-important. Extinguishing systems using water must be carefully designed so that all the

TABLE 3-15F. ***Effect of Oxygen and Storage in Oxygen on Flame Spread Rates over Various Space Cabin Materials (Edges Not Inhibited)****

Material	Flame spread rate (in./sec)§		
		In 258 mm Hg oxygen	
	In air	Before storage	After 30 day storage
Aluminized Mylar tape	—	1.95	—
Aluminized vinyl tape	NI†	3.1 ± 0.4	3.0 ± 0.4
Asbestos insulating tape	NI	0.08	0.05
Chapstick	NI	1.82	—
Cotton shirt fabric	NP‡	1.50 ± 0.05	2.10 ± 0.3
Electrical insulating resin	NI	0.27	0.20
Electrical terminal board	NI	0.06 ± 0.01	0.06 ± 0.01
Fiberglas insulating tape	NI	4.2 ± 0.6	2.0 ± 0.8
Foam cushion material	0.19	12.4	11.3
Foamed insulation	0.002	2.2 ± 0.2	3.0 ± 0.3
Food packet, aluminized paper	NI	0.28 ± 0.05	0.26 ± 0.05
Food packet, brown aluminum	NI	0.7 ± 0.30	0.8 ± 0.20
Food packet, plastic	0.33	0.55	0.47
Glass wool	NI	NI	NI
Masking tape	0.17	1.82	—
Paint, 3-M velvet	NI	0.15 ± 0.01	0.31 ± 0.02
Paint, Capon ivory	NI	0.38 ± 0.04	0.35 ± 0.02
Paint, Pratt & Lambert, grey	NI	0.60 ± 0.2	0.24
Pump oil	NI	0.89	—
Refrigeration oil	NI	0.82 ± 0.07	—
Rubber tubing	0.03	0.24	0.25 ± 0.05
Silicone grease	NI	0.92	—
Solder, rosin core	NI	0.18	0.25
Sponge, washing	0.07	8.1 ± 0.1	10 ± 2
Teflon pipe sealing tape	NI	NI	NI
Teflon tubing	NI	NI	NI
Tygon tubing	0.18	0.50 ± 0.05	0.52 ± 0.05
Wire, Mil W76B, orange	NI	0.57 ± 0.05	0.54
Wire, Mil W76B, blue	NI	—	0.57
Wire, Mil W76B, yellow	NI	—	0.54
Wire, Mil W16878, green	NI	NI	NI
Wire, Mil W16878, black	NI	NI	NI
Wire, Mil W16878, yellow	NI	NI	NI
Wire, Mil W16878, white	NI	NI	NI
Wire, misc., white, 3/32	NI	0.33	0.25
Wire, misc., black, 3/16	NI	—	0.40
Wire, misc., brown, 7/32	NI	0.51 ± 0.05	—
Wire, misc., yellow, 7/64	NI	0.89	—
Wire, misc., yellow, 5/32	NI	0.41	—

* (Hugget *et al* 1965).
† NI—No ignition of material.
‡ NP—No sustained propagation of flame.
§ 1 in./sec = 25.4 mm/sec.
Note: See bibliography for source.

protected space is covered by the minimum spray density and that water is distributed to a depth sufficient to extinguish stratified fires in nonhomogeneous materials, e.g., layers of cloth in clothing.

Several halogenated hydrocarbons have been found useful for extinguishing fires in normal atmospheres. Table 3-15H indicates their behavior in pure oxygen, as well as their toxicity ratings as given by Underwriters Laboratories Inc. (Toxicity ratings for undecomposed vapor range from 1, the most toxic, to 6, the least hazardous.)

Bromotrifluoromethane (Halon 1301) appears to be useful in oxygen-enriched atmospheres. Testing has shown that it will extinguish fires in pure oxygen when used at 50 percent concentration, and in compressed air at 5 percent by volume.[5] Generally, it is effective against few truly deep-seated fires in oxygen-enriched atmospheres. NFPA 12A, *Halon 1301 Fire Extinguishing Systems,* states that concentrations greater than 10 percent are not used in normally occupied areas and, even then, are used only where evacuation can be accomplished immediately.

Generally, halogenated agents are not recommended against fires that involve highly reactive metals or fuels that contain their own oxidizing agent. Such metals as magnesium and aluminum are known to present an increased fire or explosion hazard with certain halogenated hydrocarbons. The hazard posed by these materials will depend upon their quantity, distribution, and physical form, as well as the composition of the extinguishant; the presence of other combustibles can cause a further complication. All such factors must be weighed by the designer in making any recommendation.

Available data regarding the effectiveness of carbon dioxide is inconclusive.

TABLE 3-15G. ***Typical Measured Burning Rates for Strips of Filter Paper at 45-Degree Angle****

			Burn Rate, cm/sec					
Total pressure		Atm. abs. (kPa abs) Ft. of sea water	0.21 Atm. 21.28 —	0.53 Atm. 53.70 —	1.00 Atm. 101.33 0 ft.	4.03 Atm. 408.34 100 ft.	7.06 Atm. 715.35 200 ft.	10.09 Atm. 1022.37 300 ft.
Gas Composition (dry basis)								
%O^2	%N_2†	%He						
99.6	0.4	0.0	2.32	3.13	4.19	‖	‖	‖
50.3	49.7	0.0	1.13 1.17	1.44	2.36	3.72 3.77	5.10 4.06	6.34
20.95‡	79.05	0.0	§	0.80	1.17 1.17 1.10	1.82 1.78	2.80 2.28	3.13 3.25
49.5	0.0	50.5	1.24	1.87 1.90	2.96 2.89 2.89	4.06	4.90 4.82	‖
20.3	0.0	79.7	§	§	§	2.23	2.61	2.49
47.0	24.6	28.4	‖	‖	2.74 2.68	3.66	4.41 4.64	5.53 6.78
20.9	39.6	39.5	‖	‖	1.38 1.38 1.35 1.27	2.28 2.28 1.97 2.28 1.81 1.72	2.71 2.83 2.74	3.72 3.13 3.56 3.33 3.00

* (Cook *et al* 1967).
† Includes any argon that was present.
‡ Compressed air.
§ Sample would not burn, even with brightly glowing igniter grid.
‖ No run was made under these conditions.
Note: See bibliography for source.

TABLE 3-15H. ***Behavior of Halons in Pure Oxygen***

Compound	Halon No.	Toxicity	Behavior in Pure Oxygen*
Carbon tetrachloride, CCl_4	104	3	
Methyl bromide, CH_3Br	1001	2	Flammable
Chlorobromomethane, CH_2BrCl	1011	3	Flammable, decomposes
Dibromodifluoromethane, CBr_2F_2	1202	4	Flammable
Bromochlorodifluoromethane, $CBrClF_2$	1211	5	Nonflammable over tested concentration (14–95%)
Bromotrifluoromethane, CF_3Br	1301	6	Nonflammable over tested range (12–98%)

* (Perlee *et al* 1966)
Note: See bibliography for source.

High-expansion foam has been shown to be effective and that respiration in the foam atmosphere is possible.[6] However, the applicability of this agent to each particular candidate system must be evaluated separately with regard to available space and required time.

Little or no data is available on the use of low-expansion foam or dry chemical in oxygen-enriched atmosphere fires. No reliance should be placed on ordinary fire blankets made of wool or asbestos (with an organic binder).

Because of the rapid flame spread in oxygen-enriched atmospheres, fire extinguishing systems must be capable of fast automatic actuation by fire detectors, as well as by manual actuation. Fixed systems utilize an extinguishing agent acceptable for use on fires in oxygen-enriched atmospheres, and automatic activation occurs in less than one second of the perception of detectable flame development. In addition to the automatic fixed system in occupied areas, a manually operated water hose not less than ½ in. (approxiately 13 mm) inside diameter (ID), and with an effective nozzle pressure not less than 50 psi (345 kPa) above the ambient pressure, is usually provided.

BIBLIOGRAPHY

References Cited

1. Dorr, V. A., "Fire Studies in Oxygen-Enriched Atmospheres," *Journal of Fire and Flammability*, Vol. 1, 1970, pp. 91-106.
2. Scott, G. S., Jones, G. W., and Scott, F. E., "Determination of Ignition Temperatures of Combustible Liquids and Gases," *Analytical Chemistry*, Vol. 20, Mar. 1948, p. 238.
3. Denison, D., and Cresswell, A. W., "The Fire Risks to Man of Oxygen- and Rich Gas Environments," IAM Report No. 320, Apr. 1965, and Report No. 343, Sept. 1965, Civil Aeromedical Institute, Aeronautical Center, Oklahoma City, OK.
4. Botteri, B. P., "Fire Protection in Oxygen-Enriched Atmospheres," *Fire Journal*, Vol. 62, No. 1, Jan. 1967, pp. 48-55.

5. Eggleston, L. A., "Firesafety in Hyperbaric Chambers," *Fire Technology*, Vol. 6, No. 4, Nov. 1970.

6. Charno, R. J., "Evaluation of High-Expansion Foam for Spacecraft Fire Extinguishment," N69-20776, Feb. 3, 1969, E. W. Bliss Co., Swarthmore, PA; prepared for NASA/JSC (Johnson Space Center).

References

Blanc, M. V., *et al*, "Ignition of Explosive Gas Mixtures by Electrical Sparks—Minimum Ignition Energies and Quenching Distances of Methane, Oxygen, and Inert Gases," *Journal of Chemical Physics*, Vol. 15, 1947, p. 798.

Calcote, H. F., *et al*, "Spark Ignition," *Industrial and Engineer Chemistry*, Vol. 44, No. 11, Nov. 1952, p. 2656.

Cook, G. A., Meierer, R. E., and Shields, B. M., "Screening of Flame-Resistant Materials and Comparison of Helium with Nitrogen for Use in Diving Atmospheres," First Summary Report on Combustion Safety in Diving Atmospheres, Mar. 31, 1967, U.S. Department of the Navy, Office of Naval Research and Naval Ship Systems Command, Washington, DC.

Dorr, V. A., "Fire Studies in Oxygen-Enriched Atmospheres," *Journal of Fire and Flammability*, Vol. 1, 1970, pp. 91-106.

Fenn, J. B., "Lean Flammability Limit and Minimum Spark Ignition Energy," *Industrial and Engineering Chemistry*, Vol. 43, No. 12, Dec. 1951, p. 2865.

Hugget, C., *et al*, "The Effects of 100% Oxygen at Reduced Pressure on the Ignitibility and Combustibility of Materials," SAM-TR-65-78, Dec. 1965, Brooks Air Force Base, TX.

Humphrey, H. B., and Morris, G., "Safety with Solvents," USDI Bureau of Mines Information Circular 7757, 1957, Washington, DC.

Lewis, B., and Von Elbe, G., *Combustion Flames and Explosion of Gases*, Academic Press, New York, pp. 323-346, 1961.

Litchfield, E. L., Kuchta, J. M., and Furno, A. L., "Flammability of Propellant Combinations," USDI Bureau of Mines Explosives Research Report 3997, Oct. 30, 1966, Washington, DC; USDI Bureau of Mines Research Report 3958, June 30, 1965, Washington, DC.

NACA, "Basic Considerations in the Combustion of Hydrocarbon Fuels with Air," NACA Report 1300, 1957, National Advisory Committee for Aeronautics, Washington, DC.

Perlee, H. E., Martindill, G. H., and Zabetakis, M. G., "Flammability Characteristics of Selected Halogenated Hydrocarbons," USDI Bureau of Mines RI 6748, 1966, Washington, DC.

Zabetakis, M. G., "Flammability Characteristics of Combustible Gases and Vapors," USDI Bureau of Mines Bulletin 627, 1965, Washington, DC.

NFPA Codes, Standards, and Recommended Practices

Reference to the following NFPA codes, standards, and recommended practices will provide further information on oxygen-enriched atmospheres discussed in this chapter. (See the latest *NFPA Catalog* for availability of current editions of the following documents.)

NFPA 12A, *Halon 1301 Fire Extinguishing Systems.*

NFPA 50, *Bulk Oxygen Systems at Consumer Sites.*

NFPA 51, *Oxygen-Fuel Gas Systems for Welding, Cutting, and Allied Processes.*

NFPA 53M, *Fire Hazards in Oxygen-Enriched Atmospheres.*

NFPA 99, *Health Care Facilities.*

NFPA 255, *Method of Test of Surface Burning Characteristics of Building Materials.*

NFPA 325M, *Fire Hazard Properties of Flammable Liquids, Gases, and Volatile Solids.*

NFPA 491M, *Manual of Hazardous Chemical Reactions.*

Additional Reading

Aerospace Medical Division, *Proceedings* of Fire Hazards and Extinguishment Conference, Brooks Air Force Base, TX, May 23, 1967.

Attallah, S., and DeRis, J. N., "Pressure Rise Due to a Fire in an Enclosure," *Fire Technology*, Vol. 5, No. 2, May 1969, pp. 112-121.

Ault, W. E., and Carter, D. L., "The Influence of Hyperbaric Chamber Pressure on Water Spray Patterns," *Fire Journal*, Vol. 61, No. 6, Nov. 1967, p. 48.

Brenneman, J. J., "Oxygen Induced Cabin Fire," *Fire Journal*, Vol. 65, No. 5, Sept. 1971, pp. 26-28.

Eggleston, L. A., "Evaluation of Fire Extinguishing Systems for Use in Oxygen Rich Atmospheres," Final Report prepared for Aerospace Medical Division, Brooks Air Force Base, May 1967, Southwest Research Institute, San Antonio, TX.

Fitt, P. W., Collings, N., and O'Neill, D., "The Ignition of Solid Materials in Oxygen by Electrical Sparks," *Fire Prevention and Suppression*, Hilado, C. J., ed., Technomic, Westport, CT, 1974, pp. 62-73.

Flammability and Sensitivity of Materials in Oxygen-Enriched Atmospheres, Vols.1-4, American Society for Testing and Materials, Philadelphia, PA, 1989.

Harter, J. V., "The Problem of Fire at High Pressure," *Proceedings* of the Third Symposium on Underwater Physiology, ed. by C. J. Lambertsen, The Williams and Wilkins Company, Baltimore, 1967, pp. 76-77.

Johnson, J. E., and Woods, F. J., "Flammability in Unusual Atmospheres, Part I—Preliminary Studies of Materials in Hyperbaric Atmospheres Containing Oxygen, Nitrogen, and/or Helium," NRL Report 6470, Oct. 31, 1966, Naval Research Laboratory, Washington, DC.

Kuchta, J. M., *et al*, "Flammability of Materials in Hyperbaric Atmospheres," USDI Bureau of Mines Final Report 4016, Aug. 30, 1967, Explosive Research Center, Pittsburgh.

Kuchta, J. M., Furno, A. L., and Martindill, G. H., "Flammability of Fabrics and Other Materials in Oxygen-Enriched Atmospheres, Part I. Ignition Temperature and Flame Spread Rates," *Fire Technology*, Vol. 5, No. 3, Aug. 1969, pp. 203-216.

Litchfield, E. L., and Kubala, T. A., "Flammability and Ignition of Fabrics and Other Materials in Oxygen-Enriched Atmospheres, Part II. Minimum Ignition Energies," *Fire Technology*, Vol. 5, No. 4, Nov. 1969, pp. 341-345.

Nakakuki, A., "Extinction of Fires in Hyperbaric Chambers: Part I, Water Spray Properties and Extinction with Single Spray Nozzles," *Fire Technology*, Vol. 8, No. 1, Feb. 1972, pp. 5-18.

Purser, P. R., "Ignition by Electrostatic Sparks in Hyperbaric Oxygen," *The Lancet*, Dec. 24, 1966.

Segal, L., *et al*, "Fire Suppression in Hyperbaric Chambers," *Fire Journal*, Vol. 60, No. 3, May 1966, pp. 17-18.

Turner, H. L., and Segal, L., "Fire Behavior and Protection in Hyperbaric Chambers," *Fire Technology*, Vol. 1. No. 4, Nov. 1965, pp. 269-277.

Werley, B. L., "Fire Safety Standard for Polymers in Oxygen Environments," *Materials Engineering*, Vol. 104, No. 4, 1987, pp. 54, 58.

Widawsky, A., "Fire Protection System for a Hyperbaric Chamber," *Fire Technology*, Vol. 9, No. 2, May 1973, pp. 85-90.

Wilson, R., and Ledoux, E. F., "High-Speed Protection for Personnel in Oxygen-Enriched Atmospheres," *Fire Journal*, Vol. 62, No. 2, Mar. 1968, pp. 23-25.

Zallen, D. M., and Morehouse, E. T., "Fire Extinguishing Agents for Oxygen-Enriched Atmospheres," *Proceedings* of the Third International Symposium on Flammability and Sensitivity of Materials in Oxygen-Enriched Atmospheres, 3rd Vol., American Society for Testing and Materials, 1988, pp. 391-412.

PESTICIDES

William J. Keffer

Pesticides are extremely diverse in chemical composition and formulation, reflecting the enormous diversity of pests, pest management problems, and application conditions. These "tools" of pest management are closely regulated under a variety of federal and state regulations. The principal federal regulations of concern to fire prevention and response personnel are:

- *Federal Insecticide, Fungicide, and Rodenticide Act (FIFRA).* Since 1970 this act has been administered by the Environmental Protection Agency (EPA). FIFRA controls the registration, classification, suspension, and cancellation of all pesticide products. This act is also responsible for the presence of a registration number on each container; this number allows the user to identify the manufacturing facility.
- *Resource Conservation and Recovery Act (RCRA).* This act, administered by EPA, identifies many pesticide products as hazardous wastes and provides regulations for the environmentally safe disposal of these materials.
- *Hazardous Materials Transportation Act (HMTA).* This act, administered by the Department of Transportation (DOT), provides for the identification and packaging conditions under which many hazardous pesticides may be offered or carried in commercial transportation.
- *Occupational Safety and Health Act.* This act, administered by the Occupational Safety and Health Administration (OSHA), regulates limits for worker exposure to many pesticide-type substances and also provides requirements for identification and training of potentially exposed workers under the Hazard Communication Standard (HCS).
- *Comprehensive Environmental Response Compensation and Liability Act (CERCLA/Superfund).* This act, administered by the EPA, identifies many pesticide products as hazardous materials. These products must be reported when released to the air, water, or land of the United States for other-than-normal agricultural applications, and must be cleaned up and disposed of properly.
- *Emergency Planning and Community Right-to-Know (SARA Title III).* This act, administered by the EPA, identifies many pesticides as extremely hazardous substances. It also requires that commercial manufacturers, storers, and users of certain quantities identify themselves to state and local emergency planning commissions. They must also report releases of these extremely hazardous substances to local authorities *immediately* upon release.

Additional information relevant to the hazards of storage and use of pesticides can be found in this handbook. See the following sections and chapters:

Section 2

2-25 Storage of Flammable and Combustible Liquids

2-26 Storage of Gases

2-27 Storage and Handling of Chemicals

2-34 Housekeeping Practices

Section 3

3-2 Fire Hazards of Materials: An Overview

3-5 Flammable and Combustible Liquids

3-7 Gases

3-8 Chemicals

Section 8

8-4 Warehouse Pre-fire Planning and Fire Fighting Operations

8-5 General Indoor Storage

8-7 Outdoor Storage Practices

8-9 Environmental Issues in Fire Protection

Section 9

9-12 The Role of the Fire Protection Community in Hazardous Waste Control

9-13 Identification of the Hazards of Materials

William J. Keffer is senior engineering advisor, U.S. Environmental Protection Agency, Kansas City, KS.

DEFINITION OF PESTICIDES

The definition of a pesticide as provided in the FIFRA Act is comprehensive, and includes a chemical or mixture of chemicals or substances used to repel or combat an animal or plant pest. This includes insects and other invertebrate organisms; all vertebrate pests, e.g., rodents, fish, pest birds, snakes, gophers; all plant pests growing where not wanted, e.g., weeds; and all microorganisms which may or may not produce disease in humans. Household germicides, plant growth regulators, and plant root destroyers are also included in the definition.

Pesticides are typed according to their primary or specific control purposes or to reflect the manner in which they are used. Insecticides (insect control), fungicides (fungus and bacteria control), herbicides (unwanted plant control), nematocides (earth and water worm control), and rodenticides (rodent control) are examples of pesticides classified by control purposes. Fumigants are an example of pesticides that are classified by the manner in which they are used, in that a fumigant is a pesticide that acts in the gaseous, or "fume," state.

Pesticides are also classified by the hazard to users or the environment. Many concentrations and specific poisons are only available to trained and licensed applicators.

Well over one billion pounds of pesticides are produced and sold annually in the United States. In addition to their manufacturing facilities, pesticides can be found stored in commercial warehouses, agricultural chemical warehouses, farm supply stores, nurseries, farms, supermarkets and discount stores, hardware stores and other retail outlets, on the premises of commercial pest control and lawn-care operators, and in the home. Large quantities are continually being transported as liquids, solids, and gases in highway and rail transportation.

HAZARDS AND HAZARD IDENTIFICATION

In addition to the obvious health hazard of the pesticide active ingredient (because what can kill other forms of life can also kill humans), pesticide formulations (i.e., active ingredients, carriers, and adjuvants) can also be corrosive, reactive, flammable, or combustible. The products of combustion of some formulations may present a significant toxic hazard. Some formulations may act as oxidizing agents that can accelerate combustion. Runoff water from fires involving pesticide products may be highly contaminated and may represent a human health and environmental hazard. It is not uncommon to find pesticides stored in close proximity to other agricultural products, swimming pool chemicals, and various fuels. This is especially common in large discount stores in urban and suburban areas.

Pesticide formulations are encountered in all three states of matter: liquid, solid, and gaseous. Flammable or combustible liquids are widely used to dissolve solid pesticides in order to facilitate application. Adjuvants are frequently added to reduce surface tension, increase uptake by target, and protect against wash off/abrasion, all of which may also increase the hazard during fire or other release incidents. The hazards of flammable or combustible liquids when released from containers can range from a simple spill fire to a combustible explosion of vapors, fogs, or mists during application. Solids are usually stored and handled as granules, dusts, and powders. If they are combustible, they can present a dust explosion hazard when dispersed into the air. Most pesticide powders, however, are specific formulations absorbed into an inert material, such as clay.

The intrinsic toxicity of the active ingredient in pesticides varies considerably. Table 3-16A lists the toxicity of the active ingredients of some common pesticides routinely offered for retail sale to the general public, and provides information on a few other common substances for comparative purposes.

TABLE 3-16A. ***Common Pesticide Toxicities***

	Oral LD 50* mg/kg	Dermal LD 50* mg/kg
Fungicides		
captan	9,000	—
chlorothalinol	>10,000	>10,000
Herbicides		
2,4-D	375	—
glyphosate	4,300	—
prometron (tech-Pramitol)	2,980	>2,000
Calcium acid methanearsonate	4,000	—
Insecticides		
acephate (tech-Orthene)	945	>10,250
carbaryl (tech-Sevin)	283	—
chloropyrifos (Dursban)	270	2,000
diazanon (tech)	400	3,600
disulfuton (tech-Disyston)	12	25
lindane	125	1,000
malathion	1,375	4,100
methyoxychlor	6,000	—
rotenone	1,500	—
EPA definition of extremely hazardous substances	50	
Table salt	3,320	
Aspirin	1,200	

*LD_{50} is a measurement value used in toxicity tests to specify the dose of a substance which is most likely to cause death within 14 days in one half of the test animals.

It is very difficult for safety program managers and local emergency planners to obtain adequate hazard information on occupancies for several reasons. Hazard information provided on labels is frequently based only on the active ingredient and does not include fire, health, or reactivity hazard of the complete formulation consisting of active ingredients, carriers, and adjuvants. Information on the synergistic effects of releases involving a mixture of pesticide materials is not available. Concentrations of active ingredients vary widely in the various formulations. The system of hazard identification required by EPA is based on the active ingredient testing only and is not compatible with the NFPA 704, *Identification of the Fire Hazards of Materials*, system. Many manufacturers have not prepared material safety data sheets (MSDS) for commonly encountered formulations.

Table 3-16B lists the current EPA-required warning systems for labeling pesticide containers based on active ingredients.

TABLE 3-16B. ***EPA Toxicity Categories***

Category 1: POISON/DANGER

All pesticide products meeting the following criteria:
Oral LD_{50} up to and including 50 mg/kg,
Inhalation LD_{50} up to and including 0.2 mg/liter,
Dermal LD_{50} up to and including 200 mg/kg,
Eye effects—corneal opacity not reversible within 7 days, and
Skin effects corrosive.

Must bear on the front panel the signal word "Danger." In addition, if the product was assigned to category 1 on the basis of its oral, inhalation, or dermal toxicity (as distinct from skin and eye local effects), the word "Poison" must appear in red on a background of distinctly contrasting color and the skull and crossbones must appear in immediate proximity to the word "Poison."

Category 2: WARNING

All pesticides meeting the following criteria:
Oral LD_{50} from 50 through 500 mg/kg,
Inhalation LD_{50} from 0.2 through 2.0 mg/liter,
Dermal LD_{50} from 200 through 200 mg/kg,
Eye effects—corneal opacity reversible within 7 days (irritation persisting for 7 days) and
Skin effects—severe irritation at 72 hours

Must bear on the front panel the signal word "Warning."

Categories 3 and 4: CAUTION

All pesticide products meeting the following criteria:
Oral LD_{50} greater than 500 mg/kg,
Inhalation LD_{50} greater than 2.0 mg/liter,
Dermal LD_{50} greater than 2,000 mg/kg,
Eye effects—no corneal opacity, and
Skin effects—moderate irritation at 72 hours

Must bear on the front panel the signal word "Caution."

One additional pesticide categorization system may be helpful. There has been a considerable effort on the part of the federal government to limit accessibility of the general public to many of the more toxic formulations of pesticide products. It may be assumed that, in general, those products and formulations that require licensed applicators may present a more serious health risk than the same chemicals formulated in more dilute concentrations for general retail sales. Many of the more toxic and persistent pesticides have been canceled for any use by EPA but may still be found by fire personnel. These older pesticide stocks may present a very serious fire and/or health hazard for personnel involved in an emergency response to any occupancy containing these materials. Information on the restrictions on pesticides can be obtained from the nearest regional EPA office. Information on toxic effects for emergency personnel is available from the Agency for Toxic Substances and Disease Registry, from health and safety groups, from major manufacturers, and from the National Pesticide Telecommunication Network (NPTN).

PESTICIDE STORAGE SAFEGUARDS

Pesticides should be segregated in well-identified areas of structures designed to minimize effects from fire or release of the chemicals. Storage orders should include consideration of the intrinsic fire, corrosive, health, and reactive hazards of the pesticides. NFPA 43D, *Pesticides in Portable Containers*, presents basic guidelines for storing containers up to 660 gal (2.5 m^3) in size.

Where practical, and if large quantities are involved, a detached single-story, noncombustible structure or a first-story corner room with direct outside access should be used. Considerations for control of released materials and for fire runoff water are important. Basement storage locations are to be avoided as much as possible because of difficulties in ventilation of vapor hazards, fire fighting, salvage, decontamination, and controlling water runoff. Adequate facility preplanning, employee training, placarding, and security are important.

Due to the high risks of economic loss, environmental contamination, and health hazards of pesticides, serious consideration must be given to facility design for pesticide-containing occupancies. Segregated storage, runoff containment, and automatic sprinklers must be designed to minimize the hazards to employees and public responders from fire or nonfire releases of these materials. Ideally, all runoff from the pesticide storage area should drain into an impervious impounding basin that provides for testing, treatment, and proper disposal of the runoff.

Reactive pesticides, and the chemicals associated with them, should be further segregated. These include ammonium nitrate fertilizers, oxidizers, and, especially, swimming pool chemicals. (See NFPA 490, *Ammonium Nitrate*, and NFPA 43A, *Liquid and Solid Oxidizing Materials*.) Chlorates (oxidizing agents) are commonly found in herbicides, so herbicides should be segregated from other pesticides, especially those with significant concentrations of flammable or combustible carriers.

USAGE SAFEGUARDS

The safeguards outlined below are applicable to the routine use of pesticides for agricultural applications, manufacture, and warehousing, and should be considered for public agency responders and retail establishment employees who may be assigned cleanup duties for nonfire considerations. Normal usage considerations should include consideration of:

- Waterproof aprons made from rubber or synthetic materials for use in mixing operations.
- Waterproof boots or foot coverings made from rubber or synthetic materials with appropriate compatibility to all constituents of the formulations being handled.
- Daily clothing changes with controlled washing and testing, or provision of disposable garments. Where spray applications are being conducted, provisions for impermeable garments should be considered. In these cases, one-piece coveralls are preferred to jacket-and-trouser sets.
- Face shields, goggles, or respiratory protection may be necessary. Goggles with side shields or a full-face respirator are required if handling or applying dusts, wettable powders, or granules exposed to mists or spray.
- Waterproof gloves made from rubber or compatible synthetic materials are required.
- Waterproof, wide-brimmed hats with nonabsorbent headbands may be necessary.
- Respirator cartridges or canisters must be approved for pesticide vapors, unless the label or MSDS specifies another type.

The normal fire fighter protective clothing and attack procedures (which call for a close-to-the-floor entry to smoke-filled occupancies where pesticides may have been released) may result in the bunker gear performing as a sponge, possibly allowing significant exposure to fire fighters long after they have exited the structure. Several cases have been reported in the literature in recent years where fire companies were out of service for extended periods due to contamination of hoses and personnel bunker gear. Occupancies that contain pesticides with NFPA 704, *Identification of the Fire Hazards of Materials*, risk levels for category 3 or higher, or contain the signal words "POISON/DANGER," "WARNING," or "CAUTION," should be pre-planned for both fire and nonfire emergency incidents. Technical specialists from public or private hazardous materials teams, manufacturers, or government agencies may be needed to assist with development of pre-plans. The pre-plan should identify appropriate tactics, sorbents, neutralizers, toxic vapor emission monitors, and chemical protective clothing ensembles.

Flammable fumigants may present a special fire hazard. A list of commercial fumigants under their various trade names is published annually by Underwriters Laboratories Inc. This list specifies the composition of the material and provides a relative fire hazard classification.

Insecticidal fogging presents combustion, explosion, and flash fire hazards. Safeguards include: (1) the use of solvents having flash points well above normal ambient temperatures, and (2) limiting the quantities applied to structures in relation to their volume. Some fogging applicators are examined and listed by testing agencies.

EMERGENCY HANDLING

For fire and nonfire releases of pesticides, it is important to recognize the differences from normal incident responses. Recommended response actions include:

- Consultation with the facility pre-plan.
- Notification of public agency hazardous materials specialists.
- Contact with the facility operator to determine the specific material(s) released, conditions of release, fire or nonfire potential, and entry precautions.
- Notification of a physician specializing in occupational medicine and appropriate medical care facilities.
- Contact with appropriate manufacturers and other technical resources.
- Evacuation or shelter-in-place for downwind populations and taking steps to protect public agency personnel conducting evacuations or managing site access control.
- Selection of and wearing appropriate chemical and fire protective equipment.
- Establishment of appropriate decontamination procedures for response personnel.
- Evaluation of appropriate tactics based on flammability, toxicity, reactivity, and physical hazards after consultation with the technical authorities.
- Consideration of environmental damage if runoff will occur.

The importance of appropriate use of water cannot be overemphasized. Large-scale groundwater pollution or other environmental damage by fire fighting runoff water is a distinct possibility. In fact, if a pesticide occupancy is so heavily involved that control is doubtful, efforts should be directed at protecting exposures, thus sacrificing the structure with the pesticides. This provides two benefits: (1) the fire is allowed to reach higher temperatures, thus resulting in more efficient combustion and more complete thermal decomposition of the pesticides to the least toxic combustion products; and (2) the possibility of groundwater contamination is almost eliminated. Of course, protection of downwind populations from toxic exposures is critical in such situations.

BIBLIOGRAPHY

Reference

UL, *Classified Products Index*, Underwriters Laboratories Inc. (issued annually in July).

NFPA Codes, Standards, and Recommended Practices

Reference to the following NFPA codes, standards, and recommended practices will provide further information on pesticides discussed in this chapter. (See the latest *NFPA Catalog* for availability of current editions of the following documents.)

NFPA 43A, *Liquid and Solid Oxidizing Materials*.

NFPA 43D, *Pesticides in Portable Containers*.

NFPA 490, *Ammonium Nitrate*.

NFPA 704, *Identification of the Fire Hazards of Materials*.

Additional Reading

Agricultural Chemical Label Book, published annually by Pueblo Chemical and Supply Company, North Kansas City, MO.

Bahme, C. W., *Fire Officer's Guide to Dangerous Chemicals*, 2nd ed., National Fire Protection Association, Quincy, MA, 1978.

Bowen, J. E., "Pre-Incident Planning for Pesticide Fires," *Fire Engineering*, Vol. 141, No. 2, 1988, pp. 36-39.

Farm Chemicals Handbook, published annually by Meister Publishing Company, Willoughby, OH.

"Fire Protection for Pesticide Storage," *NAC News and Pesticide Review* (National Agricultural Chemicals Association), Vol. 28, No. 2, Dec. 1969.

"Hazardous Materials: The Pesticide Challenge," 10-unit audiovisual training program, National Fire Academy, Emmitsburg, MD, 1984.

Meskimen, A. L., and Cullom, K. D., "Pesticide Storage Fire," *Fire Engineering*, Vol. 140, No. 2, 1987, pp. 20-21, 23.

"Recognition and Management of Pesticide Poisonings," 4th ed., EPA 540/9-88-001, Mar. 1989, U.S. Environmental Protection Agency, Washington, DC.

Safety Manual for Handling and Warehousing Class B Poison Pesticides, National Agricultural Chemicals Association, Washington, DC, 1969.

"Unstable Insecticide," *Fire Journal*, Vol. 62, No. 2, Mar. 1968, pp. 5-9.

FIRE-RETARDANT AND FLAME-RESISTANT TREATMENTS OF CELLULOSIC MATERIALS

Revised by James R. Shaw

This chapter discusses the basic principles of fire-retardant and flame-resistant treatments, their uses and limitations, and methods of treatment for wood, wood-based composite panels, fiberboard, paper, and miscellaneous decorative materials.

Related information can be found in the following chapters: Section 3, Chapter 3, "Wood and Wood-Based Products"; Section 3, Chapter 4, "Fibers and Textiles"; Section 3, Chapter 10, "Plastics and Rubber"; Section 6, Chapter 4, "Interior Finish"; and Section 8, Chapter 32, "Wildland Fires."

Cellulosic materials are an integral part of the living environment. Homes, schools, factories, offices, shops, etc., utilize large quantities of cellulosic products in construction, furnishings, and decorations. Fire-retardant and flame-resistant treatments for these cellulosic materials can increase fire protection.

Popular usage has created a variety of terms associated with this subject, resulting in frequent misconceptions, misunderstandings, misuses, and an undesirable degree of ambiguity. Terms such as "fire resistant," "fire retardant," "flame resistant," "flame retardant," and "flameproof" are often used indiscriminately and incorrectly.

The term "fire resistant" should not be used in reference to the fire-retardant treatment of combustibles. Fire resistant is used properly only to signify the ability of a structure, material, or assemblage to resist the effects of a large-scale severe fire exposure. The American Society for Testing and Materials (ASTM) defines fire resistance as "the property of a material or assembly to withstand fire or give protection from it."[1] Fire-resistance rating or fire endurance is the time, in minutes or hours, that materials or assemblies have withstood a fire exposure, as established in accordance with the test procedures of NFPA 251 (ASTM E119), *Standard Methods of Fire Tests of Building Construction and Materials.* "Flameproof" and its derivatives are also misleading and subject to abuse and misunderstanding; their use should be discouraged.

"Fire retardant" signifies a lesser degree of protection than fire resistant. It should be used in reference to chemicals, treatments, or coatings used to reduce the combustibility of building materials, and to such treated materials. ASTM suggests "fire retardant" be used as a modifier only with defined compound terms, such as fire-retardant barrier, fire-retardant chemical, fire-retardant coatings, and fire-retardant treatments.[1] Flame spread rating refers to numbers or classifications obtained according to NFPA 255 (ASTM E84), *Method of Test of Surface Burning Characteristics of Building Materials.* "Flame retardant" and "flame resistant" may be used more or less interchangeably and denote decorative materials that, due to chemical treatment or inherent properties, do not ignite readily or propagate flaming under small-to-moderate fire exposure. "Flame retardant" is the preferred term to denote chemicals, processes, or coatings used for the treatment of decorative materials, including fabrics, foliage, Christmas trees, and similar materials that are decorations or furnishings.

Fire retardants and flame-retardant treatments frequently have been misused. They have a widespread appeal due perhaps in part to a general lack of understanding about the limitations of the treatments, and a failure to differentiate between those that are effective and those that are not. One popular misconception is that all fire-retardant treatments give a fire-resistance rating. This is not true. While some fire-resistive coatings may improve the fire endurance of combustible materials and assemblies, other treatments are only effective in retarding the rate of burning and the rate at which fuel is contributed by the treated material. This action, however, can reduce the fire intensity of some materials that otherwise might be very fast burning.

In other words, there are practical limits to fire-retardant treatments. They are not all permanent, they affect other properties of the treated material, and they add expense. They do, however, provide protection on a competing basis with nonfire-retardant treatments and coatings. For example, fire-retardant paints have been improved to the point where many provide a colorful, protective coating with comparable wear resistance and strength of normal oil paints.

James R. Shaw, Ph.D., is the director of the fire technology laboratory of Weyerhaeuser Company.

BASIC PRINCIPLES

Treatments to reduce the combustibility of wood, fabrics, and other natural materials have a long history reaching back to at least the time of Moses. The early use and development of chemical retardants was limited to materials that were accidentally found to be effective. Research in basic combustion processes and action of retardants was greatly expanded during World War II due to increased military needs for flame-resistant fabrics and fire-retardant wood; this expansion has continued. Because cotton textiles and wood have by far the longest history of use and are of great economic importance, research has been directed toward these cellulosic materials.

Burning of Cellulose

The chemical reactions and the mechanisms involved in the combustion of untreated cellulose are, by themselves, highly complex and not yet fully understood. The complexity is magnified by the addition of fire-retardant chemicals.

Wood (cellulose) normally does not burn directly. The initial reaction to high heat exposure is pyrolysis, in which some of the products given off are gases, vapors, or mists that can form flammable mixtures with air. On ignition, the combustion of these products is evidenced by visible flames. The solid residues include charcoal, which can undergo a different form of combustion by combining directly with oxygen, as evidenced by glowing. This is an important distinction, since many chemicals that are effective flame inhibitors have little or no effect in retarding flameless combustion, or afterglow. For most applications, flame retardance is more important, but there are some instances where glow resistance is equally necessary.

Theories of Fire-Retardant Mechanisms

Four general theories have evolved to explain the mechanisms by which chemicals retard flaming or glowing of cellulosic materials. It is agreed that no single theory is adequate to explain these mechanisms, and that, in most cases, more than one mechanism is involved. The four theories that offer the most satisfactory explanations for the function of fire-retardant chemicals are as follows.

Thermal: There are three possible ways that fire-retardant materials work to reduce thermal buildup of the treated combustible: (1) they increase thermal conductivity to dissipate the heat of combustion, (2) they increase thermal absorption to reduce the amount of heat available for pyrolysis, and/or (3) they provide thermal insulation to reduce heat access to the substrate. Thermal insulation is the most important mechanism and is also discussed below, under coating theories.

Coating: Some retardants melt or fuse at relatively low temperatures, and it is believed that they may form an insulating coating over the fibers of the treated material, acting to exclude oxygen and inhibit the escape of combustible gases. More effective retardants exhibit a bubbling or foaming action, creating an insulating barrier. Intumescent paints and coatings protect substrates by this mechanism.

Gas: Some chemicals function by releasing nonflammable gases, such as water, ammonia, and carbon dioxide, under heat exposure that dilute the combustible gases sufficiently to render the mixture nonflammable in air. Other retardants catalytically inhibit the fire radical chain reactions that occur in the gas phase (flaming combustion). Halogen-containing retardants exhibit this type of mechanism and, when combined with antimony, a synergistic (more than additive) effect is observed.

Chemical: Simplified representations of the chemical mechanism are shown in Figures 3-17A and 3-17B. These diagrams illustrate the different effects of fire on untreated and treated cellulose and are diagramatically explained in "Flameproofing Textile Fabrics."[2] Untreated cellulose breaks down into liquids and a smaller amount of solids. The liquids in turn break down into flammable gases and a little char, and the solids decompose into char and gases, some of which are flammable, some not. The flammable gases volatilized from the liquids combine with those from the solids to cause flaming and the emission of additional heat which continues the reaction.

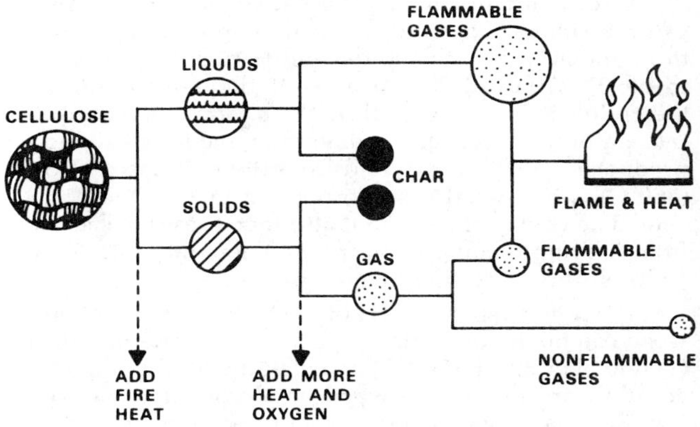

FIG. 3-17A. Schematic diagram of the burning sequence of untreated cellulose. The size of the circle is representative of the volume of product. Note predominance of liquid and flammable gas products.

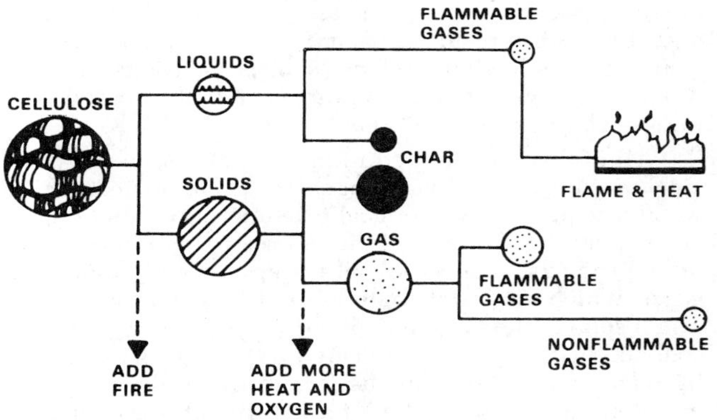

FIG. 3-17B. Schematic diagram of the burning sequence of treated cellulose. The size of the circle is representative of the volume of product. Note the predominance of solids and the severe reduction in liquids and flammable gases emanating from the liquids, as compared with the same burning sequence for untreated cellulose as illustrated in Figure 3-17A.

With treated cellulose, fewer liquids and more solids are formed, and more of the solids become char. The reduced amount of liquids creates some char and some flammable gases. Because the amount of flammable gases from both the liquid and solid phases is now significantly less with treated cellulose, there is less and less heat released. Therefore, flame resistance or at least a reduced burning rate is achieved. Another postulate, an expansion of the chemical theory known as the catalytic dehydration theory, has been advanced.[3]

Studies at the U.S. Forest Products Laboratory[4] have shown that pyrolysis reactions (without the presence of oxygen) for the lignin component of wood start at approximately 428°F (220°C), while that for the cellulose fraction starts near 518°F (270°C). However, once pyrolysis for the cellulose fraction is started, its decomposition is primarily an endothermic reaction and is nearly completed when 752°F (400°C) is reached. The lignin decomposes more slowly, almost in an entirely exothermic reaction, and loses less than half its weight in pyrolysis up to 1112°F (600°C).

Fire-retardant chemicals greatly influence the pyrolysis reaction of the cellulose fraction, frequently reducing the temperature at which decomposition starts from 518 to 446°F (270 to 230°C). As a result, the decomposition of the cellulose is promoted directly to form char and water, instead of forming intermediate flammable gases and tar products; and the char yield from the cellulose at 680°F (360°C) is increased from 15 percent up to 30 to 35 percent. The chemical treatment also increases the char yield from the lignin component from 49 percent up to 57 percent, but here the significance is less.

It was further shown that the combustion reactions for wood can be divided primarily into two exothermic stages: (1) one near 626°F (330°C) associated with flaming as the cellulose fraction of the wood undergoes decomposition into flammable gases and tars and becomes ignited, and (2) a second reaction near 806°F (430°C) associated with glowing as the lignin fraction of the wood, which has been changed to charcoal, undergoes oxidation. Fire-retardant chemicals greatly reduce the intensity of the first peak, and some chemicals also reduce the intensity of the second peak, thus reducing the heat released by the treated wood over a wide temperature range. Other chemicals reduce the first peak and intensify the second, thus requiring a second chemical to result in maximum fire-retardant performance. Heat release during the pyrolysis reactions for wood was found to be less than 5 percent of that released during the combustion reactions.

All of this data tended to prove that one of the principal reactions of fire-retardant chemicals impregnated into wood is to accelerate chemical reactions at certain temperature ranges. This reduces the release of certain intermediate products, such as levoglucosan tars and flammable gases, which may contribute to the flaming of wood, and also results in the formation of greater percentages of charcoal and water. Some chemicals are then further effective in reducing the oxidation rate for the charcoal residue. An excellent discussion of these basic principles is contained in the Forest Products Laboratory report, "Theories of the Combustion of Wood and Its Control."[5]

FIRE-RETARDANT TREATING METHODS

There are four basic methods of treatment to produce fire retardance in materials: (1) chemical changes (substitutions, admixtures), (2) impregnation (saturation, absorption), (3) pressure impregnation, and (4) coating. Chemical changes and pressure impregnation are limited to manufacturing processes and procedures, and are not adaptable for field use. Impregnation and coating methods may be used in the field. Generally, methods employed in manufacturing processes are to be preferred, because they provide greater uniformity, permanence, and dependability. Applications in the field, or subsequent to manufacture of the basic material, are more subject to variation in skill and integrity of the processor or applicator. Treatments of the coating- and pressure-impregnation type are covered in NFPA 703, *Fire-Retardant Impregnated Wood and Fire-Retardant Coatings for Building Materials.*

Chemical Changes

Fire-retardant chemical changes are primarily effective with plastics and with synthetic fibers, because different elements and compounds can be chosen that will alter the burning characteristics of the final product. Since the fire-retardant elements are an integral part of the chemical composition, these materials are said to be "inherently" fire retardant. Naturally occurring polymers, such as cellulose, cannot be made fire retardant by this method. However, another type of chemical fire-retardant treatment, known as chemical grafting, can be applied to natural polymers. It is still in the developmental stage, but shows great promise and utility. In chemical grafting, the material is treated by a multi-stage process in which the material is chemically activated so that molecules of fire-retardant chemical are bonded to molecules of the material being treated. A followup curing step ensures permanence.

Impregnation

Impregnation refers to a technique for treating absorbent materials. The flame-retardant chemicals are either dissolved or dispersed in a solvent, usually water, and the material to be treated is thoroughly wetted or saturated with the solution. The solution may be applied by spraying or by immersion of the material. The latter process is used for treatment of large volumes of fabric yardage. The excess solution is extracted by passing the saturated material through squeeze rollers before drying.

In the simple water-soluble salt impregnation processes, the result is merely to deposit minute crystals of the salts within or on the surface of the fibers. The process is purely physical, i.e., no chemical reaction is involved. With durable treatments, insoluble deposits are formed by chemical reactions or other means.

Certain cellulose-based products, such as paper, acoustical tile, and wood-based compositions, incorporate a wet pulp stage during the manufacturing process. It is possible to add fire-retardant chemicals at the wet pulp stage, resulting in even distribution of the chemicals through the entire mass of the finished product. This practice is prevalent in manufacturing treated papers of many types, and is currently in use by several producers of building materials. Wood-fiber acoustical tile and building panels processed by this method have an NFPA 255/ASTM E84 flame spread rating of less than 25.

Pressure Impregnation

Fire-retardant pressure impregnation is used for treating relatively dense nonabsorbent materials, such as wood. This process replaces the air in the wood cells with fire-retardant chemical solutions. (The chemicals are deposited as the solutions dry.) The treating solution is usually forced into the wood by the standard vacuum pressure methods used in the wood preserving industry.[6] Compared to simple impregnation techniques, pressure impregnation provides for deeper penetration and much greater chemical retention.

Coating

There are several types of fire-retardant coatings that are useful in treating many materials. Coatings may be applied at any stage from manufacture to use. They may either actively inhibit flame spread to some degree or present a noncombustible surface over which flame cannot spread. They are used predominately on nonabsorbent building materials that cannot be treated by any other method; on Christmas trees and similar decorative materials; and, to a limited extent, on paper and fabrics that for various reasons cannot be treated effectively by impregnation.

The effectiveness of a coating depends on the chemical and physical properties of the material to which the coating is applied, the effectiveness of the coating on this material, the ability of the applier, and the thoroughness of the treatment. Since types of coatings and their effects vary depending on the material treated, they are discussed in the subsections of this chapter that cover materials.

PRACTICAL LIMITATIONS OF TREATMENTS

Ideally, a fire-retardant treatment would permanently eliminate all flame spread and smoke generation characteristics from a material; the color, feel, strength, weight, and other key characteristics of the basic material would not suffer from the treatment; and the method would be inexpensive, easy, and safe. There are no present-day treatments meeting all of these qualifications. As the different materials are discussed, the limitations of fire-retardant treatments will be identified.

WOOD

Wood can be made fire retardant by either pressure impregnation or coatings. While both of these treatments will reduce the flame spread of wood, only some fire-retardant coatings are significantly effective in increasing the resistance of wood to degradation under sustained fire exposure or in delaying reduction of its load-bearing capacity.

While the fire-retardant treatment that would make wood noncombustible does not exist, the spread of flame from the immediate area of an incipient fire can be retarded and, in some cases, prevented by present-day treatments, with a corresponding substantial reduction in smoke contribution. Also, the fire-resistance rating of wood structural members in buildings may be improved through the use of fire-resistive coatings.[7,8,9]

Fire-Retardant Pressure Impregnation

Pressure impregnation treatments deposit chemicals within the fibrous passages of wood. Many chemicals exhibit fire-retardant properties, but because of cost limitations or various other objectionable characteristics, comparatively few are considered practical. Chemicals commonly used in the past include monobasic and dibasic ammonium phosphates, ammonium sulfate, borax, boric acid, zinc chloride, and sodium dichromate, usually in various combinations. Newer formulations tend to exclude hygroscopic salts, such as ammonium sulfate and zinc chloride, and, in some cases, include organophosphorus compounds and amino resins. The most significant improvements in the new formulations are the high tolerance for high relative humidity (RH) conditions (up to 95 percent RH) and exterior application due to their nonleachability. The impregnation operation can be controlled to secure a predetermined absorption of solution. The important considerations are the depth of penetration and the amount of chemical deposited per unit volume of the wood.

Since the fire-retarding effect of the treatment is directly related to the amount of the chemical deposited within the wood, it is interesting to compare the effect of an ordinary brush treatment with a pressure-impregnation treatment. A 10-ft (3 m) high fence 50 ft (15.25 m) long of nominal 1-in. (25 mm) pine boards would absorb about 4 gal (15 L) of treating solution if applied by brush. The effect on flame spread would be minor [flame spread index (FSI) = 130 to 195, Class III]. When the same boards are pressure impregnated to refusal (i.e., the point at which no more salts are absorbed by the wood), they absorb about 225 gal (852 L) of chemical and the flame spread is cut to one-fourth or less of the original (FSI <25, Class I).

A load or "charge" of wood is locked in a large cylinder that can be up to 8 ft (2.5 m) in diameter and over 140 ft (43 m) long. The air is then withdrawn, and the resulting vacuum draws much of the entrapped air from the wood cells. After a delay to allow the vacuum to stabilize, the fire-retardant chemical solution is bled into the cylinder. After the cylinder has been filled with the treating solution, additional chemicals are forced into it under pressure. As the pressure is raised [up to 200 psi (1379 kPa)], the chemicals are forced into the empty wood voids. The process can be run to refusal and the unabsorbed salt solution drained from the cylinder. A slight vacuum may then be drawn to remove surface chemicals that would cause dripping and slow drying. After the charge is removed and dried, it is ready for shipment and use. Additional details are available from the American Wood Preservers Association.

Advantages: Pressure impregnation permits a large amount of fire-retardant chemical to be deposited in the wood under close control and with uniform and predictable results. Samples for tests are readily available. Of primary importance, the treatment can be considered permanently effective under normal and proper conditions of use. Since both water-soluble and nonleachable fire retardants are available, it is important that nonleachable treatments be chosen for exterior use. Treatments with low hygroscopicity should be used for interior applications where high humidity conditions exist.

Disadvantages: In recent years, the fire-retardant chemical producers changed to "new generation," low-hygroscopicity formulations that dramatically improved the resistance to corrosion of metal fasteners. However, there have been reports of structural failures in fire-retardant treated plywood roofs where high temperature and humidity conditions exist. Research efforts at the Forest Products Laboratory have shown that acidic fire-retardant chemicals, such as monoammonium phosphate, can cause premature degradation and simultaneous strength loss at elevated temperatures [>150°F (66°C)] and humidities. It is important to note that not all fire-retardant formulations currently being used for wood show the same degree of strength losses under the chosen laboratory conditions. Therefore, it is necessary for the user of fire-retardant treated wood and fire-retardant treated plywood to review the available literature on this subject, including the information available from the American Plywood Association and the fire-retardant chemical producers. A technical report on this problem has been published.[10]

Another disadvantage of pressure impregnation is that the wood must be treated before use and after dimensioning.

Fire performance characteristics: The pressure impregnation process can substantially improve the fire performance characteristics of wood, as measured by the tunnel test, the room fire test, and heat-release rate tests. The effect can be illustrated by a study of a typical wood, Douglas fir, as shown in Tables 3-17A and 3-17B.

TABLE 3-17A. ***Maximum Effect of Pressure Impregnation on Douglas Fir***

	Untreated	Pressure-Impregnated
Flame spread	100	As low as 15
Fuel contribution	100	As low as 10
Smoke generation	100	As low as 0

TABLE 3-17B. ***Effect of Pressure Impregnation on Douglas Fir Plywood in the Room Fire Test****

	Untreated	Pressure Impregnated
Flashover Time	3.3 min	None
Maximum Heat Release Rate	7.3 mW	0.6 mW
Maximum Smoke Generation (O.D.†)	1.11	0.76

* The ignition exposure was 40 kW (net) for 5 min., 160 kW (net) for 5 min. and 0 kW (net) for 5 min.

† Optical Density.

Testing: The effectiveness of fire-retardant pressure impregnation treatments is tested by several methods. The tunnel test (NFPA 255/ASTM E84) has been used to determine the fire performance characteristics of many pressure impregnation treatments. A standard room fire test of wall and ceiling materials[11] is being developed at the National Institute of Standards and Technology Center for Fire Research, and is used to evaluate treated panel products. The test utilizes the oxygen depletion method for calculating the rate of heat release. Data collected by this method is used in the validation of fire mathematical models. The City of New York originally established three tests: (1) crib (ASTM E160), (2) shavings, and (3) timber, for evaluating fire-retardant-treated wood. The fire tube test (ASTM E69), developed at the Forest Products Laboratory, has been used extensively both in the United States and in several other countries to measure the effectiveness of fire-retardant treatments. Other tests, such as fire penetration, rate of heat release, and ignition tests, have been used by different organizations and individuals.

Model codes allow the use of fire-retardant-treated wood in noncombustible construction, with some limitations. Lumber and plywood for construction can be treated by pressure impregnation to achieve a flame spread rating as low as 15 and to perform well in rated assemblies.

Plywood: Fully treated plywood is satisfactory only when surface appearance is unimportant. For decorative purposes where the face veneer must have the beauty of natural wood, untreated face veneers of various species are laminated to treated cores. The flame spread classification of these treated plywood products varies in approximately inverse proportion with the density of the face veneer, and ranges generally from 20 to 75, satisfying all but the most restrictive requirements. Fully treated plywood generally has a flame spread index less than 25 (Class I).

Relative Toxicity

Combustion toxicity testing of treated and untreated wood suggests that smoke from treated wood is "no more toxic than untreated Douglas fir." This is true even though minor amounts of toxic vapors, such as HCN and nitrogen oxides, are expected to be liberated from some treatments upon degradation.[12]

Smoke toxicity values are now required by the State of New York on all wood products to be sold in-state that are used for interior finish and interior floor finish.[13] These values are generated using the University of Pittsburgh Test Method. Treated and untreated wood products tested to date range in LC_{50} values of 7 to 72 g.[13] Many treated and untreated wood products have also been tested by the radiant furnace method. These results also indicate that smoke from treated wood is less toxic than from untreated.[14] The National Institute of Building Sciences is developing a toxic hazard test method based on the radiant furnace apparatus. The limited data collected thus far by this method shows no difference in toxic hazard between fire-retardant-treated and untreated wood.[15]

Fire-Retardant Coatings

In existing structures of untreated wood, or in cases where fire-retardant pressure impregnations are impracticable, fire-retardant coatings can be used. Coatings can be applied to any exposed surface of structural members, interior finish, or contents. They may be applied by means of brush, roller, sprayer, or trowel. As in the case of pressure impregnations, the degree of the flame spread reduction secured by a coating is dependent upon the original combustibility of the surface to be protected, the effectiveness of the coating material used, the amount of coating used, the thoroughness of the application, and the size and severity of the exposing fire.

With normal paints, the usual aim is to get maximum coverage with minimum material. The approach is different in the application of fire-retardant coatings. Here, the objective is to provide the needed amount of coating per unit area required to ensure a definite degree of protection. Film thickness for intumescent coatings is a very important factor in their ultimate performance.

Among the many proprietary fire-retardant coatings, several have been listed by testing laboratories. Beware of any so-called fire-retardant or "fireproof" paint that has not been certified as to its flame spread characteristics by an independent testing laboratory. There are four types of fire-retardant coatings for wood, as follows.

1. *Intumescent paints.* These coatings, upon the action of heat, expand from a thin, paint-like coating to a thick, puffy, burnt-marshmallow-type coating. The puffy coating results in one or all of the following effects: insulation of fuel from heat, exclusion of oxygen from fuel, production of diluent gases, and reduction of flammable gases. It will retain its effectiveness until broken up either by high heat or by sustained heat.

2. *Mastics.* These materials are applied by trowel or by heavy-duty spray equipment and form a thick coating on the surface of the combustible material. They vary from hard, ceramic-like materials to soft, tar-like coatings. All withstand significant amounts of heat and inhibit flame spread by the impervious noncombustible membrane they form.
3. *Gas-forming paints.* These coatings, when heated, release quantities of noncombustible gas that dilute the oxygen at the protected surface so there is not sufficient oxygen to support combustion.
4. *Cementitious and mineral-fiber coatings.* Limited research has been conducted on the potential use of cementitious and mineral-fiber coatings on wood to improve its fire endurance characteristics. These coatings are commonly used on structural steel to enhance fire endurance by protecting the steel from the intense heat of a fire. Some researchers feel that structural wood systems may be protected in the same manner.

The customary finishing materials for wood, such as ordinary stains, oil paints, enamels, varnishes, shellac, lacquer, and waxes, are of no appreciable value in protecting wood against fire, and, in some cases, increase combustibility. Paint, however, may be of value in preventing absorption of oil and in promoting cleanliness. It should also be noted that dry, decayed wood is more susceptible to ignition by small sparks from cigarettes than is sound wood, and that paint coatings tend to prevent surface decay.

Advantages: Fire-retardant coatings have the following advantages: (1) they can be used on combustible materials already in place, (2) they are relatively inexpensive, (3) they may be easily applied, and (4) they do not cause strength loss at high temperatures and humidities.

Disadvantages: Fire-retardant coatings have the following disadvantages: (1) ease of application can lead to thin and ineffective treatments, (2) unexposed surfaces cannot be treated, (3) limited life and durability, (4) susceptibility to damage, and (5) required maintenance.

Fire performance characteristics: The fire performance of wood can be improved through the use of fire-retardant coatings. The amount of improvement is determined by the effectiveness of the treatment. Underwriters Laboratories Inc. has established a minimum standard of effectiveness for listed coatings to be a flame spread rating of 50 or less in the tunnel test, or a 50 percent reduction in flame spread as compared to the untreated surface, whichever is lower.

Listed coatings, when properly applied, are effective in improving fire performance characteristics, some to a point well below the limits noted above. The variations in effect of listed fire-retardant coatings on Douglas fir are shown in Table 3-17C.

Permanence: Some fire-retardant paints and coatings have good permanence when used in interior locations of relatively normal humidity and temperatures. Water-resistant, oil-based, intumescing fire-retardant coatings have been developed.[16] But the use of fire-retardant coatings in exterior locations, in areas of relatively high humidity, and in areas of high temperature has not been thoroughly tested. One difficulty in testing these exterior paints is the problem of weathering samples. Samples for small-scale tests can be placed in a weather accelerator or weatherometer, and the results measured. These small-scale tests, however, do not produce significant flame spread results. There is also doubt as to the comparability of weatherometer exposures and actual long-term weathering. The samples required for the acceptable large-scale tests are too large for accelerated weathering and thus must be exposed to actual weathering, which requires long periods of time. Until this testing problem can be solved, the use of fire-retardant coatings in exterior locations is questionable.

Strength and deterioration: Strength and deterioration of both the materials coated and their fastenings is not a problem with most fire-retardant coatings.

Moisture: Only those coatings that use hygroscopic fire-retardant chemicals are vulnerable to absorbing moisture, thus reducing their effectiveness.

Toxicity: The reactive toxicity of the total products of combustion of the coated material as compared to the uncoated material should be considered when examining fire-retardant coatings.

Preservative Treatments

Where subject to decay or insect attack, or to attacks by marine borers, timber and lumber commonly are pressure treated with coal tar creosote, pentachloro phenol, chromated copper arsenate, and ammonical copper arsenate. Such treatments are used in piers, bridges, trestles, decks and similar structures, and to some extent in buildings.

Oil-type preservatives, such as creosote, cause an increase in fire hazard as compared with untreated wood. Fire retardants utilizing the proper ratio of phosphorous-halogen mixture are effective in reducing the combustibility of the treated wood to that of untreated wood; however, there is an initial flash of "light ends" not observed in untreated wood.[17]

Fire is reported to spread more rapidly and generate higher surface temperatures in structures containing newly creosoted wood than in structures of untreated wood, particularly where general fire temperatures are sufficiently high to vaporize the creosote oils. The adverse fire experience in fires in creosoted pier substructures, however, is due primarily to the excessive areas of wood construction without firebreaks, which are inaccessible for manual fire fighting and lack automatic sprinkler protection.

Water-borne salt preservatives can provide some fire-retardant effect, but normal preservative concentrations are not recognized as effective fire-retardant treatments. Conversely, some fire-retardant formulations combine fire retardance and resistance to decay or to attack by insects.

Christmas Trees

Christmas trees become extremely flammable when cut long in advance of use and then brought indoors where heat and low humidity accelerate drying. To reduce the hazard, the tree should be kept indoors only as long as absolutely necessary, the trunk sawed off at an angle at least 1 in. (25 mm) above the original cut end, and the tree placed in water while it is in the house. Water should be added at intervals to the pail, tub, or tree stand in which the tree is placed so that the water level is always above the cut. To achieve a satisfactory degree of flame resistance in any combustible material, including Christmas trees, it is essential to get a certain minimum quantity of effective flame-retardant chemical either into or on the surface of the material to be treated. Since Christmas trees by their nature are not absorbent, the only way to effectively treat

TABLE 3-17C. ***Variations in Effect of Different Fire Retardant Coatings on Unprimed Douglas Fir***

	Untreated	Painted with Coating X†	Painted with Coating Y†	Painted with Coating Z†
Total coverage (sq ft per gal)	—	100	100	200
(L /m2)	—	2.45 L /m^2	2.45 L /m^2	1.23 L /m^2
Flame spread*	100	60	10	25
Fuel contributed*	100	35	15	10
Smoke developed*	100	40	5	10
Rate per coat (sq ft per gal)	—	300	200	200
(L /m^2)	—	0.82 L /m^2	1.23 L /m^2	1.23 L /m^2
Number of coats	—	3	2	1

* Where a range of values was obtained, the figure given here is the highest obtained.
† Each coating is listed by Underwriters Laboratories Inc., as meeting the minimum requirements for a fire retardant coating.

them is to apply a surface coating. Treating Christmas trees with simple solutions of water-dissolved chemicals, such as borox-and-boric acid, diammonium phosphate, or ammonium sulfate, is not effective. In order to provide a significant flame-retardant value, the testing solution or coating must be thick or syrupy enough to form a fairly heavy coating.

Much misunderstanding in this area results from tests of fresh trees treated with simple water-thin solutions of the type described above. Such tests lead to the erroneous conclusion that the treatment is effective, when the fact is that the tree was naturally flame resistant due to its water content.

Pressurized aerosol containers of flame-retardant Christmas tree coatings may be convenient, but their value is questionable due to the very limited quantity of the contents. Many cans would be necessary to adequately treat all parts of larger trees, but the high cost leads the user to apply only a token (and useless) coating.

WOOD-BASED COMPOSITE PANELS

The group of materials referred to here as "wood-based composite panels" includes products such as insulation boards, hardboards, particleboards, oriented strand boards, and laminated paper boards. They consist of a mixture of fibers, particles, or flakes and binder formed under pressure into board-like panels or tiles. These board or panel materials in final form retain some of the properties of the original wood but, because of the manufacturing methods, gain new and different properties from those of the wood.

Wood-based composite panels can be fire-retardant treated by chemical admixtures, impregnations, and coatings. These treatments vary in their effectiveness and are somewhat limited in their use by their effect on the physical properties of the untreated panel.

Admixtures

When mineral fibers, such as glass or rock wood, are added to a mixture of organic fibers, they will reduce the combustibility of the mixture, depending upon the amount of mineral fiber used. If mineral fibers completely replace the organic fibers, then the product becomes noncombustible, provided the binder used to join the fibers is noncombustible or has a sufficiently high ignition temperature. Mixtures of alumina trihydrate, boric acid, and wood fibers have been successfully combined into panel products with very low flamespread, fuel-contributed, and smoke-developed values. Fire-retardant particleboard and oriented strand board are prepared by adding the fire-retardant chemicals to the furnish prior to board making. These products give very consistent flamespread and smoke-developed values.

Impregnations

Attempts have been made to reduce the combustibility of organic composite boards by pressure impregnation of the finished product and by treatment of the raw fiber product itself. Treatments have included soluble salts, insoluble complexes, and chemical reactions with the organic materials themselves. The effect of these treatments on combustible composite boards varied with respect to the type of treatment and type and quantity of chemicals used. Treatment by pressure impregnation has not yet proved to be commercially feasible. At least one manufacturer has developed a successful wood pulp treatment process for both composite boards and acoustical tile, and similarly treated wood fiber acoustical tile is produced by other manufacturers.

Coatings

The treatments previously discussed are made during the manufacture of the material. Coatings can be applied during manufacture or to material already in use. Factory-applied coatings are usually fire-retardant paints; however, many are of questionable effectiveness when exposed to severe fire conditions. Their main effect is to cover the fuzzy surface of the untreated material.

The application of fire-retardant paints of the intumescent variety to existing composite board will provide good protection for the exposed side of the board, provided the coatings are maintained. Some composite boards exhibit considerable dimensional instability, expanding when damp and contracting when dry. This movement may expose cracks and gaps in the material that will open untreated areas to the action of heat and rapid flame spread.

Fire Performance Tests of Wood-based Composites

The effectiveness of the treatments of composite boards can be shown with a fire test. Most of the methods listed under the section on wood can be used to evaluate their fire performance characteristics.

PAPER

Paper can be treated by impregnation to make it flame and glow retardant after the ignition source has been removed. In addition to treating various forms of paper, e.g., building paper, wrapping, packing, and decorative paper, these same treatments can be used to preserve foliage, leaves, grass skirts, broom straw, excelsior, and similar materials if they are sufficiently absorbent. Adequate wetting may be achieved by dipping or spraying with some materials, while others may require soaking for several hours or even days.

The development of flame-retardant products has been given impetus by the requirements for nonflammable display and decorative material in hotels, theaters, schools, hospitals, nursing homes, and other high-occupancy buildings. Decorative crepe paper, corrugated display cardboard, textiles, and window-shade materials may be made flame resistant during manufacture, which is the most reliable method. Field treating paper is difficult due to variations in paper finishes, sizing, and color fastness. It is preferable to purchase factory-treated materials.[18]

MISUSE OF FIRE RETARDANTS

Fire-retardant treatments are used for reduction of flame spread on structural wood members, and combustible interior finish, such as wood paneling, acoustical tile, and wood-based composite panels. Flame-retardant treatments are used for reducing the flammability of contents, furnishings, and decorative materials, such as curtains, draperies, upholstery, crepe and corrugated papers, Christmas trees, and miscellaneous dried or artificial plants and foliage. In all these applications, there are opportunities for misuse or misrepresentation. Some of the more prevalent kinds of misuse are described as follows.

1. Promoting pressure-impregnated wood for uses where noncombustible materials are conventionally required. Such substitutions are appropriate in certain limited applications, but even the most effective treatments cannot entirely eliminate some contribution of fuel and smoke.
2. Using pressure-impregnated or coated materials that are not intended for use in locations that are exposed to the weather or unusually high humidity conditions.
3. Attempting to treat the newer synthetic fiber fabrics with common water-soluble-salt flame-retardant solutions. Such solutions are effective only on cellulose fibers, such as cotton and rayon, and the common animal fibers, such as wool and silk. They are not effective for the treatment of nylon, acetate, Orlon®, Dacron®, Acrilan®, or any of the similar synthetics presently in wide use.
4. Marketing flame-retardant solutions in small aerosol spray containers for home use. This practice is subject to many abuses, including the lack of product labels to indicate the limitations of the contents and instructions for proper application. Advertising frequently contains wildly exaggerated claims for the product's utility, giving the impression that the contents of one can will "flameproof" virtually everything in the home. The product itself may be excellent and convenient to use, but there is a great risk that the average user will not achieve an effective degree of flame resistance. With few exceptions, flame-retardant treatments should be left to skilled persons.
5. Advocating the use of ordinary water-soluble-salt solutions for the treatment of nonabsorbent materials. Effective treatment of nonabsorbent materials can be achieved only by means of a substantial surface coating, requiring that the treating solution be of a syrupy or paint-like consistency.

The technology of flame-retardant treatment is highly useful and can do much to increase firesafety. But because it is also a field vulnerable to entry by unskilled entrepreneurs and charlatans, the buyer should be alert to its limitations. Products that have been tested, rated, and labeled by reputable, independent testing laboratories are the consumers' best safeguard against the pitfalls listed above.

BIBLIOGRAPHY

References Cited

1. ASTM, "Standard Terminology Relating to Fire Standards," E176-83a, *1986 Annual Book of ASTM Standards*, Vol. 04.07, American Society for Testing and Materials, Philadelphia, PA, 1986, pp. 416-420.
2. Little, R. W., Church, J. M., and Coppick, S., "Flameproofing Textile Fabrics," ACS Monography 104, 1947, American Chemical Society, Reinhold, NY.
3. Schuyten, H. A., Weaver, J. W., and Reid, J. D. , "Some Theoretical Aspects of the Flameproofing of Cellulose," *Advances in Chemistry Series No. 9*, American Chemical Society, Washington, DC, 1954.
4. U.S. Forest Products Laboratory, 1962-64: Eickner, H. W., "Basic Research on the Pyrolysis and Combustion of Wood," *Forest Products Journal*, Apr. 1962; Browne, F. L., and Tang, W. K., "Thermogravimetric and Differential Thermal Analysis of Wood and of Wood Treated with Inorganic Salts During Pyrolysis," *Fire Research Abstracts and Reviews*, Vol. 4, Nos. 1 and 2, 1962, pp. 76-91; Tang, W. K., and Neill, W. K., "Effect of Flame Retardants on Pyrolysis and Combustion of Alpha-Cellulose," *Journal of Polymer Sciences*, Part C6, 1964, pp. 65-81; Brenden, J., "The Influence of Inorganic Salts on the Products of Pyrolysis of Ponderosa Pine," Masters thesis, University of Wisconsin, 1963; Tang, W. K., "Effect of Inorganic Salts on the Pyrolysis, Ignition and Combustion of Wood, Cellulose, and Lignin," Ph.D. thesis, University of Wisconsin, 1964; Browne, F. L., and Tang, W. K., "Effect of Various Chemicals on the Thermogravimetric Analysis of Ponderosa Pine," U.S. Forest Service Research Paper RPL-6, May 1963, Forest Products Laboratory, Madison, WI.
5. Browne, F. L., "Theories of the Combustion of Wood and Its Control," Report No. 2136, 1958, Forest Products Laboratory, Madison, WI.
6. American Wood Preservers, "All Timber Products—Preservative Treatment by Pressure Processes," C1-77, 1977, American Wood-Preservers Association, Vienna, VA.
7. White, R. H., "Use of Coatings to Improve Fire Resistance of Wood," *Fire-Resistive Coatings: The Need for Standards*, ASTM STP 826, Morris Lieff and F. M. Stumpf, eds., American Society for Testing and Materials, Philadelphia, PA, 1983, pp. 24-39.
8. Lieff, M., "Fire-Resistant Coverings," *Fire-Resistive Coatings: The Need for Standards*, ASTM STP 826, Morris Lieff and F. M. Stumpf, eds., American Society for Testing and Materials, Philadelphia, PA, 1983, pp. 3-13.
9. Stumpf, F. M., "Spray-Applied Fibrous Material Fire-Resistive Coatings," *Fire Resistive Coatings: The Need for Standards*, ASTM STP 826, Morris Lieff and F. M. Stumpf, eds., American Society for Testing and Materials, Philadelphia, PA, 1983, pp. 14-23.
10. LeVan, S., and Collet, M., "Choosing and Applying Fire-Retardant-Treated Plywood and Lumber for Roof Designs,"

General Technical Report FPL-GTR-62, 1989, U.S. Department of Agriculture, Forest Service, Forest Products Laboratory, Madison, WI.

11. ASTM, "Proposed Method for Room Fire Test of Wall and Ceiling Materials and Assemblies," *1982 Annual Book of ASTM Standards*, Part 18, American Society for Testing and Materials, Philadelphia, PA, 1982, pp. 1618-1638.
12. Leiu, P. J., Magill, J. H., and Alarie, Y. C., "An Evaulation of Some Polyphosphazenes and Commercial Fire Retardants for Wood," *Journal of Combustion Toxicology*, Vol. 9, May 1982, p. 65.
13. New York State Uniform Fire Prevention and Building Code, Article 15, Lenz and Riecker, Albany, NY.
14. Alexeeff, G. V., and Packham, S.C., "Use of Radiant Furnace Fire Model to Evaluate Acute Toxicity of Smoke," *Journal of Fire Sciences*, Vol. 2, 1984, pp. 306-320.
15. Memorandum to the National Institute of Building Sciences Com/Tox Steering Committee from Wayne Ellis, June 15, 1989.
16. Verburg, G. B., *et al*, "Water-Resistant, Oil-Based, Intumescing Fire-Retardant Coatings, Part I, Developmental Formulations," *Journal of the American Oil Chemists' Society*, Vol. 41, Oct. 1964.
17. Gooch, R. M., Kenaga, D. L., and Tobey, H. M., "The Development of Fire Retardants for Wood Treated with Oil-Type Preservatives," *Forest Products Journal*, Vol. 9, No. 10, Oct. 1959.
18. Segal, L., "Flameproofing: Facts and Fallacies," *Fire Journal*, Vol. 60, No. 6, Nov. 1966, pp. 41-45.

NFPA Codes, Standards, and Recommended Practices

Reference to the following NFPA codes, standards, and recommended practices will provide further information on fire-retardant and flame-resistant treatments of cellulosic materials discussed in this chapter. (See the latest *NFPA Catalog* for availability of current editions of the following documents.)

NFPA *101*®, *Life Safety Code*.®

NFPA 220, *Standard Types of Building Construction.*

NFPA 251, *Standard Methods of Fire Tests of Building Construction and Materials.*

NFPA 703, *Fire-Retardant Impregnated Wood and Fire-Retardant Coatings for Building Materials.*

Additional Reading

ASTM E160-50, *Standard Method of Test for Combustible Properties of Treated Wood by the Crib Test*, American Society for Testing and Materials, Philadelphia, PA, 1969.

ASTM E-69-50, *Standard Method of Test for Combustible Properties of Treated Wood by the Fire-Tube Apparatus*, American Society for Testing and Materials, Philadelphia, PA, 1969.

Bescher, R. H., "Fire-Retardant Treated Wood," *The Construction Specifier*, Vol. 23, No. 3, Mar. 1970, pp. 59-62.

Camino, G., Costa, L., and Martinasso, G., "Intumescent Fire-Retardant Systems," *Polymer Degradation and Stability*, Vol. 23, No. 4, 1989, pp. 359-376.

Canadian Wood Council, *Wood Fire Behavior and Fire Retardant Treatment: A Review of the Literature*, Ottawa, 1966.

Chen, Y., "An Experimental Study of the Pyrolysis of Pure and Fire-Retarded Cellulose," NIST-GCR-89-566, June 1989, National Institute for Standards and Technology, Gaithersburg, MD.

Cisek, T., and Piechocki, J., "Influence of Fire Retardants on Smoke Generation from Wood and Wood Derived Materials," *Fire Technology*, Vol. 21, No. 2, 1985, pp. 122-133.

Cullis, C. F., and Hirschler, M. M., *The Combustion of Organic Polymers*, Oxford University Press, New York, 1981.

Day, T., "Surface Coatings: Will Time Affect Their Performance?," *Fire Prevention*, No. 222, Sept. 1989, pp. 40-41.

Eichner, H. W., and Schaffer, E. L., "Fire-Retardant Effects of Individual Chemicals on Douglas Fir Plywood," *Fire Technology*, Vol. 3, No. 2, May 1967, pp. 90-104.

Fire Retardant Chemicals Association, *Fire Safety Problems Leading to Current Needs and Future Opportunities*, Technomic, Lancaster, PA, 1989.

"Flame Retardant Chemicals—The Current Picture," *Fire Prevention*, No. 199, May 1987, pp. 33-35.

George, C. W., and Aylmer, D. B., "Energy Release Rates in Fire-Retardant Evaluation," *Fire Technology*, Vol. 6, No. 3, Aug. 1970, pp. 203-210.

Gillon, R. D., "Intumescent Coatings: Their Uses and Future Development," *Fire Surveyor*, Vol. 18, No. 2, April 1989, pp. 13-20.

Hastie, J. W., "Molecular Basis of Flame Inhibition," *Journal of Research of the National Bureau of Standards*, 77A, No. 6, Nov.-Dec. 1973, pp. 733-754.

Hastie, J. W., "Chemical Aspects of Flame Inhibition," *NBS Special Pub. 411*, National Bureau of Standards, Washington, DC, Nov. 1974, pp. 30-36.

Hirano, T., and Nakaya, I., "Strategy of Fire Suppression by Using Fire Retardants," *9th Joint Panel Meeting* of the UJNR Panel on Fire Research and Safety, NBSIR 88-3753, Center for Fire Research, April, 1988, pp. 397-404.

Hirato, T., and Kawamoto, S., "Toxic Gases from Combustion of Wood Treated with Retardants," *9th Joint Panel Meeting* of the UJNR Panel on Fire Research and Safety, NBSIR 88-3753, Center for Fire Research, April 1988, pp. 417-427.

"Intumescent Fire Seals Product Review," *Fire Surveyor*, Vol. 17, No. 2, April 1988, pp. 17-19, 22-29.

James, R., "Intumescent Fire Seals," *Fire Surveyor*, Vol. 17, No. 2, April 1988, pp. 13-15.

Jensen, R., ed., *Fire Protection for the Design Professional*, Cahners, Boston, 1975, pp. 181-189.

Kirkpatrick, A. T., Curtis, H., and Adelgren, A., "Experimental Measurements of the Thermal Effectiveness of Two Types of Protective Clothing for Fire Fighters," *Fire Technology*, Vol. 18, No. 3, Aug. 1982, pp. 259-267.

Krasny, J. F., Singleton, R. W., and Pettengill, J., "Performance Evaluation of Fabrics Used in Fire Fighters' Turnout Coats," *Fire Technology*, Vol. 18, No. 4, Nov. 1982, pp. 309-318.

Lucas, C. L., "Improved Intumescent Fire Protection for Hazardous Environments," *Proceedings* of the Conference on Offshore Passive Fire Protection, Plastics and Rubber Institute, 1987, p. 8.

Lyon, D. E., *et al*, "Evaluation of Strength Properties of Fire-Retardant Treated Wood Using the 1983 National Forest Products Association Protocol," *Forest Products Journal*, Vol. 38, No. 6, 1988, pp. 13-18.

Lyons, J. W., *The Chemistry and Uses of Fire Retardants*, reprint, R. E. Krieger, Malabar, FL, 1987.

Mischutin, V., "Flame-Retardant Home Furnishings," *American Dyestuff Reporter*, Vol. 76, No. 3, 1987, pp. 38-42, 49.

Montle, J. F., "The Role of Magnesium Oxychloride as a Fire-Resistive Material," *Fire Technology*, Vol. 10, No. 3, Aug. 1974, pp. 201-210.

Needles, H. L., *et al*, "Assessment of Flame Retardant Coated Fabric Flammability by Small Scale Test Methods," *Journal of Coated Fabrics*, Vol. 17, Oct. 1987, pp. 129-134.

Saville, N., "Overview of Fire Blocking Fabrics," *Proceedings* of the 32nd International SAMPE Symposium and Exhibition: Advanced Materials Technology '87, SAMPE, Covina, CA, 1987, pp. 1347-1359.

"Sprayed Passive Fire Protection," *Insulation Journal*, Vol. 30, No. 8, 1986, p. 14.

Tewari, S. S., "An Experimental Study of the Burning of Pure and Fire Retarded Cellulose," NBS-GCR-84-485, Jan. 1985, Center for Fire Research, Gaithersburg, MD.

Topf, R., "New Developments in Intumescent Materials," *Proceedings* of the Conference on New Technologies to Reduce Fire Losses and Costs, Elsevier, 1986, pp. 155-161.

Tryon, G. H., "Looking at Fire Hazards—Christmas Trees," *Fire Journal*, Vol. 60, No. 6, Nov. 1966, p. 29.

Underwriters Laboratories Inc., *Building Materials List*, Part I, Underwriters Laboratories Inc., Chicago. (Published annually.)

Vandersall, H. L., "Intumescent Coating Systems, Their Development and Chemistry," *Fire Prevention and Suppression*, Vol. 10, Hilado, C. J., ed., Technomic, Westport, CT, 1974, pp. 116-159.

DETECTION AND ALARM

When fire occurs, every subsequent action or reaction that serves to mitigate the fire's severity is triggered by some transfer of information about the fire or the response to it. Detection and alarm systems, including all associated systems of communications, are the means by which that information is transferred. Detection is necessary to trigger automatic or manual suppression, some types of active fire confinement systems, and evacuation. The sooner this detection and triggering can occur, the sooner these reactions and the resulting fire mitigation can begin. This section addresses the principal detection, alarm, and communications systems and options.

Chapter 1 addresses the emergency communications systems of the fire department. Notifying the right people that a fire exists is only the beginning. Most of the information exchanges that make fire protection work actually occur during the response of the fire department, which must receive notification of the fire; respond in a coordinated manner, possibly from several locations; find the property with the fire and the fire in it; and perform a number of complex tasks, often in parallel, usually involving many personnel and multiple pieces of equipment, and often from multiple vantage points that cannot see each other. The military concepts of command, control, and communications are essential to successful fire department operations, and the bigger the "battlefield"—a large wildfire for example—the more essential these elements become. Chapter 1 covers these systems for a single fire department.

Chapter 2 addresses protective signaling systems, the umbrella term for those systems that pass information between points in the fire-involved building or between that building and a remote monitoring location. The form of information transmitted, such as voice or data, and the information needs of the recipients can take many forms. Whatever the system, its reliability must be assured under any conceivable fire or emergency condition.

Chapter 3 covers the detection side of sprinkler systems, which includes waterflow alarms to signal that the system has been activated and supervisory systems that monitor its status and readiness. As Chapter 3 says, "It is obviously necessary to ensure that the automatic sprinkler system is maintained in such a condition that it is always ready to discharge water on a hostile fire, holding the fire to its area of origin."

Chapters 4 and 5 describe fire detection systems for households and for everything else, respectively. Chapter 4 discusses the revolution of the past couple decades that put smoke detectors into most American homes and that, in so doing, contributed greatly to the reduction of fire deaths and injuries. Chapter 5 reviews the much longer history—a century and a half—of fire detectors in general and the multitude of principles now used to detect fires. Special considerations regarding the effective use of fire detectors are reviewed in both chapters.

Chapter 6 extends the discussion to detectors for gases and vapors. These systems can detect certain hazardous conditions, even before fire breaks out. They also provide a hint of the remarkable diversity of possibilities for future developments in the area of detection.

Finally, Chapter 7 discusses the oldest detection system of all—human beings. This is done in the context of the modern systematic approach to surveillance and guard service as a part of fire protection and security. Remembering that earlier chapters have established the large share of fires, deaths, and especially property loss caused by arson fires and considering that the most skillful of arsonists may include disabling or evasion of automatic fire protection systems in their plans, the value of well-trained guards should be clear. Chapter 7 covers everything from routes to reliability to resourcefulness.

Also look for these: Anyone whose work requires in-depth knowledge of detection and alarm systems will need the more detailed information provided in such NFPA resources as the *Fire Alarm Signaling Systems Handbook* and the alarm systems seminar. Also, see the more detailed information on systems design calculation methods in *The SFPE Handbook of Fire Protection Engineering* from NFPA. Some detection features of suppression and fire confinement systems are addressed briefly in the appropriate chapters in Sections 5 and 6. Also, Chapter 9 of Section 10 includes a brief discussion of computer models for predicting detector activation times. This provides a starting point for the larger objective of modeling all of fire protection, with the stages of detection and alarm placed in their proper context and treated quantitatively.

FIRE DEPARTMENT EMERGENCY COMMUNICATIONS SYSTEMS

Revised by Evan E. Stauffer

This chapter is intended to provide the handbook user with an overview of the total emergency communications responsibilities of the fire service, together with some of the principal management and operational systems and/or techniques through which the respective responsibilities may be achieved. The fire service relies upon four major elements for success: (1) intelligence, (2) personnel, (3) supplies, and (4) good communications.

Intelligent and well-trained personnel are of no value if there are no reliable means to direct them to the right place at the right time. The fire department's communications divisions are entrusted to provide this direction.

For additional information, consult the NFPA documents referenced in this chapter and review the experiences of other similar organizations. One should then make an individual needs assessment of the community and fire department, and from that, determine the adequacy of the emergency communications services provided. In all cases, the requirements of NFPA 1221, *Installation, Maintenance, and Use of Public Fire Service Communications Systems*, should be followed. Also, see Section 4, Chapter 2, "Protective Signaling Systems."

COMMUNICATIONS CENTERS

In creating any communications network, one must first establish a center point (communications center) through which all related process and control functions will be directed. (See Figure 4-1A.) A communications center may serve a single agency or area, multiple agencies under the control of a single political subdivision, several similiar agencies from adjacent political subdivisions, an entire county, or any other large political jurisdiction. Combining fire and police communications within a specific political jurisdiction (and fire communications for several adjacent jurisdictions) has become an increasingly common management concept. If properly planned, such consolidations can provide positive results.

Evan E. Stauffer, P.E., is chairman of the NFPA Committee on Public Fire Service Communications. He is a fire protection engineer employed by the U.S. Navy.

FIG. 4-1A. A communications center equipped with an automated status board (top left). The status board is controlled by a fully computerized, multiple-operator dispatching network. (Source: Phoenix, AZ, Fire Department)

The communications center is where all requests for emergency assistance under the jurisdiction of a fire department are received and translated into an appropriate response. Further, the communications center should be structured to provide logistical support to the responding units until the situation is under control. Accordingly, as an operating entity, the communications center must ensure that the equipment, personnel, and established procedures are adequate to satisfactorily perform in emergencies.

Even the smallest fire department must have some means of receiving notice of a fire. In small communities, the communications center may consist of a telephone in a prvate residence or business establishment where someone is always available and where there is a switch to sound a siren or other device to alert fire fighters. Quite frequently, the police station serves as the communications center. As fire departments grow, a room should be provided to house the fire alarm dispatcher and related facilities in a fire station or other suitable structure.

Site Selection and Configuration Considerations

The following is a list of items that should be considered in the development of a communications center complex:

1. Location,
2. Seismic stability,
3. Security,
4. Emergency electrical power,
5. Wiring access (computer floor),
6. Lighting,
7. Air conditioning (computers/dispatch),
8. Air conditioning backup,
9. Console layout [per Occupational Safety and Health Administration (OSHA) Regulations],
10. Console arrangement,
11. Acoustics (background noise suppression),
12. Restroom facilities,
13. Kitchen facilities,
14. Decoration,
15. Rest areas (lounges),
16. Dormitories (sleeping quarters),
17. Emergency rations, and
18. Alternate locations.

The communications center should be designed and constructed so the probability of interruption to operations due to fire or other causes will be minimized. A building in a park or other open space is most desirable and can often be designed in harmony with the surroundings. When a separate building is not feasible and the communications center must be housed with other operations, such as city hall offices or in a fire station, the center should be properly separated from the remainder of the building by vertical and horizontal separations with a fire-resistance rating of at least two hours, and preferably with entrance only from the outside. Protection should be provided against fire exposures and unauthorized entry.

Alternate Dispatch Location

Serious consideration should be given to an alternate dispatch location. For example, a bomb threat or an actual fire in the center requires developing an alternate dispatch center and planning when to evacuate the communications center. This alternate location should be totally removed from the primary location, and should have all the necessary requirements for long-term usage. In the event of fire in the center, provisions should be made to continue operations long enough to transfer operations to the alternate dispatch location.

Communications Center Protection

Because of the types of activities conducted and the records maintained in any modern communications center, building and systems protection must be provided. Security begins at the entrance to the communications center, and can be as simple as a dead-bolt lock or as complex as a computerized entry control system. Only authorized personnel should be allowed access to the center. The center should be protected against damage due to vandalism, sabotage, and civil disturbances. If the center is located on the first floor (grade level) of the building, windows should not be permitted. Entrances into the center directly from the exterior, if provided, should be protected by two doors and a vestibule. The communications center should be located in a fire-resistive building, or in a fully sprinklered noncombustible building. Alarms and supervisory signals from the building sprinkler system(s) should be monitored in the center. If sprinkler protection is not required, the spaces adjoining the center should be provided with an automatic fire detection system that is monitored in the center. In any case, hazardous areas and the center itself should be protected by supervised automatic fire detection and fire suppression system(s). Portable fire extinguishers should be provided throughout. Heating, ventilating, and air-conditioning (HVAC) systems serving the center should be independent of the main building HVAC systems to avoid the possibility of smoke contamination from a fire elsewhere in the building. Fresh-air intakes should be located to minimize the possibility of drawing in smoke from a fire inside or outside the building. Consideration should be given to providing operator-controlled smoke-control modes for the center HVAC system. Interior finishes in the center should be noncombustible. Emergency lighting of sufficient intensity to permit operators to perform their duties during a total failure of normal lighting should be provided. Records must be properly safeguarded. Access to records should be limited to authorized personnel only. Off-premises storage of backup records, software, etc., is essential. This backup information should be updated on a regular basis.

Emergency Power

The communications center must be able to operate in the event of a primary power failure. If the primary power is provided from a utility distribution system, the secondary power may be either an engine-driven generator with a four-hour battery, a circuit from an independently different utility, or two standby generators. Standby generators should be tested weekly for at least one hour and should be able to power the system for at least four hours. Fuel storage should be adequate for 24 hours of operation, unless a reliable source of fuel resupply is available on two-hours' notice, even under adverse conditions.

Uninterruptable Power Source

A computer-aided dispatch (CAD) system cannot tolerate the power surges and interruptions normally associated with commercial power systems. A momentary power surge or outage could blank the computer's memory or damage its many sensitive circuits. To prevent this, an uninterruptable power source (UPS) is used as an isolator element between the commercial ac power lines and the computer system. This UPS consists of a set of batteries, a battery charger, and a dc to ac inverter. The inverter is phased to the commercial power frequency and produces the same power. Thus, any fluctuations or interruptions in commercial power would not affect the computer.

FIRE DEPARTMENT RADIO COMMUNICATIONS SYSTEMS

Radio System Selection

Considerable thought should be given to selecting the proper radio system, and professional personnel should be used to ensure the proper functioning of each system.

Radio Frequency Selection

Several bands of radio frequencies are available to the fire radio service. These bands are VHF low band, VHF high band, UHF 450 MHz and UHF 800 MHz bands. Each band of frequencies has its advantages and disadvantages, and the selection of a particular band will depend upon factors such as frequency availability, area to be covered, type of terrain, number of radio units required, frequencies used by bordering fire districts, mutual-aid agreements, type of operation, and use of emergency medical radios.

Due to the lack of available frequency bands, it may be necessary for fire departments or districts to share radio frequencies. For small fire districts, sharing radio channels with neighboring departments could be advantageous.

Type of Radio System Operation

The several types of radio systems available are as follows.

Simplex: This system utilizes a single radio frequency for both transmitting and receiving in all radios for each channel. With a simplex system, only one radio can transmit at any time and all others must receive.

Two-frequency half duplex: This system utilizes separate frequencies for transmitting and receiving. As in the simplex system above, half duplex allows only one radio to transmit at any one time.

Two-frequency full duplex: The two-frequency full duplex system utilizes separate transmit and receive frequencies and permits simultaneous conversations in two directions.

Two-frequency repeater system: With this system, a high-powered base station "repeater" is centrally located at a favorable site overlooking the area to be covered, preferably on a mountaintop, a tall building, or a tower. The repeater receives a transmission from any radio in the system on one radio frequency and instantly retransmits or "repeats" the message on a second frequency that is received by all other radios in the system. A repeater system greatly increases the range of all of the radios in the system. It is especially useful in hilly or mountainous terrain where it might be impossible to talk directly from unit to unit. Repeater systems are two-frequency half duplex systems as described above.

Trunking systems: The trunking system uses a group of radio frequencies. The system is controlled by a computer at the communications center or at the base station transmitter site. When a transmitter is keyed, it transmits its unique identity code to the computer. The computer instantaneously selects an available communications frequency and automatically directs the transmitting radio to use that frequency for the transmission. The advantage of this type of system is that it uses a group of available frequencies more efficiently by utilizing the capabilities of the computer to manage the radio traffic on each frequency. Thus, more radio traffic can be handled on the available frequencies, without causing congestion and interference. The computer can prioritize traffic from competing transmitters, based on their individual identity codes. For example, a request for a clear frequency transmitted by a fire department radio can receive a higher priority than a request from a non-fire agency's radio. Provisions should be included to keep the system operational in the event of failure of the computer controlling the system.

Tone-coded squelch: In a tone-coded squelch system, each radio transmits a subaudible tone along with the voice signal. This audio tone is used to "turn on" the receiver so the conversation will be heard. Only the proper tone will activate the receiver, which eliminates the reception of radio interference.

Radio paging systems: Contacting fire department personnel who do not normally listen to the radio system can be easily accomplished by a radio paging system. This system consists of a paging "encoder," which is located in the communications center, and individual personnel pagers. Pagers are also available that will respond to both an individual and group call.

Pagers are available for tone-only or tone-and-voice operation. When utilizing tone-only pagers, each individual is given a telephone number to call or location to respond to when the tone activates. With tone-and-voice pagers, the tone alerts the individual and turns on the receive audio. At that time, the dispatcher can relay a verbal message to the individual.

Multichannel Use of Radio Frequencies

The size and complexity of each fire department will determine the number of radio channels necessary for adequate communications. Very small departments should require only one radio channel for their private use, while departments in large metropolitan areas may require several. The Federal Communications Commission (FCC) has definite rules regarding channel loading, and excessive radio congestion must be proved before another radio channel will be licensed. In a large department, it is customary to have one or more dispatch radio channels and one or more tactical radio channels for controlling units in the field. In this case, the jurisdiction is divided into districts and each district is given a tactical radio channel. In addition, all departments adjacent to one another should share a common mutual-aid radio channel. This is provided for by the FCC and is usually managed on a statewide basis.

Base Station or Repeater Location

Care should be taken in selecting the main base station or repeater location for the radio system. Each radio coverage area is unique and must be dealt with on an individual basis. A high, central location, such as a mountaintop or large hill overlooking the area to be covered, a tall building, or similar structure, is generally the ideal site for the main base station location. (This depends upon coverage requirements, frequency availability, and requirements for channel sharing.) Where none of the above is present, a high antenna tower can be utilized. Towers are required, even on mountaintops, to ensure proper antenna system operation.

The availability of commercial power and telephone access is also desirable when locating the main base station site. Standby power supplied by a generator or batteries (or both) must be provided to ensure the site remains "on the air" in the event of a commercial power outage.

In some locations, where commercial power is unavailable, solar power (solar cells), batteries, or generators may be used as the primary source of power for the site. If the base station or repeater location is remote and unattended, provisions should be made to secure the area against weather, vandals, etc. A chain-link fence should surround the area and all radio equipment should be located inside a proper building, out of sight, and protected from the weather. Security and fire protection considerations are similar to those of the communications center.

Standby base station or repeater location: A separate location should be provided for a standby base station or repeater. This standby location should have the same complement of radios as the main station. A good high central location is also desirable for this site. These standby radios will be used if one or all of the radios at the main site fail. A separate commercial power source should be provided, if possible, and standby power should also be available.

The communications center should have the capability of selecting either the main or standby radios. The standby radios should be used periodically to ensure they are operable and ready for use in case of an emergency.

Radio Site Antenna Configuration

When more than one radio is installed at a single site, an antenna system may be required. It may be impractical for each radio to have its own separate antenna, because considerable interference could be generated using separate antennas. When several compatible radios are used, it is customary to provide one or more transmit antenna systems and a separate receive antenna system. A base station repeater using a single antenna requires a duplexer in order to transmit and receive simultaneously. Several transmitters can be connected to a single antenna by use of an antenna combiner; several receivers can be connected to a single antenna through the use of a multicoupler. Professional assistance should be utilized to design the antenna system for all radio sites.

The antenna design should provide maximum radio frequency (RF) isolation between transmitting and receiving antennas. This is usually accomplished by mounting them one above the other on the antenna structure. Coaxial cables should be used for connections between radios and antennas. These cables should be high quality, low loss with length as short as practical. Good grounding of the antenna system is required to prevent damage due to lightning.

Access from Communications Center to Radio Site

If base station radios are located at the communications center, individual wires or "house cables" can be used to connect the dispatcher's consoles to the proper base station. If the base station radios are located remotely from the communications center, radios can be connected by leased telephone lines, a microwave radio system, or a point-to-point radio. Redundant links should be provided so that failure of a single link will not prevent operation of the remote transmitter site from the communications center.

Mobile Radios

Mobile radios are ideal for use in fire apparatus or sedans. They have high RF power output (30 to 50 watts) and, therefore, considerable range. Their use, however, is restricted to vehicles, and they cannot be carried into buildings or structures. All fire department vehicles should have two-way radios. Mobile radios should be water resistant. Radios should be equipped with carrier-control timers to disable a transmitter that remains on the air due to a malfunction. If scanning devices are used, they should have an automatic priority feature whereby the radio will revert to its primary channel automatically when the channel is being used.

Portable Radios

Portable radios are much lower in RF power than mobile radios (0.1 to 7 watts), and, therefore, have a considerably shorter operating range. Their main advantage is portability. They can be hand-carried and allow communications outside the vehicle, giving the user considerable flexibility. The reduced RF power, however, can cause problems in communications reliability inside structures in some areas. Portable radios should have carrier-control timers to disable a transmitter that remains on the air due to a malfunction.

Diversity receiver-voter system: Since portable radios have a very low RF power output, this low power creates problems for communications over large areas. Portables can normally receive the high-power base station, but they do not always have sufficient power to transmit back to the main radio site. This problem can be eliminated by a diversity receiver-voter system in which radio receivers are installed in a uniform manner at various locations throughout the coverage area. This provides a receiver for each subarea in the system. In this manner, a portable radio should not be more than a mile or two from one of the receivers in its subarea.

The signal from each of these receivers is fed to the communications center. The voter is capable of switching from receiver to receiver in midsyllable, so, as the RF signal rises and fades at each receiver, the dispatcher hears only the best signal received. A diversity receiver-voter system can also be incorporated into a repeater system to greatly exceed portable-to-portable communications. A block diagram of a simple diversity (satellite) receiver-voter system is shown in Figure 4-1B.

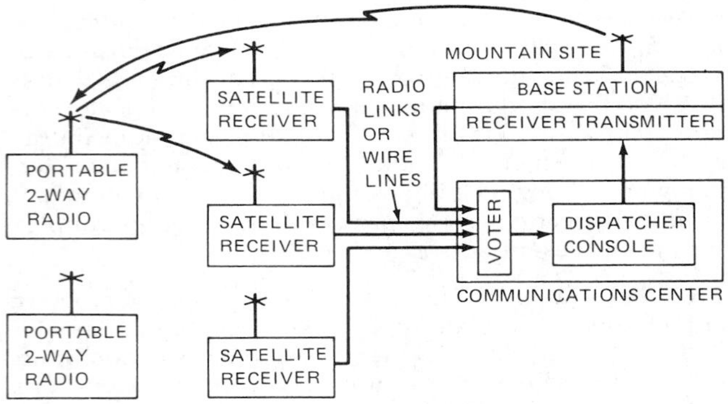

FIG. 4-1B. Block diagram of a simple diversity (satellite) receiver-voter system.

Mobile repeaters or extenders: An extender is simply a radio that receives on one frequency and immediately retransmits the signal on another frequency, usually in a different band. For example, in a rural area with a low-band simplex radio system, high-band portable radios could be used near a fire engine equipped with a mobile repeater, operating at 50 to 100 watts, to increase the range of the portable radios.

Mobile data terminals: Mobile data terminals are small computer terminals that may be connected to a radio system, allowing that unit to access another mobile terminal, base station terminal, or computer. These units generally consist of a small computer system that converts digital information into a signal that a radio can transmit or receive. These units may have preprogrammed display capabilities where by pressing one key, a "canned" message, such as unit status, condition, operator name, or even the time of day, can be sent. These units are so reduced in size they can be hand-held (including the radio).

Screen formats vary from simple light indicators to complex visual images including text and graphic characters. Some systems even have city maps or building drawings showing specific items relative to access, hydrant location, standpipes, and hazardous materials storage. One major consideration, however, is that these units require dedicated, conventional radio channels.

Station dispatch notification: There are three items that should be included as part of a fire department dispatch/alerting system: (1) a voice announce or public address system to alert the company(s) to an emergency response requirement; (2) a remote control, either wire or radio controlled, for station lights/annunciators; (3) failsafe communications to ensure the proper sending of the dispatch message. Vehicles may even be included in this alerting process by the use of digital decoders or other suitable audible alarms.

Mobile Communications

There are several factors to consider when establishing a mobile communications system. This chapter cannot specify the exact number of channels or frequencies needed; a fire department should be aware of the various requirements so a system can be selected more knowledgeably.

An analysis of service area and system configuration will help determine the wattage rating needed and the number of channels or frequencies required to support current usage and provide for future expansion. Small departments may be able to operate with one or two frequencies. However, if a department is considering the possible need of a mutual- or automatic-aid frequency, a police or interagency frequency, a disaster communications frequency, or the required individual departmental frequencies, it is quickly obvious why careful planning is needed.

To ensure quality communications, headsets should be considered for the driver, company officer, and fire fighters. To further support the suppression personnel as much as possible, each apparatus should be equipped with at least two radio units, one of which should be a portable radio and charger unit for the company officer. A portable unit will allow the officer to leave the vehicle while maintaining communications with the apparatus, other units, and the communications center, without returning repeatedly to the vehicle.

Emergency Medical Service Communications

From the early 1970s, the fire service has become more involved in providing emergency medical services (EMS), both basic and advanced life support, to the citizens they serve. Each state has an EMS communications plan on file with the FCC, and these plans identify how the EMS communications system will be implemented in that state. The EMS system differs from the normal fire communications system in the approach the FCC has taken to frequency allocation. The FCC has set aside ten UHF frequency pairs for communications between field EMS personnel and base hospital personnel. These ten channels are shared and used in all fifty states. Therefore, to ensure quality, noninterfering communications on these ten channels during critical life-threatening incidents, it is imperative that local coordination prevail. The ten frequency pairs are outlined in Table 4-1A.

TABLE 4-1A. ***EMS Frequency Pairs***

Channel #	Base Frequency	Mobile Frequency	Channel Name
1	463.000	468.000	MED-ONE
2	463.025	468.025	MED-TWO
3	463.050	468.050	MED-THREE
4	463.075	468.075	MED-FOUR
5	463.100	468.100	MED-FIVE
6	463.125	468.125	MED-SIX
7	463.150	468.150	MED-SEVEN
8	463.175	468.175	MED-EIGHT
9	462.950	467.950	MED-NINE
10	462.975	467.975	MED-TEN

Hazardous Materials Team Communications

The development of hazardous materials (HAZMAT) response teams in the fire service has resulted in new communications requirements for safety. These new requirements are in two major areas: (1) hazardous materials information, and (2) HAZMAT team communications from within encapsulating suits.

A major element in the successful outcome of hazardous materials incidents is the ability to rapidly obtain information about the material(s) involved. This generally involves contacting outside agencies for a variety of information. Mobile radio telephone patch(es) may be considered, but this usually ties up the only available radio channel. Mobile cellular telephones should be installed in the hazardous materials team apparatus to facilitate this need for information. This approach also allows a printer to be installed along with the telephone so that one of the hazardous materials computerized information services can be used for on-scene, rapid-printed information.

Mobile telephones also allow the hazardous materials team members direct access to HAZMAT information services, reducing the potential for errors. The medical component of the HAZMAT team should be equipped with a UHF MED radio for medical control or to obtain toxicological information from base hospitals.

Many hazardous materials team members must work inside encapsulating suits. They require special communications systems designed to meet their requirements for operational safety. Two-way wireless communications, preferably hands-free, should be considered. A variety of radio systems that use bone, ear, or throat microphones for voice transmission are available to meet these needs. These radio systems come in simplex, half duplex, or full duplex. They use push-to-talk or voice-actuated circuits to transmit, and mobile repeaters may be integrated into them. The fire department should thoroughly examine its needs in this area prior to purchase.

PERSONNEL

No matter how well designed, installed, and maintained, no system is better than the people who operate it. Communications systems should be supervised by responsible and competent people whose duties include directing, testing, and inspection programs. Fire alarm dispatchers should be healthy, temperamentally suited to the position, and be able to efficiently handle assigned duties. They should have the ability to remain calm, take decisive action during emergencies, remain alert during periods of inactivity and while carrying out normal repetitive operations, and work harmoniously with other people. They should also be familiar with general fire department operations.

Work schedules should be structured to provide for maximum efficiency. Stress and high activity lead to dispatcher fatigue. Therefore, dispatchers should be provided with a place to take work breaks away from the communications center.

Communications personnel should not become isolated from the fire department. Their structured training should be directed toward maintaining and improving their dispatching skills, but it must also include a full understanding of all department operations, the most important being fire suppression. All standard operating procedures should be in writing to ensure standard performance.

An adequate number of qualified communications operators should be on duty at all times to handle the expected alarm load. For jurisdictions receiving fewer than 600 alarms per year, there should be at least one operator on duty at all times. This operator may be a designated employee of the telephone company; a member of another government agency; or the house watch at a fire station, provided an alternate means is provided to handle alarms if the house watch responds to emergencies. For jurisdictions receiving 600 to 2,500 alarms per year, at least one full-time operator should be on duty in the communications center at all times. For jurisdictions receiving 2,500 to 10,000 alarms per year, at least two operators should be on duty at all times. For jurisdictions receiving more than 10,000 alarms per year, NFPA 1221, *Installation, Maintenance, and Use of Public Fire Service Communications Systems*, should be consulted for specific requirements for additional operators.

Provisions should be made for recalling off-duty operators in event of an unexpectedly high alarm load. Extra operators should be placed on duty in advance to deal with anticipated natural disasters, such as blizzards and hurricanes. Arrangements should be made to provide meals and rest periods for operators during natural disasters, since operators may be unable to leave the communications center for extended periods.

CONSOLIDATION OF COMMUNICATIONS CENTERS

Many small-to-medium-sized fire jurisdictions have found that, by consolidating communications functions with other agencies, they can provide a higher level of service to their citizens at a lower overall cost. One of the major benefits of consolidation for these agencies is the ability to provide highly trained, alert radio dispatchers who are on duty 24 hours a day. A larger communications center will also have adequate backup to handle multiple, simultaneous incoming alarms, while the smaller center may not have the personnel to cope with them. The major benefit of consolidation is to provide an increased level of service at reduced costs.

A fire communications center is labor intensive. If a combined communications center can handle the same workload with fewer employees, the result can be a substantial savings to the jurisdictions involved. For example, suppose there are four medium-sized fire departments operating independently in the same valley, each with its own communications center. Typical staffing for the individual centers might be three full-time dispatchers, each working a 24-hour shift. Their time would be supplemented by overtime pay and/or the assignment of fire suppression personnel to cover vacations, sick leave, etc. In this case, the four individual fire departments would be served by twelve dispatchers. By combining the four communications operations into one central communications center, the same workload could be handled by nine dispatchers working 24-hour shifts.

Methods of consolidating fire communications centers vary, but the two most popular are: (1) forming a joint powers authority (JPA) to provide this service as an independent agency, or (2) one or more departments contracting with another fire department to provide this service. Either system can work well and provide the same benefits to the participants.

Joint Powers Authority

A joint powers authority is an independent government entity, established to provide specific services. There are several benefits of a JPA arrangement for combined fire communications *versus* other arrangements, but the major benefit is shared administration. With a JPA operating with an independent board of directors, no one agency that might set policy unacceptable to another agency is "in control." In this way, each participant has equal representation and equal responsibility to make the operation a success.

REPORTING A FIRE OR EMERGENCY

Reports of fires and other emergencies under the jurisdiction of the fire service originate from three principal sources: (1) the general public, (2) the business community (industrial, institutional, commercial, and mercantile), and (3) other public service/safety agencies. The reporting process may utilize any of the following four means, individually or in combination: (1) public commercial telephone systems, (2) public emergency reporting/fire alarm systems, (3) privately operated automatic alarm systems, and (4) two-way radio communications systems.

Commercial Telephone Facilities

The most common method, and no doubt the least costly to the community involved, is the conventional commercial telephone network. However, the important factor of automatic location identification is not obtainable in a majority of the areas presently served.

The "911" system, where adopted, provides a universal, easily remembered telephone for use by the public to summon emergency services. Only the "enhanced 911" system provides both the calling number and the location of the related telephone instrument directly to the dispatcher. This indication is presented visually on a cathode-ray tube (CRT), and can be automatically recorded if the communications center includes CAD or computerized logging support systems.

Although there are some disadvantages to total dependency upon a utility-owned, -operated, and -maintained communications network, specifically with regard to emergency reporting, telephones are often the only means of communication available in urban centers, as well as in suburban and rural areas. The installation of outdoor telephone booths increases the availability of telephones for emergency reporting. In general, the public telephone system, widely used for reporting fires and other emergencies, provides a very viable function.

Municipal Fire Alarm Systems

Scope, installation, maintenance, and use of all municipal fire alarm systems, regardless of the principles of operation, are covered in detail in NFPA 1221, *Installation, Maintenance, and Use of Public Fire Service Communications Systems*. This standard makes no distinction among a coded, voice, or code-voice alarm system, because each must perform the same function, i.e., providing a means by which an alarm can be transmitted from a street alarm box to the communications center.

From the standpoint of the dispatcher responsible for receiving the alarm, the use of a public emergency reporting station (fire alarm box) eliminates the difficulty of determining the location from which the alarm is being transmitted. When actuated, each device must transmit a distinct numerical code, in addition to any other functions or capabilities provided.

A general abandonment of jurisdictionally owned municipal fire alarm systems, or, more aptly, public emergency reporting systems, began to take place in many major metropolitan centers in the mid 1970s. The movement, based on economics and the efficiency of the service provided, has since spread to smaller suburban jurisdictions.

The average metropolitan system consisted of a mix of public reporting stations (street boxes) and auxiliarized fire alarm systems interconnected to master boxes. In most cases, the operational jurisdictions reduced their obligations toward auxiliarized interconnects by referring all risks, exclusive of schools, hospitals, churches, government buildings, and major hotels, to privately operated central stations. Public reporting stations were eliminated shortly thereafter. Those agencies that still maintain and operate such systems have essentially directed their applications toward auxiliarized systems.

The expanding implementation of "911" systems has eliminated the necessity of public reporting stations (street boxes), at least in those areas where publicly accessible phones are well distributed and functionally usable. Public emergency reporting systems are electrically operated networks divided into three basic categories: (1) coded, (2) voice, and (3) coded-voice combination.

A public emergency reporting system may be used for the transmission of other emergency signals or calls, provided such transmission does not interfere with the proper handling of fire alarms. For example, systems employing voice communications between the street alarm box and communications center can be used to transmit alarms of nonfire emergency nature. Fire alarm boxes in a radio-type system can be provided with pushbuttons for calling the police department, the ambulance service, or other emergency services, and signals can be transmitted directly to the service called. With parallel-type telephone systems (each box served by a separate circuit), the dispatcher can crossconnect to the proper emergency service, such as the police department, or systems can be arranged so authorized persons, such as law enforcement personnel, can be connected directly to their own departments.

Coded Systems

The coded category is divided into two classifications: (1) the wired telegraphic system, and (2) the radio (wireless) system.

The wired telegraph-type box is actuated by depressing a lever that is accessible through a small door. (See Figure 4-1C.) This starts a spring-wound clockwork mechanism and transmits a code number by the rotation of a code wheel that opens and closes the circuit. The transmitted code number of each box is different, so the location of the box transmitting the alarm can be determined. If a circuit wire is broken, the telegraph box system usually is designed to transmit the coded signal through a ground connection.

***FIG. 4-1C.** (Left) A coded telegraphic-type box. (Right) An interior view of the telegraphic alarm box, showing the actuating lever (arrow) that normally protrudes through the hole shown on the inner door at right. When depressed, the handle releases the spring-wound mechanism and sends a coded signal from the code wheel shown at center. (Source: Gamewell Corp.)*

Radio boxes are similar to wired telegraphic boxes. (See Figure 4-1D.) When activated, they transmit a coded signal, representative of their geographical location; however, in addition to the basic numerical identification code, each box must be equipped to send at least three specific messages identifying the actuation cause. A "test" message must be transmitted at least once in each 24-hour period, assuring the monitoring point (communications center) that the box is working. If a box is stuck or physically battered, a specific "tamper" message must be transmitted. If the box is used for public reporting only, the third required message would be "fire." Radio boxes are available that allow transmission of up to 50 messages actuated either publicly (fire, police, medical aid, etc.), privately (through auxiliarized connections), or a combination of both.

Voice Systems

Voice systems are wired telephone networks. The fire alarm box is essentially a telephone handset installed in a specially designed housing. (See Figure 4-1E.) The location from which the alarm is transmitted is definitely established, without dependence upon voice transmission and without interference from other boxes. Removing the handset from its cradle in the box lights a lamp on the communications center switchboard, where the number of the box and the time of message can be recorded.

FIG. 4-1D. (Left and Center) Typical battery/dc-powered coded radio-type alarm boxes equipped for multiple messages (fire, police, ambulance, etc.). (Source: King Fisher Co.). (Right) A user-power-coded radio box. This type of device must incorporate an automatic test feature to meet standard requirements. (Source: Signal Communications Corp.)

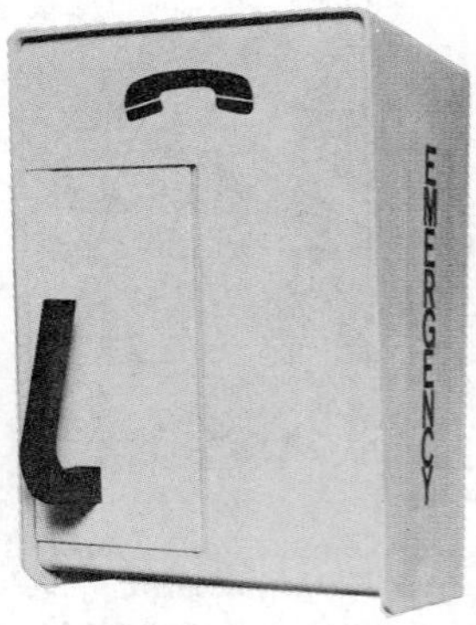

FIG. 4-1E. A voice-telephone alarm box, series type, for handset operation only. (Source: Gamewell Corp.)

Voice systems technology is divided into parallel and series classifications.

Coded-voice combination: Boxes that also contain a telegraph mechanism are called combination telephone-telegraph type, and both voice and coded signals can be transmitted over the same circuit to the communications center. (See Figure 4-1F.) The series telephone box may be intermixed with telegraph street boxes and master boxes.

FIG. 4-1F. A combination telephone-and-coded telegraphic-type alarm box. (Source: Gamewell Corp.)

Privately Operated Automatic Alarm Systems

There are two sources of alarms that constitute a private agency notification to a governmentally operated communications center: (1) central station, and (2) remote station systems. Proprietary systems may be auxiliarized to the municipal system or may rely on manual notification of the communications center. These operations are described in Section 4, Chapter 2, "Protective Signaling Systems."

Two-Way Radio Communications

A commonly overlooked alarm/emergency notification source is the two-way radio network of the responding service(s). Notification of incidents in watershed areas are typically reported by mobile patrols. Similarly, requests for supplemental dispatches to multiple-alarm fires usually originate from units in the field.

Contact between agencies in adjacent jurisdictions, as well as contact between agencies of a single jurisdiction, may often utilize radio to expedite communications.

PROCESSING COMMUNICATIONS WITHIN THE DEPARTMENT

Regardless of the method by which an alarm is received, the location of the emergency is the minimum information required to respond to an emergency. The nature of the incident being reported is also obviously essential. However, one must bear in mind that thousands of responses to numerically coded (location) nonvoice notifications are made each year.

Data Collection Systems

To efficiently operate a fire department communications center, reliable data must be available. To be useful, this data must be both accurate and readily available. The data may take a wide variety of forms, from card indexes to sophisticated computer files, and may include such categories as the status of vehicles, the availability of resources, geographic information, and personnel information. The following categories outline the various types and uses of data that can be collected and maintained by a communications center.

Incident-related data: It is important (and often a legal responsibility) to keep accurate records of fire and emergency medical incidents to which the department responds. The type of data worth collecting include:

1. Time of dispatch,
2. Address,
3. Identifications and times of responding units,
4. Arrival times at the scene,
5. Departure times from the scene,
6. Radio traffic tape logs,
7. Telephone tape logs, and
8. Times of significant events at the scene.

Operational-related data: This data consists of information that must be rapidly available at all times to maintain efficient operation of the communications center. The data include:

1. Geographic data,
2. Equipment data,
3. Response order data, and
4. Additional resource data.

Administrative/management data: This category includes data that may be required for the general fire department management:

1. Personnel records,
2. Personnel scheduling data,
3. Personnel specialty skills information, and
4. Occupancy information.

Reports: Many types of reports are necessary for overall fire department management. Some of these reports will be required at regular intervals, while others will be required on demand to fill a specific departmental information need. A list of probable reports are:

1. Response time reports,
2. Emergency activity reports,
3. Occupancy activity reports,
4. Specific incident reports,
5. Personnel staffing reports,
6. Reports for outside agencies,
7. Fire loss/injury reports, and
8. Equipment-related reports.

These reports can be used to project future needs of the department, such as location of new fire stations, hiring of additional personnel, and relocation of existing equipment.

Receipt of Alarms

Most alarms or emergency notifications are received by telephone over a conventional commercial telephone network. Automatic recording devices must be interconnected to all types of voice-reporting circuits, including radio systems. However, recording devices cannot ensure the credibility or accuracy of the information received.

Correct telephone numbers are the only means of positively identifying the location of an informant. The cross-matching of telephone numbers to addresses is a telephone company service, provided on a select basis, to public safety agencies.

The enhanced 911 systems are designed to provide the answering dispatcher with an immediate reference to the number of the telephone in use and its specific location. The data is usually displayed on a CRT device. The data input is formulated for electronic data processing (EDP) usage and can be fed concurrently to a departmental CAD system.

All public emergency reporting systems (municipal fire alarm systems) provide an individual numeric code for each unit installed, and the proper numeric code is transmitted when use of a specific unit is initiated. All incoming coded signals are permanently recorded on printers integral to the specific systems and, in some cases, are also displayed on direct readout (LED, CRT, etc.) devices.

The translation of the numerically coded data into a usable address is performed with the aid of a running-card file, which is a necessary factor in the processing of all alarms and requests for emergency assistance.

Voice Recording and Reproducing Systems

The voice recording and reproducing system should consist of a multichannel recording device that provides a permanent, time-referable, unalterable, and court-admissible recording of all telephonic/radio communications within a fire department.

The watch commander and one of the dispatchers should be totally familiar with the operation and maintenance of the multichannel recording device. Familiarizing other department personnel is advisable, but responsibility should lie with no more than two individuals per watch/shift.

A multichannel recording system will provide:

1. Verification of emergency messages,
2. A log of all communications within the department,
3. Protection of the department against civilian or other department complaints,
4. Substantiation or negation of claims against the department,
5. Added protection to the civilian population,
6. A training tool for dispatch personnel, and
7. Validation of response time.

The importance of these various benefits will differ from department to department.

Running-Card Files

A running-card file contains a dispatch plan for every area of the jurisdiction served. The number of running cards in a given file is dependent upon the size of the jurisdiction and the manner in which it has been indexed for responses. The most common method of indexing is to assign numeric designations to all intersections or cadastral networks of horizontal and vertical crosspoints. There is a specific running-card to each intersection or crosspoint. Public emergency reporting stations (alarm boxes) are normally assigned an identity code corresponding to the intersection or crosspoint site closest to their physical location.

When an emergency notification is received over a conventional commercial telephone network, through a 911 system, or by two-way radio, the dispatcher utilizes the addresses and/or intersection data obtained from the informant to find the correct running-card.

Status-Keeping Systems

The ability to maintain an accurate record of the current status of all emergency units in the system is essential to a successful fire dispatch system and will aid in: (1) minimizing response times, (2) ensuring appropriate response, and (3) collecting nonemergency unit activity information.

Status-keeping systems may involve the tracking of various pieces of information, such as:

1. Availability of the unit for emergency response,
2. Service capabilities of the unit (paramedic service, extrication equipment, all-terrain capability, etc.),
3. Location of the unit,
4. Means of contacting the unit (radio, phone, etc.), and
5. Miscellaneous items based on the particular department's operating philosophy.

The mechanism of a status-keeping system will vary, depending upon the number of units on which status must be kept and the actual dispatch process utilized by a department. A small department might utilize a manual system with a small "clipboard," while a large department may require a computer.

Computer-Aided Dispatch (CAD)

Computers are being used in all areas of the fire service. These areas include personnel management, budgeting, fire prevention, training, inventory, etc. One major use is the dispatching of fire units. The degree to which a CAD system can be implemented depends upon the size of the department. A small fire department with one to three stations does not require a complex CAD system with mobile digital terminals, station terminals, and printers. Dispatch software packages are available for personal computers, and small departments can use them to rapidly recover the information needed to expeditiously dispatch fire units. This information includes preplans, hazardous materials information, lists of other responsible public safety agencies, names, addresses, and phone numbers of responsible parties, etc. (See Figure 4-1G.)

NFPA 1221, *Installation, Maintenance, and Use of Public Fire Service Communications Systems*, categorizes CAD systems as Class 1, 2, or 3. The Class 1 system is the most complex, utilizing computers to automatically track the status of all fire apparatus, and to select and recommend the appropriate units for dispatch. Upon approval of the operator, signals are then transmitted to the appropriate stations and field units to dispatch the appropriate personnel and equipment. A Class 1 CAD system requires complete redundancy and automatic switchover to an on-line backup computer, in event of failure of computer hardware or software. A Class 2 CAD system uses computers to support dispatching operations. Redundancy, but not automatic switchover, is required. A Class 3 CAD system requires manual entry from the operator, and is used primarily to keep track of unit status and related information. In a Class 3 system, computer redundancy is not required. In all classes of CAD systems, manual backup facilities should be provided and be readily available for use in the event of problems with, or failure of, the CAD system. There also should be an up-to-date hard copy file of stored information located on the premises to support the dispatch function should the CAD system fail. For more detail on CAD systems, the reader should refer to NFPA 1221, *Installation, Maintenance, and Use of Public Fire Service Communications Systems*.

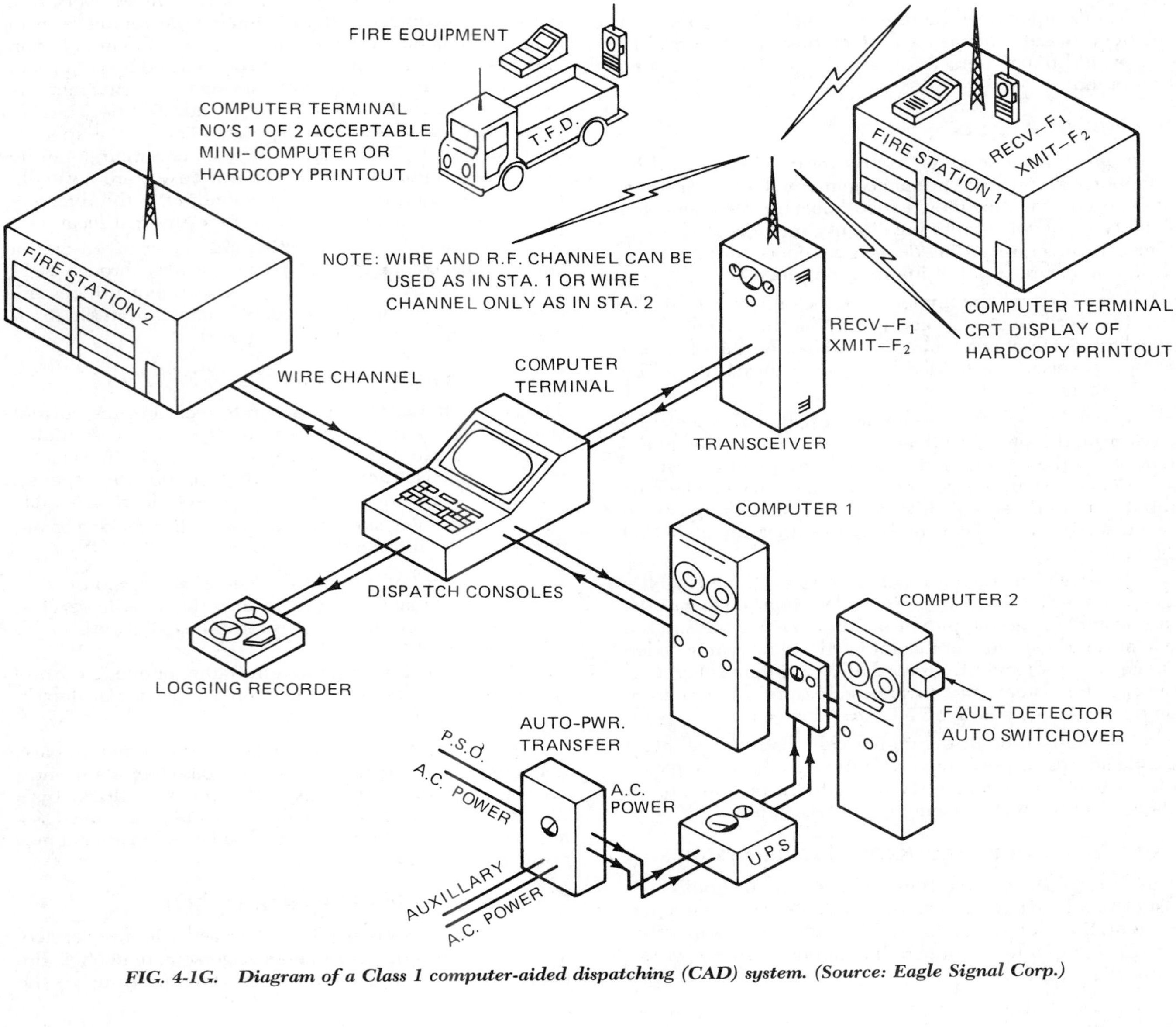

FIG. 4-1G. Diagram of a Class 1 computer-aided dispatching (CAD) system. (Source: Eagle Signal Corp.)

Caution must be used in both the selection and use of personal computers. Computer professionals should match the application to the proper computer. The dispatch computer should not be used for other department applications. It should be kept free of time-consuming processes to allow for rapid retrieval of dispatch information. CAD systems for medium-to-large departments are more complex and must be designed for the needs of an individual department.

Dispatch Circuits and Equipment

A dispatch circuit is the means by which the fire alarm dispatcher notifies fire companies to respond to an alarm. The location from which the alarm was received is the minimum information that must be transmitted.

NFPA 1221, *Installation, Maintenance, and Use of Public Fire Service Communications Systems*, provides requirements, some of which are:

1. Two separate means of transmitting alarms to fire stations must be provided at the communications center. However, only one means of transmittal is required when fewer than 600 alarms per year are received.
2. Each alarm transmitted and its date and time must be automatically recorded.
3. Devices for transmitting coded or other types of signals must be arranged for manual setting and operation. (The automatic dispatching of fire companies by the use of computers is under development.)

It should be noted that CAD, unlike fully automated dispatching systems, is not a circuit. CAD is a method used to assess related response information. CADs identify the companies normally assigned, and the current status of each of the companies.

Types of Dispatch Circuits

Telegraph circuits: Telegraph dispatch circuits are wired circuits, arranged for transmitting and receiving coded alarm signals. Signals are received at fire stations on a variety of instruments, including gongs, bells, or tappers, and punch or printing registers that register the coded signal with holes in, or marks on, a paper tape.

Teletype circuits: The teletypewriter dispatch circuit (either wired or microwave) is another form of dispatch circuit, where a fire alarm dispatcher transmits alarm information to various fire stations by means of a teletypewriter. The alarms are received by the teletypewriter, which reproduces the information on a roll of paper. Their major advantage is that more information, if available, can be transmitted to the fire station.

Facsimile circuits: Facsimile dispatch circuits are wired circuits that incorporate the telewriter, a device formerly used by hotels and railroads. The dispatcher writes out instructions on pressure-sensitive paper tape with a special stylus, and the instructions are reproduced at the fire stations on a roll of paper tape.

The teleprinter is a facsimile device that reproduces hardcopy information, including drawings. Receiving units are generally installed in fire stations, and also installed in fire department vehicles when radio is used.

Voice amplification circuits: Voice amplification dispatch circuits are wired circuits. As the name implies, this is an arrangement whereby the dispatcher talks into a microphone at the communications center and the information is amplified and received on loudspeakers located in the fire stations.

Radio channel: A radio channel is another form of dispatch circuit for the transmission of fire alarm signals. Transmitting equipment is located at the communications center, with receivers in each fire station. Transceivers on fire apparatus provide communications with companies in the field. A radio system has the advantage of not being connected to, or dependent upon, wires, unless the transmitter is located at a point remote from the dispatcher.

Telephone alerting systems: Various types of telephone alerting systems are available from telephone companies. Telephone systems are flexible and can be zoned to alert specific people or areas, rather than alerting the general public.

Other Alerting Facilities

Because they are operated entirely by volunteer fire fighters, many fire departments have no one on duty at a fire station to receive an alarm. In these instances, bells, air horns, whistles, or sirens are commonly used to alert the volunteers when an alarm has been received. A satisfactory arrangement is to sound coded signals that communicate the location of the fire. Radio receivers in volunteer fire fighter residences or places of business and radio pagers (i.e., portable receivers carried on the person) are frequently used for receiving alarms.

Supervision and Testing Facilities

The communications center is where trouble signals are received and testing facilities are generally provided. In a leased telephone system, some test facilities are located in telephone buildings. In the event of trouble, both an audible and a visual signal should be provided. An audible signal may be shut off, but it should be designed to operate again in the event of trouble in any of the other circuits connected to the same supervisory device.

BIBLIOGRAPHY

NFPA Codes, Standards, and Recommended Practices

Reference to the following NFPA codes, standards, and recommended practices will provide further information on fire department emergency communications systems discussed in this chapter. (See the latest *NFPA Catalog* for availability of current editions of the following documents.)

NFPA 70, *National Electrical Code®*.

NFPA 71, *Installation, Maintenance, and Use of Signaling Systems for Central Station Service*.

NFPA 72, *Protective Signaling Systems*.

NFPA 1221, *Installation, Maintenance, and Use of Public Fire Service Communications Systems*.

Additional Reading

Bahme, C. W., "The Watts Fires and Their Lessons," *Fire Journal*, Vol. 60, No. 2, Mar. 1966, pp. 10-14.

"Communications: Scanning the Equipment," *Fire Command*, Vol. 56, No. 9, Sept. 1989, p. 29.

Foot, N., "Radio Interference to Alarm Systems," *Fire Surveyor*, Vol. 17, No. 6, Dec. 1988, pp. 36-39.

Glicksman, M., "Voice Alarms," *Specifying Engineer*, Vol. 49, No. 5, May 1983, pp. 67-73.

"How One City Is Dealing with the Nuisance Alarm Problem," *Fire Journal*, Vol. 82, No. 1, 1988, p. 57.

Maillet, M., "Microprocessors and New Communications Systems in Improved Detection Systems," *Proceedings* of the Conference on New Technology to Reduce Fire Losses and Costs, Elsevier, 1986, pp. 243-247.

"Malicious Alarms or Nuisance Alarms: Which Is the Larger Problem," *Fire Journal*, Vol. 83, No. 1, 1989, p. 5.

Nesse, T., "Digital Alarm Communications: Where They Come From, Where They're Going," *Fire Journal*, Vol. 82, No. 4, 1988, p. 47.

Nielsen, D. J., and Ryland, H. G., "Computer Command-Control," *Fire Journal*, Vol. 62, No. 3, May 1968, pp. 43-48.

Singer, E. N., "Radio Communications in High-Rise Buildings," *With NY Firefighters*, Vol. 42, No. 1, 1981, pp. 10-12.

Spahn, E., "Increasing Your Fire Alarm Literacy," *Fire Engineering*, Vol. 143, No. 6, 1990, p. 75.

Szymanski, D. J., and Stacey, J. W., "Lesson Plan: Computer-Aided Dispatch System," *Fire Engineering*, Vol. 141, No. 7, 1988, pp. 32-35.

Todd, C. S., "Remote Monitoring of Alarm Signals, Part 2: Monitoring by Central Stations," *Fire Surveyor*, Vol. 17, No. 1, Feb. 1989, pp. 18-31.

Todd, C. S., "Remote Monitoring of Alarm Signals, Part 4: Central Station Operations and Communications with Fire Controls," *Fire Surveyor*, Vol. 17, No. 2, Apr. 1988, pp. 32-37.

Todd, C. S., "Remote Monitoring of Alarm Signals, Part 5: The Future," *Fire Surveyor*, Vol. 17, No. 3, June 1988, pp. 16-21.

Walsh, C. P., "Radio Communications: Coming In Loud and Clear," *Fire Engineering*, Vol. 143, No. 11, 1989, pp. 32-36.

PROTECTIVE SIGNALING SYSTEMS

Revised by Dean K. Wilson

A fire detection and alarm system is a key element among the fire protection features of any building. Properly designed, installed, operated, tested, and maintained, a fire alarm system can help limit property fire losses in buildings, regardless of occupancy. Since many of the fire deaths in the United States result from building fires, the use of detection and alarm systems in buildings also can reduce the loss of life from fire. This chapter will discuss the operational characteristics of the various types of protective signaling systems currently in use.

TYPES OF SYSTEMS

Fire protective signaling systems are classified according to the functions they are expected to perform. Their installation, maintenance, and use are specified in the several NFPA standards listed in the bibliography at the end of this chapter.

The basic features of each system are:

1. A system control unit.
2. A primary, or main, power supply that usually is a connection to the local public electric utility.
3. A secondary, or standby, power supply.
4. A "trouble" power supply.
5. One or more initiating device circuits to which manual fire alarm boxes, sprinkler waterflow alarm devices, automatic fire detectors, and other fire alarm initiating devices are connected.
6. One or more alarm indicating appliance circuits to which alarm indicating appliances, such as bells, horns, and speakers, are connected, or to which an off-premises alarm is connected, or both.

The secondary, or standby, power supply is required automatically to supply the energy to the system within 30 sec whenever the primary, or main, power supply is incapable of providing the minimum voltage required for proper system operation. Since fire protective signaling systems are required to operate properly when the applied voltage rises to 110 percent of normal, as well as when the voltage falls as low as 80 percent of normal, the secondary supply must not supply energy as long as the primary voltage remains above 85 percent of the rated voltage. The size of the secondary supply usually is measured in the amount of time that the secondary supply will operate the system. Each system type has its own standby time requirement, which is explained in the appropriate sections of this chapter.

The secondary supply can be a storage battery, generators, or a combination of a battery and a generator. The secondary supply may be used to power the trouble signals on the system.

Many control units have more than one initiating device circuit, so that the fire location can be indicated on an annunciator panel by floor, wing, subsection, or room. The annunciator can be built into the control unit or located in a lobby, maintenance area, telephone switchboard room, or some other space where it is accessible to building and fire service personnel.

Central Station Systems

A signaling system for central station service is designed to receive signals from a protected premises at a constantly attended location operated by a company whose purpose is providing central station service. Signals may be transmitted from a protected premises using either traditional direct-current-coded circuits, often referred to as McCulloh circuits; by means of three types of multiplex signaling systems, including telephone-company-provided derived local channel systems; by means of digital alarm communicator systems; by means of two-way radio frequency (RF) multiplex communications systems; by means of a combination of a single-line digital alarm communicator transmitter and a one-way RF transmitter system; or by means of a one-way RF communications system.

When they receive fire alarm signals, operators at the central station retransmit those signals to the public fire service communications center. In addition, the central station either directly or through a subcontractor provides emergency runner response to the various signals received, the central station also must supply repair service in case

Dean K. Wilson is director of Loss Prevention Training, at Industrial Risk Insurers (IRI), Hartford, CT, and co-editor of the bimonthly fire alarm/burglary alarm newsletter, *The Moore-Wilson Signaling Report*.

of a trouble signal, with the repair person reaching the protected premises within 4 hrs.

The power supply at the protected premises must provide 24-hr standby operation from rechargeable or dry-cell batteries. The standby power supply at the central station must supply energy to operate the system for 24 hrs. This standby supply at the central station may consist of rechargeable batteries, a combination of a single-engine-driven generator and 4-hr-capacity rechargeable batteries, or multiple-engine-driven generators. The high level of systems security and personnel response of signaling systems for central station service is most often employed by high-valued facilities, such as those commercial and industrial properties insured under the highly protected risk (HPR) property insurance plan. For this reason, central station systems are generally considered to be principally for property protection.

Central station systems may handle fire alarms, supervisory signals, guard patrol tours, and trouble signals. One of the greatest values of signaling systems for central station service is their ability to supervise the availability of other fire protection systems, such as automatic sprinkler systems or special-hazard fire extinguishing systems. For example, the ability of a central station system to supervise the position of an automatic sprinkler system control valve adds significantly to the overall management capability of a building fire protection system.

Local System

The main purpose of a local protective signaling system is to sound local alarm signals for evacuation of the protected building. (See Figure 4-2A.) A system could be limited to the basic features indicated earlier. A local system standby power supply must operate the system for 24 hrs under normal load and then be able to operate the alarm system for 5 min in an alarm condition.

In a local system, the alarm is not relayed automatically to a fire department. Instead, when the alarm sounds, someone must use some other means to notify the fire department. If the building is unoccupied at the time of the alarm, fire department response would depend upon a neighbor or passerby hearing the audible fire alarm signaling appliances and notifying the department.

Auxiliary System

An auxiliary protective signaling system has circuitry that connects a building's fire alarm initiating device(s) to a public fire reporting system installed in accordance with the requirements of NFPA 1221, *Installation, Maintenance, and Use of Public Fire Service Communications Systems*. This is done either through a nearby master fire alarm box or through a dedicated telephone line run directly to the public fire communications center switchboard. (See Figure 4-2B.) The signal received by the fire department is the same received when someone manually activates the municipal fire alarm box. Because fire department personnel know which municipal boxes are auxiliarized, responding fire fighters can check for an alarm originating within the protected premises.

The standby power supply for an auxiliary system is required to operate the system for 60 hrs of normal operation, followed by 5 min of alarm. Since this system has been installed primarily for building protection, the 60-hr span is needed to carry the system over a normal weekend. In an auxiliary system, the protected building may or may not have an evacuation alarm.

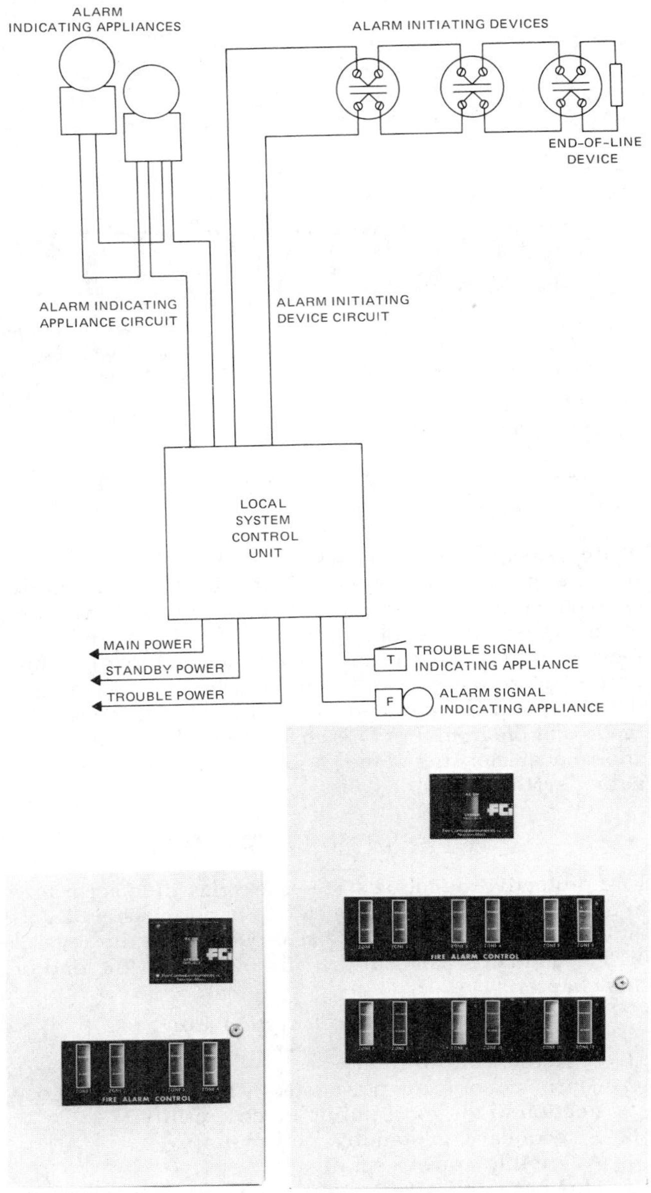

FIG. 4-2A. A typical arrangement of a local protective signaling system (top). A local system control unit (bottom). (Source: Fire Control Instruments)

Remote Station System

A remote station protective signaling system has an alarm signal that is received at a remote location, acceptable to the authority having jurisdiction, which is attended by trained personnel 24 hrs a day. (See Figure 4-2C.) The receiving equipment usually is located at a public fire service communications center, police station, or telephone answering service. The signal is transmitted over a leased telephone line or by means of a digital alarm communicator system (DACS), and is indicated audibly and visually at the remote station. If the remote station is not at the public fire service communications center, the remote station personnel must notify the center of the alarm. System

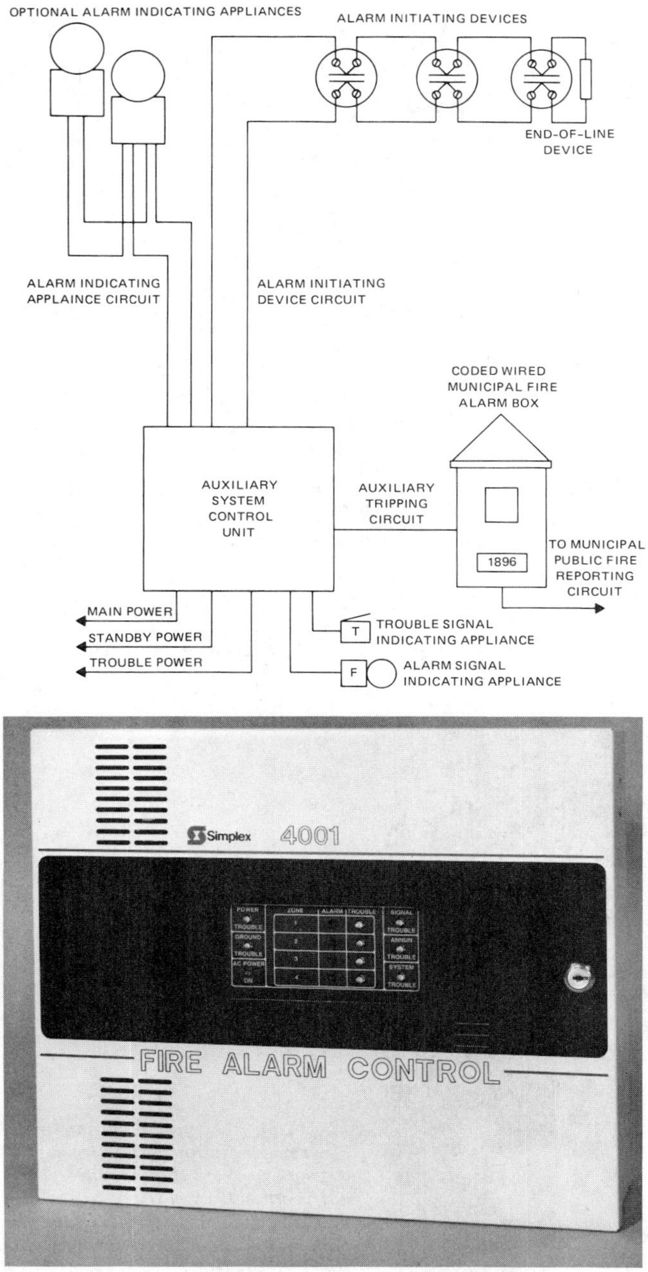

FIG. 4-2B. A typical arrangement of an auxiliary protective signaling system (top). An auxiliary system control unit (bottom). (Source: Simplex Time Recorder Company)

trouble signals usually are transmitted automatically to the remote receiving station. The control unit at the remote station, and, if needed, at the protected premises, also is required to have an independent secondary power supply that will operate the system for 60 hrs, followed by 5 min of alarm. The protected premises of a remote station system may or may not have an evacuation system.

Proprietary System

The proprietary protective signaling system is widely used in large commercial or industrial occupancies. (See Figure 4-2D.)

Signals transmitted over a proprietary system are received and automatically and permanently recorded at a constantly attended central supervising station located either at the protected premises or at another location of the property owner. In very simplistic terms, a proprietary system is a central station system with the central station located at the protected premises.

Many existing proprietary systems have separate initiating device circuits for each building zone or subsection, similar to the local, auxiliary, and remote station systems. However, due to the increasing use of electronics, newer proprietary systems for larger buildings often have signal multiplexing and built-in minicomputer systems. These systems receive all signals from the building over one or more pairs of wires, and determine the exact location of the fire by use of different frequencies or digitally coded information transmitted over the wires. Figure 4-2E shows the complexity and interrelationship among the many facets of a modern computer-controlled proprietary/high-rise communications system.

Large proprietary multiplex and computer-controlled systems usually do much more than indicate fire alarms to the operator and sound an alarm. These systems often provide for smoke control within the building by automatically closing and opening dampers in heating, ventilating, and air-conditioning (HVAC) systems and turning on exhaust fans. They also may adjust elevator controls so that elevators bypass fire floors and are automatically routed to the lobby floor for fire department use. In addition to increasing flexibility, multiplexing signals greatly reduce the amount of wire used in a building. Computer-based proprietary systems often include energy management capabilities resulting in energy savings—a major factor in the recent sizeable increase in the use of these systems in large buildings.

Proprietary control units are required to transmit trouble and alarm signals to the central supervising station. The control unit at the central supervising station, as well as remotely located control equipment, must have a secondary power supply that will operate the system for 24 hrs of normal signal traffic. Since operators are constantly on duty with a proprietary system, 24 hrs of standby is considered sufficient.

Emergency Voice/Alarm Communication System

This system is used to supplement a local, auxiliary, remote station, or proprietary protective signaling system where it is necessary to relocate occupants to areas of refuge, rather than evacuate them. Its standby power supply must operate the system for 24 hrs, followed by 2 hrs of operation in an alarm condition. Because of the emergency nature of a voice communication system, special requirements in NFPA 72, *Protective Signaling Systems*, also cover the survivability of the system, so that fire damage to one paging zone will not result in loss of communication to another. (See Figure 4-2F.)

The voice/alarm system consists of a series of high-reliability speakers located throughout the building. They are connected to, and controlled from, the fire alarm communication console located in an area designated as a building fire command station. From the building fire com-

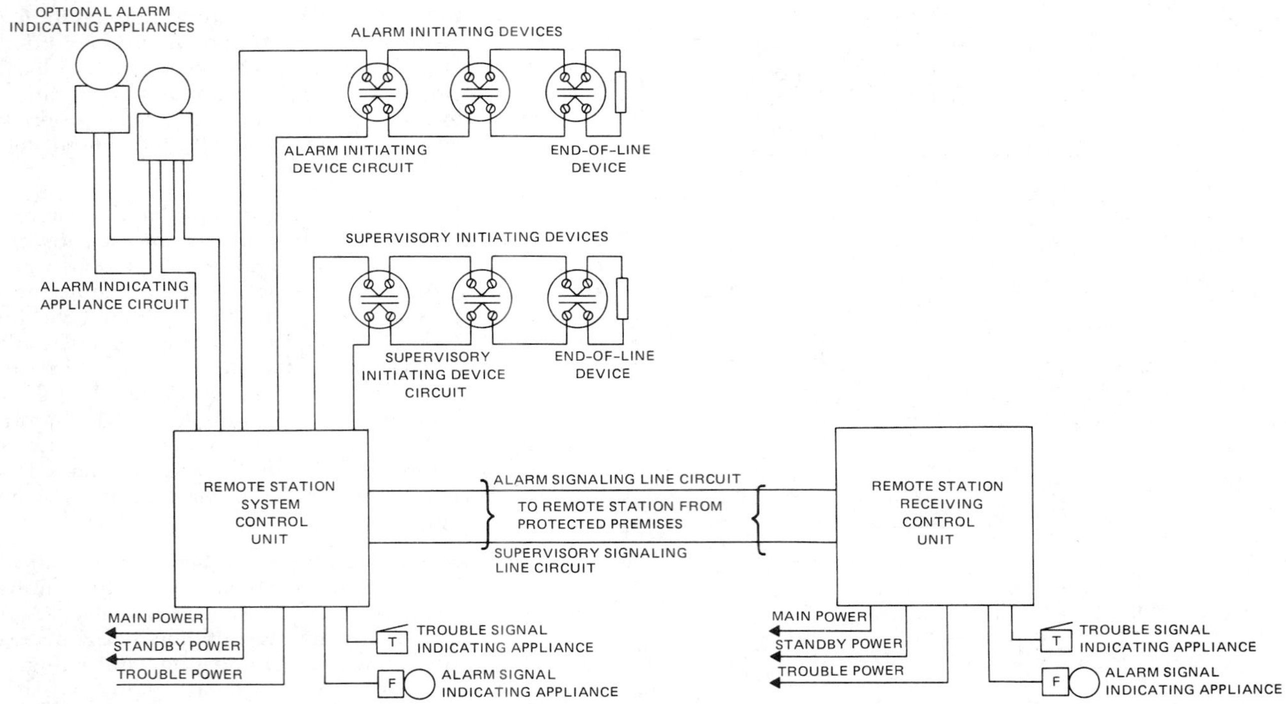

FIG. 4-2C. A typical arrangement of a remote station protective signaling system. Note that, if a direct circuit connection is used, fire alarm and supervisory signals must be transmitted over separate signaling line circuits (top). Upon receipt of a remote station sprinkler waterflow alarm, the fire dispatcher prepares to retransmit the alarm to the fire companies that will respond (bottom).

mand station, individual speaker zones or the entire building can be selected to receive voice messages that give specific instructions to the occupants. Some systems have fire warden stations on each floor, or fire zones, to which a fire warden would go to assume local command and pass on specific evacuation instructions. Operation of the fire command station usually is assumed by a trained building employee until the fire department arrives, at which time the officer in charge takes over. The system may also be used during fire fighting operations for communication with the fire fighters.

One important aspect of a voice communication system is that, since complete building evacuation is not always feasible, it can instruct occupants to relocate to "safe" areas in which to wait out the fire. In such cases, communication with these people must be maintained to prevent panic and to facilitate further relocation if necessary.

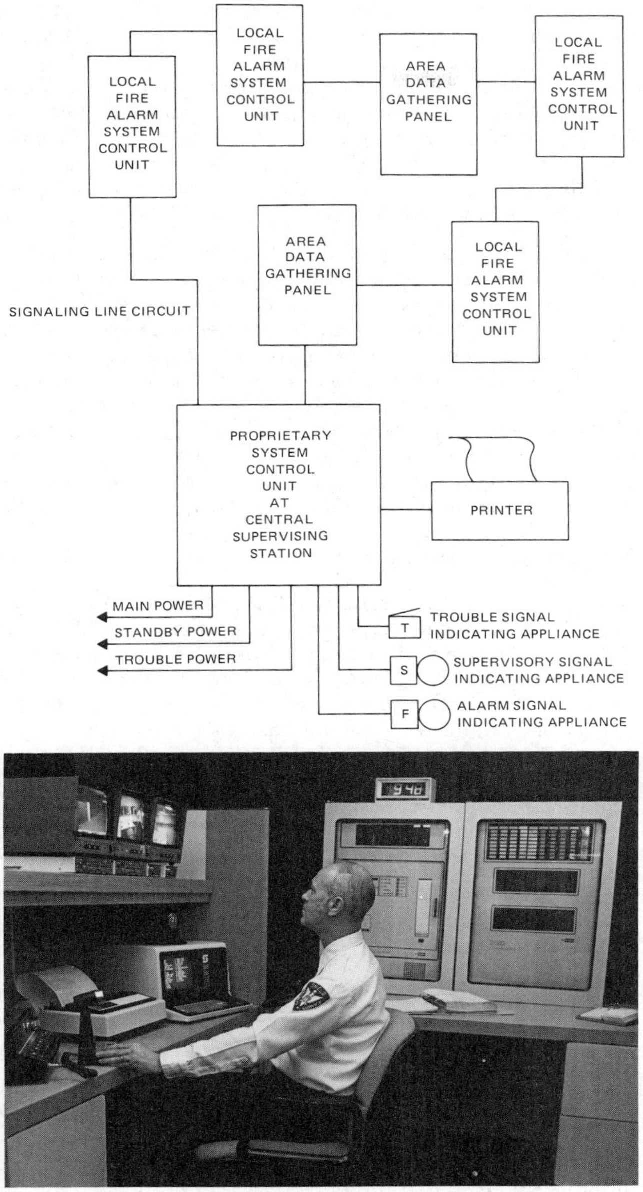

FIG. 4-2D. A typical arrangement of a proprietary protective signaling system (top). At the central supervisory station, an attendant constantly monitors the proprietary protective signaling system (bottom). The printer on the desk provides a permanent record of signaling traffic. (Source: Simplex Time Recorder Company)

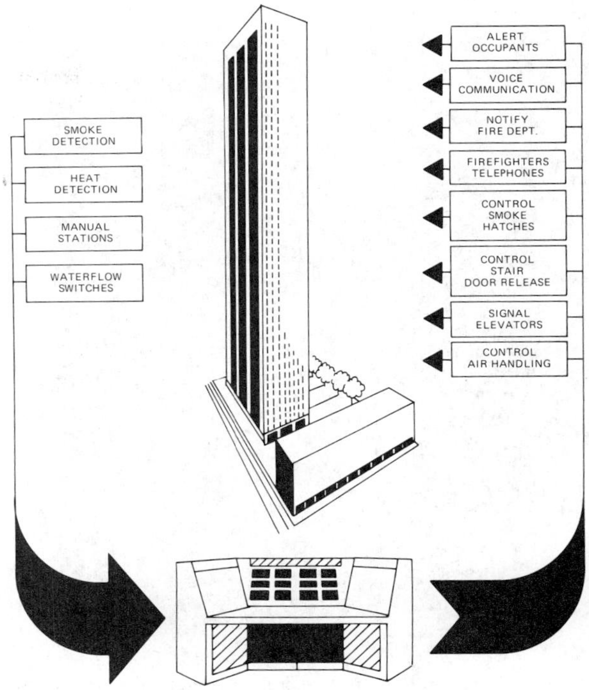

FIG. 4-2E. Typical high-rise emergency voice/alarm and communication system.

FIG. 4-2F. Using an emergency voice/alarm communication system, a fire officer gives building occupants specific instructions during a fire. (Source: Simplex Time Recorder Company)

TYPES OF SIGNALS

Protective signaling systems provide three distinct categories of signals: (1) fire alarm signals, (2) supervisory signals, and (3) trouble signals.

Fire Alarm Signals

When a manual fire alarm station is actuated, when an automatic fire detector operates, or when a waterflow or other extinguishing system alarm-initiating device is operated by the discharge of that system, a fire alarm signal is initiated to the fire alarm system control unit. Depending upon the particular protective signaling system installed, the control unit will then interpret and indicate either locally or remotely, or both, that a signal has been received indicating the presence of a hostile fire.

In some cases, fire alarm signals are extended throughout a protected premises for the purpose of alerting occupants so that they may evacuate the building safely. In such a case, the indication of fire is given by audible and visible alarm indicating appliances. For emergency voice/alarm communications systems, the alarm signal may be a tape-recorded, digitized, or live-voice message broadcast to the building occupants by listed textual alarm-indicating appliances, such as speakers.

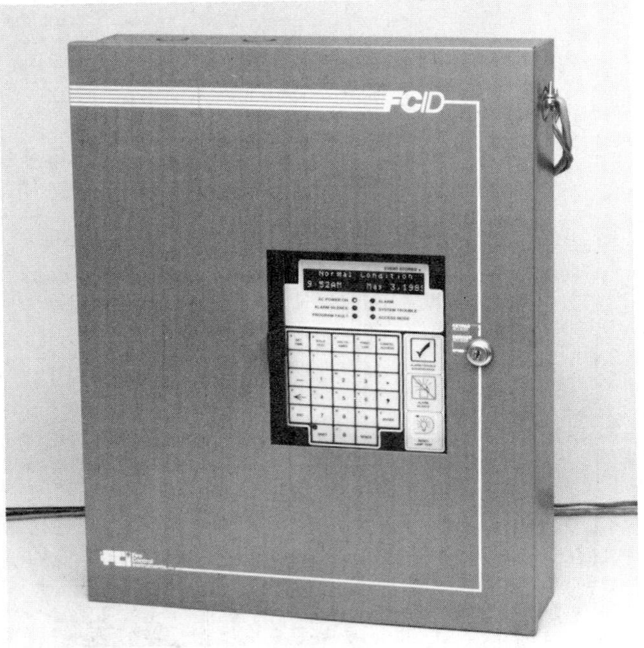

FIG. 4-2G. Technology increasingly impacts fire alarm systems as evidenced by this solid-state, microprocessor-based fire alarm system control unit. An alpha-numeric visible display provides detailed information from the system. (Source: Fire Control Instruments)

Information on the suitability of audible and visible alarm indicating appliances can be found in NFPA 72, *Protective Signaling Systems*.

Non-textual alarm signals may be non-coded or coded. Non-coded audible or visible alarm signals are produced by the continuous operation of audible or visible alarm indicating appliances. Coded alarm signals are produced by the intermittent operation of audible and visible alarm indicating appliances, in accordance with a prescribed pattern or code. Coded signals may be used to indicate the specific location from which a fire alarm signal has been initiated. This information would be particularly useful to building security forces and to the private fire brigade assigned to protect a particular facility.

Visible alarm indicating appliances may be viewed either directly or indirectly. Such appliances notify occupants that the signal they are hearing is specifically a fire alarm signal. Or such appliances may be used to provide fire alarm notification for persons who are hearing-impaired. In the latter case, ongoing research seems to favor the use of indirectly viewed, high-intensity stroboscopic visible alarm indicating appliances.

Normally, audible and visible alarm indicating appliances are used to warn facility occupants that they must evacuate that facility because of the presence of a hostile fire. It is necessary that the signals clearly indicate their purpose. To aid in this effort, a distinctive audible and visible signal has been recommended, using a uniform Code 3 temporal pattern, which may be reproduced on any of the existing audible and visible alarm indicating appliances. As described in the appendix of NFPA 72, *Protective Signaling Systems*, this temporal pattern is keyed $1/2$ to 1 sec on, $1/2$ sec off, $1/2$ to 1 sec on, $1/2$ sec off, $1/2$ to 1 sec on, and $2^1/2$ sec off. Such a signal should be repeated for not less than 3 min, though it may be necessary when using an emergency voice/alarm communications system to interrupt that signal manually for verbal instructions to the occupants. This would be the case in buildings where, because of the particular construction or because of the significantly large occupant load, such as would be found in a high-rise building, it may be advisable to relocate occupants to areas of refuge rather than evacuate them from the building.

Protective signaling systems that are installed for property protection purposes, such as signaling systems for central station service, auxiliary protective signaling systems, remote station protective signaling systems, and proprietary protective systems, are not required to provide audible and visible signaling appliances throughout the protected premises. Rather, these systems extend or transmit the fire alarm signal to some constantly attended receiving location either off-premises or, in the case of a proprietary system, at a designated location on the protected premises or at a premises under the same ownership.

Supervisory Signals

Supervisory signals generally fall into two specific categories: (1) protective systems supervisory signals, or (2) guard patrol tour supervisory signals. Protective systems supervisory signals are initiated by devices that monitor the integrity of other fire protective systems, such as automatic sprinkler systems and special hazards extinguishing systems using such agents as carbon dioxide, dry chemical, Halon 1301, high-expansion foam, aqueous-film-forming-foam (AFFF), or similar agents. The purpose of these signals is to indicate that some feature of the protective system is "off-normal" and to further indicate when that feature has been restored to normal.

Guard patrol tour supervisory signals are initiated by systems that monitor the fire patrol tour of guards as they provide manual surveillance of a protected premises. These systems may either signal from one or more specific locations throughout the course of the guard's tour, or they may be arranged to initiate a signal if the guard fails to make the tour within a prescribed time limit.

It is essential that such signals be arranged so that they do not interfere with fire alarm signals. It is also important that they be arranged so as to transmit information in suitable detail so that the person receiving the signals can take appropriate action.

Trouble Signals

Trouble signals are initiated either by the disarrangement of protective signaling system wiring or by the failure of the protective signaling system's primary power supply. Historically, protective signaling systems have been said to be "supervised." The word "supervised" has been replaced in more recent editions of the standards with the term "monitored for integrity." Formerly, it would have been said that the alarm initiating circuits and alarm indicating appliance circuits of a protective signaling system were supervised. Current terminology would say that alarm initiating device circuits and alarm indicating appliance circuits are monitored for system integrity. The disarrangement of these circuits by an open fault, a ground fault, or, in the case of alarm indicating appliance circuits, a short circuit must be signaled to the system control unit as a "trouble" signal.

Protective signaling systems installed for property protection purposes, such as signaling systems for central station service, auxiliary protective signaling systems, remote station protective signaling systems, or proprietary protective signaling systems, generally extend "trouble" signals to the constantly attended receiving location. A possible exception is the case of auxiliary protective signaling systems, where the trouble signal may be indicated only at the protected premises. Some authorities having jurisdiction require the trouble signals from auxiliary protective signaling systems to be transmitted by means of a remote station protective signaling system to a location suitable to that authority.

PROTECTIVE SIGNALING SYSTEMS CIRCUITS

Protective signaling systems have three basic types of circuits: (1) initiating device circuits, (2) indicating appliance circuits, and (3) signaling line circuits.

Initiating device circuits connect fire alarm and supervisory initiating devices to the system control unit. Alarm indicating appliance circuits connect alarm indicating appliances to the system control unit. Signaling line circuits connect the system control unit to a constantly attended receiving location, such as a central station, a public fire service communications center, a remote station, or a central supervising station.

In the examples that follow, some very rudimentary circuits are described. It is important to note that these circuits are included simply for illustration. They should not be used as indications of proper design for a specific application. It should also be recognized that not all of the components of the system have been shown in these figures, but only those portions of the circuits necessary to understand how each functions.

Basic Alarm Initiating Device Circuit

A typical basic alarm initiating device circuit (styles "A" or "B") consists of a two-wire circuit with an end-of-line resistor. Initiating devices, with normally open contacts, are connected in parallel. [See Figure 4-2H(a).] A small supervisory current normally flows through both relays (or an equivalent solid-state circuit), the field installation, wires, and resistor. The current is sufficient to energize the "trouble" relay, but not the "alarm" relay. Operation of an initiating device (detector) shunts the resistor. [See Figure 4-2H(b).] This increases the current in the circuit and energizes the "alarm" relay to initiate the alarm. A short between the wires or a ground fault on both wires also will cause an alarm.

A single open fault on the circuit would deenergize the "trouble" relay and initiate a trouble signal. [See Figure 4-2H(c).] It also would render inoperable all initiating devices that are electrically beyond the open fault.

Operation with open fault condition: To permit continued operation of the alarm initiating device circuit, a feature may be added to the Style "A" or "B" circuit that will give it the ability to initiate an alarm even with a single open fault. Such a circuit (Style "D") is shown in Figure 4-2I(a). In this case, since the end of the line also is at the fire alarm control panel, the "trouble" relay deenergizes when an open on the wire occurs, sounding the trouble signal and conditioning the alarm initiating device circuit so that power flows from the control unit in both directions toward the single open fault. [See Figure 4-2I(b).]

When the contacts of an alarm initiating device close to initiate an alarm, the coil of the "trouble" relay is shunted, allowing the resultant increase in current to operate the "alarm" relay. [See Figure 4-2I(c).]

Alarm Indicating Appliance Circuits

A typical, basic alarm indicating appliance circuit is shown in Figure 4-2J(a). In the normal supervisory condition, current flows through the circuit so that the end-of-line diode mounted inside the last alarm indicating appliance is forward-biased, allowing the "trouble" relay to be operated. A reverse-biased blocking diode inside each alarm indicating appliance prevents the actuation of the appliance. If an open fault occurs on the wiring, the "trouble" relay becomes deenergized, actuating an audible trouble-indicating appliance. [See Figure 4-2J(b).]

Short-circuit supervision is accomplished by a fuse that opens the circuit when sufficient short-circuit current flows. The "trouble" relay then detects the open fuse and becomes deenergized, actuating the audible trouble indicating appliance. [See Figure 4-2J(c).]

When the system control unit operates into an "alarm" condition, the "alarm" relay becomes energized, and its contacts reverse the polarity to the alarm indicating appliance circuit. This reversal causes the blocking diode inside each alarm indicating appliance to be forward-biased, allowing the current to flow and to actuate the appliance. [See Figure 4-2J(d).]

Signaling Line Circuits (Channels)

Signaling systems use signaling line circuits or channels to transmit signaling information from the system control unit to some central location, either on or off the premises. The performance characteristics of the signaling line circuit (channel) depend upon the type of signaling system employed. The various NFPA signaling standards state specific requirements for signaling line circuits (channels).

Signaling systems for central station service may employ multiplex signaling line circuits or channels; digital alarm communicator systems, including digital alarm radio system channels; McCulloh circuits; two-way radio frequency multiplex channels; or a one-way radio alarm system channel. (See NFPA 71, *Installation, Maintenance, and Use of Signaling Systems for Central Station Service*.)

Auxiliary protective signaling systems use connections to the public fire reporting system and should be installed in accordance with the requirements of NFPA 1221, *Installation, Maintenance, and Use of Public Fire Service Communications Systems*. The signaling line circuit of the auxiliary system should be the circuit connection between the system control unit and the device that interfaces with the public fire reporting system.

Remote station systems generally employ either a direct circuit connection to the remote station receiving location or a digital alarm communicator system. Most often, the direct circuit connection is accomplished by leasing such a circuit from the public telephone utility and connecting it to a polarity-reversing relay in the system control unit at the protected premises and to suitable receiving equipment at the remote station.

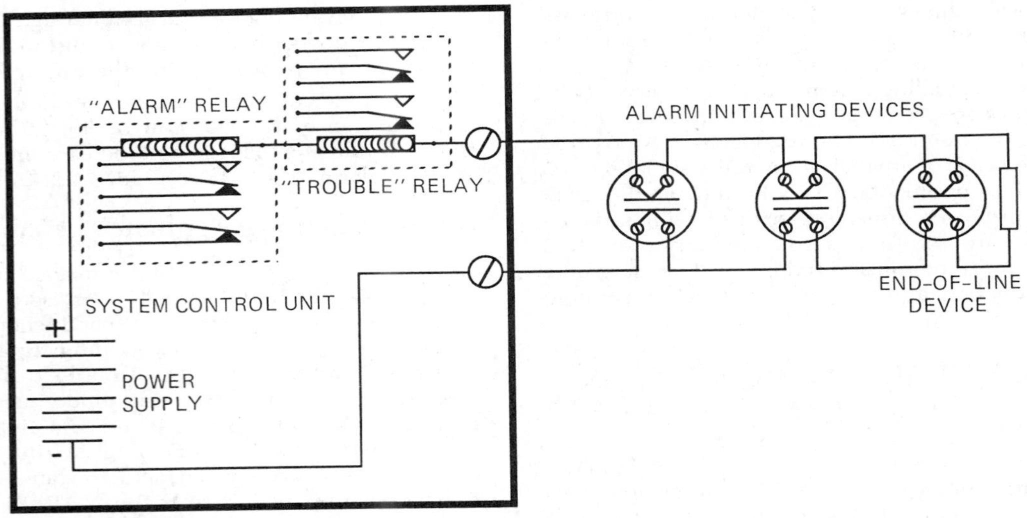

FIG. 4-2H(a). Style "A" or "B" alarm initiating device circuit, "normal" mode.

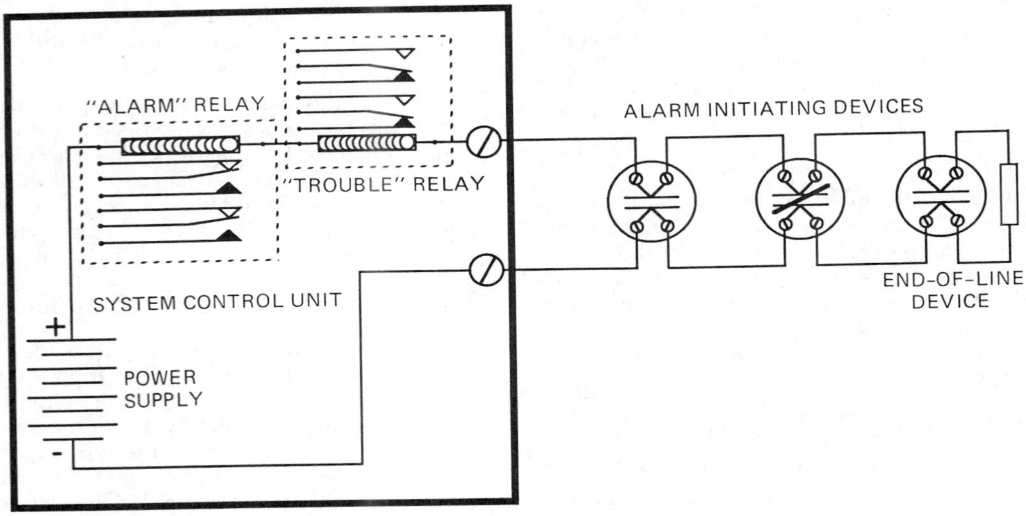

FIG. 4-2H(b). Style "A" or "B" alarm initiating device circuit, "alarm" mode.

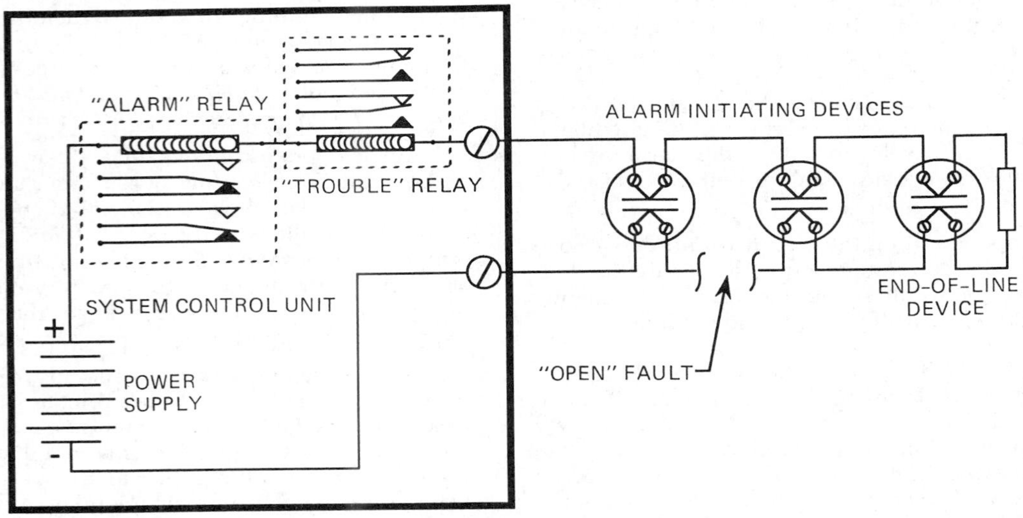

FIG. 4-2H(c). Style "A" or "B" alarm initiating device circuit, "trouble" mode.

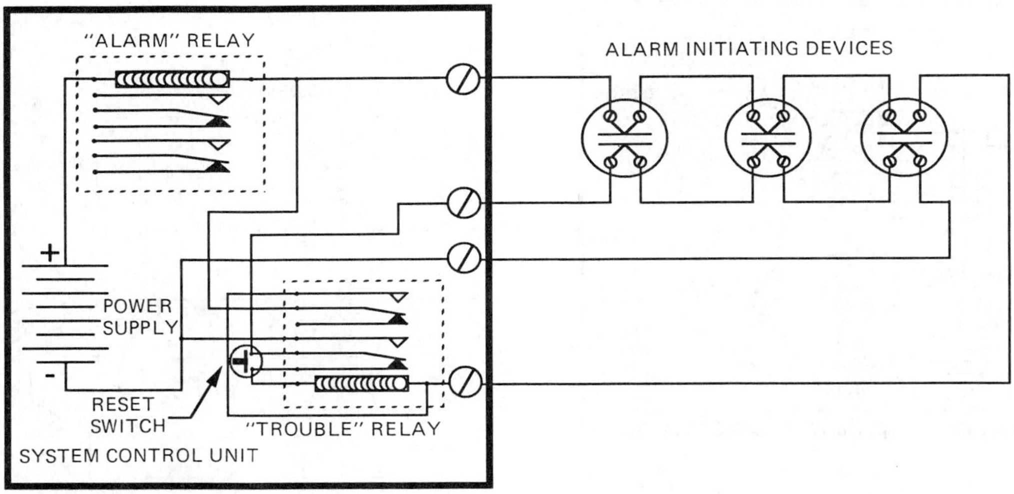

FIG. 4-21(a). Style "D" alarm initiating device circuit, "normal" mode.

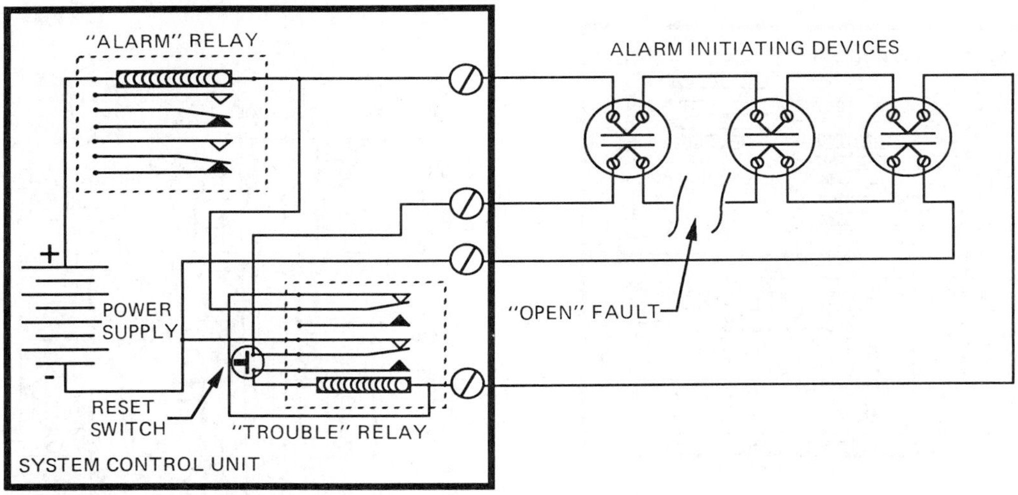

FIG. 4-21(b). Style "D" alarm initiating device circuit, "trouble" mode.

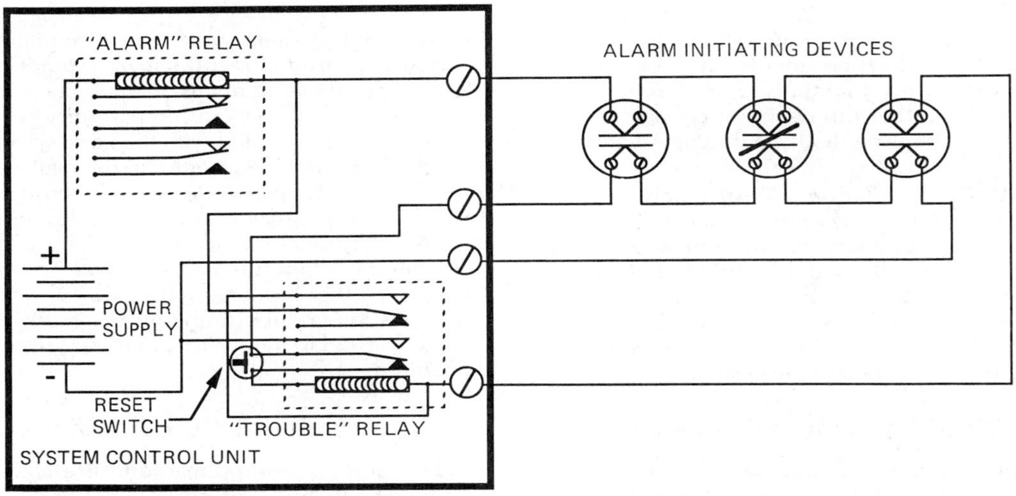

FIG. 4-21(c). Style "D" alarm initiating device circuit, "alarm" mode.

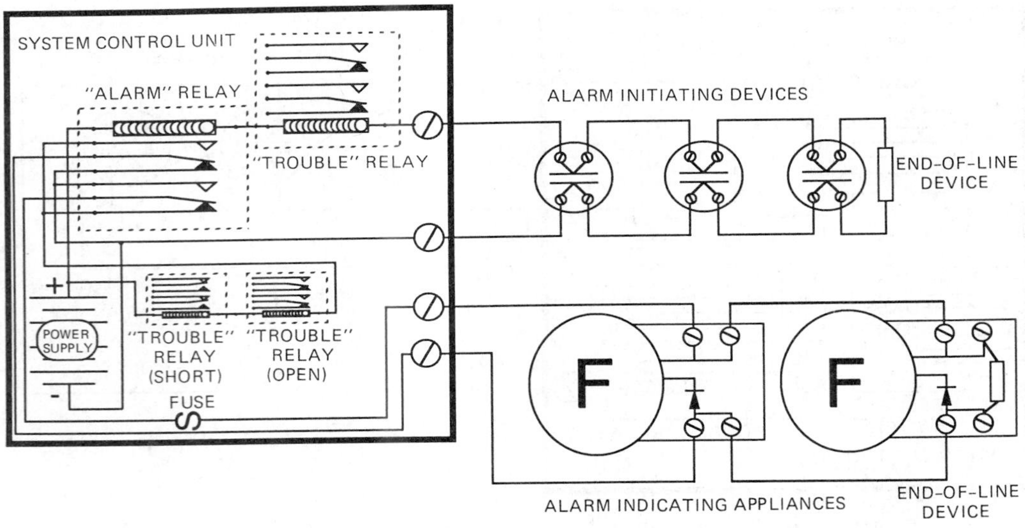

FIG. 4-2J(a). Style "W" or "Y" alarm indicating appliance circuit, "normal" mode.

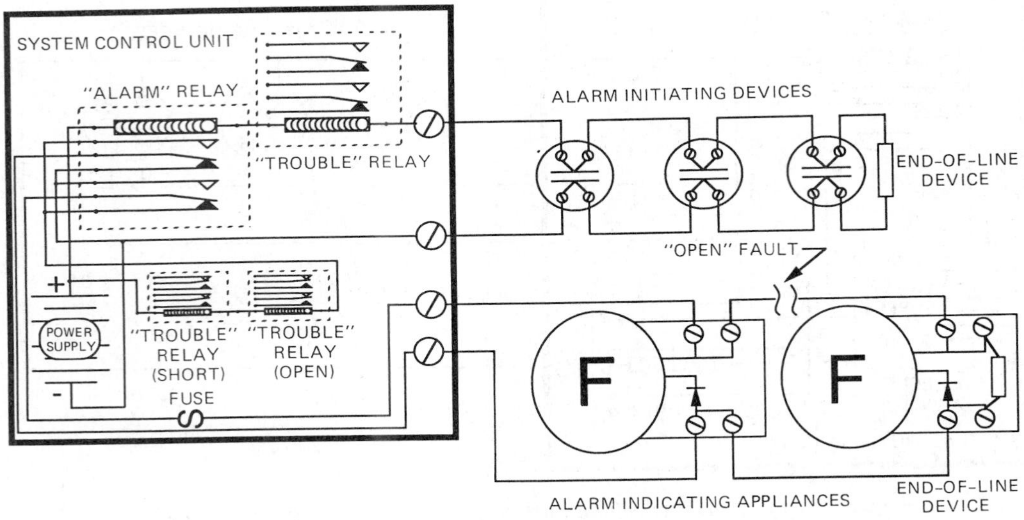

FIG. 4-2J(b). Style "W" or "Y" alarm indicating appliance circuit, "trouble" mode.

Proprietary protective signaling systems may utilize one of ten styles of signaling line circuits (channels). These performance-based styles essentially describe signaling methods that employ either direct-circuit connections or multiplex communications methods, including microwave radio or fiber-optic links.

While NFPA 71, *Installation, Maintenance, and Use of Signaling Systems for Central Station Service*, has created a special circuit category for multiplex initiating devices (sometimes called "smart" initiating devices), NFPA 72, *Protective Signaling Systems*, terms the circuit to which such initiating devices are connected a "signaling line circuit." All of the specific requirements for signaling line circuits apply equally, however.

COMPATIBILITY AMONG SYSTEMS

One frequent question from building designers and equipment owners pertains to compatibility among equipment produced by various manufacturers. For example, if the control unit is manufactured by one company, how is compatibility determined with regard to other manufacturers' detectors, indicating devices, annunciator panels, and so on? The key to all system compatibility is the installation wiring diagram provided with the basic system control unit. If a given circuit extending from the control panel is compatible only with particular devices, those devices will be specified by manufacturer and model number. If a circuit contains only an electrical rating and does not indicate specific devices, then it most likely will be compatible with any device that has a similar electrical rating. If there is any question about equipment compatibility, the recognized testing laboratory listing the equipment should be consulted.

CODE REQUIREMENTS

Code requirements applicable to fire alarm systems can often be confusing, because a number of different codes all apply to a given circumstance.

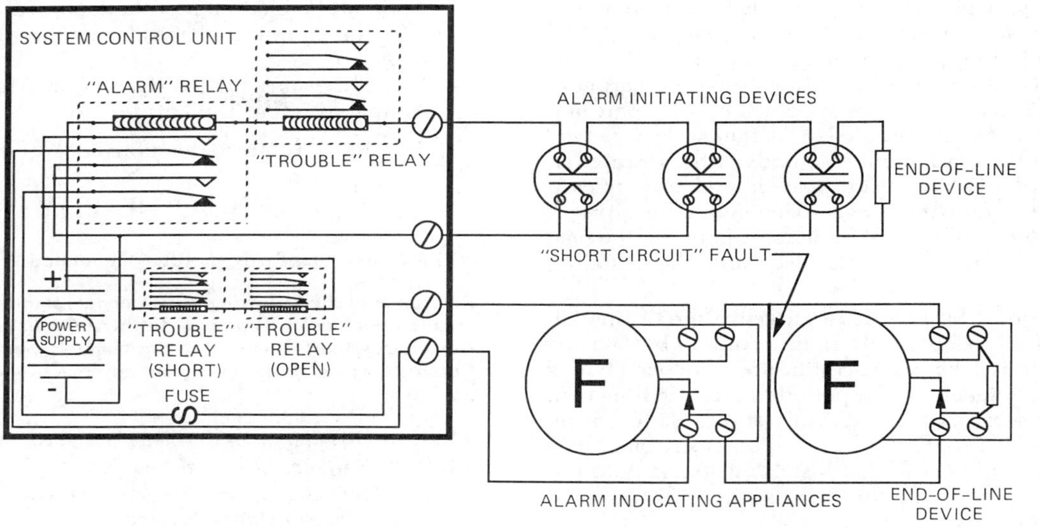

FIG. 4-2J(c). Style "W" or "Y" alarm indicating appliance circuit, "trouble" mode.

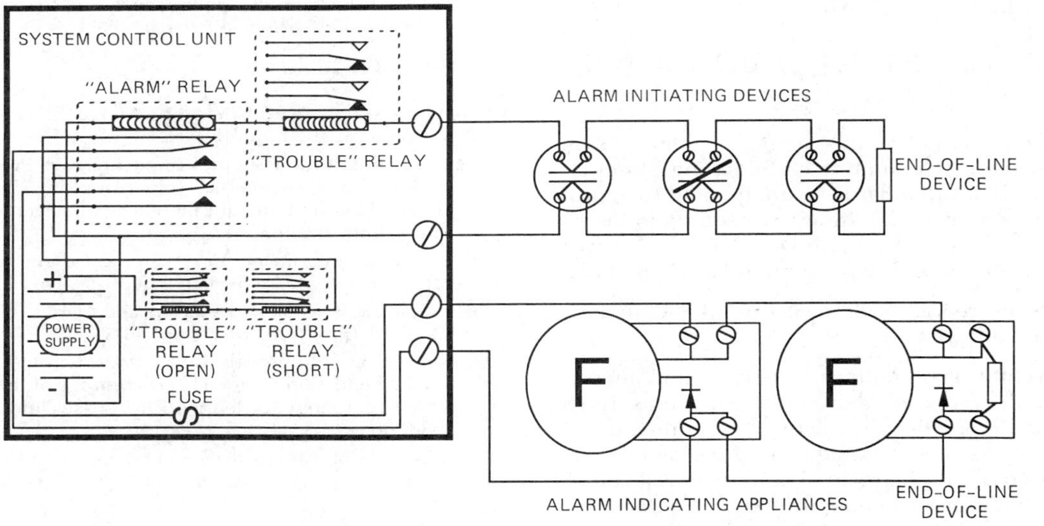

FIG. 4-2J(d). Style "W" or "Y" alarm indicating appliance circuit, "alarm" mode.

First, it is important that all equipment be "listed" by a recognized testing laboratory. In many cases, use of listed equipment is mandated by the NFPA signaling standards. Even if it is not mandated, listing is one way to ensure that an independent agency has evaluated the equipment.

To determine the type of system required for a given occupancy, consult a code, such as NFPA *101®*, *Life Safety Code®*. The occupancy code will specify the type of system and the type of detection required. For example, a nursing home would be required to have a fire alarm system that provides evacuation signals, contains smoke detectors in the corridors as a minimum, and is connected to the fire department. Once the type of system and the type of detection required by the occupancy have been determined, guidelines from NFPA 72, *Protective Signaling Systems*, should be followed.

In addition to occupancy and device standards, the applicable system standard, including system maintenance and testing, should be consulted for the installation requirements of the system (e.g., system control unit, initiating devices, indicating appliances, etc.).

Maintenance and Testing

After a protective signaling system has been installed, it is extremely important to conduct a proper acceptance test and regular periodic tests on all parts of the system. (Consult appropriate standards for testing requirements.) Guidelines for several tests can be found in NFPA 72, *Protective Signaling Systems*. Maintaining and testing signaling equipment are as important as installating the system was in the first place. Maintenance must not be overlooked in the overall fire protection plan.

CERTIFICATION

At least one recognized testing laboratory makes available to those companies that have been specifically listed to install, maintain, and test either central station systems or local, auxiliary, remote station, proprietary, and emergency voice/alarm communications systems a program in which the listed installing company may apply for the issuance by the testing laboratory of a certificate for the particular installation. Such a certificate specifies that the pertinent requirements of the applicable NFPA standards have been met, as have the equipment standards of the testing laboratory. In order to have a certificate issued, a contract for maintenance and testing in accordance with the appropriate NFPA standard also must be in force between the management of the protected premises and the installing company.

On a periodic basis, at least annually, the testing laboratory inspects a statistically significant number of those protected premises for which certificates have been issued. Any noted deficiencies are reported to the installing company for correction. Consistent misrepresentation of the character of the installations for which certificates have been issued would cause that installing company to lose the privilege of applying for the reissuance of the certificate on future jobs.

Such certification policies can verify that proper installation, maintenance, and testing procedures were followed and will continue to be followed.

FUTURE CHANGES TO SIGNALING STANDARDS

Following the presentation of specific recommendations from the Correlating Committee on Signaling Systems in late 1989, the NFPA Standards Council voted to approve the reorganization plan that ultimately resulted in the production of a single signaling standard, NFPA 72, *Protective Signaling Systems*. The recommendations included:

1. Approve the reorganization of the NFPA Signaling Project as follows:

   Seven technical committees, meeting simultaneously to process public proposals and public comments, reporting through a 15-member Correlating Committee on Signaling Systems. Said correlating committee membership to be comprised of the chairman of each technical committee, plus one additional member from each technical committee having a different membership classification than the chairman, and a separately appointed correlating committee chairman who is not the chairman of a technical committee. The seven technical committees are:

   - Technical Committee on Fundamentals of Signaling Systems.
   - Technical Committee on Household Fire Warning Equipment.
   - Technical Committee on Protected Premises Signaling Systems.
   - Technical Committee on Off-Premises Signaling Systems.
   - Technical Committee on Initiating Devices for Signaling Systems.
   - Technical Committee on Notification Appliances for Signaling Systems.
   - Technical Committee on Testing and Maintenance of Signaling Systems.

2. Approve the scopes for these seven technical committees.
3. Appoint the chairmen of the technical committees to serve on an interim basis during the first cycle of the new project.
4. Permit the consolidated signaling standard to enter the Annual Meeting 1992 cycle.

   The above requested actions took effect in 1990.

BIBLIOGRAPHY

NFPA Codes, Standards, and Recommended Practices

Reference to the following NFPA codes, standards, and recommended practices will provide further information on protective signaling systems discussed in this chapter. (See the latest *NFPA Catalog* for availability of current editions of the following documents.)

NFPA 13, *Installation of Sprinkler Systems*.

NFPA 70, *National Electrical Code®*.

NFPA 71, *Installation, Maintenance, and Use of Signaling Systems for Central Station Service*.

NFPA 72, *Protective Signaling Systems*.

NFPA *101®*, *Life Safety Code®*.

NFPA 1221, *Installation, Maintenance, and Use of Public Fire Service Communications Systems*.

Additional Reading

"A Proposed Standard Fire Alarm Signal," *Fire Journal*, Vol. 69, No. 5 (Sept. 1973), p. 24.

"Assessment of the Potential Impact of Fire Protection Systems on Actual Fire Incidents," Johns Hopkins University, *Report* prepared for the Federal Emergency Management Agency, U.S. Fire Administration, May 1980.

Bellamy, L., "Informative Fire Warning Systems: A Study of Their Effectiveness," *Fire Surveyor*, Vol. 18, No. 4, pp. 17-23.

Bertschinger, S., "Smoke Detectors and Alarms," *Fire Journal*, Vol. 82, No. 1 (Jan.-Feb. 1988), pp. 43-53.

Breen, D. E., "Improved Life Safety Through More Reliable Smoke Detection Systems," *Proceedings* of the Conference on New Technology to Reduce Fire Losses and Costs, Elsevier, 1986, pp. 227-334.

Brooks, J., "Software Adds New Dimension to Fire Alarm Equipment," *Fire Journal*, Vol. 82, No. 6 (Nov./Dec. 1988), pp. 49-50, 52.

Bukowski, R. W., *Fire Alarm Signaling Systems Handbook*, National Fire Protection Association, Quincy, MA, 1987.

Bukowski, R. W., "Fire Detection and Alarm Systems," *NBSIR 86-3360*, National Bureau of Standards, Gaithersburg, MD, Apr. 1986.

Butler, H., Bowyer, A., and Kew, J., "Locating Fire Alarm Sounders for Audibility," Building Services Research and Information Association, United Kingdom, Aug. 1981.

Cellantani, E. N., "A Coordinated Detection/Communication Approach to Fire Protection," *Specifying Engineer*, Vol. 48, No. 5 (May 1982), pp. 58-62.

Chohan, R. K. and Upadhyaya, B. R., "Safety and Fault Detection in Progress Control Systems and Sensors," *Fire Safety Journal*, Vol. 14, No. 3 (Jan. 1989), pp. 167-177.

Gupta, Y. P., "Automatic Fire Detection Systems: Aspects of Reliability, Capability and Selection Criteria," *Fire Safety Journal*, Vol. 8, No. 2, 1985, pp. 105-118.

Halliwell, R. E. and Sultan, M.A., "Attenuation of Smoke Detector Alarm Signals in Residential Buildings," *Proceedings* of the First International Symposium on Fire Safety Science, Hemisphere, Washington, DC, 1986, pp. 689-697.

"High-Rise Fire Alarm Systems—Recommendations for State and Local Codes," National Electrical Manufacturers Association, Washington, DC, Aug. 1984.

High-Rise Fire Alarm Systems, National Electrical Manufacturers Association, Washington DC, 1984.

Humphreys, W. L., "The Alarming Problem," *Fire Journal*, Vol. 67, No. 5 (Sept. 1973), pp. 15ff.

"Implementing a Community-Wide Automatic Residential Remote Alarm System: The Westland Plan," *Report* prepared for the Federal Emergency Management Agency, U.S. Fire Administration, Nov. 1980.

Johnson, E. R., "Accidental Power Cross Results in Improved Alarm System Design," *Fire Journal*, Vol. 68, No. 2 (Mar. 1974), p. 7.

Kravontka, S. J., "False Fire Alarms in Urban Public Schools," *Fire Technology*, Vol. 10, No. 3 (Aug. 1974), pp. 220-227.

Kravontka, S. J., "A Fire Signal for Deaf School Children," *Fire Technology*, Vol. 11, No. 1 (Feb. 1975).

Letts, J. B., "Fire Alarm Control and Indicating Equipment," *Fire Surveyor*, United Kingdom, Aug. 1982.

Maillet, M., "Microprocessors and New Communications Systems in Improved Detection Systems," *Proceedings* of the Conference on New Technology to Reduce Fire Losses and Costs, Elsevier, 1986, pp. 243-247.

Martin, R. L., "Alarm Sounders—Requirements and Selection," *Fire Surveyor*, Vol. 18, No. 5 (Oct. 1989), pp. 21-23.

McPherson, R. W., "A New Concept of Evacuation Alarm Signaling in High-Rise Buildings," *Fire Journal*, Vol. 65, No. 6 (Nov. 1971), pp. 8, 9.

Melhuish, C., "Fast-tracking the Fire and Security Perspective," *Fire Prevention*, No. 214 (Nov. 1988), pp. 31-32.

Moore, W., "When the Fire Alarm Sounds, Will Anyone Leave the Building,?" *Fire Journal*, Vol. 82, No. 1 (Jan.-Feb. 1988), p. 54.

Moore, W. D., and Wilson, D. K., *The Moore-Wilson Signaling Report*, published bimonthly by Focus Publishing Enterprises.

Nasenbeny, R. J., "Fire Alarm Control Panels," *Specifying Engineer*, Vol. 54, No. 3, 1985, pp. 85-87.

Nober, E. H., Well, A. D., and Moss, S., "Does Light Work as Well as Sound?," *Fire Journal*, Vol. 84, No. 1 (Jan.-Feb. 1990), p. 26.

Pate, M. E., "Warning Systems in Risk Management," *Risk Analysis*, Vol. 6, No. 2, 1986, pp. 223-234.

Pati, V. B., *et al*., "Simulation of Intelligent Fire Detection and Alarm System for a Warship," *Defense Science Journal*, Vol. 39, No. 1 (Jan. 1989), pp. 79-94.

Pezoldt, V. J. and Van Cott, H. P., "Arousal from Sleep by Emergency Alarms: Implications from the Scientific Literature," *NBSIR 78-1484*, National Bureau of Standards, Washington, DC, 1978.

"Remote Detection and Alarm for Residences: The Woodlands System," *Report* prepared for Federal Emergency Management Agency, U.S. Fire Administration, May 1980. (Reprint Mar. 1981.)

Robinson, D. A., "Sound Attenuation in Buildings: Implications for Fire Alarm System Design," *Fire Safety Journal*, Vol. 14, Nos. 1&2, 1988, pp. 5-12.

Robinson, D. A., "Sound Transmission Loss from Corridors to Rooms: Implications for Locating Fire Alarm Sounders," *Fire Technology*, Vol. 22, No. 2, 1986, p. 22.

Salamone, R., "Retrofitting High-Rise Dorms with Alarm and Detection Systems," *Fire Journal*, Vol. 84, No. 1 (Jan.-Feb. 1990), p. 37.

Sanderford, H. B., "Spread Spectrum Radio Alarms—Give Hardwire Performance," *Fire Journal*, Vol. 84, No. 1 (Jan.-Feb. 1990), p. 57.

Schifiliti, R. P., "Designing Fire Alarm Audibility," *Fire Technology*, Vol. 24, No. 2, 1988, pp. 181-188.

Schifiliti, R. P., "Design of Detection Systems," *SFPE Handbook of Fire Protection Engineering*, National Fire Protection Association, Quincy, MA, 1988.

Snow, A. W., "Integrated Security Systems," *Fire Prevention*, No. 198 (Apr. 1987), pp. 23-25.

Solomon, E. E., "Fire Alarm System Reliability," *Consulting Specifying Engineer*, Vol. 1, No. 5, 1987, pp. 61-65.

Solomon, E., "Alarm Verification and Design Considerations for Reliable Fire Alarm Systems," *Fire Journal*, Vol. 80, No. 2 (Mar. 1986), p. 26.

Spahn, E., "Increasing Your Fire Alarm Literacy," *Fire Engineering*, Vol. 143, No. 11, 1989, pp. 47-49.

Stroke, J. P., "Flexibility Is Key to Fire Alarm System," *Electrical System Design*, Vol. 67, No. 4 (May 1987), pp. 36, 38-40.

"Today's Alarm Systems," *Fire Journal*, Vol. 83, No. 5 (Jul.-Aug. 1989), p. 55.

Tong, D. and Canter, D., "Informative Warnings: *In Situ* Evaluations of Fire Alarms," *Fire Safety Journal*, Vol. 9, No. 3, 1985, pp. 267-279.

Training Manual on Fire Alarm Systems, National Electrical Manufacturers Association, Washington, DC, 1985.

WATERFLOW ALARMS AND SPRINKLER SYSTEM SUPERVISION

Dean K. Wilson

The value of installing an automatic sprinkler system for life safety and property protection has been well documented over many years of service in a variety of specific applications. It is obviously necessary to ensure that the automatic sprinkler system is maintained in such a condition that it is always ready to discharge water on a hostile fire, holding the fire to its area of origin. One way of making certain that an automatic sprinkler system remains fully in service is to supervise its operational features. At the same time, it is necessary to initiate an alarm signal whenever the sprinkler system does operate so that personnel may respond promptly and take whatever action is needed. Thus, these two functions — waterflow alarm and automatic sprinkler system supervision — are vital elements of an overall fire protection program.

AUTOMATIC SPRINKLER SYSTEM WATERFLOW ALARMS

Waterflow alarm systems may be as simple as a hydraulically operated water motor gong serving a single sprinkler riser, or as complex as a multiplex proprietary protective signaling system covering several hundred sprinkler risers at a very large industrial facility. In either case, there are certain basic functions that must be provided by whatever waterflow alarm equipment is installed. These include:

1. The prompt detection of the discharge of a certain number of gallons per minute at nominal pressure that would be equivalent to the amount of water discharged from a single operating sprinkler having the smallest orifice of those sprinklers installed in that particular system.
2. The reliable operation of a suitable audible alarm indicating appliance. The exact nature of the particular appliance will depend on the purpose of the specific waterflow alarm system.
3. The provision of suitable facilities to test the operation of the waterflow alarm device, preferably by an actual flow of water equivalent to the discharge from a single automatic sprinkler having the smallest orifice of those sprinklers installed in the system.

Categorizing Waterflow Alarms

Waterflow alarm systems can be categorized according to their purpose and according to their method of operation. For example, the waterflow alarm system may be installed to provide an alarm signal that will alert someone outside the building. Or the waterflow alarm system may be installed to provide an alarm signal that will alert someone in the immediate area of the sprinkler riser. Such a signal would normally be produced by the operation of either a hydraulically operated or an electrically operated bell. The waterflow alarm system also may be installed to provide an alarm signal that will sound throughout the protected building. This will normally be achieved by connecting the waterflow alarm initiating device to a local protective signaling system. The waterflow alarm system may be installed to provide an alarm signal that will be transmitted off-premises to some constantly attended location by means of a signaling system for central station service, an auxiliary protective signaling system, or a remote station protective signaling system. The waterflow alarm system may be installed to provide an alarm signal that will be transmitted to a constantly attended location on the protected premises or to another location of the same owner. This will normally be accomplished by connecting the waterflow alarm initiating device to a proprietary protective signaling system.

Hydraulically Operated Waterflow Alarms

Hydraulically operated waterflow alarm indicating appliances are called "water motor gongs." These devices operate very much like a miniature version of the water wheel that operated the mill shafting of a textile mill at the turn of the century. When an automatic sprinkler fuses in a fire, when a pipe breaks, or when a fitting develops a signifi-

---

Dean K. Wilson is director Loss Prevention Training for Industrial Risk Insurers in Hartford, CT. He is chairman of the NFPA Technical Committee on Off-Premises, Signaling Systems. He is also co-editor of *The Moore-Wilson Signaling Report*, a bimonthly fire/burglary alarm newsletter.

cant leak, water is diverted through an open alarm control valve to a nozzle assembly that directs a stream of water against the paddles of a water wheel. As the wheel turns, it operates a striking mechanism that repeatedly strikes the shell of a large gong. This produces a loud clanging sound that can be heard in the vicinity of the sprinkler riser. Most often, water motor gongs are mounted so that the gong shell is actually on the outside of the building. In countless instances of sprinkler operation, passersby have heard the water motor gong ringing and have telephoned the police or fire department. (See Figure 4-3A.)

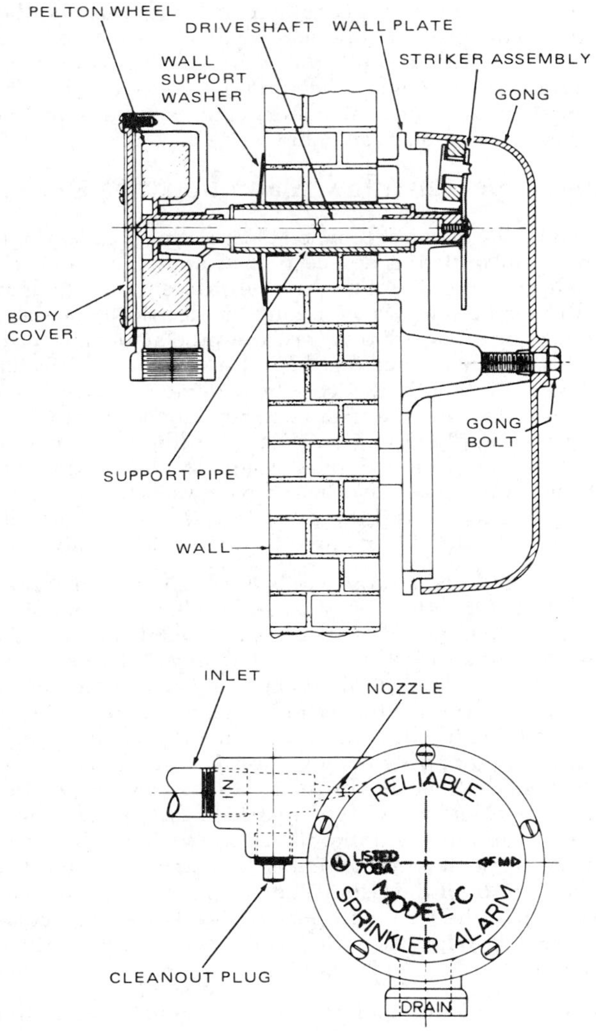

FIG. 4-3A. A representative water motor gong. Shown is the Reliable Automatic Sprinkler Co., Inc., Model C. Other manufacturers have similar arrangements of proprietary equipment for water motor gong installations.

Electrically Operated Waterflow Alarms

Waterflow alarms may be signaled using electrically operated fire alarm indicating appliances, such as vibrating bells, horns, sirens, chimes, and several varieties of flashing lights. Such signals usually are initiated by electrical switches incorporated into some type of pressure- or flow-operated device.

Waterflow Alarms for Wet-Pipe Automatic Sprinkler Systems

For wet-pipe automatic sprinkler systems, the flow of water is generally detected either hydraulically by an alarm check valve or electrically by a vane-type waterflow alarm initiating device. Either of these would be installed at the point the water supply piping enters the building from the underground. Supplementary vane-type devices could also be installed at various points in the piping system, e.g., on each floor of a high-rise building.

Alarm Check Valves

Depending on the specific design, alarm check valves are generally referred to as being either "plain type" or "differential type." (See Section 5, Chapter 9, "Automatic Sprinkler Systems," for more information on alarm check valves.) The basic design of most alarm check valves incorporates a clapper that lifts from its seat when water is discharged from sprinkler system piping above the valve. The movement of the clapper is used in one of the following ways:

1. The valve seat ring can have a concentric groove with a pipe connection from the groove to an alarm outlet or port to which piping can be connected. Such valves are commonly called "differential" or "divided seat ring" alarm check valves. When the clapper of the alarm valve rises in response to discharge from the sprinkler piping above the valve, water also flows through the groove in the divided seat ring, out of the alarm port, and into the alarm piping. (See Figure 4-3B.)

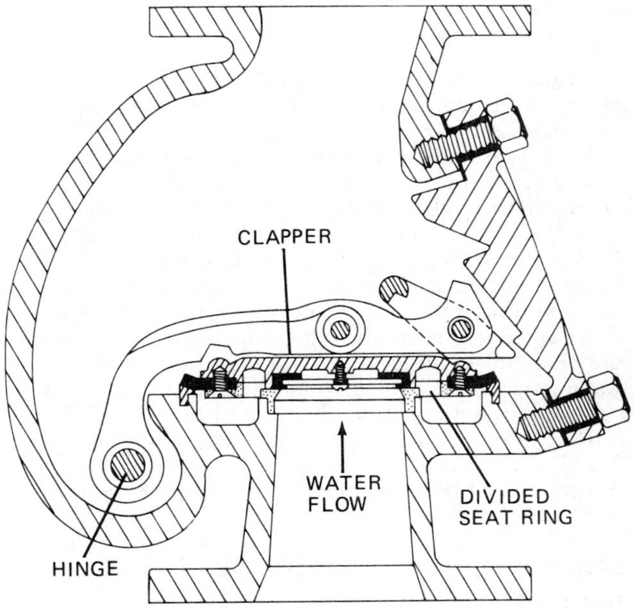

FIG. 4-3B. A waterflow alarm check valve of the differential type. (Source: Firematic Sprinkler Devices Inc.)

2. The clapper of the alarm check valve may have an extension arm with a smaller clapper that covers the seat of a small pilot valve connected to an alarm out-

let or port. Alarm piping may be connected to this port. When the clapper of the alarm valve rises in response to discharge from the sprinkler piping above the valve, the extension arm also rises, lifting the smaller clapper off the seat of the pilot valve. Water flows through the pilot valve, out of the alarm port, and into the alarm piping. (See Figure 4-3C.)

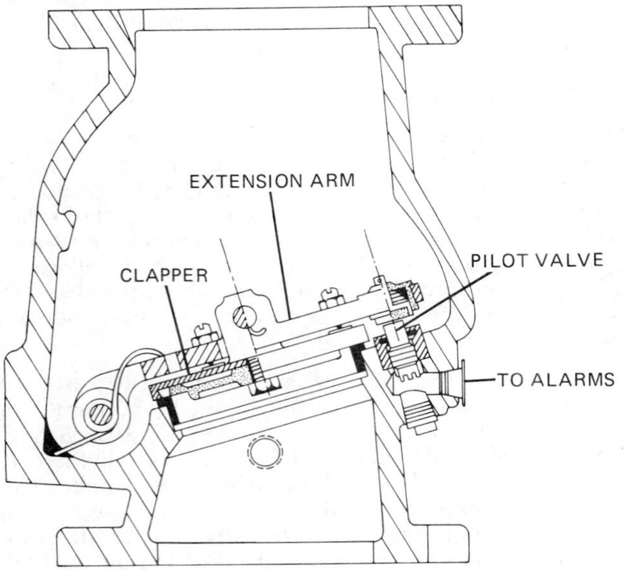

FIG. 4-3C. An alarm check valve with an auxiliary valve and pipe connection to alarms. Shown is the "Automatic" Sprinkler Co. Model 253 alarm check valve (no longer manufactured).

In either case, as the clapper lifts, it uncovers a passageway through which water can flow through an open alarm control valve to the water motor gong. To help reduce false alarms due to surges, the water may pass through a retard chamber after it passes through the open alarm control valve on its way to the water motor gong. This device is simply a large cast-iron or steel "bottle" that is equipped with a normally open automatic drain. As water flows into the retard chamber, the automatic drain shuts off. The time it takes for the water to fill up the chamber is the amount of retard time provided for the system. Once the chamber is filled, the water continues to flow to the water motor gong, operating that appliance. Once the water stops flowing, the automatic drain of the retard chamber returns to its normally open position, allowing the retard chamber to drain so that it is ready to be used the next time the clapper of the alarm check valve opens. (See Figure 4-3D.)

Pressure-Operated Switch Waterflow Alarm Initiating Devices

A pressure-operated switch may be mounted at the top of the retard chamber to provide a means of initiating the operation of an electric bell mounted in the vicinity of the riser. (See Figure 4-3E.) It is important to understand that such a switch mounted at the top of the retard chamber would not be permitted to initiate an alarm signal for a central station, local, auxiliary, remote station, or proprietary signaling system. Each of these systems requires that the waterflow alarm initiating device be located on the system in such a way that it cannot be tampered with or removed without initiating a signal. Because the water flowing to the retard chamber passes through a small alarm control valve that could be shut off—stopping the flow of water—this non-tamper/non-removal requirement of the signaling standards could not be met.

A pressure-operated switch could be mounted on a fitting connected to the alarm port of the alarm check valve, as long as there is no shut-off valve in the connection. In such a case, it would normally be necessary to provide an electronic or electro-pneumatic retard mechanism, either built into the pressure-operated switch or installed at the fire alarm system control unit, if one exists. A pressure-operated switch so located could be used to initiate a fire alarm signal on a central station, local, auxiliary, remote station, or proprietary signaling system.

Vane-Type Waterflow Alarm Initiating Devices

Far and away the most common electrically operated waterflow alarm initiating device is the vane-type waterflow switch. (See Figure 4-3F.) As a substitute for the hydraulically operated water motor gong, an electrically operated bell may be arranged to serve a wet-pipe automatic sprinkler system by connecting the bell to a vane-type waterflow alarm initiating device. These devices are designed to be inserted into the riser just above the point at which the water supply piping enters the building from underground. Even if the wet-pipe system has been equipped with an alarm check valve, a vane-type waterflow alarm initiating device may still be used. In this case, it normally would be installed just above the alarm check valve.

A small hole approximately 1 in. (25 mm) in diameter is drilled into the riser. The drill bit has a special piece of spring steel wire that captures the metal center of the hole, which is called the "coupon." Once the coupon is removed from the drill bit, it is usually attached to one of the mounting bolts of the waterflow alarm initiating device to show future inspectors that it was not left inside the pipe where it might possibly move upward into the sprinkler system and become an obstruction to the proper operation of the sprinkler system. The plastic or thin metal vane is rolled up and inserted into the riser. Once it resumes its original shape, it forms a thin barrier that covers almost all of the interior of the riser. When a sprinkler fuses, water flowing past the vane will push the vane upward, actuating a switch. When the switch contacts close, they initiate an alarm.

Two problems that may occur occasionally with vane-type waterflow alarm initiating devices are leaks around the point of entrance into the riser and detached vanes. The laboratories that test and list such devices require that each vane have a supplementary means of attaching the vane to the device so that, even if the vane breaks off, it will be retained near its original point of connection.

Waterflow Alarms for Dry-Pipe, Preaction, and Deluge Automatic Sprinkler Systems

Automatic sprinkler systems equipped with dry-pipe valves, preaction valves, or deluge valves also must have appropriate waterflow alarms. Each of these types of valves has a passageway that is uncovered when the clapper of the

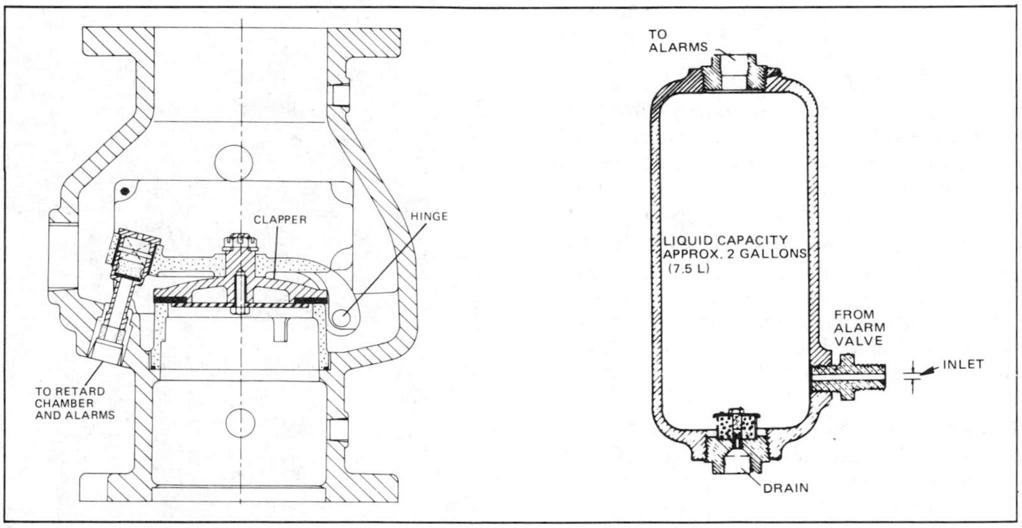

FIG. 4-3D. A waterflow alarm valve and retard chamber. Shown are Viking Models F-1 and B-3.

FIG. 4-3E. A pressure-operated waterflow alarm switch.

valve trips into the open position. Since these three types of valves are not affected generally by surges in the water system, no retard chamber is necessary. Piping connected to the outlet from the alarm passageway of these valves may be attached to a water motor gong or to a pressure-operated switch.

Vane-type waterflow alarm initiating devices are not permitted to be used for dry-pipe valve, preaction, or deluge sprinkler systems. This prohibition comes from concern that the hydraulic shock that occurs when these valves trip would increase the possibility that the vane might become detached.

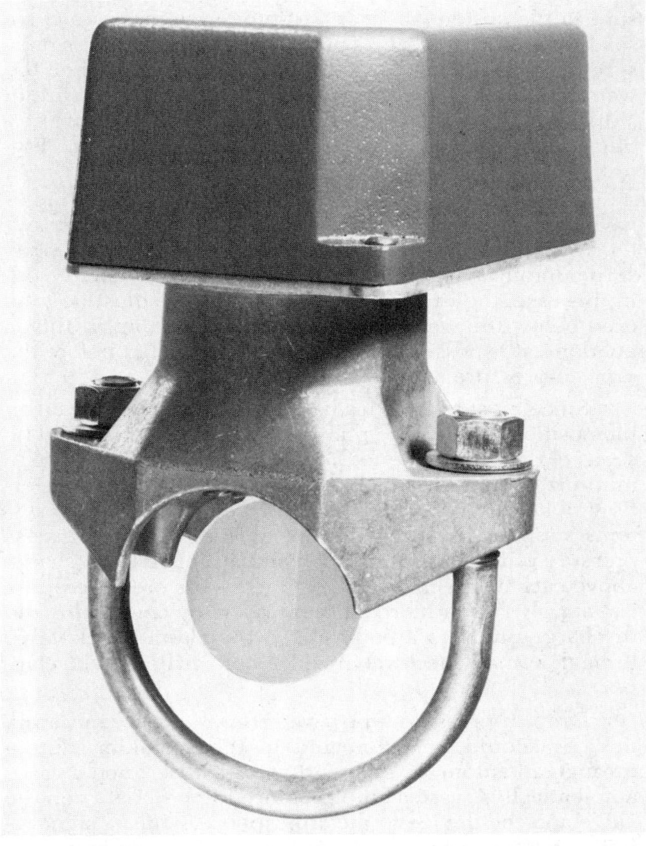

FIG. 4-3F. A vane-type waterflow alarm switch.

Drop-in-Pressure Waterflow Alarms

An alternative arrangement designed to initiate a waterflow alarm, even if the main automatic sprinkler system control valve is shut, is the "drop-in-pressure" waterflow alarm. The supervision of all fire protective system control valves $2\frac{1}{2}$-in. (63.5 mm) nominal size or larger is considered very important, especially when a protective signaling system is used to supplement or supplant standard guard service. Occasionally, it is simply not possible to obtain this valuable supervision. In such cases, it is essential that some method of detecting sprinkler system waterflow be used that will initiate an alarm even if the sprinkler control valve is shut. One method of accomplishing this is to use a waterflow alarm initiating device that detects a drop in sprinkler system pressure as a means of detecting the discharge of water from the system.

Such devices may use an ancillary storage chamber connected to the sprinkler system through a restricted orifice. Under normal conditions, the pressure in the ancillary chamber is the same as that in the sprinkler system. When system pressure drops, the pressure stored in the chamber acts on a diaphragm to activate an alarm initiating switch.

Other such devices may employ a pressure-sensing transducer and associated electronic circuitry to detect the rate of pressure change in the system. A slow rate of change is reported as a trouble signal, while a rapid rate of change is reported as an alarm.

The most common drop-in-pressure waterflow alarm initiating device uses a pressure switch to sense the pressure in the system and, for wet-pipe systems, employs a small riser-mounted excess pressure pump. (An excess pressure pump is not needed for dry-pipe systems.) When the water pressure in a wet-pipe system or the air pressure in a dry-pipe system drops to a predetermined pressure setting, the pressure switch initiates an alarm signal. (See Figure 4-3G.)

Occasionally, drop-in-pressure-type waterflow switches have been discovered incorrectly installed on sprinkler systems supplied by fire pumps where the small excess pressure pump has not been provided. For the switch to work in this case, the fire pump starting pressure must be lowered below the waterflow alarm switch setting. If this is not done, it is possible for the fire pump to start before the drop-in-pressure switch initiates an alarm.

Since most authorities having jurisdiction have taken the position that the fire pump starting pressure should be set as close as possible to the fire pump churn pressure to minimize hydraulic shock, a drop-in-pressure-type waterflow switch should not be used on wet-pipe sprinkler systems supplied by a fire pump, unless the small excess pressure pump is also installed and arranged to discharge above each alarm check valve. One excess pressure pump can supply two or more adjacent risers by connecting the discharge pump to a point above the alarm check valve through a small check valve with a hole drilled in the clapper.

Drop-in-pressure-type waterflow alarm initiating devices should be connected to the sprinkler system through an automatic stop-and-waste valve. Such a valve automatically "wastes" the pressure trapped between the valve and the device to the atmosphere. Thus, a signal is initiated whenever the valve is closed. This eliminates the possibility of tampering with the device without producing a signal.

Testing Waterflow Alarm Initiating Devices

The piping connected to the alarm outlet from alarm check valves, dry-pipe valves, preaction valves, or deluge valves usually is connected also through a normally closed valve to a point of water supply below the alarm check valve, dry-pipe valve, preaction valve, or deluge valve. Opening this test bypass valve will allow water to flow into the alarm piping, actuating the water motor gong or pressure-operated switch. Unless the dry-pipe valve, preaction valve, or deluge valve is going to be performance tested with a full actuation of the system, opening the alarm test bypass valve is the only way to test the alarms. In the case of a dry-pipe valve, care must be taken to be certain that the automatic velocity drain from the intermediate chamber of the dry-pipe valve is not stuck in the closed position and that the check valve at the alarm outlet from the dry-pipe valve intermediate chamber is not stuck in the open position. The combination of these two faults will most likely cause the dry-pipe valve to trip when the alarm test bypass valve is opened. This tripping occurs when water from the test bypass valve flows back into the intermediate chamber of the dry-pipe valve, destroying the differential between the air seat and the water seat inside the valve.

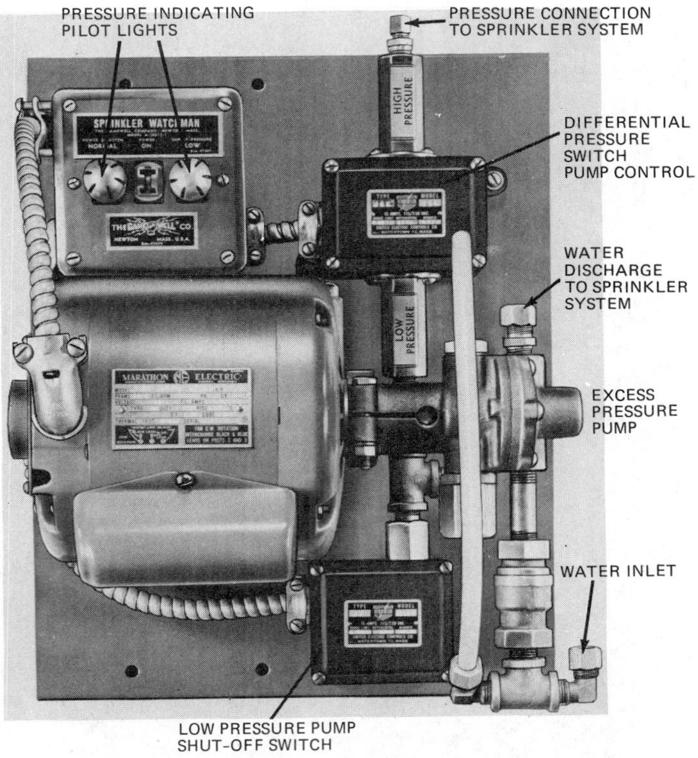

FIG. 4-3G. An excess pressure pump for installation on a wet-pipe sprinkler system. The automatic excess pressure pump maintains a pressure 29 to 47 psi (200 to 325 kPa) in excess of the water supply pressure above an alarm check valve. A continuous white pilot light, controlled by a differential switch, indicates when the pressure in the sprinkler system is more than 29 psi (200 kPa) above the supply pressure. Should the water supply fail, a low-pressure switch shuts off the current to the pump so that it will not run without water. This switch also controls a red pilot light to show when the supply pressure drops below 29 psi (200 kPa). A second pressure switch on the sprinkler system (not a part of the pump unit) is connected into the sprinkler system alarm circuit and gives an alarm if system pressure fails completely (e.g., a closed water control valve) when a sprinkler operates. A third pressure switch gives a warning by a local bell or other means in the event the pressure pump fails to maintain system pressure within the established excess pressure range. (Source: Gamewell Corp.)

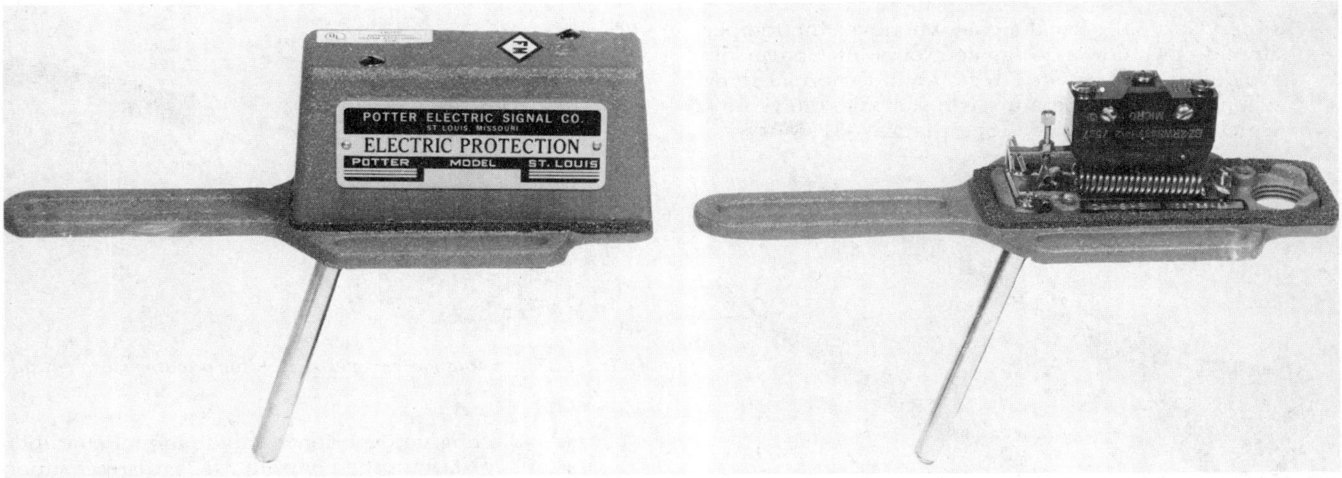

FIG. 4-3H. A valve supervisory switch for an outside screw and yoke (OS&Y) valve.

For wet-pipe automatic sprinkler systems, the only proper way to test the operation of a vane-type waterflow alarm initiating device, and the preferable way to test all other types of waterflow alarm initiating devices, is to open the valve at the inspector's test connection. This valve, installed on a 1-in. (25 mm) piece of pipe—for older installations, it is often located at the most remote point of the sprinkler system, and, for more modern installations, it is often located at the top of the riser—terminates outside the building in an orifice that can simulate the discharge from a single sprinkler having the smallest orifice used by those sprinklers installed on the system. Thus, opening the inspector's test connection will simulate the fusing of a single sprinkler.

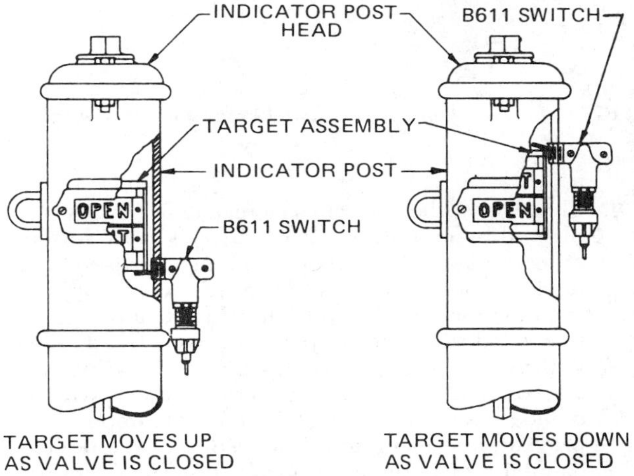

FIG. 4-3I. A valve supervisory switch for a post indicator valve (PIV).

SPRINKLER SYSTEM SUPERVISION

To ensure that an automatic sprinkler system is ready to discharge water on a hostile fire and hold the fire to its area of origin, a central station, local, remote station, or proprietary signaling system may be connected to supervisory initiating devices that will supervise critical operating features of the sprinkler system. Such devices may include the supervision of:

1. The position of sprinkler shut-off valves. Normally, only those valves that are 2½ in. (63.5 mm) or larger are supervised. This supervision is provided by mounting a supervisory initiating device on the valve that will initiate an off-normal signal whenever the valve is operated into a closed position, and that will initiate a restoration-to-normal signal whenever the valve is returned to a fully open position. When mounting such an initiating device where it will come in contact with the threaded shaft of the valve, care must be taken that the device is adjusted so that it will not falsely initiate a restoration signal if the shaft stops turning with the sensing portion of the device between two of the threads. This is a particularly troubling problem with larger sizes of control valves. (See Figures 4-3H and 4-3I.)
2. The air pressure in a dry-pipe sprinkler system or water pressure tank and the supervisory air pressure in a preaction sprinkler system. This is accomplished by connecting an air pressure supervisory initiating device to the system being supervised. Such a device is designed to initiate a supervisory off-normal signal whenever the air pressure climbs above or drops below a designated set-point. Conversely, the device will initiate a restoration-to-normal signal whenever the air pressure is restored to the valve at which the device is set. During installation, it is important that provision be made to allow testing of the device by simulating its operation during abnormal conditions. One method of accomplishing this is to connect the device to the sprinkler system through a stop-and-waste valve. When operated, such a valve automatically "wastes" the pressure trapped between the valve and the device to the atmosphere. Thus, whenever the valve is closed, a signal is initiated. This eliminates the possibility of tampering with the device without producing a signal.
3. Low temperature in a building equipped with a wet-pipe automatic sprinkler system, in a closet protecting a dry-pipe valve, preaction valve, or deluge valve from freezing, or of the water inside a storage tank. This is accomplished by mounting a temperature supervisory initiating device at the location to be supervised. Such a device is designed to initiate a

supervisory off-normal signal whenever the temperature drops below a designated set-point. Conversely, the device will initiate a restoration-to-normal signal whenever the temperature is restored to the value at which the device is set. (See Figure 4-3J.)

FIG. 4-3J. Low-temperature switches for a water storage tank.

4. The level of the water in a storage tank. This is accomplished by mounting a water-level supervisory initiating device at the location to be supervised. Such a device is designed to initiate a supervisory off-normal signal whenever the water level rises above or drops below a designated set-point. Conversely, the device will initiate a restoration-to-normal signal whenever the water level is restored to the value at which the device is set. During installation, it is important that provision be made to allow testing of the device by simulating its operation during abnormal conditions. (See Figure 4-3K.)

5. The operation and integrity of a fire pump. This is accomplished by connecting supervisory initiating device circuits to the "remote signal" contacts inside the fire pump controller. When an electric motor-driven fire pump operates into a running condition or when the power to the motor is interrupted, distinct supervisory signals are initiated. Similarly, when an engine-driven fire pump operates into a running condition — that is, its main switch is placed in a position other than "automatic start" — the battery charger

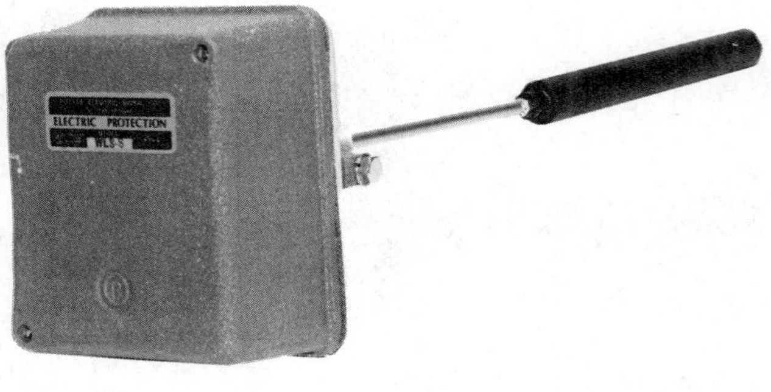

FIG. 4-3K. A low water level switch for a water storage tank.

fails, the engine experiences an abnormal condition or fails to start, or the controller fails, distinct supervisory signals are initiated. Conversely, a restoration-to-normal signal will be initiated whenever the particular feature of the fire pump that is off-normal is restored to normal.

BIBLIOGRAPHY

NFPA Codes, Standards, and Recommended Practices

Reference to the following NFPA codes, standards, and recommended practices will provide further information on waterflow alarms and sprinkler system supervision discussed in this chapter. (See the latest *NFPA Catalog* for availability of current editions of the following documents.)

NFPA 13, *Installation of Sprinkler Systems.*

NFPA 70, *National Electrical Code®.*

NFPA 71, *Installation, Maintenance, and Use of Signaling Systems for Central Station Service.*

NFPA 72, *Installation, Maintenance, and Use of Protective Signaling Systems.*

Additional Reading

Bryan, J. L., "Supervision of Automatic Sprinkler Systems," *Automatic Sprinkler and Standpipe Systems*, National Fire Protection Association, Quincy, MA, 1976, pp. 362-377.

Fire Protection Equipment List, Underwriters Laboratories Inc., Northbrook, IL. (published annually, with bimonthly supplements)

Factory Mutual Approval Guide, Factory Mutual Research Corporation, Norwood, MA. (published annually)

Higgins, P. J. and Ballanco, J. A., "Backflow Protection for Water Supply to Fire Sprinkler Systems," *Plumbing Engineer*, Vol. 17, No. 6 (Jul.-Aug. 1989), pp. 40-42, 46-47.

HOUSEHOLD WARNING SYSTEMS

Revised by Walter F. Schuchard

Why are household warning systems needed? Because America's unusually high fire death rate is dominated by fires in U.S. homes, and household warning systems, specifically smoke detectors, provide a rare combination of effectiveness and affordability in reducing the risk of death in home fires. The dominance of U.S. homes in fire deaths is demonstrated each year. In 1989, 80 percent of all fire deaths occurred in U.S. homes and 93 percent of fire deaths in any type of building. Analyses by NFPA indicate that, when a fire occurs, detectors cut the chances of dying in half. The potential impact of detectors is far greater still because the 50 percent reduction reflects all the current gaps, such as households that fail to provide enough detectors or proper locations or working batteries.

Why do smoke detectors have such great performance and even greater potential? Actual fire tests in residential occupancies have shown that measurable amounts of smoke have preceded measurable amounts of heat in almost all cases. In the other cases, the smoke and heat appeared almost simultaneously.

This chapter will discuss the reasons household fire warning systems are needed, the history of residential fire warning systems, research into system effectiveness, the importance of having a system in the home and how to make the best use of it, and the importance of an effective escape plan. The types of systems and detectors will also be covered, along with guidelines for installing and testing household fire warning equipment.

Although heat detectors for residential use have been available since 1921, field tests have shown that they are not as effective as smoke detectors in detecting fires in the home.

Residential smoke detectors were relatively expensive when they began to appear in the marketplace in the late 1960s. In 1970, however, the introduction of a battery-operated smoke detector, along with several new line-powered smoke detectors, initiated a period of public acceptance of single-station residential smoke detectors. By 1989, 85 percent of U.S. homes had at least one smoke detector.

Walter F. Schuchard is director of industry affairs for Electro Signal Lab, Inc., Hingham, MA.

RESIDENTIAL FIRE DETECTOR RESEARCH

Current performance requirements and installation practices for residential fire detectors are the result of knowledge and experience gained from several test programs. The first major test programs using heat and smoke detectors were "Operation School Burning" and "Operation School Burning No. 2," conducted by the Los Angeles Fire Department in 1959 and 1961, respectively. These tests had a major impact on fire protection and illustrated two significant points: (1) the tests proved that smoke detectors could provide a high level of life safety due to their fast response to a fire, and (2) detectable quantities of smoke usually preceded detectable levels of heat.

The next significant test series was conducted by the Bloomington (MN) Fire Department in May 1969. Although all detectors employed in the Bloomington tests were system-connected units, the results of these tests—such as time of detector response, order of response as a function of detector and fire type, and conditions at time of response—correlated well with subsequent tests.

In 1974, NFPA members adopted a major change to NFPA 74, *Household Fire Warning Equipment*. Prior to this, NFPA 74 required that in addition to a smoke detector, a home be protected with a heat detector in every major room of the dwelling. The 1974 edition recognized two facts: (1) the mandatory total system approach was impractical for the majority of the population, and (2) heat detectors were not the most effective detectors for the home. Therefore, an NFPA committee developed a matrix of four "levels of protection" from which the homeowner could choose. The four levels of protection concept was finally adopted by the NFPA membership, but not without a fight. The opposition (principally some fire chiefs and fire marshals) felt that they could not recommend anything less than complete protection, and that effectiveness of Level 4, which provided for one or two smoke detectors in the home, had not been proved by test data.

Based on this latter argument, the National Bureau of Standards (NBS) [now the National Institute for Standards and Technology (NIST)] contracted with ITT Research

Institute and Underwriters Laboratories (UL) to provide just such test data. The results of the first phase of this test program were published in August 1975 under the title "Detector Sensitivity and Siting Requirements for Dwellings." The study, more commonly known as the "Indiana Dunes Report," showed, in fact, that Level 4 coverage was inadequate under certain conditions. The report recommended that at least one smoke detector on each story of the residence be used as a minimum requirement. This was referred to as the "every level" smoke detection system. Based primarily on the results of this report, NFPA 74, *Household Fire Warning Equipment*, was revised again in 1978 by dropping the four levels of protection and adopting a minimum required system of one smoke detector on each story (floor level) of a home. Also, because of the slow response of heat detectors when compared to smoke detectors, NFPA 74 no longer permitted the use of heat detectors as the prime method of fire detection.

Shortly after publication of the first phase of the Indiana Dunes Report, the Minneapolis Fire Department conducted a similar independent study on smoke detector performance. The Minneapolis and Dunes tests were very similar in that each was conducted in a two-story house with basement, with detectors installed on each floor. Likewise, the conclusions of the Minneapolis and Dunes tests were essentially identical; thus, the Minneapolis tests provided an independent verification of many of the conclusions of the Dunes tests.

ELEMENTS OF RESIDENTIAL FIRE PROTECTION

As the first chapter of this handbook stated, the many elements of firesafety and fire protection can be grouped into six elements that need to work together in an integrated system for best results: (1) fire prevention, (2) prevention of unusually rapid early growth or spread, (3) automatic detection, (4) automatic suppression, (5) compartmentation or containment, and (6) evacuation or escape. Each is important individually, and all are interdependent in any successful residential fire protection scheme. From the perspective of household early warning systems, these six elements need to be examined in terms of the essential steps that make the automatic detection element successful and the other fire elements that can render detector protection unsuccessful. Taking them in order, one may focus on prevention of ignition and of rapid early growth or spread under a generic title of minimizing fire hazards. Also, automatic suppression is still rare in homes, so its advantages as a complement to automatic detection need not be addressed here.

Minimizing Fire Hazards

It is always easier to prevent a fire before it occurs than to detect it once it has occurred; therefore, minimizing fire hazards in and around the home is the first key element to minimizing hazards. This includes care in the selection and use of all potential heat sources (e.g., tobacco products, heating and cooking equipment, the electrical system, appliances, lighting implements) and fuel sources (e.g., furnishings and contents, interior finishes). Preventing rapid early growth or spread implies special attention to removing all unessential flammable liquids and other highly combustible items from the home. Further, it should also mean strict adherence to and enforcement of building and fire codes in the construction of residential occupancies, use of only low flame-spread materials for interior finish, and use of low-flammability or fire-retardant-treated materials in residential furnishings. Proper compartmentation is also essential to slow the fire as it moves from zone to zone, extending the time to hazardous exposure for most occupants. It must be realized that, if a fire develops rapidly enough, residential smoke detectors may not provide enough time for the occupants of a dwelling to escape before their exit routes are cut off. Therefore, it is highly dangerous for people to be careless, thinking smoke detectors will protect them.

Installation of Smoke Detectors

Full effectiveness for household warning systems means the right number of the right kind of detectors, located in the right places and operating properly. As required by NFPA 74, *Household Fire Warning Equipment*, the acceptable minimum consists of one smoke detector outside each sleeping area, one on each habitable story, and one in the basement of the home. It is also recommended that the minimum package be supplemented by additional smoke detectors in other areas as needed. For example, a smoke detector could be located inside each bedroom (especially if the occupants sleep with their bedroom doors closed) or in living and family rooms, and smoke or heat detectors could be located in the kitchen, attached garage, attic, and furnace room. Each additional detector could provide more time for the family to escape. When more than one smoke detector is installed, the detectors should be arranged so all of the alarm devices sound when any one device detects smoke. This can be done either by installing multiple-station smoke detectors or a complete system with smoke detectors, panel, and separate alarm sounding devices.

Equally as important as the installation is proper care and maintenance of the detectors. Each residential smoke detector comes with an owner's booklet describing the necessary maintenance procedures. A smoke detector with a dead or missing battery will be useless in a fire. In fact, analysis of fire reports at NFPA has shown roughly one-third of U.S. home detectors are not working, typically because of dead or missing batteries. This is a major obstacle to achievement of full success with home detectors. Because of the battery problem, NFPA 74, *Household Fire Warning Equipment*, mandates use of an ac primary power source in all new construction. It would follow that, even in existing households, smoke detectors should be powered by the ac house current, not only by batteries.

Escape Planning

The last key element in residential fire protection is the development and practice of a family escape plan. Remember, residential smoke detectors can do no more than warn occupants of a fire in the home. Detectors will not extinguish the fire. Also, depending upon the speed at which the fire is developing, the amount of time available for escape may be limited. It is critical that all occupants leave the home immediately and *call the fire department from a neighbor's house*. Many deaths have been reported in fires where people have unwisely taken extra time to get dressed, gather valuables, or look for pets. Also, it is important that everyone have an alternate way out of each room in case the primary exit is blocked by fire. There must be a prearranged outside meeting place so everyone will know that the entire family has escaped the fire. Deaths have resulted because people reluctant to climb out of windows were overcome by smoke, and, equally tragic, many have died when they reentered a burning home to look for people who had, in fact, already escaped.

Information on how to formulate a family escape plan is contained in the homeowner's booklet provided with each residential smoke detector and by NFPA in its "E.D.I.T.H." (Exit Drills in the Home) materials.

TYPES OF SYSTEMS

A residential fire detection system may range in size from one single-station smoke detector in an apartment, mobile home, or recreational vehicle to a centrally wired system containing numerous detectors and separate alarm signaling devices. The fire detection system may be combined with a burglar alarm system and an emergency medical alert system. It may be connected to a central receiving headquarters by leased telephone lines or by a digital alarm communication transmitter. The number of devices and the complexity of the system are determined, on the low end, by the minimum acceptable for a given dwelling, and, on the high end, by the extent of the occupant's needs and finances.

Single- and Multiple-Station Detectors

A single-station detector (Figures 4-4A and 4-4B) is a self-contained device that consists of a detecting element, electrical control components, an alarm-sounding appliance, and provision for connection to a separate power supply source or an integral power source, or both. In new construction, the detector is mounted to an outlet box and directly connected to unswitched house power. Detectors are also available with a line cord and plug that can be plugged into a convenient wall receptacle.

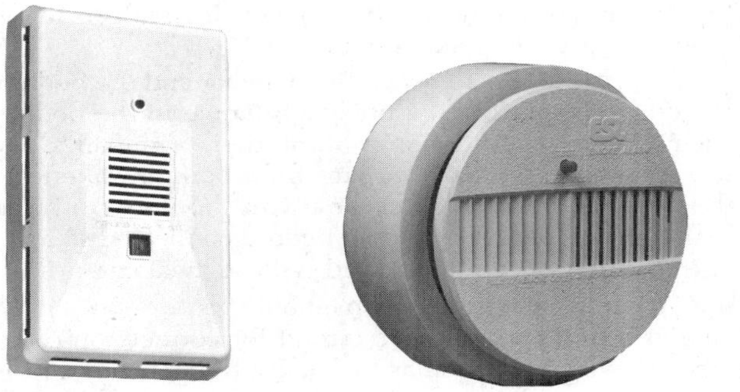

FIG. 4-4A. Single-station photoelectric smoke detectors. (Sources: Chloride Pyrotector, left, and Electro Signal Lab, Inc., right)

A direct-wired type, when provided with one or more additional wires for interconnection with other similar detectors, is referred to as a multiple-station detector. (See Figure 4-4C.) When interconnected according to the instructions provided, an alarm from any one of the interconnected detectors sounds the alarm in all the detectors. This is important because the detector near the bedrooms should sound when a detector located in another area senses smoke. The number of detectors that can be interconnected varies from one model to another. In addition, some interconnection methods are so arranged that a closure of a simple normally open contact, such as normally provided in manual non-coded fire alarm boxes and both fixed-temperature and rate-of-rise heat detectors, will also

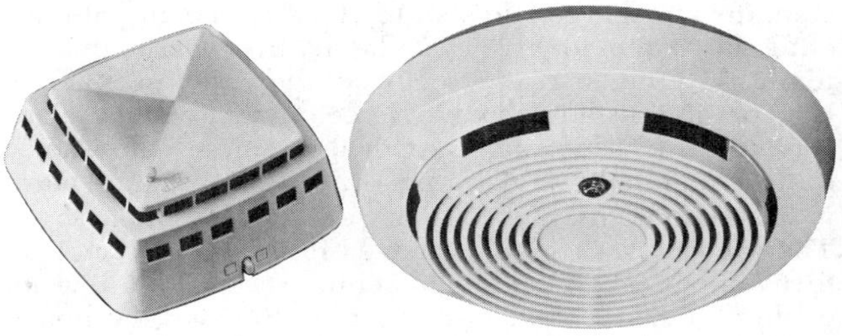

FIG. 4-4B. Single-station ionization smoke detectors. (Sources: Statitrol Division, Emerson Electric—left, and BRK Electronics—right)

sound the alarm signals in all of the smoke detectors. While this configuration is not sanctioned by NFPA 74, *Household Fire Warning Equipment*, because the installation wiring conductors connecting the contact devices are not electrically supervised and an open fault would render them inoperative and no signal would be sounded, it is extensively used in small residential occupancies to provide a household fire warning system.

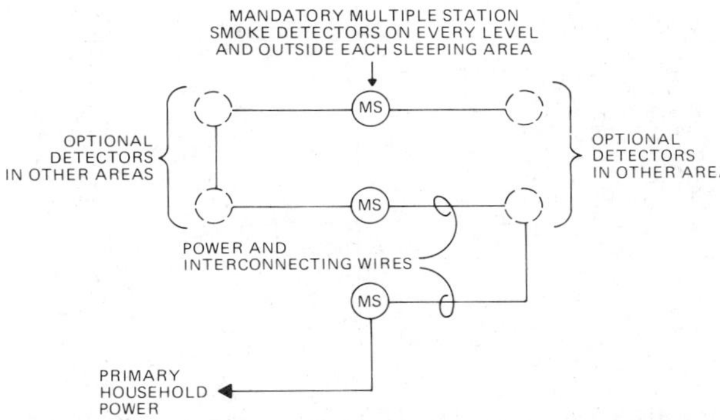

FIG. 4-4C. Typical household multiple-station smoke detector system.

Some smoke detectors are equipped with a transmitter that sends a signal to a receiver unit, which is usually located in a bedroom. If the detector is an ac plug-in model, a line carrier transmitter impresses a high-frequency signal on the house wiring. The receiver unit detects the signal as long as both are on the same power company transformer. If the detector is battery powered, it may contain a radio transmitter (similar to those used in garage door openers) with a range up to 200 ft (61 m). The receiver unit is usually ac powered. Some models also send a periodic signal to indicate to the receiver that the smoke detector is still functioning. These detectors will also send a signal when a battery needs replacement.

Household Fire Warning System

In addition to single- and multiple-station detectors, there are household fire warning systems similar in makeup and operation to the local fire alarm systems described in Chapter 6 of NFPA 72, *Installation, Maintenance, and Use of Protective Signaling Systems*. Such a system typically consists of a household system control unit (Figure 4-4D) that derives main power from the ac house wiring, and usually contains a rechargeable standby battery capable of operating the system for at least 24 hours. In addition, this system uses either smoke detectors of the system-connected type or single-station smoke detectors that contain alarm contacts. The fire warning system also could use heat detectors and manual fire alarm boxes, and has separate alarm indicating devices, such as bells, horns, or electronic sirens. The control unit also might have provision for connection to an automatic digital dialer, central station, or television cable to transmit the alarm to a point beyond the household. However, when a residential system is required to be connected to some other alarm point, the requirements of the other signaling system standard also must be met. Such standards include NFPA 71, *Installation, Maintenance, and Use of Signaling Systems for Central Station Service*, and NFPA 72, *Installation, Maintenance, and Use of Protective Signaling Systems.*

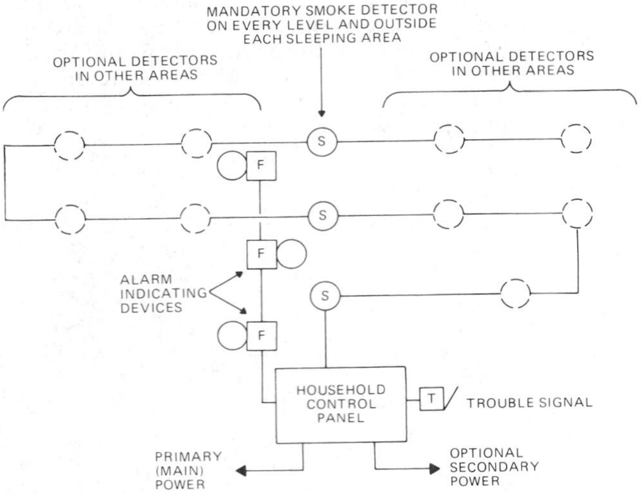

FIG. 4-4D. Typical household fire alarm system, with separate control panel.

Combination Systems

Both wired and wireless household systems often include a burglar alarm in addition to fire alarm functions. This could make the system more cost effective. In combined systems, the fire alarm signal must take precedence over the burglar alarm signal. The audible alarms are required to be distinctive so the homeowner can immediately discern the difference between a fire and a burglary. In addition, a system that provides for transmission of alarms to a point beyond the household by means of a digital dialer will sometimes have a medical alert feature that can be used to summon medical help.

DETECTION SYSTEM COMPONENTS

Smoke Detectors

A single-station smoke detector is a self-contained fire alarm device that consists of an assembly of electrical components, including a smoke sensing chamber, an alarm sounding appliance, and either integral batteries or provision for connection to a separate power supply source. Single- and multiple-station residential smoke detectors may be either of the ionization or photoelectric type.

Tests have shown that listed smoke detectors of either the ionization or photoelectric type should provide adequate warning to the occupants for most residential fires. It might be noted that, as a class, ionization detectors respond slightly faster to open flaming fires than photoelectric detectors. Conversely, the photoelectric detectors respond faster to smoldering fires. Since residential occupancies experience both flaming and smoldering fires, an extra margin of occupant safety might be achieved if the home is equipped with one detector of each type. However, both types of smoke detectors are subjected to, and must pass, the same test fires for listing by a testing laboratory. Typical test fires are described in ANSI/UL 217, *Safety Standard for Single- and Multiple-Station Smoke Detectors*, and ANSI/UL 268, *Safety Standard for Smoke Detectors for Fire Protective Signaling Systems.*

It is well known that compliance with strong smoke detector laws offers the potential of significant reduction in loss of life and property from fire. For uniformity, laws adopted statewide are preferable to local ordinances. Many states and communities now require residential units from single-family dwellings to hotels and motels to be equipped with smoke detectors.

Sounding Devices (Appliances)

A single-station smoke detector sounds an audible alarm at the device itself. The sound level output must be at least 85 dBA at a distance of 10 ft (3.05 m). This should be sufficient to alert most sleeping people as long as the detector is located on the same floor and near those who are sleeping. A general rule of thumb is that a device should provide at least 15 dBA above the maximum ambient sound level at the ear of the sleeping person. (For comparison, conversational speech has been shown to register 65 dBA and traffic on an "average" street corner 75 dBA). In addition to background noise, the stage of sleep affects the volume necessary to wake a person.

Long distances between the detector and the bedroom, closed bedroom doors, a noisy appliance in the bedroom such as an air conditioner or humidifier, or impaired hearing could prevent an occupant from being awakened by the detector. In such cases, an alarm should sound in the bedroom and detectors should be interconnected so at least one member of the household will be awakened.

A wired or wireless household system normally has an alarm indicating device circuit for connection of various alarm signals, such as fire alarm bells, horns, or electronic sirens. These devices can produce higher sound levels and can be located independently of the detectors. They can be clearly audible throughout the house or even outside, where neighbors might hear the alarm.

The sound frequencies produced by the alarm horn should be considered when selecting a device. Regardless of the type of detector installed in the home, each alarm should be tested with someone in each bedroom. This can ensure that alarms can be heard from all bedrooms.

INSTALLATION PRACTICES

Detector Location Guidelines

Detectors should be located on the ceiling at least 4 in. (100 mm) from the wall; or on the side wall, 4 to 12 in. (100 to 300 mm) from the ceiling to the top of the detector. (See Figures 4-4E, 4-4F, and 4-4G.) On floors containing bedrooms, the ceiling of the hallway serving the bedrooms is the usual detector location. On other floors, detectors should be located near the stairways to intercept smoke rising from lower floors.

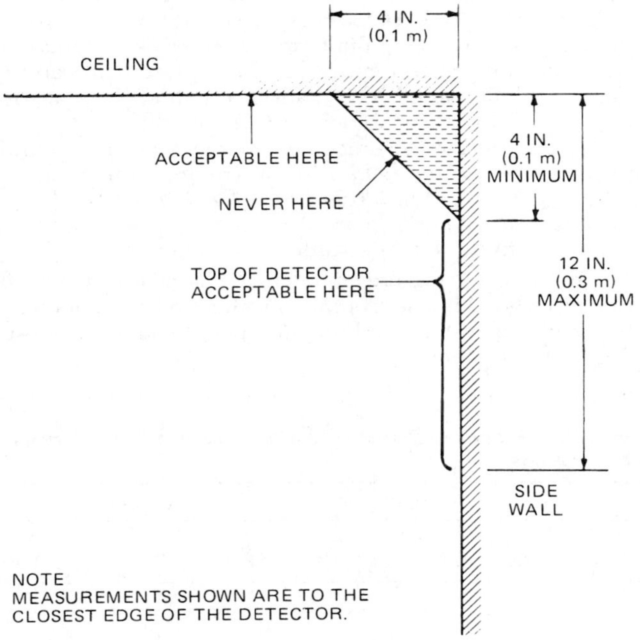

FIG. 4-4E. Proper mounting of detectors.

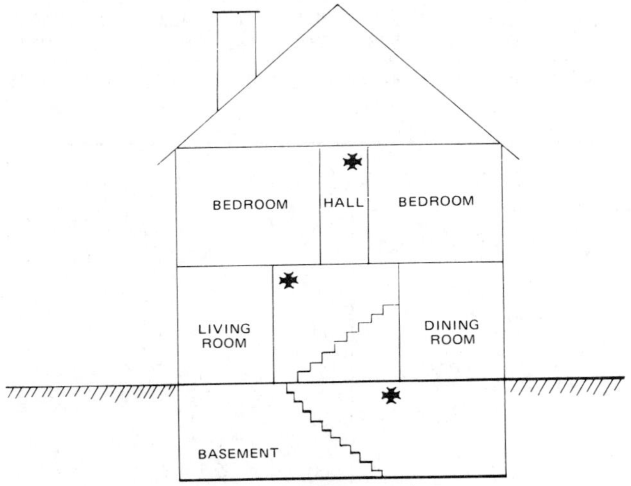

FIG. 4-4F. A smoke detector (indicated by cross) should be located on each story.

Detectors should be located no closer than 3 ft (0.9 m) from heating vents so that air issuing from the vent will not blow the smoke away from the detector. Some smoke detectors are not suitable for location within kitchens, because of false alarms from cooking vapors. Also, some smoke detectors are not recommended for garages, where automobile exhaust might cause alarms, or for attics or other unheated spaces where extremes of temperature or humidity might affect their operation. Before a smoke detector is installed in any of these locations, its specifications should be checked to ensure it is appropriate for the intended area.

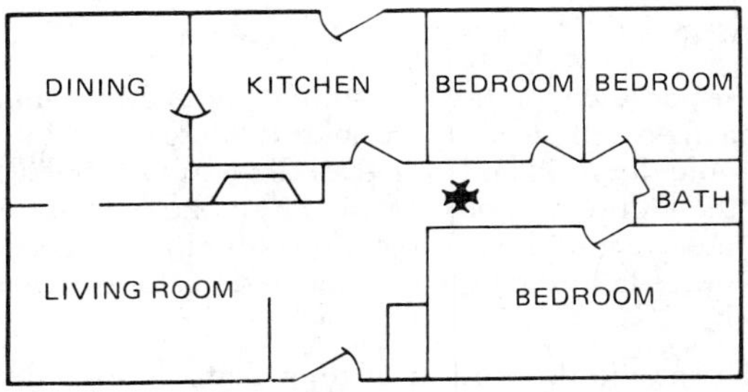

FIG. 4-4G. A smoke detector (indicated by cross) should be located between the sleeping area and the rest of the family living unit.

Another consideration is the temperature of the mounting surface. If a smoke detector is installed on a surface that can be even a few degrees warmer or cooler than the room temperature, its response may be delayed by the cold or warm air layer at the mounting surface. Smoke detectors should not be installed on uninsulated exterior walls, ceilings below uninsulated attics, or ceilings containing radiant heating coils. If the detector is colder than the air temperature and if the relative humidity is high, condensation of water vapor may occur in the detector and either produce a false alarm or put the detector to "sleep." Condensation, dust, and insects are the three most common things that lead to detector malfunction.

Special Considerations for the Handicapped

In general, households with handicapped or elderly occupants need a higher level of protection to provide additional escape time. If the handicapped person could not escape without assistance, provisions should be made for someone to provide help. Detectors that signal to remote receivers could be used, for instance, to sound the alarm in a neighbor's home. For hearing-impaired occupants, some detectors can be connected to bed vibrators, flashing lights, or fans to provide tactile or visual as well as aural stimulation.

MAINTENANCE

Household fire warning equipment should be maintained in accordance with the recommendations of the equipment manufacturer. In general, this means little more than keeping the equipment clean and free of dust, and replacing the batteries when needed. Detectors should never be disconnected due to nuisance alarms. If a detector is removed from its mounting bracket to stop a nuisance alarm caused by cooking, place the detector in an obvious location as a reminder to remount it. Most such nuisance alarms can be corrected either by moving the detector to another location, farther from the cooking source, or by replacing it with a smoke detector that is not as sensitive to cooking smoke. Also, unless the detector has a built-in sensitivity adjustment, an individual should never tamper with the factory-set sensitivity of a detector.

Testing

The importance of testing smoke detectors cannot be emphasized too strongly. Smoke detectors are basically electronic devices, and, since all devices will fail at some time, the failure rate projection of a smoke detector can be calculated. From these projections, the life expectancy or the average failure rate of the smoke detector can be determined.

To reduce the period of time that a smoke detector could be out of service because of failure, the detector that has failed can best be identified by periodic testing and then replaced. The following example is merely illustrative and is not illustrative of currently available units. Table 4-4A shows that over a 30-year period, if a detector with a calculated failure rate of 3.5 failures per million hours is not tested, the probability of it failing is 60 percent. If so, the owner could be unprotected for a period of almost 900 weeks, or almost 17½ years.

Notice that over the same 30-year period, with a test only once a year, the unprotected time would fall from almost 900 weeks to approximately 43 weeks. Referring to Figure 4-4H, notice that, if the frequency of testing is increased from one year to one month, the out-of-service time would drop from 43 weeks to about 6 weeks. All of these figures have a built-in factor of two weeks, so a defective detector can be removed and a replacement can be obtained and installed. This dramatically shows how important it is to test a smoke detector frequently.

Guidelines for testing smoke detectors can be found in NFPA 74, *Household Fire Warning Equipment*; in NFPA 72H, *Testing Procedures for Local, Auxiliary, Remote Station, and Proprietary Protective Signaling Systems*; and in the manufacturers' instructions.

In summary, fire prevention in the home involves good planning, good housekeeping, installation of an adequate fire warning system, and ongoing maintenance and testing for the system.

TABLE 4-4A. ***Probability of Failure and Average Unprotected Time for Typical Ranges of Detector Failure Rates and Test Intervals for Various Service Life Periods***

Service period	1 Year				10 Years				20 Years				30 Years			
Failures per million hours	2.0	3.0	3.5	4.0	2.0	3.0	3.5	4.0	2.0	3.0	3.5	4.0	2.0	3.0	3.5	4.0
Unprotected time (weeks)																
Test interval																
1 week	2.5	2.5	2.5	2.5	2.7	2.8	2.9	3.0	3.0	3.2	3.3	3.5	3.2	3.6	3.8	4.0
2 weeks	3.0	3.0	3.0	3.1	3.3	3.4	3.5	3.6	3.6	3.9	4.0	4.2	3.9	4.3	4.6	4.9
1 month	4.2	4.2	4.2	4.2	4.5	4.7	4.8	5.0	4.9	5.4	5.6	5.8	5.4	6.0	6.4	6.7
3 months	8.6	8.6	8.7	8.7	9.3	9.7	9.9	10.1	10.1	10.9	11.4	11.9	10.9	12.3	13.0	13.8
6 months	15.2	15.2	15.3	15.3	16.4	17.1	17.5	17.9	17.8	19.3	20.1	21.0	19.3	21.7	23.0	24.4
1 year	28.2	28.6	28.6	28.7	30.6	32.0	32.7	33.5	33.3	36.1	37.6	39.3	36.1	40.6	43.0	45.6
No test	28.2	28.6	28.6	28.7	268	271	273	276	550	565	573	581	848	881	898	914
Probability of failure during service period (%)	1.7	2.6	3.0	3.4	16.1	23.1	26.4	29.6	29.6	40.1	45.8	50.4	40.1	54.4	60.1	65.0

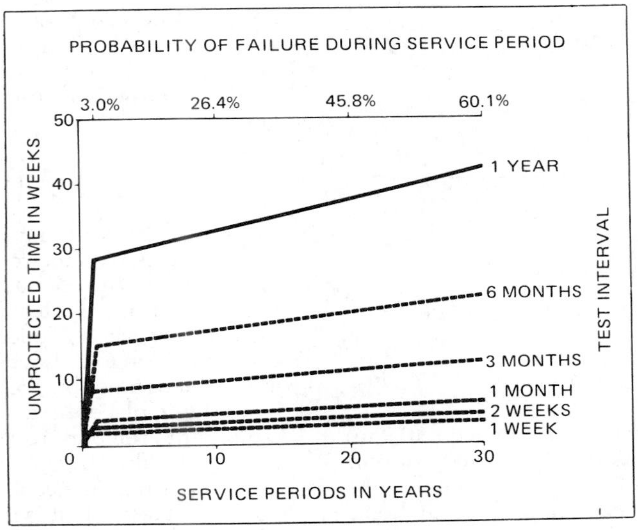

FIG. 4-4H. ***A plot of unprotected time versus service life with different test intervals. The typical case of 3.5 failures per million hours is used, with the expected percent failure also indicated.***

BIBLIOGRAPHY

NFPA Codes, Standards, and Recommended Practices

Reference to the following NFPA codes, standards, and recommended practices will provide further information on household warning systems discussed in this chapter. (See the latest *NFPA Catalog* for availability of current editions of the following documents.)

NFPA 71, *Installation, Maintenance, and Use of Signaling Systems for Central Station Service.*

NFPA 72, *Installation, Maintenance, and Use of Protective Signaling Systems.*

NFPA 72H, *Testing Procedures for Local, Auxiliary, Remote Station, and Proprietary Protective Signaling Systems.*

NFPA 74, *Household Fire Warning Equipment.*

Additional Reading

ANSI/UL 217, *Safety Standard for Single- and Multiple-Station Smoke Detectors.*

ANSI/UL 268, *Safety Standard for Smoke Detectors for Fire Protective Signaling Systems.*

Berry, C. H., "Will Your Smoke Detector Wake You?," *Fire Journal*, July 1978, pp. 105-108.

Bills, Robert G., Jr., "The Response of Smoke Detectors to Smoldering-Started Fires in a Hotel Occupancy," FMRC J.I. 0Q0R4.RA, Factory Mutual Research Corporation, Norwood, MA.

Brannigan, V., "The Legal Implications of Mandatory Home Fire Detection," *Fire Journal*, Vol. 71, No. 2, Mar. 1977, pp. 59-65.

Brien, D. E., "Toward More Reliable Residential Smoke Detection Systems," *Journal of Fire Protection Engineering*, Vol. 2, No. 1, 1990, pp. 1-10.

Bright, R. G., "NBS Answers FEMA's Criticisms of the Indiana Dunes Test of Residential Smoke Detectors," *Fire Journal*, Vol. 71, No. 5, Sept. 1977, p. 47.

Bukowski, R. W., *et al*, "Detector Sensitivity and Siting Requirements for Dwellings," NBSGCR 75-51, National Bureau of Standards, Washington, DC, 1975.

Bukowski, R. W., "Testing Residential Fire Detectors: Field Investigation of Residential Smoke Detectors," *Fire Journal*, Vol. 71, No. 2, Mar. 1977, p. 18.

Bukowski, R. W., "Investigation of the Effects of Heating and Air Conditioning on the Performance of Smoke Detectors in Mobile Homes," NBSIR 79-1915, National Bureau of Standards, Washington, DC, 1979.

Christian, W. J., and Dubivsky, P. M., "Household Fire Detection and Warning: The Key to Improved Life Safety," *Fire Journal*, Vol. 67, No. 1, Jan. 1973, p. 55.

Custer, R., and Bright, R. G., "Fire Detection, the State-of-the-Art," NBS Technical Note 839, National Bureau of Standards, Washington, DC, 1974.

"Fire Detection Systems in Dwellings," Los Angeles Fire Department Tests, *NFPA Quarterly*, Jan. 1963.

Gancarski, J. L., and Timoney, T., "Home Smoke Detector Effectiveness," *Fire Technology*, Vol. 20, No. 4, Nov. 1984, pp. 57-62.

Garner, B. W., and LiCalsi, J., "Conceptual Design for an Automatic Residential Remote Fire Alarm System," prepared for Federal Emergency Management Agency, U.S. Fire Administration, Mar. 1980.

Gawin, W. M., and Bright, R. G., "Mobile Home Smoke Detector Siting Study," NBSIR 76-1016, National Bureau of Standards, Washington, DC, May 1976.

Hall, J. R., "The Latest Statistics on U.S. Home Smoke Detectors," *Fire Journal*, Vol. 83, No. 1, 1989, pp. 39-41.

Hall, J. R., "The Most Recent Statistics on Smoke Detector Installation and Maintenance in U.S. Homes," *Fire Prevention*, No. 215, Dec. 1988, pp. 30-32.

Hall, J. R., Jr., *U.S. Experience with Smoke Detectors*, National Fire Protection Association, Quincy, MA, annual.

Harpe, S. W., Waterman, T. E., and Christian, W. J., "Detector Sensitivity and Siting Requirements for Dwellings," NFPA SPP-43A, National Fire Protection Association, Quincy, MA, July 1976.

Hygge, S., "Smoke Detectors in Apartments and One-Family Houses: A Comparison Between the Maintenance, Care, and Performance of Free and Purchased Smoke Detectors," *Fire Safety Journal*, Vol. 15, No. 3, 1989, pp. 195-210.

Johnson, P. F., and Brown, S. K., "Smoke Detection of Smoldering Fires in a Typical Melbourne Dwelling," *Fire Technology*, Vol. 22, No. 4, 1986, pp. 295-310.

Kahn, M. J., "Detection Times to Fire-Related Stimuli by Sleeping Subjects," NBS-GCR-83-435, National Bureau of Standards, Washington, DC, June 1983.

LeCoque, P. G., and Harris, K., "State by State...An Update of Residential Smoke Detector Legislation," *Fire Journal*, Vol. 84, No. 1, 1990, p. 40.

Moore, D. A., "Remote Detection and Alarm for Residences: The Woodlands System," *Fire Journal*, Vol. 74, No. 1, Jan. 1980.

Nober, E. H., *et al*, "Waking Effectiveness of Household Smoke and Fire Detection Devices," NBS-GCR-83-439, National Bureau of Standards, Washington, DC, July 1983.

Nelson, H. N., Jr., "The Need for Full Function Test Features in Smoke Detectors," *Fire Technology*, Vol. 15, No. 1, Feb. 1979.

Pezoldt, V. J., and Van Cott, H. P., "Arousal from Sleep by Emergency Alarms: Implications from the Scientific Literature," NBSIR-78-1484 (HEW), National Bureau of Standards, Washington, DC, 1978.

"Residential Smoke Alarm Report," *The International Fire Chief*, Sept. 1980, pp. 62-67.

"Survey and Analysis of Occupant Installable Smoke Detectors: A Summary Report," U.S. Dept. of Commerce, June 1978.

Waterman, T. E., "Fire Detector Response Versus Available Escape Time in Residences," ITT Research Institute, Chicago, IL.

"What You Should Know About Smoke Detectors," U.S. Consumer Product Safety Commission, Apr. 1982.

Willey, A. E., "Reducing Home Fire Deaths in the 1990s," *Fire Journal*, Vol. 81, No. 5, 1987, pp. 12-13.

AUTOMATIC FIRE DETECTORS

Revised by Wayne D. Moore

As soon as a fire starts, it produces a variety of environmental changes that help make its presence known. Human beings are excellent fire detectors—they possess the senses of smell, sight, hearing, taste, and touch. However, human senses can also be unreliable. Beginning in the mid-19th century, a number of mechanical, electrical, and electronic devices have been developed to mimic human senses in detecting the environmental changes created by fire.

The most common elements of a fire that can be detected are heat, smoke (aerosol particulate), and light radiation. Complicating the matter are two facts: (1) not all fires produce all of the elements, and (2) nonfire conditions can produce similar ambient conditions. The fire protection engineer must decide which of the elements produced by a fire might be expected from hostile fires and which similar ambient conditions might result from nonfire situations.

Even if all of these elements—heat, smoke, and light—are present in a given fire, the magnitude of the different elements must exceed some theoretical basic level during fire development. It is also helpful to determine which element will appear first. This is especially true if life safety is involved. This chapter will discuss various automatic fire detectors and their principles of operation.

HEAT DETECTORS

Heat detectors are the oldest type of automatic fire detection device. They began with the development of automatic sprinklers in the 1860s and have continued to the present with a proliferation of various types of devices. A sprinkler can be considered a combined heat-activated fire detector and extinguishing device when the sprinkler system is provided with waterflow indicators connected to the fire alarm control system. Waterflow indicators detect either the flow of water through the pipes or the subsequent pressure change upon actuation of the system.

Heat detectors that only initiate an alarm and have no extinguishing function are still in use. Although they are the least expensive fire detectors, and have the lowest false alarm rate of all automatic fire detector devices, they also are the slowest in detecting fires. A heat detector is best suited for fire detection in a small confined space where rapidly building high-heat-output fires are expected, in areas where ambient conditions would not allow the use of other fire detection devices, or where speed of detection is not a prime consideration.

Heat detectors are generally located on or near the ceiling and respond to the convected thermal energy of a fire. They respond either when the detecting element reaches a predetermined fixed temperature or to a specified rate of temperature change. In general, heat detectors are designed to operate when heat causes a prescribed change in a physical or electrical property of a material or gas.

Operating Principles of Fixed-Temperature Heat Detectors

Fixed-temperature heat detectors are designed to alarm when the temperature of the operating element reaches a specified point. The air temperature at the time of alarm is usually considerably higher than the rated temperature because it takes time for the air to raise the temperature of the operating element to its set point. This condition is called thermal lag. Fixed-temperature heat detectors are available to cover a wide range of operating temperatures—from about 135°F (57°C) and higher. Higher temperature detectors are also necessary so that detection can be provided in areas normally subjected to high ambient (nonfire) temperatures, or in areas zoned so that only detectors in the immediate fire area operate.

Fusible-element-type: Eutectic metals—alloys of bismuth, lead, tin, and cadmium that melt rapidly at a predetermined temperature—can be used as operating elements for heat detection. The most common use is the fusible element in an automatic sprinkler. Fusing of the element allows the cover on the orifice to fall away, water to flow in the system, and the alarm to be initiated.

An eutectic metal may also be used to actuate an electrical heat detector. The eutectic metal is often used as a

Wayne D. Moore is president of Mass Fire Alarms of New England, Lowell, MA.

solder to secure a spring under tension. When the element fuses, the spring action closes contacts and initiates an alarm. (See Figure 4-5A.) Devices using eutectic metals cannot be restored; either the device or its operating element must be replaced following operation.

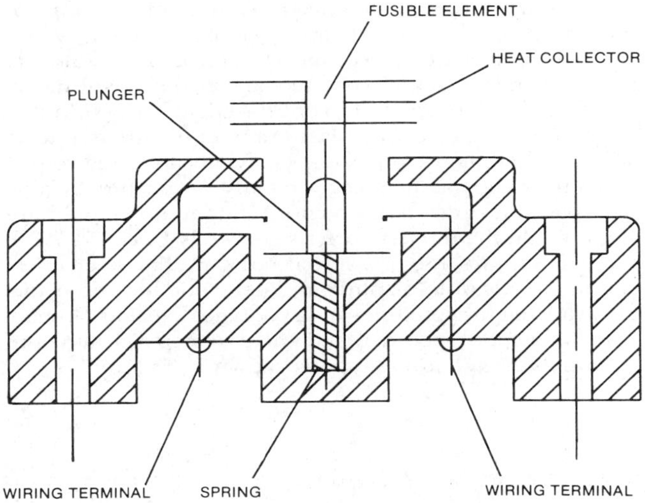

FIG. 4-5A. Fixed-temperature heat detector, spot-type, fusible element.

Continuous line-type: As alternatives to spot-type fixed-temperature detection, various methods of line-type detection have been developed. The detector shown in Figure 4-5B uses a pair of steel wires in a normally open circuit. The conductors are held apart by a heat-sensitive insulation. The wires, under tension, are enclosed in a braided sheath to form a single cable assembly. When the design temperature is reached, the insulation melts, the two wires contact, and an alarm is initiated. Following an alarm, the fused section of the cable must be replaced to restore the system.

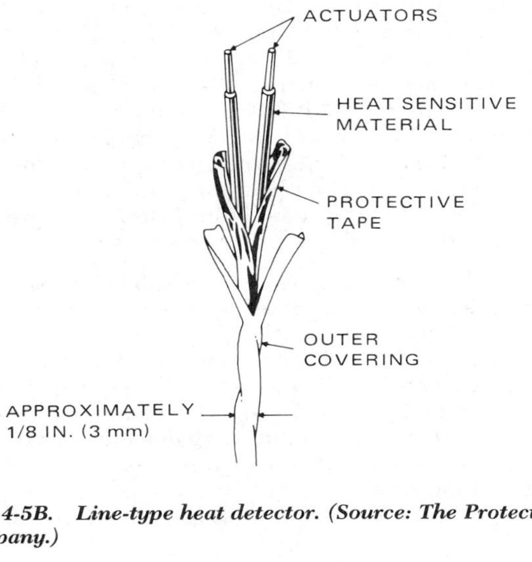

FIG. 4-5B. Line-type heat detector. (Source: The Protectowire Company.)

A similar alarm device utilizing a semiconductor material and a stainless steel capillary tube has been used where mechanical stability is also a factor. (See Figure 4-5C.) The capillary tube contains a coaxial center conductor separated from the tube wall by a temperature-sensitive glass semiconductor material. Under normal conditions, a small current (i.e., below alarm threshold) flows in the circuit. As the temperature rises, the resistance of the semiconductor decreases, allows more current flow, and initiates the alarm.

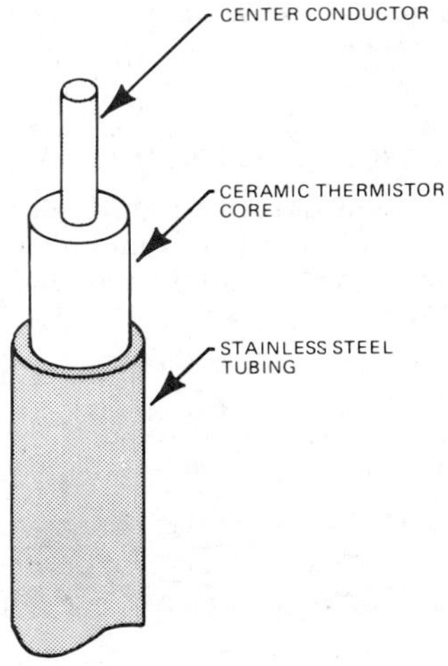

FIG. 4-5C. View of the construction of the continuous thermal sensor showing outer tubing, ceramic thermistor core, and center wire. (Source: Alison Control, Inc.)

Bimetallic-type: When two metals with different coefficients of thermal expansion are bonded together and then heated, differential expansion causes bending or flexing toward the metal having the lower expansion rate. This action closes a normally open circuit. The low-expansion metal commonly used is invar, an alloy of 36 percent nickel and 64 percent iron. Several alloys of manganese-copper-nickel, nickel-chromium-iron, or stainless steel may also be used for the high-expansion component of a bimetal assembly. Bimetals are used for the operating elements of a variety of fixed-temperature detectors. These detectors are generally of two types: (1) the bimetal strip, and (2) the bimetal snap disc.

As it is heated, a bimetal strip deforms in the direction of the contact point. With a given bimetal, the width of the gap between the contacts determines the operating temperature: the wider the gap, the higher the operating point. The operating element of a snap disc device is a bimetal disc formed into a concave shape in its unstressed condition. (See Figure 4-5D.) Generally, a heat collector is attached to the detector frame to speed the transfer of heat from the room air to the bimetal. As the disc is heated, the stresses developed cause it to suddenly reverse curvature and become convex. This provides a rapid positive action that closes the alarm contacts. The disc itself usually is not part of the electrical circuit.

All heat detectors using bimetal elements are automatically self-restoring after operation, when the ambient temperature drops sufficiently below the operating point.

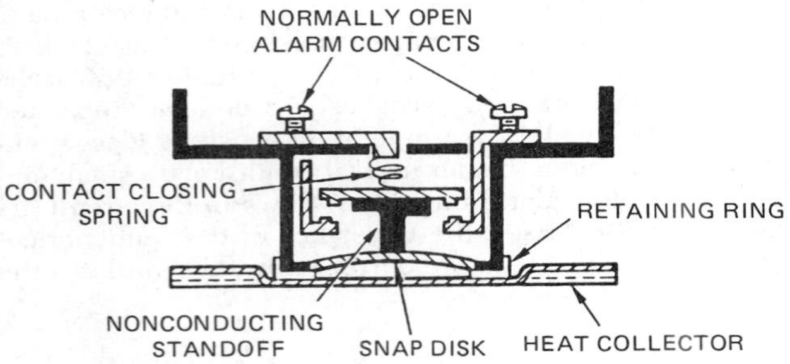

FIG. 4-5D. Spot-type fixed-temperature snap disc detector. (Source: Edwards Company.)

Rate Compensation Detectors

A rate compensation detector is a device that responds when the temperature of the surrounding air reaches a predetermined level, regardless of the rate of temperature rise. (See Figure 4-5E.)

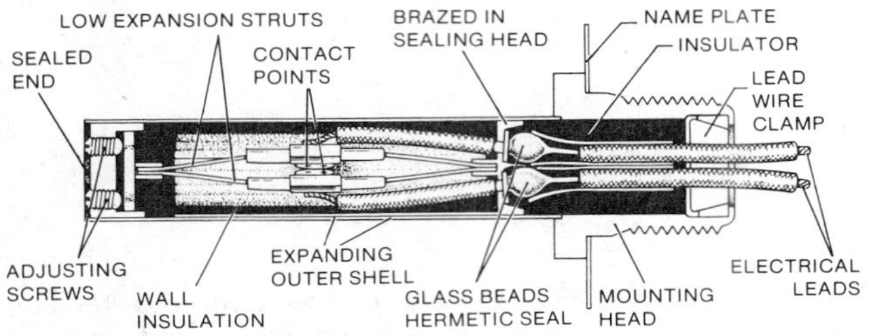

FIG. 4-5E. Section of spot-type rate compensation detector. (Source: Fenwal, Inc.)

A typical example is a spot-type detector with a tubular casing of metal that tends to expand lengthwise as it is heated, and an associated contact mechanism that will close at a certain point in the elongation. A second metallic element inside the tube exerts an opposing force on the contacts, tending to hold them open. The forces are balanced so that, with a slow rate of temperature rise, there is more time for heat to penetrate to the inner element. This inhibits contact closure until the total device has been heated to its rated temperature level. However, with a fast rate of temperature rise, there is less time for heat to penetrate to the inner element. The element therefore exerts less of an inhibiting effect, so contact closure is obtained when the total device has been heated to a lower level. This, in effect, compensates for thermal lag.

Thermal detectors using expanding metal elements are also automatically self-restoring after operation, when the ambient temperature drops to some point below the operating point.

Rate-of-Rise Detectors

One effect that a flaming fire has on the surrounding area is to rapidly increase air temperature in the space above the fire. Fixed-temperature heat detectors will not initiate an alarm until the air temperature near the ceiling exceeds the design operating point. The rate-of-rise detector, however, will function when the rate of temperature increase exceeds a predetermined value, typically around 12 to 15°F (7 to 8°C) per minute. Rate-of-rise detectors are designed to compensate for the normal changes in ambient temperature [less than 12°F (6.7°C) per minute] which are expected under nonfire conditions.

In a pneumatic fire detector, air heated in a tube or chamber expands, increasing the pressure in the tube or chamber. This exerts a mechanical force on a diaphragm that closes the alarm contacts. If the tube or chamber were hermetically sealed, slow increases in ambient temperature, a drop in the barometric pressure, or both, would cause the detector to initiate an alarm regardless of the rate of temperature change. To overcome this, pneumatic detectors have a small orifice to vent the higher pressure that builds up during slow increases in temperature or during a drop in barometric pressure. The vents are sized so that when the temperature changes rapidly, as in a fire, the rate of expansion exceeds the venting rate and the pressure rises. When the temperature rise exceeds 12 to 15°F (7 to 8°C) per minute, the pressure is converted to mechanical action by a flexible diaphragm. Pneumatic heat detectors are available for both line- and spot-type detectors. A schematic of a spot-type pneumatic heat detector is shown in Figure 4-5F, and a line-type is shown in Figure 4-5G.

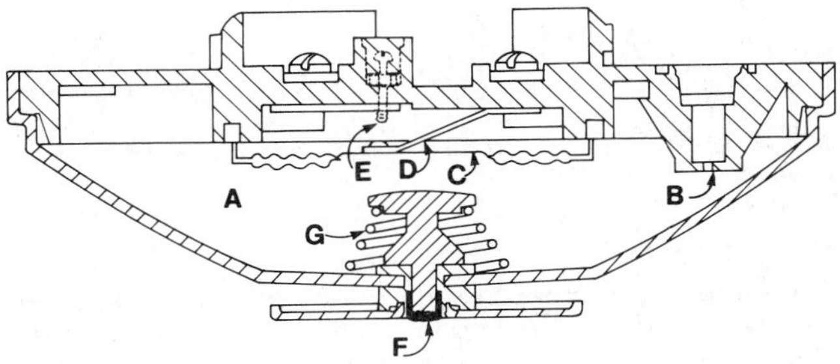

***FIG. 4-5F.** A spot-type combination rate-of-rise, fixed-temperature device. The air in chamber A expands more rapidly than it can escape from vent B. This causes pressure to close electrical contact D between diaphragm C and contact screw E. Fixed-temperature operation occurs when fusible alloy F melts, releasing spring G which depresses the diaphragm closing contact points. (Source: Edwards Company.)*

Line-type: The line-type consists of metal tubing, in a loop configuration, attached to the ceiling or side wall near the ceiling of the area to be protected. (See Figure 4-5G.) Lines of tubing are normally spaced not more than 30 ft (9.1 m) apart, not more than 15 ft (4.5 m) from a wall, and with no more than 1000 ft (305 m) of tubing on each circuit. Also, a minimum of at least 5 percent of each tube circuit or 25 ft (7.6 m) of tube, whichever is greater, must be in each protected area. Without this minimum amount of tubing exposed to a fire condition, insufficient pressure would build up to achieve proper response.

In small areas where the line-type tube detectors might have insufficient tubing exposed to generate sufficient pressures to close the alarm contacts, air chambers or rosettes of tubing are often used. These units act like a spot-type detector by providing the volume of air required to meet the 5-percent or 25-ft (7.6 m) requirement. Since a line-type rate-of-rise detector is an integrating detector, it will actuate either when a rapid heat rise occurs in one area of exposed tubing, or when a slightly less rapid heat rise takes place in several areas where tubing on the same loop is exposed.

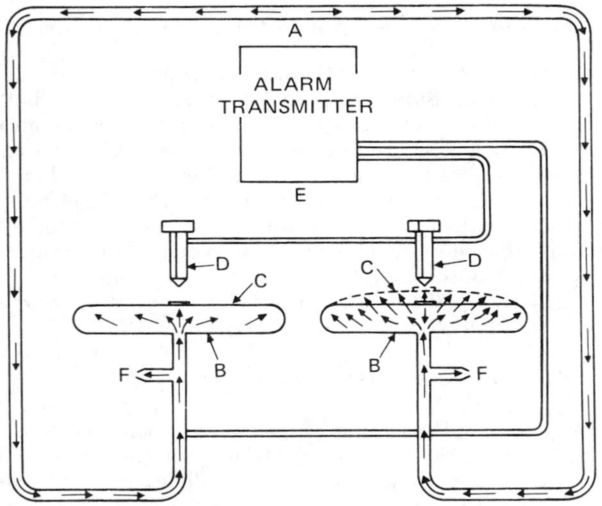

FIG. 4-5G. Line-type rate-of-rise heat detector. The copper tubing A is fastened in a continuous loop to ceilings or walls and terminates at both ends in chambers B having flexible diaphragms C which control electrical contacts D. When air in the tubing expands under the influence of heat, pressure builds within the chambers, causing the diaphragms to move and close a circuit to alarm transmitter E. Vents F compensate for small pressure changes in the tubing brought about by small changes in temperature in the protected spaces. (Source: American District Telegraph Co, and its associated companies.)

Spot-type: The pneumatic principle is also used to close contacts within spot detectors. (See Figure 4-5F.) The difference between the line- and spot-type detectors is that the spot-type contains all of the air in a single container rather than in a tube that extends from the detector assembly to the protected area(s).

Sealed Pneumatic Line-Type Detectors

A pneumatic line-type heat detector that is not vented to the air is shown in Figure 4-5H. The unit consists of a capillary tube containing a special salt that is saturated with hydrogen gas. At normal temperatures, most of the hydrogen is held in the porous salt, and the pressure in the tube is low. As the temperature increases, at any point along the tubing, hydrogen is released from the salt, increases the internal pressure, and eventually trips a diaphragm pressure switch. This system supervises the integrity of the capillary tube with a second pressure switch, which monitors the low pressure present at normal temperatures.

Combination Detectors

Combination detectors contain more than one element which responds to a fire. These detectors may be designed to respond from either element, or from the combined partial or complete response of both elements. An example of the former is a heat detector that operates on both the rate-of-rise and fixed-temperature principles. Its advantage is that the rate-of-rise element will respond quickly to a rapidly developing fire, while the fixed-temperature element will respond to a slowly developing fire when the detecting element reaches its set point temperature. The most common combination detector uses a vented air chamber and a flexible diaphragm for the rate-of-rise function, while the fixed-temperature element is usually leaf-spring

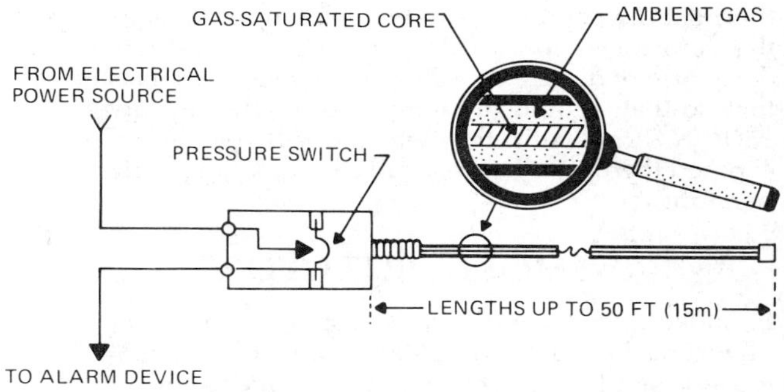

FIG. 4-5H. Line-type overheat detector. (Source: Systron-Donner.)

restrained by an eutectic metal. (See Figure 4-5F.) When the fixed-temperature element reaches its design operating temperature, the eutectic metal fuses and releases the spring, which closes the contacts.

Thermoelectric Effect Detectors

A thermoelectric effect detector is a device that utilizes a sensing element consisting of one or more thermistors which produce a change in electrical resistance in response to an increase in temperature. (See Figure 4-5I.) This resistance change is monitored by associated electronic circuitry, and the detector responds when the resistance changes at an abnormal rate (rate-of-rise type) or when the resistance reaches a specific value (fixed-temperature type).

Rate-of-rise detectors of this type use two thermistors. One is exposed to changes in atmospheric temperature. When the temperature rapidly changes as in a fire situation, the temperature of the exposed thermistor increases faster than the temperature of the unexposed reference

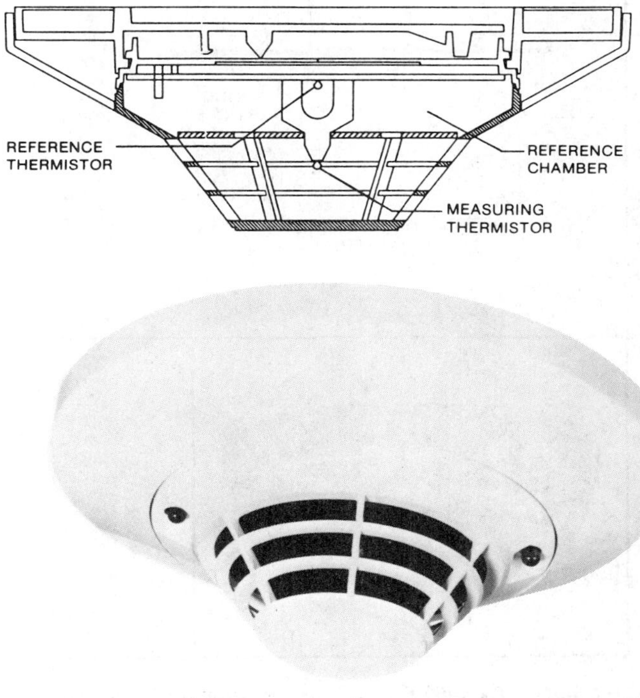

FIG. 4-5I. Thermal electric effect detector. (Source: System Sensor/Division BRK.)

thermistor, generating a net change in resistance causing the detector to go into alarm condition. Most rate-of-rise detectors are designed with a fixed-temperature backup feature so that, should the temperature rise be slower than 15°F (8°C) per min, the detector will operate when the exposed thermistor has reached a predetermined fixed temperature.

SMOKE DETECTORS

A smoke detector will detect most fires much more rapidly than a heat detector. This section will describe the various principles of smoke detector operation and their applications.

Smoke detectors are identified by their operating principle. Two of the operating principles are: (1) ionization and (2) photoelectric. As a class, smoke detectors using the ionization principle provide somewhat faster response to high-energy (open-flaming) fires, since these fires produce large numbers of the smaller smoke particles. As a class, smoke detectors operating on the photoelectric principle respond faster to the smoke generated by low-energy (smoldering) fires, as these fires generally produce more of the larger smoke particles. However, each type of smoke detector is subjected to, and must pass, the same test fires at testing laboratories in order to be listed.

Ionization Smoke Detectors

Smoke detectors utilizing the ionization principle are usually of the spot type. An ionization smoke detector has a small amount of radioactive material that ionizes the air in the sensing chamber, rendering the air conductive and permitting a current flow through the air between two charged electrodes. This gives the sensing chamber an effective electrical conductance. When smoke particles enter the ionization area, they decrease the conductance of the air by attaching themselves to the ions, causing a reduction in ion mobility. When the conductance is below a predetermined level, the detector responds. (See Figure 4-5J.)

Photoelectric Smoke Detectors

The presence of suspended smoke particles generated during the combustion process affects the propagation of a light beam passing through the air. The effect can be utilized to detect the presence of a fire in two ways: (1) obscuration of light intensity over the beam path, or (2) scattering of the light beam.

Light obscuration principle: Smoke detectors that operate on the principle of light obscuration consist of a light source, a light beam collimating system, and a photosen-

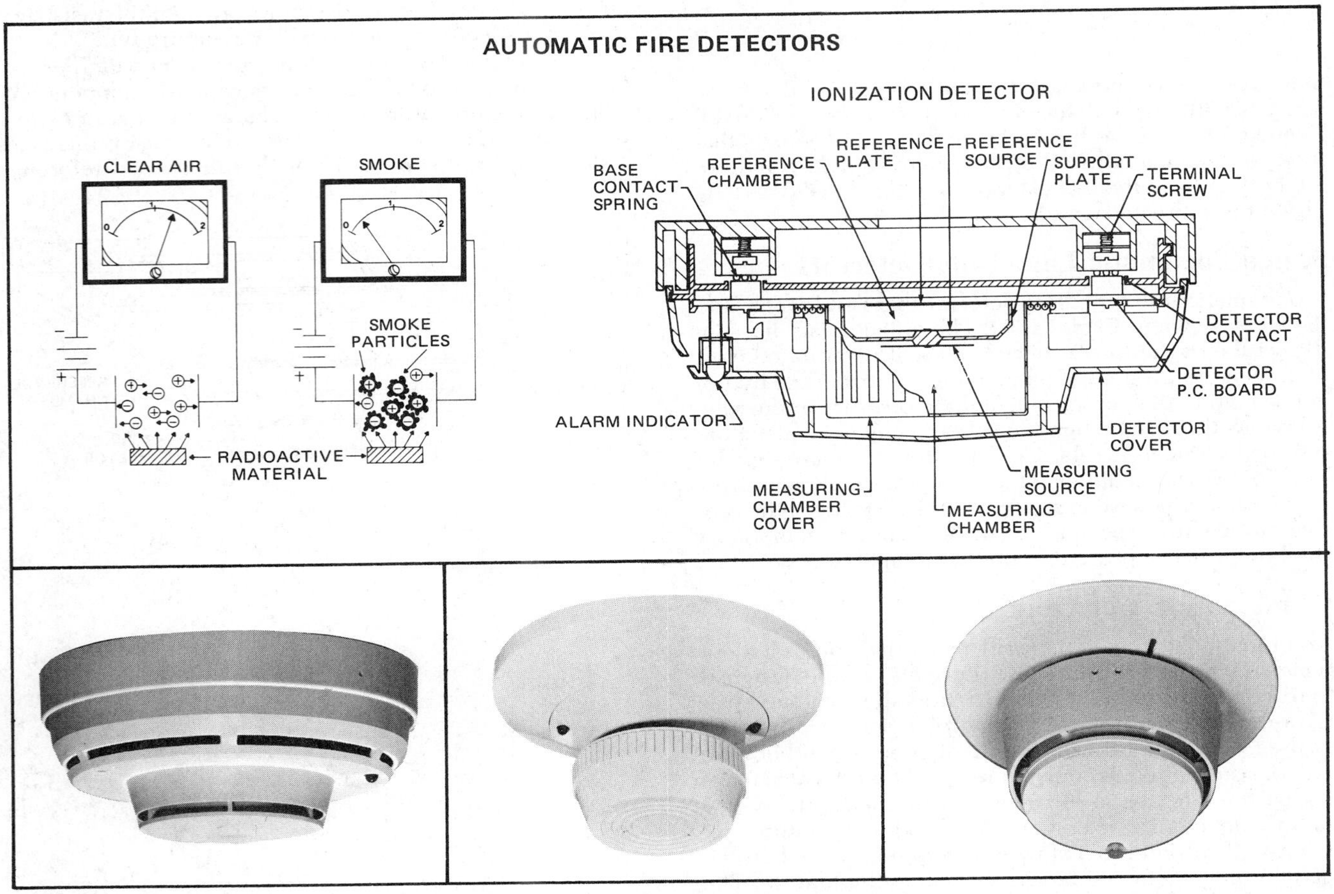

FIG. 4-5J. (Top left) Principle of operation for ionization smoke detector; (Top right) Cross-section view of an ionization smoke detector (Source: Pyrotronics); (Lower left) Ionization smoke detector (Source: Pyrotronics); (Lower center) Ionization smoke detector (Source: System Sensor/Division BRK); (Lower right) Ionization smoke detector (Source: Fire Control Instruments, Inc.).

sitive device. When dense smoke obscures part of the light beam, or less dense smoke obscures more of the beam, the light reaching the photosensitive device is reduced, and this initiates the alarm. (See Figure 4-5K.)

Most light obscuration smoke detectors are the beam type and are used to protect large open areas. They are installed with the light source at one end of the area to be protected and the photosensitive device at the other. Projected beam detectors are generally installed in accordance with the manufacturer's instructions.

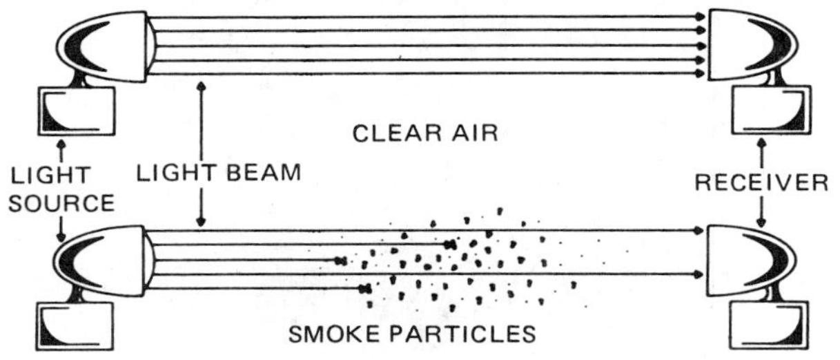

FIG. 4-5K. (Top) Principle of operation for photoelectric obscuration smoke detector. (Bottom) Typical photoelectric obscuration-type smoke detector. (Source: Hochiki America)

Light scattering principle: When smoke particles enter a light path, scattering results. Smoke detectors utilizing the photoelectric light scattering principle are usually of the spot type. They contain a light source and a photosensitive device arranged so the light rays normally do not fall onto the device. When smoke particles enter the light path, light strikes the particles and is scattered onto the photosensitive device, causing the detector to respond. (See Figure 4-5L.) The photosensitive device used in scattering detectors usually is a photodiode or a phototransistor.

Cloud chamber smoke detection principle: A smoke detector utilizing the cloud chamber principle is usually of the sampling type. An air pump draws a sample of air from the protected area(s) into a high-humidity chamber within the detector. After the air sample has been raised to a high humidity, the pressure is lowered slightly. If smoke particles are present, the moisture in the air condenses on them, forming a cloud in the chamber. The density of this cloud is then measured by a photoelectric principle. The detector responds when the density is greater than a predetermined level.

GAS-SENSING FIRE DETECTORS

Many changes occur in the gas content of the environment during a fire. In large-scale fire tests, it has been observed that detectable levels of gases are reached after detectable smoke levels and before detectable heat levels. One of two operating principles, i.e., semiconductor and catalytic element, may be used in a gas-sensing fire detector.

Semiconductor Principle

Fire-gas detectors of the semiconductor type respond to either oxidizing or reducing gases by creating electrical changes in the semiconductor. The subsequent conductivity change of the semiconductor causes actuation of the detector.

Catalytic Element Principle

Fire-gas detectors of the catalytic element type contain a material which, in itself, remains unchanged, but which accelerates the oxidation of combustible gases. The resulting temperature rise of the element causes detector actuation.

FLAME DETECTORS

A flame detector responds either to radiant energy visible to the human eye (approximately 4000 to 7700 angstroms) or outside the range of human vision. Such a detector is sensitive to glowing embers, coals, or flames which radiate energy of sufficient intensity and spectral quality to actuate the alarm.

Due to their fast detection capabilities, flame detectors are generally used only in high-hazard areas, such as fuel-loading platforms, industrial process areas, hyperbaric chambers, high-ceiling areas, and atmospheres in which explosions or very rapid fires may occur. Because flame detectors must be able to "see" the fire, they must not be blocked by objects placed in front of them. The infrared-type flame detector, however, has some capability for detecting radiation reflected from walls.

Infrared Flame Detectors

An infrared (IR) detector basically is composed of a filter and lens system used to screen out unwanted wavelengths and focus the incoming energy on a photovoltaic or photoresistive cell sensitive to infrared energy. (See Figure 4-5M.) IR flame detectors can respond to the total IR component of the flame alone or in combination with flame flicker in the frequency range of 5 to 30 Hz.

A major problem in the use of infrared detectors receiving total IR radiation is the possible interference of solar radiation in the infrared region. When detectors are located in places shielded from the sun, such as vaults, filtering or shielding the unit from the sun's rays is unnecessary.

Ultraviolet Flame Detectors

Ultraviolet (UV) detectors generally use either a solid-state device, such as silicone carbide or aluminum nitride, or a gas-filled tube as the sensing element. (See Figure 4-5N.) UV detectors are essentially insensitive to both sunlight and artificial light.

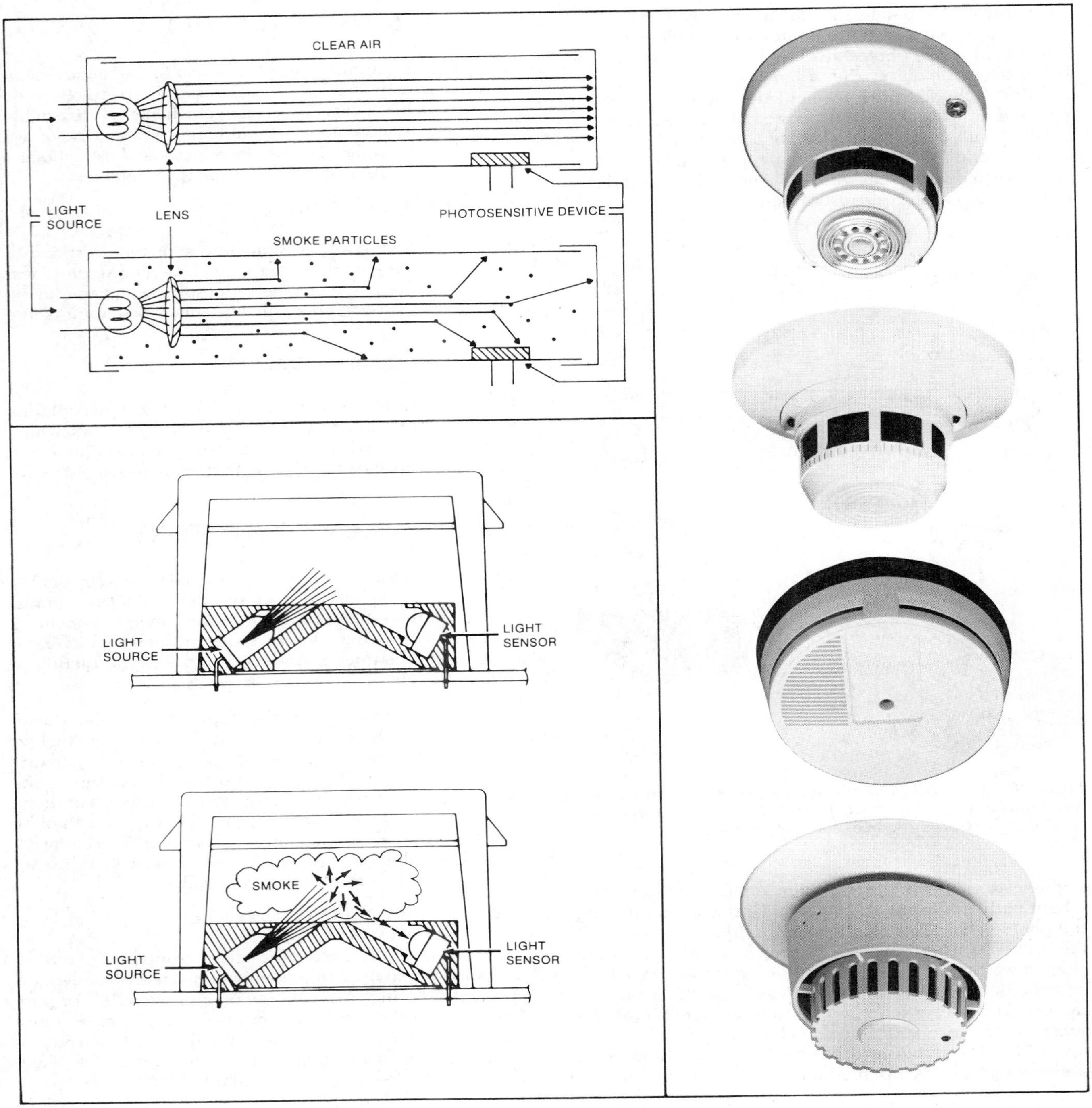

***FIG. 4-5L.** (Top left) Principle of operation for photoelectric scattering smoke detector; (Lower left) Cross-section view of a photoelectric scattering smoke detector (Source: Electro Signal Lab, Inc.); (Top right) Photoelectric smoke detector (Source: Electro Signal Lab, Inc.); (First center right) Photoelectric smoke detector (Source: System Sensor/Division BRK); (Second center right) Photoelectronic system smoke detector (Source: Electro Signal Lab, Inc.); (Bottom right) Photoelectric smoke detector. (Source: Fenwal, Inc.)*

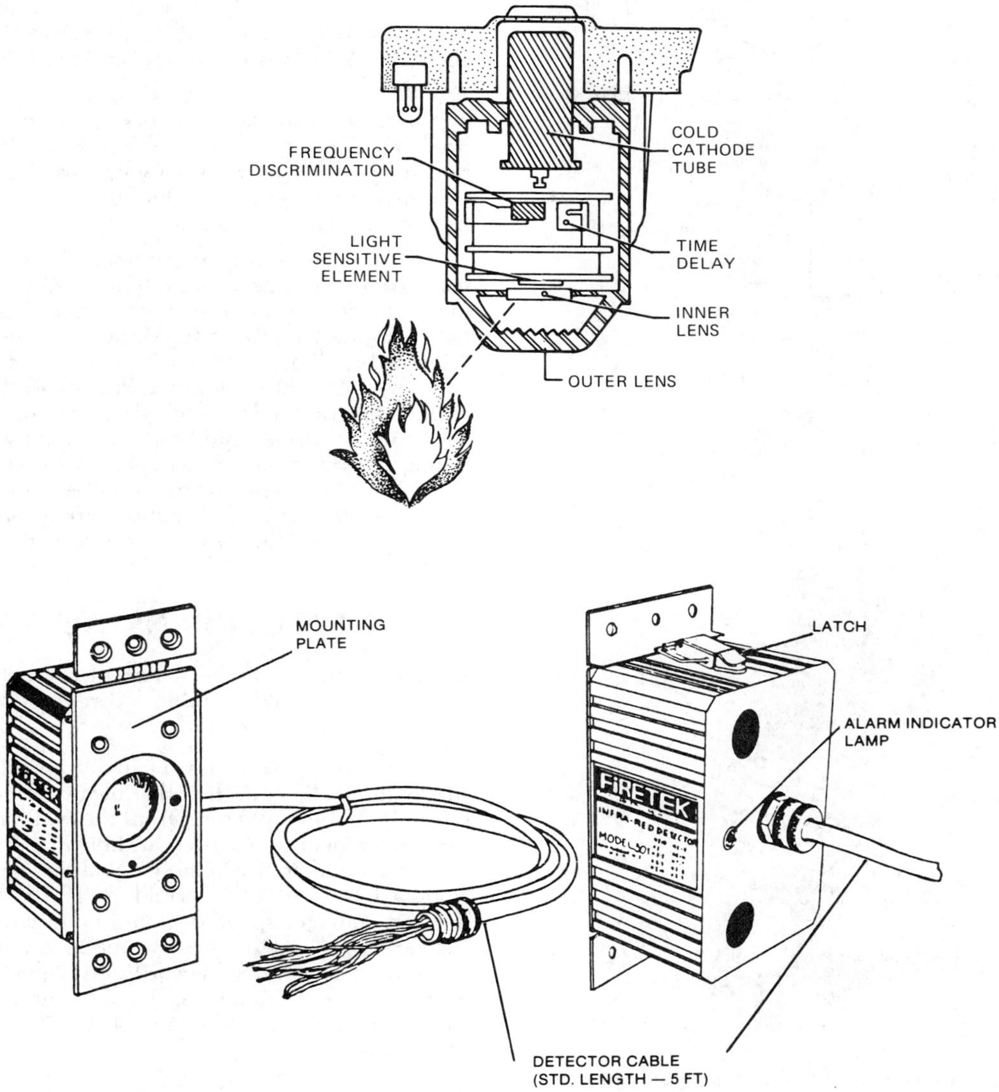

FIG. 4-5M. *(Top) Cross-section of an infrared flame detector (Source: Pyrotronics); (Bottom) Infrared flame detector. (Source: Firetek Corp.)*

AMBIENT CONDITIONS AFFECTING DETECTOR RESPONSE

Ambient conditions need to be considered in the selection, placement, and response capability of detectors. The improper selection of a class of detector or the improper placement of a detector can create problems ranging from no alarm to excessive false alarms.

Ambient Background Level

When selecting a detector for a specific location, consider the ambient background to which the detector might be exposed under nonfire conditions. For example, an IR or UV detector used where there is gas or arc welding can generate false alarms due to the presence of radiant energy, which the unit was designed to detect. These responses are considered false alarms, since they do not result from a "hostile" fire. Detectors that respond to smoke particles are especially prone to false alarms from such sources as cooking fumes, cigarette smoke, and automobile exhaust fumes.

Heating, Ventilating, and Air Conditioning (HVAC)

In buildings or portions of buildings where forced ventilation is present, smoke detectors should not be located where air from supply diffusers could dilute smoke before it reaches the detector. Detectors should be located to favor the airflow toward return openings. This may require additional detectors, since placing detectors only near return air openings may leave the balance of the area with inadequate protection when the air-handling system is shut down.

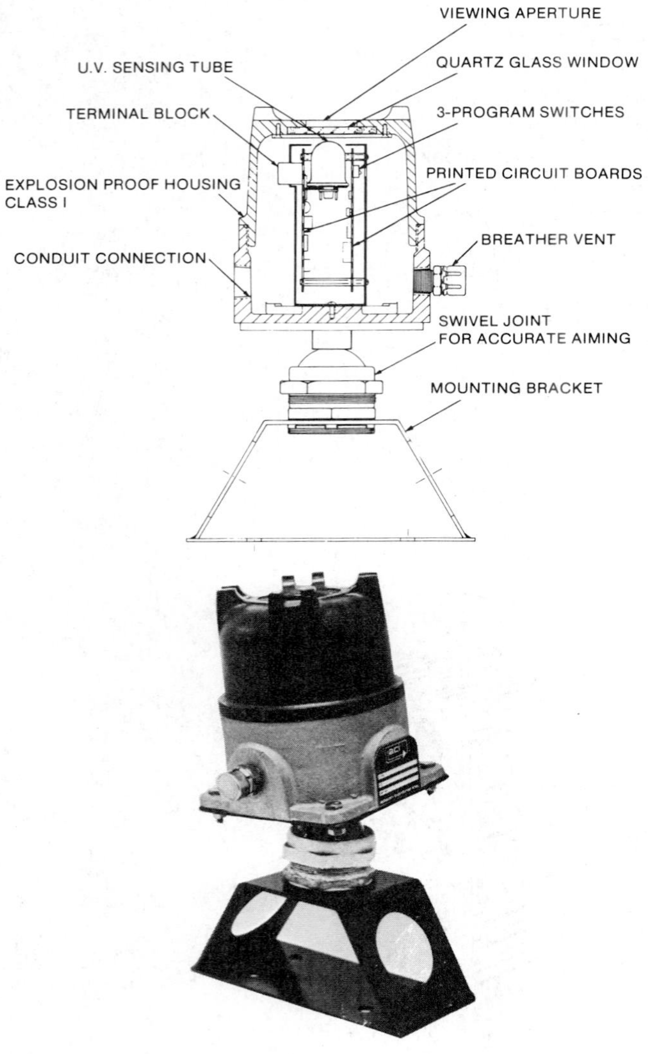

***FIG. 4-5N.** (Top) Cross-section of an ultraviolet flame detector. (Bottom) Ultraviolet flame detector. (Source: Alison Control, Inc.)*

SELECTION OF DETECTORS

When planning a fire detection system, the choice of detectors should be based on the kinds of potential fires expected. The type and quantity of fuel, possible ignition sources, ranges of ambient conditions, and the value of the protected property should all be considered.

In general, heat detectors have the lowest cost and false alarm rate, but they also have the slowest response time. Since the heat generated by small fires tends to dissipate fairly rapidly, heat detectors are best used either to protect confined spaces or directly over hazards where flaming fires could be expected. They are usually installed in a grid pattern according to their recommended spacing schedule or with reduced spacing for faster response. The operating temperature of a heat detector should be a minimum of 25°F (14°C) above the maximum expected ambient temperature in the area protected.

Smoke detectors are more expensive than heat detectors, but have a faster response time. They are better suited than heat detectors to protect large open spaces because smoke does not dissipate as rapidly as heat does in the same sized space. Smoke detectors are installed either according to prevailing air current conditions or in a grid layout.

Ionization smoke detectors are useful where flaming fires are a possibility. Photoelectric smoke detectors are best used in places with potential for smoldering fires or fires involving low-temperature pyrolysis of polyvinylchloride (PVC) wire insulation.

Flame detectors offer extremely fast response, but will warn of any source of radiation within their sensitivity range. False-alarm rates can be high if this kind of detector is applied improperly. Because flame detectors are "line-of-sight" devices, care must be taken to ensure they can "see" the entire protected area and they will not be accidentally blocked by stacked material or equipment. The sensitivity of these units is determined by flame size and flame distance from the detector. Although fairly expensive, flame detectors are well suited to protecting areas where explosive or flammable vapors or dusts may be present because they are usually available in "explosion-proof" housings.

DETECTOR INSTALLATION

After selection of the most suitable detectors for the job, the next step is to determine where to locate them within the space to be protected.

Spot-type detectors are usually installed on the ceiling or the wall, with the edge of the detector located no closer than 4 in. (100 mm) from the wall or ceiling. When heat detectors are installed at their listed spacing, detection times will approximately equal the operating times of standard 165°F (74°C) sprinklers. If a faster response is desired, detector spacing should be reduced. Where ceilings are high or ceiling construction is not smooth, spacing should be reduced accordingly. Specific information on the treatment of joisted, beamed, and sloped ceilings can be found in Appendix A of NFPA 72E, *Automatic Fire Detectors*.

Spacing of Heat Detectors on High Ceilings

Because hot air is diluted by colder air as it rises from a fire, it has always been assumed that heat detectors should be spaced closer together on a high ceiling to achieve the same response time that they would provide on an 8- to 10-ft (2.5 to 3 m) ceiling. To determine how much closer the detectors should be, a series of test fires were conducted using fires of various sizes and taking into consideration ceiling height, ambient temperature, and fire development. The data clearly show that heat detectors must be spaced closer together on a high ceiling to achieve the same response time they would have on a 10-ft (3 m) ceiling.

A typical chart (Figure 4-5O) from Appendix C of NFPA 72E, *Automatic Fire Detectors*, shows a heat detector with a listed spacing of 30 ft (9.1 m) responding to a slowly developing fire. The example shown indicates that, to detect a fire with a heat-release rate of 500 Btu per second (527 kW) on a 10-ft (3 m) ceiling, a detector with a listing of 30 ft (9.1 m) should be placed on 17-ft (5.2 m) centers. If the ceiling is 20 ft (6.1 m) high, the same detector should be placed on 8-ft (2.4 m) centers to achieve the same response time it would have on a 10-ft (3 m) ceiling.

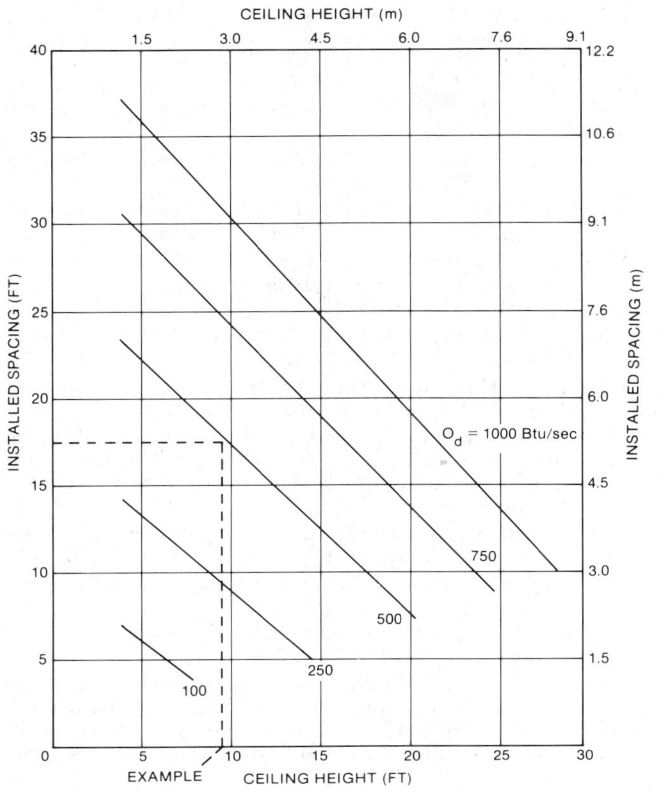

FIG. 4-50. Example of a design curve for a fixed-temperature heat detector with a listed spacing of 30 ft (9.1 m) for slow fires.

One might ask why a detector with a listing of 30 ft (9.1 m) is not spaced on 30-ft (9.1 m) centers when mounted on a 10-ft (3 m) ceiling. The answer is that the above example considered detecting a smaller fire. The test fires used by the testing laboratories more nearly approximated the 1000 Btu/sec (1055 kW) fire line on the chart. To detect a slowly developing fire with a heat release rate of 1000 Btu/sec (1055 kW), the chart shows that on a 10-ft (3 m) ceiling the recommended spacing would be 30 ft (9.1 m). On a 20-ft (6 m) ceiling, the recommended spacing would be 19 ft (5.8 m). NFPA 72E, *Automatic Fire Detectors*, requires the reduction of spacing for heat detectors mounted on ceilings higher than 10 ft (3 m). This reduction is shown in Table 4-5A.

TABLE 4-5A. *Heat Detector Spacing Reduction for High Ceilings*

Ceiling Height (ft) Above	Up To	Percent of Listed Spacing
0	10	100
10	12	91
12	14	84
14	16	77
16	18	71
18	20	64
20	22	58
22	24	52
24	26	46
26	28	40
28	30	34

For SI Units: 1 ft = 0.305 m.

Appendix C of NFPA 72E also contains charts for smoke detectors, which can be used as very expensive heat detectors to detect flaming fires only. The information regarding smoke detectors in Appendix C is intended only for flaming fires, not smoldering fires.

When installing any type of heat detector, consideration should be given to sources of heat within the protected space which might cause false alarms. For example, heat detectors should be located away from unit heaters and ovens where surges of hot air might be expected.

Proper installation is more critical for smoke detectors than it is for heat detectors because in a smoldering fire, smoke transport is strongly influenced by the convective airflow patterns within the protected area. For this reason, smoke detectors are not assigned a listed spacing by the testing laboratories. Although a grid pattern can be used as a starting point, care must be taken to appropriately locate smoke detectors with respect to the heating supply registers and return air registers. Smoke detectors should be located away from turbulence caused by supply air outlets. Their location should favor return air, because the return air will draw smoke toward the detector, and air velocity at the return tends to be lower.

Special Applications

Air duct smoke detectors are installed either in or on return air ducts or at the return air openings of HVAC systems in buildings. These detectors are used to prevent recirculation of smoke from a fire through the HVAC system within the building. Upon detection of a fire, the associated control system initiates an alarm and either shuts down the circulating blowers or switches them to a smoke exhaust mode. Detectors installed in air duct systems must never be considered substitutes for open-area protection. This is because of dilution of smoke-laden air by clean air from other parts of the building, and because the smoke may not be drawn into the HVAC system when the system is shut down.

Smoke-activated devices also are used to automatically close smoke doors in buildings to limit the spread of smoke in case of fire. Separate corridor ceiling-mounted smoke detectors can be connected to electrically operated hold-open devices on the doors, or smoke detectors can be built into the door closure units themselves.

Smoke stratification should also be considered when smoke detectors are installed. Smoke may stratify below a ceiling due to temperature gradients or airflow along the ceiling. Where stratification is possible, additional smoke detectors can be installed at alternate levels.

Installation of gas-sensing detectors is similar to that of smoke detectors. Fire gases tend to flow with smoke and are similarly affected by convected flows within the protected space. Gas detectors must also be located away from sources of oxidizable gases or vapors, such as aerosol sprays or hydrocarbon solvents, as these could cause false alarms.

The requirements of flame detectors are unlike those of heat or smoke detectors because spacings are not relevant for line-of-sight devices. Rather, flame detectors must be located so they can "see" light radiation emanating from any point within the protected space. Because the "cone of vision" for a given flame detector varies with the detector design, manufacturer's recommendations for area coverage must be followed. Flame detectors need to be shielded or located so they will not "see" radiant energy from nonfire sources that might cause false alarms.

DETECTOR MAINTENANCE AND TESTING

A thorough maintenance and testing program of all fire detectors is essential to provide continuous detector operation. A regular test of every smoke detector is of utmost importance because testing is the best way to determine that the detector has not failed.

BIBLIOGRAPHY

NFPA Codes, Standards, and Recommended Practices

Reference to the following NFPA codes, standards, and recommended practices will provide further information on automatic fire detectors discussed in this chapter. (See the latest *NFPA Catalog* for availability of current editions of the following documents.)

NFPA 72E, *Automatic Fire Detectors*.

NFPA 72H, *Local, Auxiliary, Remote Station, and Proprietary Protective Signaling Systems*.

NFPA 74, *Household Fire Warning Equipment*.

Additional Reading

Alpert, R. L., "Response Time of Ceiling-Mounted Fire Detectors," *Fire Technology*, Vol. 8, No. 3 (Aug. 1972) pp. 181-195.

Bankston, C. P., *et al.*, "Review of Smoke Particulate Properties," *NBS-GCR-78-147*, National Bureau of Standards, Washington, DC, 1978.

Beever, P. F., "Estimating the Response of Thermal Detectors," *Journal of Fire Protection Engineering*, Vol. 2, No. 1, 1990, pp. 11-24.

Benjamin, I. A., "Detector Response in Large Buildings," *Engineering Applications of Fire Technology Workshop Proceedings*, Gaithersburg, MD, Apr. 16-18, 1980. (Published by Society of Fire Protection Engineers, Boston, 1983.)

Bertshinger, S., "Smoke Detectors and Alarms," *Fire Journal*, Vol. 81, No. 1 (Jan.-Feb. 1988) pp. 43-53.

Beyler, C., "A Design Method for Flaming Fire Detection," *Fire Technology*, Vol. 20, No. 4, 1984, p. 5.

Breen, D. E., "Improved Life Safety Through More Reliable Smoke Detection Systems," *Proceedings* from the Conference on New Technology to Reduce Fire Losses and Costs, Elsevier, New York, 1986, pp. 227-234.

Bright, R. G., "A New Test Method for Automatic Fire Detection Devices," *Fire Technology*, Vol. 13, No. 2 (May 1977) pp. 105-113.

Bright, R. G., "Report of Fire Tests on Eight TGS Semiconductor Gas Sensor Residential Fire/Smoke Detectors," *NBSIR-76-990*, National Bureau of Standards, Washington, DC, 1976.

Bright, R. G. and Custer, R. L. P., "Fire Detection, The State of the Art," *Technical Note 839*, National Bureau of Standards, Washington, DC, 1974.

Bryan, J. L., *Fire Suppression and Detection Systems*, 2nd ed., MacMillan, New York, 1982.

Bukowski, R. W., "An Evaluation of Light Emitting Diodes as Source Lamps in Photoelectric Smoke Detectors," *Fire Technology*, Vol. 11, No. 3 (Aug. 1975) pp. 157-163.

Bukowski, R. W., "Fire Detection and Alarm Systems," *NBSIR 86-3360*, Center for Fire Research, Gaithersburg, MD, Apr. 1986.

Bukowski, R. W., "Techniques for Fire Detection," *Spacecraft Fire Safety*, NASA CP 2476, National Aeronautics and Space Administration, 1987.

Bukowski, R. W. and Bright, R. G., "Taguchi Semiconductor Sensors as Residential Fire/Smoke Detectors," *Fire Journal*, Vol. 69, No. 3 (May 1975) p. 30.

Bukowski, R. W. and Mulholland, G. W., "Smoke Detector Design and Smoke Properties," *Technical Note 973*, National Bureau of Standards, Washington, DC, Nov. 1978.

Chohan, R. K. and Upadhyaya, B. R., "Safety and Fault Detection in Progress Control Systems and Sensors," *Fire Safety Journal*, Vol. 14, No. 3 (Jan. 1989) pp. 167-177.

Cholin, J., "The Current State of the Art in Optical Fire Detection," *Plant/Operations Progress*, Vol. 8, No. 1 (Jan. 1989) pp. 12-18.

Cholin, J., "Optical Fire Detection," *Chemical Engineering Progress*, Vol. 85, No. 7 (Jul. 1989) pp. 62-68.

Cooper, L., "Why We Need to Test Smoke Detectors," *Fire Journal*, Vol. 80, No. 6 (Nov.-Dec. 1986) pp. 43-45.

Drake, A., "Detecting Incipient Fires—A New Approach," *Fire Surveyor*, Vol. 18, No. 5 (Oct. 1989) pp. 5-11.

Drouin, J. A. and Cote, A. E., "Smoke and Heat Detector Performance: Field Demonstration Test Result," *Fire Journal*, Vol. 78, No. 1 (Jan. 1984) pp. 34-38, 69.

Dubivsky, P. M., "Underwriters Laboratories' Smoke Detector Standards and Tests," *Fire Journal*, Vol. 82, No. 1, 1988, p. 45.

Evans, D. D. and Stroup, D. W., "Methods to Calculate the Response Time of Heat and Smoke Detectors Installed Below Large Unobstructed Ceilings," *Fire Technology*, Vol. 22, No. 1, 1986, pp. 54-66.

"Fire Detection and Suppression: Today's Technology," *Fire Safety Journal*, Vol. 14, Nos. 1 & 2 (July 1988) p. 1-125.

"Fire Detector Systems: The Range of Choice," *NFPA Journal*, No. 91, pp. 18-23.

Fry, J. F., "The Behavior of Automatic Fire Detection Systems," *Fire Research Note 310*, UK, 1970.

Gulland, W. G., "Application of a State-of-the-Art Fire and Gas Detection and Control System," *Proceedings* of the Conference on Facilities, Pipelines, and Measurements: A Workbook for Engineers, American Society of Mechanical Engineers, 1985, pp. 71-73.

Hall, J. R., "A Decade of Detectors: Measuring the Effect," *Fire Journal*, Vol. 79, No. 5 (Sept. 1985) p. 37.

Hall, J. R., "When Fire Detectors Don't Operate—A Growing Problem," *Fire Safety Journal*, Vol. 14, Nos. 1 & 2, 1988, pp. 25-32.

Hall, J. R., "U.S. Experience with Smoke Detectors: Who Has Them? How Well Do They Work? When Don't They Work?," National Fire Protection Association, Quincy, MA, 1988.

Halliwell, R. E. and Sultan, M. A., "Attenuation of Smoke Detector Alarm Signals in Residential Buildings," *Proceedings* of the First International Symposium on Fire Safety Science, Hemisphere, Washington, DC, 1986, pp. 689-697.

Hertzberg, M., *et al.*, "The Spectral Growth of Expanding Flames—The Infrared Radiance of Methane-Air Ignitions and Coal Dust-Air Explosions," RI 7779, U.S. Bureau of Mines, 1973.

Hertzberg, M. and Litton, C. D., "The Optical Detection of Underground Fires and Explosions," Storch Award Symposium, 164th American Chemical Society Meeting, New York, Aug. 1972.

Hertzberg, M. and Litton, C. D., "An Optical Infrared Detection System for Methane-Air Explosions," U.S. Bureau of Mines, 1973.

Heskestad, G. and Delichatsios, M. A., "Environments of Fire Detectors—Phase II-Effect of Ceiling Configuration. Vol. I. Measurements," *NBS-GCR-78-128*, National Bureau of Standards, Washington, DC, 1978.

Heskestad, G. and Delichatsios, M. A., "Environments of Fire Detectors. Vol. II. Analysis," *NBS-GCR-78-129*, National Bureau of Standards, Washington, DC, 1978.

Holker, J. R. and Lomax, G. R., "Sensory Early Warning Systems in Fire Detection," *Proceedings* of the Conference on New Technology to Reduce Fire Losses and Costs, Elsevier, 1986, pp. 246-255.

Hygge, S., "Installation and Reliability of a Free Smoke Detector," *Proceedings* of the First International Symposium on Fire Safety Science, Hemisphere, Washington, DC, 1986, pp. 739-748.

Jernigan, W., "Keeping the Smoke Detectors Operational: The Dallas Experience," *Fire Journal*, Vol. 81, No. 4 (July 1987) p. 57.

Johnson, J. E., "Fire Detection: Past, Present, and Future," *Fire Journal*, Vol. 81, No. 5 (Sept. 1987) p. 49.

Katzel, J., "An Overview of Automatic Fire Detectors," *Plant Engineering*, Sept. 27, 1984.

Lawson, D. I., "A Laser Beam Fire Detection System," *Fire Technology*, Vol. 6, No. 4 (Nov. 1970) pp. 305-311.

Lee, T. G. K., "An Instrument to Evaluate Installed Smoke Detectors," *NBSIR-78-1430*, National Bureau of Standards, Washington, DC, 1978.

Lee, T. G. K. and Mulholland, G. W., "Physical Properties of Smokes Pertinent to Smoke Detector Technology," *NBSIR 77-1312*, National Bureau of Standards, Washington, DC, 1977.

Luck, H., "Economics of Fire Protection with Fire Detectors," *Fire Technology*, Vol. 9, No. 1 (Feb. 1973) pp. 56-64.

Mniszewski, K. R., *et al.*, *Analysis of Fire Detectors Test Methods/ Performance: A Summary Report*, Federal Emergency Management Agency, U.S. Fire Administration, June 1980.

Moore, W. D., "Automatic Fire Detection: False Alarms," *NFPA Journal*, No. 88, pp. 146-148.

Nelson, H. N., "The Need for Full-Function Test Features in Smoke Detectors," *Fire Technology*, Vol. 15, No. 1 (Feb. 1979) pp. 10-19.

Newman, J. S., "Prediction of Fire Detector Response," *Fire Safety Journal*, Vol. 12, No. 3, 1987, pp. 205-211.

Newman, J. S., "Principles of Fire Detection," *Fire Technology*, Vol. 24, No. 2, 1988, pp. 116-127.

O'Sullivan, E. F., Gohosh, B. K., and Turner, J., "Experiments on the Use of a Laser Beam for Heat Detection," *Fire Technology*, Vol. 7, No. 2 (May 1971) pp. 133-134.

Pati, V. B., *et al.*, "Simulation of Intelligent Fire Detection and Alarm System for a Warship," *Defense Science Journal*, Vol. 39, No. 1 (Jan. 1989) pp. 79-94.

Pomroy, W. H., "Spontaneous Combustion Fire Detection for Deep Metal Mines," *Report 9144*, U.S. Bureau of Mines, Minneapolis, 1987.

Powell, B. D., Spring, D. J., and Adams, S. J., "Infrared Flame Detector with Fire-Ranging Ability," *Proceedings* of the Conference on Infrared Systems and Technology, International Society for Optical Engineering, Vol. 807, Bellingham, WA, 1987, pp. 69-72.

Raber, S. and Ellner, I., "Battery-Operated Smoke Detectors, The Need for Effective Battery Supervision," *Fire Journal*, Vol. 72, No. 5 (Sept. 1978) pp. 104-108.

Ramachandran, G., "Economic Value of Automatic Fire Detectors," *Building Research Establishment Information Paper 27/80*, Fire Research Station, Borehamwood, Herts., UK, 1980.

Rochholz, M. L., "Fire Detection State-of-the-Art," *Consulting Engineer*, Vol. 64, No. 4, 1985, pp. 54-57.

"Results of Tests Made from Six Separate Fires in a Three-Bedroom Single-Family Dwelling," Bloomington Fire Department, Bloomington, MN, May 1979.

Rickers, H. C., *Residential Smoke Detector Reliability Handbook*, Reliability Analysis Center, Griffiss Air Force Base, New York, 1979. (Also available as *NBS-GCR-79-161* and *NBS-GCR-79-162*, National Bureau of Standards, Washington, DC.)

Salamone, R., "Retrofitting High-Rise Dorms with Alarm and Detection Systems," *Fire Journal*, Vol. 84, No. 1 (Jan.-Feb. 1990) p. 37.

Schierau, K., "Detection Equipment for Fire Prevention, A Standard Solution?," *Proceedings* of the Conference on New Technology to Reduce Fire Losses and Costs, Elsevier, 1986, pp. 256-263.

Shalna, A. J., "What a Combination: Beam Smoke Detectors and Hostile Environments," *Fire Journal*, Vol. 82, No. 4 (Jul.-Aug. 1988) p. 53.

Shifiliti, R. P., "Design of Detection Systems," *SFPE Handbook of Fire Protection Engineering*, National Fire Protection Association, Quincy, MA, 1988.

Smoke Detectors: A Bibliographical Overview, Vance Bibliographies, Monticello, IL, 1985.

"Smoke Detectors," *Consumer Reports*, Aug. 1980, pp. 475-479.

Stroup, D. W., Evans, D. D., and Martin, P. M., "Evaluating Thermal Fire Detection Systems," *NBS SP 712* and *NBS SP 713*, Center for Fire Research, Gaithersburg, MD, Apr. 1986.

Stroup, D. W. and Evans, D. D., "Use of Computer Fire Models for Analyzing Thermal Detector Spacing," *Fire Safety Journal*, Vol. 14, Nos. 1 & 2, 1988, pp. 33.

Watanabe, A., Sasaki, H., and Unoki, J., "Overview of Fire Detection in Japan," *Proceedings* of the First International Symposium on Fire Safety Science, Hemisphere, Washington, DC, 1986, pp. 679-688.

Waterman, T. E., Mniszewski, K. R., and Spadoni, D. J., *Cost/ Benefit Analysis of Fire Detectors*, IIT Research Institute for the U.S. Fire Administration, Sept. 1978.

Wickham, R. T., "Detectors," *Specifying Engineer*, Vol. 49, No. 5 (May 1983) pp. 86-88.

Wilton, R., "Recent Developments in the Fire Detection Field," *Fire Engineers Journal*, Vol. 47, No. 144, 1987, pp. 8-10.

Zallen, D. M., *et al.*, "Evaluation of Optical Fire Detectors," *Proceedings* of the 34th International Instrumentation Symposium, ISA, 1988, pp. 121-128.

Zimmerman, C. E., "Development of Light Emitting Diodes for Photoelectric Smoke Detectors," *Fire Technology*, Vol. 11, No. 3 (Aug. 1975) pp. 153-156.

GAS AND VAPOR TESTING

Revised by Stuart B. Eynon

Prevention of accidental fire involving combustible gases requires an accurate knowledge of where and when ignition of a mixture within the flammable range can occur, so additional precautions can be taken to prevent ignition. A combustible gas is defined as any flammable or combustible gas or vapor that can, in sufficient concentrations by volume in air, become the fuel for an explosion or fire. Measurement of the oxygen concentration is important for three reasons: (1) as a means of evaluating the effectiveness of inerting processes, (2) as a means of protecting personnel from the effects of oxygen deficiency, and (3) as a means of determining that sufficient oxygen is present in the atmosphere to ensure reliable combustible gas readings. Of increasing importance is the need for an awareness of the toxic properties of gases or vapors that may also be present in the atmosphere.

Enclosed areas where combustible gases or vapors can be present are found in public utility operations; petroleum production, refining, and marketing; chemical and petrochemical plants; metallurgical industries; distilleries; paint and varnish making; marine operations; and many other industrial activities. In addition, combustible gases may be found in the atmosphere as a result of leakage from above- or below-ground piping systems or from spillage of flammable liquids. They may also be found in the soil atmosphere due to leakage from below-ground piping systems, spillage of flammable leakage onto the soil surface, or the decomposition of natural organic material in the soil or sanitary landfills. Combustible gases may be detected by instruments such as combustible gas indicators, flammable vapor detectors, combustible gas analyzers, flame-ionization detectors, infrared-type analyzers, and the like. All of these instruments operate by sensing the characteristics of a sample and translating these characteristics into appropriate data.

In this chapter, portable instruments are defined as those requiring no external power source. Such devices may operate continuously for several days or longer. Stationary instruments are those that are permanently installed and, in general, operate on line power.

Stuart B. Eynon is senior vice president of Heath Consultants, Inc., Stoughton, MA.

COMBUSTIBLE GAS INDICATORS

Operating Principles

Many of the instruments in current use utilize the principle of "catalytic combustion." Mixtures of combustible gas and air cannot be ignited to cause self-sustaining flame unless the concentration of gas exceeds a minimum value called the lower flammable limit (LFL) or lower explosive limit (LEL). (The two terms are synonymous and are used interchangeably.) Mixtures containing much lower concentrations, approaching zero, can "burn" on the surface of heated platinum, yielding heat in direct proportion to the gas or vapor concentration. This is called "surface" or "catalytic" combustion.

If the heated surface is an electrically heated platinum wire connected in an appropriate circuit (e.g., the Wheatstone bridge circuit, see Figure 4-6A), the heat released by catalytic combustion can further increase the temperature of the wire, resulting in a change in electrical resistance, and a corresponding indication on an electric meter. The meter may be analog (scale with needle) or digital. The usual combustible gas indicator (hot-wire type) operates in this manner. Other somewhat similar devices may employ a solid or porous catalytic mass instead of a wire and may sense the temperature by means other than the increase in electrical resistance.

A more recent development is a type of instrument using solid-state sensors (semiconductors). These sensors are generally less specific to combustible gases and may respond to changes in atmospheric moisture content and temperature. Such instruments do not commonly provide a meter or digital read-out in percent of the lower explosive level of percent gas-in-air, but produce an audible or visual alarm at one or more pre-selected alarm levels. Generally, semiconductor instruments respond to various gases in the parts per million (ppm) range, but do not display exact repeatability and cannot be calibrated in the field.

In operation, gas diffuses through a porous metal disc and comes into contact with the heated surface of a silicone chip. As gas concentrations increase, the resultant

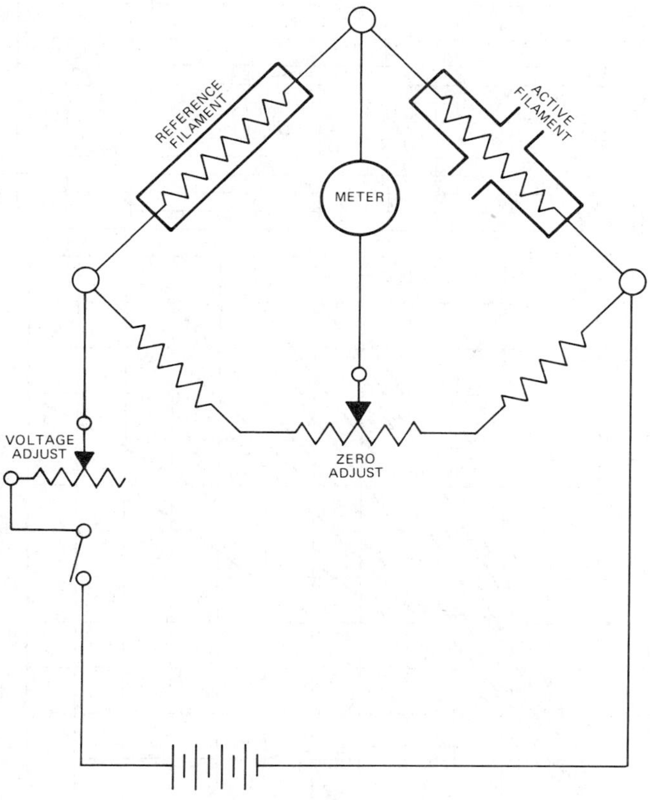

FIG. 4-6A. The Wheatstone bridge circuit in which the "active filament" is a platinum wire on which catalytic combustion takes place when a sample of the atmosphere being tested is passed across it. The resultant change in resistance in that arm of the circuit is translated into a corresponding deflection of an electric meter.

chemical reaction reduces the semiconductor resistance logarithmically, producing an output voltage that can be linearized by the instrument's microelectronic circuits.

The combustible gas instrument must be set to read "zero" when uncontaminated air is drawn into it. When making tests, the amount of gas present in the sample is read on a scale that shows the amount in terms of the fraction or percent of the lower flammable limit concentration, usually abbreviated as "percent LFL," or lower explosive limit, abbreviated as "percent LEL." This is practical, since the heat of combustion at the LFL/LEL concentration of most combustible gases is approximately the same. Some vapors, e.g., carbon disulfide, give somewhat low readings in terms of true explosibility; others, such as natural gas, may give readings on the high side. Special calibrations are used where exact readings at the upper part of the scale are required. For most purposes, where the sought-after condition is a gas-free atmosphere, these differences disappear as the reading approaches the previously set zero.

The fact that the hot-wire type of instrument responds to all combustible gases or mixtures of combustible gases, irrespective of chemical composition, is usually advantageous in that it is unnecessary to know the exact identity of a gas to evaluate its fire and explosion risk. Where it is desirable to selectively measure the presence of some specific combustible gas in the possible presence of other combustibles, special or more refined techniques are necessary. Infrared absorption and gas chromotography are some of the principles that may be used.

Other instruments, some generally similar in appearance to the ordinary combustible gas indicator, depend for their operation upon properties of a gas or vapor other than combustibility, such as refractive index, density, diffusion, or thermal conductivity of a gas. Calibrated upon a specific gas, these instruments can be designed to give readings on higher concentrations up to pure gas. The instruments are not selective, however, and will respond to almost any gas or vapor, regardless of combustibility.

In some instruments, the catalytic combustion principle and the thermal conductivity principle are combined in a single device to permit extending the useful range into and beyond the flammable range. However, each section of the instrument retains the limitations of the particular method employed.

Operation and Limitations

As actual ignition of flammable mixtures may occur within the instrument, flame arresters are provided in the inlet and outlet connections to the chamber housing the catalytic filament to prevent combustion within the chamber from traveling outside and igniting the atmosphere being sampled. Flame arresters are suitable for conventional gas-air mixtures. If the atmosphere is oxygen enriched, i.e., the atmosphere contains more than 21 percent oxygen by volume or the partial pressure of oxygen exceeds 160 mm of mercury (21.27 kPa), special arresters may be necessary.

Tests may be made remotely by drawing a sample from a suspect location through a hose to an indicator, or on site by carrying the instrument (previously set to zero in fresh air) into the suspect area. The former is preferred as a preliminary test because the operator is not exposed to possible flammable or toxic concentrations of gas.

Instruments of the hot-platinum-filament type are designed specifically for measuring combustibles in air. They depend upon an oxidation reaction to operate. The oxygen in the air is necessary for proper instrument function. They will give a reasonably accurate indication of the presence of combustible gas even when the oxygen concentration has been substantially reduced by oxidation, biological action, or displacement. As a rule of thumb, if the oxygen content of the atmosphere tested is less than 10 percent, a catalytic-filament-type instrument may not give a true reading. Without special adaptation, they cannot be relied upon to demonstrate whether or not the objective of an inerting procedure, i.e., the elimination of an explosive mixture, has actually been achieved.

Sampling steamy atmospheres is not recommended, since readings normally will be erroneously high and condensation of water within the instrument is likely to cause problems. Sampling from ovens or dryers at substantially elevated temperatures should be avoided unless it is known that the vapor is so dilute that condensation will not occur at the temperature of the instruments. However, if the solvent involved has a flash point below atmospheric temperature, explosibility readings can be relied upon irrespective of the oven temperature.

The sample should always be drawn into the instrument by the aspirator bulb or pump supplied by the manufacturer. Sampling directly from a pressurized system should be avoided, as pressurized samples may damage the instrument and will produce inaccurate readings of the combustible gas being sampled.

Some catalytic filaments lose their catalytic properties if exposed to substances such as silicones, dust, and the vapors of tetraethyl lead. The listings of testing laboratories specify which instruments utilize filaments with sufficiently high temperatures to make them suitable for use on the vapors of gasoline containing tetraethyl lead. Some manufacturers supply an accessory chemical filter whose vapors will combine with the lead to form a compound that will prevent poisoning of the filament. Recent research and development has produced filaments that are less susceptible to poisoning. Manufacturer's literature and instruction manuals should be checked for the latest information about specific instruments.

CALIBRATION CHECKS

The response of these instruments to combustible gases must be verified regularly. Some authorities recommend verification be performed daily before use. Such verification, usually called a calibration check, is accomplished by passing a known concentration of a combustible gas in air through the instrument. The response is then compared with performance data supplied by the manufacturer, and adjustments are made in accordance with that manufacturer's instructions. Most suppliers of combustible gas detection equipment have available pressurized cylinders that contain calibration gas-air mixtures. Such cylinders are equipped with regulators to deliver the mixture to the instrument at the proper pressure. A typical calibration gas-air supply is shown connected to a portable combustible gas indicator in Figure 4-6B. Similar equipment can be used to check a remote sampling head.

FIG. 4-6B. ***A calibration gas-air supply connected to a portable combustible gas indicator through a pressure regulator and adapter hose. (Source: Mine Safety Appliances Co.)***

Some instruments are supplied with calibration curves showing the response of the particular unit to combustible gases other than that on which the device was calibrated. Calibration curves for one particular model of combustible gas indicator are shown in Figure 4-6C. Since all manufacturers do not use the same gas for base factory calibrations, the curves for one instrument cannot be used with curves of another type.

CALIBRATION CURVES FOR FIELD REFERENCE

GAS OR VAPOR	L.E.L. % BY VOL.	CURVE NO.	GAS OR VAPOR	L.E.L. % BY VOL.	CURVE NO.
ACETONE	2.5	5	HYDROGEN	4.0	1
ACETYLENE	2.3	3	METHYL ALCOHOL	6.7	2
BENZENE	1.4	5	METHYL ETHYL KETONE	1.8	6
CARBON DISULFIDE	1.0	10	NATURAL GAS	4.8	3
CARBON MONOXIDE	12.5	1	OCTANE	1.0	9
ETHYL ACETATE	2.2	7	PENTANE	1.4	5
ETHYL ETHER	1.7	7	PROPANE	2.2	4
GASOLINE	1.3	8	TOLUENE	1.3	4
HEXANE	1.2	7	XYLENE	1.0	7

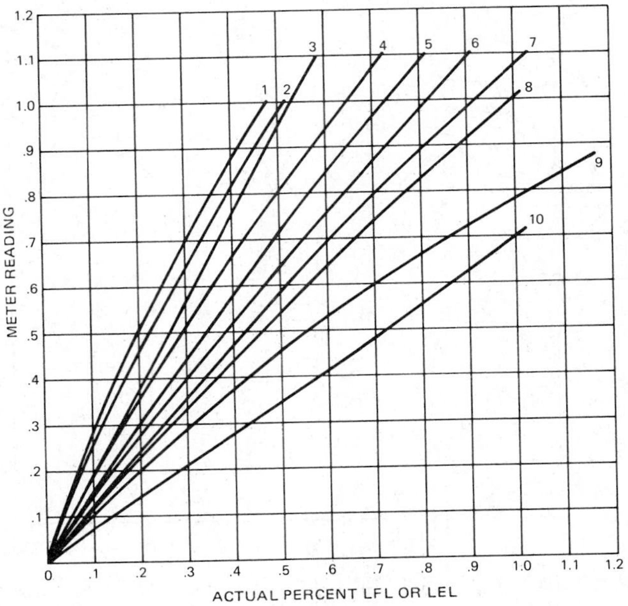

FIG. 4-6C. ***Calibration curves for one particular make of combustible gas indicator. Calibration curves for other manufactured indicators may be different because of physical arrangement of the catalytic unit. Note that, despite wide variations at higher concentrations, the error becomes negligible as the zero concentration is approached.***

TYPES OF INSTRUMENTS

Portable Indicators

Portable indicators are generally lightweight, battery-powered devices intended for field use such as testing the confined atmosphere in buildings or structures, e.g., sewers, manholes, ducts, containers, tanks, or the soil atmosphere, where the presence of a combustible gas mixture is suspected. The batteries used may be carbon-zinc, alkaline, mercury, nickel-cadmium, or lead-acid. Samples are drawn through a hose or tube, which is frequently equipped with a rigid extension or "probe" for ease in reaching inaccessible points. Suction is provided by a hand-operated rubber aspirator bulb or a battery-powered built-in motor-driven pump.

There are portable combustible gas indicators equipped with audible and visual alarms. Usually powered by rechargeable batteries, they are designed to run continuously for eight to ten hours on a full charge. The alarm circuits are energized when a preset concentration of combustible gas is reached. These instruments usually depend upon diffusion and convection to bring the sample to the filament chamber, but may also have battery-operated pumps to draw a sample through the filament chamber. (See Figure 4-6D.)

FIG. 4-6D. A portable combustible gas alarm device.

The most recent development in portable gas indicators is combination instruments that provide multiple ranges of sensitivity for combustible gases in ppm, percent of LFL/LEL, and percent gas by volume, combined with an additional sensor for oxygen level or carbon monoxide. (See Figure 4-6E.)

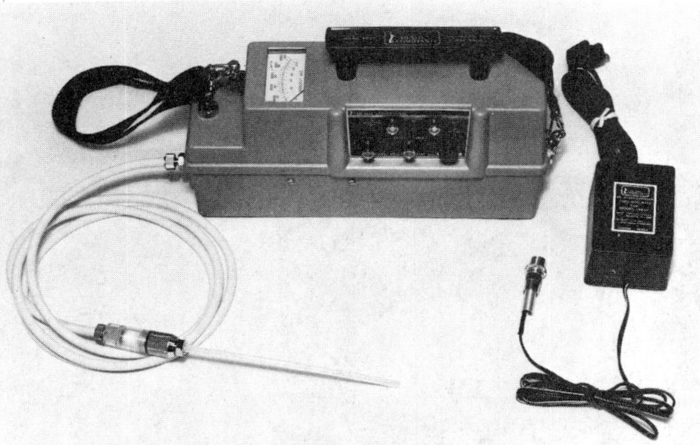

FIG. 4-6E. A portable multiple-range gas indicator. (Source: Heath Consultants, Inc.)

A number of portable indicators are available for use in hazardous locations. (See Figure 4-6F.) The electrical circuits have been designed to meet the requirements of Article 500 of NFPA 70, *National Electrical Code*®, and have been tested and listed by testing agencies. The manufacturer's label and instructions indicate the type of approval granted for the particular instrument.

Stationary Analyzers

Stationary analyzers are permanently installed line-powered devices for continuously analyzing air samples from one to as many as twenty or more points. The analyzers may be either of the remote detection (diffusion) type (Figure 4-6G) or may draw samples through tubing to a central location by means of a suction pump or equivalent. Functions may include audible or visible alarms in addition to continuous recording of data, such as two-level alarms, e.g., a warning light at 20 percent and/or 40 percent LFL/LEL; an audible alarm at 50 percent of LFL/LEL; automatic shutdown or startup of equipment; and similar features as required by individual applications.

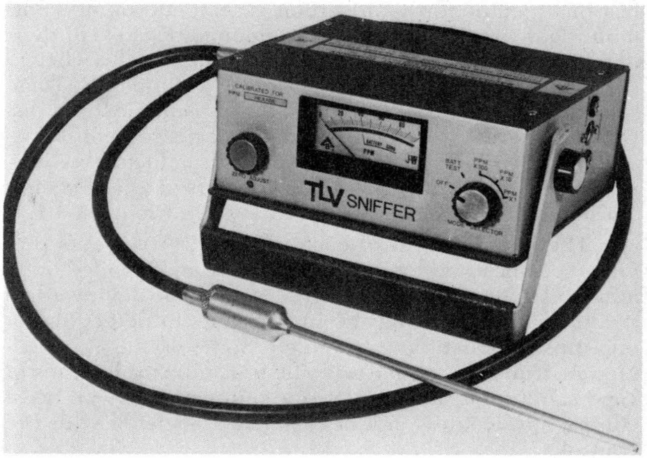

FIG. 4-6F. A portable flammable and combustible gas detector. (Source: Bacharach Instrument Co.)

FIG. 4-6G. A continuous type of combustible gas analyzer for multiple location sampling. Inset shows a typical sensing for remote mounting. (Source: Mine Safety Appliances Co.)

The central equipment is available either for installation in nonhazardous locations, such as control rooms, or in listed explosion-proof enclosures for hazardous areas.

Stationary analyzers are frequently tailored to meet the exact requirements of the particular installation, and may also employ operating principles other than catalytic combustion. The output signals from such instruments can also be incorporated into computer-controlled data acquisition networks.

Other Types of Indicators

Numerous devices are available, some reasonably portable, that are suitable for determining the presence of contaminating gaseous substances in air. Among those are ones depending upon refractive index, density, diffusion, or thermal conductivity of gases. Other operating principles include glass tubes filled with granular material, where a color change indicates the presence of some specific substance; gas chromatography; infrared absorption; flame ionization (specific for hydrocarbon gases); and others. Portable flame-ionization-type instruments, because of their excellent sensitivity in ppm, pumped sample systems, field stability, and reliability, have become a standard leakage search instrument in the natural gas transmission and distribution industry. Because this type of instrument is specific to hydrocarbon gases and largely unaffected by heat, moisture, and airflow, it is also widely used as an accelerant detector in arson investigations. (See Figure 4-6H.)

The manufacturer of each of these instruments provides specifications, proper applications, and detailed operating instructions. This material should be reviewed in detail by anyone using the instruments to detect and/or measure combustible gases in air. Some of these specialized instruments are not specific to combustible gases or vapors, but serve as special-purpose instruments in process control applications, not necessarily associated with fire control.

Oxygen Indicators

Devices similar in appearance to combustible gas indicators are available for measuring the oxygen content of the atmosphere in a closed space. The devices operate either as an individual unit or as a combination unit also incorporating a combustible gas indicator.

The portable oxygen indicator operates on an electrochemical principle, the partial pressure of the oxygen in the atmosphere controlling the rate of diffusion through a porous membrane and into an electrochemical cell with suitable electrolytes and electrodes. (See Figure 4-6I.) The oxygen enters into an electrochemical reaction, generating a current that, in turn, reads the percentage of oxygen directly on a scale graduated from 0 to 25 percent.

Except for setting the meter to read 20.8 percent while aspirating fresh air at the elevation (atmospheric pressure) where tests are to be made, no other calibration is necessary for accurate reading in the range of oxygen concentrations in which it is permissible for people to work. (Current regulations require a minimum of 19.5 percent oxygen, otherwise air supplied or self-contained breathing equipment must be used.) Enclosed spaces should also be tested to ensure sufficient oxygen is present to permit reliable gas measurements. Where readings are intended to be significant in the low range, i.e., with inerting systems, the zero setting can be confirmed by sampling an oxygen-free gas, such as propane or nitrogen.

Some models use an aspirator bulb or pump to draw the sample into the instrument, and have an appearance and configuration very similar to the standard combustible gas indicator. Other models utilize diffusion sampling, with the oxygen cell suspended at the end of a flexible cable. In either case, the electrical energy levels available from the cell are far below those that could constitute a source of ignition. Figure 4-6J shows a combination combustible gas and oxygen detector.

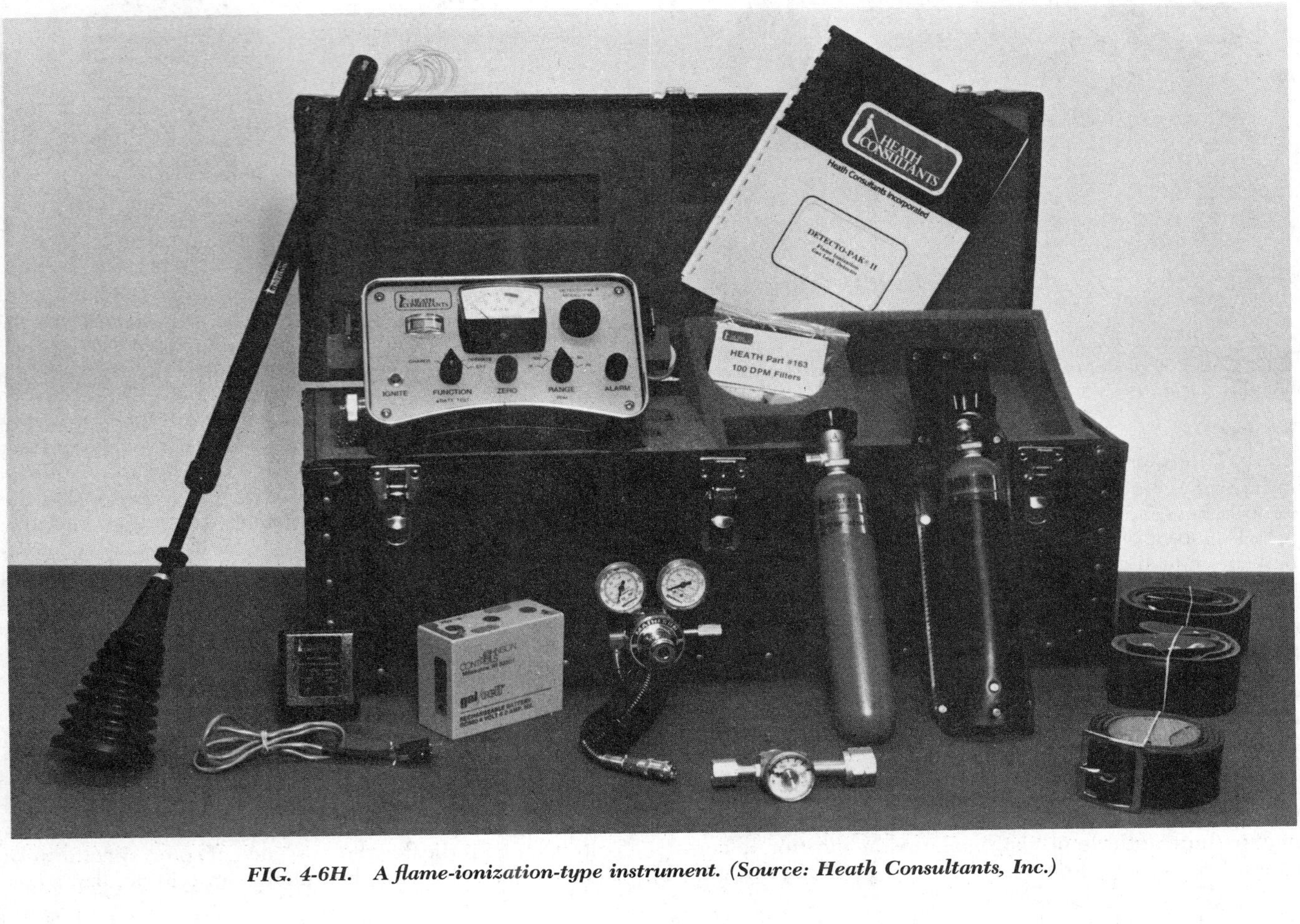

FIG. 4-6H. A flame-ionization-type instrument. (Source: Heath Consultants, Inc.)

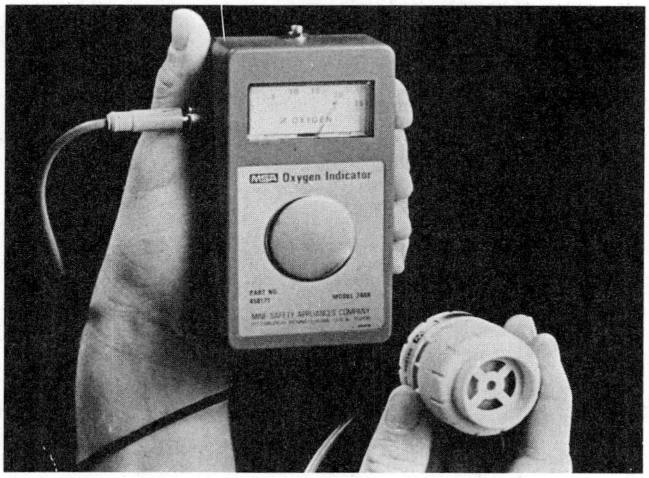

FIG. 4-6I. An individual oxygen indicator for remote sampling. (Source: Mine Safety Appliances Co.)

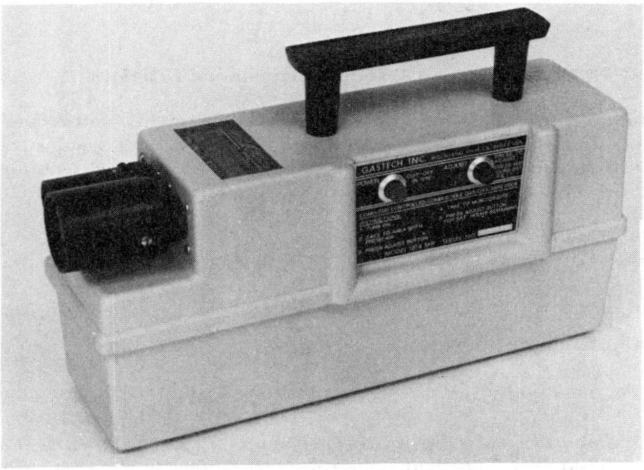

FIG. 4-6J. A microprocessor-controlled dual-range combustible gas oxygen monitor that uses synthesized speech to produce vocal instructions and alarm warning statements and sounds. Computerization has simplified operation to two push-button controls. (Source: Gas Tech, Inc.)

Toxic Gases and Vapors

Many combustible substances also present a health hazard. A concentration of a gas in air might not be flammable but could be a very serious toxic (health) hazard. As previously stated, combustible hazards are expressed as percent of LFL/LEL or a percent by volume. Toxicity is expressed in ppm, where one percent by volume equals 10,000 ppm. Many toxic gases are health hazards in concentrations of less than 100 ppm.

The presence of toxic gases in confined spaces must be considered, either because of normal manufacturing procedures or as products of combustion resulting from a fire. Carbon monoxide is one byproduct that is almost always present.

A wide variety of instruments, including both portable indicators and stationary analyzers, exist for the measurement of toxic gases. Ranging from simple chemical-filled detector tubes (Figure 4-6K) to complicated electrochemical systems (Figure 4-6L), they are relatively specific to individual chemicals or families of chemicals. Figure 4-6M shows a portable diffusion-type indicator that simultaneously tests for combustible gas, oxygen, and a toxic gas. Figure 4-6N depicts a sample-draw-type portable instrument for similar testing.

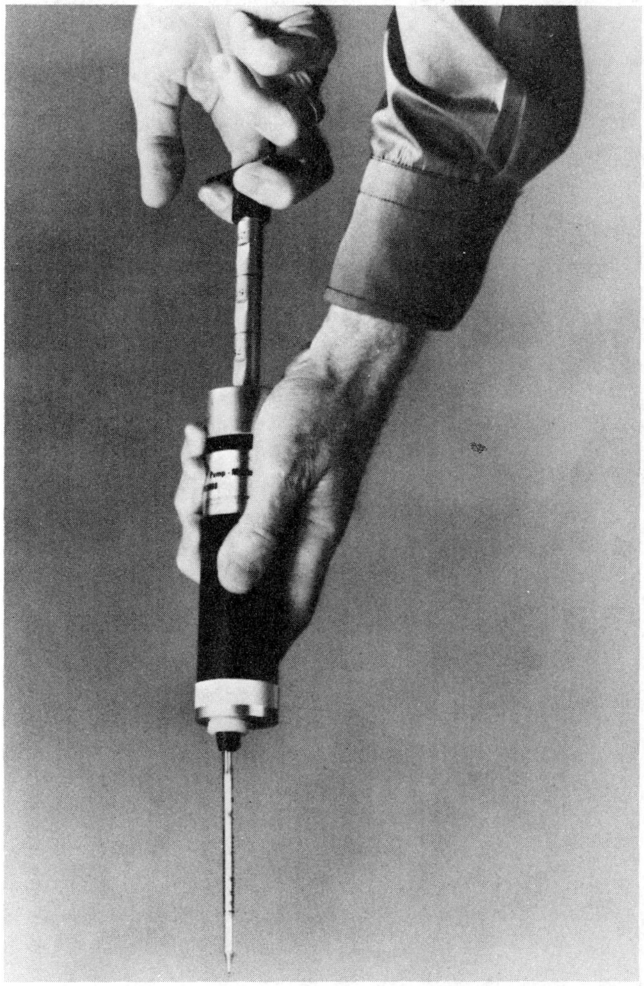

FIG. 4-6K. Length-of-stain toxic gas detector tube and sampling pump.

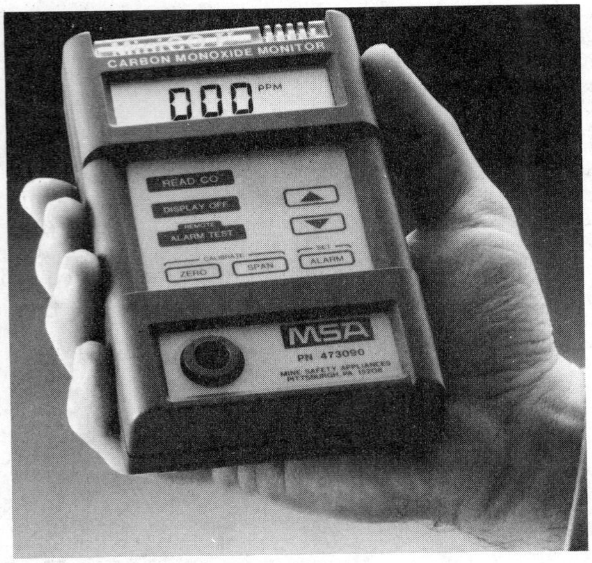

FIG. 4-6L. Electrochemical-type toxic gas indicator and alarm for carbon monoxide monitoring.

FIG. 4-6M. Diffusion sampling combustible gas, oxygen, and toxic gas indicator. (Source: Scott Aviation)

FIG. 4-6N. Sample-draw combustible gas, oxygen, and toxic gas indicator. (Source: Mine Safety Appliances Co.)

BIBLIOGRAPHY

NFPA Codes, Standards, and Recommended Practices

Reference to the following NFPA codes, standards, and recommended practices will provide further information on gas and vapor testing discussed in this chapter. (See the latest *NFPA Catalog* for availability of current editions of the following documents.)

NFPA 70, *National Electrical Code.*

NFPA 325M, *Fire Hazard Properties of Flammable Liquids, Gases, and Volatile Solids.*

Additional Reading

"Air Sampling Instruments," American Conference of Governmental Industrial Hygienists, Cincinnati, OH, latest ed.

"Combustible Gas Detection Instruments, Standard C22.2, No. 152-M1984, Canadian Standards Association, Rexdale, Ontario, 1984.

ANSI Standard 117.1-1989, Safety Requirements for Confined Spaces.

Bukowski, R. W., and Bright, R. G., "Taguchi Semiconductor Sensors as Residential Fire/Smoke Detectors," *Fire Journal*, Vol. 69, No. 3, May 1975, pp. 30-33.

Davidson, R. S., and Peacock, S. J., "Smoke, Fire, and Gas Detection at British Gas Installations," *Communication* of the 52nd Autumn Meeting of the Institution of Gas Engineers, Communication 1298, Institution of Gas Engineers, 1986.

Donohue, M. L., "Working Safely in Confined Spaces," *Fire Chief*, Oct. 1984, pp. 44-46.

Eicker, H., "Early Fire Detection Using Trace Gases in the Airstream," *Glueckauf and Translation*, Vol. 124, No. 10, 1988, pp. 304-309.

Gulland, W. G., "Application of a State-of-the-Art Fire and Gas Detection and Control System," *Proceedings* of the Conference on Facilities, Pipelines, and Measurements: A Workbook for Engineers, American Society of Mechanical Engineers, 1985, pp. 71-73.

Hartz, N. W., "Use of Combustible Gas Indicators," *NFPA Quarterly*, Vol. 52, Apr. 1959, pp. 357-365.

Holtzberg, J. T., "Carbon Monoxide Detectors Revolutionize Fire Protection," *Coal Mining and Processing*, Vol. 18, No. 4, Apr. 1981, pp. 118-120.

Riley, J. F., "Detection and Analysis of Binary Gas Phase Mixtures," *Fire Technology*, Vol. 9, Feb. 1973, pp. 15-23.

Sinha, A. K., Rajwar, D. P., and Ghosh, A. K., "Underground Fire Hazard Detection Through Carbon-Monoxide Monitors," *Journal of Mines, Metals, and Fuels*, Vol. 35, No. 8, Aug. 1987, pp. 365-367.

Srivastava, S. C., *et al*, "Development of the Electrochemical Cell for Carbon Monoxide Measurement," *Journal of Mines, Metals, and Fuels*, Vol. 35, No. 8, Aug. 1987, pp. 184-385.

Swift, R. L., "Testing Equipment for Air Contaminants in the Marine Industry," *Proceedings* of the Marine Chemists Association, National Fire Protection Association, Quincy, MA, 1978.

Welby, P., and Dickinson, K. R., "Monitoring Work Areas for Explosive and Toxic Hazards," *Chemical Engineering*, Vol. 83, No. 22, 1976, pp. 139-145.

Zatek, J. E., "Instruments for Measuring Hazardous Atmospheres," *Fire Journal*, Vol. 64, Sept. 1970, pp. 76-80.

FIRE GUARD SERVICES AND FIRE PROTECTION SURVEILLANCE

Revised by Dean K. Wilson

Containment of fire to its area of origin is made possible by several factors, one of the most important of which is early fire detection.

During normal business hours, most areas of most facilities are occupied. By their presence, the occupants provide fire protection surveillance because they are able to detect a fire when it occurs. A carelessly discarded cigarette, for example, may ignite the contents of a wastebasket; that fire may spread until the entire building is involved. However, someone who discovers the fire while it is still in its incipient stage may be able to extinguish it with a portable fire extinguisher. In some cases, the occupants can also detect conditions, such as a malfunctioning machine, that might lead to a fire.

Similarly, most companies have come to realize that increased security surveillance is vital in guarding against fires of incendiary origin, the numbers of which have already risen at an alarming rate.

Guard services generally serve three purposes in protecting a property against fire loss: (1) to protect the property at times when the management is not present; (2) to facilitate and control the movement of persons into, out of, and within the property; and (3) to carry out procedures for the orderly conduct of some operations on the property. Guards may be facility employees or employees of outside firms established to provide these services on a contract basis. The duties of these individuals may be supplemented or, in some cases, replaced in part by various approved fire and security protective signaling systems.

GUARD SERVICE DIRECTION

In conjunction with fire and explosion protective systems and various other management programs for loss prevention and control, a comprehensive program of fire protection and security surveillance provides a means of: (1) continually monitoring the facility for conditions that might lead to a fire or explosion, (2) promptly notifying the public fire department or private fire brigade that a fire or explosion has occurred, and (3) effectively inhibiting unauthorized access to the facility. Thus, management must determine how this surveillance can be best achieved.

In concept, guards should patrol thoroughly all unoccupied areas of a facility often enough to be able to detect conditions likely to result in a fire or other emergency. These patrols should be supervised in some way so management can verify that the guard is indeed making the patrol tours.

The highly protected risk (HPR) property insurance carriers generally recommend that the first patrol tour begin within one-half hour of vacancy and that subsequent patrol tours be made every hour at night and every other hour (bihourly) during the day. Each tour should not exceed 45 min in actual length, allowing the guard 15 min of rest.

Management should develop a written surveillance plan for both fire protection and security in the facility. To do this, the property manager should determine which areas of the facility are unoccupied during both working and nonworking hours. The property manager should also designate a management representative who will be responsible for overseeing the surveillance program. It is very important that management retain supervisory control of surveillance to maintain program integrity. This representative should review surveillance reports daily and evaluate changes in the facility that might require modification of the surveillance plan.

The facility's fire loss prevention and control manager should be consulted during the establishment of procedures to be followed by guard service personnel. Procedures and instructions to guards should be geared to the specific actions required. General instructions or superficial training are of little value. Meaningful, specific instructions cannot be prepared, however, without an investment of both time and thought by the management of the property.

Management should establish a clear line of succession in event of absences. Even when there are only two guards employed, one should be designated as the leader.

Supervision of guards provided under contract with outside firms should be through the designated representatives of the company providing the guard service. In its

Dean K. Wilson is director of loss prevention training at Industrial Risk Insurers (IRI), Hartford, CT. He is also former chairman of the NFPA Technical Committee on Loss Prevention Procedures and Practices.

contract or supplementary documents, that company should be given details as specific and complete as possible regarding the services expected.

When guards are assigned to patrol a property, management is responsible for providing them with adequate equipment and information with which to safeguard their own health and safety. Potential situations that must be considered include:

1. Sudden illness or injury while the guard is alone at the property.
2. The possibility of a guard being overpowered by an intruder.
3. The development of a situation requiring management decisions.

The first situation can be addressed by equipping guards with a means of prompt, efficient communication, such as portable two-way radios, which would allow them to summon aid.

In the second situation, an intruder may prevent the guard from using any communications equipment. It then becomes necessary to have a system or procedure whereby the guard's failure to transmit a signal or meet a predetermined schedule will be investigated promptly.

Thirdly, situations that require management decisions may arise at times when the property is attended by guards only. Such decisions may involve conditions ranging from the unscheduled arrival of merchandise or supplies to anonymous bomb threats. Guards must have instructions and the means for contacting management personnel.

COMMUNICATIONS EQUIPMENT

Guards should be provided with facilities for communication within and outside the property. A control center should provide a point with which guards may communicate, and the center should have communications facilities to points outside the property. Such a center is needed even when there is very limited guard service. For example, in a facility with only one or two guards, this control center might simply be a room with a telephone. Even with a complete fire and security protective signaling system covering all areas of the property, a control center on the property is necessary.

Where the equipment for guard communications, including guards on watch patrol, requires that signals from guards be monitored, the control center should be provided with an operator. Additional operators needed to effect a 24-hour operator service should be provided at the control center, according to the character of guard service provided. For some services, runners, or guards who can be dispatched to investigate signals, should also be provided.

A directory of names and telephone numbers (including any other information to assist in making emergency calls to the outside) should be kept at the control center in a visible index or other quickly accessible form. This directory should give information about the public fire and police departments, key management personnel, and other outside agencies that may have to be contacted in an emergency.

GUARD PATROL TOUR SUPERVISION

Off-premises guard supervisory service designed to report the performance of a guard may be provided by signaling systems for central station service, remote station protective signaling systems, or proprietary protective signaling systems. Portable watchclocks may also be used to supervise the guard if centralized, immediate supervision is not required.

Tour supervisory systems generally consist of guard patrol tour supervisory initiating devices of some type and a means of recording signals initiated from these devices. Two types of supervisory service systems are: (1) compulsory, and (2) noncompulsory.

Compulsory Tour Supervisory Systems

This system involves one or more "active" guard patrol tour supervisory initiating devices that are installed in conjunction with several "passive" guard patrol tour supervisory initiating devices. These devices are arranged so that the guard must progress in a fixed route from one station to another. Ordinarily, the guard carries some type of device called a "key." The initiating devices are arranged so that the passive devices condition the key so that it may operate the next device, whether that device is active or passive. In addition to conditioning the key for the next device, active initiating devices also either transmit a signal to an on- or off-premises central recording location, or cause a signal to be recorded inside the key which indicates the date and time that the active initiating device was operated. This system is particularly useful when, because of the nature of the facility, it is essential that the guard follow a carefully prescribed route. One disadvantage to this system from a security standpoint is that the tour may not be varied. This is sometimes felt undesirable because a potential intruder who is observing the movement of the guard might be able to readily discern a pattern to the guard's movement.

In many compulsory tour systems, the guard initiates a starting signal at the beginning of a round and initiates a finishing or completion signal at the end of the round. All of the other stations in between would be passive initiating devices.

A fixed schedule of starting and finishing times is arranged in advance when a compulsory tour is monitored by an off-premises facility. If the guard fails to either begin or end a round within the prescribed times, upon the expiration of a "grace" period of usually no more than 10 or 15 min in length, the off-premises monitoring facility will initiate action. Normally, an attempt will be made to contact the guard by telephone. Upon failure to reach the guard, the off-premises monitoring facility will normally dispatch the police department and notify the management of the facility that the guard has failed to respond.

When a compulsory tour system is used in conjunction with a proprietary protective signaling system, the process works much the same, except that, since the receiving location is normally located on the protected premises, the operator at the receiving location will be more readily able to determine why the guard has not begun or ended his/her round.

Noncompulsory Tour Supervisory Systems

In this system, all of the initiating devices are active. The guard progresses from station to station with each initiating device indicating the date and time of the guard operating the station. By following the progression of signals, the off-premises or on-premises monitoring station can follow the progress of the guard during the course of the round. In some cases, combination manual fire alarm stations/guard patrol tour supervisory initiating stations are grouped in the same physical housing. These stations are arranged so that they may be actuated by any person to indicate a fire, but may also be operated by a guard to indicate the progress of his/her tour.

Delinquency Reporting Systems

Some compulsory or noncompulsory tour supervisory systems are arranged so that, rather than reporting every time the guard operates an active initiating device, the system only transmits a signal when the guard has failed to operate the device within a prescribed time period. Such delinquency reporting systems are utilized when it is desired to reduce the amount of signal traffic associated with the guard patrol tour supervisory system. Many remote station protective signaling system guard patrol tour supervisory systems are arranged in this fashion.

Telephone, Radio, and Other Voice Reporting Systems

Occasionally, a guard patrol tour is supervised by means of the guard reporting from a specific location by means of a voice reporting system. Probably the most common system utilizes a telephone system equipped with calling subset identification. When the guard initiates voice communication over such a system, the system indicates and records the specific location from which the guard is calling. Other systems employing means of voice communication, including radio systems, can also be utilized. In some radio systems, a tour supervisory initiating device must be inserted into the radio before the guard establishes patrol tour contact. This device transmits a digital code that gives a specific location, thus indicating that the guard is at the prescribed tour station.

Portable Watchclocks

In many cases, management determines that it is not necessary to provide immediate supervision of the guard patrol tours, and elects to provide retrospective guard patrol tour supervision by means of a stationary or portable watchclock. (See Figure 4-7A.) The records from these devices must be reviewed the following day to determine that the guard has indeed made the prescribed tours and operated all of the tour supervisory initiating devices. While this method lacks the immediacy of the other tour supervisory methods, it is particularly cost effective and is the most common tour supervisory method employed. Traditionally, a spring-wound clock mechanism—either at a single location in the case of a stationary watchclock, or in a portable case that the guard can carry from location to location—is used to drive some type of recording medium. The most common recording medium is a paper disk or a paper tape. In this case, the tour supervisory initiating devices are embossing keys that must be inserted into the portable watchclock and turned, making their impression on the paper tape. The tour supervisory initiating devices for the stationary clock are usually some type of electric switch or, in at least one design, a magneto that must be operated by the guard, causing the stationary clock to record the specific location.

The portable watchclock can be an effective supervisory tool if the control of access to the clock is carefully limited so that the guard cannot have access to the internal mechanism of the watchclock. This means that someone in management should actually open the clock and retrieve the record each day. To safeguard the premature opening of the clock, a tell-tale device places a mark on the paper disk or tape whenever the clock is opened.

Even when a guard service company provides the guard patrol tour service, it is advisable to have management supervise the retrieval of records from the watchclock to prevent any collusion between upper level guards, such as sergeants or lieutenants, and the guards themselves.

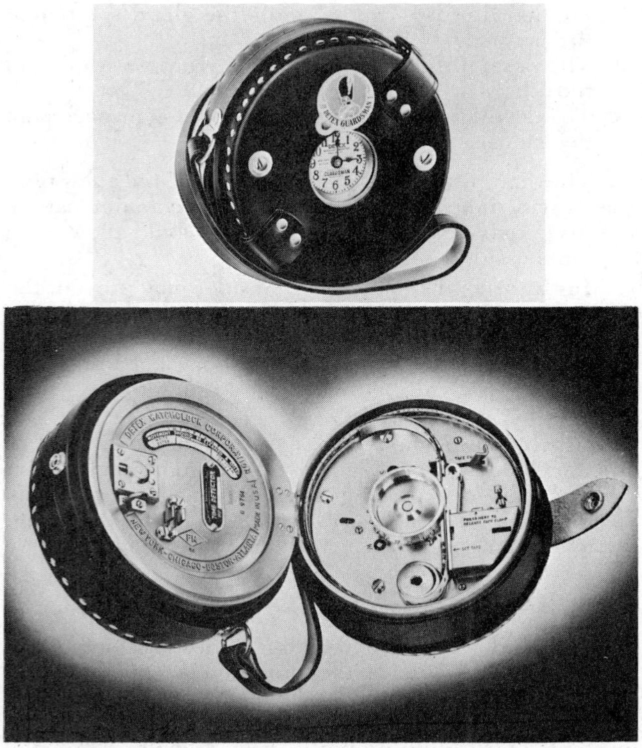

FIG. 4-7A. Front view (top), interior view (bottom) of a portable watchclock. This clock provides an embossed record tape, made directly from type on the recording key. The tape has 24 ruled segments and is synchronized with the clock mechanism. If a guard fails to punch in, the omission is indicated by a prominent white space on the tape. This clock indicates when it was opened. (Source: Detex Corp.)

GUARD SERVICE FUNCTIONS

A sufficient number of guards should be provided to accomplish the needed services. If guards are assigned to other part-time duties in addition to their regular guard services, these duties should be chosen so they will not interfere with regular guard duties.

Guard service can facilitate and control the movement of persons within a property when the number of persons in the property requires such a service. Duties in this category include:

1. Preventing the entry of unauthorized persons who might set a fire or do damage to the facility.
2. Controlling the activities of people authorized to be on the property, but who may not be aware of procedures established for the prevention of fire.
3. Controlling pedestrian and vehicular traffic during exit drills, and evacuating the property or parts of it during emergencies.

4. Controlling gates and vehicular traffic to facilitate access to the property by the public fire department, members of a private fire brigade, and off-duty management personnel in case of fire or emergency.

Guard service should be established to carry out certain procedures for the orderly conduct of the operations on the property, including procedures for fire loss prevention and control, both by personnel associated with the property and outside contractors. Duties in this category include:

1. Checking permits for "hot work," including cutting and welding, and standing by to operate fire extinguishing equipment where necessary.
2. Detecting conditions likely to cause a fire, such as leaks, spills, and faulty equipment.
3. Detecting conditions likely to reduce the effectiveness with which a fire may be controlled, such as portable fire extinguishers not in place, sprinkler valves not open, and water supplies impaired.
4. Performing operations to ensure that fire equipment will function effectively. These may include testing automatic sprinkler and other fixed fire protection systems, including fire pumps, and other equipment related to these systems and assisting in the maintenance of this equipment; checking portable fire extinguishers and fire hose and assisting in pressure tests and maintenance service on these items; testing fire alarm equipment by actuating transmitting devices as required; and checking equipment provided on any fire apparatus and carrying out the periodic tests and maintenance operations required for the apparatus.
5. Promptly discovering a fire and calling the public fire department (also the fire brigade of the property, where there is such a brigade).
6. Operating equipment provided for fire control and extinguishment after giving the alarm and before the response of other persons to the alarm.
7. Monitoring signals of protective signaling systems, such as alarms from manual fire alarm boxes, signals for water flow in sprinkler systems, and signals from systems for detecting fires and abnormal conditions, including trouble signals.
8. Patrolling routes chosen by management to ensure surveillance of all the property at appropriate intervals.
9. Starting up and shutting down certain equipment when no other personnel are provided for this purpose.

PATROL ROUTES AND ROUNDS

Each route to be patrolled should be laid out by the responsible manager. The guard responsible for each route should be given instructions as to all details of the route, and what is expected in covering it. The route should be laid out to prevent shortcuts so that the guard is required to pass through the entire patrol area. A rest period between rounds is reasonable.

Guards should make rounds at intervals determined for the particular situation by management. When operations in the property are normally suspended, rounds should be made hourly, unless management is willing to accept rounds at less frequent intervals. When there are special conditions, such as the presence of exceptional hazards or when protection is impaired, management should institute as many additional rounds as necessary to meet the firesafety requirements of such conditions.

The first round of a patrol should begin as soon as possible after the end of activities of the preceding work shift. The guards should be instructed to make a thorough inspection of all buildings or spaces on the route during their first round. Their instructions should cover the following:

1. Outside doors and gates should be closed and locked. Windows, skylights, fire doors, and fire shutters should be closed.
2. All oily waste, rags, paint residue, rubbish, and similar items should be removed from buildings or placed in approved containers.
3. All fire apparatus should be in place and not obstructed.
4. Aisles should be clear.
5. Motors or machines carelessly left running should be shut off and reported.
6. All offices, conference rooms, and smoking areas should be checked for carelessly discarded smoking materials.
7. All gas and electric heaters, coal and oil stoves, and other heating devices on the premises should be checked.
8. All hazardous manufacturing processes should be left in a safe condition. The temperature of dryers, annealing furnaces, and similar equipment that continue to operate during the night, holidays, and weekends should be noted on all rounds.
9. Hazardous materials, such as gasoline, rubber cement, and other flammable and highly volatile combustibles, should be kept in proper containers or removed from buildings.
10. All sprinkler valves should be open, with gages indicating proper pressures. If not open, the fact should be reported immediately.
11. During cold weather, all rooms should be checked to determine if they are heated properly.
12. All water faucets and air valves found leaking should be closed. If leaks cannot be stopped, the condition should be reported.
13. Particular attention should be given to new construction or alterations that may be in progress.

SELECTION OF GUARDS

Management should require individuals considered for guard service to satisfactorily pass a character investigation. This investigation should attempt to evaluate the individual's reliability, self-control, and potential loyalty to the employer. Applicants for a guard position should be required to be fingerprinted and to give particulars of any police records. The local police should be furnished with this information, should corroborate it, and should ask for checks by other police agencies. The fingerprint data should be cleared with state, national, or appropriate international agencies that maintain clearing facilities for police records. All applicants for a position as a fire or security guard or patrol person should be required to state any military service record and to submit evidence of such service that may assist in an evaluation of the individual's suitability for guard service.

Contracts for guard service should include a provision that the company furnishing guard service will replace any of its employees who, in the judgment of the company purchasing the service, are not qualified.

Management should be satisfied that individuals considered for guard service are mentally alert and have good powers of observation, intelligence, and judgment. Investigation should attempt to evaluate the individual's personality and temperament. Such an evaluation is more realistic than arbitrarily testing education or intelligence, or setting an age limit. Very young people may not qualify because they have not acquired a sense of responsibility or judgment. Very old people may have impaired alertness. Individuals should be sought who are known to be "clear-headed" in an emergency.

Guards should be required to pass an annual written examination dealing with information about the property protected and procedures for fire loss prevention with which they are expected to be familiar.

Management should require that individuals considered for guard service pass an examination to determine whether they are physically able to perform the guard duties to which they will be assigned. Guards should also be required to pass an annual physical examination. The guards do not need to be athletes, but they should not have a heart condition or other physical ailment that might work to their disadvantage in moments of stress.

TRAINING

Management should establish a continuing training program for its guards. Its scope should be established by the manager or by a fire loss prevention and control manager acting for the manager. Courses for guards and fire fighters, available through training programs of vocational training agencies, schools, universities, and other training and educational agencies, should be considered in any training program for guards.

Management should require guards to have completed at least elementary courses of instruction in the use of portable fire equipment and emergency first aid. The time spent in such preliminary training should be a minimum of two working days in each subject. During service, guards should be given not less than the equivalent of two full working days per year of training to increase their knowledge and experience in the use of portable fire extinguishers, first aid, and other useful training. Guards should be required as part of their training to participate in appropriate meetings devoted to prefire planning with operating personnel. Guards can help accomplish this by working together with the public fire department when it establishes its plan for the premises.

Management should require guards to know the location of portable fire extinguishers, hand hoses, standpipes and hydrants, valves controlling sprinkler systems, inside riser valves, post-indicator valves, and sectional valves in the property's own water system. (They also should know how to start fire pumps.) Guards may also need to know the location and purpose of valves controlling water for purposes other than for fire protection, and valves controlling steam, gas, and other services. Management should require guards to know the locations of dangerous machinery or materials and inform them of hazardous manufacturing processes, especially those continuing during the night, holidays, or weekends.

EVALUATING GUARD SERVICE

There are several items to be considered when evaluating guard service.

Tour Records

Management's representative should ensure that:

1. All unoccupied areas of the facility are included in each tour.
2. All key stations or tour supervisory transmitters in each tour have been recorded clearly in a regular hourly pattern at night and in a bi-hourly pattern during the day.
3. Tours last no longer than 45 minutes, allowing for a rest period of at least 15 minutes each hour.
4. Tours begin within one-half hour of the time the area becomes unoccupied and continue to within one-half hour of the resumption of occupancy.
5. The "tell-tale" of a portable or stationary watchclock is recording each time the clock is opened. Look for indications that the clock has been opened more than once a day or at unusual times. This might indicate that unauthorized persons have access to a clock key.

Inspecting Tour Supervisory System Initiating Devices

Key stations, tour supervisory transmitters, or intermediate stations should be inspected once a month to ensure they are firmly attached and sealed with a "tamper" seal and have not been relocated or removed. The key should be checked for damage. If there is evidence of tampering, the key stations, tour supervisory transmitters, or intermediate stations should be checked more often and suitable action taken.

Guards

Management should expect, and is entitled to receive, guard service of the highest quality. Guards must be conscientious in the performance of their duties, note and report all infractions of company regulations, and closely follow the orders given to them.

1. Guards hold positions of trust, which require individuals who are physically able, mentally alert, and morally responsible. Therefore, their physical and emotional stability should be evaluated by appropriate management personnel.
2. Guards must be sufficiently intelligent, calm in the face of an emergency, mature with sound judgment, and possess the physical stamina required for the job.
3. A sufficient number of guards should be provided to maintain proper surveillance in the facility. It is undesirable for guards to be assigned part-time duties unrelated to surveillance. If they are so assigned, however, these duties must not interfere with surveillance responsibilities.
4. Guards should receive full support of management in the performance of their duties.
5. When the guards are facility employees, management should establish the scope of the service and provide necessary training and supervision for the guards.
6. If a contract guard service is used, management should not assume that it will be adequate. Rather, management should prepare detailed specifications and investigate the ability of prospective contractors to meet these specifications. When the contract has been met, management should make sure that its intent is being carried out.
7. Initial and continued training of guards should be by a formal, comprehensive, written program covering all applicable protection procedures. Each guard must be:

- Acquainted with the general nature of the facility's operations, and possess specific knowledge of any hazardous operations.
- Familiar with all of the facility's manual and automatic fire protection equipment. They should be especially aware of the location of all sprinkler valves and know which area each controls. Guards should periodically accompany the person making fire protection equipment inspections, in order to gain a working knowledge of facility protection features and hazards.
- Familiar with the location and operation of manual fire alarm stations and other means of transmitting fire alarms. Such means should be provided throughout the facility so guards can easily report a fire.
- Taught to notify the fire department before attempting to fight the fire.
- Taught how to admit public fire apparatus to the property and how to direct fire department officers to the location of the fire.
- Taught to properly notify company officials when an emergency occurs or when potential trouble is observed.
- Taught to maintain a shift log and to prepare reports to management of observations made and actions taken during tours.

8. Guard service should be integrated into the overall pre-emergency planning program.
9. General and special instructions and other data required by the guards should be written down and kept up-to-date. (See NFPA 601, *Guard Service in Fire Loss Prevention*, and NFPA 602, *Guard Operations in Fire Loss Prevention.*)

While making regular tours throughout the facility, guards must be alert for all emergencies, paying special attention to known hazardous areas. Guards are in a position not only to detect and correct unsafe conditions that might develop into or contribute to a serious fire, but also to discover an incipient fire. Therefore, the guards should be familiar with the fundamentals of fire control and with the proper use of all available extinguishing equipment.

The importance of notifying the fire department before attempting to fight a fire should be stressed in guard training. Guards should report any situation that may endanger the facility, e.g., an exposing fire in adjacent properties. Any unusual condition that the guards cannot correct without assistance must be reported immediately to the proper official so the situation can be remedied without undue delay. Such situations include the interruption of sprinkler service or the failure of heating equipment.

In addition to carefully following written pre-emergency plans, guards must be resourceful and capable of applying common sense to any unusual conditions, e.g., "natural" hazard threats, they may encounter. If the facility is being subjected to freezing weather, for example, the guard should be alert to those areas of the facility where protective systems or process equipment might be vulnerable to freezing damage. Such areas should be checked frequently to ensure the heating system is properly maintaining the temperature necessary to avoid damage. If a thermometer is unavailable, a resourceful guard might set out a small container of water to observe whether the area is approaching a dangerously low temperature. See NFPA 601, *Guard Service in Fire Loss Prevention*, and NFPA 602, *Guard Operations in Fire Loss Prevention*, for further details.

BIBLIOGRAPHY

NFPA Codes, Standards, and Recommended Practices

Reference to the following NFPA codes, standards, and recommended practices will provide further information on fire guard services and fire protection surveillance discussed in this chapter. (See the latest *NFPA Catalog* for availability of current editions of the following documents.)

NFPA 71, *Signaling Systems for Central Station Service.*

NFPA 72, *Protective Signaling Systems.*

NFPA 601, *Guard Service in Fire Loss Prevention.*

NFPA 602, *Guard Operations in Fire Loss Prevention.*

Additional Reading

Accident Prevention Manual, National Safety Council, Chicago, IL, 1981.

"Introduction to Fire Protection," (training course for employees involved in facility safety programs), National Fire Protection Association, Quincy, MA, 1982.

Cote, A. E., ed., *Industrial Fire Hazards Handbook*, 3rd ed., National Fire Protection Association, Quincy, MA, 1990.

Overview Manual, 3rd ed., Industrial Risk Insurers, Hartford, CT, 1989.

Planner, R. G., *Fire Loss Control*, Marcel Dekker, New York, 1979.

"Self Fire Inspection—A New Concept in Fire Safety," *Fire Chief*, Vol. 24, No. 5, May 1980, pp. 34-35.

Moulton, G. A., ed., *NFPA Inspection Manual*, 6th ed., National Fire Protection Association, Quincy, MA, 1989.

SUPPRESSION

Sooner or later, with rare exceptions, someone or something has to extinguish the fire. There are fires that self-extinguish with no specific outside intervention, but each year in the U.S.A., millions of unwanted fires go unstopped until a fire department extinguishes them, and tens of millions of unwanted fires go unstopped until someone or some system on-site extinguishes them. Chapter 6 in Section 1 described the basic physics and chemistry of fire extinguishment (building on the description in Chapter 4 of Section 1 of the basic physics and chemistry of fire initiation and development). Section 5 provides details on extinguishing agents, suppression systems, and the related systems aspects of fire suppression, broadly considered.

As Chapter 1 says, "Water is the most common extinguishing agent." Chapter 1 describes the physical properties of water and the various means by which those properties make fire extinguishment possible. Chapter 1 also addresses the use of additives to enhance the effectiveness of water in extinguishment. Completing the picture of water and fire, Chapter 1 discusses situations where water is ***not*** the extinguishing agent of choice or when it must be applied with unusual care (e.g., to avoid hazards of electric shock). This description of water as a material leads into Chapter 2 (Hydraulics), which reviews the physics of water (and other fluid media) in motion through orifices, nozzles, pipes, and the like.Chapters 3 through 8 describe the elements of the system that fire departments use to deliver water for suppression—quantity of water supply required (Chapter 3), public systems for water distribution (Chapter 4), specialized storage tanks and devices for pulling water from surface sources (Chapter 5), pumps (Chapter 6), methods of conversion of water into a stream to be delivered from nozzle to fire (Chapter 7), and test procedures to make sure everything will work as expected when it is needed (Chapter 8). An additional element involved with delivering outside water to fires in large buildings, standpipes and associated hose systems, is discussed in Chapter 14. Chapters 9 through 12 describe essential aspects of automatic on-site water-based suppression systems (i.e., sprinklers). Chapter 9 reviews the key issues in designing a sprinkler system that is right for its environment, taking into account such factors as the size and configuration of the building and the special hazards that its particular combination of combustibles and activities may present. Chapter 10 provides more mathematical concepts relevant to sprinkler design and effectiveness, including some of the more recently developed concepts, such as response time indexes. Chapter 11 focuses on the special water supply needs of a sprinkler system, and Chapter 12 discusses the many types of sprinkler hardware. Care and maintenance requirements are covered in Chapter 16.

Chapters 13 and 15 address two major specialized systems among sprinklers—fast-response sprinklers (Chapter 13) and systems that deliver water in a fog or specialized water spray (Chapter 15). Then, Chapters 17 through 22 address non-water-based systems—carbon-dioxide-based systems (Chapter 17), halogenated agents and associated systems (Chapter 18), dry-chemical agents and associated systems (Chapter 19), foams and their systems (Chapter 20), the diverse agents and systems designed for extinguishing fires in specific combustible metals (Chapter 21), and miscellaneous other agents and systems (Chapter 22).

Finally, Chapters 23 and 24 address fire extinguishers—the different types and how they should and should not be used.

Also look for these: As noted, Chapters 4 and 6 of Section 1 provide necessary basic science, which is further elaborated in *The SFPE Handbook of Fire Protection Engineering.* The latter also has more detailed guidance on design calculation methods for automatic sprinkler systems, foam systems, and halon systems. Those who work with suppression systems in detail will need The *Automatic Sprinkler Systems Standard and Handbook*; may need other specialized resources, such as NFPA's books on *Automatic Sprinkler and Standpipe Systems* and *Residential Sprinkler Systems*; and are likely to want detailed formal training through seminars, videotapes, manuals, and the like, to produce a working familiarity with these very complex systems. Also, see Chapter 3 of Section 4 for a discussion of the detection and alarm aspects of suppression systems, such as waterflow alarms and supervised systems. Some of the chapters in Section 8 raise special concerns for suppression systems in particular occupancies, and consideration of fire department water delivery systems may be affected by the discussion of fire apparatus in Chapter 10 of Section 9. Finally, in Chapter 9 of Section 10, there is a brief discussion of ways to model the actuation time and conditions for the thermal sensors used in most automatic suppression systems.

WATER AND WATER ADDITIVES FOR FIRE FIGHTING

Revised by Andrew M. Wahl

Water is the most common extinguishing agent. This chapter discusses the properties of water as an extinguishing agent, including both its advantages and limitations.

The basic principles of extinguishment of fire are contained in Section 1, Chapter 4, "Chemistry and Physics of Fire," and Section 1, Chapter 6, "Theory of Fire and Explosion Control." The systems and devices employed for the transportation and application of water as an extinguishing agent are contained in other chapters in this Section. The use of water on specific types of materials, e.g., chemicals, flammable liquids, gases, metals, etc., is covered in more detail in the chapters of Section 3, "Materials, Products, and Environments." See Section 8, Chapter 25, "Nuclear Facilities," for guidance on planning fire protection, including the use of water, for facilities containing radioactive materials.

PHYSICAL PROPERTIES

The physical properties that make water a good extinguishing agent are:

1. At ordinary temperature water is a heavy, relatively stable liquid.
2. The melting of 1 lb (0.45 kg) of ice into water at 32°F (0°C) absorbs 143.4 Btu (151.3 kJ), which is the heat of fusion of ice.
3. One Btu is required to raise the temperature of 1 lb of water 1°F, which is the specific heat of water. Therefore, raising the temperature of 1 lb of water from 32°F to 212°F requires 180 Btu. (In S.I. units, the specific heat capacity of water is 4.186 kJ/kg K.)
4. The latent heat of vaporization of water, i.e., converting 1 lb (0.45 kg) of water to steam at a constant temperature is 970.3 Btu per lb (2254.8 kJ/kg) at atmospheric pressure.
5. When water is converted from liquid to vapor, its volume at atmospheric pressure increases about 1,600 times. This large volume of water (saturated steam) displaces an equal volume of air surrounding a fire, thus reducing the volume of air (oxygen) available to sustain combustion.

Other than water, there is no material readily available which has all these characteristics. Water applied in the form of ice or snow would provide even better cooling effect than plain water because the energy from the fire must first convert the ice or snow to water [143.4 Btu/lb (333.2 kJ/kg)], and then the energy is needed to convert the water to steam [970.3 Btu/lb (2254.8 kJ/kg)].

EXTINGUISHING PROPERTIES

A fire can be extinguished only if an effective agent is applied at the point where combustion is occurring. For hundreds of years, the principal method of extinguishing fires has been to direct a stream of water at the base of the fire, and this method is still used widely today. A more efficient method is to apply water in spray form, which increases the cooling effect and conversion of water to steam.

Extinguishment by Cooling

In most cases, if the surface of the burning material is cooled below the temperature at which it will give off sufficient vapor to support combustion, the fire will be extinguished. Surface cooling is not usually effective on gaseous products and flammable liquids that have flash points below the temperature of the applied water. Water is generally not recommended for flammable liquids with a flash point below 100°F (37.8°C).

The amount of water required to extinguish a fire depends on how hot the fire is. How quickly a fire is extinguished depends on how quickly the water is applied, how much of it is applied, and what form of water is applied. It is best to apply water so that the maximum amount of heat will be absorbed. Water absorbs the most heat when it is converted into steam, and it will be converted into steam more easily from droplets (spray) than from a solid stream.

Much theoretical information is available on the factors that affect the rates of heat absorption and vaporization of water droplets. Because these factors cannot be

Andrew M. Wahl, P.E., is a professional fire protection engineering consultant with Rolf Jensen & Associates, Inc., Fairfax, VA, and serves as a member of the NFPA Foam-Water Sprinkler Committee.

closely controlled under most actual fire conditions, they cannot be used for accurate fireground calculations.

Water spray cools a fire according to the following principles:

1. The rate of heat transfer is proportional to the exposed surface of the liquid. For a given quantity of water, the surface is greatly increased by conversion to droplets.
2. The rate of heat transfer depends on the temperature difference between the water and the surrounding air or burning material.
3. The rate of heat transfer also depends on the vapor content of the air.
4. The heat absorbing capacity of water depends upon the distance it traveled and its velocity near the fire (heat source) and fire plume. (This factor must take into account the necessity for projecting a suitable volume of water to the fire.)

When the heat absorption rate of the water spray approaches the total heat release rate of the fire, fire control begins. When the heat absorption rate of the water spray exceeds the heat release rate of the fire, fire extinguishment is achieved. Other factors to consider in fire control and extinguishment include heat losses through openings, and heat losses to walls, ceilings, and floors.

Droplet size: Calculations show that the optimum diameter of a water droplet is in the range of 0.01 to 0.04 in. (0.3 to 1.0 mm), and that the best results are obtained when the droplets are fairly uniform in size. (See Figure 5-1A.) No present discharge device is capable of producing completely uniform droplets, although many discharge devices spray droplets that are fairly uniform over a broad range of pressures. The droplet must be formed near the base of the flame or be large enough to have sufficient energy to reach the point of combustion despite air resistance, the opposing force of gravity, any air currents, and the fire plume. When water droplets are too small, they can be deflected by the fire plume, or evaporate before they reach the base of the fire.

Wetting combustible materials is a method often employed to prevent ignition of unburned materials. If combustibles absorb water, it takes longer to ignite them because the water must be evaporated before they can get hot enough to burn.

Extinguishment by Smothering

When water is applied to a fire and enough steam is generated, air can be displaced or excluded. Fires in certain materials can be extinguished by this smothering action, which is quicker if the steam generated can be confined to the flame/combustible gases/fuel interface. The process of heat absorption by steam ends when the steam starts to condense, a change which requires heat release from the steam. When this happens, visible clouds of water vapor form. When such condensation occurs above the fire, it has no cooling effect on the burning material. However, the steam can carry heat away from the fire if it can dissipate itself into clouds of water vapor above the fire.

Fires in ordinary combustibles are normally extinguished by the cooling effect of water—not by the smothering effect created by the generation of steam. Although the latter might suppress flames, it usually cannot extinguish such fires.

Water may be used to smother a burning flammable liquid when the liquid has a flash point above 100°F (37.8°C), a specific gravity of 1.1 or heavier, and is not water soluble. To achieve this most effectively, a foam concentrate is added to the water, forming a foam solution. The water must then be applied gently to the surface of the flammable liquid.

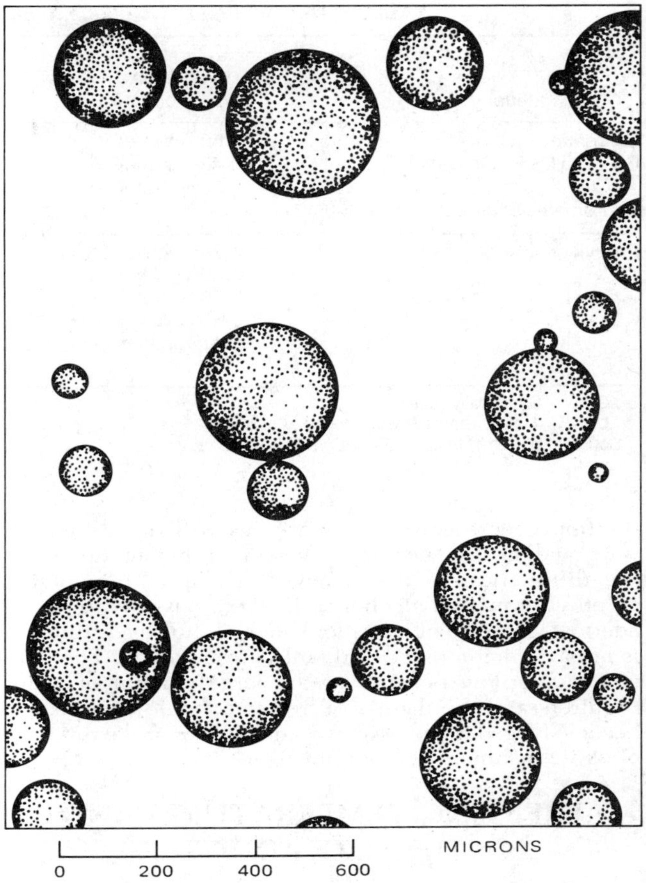

FIG. 5-1A. Diameters of typical droplets of water spray. (Source: National Board of Fire Underwriters, Research Report No. 10)

In cases where oxygen is produced while a burning material decomposes, smothering by any agent is not possible.

Extinguishment by Emulsification

An emulsion is formed when immiscible liquids are agitated together and one of the liquids is dispersed throughout the other. Extinguishment by this process can be achieved by applying water to certain viscous flammable liquids, since the effect of cooling the surfaces of such liquids prevents the release of flammable vapors. With some viscous liquids (such as No. 6 fuel oil), the emulsification is a "froth" which retards the release of flammable vapors. Care must be used on liquids of appreciable depth, however, because frothing may spread the burning liquids over the sides of the container. A relatively strong, coarse water spray is normally used for emulsification. Avoid a solid stream of water, as it will cause violent frothing.

Extinguishment by Dilution

Fires in water-soluble flammable materials may, in some instances, be extinguished by dilution. The percentage of

TABLE 5-1A. ***Antifreeze Solutions to be Used if Public Water is Connected to Sprinklers***

Material	Solution (By Volume)	Specific Gravity at 60°F (15.6°C)	Freezing Point SDF	Freezing Point SDC
Glycerine C.P. or U.S.P. Grade*	50% Water	1.133	−15	−26.1
	40% Water	1.151	−22	−30.0
	30% Water	1.165	−40	−40.0
Hydrometer Scale 1.000 to 1.200				
Propylene Glycol	70% Water	1.027	± 9	−12.8
	60% Water	1.034	− 6	−21.1
	50% Water	1.041	−26	−32.2
	40% Water	1.045	−60	−51.1
	Hydrometer Scale 1.000 to 1.200 (Subdivisions 0.002)			

* C.P. —Chemically pure.
U.S.P.—United States Pharmacopoeia 96.5%.
Source: NFPA 13, *Installation of Sprinkler Systems.*

dilution necessary varies greatly, as will the volume of water and the time necessary for extinguishment. For example, dilution can be used successfully in a fire involving an ethyl or methyl alcohol spill if it is possible to get an adequate mixture of water and alcohol; however, dilution is not a common practice if tanks are involved. The danger of overflow because of the large amount of water required, and the danger of frothing should the mixture become heated to the boiling point of water, make this form of extinguishment seldom practical.

FREEZING TEMPERATURES AND ANTIFREEZE ADDITIVES

Because water freezes at 32°F (0°C), its use as an extinguishing agent is limited in climates or situations where freezing temperatures are encountered. There are several methods commonly used to prevent problems of freezing. These include using dry pipe sprinkler systems in lieu of wet pipe systems, circulating or heating tank water supplies held for fire protection purposes, adding freezing-point depressants to the water, or a combination of these.

The water-soluble freezing-point depressant in fire equipment most widely used is calcium chloride with a corrosion-inhibitor additive. Calcium chloride solutions are not used when fire protection systems are supplied by public water connections. Table 5-1A gives data on antifreeze solution amounts needed for various low temperatures.

Sodium chloride (common salt) is unsatisfactory because of its limited ability to depress the freezing point of water and because it is highly corrosive.

Sprinkler Systems

Chemically pure glycerine (U.S. Pharmacopoeia 96.5 percent grade) or pure propylene glycol can be used to depress the freezing point of water in portions of water suppression systems connected to public water supplies if authorized by local health or water authorities. Diethylene glycol, ethylene glycol, or calcium chloride, as well as glycerine or propylene glycol, can be used for the same purposes where public water is not connected to the system. Both ethylene and diethylene glycol are poisonous, and cannot be permitted to contaminate drinking water. Tables 5-1A and 5-1B give data on the amounts needed for the various low temperatures.

Water-type Extinguishers

Alkali-metal salt solutions provide protection against low temperatures as low as –40°F (–40°C). Only the antifreeze solutions specified by the manufacturers should be used. Glycol solutions should not be used in extinguishers because the amount required to protect against freezing would be high, i.e., a 52.5 percent solution of ethylene glycol would be needed to achieve –40°F (–40°C) freezing point. Such amounts would alter the effectiveness of the extinguisher and could also lead to complications if the water should "boil off" and leave a strong concentration of the glycol which, under certain conditions, could be ignited.

Efforts have been made to develop other additives that can be mixed with water to lower the freezing point to –65°F (–54°C). This work has been largely stimulated by increased activity in extremely low-temperature areas, with most of the research being done by the U.S. armed forces. To date, formulas of lithium chloride, lithium chloride-calcium chloride, and lithium chloride-anhydrous sodium chromate have been used successfully. No commercial use of these solutions is known, although the U.S. Naval Research Laboratory has developed a lithium chloride solution for fire extinguishers exposed to low temperatures of –65°F (–54°C).

SURFACE TENSION AND WETTING AGENT ADDITIVES

The relatively high surface tension of plain water slows its ability to penetrate burning combustibles, and impedes its spread throughout any closely packed, baled, or stacked materials. Immersion of burning combustibles in water is rarely practical. If a fire originates or burrows in a mass of combustibles, it is necessary either to dismantle the mass or use a wetting agent additive to lower the surface tension of the water. Many chemicals can be used as wetting agents, but few are good extinguishing agents because they are toxic, corrosive, or unstable when mixed with water so it can penetrate the dense material. Minimum requirements for wetting agents for fire protection purposes are contained in NFPA 18, *Wetting Agents*. The purpose of NFPA 18 is to set forth requirements for wetting agent additives that will improve the fire fighting properties of plain water without making it harmful to personnel, property, or equipment.

TABLE 5-1B. ***Antifreeze Solutions to be Used if Public Water is not Connected to Sprinklers***

Material	Solution (By Volume)	Specific Gravity at 60°F (15.6°C)	Freezing Point SDF	Freezing Point SDC
Glycerine		If glycerine is used, see Table 5-1A.		
Diethylene Glycol	50% Water	1.078	−13	−25.0
	45% Water	1.081	−27	−32.8
	40% Water	1.086	−42	−41.1
	Hydrometer Scale 1.000 to 1.120 (Subdivisions 0.002)			
Ethylene Glycol	61% Water	1.056	−10	−23.3
	56% Water	1.063	−20	−28.9
	51% Water	1.069	−30	−34.4
	47% Water	1.073	−40	−40.0
	Hydrometer Scale 1.000 to 1.120 (Subdivisions 0.002)			
Propylene Glycol		If propylene glycol is used, see Table 5-1A		
Calcium Chloride 80 ***"Flake"***	Lb $CaCl_2$ per gal of Water			
*Fire Protection Grade**	2.83	1.183	0	-17.8
Add corrosion inhibitor	3.38	1.212	-10	-23.3
of sodium bichromate	3.89	1.237	-20	-28.9
1/4 oz per gal water	4.37	1.258	-30	-34.4
	4.73	1.274	-40	-40.0
	4.93	1.283	-50	-45.6

* Free from magnesium chloride and other impurities.
Source: NFPA 13, *Installation of Sprinkler Systems.*

Wetting agents are effective because they decrease the surface tension of the water, thus increasing the amount of free surface available for heat absorption. There is less water run-off, and the water is therefore more efficient. In the United States, UL lists wetting agents according to their qualities and their extinguishing abilities on Class A or Class B fires, or both. Wetting agents used in fire fighting and fire protection are no more corrosive than plain water to brass, bronze, and copper, although they tend to accelerate corrosion of some metals due to the cleaning and penetrating action of the concentrates. The use of containers made of materials such as cast iron, aluminum, zinc, galvanized steel, lead or lead-coated iron, die-cast alloys (such as white metal, zinc, etc.), or "air-dried" types of coatings (which may include plastics, oil paint, lacquers, or asphalt) should be avoided. Wetting agent solutions should only be used with appropriate equipment.

"Wet water" (plain water plus a wetting agent) is chiefly used to penetrate porous surfaces and allow the solution to reach hidden areas of burning combustibles (e.g., a "fire-packed" bale of cotton or stacked hay) and to penetrate the subsurface of ordinary combustibles to prevent rekindling. Wet water is sometimes used on grass, brush, or forest fires. Generally, these fires are more properly and easily handled by "thickened" water. (See the following section.)

Wet water has the same limitations as plain water on fires in chemicals that react with water, such as sodium, calcium carbide, etc. The use of wetting-agent solutions on flammable and combustible liquid fires is not common since Halon 1301, Halon 1211, carbon dioxide, dry chemicals, or foam are normally used on these types of fires. Wet water should not be used on flammable or combustible liquid fires if the liquids are water soluble (such as the alcohols, glycols, and some ketones).

In general, wet-water solutions should not be used on live electrical equipment because of the conductivity of the solution. Spray or fog, however, might be used with caution. Wet water, due to its penetrating characteristics, may have more harmful effects on motors, transformers, and similar equipment than plain water. Any electrical equipment that has been penetrated by wet water should be thoroughly flushed and cleaned before it is returned to service.

Wetting agents may be either premixed with water or added to the water through suitable proportioning equipment at the time the water is being used. Mixing wetting agents from different manufacturers, or mixing a wetting agent with mechanical or chemical foam concentrates, is not recommended. Distinction must be made between wetting agents and wetting-agent foams and other detergent-type foams (high-expansion foam) and film-forming foam agents. Methods of measuring the effect of the addition of a wetting agent to water to lower the surface tension are given in the appendix of NFPA 18, *Wetting Agents*.

VISCOSITY AND ADDITIVES TO THICKEN WATER

The relatively low viscosity of water makes it tend to run off surfaces quickly and limits its ability to blanket a fire by forming a barrier on the surface of combustible materials. Additives to make water more viscous ("thickened" water) make the use of water more efficient on certain types of fires.

Viscous water has had one of several thickening agents added to it. In proper proportions, viscous water seems to have the following advantages over plain water in that it:

1. Sticks and clings more readily to the burning fuel.
2. Spreads itself out in a continuous coating or film over the fuel surface.
3. Develops in a layer several times the thickness of plain water.
4. Absorbs heat proportional to the amount of water present.

5. Projects somewhat farther and higher from straight-stream nozzles.
6. Forms a tough, dry film after drying which helps seal the fuel from oxygen.
7. Resists wind drift in some applications (such as from aircraft in forest fire fighting).

Disadvantages of viscous water may be that it:

1. Does not penetrate the fuel as well as plain or wet water.
2. Increases friction loss in hose or pipe.
3. Increases water droplet size (where fine sprays are needed, they cannot be secured as readily).
4. Increases the slipperiness of surfaces, making it more difficult to walk in areas where it has been applied.
5. Increases handling problems and logistics of fire operations because it takes time to mix viscosity agents with water. (Under some conditions, stored solutions can lose viscosity, principally through water temperature changes and possible bacterial or chemical contamination.)

To date, most of the application research has been directed at fighting forest fires. A detailed report was prepared by the NFPA Forest Committee in cooperation with the U.S. Forest Service and other forest fire control specialists.[1] Plain water is often capable of handling ordinary brush, grass, and forest fires; in some situations, such as burrowing fires in a mass of combustibles, "wet" water is preferred. Viscous water is most effective on very hot fires, whether in forests or structural fuels, and where radiation may spread the fire.

Two viscosity agents used in forest fire control are CMC (sodium carboxymethylcellulose) and Gelgard (a trade-name product of the Dow Chemical Company). Other viscosity agents are available. The agents are desirable for the following reasons:

1. Only a small quantity of dry powder is necessary for a batch mix.
2. It takes only a few minutes to mix an adequate batch.
3. Near-maximum viscosity is reached within the batch mix period, and the viscosity is retained indefinitely (assuming no contamination or spoilage).
4. Their cost is reasonable.
5. They are nontoxic and noncorrosive.
6. They pump easily.
7. They provide a good stream pattern.
8. They provide good coverage over the fuels.

Bentonite clay (montmorillonite) has been used as a short-term fire retardant and a slurry in water and produces a heavy coat of water. Longer-term retardants are ammonium phosphates and ammonium sulfates. The phosphates are about 1.5 times as effective as ammonium sulfate, since the former seem effective against both flaming and glowing ignition, while the sulfates seem to be effective only in flaming ignition. Two solid ammonium phosphate chemicals notable for their fire-retardant and fire-extinguishing capabilities are DAP (diammonium phosphate) and MAP (monoammonium phosphate). Viscous retardant solutions employing DAP and CMC are available commercially, as are a liquid ammonium phosphate concentrate and an ammonium sulfate fire retardant.

The NFPA Forest Committee has prepared a special publication covering the use of aircraft for reconnaissance, fire attack, and control of these types of fires.[2]

ADDITIVES TO MODIFY FLOW CHARACTERISTICS

Friction loss in fire hose is always a problem for fire fighters. The longer the hose or the more water pumped through it, the greater the pressure loss. With a smooth fire hose lining, most of the pressure loss is the result of friction between particles of water generated by the turbulence in the flowing stream. When flow is either smooth or laminar, the friction loss tends to be very low with a slow stream of water; however, the amount of water delivered under laminar flow is generally too low for fire fighting. Fire fighting requires high-velocity streams that generate turbulence which, in turn, results in friction between water particles. This friction accounts for about 90 percent of the pressure loss in fire hose. The friction between the flowing water and the interior hose wall accounts for only 5 to 10 percent of the loss.

Until 1948 it was generally believed that not much could be done to reduce friction loss. At that time, trace quantities of certain polymers were found to reduce friction loss of turbulent streams. Most researchers report that linear polymers (polymers that form a single straight-line chemical chain with no branches) are the most effective in reducing turbulent frictional losses and, of these, poly (polyethylene oxide) is the most effective. Friction-reducing efficiency is a direct function of polymer linearity.

Poly is nontoxic, has no effects on plants or marine life, and will degrade in sunlight. It is a long linear chain, high molecular weight polymer, and is 2 to 3 times more effective as a friction reduction agent than other materials tested to date. It is an opaque, white slurry that has no odor and weighs 9.1 lb per gal (1.1 kg/L) and must be kept within 0 to 120°F (–17 to 49°C). When it is injected into the hose stream, it dissolves completely and does not separate. It is compatible with all fire fighting equipment and is useful in both fresh and salt water. One gallon of additive treats 6,000 gal (22 710 L) of water and achieves at least a 40 percent greater water delivery.

Tests conducted by the New York City Fire Department and Union Carbide Corporation[3] found that in present systems without poly, a 1-in. (25 mm) booster hose will deliver approximately 20 gpm (76 L/min). However, with poly and a change in nozzle design, 75 gpm (284 L/min) were delivered during the test. A 1½-in. (38 mm) hose delivered 250 gpm (946 L/min), or as much as a 2½-in. (64 mm) hose without the additive. With the additive, a 2½-in. (64 mm) hose was able to deliver more water than a 3-in. (76 mm) hose, and nearly as much water as a 3½-in. (89 mm) hose.

These tests also showed that the additive nearly doubled the nozzle pressure. The stream's reach was increased by nearly 30 percent, and the stream was more coherent. Little effect was found on the fog nozzle sprays other than that the water spray seemed to be more dense.

OPACITY AND REFLECTIVITY

Tests conducted at UL using water spray to provide exposure protection to a sheet metal surface from a gasoline fire indicate that, when the spray is applied as a thin film of water over the sheet metal, the temperature of the metal was contained within limits which protected the metal from significant damage. This was not true, however, when the water spray was adjusted so that it did not touch the sheet metal but did provide a water curtain between the metal and the fire. In this latter case, the temperatures of the metal were three to four times greater than when the water flowed over the metal. These tests may indicate that, because of its lack of opacity, water does not prevent the passage of radiant heat well. The principal value of water used to protect exposures is from the cooling obtained by evaporation of a water film on the exposed surfaces.

NFPA 13, *Installation of Sprinkler Systems*, calls for outside sprinklers for protection against exposure fires to be positioned so that the water will thoroughly wet exposed glass windows and run down over the window sash and the glass, wetting the entire window as much as possible. Similar recommendations require that as much of the cornice as possible be wetted when cornice sprinklers are installed. These rules reflect the experimental evidence.

In England, tests have been run to measure the transmission of radiant heat through water sprays from two types of nozzles.[4] The tests proved that the transmission of this kind of heat depends mostly on nozzle design, and that, with certain nozzles, a water curtain of low transmission could be produced for water flows comparable to those of sprinkler installations. Fire fighters have, of course, used water curtains in situations where it was too hot or dangerous for them to remain exposed to flames and heat.

ELECTRICAL CONDUCTIVITY OF WATER

Water in its natural state contains impurities that make it conductive. If water is applied to fires involving live electrical equipment, a continuous circuit might be formed which would conduct electricity back to the user and cause a shock, especially if there are high voltages or potentials. Foam-type extinguishing agents are very conductive. The amount of current, rather than the voltage, determines the extent of the shock. Principal variables, assuming contact with a live electrical charge, are:

1. The voltage and amount of current flowing.
2. The "break-up" of the stream as a result of the nozzle design, the pressures used, and the wind conditions. This break-up influences the conductivity of the stream because the air spaces formed between the droplets interrupt the electrical path to ground. Modern water spray nozzles and combination straight-stream spray nozzles, the latter in the spray position, provide for effective dispersion of the water droplets. The hazards of these are less than those of solid streams of water.
3. The purity of the water and the relative resistivity of the water.
4. The length and cross-sectional area of the water stream.
5. The resistance to ground through a person's body as influenced by location (whether on wet ground or not), skin moisture, the amount of current the body can endure, the length of exposure to the current, and other factors, such as protective clothing.
6. The resistance to ground through the hose.

Conductivity and Hazard of Shock

There is some danger to fire fighters directing streams of water onto wires of less than 600 V to ground from any distance likely to be met under ordinary fire fighting conditions. But it is dangerous if fire fighters, standing either in puddles of water or on moist surfaces, come into contact with live electrical equipment. In such cases, the fire fighters' bodies complete an electrical circuit, and the current from the electrical equipment relayed through their bodies is more readily grounded than if it were conveyed through dry, nonconductive surfaces. Rubber boots often contain enough carbon black to permit the passage of current through the body, and should not be relied upon for protection.

Research conducted by Underwriters Laboratories Inc. on electric fences indicates that there are differences in the electric current to which individuals may be safely subjected, and that the maximum continuous (uninterrupted) current to which an individual may be safely subjected is 5 ma (milliamperes) ac applied on the surface of the body.[5]

Impurities in water (mostly the mineral content) also affect its conductivity. Tests of the resistivity of public water supplies in Indiana showed results ranging from 710 to 5,400 ohms per cm^3; the lowest values were found in supplies from deep wells. The resistivity of deep well supplies ranged between 1,000 and 2,000 ohms per cm^3, and the resistivity of river waters was about 4,000 ohms per cm^3. In tests conducted by the Commonwealth Edison Company in cooperation with the Chicago Fire Department, the resistivity of Chicago River water ranged from 1,671 to 2,393 ohms per cm^3.[6] At the time the tests were made, the normal hydrant water in the Chicago area had a resistivity of about 3,800 ohms per cm^3.

Safe Distances from Live Equipment

From time to time many authorities have tried to determine safe distances between nozzles and live electrical equipment. The bibliography at the end of this chapter cites some of the more important papers on this subject.

The conductivity of water streams varies according to the type of equipment from which they are expelled, such as: (1) hand-held or manually supported solid-stream nozzles, (2) hand-held water spray (water fog) nozzles, (3) fixed water spray systems for fire protection services, and (4) plain water and water solution portable fire extinguishers.

Data available on the minimum safe distances between manually supported solid-stream hose lines and live electrical equipment carrying voltages higher than 600 V are not wholly consistent, because the results of different tests vary. The reasons for these variances are: the different testing methods used, the variances in the purposes of the tests, the limitations of the tests (necessitated by the physical circumstances and available equipment), and the fact that the same voltages were not used in all of the tests.

The American Insurance Services Group (AISG) (formerly AIA) suggests the distances given in Table 5-1C between solid-stream nozzles (dispensing fresh water) and electrical conductors or equipment carrying voltages higher than 600 V to be the minimum for safety.[7] The AISG data are based on tests run in the 1930s; thus, the voltages given do not correspond to present-day, commonly encountered ranges, nor does the data extend to the higher ranges now widely used. The AISG cautions that, for streams from contaminated or salt water, or where additives have been introduced into the water, it is not possible to give simple rules due to the variances in the conductivity of the water.

Some limited tests made in 1958 by the Hydroelectric Power Commission of Ontario, in cooperation with the Office of the Fire Marshal of Ontario, Canada,[8] resulted in recommendations for minimum safe distances from live electrical equipment for a ⅝-in. (16 mm) solid-stream nozzle. (See Table 5-1D.) The report recommends that solid streams greater than ⅝ in. (16 mm) should not be used near

TABLE 5-1C. *Distances Between Solid Stream Nozzles (Fresh Water) and Electrical Conductors*

		Diameter of Nozzle Orifice			
		1⅛ in. (29 mm)		1½ in. (38 m)	
	Voltage	Minimum Safe Distance			
Voltage To Ground	Between Conductors	Feet	Meters	Feet	Meters
635	1,100	6	1.8	9	2.7
1,270	2,200	11	3.6	16	4.9
1,905	3,300	15	4.6	22	6.7
3,175	5,500	18	5.5	27	8.2
4,215	6,600	19	5.8	29	8.8
6,350	11,000	20	6.1	30	9.1
12,700	22,000	25	7.6	33	10.1
19,050	33,000	30	9.1	40	12.2

TABLE 5-1D. *Limit of Safe Approach to Live Electrical Equipment*[8]

		⅝ in. (16 mm) Solid Stream Nozzle*	
		Minimum Safe Distance	
Voltage To Ground	Voltage Between Conductors	Feet	Meters
2,400	4,160	15	4.6
4,800	8,320	20	6.1
7,200	12,500	20	6.1
8,000	13,800	20	6.1
14,400	24,900	25	7.6
16,000	27,600	25	7.6
25,000	44,000	30	9.1
66,000	115,000	30	9.1
130,000	230,000	30	9.1

* Nozzle pressure 100 psi (690 kPa) water resistance 600 ohms per cubic inch.

live electrical equipment, but the tests were limited to a maximum stream distance of 30 ft (9.1 m). Larger nozzles might produce sufficient stream dispersion over longer distances, which would permit their use.

The results of tests made in 1934 for the Fire Brigade of Paris, France,[9] present perhaps the most comprehensive guide. (See Table 5-1E.) The distances are based on preventing the transmission of a 1-ma current to a fire fighter in contact with a nozzle or hose. The tests covered only voltages to ground ranging from 115 to 150,000 V, and the groupings of the voltages do not correspond to current standard U.S. voltages. The maximum size of the nozzle used is also nonstandard in the United States.

The preceding information indicates that definite shock hazards exist unless adequate distances are kept, and that these distances can only be estimated from the available data. It is difficult for fire fighters in the field to know precisely what electrical potentials exist in any given situation. For this reason, and those given below, it is best, whenever possible, to use water spray streams rather than solid streams.

As noted before, water spray reduces the conductivity hazard. The design of the nozzle and the character of the spray determines the amount of leakage current that can actually flow in the stream, and each nozzle should be tested to determine precisely the characteristics it possesses. Tests that have been made on various commercial water spray nozzles indicate that a minimum distance of 4 ft (1.2 m) should be maintained for voltages to ground up to about 10 kV. This distance is actually no greater than is sensible to prevent an operator from getting dangerously close to live electrical equipment. Distances should be increased when attacking fires involving live electrical equipment operating above this voltage. Figure 5-1B shows the results of four researchers, as analyzed by the UK Fire Offices' Committee, Joint Fire Research Organization.[10]

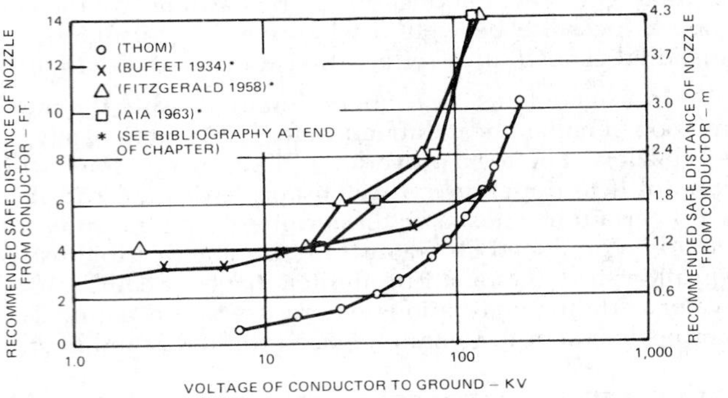

FIG. 5-1B. ***Variation of safe distance with conductor voltage for spray nozzles.***

The Toledo Edison Company made tests in which water was discharged onto a screen at a potential to ground of 80,500 V (equivalent to a system or line voltage of 138 kV phase-to-phase). As a consequence, the Edison Electric Institute in 1967 adopted the following safety rules (the distance in these rules will limit leakage currents to less than 1 ma):

1. Using all hand-held water spray nozzles, the minimum approach distance is 10 ft (3 m).
2. Using hand-held, 1½-in. (38 mm) straight (solid) stream nozzles, the minimum approach distance is 20 ft (6 m).
3. Using hand-held, 2½-in. (64 mm) straight (solid) stream nozzles, the minimum approach distance is 30 ft (9 m).

It is better not to use combination nozzles to fight fires in live electrical equipment because a solid stream could accidentally be used instead of a spray. When such hand-held nozzles must be used on live electrical equipment, fire fighters should be sure they have the desired spray pattern before applying the stream. The use of spray nozzles on "applicators" increases the possibility of accidental contact between the nozzle and live electrical equipment, and most authorities recommend that they not be used.

Clearance from Fixed Water Spray Systems

Fixed water spray systems are used extensively to protect high-value and/or critical electrical equipment, such as transformers, oil switches, and motors. These systems are designed to provide effective fire control, extinguishment, prevention, or exposure protection. NFPA 15, *Water-Spray Fixed Systems for Fire Protection*, gives installation recommendations for such systems, and includes a table of recommended clearances between water spray equipment and unenclosed or uninsulated live electrical components at other-than-ground potential. (See Table 5-1F.) Modern prac-

TABLE 5-1E. ***Minimum Safe Distances Between Hose Nozzles and Live Electrical Equipment Recommended for the Paris, France, Fire Brigade*** [9]

		Diameter of Nozzle Orifice					
		¼ in. (6 mm)		¾ in. (19 mm)		1¼ in. (32 mm)	
		Safe Distance					
Voltage to Ground	Voltage Between Conductors	Feet	Meters	Feet	Meters	Feet	Meters
115	230	1.6	0.50	3.3	1.00	6.6	2.00
460	480	2.5	0.75	9.8	3.00	16.4	5.00
3,000	5,195	6.6	2.00	16.4	5.00	32.8	10.00
6,000	10,395	8.2	2.50	19.7	6.00	39.4	12.00
12,000	20,785	9.8	3.00	21.4	6.50	49.2	15.00
60,000	103,820	14.8	4.50	39.4	12.00	72.2	22.00
150,000	259,800	19.7	6.00	49.2	15.00	82.0	25.00

TABLE 5-1F. ***Clearance From Water Spray Equipment to Live Uninsulated Electrical Components***

Nominal System Voltage (kv)	Maximum System Voltage (kv)	Design BIL (kv)	Minimum* Clearance (in.)	(mm)
To 13.8	14.5	110	7	178
23	24.3	150	10	254
34.5	36.5	200	13	330
46	48.3	250	17	432
69	72.5	350	25	635
115	121	550	42	1067
138	145	650	50	1270
161	169	750	58	1473
230	242	900	76	1930
		1050	84	2134
345	362	1050	84	2134
		1300	104	2642
500	550	1500	124	3150
		1800	144	3658
765	800	2050	167	4242

* For voltages up to 161 kv the clearances are taken from NFPA 70, *National Electrical Code®*. For voltages above the clearances are taken from Table 124 of ANSI C-2, *National Electrical Safety Code*.

NOTE: BIL values are expressed as kilovolts (kv), the number being the crest value of the full wave impulse test that the electrical equipment is designed to withstand. For BIL values that are not listed in the table, clearances can be found by interpolation.

Source: NFPA 15, *Water-Spray Fixed Systems for Fire Protection.*

tice is to coordinate the required clearance with the electrical design. The basic insulation level (BIL) values of the equipment are used as the basis, although the clearance between uninsulated live parts of the equipment and any portion of the water spray system should not be less than the minimum clearances provided elsewhere for electrical system insulation on any individual component (the minimum unshielded straight line distance from the exposed electrical parts to nearby grounded objects). The BIL (expressed in kilovolts) is the crest value of the full wave impulse test.

Portable Extinguishers and Hazard of Shock

Water-based or water-solution portable fire extinguishers are not recommended for use on fires involving live electrical equipment (Class C). NFPA 10, *Portable Fire Extinguishers*, recommends that extinguishers specifically tested for use on Class C fires be used for such fires. When electrical equipment is de-energized, extinguishers for Class A or B fires may be used safely. Tests on the conductivity of portable fire extinguishers containing water indicate that soda-acid (now discontinued), loaded-stream (now discontinued), foam, and antifreeze solution extinguishers, which produce solid streams and have a short range, are particularly hazardous. One test involving an antifreeze solution extinguisher showed a current of 157 ma for a potential of 1 kV with a 3/32-in. (2.4 mm) stream at a distance of 1 ft (0.3 m). To reduce the current to below 1 ma, it would be necessary to use the device from a distance at which the stream is dispersed; it is generally agreed that for such extinguishers the minimum distance should be 4 ft (1.2 m) for voltages up to 1 kV. Extinguishers containing plain water might, in theory, be used at shorter distances, but it is best to maintain a 4-ft (1.2 m) distance if it is necessary to use this kind of extinguisher.

Water on Electrical, Electronic, and Computer Equipment

Automatic sprinkler protection and water spray fixed systems are valuable for fire control, even where electrical, electronic, or computer equipment may be present. There should be little concern about the possibility of shock, or of the water causing excessive damage to the equipment. Experience has proven that, if a fire activates sprinklers, the sprinklers, if properly installed and maintained, provide effective protection with virtually no hazard to personnel and with no measurable increase in damage to the equipment, as compared with the damage done by heat, flame, smoke, and the manual hose streams.[11]

NFPA 75, *Electronic Computer/Data Processing Equipment*, recognizes the importance of automatic sprinkler protection in computer rooms. It recommends that, where sprinklers are installed to protect electronic computer equipment, the power to the equipment should be shut off prior to the application of water.

USE OF WATER ON SPECIAL HAZARDS

While water is generally a universal extinguishing agent, there are certain prohibitions and precautions that must be observed when it is applied manually on some burning materials that either react chemically or explosively on contact with water. In other instances, the mechanical action of applying water must be carefully monitored so as not to create conditions that intensify the hazard, rather than controlling it.

The following paragraphs give summary guidance on using water on different materials that can present problems if water is used indiscriminately as an extinguishing agent. A good reference to consult for recommendations on use of water on specific materials where problems could be encountered is the NFPA *Fire Protection Guide to Hazardous Materials*.[12]

Chemical Hazards

As a general rule, water should not be used on certain materials, such as carbides, peroxides, etc., because the reaction may release flammable gases and heat. When wet, certain materials, such as unslaked lime, will heat spontaneously over a period of time if heat cannot be dissipated due to storage conditions.

Combustible Metals

As a rule, water should not be used on fires involving combustible metals, such as magnesium, titanium, metallic sodium, and hafnium, or on metals that are combustible under certain conditions, such as calcium, zinc, and aluminum.

Radioactive Metals

Water should not be used continuously on radioactive metals. The requirements for fire protection for radioactive metals are generally consistent with their nonradioactive counterparts (for all practical purposes, radioactivity does not influence, nor is it influenced by, the fire properties of a metal). Control of contaminated runoff water is a complicating factor in using water on radioactive metals.

Gas Fires

Water used on gas-fire emergencies is generally used for the control of heat from the fire while efforts are made to shut off, or stop, the flow of escaping gas. Water in the form of spray applied from hose lines or monitor nozzles or by fixed water spray systems is commonly used for dispersement or dilution of concentrations of flammable gases.

Combustible and Flammable Liquids Fires

Heavy fuel oil, lubricating oil, asphalt, and other high-flash-point liquids do not produce flammable vapors unless heated. Once ignited, the heat of the fire will cause enough vaporization for continued burning. If water in spray form is applied to the surface of such high-flash-point burning liquids, cooling will slow down the rate of vaporization—possibly enough to extinguish the fire. If water is applied to high-flash-point burning liquids by means of a coarse spray, extinguishment may be obtained by emulsification.

The ability of water without additives (foaming agents) to extinguish a fire is limited on low-flash-point flammable liquids, such as Class I flammable liquids [flash points below 100°F (37.8°C)], as defined in NFPA 30, *Flammable and Combustible Liquids Code*. Sprinklers and water spray are usually effective in extinguishing fires in combustible liquids with flash points of 200°F (93.3°C) and higher at normal room temperatures, in heavy flammable liquids (specific gravity greater than water), and in water-soluble liquids. Control of fire, but not extinguishment, is possible in low-flash-point [under 200°F (93.3°C)] flammable liquids. Any water that reaches the surface of a burning, low-flash-point flammable liquid in a tank may sink and cause the tank to overflow. In the case of a spill fire, the water will probably cause the fire to spread. Professional handling of certain types of water spray nozzles can result in extinguishment of fires in these liquids or, at a minimum, effective fire control.

The uses of water on petroleum product fires can be summarized as follows:[13]

1. As a cooling agent, water may be used to:
   (a) Cut off the release of vapor from the surface of a high-flash-point oil, thus extinguishing the fire.
   (b) Protect fire fighters from flame and radiant heat when closing a valve or doing other work requiring close approach to the fire.
   (c) Protect flame-exposed surfaces; most effective when the surface is above 212°F (100°C).
2. As a mechanical tool, a water stream can do work at a distance to:
   (a) Control leaks.
   (b) Direct the flow of petroleum product to prevent its ignition, or to move the fire to an area where it will do less damage.
3. As a displacing medium, water may be used to:
   (a) Float oil above a leak in a tank either before or during a fire.
   (b) Cut off fuel escape by pumping it into a leaking pipe ahead of a leak.

BIBLIOGRAPHY

References Cited

1. NFPA, "Chemicals for Forest Fire Fighting," A Report of the NFPA Forest Committee, 3rd ed., 1977, National Fire Protection Association, Quincy, MA.
2. NFPA, "Air Operations for Forest, Brush, and Grass Fires," A Report of the NFPA Forest Committee, 1975, National Fire Protection Association, Quincy, MA.
3. Clough, T. C., "Research on Friction Reducing Agents," *Fire Technology*, Vol. 9, No. 1, Feb. 1973, pp. 32-45.
4. Heselden, A. J. M., and Hinkley, P. L., "Measurement of the Transmission of Radiation Through Water Sprays," Fire Research Note No. 520, 1963, Dept. of Scientific and Industrial Research and Fire Offices' Committee, Joint Fire Research Organization, Boreham Wood, Herts, England.
5. UL, "Electric Shock as It Pertains to the Electric Fence," Bulletin of Research No. 14, 1939, Underwriters Laboratories Inc., Chicago, IL.
6. Commonwealth Edison Co., "Conductivity of Electricity Through Various Sizes and Types of Fire Streams," 1947. (An Engineering Report of Tests Conducted in Cooperation with the Chicago Fire Department.)
7. AIA, "Fire Streams and Electrical Circuits," Special Interest Bulletin No. 91, 1963, American Insurance Association, NY.
8. Fitzgerald, G. W. N., "Fire Fighting Near Live Electrical Apparatus," Research Division Report No. 58-160, 1958, Hydro-Electric Power Commission of Ontario.
9. Buffet, "Peut-on Employer les Lances d'Incendie sur des Conducteurs Electriques?," 1934.
10. O'Dogherty, M. J., "The Shock Hazard Associated with the Extinction of Fires Involving Electrical Equipment," Fire Research Technical Paper No. 13, 1965, Ministry of Technology and Fire Offices' Committee, Joint Fire Research Organization. (Published by Her Majesty's Stationery Office.)
11. Keigher, Donald J., "Water and Electronics Can Mix," *Fire Journal*, Vol. 62, No. 6, 1968, pp. 68-72.
12. NFPA, *Fire Protection Guide to Hazardous Materials*, 7th ed., National Fire Protection Association, Quincy, MA, 1984.
13. Johnson, Oliver W., "Water on Oil Fires," *NFPA Quarterly*, Vol. 55, No. 2, 1961, pp. 141-146.

References

NBFU, "The Mechanism of Extinguishment of Fire by Finely Divided Water," Research Report No. 10, National Board of Fire Underwriters.

You, H. Z., Kung, H. C., and Han, Z., *Spray Cooling in Room Fires*, National Bureau of Standards, Washington, DC, 1986.

NFPA Codes, Standards, and Recommended Practices.

Reference to the following NFPA codes, standards, and recommended practices will provide further information on water and water additives for fire fighting discussed in this chapter. (See the latest *NFPA Catalog* for availability of current editions of the following documents.)

NFPA 10, *Portable Fire Extinguishers*.

NFPA 13, *Installation of Sprinkler Systems*.

NFPA 15, *Water-Spray Fixed Systems for Fire Protection*.

NFPA 18, *Wetting Agents*.

NFPA 30, *Flammable and Combustible Liquids Code*.

NFPA 75, *Electronic Computer/Data Processing Equipment*.

Additional Reading

Aidun, A. R., and Grove, C. S., Jr., "Additives to Improve the Fire Fighting Characteristics of Water," Report No. Ch. E 504-6112F, Syracuse University Research Institute (sponsored by U.S. Dept. of the Navy), 1961.

Beyler, C. L., *The Interaction of Fire and Sprinklers*, National Bureau of Standards, Washington, DC, 1977.

Davis, J. B., Dibble, D. L., Richards, S. S., and Steck, L. V., "Gelgard—A New Fire Retardant for Air and Ground Attack," *Fire Technology*, Vol. 1, No. 3, Aug. 1965, pp. 216-224.

"High Voltage Electrical Conductivity Tests with Nu-Swift Dry Powder and Water Type Extinguishers," conducted at Institute of High Voltage and Measuring Technique, Technical High School, Darmstadt, Germany, 1962.

Hopping, R., and Knox, C., "Tests of Fire Fighting Streams," The Electricity Commission of New South Wales, Fire Protection Organization, File No. 8610, 1960.

Jacobson, Dan W., "Automatic Sprinkler Protection for Essential Electrical and Electronic Equipment," *Fire Journal*, Vol. 61, No. 1, Jan. 1967, pp. 48-53.

Keigher, Donald J., "Water and Electronics Can Mix," *Fire Journal*, Vol. 62, No. 6, Nov. 1968, pp. 68-72.

Reiner, J., "New Additives to Extinguishing Water for Fire Fighting," *Proceedings* of the Conference on New Technology to Reduce Fire Losses and Costs, Elsevier, New York, 1986, pp. 280-287.

Reischl, Uwe, "Water Fog Stream Heat Radiation," *Fire Technology*, Vol. 15, Nov. 1979, pp. 262-270.

Stratta, J. J., "Ablative Fluids in the Fire Environment," *Fire Technology*, Vol. 1, No. 3, Aug. 1969, pp. 181-192.

"Study to Optimize Gellant Polymer-Water Systems for the Control of Hypergolic Spills and Fires," Report CR-2198, 1972, National Aeronautics and Space Administration.

"Use of Water on Electronic Equipment Fires," *NASA Safety Journal*, 68-9, Sept. 6, 1968.

HYDRAULICS

Revised by Kenneth W. Linder

Fire protection hydraulics, a category of fluid mechanics, involves the flow of water through pipes and orifices, such as hydrant outlets, hose nozzles, or sprinklers. This chapter describes the physical properties of water that are pertinent to hydraulic calculations and the formulas used to calculate flow and pressure loss in fire protection systems.

HYDRAULIC PROPERTIES OF WATER

As used in this handbook, water refers to fresh water unless otherwise specified. All calculations are made in U.S. gallons, unless otherwise indicated. A U.S. gallon equals 3.78 L. An Imperial gallon equals 1.20 U.S. gallons (4.54 L).

Material Properties

Density: Density ρ is defined as mass per unit volume;

$$\rho = \frac{\text{mass}}{\text{volume}}$$

The density of water, as with many other liquids, varies with temperature. The maximum density of water occurs at 39.2°F (4.0°C) and is 62.43 lbm (pound mass) per cu ft [1000 kg/m^3 (kilograms per cubic meter)] in vacuum or 62.35 lbm per cu ft (998.7 kg/m^3) in air. For most hydraulic calculations, an approximate value of 62.4 lbm per cu ft (1000 kg/m^3) is usually used. Average seawater has a density of 64.1 lbm per cu ft (1030 kg/m^3) at 39.2°F (4.0°C).

Specific weight: The specific weight of a material (w) is defined as $w = \rho\, g$ where g is the acceleration due to gravity. The specific weight is usually measured in lbf (pound force) per cu ft in U.S. customary units and kgf (kilogram force)/m^3 in SI units and is:

$$w = \rho g = 62.4\,\frac{\text{lbm}}{\text{ft}^3} \times 32.2\,\frac{\text{ft}}{\text{sec}^2} \times 1\,\frac{\text{lbf sec}^2}{32.2\text{ lbm ft}}$$

$$= 62.4\,\frac{\text{lbf}}{\text{ft}^3}\,(1000\text{ kgf per m}^3)$$

A common, though incorrect, practice is to use the terms pound mass (lbm) and pound force (lbf) interchangeably since one lbm has a weight of one lbf under standard gravity. [A similar situation exists in SI units with kg (kilogram) and kgf (kilogram force.] In this chapter, pound (lb) means pound force (lbf) and kilogram (kg) means kilogram force (kgf), as is common in engineering practice.

One cu ft (0.28 m^3) equals 7.48 U.S. gallons. Assuming the specific weight of water is 62.4 lb per cu ft (1000 kg/m^3), one gallon of water therefore weighs (62.4 lb per cur ft ÷ 7.48 gal per cu ft) or 8.34 lbs (3.78 kg).

Viscosity: Viscosity is a measurement of a fluid's resistance to flow, and is usually measured in pound sec per square foot (lb sec/ft^2) in U.S. customary units or newton sec per square meter (N sec/m^2) in SI units. Viscosity, like density, varies with temperature. At 32°F (0.0°C), water has an absolute viscosity, μ, of 3.746×10^{-5} lb sec/ft^2 (1.793×10^{-5} N sec/m^2). In hydraulic problems, viscosity is often divided by density. This relative viscosity, called kinematic viscosity, v, is defined as:

$$\nu = \frac{\mu}{\rho}$$

While viscosity is an important factor in fluid flows, most fire protection hydraulics applications assume water at ambient conditions, and the empirical formulas normally used to calculate losses do not take into account changes in viscosity.

Pressure

Pressure, p, is the unit that measures the force, caused by compression, per unit area in a fluid. In fire protection hydraulics, pressure is normally measured in pounds per square inch (psi) or in kilopascals (kPa), as indicated by a pressure gage, or as head, h, in feet (ft) or meters (m) of

Kenneth W. Linder is assistant director of research for Industrial Risk Insurers, Hartford, CT.

water. Pressure is also commonly measured as a head of mercury.

For water flow in pipes, the total pressure (p_t) is the sum of normal pressure (p_n) and velocity pressure (p_v).

$$p_t = p_n + p_\nu$$

Normal pressure: Net or normal pressure is the pressure exerted against the side of a pipe or container by the liquid in the pipe or container with or without flow. Without flow, this pressure is called "static pressure" or "static head." With flow, this pressure is called "residual" pressure.

The pressure exerted by a column of water is related to its specific weight. Expressed slightly differently, the specific weight is:

$$\frac{62.4 \text{ lbs}}{\text{ft}^3} = \frac{62.4 \text{ lbs}}{\text{ft}^2 \text{ ft}} \times \frac{1 \text{ ft}^2}{144 \text{ in.}^2} = 0.433 \text{ psi per ft}$$

It follows that pressure and static head are related by the following formulas:

$$p = wh = 0.433h.$$

$$h = \frac{p}{w} = \frac{p}{0.433} = 2.31p$$

For SI units, the weight of a 1-m column of water equals of force of 9.81 kPa or:

$$p = 9.81h$$

$$h = \frac{1}{9.81} = 0.102p$$

A 1-in. (25.4 mm) head of mercury generates a pressure of 0.491 psi (3.39 kPa) and is equivalent to a 1.135-ft (0.3456 m) head of water.

Normal atmospheric pressure is taken as 14.7 psi (101.4 kPa), equivalent to a head of water of 33.95 ft (10.35 m) and a head of mercury of 29.94 in. (760.5 mm).

Velocity head or velocity pressure: The velocity (v) produced in a mass of water by pressure acting upon it is the same as if the mass was to fall freely, starting from rest, through a distance equivalent to the pressure head in feet. This relationship is represented by Torricelli's equation:

$$v = \sqrt{2gh}$$

v being the velocity produced in feet per second (m/sec), g being the acceleration due to gravity or 32.2 ft/sec^2 (9.81 m/sec^2), and h being the head in feet (m) producing the velocity.

Just as a static head can be converted into a velocity head, velocity head can be converted to an equivalent static pressure head. This relation is:

$$h_\nu \text{ (velocity head)} = \frac{\nu^2}{2g} \text{ (ft)}$$

Because

$$p_\nu = 0.433h_\nu$$

the velocity pressure can be expressed as:

$$p_\nu = 0.433 \frac{\nu^2}{2g} \text{ (psi)}$$

In SI units:

$$p_{\nu m} \text{ (kPa)} = 9.81 \frac{\nu^2}{2g}$$

for v in m/sec.

Values of velocity pressure for different rates of flow in various pipe sizes are shown in Figure 5-2A. (For SI units see Figure 5-2B.) Velocity head or velocity pressure may be calculated by formulas involving velocity and pipe diameter:

$$h_\nu = \frac{\nu^2}{64.4} \quad \text{or} \quad p_\nu = \frac{0.433\nu^2}{64.4} = \frac{\nu^2}{149}$$

In SI units:

$$h_{\nu m} = 0.0151\nu^2 \quad \text{and} \quad p_{\nu m} = 0.5\nu^2$$

A convenient equation for calculating velocity in feet per second (fps) from the rate of flow can be developed from the principle of conservation of mass. For a steady-state one-dimensional flow with average velocity v, this principle can be stated as

$$Q = av$$

It follows that:

$$\nu = \frac{Q}{a}$$

in which v is the average velocity in feet per second, Q is the flow in cubic feet per second, and a is the cross-sectional area of the pipe in square feet.

For a pipe with flow in gpm and diameter in inches, the velocity is:

$$\nu \text{ (fps)} = \frac{Q \text{ (gal/min)}}{60 \text{ sec/min} \times 7.48 \text{ gal/ft}^3} \div \frac{\pi\, d^2\text{(in)}^2}{4 \times 144 \text{ in}^2\text{/ft}^2}$$

$$= \frac{Q \times 4 \times 144}{60 \times 7.48 \times \pi\, d^2} = \frac{0.4085 \times Q}{d^2}$$

It follows that h_v *and* p_v *are:*

$$h_\nu = \frac{\nu^2}{2g} = \frac{(0.4085Q)^2}{(d^2)^2} \div 64.4 = \frac{Q^2}{d^4}\frac{(0.4085)^2}{64.4} = \frac{Q^2}{386d^2}$$

$$p_\nu = \frac{Q^2}{d^4} \times \frac{0.433}{386} = \frac{Q^2}{891d^4}$$

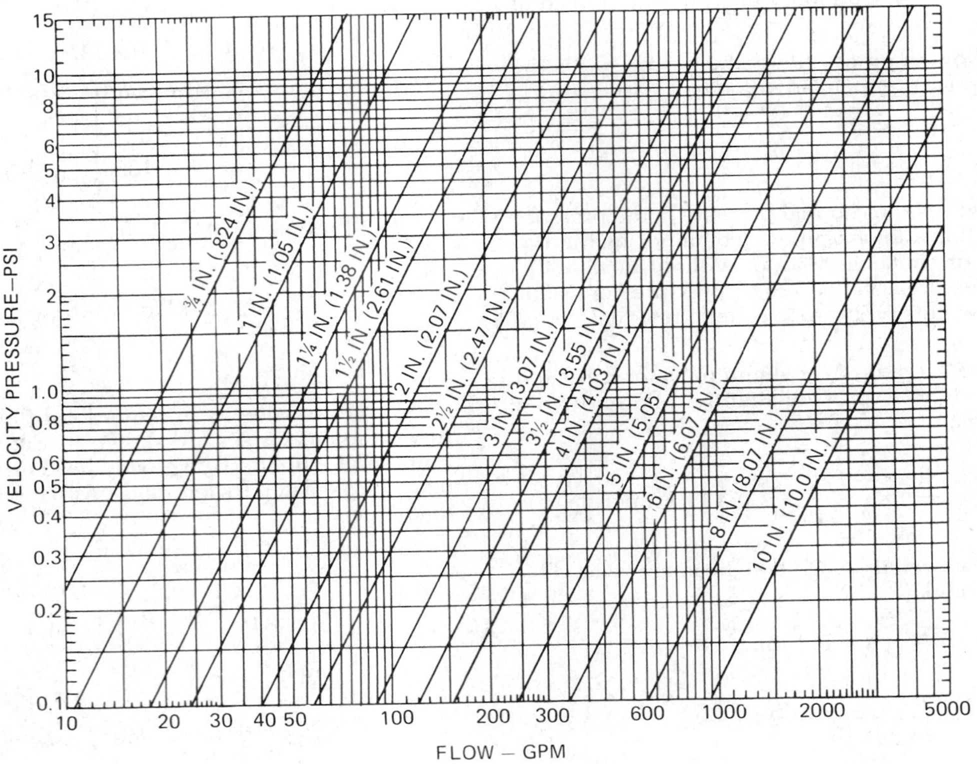

FIG. 5-2A. Graph for the determination of velocity pressure.

In SI units, the formula for velocity pressure is expressed as:

$$p_{vm} = 225 \frac{Q_m{}^2}{d_m{}^4}$$

where:

p_{vm} = velocity pressure, kPa

Q_m = flow, L/min.

d_m = inside diameter, mm

EXAMPLE 1: Find the velocity pressure in 1-in. Schedule 40 pipe with 36 gpm flowing. The actual diameter of the pipe is 1.049 in.

SOLUTION:

$$p_v = \frac{Q^2}{891\,(d)^4} = \frac{36^2}{891\,(1.049)^2} = 1.20 \text{ psi}$$

Eq 20

EXAMPLE 2: Find the velocity in a 25-mm (actual diameter) pipe with 100 L/m flowing:

SOLUTION:

$$p_{vm} = 225 \frac{Q_m{}^2}{(d_m)^4} = \frac{225 \times (100)^2}{(25)^4} = 5.8 \text{ kPa}$$

Total head: At any point within a piping system that contains water in motion, there is a pressure head h_p (normal pressure head) acting perpendicular to the pipe wall independent of velocity, and a velocity head h_v acting parallel to the wall but exerting no pressure against the wall. Therefore, as previously stated, the total head, $H = h_p + h_v$, expressed as pressure (psi) instead of feet is:

$$p_t = 0.433 h_p + 0.433 \frac{v^2}{2g}$$

In SI units, total head expressed in kPa is:

$$p_{tm} = 9.81 h_{pm} + 9.81 \frac{v_m{}^2}{2g}$$

where:

p_{tm} = total pressure, kPa

h_{pm} = head, meters

v_m = velocity, meters per sec

Pressure Sources

The sources of pressure head commonly found in fire protection hydraulic systems include the following.

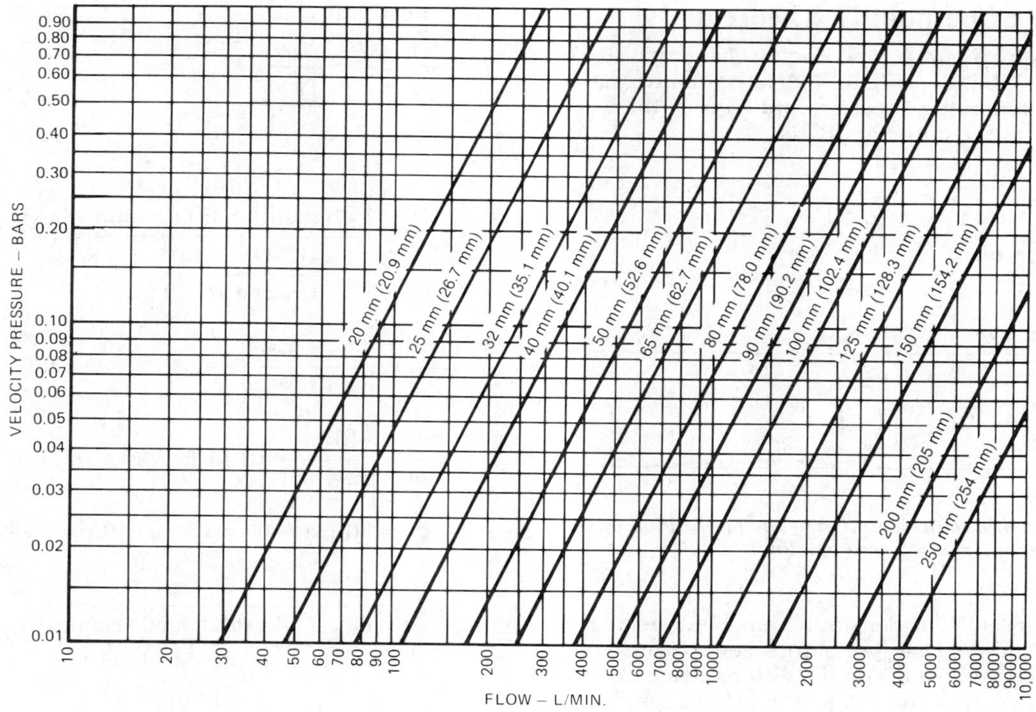

FIG. 5-2B. Graph for the determination of velocity pressure (SI units).

Gravity (elevated tanks, reservoirs, standpipes): Head is the elevation of the water supply surface above the point under consideration, measured directly in feet (m) or converted from a pressure gage reading.

Pumping: Head is the combination of pump discharge pressure and any difference in elevation between the pump discharge gage and the point under consideration.

Pneumatic (pressure tanks): Head is the tank air pressure combined with any difference in elevation in tank water surface and the point under consideration.

Combination: Any combination of the above pressure sources.

BERNOULLI'S THEOREM

Bernoulli's theorem expresses the physical law of conservation of energy applied to problems of incompressible fluid flow. The theorem can be defined as follows: "In steady flow without friction, the sum of the velocity head, pressure head, and elevation head is constant for any incompressible fluid particle throughout its course." In other words, the total pressure (head) is the same at all locations within the system.

[Note that in Bernoulli's theorem, all of the individual head terms, i.e., velocity head, pressure head, elevation head, and lost head are expressed in feet (m). When using velocities in feet per second (m/s) and gage pressure in psi (kPa), they must be converted to feet, or all of the terms expressed as pressures.]

Real systems are not frictionless, however, and in practice losses due to pipe friction and other factors are accounted for. Expressed mathematically, Bernoulli's theorem, when applied to locations "A" and "B," is:

$$\frac{v_A^2}{2g} + \frac{p_A}{w} + z_A = \frac{v_B^2}{2g} + \frac{p_B}{w} + z_B + h_{AB}$$

where:

v (v_m) = *velocity in feet per second (m/s)*

g (g_m) = *acceleration of gravity - 32.2 feet per second per second (9.81 m/sec²)*

p (p_m) = *pressure, pounds per square foot (kPa)*

z (z_m) = *elevation head (distance above assumed datum), in feet (m)*

w (w_m) = *specific weight of the fluid in pounds per cubic foot (64.4 pcf or 9.81 kN/m³ for water)*

$$\frac{v^2}{2g}\left(\frac{v_m^2}{2g}\right) = \text{velocity head in feet (m)}$$

$$\frac{p}{w}\left(\frac{p_m}{w_m}\right) = \text{pressure head in feet (m)}$$

h_{AB} (h_{ABm}) = *lost head between location "A" and location "B" in feet (m).*

Application of Bernoulli's Theorem

Consider a reservoir and a pipe line discharging water to atmosphere at "B." (See Figure 5-2C.) Assuming datum through "B," Bernoulli's theorem applied from the water surface at "A" to the outlet at "B" is:

$$\frac{v_A^2}{2g} + \frac{p_A}{w} + z_A = \frac{v_B^2}{2g} + \frac{p_B}{w} + z_B + h_{AB}$$

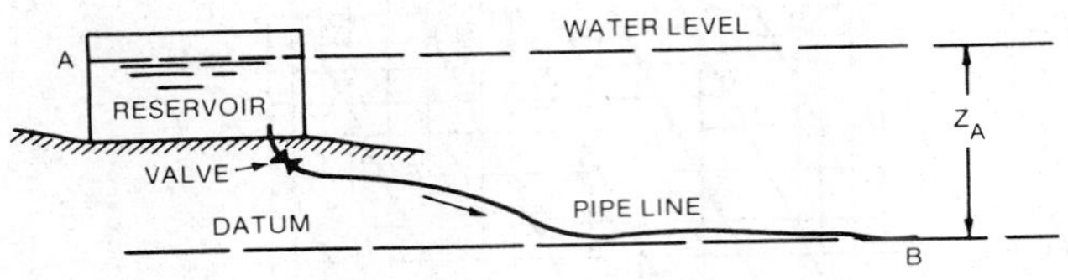

FIG. 5-2C. Graphic respresentation of the application of Bernoulli's theorum to a resevoir and pipelines.

The velocity at "A" is practically zero, because the tank is very large, and the gage pressure is zero because only atmospheric pressure works on the water surface. At "A," the elevation is z_A measured in feet (m) above the datum.

At "B," the elevation above the datum is zero, the gage pressure is zero, since the water is discharging to atmosphere, and only velocity pressure is available as the water leaves the outlet. (A gage at a right angle to the emerging stream would register zero pressure).

Therefore:

$$0 + 0 + z_A = \frac{v_B^2}{2g} + 0 + 0 + h_{AB}$$

or:

$$\frac{v_B^2}{2g} = z_A - h_{AB}$$

Lost head h_{AB} is the sum of: (1) hydraulic losses at the reservoir where water enters the pipeline, at the valve, and at the discharge outlet, plus (2) the friction loss in the pipeline. The values of the components producing lost head can be estimated, as discussed later in the chapter.

As another example, calculate the head loss across 1,000 ft of 8-in. pipe with 750 gpm flowing from a 2½-in. hydrant outlet at "B" and a residual pressure at hydrant "A" of 40 psi. With no flow, hydrant "A" has a 60 psi static pressure and hydrant "B" has an 80 psi static pressure. Assume a datum through hydrant "B." Again, Bernoulli's theorem applied from point "A" to point "B" applies:

$$\frac{v_A^2}{2g} + \frac{p_A}{w} + z_A \frac{v_B^2}{2g} + \frac{p_B}{w} + z_B + h_{AB}$$

Rearranging:

$$h_{AB} = \frac{v_A^2}{2g} + \frac{p_A}{w} + z_A - \frac{v_B^2}{2g} - \frac{p_B}{w} - z_B$$

Substituting,

$$v_A = \frac{Q}{a} = \frac{q}{\dfrac{\pi\, d^2}{4 \times 144}}$$

$$= \frac{\dfrac{750 \text{ gpm}}{7.48 \text{ gal/ft}^2 \times 60 \text{ sec/min}}}{\dfrac{3.1416 \times (8)^2}{4 \times 144 \text{ in.}^2/\text{ft}^2}} = 4.79 \text{ fps}$$

$$\frac{v_A^2}{2g} = \frac{(4.79 \text{ fps})^2}{64.4 \text{ fps/sec}} = 0.36 \text{ ft} = 0.4 \text{ ft}$$

$$\frac{p_a}{w} = \frac{40 \text{ psi}}{62.4 \text{ pcf}} = 144 \text{ in.}^2/\text{ft}^2 = 92.3 \text{ ft}$$

$$z_A = 80 \text{ psi} - 60 \text{ psi} \times 2.31 \text{ ft/psi} = 46.2 \text{ ft}$$

$$v_B = \frac{Q}{a} = \frac{\dfrac{750 \text{ gpm}}{7.48 \text{ gal/ft}^2 \times 60 \text{ sec/min}}}{\dfrac{3.1416 \times (2.5)^2}{4 \times 144 \text{ in.}^2/\text{ft}^2}} = 49.02 \text{ fps}$$

$$\frac{v_B^2}{2g} = \frac{(49.02)^2}{64.4} = 37.3 \text{ ft}$$

$$\frac{p_B}{w} = 0.$$

There is no normal pressure as the flow discharges to atmosphere.

$z_B = 0$, since the datum goes through hydrant "B."

Thus:

$$h_{AB} = 0.4 + 92.3 + 46.2 - 37.3 - 0 - 0 = 101.6 \text{ ft}$$

One further problem is expressed in SI units. Water is pumped via a pipeline, up a 5.0 m incline from "A" to "B." The pipeline at "A" has an inside diameter of 80 mm and a static pressure of 300 kPa. If the pipeline has changed in diameter to 70 mm at "B" and there is frictional head loss over the length of the pipe (h_{AB}) of 12 m, determine the residual pressure at "B" for a flow rate of 4200 L/min.

The solution is expressed as:

$$\frac{v_A^2}{2g} + \frac{p_A}{w} + z_A = \frac{v_B^2}{2g} + \frac{p_B}{w} = z_B + h_{AB}$$

Rearranging for the static at "B":

$$\frac{p_B}{w} = \frac{v_A^2}{2g} + \frac{p_A}{w} + z_A - \frac{p_B^2}{2g} - z_B - h_{AB}$$

Substituting:

$$v_A = \frac{Q}{a_A} = \frac{\dfrac{4200 \text{ L/min}}{60 \text{ sec/min} \times 1000 \text{ L/m}^3}}{\dfrac{\pi (80 \text{ mm})^2}{4 \times 10^6 \text{ mm}^2/\text{m}^2}} = 13.9 \text{ m/sec}$$

$$\frac{v_A^{\ 2}}{2g} = \frac{(13.9)^2}{2 \times 9.81} = 9.9 \text{ m}$$

$$\frac{p_A}{w} = \frac{300 \text{ kPa}}{9.81 \text{ kPa/m}} = 30.6 \text{ m}$$

$$z_A = 0 \quad \text{(datum through "A")}$$

$$v_B = \frac{Q}{a_B} = \frac{\dfrac{4200 \text{ L/min}}{60 \text{ sec/min} \times 1000 \text{ L/min}^3}}{\dfrac{\pi (70 \text{ mm})^2}{4 \times 10^6 \text{ mm}^2/\text{m}^2}} = 18.2 \text{ m/sec}$$

$$\frac{v_B^{\ 2}}{2g} = \frac{(18.2)^2}{2 \times 9.81} = 16.9 \text{ m}$$

$$z_B = 5.0 \text{ m}$$

$$h_{AB} = 12 \text{ m} \quad \text{(friction loss)}$$

Then:

$$\frac{p_A}{w} = 9.9 + 30.6 + 0 - 16.9 - 5 - 12 = 6.6 \text{ m}$$

In pressure terms:

$$p_A \text{ (kPa)} = 9.81\ h\text{(m)} = 9.81 \times 6.6 = 65 \text{ kPa}$$

i.e., the residual pressure at "B" is 65 kPa.

FLOW OF WATER THROUGH ORIFICES

As a liquid leaves a pipe, conduit, or container through an orifice and discharges to atmosphere, the normal pressure is converted to velocity pressure. The rate of flow though an orifice can be expressed in terms of velocity and cross-sectional area of the stream, the basic relations being $Q = av$, where Q = rate of flow in cubic feet per second, (m^3/sec); a = area of cross section in square feet (m^2); and v = velocity at the cross section in feet per second (m/sec). (See Table 5-2A.) From the previous discussion in this chapter on velocity head, it is known that

$$Q = a\sqrt{2gh}$$

and h = 2.307p. It follows that with the orifice diameter in inches, Q in gallons per minute would equal:

$$Q = 60 \times 7.4805 \times \frac{\pi d^2}{4 \times 144} \sqrt{64.4 \times 2.30 p_v}$$

$$Q = 29.84 d^2 \sqrt{p_v}$$

In SI units, the flow formula is expressed as:

where

$$Q_m = 0.0666 d_m^{\ 2} \sqrt{p_{vm}}$$

Q_m = flow rate (L/m)

d_m = inside diameter (mm)

p_{vm} = velocity pressure (kPa)

The above equations (and tables derived therefrom) assume that: (1) the jet is a solid stream the full size of the discharge orifice, and (2) 100 percent of the available total head is converted to velocity head which is uniform over the cross section. This is a theoretical situation only, however, as these two conditions are not totally attainable, as the following discussion will show.

Coefficients of Flow

In actual flow from nozzles or orifices, the velocity, considered to be average velocity across the entire cross section of the stream, is somewhat less than the velocity calculated from the head. The reduction is due to friction of the water against the nozzle or orifice and turbulence within the nozzle, and is accounted for by a coefficient of velocity, designated c_v. Values of c_v are determined by laboratory tests. With well-designed nozzles, the coefficient of velocity is nearly constant and is approximately equal to 0.98.

Some nozzles are designed so that the actual cross-sectional area of the stream is somewhat less than the cross-sectional area of the orifice. This difference is accounted for by the coefficient of contraction, designated as c_c. Coefficients of contraction vary greatly with the design and quality of the orifice or nozzle. For a sharp-edged orifice, the value of c_c is about 0.62.

The coefficients of velocity and contraction are usually combined as a single coefficient of discharge, designated c_d:

$$c_d = c_v \times c_c$$

The basic flow equation can now be written as:

$$Q = 29.84 c_d\, d^2 \sqrt{p_v}$$

In SI units the formula is:

$$Q = 0.666 c_d\, dm^2 \sqrt{p_{vm}}$$

TABLE 5-2A. *Theoretical Flow Through Circular Orifices–GPM (L/min)*

This table is computed from the formula $Q = 29.84cd^2\sqrt{p}$ ($Q_m = 0.0666cd_m^2\sqrt{p_{vm}}$) with c = 1.00. The theoretical discharge of sea water, as from fireboat nozzles, may be found by subtracting 1 percent from the figures in the following table, or from the formula $Q = 29.47cd^2\sqrt{p}$ ($Q_m = 0.065cd_m^2\sqrt{p_{vm}}$).

When pressures are read with a Pitot gage at a nozzle, the nozzle discharge in most cases will correspond to the values in the tables within a range of 1 to 3 percent for nozzles up to 1⅜ in. in diameter For larger diameter nozzles, the principles discussed in "The Nozzle Method of Measuring Flow" in this chapter of the *Handbook* apply. Appropriate coefficients should be applied where it is read from a hydrant outlet. Where more accurate results are required, a coefficient appropriate to the particular nozzle must be selected and applied to the figures of the table.

The discharge from circular openings of sizes other than those in the table may readily be computed by applying the principle that quantity discharged under a given head varies as the squre of the diameter of the opening.

Pres.	Velocity	Orifice Diameter Inches (mm)																					
PSI (kPa)	ft/sec (m/sec)	3/8 (9.53)	1/2 (12.7)	5/8 (15.9)	3/4 (19.1)	7/8 (22.2)	1 (25.4)	1-1/8 (28.6)	1-1/4 (31.8)	1-1/2 (38.1)	1-3/4 (44.5)	2 (50.8)	2-1/4 (57.2)	2-3/8 (60.3)	2-1/2 (63.5)	2-5/8 (66.7)	2-3/4 (69.9)	3 (76.2)	3-1/4 (82.6)	3-1/2 (88.9)	3-3/4 (95.3)	4 (102)	4-1/2 (114)
1	12.2	4.20	7.46	11.7	16.8	22.8	29.8	37.8	46.6	67.1	91.4	119	151	168	187	206	226	269	315	366	420	477	604
(6.90)	(3.72)	(15.9)	(28.2)	(44.1)	(63.5)	(86.5)	(112.9)	(143)	(176)	(254)	(346)	(452)	(572)	(637)	(706)	(778)	(854)	(1020)	(1190)	(1380)	(1590)	(1810)	(2290)
2	17.2	5.93	10.6	16.5	23.7	32.3	42.2	53.4	65.9	95.0	129	169	214	238	264	291	319	380	446	517	593	675	855
(13.8)	(5.30)	(22.5)	(39.9)	(62.4)	(89.8)	(122)	(159.7)	(202)	(250)	(359)	(489)	(639)	(809)	(901)	(998)	(1100)	(1210)	(1440)	(1690)	(1960)	(2250)	(2560)	(3230)
3	21.1	7.27	12.9	20.2	29.1	39.6	51.7	65.4	80.8	116	158	207	262	292	323	356	391	465	546	633	727	827	1050
(20.7)	(6.44)	(27.5)	(48.9)	(76.4)	(110)	(150)	(195.6)	(248)	(306)	(440)	(599)	(783)	(990)	(1100)	(1220)	(1350)	(1480)	(1760)	(2070)	(2400)	(2750)	(3130)	(3960)
4	24.4	8.39	14.9	23.3	33.6	45.7	59.7	75.5	93.3	134	183	239	302	337	373	411	451	537	630	731	839	955	1210
(27.6)	(7.43)	(31.8)	(56.5)	(88.2)	(127)	(173)	(225.9)	(286)	(353)	(508)	(692)	(904)	(1140)	(1270)	(1410)	(1560)	(1710)	(2030)	(2390)	(2770)	(3180)	(3610)	(4570)
5	27.3	9.38	16.7	26.1	37.5	51.1	66.7	84.4	104	150	204	267	338	376	417	460	505	601	705	817	938	1070	1350
(34.5)	(8.31)	(35.5)	(63.1)	(98.7)	(142)	(193)	(252.6)	(320)	(395)	(568)	(773)	(1010)	(1280)	(1420)	(1580)	(1740)	(1910)	(2270)	(2670)	(3090)	(3550)	(4040)	(5110)
6	29.9	10.3	18.3	28.6	41.1	56.0	73.1	92.5	114	164	224	292	370	412	457	504	553	658	772	895	1030	1170	1480
(41.4)	(9.11)	(38.9)	(69.2)	(108)	(156)	(212)	(276.7)	(350)	(432)	(622)	(847)	(1110)	(1400)	(1560)	(1730)	(1910)	(2090)	(2490)	(2920)	(3390)	(3890)	(4430)	(5600)
7	32.3	11.1	19.7	30.8	44.4	60.4	78.9	99.9	123	178	242	316	400	445	493	544	597	711	834	967	1110	1260	1600
(48.3)	(9.83)	(42.0)	(74.7)	(117)	(168)	(229)	(298.8)	(378)	(467)	(672)	(915)	(1200)	(1510)	(1690)	(1870)	(2060)	(2260)	(2690)	(3160)	(3660)	(4200)	(4780)	(6050)
8	34.5	11.9	21.1	33.0	47.5	64.6	84.4	107	132	190	258	338	427	476	528	582	638	760	891	1030	1190	1350	1710
(55.2)	(10.5)	(44.9)	(79.9)	(125)	(180)	(245)	(319.5)	(404)	(499)	(719)	(978)	(1280)	(1620)	(1800)	(2000)	(2200)	(2420)	(2880)	(3370)	(3910)	(4490)	(5110)	(6470)
9	36.6	12.6	22.4	35.0	50.4	68.5	89.5	113	140	201	274	358	453	505	560	617	677	806	946	1100	1260	1430	1810
(62.1)	(11.2)	(47.6)	(84.7)	(132)	(191)	(259)	(338.8)	(429)	(529)	(762)	(1040)	(1360)	(1720)	(1910)	(2120)	(2330)	(2560)	(3050)	(3580)	(4150)	(4760)	(5420)	(6860)
10	38.6	13.3	23.6	36.9	53.1	72.2	94.4	119	147	212	289	377	478	532	590	650	714	849	997	1160	1330	1510	1910
(69.0)	(11.8)	(50.2)	(89.3)	(140)	(201)	(273)	(357.2)	(452)	(558)	(804)	(1090)	(1430)	(1810)	(2010)	(2230)	(2460)	(2700)	(3210)	(3770)	(4380)	(5020)	(5710)	(7230)
11	40.4	13.9	24.7	38.7	55.7	75.8	99.0	125	155	223	303	396	501	558	619	682	748	891	1050	1210	1390	1580	2000
(75.9)	(12.3)	(52.7)	(93.6)	(146)	(211)	(287)	(374.6)	(474)	(585)	(843)	(1150)	(1500)	(1900)	(2110)	(2340)	(2580)	(2830)	(3370)	(3960)	(4590)	(5270)	(5990)	(7590)
12	42.2	14.5	25.8	40.4	58.1	79.1	103	131	162	233	317	413	523	583	646	712	782	930	1090	1270	1450	1650	2090
(82.8)	(12.9)	(55.0)	(97.8)	(153)	(220)	(300)	(391.3)	(495)	(611)	(880)	(1200)	(1570)	(1980)	(2210)	(2450)	(2700)	(2960)	(3520)	(4130)	(4790)	(5500)	(6260)	(7920)
13	44.0	15.1	26.9	42.0	60.5	82.4	108	136	168	242	329	430	545	607	672	741	814	968	1140	1320	1510	1720	2180
(89.7)	(13.4)	(57.3)	(102)	(159)	(229)	(312)	(407.2)	(515)	(636)	(916)	(1250)	(1630)	(2060)	(2300)	(2550)	(2810)	(3080)	(3670)	(4300)	(4990)	(5730)	(6520)	(8250)
14	45.6	15.7	27.9	43.6	62.8	85.5	112	141	174	251	342	447	565	630	698	769	844	1000	1180	1370	1570	1790	2260
(96.6)	(13.9)	(59.4)	(106)	(165)	(238)	(324)	(422.6)	(535)	(660)	(951)	(1290)	(1690)	(2140)	(2380)	(2640)	(2910)	(3200)	(3800)	(4460)	(5180)	(5940)	(6760)	(8560)
15	47.2	16.3	28.9	45.1	65.0	88.5	116	146	181	260	354	462	585	652	722	796	874	1040	1220	1420	1630	1850	2340
(103)	(14.4)	(61.5)	(109)	(171)	(246)	(335)	(437.4)	(554)	(683)	(984)	(1340)	(1750)	(2210)	(2470)	(2730)	(3010)	(3310)	(3940)	(4620)	(5360)	(6150)	(7000)	(8860)
16	48.8	16.8	29.8	46.6	67.1	91.4	119	151	187	269	366	477	604	673	746	822	903	1070	1260	1460	1680	1910	2420
(110)	(14.9)	(63.5)	(113)	(176)	(254)	(346)	(451.8)	(572)	(706)	(1020)	(1380)	(1810)	(2290)	(2550)	(2820)	(3110)	(3420)	(4070)	(4770)	(5530)	(6350)	(7230)	(9150)
17	50.3	17.3	30.8	48.1	69.2	94.2	123	156	192	277	377	492	623	694	769	848	930	1110	1300	1510	1730	1970	2490
(117)	(15.3)	(65.5)	(116)	(182)	(262)	(357)	(465.7)	(589)	(728)	(1050)	(1430)	(1860)	(2360)	(2630)	(2910)	(3210)	(3520)	(4190)	(4920)	(5700)	(6550)	(7450)	(9430)
18	51.7	17.8	31.7	49.5	71.2	96.9	127	160	198	285	388	506	641	714	791	872	957	1140	1340	1550	1780	2030	2560
(124)	(15.8)	(67.4)	(120)	(187)	(270)	(367)	(479.2)	(606)	(749)	(1080)	(1470)	(1920)	(2430)	(2700)	(2990)	(3300)	(3620)	(4310)	(5060)	(5870)	(6740)	(7670)	(9700)

TABLE 5-2A. ***Theoretical Flow Through Circular Orifices–GPM (L/min) (Continued)***

This table is computed from the formula $Q = 29.84cd^2\sqrt{\rho}$ ($Q_m = 0.0666cd_m^2\sqrt{\rho_{vm}}$) with c = 1.00. The theoretical discharge of sea water, as from fireboat nozzles, may be found by subtracting 1 percent from the figures in the following table, or from the formula $Q = 29.47cd^2\sqrt{\rho}$ ($Q_m = 0.065cd_m^2\sqrt{\rho_{vm}}$).

When pressures are read with a Pitot gage at a nozzle, the nozzle discharge in most cases will correspond to the values in the tables within a range of 1 to 3 percent for nozzles up to 1⅜ in. in diameter. For larger diameter nozzles, the principles discussed in "The Nozzle Method of Measuring Flow" in this chapter of the *Handbook* apply. Appropriate coefficients should be applied where it is read from a hydrant outlet. Where more accurate results are required, a coefficient appropriate to the particular nozzle must be selected and applied to the figures of the table.

The discharge from circular openings of sizes other than those in the table may readily be computed by applying the principle that quantity discharged under a given head varies as the squre of the diameter of the opening.

Pres.	Velocity	Orifice Diameter																					
		Inches (mm)																					
PSI (kPa)	ft/sec (m/sec)	3/8 (9.53)	1/2 (12.7)	5/8 (15.9)	3/4 (19.1)	7/8 (22.2)	1 (25.4)	1-1/8 (28.6)	1-1/4 (31.8)	1-1/2 (38.1)	1-3/4 (44.5)	2 (50.8)	2-1/4 (57.2)	2-3/8 (60.3)	2-1/2 (63.5)	2-5/8 (66.7)	2-3/4 (69.9)	3 (76.2)	3-1/4 (82.6)	3-1/2 (88.9)	3-3/4 (95.3)	4 (102)	4-1/2 (114)
19	53.2	18.3	32.5	50.8	73.2	99.6	130	165	203	293	398	520	658	734	813	896	984	1170	1370	1590	1830	2080	2630
(131)	(16.2)	(69.2)	(123)	(192)	(277)	(377)	(492.3)	(623)	(769)	(1110)	(1510)	(1970)	(2490)	(2780)	(3080)	(3390)	(3720)	(4430)	(5200)	(6030)	(6920)	(7880)	(9970)
20	54.5	18.8	33.4	52.1	75.1	102	133	169	209	300	409	534	676	753	834	920	1010	1200	1410	1630	1880	2140	2700
(138)	(16.6)	(71.0)	(126)	(197)	(284)	(387)	(505.1)	(639)	(789)	(1140)	(1550)	(2020)	(2560)	(2850)	(3160)	(3480)	(3820)	(4550)	(5340)	(6190)	(7100)	(8080)	(10200)
21	55.9	19.2	34.2	53.4	76.9	105	137	173	214	308	419	547	692	771	855	942	1030	1230	1440	1680	1920	2190	2770
(145)	(17.0)	(72.8)	(129)	(202)	(291)	(396)	(517.6)	(655)	(809)	(1160)	(1590)	(2070)	(2620)	(2920)	(3230)	(3570)	(3910)	(4660)	(5470)	(6340)	(7280)	(8280)	(10500)
22	57.2	19.7	35.0	54.7	78.7	107	140	177	219	315	429	560	709	789	875	964	1060	1260	1480	1710	1970	2240	2830
(152)	(17.4)	(74.5)	(132)	(207)	(298)	(406)	(529.8)	(670)	(828)	(1190)	(1620)	(2120)	(2680)	(2990)	(3310)	(3650)	(4010)	(4770)	(5600)	(6490)	(7450)	(8480)	(10700)
23	58.5	20.1	35.8	55.9	80.5	110	143	181	224	322	438	572	724	807	894	986	1080	1290	1510	1750	2010	2290	2900
(159)	(17.8)	(76.2)	(135)	(212)	(305)	(415)	(541.7)	(686)	(846)	(1220)	(1660)	(2170)	(2740)	(3060)	(3390)	(3730)	(4100)	(4870)	(5720)	(6640)	(7620)	(8670)	(11000)
24	59.7	20.6	36.5	57.1	82.2	112	146	185	228	329	448	585	740	825	914	1010	1110	1320	1540	1790	2060	2340	2960
(166)	(18.2)	(77.8)	(138)	(216)	(311)	(424)	(553.3)	(700)	(865)	(1240)	(1690)	(2210)	(2800)	(3120)	(3460)	(3810)	(4180)	(4980)	(5840)	(6780)	(7780)	(8850)	(11200)
25	61.0	21.0	37.3	58.3	83.9	114	149	189	233	336	457	597	755	842	933	1030	1130	1340	1580	1830	2100	2390	3020
(172)	(18.6)	(79.4)	(141)	(221)	(318)	(432)	(564.7)	(715)	(882)	(1270)	(1730)	(2260)	(2860)	(3190)	(3530)	(3890)	(4270)	(5080)	(5960)	(6920)	(7940)	(9040)	(11400)
26	62.2	21.4	38.0	59.4	85.6	116	152	193	238	342	466	609	770	858	951	1050	1150	1370	1610	1860	2140	2430	3080
(179)	(19.0)	(81.0)	(144)	(225)	(324)	(441)	(575.9)	(729)	(900)	(1300)	(1760)	(2300)	(2920)	(3250)	(3600)	(3970)	(4360)	(5180)	(6080)	(7050)	(8100)	(9210)	(11700)
27	63.4	21.8	38.8	60.6	87.2	119	155	196	242	349	475	620	785	875	969	1070	1170	1400	1640	1900	2180	2480	3140
(186)	(19.3)	(82.5)	(147)	(229)	(330)	(449)	(586.9)	(743)	(917)	(1320)	(1800)	(2350)	(2970)	(3310)	(3670)	(4040)	(4440)	(5280)	(6200)	(7190)	(8250)	(9390)	(11900)
28	64.5	22.2	39.5	61.7	88.8	121	158	200	247	355	484	632	799	891	987	1090	1190	1420	1670	1930	2220	2530	3200
(193)	(19.7)	(84.0)	(149)	(233)	(336)	(458)	(597.6)	(756)	(934)	(1340)	(1830)	(2390)	(3030)	(3370)	(3740)	(4120)	(4520)	(5380)	(6310)	(7320)	(8400)	(9560)	(12100)
29	65.7	22.6	40.2	62.8	90.4	123	161	203	251	362	492	643	814	906	1000	1110	1220	1450	1700	1970	2260	2570	3250
(200)	(20.0)	(85.5)	(152)	(238)	(342)	(466)	(608.2)	(770)	(950)	(1370)	(1860)	(2430)	(3080)	(3430)	(3800)	(4190)	(4600)	(5470)	(6420)	(7450)	(8550)	(9730)	(12300)
30	66.8	23.0	40.9	63.8	91.9	125	163	207	255	368	501	654	827	922	1020	1130	1240	1470	1730	2000	2300	2620	3310
(207)	(20.4)	(87.0)	(155)	(242)	(348)	(474)	(618.6)	(783)	(967)	(1390)	(1890)	(2470)	(3130)	(3490)	(3870)	(4260)	(4680)	(5570)	(6530)	(7580)	(8700)	(9900)	(12500)
31	67.9	23.4	41.5	64.9	93.5	127	166	210	260	374	509	665	841	937	1040	1140	1260	1500	1750	2040	2340	2660	3360
(214)	(20.7)	(88.4)	(157)	(246)	(354)	(481)	(628.8)	(796)	(983)	(1410)	(1930)	(2520)	(3180)	(3550)	(3930)	(4330)	(4760)	(5660)	(6640)	(7700)	(8840)	(10100)	(12700)
32	69.0	23.7	42.2	65.9	95.0	129	169	214	264	380	517	675	855	952	1060	1160	1280	1520	1780	2070	2370	2700	3420
(221)	(21.0)	(89.8)	(160)	(250)	(359)	(489)	(638.9)	(809)	(998)	(1440)	(1960)	(2560)	(3230)	(3600)	(3990)	(4400)	(4830)	(5750)	(6750)	(7830)	(8980)	(10200)	(12900)
33	70.1	24.1	42.9	67.0	96.4	131	171	217	268	386	525	686	868	967	1070	1180	1300	1540	1810	2100	2410	2740	3470
(228)	(21.4)	(91.2)	(162)	(253)	(365)	(497)	(648.8)	(821)	(1010)	(1460)	(1990)	(2600)	(3280)	(3660)	(4060)	(4470)	(4910)	(5840)	(6850)	(7950)	(9120)	(10400)	(13100)
34	71.1	24.5	43.5	68.0	97.9	133	174	220	272	391	533	696	881	981	1090	1200	1320	1570	1840	2130	2450	2780	3520
(234)	(21.7)	(92.6)	(165)	(257)	(370)	(504)	(658.6)	(834)	(1030)	(1480)	(2020)	(2630)	(3330)	(3710)	(4120)	(4540)	(4980)	(5930)	(6960)	(8070)	(9260)	(10500)	(13300)
35	72.1	24.8	44.1	69.0	99.3	135	177	223	276	397	541	706	894	996	1100	1220	1340	1590	1860	2160	2480	2820	3570
(241)	(22.0)	(94.0)	(167)	(261)	(376)	(512)	(668.2)	(846)	(1040)	(1500)	(2050)	(2670)	(3380)	(3770)	(4180)	(4600)	(5050)	(6010)	(7060)	(8190)	(9400)	(10700)	(13500)
36	73.2	25.2	44.8	69.9	101	137	179	227	280	403	548	716	906	1010	1120	1230	1350	1610	1890	2190	2520	2860	3630
(248)	(22.3)	(95.3)	(169)	(265)	(381)	(519)	(677.7)	(858)	(1060)	(1520)	(2080)	(2710)	(3430)	(3820)	(4240)	(4670)	(5120)	(6100)	(7160)	(8300)	(9530)	(10800)	(13700)

TABLE 5-2A. *Theoretical Flow Through Circular Orifices–GPM (L/min) (Continued)*

This table is computed from the formula $Q = 29.84cd^2\sqrt{p}\,(Q_m = 0.0666cd_m^2\sqrt{p_{vm}})$ with c = 1.00. The theoretical discharge of sea water, as from fireboat nozzles, may be found by subtracting 1 percent from the figures in the following table, or from the formula $Q = 29.47cd^2\sqrt{p}\,(Q_m = 0.065cd_m^2\sqrt{p_{vm}})$.

When pressures are read with a Pitot gage at a nozzle, the nozzle discharge in most cases will correspond to the values in the tables within a range of 1 to 3 percent for nozzles up to 1⅜ in. in diameter. For larger diameter nozzles, the principles discussed in "The Nozzle Method of Measuring Flow" in this chapter of the *Handbook* apply. Appropriate coefficients should be applied where it is read from a hydrant outlet. Where more accurate results are required, a coefficient appropriate to the particular nozzle must be selected and applied to the figures of the table.

The discharge from circular openings of sizes other than those in the table may readily be computed by applying the principle that quantity discharged under a given head varies as the squre of the diameter of the opening.

Pres.	Velocity	Orifice Diameter, Inches (mm)																					
PSI (kPa)	ft/sec (m/sec)	3/8 (9.53)	1/2 (12.7)	5/8 (15.9)	3/4 (19.1)	7/8 (22.2)	1 (25.4)	1-1/8 (28.6)	1-1/4 (31.8)	1-1/2 (38.1)	1-3/4 (44.5)	2 (50.8)	2-1/4 (57.2)	2-3/8 (60.3)	2-1/2 (63.5)	2-5/8 (66.7)	2-3/4 (69.9)	3 (76.2)	3-1/4 (82.6)	3-1/2 (88.9)	3-3/4 (95.3)	4 (102)	4-1/2 (114)
37	74.2	25.5	45.4	70.9	102	139	182	230	284	408	556	726	919	1020	1130	1250	1370	1630	1920	2220	2550	2900	3680
(255)	(22.6)	(96.6)	(172)	(268)	(386)	(526)	(687)	(870)	(1070)	(1550)	(2100)	(2750)	(3480)	(3880)	(4290)	(4730)	(5200)	(6180)	(7260)	(8420)	(9660)	(11000)	(13900)
38	75.2	25.9	46.0	71.9	103	141	184	233	287	414	563	736	931	1040	1150	1270	1390	1660	1940	2250	2590	2940	3720
(262)	(22.9)	(97.9)	(174)	(272)	(392)	(533)	(696.2)	(881)	(1090)	(1570)	(2130)	(2780)	(3520)	(3930)	(4350)	(4800)	(5270)	(6270)	(7350)	(8530)	(9790)	(11100)	(14100)
39	76.2	26.2	46.6	72.8	105	143	186	236	291	419	571	745	943	1050	1160	1280	1410	1680	1970	2280	2620	2980	3770
(269)	(23.2)	(99.2)	(176)	(276)	(397)	(540)	(705.3)	(893)	(1100)	(1590)	(2160)	(2820)	(3570)	(3980)	(4410)	(4860)	(5330)	(6350)	(7450)	(8640)	(9920)	(11300)	(14300)
40	77.1	26.5	47.2	73.7	106	144	189	239	295	425	578	755	955	1060	1180	1300	1430	1700	1990	2310	2650	3020	3820
(276)	(23.5)	(100)	(179)	(279)	(402)	(547)	(714.3)	(904)	(1120)	(1610)	(2190)	(2860)	(3620)	(4030)	(4460)	(4920)	(5400)	(6430)	(7550)	(8750)	(10000)	(11400)	(14500)
41	78.1	26.9	47.8	74.6	107	146	191	242	299	430	585	764	967	1080	1190	1320	1440	1720	2020	2340	2690	3060	3870
(283)	(23.8)	(102)	(181)	(282)	(407)	(554)	(723.2)	(915)	(1130)	(1630)	(2210)	(2890)	(3660)	(4080)	(4520)	(4980)	(5470)	(6510)	(7640)	(8860)	(10200)	(11600)	(14600)
42	79.0	27.2	48.3	75.5	109	148	193	245	302	435	592	774	979	1090	1210	1330	1460	1740	2040	2370	2720	3090	3920
(290)	(24.1)	(103)	(183)	(286)	(412)	(560)	(732)	(926)	(1140)	(1650)	(2240)	(2930)	(3710)	(4130)	(4570)	(5040)	(5540)	(6590)	(7730)	(8970)	(10300)	(11700)	(14800)
43	80.0	27.5	48.9	76.4	110	150	196	248	306	440	599	783	991	1100	1220	1350	1480	1760	2070	2400	2750	3130	3960
(297)	(24.4)	(104)	(185)	(289)	(417)	(567)	(740.6)	(937)	(1160)	(1670)	(2270)	(2960)	(3750)	(4180)	(4630)	(5100)	(5600)	(6670)	(7820)	(9070)	(10400)	(11900)	(15000)
44	80.9	27.8	49.5	77.3	111	152	198	251	309	445	606	792	1000	1120	1240	1360	1500	1780	2090	2420	2780	3170	4010
(303)	(24.7)	(105)	(187)	(293)	(421)	(574)	(749.2)	(948)	(1170)	(1690)	(2290)	(3000)	(3790)	(4230)	(4680)	(5160)	(5670)	(6740)	(7910)	(9180)	(10500)	(12000)	(15200)
45	81.8	28.1	50.0	78.2	113	153	200	253	313	450	613	801	1010	1130	1250	1380	1510	1800	2110	2450	2810	3200	4050
(310)	(24.9)	(107)	(189)	(296)	(426)	(580)	(757.7)	(959)	(1180)	(1700)	(2320)	(3030)	(3840)	(4270)	(4740)	(5220)	(5730)	(6820)	(8000)	(9280)	(10700)	(12100)	(15300)
46	82.7	28.5	50.6	79.1	114	155	202	256	316	455	620	810	1020	1140	1260	1390	1530	1820	2140	2480	2850	3240	4100
(317)	(25.2)	(108)	(192)	(299)	(431)	(586)	(766)	(970)	(1200)	(1720)	(2350)	(3060)	(3880)	(4320)	(4790)	(5280)	(5790)	(6890)	(8090)	(9380)	(10800)	(12300)	(15500)
47	83.6	28.8	51.1	79.9	115	157	205	259	320	460	627	818	1040	1150	1280	1410	1550	1840	2160	2510	2880	3270	4140
(324)	(25.5)	(109)	(194)	(302)	(436)	(593)	(774.3)	(980)	(1210)	(1740)	(2370)	(3100)	(3920)	(4370)	(4840)	(5340)	(5860)	(6970)	(8180)	(9490)	(10900)	(12400)	(15700)
48	84.5	29.1	51.7	80.8	116	158	207	262	323	465	633	827	1050	1170	1290	1420	1560	1860	2180	2530	2910	3310	4190
(331)	(25.8)	(110)	(196)	(306)	(440)	(599)	(782.5)	(990)	(1220)	(1760)	(2400)	(3130)	(3960)	(4410)	(4890)	(5390)	(5920)	(7040)	(8270)	(9590)	(11000)	(12500)	(15800)
49	85.4	29.4	52.2	81.6	117	160	209	264	326	470	640	836	1060	1180	1310	1440	1580	1880	2210	2560	2940	3340	4230
(338)	(26.0)	(111)	(198)	(309)	(445)	(605)	(790.6)	(1000)	(1240)	(1780)	(2420)	(3160)	(4000)	(4460)	(4940)	(5450)	(5980)	(7120)	(8350)	(9680)	(11100)	(12600)	(16000)
50	86.2	29.7	52.8	82.4	119	162	211	267	330	475	646	844	1070	1190	1320	1450	1600	1900	2230	2580	2970	3380	4270
(345)	(26.3)	(112)	(200)	(312)	(449)	(611)	(798.6)	(1010)	(1250)	(1800)	(2450)	(3190)	(4040)	(4500)	(4990)	(5500)	(6040)	(7190)	(8440)	(9780)	(11200)	(12800)	(16200)
52	87.9	30.3	53.8	84.1	121	165	215	272	336	484	659	861	1090	1210	1340	1480	1630	1940	2270	2640	3030	3440	4360
(359)	(26.8)	(115)	(204)	(318)	(458)	(624)	(814.5)	(1030)	(1270)	(1830)	(2490)	(3260)	(4120)	(4590)	(5090)	(5610)	(6160)	(7330)	(8600)	(9980)	(11500)	(13000)	(16500)
54	89.6	30.8	54.8	85.7	123	168	219	278	343	493	672	877	1110	1240	1370	1510	1660	1970	2320	2690	3080	3510	4440
(372)	(27.3)	(117)	(207)	(324)	(467)	(635)	(830)	(1050)	(1300)	(1870)	(2540)	(3320)	(4200)	(4680)	(5190)	(5720)	(6280)	(7470)	(8770)	(10200)	(11700)	(13300)	(16800)
56	91.3	31.4	55.8	87.2	126	171	223	283	349	502	684	893	1130	1260	1400	1540	1690	2010	2360	2740	3140	3570	4520
(386)	(27.8)	(119)	(211)	(330)	(475)	(647)	(845.2)	(1070)	(1320)	(1900)	(2590)	(3380)	(4280)	(4770)	(5280)	(5820)	(6390)	(7610)	(8930)	(10400)	(11900)	(13500)	(17100)
58	92.9	32.0	56.8	88.8	128	174	227	288	355	511	696	909	1150	1280	1420	1570	1720	2050	2400	2780	3200	3640	4600
(400)	(28.3)	(121)	(215)	(336)	(484)	(659)	(860.2)	(1090)	(1340)	(1940)	(2630)	(3440)	(4350)	(4850)	(5380)	(5930)	(6500)	(7740)	(9090)	(10500)	(12100)	(13800)	(17400)

TABLE 5-2A. *Theoretical Flow Through Circular Orifices–GPM (L/min) (Continued)*

This table is computed from the formula $Q = 29.84cd^2\sqrt{p}\,(Q_m = 0.0666cd_m^2\sqrt{p_{vm}})$ with c = 1.00. The theoretical discharge of sea water, as from fireboat nozzles, may be found by subtracting 1 percent from the figures in the following table, or from the formula $Q = 29.47cd^2\sqrt{p}\,(Q_m = 0.065cd_m^2\sqrt{p_{vm}})$.

When pressures are read with a Pitot gage at a nozzle, the nozzle discharge in most cases will correspond to the values in the tables within a range of 1 to 3 percent for nozzles up to 1⅜ in. in diameter. For larger diameter nozzles, the principles discussed in "The Nozzle Method of Measuring Flow" in this chapter of the *Handbook* apply. Appropriate coefficients should be applied where it is read from a hydrant outlet. Where more accurate results are required, a coefficient appropriate to the particular nozzle must be selected and applied to the figures of the table.

The discharge from circular openings of sizes other than those in the table may readily be computed by applying the principle that quantity discharged under a given head varies as the squre of the diameter of the opening.

Pres. PSI (kPa)	Velocity ft/sec (m/sec)	3/8 (9.53)	1/2 (12.7)	5/8 (15.9)	3/4 (19.1)	7/8 (22.2)	1 (25.4)	1-1/8 (28.6)	1-1/4 (31.8)	1-1/2 (38.1)	1-3/4 (44.5)	2 (50.8)	2-1/4 (57.2)	2-3/8 (60.3)	2-1/2 (63.5)	2-5/8 (66.7)	2-3/4 (69.9)	3 (76.2)	3-1/4 (82.6)	3-1/2 (88.9)	3-3/4 (95.3)	4 (102)	4-1/2 (114)
		Orifice Diameter Inches (mm)																					
60	94.5	32.5	57.8	90.3	130	177	231	293	361	520	708	925	1170	1300	1440	1590	1750	2080	2440	2830	3250	3700	4680
(414)	(28.8)	(123)	(219)	(342)	(492)	(670)	(874.9)	(1110)	(1370)	(1970)	(2680)	(3500)	(4430)	(4930)	(5470)	(6030)	(6620)	(7870)	(9240)	(10700)	(12300)	(14000)	(17700)
62	96.0	33.0	58.7	91.8	132	180	235	297	367	529	720	940	1190	1330	1470	1620	1780	2110	2480	2880	3300	3760	4760
(428)	(29.3)	(125)	(222)	(347)	(500)	(681)	(889.3)	(1130)	(1390)	(2000)	(2720)	(3560)	(4500)	(5020)	(5560)	(6130)	(6730)	(8000)	(9390)	(10900)	(12500)	(14200)	(18000)
64	97.6	33.6	59.7	93.3	134	183	239	302	373	537	731	955	1210	1350	1490	1640	1810	2150	2520	2920	3360	3820	4830
(441)	(29.7)	(127)	(226)	(353)	(508)	(692)	(903.6)	(1140)	(1410)	(2030)	(2770)	(3610)	(4570)	(5100)	(5650)	(6230)	(6830)	(8130)	(9540)	(11100)	(12700)	(14500)	(18300)
66	99.1	34.1	60.6	94.7	136	186	242	307	379	545	742	970	1230	1370	1520	1670	1830	2180	2560	2970	3410	3880	4910
(455)	(30.2)	(129)	(229)	(358)	(516)	(703)	(917.6)	(1160)	(1430)	(2060)	(2810)	(3670)	(4650)	(5180)	(5730)	(6320)	(6940)	(8260)	(9690)	(11200)	(12900)	(14700)	(18600)
68	101	34.6	61.5	96.1	138	188	246	311	384	554	754	984	1250	1390	1540	1700	1860	2210	2600	3010	3460	3940	4980
(469)	(30.7)	(131)	(233)	(364)	(524)	(713)	(931.4)	(1180)	(1460)	(2100)	(2850)	(3730)	(4720)	(5250)	(5820)	(6420)	(7040)	(8380)	(9840)	(11400)	(13100)	(14900)	(18900)
70	102	35.1	62.4	97.5	140	191	250	316	390	562	765	999	1260	1410	1560	1720	1890	2250	2640	3060	3510	3990	5060
(483)	(31.1)	(133)	(236)	(369)	(532)	(723)	(945)	(1200)	(1480)	(2130)	(2890)	(3780)	(4780)	(5330)	(5910)	(6510)	(7150)	(8500)	(9980)	(11600)	(13300)	(15100)	(19100)
72	103	35.6	63.3	98.9	142	194	253	320	396	570	775	1010	1280	1430	1580	1740	1910	2280	2670	3100	3560	4050	5130
(497)	(31.5)	(135)	(240)	(374)	(539)	(734)	(958.4)	(1210)	(1500)	(2160)	(2930)	(3830)	(4850)	(5410)	(5990)	(6600)	(7250)	(8630)	(10100)	(11700)	(13500)	(15300)	(19400)
74	105	36.1	64.2	100	144	197	257	325	401	578	786	1030	1300	1450	1600	1770	1940	2310	2710	3140	3610	4110	5200
(510)	(32.0)	(137)	(243)	(380)	(547)	(744)	(971.6)	(1230)	(1520)	(2190)	(2980)	(3890)	(4920)	(5480)	(6070)	(6690)	(7350)	(8740)	(10300)	(11900)	(13700)	(15500)	(19700)
76	106	36.6	65.0	102	146	199	260	329	406	585	797	1040	1320	1470	1630	1790	1970	2340	2750	3190	3660	4160	5270
(524)	(32.4)	(138)	(246)	(385)	(554)	(754)	(984.6)	(1250)	(1540)	(2220)	(3020)	(3940)	(4980)	(5550)	(6150)	(6780)	(7450)	(8860)	(10400)	(12100)	(13800)	(15800)	(19900)
78	108	37.1	65.9	103	148	202	264	334	412	593	807	1050	1330	1490	1650	1820	1990	2370	2780	3230	3710	4220	5340
(538)	(32.8)	(140)	(249)	(390)	(561)	(764)	(997.5)	(1260)	(1560)	(2240)	(3050)	(3990)	(5050)	(5630)	(6230)	(6870)	(7540)	(8980)	(10500)	(12200)	(14000)	(16000)	(20200)
80	109	37.5	66.7	104	150	204	267	338	417	601	817	1070	1350	1510	1670	1840	2020	2400	2820	3270	3750	4270	5400
(552)	(33.2)	(142)	(253)	(395)	(568)	(773)	(1010)	(1280)	(1580)	(2270)	(3090)	(4040)	(5110)	(5700)	(6310)	(6960)	(7640)	(9090)	(10700)	(12400)	(14200)	(16200)	(20500)
82	110	38.0	67.6	106	152	207	270	342	422	608	828	1080	1370	1520	1690	1860	2040	2430	2850	3310	3800	4320	5470
(566)	(33.7)	(144)	(256)	(400)	(575)	(783)	(1020)	(1290)	(1600)	(2300)	(3130)	(4090)	(5180)	(5770)	(6390)	(7050)	(7730)	(9200)	(10800)	(12500)	(14400)	(16400)	(20700)
84	112	38.5	68.4	107	154	209	273	346	427	615	838	1090	1380	1540	1710	1880	2070	2460	2890	3350	3850	4380	5540
(579)	(34.1)	(146)	(259)	(404)	(582)	(793)	(1040)	(1310)	(1620)	(2330)	(3170)	(4140)	(5240)	(5840)	(6470)	(7130)	(7830)	(9320)	(10900)	(12700)	(14600)	(16600)	(21000)
86	113	38.9	69.2	108	156	212	277	350	432	623	847	1110	1400	1560	1730	1910	2090	2490	2920	3390	3890	4430	5600
(593)	(34.5)	(147)	(262)	(409)	(589)	(802)	(1050)	(1330)	(1640)	(2360)	(3210)	(4190)	(5300)	(5910)	(6550)	(7220)	(7920)	(9430)	(11100)	(12800)	(14700)	(16800)	(21200)
88	114	39.4	70.0	109	157	214	280	354	437	630	857	1120	1420	1580	1750	1930	2120	2520	2960	3430	3940	4480	5670
(607)	(34.9)	(149)	(265)	(414)	(596)	(811)	(1060)	(1340)	(1660)	(2380)	(3240)	(4240)	(5360)	(5980)	(6620)	(7300)	(8010)	(9540)	(11200)	(13000)	(14900)	(17000)	(21500)
90	116	39.8	70.8	111	159	217	283	358	442	637	867	1130	1430	1600	1770	1950	2140	2550	2990	3470	3980	4530	5730
(621)	(35.3)	(151)	(268)	(419)	(603)	(820)	(1070)	(1360)	(1670)	(2410)	(3280)	(4290)	(5420)	(6040)	(6700)	(7380)	(8100)	(9640)	(11300)	(13100)	(15100)	(17100)	(21700)
92	117	40.2	71.6	112	161	219	286	362	447	644	877	1140	1450	1610	1790	1970	2160	2580	3020	3510	4020	4580	5800
(634)	(35.7)	(152)	(271)	(423)	(609)	(829)	(1080)	(1370)	(1690)	(2440)	(3320)	(4330)	(5480)	(6110)	(6770)	(7460)	(8190)	(9750)	(11400)	(13300)	(15200)	(17300)	(21900)
94	118	40.7	72.3	113	163	222	289	366	452	651	886	1160	1460	1630	1810	1990	2190	2600	3060	3540	4070	4630	5860
(648)	(36.0)	(154)	(274)	(428)	(616)	(838)	(1100)	(1390)	(1710)	(2460)	(3350)	(4380)	(5540)	(6180)	(6840)	(7550)	(8280)	(9860)	(11600)	(13400)	(15400)	(17500)	(22200)

TABLE 5-2A. *Theoretical Flow Through Circular Orifices–GPM (L/min) (Continued)*

This table is computed from the formula $Q = 29.84cd^2\sqrt{\rho}$ ($Q_m = 0.0666cd_m^2\sqrt{\rho_{vm}}$) with c = 1.00. The theoretical discharge of sea water, as from fireboat nozzles, may be found by subtracting 1 percent from the figures in the following table, or from the formula $Q = 29.47cd^2\sqrt{\rho}$ ($Q_m = 0.065cd_m^2\sqrt{\rho_{vm}}$).

When pressures are read with a Pitot gage at a nozzle, the nozzle discharge in most cases will correspond to the values in the tables within a range of 1 to 3 percent for nozzles up to 1⅜ in. in diameter. For larger diameter nozzles, the principles discussed in "The Nozzle Method of Measuring Flow" in this chapter of the *Handbook* apply. Appropriate coefficients should be applied where it is read from a hydrant outlet. Where more accurate results are required, a coefficient appropriate to the particular nozzle must be selected and applied to the figures of the table.

The discharge from circular openings of sizes other than those in the table may readily be computed by applying the principle that quantity discharged under a given head varies as the squre of the diameter of the opening.

Pres. PSI (kPa)	Velocity ft/sec (m/sec)	Orifice Diameter Inches (mm) 3/8 (9.53)	1/2 (12.7)	5/8 (15.9)	3/4 (19.1)	7/8 (22.2)	1 (25.4)	1-1/8 (28.6)	1-1/4 (31.8)	1-1/2 (38.1)	1-3/4 (44.5)	2 (50.8)	2-1/4 (57.2)	2-3/8 (60.3)	2-1/2 (63.5)	2-5/8 (66.7)	2-3/4 (69.9)	3 (76.2)	3-1/4 (82.6)	3-1/2 (88.9)	3-3/4 (95.3)	4 (102)	4-1/2 (114)
96	119	41.1	73.1	114	164	224	292	370	457	658	895	1170	1480	1650	1830	2010	2210	2630	3090	3580	4110	4680	5920
(662)	(36.4)	(156)	(277)	(432)	(622)	(847)	(1110)	(1400)	(1730)	(2490)	(3390)	(4430)	(5600)	(6240)	(6920)	(7630)	(8370)	(9960)	(11700)	(13600)	(15600)	(17700)	(22400)
98	121	41.5	73.9	115	166	226	295	374	462	665	905	1180	1500	1670	1850	2040	2230	2660	3120	3620	4150	4730	5980
(676)	(36.8)	(157)	(280)	(437)	(629)	(856)	(1120)	(1420)	(1750)	(2520)	(3420)	(4470)	(5660)	(6310)	(6990)	(7700)	(8460)	(10100)	(11800)	(13700)	(15700)	(17900)	(22600)
100	122	42.0	74.6	117	168	228	298	378	466	671	914	1190	1510	1680	1870	2060	2260	2690	3150	3660	4200	4770	6040
(690)	(37.2)	(159)	(282)	(441)	(635)	(865)	(1130)	(1430)	(1760)	(2540)	(3460)	(4520)	(5720)	(6370)	(7060)	(7780)	(8540)	(10200)	(11900)	(13800)	(15900)	(18100)	(22900)
105	125	43.0	76.4	119	172	234	306	387	478	688	936	1220	1550	1720	1910	2110	2310	2750	3230	3750	4300	4890	6190
(724)	(38.1)	(163)	(289)	(452)	(651)	(886)	(1160)	(1460)	(1810)	(2600)	(3540)	(4630)	(5860)	(6530)	(7230)	(7970)	(8750)	(10400)	(12200)	(14200)	(16300)	(18500)	(23400)
110	128	44.0	78.2	122	176	240	313	396	489	704	958	1250	1580	1770	1960	2160	2370	2820	3310	3830	4400	5010	6340
(759)	(39.0)	(167)	(296)	(463)	(666)	(907)	(1180)	(1500)	(1850)	(2670)	(3630)	(4740)	(6000)	(6680)	(7400)	(8160)	(8960)	(10700)	(12500)	(14500)	(16700)	(19000)	(24000)
115	131	45.0	80.0	125	180	245	320	405	500	720	980	1280	1620	1800	2000	2200	2420	2880	3380	3920	4500	5120	6480
(793)	(39.9)	(170)	(303)	(473)	(681)	(927)	(1210)	(1530)	(1890)	(2730)	(3710)	(4840)	(6130)	(6830)	(7570)	(8350)	(9160)	(10900)	(12800)	(14800)	(17000)	(19400)	(24500)
120	134	46.0	81.7	128	184	250	327	414	511	735	1000	1310	1650	1840	2040	2250	2470	2940	3450	4000	4600	5230	6620
(828)	(40.7)	(174)	(309)	(483)	(696)	(947)	(1240)	(1570)	(1930)	(2780)	(3790)	(4950)	(6260)	(6980)	(7730)	(8530)	(9360)	(11100)	(13100)	(15200)	(17400)	(19800)	(25100)
125	136	46.9	83.4	130	188	255	334	422	521	751	1020	1330	1690	1880	2090	2300	2520	3000	3520	4090	4690	5340	6760
(862)	(41.6)	(178)	(316)	(493)	(710)	(967)	(1260)	(1600)	(1970)	(2840)	(3870)	(5050)	(6390)	(7120)	(7890)	(8700)	(9550)	(11400)	(13300)	(15500)	(17800)	(20200)	(25600)
130	139	47.8	85.1	133	191	260	340	431	532	766	1040	1360	1720	1920	2130	2340	2570	3060	3590	4170	4780	5440	6890
(897)	(42.4)	(181)	(322)	(503)	(724)	(986)	(1290)	(1630)	(2010)	(2900)	(3940)	(5150)	(6520)	(7260)	(8050)	(8870)	(9740)	(11600)	(13600)	(15800)	(18100)	(20600)	(26100)
135	142	48.8	86.7	135	195	265	347	439	542	780	1060	1390	1760	1960	2170	2390	2620	3120	3660	4250	4880	5550	7020
(931)	(43.2)	(185)	(328)	(513)	(738)	(1000)	(1310)	(1660)	(2050)	(2950)	(4020)	(5250)	(6640)	(7400)	(8200)	(9040)	(9920)	(11800)	(13900)	(16100)	(18500)	(21000)	(26600)
140	144	49.7	88.3	138	199	270	353	447	552	794	1080	1410	1790	1990	2210	2430	2670	3180	3730	4330	4970	5650	7150
(966)	(44.0)	(188)	(334)	(522)	(752)	(1020)	(1340)	(1690)	(2090)	(3010)	(4090)	(5350)	(6770)	(7540)	(8350)	(9210)	(10100)	(12000)	(14100)	(16400)	(18800)	(21400)	(27100)
145	147	50.5	89.8	140	202	275	359	455	561	808	1100	1440	1820	2030	2250	2480	2720	3230	3800	4400	5050	5750	7280
(1000)	(44.8)	(191)	(340)	(531)	(765)	(1040)	(1360)	(1720)	(2130)	(3060)	(4170)	(5440)	(6890)	(7670)	(8500)	(9370)	(10300)	(12200)	(14400)	(16700)	(19100)	(21800)	(27500)
150	149	51.4	91.4	143	206	280	365	463	571	822	1120	1460	1850	2060	2280	2520	2760	3290	3860	4480	5140	5850	7400
(1030)	(45.5)	(195)	(346)	(540)	(778)	(1060)	(1380)	(1750)	(2160)	(3110)	(4240)	(5530)	(7000)	(7800)	(8650)	(9530)	(10500)	(12400)	(14600)	(16900)	(19500)	(22100)	(28000)

The coefficient of discharge, c_d, is defined as the ratio of the actual discharge to the theoretical discharge. For any specific orifice or nozzle, values of c_d are determined by standard test procedures using this definition. The actual rate of flow is measured by calibrated meters, or "weigh tanks." The theoretical flow is calculated using, $c_d = 1$, the carefully measured orifice or nozzle diameter, and the measured velocity pressure in the flow equation.

Standard orifice: An orifice with a sharp entrance edge, shown as form (1) in Figure 5-2D, is known as a standard orifice, and is commonly used to measure water flow. As water leaves the orifice, it contracts to form a jet whose cross-sectional area is less than that of the orifice. The contraction is complete at the plane a' (see Figure 5-2E), which is located a distance from the plane of the orifice equal to approximately half the diameter of the jet.

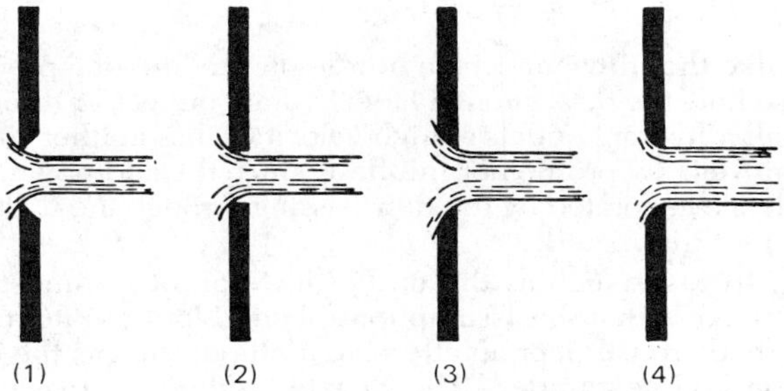

FIG. 5-2D. Orifices of various shapes. If the shape of the orifice is changed so as to decrease the contraction, its capacity will be increased. Form 1 in the illustration is a standard orifice having a sharp edge on the approach side. Form 2, when in a thin plate, gives the same stream characteristics as Form 1. Form 3 is the reverse of 1. In Form 4, the edge is rounded to conform to the shape of the stream. The coefficients of discharge of 3 and 4 are greater than those of the standard orifices, approaching a value of 1.0 in the case of 4.

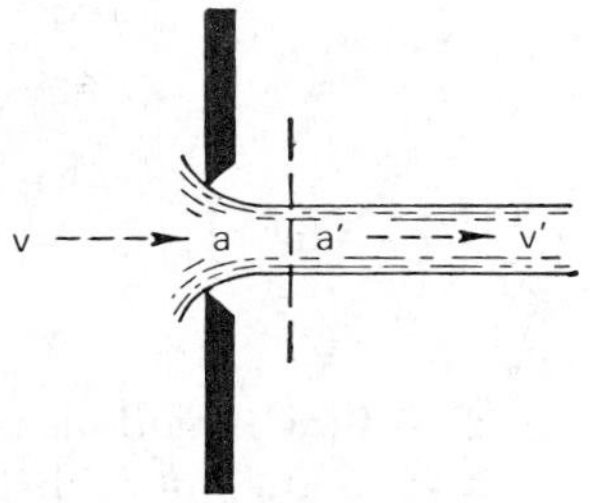

FIG. 5-2E. Flow through a standard orifice.

The quantity flowing is obviously the same at the orifice a as at the contracted section a', so the quantity flowing could be obtained by measuring the velocity and area at either of these planes. Expressed in a formula, where Q is cubic feet per second (m^3/sec), v is velocity in feet per second (m/sec), and a is the area in square ft (m^2):

$$Q = va = v'a'$$

The coefficient of discharge for a standard orifice is the product of the coefficient of velocity and the coefficient of contraction, or $c = 0.98 \times 0.62 = 0.61$.

Other orifices: The hydraulic characteristics of good solid-stream nozzles are consistent within a wide range of flow conditions. The velocity at the surface of the stream of most such nozzles is reduced slightly by friction against the orifice or nozzle. A coefficient of velocity of 0.97 is usually applied to nozzles of fire stream sizes to account for this friction.

Coefficients of discharge are available for the flow through hydrants, hose nozzles, automatic sprinklers, and other common fire protection discharge outlets. Representative values for the coefficients of discharge are given in Table 5-2B. Again, these coefficients only apply when there is flow through the full orifice or nozzle opening with a reasonably uniform velocity profile.

TABLE 5-2B. ***Typical Discharge Coefficients of Solid Stream Nozzles***

Spray sprinkler, average (nominal ½ in. dia.)	0.75
/Spray Sprinkler, average (nominal 17/32 in. dia.)	0.95
/Large Drop Sprinkler, (0.64 in. dia.)	0.90
Standard orifice (sharp edge)	0.62
Smooth bore nozzles, general	0.96–0.98
Underwriter playpipes or equal	0.97
Deluge or monitor nozzles	0.997
Open pipe, smooth, well rounded	0.90
Open pipe, burred opening	0.80
* Hydrant butt, smooth and well-rounded outlet, flowing full	0.90
* Hydrant butt, square and sharp at hydrant barrel	0.80
* Hydrant butt, outlet square, projecting into barrel	0.70

* See Figure 5-2F.

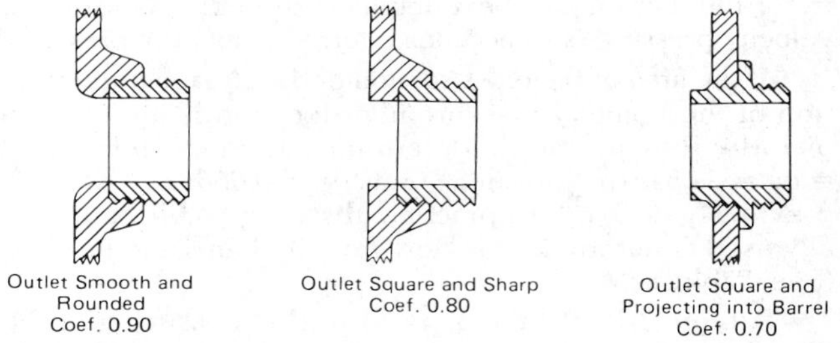

FIG. 5-2F. Three general types of hydrant outlets and their coefficients of discharge.

Flow in short tubes: A tube attached to an orifice is known as a standard short tube if it is 2½ to 3 times longer than the diameter of the orifice, and its diameter is the same as the orifice. A shorter tube will not flow full, and friction losses in a longer tube will affect results when used as a measuring device, hence the specified length limit.

The characteristics of a standard short tube and a short conical converging tube are shown in Figures 5-2G and 5-2H, respectively. The principles of flow in orifices apply, but with different coefficients. With the conical tube, the coefficients c_v and c_c vary with the angle ß. When ß is 0 degrees, the converging tube becomes a cylindrical tube, with $c_c = 1$ and $c_v = 0.82$; c_d is then 0.82. As the angle ß increases, the coefficient of contraction (c_c) develops and the coefficient of velocity (c_v) increases, approaching the

0.98 value for a sharp edge orifice. Relations are such that the coefficient of discharge attains a maximum value of 0.94 with a ß angle of about 13 degrees.

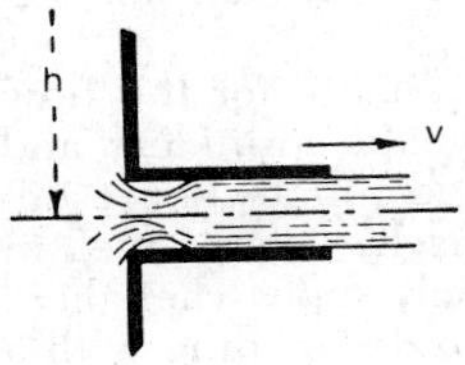

FIG. 5-2G. Flow in cylindrical short tube.

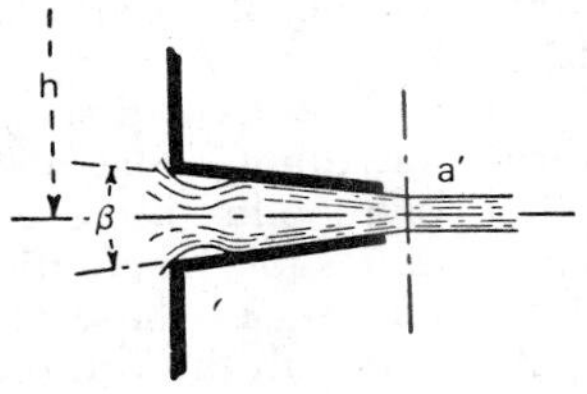

FIG. 5-2H. Flow in conical converging tube.

FLOW MEASUREMENT

Pitot Tube Method of Measuring Flow

The most commonly used method of measuring flow in an open stream discharging from an orifice, nozzle, or open pipe is by direct measurement of the velocity head that produces the flow. This measurement process makes use of the well-known Pitot tube and pressure gage combination of which representative forms are shown in Section 5, Chapter 8, "Tests of Water Supplies."

When the small opening [usually not over 1/16 in. (1.6 mm) in diameter] is inserted into the center of a stream at the point of maximum contraction, with the opening directly in the line of flow, the gage will indicate the total head at that location. With the stream open to the atmosphere, there will be no pressure head, so the indicated reading will be velocity head alone, and thus the velocity of the stream can be calculated directly. As a result, velocity pressure is sometimes referred to as Pitot pressure.

If the area of the cross section of the stream at the location of the velocity measurement location is known, the quantity flowing can be determined from the relation $Q = av = 29.84c_d d^2 \sqrt{p}$ or in SI units $q_m = 0.0666\, c_d\, d_m 2 \sqrt{p_{vmp}}$ previously derived. In practice, discharge tables are usually used to determine the flow from hydrants and nozzles. (See Table 5-2A.)

A typical Pitot tube as used in the measuring of the flow from a fire stream nozzle is shown in Figure 5-2I. For the usual forms of orifices and nozzles, the coefficient of discharge (c_d) is accurately known, so that $a = c_d \times$ actual discharge opening. For example, with a sharp edge orifice the area of the stream may be determined from the actual diameter of the orifice opening and the use of the 0.62 coefficient of discharge as outlined in the previous section on flow through orifices.

When measuring flow from a straight stream fire nozzle, the use of the Pitot tube method only holds with reasonable accuracy for tip sizes up to 1³/₈-in. (35 mm) supplied from 2¹/₂-in. (64 mm) hose. Above that, the error rate increases beyond acceptable limits, as the assumptions of uniform velocity and full flow become less valid. An exception is the Underwriters playpipe which maintains a uniform coefficient over a wide range of flows and pressures for tip sizes of 1¹/₈ or 1³/₄ in. (29 or 45 mm).

The Pitot tube method is also commonly used to measure the flow discharging from the outlets of fire hydrants to determine the water supply available for fire protection.

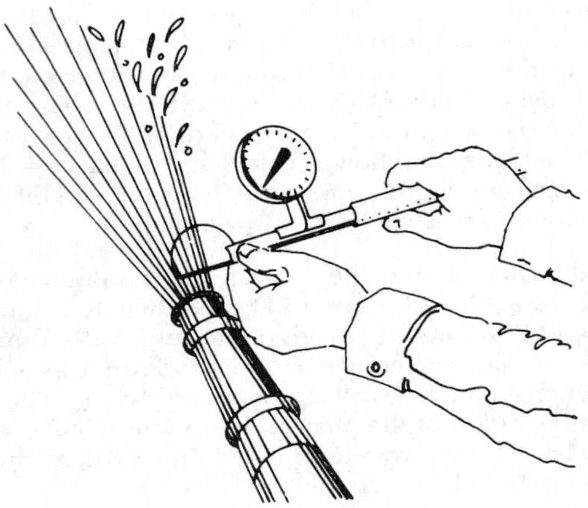

FIG. 5-2I. Taking nozzle pressure with a Pitot tube.

Unlike the flow entering a nozzle on the end of a pipe or hose line, the flow through large hydrant outlets, or through smaller hydrant outlets at high velocities, has neither a uniform velocity profile nor full flow, since the additional turbulence generated by the flow passing through the hydrant has not dissipated.

In cases such as these, the flow conditions must be changed so that the assumptions needed for the Pitot tube method are valid, or an alternate method, such as the one described next under "The Nozzle Method of Measuring Flow," should be used. If flow is from an open hydrant outlet, hoses and nozzles, a reducer, or a short tube can often be connected to the outlet to improve the flow characteristics.

The Nozzle Method Of Measuring Flow

The rate of discharge can also be calculated from the gage pressure at the base of the nozzle. The flow formula for using base pressure is:

$$Q = \frac{29.84cd^2\sqrt{p_1}}{\sqrt{1 - c^2\left(\frac{d}{D}\right)^4}}$$

where:

Q = flow in gallons per minute
c = coefficient of discharge
d = diameter of outlet, in inches
p_1 = gage pressure at base of nozzle, in psi
D = inside diameter of fitting to which gage is attached, in inches

For SI units, the formula is expressed as:

$$Q_m = \frac{0.0666cd_m^2\sqrt{p_{1m}}}{\sqrt{1 - c^2\left(\frac{d_m}{D_m}\right)^4}}$$

where:

Q_m = flow in liters per minute

c = coefficient of discharge

d_m = diameter of outlet, in mm

p_{1m} = gage pressure at base of nozzle, in kPa

D_m = inside diameter of fitting to which gage is attached, in mm.

This is the same formula that is used for discharge from an orifice, except that: (1) gage pressure at the base of the nozzle is substituted for Pitot pressure, and (2) a factor is added that represents the ratio between gage pressure (normal) and total pressure at the nozzle base. (Total pressure is gage plus velocity pressure.)

When base pressure is to be used, the gage is attached to a fitting close to the nozzle with a straight piece of approach pipe or hose to eliminate turbulence or unstable flow conditions. To obtain greater accuracy than provided by a simple fitting, a piezometer fitting may be used. With this device, the gage is connected to an annular tube or channel having a number of small holes drilled into the waterway around the circumference. The mean or resultant static pressure indicated by the gage is p_1 in the formula above.

Although accurate and convenient for fixed test arrangements, the measurement of pressure at the base of a nozzle is not practical for usual hose stream operations. However, because a Pitot gage is useless with spray-type nozzles, or other devices producing special types of discharge, the base pressure method is necessary.

Discharge Calculations

The most common method of estimating nozzle or orifice discharge is to use Table 5-2A. The flow from the table, corresponding to the measured Pitot pressure and orifice diameter, is multiplied by the discharge coefficient. (See Table 5-2B.)

EXAMPLE 1: A Pitot reading of 20 psi was measured on an open 2½-in. smooth and rounded hydrant butt. From Table 5-2B, the discharge coefficient is 0.90. The theoretical flow for a 20 psi velocity head is 834 gpm. The discharge is:

Q = 834 ×0.90 = 751 gpm. (Or subtract 10 percent from 834 and get 751 gpm.)

EXAMPLE 2: A pitot reading was 200 kPa at a 38.1 mm pipe with a square sharp opening (discharge coefficient = 0.80). From Table 5-2A, 200 kPa gives a theoretical flow of 1370 L/min. The actual flow would be 0.8 × 1370 = 1100 L/min.

Discharge curves, such as those shown in Figure 5-2J, are available for many nozzles and are sufficiently accurate for most fire flow calculations. These usually incorporate the specific discharge coefficients for the nozzle involved, but occasionally plot theoretical flow. Nozzle discharge can also be determined by the standard formulas previously discussed. (See "Flow of Water Through Orifices" and "The Nozzle Method of Measuring Flow," in this chapter).

EXAMPLE: Calculate the rate of discharge from a 2-in. (51 mm) nozzle with a pressure measured by a 2½-in. (64 mm) piezometer ring and gage of 80 psi (552 kPa) at the base of the nozzle. The nozzle has a coefficient of discharge of 0.99.

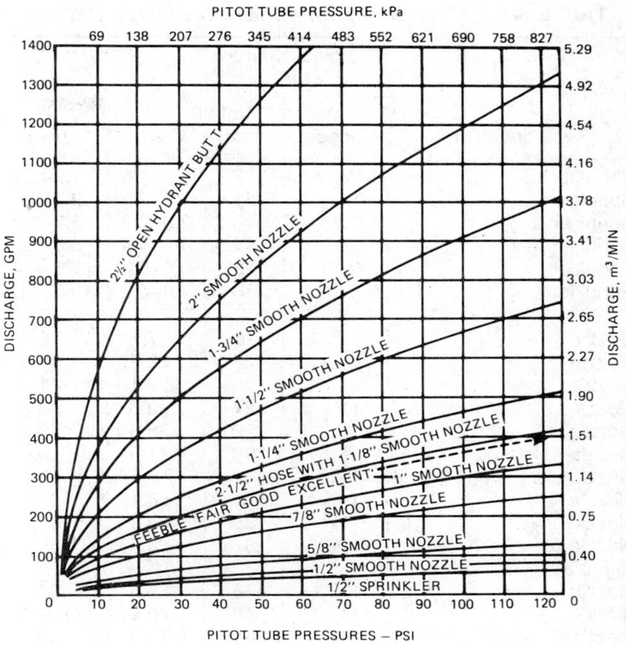

FIG. 5-2J. ***Relative discharge curves. (Source: Chemical Engineers' Handbook, McGraw-Hill Book Co.)***

Using the formula for the nozzle method of measuring flow:

$$Q = \frac{29.84cd^2\sqrt{p_1}}{\sqrt{1 - c^2\left(\dfrac{d}{D}\right)^4}}$$

$$Q = \frac{29.84 \times 0.99 \times (2)^2\sqrt{80}}{\sqrt{1 - (0.99)^2\left(\dfrac{2}{2.5}\right)^4}}$$

Q = 1366 gpm (5170 L/min).

To simplify calculations for a specific orifice or nozzle, the constants in the flow formula can be combined, reducing the formula to:

$$Q = k\sqrt{p}$$

where k combines the constants 29.84 (0.0666 in SI units), c_d, and d^2. Table 5-2C lists k factors of some common discharge orifices used for fire protection. For SI units, use the k_m values.

Because,

$$k = \frac{Q}{\sqrt{p}}$$

the k values of spray nozzles can be calculated from data in testing laboratory listings of nozzles. For some nozzles,

TABLE 5-2C. *Values of k for Various Discharge Orifices*

Type of Orifice	Nominal Diameter (Inches)	(mm) km	*k*	(S-I)
Sprinkler	1/4	7	1.3–1.5	1.9–2.2
Sprinkler	5/6	21	1.8–2.0	2.6–2.9
Sprinkler	3/6	10	2.6–2.9	3.7–4.2
Sprinkler	7/16	11	4.0–4.4	5.8–6.3
Sprinkler	1/2	13	5.3–5.8	7.6–8.4
Sprinkler	17/32	39	7.4–8.2	10.6–11.8
Nozzle	1/2	13	7.2	10.3
Nozzle	7/8	22	22.2	32.0
Nozzle	1	25	29.1	41.9
Nozzle	1 1/16	27	32.8	47.2
Nozzle	1 1/8	29	36.8	53.0
Nozzle	1 3/16	30	41.0	59.0
Nozzle	1 1/4	32	45.4	65.4
Nozzle	1 5/16	33	50.1	72.1
Nozzle	1 3/8	35	54.9	79.1
Nozzle (*c* = 0.97 for all nozzles)	1 7/16	37	60.0	86.4
Nozzle	1 1/2	38	65.4	94.2
Nozzle	1 9/16	40	70.9	102.0
Nozzle	1 5/8	41	76.8	110.6
Nozzle	1 11/16	43	82.8	119.2
Nozzle	1 3/4	44	89.0	128.2
Nozzle	1 13/16	46	95.5	137.5
Nozzle	1 7/8	48	102.0	146.9
Nozzle	1 15/16	49	109.0	157.0
Nozzle	2	51	116.0	167.0
Hydrant butt (*c* = 0.90)	2	51	107.4	154.7
Hydrant butt (*c* = 0.90)	2 1/4	57	135.9	195.7
Hydrant butt (*c* = 0.90)	2 1/2	64	167.8	241.6

the flow rate at 25 and 125 psi (170 and 162 kPa) pressure is given, from which the *k* factor can be calculated.

EXAMPLE 1: A certain fire service spray nozzle is rated for 83 gpm at 50 psi. Therefore,

$$k = \frac{83}{\sqrt{50}} = \frac{83}{7.07} = 11.7$$

At 25 psi pressure, the discharge would be

$$11.7\sqrt{25} = 11.7 \times 5 = 58.5 \text{ gpm}$$

EXAMPLE 2: Determine the discharge from a 51 mm hydrant butt (c_d = *90)* at a pressure of 350 kPa.

$$k_m = 0.0666 c d_m{}^2 = 0.0666 \times 0.90 \times 51^2 = 156$$

Thus,

$$Q_m = k_m \sqrt{p_m} = 156\sqrt{350} = 2918 \text{ L/min}$$

Flow Meters

When it is not convenient to discharge water to the atmosphere, meters are used to determine flow.

Venturi tube: The Venturi principle has a number of applications in fire protection. The Venturi tube is essentially a tapered constriction in a pipe. In the constricted part, the velocity must be greater than in the straight tube, and the pressure is correspondingly less in accordance with Bernoulli's theorem. If the increase in velocity through the restricted portion is sufficient, the pressure at that point will be less than atmospheric, and a suction will be created at any opening into the side of the tube. The Venturi tube is illustrated in Figure 5-2K. The diverging portion of a Venturi tube serves only to restore the system pressure with a minimum of friction loss.

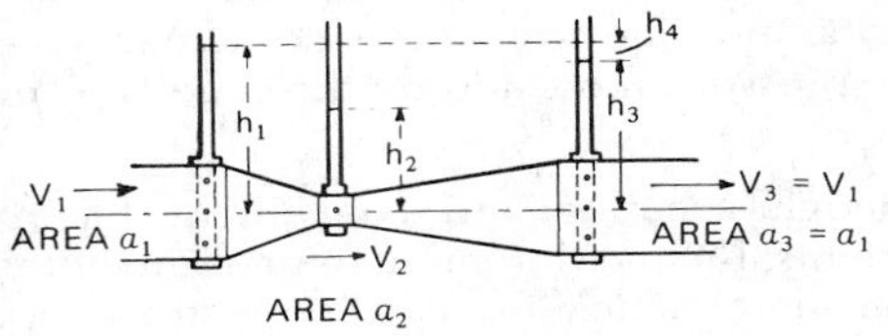

FIG. 5-2K. The Venturi tube.

Venturi meter: The Venturi principle as applied in the Venturi meter for the measurement of flow in closed pipe lines under pressure is as follows.

With no elevation difference along the line of flow, Bernoulli's theorem becomes:

$$\frac{v_1{}^2}{2g} + \frac{p_1}{w} + 0 = \frac{v_2{}^2}{2g} + \frac{p_2}{w} + 0$$

In Figure 5-2K,

$$\frac{p_1}{w}$$

is represented by h_1, and

$$\frac{p_2}{w}$$

by h_2 which are used in the following equations.

The quantity of liquid passing through all portions of the Venturi must be the same. Therefore,

$$Q = a_1 v_1 = a_2 v_2 \quad \text{or} \quad v_1 = \frac{Q}{a_1} \quad \text{or} \quad v_2 = \frac{Q}{a_2}$$

Substituting in Bernoulli's theorem,

$$\frac{\left(\frac{Q}{a_1}\right)^2}{2g} + h_1 = \frac{\left(\frac{Q}{a_2}\right)^2}{2g} + h_2$$

$$\frac{\left(\frac{Q}{a_2}\right)^2}{2g} - \frac{\left(\frac{Q}{a_1}\right)^2}{2g} = h_1 - h_2$$

$$Q^2\left(\frac{1}{a_2^{\,2}} - \frac{1}{a_1^{\,2}}\right) = 2g(h_1 - h_2)$$

$$Q^2\left(\frac{a_1^{\,2} - a_2^{\,2}}{a_1^{\,2}a_2^{\,2}}\right) = 2g(h_1 - h_2)$$

$$Q = \frac{a_1a_2}{\sqrt{a_1^{\,2} - a_2^{\,2}}}\sqrt{2g(h_1 - h_2)}$$

For any specific Venturi, a_1 and a_2 are known constant values. There is also a friction loss coefficient which is usually determined by test and which does not remain constant with very low velocities. Combining the known constant values, the Venturi meter formula is generally expressed as:

$$Q = k\sqrt{h_1 - h_2}, \quad \text{or} \quad Q = k\sqrt{\frac{p_1}{w} - \frac{p_2}{w}}$$

By test, a value of k for any specific meter can be established with reasonable accuracy, thus allowing the measurement of flow to be calculated from the pressure differential across the meter.

When used as a device for inducing gas or liquid into the stream, as is made possible by the reduced pressure, in the throat section, the hydraulic performance will not be in strict accordance with the above theoretical calculations because energy is expended on the induced substance.

Orifice meters: When water flows through a thin sharp-edged orifice (such as the standard orifice discussed earlier) within a pipe, the flow diameter contracts the same way it does when the flow discharges to atmosphere, and then increases back to the full pipeline diameter. The pressure at the pipe wall is reduced due to this change in flow, and is related to the flow rate. (See Fig. 5-2L.)

Bernoulli's equation can be applied to an orifice meter in the same way as it is applied to the Venturi meter. The resultant k factor or discharge coefficient depends upon several factors, including the ratio of orifice/pipe diameter and the location of the pressure taps upstream and downstream of the orifice.

ASME flow nozzle: Flow can also be measured by an ASME flow nozzle, as shown in Figure 5-2M. The pressure taps for this device are normally one pipe diameter upstream of the nozzle and one-half pipe diameter downstream from the nozzle inlet. Combining known constant values, the Venturi meter formula is generally expressed as:

$$Q = k\sqrt{h_1 - h_2}, \quad \text{or} \quad Q = k\sqrt{\frac{p_1}{w} - \frac{p_2}{w}}$$

FLOW OF WATER IN PIPES

The theory of liquid flow in pipes involves the same continuity principles used in the previous discussions. These include continuity of energy (Bernoulli's theorem with friction) and continuity of flow.

When water flows through a pipe, there is always a drop in pressure. Theoretically the lost head between two points is caused by: (1) friction between the moving water and the pipe wall, and (2) friction between water particles, including that produced by turbulence when flow changes direction or when a rapid increase or decrease in velocity takes place, such as at abrupt changes in pipe diameter. A change in velocity results in some conversion of velocity head to pressure head, or *vice versa*.

At low velocity in a smooth pipe, very little turbulence is produced, and the flow is called "laminar" or "streamline" flow. With this condition, all particles of water move along the pipe in definite paths which are essentially straight lines, in concentric layers. Friction loss occurs due to shear stress, mainly in a thin boundary layer at the pipe wall, and also between adjacent stream layers. The friction loss is small compared to that of turbulent flow.

The flow within either a smooth or a rough pipe remains laminar until the velocity reaches what is called critical velocity. At this point, there is a range of unstable flow which is neither laminar nor completely turbulent. This is called the transition zone.

As the flow continues to increase, it becomes turbulent. In turbulent flow the fluid moves in an eddying mass, and, at any point, the individual water particles move rapidly in a random manner rather than in a straight line.

Reynolds demonstrated that, for any fluid, the critical point at which the flow changes from laminar to turbulent could be predicted. In circular pipes, the critical point occurs when the dimensionless parameter $dv\rho/\mu$ (called the Reynolds Number) is approximately 2000. The transition to complete turbulence is complete for Reynolds numbers exceeding 4000.

Most fire protection systems and water distribution mains function under turbulent flow conditions, and friction losses within the pipe itself account for most of the lost head. Other losses are usually considered together and are called "minor losses" or "losses in fittings."

Friction (Head) Loss Flow Formulas

Experimental data have established that frictional resistance in a pipe is:

1. Independent of pressure in the pipe.
2. Proportional to the amount and character of the flow.
3. Variable with the velocity of the flow (nearly proportional to the second power of the velocity for velocities above the critical; if velocity is below critical, resistance varies with the first power).

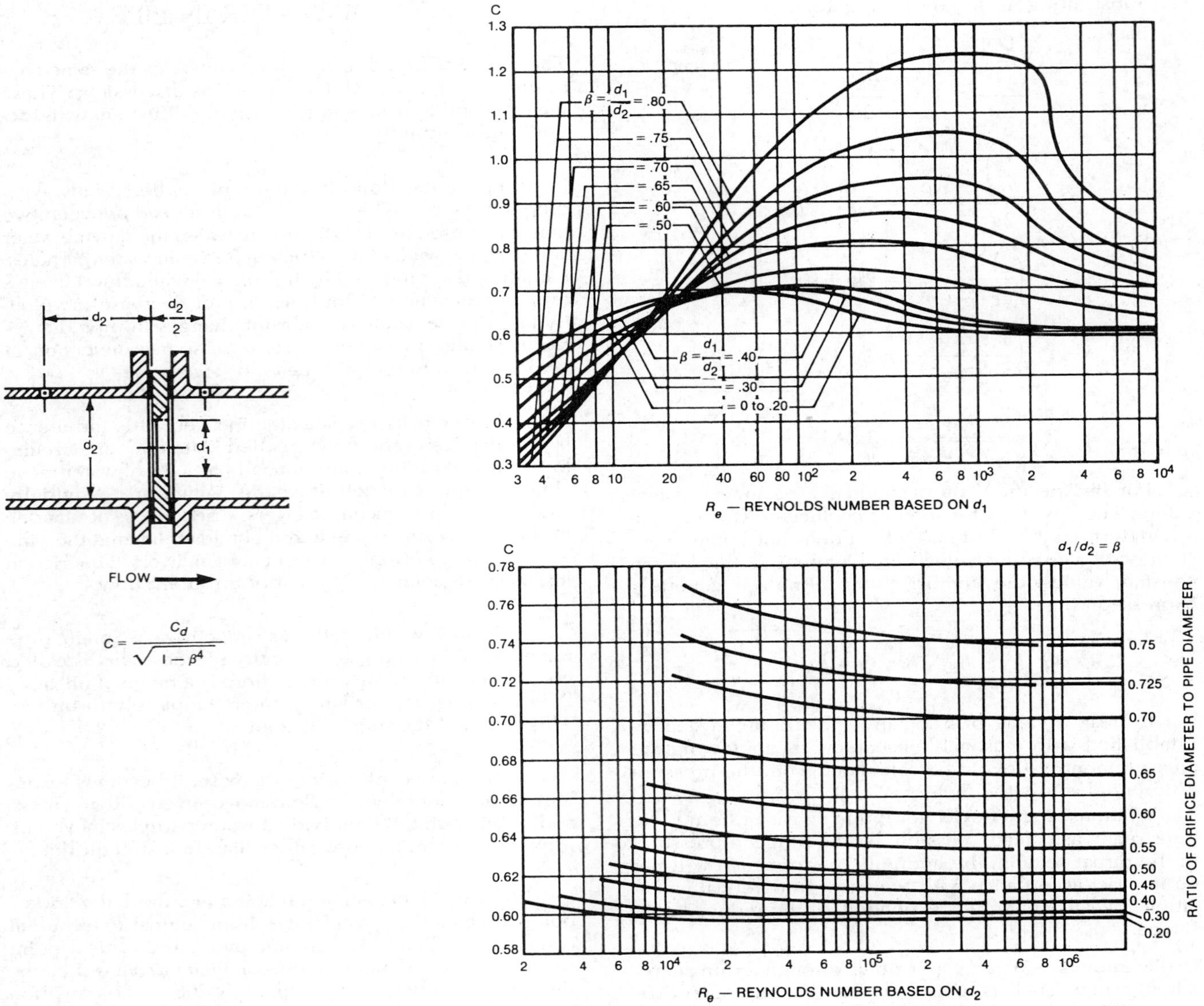

FIG. 5-2L. Flow coefficient C for square-edged orifice meters. (Source: Crane Technical Paper No. 410, 1976)

The Chezy formula: One of the best-known and oldest expressions relating velocity to friction loss in piping is known as the Chezy formula:

$$v = c\sqrt{rs}$$

where:

c = a factor that is dependent on the kind and roughness of the pipe

r (the hydraulic radius) = area/circumference = $d/4$, where d = diameter of the pipe in feet (m)

s = the hydraulic slope = h/l = slope of hydraulic gradient in which h is the head loss in length of pipe l in feet (m). (See Section 5, Chapter 5 for a discussion of hydraulic gradients.)

Therefore:

$$v = c\sqrt{d/4 \times h/l} \quad \text{or} \quad h = \frac{4lv^2}{c^2 d}$$

The Darcy-Weisbach formula: Another classical formula for friction loss, applicable to long, straight pipes of uniform diameter and roughness, is ascribed to Darcy, Manning, Fanning, and others. In modern textbooks, the formula is derived by analysis of forces acting on a flowing particle of water in a pipe. Often called the Darcy-Weisbach formula, it is a variation of Chezy's formula, with a friction factor f replacing c, and expressed as follows:

$$h = f\frac{l}{d}\frac{v^2}{2g}$$

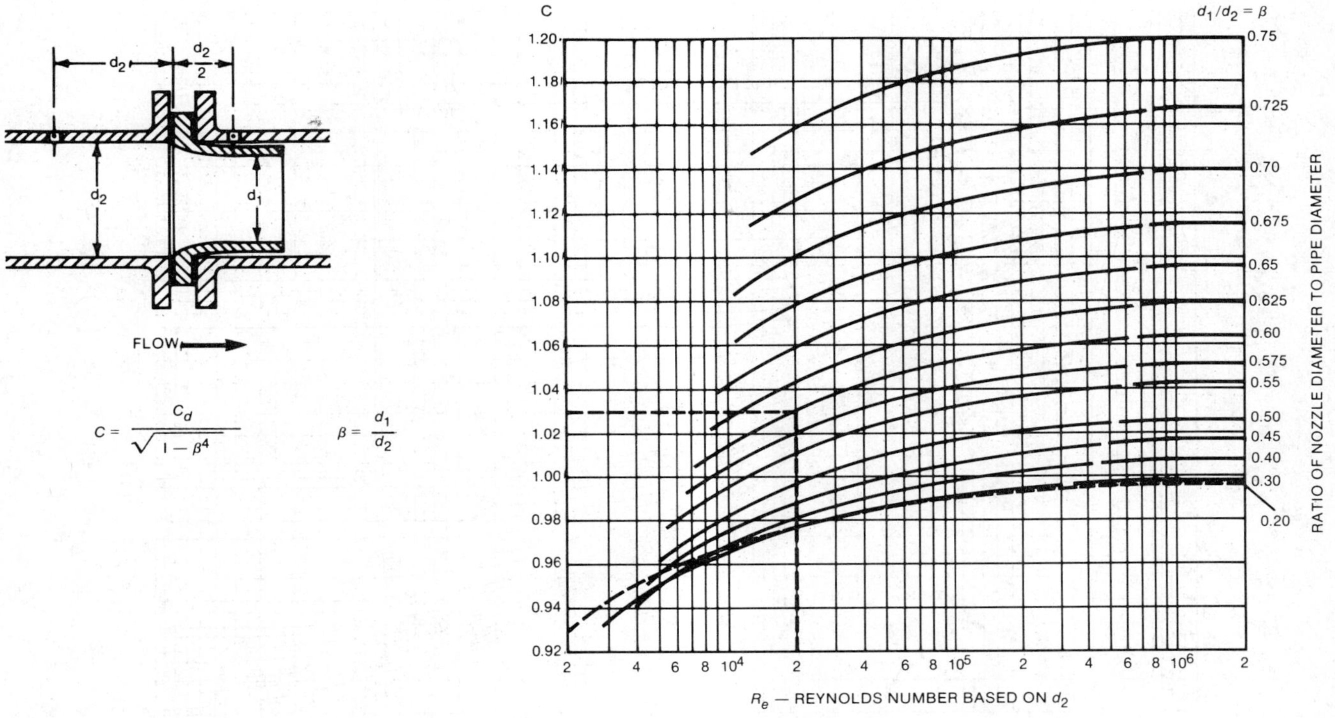

FIG. 5-2M. Flow coefficient C for ASME flow nozzles. (Source: Crane Technical Paper No. 410, 1976)

where:

h = friction head

l = length of pipe

d = diameter of pipe

v = velocity

g = acceleration of gravity

The Darcy-Weisbach formula is suitable for all Newtonian fluids. (A Newtonian fluid is one where the viscosity is constant at a specific temperature regardless of pressure and the rate of shear.) The friction factor f is dimensionless and variable, and depends on the pipe roughness and the Reynolds number.

The value of f can be computed by the Colebrook-White equation which is neither a completely empirical nor rigidly theoretical formula. This equation is usually written as follows:

$$\frac{1}{\sqrt{f}} = -2 \log_{10}\left[\frac{\varepsilon}{3.7D} + \frac{2.51}{R\sqrt{f}}\right]$$

where:

ε = a linear measure of roughness

f = the Darcy-Weisbach friction factor

D = the pipe diameter in feet

R = the Reynolds number

Computing f by the formula can be avoided by using tables and charts known as "Moody" diagrams.

Figure 5-2N is a Moody diagram (© The Hydraulic Institute, 1954) from which f can be read directly off the chart. The dimensionless parameter ϵ/D is sometimes difficult to obtain, and it may be necessary to assume a value for, ϵ/D based on experience and judgment. The roughness factor of new pipe usually can be provided by the manufacturer.

The Hazen-Williams formula: The friction-flow formulas commonly used in fire protection hydraulics have been developed by experiment and experience. These formulas (which are variations of the Chezy formula) are usually exponential in the form $V = Cr^xs^y$, where V is velocity, C the coefficient of friction, r the hydraulic radius (area divided by circumference), and s the hydraulic slope (loss of head divided by length). The most popular exponential formula is the Hazen-Williams, its basic form being $V = 1.31Cr^{0.63}S^{0.54}$. The friction coefficients in formulas of this type are constant for a specific roughness of pipe, and are independent of velocity, and thus the accuracy of these formulas is variable. However, the fixed values generally assumed for viscosity and density are considered adequate for most fire protection hydraulic work.

The basic form of the Hazen-Williams formula ($V = 1.31Cr^{0.63}S^{0.54}$) is not practical for ordinary fire protection flow calculations. Given pressure loss in psi and flow in gpm, the formula becomes:

$$p = \frac{452Q^{1.85}}{C^{1.85}d^{4.87}}$$

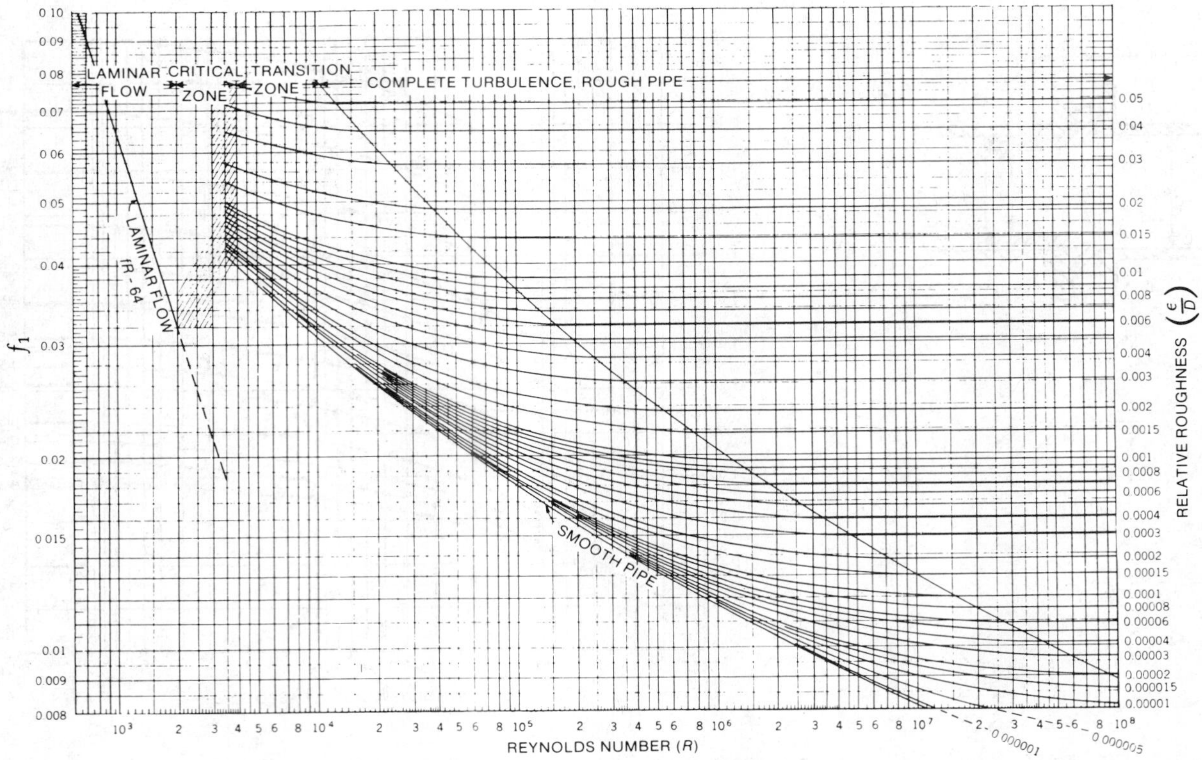

FIG. 5-2N. Moody Diagram for friction in pipe. The values for friction factor are on the vertical scale at left. (See Friction Manual © Hydraulic Institute.)

in which p is the pressure loss in psi per 100 ft of pipe; Q is the rate of flow in gpm; and d is the inside diameter of the pipe in inches. (Numbers to the 1.85 power are given in Table 5-8C.)

In SI units the formula is:

$$p_m = 6.06 \times \frac{Q_m^{1.85}}{c^{1.85} d_m^{4.87}} \times 10^9$$

where:

p_m = pressure loss (kPa) per 100 m of pipe

Q_m = rate of flow (L/min)

d_m = inside diameter (mm)

Friction loss calculations: The solution of many fire protection problems involving pipe flow and friction do not require direct calculation using formulas, since tables and charts are readily available. However, in using the simplifying charts and tables, great care must be taken to identify the C value (coefficient of friction) on which the chart or table is based. Where the type or condition of a pipe necessitates the use of a different C value, the friction loss from the table must be multiplied by a conversion factor to obtain the correct results for the desired C value.

By way of illustration, Table 5-2D gives values of p when $C = 100$ for standard pipe sizes from ½ in. to 30 in. in diameter. For values of C other than 100, the tabular value losses are multiplied by the corresponding factor in Table 5-2E.

EXAMPLE: Determine the friction loss with 700 gpm, flowing in 700 ft of 8-in. cast-iron pipe having a C value of 80.

SOLUTION: From Table 5-2D, the loss for 700 gpm per 100 ft of 8-in. pipe with $C = 100$ is 0.662 psi. From Table 5-2E, the factor for $C = 80$ is 1.51. Because friction loss is directly proportional to the length of pipe, multiply 0.662 $\times$ 7 $\times$ 1.5 = 6.95 psi (answer).

The Hazen-Williams diagram: Figure 5-2O is a graphical representation of Table 5-2D, except that it is based upon a Hazen-Williams coefficient of $C = 120$ rather than $C = 100$, as used in the table. It is limited in scope to pipes not over 10 in. in diameter, and due to the reduced scale is less accurate than the table.

Figure 5-2P gives data in SI units for pipes up to 10 in. (254 mm) in diameter, again based on a $C = 120$.

EXAMPLE OF USE: What is the friction loss in 300 ft (90 m) of 8-in. cement-lined cast-iron pipe, at 1,500 gpm (5678 L/min)?

SOLUTION: From the intersection of the 1,500 gpm vertical line with the sloping 8-in. pipe diameter line in Figure 5-2O, read left horizontally for a loss of head value, which is found to be 0.019 psi per foot. For 300 ft, the loss would be 300 $\times$ 0.019 psi or 5.7 psi. The probable C value of cement-lined pipe is 140 (Table 5-2G), and the conversion factor is 0.75 (Figure 5-2O). Therefore, the friction loss is 5.7 $\times$ 0.75 = 4.3 psi.

TABLE 5-2D. *Friction Loss in Pipe*

Pounds per Square Inch per 100 Feet of Pipe
Hazen-Williams $C = 100$*

	Actual Diameter of Pipe ½ through 3½ in.†‡ Nominal Diameter of Pipe for 4 through 30 in.‡									
Gpm‡	½	¾	1	1¼	1½	2	2½	3	3½	4	Gpm
5	17.9	4.55	1.40	.369	.174	.052	—	—	—	—	5
10	64.5	16.4	5.06	1.33	.629	.186	.078	.030	—	—	10
15		34.7	10.7	2.82	1.33	.394	.166	.064	.028	—	15
20	*5*	59.1	18.2	4.89	2.27	.671	.282	.109	.048	.027	20
30	.019	*6*	38.6	10.2	4.80	1.42	.598	.231	.102	.057	30
40	.033	—	65.8	17.3	8.17	2.42	1.02	.393	.174	.097	40
50	.050	.020	*8*	26.2	12.3	3.66	1.54	.593	.263	.147	50
60	.069	.029	—	36.6	17.3	5.12	2.16	.831	.369	.206	60
70	.092	.038	—	48.7	23.0	6.81	2.87	1.11	.490	.274	70
80	.118	.049	—	62.4	29.4	8.72	3.67	1.41	.628	.350	80
90	.147	.060	—	77.6	36.6	10.8	4.56	1.76	.781	.435	90
100	.178	.074	—	*10*	44.5	13.1	5.55	2.14	.949	.529	100
120	.250	.103	—	—	62.3	18.5	7.77	3.00	1.33	.741	120
140	.333	.137	.034	—	82.9	24.6	10.3	3.98	1.77	.986	140
160	.426	.175	.043	—	106.0	31.4	13.2	5.10	2.26	1.26	160
180	.529	.218	.054	.018	*12*	39.1	16.5	6.34	2.81	1.57	180
200	.643	.265	.065	.022	—	47.5	20.0	7.71	3.42	1.91	200
220	.768	.316	.078	.026	—	56.7	23.9	9.19	4.08	2.28	220
240	.902	.371	.091	.031	.013	*14*	28.0	10.8	4.79	2.67	240
260	1.05	.430	.106	.036	.015	—	32.5	12.5	5.56	3.10	260
280	1.20	.493	.122	.041	.017	—	37.3	14.4	6.37	3.55	280
300	1.36	.562	.138	.047	.019	—	42.3	16.3	7.24	4.04	300
350	1.81	.746	.184	.062	.026	.012	*16*	21.7	9.63	5.37	350
400	2.32	.955	.235	.079	.033	.015	—	27.8	12.3	6.88	400
450	2.88	1.19	.292	.099	.041	.019	—	34.6	15.3	8.55	450
500	3.51	1.44	.353	.120	.049	.023	.012	42.0	18.6	10.4	500
550	4.18	1.72	.424	.143	.059	.028	.015	50.1	22.2	12.4	550
600	4.91	2.02	.498	.168	.069	.033	.017	58.8	26.1	14.6	600
650	5.70	2.34	.577	.195	.080	.038	.020	68.2	30.3	16.9	650
700	6.53	2.69	.662	.223	.092	.043	.023	*18*	34.7	19.4	700
750	7.42	3.05	.752	.254	.104	.049	.026	—	39.4	22.0	750
800	8.36	3.44	.848	.286	.118	.056	.029	—	44.5	24.8	800
850	9.35	3.85	.948	.320	.132	.062	.032	—	49.7	27.7	850
900	10.4	4.28	1.05	.356	.146	.069	.036	—	*20*	30.8	900
950	11.5	4.73	1.17	.393	.162	.076	.040	—	—	34.1	950
1,000	12.6	5.20	1.28	.432	.178	.084	.044	—	—	37.5	1,000
1,250	19.1	7.85	1.94	.653	.269	.127	.066	—	—	*24*	1,250
1,500	*30*	11.0	2.71(18.7)	.914	.376	.178	.093	—	—	—	1,500
1,750	—	—	3.61	1.22	.501	.236	.123	—	—		1,750
2,000	.007	—	4.62	1.56	.641	.303	.158	.089	.053	.022	2,000
2,250	.009	—	—	1.94	.797	.376	.196	.111	.066	.027	2,250
2,500	.011	—	—	2.35	.969	.457	.239	.134	.081	.033	2,500
2,750	.013	—	—	2.81	1.16	.545	.285	.160	.096	.040	2,750
3,000	.016	—	—	3.30	1.36	.641	.334	.188	.113	.046	3,000
4,000	.027	—	—	—	2.31	1.09	.569	.321	.192	.079	4,000
5,000	.040	—	—	—	3.49	1.65	.860	.485	.290	.119	5,000

* To convert friction loss at $C = 100$ or other values of C, see Table 5-2E.
† Schedule 40 pipe sizes ½ through 3½ in. steel pipe.
‡ SI units: 1 psi = 6.895 kPa; 1 gpm = 0.378 L/min; 1 in = 25.4 mm.
Note: Actual inside diameter for sizes ½ in. through 3½ in. is given for greater accuracy as these sizes include sprinkler branch lines and the smaller sizes of cross mains. For sizes 4 in. and greater, the nominal diameters were used as a fairly safe average for the diameters of various types of underground pipes as follows: cast iron unlined and Enameline, greater than nominal; cast iron cement lines and Class 200 asbestos cement, less than nominal; Class 150 asbestos-cement sizes 6 and 8 in. less than nominal, and other sizes even nominal. (A 0.10 variation is true for Class 150 cement lined only—see ASHD FT-9 through 45 for actual IDs.)

This table will be useful in approximating friction loss in flow through existing underground piping where the type, inside diameter, and condition are frequently unknown. However, in such cases, a flow test is recommended.

When the type, inside diameter, and condition are known, and in designing new systems for all sizes and types of pipes, the friction loss tables should be used. Friction tables based on Hazen-Williams formula are published in *Automatic Sprinkler Hydraulic Data* by "Automatic" Sprinkler Corporation of America, and tables based on Darcy-Weisbach formula are published in *Standards of the Hydraulic Institute.*

TABLE 5-2E. ***Conversion Factors for Friction Loss in Pipe for Values of Coefficient Other Than 100***

C	Factor	C	Factor	C	Factor
150	0.472	110	0.838	70	1.93
145	0.503	105	0.914	65	2.22
140	0.537	100	1.00	60	2.57
135	0.574	95	1.10	55	3.02
130	0.615	90	1.22	50	3.61
125	0.662	85	1.35	45	4.38
120	0.714	80	1.51	40	5.48
115	0.772	75	1.70	35	6.97

METRIC EXAMPLE: What is the friction loss in 400 m of 150 mm 30-year-old unlined cast-iron pipe (C = 80) for a flow of 10,000 L/min?

SOLUTION: From the intersection of the 10,000 L/min vertical line with the sloping 150 mm pipe diameter line in Figure 5-2P, read left horizontally for a loss of head value, which is 480 kPa per 100 meters. For 400 m, the loss would be 4 × 480 kPa or 1920 kPa, based on C = 120. For the cast-iron pipe, C = 80 and the conversion factor is 2.12. (See Figure 5-2P). Therefore the friction loss is 1920 × 2.12 = 4070 kPa.

Equivalent pipes: Problems involving piped water supplies and fire protection systems occasionally require substitution of one pipe for another. The term "equivalent pipe" usually means a pipe having the same friction loss as the pipe for which it is being substituted. The formula for using the friction loss table is applicable here.

EXAMPLE:

What length of 8-in. pipe (C = 110) is equivalent to 700 ft of 6-in. pipe (C = 85)?

SOLUTION:

$$N_1 \times \frac{L_1}{100} \times T_1 = N_2 \times \frac{L_2}{100} \times T_2$$

Assume a rate of flow (say 1000 gpm) and substitute known values:

$$1.35 \times \frac{700}{100} \times 5.20 = 0.838 \times \frac{L_2}{100} \times 1.28$$

Solving for L_2:

$$\frac{1.35 \times 700 \times 5.20}{0.838 \times 1.28} = 4581 \text{ ft}$$

which can be rounded off to 4,600 ft.

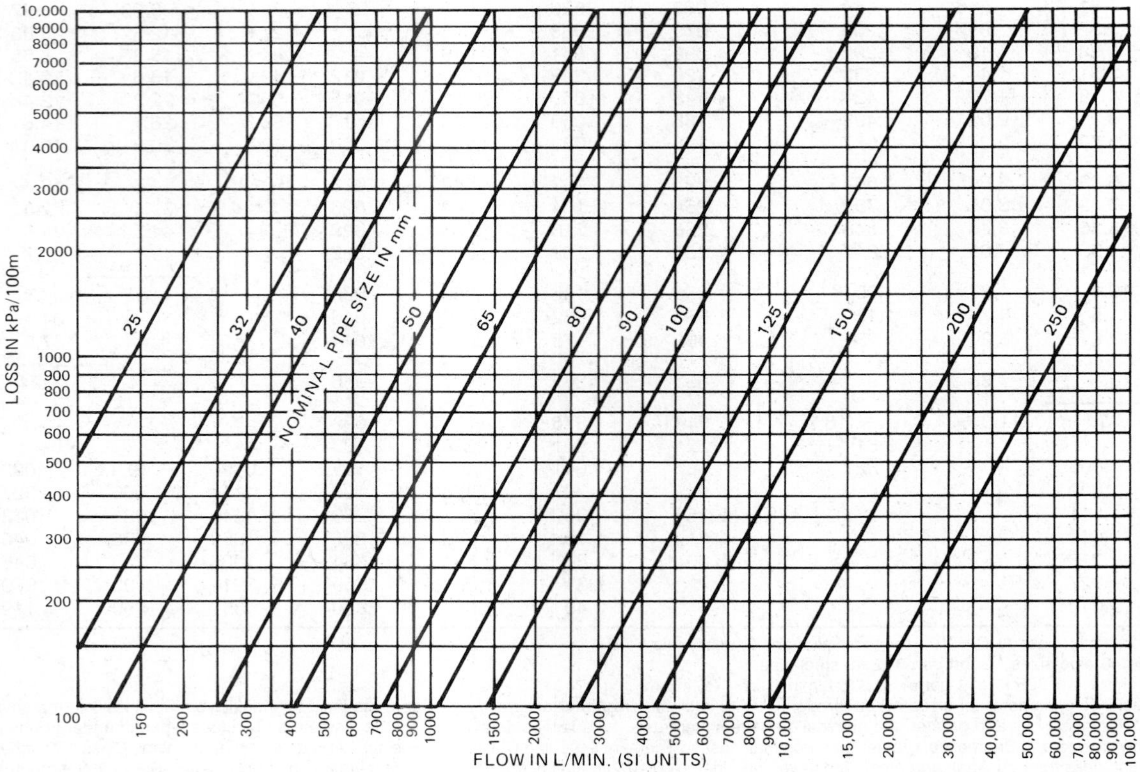

FIG. 5-2O. Friction loss in Schedule 40 steel pipe, Hazen & Williams C-120. For other c values use: Value of c: 80 100 120 130 140 150, Multiplying factor: 2.12 1.40 1.00 0.86 0.75 0.66.

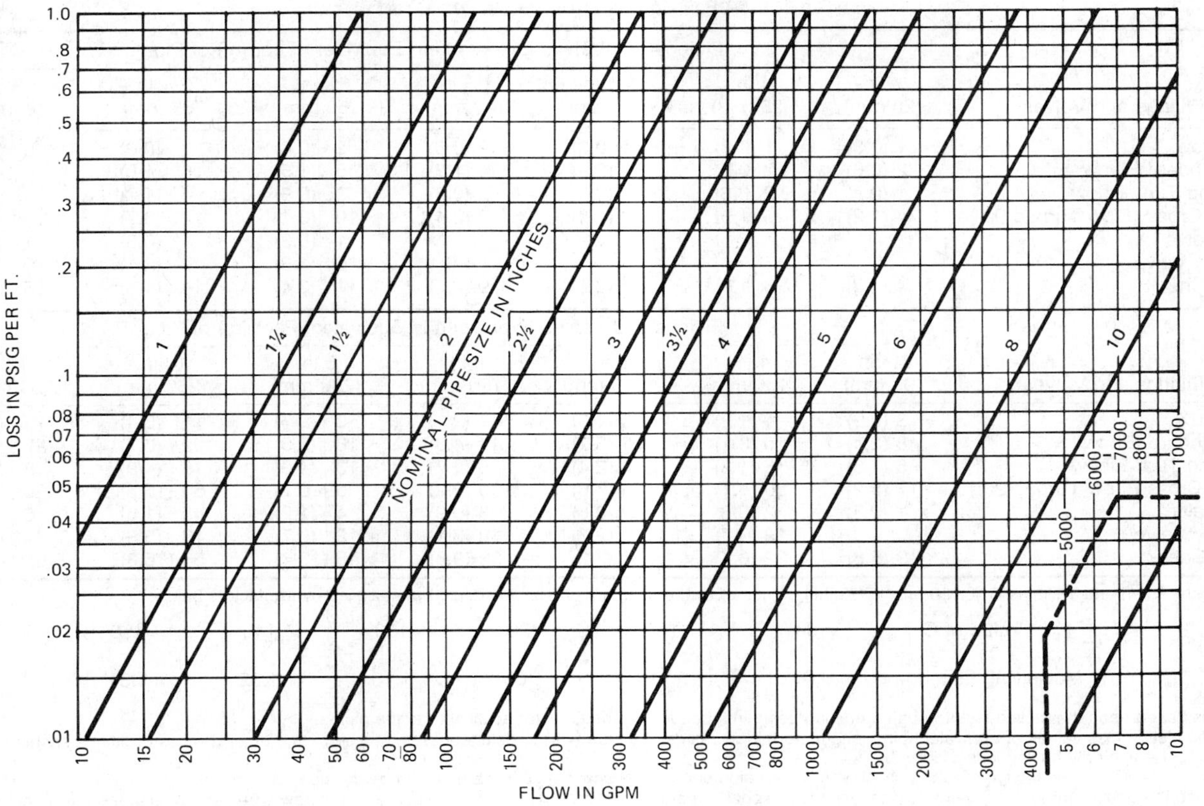

FIG. 5-2P. ***Friction Loss (SI units) in Schedule 40 Steel Pipe, Hazen & Williams C-120. For other c values use: Value of c 80 100 120 130 140 150, Multiplying factor 2.12 1.40 1.00 0.86 0.75 0.66.***

Minor Losses

While the friction loss within the pipe normally accounts for most of the lost head, head losses also occur when the flow in a pipe changes direction, the pipe size changes, or a valve or other fitting is encountered. These losses are typically referred to as minor losses even though they can be significant for some fittings, such as swing check valves or backflow preventers, that are commonly found in fire protection systems.

The amount of minor losses from fittings can be found in many references and are often expressed in various forms. The most common are as an equivalent length (*l*/*d*), a resistance coefficient (*k*), or a flow coefficient (C_v).

Equivalent length: For most fire protection calculations, friction loss is obtained by using the equivalent length method from a table such as Table 5-2F which expresses the friction loss of the fitting as an "equivalent pipe length" having the same friction loss as the fitting. This length is then added to the length of the pipe to which the fittings are connected to obtain the total friction loss of pipe and fittings.

EXAMPLE: Calculate total friction loss for 600 L/min flow through 200 m of nominal 2-in. (50 mm) pipe (C = 120) which incorporates three 90-degree elbows, one tee junction (90-degree turn), and two butterfly valves.

SOLUTION: Using Table 5-2F for equivalent lengths of fittings (C = 120):

Fittings or pipe	Number	Equivalent length per fittings (m)	Total Equivalent Length (m)
Std. elbow	3	1.5	4.5
T-junction	1	3.1	3.1
Butterfly	2	1.8	3.6
Pipe	1	200.0	200.0
	Total equivalent pipe length		211.2

From Figure 5-2P, the total friction loss of 600 L/min flow in 50 mm (2 in. norm) pipe is 500 kPa per 100 m of pipe. Brcause friction loss is directly proportional to length of pipe, total loss is given by :

$$\frac{211.2}{100} \times 500 = 1056 \text{ kPa}$$

The loss due to fittings is given by

$$\frac{11.2}{100} \times 500 = 56$$

kPa or 5.3 percent of the total friction·loss.

TABLE 5-2F. *Equivalent Pipe Length Chart*

Fittings and Valves	Fittings and Valves Expressed in Equivalent Feet (m) of Pipe						
	¾ in. (20 mm)	1 in. (25 mm)	1¼ in. (32 mm)	1½ in. (40 mm)	2 in. (50 mm)	2½ in. (65 mm)	3 in. (80 mm)
45° Elbow	1 (0.3)	1 (0.3)	1 (0.3)	2 (0.6)	2 (0.6)	3 (0.9)	3 (0.9)
90° Standard Elbow	2 (0.6)	2 (0.6)	3 (0.9)	4 (1.2)	5 (1.5)	6 (1.8)	7 (2.1)
90° Long Turn Elbow	1 (0.3)	2 (0.6)	2 (0.6)	2 (0.6)	3 (0.9)	4 (1.2)	5 (1.5)
Tee or Cross (Flow Turned 90°)	4 (1.2)	5 (1.5)	6 (1.8)	8 (2.4)	10 (3.1)	12 (3.7)	15 (4.6)
Gate Valve	—	—	—	—	1 (0.3)	1 (0.3)	1 (0.3)
Butterfly Valve	—	—	—	—	6 (1.8)	7 (2.1)	10 (3.1)
Swing Check*	4 (1.2)	5 (1.5)	7 (2.1)	9 (2.7)	11 (3.4)	14 (4.3)	16 (4.9)

Fittings and Valves	Fittings and Valves Expressed in Equivalent Feet (m) of Pipe						
	3½ in. (90 mm)	4 in. (100 mm)	5 in. (125 mm)	6 in. (150 mm)	8 in. (200 mm)	10 in. (250 mm)	12 in. (300 mm)
45° Elbow	3 (0.9)	4 (1.2)	5 (1.5)	7 (2.1)	9 (2.7)	11 (3.4)	13 (4.0)
90° Standard Elbow	8 (2.4)	10 (3.1)	12 (3.7)	14 (4.3)	18 (5.5)	22 (6.7)	27 (8.2)
90° Long Turn Elbow	5 (1.5)	6 (1.8)	8 (2.4)	9 (2.7)	13 (4.0)	16 (4.9)	18 (5.5)
Tee or Cross (Flow Turned 90°)	17 (5.2)	20 (6.1)	25 (7.6)	30 (9.2)	35 (10.7)	50 (15.3)	60 (18.3)
Gate Valve	1 (0.3)	2 (0.6)	2 (0.6)	3 (0.9)	4 (1.2)	5 (1.5)	6 (1.8)
Butterfly Valve	—	12 (3.7)	9 (2.7)	10 (3.1)	12 (3.7)	19 (5.8)	21 (6.4)
Swing Check*	19 (5.8)	22 (6.7)	27 (8.2)	32 (9.8)	45 (13.7)	55 (16.8)	65 (19.8)

Use with Hazen and Williams C = 120 only. For other values of C, the figures in this table should be multiplied by the factors below:

Value of C	80	100	120	130	140	150
Multiplying factor	0.472	0.713	1.00	1.16	1.32	1.51

(This is based upon the friction loss through the fitting being independent of the C factor applicable to the piping.)

Specific friction loss values or equivalent pipe lengths for alarm valves, dry pipe valves, deluge valves, strainers, and other devices or fittings should be made available to the authority having jurisdiction.

* Due to the variations in design of swing check valves, the pipe equivalents shown in this table should be considered average.

NOTE: Use the equivalent feet (m) value for the "standard elbow" on any abrupt ninety-degree turn such as the screw-type pattern. Use the equivalent feet (m) value for the "long turn elbow" on any sweeping ninety-degree turn such as a flanged, welded or mechanical joint elbow type.

TABLE 5-2G. *Guide for Estimating Hazen-Williams C*

Kind of Pipe	Value of *C*		
	1*	2†	3‡
Cast Iron, unlined:			
10 years old	110	90	75
15 years old	100	75	65
20 years old	90	65	55
30 years old	80	55	45
50 years old	70	50	40
Cast Iron, unlined, new		120	
Cast Iron, cement-lined		140	
Cast Iron, bitumastic enamel-lined		140	
Average steel, new		140	
Riveted steel, new		110	
Asbestos-cement		140	
Reinforced concrete		140	

* 1. Water mildly corrosive. Use same values for fire-protection mains having no mill-use or domestic draft.

† 2. Water moderately corrosive.

‡ 3. Water severely corrosive.

Note: *C* values chosen for design of piping systems should be based on applicable standards of NFPA or the authority having jurisdiction.

Resistance coefficients: Resistance coefficients are sometimes used to express the head loss in a fitting as a function of velocity according to the relationship:

$$h_f = k\frac{v^2}{2g}$$

The equivalent length and the resistance coefficient methods are related. Using the basic Darcy-Weisbach formula:

$$h = f\frac{1}{d}\frac{v^2}{2g} = k\frac{v^2}{2g}$$

or:

$$k = f\frac{1}{d}$$

Most entrance losses are calculated using resistance coefficients. Figure 5-2Q provides resistance coefficients for some common entrance conditions and fittings.

Flow coefficients: Where the loss in a fitting is defined by a flow coefficient C_v, the coefficient is defined as the flow of water that will produce a known friction loss (usually 1 psi) through the fitting. The relationship is usually shown as:

$$Q = C_v\sqrt{h}$$

Substituting p/w for h, and solving for p:

$$p = 0.433\frac{Q^2}{C_v^{\,2}}\ \text{psi}$$

The flow coefficient can be shown to be related to the resistance coefficient k by:

$$C_v = \frac{29.9\,d^2}{\sqrt{k}}$$

FRICTION LOSS COEFFICIENTS

HEAD LOSS = h = K $\frac{v^2}{2g}$

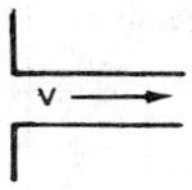

SHARP-EDGED INLET

K = 0.5

INWARD PROJECTING PIPE

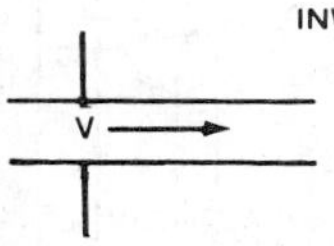

K = 0.8 - 1.0

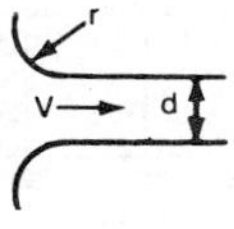

ROUNDED INLET

r/d	0.05	0.1	0.2	0.3	0.4
K	0.20-0.25	0.09-0.17	0.08	0.05	0.04

SUDDEN CONTRACTION

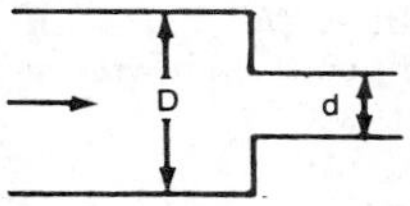

D/d	1.1	1.5	2.0	3.0	10
K	.15	0.28-0.30	0.36-0.40	0.42-0.50	0.50

GRADUAL CONTRACTION

NOTE: USE K WITH V OF SMALL PIPE SECTION

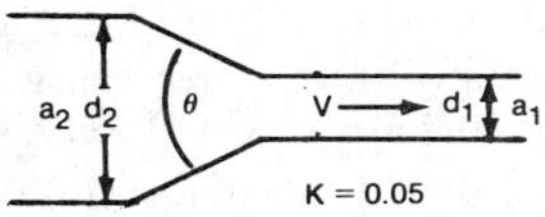

NOTE: USE K WITH V FROM LARGE PIPE

K = 0.05

$$\beta = \frac{d_1}{d_2}$$

IF $\theta \leq 45°$

$$K = \frac{0.8 \sin \frac{\theta}{2} \left(1 - \beta^2\right)}{\beta^4}$$

$\theta > 45$

$$K = \frac{0.5 \left(1 - \beta^2\right) \sqrt{\sin \frac{\theta}{2}}}{\beta^4}$$

SUDDEN ENLARGEMENT

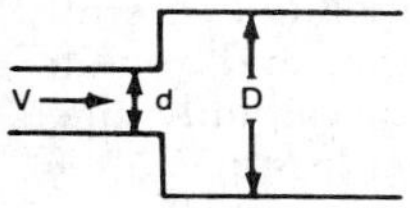

d/D	0.1	0.2	0.3	0.4	0.5	0.6	0.7	0.8	0.9
K	0.98	0.92	0.83	0.71	0.56	0.41	0.28	0.13	0.04

GRADUAL ENLARGEMENT

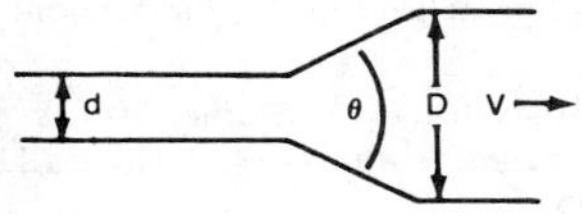

NOTES: USE K WITH V IN LARGE PIPE

$\beta = d/D$

IF $\theta \leq 45°$

$$K = \frac{2.6 \sin \frac{\theta}{2} \left(1 - \beta^2\right)}{\beta^4}$$

IF $\theta > 45°$

$$K = \frac{\left(1 - \beta^2\right)^2}{\beta^4}$$

FIG. 5-2Q. Friction loss coefficients.

WATER HAMMER

Water hammer is an effect of the pressure rise (surge) that accompanies a sudden change in the velocity of water flowing in a pipe. When deceleration of velocity is rapid or completely stopped, the kinetic energy of the moving water column is absorbed temporarily by elastic deformation of the pipe and by the compressibility of water. A pressure wave is then formed that is reflected back and forth within the pipe.

Pressure surges may be initiated by the closing of a valve, stopping of a pump, or by the sudden development of abnormal water demand when a water main breaks. Occasionally, the operation of automatic control valves in sprinkler systems may result in the reversal of flow and a buildup of high pressure in the fire protection system.

Consideration of water hammer and transient pressure surges is traditionally based on the elastic wave theories of Joukowski and Allievi. The *SFPE Handbook of Fire Protection Engineering* provides an alternative discussion based on the elastic wave theories of Zhukovsky.

The force of water hammer is sometimes sufficient to rupture pipes, fittings, or hose lines. Theoretically, the resultant forces could be infinite if the system were totally inelastic.

The elasticity of hose tends to reduce the danger from water hammer, but the sudden closing of shutoff nozzles on long hose lines may cause a pressure rise sufficient to rupture the hose. Tests conducted by the New York City Fire Department indicated that pressure surges from closing of nozzles approximated twice the hydrant pressure. These tests point to the advantage of operating nozzle valves slowly.

Discharge lines from pumps are subject to water hammer caused by water column separation. This may occur when a pump suddenly stops (due to power failure, manual shutdown, etc.), or if the discharge valve is closed too quickly with the pump operating. Separation takes place somewhere downstream, especially at a summit, or where the downward slope of the pipe increases sharply. When forward movement becomes exhausted, the flow reverses direction and closes the gap.

When a pump is located at an elevation above the system outlet, a vacuum breaker in the line may provide effective control. When there is static head on a pump at discharge, it is practically impossible to completely eliminate a water column reversal. Surge suppressors or special-type vacuum breakers designed to bypass a portion of the reverse flow water column around the check valve or control valve may be effective.

The restarting of a fire pump too quickly after a tripout may cause excessive surging, and installations subject to intermittent operation should be protected by time-delay relays. Simple relief valves are considered useless, because their operation is too slow to counteract the speed of the pressure rise. In fire protection systems, a jockey pump is used to maintain a high pressure on the system and reduce the water hammer causing surge when the fire pump starts.

The principle factors contributing to water column separation are: (1) rate of flow stoppage, either by rapid closing of a valve, or the fast deceleration of a pump; (2) length of pipe system (this determines the time that pressure continues to fall before positive-pressure waves returning from the far end of the line counteract the initial pressure drop); (3) the normal operating pressure at critical points, such as the crests of hills; and (4) the velocity of the water just before pump stoppage or valve closure occurs; the greater the velocity the larger the size of the void, reverse flow velocity, and the final pressure rise.

Elastic Wave Theory

The basic concepts of elastic wave theory (EWT) are:

1. The magnitude of the pressure rise is proportional to the fluid velocity destroyed and to the velocity of the pressure wave.
2. The pressure rise is independent of the length and profile of the pipe.
3. The velocity of the pressure wave is the same as the velocity of sound through water.

The theoretical pressure rise when flow is stopped instantly may be calculated by the formula:

$$\Delta p_m = \frac{0.433 a \nu}{g}$$

where:

Δp = pressure rise in pounds per square inch
a = velocity of the pressure wave in feet per second
v_m = water flow velocity in feet per second
g = acceleration of gravity in feet per second per second.

In SI units, the formula is:

$$\Delta p = \frac{9.81 a_m \nu_m}{g_m}$$

where:

Δp_m = pressure rise in kPa
a_m = velocity of the pressure wave in m/sec
v = water flow velocity in mm/sec
g = acceleration of gravity in mm/sec^2

In practice, the calculated Δp may be reduced, allowing for valve closure characteristics, and friction loss in the pipe. Usually, this is a matter of judgment and experience. For the pipe sizes used in fire protection systems, an allowance of 100 to 125 psi (690 to 860 kPa) is suggested.

The pressure rise Δp is at maximum when the flow is stopped in a time equal to or less than the critical time of the pipe, which is the time required for the pressure wave to travel from the point of closure to the end of the pipe and return. The formula for the critical time is:

$$a = \sqrt{\frac{w}{g}\left(\frac{1}{k}\frac{d}{Ee}\right)}$$

where:

w_m = weight of water in pounds per cubic ft (L/m^3)
g_m = acceleration of gravity, feet per second per second (m/sec^2)
k_m = bulk modulus of compressibility of water in pounds per square inch (kPa)
E_m = Youngs modulus of elasticity of pipe wall material in pounds per square inch (kPa)
e_m = thickness of the pipe wall in inches (mm)

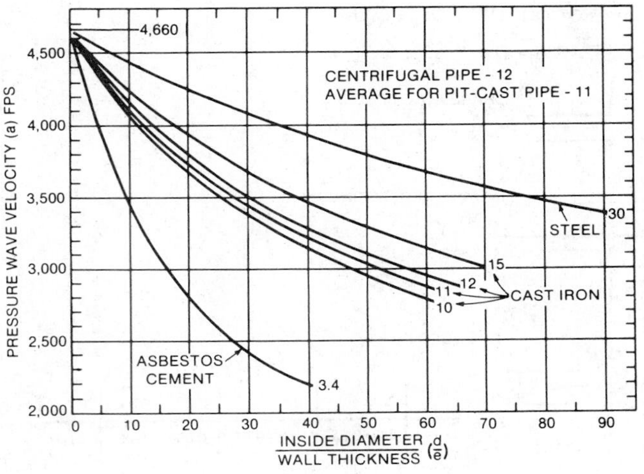

FIG. 5-2R. Surge wave velocity chart for water. The figures on the curves represent values of E in millions of pounds per square inch (bulk modules of elasticity).

d_m = inside diameter of the pipe in inches (mm)

To avoid calculating a, use the chart in Figure 5-2R.

The calculated pressure rise in a 6-in. cast-iron pipe is about 60 psi per foot (1357 kPa/m) of arrested velocity.

The water hammer potential of distribution systems, especially those with automatic pumps, should be examined, and practical steps taken to reduce the probability of destructive pressure surges. It should be noted, however, that the conditions under which dedicated fire protection distribution systems are designed (automatic operation of pumps with check valves in their discharge lines), the potential for water hammer cannot be completely eliminated.

To prevent water hammer, valves and hydrants should be maintained in good condition, and operated carefully to prevent an abrupt reduction in flow; and remote-controlled power-operated valves should be carefully timed to prevent them from closing too fast (never less than 5 sec).

BIBLIOGRAPHY

References

AWWA M11 Steel Pipe Manual, American Water Works Association, New York, 1964.

Baumeister, T., Avallone, E. A., Baumeister, T. III, eds., *Marks' Standard Handbook for Mechanical Engineers*, 8th ed., McGraw-Hill, New York, 1978.

Casey, James F., *ed.*, *Fire Service Hydraulics*, 2nd ed., Dun-Donnelley, New York, 1970.

Crocker, S. and King, R. C., *eds.*, *Piping Handbook*, McGraw-Hill, New York, 1967.

DeNevers, N., *Fluid Mechanics*, Addison-Wesley, Reading, 1970.

DiNenno, P. J., *ed.*, *SFPE Handbook of Fire Protection Engineering*, National Fire Protection Association, Quincy, 1988.

Flow of Fluids Through Valves, Fittings and Pipe, *Crane Technical Paper No. 410*, Crane Co., Chicago, 1976.

Hydraulic Institute. 1970 *Engineering Data Book*. Hydraulic Institute. Cleveland, OH.

Idelchik, I. E., *ed.*, *Handbook of Hydraulic Resistance*, 2nd ed., Hemisphere, Washington, 1986.

Jeppson, R. W., *Analysis of Flow in Pipe Networks*, Butterworth, Boston, 1976.

Parmakian, J., *Waterhammer Analysis*, Dover, New York, 1963.

Perry, R. H. and Chilton, C. H., *Chemical Engineers Handbook*, 5th Ed., McGraw-Hill, New York, 1973.

Wass, H. S., *Sprinkler Hydraulics*, IRM Insurance, White Plains, 1983.

Additional Reading

Albertson, M. L., Barton, J. R., and Simons, D. B., *Fluid Mechanics for Engineers*, Prentice-Hall, Inc., Englewood Cliffs, N.J., 1960.

Benedict, R., P., *Fundamentals of Pipe Flow*, Wiley, New York, 1980.

Caulfield, H. J., "Hydraulics," *Fire Engineering*, Vol. 138, No. 6, 1987, p. 56.

Cozad, F. D., *Water Supply for Fire Protection*, Prentice-Hall, Englewood Cliffs, N.J., 1981.

"Data Sections," *Standards of Hydraulic Institute*, 11th ed., Hydraulic Institute, New York, 1965.

Davis, C. V. and Sorensen, K. E., eds, *Handbook of Applied Hydraulics*, 3rd ed. reprint, McGraw-Hill, New York, 1984.

Edwards, C. C., "Fireground Hydraulics in Your Head," *Fire Engineering*, Vol. 142, No. 3, 1989, pp. 79-80, 82-83.

Giles, R. V., *Fluid Mechanics and Hydraulics*, 2nd ed., Schaum's Outline Series, McGraw-Hill, New York, 1977.

Howard, C. D. D., "Pipe Friction Coefficients from Measured Velocity Profiles," *American Water Works Association Journal*, Vol. 59, No. 5, May 1967, pp. 645-650.

Jedlicka, J. R., "Pressure Surge Protection," *Fire Technology*, Vol. 2, No. 3, August, 1966, pp. 239-245.

"Hydraulics of Pipelines," Chapter 5 in *AWWA M11 Steel Pipe Manual*, American Water Works Association, New York, 1964.

Kandola, B. S., "Intoduction to Mechanics of Fluids," *SFPE Handbook of Fire Protection Engineering*, National Fire Protection Association, Quincy, MA., 1988.

King, H. W., and Brater, E. F., *Handbook of Hydraulics*, 5th ed., McGraw-Hill, New York, 1963.

Lescovich, J. E., "The Control of Water Hammer by Automatic Valves," *American Water Works Association Journal*, Vol. 59, No. 5, May 1967, pp. 632-644.

McJunkin, F. E., and Vesilind, P. A., "Practical Hydraulics for the Public Works Engineer," reprinted from *Public Works Magazine*, Sept., Oct., Nov., 1968.

Mahoney, E. F., *Fire Department Hydraulics*, Allyn and Bacon, Boston, 1980.

Melley, B. W., "Comparison of Several Computer Hydraulics Programs for the IBM PC and Compatibles," *Fire Technology*, Vol. 25, No. 4, 1989, pp. 336-363.

Purington, R. G., *Fire-Fighting Hydraulics*, McGraw-Hill, New York, 1980.

Richard, R. T., "Water Hammer," *Transactions of American Society of Mechanical Engineers*, Vol. 78, No. 6, August 1956.

Rosenhan, A. K., "Water-Net-A Computerized Design Aid," *Fire Technology*, Vol. 4., No. 3, August 1968, pp. 179-184.

Streeter, V. L., ed., *Handbook of Fluid Dynamics*, reissue, McGraw-Hill, New York, 1982.

"Water Hammer and Surge," Chapter 7, *Ibid*.

Titus, J. J., "Hydraulics," *SFPE Handbook of Fire Protection Engineering*, National Fire Protection Association, Quincy, MA., 1988.

Winn, W. P. "Techniques in Water Hammer Control and Surge Supression," *American Water Works Association Journal*, Vol. 59, No. 5, May 1967, pp. 620-624.

Wood, C. M., *"Automatic" Sprinkler Hydraulic Data*, 1964 ed., "Automatic" Sprinkler Corporation of America (reprinted 1980).

Wood, D. J., "Calculation of Water Hammer Pressure Due to Valve Closure," *American Water Works Association Journal*, Vo. 60, No. 11, Nov. 1968, pp. 1301-1306.

Wood, M. S., "Full Hydraulic Calculations for Sprinkler Systems," *Fire Surveyor*, Vol. 17, No. 4, Aug. 1988, pp. 64-73.

WATER SUPPLY REQUIREMENTS FOR FIRE PROTECTION

Revised by Kenneth W. Linder

The amount of water needed and the economics of supplying it are basic questions underlying the planning of water supply systems for fire suppression.

This chapter gives information on planning for public water supply systems and outlines the methods used to evaluate public supplies for their adequacy and reliability. The chapter does not cover the specifics of water supply requirements for automatic extinguishing systems within individual properties. They are covered in the following chapters of Section 5: Chapter 11, "Water Supplies for Sprinkler Systems;" Chapter 13, "Residential Quick-Response Sprinklers;" Chapter 14, "Standpipe and Hose Systems;" and Chapter 15, "Water Spray Protection."

Components of a water supply system are covered in Section 5, Chapter 4, "Water Distribution Systems." Testing procedures to determine adequacy of flows can be found in Section 5, Chapter 8, "Test of Water Supplies."

FACTORS AFFECTING PUBLIC WATER SUPPLY DESIGN

Most public water supply systems serving a substantial number of customers are, and should be, designed for a dual purpose: (1) to supply water for normal domestic demands, such as drinking and sanitary purposes, as well as for processing and industrial uses, and (2) to provide water to fire hydrants for emergency use by fire departments and to supply fixed fire protection systems, such as automatic sprinklers, foam systems, and standpipe systems.

The variety of hazards encountered in most communities and the need to plan for future growth must be considered when evaluating these objectives. In some cities, there may be a heavy industrial demand. At the same time, demands for air conditioning and lawn sprinkling may affect the required capacity of the system. The adequacy of a public water system for fire protection cannot be taken for granted, and the other demands must be determined to estimate their effects on the capacity of the system.

Public water systems also must be reliable. Since the occurence of a fire should not affect domestic demands, the water system must be designed to meet the simultaneous demand rates for both purposes. In addition, portions of the pumping or distribution system may be out of service due to breakdown or scheduled maintenance, so the consequences of these interruptions must be examined for acceptability when evaluating system reliability.

DEMANDS FOR DOMESTIC PURPOSES

To determine the domestic demands on a public water supply, it is necessary to focus on variations in water consumption with respect to the time of year, the day of the week, and even the hour of the day. Obviously, as more water is used in a given system for normal consumption, less remains for fire protection. Normal consumption demands are usually expressed in the following terms:

1. Average daily demand, or the average of the total amount of water used each day during a 1-year period.
2. Maximum daily demand, or the maximum total amount of water used during any 24-hr period in a 3-year period. Unusual situations that might have caused an excessive use of water, such as refilling a reservoir after cleaning, should not be considered when determining this figure.
3. Peak hourly demand, or the maximum amount of water used in any given hour of a day.

A joint report of committees from the American Society of Civil Engineers, the American Water Works Association (AWWA), and others suggested that the maximum general service demand on a waterworks system be taken as the peak hourly demand during a test year.[1] This, the report noted, was the only figure that can be fairly compared with the maximum fire flow requirement.

The maximum daily demand can be estimated as 1.5 times the average daily consumption if the actual maximum is not known. The peak hourly rate usually varies from two to four times the normal hourly rate. The effect these varying consumption rates have on the ability of the system to deliver required fire flows varies with the system design.

Kenneth W. Linder is assistant director of research, Industrial Risk Insurers, Hartford, CT.

Both maximum daily consumption and peak hourly consumption should be considered to ensure that water supplies and pressures do not reach dangerously low levels during these periods and that adequate water will be available if there is a fire.

WATER REQUIREMENTS FOR FIRE FIGHTING

The water requirements for fire fighting include the rate of flow, the residual pressure required at that flow, and the total quantity required. The American Water Works Association defines the required fire flow as "the rate of water flow, at a residual pressure of 20 psi and for a specified duration that is necessary to control a major fire in a specific structure."[2]

Calculating Fire Flow Rates

The required flow rate for properties protected by automatic sprinklers is based on the sprinkler system design as required by NFPA 13, *Installation of Sprinkler Systems*. (Also see NFPA 13R, *Installation of Sprinkler Systems in Residential Occupancies Up to Four Stories in Height*, and NFPA 13D, *Installation of Sprinkler Systems in One- and Two-Family Dwellings and Mobile Homes*.) The flow required is that of the sprinkler system plus the anticipated hose stream, or manual fire fighting requirements.

There are several methods currently used to calculate required water flow rates for non-sprinklered properties. These include:

- The Insurance Services Office (ISO) method
- The Iowa State University (ISU) method
- The Illinois Institute of Technology Research Institute method

Insurance Services Office (ISO) method: One of the most comprehensive and widely recommended methods for estimating fire flow requirements is found in the Insurance Services Office's *Fire Suppression Rating Schedule*.[3] It provides guidance for estimating fire flow requirements for specific structures and was designed for insurance rating purposes. The flows determined by this method are generally considered a good estimate, and, as a result, the ISO method has received widespread use. The ISO method considers building construction, occupancy, adjacent exposed buildings, and communication paths between buildings.

The basic formula in the schedule is:

$$NFF_i = (C_i)(O_i)(X + P)_i$$

where NFF_i is needed fire flow (NFF) in gallons per minute (L/min); C_i is a construction factor that depends upon the construction of the structure under consideration; O_i is an occupancy factor that depends upon the combustibility of the occupancy; and $(X + P)_i$ is an exposure factor that depends upon the extent of exposure from and to adjacent structures.

The subscripts in the formula indicate that, where portions of a building have differing characteristics, a factor can be calculated for each section and multiplied by the percentage it represents of the effective area to obtain a weighted factor. The weighted C_i factor should not be less than the individual factor required for any individual section.

Construction factor. The construction factor C_i is calculated from the following formula:

$$C_i = 18F\sqrt{A_i}$$

where:

F = coefficient related to the class of construction
F = 1.5 for construction class 1 (frame)
F = 1.0 for construction class 2 (joisted masonry)
F = 0.8 for construction class 3 (noncombustible) or construction class 4 (masonry, noncombustible)
F = 0.6 for construction class 5 (modified fire-resistive) or construction class 6 (fire-resistive)
A_i = effective building area

The effective building area is the total square foot area of the largest floor plus:

- Construction classes 1 through 4—50 percent of all other floors.
- Construction classes 5,6—25 percent of the area not exceeding the two other largest floors when all of the vertical openings have at least 1½-hr-rated protection, or 50 percent of the area not exceeding eight other floors when vertical openings are unprotected or have less than 1½-hr protection.

The value of C_i should not be less than 500 gpm nor greater than 8000 gpm for construction classes 1 and 2, and 6000 gpm for construction classes 3,4,5, and 6, or any single, one-story building, regardless of construction.

Occupancy factor. The occupancy factor O_i reflects the combustibility of the occupancy on the needed fire flow and is determined from the occupancy combustibility class. Occupancy factors can be found in Table 5-3A.

TABLE 5-3A. ***Occupancy Factors***

Occupancy Combustibility Class	Occupancy Factor (O_i)
C-1 (Non-combustible)	0.75
C-2 (Limited-combustible)	0.85
C-3 (Combustible)	1.00
C-4 (Free burning)	1.15
C-5 (Rapid burning)	1.25

Exposure and communication $[(X + P_i)]$ factors. The exposure and communication factors are determined as:

$$X_i = 1 + \sum_{i=1}^{n} X_i + P_i$$

The exposure factor, X_i, reflects the need for additional water to reduce the exposure to adjacent buildings. It depends on the separation distance, the construction of the exposed building wall, and a length-height value—that is, the length of the exposed wall in feet multiplied by the height in stories. Values can be obtained from Table 5-3B.

The communication factor, P_i, reflects the potential fire spread through open or enclosed communicating passageways between buildings and is taken from Table 5-3C. Where there is more than one connection, only the one with the largest factor is used.

Needed fire flow (NFF). The needed fire flow is calculated from the formula given previously and from the above factors. The NFF calculated from the formula should be rounded to the nearest 250 gpm for flows under 2500

TABLE 5-3B. *Factors for Exposure X_i*

Construction of Facing Wall of Subject Bldg.	Distance Feet to the Exposed Building	Length-Height of Facing Wall of Exposed Building	Construction of Facing Wall of Exposed Building Classes: 1,3	2, 4, 5, & 6: Unprotected Openings	2, 4, 5, & 6: Semi-Protected Openings (wired glass or outside open sprinklers)	2, 4, 5, & 6: Blank Wall
Frame, Metal or Masonry with Openings	0-10	1-100	0.22	0.21	0.16	0
		101-200	0.23	0.22	0.17	0
		201-300	0.24	0.23	0.18	0
		301-400	0.25	0.24	0.19	0
		Over 400	0.25	0.25	0.20	0
	11-30	1-100	0.17	0.15	0.11	0
		101-200	0.18	0.16	0.12	0
		201-300	0.19	0.18	0.14	0
		301-400	0.20	0.19	0.15	0
		Over 400	0.20	0.19	0.15	0
	31-60	1-100	0.12	0.10	0.07	0
		101-200	0.13	0.11	0.08	0
		201-300	0.14	0.13	0.10	0
		301-400	0.15	0.14	0.11	0
		Over 400	0.15	0.15	0.12	0
	61-100	1-100	0.08	0.06	0.04	0
		101-200	0.08	0.07	0.05	0
		201-300	0.09	0.08	0.06	0
		301-400	0.10	0.09	0.07	0
		Over 400	0.10	0.10	0.08	0

Blank Masonry Wall — Facing wall of the exposed building is higher than subject building.

Use the above table EXCEPT use only the length-height of facing wall of the exposed building ABOVE the height of the facing wall of the subject building. Building five stories or over in height consider as five stories.

When the height of the facing wall of the exposed building is the same or lower than the height of the facing wall of the subject building, $X_i = 0$.

Source: Insurance Services Office © 1980.

TABLE 5-3C. *Factors for Communications P_i*

Description of Protection of Passageway Openings	Fire-Resistive, Non-Combustible or Slow-Burning Communications: Open				Communications with Combustible Construction: Open			Enclosed		
	Open	Enclosed			Open			Enclosed		
	Any Length	10 Ft or Less	11 ft or 20 ft	21 ft to 50 ft +	10 ft or Less	11 ft to 20 ft	21 ft to 50 ft +	10 ft or Less	11 ft to 20 ft	21 ft to 50 ft +
Unprotected	0	+ +	0.30	0.20	0.30	0.20	0.10	+ +	+ +	0.30
Single Class A Fire door at One End of Passageway	0	0.20	0.10	0	0.20	0.15	0	0.30	0.20	0.10
Single Class B Fire Door at One End of Passageway	0	0.30	0.20	0.10	0.25	0.20	0.10	0.35	0.25	0.15
Single Class A Fire Door at Each End or Double Class A Fire Doors at One End of Passageway	0	0	0	0	0	0	0	0	0	0
Single Class B Fire Door at Each End or Double Class B Fire Doors at One End of Passageway	0	0.10	0.05	0	0	0	0	0.15	0.10	0

\+ For over 50 ft, $P_i = 0$.

\+ + For unprotected passageways of this length, consider the two buildings as a single fire division.

Note: When a party wall has communicating openings protected by a single automatic or self-closing Class B fire door, it qualifies as a division wall* for reduction of area.

Note: Where communications are protected by a recognized water curtain, the value of P_i is 0.

*When an asterisk is shown next to a term in this table, the term is defined in greater detail in the ISO Commercial Fire Rating Schedule.

gpm and to the nearest 500 gpm for larger flows and then adjusted by the following:

- For buildings with a wood roof, add 500 gpm.
- The needed flow should not exceed 12,000 gpm (45 425 L/min) nor be less than 500 gpm (1893 L/min). The practical reason for these figures is that manual fire fighting methods using hose streams and heavy stream appliances are not likely to need a larger supply, considering the general arrangement of buildings and the availability of hydrants.
- For habitational buildings, use the calculated NFF up to 3500 gpm maximum.
- For groupings of one-family and small two-family dwellings not more than two stories high, the required fire flow given in Table 5-3D may be used.

TABLE 5-3D. ***Fire Flows for Groups of Dwellings***

Exposure Distances		Suggested Required Fire Flow	
Ft	m	gpm	L/min
Over 100	30	500	1893
31 to 100	9.5–30	750–1,000	2839–3785
11 to 30	3.4–9.1	1,000	3785
10 or less	3 or less	1,500	5678

Iowa State University method: The Iowa State University method is another common method used to determine water flow rates for fire fighting. It uses a more theoretical approach and is based on the amount of water needed to deplete the oxygen in a confined area when the water is vaporized into steam by the heat of the fire. Tests conducted by the university indicate that a fire is best controlled if the amount of water necessary to deplete the oxygen is applied within 30 sec.

The required flow in gpm is given as:

$$\text{Required Flow} = \frac{V}{100}$$

where V is the enclosed volume in cubic feet.

This method is unique, in that it does not consider the occupancy hazard, only the volume of the building to be filled with steam.

Due to inefficiencies in applying water, some experts feel that the rate should be 2 to 4 gal per 100 cu ft of building volume, rather than the 1 gal per 100 cu ft in the formula. Other variations include changing the value in the denominator based on the occupancy hazard.

This formula has been used for approximately 30 years and is extremely simple to apply. For most buildings, the entire volume of the structure should be used, including the volume of basements, attics, crawl spaces, and other concealed spaces. For groups of buildings, the largest flow rate should be used.

Illinois Institute of Technology Research Institute method: The Illinois Institute of Technology method was based on a survey of 134 fires in the Chicago area. The results of the survey were used with regression analysis to develop fire flow formulas based on building area. The fire flow rate is based on one of the following formulas:

$$\text{Flow for residential occupancies} = 9 \times 10^{-5} A^2 + 50 \times 10^{-2} A$$

$$\text{Flow for other occupanices} = -1.3 \times 10^{-5} A^2 + 42 \times 10^{-2} A$$

where A is the area of the fire in square feet.

Other Flow Considerations

Regardless of the method used to determine the flow rate, the required fire flow should be available simultaneously with consumption at the maximum daily rate.

When evaluating the flow required for general public protection, both the AWWA and the ISO suggest that 3500 gpm is the upper limit to be provided and that large facilities or those with severe hazards that need flow rates up to 12,000 gpm be individually analyzed to determine the required flow rate.

There are fires in which quantities of water in excess of the required fire flow are used. Water supplies of 50,000 gpm (190 000 L/min) or greater have been used in fire suppression, but designing systems capable of delivering flows of that magnitude is not cost-effective.

Fire Water Duration

The number of hours during which the required fire flow should be available varies from 2 to 10 hrs, as indicated in Table 5-3E. It should be noted that many water authorities place an upper limit of 2 to 4 hrs on fire water supply duration due to economics.

Evaluating System Capacity

The capacity of a water system is determined by the total amount of water it must furnish. This is the sum of water required for domestic or industrial uses and water required for the fire service. In small towns, the requirements for fire protection exceed other requirements.

The AWWA recommends that the rate used be either the peak hourly rate or the maximum daily rate plus fire flow, whichever is larger. In most large cities, the peak hourly rate exceeds the maximum daily consumption rate plus fire flow and is therefore the controlling factor in the supply system design. In smaller communities, however, the reverse is true and the maximum daily consumption rate plus fire flow is the controlling factor. For many years, water consumption has been increasing in most municipalities, resulting in increased peak hourly rates. Consequently, there has been an increase in the number of municipalities in which the peak hourly rate controls designs of the supply system. However, there is no guarantee that a fire will not occur at the peak hour, and some recommend that the capacity of the system be sufficient to meet the peak hourly rate plus the fire flow rate.

Fire flows are a very important consideration in all areas served by the distribution system and, in many instances, they govern the size of pipe used in these locations. In all systems, the supply should be sufficient to provide for automatic sprinklers and other automatic fire protection systems, in addition to the other demand rates imposed upon the system. For example, many smaller cities and large towns restrict lawn watering in summer months to specified periods, usually 2 to 4 hrs in the

TABLE 5-3E. *Duration of Required Fire Flow*

Required Fire Flow					Required Fire Flow				
gpm	L/min	Million gallons per day	Million liters per day	Duration hours	gpm	L/min	Million gallons per day	Million liters per day	Duration hours
1,000	3785	1.44	5.45	2	4,500	17 034	6.48	24.53	4
1,250	4732	1.80	6.81	2	5,000	18 927	7.20	27.25	5
1,500	5678	2.16	8.18	2	5,500	20 820	7.92	29.99	5
1,750	6624	2.52	9.54	2	6,000	22 712	8.64	32.71	6
2,000	7571	2.88	10.90	2	7,000	26 498	10.08	38.16	7
2,250	8517	3.24	12.26	2	8,000	30 283	11.52	43.61	8
2,500	9463	3.60	13.63	2	9,000	34 069	12.96	49.06	9
3,000	11 356	4.32	16.35	3	10,000	37 854	14.40	54.51	10
3,500	13 249	5.04	19.08	3	11,000	41 639	15.84	59.96	10
4,000	15 142	5.76	21.80	4	12,000	45 425	17.28	65.41	10

evening. The demand rates imposed by lawn watering are excessive in many water supply systems depleting storage facilities and reducing pressure throughout the system for many hours. In such situations, there would be little or no water available for fire protection systems, particularly at higher elevations.

Pressure Characteristics of Systems

The pressures for which systems are normally designed are the result of practical attempts to provide adequate pressures for both domestic consumption and for fire protection. If either demands special ranges of pressure, materials and design methods are available that will allow almost any desired range.

For example, San Francisco has a separate system, designated the "high-pressure system," that is under the control of the fire department. All of the pipe is heavy cast-iron, tar-coated and lined, and it is tested on installation and repair to 450 psi (3103 kPa). Two steam-operated pump stations can pump water from San Francisco Bay into the system, and 20,000 gpm (75 700 L/min) at 250 psi (1724 kPa) can be delivered to most of the principal mercantile district. San Francisco provided this system primarily because an earthquake might put the regular public water system out of service. A few other cities have similar high-pressure systems.

Modern fire department pumpers make heavy streams and high pressures available from ordinary water systems where adequate volume is provided. Cities that formerly had separate systems of fire mains operating at so-called high pressures now generally keep them at normal public water pressures. The second system still provides an advantage, though, even if it is not at high pressure, because it is still available.

Public water systems reflect a compromise on the question of pressures. Pressures in the range of 65 to 80 psi (448 to 552 kPa) are common. This range, which is adequate for ordinary consumption in buildings up to about ten stories, will provide a good supply of water for automatic sprinkler systems in buildings of about four stories, in which occupancies are classified as "ordinary." Where pressures of this order are provided, it is reasonably easy to compensate for local fluctuations in draft.

Because of the increased cost of energy, greater care is being given to the water pressure that systems should provide. A reduction in water pressure will substantially reduce pumping costs. Before a general reduction is made, however, a study should be conducted as to the effects it could have on sprinklers and other fixed fire protection systems. If a reduction in pressure is planned, it is imperative that the system remain capable of meeting anticipated demand rates, or steps must be taken to lower the demand rates to a point where they will be within the capability of the system.

A minimum residual pressure of least 20 psi (138 kPa) should be maintained at hydrants delivering the required fire flow. Pumpers can be operated, but with difficulty, where hydrant pressures are less. Where hydrants are well distributed and of the proper size and type so that friction losses in the hydrant and suction line will not be excessive, it may be possible to set 10 psi (69 kPa) as the minimum pressure. Sufficient hydrant pressure should be maintained to prevent a negative pressure from developing in the street mains, which might cause back siphonage of polluted water from some interconnected source. Using residual pressures less than 20 psi (138 kPa) is prohibited by most state health departments.

Pressures in a public water system may be considered excessive as they approach 150 psi (1034 kPa). As pressures increase, they tend to cause leaks in domestic plumbing, and special attention is required to restrain pipelines in the ground. Pipe and fittings used in ordinary public water systems are designed for maximum working pressures of 150 psi (1034 kPa), but it is not good practice to operate with pressures that high. Pressure-reducing valves can be used in sections of a system where variations in topography result in excessive pressures. Individual water services to buildings may require pressure-reducing valves to keep the pressure on domestic piping at safe levels.

Systems for Higher Elevations

When water must be supplied to high elevations, a separate water distribution system is usually provided for the elevated section so that normal pressures are maintained. In such cases, the elevated area should be provided with its own water storage facility, and pumps may be provided to boost the water from other parts of the system.

Likewise, the upper stories of a high-rise building should be provided with self-contained water supplies. High-rise structures are normally divided into a number of pressure zones, and zones of more than 12 stories tend to get outside the normal pressure ranges. In any case, each pressure zone must be provided with water in the amounts needed for sprinkler system and hose stream use, and each system is usually supplied by a series of pumps and tanks arranged so that each zone is fed from the zone below. Care should be taken to ensure that pumps will be able to operate even during power failures.

For information and guidance concerning water supplies for high-rise structures, see NFPA 13, *Installation of Sprinkler Systems*; NFPA 14, *Installation of Standpipe and Hose Systems*; and NFPA 20, *Installation of Centrifugal Fire Pumps*.

ADEQUACY AND RELIABILITY OF SUPPLY

The adequacy of any given water supply system can be determined by engineering estimates. The source (e.g., storage facilities and distribution system) must be sufficient to furnish all the water that combined fire and domestic needs may call for at any one time. The arrangement of the supply and pumping facilities may render the supply inadequate or affect its reliability.

Pumping systems commonly are arranged so that one set of pumps takes suction from wells or from a river, lake, or other body of water. If the water does not have to be filtered, the pumps may discharge directly into the distribution system. Where filtration or other treatment is necessary, pumps take suction from the primary or raw water source and discharge to sedimentation basins or other facilities and then to filter beds. After the water is processed, it flows to clear-water reservoirs from which a second set of pumps takes suction and discharges the water directly into the supply system. Unfortunately, failure of any part of the equipment may affect the entire system.

When assessing the reliability of the supply works, one should evaluate: minimum yield; the frequency and duration of droughts; the condition of intakes; the possibility of earthquakes, floods, and forest fires; ice formations; silting up or shifting of river channels; and the absence of guards or watchmen, where needed, to protect the facility from physical injury. Reservoirs out of service for cleaning and the interdependence of parts of waterworks also affect reliability. The condition, arrangement, and dependability of individual units of plant equipment, such as pumps, engines, generators, electric motors, fuel supply, electric transmission facilities, and similar items, are also factors. Pumping stations of combustible construction may be destroyed by fire unless they are protected by automatic sprinkler systems.

Duplication of pumping units and storage facilities, and arrangement of mains and distributors so that water may be supplied to any area from more than one direction, are measures that can ensure continuous operation. The importance of duplicate facilities is shown by the frequency of their use. Many utilities design their systems so that the peak hourly rate and required fire flow rate can be supplied when any pump or section of the distribution system is out of service.

The amount of water needed to control and extinguish a fire in a given property currently cannot be established in precise terms. Better fire experience data bases should make it possible to tailor fire flows more specifically to conditions that might be expected at the time of a fire. Better analysis may indicate a need to increase fire flow beyond what is presently required, or it may result in a water system design based upon a balance between the risk involved and the economics of maintaining the water system.

A detailed discussion of all the factors to be considered in designing a water supply system is beyond the scope of this handbook. An overview of the subject can be found in AWWA M24, *Dual Water Systems*, and AWWA M31, *Distribution System Requirements for Fire Protection*.

THE ROLE OF CODES AND ORDINANCES

Fire prevention codes can effectively limit hazards and ignition sources within buildings which, in turn, limits the number and size of fires by controlling combustibles in a fire area. A good building code further reduces the chance for a serious fire by requiring construction materials and building assemblies that will contain a developing fire to a given area. Codes alone can reduce considerably the amount of water needed for fire fighting. Zoning ordinances that establish distances between properties can be effective in controlling exposure situations.

THE ROLE OF FIRE DETECTION AND EXTINGUISHING SYSTEMS

The increased use of automatic extinguishing systems, whether they use water or some other agent, will affect the quantities of water required. Until more widespread use is made of early warning systems and automatic extinguishing systems, however, it will not be possible to equate the effect of these systems with required fire flow. Water supply requirements are just one factor in a system that determines what the potential for a fire is, how extensive that fire will be, and what measures will be needed to suppress it. Someday, research will measure all these factors and allow us to establish fire flows on the basis of thoroughly researched and documented principles.

HISTORY

Historically, water supply systems for cities and towns were developed primarily to provide drinking water and water for sanitary purposes, rather than for fire protection. However, it was found that large cities that required substantial amounts of water for domestic purposes usually had enough water to provide a useful supply for fire fighting purposes.

This led to inquiries in the late 19th century into the additional cost of waterworks that could provide water for fire fighting, as well as other uses. A number of distinguished engineers associated with individual waterworks examined the problem and presented their findings in technical papers at engineering society meetings. Papers by J. Herbert Shedd,[4] J. T. Fanning,[5] and Emil Kuichling[6] give the details of discussions in which standards for American and Canadian waterworks were first developed. (See Table 5-3F.)

Number of Hose Streams

In these discussions, the starting point for computing the cost of water for fire protection was to estimate the number of hose streams that a fire department might need for fire fighting. This was usually estimated using are basis the central portion of a city where the largest buildings were

TABLE 5-3F. ***Estimates of Fire Flow***[4,5,6,7,8]

	Number of Fire Streams Required Simultaneously				
Populations Thousands	Shedd 1889[4]	Fanning 1892[5]	Freeman 1892[7]	Kuichling 1897[6]	NBFU 1911[8]
1			2–3	3	4
4		7		6	8
5	5		4–8	6	9
10	7	10	6–12	9	12
20	10		8–15	12	17
40	14		12–18	18	24
50		14		20	26
60	17		15–22	22	28
100	22	18	20–30	28	36
150		25		34	44
180	30			38	48
200			30–50	40	48

located and where there was the greatest building congestion. The number of streams was found to be related, in a very rough way, to the population. Shedd's proposal,[4] which was the first, used hose streams discharging 200 gpm (757 L/min). He suggested that a community of 5000 would need about five such streams and that the needs of other cities could be graduated up to 30 streams in a city of 180,000. Fanning[5] proposed streams requiring about 54 psi (372 kPa) pressure. His figures were similar to Shedd's,[4] beginning at seven streams for a community of 4000 and going up to 25 streams for a city of 150,000.

Kuichling[6] suggested a formula in which the number of streams required would be the square root of the population in thousands multiplied by 2.8. There were arithmatical differences as to how these estimates worked out for individual cities, but they were all of the same general order. (See Table 5-3F.) Most important, they provided a basis from which waterworks designers could estimate costs.

The most important paper produced during this time was John R. Freeman's "The Arrangement of Hydrants and Water Pipes for the Protection of a City Against Fire," published in 1892.[7] Freeman had done the fundamental work on water flow through hose and nozzles, so he was able to pin down the definition of a standard fire stream to one with a discharge of 250 gpm (946 L/min) at 40 to 50 psi (276 to 345 kPa) pressure. He said that the relationships suggested by Shedd[4] and Fanning[5] between population and the number of streams required were of the right order, but he did not think the needs of individual cities could be quite so definitely ascertained. He suggested two to three streams as a minimum for a population of 1000, graduated up to 30 to 50 streams at 200,000. (See Table 5-3F.) Most significantly, he warned that, "Ten streams, or as large a proportion thereof as the financial consideration will permit, may be recommended for a compact group of large, valuable buildings, irrespective of a small population."[7]

ENGINEERING: DISTRIBUTION NETWORK, HYDRANT SPACING, STORAGE

Freeman[7] noted a fundamental difference between systems designed to supply ordinary water needs and those for fire protection: Fire draft required concentration of the water, whereas domestic draft was a matter of distribution.

Freeman[7] asserted that, if a water system was to supply fire protection needs, the distribution system should be designed to concentrate the needed amounts of water. Small pipes were sufficient for distribution, but larger ones were needed to concentrate supply to fire streams. He suggested 6-in.-diameter pipe as the minimum for residential districts and noted that 8-in. pipe was adequate only if it formed part of a network of distribution pipes whose intersections were not far apart.

Another important point Freeman[7] made was that hydrants should be placed where they could concentrate streams at specific blocks or groups of buildings, rather than placed arbitrarily a certain number of feet apart on the street mains. His work on hose streams showed how long hose lines reduced the water that can be delivered promptly to a fire. He therefore suggested a working rule for hydrant spacing of 250 ft (76 m) between hydrants in compact mercantile and manufacturing districts and 400 ft (122 m) to 500 ft (152 m) in residential districts. These working rules can still be used as guides for good design.

Freeman[7] further insisted that fire supply should be in addition to maximum domestic consumption, and laid the foundation for the eventual recognition of this principle. He also calculated how much water should be stored in standpipes or in elevated reservoirs. He figured that flow for all of the hose streams required should be supplied from a reliable source, such as an elevated storage reservoir, for at least 6 hr when the system was also furnishing maximum demands for domestic and other uses and he calculated that, to supply the combined fire and domestic needs in a system provided with reliable pump capacity, a 1-hr supply in a standpipe or elevated reservoir would be acceptable.

The Insurance Grading Schedule

As early as 1889, the National Board of Fire Underwriters (NBFU) began to make fire protection surveys of municipalities. This work was intensified in 1904 after a conflagration in Baltimore. Today, the ISO surveys communities in all but a few states. The ISO survey, called the "Fire Suppression Rating Schedule,"[3] was discussed in detail earlier in this chapter.

The current ISO procedure for establishing fire flows is different from the original NBFU formula, which was commonly used for many years as a guide to determine the fire flow required in downtown business districts of municipalities. (See Table 5-3F.) The formula gave the fire flow, G, in gal per min as a function of the population, P, in thousands.

$$G = 1020\sqrt{P}\,(1 - 0.01\sqrt{P})$$

In making fire protection surveys, engineers from the NBFU and insurance bureaus estimated the fire flow requirements in sections of municipalities outside the downtown business district.

As cities became more decentralized, the formula based on population became less reliable as a guide for the fire flow needed downtown. In addition, it became apparent that a guide to engineering judgment was needed for the other sections of the cities. In 1948, a paper by A. C. Hutson,[9] assistant chief engineer of the NBFU, provided some specific suggestions for estimating fire flow requirements in these sections, based on the type of construction and the area of a building. This eventually led to the current ISO rating system.

BIBLIOGRAPHY

References Cited

1. ASCE, "Fundamental Considerations in Rates and Rate Structures for Water and Sewage Works: A Joint Report of Committees of the American Society of Civil Engineers and the Section of Municipal Law of the American Bar Association and of Representatives of the American Water Works Association, National Association of Railroad and Utilities Commissioners, Municipal Finance Officers Association, Federation of Sewage Works Association, American Public Works Association, and Investment Bankers Association of America," *ASCE Bulletin No. 2*, American Society of Civil Engineers, NY, 1951.
2. AWWA Manual M31, *Distribution System Requirements for Fire Protection*, American Water Works Association, Denver, CO, 1989.
3. *Fire Suppression Rating Schedule*, Insurance Services Office, NY, 1980.
4. Shedd, J. H., *Discussion* on a paper by William B. Sherman, "Ratio of Pumping Capacity to Maximum Consumption," *Journal of New England Water Works Association*, Vol. 3, 1889, p. 113.
5. Fanning, J. T., "Distribution Mains and the Fire Service," *Proceedings* of the American Water Works Association, Vol. 12, 1892, p. 61.
6. Kuichling, E., "The Financial Management of Water Works," *Transactions* of the American Society of Civil Engineers, Vol. 38, 1897, p. 16.
7. Freeman, J. R., "The Arrangement of Hydrants and Water Pipes for the Protection of a City Against Fire," *Journal of the New England Water Works Association*, Vol. 7, 1892, p. 49.
8. Metcalf, L., Kuichling, E., and Hawley, W. C., "Some Fundamental Considerations in the Determination of a Reasonable Return for Public Fire Hydrant Service," *Proceedings* of the American Water Works Association, Vol. 31, 1911, p. 55.
9. Hutson, A. C., "Water Works Requirements for Fire Protection," *Journal of the American Water Works Association*, Vol. 40, No. 9, 1948, p. 936. [Also reprinted in *Special Interest Bulletin No. 266*, National Board of Fire Underwriters (now American Insurance Service Group), NY.]

Reference

Davis, L. W., *Rural Firefighting Operations*, International Society of Fire Service Instructors, Ashland, MA, 1986.

NFPA Codes, Standards, and Recommended Practices

Reference to the following NFPA codes, standards, and recommended practices will provide further information on water supply requirements for fire protection discussed in this chapter. (See the latest *NFPA Catalog* for availability of current editions of the following documents.)

NFPA 13, *Installation of Sprinkler Systems*.

NFPA 14, *Installation of Standpipe and Hose Systems*.

NFPA 20, *Installation of Centrifugal Fire Pumps*.

NFPA 24, *Private Fire Service Mains and Their Appurtenances*.

NFPA 1231, *Water Supplies for Suburban and Rural Fire Fighting*.

Additional Reading

AWWA M24, *Dual Water Systems*, American Water Works Association, Denver, CO.

Babbit, H. E. and Doland, J. J., *Water Supply Engineering*, 6th ed., McGraw-Hill, NY, 1962.

Carl, K. J. Young, R. A. and Anderson, G. C., "Guide for Determining Fire Flow Requirements," *American Water Works Association Journal*, Vol. 65, 1973, pp. 335-344.

Costigan, E. J., "Rural Water Supply," *Fire Engineering*, Vol. 142, No. 3, 1989, pp. 93-95.

Laughlin, J. W. and Williams, C., eds., *Water Supplies for Fire Protection*, 4th ed., IFSTA, Oklahoma State University, Stillwater, OK, 1988.

Maatman, G. L., "Systems Approach to Evaluating Public Fire Fighting Operations," *Fire Technology*, Vol. 1, No. 3 (Aug. 1965), pp. 187-193.

Patek, N. J., "Hydraulics for Fire Protection," *Fire Journal*, Vol. 67, No. 2 (Mar. 1973), p. 13ff.

Salzberg, F. Vodvarka, F. J. and Maatman, G. L., "Minimum Water Requirements for Suppression of Room Fires," *Fire Technology*, Vol. 6, No. 1 (Feb. 1970), pp. 22-28.

Seiffert, D. J., "Increase Your Water Supply Options," *Fire Engineering*, Vol. 138, No. 12, 1985, pp. 50-51.

Smith, P. D., "Elements of Fire Protection Systems for Isolated Facilities," *Fire Journal*, Vol. 66, No. 4 (July 1972), pp. 45-51.

Smith, P. D., "What Are the "Real" Fire Flow Requirements," *Fire Journal*, Vol. 69, No. 2 (Mar. 1975), pp. 93-96.

WATER DISTRIBUTION SYSTEMS

Revised by Gerald R. Schultz

Most public waterworks systems of any size are designed to provide water for fire protection and normal consumption demands. Many water distribution systems on private property providing water for fire protection also supply water for sanitary purposes. In some large private plant installations, extensive water distribution systems exist primarily to provide process water for elements of manufacturing or purification and additionally provide water for fire protection. In other private plants, large or small, water distribution systems exist for the sole purpose of providing fire protection.

This chapter includes information on components that make up a system for the distribution of water from sources of supply to specific areas of use for the purpose of providing fire protection, and, in dual systems, information on simultaneously supplying water for normal consumption demands. Specifically, subjects covered are: the sources of supply, the distribution systems, the rules for laying pipe, and the types of pipe and equipment used in the systems for control and distribution purposes. The principles are the same whether the distribution system is owned by a municipality, is owned by a public utility, or is privately owned to provide water to a single property.

Water supply requirements, i.e., the amount of water necessary for adequate fire control, are covered in Section 5, Chapter 3, "Water Supply Requirements for Fire Protection," and test procedures for adequacy of supply for fire protection can be found in Section 5, Chapter 8, "Test of Water Supplies."

A list of NFPA standards and recommended practices having application to water distribution systems can be found in the bibliography. The bibliography also includes standards and manuals of the American Water Works Association, Underwriters Laboratories Inc., and Underwriters Laboratories of Canada that refer to water distribution systems and their components. Many of these standards are also approved by the American National Standards Institute (ANSI).

Gerald R. Schultz, P.E., is a regional engineering manager for Schirmer Engineering, based in Deerfield, IL.

SEPARATE AND DUAL DISTRIBUTION SYSTEMS

There are many advantages to providing a completely separate distribution system for fire protection; there are also some disadvantages.

Among the advantages are:

1. Complete control over the system by those responsible for fire protection.
2. Proper design of the system to meet all fire demands.
3. The system is not subject to reduced supply when increases in population increase the use of water for normal demands or when processes using increased amounts of water are experienced.
4. There is little danger of introducing a nonpotable fire supply into a potable supply through faulting cross connections.

One of the disadvantages, however, is that pumps, prime movers, and other machinery and equipment are usually in a "non-operating" mode. This equipment must be started, controlled, and operated successfully during a fire emergency.

In combined systems, an advantage is that pumping machinery is in operation almost continuously and in many cases equipment is duplicated. Further, in combined systems, a malfunction surfaces quickly, as customers will likely be without water. In addition, public water systems have trained personnel readily available and not just for emergency operations.

In systems providing for normal consumption demands and for fire protection, that portion of the system extending into private property may be required to be isolated from the public portion of the system. This is usually done by the installation of listed or approved backflow prevention devices to provide protection from the possibility of contamination of the potable source.

Systems on private property that provide water for process use should be made available to fire systems through the opening of normally closed valves or other cross ties. Process water systems usually have substantial capacities and could be of significant value in augmenting the adequacy and reliability of fire protection systems.

FUNCTION OF SUPPLY AND DISTRIBUTION SYSTEMS

It is generally accepted that water systems are subdivided into two divisions: (1) supply systems, and (2) distribution systems. However, in small water systems there may be no way of differentiating between supply and distribution systems since the functions of both may be carried out in a single element of the system.

Supply System

The supply portion of a water system is usually that part of the system where the source or sources of supply are found. It also includes the storage and transmission of that supply through large conduits and aqueducts, and, in some cases, includes the arterial feeders extending to the distribution system.

Distribution System

The distribution system is that portion of the works that actually delivers water to the individual consumer connections and to which fire hydrants are attached.

SOURCES OF SUPPLY

Sources of supply have two major divisions: (1) groundwater supplies, and (2) surface water supplies.

Groundwater Supplies

Of the total quantity of fresh water available for use in the world, by far the large majority is available from groundwater supplies. Groundwater supply is that water that percolates into the ground from precipitation and is stored in underground strata. The underground stratum holding water can be defined as an aquifer. The free surface of water in the underground stratum is referred to as the water table. The height of the water table varies throughout the year, depending upon variations in precipitation, water movement in the aquifer, and water withdrawn from the aquifer through springs or wells.

There are locations, now greatly diminished in number because of usage, where water is stored in the underground strata under a positive head. When this aquifer is penetrated, water will rise to an elevation higher than that in the aquifer, resulting in free flow at the surface.

The amount of water in the underground strata and its availability depends upon the nature of the material of the strata. For example, the porosity of natural sand and gravel may exceed 40 percent, while the porosity of igneous rock is approximately 1 percent.

While porosity is important, perviousness, i.e., the ability of a substance to allow water to flow through it, is of greater importance insofar as the movement of water through the strata to drilled or dug wells is dependent upon the perviousness of the soil. For example, some clays have a porosity in excess of 40 percent but are impervious to waterflow.

The supply available from underground aquifers to wells is influenced, among other factors, by the precipitation falling on the area of recharge and the amount of water drawn from all of the wells penetrating the same aquifer. When the aquifer is of substantial size, static water levels usually delay the effects of drought and also delay the effects of increased precipitation. There are many different types of wells that may be constructed; however, high-capacity wells that are used for municipal water supplies are usually drilled and are equipped with deep-well turbine or submersible pumps.

NFPA 20, *Installation of Centrifugal Fire Pumps*, permits the installation of vertical turbine pumps in properly developed and tested wells under conditions described in the standard.

Surface Supplies

Surface supplies consist of rivers, lakes, streams, and impounded supplies. As with underground supplies, the availability and reliability of the supply is dependent upon precipitation falling within the drainage area or watershed of the supply. Usually, however, surface supplies respond more quickly to diminished precipitation or drought. Water levels may vary substantially between wet and dry periods. At certain times of the year, there may be excessive runoff from the watershed, resulting in high water levels at intake structures and low lift pumping stations. At other times, under drought conditions, water levels in surface supplies could be so low as to require the installation of pumps in a reservoir discharging into normally gravity-supplied intake structures. Large surface reservoirs supplied by substantial watersheds or runoff areas are reliable sources, provided water consumption demands do not increase beyond the recharge capabilities of the watershed.

There are several factors that may affect the operation of the intake structures of surface supplies, particularly in colder climates. For example, ice formation is a hazard. There are several kinds of ice that may form and affect the functioning or threaten the stability of intake structures or cribs. Anchor ice, which forms on submerged dark metallic pipe, fittings, or gratings, can restrict flow into the intakes. Surface ice and surface ice forming ice dams may impose considerable thrust upon intake structures and cribs. Frazil ice, i.e., displaced anchor ice, or ice that has formed about small suspended particles, may clog intake parts.

When anchor or frazil ice begins to clog an intake, a relatively small change in temperature will free the obstruction. There are some intakes designed with a grid which is in essence a heating coil. In such cases, all that is required is the activation of the circuit which in turn will heat the intake element sufficiently to keep it free from ice. This method has been found economical in a number of locations, since it requires small amounts of electric power and is used only a relatively few times per year. When the intake is designed so that there is a continuous temperature recording, the imminence of the formation of anchor or frazil ice can be predicted.

A river can also be a reliable source of supply if the flow rates during drought periods are not seriously affected. A river can be susceptible to ice hazard, scouring of the bottom, changing of the channel, and silting. Before a river intake is constructed, a careful study must be made of the stream bottom, the degree of scour, and the extent of formation of surface ice, and the likelihood of the formation of ice jams must be established. An intake can easily be destroyed by an ice jam, or the entire flow of a river may be stopped by ice. Provision must be made in the design of the intake to ensure that it can withstand the forces that will act upon it during times of flood, heavy silting, or ice conditions.

GRAVITY AND PUMPING SYSTEMS

There are two basic types of water distribution systems: (1) gravity systems, and (2) direct pumping systems. Most water systems are a combination of the two types.

Gravity Systems

A true gravity system is one which delivers a supply from the source directly to the distribution system without the use of pumping equipment. This type of system is usually ideal for a fire supply, provided pressures are adequate to supply fire demands and normal consumption rates. A gravity system is extremely reliable because the supply is not dependent upon the operation of mechanical equipment; however, the reliability of a well-designed and safeguarded pumping system can be developed to the extent that no distinction is made between gravity and pumping systems.

Pumping Systems

When water cannot be obtained at an elevation sufficient to provide working pressures from the elevation head, it is necessary to provide pumps on the system. These pumps are normally located at the source of supply and are used to develop the pressure needed to overcome friction loss in the supply system and to provide satisfactory working pressures in the distribution system. Public systems sometimes have water treatment facilities associated with the pumping station. Water treatment facilities will affect flow rates and quantities of water available to the distribution system. Many times, limiting features of supply are due to some element of water treatment. Therefore, it is imperative that the effects of water treatment on the availability of supply be thoroughly understood and considered. (See Section 8, Chapter 1, "Protection of Wastewater Treatment Plants.")

Combination Systems

Often associated with pumping systems are elevated water distribution storage facilities. These provide for storage of water during times of least demand and then supply water during times of peak demand.

Storage can be located so that pumps directly supply the elevated storage facility, and water flows to the distribution system from the storage facility. Elevated storage can also be provided at a remote location within the distribution system, and water can be pumped directly into the distribution system, with any excess automatically dumping into the elevated storage facility. The more water that can be maintained in elevated storage, the more reliable a system can be considered because water flowing from an elevated storage facility is a gravity system. Any failure of pumping equipment will not prevent this water from being available for fire protection purposes.

Distribution storage may also consist of large water tanks located at surface elevations equal to or even somewhat lower than the areas of the distribution system they serve. These tanks are filled during periods of relatively low consumption in the system. When demand rates are high, pumps deliver water from these storage facilities to the distribution system. Duplication of pumping equipment and proper design and operation can improve the reliability of these facilities to approach that provided by elevated storage.

SUPPLY CONDUITS, AQUEDUCTS, AND PIPELINES

Two terms sometimes used to describe the conveyor of water from the source of supply to the distribution system are "conduit" and "aqueduct." A conduit is an enclosed pipe capable of withstanding internal water pressures, while an aqueduct is either a closed tube or an open trench, canal, or channel in which water flows but which has no pressure on the side or bottom except that caused by the weight of the water. Aqueducts are not usually designed to withstand internal pressure other than atmospheric.

Pipelines

Pipelines are designed to withstand pressure and to distribute water to the point of use. Three classes of pipelines, or distribution mains, in a large system are:

1. Primary feeders consisting of large pipes with relatively wide spacing. They convey large quantities of water to various points of the system for local distribution to the smaller mains.
2. Secondary feeders forming a network of pipes of intermediate size. They reinforce the distribution grid within the various panels of the primary feeder system and aid the concentration of the required fire flow at any point.
3. Distributors consisting of a gridiron arrangement of small mains. They serve the individual fire hydrants and blocks of consumers.

In order to provide for reliability, two or more primary feeders should extend by separate routes from the source of supply to the high-value districts of the city. Similarly, secondary feeders should be arranged as much as possible in loops to give two directions of supply to any point. This practice increases the capacity of the supply at any given point and ensures that a break in a feeder main will not completely cut off the supply.

Secondary feeders should generally be installed not over 3000 ft (914 m) apart in built-up areas.

Where water systems are divided into pressure zones, water can be transferred from one zone to another by operating valves or by using fire department pumpers to pump from the hydrants in one zone to hydrants in the other. The same sort of thing can be done between the water systems of adjoining communities or between a private system and the public system. However, great care must be taken to prevent damage from occurring by subjecting parts of the system to excessive pressures and possible contamination. Usually this is not a good practice and should not be attempted without advance planning, adequate controls, and specific written approval from health authorities.

The Size of Pipe

Pipe less than 6 in.* (150 mm) in diameter is not recommended for fire service, and 6-in. (150 mm) pipes should only be used when looped in a gridiron where no leg is

*Nominal pipe sizes are not directly convertible into metric sizes. The following metric equivalents for common pipe sizes (rounded off for convenience in use) may be useful as points of reference: 4 in. = 100 mm; 5 in. = 125 mm; 6 in. = 150 mm; 8 in. = 200 mm; 10 in. = 250 mm; 12 in. = 300 mm; 16 in. = 400 mm; and 20 in. = 500 mm.

greater than 600 ft (183 m) in length. In congested districts, it is recommended that distributors should be not less than 8 in. (200 mm) in diameter and interconnected within every 600 ft (183 m). On principal streets and for all long lines, the distributors should be 12 in. (300 mm) or larger.

The cost of a line of pipe includes such factors as trenching (sometimes with piling), laying the pipe, backfilling, and testing. All of these factors are present regardless of the size of pipe used. To them is added the cost of the pipe delivered on the job. It is usually good practice, therefore, to install pipe for fire protection which is one or more sizes larger than the bare minimum might require. Increasing the pipe diameter only one size will often nearly double the possible flow. The figures in Table 5-4A show the relative capacity of pipe obtained by increasing sizes above 6 in. (150 mm).

TABLE 5-4A. ***Comparison of Pipe Capacity***

Size of Pipe, Inches (cm)	Relative Capacity
6 (15.2)	1.0
8 (20.3)	2.1
10 (25.4)	3.8
12 (30.5)	6.2
14 (35.5)	9.3
16 (40.6)	13.2

In designing a system, it is also important to consider the probable development of the area under consideration; to plan, in a general way at least, protection for its ultimate development; then to install that part of the system for which there is immediate need.

The actual size of pipe needed is based on the rate of water flow required (domestic consumption plus fire flow) and the hydraulic gradient in the area.

Another way to show advantages of larger pipe is to indicate the better performance of four sizes by comparing their friction loss characteristics under a simple range of fire demands. (See Table 5-4B.)

Arrangements of Pipe Systems

Pipe systems should be arranged in loops wherever possible. This allows hydrants and other connections to be fed from at least two directions and greatly increases the possible delivery of water without excessive friction loss.

In private water systems where pipelines supply hydrants only and where there are adequate pressures for good streams at the hydrants, it is general practice to use 6-in. (150 mm) pipe to supply two-outlet hydrants, and 8-in. (200 mm) or larger pipe under the following conditions: dead-end mains, if more than one hydrant is to be supplied or the distance is more than 500 ft (152 m); looped mains, if two hydrants are to be supplied on a loop with over 1500 ft (457 m) of pipe; if three hydrants are to be supplied on a loop with over 1000 ft (305 m) of pipe; or if four or more hydrants are to be supplied.

Where pressures are low, or where three-outlet or four-outlet hydrants only are installed, pipes should be larger. However, the design and layout of the pipe system must provide for the delivery of the maximum fire flow rates to all locations coincident with maximum daily consumption demands.

Internal Condition of Pipe Systems

In the course of time, the internal cross-section of unlined cast-iron pipe may be reduced or its interior surface roughened because of tuberculation, incrustation, or sedimentation. Tuberculation is caused by internal pipe corrosion and a build-up of rust. Incrustations may be due to: (1) tubercular growth, (2) the depositing of chemical constituents normally in solution in the water, or (3) growth of biological or living organisms. Sedimentation can be due to the accumulation of mud, clay, leaves, or vegetable decay. Additionally, foreign matter other than sediment can adversely affect flow capacity.

The existence of serious trouble can generally be detected by careful flushing tests. Flushing the system will remove ordinary sediment. Operation of valves will sometimes show presence of sediment or corrosion. Local water conditions are taken into account in establishing a regular procedure of flushing and testing. Pipes can be cleaned by the use of a scraper or rotating auger. The cleaning device can be pulled through the pipe by a cable or forced through by water pressure.

When pipe has been cleaned in this manner, the rate of tuberculation following cleaning will usually be very rapid, quickly resulting in decreased carrying capacities. The addition of cement lining will retard or prevent further deterioration of capacity. Therefore, a cost analysis should be made to determine if the pipe should be lined or cleaned periodically throughout its life.

TYPES OF PIPES

Underground pipe and fittings for fire protection should be suitable for the working pressures and conditions under which the pipe is to be installed, and in accordance with American Water Works Association (AWWA) specifications. Pipe is mostly installed without blocks in flat-bottomed trenches with selected tamped backfill. The required earth cover over pipe varies depending on pipe size, soil type, and geographical location. Generally, because of frost penetration in the northern states, a minimum cover of 4 to 5 ft (1.2 to 1.5 m) is required for large-diameter mains and

TABLE 5-4B. ***Friction Loss in Cast-Iron Pipe (Nominal Size)***
Hazen Williams Coefficient C=100

Flow		Loss per 1000 ft (305 m) of Pipe							
		6 in.* (150 mm)		8 in.* (200 mm)		10 in.* (250 mm)		12 in.* (300 mm)	
GPM	L/min	psi	kPa	psi	kPa	psi	kPa	psi	kPa
500	1892	12.9	89	3.1	21	1.1	7.6	.4	02.7
1000	3785	46.4	320	11.1	76	3.9	26.9	1.6	11.0
1500	5678	98.0	676	23.6	163	8.2	56.5	3.4	23.4

* Nominal pipe sizes.

as much as 7 or 8 ft (2.1 to 2.4 m) for small-diameter mains. Classes of pipe for working pressures above 150 psi (1034 kPa) are often used if heavier and thicker pipe is desired, e.g., in unstable or corrosive soils or in locations that would be difficult to reach should leaks or breaks occur. Flexible construction is advantageous in difficult situations, such as under railroad tracks, in areas with heavy industrial machinery, in earthquake areas, or where steep slopes or unstable soil conditions are encountered.

Pipe and fittings used for underground fire service mains should be listed by a recognized testing laboratory.

The titles and availability of design and installation standards and manuals for the various types of pipe and fittings discussed in the following paragraphs can be found in the bibliography at the end of this chapter.

Asbestos Cement Pipe

Asbestos cement pipe is particularly well adapted for locations where ferrous types without special protective linings or coverings would be attacked by corrosive soil conditions or by electrolysis. Where asbestos cement pipe must be buried in highly acid or alkaline soils, coatings can be provided that will protect the pipe from soil conditions.

The usual joint for asbestos cement pipe is an asbestos cement sleeve into which a specially shaped rubber gasket is inserted in a circumferential groove near each end of the sleeve. (See Figure 5-4A.) Cast-iron fittings may be used in asbestos cement pipelines.

Environmental concerns (personal health) exist when working with asbestos cement pipe. Care must be taken in the handling and preparation of the pipe.

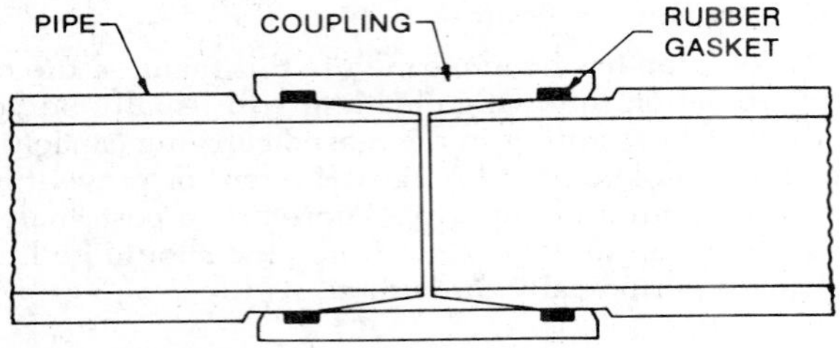

FIG. 5-4A. Coupling for asbestos cement pipes.

Polyvinyl Chloride (PVC) Pipe

PVC pressure pipe, manufactured in accordance with AWWA C900, is acceptable for fire service. PVC pipe often is specified in situations where severe corrosion problems are anticipated. PVC pipe is not subject to electrolytic corrosion, nor to tuberculation from corrosion byproducts.

Because of its flexibility and high-impact strength, PVC pipe manufactured to AWWA C900 specifications is not susceptible to beam, sheer, or impact failure in unstable soil conditions. The product is considered particularly suitable where shifting or heaving soils, live loading, or earthquake shock is anticipated.

AWWA C900 specifies PVC pipe with three pressure classes—100, 150, and 200. The pressure class designations define the maximum working pressure ratings for the pipe. The product is available in two series of outside diameters—cast-iron pipe (CI) and steel pipe (IPS). AWWA C900 PVC pipe is available in nominal diameters from 4 in. through 12 in. (approximately 100 to 300 mm).

PVC pipe used in potable water distribution and fire protection systems is commonly provided with gasketed (push-on) joints. Either integral bell gasketed joints or gasketed couplers that satisfy the requirements of ASTM D 3139 may be specified. When installing PVC pipe with gasketed joints, thrust restraint or blocking should be provided as necessary to prevent movement of pipe or appurtenances in response to thrust.

Cast-Iron Pipe

Table 5-4C gives dimensions and weights for cast-iron pipes of thickness class 22, which is designed for standard laying conditions. The complete AWWA specifications have additional data on pipe sizes, weights, pressure classes, and thickness classes for other laying conditions. Pipe should be selected on the basis of maximum working pressure, with consideration for transient pressures and the laying condition. Cast-iron pipe is seldom used in new installations and has limited availability. Ductile iron has largely replaced it.

There are several acceptable types of joints. The most common are single gasket push-on and standard mechanical. Poured bell-and-spigot joints are seldom used now. All these joints depend on friction between the parts and surrounding earth fill to prevent separation. (See Figures 5-4B, 5-4C, and 5-4D.)

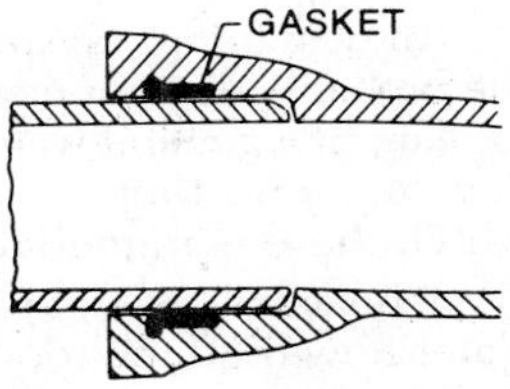

FIG. 5-4B. A push-on joint.

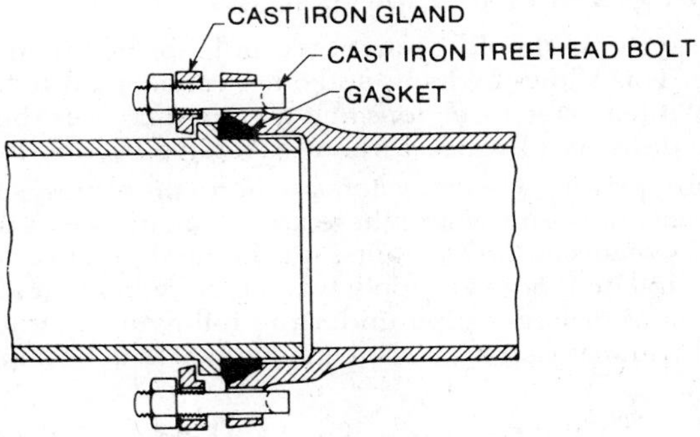

FIG. 5-4C. A standardized mechanical joint using anchoring fittings.

Push-on joints: The push-on joint is made up by seating a circular rubber gasket of special cross section in the valve and then forcing the spigot end of the pipe past the gasket to the bottom of the valve socket. No packing or caulking is required.

TABLE 5-4C. ***Standard Dimensions and Weights of Cast Iron Pipe****

Nominal Size		Outside Diameter		Class 150 (150 Psi or 1034 kPa)				Class 200 (200 Psi or 1379 kPa)				Class 250 (250 Psi or 1723 kPa)			
				Thickness		Weight per 18 ft (5.5 m) Laying Length†		Thickness		Weight per 18 ft (5.5 m) Laying Length†		Thickness		Weight per 18 ft (5.5 m) Laying Length†	
In.	mm#	In.	mm	In.	mm	Lbs	kg	In.	mm	Lbs	kg	In.	mm	Lbs	kg
4	100	4.80	122	0.35	8.89	290	131	0.35	8.89	290	131	0.35	8.89	290	131
6	150	6.90	175	0.38	9.65	460	209	0.38	9.65	460	208	0.38	9.65	460	208
8	200	9.05	130	0.41	10.41	655	297	0.41	10.41	655	297	0.41	10.41	655	297
10	250	11.10	282	0.44	11.18	870	395	0.44	11.18	870	395	0.44	11.18	870	395
12	300	13.20	335	0.48	12.19	1,125	510	0.48	12.19	1,125	510	0.52	13.20	1,215	551
14	350	15.30	388	0.51	12.95	1,410	639	0.55	13.97	1,510	685	0.59	14.99	1,610	730
16	405	17.40	442	0.54	13.71	1,700	771	0.58	14.73	1,815	823	0.63	16.00	1,960	889
18	460	19.50	495	0.58	14.73	2,050	930	0.63	16.00	2,210	1002	0.68	17.27	2,370	1075
20	510	21.60	548	0.62	15.75	2,430	1102	0.67	17.02	2,610	1184	0.72	18.28	2,785	1263
24	610	25.80	655	0.73	18.54	3,415	1549	0.79	20.07	3,665	1662	0.79	20.07	3,665	1662

* ANSI/SWWA C150/A21.50-1981 (R86). Based on standard laying conditions [5 ft (1.5 m cover), flat-bottomed trench and tamped backfill].
† Includes bell.
# Rounded off for convenience.

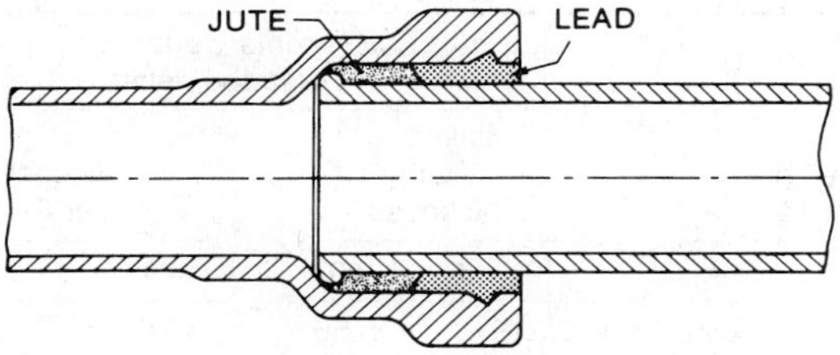

FIG. 5-4D. A poured bell-and-spigot lead joint.

Standard mechanical joints: These are joints in which a rubber ring gasket is held in place by a follower ring bolted to the bell. A mechanical joint provides for a limited amount of flexibility; a ball-and-socket joint of similar design provides a little more. Because of the flexibility, pipe with these joints is often selected for lines across bridges or in unstable soil.

Poured bell-and-spigot joints: These joints have a ring packing of jute or other material and are caulked with lead. Special joint compounds are available that require no caulking.

When using bell-and-spigot pipe and fittings, changes in grade or direction should never be made by shifting the pipe in the joints. This would result in uneven packing and caulking, and such joints are likely to leak. Only a very slight variation from normal is tolerable.

Ductile-Iron Pipe

Ductile iron has the corrosion resistance of cast iron and approaches the strength and ductility of steel. Ductile iron is now used in place of cast iron. Table 5-4D gives the minimum available thicknesses for ductile-iron pipe 4 to 24 in. (100 to 610 mm) in diameter. Ductile-iron pipe is made with push-on and mechanical joints.

Cast-iron fittings are used with ductile-iron pipe. Coating or cathodic protection is not needed, except where extremely corrosive conditions exist. Cement-lined pipe is recommended for all new or replacement installations of cast-iron or ductile-iron pipe to offset the corrosive action of water. Portland cement is used extensively for lining. Coal-tar enamel linings are available but less common. A large percentage of all cast-iron pipe is cement lined at the foundry.

Steel Pipe

Steel pipe of suitable wall thickness and manufacture, when lined and coated, can be used for fire service, both for underground mains and for supply lines in tunnels and buildings. Because of its high tensile strength, steel pipe is particularly suitable where it may be exposed to shock or to impact from railroad tracks, highways, drop-forge equipment, etc. The greater strength of steel is also advantageous in unstable soil or on steep slopes. Approximate dimensions and weights are given in Table 5-4E.

Steel pipe joints are welded, made with flanges or mechanical couplings. (See Figure 5-4E.) Expansion joints may be needed in long runs of pipe in tunnels. Hangers and supports should conform to good engineering practice and applicable standards.

Reinforced Concrete Pipe

Several designs of pipe of concrete and steel 24 in. (610 mm) and larger in diameter are available. Concrete pipe is often used for long supply and arterial feeders, but it is not normally used in distribution systems. A "nonprestressed" design is a steel cylinder with one or two steel-cage reinforcements encased in concrete. A "modified prestressed" design is a steel cylinder with a spirally wound steel rod reinforcement prestressed to provide a slight initial tension in the cylinder and concrete lining. "Prestressed" designs consist of a concrete-lined cylinder or steel cylinder helically wrapped under tension with a high tensile strength wire. External coatings are cement mortar. Details of a reinforced concrete pipe joint are shown in Figure 5-4F.

Fittings

Fittings used should be appropriate for the same range of working pressures as the pipe with which they are used. A single class of cast-iron fittings for sizes 3 to 12 in. (76 to 300 mm) is now used generally. These are for work

TABLE 5-4D. *Standard Dimensions and Weights of Ductile-Iron Pipe**

Nominal Size		Outside Diameter		Working Pressure		Thickness		Weight per 18 ft (5.5 m) Laying Length‡	
In.	mm	In.	mm#	Psi	kPa	In.†	mm	Lbs	kg
4	100	4.80	122	350	2413	0.29	7.37	240	109
6	150	6.90	175	350	2413	0.31	7.87	380	172
8	200	9.05	230	350	2413	0.33	8.38	535	243
10	250	11.10	282	350	2413	0.35	8.89	700	317
12	300	13.20	335	350	2413	0.37	9.40	885	401
14	350	15.30	338	350	2413	0.36	9.14	1,005	456
16	400	17.40	442	350	2413	0.37	9.40	1,185	537
18	460	19.50	495	300	2068	0.38	9.65	1,370	621
20	510	21.60	548	250	1723	0.39	9.91	1,560	708
24	610	25.80	655	250	1723	0.41	10.41	1,975	896

* ANSI/AWWA C151/A21.51-1986. Based on standard laying conditions [5 ft (1.5 m) cover, flat-bottomed trench and tamped backfill].
† Minimum distance.
‡ Includes bell.
# Rounded off for convenience.

TABLE 5-4E. *Recommended Minimum Dimensions and Weights of Steel Pipe for Fire Protection Mains*

Nominal Diameter		Outside Diameter		For Welded Joints: Minimum Wall Thickness		For Welded Joints: Weight per Ft*		For Flexible Couplings or Threaded Joints: Minimum Wall Thickness		For Flexible Couplings or Threaded Joints: Weight per Ft*	
In.	mm†	In.	mm	In.	mm	Lbs	kg	In.	mm	Lbs	kg
6	150	6.625	168	0.188	4.77	12.9	5.85	0.219	5.56	15.0	6.8
8	200	8.625	219	0.188	4.77	16.9	7.67	0.239	6.07	21.4	9.7
10	250	10.750	273	0.188	4.77	21.2	9.61	0.250	6.35	28.0	12.7
12	300	12.750	324	0.188	4.77	25.1	11.38	0.281	7.14	37.0	16.78
14	350	14,000	355	0.239	6.07	35.1	15.92	0.281	7.14	41.2	18.69
16	405	16.000	406	0.250	6.35	42.0	19.05	0.312	7.92	52.4	23.77

* One foot equals 305 mm
† Rounded off for convenience.

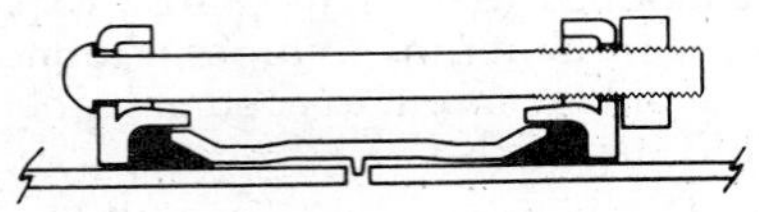

FIG. 5-4E. A steel mechanical coupling for plain-end steel pipe.

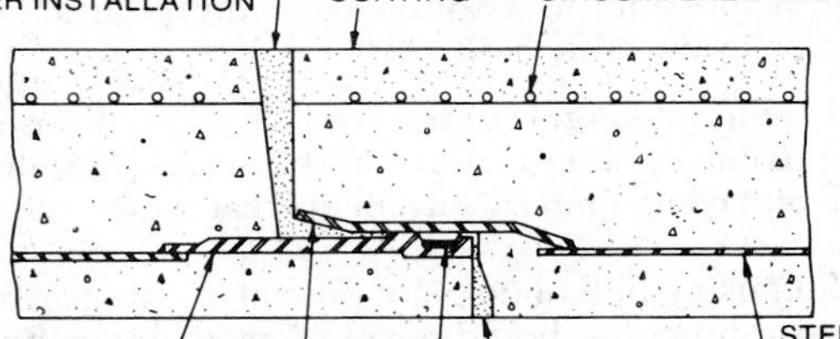

FIG. 5-4F. A reinforced concrete pipe joint.

ing pressures of 250 psi (1723 kPa). Cast-iron fittings (bends and tees) are used with asbestos cement pipe. They have bells designed to be used with the asbestos cement gasket-type joint.

Cast-iron and steel fittings for underground water lines for fire protection are approved by testing laboratories.

Pipe Corrosion

Water is corrosive to cast-iron, ductile-iron, and steel pipe, and to fittings. The initial rate of corrosion for steel pipe may be more rapid than for cast- or ductile-iron, but after several years exposure, there is little difference.

External corrosion of buried iron and steel pipe is the direct result of complicated electrochemical reactions. Soil containing metallic salts, acids, or other substances in combination with moisture causes iron ions to separate from the pipe. The mass of the metal at the pipe surface is diminished, and the pipe becomes pitted or corroded. Iron or steel pipe should not be installed under coal piles, in cinderfill, or wherever acids, alkalies, pickling liquors, etc., can penetrate the soil.

Stray electric currents from external sources may reach and follow buried pipelines to locations where the resistance to ground is less than that of the pipeline. Ionization then occurs at points where the current leaves the pipe, producing an effect similar to that of soil corrosion.

When stray electric currents are suspected, the extent and origin should be determined by professional ground surveys. If the stray currents cannot be eliminated or diverted, the pipe, if not yet seriously corroded, can be protected by bonding all the joints and by providing direct low-resistance metallic ground connections.

Cathodic methods are widely used for the external protection of iron and steel water mains. Cathodic protection is a technique of imposing direct electric current from a galvanic anode to the buried pipeline. In many instances, cathodic protection is more economical than coating and wrapping. Cast-iron or ductile-iron pipe used in water systems should be cement-lined in accordance with AWWA standards.

A smooth lining is necessary to minimize loss of carrying capacity. Buried piping needs a coating to protect against soil corrosion. An outside coating may be applied in the field if desired, but it is practical only on large jobs. Exposed piping should be painted or otherwise protected as required by atmospheric conditions. Nuts and bolts of buried joint assemblies should be heavily coated. Any damage resulting to lining or coating should be thoroughly repaired.

RULES FOR LAYING PIPE

The depth of cover to provide protection against freezing will vary from about 2½ ft (0.76 m) in the southern states to about 10 ft (3.05 m) in northern Canada. Because there is normally no circulation of water in fire protection mains, they require greater depth of covering than do public mains. The 2½-ft (0.76 m) minimum should always be maintained to prevent mechanical damage. Depth of covering should be measured from top of pipe to ground level, and consideration should always be given to future or final grade and nature of soil. A greater depth is required in a loose, gravely soil (or in rock) than in compact or clay soil. A safe rule to follow is to bury the top of the pipe not less than 1 ft (0.3 m) below the lowest frostline for the locality.

Placing pipes over raceways or near embankment walls should be avoided. Keep mains back a sufficient distance from the banks of streams or raceways to avoid any danger of freezing through the side of the bank. Where mains are laid in raceways or shallow streams, care should be taken that there will be running water over the pipe during all seasons of frost; a safer method is to bury the main 1 ft (0.3 m) or more under the bed of the waterway.

Protection Against Pipe Breakage

In general, it is advisable to avoid running pipe under buildings. Where mains necessarily pass under a building, the foundation walls can be arched over the pipe. Pipes passing under building walls with ground floors at grade are buried to the same depth as outdoors. Pipes under basement floors below grade may require less depth, but in no case should the cover be less than 2½ ft (0.76 m).

Any pipe that passes through a wall or foundation must be protected from fracture. This is done by keeping a clear 1- to 3-in. (25 to 75 mm) annular space around the pipe and sealing it with coal tar or asphalt. (See Figure 5-4G.)

Special care is necessary in running pipes under railroad tracks, highways, large piles of iron, and under buildings housing heavy machinery that could subject the buried pipes to shock or vibration. Where subject to such breakage, pipes should be run in a covered pipe trench, be sleeved, or be otherwise properly guarded. While flanged cast-iron pipe with metallic gaskets is sometimes used under buildings, it is not recommended because of its lack of flexibility, higher cost, and almost impossible access.

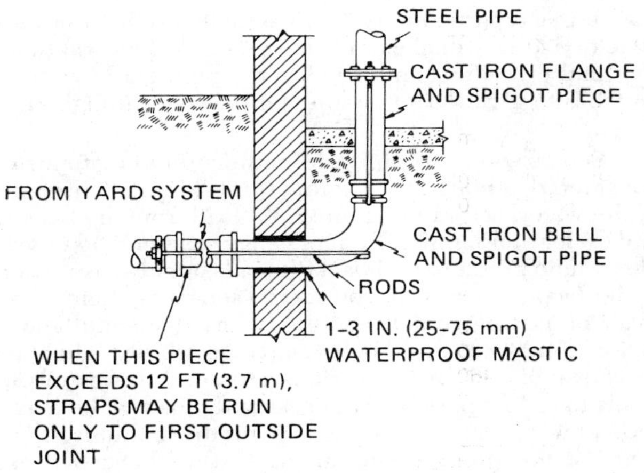

FIG. 5-4G. A common arrangement of pipe is through a foundation to feed a sprinkler or standpipe riser. The anchorage of the horizontal run is determined by soil conditions. In some cases, as in earthquake areas, considerable flexibility is desirable in this run and in the first two joints outside the building. Often the run is brought into the building with the first joint of a flexible type, particularly if the pipe openings through foundation and floors are sealed with grouted concrete instead of mastic. The anchorages shown would be the usual ones.

Frost loading is also recognized as a substantial factor that must be considered in pipe installation. Frost loading may exceed earth and live loads for which the pipe was designed. Other loads must also be considered, such as those which result from seismic shifts and tremors, unequal settlement and expansion, and subsidence of specific clay soils with changes in moisture content.

Care in Laying Pipe

Pipes should be clean inside when put in trenches, and open ends should be plugged when work is stopped to prevent stones or dirt from entering.

Pipes should be supported throughout their length and not by the bell ends only. Superior support is obtained where the bottom of the trench is shaped to fit the pipe. If the ground is soft or of a quicksand nature, special provision must be made for supporting pipe. For ordinary conditions of soft ground, longitudinal wood stringers with cross ties will give good results. A reinforced concrete mat 3 or 4 in. (75 to 100 mm) thick in the bottom of the trench can also be used. In extreme cases, the stringers and cross ties or concrete mat may have to be supported on piles. The most important aspect of laying pipe, though, is to follow the manufacturer's instructions for trench preparation, maximum deflection, and method of joining.

Pipe Anchorage

Most conventional pipe joints are not designed to resist unusual forces tending to pull them apart. Joints are expected to be kept in place by the soil in which the pipe is buried. It is necessary to determine, by tests in case of doubt, that a particular soil will actually do this. In unsatisfactory soils, trenches may have to be excavated below the final pipe level and filled to the pipe grade with soil suitable to give the pipe an even bearing throughout its length.

Forces acting on pipe laid in the ground that must be considered, among others, are: (1) internal static pressure of the water, (2) water hammer, (3) load from the backfill, and (4) load and impact from passing trucks and other vehicles. Static pressure and backfill loads are always present. Water hammer loads are considered separately from impact loads of passing vehicles on the theory that simultaneous action of the two would be a remote possibility. The thickness designated for the various pressure classes of pipe tends to reflect possible water hammer loads. The magnitude of water hammer depends upon the modulus of elasticity of the piping material, pipe wall thickness, pipe diameter, flow velocity, and the rate of change in velocity. Anchorages are needed to take care of additional loads due to water hammer and other forces. Trenches, which have to be unusually wide or deep, impose additional loads which may affect the choice of pipe thickness for the particular installation.

To prevent joints in cast-iron pipes from coming apart, they should be securely braced or clamped unless anchoring fittings or locked joints are used. Typical methods of anchoring joints at elbows, tees, and bends, and plugs at blanked openings are shown in Figures 5-4H through 5-4O. Clamps and rods and other steel fittings at anchors should be protected against corrosion by a thick covering of asphalt.

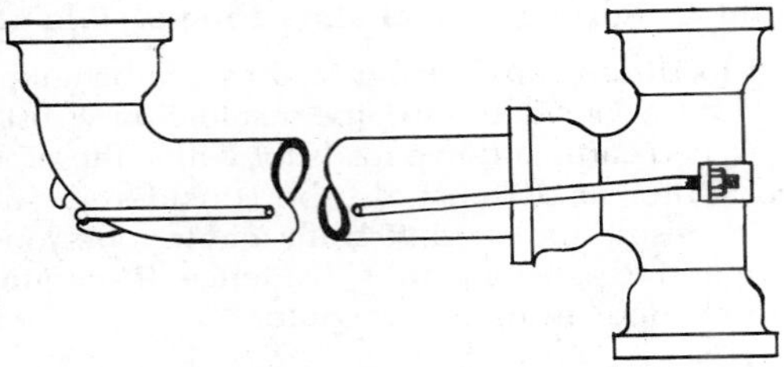

FIG. 5-4H. Strap for bend anchor to tee.

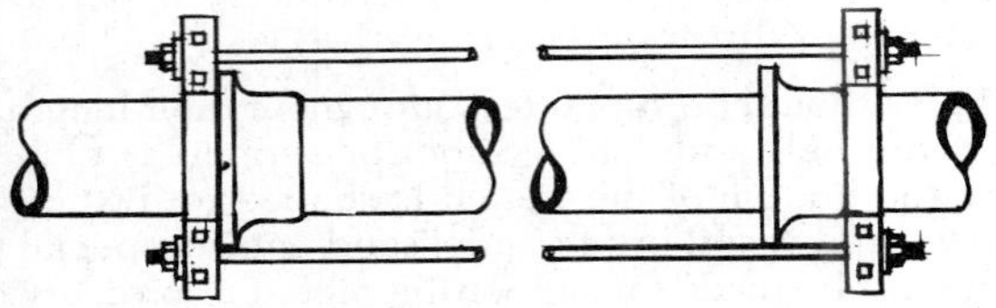

FIG. 5-4I. Anchor rods for bell-and-spigot pipe. When distance between bells is less than 12 ft (3.6 m), the next length of pipe is also anchored.

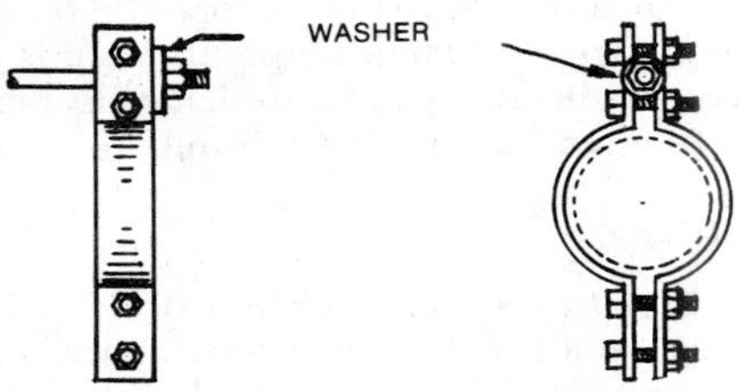

FIG. 5-4J. Clamps for bell-and-spigot and short-body fittings.

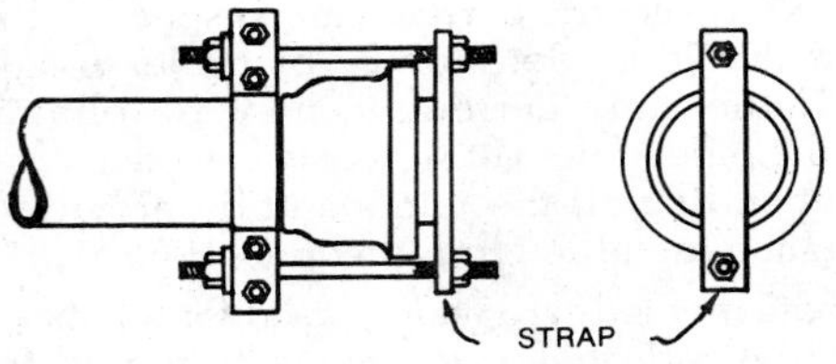

FIG. 5-4K. A plug for the bell end of a pipe.

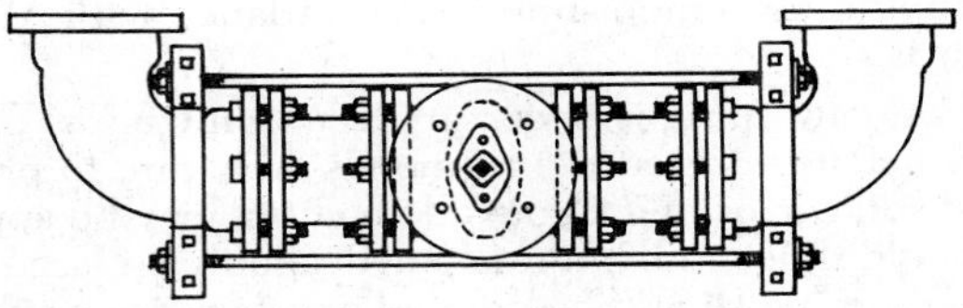

FIG. 5-4L. A general form of an anchor for indicator post valves. A mechanical joint pipe is illustrated.

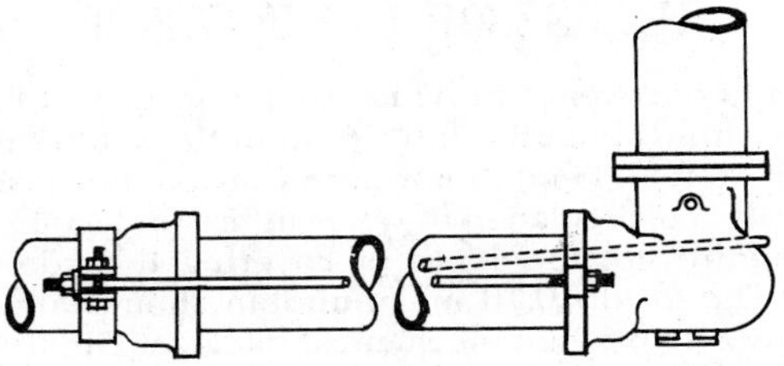

FIG. 5-4M. Hydrants are connected with a double-spigot connection anchored as illustrated. Anchor fittings and locked joints are often more convenient alternatives for rodded anchors. When the hydrant does not have lugs, the anchor rods are arranged as indicated by the dotted lines.

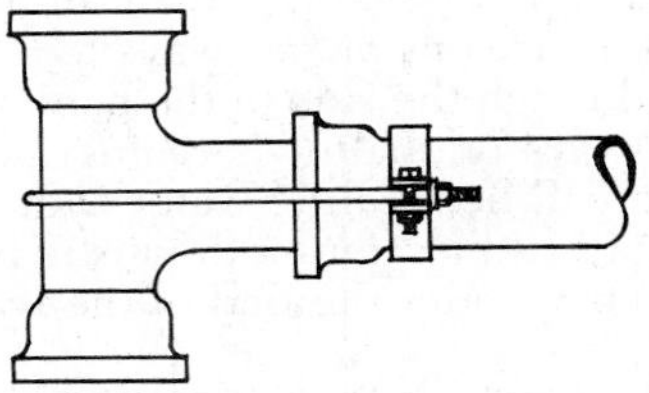

FIG. 5-4N. An anchor at a spigot end of a tee fitting.

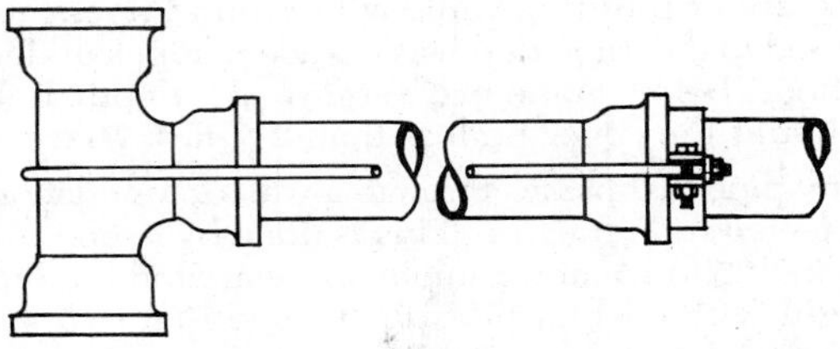

FIG. 5-4O. An anchor at a bell end of a tee fitting. If the distance between joints is less than 12 ft (3.6 m), rods also should be run to a clamp on the next bell.

Thrust Blocks

It is also necessary to consider the loads imposed by water moving in the pipe. This is why at bends, tees, and pipe ends, and wherever the piping changes direction, the pipe assembly must actually bear on a surface that will resist the loads imposed. Thrust blocks are used to keep the pipe assemblies in place. Guidance on sizing thrust blocks can be found in NFPA 24, *Private Fire Service Mains and Their Appurtenances*.

The usual thrust block is made of concrete and is placed between the fitting and the trench wall. Thrust blocks may be tied to foundations where these are of sufficient size to provide a bearing.

A thrust block under a hydrant or valve to prevent upward movement in newly laid soil would require rods bent over the bells to hold the valve or hydrant to the block. Blocks under hydrants should be located so as not to prevent the hydrant from draining properly when drains are installed. Thrust blocks are shown in Figures 5-4P and 5-4Q.

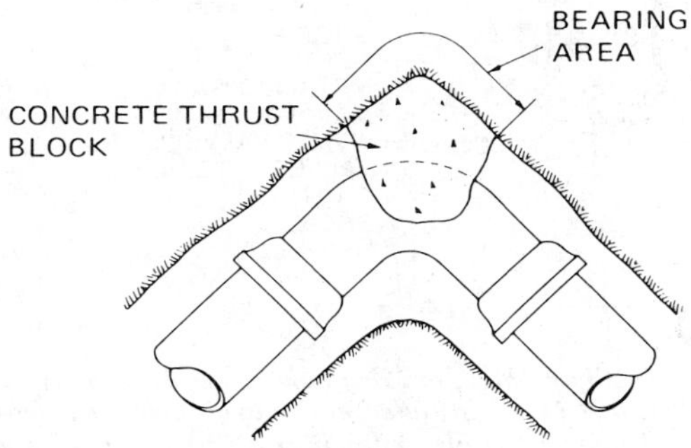

FIG. 5-4P. A thrust block at a one-quarter bend.

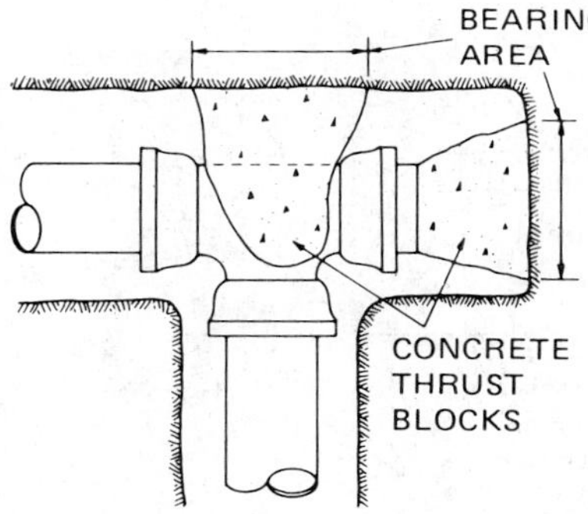

FIG. 5-4Q. A thrust block at a tee and plug.

Testing

All pipelines, of whatever material, should be subjected to hydrostatic tests, either by sections as completed or as a whole after completion. Such testing is usually done after the trench has been partially backfilled. All tests should be conducted in accordance with AWWA standards and NFPA 24, *Private Fire Service Mains and Their Appurtenances*.

Backfilling

Earth should be well tamped under and around pipes (and puddled where possible) to prevent settlement or lateral movement, and should contain no ashes, cinders, or other corrosive materials. If the ground in which the pipe is laid is partly or wholly cinderfill, care should be taken that about a foot of cinder-free dirt is put in the trench below the pipe and no dirt containing cinders is used in backfilling around the pipe. Cinders stimulate galvanic actions which may cause the pipe to fail in a relatively short period. There are similar considerations in occupancies where salt or industrial wastes, e.g., from cattle sheds, packing operations, and chemical plants, might seep into the ground.

Rocks should not be rolled into trenches nor allowed to drop on pipes. In trenches cut through rock, backfilling is normally entirely of earth. In any case, earth should be used under and around pipe and at least 2 ft (0.6 m) above it.

Flushing

After a system of underground pipe for fire protection has been completed and before it is permanently filled with water, the entire system should be thoroughly flushed out under pressure through hydrants or other outlets. Mains supplying sprinkler systems should be flushed at the following rates: 6-in. (150 mm) pipe, 750 gpm (2839 L/min); 8-in. (200 mm), 1000 gpm (3785 L/min); 10-in. (250 mm), 1500 gpm (5678 L/min); and 12-in. (300 mm), 2000 gpm (7571 L/min).

NFPA 13, *Installation of Sprinkler Systems*, contains information on the requirements for flushing underground connectors to ensure their reliability.

During flushing, the valves to any inside sprinkler or standpipe equipment should be closed to avoid washing stones or other debris into the inside system. Branches from the outside system should be flushed before they are connected to sprinkler or standpipe risers.

HYDRANTS

The most important features of good hydrants for fire protection are:

1. Normal diameter of bottom valve opening at least 4 in. (100 mm) for two $2\frac{1}{2}$-in. (64 mm) or larger outlets, 5 in. (125 mm) for three $2\frac{1}{2}$-in. (64 mm) or larger outlets, and 6 in. (150 mm) for four $2\frac{1}{2}$-in. (64 mm) or larger outlet hydrants. Hydrants having a bottom valve less than 4 in. (100 mm), or outlets less than two $2\frac{1}{2}$-in. (64 mm), are usually not approved by testing laboratories. The connection between a water main and a hydrant should not be less than 6 in. (150 mm) in diameter.
2. The net area of the hydrant barrel and foot piece at the smallest part is not less than 120 percent of that of the net opening of the main valve.
3. A liberal-sized waterway and low friction loss. With the hydrant discharging 250 gpm (946 L/min) through each of two $2\frac{1}{2}$-in. (64 mm) hose outlets, the total head loss at the hydrant should not exceed 2 psi (13.8 kPa). For a hydrant with a $4\frac{1}{2}$-in. (114 mm) outlet, at a discharge rate of 1000 gpm (3785 L/min), the maximum permissible head loss is 5 psi (34.5 kPa). For hydrants designed or intended to deliver more than 1000 gpm

(3785 L/min), the maximum permissible head loss should not exceed 5 psi (34.5 kPa) when discharging at the intended flow rate.

4. A positive-operating, corrosion-resistant drain or drip valve.
5. A uniform-sized pentagonal operating nut measuring 1½ in. (38 mm) from point to flat at the base and 1⁷⁄₁₆ in. (36 mm) at the top. The faces should be tapered uniformly, and the height of the nut should not be less than 1 in. (25.4 mm).

Hydrant bonnets, barrels, and foot pieces are generally made of cast iron with internal working parts of bronze. Valve facings should be of a suitable, yielding material, such as rubber or a composition material. Hydrants are available with various configurations of outlets.

Types of Hydrants

There are two types of fire hydrants in general use today. The most common is the base valve (dry barrel) in which the valve controlling the water is located below the frost line between the foot piece and the barrel of the hydrant. (See Figure 5-4R.) The barrel on this type hydrant is normally dry with water being admitted only when there is a need. A drain valve at the base of the barrel is open when the main valve is closed, allowing residual water in the barrel to drain out. This type of hydrant is used whenever there is a chance the temperature will go below freezing, because the valve and water supply are installed below the frost line.

The other type of hydrant is the wet barrel (California) type, which is sometimes used where the temperature remains above freezing. These hydrants usually have a compression valve at each outlet, but they may have another valve in the bonnet that controls the water flow to all outlets. (See Figure 5-4S.)

Fire hydrants are covered by standards of the American Water Works Association (AWWA C502-85 and AWWA C503-88) and Underwriters Laboratories Inc. (UL 246), all listed in the bibliography at the end of this chapter.

Location

Hydrant spacing is usually determined by fire flow demand established on the basis of the type, size, occupancy, and exposure of structures. At present, there is no universally accepted method for establishing fire flows for other than fixed extinguishing systems. Insurance Services Office (ISO) has a procedure that was developed for insurance rate-making purposes only. The procedure has been in effect for many years and is of value in arriving at hydrant spacing recommendations. Its use should be based upon sound engineering judgement that addresses the field situations that are encountered.

As a general rule, however, spacing should not exceed 800 ft (245 m) between hydrants. In closely built areas, 500 ft (150 m) or less between hydrants is more realistic. Hydrants should be located as close to a street intersection as possible, with intermediate hydrants along the street to meet the area requirements.

Where hydrants are located on a private water system and hose lines are intended to be used directly from the hydrants, they should be so located as to keep hose lines short, preferably not over 250 ft (75 m). At a minimum, there should be enough hydrants to make two streams available at every part of the interior of each building not covered by standpipe protection. They should also provide hose stream protection for exterior parts of each building using only the lengths of hose normally attached to the hydrants. It is desirable to have a sufficient number of hydrants to concentrate the required fire flow about any

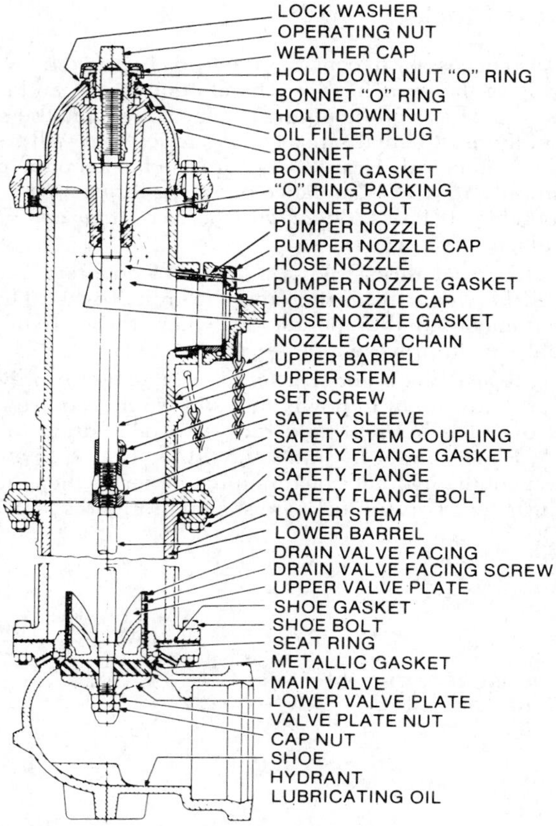

FIG. 5-4R. A base valve, or "dry barrel," hydrant with nomenclature identified. When installed, the valve is below the frost line. This type of hydrant is also known as a "frost-proof" hydrant. (Source: Mueller Company)

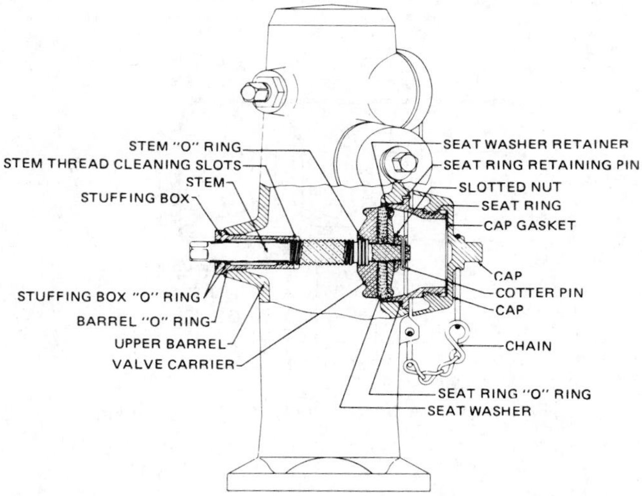

FIG. 5-4S. A wet barrel, or "California," hydrant used where freezing is not encountered. There is a compression valve at each hydrant outlet. (Source: Mueller Company)

important building with no hose line exceeding 500 ft (150 m) in length.

For average conditions, hydrants normally are placed about 40 ft (12.2 m) from the buildings to be protected. When that is impossible, they are set where the chance of injury by falling walls is small and where fire fighters are not likely to be driven away by smoke or heat. In crowded industrial yards, hydrants usually can be placed beside low buildings, near substantial stair towers, or at corners formed by masonry walls that are not likely to fall.

Hydrants that must be located in areas subject to heavy traffic need protection against damage from collision. The parking lots of shopping centers and mill yards are good examples.

Setting of Hydrants

Hydrants should be set plumb with outlets about 18 in. (0.46 m) above the ground and 18 in. (0.46 m) above the floor in hose houses. When hydrants are installed before grading is completed, the final grade line and accessibility should be considered. Most hydrants have a grade line indicated on the barrel of the hydrant.

Drainage is necessary for hydrants equipped with drain ports and can be provided by excavating a pit about 2 ft (0.61 m) in diameter and 2 ft (0.61 m) deep below the base of the hydrant, and filling it compactly with coarse gravel or stones placed around the bowl of the hydrant to a level of 6 in. (150 mm) above the waste opening. If the drip valve of the hydrant is below groundwater level, it may be plugged to exclude groundwater. In that case, water remaining in the hydrant after use should be pumped out to prevent freezing.

The bowl of a hydrant should be secured to the next preceding bell with anchoring or locking joints or rods and clamps, or securely anchored by means of concrete backing. (See Figure 5-4M.)

Maintenance and Testing

Private hydrants should be tested and maintained in accordance with NFPA 13A, *Inspection, Testing, and Maintenance of Sprinkler Systems*, which recommends that private hydrants be visually inspected monthly, lubricated twice yearly, and opened and closed yearly to ensure proper water flow and drainage.

Well-designed and properly installed hydrants present a minimum of maintenance difficulties. The dry barrel hydrant, for example, has a small drain near the base of the barrel arranged to permit water to drain out when the main valve is shut. When the main valve is opened several turns, this drain is closed. If this drain is working properly and the main valve is tight, the difficulty of water freezing in the barrel is avoided. Occasionally situations are found where ground drainage is unsatisfactory or where groundwater may stand at dangerous levels. In those cases, drains may be closed entirely and hydrant barrels pumped out periodically.

The use of salt or salt solutions to prevent freezing is not recommended because of their corrosive effect and limited usefulness. If antifreeze is used in hydrant barrels, its use must be confined to hydrants that are not part of a system supplying water for domestic consumption.

Ethylene glycol is extremely toxic, with as little as 0.1 mg/L ingested for a period of a week being fatal. This substance should not be used. Propylene glycol is not as toxic and may be used to prevent freezing but with proper precautions and in accordance with local health regulations.

Suggestions for detecting freezing in hydrants include:

1. Sounding by striking the hand over an open outlet. Water or ice shortens the length of the "organ tube" and raises the note.
2. Try turning the hydrant stem. If solidly frozen, the stem will not turn. If only slightly bound by ice, placing a hydrant wrench on the nut and tapping smartly may release the stem. Blows should be moderate to prevent breaking the valve rod.
3. Lowering a weight on a stout string into the hydrant. It may strike ice or come up wet, showing water in the barrel.

Probably the most satisfactory method of thawing a hydrant is by means of a steam hose. A thawing device in which steam may be rapidly produced should be standard equipment for fire departments in cold-weather climates. The steam hose is introduced into the hydrant through an outlet and pushed down, thawing as it goes.

A major item of periodic maintenance is a check for leaks in: (1) the main valve when the hydrant is closed, (2) the drip valve when the main valve is open but outlets capped, and (3) the mains near the hydrant. Stethoscope-like listening devices are available to make these checks. Maintenance routines provide for an operating test, repair of leaks, and pumping out of the hydrants where necessary. Threads of the outlet, caps, and valve stem should be lubricated with graphite. Hydrants should be kept painted, but care should be taken to avoid accumulations of paint that might prevent easy removal of caps or operation of valve stems.

Uniform Marking of Fire Hydrants

Color coding of hydrants is based on water flow available from them. Color coding is of substantial value to water and fire departments. A test of an individual hydrant does not give as complete and satisfactory results as group testing, but such a test is a start in the right direction. The colors signify the capacity of the individual hydrant as tested, not group hydrant effect.

NFPA 291, *Fire Flow Testing and Marking of Hydrants*, recommends that hydrants be classified as shown in Table 5-4F.

TABLE 5-4F. ***Hydrant Classification***

Class	Flow	Color of Bonnets and Nozzle Caps
AA	1500 gpm or greater	Light Blue
A	1000 to 1499 gpm	Green
B	500 to 99 gpm	Orange
C	Less than 500 gpm	Red

Capacities are rated by flow measurement and tests of individual hydrants during a period of ordinary water consumption. Rating is based upon the flow rate available at 20 psi (138 kPa) residual pressure.

The capacity-indicating color scheme provides simplicity and consistency with colors used in signal work for safety, danger, and intermediate conditions. (See Figure 5-4T.) Barrels of all public hydrants are normally chrome yellow, except in cases where another color has already been adopted.

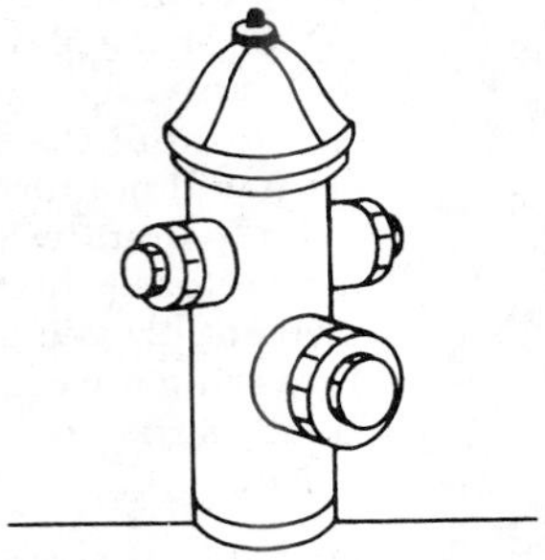

FIG. 5-4T. Shaded areas are color coded to show the hydrant's flow capacity.

Within private enclosures, marking of private hydrants is at the discretion of the owner. Private hydrants on public streets are normally painted red to distinguish them from public hydrants.

Location markers for flush hydrants carry the same color background for class indication, with such data stenciled or painted on them as may be necessary.

CONTROL VALVES FOR WATER DISTRIBUTION SYSTEMS

Water distribution systems require valves at strategic locations and intervals to control flow as circumstances dictate. Nonindicating gate valves, butterfly valves, check valves, and pressure-reducing or altitude valves are the types of controlling valves used in supply systems.

Required features for gate valves, check valves, and indicator posts listed by a testing laboratory include:

For Gate Valves:

1. Stems of bronze with a minimum tensile strength of 32,000 psi (220 640 kPa).
2. Stuffing boxes with good-sized packing space.
3. Bronze-lined gland and bonnet opening, and a valve capable of being repacked under pressure.
4. Yokes bolted on bonnets in valves larger than 4 in. (100 mm).

For Check Valves:

1. Large clearances between moving parts and valve body.
2. A clapper that moves entirely out of the waterway.
3. Bronze-to-bronze bearings having large wearing surfaces.
4. Valves of the straightaway type, and iron body valves having a waterway equal to the area of the pipe.

For Indicator Posts:

1. A uniform flange to suit all sizes of gate valves.
2. Interchangeable operating stems.
3. Adjustable and interchangeable target plates.
4. Uniform-sized square operating nut measuring 1 in. (25.4 mm) square by 1 in. (25.4 mm) high.

Gate Valves

Gate valves of the nonindicating type are provided in distribution systems to allow segments to be shut off for repairs or extensions without reducing protection over a wide area. Such valves are normally a nonrising-stem-type which require a key wrench to operate. A valve box is located over the valve to keep dirt from the valve and to provide a convenient access point for the valve wrench to the valve nut. (See Figure 5-4U.)

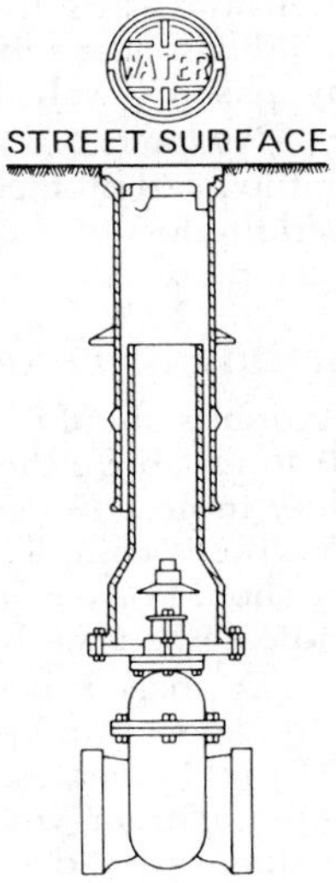

FIG. 5-4U. A nonindicating-type gate valve for underground installation.

A complete record should be made for each valve in the system, including date installed, make, size, direction of opening, number of turns to open, any maintenance performed, and location by triangulation from fixed bounds, preferably under the control of the water system management. Permanent valve records should be stored in a secure place, and copies suitably indexed should be available in all water supply vehicles that respond to emergency calls. Copies should also be available to each fire station.

Good practice dictates that valves are provided so that no single accident, break, or repair will necessitate shutting down a length of pipe greater than 500 ft (150 m) in high-value districts or greater than 800 ft (245 m) in other sections, and so that flow may be maintained through other arterial mains.

PRIVATE FIRE SYSTEMS

This part of the chapter covers the valving arrangement on a private fire protection water distribution system from the point where it connects with its supply.

Indicating Valves

The first valve in the fire line on private property should be a valve of the indicating type. It may be one of three kinds: (1) underground gate valve with indicator post attached, (2) underground butterfly indicating type with post, or (3) outside screw and yoke (O.S.&Y.) gate valve in a pit.

The type of underground gate valve commonly used in domestic and industrial water lines (which requires a key wrench to operate) should be avoided in fire lines. The difficulties of finding such valves, getting up cover plates, and locating a key wrench that will fit are detriments to its use. If used, underground gate valves should open counter-clockwise and have the same size nut on all valve stems. The valve locations should be clearly marked on nearby buildings.

Indicator posts should have a metal plate showing what they control. Painting building names or numbers on them is advisable. The proper direction to turn for opening should be shown. Posts are often locked in the open position to prevent tampering. Lock shackles should, however, be brittle so that they can be removed readily if they are frozen and the keys will not work. Posts should have a handle, wheel, or wrench attached. A typical indicator post valve is shown in Figure 5-4V. Figure 5-4W shows a butterfly post indicator valve.

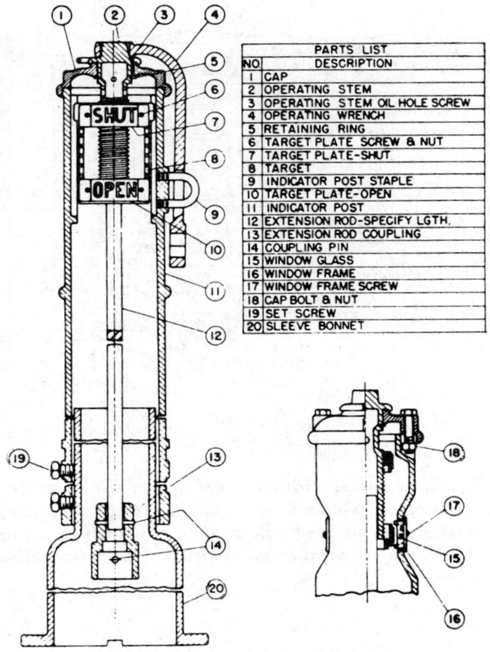

PARTS LIST	
NO.	DESCRIPTION
1	CAP
2	OPERATING STEM
3	OPERATING STEM OIL HOLE SCREW
4	OPERATING WRENCH
5	RETAINING RING
6	TARGET PLATE SCREW & NUT
7	TARGET PLATE-SHUT
8	TARGET
9	INDICATOR POST STAPLE
10	TARGET PLATE-OPEN
11	INDICATOR POST
12	EXTENSION ROD-SPECIFY LGTH.
13	EXTENSION ROD COUPLING
14	COUPLING PIN
15	WINDOW GLASS
16	WINDOW FRAME
17	WINDOW FRAME SCREW
18	CAP BOLT & NUT
19	SET SCREW
20	SLEEVE BONNET

FIG. 5-4V. A standard post indicator valve. Nearly all manufacturers of valves furnish standard valves, and their catalogs should be consulted for details of each. (Source: Henry Pratt Company)

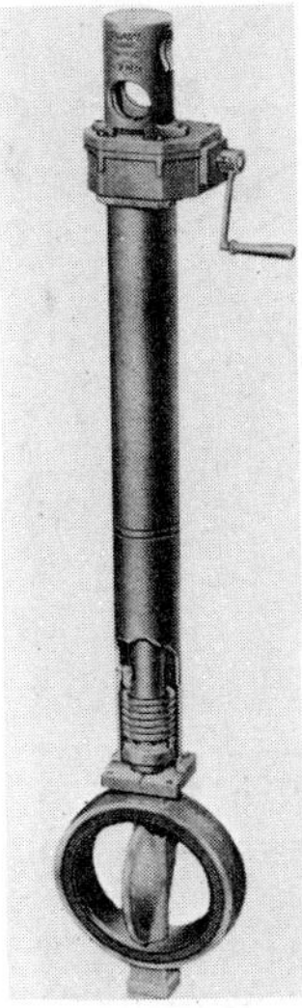

FIG. 5-4W. A butterfly post indicator valve. (Source: Henry Pratt Company)

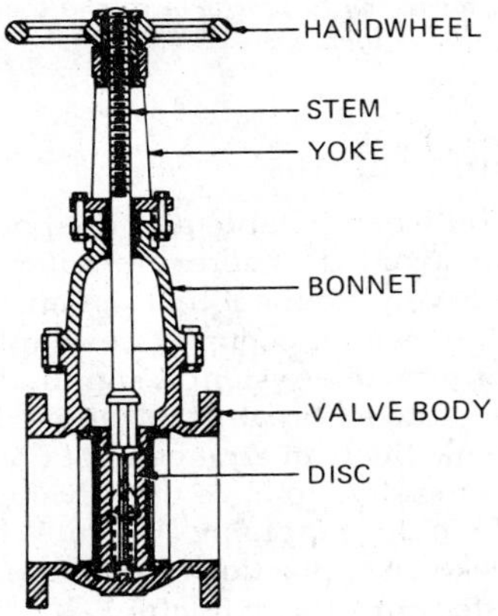

FIG. 5-4X. A typical outside screw and yoke (O.S.&Y.) valve in the closed position. The spindle on the valve stem indicates whether the valve is open or shut.

O.S.&Y. gate valves, if underground, should be in pits. Important junction points often warrant the use of pits to cover several valves. Indicating valves are used on all shutoffs. They are universally used on inside piping because they show the position of the gates at a glance. They are commonly strapped or otherwise sealed open. Where O.S.&Y. gate valves are located in pits, a metal sleeve with the upper end closed may be slipped over the valve stem to keep off dirt. An O.S.&Y. gate valve is shown in Figure 5-4X.

Check Valves

A check valve is installed next to the main control valve inside the property. The check valve must be installed in a pit unless it is located inside a building, even when the main control valve is a conventional buried valve with an indicating post. The check valve also needs to be accessible, so the size of the pit, the arrangement of its manhole and ladder, and the size of working space around the valve or valves in the pit should be large enough for convenient access. (See Figure 5-4Y.)

A check valve allows water to flow from the public system to the private system but not from the private system into the public system. It also permits water at higher pressures in the private system than the normal pressures in the connecting public water mains in case of fire. Higher pressures can be provided in a private system through its own fire pumps, where these are provided, or by fire department pumpers when they pump through the fire department connections on automatic sprinkler systems and standpipe systems in buildings or on a private yard system.

Check valves are also installed at the base of gravity tanks and in the private or fire department pumper connections. The check valves at these points ensure flow of water one way only.

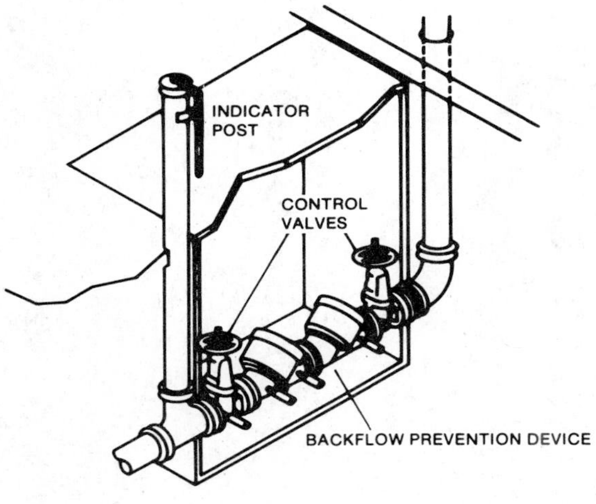

FIG. 5-4Y. ***A valve pit is usually provided for a check valve or a backflow device (as shown) and for O.S.&Y., gate valves, meters, and other equipment on underground mains. Clearance should be 18 in. (0.46 m) around all valves and equipment in the pit. Pits are as deep as necessary to conform to the location of the pipe in which the valve is located.***

Air Gap Connections

Connections between potable and nonpotable water systems should be avoided. Where one water system must be separated positively from another, an air gap is provided so that backflow cannot occur. An example of an air gap is where water from one system is supplied through a pipe that discharges into a "break" tank above the level of the water in the tank. Such an arrangement does not allow the receiving water system to have the advantage of the pressures available in the supplying system. With a connection through a check valve, practically all of the pressure in the supplying system may be available.

Additional information can be found on cross connections in AWWA M14, *Recommended Practice for Backflow Prevention and Cross-Connection Control*.

Double Check Valves

For situations where there is some question of leaks, double check-valve equipment is available. (Double check valves are required for certain situations by the regulations of some health departments.) Check valves in double installations are made with bronze working parts and rubber facings so that they will have tight seats. For each connection, two of these valves are installed in series, thus increasing the efficiency because the probability that both will leak at the same time is extremely remote. The two check valves are installed between valves in a pit where they are readily accessible for examination. In addition, the valves are provided with pressure gages and test cocks so arranged that the tightness of each check valve may be verified in a few minutes. Figure 5-4Z shows a typical double check valve installation in a pit. A double check valve assembly is shown in Figure 5-4AA.

When the two check valves are bolted together, an 18-in. (0.46 m) space is provided between clappers, which is sufficient to prevent any ordinary material found in a pipeline from holding both clappers open at the same time. To improve further the efficiency of the equipment, a filling piece of pipe or spacer from 3 to 5 ft (0.9 to 1.5 m) long installed between the check valves is advised where space is available.

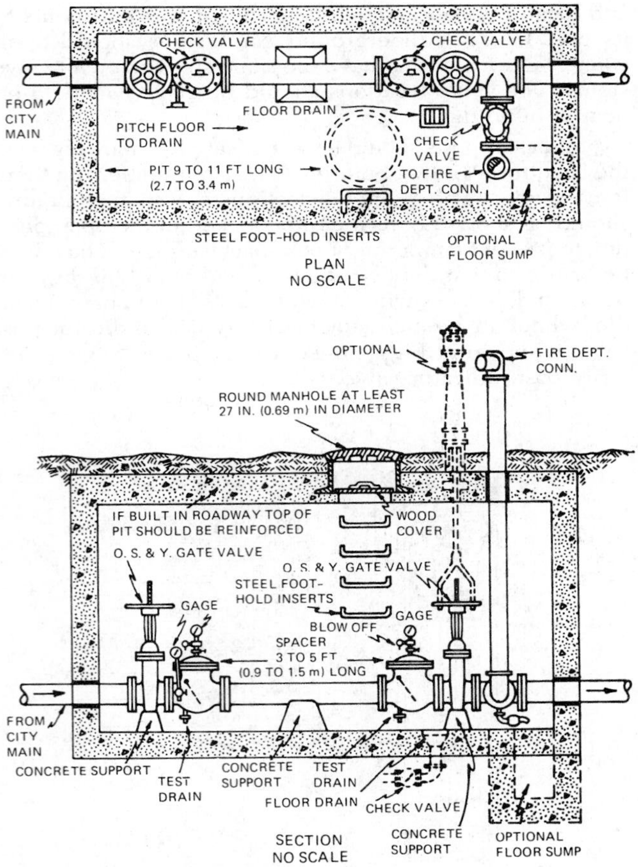

FIG. 5-4Z. ***Plan and section views showing the arrangement of double check valves in a connection for fire protection from a public water system. Indicating valves of the butterfly-type designed for fire service may be used in place of the gate valves illustrated.***

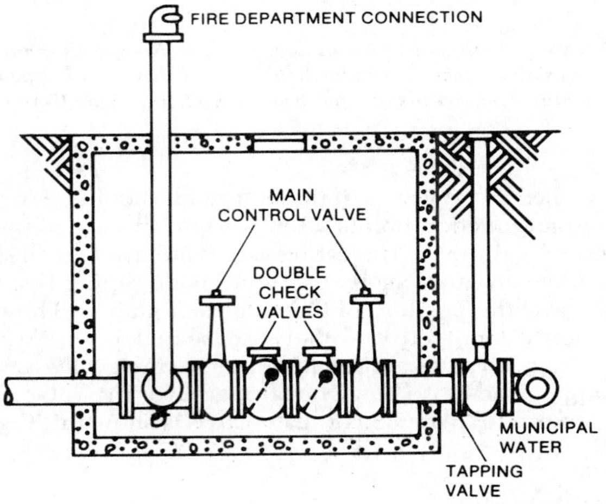

FIG. 5-4AA. ***A double check valve assembly.***

Certain manufacturers have developed a double check valve assembly where the 18-in. (0.46 m) space is not provided. In these devices, the design attempts to minimize the possibility of simultaneous failure.

Note: Check valves do not always work properly. Whenever there is any possibility of backflow from a fire service main into a potable supply, a listed backflow prevention device should be installed or an air gap provided, depending upon local health regulations.

Reduced-Pressure Backflow Preventers

Figure 5-4BB shows a reduced-pressure backflow preventer assembly which is intended to maintain pressure between two check valves at less than the supply pressure in the pipeline. (Figure 5-4CC shows a cutaway view of Figure 5-4BB.) The assembly consists of two independently acting approved check valves interspaced by an automatically operated pressure differential relief valve. In case of leakage at either check valve, the relief valve operates to maintain the pressure between the check valves at less than supply pressure. There is some loss of head [generally 5 to 15 psi (34.5 to 103.4 kPa)] in such backflow preventers, but there may be situations where sacrificing some loss of head is preferable to sacrificing all of it as would be necessary with an air gap separation. An additional concern on the part of many fire protection professionals is that the device fails in the open position, thereby discharging directly to the drain.

FIG. 5-4BB. A reduced-pressure backflow preventer assembly for installation between two gate valves. (Source: Hersey Products, Inc.)

Location of Valves in Private Fire Service Systems

Opinions vary on how many valves should be used in a system of underground mains. More plants have probably been destroyed because a sectional control valve was shut than because a large part of the system was out of commission by reason of too few sectional valves. Nevertheless, the modern tendency is to make fairly liberal use of valves. A few well-established principles are shown in Figure 5-4DD. They include:

1. A city supply check valve (and meter, if required) located between indicating valves so it can be repaired without affecting city or plant systems.
2. A pump check valve located between pump and indicating valves so that the latter can be used to shut off the connection to the system when making check valve and pump repairs.
3. Three sectional valves (two, G and H, to take care of present loop and one, J, for a short branch supplying a small detached building) in addition to the main water supply valve. (See Detail of Pit 1.) The branch will ultimately be part of a second loop. There should be a loop valve on each side of every valuable water supply to permit cutting off a part of the loop without cutting the water supply off altogether. Best practice requires that post indicators be attached to valves in pits, with the posts cemented into the concrete tops.
4. Sectional control valves (indicator posts C, E, and F) can cut the loop into four sections (in connection with valves H and G). In large or complicated underground systems, it is recommended that indicator posts controlling risers to sprinklers or standpipes be painted a different color from sectional control valves. Generally, no more than six hydrants or indicator posts should be located between section valves.
5. Gate valves must be provided on hydrant laterals to isolate the hydrant in the event it malfunctions or when repairs are necessary.

Records

Records for water systems should include the following:

1. A complete map and satisfactory sectional views of the distribution system made on a suitable scale, showing all the features of the distribution system, including size and location of pipelines; location of gate, check, and altitude valves, and pressure reducers; and hydrants. There should also be sectional maps showing the location of all gate valves by triangulation to fixed reference points. Copies of these maps should be distributed to the personnel who would be working on the system.

In the event of a break in the underground system or the abandonment of a flowing hydrant during a fire, it is essential that water be shut off promptly to protect the supply to other hydrants or sprinkler connections and to avoid flooding. Operating valves correctly and rapidly at the time of a fire, especially at night and under adverse weather conditions, requires accurate knowledge of the system.

2. Complete records should be kept for each fire hydrant in the system. They should show the date of installation; location, number, and size of outlets; size of the hydrant valve; size and location of the gate valve between the hydrant and street connection; the size of pipe to which it is connected, including the length of the branch connection; and inspection dates. The records should note if the hydrant is equipped with drains, if the drains have been plugged or omitted, and if there has been any problem with drainage or with groundwater entering the hydrant barrel. Records of all maintenance performed should also be kept.

Permanent hydrant records should be stored in a safe place with copies indexed for field use located in all vehicles responding to an emergency. Also, copies should be available to each fire station providing protection in the area served by the water distribution system.

Copies of the distribution map and hydrant and valve records should be used by the fire department in preplanning and developing a familiarity with the water system.

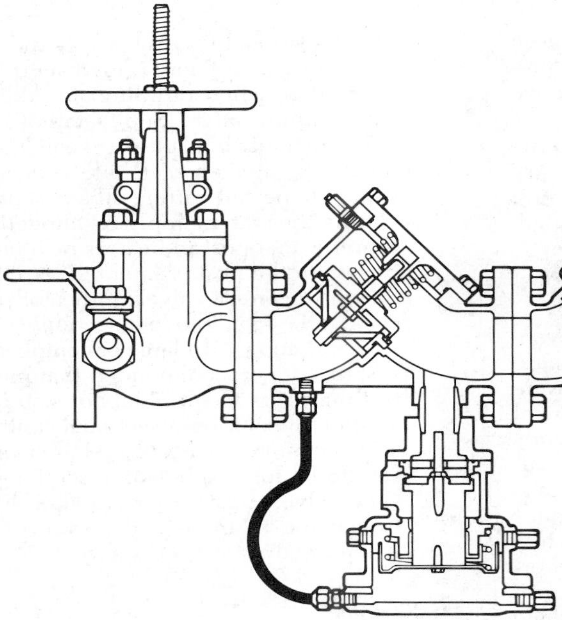

FIG. 5-4CC. A cutaway view of a reduced-pressure backflow preventer.

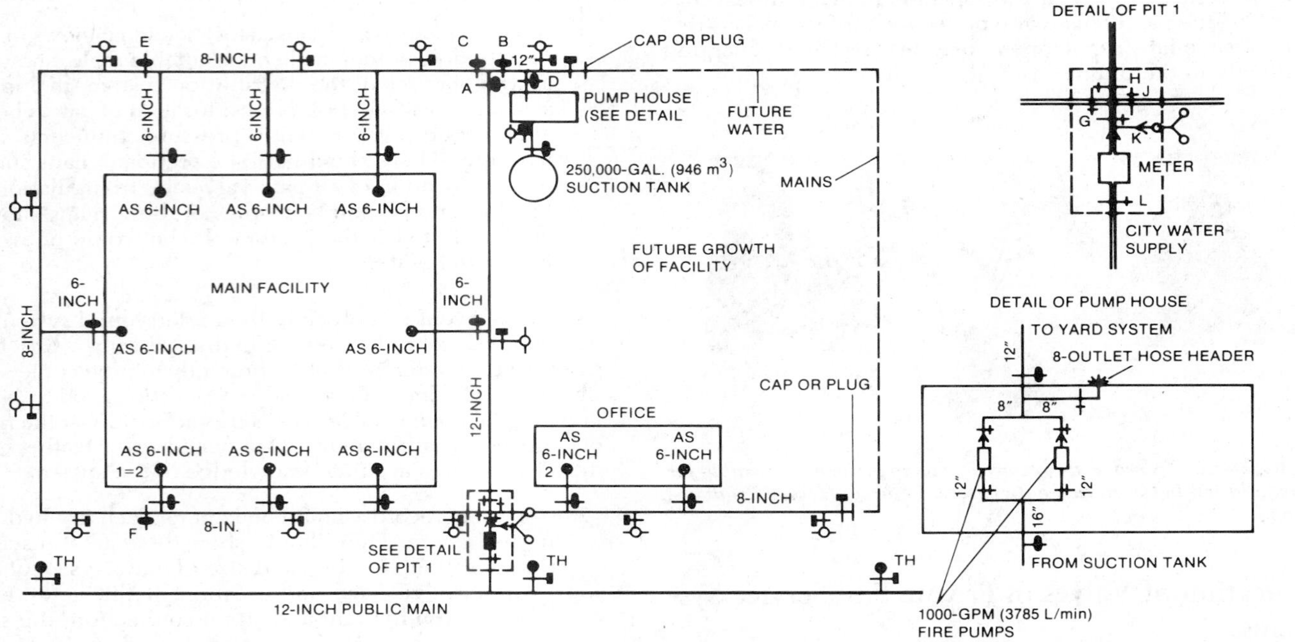

FIG. 5-4DD. Water piping for fire protection of an industrial site. Typical details shown are connections to public mains and supplies for a private fire pump, looped water mains, sectional control valves (lettered), and hydrants. (1 in. = 25.4 mm.)

Maintenance and Testing

Check valves should be checked and tested for tightness monthly, particularly where double check valves are used to prevent backflow between potable water and yard systems. The test drains and gages provide a means for determining where a leak may exist. Even though found tight when tested periodically, check valves should be thoroughly cleaned once a year, so they will remain tight.

Where there are several sets of check valves in fire connections from public mains, only one set of check valves should be overhauled and cleaned at a time, the others being left in service.

Gate valves should be operated periodically to ensure that they are in proper working condition and that gate boxes are not silted up or tarred over.

METERS FOR FIRE CONNECTIONS

Fire flow meters are devices capable of measuring small and large flows with a minimum loss of head for heavy demands. They are offered in two types: (1) detector check-valve meters that detect only small rates of flow, and (2) full registration meters that measure the entire flow throughout the line in which they are installed. Meters of types other than the fire-flow type have been found to be unsatisfactory for fire protection water supplies.

Detector Check Valves

These devices consist of a check valve with a weighted clapper in the main passage and a meter in a bypass around the check. In operation, the smaller flows pass through the meter in the bypass and are accurately registered. Meters may be furnished up to 3 in. (76 mm) in size to serve specific needs. For heavy flows, the check valve opens, and a free unmetered waterway is provided. Beyond the point where the weighted check valve lifts, the bypass meter registers only a small part of the flow. In many situations, detector check valves give the waterworks assurance about the proper use of water. Figure 5-4EE shows a detector check valve.

FIG. 5-4EE. A detector check valve assembly. (Source: Febco)

Full Registration Meters

These devices are of three general types, each produced by a different manufacturer, and they have been designed for small friction loss with large flows and for a main passageway practically unobstructed when open. The three types are: (1) proportional-type meters, (2) meters of the displacement type in a bypass, and (3) turbine-type meters.

Proportional-type, Hersey detector meter, Model MFM II: This meter is a special meter of the compound type in which a "proportional meter" and an automatic valve in the main line of the meter are combined with a disc or compound meter in a bypass. (See Figure 5-4FF.)

In the Model MFM II, the smaller flows pass through and are measured by the bypass meter. When the demand for water reaches a rate of flow that causes a difference in pressure of 4 psi (28 kPa) in the bypass, the automatic check valve opens and provides a practically free waterway through the main line. When water begins to flow through the line in which the automatic valve has opened, it is slightly retarded by a restricting orifice placed a little upstream from the automatic valve, and a part of the water is diverted through a metering unit. This diverted flow is a fixed percentage of the total flow through the

FIG. 5-4FF. A detector meter of the proportional type. (Source: Hersey Products, Inc.)

restricting orifice. The metering unit is calibrated to record the total quantity through the line—the sum of the readings of the bypass meter and the main line metering unit gives the total flow.

Displacement-type, Neptune Trident Protectus III meter: This meter has all of the working parts in one casing. A disc meter is installed in a bypass on one side of the main waterway, with a current meter on the other side. Small flows pass through the disc meter and are recorded when the check valve is closed. With larger flows, the main check valve opens and gives a free waterway. The opening of the check valve stops the flow through the disc meter and opens the bypass to the current meter so that the flow through the open waterway is measured proportionately. The sum of the readings gives the total flow. (See Figure 5-4GG.)

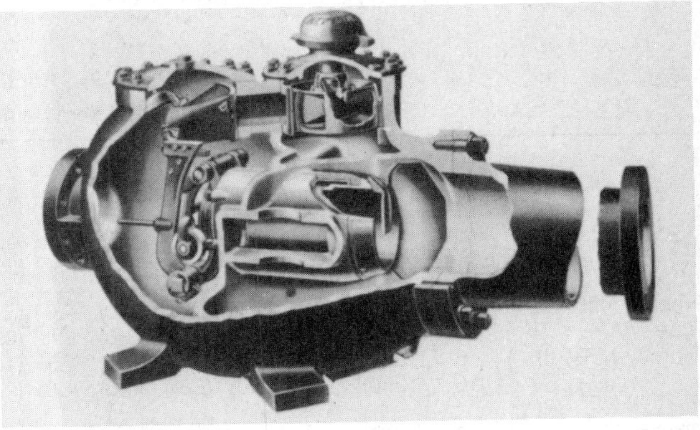

FIG. 5-4GG. A fire flow meter of the displacement type. (Source: Neptune Water Meter Company)

Turbo-type, Rockwell W-1000DR, W-2000DR, W-3500DR, and W-5500DR Turbo Meter: This meter is based on the turbine principle of measurement. (See Figure 5-4HH.) The meter is composed of two principal assemblies: (1) the main case, and (2) the measuring chamber. The main case contains the flow-straightening vane assembly. The measuring chamber includes rotor, adjusting vane, and register. The meter can be equipped with either a direct reading register or a pulse transmitting register (which also contains a direct reading odometer and test circle) for sending signals to remote reading registers and other instruments. The manufacturer recommends that, for fire service applications, the meter be used only with an approved fire service strainer placed immediately upstream of the meter.

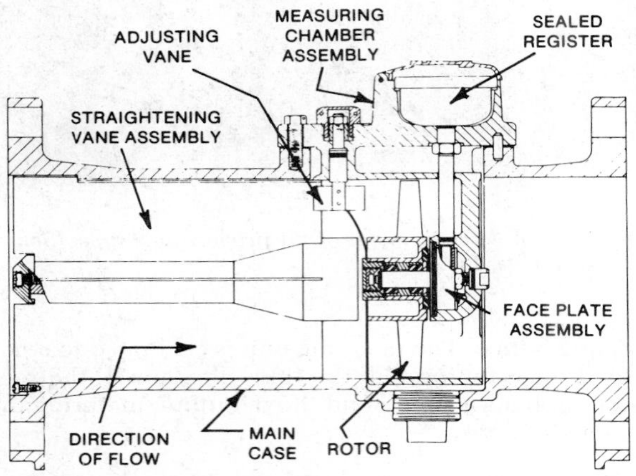

***FIG. 5-4HH.** A fire flow meter of the turbo type. (Source: Rockwell International)*

Friction Loss in Fire Flow Meters and Detector Check Valves

The standard specifications for cold-water meters adopted by both the American Water Works Association and the New England Water Works Association limit the friction loss for fire flow meters to 4 psi (28 kPa) at rated flow capacities. Table 5-4G gives friction loss values for the three currently available types of fire flow meters.

Friction loss values for meters of the disc, current, and compound type that are used commonly in waterworks systems for general purposes are relatively high and not suited for fire protection purposes. AWWA limits their friction loss values to 20 psi (138 kPa).

Detector check valves: The friction loss in detector check valves listed by testing laboratories is less than 3 psi (21 kPa) for the following flows:

Size (in.)	(mm)	Flow (gpm)	(L/min)
4	(100)	750	(2839)
6	(150)	1500	(5678)
8	(200)	3000	(11,356)
10	(250)	4500	(17,034)
12	(300)	6500	(24,605)

The pressure required to open the clapper is less than 20 psi (138 kPa).

CONNECTION BETWEEN PUBLIC AND PRIVATE WATER

Connections from public water systems for fire protection are for the purpose of providing water supply to the following:

1. Automatic sprinkler systems.
2. Standpipes for hand hose or fire department use.
3. Open sprinklers.
4. Yard systems with private hydrants.
5. Fire pumps.
6. Private storage reservoirs or tanks for fire protection.

A fundamental principle is that, within the property, piping systems from which water is used for fire must be independent of systems supplying domestic and industrial service. Special conditions where this is not the case are rare and may be dealt with individually.

In public water systems, except in some unusual situations, economics favor a single water system for combined fire use and domestic service. In private properties,

TABLE 17-4G. ***Friction Loss in Fire Flow Meters***

Compiled from data supplied by manufacturers

Meter Name and Type	Size of Meter Inches	(mm)*	Loss of Pressure Caused by Meter Pounds per Square Inch (kPa) — Gallons per Minute Flowing (L/min): 250	(946)	500	(1892)	750	(2839)	1000	(3785)	1250	(4732)	1500	(5678)	2000	(7571)	2500	(9463)
Proportional	4	(100)	2.2	(15.1)	1.9	(13.1)	4.0	(27.6)										
Type	6	(150)	3.8	(26.2)	2.7	(18.6)	1.4	(09.7)	1.8	(12.4)	2.2	(15.1)	2.9	(20.0)	3.9	(26.9)		
(Hersey-MFM II)	8	(200)	3.0	(20.7)	3.7	(25.5)	1.9	(13.1)	1.0	(06.9)	0.8	(05.5)	0.8	(05.5)	1.3	(09.0)	2.2	(15.2)
	10	(250)	1.6	(11.0)	3.6	(24.8)	4.0	(27.6)	3.7	(25.5)	2.6	(17.9)	1.4	(09.7)	0.8	(05.5)	1.1	(07.9)
Differential	4	(100)	2.2	(15.2)	2.0	(13.8)	3.9	(26.9)										
Type	6	(150)	2.9	(20.0)	1.9	(13.1)	1.8	(12.4)	1.8	(12.4)	1.8	(12.4)	1.8	(12.4)	2.2	(15.2)	3.3	(22.8)
(Trident	8	(200)	3.2	(22.1)	1.8	(12.4)	1.5	(10.3)	1.5	(10.3)	1.5	(10.3)	1.6	(11.0)	1.8	(12.4)	2.2	(15.2)
Protectus III)	10	(250)	3.0	(20.7)	2.3	(15.9)	1.8	(12.4)	1.3	(09.0)	1.2	(08.3)	1.1	(07.9)	1.1	(07.9)	1.2	(08.3)
Turbo Type (Rockwell W-1000 Dr, W-2000 Dr, W-3500 Dr, W-5500 Dr Turbo)	6	(150)	0.2	(01.4)	0.3	(02.1)	0.6	(04.1)	0.85	(05.9)	1.2	(08.3)	1.6	(11.0)	3.5	(24.1)		

* Rounded off for convenience of use.

it is economically practicable to have separate systems; the advantages of a definite, dependable supply, free from interruptions of service inevitable in a domestic system, strongly favor the established practice. However, it should be remembered that a failure in any portion of the public system supplying the private and separate fire system may result in reduced flows or no flow into the private system.

Occasionally, a property will have two sources of water supply for fire protection: one from the public supply; the other from a private source, many times nonpotable. When this happens, adequate measures must be followed in accordance with local health department regulations to prevent the public water supply from becoming contaminated. Means of achieving this have been discussed previously in this chapter. Some communities do not allow any direct connection, and, if two supplies are required or desired, separate systems must be maintained with an air gap or backflow prevention device between the two systems.

Charges for Connections to Private Fire Protection Systems

The question of annual standby charges for connections from a public water system to fire protection systems may be controversial, largely because the nature of automatic sprinkler systems is not always understood by public officials. Whatever charges are made should be based on actual cost to the utility and not on the possible value of the installation to the customer. Annual charges for connections to fire protection systems are often established in water rate schedules for the sole purpose of obtaining additional revenue.

Although many waterworks, both public and private, make no standby charge for connections for fire protection, there may be no objections to charges that fairly reflect actual cost to the waterworks of the connection itself and the expense of servicing it, including necessary pits, valves, and meters. There could be costs to the waterworks for amortization of costs of its part of the connection and for its maintenance and inspection. However, it is usual to charge for the installation when it is made, and if repairs, maintenance, and inspection are charged for when done, there is little other cost involved.

Since the amount of water used for fire fighting is usually very small when compared to normal consumption, it is almost universal practice to make no charge to property owners for the water actually used in the extinguishment of fire or for authorized hydrant flow testing.

Control of Connections During Fires

The safe location of control valves for connections for fire protection is important so that they may be shut off promptly after water extinguishing systems have put out the fire, or to conserve water and pressure if pipes have been broken.

Sprinkler systems have outside indicating valves where yard space is available. This is the preferable arrangement. In many city properties having no yard space, valves are installed in a stair tower or other sufficiently cut off area. Sometimes the control valves are located outside the area protected as, for example, on the other side of a fire wall. In a relatively few instances, dependence must be placed on the accessibility of the valve on the connection to the street main.

Experience has shown that, in practically all fires, sprinkler control valves on private property have been adequate to serve their intended use and allow prompt and safe control of fire protection.

Control of Water Waste

There are a number of conditions under which flow of water from private fire protection equipment other than for fire or testing purposes may occur. These are:

1. Leakage.
2. Wrongful use, such as wetting down roofs, watering lawns, or waste through ignorance.
3. Emergency use.
4. Theft.

Fire protection equipment should be inspected several times a year to ensure that the systems will be kept free from material leakage or unauthorized connections. Maintenance rules enforced by inspection authorities tend to discourage wrongful uses of these systems. These are further enforced in many places by fire department inspections, which are made to ensure that valves controlling extinguishing systems and other fire supplies are kept open and that hose and other equipment are not used for any purpose other than that intended. Occasional inspections by waterworks inspectors are desirable.

In cases where inspections alone are not a sufficient safeguard against water waste, a plan involving the securing of valves and outlets would be effective. In such cases, all sprinkler drains, hydrants, and hose outlets are sealed by the water utility which may require:

1. A report from the owner when a seal is broken.
2. A notice from the user before testing through outlets on hydrants or sprinkler drains.
3. Payment of a nominal charge for resealing.

As a further safeguard, indemnity to the water utility may be secured by requiring the user to file a bond or deposit to be forfeited in the event of willful or persistent violation of the rules, or abuse of the fire service furnished by the water utility.

The simplest cases of control of water waste to deal with are fire connections in single buildings such as those serving:

1. One or more standpipes for hand hose or fire department use.
2. Automatic extinguishing systems only.
3. Combined automatic sprinkler systems and standpipes.

In connections of these types, any regulation on the part of a water utility (for the ostensible purpose of preventing water waste) that involves an excessive annual charge or a costly meter installation may impose an expense to the property owner so large as to discourage the installation of extinguishing systems or standpipes. This particularly affects a class of property—small industrials and mercantiles—in which the bulk of current fire losses occur, and which greatly needs the protection.

Ordinarily inspections, or at least a valve securing procedure, will give adequate protection to the utility. In extreme cases, special action may be taken by a utility against any individual violator. In adopting any procedure to apply to all users of private fire protection, the relative unimportance of a very small amount of water improperly used, as against the greater public good in the extensive installation of automatic sprinklers and other private fire equipment, should be considered.

Fire protection connections that serve several buildings with extinguishing systems and standpipes, or, in addition, a yard system with private hydrants, fire pump, and tank supplies, may introduce a slightly more difficult problem of water waste control. In general, inspection or sealing procedures will suffice, and both may be appropriate in some cases. Where meters are employed on fire connections, the extent to which they reduce pressures and obstruct or reduce flows must be determined.

BIBLIOGRAPHY

NFPA Codes, Standards, and Recommended Practices

Reference to the following NFPA codes, standards, and recommended practices will provide further information on water distribution systems discussed in this chapter. (See the latest *NFPA Catalog* for availability of current editions of the following documents.)

NFPA 13, *Installation of Sprinkler Systems.*

NFPA 13A, *Inspection, Testing, and Maintenance of Sprinkler Systems.*

NFPA 20, *Installation of Centrifugal Fire Pumps.*

NFPA 24, *Private Fire Service Mains and Their Appurtenances.*

NFPA 26, *Supervision of Valves Controlling Water Supplies for Fire Protection.*

NFPA 291, *Fire Flow Testing and Marking of Hydrants.*

Other Codes, Standards, and Manuals

American Society for Testing and Materials

ASTM D3139, *Standard Specification for Joints for Plastic Pressure Pipes Using Flexible Elastomatic Seals,* American Society for Testing and Materials, Philadelphia, PA, 1989.

American Water Works Association

The following are published by American Water Works Association, 6666 W. Quincy Ave., Denver, CO 80235:

AWWA C200-86, *Standard for Steel Water Pipe 6 In. and Larger.*

AWWA C203-86, *Standard for Coal-Tar Protective Coatings and Linings for Steel Water Pipelines—Enamel and Tape—Hot Applied.*

AWWA C205-85, *Standard for Cement-Mortar Protective Lining and Coating for Steel Water Pipe—4 In. and Larger—Shop Applied.*

AWWA C300-82, *Standard for Reinforced Concrete Pressure Pipe—Steel Cylinder Type, for Water and Other Liquids.*

AWWA C301-84, *Standard for Prestressed Concrete Pressure Pipe—Steel Cylinder Type, for Water and Other Liquids.*

AWWA C302-87, *Standard for Reinforced Concrete Pressure Pipe—Noncylinder Type, for Water and Other Liquids.*

AWWA C303-87, *Standard for Reinforced Concrete Pressure Pipe—Steel Cylinder Type, Pretensioned, for Water and Other Liquids.*

AWWA C400-80/(R86), *Standard for Asbestos Cement Distribution Pipe 4 In. through 16 In. NPS for Water and Other Liquids.*

AWWA C401-83/(R86), *Standard Practice for the Selection of Asbestos Cement Distribution Pipe; 4 In. through 16 In. for Water and Other Liquids.*

AWWA C500-86, *Standard for Gate Valves 3 In. through 48 In. NPS for Water and Sewage Systems.*

AWWA C502-85, *Standard for Dry Barrel Fire Hydrants.*

AWWA C503-88, *Standard for Wet Barrel Fire Hydrants.*

AWWA C506-78/(R83), *Standard for Backflow Prevention Services—Reduced Pressure Principle and Double Check Valve Types.*

AWWA C600-87, *Standard for Installation of Ductile-Iron Water Mains and Appurtenances.*

AWWA C603-78, *Standard for Installation of Asbestos Cement Pressure Pipe.*

AWWA C703-86, *Standard for Cold Water Meters—Fire Service Type.*

AWWA C900-89, *Standard for Polyvinyl Chloride (PVC) Pressure Pipe, 4 In. through 12 In. for Water.*

AWWA C104/A21.4-85, *American National Standard for Cement-Mortar Lining for Ductile-Iron Pipe and Fittings for Water.*

AWWA C110/A21.10-85, *American National Standard for Ductile-Iron and Gray-Iron Fittings, 3 In. through 48 In., for Water and Other Liquids.*

AWWA C111/A21.11-85, *American National Standard for Rubber Gasket Joints for Ductile-Iron and Gray-Iron Pressure Pipe and Fittings.*

AWWA C150/A21.50-81/(R86), *American National Standard for the Thickness Design of Ductile-Iron Pipe.*

AWWA C151/A21.51-86, *American National Standard for Ductile-Iron Pipe, Centrifugally Cast in Metal Molds or Sand-Lined Molds, for Water or Other Liquids.*

AWWA M6 (30006)-86, *Water Meters—Selection, Installation, Testing, and Maintenance.*

AWWA M9 (30009)-79, *Concrete Pressure Pipe.*

AWWA M11 (30011)-89, *Steel Water Pipe—Design and Installation.*

AWWA M14 (30014)-66, *Recommended Practice for Backflow Prevention and Cross-Connection Control.*

AWWA M17 (30017)-80, *Installation, Field Testing, and Maintenance of Fire Hydrants.*

AWWA M23 (30023)-80, *PVC Pipe.*

Underwriters Laboratories of Canada

The following are published by Underwriters' Laboratories of Canada, 7 Crouse Road, Scarborough, Ontario:

ULC No. C-246, *Hydrants,* 1974.

ULC No. C-312, *Check Valves for Fire Protection,* 1981.

ULC No. C-789, *Indicator Posts for Fire Protection,* 1975.

Underwriters Laboratories Inc.

The following are published by Underwriters Laboratories Inc., 333 Pfingsten Road, Northbrook, IL 60062:

UL No. 107, *Asbestos Cement Pipe and Couplings,* 1980.

UL No. 246, *Hydrants for Fire Protection Service,* 1986.

UL No. 262, *Gate Valves for Fire Protection Service,* 1988.

UL No. 312, *Check Valves for Fire Protection Service,* 1980/(R85).

UL No. 385, *Clay Pipes for Water Supply Testing in Fire Protection Service,* 1988.

UL No. 789, *Indicator Posts for Fire Protection Service,* 1987.

UL No. 888, *Steel Pipe for Underground Water Service,* 1978.

UL No. 194, *Gasketed Joints for Ductile-Iron and Gray-Iron Pressure Pipe and Fittings, for Fire Protection Service,* 1980/(R81).

UL No. 753, *Alarm Accessories for Automatic Water Supply Control Valves for Fire Protection Service,* 1982/(R88).

Additional Reading

AWWA Committee on Financial Aspects of Fire Prevention and Protection, *A Business-like Approach to Fire Protection Changes,* American Water Works Association, Denver, CO, 1974.

Angele, G. J., "Backflow Prevention and Cross-Connection Control," *American Water Works Association Journal,* Vol. 62, No. 6 (June 1970).

Babbit, H. E., Cleasby, J. L., and Doland, J. J., *Water Supply Engineering*, 6th ed., McGraw-Hill, New York, 1962.

Crocker, C., ed., *Piping Handbook*, 5th ed., McGraw-Hill, New York, 1967.

Handbook of Ductile Iron Pipe, 6th ed., Ductile Iron Pipe Research Association, Birmingham, AL, 1984.

Jensen, R., ed., *Fire Protection for the Design Professional*, Cahners, Boston, 1975, pp. 41-57.

"Liability for Hydrant Maintenance," *Fire Journal*, Vol. 59, No. 5 (Sept. 1965), p. 23.

Vance, M., *Drinking Water Standards: A Bibliography*, Vance Bibliographies, Monticello, IL, 1989.

Walski, T. M., *Analysis of Water Distribution Systems*, Van Nostrand Reinhold, New York, 1984.

WATER STORAGE FACILITIES AND SUCTION SUPPLIES

Revised by William E. Wilcox

In a broad sense, water storage facilities and suction supplies include all bodies of water available as sources of supply, whether they are contained by constructed or natural barriers. Elevated or ground-level storage tanks of metal, wood, or rubberized fabric are examples of constructed storage facilities; rivers, ponds, and harbors are examples of natural storage facilities.

Open bodies of water, such as reservoirs created by the damming of streams, are sometimes used in private fire protection to supplement public water supplies or furnish the primary source of water for fire protection if public supplies are insufficient in volume or pressure, or both, or if they lack dependability. Such arrangements are, however, feasible only in special situations. A common method is to use elevated gravity tanks or ground-level suction tanks with fire pumps. Pressure tanks, with their limited capacity, may be used where storage requirements are relatively small.

This chapter contains information on the design, installation, and maintenance of contructed water storage facilities and the ways in which naturally occurring surface and ground-water supplies can be used for fire protection. Of particular interest are the provisions described for preventing water in storage from freezing during cold weather.

Water distribution systems and fire pumps (depending on the nature of the storage facilities), both integral parts of water supplies for fire protection systems, are covered in Chapters 4 and 6, respectively, in this section. Water-based extinguishing systems are covered in other chapters of this section.

STORAGE TANKS (GRAVITY AND SUCTION)

At the outset, it is well to recognize that, with the advent of hydraulically designed sprinkler systems, the use of elevated tanks for fire protection has declined; however, the use of ground-level suction tanks, combined with fire pumps, has increased. Nevertheless, there are many elevated gravity tanks still in service used solely for fire protection service, and they require high standards of maintenance to continue their reliability as primary sources of water for extinguishing systems.

It is best if tanks for fire protection are not used for any other purpose. Tanks used for other purposes must usually be refilled frequently, and they become settling basins that collect large accumulations of sediment. When water is drawn from the tank, the sediment also is drawn into the yard or extinguishing system and may block the system.

If the tank is wood and is refilled frequently, the alternate drying and wetting of the lumber may appreciably shorten the life of the tank; with a steel tank, more frequent painting is required, which means not only greater expense, but more time out of service.

Another important consideration involving dual-purpose tanks is the water available at the time of the fire. Such tanks will seldom be full, because domestic and industrial consumption constantly draws it down. In addition, the normal water level may drop lower and lower if the industry grows. If a fire occurs several years after the tank is installed, sufficient water at sufficient pressure might not be available. To overcome this problem, the outlet for the domestic and industrial supply should be set at a water level above the water dedicated for fire protection service.

Location

A gravity tank supported on an independent steel tower with foundations placed in the ground rather than on a building is the best arrangement. The tank should be built so that it will not be subject to fire exposure from adjacent buildings or yard storage. If lack of yard room makes this impossible, the exposed steelwork should be suitably protected by fire-resistive construction or coverings. The steel protection, when necessary, should include steelwork within 20 ft (6 m) of combustible buildings or openings from which fire might issue.

If the tank or supporting trestle is to be placed on the walls of a new building, the building should be designed and built to carry the maximum loads.

William E. Wilcox, P.E., is a senior engineer in the Standards Division at the Factory Mutual Research Corporation, Norwood, MA.

Suction tanks should be located so as to minimize yard piping. The pump house is generally placed close to the tanks to minimize suction piping. The tanks should not be put where they will be exposed to fires in combustible construction, or fires issuing from windows or yard storage. (See Figure 5-5A.)

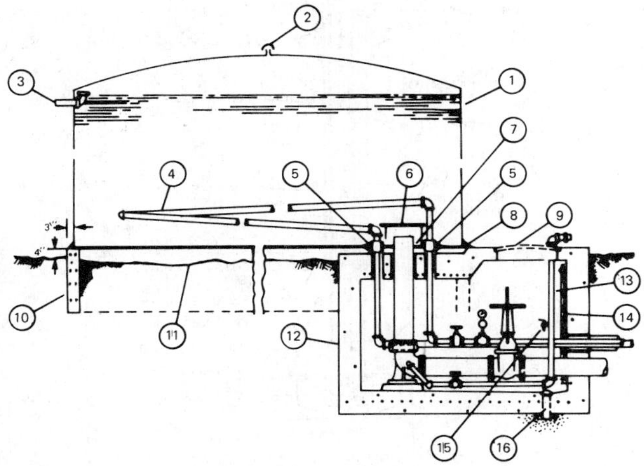

FIG. 5-5A. A ground-level suction tank showing the discharge pipe connected to the bottom of the tank in a valve pit. Nomenclature: (1) pump suction tank, (2) screened vent, (3) stub overflow pipe, (4) steam coil for heating, (5) extra-heavy couplings welded to tank bottom, (6) vortex plate, (7) watertight lead slip joint, (8) flashing around tank, (9) manhole with cover, (10) concrete ring wall, (11) sand or concrete pad (depending on soil condition), (12) valve pit, (13) drain pipe, (14) ladder, (15) drain cock, and (16) valve pit drain. (Source: Factory Mutual Research Corp.)

Design for Earthquake Resistance

Storage tanks can be designed to resist earthquakes. In an earthquake, the motion of Earth sets up a whip-like action in elevated tanks and a sloshing of water in all storage tanks. These motions produce stresses beyond those provided for in a design that allows only for ordinary dead, live, and wind loads.

In areas where earthquakes are likely, the tanks, including tower and foundation, should meet the requirements for resisting earthquake damage by complying with the earthquake design provisions of the American Water Works Association's *Standard for Welded Steel Tanks for Water Storage*[1] or *Standard for Factory-Coated Bolted Steel Tanks for Water Storage*.[2]

There are three earthquake design categories: (1) cross-braced, (2) pedestal-type for elevated tanks, and (3) ground-supported for suction tanks. Cross-braced elevated tanks rely on the cross-bracing system to resist lateral forces. Pedestal tanks rely on the cantilever action of the shaft to resist earthquake forces. Suction tanks are affected less by earthquakes than elevated tanks; however, they may need to be anchored to resist earthquakes. The maximum load in the foundation is dependent on the column or shaft reactions of elevated tanks and whether suction tanks are anchored. Pipe connections, especially between suction tanks and the pumps, should be designed to protect against earthquakes.

Tank Capacities

Today it is usually uneconomical to install a gravity tank big enough and tall enough that it can be connected directly into the fire protection system and furnish an adequate supply for both hose streams from hydrants and automatic fire extinguishing systems.

Years ago, because of limited capacity and pressure requirements, a gravity tank holding at least 30,000 gal (110 m^3) with its bottom at least 75 ft (23 m) above the ground could adequately supply both hose lines from hydrants and the extinguishing systems. Storage tank selection is still determined by the capacity and pressure required for both hose streams and sprinklers for the possible duration of a fire, but, because of the increased requirements of today, the suction tank and pump is more economical than a gravity tank or gravity tank and booster pump.

Gravity and suction tanks are generally erected in standard sizes. (See Tables 5-5A and 5-5B.) The capacity required is determined by the intended use of the tank and is specified in the number of gallons (cubic meters) available from the tank (1 gal = 0.00378 m^3).

TABLE 5-5A. *Standard Sizes of Gravity Tanks*

Steel Tanks		Wooden Tanks		Standard Height	
gal	m^3*	gal	m^3*	ft	m*
30,000	115	30,000	115	75	22.9
40,000	150	40,000	150	100	30.5
50,000	190	50,000	190	125	38.1
60,000	230	60,000	230	150	45.7
75,000	290	75,000	290		
100,000	380	100,000	380		
150,000	570				
200,000	760				
300,000	1100				
400,000	1480				
500,000	2000				

* Figures rounded off as approximations from nominal customary American tank sizes.

TABLE 5-5B. *Common Sizes of Steel Pump Suction Tanks*

gal	m^3*	gal	m^3*
50,000	190	250,000	950
75,000	290	300,000	1100
100,000	380	400,000	1500
125,000	475	500,000	2000
150,000	575	750,000	3000
200,000	750	1,000,000	4000

* Figures rounded off as approximations from nominal customary American tank sizes.

Steel gravity tanks with suspended bottoms are usually erected on towers with four columns for capacities from 50,000 to 200,000 gal (190 to 750 m^3) inclusive, six columns for capacities from 200,000 to 300,000 gal (750 to 1100 m^3) inclusive, and eight columns for tanks over 300,000 gal (1135.50 m^3).

Construction of Tanks

Gravity tanks are usually built of wood or steel and are supported by steel towers. Reinforced concrete towers are sometimes used, and tanks can also be placed directly on

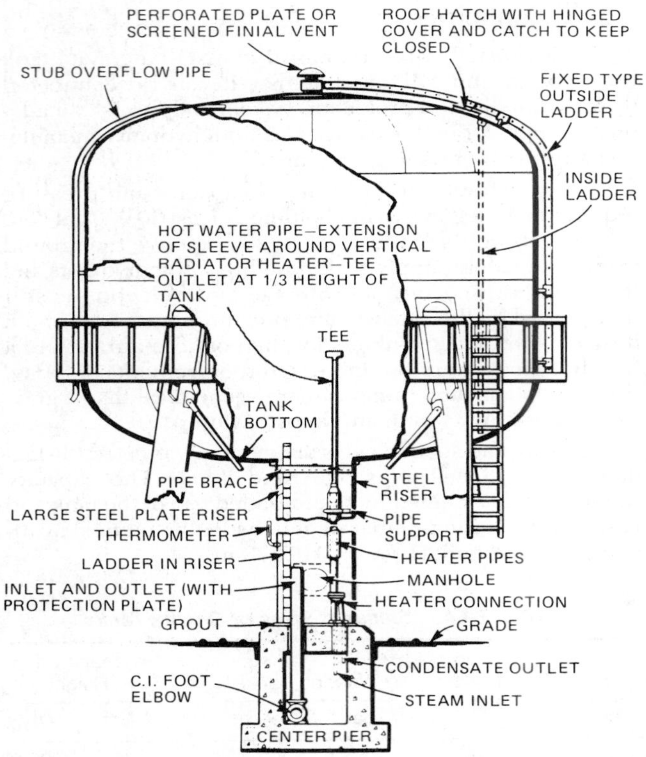

FIG. 5-5B. A typical tower-supported double ellipsoidal tank.

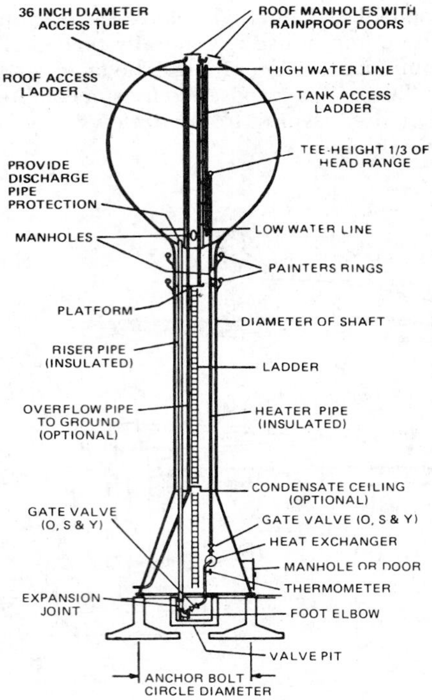

top of the structures they supply. In a few cases, concrete has also been used for the tank shells themselves. Typical gravity tanks are shown in Figures 5-5B and 5-5C.

Tanks should be designed and installed according to NFPA 22, *Water Tanks for Private Fire Protection*, which gives full requirements for construction materials, loads, unit stresses, details of design, foundations, accessories, and workmanship. Welding of towers should conform to code requirements for welding in building construction.[3]

Steel for tanks and towers should conform to the specifications in NFPA 22, *Water Tanks for Private Fire Protection*. Chief among these specifications are the American Water Works Association standards for steel tanks,[1,2] which give the thickness of steel plates and the welding and bolting practices that should be followed. Other standards referenced in NFPA 22 cover steel shapes, plate materials, bolts, anchor bolts and rods, forgings, castings, reinforcing steel, and filler material for welding.

NFPA 22, *Water Tanks for Private Fire Protection*, also gives information on wood tanks, including types and dimensions of wood suitable for use, processes that should be used, and proper hoop materials and design, as well as unit loads and unit stresses for steel tanks and towers, and working stresses for timber for wood tanks.

Steel tanks and towers should be riveted, welded, or bolted if factory-coated. Unfinished bolts should only be used in field connections of nonadjustable tension members carrying wind stress and in-field connections of compression members and grillages in towers supporting tanks of 30,000-gal (110 m^3) or less capacity.

During assembly and erection, plates should be bolted firmly together before riveting. Drift pins should not be used to bring parts together or to enlarge unfair holes.

FIG. 5-5C. A typical pedestal tank. The higher the tank, the greater the water pressure at the base of the tank.

No waste material, such as boards, roofing, paint cans, etc., should be left in the tank or in the space at the top of the tank after its completion, because it may get into the water and obstruct the piping.

Tanks should be put in service promptly after completion. Wood tanks may be damaged by shrinkage if left empty.

TANK AND TOWER FOUNDATIONS

The following are principles of good foundations for suction tanks and gravity tank towers.

Foundations in the Ground

Material: Foundations should be built of concrete with compressive strength not less than 3000 psi (20.69 mPa). The cement and aggregates, and the mixing and placing of the concrete, should conform to the current American Concrete Institute requirements for reinforced concrete.[4] Concrete work should conform to all requirements of ACI 301.[5]

Steel or wood pump suction tanks should be set upon crushed stone, sand, or concrete foundations. If the soil is good, at least 4 in. (100 mm) of crushed stone or sand is suggested. The material should then be saturated with oil and laid on moistened and compacted gravel after removing unsuitable soil. Special consideration (outlined below) must be given if soil is poor.

A concrete ring wall at least 2½ ft (760 mm) deep and 10 in. (250 mm) thick should surround the tank foundation. This ring normally projects 6 in. (150 mm) above grade and includes hoop tension reinforcing steel equal to 0.25 percent of the cross-sectional area, or as required. If the ring wall is outside of the tank shell, asphalt flashing should be installed between the tank and the ring wall at ground level.

For poor soil, an 8-in. (200 mm) reinforced concrete slab with a concrete ring wall directly beneath the tank sides and extended below the frost line is advised. For riveted tanks, a 1½-in. (38 mm) layer of a dry mixture of sand and cement should be placed on top of the concrete slab. For tanks of welded construction, no sand cushion is needed on the concrete slab. Piles can be used in addition to the reinforced concrete slab if the soil is very poor.

Form: The tops of foundations should be level and at least 6 in. (150 mm) above ground. The bottoms of foundation piers for towers should be located below the frost line, and, in the case of piers, at least 4 ft (1.2 m) below grade, resting on thoroughly tamped soil or rock.

Piers: Pier foundations may be of any suitable shape and may be either plain or reinforced concrete. If they support a tower, their center of gravity should lie in the continued center of gravity line of the tower column or else be designed for eccentricity. The height of piers should not be less than the mean width. The top surface should extend at least 3 in. (75 mm) beyond the bearing plates on all sides and is generally chamfered at the edges.

Anchorage: The weight of piers should be sufficient to resist the maximum net uplift that occurs when the wind blows from any direction on the empty tank. The weight of dirt directly above the base of the pier may be included in the calculations.

Anchor bolts should be arranged to engage a weight at least equal to the net uplift with the tank empty and the wind blowing from any direction. Their lower ends should be hooked or fitted with anchor plates.

Anchor bolts should be accurately located with sufficient free length of thread to fully engage their nuts. Expansion bolts are not acceptable. The minimum size of anchor bolts should be 1½ in. (38 mm).

Grouting and flashing: Bearing or base plates should have complete bearing on the foundation or be laid on cement grout to secure a complete bearing. The stressed portion of anchor bolts should not be exposed except where necessary. If the stressed portions of anchor bolts must be exposed, they should be encased in cement mortar to protect against corrosion unless they are accessible for complete cleaning and painting. If structural shapes, plates, and bolts enter or are supported by masonry or concrete, the joint between the metal and masonry or concrete should be flashed with asphalt. (This does not refer to base plates under columns.)

Soil-bearing pressure: In order to find the proper depth of the foundation, the soil-bearing pressure must be determined by analyzing the subsurface and checking the foundations of other structures in the area. Test borings should be made by or under the supervision of an experienced soils engineer or soils testing laboratory. The borings should be made deep enough to determine the adequacy of the support, which is usually a minimum of 20 to 30 ft (6 to 9 m).

Foundations: The foundations should be designed to carry the maximum loads without excessive settlement. If wood piles are used above permanent low ground-water level, they should be protected as specified by the American Wood Preservers Association.[6]

Foundations should not be constructed over buried pipes or immediately adjacent to existing or former deep excavations unless the foundation bases go below the excavation.

Center pier: In addition to the weight of the water in a large plate riser, the weight of the column of water directly above the riser in the tank, and the weight of the steel plate, the center pier should be considered as supporting a hollow cylinder of water in the tank. If the hemispherical or ellipsoidal bottom is rigidly attached to the top of the large riser by a flat horizontal diaphragm plate, the radius of the hollow cylinder of water should be determined as specified under large risers discussed later in this chapter.

TANK TOWERS

Steel is generally used for the construction of tank towers. Details on the specific types of steel used in tanks can be found in NFPA 22, *Water Tanks for Private Fire Protection.*

Both live loads and dead loads should be considered when designing towers. The dead load is an estimate of the weight of the structure and all its fittings. The live load is considered as the weight of the water when the tank is filled and overflowing. Consideration should also be given to temporary loading, such as ice and snow.

The weight of the water in the riser need not be considered when figuring loads unless the riser is suspended from the tank bottom. If the riser is used to support the tank bottom, the entire weight supported by the riser should be considered, including the weight of the water.

Additional factors to consider are wind, balcony, and earthquake loads. Wind loads are based on 30 psi (207 kPa) for vertical plain surfaces and 18 psi (124 kPa) over the vertical projection of cylindrical surfaces. These loads are applied to the center of gravity of the projected areas. The balcony load consists of the weight of the balcony railing and ladder material and, if exposed, the weight of snow. Earthquake loading must be designed specifically for local conditions.

Ladders and Balconies

All tanks should have ladders on both the outside and inside, with convenient passage from one ladder to the other. Ladders are for inspection and maintenance of the tank's interior and exterior surfaces; they should be constructed of materials compatible to those of the tank and tower, and they should be easily accessible. Ladders more than 20 ft (6 m) long should be equipped with a cage or other safety device designed to protect the climber.

Balconies and walkways are recommended for towers over 20 ft (6 m) high. Normally, balconies should not be less than 24 in. (600 mm) wide and walkways not less than 18 in. (450 mm) wide. Railings should be at least 42 in. (1050 mm) high. Balconies and walkways should also be made of materials compatible with the tank and tower materials.

Tower Construction

During field erection, the columns of towers should be built on thin metal wedges driven to equal resistance so that all columns will be loaded equally after the structure is completed. The spaces beneath the base plates and the anchor holes should be completely filled with cement mortar.

Sections of structural members for towers should be symmetrical and built of standard structural shapes or tubular sections. Structural shapes should be designed with open sections so that all corrosible surfaces that will be exposed to air or moisture can be painted. Tubular sections of columns and struts should be airtight.

TANK HEATING EQUIPMENT

Adequate heating of tank equipment ranks next to structural design in importance. An ice plug in a riser pipe may make the tank water unavailable in case of fire and may break the pipe. Ice in or on tank structures has been the direct cause of collapse in several cases. The heating system must therefore be reliable and allow convenient and economical operation to 50°F (10°C). However, overheating can seriously damage wood tanks and the paint on steel tanks, and should be avoided.

Determination of Heater Capacity

To prevent freezing in any part of a tank during the coldest weather, the heating system must be of such capacity that the temperature of the coldest water in the tank or riser, or both, will be maintained at or above 42°F (5.6°C). The coldest weather temperature used to determine the need of heating should be based upon the lowest mean temperature for one day, as shown on the isothermal map, Figure 5-5D.

Tables 5-5C and 5-5D show the heat losses from tanks of common sizes exposed to various atmospheric temperatures. The following is an example of the method used to determine required heating capacities for various types and sizes of tanks:

Question: What heater capacity would be needed for a 75,000-gal (284 m^3) steel tank at Duluth, MN?

Answer: A heater capable of delivering 659,000 Btu per hr (193,000 W) under field conditions. Answer formed by interpolating from Figure 5-5D. The lowest mean temperature for one day at Duluth is –28°F (–33°C), and by interpolating from Table 5-5D, it is found that the heat loss at –28°F (–33°C) for a 75,000-gal (284 m^3) steel tank is approximately 659,000 Btu per hr (193,000 W).

Selection of Heating Method

The selection of a heating method depends chiefly upon a tank's height, construction material, size, and shape, and on the lowest temperature of exposure. The recommended methods of heating are covered in detail in NFPA 22, *Water Tanks for Private Fire Protection.*

There are three basic methods of heating tank water: (1) gravity circulation of hot water, (2) steam coils inside tanks, and (3) direct discharge of steam into the water.

Gravity Circulation of Hot Water

Heating by gravity circulation is dependable and economical if correctly planned. Cold water received through a connection from the discharge pipe or from near the bottom of a suction tank or standpipe is heated and rises through a separate hot water pipe into the tank. Steam, coal burning, or oil heaters are ordinarily used; gas heaters or electric heaters are also satisfactory.

A steam heater ordinarily consists of a cast-iron or steel shell through which water circulates by gravity around steam tubes or coils of brass or copper. It should be located in a valve pit, heater house, or in a nearby building at or near the base of the tank. When the tank is over a building, the steam heater should be located in the top story.

Heater thermometer: The convenience of a gravity system is that it permits discovery of the temperature of the coldest water in the system. A recording thermometer should be placed in the cold water return pipe near the heater; it should be checked frequently to make sure that the temperature does not fall below 42°F (5.6°C). To fail to observe the temperature is to risk freezing the equipment. [Water has its maximum density at 39.2°F (4°C). When the temperature of the water falls below 39.2°F (4°C), there is an inversion, and the warmer water settles to the bottom of the tank while the colder water rises. Therefore, if the circulation heater is to be effective, sufficient heat must be provided so that the temperature of the coldest water will be above 42°F (5.6°C).]

Water circulating pipes: The size of pipe used for the circulation of heating water is given in Table 5-5E. Pipe should be either copper water tubing or brass (85 percent copper) throughout. The hot water discharges into the tank through a tee fitting at the end of the hot water pipe at a height about one-third up from the bottom of the tank. The return pipe connects into the discharge pipe at a point that guarantees circulation throughout the portion of the discharge pipe subject to freezing. A typical arrangement of a circulating heater and piping in a valve pit is shown in Figure 5-5E.

Steam Coils Inside Tanks

Steam coils inside the tank do not permit convenient observation of water temperatures and have other faults that make them unsuited for heating elevated tanks except in areas of the South where only intermittent heating is necessary. This method may, however, be used for heating suction tanks and standpipes with flat bottoms supported near the ground level if coils are submerged continuously. The coil consists of at least 1¼-in. (32 mm) brass or copper pipe,

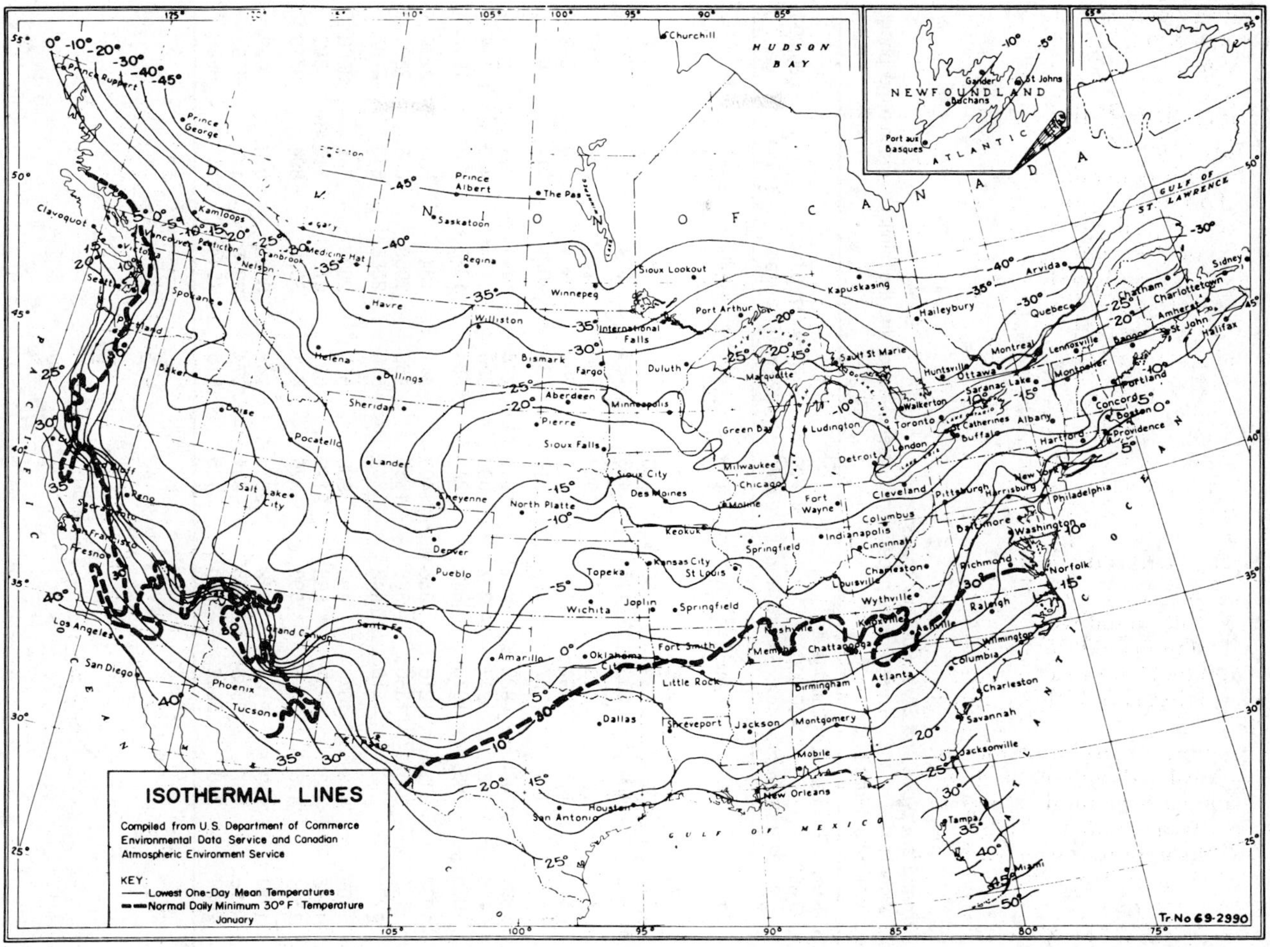

FIG. 5-5D. Isothermal lines—lowest one-day temperature mean temperature.

pitched to drain, supplied with steam at not less than 10 psi (69 kPa) pressure through a pipe of sufficient size to furnish the required quantity of steam from a reliable source.

Direct Discharge of Steam

Steam from a reliable supply is blown directly into the tank water through a pipe that enters the tank through the bottom, extends to above the maximum water level, and then returns to a point 3 or 4 ft (0.9 or 1.2 m) below the normal fire service level. An air vent and check valve in the pipe above the surface of the water keeps the water from siphoning back down the steam line. This method is employed where the lowest mean temperature for one day is 5°F (–15°C) or above.

Solar Heating of Elevated Steel Tanks

With the increase in fossil fuel prices, work was done in Canada on the feasibility of solar heating of elevated steel tanks.[7] The basic technique is to insulate the entire tank, leaving a window on the south side through the insulation. The tank shell in the opening is painted flat black to absorb heat from the sun and the opening is double-glazed.

Retrofit installations of solar systems on existing tanks involves special precautions in the attachment of components to the tank, such as the use of adhesives. The costs would be relatively high and the payback period long.

For new tanks, low-cost welding techniques can be used for attachment of collector components to the tank. With substantially all energy being supplied by the sun, a backup heating system can be a low-cost electrical system. Compared to a conventional tank with a fossil-fuel-fired boiler heating system, a solar-heated tank with an electrical backup heating system is likely to have a lower capital cost.

The preliminary findings indicate that solar-heated water tanks would seem appropriate for new installations.

TANK EQUIPMENT AND ACCESSORIES

A complete installation of a gravity or suction tank includes the necessary pipe connections, valve enclosures, and, where appropriate for the particular tank, such features as a frostproof casing for the riser.

TABLE 5-5C. ***Heat Loss from Standpipes and Steel Suction Tanks***

Thousands of British thermal units lost per hour when the temperature of the coldest water is 42°F (5.6°C). To determine capacity of heater needed, find the minimum mean atmospheric temperature for one day from the isothermal map, Figure 5-5D, and note the corresponding heat loss below.

Temperature		100,000 gal	378 m³	150,000 gal	567 m³	200,000 gal	757 m³	300,000 gal	1135 m³	400,000 gal	1514 m³	500,000 gal	1892 m³	750,000 gal	2838 m³	1,000,000 gal
		TANK CAPACITIES—Thousands of Gallons														
Deg. F	Deg. C	Btu/hr	W	Btu/hr	W	Btu/hr	W	Btu/hr	W	Btu/hr	W	Btu/hr	W	Btu/hr	W	Btu/hr
35	2	85	25	114	33	135	40	175	51	206	60	238	70	312	91	380
30	-1	121	35	162	47	193	57	248	73	294	86	340	100	445	130	542
25	-4	161	47	216	63	257	75	330	97	393	115	453	133	594	174	722
20	-7	202	59	271	79	323	95	414	121	493	144	568	166	745	218	907
15	-9	245	72	329	96	391	115	502	147	597	175	689	202	904	265	1099
10	-12	290	85	389	114	463	136	595	174	707	207	816	239	1071	314	1032
5	-15	337	99	452	132	539	158	691	202	822	241	949	278	1244	364	1514
0	-18	388	114	521	153	620	182	796	233	947	277	1093	320	1434	420	1744
-5	-21	441	129	592	173	705	207	905	265	1076	315	1241	364	1628	477	1987
-10	-23	498	146	669	196	797	234	1023	300	1216	356	1403	411	1841	539	2239
-15	-36	557	163	748	219	891	261	1143	335	1360	398	1569	460	2058	603	2503
-20	-29	619	181	830	243	989	290	1270	372	1510	442	1742	510	2286	670	2787
-25	-32	685	201	920	270	1096	321	1406	412	1673	490	1930	565	2532	742	3080
-30	-34	752	220	1010	296	1203	352	1545	453	1837	538	2119	621	2781	815	3383
-35	-37	825	242	1108	325	1320	387	1694	496	2015	590	2325	681	3050	894	3710
-40	-40	898	263	1206	353	1437	421	1844	540	2193	643	2531	742	3320	973	4039
-50	-46	1059	310	1422	417	1694	496	2175	637	2586	758	2984	874	3915	1147	4762
-60	-51	1229	360	1651	484	1966	576	2524	740	3002	880	3463	1015	4544	1331	5528

TABLE 5-5D. *Heat Loss from Elevated Tanks*

Thousands of British thermal units lost per hour when the temperature of the coldest water is 42°F (5.6°C). To determine capacity of heater needed, find the minimum mean atmospheric temperature for one day from the isothermal map, Figure 5-5D, and note the corresponding heat loss below.

Atmospheric Temperature		Wooden Tanks 10,000 gal ($38\ m^3$)		15,000 gal ($57\ m^3$)		20,000 gal ($76\ m^3$)		25,000 gal ($95\ m^3$)		30,000 gal ($114\ m^3$)		40,000 gal ($151\ m^3$)		50,000 gal ($189\ m^3$)		75,000 gal ($284\ m^3$)		100,000 gal ($378\ m^3$)	
Deg F	Deg C	Btu/hr	W	Btu/hr	W	Btu/hr	W	Btu/hr	W	Btu/hr	W	Bru/hr	W	Btu/hr	W	Btu/hr	W	Btu/hr	W
35	-2	8	2	10	3	11	3	13	4	14	4	19	6	21	6	28	8	33	10
30	-1	11	3	14	4	16	5	19	6	21	6	27	8	31	9	40	12	49	14
25	-4	15	4	20	6	21	6	25	7	28	8	36	11	42	12	54	16	65	19
20	-7	19	6	25	7	27	8	32	9	35	10	46	13	54	16	69	20	83	24
15	-9	24	7	31	9	34	10	39	11	44	13	57	17	66	19	85	25	102	30
10	-12	28	8	36	11	40	12	46	13	51	15	68	20	78	23	100	29	121	35
5	-15	33	10	43	13	47	14	54	16	60	18	78	23	92	27	117	34	142	42
0	-18	38	11	49	14	53	16	62	18	69	20	90	26	106	31	135	40	164	48
-5	-21	43	13	56	16	61	18	71	21	79	23	103	30	120	35	154	45	187	55
-10	-23	49	14	63	18	69	20	80	23	89	26	116	34	136	40	174	51	211	62
-15	-26	54	16	71	21	77	23	89	26	100	29	130	36	153	45	195	57	236	69
-20	-29	61	18	79	23	86	25	99	29	111	33	145	42	169	50	217	64	262	77
-25	-32	68	20	87	25	95	28	110	32	123	36	160	47	188	55	240	70	291	85
-30	-34	74	22	96	28	104	30	121	35	135	40	176	52	206	60	264	77	319	93
-35	-37	81	24	105	31	115	34	133	39	148	43	193	57	226	66	289	85	350	103
-40	-40	88	26	114	33	125	37	144	42	162	47	210	62	246	72	317	93	382	112
-50	-46	104	30	135	40	147	43	170	50	190	56	246	72	290	85	372	109	450	132
-60	-51	122	36	157	46	171	50	197	58	222	65	266	78	307	90	407	119	490	144

Atmospheric Temperature		Steel Tanks 30,000 gal ($114\ m^3$)		40,000 gal ($151\ m^3$)		50,000 gal ($189\ m^3$)		75,000 gal ($284\ m^3$)		100,000 gal ($284\ m^3$)		150,000 gal ($568\ m^3$)		200,000 gal ($757\ m^3$)		250,000 gal ($946\ m^3$)		See Note Below	
Deg F	Deg C	Btu/hr	W	Btu/hr	W	Btu/hr	W	Btu/hr	W	Btu/hr	W	Bru/hr	W	Btu/hr	W	Btu/hr	W	Btu/hr	W
35	17	43	13	51	15	59	17	77	23	92	27	120	35	145	42	168	49	69	20
30	12	62	18	72	21	83	24	110	32	132	39	171	50	207	61	242	71	192	56
25	7	82	24	96	28	111	33	146	43	175	51	228	67	275	81	323	96	340	100
20	2	103	30	120	35	139	41	183	54	220	64	287	84	346	101	405	119	506	148
15	-3	125	37	146	43	169	50	222	65	267	78	347	102	419	123	491	144	692	203
10	-8	147	43	172	50	200	59	263	77	316	93	411	120	496	145	582	171	893	262
5	-13	171	51	200	59	233	68	306	90	367	108	478	140	577	169	676	198	1092	320
0	-18	197	58	231	68	268	79	352	103	423	124	551	161	664	195	779	228	1309	384
-5	-23	224	66	262	77	304	89	400	117	480	141	626	183	755	221	884	259	1536	450
-10	-28	253	74	296	87	344	101	452	132	543	159	707	207	853	250	1000	293	1771	519
-15	-33	283	83	331	97	384	113	506	148	607	178	790	231	954	280	1118	328	2020	592
-20	-38	314	92	368	108	427	125	562	165	674	197	878	257	1059	310	1241	364	2291	671
-25	-43	348	102	407	119	473	139	622	182	747	219	972	285	1173	344	1375	403	2568	752
-30	-48	382	112	447	131	519	152	683	200	820	240	1068	313	1288	377	1510	442	2860	838
-35	-53	419	123	490	144	569	167	749	219	900	264	1171	343	1413	414	1656	485	3174	930
-40	-58	456	134	534	156	620	182	816	239	979	287	1275	374	1538	451	1803	528	3494	102
-50	-68	538	158	629	184	731	214	962	282	1154	338	1503	440	1814	532	2126	623	4186	122
-60	-78	624	183	730	214	848	248	1116	327	1340	393	1745	511	2105	617	2467	723	4936	144

Note: For each lineal foot of uninsulated riser 4 ft (1.2 m) in diameter, add the number of Btus or W in this column to the total heat loss at the different temperatures of the various tank capacities.

TABLE 5-5E. ***Sizes of Circulating Pipes Required for Elevated Steel Tanks***

Minimum One-Day Mean Temp.		TANK CAPACITY																	
		Gallons 15,000	m^3 568	Gallons 20,000	m^3 757	Gallons 25,000	m^3 946	Gallons 30,000	m^3 1136	Gallons 40,000	m^3 1514	Gallons 50,000	m^3 1893	Gallons 60,000	m^3 2271	Gallons 75,000	m^3 2839	Gallons 100,000	m^3 3785	Gallons 150,000	m^3 5678
Deg F°	Deg C°	inches	mm	inches	mm	inches	mm	inches	mm	inches	mm	inches	mm	inches	mm	inches	mm	inches	mm	inches	mm
10	−12	2	51	2	51	2	51	2	51	2	51	2	51	2	51	2	51	2	51	2½	64
5	−15	2	51	2	51	2	51	2	51	2	51	2	51	2	51	2	51	2	51	2½	64
0	−18	2	51	2	51	2	51	2	51	2	51	2	51	2	51	2	51	2½	64	2½	64
−5	−21	2	51	2	51	2	51	2	51	2	51	2	51	2	51	2	51	2½	64	2½	64
−10	−23	2	51	2	51	2	51	2	51	2	51	2	51	2	51	2½	64	2½	64	2½	64
−15	−26	2	51	2	51	2	51	2	51	2	51	2	51	2½	64	2½	64	2½	64	3	76
−20	−29	2	51	2	51	2	51	2	51	2	51	2½	64	2½	64	2½	64	2½	64	3	76
−25	−32	2	51	2	51	2	51	2	51	2½	64	2½	64	2½	64	2½	64	3	76	3	76
−30	−34	2	51	2	51	2	51	2	51	2½	64	2½	64	2½	64	2½	64	3	76	3	76
−35	−37	2	51	2	51	2	51	2½	64	2½	64	2½	64	2½	64	3	76	3	76	3	76
−40	−40	2	51	2	51	2	51	2½	64	2½	64	2½	64	2½	64	3	76	3	76	3	76

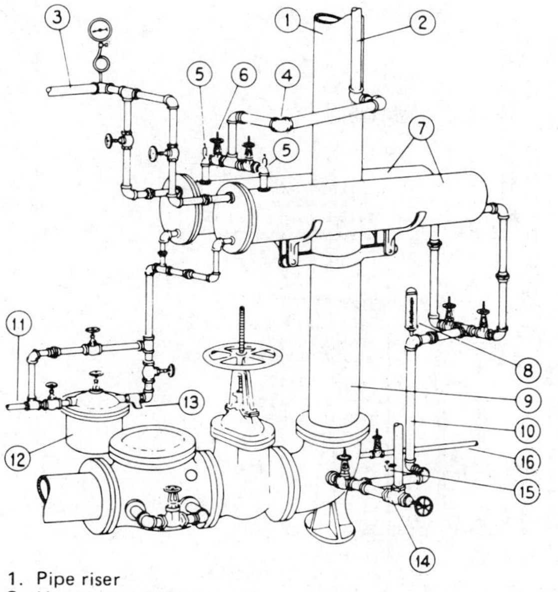

1. Pipe riser
2. Hot water circulating pipe
3. Steam supply pipe
4. Four-elbow swing joint
5. Relief valves
6. Approved OS&Y gate valves
7. Steam-heated water heaters
8. Thermometer
9. Pipe riser or discharge pipe from large steel-plate riser
10. Cold water circulating pipe
11. Condensate return
12. Steam trap
13. Strainer
14. Drain valve
15. Drain cock
16. From mercury gage

FIG. 5-5E. The piping arrangement for a multi-unit, steam-heated water heater for a gravity circulation system. Nomenclature: (1) pipe riser, (2) hot water circulating system, (3) steam supply line, (4) four-elbow swing joint, (5) relief valves, (6) O.S.&Y. valve, (7) steam-heated water heaters, (8) thermometer, (9) pipe riser, (10) cold water circulating pipe, (11) condensate return, (12) steam trap, (13) strainer, (14) drain valve, (15) drain cock, and (16) pipe from mercury gage. (Source: Factory Mutual Research Corp.)

Valve Pits

A pit 7 ft (2.1 m) deep and 6 ft by 9 ft (1.8 by 2.7 m) inside is usually large enough to house the necessary valves, tank heaters, and other fittings. Details of the construction of the pit and its arrangement, including clearance around equipment, waterproofing, manhole and ladder, and drainage, should conform to the recommendations given for valve pits. (See Figure 5-5F.)

ValveEnclosures

The tank heater and other fittings are sometimes installed in an enclosure above grade. In such a case, the indicating valve and the check valve are generally placed in the horizontal pipe below the frost line in a small pit heated sufficiently to maintain a temperature of at least 40°F (4.4°C) during the most severe weather.

The enclosure may be of concrete, brick, cement plaster on metal lath, or any other noncombustible material with suitable heat-insulating properties. The roof should be strong enough to support the frostproof casing and other loads without excessive deflection.

Frostproof Casings

Except in the case of a large steel riser, a frostproof casing around all exposed tank piping is necessary in localities where the lowest mean atmospheric temperature for one day as shown by the isothermal map (Figure 5-5D) is 20°F (–6.7°C) or lower. Tank piping subjected to temperatures below freezing within unheated buildings must also be adequately protected. Noncombustible frostproof casings should be used where there is danger of serious fire exposure.

Large Risers

Large steel-plate riser pipes 3 ft (0.9 m) or more in diameter, without frostproof casings, are often desirable. The fire hazard and upkeep of the frost casing are thereby avoided, the expansion joint in the discharge pipe is eliminated, and it is not necessary to have a walkway to reach the valves. When the tank is on an independent tower, a concrete valve pit at the base of the discharge pipe and the pier are usually built as a single unit to support the riser. (See Figure 5-5B.) On the other hand, the larger valve pit at the base of the riser makes the initial cost higher than it is for equipment with small risers.

Water-Level Indicators

A water-level gage of suitable design should be provided. A mercury gage is the most reliable water-level indicator for tanks. A dependable, closed circuit, high- and low-water electrical alarm is a suitable substitute for the mercury gage in certain installations. The mercury gage is normally installed in a heated room, such as a boiler room, engine room, or office, where it will be readily accessible.

The gage should be accurately installed so that, when the tank is filled to the level of the overflow, the mercury level is opposite the "FULL" mark on the gage board. The procedures for installing and testing mercury gages are given in detail in NFPA 22, *Water Tanks for Private Fire Protection.*

Overflow Pipes

The overflow pipe located at the top capacity or high-water line of the tank should not be less than 3 in. (7.6 mm) in diameter. If dripping water or a small accumulation of ice is not objectionable, the overflow may pass through the side of the tank near the top and extend not more than 4 ft (1.2 m), with a slight downward pitch to discharge beyond the balcony and away from the ladders.

When a stub pipe is undesirable, the overflow pipe can be extended down through the tank bottom and inside the frostproof casing or steel-plate riser, discharging through the casing near the ground or roof level. The section of the pipe inside the tank should be brass except on tanks with steel-plate risers, when overflow pipes 3½ in. (89 mm) or larger may be of extra-heavy wrought iron or of flanged cast-iron pipe.

Cathodic Protection

Cathodic protection can be used instead of painting to prevent interior corrosion on surfaces that are wetted by the tank's contents. Other surfaces inside the tank should be painted.

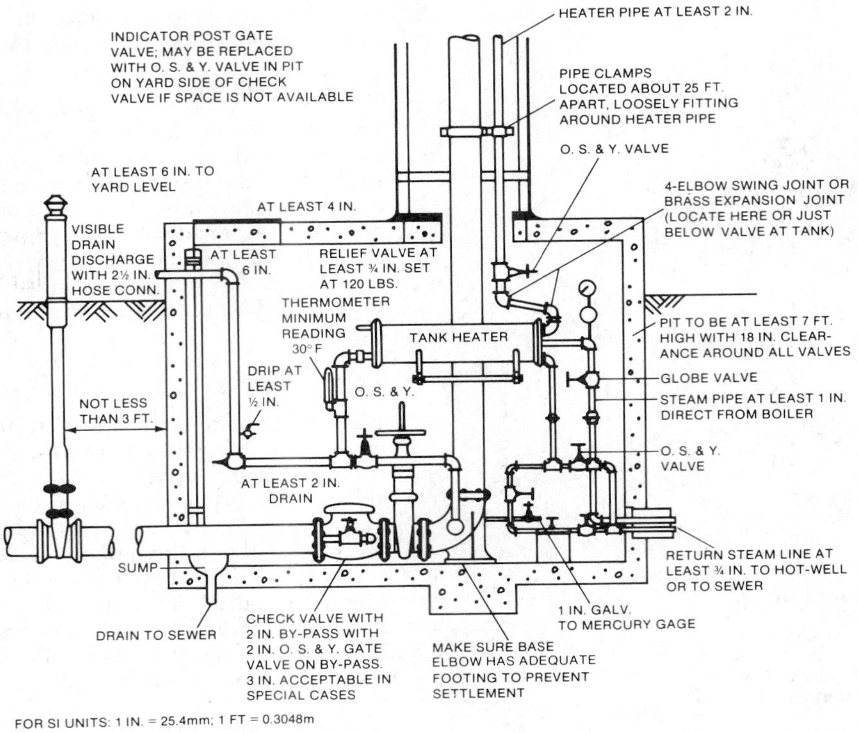

FIG. 5-5F. Valve pit and tank connections at base of riser.

Internal corrosion is caused by galvanic current flowing from numerous anodic areas of the tank shell through the water to adjacent cathodic areas. Cathodic protection counteracts this process by passing sufficient direct current from an outside source (anodes suspended in the water) to the tank shell to keep the whole of the interior wetted surfaces of the tank at a negative potential. Low-voltage direct current is supplied from a rectifier. Frequent and regular checking of the ammeter and voltmeter readings is advisable to determine whether the electrical system is functioning.

Aluminum anodes, which are common, require renewal annually. In unheated tanks, ice may damage the anodes in winter, and early servicing in the spring is necessary. Broken parts of the anodes should be removed from the tank.

For heated tanks, anodes of fine platinum wire (which is not deteriorated by the electric current) are sometimes used, but they cost much more than aluminum anodes.

EMBANKMENT-SUPPORTED RUBBERIZED FABRIC SUCTION TANKS

Embankment-supported rubberized fabric (ESRF) tanks can be used as suction tanks for fire protection. NFPA 22, *Water Tanks for Private Fire Protection*, contains details on construction, installation, and maintenance of ESRF tanks.

ESRF tanks are available in 20,000- and 50,000-gal (75 and 190 m^3) sizes, and in 100,000-gal (378.5 m^3) increments up to 1 million gal (3785 m^3). The tank is usually composed of a reservoir liner with an integral flexible roof and is designed to be supported by earth underneath and on all four sides. The material of ESRF tanks is a nylon fabric coated with an elastomer compounded to provide resistance to abrasion and weather. Support is provided by a specifically prepared excavation and earthen berm.

Preparation of the installation site is critical to the reliability of an ESRF tank. Usually, a shallow excavation the size of the bottom of the tank is made. The excavated earth is then graded to form the berm, or embankment, for the upper sides of the tank. The exterior of the berm should be graded to allow for rain and snow drainage and pipe connections, and the interior graded to match the contour of the tank, including rounded corners. ESRF tanks may be placed underground with the top of the tank at grade level, or they may be placed above ground where the earthen berm provides the entire support.

When the excavation meets the shape requirements of the tank and all sharp objects have been carefully removed from the floor of the tank excavation, a 6-in. (150 mm) layer of sand or clean soil is spread over a 3-in. (75 mm) underlayment of pea gravel which provides a firm base with good drainage. The tank is then placed in the foundation, and all connections are made. (Tanks are shipped to the site fully constructed.) After the tank is filled, a coating is applied to the exposed surface to protect it from the atmosphere. (See Figure 5-5G for a typical ESRF installation.)

As with other types of storage tanks, water temperature in ESRF tanks should be maintained at not less than 42°F (5.6°C). An acceptable method of providing heat is a water recirculation system with a heat exchanger. (See Figure 5-5H.) When the ambient water temperature drops below 42°F (5.6°C), a thermostat activates a pump which

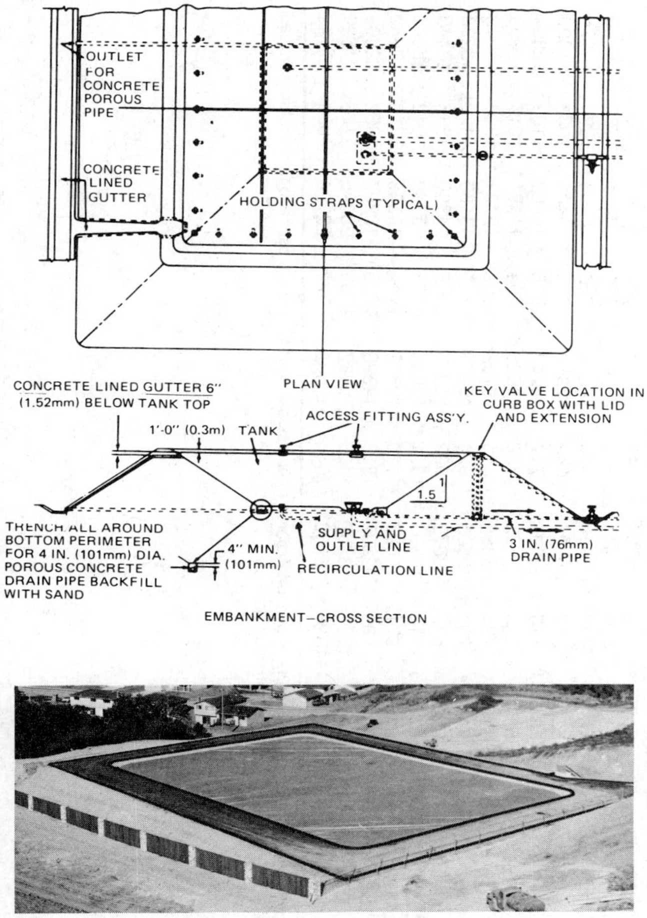

*FIG. 5-5G. **Installation details of a typical embankment-supported rubberized fabric (ESRF) tank, including fittings.***

draws water from the tank through an inlet-outlet fitting and pumps the heated water back into the tank through a recirculation fitting located in the bottom of the tank diagonally opposite the inlet-outlet fitting. Heat losses in ESRF tanks are given in Table 5-5F.

PRESSURE TANKS

Pressure tanks are used for limited private fire protection services, such as sprinkler systems, standpipe and hose systems, and water spray systems. They are sometimes used with fire pumps and gravity tanks that are located at as high an elevation as possible for quicker discharge. A typical pressure tank installation is shown in Figure 5-5I.

Tank capacity is considered to be the total contents, both air and water, not including dished ends. For light-hazard occupancies only, the tank may have a minimum capacity of 3000 gal (11 m^3), of which 2000 gal (7.5 m^3) is water, but the tank capacity ordinarily should be at least 4500 gal (17 m^3) for ordinary-hazard occupancies. Tanks for this service generally are not over 9000 gal (34 m^3) capacity. For larger supplies, more than one tank would be employed. (See Table 5-5G.)

The tank is normally kept two-thirds full of water, and an air pressure of at least 75 psig (517 kPa) is maintained. As the last of the water leaves the pressure tank, the residual pressure shown on the gage should not be less than zero, and should give at least 15 psig (103 kPa) pressure at the highest automatic discharge device under the main roof of the building.

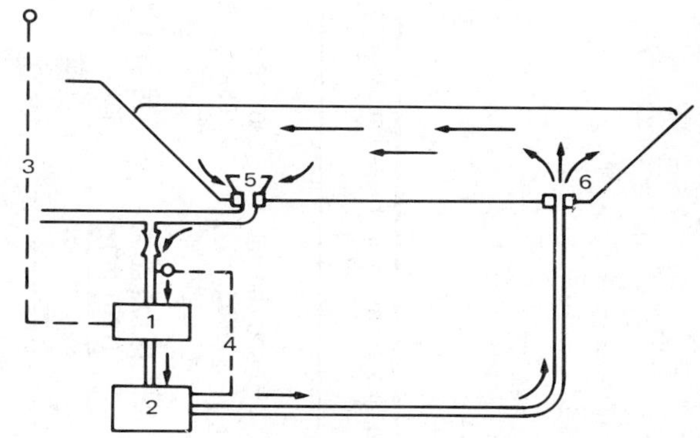

*FIG. 5-5H. **A schematic of a recirculation and heating system for an ESRF tank. Nomenclature and operation sequence are: (1) recirculation pump, (2) heat exchanger, (3) unit sensing atmosphere temperature starts pump and water recirculation, enabling heat stored in the ground to transfer into water at a higher rate, (4) unit sensing water temperature starts heat exchanger when required, (5) inlet-outlet fitting, and (6) recirculation fitting.***

Air for pressure tanks is supplied by compressors capable of delivering not less than 16 cu ft/min (0.045 m^3/min) of free air for tanks of 7500 gal (28 m^3) total capacity, and not less than 20 cu ft/min (0.057 m^3/min) for larger sizes. The compressors are located in the tank house.

Relationship of Air Pressure and Volume in Tanks

The volume of air in the tank at any time varies inversely with the pressure:

$$\frac{P_1}{P_2} = \frac{V_2}{V_1}$$

Pressures are absolute pressures, not gage pressures, as used in the above general formula. Let us apply this formula to the special condition which exists in a tank used to supply water for sprinklers. Except where there is danger of air lock, it is desirable to have 15 psig (103 kPa) pressure in the tank when the last water leaves. Thus,

$$P_2 = \text{residual pressure required} + \text{atmospheric pressure},$$
$$= 15 \text{ psi} + 15 \text{ psi}$$
$$= 30 \text{ psi},$$

Since at this condition the tank is full of air,

$$V_2 = 1.$$

If the tank is at or above the top line of sprinklers, the tank will be normally kept two-thirds full of water, so,

$$V_1 = 1/3.$$

Therefore,

$$P_1 = P_2 \times \frac{V_2}{V_1} = 30 \times \frac{1}{1/3} = 30 \times 3 = 90 \text{ psi}.$$

The corresponding gage pressure would be 90 psi (710 kPa), minus the atmospheric pressure, 15 psi (103 kPa), or 75 psi (517 kPa).

TABLE 5-5F. ***Heat Loss from Embankment Supported, Rubberized Fabric Suction Tanks***

Thousands of British thermal units lost per hour when the temperature of the coldest water is 42°F (5.6°C). To determine capacity of heater needed, find the minimum mean atmospheric temperature for one day from the isothermal map, Figure 5-5D, and note the corresponding heat loss below.

Atmospheric Temperature		Heat Loss Tank Radiating Surface		Tank Capacities / Exposed Tank Surface / Loss Per Hour—Thousands															
				100,000 gal (378 m³)		200,000 gal (757 m³)		300,000 gal (1136 m³)		400,000 gal (1514 m³)		500,000 gal 1893 m³)		600,000 gal (227 m³)		800,000 gal (3407 m³)		1,000,000 gal (3785 m³)	
				2746 sq ft 255 m²)		4409 sq ft (410 m²)		6037 sq ft (561 m²)		7604 sq ft (706 m²)		9139 sq ft (849 m²)		10,630 sq ft (988 m²)		13,572 sq ft (1261 m²)		16,435 sq ft (1527 m²)	
Deg F	Deg C	Btu	k/m²	Btu	W	Btu	W	Btu	W	Btu	W	Btu	W	Btu	W	Btu	W	Btu	W
35	-2	22	252	61	693	98	1113	134	1522	168	1908	202	2294	235	2669	300	3407	363	4122
30	-1	29	324	78	886	126	1431	173	1965	217	2464	261	2964	304	3452	389	4417	470	5337
25	-4	35	399	96	1090	155	1760	212	2407	266	3021	320	3634	372	4224	476	5405	576	6541
20	-7	42	472	114	1295	183	2078	251	2850	315	3577	379	4304	441	5008	564	6405	682	7745
15	-9	48	545	132	1499	212	2407	290	3293	364	4134	438	4974	510	5792	652	7404	789	8960
10	-12	55	619	149	1692	241	2737	329	3736	413	4690	497	5644	579	6675	740	8403	896	10175
5	-15	61	693	167	1896	269	3055	369	4190	463	5258	557	6325	648	7359	828	9403	1003	11390
0	-18	68	767	185	2101	298	3384	408	4633	512	5814	616	6995	717	8142	916	10402	1109	12594
-5	-21	74	839	203	2305	326	3702	447	5076	561	6371	675	7665	786	8926	1004	11401	1216	13809
-10	-23	80	913	220	2498	355	4031	486	5519	610	6927	734	8335	855	9709	1092	12401	1322	15013
-15	-26	87	986	238	2703	384	4361	525	5962	659	7484	793	9005	924	10493	1180	13400	1429	16228
-20	-29	93	1060	256	2907	412	4679	564	6405	708	8040	852	9675	992	11265	1268	14399	1536	17443
-25	-32	100	1134	273	3100	441	5008	604	6859	758	8508	912	10357	1061	12049	1356	15399	1642	18647
-30	-34	106	1206	291	3205	469	5326	643	7302	807	9164	971	11027	1130	12832	1444	16398	1749	19862
-40	-40	119	1355	327	3713	526	5973	721	8188	905	10277	1089	12367	1268	14399	1620	18397	1962	22809
-50	-46	132	1498	362	4111	584	6632	799	9073	1003	11390	1207	13707	1406	15967	1796	20395	2175	24699
-60	-51	145	1648	397	4508	641	7279	878	9971	1102	12514	1326	15058	1544	17534	1972	22394	2389	27129

Heat loss for a given capacity with a different radiating surface than shown above is obtained by multiplying the radiating surface by the tabulated heat loss per sq ft for the atmospheric temperature involved. The minimum radiation surface area is the wetted surface exposed to atmosphere. No heat loss is figured for tank bottoms resting on grade.

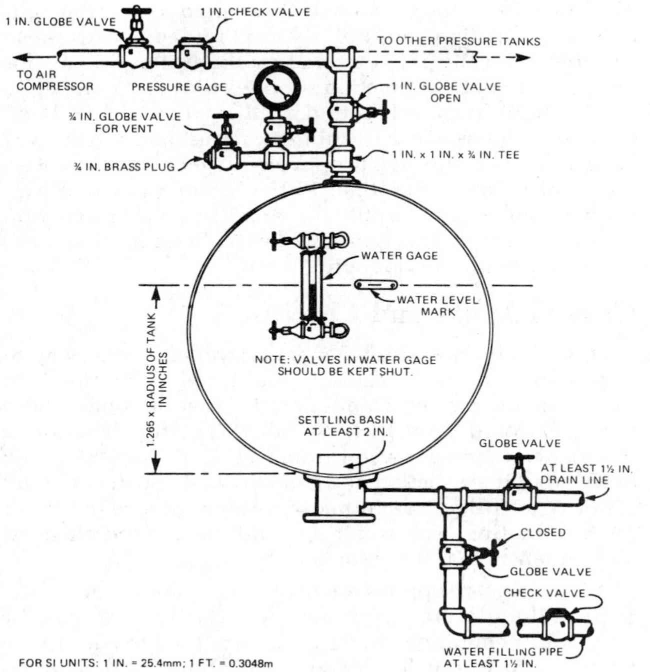

FIG. 5-5I. A typical pressure tank installation.

If the bank is below the top line of sprinklers, P_2, the required residual pressure would be increased 0.434 psi for every foot (0.912 kPa/m) of head represented in the distance between the base of the tank and the highest sprinkler. If we call this head *H*, we have

$$P_1 = P_2 \times \frac{V_2}{V_1} = (30 + 0.434H)\frac{V_2}{V_1}.$$

Gage pressure to be carried in the tank would be P_1–15, or

$$(30 + 0.434H)\frac{V_2}{V_1} - 15.$$

For a tank 1/3 full of air $\frac{V_2}{V_1}$–3, and gage pressure would be 3(30 + 0.434H) –15 = 75 + 1.30 H.

For a tank 1/2 full of air $\frac{V_2}{V_1}$–2, and gage pressure would be 2(30 + 0.434H) – 15 = 45 + 0.87H.

Air Lock

A condition known as air lock can occur when a pressure tank and a gravity tank are connected to a sprinkler system through a common riser. Air lock occurs if the gravity water pressure at the gravity tank check valve is less than the air pressure trapped in the pressure tank and the common riser by a column of water in the sprinkler system, after water has been drained from the pressure tank. For instance, if the pressure tank is kept two-thirds full of water with an air pressure of 75 psi (517 kPa), and a sprinkler opens 35 ft (10.5 m) or more above the point where connections from both tanks enter the common riser supplying the sprinkler system, the pressure tank drains, leaving an air pressure of 15 psi (103 kPa) balanced by a column of water of equal pressure [35 ft (10.5 m) head] in the sprinkler system. The gravity tank check valve is held closed unless the water pressure from the gravity tank is more than 15 psi (103 kPa) [35 ft (10.5 m) head].

Air lock can be prevented by increasing the volume of water and decreasing the air pressure in the pressure tank so that little or no air pressure remains after water has been exhausted. For example, if the pressure tank is kept four-fifths full of water, with an air pressure of 60 psi (414 kPa), the air pressure remaining in the tank after water has been drained is zero, and the gravity tank check valve opens as soon as the pressure at that point from the pressure tank drops below the static head from the gravity tank.

TABLE 5-5G. *Typical Dimensions of Horizontal Pressure Tanks of Standard Sizes*

Approx Gross Capacity		Approx Net Cap ⅔ Full		Inside Diam		Inside Length		Approx Wt of Water ⅔ Full	
Gal	L	Gal	L	in.	m	Ft	m	Lbs	Kg
3,000	11355	2,000	7570	60	1.5	20.2	6.2	16,670	7568
3,000	11355	2,000	7570	66	1.7	17.0	5.2	16,670	7568
3,000	11355	2,000	7570	72	1.8	14.2	4.3	16,670	7568
4,500	17033	3,000	11355	66	1.7	25.4	7.7	25,000	11350
4,500	17033	3,000	11355	72	1.8	21.3	6.5	25,000	11350
4,500	17033	3,000	11355	78	2.0	18.2	5.5	25,000	11350
6,000	22710	4,000	15140	72	1.8	28.2	8.6	33,340	15136
6,000	22710	4,000	15140	78	2.0	24.2	7.4	33,340	15136
6,000	22710	4,000	15140	84	2.1	21.0	6.4	33,340	15136
7,500	28388	5,000	18925	78	2.0	30.3	9.2	41,670	18918
7,500	28388	5,000	18925	84	2.1	26.2	8.0	41,670	18918
7,500	28388	5,000	18925	90	2.3	22.7	6.9	41,670	18918
9,000	34065	6,000	22710	84	2.1	31.4	9.6	50,000	22700
9,000	34065	6,000	22710	90	2.3	27.3	8.3	50,000	22700
9,000	34065	6,000	22710	96	2.4	24.0	7.3	50,000	22700

Note: 4,500 gals (17 m3) gross capacity is the minimum ordinarily accepted for pressure tanks for automatic sprinkler systems.
In the above table the length of the tank has been figured as though the ends were flat instead of dished.
The actual length of tanks of the above capacities and diameters will therefore be slightly greater.

Air lock may be conveniently prevented in new equipment by connecting the gravity tank and pressure tank discharge pipes together 40 ft (12 m) or more below the bottom of the gravity tank. (See Figure 5-5J.)

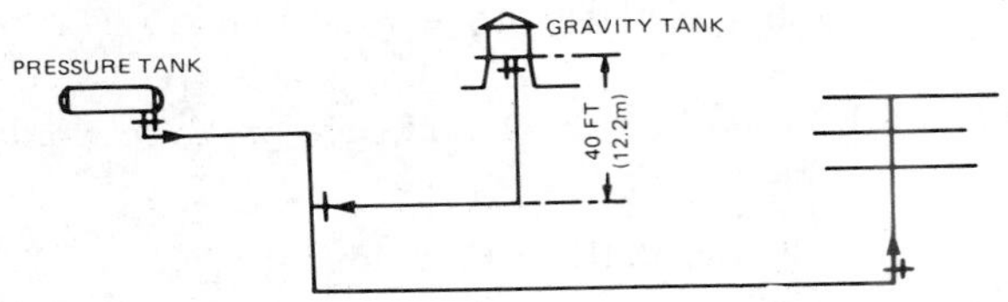

FIG. 5-5J. A gravity tank and a pressure tank showing how risers are connected to avoid air lock.

Construction of Pressure Tanks

Standard pressure tanks are constructed in accordance with the ASME *Boiler and Pressure Vessel Code*,[8] with modifications given in NFPA 22, *Water Tanks for Private Fire Protection.* Important modifications are a minimum hydrostatic test at 150 psi (1034 kPa) and a test for tightness.

Tanks should be located in substantial noncombustible housings unless they are within a heated room in a building. They should be large enough to provide free access to all connections, fittings, and manholes, with at least 3 ft (0.9 m) of clearance around the valves and gages and at least 18 in. (451 mm) around the rest of the tank. The distance between the floor and any part of a tank should be at least 3 ft (0.9 m).

The interiors of pressure tanks are inspected at three-year intervals to determine if corrosion is taking place and if repainting or repairing is needed. When necessary, tanks should be scraped, wire brushed, and repainted with an approved metal protective paint. Relief valves should be tested at least once each month.

Provisions should be made to drain each tank independently of all other tanks and have the sprinkler system drained by a pipe not less than 1½ in. (38 mm) in diameter.

The filling supply or pump should be reliable and capable of replenishing the water to be maintained in the tank against the normal tank pressure in not more than four hours.

NATURAL AND CONSTRUCTED SUCTION FACILITIES

The advantages of piped systems make them the first choice for a water supply for fire protection, but sometimes other water may be more convenient or less expensive.

Examples are suburbs or farms and resorts that are not near a community with a piped water system for fire protection. In many of these, however, water is available for fire protection in the ocean, lakes and ponds, rivers, and streams. Cisterns or tanks can be used at locations distant from natural water sources. Water that is provided for other uses in fairly large quantities, such as the stock tanks on a farm, can be used for fire protection if the tanks are kept full. Conversely, small ponds in parks and swimming pools are not particularly good sources of emergency water because this competes with their regular purposes.

For water sources such as those mentioned, the general term "suction supplies" is used to distinguish these supplies from the conventional public water systems for fire protection. Static suction supplies must, in general, be used where they are found. While there have been instances where water in suburbs, farms, and forests was used to provide effective fire streams at very long distances, laying hose lines more than 750 to 1000 ft (225 to 300 m) seldom makes it possible to provide good protection because of the time required to lay the long lines and the greater difficulty in operating them.

Ground Tanks and Cisterns

If no hydrant on a water system is available, one way to ensure the amount of water required for fire fighting is to store it in underground tanks or cisterns at locations where hydrants would normally be installed. The fire department pumper can then get water from a connection on the tank or by dropping a suction hose into the tank. Such tanks and cisterns are filled from domestic water sources too small for fire fighting. The water does not have to be changed so frequently that it presents difficulties.

Static water supplies are of obvious value in suburban, farm, and forest areas, but they are equally important for emergency conditions in cities. Before the present public water systems were developed, some cities provided underground reservoirs or cisterns for fire protection. When water was needed for fire fighting, a pumper suction hose was simply dropped through a manhole. Some of these cisterns are still used in San Francisco and Chicago. Even though San Francisco has a regular water system and a separate system of high-pressure mains, it has been considered prudent, because of the threat of earthquake, to keep over 100 cisterns in service, most of which hold 75,000 gal (284 m^3). Some of the oldest cisterns have brick walls. Newer ones are reinforced concrete.

Rivers and Ponds

Rivers and ponds are important auxiliary water sources, but merely because the water can be seen does not mean that it can be used for fire fighting. These sources of water must have suitable approaches so that fire apparatus can get near the water without becoming mired. A cleared space and some fill in many cases will provide access. These sources must be studied to determine that the water is available all year round and to select the best possible approach. They should also be recorded and mapped and given periodic attention in much the same manner that hydrants are maintained.

At such locations, it is usually necessary to provide a basin or cistern into which water can flow and the pumper suction strainer can be placed. There should be a screen or weir so that large objects will not interfere with the suction strainer. In some places, a permanent suction pipe and strainer can be installed. The details of such an arrangement are the same as those for a fire pump operating under a lift. The suction pipe should be laid with enough cover so that it will not freeze. It can be connected at the top to a hydrant with one or more pumper suction connections.

Small Streams and Brooks

Where water supply comes from a brook or stream, it is usually best to drain the water into a sump rather than attempt to use it straight from the flowing stream. If there is a marshy bank or shore, it may be best to go out into the pond or stream to a point where water can be collected in a sump. From the sump in the pond or stream, a pipe should be laid for draining to another sump, the latter located near where the fire apparatus will stand.

In some sumps, and particularly in open water that freezes over in winter, covers may not be feasible at the point where the sump is provided for pumper suction. At such locations, an anchored plug of wood can be floated where the pumper suction should be taken. Such a plug should have a minimum diameter larger than the pumper suction hose and be tapered so that, when frozen in ice, it can be driven down and out of position with a sledge hammer.

In some parts of the country, streams do not flow continuously. A covered cistern of generous capacity may be filled when water flows. Thus, the water may be stored for a longer period than it would keep in an open reservoir.

Water from streams and ponds is more important in areas without public water systems than in a city. There are small groups of farm buildings and small communities where even a brook, if dammed, and with a proper pumper approach and a suction basin, can provide good protection at little cost.

For projects in which a stream will be dammed to form static water, experienced local engineers should be consulted. Details of the dam construction and decisions about the amount of water to be impounded depend upon many factors and may require a comprehensive engineering survey. Its effect on users of the stream and flood conditions also have to be considered.

Harbors and Rivers

The principal problem with using harbors and rivers as suction supplies is that their water levels change. In harbors, ocean tide levels vary continuously throughout any given 24-hr period. River water levels are seasonal, but the problem is generally the same.

Where there is little fluctuation in the level of a natural water source, a simple pier or platform may be all that is needed to make the water available. If a pumper can be driven onto a sturdy pier, it can go to work when its suction line is dropped over the side. But where the water level varies, special arrangements are needed. If the water is always deep enough for drafting, a hinged ramp leading down to a large float is feasible. But more common is a sloping beach down which the water recedes too far to be accessible at all times. Reservoirs that can be filled at high tide are one solution to this problem.

Where a bridge passes over tidewater, water can be obtained by permanently installing a deep-well pump with a discharge pipe to a point convenient for fire department pumper use. The most practical way to use tidewater supplies is to provide pumps on boats, supplementary to any fireboats in service. Relatively large quantities of water for fire fighting can be obtained from river and harbor sources because large-capacity pumps are normally provided on fireboats, and where there are no fireboats, large pumps can be installed on a boat or barge and pressed into use to supply water for fire protection. To use the water on land, it is necessary to provide a place at which a fireboat or a barge with pumps can tie up and discharge into tanks or a special pipe system with hydrants from which land-based pumping equipment can take the water.

Wells

Wells have become increasingly popular for both domestic use and fire supply for industrial sites, shopping centers, etc., located beyond the reach of a piped water supply. Before a well is constructed, a thorough examination of the groundwater must be made. This examination generally includes an aquifer performance analysis and a review of the history of nearby wells. The water in the ground must be of sufficient capacity and dependability, and of reasonably good quality.

A vertical shaft turbine pump is used to draw the water from wells into the fire system or into a storage tank.

BIBLIOGRAPHY

References Cited

1. AWWA D100-84 (AWS D5.2-84), *Standard for Welded Steel Tanks for Water Storage,* American Water Works Association, Denver, CO.
2. AWWA D103-87, *Standard for Factory-Coated Bolted Steel Tanks for Water Storage,* American Water Works Association, Denver, CO.
3. AWS D5.2, *Structural Welding Code, Steel*, American Welding Society, Miami, FL, 1984.
4. ACI 318-1983, *Building Code Requirements for Reinforced Concrete,* American Concrete Institute, Detroit, MI.
5. ACI 301, *Specification for Structural Concrete for Buildings,* American Concrete Institute, Detroit, MI.
6. *Standard Specifications of the American Wood Preservers Association,* American Wood Preservers Association, Washington, DC, 1983.
7. *Testing and Monitoring Program for Solar-Heated Water Storage Tanks,* Prepared for the National Research Council of Canada, Ottawa, Ontario, 1984.
8. *Boiler and Pressure Vessel Code,* American Society of Mechanical Engineers, New York, 1983.

NFPA Codes, Standards, and Recommended Practices

Reference to the following NFPA codes, standards, and recommended practices will provide further information on water storage facilities and suction supplies discussed in this chapter. (See the latest *NFPA Catalog* for availability of current editions of the following documents.)

NFPA 13, *Installation of Sprinkler Systems.*

NFPA 22, *Water Tanks for Private Fire Protection.*

Additional Reading

"Embankment Supported Fabric Tanks," *Loss Prevention Data 3-4*, Factory Mutual Research Corp., Norwood, MA, Apr. 1971.

"Isothermal Map for Europe," *Loss Prevention Data* 3-2S, Factory Mutual Research Corp., Norwood, MA, 1978.

"Lined Earth Reservoirs for Fire Protection," *Loss Prevention Data 3-6*, Factory Mutual Research Corp., Norwood, 1977.

"Water Tanks for Fire Protection," *Loss Prevention Data* 3-2, Factory Mutual Research Corp., Dec. 1977.

FIRE PUMPS

Revised by W. L. Ingles

This chapter covers the operating principles of stationary pumps used for fire protection, the methods of driving and controlling them, and the testing and maintenance procedures that should be followed to keep them in top operating condition.

Fire pumps are used to enhance the water supply pressure available from public mains, gravity tanks, reservoirs, or other sources. The first modern fire pumps were the wheel-and-crank reciprocating-type, belt-driven from mill machinery. If plant operations were stopped during a fire, the pump could not operate. At best, these pumps were inadequate.

Better water supplies became necessary as automatic sprinkler systems became more common, and mill pumps were replaced by rotary, or displacement, pumps driven by friction drive from horizontal water wheels supplying power to the plant. As steam supplanted water power, the reciprocating steam pump was adopted for fire protection. For many years the Underwriter duplex, double-acting, direct-steam-driven unit was universally accepted as the "standard" fire pump.

Today, the centrifugal fire pump is standard. (See Figures 5-6A and 5-6B.) Its compactness, reliability, easy maintenance, and hydraulic characteristics, and the variety of available drivers—electric motors, steam turbines, and internal combustion engines—have made the Underwriter pump obsolete, although not entirely extinct.

The NFPA standard on fire pumps is NFPA 20, *Installation of Centrifugal Fire Pumps*. Other NFPA documents that contain information on fire pumps include NFPA 11, *Low Expansion Foam and Combined Agent Systems*; NFPA 11A, *Medium- and High-Expansion Foam Systems*; NFPA 13, *Installation of Sprinkler Systems*; NFPA 13A, *Inspection, Testing, and Maintenance of Sprinkler Systems*; NFPA 13D, *Installation of Sprinkler Systems in One- and Two-Family Dwellings and Mobile Homes*; NFPA 13E, *Fire Department Operations in Properties Protected by Sprinkler and Standpipe Systems*; NFPA 14, *Installation of Standpipe and Hose Systems*; NFPA 14A, *Testing, Inspection, and Maintenance of Standpipe and Hose Systems*; NFPA 15, *Water-Spray Fixed Systems for Fire Protection*; NFPA 16, *Deluge Foam-Water Sprinkler and Foam-Water Spray Systems*; NFPA 16A, *Installation of Closed-Head Foam-Water Sprinkler Systems*; NFPA 22, *Water Tanks for Private Fire Protection*; NFPA 24, *Private Fire Service Mains and Their Appurtenances*; and NFPA 26, *Supervision of Valves Controlling Water Supplies for Fire Protection*.

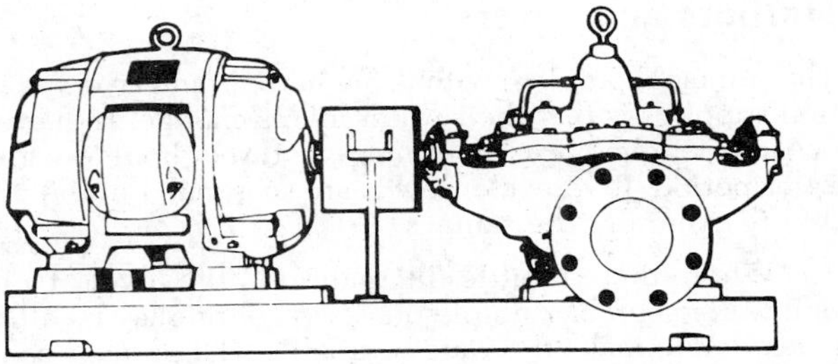

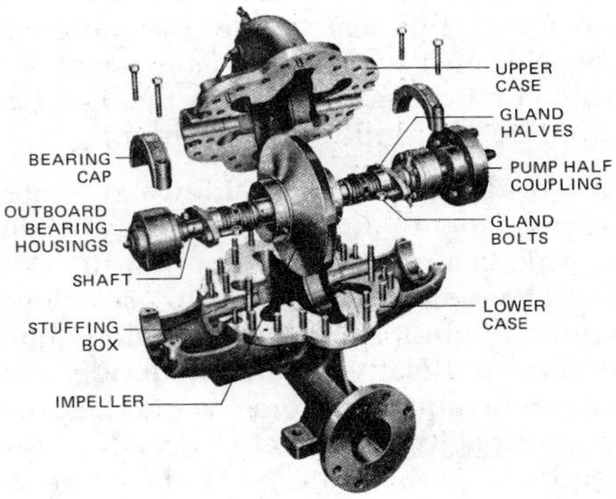

FIG. 5-6A. A horizontal shaft single-stage centrifugal pump, with cutaway view of the pump. (Source: Peerless Pump)

W. L. Ingles, P.E., is a fire protection engineer for Duke Power Co., Charlotte, NC.

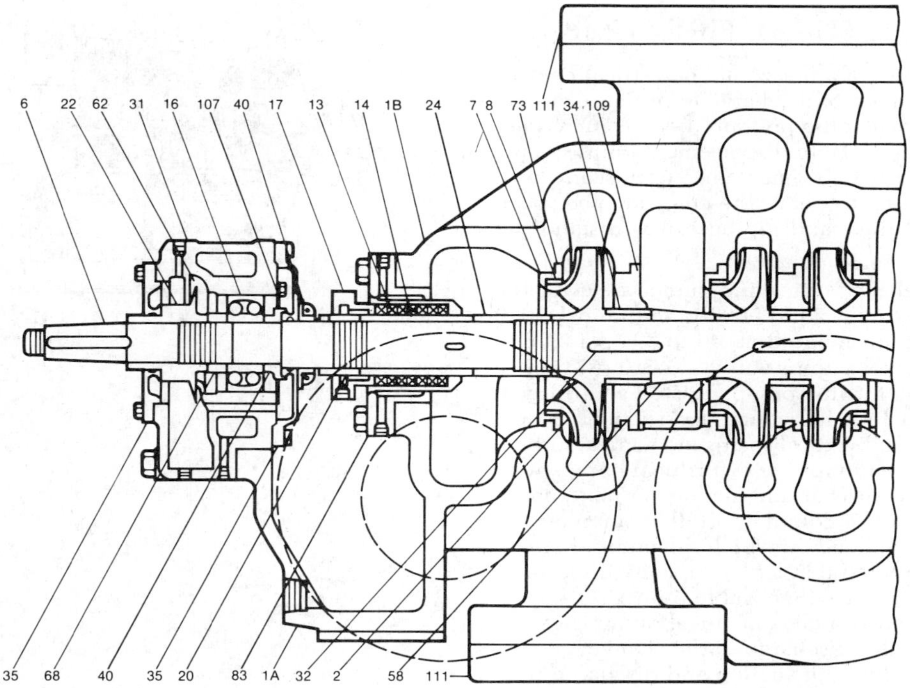

1A Casing, Lower Half
1B Casing, Upper Half
2 Impeller
5 Diffuser
6 Shaft, Pump
7 Ring, Casing
8 Ring, Impeller
13 Packing
14 Sleeve, Shaft
16 Bearing, Inboard
17 Gland
18 Bearing, Outboard
20 Nut, Shaft Sleeve
22 Locknut, Bearing
24 Nut, Impeller
31 Housing, Bearing, Inboard
32 Key, Impeller
33 Housing, Bearing, Outboard
34 Sleeve, Impeller Hub
35 Cover, Bearing, Inboard
37 Cover, Bearing, Outboard
40 Deflector
45 Cover, Oil, Bearing Cap
56 Disc or Drum, Balancing
58 Sleeve, Interstage
62 Thrower (Oil or Grease)
63 Bushing, Stuffing Box
68 Collar, Shaft
72 Collar, Thrust
73 Gasket
83 Stuffing Box
107 Shield, Oil Retaining
109 Diaphragm, Interstage
111 Crossover, Interstage
113 Bushing, Interstage Diaphragm
115 Ring, Balancing
117 Bushing, Pressure Reducing
119 Coupling, Oil Pump
121 Pump, Oil

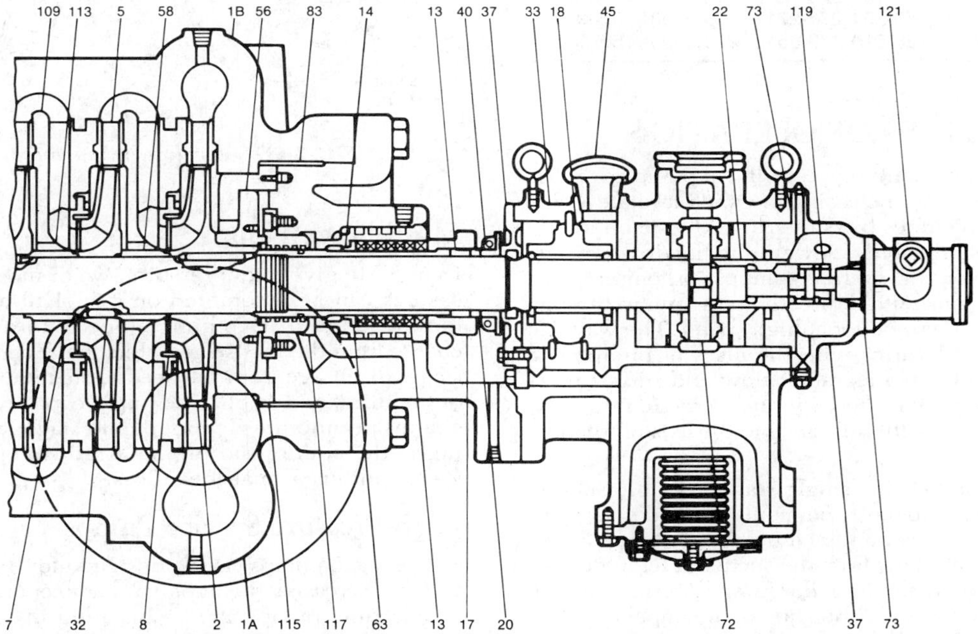

***FIG. 5-6B.* Cross section of a typical multi-stage centrifugal pump. The numbers shown on this drawing do not necessarily represent standard part numbers in use by any manufacturer.**

THE CENTRIFUGAL FIRE PUMP

An outstanding feature of a horizontal or vertical centrifugal pump is the relation of discharge to pressure at constant speed, that, as when the pressure head is increased, the discharge is reduced. With displacement pumps, however, the rated capacity can be maintained against any head if the power is adequate to operate the pump at rated speed and if the pump, fittings, and piping can withstand the pressure.

Listed horizontal and vertical fire pumps are available with rated capacities from 25 to 5000 gpm (95 to 18 925 L/min). Pressure ratings range from 40 to 394 psi (276 to 2758 kPa) for horizontal pumps and 26 to 510 psi (517 to 3448 kPa) for vertical turbine pumps. Listed centrifugal fire pump designs include horizontal-end-suction, in-line, split-case (horizontal and vertical shaft), and vertical-turbine types. Vertical turbine pumps are centrifugal pumps with one or more impellers discharging into one or more bowls and a vertical educator or column pipe that connects the bowls to the discharge head on which the pump driver is mounted. It is anticipated that larger-capacity fire pumps will be listed in the future. (See Table 5-6A.)

The "size" of a horizontal centrifugal pump is generally the diameter of the discharge outlet. However, it is sometimes indicated by both suction and discharge pipe flange diameters. The size of a vertical turbine pump is the diameter of the pump bowl. (See Figure 5-6C.)

TABLE 5-6A ***Pump Types and Their Pressure and Capacity Ranges***

Pump Type	Pressure Range PSI	Pressure Range kPa	Capacity Range gpm	Capacity Range L/s
Horizontal-End-Suction	40-186	276-1282	25-499	1.6-31.5
In-line	40-186	276-1296	25-499	1.6-31.5
Split case	40-294	276-2717	150-5000	9.5-315.4
Vertical turbine	26-510	179-3516	250-5000	15.8-315.4

PRINCIPLES OF OPERATION

The two major components of a centrifugal pump are a disc called the impeller and the casing in which it rotates. (See Figure 5-6D.) It operates by converting kinetic energy to velocity and pressure energy. Power from the driver, which is an electric motor, an internal combustion engine, or a steam turbine, is transmitted directly to the pump through the shaft, rotating the impeller at high speed. The way that energy is converted varies with the class of pump. The major classes are known as radial flow and mixed flow. These pumps are identified by the direction of flow through the impeller with reference to the axis of rotation. (See Figure 5-6E.)

The horizontal-shaft, single-stage, double-suction volute pump is the type most commonly applied to fire protection service and to commercial use. (See Figure 5-6A.) In these pumps, waterflow from the suction inlet in the casing divides and enters the impeller from each side through an opening called the "eye." Rotation of the impeller drives the water by centrifugal force from the eye to the rim and through the casing volute to the pump discharge outlet. The kinetic energy acquired by the water in its passage through the impeller is converted to pressure energy by gradual reduction of velocity in the volute.

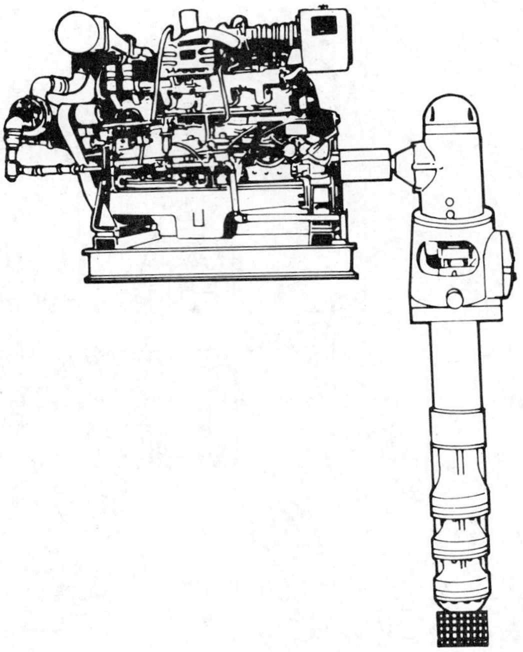

FIG. 5-6C. A vertical turbine fire pump with a right-angle gear and engine drive. (Source: Peerless Pump)

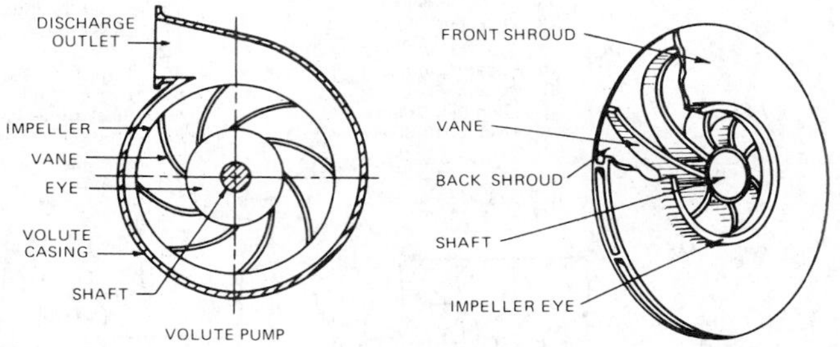

FIG. 5-6D. A volute casing and impeller.

Multi-Stage Pumps

In order to give high pressure, two or more impellers and casings can be assembled on one shaft as a single unit, forming a multi-stage pump. (See Figure 5-6B.) The discharge from the first stage enters the suction of the second stage, discharge from the second stage enters the suction of the third, and so on. The pump capacity is the rating in gallons per minute (L/min) of one stage; the pressure rating is the sum of the pressure ratings of the individual stages, minus a small head loss.

High-Pressure Service Pumps

Single-stage pumps can be designed for high-pressure service by increasing the impeller diameter or the rated speed. In addition, pumps can be installed in series to achieve the necessary pressure. In some high-rise buildings, vertical turbine pumps are installed in a sub-basement and take suction from a sump pit. As shown in Table 5-6A, these pumps are capable of developing pressures in excess of 500 psi (527 kPa).

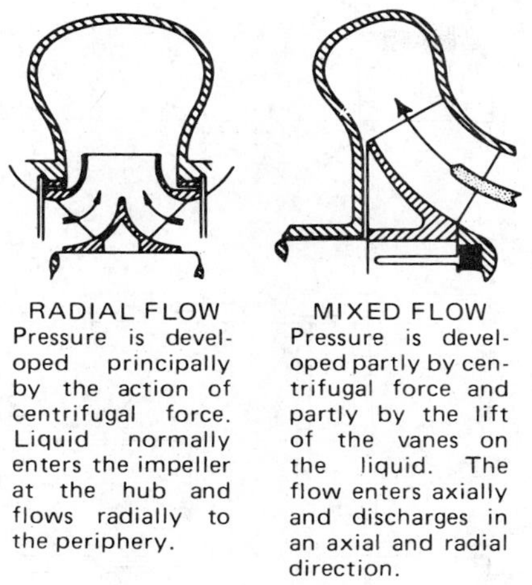

FIG. 5-6E. The two major classes of fire pumps.

CHARACTERISTIC PUMP CURVES

The characteristic curves (Figure 5-6F) of a horizontal-centrifugal- or a vertical-turbine-type pump are:

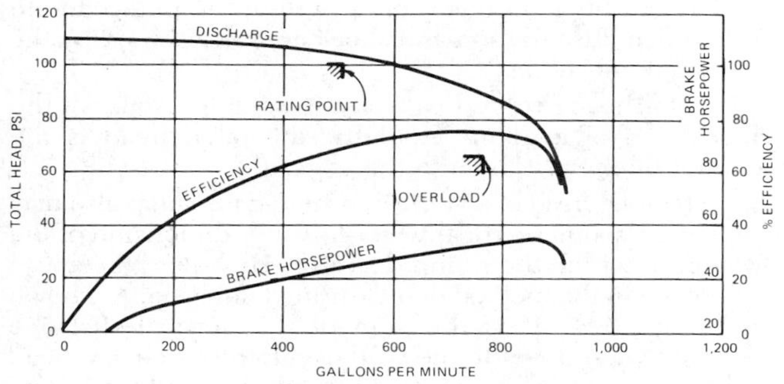

FIG. 5-6F. Typical fire pump characteristic curves. Illustrated curves are for a 500-gpm, 100-psi, 2000-rpm, gasoline-engine-drive pump with a 14-in. impeller and a maximum suction lift of 6.4 ft. Note that the shutoff point is 110 psi, the maximum brake horsepower is 55, and the maximum efficiency is 75 percent at overload capacity. Head is 90 psi over the 65 percent minimum required. SI units: 1 psi = 6.89 kPa; 1 gpm = 0.38 L/min.

1. Total head *vs* discharge (feet of head or pounds per square inch of pressure vs gallons per minute).
2. Brake horsepower *vs* discharge.
3. Efficiency *vs* discharge $\left(\dfrac{\text{Water Hp}}{\text{Input Hp}}\ vs\ \text{gpm}\right)$

These curves assume that the pump is operated at a constant speed equal to its rated rpm (revolutions per minute). In actual service, however, the speed of the driver may vary with changes in the load.

The flow and pressure ratings of commercial pumps are usually established on the basis of maximum efficiency and desired speed. Impellers can be designed for flat, medium, or steep head-discharge characteristics, as required for various uses. Figure 5-6G illustrates how the head-discharge curve is affected by the diameter of the eye, the width of the impeller, the number of vanes, and the shape or angle of the vanes.

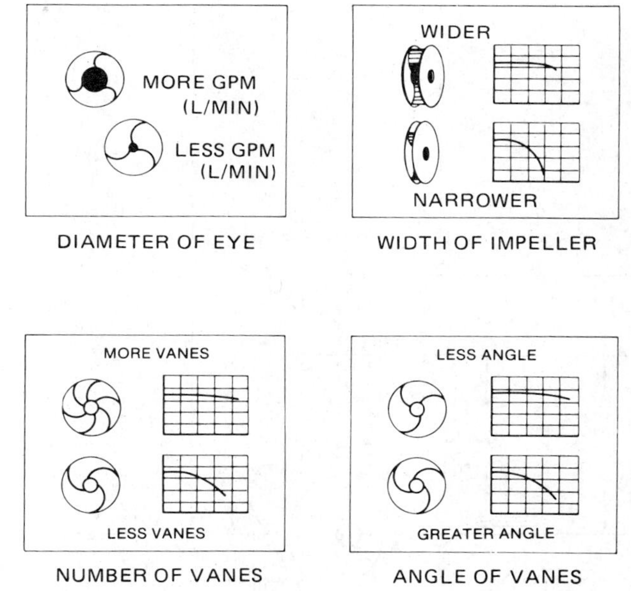

FIG. 5-6G. Effect of impeller design on head-discharge curves for fire pumps.

TOTAL HEAD

The total head of a pump is the energy imparted to the liquid as it passes through the pump. It may be expressed in various units of pressure, but for fire protection it is generally given in pounds per square inch (psi) or kilopascals (kPa), or in feet (ft) or meters (m) of liquid measured vertically. The total head is calculated by subtracting the energy in the incoming liquid from the energy in the discharging liquid. The total head (H) of a pump is calculated by the formula:

$$H = h_d + h_{vd} - h_s - h_{vs}$$

in which:

H = total head, feet (m)
h_d = discharge head, feet (m)
$h_{vd} = \dfrac{v_d^2}{2g}$ = discharge velocity head, feet (m)
h_s = suction head, feet (m)
$h_{vs} = \dfrac{v_v^2}{2g}$ = suction velocity head, feet (m)
v = average velocity, feet per second (m/sec)
g = acceleration due to gravity, 32.2 ft/sec² (9.81 m/sec²).

For a horizontal split-case pump, the individual heads (h_v) are measured at the pump discharge nozzle flange and at the suction flange. (See Figure 5-6H.) The heads are read from pressure gages attached to the pump flanges. The velocity head must be calculated for the volume of liquid passing through the flanges:

$$\left(h_v = \frac{v^2}{2g}\right)$$

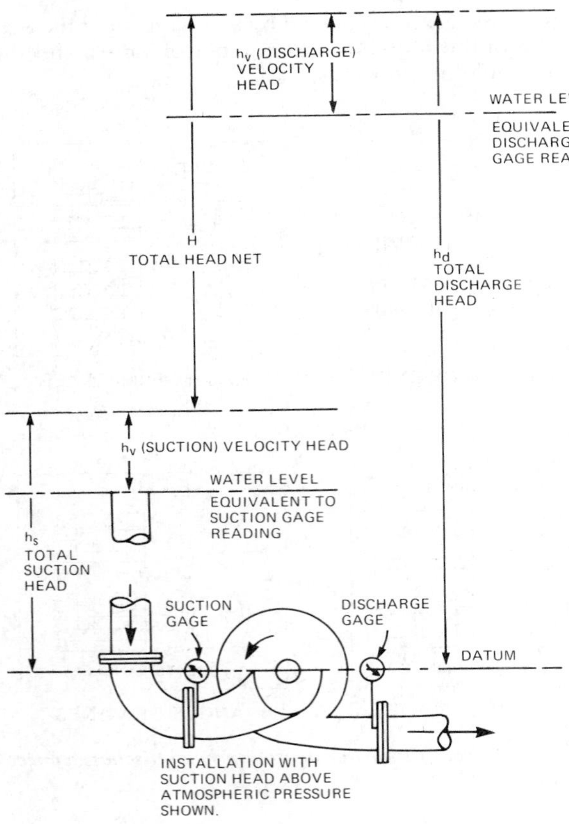

FIG. 5-6H. Typical head of horizontal shaft centrifugal fire pumps.

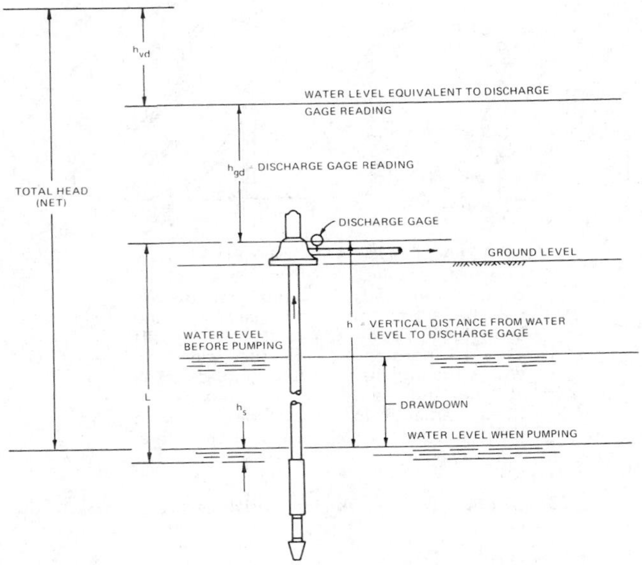

FIG. 5-6I. Total head of vertical-turbine-type fire pumps.

If the flanges have the same diameters, there will be no difference between the incoming and outgoing velocity, and the calculation can be omitted.

For a vertical turbine pump, the discharge head is theoretically read at the discharge flange of the pump. Since this flange usually is inaccessible for gage readings, a gage is used at the discharge fitting at the top of the pump column pipe. (See Figure 5-6I.) The discharge pressure at the pump discharge flange therefore equals the pressure at the gage above, plus the pressure effect of the vertical distance between the two points, plus the friction loss between the two points. In most cases, the friction loss is so small that it may be disregarded.

The suction head is the vertical distance from water level to the pump discharge flange. The velocity head of the incoming liquid is assumed to be zero. Hence, the formula would now take the following form:

$$H = h_d + h_{vd} - h_s$$
$$= (h_{gd} + L) + h_{vd} - h_s$$

where:

h_{gd} = discharge gage reading, feet (m)
L = gage to pump flange, feet (m)
h_s = water level when pumping to pump flange, feet (m).

However $L - h_s = h$ = the vertical distance between the discharge gage and water level.

Therefore the formula becomes:

$$H = h_{gd} + h_{vd} + h$$

Hydraulic and power losses within the pump due to turbulence, disc friction and shock are represented by the efficiency rating.

Total head at rated capacity is used to establish the rated head of a pump. Actually, the rated head is the amount of energy given to the water.

The total head of a vertical-turbine-type pump also may be defined as the vertical water-to-water dimension of the system in which the pump operates. However, there is a difference in the method of measuring total head. As shown in Figure 5-6I, it is the sum of the vertical distance between water level in the well or pit, the discharge head indicated by the gage on the pump outlet, and the velocity head at the gage connection.

SPECIFIC SPEED (N_s)

Specific speed is a number relating the head, capacity, and speed of a centrifugal pump for design purposes. Actually, specific speed is the revolutions per minute of a geometrically similar impeller that will discharge 1 gpm (3.8 L/min) at 1 ft (0.3 m) total head. The formula for calculating specific speed of a centrifugal pump is:

$$N_s = \frac{rpm \times gpm^{1/2}}{H^{3/4}}$$

where:

N_s is the specific speed number, and
H is the head in feet (m).

When values of head, speed, and capacity in the formula correspond to pump performance at optimum efficiency, the specific speed is an index to the type of pump. Impellers for high heads usually have low specific speeds, and impellers for low heads have high specific speeds.

A pump of low specific speed will operate satisfactorily with greater suction lift than a pump of the same head and capacity with a higher specific speed. Experience shows that specific speed is a useful guide for determining maximum suction lift or minimum suction head.

When suction lift exceeds 15 ft (4.5 m), it may be necessary to provide a larger pump at less speed. With low lift or positive head on the suction, a smaller pump operating at greater speed may be used. Abnormally high suction lifts may seriously reduce pump capacity and efficiency or cause excessive vibration and cavitation.

NET POSITIVE SUCTION HEAD

Net positive suction head (NPSH) is the pressure head that causes liquid to flow through the suction pipe and fittings into the eye of a pump impeller. The pump itself has no ability to "lift," and the suction pressure depends on the nature of the supply.

If a pump is supplied from a pond, stream, open well, or uncovered reservoir where the water level is below the pump, the suction head is atmospheric pressure minus the lift. If the water level is above the pump, as from a water main, penstock, or aboveground tank, the suction head is atmospheric pressure plus static pressure.

Pressure readings at the inlet flange of a pump operating under lift are negative with respect to the gage, but positive when referred to absolute pressure. Hence the expression, "net positive suction head." Absolute pressure is gage pressure plus barometric pressure.

There are two kinds of NPSH to consider. Pump NPSH is a function of the pump design and varies with the capacity and speed of any one pump and with the designs of different pumps. Curves of NPSH *vs* gallons per minute usually can be obtained from pump manufacturers. (See Figure 5-6J.) Available NPSH is a function of the system in which the pump operates and can be calculated readily.

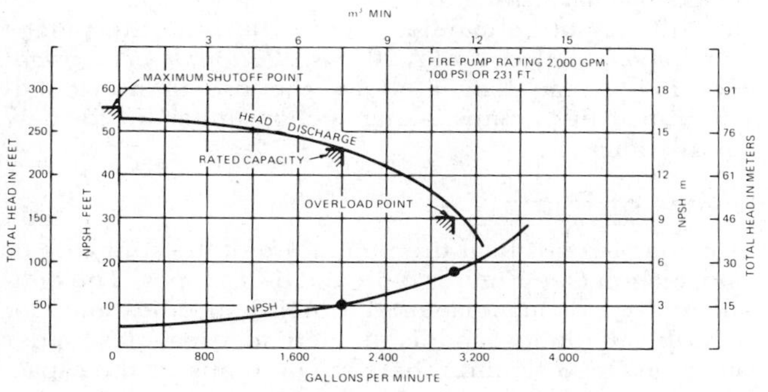

FIG. 5-6J. NPSH curve of a typical fire pump. Note that the required NPSH at 2000 gpm is 10 ft and 18 ft at 3000 gpm. SI units: 1 gpm = 0.38 L/min; 1 ft = 0.30 m.

When the water source is above the pump, available NPSH = atmospheric pressure (ft or m) + static head on suction (ft or m) – friction and fitting losses in suction piping (ft or m) – vapor pressure of liquid (ft or m). Note that the vapor pressure of water at 90°F (32°C) is 1.6 ft (0.48 m).When the water source is below the pump, available NPSH = atmospheric pressure (ft or m) – static lift (ft or m) – friction loss in piping and head loss in the fittings (ft or m)—vapor pressure of liquid (ft or m).

For any pump installation, the available system NPSH must be equal to or greater than the pump NPSH at the desired operating conditions.

CAVITATION

Cavitation is a complex phenomenon that may take place in pumps or other hydraulic equipment. As liquid flows through the suction line of a centrifugal pump and enters the eye of the impeller, the velocity increases and pressure decreases. If the pressure falls below the vapor pressure corresponding to the temperature of the liquid, pockets of vapor will form. When the vapor pockets in the flowing liquid reach a region of higher pressure, they collapse with a hammer effect, causing noise and vibration. Tests have shown that the extremely high instantaneous pressures that may be developed in this manner, may pit various parts of the pump casing and impeller. Conditions may be mild or severe, and mild cavitation may occur without much noise. Severe cavitation can cause reduced efficiency and, ultimately, failure of the pump if it is not corrected.

AFFINITY LAWS

The mathematical relationships among head, capacity, brake horsepower, and impeller diameter are called affinity laws. Law 1 assumes constant impeller diameter with change of speed. Law 2 assumes constant speed with change in diameter of the impeller. These laws are expressed by proportion as follows:

Law 1.

$$\frac{Q_1}{Q_2} = \frac{N_1}{N_2} \qquad \frac{H_1}{H_2} = \frac{N_1^2}{N_2^2} \qquad \frac{\text{bhp}_1}{\text{bph}_2} = \frac{N_1^3}{N_2^3}$$

Law 2.

$$\frac{Q_1}{Q_2} = \frac{D_1}{D_2} \qquad \frac{H_1}{H_2} = \frac{D_1^2}{D_2^2} \qquad \frac{\text{bhp}_1}{\text{bph}_2} = \frac{D_1^3}{D_2^3}$$

The nomenclature for the relationship is: Q = capacity; H = head; N = speed; D = impeller diameter; and bhp = brake horsepower. Thus:

Q_1 = gpm (L/min) at N_1 or D_1 $\quad$ Q_2 = gpm (L/min) at N_2 or D_2

H_1 = head in ft (m) at N_1 or D_1 $\quad$ H_2 = head in ft (m) at N_2 or D_2

bhp_1 = brake horsepower (kW) at N_1 or D_1 $\quad$ bhp_2 = brake horsepower (kW) at N_2 or D_2.

Law 1 applies to common types of pumps, including horizontal centrifugal pumps and vertical turbine pumps. Law 2 applies to centrifugal pumps with reasonably close agreement between calculated and tested performance. Generally, pumps with low specific speeds show closer agreement than pumps with high specific speeds.

The affinity laws should be applied when proposed changes in a fire pump installation would increase the speed or significantly raise the pressure of the suction supply. Greater speed would increase the power demand, and high discharge pressure might be undesirable. In some instances, it is possible to trim the impeller or to install a speed-reducing gear between the pump and driver. However, this should not be done without the approval of the pump manufacturer. For pumps operating under lift, possible changes in performance should be studied carefully, because greater velocity in the suction line could cause cavitation and substantially alter the characteristic curve.

FIRE PUMP APPROVAL AND LISTING

NFPA standards for design and installation of various fire protection systems recommend the use of approved equipment, or listed equipment, or both, including fire pumps, for installations requiring them.Under the testing and listing approval system, the manufacturer is responsible for providing a listed or approved shop-tested pump that will perform satisfactorily when installed in conformance with NFPA 20, *Installation of Centrifugal Fire Pumps*. Contractors or others are responsible for installing the driver-pump combination in accordance with the provisions of NFPA 20, while it is the customer's obligation to provide adequate data about the pump driver, power supply, water supply, location, and so on.

Fire pumps are designed to provide maximum reliability and specific net head-discharge characteristics. Except for periodic inspections and tests, fire pumps are idle most of the time. Pumps for commercial use, on the other hand, are chosen for maximum efficiency and economy.

To obtain an official listing of a new pump, the manufacturer submits plans and specifications to a testing agency for review and comment. After any revisions or corrections have been agreed to, arrangements are made for representatives of the testing agency involved to witness the required approval tests at the manufacturer's plant.

If the results are satisfactory, the new pumps are listed in the usual manner or with any restrictions considered desirable. It is the duty of the manufacturer to shop-test every unit sold and to furnish certified curves of head, efficiency, and brake horsepower *vs* discharge. Although not ordinarily shown, the NPSH curve of the pump, if available, should be provided upon request.

Many of the listed fire pumps used today are top-quality commercial units. These pumps are upgraded when necessary, trimmed, and fitted to meet all the approval requirements for fire protection.

STANDARD HEAD DISCHARGE CURVES

The shape of the standard head discharge curve of a fire pump is determined by three limiting points as follows.

Shutoff

With the pump operating at rated speed and the discharge valve closed, the total head of a horizontal centrifugal pump at shutoff must not exceed 120 percent or 140 percent, depending on the testing agency requirements, of the rated head at 100-percent capacity. For a vertical or end-suction pump, the total head at shutoff must not exceed 140 percent of the rated head at 100-percent capacity.

The shutoff point represents the maximum allowable total head pressure. Otherwise, the pump would have a rising or convex characteristic curve. Such pumps are not listed. With a convex curve, there could be two flow points for one pressure.

Rating

The curve should pass through or above the point of rated capacity and head. (See Figure 5-6K.)

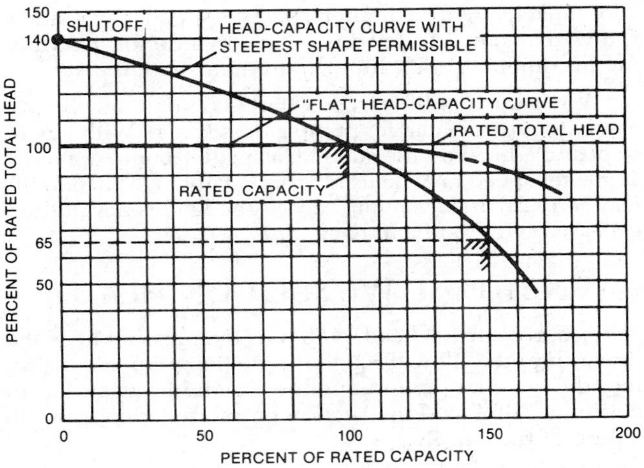

FIG. 5-6K. Pump characteristic curves.

Overload

At 150 percent of rated capacity, the total head should not be less than 65 percent of the rated total head. Here, also, the curve should pass through or above the overload point. Most modern fire pumps have curves with a significant margin above the theoretical overload, and some models have a cavitation or "break" point in the curve just beyond overload.

HORIZONTAL-SHAFT CENTRIFUGAL FIRE PUMPS

Horizontal-shaft fire pumps should be installed to operate under positive suction head, especially with automatic or remote-manual starting. If the water supply is such that suction lift cannot be avoided, vertical turbine fire pumps should be installed. NFPA 20, *Installation of Centrifugal Fire Pumps*, no longer allows the use of horizontal-centrifugal fire pumps taking suction under lift for new installations.

Types of Pump

Horizontal centrifugal fire pumps are of the split-case or end-suction (see Figures 5-6A and 5-6L) types. The end-suction type is manufactured to ANSI specifications[1] for centrifugal pumps and is limited to capacities under 500 gpm (1893 L/min). There are no limits on the capacities of split-case fire pumps, but the maximum capacity for listed fire pumps is currently 5000 gpm (18 925 L/min).

Suction Facilities

When streams, ponds, and other open bodies of water are used, properly screened intakes should be provided to prevent fish, eels, and foreign material from entering the pump and the fire protection system. A foot valve of proper design should be provided on each suction inlet. (See Figure 5-6M.)

Use of nonpotable water should be avoided when fire pumps discharge into a system that is also connected to public mains or to other potable supplies. Otherwise, there will be cross-connections, which are restricted in some locations by either health or water utility authorities, or both,

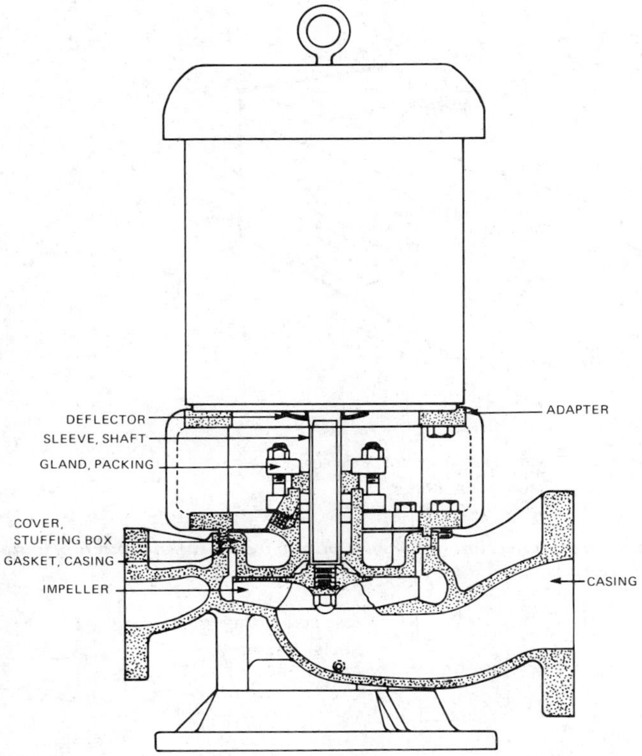

FIG. 5-6L. An over-hung impeller, close-coupled, single-stage, inline, horizontal end-suction fire pump.

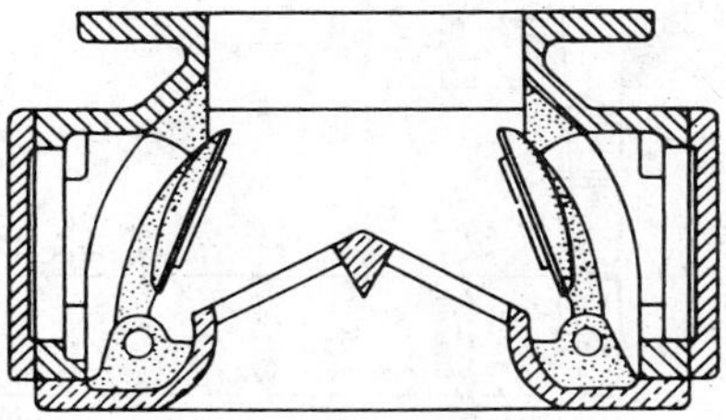

FIG. 5-6M. A typical foot valve of good design shown in the open position.

in most states and provinces. In those cases where cross-connections cannot be avoided, suitable backflow prevention devices acceptable to health and water authorities should be provided to prevent contamination of potable water supplies. Such devices should be installed on the discharge side of the pump. Aboveground covered tanks filled with potable water are recommended for supplying fire pumps.

The volume of suction storage should be sufficient to supply the pump at overload rate for the estimated duration of the water demand.

Break Tanks

At locations where a direct connection between a public water supply and a private fire protection system is prohibited, either for public health or hydraulic reasons, a break tank installation may be desirable. A break tank is an automatically filled tank that provides a suction supply for a fire pump without a direct connection to a public supply. (See Figure 5-6N.) This is done by an actual physical break or gap between the public supply and a private protection system. Water from the public supply enters the break tank from a height above the tank's overflow outlet and falls freely to the surface of the water in the tank. A fire pump is needed to take suction from the tank, as the water is no longer under pressure from the public supply.

A separate break tank should be provided for each fire pump in an installation, and they should be large enough to supply pump operation at 150 percent of the pump rated capacity for 15 minutes. The flow into the tank from the public supply is controlled by an automatic fill mechanism, and, since the water in the tank is considered potable, the top of the tank should be closed.

Break tanks are less reliable than a good, full-sized suction tank, as the automatic fill mechanisms could fail. There is no NFPA standard for the design and installation of break tanks, although recommendations have been made on them by an insurance engineering service.[2]

Booster Pumps

These are fire pumps taking suction from public water mains, industrial systems, or power penstocks. (In a mechanical sense, all pumps are booster pumps.) As a prelude to installation, the available fire flow in the area is obtained by testing. Full overload capacity of the pump, plus the probable flow drawn from area hydrants by the fire department, are calculated, and they should not drop the pressure in the water mains below 20 psi (138 kPa) or that allowed by the public health authorities. Head rating of the pump should be sufficient to meet all pipe friction in the connection plus pressure demand.

Pump Accessories

Auxiliary devices have an important bearing on the complete functioning of a pump as a fire protection water supply, and their provision or omission should never be decided solely on the basis of cost. NFPA 20, *Installation of Centrifugal Fire Pumps*, gives detailed information concerning their installation. The following items are worthy of special consideration.

Relief valves: These are necessary on the pump discharge line when the operation of the pump results in excess pressure. Pumps with adjustable speed drivers need relief valves, as do those where suction pressure plus shutoff pressure would exceed the pressure rating of the fire protection equipment.

Hose valves: Approved $2\frac{1}{2}$-in. (64 mm) hose valves are used in testing pumps and for hose stream fire protection. The valves should be attached to a header or manifold outside the pump room, or otherwise located to avoid water damage to the pump, driver, and controller. The number of valves needed depends on the pump capacity. For details, see NFPA 20, *Installation of Centrifugal Fire Pumps*.

Automatic air release valves: These are necessary on the top of the casing of pumps arranged for automatic or remote-control operation. An umbrella cock may be adequate for a pump that can be started only manually by an operator in the pump room, but an automatic air release is desirable on any pump with a casing that is normally full of water.

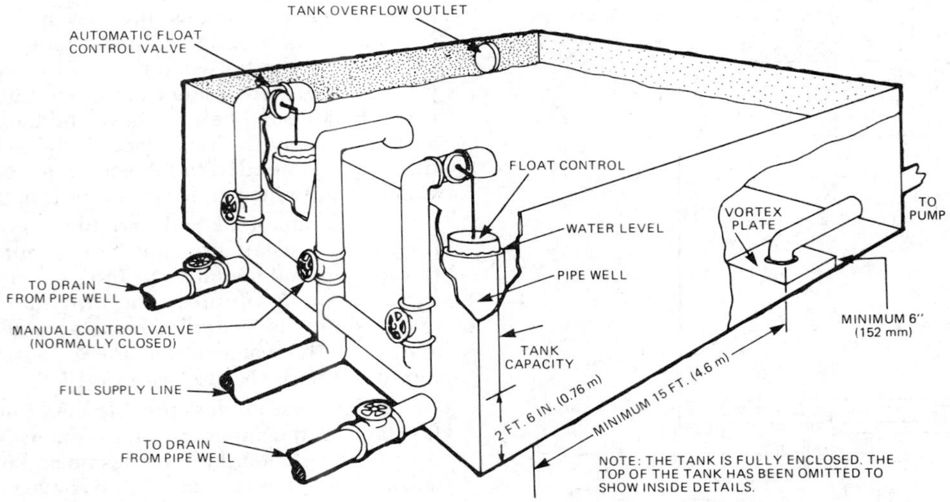

FIG. 5-6N. A break tank used in connection with a fire pump when a direct connection between a public water supply and a private fire protection system is prohibited. (Source: Factory Mutual Research Corp.)

Circulation relief valves: These are necessary for pumps that may be started automatically or by remote control. Their function is to open at slightly above rated pressure, when there is little or no discharge, so that sufficient water is discharged to prevent the pump from overheating. These valves are not needed on engine-driven pumps where cooling water is taken from the pump discharge.

VERTICAL TURBINE-TYPE FIRE PUMPS

Vertical turbine pumps were originally designed to pump water from bored wells. As fire pumps, they are recommended in instances where horizontal pumps would operate with suction lift. An outstanding feature of vertical pumps is their ability to operate without priming. (See NFPA 20, *Installation of Centrifugal Fire Pumps*, for required submergence.) Vertical pumps may be used to pump from streams, ponds, wet pits, and so on, as well as in booster service.

Suction from wells is not recommended for fire service, although it is acceptable if the adequacy and reliability of the well has been established and the entire installation has been made in conformance with NFPA 20, *Installation of Centrifugal Fire Pumps*. In many instances, the cost of a deep-well fire pump installation would be prohibitive, especially if the pumping level at maximum rate is more than 50 ft (15 m) below ground level; 200 ft (60 m) is the limit.

If the yield from a reliable well is too small to supply a standard fire pump, low-capacity well pumps could be used to fill conventional ground-level tanks or reservoirs for the fire pump supply.

A typical vertical fire pump consists essentially of a motor head or right-angle gear drive, a column pipe and discharge fitting, an open or enclosed drive shaft, a bowl assembly containing the impellers, and a suction strainer. (See Figures 5-6O and 5-6P.) The principle of operation is comparable to that of a multi-stage horizontal centrifugal pump. Except for shutoff pressure, the characteristic curve is the same as it is for horizontal pumps. (See Figure 5-6K.)

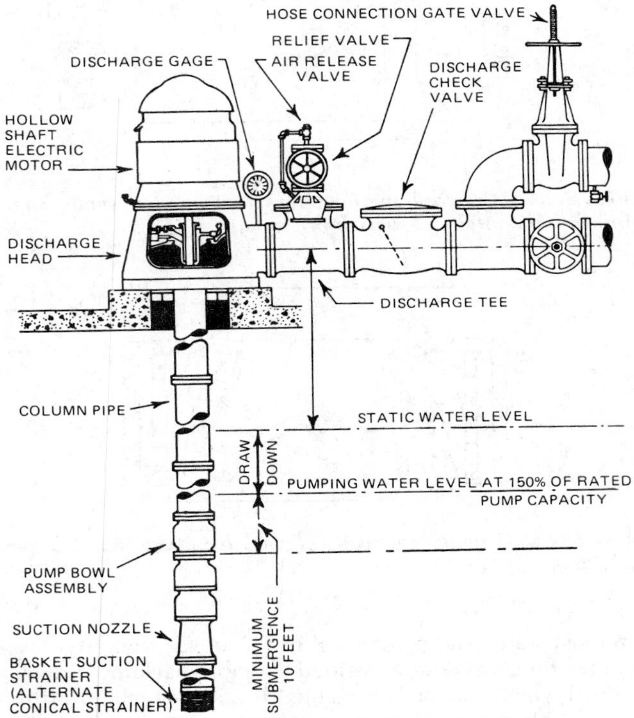

FIG. 5-6O. Vertical-shaft-turbine-type pump installation.

Vertical Turbine Barrel or Can Pump

Sometimes vertical-type multi-stage pumps are installed in a casing called a "barrel" or "can" for high-pressure installations. (See Figure 5-6Q.) Where pumps with adequate pressure ratings are available, horizontal split-case pumps are normally used.

Vertical pumps have the same standard capacity ratings that horizontal fire pumps have. Pressure ratings are not standardized. By changing the number of stages, or the impeller diameters, or both, the pump manufacturer can provide a specific total head at rated speed.

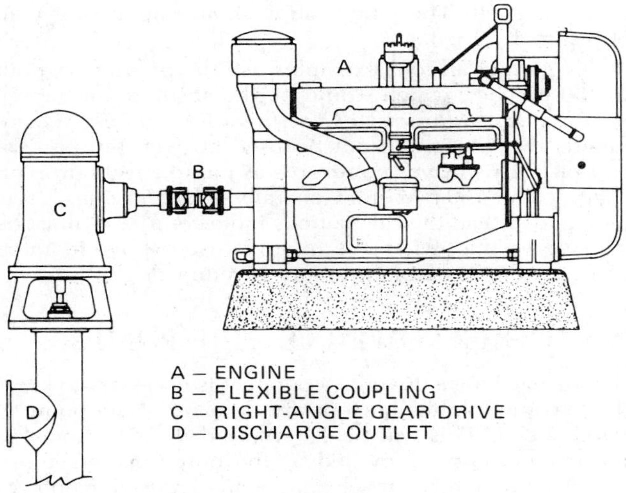

FIG. 5-6P. Engine-driven vertical fire pump.

For electrically driven pumps, hollow shaft motors are used. Diesel engines or steam turbines can be used by means of right-angle gear heads.

FIRE PUMP CAPACITY AND HEAD RATING

The capacity and pressure ratings of fire pumps should be adequate to meet flow and pressure demands consistent with water supply requirements for the property in question. Fire pumps are designed to provide their rated capacity with a safety factor built in (150 percent of rated capacity at 65 percent of rated pressure) to provide some protection in case of greater-than-expected demand at the time of a fire. The following examples show one method of how rated capacity and pressure can be determined by using the standard fire pump curve for a typical manufacturer's pump characteristic curve. (See Figure 5-6K.)

Example No. 1: Horizontal centrifugal pump. The estimated water demand for sprinklers and hose streams is 1400 gpm at 90 psi pump discharge pressure. The suction supply is a ground-level storage tank, and the minimum inlet pressure is 0 psig at maximum flow.

PROBLEM: Determine the required rated capacity and pressure of the pump.

SOLUTION:

1. Meet the demand of 1400 gpm with the overload capacity of the pump, which is 150 percent of rated capacity;
2. Thus, 1400 ÷ 150 percent = 933 gpm. The nearest standard pump rating is approximately 1000 gpm;
3. Therefore, 1400 gpm demand would be 140 percent of capacity;
4. From the manufacturer's pump characteristic curve, it is determined that, at 140 percent capacity, the total pressure is 73 percent of rated pressure;
5. Under conditions of operation, the total pressure equals the discharge pressure (90 psi) plus suction pressure (0 psi);
6. Therefore, net pressure at 1400 gpm equals 90 + 0 = 90 psi, and rated pressure at 1000 gpm = 90 ÷ 73 percent = 125 psi.

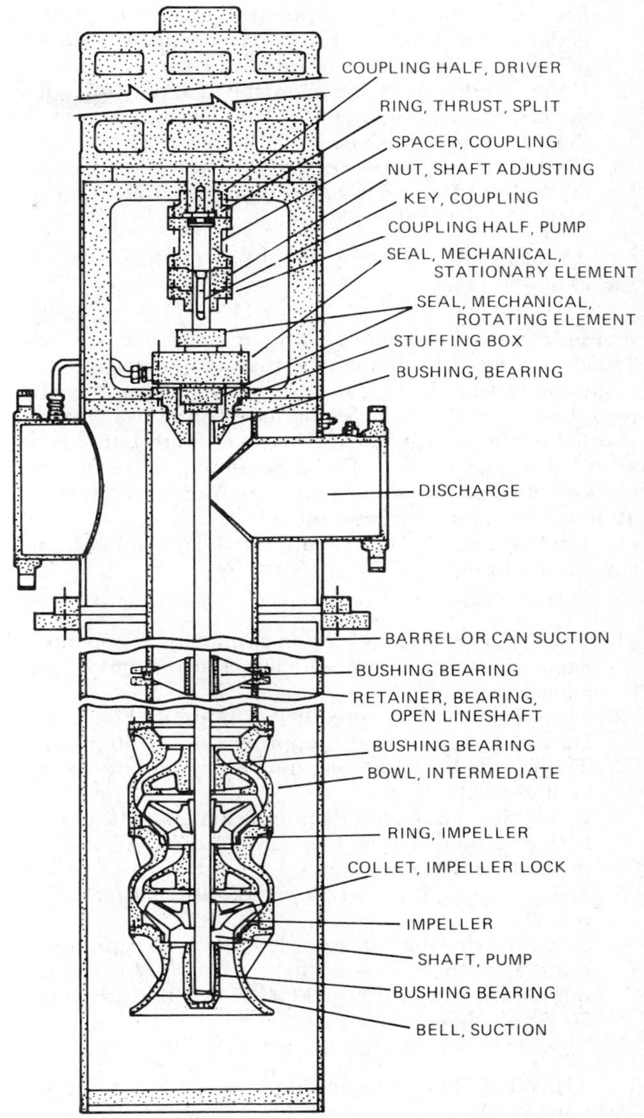

FIG. 5-6Q. A turbine-type, vertical, multi-stage, barrel or can pump.

ANSWER: Pump rating should be not less than 1000 gpm at 125 psi.

Example No. 2: Horizontal centrifugal pump (SI units). The estimated water demand for a sprinkler system is 2000 L/min at a pump discharge pressure of 400 kPa. The suction supply is a well with a lift of 5m from water surface to the pump.

PROBLEM: Determine the required rated capacity and pressure of the pump.

SOLUTION:

1. Meet the demand of 2000 L/min with the overload capacity of the pump which is 150 percent of rated capacity;
2. Thus, 2000 ÷ 150 percent = 1330 L/min. The nearest standard pump rating is approximately 1500 L/min;
3. Therefore, 2000 L/min demand would be 2,000/1500 × 100 percent = 133 percent of rated capacity;

4. From the manufacturer's pump characteristic curve, it is determined that, at 133 percent capacity, the total pressure is 78 percent of rated pressure;
5. Under conditions of operation, the total pressure equals the discharge pressure (400 kPa) plus suction pressure (5 m head = 5 × 9.81 kPa = 50 kPa);
6. Therefore, net pressure at 2000 L/min equals 400 + 50 = 450 kPa, and rated pressure at 1500 L/min = 450 ÷ 78 percent = 580 kPa.

ANSWER: Pump rating should be not less than 1500 L/min at 580 kPa.

Example No. 3: Vertical turbine pump in a driven well. The estimated water demand at the pump discharge gage at ground level is 1100 gpm at 100 psi. Tests and weather records show that the aquifer, or underground water source, is reliable and adequate at all seasons. The static level is 45 ft below the surface. The draw down, or vertical distance, between the static and pumping water levels is 40 ft at 1100 gpm pumping rate.

PROBLEM: Determine the rated capacity and pressure of the pump.

SOLUTION:

1. Meet the demand of 1100 gpm with the overload capacity of the pump, which is 150 percent of rated capacity;
2. Thus 1100 ÷ 150 percent = 733 gpm. The nearest standard pump rating is approximately 750 gpm;
3. Therefore, the 1,100 gpm demand would be 147 percent capacity;
4. From the manufacturer's pump characteristic curve, it is determined that at 147 percent capacity, the total pressure is 70 percent rated pressure;
5. At 1,100 gpm, pressure demand at the surface = 100 psi;
6. Since the distance to water level at 1,100 gpm pumping rate is 45 + 40 = 85 ft × 0.434 = 37 psi, pumping pressure would be 100 + 37 = 137 psi, which is 70 percent of rated pressure;
7. Therefore, 137 ÷ 70 percent = 195 psi.

ANSWER: The pump rating should be not less than 750 gpm at 195 psi.

Example No. 4: Booster pump on public water connection. A sprinklered building in a city has an estimated sprinkler demand of 750 gpm at 60 psi pump discharge. Based on fire flow tests from nearby street hydrants, 750 gpm at 27 psi would be available for sprinklers at the inlet flange of the pump. Allowance has already been made for hose streams.

PROBLEM: Determine the rated capacity and pressure of the pump.

SOLUTION:

1. Meet the demand of 750 gpm with the overload capacity of the pump, which is 150 percent of rated capacity;
2. Thus, 750 ÷ 150 percent = 500 gpm, a standard pump rating;
3. The total pressure at 150 percent capacity is 65 percent rated net pressure;
4. With positive head suction supply, the net pressure equals discharge pressure minus suction pressure; thus, at 750 gpm flow, net pressure equals 60 – 27 = 33 psi;
5. Therefore, 33 ÷ 65 percent = 51 psi.

ANSWER: The pump rating should be greater than 500 gpm at 51 psi.

Note that all four examples use the pump curve out to 150 percent, which would be the absolute maximum. NFPA 20, *Installation of Centrifugal Fire Pumps*, recommends that the pump not be used at over 140 percent capacity. This leaves no reserve as pump curves drop off sharply after 150 percent. Generally, a larger pump is recommended than the calculations indicate. Also, it must be considered that, when the pump is used above its rated capacity, the available pressure is reduced.

HORSEPOWER OF FIRE PUMPS

Before matching a driver to a pump, it is necessary to know the maximum brake horsepower demand of the pump at rated speed. This can be determined directly from the horsepower curve provided by the pump manufacturer. Typical fire pumps reach maximum brake horsepower between 140 and 170 percent of rated capacity.

If the curves are not available, horsepower can be calculated, by the formula (in U.S. customary units):

$$\text{bhp} = \frac{5.83QP}{10{,}000 \times E} \quad \text{or} \quad \text{bhp} = \frac{QP}{1{,}710 \times E}$$

where:

bhp = brake horsepower

Q = gallons per minute

P = total head (psi) or net pressure

$E = \text{efficiency} = \dfrac{\text{Water Horsepower}}{\text{Input Horsepower}}$

The efficiency at maximum brake horsepower is usually 60 to 75 percent.

EXAMPLE: Find by formula the minimum horsepower needed to drive a 1000-gpm, 100-psi, 1760-rpm horizontal centrifugal fire pump.

SOLUTION:

1. Assume 65 percent efficiency at 160 percent capacity;
2. From a standard pump curve, the pressure is 55 percent at 160 percent capacity or 55 psi at 1600 gpm;
3. By formula,

$$\text{bhp} = \frac{5.83 \times 1{,}600 \times 55}{10{,}000 \times .65} = 79$$

ANSWER: Not less than 79 usable brake horsepower.

IN SI UNITS:

$$\text{Output power} = \frac{0.167 Q_m P_m}{10{,}000\ E}$$

where:

kW = power output (kilowatts)

Q_m = liters per minute

P_m = total head (kPa) or net pressure

$E = \text{efficiency} = \dfrac{\text{Water Power Output}}{\text{Input Power}}$

EXAMPLE (SI units): Find by formula the minimum power output needed to drive a 4000-L/min, 700-kPa, 1760 rpm horizontal centrifugal fire pump.

SOLUTION:

1. Assume 65 percent efficiency at 160 percent capacity;
2. From a standard pump curve, the pressure is 55 percent at 160 percent capacity or 385 kPa at 6400 L/min;
3. By formula,

$$\text{power output} = \frac{0.167 \times 6400 \times 385}{10{,}000 \times 0.65}$$
$$= 63\ kW$$

ANSWER: Not less than 63 kW output.

FIRE PUMP DRIVERS

Power for driving fire pumps is selected on the basis of reliability, adequacy, safety, and economy. The reliability of utility electric power may be judged by the record of outages and by review of the power sources and distribution layout of the system in question.

Gas utility systems may be subject to periods of restricted use because of high seasonal demand. To offset this, standby gas storage can be provided, or arrangements can be negotiated with utilities to supply the fire pump with gas even though the general use of gas is restricted.

Many public utilities operate steam distribution systems. When high-pressure steam is available, it would be practical for large consumers to use turbine-driven fire pumps.

Many industrial plants generate their own steam-electric or hydroelectric power, or both. Utility power also may be used, possibly on a standby basis.

Diesel engines have the advantage of not being dependent upon outside sources of power.

Electric Motors

Electric motors for driving fire pumps are required to be listed for fire pump service. These motors are designed in accordance with specifications of National Electrical Manufacturers Association (NEMA) or Electrical Manufacturers Association of Canada (EMAC). All electrical equipment and wiring in a fire pump installation should comply with NFPA 70, *National Electrical Code®*, except as modified by NFPA 20, *Installation of Centrifugal Fire Pumps*.

Fire pumps that are driven by electric motors are designed to withstand rather severe ranges of operating conditions. As a result, the power supply for these pumps is designed to accomodate large electrical loads, and pump configurations will sacrifice the pump motor. Such design is contrary to the design of most other electrical motors and results in an extremely high level of pump reliability.

The pump manufacturer or the installing contractor is responsible for providing a motor of sufficient capacity to avoid overloading beyond the limit of the service factor at maximum brake horsepower and rated speed. The service factor is a numerical value, and it depends on the type of motor—open, splashproof, or totally enclosed—and on the resistance of the insulation on the windings to heat and breakdown.

When the service factor exceeds 1.0, the excessive amount is stamped on the nameplate along with the voltage and the full-load ampere rating. For example, a 75-hp (56 kW) motor with 1.15 service factor, could safely meet a demand of 75 × 1.15 = 86.25 bhp (64 kW).

Another use for the service factor is to estimate the maximum allowable ampere demand. For example, with a 40-amp full-load rating and a 1.12 service factor, the maximum ammeter reading should not exceed 40 × 1.12 = 45 amps. Note also that, for a given voltage, horsepower is proportional to amperes.

Only motors wound for 208 volts should be used on 208-volt services.

Direct-current motors for pumps are either of the stabilized shunt type or of the cumulative compound-wound type. The speed of the motor with no load at operating temperature must not exceed the speed of the motor under full load at operating temperature by more than 10 percent.

The most commonly used alternating current motors are of the squirrel-cage induction type. They usually are equipped with across-the-line starting equipment unless their starting characteristics would be objectionable to the company furnishing the power. In the latter case, primary resistance starting may be employed, or a wound-rotor-type of motor with appropriate starting equipment may be substituted. When squirrel-cage motors are used, the voltage drop must not be so great as to prevent the motor from starting; that is, it should not be more than 10 percent below normal voltage at moment of start. While the motor is running at rated pump capacity, pressure, and speed, the line voltage should not drop more than 5 percent below motor nameplate voltage.

This type of motor should have normal starting and breakdown torque. The locked rotor currents for motors of various horsepower ratings are specified in NFPA 20, *Installation of Centrifugal Fire Pumps.*

When an electric-driven pump is used as a part of a high-rise building fire protection system, it will normally be required to have a backup power supply. The capability of fire apparatus to effectively pump into a high-rise standpipe or sprinkler riser is restricted. Thus, the reliability of pumps used in this environment is especially important. In some instances, special circumstances may warrant the installation of a non-listed fire pump to achieve the necessary high-pressure service.

If power supplies to the pump are not reliable, the use of an emergency generator, in conjunction with a permanent power supply, may be necessary. The installation of this generator must be done in accordance with NFPA 20, *Installation of Centrifugal Fire Pumps*, and NFPA 37, *Stationary Combustion Engines and Gas Turbines*. A transfer switch is required to be installed for the pump and is necessary to switch the pump energy source from the permanent supply to the emergency source. This transfer switch may be provided as an integral part of the fire pump controller, or it may be installed as a separate piece of equipment. No matter which method is selected, it must be installed such that it does not reduce the degree of reliability for the entire system.

Electric Motor Controllers

The fire pump controller used for an electric-driven pump is a critical component to ensure the successful operation of the pump. Such controllers are equipped with a variety of internal components to achieve this level of reliability. These components may include elements such as circuit breakers, disconnecting means, timers, and similar devices.

Motor controllers are available for alternating-current fire pump motors operating at standard voltages up to

600 V. A controller is a complete, assembled unit, wired and tested, and ready for service by connecting to the power supply and the proper motor terminals. Detailed specifications are described in NFPA 20, *Installation of Centrifugal Fire Pumps*. Higher voltages are not recommended, but acceptable controllers conforming to special requirements of NFPA 20 can be provided.

Controllers are available for combined manual and automatic operation or for manual operation only. They also are available for either squirrel-cage or wound-rotor motors and for two-phase or three-phase power. Across-the-line starting is recommended for most industrial applications, but controllers for reduced voltage starting are also available. Reduced voltage starting is normally used when electric-driven pumps are served by engine generator sets.

The circuit breaker of a fire pump controller permits normal starting without tripping and provides stalled rotor and instantaneous short circuit protection. The interrupting capacity of the breaker should be adequate for the circuit in which it is located, but not less than 15,000 amps in any case.

Automatic controllers known as limited-service controllers are available for across-the-line squirrel-cage motors of 30 hp (22 kW) or less driving special-service booster fire pumps.

Steam Turbine

When adequate and reliable steam supplies are available, turbine-driven fire pumps are acceptable. Only well-built machines of good design with industrial records of proven reliability are used. Special arrangements are needed for automatic operation. Speed rating should not exceed 3600 rpm, because this is the maximum speed of listed fire pumps. Detailed requirements for steam supply, speed governors, and controls are contained in NFPA 20, *Installation of Centrifugal Fire Pumps*.

Internal Combustion Engines

Engines that are powered by diesel fuel or natural gas are used for fire pump service. However, engines powered by gasoline, natural gas, or LP-Gas are not recognized by NFPA 20, *Installation of Centrifugal Fire Pumps*. Only the vapor-withdrawal method of supplying an engine with LP-Gas should be allowed.

Natural gas and LP-Gas engines differ from gasoline engines only in the design of the carburetors, intake manifolds, and cylinder heads. Large industrial consumers of natural or LP-Gas often prefer engine-driven fire pumps using these fuels.

In addition to NFPA 20, *Installation of Centrifugal Fire Pumps*, reference should be made to NFPA 37, *Stationary Combustion Engines and Gas Turbines*; NFPA 54, *National Fuel Gas Code*; NFPA 58, *Storage and Handling of Liquefied Petroleum Gases*; and NFPA 31, *Oil Burning Equipment*. Installations should be made in conformance to local codes.

NFPA 37, *Stationary Combustion Engines and Gas Turbines*, specifically recognizes the need for special provisions covering engines driving fire pumps. In general, manual and automatic devices intended to limit or prevent the accidental discharge of flammable gases are needed, but the development of other unsatisfactory conditions, such as high cooling water temperature and low oil pressure, should be indicated by alarms, not by shutting down the engine. The intent is to keep the pump operating just as long as possible. The importance of supervision, especially for automatic pumps, is obvious.

Cooling systems: An adequate cooling system is vital to the reliable operation of an internal combustion engine. A closed pipe system with a heat exchanger or a thermally insulated manifold is the usual cooling arrangement for a fire pump recognized in NFPA 20, *Installation of Centrifugal Fire Pumps*. Only clean or potable water should be circulated through the engine block. Raw water is piped from the fire pump through the heat exchanger tubes to free discharge in a visible location, such as the cone of the fire pump relief valve. On some engines, the manifolds, oil coolers, and other parts are equipped with water jackets, as recommended by the engine manufacturer. (See Figure 5-6R.) Most engines require a raw water flow of 15 to 30 gpm (57 to 114 L/min) or even more.

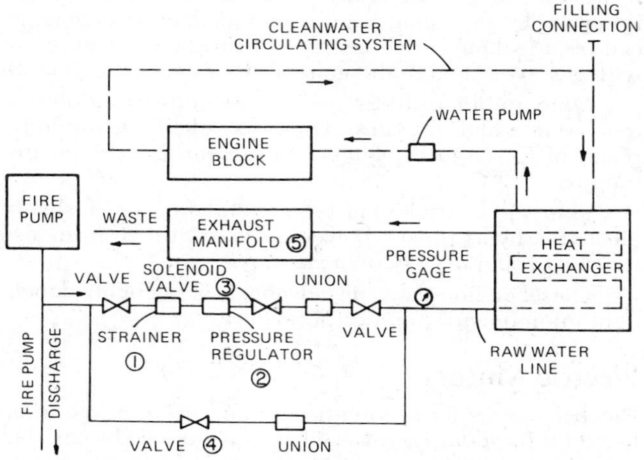

FIG. 5-6R. A typical heat-exchanger cooling system for an automatically controlled engine-driven fire pump. Raw water from the fire pump enters the system through the strainer (1), which prevents sediment from entering the system, and the pressure regulator (2), which protects the heat exchanger from excessive pressure. The solenoid valve (3) is required with automatic control of the engine. Valve (4), normally closed, may be used to bypass the regulator and solenoid valve. The exhaust manifold (5) may be cooled by the clean water circulating system.

Fuel tanks: The storage tank for liquid or gas fuel should contain at least an 8-hr supply; greater capacity should be provided if facilities for prompt refilling are not available. Tank capacity may be estimated by allowing 1 pt of diesel oil or LP-Gas per horsepower per hour. (See diagrams of typical fuel systems in NFPA 20, *Installation of Centrifugal Fire Pumps*.)

Battery chargers: The energy source needed to permit automatic starting of a diesel-driven fire pump is dependent upon a sufficient capacity from the battery system. The charges used to satisfy this requirement are specifically listed for fire pump service, and consist of rectifiers, transformers, and relays.

Engine Horsepower

Engines specifically designed for use with fire pumps are rated by measuring the horsepower developed with all accessories in operation and then making some allowance for wear and tear. Other engines used with fire pumps outside the power range and type of listed engines must have a horsepower capability, when equipped for fire pump driver service, of not less than 10 percent greater than the maximum brake horsepower required by the pump under any conditions of pump load. The engine must meet all the other requirements of listed engines. Typical bare engines and usable horsepower curves are shown in Figure 5-6S.

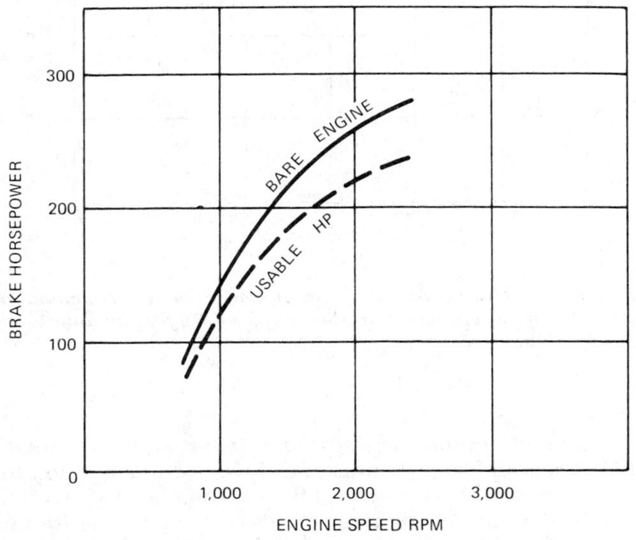

FIG. 5-6S. Typical engine horsepower curves. SI units: 1 bph = 745.70 W.

The engine manufacturer's test curves are based on barometric pressure of 29.61 in. (752 mm) Hg, which approximates 300 ft (90 m) above sea level and 77°F (25°C). The usable horsepower of a fire pump engine should be reduced for each 1000-ft (300 m) rise in altitude above 300 ft (90 m) by 3 percent for a diesel engine and 1 percent for each 10°F- (5.6°C) rise above 77°F (25°C).

Engine Controllers

Controllers are used for automatic operation of engine-driven fire pumps. The specifications for construction, location, and methods of actuation of engine controllers are the same as for electric motor controllers. Automatic controllers are equipped with manual starting and stopping switches.

Alarm devices are provided to indicate low oil pressure in the lubrication systems, high engine-jacket water temperature, failure of the engine to start automatically, and shutdown from overspeed (diesel only).

There are optional features for controllers as given in NFPA 20, *Installation of Centrifugal Fire Pumps*. A weekly program timer can be provided. This device may be arranged to start the unit automatically once a week and to run for a predetermined number of minutes. A recording pressure gage records this performance.

Controllers are operated on low-voltage direct-current power from the engine's batteries. The program timer, battery charger, or other auxiliary devices not essential to pump control are powered by the regular alternating current power supply at the property.

Automatic Pump Control

Most fire pump installations normally are arranged for automatic operation, preferably with automatic start and manual shutdown. The choice between manual and automatic shutdown depends on the specific conditions involved in a pump's installation and use. Horizontal centrifugal pumps under automatic control should always operate under a head to avoid the need for priming.

Each motor or engine controller is equipped with a pressure switch that actuates the pump unit when pressure in the water system piping drops to a preset level. Unless the normal water supply static pressure is higher than the pump starting pressure, an automatic jockey pump must be provided to maintain pressure in the system at the higher level.

Actuation of a pump by water flow instead of by pressure drop is desirable for certain installations, such as those in which the opening of a moderate number of sprinklers would not drop the system pressure enough to move the pressure switch; high-hazard occupancies in which a fire would demand fire pump service without delay; combined fire protection and plant service systems where a pressure maintenance pump would be impractical; and occupancies in which pressure fluctuates so much that a stable cut-in pressure could not be obtained.

The wiring system of a pump controller includes terminals for connection of a relay to an external alarm circuit from a sprinkler, deluge, or special fire protection system. To secure reliable pump actuation, external circuits should be installed in conformance with one of the following NFPA standards, depending upon the nature of the signaling system:

NFPA 71, *Signaling Systems for Central Station Service*.

NFPA 72, *Protective Signaling Systems*.

NFPA 72A, *Local Protective Signaling Systems for Guard's Tour, Fire Alarm, and Supervisory Service*.

Circuits for remote automatic starting of fire pumps should be powered from the controller power.

FIELD ACCEPTANCE TESTS

After a new fire pump has been installed, it is general practice to make a performance test. Defects and faults can be discovered, and steps taken to remedy them. These tests enable the purchaser to determine that the contract has been properly concluded. They also demonstrate the need for future maintenance tests.

Details of the acceptance tests are given in NFPA 20, *Installation of Centrifugal Fire Pumps*. The test demonstrates the adequacy of the pump suction and the ability of the pump to deliver water in accordance with its head capacity curve. The prime mover also is operated under various conditions and its performance noted. There are separate provisions for electric motors, steam turbines, and diesel engines. Repeated operation of the controlling equipment is required to ensure that full operation of the unit will result from either manual or automatic operation of the controller.

Flow tests are made to develop the pressure-discharge characteristic curve of the pump. The procedure followed is to run the pump at five or six different flows, including shutoff with no water flowing. The rate in gallons per minute is determined with a Pitot gage at the nozzles [preferably standard 30-in. (762 mm) long Underwriter playpipes] attached to hose lines from an outside hose-valve header. The discharge is varied by changing the number of lines, the size of nozzle tips, or both.

For every flow, pressure readings are taken at the suction gage and the discharge gage. The revolutions per minute are also measured using a revolution counter or a tachometer, if available. (The tachometer on a fire pump engine is not sufficiently accurate.)

The net pressures are calculated from the pump gage readings, and the flows in gallons per minute corresponding to the Pitot readings are obtained from discharge tables. The flow required for coolant purposes for internal combustion engine-driven pumps can be added to the measured flow. However, it is usually difficult to accurately measure this flow, so an estimate based on the manufacturer's recommendations may have to be used. In many cases, this flow is small enough to be considered negligible.

The nozzles may be attached directly to outdoor headers, without hose lines, if water damage can be avoided. Disposal of test water is often a problem, and the length of hose lines depends on the drainage facilities available and the exposure to property and people.

With the growing problems of waste water disposal, many pump installations are equipped with water meters for the acceptance test and the periodic service tests. The meters should be installed in conformance with NFPA 20, *Installation of Centrifugal Fire Pumps*, in order to function properly and not interfere with the operation of the pump.

Vertical turbine fire pumps are tested in the same manner as horizontal pumps, except that there is no suction gage. In addition, the pumping water level should be recorded at the several test points, unless it is more or less constant.

Figure 5-6T is a tabulation of data obtained by a typical field acceptance test of a horizontal 1500-gpm, 100-psi, 1760-rpm (5678 L/min, 689 kPa, 1760 rpm) engine-driven centrifugal pump. The net pressure and total flows are calculated from the observed data and plotted. (See Figure 5-6U.) The curve best fitting the plotted points is then drawn (Curve A). In this installation, the engine governor appeared to be out of adjustment, restricting the average speed to 1689 rpm, whereas the rated speed was 1760 rpm.

Acceptance Test 1,500 gpm, 100 psi, 1,760 rpm Fire Pump

				Streams				corrected to 1,760 RPM		
RPM	Discharge psi	Suction psi	*Net psi	No.	Size in.	Pitot Pressure psi	GPM*	Total*	GPM*	Net* psi
1,700	125	+16	109	0	—	—	—	0	0	118
1,695	120	+18	102	1	1 ¾	70	742	742	772	110
1,690	110	+16	94	2	1 ¾	60, 60	687, 687	1,374	1,420	101
1,686	95	+17	79	3	1 ¾	55, 55, 55	657, 657 657	1,971	2,060	85
1,675	85	+16	69	4	1 ¾	35, 37, 48, 48	525, 540 614, 614	2,293	2,410	76

* Calculated from observed data.

FIG. 5-6T. ***An example of a log for a fire pump acceptance test.***

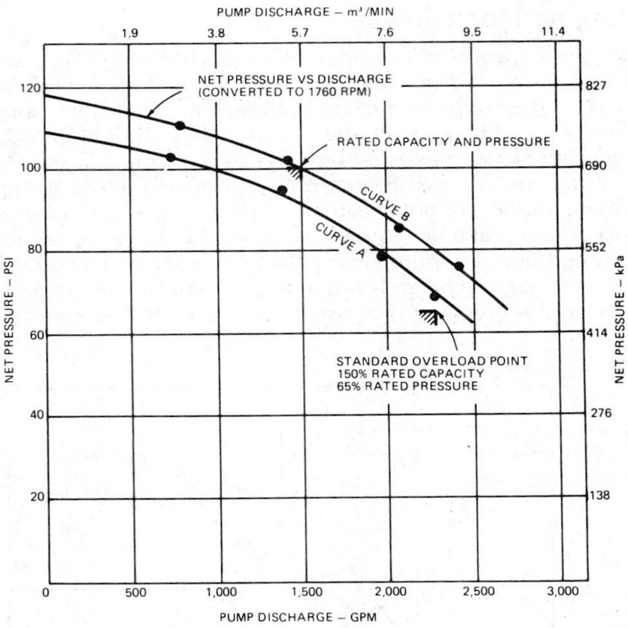

FIG. 5-6U. ***Head capacity curves plotted from data compiled in a fire pump acceptance test. (See Figure 5-6T for the data used to plot these curves.)***

Since the pump was tested at less than rated speed, the observed net pressures and flows were converted to what they would have been at the rated speed of 1760 rpm. Curve B is the characteristic curve at rated conditions. Although the rating point was barely reached, the overload point exceeded the minimum by a good margin. With the engine adjusted to operate at full speed, the pump performance would be acceptable. The following is the conversion calculation procedure that was followed:

Flow is directly proportional to revolutions per minute
Net pressure is proportional to $(\text{rpm})^2$

EXAMPLE: Test flow 1,971 gpm at 1,686 rpm

$$\text{Flow at 1,760 rpm} = 1.971\left(\frac{1{,}760}{1{,}686}\right) = 2{,}060 \text{ gpm}$$

Net pressure for 1,971 gpm at 1,686 rpm is 78 psi

$$\text{Net pressure for 2,060 gpm at 1,760 rpm is } 78\left(\frac{1{,}760}{1{,}686}\right)^2 = 85 \text{ psi.}$$

Similar calculations can be carried out in SI units using the affinity laws mentioned previously in this chapter.

Water Meters

As an alternative to the hose valves previously described, a listed water meter may be installed in the fire pump test header line. This method of test requires that the water being discharged through the meter terminate at atmospheric pressure. For a self-contained water supply, the water can be discharged back into the storage tank, thereby conserving water.

In theory, the characteristic curve assumes operation at constant rated speed. Actually, the speed of internal combustion engines and steam turbines is permitted to vary within a range of 8 to 10 percent between shutoff and maximum load. Electric motor speed is more nearly constant. Speed reduction may occur if the power supply is overloaded.

LOCATION AND HOUSING OF CENTRIFUGAL PUMPS

Fire pumps are housed in buildings of fire-resistive or noncombustible construction. Even when the climate is so mild that there is no danger of freezing, sufficient enclosure is needed to protect against dirt, corrosion, and tampering. Structural separation of the pump room from other parts of a property is desirable.

Pump rooms and power facilities should be as free as possible from exposure to fire, explosion, flood, and windstorm damage.

Light, heat, ventilation, and floor drainage should be provided for pump rooms. A dry location above-grade is preferred. For an internal combustion engine-driven unit, heat, ventilation, and above-grade location are essential.

Pump rooms should be large enough to facilitate easy access to all equipment and devices for inspection and maintenance.

Fire pumps preferably are located as close as possible to those areas where protection is most important. In some large properties, it may be necessary to have water supplies at more than one point to obtain the most favorable distribution system. When this results in placing a pump in a somewhat isolated pump room, the requirements for housing and supervision are of special importance.

ANNUAL PUMP TESTS

A fire pump should be tested annually to make certain that the pump, driver, suction, and power supply function properly and to correct faults that may be revealed. The hydraulic performance of the pump is measured by a flow test with hose and nozzles connected to the pump header or yard hydrants. Three points on the standard curve are checked: (1) shutoff, (2) overload (150 percent of rated capacity or more), and (3) a convenient rate of flow at or near capacity rating.

Automatic operation is tested by opening yard hydrants or sprinkler riser drains, giving due consideration to the layout of the fire protection system—pressure drop or water flow actuation, jockey pump, and so on. It is not sufficient to initiate pressure drop by the test cock on the controller.

The water level of ponds and reservoirs and the condition of suction screens and intakes, aboveground tanks, and so on, should be carefully examined.

The history of power outages, low water, and failure of any kind involving pump, driver, or associated equipment, also should be investigated and gage records from engine controllers, when so equipped, examined.

PUMP OPERATION AND MAINTENANCE

A fire pump can be depended upon to work in an emergency only if it is properly operated and maintained. It is recommended that an inspection and testing program that includes written instructions and recordkeeping be implemented. It is desirable to have someone at the property at all times who has been designated and instructed to operate the pump and its driver. A short test by the regular pump operators should be made each week by discharging water from some convenient outlet.

When a fire alarm is given or an alarm indicates an automatic fire pump is operating, the person responsible for the fire pump should proceed to its location immediately. The pump preferably should be put in manual operation and allowed to run until the emergency is over, when it may be shut down manually. During this and every other operating period, the equipment should be checked carefully to see whether it is performing properly.

To prevent too-frequent starting and stopping, an electric motor controller has a timer that keeps the motor running for at least 1 min for each 10-hp motor rating; not more than 7 min is required. It is preferable with all types of pump drivers to permit the unit to run until it is shut down manually. When there is more than one automatic fire pump, the control is arranged to operate the pumps in a predetermined sequence. Control of the pump from one or more remote pushbuttons, which will start but not stop the pump, may be provided if desired. If there is deluge valve control of an open discharge device system, the pump may be started by a drop-out relay in a closed circuit.

The cooling and lubrication of a centrifugal fire pump is so dependent upon water that the pump must never be run unless the pump casing is full of water. Close attention should be given to the bearings and stuffing boxes during the first few minutes of running to see that they do not heat up and need no adjustment. When water reaches the water seal, a small leak at the stuffing box glands is desirable. The suction inlet and discharge outlet pressure gages should be read occasionally to see that the inlet is not obstructed by a choked screen or foot valve.

With a vertical-shaft-turbine-type fire pump, the water level can be observed if suction is from a visible supply. If the pump takes suction from a well, water level testing equipment must be used. The groundwater level at the pump should be checked at intervals during the year and the draw down should be determined during the annual 150 percent capacity test. These tests should indicate any important change in the groundwater supply.

The direction of rotation of the pump and the speed of operation should always be checked.

Power Supply Maintenance

The source of power for the pump should also be checked. With an electric motor drive this means current supply for the motor and its auxiliary equipment. For steam turbine drive, it means the steam supply up to the control valve and the absence of condensate from supply, turbine, and exhaust. If the pump is driven by a diesel engine, there must be adequate fuel for 8 hr of operation. The batteries must be fully charged.

The starting equipment must be test-operated and its functioning carefully checked. Any evidence of a drop in voltage to an electric motor or a drop in steam pressure to a turbine must be investigated.

With a diesel engine drive, the crankcase oil must be replenished or renewed as needed, the oil filter and air cleaner given the necessary attention, the automatic battery charging equipment checked, and the specific gravity of battery electrolyte determined at least once a month.

RECIPROCATING STEAM FIRE PUMPS

Although no new reciprocating steam fire pumps have been installed in recent years, a few may still be in service. These fire pumps are commonly referred to as Underwriter steam fire pumps.

The general features of a direct-acting duplex steam pump are shown in Figure 5-6V. The size of the steam and exhaust ports of this type of pump is larger than it is in the general-purpose steam pump, thus permitting higher speeds. The steam supply pipe should be an independent line run from boiler to pump in such a way that it will not be damaged by fire or other hazards.

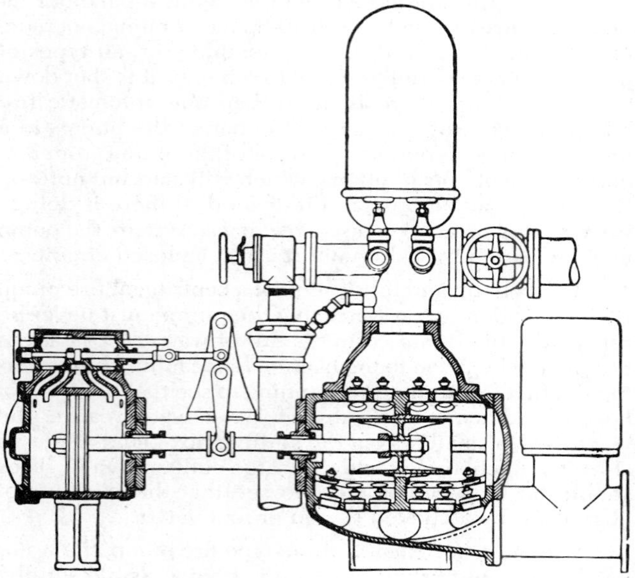

FIG. 5-6V. Sectional view of an approved duplex steam pump.

Automatic Control

Automatic control can be provided by a pressure governor to regulate steam supply to the pump in accordance with the water pressure on the pump discharge. For successful operation, it is nearly always necessary to provide a small, automatically controlled jockey pump to maintain system pressure, control supply leakage, and avoid continuous operation of the large pump.

BIBLIOGRAPHY

References Cited

1. ANSI B73.1, *Specifications for Horizontal End-Suction Centrifugal Pumps*, American National Standards Institute, 1973.
2. "Break Tanks," *Loss Prevention Data 3-251*, Factory Mutual Research Corp., Norwood, MA, May 1983.

NFPA Codes, Standards, and Recommended Practices

Reference to the following NFPA codes, standards, and recommended practices will provide further information on fire pumps discussed in this chapter. (See the latest *NFPA Catalog* for availability of current editions of the following documents.)

NFPA 11, *Low Expansion Foam and Combined Agent Systems*.

NFPA 11A, *Medium- and High-Expansion Foam Systems*.

NFPA 13, *Installation of Sprinkler Systems*.

NFPA 13A, *Inspection, Testing, and Maintenance of Sprinkler Systems*.

NFPA 13D, *Installation of Sprinkler Systems in One- and Two-Family Dwellings and Mobile Homes*.

NFPA 13E, *Fire Department Operations in Properties Protected by Sprinkler and Standpipe Systems*.

NFPA 14, *Installation of Standpipe and Hose Systems*.

NFPA 14A, *Testing, Inspection, and Maintenance of Standpipe and Hose Systems*.

NFPA 15, *Standard for Water-Spray Fixed Systems for Fire Protection*.

NFPA 16, *Deluge Foam-Water Sprinkler and Foam-Water Spray Systems*.

NFPA 16A, *Installation of Closed-Head Foam-Water Sprinkler Systems*.

NFPA 20, *Installation of Centrifugal Fire Pumps*.

NFPA 22, *Water Tanks for Private Fire Protection*.

NFPA 24, *Private Fire Service Mains and Their Appurtenances*.

NFPA 26, *Supervision of Valves Controlling Water Supplies for Fire Protection*.

NFPA 31, *Oil Burning Equipment*.

NFPA 37, *Stationary Combustion Engines and Gas Turbines*.

NFPA 54, *National Fuel Gas Code*.

NFPA 58, *Storage and Handling of Liquefied Petroleum Gases*.

NFPA 70, *National Electrical Code®*.

NFPA 71, *Signaling Systems for Central Station Service*.

NFPA 72, *Protective Signaling Systems*.

NFPA 72A, *Local Protective Signaling Systems for Guard's Tour, Fire Alarm, and Supervisory Service*.

Additional Reading

American Standard Specifications for Deep Well Vertical Turbine Pumps, AWWA, NY.

Borland, G. S. and Greig, A., "Fire Pumps for the Oil and Gas Industry," *Proceedings* of the Institution of Mechanical Engineers Third European Congress on Fluid Machinery for Oil, Petrochemical, and Related Industries, Institution of Mechanical Engineers, London, 1987, pp. 147-155.

Cameron Hydraulic Data, 17th ed., Ingersoll Rand Co., NY, 1988.

Clark, W. G., "Applying Motor-Driven Fire Pump Controllers," *Electrical Construction and Maintenance*, Vol. 88, No. 7, (July 1989), pp. 57-61.

"Underwriter Steam Fire Pumps," Loss Prevention Data Sheet 3-9, Factory Mutual Engineering Corp., Norwood, MA., Dec. 1973

Hydraulic Institute, "Centrifugal Pump Suction," *Standards of Hydraulic Institute,* 14th ed., Hydraulic Institute, NY, 1969.

Isman, W. E., *Fire Service Pump Operations Handbook*, Fire Engineering, NY, 1984.

Jensen, R., ed., *Fire Protection for the Design Professional*, Cahners, Boston, 1975, pp. 47-57.

Karassik, I. J., *Pump Handbook*, McGraw-Hill, NY, 1986.

Leibman, J. G. and Conover, K. L., "Fire Pumps and Controllers," *Plumbing Engineer*, Vol. 17, No. 4 (May 1989), pp. 19-22, 47.

Mills, R., "The Packaged Pumphouse," *Fire Surveyor*, Vol. 18, No. 6, (Dec. 1989), pp. 23-24.

Rotary and Centrifugal Pump Theory and Design, Worthington Pump Corp., East Orange, NJ, 1971.

SFPE Handbook of Fire Protection Engineering, 1st ed., National Fire Protection Association, 1988, pp. 1-22, 1-26.

Smith, P. D., "Talking Fire Protection Systems," *Fire Journal*, Vol. 73, No. 3 (May 1979), pp. 11, 117.

FIRE STREAMS

Revised by Robert G. Purington

Water has always been and remains the primary fire extinguishing agent; therefore, the movement of water from its source to the fire is a significant operation in most kinds of fire fighting. A typical fire department delivery system consists of suction hose, a pumper to increase the water pressure to overcome friction loss and provide nozzle pressure, a supply line to move the water from the pump to the fire scene, and "working lines" and nozzles for the final delivery. Water is used in a number of forms and with various additives, and there are numerous combinations in which the water can be delivered to the fire scene.

This chapter includes a description of the most important details of good fire streams, including fire apparatus pumps, nozzles, fire hose friction loss, pump pressure calculations, friction-reducing additives, and reaction forces.

FIRE DEPARTMENT PUMPS

The primary purpose of fire department pumpers is to move water with adequate pressure from a source to the fire. Sources include hydrants, lakes, streams, rivers, or storage tanks in fixed locations or in vehicles. Pumpers serve other functions, including transporting fire fighters, water and other extinguishing agents, and equipment. Pumps are also installed on specialized apparatus, such as tank trucks, aerial ladders, elevating platforms, aircraft crash vehicles, forestry trucks, and fire boats.

Pumpers, or "engines," are generally equipped with a centrifugal pump and the necessary fittings for pressure regulation and priming operations. Piston, rotary gear, and rotary vane pumps are used for special purposes, such as high-pressure booster pumps and priming. Requirements for standard pumpers are given in NFPA 1901, *Pumper Fire Apparatus*.

Two important characteristics of fire pumps are: (1) the discharge rate, and (2) the discharge pressure. They comprise the final output of the pump. The discharge rate, also known as the quantity, flow rate, or volume, is the amount of water pumped per unit time, such as gallons per minute (gpm) or liters per minute (L/min). The discharge pressure, indicated by gages, is the pressure at which the pump is pumping water. The discharge pressure is in pounds per square inch (psi) or kilopascals (kPa). Pumps are rated according to their flow rate at 150 psi (1034 kPa) discharge and generally range from 500 gpm (1893 L/min) to 2,000 gpm (7571 L/min). These pumps are also required to provide 70 percent of their rated capacity at 200 psi (1379 kPa) and 50 percent of their rated capacity at 250 psi (1724 kPa). These ratings are summarized in Table 5-7A.

TABLE 5-7A. *Standard Pumps*

Rated Flow Rate		70 Percent of Rated Flow Rate		50 Percent of Rated Flow Rate	
gpm @ 150 psi	L/min @ 1034 kPa	gpm @ 200 psi	L/min @ 1379 kPa	gpm @ 250 psi	L/min @ 1724 kPa
500	1893	350	1325	250	946
750	2839	525	1987	375	1419
1000	3785	700	2650	500	1893
1250	4732	875	3312	625	2366
1500	5678	1050	3975	750	2839
1750	6624	1225	4637	875	3312
2000	7571	1400	5300	1000	3785

The centrifugal pump, a nonpositive displacement pump, consists essentially of a pair of rotating discs called shrouds, separated by curved partitions which are called vanes. This assembly makes up the impeller. Typically, fire apparatus pumps are multi-stage, usually two, thus permitting discharge at either higher flow rates with lower pressures or lower flow rates with higher pressures. The purpose of the multi-stage pump is to obtain the most effective operation at the lowest possible engine speed.

Pumping operations start with water from either a pressure source, such as a hydrant, or from a static water source, such as a pond. Drafting operations are required in the latter case. The factors that affect the height (lift) limitations to which water can be drafted and the flow rate are interrelated. These factors are: (1) atmospheric pressure, (2) water temperature, (3) friction loss in the suction hose and strainer, and (4) velocity energy.

Robert G. Purington is a retired fire chief and is a consulting engineer based in Arnold, CA.

The lift at a given flow rate can be determined by: Lift = atmospheric pressure − water vapor pressure − strainer and suction hose friction loss − velocity energy.

Atmospheric pressure varies from day to day according to the weather conditions and the elevation above sea level. Since drafting is essentially the creation of a vacuum or partial vacuum in the pump and suction hose, the total energy available for moving the water from the source to the pump is the atmospheric pressure. The nominal atmospheric pressure, 14.696 psia (101.333 kPa) at sea level, usually rounded to 14.7 psia (100 kPa), can theoretically provide a lift of almost 34 ft (10.5 m). Under actual conditions, a pump in excellent condition and pumping its rated capacity at sea level should be able to draft water at least 25 ft (7.6 m).

Often atmospheric pressure is given in inches of mercury. If this is the case, it must be converted to feet of water using:

$$h_w = 1.13h'_{Hg}$$

where:

h_w = feet of water
h'_{Hg} = inches of mercury.

The vapor pressure reduces the amount of vacuum that is possible and consequently reduces the total lift. Vapor pressure depends on the water temperature and is measured in terms of feet (meters) of water. Table 5-7B lists common values of vapor pressure as a function of water temperature.

TABLE 5-7B. ***Vapor Pressure***

Water Temperature		Vapor Pressure	
°F	°C	Ft of water	kPa
60	16	0.59	1.7
80	27	1.20	3.5
100	38	2.20	6.6
120	49	3.90	11.6

Another factor affecting the total lift is the friction loss in the suction hose and the strainer. The friction loss in the suction hose depends on the hose diameter, hose length, and the flow rate of the water. Equations for the friction loss in various sizes of suction hose are shown in Table 5-7C. The friction loss through the strainer is a function of the flow rate and the strainer diameter. The friction equations for the various strainer sizes are shown in Table 5-7D.

The velocity head also affects the total lift of the pump. The velocity head is given by $V^2/2g$, where V is the water velocity in feet per second (meters per second) and g is the acceleration due to gravity and is equal to 32.2 ft/sec^2 (9.81 m/sec^2). The velocity can be found by using the continuity equation, $Q = VA$, where Q is the flow rate in cubic feet per second (cubic meters per second) and A is the cross section of the suction hose in square feet (square meters). However, the flow rate is usually given in gallons (liters) per minute and the suction hose diameter is in inches (millimeters). Consequently, Table 5-7E can be used to determine the velocity head in the suction hose without tedious calculations.

In solving the lift equation, all units must be converted to the equivalent feet (or meters) of water. Atmospheric pressure is usually given in terms of inches of mercury (or kilopascals). Table 5-7F can be used to convert the atmospheric pressure to the equivalent feet (or meters) of water.

TABLE 5-7C. ***Suction Hose Friction Losses per 10 ft (3 m) Length***

Suction Hose Diameter		Friction Loss			
in.	mm	psi	kPa	ft	m
3	76	$0.083q^2$*	$0.0400q^2$**	$0.191q^2$	$0.00408q^2$
3½	88	$0.0385q^2$	$0.0186q^2$	$0.0886q^2$	$0.00189q^2$
4	102	$0.0197q^2$	$0.0095q^2$	$0.0454q^2$	$0.00978q^2$
4½	114	$0.0109q^2$	$0.0053q^2$	$0.0251q^2$	$0.00054q^2$
5	127	$0.00646q^2$	$0.0031q^2$	$0.0149q^2$	$0.00033q^2$
6	152	$0.0026q^2$	$0.0014q^2$	$0.006q^2$	$0.00014q^2$

* q = gpm × 100
**q = L/min × 100

TABLE 5-7D. ***Suction Strainer Friction Losses (Loss = Cq^2)***

Suction Hose Diameter		Friction Loss			
in.	mm	psi	kPa	ft	m
3	76	$0.147q^2$*	$0.0708q^2$**	$0.339q^2$	$0.00722q^2$
3½	88	$0.0793q^2$	$0.0353q^2$	$0.1827q^2$	$0.00390q^2$
4	102	$0.0465q^2$	$0.0225q^2$	$0.1071q^2$	$0.00229q^2$
4½	114	$0.0290q^2$	$0.0139q^2$	$0.0668q^2$	$0.00142q^2$
5	127	$0.0190q^2$	$0.0092q^2$	$0.0438q^2$	$0.00093q^2$
6	152	$0.00918q^2$	$0.0053q^2$	$0.0212q^2$	$0.00054q^2$

* q = gpm × 100
**q = L/min × 100

EXAMPLE: Convert atmospheric pressure to feet of water (lift).

Atmospheric pressure = 27.00 in. of mercury (91 kPa)
Water temperature = 60°F (15.5°C)
Flow rate = 1,100 gpm (4163 L/min)
Suction hose diameter (and strainer diameter) = 5 in. (127 mm)
Suction hose = two lengths of 10 ft (3 m) each.

SOLUTION: From Table 5-7F atmospheric pressure of 27.00 in. of mercury (91 kPa) equals 30.556 ft (9.31 m) of water. From Table 5-7B the vapor pressure [at 60°F (16°C)] equals 0.59 ft (0.18 m) of water. Using Table 5-7C, the friction loss for 10 ft (3 m) of 5-in. (127 mm) suction hose is $0.0149q^2$ in feet and $0.00033q^2$ in meters.

Q = 1,100 gpm (4163 L/min). However, the equation is for Q in 100s of gpm or L/min, and $Q/100 = q$. Therefore, use q = 11 (41.63). Thus:

$FL = (0.0149)(11)^2 = 1.8$ ft for 10 ft or $(2)(1.8) = 3.6$ ft for 20 ft.

In SI units: $FL = (0.00033)(41.63)^2 = 0.57$ m for 3 m or $(2)(0.57) = 1.14$ m for 6 m.

From the suction strainer equation listed in Table 5-7D:

$FL = 0.0438q^2$, where $q = 11$ as in the suction equation.

$FL = (0.0438)(11)^2 = 5.3$ ft.

In SI units: $FL = 0.00093q^2$, where $q = 41.63$.
$FL = (0.00093)(41.63)^2 = 1.6$ m.

TABLE 5-7E. *Velocity Head (V) For Suction Hose, ft (m) Water*

FLOW, *Q*		Suction Hose Diameter, (D) in inches and mm											
		3.0 in.	76 mm	3.5 in.	88 mm	4.0 in.	102 mm	4.5 in.	114 mm	5.0 in.	127 mm	6.0 in.	152 mm
gpm	L/min	ft.	m	ft	m	ft	m	ft	m	ft	m	ft	m
100	378	0.32	0.09	0.17	0.05	0.10	0.03	0.06	0.02	0.04	0.01	0.02	0.006
200	757	1.28	0.39	0.69	0.21	0.40	0.12	0.25	0.05	0.17	0.05	0.08	0.02
300	1136	2.88	0.88	1.55	0.47	0.91	0.28	0.57	0.17	0.37	0.11	0.18	0.05
400	1514	5.11	1.56	2.76	0.84	1.62	0.49	1.01	0.31	0.66	0.20	0.32	0.09
500	1892	7.99	2.44	4.31	1.31	2.53	0.78	1.58	0.48	1.04	0.32	0.50	00.15
600	2271	11.51	3.51	6.21	1.90	3.64	1.11	2.57	0.78	1.49	0.45	0.72	0.22
700	2650			8.45	2.58	4.96	1.51	3.09	0.94	2.03	0.62	0.98	0.30
800	3028			11.04	3.36	6.47	1.97	4.04	1.23	2.65	0.81	1.28	0.39
900	3407					8.19	2.50	5.11	1.56	3.36	1.02	1.62	0.49
1000	3785					10.11	3.08	6.31	1.92	4.14	1.26	2.00	0.61
1100	4163					12.24	3.73	7.64	2.33	5.01	1.53	2.42	0.74
1200	4542							9.09	2.78	5.97	1.82	2.88	0.88
1300	4921							10.67	3.25	7.00	2.13	3.38	1.03
1400	5300							12.37	3.78	8.12	2.47	3.92	1.19
1500	5677									9.32	2.84	4.49	1.37

TABLE 5-7F. *Inches of Mercury Vacuum Compared with Height of Water and Corresponding Pressure*

Vacuum Inches of Mercury	Pressure psig	Pressure psia	Height of Water (ft)
0.00	0.000	14.696	.000
1.00	-0.491	14.205	1.132
2.00	-0.982	13.714	2.263
3.00	-1.473	13.223	3.395
4.00	-1.965	12.731	4.527
5.00	-2.456	12.240	5.658
6.00	-2.947	11.749	6.790
7.00	-3.438	11.258	7.922
8.00	-3.929	10.767	9.054
9.00	-4.420	10.276	10.185
10.00	-4.912	9.784	11.317
11.00	-5.403	9.293	12.449
12.00	-5.894	8.802	13.580
13.00	-5.385	8.311	14.712
14.00	-6.876	7.820	15.844
15.00	-7.367	7.329	16.975
16.00	-7.858	6.838	18.107
17.00	-8.350	6.346	19.239
18.00	-8.841	5.855	20.370
19.00	-9.332	5.364	21.502
20.00	-9.823	4.873	22.634
21.00	-10.314	4.382	23.766
22.00	-10.805	3.891	24.897
23.00	-11.297	3.399	26.029
24.00	-11.788	2.908	27.161
25.00	-12.279	2.417	28.292
26.00	-12.770	1.926	29.424
27.00	-13.261	1.435	30.556
28.00	-13.752	0.944	31.687
29.00	-14.244	0.453	32.819
29.92	-14.696	0.000	32.862

SI Units: 1 in. of Mercury = 3.385 kPa; 1 psi = 6.895 kPa; 1 ft = 0.305 m.

The velocity head (from Table 5-7E) is 5 ft (1.53 m) of water. Therefore, the total lift is:

$$\text{Lift} = 30.56 - 0.59 - 3.6 - 5.3 - 5 = 16.1 \text{ ft.}$$

In SI units: Lift = 9.31 – 0.18 – 1.14 – 1.6 – 1.53 = 4.9 m (16.1 ft).

NOZZLES

The purpose of a nozzle is to shape the stream and convert pressure energy to velocity (kinetic) energy. In this way, the water can be applied to the fire in the appropriate quantity and from an adequate distance. There are many specialized nozzles. However, they all can be classified in two ways: (1) solid stream, and (2) fog (spray) nozzles. (See Figure 5-7A.) They both have advantages and disadvantages. These characteristics will be discussed.

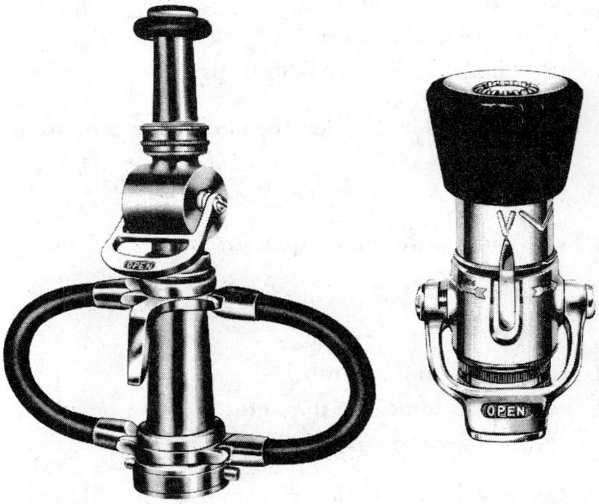

FIG. 5-7A. Straight stream nozzle (left) and fog nozzle (right). (Source: W. S. Darley and Co.)

The governing hydraulic characteristics of nozzles are the flow rate, diameter, and the nozzle pressure. The flow rate is the amount of water flowing out of the nozzle per unit time and is measured in gallons per minute or liters per minute.

Nozzle pressure is defined as the Pitot pressure (the stagnation pressure of the water coming from the nozzle tip), or the pressure at the base of the nozzle (pressure energy only). The Pitot pressure is used only for solid-stream nozzles, and the pressure at the base of the nozzle can be used for both kinds of nozzles. Practically speaking, there is usually little numerical difference in the two definitions. The unit of nozzle pressure is pounds per square inch (psi) or kilopascals (kPa).

Solid-Stream Nozzles

Solid-stream nozzles are classified according to the nozzle diameter. The diameters range from 1/4 in. to 2 1/2 in. (6 mm to 64 mm) or larger. The nozzle sizes are generally available in 1/8 in. (3 mm) graduations. Nozzles up to 1 1/8 in. (29 mm) or perhaps 1 1/4 in. (32 mm) are generally considered to be for "handlines," i.e., those manually held. Nozzles larger than about 1 1/4 in. (32 mm) have such large reaction forces that they must be mechanically restrained. These are usually called master streams, monitors, deluge, or deck guns. The 1 1/8-in. (29 mm) nozzle produces the so-called standard stream of 250 gpm (946 L/min) at about 45 psi (310 kPa) nozzle pressure.

Solid streams are useful where extreme range is desired, where it is necessary to penetrate soft material, such as peat, or when thermal degradation of spray streams prevents proper penetration.

Solid-stream nozzles are also useful in measuring water flows, since both their diameter and the Pitot pressure can be measured. From this information, the flow rate can be computed. It is related to the diameter and nozzle pressure by the following equations:

$$Q = 29.7d^2 \sqrt{p}$$

where:

Q = flow rate, gpm

d = nozzle diameter, in.

P = nozzle pressure (Pitot), psi

For most field hydraulics, the equation can be rounded to:

$$Q = 30d^2 \sqrt{p}$$

For SI units, the flow equation is:

$$Q = 0.0666{d_m}^2 \sqrt{P_m}$$

where:

Q = flow rate, (L/min)

d_m = inside nozzle diameter, (mm)

P_m = nozzle pressure, (kPa).

Theoretical flows from various nozzles at different nozzle pressures can be found in Section 5, Chapter 2, "Hydraulics."

Solid streams, with a lower surface-area-to-volume ratio, do not have as good heat-transfer characteristics as spray nozzles and, consequently, are not as effective in absorbing heat. Another disadvantage of a solid stream is that it is a better conductor of electricity than a spray.

Spray Nozzles

Spray nozzles, or fog nozzles as they are often called, produce varying degrees of water spray. They may have a fixed-spray angle, or may be adjustable from almost a straight stream to a very wide angle spray. The spray angle is customarily measured at the angle between the outer limits of the spray core. Many spray nozzles have predetermined pattern settings, usually at straight-stream, 30-, 60-, and 90-degree spray angles; however, most of them can also be set at intermediate angles.

Spray nozzles are generally classified according to the size of their hose coupling and their flow rate in gpm. Table 5-7G shows typical flow rates from spray nozzles.

TABLE 5-7G. ***Flows from Typical Fog Nozzles***

Nozzle Type	Flow Rate gpm	Flow Rate L/mm
3/4 to 1 in. (19 to 25 (mm) booster spray nozzle	10–40	38–151
1 1/2 in. (38 mm) spray nozzle	70–150	265–568
2 1/2 in. (64 mm) spray nozzle	200–300	757–1136
Master stream nozzles	500	1893
	750	2839
	1000	3785
	1250	4732
	1500	5678
	2000	7570

The designated flow from a spray nozzle is usually rated at 100 psi (690 kPa) nozzle pressure. Some spray nozzles have different flows at various angles. Generally, the flow increases as the angle widens. Other spray nozzles are "constant gallonage," i.e., they have the same flow at all spray angles. In addition, some models have a flow rate setting; they can be set for several different flow rates.

Flow rates are determined experimentally, either by a flow meter or by flowing water into a tank and measuring the time for a given quantity. Flow rate information is obtained from the manufacturer, and is usually reported as the flow rate at 100 psi (690 kPa) nozzle pressure for the various spray angles.

Flows for other pressures may be obtained by using the flow equation:

$$Q = 29.7d^2 \sqrt{P}$$

and finding the equivalent nozzle diameter d_e, using

$$d_e = \sqrt{Q/29.7 \sqrt{P}}$$

where:

d_e = equivalent nozzle diameter, in inches.

For SI units the flow formula is:

$$Q = 0.066\, {d_m}^2 \sqrt{P_m}$$

Where:

Q = flow rate (L/min);

d_m = inside nozzle diameter, (mm);

P_m = nozzle pressure (kPa).

HOSE LINE FIRE STREAM CALCULATIONS

The pump pressure (commonly called "engine pressure") is usually the end result of hose stream calculations. The methods for obtaining pump pressure are described below.

However, algebraic manipulation of the equations can yield any variable, providing the other quantities are known.

Special techniques, known as "field hydraulics" or "rule-of-thumb," are used by pump operators for approximate results. The methods shown below give more precise results, but are generally too involved for field applications. Details on rule-of-thumb fire stream calculations can be found in the fire fighting hydraulic texts listed in the bibliography of this chapter.

The calculation of the pump pressure depends on a number of variables: discharge pressure, hose friction loss, and back pressure due to elevation changes.

As shown previously, the discharge pressure is a function of the nozzle pressure and nozzle diameter. The hose friction loss is a function of the hose diameter and the hose length, in addition to losses in various appliances, such as monitors and ladder pipes.

Back pressure is the loss or gain of potential energy due to elevation changes between the pump and the nozzle. This is determined by the equations:

$BP = 0.434h$ (SI units: $BP_m = 9.81\ h_m$)

where:

BP = back pressure, psi (kPa)

h = elevation change or head, feet (m) of water.

The basis of these calculations revolves around three fundamental hydraulic principles:

Bernoulli's Equation: A special form of conservation of energy. For a pumper hose line system this becomes:

$$EP = NP + FL + BP$$

where:

EP = pump pressure, psi (kPa)

NP = nozzle pressure, psi (kPa)

FL = friction loss, psi (kPa)

BP = back pressure, psi (kPa).

The Darcy-Weibach Equation:

$$FL = (fV^2L)/(2gD)$$

where:

g = acceleration due to gravity, ft/sec^2 (m/s^2)

f = friction factor, a dimensionless number

L = hose length, ft (m)

D = hose diameter, in. (mm).

The Continuity Equation: This is a special form of conservation of mass.

$$Q = VA$$

where:

Q = flow rate, ft^3/sec (m^3/sec)

V = velocity, ft/sec (m/sec)

A = area, ft^2 (m^2).

These equations can be manipulated to result in friction loss equations and a modern version of the Underwriters equation.[1]

Friction loss is the loss of energy resulting from the internal friction between the moving particles of water and the friction between the water and the lining of the hose. The friction loss depends on water viscosity, flow rate, hose diameter, hose length, and the roughness characteristics of the hose lining. While the viscosity is partly a function of the water temperature, the change is insignificant in the ranges of the temperature of water commonly used for fire fighting. The flow rate, hose diameter, and length are variables that are determined by the fire fighting requirements. The roughness of the hose lining cannot be easily measured and is generally determined experimentally and reported as the friction factor. Consequently, all variables, except the flow rate, hose diameter, and hose length, are embodied in the friction factor, f, of the Darcy-Weibach equation and in the continuity equation. Putting all constants into one constant factor results in $FL = cq^2L$ for a given hose diameter, where L is traditionally given in hundreds of feet (meters) of hose and q is hundreds of gallons per minute or hundreds of liters per minute ($q = Q/100$).

TABLE 5-7H. *Recommended Friction Loss Equations*

Hose Diameter and Type Inches (mm)	Friction Loss Equation psi	kPa
¾ (19) booster	$FL = 1100q^2L$*	$FL = 1741q^2L$**
1 (25) booster	$FL = 150q^2L$	$FL = 238q^2L$
1¼ (32) booster	$FL = 80q^2L$	$FL = 127q^2L$
1¼ (32) linen	$FL = 127q^2L$	$FL = 201q^2L$
1½ (38) rubber-lined	$FL = 24q^2L$	$FL = 38q^2L$
1½ (38) linen	$FL = 51.2q^2L$	$FL = 81q^2L$
1¾ (45) with 1½ (38) couplings	$FL = 15.5q^2L$	$FL = 24.6q^2L$
2 (51) rubber-lined	$FL = 8q^2L$	$FL = 12.7q^2L$
2 (51) linen	$FL = 12.5q^2L$	$FL = 19.8q^2L$
2½ (64) linen	$FL = 4.26q^2L$	$FL = 6.75q^2L$
2½ (64) rubber-lined	†$FL = 2q^2L$	$FL = 3.17q^2L$
2¾ (70) with 3 (76) couplings	$FL = 1.5q^2L$	$FL = 2.36q^2L$
3 (76) with 2½ (64) couplings	$FL = 0.80q^2L$	$FL = 1.27q^2L$
3 (76) with 3 (76) couplings	$FL = 0.677q^2L$	$FL = 1.06q^2L$
3½ (88)	$FL = 0.34q^2L$	$FL = 0.53q^2L$
4 (102)	$FL = 0.2q^2L$	$FL = 0.305q^2L$
4½ (114)	$FL = 0.1q^2L$	$FL = 0.167q^2L$
5 (127)	$FL = 0.08q^2L$	$FL = 0.138q^2L$
6 (152)	$FL = 0.05q^2L$	$FL = 0.083q^2L$

** q = qpm × 100
L= Hose length in hundreds of ft (m)
† The equation replaces the old, less accurate and more complex equation $Fl = (2q^2 + q)\ L$. The old equation is still used. Those interested in it are referred to the bibliography.

For a standard 2½-in. (64 mm) double jacket, lined hose, the currently recommended constant is $c = 2$, or $FL = 2q^2L$. (For SI units, $FL = 3.17q^2L$.) Suggested constants for other hose sizes and friction loss equations are shown in Table 5-7H.

An approximate constant can be determined from $FL = (fQ^2L)/(2gD^5)$ by assuming the same friction characteristics for both hose sizes, so:

$k_h = (D_1)^5/(D_2)^5$
If D_1 is 2½ in., then:
$k_h = (2.5)^5/(d_2)^5 = 97.9/(D_2)^5$,

k_h can then be used to convert a given hose diameter (and length) to 2½ in. equivalent length.

$$L' = k_hL$$

Where L' is the equivalent 2½ in. length, k_h is the hose conversion factor and L is the given hose length.

[For SI units, $k_h = (64)^5/D_2)^5$ where $D_2)^5$ where D_2 is the given hose diameter required to be converted to the 64 mm equivalent length.]

TABLE 5-7I. ***Factors for Converting Hose to 2½ in. (64 mm) Equivalent (k^h)***

Hose Diameter in. (mm)	References*						
	IFSTA 1980	Gaskill 1966	Erwin 1972	Holwege 1961	Other	$97.7/D^5$	Recommended Factors
¾ (19)	344	550	590	345		412	500
1 (25)	91	75	78.5	90.9		97.7	75
1¼ (32)	40					32	40
1¼ (32) linen	63.6					32	63.6
1½ (38) rubber-lined	13.5	12	12.25	13.5	9.81	12.86	12
1½ (38)	25.6					12.86	25.6
1¾ (45) with 1½ (38)					7.76	5.95	7.76
2 (51) rubber-lined	2.94				4.0	3.05	4
2 (51) linen	6.25					3.05	6.25
2½ (64) linen	2.13					1.0	2.13
2¾ (70) with 3 (76)					0.75	0.62	0.75
3 (76) with 2½ (64)	0.4	0.4	0.4	0.4	0.4	0.4	
3 with 3 (76)	0.385	0.333		0.385		0.4	0.333
3½ (88)	0.17			0.172		0.186	0.17
4 (102)	0.09			0.09	0.1	0.095	0.1
4½ (114)	0.051			0.0513	0.05	0.053	0.05
5 (127)	0.031			0.031	0.03	0.033	0.04
					0.0446		
					0.333		
6 (152)						0.0125	0.0125

* See references cited 4 through 7 in bibliography.

The hose conversion factor, k_h, and the friction loss equation constant, c, are functions of both the hose diameter and the friction characteristics of the hose. These two constants are determined experimentally. The classical hose experimentation was done by John R. Freeman.[2] Subsequent tests were made by Underwriters Laboratories Inc.,[3] James Gaskill,[4] and many fire departments. The values in Table 5-7I are based on the best current information, and should be used until more current data becomes available.

The pump pressure can be found using the appropriate equations shown below:

Given NP, L, D, and d,

1. Find $Q = 29.7d^2\sqrt{P}$
(SI): $Q = 0.0666\, d_m^{\,2}\sqrt{P_m}$)

Convert hose to 2½ in. (64 mm) equivalent
$k_h = 97.7/D^5$ [SI: $= (64)^5/D^5$]
or
$L' = k_hL$
from Table 5-7I

2. Find $FL = cq^2L$
$FL = 2q^2$(SI $= 3.17\, q^2$)

BP = $0.43h$ [SI = $9.81h$]
up is +
down is –
h = distance above or below the pump in ft (m)

3. EP = $NP + FL$ + BP

EXAMPLE: What pump pressure is required to establish a theoretical nozzle pressure of 10 psi (69 kPa) at the end of 400 ft (122 m) of 4-in. (102 mm) hose if it rises up through an elevation of 10 ft (3.05 m) from engine to nozzle?

SOLUTION:

U.S. customary units:

$Q = 29.7\,(4.0)^2\sqrt{10}$

$Q = 1502$ gpm,

i.e.,

$$q = \frac{1502}{100} = 15.02$$

$FL = 0.2\, q^2L$ (for 4-in. hose)

$FL = 0.2\,(1502)^2\,(400/100)$

$FL = 180$ psi.

$BP = 0.434\, h$

$BP = 0.434 \times 10$

$BP = 4.34$ psi.

$EP = NP + F + BP$

$EP = 10 + 180 + 4.3$

$EP = 194.3$ psi.

SI units:

$Q = 0.0666\,(102)^2\sqrt{69}$

$Q = 5756$ (L/min)

$Q = 5756/100 = 57.6.$

$FL = 0.305\, q^2L$ (for 102 mm hose)

$FL = 0.305\,(57.6)^2\,(122/100)$

$FL = 1234$ kPa.

$BP = 9.81\, L$

$BP = 9.81 \times 3.05$

$BP = 29.9$ kPa.

$EP = NP + FL + BP$

$EP = 69 + 1234 + 29.9$

$EP = 1333$ kPa (this converts to 193 psi).

This scheme works well for simple straight lines, particularly if the flow rate is given. However, for more complex setups, the following is recommended:[1]

For 2½-in. (64 mm) rubber-lined hose

$$EP = NP\,(1 + 1.76\,k_nL) + BP$$

where:

EP = engine pressure, psi
NP = nozzle pressure, psi
k_n = *nozzle constant (see Table 5-7K)*
L = hose length, 100s of feet
BP = back pressure due to elevation change, psi.

In SI units, for the equivalent 64 mm rubber-lined hose

$$\text{EP} = NP\,(1 + 2.99\,k_{nm}L) + BP$$

where:

EP = engine pressure, kPa
NP = nozzle pressure, kPa
k_{nm} = *nozzle constant (see Table 5-7K)*
L = hose length in 100s of meters
BP = back pressure due to elevation change, kPa.

For other sizes, use either 2½-in. (64 mm) equivalent length or a special equation for the particular hose size (shown in Table 5-7J).

The nozzle constant, k_n, *is numerically equal to* $k_n = d^4/10$ (in SI units, $k_{nm} = d^4/10^6$). Table 5-7K shows values of k_n *for solid-stream nozzles and the equivalent* k_n *for several spray nozzles.*

For siamese or parallel lines, a single 2½-in. (64 mm) equivalent length must be determined:

$$L' = k_sL$$

where:

L' = 2½-in. (64 mm) equivalent length

k_s = the siamese constant which is generally taken as the number of lines, assuming that all lines are the same diameter.[8] (However some authorities use a slightly modified siamese constant to account for friction in fittings and appliances. Suggested values for k_s are given in Table 5-7L.)

Where siamesed lines are of unequal length and/or diameter, find the average length and the 2½-in. (64 mm) equivalent lengths, respectively. For two lines, all of the above can be combined in one equation:

$$L'' = k_s\,(k_{h1}L_1 + k_{h2}L_2)/2$$

L'' is another way of expressing equivalent length. For more than two lines, the equation can be expanded. If the lines are the same diameter, a precise equivalent length can be found from:

$$L'' = \frac{L_1}{\left[1 + \left(\sqrt{\frac{L_1}{L_2}}\right)\right]^2}$$

For more than two lines, the general equation is:

$$L'' = \frac{L_1}{\left[1 + \sqrt{\frac{L_1}{L_3}} + \sqrt{\frac{L_1}{L_3}} + \sqrt{\frac{L_1}{L_4}} + \ldots \sqrt{\frac{L_1}{L_n}}\right]^2}$$

TABLE 5-7J. ***Engine Pressure Formulas for Various Hose Sizes***

Hose Size in. (mm)	Formulas: Customary Units	Formulas: SI Units
¾ (19) booster	$EP = NP\,(1 + 968k_nL)$	$EP = NP\,(1 + 782k_{nm}L)$
1 (25) booster	$EP = NP\,(1 + 132k_nL)$	$EP = NP\,(1 + 106k_{nm}L)$
1¼ (32) booster	$EP = NP\,(1 + 70.4k_nL)$	$EP = NP\,(1 + 54.5k_{nm}L)$
1¼ (32) linen	$EP = NP\,(1 + 112k_nL)$	$EP = NP\,(1 + 86.3k_{nm}L)$
1½ (38) rubber-lined	$EP = NP\,(1 + 21.1k_nL)$	$EP = NP\,(1 + 16.8k_{nm}L)$
1½ (38) linen	$EP = NP\,(1 + 45k_nL)$	$EP = NP\,(1 + 35.9k_{nm}L)$
1¾ (45) with 1½ (38) couplings	$EP = NP\,(1 + 13.6k_nL)$	$EP = NP\,(1 + 11.0k_{nm}L)$
2 (51) rubber-lined	$EP = NP\,(1 + 7.04\,k_nL)$	$EP = NP\,(1 + 5.63k_{nm}L)$
2 (51) linen	$EP = NP\,(1 + 11k_nL)$	$EP = NP\,(1 + 8.78k_{nm}L)$
2½ (64) rubber-lined	$EP = NP\,(1 + 1.76k_nL)$	$EP = NP\,(1 + 2.99k_{nm}L)$
2½ (64) linen	$EP = NP\,(1 + 3.75k_nL)$	$EP = NP\,(1 + 1.40k_{nm}L)$
2¾ (70) w/3 (76) couplings	$EP = NP\,(1 + 1.32k_nL)$	$EP = NP\,(1 + 1.05k_{nm}L)$
3 (76) w/2½ (64) couplings	$EP = NP\,(1 + 0.704k_nL)$	$EP = NP\,(1 + 0.56k_{nm}L)$
3 (76) w/3 (76) couplings	$EP = NP\,(1 + 0.586k_nL)$	$EP = NP\,(1 + 0.47k_{nm}L)$
3½ (88)	$EP = NP\,(1 + 0.3k_nL)$	$EP = NP\,(1 + 0.235k_{nm}L)$
4 (102)	$EP = NP\,(1 + 0.17k_nL)$	$EP = NP\,(1 + 0.135k_{nm}L)$
4½ (114)	$EP = NP\,(1 + 0.88k_nL)$	$EP = NP\,(1 + 0.074k_{nm}L)$
5 (127)	$EP = NP\,(1 + 0.07k_nL)$	$EP = NP\,(1 + 0.061k_{nm}L)$
6 (152)	$EP = NP\,(1 + 0.022k_nL)$	$EP = NP\,(1 + 0.037k_{nm}L)$

TABLE 5-7K. *Nozzle Factors*

Nozzle Diameter in.	Customary Units *kn**	Nozzle Diameter mm	SI Units k_{nm}
1/16	1.53×10^{-6}	2	1.6×10^{-5}
1/8	2.44×10^{-6}	3	8.1×10^{-5}
3/16	1.24×10^{-4}	5	6.25×10^{-4}
1/4	3.91×10^{-4}	6	1.30×10^{-3}
5/16	9.54×10^{-4}	8	4.10×10^{-3}
3/8	1.98×10^{-3}	10	0.010
7/16	3.66×10^{-3}	11	0.015
1/2	6.3×10^{-3}	13	0.029
9/16	0.01	14	0.038
5/8	0.0153	16	0.066
11/16	0.0223	17	0.084
3/4	0.0316	19	0.130
13/16	0.0436	21	0.194
7/8	0.0586	22	0.234
1	0.1	25	0.416
1 1/8	0.16	29	0.707
1 1/4	0.244	32	1.05
1 3/8	0.357	35	1.50
1 1/2	0.506	38	2.11
1 5/8	0.697	41	2.83
1 3/4	0.938	44	3.90
1 7/8	1.24	48	5.31
2	1.6	51	6.66
2 1/2	3.9	64	16.3
3	8.1	76	33.7
3 1/2	15.0	89	62.4
4	25.6	102	107.0
4 1/2	41.0	114	171.0
5	62.5	127	260.0
6	130.0	152	539.0

$^*k_n = \frac{d^4}{10}$ $\left(k_{nm} = \frac{d^4}{10^6}\right)$

TABLE 5-7L. *Siamese Conversion Factors (k_s)* to Single 2-1/2 in. (64 mm) Equivalent Length

Number of Hose Lines	Siamese Conversion Factor To Single 2 1/2 in. Equivalent Length
Two 2 1/2 in.	0.25
Three 2 1/2 in.	0.11
Four 2 1/2 in.	0.0625
Five 2 1/2 in.	0.04
Two 3 in. with 2 1/2 in. couplings	0.08
Three 3 in. with 2 1/2 in couplings	0.0307

Figure 5-7B is a schematic illustrating the solution of siamese line problems, and Figure 5-7C includes hose sizes other than 2 1/2 in. (64 mm).

A common hose lay is the wyed or branch lines. This set-up involves a 2 1/2-in. (64 mm) or larger supply or lead line branched into two or more lines. The legs or branches are typically smaller diameter hoses than the supply line. A typical set-up involves a 2 1/2-in. (64 mm) supply line and two 1 1/2-in. (38 mm) branches, each 100 or 150 ft (30 or 45 m) in length.

The solution to engine pressure problems depends on whether or not the branches or legs are symmetrical, i.e., hose length, diameters, and nozzles equal. (See Figure

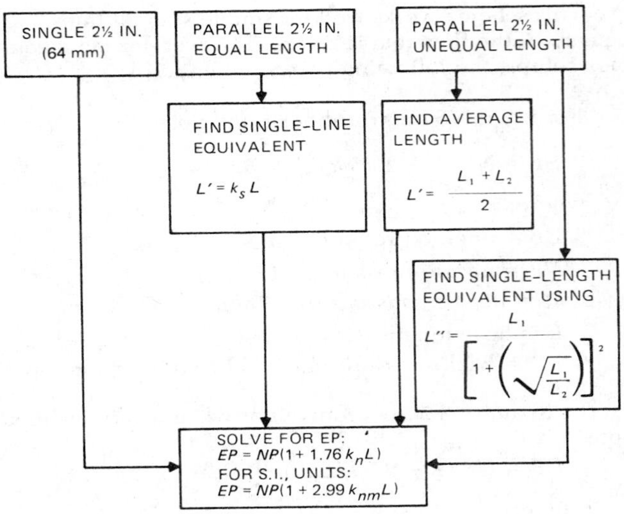

FIG. 5-7B. Solving for engine pressure, 2 1/2-in. (64 mm) hose.

5-7D for outline of the solution.) If the legs are symmetrical, the solution can be easily determined by finding an equivalent nozzle diameter and equivalent nozzle constant from:

$$L'' = \frac{L_1}{\left[1 + \left(\sqrt{\frac{L_1}{L_2}}\right)\right]^2}$$

If the lines are not symmetrical, a more involved calculation is required for an exact solution. (The method described above for symmetrical lines can be used for an approximate solution.)

The technique involves finding the flow through one of the legs and determining the friction loss in that leg and the pressure at the wye. Using the pressure at the wye as engine pressure, calculate the nozzle pressure on the other line and the flow from the second line and then sum up the flow from all the lines. With this flow known, the friction loss in the supply line can be found. The engine pressure is the supply line friction loss plus the pressure at the wye. This technique is also shown in Figure 5-7D.

LARGE-DIAMETER HOSE

Many fire departments are now using large-diameter hose. The most popular sizes in use include:

- 3-in. (76 mm) hose with 2 1/2-in. (64 mm) couplings
- 3-in. (76 mm) hose with 3-in. (76 mm) couplings
- 4-in. (101 mm) hose with 4-in. (101 mm) couplings
- 5-in. (127 mm) hose with 5-in. (127 mm) couplings
- 6-in. (152 mm) hose with 6-in. (152 mm) couplings

The main advantage of large-diameter hose is its lower friction loss. It is especially useful as a supply line with large flows. Because of the low friction loss, some fire departments use large-diameter hose for supply lines into a portable hydrant, from which smaller working lines [2 1/2 in. (64 mm), 1 1/2 in. (38 mm), etc.] are then taken off.

Large-diameter hose is also useful for relaying water, i.e., one pumper supplying a second.

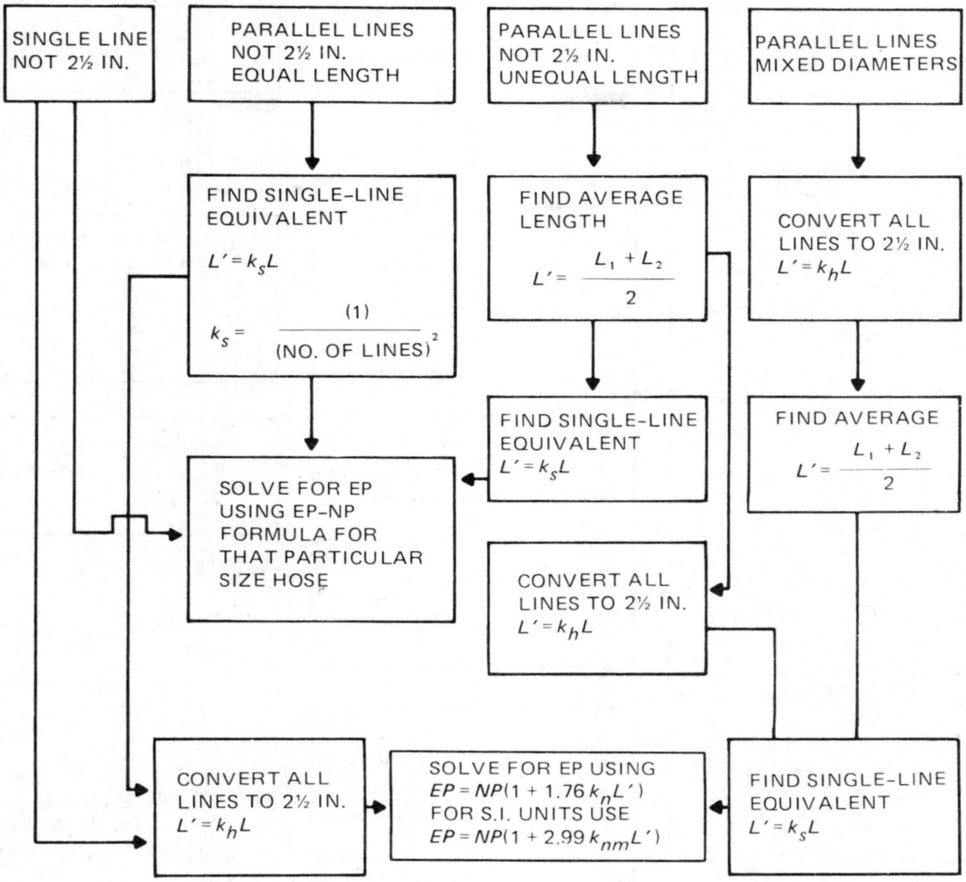

FIG. 5-7C. Solving for engine pressure, all hose sizes.

There have been some complaints that the large-diameter hose is difficult to handle and, in some cases, wears out rapidly. Nevertheless, even if these disadvantages are not overcome, they appear to be overshadowed by the advantages, at least for certain applications.

FRICTION-REDUCING ADDITIVES

Certain high-molecular-weight polymers injected into a pump or hoseline have the capacity of reducing friction. These polymers include polyethylene oxide, polyacrylamide, polysulfonates, and hydroxethyl cellulose, the first being the most prevalent in current use. Several trade names are used to describe friction-reducing additives. Polymer additives reduce friction loss by as much as 50 percent. This permits flowing greater amounts of water in smaller diameter hose ("rapid water").

For example, 200 gpm (757 L/min) of plain water flowing in 1½-in. (38 mm) hose has a friction loss of about 96 psi (662 kPa). With such high friction loss, and assuming a nozzle (spray type) pressure of 100 psi (690 kPa), the maximum distance 200 gpm (757 L/min) could be pumped through 1½-in. (38 mm) hose without exceeding the hose test pressure of 250 psi (1724 kPa) is about 150 ft (45.7 m). On the other hand, with polyethylene oxide additive the friction loss of 200 gpm (757 L/min) through 100 ft (30.5 m) of 1½-in. (38 mm) hose is about 25 psi (172 kPa). Adding the friction-reducing polymer permits 1½-in. (38 mm) lines to provide 200-gpm (757 L/min) flows at 100 psi (690-kPa) nozzle pressures up to 600 ft (183 m) without exceeding pump pressure of 250 psi (1724 kPa). In other words, 1½-in. (38 mm) hose with the friction-reducing additive can have almost the same "punch" as 2½-in. (64 mm) hose lines, for at least distances up to 600 ft (183 m).

The use of the smaller-diameter hose can be a significant advantage, since water in 2½-in. (64 mm) hose weighs about 2 lb/ft (3 kg/m) as compared to ¾ lb/ft (1.1 kg/m) for 1½-in. (38 mm) hose. For a 50-ft (15 m) length, this is 100 lb (45 kg) *vs* about 35 lb (16.8 kg) (neglecting the weight of the hose). This weight reduction is crucial to the fire fighter who is dragging a hose line into position.

The City of New York Fire Department has considerable experience using 1¾-in. (44 mm) hose [with 1½-in. (38 mm) couplings] in conjunction with a friction-reducing agent. With this arrangement, they combined the fire extinguishing capability of a 2½-in. (64 mm) line with the mobility of a 1½-in. (38 mm) line.

There are some technical difficulties with some of the additives that are apparently being overcome. For example, the polymer is nontoxic, but it is difficult to inject into the hose stream. Also, the polymer is subject to deterioration at temperatures exceeding 120°F (48.9°C), or less than 32°F (0°C).

Some equations are shown in Table 5-7M that can be used to establish the friction loss in hose with rapid water. These equations should be used with discretion, however,

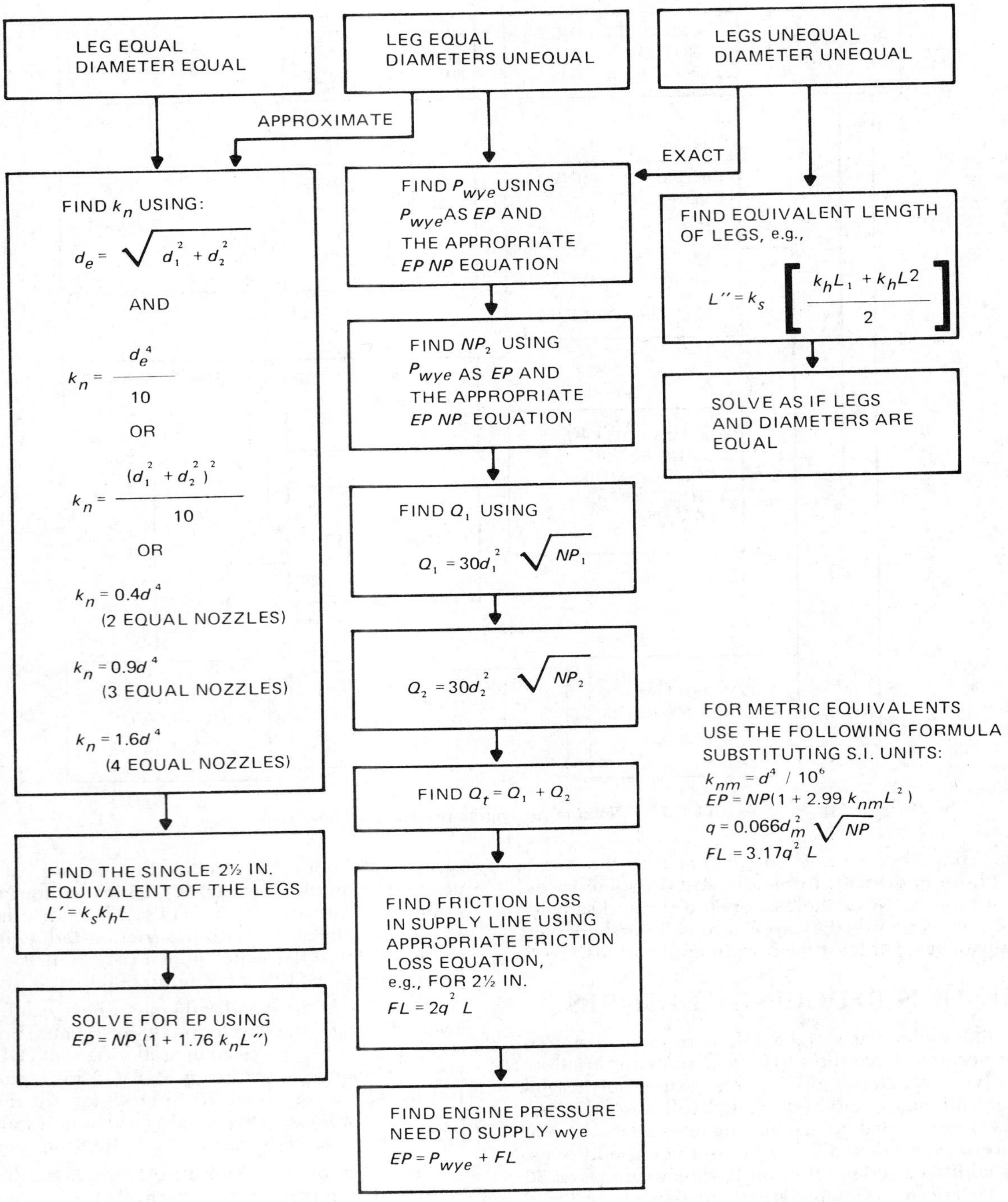

FIG. 5-7D. Solving for engine pressure for wyed lines.

since the friction loss is a function of polyethylene oxide concentration, which is not reflected in these equations.

REACTION FORCES IN HOSE LINES AND NOZZLES

When water is discharged from a hose line, there are two reaction forces acting on the line: (1) hose line reaction, and (2) nozzle reaction. Both contribute in varying degrees to the total reaction that is present in any hose nozzle flow configuration. For purposes of simplicity, each is treated separately in this chapter.

Hose Line Reaction

Reaction forces occur in hose lines when the direction of waterflow is changed by a bend in the hose. Between the hydrant and nozzle, the velocity is constrained in the hose and the acceleration is zero as shown by the equation $Q = AV$, where Q is the flow rate, A is the cross-section area, and V is the average velocity.

TABLE 5-7M. *Friction Loss, Using "Rapid Water"*

Hose Size in. (mm)	psi	kPa
1½-in. (38) rubber-lined hose*	$FL = 7.5q2L$	$FL = 11.8q^2L$
1¾ in. (45) with 1½ in. (38) couplings	$FL = 6.2q^2L$	$FL = 9.8q^2L$
2½-in. (64) rubber-lined hose*	$FL = 0.7q^2L$	$FL = 1.1q^2L$
	q = 100s of gpm; L = 100s of feet	q = 100s of L/min; L = 100s of meters

* Derived from D. B. Brown, "Reducing Friction Loss in Fire Fighting Streams Using Poly (Ethylene Oxide) Slurry," presented at the 1974 NFPA Meeting, Miami Beach, FL.

Figure 5-7E illustrates a typical hand-line situation where enough push must be applied at the bend to resist the reaction force F_3. There is no problem where the hose bends off the ground.

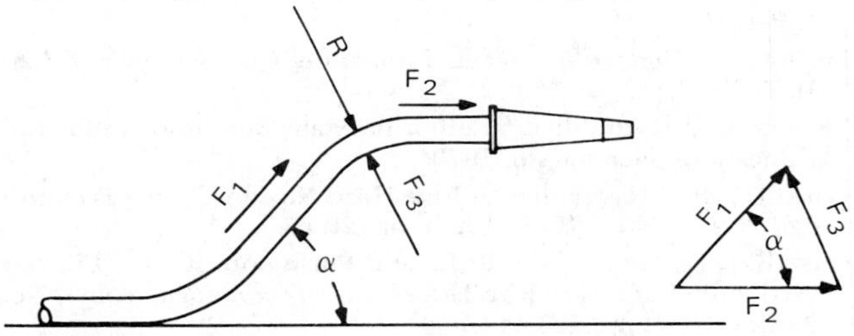

FIG. 5-7E. **Reaction in a hose line.** **a = deflection angle at bend. F_3 = *resultant of forces F_1, and F_2 (reaction in lbs).* R = *force needed to hold hose against F_3.***

Figures 5-7F(a) and 5-7F(b) are charts by which values of the reaction F_3, in pounds force, can be directly determined. To obtain reactions in other sizes of hose, Figures 5-7F(a) and 5-7F(b) each include a table of conversion factors.

EXAMPLE: What is the reaction at a 55-degree bend in 1½-in. (38 mm) hose if the pressure is 100 psi (690 kPa)?

SOLUTION: On the deflection angle side, move horizontally from the 55-degree bend to intersection with the 100 psi (690 kPa) curve. From there go down vertically to the reaction scale and read 450 lb (204 kg). From Figures 5-7F(a) and (b), note that the factor for 1½-in. (38 mm) hose is 0.36. Multiplying 450 (204 kg) by 0.36, the answer is 162 lb (73 kg).

Nozzle Reaction

Water discharging from a nozzle produces a reaction that is opposite the flow of water and known as nozzle reaction. As flow and pressure are increased, the nozzle reaction increases. Nozzle reaction of solid-stream nozzles may be calculated by means of the following formula:

$$NR = 1.5d^2NP$$

where:

NR = nozzle reaction, lb
d = nozzle diameter, in.
NP = nozzle pressure, psi.

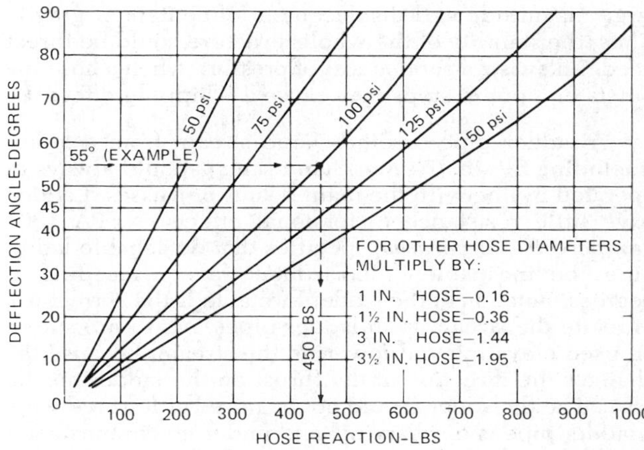

FIG. 5-7F(a). ***Reaction forces in 2½-in. hose. (See table within the graph for onversion factors to use in calculating reaction forces, expressed as pounds force, in hose of other diameters.)***

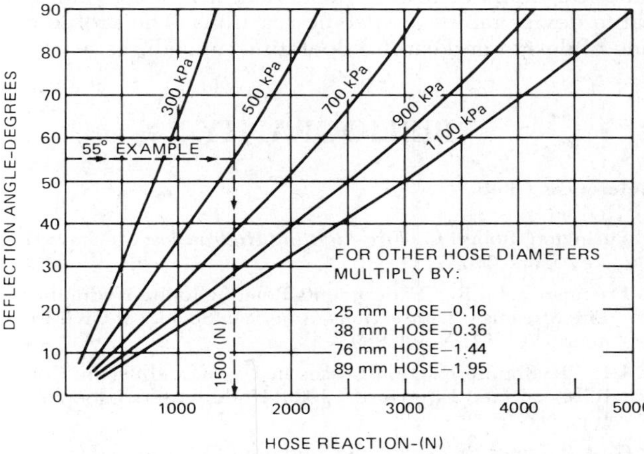

FIG. 5-7F(b). ***Reaction forces in 64-mm hose. (See table within the graph for conversion factors to use in calculating reaction forces, expressed in newtons, in hose of other diameters.)***

Another formula that may be used for both solid-stream and spray nozzles is:

$$NR = 0.0505\,Q\sqrt{NP}$$

where:

Q = flow rate, gpm.

For SI units:

$NR = (1.6 \times 10\text{-}3)\, d^2NP$

where:

NR = nozzle reaction, N (Newton)
d = nozzle diameter, mm
NP = nozzle pressure, kPa.

Reaction Forces in Ladder and Tower Streams

The reaction of heavy streams, either solid or spray, discharged from ladder pipes, platform booms, and towers can easily cause serious problems, such as leverage effects of large magnitude and displacement of centers of gravity. Thus, the stability of the whole structure could be threatened. Likewise, a sudden loss of pressure when a hose line bursts or a pump stops may cause a whipping effect.

A ladder pipe or other large stream from a ladder [including 2½-in. (64 mm) hand lines] should always be operated in line with the main beams or trusses. Ladders have little resistance to torsional effects. NFPA 1901, *Pumper Fire Apparatus*, specifies that detachable ladder pipes be incapable of horizontal travel exceeding 15 degrees. Rotation of the ladder turntable is the correct way to rotate the stream from ladder pipes. Also, care should be used elevating and lowering the stream, because this changes the direction of the thrust on the ladder mechanism. The fly ladder should not be raised or lowered while a ladder pipe is discharging, and under no circumstances should the vehicle be moved with the ladder pipe discharging. All such streams should be gated to permit movement of the ladder and vehicle without shutting down the pump.

Because there are many variable forces acting on mobile ladders or towers in service, it is quite impractical to devise tables of specific reactions. The problem is one of design and careful operating procedures.

BIBLIOGRAPHY

References Cited

1. Purington, Robert G., *Fire-Fighting Hydraulics*, McGraw-Hill, New York, 1974.
2. Freeman, John R., "Experiments Relating to the Hydraulics of Fire Streams," *Transactions*, American Society of Civil Engineers, Vol. 21, Nov. 1889.
3. UL, "Hydraulic Friction Losses in 1½-in. and 2½-in. Cotton Rubber-Lined Fire Hose," 1939, Underwriters Laboratories Inc., NY.
4. Gaskill, James R., "Hydraulic Studies of Fire Hose," *Fire Technology*, Vol. 2, No. 1, 1966.
5. IFSTA, *Fire Stream Practices*, International Fire Service Training Association, Stillwater, OK, 1980.
6. Erwin, Lawrence W., *Fire Hydraulics*, Glencoe Press, Beverly Hills, CA, 1972.
7. Holwege, J., "What Size Fire Hose," *Washington Comm. and School*, 1961.
8. Vennard, John K., *Elementary Fluid Mechanics*, 4th ed., John Wiley & Sons, New York, 1961.

NFPA Codes, Standards, and Recommended Practices

Reference to the following NFPA codes, standards, and recommended practices will provide further information on fire streams discussed in this chapter. (See the latest *NFPA Catalog* for availability of current editions of the following documents.)

NFPA 1901, *Pumper Fire Apparatus*.

NFPA 1911, *Service Tests of Pumps on Fire Department Apparatus*.

NFPA 1961, *Fire Hose*.

NFPA 1962, *Care, Use, and Maintenance of Fire Hose, Including Connections and Nozzles*.

NFPA 1964, *Spray Nozzles (Shutoff and Tip)*.

Additional Reading

Bonadio, G. E., *Firefighting Hydraulics*, Arco Publishing Co., New York, 1979.

Casey, J. F., ed., *Fire Service Hydraulics*, 2nd ed., Fire Engineering, Bode Service, Tulsa, OK, 1984.

Cozad, D., *Water Supply for Fire Protection*, Prentice-Hall, Englewood Cliffs, NJ, 1981, pp. 79-160, 215-257.

"Developing Good Solid Fire Streams," American Insurance Association Bulletin 50, rev. ed., American Insurance Association, NY, 1970.

Firefighters Hydraulics, Davis Publishing Co., Santa Cruz, CA, 1962.

"Fireground Hydraulics," California State Bureau of Industrial Education, Sacramento, 1970.

Gaskill, J. R., "Hydraulics of Fire Hose Nozzles," *Fire Technology*, Vol. 3, No. 1 (Feb. 1967), pp. 20-28.

Gaskill, J. R., Henderson, R. L., and Purington, R. G., "Further Hydraulic Studies of Fire Hose," *Fire Technology*, Vol. 3, No. 2 (May 1967) pp. 105-114.

"Heavy Stream Appliances and Their Effective Use," American Insurance Association Bulletin 147, rev. ed., American Insurance Association, NY, 1963.

Hickey, H. E., *Hydraulics for Fire Protection*, National Fire Protection Association, Quincy, MA, 1980.

Kimball, W. Y., *Effective Streams for Fighting Fires*, 2nd ed., National Fire Protection Association, Quincy, MA, 1976.

Mahoney, E. F., *Fire Department Hydraulics*, Allyn and Bacon, Boston, 1980, pp. 85-252.

Operating Fire Department Aerial Ladders, National Fire Protection Association, Quincy, MA, 1967.

Purington, R. G., *Fire-Fighting Hydraulics*, McGraw-Hill, New York, 1974, pp. 127-286.

Purington, R. G., "Friction Loss Studies Using a 0.0127-m Fire Hose," *Fire Technology*, Vol. 11, No. 3 (Aug. 1975) pp. 184-190.

Salzberg, F., Vodvarka, F. J., and Maatman, G. L., "Minimum Water Requirements for Suppression of Room Fires," *Fire Technology*, Vol. 6, No. 1 (Feb. 1970) pp. 22-28.

TEST OF WATER SUPPLIES

Revised by John R. Anderson

An existing water supply system is one of the most important factors in public or private protection. Fire departments and fire protection engineers, as well as those responsible for the design, operation, and maintenance of water systems, are concerned with two aspects of the water supply: (1) its adequacy, and (2) its reliability.

Adequacy in the case of a water system supplying water for normal consumption and for fire protection can be defined as having the capability of simultaneously supplying water for maximum normal consumption demands and water that may be needed to combat and extinguish a major fire within the area served by the water system.

Reliability of a water system can be defined as having the capability of supplying the maximum daily consumption plus a required fire demand, even in the event of a malfunction or the outage of important system components, such as a pipe line break, valve failure, power failure, or pump outage.

This chapter explains the objectives of water supply testing, test procedures, and graphical solutions to test and flow problems.

The hydraulics principles underlying waterflow and pump testing can be found in Chapter 2, "Hydraulics," and Chapter 6, "Fire Pumps," in this section. Information on water supply requirements and systems can be found in Chapter 3, "Water Supply Requirements for Fire Protection," and Chapter 4, "Water Distribution Systems," also in this section of the handbook.

TEST OBJECTIVES

Hydrant flow tests conducted on public water systems are usually made to determine the rate at which water is available at specific locations within the distribution system to determine points of connection for pipe line extensions, for booster pump applications, to verify the accuracy of distribution models, and for a variety of other purposes.

Of particular interest to fire departments and insurance companies is the rate and quantity at which water is available to concentrated high-value areas, such as shopping centers, industrial parks, institutions, and built-up residential areas.

Private fire systems are usually tested for water flow and integrity annually. This includes testing the operating performance of fire pumps, standpipes or elevated tanks, municipal connections, other water sources, and the overall adequacy of the system.

Flow testing of public water systems should not be conducted without the consent and assistance of waterworks personnel, and possibly the local police and fire departments. Fire departments will usually aid in the test work; police may be needed to control vehicular and pedestrian traffic.

Hydrant and flow tests are made so frequently and the results obtained are so important that it is imperative for anyone charged with the responsibility for operation, management, or maintenance of a water supply system to be aware of how tests are conducted and to be able to interpret the results correctly.

Hydrant flow tests should not be attempted until all the operational characteristics of a water system are known. Results may differ substantially depending upon the operation of pumping equipment, water levels in the system's storage facilities, rates of consumption, and points of demand in the system. Even though it is possible to conduct accurate tests within acceptable tolerances, the results obtained will often vary from day to day and even at different periods during the same day because of the many variables involved.

TEST EQUIPMENT

In order to conduct hydrant flow tests, the following equipment should be provided, calibrated in customary American units or appropriate SI units.

1. 6-in. steel rule with $^1/_{16}$-in. divisions.
2. A Pitot tube, together with a test-pressure gage, suitable for the pressures to be expected, with $^1/_2$-lb graduations (usually a 60-psi gage is satisfactory). (See Figure 5-8A.)

John R. Anderson, P.E., is a consulting engineer, based in Marshfield Hills, MA.

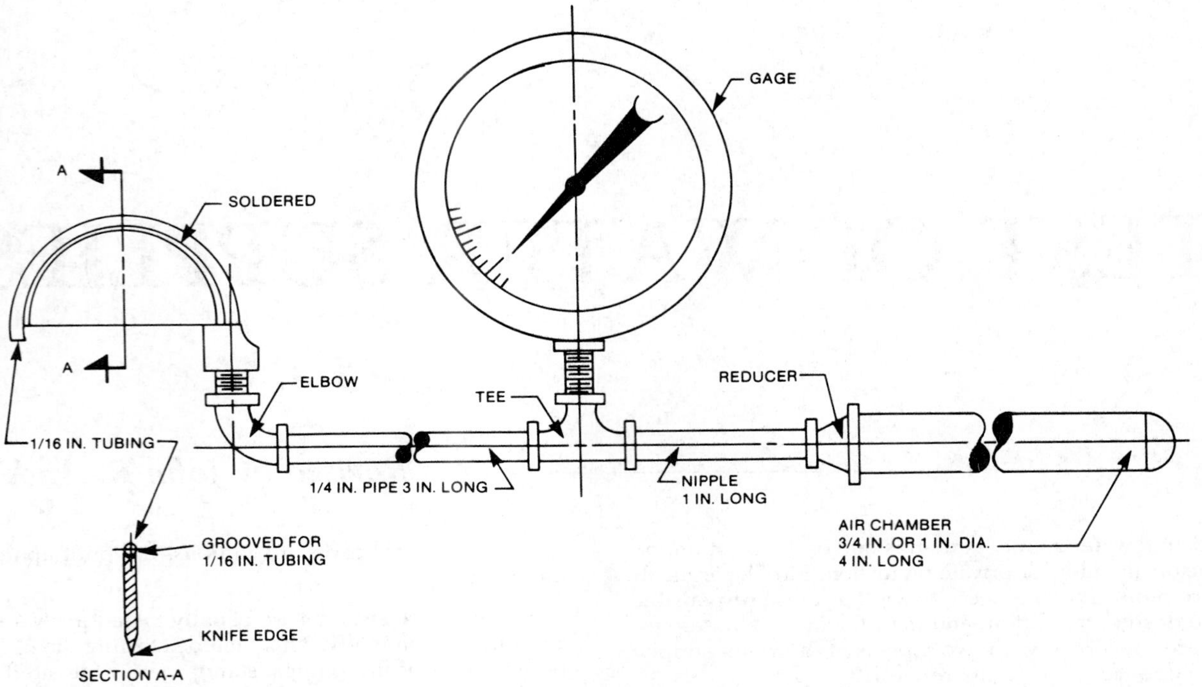

FIG. 5-8A. A typical Pitot tube assembly.

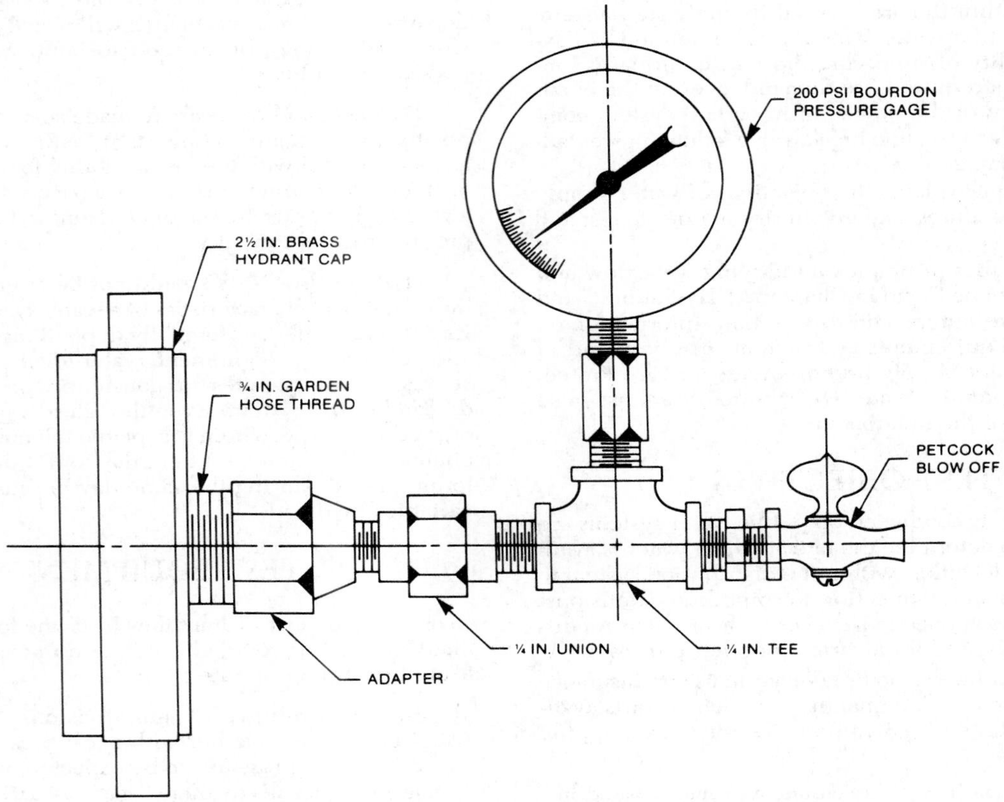

FIG. 5-8B. A typical hydrant cap and gage.

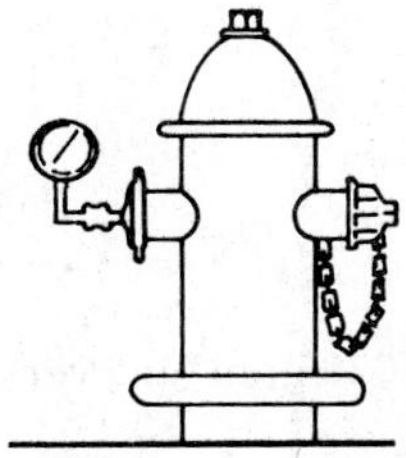

FIG. 5-8C. Gage on nonflowing hydrant to measure pressure.

3. A 2½-in. hydrant cap with fittings, together with a test-pressure gage suitable for the pressures to be expected, with 1-lb graduations (usually a 200-psi gage is satisfactory). (See Figure 5-8B.)
4. A convenient form to record test data and to include a sketch of the location at which the test was conducted showing hydrants and any other salient features.

A Pitot-tube-and-gage combination is indispensable in conducting flow tests from hydrants and nozzles. The small opening at the end of the tube, not over 1/16 in. (1.6 mm) in diameter, is inserted in the center of the stream, with the opening in a direct line with the flow and at a distance in front of the opening of one half the diameter of the opening. Velocity pressure is registered on the gage attached to the tube.

Note in Figure 5-8B the petcock blow-off. Its operation will permit air from the hydrant barrel to be vented when the hydrant is opened and will allow air to re-enter when the hydrant is closed. Failure to open the petcock during hydrant closing may subject the pressure gage to a partial vacuum which may introduce errors in future gage readings. Also note the ¾-in. (19 mm) garden-hose thread on the 2½-in. (64 mm) hydrant cap. Removal of the cap from the remainder of the fitting allows the gage assembly to be attached to a house silcock connection.

Test-quality gages should be used in accordance with ASME Standard B40.1-1985, grade AA. The use of good quality test gages has produced results that are considered reasonably accurate within the scope of the test procedure. However, care should be taken to protect the gages from rough handling. They should be tested periodically by means of a dead-weight tester throughout the range of operation. Calibration sheets should be kept for each gage and correction factors affixed to the back of each gage before a test series is begun. All test data should be recorded in a neat, systematic fashion, along with any system operating conditions that might affect the test results.

CONDUCTING FLOW TESTS

Hydrant flow tests are fairly simple to conduct and the results usually and easily interpreted. Once the objective of the test has been determined, it is only necessary to discharge water at a known rate from one or more hydrants. The pressure drop the discharge produces is observed simultaneously at a second hydrant or at other points of connection to the system that is supplying the flowing hydrants.

The usual procedure for conducting a flow test on a water system is to flow a sufficient number of hydrants to determine the capacity of the system in the area tested. Pressures observed without test hydrants flowing are called "static pressures"; those obtained with hydrants flowing are "residual pressures." One hydrant is chosen for observing the static and residual pressures, preferably located in the center of the group or where the best average pressure conditions might be expected. (See Figure 5-8C.) Avoid using a flowing hydrant for this purpose.

Once flow and pressure have stabilized, Pitot readings are taken simultaneously on the flowing hydrants. Residual pressure at the nonflow hydrant should be recorded at the same time. After the flowing hydrants have been slowly shut off, the static pressure should be observed and compared with the initial reading.

Pitot readings of less than 10 psi (69 kPa) or over 30 psi (207 kPa) at any open hydrant should be avoided. To keep within these pressure limits, the rate of flow can be controlled by throttling the hydrant or opening a second outlet, or both. However, the flow hydrants should be opened sufficiently so that hydrant drains are closed. Water continuously discharged through the drains tends to erode the soil from the base of the hydrant. Avoid using the larger pumper connection on a hydrant for testing unless flow and pressure are strong enough to produce a full stream. When pumper outlets are used, a proper coefficient of discharge must be determined, based upon the extent to which the orifice is completely filled with water. On occasion, it may be desirable to obtain an average velocity pressure by moving the Pitot tube through the entire vertical dimension of the orifice.

Figure 5-8D is the record of a typical flow test. Hydrant No. 1 was the gaging point, and Hydrant No. 2 was the point where flow tests were actually made. Figure 5-8E is a graphical plot of the results of the tests.

LOCATION: *Adams St. between Cox St. and Baker St.*

HYDRANTS: *2 ½ In. Square Sharp Assumed C = 80*

PRESSURE	PITOT PRESSURE				GPM	TOTAL GPM
HYD 1	HYD 2	HYD 3	HYD 4			
72	—	—	—		0	0
62	18	—	—		633	633
50	10 10		—		472 472	944

GAGE 103 AT HYDRANT No.1 – GAGE 79 FOR PITOT READINGS

FIG. 5-8D. Log of a public waterflow test.

Tests of this kind show the available flow over and above water consumption that occurs during the test. To evaluate the adequacy and reliability of a system properly, consideration is given to the sources of supply, the levels of water in distribution storage, and the overall operating condition of the system. The hour of the day, the day of the week, the month of the year, the weather, or an impairment made necessary by construction or system expansion are all factors that may affect the results of flow tests. Fire flow may be adequate one time and inadequate another because of variations in consumption or in the mode of operation of the system.

Sometimes unsuspected faults other than insufficient supplies are disclosed by hydrant flow tests. Valves may be partly or entirely shut; sometimes, they are found broken or with bent valve stems. Valve boxes may be filled with muck or sand, or even paved over with concrete or

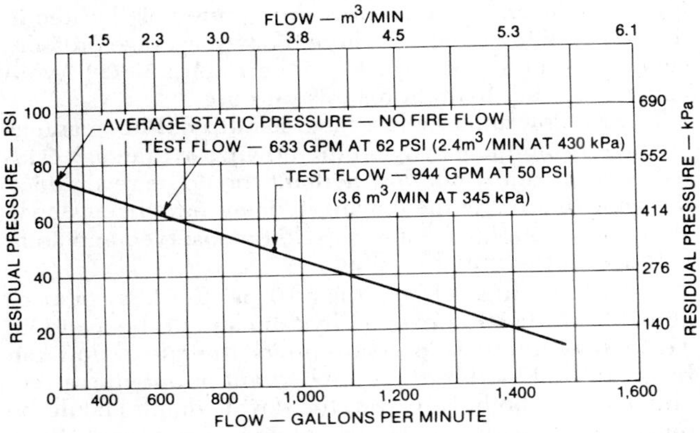

***FIG. 5-8E.** Curve plotted from flow test data given in Figure 5-8D.*

asphalt cement. Silt, stones, fish, and other foreign material may be found in pipe systems or hydrants, effectively reducing the available water supply. Many or all of these faults may be due to lack of maintenance and operational control.

It is customary to report the results of hydrant flow tests conducted in public systems in gallons per minute (L/min) available at 20-psi (138 kPa) residual pressure, which is the minimum recommended residual pressure at hydrants for fire engine use. The observed flow and pressures can be converted to any desired residual pressure or flow rate by a simple proportion derived from the Hazen-Williams pipe flow formula. This formula shows that the flow rate in gallons per minute is directly proportional to the 0.54 power of the head loss or the drop in pressure from static to residual observed during the test.

Head loss, which is mostly pipe friction, is the difference between the observed static pressure S and the residual pressure R. The gage value of S seldom indicates the true static (no flow) pressure; actually, it is the residual pressure for the normal pipe flow occurring before and during the test flow. Observed residual pressure is a function of total flow or $Q \pm DQ$, where Q is the normal rate of flow and DQ is the measured discharge during the test.

For many fire flow tests, the difference between the true and observed values of S is not usually significant. When meter readings or other consumption data are not available for the period of time during which flow tests were conducted, rates of water consumption may be estimated using records of consumption on preceeding days or by comparing similar water systems.

Examples of Calculating Flow and Pressure Conversion

Example A.

A 2500-gpm test flow from a group of street hydrants dropped the pressure from 69 to 44 psi. (1) What flow would be available at 20 psi? (2) What would the residual pressure be if flow were increased to 3000 gpm?

SOLUTION 1: Since the flow rate (Q) is directly proportional to the 0.54 power of the head (friction) loss, by proportion

$$\frac{Q_2}{Q_1} = \frac{(S - R_2)^{0.54}}{(S - R_1)^{0.54}} \text{ and } Q_2 = Q_1 \frac{(S - R_2)^{0.54}}{(S - R_1)^{0.54}}$$

Substituting the known values:

$S - R_2 = 69 - 20 =$ psi.

From Table 5-8A $49^{0.54} = 8.18$

$S - R_1 = 69 - 44 = 25$ psi.

From Table 5-8A $25^{0.54} = 5.59$

$$Q_2 = 2{,}500 \frac{8.18}{5.69} = 2{,}500 \times = 1.445 = 3{,}620 \text{ gpm (answer).}$$

Solution 2: Calculate R_2 when $W_2 - 3{,}000$ gpm.

$$3{,}000 = 2{,}500 \frac{(69 - R_2)^{0.54}}{(69 - 44)^{0.54}}$$

or

$$(69 - R_2)^{0.54} = \frac{3{,}000}{2{,}500} (69 - 44)^{0.54}$$

Since $(69 - 44)^{0.54} = 5.69$, then

$$(69 - R_2)^{0.54} = 1.20 \times 5.69 = 6.83.$$

From Table 5-8A, it is found by interpolation that 6.83 is $35.1^{0.54}$. Therefore, $69 - R_2 = 35.1$ and $R_2 = 69 - 35.1 = 33.9$ psi, residual pressure at 3000 gpm.

TABLE 5-8A. ***Numbers to 0.54 Power***

h	$h^{0.54}$	h	$h^{0.54}$	h	$h^{0.54}$	h	$h^{0.54}$	h	$h^{0.54}$
1	1.00	36	6.93	71	9.99	106	12.41	141	14.47
2	1.45	37	7.03	72	10.07	107	12.47	142	14.53
3	1.81	38	7.13	73	10.14	108	12.53	143	14.58
4	2.11	39	7.23	74	10.22	109	12.60	144	14.64
5	2.39	40	7.33	75	10.29	119	12.66	145	14.69
6	2.63	41	7.43	76	10.37	111	12.72	146	14.75
7	2.86	42	7.53	77	10.44	112	12.78	147	14.80
8	3.07	43	7.62	78	10.51	113	12.84	148	14.86
9	3.28	44	7.72	79	10.59	114	12.90	149	14.91
10	3.47	45	7.81	80	10.66	115	12.96	150	14.97
11	3.65	46	7.91	81	10.73	116	13.03	151	15.02
12	3.83	47	8.00	82	10.80	117	13.09	152	15.07
13	4.00	48	8.09	83	10.87	118	13.15	153	15.13
14	4.16	49	8.18	84	10.94	119	13.21	154	15.18
15	4.32	50	8.27	85	11.01	120	13.27	155	15.23
16	4.48	51	8.36	86	11.08	121	13.33	156	15.29
17	4.62	52	8.44	87	11.15	122	13.39	157	15.34
18	4.76	53	8.53	88	11.22	123	13.44	158	15.39
19	4.90	54	8.62	89	11.29	124	13.50	159	15.44
20	5.04	55	8.71	90	11.36	125	13.56	160	15.50
21	5.18	56	8.79	91	11.43	126	13.62	161	15.55
22	5.31	57	8.88	92	11.49	127	13.68	162	15.60
23	5.44	58	8.96	93	11.56	128	13.74	163	15.65
24	5.56	59	9.04	94	11.63	129	13.80	164	15.70
25	5.69	60	9.12	95	11.69	130	13.85	165	15.76
26	5.81	61	9.21	96	11.76	131	13.91	166	15.81
27	5.93	62	9.29	97	11.83	132	13.97	167	15.86
28	6.05	63	9.37	98	11.89	133	14.02	168	15.91
29	6.16	64	9.45	99	11.96	134	14.08	169	15.96
30	6.28	65	9.53	100	12.02	135	14.14	170	16.01
31	6.39	66	9.61	101	12.09	136	14.19	171	16.06
32	6.50	67	9.69	102	12.15	137	14.25	172	16.11
33	6.61	68	9.76	103	12.22	138	14.31	173	16.16
34	6.71	69	9.84	104	12.28	139	14.36	174	16.21
35	6.82	70	9.92	105	12.34	140	14.42	175	16.26

For a graphical solution to the two problems described above, see Figure 5-8H(a) which is a hydraulic flow curve plotted on semiexponential paper.

Example B. SI Units.

A 5000 L/min test flow from a group of street hydrants dropped the pressure from 500 to 350 kPa. What flow would be available at 140 kPa (approximately 20 psi)?

SOLUTION: Again, flow rate (Q) is directly proportional to the 0.54 power of the head (friction) loss, by proportion:

$$\frac{Q_2}{Q_1} = \frac{(S - R_2)^{0.54}}{(S - R_1)^{0.54}} \text{ and } Q_2 = Q_1 \frac{(S - R_2)^{0.54}}{(S - R_1)}.$$

Substituting known values:

$S\text{-}R_2 = 500 - 140 = 360$ kPa and $360^{0.54} = 24.01$

$S\text{-}R_1 = 500 - 350 = 150$ kPa and $150^{0.54} = 14.97$

$$Q_2 = 5000 \cdot \frac{24.01}{14.97} = 8019 \text{ L/min.}$$

See Figure 5-8H(b) for a graphical solution on semiexponential paper to the problem in SI units described above in Example B.

Flow Test of Public Main at Plant Site

A common procedure for using street hydrants to test the water supply for a connection to an industrial plant follows, using an example to describe the step-by-step testing procedures. The sprinkler system in the example is connected to the dead-ended Adams Street main (Figure 5-8F.) Therefore, the entire supply comes from the 10-in. main in Baker Street. There are no yard hydrants. The test was conducted as follows:

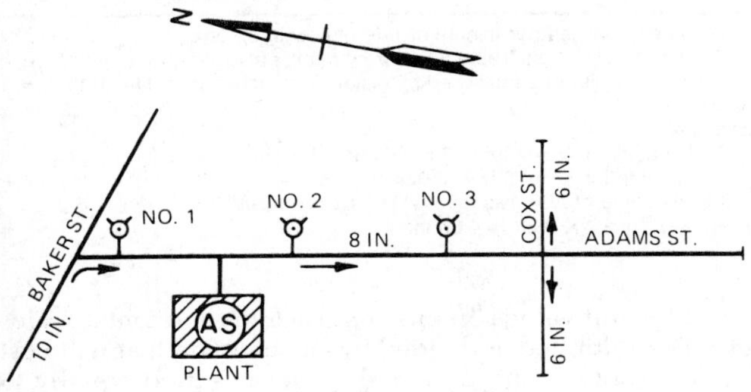

FIG. 5-8F. Data and sketch of a flow test of a public main at a plant site.

Step No. 1: A gage was attached to No. 1 hydrant with a cap. The hydrant was opened, and the static pressure [72 psi (496 kPa)] was recorded. (See Figure 5-8D.) No. 1 hydrant was chosen for the gaging point. The gage could have been located on the sprinkler riser in the building, but the hydrant location probably was more convenient.

Step No. 2: The caps were removed from No. 2 hydrant. The diameter of the outlets was measured, and the outlets were found to be square and sharp. (See Figure 5-2F.) After one cap was replaced, the hydrant was opened, and a Pitot reading of 18 psi (124 kPa) was made and recorded. Before the flow was shut off, the residual pressure at No. 1 hydrant was recorded as 62 psi (235 kPa).

Step No. 3: The second butt at No. 2 hydrant was opened, and 10-psi (69 kPa) Pitot readings were noted on both streams. At No. 1 hydrant, the residual pressure was now 50 psi (345 kPa). It is always desirable to obtain data for at least two rates of flow, one of which should be as heavy as facilities, conditions, and time will allow.

Step No. 4: No. 2 hydrant was shut down slowly and carefully, and the caps were replaced. The static pressure at No. 1 hydrant was read and found to be 72 psi (496 kPa), as before the test. The hydrant was then shut down, the gage cap removed, and the regular cap replaced.

Computing the flow: The rate of discharge is best determined by using the table of theoretical discharge (Table 5-2A) and by applying a suitable coefficient from Table 5-2B. In this instance, the hydrant outlets justified the use of c = 0.80 (square and sharp hydrant outlets in Figure 5-2F). Table 5-2A shows that, when the Pitot gage reading of velocity pressure from a 2½-in. (64 mm) orifice is 18 psi (124 kPa), the flow will be 791 gpm (2990 L/min). The actual flow then would be 791 × 0.8 or 634 gpm (2990 × 0.8 or 2392 L/min) at a residual pressure of 62 psi (235 kPa). With both outlets flowing, the Pitot reading on each was 10 psi (69 kPa), corresponding to 590 gpm (2233 L/min). The total actual flow was 2 × 590 × 0.8 = 944 gpm (2 × 2233 × 0.8 = 3573 L/min) at a residual pressure of 50 psi (345 kPa). It is now possible to calculate a flow at any residual pressure. It should be remembered, however, that this flow test procedure establishes the available flows to the point of connection of No. 1 hydrant to Adams Street and *not* to the point of connection of the sprinkler supply line to Adams St.

There may be times when a hydrant's open outlet cannot be flowed because of the damage it will do. In that case, additional or alternate hydrants should be flowed. When water supplies are very weak and the available water does not give a good Pitot reading with an open hydrant outlet flowing, a nozzle with a diameter less than the hydrant outlet may be attached directly to the hydrant outlet. Be sure to measure accurately the diameter of the nozzle used.

Annual Tests

Insurance companies usually require annual tests of private water supplies. When there are multiple sources, each source should be tested separately and in combination to determine if the total supply is sufficient to meet the maximum required fire flow.

Many faults are disclosed by flow tests. Among them are:

1. Valves partly or wholly closed, or inoperative.
2. Stones, silt, and other foreign material in the mains.
3. Tuberculated mains causing high friction loss.
4. Empty or partly filled gravity tanks.
5. Check valves leaking or installed backward.
6. Mains smaller than indicated on plans.
7. Broken meters or clogged strainers.
8. Existence of meters and valves not previously known.
9. Inoperative hydrants.

Hydrants and gaging points are carefully chosen. Tests should be conducted so that the available flow and pressure at high-value or hazardous areas can be determined readily. Make sure that water from the test streams does not cause flooding or property damage. Do not use flowing hydrants for pressure readings: Loss of head in hydrant and connection is not determined and is difficult to estimate.

Care should be taken not to drop the residual pressure in a public water supply system to less than 20 psi (140 kPa), or the minimum pressures that are established by municipal authorities.

Because of the probability of introducing contaminated water into a public water supply system from a fire protection system, backflow prevention devices are sometimes required to be installed at the point of connection to the public supply. It is quite possible that fire department pumping engines augmenting a sprinkler supply from an adjacent pond through a pumper connection with partial failure at the check valve could contaminate the public water system.

However, backflow prevention devices will introduce additional hydraulic losses, and these additional losses should be considered when determining the available flow to sprinkler and other fixed-water extinguishing systems.

Because flow testing may involve valve operations, all control valves should be carefully checked after the tests to ensure that they are open and that the system is left in normal condition. Faults should be corrected as soon as possible, and recommendations made for desirable improvements.

Figure 5-8G illustrates how a private system supplied with public water would be tested.

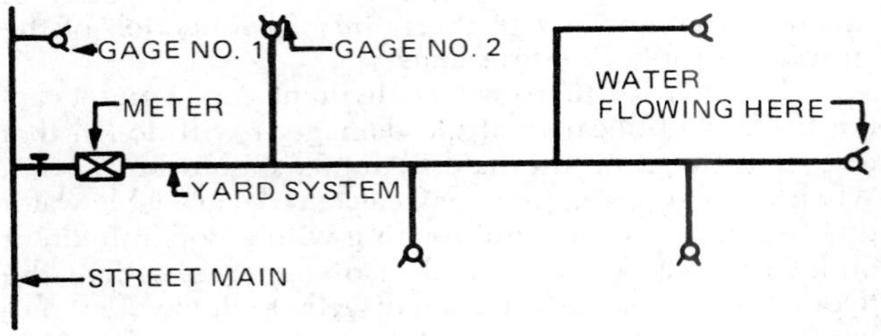

***FIG. 5-8G.** Method of testing city water supply to private system. Gage No. 1 shows street pressure and should, for gallons discharged, be consistent with data previously secured by street tests, if such tests have been made. Gage No. 2 on branch line will show flowing pressures in main at the point where the branch takes off. The difference in pressure between Gages No. 1 and No. 2 equals the loss in meter, pipe, and fittings. Friction losses to be expected in fittings and pipes can be estimated from Tables 5-2D and 5-2F. Fire-flow meter friction loss can be checked to see if it is unusually high by consulting Section 5, Chapter 4.*

HYDRAULIC FLOW CURVES

Many problems involving water tests and flow in pipes can be solved readily by graphs plotted on semiexponential, semilogarithmic, or linear cross-section paper. Semiexponential paper, commonly called $N^{1.85}$ or "hydraulic" paper, is recommended because a master sheet can be drawn easily, and copies easily made by duplicating equipment.

The problems can be solved equally well in U.S. customary units or SI units, although only problem examples in U.S. customary units will be presented in the remainder of this chapter. The Factory Mutual Research Corporation has a data sheet with examples worked graphically in both sets of units. (See bibliography.)

The design of $N^{1.85}$ paper is based on the Hazen-Williams pressure-drop relation: Head loss, which is static pressure less residual pressure, is proportional to the 1.85 power of flow. This relationship holds equally for head loss and flow calculations in SI units. Table 5-8B gives values of unit flows from 1 to 20 gpm in ½-gal increments raised to the 1.85 power (see Table 5-8C), and the corresponding scale values when the distance from 0 to the 1-gpm point is 0.05 in. For plotting pressure, the vertical spacing is linear.

TABLE 5-8B. ***Data for Making $N^{1.85}$*** **Hydraulic Graph Paper**

1	2	3	1	2	3
Gpm N	$N^{1.85}$	Scale value, inches from 0	Gpm N	$N^{1.85}$	Scale value, inches from 0
1	1.00	0.05	10.5	77.48	3.87
1.5	2.12	0.11	11	84.44	4.22
2	3.60	0.18	11.5	91.68	4.59
2.5	5.45	0.27	12	99.19	4.96
3	7.63	0.38	12.5	107.0	5.35
3.5	10.15	0.50	13	115.0	6.75
4	13.00	0.65	13.5	123.3	6.16
4.5	16.16	0.81	14	131.9	6.59
5	19.64	0.98	14.5	140.8	7.04
5.5	23.42	1.17	15	149.9	7.49
6	27.52	1.37	15.5	159.2	7.96
6.5	31.90	1.60	16	168.9	8.44
7	36.60	1.83	16.5	178.8	8.95
7.5	41.58	2.08	17	189.0	9.45
8	46.85	2.34	17.5	199.5	9.96
8.5	52.40	2.62	18	210.0	10.50
9	58.26	2.91	18.5	221.0	11.05
9.5	64.39	3.22	19	232.1	11.60
10	70.80	3.54	19.5	243.5	12.18
			20	255.2	12.76

Column 1. Gallons per minute or rate of flow in other units.
Column 2. $N^{1.85}$ from Table 5-8C or by interpolation from that table.
Column 3. Column 2 multiplied by distance in inches from $N = 0$ to $N = 1$ (0.05 in.).
Examples:
Scale value for $N = 7$ is $36.60 \times 0.05 \times 1.83$ in.
Scale value for $N = 16$ is $168.9 \times 0.05 = 8.44$ in.
If scale value of $N = 1$ is 0.08, what is scale for $N = 9$?
Answer: $58.26 \times 0.08 = 4.66$ in.

The unit values on either vertical or horizontal scales may be multiplied or divided by any constant that will best fit the problem, and the graph paper is suited equally to U.S. customary and SI units.

See Figure 5-8H(a) for an example of a flow curve in customary American units plotted on $N^{1.85}$ semiexponential scale. Figure 5-8H(b) is an example in SI units.

FLOW IN LOOP SYSTEMS

It is sometimes necessary to estimate the friction loss and flow characteristics of loops or parallel pipe systems. Such problems are readily solved graphically by procedures based on the principle that pressure drop through a simple loop is the same in every leg; this is true regardless of size, condition, and length of pipe. The method described is not applicable to grid or network systems, although it is sometimes possible to treat a grid as a loop

TABLE 5-8C. *Numbers to 1.85 Power*

N	$N^{1.85}$	*N*	$N^{1.85}$	*N*	$N^{1.85}$
5	19.64	39	877.9	230	23,400
6	27.52	40	920.1	240	25,320
7	36.60	41	963	250	27,300
8	46.85	42	1.007	260	29,360
9	58.26	43	1.052	270	31,480
10	70.80	44	1,097	280	32,910
11	84.44	45	1,144	290	34,310
12	99.19	46	1.192	300	38,250
13	115.0	47	1,240	350	50,880
14	131.9	48	1,289	400	65,150
15	149.9	49	1,339	450	80,990
16	168.9	50	1,390	500	98,440
17	189.0	55	1,658	550	117,400
18	210.0	60	1,948	600	137,900
19	232.1	65	2,259	650	159,900
20	255.2	70	2,591	700	183,400
21	279.3	75	2,944	750	208,400
22	304.4	80	3,317	800	234,800
23	330.5	85	3,710	850	262,700
24	357.6	90	4,124	900	291,900
25	385.7	95	4,558	950	322,700
26	414.7	100	5,012	1,000	354,800
27	444.7	110	5,979	1,200	497,200
28	475.6	120	7,022	1,400	661,100
29	507.5	130	8,144	1,600	846,400
30	540.4	140	9,339	1,800	1,053,000
31	574.1	150	10,610	2,000	1,279,000
32	608.9	160	11,960	2,200	1,526,000
33	644.5	170	13,370	2,400	1,792,000
34	681.2	180	14,870	2,600	2,079,000
35	718.7	190	16,440	2,800	2,384,000
36	757.1	200	18,070	3,000	2,708,000
37	794.6	210	19,770	4,000	4,611,000
38	836.7	220	21,550	5,000	6,968,000

Figures in this table are for use with the Hazen-Williams formula.
Determining the 1.85 power of numbers by proportional parts between the figures given (linear interpolation) will produce results with error of less than 2 percent.

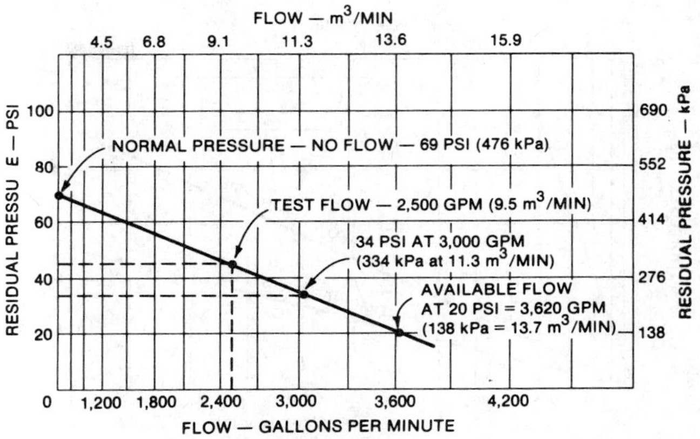

FIG. 5-8H(a). An example of a flow curve plotted on $N^{1.85}$ semiexponential paper. The illustration is a graphical plot of data involved in Example A of a flow test of a public water system described earlier in this chapter.

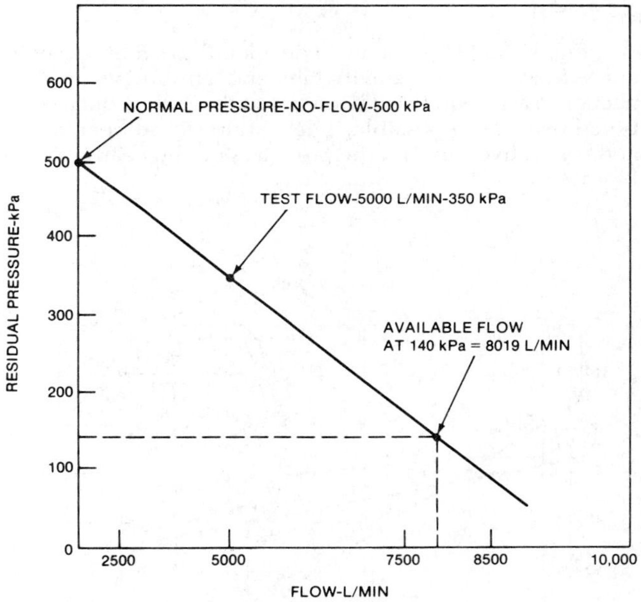

FIG. 5-8H(b). A graphical solution to the flow problem (Example B described earlier), expressed in SI units on $N^{1.85}$ semiexponential paper.

system by making certain assumptions. Grids can be solved by network analyzers or computers, or they can be calculated by the Hardy Cross method and other relaxation formulas. Because these matters are outside the scope of this handbook, the words of John R. Freeman might well be recalled: "A day of (flow) testing is worth a week of calculating."

Figure 5-8I illustrates a graphical solution of a simple loop having two legs, one 800 ft of 8-in. pipe and the other 1200 ft of 6-in. pipe. The Hazen-Williams coefficient is C = 100 (unlined cast-iron pipe about 15 to 20 years old and in good condition). Using Table 5-2D, the calculations would be as follows:

Step No. 1: Friction loss in the 8-in. pipe was calculated for an assumed flow of 1500 gpm as follows: 1 × 8 × 2.71 = 21.6 psi in 800 ft of 8-in. pipe. Friction loss of 21.6 was plotted as Point "a" on the vertical 1500 gpm line in Figure 5-8I. A straight line was drawn to connect Point "a" with 0, forming the Loss Curve "A" for the 8-in. leg.

Step No. 2: Assuming a flow of 600 gpm, follow the same procedure as followed in Step No. 1: 1 × 12 × 2.02 = 24.2 psi loss in 1200 ft of 6-in. pipe. Friction loss of 24.2 was plotted as Point "b" on the vertical 600-gpm line and connected to 0, thus forming Loss Curve "B" for the 6-in. pipe.

Step No. 3: The flows corresponding to a convenient pressure of 10 psi on each curve (Points "c" and "d") were added together, and Point "e" plotted at 1400 gpm. This represents 400 gpm at Point "d" + 1000 gpm at Point "c." The straight line connecting Point "e" with 0 is the Curve C for the whole loop.

GRAPHICAL DETERMINATION OF YIELD FROM COMBINED SUPPLIES

Determination of the yield from combined water supplies made by actual testing is not always possible. A supply may be impaired, as when a gravity tank is emptied for repairs or painting, or it may be necessary to estimate the yield when a new supply is to be added to a one-source system.

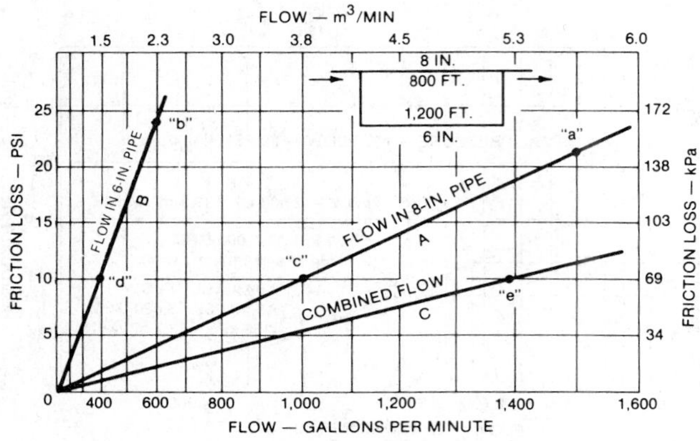

FIG. 5-8I. Graphical demonstration of flow in loop piping. The assumed friction coefficient is C = 100. Curve A represents flow in 800 ft of 8-in. pipe; Curve B represents flow in 1200 ft of 6-in. pipe.

Figure 5-8J shows how to develop the combined yield curve from a private gravity tank and a public water connection. Each source had been tested separately, but a combined test was impossible. The test flows had been taken at the yard hydrant, and the pressures on the nearby sprinkler riser.

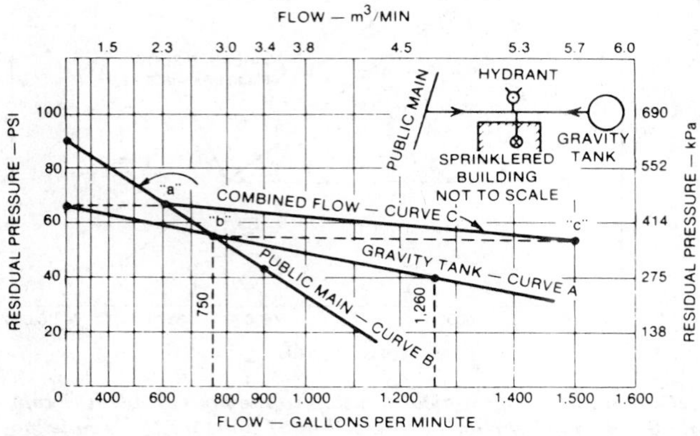

FIG. 5-8J. Graph of a combined water supply from a public system and a private gravity tank.

The curves were plotted from the test data as follows: 1260 gpm flowing from the tank (Curve A) reduced pressure from 65 to 40 psi; 900 gpm flowing from the public supply (Curve B) reduced pressure from 90 to 43 psi.

All the water would come from the public main until the residual pressure dropped to the static pressure of the tank—in this case, to 65 psi at approximately 600 gpm plotted as Point "a." From then on, water would come from both sources.

The curves cross at 750 gpm at 55 psi, plotted as Point "b." With 750 gpm from each, the total flow at 55 psi would be 1500 gpm, plotted as Point "c." Connecting Points "a" and "c" with a straight line produces Curve C, which is the desired combined curve.

ANALYZING TEST DATA

A major purpose of flow testing is to determine whether the available water supply can meet the water demand required for acceptable protection. Plotting test data on $N^{1.85}$ hydraulic graph paper offers a simple and convenient method of analyzing water supply and demand. (See "Hydraulic Flow Curves," in this chapter.)

As an example of analyzing data, assume that flow tests have been made on a water supply to a sprinklered building and that the following data have been recorded: no flow at 72 psi; 633 gpm at 62 psi; and 944 gpm at 50 psi. Curve A in Figure 5-8K was drawn by fitting a straight line to the three points. By extending the curve, residual pressures at larger flows can be read off directly. For example, the residual pressure at 1200 gpm would have been 40 psi. It is not necessary to extrapolate much beyond the maximum flow point, because tests from networks often produce supply curves that flatten out as the rate of flow increases.

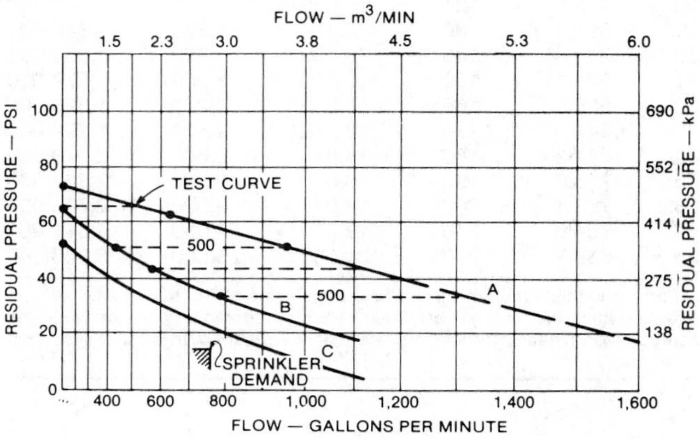

FIG. 5-8K. An example of a graphic water supply evaluation. Curve A is the test flow; Curve B the test flow, less 500 gpm for hose streams; and Curve C is Curve B corrected for elevation (30-ft elevation in this example).

The fact that all three test points fix a practically straight line indicates that the observed static of 72 psi was close to a true figure and that the normal rate of flow was relatively small.

Curve B in Figure 5-8K represents the available supply at street level to the sprinkler system over and above a 500-gpm allowance for probable hose stream use by the fire department. Obviously, if more water were taken for hose streams, there would be less remaining for the sprinklers.

Curve B was developed by subtracting 500 gpm from Curve A at various pressures. The point at zero flow was obtained by moving horizontally from the intersection of Curve A and the vertical 500-gpm line. (See Figure 5-8K.) The next point was found by plotting 444 gpm (944 – 500 gpm) at 50 psi, which was the residual pressure for the 944-gpm test. Other points were plotted in the same way.

Curves developed by this method are approximations at best, because the rate of flow is dependent on the 0.5 power of discharge pressure (see Section 5, Chapter 2,

"Hydraulics") and the 0.54 power of head loss (see Table 5-8A). However, this manner of evaluating the water supply to sprinkler systems is practical and acceptable.

Curve C in Figure 5-8K is actually Curve B corrected for a 30-ft (9.1 m) elevation difference between the residual pressure at street level and the top line of sprinklers. Therefore, every point of Curve C is 13 psi (89.6 kPa) below the corresponding point of Curve B. Friction loss in pipe and fittings between the city main and the top of the sprinkler riser in the building was not considered, but the losses could have been estimated with certain details assumed, as follows (no meter or fire department connection to sprinklers or backflow prevention device):

System Component	Equivalent Length (ft) (see Section 5, Chapter 2)
Eighty feet of 6 in.-pipe, C = 120 (riser and connection)	80.0
One 8 × 8 × 6 in.-tee (connection to main)	21.5
Two 6 in.-standard elbows (top and bottom of riser)	20.0
Two 6 in. gate valves (waterworks valve and sprinkler valve)	04.0
One 6 in.-check valve	23.0
	Total 148.5 ft.

It is assumed in the foregoing example that the sprinkler system in the building requires a flow of 750 gpm at the point of supply to the sprinklers, while residual pressure at the top line of sprinklers does not drop below 15 psi. Curve C of Figure 5-8K shows that 750 gpm would be available at approximately 20 psi residual pressure.

HYDRAULIC GRADIENT

A hydraulic gradient is a profile of residual pressure whose function is to present graphically the flow characteristics of a pipe line. The hydraulic gradient is an important factor in the design of water supply conduits and trunk mains, and is useful for investigating the condition of a public or private main when tests produce less than the expected flow.

The relationships between pressure and elevation in a pipe having uniform flow are shown in Figure 5-8L. The axioms accompanying the diagram should be noted carefully.

Hydraulic gradient tests of a private fire protection system usually involve shorter runs of pipe than tests of public mains. To reduce the number of tests, pipes should be chosen that are typical of the age and condition of the system. Relatively heavy flows should be induced through the test section to obtain a maximum pressure drop, thereby minimizing the effect of fluctuating pressure or inaccurate gage readings.

In public water supply systems, residual pressures should not be lowered to a value less than that required by municipal authorities.

The data obtained from a hydraulic gradient are readily applied to calculating the C values (internal pipe roughness coefficient) of the pipes tested. The head loss in valves and fittings, if any, should be deducted from the observed pressure drop before calculating C or the value obtained would be too low. (See Section 5, Chapter 2, "Hydraulics.")

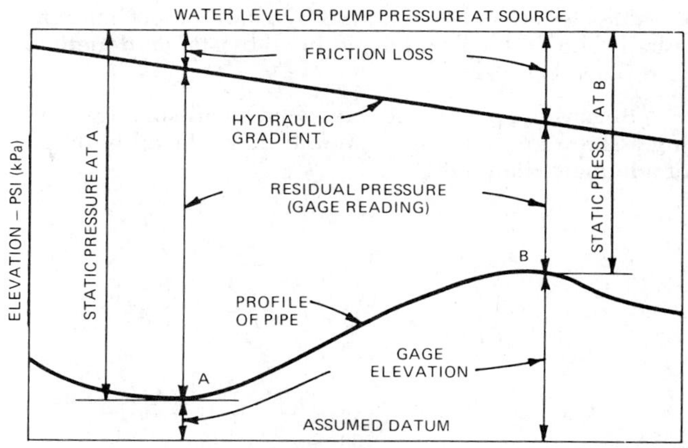

FIG. 5-8L. Principle of a hydraulic gradient. The following axioms apply: Static-pressure readings measure distance below source. The higher the pipe elevation, the lower the static pressure. Static pressure plus gage elevation [expressed in psi (kPa)] is constant for all points along pipe. Static pressure minus residual pressure equals total friction loss from source to point of measurement. Residual pressure plus gage elevation equals hydraulic-gradient elevation. Friction loss is independent of elevation.

In municipal water supply systems, however, this deduction is not made, as tested pipe lengths are relatively long and losses due to fittings are considered to be minor. Obviously, consideration of the C value is not part of gradient development; it is a convenient and widely used measure in determining the condition of the interior of the pipe.

If there are more than two gaging points, an attempt should be made to take simultaneous readings, but satisfactory results can usually be obtained (if rates of consumption are relatively low and steady) by moving the gage progressively from hydrant to hydrant while the test flow is maintained in the pipe. True static pressure obtained under no-flow conditions would plot as a horizontal line.

In a municipal system with normal flow, the observed static pressures are actually residual pressures and would trace the normal gradient. Therefore, efforts should be made to find the true static pressure. If the system is supplied by gravity, it may be possible to determine the static by elevation differences, topographic maps, or other survey data. If it is necessary to depend on the static readings, it would be desirable to take readings between 1 a.m. and 3:30 a.m., when normal draft is at a minimum and observed static pressures are closer to the true levels.

Static pressure on fire protection mains usually can be obtained readily because there is little or no normal flow except in properties with combined fire and industrial systems. With street mains, it is often possible to close a valve below the downstream end of the section being tested, thereby reducing the normal flow temporarily.

It is usually desirable to plot the profile of the pipe being tested, along with the gradient. When improvements and changes are in order, it is desirable to plot a calculated gradient for comparison with the one tested. Both gradients must be based on the same rate of flow. Figure 5-8M is a graph of a gradient test, together with a pipe profile and a calculated gradient. A uniform flow of 750 gpm is assumed. If a gradient falls below the pipe line, pressure in the pipe is less than atmospheric. This condition could impair the flow and cause dangerous pressure surges. When

C values less than 80 are found by gradient tests, the pipe usually should be cleaned and lined by standard methods, or replaced.

Regardless of C value, however, small-size pipe causing a steep gradient slope should be replaced with pipe of adequate diameter.

The choice of method depends on the relative costs of cleaning and lining, as opposed to replacement, and on other practical considerations.

Table 5-8D shows the data for Figure 5-8M and explains the calculation.

Table 5-8E covers the calculated gradient.

Table 5-8F explains the calculation of C values.

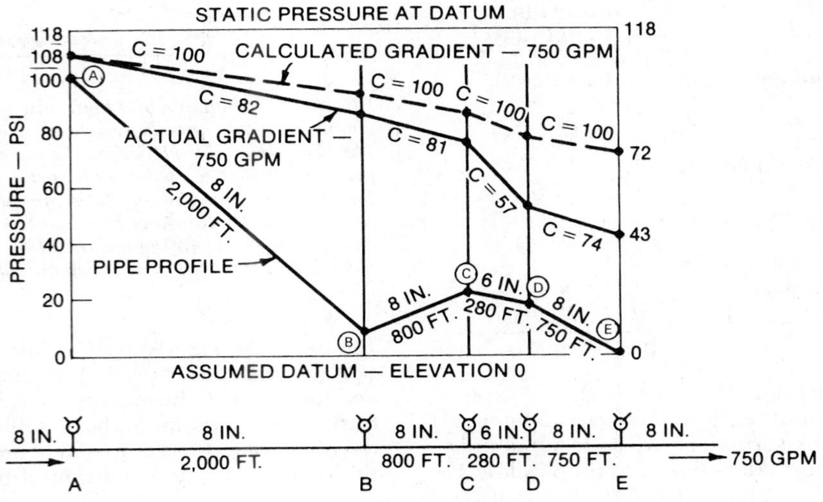

FIG. 5-8M. Hydraulic gradient and pipe profile.

TABLE 5-8D. *Data for Hydraulic Gradient*

(1)	(2)	(3)	(4)	(5)	(6)	(7)	(8)	(9)
			Gage Pressure					
Gage Location	Actual Pipe Length	(Ft) Pipe Diameter (In.)	Static (Psi)	Residual (Psi)	Total Loss (Psi)	Loss Between Stations (Psi)	Gage Elevation Above Datum (Psi)	Gradient Elevation (Psi)
A	—	—	18	8	10	—	100	108
B	A − B = 2000	8	110	78	32	A − B = 22	8	86
C	B − C = 800	8	95	54	41	B − C = 9	23	77
D	C − D = 280	6	100	35	65	C − D = 24	18	53
E	D − E = 750	8	118	43	75	D − E = 10	0	43

Explanation:
Columns 1–5: Data from actual gradient test.
Column 6: Static pressure − residual pressure = total loss.
Column 7: Difference in total loss, station to station.
Column 8: Gage elevation above datum = static pressure at datum (118 psi in this example) minus observed static at each location. Thus A = 118 − 18 = 100; B = 118 − 100 = 8; C = 118 − 95 = 23; D = 118 − 100 = 18; and E = 118 − 118 = 0.
Column 9: Gradient elevation = gage elevation + residual pressure. Thus A = 100 + 8 = 108; B = 8 + 78 = 86; C = 23 + 54 = 77; D = 18 + 53; E = 0 + 43 = 43.

TABLE 5-8E. ***Data for Calculated Hydraulic Gradient***

(Rate of Flow – 750 Gpm – C = 100)

(1)	(2)	(3)	(4)	(5)	(6)	(7)	(8)	(9)
Gage Location	Actual Pipe Length (Ft)	Pipe Diameter (In.)	Gage Elevation Above Datum (Psi)	Static Pressure (Psi)	Calculated Loss Station to Station (Psi)	Total Loss (Psi)	Residual Pressure (Psi)	Gradient Elevation (Psi)
A	—	—	100	18	10	10	8	108
B	A – B = 2000	8	8	110	15	25	85	93
C	B – C = 800	8	23	95	6	31	64	87
D	C – D = 280	6	18	100	9	40	60	78
E	D – E = 750	8	0	118	6	46	72	72

Explanation:

Columns 1–5: Data taken from Columns 1, 2, 3, 8, and 4 of Table 5-8D respectively.

Column 6: Calculated pressure loss from station to station. (See Section 5, Chapter 2 for friction loss calculations). The losses are:

$$\text{A to B} = 1 \times \frac{2000}{100} \times .752 = 15$$

$$\text{B to C} = 1 \times \frac{800}{100} \times .752 = 6$$

$$\text{C to D} = 1 \times \frac{280}{100} \times 3.05 = 9$$

$$\text{D to E} = 1 \times \frac{750}{100} \times .752 = 6$$

Column 7: Total loss (accumulative loss at each location): Thus:

A = 10 psi
B = Loss A to B + Loss A = 15 + 10 = 25
C = Loss B to C + Loss B = 6 + 25 = 31
D = Loss C to D + Loss C = 9 + 31 = 40
F = Loss D to E + Loss D = 6 + 40 = 46

Column 8: Residual pressure: equals the static pressure (Column 5) minus the total loss (Column 7) at each location

Column 9: Gradient elevation is gage elevation (Column 4) plus the residual pressure (Column 8).

TABLE 5-8F. ***Calculations for C Values***

(Rate of Flow–750 Gpm)

(1)	(2)	(3)	(4)	(5)	(6)	(7)
Gage Location	Actual Pipe Length (Ft)	Pipe Diameter (In.)	Loss Station to Station (Psi)	Loss per 100 ft (Psi)	C Factor	C
A	—	—	—	—	—	—
B	A – B = 2000	8	A – B = 22	1.10	1.46	82
C	B – C = 800	8	B – C = 9	1.125	1.49	81
D	C – D = 280	6	C – D = 24	8.6	2.82	57
E	D – E = 750	8	D – E = 10	1.35	1.76	74

Explanation:

Columns 1–4: Data taken from Columns 1, 2, 3, and 7 in Table 5-8D, respectively.

Column 5: Pressure loss from station to station (Column 4) divided by the actual pipe length (Column 2) multiplied by 100.

Column 6: The actual pressure loss by test for each 100 ft of pipe (Column 5) divided by friction loss for 100 ft of pipe with *C* = 100 (Table 16-2E).

Column 7: Values for *C* interpolated from Table (Approximate linear interpolation is acceptable.) Example: For Station C the *C* factor is 1.49. Find *C:*

C	Factor	Factor
85	1.35	1.35
?		1.49
80	1.51	
5	14	16

$$\frac{14}{16} \times 5 = 4.4$$

85 – 4.4 = 80.6 = 81 (answer).

BIBLIOGRAPHY

References

"Hydraulics of Fire Protection Systems," *Loss Prevention Data Sheet 3-0*, Factory Mutual Research Corp., Norwood, MA, 1977.

American Society of Mechanical Engineers, Gauges—Pressure Indicating Dial Type Elastic Element, NAS Standard B40.1-1985, NY.

NFPA Codes, Standards, and Recommended Practices

Reference to the following NFPA codes, standards, and recommended practices will provide further information on test of water supplies discussed in this chapter. (See the latest *NFPA Catalog* for availability of current editions of the following documents.)

NFPA 24, *Private Fire Service Mains and Their Appurtenances*.

NFPA 291, *Fire Flow Testing and Marking of Hydrants*.

NFPA 292M, *Water Charges for Private Fire Protection*.

Additional Reading

ANSI B40.1, *Gages, Pressure and Vacuum, Indicating Dial-Type Elastic Element*, American National Standards Institute, Philadelphia, PA, 1968.

Casey, J. F., ed., *Fire Service Hydraulics*, 2nd ed., Reuben H. Donnelley Corp., NY, 1970.

Cozad, D., *Water Supply for Fire Protection*, Prentice-Hall, Englewood Cliffs, NJ, pp. 181-214, 1981.

Fire Department Pumper Tests and Fire Stream Tables, 9th ed., National Fire Protection Association, Quincy, MA, 1981.

Fire Flow Tests, National Fire Protection Association, Quincy, MA, 1981.

Mahoney, E. F., *Fire Department Hydraulics*, Allyn and Bacon, Boston, 1980, pp. 51-83.

Purington, R. G., "Fire Hydrant Efficiency Measurements," *Fire Technology*, Vol. 7, No. 1 (Feb. 1971) pp. 57-60.

Simplified Water Supply Testing, Alliance of American Insurers, Chicago, IL, 1982.

AUTOMATIC SPRINKLER SYSTEMS

Revised by Robert Solomon

Automatic sprinkler systems are one of the most reliable methods available for controlling fires. The rate of effectiveness of sprinkler systems has been very good during the more than 100 years they have been in use. In order to understand the capabilities of these systems, a thorough understanding of their components and uses is essential.

This chapter is an introduction to sprinkler systems, which may be automatic or, in some cases, manual. It covers the fundamentals of good sprinkler protection by giving information on: (1) the value of sprinkler protection, (2) the standardizing of sprinkler protection, (3) building features that must be considered in planning sprinkler protection, (4) occupancy hazards and conditions that have a bearing, (5) the types of sprinkler systems that are available, (6) the materials used in these systems, and (7) an overview of installation practices that must be observed.

For related information, see Section 5, Chapter 11, "Water Supplies for Sprinkler Systems;" Section 5, Chapter 12, "Automatic Sprinklers;" Section 5, Chapter 13, "Fast Response Sprinkler Technology;" and Section 4, Chapter 3, "Water Flow Alarms and Sprinkler System Supervision." Maintenance of sprinkler systems is covered in Section 5, Chapter 16, "Care and Maintenance of Water-Based Extinguishing Systems."

Because of the wide application of sprinklers as suppression devices, it is difficult to single out other specific chapters in this handbook for additional guidance on the installation and use of sprinklers. Special mention must be made of Section 5, Chapter 15, "Water Spray Protection," where deluge and other special control valves associated with sprinklers are mentioned as part of the water spray systems for extinguishing flammable liquid and other intense fires; of Section 8, Chapter 24, "Storage Occupancies," which covers protection of storage occupancies; and of Section 4, Chapter 5, "Automatic Fire Detectors," for illustrations and descriptions of heat- and smoke-responsive devices that can be used to actuate preaction and deluge sprinkler systems.

Robert Solomon, P.E., is senior fire protection engineer in the NFPA General Engineering Department, Quincy, MA.

DEVELOPMENT OF AUTOMATIC SPRINKLERS

Automatic sprinklers are devices for automatically distributing water on a fire in sufficient quantity to control the fire. While current sprinkler system designs are not devised to extinguish a fire, many systems have accomplished complete fire extinguishment.

The water is supplied to the sprinklers through a system of piping, ordinarily suspended from the ceiling, with the sprinklers placed at intervals along the pipes. The orifice of the automatic sprinkler is normally closed by a disk or cap held in place by a temperature-sensitive releasing element. Figure 5-9A shows in stop-action sequence the operation of a typical fusible-link, upright automatic sprinkler. For more information on automatic sprinklers, see Section 5, Chapter 12, "Automatic Sprinklers."

The forerunners of the automatic sprinkler were the perforated pipe and the open sprinkler. These were installed in a number of mill properties from 1850 to 1880. The systems were not automatic, the discharge openings in the pipes often clogged with rust and foreign materials, and water distribution was poor.

Open sprinklers, an improvement over perforated pipes, consisted of metal bulbs with numerous perforations attached to piping and intended to give improved water distribution. This system was only slightly better than the perforated pipe.

The idea of automatic sprinkler protection, whereby heat from a fire opens one or more sprinklers and allows the water to flow, dates back to about 1860. However, its practical application in the United States began about 1878 when the Parmelee sprinkler was first installed. This sprinkler, while very crude when compared with modern devices, generally gave good results and proved conclusively that automatic sprinkler protection was both practical and valuable. (See Figure 5-9B.)

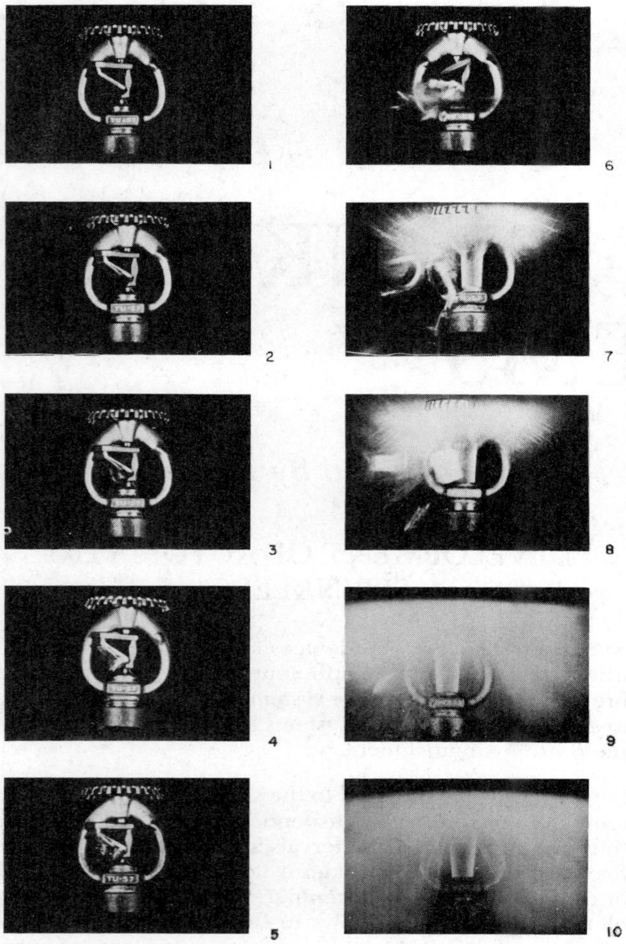

FIG. 5-9A. Operation of a typical fusible-link automatic sprinkler is shown in this sequence of photos. As heat melts the solder, members of the soldered link (the sloping side of the triangle in photos 1 to 5) separates, followed by complete separation of the link and lever arrangement (photo 6), which releases the cap over the sprinkler orifice, allowing water to escape and strike the deflector (photos 7 to 10).

Value of Automatic Sprinkler Protection

Automatic sprinkler protection helped modern industrial, commercial, and mercantile practices to develop. Large areas, high buildings, hazardous occupancies, large content value, or many people concentrated in one area all tend to develop conditions that cannot be tolerated without automatic sprinkler systems.

Automatic sprinklers are particularly effective for life safety because they warn of the existence of fire and, at the same time, apply water to the burning area. With sprinklers, there are seldom problems of access to the seat of the fire or of interference with visibility for fire fighting due to smoke. While the downward force of the water discharged from sprinklers may lower the smoke level in a room where a fire is burning, the sprinklers also serve to cool the smoke and make it possible for persons to remain in the area much longer than they could if the room were without sprinklers.

Extensive testing and research has been completed to show the effectiveness of sprinklers in the home. This culminated with the development of the residential sprinkler

FIG. 5-9B. An early automatic sprinkler. Water is shown discharging from a Parmelee No. 3 upright sprinkler, which was first used in 1875. It consisted of a brass cap soldered over a perforated distributor and was designed to screw onto a nipple. A cross-sectional view of the sprinkler is at right.

that may be installed in any dwelling unit, from a single-family home to a high-rise condominium. Section 5, Chapter 13, "Fast Response Sprinkler Technology," further discusses residential sprinklers. In rural areas where water supplies are limited, a pressure tank can be provided with a self-contained tank and pump unit, making it acceptable for water supplies of sufficient capacity to control a fire during evacuation. NFPA 13D, *Installation of Sprinkler Systems in One- and Two-Family Dwellings and Mobile Homes*, gives guidance on sprinkler systems for dwellings.

NFPA *101*,® *Life Safety Code*,® recognizes sprinklers in numerous ways, particularly to offset deficiencies in existing buildings. For example, longer travel distances to exits and interior finish of a higher combustibility than would otherwise be permitted are allowed with sprinklers.

Automatic sprinklers, properly installed and maintained, provide a highly effective safeguard against the loss of life and property from fire.

NFPA has no record of a multiple-death fire (a fire which kills three or more people) in a completely sprinklered building where the system was operating properly, except in an explosion or flash fire or where industrial fire brigade members or employees were killed during fire suppression operations. In some cases, victims of fatal fires in sprinklered properties were involved in the ignition of the fire and received their injuries before the sprinklers operated, or they were unable to escape due to a physical or mental impairment.

For many years, NFPA published summaries of sprinkler performance. This practice was stopped after 1970 when it became apparent that the data being used were biased by collection criteria that concentrated on fires causing large dollar loss. This bias led to a perception of a decline in sprinkler effectiveness. Information on sprinkler effectiveness from insurers is also biased toward the larger property loss and the possible sprinkler failure because of the widespread use of deductibles. Many fires that are extinguished by a small number of sprinklers and result in small property loss are never reported to the insurer.

A fair percentage of fires are still controlled by a relatively small number of sprinklers operating. Table 5-9A shows the number of sprinklers that operate in comparison to the total number of fires. The reader is reminded that Table 5-9A is also biased toward the large-fire-high-value loss scenario.

TABLE 5-9A. *Sprinkler Operation 1978–1987*

Number Operating	Fires	Cumulative Number	Percent of Total	Cumulative Percent
1	797	797	28	28
2	520	1317	18	46
3	291	1608	10	56
4	221	1829	8	64
5	147	1976	5	69
6	146	2122	5	74
7	74	2196	3	77
8	77	2273	3	80
9	44	2317	1	81
10	55	2372	2	83
11–15	172	2544	6	89
16–20	100	2644	3	92
21–25	49	2693	2	94
26+	167	2860	6	100

Source: Factory Mutual Research Corp.

While comprehensive statistics on sprinkler effectiveness are not available currently, documentation of their effectiveness in the protection of property can be found in numerous examples of successful operation in the files of the National Fire Protection Association, the United States Fire Administration, and various insurers.

In many situations, however, sprinkler protection is required by law for specific parts of the building only. Partial systems generally are neither cost-effective nor reliable. Should a fire start in an area not protected by the system, sprinklers will have no effect on the growing fire. A fire burning into the protected area generally will have developed sufficient intensity to overpower the sprinklers, thereby wasting water needed by the fire service to fight the fire.

Minimizing Business Interruption and Water Damage

In addition to the savings in direct fire losses due to sprinkler protection, there is a saving represented by the freedom from business interruption. Indirect business losses may be incurred in any building. These losses include rental of, and relocation of employees to temporary quarters; rental of equipment such as business machines, cars, trucks, utility equipment, and space to maintain some form of operation; and the almost-ever-present threat of litigation that may arise from a destructive fire. There also is an undetermined but possibly even greater reduction in exposure losses, which reasonably may be attributed to automatic sprinkler protection. The destruction of property and its adverse and sometimes permanent effect on business often is a great hardship, not only to the owner, tenants, and employees, but also to the community as a whole. Safeguarding a business from serious interruption by fire is often a determining factor in the decision to install sprinkler protection.

Standard sprinkler systems have devices that automatically give an alarm in case of sprinkler operation. Thus, they not only apply water at the point most needed, but they also give an audible signal on the premises and, in many cases, an alarm at a remote location, such as the local fire department or a central station. This permits an immediate check of fire conditions and minimizes water damage.

A properly installed sprinkler system operating in a timely manner will generate less water damage than the later application of hose streams by the fire service. Sprinklers are not hampered in their operation by smoke or heat, as is the fire service. Sprinklers can apply water efficiently and promptly to the seat of the fire.

A common misconception is that all sprinklers in a system discharge water at the time of fire. This is not the case; most fires are controlled by a few automatic sprinklers in their immediate vicinity. Fear of water damage sometimes is offered as an objection to the installation of automatic sprinkler protection. This fear comes in part from the emphasis, often in ignorance, placed upon water damage in news reports of fires. Statements that a fire was of insignificant size, but that water damage was severe, have been frequent. The probability of very severe destruction by fire in the absence of automatic sprinkler protection is seldom mentioned in these news accounts.

Accidental discharge of water from an automatic sprinkler system or other parts of a fire protection water system due to defects in sprinklers, water control devices, piping, or associated equipment is very rare. Precautions that may be taken to prevent unnecessary discharge of water as a result of mechanical injury, freezing or overheating, or corrosion are covered in Section 5, Chapter 16, "Care and Maintenance of Water-Based Extinguishing Systems."

It is estimated that 1 in 16,000,000 installed sprinklers will fail and allow water discharge, and that 1 in 2,500,000 installed systems will fault and permit water discharge. More often than not, such failures are a result of poor quality control during initial installation or of lack of maintenance.

Economics of Sprinkler Protection

In addition to the protection against destruction of property values and interruption to business, the savings in insurance costs often make the expenditure for automatic sprinkler protection a sound business investment.

Many buildings do not have automatic sprinkler protection because the per dollar cost of the protection appears unjustifiably high to the building owners in relation to the value of the building. In numerous cases, however, savings in insurance premiums alone could be adequate to finance the installation of automatic sprinkler protection over a few years' time. Of equal importance are the many building code modifications that are allowed when sprinklers are installed. These modifications permit an increase in undivided area and, often, less fire resistance for the building construction and therefore lower construction costs. No value can be placed on the life safety aspects of total sprinkler protection or on the security occupants feel when such systems are installed.

STANDARDIZING SPRINKLER INSTALLATIONS

The terms "sprinkler protection," "sprinkler installations," and "sprinkler systems" usually signify a combination of water discharge devices, or sprinklers; one or more sources of water under pressure; waterflow controlling devices, or valves; distribution piping to supply the water to the discharge devices; and auxiliary equipment, such as alarms and supervisory devices. Outdoor hydrants, indoor hose standpipes, and hand hose connections also are frequently a part of the system that provides protection. Figure 5-9C is an illustration of a typical sprinkler installation with all common water supplies, outdoor hydrants, and underground piping.

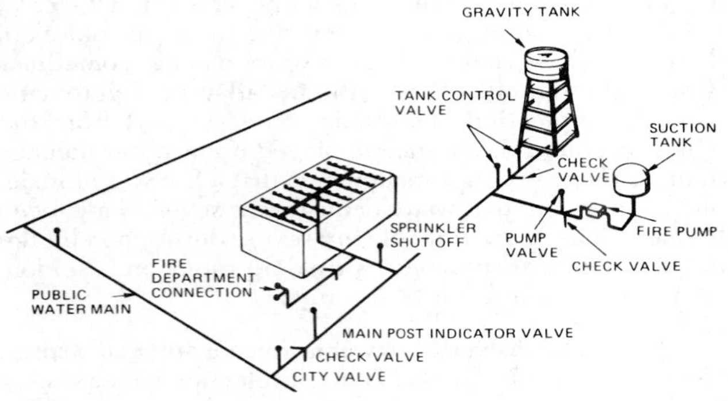

FIG. 5-9C. A typical sprinkler installation showing all common water supplies, outdoor hydrants, and underground piping.

When considering the water supply, the performance of sprinklers, dry-pipe or wet-pipe systems, or special arrangements of sprinkler protection, the designation "sprinkler system" applies to the sprinklers controlled by a single water supply valve. Under this definition, large buildings require several sprinkler systems, and a single water system may supply a number of sprinkler systems.

The fundamentals of sprinkler protection are based on the principle of the automatic discharge of water in sufficient density to control or extinguish a fire in its incipiency. In planning for a system that fulfills this objective, many factors must be considered. However, these factors can be broadly grouped into four categories: the sprinkler system itself, features of building construction, hazards of occupancy, and water supplies.

Automatic sprinkler systems of one type or another have been designed to extinguish or control practically every known type of fire in practically all materials in use today. It is essential, however, that the proper system be used for a given hazard. A sprinkler system designed to control and extinguish fire in an office occupancy with a relatively small amount of combustibles cannot be expected to be as effective in protecting a hazardous process involving considerable combustible materials or a storage area where the fire loading is severe. On the other hand, it is not economical to overprotect by installing sprinkler equipment capable of controlling and extinguishing fire of a magnitude beyond any conceivable situation that could arise in the lifetime of a building.

The NFPA Sprinkler Systems Standard

NFPA 13, *Installation of Sprinkler Systems*, covers the planning and design of sprinkler protection, the type of materials and components used in systems, and the operations carried on in making the installation. Compliance with NFPA 13 is often required by enforcement agencies, and it is used by insurance companies and insurance rating organizations. Property owners themselves often specify compliance with NFPA 13 in order that the protection provided will be in accordance with the best-known practices.

While NFPA 13, *Installation of Sprinkler Systems*, is the primary standard for guidance on installation of sprinklers, other NFPA standards, recommended practices, and guides also have a direct bearing on certain phases of sprinkler protection. They should be referred to during design and construction of sprinkler systems. (See the bibliography at the end of this chapter.)

Listing of sprinkler system devices by a testing laboratory is a separate procedure. Listing helps to reassure the public that the claims made for a particular product or device are true and that the device will perform as intended. The use of devices and equipment listed by such a laboratory after they have passed rigorous tests is often required by NFPA 13, *Installation of Sprinkler Systems*.

In 1975, NFPA published the first edition of NFPA 13D, *Installation of Sprinkler Systems in One- and Two-Family Dwellings and Mobile Homes*. This standard was a direct result of the "America Burning Report," which was released in 1973. The first edition of NFPA 13R, *Installation of Sprinkler Systems in Residential Occupancies up to Four Stories in Height*, was published in 1989. This standard was developed in response to the lower threshold values for residential occupancies that have been established in the last few years.

CONSIDERATION OF BUILDING FEATURES

When sprinkler protection is being planned, it is necessary to evaluate construction, design, and certain features of a building in order to ensure effective operation of the sprinkler system. In older buildings, some typical modifications often are needed. These include enclosing vertical openings to divide multi-storied structures into separate fire areas; removing unnecessary partitions that could interfere with sprinkler discharge; removing needless sheathing and shelving; checking concealed areas to see whether they need sprinkler protection or heat, if such areas are to be sprinklered with wet-pipe systems; and pinpointing areas requiring intermediate- and high-temperature sprinklers.

Older buildings often require some renovation to prepare them for sprinkler protection. On the other hand, designs for new buildings can incorporate features of construction and finish that are compatible with good sprinkler protection. Adding sprinklers as an afterthought is more expensive.

Further details concerning features of building design and construction as they relate to fire protection can be found in Section 1 of this handbook. The following paragraphs give information on some of the more prominent building features that deserve special mention.

Floor Cutoffs—Multi-Story Buildings

Sprinkler systems in multi-story buildings are designed to extinguish fire in any one story, but not in several stories at once. Therefore, the cutoffs for vertical openings must be complete to prevent the spread of heat to upper stories. Unprotected vertical openings can allow fire to spread upward and cause an excessive number of sprinklers to open which, in turn, can overtax the water supply.

Hourly fire-resistant enclosures around stairways, elevator shafts, utility shafts, and so on, with fire doors at all interior openings into the enclosures, are the preferred protection. Nevertheless, there may be instances in which special arrangements would permit openings of various sizes between floors. An example is the water curtain method of protecting escalator or conveyor openings. NFPA 13, *Installation of Sprinkler Systems*, suggests close-spaced sprinklers for water curtains for this purpose.

High Ceilings

Sprinkler action may be delayed by excessive distance between sprinklers at the ceiling and combustible materials on the floor. As the hot products of combustion from a flaming fire rise, air from the surrounding atmosphere mixes with the gases so that the temperature of the mixture decreases. When a fire occurs in a room with an unusually high ceiling, the temperature at the ceiling directly over the fire is initially lower than it would be under a low ceiling, when system activation is delayed.

Large clearances between sprinklers and combustibles below also can magnify the problem of obtaining the correct density and breakup of water discharge from sprinklers for the maximum effect on fires, particularly in high-challenge fires, such as might occur in a warehouse. The upward travel of combustion products creates temperature and draft conditions which water droplets may have difficulty penetrating if the distance between a relatively intense flaming fire and the sprinklers is too great.

Fire tests have shown the relationship between varying clearances and varying water pressures, the latter governing the density and degree of atomization of the water droplets.[1] The tests showed that high water pressures for sprinklers are of somewhat dubious advantage in compensating for extremes of height. Finely atomized water that must travel down through a strong fire plume is slowed by the upward velocity of the fire gases; at the same time, the size of the droplets is reduced continually by evaporation.

Tests made in the 1960s showed that a relatively coarse discharge density of 0.20 gpm per sq ft [8 (L/min)/m^2] from sprinklers at ceiling heights of 30 and 50 ft (9 and 15 m) was sufficient for fire control.[2] The test conditions simulated display booths in an exhibition hall representing a fire loading of 15 to 20 lb per sq ft (73 to 98 kg/m^2). The tests indicated that the ratio of sprinklers that open during a fire will increase proportionately with ceiling height, assuming a constant discharge density. Higher fire loadings would require correspondingly higher discharge densities. The concept of sprinklers with relatively coarse discharge was verified with the development of the large drop sprinkler, which was designed specifically to produce large drops to penetrate the high-velocity fire plume present in high-challenge fires.

The development of the early suppression-fast response (ESFR) sprinkler in the 1980s also was concerned with this phenomenon. The ability of water droplets to penetrate the fire plume was studied and tested in depth to develop the concept of ADD-RDD. ADD is the actual delivered density, a measurement of the rate at which water is placed on the surface of a burning combustible array. RDD is the required delivered density, a measurement of a particular material's ability to be suppressed once ignited.

In basic terms, once the RDD is know, a number of ADD values can be established to determine the appropriate design criteria. These two properties are closely related to the sensitivity of the sprinklers, as measured by the response time index (RTI). Any given fire hazard may be suppressed by a number of ADD-RDD combinations. Figure 5-9D presents a generalization of ADD-RDD properties.

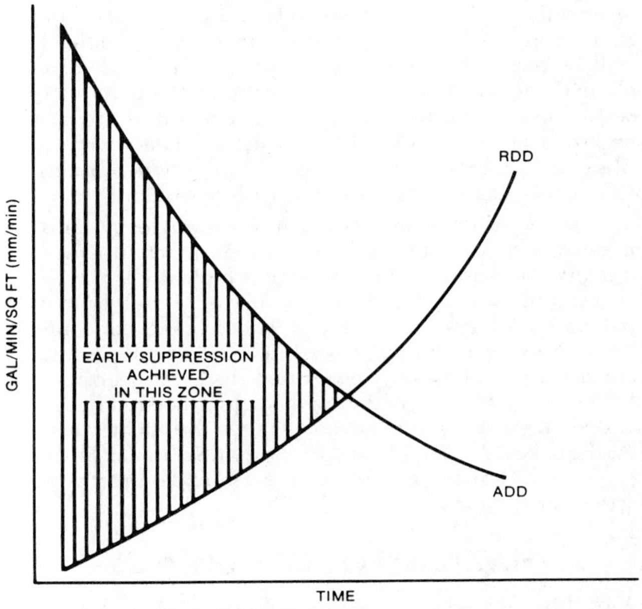

FIG. 5-9D. Generalized RDD-ADD concept.

Concealed Spaces

Sprinklers should be installed in combustible spaces above ceilings because fires that ignite in such areas can spread in an uncontrolled manner. Sprinklers installed below such areas will have no effect on such fires. Fire may also spread into these spaces when they are shielded by construction from sprinklers in the main area. It is important to minimize ignition sources in such spaces, and it is desirable to provide firestopping to prevent the entrance and spread of fire. Before sprinklers are installed in an older building, it is important to examine the interior finish closely; some of the ceiling sheathing or hollow siding could be removed. The use of fire-retardant, noncombustible, and fire-resistive materials does not require this form of sprinkler protection.

Shielded Fires

Wide shelves or tables, partitions, conveyors, ducts, light fixtures, and other equipment that shield fire from sprinkler discharge may delay activation and cause an excessively large number of sprinklers to operate. In some cases, these conditions require additional sprinklers. Architectural features, such as soffits or decorative ceilings, may also cause some obstruction to the sprinkler spray pattern.

Building Location

A frequently unanticipated or neglected handicap to automatic sprinkler protection comes from exposure fires that occur outside the sprinklered building. Heat transfer to the protected building by means of radiation, convection, and conduction may cause sprinklers to operate. The majority of sprinkler systems are designed to protect the building from fires originating in the building itself. Additional protection features are necessary to protect the building from exposure fires. Protection against exposure fires may consist of outside sprinklers, window sprinklers, cornice sprinklers, or various combinations of these.

Sprinkler systems in buildings subject to flood require special attention to the following: (1) the location and arrangement of piping so that it will not be washed out or its supports weakened; (2) the location of valves so that they will be accessible during high water; (3) the location of alarm devices so that they will remain operable during high water; and (4) the location and arrangement of fire pumps and their power supply and controls, secondary water supplies, and other auxiliary equipment to provide reasonable safeguards against interference with operation.

Earthquake bracing provisions for sprinkler systems are necessary to keep the pipe network in place during seismic events. Additional pipe support typically is necessary and can be provided through the use of lateral, longitudinal, and transverse sway braces. These braces, in conjunction with various types of flexible fittings, will permit the sprinkler piping to stay in position during an earthquake. Sprinkler systems provided with such protection have prevailed after some rather severe—7.0 on the Richter Scale—earthquakes. NFPA 13, *Installation of Sprinkler Systems*, provides extensive guidance on earthquake protection of sprinkler systems.

HAZARDS OF OCCUPANCY

A building's use is an essential consideration in designing a sprinkler system that is adequate to protect against the hazards inherent in the type of occupancy. NFPA 13, *Installation of Sprinkler Systems*, currently takes an occupancy approach to system design. All buildings that fall within the scope of NFPA 13 can be broken down into six "occupancy hazards." For each of these hazards, the spacing of sprinklers, sprinkler discharge densities, and water supply requirements differ in order to provide protection appropriate for the hazard while avoiding unnecessary expense.

Classification of Occupancies

The three general classifications are light hazard, ordinary hazard, and extra hazard.

Light-hazard class: This includes occupancies in which the quantity, or combustibility, or both, of materials is low, and fires with relatively low rates of heat release are expected. Examples are apartments, churches, dwellings, hotels, public buildings, office buildings, and schools.

Ordinary-hazard class: This class is subdivided into three groups, mainly because each requires a somewhat different water supply for sprinklers. In general, this class includes ordinary mercantile, manufacturing, and industrial properties. Group 1 includes properties where combustibility is low, the quantity of combustibles is moderate, stockpiles of combustibles are no higher than 8 ft (2.4 m), and fires with moderate rates of heat release are expected. Examples are canneries, laundries, and electronics plants. Group 2 includes properties where the quantity and combustibility of contents is moderate, stockpiles do not exceed 12 ft (3.6 m), and fires with moderate rates of heat release are expected. Examples are cereal mills, textile plants, printing and publishing plants, and shoe factories. Group 3 includes a small number of occupancies where the quantity and/or combustibility of the contents is high and fires of high rates of heat release are expected. Examples are flour mills, piers and wharves, paper manufacturing and processing plants, rubber tire manufacturing, and storage warehouses holding paper, household furniture, paint, and so on.

Extra-hazard class: Extra-hazard occupancies involve a wide range of variables subdivided into two groups that may produce severe fires. Group 1 includes occupancies with little or no flammable or combustible liquids. Some examples are die casting, metal extruding, rubber production operations, sawmills, and upholstering operations using plastic foams. Group 2 includes occupancies with moderately substantial amounts of flammable or combustible liquids or occupancies in which shielding of combustibles is extensive. Some examples are asphalt saturating, flammable liquid spraying, open oil quenching, solvent cleaning, and varnish and paint dipping.

While classification of occupancies into three broad categories serves as a good basic guide, it does not rule out the necessity of evaluating separately certain portions of an occupancy that may contain hazards more severe than in the remainder of the building. For example, a hotel is listed in NFPA 13, *Installation of Sprinkler Systems*, as a light-hazard occupancy. But certain areas in a hotel, such as kitchens and laundries, obviously are more hazardous than guest rooms. Consequently, the sprinkler protection for these more hazardous areas must be increased, and, in this particular example, the design in the kitchen and laundry areas would conform to that required for ordinary-hazard occupancies.

In each of the three broad groups, the system may be designed according to hydraulic calculation techniques or using a set of predetermined pipe schedule tables. Hydraulically designed systems are preferable from a protection standpoint in all occupancies.

SPECIAL OCCUPANCY CONDITIONS

Some conditions require more than ordinary sprinkler protection in order to provide dependable fire extinguishment and control. Sprinkler experience shows that occupancies involving high-piled combustible stocks, flammable and combustible liquids, combustible dusts and fibers, large quantities of light or loose combustible materials, and chemicals and explosives can permit rapid spread of fire, and often cause the opening of excessive numbers of sprinklers, with disastrous results. Complete automatic sprinkler protection with strong water supplies usually will control fires in occupancies containing these hazardous conditions, provided the severity of the hazards is recognized plainly and the sprinkler system is designed appropriately for the hazards.

High-Piled Combustible Material

Practices in storage and warehousing lead to high piling for many combustible solid or packaged commodities.[3] It is a matter of record that disastrous fires have occurred in sprinklered warehouses where combustible materials were stored to heights over 50 ft (15 m). One of the principal factors contributing to the difficulty sprinklers have in controlling or extinguishing fires in high-piled stock is that water discharged from the sprinklers cannot penetrate to the interior or lower portions of high piles, the areas where fires most frequently originate. High, closely packed piles, particularly those over 12 ft (3.6 m) high shed water so the bottom parts of the piles may not be adequately wetted to control fire spread.

Storage of materials more than 12 ft (3.6 m) high usually presents a severe challenge to the sprinklers. NFPA 13, *Installation of Sprinkler Systems*, governs the design of systems to 12 ft (3.6 m); storage piles beyond this are the subject of NFPA 231, *General Storage*, or, if racks are involved, NFPA 231C, *Rack Storage of Materials*. These NFPA standards require higher densities than those addressed in NFPA 13. NFPA 231C also addresses mandatory provisions for the installation of in-rack sprinklers for certain commodities. Higher densities and building requirements for hose stations are necessary in the NFPA storage standards to compensate for the severe obstruction to discharge which typically is found in high-piled storage warehouse.

Special types of sprinklers, such as large drop and ESFR, were specially designed to combat the high-challenge warehouse fire. Each sprinkler was evaluated on its ability to penetrate the high-velocity fire plumes associated with fires in storage facilities.

Flammable and Combustible Liquids

The effectiveness of automatic sprinklers on flammable and combustible liquid tank and spill fires depends on the flash point, physical and combustion characteristics, temperature, areas of burning surface, and quantity of liquid involved. Sprinklers usually are effective in extinguishing fires in combustible liquids with flash points of 200°F (93.3°C) and higher at normal room temperatures; in heavy flammable liquids whose specific gravity is greater than water, and in water-soluble liquids. Automatic sprinklers can also control, but not extinguish fires in flammable liquids with low flash points [under 100°F (38°C)].

Combustible liquids: The basic action of water spray from sprinklers in extinguishing fire in liquids with a high flash point is considered to be cooling of the liquid surface to a point where it cannot produce a sufficient quantity of vapors for combustion. Most of the cooling is obtained by the absorption of about 8000 Btu (8440 kJ) of heat through conversion of each gallon (1 gal = 3.78 L) of water to steam. The vaporization of the spray should occur near the burning liquid surface; consequently, the size and velocity of the water droplets are critical factors in ensuring that the water penetrates upward fire drafts and reaches the combustion zone at the right size for the maximum cooling effect. For this reason, water-based extinguishment of flammable liquids fires may best be accomplished using water spray designed in accordance with NFPA 15, *Water-Spray Fixed Systems for Fire Protection*. Other design options may include the enhancement of the water's extinguishing ability through the use of water additives, such as AFFF or FFFP. See Section 5, Chapter 20, "Foam Extinguishing Agents and Systems," for more details on this option. Some of the many combustible liquids in this category are medium and heavy fuel oils, quench oils, asphalts, and lubricating oils.

"Heavy" flammable liquids: A few flammable liquids, such as carbon disulfide, are heavier than water and are not soluble in water. As a consequence, spill and tank fires in such liquids are extinguished by the vapor-air separation a layer of water from sprinkler discharge floating on the liquid produces.

Water-soluble liquids: Certain flammable liquids, such as methyl alcohol and acetone, are soluble in water and may be extinguished by dilution with water from sprinklers. The resulting liquid-water solution is less volatile than the liquid alone, depending on the degree of dilution with water. This eventually raises the flash and fire point temperatures higher than the actual solution temperatures. Combustion ceases because there are not enough flammable vapors. However, extinguishment by dilution is not commonly relied upon due to the amount of water required to make most liquids nonflammable, and there may be the danger of frothing if the burning liquid is heated to over 212°F (100°C). For example, as many as 4 gal (15 L) of water may be needed to dilute each gallon (1 gal = 3.78 L) of alcohol.

Liquids with a low flash point: Fires in flammable liquids with a low flash point that are not water soluble, and those with a specific gravity greater than water cannot, as a rule, be extinguished with water because the relationship between the flash point and the water temperature precludes adequate cooling. However, water spray from sprinklers can exert a degree of control short of extinguishment on fires that involve flammable liquids with low flash points. Control principally is due to the absorption of the heat by the water when it converts to steam. For example, a burning gasoline fire 100 sq ft (9.3 m^2) in area will liberate about one million Btu per min (1055 MJ/min). [Theoretically, it would take only 120 gpm (454 L/min) of sprinkler water to absorb that amount of heat. Although 100-percent efficiency in converting water to steam in a combustion zone is rarely achieved, a substantial amount of water can be vaporized with absorption of considerable heat, provided the discharge from the sprinklers is finely dispersed for maximum cooling effect.] Thus, a good portion of the million Btu per minute (1055 MJ/min) released from the fire is absorbed in the formation of steam.

Other factors that contribute to the controlling effect sprinkler discharge has are the deposition of a protective film of water on exposed materials and the reduction of the rate of combustion. As a result, the zone of high temperature is limited to a relatively small area in the immediate vicinity of the burning liquid.

Normally, all equipment containing flammable liquids or vapors is enclosed. However, accidents or mistakes in operating procedures may release vapors which, on ignition, may result in an explosion that can cripple a sprinkler system or in a flash fire that may open an excessively large number of sprinklers. Efficient and reliable ventilation and explosion protection equipment are important in reducing explosion hazards and the consequent damage to sprinkler systems. Strong water supplies capable of supplying all the sprinklers in a single hazardous area at higher than usual discharge densities are essential. Densities ranging from 0.2 to 0.5 gpm per sq ft [8 to 20 (L/min)/m^2] are common. Although excessively high discharge pressures yield high discharge rates, they may produce too fine a spray for effective extinguishment or control.

Combustible Dusts

Severe dust explosions may cripple sprinkler systems. A local dust explosion within equipment or a building can dislodge and ignite additional dust as the disturbance progresses to other areas. The explosion and flame may extend throughout a large area almost instantaneously.

Ordinary automatic sprinkler protection in properties where dust explosion hazards exist can be effective for fire control, provided it has been installed in a manner that will reduce the probability that an explosion will break to piping. To obtain the full benefit of sprinkler protection, efficient dust removal systems and good housekeeping, combined with explosion venting construction, also are essential. NFPA standards for the prevention of dust explosions cover essential precautions.

Chemicals and Explosives

The production and handling of hazardous chemicals and explosives frequently involve materials that are unusually sensitive to shock or to elevated temperatures. To keep the hazards moderate, such materials ordinarily are handled in small amounts and in closed or covered containers.

Fire in cellulose nitrate film, pyroxylin plastic, rocket propellants, and other chemicals subject to decomposition may generate much heat and produce flammable or explosive vapors. Proper handling, process, and storage arrangements are thus primary operating principles to prevent excessive release of these vapors.

Conventional automatic sprinkler protection will not arrest a detonation once it starts. In some cases, it may disrupt a deflagration if specifically designed to do so. However, strong water supplies and closely spaced sprinklers [90 sq ft (8.4 m^2) or less] on piping designed and installed to resist damage, insofar as possible, are helpful in preventing an extension of damage. Water from sprinklers can protect combustible construction and equipment in the vicinity of an explosion and can cool the atmosphere, reducing the spread of an initial fire or other heat-producing disturbance. It is essential that good explosion venting practices are followed to minimize explosion damage, not only to the building and process equipment that may be involved, but to the sprinkler system itself.

Rocket propellants used in the aerospace industry and in defense systems are examples of chemical hazards requiring more than ordinary sprinkler protection. High-speed water deluge systems employing special discharge devices and fast-acting water control valves that respond to rate-of-pressure increases or visual detection, either infrared or ultraviolet, are used in locations where rocket propellants are manufactured, on missile launching pads, and in missile silos. However, mass detonating fuels cannot be protected by any fire protection system. Proper handling, care, and prevention are the best protection features for such fuels.

LOCATION AND SPACING OF SPRINKLERS

The fundamental idea in locating and spacing sprinklers in a building is to make sure there is no area unprotected, where a fire, however unexpected, can start. In other words, no matter where a fire starts, there must be one or more sprinklers located in relation to that particular point that will operate promptly and discharge water when heat from the fire reaches them. Proper placement of sprinklers in a building to ensure that a fire will be kept in check is necessary to prevent unnecessary fire damage.

Complete Protection

It is obvious, in theory at least, that complete installation of sprinklers throughout a building is necessary for complete protection of life and property. No areas should be left unprotected. NFPA 13, *Installation of Sprinkler Systems*, specifically treats a number of locations where the need for sprinklers is sometimes questioned. These include areas such as stairways and vertical shafts; deep, blind, and combustible concealed spaces; ducts; basements or subfloor spaces; attics and lofts; electrical equipment rooms; small closets; walk-in coolers; and the spaces under decks, tables, exhaust hoods, canopies, and outdoor platforms. It is risky to omit sprinklers from any single area because the hazard does not seem sufficient to warrant them. Such omissions are the weak links in otherwise complete protection.

Frequently, building codes and ordinances require partial sprinkler protection for specific areas, as a way of providing limited protection for certain hazardous areas and as a life safety measure. But the limitations of partial protection often outweigh the supposed advantages they offer.

Area and Spacing Limitations

The location of sprinklers on a line of pipe and the location of the lines in relation to each other determine the size of area protected by each sprinkler. NFPA 13, *Installation of Sprinkler Systems*, gives a definite maximum area of coverage for each sprinkler, depending principally upon the severity of the occupancy hazard and, to a lesser degree, on the type of ceiling or roof construction above the sprinklers. The five types of ceiling or roof construction and variations found in each type are smooth ceiling, beam and girder, bar joist, wood joist, and wood truss.

NFPA 13, *Installation of Sprinkler Systems*, covers the maximum permissible distances between the sprinklers on lines and between sprinkler lines and the maximum area of protection for each sprinkler. The maximum area of coverage permitted for each sprinkler must not be exceeded. However, NFPA 13 allows for use of special sprinklers with greater areas of coverage when they have been tested and listed for this greater coverage. These types of sprinklers are referred to as "extended coverage." Such sprinklers require higher discharge pressures and flow rates than the standard spray upright and pendent sprinklers and the horizontal sidewall sprinkler.

On the other hand, sprinklers and lines should not be spaced too closely together. If sprinklers are less than 6 ft (1.8 m) apart, baffles are required to prevent an operating sprinkler from wetting, and thereby delaying the operation of, adjacent sprinklers. This condition is referred to as the "cold solder effect."

Obstruction to Distribution

In addition to limits on the maximum distance between sprinklers, certain limits of clearance have been established between sprinklers and structural members such as beams, girders, and trusses to keep them from obstructing water discharged from sprinklers. If a sprinkler is placed too close to a beam that deflects the normal discharge pattern of the water, the area of protection for that sprinkler is considerably reduced, and fire has a chance for additional growth.

This causes more sprinklers to operate than should have been necessary. NFPA 13, *Installation of Sprinkler Systems*, is explicit in the limitations it places on distances between sprinklers and structural members to avoid obstruction of lateral distribution of water.

Clearance Between Sprinklers and Ceilings

The distance between sprinklers and the ceiling is important. The closer sprinklers are to the ceiling, the faster they will operate. (See Figure 5-9E). However, locating sprinklers too close to any ceiling but a smooth continuous ceiling is more likely to result in serious interference with lateral distribution of water from sprinklers by structural members. When a combustible ceiling is broken up into bays by beams framed into girders or into narrow channels by beams, purlins, or joists, it is also quite possible for a fire of moderate to severe intensity to ignite the ceiling and spread for considerable distances if the sprinklers are not located at the correct distance below the ceiling. Some types of ceiling construction, such as panel construction, actually allow the sprinkler to operate in a timely manner. In this type of construction, the heat has a well-defined volume in which to accumulate, thereby allowing heat to accumulate near the sprinkler much more quickly. NFPA 13, *Installation of Sprinkler Systems*, gives maximum distances below ceilings for a variety of construction types.

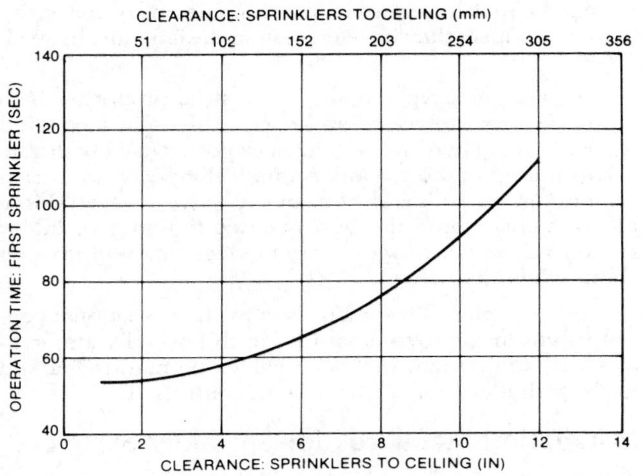

FIG. 5-9E. Effect of clearance between ceiling and sprinklers on operating time of sprinklers.

Sprinkler Piping

Sprinkler piping must be carefully planned and installed in accordance with NFPA 13, *Installation of Sprinkler Systems*. Lines of pipe in which the sprinklers are placed directly are designated branch lines. The pipe directly supplying branch lines is designated as a cross main. The pipe supplying a cross main is designated as a feed main. (See Figure 5-9F.)

The size of piping supplying automatic sprinklers is determined either on the basis of hydraulic calculations or from the pipe schedule tables.

General Pipe Schedule Requirements

No practical sprinkler piping arrangement can produce a completely uniform protective water discharge from sprinklers in different locations or with various numbers of sprinklers simultaneously discharging water. The piping schedules listed in NFPA 13, *Installation of Sprinkler Systems*, are based on extensive and carefully controlled tests and will provide consistently dependable sprinkler protection with practical economy in installation costs and water supply. Hydraulically designed systems usually will provide a more uniform water distribution with additional economy.

If conditions call for either unusually long runs of pipe or many bends, an increase in the size of risers or feed mains may be required to compensate for friction loss.

Wet-pipe and dry-pipe installations follow the same schedule of piping, except that the longer average time between the operation of sprinklers and the discharge of water required in dry-pipe over wet-pipe systems calls for specific restrictions on the air capacity of dry-pipe system piping.

Arrangement of Sprinkler Supply Piping

Figure 5-9G illustrates various configurations for sprinkler system piping. Although it is permissible to supply water to sprinklers in one fire area with an overhead feed main which also supplies adjoining areas, this is not generally done, except for small areas. Adjacent horizontal fire areas usually should have individual risers, each with its own control valve.

Many hydraulically designed sprinkler systems employ gridded or looped piping arrangements in order to reduce friction loss in piping, which results in less costly piping systems to deliver a given quantity of water to the design area. Figure 5-9H illustrates both gridded and looped piping configurations.

Risers

The proper location, arrangement, and size of risers at any given property require skilled judgment. Construction, height, area, occupancy, and fire hazards must be considered carefully .

In multi-story buildings that have fire-rated assemblies between floors, the size of the system riser usually is determined hydraulically by calculating the maximum number of sprinklers expected to operate on one floor during a fire. The size of the riser in a pipe schedule system is determined by the maximum number of sprinklers supplied by the riser on one floor. Both of these methods are based on the assumption that the system will handle one fire at a time on any given floor.

NFPA 13, *Installation of Sprinkler Systems*, covers methods of making riser connections to underground mains, the permissible location of connections to domestic supplies, and special piping arrangements needed when pressure tank supplies are used.

Water Supply Connections

Piping from the water supply to the sprinkler risers should be at least as large as the riser. In private underground piping for buildings having other than light-hazard occupancies, no dead-end pipe that supplies both sprinklers and hydrants should be less than 8 in. (203 mm) in size. Underground pipe should conform to the specifications and rules for laying pipe given in NFPA 24, *Private Fire Service Mains and Their Appurtenances*. Steel pipes used underground may corrode and develop leaks in a short time, unless special protection against corrosion is provided.

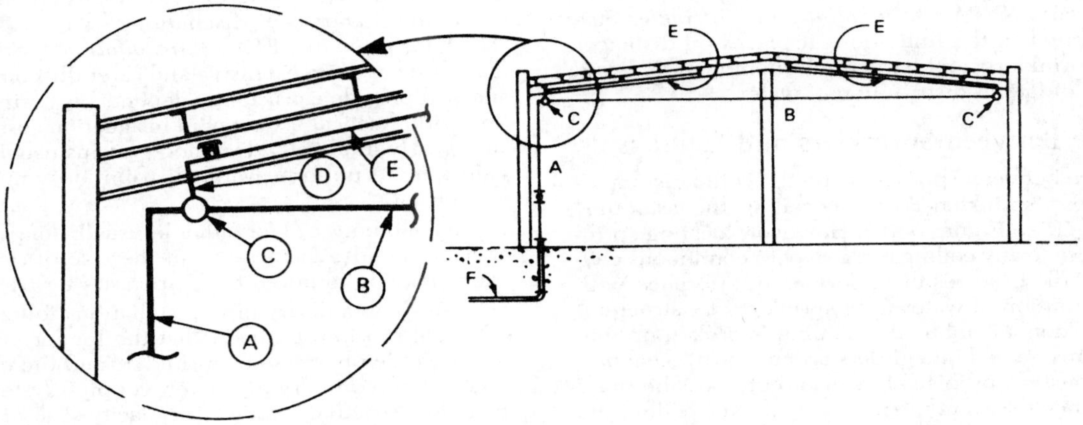

FIG. 5-9F. Building elevation showing parts of sprinkler piping system. (A) Riser; (B) feed main; (C) cross main; (D) riser nipple; (E) branch lines; and (F) underground supply.

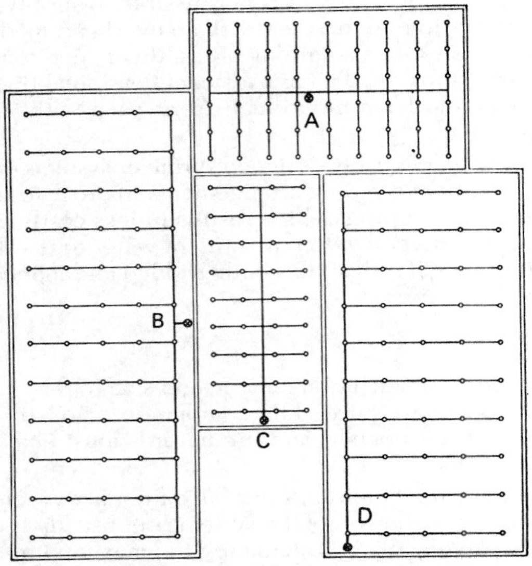

FIG. 5-9G. Location of risers. (A) central feed; (B) side central feed; (C) central end feed; and (D) side end feed.

Each sprinkler system should have an accessible control valve to control flow of water to the system from all sources other than fire department connections. If there is more than one source of water supply, a check valve is needed in the connection from each source.

Many municipal water authorities require some form of backflow prevention device on piping that is common to a potable water supply and the sprinkler system. While the need for such devices is questionable on sprinkler systems, the impact they have on system design must be evaluated.

A common arrangement in industrial properties is to locate water supply gate and check valves in a covered valve pit. An above-ground indicator post is used with gate valves buried in the ground. An indicator post also is used sometimes, even though the control valve is located in a pit. It is considered the best practice to equip sprinkler shutoff valves with supervisory devices that will give an alarm when the valve is closed.

In large plants, fire main systems have sectional control valves to improve flexibility in the use of water supplies. It is important that such valves be plainly marked to show the location of the system controlled.

Installation Standards for Sprinkler System Piping

Piping used in sprinkler systems should be of a type that can withstand a working pressure of not less than 175 psi (1207 kPa).[4] Piping should conform to Table 5-9B.

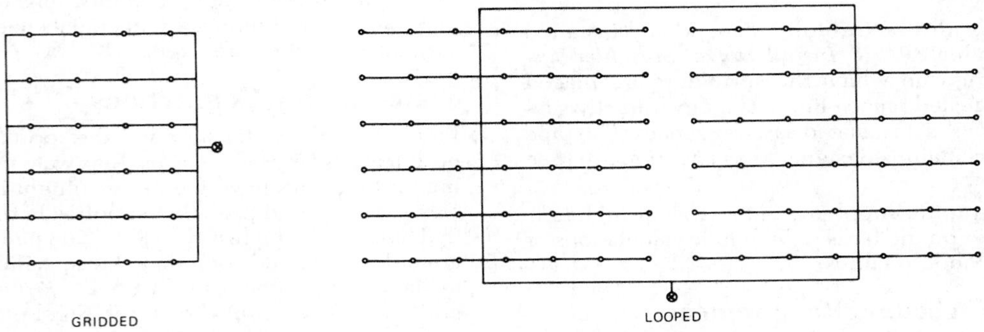

FIG. 5-9H. Low-friction-loss piping configurations showing gridded and looped systems.

Other types of pipe or tube may be used, but only if they have been tested and listed by a testing laboratory as suitable for use as sprinkler piping.[5]

TABLE 5-9B. ***Pipe or Tube Materials and Dimensions***

Materials and Dimensions	Standard
Ferrous Piping (Welded and Seamless)	
*Spec. for Black and Hot-Dipped Zinc Coated (Galvanized)	ASTM A795
Welded and Seamless Steel Pipe for Fire Protection Use	
*Spec. for Welded and Seamless Steel Pipe	ANSI/ASTM A53
Wrought Steel Pipe	ANSI B36.10M
Spec. for Elec-Resistance Welded Steel Pipe	ASTM A135
Copper Tube (Drawn, Seamless)	
*Spec. for Seamless Copper Tube	ASTM B75
*Spec. for Seamless Copper Water Tube	ASTM B88
Spec. for General Requirements for Wrought Seamless Copper and Copper-Alloy Tube	ASTM B251
Brazing Filler Metal (Classification BCuP-3 or BCuP-4)	AWS A5.8
Solder Metal, 95-5 (Tin-Antimony-Grade 95TA)	ASTM B32

* Denotes pipe or tubing suitable for bending, according to ASTM standards.

At present, two types of non-metallic piping have been listed for use in sprinkler systems in light-hazard occupancies. Polybutyalene and chlorinated polyvinyl chloride (CPVC) pipe is rapidly gaining wide acceptance in system design and installation. First used in one- and two-family dwellings, the pipe has proved popular among building owners, installers, and designers. Its light weight and favorable hydraulic characteristics make it a viable option to steel pipe and copper tubing.

Special installation requirements for this pipe must be followed closely . This piping is restricted for use in light-hazard occupancies and not permitted in concealed combustible spaces which require sprinklers. It must be concealed by a protective membrane, although CPVC pipe may be installed exposed when quick-response or residential sprinklers are installed. And strict adherence to manufacturers' instructions for assembly of pipe and fittings is necessary.

Pipe fittings: If fittings are of cast iron, they should be of extra-heavy pattern for sizes larger than 2 in. (50.8 mm) if the normal pressure in the piping system exceeds 175 psi (1207 kPa). If fittings are of malleable iron, standard-weight pattern is acceptable in sizes up to and including 6 in. (152.4 mm) if the normal pressure in the pipe system does not exceed 300 psi (2069 kPa).

Fittings should be of types designed for use in sprinkler systems. Pipe size should not be reduced by the use of bushings. Bushings should only be used as a last resort when a particular prefabricated fitting is not available.

Cast-iron screwed fittings (Class 125 and 250) and malleable-iron screwed fittings (Class 150 and 300) are covered by American National Standard Institute (ANSI) piping standards.[6,7]

All inside piping is installed by means of screwed, flanged, mechanical joint, or brazed fittings or, with specific approval, by welding or flexible couplings. Specifications for such welding are given in the American Welding Society Standard.[8] Where welding of joints is allowed, or where fittings are brazed, the fire hazard of indoor welding must be suitably safeguarded.

Installation methods for joining non-metallic pipe are unique to the type of pipe used. These joining methods are evaluated as a part of the listing of the particular product. The manufacturer's instructions are critical to ensuring a correct installation.

The CPVC product is joined together using a listed bonding agent. The agent is applied in a two-step process which results in a sturdy chemical bond. It is important to use only those materials that have been listed for use with the product. The fittings available can be used to join abutted pipe segments, supply branch lines, or directly supply sprinklers.

The polybutylene product is joined together using a heat fusion process. which requires the use of a specific tool that can physically melt and bond the layer of material between the pipe and the fitting. It is very important to use only those devices that are recommended in the manufacturer's technical data sheets. Fittings are available to accomplish the same results noted for CPVC pipe.

Approved flexible couplings are used for earthquake resistance. Couplings, bends, and tees of this type are sometimes employed in risers and feed mains if their use is of particular advantage.

Pipe hangers and clamps: These are used to attach sprinkler system piping to substantial structural elements of a building. The support offered by ceiling construction often is inadequate to carry the load of sprinkler piping without additional connections.

The types of hangers necessary to meet various conditions of construction have been tested and listed by testing laboratories. Representative types are shown in Figure 5-9I. For the larger pipe, trapeze bars of steel angle or pipe supported by double hanger rods are used frequently. Expansion shields for attaching hangers to concrete preferably are installed horizontally, although vertical installation may be used in some instances. The adequate support of sprinkler piping is an important consideration. NFPA 13, *Installation of Sprinkler Systems*, provides detailed information.

Corrosive conditions: Corrosive conditions call for the use of pipe, fittings, and hangers designed to resist the particular corrosive environment, or for the application of a protective coating over the susceptible components. Threaded, thin-wall steel pipe should not be used where severe corrosive conditions exist. The choice depends on the kind and severity of the corrosive condition. Care must be taken that paint is not applied to the sprinklers when piping or other adjacent installations are being painted as protection against corrosion.

If it is necessary to use steel pipe underground as a connection from a system to the sprinklers in a detached building, the pipe should be protected against corrosion before it is buried.

Test Equipment

It is essential that the condition of a sprinkler system and its water supply are known at all times. Testing of the supply and the system itself at stated intervals is the best way of doing it. Special fittings and piping on the supply and system are required.

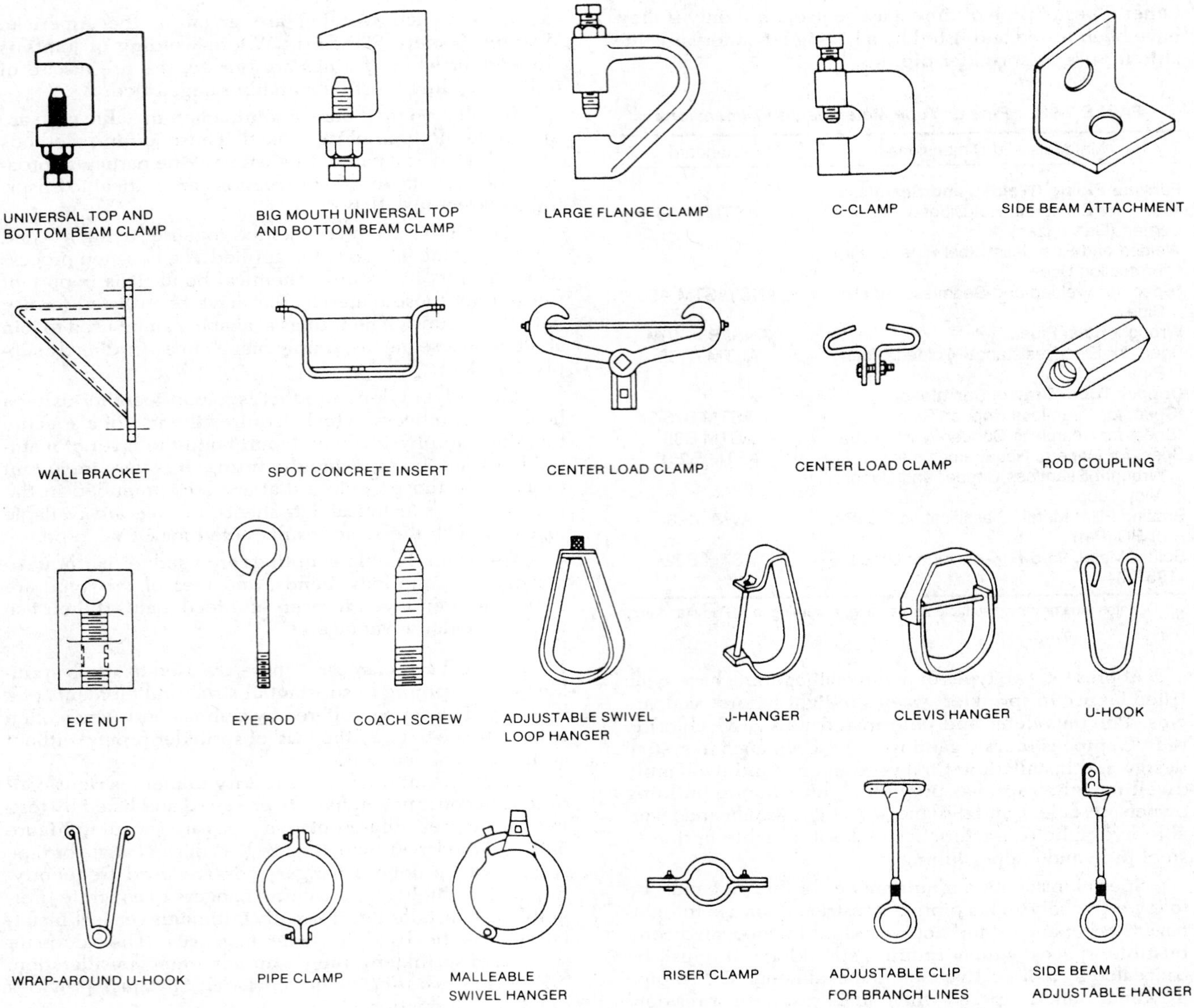

FIG. 5-9I. Common types of acceptable hangers.

Water supply drain pipes and pressure gages: These are supplied for each sprinkler system installation. Drain pipes, which may also serve as test pipes, must be provided to permit flow tests. Drain pipes range in size from 3/4 in. (19.0 mm) to 2 in. (50.8 mm) and are equipped with a shutoff valve. The arrangement permits a test with the system's main water control valve wide open without its discharge causing damage. A gage must be installed to show the pressure in the riser at or near the drain connection. A typical arrangement of a drain connection with a pressure gage for a riser is shown in Figure 5-9J.

Sprinkler system alarm test pipe: An alarm test pipe that is not less than 1 in. (25.4 mm) in size, terminates in a corrosion-resistant outlet, and will give a flow equivalent to the flow from one sprinkler should be installed in the top story. This provides a proper method of testing alarm devices and of tripping dry-pipe valves and also shows that water can flow through the system. Typical arrangements are shown in Figure 5-9K, parts (a) and (b).

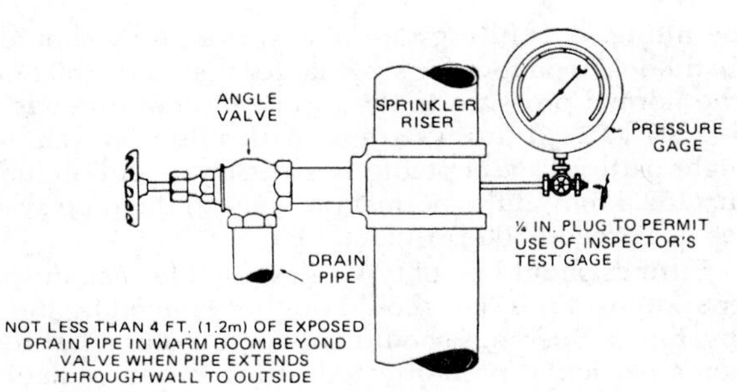

FIG. 5-9J. Drain connection for wet pipe sprinkler system riser.

Other Connections and Features

Other connections to the sprinkler system piping should be limited to hand hose reserved exclusively for fire use. Circulation of water in sprinkler pipes is objectionable

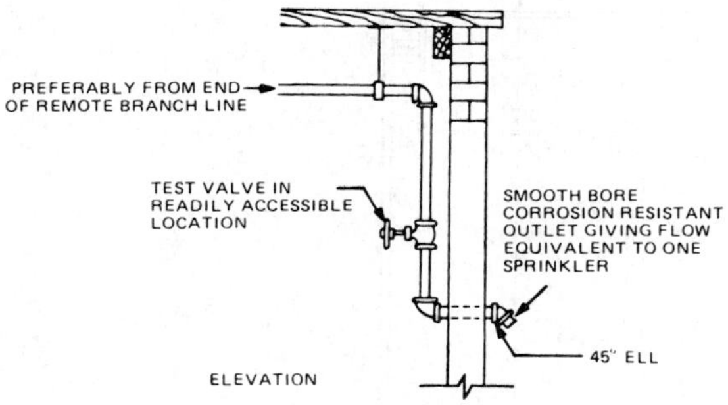

FIG. 5-9K(a). Wet-pipe sprinkler system test pipes.

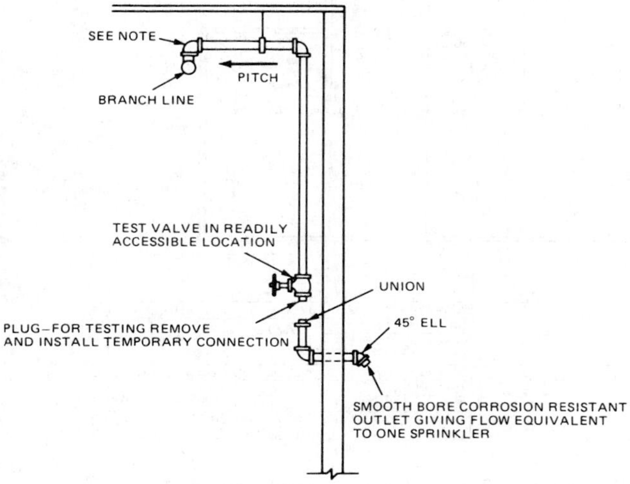

FIG. 5-9K(b). One-inch (25.4 mm) system test pipes on dry pipe system.

because of increased corrosion, which may impair the efficiency of the system. (See Circulating Closed Loop Systems later in this chapter for permitted uses of sprinkler piping for circulation of water.) Sprinkler system piping must not be used in any way for domestic or utility water service because demands at peak periods could deplete the water supply required for fire service during a fire. Hand hose attached to sprinkler pipes within a room should never be attached to a dry-pipe deluge or preaction sprinkler system, and the piping and hose valve should be at least 1 in. (25.4 mm), with a hose not larger than 1½ in. (38 mm).

Waterflow alarm valves, dry-pipe valves, and other special features are covered separately in other chapters of this section.

Signs should be provided on all control, drain, test, and alarm valves to identify their purpose and function. Fire department connections should be identified properly to show whether they supply sprinkler systems, outside sprinklers, or hose standpipes. Manufacturers' instruction charts describing the operation and maintenance of equipment should be located near major sprinkler devices. Identification signs are shown in Figure 5-9L.

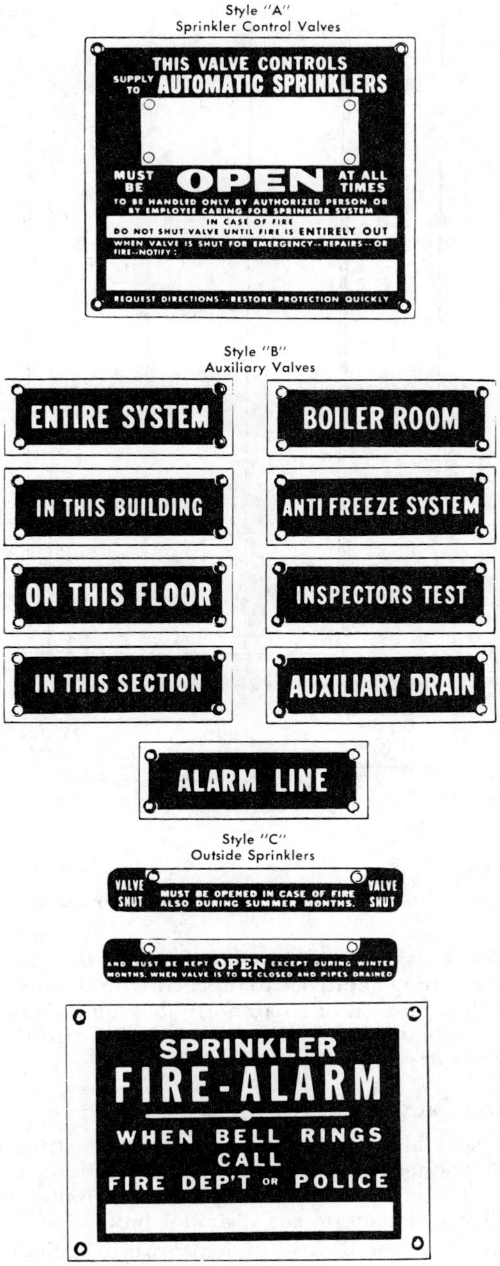

FIG. 5-9L. Identification signs.

INSTALLING SPRINKLER SYSTEMS

Sprinkler system design and installation should be entrusted only to fully qualified and responsible parties. The installation of sprinkler systems is a trade by itself. However, some large industrial properties may have engineering and construction staffs to design and install automatic sprinkler systems and their water supplies.

Before a sprinkler system is installed or remodeled, a working plan is prepared. The plan identifies pertinent features of building construction and occupancy, water supplies, and system piping and equipment. NFPA 13, *Installation of Sprinkler Systems*, is quite precise on the data

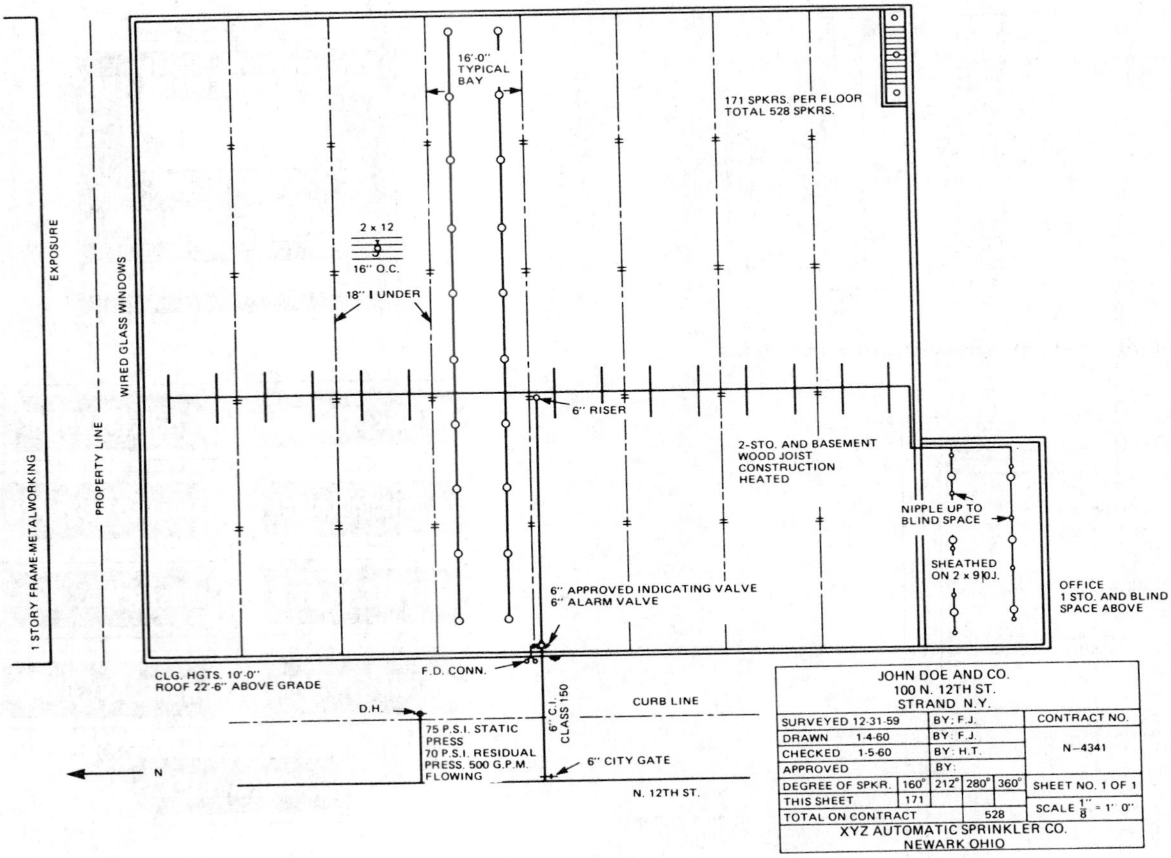

FIG. 5-9M. Typical sprinkler system working plan. (SI units: 1 ft = 0.3048 m; 1 psi = 6.89 kPa.)

that must be shown on the plan, because the plan is the basis for issuing approvals to proceed with the installation where the approval of an authority having jurisdiction is required. Figure 5-9M illustrates a typical sprinkler system working plan.

Testing New Installations

Before sprinkler risers are connected for testing, underground connections to sprinkler installations must be flushed thoroughly. Obstructing materials in underground pipes can seriously impair sprinkler protection.

All piping and devices under pressure, (including yard piping and fire department connections), should be tested hydrostatically for strength and leakage at not less than 200 psi (1379 kPa) pressure for 2 hr, or at 50 psi (345 kPa) pressure in excess of the maximum static pressure when that pressure is in excess of 150 psi (1034 kPa).

Any blank gasket used in testing should be of a special self-indicating type having red lugs protruding beyond the flange in such a way as to clearly mark its presence. These should be numbered to ensure their return after the work is completed.

Tests of drainage facilities are made by opening the main drain valve while the control valve is wide open. This ensures that main control valves are open and that the water will be disposed of safely.

When the weather is too cold for testing with water, dry-pipe systems are tested by maintaining at least 40 psi (2.8 bars) air pressure for 2 hrs. During such a test, the clappers of differential-type dry-pipe valves should be held off their seats whenever a pressure in excess of 50 psi (3.4 bars) is used, in order to prevent damage to the valves. When the weather warms up, it will be necessary to perform the hydrostatic test at a minimum of 200 psi (13.8 bars).

Dry-pipe valves, quick-opening devices, and water flow alarms should be given a complete working test.

TYPES OF SPRINKLER SYSTEMS

There are six major classifications of automatic sprinkler systems. Each type of system includes piping for carrying water from a source of supply to the sprinklers in the area under protection. The six major classifications of systems are:

Wet-pipe systems: These systems employ automatic sprinklers attached to a piping system that contains water under pressure at all times. When a fire occurs, individual sprinklers are actuated by the heat, and water flows through the sprinklers immediately.

Dry-pipe systems: These systems have automatic sprinklers attached to piping that contains air or nitrogen under pressure. When a sprinkler is opened by heat from a fire, the pressure is reduced to the point where water pressure on the supply side of the dry-pipe valve can force open the valve. Then water flows into the system and out any opened sprinklers.

Preaction systems: These are systems in which there is air in the piping that may or may not be under pressure. When a fire occurs, a supplementary fire-detecting device in the protected area is actuated. This opens a water control valve, which permits water to flow into the piping system before a sprinkler is activated. When sprinklers are subsequently opened by the heat of the fire, water flows through the sprinklers immediately, as it does in a wet-pipe system.

Combined dry-pipe and preaction systems: These include the essential features of both types of systems. The piping system contains air under pressure. A supplementary heat-detecting device opens the water control valve and an air exhauster at the end of the unheated feed main. The system then fills with water and operates as a wet-pipe system. If the supplementary heat-detecting system should fail, the system will operate as a conventional dry-pipe system.

Deluge systems: In these systems, all sprinklers are open at all times. When heat from a fire actuates the fire-detecting device, the deluge valve opens and water flows to, and is discharged from, all the sprinklers on the piping system, thus deluging the protected areas.

Special types: Special types of systems depart from requirements of NFPA 13, *Installation of Sprinkler Systems*, in such areas as special water supplies and reduced pipe sizes. They are installed according to the instructions that accompany their listing by a testing laboratory. These include systems for exterior exposure protection and circulating closed loop systems.

Wet-Pipe Sprinkler Systems

This type of system generally is used wherever there is no danger that the water in the pipes will freeze, and wherever there are no special conditions requiring one of the other types of systems.

Where subject to temperatures below freezing, even for short periods, the ordinary wet pipe system cannot be used because it contains water under pressure at all times. (See Fig. 5-9N.) There are two recognized methods of maintaining automatic sprinkler protection in such locations. One is using systems in which water enters the sprinkler piping only after the operation of a control valve, as happens in dry pipe, preaction systems, and so on, and the other is using an antifreeze solution in a portion of the wet-pipe system.

Antifreeze solutions: When a recommended antifreeze solution is maintained in the piping from the riser, the normal water supply does not flow except when the solution is discharged from an opened sprinkler. Because antifreeze solutions are costly and may be difficult to maintain, their use is usually limited to small, unheated areas served by a wet-pipe system where the volume of the section involved is not more than 40 gal (150 L) and where the piping would otherwise have to be shut off and drained during cold weather. Where the section involved is more than 40 gal (150 L), the cost of refilling the system or even of replenishing losses from small leaks makes it advisable to use small dry-pipe valves. In any event, antifreeze solutions should be used only in accordance with applicable local health regulations.

The antifreeze solution generally consists of water and a water-soluble liquid, such as glycerine or certain glycols. The proportions specified in NFPA 13, *Installation of Sprinkler Systems*, give the desired reduction in freezing temperature without producing a combustible mixture. Where the system is supplied from public water connections, the use of antifreeze solutions other than chemically pure glycerine (U.S. Pharmacopoeia 96.5 percent grade) or propylene glycol must not be permitted. In other systems, diethylene glycol, glycerine, propylene glycol, ethylene glycol, or a calcium chloride solution containing a corrosion inhibitor such as sodium chromate may be used.

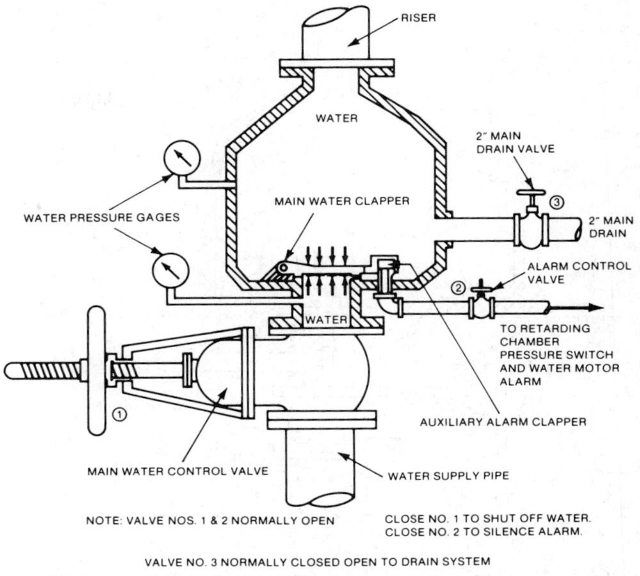

FIG. 5-9N. A wet-pipe sprinkler system is under water pressure at all times so that water will be discharged immediately when an automatic sprinkler operates. The automatic alarm valve shown causes a warning signal to sound when water flows through the sprinkler piping.

Dry-Pipe Sprinkler Systems

Dry-pipe sprinkler systems, in which the piping contains air under pressure until the dry-pipe valve operates, are used only in locations that cannot be heated properly or that have controlled environments maintained at or below 40°F (4°C). The principle of a dry-pipe system is illustrated in Figure 5-9O.

Dry-pipe systems are often converted to wet-pipe systems when they become unnecessary because adequate heat is provided.

Efficiency of dry-pipe systems: According to fire records, more sprinklers open, on average, at fires with dry-pipe systems than at those with wet-pipe systems, which tends to show that the control of fire is not as prompt with dry-pipe systems. In most classes of occupancy; however, and especially those of light and ordinary hazard, dry-pipe systems have shown generally good results and, when properly maintained, can be relied upon to control or extinguish fires satisfactorily.

Dry-pipe valve designs: Most dry-pipe valves are designed so that a moderate air pressure in the dry-pipe system will hold back a much greater water pressure. The difference between the air pressure and the water pressure, expressed as the ratio of these pressures when the air pressure is reduced to the value at which the valve opens, is called the "differential."

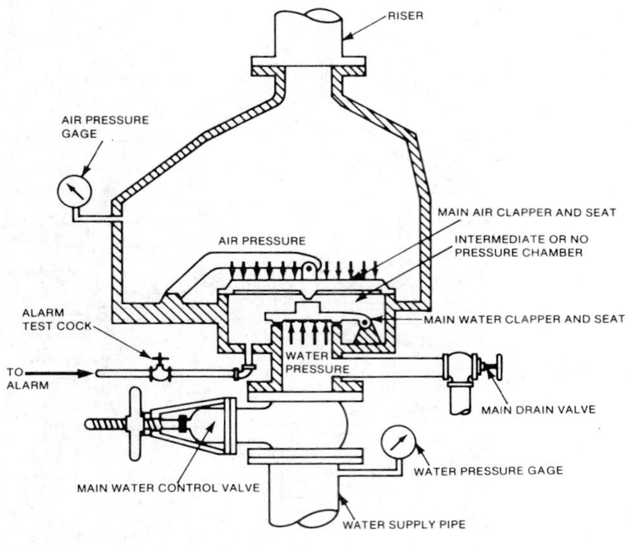

FIG. 5-9O. The principle of a dry-pipe system is illustrated by this simplified drawing of a dry-pipe valve. Compressed air in the sprinkler system holds the dry valve closed, preventing water from entering the sprinkler piping until the air pressure has dropped below a predetermined point.

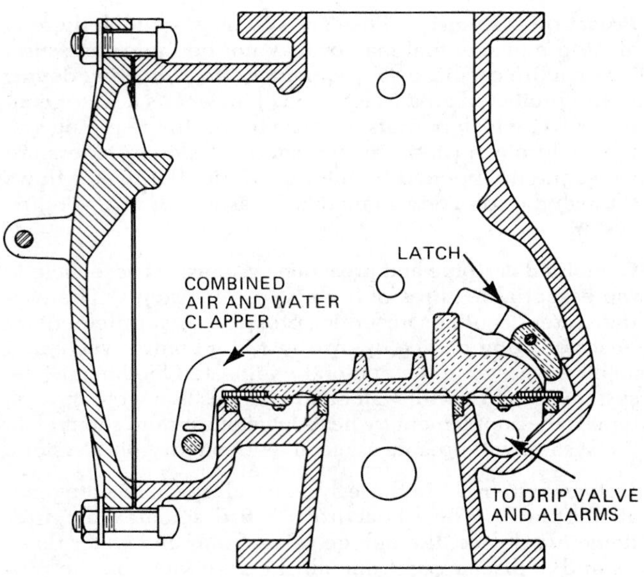

FIG. 5-9P. Differential-type dry-pipe valve. When the downward force exerted on the combined air and water clapper by the system air pressure is reduced to the value of the upward force exerted by the water supply upon the clapper, the valve will open to permit the flow of water into the sprinkler system. The latch prohibits the valve from returning to the closed position. Shown is the Hodgman Manufacturing Co., Inc., Model C dry-pipe valve, which is no longer manufactured.

If the differential is obtained by having a large-diameter air clapper in a valve bear directly upon a smaller water clapper, the valve is often referred to as a differential-type dry-pipe valve. Figures 5-9P and 5-9Q show the arrangement of parts and the relative sizes of air and water clappers in ordinary differential-type dry-pipe valves of recent and early manufacture. Large valve bodies are usually needed to accommodate the relatively large air clappers.

If the air pressure in the sprinkler system acts upon a small disc, diaphragm, or clapper that is arranged with levers, links, and latches to provide the necessary closing force upon the water clapper, the valve may be designated as a mechanical-type or a latched-clapper-type. Mechanical dry-pipe valves of early design are shown in Figure 5-9R. Such valves were mechanically complicated and difficult to keep in good operating condition. A latched-clapper-type dry-pipe valve is shown in Figure 5-9S.

Originally, a differential of 5 or 6 to 1 (water pressure to air pressure) was accepted practice, but this has been altered with some designs so that higher air pressures may be used. In a low-differential dry-pipe valve, the differential is usually 1.0 and 1.2 to 1, rather than the 5 or 6 to 1 common with ordinary differential dry-pipe valves. The low-differential valve, which resembles a check valve or alarm valve, is kept closed by air pressure on the sprinkler system side of the valve clapper, which exceeds the pressure on the water supply side of the clapper. The valve operates when the air pressure is reduced to only about 10 percent less than the water pressure at the point of operation. A low-differential-type dry-pipe valve is shown in Figure 5-9T.

To reduce the danger of accidentally tripping ordinary dry-pipe valves subjected to higher-than-normal water pressure or to water hammer, it is usual practice to maintain an air pressure well above the normal trip point pressure. For example, with a valve that has a 6 to 1 differential and is used with a normal maximum water supply pressure of

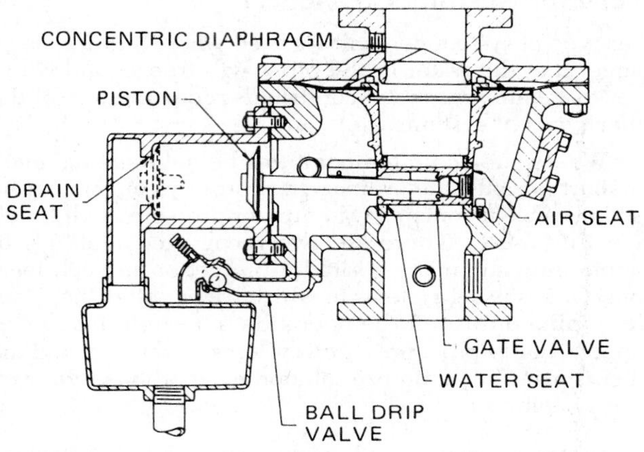

FIG. 5-9Q. Early-type differential dry-pipe valve manufactured from 1905 to 1920. Air pressure on the concentric diaphragm and on the air seat of the gate valve holds the gate on the water seat. The ball drip valve prevents water leakage by the water seat from accumulating in the intermediate chamber. Release of air pressure allows the gate valve to lift slightly from the water seat. The pressure of the water acts on the loosely fitting piston to withdraw the gate valve from the air seat and the water seat. The piston against the drain seat prevents escape of water. (Grinnell Company, Inc.)

100 psi (689 kPa), the air pressure of the trip point would be approximately 100 ÷ 6 or 17 psi (117 kPa), but an air pressure of 30 to 35 psi (207 to 241 kPa) would be maintained. Unless a valve has been designed for especially low pressures, in which case the manufacturer's instructions regarding pressures should be followed, it is customary to

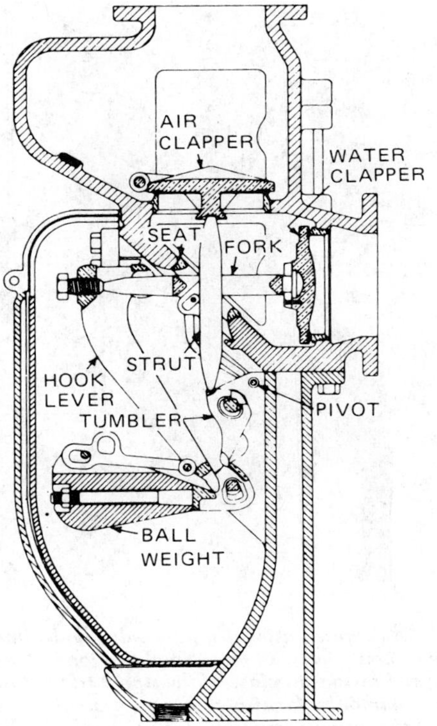

FIG. 5-9R. ***Mechanical-type dry-pipe valve manufactured from 1909 to 1924. Water supply pressure on the water clapper is resisted by the fork hook lever, ball weight, tumbler, and strut, and by air pressure on the air clapper. When the valve trips, the strut and the fork hinge on the pivot, carrying the water clapper back to rest on the seat and thus preventing leakage into that portion of the valve containing the mechanical linkage assembly. ("Automatic" Sprinkler Corp. of America, International)***

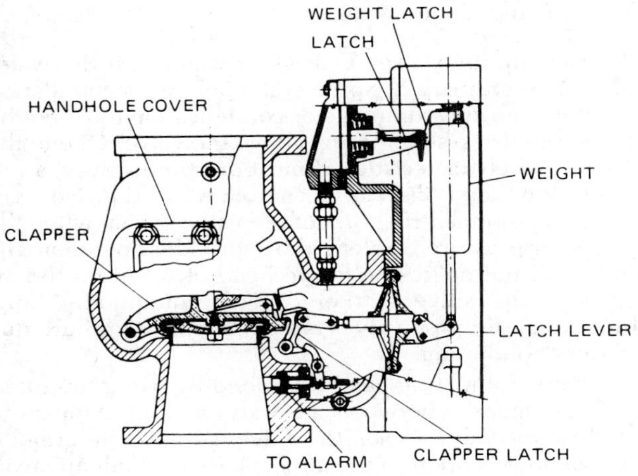

FIG. 5-9S. ***Latched-clapper-type mechanical dry-pipe valve. The pressure of the water supply is resisted by a positive clapper latch that is released by the falling weight when a reduced system air pressure releases the diaphragm-actuated weight latch. An automatic float drain may be provided to prevent water columning by possible leakage at the water valve seat or condensate drainage in the sprinkler piping. (See Figure 5-9Y.) Shown is the "Automatic" Sprinkler Corp. of American Model 141 dry-pipe valve, which is no longer manufactured.***

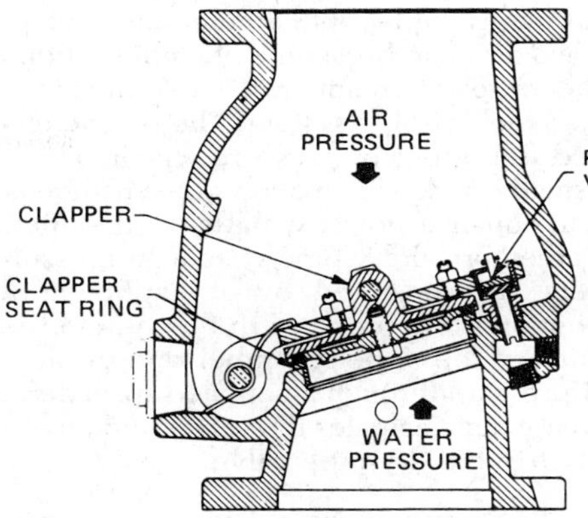

FIG. 5-9T. ***A low-differential dry-pipe valve. Air pressure 15 to 20 psi (103 to 140 kPa) higher than the water pressure supplying the sprinkler system holds the clapper shut on the clapper seat ring. When the air pressure is reduced to about 10 percent below the water pressure, the clapper is lifted off its seat, and water enters the sprinkler system and flows out through the pilot valve to operate alarm devices. Low-differential valves are similar to the alarm check valves used in wet-pipe sprinkler systems. Shown is the "Automatic" Sprinkler Corp. of America Model 15 valve, which is no longer manufactured.***

maintain the dry system air pressure 15 to 20 psi (103 to 138 kPa) above the value at which the dry-pipe valve would trip. About the same amount of excess pressure is carried in low-differential dry-pipe systems.

After a dry-pipe valve has tripped and the piping has filled with water, the air and water clappers of ordinary differential valves must be prevented from returning to the set position if the water flow is interrupted, because the weight of the water column would restrict the valve. Reseating under temporary backflow can produce water hammer sufficient to break the valve or its fittings. An automatic mechanical latch is provided to prevent a clapper from returning to its seat after it has opened appreciably.

Quick-opening devices: One characteristic of a dry-pipe system is a delay between the opening of a sprinkler and the discharge of water, a delay which may allow the fire to spread and more sprinklers to open. The delay is due to the time required to exhaust the air from the sprinkler piping. The difficulty may be partly overcome by installing quick-opening devices which either increase the rate of discharge of air from the piping or accelerate the opening of the dry-pipe valve when one or more sprinklers operate.

Other steps are also taken to reduce the impact of this ever-present delay. They include a prohibition on gridded-type systems, limiting the capacities of the systems to 750 gal (2840 L) unless the systems will deliver water to the inspectors test in 60 sec or less, and increasing the design area of a hydraulically calculated system by 30 percent.

Dry-pipe valves controlling systems with a capacity of more than 500 gal (1893 L) must have quick-opening devices. These are generally called accelerators or exhausters, and they operate when the opening of one or more sprinklers produces a prompt, but not large, drop in system air pressure. The failure of an accelerator or exhauster to operate does not prevent normal tripping of a dry-pipe valve.

In operating principle, both accelerators and exhausters employ two air chambers. One chamber, often designated the inlet or lower chamber, has a connection that is always open to the dry-pipe system. The second chamber, usually called the upper or pressure chamber, is closed except for a small orifice which allows the chamber's internal pressure to equalize slowly with that of the inlet chamber, which is the normal dry-pipe system air pressure. The two chambers are separated by a diaphragm that is deflected whenever the pressure in the system becomes lower than that of the upper chamber due to the escape of system air pressure through an opened sprinkler. Movement of the diaphragm actuates the valves and mechanisms that promptly trip the dry-pipe valve.

Figure 5-9U shows an accelerator and explains how it trips a dry-pipe valve. See Figure 5-9V for a view of the same accelerator attached to a dry-pipe valve as one of the latter's trimmings. An exhauster is shown in Figure 5-9W.

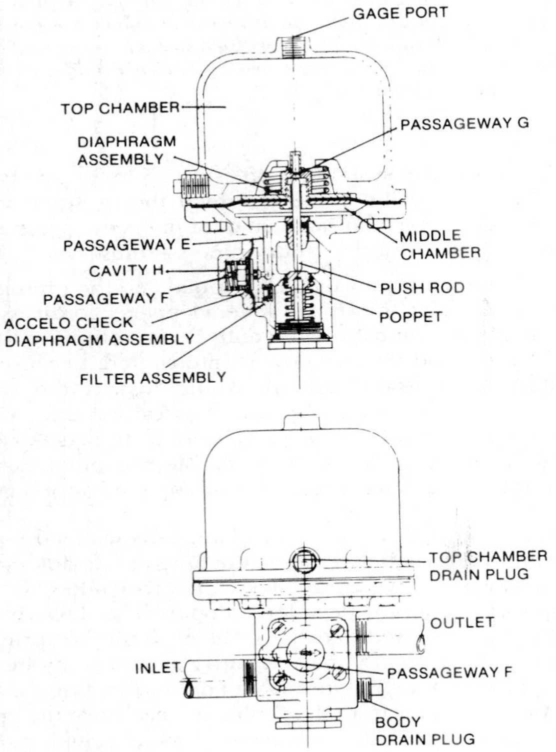

FIG. 5-9U. A dry-pipe system accelerator with integral anti-flooding device. System air pressure enters the top chamber from the inlet through passageways E and G. Once pressurized, the diaphragm assembly closes on the push rod, restricting air flow from the top chamber. The opening of an automatic sprinkler reduces the air pressure in the sprinkler system and the middle chamber. The top chamber, being restricted from losing air, instead moves the diaphragm assembly and push rod. This movement opens the poppet, which admits system air pressure to the outlet and dry-pipe valve intermediate chamber. The buildup in pressure in the outlet backs up through passageway F to close the Accelocheck diaphragm assembly against passageway E, preventing any water or contamination from flowing upward to the middle and top chamber. Shown is the Reliable Automatic sprinkler Co., Inc. Model B1 accelerator.

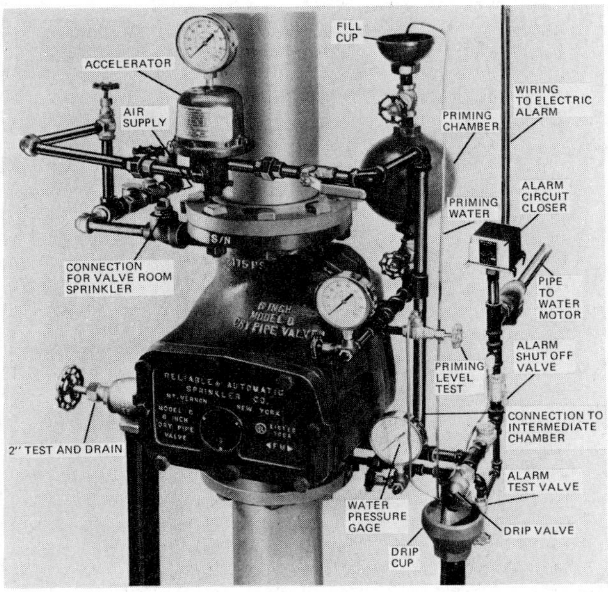

FIG. 5-9V. A representative dry-pipe valve and trimmings. The arrangement shown includes some simplification in the use of copper tubing and fittings in place of the standard steel pipe and fittings still commonly furnished by most manufacturers. The functions of the various components have not been changed, and the arrangement is recognized by testing laboratories. Shown is Reliable Automatic Sprinkler Co., Inc., Model D differential-type dry-pipe valve.

The reduction in operating time of a dry-pipe valve due to the use of a quick-opening device is recognized in NFPA 13, *Installation of Sprinkler Systems*, which permits an increase in the allowable size and capacity of a dry-pipe sprinkler system over that allowed if no accelerating or exhausting device is used.

Water columning: Any leakage of water past the water valve of an ordinary dry-pipe system or any accumulation of water from slow drainage or condensation must not be allowed in dry system piping above the valve. Due to the differential characteristics of most dry-pipe valves, a relatively low head of water accumulated in the riser will exceed the normal trip point of the valve so that when the system air pressure is released by sprinkler operation, the valve will not open due to the head of water on the air clapper. The valve is then "water columned." Low-differential dry-pipe valves are not subject to failure due to water columning.

Water columning can be avoided by using the intermediate chamber between the water and air clappers in the dry-pipe valve. When the valve is set, the intermediate chamber is open to the atmosphere through an auxiliary drip valve. Thus, water entering the chamber through a leaky water clapper can escape through the auxiliary valve. When the valve trips, the auxiliary valve closes automatically. Two designs of auxiliary valves are shown in Figures 5-9X and 5-9Y. These valves reopen by gravity when the dry-pipe valve is reset.

Location of dry-pipe valves: The dry-pipe valve should be located in an accessible place as near as practicable to the sprinkler system it supplies. It should be protected from

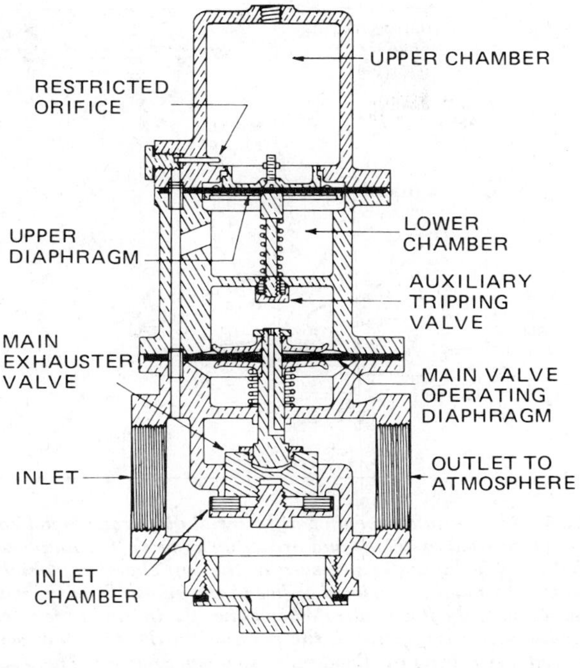

FIG. 5-9W. A dry-pipe system exhauster. The inlet is connected to the sprinkler system side of the dry-pipe valve. System air pressure enters the lower chamber by way of an open passage from the inlet chamber. Pressure can also build up in the upper chamber slowly through the restricted orifice between the upper and lower chambers, so that normally their pressures are equal. The opening of an automatic sprinkler reduces the air pressure in the lower chamber. The higher pressure remaining in the upper chamber moves the upper diaphragm in the direction to open the auxiliary tripping valve. This allows the pressure in the lower chamber and sprinkler system to enter the chamber above the main valve-operating diaphragm where the pressure previously was kept at atmospheric pressure by a small passage to the outlet to atmosphere. The pressure below the main valve-operating diaphragm is kept at atmospheric pressure through a piped connection to the intermediate chamber of the dry-pipe valve. Because the area of the main valve-operating diaphragm is much greater than that of the main exhauster valve, the latter opens and allows the system air pressure to drop rapidly to the pressure at which the dry-pipe valve trips. Water pressure through the connection to the intermediate chamber of the dry-pipe valve then enters the chamber below the main valve-operating diaghragm, balancing the pressure above it, so that the main exhauster valve is closed by the spring, aided by the flow that has been passing through the valve. Shown is Central Automatic Sprinkler Company's Lewis Model A exhauster, which is no longer manufactured.

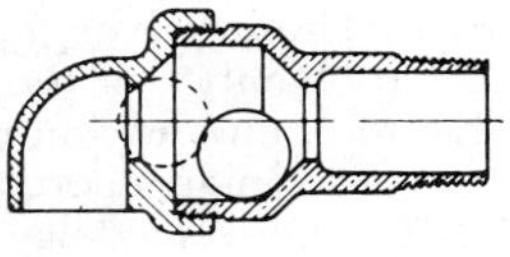

FIG. 5-9X. Automatic ball drip.

mechanical injury, and when exposed to cold, it must be housed in a well-constructed, lighted, and heated enclosure that will allow ready access to the valve. The water supply pipe below the dry-pipe valve contains water at all times and must be protected properly from freezing.

An example of construction for a dry-pipe valve enclosure inside a sprinklered building is shown in Figure 5-9Z.

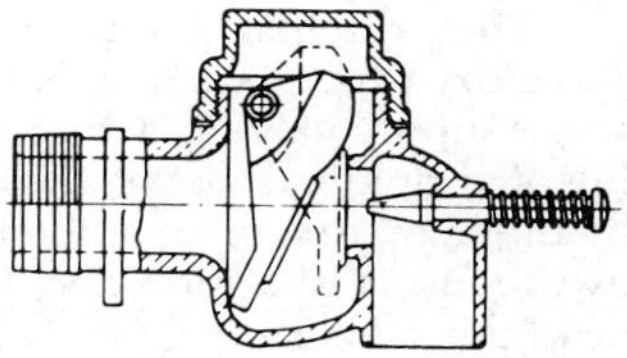

FIG. 5-9Y. Clapper-type automatic drip.

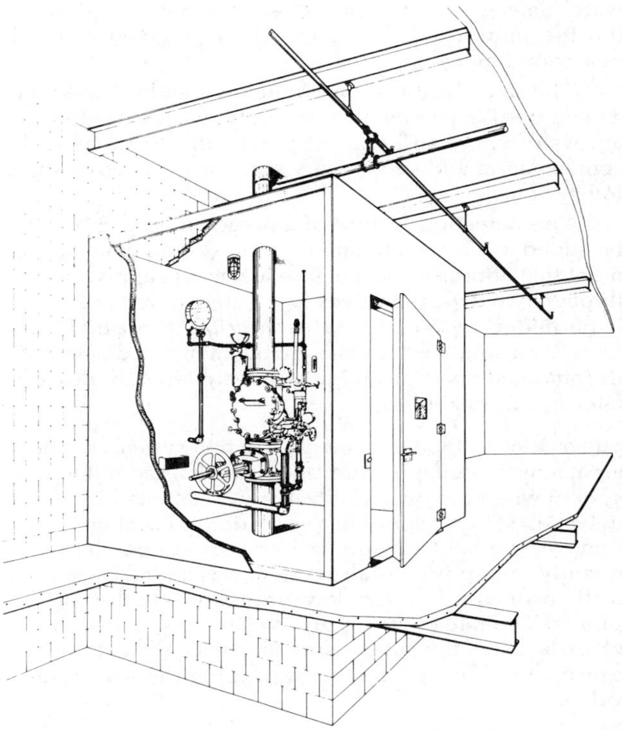

FIG. 5-9Z. A permissible type of indoor dry-pipe valve enclosure. (Source: Factory Mutual System)

If the water control valve is located at the dry-pipe valve, the dry valve enclosure should be of fire-resistive construction and located outdoors or accessible from outdoors.

In cold storage rooms where temperatures are kept at 32°F (0°C) or lower, special arrangements of piping and devices are needed to prevent frost and ice from accumulating inside the sprinkler piping and to permit ready inspection for these conditions. Replacing air with dry, compressed nitrogen from cylinders will reduce the accumulation of moisture in the system, or propylene glycol or some other suitable material may be substituted for the priming water. A small amount of mineral oil added to the surface of the priming water will prevent evaporation.

Preaction Sprinkler Systems

Preaction systems are designed primarily to protect properties where there is danger of serious water damage as a result of damaged automatic sprinklers or broken piping.

The principal difference between a preaction system and a dry-pipe system is that, in the preaction system, the water supply valve is actuated independently of the opening of sprinklers; that is, the water supply valve is opened by the operation of an automatic fire detection system, not by the fusing of a sprinkler. The fire detection system may be of the smoke, heat, infrared, or ultraviolet-sensing types. The valve also can be operated manually.

The preaction system has several advantages over a dry-pipe system. The valve is opened sooner because the detection devices tend to operate before the sprinklers. The detection system also automatically rings an alarm. Fire and water damage are decreased because water is placed on the fire more quickly and the alarm is given when the detection device operates.

The same heat-responsive devices and release mechanisms used in preaction systems also can be used to operate water spray and foam extinguishing systems and to actuate alarm and supervisory systems (protective signaling systems).

The detection feature of a preaction system can also be added to a conventional dry-pipe system in an arrangement that affords an acceptable means of supplying water through two dry-pipe valves to a system of larger size than is permitted by NFPA 13, *Installation of Sprinkler Systems*, for a single valve. The arrangements of devices used in combined dry-pipe and preaction systems are described later in this chapter.

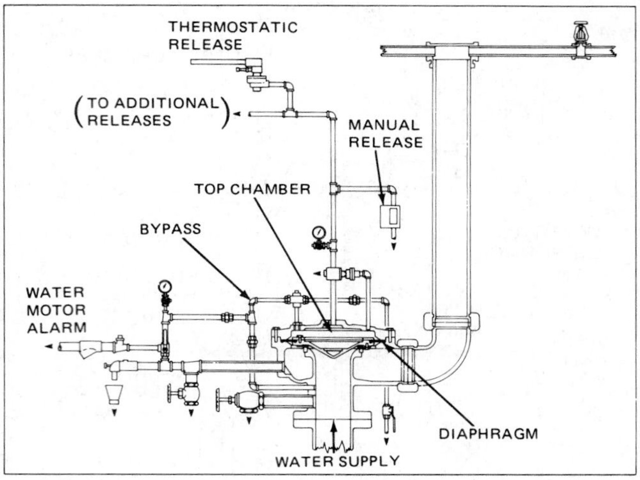

FIG. 5-9AA. A quick-opening, differential-diaphragm flood valve that can be used in deluge and preaction systems. The diaphragm is held closed by water pressure in the top chamber, which is admitted through a restricted orifice in the bypass from the water supply side of the flood valve. When either the thermostatic release or manual release operates, the pressure in the top chamber is released, permitting the flood valve to open. Shown is The Viking Corporation Model E-1 valve.

Supervision: Piping on early preaction systems contained air at atmospheric pressure, and water was admitted to the system when the preaction valve was actuated by the fire detection system. Sprinklers or sections of piping could be removed without causing the system to operate. Subsequently, supervision of the system was added by automatically maintaining a very low air pressure in the sprinkler piping. The rate of air supply is made low so that, in case of air leakage, the supervisory air pressure will drop and cause a trouble signal without tripping the water control valve.

Devices and equipment: The water supply requirements and the rules for sprinkler spacing, as given in NFPA 13, *Installation of Sprinkler Systems*, generally are followed for preaction systems. However, no more than 1000 automatic sprinklers can be controlled by one preaction valve.

Automatic valves control the supply of water in a preaction system. Manufacturers use a wide variety of mechanical, pneumatic, hydraulic, and electrical devices for this purpose. In general, each manufacturer provides a particular complete combination of water control valve release, detection system, and supervisory equipment. A control valve for a preaction system is shown in Figure 5-9AA.

Smoke-sensing devices are the most common means of actuating a preaction system. Smoke detection equipment is usually of the photoelectric or ionization type. A detailed discussion of these is found in Section 4, Chapter 5, "Automatic Fire Detectors." NFPA 13, *Installation of Sprinkler Systems*, permits a wide range of options for operating a preaction system. The system may be operated by activation of a single detector or by a combination of any two detectors. This option exists for the range of detection devices previously mentioned: smoke, heat, ultraviolet, and infrared.

Alarms are standard accessory equipment on water control valves to provide an audible signal on the premises if the valve operates from any cause. Supervised preaction systems also give an audible alarm when the supervisory means is lost, or when an accident makes the detection system inoperative. Alarm systems that give signals at a central station office or that are connected to public fire alarm systems are advantageous and often required.

Preaction System with a Recycling Feature

A further refinement of the preaction principle is a recycling system for controlling sprinklers. It shuts off the water when the fire has been extinguished, reactivates itself if the fire rekindles, and continues cycling as long as fire persists.

Automatic sprinklers are used in the conventional manner. Supply water is held back by a flow control valve that is kept closed by water pressure. Operation of the flow control valve is controlled by an electrical panel that is activated by a system of heat detectors located in much the same way as sprinklers, but with a specific ratio of detectors to sprinklers, depending on the type and use of building and the degree of hazard.

Heat from a fire activates the detectors at 140°F (60°C) which, through closed circuitry, activates two solenoid valves. These valves, upon opening, exhaust water from the top chamber of the flow control valve, causing that valve to open and water to flow into the system piping. Because sprinklers normally do not fuse until at least 160°F (71.1°C), there is a delay during which water can reach the sprinklers in the fire area before the sprinklers fuse and begin discharging water on the fire. As the sprinklers bring the fire under control, the temperature decreases until, at 140°F (60°C), the detectors again close the detector circuit. At this point, a safety timer is activated, permitting the water to supply the system for a predetermined time. On completion of the timer cycle, the dual solenoid valves close, pressure builds up in the top chamber of the flow control valve, and this valve closes. In case the fire rekindles or breaks out in another area, the detectors again turn on the water when the temperature reaches 140°F (60°C), and continue to repeat the cycle as long as a temperature of 140°F (60°C) or higher persists. The system can be reset when the fire has been extinguished completely. Any damage to the closed detector circuit automatically will cause water to be supplied to the sprinklers, which will then operate as a conventional wet-pipe system. To ensure uninterrupted detector circuit service, Type MI cable is used for the detector circuit. This cable consists of a copper wire that is surrounded by magnesium oxide insulating material and enclosed in a special copper sheath. A recycling preaction system is shown in Figure 5-9BB.

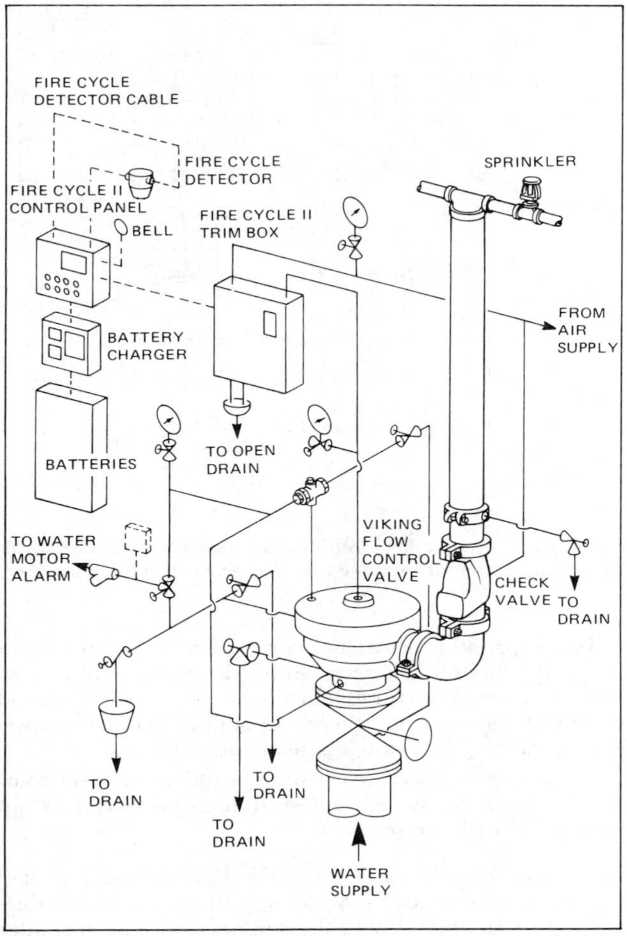

FIG. 5-9BB. The principal components of the Viking Corp. "Fire-cycle" system, a preaction system with a recycling feature for controlling water to sprinklers. Water is automatically shut off when heat drops below the detector operating temperature, and the water is turned back on when the temperature is exceeded. A time delay reduces excessive cycling.

Combined Dry-Pipe and Preaction Systems

The purpose of a combined dry-pipe and preaction system is to provide an acceptable means of supplying water through two dry-pipe valves connected in parallel to a sprinkler system of larger size than is permitted for a single dry-pipe valve by NFPA 13, *Installation of Sprinkler Systems*.

Although NFPA 13, *Installation of Sprinkler Systems*, does not restrict the use of combined systems to any particular classes of property, such systems were originally developed to protect piers where long lines of supply piping could have been subject to freezing if a number of conventional dry-pipe systems had been installed along the length of the pier. Due to the complications of combined dry-pipe and preaction systems and to the increased possibility of delayed water discharge, it is general practice to install them only where it is difficult to protect a long supply main from freezing.

The main features of a combined system are as follows:

1. A dry-pipe automatic sprinkler system, usually with more than 600 sprinklers and supplied by a long feed main in an unheated area.
2. Two approved or listed dry-pipe valves connected in parallel can be used to supply water to a single large sprinkler system. Two 6-in. dry-pipe valves, interconnected with the tripping means for simultaneous operation, are required if a system has more than 600 sprinklers or more than 275 in one fire area. A combination system must have a quick-opening device at the dry-pipe valves.
3. A supplemental heat detection system of generally more sensitive characteristics than the automatic sprinklers themselves is installed in the same areas as the sprinklers. Operation of the heat detection system, as from a fire, actuates tripping devices which open the dry-pipe valves simultaneously without loss of air pressure in the system. The heat detection system also is used to give an automatic fire alarm.
4. Approved air exhaust valves installed at the end of the feed main are opened by the heat detection system to hasten the filling of the system with water, usually in advance of the opening of sprinklers.
5. Systems with more than 275 sprinklers in one fire area are divided into sections of 275 sprinklers or fewer by check valves at connections to the feed main. However, no more than 600 sprinklers can be supplied through a single check valve.
6. A means is provided for manual actuation of the system.

Advantages of a combined system: Some advantages of a combined system include:

1. Elimination of the wrapping and heating required for long runs of exposed supply piping carrying water to dry-pipe valves.
2. A substantial reduction in the number of dry-pipe valves required for adequate protection for a given area, and a corresponding reduction in the number of dry-pipe valve enclosures required.
3. Elimination of extensive air-line piping from the compressor to dry-pipe valves.
4. Quick action of the rate-of-rise heat detection system enables water to enter the system piping by the time sprinklers operate.
5. Failure of the heat detection system does not prevent the sprinkler system from operating properly as a conventional dry-pipe system, while failure of the dry-pipe system does not prevent the heat detection system from giving an automatic fire alarm.

Devices and equipment: To ensure the expected action of the system, NFPA 13, *Installation of Sprinkler Systems*, requires that water reach the farthest sprinklers within 1 min after the action of the independent detection device for each 400 ft (120 m) of common feed main. The total time for the system must not exceed 3 min.

Combined dry-pipe and preaction systems are not listed as single complete units by testing laboratories, but are assembled from individually tested and approved components. Details of a typical installation supplying more than a total of 600 sprinklers or more than 275 in one fire area are shown in Figures 5-9CC, 5-9DD, and 5-9EE.

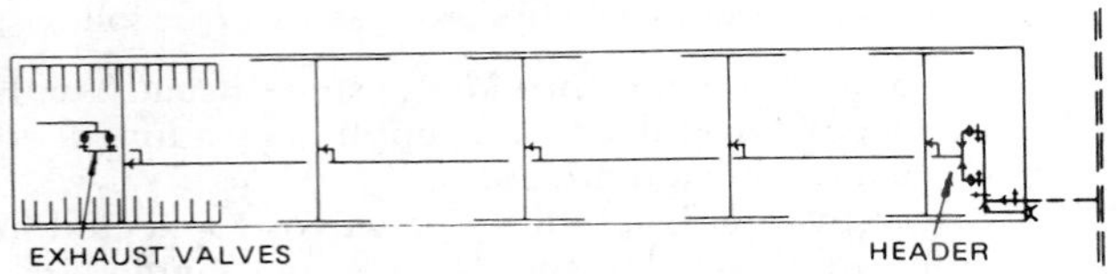

***FIG. 5-9CC.** Typical piping layout for combined dry-pipe and preaction sprinkler system. See Figure 5-9DD for details of the exhaust valves and Figure 5-9EE for details of the header.*

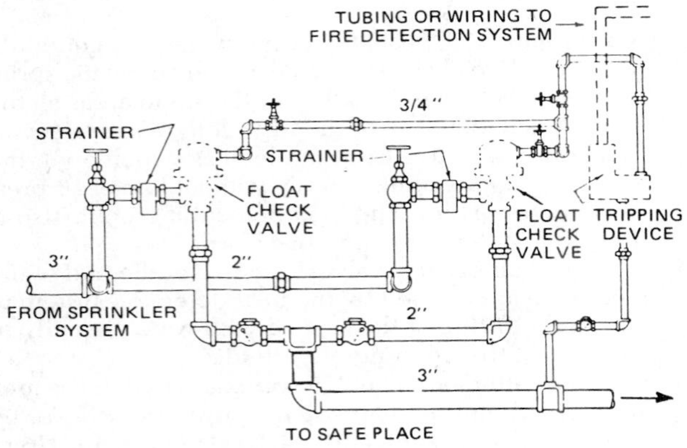

***FIG. 5-9DD.** Arrangement of air exhaust valves for combined dry-pipe and preaction sprinkler system.*

Figure 5-9FF shows an arrangement of devices that make up the basic combination of a single conventional dry-pipe valve and an auxiliary heat-responsive preaction system for a sprinkler system of no more than 275 sprinklers.

Deluge Sprinkler Systems

The purpose of a deluge system is to wet down an entire fire area by admitting water to sprinklers that are open at all times. By using sensitive detectors operating on the rate-of-rise or fixed temperature principle, or controls designed for individual hazards, it is possible to apply water to a fire more quickly and with wider distribution than with systems whose operation depends on the opening of sprinklers only as the fire spreads.

Deluge systems are suitable for various extra-hazard occupancies in which flammable liquids or other hazardous materials are handled or stored and where there is a possibility that fire may flash ahead of the operation of ordinary automatic sprinklers. They are also often used in aircraft hangars and assembly plants where ceilings are unusually high and where drafts, as from hangar doors, may deflect the direct rise of heat from an incipient fire so that

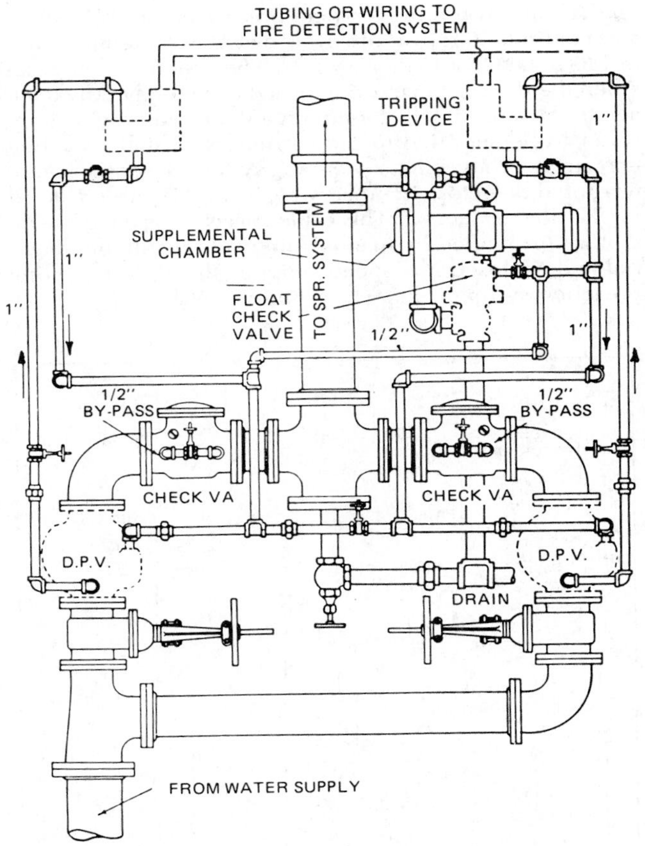

***FIG. 5-9EE.** Header for combined dry-pipe and preaction sprinkler system. Standard trimmings for dry-pipe valves are not shown.*

ordinary sprinklers directly over the fire would not open promptly, though others at some distance would open without effect on the fire. Deluge systems may also be used to control automatically the water supply to outside open sprinklers for protection against exposure fires.

Open sprinklers and closed sprinklers may be combined in a single system where deluge protection is not needed over the entire area.

Design and installation: Where deluge systems are used to protect large areas, the water supply requirements may be large as compared with those for closed-type sprinkler systems. In addition, the design of piping systems and the hydraulic problems involved, particularly where sprinklers are on different levels, as in an arched-roof hangar, call for careful engineering.

Because all the sprinklers on a deluge system must be supplied simultaneously with water at effective pressure, NFPA 13, *Installation of Sprinkler Systems*, recommends that such systems be hydraulically designed. Systems with fewer than 20 sprinklers may use the extra-hazard pipe schedule. Other special requirements given in NFPA 13 also must be followed.

It may be necessary to space sprinklers closer than usual to give the desired density of discharge. The sprinkler piping and the water supply should be designed and coordinated so that it is appropriate for the specific density requirements.

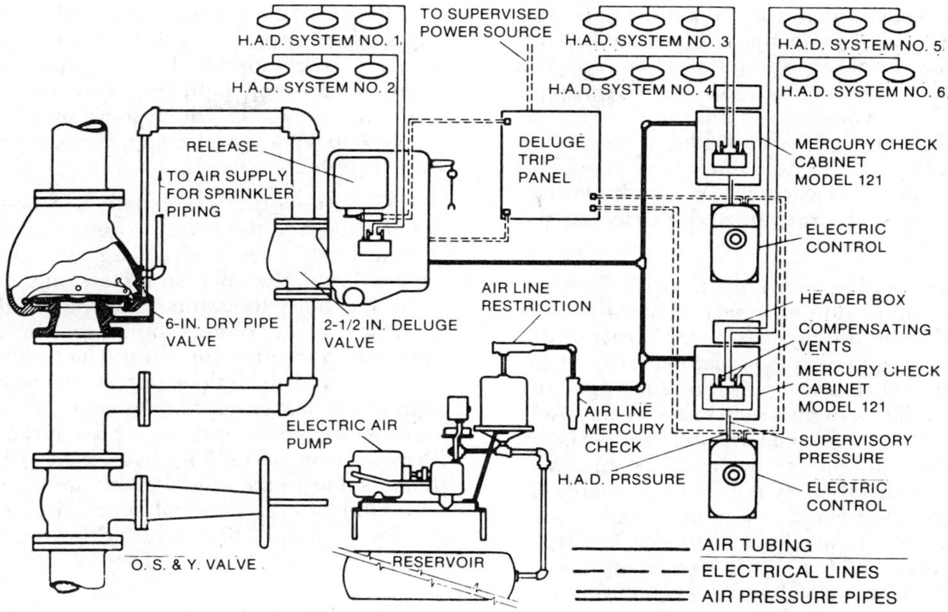

FIG. 5-9FF. ***Components of a combined dry-pipe and preaction sprinkler system of fewer than 275 sprinklers. Manufacturers have various arrangements of proprietary equipment for operation of combined dry-pipe and preaction systems.***

Devices and equipment: Valves controlling the water supply to deluge systems include a wide variety of mechanical, pneumatic, hydraulic, electrical, and explosive squib devices. In general, each manufacturer provides a particular combination of water control valve, releasing mechanism, fire detection system, and supervisory equipment.

Fire detection devices should be located and spaced in accordance with their listing unless conditions call for closer spacing or special location. Detection devices that sense heat are the most commonly used to operate a deluge system. For unusual fire hazards, special arrangements often are needed.

Alarms are required accessory equipment on control valves. Their purpose is to give an audible alarm on the premises if the valve operates for any reason. Alarm systems that give signals at a central station office often are advantageous.

Circulating Closed-Loop Systems

Sprinkler systems piping in some instances can be used to circulate water for heating and cooling purposes. The closed-loop piping is used only to circulate the water; none is removed for manufacturing processes or other nonfire uses.

A prominent feature of a closed-loop system is that water for sprinklers is not required to pass through any heating or cooling equipment when sprinklers operate. The system contains provisions for water to flow from the sprinkler water supply to each sprinkler without compromising the sprinkler system design pressure or causing any loss of outflow of water from the system because of operation of heating or cooling equipment.

Another critical feature of a circulating system is that the temperature of the water must not have any affect at all on the operating temperature of sprinklers in the system. This protection is provided by tested or approved control devices that shut down ancillary heating equipment when the temperature of the water exceeds 120°F (49°C). Conversely, when cooling is involved, precautions must be taken to ensure that the temperature of the water does not fall below 40°F (4°C).

Sometimes, additives are required for heating and cooling purposes. Care must be taken that the additives do not adversely affect the fire fighting properties of the water. Some additives may remove and suspend scale from older piping, which could lead to obstructions at critical points in the systems.

Guidance for the installation of circulating closed-loop systems can be found in NFPA 13, *Installation of Sprinkler Systems*.

Special Types of Systems

There are many situations in which the installation of sprinklers is advisable, especially for life safety, even though it may not be possible to meet all the requirements of NFPA 13, *Installation of Sprinkler Systems*. This type of installation, commonly called nonstandard, or limited area, involves features that depart from generally accepted practices. This does not necessarily imply questionable reliability or ability to handle the specific fire problems for which they are intended. However, their use does require very careful evaluation by qualified individuals to determine their suitability.

Nonstandard sprinkler installations may involve water supplies of limited capacity, partial protection, sprinklers installed in a manner different from that generally used, and other features not typical of standard installations.

Small-capacity pressure tanks: A sprinkler system may have a single water supply from a pressurized tank where capacity [2000 gal (7570 L)] is smaller than is recognized by NFPA 13, *Installation of Sprinkler Systems*, for limited water supply systems, and may also depart from the standard by permitting limited protection to small areas. These special systems may employ a water supply tank pressurized by air or by compressed inert gas, such as nitrogen or carbon dioxide, from cylinders. Manufacturers of fire protection equipment have supplied, and laboratories have tested, systems of the latter type, which have the advantage of using the full water capacity of a tank, with the water being discharged at a preselected, nearly constant pressure.

Substandard water supplies: Automatic sprinklers supplied from public mains, domestic or industrial systems, or other sources that do not meet NFPA 13, *Installation of Sprinkler Systems* requirements, sometimes are installed. Such water supplies having the pressure and capacity to supply effectively a few automatic sprinklers can provide limited protection for light fire hazards in small areas, provided the supply is available continuously. Public water supplies of limited capacity may not be dependable due to varying supply-and-demand relations, small sizes of mains, and, frequently, long pipelines. Occasionally, an automatic, limited-service fire pump can strengthen the supply pressure if sufficient volume is available.

Limited Water Supply Systems

Limited water supply systems are used where a public water supply or other conventional type of supply, such as a gravity tank or fire pump, is not available for sprinklers with sufficient volume or pressure to satisfy the water supply requirements in NFPA 13, *Installation of Sprinkler Systems*.

A pressure tank of limited capacity is one source of supply in this type of system which, in other respects, is the same as a conventional system because standard sprinkler system piping and standard sprinklers are used. The minimum sizes of pressure tanks recognized by NFPA 13, *Installation of Sprinkler Systems*, for supplemental supply for limited supply systems contain 4500 gal (17 032 L) of water for light-hazard occupancies and 6750 gal (25 550 L) for ordinary-hazard occupancies. Approval of plans for all proposed limited supply systems, including the amount of water available for pressure tanks, should be obtained from the appropriate authority having jurisdiction.

Outside Sprinkler Systems

The use of a water curtain on the outside wall of a building probably predates automatic sprinklers. In the early years of sprinkler protection, ordinary sprinklers with the caps removed were used at the peaks of combustible roofs and at the eaves of buildings, particularly wooden buildings. Special types of open sprinklers have since been designed to protect window openings in brick walls. Others have been designed to protect combustible cornices. These sprinklers are placed near the top of the window or under the cornice, and the water is discharged against the glass and frame or the cornice, thus providing the desired protection.

To be effective, outside sprinklers must wet the entire surface being protected. A water curtain that is not in contact with the window, the wall, or the cornice is of little value because the water is broken up into drops through which radiated heat can pass. The water discharge patterns from open sprinklers are fan shaped or quarter-spherical, rather than hemispherical, as with standard sprinklers.

Because of the large volume of water required to supply an open sprinkler system, this form of protection ordinarily is recommended only when sufficient water is available to supply both open and automatic sprinklers and any other needs for which there may be a demand at the same time. Where water supplies are limited, other methods of protection are preferable.

Outside sprinklers usually are needed at each floor level, except in the lower stories of multi-story buildings. In the latter case, such a large volume of water is discharged from the open sprinklers on the upper stories that it is customary to assume that there will be ample water flowing down to protect the lower windows. Because window sills and other building structural details commonly are designed to deflect rain water from the wall of the building, a larger quantity of water is required than might otherwise be necessary to wet the surface being protected. Provisions in NFPA 13, *Installation of Sprinkler Systems*, for outside sprinkler installations are based on building construction of conventional type with recessed windows. NFPA 13 should be consulted for the details of installation.

Partial Installations

Installation of sprinklers throughout the premises is necessary for complete protection to life and property. In some cases, however, partial sprinkler installations covering hazardous sections and other areas are specified in codes or standards for limited protection in the belief that they provide an opportunity for safe exit from the building, help reduce fire spread, and improve access for manual fire control.

Just what portions of such buildings should be equipped depends on construction features, as well as type of occupancy and fire hazards. In multiple-occupancy mercantile and apartment buildings, for example, all portions occupied by stores or similar occupancies, as well as all basement areas, frequently are sprinklered to meet local codes. Many cities have passed special ordinances, some retroactive, calling for sprinklers in the basements of all mercantile buildings. These ordinances are predicated on the life hazard of fires originating in such areas, the heavy concentration of storage frequently found in these areas, the inaccessibility of many basements for manual fire fighting, and the frequency of fires, as shown by the fire records.

In apartment houses, tenements, dormitories, and similar properties of ordinary construction, partial sprinkler protection frequently has been called for to cover basements, kitchens, laundries, storerooms, and corridors, stairways, elevators, and other floor openings. In some cases, it is recommended that a single additional sprinkler be installed just inside the entry door to the dwelling unit. However, residential sprinklers are now being encouraged for use in the residential portions of these occupancies.

Attics or spaces between the roof and ceilings of top floors present a special problem, because these areas may not be heated. A dry-pipe system may be required if sprinklers are installed.

Such partial sprinklers cannot be relied on to prevent the spread of fire when the fire originates in an unsprinklered area, except in unusual cases. NFPA fire records contain many case histories where such partial systems have been overtaxed by fires that began in such unsprinklered spaces.

Self-Contained Systems

So-called package-type systems, all supplied by pressure tanks, can, in some instances, meet NFPA 13, *Installation of Sprinkler Systems* requirements for a standard limited water supply sprinkler system. Other systems, because of the smaller capacity of pressure tanks supplying them and other features that depart from NFPA 13 requirements, are limited to use in situations where it is impractical to meet all the provisions of NFPA 13.

Special systems with pressure tank water capacities below the minimum requirements of NFPA 13, *Installation of Sprinkler Systems*, may be listed by testing laboratories and recognized by regulating agencies for the limited service for which they were designed. Some of the systems may employ a pressure source from separate compressed gas storage cylinders controlled by regulating valves for expelling water from the tank, while others have the gas supply approved and listed as a complete unit. In still other cases, the individual devices making up the system are listed.

BIBLIOGRAPHY

References Cited

1. Thompson, N. J., *Fire Behavior and Sprinklers*, National Fire Protection Association, Quincy, MA, 1964, pp. 104-110.
2. Webb, W. A., "Automatic Sprinklers in Exhibition Halls," *Fire Technology*, Vol. 4, No. 2, 1968, pp. 115-125.
3. Thompson N. J., "Hazard of High-Piled Combustible Stock," *NFPA Quarterly*, Vol. 43, No. 1, 1949, pp. 38-46.
4. "Wrought Steel and Wrought Iron Pipe," ANSI B36.10, American National Standards Institute, NY, 1985.
5. "Black and Hot-Dipped Zinc-Coated (Galvanized) Welded and Seamless Steel Pipe for Ordinary Uses," ASTM A.795, American Society for Testing and Materials, Philadelphia, 1990.
6. "Cast-Iron Screwed Fittings (125 and 250 lb)," ANSI B16.4, American National Standards Institute, NY, 1985.
7. "Malleable-Iron Screwed Fittings (150 and 300 lb)," ANSI B16.3, American National Standards Institute, NY, 1985.
8. "Standard for Qualifications of Welding Procedures and Welders for Piping and Tubing," AWSD10.9, American Welding Society, 1980.

NFPA Codes, Standards, and Recommended Practices

Reference to the following NFPA codes, standards, and recommended practices will provide further information on automatic sprinkler systems discussed in this chapter. (See the latest *NFPA Catalog* for availability of current editions of the following documents.)

NFPA 13, *Installation of Sprinkler Systems.*

NFPA 13A, *Inspection, Testing, and Maintenance of Sprinkler Systems.*

NFPA 13D, *Installation of Sprinkler Systems in One- and Two-Family Dwellings and Mobile Homes.*

NFPA 13R, *Installation of Sprinkler Systems in Residential Occupancies Up to Four Stories in Height.*

NFPA 14, *Installation of Standpipe and Hose Systems.*

NFPA 15, *Water-Spray Fixed Systems for Fire Protection.*

NFPA 20, *Installation of Centrifugal Fire Pumps.*

NFPA 22, *Water Tanks for Private Fire Protection.*

NFPA 24, *Private Fire Service Mains and Their Appurtenances.*

NFPA 71, *Signaling Systems for Central Station Service.*

NFPA 72, *Protective Signaling Systems.*

NFPA 80, *Fire Doors and Windows.*

NFPA *101, Life Safety Code.*

NFPA 204M, *Smoke and Heat Venting.*

NFPA 231, *General Storage.*

NFPA 231C, *Rack Storage of Materials.*

Additional Reading

"Automatic Sprinkler System Performance and Reliability in United States Department of Energy Facilities," *DOE-EP-0052*, 1952-1980, U.S. Department of Energy, Washington, DC, June 1982.

Ballast, D.K., *Sprinkler Use in Buildings for Fire Protection: Recent Periodical Literature*, Vance Bibliographies, Monticello, IL.,1988.

Budnick, E. K. and Fleming, R. P., "How Quick Response Sprinklers Perform and What it Means for Their Applications," *Fire Journal*, Vol. 83, No. 5 (Sept/Oct 1989), p. 48.

Bryan, J.L., *Automatic Sprinkler and Standpipe Systems*, 2nd ed., National Fire Protection Association, Quincy, MA, 1990.

Cheng, Y., "The Development of the ESFR Sprinkler System," *Fire Safety Journal*, Vol. 14, Nos. 1&2, 1988, pp. 65-73.

Chow, W.K., "Sprinklers in Atrium Buildings," *Hong Kong Engineer*, Vol. 16, No. 9 (Sept.1988), p. 41, 43.

Cote, A. E., "Fifty Editions of NFPA 13," *Fire Journal*, Vol. 77, No. 3 (May 1983), pp. 36-38, 124-126.

Cote, A. E., "Final Report of Field Test of a Retrofit Sprinkler System," National Fire Protection Research Foundation, Washington, D.C., Feb. 1983.

Damon, W. A., "Preventing Pitfalls in Fire Protection Systems," *Heating/Piping/Air Conditioning*, April 1985, pp. 61-64, 69-71.

Factory Mutual Approval Guide, Factory Mutual Engineering Corporation, Norwood, MA, published annually.

Fire Protection Equipment Directory, Underwriters Laboratories Inc., Northbrook, IL, published annually in January with one supplement in July.

Fleming, R., "Bracing for Earthquake," *Sprinkler Quarterly*, No. 49, Spring 1984, p. 43.

Fleming, R. P., "A Closer Look at the NFPA Residential Sprinkler Standards," *Fire Journal*, Vol. 82, No. 2 (Mar.-Apr. 1988), p.51.

Fleming, R. P., "Automatic Sprinkler System Calculations," *SFPE Handbook of Fire Protection Engineering*, NFPA, Quincy, MA., 1988.

Hodge, B. K., "Analysis and Design Program for Series Piping Systems," *Fire Technology*, Vol. 21, No. 4, 1985, pp. 310-319.

Hoffmann, N., Galea, E. R., and Markatos, N. C., "Mathematical Modeling of Fire Sprinkler Systems," *Applied Mathematical Modeling*, Vol. 13, No. 5 (May 1989), pp. 415-424.

Marryatt, H. W., *Fire-Automatic Sprinkler Performance in Australia and New Zealand, 1886-1968*, Australian Fire Protection Associations, Melbourne, Australia, 1971. (Available from NFPA.)

Marryatt, H. W., "Suppression and Extinguishment of Fire-98 Years of Experience with Automatic Sprinkler Systems in Australia," *SFPE Bulletin*, Vol. 85, No. 1 (Jan. 1985), pp. 19-23.

Moore, J., "Why Sprinkler Systems Fail," *Fire Engineering*, Vol. 142, No. 5, 1989, pp. 36-40.

Morris, J., "Life Safety and Sprinkler Protection," *Fire Prevention*, No. 209 (May 1988), pp. 18-21.

Nash, P. and Young, R. A., *Automatic Sprinklers for Fire Protection*, Victor Green, London, 1982.

O'Rourke, G., "Polybutylene Piping for Automatic Sprinkler Systems," *Heating/Piping/Air Conditioning*, April 1985, pp. 54-58.

Pennel, G., "Computer Based Sprinkler Plans," *Fire Safety Journal*, Vol. 9, No. 2, 1985, pp. 165-170.

Richardson, J. K., "An Assessment of the Performance of Automatic Sprinkler Systems," *Fire Technology*, Vol. 19, No. 4 (Nov. 1983), pp. 275-279.

Smith, W. W., "Computerized Sprinkler Calculations...The Advantages Are Too Great to Ignore," *Fire Journal*, Vol. 83, No. 3 (May-June 1989), p. 67.

Smith, W. W., "Integrating Hydraulic Sprinkler Calculations and CAD," *Fire Journal*, Vol. 84, No. 2 (Mar.-Apr. 1989), p. 56.

Smoluk, G. R., "What Makes Plastic the Choice in, of All Things, Fire Sprinkler Systems ?" *Modern Plastics*, Vol. 66, No. 7 (July 1989), pp. 55-56.

Solomon, R., *ed.*, *Automatic Sprinkler Systems Handbook*, 4th ed., National Fire Protection Association, Quincy, MA, 1989.

Spees, P. L. and Wright, J. R., "Cycling Waterflow in Sprinkler Systems," *Fire Engineering*, Vol. 142, No. 4 (Apr. 1989).

Tuten, H. A., "Computer—Assisted Sprinkler Design," *Plumbing Engineer*, Vol. 15, No. 4 (May 1987), pp. 22-29.

Watson, F., "Trip Times for Dry Pipe Valves in Grid Systems—A Theoretical Analysis," *Sprinkler Quarterly*, March 1982.

Yao, C., "The ESFR Sprinkler System—A New Approach to High-Challenge Storage Protection," *Fire Journal*, Vol. 79, No. 2 (March 1985), pp. 30-33, 70-72.

THEORY OF AUTOMATIC SPRINKLER PERFORMANCE

Russell P. Fleming

Most fire sprinkler systems are designed so that each individual sprinkler can react to heat from a fire, operating to distribute water over the source of that heat. The complex nature of the interaction of fire and sprinklers historically has prevented an analytical approach to sprinkler system design, but today there is a growing appreciation for measuring the performance characteristics of sprinklers and for using those characteristics in new combinations to achieve specific fire protection goals. The characteristics include thermal response, water distribution, and fire suppression and control capability.

This chapter discusses the response, distribution, and fire extinguishing characteristics of automatic sprinkler systems, and the mechanisms by which it is believed that those characteristics work together for successful sprinkler system performance.

General information on fire sprinklers can be found in Section 5, Chapter 9, "Automatic Sprinkler Systems," and Section 5, Chapter 12, "Automatic Sprinklers." Additional information on sprinkler response and sensitivity ranges appears in Section 5, Chapter 13, "Fast Response Sprinkler Technology." Related information also is contained in Section 1, Chapter 4, "Chemistry and Physics of Fire;" Section 5, Chapter 1, "Water and Water Additives for Fire Fighting;" Section 5, Chapter 2, "Hydraulics;" and Section 5, Chapter 15, "Water Spray Protection."

THERMAL RESPONSE OF SPRINKLERS

While it is possible to equip sprinkler systems with elaborate detection systems intended to recognize other fire products or signatures, it is heat detection that serves as the basis of sprinkler system response. Therefore, a basic understanding of heat production and movement in a fire is an important first step in an analysis of the way fire sprinkler systems work.

Russell P. Fleming, P.E., is vice president of engineering for the National Fire Sprinkler Association, Patterson, NY. He has served on nine different NFPA Technical Committees, including the Committee on Automatic Sprinklers.

Convective Heat Flow in Fires

Since combustion is an exothermic process, burning fuels produce heat. Even smoldering fires produce heat, although the level of heat can be so low as to be ineffective in actuating thermal detectors. However, smoldering fires generally develop to a flaming stage before producing untenable room conditions, at which point the heat release rate of the fire will grow in a manner related to the nature of the fuel and its arrangement, the ventilation conditions, and other factors.

Heat is released from a fire in several forms: radiation, conduction, and convection. It has been determined that convective heat transfer is most important in activating sprinklers.[1] Convective heat transfer involves heat transfer through a circulating medium, which, in the case of fire sprinklers, is the room air. The air heated by the fire rises in a plume, entraining other room air as it rises. When the plume hits the ceiling, it generally splits to produce a ceiling gas jet. (See Figure 5-10A.) The thickness of this ceiling jet flow is approximately 5 to 12 percent of the height of the ceiling above the fire source, with the maximum temperature and velocity occurring 1 percent of the distance from the ceiling to the fire source.[2] The heat-sensing elements of sprinklers within this ceiling jet are then heated by conduction of the heat from the air.

Quantifying Sprinkler Sensitivity

Tremendous effort has been made in recent years to quantify the thermal sensitivity of sprinklers and other heat-actuated detectors. This effort is aimed at making it possible to use analytical methods to predict the time of sprinkler response.

Several terms have come into use as part of this process. One is the time constant τ (tau), which is a measure of the thermal sensitivity of a body and is defined as:

$$t = mc/h_c\,a$$

where:

m = mass of the body
c = specific heat of the body
h_c = convective heat transfer coefficient, and
a = area of the body exposed to gas flow.

Figure 5-10A. The plume-ceiling interaction.

The time constant has units of seconds but cannot be determined readily for any specific body due to difficulties in estimating the convective heat transfer coefficient. This term varies with the velocity of the gases that pass by the body. As a result, the time constant is measured using a plunge test apparatus, first developed for use with sprinklers in 1976.[3] This apparatus generally consists of a circulating air oven with a known air temperature and velocity. (See Figure 5-10B.) The air temperature is set well above the nominal operating temperature of the sprinkler. At time t=0, a sprinkler is "plunged" into the heated air. The amount of time it takes for the sprinkler to operate is recorded and is presumed to be the time necessary for the sprinkler operating mechanism to move from room temperature to the nominal operating temperature.

The use of the plunge test permits determination of the time constant, because it provides two data points with regard to the sensitivity of a sprinkler. It is known that the sprinkler was at ambient room temperature, T_a, at t=0, and it is known that the sprinkler reached its nominal operating temperature, T_L at time $t=t_{act}$. Based on the known shape of the curve by which a body takes on or loses heat to its environment, the time constant can be determined. Under plunge test conditions, involving a constant environmental temperature, the time constant is effectively the amount of time that would be needed for the body to move 62.8 percent of the way to the temperature of its heated environment. (See Figure 5-10C.) In an environment in which the temperature is constantly increasing, the time constant is the amount of time by which the body lags behind its environment after some initial period of time equal to approximately four times the time constant. (See Figure 5-10D.)

Due to the fact that the time constant varies with the velocity at which it is measured, it is not a particularly useful term. Factory Mutual Research Corporation (FMRC) researchers therefore developed a new term, "response time index" (RTI), as a measure of sprinkler sensitivity

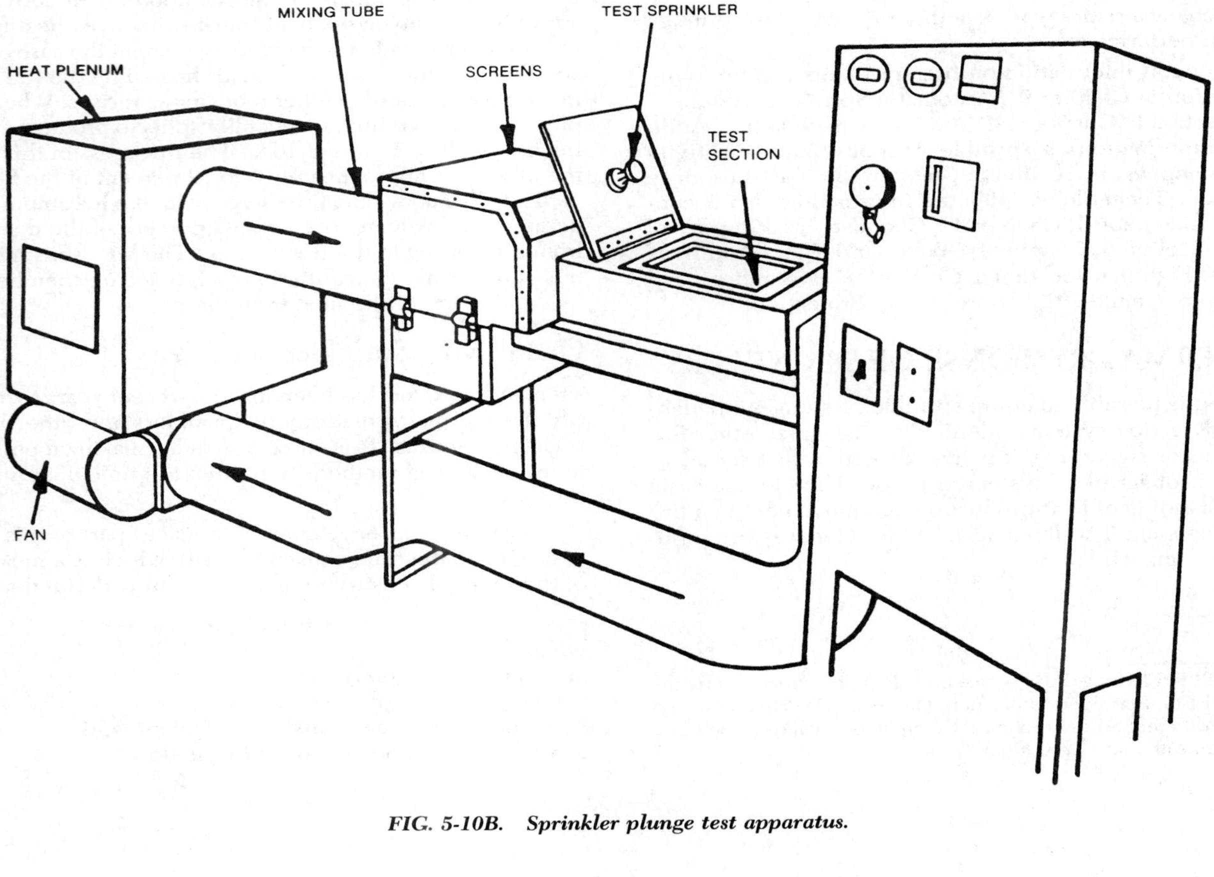

FIG. 5-10B. Sprinkler plunge test apparatus.

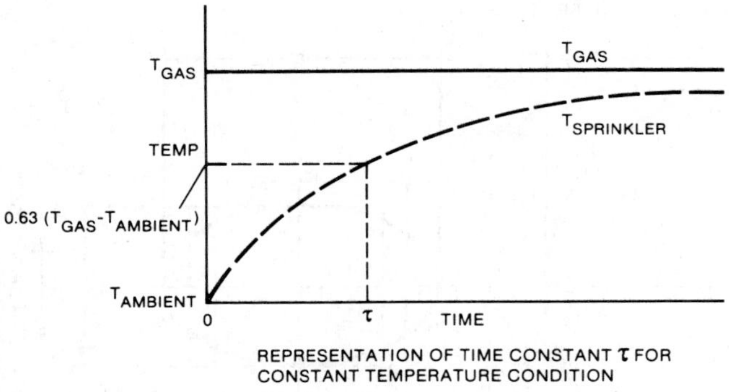

FIG. 5-10C. ***Representation of time constant*** τ ***for constant temperature condition.***

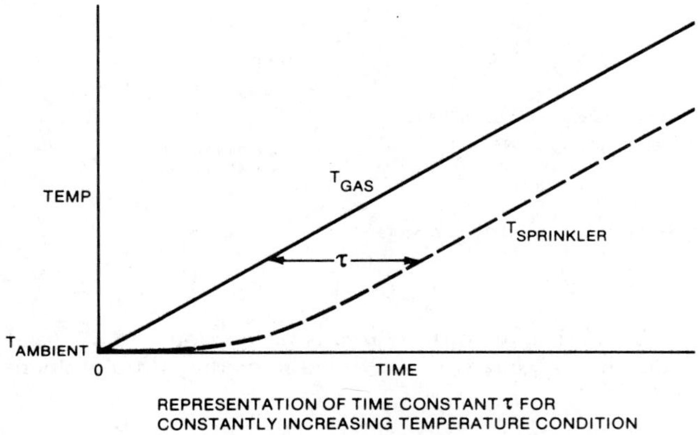

FIG. 5-10D. ***Representation of time constant*** τ ***for constantly increasing temperature condition.***

independent of velocity.[4] FMRC observed that the convective heat transfer coefficient of blunt bodies in cross-flows was roughly proportional to the square root of the velocity of those flows. By multiplying the time constant by the square root of its corresponding velocity, FMRC could eliminate the effects of the convective heat transfer coefficient:

$$\text{RTI} = \tau\, u^{1/2} = \text{a constant}$$

It should be noted that, depending on the units of velocity used, the actual units of RTI are either $m^{1/2}sec^{1/2}$ or $ft^{1/2}sec^{1/2}$.

Determination of the RTIs of various devices has permitted the development of computer programs that predict the operating time of heat detectors and sprinklers based on the heat release history of a fire in conjunction with the ceiling height and radial distance of the detector or sprinkler from the fire.[5] These programs must be used with caution, since they represent only a rough correlation to actual conditions. It should also be noted that they are not appropriate for use with sprinklers following the start of water discharge.

The models of sprinkler sensitivity have recently been modified to account for conduction losses from the sprinkler operating mechanism to the sprinkler frame, fittings, and water in the adjacent piping. These new complexities are not taken into account by the original computer models.

The importance of conduction losses was established in 1986 sprinkler industry test work comparing various sprinklers.[6] These tests showed that the apparent RTI of some sprinklers increased at low velocities, particularly for sprinklers with high conductivity between the sprinkler operating mechanism and the sprinkler body. (See Figure 5-10E.)

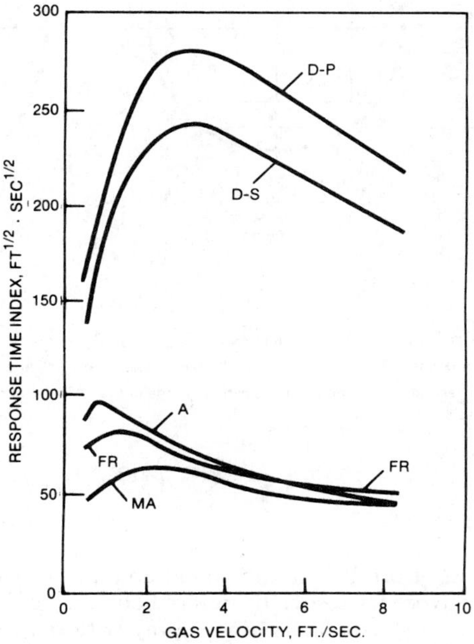

FIG. 5-10E. ***Response time indexes as a function of velocity***[6]***. Sprinklers D-P and D-S represent standard pendent and sidewall sprinklers, A and MA represent flush-type pendent and sidewall sprinklers, and FR represents quick-response sprinklers with conventional frame arms.***

While it might seem beneficial to seek to control the conduction effect to maintain a constant RTI, the tests also demonstrated that the phenomenon could be helpful in preventing excessive sprinkler operations, since velocities tend to decrease with distance from the fire.

Following those tests, the FMRC researchers reviewed the original thermal response model, leading to the RTI concept and the plunge test devised for measuring RTI. They then introduced a modified model that incorporated a conductive heat loss factor.[7]

The revised model assumes that the sprinkler fitting is essentially at ambient temperature and that the conductive heat loss rate is proportional to the temperature rise of the sprinkler operating element. Experimental programs have demonstrated the accuracy of the revised model.

WATER DISTRIBUTION AND SPRAY COOLING CHARACTERISTICS OF SPRINKLERS

Relatively little can be accomplished from a design engineering standpoint with regard to the specific spray patterns produced by sprinklers. The distribution pattern of most types of sprinklers is tested only for overall coverage under specific geometric conditions. At present, there is

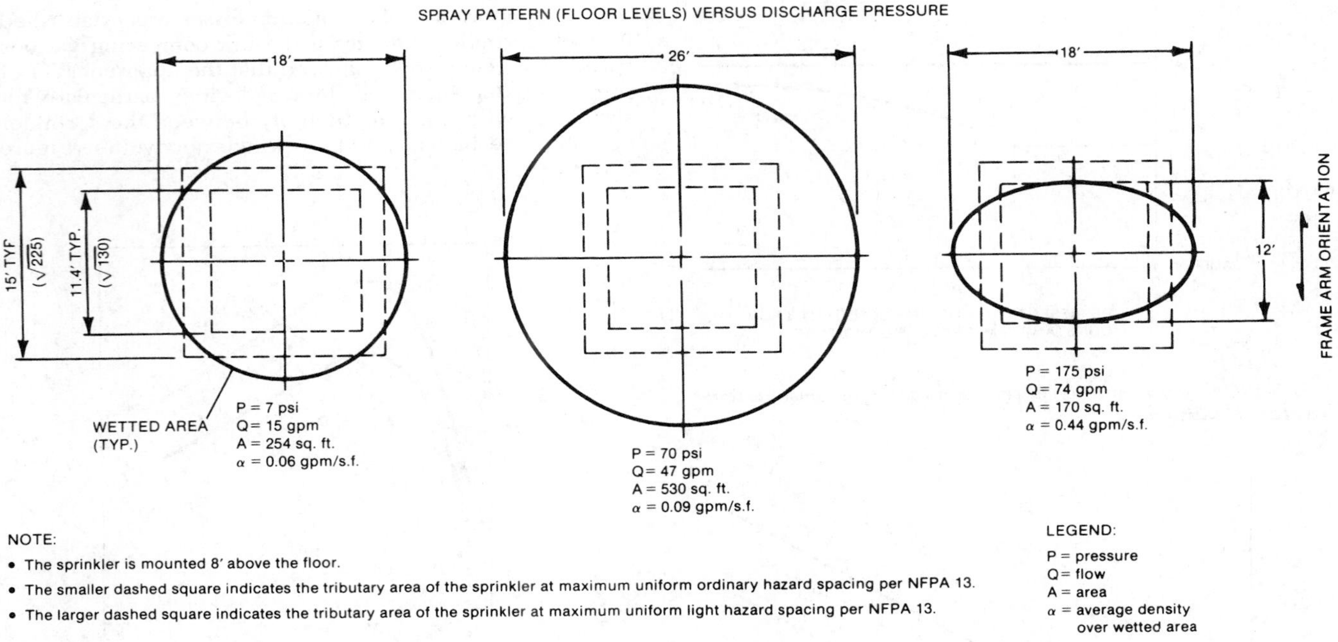

***FIG. 5-10F.** Spray pattern (floor level) versus discharge pressure.*

no method of predicting the actual amount of water that will be delivered to a specific unit of floor area under actual fire conditions, especially since spray patterns vary with water discharge pressures.

Figure 5-10F demonstrates the variability of the spray pattern of a typical ½-in. (12.7 mm) pendent spray sprinkler when discharged under nonfire conditions at selected pressures. A 7-psi (48.3-kPa) operating pressure is considered minimum by NFPA 13, *Installation of Sprinkler Systems*. At that minimum pressure, the extent of the spray pattern roughly approximates that of the maximum light-hazard spacing permitted by NFPA 13, when the sprinkler is located 8 ft (2.4 m) above the floor. The spray pattern enlarges as the operating pressure is increased to about 70 psi (483 kPa), then begins to contract at higher pressures, becoming more elliptical in shape at the upper end of the allowable pressure range. Within the wetting area, the water application rates vary considerably, such that the concept of an average density over the coverage area of a sprinkler provides only the roughest approximation of the amount of water that might actually be reaching a particular unit of floor area.

Some studies have been made of individual droplet size and motion. For geometrically similar sprinklers, the median droplet diameter in the sprinkler spray has been found to be inversely proportional to the ⅓ power of water pressure and directly proportional to the ⅔ power of sprinkler orifice diameter,[8] such that:

$$d_m \sim D^{2/3} / p^{1/3} \sim D^2 / Q^{2/3}$$

where:

d_m = mean droplet diameter
D = orifice diameter
p = pressure, and
Q = rate of water flow.

Total droplet surface area is proportional to the total water discharge rate, divided by the median droplet diameter

$$A_s \sim Q \backslash d_m$$

where:

A_s = total droplet surface area.

Combining these relationships, it can be seen that:
$A_s \sim (Q^3\ p\ D^{-2})^{1/3}$

The heat absorption rate of a sprinkler spray can be expected to depend on the total surface area of the water droplets, A_s, and the temperature of the ceiling gas layer, in excess of the droplet temperature. The total cooling ability of a sprinkler also depends on the depth of the ceiling jet or smoke layer through which the droplets pass.

INTERACTION OF SPRINKLER DISTRIBUTION AND BURNING FUEL

Sprinklers can be effective against fires in a number of ways. One of the most efficient, in terms of use of water, is simply through the cooling effects of the water spray. The production of a mist of fine water droplets can cause significant cooling, which reduces the radiative feedback to the fire below that which is needed to sustain combustion. In addition, the evaporation of water droplets can produce steam with a volume more than 1700 times that of the water and can deprive the fire of needed oxygen. This combination of "spray cooling" and "smothering," while efficient, has its limitations. It generally works well only if the fire is contained within an unventilated enclosure.[9]

The greatest efficiency is in the smallest enclosures, since almost all water droplets can be evaporated by contact with enclosing surfaces, and smothering is enhanced.[10]

In 1955, Nash and Rasbash[10] reviewed extensive tests of manual water extinguishment of fully developed room fires, and suggested that there is a minimum "critical rate" of water application below which the fire cannot be extinguished. With increased rate of water application above the critical rate, the time needed to control or extinguish the fire falls rapidly. With further increases in the rate of water application, the time to extinguish diminishes more slowly. (See Figure 5-10G.) Under the best of conditions, fires in model rooms could be extinguished with scanned jets or sprays with about 1 (imperial) gal per 1000 ft^3 (4.5 L/28.4 m^3) of room volume. It was found that a fixed spray with a medium degree of ventilation could extinguish the fire with about 2 (imperial) gal per 1000 ft^3 (9 L/28 m^3) of room volume.

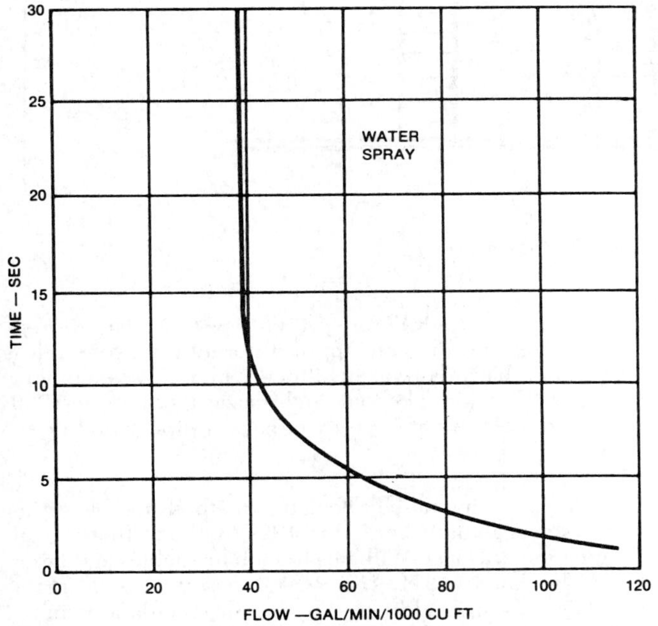

FIG. 5-10G. Time to extinguish fire in model room at various flows.[10]

Automatic sprinklers, of course, are expected to operate before total room involvement. To some extent, this makes their job more difficult, since the sprinkler spray is not readily evaporated to steam.

In a large, open or well-ventilated area, a strong fire can create updrafts which sweep away the small droplets, making them ineffective. For this reason, traditional sprinkler system design is based on the idea of distributing a variety of droplet sizes over the burning fuel area to maintain relatively low ceiling temperatures while controlling or extinguishing the fire.

FIRE CONTROL BY SPRINKLERS

The traditional method by which sprinkler systems control fires currently is being termed the "fire control" approach. This method anticipates that a certain number of sprinklers will be opened surrounding the fire area. While the sprinklers immediately over the fire may not be able to actually extinguish the fire, they will work with other open sprinklers to cool the atmosphere and to prevent sprinklers outside the general vicinity of the fire from operating. In the meantime, the open sprinklers outside the immediate fire area also can be expected to pre-wet adjacent combustibles, helping to prevent the spread of fire.

Figure 5-10H represents the fire control condition that can be achieved by sprinklers. In this steady-state condition, two separate energy balances must take place. At the level of the fuel, the water reaching the fire must be capable of reducing the burning rate to the point at which, in combination with the pre-wetting of adjacent combustibles that has taken place, the fire will not spread to additional fuel. Simultaneously, at the ceiling level, the cooling effect of the water spray from open sprinklers must be sufficient to absorb the heat of the fire plume so as to prevent additional sprinklers from operating and to maintain temperatures below those which would result in structural damage to the building.

In the fire control condition, the area over which sprinklers open generally exceeds the maximum area of the fire. The appendix of NFPA 231C, *Rack Storage of Materials*, provides typical examples of relative sizes of damaged areas of the test array and sprinkler operating areas. (See Table 5-10A.)

TABLE 5-10A. ***Sprinkler Operation in Test Array***

Density GPM/Sq Ft		Fire Damage in Test Array %	Sq Ft	Sprinkler Operation (165°F) Area—Sq Ft
0.30	(Ceiling only)	22	395	4500-4800
0.375	(Ceiling only)	17	306	1800
0.45	(Ceiling only)	9	162	700
0.20	(Ceiling only)	28-36	504-648	13,100-14,000
0.20	(Sprinklers at ceiling and in racks)	8	144	4100
0.30	(Sprinklers at ceiling and in racks)	7	126	700

For SI Units: 1 ft = 0.3048 m; C = $\frac{5}{9}$ (F-32); 1 gpm/ft^2 = 40.746 (L/min)/m^2.

With sprinklers operating in the fire control mode, the central fuel package is eventually depleted, and the fire is extinguished. For fire control by sprinklers, the heat release rate of the fire over time can be characterized as shown in Figure 5-10I.

Various studies have been made of the water application rate needed to extinguish or control fires in fully ventilated areas, both on simple surfaces and in complex fuel arrangements.

The critical rate for wood appears to be between 0.0022 and 0.0044 gpm/ft^2 [0.09 and 0.18 (L/min/m^2], increasing to a degree with preburn.[11] For some plastic surfaces, the critical rate appears to be in the range of 0.02 to 0.065 gpm/ft^2[0.8 and 2.65 (L/min/m^2], higher with external radiation.[12] These values are per unit of burning surface area, not floor area, and are determined under laboratory conditions.

For realistic fuel arrangements, the unit surface area of burning combustibles can be many multiples of the unit floor area protected by sprinklers. British fire tests have indicated that, for midsize wood cribs, water applied through impinging jet nozzles at rates less than 0.275 gpm/

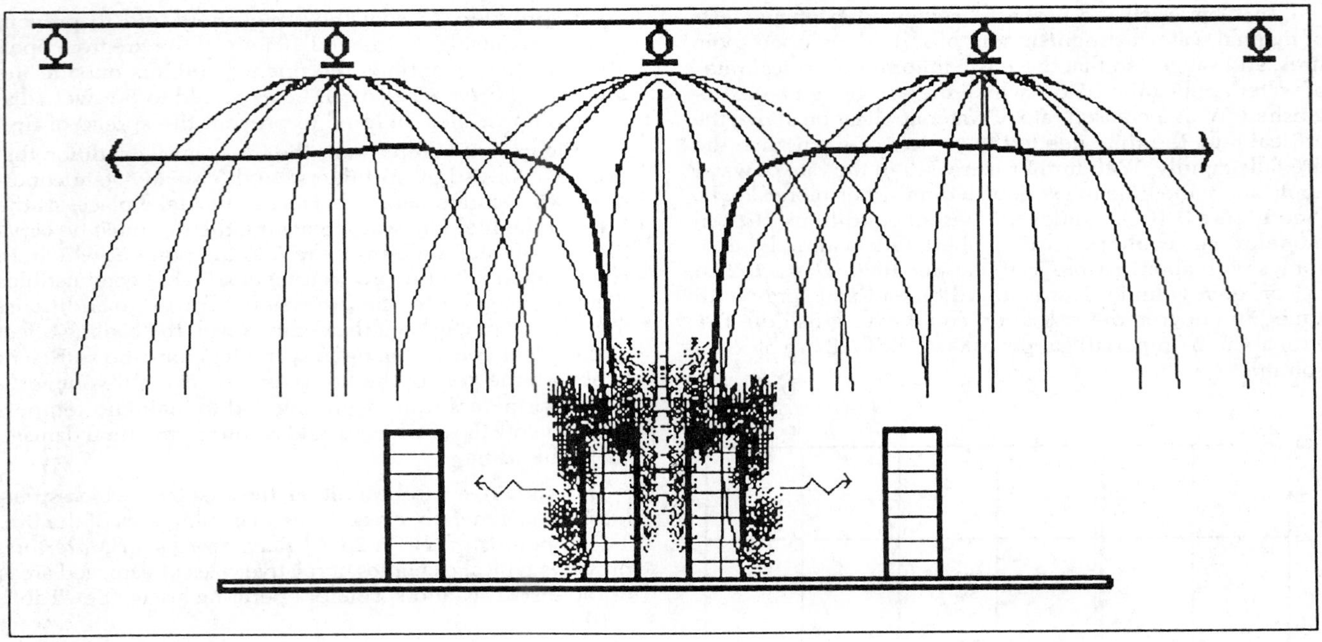

FIG. 5-10H. Fire control by sprinklers (conceptual).

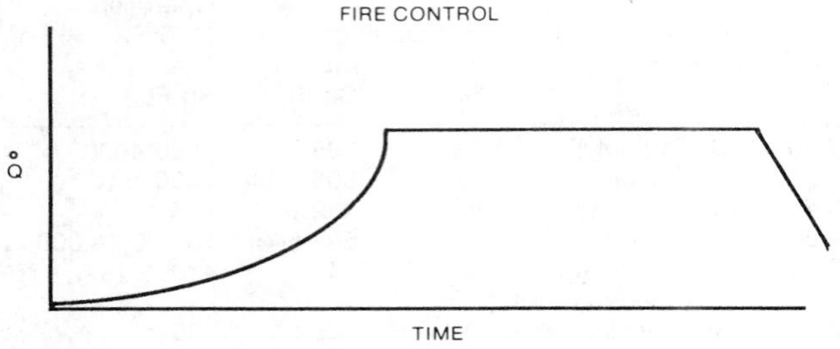

FIG. 5-10I. Representation of fire control by sprinklers, heat release rate (Q) vs time.

ft² [11.2 (L/min)/m²] of unit surface area had little effect on the actual burning zone.[13] The tests also indicated that application rates as low as 0.0625 gpm/ft² [2.56 (L/min)/m²] of unit surface area were found to be sufficient to limit flame spread within the crib.

Area/Density Curves

The area/density curves that form the basis of standard sprinkler system design can be considered to reflect historical experience with the fire control concept. Although most fires are extinguished or contained by only a few sprinklers, the more troublesome deep-seated fires historically have opened more sprinklers and justifiably have influenced the standards writers. System design criteria must address a reasonably "worst-case" situation.

The first edition of NFPA 13, *Installation of Sprinkler Systems*, published in 1896, contained simple pipe schedules which limited the maximum number of sprinklers that could be fed through each size of pipe. Combined with a minimum supply pressure of 25 psi (3.6 kPa) at the highest line of sprinklers, the pipe schedule was expected to adequately provide water to at least 15 sprinklers.

The pipe schedule for sprinkler systems was altered many times, and the concept of different pipe schedules for various "hazards" was instituted with the development of "Class B" (later to become light-hazard) criteria in 1930 and the development of an extra-hazard pipe schedule in 1940.

The use of hydraulic calculation methods for fire sprinkler systems actually started in 1929, with the first formal compilation of Hazen-Williams friction loss tables and other hydraulic data in 1931.[14] NFPA 13, *Installation of Sprinkler Systems*, first addressed hydraulic calculations in its 1955 edition, but the use of such calculations was limited essentially to deluge system and water spray applications until the inclusion of area/density criteria in the 1972 edition of the standard. NFPA 231C, *Rack Storage of Materials*, the first standard developed based on fire test data, was adopted in 1971, and 1972 saw the insertion of area/density curves into NFPA 231, *General Storage*, although basic criteria had appeared as early as 1965.

The area/density curves in NFPA 13, *Installation of Sprinkler Systems*, were modified significantly in 1974 and again in 1991 as part of an overall reorganization and simplification of the standard. As developed in 1974, the curves reflect the hydraulic capability of pipe schedule designs which had proved satisfactory in nearly a century of experience.

The merging of ordinary-hazard groups 2 and 3 in the 1991 edition of NFPA 13, *Installation of Sprinkler Systems*, created a system design point of 0.2 gpm/ft² [8.18 (L/min)/m²] over 1500 sq ft (135 m²) for a hazard that could essentially be considered the processing and display of ordinary combustibles. This relates well to the historical development and use of the standard sprinkler system. The 1991 area/density curves are shown in Figure 5-10J.

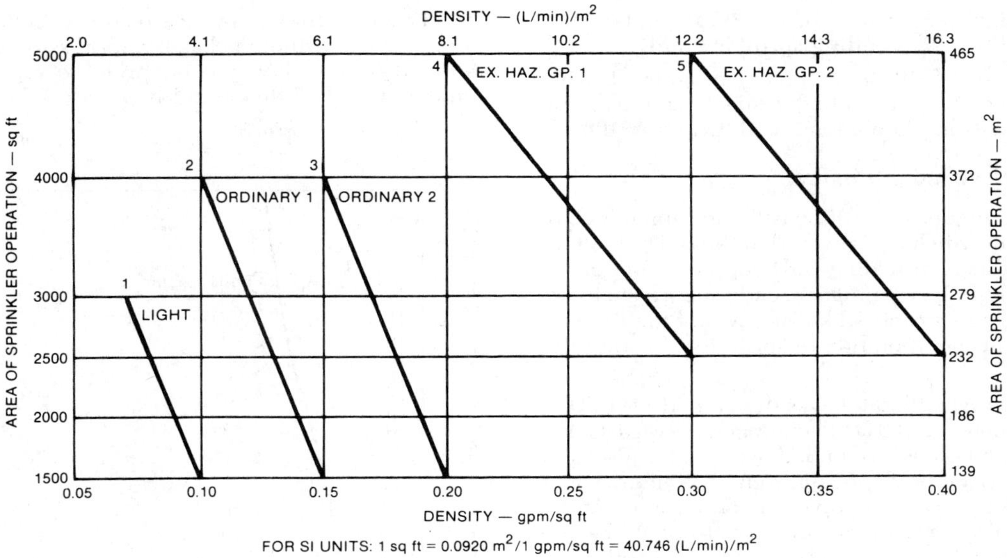

FIG. 5-10J. Area/density curves.

Compartmentation and Fire Control

It has been observed in a number of test programs that walls tend to assist the sprinkler system in the control mode by limiting the number of sprinklers that can operate. If a fire takes place near a wall, the total number of sprinklers that operate will tend to be reduced by the fact that presumed "outer ring" sprinklers are not available on at least one side.

This will tend to conserve water for the operating sprinklers, resulting in higher application rates and earlier achievement of the fire control energy balances. Carried to an extreme, it is the benefit of walls that is recognized in the "room design method" permitted by NFPA 13, *Installation of Sprinkler Systems*, as an alternate to the area/density method.

However, one might ask how the same amount of heat can be absorbed by fewer operating sprinklers. In other words, if those fringe sprinklers are not available to operate and absorb some of the heat from the fire plume, doesn't that same heat flow back across the room in the other direction and simply open more sprinklers on the opposite side?

Two factors argue against this. One is that, unless the fire is almost exactly along the wall, it will entrain the same amount of air as a centered fire, producing the same amount of ceiling jet gases. However, the wall will prevent it from breaking into an axisymmetric ceiling jet, and the resulting ceiling jet or smoke layer will be thicker. The thicker smoke layer actually will permit more cooling to take place from the discharge of each sprinkler, since the path of each droplet through the layer is longer.

The other factor is that the spray cooling ability of each sprinkler is enhanced at higher pressures. Cooling depends on droplet surface area, which is increased with flow and with the production of smaller-diameter droplets, both of which result from higher pressures. With fewer sprinklers operating in the vicinity of the fire, higher water supply pressures are available and more cooling takes place.

FIRE SUPPRESSION BY SPRINKLERS

Recent years have seen the development of new types of sprinklers that purport not only to control a fire but to actively suppress the fire. To achieve fire suppression, water must be delivered by sprinklers to the burning fuel surface in sufficient quantity to disrupt the combustion process, knocking down the rate of heat release and preventing fire regrowth. (See Figure 5-10K.) If suppression is achieved at an early stage of the fire, only the sprinklers immediately over the fire area are expected to operate.

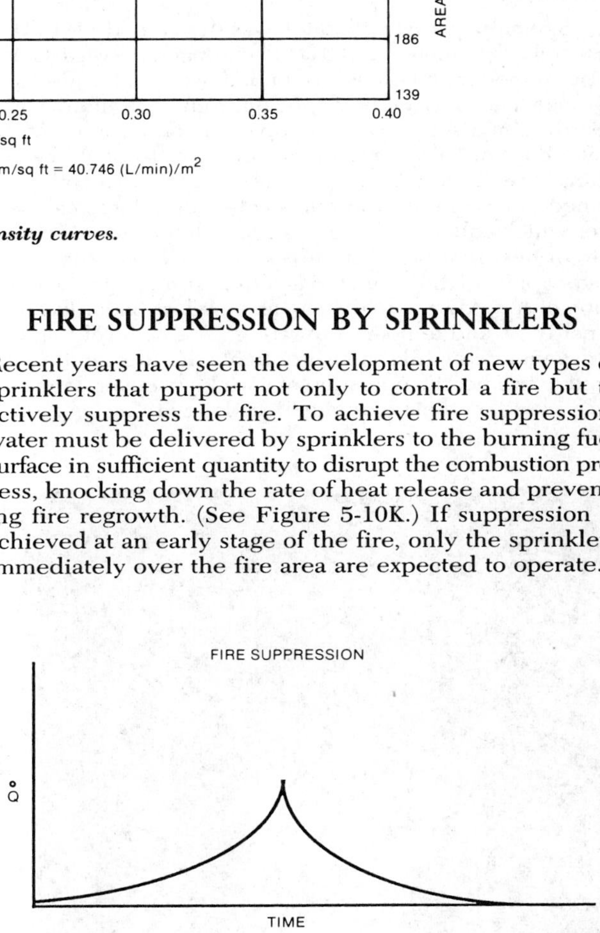

FIG. 5-10K. Representation of fire suppression by sprinklers, heat release rate (Q) vs time.

For this reason, the term "early suppression" has been developed. Today the term is being used both as the name for a concept and for a particular type of sprinkler. The concept is that fast response of sprinklers can produce an advantage in a fire if the response is accompanied by an effective discharge density—that is, a sprinkler spray capable of fighting its way down through the fire plume in sufficient quantities to suppress the burning fuel package.

The first sprinkler to include the term in its name, the early suppression fast response (ESFR) sprinkler, was developed to apply the concept to a particular class of fire:

protection of high-rack storage of FMRC's standardized plastic commodity, using ceiling sprinklers only.

As part of the ESFR development program, FMRC researchers created new terms to investigate and to define the early suppression phenomenon: RDD and ADD.

Required Delivered Density

Required delivered density (RDD) is the minimum rate of water application which, if delivered to the top of the fuel package, is capable of providing early suppression. For the purposes of FMRC's ESFR program, early suppression was, in turn, defined as a sustained knockdown of the fire sufficient to prevent the operation of sprinklers beyond the initial ring.

Specialized test apparatus was developed by FMRC researchers to measure RDD. The apparatus consists of a series of perforated pipes suspended over the burning fuel package that are capable of spreading a fairly uniform water distribution directly over the top of the fuel, such that the water does not have to fight its way down through the fire plume. (See Figure 5-10L.) The pipes and fuel are all positioned below the fire products collector, a large calorimeter which collects all fire gases and determines the total rate of heat release of the fire as a function of time. The water application is initiated at a time simulating the operation of sprinklers, based on an assumed sprinkler location, sensitivity, and temperature rating. The heat-release history generated while the water fights the fire can then be used to predict the operation of sprinklers beyond the first ring, based on their presumed location with respect to the fire.

FIG. 5-10L. RDD test apparatus. (©Factory Mutual Engineering Corp. Reprinted with permission.)

Figure 5-10M shows the results of several RDD tests for a particular fuel package. Suppression can be considered to occur when the heat-release rate of the fire is quickly knocked down and is prevented from resurging.

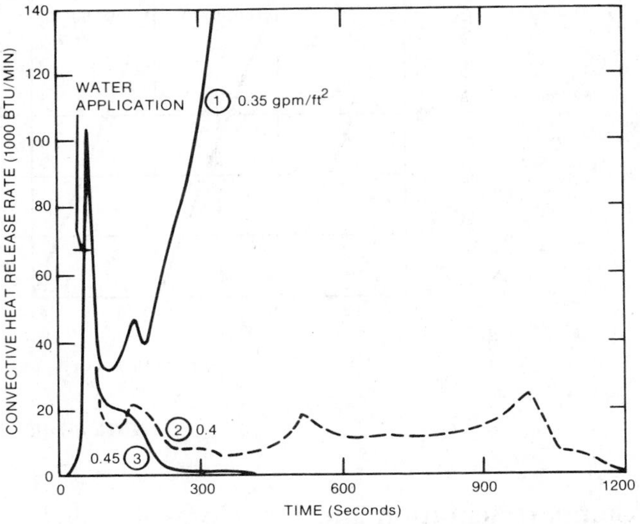

FIG. 5-10M. RDD test results using three different water application rates. (©Factory Mutual Research Corp. Reprinted with permission.)

With regard to the standard plastic commodity stored in racks, FMRC confirmed that a relationship existed between RDD and height of storage:

Standard Plastic Commodity—RDD Determination

Storage Height in Racks	*RDD*
(Fast response sprinklers — 30-ft racks)	
3 tiers (15 ft)	0.35 gpm/ft^2
4 tiers (20 ft)	0.45 gpm/ft^2
5 tiers (25 ft)	0.65 gpm/ft^2

Under the sponsorship of the National Fire Protection Research Foundation, there has been an attempt to extend the early suppression concept to sprinkler protection of ordinary hazards.

Prior freeburn testing had been performed to determine the heat release histories of selected fuel packages. Among the fuel packages tested were the upholstered furniture corner scenario used during the development of the residential sprinkler and a 6.7-ft (2.0 m) high storage configuration of the standardized plastic commodity in corrugated cardboard cartons that was used in the ESFR sprinkler program. Nineteen RDD tests were conducted by Underwriters Laboratories Inc. under the Foundations's sponsorship to compare the relative suppressibilities of the two different fuel packages.[15,16]

In the freeburn testing, both these fuel packages were found to produce a total heat release history that could be approximated by an "ultra-fast t-squared" fire, with a maximum heat release rate of about 5 MW. This refers to a standardized curve in which heat release grows proportionally to the square of time. (See Figure 5-10N.)

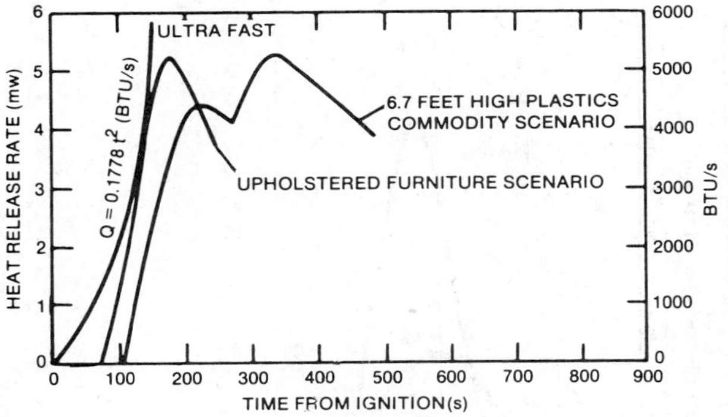

FIG. 5-10N. Comparison of fire growth rates for selected fuel packages and the "ultra-fast" t^2 fire.

The specific water application rates needed to provide early suppression are still under study. However, it was observed clearly that the densities required for suppression of the plastic commodity were considerably higher than those required for the upholstered furniture for the same size fires. The tests conclusively demonstrated that some fuel packages are more easily suppressed than others, even if their heat-release rate histories appear to be similar.

Actual Delivered Density

Actual delivered density (ADD) is the actual rate of water application that a particular configuration of flowing sprinklers is capable of delivering to the top of a fuel package, depending on the strength of the upward fire plume.

The ADD measuring apparatus consists of a series of collection pans situated over a gas burner. (See Figure 5-10O.) The 0.5 m^2 pans simulate the top of a storage array and measure the rate at which each such area receives water from any particular configuration of flowing sprinklers. The gas burner is used to produce upward fire plume forces through the simulated flue spaces between the pans. In this manner, the ability of the flowing sprinkler(s) to deliver water to the fuel package can be checked against a wide range of fire strength conditions, simulating different points in the fire history. Typically, ADD decreases as the fire gets larger.

Since the water spray distribution of a sprinkler is not uniform, the collection pans collect different quantities of water during an ADD test. The development of ADD values from test results is accomplished using a probability distribution developed by, and named for, W. Weibull of Sweden. It was first applied to the distribution of liquid droplet sizes in 1951.[17] Using the Weibull distribution, the pan collections of each sprinkler spray acting through a fire plume of a given strength are fitted to a probability curve with a characteristic or average ADD (Φ) and a uniformity value (b). The higher the uniformity value, the more likely it is that a characteristic ADD (Φ) higher than the RDD will suppress the fire, since the needed water is being distributed in usable fashion.

The uniformity factor affects the basic shape of the probability distribution curve. Figures 5-10P and 5-10Q indicate the relative effects of changing the scale parameter Φ and the uniformity parameter b on the frequency distribution of the statistical model. The variable x represents any given measurement. Typically, the ADD uniformity values range from about 1 to 7. A uniformity value of infinity would represent a perfectly uniform distribution.

FIG. 5-10O. ADD measuring apparatus for rack storage. (Factory Mutual Engineering Corp. Reprinted with permission.)

The probability concept can also be applied to RDD data. A uniformity value b can be determined despite the fact the RDD is measured in a test using the special water applicator intended to provide fairly uniform distribution. A "characteristic" RDD can be calculated as:

$$\Phi_{RDD} = \frac{\text{RDD (proposed)}}{(1/b)!}$$

The probability distribution concept can also be used to rank the relative suppression capability of sprinklers. If ADD measurements are taken for three prototype sprinklers under the same fire, spacing, and flow conditions, and values of characteristic ADD and uniformity are found for each, the probability that each sprinkler will meet or exceed the characteristic RDD at any selected point on the fuel surface can be calculated from the relationship:

$$P(\text{ADD} \geq \Phi_{RDD}) = \exp\left[-(\Phi_{RDD}/\Phi_{ADD})b^{ADD}\right]$$

FUTURE DEVELOPMENTS

The preceding discussion shows that the present understanding of the theory of fire sprinkler performance is incomplete. For some aspects of sprinkler system performance, such as thermal response and the hydraulics of

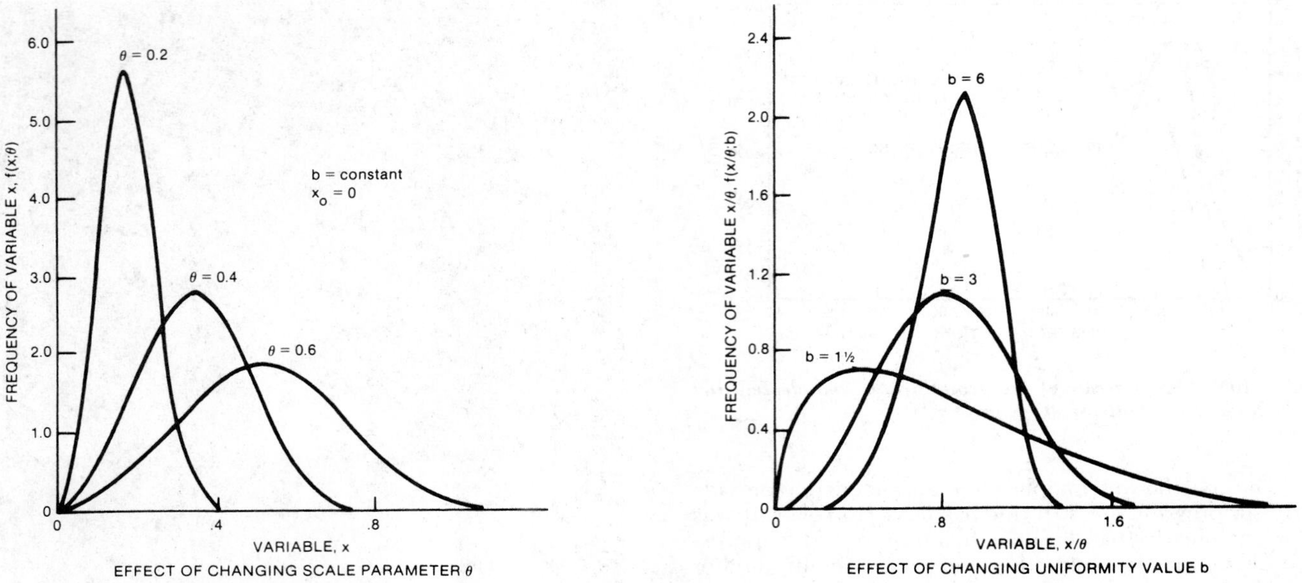

FIG. 5-10P. Effect of changing scale parameter Φ (left) and uniformity value b (right).

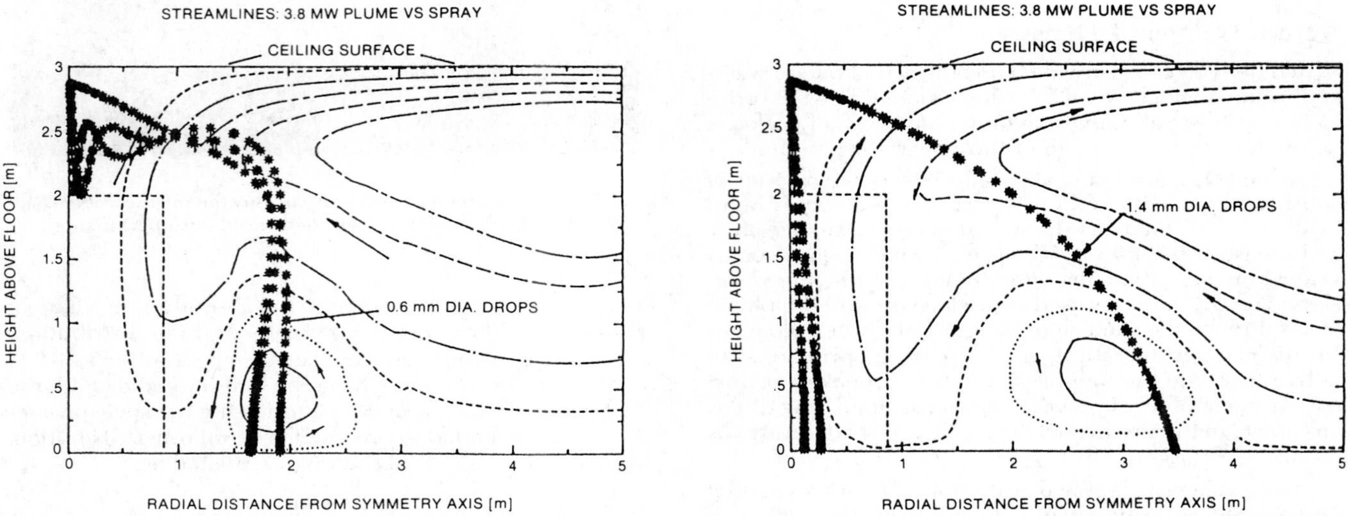

FIG. 5-10Q. These computer-generated figures demonstrate the superior ability of larger water droplets to penetrate the fire plume when a large fire is located directly below a sprinkler. At left, the 0.6-mm diameter drops are swept away by the upward plume velocities, while, at right, the 1.4-mm diameter drops are able to follow their trajectories.[18]

water delivery, research has led to a good understanding of the mechanisms at work. On the other hand, the science of understanding how the water is distributed remains very weak. Almost all the advances made in mathematical modeling of sprinkler performance in the past 15 years deal only with the time up to which the sprinkler starts to put water on the fire.

Research over the past few years at FMRC, funded partly through the National Institute of Standards and Technology (NIST), has been aimed at using computers to analyze the complex interaction between water droplet sprays and the gas flows induced by a building fire.[18] So far, the results are promising, but the work has been based on very simplified assumptions, with the presumed fire located directly under a single sprinkler producing droplets of uniform size in a few specific directions. (See Figure 5-10Q.) Much more work will be needed before this research can help build a better sprinkler.

BIBLIOGRAPHY

References Cited

1. Heskestad, G. and Smith, H. F., "Investigation of a New Sprinkler Sensitivity Approval Test: The Plunge Test," *FMRC No.*

22485, Factory Mutual Research Corp., Norwood, MA, Dec. 1976.

2. Alpert, R. L., "Calculation of Response Time of Ceiling-Mounted Fire Detectors," *Fire Technology*, Vol. 8, No. 3 (Aug. 1972).
3. Heskestad, G. and Smith, H. F., "Plunge Test for Determination of Sprinkler Sensitivity," *J.I. 3A1E2.RR, Dec. 1980*, Factory Mutual Research Corp., Norwood, MA, Dec. 1980.
4. Heskestad, G., "The Sprinkler Response Time Index (RTI)," *Paper (RC81-TP-3)* presented at the Technical Conference on Residential Sprinkler Systems, Factory Mutual Research Corp., Apr. 28-29, 1981.
5. Evans, D. D. and Stroup, D. W., "Methods to Calculate the Response Time of Heat and Smoke Detectors Installed Below Large Unobstructed Ceilings," *NBSIR 85-3167*, National Bureau of Standards, Gaithersburg, MD, 1985.
6. Pepi, J. S., "Design Characteristics of Quick-Response Sprinklers," Grinnell Fire Protection Systems Co., Providence, RI, May 1986.
7. Heskestad, G. and Bill, R. G., "Conduction Heat-Loss Effects on Thermal Response of Automatic Sprinklers," *FMRC J.I. ONOJ5.RU*, Factory Mutual Research Corp., Norwood, MA, Sept. 1987.
8. Dundas, P. H., "Optimization of Sprinkler Fire Protection, Progress Report No. 10, The Scaling of Sprinkler Discharge: Prediction of Drop Size," *FMRC No. 18792*, Factory Mutual Research Corp., Norwood, MA, June 1974.
9. Braidech, M. M. and Neale, J. A., "The Mechanism of Extinguishment of Fire by Finely Divided Water," *NBFU Research Report No. 10*, Underwriter Laboratories Inc., Chicago, IL, 1955.
10. Nash, P. and Rasbash, D. J., "The Use of Water in Fire Fighting," *F.R. Note No.* 202/1955, Fire Research Station, Borehamwood, England.
11. Heskestad, G., "The Role of Water in Suppression of Fire: A Review," *CIB/W14/80-35*, Factory Mutual Research Corp., Norwood, MA, 1980.
12. Magee, R. S. and Reitz, R. D., "Extinguishment of Radiation-Augmented Plastic Fires by Water Sprays," Fifteenth Symposium (International) on Combustion, The Combustion Institute, 1975.
13. O'Dogherty, M. J., Nash, P., and Young, R. A., "A Study of the Performance of Automatic Sprinkler Systems," *Fire Research Technical Paper No. 17*, Joint Fire Research Organization, London, 1967.
14. Wood, Clyde M., *Hydraulic Data for Fire Protection Systems*, Automatic Sprinkler Corp. of America, Youngstown, OH, 1961.
15. Carey, W., *Group 2 RDD Test Program*, National Fire Protection Research Foundation, Quincy, MA, 1989.
16. Budnick, E. and Fleming, R., "How Quick-Response Sprinklers Perform," *Fire Journal*, Vol. 83, No. 5, National Fire Protection Association, Quincy, MA (Sept./Oct. 1989).
17. Goodfellow, David G., "A Statistical Model for Analysis of Sprinkler Water-Spray Distributions," Factory Mutual Research Corp. Norwood, MA, Aug. 1985.
18. Alpert, R. L. and Delichatsios, M. M., "Calculated Interaction of Water Droplet Sprays with Fire Plumes in Compartments," *NBS-GCR 86-520*, National Bureau of Standards, Gaithersburg, MD, Dec. 1986.

Reference

Fleming, Russell P., "Group 2 Test Results Show RDD Differences," *The QRS Link*, No. 6, National Fire Protection Research Foundation, July/Aug. 1987.

NFPA Codes, Standards, and Recommended Practices

Reference to the following NFPA codes, standards, and recommended practices will provide further information on the theory of automatic sprinkler extinguishment discussed in this chapter. (See the latest *NFPA Catalog* for availability of current editions of the following documents.)

NFPA 13, *Installation of Sprinkler Systems*.

NFPA 231, *General Storage*.

NFPA 231C, *Rack Storage of Materials*.

Additional Reading

Cooper, L. Y. and Stroup, D. W., "Test Results and Procedures for the Response of Near Ceiling Sprinkler Links in a Full-Scale Compartment Fire," *NBSIR 87-3633*, National Bureau of Standards, Gaithersburg, MD, Sept. 1987.

Evans, D. D. and Madrzykowski, D., "Characterizing the Thermal Response of Fusible-Link Sprinklers," *NBSIR 81-2329*, National Bureau of Standards, Washington, DC, Aug. 1981.

Evans, D. D., "Calculating Sprinkler Actuation Time in Compartments," National Bureau of Standards, Washington, DC, 1984.

Evans, D. D., "Calculating Sprinkler Actuation Times in Compartments," *Fire Safety Journal*, Vol. 9, No. 2, 1985, pp. 147-156.

Evans, D. D., Walton, W. D., and McCaffrey, B., "Progress in Modeling Sprinkler Performance," *9th Joint Panel Meeting* of the UJNR Panel on Fire Research and Safety, NBSIR 88-3753, National Institute of Standards and Technology, Gaithersburg, MD, Apr. 1988, pp. 325-335.

Hayes, W. D., and Zile, R. H., "Full-Scale Study of the Effect of Pendent and Sidewall Location on the Activation Time of an Automatic Sprinkler," *NBSIR 82-2521*, National Bureau of Standards, Gaithersburg, MD, July 1982.

Heskestad, G. and Bill, R. G., "Quantification of Thermal Responsiveness of Automatic Sprinklers Including Conduction Effects," *Fire Safety Journal*, Vol. 14, Nos. 1&2 (July 1988), pp. 113-125.

Hestestad, G. and Smith, H. F., "Investigation of a New Sprinkler Sensitivity Approval Test: The Plunge Test," *FMRC Technical Report 22485*, Factory Mutual Research Corp., Norwood, MA, Dec. 1976.

Heskestad, G., "The Sprinkler Response Time Index (RTI)," presented at the Technical Conference on Residential Sprinkler Systems, Factory Mutual Research Corp., Norwood, MA, April 1981.

Labes, W. G., "Evaluation of Fire Protection Spray Devices: The State of the Art," *NBS-GCR-76-72*, National Bureau of Standards, Washington, DC, June 1976.

Morehart, J. L., "Sprinklers in the NIH Atrium: How Did They React During the Fire Last May?," *Fire Journal*, Vol. 83, No. 1 (Jan-Feb. 1989), pp. 56-57.

Suchomel, M. R., "Factors Influencing the Use of High-Temperature Sprinklers," *Fire Technology*, Vol. 1, No. 1 (Feb. 1965), pp. 15-22.

Theobald, C. R., "FRS Ramp Test for the Thermal Sensitivity of Sprinklers," *Journal of Fire Protection Engineering*, Vol. 1, No. 1, 1989, pp. 23-34.

Theobald, C. R. and Westley, S. A., "Factors Affecting the Sensitivity of Sprinklers," *Fire Surveyors*, Vol. 17, No. 3 (June 1988), pp. 5-11.

Thorne, P. F., Theobald, C. R., and Melinek, S. J., "Thermal Performance of Sprinkler Heads," *Fire Safety Journal*, Vol. 14, Nos. 1&2 (July 1988), pp. 89-99.

Yao, C. and Kalelkar, A. S., "Effect of Drop Size on Sprinkler Performance," *Fire Technology*, Vol. 6, No. 4 (Nov. 1970), pp. 254-268.

WATER SUPPLIES FOR SPRINKLER SYSTEMS

Revised by Robert Solomon

Every automatic sprinkler system must have at least one automatic water supply of adequate pressure, capacity, and reliability. An "automatic" supply is one that is not dependent on any manual operation, such as making connections, operating valves, or starting pumps, to supply water at the time of a fire. Both the rate of flow and the duration of that flow must be considered.

This chapter identifies the types of water supplies that are acceptable for sprinkler systems; the variables that must be considered, including the hazards of occupancies, in evaluating requirements for both sprinklers and supplementary hose line supplies; and the fundamentals of hydraulically designing sprinkler systems to match sprinkler piping sizes with the characteristics of available water supplies.

Other chapters in this handbook of interest in understanding the complexities of providing adequate water supplies for sprinkler systems are those chapters in this section covering water supplies for fire protection. Of particular interest are Chapter 2, "Hydraulics," which discusses the fundamentals of water flow through pipes and orifices; Chapter 5, "Water Storage Facilities and Suction Supplies;" Chapter 6, "Fire Pumps;" and Chapter 15, "Water Spray Protection," which is of value, because there is no definitive line between sprinkler systems and water spray systems, and many of the water supply requirements pertaining to sprinkler systems apply equally well to spray systems.

TYPES OF SUPPLIES

Sprinkler systems may be supplied with water from one source or a combination of sources, such as street mains, gravity tanks, reservoirs, fire pumps, pressure tanks, rivers, lakes, and wells.

In theory, a single water supply would seem to be all that is necessary for satisfactory protection. However, a single supply may be temporarily out of service; it may be disabled at the time of a fire or before a fire is completely extinguished; or its pressure or capacity may be below normal during an emergency. Therefore, a secondary supply may be necessary depending on the strength and reliability of the primary supply; the value and importance of the property; the area, height, and construction of the building; the occupancy; and the outside exposures.

Connections to Public Water Works Systems

A connection from a reliable public water works system of adequate capacity and pressure is the preferred single or primary supply for automatic sprinkler systems. In determining its adequacy, one must consider not only the normal capacity and pressure of the system, but also the probable minimum pressures and flows available at unfavorable times, such as the summer months, periods of heavy demand on the system, or periods of impairment caused by flood or by winter conditions. These conditions are typically referred to as seasonal lows.

The size and arrangement of street mains and feeders from public water supplies are also important. Connections from large mains fed two ways or from two mains on a grid system may provide an excellent supply. Street mains less than 6 in. (15 mm) in diameter are usually considered inadequate and unreliable. Feeds from dead-end mains are also undesirable. Water meters, if required by the water supply authority, should be of types listed for the fire service. Flow and pressure tests under varying conditions of demand are generally necessary to determine the amount of public water available for fire protection.

Cross-Connections Between Public and Private Supplies

Where a secondary supply is needed to supplement the public water supply, public and private fire service mains can be connected to feed into a single fire protection system. When the private fire service main is from a nonpotable source and it is connected to the public main, the systems are said to be cross-connected.In some localities, cross-connections may be prohibited or closely regulated by health authorities.

Robert Solomon, P.E., is senior fire protection engineer on the staff of NFPA.

Federal regulations approved in 1986 require states to protect closely all water supplies intended for public consumption. States and municipal governments have taken various steps to protect the potable water supply. Double check valves and reduced pressure zone (RPZ) backflow prevention devices may be required any time the sprinkler system will be supplied by a potable water source.

These devices may protect the public water supply from potential contamination, but designers must be aware of their cost and maintenance, and their negative impact on the available water supply and pressures to the sprinkler system. NFPA 24, *Private Fire Service Mains and Their Appurtenances*, provides guidance for the installation of these devices.

Gravity Tanks

Gravity tanks of adequate capacity and elevation make a good primary supply and may be acceptable as a single supply. Details of the construction, heating, and maintenance of gravity tanks are given in NFPA 22, *Water Tanks for Private Fire Protection*. In determining tank size and elevation, consideration should be given to the number of sprinklers expected to operate, the duration of operation, the arrangement of underground supply piping, and the provision of hose standpipes, hydrants, and fire department connections.

Suction Tanks

With the advent of hydraulically designed sprinkler systems, the use of gravity tanks for fire protection has declined. The use of fire pumps combined with suction tanks has increased. These tanks are typically constructed of steel, concrete, or fiberglass. NFPA 22, *Water Tanks for Private Fire Protection*, should be consulted for details.

Fire Pumps

A fire pump with a reliable source of power and a reliable suction water supply is a desirable piece of equipment. Fire pumps are used to a great extent because of the hydraulic advantages of having a water supply available at high pressure. With ample water, a fire pump can maintain a high pressure over a long period of time and may be a necessary part of some installations requiring greater water pressure than would be available otherwise. For details of power sources, pump construction, installation, and methods of control and operation, consult NFPA 20, *Installation of Centrifugal Fire Pumps*.

Automatic control of fire pumps is usually needed where a high water demand may occur immediately, as with a deluge system. Automatic fire pumps must have their suction under a positive pressure to avoid the delays and uncertainties of priming.

Most fire pumps are powered by electric motors or diesel engines. Where a reliable source of power is available at all times, an electrically driven installation may be the most desirable. Where the power supply is questionable, a diesel-driven fire pump would be preferred. In some critical installations, such as hospitals, a diesel-driven emergency power generator may be used to supply secondary power to the electric motor. The use of a diesel-driven fire pump in a critical installation would eliminate the need for a good portion of the output of the emergency generator.

The automatic control of electrically driven centrifugal pumps must be arranged to prevent frequent, repeated starting of the motor, either by initiating continuous running until stopped manually or by using a timing device that stops the motor automatically only after a predetermined period of operation.

Pressure Tanks

Pressure tanks have several possible uses in automatic sprinkler protection. An important limitation is the small volume of water that can be stored in such tanks.

In situations where an adequate volume of water can be supplied by a public or private source but where the pressure is not sufficient to serve a sprinkler system directly, the pressure tank gives a good starting pressure for the first sprinklers that operate.In tall buildings where the public water pressure is too low for effective water distribution from the highest sprinklers, pressure tanks may be used to supply such sprinklers during the time required for a public fire department to begin supplying water through fire department connections.

Each proposed use of pressure tanks calls for special consideration and analysis of water capacity, location, and arrangement of the connection to the sprinkler system. Each installation must usually have specific approval. Details on the construction, installation, and maintenance of pressure tanks are given in NFPA 22, *Water Tanks for Private Fire Protection*.

Fire Department Connections

Under fire conditions that cause a considerable number of sprinklers to operate, public water or tank supplies may not provide water at sufficient pressure for effective sprinkler discharge and distribution. In addition, the pressure in many public water supplies to sprinkler systems may be reduced materially by hose streams from hydrants. In such cases, a connection through which the public fire department can pump water into the sprinkler system provides an important secondary supply. Fire department connections are therefore a standard part of sprinkler systems.

Fire department connections must be readily accessible and properly marked. Each connection must be fitted with a check valve, but not with a gate valve, so that the connection will not be shut off inadvertently. There should be a proper drain, as well as a drip device between the check valve and the outside hose coupling. Figures 5-11A and 5-11B show the main features of a fire department connection. Other details of installation and pipe size are given in NFPA 13, *Installation of Sprinkler Systems*.

Where a wet-pipe sprinkler system has a single riser, the fire department connection should be attached to the system side of the controlling valve. For a dry-pipe system, the connection should be between the dry-pipe controlling valve and the valve. This makes it possible to pump water into the system even if the valve is closed. If there are two or more sprinkler system risers, each with its own separate connection to a public main, each system must have its own fire department connection. If more than one riser is connected to a yard system, the fire department connection should feed into the yard system on the supply side of all riser shutoff valves, and there must be a check valve in all other water supply connections into the yard system to prevent backflow and loss of water supplied through the fire department connection. If one riser is shut off, the fire department connection can still supply all other riseres.

FIG. 5-11A. Fire fighters attaching hose lines to a fire department (siamese) connection supplying a sprinkler system. The inset shows typical siamese connections for sprinkler systems and standpipes. A check valve allows the use of a single hose line.

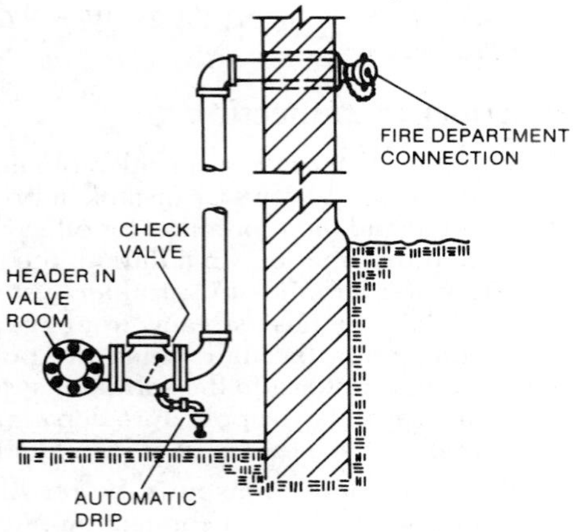

FIG. 5-11B. Typical fire department connection.

If two or more sprinkler system risers are fed by one sprinkler connection, one fire department connection can supply both risers.

In an emergency, a fire department can pump water from public hydrants or other sources of water into a sprinkler system through hose connected to a yard hydrant or other hose connection using a double female hose coupling, if other supply connections have a check valve or a gate valve that can be closed.

INFLUENCE OF VARIOUS FACTORS ON WATER SUPPLY NEED

Determining the water supply requirement for most sprinkler systems is not always easy because of the many variables involved. If a water source that can supply all the sprinklers is available, there is no problem, but such a water supply is seldom practical except in the case of small systems. The water supply requirement for any sprinkler system is directly related to the number of sprinklers expected to operate, which is determined by the hazard classification and the anticipated use of outside and inside hose stream demands. This, in turn, depends on so many other variables and uncertain factors that no exact mathematical solution is possible.

Records kept by NFPA before 1970 show that 20 or fewer sprinklers opened in 93 percent of all fires in sprinklered buildings, Experience shows that, with an adequate water supply, the percentage of unsatisfactory sprinkler performance is extremely small. Thus, water supply is a significant concern, particularly with large sprinkler systems and with systems protecting greater-than-ordinary hazards.

Establishing the water supply requirement for any particular sprinkler system requires good engineering judgment based on all the factors relating to sprinkler control. Where the cooling effect from the water discharged by sprinklers is greater than the heat liberated by the fire, the sprinklers can gain control. When the reverse occurs, as when a water supply is overtaxed or system design is inadequate, the sprinklers cannot control the fire and the sprinkler system may fail. Where all conditions are favorable, the fire should be controlled by the operation of only a small number of sprinklers. Because conditions vary with different classes of occupancy, areas, and types of buildings, the number of sprinklers expected to operate to control a fire may range up to the total number in the area, and the water supply should be provided accordingly.

The primary factors affecting the number of sprinklers that might open in a fire, and which therefore must be considered in determining the water supply requirement, include the following.

Hazard of Occupancy (Including Flash Fire Hazard and Potential Rate of Heat Release)

This is the most important factor and one requiring experienced judgment to evaluate. Where the flash fire hazard is present, it is usually necessary to provide enough water to operate of all the sprinklers in any individual fire area.

Initial Water Pressure

At a pressure of 15 psi (103 kPa), a standard ½-in. (13 mm) sprinkler will discharge 22 gpm (83 L/min), or an average of approximately 0.17 gal per sq ft per min [6.8 (L/min)/m^2] over an area of 130 sq ft (12 m^2). At 30 psi (207 kPa), the discharge is 31 gpm (125 L/min), and at 50 psi (345 kPa), 40 gpm (155 L/min). At higher pressures, the discharge is correspondingly greater. With a greater discharge, there is a better chance of fire control from a small number of sprinklers and less need for large volumes of water to supply a large number of sprinklers.

Obstructions to Distribution of Water from Sprinklers

With obstructions, such as high-piled stocks, pallets, racks, and shelving, there is less likelihood that fire will be controlled in its initial stages, and a greater chance that a large number of sprinklers needing large water supplies will open.

High Ceilings and Draft Conditions

With ceilings of unusual height, there is a greater chance that drafts will carry heat away from the sprinklers immediately over a fire, resulting not only in a delay in the application of water, but also in the opening of sprinklers remote from the fire's place of origin. More water is usually needed under such conditions. The same situation exists wherever there are drafts, such as in areas open on the sides to the outside where winds can divert heat from sprinklers over the fire.

Unprotected Vertical Openings

Sprinkler systems in multistory buildings are usually designed on the assumption that fire will be controlled on the floor of origin. Where there are unprotected openings up through which heat and fire may spread, it may be expected that more sprinklers will open, particularly in the case of a fire originating near the vertical opening. In the case of high combustibility, the interconnected floors may need to be considered as one fire area. This means more water and larger pipe sizes in risers and supply.

Wet-Pipe *vs* Dry-Pipe Systems

Because of the delay due to exhausting air from dry-pipe systems, more sprinklers open on dry-pipe systems than on wet-pipe systems. This may call for greater water supplies. Design areas are increased by 30 percent to account for this delay.

Size of Undivided Areas

A large undivided area has a greater number of sprinklers, a possibility of a greater maximum number of sprinklers operating, and, consequently, a greater water demand than with a small area.

Floor-Mounted and Ceiling-Mounted Obstructions and Concealed Spaces

Beams, girders, light fixtures, and HVAC ducts can obstruct water distribution to the point where additional sprinklers may be necessary to account for the obstruction, the result being more sprinklers in the design area. Floor-mounted obstructions, such as privacy partitions, require similar special treatment.

Concealed combustible spaces also have an impact on sprinkler design areas. When they are unprotected, the sprinkler design area is usually doubled to account for the uncontrolled movement of fire in such areas.

Extent of Coverage and Exposures

Any fire in an unsprinklered space extending to an area with automatic sprinklers places an abnormal demand on the sprinkler system and requires increased water supplies so that the system may function effectively.

The preceding factors must be considered individually and collectively, and it is not feasible to derive any general formula or simple method of arriving at water supply requirements. However, certain general statements on this subject may be made. One is that any situation may be protected effectively with much less water where the water is applied automatically instead of manually. Another is that it is good practice to provide more water at higher pressure than will probably be needed to extinguish any fire. Hose streams may be used to supplement sprinklers, even when it is not necessary, and an ample supply of water provides a margin of safety.

Regardless of the size of the building, NFPA 13, *Installation of Sprinkler Systems*, requires a specific design area which relates to the occupancy fire hazard rather than the size of the building. The idea behind this concept is to provide a water supply that is adequate to cover this design area for a given period. The sprinklers in the most remote portion (hydraulically remote areas) of this area are used as the basis of design. The capability of supplying sprinklers in this area automatically means that sprinklers that are physically closer to the water supply source can be supplied, as well.

WATER SUPPLY REQUIREMENTS FOR SPRINKLER SYSTEMS

Notwithstanding the general problems involved in arriving at water supply requirements, the fire hazard represented by different building occupancies has made it possible to establish guides to water supply requirements for sprinkler systems. The occupancy factor is the primary consideration, with latitude allowed for the contributing factors.

The established guide tables in NFPA 13, *Installation of Sprinkler Systems*, divide hazards of occupancy for the purpose of determining water supplies into several groups with specified minimum water supplies for each group. (See Table 5-11A.)

The total water supply required is determined from Table 5-11A, and the water for hose streams is added if required. If stored water is used, the total water flow required would have to be multiplied by the duration of flow to determine whether the capacity of the stored supply is adequate, a factor that would not be pertinent for a reliable municipal water source.

The guide should be used only with experienced judgment, but it can serve for all cases qualifying as the light-hazard and ordinary-hazard (Groups 1 and 2) occupancy classifications which constitute the larger percentage of sprinkler installations. The other occupancy classifications usually involve more complex factors and therefore require special consideration.

Where fire pumps contribute to the water supply, pumps of standard size used with adequate rates of discharge are required. A suction supply for a pump should preferably be large enough for continuous operation.

Where pressure tanks furnish the water supply, the tank installation should comply with the appropriate provisions of NFPA 22, *Water Tanks for Private Fire Protection*. Where a combination of different water supplies is provided in the interest of reliability, it is good practice to have the rate of supply from each source at least equal to the minimum requirement for the system.

Light-Hazard Occupancies

Examples of light-hazard occupancies are apartment buildings, dormitories, office buildings, the seating areas of restaurants, and hospitals. In these occupancies, the potential rate of heat release is low, areas are usually subdivided, and a small number of sprinklers normally should control any fire. For hydraulically designed systems, 150 gpm,

TABLE 5-11A. ***Guide to Water Supply Requirements for Pipe Schedule Sprinkler Systems***

Occupancy Classification	Residual Pressure Required (See Note 1)	Acceptable Flow at Base of Riser (See Note 2)	Duration in Minutes (See Note 4)
Light Hazard	15 psi	500–750 gpm (See Note 3)	30–60
Ordinary Hazard (Group 1)	15 psi or higher	700–1000 gpm	60–90
Ordinary Hazard (Group 2)	15 psi or higher	850–1500 gpm	60–90
Ordinary Hazard (Group 3)	Pressure and flow requirements for sprinklers and hose streams to be determined by authority having jurisdiction.		60–120
Warehouses	Pressure and flow requirements for sprinklers and hose streams to be determined by authority having jurisdiction. Also see Chapter 7 of NFPA 13, NFPA 231, and NFPA 231 C.		
High-Rise Buildings	Pressure and flow requirements for sprinklers and hose streams to be determined by authority having jurisdiction. Also see Chapter 8 of NFPA 13.		
Extra Hazard	Pressure and flow requirements for sprinklers and hose streams to be determined by authority having jurisdiction.		

For SI Units: 1 psi = 6.89 kPa; 1 gpm = 3.785 L/min.

NOTES:
1. The pressure required at the base of the sprinkler riser(s) is defined as the residual pressure required at the elevation of the highest sprinkler plus the pressure required to reach this elevation.
2. The lower figure is the minimum flow including hose streams ordinarily acceptable for pipe schedule sprinkler systems. The higher flow should normally suffice for all cases under each group.
3. The requirement may be reduced to 250 gpm if building area is limited by size or compartmentation or if building (including roof) is noncombustible construction.
4. The lower-duration figure ordinarily is acceptable where remote station water-flow alarm service or equivalent is provided. The higher-duration figure normally should suffice for all cases under each group.

(568 L/min) for sprinkler operation and an additional 100 gpm (378 L/min) for hose stream demand will generally make a good starting point for system demand. A total of 500 to 750 gpm (1893 to 2839 L/min) for pipe schedule systems may be necessary for the same hazard, thereby making this a less desirable design approach.

Ordinary-Hazard Occupancies

Group 1: This ordinary-hazard classification includes occupancies such as in garages, bakeries, laundries, and canneries, in which the combustibility of contents, though generally low, is greater than that for the light-hazard classification. Ordinary-hazard Group 1 occupancies will require a minimum of 240 gpm (908 L/min) for sprinkler operation, and an additional 250 gpm (946 L/min) to support exterior hose streams. If a pipe schedule approach is selected, a minimum flow of 700 gpm (2650 L/min) is necessary.

Group 2: This ordinary-hazard classification includes occupancies such as clothing factories, mercantiles, pharmaceutical manufacturing, and shoe factories. With this group, the combustibility of contents, storage heights, and obstruction features are generally unfavorable. Ordinary-hazard Group 2 occupancies will require a minimum flow of 285 gpm (1079 L/min) for sprinkler operation, plus an additional 250 gpm (946 L/min) to operate the exterior hose streams. If design is based upon the pipe schedule method, a minimum total flow of 850 gpm (3217 L/min) is necessary.

Group 3: This classification consists of occupancies where standard sprinkler spacing and pipe schedules are considered satisfactory, but where more-than-ordinary water supplies are advisable. This group includes certain woodworking occupancies and others such as flour and feed mills, paper mills, piers and wharves, and tire storage.

Extra-Hazard Occupancies

Extra-hazard occupancies consist of properties where flash fires opening all the sprinklers in a fire area are probable, calling for close sprinkler spacing and larger pipe sizes. They are divided into two groups:

1. Extra-hazard occupancies (Group 1) include those that may produce severe fires where few or no flammable or combustible liquids are present. These include such occupancies as die casting, plywood and particle board manufacturing, printing [using inks with below 100°F (37.8°C) flash points], rubber manufacturing operations, saw mills, textile operations, and plastic foam manufacturing.
2. Extra-hazard occupancies (Group 2) include those that may produce severe fires where moderate to substantial amounts of flammable or combustible liquids are present, or where shielding of combustibles is extensive. These include such occupancy hazards as asphalt saturating, flammable liquids spraying, flow coating, open oil quenching, solvent cleaning, and varnish and paint dipping.

In any treatment of hazards by general groups of occupancy, it must be noted that individual properties differ markedly and that buildings of the same nominal occupancy classification may show widely different individual hazards that should be considered in any determination of water supply.

WATER SUPPLY REQUIREMENTS FOR HOSE STREAM PROTECTION

The values given in Table 5-11A include hose stream requirements. In considering water requirements for hose streams, one should realize that, if sprinklers perform effectively, little hose stream assistance is required. Although this is generally the case, a realistic view must be taken of possible contingencies and of the amount of water that might be needed for hose stream protection under adverse conditions. Hose streams may also be necessary to accomplish final extinguishment of the fire. However, it should be noted that, current sprinkler system technology is intended to control a fire, not necessarily to extinguish it.

In evaluating hose stream requirements, one should consider several possibilities, such as the amount of water necessary for final extinguishment and clean-up operations, or the steps that may have to be taken in the event that sprinklers are retarding fire spread but are not fully effective in gaining control of the fire and extinguishing it.

HYDRAULICALLY DESIGNED SPRINKLER SYSTEMS

Planning new water supplies or evaluating existing supplies for sprinkler systems requires information about the hydraulic behavior of sprinkler piping systems.

Hydraulic Calculations

A hydraulically designed sprinkler system is one in which pipe sizes are selected on a pressure-loss basis to provide a prescribed density in gallons per minute per square foot [(L/min)/m^2] distributed with a reasonable degree of uniformity over a specified area. This permits the selection of pipe sizes in accordance with the characteristics of the water supply available. The stipulated design density and area of application will vary with occupancy hazard. This is the verbatim definition of a hydraulically designed system, taken from NFPA 13, *Installation of Sprinkler Systems*. This definition sets the basic premise for the preferred method of sprinkler system design.

Table 5-11B is used to determine density, area of sprinkler operation, and water supply requirements for hydraulically designed sprinkler systems. Systems must be calculated to satisfy a single point on the appropriate design curve, and interior piping must be based on this design point. It is not necessary to meet all points on the selected curve. In some cases where a large water supply is available, it might be advantageous, because of the elimination of a fire pump, to design the system using the top portion of the curve. In other cases, it might be better to design with smaller areas of application and higher densities, because these tend to limit fire size, even though a fire pump is required.

When selecting a point on the curve in Figure 5-11B, it should be noted that more total water is necessary in terms of flow and capacity as one moves up the curve. As an example, for a light-hazard system, a 1500-sq-ft (139 m^2) area requires a density of 0.1 gpm/sq ft [4.1 (L/min)/m^2], or a flow of 150 gpm (568 L/min). If a 2500-sq-ft (232 m^2) area is selected, the density is only 0.075 gpm/sq ft [3.0 (L/min)/m^2], but the total flow is increased to 188 gpm (710 L/min).

The same hazard occupancy classifications that apply to pipe schedule sprinkler systems apply to hydraulically designed sprinkler systems, as mentioned in this chapter. However, the recommended water supply figures are somewhat lower due to the greater efficiency of a calculated system.

The water allowances for inside and outside hose streams may be combined and added to the system requirement at the system connection to the underground main. The total water requirement must be calculated through the underground main to the point of supply.

For deluge and water spray systems with open orifices, calculations are essential. Automatic sprinkler systems protecting high-piled storage require a specific water density for fire control. Because the hydraulic design approach results in superior design, it always should be selected as the preferred method.

Hydraulic calculation programs: Since NFPA 13, *Installation of Sprinkler Systems*, first permitted the use of hydraulic calculations, several computer programs have been developed that can assist the designer with this particular task. These programs are not required to be listed nor are they governed by NFPA 13. They must, as a minimum, be capable of providing the information required for any hydraulic calculation procedure. This information includes, but is not limited to, the hydraulic reference points, the flow and pressure at specific points, the pipe diameter, and, for a grid system, a printout showing the flow direction and quantities.

The capabilities and limitations of computer programs are as wide-ranging as the cost differences among them. Before buying one of these programs, the user should be aware of the type of sprinkler system design addressed. *A Comparison of Several Computer Hydraulics Programs for the IBM PC and Compatibles*[1] is considered the "consumer's report" for hydraulic software programs, and it should be consulted.

Flow Calculation Methods

Methods of making flow calculations for sprinkler systems are given in NFPA 13, *Installation of Sprinkler Systems*; NFPA 15, *Water-Spray Fixed Systems for Fire Protection*; *Sprinkler Hydraulics*[2]; *Hydraulic Design and Estimation of Fire Sprinkler Systems*[3]; *Automatic Sprinkler Hydraulic Data*[4]; "Hydraulics of Fire Protection Systems"[5]; and "Water Flow Characteristics of Sprinkler Systems".[6]

The design area for flow calculations is the most hydraulically demanding area for the sprinkler system. The area should have a dimension parallel to the branch line of 1.2 times the square root of the area of anticipated sprinkler operation (except grid systems). The 1.2 times the square root of the area is added to ensure that the long side of the rectangle would be along the branch line. In grid systems, the hydraulically most demanding area must be verified using at least two additional sets of calculations. This technique is referred to as "peaking," and it is merely a check to prove that the most demanding area has been calculated.

Each sprinkler in the design area must discharge at a flow rate at least equal to the stipulated minimum water application rate or density. Begin calculations at the sprinkler hydraulically farthest from the supply connection. In common system configurations, this will be the end sprinkler on the end branch line. The minimum operating pressure for any sprinkler must not be less than 7 psi (48 kPa). Special sprinklers, such as extended-coverage-types, will require operating pressures well in excess of this 7-psi (48 kPa) minimum.

TABLE 5-11B. *Density, Area of Sprinkler Operation, and Water Supply Requirements for Hydraulically Designed Sprinkler Systems*

Minimum Water Supplies

Hazard Classification	Sprinklers gpm†	Inside Hose gpm†	Combined Inside & Outside Hose—gpm†	Duration in Minutes
Light	See Density Curves Below	50 or 100	100	30
Ord.—Gp. 1		50 or 100	250	*60–90
Ord.—Gp. 2		50 or 100	250	*60–90
Ord.—Gp. 3		50 or 100	500	*60–120
Ex. Haz.—Gp. 1		50 or 100	500	*90–120
Ex. Haz.—Gp. 2		50 or 100	1,000	120

* The lower duration figure is ordinarily acceptable where remote station water flow alarm service or equivalent is provided.
† 1 gpm = 3.785 L/min.

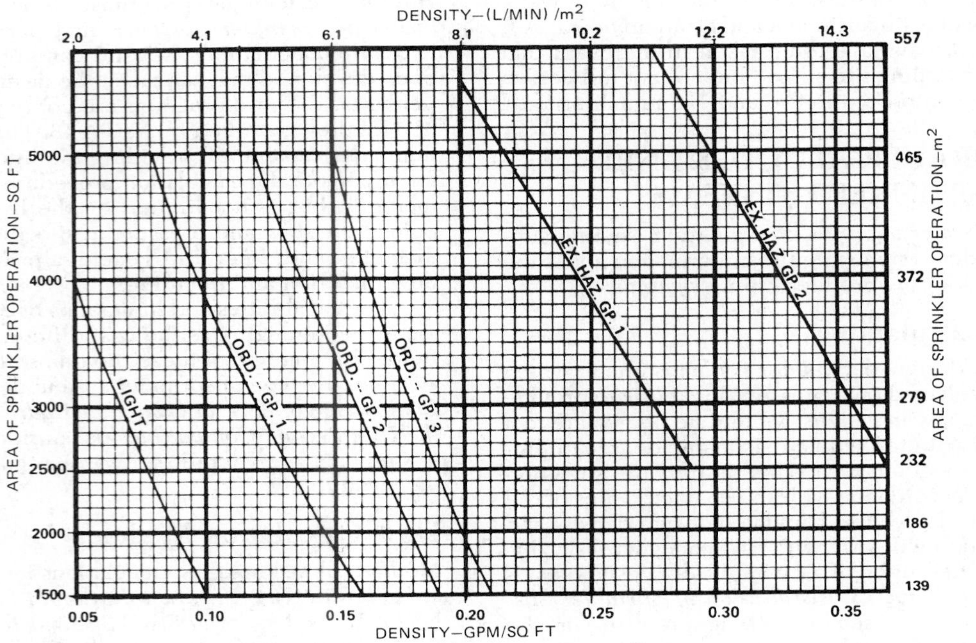

FOR SI UNITS: 1 SQ FT = 0.0920 m²; 1 GPM/SQ FT = 40.746 (L/MIN)/m²

The Most Remote Sprinkler

Assuming a minimum pressure of 10 psi (69 kPa) at the most remote sprinkler and a discharge coefficient of 0.75 for a standard ½-in. (12.7 mm) orifice sprinkler, there is a discharge of 17.7 gpm (67 L/min) calculated from the formula

$$Q = 29.8\, cd^2 \sqrt{P}$$

used in calculating flows through orifices and short tubes. For a given sprinkler, the product of these numbers in the equation—29.8 cd^2—becomes a constant and is denoted as the sprinkler K-factor. In the case of a ½-in. (12.7 mm) orifice sprinkler, the constant is 5.6 and is derived by multiplying the following numbers: $29.8 \times 0.75 \times (1/2)^2 = 5.6$. A simplied equation may now be used to describe flow through the sprinkler orifice. The new equation is:

$$Q = K\sqrt{P}.$$

Velocity pressure is not a factor at the most remote sprinkler, but it may be considered at all the other sprinklers in the example that follows. Some organizations ignore velocity pressure in their calculations. The error introduced is on the safe side. NFPA 15, *Water-Spray Fixed Systems for Fire Protection*, recommends considering velocity only when it is more than 5 percent of the total pressure.

Example for Second Sprinkler from the End

Assuming sprinklers 10 ft (3.05 m) apart on branch lines, with the end section of pipe 1 in. (25.4 mm) nominal diameter, the friction loss at 17.7 gpm (67 L/min) flow with a Hazen-Williams formula coefficient of 120 (value for black steel pipe) will be 1.0 psi (7 kPa).

The total pressure at the second sprinkler will be 10.0 + 1.0 psi (69 + 7 kPa) = 11.0 psi (76 kPa). Velocity pressure, if used in the procedure, is calculated from the formula

$$P_v = 0.001123 \frac{Q^2}{D^2}$$

where:

P_v =velocity pressure in psi

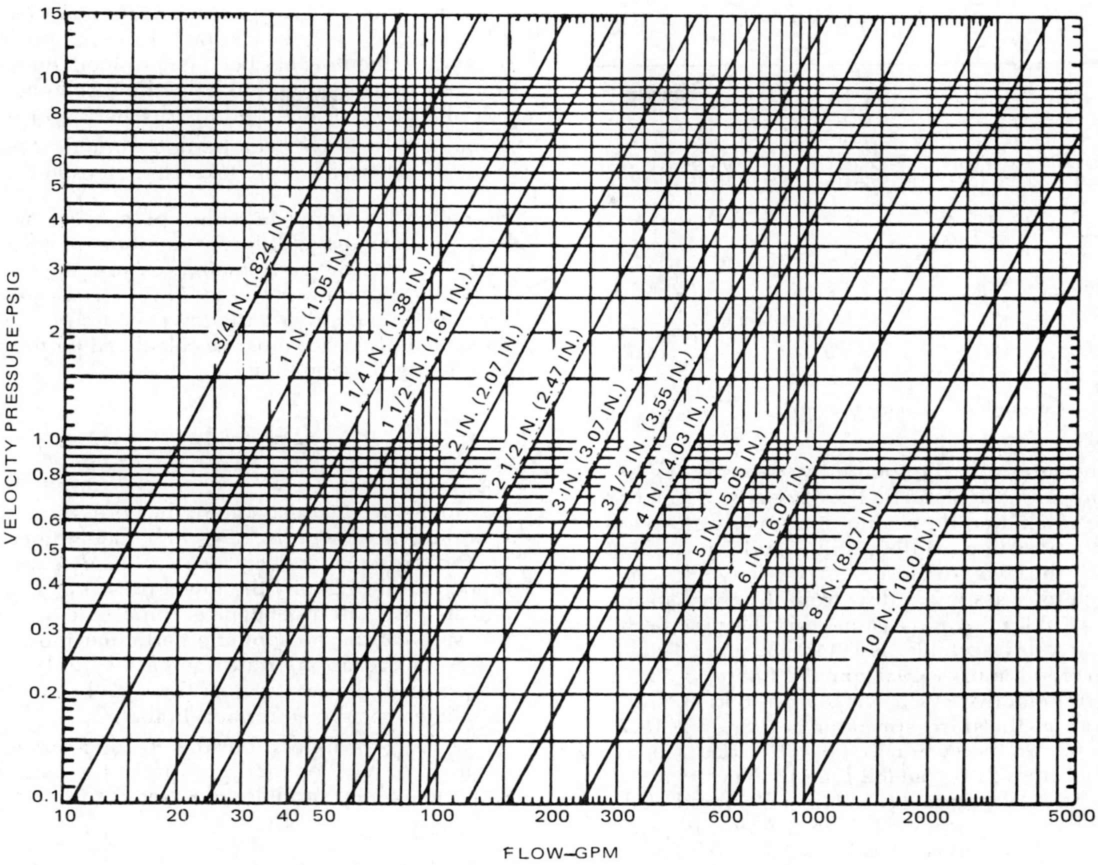

FIG. 5-11C. Graph for the determination of velocity pressure.

Q = flow in gpm

D = inside pipe diameter in inches.

The velocity pressure relates to the system design by:

$$P_n = P_t - P_v$$

where:

P_n = normal pressure

P_t = total pressure

P_v = velocity pressure.

Of this, velocity pressure based on a flow of 17.7 gpm (67 L/min) will be 0.3 psi (2 kPa). The normal pressure (pressure acting perpendicular to the pipe wall) acting on the second sprinkler is the total pressure of 11.0 psi (76 kPa), less the velocity pressure of 0.3 psi (2 kPa), which equals 10.7 psi (74 kPa). On all sprinklers except the end sprinkler, only normal pressure is considered as acting on the sprinklers. The discharge from the second sprinkler, at a pressure of 10.7 psi (74 kPa), will be 18.3 gpm (69 L/min).

The pipe between the second and third sprinkler, also 1 in. (25.4 mm) in diameter, 10 ft (3.05 m) long, and with a flow of 17.7 gpm (67 L/min) + 18.3 gpm (69 L/min) = 36.0 gpm (136 L/min), will have a friction loss of 3.8 psi (26 kPa) and a velocity pressure of 1.2 psi (8 kPa). Normal pressure at the third sprinkler is 10.7 psi (74 kPa) + 3.8 psi (26 kPa) – 1.2 psi (8 kPa), or 13.3 psi (92 kPa).

Other Sprinklers on a Branch Line

Figure 5-11C can be used to establish the velocity pressure correction needed for various pipe sizes and flows. This figure may be used for any pipe type, but it is based on the use of schedule 40 pipe. The difference in velocity pressure is miniscule as it relates to schedule of pipe.

Figure 5-11D is an example of the velocity pressure component, determined as follows: The flow between the last sprinkler and the next to last sprinkler on the branch line was determined to be 17.7 gpm (67 L/min), and the pipe size is 1 in. (25.4 mm). The graph in Figure 5-11C is now used to locate a flow of 17.7 gpm (67 L/min) on the x-axis, going vertically from this point until the 1-in. (25.4 mm) line is intercepted. The corresponding pressure is taken from the y-axis, and is determined to be 0.3 psi. This procedure can now be repeated for each combination of pipe sizes and flows.

Up to this point, velocity pressure has been based on flow downstream from the sprinkler being considered; this has been confirmed by tests.[6] It has also been shown by those tests that, beyond the second sprinkler, velocity pressure should be figured from the flow on the upstream side of the sprinkler being considered. This is done by trial and error, assuming a flow from the sprinkler, calculating the

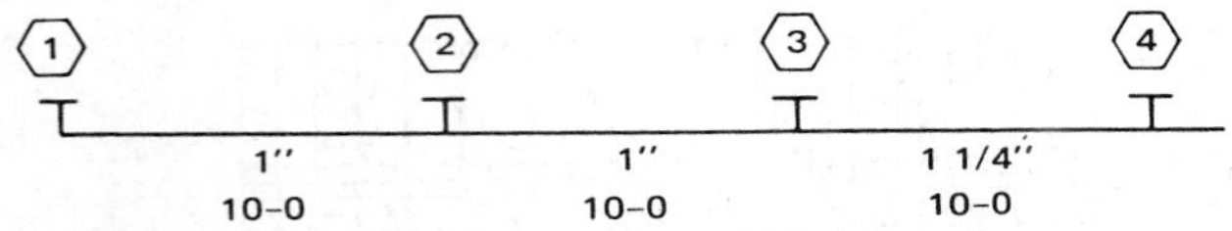

SUMMARY

	FLOW (gpm)	FRICTION LOSS (PSI)	VELOCITY PRESSURE (PSI)	NORMAL PRESSURE (PSI)
1 2	17.7	1	0.3	11
2 3	36	3.8	1.2	13.3
3 4	57.5	3.9	1.0	15.0

FIG. 5-11D. Example of velocity pressure.

velocity pressure from the total flow, determining a normal pressure, and calculating a flow from the normal pressure. If the calculated flow is not reasonably close to the assumed flow, assume a different flow and repeat the procedure until the two are close.

For example, assume a flow from the third sprinkler of 19.0 gpm (72 L/min) and assume that the pipe between the third and fourth sprinkler is 1¼ in. (32 mm). Total flow is 36.0 gpm (136 L/min) + 19.0 gpm (72 L/min) = 55.0 gpm (208 L/min). Velocity pressure is 0.9 psi (6 kPa), and normal pressure at the third sprinkler is therefore 15.7 psi (108 kPa) – 0.9 psi (6 kPa), or 14.8 psi (102 kPa). Corrected flow then becomes 21.6 gpm (82 L/min), which is not close enough to the 19.0 gpm (72 L/min) assumed. Try an assumed flow of 21.4 gpm (81 L/min). Velocity pressure at 57.4 gpm (217 L/min) is 1.0 psi (7 kPa); normal pressure is 14.7 psi (101 kPa), and the new corrected flow is 21.5 gpm (81 L/min). Total flow at the third sprinkler then becomes 36.0 gpm (136 L/min) + 21.5 gpm (81.4 L/min) = 57.5 gpm (217.6 L/min). The calculating procedure for the other sprinklers on the branch line is the same as it is for the third sprinkler.

If this set of conditions is compared to pipe schedule design, it will be seen that the 15- psi (103 kPa) minimum riser pressure has been exceeded, unless, as is quite probable, the pressure with 57.5-gpm (217.6 L/min) flow is substantially higher than that with a 500-gpm (1893 L/min) flow. Whether the pressure with 57.5-gpm (217.6 L/min) flow is higher than 15 psi (103 kPa) depends on the characteristics of the water supply. In any case, it appears that, with not many more sprinklers open, the pressure at the most remote sprinkler will be less than the 10 psi (69 kPa) selected in this example.

Branch Lines, Cross Mains, Risers, and Fittings

Cross main pressure at the branch line connection: This is the normal pressure at the nearest open sprinkler increased by the friction loss and the velocity pressure in the intervening pipe. If the branch line is fed through a tee and nipple, additional friction loss allowances must be made, although the friction loss in nipples less than 6 in. (152 mm) long is customarily neglected.

Two branches in one line of sprinklers: These may have the same or different numbers of sprinklers. The pressure at the entrance to the two branches will always be the same. The computations starting at the end sprinklers will be duplicated for the number of open sprinklers.

After the discharge from any number of sprinklers on a branch line has been computed and the pressure needed to produce the flow has been determined, the entire branch line can be considered to have the discharge characteristics of a single orifice, and the discharge constant K in the formula $Q = K\sqrt{P}$ can be determined, P being the net pressure where flows are taken from tees in the cross main.

Branches on opposite sides of a cross main: These branches may have different numbers of sprinklers open, in which case the cross-main pressure must be the higher of the two computed values. This increases the discharge from the branch giving the lower computed pressure, and the actual discharge must be calculated for the higher pressure using the equation:

$$\frac{Q_1}{Q_2} = \sqrt{\frac{P_1}{P_2}}$$

in which P_2 is taken as the higher pressure, Q_2 the corresponding increased discharge to be determined, and P_1 and Q_1 the pressure and corresponding discharge from the branch requiring only the lower pressure. This proportion and its associated concept is important in that only one pressure can be present at a particular junction point.

After the appropriate increased discharge has been determined, the two rates of flow can be combined and K calculated for the combined branches.

When sprinklers on the second branch line are assumed to have opened, starting at the cross-main sprinkler, the opened sprinkler most remote from the cross main

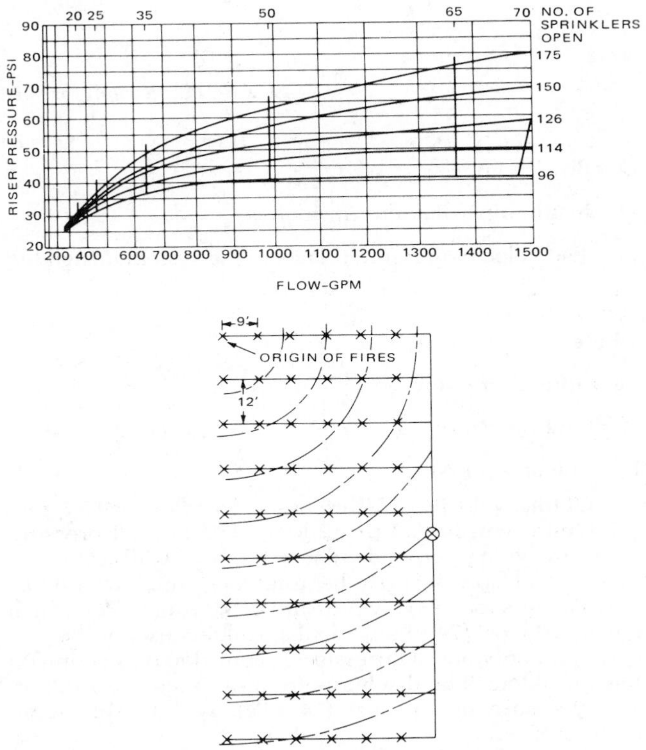

FIG. 5-11E. A flow curve for a side-central feed to sprinklers on a system having six sprinklers on each branch line is shown on the above graph. Below is the pattern of sprinklers opening on a side-central feed system. (Source: Factory Mutual Research Corp.)

is considered as the end sprinkler in the branch line computation, the next opened is the second, and so on, regardless of nonoperating sprinklers on the outer end of the branch.

Cross-main pressures: Cross main pressures are calculated with the same procedure used for sprinklers on a single branch line, except that it is not necessary to use the trial-and-error procedure for the third and additional branch lines since the effect of change in velocity pressure with flows passing through tees in the cross main is usually negligible. The net pressure producing the flow in successive branch lines is taken as the normal pressure at the end branch line, increased by the friction loss in the pipe between the branches.

Riser pressure: Riser pressure is taken as the normal pressure at the nearest flowing branch, increased by the total friction loss between this branch and the riser and by the velocity pressure in the cross main at the riser connection.

Friction loss in fittings: This is generally included in calculations only when the fitting involves a change in the direction of flow. An exception to this is the fitting immediately preceding the sprinkler. Friction loss in control, gate, and check valves and in strainers, meters, backflow devices, and similar devices is always included. The friction loss in piping between the source of supply and the opened sprinklers obviously must be included in all calculations.

Differences in elevation must be allowed for on the basis that each foot (meter) of height represents 0.434 psi (9.82 kPa/m). In multistory buildings, this may be a substantial factor. Feed mains, cross mains, and branch lines within the same system may be looped or gridded to divide the total water flowing to the design area.

Grid systems: Many grid systems are currently being installed. The use of grid systems means that every sprinkler is fed from several directions, with a resulting reduction in pipe sizing. The hydraulic calculations required for a grid system are complex and almost impossible without the use of computers.

Sprinkler System Waterflow Curves

To avoid repetition of laborious computation of water flows and pressures when such information is needed in cases involving standard sprinkler, spray, or open-device systems, it is possible to prepare diagrams or waterflow curves from which riser pressures and corresponding total sprinkler flows may be determined for different numbers of opened sprinklers. One such series of curves, developed by the Factory Mutual Research Corporation, and the piping arrangement and assumed pattern of opened sprinklers are shown in Figure 5-11E. Programmable, hand-held calculators are also useful, fast, and accurate.

BIBLIOGRAPHY

References Cited

1. *A Comparison of Several Computer Hydraulics Programs for the IBM PC and Compatibles*, Society of Fire Protection Engineers, Boston, MA.
2. Wass, H. E., *Sprinkler Hydraulics*, IRM Insurance, White Plains, NY, 1983.
3. Crowley, J. E., *Hydraulic Design and Estimation of Fire Sprinkler Systems*, Crowley Design Group, Inc., King of Prussia, PA, 1982.
4. Wood, C. M., *Automatic Sprinkler Hydraulic Data*, "Automatic" Sprinkler Corporation of America, Cleveland, OH, 1980.
5. "Hydraulics of Fire Protection Systems," *Loss Prevention Data Sheet 3-0*, Factory Mutual Research Corp., Norwood, MA, 1977.
6. Nickerson, M. H., "Water Flow Characteristics of Sprinkler Systems," *Proceedings* of the fifty-eighth Annual Meeting, National Fire Protection Association, May 17-21, 1954, Washington, DC, pp. 140-152.

NFPA Codes, Standards, and Recommended Practices

Reference to the following NFPA codes, standards, and recommended practices will provide further information on water supplies for sprinkler systems discussed in this chapter. (See the latest *NFPA Catalog* for availability of current editions of the following documents.)

NFPA 13, *Installation of Sprinkler Systems.*

NFPA 15, *Water-Spray Fixed Systems for Fire Protection.*

NFPA 20, *Installation of Centrifugal Fire Pumps.*

NFPA 22, *Water Tanks for Private Fire Protection.*

NFPA 24, *Private Fire Service Mains and Their Appurtenances.*

NFPA 231, *General Storage.*

NFPA 231C, *Rack Storage of Materials.*

NFPA 231D, *Storage of Rubber Tires.*

NFPA 231E, *Storage of Baled Cotton.*

NFPA 231F, *Storage of Roll Paper.*

NFPA 291, *Fire Flow Testing and Marking of Hydrants.*

Additional Reading

Brown, J. R., *Field Test to Compare Sprinkler Demands of Wet-Pipe and Dry-Pipe Systems*, Factory Mutual Research Corp., Norwood, MA, May 1980.

Bryan, J. L., *Automatic Sprinkler and Standpipe Systems*, Chapter 4, National Fire Protection Association, Quincy, MA, 1990.

Chicarello, P. J., Jr., "Analytical Methods for Calculating Sprinkler Discharge," *Fire Technology*, Vol. 8, No. 1 (Feb. 1972), pp. 45-52, Crane Hydraulic Data.

Damon, W. A., "Preventing Pitfalls in Fire Protection Systems," *Heating/Piping/Air Conditioning*, Apr. 1985, pp. 61-64, 69-71.

Gomberg, A. and Cote, A. E., "The Computer Approach to Fire Protection Problems," *Fire Technology*, Vol. 3, No. 1 (Aug. 1967), pp. 202-212.

Hasegawa, H. K. and Lambert, H.E., "Reliability Study on the Lawrence Livermore National Laboratory Water-Supply System," *Proceedings* of the First International Symposium on Fire Safety Science, Hemisphere, 1986, pp. 611-620.

Milke, J. A. and Bryan, J. L., "Development of Cost Effective Techiques for Alleviating Water Supply Deficiencies in a Residential Sprinkler System," *NBS-GCR-87-533*, National Institute of Standards and Technology, Gaithersburg, MD, Nov. 1987.

Ng, W., *Fire Sprinkler System Hydraulic Calculations and Computer-Aided Design Methods*, (privately published) available from author, Oakland, CA, 1982.

NFPA, *Automatic Sprinkler Systems Handbook*, National Fire Protection Association, Quincy, MA 1989.

SFPE Handbook of Fire Protection Engineering, Society of Fire Protection Engineers, Boston, MA, 1988.

"Water *vs* Fire: The Essential Components of a Good Water Supply," *The Sentinel*, Industrial Risk Insurers, Vol. 367, No. 4, July/Aug. 1980, pp. 3-9.

Wright, V. E., "Hydraulic Graphing on a Microcomputer for Fire Protection Analysis," *Heating, Piping, and Air Conditioning*, Apr. 1984, pp. 83-90.

AUTOMATIC SPRINKLERS

Revised by Russell P. Fleming

Automatic sprinklers are thermosensitive devices designed to react at predetermined temperatures by automatically releasing a stream of water and distributing it in specified patterns and quantities over designated areas. The automatic distribution of water is intended to extinguish a fire or to prevent its spread in the event that the initial fire is out of range of the sprinklers or is of a type that cannot be extinguished by water discharged from sprinklers. The water is fed to the sprinklers through a system of piping, ordinarily overhead, with the sprinklers placed at intervals along the pipes.

This chapter covers the operating principles, including operating temperatures, of the various types of automatic sprinklers currently available and describes their construction in some detail. Sprinklers for special service conditions are also covered.

The National Fire Protection Association does not have standards that cover the manufacture of sprinklers. However, it does insist through requirements in its many fire protection standards containing sprinkler protection requirements that only sprinklers listed by reputable product evaluation organizations be used in sprinkler systems meeting the requirements of NFPA 13, *Installation of Sprinkler Systems*. Listing of sprinklers in a national organization's listing service is an indication that the sprinklers have been scrutinized for their reliability and compliance with the organization's test criteria for sprinklers.

Since they were introduced in the latter part of the 19th century, the performance and reliability of automatic sprinklers have been improved continually through experience and the efforts of manufacturers and testing organizations.

In 1952 and 1953, a new sprinkler was developed with a more efficient umbrella-shaped spray pattern. This "spray sprinkler" became the standard sprinkler in 1958 for use in conformance with NFPA 13, *Installation of Sprinkler Systems*, and sprinklers of the older design became known as "old-style" sprinklers. Redesign of the deflector was the principal feature of the new standard sprinklers.

Due to the development of many new types of sprinklers during the 1980s, it became questionable whether any single type of sprinkler could be considered standard in the future. As such, the term "spray sprinkler" was brought back into use with the 1991 edition of NFPA 13, *Installation of Sprinkler Systems*. This also conforms better to internationally accepted terminology.

Russell P. Fleming, P.E., is vice president of engineering for the National Fire Sprinkler Association, Patterson, NY. He has served on nine different NFPA technical committees, including the Committee on Automatic Sprinklers.

OPERATING PRINCIPLES OF AUTOMATIC SPRINKLERS

In order to appreciate the ruggedness, mechanical simplicity, reliability in operation, and freedom from premature operation of an automatic sprinkler, a familiarity with the basic principles of its design, construction, and operation is necessary.

Operating Elements

Under normal conditions, the discharge of water from an automatic sprinkler is restrained by a cap or valve held tightly against the orifice by a system of levers and links or other releasing devices pressing down on the cap and anchored firmly by struts on the sprinkler.

Fusible sprinklers: A common fusible-style automatic sprinkler operates when a metal alloy of predetermined melting point fuses. Various combinations of levers, struts, and links or other soldered members are used to reduce the force acting upon the solder so that the sprinkler will be held closed with the smallest practical amount of metal and solder. This minimizes the time of operation by reducing the mass of fusible metal to be heated.

The solders used with automatic sprinklers are alloys of optimum fusibility composed principally of tin, lead, cadmium, and bismuth; all have sharply defined melting points. Alloys of two or more metals may have a melting point that is lower than that of the individual metal with the lower melting point. The mixture of two or more metals that gives the lowest melting point possible is called an "eutectic" alloy.

Bulb sprinklers: A second style of operating element utilizes a frangible bulb. (See Figure 5-12A.) The small bulb, usually of glass, contains a liquid which does not completely fill the bulb, leaving a small air bubble trapped in it. As heat expands the liquid, the bubble is compressed and finally absorbed by the liquid. Once the bubble disappears, the pressure rises substantially, and the bulb shatters, releasing the valve cap. The exact operating temperature is regulated by adjusting the amount of liquid and the size of the bubble when the bulb is sealed.

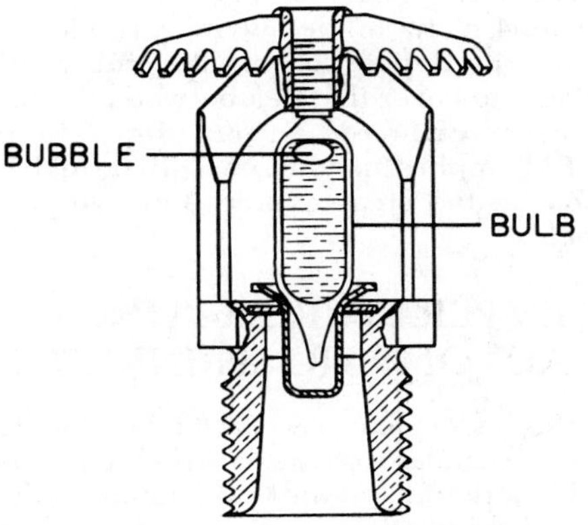

FIG. 5-12A. Grinnell Quartzoid, Issue D.

Other thermosensitive elements: Other styles of thermosensitive operating elements employed to provide automatic discharge include bimetallic discs, fusible alloy pellets, and chemical pellets. (See Figure 5-12B.)

FIG. 5-12B. Central "Flow Control" (on-off) sprinkler.

Sprinkler Dynamics

Figure 5-12C shows how the mechanical force exists in the link-and-lever-style automatic sprinkler. The construction shown is diagrammatic and does not represent any particular sprinkler.

The mechanical force normally exerted on the top of the cap or valve is many times that developed by the water pressure below, so that the possibility of leakage, even from water hammer or exceptionally high water pressure, is practically eliminated. The mechanical force in a link-and-lever sprinkler is produced by tension in the sprinkler frame, usually created by tightening the screw that holds the

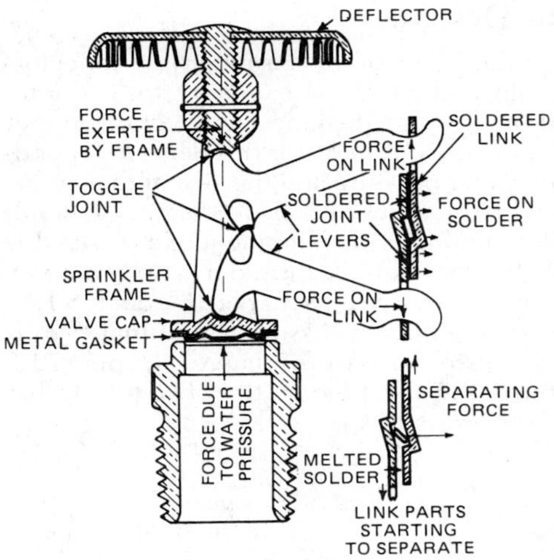

FIG. 5-12C. Representative arrangement of a soldered link-and-lever automatic sprinkler.

deflector down against the toggle joint formed by the levers. This pressure is applied against the valve or cap, but the line of force is not direct. The eccentricity of the loading permits a leveraged reduction of the force, first by the toggle effect of the two levers, and second by the mechanism of the link parts. The force resisted by the solder is made relatively low because solder of the composition needed to give the desired operating temperatures is subject to cold flow under high stress. The sprinkler frame or other parts usually possess a degree of elasticity to provide the energy that produces a positive, sharp release of the operating parts.

Sprinklers illustrated in Figure 5-12D use modifications of the common link-and-lever construction, some of which employ solder under compression, tension, and tension and shear.

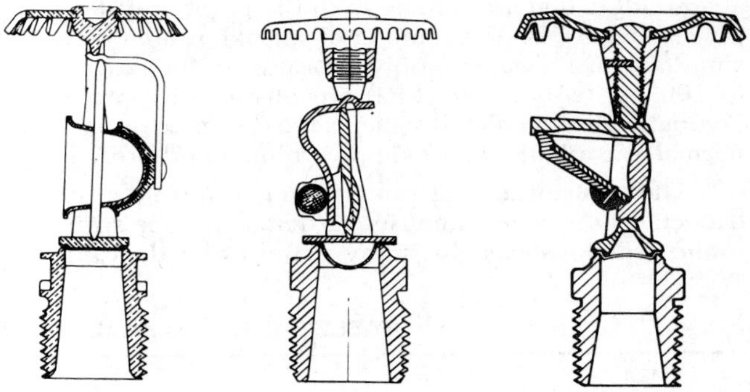

FIG. 5-12D. Some modifications of the common link-and-lever construction. At left is Grinnell F950 Duraspeed; at center is Reliable Model G; and at right is Firematic Type S.

To ensure that cold flow will not be a problem, the laboratories that test and list sprinklers use statistical methods to simulate long-term loading of heat-responsive elements. Statistical methods are also employed to make sure that the crush strength of glass bulbs is sufficiently higher than the frame loads which will be applied to the bulbs.

Deflector Design

Attached to the frame of the sprinkler is a deflector or distributor against which the stream of water is directed and converted into a spray designed to cover or protect a certain area. The amount of water discharged depends upon the flowing water pressure and the size of the sprinkler orifice. A flowing pressure of 7 psi (48 kPa) is generally considered a minimum for development of a reasonable spray pattern. At this pressure, a sprinkler having a nominal ½-in. (12.7 mm) orifice will discharge 15 gpm (58 L/min). At the same 7-psi (48 kPa) pressure, a nominal 17/32-in. (13.5 mm) orifice sprinkler will discharge 21 gpm (79 L/min). (See Figure 5-12E for the quantity of water discharged at various water pressures.)

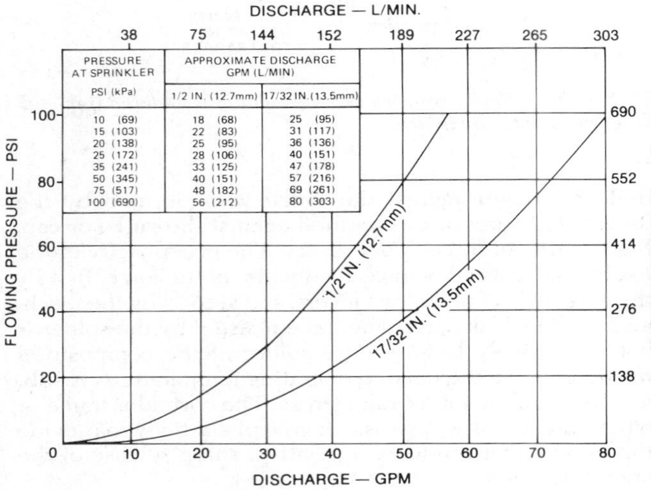

FIG. 5-12E. Water discharge rates of typical nominal ½-in. (12.7 mm) and 17/32-in. (13.5 mm) orifice automatic sprinklers.

In order to have even the minimum flowing pressure at sprinklers that are remote from the point of water supply, especially when a number of sprinklers are operating simultaneously, water supply pressures in the range of 30 to 100 psi (316 to 690 kPa) are customarily provided. Hydraulically calculated systems are designed around the normally available water supply volume and pressure.

The distribution of water from a sprinkler is not expected to be axisymmetric, particularly since sprinkler frame arms obstruct the spray pattern and the serrated edges of the deflector create a "fingering" effect. A contour plot of the flow pattern of a pendent spray sprinkler is shown in Figure 5-12F.[1]

Because the distribution of water from sprinklers is a complex phenomenon, the testing laboratories have fairly broad requirements in this area. For upright and pendent spray sprinklers, for example, Underwriters Laboratories Inc. (UL) requires a turntable test to "fingerprint" the spray pattern. For a ½-in. (12.7 mm) orifice sprinkler flowing 15 gpm (58 L/min), or a large 17/32-in. (13.5 mm) orifice sprinkler flowing 21 gpm (79 L/min), water distribution is not permitted outside a 16-ft (4.9 m) diameter circle in a horizontal plane 4 ft (1.2 m) below the sprinkler. A separate "16 pan" distribution test checks the ability of four flowing sprinklers to cover the area between them with their overlapping spray patterns. Factory Mutual Research Corporation (FM) applies an additional six-sprinkler flow test, which looks at the area covered between two adjacent sprinklers.

TEMPERATURE RATINGS OF AUTOMATIC SPRINKLERS

Automatic sprinklers have various temperature ratings that are based on standardized tests in which a sprinkler is immersed in a liquid and the temperature of the liquid is raised very slowly until the sprinkler operates. (See Table 5-12A.)

The temperature rating of all fusible-element-style automatic sprinklers is stamped upon the soldered link. For bulb sprinklers, the temperature rating must be stamped or cast on some visible part. Color codes are also used for glass bulbs and for frame arms of fusible-element sprinklers.

The recommended maximum room temperature is restricted for both bulbs and fusible-element sprinklers. This is because solder begins to lose its strength somewhat below its actual melting point. Premature operation of a solder sprinkler usually depends on the extent to which the normal room temperature is exceeded, the duration of the excessive temperature, and the load on the operating parts of the sprinkler. While glass bulb sprinklers do not lose strength at temperatures close to their operating temperatures, using them at such temperatures can result in continuous loss and reforming of the air bubble, which creates stresses on the bulb.

The general rule of not using sprinklers of ordinary [135 to 170°F (57 to 77°C)] temperature rating where temperatures exceed 100°F (38°C) is necessary to provide a

TABLE 5-12A. ***Temperature Ratings, Classification and Color Codings****

Max. Ceiling Temp. °F	°C	Temperature Rating °F	°C	Temperature Classification	Color Code	Glass Bulb Colors
100	38	135 to 170	59 to 77	Ordinary	Uncolored	Orange or Red
150	66	175 to 225	79 to 107	Intermediate	White	Yellow or Green
225	107	250 to 300	121 to 149	High	Blue	Blue
300	149	325 to 375	163 to 191	Extra High	Red	Purple
375	191	400 to 475	204 to 246	Very Extra High	Green	Black
475	246	500 to 575	260 to 302	Ultra High	Orange	Black
625	329	650	343	Ultra High	Orange	Black

* Source: NFPA 13, Sprinkler Systems Standard.

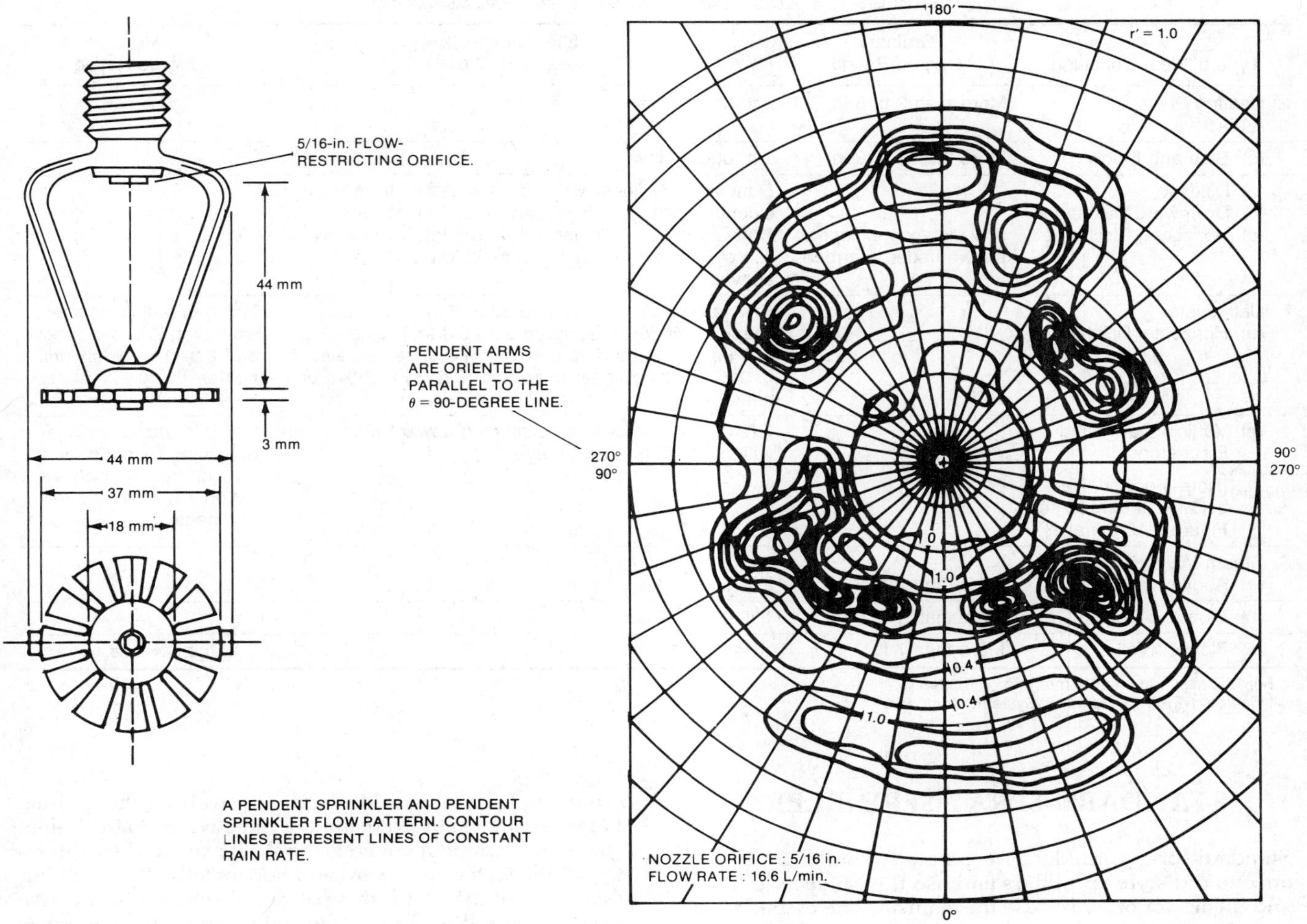

FIG. 5-12F. Pendent spray sprinkler and flow contours.[1]

margin of safety. General practices regarding the use of automatic sprinklers of higher than the ordinary rating are given in Tables 5-12B and 5-12C. Sprinklers of ordinary temperature rating can be used inside buildings and other places where they are not subject to direct sun rays, except in monitors and in blind attics without ventilation, under metal or tile roofs, near or above heat sources, or in confined spaces where normal temperatures may be exceeded.

When there is doubt as to maximum temperatures at sprinkler locations, maximum reading thermometers should be used and the temperature determined under conditions which would show the highest readings to be expected.

Sprinklers with high temperature ratings are often used in place of ordinary-rated sprinklers in situations where a high rate of heat release can be anticipated. The sprinklers rated for higher temperatures may have the advantage of reducing the number of sprinklers that would otherwise operate outside the fire area.

Automatic sprinklers may require a longer time period to operate when exposed to a slowly developing fire as opposed to the high heat release of a rapidly developing fire. They are designed to operate quickly enough to control a fire and prevent its spread.

The speed of operation depends on the physical properties of the sprinkler's mechanism. The time involved to operate depends, among other factors, upon the shape, size, and mass of the thermosensitive mechanism, the temperature differential between the surrounding atmosphere and the operating temperature of the sprinkler, and the velocity of the heated fire gases past the sprinkler operating element.

In cases where extreme speed of operation is necessary owing to the likelihood of a rapidly developing and spreading fire as, for example, in explosives manufacturing, the practice is to use deluge systems incorporating open sprinklers. These systems can be activated by special detection systems using infrared or ultraviolet light detection, smoke detection, or other means to open a valve and quickly allow water to enter the system and discharge through the open sprinklers. In cases where extremely fast response is required, the sprinkler piping is pre-filled with water up to the open sprinklers, which are equipped with blow-off plugs or caps.

TABLE 5-12B. ***Distance of Sprinklers from Heat Sources****

Type of Heat Condition	Ordinary Degree Rating	Intermediate Degree Rating	High Degree Rating
1. Heating Ducts (a) Above	More than 2 ft. 6 in.	2 ft. 6 in. or less	—
(b) Side and Below	More than 1 ft. 0 in.	1 ft. 0 in. or less	—
(c) Diffuser (c) Downward Discharge (c) Horizontal Discharge	Any distance except as shown under Intermediate	*Downward:* Cylinder with 1 ft. 0 in. radius from edge, extending 1 ft. 0 in. below and 2 ft. 6 in. above *Horizontal:* Semicylinder with 2 ft. 6 in. radius in direction of flow, extending 1 ft. 0 in. below and 2 ft. 6 in. above.	—
2. Unit Heater (a) Horizontal Discharge	—	*Discharge Side:* 7 ft. 0 in. to 20 ft. 0 in. radius pie-shaped cylinder [see Figure 3-16.6.3 (a)†] extending 7 ft. 0 in. above and 2 ft. 0 in. below unit heater; also 7 ft. 0 in. radius cylinder more than 7 ft. 0 in. above unit heater	7 ft. 0 in radius cylinder extending 7 ft. 0 in. above and 2 ft. 0 in. below unit heater
(b) Vertical Downward Discharge [Note: For sprinklers below unit heater, see Figure 3.16.6.3(a).†]	—	7 ft. 0 in. radius cylinder extending upward from an elevation 7 ft. 0 in. above heater	7 ft. 0 in. radius cylinder extending from the top of the unit heater to an elevation 7 ft. 0 in. above unit heater
3. Steam Mains (Uncovered) (a) Above	More than 2 ft. 6 in.	2 ft. 6 in. or less	—
(b) Side and Below	More than 1 ft. 0 in.	1 ft. 0 in. or less	—
(c) Blow-off Valve	More than 7 ft. 0 in.	—	7 ft. 0 in. or less

For SI Units: 1 in. = 25.4 mm; 1 ft. = 0.3048 m.
* Source: NFPA 13, Sprinkler Systems Standard

STANDARD SPRAY SPRINKLERS

Standard spray sprinklers are generally similar in appearance to old-style sprinklers and use the same style frame and linkage or other release mechanism. The essential difference is in the deflector; seemingly minor differences in deflector design make major differences in discharge characteristics. Several representative standard spray sprinklers are illustrated in Figure 5-12G.

On the assumption that discharging water against the ceiling was essential to fire extinguishment, early research on automatic sprinklers was largely concerned with securing reasonably uniform distribution of water over the area protected by one sprinkler and with wetting the ceiling. Later research showed that more effective extinguishment and a larger area of coverage could be secured by directing all the water downward and horizontally. Research further showed that, with this pattern, discharge is effective even in controlling fires on the ceiling above the sprinklers because of the improved cooling effect of the spray, better high-level water distribution, and decreased exposure to the ceiling because of more effective direct discharge of water on burning materials below.[2]

The design of the deflector causes the solid stream of water issuing from the orifice of a standard sprinkler to break up to form an umbrella-shaped spray. The pattern is roughly that of a half-sphere filled with spray.

TABLE 5-12C. ***Ratings of Sprinklers in Specified Locations****

Location	Ordinary Degree Rating	Intermediate Degree Rating	High Degree Rating
Skylights	—	Glass or plastic	—
Attics	Ventilated	Unventilated	—
Peaked Roof: Metal or thin boards; concealed or not concealed; insulated or uninsulated	Ventilated	Unventilated	—
Flat Roof: Metal; not concealed; insulated or uninsulated	Ventilated or unventilated	Note: For uninsulated roof, climate and occupancy may require Intermediate sprinklers. Check on job.	—
Flat Roof: Metal; concealed; insulated or uninsulated	Ventilated	Unventilated	—
Show Windows	Ventilated	Unventilated	—

NOTE: A check of temperatures by means of thermometers may be necessary.
*Source: NFPA 13, Sprinkler Systems Standard.

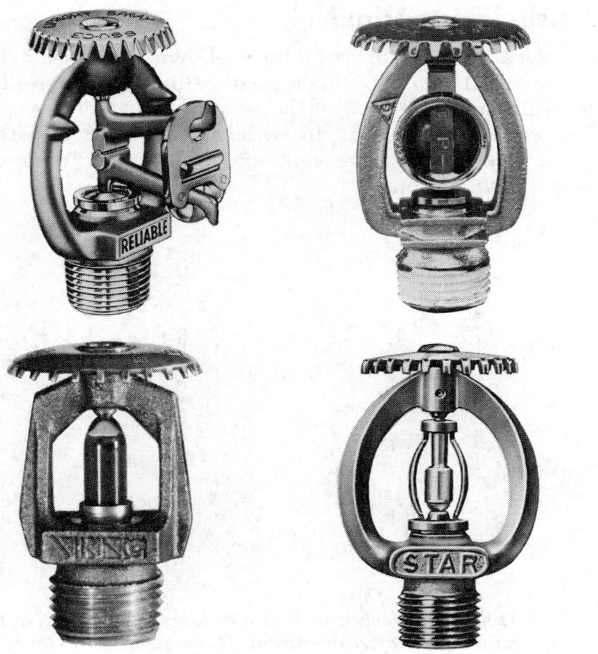

FIG. 5-12G. Standard spray sprinklers showing the various arrangements of releasing mechanisms. Clockwise from upper left is a fusible link-and-lever style (Reliable Issue C); a perforated heat-collector style, which is a variation of the link-and-lever style (Grinnell F950 Duraspeed); a center-strut style with solder under compression (Chemetron Stargard Model H); and a frangible-bulb style (Viking Model M).

Standard spray sprinklers are made for installation in an upright or pendent position and must be installed in the position for which they are designed. (See Figure 5-12H.) It is customary to replace old-style sprinklers with spray sprinklers in existing installations, although NFPA 13, *Installation of Sprinkler Systems*, permits replacing old-style sprinklers with similar devices. Some manufacturers, however, have discontinued producing old-style sprinklers.

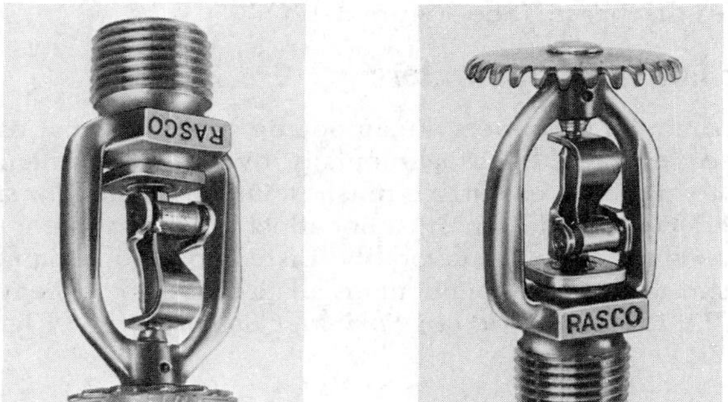

FIG. 5-12H. A listed sprinkler showing upright (right) and pendent (left) models of the same issue; note the difference in design of the deflectors. The sprinklers shown are Reliable Model G.

Double Deflectors

Several manufacturers developed a double deflector as their first design for use as standard spray upright sprinklers. A typical double deflector is shown in Figure 5-12I. Such sprinklers are no longer manufactured but, if previously "listed," are as acceptable as the currently approved upright spray sprinklers with a one-piece deflector.

FIG. 5-12I. Standard upright spray sprinkler with double deflector.

The general patterns of water discharge from the old-style and from the standard spray sprinklers are shown in Figures 5-12J and 5-12K, respectively.

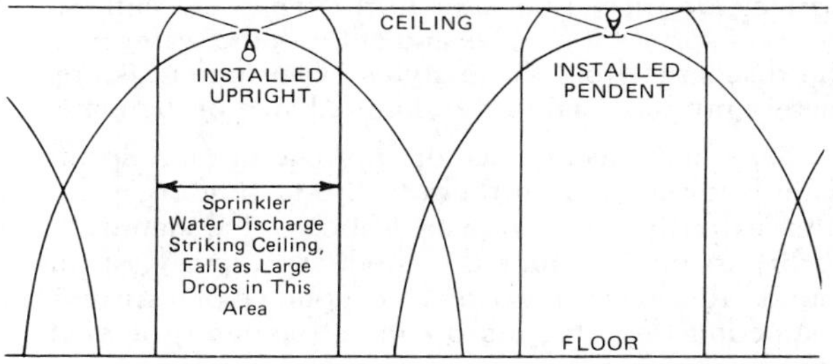

FIG. 5-12J. Principal distribution pattern of water from old-style/conventional sprinklers.

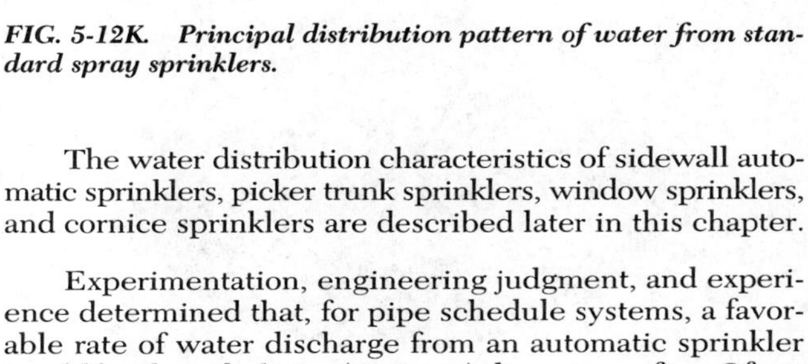

FIG. 5-12K. Principal distribution pattern of water from standard spray sprinklers.

The water distribution characteristics of sidewall automatic sprinklers, picker trunk sprinklers, window sprinklers, and cornice sprinklers are described later in this chapter.

Experimentation, engineering judgment, and experience determined that, for pipe schedule systems, a favorable rate of water discharge from an automatic sprinkler would be that of a ½-in. (12.7 mm) diameter orifice. Often, this is not the case with hydraulically designed systems.

Therefore, sprinklers of various orifice sizes are used. Standard automatic sprinklers have a nominal ½-in. (12.7 mm) orifice which may be of the ring-nozzle or tapered-nozzle style. (See Figure 5-12L.)

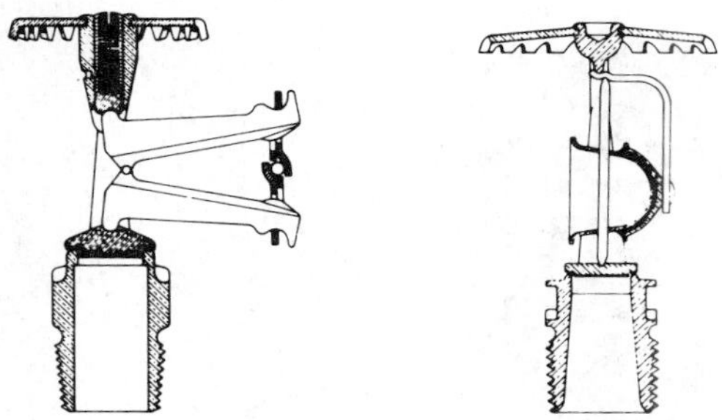

FIG. 5-12L. Typical sprinklers, showing a straight discharge orifice (ring style) at left and tapered-nozzle orifice at right.

The rate of water discharge from a sprinkler follows hydraulic laws and depends upon the size of the orifice or nozzle and on the water pressure. Approximate rates of discharge at different pressures may be obtained from the plotted curve or from the table given in Figure 5-12E.

Sprinklers discharging water through smaller or larger orifices are discussed later in this chapter. With similar forms of sprinkler nozzles and at the same water pressure, the discharge from these styles of sprinklers is approximately proportional to the nominal size of the orifice.

To obtain acceptance or approval of their sprinklers, manufacturers submit them to fire-testing organizations. After extensive tests and verification of the manufacturer's ability to manufacture the product properly, sprinklers found satisfactory are listed. Acceptance of a sprinkler by inspection departments or other regulatory agencies is based on such a listing.

Standard spray sprinklers are designed to be installed and operated in their proper position—that is, upright or pendent, as indicated by a stamping upon the deflector bearing the appropriate word or the letters "SSU" (spray sprinkler upright) or "SSP" (spray sprinkler pendent).

Recessed Sprinklers

A recessed sprinkler is a type of ceiling sprinkler in which part or most of the body of the sprinkler, other than the part that connects to the piping, is mounted in a recessed housing. Its operation is similar to that of a standard pendent sprinkler. (See Figure 5-12M.)

FIG. 5-12M. A Central Model H recessed sprinkler.

Flush-Type Sprinklers

A typical flush-style sprinkler is shown in Figure 5-12N. The special design of this type of ceiling sprinkler allows a minimum projection of the working parts of the sprinkler below the ceiling in which it is installed without adversely affecting the heat sensitivity or the pattern of water distribution.

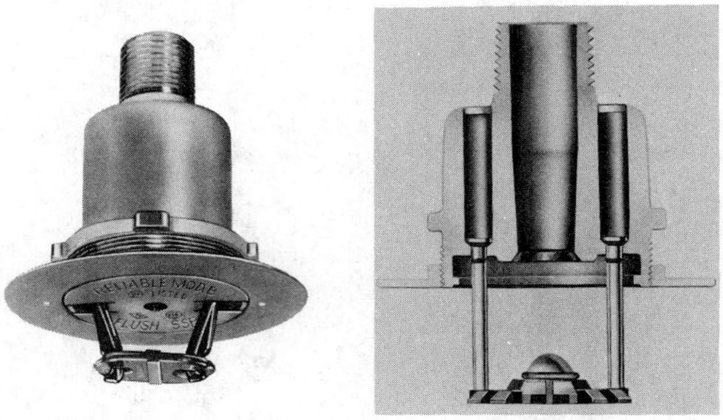

FIG. 5-12N. A flush-style ceiling sprinkler; the diagram at right shows the sprinkler after operation. This style of sprinkler is used where appearance is considered to be of prime importance. Shown is Reliable Model B.

In an effort to provide sprinkler protection in low-risk occupancies where aesthetics are important, sprinklers have been designed that attractively blend with the ceiling. Only the ceiling plate and thermosensitive assembly are visible from the floor when these sprinklers are installed. When a fire occurs and the thermosensitive element operates, the deflector drops to a position below the ceiling, and water discharge commences.

Concealed Sprinklers

A concealed sprinkler is a type of ceiling sprinkler whose entire body, including the operating mechanism, is above its concealing cover plate. When a fire occurs, the cover plate drops, exposing the thermosensitive assembly. The subsequent operation of the thermosensitive assembly initiates discharge. (See Figure 5-12O.)

Ornamental Sprinklers

Ornamental sprinklers are automatic sprinklers that have been decorated by attachments or by plating or enameling to give desired surface finishes. Ornamentation or special decorative design must not affect the operation or the water distribution unfavorably. Listed styles of ornamental sprinklers are for pendent installation in accordance with NFPA 13, *Installation of Sprinkler Systems*. (See Figure 5-12P.)

Dry Pendent and Dry Upright Sprinklers

Dry pendent and dry upright sprinklers are used to provide sprinkler protection in unheated areas, such as freezers, where individual sprinklers are supplied from a drop or riser pipe from a wet-pipe system outside the unheated area. To prevent damage to the system, the drop/riser must remain free of water. Dry pendent sprinklers may also be used in low areas of a dry-pipe system where water must not be allowed in the drop pipe supplying the sprinkler.

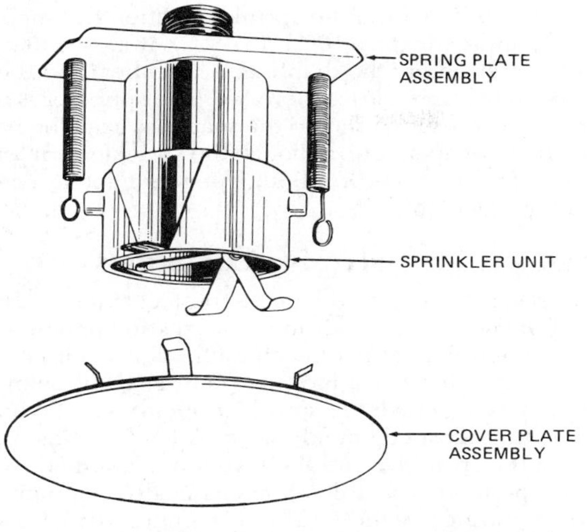

FIG. 5-12O. Concealed ceiling sprinkler. Cover plate drops away when heat is applied to bottom side of plate. (Stargard Model G.)

FIG. 5-12P. Prussag SFH glass-bulb-style decor sprinkler.

Sprinklers designated and listed by testing organizations as dry pendent or dry upright automatic sprinklers may be used. A seal is provided at the entrance of the dry sprinkler to prevent water from entering until the sprinkler fuses. The heat-sensitive operating mechanisms are adaptations of those used with automatic standard sprinklers. See Figure 5-12Q for an example of a dry pendent automatic sprinkler.

SPRINKLERS FOR SPECIAL SERVICE CONDITIONS

The sprinkler system using approved upright or pendent spray sprinklers is adaptable to a wide variety of conditions. However, there are situations for which special styles of sprinklers and special sprinkler arrangements are suited. In some cases, such as with sidewall sprinklers, special patterns of water distribution are necessary; in others, unusual temperatures or corrosive atmospheres call for special design or construction features.

Residential Sprinklers

Residential sprinklers are sprinklers that have been specifically listed for use in residential occupancies. These fast-response sprinklers have special low-mass fusible links or bulbs that make the time of temperature actuation much less than that of a sprinkler with a conventional fusible link.

Because of the life safety aspects of fast response, these sprinklers very often are used in residential occupancies where a conventional system installed according to the provisions of NFPA 13, *Installation of Sprinkler Systems*, might not be as practical. NFPA 13D, *Installation of Sprinkler Systems in One- and Two-Family Dwellings and Mobile Homes*, and NFPA 13R, *Installation of Sprinkler Systems in Residential Occupancies Up to Four Stories in Height*, have been developed specifically around the life-safety capabilities of the residential sprinkler. A representative residential sprinkler is shown in Figure 5-12R. (Residential sprinkler installations are discussed in detail in Section 5, Chapter 13, "Fast-Response Sprinkler Technology.")

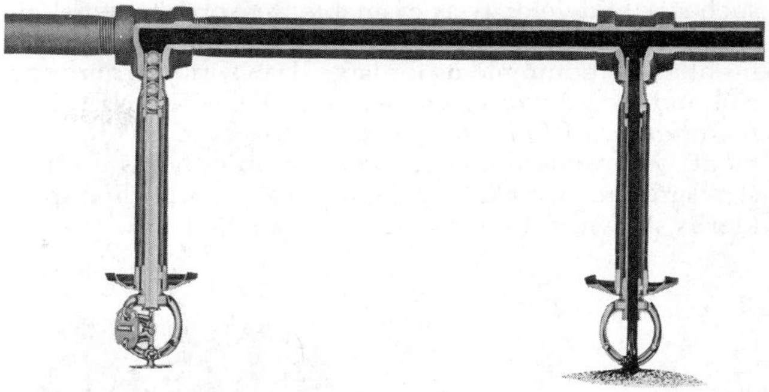

FIG. 5-12Q. Representative dry pendent automatic sprinkler. When the ambient temperature rises beyond the operating temperature of the soldered link, the solder melts and the link plates separate on roller key. Levers held in place by a deflector screw are released, and the fixed tension of the frame, acting as a spring, ejects the levers and link parts clear of the sprinkler. Since the inner tube, which also serves as a discharge orifice, is no longer held in place by the levers, it moves to a predetermined position. With the support of the inner tube eliminated, the elements forming the watertight seal at the piping inlet pass through the inner tube and away from the sprinkler, allowing water to flow through the unobstructed waterway and strike the deflector, which distributes it in a spray pattern comparable to that of a 1/2-in. (12.7 mm) standard sprinkler. Shown is Reliable's Model C Dry Pendent. Other manufacturers have similar arrangements of proprietary equipment for dry pendent automatic systems.

FIG. 5-12R. A representative residential sprinkler.

Large Drop Sprinklers

Large drop sprinklers are special sprinklers with a K factor between 11.0 and 11.5. [K factors for standard 1/2-in. (12.7 mm) sprinklers range from 5.3 to 5.8.] The deflector of a large drop sprinkler is specially designed and, combined with the greater discharge, produces large drops of such size and velocity as to enable the spray to penetrate strong updrafts generated by high-challenge fires. The installation requirements for large drop sprinklers are special and are covered in a separate chapter in NFPA 13, *Installation of Sprinkler Systems*, because the requirements supersede the density/area requirements used for standard spray sprinklers. A representative large drop sprinkler is shown in Figure 5-12S.

***FIG. 5-12S.** A representative large drop sprinkler.*

On/Off Sprinklers

An on/off sprinkler cycles on and off as needed. The model shown in Figure 5-12T operates as a normal fusible element sprinkler, but with a supplemental activation system based on a pilot valve principle. Under normal conditions, the pilot valve is held closed by the bimetallic snap disc. Water in the diaphragm chamber holds the diaphragm closed. When the snap disc is heated to the rated temperature, it opens the pilot valve and releases the water from the diaphragm chamber. This allows the diaphragm to open and water to flow from the sprinkler. When the snap disc cools to approximately 100°F (37.8°C), it closes the pilot valve. Water enters the diaphragm chamber, and the difference in pressure closes the valve. The sprinkler is ready for repeated operation should the snap disc again be heated to the rated temperature, although the sprinkler is intended to be replaced after a fire. Both a pendent and a recessed model are available.

Sprinklers for Corrosive Conditions

Measures have been developed to protect automatic sprinklers from corrosive conditions, and testing organizations have studied the value of each method. A complete covering of wax that has a melting point slightly below the temperature at which the sprinkler operates is the protective coating most commonly used. A lead coating for the body of the sprinkler and the levers in combination with wax for protecting fusible elements is also common. Traditional coatings include wax only (Figure 5-12U), asphalt only, lead only, wax over lead, and asphalt over lead. In recent years, sprinklers have been listed with enamel, polyester, and Teflon® coatings. Stainless steel sprinklers are available from some manufacturers. Other coatings are also available and should be selected on the basis of the expected environment.

Whatever the protective measures taken, they must not delay the operation of the sprinkler, nor interfere with the release of operating parts, nor significantly alter the pattern of water distribution.

Sidewall Sprinklers

Sidewall sprinklers have the components of standard sprinklers except for a special deflector which discharges most of the water toward one side in a pattern somewhat resem-

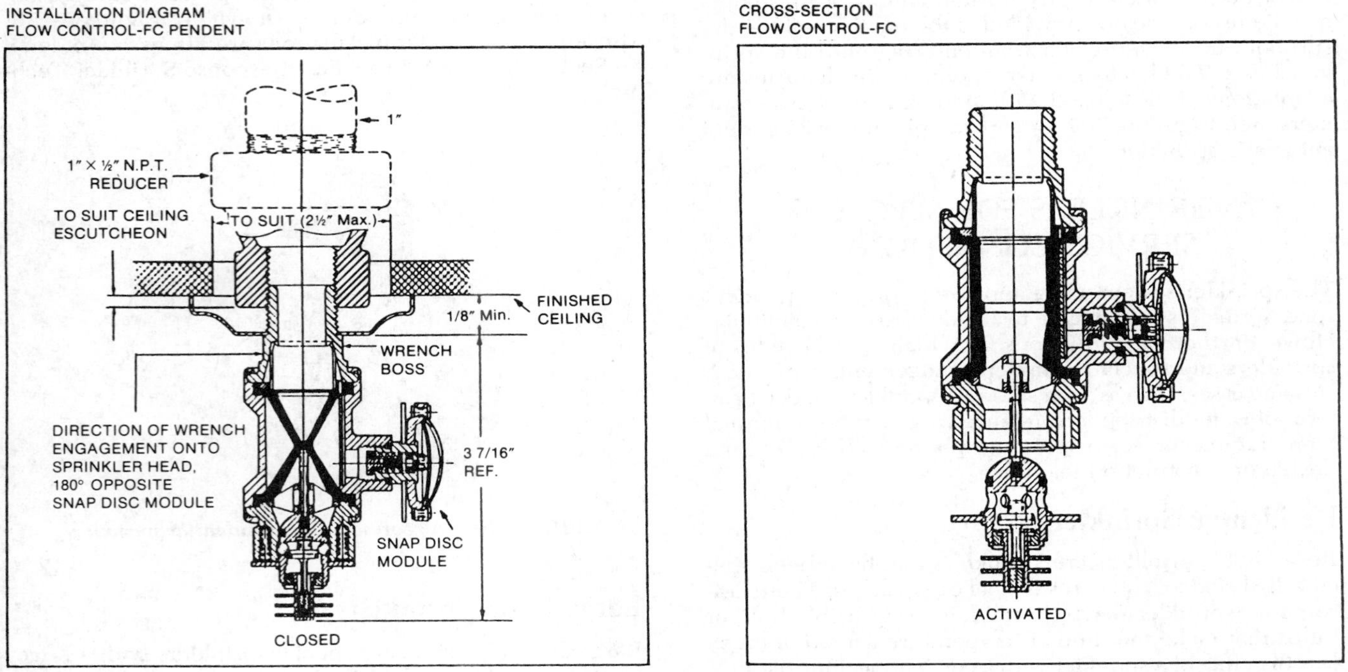

***FIG. 5-12T.** An on/off sprinkler showing its operating elements. In a fire, the melting of the fusible element opens the main waterway, and the bimetallic snap disc responds by opening the pilot valve, which relieves pressure from the diaphragm chamber. (Source: Central Sprinkler Corp.)*

FIG. 5-12U. A wax-coated upright sprinkler for corrosive atmospheres. (Source: "Automatic" Sprinkler Corporation of America)

bling one-quarter of a sphere. A small proportion of the discharge wets the wall behind the sprinkler. Located and mounted either vertically or horizontally along the junction between a ceiling and sidewall, sidewall sprinklers provide protection adequate for light-hazard occupancies, such as hotel lobbies, dining rooms, executive offices, and other areas where the usual sprinkler pipes would be objectionable in appearance. Some sidewall sprinklers have been tested and listed for use in ordinary-hazard occupancies.

The directional character of the discharge from sidewall sprinklers makes them applicable to occasional special protection problems. They may be installed to give discharge in any desired direction.

Figure 5-12V shows typical sidewall sprinklers. Selection has been made to show the different shapes of a variety of deflectors. Many vertically mounted sidewall sprinklers may be installed in either the pendent or upright position.

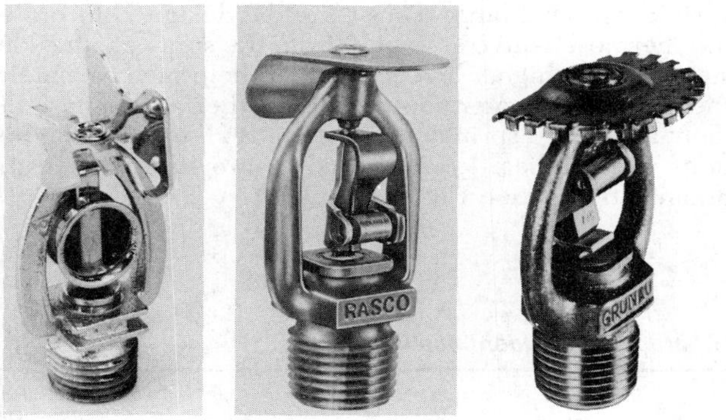

FIG. 5-12V. A representative selection of listed sidewall sprinklers showing various shapes of deflectors.

Extended coverage sidewall sprinklers: These are special sidewall sprinklers, used in the horizontal position, that have larger areas of coverage than those allowed for conventional sidewall sprinklers. They are used in light-hazard occupancies, particularly in hotels and similar occupancies where a sprinkler system can be installed in an existing building without having piping exposed in living areas, which could be objectionable aesthetically.

The water pressure required to obtain the greater coverage is specified in the listings for the sprinklers and is greater than that required for conventional sidewall sprinklers. Installation requirements are also a part of the listing.

An extended coverage sidewall sprinkler with a conventional link release is shown in Figure 5-12W.

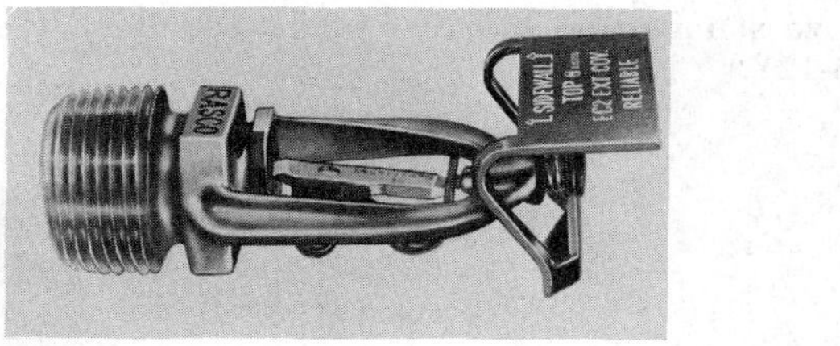

FIG. 5-12W. A representative extended coverage sidewall sprinkler.

Open Sprinklers

Automatic sprinklers from which the valve cap and heat-responsive elements have been omitted, are used in deluge sprinkler systems where the water supply is controlled by an automatic water control valve actuated independently of the automatic sprinklers. (See Figure 5-12X.) The water distribution pattern and the density of the discharge are designed to be appropriate for the hazard to be protected.

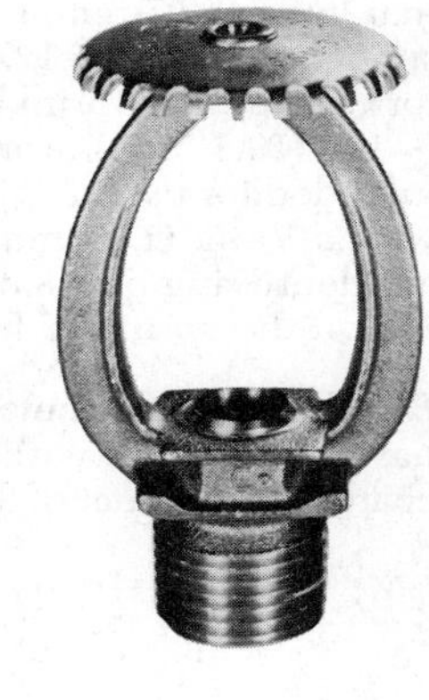

FIG. 5-12X. A standard upright sprinkler with its operating elements removed.

Small- and Large-Orifice Sprinklers

Automatic sprinklers having a water discharge rate greater or less than that of a standard ½-in. (12.7 mm) orifice sprinkler operating at the same pressure have characteristics desirable in protecting certain occupancies. High-discharge, large-orifice sprinklers operating at discharge densities of 0.45 gpm/sq ft [18 (L/min)/m^2] and greater provide a quantity discharge not available from standard nominal ½-in. (12.7 mm) orifice sprinklers. The pattern of the water discharge from small- and large-orifice sprinklers is similar to that of the standard ½-in. (12.7 mm) sprinkler.

Whenever sprinklers are replaced, care must be taken to replace them with the proper styles. Replacement of sprinklers with others of the correct orifice size is critical in hydraulically calculated systems.

Small-orifice automatic sprinklers: These sprinklers have been listed with orifices ranging from 1/4 through 7/16 in. (6.4 through 11.1 mm). Small-orifice sprinklers are identified by a pintle extending above the deflector and by the size stamped on the base of the sprinkler. (See Figure 5-12Y.)

FIG. 5-12Y. A small-orifice sprinkler in the pendent position. Note the pintle extending from deflector.

Large-orifice automatic sprinklers: These sprinklers have a discharge rate of 140 percent of that of the standard nominal 1/2-in. (12.7 mm) sprinkler operating at the same pressure. (See Figure 5-12Z.) Large-orifice sprinklers intended for use in new sprinkler installations are identified by a 3/4-in. (19.1 mm) iron pipe thread connection. Those intended for use in existing installations are manufactured with a 1/2-in. (12.7 mm) iron pipe thread connection and an identifying pintle on the deflector and with size marking on the sprinkler frame.

Extra-large-orifice automatic sprinklers: These sprinklers have been listed with a K factor of 11.0 to 11.5, and discharge 200 percent of the standard nominal 1/2-in. (12.7 mm) sprinkler operating at the same pressure. Manufactured with either a 1/2-in. (12.7 mm) or 3/4-in. (19.1 mm) iron pipe thread connection, they are identified with a pintle.

FIG. 5-12Z. A representative large-orifice sprinkler. (Source: Viking Corporation)

The discharge characteristics of various large- and small-orifice sprinklers are given in Table 5-12D.

Picker Trunk Sprinklers

Picker trunk automatic sprinklers (Figure 5-12AA) have a small, smooth deflector which aids in reducing collections of lint and fiber on the sprinklers when they are placed inside ducts or enclosures where moving air carries such foreign materials in suspension. Freedom from obstruction and a general breakup of the water stream are of more importance than any specific pattern of distribution.

Intermediate-Level Sprinklers

Intermediate-level sprinklers, also referred to as in-rack sprinklers, have large discs (shields) designed to protect the thermosensitive assembly from the spray of sprinklers suspended at higher levels. Without the protective shields, the impinging water could cool the thermosensitive element and retard sprinkler operation. Both upright and pendent intermediate-level sprinklers are listed by testing organizations. (See Figure 5-12BB.)

TABLE 5-12D. ***Sprinkler Discharge Characteristics Identification***

Nominal Orifice Size (in.)	Orifice Type	"K" Factor*	Percent of Nominal 1/2 in. Discharge	Thread Type	Pintle	Nominal Orifice Size Marked On Frame
1/4	Small	1.3–1.5	25	1/2 in. NPT	Yes	Yes
5/16	Small	1.8–2.0	33.3	1/2 in. NPT	Yes	Yes
3/8	Small	2.6–2.9	50	1/2 in. NPT	Yes	Yes
7/16	Small	4.0–4.4	75	1/2 in. NPT	Yes	Yes
1/2	Standard	5.3–5.8	100	1/2 in. NPT	No	No
17/32	Large	7.4–8.2	140	1/4 in. NPT	No	No
				or 1/2 in. NPT	Yes	Yes

For SI Units: $Qm = K_m P_M$, Where Q_m = Flow in L/min, P_m = Pressure in bars, and $K_m = 14\ K$

* K factor is the constant in the formula $Q = K P$, where Q equals flow in gpm and P equals pressure in psi.

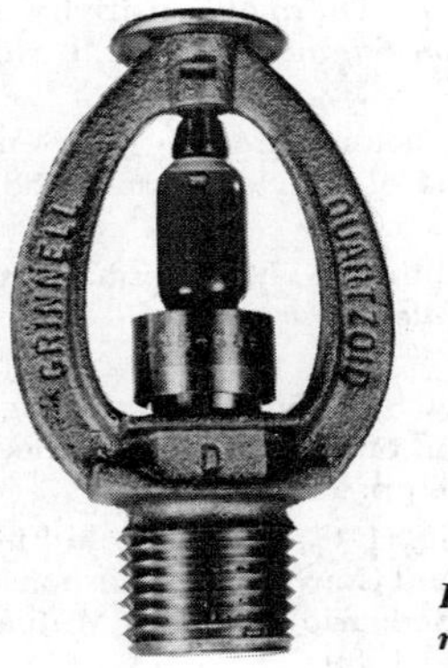

FIG. 5-12AA. A picker trunk automatic sprinkler. (Source: Grinnell)

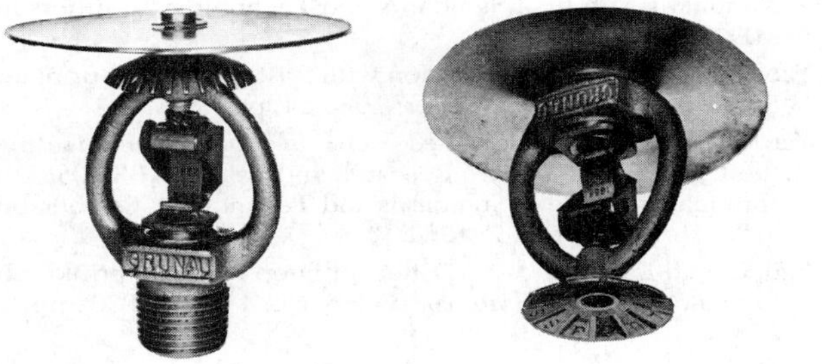

FIG. 5-12BB. Intermediate-level (rack storage) sprinklers showing integral shields that protect operating elements from the discharge of sprinklers installed at higher levels. (Star Model LD.)

BIBLIOGRAPHY

References Cited

1. Wendt, B., and Prahl, J. M., "Discharge Distribution Performance for an Axisymmetric Model of a Fire Sprinkler Head," *NBS-GCR-86-517*, Case Western Reserve University, sponsored by National Bureau of Standards, Gaithersburg, MD, Oct. 1986.
2. Thompson, N. J., *Fire Behavior and Sprinklers*, National Fire Protection Association, Quincy, MA, 1964.

NFPA Codes, Standards, and Recommended Practices

Reference to the following NFPA codes, standards, and recommended practices will provide further information on automatic sprinklers discussed in this chapter. (See the latest *NFPA Catalog* for availability of current editions of the following documents.)

NFPA 13, *Installation of Sprinkler Systems.*

NFPA 13A, *Inspection, Testing, and Maintenance of Sprinkler Systems.*

NFPA 13D, *Installation of Sprinkler Systems in One- and Two-Family Dwellings and Mobile Homes.*

NFPA 13R, *Installation of Sprinkler Systems in Residential Occupancies Up to Four Stories in Height.*

Additional Reading

"An Overview of Sprinkler Technology," *Fire Journal*, Vol. 83, No. 6 (Nov.-Dec. 1989), p. 48.

Beitel, J. J., "Quick-Response Sprinkler Tests, Group 2 Performance Tests," National Fire Protection Research Foundation, Quincy, MA, Dec. 1988.

Beyler, C. L., "Effect of Selected Variables on the Distribution of Water from Automatic Sprinklers," NBS-GCR-77-105, National Bureau of Standards, Washington, DC, June 1977.

Bill, R. G. and Kung, H. C., "Evaluation of an Extended Coverage Sidewall Sprinkler and Smoke Detector in a Hotel Occupancy," *Journal of Fire Protection Engineering*, Vol. 1, No. 3, 1989.

Bryan, J. L., "Automatic Sprinklers," *Automatic Sprinkler and Standpipe Systems*, 2nd ed., NFPA, Quincy, MA, 1990, pp. 193-269.

Budnick, E. K. and Fleming, R. P., "Developing an Early Suppression Design Procedure for Quick-Response Sprinklers," *Fire Journal*, Vol. 83, No. 6 (Nov.-Dec. 1989), p. 41.

Budnick, E. K. and Fleming, R. P., "How Quick-Response Sprinklers Perform and What It Means for Their Application," *Fire Journal*, Vol. 83, No. 5 (Sept.-Oct. 1989), p. 48.

Campbell, L. E., "A Study of Sprinkler Sensitivity," *Fire Technology*, Vol. 5, No. 2 (May 1969), pp. 93-99.

Carey, W. M.,"Report of the Quick-Response Sprinkler Project, Group 2 Performance Tests," National Fire Protection Research Foundation, Quincy, MA, March 1988.

Cooper, L. Y. and Stroup, D. W., "Test Results and Procedures for the Response of Near Ceiling Sprinkler Links in a Full-Scale Compartment Fire," *NBSIR 87-3633*, National Bureau of Standards, Gaithersburg, MD, Sept. 1987.

Cote, A. E., "QRS: Do You Understand the Technology?," *Fire Journal*, Vol. 81, No. 1 (Jan. 1987), p. 27.

Evans, D. D. and Madrzykowski, D., "Characterizing the Thermal Response of Fusible-Link Sprinklers," *NBSIR 81-2329*, National Bureau of Standards, Washington, DC, Aug. 1981.

Evans, D. D., "Calculating Sprinkler Actuation Time in Compartments," National Bureau of Standards, Washington, DC, 1984.

Evans, D. D., "Calculating Sprinkler Actuation Times in Compartments," *Fire Safety Journal*, Vol. 9, No. 2, 1985, pp. 147-156.

Evans, D. D., Walton, W. D., and McCaffrey, B., "Progress in Modeling Sprinkler Performance," *9th Joint Panel Meeting* of the UJNR Panel on Fire Research and Safety, NBSIR 88-3753, National Institute of Standards and Technology, Gaithersburg, MD, Apr. 1988, pp. 325-335.

Factory Mutual Approval Guide, Factory Mutual Research Corporation, Norwood, MA, (published annually).

"Final Report on Development of a Nitinol-Actuated Fire Sprinkler," Battelle Columbus Laboratories, Columbus, OH, Sept. 15, 1982.

"Fire Protection—Automatic Sprinkler Systems—Part I: Requirements and Test Methods for Sprinklers," *DIS 6182/1*, International Standards Organization, Geneva, Switzerland, 1984.

Fire Protection Equipment List, Underwriters Laboratories Inc., Northbrook, IL (published annually).

Fleming, R. P., "Quick-Response Sprinklers: A Technical Analysis," National Fire Protection Research Foundation, Quincy, MA, Apr. 1985.

Goodfellow, D. G., "Apparatus and Procedure for Measuring the Actual Delivered Density (ADD) of Sprinklers in Simulated Rack Storage Fires," Factory Mutual Research Foundation, Norwood, MA, Jan. 1985.

Groos, R. T., "Large-Drop Sprinklers: High Challenge," *Plumbing Engineer*, Vol. 13, No. 2 (Mar./Apr. 1985), pp. 32-36.

Guenther, P., "Sprinklers—A German Viewpoint," *Fire Prevention*, No. 200 (June 1987), pp. 23-24.

Hammerman, D. M., "Project Home—A Pilot Program for a Low-Cost Residential Sprinkler System," *Fire Journal*, Vol. 75, No. 2 (Mar. 1981), pp. 66-69.

Hayes, W. D., and Zile, R. H., "Full-Scale Study of the Effect of Pendent and Sidewall Location on the Activation Time of an Automatic Sprinkler," *NBSIR 82-2521*, National Bureau of Standards, Gaithersburg, MD, July 1982.

Heskestad, G. and Bill, R. G., "Quantification of Thermal Responsiveness of Automatic Sprinklers Including Conduction Effects," *Fire Safety Journal*, Vol. 14, Nos. 1&2 (July 1988), pp. 113-125.

Hestestad, G. and Smith, H. F., "Investigation of a New Sprinkler Sensitivity Approval Test: The Plunge Test," *FMRC Technical Report 22485*, Factory Mutual Research Corp., Norwood, MA, Dec. 1976.

Heskestad, G., "The Sprinkler Response Time Index (RTI)," presented at the Technical Conference on Residential Sprinkler Systems, Factory Mutual Research Corp., Norwood, MA, April 1981.

Kirson, D., "Automatic Sprinklers in Exhaust Systems," *Heating, Piping and Air Conditioning*, Vol. 61, No. 1 (Jan. 1989), pp. 163-166.

Labes, W. G., "Evaluation of Fire Protection Spray Devices: The State of the Art," *NBS-GCR-76-72*, National Bureau of Standards, Washington, DC, June 1976.

Lougheed, G. D. and Richardson, J. K., "Sprinklers in Combustible Concealed Spaces," *Journal of Fire Protection Engineering*, Vol. 1, No. 2, 1989, pp. 49-62.

Merdinyan, P. H., "A Fully Approved On-Off Sprinkler," *Fire Journal*, Vol. 67, No. 1 (Jan. 1973), p. 10.

Pepi, J. S., "Design Charecteristics of Quick-Response Sprinklers," *TR 86-3, 1986*, Society of Fire Protection Engineers, Boston, MA.

Soloman, R. E., ed., *Automatic Sprinkler Handbook*, 4th ed., National Fire Protection Association, Quincy, MA, 1989.

Standard for Automatic Sprinklers for Fire Protection Service, 8th ed., Underwriters Laboratories Inc., Northbrook, IL, 1990.

Suchomel, M. R., "Factors Influencing the Use of High-Temperature Sprinklers," *Fire Technology*, Vol. 1, No. 1 (Feb. 1965), pp. 15-22.

Suchomel, M. R. and Castino, G. T., "Sprinkler Performance Tests—The Extended Coverage Panacea," *Fire Technology*, Vol. 16, No. 2 (May 1980), pp. 85-93.

Theobald, C. R., "FRS Ramp Test for the Thermal Sensitivity of Sprinklers," *Journal of Fire Protection Engineering*, Vol. 1, No. 1, 1989, pp. 23-34.

Theobald, C. R. and Westley, S. A., "Factors Affecting the Sensitivity of Sprinklers," *Fire Surveyors*, Vol. 17, No. 3 (June 1988), pp. 5-11.

Thorne, P. F., Theobald, C. R., and Melinek, S. J., "Thermal Performance of Sprinkler Heads," *Fire Safety Journal*, Vol. 14, Nos. 1&2 (July 1988), pp. 89-99.

Unoki, J., "Fire Extinguishing Time by Sprinkler," *Proceedings* of the First International Symposium on Fire Safety Science, Hemisphere, Washington DC, 1986, pp. 1187-1196.

Vincent, B. G., Stavrianidis, P., and Kung, H. C., "Large-Scale Fire Testing of Fast Response Sprinklers and Conventional Response Sprinklers in a Fire-Control-Mode Scenario," Factory Mutual Research Corp., Norwood, MA, June 1989.

Walton, W. D. and Budnick, E. K., "Quick-Response Sprinklers in Office Configurations: Fire Test Results," *NBSIR 88-3695*, National Institute of Standards and Technology, Gaithersburg, MD, 1988.

Yao, C., "Early Fire Suppression with Fast-Response Sprinklers," *Sprinkler Quarterly*, Winter, 1983-84, pp. 19-23.

Yao, C., "FMRC Sprinkler Research," *9th Joint Panel Meeting* of the UJNR Panel on Fire Research and Safety, *NBSIR 88-3753*, National Institute of Standards and Technology, Gaithersburg, MD, Apr. 1988, pp. 314-324.

Yao, C. and Kalelkar, A. S., "Effect of Drop Size on Sprinkler Performance," *Fire Technology*, Vol. 6, No. 4 (Nov. 1970), pp. 254-268.

FAST RESPONSE SPRINKLER TECHNOLOGY

Arthur E. Cote and Russell P. Fleming

The ability to evaluate and control sprinkler sensitivity was the single most significant development in sprinkler technology in the 1980s. This ability has led to the development of new fast response sprinkler technology that holds the promise of improved fire protection for both life and property.

This chapter covers the development of residential and other fast response sprinklers, first for the residential environment and later for other applications. It also discusses the specific types of fast response sprinklers currently available and some of the incentives that have been considered to encourage the widespread use of residential sprinklers.

General information on fire sprinklers can be found in Section 5, Chapter 9, "Automatic Sprinkler Systems," and Section 5, Chapter 12, "Automatic Sprinklers." A discussion of the theory of fire sprinkler performance is in Section 5, Chapter 10, "Theory of Automatic Sprinkler Performance."

MEASURING SPRINKLER SENSITIVITY

Much of the original work in the area of measuring sprinkler sensitivity was done at Factory Mutual Research Corporation (FMRC) under the sponsorship of the United States Fire Administration (USFA) during the development of the residential sprinkler. Important contributing research was also performed at the British Fire Research Station and the National Institute of Standards and Technology (NIST).[1,2]

The decade of progress in this area climaxed late in 1990, when tentative agreement was reached within the working group on sprinkler and water spray equipment of the International Standards Organization (ISO) for a standardized approach to sprinkler sensitivity requirements and testing. The agreement, which is expected to be processed as an amendment to Draft International Standard 6182/1, "Requirements and Methods of Tests for Sprinklers," uses a combination of sprinkler test procedures developed by laboratories in the United States and Europe and establishes the three ranges of sprinkler sensitivity characteristics shown in Figure 5-13A.

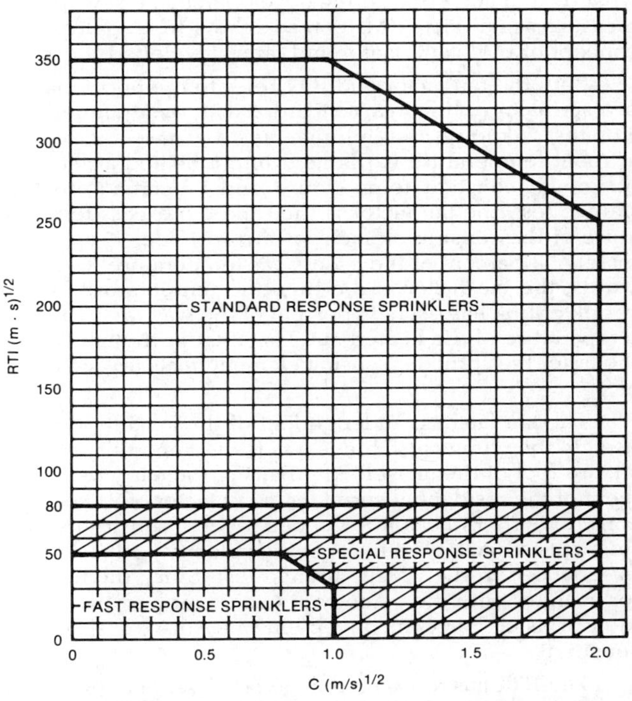

5-13A. Tentative international sprinkler sensitivity ranges, RTI vs conductivity.

These ranges of sensitivity are based both on the response time index (RTI) of the device and on its conductivity (C). RTI is a measure of pure thermal sensitivity, which indicates how fast the sprinkler can absorb heat from its surroundings sufficient to cause activation. The conductivity factor is important in measuring how much of the heat

Arthur E. Cote, P.E., is assistant vice president and chief engineer of the NFPA. Russell P. Fleming, P.E., is vice president of engineering of the National Fire Sprinkler Association.

picked up from the surrounding air will be lost to the sprinkler fittings and waterway.

Figure 5-13A shows three broad ranges of sprinkler sensitivity: standard, special, and fast response. Traditional sprinkler hardware falls into the standard-response category. The fast response category is being used for new types of sprinklers for which fast response is considered important. The special-response category is being used in some countries for special types of sprinkler that may be installed in conformance with appropriate national installation standards. In the United States, this includes some of the extended coverage sprinklers that are listed as special sprinklers.

Sprinkler response time as a function of the temperature rating of the operating element is well understood, - that is, a 165°F (74°C) rated sprinkler would operate when its temperature reaches 165°F (74°C), plus or minus a few degrees. Because of the "thermal lag" of the link or bulb mass, however, the air temperature may be as high as 1000°F (538°C) before the element operates. The smaller mass of the operating element of a fast response sprinkler permits it to follow a temperature rise in the surrounding air more rapidly, resulting in faster operation.The actual sensitivity requirements of the first fast-response sprinklers, intended as residential sprinklers, were arrived at somewhat by trial and error during developmental test work. To measure sensitivity, FMRC researchers first applied the concept of the "tau" factor and later developed the RTI.

Both the tau factor and RTI refer to the performance of a sprinkler or link in a standardized air oven tunnel test. The test is known as a "plunge" test because a sprinkler at room temperature is plunged into a heated air stream of known constant temperature and velocity.[3,4] In the plunge test, the tau factor is the time the excess temperature of the sensing element of the sprinkler is approximately 63 percent of the excess gas temperature. In other words, the tau factor is the time the temperature of the sprinkler link has risen 63 percent of the way to the higher temperature of the heated air. The smaller the tau factor, the faster the sprinkler sensing element heats up and operates.

The tau factor is independent of the air temperature used in the plunge test, but is inversely proportional to the square root of the air velocity. During the early development of the residential sprinkler, a tau factor of 21 sec was considered to indicate the needed level of sensitivity, but this was associated with a specific velocity - 5 ft/sec (1.52 m/sec) used in the FMRC plunge test. Since the tau factor changes with the velocity of heated air past the sprinkler, it is a fairly inconvenient measure of sprinkler sensitivity.

The RTI has replaced the tau factor as the measure of sensitivity and is determined simply by multiplying the tau factor by the square root of the air velocity at which it is found. The RTI is therefore practically independent of both air temperature and air velocity. Comparisons of RTI give a good indication of relative sprinkler sensitivity.

The smaller the RTI, the faster the sprinkler operation. Standard response sprinklers have RTIs in the range of 225 to 700 $sec^{1/2}ft^{1/2}$ (100 to 400 $sec^{1/2}m^{1/2}$), while the RTI range for residential sprinklers is about 50 to 90 $sec^{1/2}ft^{1/2}$ (28 to 50 $sec^{1/2}m^{1/2}$).

The need to add a conductivity term to the model of sprinkler response was recognized in 1986.[5,6] This term accounts for the loss of heat from the sprinkler operating element to the sprinkler frame, its mounting, and even the water in the pipe. These losses can become significant under low-velocity conditions, particularly for some of the flush-type sprinkler designs with little insulation between the operating element and the sprinkler body.

HISTORICAL DEVELOPMENT

Sensitivity was recognized as a key attribute of automatic sprinklers almost from the start. An evaluation of "sensitiveness" was included among the first comprehensive tests ever performed by C.J.H. Woodbury of the Factory Mutual Fire Insurance Companies in 1884. Many of the refinements to the automatic sprinkler during its first century of use were made with thermal sensitivity in mind.

Yet the standard sprinkler of the 1970s was really little changed from its ancestors. Except for the introduction of the spray sprinkler in the early 1950s to improve the sprinkler discharge pattern, sprinkler design, including the sensitivity of release mechanisms, remained about the same. Sprinklers were essentially devices intended to protect property, although their effectiveness in providing life safety from fires was outstanding.

Development of NFPA 13D

In 1973, in response to recommendations in the Presidential Commission report, "America Burning," the NFPA Committee on Automatic Sprinklers appointed a Subcommittee on Residential and Light-Hazard Occupancies to prepare a residential sprinkler standard. In 1975, the first edition of NFPA 13D, *Installation of Sprinkler Systems in One- and Two-Family Dwellings and Mobile Homes*, was published, based on expert judgment and the best information available at that time.

The purpose of the standard was "to provide a sprinkler system that will aid in the detection and control of dwelling fires and thus provide improved protection against injury, life loss, and property damage." The standard required the use of an NFPA 13, *Installation of Sprinkler Systems*, light-hazard water application density of 0.10 gpm/ft^2 [4 L/min)/m^2], but it permitted other concessions. The water supply could be based on the area of the largest room or 25 gpm (95 L/min), whichever was less; the total water supply required was to be only 250 gal (946 L); and sprinkler spacing of 256 sq ft (23.7 m^2) was permitted, even though NFPA 13 allowed only 225 sq ft (20.9 m^2). Further, 13D, *Installation of Sprinkler Systems in One- and Two-Family Dwellings and Mobile Homes*, permitted sprinklers to be omitted from certain areas where the incidence of life loss from fires was shown statistically to be low. NFPA 13 had always required complete sprinkler protection in order to safeguard property properly. In departing from this ideal, the 1975 edition of NFPA 13D became the first attempt at a "life safety" sprinkler standard. In spite of these concessions, actual installations based on this standard were rare, primarily due to cost.

Residential Sprinkler Research

Beginning in 1976, the National Fire Prevention and Control Administration (NFPCA), which was later renamed the U.S. Fire Administration (USFA), acted on its mandate to reduce the nation's fire losses and funded research programs focusing on the residential fire problem in general and residential sprinkler protection in particular. The NFPCA/USFA programs included studies to assess the impact sprinklers would have on reducing deaths and injuries in residential fires.[7] Other studies evaluated the design, installation, practical usage, and water acceptance factors that would have an impact on achieving reliable and acceptable systems[8]; the minimum water discharge rates and automatic sprinkler flow required, and response sensitivity and design criteria[9,10,11]; and full-scale tests of prototype residential sprinkler systems.[12,13,14,15,16]

The research showed that a more sensitive sprinkler was needed to respond faster to both smoldering and fast-developing residential fires for two reasons. First, fires had to be controlled quickly in order to prevent the development of lethal conditions in small residential compartments. In addition, fires had to be attacked while still small if they were to be controlled with the water supplies typically available in residences, - 20 to 30 gpm (76 to 114 L/min) - and if low costs were to be achieved.

Full-scale tests conducted by FMRC resulted in the development of a prototype fast response sprinkler that could control or suppress typical residential fires with the operation of not more than two sprinklers. It could also operate fast enough to maintain survivable conditions within the room of fire origin.[12] Survivable conditions were established as follows:

1. Maximum gas temperature at eye level of 200°F (93°C).
2. Maximum ceiling surface temperature of 500°F (260°C).
3. Maximum carbon monoxide concentration of 1,500 parts per million.

Thus, the sprinkler concept expanded from the traditional role of property protection to include life safety. Full-scale field tests were then conducted in Los Angeles to establish system design parameters using the new prototype fast response "residential sprinkler."[13,14,15,16]

The data from these tests were studied by the National Fire Protection Association Technical Committee on Automatic Sprinklers and used to establish the criteria for the 1980 edition of NFPA 13D, *Installation of Sprinkler Systems in One- and Two-Family Dwellings and Mobile Homes*.

Revised NFPA 13D Design Requirements

The design criteria in the 1980 edition of NFPA 13D, *Installation of Sprinkler Systems in One- and Two-Family Dwellings and Mobile Homes*, included for the first time the requirement that all sprinklers be "listed residential sprinklers." Figure 5-13B shows the first two listed residential sprinklers.

Other initial basic design requirements in the revamped NFPA 13D, *Installation of Sprinkler Systems in One- and Two-Family Dwellings and Mobile Homes*, were as follows:

Performance criteria: To prevent flashover in the room of fire origin, when sprinklered, and to improve the chance for occupants to escape or be evacuated.

Design criteria:

1. Only listed residential sprinklers to be used.
2. Minimum 18 gpm (68 L/min) to any single operating sprinkler and 13 gpm (49 L/min) to all operating sprinklers in the design area up to a maximum of two sprinklers.
3. Maximum area protected by a single sprinkler of 144 sq ft (13.4 m^2).

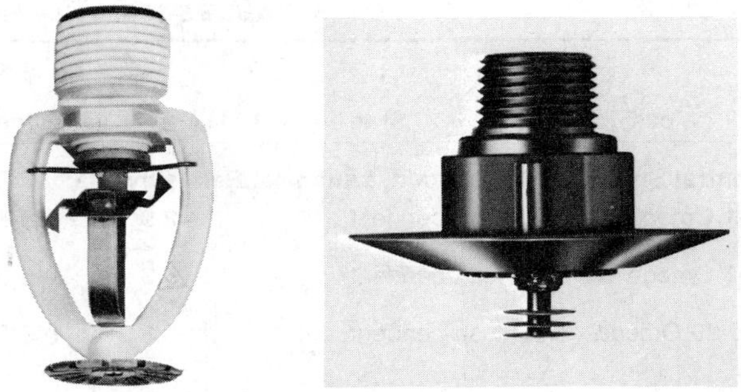

FIG. 5-13B. The first two listed residential "quick response" sprinklers. Shown are the Grinnell Model F954 (left) and Central "Omega" Model R-1 (right) pendent sprinklers.-

4. Maximum distance between sprinklers of 12 ft (3.7 m).
5. Minimum distance between sprinklers of 8 ft (2.4 m).
6. Maximum distance from a sprinkler to a wall or partition of 6 ft (1.8 m).

Application rates, design areas, areas of coverage, and minimum design pressures other than those specified above were permitted to be used with special sprinklers listed for such special residential installation conditions.

Sprinkler coverage: Sprinklers to be installed in all areas with the following exceptions.

Exception No. 1: Sprinklers allowed to be omitted from bathrooms no larger than 55 sq ft (5.1 m^2).

Exception No. 2: Sprinklers allowed to be omitted from closets where the least dimension does not exceed 3 ft (0.9 m), the area does not exceed 24 sq ft (2.2 m^2), and the walls and ceiling are surfaced with noncombustible materials.

Exception No. 3: Sprinklers allowed to be omitted from open-attached porches, garages, carports, and similar structures.

Exception No. 4: Sprinklers allowed to be omitted from attics and crawl spaces that are not used or intended for living purposes or storage.

Exception No. 5: Sprinklers allowed to be omitted from entrance foyers that are not the only means of egress.

TYPES OF FAST RESPONSE SPRINKLERS

Today, fast response sprinkler technology has been incorporated into several different types of sprinklers, each with unique attributes and applications.

Residential Sprinklers

In the ten years following the development of the residential sprinkler, the special listings proliferated, to the point where the original sprinkler flow and spacing criteria have almost become obsolete. Residential sprinklers are now listed for coverage areas up to 400 sq ft (37.2 m^2) per sprinkler. Table 5-13A contains a 1990 compilation of residential sprinklers listed by Underwriters Laboratories Inc. (UL), along with their pressure and flow requirements.

TABLE 5-13A. ***UL-Listed Residential Sprinklers (1990)***

Model	Style	K	Temperature	Maximum Spacing	1-spr Flow (gpm)	Pres (psi)	Multiple Sprinkler Flow	Pres (psi)
Central Sprinkler Corporation, Lansdale, Pennsylvania:								
R-1 Omega	Flush pendent	3.9	145 & 160	14x14	18	(21.9)	13	(11.4)
				16x16	24	(38.9)	17	(19.5)
C-1 Omega	Flush pendent	5.3	145 & 160	12x12	25	(22.2)	18	(11.5)
				14x14	30	(31.9)	21	(15.6)
EC-20 Omega	Flush pendent	5.3	145 & 160	14x14	23	(18.8)	16	(9.1)
				16x16	25	(22.2)	18	(11.5)
				18x18	32	(36.3)	22.5	(17.9)
EC-20A	Flush pendent or Recessed pendent	4.1	160	14x14	21	(26.2)	15	(13.4)
EC-20A Omega	Flush pendent	5.6	160	14x14	25	(19.9)	18	(10.3)
				16x16	30	(28.7)	21	(14.1)
				18x18	32	(32.7)	29	(26.8)
C1A	Flush pendent	5.6	160	12x12	25	(19.9)	20	(12.8)
				14x14	30	(28.9)	26	(21.6)
GB-R	Recessed pendent	4.3	155	14x14	17	(15.6)	13	(9.1)
				16x16	18	(17.5)	13	(9.1)
GB-R1	Pendent or Recessed pendent	5.3	155	14x14	24	(20.5)	17	(10.3)
				16x16	30	(32.0)	21	(15.7)
GB-R	Horizontal sidewall	5.3	155	14Wx16L	30	(32.0)	21	(15.7)
	Recessed horizontal sidewall	5.3	155	14x14	27	(26.0)	19	(12.9)
HEC-12	Flush horizontal side-wall	5.6	160	12x12	27	(23.6)	19	(11.7)
			145 & 160	14x14	30	(29.1)	21	(14.3)
Firematic, Shrewsbury, Massachusetts:								
A	Pendent or Recessed pendent	5.7	135 & 155	14x14	24	(17.7)	17	(8.9)
A	Horizontal sidewall	5.7	155	14x14	25	(19.2)	20	(12.3)
A	Recessed horizontal sidewall	5.7	155	14x14	26	(20.8)	20	(12.3)
Grinnell Corporation, Exeter, New Hampshire:								
F954	Pendent	2.8	165	12x12	18	(41.3)	13	(21.6)
F958	Horizontal sidewall	4.2	165	16Wx14L	24	(32.7)	17	(16.4)
FR-1	Horizontal sidewall	5.6	140 & 165	16Wx20L	40	(51.0)	37	(43.7)
		8.0	140 & 165	16Wx20L	50	(39.1)	45	(31.6)
F991 Aquarius	Flush pendent	4.2	160	14x14	18	(18.4)	13	(9.6)
				16x16	22	(27.4)	16	(14.5)
F992 Aquarius	Flush pendent	5.6	160	14x14	20	(12.8)	17	(9.2)
				16x16	22	(15.4)	19	(11.5)
				18x18	31	(30.6)	24	(18.4)
F993 Aquarius	Flush horizontal side-wall	5.55	160	14x14	30	(29.2)	21	(14.3)
Reliable Automatic Sprinkler Co., Mt. Vernon, New York:								
A	Pendent	4.2	165	14x14	18	(18.8)	13	(9.38)
				16x16	25	(36.3)	18	(18.8)
		5.5	165	12x12	21	(14.6)	15	(7.4)
				14x14	24	(19.0)	17	(9.6)
A	Recessed pendent	4.2	165	14x14	19	(21.0)	13.5	(10.6)
				16x16	25	(36.3)	18	(18.8)
		5.5	165	12x12	21	(14.6)	15	(7.4)
				14x14	24	(19.0)	17	(9.6)
A	Horizontal sidewall or Recessed horizontal sidewall	4.1	165	12x12	21	(25.6)	15	(13.1)
				14x14	25	(36.3)	18	(18.8)
ZX	Flush pendent	4.1	165	14x14	18	(19.3)	13	(10.1)
				16x16	24	(34.3)	17	(17.2)
		5.4	165	14x14	26	(23.2)	18	(11.1)
				16x16	30	(30.9)	21	(15.1)
				18x18	32.5	(36.2)	23	(18.1)
ZX	Horizontal sidewall	5.4	165	14x14	24	(19.0)	17	(9.6)
F1/Res	Pendent	5.6	135 & 155	14x14	20	(12.8)	14	(6.3)
				16x16	20	(12.8)	20	(12.8)
				18x18	28	(25.0)	22	(15.4)
F1/Res/F2	Recessed pendent	5.6	135 & 155	14x14	20	(12.8)	14	(6.3)
				16x16	20	(12.8)	20	(12.8)

TABLE 5-13A. *UL-Listed Residential Sprinklers (1990) (Continued)*

Model	Style	K	Temperature	Maximum Spacing	1-spr Flow (gpm)	Pres (psi)	Multiple Sprinkler Flow	Pres (psi)
F1/Res	Horizontal sidewall	5.6	135	14x14	27	(23.3)	19	(11.5)
			135	14x14	25	(19.9)	18	(10.3)
			135 & 155	16x16	30	(28.7)	21	(14.1)
				16Wx18L	34	(36.9)	24	(18.4)
				16Wx20L	37	(43.7)	26	(21.6)
F1/Res/F2	Recessed horizontal sidewall	5.6	135 & 155	14x14	28	(25.0)	20	(12.8)
Star Sprinkler Corporation, Milwaukee, Wisconsin								
LD-2	Pendent or Recessed pendent	4.5	165	14x14	18	(16.0)	13	(8.3)
				16x16	25	(30.9)	18	(16.0)
LD-2	Horizontal sidewall or Recessed horizontal sidewall	4.5	165	14x14	21	(21.8)	15	(11.2)
				16x16	25	(30.9)	18	(16.0)
		4.8	165	16Wx20L	38	(62.7)	27	(31.6)
Viking Corporation, Hastings, Michigan:								
M	Pendent or Recessed pendent	4.2	155	14x14	18	(18.4)	13	(9.6)
				16x16	24	(32.7)	17	(16.4)
M-2	Pendent or Recessed pendent	5.5	155	12x12	23	(17.5)	16	(8.5)
				14x14	24	(19.0)	17	(9.6)
M	Horizontal sidewall	5.5	155	14x14	25	(21.0)	18	(10.7)
H	Flush pendent	4.2	165	16x16	17	(16.4)	12	(8.2)
				18x18	20	(22.7)	14	(11.1)
				20x20	29	(47.7)	21	(25.0)
		5.5	165	12x12	18	(10.7)	13	(5.6)
				16x16	22	(16.0)	16	(8.5)
				18x18	22	(16.0)	18	(10.7)
				20x20	30	(29.8)	21	(14.6)
A-1	Concealed pendent	4.2	155	14x14	18	(18.4)	13	(9.6)
		5.5	155	14x14	24	(19.0)	17	(9.6)

It is important to recognize that, in addition to their fast response characteristics, residential sprinklers have a special water distribution pattern.[12] Because the effective control of residential fires often depends on a single sprinkler in the room of fire origin, the distribution of residential sprinklers is required to be more uniform than that of standard spray sprinklers, which in large areas can rely upon the overlapping patterns of several sprinklers to make up for voids. Additionally, residential sprinklers are required to protect sofas, drapes, and similar furnishings at the periphery of the room. In their discharge patterns, therefore, the sprinklers must not only be capable of throwing water to the walls of their assigned areas, but high enough up on the walls to prevent the fire from getting "above" the sprinklers. The water delivered close to the ceiling not only protects the portion of the wall close to the ceiling, but also enhances the capacity of the spray to cool gases at the ceiling level, thus reducing the likelihood of excessive sprinkler openings.[12]

Because of their differences, residential sprinklers are not listed by product evaluation organizations under the same product standards as standard sprinklers. Underwriters Laboratories Inc., for example, has developed UL 1626 for residential sprinklers, and FMRC has published its Approval Standard FM 2030 for residential sprinklers. Both of these standards include a plunge test with specific sensitivity requirements and a distribution test that checks the spray pattern in the vertical plane, as well as the horizontal plane. The product standards for standard spray sprinklers contain neither test.

Both UL 1626 and FM 2030 also include a fire test that is intended to simulate a residential fire in the corner of a room containing combustible materials representative of a living room environment. The fire test arrangements for UL 1626 are shown in Figure 5-13C.

The UL 1626 test procedure contains a time-temperature curve that is reproducible in actual tests. The curve parallels the time-temperature relationship developed during the tests of the prototype residential sprinkler in Los Angeles that was part of the on-going residential sprinkler research effort.[13,15,16]

In summary, to meet the UL 1626 test criteria, residential sprinklers, installed in a fire test enclosure with an 8-ft (2.4 m) ceiling are required to control a fire for 10 min with the following limits:

1. The maximum gas or air temperature adjacent to the sprinkler—3 in. (76.2 mm) below the ceiling and 8 in. (203 mm) horizontally away from the sprinkler—must not exceed 600°F (316°C).
2. The maximum temperature—5 ft, 3 in. (1.6 m) above the floor and half the room length away from each wall— must be less than 200°F (93°C) during the entire test. This temperature must not exceed 130°F (54°C) for more than a 2-min period.
3. The maximum temperature 1/4 in. (6.3 mm) behind the finished surface of the ceiling material directly above the test fire must not exceed 500°F (260°C).
4. No more than two residential sprinklers in a test area can operate.

The test enclosure is twice the size of the proposed maximum spacing of the residential sprinkler. In a typical test, the walls of one corner of the test enclosure are covered with combustible cellulosic acoustical panels 1/8 in. (3.2 mm) thick . Two combustible structures with urethane foam, representing stuffed furniture, are positioned

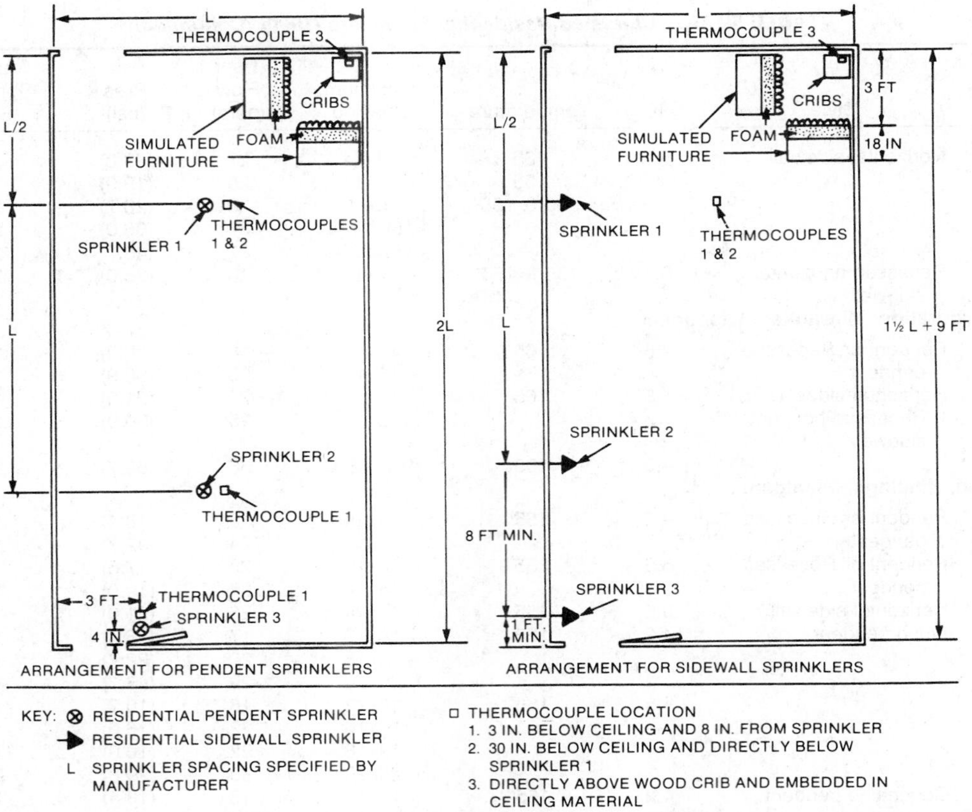

FIG. 5-13C. Fire test arrangements for UL 1626 for pendent sprinklers (left) and sidewall sprinklers (right). The simulated furniture consists of 3 in. (76 mm) thick uncovered urethane foam cushions 30 in. (762 mm) high by 30 in. (762 mm) wide. The foam has a density of 1.25 lbs/ft^3 (6.1 kg/m^3) and is attached to a wood frame. The walls of the test room are covered with 4 by 8 ft by 1/8 in. (1.2 × 2.4 m × 3.2 mm) decorative plywood paneling (flame spread rating 200) attached to wood furring strips. The fire source consists of 12 by 12 by 12 in. (0.3 × 0.3 × 0.3 m) wood cribs weighing 12 to 13 lbs (5.4 to 5.9 kg). The ceiling of the test room is 8 ft (2.4 m) high and covered with 2 × 4 ft × 1/2 in. (6.1 × 1.2 m × 12.7 mm) thick acousticalpanels attached to wood furring strips.

at the same corner. (See Figure 5-13C.) The enclosure is kept at an initial ambient temperature of 80°F (27°C) ± 5°F (3°C), and it is ventilated through two door openings on opposite walls. The fire source is a wood crib of 12 to 13 lb (5.4 to 5.9 kg) mass, measuring approximately 12 by 12 by 12 in. (0.3 by 0.3 by 0.3 m).

The wood crib is ignited by 8 oz. (24 mL) of N-heptane in a pan directly below the crib. Forty sec after ignition, the excelsior [1/4 lb (0.11 kg)] on the floor next to the simulated furniture is ignited.

The fire test is conducted for 10 min after the ignition of the wood crib. The water flow to the first sprinkler that operates and the total water flow when the second sprinkler operates are specified as part of the listing limitations for the sprinklers in the test. The total water flow for two sprinklers must be a minimum of 1.2 times the minimum flow for a single sprinkler.

The water distribution test requirements are based on the distribution pattern of the prototype residential sprinkler used in the Los Angeles test fires.[16] The distribution requirements involve collections in both the horizontal and vertical planes.

All residential sprinklers in the test must discharge water at the flow rate specified by the manufacturer for a 10-min period simulating one sprinkler operating and two sprinklers operating. The quantity of water collected on both the horizontal and vertical surfaces is measured and recorded.

Sprinklers being tested are required to discharge a minimum of 0.02 gpm per sq ft [0.8(L/min)/m^2] at both flow rates over the entire design area, plus an area 2 ft (0.61 m) beyond the listed coverage area in each direction (only three directions for horizontal sidewall-type sprinklers). They must also wet the walls of the test enclosure to a height not less than 28 in. (711 mm) below the ceiling with one sprinkler operating and not less than 36 in. (914 mm) with two sprinklers operating. Each wall surrounding the coverage area is required to be wetted with a minimum of 5 percent of the sprinkler application densities at both flow rates.

Since 1983, the use of residential sprinklers has also been permitted under some conditions in accordance with NFPA 13, *Installation of Sprinkler Systems*. Essentially, NFPA 13 allows residential sprinklers in dwelling units located in any occupancy provided they are installed in conformance with the requirements of their listing and the positioning requirements of NFPA 13D, *Installation of Sprinkler Systems in One- and Two-Family Dwellings and Mobile Homes*. A dwelling unit is defined as one or more rooms arranged for the use of one or more individuals living together, as in a single housekeeping unit normally having cooking, living, sanitary, and sleeping facilities. Dwelling units include hotel rooms, dormitory rooms, sleeping rooms in nursing homes, and similar living units. Occupancies encompassing dwelling units include apartment buildings, board and care facilities, dormitories, condominiums, lodging and rooming houses, and other multiple-family dwellings.

For NFPA 13, applications involving residential sprinklers in dwelling units, the design area is required to consist of the four most hydraulically demanding sprinklers. (See Figure 5-13D).

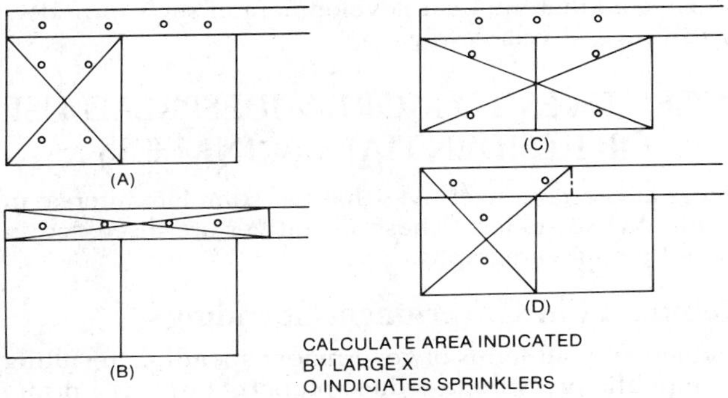

FIG. 5-13D. Examples of design areas for dwelling units within NFPA 13 occupancies.

Other areas, such as attics, basements, or other types of occupancies outside of dwelling units but within the same structure, are required to be protected in accordance with regular provisions of NFPA 13, *Installation of Sprinkler Systems*, including the appropriate water supply requirements. The decision as to which areas are to be protected with sprinklers is also regulated in accordance with the normal provisions of NFPA 13. This means, for example, that combustible concealed spaces generally require sprinklers, although the four-sprinkler design area is extended to such spaces above dwelling units when protected with residential sprinklers.

Residential sprinklers installed in systems designed to NFPA 13 requirements are spaced and positioned in accordance with their residential listings, not with the spacing requirements of NFPA 13. The water demands for the residential sprinklers are the same as in NFPA 13 applications, except that the multiple sprinkler flow requirement is extended to four sprinklers rather than the two stipulated for one- and two-family dwellings and mobile homes in NFPA 13D, *Installation of Sprinkler Systems in One- and Two-Family Dwellings and Mobile Homes*. The more liberal piping, component, hanger, and water supply duration allowances of NFPA 13D are not permitted in these systems.

In summary, NFPA 13, *Installation of Sprinkler Systems*, does not require residential sprinklers in residential areas, but it encourages their use through the four-sprinkler design area.

In 1989, a new standard was developed to bridge the gap between NFPA 13, *Installation of Sprinkler Systems*, and NFPA 13D, *Installation of Sprinkler Systems in One- and Two-Family Dwellings and Mobile Homes*. The new standard is NFPA 13R, *Installation of Sprinkler Systems in Residential Occupancies Up to Four Stories in Height*.

Like NFPA 13D, NFPA 13R is oriented toward economical life safety protection. Sprinklers are omitted from building areas that have been found to have a low incidence of fatal fires, including combustible concealed spaces, small bathrooms and closets, and attached porches. As with NFPA 13D, residential sprinklers are required throughout dwelling units, with some minor exceptions. A four-sprinkler design area is required unless the largest compartment contains fewer sprinklers.

In recognition of the greater risk associated with multifamily occupancies, however, NFPA 13R, is more conservative than NFPA 13D, in some areas. Requirements for plans, hydraulic calculations, and system acceptance certificates parallel those of NFPA 13, *Installation of Sprinkler Systems*. Unlike NFPA 13D, NFPA 13R requires a consideration of the likelihood that simultaneous domestic flows might occur through combined service piping. In addition, pumps and other key equipment are required to be listed.

In NFPA 13R, *Installation of Sprinkler Systems in Residential Occupancies Up to Four Stories in Height* systems, areas outside dwelling units can be protected with standard spray sprinklers, using NFPA 13 design criteria.

Quick Response Sprinklers

Quick response sprinklers are designed to be used in hotels, motels, offices, and other buildings where faster sprinkler operation could enhance life safety. UL first listed these sprinklers as quick response sprinklers based on performance comparable to a standard response sprinkler equipped with a quick response electronic squib actuator, a device marketed by one sprinkler manufacturer in the 1970s.

Quick response sprinklers, which are essentially standard spray sprinklers equipped with fast response operating mechanisms, were first introduced in 1983. They were developed by manufacturers in two different ways. One was to replace the actuating mechanism of standard spray sprinklers with the more sensitive heat responsive element used in residential sprinklers. This sprinkler was then resubmitted to a testing laboratory for testing and listing under the product standard for standard spray sprinklers. The other way was to simply submit a residential sprinkler to a testing laboratory for testing and listing under the provisions of a product standard for standard spray sprinklers.

It was not until 1988 that full-scale testing showed that quick response sprinklers could be used effectively with the traditional area/density design approaches found in sprinkler installation standards.[17,18] In "control-mode" testing of a 6 ft, 8-in. (2.0 m) arrangement of a standard plastic commodity under a 20-ft (6.1 m) ceiling, multiple tests involving sprinklers identical in all respects except sensitivity indicated that fewer average quick response sprinklers activated to control the fire than standard response sprinklers.

Current NFPA standards permit the use of quick-response sprinklers throughout buildings of light- and ordinary-hazard occupancy, but they have not yet recognized their use in extra-hazard occupancies or occupancies involving high-piled storage. Research is currently underway to determine if quick response sprinklers can be used successfully in dry systems as well as wet systems.

Early Suppression Fast Response Sprinklers

The early suppression fast response (ESFR) sprinklers were first envisioned by the Factory Mutual Research Corporation.[19,20] Working with FMRC, the National Fire Protection Research Foundation funded full-scale testing to prove that fast response sprinklers made suppression of a high-challenge fire feasible.[21]

Like its predecessor, the large drop sprinkler, the ESFR sprinkler is intended to prevail against the strong fire plumes associated with fires in industrial and warehouse occupancies. However, its delivery of water to the burning fuel surfaces is accomplished by means of spray momentum rather than the gravitational effects of large droplets.

Operating at a minimum pressure of 50 psi (7.25 kPa) so as to produce a minimum flow per sprinkler of 100 gpm (380 L/min), the ESFR sprinkler can protect challenges up to and including 25 ft (7.6 m) of plastics storage under a 30-ft (9.1 m) ceiling, without the use of in-rack sprinklers. The sprinkler has also been tested successfully for use in protecting aerosols and other special hazards, and it is currently being evaluated for use with storage more than 30 ft (9.1 m) high.

"Quick Response, High-Challenge" Large-Drop Sprinklers

The "quick response, high-challenge" sprinkler resulted from one manufacturer's insertion of a fast response link into an approved large-drop sprinkler. The large-drop sprinkler concept, pioneered during the 1970s by FMRC, was based on the theory that larger spray droplets would be more capable of achieving gravitational penetration of a strong upward fire plume.

Product approval and installation standards were developed, and specialized system design criteria found its way into NFPA standards beginning with the 1985 edition of NFPA 13, *Installation of Sprinkler Systems*. The large-drop sprinkler has a characteristic large deflector and is an upright sprinkler with a 0.64-in. (1.6 cm) diameter orifice.

The concept of combining the penetration capabilities of the large-drop sprinkler with fast response was basic to the development of the ESFR sprinkler program. In tests of the large-drop sprinklers with and without fast response links, the addition of fast response to the penetration abilities of the sprinkler provided superior protection against a high-challenge fire.

This particular sprinkler, however, later referred to as the "quick response, high-challenge" sprinkler, fell by the wayside during the screening for the ESFR prototype sprinkler due to its inability to provide sufficient water directly under the sprinkler. As an upright sprinkler, it could not handle the scenario in which a fire is started directly under a single sprinkler with 5 to 15 ft (1.5 to 4.6 m) of clearance below a 30-ft (9.1 m) ceiling. The sprinkler's water penetration capability was considered insufficient, due to an opening of the spray umbrella. The ESFR prototype eventually selected was a pendent with a larger orifice.

Nevertheless, this sprinkler had already established its worth in the eyes of many. A variation of that sprinkler is now listed by UL as a "specific application" sprinkler, intended for use within the constraints of demonstrated performance in full-scale fire tests.[22]

Quick Response, Early Suppression Sprinklers

Quick response, early suppression (QRES) sprinklers are currently being developed in the United States.[18] With the QRES sprinkler, the same principles used in the development of the ESFR sprinkler are being applied to a smaller-orifice sprinkler, which could be used in a wide variety of business, mercantile, public assembly, educational, and other applications. The proposed NFPA definition of QRES sprinklers is "fast response sprinklers that are listed for their ability to provide fire suppression of specific hazards." It is expected that the final development of such sprinklers is still several years away.

INCENTIVES TO MORE WIDESPREAD USE OF RESIDENTIAL SPRINKLERS

There are certain incentives that can stimulate interest in residential sprinklers. These incentives are discussed in the following paragraphs.

Reduction in Government Spending

Reduction in all forms of government spending, resulting from public pressure to reduce property taxes, is a prime factor in the future growth of the residential sprinkler concept. Many fire departments are forced to protect larger areas and more subdivisions with the same number of or even fewer people since financial restrictions hamper a fire department's ability to grow with the community. As a result, alternates to traditional fire fighting techniques must be found. One of them is the use of residential sprinklers.

San Clemente, CA, was the first community in the United States to pass a residential sprinkler ordinance in 1980 as part of the fire department's master plan. This ordinance requires automatic sprinkler systems to be installed in all new residential construction. The prime motivation for the passage of this ordinance was San Clemente's cutbacks in government spending brought about by Proposition 13, the state's tax-capping measure. Many communities across the country face similar situations. Automatic sprinklers in residences may be the answer to fewer fire fighters and longer response times from the fire department.

Insurance Savings

Although the greatest benefit from widespread installation of residential sprinklers will be the lives saved and injuries prevented, lower property losses will be a secondary and substantial benefit. An ad-hoc committee from the insurance industry sponsored a number of the test fires in Los Angeles and concluded that residential sprinklers have the potential for reducing homeowners' claim payment expenses.[23] As a result, the Insurance Services Office (ISO) Personal Lines Committee recommended that a 15-percent reduction in the homeowner's policy premium be given for installation of an NFPA 13D, *Installation of Sprinkler Systems in One- and Two-Family Dwelling and Mobile Homes*, residential sprinkler system. While this would not pay for the system over a short period of time, as is the case in many commercial installations, the continuing increases in the cost of insuring a single-family home make this a significant incentive nonetheless.

Real Estate Tax Reductions

In 1981, the State of Alaska enacted into law a significant piece of legislation that has a dramatic impact on the installation of sprinkler systems throughout that state. The law provides that 2 percent of the assessed value of any structure is exempt from taxation if the structure is protected with a fire protection system. The word "structure" is significant in the law, since it also applies to homes. In effect, if a home were assessed at $100,000 for purposes of taxation, the assessed value would be computed at $98,000, provided that it contained a fire protection system.

Buyers' Attitude

While one study indicated that 30 percent of the people interviewed perceived no need for a residential sprinkler system,[8] a survey published by the National Association of Home Builders on luxury features that buyers want in a new home showed that 14.3 percent indicated "fire suppression systems" as a choice. For potential buyers with incomes over $50,000, the percentage rose to over 20 percent.

Zoning

Greater land use may be possible with zoning changes that would permit fully sprinklered residences to be built on smaller parcels of land. The assumption is that the space between houses will not be as important from a fire protection standpoint if an entire street or neighborhood is fully sprinklered. One could argue, however, that if the sprinkler system fails, the resultant fire involving a number of residences could be much greater.

Sprinkler Legislation

In addition to the San Clemente, a number of other California communities have passed residential sprinkler legislation, including Orange County and Los Angeles County.

Since 1982, Greenburgh, NY, and several surrounding communities have enacted sprinkler ordinances that require the installation of automatic sprinklers in virtually all new construction, including all new multiple- and one- and two-family dwellings.

The State of Florida in 1983 passed a law requiring that all public lodging and time-share units three stories or more high in the state be sprinklered. It also required that all existing units be sprinklered by 1988.

In 1983, the City of Honolulu, HI, adopted legislation that required all new and existing high-rise hotels, which are those more than 75 ft (23 m) above grade, to be sprinklered.

In the late 1980s, additional jurisdictions, including Atlanta, GA, the State of Connecticut, and the Commonwealth of Massachusetts, acted to retroactively require the installation of sprinkler systems in high-rise residential buildings.

In 1990, the federal government enacted the Hotel and Motel Fire Safety Act, which contains strong incentives for complete sprinkler protection of hotels, since only hotels with satisfactory levels of fire protection will be eligible for federal employee travel.

Trade-Offs

Many "authorities having jurisdiction" have used building code trade-offs as an incentive to install sprinklers. Cobb County, GA, was one of the first communities to amend its Buildings and Construction Code to include trade-offs for multi-family structures equipped with residential sprinkler systems.

While these trade-offs can be a major incentive to install residential sprinklers, the disaster potential must always be considered if a fire, for whatever reason, should overpower the sprinkler system. This is especially true if the system is designed with the minimal water supplies required by NFPA 13D, *Installation of Sprinkler Systems in One- and Two-Family Dwellings and Mobile Homes*.

The City of Dallas, TX, adopted a building code that requires all new buildings or those undergoing major renovation, having an area greater than 7500 sq ft (697 m^2), to have automatic sprinklers. At the same time, this building code encourages trade-offs by allowing design options that trade "passive" fire protection features for "active" automatic sprinkler alternatives.

Mobile Homes

At least one major mobile home manufacturer is installing residential sprinkler systems in all of its mobile homes at the factory.

BIBLIOGRAPHY

References Cited

1. Pickard, R. W., Hird, D., and Nash, P., "The Thermal Testing of Heat-Sensitive Fire Detectors," *F.R. Note No. 247,* Fire Research Station, Borehamwood, Herts, England Jan. 1957,.
2. Evans, D. D. and Madrzykowski, D., "Characterizing the Thermal Response of Fusible-Link Sprinklers," *NBSIR 81-2329,* National Bureau of Standards, Washington, DC Aug. 1981.
3. Heskestad, G. and Smith, H., "Investigation of a New Sprinkler Sensitivity Approval Test: The Plunge Test," *FMRC No. 22485,* Factory Mutual Research Corp., Norwood, MA Dec. 1976.
4. Heskestad, G. and Smith, H., "Plunge Test for Determination of Sprinkler Sensitivity," *FMRC J.I.3A1E2.RR,* Factory Mutual Research Corp., Norwood, MA 1980.
5. Pepi, J. S., "Design Characteristics of Quick Response Sprinklers," Grinnell Fire Protection Systems Co., Providence, RI, May 1986.
6. Heskestad, G. and Bill, R. G., "Conduction Heat-Loss Effects on Thermal Response of Automatic Sprinklers," *FMRC J.I. OMOJ5.RU,* Factory Mutual Research Corp., Norwood, MA, Sept. 1987.
7. Halpin, B. M., Dinan, J. J., and Deters, O. J., "Assessment of the Potential Impact of Fire Protection Systems on Actual Fire Incidents," Johns Hopkins University—Applied Physics Laboratory (JHU/APL), Laurel, MD, Oct. 1978.
8. Yurkonis, P., "Study to Establish the Existing Automatic Fire Suppression Technology for Use in Residential Occupancies," Rolf Jensen & Associates, Inc., Deerfield, IL., Dec. 1980.
9. Kung, H. C., Haines, D., and Green, R., Jr., "Development of Low-Cost Residential Sprinkler Protection," Factory Mutual Research Corp., Norwood, MA, Feb. 1978.
10. Henderson, N. C., Riegel, P. S., Patton, R. M., and Larcomb, D. B., "Investigation of Low-Cost Residential Sprinkler Systems," Battelle Columbus Laboratories, Columbus, OH, June 1978.
11. Clark, G., "Performance Specifications for Low-Cost Residential Sprinkler System," Factory Mutual Research Corp., Norwood, MA, Jan. 1978.
12. Kung, H. C., Spaulding, R. D., and Hill, E. E., Jr., "Sprinkler Performance in Residential Fire Tests," Factory Mutual Research Corp., Norwood, MA, Dec. 1980.
13. Cote, A. E. and Moore, D., "Field Test and Evaluation of Residential Sprinkler Systems," Los Angeles Test Series (A report for the NFPA 13D Subcommittee), National Fire Protection Association, Quincy, MA, April 1980.

14. Moore, D., "Data Summary of the North Carolina Test Series of USFA Grant 79027 Field Test and Evaluation of Residential Sprinkler Systems, (a report for the NFPA 13D Subcommittee)," National Fire Protection Association, Quincy, MA, Sept. 1980.

15. Kung, H. C., Spaulding, R. D., Hill, E. E., Jr., and Symonds, A. P., "Technical Report, Field Evaluation of Residential Prototype Sprinkler Los Angeles Fire Test Program," Factory Mutual Research Corp., Norwood, MA, Feb. 1982.

16. Cote, A. E., "Final Report on Field Test and Evaluation of Residential Sprinkler Systems," National Fire Protection Association, Quincy, MA, July 1982.

17. Vincent, B. G., Stavrianidis, P., and Kung, H. C., "Large-Scale Fire Testing of Fast Response Sprinklers and Conventional Response Sprinklers in a Fire-Control-Mode Scenario," *FMRC J.I. OQ2P6.RA,070(A)*, Factory Mutual Research Corp., sponsored by National Fire Sprinkler Association, June 1989.

18. Budnick, E. and Fleming, R., "Developing an Early Suppression Design Procedure for Quick Response Sprinklers," *Fire Journal*, Vol. 83, No. 6 (Nov. 1989).

19. Yao, C. and Marsh, W., "Early Suppression—Fast Response: A Revolution in Sprinkler Technology," *Fire Journal*, Vol. 78, No. 1 (Jan. 1984).

20. Yao, C., "ESFR Sprinkler System—A New Approach to High-Challenge Storage Protection," *Fire Journal*, Vol. 79, No. 2 (Mar., 1985).

21. Chicarello, P., Troup, J., and Dean, R., "Large-Scale Fire Test Evaluation of Early Suppression Fast Response (ESFR) Automatic Sprinklers," *FMRC J.I. OM2R5.RR/OMJ7.RR*, Factory Mutual Research Corp., sponsored by National Fire Protection Research Foundation, May 1986.

22. Beitel, J., "Quick Response Sprinkler Tests, Group 1 Performance Tests: Tests Nos. 14-17," Southwest Research Institute, sponsored by the National Fire Protection Research Foundation, Quincy, MA, Dec. 1988.

23. Jackson, R. J., *Report of 1980 Property Loss Comparison Fires*, FEMA/USFA, Washington, DC, 1980.

NFPA Codes, Standards, and Recommended Practices

Reference to the following NFPA codes, standards, and recommended practices will provide further information on fast response sprinkler technology discussed in this chapter. (See the latest *NFPA Catalog* for availability of current editions of the following documents.)

NFPA 13, *Installation of Sprinkler Systems.*

NFPA 13D, *Installation of Sprinkler Systems in One- and Two-Family Dwellings and Mobile Homes.*

NFPA 13R, *Installation of Sprinkler Systems in Residential Occupancies Up to Four Stories in Height.*

Additional Reading

Anderson, N., "Sprinklers in the Home—A Life Saver," *Fire International*, Vol. 12, No. 108, (Dec.-Jan. 1988), pp. 54-55.

Beitel, J. J., "Quick-Response Sprinkler Tests, Group 2 Performance Tests," National Fire Protection Research Foundation, Quincy, MA, Dec. 1988.

Benjamin/Clarke Associates, "Operation San Francisco Smoke/Sprinkler Test Technical Report," International Association of Fire Chiefs, Washington, DC, April 1984.

Beitel, J. J., "Quick-Response Sprinkler Tests, Group 2 Performance Tests," National Fire Protection Research Foundation, Quincy, MA, Dec. 1988.

Budnick, E. K., "Estimating Effectiveness of State-of-the-Art Detectors and Automatic Sprinklers on Life Safety in Residential Occupancies," *NBSIR 84-2819*, National Bureau of Standards, Washington, DC, Jan. 1984.

Carey, W. M.,"Report of the Quick-Response Sprinkler Project, Group 2 Performance Tests," National Fire Protection Research Foundation, Quincy, MA, March 1988.

Casaccio, E. K., "ESFR Installation Guidelines Set," *Building Standards*, Vol. 57, No. 2, Mar.-Apr. 1988), pp. 20-21.

Chopra, I. S., "Subject 1626: Residential Automatic Sprinklers," *Lab Data*, Underwriters Laboratories, Northbrook, IL, Vol. 15, No. 2, 1984.

Coleman, R. J., *Alpha to Omega: The Evolution in Residential Fire Protection*, Phenix, San Clemente, CA, 1985.

Coleman, R. F., "Sprinklers in the Home—The Evolution of an Idea," *Fire International*, Vol. 11, No. 102, 1987, pp. 43, 46-47.

Cote, A. E., "Final Report on Field Test of a Retrofit Sprinkler System," National Fire Protection Research Foundation, Washington, DC, Feb. 1983.

Cote, A. E., "QRS: Do You Understand the Technology?," *Fire Journal*, Vol. 81, No. 1 (Jan. 1987), p. 27.

Cote, A. E., "Behind the Technology of Quick Response Sprinklers," *Consulting Specifying Engineer*, Vol. 1, No. 5, 1987, pp. 68-71.

Cote, A. E., "Use of Quick Response Sprinklers in Residential Occupancies—What You Should Know," *Sprinkler Quarterly*, Spring 1985.

Cote, A. E., "Highlights of a Field Test of a Retrofit Sprinkler System," *Fire Journal*, Vol. 77, No. 3 (May 1983).

Cote, A. E., "Update on Residential Sprinkler Protection," *Fire Journal*, Vol. 77, No. 6 (Nov. 1983), p. 69.

Cote, A. E., Field Test and Evaluation of Residential Sprinkler Systems, Part I, *Fire Technology*, Vol. 19, No. 4, (Nov. 1983), pp. 221-232.

Cote, A. E., Field Test and Evaluation of Residential Sprinkler Systems, Part II, Vol. 20, No. 1, (Feb. 1984), pp. 48-58.

Cote, A. E., Field Test and Evaluation of Residential Sprinkler Systems, Part III, Vol. 120, No. 2, (May 1984), pp. 41-46.

"Development of an Experimental Prototype Low-Cost Electronic Sensor/Actuator for a Residential Automatic Sprinkler Head," Battelle Columbus Laboratories, Columbus, OH, 1982.

Evans, D. D., "Calculating Sprinkler Activation Time in Compartments," National Bureau of Standards, Washington, DC, 1984.

Approval Standard—Residential Automatic Sprinklers, Factory Mutual Research Corporation, Class No. 2030, Sept. 1983.

Fleming, R. P., "Applications/limitations of QRS Technology," *Fire Safety Journal*, Vol. 14, Nos. 1&2 (July 1988), pp. 75-88.

Fleming, R. P., "Quick Response Sprinklers—A State of the Art Technical Report," National Fire Protection Research Corporation, Quincy, MA, 1985.

Fleming, R. P., "The Special Listings," *Sprinkler Quarterly*, No. 52, Spring 1985.

Fleming, R. P., "Understanding the New Sprinklers," *Sprinkler Quarterly*, National Fire Sprinkler Association, No. 47, Fall 1983.

Foehl, J. M., "In Quest of an Economical Automatic Fire Suppression System for Multi-Family Residential Complexes," *Fire Journal*, Vol. 70, No. 1 (Jan. 1976), pp. 48-57.

Fuller, S. K. and Ruegg, R. T., "Economics of Fast-Response Residential Sprinkler Systems," *Fire Journal*, Vol. 79, No. 3 (May-June 1985), pp. 18-22, 115.

Goodfellow, D. G., "Apparatus and Procedure for Measuring the Actual Delivered Density (ADD) of Sprinklers in Simulated Rack Storage Fires," Factory Mutual Research Foundation, Norwood, MA, Jan. 1985.

Hammerman, D. M., "Project Home—A Pilot Program for a Low-Cost Residential Sprinkler System," *Fire Journal*, Vol. 75, No. 2 (Mar. 1981), pp. 66-69.

Harmathy, T. Z., "On the Economics of the Mandatory Sprinklering of Dwellings," *Fire Technology*, Vol. 24, No. 3, 1988, pp. 245-261.

Isner, M. S., "Successful Residential Sprinkler Activation," *Fire Command*, Vol. 53, No. 1 (Jan. 1986), pp. 22-27.

Kung, H. C., Spaulding, Robert D., and Hill, E. E., "Sprinkler Performance in Living-Room Fire Tests: Effect of Link Sensitivity and Room Size," Factory Mutual Research Corporation, July 1983.

Kung, H. C., "Low-Cost Residential Sprinkler Protection," *Fire Technology*, Vol. 12, No. 2 (May 1976), pp. 85.

Miller, C., "Early Suppression-Fast Response Sprinklers: A New Level of Industrial Fire Protection," *National Engineer*, Vol. 93, No. 9 (Sept. 1989), pp. 18-19.

Moore, D. A., "Field Test and Evaluation of Residential Sprinkler Systems," *Fire Journal*, Vol. 74, No. 6 (Nov. 1980).

O'Neil, J. G., "Fast Response Sprinklers in Patient Room Fires," *Fire Technology*, Vol. 17, No. 4 (Nov. 1981).

O'Rourke, G. W., "Automatic Sprinkler Systems: What's New?" *Heating/Piping/Air Condition*, Vol. 55, No. 4 (April 1983), pp. 37-41.

Pepi, J. S., "Design Charecteristics of Quick-Response Sprinklers," *TR 86-3, 1986*, Society of Fire Protection Engineers, Boston, MA.

Ruegg, R. T. and Fuller, S. K., "A Benefit-Cost Model of Residential Fire Sprinkler Systems," *NBS Technical Note 1203*, National Bureau of Standards, Washington, DC, Nov. 1984.

"Outline of Proposed Investigation for Residential Automatic Sprinklers for Fire Protection Service," Subject 1626, Underwriters Laboratories, Oct. 27, 1980.

Pepi, J. S., "Concept and Development of the Residential and Fast Response Sprinklers," *Sprinkler Quarterly*, No. 52, Spring 1985.

Proceedings of the Fourth Conference on Low-Cost Residential Sprinkler Systems, September 26-27, 1979, Federal Emergency Management Agency/U.S. Fire Administration, Aug. 1980.

Proceedings of the Third Conference on Low-Cost Residential Sprinklers, November 29-30, 1977, National Fire Prevention and Control Administration, June 1978.

"Residential Automatic Sprinklers for Fire Protection Service," *UL 1626*, Underwriters Laboratories, Northbrook, IL, 1986.

Shaw, H., "Fast Response Sprinklers—The Answer to the Toxicity Problem," *Sprinkler Quarterly*, No. 47, Fall 1983.

Teague, P. E., "Residential Sprinklers: An Idea Whose Time Has Almost Come," *Fire Journal*, Vol. 82, No. 5 (Sept.-Oct.) 1988, p. 46.

Viniello, J. A., "Residential and Quick Response Fire Sprinklers—You Need to Know the Difference!" *Sprinkler Quarterly*, No. 52, Spring 1985.

Walton, W. D. and Budnick, E. K., "Quick-Response Sprinklers in Office Configurations: Fire Test Results," *NBSIR 88-3695*, National Institute of Standards and Technology, Gaithersburg, MD, 1988.

Weber, R. A. and Smith, D. T., "Evaluation of Residential Sprinklers for Use in Military Housing," *Technical Report*, U.S. Army Corps of Engineers, Champaign, IL., Sept. 1987, p.28.

"What Residential Sprinklers Can Do," *Fire Journal*, Vol. 82, No. 5 (Sept.-Oct. 1985), p. 60.

Yoa, C., "Development of the ESFR Sprinkler System," *Fire Safety Journal*, Vol. 14, Nos. 1&2, (July 1988), pp. 75-73.

Yao, C., "Early Fire Suppression with Fast-Response Sprinklers," *Sprinkler Quarterly*, Winter, 1983-84, pp. 19-23.

STANDPIPE AND HOSE SYSTEMS

Jeffrey M. Shapiro

As long as there are buildings, there will be building fires and a need for fire extinguishing equipment. In tall and large-area buildings, such equipment should include a standpipe system. Standpipe systems provide a fixed means of transporting water for fire fighting from a reliable water supply to designated areas of buildings, thus significantly improving the efficiency of manual fire fighting operations. Even in tall and large-area buildings that are protected by automatic sprinklers, standpipe systems play an essential role in building firesafety by serving as a backup for, and complement to, sprinklers.

Information related to standpipe systems can be found in NFPA 14, *Installation of Standpipe and Hose Systems*, which contains specific design, installation, and testing requirements. Note that NFPA 14 does not cover where standpipe systems are required. Required installations are set forth in code documents, such as NFPA *101®*, *Life Safety Code®*; NFPA 1, *Fire Prevention Code*; and the model building codes. NFPA 13, *Installation of Sprinkler Systems*, is a useful reference when considering hydraulically designed systems or combined sprinkler and standpipe systems. Other NFPA standards and recommended practices that may be helpful when dealing with standpipe systems are included in the bibliography at the end of this chapter.

For other information relevant to standpipe systems, see Section 4, Chapter 2, "Protective Signaling Systems"; Section 5, Chapter 5, "Water Storage Facilities and Suction Supplies"; Section 5, Chapter 6, "Fire Pumps"; and Section 5, Chapter 16, "Care and Maintenance of Water-Based Extinguishing Systems."

STANDPIPE SYSTEM DESIGN CONSIDERATIONS

All standpipe systems share the common purpose of delivering water for manual fire fighting. However, system designs used to accomplish this purpose will vary. While one system may involve a simple pipe network for conveying water from fire department apparatus to inside hose connections, another may involve a fully automatic water supply and preconnected hoses.

The design of a standpipe system is usually dictated by a local, state, or model building code, by NFPA 14, *Installation of Standpipe and Hose Systems*, or by the insurance standards.. In many cases, the requirements among these codes and standards will vary greatly, so it is essential that an individual interested in standpipe system design requirements determine the applicable code or standard adopted by the regulations entity. Because of the numerous and varied codes and standards, the following discussion on design considerations does not focus on the regulatory requirements in any one code or standard. Instead, requirements in all of the model codes and standards are considered along with engineering and historical perspectives.

The design process begins by determining the intended use of a system, i.e., whether it is for full-scale fire fighting, first-aid fire fighting, or both. These three uses correspond with the three categories of standpipe systems, commonly referred to as "classes" of systems. Most aspects of system design, such as the water supply, layout, and system components, are affected or dictated by the class of system. Other aspects, such as whether piping is wet or dry, can be determined independently of the class of system.

Classes of Systems

The three classes of standpipe systems are designated as Class I, Class II, and Class III. Some sources refer to a fourth class of system called a "combined" system. Combined systems are Class I or Class III standpipe systems that also supply water to a sprinkler system. Note that sprinkler systems with occasional hose connections are not considered to be combined systems. The design of a combined system is similar to any other Class I or Class III system, except that the water supply and pipe sizes may have to be modified to accommodate the sprinkler system demand.

Class I systems: Class I systems provide 2½-in. (64 mm) hose connections at designated locations in a building for full-scale fire fighting. These systems are generally

Jeffrey M. Shapiro, P.E., is fire code coordinator for the International Conference of building Officials/Western Fire Chiefs Association based in Whittier, CA.

intended for use by fire departments. Class I systems reduce the need for fire fighting personnel to lay extended lengths of hose from exterior locations to reach an interior fire, thereby reducing the time and personnel required to begin attacking a fire.

Class I systems are generally required in sprinklered and non-sprinklered buildings which are more than three stories high because of the excessive time and personnel required to lay hoses from outside to floors above the third story. Class I systems are commonly required in malls for similar reasons.

Class II systems: Class II systems provide 1½-in. (38 mm) hose connections at designated locations in a building for first-aid fire fighting. These systems are generally intended for use by fire brigades and perhaps building occupants before the fire department arrives. They are occasionally provided for use by fire departments, as well. With Class II systems, a hose, a nozzle, and a hose rack are typically installed on each hose connection.

Class II systems are often required in large unsprinklered buildings. They may also be required to protect special hazard areas, such as exhibit halls and stages.

Presently, members of the fire protection community disagree about the desirability of having standpipe systems available for occupant use. Concerns focus on the ability of untrained occupants to use safely a 100-ft (30.5 m) long hose flowing up to 100 gpm (378 L/min) and on the wisdom of encouraging occupants to fight a fire instead of evacuating. These concerns have led to a trend of reducing the requirements for, or eliminating the installation of, standpipe systems with preconnected hoses. Consequently, the use of Class II systems is becoming less frequent.

Class III systems: Class III systems combine the features of Class I and Class II systems. They are provided for both full-scale and first-aid fire fighting. These systems are generally intended for use by fire departments, fire brigades, and perhaps building occupants. Because of their multiple uses, Class III systems are provided with both Class I and Class II hose connections with associated equipment. This is sometimes accomplished by using 2½-in. (64 mm) hose valves with easily removable 2½-in. (64 mm) to 1½-in. (38 mm) adapters which are permanently chained to hose connections. Class III systems are sometimes used when both Class I and Class II systems are required and no useful purpose would be served by installing separate systems. Like Class II systems, the use of Class III systems is declining because of concerns about the safety and effectiveness of untrained occupants fighting fires.

Water Supply Requirements

Once the required class of system has been determined, the most critical feature of a system that must be determined is the water supply. Before the means of supply can be determined, the designer must assess just how much water a system will require and at what pressure. The minimum required flow and pressure are referred to as "system demand."

System demand: The system demand for a standpipe system is a function of several variables:

1. The required flow rate and pressure at the hydraulically most remote hose connections.
2. Required flow rates for additional standpipes.
3. The water supply requirements for automatic sprinklers sharing common piping.
4. Required flow duration.
5. Pressure losses from friction and changes in elevation.

Flow rate, pressure, and duration requirements for standpipe systems are determined by the class of system. According to the 1990 edition of NFPA 14, *Installation of Standpipe and Hose Systems*, Class I and Class III systems must be capable of delivering 500 gpm (1893 L/min) for the first standpipe plus 250 gpm (947 L/min) for each additional standpipe, up to a maximum of 2500 gpm (9463 L/min). This standard also requires the water supply to be capable of providing the minimum flow rate for 30 min. Figure 5-14A illustrates these design flow rate requirements for Class I and Class III systems. In addition, NFPA 14 requires that a water supply for Class I and Class III systems be able to deliver a residual pressure of 65 psi (448 kPa) at the outlet of the topmost hose connection of each standpipe, with 250 gpm (947 L/min) flowing from each of the two topmost hose connections of the hydraulically most remote standpipe, plus 250 gpm (947 L/min) from each additional standpipe, up to the 2500 gpm (9463 L/min) maximum. For Class II systems, NFPA 14 requires that water supplies be capable of delivering 100 gpm (378 L/min) for 30 min and that they be strong enough to maintain a residual pressure of 65 psi (448 kPa) at the outlet of the hydraulically most remote hose connection with 100 gpm (378 L/min) flowing.

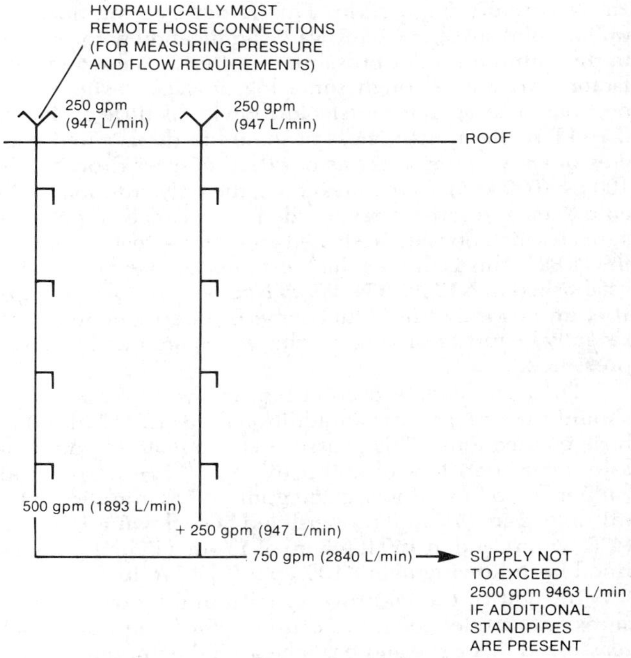

FIG. 5-14A. Basic flow rate requirements for Class I and Class III systems in a non-sprinklered building.

In recent years, some disagreement has developed within the fire protection community and among some codes and standards regarding the adequacy of a 65-psi (448 kPa) design pressure for the oulet of the hydraulically most remote hose connection on a standpipe system. From a performance perspective, all agree that the minimum pressure at any hose connection should be adequate to operate a nozzle properly while overcoming friction loss in a hose. From a design perspective, the establishment of a minimum design pressure for hose connections has proven difficult because nozzle operating pressures and friction losses in hoses vary depending upon the equipment used.

The concern over nozzle pressure became an issue when fog nozzles were introduced for fire fighting in the mid-1900s. Before using fog nozzles, fire fighters used solid stream nozzles, which operated well at fairly low pressures. As the use of fog nozzles became more common, the fire protection community moved to increase the minimum pressure required at the hydraulically most remote hose connections on standpipe systems to accommodate the greater nozzle pressures required by fog nozzles. The NFPA Committee on Standpipe and Hose Systems recommended a pressure of 65 psi (448 kPa), which was later widely implemented. In establishing this pressure, the committee had tried to minimize the pressure required for standpipe system water supplies and assumed that nozzle designers and testing laboratories would establish criteria to ensure that fog nozzles would operate satisfactorily with a 65-psi (448 kPa) pressure at hose connections. Unfortunately, this assumption never materialized, and many have since questioned the 65-psi (448 kPa) minimum pressure requirement.

Until such time as a nationally recognized standard is developed to establish a minimum inlet pressure at which fog nozzles will satisfactorily perform, identification of the actual minimum pressure necessary to supply a fog nozzle is virtually impossible. This is because fog nozzles, unlike solid stream nozzles, vary significantly with respect to the minimum inlet pressure required to achieve satisfactory streams. Though some fog nozzles designed for occupant use operate satisfactorily with as little as 40 psi (276 kPa), the effectiveness of some fire department nozzles quickly deteriorates as nozzle pressures drop below 100 psi (690 kPa). In the meantime, the only criterion available to ensure satisfactory nozzle performance is the pressure at which nozzles are tested and rated—that is, 100 psi (690 kPa). This is the residual test pressure for fog nozzles established in NFPA 1964, *Spray Nozzles (Shutoff and Tip)*. It is interesting to note that some fire departments have recently begun specifying nozzles which are rated at lower pressures.

To accommodate friction loss in fire hose, a design should provide at least an additional 25 psi (172 kPa) at hose connections. This pressure is adequate to compensate for friction loss in 200 ft (61 m) of 2½-in. (64 mm) rubber-lined hose flowing 250 gpm (947 L/min), in 200 ft (61 m) of 2-in. (51 mm) rubber-lined hose flowing 125 gpm (473 L/min), and in 150 ft (46 m) of 1¾-in. (45 mm) rubber-lined hose flowing about 100 gpm (379 L/min).

In light of the controversy surrounding outlet pressures, one model code, the *Uniform Building Code*,[1] has reassessed this issue and has increased the minimum pressure requirement for hose connections. It is likely that other codes and standards will follow suit at some point. Based on the foregoing discussion, a prudent design would provide a minimum of 125 psi (862 kPa) at the hydraulically most remote hose connection without preconnected hoses to allow for some friction loss in a hose while delivering 100 psi (690 kPa) at a nozzle. Though this pressure may be considered excessive when compared to that specified in the past, fire departments for decades have used 100 psi (690 kPa) as the target nozzle pressure when pumping hoses supplying fog nozzles. This often means that hoses supplying fog nozzles have to be pumped at 150 psi (1034 kPa) or more to accommodate friction loss.

For hose connections with preconnected hoses, nozzles with operating pressures in the 50-psi (345 kPa) range should be specified, recognizing that this may require additional testing. By limiting nozzle pressures, the minimum pressure at the hydraulically most remote hose connection with preconnected hoses can be limited to 65 psi (448 kPa), which will allow occupants to manage hoses.

Another aspect of system demand on which codes and standards do not agree is the minimum water supply required for combined systems in fully sprinklered buildings. According to NFPA 14, *Installation of Standpipe and Hose Systems*, the system demand for sprinklers need not be added to the system demand for standpipes if a building is completely sprinklered. This standard calls for the greater amount that is required for the standpipe or the sprinkler system to be provided, but reduces the maximum required flow for standpipes to 1500 gpm (5678 L/min) in light-hazard occupancies and 2000 gpm (7570 L/min) in ordinary-hazard occupancies.

However, some of the model building codes allow significant reductions in the standpipe system water supply requirements when buildings are equipped with automatic sprinklers throughout. In part, these reductions result from an interpretation of a provision in NFPA 13, *Installation of Sprinkler Systems,* thought by many to allow significant reductions in the water supply for combined systems. This interpretation appears to be an improper extrapolation of the intent of NFPA 13, which was to specify hose demands for occasional hose stations connected to a sprinkler system as opposed to the total hose demand for a complete standpipe system combined with a sprinkler system. Until this issue is resolved, the authority having jurisdiction should be consulted to determine the water supply criteria for combined systems in fully sprinklered buildings.

For combined systems in partially sprinklered buildings, codes and standards generally agree that the demands for each system must be added.

Types of water supplies: Standpipe systems require a minimum of one water supply that is capable of supplying a standpipe system's hydraulic demand for the minimum required duration. Several types of water supplies may be acceptable. These include:

1. Public water works systems, with a booster pump when higher pressures are required.
2. Fire pumps connected to a reliable fixed water source.
3. Pressure tanks.
4. Gravity tanks.
5. Fire department apparatus with access to a reliable water source.

Many factors must be considered in selecting the type of water supply for a standpipe system. Foremost is whether the water supply capable of supplying the system demand must be permanent or whether exclusive reliance on fire department apparatus is adequate. Standpipe systems should be provided with permanent water supplies when they are intended for use before the fire department arrives; examples are Class II and Class III systems with preconnected hoses. Permanent water supplies should be provided for Class I systems when it is considered undesirable to rely on fire department apparatus as the sole water supply. Such cases may include high-rise buildings, buildings with glass curtain walls which could cut supply hoses if the glass fails during a fire, and buildings in active seismic areas. Buildings in active seismic areas are often required to use in-house tanks to supply standpipe systems rather than relying on public water supplies, which are susceptible to earthquake-induced failure. If none of these conditions are present, there is minimal benefit to providing a permanent water supply, since most fire departments will primarily rely on fire apparatus to pump into a standpipe system, as opposed to relying on an in-house supply.

Even when a permanent water supply is provided, at least one fire department connection should still be installed to provide a secondary water supply on Class I and Class III systems if the system serves areas within the pumping range of fire department apparatus. When areas of a building are located beyond the pumping range of fire department apparatus, additional measures, such as a permanent secondary water source, should be considered since failure of the primary supply would render a building completely unprotected. If the primary water supply uses a pump, the backup arrangement could consist of a second pump, driver, and controller. The point where a system requires a water supply beyond the capability of fire department apparatus depends on the apparatus' pump and the residual pressure available from the water source. This can be evaluated using the formula:

$$AP + RS = SD$$

where:

AP = apparatus pressure available at the system demand flow rate

RS = residual pressure from the public or private water supply at the system demand flow rate

SD = system demand pressure (calculated to fire apparatus) at the system demand flow rate.

As a rule, systems serving areas beyond 400 ft (122 m) above the lowest level of fire department access should be evaluated to determine whether the pumping range of the fire department apparatus has been exceeded.

System Layout

Number and location of hose connections: The required number of hose connections is primarily a function of building design. In general, codes and standards have employed two approaches to determine hose connection locations. The first method, termed the "actual length" method, locates hose connections such that enough connections are provided to reach all portions of the area served with a 100-ft (30.5 m) hose that has a nozzle with a 30-ft (9 m) reach. These distances should be measured around partitions and obstructions for hose length, but along unobstructed straight-line paths for nozzle reach. Figure 5-14B illustrates this method of locating hose connections.

The second method, termed the "exit location" method, locates hose connections based upon a building's exiting system. Using this method, hose connections are located at doors leading to exit stairs, horizontal exits, and, in the case of malls, doors leading to exit passageways. Since exits must be reasonably distributed within buildings to provide adequate egress, it is assumed that hose connections will be adequatly distributed by locating them at the points of egress from areas served. Figure 5-14C illustrates the exit location method of locating hose connections.

The exit location method is preferred over the actual length method for locating hose connections without preconnected hoses, since the actual length method encourages locating hose connections in unprotected areas to meet distance requirements. When locating hose connections

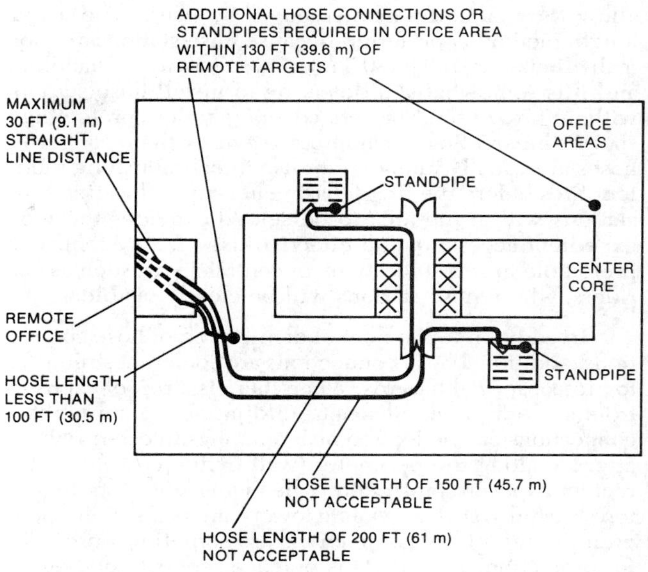

FIG. 5-14B. ***Actual length method for locating hose connections in a building having a maximum travel distance to an exit or 150 feet (45.7m).***

without preconnected hoses, such as 2½-in. (64 mm) hose connections for fire department use, it is preferable to locate them where they will be protected from a fire, such as within protected stair enclosures or on opposite sides of horizontal exits. This allows fire fighters to hook up to a system in relative safety and to have a charged hose before entering a fire area when necessary. Though some may argue that the use of a hose from an exit enclosure violates the enclosure and places occupants at risk, the alternative would be an unreasonable expectation of fire fighters to enter an area filled with smoke and heated gases to search for a hose connection. In addition, time lost while searching would prolong an uncontrolled fire, potentially posing a much greater threat to occupants.

When locating 1½-in. (38 mm) hose connections with preconnected hoses, often called hose stations, it is preferable to use the actual length method, though some codes

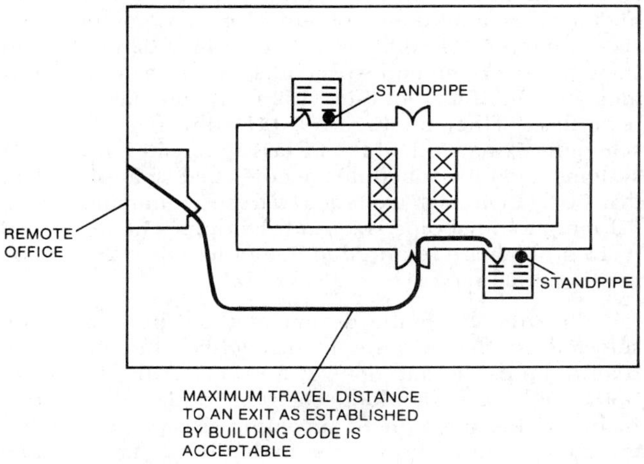

FIG. 5-14C. ***Exit location method for locating hose connections.***

allow the exit location method to be used. The actual length method is preferred because hose stations are normally limited to 100 ft (30.5 m) of hose for ease of handling, and it is somewhat self-defeating to install hose stations without providing complete coverage unless protecting a specific hazard. Since standpipe systems with preconnected hoses are usually intended for use in extinguishing incipient fires before the fire department arrives, locating hose stations within the area to be served provides the most expedient access to, and effective use of, a system. It is preferable to select locations in central areas, such as corridors, where hose stations will be clearly visible.

In addition to the normal distribution of hose connections, additional hose connections are sometimes required to protect special hazards. When there is a risk of exposure from a fire from an adjacent building, for example, hose connections can be located near openings in exterior walls, at grade along the perimeter (wall hydrants), and on the roof for exposure protection. When large combustible rooftop structures, such as cooling towers, are present, multiple-outlet rooftop hose connections are sometimes provided for protection, as well. This practice seems to be becoming less frequent due to the increased use of noncombustible construction materials for structures on roofs. Rooftop hose connections may also be provided for system testing, since water is easily disposed of from most roofs. An alternative to providing rooftop hose connections is to provide additional hose connections at the top landings of stair enclosures having stairway access to the roof. From such connections, hoses easily can be extended to a roof when necessary, and the need to make roof penetrations and provide freeze protection for piping is avoided.

Sizing pipe: There are two methods of sizing standpipe system piping: (1) the pipe schedule method, and (2) the hydraulic method. Though the hydraulic method, is universally accepted, the pipe schedule method is not. For example, the *Uniform Building Code*[1] no longer allows pipe schedule sizing. Those codes and standards that do use the pipe schedule method all contain the same provisions.

With the pipe schedule method, pipe sizes are prescribed by a schedule based upon the class of system and the height of the standpipe. According to the pipe schedule for Class I and III systems, standpipes not exceeding 100 ft (30.5 m) in height must be a minimum of 4-in. (102 mm) nominal pipe size. Standpipes over 100 ft (30.5 m) high must be a minimum of 6-in. (152 mm) nominal pipe size [the top 100 ft (30.5 m) may be 4 in. (102 mm)]. And standpipes serving both sprinklers and hose connections must be a minimum of 6-in. (152 mm) nominal pipe size regardless of height. Figure 5-14D illustrates the pipe schedule sizing method for a Class I system. For Class II systems, the pipe schedule specifies that standpipes less than 50 ft (15 m) high are required to be a minimum of 2-in. (51 mm) nominal pipe size, and standpipes more than 50 ft (15 m) high are required to be not less than 2½-in. (64 mm) nominal pipe size.

With the hydraulic design method, pipe sizes are selected so that a system will deliver the minimum required pressure and flow. More specifically, the selection of pipe sizes should be such that each water supply, including fire department apparatus, is capable of delivering the required flow at the hydraulically most remote hose connection.

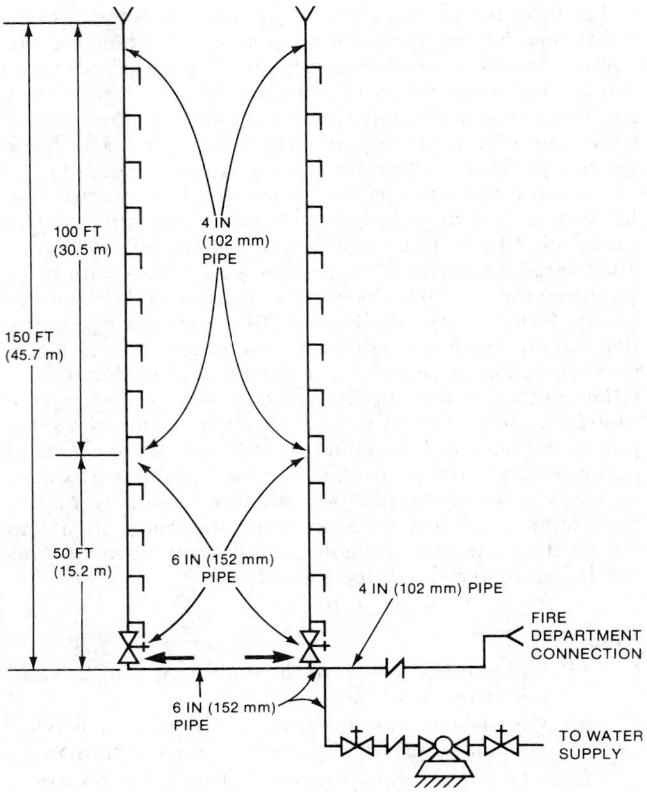

FIG. 5-14D. ***Pipe schedule sizing method for a Class I system.***

When performing a hydraulic design, the hydraulic characteristics of each water supply must be known. The procedure for determining the hydraulic characteristics of permanent water supplies, such as pumps, is fairly straightforward and is described in other chapters of this handbook. The procedure for determining the hydraulic characteristics of fire apparatus supplying a standpipe system are similar. Lacking better information about local fire apparatus, a conservative design would accommodate a 1000-gpm (3785 L/min) fire department pumper performing at the level of design specifications set forth in NFPA 1901, *Pumper Fire Apparatus*. NFPA 1901 specifies that fire department pumpers must be able to achieve three pressure/flow combinations. These are 100 percent of rated capacity at 150 psi (1034 kPa) net pump pressure, 70 percent of rated capacity at 200 psi (1379 kPa) net pump pressure, and 50 percent of rated capacity at 250 psi (1724 kPa) net pump pressure. Therefore, a 1000-gpm (3785 L/min) pumper can be expected to deliver no less than 1000 gpm (3785 L/min) at 150 psi (1034 kPa), 700 gpm (2650 L/min) at 200 psi (1379 kPa), and 500 gpm (1893 L/min) at 250 psi (1724 kPa). Residual supply pressure on the suction side of a pump can also be added.

To perform a hydraulic design, one should calculate the minimum required pressure and flow at the hydraulically most remote hose connection back through system piping to each water supply, accumulating losses for friction and elevation and adding flows for additional standpipes and sprinklers at each point where such standpipes or sprinklers connect to the hydraulic design path. When considering fire apparatus as a water supply, flows must be calculated from system piping through the fire department connection and back through connecting hoses to the pump. If the pressure available at each supply source exceeds a standpipe system's pressure demand at the designated flow, the design is acceptable. Otherwise, the piping design or the water supply must be adjusted.

Maximum pressures and zoning in tall buildings: In tall buildings, standpipe systems are often divided into subsystems to limit the maximum system pressure by controlling the maximum height of a water column. These subsystems are called zones. The goal of zoning systems is basically opposite that of hydraulically sizing piping. When sizing piping for a standpipe system, the goal is to maintain high system pressure to deliver a system's hydraulic demand without requiring large pumps. When zoning a standpipe system, the goal is to minimize the pressure that can be developed at connections to, and within, system piping to reduce the need for high pressure fittings and pressure reducing valves.

Codes and standards have established a commonly accepted maximum zone height of 400 ft (122 m) when outlet pressures are controlled properly. The 400-ft (122 m) limit is adequate to prevent system pressures from exceeding the pressure ratings of available standpipe equipment while delivering 65 psi (448 kPa) to the hydraulically most remote hose connection. Caution should be exercised in the selection of equipment to ensure that it is capable of withstanding the maximum possible system pressure, which will occur at pump churn when pumps are used.

Unfortunately, the use of fixed zone height limits does not allow systems to be designed with greater zone heights if the selected equipment is capable of handling the increased pressure. Nor does it recognize the need to reduce zone heights to avoid overpressurizing systems if higher pressures are desired at the hydraulically most remote hose connection.

To address these issues, the following discussion considers an alternative to the fixed zone height limits contained in codes and standards. The method uses a performance approach, limiting maximum pressures within a system.

Since the purpose of subdividing standpipe systems into zones is to maintain water pressures below a reasonable safety limit, a performance approach to system zoning must first consider the maximum pressure to which a system can be subjected without creating a safety problem or a risk of failure. There are three main criteria that affect the establishment of maximum system pressures:

1. The maximum pressure rating for system components.
2. The maximum pressure that should be available at hose connections with and without preconnected hose.
3. The maximum pressure that should be available at sprinkler system connections to combined sprinkler and standpipe systems.

The maximum pressure to which system components are subjected should be commensurate with the pressure ratings of the system components. Fittings are usually the weakest link among system components, generally requiring a maximum pressure rating of 175 psi (1207 kPa), although fittings are available commercially with pressure ratings of up to 400 psi (2758 kPa). In some cases, ratings for valves and pressure-regulating devices may also be a limiting factor. Since 400 psi (2758 kPa) is the maximum pressure rating for commonly available and cost-effective equipment, the maximum pressure within a system can be reasonably extended to as much as 400 psi (2758 kPa). Therefore, the maximum zone height should be based upon limiting system pressures to 400 psi (2758 kPa).

Though the maximum zone height corresponding to a particular maximum system pressure can be calculated, it will be determined in most cases by trial and error. To determine if a single zone can be used, a designer can lay out a system with one zone and calculate the required pressures and flows from hydraulic demand points back through system piping to the supply to determine the system demand. Assuming that the supply will be a pump, a single zone could be justified if there were a pump available that would satisfy the hydraulic demand of the system without exceeding 400 psi (2758 kPa) at churn, including residual supply pressure. If a pump could not be found to meet these criteria, subdivision into zones would be required.

Standpipe system pressures in the 400 psi (2758 kPa) range pose some danger to users and a risk of failure of sprinkler system components on combined systems. Therefore, additional factors, such as pressure control devices, must be incorporated into a system design when systems are zoned such that pressure could exceed safety limits at connections.

The determination of safety limits at hose connections logically should consider two criteria: (1) hose burst pressure, and (2) handling. Hoses for fire department use are required to be tested periodically to 250 psi (1724 kPa) or more, according to NFPA 1962, *Care, Use, and Maintenance of Fire Hose, Including Connections and Nozzles*. Preconnected standpipe hoses installed on new systems are required to be tested periodically to 150 psi (1034 kPa) or more, according to NFPA 1961, *Fire Hose*. Though a hose may not fail up to these pressures, experience indicates that 175 psi (1207 kPa) is about the maximum pressure on a hose that can be maneuvered by fire fighters and that 100 psi (690 kPa) is the maximum pressure that an untrained user should be expected to handle. Therefore, pressure control devices, such as pressure-regulating valves, should be used to limit pressure to 175 psi (1207 kPa) at hose connections without preconnected hoses and 100 psi (690 kPa) at hose connections with preconnected hoses. Since ultimate safety would be jeopardized at pressures over the 250-psi (1724 kPa) test pressure for fire department hose and the 150-psi (1034 kPa) test pressure for occupant-use hose, pressure relief valves should be installed as a backup to pressure-regulating valves when pressures could exceed these limits. Such pressure relief devices are intended to prevent a catastrophic failure, but not to imply use of a system at these pressures.

The safety limit for sprinkler connections is also 175 psi (1207 kPa). This is the maximum pressure for which sprinklers are listed, and is intended to act as a safety factor to prevent leakage. To allow a buffer between the pressure settings for pressure-regulating and pressure-relief valves on sprinkler connections, regulating valves should be set at 165 psi (1138 kPa) and relief valves should be set at 175 psi (1207 kPa).

Table 5-14A summarizes the limits recommended by the foregoing discussion. Figures 5-14E and 5-14F illustrate sample multiple-zone systems. Note that on multiple-zone systems, fire pumps at the same level may be used in series. In addition, two separate supply pipes are always required for high zones supplied by pumps at lower levels so that a water supply can be maintained when one supply pipe is out of service. Separate fire department connections also should be provided for each zone

TABLE 5-14A. ***Recommended Pressure Controls for Standpipe System Outlets[a]***

Outlet Use	Pressure Regulating Device Recommended When Pressure Exceeds	Pressure Relief Valve Recommended When Pressure Exceeds[b]
Hose Connection with Pre-connected hose	100 psi (690 kPa)[c]	150 psi (1034 kPa)
Hose Connection without Pre-connected Hose	100 psi (120 kPa)[d]	250 psi (1724 kPa)
Sprinkler System Connection	175 psi (120 kPa)[e]	175 psi (1207 kPa)

Notes:
[a] Pressures in system piping should not exceed the rating of any system component.
[b] Note that pressure relief valves are required for sprinkler systems by NFPA 13, *Installation of Sprinkler Systems*, for similar applications.
[c] Because this limit is less than the minimum pressure that which may be required for Class I hose connections, it may be necessary to separate hose connections with preconnected hoses from those not having preconnected hoses on Class III systems, as opposed to using reducing fittings to accommodate both Class I and Class II hose connection requirements.
[d] This setting will accommodate 200 ft (61 m) of hose connected to a hose connection with approximate flows as follows: 250 gpm (947 L/min) or more from 2- (51 mm) or 2 1/2-in. (64 mm) hose, 150 gpm (568 L/min) from 1 3/4-in. (45 mm) hose, and 125 gpm (473 L/min) from 1 1/2-in. (38 mm) hose. A setting of 165 psi (1138 kPa) can be used when installed on a combined sprinkler/hose connection on combined systems while achieving acceptable flows and nozzles pressure.
[e] Set at 165 psi (1138 kPa).

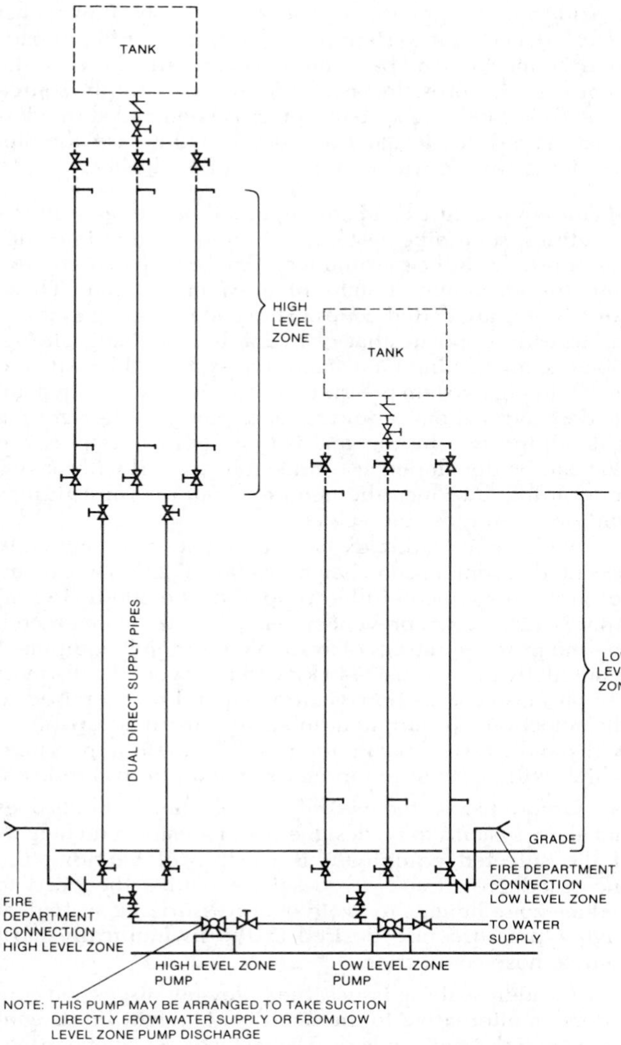

FIG. 5-14E. Sample two-zone system.

Interconnection of piping: One last item to remember when laying out a system is that standpipes must be interconnected at the bottom, or at the top when gravity tanks are used. Interconnection of standpipes ensures that water supplies can service all portions of a system.

System Components

The selection of standpipe system components is determined largely by the class of system and the system layout. Particular attention should be given to ensuring that components are rated for pressures to which they may be subjected.

Piping and fittings: Steel pipe assembled with welded joints, screwed fittings, flanged fittings, rubber-gasketed fittings, or a combination of these is the most common configuration of materials used for standpipe system piping and fittings. Ductile-iron pipe and copper tubing, the latter assembled with brazed joints, also are used occasionally. Piping should be capable of withstanding the maximum pressures that can be developed in a system.

Fittings are required to be rated to withstand either 175 psi (1207 kPa) or maximum system pressures, whichever is greater. When pressures are expected to exceed 175 psi (1207 kPa), extra-heavy fittings or fittings listed for greater pressures should be used for pressures up to 300 psi (2068 kPa), and specially designed fittings should be used for pressures exceeding 300 psi (2068 kPa).

Hose, hose racks, nozzles, and hose cabinets: When preconnected hoses are required to be installed on Class II or Class III systems, lined hose must be used. (Unlined linen hose is being phased out as of 1976, because it is subject to rapid deterioration under moist or wet conditions.) Usually, the size of choice is 1½-in. (38 mm) hose. However, the use of listed hoses smaller than 1½ in. (38 mm) is permitted by NFPA 14, *Installation of Standpipe and Hose Systems*, in light-hazard occupancies when approved by the authority having jurisdiction. The allowance for smaller hose mounted on a reel assumes that an untrained person might be less hesitant and more capable of using such equipment in the event of a fire. Similar equipment has been used in Europe for many years.

Preconnected hoses on Class II and Class III standpipes are generally limited to 100 ft (30.5 m) in length to minimize the difficulty untrained users may have advancing a hose and to minimize kinking. Such hoses are always required to be kept on compatible racks and should always be located in a readily accessible manner within convenient reach of a person standing on the floor. Hoses should be clearly visible and located in a place not likely to be obstructed. Where hoses are kept in cabinets or closets, the doors should have a glass panel or some other means to allow easy identification.

Preconnected hoses are required to be equipped with approved ⅜- or ½-in. (10 or 13 mm) open nozzles or combination spray/solid pattern nozzles. It is preferable to use nozzles that have satisfactory operating pressures in the

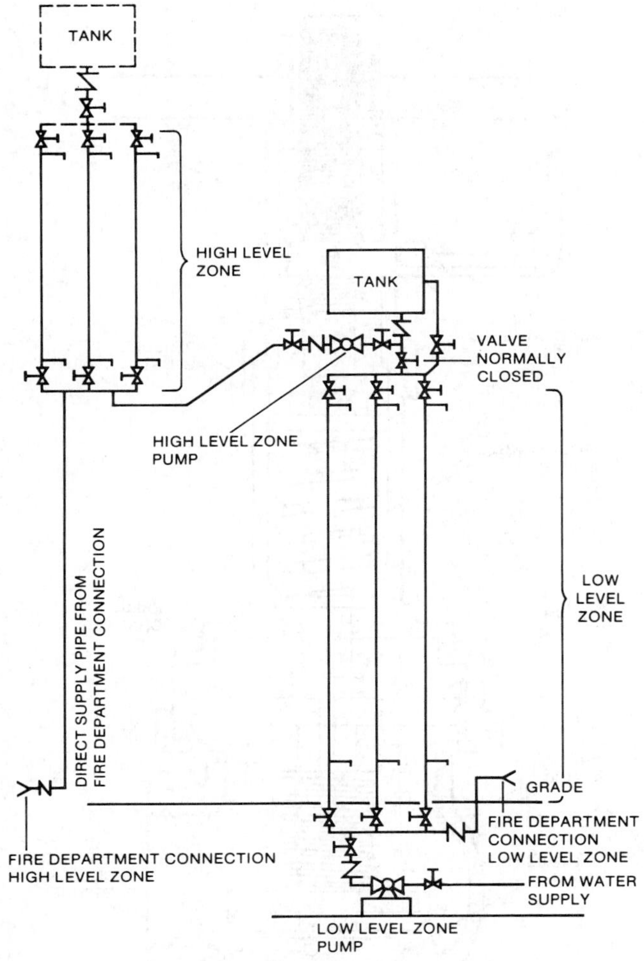

FIG. 5-14F. Sample two-zone system.

FIG. 5-14G. Typical hose racks and valve connections. (Photos courtesy of Potter-Roemer, Inc.)

50-psi (345 kPa) range to maintain hose connection pressures required to operate preconnected hoses at levels that can be handled by occupants. Since nozzle shutoff valves complicate the operation of a hose by an untrained user, they are considered undesirable unless the users are trained.

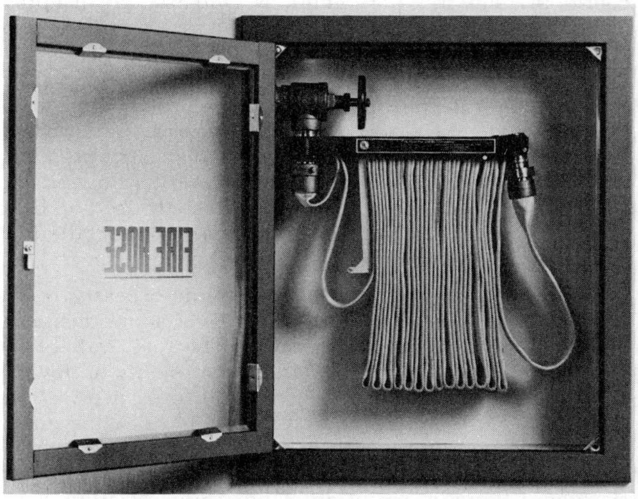

FIG. 5-14H. Typical hose cabinet.

For typical hose rack and valve connections, see Figure 5-14G. A typical hose cabinet is shown in Figure 5-14H.

Valves and pressure control devices: Several different types of valves may be used as components of standpipe systems. These include gate valves, check valves, and hose valves. Valves and pressure control devices, such as piping and fittings, must be capable of withstanding the maximum pressure that can be developed in a system. The following discussion highlights the most common valves and pressure control devices encountered.

Starting at permanent water supplies, indicating gate valves should be provided at each permanent water source to allow isolation of any water source for servicing. Note that gate valves should not be installed between a fire department connection and a system. This ensures the fire department's ability to pump into a system. Next, each permanent water source should be protected by a check valve to prevent backflow. Check valves also should be installed on pipes connecting fire department connections to systems that are normally kept filled with water. These valves allow piping that is connected to fire department connections to normally be kept dry when provided with automatic drain valves at low points.

Moving farther into a system, gate valves should be installed at supply connections to each standpipe to allow standpipes to be serviced independently without impairing entire systems.

Drain valves also should be provided to allow individual standpipes, as well as an entire system, to be drained. Finally, each outlet from a standpipe system must terminate at a hose valve or at a sprinkler control valve on combined systems. When excessive pressures are expected at outlets, pressure control devices also are required.

Pressure control devices are used to limit system discharge pressures. Pressure control devices can be categorized into three basic types: (1) pressure-restricting, (2) pressure-regulating, and (3) pressure relief. Pressure-restricting devices reduce pressures in flowing conditions, but they do not compensate for changes in input pressure to maintain a constant discharge pressure, and they do not control pressure in static conditions. One example of a pressure restricting device is an orifice plate. An orifice plate is a metal disk with a restricting orifice. Orifice plates may be inserted into connections to standpipe systems to reduce residual pressure on the downstream side. Though relatively inexpensive, orifice plates are generally undesirable because they do not maintain a steady discharge pressure, and because they can damage hoses at high flows if the pressure jet from an orifice strikes a hose. If used on hose connections, orifice plates should always be installed on hose couplings to allow easy removal if necessary.

The devices preferred for controlling excessive pressures are pressure-regulating valves, which are designed actively control discharge pressures. They are available in two types: (1) those that regulate pressure only in flowing conditions, and (2) those that regulate pressure in both static and flowing conditions. The latter are better-suited for use with standpipe systems because hoses and sprinkler systems connected to standpipes are exposed to both static and flowing conditions, and if uncontrolled static pressures were allowed, equipment failure and danger to users could result.

Pressure-regulating valves capable of controlling pressures in both static and flowing conditions generally employ an active mechanism that compensates for variations in inlet pressures by balancing water pressure in an internal chamber or chambers against a spring. Figure 5-14I illustrates one example of a pressure-regulating valve that operates in static and flowing conditions. In the case shown, the outlet pressure is a function of the setting on the regulating spring. Often, the outlet pressure is not field-adjustable, and valves are preset at the factory for use at a specific floor level in a building. In such cases, it is critical to ensure that valves are installed at the intended location.

Unfortunately, pressure-regulating valves have a history of high failure rates, so standpipe systems having such devices must be designed so that each device may be tested, and routine testing must be conducted. To accommodate the need for testing pressure-regulating valves, standpipe systems using such valves should be installed with a direct connection to a dedicated drainage system at each pressure-regulating valve, with a central means for measuring flow. Figure 5-14J shows a typical design of such an arrangement. The case shown assumes a standpipe pressure in excess of 175 psi (1207 kPa) and a combined sprinkler and standpipe system.

Where system pressures are extreme, pressure relief valves, which reduce pressures by flowing water into a drain, may be provided as a backup to pressure-regulating valves. Pressure relief valves are commonly available in two types: (1) spring operated, and (2) pilot operated. Pilot operated valves are preferred since they respond more quickly to changes in system pressures; however, these values require increased maintenance to prevent excessive accumulation of debris in strainers.

Fire department connections: Fire department connections are required for all Class I and Class III systems. In some cases, fire department connections are allowed to serve as the sole water supply for a Class I system. In other cases, they serve as an auxiliary water supply. As a rule, fire fighters rely heavily on fire department connections because they often prefer to use their own water supply, instead of an in-house system, as a primary supply.

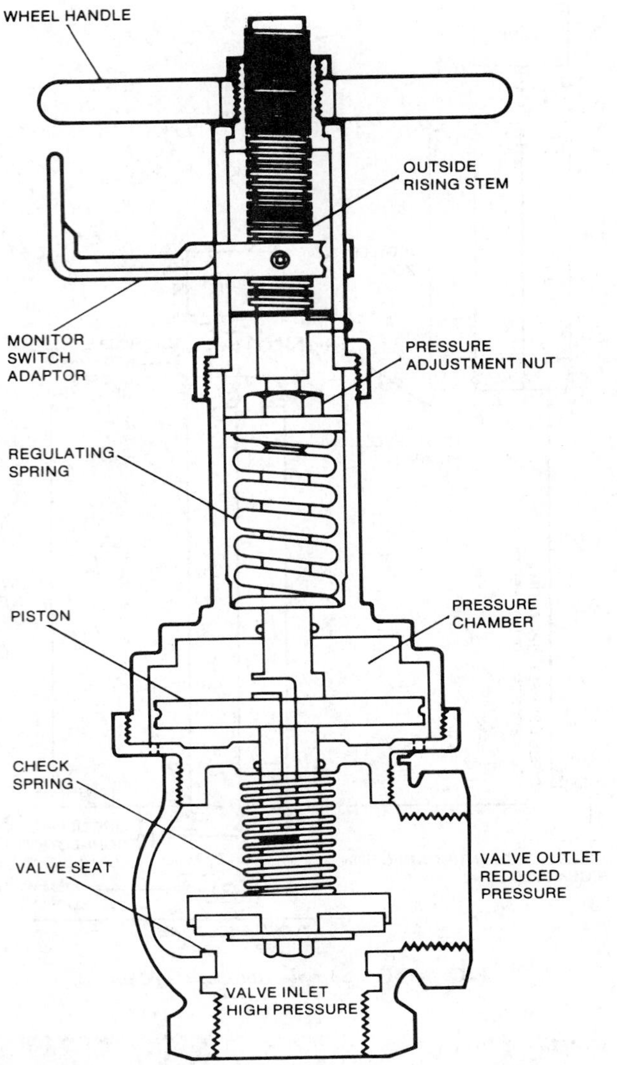

FIG. 5-14I. Cutaway of a typical in-line pressure-regulating valve.

Fire department connections should be located where they are easily accessible to fire department apparatus and nearby to a fire hydrant. They should not be obstructed from access or from view by shrubbery, vehicles, fences, or similar obstructions. It is preferable to install two or more connections, located as remotely from each other as possible, for each system. This redundancy can significantly improve a system's reliability in providing uninterrupted service during a fire, particularly in cases of high-rise buildings where falling glass from broken windows can cut supply hoses and prevent personnel from reconnecting new hoses.

As a rule, most fire department connections are provided with one 2½-in. (64 mm) inlet for each 250 gpm (947 L/min) of design flow rate. Some fire departments have switched to large-diameter inlets that are designed to connect to special high-pressure, large-diameter hoses. Even when large-diameter hoses are used, a second inlet may be desirable to allow simultaneous connection of a backup

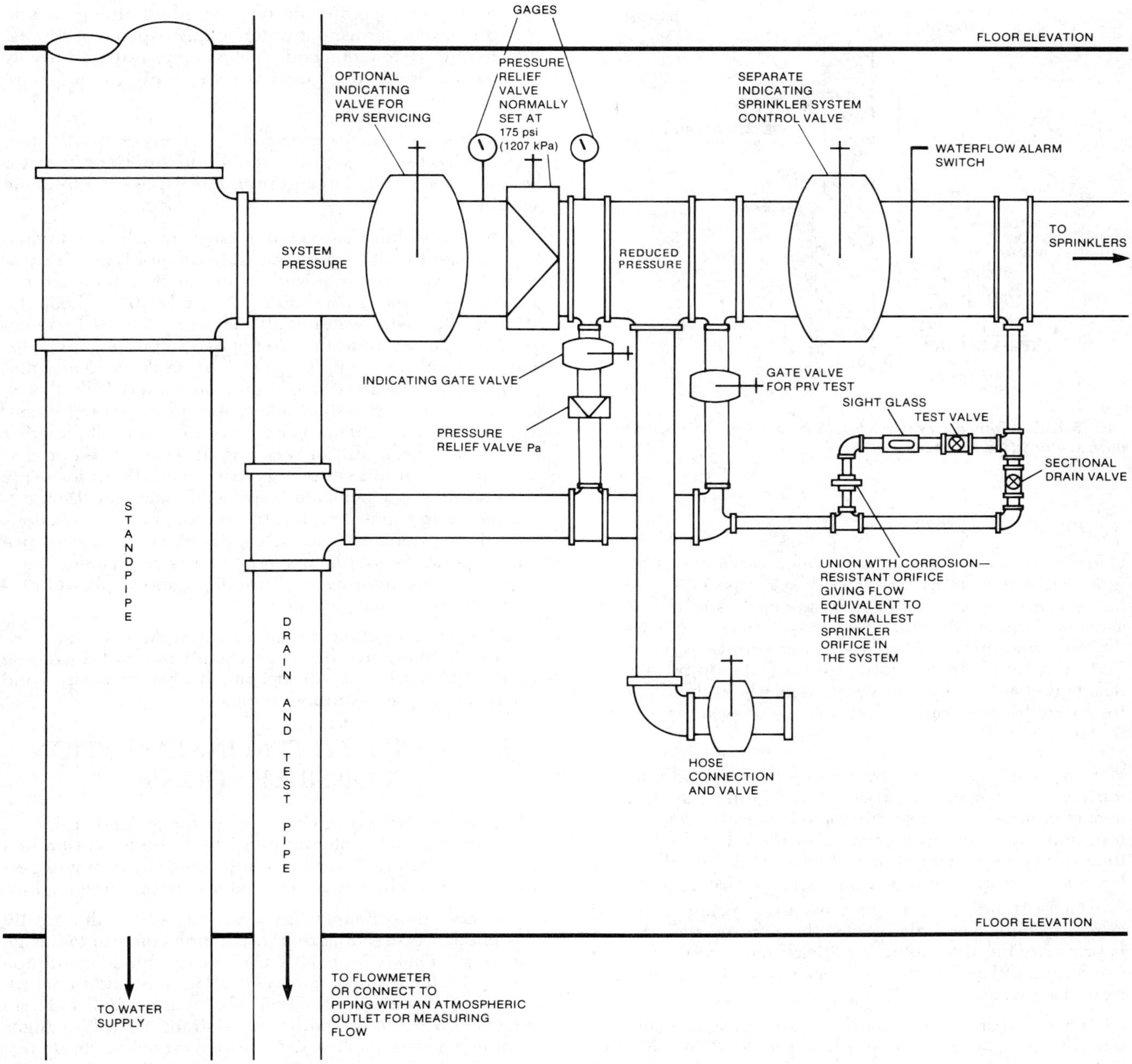

FIG. 5-14J. Sample arrangement for valving at floor connections to combined systems. (Not to scale)

hose for use should the primary hose rupture or separate from a coupling.

Another important issue that should not be overlooked is the size of the pipe connecting a fire department connection to system mains. This pipe should be sized to deliver the system demand, as discussed previously under "Sizing Pipe." It is preferable to use 4-in. (102 mm) or larger piping in all cases to inhibit obstruction by debris.

Figure 5-14K illustrates a typical arrangement for a fire department connection on a standpipe system normally having water-filled piping.

System monitoring and supervision devices: To ensure the reliability and performance of standpipe systems, provisions must be made for monitoring system pressure and supervising control valves. System pressure can be monitored by installing gages at each connection of a water supply to a system and at the top of each standpipe.

Valve supervision can be accomplished by electrical or mechanical means. Supervision is generally required for water supply isolation valves, standpipe isolation valves, and similar valves that are capable of interrupting the water supply to large portions of a system.

Occasionally, waterflow alarms are also specified for monitoring a system. Such cases are usually limited to systems having preconnected hoses where immediate notification of waterflow is desired. Also, supervision of hose cabinet doors may be provided where vandalism is a concern.

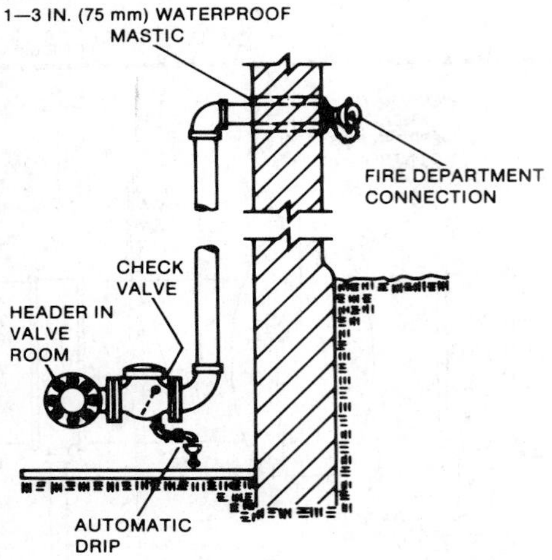

FIG. 5-14K. Typical fire department connection for a standpipe with water-filled piping.

Types of Systems

Codes and standards commonly refer to two types of systems: (1) wet systems, and (2) dry systems. These designations serve as a means of simultaneously specifying two aspects of system design, whether system piping is wet or dry and whether a permanent water supply is required. Unfortunately, these two aspects of standpipe system design do not lend themselves particularly to simultaneous treatment, so the application of types of systems is often misunderstood.

Wet standpipe systems: By definition, wet standpipe systems are those having both water-filled piping at all times and a permanent water supply capable of supplying the system demand. Wet systems are considered more reliable than dry systems, which do not have water-filled piping, because leaks in water-filled piping are very easy to detect.

Class II and Class III systems are typically designed as wet systems, particularly when hoses are installed. This is primarily because of the significant danger to untrained users from delayed water delivery while air is exhausted from dry piping.

Class I systems may also be designed as wet systems when a permanent water supply is provided and the piping is not subject to freezing.

Dry standpipe systems: Dry standpipe systems may or may not have a permanent water supply capable of supplying the system demand, and they may or may not have water-filled piping.

The three configurations of dry standpipe systems most commonly found are:

1. Systems normally having air-filled piping that are arranged to admit water automatically by means of a dry-pipe valve or some other approved device.
2. Systems normally having air-filled piping that are arranged to admit water through the manual operation of approved remote-control devices located at each hose station. For this type of system, careful consideration should be given to design of a reliable control system.
3. Systems with either air- or water-filled piping, that do not have a permanent water supply capable of supplying the system demand. Such systems rely exclusively on fire department apparatus to supply water for fire fighting.

Systems of the first two configurations are used when a permanent water supply capable of supplying the system demand is needed and piping is exposed to freezing conditions.

Systems of the third configuration may be used when a permanent water supply capable of supplying the system demand is not required. When such systems are not exposed to freezing conditions, it is preferable to keep the piping filled with water at all times to allow early detection of leaks. Systems that do not have a permanent water supply capable of supplying the system demand and that normally have water-filled piping are called "filled" systems. With a filled system, standpipe system piping is connected to a 3/4-in. (19 mm) or a 1-in. (25.4 mm) fill pipe that keeps the system full of water at all times. The one disadvantage to filled systems is that it is difficult for users to determine when a water supply adequate for fire fighting has been connected. For this reason, hose connections on filled systems should be clearly marked to warn fire fighters that the system does not have a permanent water supply for fire fighting, and fire departments should preplan the use of such systems.

Recognizing the confusion surrounding types of systems, it is likely that codes and standards will develop a revised approach that will separate the "water-in-pipe" and "permanent-water-supply" issues.

STANDPIPE SYSTEM INSTALLATION CONSIDERATIONS

Though a proper design establishes the groundwork for a reliable and usable standpipe system, the execution of a design ultimately determines how well a system will perform. A few of the key considerations are discussed below.

Since most standpipe systems are hydraulically designed, it is essential that installation conform to design drawings. This is especially true for combined standpipe and sprinkler systems. Since installation of additional fittings or pipe lengths to avoid obstructions will have an adverse effect on hydraulic calculations, as will changes in pipe sizes, installation specifications should indicate that all such changes should be reported to the designer for approval. Installation specifications should also caution the installers of systems that have preset pressure-regulating valves to ensure that such valves are installed at the proper floor levels.

To ensure operability and maintainability, it is preferable to identify piping and indicate the direction of water flow. Valve locations also should be clearly identified and accessible. Particular attention should be given to providing access space around hose connections, recognizing that fire fighters will be using large gloves when connecting hoses and operating valves. Twelve inches (0.3 m) of clear space from the valve handles and hose outlets to the walls or other obstructions is desirable.

The key concerns when locating fire department connections are accessibility and visibility. Fire department connections should be clear of shrubbery, parking vehicle, and other obstructions that could hinder their use. In addition, signs should be provided, preferably reflective, to indicate whether a connection serves standpipes, sprinklers, or both, and to indicate the area served by the connection.

During construction of a building which will have a standpipe system, it is important that the system be able to operate as soon as the work progresses to a point where deployment of hoses from fire apparatus no longer provides an efficient means of fire fighting. Local codes usually dictate the point at which standpipes must be made operable during construction.

The need for standpipes during construction has been demonstrated in many fires. Even noncombustible buildings often represent extreme fire hazards during construction because of the concurrent presence of combustible shoring and a variety of ignition sources. To provide protection during construction, the permanent system piping is typically used, along with a temporary fire department connection. In addition, at least one hose connection should be provided at each floor level, and all hose connections should be kept

capped and protected from injury. Systems providing protection during construction should be extended to keep pace with construction progress, and routine inspection should be scheduled to ensure that systems are kept operable.

TESTING AND INSPECTING STANDPIPE SYSTEMS

Since standpipe systems are essential components of manual fire fighting in large buildings, they must be tested and inspected routinely to ensure operational readiness. Testing should be conducted before system acceptance and at intervals adequate to verify reliability. There is no commonly accepted rule for frequency of testing. Some sources recommend testing every two years. Others recommend intervals of up to five years. Consequently, the authority having jurisdiction must determine local requirements based upon local climate, maintenance frequency requirements, and available resources for conducting tests.

Testing should verify that a system performs to the original installation requirements. Prior to conducting a performance test, a visual inspection should be conducted to verify that:

- Water supplies have been properly maintained.
- Valves to water supplies and standpipes are open and supervised by a chain and lock, seal, or electrical device.
- Piping is securely joined at connections. If piping will be enclosed, it should be left exposed prior to initial acceptance testing.
- Hose connections are accessible, valve wheels are present, and hose threads on fire department connections are protected by caps. On dry systems, ensure that valves are closed. Hose threads on connections must match those used by the jurisdiction.
- Hose stations are properly maintained.

Fire hose must be maintained in the proper position on racks and be in good condition. Each hose should be removed and inspected for cuts, abrasions, faulty gaskets, and loose couplings, then re-racked, at an interval not exceeding five years immediately after the purchase date and every three years thereafter. Periodic hydrostatic testing of lined hose is required; unlined linen hose should not be hydrostatically tested because it is susceptibile to rot and mildew if left even slightly damp. In addition, nozzles should be removed and examined for foreign objects. Specific inspection and maintenance instructions for fire hose are set forth in NFPA 1962, *Care, Use, and Maintenance of Fire Hose, Including Connections and Nozzles*.

Once a pre-inspection is completed, hydrostatic and flow tests should be conducted. Pressure gages should be checked on each standpipe during testing to verify the interconnection of standpipes. Dry systems should be air-tested before they are charged with water. Flow tests should be conducted to verify:

- Operation of automatic water supplies.
- Serviceability of each fire department connection.
- Proper flow rates, static pressures, and residual pressures for each standpipe and for pressure control devices.

When standpipes are flow tested by flowing water at the roof level, a flow diffuser is recommended at the point of discharge to control the water stream and intercept any debris that may be ejected. Particular attention should be paid to the adequacy of the drainage route for water.

When flow testing pressure-regulating devices, it is preferable to measure a full range of actual flows and pressures at each device to ensure that all devices perform to specifications. Using a full range of flows is also advisable to ensure that the devices are exercised. The need for testing and maintenance of pressure-regulating devices has been clearly demonstrated by the results of tests conducted by the City of Los Angeles Fire Department between 1984 and 1986. In these tests, 413 pressure-regulating valves were tested in a dozen buildings. Test results indicated that more than 75 percent of the valves tested required re-calibration, repair, or replacement.

FIRE DEPARTMENT OPERATIONS USING STANDPIPE SYSTEMS

The effectiveness of standpipe systems in assisting fire fighters is directly proportional to their familiarity with the system and operational training. Fire departments should pre-plan buildings with standpipe systems to become familiar with the locations of fire hydrants, fire department connections, water supply valves, pumps, tanks, and hose connections. This will minimize delays in utilizing the system. The presence of orifice plates in hose connections or pressure-reducing or -regulating devices should also be noted. Fire departments also should develop standard operating procedures that assign personnel and apparatus responsibilities for using standpipe systems.

Most fire departments carry "standpipe packs" on responding apparatus which contain the equipment necessary to use standpipe system hose connections. Standpipe packs are typically carried on carts or in bags and contain between 100 and 200 ft (30.5 and 61 m) of hose, a nozzle, and miscellaneous tools and wrenches. A gated wye may also be carried to allow a second hose to be connected to a single hose connection. The length of hose carried should be based upon local practices regarding which hose connections are expected to be used and the local building code requirements for locating hose connections.

Probably the most versatile hose arrangement is one that includes 1¾- or 2-in. (45 or 51 mm) hose and a high-volume nozzle capable of flowing 200 gpm (757 L/min) or more. Such an arrangement can provide a flow capability comparable to a 2½-in. (64 mm) hose with a selectable flow fog nozzle when adequate pressure is available, but it is significantly easier to handle. A fog nozzle that produces an effective pattern and flow at operating pressures less than 100 psi (690 kPa) should be used if possible to reduce the pressure necessary to support standpipe systems.

In addition to standpipe packs, fire apparatus should also carry coiled or packed sections of 2½-in. (64 mm) hose for cases where large volumes of water are necessary and the pressure available from a standpipe is limited. Such cases may occur in very tall buildings that have floor levels beyond the range of fire apparatus where exclusive reliance on in-house systems is required.

It is common to have the first fire fighting crew that arrives at the scene of an incident in a building with a standpipe system take a standpipe pack into the building when investigating the call. Meanwhile, an engine should connect to a fire department connection to supply the system. More than one supply hose should be connected to a system during a fire to prevent the water supply from being interrupted if a supply hose breaks. It is also preferable for additional apparatus to connect to different fire department connections, when more than one is present, during major fires in high-rise buildings. This reduces the risk of interruption of the water supply if glass breakage on upper floors makes conditions at some parts of a building's perimeter unsafe, perhaps cutting supply hoses.

When fire fighters determine that hoses are needed, they should select a hose connection located in a protected stairway enclosure, as opposed to a connection located in a corridor or open area, since it is desirable to have a charged hose before entering a floor if smoke or flame is detected. In multiple-story buildings, a hose connection located one floor below a fire floor is often preferred over a connection at a fire floor because it provides additional space to spread a hose before charging it, and minimizes congestion at the entrance to a fire floor. It should be noted that using a hose connection on a lower floor will create a need for additional hose to be able to reach all areas on a fire floor. Fire fighters should also be aware that, depending on desired flows, they may have to remove pressure-reducing devices or to adjust pressure-regulating devices.

The pressure to which a standpipe system is charged through a fire department connection often varies from one fire department to another based upon local preferences. Some departments use recommendations in NFPA 13E, *Fire Department Operations in Properties Protected by Sprinkler and Standpipe Systems*, which suggest that the pressure at the fire department connection be initiated at 100 psi (690 kPa) when solid-pattern nozzles will be used at elevations of 100 ft (30.5 m) or less, and at 150 psi (1034 kPa) when fog nozzles will be used at elevations of 100 ft (30.5 m) or less. For elevations above 100 ft (30.5 m), 5 psi (34.5 kPa) should be added for each floor level above 100 ft (30.5 m). Other departments simply pump 150 psi (1034 kPa) plus 5 psi (34.5 kPa) for each floor level above grade. The latter method is more commonly used and will deliver adequate pressure in all cases.

OUTSIDE HOSE SYSTEMS

Outside hose systems are appendages to water supply systems. Outside hose systems are similar to standpipe systems, since they also provide an efficient means of manually applying water to fires. Though not mandated by model building or fire codes, outside hose systems may be requested by insurance authorities or by owners as an additional safety measure to minimize potential fire losses. Outside hose systems typically are found at industrial sites, and since they usually include equipment for delivering high-volume fire streams, their installation or use is not appropriate where there is not a trained fire brigade. Systems will usually consist of yard-type fire hydrants, strategically placed around buildings, adjacent to which fire hose and fire fighting accessories are stored in hose houses. Rooftop hose houses or hose stations may also be provided when rooftop or exposure hazards are present.

Design

The design of outside hose systems should be tailored to its intended uses. These include deployment by a trained fire brigade until the fire department arrives, serving as backup protection for sprinkler systems when such systems are not in service, and serving as a backup water supply for impaired sprinkler systems by providing a ready means of supporting a fire department connection. NFPA 24, *Private Fire Service Mains and Their Appurtenances*, establishes the most commonly used design standards.

Fire hydrant spacing and placement of hose houses should be adequate to allow fire hoses to reach the desired locations while minimizing the distance which hose must be advanced. Selection of fire hydrant locations and hose lengths should consider the path of travel, as well as any obstructions between the hydrants and the target areas. When interior standpipe systems are present, it may not be necessary to provide coverage using outside hoses to all portions of a target building's interior. When rooftop hazards are present, a means of advancing hoses to the roof, such as fixed exterior ladders, hoisting ropes, and hose straps, should be provided unless there are rooftop hose houses or hose stations.

When designing outside hose systems, the needs of the fire department for on-site fire hydrants must also be considered. For large buildings, on-site hydrants may be required to serve as a water source for fire department apparatus, in addition to supplying hose systems. In such cases, underground mains must be designed for the required fire flow, and fire hydrants must be placed in locations required by the local fire code.

Equipment

NFPA 24, *Private Fire Service Mains and Their Appurtenances*, includes nationally recognized standards for fire hydrants, construction of hose houses, and equipment to be maintained in hose houses. The following is an overview of some of the major considerations for outside hose system equipment.

Fire hydrants should have outlets for use by fire brigades and fire department apparatus as necessary. Hose threads and lugs on fire hydrants should always match those used by the local fire department. It is preferable to equip each outlet with an independent valve to avoid the need to shut a fire hydrant when connecting additional hoses.

The principal features considered in hose house construction are ventilation and protection against the weather. Ventilation can be obtained by using a slatted floor and slatted shelves and by allowing space for ventilation under roof overhangs. Vents should be arranged so that rain cannot enter the structure. Hose houses should be of substantial construction and large enough to contain and provide operating space for all equipment. Where it is necessary to lock hose houses, special locks with brittle shackles or latches behind break-glass panels can be used to provide ready access in an emergency.

FIG. 5-14L. ***Typical hose houses. (Photo courtesy of Potter-Roemer, Inc.)***

FIG. 5-14M. ***Typical rooftop hose station. (Photo courtesy of Potter-Roemer, Inc.)***

Hoses for outside hose systems may be preconnected and stored in hose houses, or kept on hose carts that can deliver hose to a fire scene, or both. Preconnected hoses are often preferred to minimize the time necessary to begin fire fighting. The length of hose required will depend on hydrant locations. For hose lays greater than 150 ft (46 m), hose carts or other vehicles should be considered. One-and-three-quarter-in. (45 mm) and 2-in. (51 mm) hoses with $1\frac{1}{2}$-in. (38 mm) couplings are preferred sizes, providing high-flow characteristics with minimal friction loss and relatively easy maneuvering. Other possible arrangements include 100 to 150 ft (30.5 to 46 m) of $2\frac{1}{2}$-in. (64 mm) hose with a gated wye at the end, connecting to an additional length of smaller hose. The wye allows for subsequent connection of additional hoses closer to a fire.

Figures 5-14L and 5-14M are examples of hose houses and a rooftop hose station, respectively, that are commercially available.

Accessories

Accessory equipment in a hose house should include hydrant wrenches, nozzles, spare hose washers, gated wyes, reducing couplings, spanner wrenches, fire axes, and other tools, as necessary. When selecting nozzles, the particular fire hazard present should be considered. For example, spray nozzles are preferred for flammable liquids and electrical fires, and solid-stream nozzles may be preferred for lumber storage.

Hose Carts

Hose carts are useful where a hose supply is needed to supplement that stored in hose houses; where long travel distances are anticipated for deployment, such as in large factories or warehouses; and where there are outlying buildings or yard storage areas beyond easy reach of hose

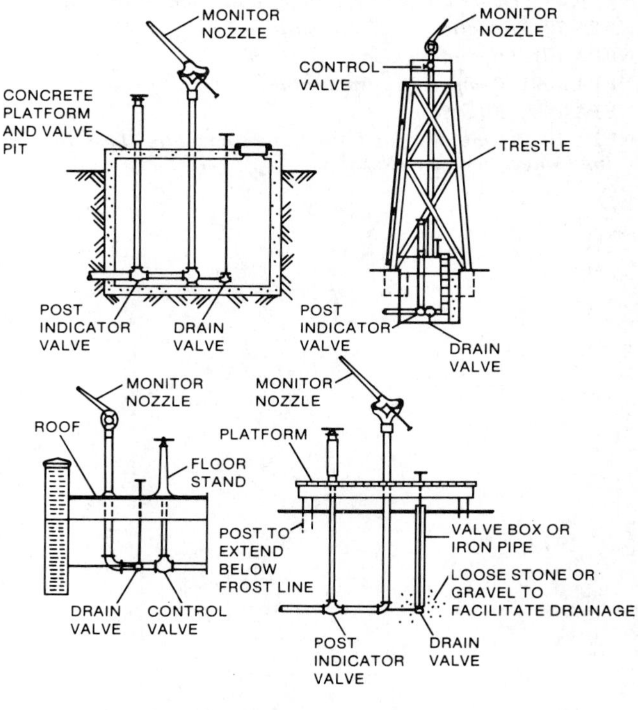

FIG. 5-14N. ***Various arrangements of monitor nozzles.***

houses. Carts may be motorized, hand-pulled, or modular devices stored for pickup and transportation by a lift truck. They should be stored in a central location.

Monitor Nozzles

Where large amounts of combustible materials, such as log piles, lumber piles, flammable or combustible liquids, or railway cars, are stored in yards, it may be necessary to provide a means of quickly delivering large volumes of water to control a fire. This can be best accomplished by installing permanent monitor nozzles around such storage at grade level, on special trestles, or on the roofs of buildings, and by having portable monitor nozzles available for use. Figure 5-14N illustrates various arrangements of monitor nozzles.

BIBLIOGRAPHY

Reference Cited

1. *Uniform Building Code*, Chapter 38, International Conference of Building Officials, Whittier, CA, 1988.

NFPA Codes, Standards, and Recommended Practices

Reference to the following NFPA codes, standards, and recommended practices will provide further information on standpipe and hose systems discussed in this chapter. (See the latest *NFPA Catalog* for availability of current editions of the following documents.)

NFPA 1, *Fire Prevention Code*.

NFPA 13, *Installation of Sprinkler Systems*.

NFPA 13E, *Fire Department Operations in Properties Protected by Sprinkler and Standpipe Systems*.

NFPA 14, *Installation of Standpipe and Hose Systems*.

NFPA 20, *Installation of Centrifugal Fire Pumps*.

NFPA 22, *Water Tanks for Private Fire Protection*.

NFPA 24, *Private Fire Service Mains and Their Appurtenances*.

NFPA 72, *Protective Signaling Systems*.

NFPA 101, *Life Safety Code*.

NFPA 1901, *Pumper Fire Apparatus*.

NFPA 1961, *Fire Hose*.

NFPA 1962, *Care, Use, and Maintenance of Fire Hose, Including Connections and Nozzles*.

NFPA 1963, *Screw Threads and Gaskets for Fire Hose Connections*.

NFPA 1964, *Spray Nozzles (Shutoff and Tip)*.

Additional Reading

National Building Code, Sec. 1012, Building Officials and Code Administrators International, Inc., Country Club Hills, IL, 1990.

Bond, H., "Water for Fire Fighting in High-Rise Buildings," *Fire Technology*, Vol. 2, No. 2, pp. 159-163.

Bryan, J. L., *Automatic Sprinkler and Standpipe Systems*, 2nd ed., National Fire Protection Association, Quincy, MA, 1990.

Carson, W. G. and Klinker, R. L., *Fire Protection Systems: Inspection, Test and Maintenance Manual,* National Fire Protection Association, Quincy, MA, 1986.

Chapman, E. F., "Standpipe Operations," *Fire Engineering*, Vol. 142, No. 1, 1989, pp. 47-49.

City of Fort Worth, Texas, *Standpipe Testing Procedure, SOP 405.1*, Sept. 1984.

Fire Protection Equipment List, Underwriters Laboratories Inc., Northbrook, IL, (published annually with bimonthly supplements).

Factory Mutual Approval Guide, Factory Mutual Research Corporation, Norwood, MA, (published annually).

Hammack, J. M., "Combined Sprinkler System and Standpipes," *Fire Journal*, Vol. 65, No. 5, pp. 68-69

Jensen, R., *ed.*, *Fire Protection for the Design Professional*, Cahners, Boston, 1975, pp. 66-71.

Kimball, W. Y., "Can Pumpers Supply Standpipes in High-Rise Buildings," *Fire Journal*, Vol. 59, No. 5, (Sept. 1965).

Loss Prevention Data Sheet 3-10, Factory Mutual Research Corporation, Norwood, MA, Mar. 1981, pp. 30-31.

Loss Prevention Data Sheet 3-11, Factory Mutual Research Corporation, Norwood, MA, Dec. 1986.

Lyons, P. R., "Dry Standpipe Survey in Los Angeles," *Fire Journal*, Vol. 63, No. 3 (May 1969), pp. 63-66.

Nolan, J. W., "How to Approach Standpipe Design," *Actual Specifying Engineer*, Vol. 24, No. 7 (July 1970), pp. 85-89.

Private Fire Protection and Detection, Fire Protection Publications, Oklahoma State University, 1979, pp. 111-114.

Standard Building Code, Sec. 902, Southern Building Code Congress International, Inc., Birmingham, AL, 1988.

Uniform Building Code and Uniform Building Code Standards, International Conference of Building Officials, Whittier, CA, 1990.

Wolfe, J. C., "Teaching notes from training session in Los Angeles City," Nov. 18, 1986.

WATER SPRAY PROTECTION

Revised by Wayne E. Ault

The term "water spray" refers to water that has a predetermined pattern, particle size, velocity, and density, and that is discharged from specially designed nozzles or devices. Water spray for fire protection has been called water fog and various trade-name designations.

The discharge from water spray nozzles differs, generally, from the discharge from sprinklers. The pattern of the water spray discharged from spray nozzles onto a surface may be elliptical or circular, and the cross section of the projected discharge is conical. The water spray is forcefully directed onto the object or surface being protected. The pattern of spray nozzle discharge must carry water spray over the distance between the nozzle and the target, compensate for wind and draft conditions, and effectively hit the surface to be protected. The required discharge density in gallons per minute per square foot and complete coverage of the area to be protected are also essential elements.

Unlike most automatic sprinkler systems, water spray systems are of the deluge type. Spray nozzles are not equipped with fusible operating elements.

Spray nozzles may be equipped with internal pilot-pressure controlled valves or with frangible or removable plugs or caps that will be displaced when the water spray deluge system is actuated. Pilot-pressure-controlled valves, plugs, or caps prevent corrosive atmospheres from entering the piping system. They may be used to retain water in the piping system for the purpose of speeding its delivery from the spray nozzles.

This chapter covers the uses and applications of water spray systems for fire prevention, control, and extinguishment and describes the components of spray systems and the specialized uses of the systems. Because of the similarities between sprinkler systems and water spray systems, their water supply requirements, some of the equipment used in the systems, and the hydraulic calculations for determining water supplies, other chapters in this section of the handbook should be consulted. These include Chapter 1, "Water and Water Additives for Fire Fighting," including the extinguishing properties of water and safe clearances from electrical equipment; Chapter 9, "Automatic Sprinkler Systems;" and Chapter 11, "Water Supplies for Sprinkler Systems."

Section 4, Chapter 5, "Automatic Fire Detectors," including releasing devices that can be used with water spray systems, and Section 8, Chapter 31, "Materials Handling Equipment," including protection of conveyor openings should also be consulted.

NFPA 15, *Water-Spray Fixed Systems for Fire Protection*, is the standard applicable to water spray systems and should be consulted on details of system design and installation not covered in NFPA 13, *Installation of Sprinkler Systems*.

USES FOR WATER SPRAY PROTECTION

Generally, water spray can be used effectively to extinguish a fire, control a fire, protect exposures and/or prevent a fire.

Extinguishment

Water spray extinguishes a fire by cooling it, smothering it with the steam produced, emulsifying or diluting some flammable liquids, or by combining these factors.

Controlled Burning

With its consequent limitation of fire spread, controlled burning may be applied if the burning combustibles can not be extinguished by water spray, or if extinguishment is not desirable.

Exposure Protection

Exposures are protected by applying water spray directly to the exposed structures or equipment to remove or reduce the heat transferred to them from the exposing fire. Water spray curtains mounted at a distance from the exposed surface are less effective than direct application.

Wayne E. Ault, P.E., is chairman of the NFPA Water Spray Committee. Formerly the manager of Research and Development for Automatic Sprinkler Corporation of America, Mr. Ault is a senior engineering consultant with Rolf Jensen and Associates, Inc., Deerfield, IL.

Prevention of Fire

It is sometimes possible to use water spray to dissolve, dilute, disperse, or cool flammable or combustible materials before they are ignited by an exposing ignition source.

APPLICATION OF WATER SPRAY SYSTEMS

Water spray can be used to protect the following types of materials or equipment:

1. Ordinary combustible materials, such as paper, wood, and textiles, particularly to extinguish fires in such materials rather than control them.
2. Electrical equipment installations, such as transformers, oil switches, and rotating electrical machinery.
3. Flammable gases and liquids, particularly to control fires in these materials and to extinguish certain types of fires involving combustible liquids.
4. Flammable liquid and gas tanks, processing equipment, and structures, as protection against exposure fires.
5. Open cable trays and runs containing electrical cables or tubing.

Fixed water spray systems are designed specifically to provide optimum control, extinguishment, or exposure protection for special fire protection problems. Limitations to the use of water spray that should be recognized involve the nature of the equipment to be protected, the physical and chemical properties of the materials involved, and the environment of the hazard.

FIXED WATER SPRAY SYSTEMS

A water spray system is a special fixed pipe system connected to a reliable supply of fire protection water, and equipped with water spray nozzles for specific water discharge and distribution over the surface or area to be protected. The piping system is connected to a water supply through a deluge valve which can be actuated both automatically and manually to initiate the flow of water.

Automatic water control valves for spray systems can be actuated electrically by the operation of automatic detection equipment, such as heat detectors, relay circuits, and gas detectors, or mechanically by hydraulic or pneumatic systems, depending upon the operating mode of the individual valves. Generally, each manufacturer of valves, most of which can do dual service in deluge systems, provides its own particular combination of water control valve, releasing mechanism, heat detection system, and supervisory service.

Application of Systems

Fixed water spray systems are most commonly used to protect equipment from exposure fires in flammable liquid and gas tankage, piping, and equipment; in electrical equipment, such as transformers, oil switches, and rotating machinery; in structural supports; and in conveyor systems and the openings in firewalls and floors through which they pass. The type of water spray required for any particular hazard will depend on the nature of the hazard and the purpose for which the protection is provided.

A water spray installation being tested at a group of liquefied petroleum gas tanks is shown in Figure 5-15A. The spray system shown is designed to give complete surface wetting with a specified water density, taking into consideration nozzle types, sizes, and spacing; the influence of wind and drafts; the probability of water rundown; the prevention of the formation of difficult-to-wet deposits of soot or carbon on surfaces; the overlap of water discharge patterns onto the surfaces; and the ability of the water supply to furnish adequate pressure to all of the nozzles. Ordinarily, it is neither desired nor expected that water spray extinguish escaping liquefied petroleum gas. However, the cooling effect of the water on the tanks may reduce and control the rate of burning and reduce the severity of the exposure until the gas supply to the fire is exhausted or can be shut off.

FIG. 5-15A. Water spray protection for LP-Gas tanks. The spray keeps the tanks cool in case of fire, prevents the liquid contents from boiling away, and protects the tank shells against rupture due to localized high-temperature flame impingement.

Water spray protection for a group of oil-filled electric transformers is shown under test in Figure 5-15B. Due to the relatively high flash point and boiling point of transformer oil, transformer fires can be extinguished quickly by properly designed water spray systems. However, the metal surfaces of the transformer case and its structural supports must be protected from radiant heat while the burning transformer oil is being extinguished. Care must be taken to locate nozzles, piping, and supports the prescribed distances from electrically charged parts of the transformer installation, and direct application of water spray to electrically charged terminals or insulating bushings should be avoided. Electricity to the transformer should be shut off automatically before water spray is applied.

Design of Systems

The practical location of the piping and nozzles with respect to the surface to which the spray is to be applied or to the zone in which the spray is to be effective is determined largely by the physical arrangement and protection needs of the installation requiring protection. Once the criteria are established, the size of the nozzles to be used, the angle of the nozzle discharge cone, and the water pressure needed can be determined.

The first factor to determine is the water density required to extinguish the fire or to absorb the expected heat from exposure or combustion. When this has been

FIG. 5-15B. A water spray system for oil-filled electric power transformers. A thick layer of crushed stone and subsurface drainage is provided around the base of the transformer installation to prevent the possibility that burning oil might flow beyond the ground area protected by the spray.

determined, a nozzle may be selected that will provide that density at a velocity adequate to overcome air currents and to carry the spray to the equipment to be protected. Each nozzle chosen must have the proper angle of discharge to cover the area to be protected by the nozzle.

Determining the proper density needed for extinguishment requires considerable engineering judgment and, in the case of flammable or combustible liquids, depends on such characteristics of the fuel as vapor pressure, flash point, viscosity, water solubility, and specific gravity. The density would vary between 0.2 gpm per sq ft and 0.5 gpm per sq ft [8.1 (L/min)/m^2 to 20.4 (L/min)/m^2] of protected surface.

For exposure protection of vessels, a density of 0.25 gpm per sq ft [10.2 (L/min)/m^2] should provide sufficient cooling to limit an exposure fire's heat input through the vessel walls to 6000 Btu per hr per sq ft (18,930 W/m^2). The water density required for exposure protection of structural supports and miscellaneous equipment, such as cable trays and runs, pipe racks, transformers, and belt conveyors, varies from 0.10 gpm per sq ft [4.1 (L/min)/m^2] to 0.3 gpm per sq ft [12.2 (L/min)/m^2] of exposed surface area. NFPA 15, *Water-Spray Fixed Systems for Fire Protection*, should be consulted for more details on required distribution densities.

Once the type of nozzle has been selected and the location and spacing to give the desired area coverage have been determined, hydraulic calculations are made to establish the appropriate pipe sizes and water supply requirements.

When water spray is to be used to protect oil-filled electrical equipment, such as transformers and large switch gear, special care must be taken to provide safe electrical clearances. Special fixed water spray nozzles have been developed to provide adequate spray density and range to accommodate wind, along with a simplified piping arrangement that is spaced safely from energized electrical parts.

Size of Water Spray Systems

Many factors govern the size of a water spray system, including the nature of the hazard or combustibles involved, the amount and type of equipment to be protected, the adequacy of other protection, and the size of the area which could be involved in a single fire. The size of the system needed may be minimized by taking advantage of possible subdivision by firewalls; by limiting the potential spread of flammable liquids with dikes, curbs, or special drainage; by installing water curtains or heat curtains; or by using a combination of these features.

The water demand will be heavy because water spray systems must perform as deluge-type systems with all nozzles open and because high densities of water are needed. Each hazard should be protected by its own water spray system to limit the cumulative demand on the water supply.

NFPA 15, *Water-Spray Fixed Systems for Fire Protection*, advises that the size of a single water spray system be limited only by the available water supply so that the designed discharge rate will be calculated at the minimum pressures for which the nozzles are effective. Experience has shown that, in most installations, a single system should not exceed a design discharge rate of 3000 gpm (11 356 L/min). Separate hazard areas should be protected by separate systems.

Water Supplies

Fixed spray systems usually are supplied from one or more of the following:

1. Connections from a reliable waterworks system of adequate capacity and pressure.
2. Automatic fire pumps with reliable power and a water supply of adequate capacity and reliability.
3. An elevated gravity tank of adequate capacity and elevation.

The capacity of pressure tanks generally is not adequate to supply water spray systems. However, they may be acceptable as water supplies to small systems whose water and pressure requirements do not exceed the tank's capabilities.

Water Demand Rate

The water supply must be adequate to supply the operating water spray system with the required gpm (L/min) at effective pressure. Water spray systems adjacent to the hazard initially protected may require additional water. The water supply should be able to supply hose streams simultaneously. The total required water supply pressure and flow rates should be considered when the system is designed. The duration of the discharge required will vary according to the nature of the hazard, the purpose for which the system is designed, and other factors which can be evaluated only for each installation.

Water demand is specified in terms of the density of a uniformly distributed spray measured in gal per min per sq ft [(L/min)/m^2] of area protected. The discharge rate per unit of area depends on whether the spray system is installed to extinguish a fire, to control a fire, or to protect an exposure, and on the characteristics of the materials involved.

Pipe Sizes

Pipe sizes must be calculated for each system so that the water at the spray nozzles will have adequate pressure. A procedure for making the hydraulic calculations for a fixed pipe water spray system is given in the Appendix to NFPA 15, *Water-Spray Fixed Systems for Fire Protection*.

Selection and Use of Spray Nozzles

The selection of spray nozzles should take into consideration such factors as the character of the hazard to be protected, the purpose of the system, and the possibility of severe winds or drafts.

High-velocity spray nozzles, generally used in piped installations, discharge in the form of a spray-filled cone, while low-velocity spray nozzles usually deliver a much finer spray in the form of a spray-filled spheroid or cone.

Nozzles of one type cannot be substituted for nozzles of another type when a water spray system is being repaired or nozzles are being replaced without taking into account the possibility of seriously affecting the effectiveness of the system. In general, the velocity and distribution of size of water droplets affects the "reach" or range and the area of coverage of the water spray pattern.

Some spray nozzles produce spray by giving the water streams a rotary motion in spiral passages inside the nozzles. These rotating streams are mixed internally with a center stream to project a solid cone of water spray from the nozzle. These nozzles are known as the internally impinging type. Sectional views of spray nozzles having internal spiral water passages are shown in Figure 5-15C.

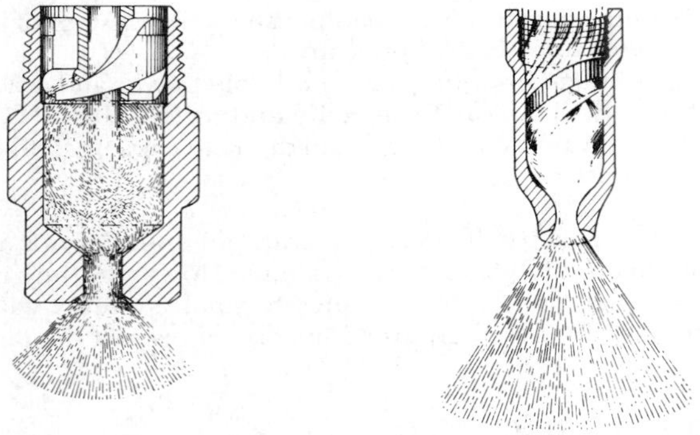

FIG. 5-15C. Water spray nozzles having internal spiral water passages.

Another type of water spray nozzle uses the deflector principle of a sprinkler. The water discharge orifice projects a solid, cylindrical stream of water onto a deflector which alters the stream into a conical distribution of water spray. This type of water spray nozzle is shown in Figure 5-15D.

One characteristically different type of water spray nozzle discharges water along the axis of a spiral of diminishing inside diameter. This spiral continuously peels off a thin layer of water from the surface of the cone, and this thin layer of water breaks into spray as it leaves the spiral. (See Figure 5-15E.)

Strainers

Strainers are ordinarily required in the supply lines of fixed piping spray systems to keep the nozzles from clogging.

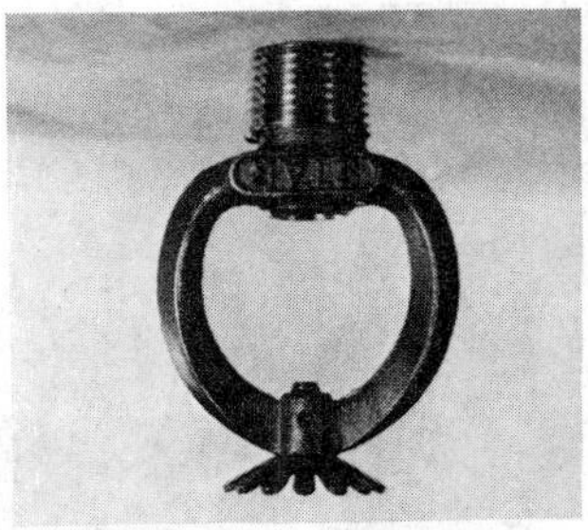

FIG. 5-15D. Water spray nozzles using the deflector principle of the standard automatic sprinkler.

FIG. 5-15E. A spiral-type water spray nozzle.

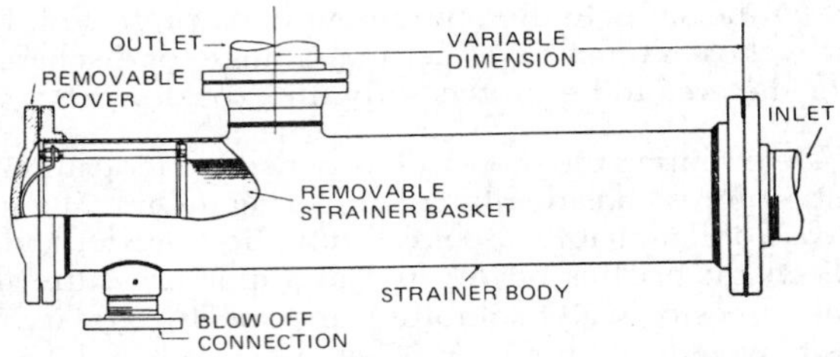

FIG. 5-15F. A Grinnell Model A strainer having a basket-type screen of corrosion-resistant metal. It is available in 3-in., 4-in., 6-in., 8-in., and 10-in. sizes. (1 in. = 25.4 mm.)

(See Figure 5-15F.) The baskets of those selected should have holes small enough to protect the smallest water passages in the nozzles used.

Water spray nozzles with very small water passages may have their own internal strainer, as well as a supply-line strainer to remove larger foreign material.

Drainage

Fixed water spray systems discharge large quantities of water. Special drainage and disposal facilities are important to control the spread of flammable or hazardous liquids to areas adjacent to the fire. Pitched floors, curbs, trenches, dikes, and sumps should be provided to direct the mixture of flammable or hazardous liquids and water runoff. These should be connected to a facility that separates flammable and hazardous liquids from the water. These liquids should be impounded in controlled areas until they can be disposed of safely.

Maintenance

It is important that fixed water spray systems be inspected and maintained on a regular basis. Included in a scheduled inspection program are such items as strainers, piping, control valves, heat-actuated devices, and the spray nozzles, particularly those equipped with strainers. Flow tests are conducted frequently to ensure satisfactory operation. After the tests have been completed, it is necessary to clean all strainers and to check all valves to be sure the system is in normal operating condition.

Nozzles with blowoff caps or plugs are provided to protect the interior of the piping and the nozzles located in areas containing paint vapor, corrosive vapors, dusts, or other foreign matter. Other blowoff caps or plugs are attached to the nozzles to allow them to retain water in the piping system, and thus reduce the time between the operation of the deluge valve and the discharge of water spray from the nozzles. (See Figure 5-15G.)

Regular inspection and maintenance should confirm that caps and plugs are in place. Priming water should be maintained in the piping of high-speed systems.

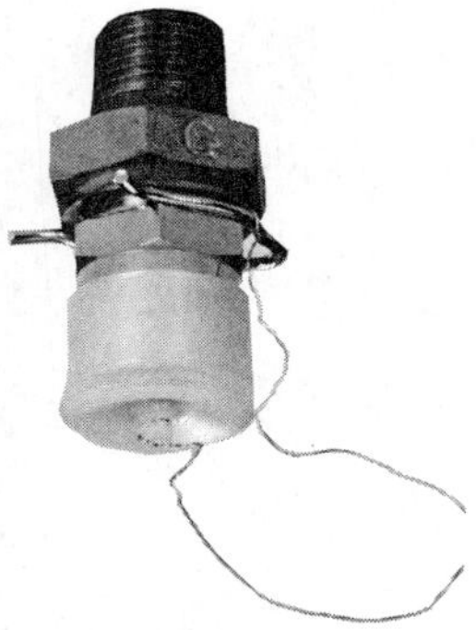

FIG. 5-15G. A Grinnell Mulsifyre nozzle with blowoff cap.

SPECIALIZED SYSTEMS UTILIZING WATER

Specialized systems using water spray have been developed to fill particular fire control needs.

Ultra-High-Speed Water Spray Systems

These systems are designed to handle extremely rapid fires of the type that can occur in solid propellants, sensitive chemicals, and industrial processes, and in oxygen-enriched atmospheres (hypo- and hyper-baric chambers). The essential features of the high-speed and ultra-high-speed water spray systems are the rapid response of photoelectric, infrared, or ultraviolet fire detectors, and electronic controls. The electronic controls actuate electric-solenoid valves which release pressure to pilot-operated spray nozzles or they may actuate explosively released deluge valves.

The piping connecting the water supply to the water spray nozzles must be kept full, or primed, and vented of all trapped air. Water is kept in the piping by plugs or caps or by pilot-pressure-operated valve mechanisms built into the water spray nozzles.

These systems can initiate water spray discharge from the spray nozzles. Response times are generally in the order of 150 milliseconds after flames are detected, because the supply water and the priming water fill the valves and all the piping connected to the nozzles. Fire tests conducted in oxygen-enriched test chambers found the time from ignition to the delivery of water to be 96 milliseconds. An ultra-high-speed water spray system installed to protect a solid rocket propellant manufacturing operation discharged water spray 240 milliseconds after fire detection.

Such installations must be carefully engineered and maintained by qualified experts.

BIBLIOGRAPHY

NFPA Codes, Standards, and Recommended Practices

Reference to the following NFPA codes, standards, and recommended practices will provide further information on water spray protection discussed in this chapter. (See the latest *NFPA Catalog* for availability of current editions of the following documents.)

NFPA 13, *Installation of Sprinkler Systems.*

NFPA 14, *Installation of Standpipe and Hose Systems.*

NFPA 15, *Water-Spray Fixed Systems for Fire Protection.* (Note especially Appendix A-4-4.3.2.)

NFPA 18, *Wetting Agents.*

NFPA 20, *Installation of Centrifugal Fire Pumps.*

NFPA 22, *Water Tanks for Private Fire Protection.*

NFPA 24, *Private Fire Service Mains and Their Appurtenances.*

NFPA 30, *Flammable and Combustible Liquids Code.*

NFPA 69, *Explosion Prevention Systems.*

NFPA 70, *National Electrical Code®.*

NFPA 71, *Signaling Systems for Central Station Service.*

NFPA 72, *Protective Signaling Systems.*

NFPA 80A, *Protection of Buildings from Exterior Fire Exposures.*

NFPA 321, *Classification of Flammable and Combustible Liquids.*

NFPA 325M, *Fire Hazard Properties of Flammable Liquids, Gases, and Volatile Solids.*

Additional Reading

Ault, W. E. and Carter, D. I., "The Influence of Hyperbaric Chamber Pressure on Water-Spray Patterns," *Fire Journal*, Vol. 61, No. 6 (Nov. 1967), pp. 48-49.

Braidech, M. M. and Neale, J. A., "The Mechanism of Extinguishment of Fire by Finely Divided Water," *NBFU Research Report No. 10*, Underwriters Laboratories Inc., Chicago, IL, 1955.

Bray, G., "Water Spray Protection of LPG Hazards," *Fire Protection*, Vol. 7, No. 4 (Dec. 1980), pp. 3-10.

Cooper, L. Y. and O'Neill, J. G., "Fire Tests of Stairwell-Sprinkler Systems, " *NBSIR 81-2202*, National Bureau of Standards, Gaithersburg, MD, Feb. 1981.

Duggan, J. J., Gilmour, C.H., and Fisher, P.F., "Requirements for Relief of Overpressure in Vessels Exposed to Fire," *Transactions* of the ASME, American Society of Mechanical Engineers, New York, 1944.

Evans, D. D., "Overview of Fire Suppression with Water," *Chemical and Physical Processes in Combustion*, 1988 Technical Meeting, Clearwater Beach, 1988.

Evans, D. D., "Water Sprays Suppress Gas-Well Blowout Fires," *Oil and Gas Journal*, Apr. 29, 1985, pp. 80-86.

Heselden, A. J. M. and Hinkley, P. L., "Measurements of the Transmission of Radiation Through Water Sprays," *Fire Technology*, Vol. 1, No. 2 (May 1965), pp. 130-137.

Kokkala, M., Andsten, T., and Bjorkman, J., "Extinguishment of Liquid Fires with Sprinklers and Water Sprays: Description of Tests," *Valtion Teknillinen Tutkimuskeskus*, No.593, 1989, Technical Research Institute of Finland, Espo, Finland.

Lev, Y., "Cooling Sprays for Hot Surfaces," *Fire Prevention*, No. 222 (Sept. 1989), pp. 42-47.

Lev, Y. and Strachan, D. C., "Dry Testing of Water Spray Systems," *Journal of Fire Sciences*, Vol. 7, No. 1 (Jan.-Feb. 1989), p. 3-21.

Milke, J. A., Evans, D. D., and Hayes, W., "Water Spray Suppression of Fully Developed Wood Crib Fires in a Compartment," *NBSIR 88-37453*, National Institute of Standards and Technology, Gaithersberg, MD, June 1988.

Nakakuki, A., "Extinction of Fires in Hyperbaric Chambers: Part I, Water Spray Properties and Extinction with Single Spray Nozzles," *Fire Technology,* Vol. 8, No. 1 (Feb. 1972), pp. 5-18.

Nishro, G. and Machida, S., "Pool Fires under Atmosphere and Ventilation in Steady-state Burning," *Fire Technology*, Vol. 23, No. 2, 1987, pp. 146-155.

O'Neill, J. G., "Sprinkler-Vent and Spray Nozzle Systems for Fire Protection of Openings in Fire Resistive Walls and Ceilings," *NBSIR 78-1571*, National Bureau of Standards, Gaithersburg, MD, 1978.

Rasbash, D. J., "Extinction of Fire with Plain Water: A Review," *Proceedings* of the First International Symposium on Fire Safety Science, Hemisphere, Washington DC, 1986, pp. 1145-1163.

Schnieder, M.E. and Kent, L.A., "Measurements of Gas Velocities and Temperatures in a Large Open Pool Fire," *Fire Technology*, Vol. 25, No. 1 (Feb. 1989), pp. 51-80.

Schoen, W. and Droste, B., "Investigations of Water Spraying Systems for LPG Storage Tanks by Full-Scale Fire Tests," *Journal of Hazardous Materials*, Vol. 20, Dec. 1988, pp. 73-82.

Schultz, N., "Fire Protection for Cable Trays in Petrochemical Facilities," *Plant/Operations Progress*, Vol. 5, No. 1, 1986, pp. 35-39.

Shokri, M.Y., *Predicting Thermal Radiation from Large Open Pool Fires*, MS Thesis, Worcester Polytechnic Institute, Worcester, MA, 1987.

Taylor, C. D. and Furno, A. L., "Evaluation of High-Pressure Front-Mounted Water Jets for Frictional-Ignition Suppression," *Report No.* 9237, United States Bureau of Mines, Pittsburgh, PA., 1989

Turner, H. L. and Segal, L., "Fire Behavior and Protection in Hyperbaric Chambers," *Fire Technology*, Vol. 1, No. 4 (Nov. 1965), pp. 269-277.

Welker, J.R., and Slipevich, C.M., "Bending of Wind-Blown Flames from Liquid Pools," *Fire Technolgy*, Vol. 2, No. 2 (May 1966), pp. 127-135.

Yow, H. Z., Kung, H. C., and Han, Z., *Spray Cooling in Room Fires*, National Bureau of Standards, Washington DC, 1986.

CARE AND MAINTENANCE OF WATER-BASED EXTINGUISHING SYSTEMS

Revised by Robert M. Hodnett

The care and maintenance of water-based extinguishing systems is vital to their performance in emergencies. Without well-conceived and executed maintenance programs, the best of systems stand a chance of failure through neglect.

Water-based extinguishing systems encompass all the different types of automatic sprinkler systems, water spray systems, and standpipe and hose systems discussed in other chapters in this section. While each of the systems has devices and equipment peculiar to its own function, much is common to all of them. Sprinkler systems have sprinklers, hose systems have hand-held nozzles, and water spray systems have spray nozzles. But none of them will work if somewhere back in the water supply system a valve is closed that should be open.

Perhaps more has been written on good practices to follow in the care and maintenance of automatic sprinkler systems than on other water-based systems, for the simple reason that they are quite common and are relatively more sophisticated than, for example, a simple standpipe installation. There are, however, the common denominators of water supply, supply delivery system (piping and valves), and discharge devices that apply to all systems. The degree of reliability rests, of course, on the complexity and extent of the system.

This chapter discusses care and maintenance of water-based systems, with a principal focus on automatic sprinkler systems. However, the Handbook user will find that many of the precepts discussed within the framework of sprinkler system care and maintenance will have application in planning and implementing maintenance for other types of water-based systems.

The principles of good maintenance procedures are detailed in NFPA 13A, *Inspection, Testing, and Maintenance of Sprinkler Systems*. NFPA 13A is a companion document to NFPA 13, *Installation of Sprinkler Systems*, the basic document governing the installation of sprinkler systems.

Robert M. Hodnett is a consultant in fire protection systems, based in South Kingstown, RI. He was NFPA staff liaison to the NFPA Committee on Automatic Sprinkler Systems prior to his retirement in 1984.

Part of good inspection and maintenance procedures is the organization that administers them. Particularly important are on-site services not under the management of outside organizations, such as commercial inspection services. Section 9, Chapter 3, "Private Emergency Organizations," will be helpful in clarifying duties and responsibilities in the maintenance of fire protection equipment.

(For the purposes of this Handbook, foam-water sprinkler and spray systems are classified as special extinguishing systems, and information on their care and maintenance can be found in Section 5, Chapter 20, "Foam Extinguishing Agents and Systems." But, again, much that applies to the care and maintenance of the water-based systems covered in this chapter also applies to foam systems.)

The maintenance of water supply equipment, such as tanks and fire pumps is treated in the chapters relating to those items.

IMPORTANCE OF EXTINGUISHING SYSTEM MAINTENANCE

Care and maintenance includes more than just the inspection and testing of system devices and equipment. If protection is to be fully effective, the proper relation between hazard and protection must be maintained. This calls for careful consideration of the fire hazards to be protected and requires a decision regarding the adequacy of the protection for the varying conditions of the property. Further, inspection must assess whether the originally installed system is adequate for the current fire hazards.

Water-based extinguishing systems employing standard devices and installed in accordance with established rules are sturdy and durable, and require minimum expenditure for maintenance. However, like other types of equipment, they may suffer deterioration or impairment through neglect or from certain conditions of service. Inspection is merely an organized, methodical procedure for determining the operating condition of devices and equipment, and, in some cases, the qualifications of personnel for the detection of conditions calling for maintenance, repair, or remedy.

Maintenance of protection involves making the inspections, as well as performing any special investigations or tests bearing on the performance of the devices and equipment; taking action to repair or keep devices and equipment in dependable operating condition; and ensuring correct procedures by personnel responsible for the performance or use of the equipment.

Inspection and maintenance functions are closely related and may overlap in some features. Management is responsible for their correlation. Inspections frequently involve matters that may be classed as maintenance, and maintenance sometimes requires its own inspections and tests beyond those made routinely during so-called fire inspections.

RESPONSIBILITY FOR MAINTENANCE

Many of the troubles experienced with extinguishing systems are due to lack of responsibility rather than lack of knowledge. The establishment of an appropriate organization is the responsibility of management. The types of organizations required to perform inspection, testing, and maintenance functions vary greatly. Size and value of the property are major considerations.

Inspection procedures may have some seasonal differences, most of which are indicated later in this chapter under the various items of equipment being considered. The following are examples of inspections governed by seasonal effects.

Spring inspection: As soon as danger of freezing is past, the spring inspection will give attention to the opening of cold-weather valves; testing, cleaning, and resetting dry pipe valves; testing water motor gongs; and conducting waterflow tests.

Fall inspection: At the approach of freezing weather, the fall inspection will give special attention to such items as:

1. Closing cold-weather valves and draining pipes exposed to freezing temperatures (drain valves on the exposed piping are left slightly open), and testing the specific gravity of the solution in antifreeze sprinkler systems.
2. Checking dry-pipe valves to make sure that the systems are holding air properly and that the electric and water motor alarms are in order, checking drains at low points of the dry piping to make sure they are properly clear of water, and checking heating provisions for the dry valves.
3. Examining gravity tanks to determine if adequate protection against freezing is ensured and that any heating system employed is in operative condition.
4. Checking the condition of fire pump reservoirs and the suction intakes from other water sources.
5. Looking over buildings to make sure that cold air will not enter or unduly expose piping to freezing.

TYPES OF SPRINKLER SYSTEM INSPECTIONS

In addition to the indispensable inspection procedures followed by the property owner, other inspection services are available.

Insurance Inspections

In insured properties, extinguishing systems are frequently given special attention by the insurance carrier. Routine testing of sprinkler systems and devices at regular intervals is a service extended by some insurance companies in the common interest of both the owner and the company. By these routine tests, the equipment can be shown to be in good operating condition, or any defects or impairments revealed. Since such tests are made at the owner's responsibility and risk, intelligent cooperation in conducting the tests serves the best interests of the owner.

Fire Department Inspections

Inspections are made of extinguishing system equipment by many fire departments at varying intervals. The inspection is principally to make sure that valves are open and to ensure familiarity with the use of the systems by the fire department. Inspections are customarily made by the fire company in whose district the installation is located.

Sprinkler Contractors' Services

Standardized sprinkler equipment inspection and maintenance services are offered by sprinkler manufacturers, sprinkler contractors, and inspection services companies. This service provides periodic examinations and reports and is of value to the property owner not only for regular checkup of the condition of sprinkler equipment, but also because of the valuable instruction that can be given to employees in the process. In addition to sprinkler devices and equipment, a contract can also cover other items, such as tanks and fire pumps that are important in the fire protection of property.

Inspection and maintenance services offered by sprinkler contractors normally follow a form acceptable to most insurance interests. Table 5-16A lists the items that should be inspected and tested and the time intervals that should be observed. Table 5-16B contains a listing of pertinent information that should be included in reports on inspections and tests that have been conducted.

Central Station Supervisory Service

Central station supervision of sprinkler alarm and control devices provided under contract is an especially valuable aid to maintenance. The reporting of each incident involving waterflow or valve closure or other supervised action keeps a constant check on the condition of the equipment and stimulates care on the part of the plant fire organization.

GENERAL MAINTENANCE OF SPRINKLERS AND SPRINKLER PIPING

Automatic sprinklers installed where they are not subjected to abnormal conditions, such as corrosion, abnormally high temperatures, or mechanical abuse, will give continued satisfaction over a great many years. Some sprinklers accepted by insurance organizations when first installed proved unreliable after years of service. Those falling into this category are identified in Section 5, Chapter 12, "Automatic Sprinklers." Sprinklers listed by leading testing laboratories since 1900 have generally given satisfactory service even though superseded by new or improved sprinklers. NFPA 13A, *Inspection, Testing, and Maintenance of Sprinkler Systems*, however, recommends testing at ten-year intervals representative samples of all sprinklers that are 50 or more years old. Sprinklers made previous to 1920 should be replaced.

TABLE 5-16A. *Summary: Minimum Inspection, Testing and Maintenance*

Records - Inspection = Visual Observation
Testing = Handling Equipment, etc.
Maintenance = Periodic Servicing and Repair

For Guidance on Specific Valves, Pumps, Hydrants, etc., Refer to the Manufacturer's Instructions.

Parts	Activity	Frequency
Flushing Piping	Test	5 Years
Fire Department-Connections	Inspection	Monthly
Control Valves	Inspection	Weekly-Sealed
	Inspection	Monthly-Locked
	Inspection	Monthly Tamper Switch
	Maintenance	Yearly
Indicator Post Valve	Test	Quarterly
Valves in Roadway Boxes	Test	Quarterly
Main Drain	Flow Test	Quarterly
Open Sprinklers	Test	Annual
Pressure Gage	Calibration Test	5 Years
Sprinklers	Test	50 Years
Sprinklers-High Temp.	Test	5 Years
Sprinklers-Residential	Test	20 years
Water Flow Alarms	Test	Quarterly
Preaction/Deluge Detection Systems	Test	Semiannually
Preaction/Deluge Systems	Test	Annually
Hydrants	Inspection	Monthly
	Test (Open and Close)	Annually
	Maintenance	Semi-Annually
Antifreeze Solution	Test	Annually
Cold Weather Valves	Open and Close Valves	Fall, Close; Spring, Open
Dry/preaction/deluge systems	Inspection	Weekly
Air Pressure and Water Pressure		
Enclosure	Inspection	Daily-Cold Weather
Priming Water Level	Inspection	Quarterly
Low-Point Drains	Test	Fall
Dry-Pipe Valves	Trip Test	Annual-Spring
Quick-Opening Devices	Test	Semi-Annually
Gravity Tank		
Water Level	Inspection	Monthly
Heat	Inspectioin	Daily-Cold Weather
Condition	Inspection	Bi-Annual
Pressure Tank		
Water Level & Pressure	Inspection	Monthly
Heat Enclosures	Inspection	Daily-Cold Weather
Condition	Inspection	3 Years
Pump	Test Flow	Annually
Engine Drive	Test Operate	Weekly
Steam Drive	Test Operate	Weekly

Source: NFPA 13A, *Inspection, Testing, and Maintenance of Sprinkler Systems.*

Representative samples of solder-type sprinklers with temperature ratings of 325°F (163°C) or greater that are exposed on a semicontinuous to continuous maximum allowable ambient temperature condition should be tested at five-year intervals for operation by a testing laboratory or the sprinkler manufacturer.

Where sprinklers are subject to loading (accumulations of foreign material) or corrosion, even to only a moderate or slight extent, they should be examined carefully and frequently. If the condition of the sprinklers appears doubtful, a representative sample (six or more) should be removed, carefully packed to avoid injury in transit, and sent for testing to testing laboratories or to the sprinkler manufacturer. The results of their testing will indicate the condition of similar sprinklers remaining in the property.

To prevent mechanical injury and distortion when installing or removing sprinklers to be cleaned and reinstalled, the special wrenches provided by manufacturers for their size and shape should be used.

Accumulation of Foreign Material on Sprinklers

In many classes of properties, conditions exist that cause an accumulation of foreign material on automatic sprinklers so that operation of the sprinkler may be retarded or prevented. This condition is commonly called loading. (See Figure 5-16A.)

Any accumulation of foreign material on sprinklers tends to retard their operation as a result of the heat-insulating effect of the loading material. If the deposit is hard, it may physically retard or prevent the sprinkler from operating. The best practice is to replace loaded sprinklers with new sprinklers rather than to attempt to clean them. Attempts at cleaning, particularly in instances where deposits are hard, are likely to damage the sprinkler, rendering it inoperative or possibly causing leakage.

Deposits of light dust, such as may be found on sprinklers in woodworking plants and grain elevators, are less serious than hard deposits. Dust may be expected to delay the operation of sprinklers but ordinarily will not prevent the eventual discharge of water. Dust deposits can be blown or brushed off, but blowing by compressed air should not be undertaken where it can create a dust explosion or ignition hazard. If a brush is used, it should be soft to avoid possible injury to sprinkler parts.

Water solution cleaning liquids of caustic or acid type are likely to be destructive to sprinklers and should not be used for cleaning. No hot solution of any kind should be used.

Sprinklers are sometimes protected when ceilings or sprinkler piping are being painted by temporarily placing small, lightweight paper or plastic bags over them, and securing the bags with a rubber band. Bags, however, are likely to delay the operation of the sprinklers and should be removed immediately after the painting is completed.

There is no known method whereby paint under the water cap or on the fusible link can be removed adequately. Sprinklers that have been painted by anyone but the manufacturer must be replaced with new units.

Sprinklers in spray booths present a special problem for which there is no wholly satisfactory solution except to conduct the spraying process in such a manner that no spray will reach the sprinklers. If so located as to minimize deposits, and if cleaned very frequently, conveniently accessible sprinklers may be cleaned without removal. Using a coating of grease, motor oil, or soft neutral soap

TABLE 5-16B. ***A Sample Report of Inspection***

(Based on Exhibit 1, Report of Inspection, as recommended in NFPA 13A, *Inspection, Testing, and Maintenance of Sprinkler Systems.)*

Owner's Section (To be answered by Owner or Occupant)

1. Explain any occupancy hazard changes since the previous inspection.
2. Describe fire protection modifications made since last inspection.
3. Describe any fires since last inspection.
4. When was the system piping last checked for stoppage, corrosion, or foreign material?
5. When was the dry piping system last checked for proper pitch?
6. Are dry pipe valves adequately protected from freezing?

Inspector's Section (All responses reference current inspection)

1. General
   a. Is the building occupied?
   b. Are all systems in service?
   c. Is there a minimum of 18 in. (457 mm) clearance between the top of the storage and the sprinkler deflector?
   d. In areas protected by wet system, does the building appear to be properly heated in all areas, including blind attics and perimeter areas, where accessible? Do all exterior openings appear to be protected, against freezing?
   e. Does the hand hose on the sprinkler system appear to be satisfactory?
2. Control Valves *(See Item 14).*
   a. Are all sprinkler system control valves and all other valves in the appropriate open or closed position?
   b. Are all control valves in the open position and locked, sealed or equipped with a tamper switch?
3. Water Supplies *(See Item 15).*
   a. Was a water flow test of main drain made at the sprinkler riser?
4. Tanks, Pumps, Fire Department Connections
   a. Are fire pumps, gravity tanks, reservoirs, and pressure tanks in good condition and properly maintained?
   b. Are fire department connections in satisfactory condition, couplings free, caps in place, and check valves right? Are they accessible and visible?
5. Wet Systems *(See Item 13).*
   a. Are cold weather valves (O.S.&Y.) in the appropriate open or closed position?
   b. Have antifreeze solutions been tested?
   c. Were the antifreeze test results satisfactory?
6. Dry Systems *(See Items 10 to 14)*
   a. Is the dry valve in service?
   b. Are the air pressure and priming water level in accordance with the manufacturer's instructions?
   c. Has the operation of the air or nitrogen supply been tested? Is it in service?
   d. Were low points drained during this inspection?
   e. Did quick-opening devices operate sufficiently?
   f. Did the dry valve trip properly during the trip pressure test?
   g. Did the heating equipment in the dry pipe valve room operate at the time of inspection?
7. Special Systems *(See Item 16).*
   a. Did the deluge or pre-action valves operate properly during testing?
   b. Did the heat-responsive devices operate properly during testing?
   c. Did the supervisory devices operate during testing?
8. Alarms.
   a. Did water motor gong test satisfactorily?
   b. Did electric alarm test satisfactorily?
   c. Did supervisory alarm service test satisfactorily?
9. Sprinklers
   a. Are all sprinklers free from corrosion, loading or obstruction to spray discharge?
   b. Are sprinklers over 50 years old, this requiring sample testing?
   c. Is stock of spare sprinklers available?
   d. Does the exterior condition of sprinkler system appear to be satisfactory?
   e. Are sprinklers of proper temperature ratings for their location?
10. Date dry pipe valve trip tested (control valve partially open) ______ *(See Trip Test Table which follows.)*
11. Date dry pipe valve trip tested (control valve fully open) ______ *(See Trip Test Table which follows.)*
12. Date quick-opening device tested ______ *(See Trip Test Table which follows.)*
13. Date deluge or preaction valve tested ______ *(See Trip Test Table which follows.)*

TRIP TEST TABLE

DRY VALVE			Q.O.D.		
MAKE	MODEL	SERIAL NO	MAKE	MODEL	SERIAL NO.

DRY PIPE OPERATING TEST		TIME TO TRIP THRU TEST PIPE		WATER PRESSURE	AIR PRESSURE	TRIP POINT AIR PRESSURE	TIME WATER REACHED TEST OUTLET		ALARM OPERATED PROPERLY	
		MIN	SEC	PSI	PSI	PSI	MIN.	SEC.	YES	NO
	WITHOUT Q.O.D.									
	WITH Q.O.D.									
	IF NO. EXPLAIN									

DELUGE & PREACTION VALVES

OPERATION	☐ PNEUMATIC	☐ ELECTRIC	☐ HYDRAULIC
PIPING SUPERVISED	☐ YES ☐ NO	DETECTING MEDIA SUPERVISED	☐ YES ☐ NO
DOES VALVE OPERATE FROM THE MANUAL TRIP AND/OR REMOTE CONTROL STATIONS			☐ YES ☐ NO
IS THERE AN ACCESSIBLE FACILITY IN EACH CIRCUIT FOR TESTING ☐ YES ☐ NO		IF NO. EXPLAIN	

MAKE	MODEL	DOES EACH CIRCUIT OPERATE SUPERVISION LOSS ALARM		DOES EACH CIRCUIT OPERATE VALVE RELEASE		MAXIMUM TIME TO OPERATE RELEASE	
		YES	NO	YES	NO	MIN.	SEC.

14. See Control Valve Maintenance Table:

Control Valve Maintenance Table

Control Valves	Number	Type	Open	Secured	Closed	Signs	Explain Abnormal Condition
City Connection Control Valves							
Tank Control Valves							
Pump Control Valves							
Sectional Control Valves							
System Control Valves							
Other Control Valves							

15. Water Flow Test at Sprinkler Riser

Water Supply Source		City		Tank	Pump
Date	Test Pipe Location	Size Test Pipe	Statis Press-sure	Residual Pressure	(Flow)
Last Water Flow Test					
This Water Flow Test					

TABLE 5-16B. ***A Sample Report of Inspection (continued)***

(Based on Exhibit 1, Report of Inspection, as recommended in NFPA 13A, *Inspection, Testing, and Maintenance of Sprinkler Systems.)*

16. Heat-Responsive Devices

Test Method ______________________________________

____

Type of Equipment ______________________________________

Manufacturer ______________________________________

Test Results:

Valve No.	A B C D E F	Valve No.	A B C D E F
Valve No.	A B C D E F	Valve No.	A B C D E F
Valve No.	A B C D E F	Valve No.	A B C D E F
Valve No.	A B C D E F	Valve No.	A B C D E F

Auxiliary Equipment? ____ Type? ____ Location? ____ Test Result? ____

17. Explain any "No" answers and comments. ______________________________________

____

____

____

18. Adjustments or corrections made during this inspection:

____

____

____

19. Although these comments are not the result of an engineering review, the following desirable improvements are recommended:

____

____

____

Signature: ______________________________________

Date: ______________________________________

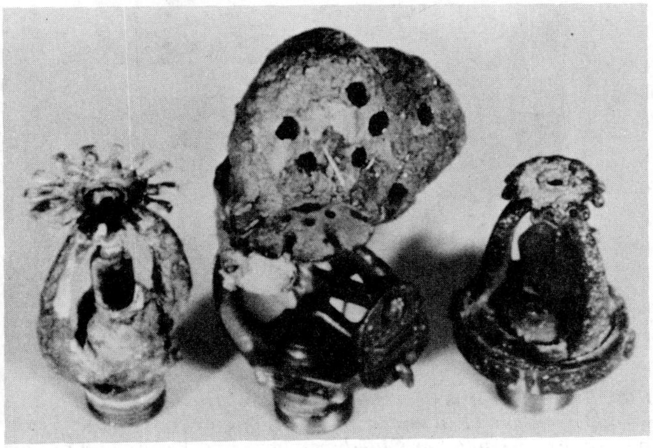

FIG. 5-16A. Examples of loaded automatic sprinklers. (Source: Factory Mutual Research Corp.)

facilitates washing or wiping off deposits. If grease is used, it should be a grease with a low melting point, such as vaseline. Unless cleaning is done very carefully, deposits are likely to accumulate to such an extent as to interfere seriously with sprinkler operation. The use of paper, polyethylene, or cellophane bags to protect sprinklers in spray booths is fairly common.

Corrosion of Automatic Sprinklers

Corrosive conditions are likely to make automatic sprinklers inoperative or to retard the speed of their operation. They can also seriously impede the waterways of spray system nozzles. Corrosive vapors may seriously affect not only the heat-actuated element and the valve retaining members of an automatic sprinkler, but also may be severe enough to weaken or destroy other portions of the sprinkler. In most instances, such corrosive action is slow but sure, and thus must be watched vigilantly. Illustrations of some typical corroded sprinklers are shown in Figure 5-16B.

Some types of sprinklers are less susceptible than others to corrosive conditions. Nonferrous metal is used for sprinkler parts, but special protective coatings are necessary for all types exposed to extreme corrosive conditions. Approved corrosion-resistant or special coated sprinklers are needed in locations where chemicals, excessive moisture, or corrosive vapors exist.

FIG. 5-16B. Examples of corroded automatic sprinklers.

Protection of Pipe Against External Corrosion

Under some conditions, corrosive vapors may cause rapid deterioration of steel pipe and hangers as well, necessitating frequent replacement unless the proper protection is provided. However, under most conditions, cast-iron fittings will not be seriously affected.

Under severe corrosive conditions, protective methods are not wholly satisfactory. Copper or special alloy noncorrosive pipe will give the best results.

Under some conditions, galvanized steel may be the best and most economical method of obtaining reasonably long life for the piping system. This might apply to chemical plants, salt works, or similar properties where corrosion may be severe. Stainless steel and copper piping have also been used in some cases.

When corrosion of existing equipment becomes a maintenance problem, replacement or the application of a recognized type of protective coating are remedial measures.

Internal corrosion conditions leading to pipe obstructions are discussed later in this chapter.

Emergency Measures for Maintaining Protection During Repairs or Alterations

Fire records show the seriousness of having extinguishing systems shut off when a fire starts. There is danger if the water supply is shut off for extensions or alterations to piping, repairs due to accidental damage to piping or sprinklers and spray nozzles, replacement of sprinklers after a fire, or maintenance or replacement of sprinklers and other system devices. When, of necessity, protection is interrupted, every effort must be made to limit the extent and duration of the interruption. A cardinal rule is to notify the fire department whenever an impairment exists so they will not place false reliance on the systems. Most insurance companies also request that owners advise them when there is interruption of protection so that alternate means of protection can be arranged if necessary or desirable.

Advance Preparations Before Shutoff

When work requires systems to be shut off, the work should be planned for a time when the least hazard exists. In industrial plants, about three times as many fires occur during operations as during idle periods; therefore, work should be done on a weekend or other idle period. Special guard service may be required, however, to help in detection of any fire that might develop while the systems are shut off.

Sectional valves, rather than main valves, should be used to reduce to a minimum the number of shutoff systems and to take advantage of multiple water supplies. All personnel, materials, and tools should be made ready before the protection is impaired.

If underground mains are involved, a tapping machine should be used when possible to avoid shutting off the water. If mains are to be opened, wood or other plugs or caps and clamps to close the ends of pipes quickly should be prepared. Emergency measures should be taken to maintain the maximum possible water supply. One possibility is to make a temporary hose connection from a hydrant still in service or from a domestic or industrial supply to the riser or risers. These connections are normally made to the nominal 2-in. drain with the drain valve and hydrant valve left open. Such arrangements are shown in Figure 5-16C. Adapters for connecting 2½-in. (64 mm) hose to sprinkler systems should be kept on hand.

Definite procedures should be followed for supervising closed valves, for notifying the fire department and insurance companies, and for making waterflow tests after the work is completed.

FIG. 5-16C. If it is necessary to shut off the water supply to a sprinkler system when repairs or extensions are to be made, a temporary supply can be provided by a hose line, keeping all or part of the system in service.

CARE AND MAINTENANCE OF SPECIFIC COMPONENTS

The following items of care and maintenance are treated in relation to routine inspection, test, and maintenance procedures. They are independent of the organization performing the inspection and maintenance functions, whether guard service, fire inspector, maintenance personnel, supervisor, or others making up the fire organization at any particular property, or outside contractors.

Public and Private Water Supply Equipment

The inspection and test of public water supplies and of private water-supply equipment, such as tanks and fire pumps, is covered in Section 5.

Control Valves and Meters

The inspection and supervision of valves in fire protection systems is covered in NFPA 26, *Supervision of Valves Controlling Water Supplies for Fire Protection*. The following paragraphs summarize some of the salient points of valve inspection and supervision.

Service valves: Service valves at private fire system connections to public systems are usually under the control of the water department and are seldom operated. Their condition is usually indicated adequately by waterflow tests made from the private protection system, as covered later in this chapter.

Meters: Meters in public water system connections are also generally under the control of the water department but are sometimes located in pits on the protected property.

Check valves: Check valves in public water connections, where needed to prevent backflow from private systems into public systems, are usually a part of the protection system for which the property owner is responsible. Tightness of check valves should be determined periodically by proper tests, depending on water supplies.

Check valves and their control valves should be arranged properly and located in accordance with the appropriate NFPA standards for sprinkler systems, water spray protection, and standpipe and hose system).

Control valves: All control valves should be readily accessible and unobstructed so they can be closed promptly and examined to see that they are open and in good operative condition, turn easily, and do not leak.

Pits for gate valves and check valves should be kept reasonably dry and clean so that valves can be tested, examined, and maintained in good condition. Manhole covers should be kept clear of snow and ice. See Section 5, Chapter 4, "Water Distribution Systems," for an example of a well-arranged check valve pit with access for inspection.

Each control valve should be numbered at the valve and listed, giving location, use, or portions of the system controlled, on a plant fire inspection report form. A plan showing valve locations should be posted at a central point known to plant and public fire officials.

Each valve should have a sign showing what it controls, with the legend "Must Be Open at All Times" or other proper wording. Underground valve locations should be shown by distance markings on nearby buildings and on accurate plans of the property.

All control valves should be sealed or locked open unless there is central station supervisory service. Wrenches should be kept at post indicator valves or at locations where they are readily accessible.

There should be someone on the premises at all times who knows the use and location of all of the control and drain valves. This includes the person on watch or any others who may be on duty at night.

Sprinklers and Sprinkler Piping

In the inspection of sprinkler systems, the following are important considerations.

Observe whether there is any building or room from which sprinklers have been omitted, including such places as basements, lofts, show windows, concealed spaces, towers, under stairs, under skylights, and inside elevator wells, vertical shafts, small enclosures such as drying and heating enclosures, and closets unless open at the top. Observe also whether there are sprinklers under large air ducts, shelves, benches and tables, overhead storage racks, platforms, and similar surfaces that might obstruct distribution of water from sprinklers above.

Additional branches and sprinklers installed after the original installation was made should be examined to make sure that the system, particularly the smaller distributing pipes, has not become overloaded by supplying too many sprinklers for the size of the supply piping and water pressure available. Where the system is hydraulically designed, calculations should be kept available on additions to the system to help in checking on the effect of these additions.

Sprinklers must not be obstructed by high-piled stock or other material, or by partitions or walls that might prevent free and proper water distribution. A clear space of not less than 18 in. (457 mm) below the deflectors of sprinklers is required. Observe whether the proper schedule of spacing is followed by referring to NFPA 13, *Installation of Sprinkler Systems*, for spacing recommendations given for the various occupancy classes.

Note whether all pipes in dry-pipe systems have the proper pitch. This feature is of special importance because water remaining in pockets or low places is likely to freeze and cripple the system.

Are any hangers loose or pipes not properly supported? Observe whether sprinkler piping is used to support stock or clothing. Sprinkler piping should not be used for such purposes.

Note whether the sprinklers are placed in an upright or pendent position. Sprinklers must be installed in the position for which they are designed and marked.

The distance of the deflectors from the ceiling or the bottom of beams or joists should conform to NFPA 13, *Installation of Sprinkler Systems*.

Note the type and design of the sprinklers, the year of their manufacture, and the date of installation. Sometimes old sprinklers are used in a new installation.

Are all sprinklers of the proper temperature rating? Ordinary-degree sprinklers should be substituted for high-degree sprinklers when the latter are unnecessary. Wherever the temperature around sprinklers exceeds 100°F (37.8°C), intermediate-degree sprinklers should be used.

Are any sprinklers corroded or loaded? Are sprinklers of a proper type, or properly protected against corrosion? If any sprinklers are in doubtful condition, samples should be removed and tested.

Sprinklers having coatings of paint, excessive deposits or incrustations, whitewash, bronzing, or other coating should be replaced by new sprinklers.

A supply of extra sprinklers should be kept in a sprinkler cabinet so that any sprinklers that have operated or have been damaged in any way may be replaced promptly. These sprinklers should correspond in type and in temperature ratings to the sprinklers in the property. The cabinet should be situated in a cool location. The number of sprinklers stocked for replacement purposes is governed by the size and number of systems, the location of the protected property relative to the source of supply for replacement sprinklers, and the number of sprinklers likely to be opened by extraordinary conditions, such as a flash fire.

Ordinarily, under average conditions, the stock of emergency sprinklers should be as follows:

- For systems having not over 300 sprinklers, 6 sprinklers
- For systems having 300 to 1000 sprinklers, 12 sprinklers
- For systems having more than 1000 sprinklers, 24 sprinklers
- For systems aboard vessels or in isolated locations, a greater number of sprinklers should be carried to permit restoring equipment to service promptly after a fire.

A special sprinkler wrench should be kept in the cabinet to be used in the removal and installation of sprinklers. This wrench should always be used for installing new sprinklers.

System Waterflow Tests

NFPA 13, *Installation of Sprinkler Systems*, calls for a water-supply test pipe and pressure gages to be provided at locations that will permit flowing tests to be made to determine whether water supplies and connections are in order. A 2-in. (51 mm) drain at the sprinkler riser may suffice as a water-supply test pipe if installed so that the valve may be opened wide for a sufficient time to ensure a proper test without causing water damage. A similar main drain valve in a water spray system can serve the same purpose.

There should be provision for checking the system's gage and its pressure recordings with an inspector's test gage.

The pressure on the sprinkler system side of alarm or check valves may be higher than that of the water supply because any momentary high pressure on the supply will be transmitted to the system and retained by the check valves. This excess pressure is relieved when a waterflow test is made.

The drop in pressure below the normal static pressure with the 2-in. (51 mm) main water-supply drain pipe wide open can be noted, and general flow conditions evaluated. For instance, if the normal static pressure is 50 psi (345 kPa), and if previous tests have shown a pressure drop to 45 psi (310 kPa) when the drain valve is opened, it will be apparent that if at inspection the pressure drops to, say, 35 psi (241 kPa) or lower, there is some obstruction to the flow which should be removed, or some other defect which should be located and remedied.

At each inspection, a flow test should be made separately for each water supply and each connection from a supply. This can be accomplished by closing all water supplies temporarily except the one under test. Too much emphasis cannot be placed on the value of flow tests to determine whether there is any obstruction to full flow. It is mandatory that all water supplies be returned to service immediately after testing.

If there is waterflow supervisory service, tests should not be made without first notifying the central station or other alarm headquarters.

There should be a 1-in. (25.4 mm) (nominal) test pipe having a standard brass ½-in. (12.7 mm) outlet at the remote point of each sprinkler system. This should be operated at each inspection of a wet system to make sure that there is free flow at good pressure and to test the waterflow alarm. In dry pipe systems, the test pipe is used to trip the dry-pipe valve, as discussed later.

Dry Pipe Sprinkler Systems

The best practice is to keep dry-pipe systems in the dry condition throughout the year. When water flows into sprinkler piping, rust and foreign materials tend to be carried into the smaller pipes where accumulation and obstruction to flow can occur. Annual tripping of the dry-pipe valve to make the system wet accelerates this behavior.

When systems are wet, with the dry-pipe valve tripped, the waterflow alarm feature of the dry valve is out of service.

Old, obsolete, and unapproved dry-pipe valves, and any in poor mechanical condition, are likely to be unreliable and should be replaced with currently approved or acceptable types.

Instruction charts are provided for the maintenance of dry-pipe valves by the sprinkler installing company and should be posted at or near these valves.

All dry pipe valves should be numbered and listed on inspection report forms.

Check the air pressure on each dry-pipe system at least once a week and pump up the systems when necessary. A daily check is recommended for the first week after a dry-pipe valve is reset. If pressure is lost rapidly, requiring frequent pumping, the piping system should be gone over and made tight. Avoid air pressure higher than that called for by the valve manufacturer's instructions.

Make sure that the priming water is maintained at the proper level above the dry-pipe valve.

Slight freezing of a dry-pipe valve may cause it to be inoperative. It is extremely important to make sure that adequate provision is made for heating the valve enclosure or the room in which it is located, and that the heating equipment is safe and in order.

Dry-pipe system piping should be thoroughly drained before freezing weather and kept clear of water during the winter. The freezing of a small amount of water in the piping may cause rupture of the piping or sprinklers and valve disfunction. Make sure that all low-point drains of the system are kept free of water and that the automatic drip or drain is clear and free to operate.

Dry pipe valves should be examined externally at frequent intervals to detect evidence of deterioration.

Thoroughly clean and reset each dry-pipe valve once yearly during the warm weather. On such occasions, the valve body should be thoroughly washed out, preferably with warm water, with care being taken to make sure that the small ports and piping leading to the alarm connections are free from obstructions.

Operating tests of dry pipe valves, including quick opening devices, if any, should be made from time to time. Such tests may be combined with the annual cleaning and resetting, and with any necessary service with respect to renewal of rubber parts or the adjustment of gages, alarm devices and connecting piping, and quick opening devices.

When dry-pipe valves are tripped for testing purposes, the procedure should be such that only the minimum flow of water needed to trip the valve is admitted to the sprinkler riser. This can usually be done by opening the control valve only one or two turns and by closing it immediately after the dry-pipe valve trips.

Operating tests and servicing of dry-pipe valves, including quick opening devices, should be conducted either by a sprinkler installing company or other fully qualified personnel.

No grease or other sealing material should be used on seats of dry-pipe valves in an effort to stop leaks. Force should not be used in an attempt to make dry-pipe valves tight.

Dry-pipe valves should carry a tag or card showing the date on which the valve was last tripped and the name of the organization making the test. Such tags are usually available from the installing company or the insurance authorities.

Quick Opening Devices

The operation of quick opening devices usually can be tested either with or without operating the dry-pipe valve itself. The manufacturer's instructions for testing and resetting the device should be followed carefully.

If the device does not operate properly on test, it can, if necessary, be removed and the sprinkler system kept in operative condition. Repair parts can be ordered from the manufacturer, or the device sent to the manufacturer for repair or adjustment.

Pressure Gages

Water pressure and air pressure gages should be tested for accuracy whenever the dry-pipe valve is cleaned and reset and at other times if the pressure indication is questionable.

Waterflow Alarm Devices

Waterflow alarm devices should be tested at regularly scheduled inspections of fire protection equipment. Electric alarms should be tested by the bypass test valve at dry-pipe valves and alarm valves, or by test switches. Actual waterflow alarm tests should be made when cold weather does not make the outdoor discharge of water from test or drain valves objectionable. Water motor gongs should not be tested in freezing weather.

Keep the small valve or cocks controlling the water supply to alarm devices sealed open.

Deluge and Preaction Systems

Complete charts are furnished by installing companies showing in detail the proper method of operating and testing thermostatically controlled systems. Only competent persons fully instructed with respect to the details and operation of such systems should be employed in their repair and adjustment. It is highly advisable for the owner to arrange with the installing company for regular periodic inspection and testing of the equipment.

The automatic valves controlling the flow of water into these systems operate through the effect of fire temperatures on actuating devices. Ordinarily, when it is necessary to repair the actuating system of a preaction system, as distinguished from the piping system itself, the piping system is run "wet," and automatic sprinkler protection is thus maintained on a preaction system, provided there is no danger of freezing.

Sprinkler System Supervisory Services

Central station, proprietary, remote station, fire alarm, and supervisory services for sprinkler systems interpret sprinkler system waterflow signals as fire alarms and immediately initiate fire department response. Signals of other types, such as valve supervision and pressure or temperature supervision, do not serve as fire alarms, but initiate appropriate courses of action as prearranged between the supervisory service and the property owner. It is extremely important that the headquarters of any of these services be notified and any special arrangements made in advance of any inspection or tests of equipment that will cause a signal to be transmitted.

Fire Department Connections

Inspect each fire department connection regularly to make sure that caps are in place, threads are in good condition, the ball drip or drain is in order, and the check valve is not leaking. A hydrostatic test should be conducted periodically on old fire department connection piping to ensure that it will withstand the required pressure.

Open Sprinkler Equipment

Outside or open sprinkler equipment should be tested once each year during warm weather. These tests should be made preferably in conjunction with the inspection department having jurisdiction and, if desired, with representatives of the fire department.

Before making operating tests, care should be exercised to make sure that all windows and doors through which water might enter are tightly closed. Proper precautions must be taken to prevent damage from discharge or accumulation of water to sidewalks, streets, pedestrian ways, or adjoining buildings.

Determine by test whether the sprinklers and the system piping are in good condition and free from plugging. Any piping or sprinklers found clogged should be removed, cleaned, and replaced at once.

OBSTRUCTIONS IN SYSTEM PIPING

Obstructions in system piping or yard mains will reduce or cut off the flow of water from a part or all of the system and will not give the protection intended; obstructed piping is one of the well-recognized causes of unsatisfactory sprinkler performance. One source of obstruction is foreign material in the water-supply system, and a second is foreign material originating within the system piping itself. Figure 5-16D is a graphic example of obstruction in system piping.

FIG. 5-16D. A stone lodged in the tee of a dry-pipe system's cross main. Good maintenance programs enable discovery of such obstructions before they can become a problem. (Source: Factory Mutual Research Corp.)

Foreign material, such as sand, gravel, stones, and pieces of wood, may enter underground mains as a result of the carelessness of workers when laying or repairing the mains. Sand, silt, or wood chips may also enter the mains through inadequately protected fire pump suction inlets. Sometimes when gravity tanks are cleaned, foreign material enters the drop pipes unless care is taken to prevent it.

Keeping foreign material out of piping for waterspray systems is particularly critical. If the waterways in the discharge nozzles are less than 3/8 in. (9.5 mm) in size or if it is suspected that the water is likely to contain obstructive material, then a strainer is required in the pipeline supplying the system. The small nozzles are prone to clogging if water-borne debris reaches them; thus, it is imperative that the strainers are maintained in good condition. Strainers used in fire protection systems should be listed by a recognized testing laboratory for fire protection service.

Scale, corrosion, and incrustations can also form in the piping. In dry-pipe sprinkler systems, for example, the condensation of moisture in the air supply may result in hard scale forming along the bottom of piping. Deep well water and water containing natural salts tend to corrode pipe interiors, and the piping of wet systems may be found obstructed by rust and corrosion. Obstructing material is carried into piping when systems operate or are refilled after draining. It may plug one or more fittings or obstruct a number of sprinklers at the end of the system. Pipe capacities may be reduced by incrustation where water contains lime or magnesia.

If the water is badly discolored during flow tests, or if gravel or stones are discharged with the water, foreign material is probably present in the piping. Finding foreign material in a fire pump suggests that there may be similar material in the system piping. Finding foreign material in resetting dry-pipe valves or examining check valves indicates a possible serious impairment of the entire fire protection system.

Obstructions to the flow of water from sprinklers usually comprise concentrations of the lighter materials, such as silt, sand, and small pebbles, piling up in the ends of the cross mains and in the nearby branch lines, with the heaviest solids collecting nearer the system risers. (See Figure 5-16E.) There are some cases where the foreign material deposits extend so far back into the system from the ends of the cross mains that complete cleaning of the entire system is necessary. More often, however, a preliminary investigation will disclose that, while foreign material may cause complete stoppage of water flow from sprinklers on branch lines connected to the ends of the cross mains, there may be no stoppage at any point on branch lines farther back in the system.

FIG. 5-16E. Silt buildup in this branch sprinkler line has totally obstructed the waterway. (Source: Factory Mutual Research Corp.)

Conditions Indicating Possible Obstruction in Piping

Evidence of possible obstruction in piping is given by any one of the following:

1. Plugging of test connections, or discharge of dirty or colored water.
2. Discharge of foreign material during routine water tests.
3. Foreign material in dry-pipe valves, check valves, or fire pumps.
4. Obstructing material found in piping dismantled for building or piping alterations.
5. Defects found in fire pump suction screens when source is from open bodies of water.
6. Repairs made in public water mains in vicinity.
7. Underground piping not flushed before connecting systems.
8. Plugged sprinklers or spray nozzles at time of fire.
9. Old equipment, especially dry-pipe systems.

Investigation of Severity and Extent of Obstruction

An investigation of conditions must be made when evidence of foreign materials in systems is found or obstruction is suspected. Where needed, cleaning or flushing procedures subsequently must be carried out to remove obstructing materials. Inspection and flushing methods outlined in this chapter are treated more completely in NFPA 13A, *Inspection, Testing, and Maintenance of Sprinkler Systems*.

Flushing Feed Main

Existing yard piping suspected of containing obstructing material should be thoroughly flushed through hydrants at dead ends of the system, blowoff valves, or groups of riser drains, by opening simultaneously as many outlets as possible and allowing the water to run until clean. If the water is supplied from more than one direction or through a looped system, divisional valves should be closed to produce a high velocity flow through each single line.

It is usually desirable to learn the nature and extent of foreign material that may be in the piping. This can best be done by fastening burlap bags securely to the flowing outlets.

The connections to system risers should next be flushed through drain valves. If the foreign material is too large to pass through a riser drain valve, some ingenuity must be used to procure a larger opening. Fire department connections can be used by removing the clappers. Flanged check valves or check valve covers, or flanged fittings can be removed and a siamese fitting substituted.

Flushing System Piping

In choosing the critical points for examination, consideration should be given to the arrangement of the piping and the probable pattern of the flow of water when a system is rapidly filled (as in a dry-pipe system), or when a large flow of water from the system occurs due to the operation of many sprinklers on a wet-pipe system.

After selection of the area in which the heaviest deposit of foreign material ordinarily would be expected, the investigation should take into consideration how much of the system's equipment in that area might be made ineffective by the obstructing material at a time of fire. It is important that the preliminary investigation indicate the extent of cleaning that may be necessary.

Flow Tests

Flow tests at critical points in a sprinkler system provide a positive means of determining whether there is foreign material in the system that may cause stoppage of flow from any of the sprinklers, and also of indicating how much of the equipment is affected. Valved hose connections are made to sprinkler fittings at the ends of two, three, or four branch lines on one side of and at the end of the cross main in the selected area. Flows are then taken simultaneously from these points.

If stoppage occurs at all of the branch lines tested simultaneously, similar tests may be necessary at points farther back on the system toward the system riser. Tests may next be extended to other floors to help make a judgment on the extent of cleaning operations that may be necessary for removing all foreign material that might cause stoppage.

Foreign deposits in sprinkler systems tend to be crowded toward the ends of the cross mains and in the end branch lines. Of course, there will be exceptions to this general statement. For example, where highly corrosive material has been introduced into the system, severe corrosion and scaling of the interior surfaces of the piping will be evident uniformly throughout the system.

Visual Examination

Visual inspection of the interior of piping is not a safe substitute for flow tests, because it is difficult to judge the behavior of a deposit within the piping from its appearance in place. However, after obstructing material has been found by flow tests, inspection of the interior may assist in determining the extent and type of flushing needed. To examine the interior of a cross main, back out several upright branch line nipples, remove the end elbow of the cross main, and inspect the interior of the pipe by means of a flashlight at the openings. A further check is to take down some of the suspected piping and clean the interior, carefully noting the character of the material removed.

EXTENT OF CLEANING REQUIRED

When preliminary tests show evidence of obstruction in sprinkler system piping, the next step is to undertake a cleaning program to remove the obstructing material. There are three degrees of cleaning: (1) complete cleaning, (2) limited cleaning, and (3) flushing extremities only. The selection of the degree required is dictated by the character, extent, and location of the obstruction.

Generally, when stoppage occurs only in the branch lines at extremities of the system, the flushing-extremities-only procedure can be used to clean the system. If stoppage occurs at several test points, but indications are that free flows are available on the other lines back toward the riser, a limited cleaning procedure may be followed. If the stoppage is more extensive, then a complete cleaning procedure should be undertaken.

Before any cleaning is undertaken, however, written specifications or procedure plans covering the entire proposed operations should be understood by all concerned. After completion of the work, the sprinkler contractor or other party performing the cleaning operation should furnish a written statement to those concerned indicating that all operations have been completed in accordance with the approved procedure, that the specified examinations and tests have been made, and that the system has been left in normal condition.

Complete Cleaning

There are some cases where the foreign material is of such character and extends so far back into the system from the ends of the cross mains that complete cleaning of the entire system will be necessary. In such cases, it is of prime importance that a plan of the piping system be prepared and be marked numerically to show the proper sequence of the cleaning operations, the size and length of hose to be used, the points where the hose is to be attached, and the number of flows to be made at each point.

Limited Cleaning

Where points of impairment of protection can be identified as occurring within restricted areas rather than throughout the system, and if these points exist in any appreciable amount only in the ends of cross mains and in the branch lines connected at or near those points, not all branch lines need to be cleaned. The cleaning procedure may be limited to the branch lines at or near these points and to the cross mains on each floor.

Limited cleaning operations serve to minimize the time during which sprinkler protection is impaired; they lessen the disturbance to normal activities within the premises where the cleaning operations are under way; and they materially lower the cost of the work as compared with the cost of more extensive cleaning. Since only a fraction of the total number of branch lines are being cleaned directly under the limited procedure, periodic flow tests should be made as the cleaning progresses, in order to determine the effectiveness of the work. The limited procedure takes into account the purging effect in branch lines not actually flushed, caused by high-velocity water and air flow along the cross main.

Cleaning System Extremities Only

This cleaning method should be used only in cases in which impairment of dry-pipe sprinkler protection has been found to occur solely at the system extremities, and it relates to every floor protected, regardless of the number of floors. Extreme care should be exercised before this cleaning method is employed. Adequate examinations and flow tests are made to make certain that only the sprinklers located at the extremities of the system are subject to plugging. It should not be used where the deposits extend back into the cross main beyond the second branch line from the end of the cross main.

CLEANING METHODS

There are two methods, in general, used for cleaning sprinkler systems: (1) water flushing, and (2) hydropneumatic. Convenience is a factor that may make the hydropneumatic method preferable to the water flushing method. With the former, there is no open discharge of water outside the building; there is less disturbance of plant operations; frequent fillings and drainings of the sprinkler system are unnecessary; there is considerably less pipe work; and a complete operation is performed at a given flush point.

Both the water flushing and hydropneumatic methods are appropriate for complete cleaning and limited cleaning procedures. Good practice is first to flush the underground piping and then to clean all private sources of water supply that might cause silting in the underground main.

Both of these methods are thoroughly covered in NFPA 13A, *Inspection, Testing, and Maintenance of Sprinkler Systems*.

Branch Line Testers

If it is anticipated that a sprinkler system may need periodic testing for obstruction or repeated flushing, a branch line tester may be installed permanently as a nippled fitting at the end of branch lines or between the last sprinkler and the end fitting on branch lines. The tester has a normally closed and capped outlet connection for hose. Turning a wrench head opens a passage to the outlet which has a 1-in. (25.4 mm) hose coupling thread. It is not necessary to remove the sprinkler.

SPRINKLER LEAKAGE

The term "sprinkler leakage" is ordinarily intended to cover all leakage or discharge of water from the sprinkler system except in case of fire. The system includes sprinklers, piping, tanks, and any other water supplies used for fire protection.

The danger of accidental water discharge is often exaggerated, because a sprinkler system is very rugged. The pipe, sprinklers, and fittings are made to stand far greater water pressures than are met with in practice. The supports are strong also, and the system is so installed that it should remain intact even under severe mechanical strain, including any anticipated earthquake shock or movement.

There is no reasonable ground for omission of sprinklers from areas in hospitals and other institutions occupied by patients. While it is true that accidental discharge of cold water from sprinklers might, for example, have an adverse effect upon certain patients in a hospital, the probability of loss of life in event of fire is infinitely more serious than any remote chance of an accidental cold shower from the sprinklers. Conditions that might result in accidental discharge of water from sprinklers are highly unlikely where ordinary hospital care would preclude the existence of either freezing temperatures or temperatures so high as to cause the opening of sprinklers except in the case of fire.

It has been estimated, based on sprinkler leakage loss reports, that the chance that a sprinkler may open accidentally because it is defective is less than one in 16 million installed sprinklers per year.

Automatic sprinkler protection for property particularly vulnerable to water damage, such as computers, finely made complicated mechanical equipment, works of art, valuable books, etc., should not be omitted due to fear of premature operation of sprinklers if reasonable precautions are taken against freezing, overheating, and mechanical injury.

Some of the more important conditions responsible for sprinkler leakage and water loss are explained in the following paragraphs.

Mechanical Injury

Automatic sprinklers are designed to withstand at least 500 psi (3448 kPa) pressure without injury or leakage. If properly installed, there is little danger of the sprinkler breaking apart unless it is injured in some way. All of the listed sprinklers are rugged and will stand considerable abuse. The frames can be bent somewhat without opening the sprinkler.

Where sprinklers are located in areas where they may suffer mechanical injury, they can be protected by commercially available metal guards. (See Figure 5-16F.)

FIG. 5-16F. Metal guard protection against mechanical injury.

The use of lift trucks or tractors in handling materials indoors must be carefully planned and supervised to avoid hitting sprinklers and sprinkler piping.

Improper Installation and Maintenance

Improper installation includes lack of proper supports for risers and feed mains, lack of proper tie rods where inside piping is connected to cast-iron fittings, and defective pipe hangers or supports.

Breaks or leaks sometimes occur in underground work due to improper laying of underground mains or poor workmanship in making joints. Sometimes breaks occur in properly installed systems due to undue stresses on the piping system, such as those caused by settling of a building or foundations or lack of clearance around pipes where they pass through foundations.

Every piping system should be frequently inspected and properly maintained. The condition of hangers and supports should be watched to determine whether they are in good order, or loose, or with screws or fastenings pulled out.

Sprinkler piping should never be used as a support for ladders, stock, or other material. Any system of piping under constant internal pressure should receive proper care and not be subject to mechanical abuse.

Freezing

The freezing of water in pipes is a common cause of trouble and the remedy in most cases is self-evident. Where this is a local condition and not unduly severe, ice in the sprinkler or fittings may rupture the sprinkler without damage to the pipe or fittings. When the ice melts, water is discharged. In other cases, the pipe or fittings may burst, causing serious damage and expensive repairs.

In some types of sprinklers, a moderate amount of freezing may not break the sprinkler open, but may cause it to leak at the seat after ice melts.

Some of the conditions that cause trouble from freezing are:

1. Insufficient heat for severe weather conditions in certain portions, such as concealed spaces under roofs or blind attics, large open doorways for trucks or railway cars, entryways, and space under buildings.
2. Windows left open during severely cold weather.
3. Insufficient heat because of shortage of fuel supply.
4. Branch lines of dry-pipe systems not correctly pitched to drain.
5. Feed mains or piping in unheated areas, or not properly protected to prevent freezing.

6. Freezing of tank risers due to lack of heat or lack of adequate protection; obstructed circulating pipes of heating systems.
7. Freezing of water in underground mains not buried deep enough.

Overheating

Overheating is the most common cause of accidental discharge from sprinklers and is the term used when an automatic sprinkler operates as a result of abnormally high temperatures but without the presence of fire. This condition is usually caused by hot manufacturing processes, artificial heating, or lack of ventilation. It may result from a sudden increase in temperature which operates the heat-responsive element, or from longer exposure to temperatures sufficiently high to cause gradual weakening. In the solder-type of sprinkler, the latter condition, sometimes termed "cold flow," is indicated by partial separation of the soldered members.

In practice, there are a number of conditions that cause unsafe temperatures, such as:

1. Climatic conditions causing temperatures well above normal [above 110°F (43.3°C)].
2. Ordinary low-temperature sprinklers located too near steam mains, unit heaters, heating ducts, etc. Temperatures higher than anticipated may occur after installation of sprinklers. Changes in heating methods, installation of unit heaters, changes in manufacturing processes or equipment, etc., after sprinklers are installed, frequently occur.
3. Changes in temperatures due to changes in occupancy or processes which cause higher temperatures than contemplated. These changes may be general or local in portions of a building.
4. In some cases, a fire that opens a number of sprinklers may weaken other sprinklers in that vicinity. This is not a common occurrence.

NFPA 13, *Installation of Sprinkler Systems*, gives some information on sprinkler temperature ratings near unit heaters. Unit heaters should never be used without a careful study of conditions, and, in most cases, sprinklers near unit heaters must be replaced by sprinklers with a higher temperature rating in order to avoid accidental operation.

When conditions occur that require sprinklers higher than ordinary-degree rating, the maximum temperature at the sprinkler level must be determined and sprinklers of the correct temperature rating installed if trouble is to be avoided.

REDUCING WATER DAMAGE

It is evident that, if leakage occurs when there is no one in the building and no proper means of alarm notification to outsiders exists, the leakage may continue for a considerable length of time and cause serious loss, even if the rate of water discharge is relatively small, as with one sprinkler operating.

While good, or "standard," guard service is of value, it may not be adequate unless there is a sprinkler alarm gong which will notify the guard if water is flowing.

Every sprinkler system should have a waterflow alarm device and properly located alarm gong, not only to give alarm in case sprinklers operate because of fire, but also to minimize loss from sprinkler leakage.

Most large losses from sprinkler leakage are due to lack or failure of local sprinkler alarm devices or gongs, or failure to notify promptly some authorized person who will investigate immediately and shut off the water if there is no fire. In some cases, water runs for many hours without anyone knowing about it, and the operation of even one sprinkler on an upper floor of a building containing expensive merchandise may cause a very heavy loss.

Sprinkler supervisory service is of great value in the prompt discovery of any leakage from the system, and in securing appropriate action to minimize the water loss.

Various provisions or safeguards may be taken to lessen the damage to stock from water used to extinguish fire. Similar provisions are of value in case of sprinkler leakage.

BIBLIOGRAPHY

NFPA Codes, Standards, and Recommended Practices

Reference to the following NFPA codes, standards, and recommended practices will provide further information on the care and maintenance of water-based extinguishing systems discussed in this chapter. (See the latest *NFPA Catalog* for availability of current editions of the following documents.)

NFPA 13, *Installation of Sprinkler Systems*.

NFPA 13A, *Inspection, Testing, and Maintenance of Sprinkler Systems*.

NFPA 14, *Installation of Standpipe and Hose Systems*.

NFPA 15, *Water-Spray Fixed Systems for Fire Protection*.

NFPA 24, *Private Fire Service Mains and Their Appurtenances*.

NFPA 26, *Supervision of Valves Controlling Water Supplies for Fire Protection*.

Additional Reading

Boyd, H. D. and Locurto, C. A., "Reliability and Maintainability for Fire Protection Systems," *Proceedings* of the First International Symposium on Fire Safety Science, Hemisphere, Washington DC, 1986, pp. 963-970.

Brannigan, F. L, "Automatic Sprinklers—Prelude to Disaster," *Fire Engineering*, Vol. 138, No. 5 (May 1985), pp. 56, 62-64.

Bryan, J. L., *Automatic Sprinkler and Standpipe Systems*, National Fire Protection Association, Quincy, MA, 1976, p 76, 81.

Carson, W. G. and Klinker, R. L., *Fire Protection Systems: Inspection, Test & Maintenance Manual*, National Fire Protection Association, Quincy, MA, 1986.

Damon, W. A., "Preventing Pitfalls in Fire Protection Systems," *Heating/Piping/Air Conditioning*, Apr. 1985, pp. 61-64, 69-71.

Factory Mutual Research Corporation, "Notes on Dry Pipe Valves," *Loss Prevention Data 2-10*, Factory Mutual Research Corp., Norwood, MA., Nov. 1977.

Factory Mutual Research Corporation, *Loss Prevention Data Sheets Nos. 2-11 through 2-95*, (various titles), information on the care and maintenance of sprinkler system components (dry-pipe valves, quick-opening devices, deluge and preaction system valves, etc.) by manufacturers' names and model numbers (various dates).

Solomon, R. E., *Automatic Sprinkler Systems Handbook*, National Fire Protection Assn, Quincy, MA, 1989.

CARBON DIOXIDE AND APPLICATION SYSTEMS

Revised by Thomas J. Wysocki

Carbon dioxide (CO_2) has been used for many years to extinguish flammable liquid fires, gas fires, fires involving electrically energized equipment, and, to a lesser extent, fires in ordinary combustibles, such as paper, cloth, and other cellulosic materials. CO_2 will suppress fire effectively in most combustible material. Exceptions are a few active metals and metal hydrides, and materials, such as cellulose nitrate, that contain available oxygen. Further, practical limitations of CO_2 are related to the method of application and to restrictions imposed by the hazard itself.

This chapter will discuss the properties of CO_2 and its proper use in fixed fire extinguishing systems, its limitations as a fire extinguishing agent, methods of application, system components, design considerations, and requirements for testing and maintenance. NFPA 12, *Carbon Dioxide Extinguishing Systems*, provides guidance to those responsible for the purchase, design, installation, testing, inspection, operation, and maintenance of carbon dioxide systems.

Other Chapters that reference CO_2 systems are Section 2, Chapter 30, "Storage and Handling of Records;" Section 6, Chapter 18, "Special Systems for Explosion Damage Control;" and Section 8, Chapter 30, "Marine."

PROPERTIES OF CARBON DIOXIDE

Carbon dioxide has a number of properties that make it a desirable fire extinguishing agent. It is noncombustible, it does not react with most substances, and it provides its own pressure for discharge from the storage container. Since carbon dioxide is a gas, it can penetrate and spread to all parts of a fire area. As a gas or as a finely divided solid called "snow" or "dry ice," it will not conduct electricity and, therefore, can be used on energized electrical equipment. It leaves no residue, thus eliminating cleanup of the agent itself.

Thomas J. Wysocki is a consultant with Guardian Services, Inc., Frankfort, IL. He is active on several NFPA technical committees, including those covering carbon dioxide and halon fire extinguishing systems.

Thermodynamic Properties

At room temperature and pressure, carbon dioxide is a gas. It is easily liquefied by compressing and cooling, and, with further compressing and cooling, it can be converted to a solid. The effect of temperature changes on compressed carbon dioxide in a closed container is shown in Figure 5-17A.

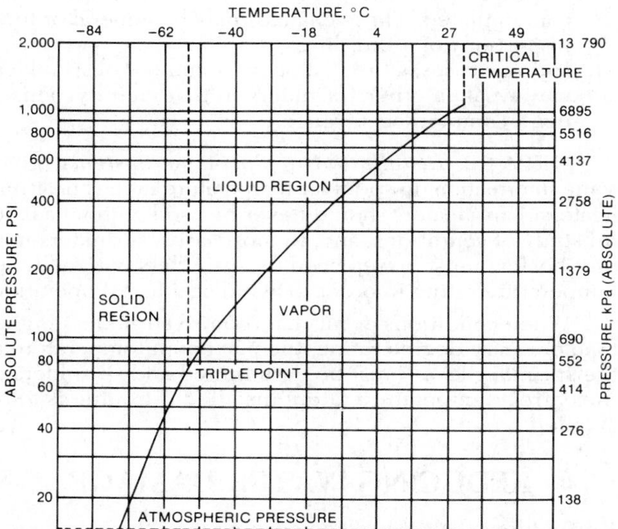

FIG. 5-17A. Effect of pressure and temperature change on the physical state of carbon dioxide. Above the critical temperature of 87.8°F (31°C), irrespective of pressure, it is entirely gas. Between 87.8°F (31°C) and the temperature of the triple point, which is −69.9°F (−57°C), in a closed container, it is part liquid and part gas. Below the triple point, it is either a solid or a gas, depending upon the pressure and temperature.

On the part of the curve between –69.9°F (–57°C) and the critical temperature of 87.8°F (31°C), carbon dioxide in a closed container may be a gas or a liquid. The pressure is related to the temperature as long as both vapor (gaseous) and liquid states are present. As the temperature and pressure increase, the density of the vapor phase increases while the density of the liquid phase decreases. At 87.8°F (31°C), the density of the vapor becomes equal to the density of the liquid, and the clear demarcation between the two phases disappears. Above the critical temperature, high-pressure carbon dioxide exists only in a gaseous form, with properties somewhat between normal vapor and liquid states.

When the temperature is reduced to –69.9°F (–57°C) at 75 psia (517 kPa), carbon dioxide may be present in vapor, liquid, and solid forms in equilibrium with each other. Hence, the term "triple point" to describe this condition. Below the triple point, only vapor and solid phases can exist. Thus, when liquid carbon dioxide is discharged to atmospheric pressure, a portion instantly flashes to vapor while the remainder is cooled by evaporation and converted to finely divided snow, or dry ice, at a temperature near –110°F (–79°C). The proportion of CO_2 converted to dry ice depends upon the temperature of the stored liquid. Approximately 46 percent of the liquid stored at 0°F (–18°C) will be converted to dry ice, compared to approximately 25 percent for liquid stored at 70°F (21°C).

Storage

Liquid carbon dioxide may be stored in high-pressure cylinders at normal ambient temperature or in low-pressure refrigerated containers designed to maintain a storage temperature near 0°F (–18°C). Freezing (solidifying) in storage is not a problem. However, any substantial reduction in storage temperature - and corresponding storage pressure - could reduce the discharge flow rate below acceptable design limits. High-pressure systems normally are designed to operate properly with storage temperatures ranging from 32 to 120°F (0 to 49°C). Low-pressure systems, which operate normally at 0°F (–18°C), would not be affected unless the ambient temperature surrounding the storage container dropped well below this level for a prolonged time. Extreme climatic environments may require special design considerations to ensure proper operation. For low storage temperatures, high-pressure cylinders may require special "winterization" treatment, while low-pressure storage units may require pressure-building vaporizers.

Discharge Properties

A typical discharge of liquid carbon dioxide has a white, cloudy appearance due to finely divided dry ice particles carried along with the flash vapor. Because of the low temperature, some water vapor from the atmosphere will condense, creating additional fog which will persist for a time after the dry ice particles have settled out or sublimed.

Static Electricity

The dry ice particles produced during a discharge of carbon dioxide can carry a charge of static electricity. Static charge can also build up on ungrounded discharge nozzles. To prevent shock hazard to personnel or unwanted static discharge in a potentially explosive atmosphere, all discharge nozzles must be grounded. This is particularly important in the case of nozzles and playpipes used in hand hose line systems.

Vapor Density

Carbon dioxide gas has a density of one and one-half times the density of air at the same temperature. The cold discharge has a much greater density, which accounts for its ability to replace air above burning surfaces and maintain a smothering atmosphere when used in local application systems. When carbon dioxide is used for total flooding, the resulting mixture of CO_2 and air will be more dense than the ambient atmosphere.

Physiological Effects

Carbon dioxide is normally present in the atmosphere at a concentration of approximately 0.03 percent. It is present in humans and animals as a normal byproduct of cellular respiration. In the human body, carbon dioxide acts as a regulator of breathing, thus ensuring an adequate supply of oxygen to the system. Up to a point, an increase in carbon dioxide in the blood causes an increase in breathing rate. The maximum increase in respiration occurs when breathing 6 to 7 percent CO_2 in air. Higher concentrations of CO_2 slow down breathing. Finally, with 25 to 30 percent CO_2 in air, a narcotic effect takes over and stops breathing almost immediately—even with a sufficient supply of oxygen in the air. Reduced oxygen supplies will cause a very much lower concentration of carbon dioxide to suppress breathing and cause death from asphyxiation. The exact concentration of carbon dioxide in air which will cause a decrease in respiration varies from person to person and is not constant even in the same person from time to time.

Six to seven percent CO_2 is considered the threshold level at which harmful effects become noticeable in human beings. At concentrations above 9 percent, most people lose consciousness within a short time. Since the minimum concentrations of CO_2 in air used to extinguish fire far exceed 9 percent, adequate safety precautions must be designed into every carbon dioxide fire extinguishing system.

The dry ice that is produced during a discharge can produce "burns" due to the extreme low temperature. Personnel should be warned not to handle any residual snow after a discharge.

EXTINGUISHING PROPERTIES OF CO_2

Carbon dioxide is effective as an extinguishing agent primarily because it reduces the oxygen content of the atmosphere by dilution to a point where the atmosphere no longer will support combustion. Under suitable conditions of control and application, the available cooling effect also is helpful, especially where carbon dioxide is applied directly on the burning material.

Extinguishment by Smothering

In any fire, heat is generated by rapid oxidation of a combustible material. Some of this heat raises the unburned fuel to its ignition temperature, while a large part of the heat is lost by radiation and convection, especially in the case of surface burning materials. If the atmosphere that supplies oxygen to the fire is diluted with carbon dioxide vapor, the rate of heat generation is reduced until it is below the rate of heat loss. When the fuel is cooled below its ignition temperature, the fire dies out and is extinguished completely.

The minimum concentration of carbon dioxide needed to extinguish surface burning materials, such as liquid fuels, can be determined accurately, since the rate of heat loss by radiation and convection is reasonably constant. Table 5-17A lists the minimum concentrations of CO_2 for some common liquid and gaseous fuels as determined by the U.S. Bureau of Mines.[1] It is difficult to obtain similar data for solid materials because the rate of heat loss by radiation and convection can vary widely, depending upon shielding effects caused by the physical arrangement of the burning material.

TABLE 5-17A. ***Minimum Carbon Dioxide Concentrations for Extinguishment***

Material	Theoretical Min. CO_2 Concentration (%)	Minimum Design CO_2 Concentration (%)
Acetylene	55	66
Acetone	27*	34
Aviation Gas Grades 115/145	30	36
Benzol, Benzene	31	37
Butadiene	34	41
Butane	28	34
Butane - I	31	37
Carbon Disulfide	60	72
Carbon Monoxide	53	64
Coal Gas or Natural Gas	31*	37
Cyclopropane	31	37
Diethyl Ether	33	40
Dimethyl Ether	33	40
Dowtherm	38*	46
Ethane	33	40
Ethyl Alcohol	36	43
Ethyl Ether	38*	46
Ethylene	41	49
Ethylene Dichloride	21	34
Ethylene Oxide	44	53
Gasoline	28	34
Hexane	29	35
Higher Paraffin Hydrocarbons		
$C_nH_{2m} + 2m - 5$	28	34
Hydrogen	62	75
Hydrogen Sulfide	30	36
Isobutane	30*	36
Isobutylene	26	34
Isobutyl Formate	26	34
JP-4	30	36
Kerosene	28	34
Methane	25	34
Methyl Acetate	29	35
Methyl Alcohol	33	40
Methyl Butene - I	32	36
Methyl Ethyl Ketone	32	40
Methyl Formate	32	39
Pentane	29	35
Propane	30	36
Propylene	30	36
Quench, Lubricating Oils	28	34

Note: The theoretical minimum extinguishing concentrations in air for the above materials were obtained from a compilation of Bureau of Mines Limits of Flammability of Gases and Vapors (Bulletins 503 and 627). Those marked with * were calculated from accepted residual oxygen values.

Extinguishment by Cooling

Although the temperatures involved in a carbon dioxide discharge may approach –110°F (–79°C), the cooling capacity of the carbon dioxide is quite small compared to an equal weight of water. The latent heat of one pound of liquid CO_2 is about 120 Btu (126 kJ) from low-pressure storage and 64 Btu (67.5 kJ) from storage at 70°F (21°C). The cooling effect is most apparent when the agent is discharged directly on the burning material by "local application." A massive application quickly covering the entire surface area smothers the fire and helps cool the fuel.

LIMITATIONS OF CO_2 AS AN EXTINGUISHING AGENT

The use of carbon dioxide on general Class A fires is limited by its relatively low cooling capacity, compared to that of water, and by enclosures incapable of retaining an extinguishing atmosphere. True surface burning fires are extinguished easily because natural cooling takes place quickly. On the other hand, if the fire penetrates below the surface or under materials that provide thermal insulation that slows down the rate of heat loss (generally referred to as "deep-seated burning"), a higher concentration of carbon dioxide and a much longer holding time are needed for complete extinguishment.

Oxygen-Containing Materials and Reactive Chemicals

Carbon dioxide is not an effective extinguishing agent for fires involving chemicals that contain their own oxygen supply, such as cellulose nitrate. Fires involving reactive metals, such as sodium, potassium, magnesium, titanium, zirconium, and the metal hydrides, cannot be extinguished by carbon dioxide because the metals and hydrides decompose CO_2.

Life Safety Considerations

Total flooding carbon dioxide should not be used in normally occupied spaces unless arrangements can be made to ensure evacuation before discharge. The same restriction applies to spaces that are not normally occupied but in which personnel may be present for maintenance or other purposes. It may be difficult to ensure evacuation if the space is large or if egress is in any way impeded by obstacles or complicated passageways. Escape is even more difficult after the discharge starts, because noise, greatly reduced visibility, and the physiological effects of the carbon dioxide concentration may confuse the occupants.

Consideration also should be given to the possibility of large volumes of carbon dioxide vapor leaking or flowing into unprotected lower levels, such as cellars, tunnels, or pits. In this event, the suffocating atmosphere would not be visible and might not be detected until too late.

METHODS OF APPLICATION

Two basic methods are used to apply carbon dioxide in extinguishing fires. One method is to discharge a sufficient amount of the agent into an enclosure to create an extinguishing atmosphere throughout the enclosed area. This is called "total flooding." The second method is to discharge the agent directly on to the burning material without relying on an enclosure to retain the carbon dioxide. This is called "local application."

Total Flooding

In total flooding systems, carbon dioxide is applied through nozzles designed and located to develop a uniform concentration of CO_2 in all parts of an enclosure. (See Figure 5-17B.) Calculation of the quantity of carbon dioxide required to achieve an extinguishing atmosphere is based upon the volume of the room and the concentration of CO_2 required for the combustible materials in it.

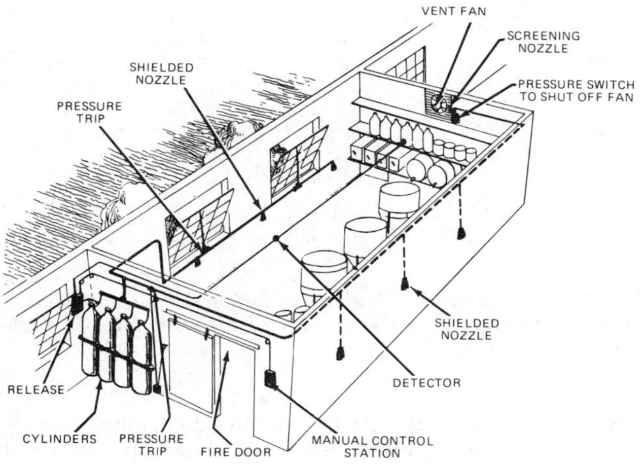

FIG. 5-17B. ***Diagram of a high-pressure carbon dioxide system for total flooding.***

The integrity of the enclosure is a very important part of total flooding, particularly if deep-seated fire potential exists in the hazard. If the room is tight, especially on the sides and bottom, the atmosphere can be retained for a long time to ensure complete control of the fire. If there are openings on the sides and bottom, however, the heavier mixture of carbon dioxide and air may leak out of the room rapidly and be replaced with air entering at higher openings. If the extinguishing atmosphere is lost too rapidly, glowing embers may remain and cause reignition when air reaches the fire zone. Therefore, it is important to close all openings to minimize leakage or to compensate for the openings by discharging additional carbon dioxide. Because of the relative weight of carbon dioxide, an opening in the ceiling helps to relieve internal air pressure during the discharge, with very little effect on leakage rate after the discharge.

Extended Discharge

An extended discharge of CO_2 is used when an enclosure is not tight enough to retain an extinguishing concentration as long as is needed. The extended discharge normally is at a reduced rate, following a high initial rate used to develop the extinguishing concentration in a reasonably short time. The reduced rate of discharge should be a function of the leakage rate, which can be calculated on the basis of leakage area, or of the flow rate through ventilating ducts that cannot be shut down.

Extended discharge is particularly applicable to enclosed rotating electrical equipment, such as generators, where it is difficult to prevent leakage until rotation stops. Extended discharge can be applied to ordinary total flooding systems, as well as to local application systems where a small hot spot may require prolonged cooling.

Local Application

In local application systems, carbon dioxide is discharged directly on the burning surfaces through nozzles designed for this purpose. The intent is to cover all combustible areas with nozzles located so they will extinguish all flames as quickly as possible. Any adjacent area to which fuel may spread also must be covered, because any residual fire could cause reignition after the CO_2 discharge ends. (See Figure 5-17C.)

FIG. 5-17C. ***A local application carbon dioxide extinguishing system that has activated. (Source: The Ansul Company)***

Discharge nozzles usually are designed for relatively low velocity to avoid splashing and air entrainment. Automatic detection is a necessity to provide fast response and minimize heat buildup. Although not essential, an enclosure would help retain carbon dioxide in the fire area. Local application of CO_2 can also be used for fast fire knockdown in an enclosure where final total flooding can provide absolute assurance that extinguishment will be complete.

Hand Hose Lines

Carbon dioxide systems can consist of hand hose lines permanently connected by means of fixed piping to a fixed supply of CO_2. Such systems frequently are provided for manual protection of small localized hazards. Although not a substitute for a fixed system, a hose line may be used to supplement a fixed system where the hazard is accessible for manual fire fighting, as well as to supplement portable equipment.

Hand hose lines are required to have a minimum bursting pressure of 5000 psi (34.5 MPa) if connected to a high-pressure supply, or 1800 psi (12.4 MPa) if the supply is low-pressure. The lines are not under pressure until the valve actuating the system is opened. There must be a sufficient carbon dioxide supply to permit the use of the

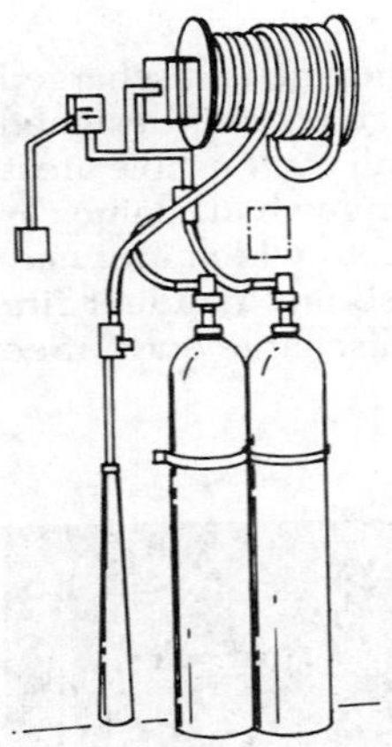

FIG. 5-17D. Carbon dioxide hand hose extinguishing system with hose mounted on a reel. This system offers flexibility for attacking fires. (Source: Walter Kidde and Company, Inc.)

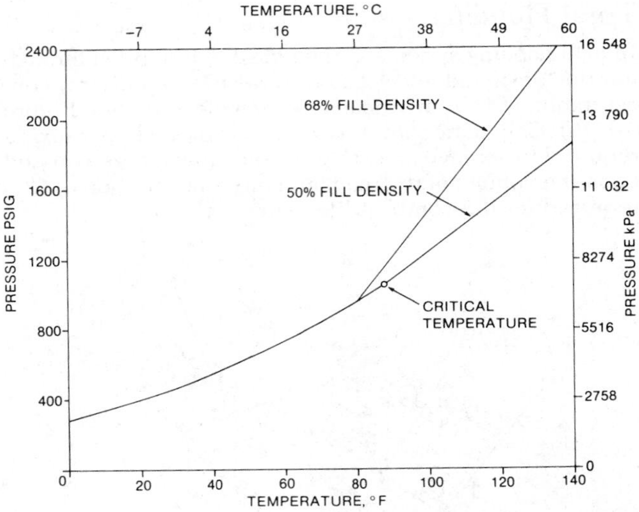

FIG. 5-17E. Variation in pressure of carbon dioxide with change in temperature, showing the effect of filling density in high-pressure storage.

hand line nozzle for at least 1 min. Nozzles should be connected to a good electrical ground to permit static electrical charges produced by the carbon dioxide discharge to drain off. The wire-braided hose properly coupled to the discharge piping can provide a path to ground. Figure 5-17D shows a hand hose line system.

Standpipe Systems and Mobile Supply

Total flooding, local application, and hand hose line systems without a permanently connected carbon dioxide supply are known as gas standpipe systems. They are supplied by containers of carbon dioxide mounted on mobile units that can be moved and quickly coupled to a standpipe, in case of fire.

Gas standpipe systems can be used as a supplement to complete fixed fire protection systems or as the only protection of hazards under certain circumstances, provided extinguishment would not be delayed adversely while the mobile supply is moved to the scene and attached to the standpipe. Mobile supplies may be equipped with hand hose lines for the protection of scattered hazards.

Special Applications

Carbon dioxide systems are sometimes used for inerting or purging. Carbon dioxide vapor is typically used in these applications. NFPA 69, *Explosion Prevention Systems*, gives guidance on these applications. Fire suppression in coal storage silos also can use carbon dioxide vapor. Low-pressure storage with an in-line vaporizer can conveniently supply the large quantities of carbon dioxide vapor often required for these applications.

COMPONENTS OF CARBON DIOXIDE SYSTEMS

The main components of a carbon dioxide system are the carbon dioxide supply, the discharge nozzles, and the piping system. These components, along with control valves and other operating devices, dispense the carbon dioxide and provide effective fire extinguishment.

Carbon Dioxide Storage

The CO_2 supply may be stored in high- or low-pressure containers. Because of the differences in pressure, system design is influenced by the storage method.

High-pressure storage: High-pressure containers, usually cylinders, are designed to store liquid carbon dioxide at atmospheric temperature. Since the maximum pressure in the cylinder or other container is affected by the ambient temperature, it is important that the container be designed to withstand the maximum expected pressure. Figure 5-17E shows the change in gage pressure with temperature.

Storage cylinders are designed, tested, and filled to U.S. Department of Transportation (DOT) specifications. The maximum filling density permitted is equal to 68 percent of the weight of water that the container can hold at 60°F (16°C). Standard cylinder capacities are 5, 10, 15, 20, 25, 35, 50, 75, and 100 lbs (2.3, 4.5, 6.8, 9.1, 11.3, 15.9, 22.7, 34, and 45.4 kg) of carbon dioxide. Fire extinguishing cylinders are fitted with an internal dip tube so that liquid will be discharged from the bottom when the cylinder is upright and the valve is opened.

Abnormally low storage temperatures adversely affect the rate of discharge. For this reason, NFPA 12, *Carbon Dioxide Extinguishing Systems*, does not permit storage temperatures below 0°F (−18°C) for total flooding systems or below 32°F (0°C) for local application systems. Lower storage temperatures may be permitted only if the design includes special features to compensate for the reduced pressure.

Low-pressure storage: Low-pressure storage containers are pressure vessels with a design working pressure of at least 325 psi (2240 kPa). These containers are maintained at a temperature of approximately 0°F (−18°C) by use of insulation and mechanical refrigeration. At this temperature, the pressure is approximately 300 psi (2069 kPa). A compressor, controlled by a pressure switch in the tank, circulates refrigerant through coils near the tank top. Tank pressure is controlled by condensation of carbon dioxide vapor by the coils. In the event of refrigeration failure, pressure-relief valves bleed off some of the vapor to keep the pressure within safe limits. This permits some of the liquid to evaporate, creating a self-refrigerating effect which reduces the pressure in the tank. Figure 5-17F shows a typical low-pressure container.

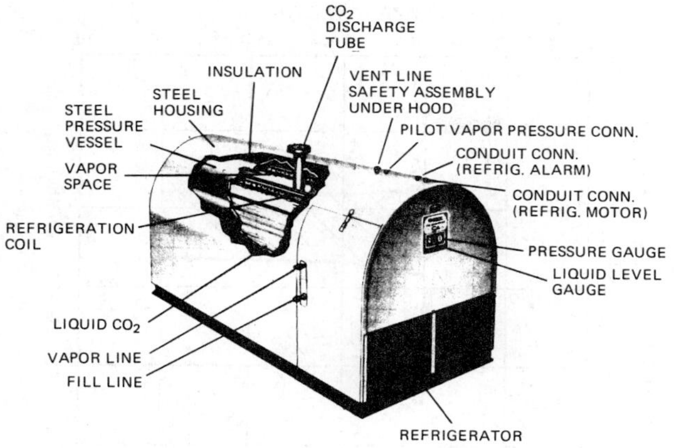

FIG. 5-17F. A low-pressure storage unit. The carbon dioxide is maintained at 0°F (−18°C) by refrigeration, and the pressure is 300 psi (2069 kPa). (Source: Cardox Division of Chemetron Corporation)

With low-pressure storage, it is common practice to protect multiple hazards from one central storage unit. The quantity of carbon dioxide discharged on a particular hazard is controlled by opening and closing the discharge valves in a preset timed sequence. Central storage units may have capacities ranging from less than one ton to a hundred tons or more (one ton equals approximately 907 kg). For large hazards, the distance between hazard and storage may be several hundred feet or more (100 ft equals approximately 30.5 m).

Piping

Piping systems, normally empty, convey carbon dioxide from the storage container to open nozzles where there is a fire. Since the proper rate of flow is a critical requirement for fire extinguishment, it is important that the piping be designed accurately. Minimum pressure in the pipeline must be kept well above the triple point pressure of 75 psia (517 kPa). If the pressure of the flowing carbon dioxide falls below the triple point pressure, dry ice will form in the pipe and block orifices in the discharge nozzles, thus stopping the flow of carbon dioxide. NFPA 12, *Carbon Dioxide Extinguishing Systems*, limits design nozzle pressures to a minimum of 300 psia (20.7 bars) for high-pressure storage and a minimum of 150 psia (10.3 bars) for low-pressure storage.

Carbon dioxide drawn from the bottom of the storage container enters the piping as a liquid. Friction causes loss in pressure. As pressure drops, the liquid boils, resulting in a mixture of liquid and vapor in the piping. The vapor increases in volume as the mixture passes through the piping, with a further drop in pressure. Thus, the flow is two-phase, a mixture of liquid and gas, a fact that pressure drop calculations must take into account.

NFPA 12, *Carbon Dioxide Extinguishing Systems*, covers the calculation of CO_2 flow in some detail and provides pertinent equations and data tables. Although charts and tables are available for manual calculation of system piping, the use of available computer programs speeds and simplifies the design of piping systems.

The piping must be adequately supported to prevent movement during the discharge, and provision must be made for its contraction and expansion. Because liquid carbon dioxide is a refrigerant, it will substantially reduce the pipe temperature during discharge. Low-pressure liquid, in particular, starts at 0°F (–18°C) and may reach temperatures as low as –50°F (–46°C) in the piping before the discharge ends.

Valves and Operating Devices

Valves for controlling the discharge of carbon dioxide must withstand the maximum operating pressure, be absolutely bubbletight when closed, and be capable of both manual and automatic operation. Valves and allied devices, such as timers and pressure switches, must be listed or approved for use in CO_2 systems.

To resist maximum anticipated pressure, valves in high-pressure systems are required to have a minimum bursting pressure of 5000 psi (34.5 MPa); valves constantly under pressure must have a minimum bursting pressure of 6000 psi (41.4 MPa). Valves for low-pressure systems must be capable of withstanding hydrostatic testing to 1800 psi (12.4 MPa) without permanent distortion. Corrosion resistance, noncombustibility and ability to withstand the expected temperature extremes are other characteristics required of the valves.

Discharge Nozzles

Many nozzle types are available for fire extinguishment applications. Nozzles used in total flooding simply may be orifices producing high-velocity jet streams, or they may be partially shielded to achieve reduced velocity or a specific discharge pattern. High-velocity types provide substantial mixing to ensure uniform concentration of carbon dioxide throughout an enclosure. Low-velocity types have a tendency to create high concentrations in the lower levels, which may be desirable under certain conditions.

Nozzle types used in local application systems normally are designed for relatively low discharge velocity. This helps to avoid splashing of liquid fuels and minimizes turbulence and air entrainment. All such nozzles must be tested for fire extinguishing characteristics and listed or approved by a testing laboratory on the basis of test performance.

Figure 5-17G shows a typical performance curve for a nozzle designed for overhead mounting. The rate of discharge used is based on the height of the nozzle above the hazard or the fuel surface and is given in listing cards or approvals. (Testing is based on the maximum rate that will not splash liquid fuels.) The maximum fire area that the nozzle will extinguish also is based on the height above the hazard surface, using the design flow rate.

Performance information enables the system designer to select and properly locate the number of nozzles necessary to cover the entire fire area of the hazard. It also establishes the design flow rate that must be used on the hazard. The effective design flow rate must continue for a minimum of 30 sec, which is part of the criteria used in performance testing.

Figures 5-17H and 5-17I show typical performance curves for nozzles designed for mounting on the sides of open tanks containing flammable liquids. In such cases, the design flow rates are based on the area of coverage for the tankside nozzles or on the width of the hazard for linear nozzles mounted to extend the full length of one side. In each case, the design flow rate must be in the shaded area of the curves.

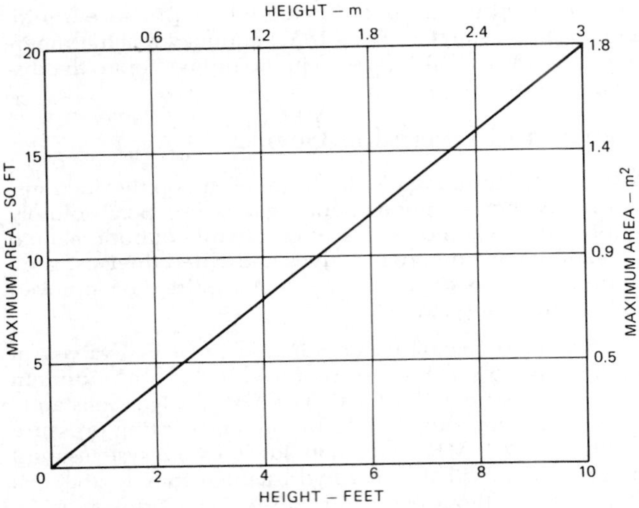

FIG. 5-17G. ***A listing or approval curve of a typical carbon dioxide nozzle showing maximum area vs. height or distance from liquid surface.***

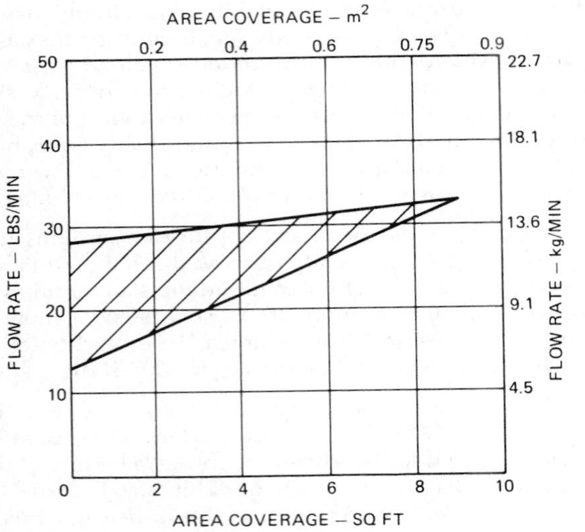

FIG. 5-17H. ***A typical listing or approval curve of a tankside carbon dioxide nozzle showing the flow rate vs. area coverage.***

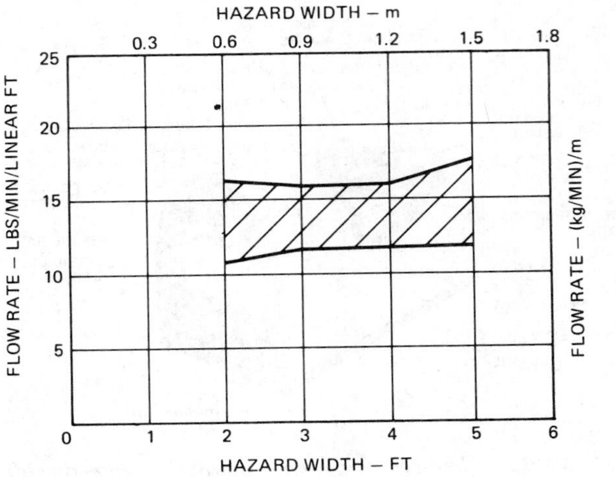

FIG. 5-17I. ***A typical listing or approval curve of a linear carbon dioxide nozzle showing flow rate vs. hazard width.***

CO_2 SYSTEM DESIGN CONSIDERATIONS

To organize basic components into a CO_2 fire protection system, a number of factors must be considered. These include the quantity of stored carbon dioxide, the method of actuation, the use of pre-discharge alarms, ventilation shutdown, pressure venting, and anything else involved in ensuring safe, prompt, and effective fire extinguishment.

Quantity Requirements

The quantity of carbon dioxide required for extinguishment depends upon the type of fire, the type of extinguishing system, and conditions in the fire area. Where continuous protection is required, the quantity of carbon dioxide on hand should be at least twice that needed for extinguishment. Detailed methods of determining the quantity required for extinguishment are covered in NFPA 12, *Carbon Dioxide Extinguishing Systems.*

Total flooding systems: The design concentration for a given enclosure should be sufficient to extinguish fires in all the fuels that are present in the hazard. The minimum concentration used in total flooding systems is 34 percent carbon dioxide by volume. Minimum design concentrations for various liquids and gases are given in Table 5-17A. NFPA 12, *Carbon Dioxide Extinguishing Systems*, requires a 50 percent concentration for electrical wiring hazards, including small electrical machines; 65 percent for bulk paper and fur storage vaults; and 75 percent for dust collectors. These are specific hazards for which there is a background of test experience. Other materials should be tested to determine minimum CO_2 concentrations and holding time.

The quantity of carbon dioxide must be sufficient to achieve a minimum design concentration and to hold it until the fire is extinguished. In an ideal enclosure, the volume of carbon dioxide vapor per unit volume of enclosure can be expressed by the equation:

$$X = \ln [100/(100 - C)]$$

where:

X = volume of vapor injected
C = concentration of carbon dioxide
ln = natural log.

This equation assumes that carbon dioxide is injected with high-velocity nozzles so that complete mixing of CO_2 with the room air is maintained throughout the discharge period. This means that some of the carbon dioxide will be lost along with the air displaced from the room. The weight of carbon dioxide required is determined by dividing the volume of vapor injected by the specific volume of carbon dioxide [near 9 cu ft/lb (0.56 m^3/kg)], and multiplying the result by the volume of the room.

Alternatively, a series of specific flooding factors has been established for surface fire hazards. These factors include an allowance for distributed leakage due to cracks around doors, porosity of the walls, and other small openings based on room size. The factors are greater for smaller rooms because the anticipated leakage would be greater relative to volume. The flooding factors are further multiplied by conversion factors to achieve design concentrations for the type of combustible involved. This procedure does not eliminate the need to compensate for leakage through obvious openings that cannot be closed or through ventilating systems that cannot be shut off in the event of a fire.

Surface burning fires, such as flammable liquid fires, are normally extinguished during a 1-min carbon dioxide discharge. Leakage compensation must be in addition to the basic quantity.

Deep-seated fires require higher concentrations and much longer holding times. The rate of discharge must be high enough to develop a concentration of 30 percent in not more than 2 min, and the final design concentration must be achieved in not more than 7 min. Enclosures for deep-seated fires must be relatively tight, or it quickly becomes uneconomical to maintain the CO_2 design concentration.

Extended discharge systems: The most efficient way to compensate for leakage where the concentration must be maintained for a substantial time is to use an extended discharge at a reduced rate equal to the rate of leakage. The quantity of carbon dioxide required is based on the rate of discharge multiplied by the time that the concentration must be maintained. This is in addition to the quantity required to develop the design concentration.

Local application systems: These systems may be designed using either "rate-by-area" or "rate-by-volume" methods. When rate-by-area is used, the hazard is considered as a number of equivalent surface areas, each protected by a single nozzle. The rate of discharge from each nozzle is determined from listing information, and the total discharge rate for the system is the sum of the design rates required for each nozzle.

Where the hazard consists of three-dimensional irregular objects that cannot be reduced easily to equivalent surface areas, the rate-by-volume method may be used. In this case, the discharge rate of the system is based on the volume of an assumed enclosure entirely surrounding the hazard. Because this method is not as precise as the rate-by-area procedure, it usually results in more carbon dioxide discharge, unless the hazard is nearly enclosed with walls.

A discharge of vapor is not considered effective for local application. The liquid portion of the discharge should be continued for a minimum of 30 sec, or longer if required for cooling. If a liquid fuel has an autoignition temperature higher than its boiling point - for example, paraffin wax and some cooking oils - the mass of liquid can become "superheated" above its autoignition temperature. For such fuels, a minimum local application time of 3 min is required to permit the mass of liquid fuel to cool.

Additional carbon dioxide must be added to storage to compensate for any initial vapor discharge produced in cooling and piping. In high-pressure systems, only approximately 70 percent of the stored quantity will be discharged as liquid. Therefore, the quantity calculated by rate and time must be increased by a factor of 1.4 to help ensure a 30-sec liquid discharge.

Hand hose line systems: In theory, the carbon dioxide supply depends upon the type and size of the hazard to be protected. As a practical matter, however, sufficient carbon dioxide should be available to counteract possible waste by inexperienced users. In any case, there should be sufficient carbon dioxide to permit operation of the system for at least one minute.

Venting Requirements

When liquid carbon dioxide is discharged into a closed room, the atmosphere will shrink initially due to the sudden refrigerating effect. At a later flooding stage, the combined volume of the carbon dioxide and air will become greater than the initial room volume. Thus, while the first result will be to create a vacuum, or draw in air, the final result must be to increase the pressure or to exhaust the excess volume through vent openings. Actual air temperatures are greatly reduced during the discharge, but they soon return to normal as heat is absorbed from solid surfaces in the room.

Experience has shown that most ordinary rooms have sufficient leakage through cracks around doors and windows and through general porosity to prevent noticeable vacuum or pressure buildup. Even so, from the viewpoint of efficient total flooding, it is better to have major vent openings in or near the ceiling rather than near the floor. In rooms that may be tightly sealed, a safe vent area for light structures can be estimated on the basis of calculated discharge flow rate:

$$X = \frac{Q}{1.3\sqrt{p}}$$

where:

X = vent area in sq in.
Q = flow rate in lbs/min
p = allowable strength of the enclosure in lbs/ft^2

For SI units:

$$X_m = \frac{23.9\, Q_m}{\sqrt{p_m}}$$

where:

X_m = vent area in sq mm
Q_m = flow rate in kg/min
p_m = allowable strength of the enclosure in kg/m^2

More information on room venting can be found in NFPA 12, *Carbon Dioxide Extinguishing Systems*.

System Control

Total flooding and local-application carbon dioxide systems normally should be designed to operate automatically. The detection device may be any of the listed or approved devices that are actuated by heat, smoke, flame, flammable vapors, or other abnormal process conditions that could lead to a fire or explosion. Automatically operated systems are required to have an independent means of manual actuation.

Modern carbon dioxide systems usually have an electric control panel. The control panel supervises the interconnections among all components necessary for control of the system and life safety. Connections among the control device and detectors, manual electric release stations, system valve actuators, and alarms are typically supervised. Standby power sources also are incorporated.

When a detector or manual station is activated, the control panel operates pre-discharge alarms to warn personnel of the impending discharge. The panel also can control shutdown of fuel lines, closure of dampers, and shutdown of ventilating and process equipment. After a suitable time delay and pre-discharge alarm, the control panel operates the system discharge valves.

Some older carbon dioxide systems used timer-driven cams to operate switches which control the various discharge functions. Totally pneumatic systems using pneumatic detection and control were also common.

Whether supplemental to automatic actuation or the sole means of placing a system in operation, manual controls must be easy to operate, accessible in case of fire, and located close to the valves they control. Remote manual controls usually are located near an exit for a total flooding installation or near a hazardous area for local application installations.

Life Safety Considerations

Every precaution must be taken to ensure that personnel in a protected area are evacuated before the area is flooded with carbon dioxide. This is the primary purpose of a predischarge alarm, which should provide a suitable time delay before the CO_2 discharge. Both audible and visual predischarge alarms should be used, as appropriate. Odorizers, such as oil of wintergreen, are sometimes added to the carbon dioxide discharge to provide an olfactory indication of the presence of a carbon dioxide discharge. Self-contained breathing apparatus should be provided. Manual controls for the system must be located so as to avoid confusion, and they must be clearly labeled with safe operating procedures. Additional life safety steps include posting warning signs of the protection status and informing personnel about operating procedures. System "lock-outs" should be provided to prevent accidental or deliberate discharge when persons unfamiliar with the system and its operation are present in the protected space. Watch procedures should be established if the protected area must be entered for maintenance or other work. Consideration should be given to any possibility that substantial volumes of carbon dioxide vapor could leak or flow into adjacent low-level areas, such as cellars, pits, or narrow hallways—spaces not included in the protected area. If this potential exists, alarms and warning signs should be extended to include these areas. Finally, arrangements for safely ventilating the flooded space following the emergency must be made.

Marine Systems

Systems used on offshore platforms and marine vessels are subject to different regulations and design procedures. Quantity calculations, piping design, nozzle sizing, and system control requirements will vary from those discussed in this chapter. The guidance of the authority having jurisdiction over the vessel must be followed for such systems.

TESTING AND MAINTAINING CO_2 SYSTEMS

An elaborate fire protection system could be worthless unless it is properly tested to demonstrate adequate performance and maintained in good working condition.

Acceptance Testing

No newly installed system should be accepted until it has been inspected properly and tested to prove performance in accordance with design specifications. The inspection should ascertain whether the system is installed in accordance with approved plans. The piping is particularly important, because any changes might affect the flow rates that were calculated on the basis of the pipe sizes shown on the plans.

The final proof of performance is to discharge the system and, for total flooding hazards, to measure the concentrations of CO_2 and the holding time in the fire zone. Local application systems cannot be subjected to concentration testing. Their effectiveness is judged by observation during the test discharge. NFPA 12, *Carbon Dioxide Extinguishing Systems*, gives the minimum requirements for approval of new installations.

Inspections

To maintain a system in proper operating condition, it is essential to conduct periodic inspections. The status of the carbon dioxide supply should be checked at least weekly for low-pressure supplies, at six-month intervals for high-pressure cylinders and immediately after the system has operated. The entire system should be inspected annually. In particular, inspectors should look for changes in the scope of the hazard, changes in the condition of any enclosure, and other changes that could affect the adequacy of the fire protection system.

Maintenance Testing

All operating devices should be tested annually. Although much of this testing can be accomplished without discharging the system, a partial discharge may be necessary in some cases. Any required maintenance found by testing should be performed without delay.

BIBLIOGRAPHY

References Cited

1. Coward, H. W. and Jones, G. W. 1952. "Limits of Flammability of Gases and Vapors." *Bulletin 503*, USDI Bureau of Mines, Pittsburgh, PA.

NFPA Codes, Standards, and Recommended Practices

Reference to the following NFPA codes, standards, and recommended practices will provide further information on carbon dioxide and application systems discussed in this chapter. (See the latest *NFPA Catalog* for availability of current editions of the following documents.)

NFPA 12, *Carbon Dioxide Extinguishing Systems.*

NFPA 69, *Explosion Prevention Systems*

Additional Reading

"Carbon Dioxide Fire Extinguishing Systems," Walter Kidde and Co., Wake Forest, NC, 1981, rev. Aug. 1984.

Fire Extinguishing Systems Design Manual: Carbon Dioxide, Walter Kidde and Co., Wake Forest, NC, 1982.

Noronha, J. A. and Schiffhauer, E. J., "Explicit Equations for Two-Phase Carbon Dioxide Flow," *Fire Technology*, Vol. 10, No. 2 (May 1974), pp. 101-109.

"Special Hazards Protection—Manufacturers and Equipment," *Fire Journal*, Vol. 81, No. 4 (July-Aug. 1987), p. 43.

HALOGENATED AGENTS AND SYSTEMS

Revised by Gary Taylor

Halogenated extinguishing agents are hydrocarbons in which one or more hydrogen atoms have been replaced by atoms from the halogen series: fluorine, chlorine, bromine, or iodine. This substitution confers not only nonflammability, but flame extinguishment properties to many of the resulting compounds. Halogenated agents are used both in portable fire extinguishers and in extinguishing systems. Streaming agents, such as Halon 1211 and 2402, have most often been used in manually applied fire equipment and local application-type fixed systems. Halon 1301 has most often been used in total flooding-type fixed systems.

Halons 1301, 2402, and 1211 have been identified as stratospheric ozone-depletion agents. The Montreal Protocol on Substances that Deplete the Ozone Layer, an international agreement, requires a complete phaseout of the production of these halons by the year 2000, except to the extent necessary to satisfy essential uses, for which no adequate alternatives are available. The Montreal Protocol establishes minimum compliance requirements; individual nations may require more stringent controls on the production, use, or disposal of ozone-depleting substances, including the halons.

The use and development of halogenated fire extinguishing agents have evolved over many years. The first member of this family of chemicals was carbon tetrachloride (Halon 104). Use as a fire extinguishant probably occurred before 1900, and by 1910 portable fire extinguishers, tested by independent agencies, had appeared. The growing popularity of the automobile, and other uses of internal combustion engines, signaled an increasing need for fire extinguishants suitable for use on flammable liquids fires.

By 1917, there were discussions regarding the possible effects that carbon tetrachloride could have on the human system. In 1919 the first recorded deaths due to carbon tetrachloride use occurred. Two men working on the construction of a submarine were killed. One man's clothing had caught fire, and the other man extinguished the fire with a carbon tetrachloride agent fire extinguisher. Both were overcome by the fumes and later died. During the 1920s the discussions regarding the toxicity of carbon tetrachloride continued, with particular attention to the possibility that freezing point depressants and impurities were contributing factors.

Methyl bromide (Halon 1001) gained popularity after it was discovered in the late 1920s. Due to its high toxicity, it was never popular for use in portable extinguishers, although it was used in British and German aircraft and ships during World War II. During World War II, Germany developed chlorobromomethane (Halon 1011) to replace methyl bromide. In 1947 a report by Underwriters Laboratories Inc. showed that the toxicity of carbon tetrachloride and chlorobromomethane (Halon 1011) were comparable, but chlorobromomethane was a more efficient fire extinguishing agent.

In the post-World War II era, the addition of stearate to sodium bicarbonate-based dry chemicals provided improved flow and moisture repellency characteristics to sodium bicarbonate-based dry chemicals. This, in turn, encouraged the use of portable dry chemical fire extinguishers as an alternative to vaporizing liquid extinguishers that used early halons as extinguishants.

By the 1950s the era of the early halons (Halons 104, 1001, and 1011) was ending. Increased popularity of dry chemicals had decreased the need for widespread use of these early halons, and growing concerns with their toxic effects resulted in their "official" death by the 1960s.

In 1947, the Purdue Research Foundation conducted a systematic evaluation of more than 60 new candidate extinguishing agents. Simultaneously, the U.S. Army Corps of Engineers undertook toxicological studies of these same compounds. As a result, four halons were selected for further study: dibromodifluoromethane (Halon 1202), bromochlorodifluoromethane (Halon 1211), bromotrifluoromethane (Halon 1301), and dibromotetrafluoroethane (Halon 2402). Testing showed that Halon 1202 was the most effective fire extinguishant, but it was also the most toxic. Halon 1301 ranked second in fire extinguishing effectiveness and least toxic. As a direct result of this program, a portable fire extinguisher employing Halon 1301 was developed for use by the U.S. Army, primarily for use

Gary Taylor is chairman of Taylor/Wagner Inc., a fire protection consulting firm located in Willowdale, Ontario, Canada.

inside armored personnel carriers and tanks. The U.S. Air Force selected Halon 1202 for military aircraft engine protection, and the U.S. Federal Aviation Administration approved the use of Halon 1301 for commercial aircraft engine fire protection.

Because of this basic research, some general conclusions were drawn, based on the contribution of the various halogens to resultant characteristics of the halon as a useful fire extinguishant. These are outlined in Table 5-18A.

TABLE 5-18A. ***Halogen Characteristics***

Characteristic/Halogen	Fluorine	Chlorine	Bromine
Stability of Compound	Enhances	–	–
Toxicity	Reduces	Enhances	Enhances
Boiling Point	Reduces	Enhances	Enchances
Thermal Stability	Enhances	Reduces	Reduces
Extinguishing Effectiveness		Enhances	Enhances

In the 1960s attention began to focus on the use of Halon 1301 as a total flooding extinguishant for the protection of computer rooms. In the past 20 years, Halon 1301 has grown in usage as an agent for use in fixed fire protection systems, primarily for the protection of vital electronics facilities, such as computer rooms and communications equipment rooms. Other significant applications for Halon 1301 systems include: museums, shipboard machinery spaces, and pipeline pumping stations.

In the United States, early Halon 1301 total flooding systems were installed using carbon dioxide equipment and technology. An example of such a system, installed in the Winterthur Museum, was described.[1]

In 1966, NFPA organized a Technical Committee on Halogenated Fire Extinguishing Agent Systems to develop standards covering installation, maintenance, and use of such systems. NFPA 12A, *Halon 1301 Fire Extinguishing Agent Systems*, and NFPA 12B, *Halon 1211 Fire Extinguishing Systems* were approved in the early 1970s. NFPA 12CT is a tentative standard for Halon 2402. Because of its rather recent recognition, there is limited experience with Halon 2402 in the U.S., and, therefore, it cannot be treated as extensively as the other agents in this handbook.

During 1966, attention began to focus on the use of Halon 1301 to protect computer rooms and electronic data processing (EDP) equipment. In 1972, following extensive testing by several major companies on the effects of Halon 1301 decomposition products on electronic equipment,[2] the NFPA Committee on Electronic Computer/Data Processing Equipment recognized Halon 1301 total flooding systems as suitable for protection of electronic computer/data processing equipment. With suitable precautions, such as time delays, Halon 1211 total flooding systems are now used in Europe.

CHEMICAL COMPOSITION AND CLASSIFICATION

The halogenated extinguishing agents are currently known simply as halons, and the halon system for naming the halogenated hydrocarbons was devised by the U.S. Army Corps of Engineers.[3] This simplified system of nomenclature describes the chemical composition of the materials without the use of chemical names or possibly confusing abbreviations (i.e., "BT" for bromotrifluoromethane and "DB" for dibromodifluoromethane). Examples of this system are shown in Table 5-18B. The first digit of the number represents the number of carbon atoms in the compound molecule; the second digit, the number of fluorine atoms; the third digit, the number of chlorine atoms; the fourth digit, the number of bromine atoms; and the fifth digit, the number of iodine atoms (if any). If the fifth digit is a zero, it is not expressed; bromotrifluoromethane ($BrCF_3$), for example, is referred to as Halon 1301 (not 13010), although its chemical formula shows one carbon atom, three fluorine atoms, no chlorine atoms, one bromine atom, and no iodine atoms.

TABLE 5-18B. ***Sample Halon Numbers for Various Halogenated Fire Extinguishing Agents***

Chemical Name	Formula	Halon No.
Methyl bromide	CH_3Br	1001
Methyl iodide	CH_3I	10001
Bromochloromethane	CH_2BrCl	1011
Dibromodifluoromethane	CF_2Br_2	1202
Bromochlorodifluoromethane	CF_2BrCl	1211
Bromotrifluoromethane	CF_3Br	1301
Carbon tetrachloride	CCl_4	104
Dibromotetrafluoroethane	$C_2F_4Br_2$	2402

The three halogen elements commonly found in extinguishing agents are fluorine (F), chlorine (Cl), and bromine (Br). Substitution of a hydrogen atom in a hydrocarbon with these three halogens influences the relevant properties in the following manner.

Fluorine: Imparts stability to the compound, reduces toxicity, reduces boiling point, increases thermal stability.

Chlorine: Imparts fire extinguishing effectiveness, increases boiling point, increases toxicity, reduces thermal stability.

Bromine: Same effects as chlorine, but to a greater degree.

Thus, compounds containing combinations of fluorine, chlorine, and bromine can possess varying degrees of extinguishing effectiveness, chemical and thermal stability, volatility, and toxicity.

The halogen is linked to the carbon atom by a "covalent" chemical bond, which means that unlike inorganic halogen compounds, such as common table salt (sodium chloride), there is no tendency to ionize or become electrically conductive in the presence of water. The presence of a fluorine atom in the molecule increases the C-Cl and C-Br strength and improves the overall chemical stability of the compound.

Because they are either gases or liquids that rapidly vaporize in fire, halons leave no corrosive or abrasive residue after use. They are nonconductors of electricity and have high liquid densities that permit use of compact storage containers. The areas of major halon use are for the protection of electrical and electronic equipment, petroleum production facilities, engine compartments (ships, military vehicles, and aircraft), and other areas where rapid extinguishment is important, or where damage to equipment or materials or cleanup after use must be minimized.

TABLE 5-18C. ***Some Physical Properties of the Common Halogenated Fire Extinguishing Agents***

Agent	Chemical Formula	Halon No.	Type of Agent	Approx. Boiling Point °F†	Approx. Freezing Point °F†	Specific Gravity of Liquid at 68°F† (Water = 1)	Approx. Critical Temp. °F†	Estimated Pressure psig‡ At 130°F†	Estimated Pressure psig‡ At Critical Temp.	Latent Heat of Vaporization cal/g Water = 540 cal/g CO_2 = 138 cal/g
Carbon tetrachloride	CCl_4	104	Liquid	170	−8	1.595	—	—	—	46
Methyl bromide	CH_3Br	1001	Liquid	40	−135	1.73	—	—	—	62
Bromochloromethane	CH_2BrCl	1011	Liquid	151	−124	1.93	—	—	—	—
Dibromodifluoromethane	CF_2Br_2	1202	Liquid	76	−223	2.28	389	23	585	29
Bromochlorodifluoromethane	CF_2BrCl	1211	Liquefied Gas*	25	−257	1.83	309	75	580	32
Bromotrifluoromethane	CF_3Br	1301	Liquefied Gas	−72	−270	1.57	153	435	560	28
Dibromotetrafluoroethane	$C_2F_4Br_2$	2402	Liquid	117	−167	2.17	—	3.8	—	25

* May be kept as a liquid at reduced temperatures.
† 5⁄9 (°F −32) = °C
‡ 1 psig = 6.895 kPa

PROPERTIES OF HALOGENATED AGENTS

Some of the physical properties of the common halogenated fire extinguishing agents referred to in this chapter are shown in Table 5-18C. More details on bromotrifluoromethane (Halon 1301) and bromochlorodifluoromethane (Halon 1211) are given in the following paragraphs.

Physical Properties

Halon 1301 is a gas at 70°F (21°C), with a vapor pressure of 199 psig (1372 kPa). Although this pressure would adequately expel the material, it decreases rapidly to 56 psig (386 kPa) at 0°F (–17°C) and to 17.2 psig (119 kPa) at –40°F (–40°C). It is, therefore, usual to increase the pressure on portable extinguishers or systems with nitrogen either to 360 psig (2482 kPa) or to 600 psig (4137 kPa), which ensures adequate performance at all temperatures. The high volatility of Halon 1301 has led to its use in total flooding systems, where rapid vaporization is an asset.

Halon 1211 is also a gas at 70°F (21°C), with a vapor pressure of 22 psig (152 kPa) and a boiling point of 25°F (–4°C). Its relatively high boiling point allows it to be projected as a liquid stream, thus enabling portable extinguishers and local application systems to have a greater range than possible with other gaseous materials. For portable extinguishers, the normal superpressurization with nitrogen is approximately 100 psig at 70°F (689 kPa at 21°C) which permits the use of inexpensive hardware. Halon 2402, with a boiling point of 117°F (47°C), is a liquid at room temperature.

Corrosion and Other Effects on Materials

The early nonfluorinated halogenated agents had significant corrosion problems. The fluorinated agents currently in use are chemically more stable, and neither Halon 1301, Halon 1211, nor Halon 2402 has any significant corrosive action on the commonly used construction metals, unless free water is present. (Free water is defined as the presence of a separate water phase in the liquid halon. When present in a small quantity, free water can provide a site for concentrating acid impurities into a corrosive liquid. It has been determined that dissolved water is not a problem.)

The effect of these agents on plastics and elastomers depends upon the precise grade or composition of the plastics and elastomers. In general, normally satisfactory effects are obtained with rigid plastics, such as polytetrafluoroethylene, nylon, and acetal copolymers. Elastomers of particular suitability are neoprene, Buna N, and "Viton" fluoroelastomer rubbers. More precise guidelines should be obtained from the manufacturers of the materials. Halon 1301 generally has considerably less effect on plastic and elastomeric materials than does Halon 1211 or Halon 2402.

EXTINGUISHING CHARACTERISTICS

The extinguishing mechanism of the halogenated agents is not clearly understood. However, a chemical reaction undoubtedly occurs that interferes with the combustion processes. The agents act by removing the active chemical species involved in the flame chain reactions (a process known as "chain breaking"). While all the halogens are active in this way, bromine is much more effective than chlorine or fluorine.

A number of possible mechanisms by which bromine inhibits combustion have been proposed. The most active species in hydrocarbon combustion are oxygen and hydrogen atoms, and hydroxyl radicals ($O^\cdot$, $H^\cdot$, and $OH^\cdot$). Under fire conditions, the halogenated agent—for example, bromotrifluoromethane (Halon 1301)—will release a bromine atom:

$$CBrF_3 \rightarrow CF_3^\bullet + Br^\bullet$$

The Br atom can react with a hydrocarbon molecule to form hydrogen bromide, HBr:

$$R\text{-}H + Br^\bullet \rightarrow R^\bullet = HBr$$

The HBr then reacts with an active hydrogen or hydroxyl radical, releasing the bromine atom for further inhibition reactions.

$$OH^\bullet + HBr \rightarrow H_2O + Br^\bullet$$

In this way, chain carriers are removed from the system while the inhibiting HBr is continuously regenerated.

Another "ionic" theory supposes that the uninhibited combustion process includes a step in which oxygen ions are formed by the capture of electrons that come from ionization of hydrocarbon molecules. Since bromine atoms have a much higher cross section for the capture of slow electrons than has oxygen, the bromine inhibits the reaction by removing the electrons that are needed for activation of the oxygen.[4]

Fire Extinguishing Effectiveness

The effectiveness of the different halons as extinguishing agents has been the subject of many studies. The initial results of some of the early studies are contained in the October 1954 issue of the *NFPA Quarterly*.[3] It is now recognized that comparison of effectiveness of agents depends upon whether portable extinguishers or fixed systems are being considered and, particularly in tests on portable units, whether the agents were evaluated with hardware of optimum nozzle and value design. Therefore, the following information should be used only as a general guide, because other considerations, such as range of the unit (which varies on the gas or liquid characteristic of the individual halon and the total weight and volume of the equipment), may be of equal importance, depending upon use.

Table 5-18D gives the approximate pounds of agent required per unit of Class B rating obtained with small portable extinguishers currently listed with Underwriters Laboratories Inc. (UL), or approved by Factory Mutual Research Corporation (FMRC).

TABLE 5-18D. ***Relative Effectiveness of Halogenated Agents on Small UL Class B Fires***

Agent	Halon No.	Weight of Agent* (pounds)	UL B:C	Pounds Per Unit B Rating*
Bromotrifluoromethane	1301	4.0	5	0.8
Bromochlorodifluoromethane	1211	2.5	5	0.5
Halon Mixture	1301/1211	0.9	1	0.9
Carbon Dioxide	—	5.0	5	1.0

* One qt = 4 lb; one lb = 0.45 kg

In total flooding systems, the effectiveness of the halogenated agents on flammable liquid and vapor fires is quite dramatic. Rapid and complete extinguishment is obtained with low concentrations of agent. On a worldwide basis, the development of systems using Halon 1301 and Halon 1211, together with the development of realistic test methods that have been applied to both these agents and recognized by NFPA, has shown that, in total flooding application for flame extinguishment or inerting, Halon 1301 requires an average of 10 percent less material on a gas volume basis than does Halon 1211 for any given fuel. Table 5-18E shows a comparison of flame extinguishment values included in NFPA 12A, *Halon 1301 Fire Extinguishing Agent Systems*, and NFPA 12B, *Halon 1211 Fire Extinguishing Systems*. It is generally recognized that on a weight-of-agent basis, both agents are approximately two and one-half times more effective than carbon dioxide.

The flame extinguishing ability of Halon 2402 vapors is very good and quite similar to that for Halon 1301 and Halon 1211. However, because it is a liquid at room temperature and is intended mainly for local application situations, its performance is not directly comparable to the data obtained for Halon 1301 and Halon 1211 with total flooding in mind.

TABLE 5-18E. ***Comparison of Flame Extinguishment Values for Halon 1301 and Halon 1211***

Fuel	Average Percent by Volume of Agent in Air Required for Flame Extinguishment: Halon 1301	Halon 1211
Methane	3.1	3.5
Propane	4.3	4.8
n-Heptane	4.1	4.1
Ethylene	6.8	7.2
Benzene	3.3	2.9
Ethanol	3.8	4.2
Acetone	3.3	3.6

Note: Design flame extinguishment concentrations for Halon 1301 and 1211 total flooding systems are calculated from the tested value by adding a 20 percent safety factor. However, they are never less than 5 percent.

The effectiveness of halogenated agents on Class A fires is less predictable. It depends to a large extent upon the specific burning material, its configuration, and how early in the combustion cycle the agent is applied. Most plastics behave as flammable liquids—they can be extinguished rapidly and completely with 4 to 6 percent concentrations of Halon 1211 or Halon 1301. Other materials, particularly cellulosic products, can, in certain forms, develop deep-seated fires in addition to flaming combustion. The flaming portion of such fires can be extinguished with low 4 to 6 percent concentrations of agent, but the deep-seated portion may continue glowing under some circumstances.[5] Even so, the deep-seated fire will be controlled in that its rate of burning and consequent heat release will be reduced. Considerably higher agent concentrations (18 percent to 30 percent) are required to achieve complete extinguishment, and these levels are seldom economical to apply. However, the concept of controlling deep-seated fires with halogenated agents has been accepted in the respective NFPA standards.

TOXIC AND IRRITANT EFFECTS

The toxicology of Halon 1301, Halon 1211, and Halon 2402 has been studied extensively in both animals and humans. As a result, safety guidelines for these agents can be written.

Early animal studies by the U.S. Army Chemical Center, summarized in Table 5-18F, determined the approximate lethal concentration (ALC) for 15-min exposures to Halon 1301, Halon 1211, and Halon 2402 to be 83 percent, 32 percent, and 13 percent by volume, respectively. The ALC for decomposed vapors of these agents is also shown.[3]

Animals exposed to halon concentrations below lethal levels exhibit two distinct types of toxic effects: (1) central nervous system changes, such as tremors, convulsions, lethargy, and unconsciousness at high airborne concentrations (above 30 percent by volume for Halon 1301, and 10 percent for Halon 1211); and (2) cardiovascular effects, including hypotension, decreased heart rate, and occasional cardiac arrhythmia (lack of rhythm in the heartbeat). Effects are transitory and disappear rapidly after exposure.

The inhalation of many halocarbons and hydrocarbons can make the heart abnormally sensitive to elevated adrenaline levels, resulting in cardiac arrhythmia and possibly death. This phenomenon has been referred to as cardiac

TABLE 5-18F. ***Approximate Lethal Concentrations for 15-min Exposure to Vapors of Various Fire Extinguishing Agents****

Agent	Formula	Halon No.	Approximate Lethal Concentration in Parts Per Million	
			Natural Vapor	Decomposed Vapor
Bromotrifluoromethane	CF_3Br	1301	83,200	14,000†
Bromochlorodifluoromethane	CF_2ClBr	1211	324,000	7,650
Carbon dioxide	CO_2	—	658,000	658,000
Dibromodifluoromethane	CF_2Br_2	1202	54,000	1,850
Bromochloromethane	CH_2ClBr	1011	65,000	4,000
Dibromotetrafluoroethane	$C_2F_4Br_2$	2402	126,000	1,600‡
Carbon tetrachloride	CCl_4	104	28,000	300
Methyl bromide	CH_3Br	1001	5,900	9,600

* Based on tests with white rats by the Medical Laboratories, U.S. Army Chemical Center.

† Subsequent tests by Kettering Laboratory of the University of Cincinnati (unpublished data) with a commercial Halon 1301 of improved quality indicated that the lethal concentration of decomposed vapor is at least 20,000 ppm. Other tests have given the ALC (Approximate Lethal Concentration) value of Halon 1301 decomposition products as low as 2,500 ppm. The variance is based on differing analytical procedures.

‡ This figure does not agree with manufacturer's data on their product.

sensitization. The halon compounds can also sensitize the heart. In the case of Halon 1301, this occurs only at high exposure levels. For example, in standard cardiac sensitization screening studies in dogs using 5-min exposures and large doses of injected adrenaline, the threshold for sensitization is in the 7.5 to 10 percent range.[6] The sensitization level for Halon 1211 is 1 to 2 percent and for Halon 2402 is 1,000 to 2,500 ppm.[7,8]

Human exposures to both Halon 1301 and Halon 1211 have shown that Halon 1301 concentrations up to 7 percent by volume and Halon 1211 concentrations of 2 to 3 percent by volume have little noticeable effect on the subject. At Halon 1301 concentrations between 7 and 10 percent and Halon 1211 concentrations between 3 and 4 percent, subjects experienced dizziness and tingling of the extremities, indicating mild anesthesia. At Halon 1301 concentrations above 10 percent and Halon 1211 concentrations above 4 to 5 percent, the dizziness becomes pronounced, the subjects feel as if they will lose consciousness (although none have), and physical and mental dexterity is reduced.[9,10,11] In human subjects exposed to 7 percent Halon 1301 for periods up to 30 min, the effects appeared within the first 5 to 10 min of exposure remained constant throughout the remainder of the exposure, then disappeared quickly after exposures were stopped.[12] When used as intended, no significant adverse health effects have been reported from the use of Halon 1301 or Halon 1211 as a fire extinguishant since their introduction into the marketplace 30 years ago.

Halon 1301 has been tested for effects on pregnant rats during the critical stages of gestation. Results showed this agent was not embryotoxic (causing growth retardation or death of the fetus) or teratogenic. In addition, Halon 1301 was not mutagenic when tested in the salmonella/microsome assay (Ames test).

A mutagen is a chemical that causes changes in the DNA structure of a cell. A standardized test, called the Ames test or assay, performed on a special strain of salmonella bacteria, provides a preliminary indication that a chemical may be a mutagen and possibly a carcinogen in humans. A high proportion of known carcinogens do exhibit mutagenic activity in the Ames assay. Halon 1301 concentrations up to 40 percent by volume did not exhibit mutagenic activity in this test.[13]

A teratogen is a chemical that causes permanent structural or functional alteration of the normal processes of fetal development. Pregnant female rats were exposed (by inhalation) to 5 percent Halon 1301 by volume. No evidence of teratogenic or embryotoxic effects was seen in their offspring.[14]

From the extensive medical data available, the following exposure guidelines have been produced for use of Halon 1301, Halon 1211, and Halon 2402. (See Table 5-18G.)

TABLE 5-18G. ***Permitted Exposure Times to Halon 1301, Halon 1211, and Halon 2402***

	Concentration Percent by Volume	Permitted Time of Exposure
Halon 1301	Up to 7	15 min
	7–10	1 min
	10–15	30 sec
	Above 15	Prevent exposure
Halon 1211	Up to 4	5 min
	4–5	1 min
	Above 5	Prevent exposure
Halon 2402	0.05	10 min
	0.10	1 min

NFPA 12A, *Halon 1301 Fire Extinguishing Agent Systems*, permits Halon 1301 design concentration up to 10 percent in normally occupied areas, and up to 15 percent in areas not normally occupied. Because the required extinguishing concentration of Halon 1211 is near or above its limit for safe exposures, Halon 1211 systems are not recognized in NFPA 12B, *Halon 1211 Fire Extinguishing Systems*, for use in normally occupied areas.

NFPA 12CT, *Halon 2402 Fire Extinguishing Agent Systems*, sets acceptable concentrations for human exposure to Halon 2402 vapors at 0.05 to 0.10 percent by volume. Additionally, the standard recognizes only local application systems that may be outdoors with appropriate personnel safeguards, or indoors in unoccupied areas.

DECOMPOSITION PRODUCTS OF HALONS

Consideration of life safety during use of halogenated agents also must include the effects of breakdown products, which have a relatively higher toxicity to humans. Decomposition of halogenated agents takes place on exposure to flame, or to surface temperatures above approximately 900°F (482°C). In the presence of available hydrogen (from water vapor or the combustion process itself), the main decomposition products of Halon 1301 are hydrogen fluoride (HF), hydrogen bromide (HBr), and free bromine (Br_2). Although small amounts of carbonyl halides (COF_2, $COBr_2$) were reported in early tests, more recent studies have failed to confirm the presence of these compounds. The decomposition products of Halon 1211 and Halon 2402 are similar, but in the case of Halon 1211 include hydrogen chloride (HCl) and free chlorine (Cl_2), as well.

The approximate lethal concentrations (ALC) for 15-min exposures to some of these compounds are given in Column 1 of Table 5-18H. Column 2 gives the concentrations of these materials that have been quoted as "dangerous" for short exposures.[15]

TABLE 5-18H. ***Approximate Lethal Concentrations for Predominant Halon 1301 and Halon 1211 Decomposition Products***

Compound	ALC for 15-min Exposure ppm by Volume in Air	Dangerous Concentrations ppm by Volume in Air*
Hydrogen Fluoride, HF	2500	50–250
Hydrogen Bromide, HBr	4750	—
Hydrogen Chloride, HCl	—	—
Bromine, Br_2	550	—
Chlorine, Cl_2	—	50
Carbonyl Fluoride, COF_2	1500	—
Carbonyl Chloride, $COCl_2$	100–150	—
Carbonyl Bromide, $COBr_2$	—	—

* Sax, 1984.

Even in minute concentrations of only a few parts per million, the decomposition products of the halogenated agents have characteristically sharp, acrid odors. This characteristic provides a built-in warning system for the agent, and at the same time creates a noxious, irritating atmosphere for those who must enter the hazard area following a fire. It also serves as a warning that other potentially toxic products of combustion (such as carbon monoxide) will be present.

It is necessary to establish the concentrations likely to be encountered when extinguishing fires with halogenated agents and to relate them not only to the absolute toxicity of the agent, but also to the toxic effects of the normal products of combustion.

The expected concentration of decomposition products depends upon many factors (i.e., size of room, size of fire, presence of large quantities of hot surfaces, and elapsed time before extinguishment). Test results, which may help to put the situation into perspective, have been made for both Halon 1301 and Halon 1211 in total flooding and portable applications. As an example of total flooding, Halon 1301 was used to extinguish 0.1-sq ft, 1.0-sq ft, and 10-sq ft (0.009 m^2, 0.09 m^2, and 0.9 m^2) n-heptane fires in a 1695-cu-ft (48 m^3) test enclosure, at agent discharge times of 15, 10, and 5 seconds. The results are shown in Table 5-18I, relating the resulting decomposition products to the ratio of fuel area to enclosure volume and flame extinguishment time.[16] It is obviously advantageous to attack the fire at an early stage while it is still small, and to release the extinguishing agent as rapidly as practical.

TABLE 5-18I. ***Halon 1301 Decomposition Produced by n-Heptane Fires†***

Enclosure volume: 1695 cu ft (48 m^3)
Halon 1301 concentration: 4% by volume

Fuel Surface Area Area Per Unit Enclosure Volume ft^2/ft^3 or m^2/m^3	Flame Extinction Time, Seconds	Total Decomposition Products* ppm
0.06	11.5–15.4	4.5–5.6
0.06	7.1–7.6	2.8–4.2
0.06	4.0–4.8	3.3–4.5
0.60	20–37	94–289
0.60	11.5–13.5	64–284
0.60	4.7–6.7	11.5–169
6.00	20–22	2252–2304
6.00	13.0–16.3	1292–1590
6.00	5.2–10.0	358–778

* Sum of HF, HBr and Br_2.
† Edmonds, 1972.

For a similar example in portable extinguishers, bromochlorodifluoromethane (Halon 1211) was used in 3-lb (1.36 kg) portable units to extinguish a 2.5-sq-ft (0.23 m^2) n-heptane fire in a 2500-cu-ft (70.8 m^3) room. The results of two tests, one normal extinguishment in 1 sec, and the second deliberately extended extinguishment in 10 sec, are given in Table 5-18J. In the case of normal extinguishment, the levels of breakdown products are below the limits allowed by Occupational Safety and Health Administration (OSHA) regulations for 8-hr continuous exposure.[17]

TABLE 5-18J. ***Concentrations of Breakdown Products Obtained from Extinguishing 2.5 sq ft (0.23 m^2) n-Heptane Fires with Halon 1211 Portable Extinguishers***

Concentration of Breakdown Products—ppm by Volume

Compounds	Test I Normal Extinction In One Second	Test II Prolonged Extinction In Ten Seconds
HCl + HBr	2	50
HF	0.5	10
Cl_2 + Br_2	Not detected*	2.5
$CoCl_2$	Not detected†	Not detected†

* Limit of detection 0.1 ppm.
† Limit of detection 0.25 ppm.

The extensive studies on the toxicological effects of halogenated agents indicate that little, if any, risk is attached to the use of Halon 1301 or Halon 1211 when used in accordance with provisions of NFPA standards governing use of these agents.

CLEAN EXTINGUISHING AGENT RESEARCH

This section presents an overview of alternative agent development and is largely extracted from the "Halon Fire Extinguishing Agents Technical Options Report" of August 11, 1989.[18] The report was prepared pursuant to Article (6) of the Montreal Protocol on Substances that Deplete the Ozone Layer, under the auspices of the United Nations Environment Program.

Approaches to Alternative Agents

The halon/ozone issue is not a single problem, and there is no single solution. Multiple alternative agents, varying according to application, are the most likely outcome. The development of one or two general-purpose "drop-in" replacements having all significant characteristics equal to those of the existing halons may not be a realistic research goal. On the other hand, alternative low or zero ozone depletion potential (ODP) clean agents for specific applications are realistic objectives.

Five requirements make halons difficult to replace: (1) cleanliness, (2) low ODP, (3) low toxicity, (4) effectiveness, and (5) low GWP (global warming potential, the calculated ability of a volatile compound to affect global climate through absorption and emission of infrared radiation). There are, of course, other considerations for replacement agents; cost, storage stability, and compatibility with engineering materials are among these.

Commonly used halon fire extinguishants can be separated into two groups according to their application: Halons 1211 and 2402 in one group, and Halon 1301 in the second. Different types of chemicals will likely be needed for replacement of each group. Halons 1211 and 2402 are usually applied by streaming (directed discharge from a nozzle positioned remote from the fire). Such agents are used in localized applications and are often applied manually. Halon 1301 is most often used in total flooding applications (filling of an enclosed volume with sufficient agent to suppress combustion). Both clean streaming agents and clean total flooding agents are needed. Some very specialized applications (e.g., fire protection systems for aircraft engines) may be best served by agents that combine characteristics of both streaming and total flooding agents. Other applications may be difficult to categorize exactly. Nevertheless, it is useful to consider and contrast streaming and total flooding agents.

Both alternative streaming agents and alternative total flooding agents must be clean and must have low ODPs. Cleanliness is the primary reason for the use of halon agents in most applications, and acceptable ODP is the primary driving force for development of new agents. However, there are important differences in certain other requirements for the two agent types. A streaming agent requires good deliverability; the material must not be too gaseous. Toxicity requirements are less stringent for streaming agents, since personnel are not usually exposed to high agent concentrations. In contrast, a total flooding agent must be more gaseous to encourage dispersion and to avoid stratification, and a very low toxicity is essential for application in normally inhabited spaces.

The steps needed to determine alternative agents have been vigorously debated. Some favor a broad-based effort with a foundation and/or parallel effort of basic research. This type of program begins with consideration of all possible families of chemicals and screens these to end up with a set of final agents. Others favor a targeted approach, directing their effort toward those chemical families considered to offer the most promise as alternative agents.

Existing Efforts to Develop Alternative Agents

Most of the work to date on alternative agents has emphasized low-ODP halocarbons, due to cleanliness, fire suppression capabilities, and relatively well-developed commercial processes for manufacture. Three major problems exist, however:

1. No limits on "acceptable" ODP values have been established. In fact, some doubt exists in the mind of many as to whether any ODP value greater than zero is acceptable. (Controversy about the reliability of ODP calculations is beyond the scope of this chapter.) While many consider very low ODP halocarbons to be a solution to the problem, rather than the source of the problem, this is not universally accepted. Unfortunately, even if the international environmental and political community were to adopt values for acceptable ODPs, there is no guarantee that these limits would not change.
2. The concern about global warming is increasing. GWPs are calculated from atmospheric models similar to those used for ODP. GWP is becoming of increasing concern, and many of the candidates being evaluated as alternative clean fire fighting agents have significant GWPs. Particularly bothersome about this is that one group of halocarbons having zero ODPs, perfluorocarbons, have very high GWPs.
3. In assessing the commercial viability of new, clean extinguishing agents, chemical manufacturers must consider trends regarding acceptability toxicity and environmental evaluations. It is likely that future environmental requirements may either be more stringent or limit production quantities. While it is difficult to fault such an approach by chemical manufacturers, this cautious attitude significantly increases the time required to introduce new halon replacements.

Research and development programs for halon alternatives have been established by a number of chlorofluorocarbons (CFC) and halon producers. Some nonindustrial development projects are also underway. Some promising candidates are now undergoing testing.

The Halon Alternatives Research Corporation (HARC) has been established in the United States to encourage and facilitate research and development activities. This consortium is a group of government and industry leaders who are supporting cooperative efforts for information exchange and complementary research programs. These efforts are intended to support the scientific basis for development and commercialization of clean, safe, and reliable fire extinguishing agents.

Conclusions

Work to date indicates that the development of general-purpose, direct replacements having attributes equal to those of the present halons may be unrealistic in the short term. On the other hand, clean alternative agents with lower ODPs for specific uses are a realistic goal, if trade-offs in fire extinguishment capability, toxicity, and/or other characteristics are acceptable. In particular, such agents could be available in the short term for selected manually applied equipment and local application systems. Toxicity considerations make total flooding agents for normally inhabited areas much more problematical. Streaming agents are inherently easier to develop since physical properties that give improved streaming performance can partially offset poorer inherent flame-suppression capabilities, and toxicity requirements are not as stringent for an agent delivered by streaming as they are for a total flooding agent.

It should be pointed out that fully halogenated chlorofluorocarbons have significant fire extinguishing capabilities. Furthermore, a number of these materials have well-defined, low toxicities. Since these CFCs have lower ODPs than do the present halon fire extinguishing agents, substitution of CFCs for halons in selected fire protection applications could reduce the threat to the ozone layer. On the other hand, these materials are regulated under the Montreal Protocol and are in a different category than are the halons. This makes substitution a highly sensitive issue and unlikely to be widely supported. Certainly, such substitutions could not be regarded as a long-term solution.

Uncertainties about future ODP, GWP, and toxicity requirements are of great concern in considering the development and commercial viability of halon alternatives.

APPLICATION SYSTEMS

A system differs from a portable or mobile appliance primarily in that the agent discharge stream is not directed by a person. The discharge stream or pattern is usually determined in advance, as is either the quantity of agent or discharge rate, or both, and the number and types of nozzles provided. A system consists of a supply of agent, a means for releasing or propelling the agent from its container, and one or more discharge nozzles to apply the agent into the hazard or directly onto the burning object. A system may also contain other elements, such as one or more detectors, remote and local alarms, a piping network, mechanical and electrical interlocks to close fire doors and to shut down ventilation, directional control valves, installed reserve agent supplies, etc. The extent of the auxiliary functions of a system is usually dependent upon the nature of the hazard, in keeping with the desires and resources of the user.

A system is usually a fixed or stationary apparatus, but some portable or mobile systems have been designed. A portable or mobile system may be moved from one hazard to a similar one, but it is placed in a stationary position while it is in service. In this regard, all systems may be considered to be "fixed," but not necessarily permanently placed.

Halogenated agent systems are broadly classified by their method of applying agent to the hazard. The two main types recognized in NFPA 12A, *Halon 1301 Fire Extinguishing Agent Systems*, and NFPA 12B, *Halon 1211 Fire Extinguishing Systems*, are total flooding and local application systems. Another category, termed "specialized systems," includes those systems that are designed to protect special or unique hazards, and which have been tested and approved under these specific conditions.

Total Flooding Systems

These systems protect enclosed, or at least partially enclosed, hazards. A sufficient quantity of extinguishing agent is discharged into the enclosure to provide a uniform fire extinguishing concentration of agent throughout the entire enclosure. Examples of total flooding systems using halogenated agents are found in computer rooms, electrical switchgear rooms, magnetic tape storage vaults, and electronic control rooms; storage areas for artwork, books, and stamps; aerosol filling rooms; machinery spaces in ships; cargo areas in large transport aircraft; processing and storage areas for paints, solvents, and other flammable liquids; etc. Halon 1301, by virtue of its lower toxicity, higher volatility, and lower molecular weight, offers particular advantages for use in total flooding systems. Halon 1211 total flooding systems, with suitable safeguards, are used outside the U.S.

Total flooding systems may be further distinguished by their method of design or installation. An engineered system is custom designed for a particular hazard, using components that are approved or listed only for their broad performance characteristics. Components may be arranged into an almost unlimited variety of configurations. (See Figure 5-18A.)

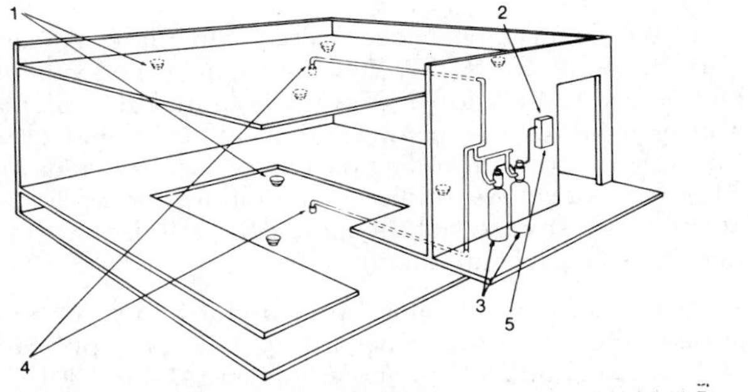

1. AUTOMATIC FIRE DETECTORS INSTALLED BOTH IN ROOM PROPER AND UNDERFLOOR AREA.
2. CONTROL PANEL CONNECTED BETWEEN FIRE DETECTORS AND CYLINDER RELEASE VALVES.
3. STORAGE CONTAINERS FOR ROOM PROPER AND UNDERFLOOR AREA.
4. DISCHARGE NOZZLES INSTALLED BOTH IN ROOM PROPER AND UNDERFLOOR AREA.
5. CONTROL PANEL MAY ALSO SOUND ALARMS, CLOSE DOORS, AND SHUT OFF POWER TO THE AREA.

FIG. 5-18A. A total flooding system installed in a room with a raised floor. (Source: The Ansul Company)

In pre-engineered systems, the number of components and configurations are determined in advance and included in the description of the system's approval or listing. While the degree of pre-engineering can differ from one system to another, the following limits of components and configurations must be considered:

1. Maximum number of cylinders per manifold.
2. Maximum and minimum size and length of piping.
3. Maximum and minimum size and number of elbows, tees, and discharge nozzles.
4. Container volume, fill density, and level of nitrogen superpressurization.

Modular systems consist of single containers connected to discharge nozzles, with minimal piping. A group of container-nozzle assemblies may be distributed throughout the protected area and interconnected electrically. Modular systems permit a more attractive and less expensive initial installation, but often result in higher maintenance costs. Figure 5-18B illustrates the installation of a typical modular system.

Central storage systems locate all agent containers in one centralized location. The agent can be stored in multiple tanks connected by a manifold arrangement (Figure 5-18C) or in a single bulk storage tank. A piping network distributes the agent to the various discharge nozzles. Ease of maintenance is the primary advantage of central storage systems.

Local Application Systems

As the name implies, these systems discharge extinguishing agent in such a manner that the burning object is surrounded locally by a high concentration of agent to

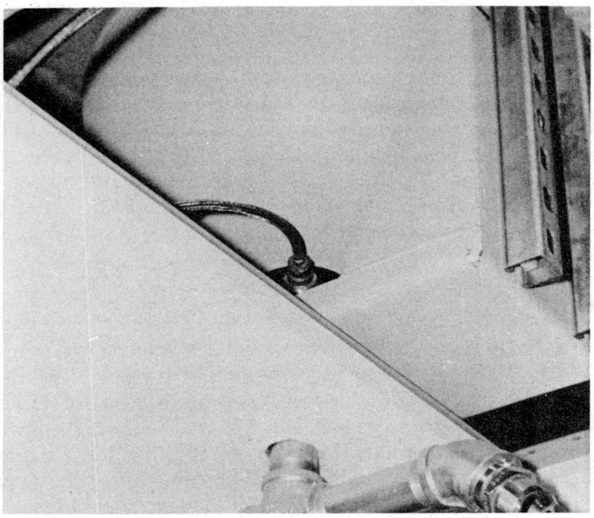

FIG. 5-18B. A modular Halon 1301 installation in a computer room. The spherical container holds 105 lb (47.6 kg) of Halon 1301 and is mounted above a false ceiling. Only a short length of pipe protrudes into the room, and it connects to two discharge nozzles. The mounting bracket of the container is visible at upper right, and braided cable in the center is the electrical connector to the release valve on the container outlet. Six identical container assemblies are installed in this room; they are interconnected to discharge simultaneously.

FIG. 5-18C. A Halon 1301 centralized storage system installed in the control room of an electrical generating plant. The large manifold has two 90-lb (40.8 kg) cylinders and discharges into the room proper. The smaller manifolds, each composed of two 56-lb (25.4 kg) cylinders, protect two individual underfloor areas. Control panels are visible at upper center and upper right. Cylinder valves are activated pneumatically through small hose connected to the top center of the valve. The large hose connected to the side of the valve is a Halon 1301 outlet.

extinguish the fire. In local application systems, neither the quantity of agent nor the type or arrangement of discharge nozzles is sufficient to achieve total flooding of the enclosure containing the object. Often, too, a local application system is required because the enclosure itself may not be suitable to provide total flooding. Examples of areas protected by local application are printing presses, dip and quench tanks, spray booths, oil-filled electric transformers, vapor vents, etc. (See Figure 5-18D.)

Because of its lower volatility, Halon 1211 is well suited for local application systems. The lower volatility, plus a high liquid density, permit the agent to be sprayed as a liquid and thus propelled into the fire zone to a greater extent than is possible with other gaseous agents. Halon 2402 also is well suited for local application systems, but its major usage has been outside the U.S.

The material relating to local application systems, in NFPA 12B, *Halon 1211 Fire Extinguishing Systems*, is largely theoretical and is intended for use by equipment manufacturers and testing laboratories in designing and evaluating components for local application systems. The component of overriding importance is the discharge nozzle, and its performance characteristics must be known with a high degree of reliability.

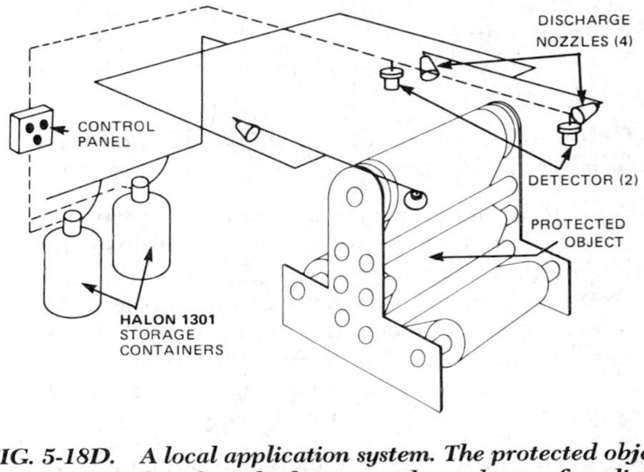

FIG. 5-18D. A local application system. The protected object is not enclosed; therefore, discharge nozzles and rate of application must be capable of enveloping the object. The agent supply must be sufficient to maintain flow for the required time of protection, usually several minutes. Nozzle design is critical and must be determined by extensive testing.

Specialized Systems

These systems, using both Halon 1301 and Halon 1211, are widely used throughout the world. Systems to protect aircraft engine nacelles, racing cars, military vehicles, emergency generator motors, etc., all fall into this category. The distinguishing characteristic of a specialized system is that it can be applied only to the specific hazard for which it was designed and tested. For example, a system designed to protect the jet engines of a Boeing 757 aircraft cannot be applied, *per se*, to a M-1 battle tank. For each such application, the system is developed by a comprehensive test program.

Systems protecting racing cars are somewhat less specialized, although they properly fit into this category. Sanctioning bodies, such as the Federation International de l'Automobile, the United States Automobile Club, and the National Hot Rod Association, have formulated general rules governing these systems. One study showed a wide variety of sizes and performance characteristics of commercially available Halon 1301 systems available in the U.S.[21] Virtually none of these systems is listed or approved by testing laboratories. In spite of this, they have been credited with saving a large number of lives in the racing field.

Another type of specialized system is a "thermatic" unit. This unit consists of a container connected directly to a thermally actuated release device, which is similar to an automatic sprinkler. When heat from the fire activates the valve, the extinguishing agent is released to attack the fire. Sizes of thermatic units range from a 1½-lb (0.68 kg) Halon 1301 unit to protect engine compartments of small pleasure boats to 150-lb (68 kg) units containing Halon 1301 and Halon 1211 designed for total flooding of small rooms.

DESIGN CONSIDERATIONS

This section highlights many of the aspects and requirements contained in NFPA 12A, *Halon 1301 Fire Extinguishing Agent Systems*, and NFPA 12B, *Halon 1211 Fire Extinguishing Systems*.

Uses and Limitations

Halogenated agent systems are generally considered useful for the following types of hazards:

1. Where a clean agent is required.
2. Where live electrical or electronic circuits exist.
3. For flammable liquids or flammable gases.
4. For surface-burning flammable solids, such as thermoplastics.
5. Where the hazard contains a process or objects of high value, and where use of other extinguishing agents could cause extensive damage or downtime.
6. Where the area is normally occupied by personnel (use of Halon 1301 only).
7. Where availability of water, or space for systems using other agents, is limited.

There are several types of flammable materials on which halogenated agents are ineffective. These are:

1. Fuels that contain their own oxidizing agent, such as gunpowder, rocket propellants, cellulose nitrate, organic peroxides, etc.
2. Reactive metals, such as sodium, potassium, NaK eutectic alloy, magnesium, titanium, and zirconium.
3. Metal hydrides, such as lithium hydride.
4. Chemicals capable of autothermal decomposition, such as organic peroxides and hydrazine.

In the first category—in which the compound contains its own oxygen supply, often built into the fuel molecule—the halogenated agent is unable to penetrate into the reaction zone quickly enough to put out the fire. The oxidizer is in too close physical proximity to the fuel to permit interaction with the extinguishing agent. Often the only effective agent for such fuels is a water deluge to dilute the fuel and attempt to remove heat ahead of the combustion front. In the second category, the reactive metals and metal hydrides are too reactive at flame temperatures for the halogenated agent to operate effectively. Also, the flame chemistry of metal fires is quite different from that of hydrocarbon fires.[20]

A more commonly encountered limitation of the capabilities of an agent is its limited effectiveness on deep-seated Class A fires at concentrations below 10 percent by volume. When the concept of control is applied to using halogenated agent systems on Class A fires, rapid response by outside help is necessary. Otherwise, a reflash potential will exist once the extinguishing concentration is dissipated.

Safety

While both Halon 1301 and Halon 1211 have low vapor toxicity, there are hazards in exposing personnel to high concentrations of either agent (above 10 percent Halon 1301, or above 4 percent Halon 1211). Further, the inhalation hazard produced by the fire itself, such as heat, smoke, oxygen depletion, and toxic combustion and decomposition products, may be substantial. Several general safety precautions are listed in the appendices of NFPA 12A, *Halon 1301 Fire Extinguishing Agent Systems*, NFPA 12B, *Halon 1211 Fire Extinguishing Systems*, and NFPA 12C-T, *Halon 2402 Fire Extinguishing Agent Systems*.

Detection and Actuation

Halogenated agent systems generally have operation requirements similar to systems using other types of agents. However, there are strong recommendations in NFPA 12A, *Halon 1301 Fire Extinguishing Agent Systems*, and NFPA 12B, *Halon 1211 Fire Extinguishing Systems*, for the use of automatically actuated systems. The primary reason behind these recommendations is to limit the size and severity of fire with which the system must deal, thus minimizing decomposition of the agent during extinguishment. In a Class A fire, automatic actuation, coupled with sensitive detectors, often can prevent the fire from becoming deep seated.

The detector portion of the system is therefore of paramount importance in system design. The detector must be sensitive enough to the fuel in question to rapidly respond to the fire at an early stage. But too great a sensitivity may produce false actuations, thus imposing an economic burden on the owner, causing unnecessary outage of fire protection, and creating a lack of confidence in the system. Designers have successfully combined sensitivity and reliability by utilizing multiple detectors connected in a double circuit or "cross-zoned" mode of operation. (See Figure 5-18E.) Actuation of either zone alone activates local and remote alarms, but does not discharge the extinguishing agent. Actuation of both zones simultaneously causes the agent to discharge. This arrangement prevents a false signal by an individual detector from discharging the entire system. The two zones may contain the same or different types of detectors. Ionization and photoelectric detectors are commonly used in computer and EDP areas.

In another arrangement, appropriate for generally attended locations, one zone of ionization detection provides early warning, and one zone of rate-compensated thermal detection releases the extinguishing agent.[21]

Particular attention must be given to locating detectors within a hazard. The amount and location of combustibles, the listed sensitivity spacing relationship of the detectors considered, and ventilation characteristics of the hazard are all important factors.

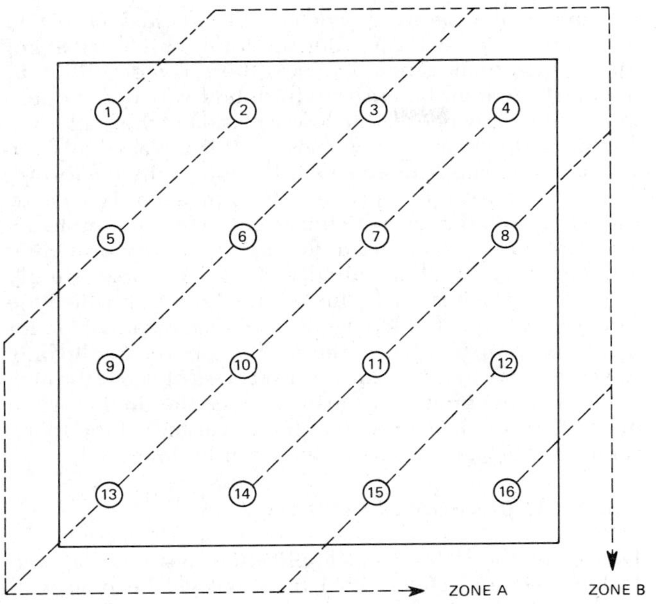

FIG. 5-18E. A cross-zoned detector circuit. Sixteen detectors in a 4 by 4 array are connected so that adjacent detectors are on different circuits, or "zones." For example, consider detector No. 7, connected to Zone A. Adjacent detectors, Nos. 3, 6, 8, and 11, are connected to Zone B.

Agent Supply

The relatively high cost of agents and the specialized nature of systems using them dictate that a specific supply of agent be provided to protect against a given hazard or set of hazards. Conventionally, the agent is contained in one or more pressurized vessels, which are installed near or within the protected area. Steel pressure cylinders or spheres containing from a few pounds to several hundred pounds of agent (1 lb equals 0.45 kg) are commonly used. Larger "bulk" tanks containing several tons (1 ton equals 907 kg) of agent are used in Europe and Canada and have been proposed in the U.S., as well.

Extra pressurization of storage containers with nitrogen is required by NFPA 12A, *Halon 1301 Fire Extinguishing Agent Systems*, and NFPA 12B, *Halon 1211 Fire Extinguishing Systems*. For Halon 1211, this extra pressurization is necessary to expel the contents of the storage container at temperatures below the atmospheric boiling point of 25°F (-4°C) and at a practical rate at higher temperatures. Two levels of extra pressurization for systems are recognized in NFPA 12B: 150 psig (1034 kPa) and 360 psig (2482 kPa) at total pressure at 70°F (21°C). Although the vapor pressure of Halon 1301 at all reasonable temperatures above -30°F (-34°C) is sufficient to completely expel the contents of the container, extra pressurization is used to flatten the pressure *versus* temperature characteristics during storage, provide a higher average pressure in the storage container during discharge, and permit the use of smaller piping. Two levels of extra pressurization of Halon 1301 are permitted by NFPA 12A: 360 psig (2482 kPa), and 600 psig (4137 kPa) total pressure at 70°F (21°C).

The fill density of a container is defined as the weight of agent divided by the internal volume of the container. NFPA 12A, *Halon 1301 Fire Extinguishing Agent Systems*, and NFPA 12B, *Halon 1211 Fire Extinguishing Systems*, permit maximum fill densities of 70 lbs per cu ft (1121 kg/m^3) for Halon 1301, and 102 lbs per cu ft (1634 kg/m^3) for Halon 1211. These limits are set by Department of Transportation (DOT) regulations for shipping containers, which require that the container not become liquid-full at temperatures below 130°F (54°C). The maximum fill densities permitted in the standards coincide with the liquid densities of the two agents at 130°F (54°C) in the presence of nitrogen at the highest level of extra pressurization, again allowing for a 5 percent maximum error in filling the container. Most manufacturers utilize a variable fill density in their design to obtain maximum economy in the system. There is no lower limit on permissible fill densities in NFPA 12A and NFPA 12B.

Flow Characteristics

The flow of Halon 1301 and Halon 1211 through pipe and tubing has been determined experimentally. For Halon 1301, the flow is two-phase liquid-vapor. Although the agent exists as a single-phase liquid in the storage container, it begins to vaporize as soon as its pressure drops during flow. By the time the agent reaches the discharge nozzle, this has substantially reduced agent density. Therefore, classical single-phase flow equations of the Moody or Fanning type cannot be used to predict the frictional pressure losses during flow of Halon 1301.

There are two methods in NFPA 12A, *Halon 1301 Fire Extinguishing Agent Systems*, to estimate flow characteristics. One is a simplified chart method to be used for balanced piping systems only. (A balanced system is one in which the actual pipeline lengths, the equivalent pipeline lengths, and the flow rates to each nozzle are equal.) The other is a rigorous two-phase equation that may be used either for balanced or unbalanced piping systems. The chart method can be applied to complex balanced systems using hand calculations, but even relatively simple unbalanced systems calculated by the two-phase equation require a computer solution. Most U.S. manufacturers of Halon 1301 systems have developed computer programs to help perform these flow calculations.

Because the solubility of nitrogen in the liquid phase of Halon 1211 is only one-half as great as for Halon 1301, the flow properties of Halon 1211 are treated as single-phase liquid flow in NFPA 12B, *Halon 1211 Fire Extinguishing Systems*.

Total Flooding Systems

The great majority of Halon 1301 and Halon 1211 systems throughout the world are of the total flooding type. As described earlier, a total flooding system is one which develops a uniform extinguishing concentration of agent throughout an enclosure, such as a room. This system is capable of extinguishing a fire within the enclosure, regardless of the location of the fire. Wickham[22] outlines the main design elements of a total flooding system as follows:

1. Define the hazard, which includes the dimensions and configuration of the enclosure, the maximum and minimum net volumes, the fuels involved, the expected temperature range in the hazard area, ventilation and unclosable openings, and occupancy status.
2. Establish a minimum design concentration, based upon the fuels involved.

3. Calculate the minimum agent quantity, based upon the minimum design concentration, the maximum net volume, the minimum expected temperature of the enclosure, and compensation for losses from ventilation and unclosable openings.
4. Calculate the maximum possible concentration that could occur if the hazard is at the conditions of minimum net volume and maximum temperature. This concentration must not be greater than that permitted by NFPA 12A, *Halon 1301 Fire Extinguishing Agent Systems*, and NFPA 12B, *Halon 1211 Fire Extinguishing Systems*, for the occupancy status of the hazard.
5. Select the agent storage container, based upon the design quantity of the agent and the sizes of standard containers available from the equipment manufacturers.
6. Determine the minimum agent flow rate by dividing the design agent quantity by the maximum permissible discharge time. This time is currently set by NFPA 12A, *Halon 1301 Fire Extinguishing Agent Systems*, and NFPA 12B, *Halon 1211 Fire Extinguishing Systems*, at 10 sec, but is subject to some discretion.
7. Determine the size of piping, considering the location of the agent storage containers and locations of the discharge nozzles. This step must be performed concurrently with the following Step 8.
8. Determine the number, size, and locations of discharge nozzles. Discharge rate and nozzle area coverage data must be obtained from laboratory listings or from design manuals of the equipment manufacturers.

Jensen regards the first of the preceding elements as the single most important.[23] Certainly it is the most important one in which the end user can usually participate. The remainder of the system is generally designed by the equipment manufacturer.

In establishing the minimum design concentration (Step 2 above), one must consider the conditions under which the fuels are used. For flammable liquids or vapors where an explosion is unlikely, a flame extinguishment concentration may be used. If an explosion potential is considered likely, a higher inerting concentration must be used. An inerting concentration is sufficient to prevent combustion of any fuel-air ratio that might occur in the enclosure. It therefore must be applied upon development of a dangerous condition, and not after ignition has occurred. Minimum design concentrations for both flame extinguishment and inertion for some flammable liquids and gases are included in NFPA 12A, *Halon 1301 Fire Extinguishing Agent Systems*, and NFPA 12B, *Halon 1211 Fire Extinguishing Systems*. Guidelines for determining which level should be used are also given in these standards.

For combustible solids or Class A fires, the possibility and consequences of developing a deep-seated fire must be considered. Rapid detection and prompt application of agent also can help prevent a Class A fire from becoming deep seated. Remote alarms to summon outside assistance should be an integral part of a fire protection system.

Enclosures with fresh air make-up ducts, and exhaust ducts to the outside must have a means of self-closure at the time of agent discharge. It is not necessary to shut down closed-loop ventilation systems in which all the exhaust air is returned to the room. In fact, continued operation of such systems will improve agent distribution and reduce the rate at which agent is lost through unclosable openings. Losses through unclosable openings are more insidious in that they often are undetected in a casual inspection of a plan of the enclosure. Because of the high density of the vapors of halogenated agents, there is a definite tendency of agent-air mixtures to find their way out of openings, particularly ones in the lower portion of the enclosure. As this mixture leaves the enclosure, it is replaced by fresh air that enters and collects near the top of the enclosure. This often gives the impression that the agent is separating itself from the air, which it is not. Also, the tendency frequently is to compensate for such losses by providing a higher concentration initially. This, of course, simply aggravates the situation by increasing the rate at which the loss occurs. An extended agent discharge or provision for mechanical mixing during the soaking period are the only effective ways to overcome a serious loss of agent through unclosable openings. Fortunately, since the fire hazard in most applications is located in the lower half of the room, some agent losses in this manner can be tolerated.

Local Application Systems

Design methods for local application systems for both Halon 1301 and Halon 1211 have not yet become well established. The information currently appearing in the NFPA halon standards on local application systems is useful only as a guide to the equipment manufacturer or testing laboratory.

The principle of local application differs greatly from total flooding. Local application is similar to a portable fire extinguisher in that the discharge nozzle is directed at the surface or object on which the fire is anticipated. For this reason, the single most important element in a local application system is the discharge nozzle. The discharge velocity and rate must be sufficient to penetrate the flames and produce extinguishment, but not so great as to cause splashing of fuel and thus increase the fire hazard. The performance of the discharge nozzle must be determined in advance by laboratory testing; the location, position, and orientation of nozzles in the installation must be in strict accordance with these listings. To date, there is no listed or approved equipment for local application systems for either Halon 1301 or Halon 1211 in the U.S.

TESTING AND MAINTENANCE SYSTEMS

Following installation, a system must first be tested to ensure that it will perform in accordance with its design, and thereafter it must be maintained to ensure its continued performance at some later time. Although minimum requirements for testing and maintenance of halogenated agent systems are given in the NFPA halon standards, some elaboration on both topics seems in order.

Testing of Halogenated Agent Systems

While the performance of individual components comprising the system has been determined by laboratory testing and listings, certain tests must be made on the completed installation to ensure that it has been installed properly and that as a whole the system will perform according to design. This process begins with the review of plans, hydraulic calculations, and specifications that have been submitted before work begins. Where field conditions necessitate a material change from the original submission, the change should be reviewed.

The complete, installed system should be tested by qualified personnel to meet the approval of the authority having jurisdiction. This testing should include all mechanical and electrical portions of the system. Specifically the following should be checked.

Hazard Configuration and Containment Capability

The configuration of the protected space should be carefully compared to the original hazard specification. Halon total flooding systems are designed to establish a concentration of halon by volume. Should the volume of the hazard change, two significant problems could result: (1) where the hazard volume has increased, the design quantity could be insufficient to provide an extinguishing concentration, and (2) where the hazard volume has decreased, personnel exposure to unacceptably high halon concentrations during discharge could result.

It is important that the enclosure be capable of containing the halon/air mixture that results from discharge for an acceptable period of time. In order to ensure this capability, the enclosure should be thoroughly inspected for sources of leakage. Air circulation systems should shut down automatically upon halon system actuation, and dampers should automatically close. Access doors to protected enclosures should be equipped with self-closing devices. Door latches should be adequate to hold the doors closed during pressure variations that may be experienced during halon discharge.

The enclosure should be tested to determine actual leakage. A method for conducting a test of enclosure integrity, using a door fan, is outlined in Appendix B of NFPA 12A, *Halon 1301 Fire Extinguishing Agent Systems*. A more thorough explanation of this methodology is also outlined in the "Enclosure Integrity Procedure for Halon 1301 Total Flooding Fire Suppression Systems,"[24] available from the National Fire Protection Research Foundation. Basically, the door fan procedure involves using a fan, mounted inside a panel that fits into a door opening to pressurize or de-pressurize the enclosure. Readings are then taken to determine the rate of leakage of air to or from the enclosure being tested. Calculations are then performed to predict the worst-case loss of a halon/air mixture from the protected enclosure. This test can be repeated on an annual basis to ensure the ongoing viability of the integrity of the enclosure.

Agent Containers

All agent containers should be properly located as shown on the drawings. The weight of halon should be verified by weighing, or calculated using liquid fill level as the basis of the calculation. All containers should be mounted in brackets and securely fastened.

Piping

The piping system should be inspected to ensure that it has been installed in accordance with the submitted hydraulic calculations and plans and that components provided are in agreement with the submissions. This should include inspection of the means of pipe size reduction and attitudes of tees. Piping joints, discharge nozzles, and piping supports should be inspected to ensure that they are securely fastened to prevent leakage or hazardous movement during system discharge. Especially ensure that nozzle discharge is not at head height of personnel in the normal work area and also that it will not impinge on any loose objects or shelves, cabinet tops, or similar surfaces where loose objects could be present and become missiles.

After a thorough visual inspection, the piping system should be subjected to a closed-circuit pneumatic pressure test to ensure tightness. Care should be taken in conducting this test and the area should be evacuated of personnel, as a rupture of the piping system could have serious consequences.

Detection and Controls

Automatic detection devices, such as heat and/or smoke detectors, should be checked for proper type and location. It is particularly important that detectors not be located near obstructions, supply air vents, humidifier discharge, or other equipment or conditions that would adversely affect their ability to respond to heat, smoke, or products of combustion emitted by a fire.

Manual stations used to cause actuation of the halon system should be securely installed, readily accessible, accurately identified as to their purpose, and properly protected to prevent damage or accidental operation. Manual stations should be located at egress points from the hazard to ensure that personnel safety is not compromised.

Where abort switches are provided, they should be of the "dead-man" type, requiring constant manual pressure to operate. Manual stations must always overide the operation of abort switches.

The control unit must be installed securely in a readily accessible location. Power to the control unit should be supplied from a dedicated circuit. Where circuit breakers are used, they should be protected to prevent accidental shutoff.

All wiring should be properly installed in accordance with local codes. During installation, the field circuitry should be measured for ground fault and short circuit conditions. This should be accomplished before electronic detection devices are connected, as this test could result in damage to these devices.

All auxiliary devices, such as audible alarm devices, graphic displays, air-handling shutdown, power shutdown, etc., should be checked for proper function.

Functional Test

A complete, non-destructive test of all system functions should be undertaken before acceptance. This should include operation of all detection devices; tests of all required sequences, including ability to actuate discharge valves; and tests of auxiliary operations, including shutdown functions and remote alarm transmission.

A "puff test" should also be considered. This involves use of compressed air or carbon dioxide in lieu of halon in the system containers for the purposes of the test only. Care must be taken to ensure that pressure safety requirements of the agent containers are not exceeded. The purpose of the puff test is to ensure valve operation against a pressure equivalent to the normal agent container pressure and to check for continuous and obstruction-free piping. Blow-off indicators should be placed over nozzles before conducting this test. Absence of the devices at the conclusion of the test indicates that test gas reached the nozzle.

Full-discharge tests using Halon 1301 should be avoided. Halon 1301 is a potent ozone depletion agent and should not be released to the atmosphere except to extinguish fire. Should there be a special need to consider a discharge test as necessary, a substitute test gas should be used. The most current edition of NFPA 12A, *Halon 1301 Fire Extinguishing Agent Systems*, should be consulted when considering the use of a test gas.

The functional test is a good opportunity to provide training for operating personnel or others who normally work in the protected area.

Upon successful completion of all tests and correction of any deficiencies to auxiliary functions, the system should be restored to, or initially placed in, full-operating condition.

Maintenance of Halogenated Agent Systems

NFPA 12A, *Halon 1301 Fire Extinguishing Agent Systems*, and NFPA 12B, *Halon 1211 Fire Extinguishing Systems*, specify certain items that must be checked at semiannual and annual intervals. Semiannually, the system should be visually inspected for evidence of corrosion or other damage, and the storage containers checked for loss of agent. This latter item involves a two-fold check. First, the pressure corrected for temperature should be measured to ensure no loss of pressurizing gas, and second, each container must be weighed to determine loss of agent. Neither check alone is sufficient; both are required. Liquid level indicators are sometimes used to indicate the quantity of agent, rather than weighing, which is often cumbersome and time-consuming.

At least annually, the operational characteristics of the system should be retested by knowledgeable and qualified personnel. It is of particular importance that all necessary measures be taken to ensure that inadvertent halon release does not occur as a result of the service procedures. Consideration should be given for the inclusion of a full functional test and test of enclosure integrity. Reports should be filed with the owner of the system. Needless to say, all impediments found in these inspections must be corrected promptly.

AT THE END OF USEFUL LIFE—RECYCLE

Halons are potent ozone depletion substances and should never be released to the atmosphere, except to extinguish actual fires. When the halon system is no longer required to provide protection for a particular hazard, the halon should be made available for recycling. Recycled halon can then be provided to protect other important facilities. Recycling halon is important—it is a wise use of an important fire protection resource and it negates the need to produce equivalent quantities of an environmentally harmful substance.

BIBLIOGRAPHY

References Cited

1. Dowling, J. and Ford, C., "Halon 1301 Total Flooding System for Winterthur Museum," *Fire Journal*, Vol. 63, No. 6 (Nov. 1969).
2. Ford, C., "Halon 1301 Computer Fire Test Program—Interim Report," E. I. duPont de Nemours & Co., Inc., Wilmington, DE, 1972.
3. "The Halogenated Extinguishing Agents," *NFPA Quarterly*, Vol. 48, No. 8, Part 3 (Oct. 1954).
4. Hough, R., "Determination of a Standard Extinguishing Agent for Airborne Fixed Systems," WADD Technical Report 60-552, Wright Air Development Division, Wright-Patterson Air Force Base, OH, 1960.
5. Ford, C., "Overview of Halon 1301 Systems," *Symposium* on the Mechanism of Halogenated Extinguishing Agents, ACS Symposia Series, 1962.
6. duPont, duPont Haskell Laboratory, unpublished data, 1969.
7. duPont, duPont Haskell Laboratory, unpublished data, 1970.
8. Beck, P. S. Clark, D. G., and Tinston, D. J., "The Pharmacologic Actions of Bromochlorodifluoromethane (BCF)," *Toxicology and Applied Pharmacology*, pp. 24, 20-29, 1973.
9. Hine, "Clinical Toxicologic Studies on Freon® FE 1301," Report No. 1, The Hine Laboratories, Inc., San Francisco, CA, 1968. (Unpublished.)
10. duPont, duPont Haskell Laboratory, unpublished data, 1966.
11. duPont, duPont Haskell Laboratory, unpublished data, 1966.
12. Stewart, R. D., Newton, P. E., Wu, A., Hake, C. L., and Krivanek, N. D., "Human Exposure to Halon 1301," Medical College of Wisconsin, Milwaukee, WI, 1978. (Unpublished)
13. duPont, duPont Haskell Laboratory, unpublished data, 1976.
14. duPont, duPont Haskell Laboratory, unpublished data, 1978.
15. Sax, N., *Dangerous Properties of Industrial Materials*, 6th ed., Van Nostrand Reinhold, New York, 1984.
16. Ford, C., "Extinguishment of Surface and Deep-Seated Fires with Halon 1301," *An Appraisal of Halogenated Fire Extinguishing Agents*, National Academy of Sciences, Washington, DC, 1972.
17. *Guide to OSHA Fire Protection Regulations*, Vol. 1, 2nd ed., National Fire Protection Association, Quincy, MA, pp. 22140-22142, 1972.
18. "Halon Fire Extinguishing Agents Technical Options Report," Aug. 11, 1989, United Nations Environment Programme, New York, Aug. 11, 1989.
19. Curry, T. H., "Halon 1301 Protects Racing Cars," *Fire Journal*, Vol. 67, No. 2 (Mar. 1973).
20. Wharry, D. and Hirst, R., *Fire Technology: Chemistry and Combustion*, Institution of Fire Engineers, Leicester, UK, 1974.
21. Grabowski, G. J., "Fire Detection and Actuation Devices for Halon Extinguishing Systems," *An Appraisal of Halogenated Fire Extinguishing Agents*, National Academy of Sciences, Washington, DC, 1972.
22. Wickham, R. T., "Engineering and Economic Aspects of Halon Extinguishing Equipment," *An Appraisal of Halogenated Fire Extinguishing Agents*, National Academy of Sciences, Washington, DC, 1972.
23. Jensen, R., "Halogenated Extinguishing Agent Systems," *Fire Journal*, Vol. 66, No. 3 (May 1972), pp. 37-39.
24. Grant, C., "Enclosure Integrity Procedure for Halon 1301 Total Flooding Fire Suppression Systems," National Fire Protection Research Foundation, Quincy, MA, 1989.

References

DiNenno, P. J. and Budnick, E. K., *Halon 1301 Discharge Testing—A Technical Analysis*, National Fire Protection Research Foundation, Quincy, MA.

"Halon Fire Extinguishing Agents Technical Options Report," United National Environment Programme, Nairobi, Kenya, Aug. 1989.

Strasiak, R., "The Development of Bromochloromethane (CB), WADC Technical Report 53-279, Wright Air Development Center, OH, 1954.

NFPA Codes, Standards, and Recommended Practices

Reference to the following NFPA codes, standards, and recommended practices will provide further information on halogenated agents and systems discussed in this chapter. (See the latest *NFPA Catalog* for availability of current editions of the following documents.)

NFPA 10, *Portable Fire Extinguishers.*

NFPA 12A, *Halon 1301 Fire Extinguishing Agent Systems.*

NFPA 12B, *Halon 1211 Fire Extinguishing Systems.*

NFPA 12CT, *Halon 2402 Fire Extinguishing Agent Systems.*

NFPA 75, *Electronic Computer/Data Processing Equipment.*

Additional Reading

Anderson, S. O., "Halons and the Stratospheric Ozone Issue," *Fire Journal*, Vol. 81, No. 3 (May 1987), p. 56.

Anderson, S. O., *et al.*, "Halons, Stratospheric Ozone and the U.S. Air Force," *Military Engineer*, Vol. 80, No. 523 (Aug. 1988), pp. 485-492.

Ashmore, F., "How Hazardous Is Halon 1301 ?" *Fire Prevention*, No. 209, May 1988, pp. 34-36.

Atallah, S. and Buccigross, H. L., "Extinction of Fire by Halogenated Compounds—A Suggested Mechanism," Fire Technology, Vol. 8, No. 2 (May 1972) pp. 131-141.

Atallah, S. and Buccigross, H. L., "Testing the Performance of Halon 1301 on Real Computer Installations," Fire Journal, Vol. 66, No. 5 (Sept. 1972), pp. 105-108.

Bischoff, B. G., "Gaseous Extinguishing Agents," *Heating, Ventilation and Air Conditioning*, Oct. 1978.

Breen, D. E., "Interactions in Binary Halon Mixtures Used as Fire Suppressants," *Fire Technology*, Vol. 13, No. 4 (Nov. 1977), pp. 261-265, 281.

Brenneman, J. J. and Charney, M., "Testing a Total Flooding Halon 1301 System in a Computer Installation," *Fire Journal*, Vol. 68, No. 6 (Nov. 1974).

Chemetron Corp., "Halon System Testing," *Hot Spots*, Cardox Products, Chicago, IL, 1974.

Chines, S. A., "Halon Design Discharge Testing—An Authority Having Jurisdiction Point of View," *Seminar Paper* for Fire Protection Halons and the Environment, NFPA Annual Meeting, Cincinnati, OH, May 1987.

Clarke, D. G., "The Toxicity of Bromotrifluoromethane (FE 1301) in Animals and Man," Industrial Hygiene Research Laboratory, Imperial Chemical Industries, Alderley Park, Cheshire, UK, 1970.

Coll, J. P., "Inerting Characteristics of Halon 1301 and 1211 with Various Combustibles," Report PSR 661, Fenwall Inc., Ashland, MA, July 16, 1976.

Creitz, E. C., "Inhibition of Diffusion Flames by Methyl Bromide and Trifluoromethyl Bromide Applied to the Fuel and Oxygen Sides of the Reaction Zones," *Journal of Research of National Business Standards*, Vol. 65, No. 4, 1961.

"Designing Halon Systems," *Plumbing Engineer*, Vol. 13, No. 2 (Mar./Apr. 1985), pp. 27-31.

DiNenno, P. and Budnick, E., "Halon 1301 Discharge Testing: A Technical Analysis," U.S. Environmental Protection Agency and National Fire Protection Research Foundation, Quincy, MA, 1988.

DiNenno, P. and Taylor, G. M., "Best and Essential Halon Use: A Methodology," National Fire Protection Research Foundation, Quincy, MA, Dec. 1989.

DiNenno, P., *et al.*, "Hydraulic Performance Tests of Halon 1301 Test Gas Simulants," *Fire Technology*, Vol. 26, No. 2 (May 1990), pp. 121-140.

DiNenno, P. J., *et al.*, "Evaluation of Halon 1301 Test Gas Simulants: Enclosure Leakage," *Fire Technology*, Vol. 25, No. 1 (Feb. 1989), pp. 24-40.

Dyer, J. H., *et al.*, "The Extinction of Fires in Aircraft Jet Engines—(Parts I through IV)," *Fire Technology*, Vol. 12, No. 4, pp. 266-275, 289 Nov. 1976; Vol. 13, No. 1, pp. 59-68 Feb. 1977; Vol. 13, No. 2, pp. 126-138 May 1977; Vol. 13, No. 3, pp. 223-230 Aug. 1977.

Echternacht, J. E., "Halon Extinguishing Systems Design Criteria," *Fire Journal*, Vol. 65, No. 6 (Nov. 1971), pp. 51-55, 66.

Eckholm, W. A., "Testing One of the World's Biggest Halon Systems...Without Using Halon," *Fire Journal*, Vol. 83, No. 4 (July 1989), p. 71.

Edmonds, A., "Use of Halon 1211 in Hand Extinguishers and Local Application Systems," An Appraisal of Halogenated Fire Extinguishing Agents, National Academy of Sciences, Washington, DC, 1972.

E. I. duPont de Nemours and Company, Inc., "Freon, Fluorocarbons, Properties and Applications," Wilmington, DE, 1985.

"Flow of Nitrogen-Pressurized Halon 1301 in Fire Extinguishing Systems," JPL Pub. 84-62, Jet Propulsion Laboratory, California Institute of Technology, Pasadena, CA, 1984.

Ford, C. L., "Halon 1301 Fire Extinguishing Agent: Properties and Applications," *Fire Journal*, Vol. 64, No. 6 (Nov. 1970).

Ford, C. L., "Halon 1301 Update: Research, Application, New Standard," Specifying Engineer, May 1977.

Ford, C. L., "Where and Why to Use Halon 1301 Systems," *Specifying Engineer*, Jan. 1972.

Franck, T. E., "Clean Room Protection Using Halon 1301," *Fire Journal*, Vol. 65, No. 2 (Mar. 1971), pp. 77-79.

Gaskill, J. R., Leonhart, E. C., and Sanborn, E. N., "A Halon 1301 Fire Extinguishing System for Trailers," Lawrence Radiation Laboratory, Livermore, CA, Aug. 19, 1969.

Gassman, J. J., and Hill, R. G., "Fire Extinguishing Methods for New Passenger-Cargo Aircraft", National Aviation Facilities Experimental Center, Atlantic City, NJ, 1971.

Gassman, J. J., and March, J. F., "Application of Halon 1301 to Aircraft Cabin and Cargo Fires," An Appraisal of Halogenated Fire Extinguishing Agents, National Academy of Sciences, Washington, DC, 1972.

Goodall, K., "Halon Fire Protection: Are Discharge Tests Necessary," *Fire Surveyor*, Vol. 17, No. 4 (Aug. 1988), pp. 57-62.

Grant, C. C., "Computer-Aided Halon 1301 Piping Calculations," *Fire Safety Journal*, Vol. 9, No. 2, 1986, pp. 171-180.

Grant, C. C., "Controlling Fire Protection Halon Emissions," *Fire Technology*, Vol. 24, No. 1, 1988.

Grant, C. C., "Enclosure Integrity Procedure," National Fire Protection Research Foundation, Quincy, MA, Jan. 1989.

Grant, C. C., "Fire Protection Halons and the Environment: An Update Symposium," *Fire Technology*, Vol. 24, No. 1 (Feb. 1988), p. 63.

Grant, C. C., "Halons and the Ozone Layer: An Overview," *Fire Journal*, Vol. 83, No. 5 (Sept. 1989), p. 58.

Grant, C. C., "Halon Design Calculations," *SFPE Handbook of Fire Protection Engineering*, National Fire Protection Association, Quincy, MA, 1988.

Grant, C. C., "Life Beyond Halon," *Fire Journal*, Vol. 84, No. 3 (May 1990), p. 52.

"Halon in the 90's? Use of Halons for Firefighting Will Continue," *Burning Issues*, Vol. 10, No. 2, Summer 1988.

Hammack, J. M., "More About Halon 1301," *Fire Journal*, Vol. 66, No. 4 (July 1972), pp. 43-44.

McDaniel, D. E., "Evaluation of Halon 1301 for Shipboard Use," An Appraisal of Halogenated Fire Extinguishing Agents, National Academy of Sciences, Washington, DC, 1972.

Peterson, P. E., "A Systems Approach to Optimum Damage Control," *Fire Journal*, Vol. 67, No. 2 (Mar. 1973), pp. 70-73.

"Plumbers Pull Plug on Halon Extinguishers," *Journal of the Institution of Engineers*, Vol. 61, No. 19 (Oct. 6, 1989), p. 21.

Poeschl, P. M., "Large-Scale Halon 1301 Fire Test Program," *Fire Journal*, Vol. 67, No. 6 (Nov. 1973), pp. 35-38.

"Report on the Halon Technical Options Committee," *Meeting of the NFPA Technical Committee on the Halogenated Fire Extinguishing Systems*, Washington, DC, May 1989.

Robinson, V. B., "Partial Flooding of Volumes with Halon 1301," Fire Technology, Vol. 14, No. 2 (May 1978), pp. 97-109.

Serb, T. J., "The Magic of Halon Protects Computers," *Security World*, Oct. 1983.

Sheehan, D. F., "An Investigation into the Effectiveness of Halon 1301 (Bromotrifluoromethane, $CBrF_3$) as an Extinguishing Agent for Shipboard, Machinery Space Fires," U.S. Coast Guard, Washington, DC, 1972.

"Special Hazards Protection—Manufacturers and Equipment," *Fire Journal*, Vol. 81, No. 4 (Jul-Aug 1987), p. 43.

Steinberg, M., "Toxic Hazards from Extinguishing Gasoline Fires Using Halon 1301 Extinguishers in Armored Personnel Carriers," An Appraisal of Halogenated Fire Extinguishing Agents, National Academy of Sciences, Washington, DC, 1972.

Strasser, A., Liebman, I., and Kuchta, J. M. "Methane Flame Extinguishment with Layered Halon or Carbon Dioxide," *Fire Technology*, Vol. 10, No. 1 (Feb. 1974), pp. 25-34.

"Taking Steps to Reduce Halon Emissions," *Fire Prevention*, No. 224 (Nov. 1989), pp. 16-17.

Taylor, G., "Achieving the Best Use of Halons ," *Fire Journal*, Vol. 81, No. 3 (May-June 1987), p. 69.

Van Stee, E. W., and Back, K. C., "Short-term Inhalation Exposure to Bromotrifluoromethane," *Tox. & Appl. Pharm.* Vol. 15, pp. 164-174, 1969.

Waters, S., "Alternative Test Agent for Halon Systems," *Fire Systems*, Vol. 2, 1987.

Whiteley, R. A., "Integrity Testing for Halon—The State of the Art," *Fire Surveyor*, Vol. 18, No. 5 (Oct. 1989), pp. 17-20.

Wiersman, S. J., "Flow Characteristics of Halon 1301 in Pipelines," *Fire Technology*, Vol. 14, No. 1 (Feb. 1978), pp. 5-14.

Willey, E. A., "Summary of International Conference on Fire Protection Halons and the Environment," National Fire Protection Association, Quincy, MA, Aug. 1988.

Williamson, H. V., "Halon 1301—Minimum Concentrations for Extinguishing Deep-Seated Fires," *Fire Technology*, Vol. 8, No. 4 (Nov. 1972).

Williamson, H. V., "Halon 1301 Flow in Pipelines," *Fire Technology*, Vol. 11, No. 4, (Nov. 1975), pp. 18-32.

DRY CHEMICAL AGENTS AND APPLICATION SYSTEMS

Revised by Walter M. Haessler

Dry chemical is a powder mixture that is used as a fire extinguishing agent. It is intended for application by means of portable extinguishers, hand hose line systems, or fixed systems. Borax- and sodium bicarbonate-based dry chemical were the first such agents developed. Sodium bicarbonate became the standard because of its greater effectiveness as a fire extinguishing agent. About 1960, sodium bicarbonate-based dry chemical was modified to render it compatible with protein-based low-expansion foams to permit a dual agent attack. Multipurpose (monoammonium phosphate base) and "Purple-K" (potassium bicarbonate base) dry chemicals then were developed for fire extinguishing use. Shortly thereafter, "Super-K" (potassium chloride base) was developed to equal "Purple-K" in effectiveness. In the late 1960s, the British developed urea-potassium-bicarbonate-based dry chemical. Presently, there are five basic varieties of dry chemical extinguishing agents.

This chapter contains information on the properties of dry chemicals affecting their use as extinguishing agents, their uses and limitations, methods of storage and handling, and quality control. Portable dry chemical extinguishers are discussed in Section 5 of this handbook. Dry powder extinguishing agents for combustible metal fires are discussed in Chapter 21 of this section, "Combustible Metal Agents and Application Techniques;" and fire and explosion control are discussed in Section 1, Chapter 6, "Theory of Fire and Explosion Control."

The terms "regular dry chemical" and "ordinary dry chemical" generally refer to powders that are listed for use on Class B and Class C fires.[1] "Multipurpose dry chemical" refers to powders that are listed for use on Class A, B, and C fires. The terms "regular dry chemical," "ordinary dry chemical," and "multipurpose dry chemical" should not be confused with "dry powder" or "dry compound," which are used to identify powdered extinguishing agents developed primarily for use on combustible metal fires.[2]

Walter M. Haessler is a consultant, based in Santa Rosa, CA. He is a member of the NFPA Technical Committee on Dry and Wet Chemical Extinguishing Systems. His activities also include teaching and writing in the field of fire protection.

Dry chemical is unusually efficient in extinguishing fires in flammable liquids. It can also be used on fires involving some types of electrical equipment. Regular dry chemical has certain limited applications in extinguishment of flash surface fires with ordinary combustibles, but the chemical requires water to put out deep-seated smoldering fires. Multipurpose dry chemical can be used on fires in flammable liquids, fires involving energized electrical equipment, and fires in ordinary combustible materials. Multipurpose dry chemical seldom needs the help of water to completely extinguish fires in Class A materials.

PHYSICAL PROPERTIES OF DRY CHEMICALS

The principal base chemicals used in the production of currently available dry chemical extinguishing agents are sodium bicarbonate, potassium bicarbonate, potassium chloride, urea-potassium bicarbonate, and monoammonium phosphate. Various additives are mixed with these base materials to improve their storage, flow, and water repellency characteristics. The most commonly used additives are metallic stearates, tricalcium phosphate, or silicones, which coat the particles of dry chemical to make them free flowing and resistant to the caking effects of moisture and vibration.

Stability

Dry chemical is stable at both low and normal temperatures. However, since some of the additives may melt and cause sticking at higher temperatures, an upper storage temperature limit of 120°F (49°C) is recommended for dry chemical. [Temperatures up to 150°F (66°C) may be acceptable for very short durations.] At fire temperatures, the active ingredients either disassociate or decompose while performing their function in fire extinguishment. Of extreme importance is the danger caused by indiscriminate mixing of the various dry chemicals. For example, mixing multipurpose (monoammonium base) dry chemical, which is acidic, with an alkaline dry chemical (most of the other dry chemicals) will result in an undesirable reaction that releases free carbon dioxide gas and causes caking. Extinguisher shells have been known to explode because of this phenomenon.

Toxicity

The ingredients presently used in dry chemical are nontoxic. However, the discharge of large quantities may cause temporary breathing difficulty during and immediately after discharge and may seriously interfere with visibility.

Particle Size

Particles of dry chemical range in size from less than 10 microns up to 75 microns (1 micron = 0.000039 in.). Particle size has a definite effect on extinguishing efficiency, and careful control is necessary to prevent particles from exceeding the upper and lower limits of this performance range. The best results are obtained by a heterogeneous mixture with a median particle size in the order of 20 to 25 microns. Underwriters Laboratories Inc. (UL) and Factory Mutual Research Corporation (FM) listings and ratings are based upon the specified use of the particular type of dry chemical set forth by the equipment manufacturer. In no case are different dry chemicals to be mixed in recharging the equipment.

EXTINGUISHING PROPERTIES

Fire tests on flammable liquids have shown potassium bicarbonate-based dry chemical to be more effective than sodium bicarbonate-based dry chemical in extinguishment. Similarly, monoammonium phosphate has been found equal to or better than sodium bicarbonate in extinguishment effectiveness.[3] The effectiveness of potassium chloride is about equivalent to potassium bicarbonate, and urea-potassium bicarbonate exhibits the greatest effectiveness of all the dry chemicals tested.

When introduced directly to the fire area, dry chemical causes the flame to go out almost at once. Smothering, cooling, and radiation shielding contribute to the extinguishing efficiency of dry chemical, but studies suggest that a chain-breaking reaction in the flame is the principal cause of extinguishment.[4]

Smothering Action

For many years it was widely held that regular dry chemical extinguishing properties relied primarily on the smothering action of the carbon dioxide released when sodium bicarbonate was heated by fire. The carbon dioxide does undoubtedly contribute to the effectiveness of dry chemical, as does the like volume of water vapor released when dry chemical is heated. However, tests have generally disproved the belief that these gases are a major factor in extinguishment.

When multipurpose dry chemical is discharged into burning ordinary combustibles, the decomposed monoammonium phosphate leaves a sticky residue (metaphosphoric acid) on the burning material. This residue seals glowing material from oxygen, thus helping to extinguish the fire and prevent reignition.

Cooling Action

It cannot be substantiated that the cooling action of dry chemical is an important reason for its ability to promptly extinguish fires. More information on this subject is contained in a paper based on studies of the heat capacities of various powders tested for extinguishing effectiveness. The heat energy required to decompose dry chemicals plays an undeniable role in contributing toward their individual extinguishing abilities, but the effect, *per se*, is minor. To be effective, any dry chemical must be heat sensitive and, as such, absorbs heat in order to become chemically active.[5]

Radiation Shielding

Discharge of dry chemical produces a cloud of powder between the flame and the fuel; this cloud shields the fuel from some of the heat radiated by the flame. Tests to evaluate this factor concluded that the shielding factor is of some significance.[5]

Chain-Breaking Reaction

The preceding extinguishing actions, when combined, exert a minimal effect. The rapidity of extinguishment is due to the interference of the dry chemical particles with the propagation of the combustion chain reaction, which reduces the concentration of "free" radicals present within the flames. To accomplish this, the dry chemical must become thermally decomposed.

The discharge of dry chemical into the flames prevents reactive particles from coming together and continuing the combustion chain reaction. The explanation is referred to as the chain-breaking mechanism of extinguishment.[6,7]

USES AND LIMITATIONS

Dry chemical is primarily used to extinguish flammable liquid fires. Because it is electrically nonconductive, it can also be used on flammable liquid fires involving live electrical equipment. Regular dry chemical extinguishers have been tested and found suitable for use on flammable liquid and electrical fires (Class B and C fires) by fire equipment testing laboratories.

Due to the rapidity with which dry chemical extinguishes flame, dry chemical is used on surface fires involving ordinary combustible materials (Class A fires). There are several areas in the textile industry, notably opener-picker rooms and carding rooms in cotton mills, where regular dry chemical has been used effectively. However, wherever regular dry chemical is provided for use on surface-type Class A fires, it should be supplemented by water spray for extinguishing smoldering embers or in case the fire gets beneath the surface. In some baled cotton storage areas, the tops of bales can be covered with regular dry chemical to prevent surface spread should fire break out. This preventive measure does not eliminate the need for automatic sprinkler protection in such areas. Since multipurpose dry chemical becomes sticky when heated, it is not recommended for textile card rooms or other locations where removal of the residue from fine machine parts may be difficult.

Dry chemical does not produce a lasting inert atmosphere above the surface of a flammable liquid; consequently, its use will not result in permanent extinguishment if reignition sources, such as hot metal surfaces or persistent electrical arcing, are present.

Dry chemical should not be used in installations where relays and delicate electrical contacts are located (e.g., in telephone exchanges and computer equipment rooms), since the insulating properties of dry chemical might render such equipment inoperative. Because some dry chemicals are slightly corrosive, they should be removed from all undamaged surfaces as soon as possible after fire extinguishment.

Regular dry chemical will not extinguish fires that penetrate beneath the surface, or fires in materials that supply their own oxygen for combustion. Dry chemical may be incompatible with mechanical (air) foam unless the dry chemical has been specially prepared to be reasonably foam compatible.

Specifications have been established by fire equipment testing laboratories to ensure the positive and consistent performance of dry chemical as an extinguishing agent. These specifications control moisture content, water repellency, electrical resistivity, storage at elevated temperatures, flow capability, caking resistivity, and abrasive action. The discharge characteristics of the device in which the dry chemical is to be used are also evaluated. Extinguishing effectiveness is determined by performance tests of the application to standard fires under conditions recommended by the manufacturer.

Though dry chemical had been used for many years in fire extinguishers, it was not until 1954 that the first dry chemical extinguishing system was tested and listed by a testing laboratory. In 1952 the NFPA Committee on Dry Chemical Extinguishing Systems was established, and in 1957 the first edition of NFPA 17, *Dry Chemical Extinguishing Systems*, was adopted.

DRY CHEMICAL EXTINGUISHING SYSTEMS

Dry chemical extinguishing systems can be used in those situations where quick extinguishment is desired and where reignition sources are not present. Dry chemical systems are used primarily for flammable liquid fire hazards, such as dip tanks, flammable liquid storage rooms, and areas where flammable liquid spills may occur. Systems have been designed for kitchen range hoods, ducts, and associated rangetop hazards, such as deep-fat fryers. Where it is necessary to extinguish a flammable liquid or gas fire being fed by fuel under pressure, dry chemical hand hose line systems can be used, followed by closure of fuel shutoff valves.

Since dry chemical is electrically nonconductive, extinguishing systems using this agent can be used on electrical equipment that is subject to flammable liquid fires, such as oil-filled transformers and oil-filled circuit breakers. Dry chemical system protection is not recommended, however, for delicate electrical equipment, such as telephone switchboards and electronic computers. Such equipment is subject to damage by dry chemical deposit and, because of the insulating properties of the dry chemical, may require excessive cleaning to restore operation.

Hand hose line systems containing regular or ordinary dry chemical have been used to a limited extent for quick-spreading surface fires on ordinary combustible material. In such applications, the dry chemical system only stops or prevents a rapid surface spread, and must be supplemented by a water-type extinguishing device to put out deep-seated smoldering fires. Fixed systems containing multipurpose dry chemical are available and are suitable for the protection of ordinary combustibles, provided the dry chemical can reach all burning surfaces.

METHODS OF APPLICATION

The two basic types of dry chemical systems are referred to as: (1) fixed systems, and (2) hand hose line systems. Other methods of applying dry chemical are by portable and wheeled-type extinguishers.

Fixed Systems

Fixed dry chemical systems consist of a supply of dry chemical, an expellant gas, an actuating method, fixed piping, and nozzles through which the dry chemical can be discharged into the hazard area. Fixed dry chemical systems are of two types: (1) total flooding, and (2) local application.

In total flooding, a predetermined amount of dry chemical is discharged through fixed piping and nozzles into an enclosed space or enclosure around the hazard. (See Figure 5-19A.) Total flooding is applicable only when the hazard is totally enclosed or when all openings surrounding a hazard can be closed automatically when the system is discharged. Total flooding can be used only where no reignition is anticipated, because the extinguishing action is transient.

***FIG. 5-19A.** This 15 by 24 ft (4.6 by 7.3 m) flammable liquids storage building is protected by a total flooding dry chemical system. Upon actuation of the system, by a heat detector, nitrogen is discharged into the 150-lb (68 kg) storage container and dry chemical is expelled through eight nozzles in the roof.*

Local application differs from total flooding in that the nozzles are arranged to discharge directly into the fire. Local application is practical in those situations where the hazard can be isolated from other hazards so that fire will not spread beyond the area protected, and where the entire hazard can be protected. The principal use of local application systems is to protect open tanks of flammable liquids. As with total flooding systems, local application is ineffective unless extinguishment can be immediate and there are no reignition sources.

Hand Hose Line Systems

Hand hose line systems consist of a supply of dry chemical and expellant gas with one or more hand hose lines to deliver the dry chemical to the fire. (See Figure 5-19B.)

The hose stations are connected to the dry chemical container either directly or indirectly by means of intermediate piping. They can provide a large quantity of extinguishing agent for quick knockdown and extinguishment of relatively large fires, such as might be experienced at gasoline loading racks, flammable liquid storage areas, diesel and gas turbine locomotives, and aircraft hangars.

***FIG. 5-19B.** A dry chemical hand hose line system consisting of an expellant gas assembly, dry chemical storage tank assembly, and a discharge assembly. Dry chemical systems of this type range from 125 to 2,000 lb (57 to 907 kg); the 2,000-lb (907 kg) system shown has four nitrogen cylinders and two 3/4-in. (19 mm) hoses with shutoff nozzles. (Source: The Ansul Company)*

DESIGN OF DRY CHEMICAL SYSTEMS

Usually, dry chemical systems consist of dry chemical and expellant gas storage tanks, piping and/or hose to carry the agent to the fire area, nozzles to ensure proper distribution of the agent into the fire or area to be protected, and automatic and/or manual actuating mechanisms. (See Figure 5-19C.)

Dry chemical systems are called either engineered or pre-engineered, depending upon how the quantity of dry chemical, rate of flow, size and length of piping, and number and size of fittings are determined. An engineered system is one in which individual calculation and design is needed to determine the flow rate, nozzle pressures, pipe sizes, quantity of dry chemical, and the number, types, and placement of nozzles for the hazard being protected. A pre-engineered system, sometimes called a package system, is one in which the size of the system (i.e., the quantity of dry chemical, pipe sizes, maximum and minimum pipe lengths, number of fittings, and number and types of nozzles) is predetermined by fire tests for specific sizes and types of hazards. Installation within these limits of hazard and system design ensures adequate flow rate, nozzle pressure, and pattern coverage without individual calculation. (See Figure 5-19D.)

Pre-engineered systems are very frequently used for kitchen range and hood fire protection, including deep-fat fryers. Only alkaline dry chemicals can be used in these cases (sodium bicarbonate, potassium bicarbonate, etc.) in order to saponify fats and oils. Multipurpose dry chemical must never be used. (See Figure 5-19E.)

Storage of Dry Chemical and Expellant

Dry chemical is stored in a pressure container, usually of welded steel construction, either under atmospheric pressure until the system is actuated or under the pressure of the internally stored expellant gas.

Containers in which dry chemical is stored separately under atmospheric pressure are equipped with an expellant gas inlet, a moisture-sealed fill opening, and a dry chemical outlet. The gas inlet leads to an internal gas tube arrangement constructed so that when it flows into the tank it agitates and permeates the powder, making it fluidlike. The dry chemical outlet is provided with a rupture disc or valve to permit buildup of proper operating pressure in the tank before the dry chemical can start to flow. The expellant gas assembly consists of a pressure storage vessel together with necessary valves, pressure regulators, and piping to deliver the expellant gas to the dry chemical storage tank at the correct pressure and rate of flow. (See Figure 5-19A.) The expellant gas is usually nitrogen, but carbon dioxide is used in some of the smaller systems. The volume and storage pressure of the expellant are dictated by the gas used and the requirements of the system. Containers in which dry chemical and the expellant gas are stored together are equipped with a moisture-sealed fill opening, a valve with integral discharge outlet and expellant gas charging inlet, and a pressure gage. (See Figure 5-19E.) The expellant gas is usually nitrogen, but dry air can be used.

It is desirable to locate the dry chemical expellant gas assemblies as near as practicable to the hazard to be protected. An area in which temperatures stay between –40 and +120°F (–40 and +49°C) is desirable to maintain the quality of the dry chemical.

Dry chemical is commercially available in various sized packages of 10 lb (4.5 kg) or more in weight, or in metal drums, plastic-lined paperboard containers, or plastic bags. Whatever the container, it should be kept tightly closed and stored in a dry location to prevent absorption of moisture. Storage in a dry location is also essential for extinguisher recharging. Once the powder has lost its free-flowing characteristic, it should be discarded.

System Actuation

Actuation of fixed systems is initiated by automatic mechanisms that incorporate sensing devices located in the hazard area and automatic, mechanical, or electrical releases which initiate the flow of dry chemical, actuate alarms, and shut down process equipment. In systems with separate dry chemical and expellant gas containers, the flow of dry chemical is started by releasing the expellant gas, which pressurizes the dry chemical chamber to the point where the rupture disc in the dry chemical outlet operates. The dry chemical is then carried by the expellant gas through the distribution system to the hazard. In stored-pressure systems, however, the flow of dry chemical is started by merely opening the valve on the dry chemical chamber. An easily accessible device for manual operation is required for all automatically operated systems.

When automatically actuated systems are used, consideration should be given to the reduced visibility and temporary breathing difficulty sometimes caused by quick

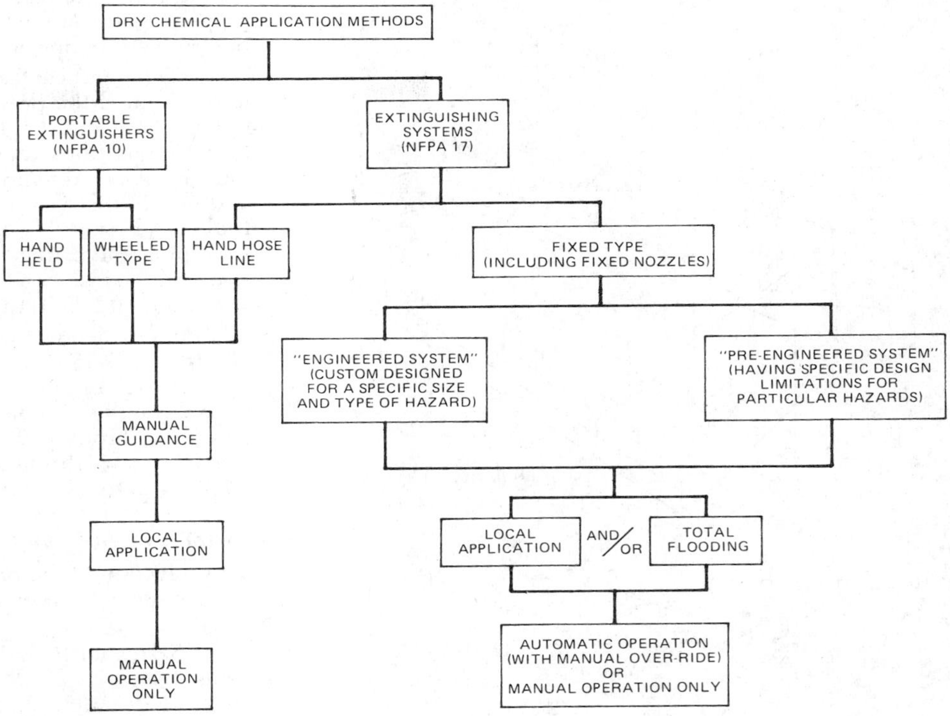

FIG. 5-19C. Methods of dry chemical application.

FIG. 5-19D. A double 30-lb (13.6 kg) stored-pressure dry chemical system with pneumatic release for automatic actuation. Each cylinder contains 30 lb (13.6 kg) of dry chemical pressurized to 350 psi (2413 kPa) with nitrogen.

discharge of large amounts of dry chemical in a restricted space. In all cases where there is a possibility that personnel may be stationed in such locations, suitable alarms and safeguards should be incorporated in the system to ensure adequate warning and prompt evacuation.

Operation of a hand hose line system requires two or, at the most, three steps. *Step one*: pressurizing the dry chemical chamber by opening the expellant gas valve (if the dry chemical and expellant gas containers are separate), or opening the main discharge valve if dry chemical is under stored pressure. *Step two*: operating the nozzle at the end of the hose line. *Step three*: if multiple hose stations are supplied by the same dry chemical supply, a distribution valve must be opened to direct the flow to the particular hose station to be used. It is extremely important to play out the hose fully (without kinks) to ensure the proper chemical discharge rate.

Fixed piping systems normally blow themselves clear. However, in hand hose line systems where the operator exercises control over the amount of dry chemical discharged, it is vital that all pipes and hose be independently blown clear before recharging to prevent blockage.

Distribution System

For fixed systems, the provisions for conveying the dry chemical to the hazard area and discharging it properly consist of piping or, for hand hose line systems, piping and hose lines or hose lines alone. Nozzles designed to emit jets or wide, flat, or round streams in desired patterns are available to meet specific hazard requirements. Adjustable nozzles permitting an operator to vary the range and shape of the discharge are also available for use with hand hose line systems.

The piping and valving for dry chemical systems are of special design because dry chemical, while tending to behave as a fluid, has distinct flow characteristics.

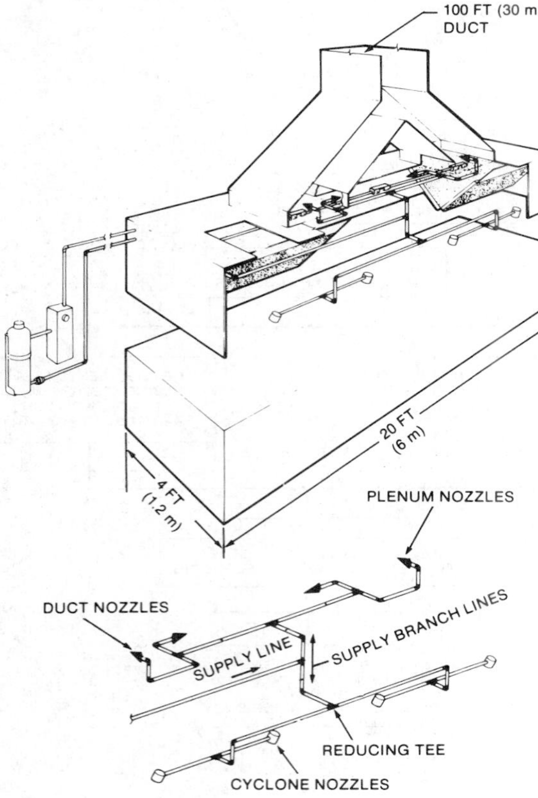

FIG. 5-19E. ***A typical single 30-lb (13.6 kg) cartridge-operated dry chemical system with fusible links for automatic operation, it is pre-engineered for kitchen range, hood, duct, and fryer fire protection. (Source: The Ansul Company)***

Control of dry chemical flow starts at the dry chemical storage tank. In systems of separate dry chemical and expellant gas containers, expellant gas must be admitted to the tank in such a way as to properly fluidize the dry chemical while the pressure builds up equally throughout the entire volume of the tank before the dry chemical is released from the tank. Should the pressure increase too rapidly above the dry chemical, the powder will not be properly fluidized and, upon release, the pressure drop in the piping or hose line will be excessive and result in a rate of dry chemical flow too low for proper extinguishing effectiveness.

If the expellant gas is permitted to channel to the outlet before the top of the dry chemical storage tank is properly pressurized, insufficient dry chemical will be carried by the flowing stream of gas, and the fire extinguishing effectiveness of the system again will be greatly reduced.

After release from the storage tank, dry chemical is carried through the piping at high velocities by the expellant gas and is thrown to the wall of the piping by centrifugal force whenever the direction of flow is sharply altered, as by an elbow. Should an elbow be directly connected to a tee and lie in the same plane as the tee, it is obvious that the two branches of the tee will carry appreciably different proportions of gas and dry chemical. This condition is overcome by installing all tees in planes perpendicular to the planes of adjacent elbows, by allowing sufficient length of straight pipe between tees and elbows, or by inserting special venturi devices between tees and elbows to ensure proper redistribution of dry chemical in the stream of gas before the mixture enters the tee.

Another critical factor in dry chemical distribution system design is the pressure drop through various lengths of pipe, hose, or fittings. Consequently, the length and size of piping and hose, and the number and size of fittings, must be selected to provide the required rate of discharge and nozzle distribution. In pre-engineered systems, this is already ensured by virtue of the limitations established for piping and fittings. In engineered systems, this selection must be made on the basis of actual calculation of pressure drop and subsequent flow rate.

For engineered systems, pressure drop data have been obtained at various rates of flow for various sizes of pipe and fittings. In one manufacturer's system, the pressure drop through a standard elbow is equivalent to the pressure drop through 20 ft (6 m) of straight pipe of the same size.[8] Pressure drop through a tee is equivalent to that of 45 ft (14 m) of straight pipe of the same size.

Nozzles

The selection of the proper types and sizes of nozzles for fixed systems is necessary to obtain proper coverage of the hazard.

Nozzles for hand hose line systems may be of either a one- or two-position type. One-position nozzles provide a modified straight stream, while two-position nozzles provide a straight stream or a fan. Since the straight stream has a longer reach than the fan discharge, it is considered better for initial attack. The shorter, wider fan-shaped stream is usually preferred for a close-range attack to complete the extinguishment. However, the present state of the art seems to prefer the use of the modified straight stream only. It is more effective and less confusing in the hands of an experienced operator.

Quantity and Rate of Application of Dry Chemical

The quantity of dry chemical and rate of flow must be sufficient to create a fire extinguishing concentration throughout all parts of the enclosure protected by a total flooding system, or over the specific fire area protected by a local application system. It must be realized that the fire extinguishing concentration accomplished throughout an enclosure (total flooding) can occur only during discharge. Following discharge, dry chemical rapidly settles out, and diminishes. This is in contrast to gaseous diffusion, where concentrations persist following discharge, such as in carbon dioxide and halon systems. Minimum rate of flow is critical because dry chemical will not extinguish a fire if applied too slowly. In local application systems, application at too high a rate may result in uneven discharge, or complete discharge of dry chemical before extinguishment is accomplished.

Optimum quantities of dry chemical and application rates have been determined by experiment for engineered total flooding and local application systems. For pre-engineered systems, the maximum sizes of hazards that can be protected by the various sizes of systems within specific piping limitations have been determined.

From tests with one manufacturer's engineered total flooding system, it has been determined that the weight in lbs (kg) of dry chemical required is obtained by multiplying the number of cu ft (m^3) in the net volume of the open space to be flooded by 0.0385 (in SI units 0.616). Net volume is the gross volume less the volume of machinery or other permanently located bulky objects.

The minimum flow rate in lbs per sec (kg/sec) is determined by multiplying the net volume in cu ft (m^3) by 0.00125 (in SI units 0.020). These volume factors apply only to this manufacturer's equipment and are cited merely to illustrate a procedure used.[8] Quantities and flow rates determined in this manner are contingent upon a nozzle arrangement that provides even distribution throughout the volume. The rates also assume that devices will be installed to close automatically all doors, windows, ventilators, or other openings through which dry chemical could escape from the enclosure.

In one manufacturer's pre-engineered total flooding system, a 1,000 cu ft (28 m^3) space not longer than 20 ft (6 m) can be protected by a 30-lb (14 kg) system with 4 nozzles and no more than 90 ft of ¾-in. pipe (27 m of 19 mm pipe), 13 elbows, 3 tees, and 3 venturi devices.[9] As with engineered systems, successful extinguishment is contingent upon proper nozzle location, shutdown of ventilation, and the closing of all openings, such as doors and windows, in addition to closure of fuel valves.

Although simultaneous shutdown of ventilation with the actuation of a total flooding system is the normal procedure, one exception exists. This exception is the special case of kitchen range hood and duct protection wherein pre-engineered systems are specifically designed to provide extinguishment, regardless of whether the ventilation is operating or not. Actually, this latter type of system is a combination of both total flooding and local application.

Quantities of dry chemical and flow rates for engineered local application systems are obtained from graphs plotted from tests using different flammable liquid surface areas, weights of dry chemical, and rates of application. These graphs are available from the manufacturer. For pre-engineered local application systems, the limitations of hazard size, system size, and piping arrangement are established by test and used in the same manner as for total flooding systems.

The minimum recommended quantity of dry chemical for hand hose line systems is sufficient to permit use of the system for 30 sec. Capacities of hand hose line systems range from 125 to 2,000 lb (57 to 900 kg), and as many as 4 hose lines can be operated from a single system. As with fixed systems, a minimum flow rate must be maintained to prevent surging or interruption of flow. Minimum rates are determined by the equipment manufacturer and depend upon the equipment used.

MAINTENANCE, INSPECTION, AND TEST PROCEDURES

In general, all dry chemical systems, including alarms and shutdown devices, should be thoroughly inspected and checked at least annually for proper operation. The frequency of inspection depends upon the type of hazard being protected. Systems subjected to process deposits (such as paint and dust) and corrosive conditions will require more frequent inspection of components.

The amount of expellant gas should be checked semiannually to ensure that there is sufficient gas to provide an effective discharge, and to automatically clean out the piping after the dry chemical has dissipated. In systems with separate expellant gas containers, this is accomplished by checking the pressure (if nitrogen) or weight (if carbon dioxide) against the manufacturer's recommended minimums. In stored-pressure systems, the pressure gage is checked to see that it is in the operable range.

At least semiannually, the quantity of dry chemical should also be checked either by visual inspection of the powder level in the separate dry chemical chamber, or by weighing the stored-pressure chamber. Except in stored-pressure systems, the dry chemical should be checked annually for any evidence of caking which could subsequently prevent proper flow.

Most dry chemicals are alkaline (sodium and potassium bicarbonate and potassium carbonate). One is neutral (potassium chloride) and the multipurpose type (monoammonium phosphate) is acidic. Inadvertent mixing of different base dry chemicals can initiate undesirable reactions, generating carbon dioxide gas and double decomposition, resulting in equipment failure or loss of discharge capability.

During the periodic inspections, the nozzles should be examined to see that they are properly aimed, free of obstruction, and in good operating condition. Nozzles in kitchen range hood and duct protection systems must be fitted with grease seals that are tight, yet easily blown clear. The system actuating devices, such as fusible links, pneumatic heat detectors, or electric thermostats, should also be checked to ensure that they are not loaded with residues, or otherwise impaired.

The inspection and maintenance of hand hose line systems will vary with the location and climate conditions. Equipment located in extremely hot or humid areas will require more frequent checking because the heat can cause cylinder pressure to increase and possibly cause leakage. Inspection of hand hose line systems consists primarily of checking the pressure of the expellant gas container, or the pressure of the unit itself (if it is of the pressurized type). It is also advisable to inspect all hose lines and nozzles to be sure that they are unobstructed and in good operating condition.

Systems containing dry chemical chambers of less than 150-lb (69 kg) nominal capacity must be hydrostatically tested every 12 years. The hydrostatic test should be applied to the auxiliary pressure containers, valve assemblies, hoses, fittings (not including field piping), check valves, directional valves, manifolds, and hose nozzles, in addition to the dry chemical chambers. The dry chemical removed from the chambers should be discarded. Care must be exercised to ensure that all equipment tested is thoroughly dried prior to recharging. If there is no automatic, connected reserve supply, alternate fire protection should be provided.

BIBLIOGRAPHY

References Cited

1. Underwriters Laboratories Inc., *Fire Protection Equipment List*, Northbrook, IL. (Published annually with bimonthly supplement.)
2. Factory Mutual Research Corp., *Factory Mutual Approval Guide*, Factory Mutual Research Corporation, Norwood, MA. (Published annually.)
3. Guise, A. B., "Potassium Bicarbonate-Based Dry Chemical," *NFPA Quarterly*, Vol. 56, No. 1, 1962, pp. 21-27.
4. Haessler, W. M., *The Extinguishment of Fire*, revised ed., National Fire Protection Association, Quincy, MA, 1974.

5. McCamy, C. S., Shoub, H., and Lee, T. G., "Fire Extinguishment by Means of Dry Powder," *Sixth Symposium on Combustion*, 1956, The Combustion Institute, Van Nostrand Reinhold, New York, pp. 795-801.

6. Guise, A. B., "The Chemical Aspects of Fire Extinguishment," *NFPA Quarterly*, Vol. 53, No. 4, 1960, pp. 330-336.

7. Haessler, W. M., "Fire and Its Extinguishment," *NFPA Quarterly*, Vol. 56, No. 1, 1962, pp. 89-96.

8. Guise, A. B., and Lindlof, J. A., "A Dry Chemical Extinguishing System," *NFPA Quarterly*, Vol. 49, No. 1, 1955, pp. 52-60.

9. Safety First, *Safe-T-Meter Automatic Dry Chemical Fixed System*, Bulletin UP-30M, (undated), Safety First Products Corp., Elmsford, NY.

NFPA Codes, Standards, and Recommended Practices

Reference to the following NFPA codes, standards, and recommended practices will provide further information on dry chemical agents and application systems discussed in this chapter. (See the latest *NFPA Catalog* for availability of current editions of the following documents.)

NFPA 10, *Portable Fire Extinguishers*.

NFPA 17, *Dry Chemical Extinguishing Systems*.

Additional Reading

Erving, C. T., "Flame Extinguishment Properties of Dry Chemicals," *Fire Technology*, Vol. 25, No. 2, May 1989, pp. 134-149.

Fire Control Engineering Co., *Dry Chemical Fire Extinguishing Characteristics*, expanded 2nd ed., Ft. Worth, TX.

Guise, A. B., "Extinguishment of Natural Gas Pressure Fires," *Fire Technology*, Vol. 3, No. 3, Aug. 1967, pp. 175-193.

Hird, D., and Fippes, D. W., *The Effect of Various Powdered Materials on the Stability of Protein Foams*, British Joint Fire Research Organization, 1960.

Jensen, R. H., "Compatibility of Mechanical Foam and Dry Chemical," *NFPA Quarterly*, Vol. 57, No. 3, Jan. 1964, pp. 296-303.

Lee, T. G., and Robertson, A. F., "Extinguishing Effectiveness of Some Powdered Materials on Hydrocarbon Fires," *Fire Research Abstracts and Reviews*, Vol. 2, No. 1, Jan. 1960.

McGarry, J. E., "Improved Fire Safety for the Indianapolis 500," *Fire Journal*, Vol. 60, No. 2, Mar. 1966, pp. 32-36.

Meldrum, D. N., "Combined Use of Foam and Dry Chemical," *NFPA Quarterly*, Vol. 56, No. 1, July 1962, pp. 28-34.

"Special Hazards Protection—Manufacturers and Equipment," *Fire Journal*, Vol. 81, No. 4, 1987, p. 43.

Standard for Dry Chemical Fire Extinguishers, 7th ed., Underwriters Laboratories Inc., Northbrook, IL, 1984.

Stauffer, E. E., "Extinguishing Toluene Di-isocyanate Fire with Dry Chemicals," *Fire Technology*, Vol. 11, No. 4, Nov. 1975, pp. 255-260.

Stevens, R. E., "Dealing with the Grease Duct Fire Problem," *NFPA Quarterly*, Vol. 56, No. 3, Jan. 1963, pp. 216-220.

Tuve, R. L., "Light Water and Potassium Bicarbonate Dry Chemical—A New Two-Agent Extinguishing System," *NFPA Quarterly*, Vol. 58, No. 1, July 1964, pp. 64-69.

Underwriters Laboratories Inc., "The Compatibility Relationship Between Mechanical Foam and Dry Chemical Fire Extinguishing Agents," *UL Bulletin of Research No. 54*, July 1963, Chicago, IL.

Wesson, H. R., "Studies of the Effects of Particle Size on the Flow Characteristics of Dry Chemical," *Fire Technology*, Vol. 8, No. 3, Aug. 1972, pp. 173-180.

Woolhouse, R. A., and Sayers, D. R., "Monex Compared with Other Potassium-Based Dry Chemicals," *Fire Journal*, Vol. 671, No. 1, Jan. 1973, pp. 85-88.

FOAM EXTINGUISHING AGENTS AND SYSTEMS

Revised by Donald N. Meldrum

Fire fighting foam is an aggregate of gas-filled bubbles formed from aqueous solutions of specially formulated concentrated liquid foaming agents. Normally, the gas used is air, but in certain applications may be an inert gas. Since foam is lighter than the aqueous solutions from which it is formed, and lighter than flammable liquids, it floats on flammable or combustible liquids, producing an air-excluding, cooling, continuous layer of vapor-sealing, water-bearing material that halts or prevents combustion.

Foam is produced by mixing a foam concentrate with water at the appropriate concentration, and then aerating and agitating the solution to form the bubble structure. Some foams are thick and viscous and form tough, heat-resistant blankets over burning liquid surfaces and vertical areas; other foams are thinner and spread more rapidly. Some foams are capable of producing a vapor-sealing film of surface-active water solution on a liquid surface. Some, such as medium- or high-expansion foam, are meant to be used as large volumes of wet gas cells for inundating surfaces and filling cavities.

Foams are defined by their expansion ratio, which is the ratio of final foam volume to original foam solution volume before adding air. They are arbitrarily subdivided into three ranges: (1) low-expansion foam—expansion up to 20:1; (2) medium-expansion foam—expansion 20 to 200:1; and (3) high-expansion foam—expansion 200 to 1000:1.

Foams are also defined according to their effectiveness on hydrocarbon fuels, water-miscible fuels, or both.

There are various methods of generating and applying foams. This chapter covers the basic characteristics of various foaming agents and the methods for producing fire fighting foams, as well as specific applications of equipment and systems useful for different types of hazards.

USES AND LIMITATIONS OF FIRE FIGHTING FOAMS

Low-expansion foam is used principally to extinguish burning flammable or combustible liquid spill or tank fires by application to develop a cooling, coherent blanket. Foam is the only permanent extinguishing agent used for fires of this type. Its application allows fire fighters to extinguish fires progressively. A foam blanket covering a tank's liquid surface can prevent vapor transmission for some time, depending upon the stability and depth of the foam. Fuel spills are quickly rendered safe by foam blanketing. The blanket may be removed after a suitable period of time; often, it has no detrimental effect on the product with which it comes into contact.

Foams may be used to diminish or halt the generation of flammable vapors from nonburning liquids or solids and may be used to fill cavities or enclosures where toxic or flammable gases may collect.

Foam is of great importance where aircraft are fueled and operated. Sudden, large fuel spills resulting from aircraft accidents or malfunction require rapid foam application. Hangar fire protection is best accomplished by properly designed foam systems.

Foams of the medium- or high-expansion type (20 to 1000 times) may be used to fill enclosures such as basement room areas or holds of ships where fires are difficult or impossible to reach. Here, foams act to halt convection and access to air for combustion. Their water content also cools and diminishes oxygen by steam displacement. Foams of this type (with expansion ratios of 400 to 500) may be used to control liquefied natural gas (LNG) spill fires and help disperse the resulting vapor cloud.

Many foams are generated from solutions with very low surface tension and penetration characteristics. Foams of this type are useful where Class A combustible materials are present. In such instances, the water solution draining from the foam cools and wets the solid combustible.

Foam breaks down and vaporizes its water content under attack by heat and flame. It therefore must be applied to a burning liquid surface in sufficient volume and rate to compensate for this loss, with an additional amount applied to guarantee a residual foam layer over the extinguished liquid. Foam is unstable and may be broken down easily by a physical or mechanical force, such as a water hose stream. Certain chemical vapors or fluids may also destroy foam quickly. When certain other extinguishing

Donald N. Meldrum is a consultant in fire protection engineering, based in Malvern, PA.

agents are used in conjunction with foam, severe breakdown of the foam may occur. Turbulent air or violently uprising combustion gases from fires may divert foam from the burning area.

Foam solutions are conductive and therefore not recommended for use on electrical fires. If foam is used, a spray is less conductive than a straight stream. However, because foam is cohesive and contains materials that allow water to conduct electricity, foam spray is more conductive than water spray.

Engineering design requirements and recommended application methods must be followed for successful use of foams. These requirements can be found in NFPA 11, *Low-Expansion Foam and Combined Agent Systems*; NFPA 11A, *Medium- and High-Expansion Foam Systems*; NFPA 11C, *Mobile Foam Apparatus*; NFPA 16, *Deluge Foam-Water Sprinkler and Foam-Water Spray Systems*; and NFPA 403, *Aircraft Rescue and Fire Fighting Services at Airports*.

In general, the following criteria for the hazardous liquid must be met for a foam to be fully effective:

1. The liquid must be below its boiling point at the ambient conditions of temperature and pressure.
2. Care must be taken in application of foam to liquids with a bulk temperature higher than 212°F (100°C). At these fuel temperatures and above, foam forms an emulsion of steam, air, and fuel. This may produce a four-fold increase in volume when applied to a tank fire, with dangerous frothing or slopover of the burning liquid.
3. The liquid must not be unduly destructive to the foam used, or the foam must not be highly soluble in the liquid to be protected.
4. The liquid must not be water-reactive.
5. The fire must be a horizontal surface fire. Three-dimensional (falling fuel) or pressure fires cannot be extinguished by foam unless the hazard has a relatively high flashpoint and can be cooled to extinguishment by the water in the foam.

TYPES OF FOAM

There are a number of types of foaming agents available, known as foam concentrates, some of which are designed for specific applications. Some are suitable for extinguishing all types of flammable liquids, including water-soluble and foam-destructive liquids. Descriptions of the common types of foam follow.

Aqueous Film-Forming Foam Agents (AFFF)

Aqueous film-forming foam agents are composed of synthetically produced materials that form air-foams similar to those produced by the protein-based materials. In addition, these foaming agents are capable of forming water solution films on the surface of flammable hydrocarbon liquids, hence the term "aqueous film-forming foam" (AFFF). AFFF concentrates are available for proportioning to a final concentration of 1 percent, 3 percent, or 6 percent by volume, with either fresh water or seawater.

The air-foams generated from AFFF solutions possess low viscosity, have fast spreading and leveling characteristics, and, like other foams, act as surface barriers to exclude air and halt fuel vaporization. These foams also develop a continuous aqueous layer of solution under the foam, maintaining a floating film on hydrocarbon fuel surfaces to help suppress combustible vapors and cool the fuel substrate. This film, which can also spread over fuel surfaces not fully covered with foam, is self-healing following mechanical disruption and continues to spread as long as there remains a reservoir of nearby foam. Film effectiveness may be reduced on hot surfaces and aromatic hydrocarbons. To ensure fire extinction, an AFFF blanket should cover the fuel surface entirely, as with other types of foam.

AFFF fluidity and film strength on kerosene makes it particularly suitable for jet aircraft fuel spill fire fighting.

AFFF concentrates contain fluorinated, long-chain synthetic hydrocarbons with particular surface active properties. They are nontoxic and biodegradable in their diluted form of use.

Because of the extremely low surface tension of the solutions draining from AFFF, these foams may be useful under mixed-class fire situations (Classes A and B), where deep penetration of water is needed in addition to the surface spreading action of foam itself.

Foam-generating devices yielding stable, homogeneous foams are not necessarily needed in the employment of AFFF. Less sophisticated foaming devices, such as water spray nozzles and sprinklers (unlike with most other foaming agents), may be used because of the inherent rapid and easy foaming capability of AFFF solutions. However, such foams drain relatively rapidly and may provide post-fire security. AFFF also may be used, without compatibility problems, in conjunction with dry chemical agents. Although AFFF concentrates must not be mixed with other types of foam concentrates, foams made from them do not break down other types of foams in fire fighting operations. The normal-use temperature range for these agents is 35 to 120°F (1.7 to 49°C).

Fluoroprotein Foaming Agents (FP)

The concentrates utilized for generating fluoroprotein foams are similar in composition to protein foam concentrates, but, in addition to protein polymers, they contain fluorinated surface active agents that confer a "fuel shedding" property to the foam generated. This makes them particularly effective for fire fighting conditions where the foam becomes coated with fuel, such as in the method of subsurface injection of foam for tank fire fighting, and nozzle or monitor foam applications where the foam may often be plunged into the fuel. Fluoroprotein foams are very effective for in-depth crude petroleum or other hydrocarbon fuel fires because of this fuel shedding property. In addition, these foams demonstrate better compatibility with dry chemical agents than do the regular protein-type foams. They also possess superior vapor securing and burnback resistance characteristics. Fluoroprotein-type concentrates are available for proportioning to a final concentration of either 3 percent or 6 percent by volume, using either fresh water or seawater. They are nontoxic and biodegradable after dilution. The normal-use temperature range for these agents is 20 to 120°F (–7 to 49°C).

Film-Forming Fluoroprotein Agents (FFFP)

Film-forming fluoroprotein (FFFP) agents are composed of protein together with film-forming fluorinated surface-active agents, which make them capable of forming water solution films on the surface of most flammable hydrocarbons and of conferring a fuel shedding property to the foam generated.

Air-foams generated from FFFP solutions have fast-spreading and leveling characteristics and, just as other foams, act as surface barriers to exclude air and prevent vaporization. Like AFFF, they generate a self-healing, continuous floating film on hydrocarbon fuel surfaces which helps suppress combustible vapors. However, to ensure fire extinction, an FFFP blanket, as with other types of foam, should cover the entire fuel surface.

Because of the rapid and easy foaming capability of FFFP solutions, water spray devices may be used in many situations. However, the foams produced drain rapidly and may not provide post-fire security.

Film-forming fluoroprotein-type concentrates are available for proportioning to a final concentration of either 3 or 6 percent by volume, using either fresh water or seawater. They may be used in conjunction with dry chemical agents without compatibility problems, and are nontoxic and biodegradable after dilution.

Protein Foaming Agents (P)

Protein-type air-foams utilize aqueous liquid concentrates proportioned with water for their generation. These concentrates contain high-molecular-weight natural proteinaceous polymers derived from a chemical digestion and hydrolysis of natural protein solids. The polymers give elasticity, mechanical strength, and water retention capability to foams generated from them. The concentrates also contain dissolved polyvalent metallic salts which aid the protein polymers in their bubble-strengthening capability when the foam is exposed to heat and flame. Protein-type concentrates are available for proportioning to a final concentration of either 3 percent or 6 percent by volume, using either fresh water or seawater. In general, these concentrates produce dense, viscous foams of high stability, high heat resistance, and good resistance to burnback, but they are less resistant to breakdown by fuel saturation than are AFFF and fluoroprotein foams. They are nontoxic and biodegradable after dilution. The normal-use ambient temperature range for these concentrates is 20 to 120°F (–7 to 49°C).

Low-Temperature Foaming Agents

This type of foam concentrate is protected for storage and use at low temperature by the inclusion of freezing-point depressants. Low-temperature foaming agents may be used at ambient temperatures as low as –20°F (–29°C). They are available for use at either 3 percent or 6 percent by volume concentration in either fresh water or seawater, and may be of the AFFF or protein-based type.

Alcohol-Type Foaming Agents (AR)

Air-foams generated from ordinary agents are subject to rapid breakdown and loss of effectiveness when they are used on fires that involve fuels that are water soluble, water miscible, or of a "polar solvent" type. Examples of this type of fuel are alcohols, enamel and lacquer thinners, methyl ethyl ketone, acetone, isopropyl ether, acrylonitrile, ethyl and butyl acetate, and the amines and anhydrides. Even small amounts of these substances mixed with common hydrocarbon fuels, such as gasohol, may cause rapid breakdown of ordinary fire fighting foams.

Therefore, certain special foaming agents, called alcohol-type concentrates, have been developed. These alcohol-resistant concentrates are proprietary compositions of several types, some containing a protein, fluoroprotein, or an aqueous film-forming foam concentrate base. The most common are usually described as polymeric alcohol-resistant AFFF concentrates which produce foams suitable for application to spill or in-depth fires of either hydrocarbon or water-miscible flammable liquids by any foam-generating device. They exhibit AFFF characteristics on hydrocarbons and produce a floating gel-like mass for foam buildup on water-miscible fuels. Agents of this type have no transit time limitations. Normal-use temperatures for any of the alcohol-type agents are 35 to 120°F (1.7 to 49°C).

Medium- and High-Expansion Foaming Agents (SYNDET)

Medium- and high-expansion foams are agents for control and extinguishment of Class A and some Class B fires, and are particularly suited as a flooding agent for use in confined spaces. The foam is an aggregation of bubbles, mechanically generated by aspiration or a blower-fan, which forces air or some other gas through a net or screen that is wetted by an aqueous solution of surface-active foaming agents. Under proper conditions, fire fighting foams of expansions from 20:1 up to 1000:1 can be generated.

Medium- or high-expansion foam is a unique vehicle for transporting wet foam masses to inaccessible places, for total flooding of confined spaces, and for volumetric displacement of vapor, heat, and smoke. Tests have shown that when used under certain circumstances in conjunction with water from automatic sprinklers, the foam will provide more positive control and extinguishment than either extinguishing agent by itself. Optimum efficiency in any one type of hazard is dependent upon the rate of application and the foam expansion and stability.

Liquid concentrates for producing medium- and high-expansion foams consist of synthetic hydrocarbon surfactants of a type that will foam copiously with a small input of turbulent action. They are generally used in approximately 2 percent proportion in water solution. Medium-expansion foam may also be generated from solutions of fluoroprotein, protein, or AFFF concentrates at 3 or 6 percent proportion.

Medium- or high-expansion foams are particularly suited for indoor fires in confined spaces. Their use outdoors may be limited because of the effects of weather. These foams have several effects on fires:

1. When generated in sufficient volume, they can prevent the air necessary for continued combustion from reaching the fire.
2. When forced into the heat of a fire, the water in the foam is converted to steam, which reduces the oxygen concentration by diluting the air.
3. The conversion of the water to steam absorbs heat from the burning fuel. Any hot object exposed to the foam will continue breaking down the foam, converting the water to steam, and being further cooled.
4. Because of its relatively low surface tension, foam solution not converted to steam will tend to penetrate Class A materials. However, deep-seated fires may require overhaul.
5. When accumulated in depth, high-expansion foam can provide an insulating barrier for protection of exposed materials or structures not involved in a fire, thereby preventing fire spread.

Research has shown that using air from inside a burning building to generate high-expansion foam has an adverse effect on the volume and stability of the foam produced. Combustion and pyrolysis products, when they react chemically with the foaming agent, can reduce the volume of foam produced and increase the drainage rate. The high temperature of the air breaks down the foam as it is generated. Physical disruption also takes place, apparently caused by vapor and solid particles from the combustion process. These factors that cause foam breakdown may be compensated for by higher rates of foam generation.

Entry to a foam-filled passage must not be attempted without use of self-contained breathing apparatus. The foam mass also reduces vision and hearing, and life lines must be used for personnel entering the foam.

Tests have shown that foam of approximately 500:1 expansion can be successfully used for control of fires and reduction of vaporization from LNG spills. As water slowly drains from the foam in small amounts, it forms a thin ice layer which floats on the LNG and supports the high-expansion foam blanket. Fixed and portable high-expansion foam facilities of this type have been provided for LNG storage and manufacturing plants.

Other Synthetic Hydrocarbon Surfactant Foaming Agents

There are many synthetically produced surface active compounds that foam copiously in water solution. When these are formulated properly, they may be used as wetting agents or as fire fighting foams and employed in much the same manner as other types of foam. (See NFPA 18, *Wetting Agents*.)

Hydrocarbon surfactant foam liquid concentrates are employed in 1 to 6 percent proportions in water. When these solutions are used in conventional foam-making devices, the resulting air-foam possesses low viscosity and spreads quickly over liquid surfaces. Its fire fighting characteristics depend upon: (1) the volume of the foam layer on the burning surface, which halts access to air and controls combustible vapor production; and (2) the minor cooling effect of the water in the foam, which becomes available due to a relatively rapid breakdown of the foam mass. This water solution does not possess film-forming characteristics on the flammable liquid surface, although, under some conditions, it may produce a temporary water emulsion due to its wetting agent or "detergent-type" properties. Because of the low surface tension and wetting properties of the water solutions of these foams, they also may be used as extinguishing agents for Class A fires, although they were primarily developed with medium- or high-expansion foam in mind.

Synthetic hydrocarbon surfactant foams are generally less stable than other fire fighting foams. Their water solution content drains away rapidly, leaving a bubble mass which is highly vulnerable to fuel heat or mechanical disruption. Usually these foams must be applied at higher rates than other fire fighting foams to achieve extinction. Many formulations of this type of foam concentrate break down other foams if used simultaneously or sequentially.

Foams for Vapor Suppression

Fire fighting foams may be used to suppress vapors from unignited flammable liquids for which the foams are proven extinguishing agents. To ensure good vapor suppression, the foam must be applied gently, so as to not mix fuel with the foam, and must cover the entire fuel surface. Care should be taken not to agitate the fuel during foam application, because static spark ignition of volatile hydrocarbons can result from plunging and turbulence from a foam or water stream.

There are flammable, toxic, or otherwise hazardous liquids on which fire fighting foams are unstable and are therefore unsuitable for use either for fire fighting or vapor suppression. Special vapor-mitigating foams have been developed that are relatively stable on many hazardous liquids; one type is an alcohol-resistant fire fighting foam of the low-expansion type, which can be additionally stabilized to enhance its effective foam life and stability on toxic, flammable, or corrosive liquids. Other types are medium-expansion foams especially formulated to be stable on either acidic or alkaline hazards. These medium-expansion foams are not effective fire fighting foams.

In general, vapor-mitigating foams should be applied to spills of toxic liquids only by trained personnel wearing suitable protective gear. These foams require special engineering consideration, and, to date, no standards have been developed for their use. The manufacturers should be consulted for use, limitations, and application data.

Chemical Foam Agents and Powders

These foam-producing materials have become obsolete because of the superior economics and ease of handling of the liquid foam-forming concentrates previously discussed. Chemical foam is formed from the chemical reaction in aqueous solution between aluminum sulfate ("A," acidic) and sodium bicarbonate ("B," basic) which also contains proteinaceous foam stabilizers. Foam is formed by the generation of carbon dioxide gas trapped in the bubbles of the foaming solution.

GUIDELINES FOR FIRE PROTECTION WITH FOAMS

The following general rules apply to the application and use of ordinary air-foams:

1. The more gently the foam is applied, the more rapid the extinguishment and the lower the total amount of agent required.
2. Successful use of foam is also dependent upon the rate at which it is applied. Application rates are described in terms of the amount by volume of foam solution reaching the fuel surface (in terms of total area) every minute. If the foam has an expansion rate of 8 to 1, an application rate of 0.1 gpm per sq ft [4.1 (L/min)m^2] will provide 0.8 gal per sq ft (32.8 L/m^2) of finished foam every minute. Increasing the foam application rate over the recommended minimum will generally reduce the time required for extinguishment. However, little time advantage is gained if application rates are increased more than three times the minimum recommended. If application rates are less than the minimum, extinguishment time will be prolonged or may not be accomplished at all. If application rates are so low that the rate of foam loss by heat or fuel attack equals or exceeds the rate of foam application, the fire will not be controlled or extinguished.
3. The minimum recommended application rate is the rate found by test to be the most practical in terms of speed of control and amount of agent required. The general curve in Figure 5-20A illustrates the rate-time

relationship for foam application to a hazard. The curve may be displaced right or left depending upon fuel and method of application; hence, the need for carefully engineered systems based on the appropriate standard and actual test information.

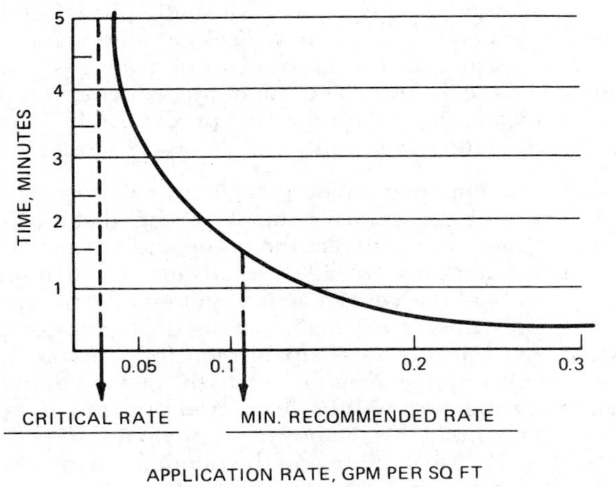

FIG. 5-20A. General relationship of foam application rate to time of application necessary for extinction. [1 gpm per sq ft equals 40.746 (L/min)/m².]

4. In general, air-foams will be more stable when they are generated with water at ambient temperature. Preferred water temperatures range from 35 to 80°F (1.7 to 27°C). Either fresh water or seawater may be used. Water containing known foam contaminants, such as detergents, oil residues, or certain corrosion inhibitors, may adversely affect foam quality.
5. Foams are adversely affected by air containing certain combustion products. While the effect is minor with ordinary air-foam and ordinary hydrocarbon fuels, it is desirable to locate fixed foam-makers on the sides of, rather than directly over, the hazard.
6. Recommended pressure ranges should be observed for all foam-making devices. Foam quality will deteriorate if these limits (high and low) are exceeded.
7. Many air-foams are adversely affected by contact with vaporizing liquid extinguishing agents, their vapors, and by some dry chemical agents.

FOAM-GENERATING METHODS

The process of producing and applying fire fighting air-foams to hazards requires three separate operations, each of which consumes energy. They are: (1) the proportioning process, (2) the foam generation phase, and (3) the distribution method. A flow diagram illustrating the relationship of the three operations is given in Figure 5-20B.

In general practice, air-foam generation and distribution occur nearly simultaneously within the same device. There are also many types of proportioning. In certain portable devices, all three functions are combined into a single device. The design and performance requirements of foam systems dictate the choice of types of proportioning, generating, and distributing equipment for the protection of specific hazards.

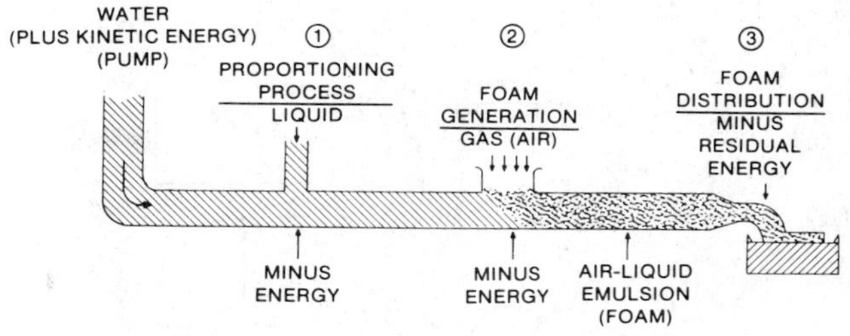

FIG. 5-20B. A diagram illustrating the steps in air-foam generation.

Foam Concentrate Proportioners

It is very important that foam concentrate be proportioned accurately into the water stream. Proportioning equipment, foam concentrate, and discharge equipment must be matched to produce the proper solution concentration at system design operating pressures. If proportioning is low, the foam will be relatively weak and unstable; if too high, the foam may be stiff and concentrate will be wasted, thus reducing effective system operating time.

So that a predetermined volume of liquid foam concentrate may be mixed with a water stream to form a foam solution of fixed concentration, the following two general methods are used:

1. Methods that utilize the pressure energy of the water stream by venturi action and orifices to induct concentrate.
2. Methods that utilize external pumps or pressure heads to inject concentrate into the water stream at a fixed ratio to flow.

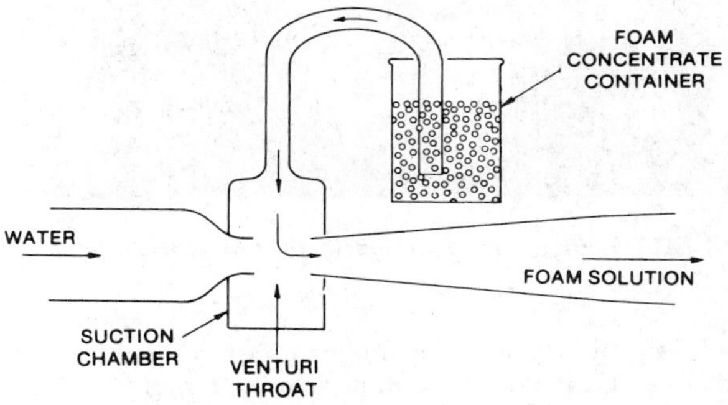

FIG. 5-20C. Venturi induction (in line) proportioner.

Figures 5-20C and 5-20D illustrate the general principles of the two different proportioning methods. Specific system designs of proportioning equipment are given below.

The nozzle eductor: This type of foam concentrate proportioner is of simple design and is widely used in portable foam-making nozzles where foam concentrate is available in 5-gal (19 L) pails or drums as shown in Figure 5-20E. Incorporating a modified venturi within the foam-making nozzle section, the nozzle eductor drafts concentrate from a portable container through a pickup tube.

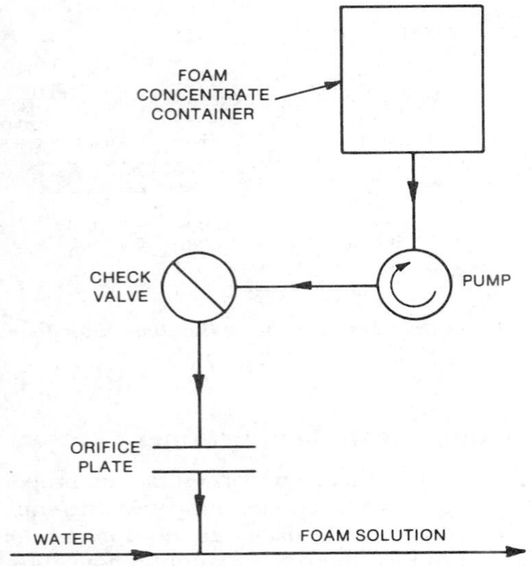

FIG. 5-20D. Foam concentrate pump proportioner.

FIG. 5-20E. Air-foam nozzle with built-in eductor.

Using a properly sized orifice or pipe section at the low-pressure cavity, the concentrate is mixed in proper proportion to the fixed flow and operating pressure of the nozzle, and foam generation proceeds.

In-line eductor: This type of proportioner educts or drafts foam concentrate from a container or tank by venturi action, utilizing the operating pressure of the hose water stream on which it is installed, and injecting concentrate into that flow of water. Its correct operation is very sensitive to water flow and pressure. Changes in either of these factors from those for which the eductor was designed will result in incorrect proportioning. Distances of more than 6 ft (1.8 m) elevation from the eductor to the lowest liquid level of the foam concentrate container also may result in incorrect proportioning. Foam-generation devices and maximum downstream lengths of hose recommended for each eductor must be carefully adhered to. This proportioning device may be used in the hose line leading to the foam-generation device. An eductor of this type may also be installed at the foam concentrate tank in a fixed system or at the pump discharge of a mobile pumper.

Some designs of this proportioning device incorporate metering valves in the foam concentrate intake line so various volume percentages of concentrate in the water stream may be obtained. A check valve is usually placed in this intake so that water cannot flow back into the foam concentrate container if a blockage occurs or a valve is closed in the downstream hose. The use of this eductor requires an allowance for a pressure loss of approximately 30 percent in the system or layout.

Around-the-pump proportioner: This type of proportioner also operates on the venturi principle, except that this proportioner must be situated at the pump and connected to both suction and pressure sides. Its advantage is that pressure recovery of the venturi action is attained, and pump delivery pressures to the foam-making device or devices downstream require no compensation for pressure loss except for that in the layout hose length. The net delivery volume of the pump will be decreased by 10 to 40 gpm (38 to 150 L/min) in this method of proportioning. (See Figure 5-20F.) The small portion of the pump discharge flows through a bypass line to the suction side of the pump. A venturi eductor in this line produces a negative pressure on the foam concentrate pickup line from the foam concentrate container. Foam concentrate is led to the eductor, where it mixes with water and is delivered to the suction side of the pump.

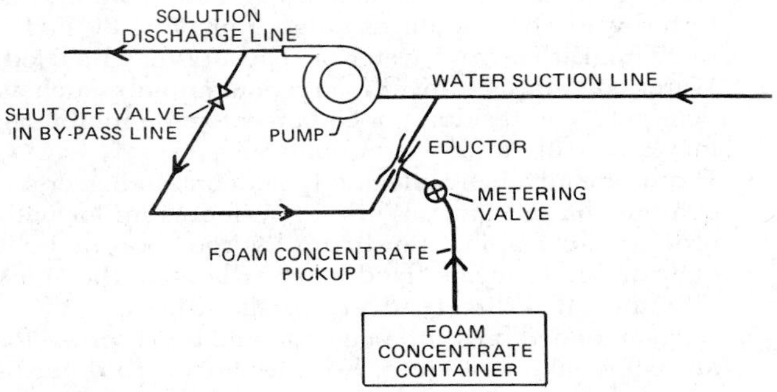

FIG. 5-20F. An around-the-pump proportioner.

Multiple foam-makers may be supplied with foam solution by this type of proportioner when it is supplied with a multiported metering valve designed for the required flows.

Pressure proportioning tank: This type of proportioner may consist of one tank or of two tanks separately connected to the water and foam solution lines. The tank or tanks in the system may each be fitted with a flexible diaphragm or bladder to separate the "driving" water from foam concentrate. Tanks may rely simply on differences in density of the two liquids to retard mixing during operation (without diaphragm or bladder), when proportioning protein or fluoroprotein concentrate.

The principle of this device is simple. A small amount of the flowing water volumetrically displaces foam concentrate into the main water stream. The design pressure of the vessel must be above the maximum static water pressure encountered in the system.

Water is allowed to enter the foam tank from the main stream with as little friction loss as possible. An orifice meters liquid in the tank into the low pressure area. Advantages of this system are its low pressure drop, automatic proportioning over range of flows and pressures, and its freedom from external power. Its disadvantages are a long refill time (since it is a "batch" method, the tank must be drained of its driving water and the tank or the bladder refilled with concentrate), and an economic limit on size.

Coupled water motor-pump proportioner: This proportioner consists of two positive displacement rotary pumps mounted on a common shaft. Water delivered to the larger pump (motor) causes it to drive the smaller pump, which is used to draft concentrate from a container and deliver it (at line pressure) to the water discharge line from the larger pump. By proportioning the sizes of the two pumps, the correct volume of concentrate is delivered to the water stream.

This proportioner is manufactured in only two sizes for water throughputs of 60 to 180 gpm (227 to 680 L/min) and 200 to 1000 gpm (757 to 3800 L/min). Both sizes are designed for proportioning foam concentrates recommended for use at 6 percent concentration. A pressure drop of 25 to 30 percent in the water stream supplied to the device is required for its operation.

Balanced pressure proportioner: The use of a separate pump for pressurizing foam concentrate to be delivered in the correct proportions to a flowing water stream offers the greatest advantage for reliable and accurate operation of a foam concentrate proportioning system which must function at varying rates of waterflow or pressure during its use. (See Figure 5-20G for a fixed design and Figure 5-20H for a foam truck-mounted design.) Many systems require manual attention to flow meters, duplex gages, or other measuring devices during system operation. These designs have been replaced by automatically operated proportioning systems that do not require continuous manual attention.

Balanced pressure proportioning systems are of two types: (1) the bypass system, and (2) the variable flow demand system. These systems are simple in principle and reliable.

Bypass system. This type of balanced pressure system relies on a hydraulically monitored pressure control valve in a bypass foam concentrate line from a pump back to the concentrate supply tank; a correctly sized venturi-type proportioning controller in the water line for correct and automatic proportioning over wide ranges of flow; and a fixed or variable metering orifice between the pump and the proportioning controller.

Variable flow demand system. This type of balanced pressure system utilizes a variable speed mechanism to drive a pump delivering foam concentrate to the system. Only a correctly sized venturi-type proportioning controller in the water line (for correct and automatic proportioning over wide ranges of flow) and a fixed or variable metering orifice between the pump and proportioning controller are used. The variable drive mechanism is controlled by a feedback system which can be designed to operate hydraulically or electronically. Once activated, the pump output is monitored automatically so foam concentrate flow and pressure are always proportional to system demand for foam solution. (See Figure 5-20I.) The variable flow demand system may be fixed or truck-mounted.

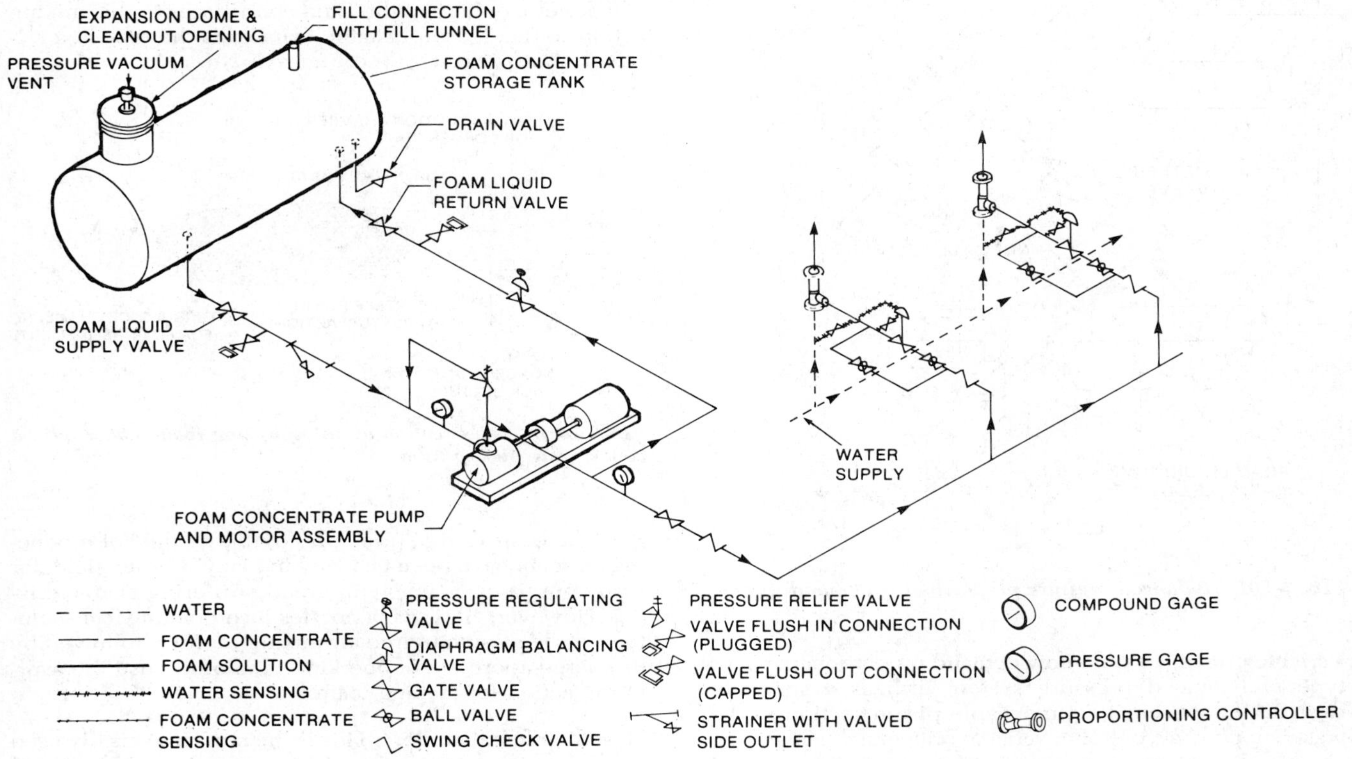

FIG. 5-20G. Balanced pressure proportioning with multiple injection points (metered proportioning).

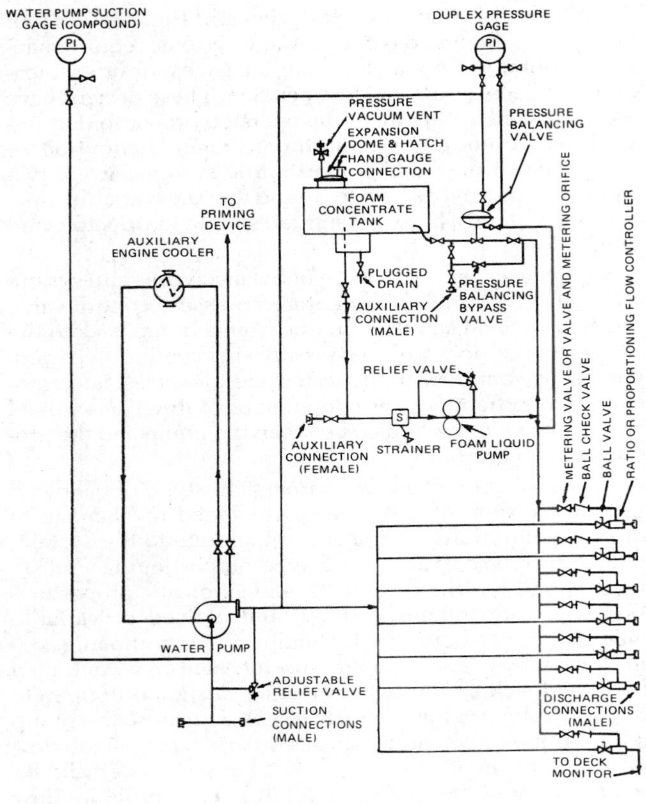

FIG. 5-20H. Balanced pressure proportioning.

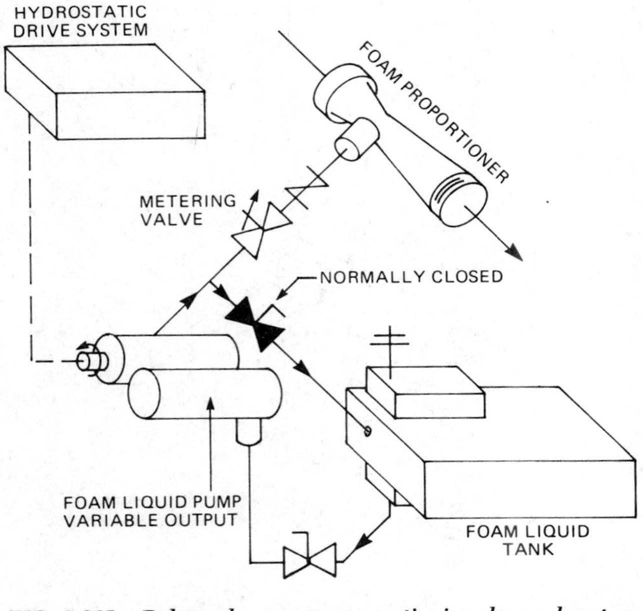

FIG. 5-20I. Balanced pressure proportioning demand system.

Variable orifice, variable flow demand proportioner: This type of balanced pressure system utilizes a specially designed, flow-sensitive, moveable piston section in the water supply that controls a variable orifice in the foam concentrate line. A pump supplies concentrate at monitored pressures to the metering orifice, which changes in size proportionally to the system demand for foam solution. The device is especially designed for large-capacity systems. Its design provides accurate proportioning over ranges of flow of water of approximately 2.3 to 1.

Premixed foam solution: This method of proportioning is a batch type of mixing of concentrate with water, usually in a container that can be pressurized. The measured volume of concentrate is poured into a measured volume of water to yield a foam solution of the recommended strength; e.g., for a 3 percent solution in a container that holds 100 gal (378.5 L) of liquid, 97 gal (367 L) of water are poured into it and 3 gal (11.5 L) of foam concentrate are mixed with it to give a solution of 3 percent by volume. The final solution mixture is then educted from a tank to a pump or placed in a pressurizing vessel.

Some foam concentrates are not suitable for storage in premix solution. Even those that are formulated for this use may show gradual loss of effectiveness. Manufacturers recommendations should be followed carefully.

Portable Aspirating Equipment and Systems

Because of the difficulties associated with pumping or transporting generated foam in pipes or hoses and the familiarity of fire fighters with nozzles, the earliest designs of air-foam generators were devised to be used in much the same manner as water nozzles. They incorporated a crude venturi design whereby a jet or jets of foam solution enter an open contracted portion of a large-diameter foam tube. This action lowers the atmospheric pressure surrounding the jets, and air is drawn or aspirated into the throat of the tube. Downstream of the contracted portion of the tube, a high turbulence and mixing of air and foam solution occurs. This turbulence may be increased by internal turbulence-accelerating devices, such as screens or baffles. The kinetic energy of the fluid contributes to this mixing action so that a useful, stable foam exits the tube at a relatively low pressure. (See Figure 5-20J.)

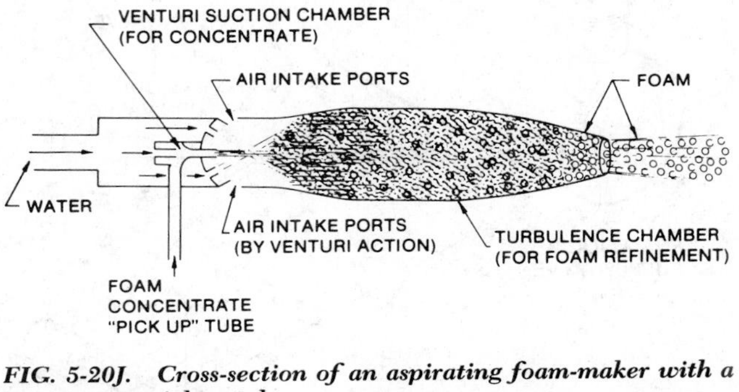

FIG. 5-20J. Cross-section of an aspirating foam-maker with a concentrate pickup tube.

The basic design principles of this method of producing air-foam have been changed in many ways to yield, for many purposes, foams with greatly differing characteristics. However, all types of nozzles incorporating foam solution jets leading into free air-mixing cavities, followed by discharge apertures of one kind or another, use the aspirating action for making foam.

Hose line foam nozzle: This is the most universally used portable, air-aspirating foam device for flammable liquid fire fighting. It is manufactured in a variety of capacities up to approximately 350 gpm (1325 L/min). (See Figure 5-20K.) Supplied with foam solution from a proportioner or by means of a pickup tube, it is used for combatting fires resulting from spills of flammable liquid, or fires in tanks or fuel pits. To provide a variety of foam stream patterns that may be needed for the extinguishment operation, these nozzles often contain built-in devices that allow continuous foam pattern variation from a solid, straight stream to an inverted, filled umbrella shape. (See Figure 5-20L.) As with water streams, foam is employed in a solid, straight stream for range or reach.) A flat or wide "bushy" shape is used for gentle "snowstorm" application on the burning fuel surface, and a very wide, circular "bushy" shape is used for radiance shielding of the operator during fire extinguishment or penetration into the fire area.

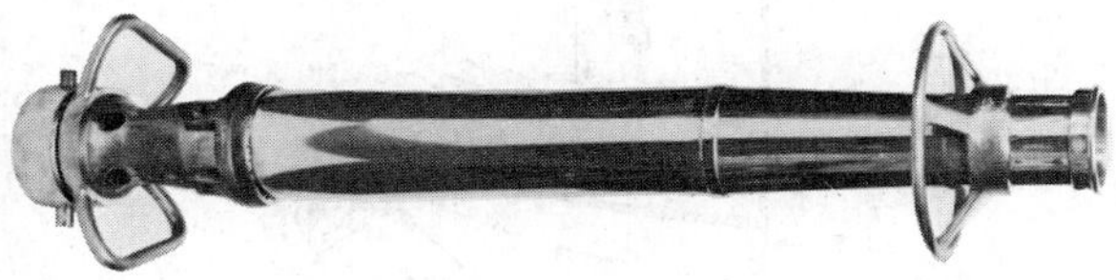

FIG. 5-20K. Hose line foam nozzle.

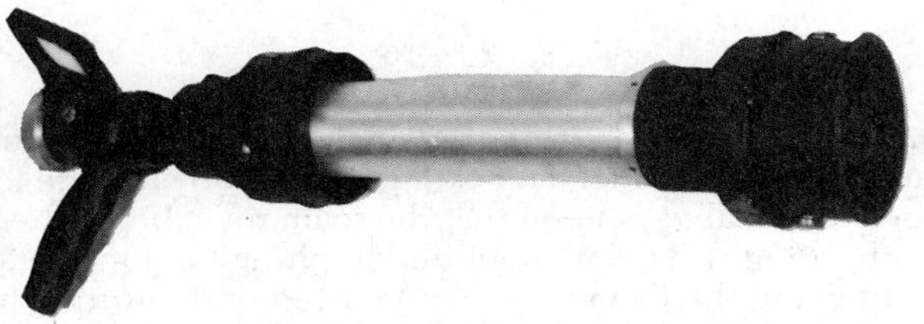

FIG. 5-20L. Adjustable hose line foam nozzle. (Source: Chubb National Foam.)

Another type of hose line foam nozzle is especially designed for quick, portable, one-person use during emergency operations from airport crash-rescue vehicles. Customarily called a handline foam nozzle, it is equipped with a foam pattern changing device, and some types are supplied with a valve control for converting the water or solution stream into a water spray for cooling purposes.

Foam and foam-water monitors: In large-scale fuel-fire fire fighting operations, it may become necessary to position a foam-making nozzle with a high discharge rate at an advantageous position for continuous application of foam to one point or over an area. Devices for this purpose are available in a variety of types, e.g., as part of mobile truck apparatus, on a trailer, wheeled, or permanently mounted. The foam pattern change is accomplished by moving a deflector into the foam stream or by opening or closing the "jaws" at the exit end of the large tube.

High backpressure foam-maker: Certain circumstances necessitate that foam be generated and supplied under pressure for transmission in pipes under a definite pressure head. The subsurface foam injection method for fuel tank fire extinguishment requires this type of foam-maker. The high backpressure foam-maker, or "forcing foam-maker," is a venturi device that is carefully designed to make foam by air aspiration, and to supply it under pressure at a carefully selected ratio (from 2:1 to 4:1) of air-to-foam solution. Approximately 20 to 40 percent of the inlet pressure is recoverable. In use, this foam device is usually brought to the fixed piping foam inlet, installed, and then supplied with foam solution by a portable or mobile pumper, or it may be permanently installed as part of a fixed system. (See Figure 5-20M.)

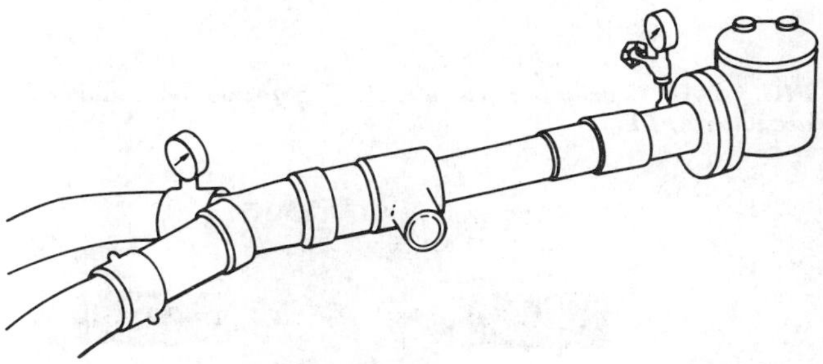

FIG. 5-20M. A "high back-pressure-type" (or "forcing"-type foam-maker.

Medium- and high-expansion foam-generating devices: There are two principal methods used for the generation of these types of fire fighting foams. One method utilizes a modified venturi action with air aspiration flow, while the other requires use of a blower and screen to form the finished foam. The latter system produces high-expansion foam containing sufficient residual kinetic energy to enable it to be forced through large tubes and passageways.

Figure 5-20N illustrates the operating principles of high-expansion foam generating devices.

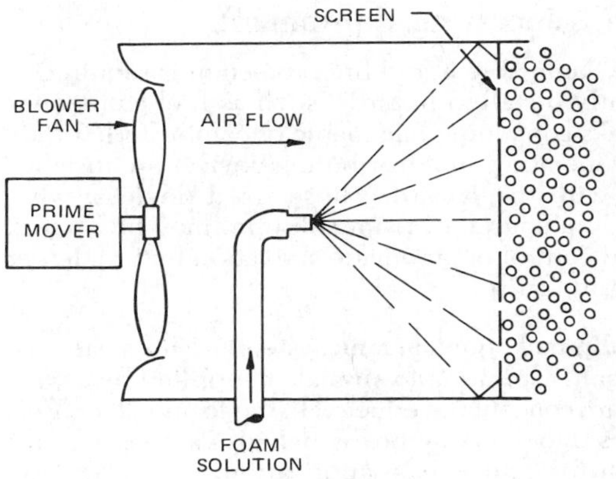

FIG. 5-20N. A fan-blower-type high-expansion foam-generator.

Water fog or spray nozzles: Several types of adjustable water fog or spray nozzles for portable use provide an acceptable fire fighting foam of adequate characteristics when supplied with certain foam concentrates. The most universal design of these is shown in Figure 5-20O. An adjustable water spray monitor nozzle designed for this purpose is shown in Figure 5-20P.

These portable water spray nozzles are used with aqueous film forming foam (AFFF) solutions for combatting flammable liquid tank and spill fires and are used in this manner on crash-rescue vehicles. The foam resulting from the discharge of AFFF solution devices that do not aspirate air is generally fast-draining and does not impart

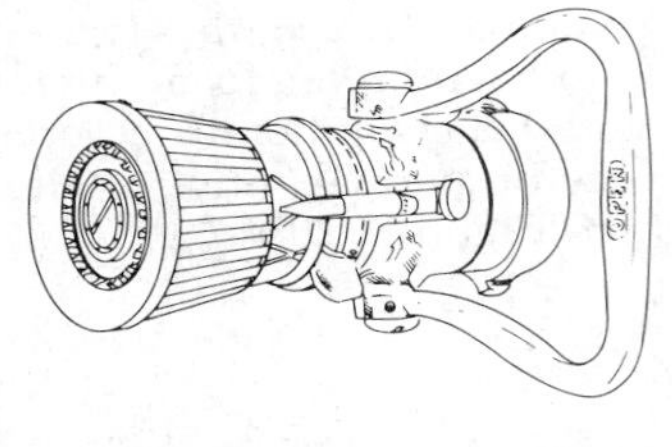

FIG. 5-20O. Variable-pattern water fog nozzle foam-maker for use with AFFF.

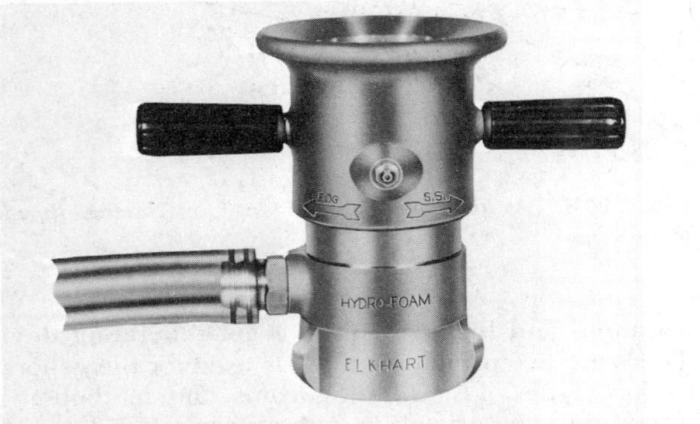

FIG. 5-20P. Adjustable 350 to 500 gpm (1325 to 1893 L/min) water spray foam monitor nozzle. (Source: Elkhart Brass Mfg. Co.)

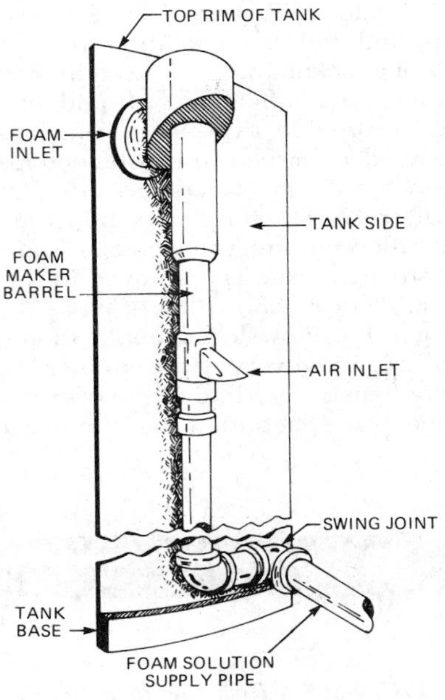

FIG. 5-20Q. Air-foam chamber at top of storage tank.

the same degree of burnback resistance as the foam produced from AFFF agents when foam-generating devices of an air-aspirating type are used.

Foam-Generating Equipment

Where flammable liquid fire protection is required for permanently installed hazards, such as fuel storage tanks or dip tanks containing flammable or combustible liquids, air-foam-generating and distributing devices are installed integrally with the hazard. These fixed devices, which are piped to a source of foam solution, may be arranged for manual control or automatic activation by fire detectors in the event of fire.

Open dip tank, quench tank system: This system consists of a small, aspirating foam-maker supplied by a water line and foam concentrate educted to the foam-maker. Foam discharges into a mixing box which also acts as a surface distributor for gentle foam application.

Foam chambers for large fuel storage tanks: Fire protection of large outdoor fuel storage tanks requires that several foam chambers with foam-makers be installed at equally spaced positions slightly below the curb angle on the top periphery of the tanks. These chambers are connected to lines on the ground that supply foam solution to each foam-maker simultaneously in case of ignition of the flammable contents of the tank. Frangible seals at the discharge outlet of the foam chamber prevent vapor from entering the foam piping. These seals are designed to burst when foam pressure is applied. A screen for the air inlet to the aspirating foam-maker prevents clogging from foreign matter, such as bird nesting material. A universal or swing pipe joint is installed at ground level in the foam solution inlet pipe to prevent fracturing of the supply piping if an explosion precedes a tank fire. (See Figure 5-20Q.)

Internal tank foam distributing devices: A prime requirement for efficient fuel tank extinguishment by topside foam devices has always been that the foam must be applied to the burning surface without undue plunging into the fuel, or allowing the foam to become coated with burning fuel. This gentle application of foam must be accomplished at any level of the contents of the tank. Many devices have been developed to gently apply foam from one point, regardless of burning fuel level. These devices are listed as "Type I" foam-discharge outlets for tanks and are required for some alcohol-type foams. When foam discharge into a tank is deflected to run down the inside tank shell to the burning fuel surface, it is called a "Type II" outlet for foam application.

Central "foam house" distributing systems: These systems, as shown in Figure 5-20R, consist of an enclosure housing a foam concentrate supply tank and a proportioning device of an automatic or balanced pressure type. Foam solution is supplied under adequate pressure from this foam house to the piping system, and controlled by appropriate valves so that the foam chambers with foam-makers on the burning tank receive foam solution.

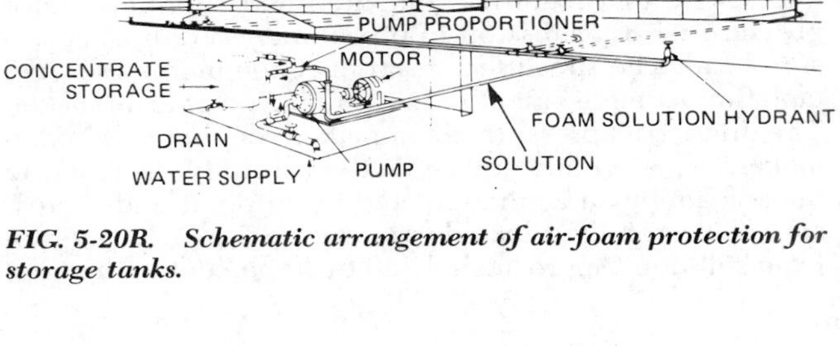

FIG. 5-20R. Schematic arrangement of air-foam protection for storage tanks.

Semifixed systems of similar design are more frequently used with mobile foam concentrate supply from foam trucks. The truck proportions and pumps foam solution to the pipe laterals feeding the foam-makers from a safe location outside the dike.

Intermediate back-pressure system: Although this system of tank protection is similar to the preceding central foam house distributing systems, it utilizes strong and well-braced foam-delivery pipes on the side of the tank which act as supports to prevent buckling of the tank from heat. This system also uses a foam truck to proportion and pump foam solution to the piping outside the dike or firewall of the burning tank.

Subsurface foam-injection systems: The problems inherent with the application of foam from above the burning surface (topside) are sometimes difficult to combat. Problems may consist of explosion or fire damage to the foam-makers or tankside piping; forceful upward fire-drafted air currents that prevent the falling foam from reaching the burning surface; hazard to workers attempting to erect portable foam distributing devices near the burning tank; or inability of foam applied from the periphery of a large tank [greater than about 200 ft (61 m) in diameter] to flow and form a complete center seal during fire attack.

The obvious solution to these problems is to apply foam from the underside of the fire, causing it to come up through the contents of the tank. The subsurface foam-injection system accomplishes this by injecting foam under the pressure of the head of fuel in the tank, using the high back-pressure foam-maker referred to previously in this chapter.

Entry of foam may be provided at several points at the base of the tank (base injection), or it may be accomplished by means of the product line. Where large tanks are involved, a branched pipe foam distributor may be installed on or slightly above the floor of the tank above any expected water level and connected to a central foam-injection point outside the tank.

Mobile foam concentrate proportioning equipment is used with these systems, pumping from a protected position outside the tank dike. (See Figure 5-20S.)

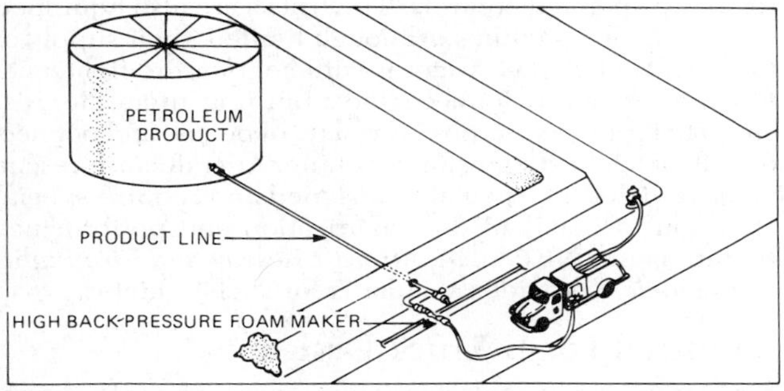

FIG. 5-20S. Semifixed subsurface foam installation.

Subsurface application of foam is recommended only for protection of cone-roof tanks containing hydrocarbon fuels. It is not recommended for use on floating-roof tanks or for protection of polar or water-miscible fuels.

These topside and subsurface injection systems require careful design. Their minimum installation requirements are found in NFPA 11, *Low-Expansion Foam and Combined Agent Systems*.

Portable foam devices for tank protection: Mobile foam monitors of high-capacity discharge (foam cannon) may be used to direct a stream of foam over the open top rim of a burning tank so foam will fall into the burning area. These devices waste foam because of cross winds, fire updrafts, and inability to place the equipment in an advantageous position. A foam-application rate 60 percent higher therefore must be included in the design; details are contained in NFPA 11, *Low-Expansion Foam and Combined Agent Systems*. Nozzles of this type also are used to extinguish fires in the overflow space inside the dike surrounding the tank. Care is needed in directing the foam stream from such devices, as shown in Figure 5-20T.

FIG. 5-20T. Portable (trailer) foam monitor (cannon). (Source: Angus Fire Armour Corporation.)

In recent years, mobile foam monitors with capacities up to 4000 gpm (15144 L/min) have been developed and used successfully for extinguishment of hydrocarbon fires in tanks up to 195 ft (60 m) in diameter. Careful planning is required to ensure availability of adequate water flow and pressure, foam concentrate, proportioning equipment, trained personnel, and safe accessibility to the hazard when relying upon such devices.

Other considerations for fuel storage tanks: The floating-roof storage tank has a good record of freedom from fire; consequently, fixed foam systems are usually not required for their protection. Under certain circumstances, however, there may be a need for a foam-flooding system to flood the rim area.

As indicated by its name, the "covered" floating-roof tank is totally enclosed above the floating roof with a properly vented steel roof. Usually Class IB flammable liquids, such as gasolines and crudes, are stored in "open top" or covered floating-roof tanks. During storage operations, there is no vapor space between the bottom of the floating roof and the stored product surface. However, during periods of initial fill, a flammable vapor space will exist until the floating roof is buoyant. In the case of covered floating-roof tanks, the space between the fixed and the floating roof will be within the flammable range during periods of initial fill and longer, depending upon atmospheric temperatures, wind, and vapor pressure of the stored product. Class II and III combustible liquids are usually stored in fixed-roof tanks.

In an open top floating-roof tank, a rim of fire is all that can be expected. Rim fires may be caused by atmospheric disturbances, such as lightning, but usually do not occur if the floating roof is bonded properly to the shell as specified in NFPA 78, *Lightning Protection Code*. Rim fires due to atmospheric disturbances do not occur in covered floating-roof tanks because of the "Faraday effect" of the fixed roof. Rim fires may occur in either type of floating-roof tank due to a serious exposure fire.

Fixed foam fire protection for the open top floating-roof consists of aspirating-type foam-makers installed in such a way that when supplied with foam solution, their foam discharge floods the annular area covered by the seal around the tank periphery. A metal foam dam may be needed to restrict the foam to this area. Further details of such construction are contained in the Appendix to NFPA 11, *Low-Expansion Foam and Combined Agent Systems*.

When foam protection is desired for covered floating-roof tanks, a foam system similar to those described for fixed-roof tanks may be provided. Subsurface injection systems are not recommended for open top or covered floating-roof tanks because of the possibility of tilted or sunken roofs resulting in improper foam distribution.

Fixed foam systems employing foam spray nozzles or monitors are used to protect large oil-water separators, pump areas, and oil piping manifolds. Fixed foam systems are not generally used to protect tank diked areas. Large wheeled monitors or trailer-mounted foam cannons, as shown in Figure 5-20T, are used for this purpose.

Certain hazardous areas, e.g., aircraft hangars, may require additional foam-making and distributing devices, such as foam monitors mounted near floor level. Often, these devices are provided with an automatic oscillator so that foam is continually distributed over the floor to extinguish burning spilled fuel under obstacles, such as aircraft wings.

Fixed foam systems are used to protect petroleum piers and wharves where products and petroleum crude are handled. Foam monitors of 1000 gpm (3800 L/min) and greater capacity are mounted on towers and remotely operated to cover both the pier and the tanker deck in the pipe manifold area. Below deck, foam spray systems or oscillating monitors are installed to keep the pier tenable in the event of a spill fire floating on the water surface under the pier.

Fixed systems consisting of automatically operated combinations of foam spray systems and foam monitors are often installed to protect chemical processing plants. Alcohol-resistant foams are usually required. In these designs, where there may be a high risk, process vessels, pumps, and piping often are all included within the foam distribution pattern for overall protection. The system can be automatically activated by heat or fire detectors. See NFPA 11, *Low-Expansion Foam and Combined Agent Systems*, for design of foam spray systems.

Foam-water sprinkler systems: In areas where flammable and combustible liquids are processed, stored, or handled, a water discharge may be ineffective for controlling or extinguishing fires. The foam-making sprinklers (aspirating-type) and deluge or spray nozzles using AFFF foams have successfully replaced water sprinkler nozzles for such systems so that fires in these occupancies may be controlled and property safeguarded.

When supplied with foam solution, sprinkler system piping grids provided with foam-water nozzles generate air-foam in essentially the same water sprinkler pattern as when water is discharged from the same nozzle. This dual capability affords the system Class A and B extinguishment ability. Design requirements can be found in NFPA 16, *Deluge Foam-Water Sprinkler and Foam-Water Spray Systems*.

Obviously, fixed sprinkler systems using these nozzles require that foam concentrate tanks, proportioners, and suitable pumps be provided to supply the system with foam solution or water. Detection devices may also be used to activate the system, or the system may be activated manually.

DELIVERING FOAM FROM VEHICLES

The majority of the mobile fire protection vehicles using foam consist of airport crash-rescue trucks and industrial foam trucks used at oil refineries and petrochemical plants. Many of these vehicles are also equipped to discharge dry chemical in combination with foam. These have combined, or "twinned," agent equipment, and are described later in this chapter.

Crash-Rescue Trucks

Mobile foam trucks, developed by military and municipal authorities in the United States and other countries, are large, custom-designed vehicles with oversize running gear which allows them to travel over all types of terrain. The trucks carry their own water supply as well as foam concentrate. Automatic balanced pressure proportioning is usually provided, although in some designs an around-the-pump proportioning system is used. The trucks are equipped with separate engine-driven water pumps and foam concentrate pumps so that the turret monitor nozzles and roadway foam nozzles can be discharged while the truck is in motion. Recent designs accomplish this using one or two engines for all necessary power requirements. Crash-rescue trucks are equipped with large-capacity, adjustable foam monitors of 500- to 1500-gpm (1900 to 5700 L/min) discharge, depending upon truck size. The foam monitors are usually installed on top of the cab with remotely operated controls. The trucks are also equipped with portable handlines. Although limited, their supply of foam concentrate and water is sufficient for fire fighters to form a passageway for access to a burning aircraft for rescue. Their primary purpose is rescue of people and not necessarily a total extinguishment of fire. Aircraft crash-rescue foam vehicles are specially designed and require special attention to detail in their fabrication and performance requirements. NFPA 414, *Aircraft Rescue and Fire Fighting Vehicles*, provides standards for such vehicles.

Industrial Foam Truck Design

Foam trucks are manufactured by vendors who make a specialty of this design and by some vendors of fire department pumpers. Generally, using NFPA 11C, *Mobile Foam Apparatus*, and NFPA 1901, *Pumper Fire Apparatus*, as a design basis, these trucks are fabricated on a suitable commercial or custom truck chassis. In the U.S., they are available with water pumps in sizes from 750 to 2000 gpm (2839 to 7570 L/min), using gasoline or diesel engine drives.

Balanced pressure proportioning is provided for maximum flexibility and simplification. A positive displacement-type foam concentrate pump takes suction from a 500- to 1000-gal (1900 to 3800 L) foam concentrate storage tank. The foam concentrate pump is driven by a power takeoff or hydraulic motor. The water pump is driven by a transfer gear from the main drive shaft behind the transmission. A metering valve at each truck outlet can vary foam proportioning from 3 to 6 percent.

In addition to the foam concentrate, each foam truck usually is equipped with a 500- to 1000-gpm (1900 to 3800 L/min) monitor and carries fire hose, foam nozzles and adjustable water spray nozzles, hose adapters, and other accessories. The maximum truck height is limited to permit passage beneath overhead obstructions. When the truck is equipped with a large-capacity nozzle on a telescopic or articulated boom, a second power takeoff is used to power the boom hydraulic system.

Foam trucks for special hazard application, instead of fixed foam systems, are popular for refinery and petrochemical plant use. Their advantages are:

1. Capability of discharging their maximum capacity at any hazard in the plant, rather than only to the limited areas covered by a fixed system.
2. Improved reliability, because their equipment is easily maintained; thus, operating procedures can be simplified and fire fighters can be trained more easily to use the equipment.

Industrial foam trucks are used to extinguish spill fires in process areas, piping runs, and tank diked areas, as well as in fighting tank fires. Their 500- to 1000-gpm (1900 to 3800 L/min) foam-water monitors and 1½-in. (38 mm) and 2½-in. (64 mm) handlines are used for fighting major spill fires. Designs that are equipped with monitor nozzles on articulated or telescopic booms enable the operator to discharge foam at various elevations in and around process equipment. In some cases, a tank fire can be extinguished with this equipment. Figure 5-20U illustrates a typical industrial foam truck with monitor. Figure 5-20V illustrates a typical foam truck with a telescopic boom, ladder, and basket. The foam trucks with booms may or may not be equipped with a ladder and/or basket.

FIG. 5-20U. A typical industrial foam truck. (Source: Chubb National Foam.)

COMBINED AGENT OR "TWINNED" EQUIPMENT

The capability of dry chemical agent (especially potassium-salt-types) for very fast flame control and three-dimensional flowing fuel extinguishment is well documented. However,

FIG. 5-20V. Foam truck with telescopic boom and nozzle with ladder and basket. (Source: Chubb National Foam.)

dry chemicals have no cooling or vapor-suppressing capability, and reflash can occur. With dry-chemical-compatible foam concentrates, it is possible to apply a coating of vapor-securing foam to a burning fuel surface that has been freshly extinguished by the chemical action of dry chemical discharges.

The logical extension of these developments has been incorporated into portable and mobile devices with dual-trigger valve nozzles and monitor nozzles discharging AFFF and dry chemical. Figure 5-20W illustrates a type of twinned pistol grip trigger valve dual-nozzle device primarily used by the U.S. Navy for dual hose line use. Figure 5-20X shows an improved industrial design used on offshore oil rigs. The use of this combined agent attack allows three-dimensional as well as spill fire extinguishment of flammable liquid, with both speed and freedom from reignition. The fire fighting vehicle shown in Figure 5-20Y is for aircraft crash-rescue purposes and for extinguishment on freeways or in plants, using combined agents.

FIG. 5-20W. A twinned nozzle applicator for combined agent use. The AFFF nozzle is in operator's left hand, and the dry chemical nozzle is in the right hand.

In use, the twinned hose from the hose reel supplies dry chemical and AFFF to a dual nozzle for one-person operation. Similarly, the turret nozzles at the front of the vehicle discharge dry chemical from the upper nozzle and AFFF from the lower. With a sweeping motion, the flames

FIG. 5-20X. ***Industrial twinned nozzle applicator for combined agent use. The AFFF nozzle is below, and the dry chemical nozzle is above. (Source: The Ansul Company.)***

FIG. 5-20Y. ***A combined-agent vehicle. (Source: Emergency One, Inc., and Feecon Corp.)***

are controlled with the dry chemical, quickly followed by a vapor-securing, cooling layer of foam to prevent reflash. This rapid action halts flame radiation and makes advancement over the fire area safe and cool.

A design especially for petroleum refinery plant protection involves the combined agent concept in a triple-use arrangement consisting of a 2000-lb (908 kg) dry chemical tank, a 200-gal (757 L) AFFF premixed solution tank, nitrogen bottles for pressurization of both tanks, a 500-gal (1900 L) foam concentrate tank, a 1500-gpm (5700 L/min) water pump, and balanced pressure proportioning up to 2000 gpm (7600 L/min). Two monitors mounted behind the truck cab are twinned for operation as a unit and consist of a 50-lb-per-sec (23 kg/sec) dry chemical turret nozzle and a 500-gpm (1900 L/min) AFFF or foam nozzle as shown in Figure 5-20Z. A different configuration uses three monitors mounted behind the truck cab—twinned 50-lb-per-sec (23 kg/sec) dry chemical and 180-gpm (680 L/min) AFFF nozzles, and one adjacent 1000-gpm (3800 L/min) adjustable foam monitor. In addition, the truck carries two hose reels, each with 100 ft (30.5 m) of twinned hose, and hose nozzles for dry chemical and AFFF arranged for twinned operation. The hose reels are equipped with an electric motor rewind. Foam nozzles, adjustable water fog nozzles, fire hose, and other accessories are carried on the truck.

FIG. 5-20Z. ***Triple-agent truck. (Source: Chubb National Foam.)***

The dry chemical turret nozzle will extinguish three-dimensional or pressure fires at a distance of 100 ft (30.5 m) and spill fires at a distance of approximately 150 ft (46 m). In addition, for long-range operation with lengthy duration, the 1000-gpm (3800 L/min) foam-water monitor has a range of more than 200 ft (61 m). The truck is capable of fighting fires in fixed-roof oil storage tanks with a maximum diameter of 160 ft (49 m). The proportioning system is designed to permit an external tank, such as a tank truck or trailer, to be used for foam concentrate supply without interrupting foam solution proportioning. (See Figure 5-20W.)

Twinned agent hose reels are often used on offshore oil platforms for equipment protection and in naval shipboard engine rooms. These systems have suitably sized potassium bicarbonate (Purple K) dry chemical containers that are pressurized by nitrogen when put into operation, and AFFF central pumped systems using balanced pressure proportioning. Similar twinned agent skid-mounted systems are used in refineries and petrochemical plants.

MEDIUM- AND HIGH-EXPANSION FOAM-GENERATING EQUIPMENT AND SYSTEMS

Medium- or high-expansion foam is an aggregation of bubbles resulting from the mechanical expansion of a foam solution by air or by other gases, with expansion ratios in the range of from 20:1 to approximately 1000:1. There are three types of systems: (1) total flooding, (2) local application, and (3) portable.

The foam generators for these systems are of two types: (1) aspirator, and (2) blower. The portable or fixed aspirator-type device utilizes jet streams of water-foam solution, entraining suitable amounts of air to produce foam. With the blower-type, foam solution is discharged onto a screen through which an air stream, developed by a fan or blower, is passing. As the air passes through the screens wetted with the foam solution, large masses of bubbles or foam are formed. The blower may be powered by a hydraulic or water motor, compressed air or gas, an electric motor, or an internal combustion engine.

System Design and Use

Detailed design information on medium- and high-expansion foam systems can be found in NFPA 11A, *Medium- and High-Expansion Foam Systems*.

Basically, medium- and high-expansion foam systems are used to control or extinguish fires involving surface fires in flammable and combustible liquids and solids, and deep-seated fires involving solid materials subject to smoldering. Three-dimensional fires in flammable liquids (falling or flowing under pressure) with flash points below 100°F (38°C) generally cannot be extinguished with this technique, although they may be kept under control. Key factors to consider in determining the design adequacy of medium- and high-expansion foam systems are:

1. The quality and adequacy of water supply, the adequacy of supply of foam liquid concentrate, and the source of the air supply.
2. Suitability of the generator and foam delivery system (piping, fittings, valves, ducts).
3. Needed submergence volume and time as influenced by the space being protected, the nature of the hazards involved, leakage of the foam, and similar factors.
4. If outdoors, the effect of wind, since some of the foam may be dissipated by air currents.

Tests have shown that high-expansion foam may be useful in controlling LNG fires and unignited spills by forming an ice layer on the liquid and by helping disperse the vapor cloud.

Total Flooding Systems

A total flooding system may be used where there is an enclosure surrounding the hazard being protected which will permit the required amount of medium- or high-expansion foam to be built up to extinguish or control the fire. Examples of such enclosures are rooms, vaults, pits, and basement areas. Even an entire building may be so protected where the foam generators are of sufficient capacity and steps are taken to ensure effective distribution and retention of the foam. Since the efficiency of the system depends upon the development and maintenance of a suitable quantity of foam within the particular enclosure, leakage of the foam from the enclosure must be avoided. Thus, it is important that doorways or windows be designed to close automatically, with consideration being given to the evacuation of personnel. High-level venting is required for the air that is displaced by the foam.

For adequate protection, sufficient high-expansion foam must be discharged at a rate to fill the space to an effective depth above the hazard before an unacceptable degree of damage occurs. The depth of the foam above the hazard will vary, depending upon the type of materials creating the hazard. Generally, the minimum depth above the hazard should be 2 ft (0.6 m). The time allowed to cover the hazard will likewise vary depending upon the type of material involved, construction features, and whether the enclosure also has an automatic sprinkler system or similar protection. Consideration has to be given to the disintegration of the foam by the heat of the fire; by normal foam shrinkage; by leakage around doors and windows, and through unclosable openings; and by the effects of sprinkler discharge where sprinkler protection is provided.

Local Application Systems

Local application systems can be used where total flooding systems may be impractical or unnecessary. Such hazards may be indoors or outdoors, where air currents are not likely to be severe. These systems are best adapted to the protection of flammable or combustible liquids in dip tanks and associated drainboards, and for pits and trenches. Medium- or high-expansion foam may be used for extinguishing spill fires where it is feasible to apply the foam from fixed or portable nozzles at adequate rates of discharge to develop a foam blanket to achieve complete extinguishment.

Precautions to Be Observed with Medium- or High-Expansion Foam

Medium- or high-expansion foam is normally nontoxic to persons who may be trapped in a space filled with it, since the air entrained in the foam is generally not contaminated. However, because of the foam bubbles, some difficulty may be experienced in breathing, and breathing discomfort will increase with reduction of foam expansion. Air is usually taken from a clean source, but, where products of combustion are introduced, the foam quality may be substandard because of the contaminants present and the temperature of the heated air. Entering a foam-filled space should be avoided unless adequate precautions are taken, because loss of vision and disorientation introduce life and injury hazards. A coarse water spray may be used to "cut" a path in the foam. Personnel should wear self-contained breathing apparatus and employ a lifeline when entering an area filled with high-expansion foam.

FOAM EQUIPMENT TESTING AND SURVEILLANCE

The continued effective emergency performance of foam equipment depends entirely upon fully adequate maintenance procedures, with periodic testing where possible. The many variations in system design and equipment applications for hazards requiring foam make it impossible to establish anything other than general procedures for periodic inspection. Because air-foam concentrates, foam equipment, and fire protection systems are subject to change, variation, and even malfunction over long unattended spans of time, they must be kept adequate for the purpose for which they are designed.

Foam Concentrate Surveillance

Because all air-foam concentrates are water solutions of organic and inorganic chemicals of one sort or another, they must be carefully observed for changes in constitution and characteristics. They must be stored in shipping containers and in storage tanks according to the manufacturer's recommendations. Exposure to extreme heat, cold, or contamination, or mixing with other materials must be avoided. Sedimentation or precipitate formation in containers or tanks of concentrate should be carefully checked periodically. The manufacturer or the manufacturer's representative is best qualified to test and determine the extent of reliability of foam concentrates under questionable conditions of deterioration. Foam concentrates should be tested at least annually.

Equipment Testing

The performance of all foam equipment under emergency conditions is guaranteed best by the initial acceptance test and periodic inspection of the equipment. Original design specifications of fixed installations should include provision for periodic testing of proportioners, pumps, and other ancillary equipment, without the trial distribution of foam to the hazard being protected.

Problems of corrosion, clogged orifices, sticky valves, and electric circuitry malfunction may be detected by suitable means without full system activation.

In the absence of an actual fire, and without full system activation, the complete testing of foam equipment performance for fire protection adequacy may be accomplished by various means. In the absence of an actual fire, complete testing may be accomplished by several physical test methods. However, because these tests are similar in nature to "fingerprint" tests, their results can only be interpreted by comparison with similar tests conducted at the installation acceptance of the equipment, or as provided for under the performance guarantee of the manufacturer.

Foam equipment performance can be tested for the following physical characteristics of foam:

1. The dimensions of the discharge pattern or patterns of the device or system.
2. The percent concentration of foam concentrate in the finished foam solution.
3. The degree of expansion of the finished foam.
4. The rate at which water drains from the foam, e.g., 25-percent drainage time. This correlates with its viscosity or rate of spreading over fuel surfaces.
5. Film-forming capacity of the foam concentrate.

The preceding tests require specially designed test equipment and standardized techniques. They require qualified operators and cannot be carried out easily in the field. Detailed information concerning the equipment required, methods used, and some interpretations of the test results can be found in the Appendices of NFPA 11, *Low-Expansion Foam and Combined Agent Systems*, and NFPA 412, *Aircraft Rescue and Fire Fighting Foam Equipment*, which includes tests for foam discharge patterns, AFFF-type foams, and protein-based foams.

The test for the concentration of the foam concentrate is very important because it indicates the efficiency of operation of the concentrate proportioning device in the system. It is performed easily in the field with a hand refractometer and volume-measuring device.

BIBLIOGRAPHY

NFPA Codes, Standards, and Recommended Practices

Reference to the following NFPA codes, standards, and recommended practices will provide further information on foam extinguishing agents and systems discussed in this chapter. (See the latest *NFPA Catalog* for availability of current editions of the following documents.)

NFPA 11, *Low-Expansion Foam and Combined Agent Systems*.

NFPA 11A, *Medium- and High-Expansion Foam Systems*.

NFPA 11C, *Mobile Foam Apparatus*.

NFPA 16, *Deluge Foam-Water Sprinkler and Foam-Water Spray Systems*.

NFPA 18, *Wetting Agents*.

NFPA 78, *Lightning Protection Code*.

NFPA 403, *Aircraft Rescue and Fire Fighting Services at Airports*.

NFPA 409, *Aircraft Hangars*

NFPA 412, *Aircraft Rescue and Fire Fighting Foam Equipment*.

NFPA 414, *Aircraft Rescue and Fire Fighting Vehicles*.

NFPA 1901, *Pumper Fire Apparatus*.

Additional Reading

Alvares, N. J. and Lipska, A. E., "The Effect of Smoke on the Production and Stability of High-Expansion Foam," *Journal of Fire and Flammability*, Vol. 3 (Apr. 1972), pp. 88-114.

"Aqueous Foams—Their Characteristics and Applications," *Industrial and Engineering Chemistry*, American Chemical Society, Vol. 48 (Nov. 1956).

Avant, C. E., "Subsurface Foam KOs Fire," *Fire Engineering*, Apr. 1973.

Ballas, T., "Electric Shock Hazard Studies of High-Expansion Foam," *Fire Technology*, Vol. 5, No. 1 (Feb. 1969), pp. 38-42.

Banerjee, S. C. and Acharya, A. K., "High-Expansion Foams—Its Use in Mine Fires," *Journal of Mines, Metals and Fuels*, Vol. 34, No. 10, 1986, pp. 448-451.

Beers, R. J., "High-Expansion Foam Fire Control for Records Storage," *Fire Technology*, Vol. 2, No. 2 (May 1966), pp. 108-117.

Beiggs, A. A., "Use of Nitrogen-Filled High-Expansion Foam to Protect a 500-Ton Fuel Tank," *Fire Research Note 1074*, Fire Research Station, Borehamwood, Herts., England, .Aug. 1977.

Bradley, M., "Heavy Foam Cover," *Fire Engineering*, Vol. 140, No. 6, 1987, p. 52.

Breen, D. E., "Hangar Fire Protection with Automatic AFFF Systems," *Fire Technology*, Vol. 9, No. 2 (May 1973), pp. 119-131.

Briggs, A. A., "The Testing of Low-Expansion Foams," *Fire*, Vol. 77, No. 48, 1984.

Briggs, A. A. and Webb, J. S., "Gasoline Fires and Foams," *Fire Technology*, Vol. 24, No. 1 (Feb. 1988) pp. 48-58.

Burford, R. R., "The Use of AFFF in Sprinkler Systems," *Fire Technology*, Vol. 12, No. 1 (Feb. 1976.)

Butlin, R. N., "High-Expansion Air-Foam, A Survey of Its Properties and Uses," *Fire Research Note No. 669*, Fire Research Station, Borehamwood, Herts., England, May 1967.

Casey, J. F., ed., "Foam," *Fire Service Hydraulics*, 2nd ed., reprint Part 4, *Fire Engineering*, NY, 1984.

CEEDO-TR-78-22, "Comparative Nozzle Study for Applying AFFF on Large-Scale Fires," Civil and Engineering Development Office, Tyndall Air Force Base, FL, 1978.

Cray, E. W., "High-Expansion Foam," *NFPA Quarterly*, Vol. 58, No. 1 (July 1964), pp. 57-63.

Erriksson, L., "Semi-Subsurface Foam System," *NFPA Quarterly*, Vol. 58, No. 1 (July 1964) pp. 54-56.

Evans, J. L., "Fire Fighting Foams," *Fire Surveyors*, Vol. 17, No. 5 (Oct. 1988) pp. 5-10.

"Evaluation of Fire Fighting Foams as Fire Protection for Alcohol Containing Fuels," *API Publication 2300*, American Petroleum Institute, Apr. 1985.

"Fighting Fuel Storage Fires with Subsurface Foam," *Fire International*, Vol. 3, No. 26 (Oct. 1969).

"Fire Extinguishing Agent, Aqueous Film Forming Foam (AFFF) Liquid Concentrate, Six Percent for Fresh and Sea Water," *Military Specification MIL-F-24385 (NAVY)*, Amendment 8, Naval Ship Engineering Center, Department of the Navy, Hyattsville, MD.

"Fire Protection in Refineries," *API Recommended Practice 2001*, American Petroleum Institute, July 1984.

Fittes, D. W., Griffiths, D. J., and Nash, P., "Extinction of Experimental Aircraft Fires with Light Water," *Fire*, Vol. 62, No. 773 (Nov. 1969), pp. 315-317.

Fittes, D. W., Griffiths, D. J., and Nash, P., "The Use of Light Water for Major Aircraft Fires," *Fire Technology*, Vol. 5, No. 4 (Nov. 1969), pp. 284-298.

"Foam Blanket Rapidly Quells Fire in Gas Storage Tank," *Volunteer Firefighter*, Mar. 1966.

A Position on Foam-Water Sprinkler Research, Foam-Water Research Coalition, Washington DC, 1989.

Frank, J. A. and Woodworth, S. P., "Foam System Considerations for Conventional Fire Apparatus," *Fire Engineering*, Vol. 141, No. 10, 1988, pp. 60-67.

Geyer, G. B., "Extinguishing Agents for Hydrocarbon Fuel Fires," *Fire Technology*, Vol. 5, No. 2 (May 1969), pp. 151-159.

"Foam and Dry Chemical Application Experiments," National Aviation Facilities Experimental Center, Federal Aviation Administration, Atlantic City, NJ, Dec. 1968.

Gillespie, P., "Protecting Petrochemical Storage Tanks with Firefighting Foam," *Fire Journal*, Vol. 83, No. 3 (May-June 1989), p. 44.

"Guide for Fighting Fires in and Around Petroleum Storage Tanks," *API Publication 2021*, American Petroleum Institute, 1980.

Hammack, J. M., "Talking Extinguishing Equipment: Effects of Low Temperatures and Combustion Products on High-Expansion Foam," *Fire Journal*, Vol. 64, No. 4 (Sept. 1970), pp. 93-94.

Herzog, G. R., "Recent Major Floating Roof Tank Fires and Their Extinguishment," *Fire Journal*, Vol. 68, No. 4 (July 1974), p. 93.

Hickey, H. E., "Foam System Calculations," *SFPE Handbook of Fire Protection Engineering*, National Fire Protection Association, Quincy, MA, 1988.

Hird, D., "Fire-Fighting Foams for Flammable Liquid Fires," *Fire Prevention*, No. 202, Sept. 1987, p. 20.

Hird, D., "The Use of Foaming Agents for Aircraft Crash Fires," *Fire*, Sept. 1974, pp. 179-180.

Hird, D., Rodrigues, A., and Smith, D., "Foam—Its Efficiency in Tank Fires," *Fire Technology*, Vol. 6, No. 1 (Feb. 1970), pp. 5-11.

Holtham, P. D., "Saponification Foam Process Proves Its Effectiveness," *Fire Engineers Journal*, Vol. 48, No. 152 (Mar. 1989), p. 14.

Hoshino, M. and Hayashi, K., "Evaluation of Extinguishing Abilities of Fire Fighting Foam Agents Applied Alone or Together," *Report of the Fire Research Institute of Japan*, No. 46, 1978.

IFSTA 206, *Aircraft Fire Protection and Rescue Procedures*, 2nd ed., International Fire Service Training Association, Oklahoma State University, Stillwater, OK, 1978.

King, C. J., "Maintenance of Low- and High-Expansion Foam Systems," *Fire Journal*, Vol. 67, No. 2 (Mar. 1973), pp. 41-43, 48.

Lev, Y., "The Use of Foam for LNG Fire Fighting," *Fire Technology*, Vol. 17, No. 1 (Feb. 1981), pp. 17-24.

Mahley, H. S., "Fire Tank Fires Subsurface," *Hydrocarbon Processing*, Aug. 1975.

Martin, G. T. O., "Fire Fighting Foam," *The Institution of Fire Engineers Quarterly*, Vol. 32, No. 86 (June 1972), pp. 165-176.

Meldrum, D. N., "Aqueous Film-Forming Foam—Facts and Fallacies," *Fire Journal*, Vol. 66, No. 1, Jan. 1972, pp. 57-64.

Meldrum, D. N., "Fire Fighting with Foam: Basics of Effective Systems," *SFPE TR 79-2*, Society of Fire Protection Engineers, Boston, MA, 1979.

Meldrum, D. N. and Williams, J. R., "Dry Chemical-Compatible Foam," *Fire Journal*, Vol. 59, No. 6 (Nov. 1965), pp. 18-22.

Meldrum, D. N., Williams, J. R., and Gilroy, D., "Foam Fire Protection of Liquid Propellants," *Fire Technology*, Vol. 2, No. 3 (Aug. 1966) pp. 234-238.

Nash, P. and Whittle, J., "Fighting Fires in Oil Storage Tanks Using Base Injection of Foam," *Fire Technology*, Part I, Feb. 1978, Part II, May 1978.

Nash, P. and Yount, R. A., *Automatic Sprinkler Systems for Fire Protection*, 1st ed., Ch. 15, Victor Green Publications Ltd., London, England, 1978.

National Fire Protection Association, "Speakers Papers, International Conference on Aviation Fire Protection," Interlaken, Switzerland, Sept. 1987.

Noll, G., "Evaluating the Use of Fire Fighting Foams," *Fire Engineering*, Vol. 139, No. 2, 1986, p. 44.

Peterson, H. F., "Suppression Capability of Foam on Runways," *NFPA Aviation Bulletin No. 250*, National Fire Protection Association, Quincy, MA.

Peterson, H. B., *et al.*, "Full-Scale Fire Modeling Test Studies of Light Water and Protein Type Foams," *NRL Report 6573*, U. S. Naval Research Laboratory, Washington, DC, 1967.

Pignato, J. A., "Enhancement of Fire Protection with Directional Cooling Spray Nozzles by Use of AFFF," *Fire Technology*, Vol. 19, No. 1 (Feb. 1983), pp. 5-13.

Pignato, J. A., "Storage Tank Protection Using AFFF," *Fire Journal*, Vol. 71, No. 6 (Nov. 1978) p. 32.

Rasbash, D. J., "Notes for Specification of High-Expansion Foam Liquid," *Fire Research Note No. 706*, Fire Research Station, Borehamwood, Herts., England, Apr. 1968.

"Results of Tests Using Low-Expansion Foams to Control and Extinguish Simulated Industrial Fires," prepared for 3M Company by Wesson and Associates, Inc., Norman, OK, Aug. 1983.

Sarkinen, C. F. and Nellis, C. L., "Electrical Tests on High-Expansion Foams," *Technical Report No. ERJ-78-67*, U. S. Dept. of Energy, Bonneville Power Administration, Vancouver, WA, May 26, 1978.

Scheffey, J. L. and Leonard, J. T., "AFFF Protection for Weapons Staging Areas," *Fire Safety Journal*, Vol. 14, Nos. 1&2, 1988, pp. 47-63.

Sherad, S. E., ed., *Fire Fighting Foams and Foam Systems*, National Fire Protection Association, Quincy, MA, 1977.

Silensky, P., "Foams Applied in Chemical Spill," *Fire Engineering*, Vol. 121, No. 6, 1988, pp. 97-99.

"Special Hazards Protection—Manufacturers and Equipment," *Fire Journal*, Vol. 81, No. 4, 1987, p. 43.

"Suffocation in High-Expansion Foam," *Fire International*, Vol. 18 (Oct. 1967), pp. 27-30.

Tabar, D. C., "Foam-Water Sprinkler Protection for Flammable Liquids," *Plant/Operations Progress*, Vol. 8, No. 4 (Oct. 1989), pp. 218-224.

"Tank Fire Extinction Tests," *Fire Protection Review*, Jan. 1977.

Timms, G. and Hagger, P., "Foam Concentration Measurement Techniques," *Fire Technology*, Vol. 26, No. 1 (Feb. 1990), pp. 41-50.

Tuve, R. L., "Light Water and Potassium Bicarbonate—A New Two-Agent Extinguishing System," *NFPA Quarterly*, Vol. 58, No. 1 (July 1964), pp. 64-69.

Tuve, R. L., Peterson, H. B., Jablonski, E. J., and Neill, R. R., "A New Vapor-Securing Agent for Flammable-Liquid Fire Extinguishment," U. S. Naval Research Laboratory, Washington, DC, Mar. 13, 1964.

"Twinned Agent Extinguishing System Uses," *Fire Engineering*, Vol. 117, No. 5 (May 1964) pp. 358-360.

UL 162, *Foam Equipment and Liquid Concentrates*, 5th ed., Underwriters Laboratories Inc., Northbrook, IL, 1985.

Wesson, H. R., Walker, J. R., and Brown, L. E., "Control LNG Spill Fires," *Hydrocarbon Processing*, Dec. 1972.

Woodman, A. L., *et al.*, "AFFF Spreading Properties at Elevated Temperatures," *Fire Technology*, Vol. 14, No. 4 (Nov. 1978) pp. 265-272.

Young, R. A. and Corrie, J. G., "The Performance of a Foam-Sprinkler Installation on Simulated Oil Rig Fires," *Report CP* 98/75, Borehamwood, Herts., England, 1975.

Young, J. R. and Fitzgerald, P. M., "The Feasibility of Using Light Water Brand AFFF in a Closed-Head Sprinkler System for Protection Against Flammable Liquid Spill Fires," *Factory Mutual Research Report No. 22352*, Factory Mutual Research Corp., Norwood, MA, Jan. 1975.

Zuber, K., "LNG Facilities-Engineered Fire Protection Systems," *Fire Technology*, Vol. 12, No. 1 (Feb. 1976).

COMBUSTIBLE METAL EXTINGUISHING AGENTS AND APPLICATION TECHNIQUES

John F. Riley and Steven W. Hansen

There are a limited number of proprietary combustible metal extinguishing agents that have been approved by recognized testing or listing agencies. The majority of agents available, and most notably those developed for special metals of limited commercial use, do not carry approvals or listings. The following agents have either been listed for use or have shown effectiveness in extinguishing fires in magnesium, aluminum, sodium, potassium, lithium, and sodium-potassium alloy.

MET-L-X POWDER

MET-L-X powder, available in 50-lb (23 kg) pails, is suitable for use on fires involving magnesium, sodium, potassium, and sodium-potassium alloy (NaK). The material is listed by Underwriters Laboratories Inc. (UL) for application by hand scoop and shovel. An approximate guide for application of agent is:

Magnesium turnings/chips	5 lbs agent/lb of fuel
Molten sodium or potassium	6 to 8 lbs agent/lb of fuel greater than 1/2 in. fuel depth
Molten NaK alloy	15 lbs/lb of fuel

For SI units, 1 lb = 0.4536 kg; 1 in. = 25.4 mm.

This dry powder, with its particle size controlled for optimum extinguishing effectiveness, is composed of a sodium chloride base with additives. A thermoplastic polymer is added to bind the sodium chloride particles into a solid mass under fire conditions.

MET-L-X powder is noncombustible, and secondary fires do not result from its application to burning metal. No known health hazard results from the use of this agent. It is nonabrasive and nonconductive.

When stored in extinguishers or original containers, MET-L-X powder is not subject to decomposition or a change in physical properties. Periodic replacement of the extinguisher charge is unnecessary. Extinguishers range from 30-lb (14 kg), carbon-dioxide-cartridge-operated hand portables through 150- and 350-lb (68 and 160 kg) wheeled units to 2000-lb (910 kg) stationary or piped systems. The wheeled units and piped systems employ nitrogen as the expellant gas.

MET-L-X powder is suitable for fires in solid chunks, such as castings, because of its ability to cling to hot vertical surfaces. To control and extinguish a metal fire, the nozzle of the extinguisher is fully opened and a thin layer of agent is cautiously applied over the burning mass from a safe distance to prevent the burning metal from blowing into other areas. Once control is established, the nozzle valve is used to throttle the stream to produce a soft, heavy flow. The metal can then be covered completely and safely from close range with a heavy layer. The heat of the fire causes the powder to cake, forming a crust that excludes air and results in extinguishment.

MET-L-X extinguishers are available for fires involving magnesium, sodium (spills in depth), potassium, and sodium-potassium alloy (NaK). In addition, MET-L-X has been successfully used where zirconium, uranium, titanium, and powdered aluminum present serious hazards.

Na-X POWDER

Na-X has been developed as a low- or non-chloride-containing agent for use on sodium metal fires. Na-X has a sodium carbonate base with various additives incorporated to render the agent resistant to moisture and to increase its fluidity for use in pressurized extinguishers. The agent also contains a polymer that will soften and form a crust over an exposed surface of burning sodium metal.

Na-X is noncombustible and does not cause secondary fires when applied to burning sodium metal above temperatures ranging from 1200 to 1500°F (649 to 816°C). No known health hazard results from the use of this agent on sodium fires, and it is nonabrasive and nonconductive.

Stored in 50-lb (23 kg) pails, 30-lb (14 kg) hand portables, and 150- and 350-lb (68 and 160 kg) wheeled and

Dr. John F. Riley is a research manager with Ansul Fire Protection, a Tyco-Grennell Company. He is president of the Halon Alternative Research Corp. (HARC) and has served on ten NFPA technical committees. Steven W. Hansen is a senior development chemist with Ansul Fire Protection.

stationary extinguishers, Na-X is UL-listed for fires involving sodium metal (spills in depth) at a fuel temperature of 1200°F (649°C). Na-X has been tested on sodium metal (spills in depth) at fuel temperatures as high as 1500°F (816°C). Stored in the supplier's metal pails and extinguishers, Na-X is not subject to decomposition, so periodic replacement of the agent is unnecessary.

OTHER COMBUSTIBLE METAL EXTINGUISHING AGENTS

G-1 Powder/MetalGuard™ Powder

"Pyrene" G-1 powder is composed of screened, graphitized foundry coke to which an organic phosphate has been added. A combination of particle sizes is used to provide good packing characteristics when applied to a metal fire. The graphite acts as a heat conductor and absorbs heat from the fire to lower the metal temperature below the ignition point, which results in extinguishment. The closely packed graphite also smothers the fire, and the organic material in the agent breaks down with heat to yield a slightly smoky gas that penetrates the spaces between the graphite particles, excluding air. The powder is nontoxic and noncombustible.

MetalGuard™ powder is identical to G-1 powder in composition and is simply a trade-name variation.

G-1 powder is effective for fires in magnesium, sodium, potassium, titanium, lithium, calcium, zirconium, hafnium, thorium, uranium, and plutonium. It has been recommended for special applications on powder fires in aluminum, zinc, and iron. The products of combustion of thorium, uranium, beryllium, and plutonium can be a health hazard, and precautions should be observed consistent with the usual procedures in combating fires in radioactive material.

G-1 powder is not commercially available at present.

Lith-X Powder

This dry powder is composed of a special graphite base with additives. The additives render it free-flowing so it can be discharged from an extinguisher. The technique used to extinguish a metal fire with this agent is the same as that used with MET-L-X. Lith-X does not cake or crust over when applied to the burning metal. It excludes air and conducts heat away from the burning mass to effect extinguishment. It does not cling to hot metal surfaces, so it is necessary to cover the burning metal completely.

Lith-X will successfully extinguish lithium fires and is suitable for the control and extinguishment of magnesium and zirconium chip fires. It will extinguish sodium spills and sodium fires in depth. It will also extinguish sodium-potassium alloy spill fires and control fires in depth.

Ternary Eutectic Chloride (TEC) Powder

Ternary eutectic chloride (REC) powder is a mixture of potassium chloride, sodium chloride, and barium chloride and is effective in extinguishing fires in certain combustible metals. The powder tends to seal the metal, excluding air. On a hot magnesium chip fire, the method of extinguishment is air exclusion by the formation of the salt melting on the metal surface. In tests reported in *Fire Technology*, TEC powder was the most effective salt for control of sodium, potassium, and sodium-potassium alloy fires.[1]

Small uranium and plutonium fires within scientific gloveboxes have been extinguished with TEC. A small plastic bag filled with powder is simply placed directly on the metal fire. The barium chloride in the mixture is toxic, but this is of no practical concern if the glovebox remains intact. In other locations, the operator should avoid inhaling the airborne powder.

Boralon

Boralon is the name given to a mixture of trimethoxyborane (TMB) and Halon 1211 (bromochlorodifluoromethane). The addition of halogenated hydrocarbons, specifically halons, reduces the problems associated with aging, low-temperature viscosity, and flammability. Although the addition of halon improves the physical characteristics of TMB, the material remains susceptible to hydrolysis; the colorless liquid hydrolyzes readily to form boric acid and methanol. Contact with moist air or other sources of water must be avoided to prevent hydrolysis.

The method of extinguishment involves the thermal breakdown of TMB. The typical application of boralon to metal fires results in the formation of molten boric oxide. TMB would ordinarily produce a secondary class B fire due to the excess methanol, but the presence of halon reduces this possibility. The molten boric oxide coating on the hot metal prevents contact with air. Cooling may then occur normally or through the cautious introduction of cooling agents, such as water. It is necessary to avoid fracturing the coating during this process.

Boralon has been developed and tested extensively for use on magnesium fires. It is applied from a sealed storage tank actuated by pressurizing with nitrogen. Because the agent is susceptible to hydrolysis, periodic maintenance and replacement of agent may be necessary.

Copper Powder

Advances in the science of alternative propulsion systems have led to the development of copper powder as a viable extinguishing agent for combustible metals. Work sponsored by the Naval Sea Systems Command was conducted to evaluate the adequacy of existing lithium fire suppression agents and to develop new agents should deficiencies exist.

Copper powder was found to be superior to known lithium fire extinguishing agents in extinguishing capacity. The dry powder is of uniform particle size and extinguishes a lithium fire more quickly and efficiently than existing agents. The process of extinction is by formation of a copper-lithium alloy, which is nonreactive and forms preferentially on the surface of the molten lithium. The alloy becomes an exclusion boundary between air and the molten metal, preventing reignition and promoting cooling of the unreacted lithium.

Copper powder can be applied from hand-portable extinguishers. The nominal charge for each extinguisher is 30 lbs (14 kg); it is 150 and 350 lb (68 and 160 kg) for wheeled units, as well as fixed systems. Argon is used as the propellant. The method of application is similar to that of other metal fire powders, in that the fuel surface is coated with the copper powder in an initial pass, with a throttled application following once control is achieved. Typical application densities are 8 lbs (3.6 kg) of copper powder per lb of lithium for complete extinguishment of the lithium. A 40-lb (18 kg) lithium fire can be fully controlled in 30 sec and completely extinguished in 9 min.

Copper powder also has demonstrated the ability to extinguish magnesium and aluminum fires.

NONPROPRIETARY COMBUSTIBLE METAL EXTINGUISHING AGENTS

Foundry Flux

In magnesium foundry operations, molten magnesium is protected from contact with air by layers of either molten or crust-type fluxes. These fluxes, which are also used as molten metal cleaning agents, consist of various amounts of potassium chloride, barium chloride, magnesium chloride, sodium chloride, and calcium fluoride. The fluxes are stored in covered steel drums. When applied to burning magnesium, they melt on the surface of the solid or molten metal, excluding air. The thin layer of protection can be provided by properly applying relatively small amounts of flux.

Fluxes are valuable in extinguishing magnesium spill fires from broken molds or leaking pots, and in controlling and extinguishing fires in heat-treating furnaces. In open fires, the flux is applied with a hand scoop or a shovel. Areas of furnaces that are difficult to reach can be coated by means of a flux-throwing device similar to those used to throw concrete onto building forms.

Although fluxes can rapidly extinguish chip fires in machine shops, they are not recommended for such use. The fluxes are hygroscopic, and the water picked up from the air combines with the salts and causes severe rusting of equipment.

Talc (Powder)

Talc, an agent that has been used industrially on magnesium fires, acts to control rather than extinguish fire. Talc acts as an insulator to retain the heat of the fire, rather than as a coolant. However, it does react with burning magnesium to provide a source of oxygen. The addition of organic matter, such as protein, to talc assists in the controlling action, but does not prevent the reaction that releases oxygen to the fire.

Graphite Powder

Graphite powder, or plumbago, has been used as an extinguishing agent for metal fires. Its action is similar to that of G-1 powder, in that the graphite acts as a coolant. Unless the powder is finely divided and closely packed over the burning metal, some air does get through to the metal, and extinguishment is not as rapid as with G-1 powder.

Sand

Dry sand often has been recommended as an agent for controlling and extinguishing metal fires. At times, it seems to be satisfactory, but hot metal, such as magnesium, usually obtains oxygen from the silicon dioxide in the sand and continues to burn under the pile. Sand is seldom completely dry, and burning metal reacting with the moisture in the sand produces steam. Under certain conditions, it may even produce an explosive metal-water reaction. By laying fine, dry sand around the perimeter of the fire, it can be used to isolate incipient aluminum dust fires.

Cast-Iron Borings

Cast-iron borings of turnings are frequently available in the same machine shops as the various combustible metals. Clean iron borings applied over a magnesium chip fire cool the hot metal and help extinguish the fire. This agent is used by some shops for handling small fires where, with normal good housekeeping, only a few combustible chips are involved. Contamination of the metal chips with iron may be an economic problem. Oxidized iron chips must be avoided to prevent possible thermite reaction with the hot metal. The iron chips must be free of moisture.

Sodium Chloride

Alkali metal fires can be extinguished by sodium chloride, which forms a protective blanket that excludes air over the metal so that the metal cools below its burning temperature. Sodium chloride is used to extinguish sodium and potassium fires. It can also be used to extinguish magnesium fires.

Soda Ash

Sodium carbonate or soda ash (not dry chemical) is recommended for extinguishing sodium and potassium fires. Its action is similar to that of sodium chloride.

Lithium Chloride

Lithium chloride is effective in extinguishing lithium metal fires. However, its use should be limited to specialized applications because the chemical is hygroscopic to a degree and the reaction between moisture and lithium may present problems.

Zirconium Silicate

This agent has been used successfully to extinguish lithium fires.

Dolomite

If zirconium or titanium in the form of dry powder ignites, neither can be extinguished easily. Control can be effected by spreading dolomite, a carbonate of calcium and magnesium, around the burning area and adding more powder until the burning pile is covered completely.

Boron Trifluoride and Boron Trichloride

Boron trifluoride and boron trichloride have both been used to control fires in heat-treating furnaces containing magnesium. The trifluoride is considerably more effective. In the case of small fires, the gases provide complete extinguishment. In the case of large fires, they control the flames and rapid burning, but the hot metal reignites on exposure to air. A combined attack of boron trifluoride gas followed by application of foundry flux completely extinguishes the fire. For details of gas application, see NFPA 48, *Storage, Handling, and Processing of Magnesium*.

Inert Gases

In some cases, inert gases, such as argon and helium, will control zirconium fires if they can be used under conditions that will exclude air. Gas blanketing with argon has been effective in controlling lithium, sodium, and potassium fires.[1] Caution should be exercised when using the agent in confined spaces because of the danger of suffocation to personnel.

Water

If automatic sprinklers open during a fire in a shop where magnesium or other combustible metals (except alkali metals or fissionable materials) are being machined or fabricated, the large volume of water from the sprinklers normally will extinguish both Class A and magnesium fires. Where automatic sprinkler protection is provided, a deflecting shield or hood should be provided over furnaces, reactors, or other places where hot molten metal may be present. Additional information on the use of sprinkler protection in shops handling magnesium or titanium can be found in NFPA 48, *Storage, Handling, and Processing of Magnesium*, and NFPA 481, *Production, Processing, Handling, and Storage of Titanium*.

When burning metals are spattered with limited amounts of water, the hot metal extracts oxygen from the water and promotes combustion. The hydrogen is released in a free state and ignites readily. Since small amounts of water accelerate combustible metal fires, particularly where chips and fines are involved, use of common portable extinguishers containing water is not recommended except to control fires in adjacent Class A materials.

However, water is a good coolant and can be used on some combustible metals, under proper conditions and applications, to reduce the temperature of the burning metals below the ignition point. The following paragraphs discuss the advantages and limitations of using water on fires involving combustible metals.

Water on sodium, potassium, lithium, NaK, barium, calcium, and strontium fires: Water applied to sodium, potassium, lithium, sodium-potassium alloys (NaK), barium, and probably calcium and strontium will induce chemical reactions that will lead to fire or explosion even at room temperature. Therefore, water must *not* be used on fires involving these metals.

Water on zirconium fires: Powdered zirconium that has been wetted with water is more difficult to ignite than dry powder. Once that ignition takes place, however, wet powder burns more violently than dry powder. Powder containing about 5 to 10 percent water is considered the most dangerous. Small volumes of water should not be applied to burning zirconium, but large volumes of water can be used successfully to completely cover solid chunks or large chips of burning zirconium. For example, the metal may be drowned in a tank or barrel of water. Hose streams applied directly to burning zirconium chips may yield violent reactions.

Water on plutonium, uranium, and thorium fires: Limited amounts of water add to the intensity of a fire in natural uranium and thorium, and greatly increase the contamination cleanup required after the fire. A natural uranium scrap fire can be fought with water by personnel, wearing face shields and gloves, using long-handled shovels to put the burning scrap into a drum of water in the open. The hydrogen formed may ignite and burn off above the top of the drum. The radioactivity hazard of natural uranium is extremely low. In reality, uranium is a metal poison, although it is considerably less toxic than lead. The use of water on enriched uranium or plutonium, which are fissionable materials, is generally prohibited. If ingested, plutonium is considerably more hazardous to humans than uranium.

Water on magnesium fires: Although water in small quantities accelerates magnesium fires, rapid application of large amounts of water is effective in extinguishing them because of the cooling effect of the water. Automatic sprinklers will extinguish a typical shop fire where the quantity of magnesium is limited. However, water should not be used on any fire involving a large number of magnesium chips when it is doubtful that there is sufficient water to handle the large area. (A few burning chips can be extinguished by dropping them into a bucket of water.) Small streams from portable extinguishers will accelerate a magnesium chip fire violently.

Burning magnesium parts, such as castings and fabricated structures, can be cooled and extinguished with coarse streams of water applied with standard hoses. A straight stream scatters the fire, but coarse drops produced by a fixed nozzle operating at a distance or produced by an adjustable nozzle flow over and cool the unburned metal. Some temporary acceleration normally takes place with this procedure, but rapid extinguishment follows if the technique is pursued. Well-advanced fires in several hundred pounds (100 lbs equals 45 kg) of magnesium scrap have been extinguished in less than 1 min with two 1½-in. (38 mm) fire hoses. Water fog, on the other hand, tends to accelerate, rather than cool, such a fire. Water should not be applied to magnesium fires where quantities of molten metal are likely to be present because the steam formation and possible metal-water reactions may be explosive.

Water on titanium fires: Water must not be used on fires in titanium fines and should be used with caution on other titanium fires. Small amounts of burning titanium other than fines can be extinguished and considerable salvage realized by quickly submerging the burning material in a large volume of water. Hose streams have been used effectively on fires outside piles of scrap, but violent reactions resulting in serious injuries have been reported in other cases where water was applied to hot or burning titanium.

MISCELLANEOUS AGENTS

Agents that have been tested for cooling capacity and ability to extinguish magnesium fires include the following; boric acid dissolved in triethylene glycol, followed by foam to extinguish the secondary fire[2]; di-isodecyl phthalate combined with chlorobromomethane[3]; and tri-cresyl phosphate, followed by foam to handle the secondary fire. To extinguish burning magnesium, a suitable powder consisting essentially of powdered polyvinyl chloride and sodium borate, was developed.[4] The powder forms a coating on the molten metal and enables a fine water spray to be used to cool the metal to extinction. Research has been conducted at two U.S. laboratories on optimum methods of controlling zirconium and uranium fires with mixed halogen organic derivatives.[5]

Among the more recent literature on combustible metals is a report on computer modeling of titanium combustion. The report describes an extensive program of analytical and experimental investigation to establish the parameters that govern the ignition and self-sustained combustion of metals, such as titanium. The analytical model allows prediction of frictional heating and exposure to high ambient temperatures.[6] Other pertinent publications include suggestions for safely machining magnesium metal[7] and for determining the pyrophorosity of the liquid mixing of combustible metal powders. The flammability of metal charges dried after liquid and dry mixing is said to be different and is connected with a substitution of oxygen absorbed on the metal surface. From the viewpoint of firesafety, maximum diluents are suggested to minimize the possibility of fire or explosion.[8]

BIBLIOGRAPHY

References Cited

1. Rodgers, S. J. and Everson, W. A., "Extinguishments of Alkali Metal Fires," *Fire Technology*, Vol. 1, No. 2 (May 1965) pp. 103-111.
2. McCutchan, R. T., "Investigation of Magnesium Fire Extinguishing Agents," *WADC Technical Report No. 55-5*, U.S. Air Force Wright Air Development Center (by Southwest Research Institute), Wright-Patterson AFB, OH, 1954.
3. Greenstein, L. M. and Richman, S. I., "A Study of Magnesium Fire Extinguishing Agents," *WADC Technical Report No. 55-107*, U.S. Air Force Wright Air Development Center (by Francis Earle Laboratories, Inc.), Wright-Patterson AFB, OH, 1988.
4. Nash, P., "A Dry Powder Extinguishing Agent for Magnesium Fires," *Institution of Fire Engineers Quarterly*, Vol. 23, No. 51 (Sept. 1963), pp. 275-276.
5. Lawrence, K. D., "New Agents for the Extinguishment of Magnesium Fires," *CEEDO Technical Report No. 78-19*, Civil and Environmental Development Office, Tyndall Air Force Base, FL, 1978.
6. Glickstein, M. R., "Computer Modeling of Titanium Combustion," *Tri-Service Conference on Corrosion, Vol II*, U.S. Air Force Wright Aeronautical Laboratories, Wright-Patterson AFB, OH, 5-7 Nov. 1980, pp. 93-122.
7. Morales, H. J., "Machining Magnesium Safely," *American Machinist*, Vol. 124, No. 10 (Oct. 1980), pp. 154-155.
8. Afanasieva, L. F., Chernenko, E. V., and Rozenband, V. I., "Pyrophorosity of Liquid Mixing of the Charge for Titanium Carbide Production," *Poroshk, Metall*, Vol. 5, May 1981, pp. 90-94.

References

Beeson, H. D., Tapscott, R. E., and Mason, B. E., "Extinguishing Agent for Magnesium Fire: Phases V and VI," *Report No. ESL-TR-86-65*, Engineering and Services Laboratory, Air Force Engineering and Services Center, Tyndall Air Force Base, FL, 1987.

Tuve, R. I., Gipe, R. L., Peterson, H. B., and Neil, R. R., "The Use of Trimethoxyboroxine for the Extinguishment of Metal Fires," *NRL Report No. 4933*, Naval Research Laboratory, Washington, DC, 1957.

Zeratsky, E. D., "Extinguishing Agents for Combustible Metals and Special Chemicals," *Safety Maintenance*, Vol. 120, No. 2 (Aug. 1960), pp. 28-32.'

NFPA Codes, Standards, and Recommended Practices

Reference to the following NFPA codes, standards, and recommended practices will provide further information on combustible metal extinguishing agents and application techniques discussed in this chapter. (See the latest *NFPA Catalog* for availability of current editions of the following documents.)

NFPA 48, *Storage, Handling, and Processing of Magnesium.*

NFPA 481, *Production, Processing, Handling, and Storage of Titanium.*

NFPA 482, *Production, Processing, Handling, and Storage of Zirconium.*

Additional Reading

Charpenel, J., *et al.*, "Combined Sodium Fires—Experiments and Code Developments," *Proceedings* of the International Conference on Science and Technology of Fast Reactor Safety, Vol. 1, Thomas Telford, London, 1986, pp. 85-88.

Cissel, D. W., *et al.*, "Guidelines for Sodium Fire Prevention, Detection, and Control: Report of the Ad Hoc Committee on Sodium Fires," *ANL-7691*, Argonne National Laboratory, Argonne, IL, 1970.

"Fire Protection For Combustible Metals," *Data Sheet 567*, National Safety Council, Chicago, IL, 1965.

Foster, K. W., *et al.*, "Clinch River Breeder Reactor Sodium Fire Protection System Design and Development," *Proceedings* of the Third International Conference on Liquid Metal Engineering and Technology, British Nuclear Energy Society, Vol. 2, 1984, pp. 272-278.

"Lithium," *Data Sheet No. D-566*, National Safety Council, Chicago, IL. 1978."Lithium Fire Fighting Study 1, July 1988 through 20 December 1989," Navy Sea Systems Command, PMS 406.

"Magnesium," *Data Sheet No. 426A*, National Safety Council, Chicago, IL, 1975.

"Methods Used by an AEC Contractor for Handling Sodium, NaK, and Lithium," *Accident and Prevention Information*, Feb. 1960, U.S. Atomic Energy Commission, Washington, DC.

Peterson, M. E., "Dry Powder for Combustible Metals," *National Safety News*, Vol. 92, No. 1 (Jan. 1963).

Riley, J. F., "Na-X, a New Fire Extinguishing Agent for Metal Fires," *Fire Technology*, Vol. 10, No. 4 (Nov. 1974).

Simpson, J. M. and Gardener, N. J. L., "Graphite-Based Extinguishants for Liquid Metal Fires," *Proceedings* of the International Conference on Science and Technology of Fast Reactor Safety, Thomas Telford, 1986, pp. 603-606.

Stout, E. L., "Safety Considerations for Handling Plutonium, Uranium, Thorium, the Alkali Metals, Zirconium, Titanium, Magnesium, and Calcium," *Report No. LA-2147*, Los Almos Scientific Laboratory, Los Alamos, NM, 1958.

"Zirconium Powder," *Data Sheet No. D-382A*, National Safety Council, Chicago, IL, 1974.

SPECIAL SYSTEMS AND EXTINGUISHING TECHNIQUES

Revised by Peter F. Johnson

A range of fire extinguishing and control systems, agents, devices, and techniques developed and used with varying degrees of success do not fit into those commonly recognized categories of systems described in previous chapters of this section. Many of the systems and techniques are novel or still in the experimental stage. Often, they are directed toward special applications, such as aircraft or coal mines, for which traditional extinguishing methods are not entirely suited. This chapter describes some of these special systems and techniques by grouping them as follows:

1. Techniques based on solids and powders.
2. Systems using water or water solutions for fire control.
3. Inerting gases used for fire or explosion suppression.
4. Combined agent systems.
5. Special applications.

For a complete discussion of the more conventional extinguishing systems, refer to these other chapters in this section: Chapter 17, "Carbon Dioxide and Application Systems;" Chapter 18, "Halogenated Agents and Systems;" Chapter 19, "Dry Chemical Agents and Application Systems;" Chapter 20, "Foam Extinguishing Agents and Systems;" and Chapter 21, "Combustible Metal Agents and Application Techniques." For information on removal of emulsifying agents, see Section 9, Chapter 17, "Hazardous Waste Control."

SOLIDS AND POWDERS

Solid materials in powder or granular form have been used for many years to extinguish fires. Use of solids to cover and suppress fires by excluding oxygen is a common technique; rows of sand-filled buckets for fire fighting were once a familiar sight. Solids in the form of dry powder systems are still a widely used extinguishing technique. Special proprietary powders and a range of common materials, such as talc, graphite, and soda ash, are capable of suppressing various metal fires, as well.

Peter F. Johnson is Principal Materials Scientist (Fire Systems) at the Scientific Services Laboratory of Australian Construction Services, Melbourne.

A number of recent developments have taken place in the use of powders and other solid materials to suppress special fire hazards.

Granules for Flammable Liquid Pool Fires

Problems associated with fighting large fires of flammable liquids, such as major spills from storage tanks, have led to considerable research in this area. One of the more dangerous fire situations occurs when a major spill of liquefied natural gas (LNG) flows into a dike surrounding a storage tank. Conventional fire fighting methods for large LNG fires have serious limitations, which include the following:

1. Vast quantities of dry chemical are required to guarantee total LNG fire extinguishment.
2. Because of their high water content, low-expansion foams are unsuitable for LNG fires.
3. High- and medium-expansion foams can control, but not extinguish, LNG fires, and large quantities of foam are required continually to replace foam destroyed by fire.

A novel concept, therefore, has been to use a "solid foam" consisting of 3/4- to 1 1/2-in. (20 to 40 mm) cubes of cellular glass in a layer about 8 in. (200 mm) deep to cover the full extent of an LNG spill where it is contained in a storage dike.[1] The granules are of nonflammable, low-density solid material and are stored within the dike in bags. Loose-filled material (with a suitable binder on the top of the liquid is also used. When a LNG spill occurs, the granules float to the top of the liquid and control the rate of burning. Both small-tray and large-scale tests have shown the glass granules to be most effective. The material shields the LNG surface from back radiation from the flames and reduces the evaporation of the fuel from the liquid surface. This limits the fuel burning rate and the overall size of the fire. In addition, radiation at a distance from the spill fire, which is the major contributor to fire spread, is reduced by approximately 90 to 95 percent, compared with LNG fires without the cellular glass granules.

Some practical difficulties with this approach to suppression of LNG fires have emerged, however. Lambert[2] reports that obtaining the cellular glass granules in the large volumes required is both difficult and costly. In addition, research in the UK has shown that, if the granules are stacked in diked areas for long periods, they deteriorate due to weathering and other means.

Carbon Microspheres for Metal Fires

Specially formulated extinguishing powders are generally used to suppress fires involving metals. Because of the reaction many metals have with water, sprinklers and the use of other water-based agents are not appropriate and, in some cases, quite dangerous.

However, many of the special agents for metal fires are at times unsatisfactory because they are corrosive, applied manually rather than by an extinguishing system, capable of clogging extinguishing nozzles, and expensive.

Studies have been undertaken to examine the effectiveness of carbon microspheres or microspheroids to extinguish fires involving alkali metals, such as sodium, sodium-potassium, and lithium.[3] These microspheres are petroleum-coke-based particles with a diameter of approximately 100 to 500 microns. The particles possess high thermal conductivity, chemical inertness, and excellent flow characteristics and are capable of being directed onto fires from dry-chemical-type extinguishers and conventional nozzles.

Tests have shown that carbon microspheres compare favorably in performance to other metal extinguishing agents.[3] In particular, experiments with carbon microspheroids incorporating neutron absorbers have been effective in extinguishing fires involving nuclear fissionable materials, such as uranium metal powder.[4] The excellent flow characteristics and noncaking properties of these microspheres suggest an effective way to extinguish radioactive metal fires within the inert atmosphere glovebox enclosures used in the nuclear industry.

Ground Cover Materials—Aircraft Fuel Fires

Aircraft fuel spill fires are another significant hazard in which solid materials have been used for extinguishment. Research in the U.S. suggests that crushed rock graded to approximately 3/8 in. (10 mm) can reduce fire growth and the spread of flames in hydrocarbon spill fires.[5] The suppression mechanism seems to be similar to that for cellular glass granules—that is, the solid material largely blocks back-radiation of the flames to the liquid surface, and prevents heat from being distributed to the fuel in front of the flame by convection currents. Ground rock materials do not float and must cover the fuel surface by 1 to 2 in. (25 to 50 mm) to retard flame growth effectively.

Dry Chemical Projectile

Since the 1940s, a number of interesting suppression techniques have been developed using projectiles of dry chemical that can be fired at a target fire from a distance.

One such system developed in the U.S. for coal mine fires used a cannon-like dispersal system. Upon an alarm from an ultraviolet detector, mono-ammonium phosphate powder was propelled from the cannon by high-pressure nitrogen to quench potential coal explosions and methane-air ignitions.[6] In reality, the devices proved somewhat impractical because of space limitations.

Dr. John L. Bryan of the University of Maryland reported on a related extinguishing technique developed some years ago that used a device known as a "gren gun." This gun consisted of cylinders that rotated in turn into the firing position. The projectiles contained 1¾ lb (0.8 kg) of dry chemical that, when fired with compressed air, could reach distances of 200 ft (60 m).[7] The gren gun was designed to operate with a minimum air pressure of 150 psi (1030 kPa) from a compressed-air cylinder carried on the back of the operator. The gun itself was constructed of lightweight aluminum, weighed approximately 10 lb (4½ kg), and was fired from the shoulder. Being portable, it was ideal as a first-attack suppression device that could place dry chemical on a target from a safe, remote distance.

Vermiculite for Flammable Liquids

Foam, dry powder, and halon systems have traditionally been used to extinguish or control flammable liquid fires. However, recent research in India[8] has examined the effectiveness of exfoliated vermiculite in gasoline and kerosene fires.

Vermiculite is a hydrated laminar mineral that is soft and flaky, and consists mainly of aluminum, iron, and magnesium silicates in proportions shown in Table 5-22A.

TABLE 5-22A. ***Chemical Composition of Vermiculite***

SiO_2	39–45%
MgO	15–20%
Al_2O_3	14–20%
Fe_2O_3–FeO	6–11%
Other compounds	4–26%

When vermiculite is heated under controlled conditions between 292 and 1832°F (700 and 1000°), its flakes exfoliate or expand from 7 to 15 times their original volume, resulting in a highly insulating material of very low density.

Tests have shown that a layer of 63 in. (160 mm) of exfoliated vermiculite can be used to blanket or smother flammable liquid fires of gasoline and kerosene up to 54 sq ft (5 m^2) in size. While comparative studies with foam have shown that 2.2 to 6.6 lbs (1 to 3 kg) of foam is required per sq ft (one sq ft = 0.09 m^2) of gasoline fire extinguished, compared with 28.6 lbs (13 kg) of exfoliated vermiculite, the latter material appears to have an indefinite shelf life and to be unaffected by fuel properties or environmental degradation. Further research obviously is needed to determine the practical aspects of supply, placement in the event of a fire, and performance on flammable liquid fires of larger area.

SYSTEMS UTILIZING WATER OR WATER SOLUTIONS

A number of specialized systems using water or water-based agents have been developed to fill particular fire control needs. These extinguishing agents remove heat from the combustion process or form a noncombustible emulsion with the fuel.

Ultra-High-Speed Water Spray Systems

These systems are designed to handle extremely rapid fires, such as those which can occur during the handling of solid propellants or sensitive chemicals, or in any industrial process or oxygen-enriched environment.

Wetting Agent Systems

Most wetting agent systems—as opposed to wetting agents used through manually operated hose lines from mobile tank supplies through portable proportioners—are designed to dispense wetting agent foam. The design, volume, and purpose of each installation depends upon the hazard being protected. Normally, wetting agent systems that meet the requirements of NFPA 18, *Wetting Agents*, can use standard water spray, sprinkler, or foam system equipment. However, this should be carefully checked to ensure maximum system efficiency.

The detergent action of a wetting agent solution may introduce some special problems. Wet-water foam is a mixture of wet water with air that forms a cellular structure foam. This foam breaks down into its original liquid state at temperatures below the boiling point of water. Breakdown is proportional to the heat exposure and is intended to cool sufficiently the surface on which the foam is applied. These properties improve the ability of water to protect exposed properties against heat transfer, and water requirements are thus appreciably reduced. Wet-water systems can introduce the potential of increased water damage to exposed stocks due to the high absorption ability of wet water, and can increase the load on any flooring affected because of the retention of large volumes of wet water. These factors must be considered in the design of such installations.

Viscous Water Systems

Systems for applying viscous, or "thickened," water vary in detailed components, depending upon whether the equipment is designed for application from the ground or from aircraft. Most ground applications are from conventional fire tankers, with some modifications. The NFPA report, "Chemicals for Forest Fire Fighting," lists the following three basic systems for ground applications.[9]

Injector-recirculating ground tanker system: In this system, water is drawn from the tank bottom through a centrifugal pump and bypassed through an added return line to the injector-disperser, where the liquid and dry powder combine and flow into the tank. The centrifugal pump serves as a mixing device, continuing until the correct amount of powder is added.

Demand viscous water tanker-mixer: This system consists of an auxiliary mixing tank, an auger feed mechanism, and a positive displacement rotary meter that acts as a power unit for the feed system. This system uses the tank, centrifugal pump, and discharge lines of a conventional tanker.

Slip-on chemical tanker-mixer: This system is a skid-mounted, all-metal unit for mounting onto a heavy-duty tractor trailer for off-road assignments. The major assemblies consist of a mixing tank, chemical hopper, hose reel, engine, pump, and pump priming tank. This system has only been used experimentally, employing a modified ordinary agricultural sprayer.

Conventional fire nozzles are used for viscous water or light gels. Those nozzles producing coarse droplets normally give satisfactory results, but fine spray nozzles should be avoided. Slurry-type fire-retardant chemicals need special nozzles because these chemicals quickly erode most conventional brass and aluminum nozzles. Cast aluminum inserts (a ceramic aluminum oxide) seem to be satisfactory, however, and can be manufactured inexpensively.

"Chemicals for Forest Fire Fighting"[9] gives additional information on equipment for mixing the chemicals, on pumps for handling the chemicals, on distribution systems, on storage of mixed and unmixed chemicals, and on means for judging the quality of the solutions in the field.

The NFPA report "Air Operations for Forest, Brush, and Grass Fires"[10] contains information on the use of aircraft for fire control operations. This manual covers air operations plans, airports, heliports, helistops, suitable aircraft, operating principles and procedures, and amphibious operations. Special equipment is needed to use aircraft for these fire control purposes.

Emulsifying Agents—Detergents

Various types of emulsifying agents or detergents have been used with varying degrees of success to extinguish or control flammable liquid spill fires on land and on water. These agents also have been used on unignited spills of such liquids to minimize the possible ignition hazard. In general, these agents mix the oil and water to form a noncombustible emulsion.

A major problem with the use of emulsifying agents and detergents in lakes, rivers, harbors, and so on is that the resultant emulsions often have a more severe effect on aquatic forms of life than does oil alone. However, relatively nontoxic emulsifying agents may be developed in the future.

One interesting example of the use of local-application emulsifying agent in cooking range hood protection is a system that uses an aqueous potassium carbonate solution with minor amounts of sodium dichromate added to inhibit corrosion, and ethylene glycol to prevent freezing. It is dispersed in the form of a dense liquid spray from conventional nozzles located in the range hood. (See Figure 5-22A.) The alkaline solution not only removes heat by steam generation, but undergoes a saponification reaction with burning fat or oil to produce a soap foam or emulsified layer that, in turn, produces inerting carbon dioxide.

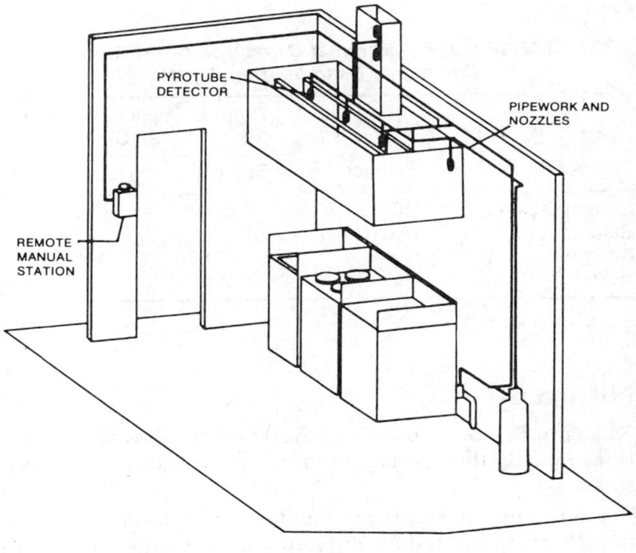

Figure 5-22A. Local emulsifying agent system in a range hood.

Similar aqueous potassium carbonate extinguishing systems have also been used for range hoods on naval vessels.[11]

A further extension of the use of emulsifying agents in kitchen range hoods has been to link this type of suppression system to a special thermal line detector that can be distributed around the inside of the range hood. When a fixed temperature of approximately 347°F (175°C) is exceeded, a pressure is generated within a ¼-in. (6 mm) diameter stainless steel line detector that automatically initiates the rapid discharge of the aqueous emulsifying agent.

INERTING GAS SUPPRESSION

For many years, a range of gases such as carbon dioxide, nitrogen, and helium has been used successfully to prevent ignition of potentially flammable mixtures or to extinguish fires, particularly those involving flammable liquids or gases. These methods are based on the knowledge that a fire can be extinguished if a sufficient volume of an inert gas is introduced into an enclosed space where the fire is burning. The concentration must be maintained in the space for an adequate period to keep the burned material from rekindling.

Traditionally, this method of extinguishment has been explained as a reduction of the fuel or oxygen concentration to the point where combustion is prevented. Modern fire dynamics show the added inerting gas acts as "thermal ballast" to reduce the temperature of the flame/vapor mixture below the limiting adiabatic flame temperature necessary to sustain combustion.[12] The gaseous extinguishing agent actually absorbs the combustion energy, and its thermal capacity is the important factor in inerting explosive or burning materials.

The thermal capacities of the more commonly used inerting agents are shown in Table 5-22B.

Table 5-22B reveals why carbon dioxide is an important gaseous extinguishing agent and why helium, with its lower heat-absorbing capacity, is not widely used. Halon extinguishing agents have not been included in the table. While they have even higher thermal capacity than carbon dioxide, their extinguishment mechanism is more related to chemical interaction in the combustion process.

TABLE 5-22B. *Thermal Capacities of the More Commonly Used Inerting Agents*

		Thermal Capacity at 340°F (727°C)	
Agent	Symbol	Btu/mol °F	J/mol-k
Carbon Dioxide	CO_2	12.9	54.3
Steam	$H_2O(g)$	9.8	41.2
Nitrogen	N_2	7.8	32.7
Helium	He	5.0	20.8

Nitrogen

Nitrogen has been used in a number of inerting applications, mostly those related to aircraft fire suppression systems.

Nitrogen has been considered for aircraft engine nacelle fires, but halons are generally far superior for this application.[13] The use of nitrogen has been directed more toward fuel tank inerting where cryogenic nitrogen in Dewar vessels is directed into the fuel tank ullage. Nitrogen up to an additional 80 percent of the gross volume to be protected is added so that a maximum oxygen concentration of 9 percent by volume is not exceeded in the atmosphere above the fuel.[14]

Nitrogen fire fighting systems have also been considered for cargo compartment underfloor areas, wheel wells, and wing areas in both military and civilian aircraft.[13] This technique is being used on U. S. Air Force C-5A transport aircraft, and consideration is being given to using nitrogen in parked aircraft to reduce oxygen concentrations to below 10 percent by volume, thus eliminating cabin fires in unattended aircraft.

One of the problems with an inerting gas is to ensure that it is well mixed and that all parts of the volume being protected have the minimum concentration required for fire suppression. This is particularly true in enclosures where the amount of extinguishing agent required for suppression must be balanced by the potential damage to equipment and injuries to personnel that could arise from too much inerting gas. Scale-model studies of nitrogen distribution within pressurizable enclosures have proved that poor distribution patterns of nitrogen can be identified and corrected.[15]

Steam Inerting Systems

Steam may be used to smother fires in the same manner as other inert gases. It effectively reduces the concentrations of fuel vapor and oxygen and absorbs sufficient heat to stop the combustion process. The use of steam systems for fire extinguishment precedes the use of other modern smothering systems, such as carbon dioxide and foam extinguishing systems, and is rarely used today. It is clearly an impractical method, except where a large steam supply is continuously available and can be tapped effectively and efficiently when a fire emergency arises. The possible burn hazard to personnel must be considered in any steam extinguishing installation.

Steam extinguishing systems are not recommended for fire protection purposes in any current NFPA standards. However, the appendix to NFPA 86, *Ovens and Furnaces*, does offer suggestions for fire protection of steam systems which may be followed "where steam flooding is the only alternative" after automatic sprinklers or water spray systems and approved types of supplementary fire protection, such as carbon dioxide, foam, or dry chemical systems, have already been considered. To protect ovens, this standard calls for steam outlets to supply at least 8 lb (3.6 kg) of steam per minute for each 100 cu ft (2.8 m^3) of oven volume. One lb (0.45 kg) of saturated steam at 212°F (100°C) and normal atmospheric pressure has a volume of 26.75 cu ft (0.76 m^3). Steam outlets should be located near the bottom of the oven, but they may be located at the top, pointing downward if the oven is not more than 20 ft (6.0 m) high. Pipe sizes and the steam supply should be sufficient to deliver the required amount of steam and to maintain a minimum pressure of 15 psi (100 kPa) at the outlet. NFPA 86 recommends manual release devices for such systems and recommends that controls be arranged to close down oven outlets as far as practicable. Additional guidance includes arrangements to reduce hazards to personnel.

Steam smothering systems used to be employed to protect cargo spaces and the holds of steamships. This method is no longer recommended. Tests indicating the relative inefficiency of such systems in controlling cotton cargo fires were conducted by the U.S. Coast Guard during "Operation Phobos."[16]

One more interesting example of the use of steam inerting is the system used to prevent explosions in certain coal pulverizers in the U.S.[17] In essence, the inerting system introduces steam into the pulverizing system to reduce the oxygen concentration below the flammability limit for ignition of a coal-dust atmosphere. Steam was chosen for this application rather than carbon dioxide or nitrogen because it was readily available, needed no storage system, was abundant from a reliable source, did not require tight enclosure of the inerted space, had no toxic effects, and was inexpensive. On-site tests and plant experience have shown the system to be quite effective in preventing coal dust explosions.

Use of Combustion Gases For Fire Extinguishment

Experiments have been conducted on use of the gases of combustion to achieve extinguishment. Inert gas was generated by an experimental turbojet engine specially designed for the test. The engine burned most of the oxygen in the air it used, and the hot combustion gases were cooled by vaporizing water introduced as a fine spray. The most efficient inert gas produced by the experimental appliance contained 46 percent nitrogen, 44 percent water vapor, 3 percent carbon dioxide, and 7 percent oxygen. The highest rate of delivery used was 45,000 cu ft/min (21 m^3/sec) when the appliance consumed 84 gal per min (320 L/min) of water and 7.8 gal per min (29.5 L/min) of kerosene. The emergent gas was cooled to 194 to 248°F (90 to 120°C). In this experimental work, either the inert gas alone was used or a high-expansion foam was made with the inert gas. By spraying a suitable detergent solution on a screen and blowing the inert gas through the wetted screen at a velocity not exceeding 5 ft/sec (1.5 m/sec), an inert gas high-expansion foam was generated with an expansion ratio of 1000 to 1. Between 50 and 80 percent of the gas was made into foam. A flexible ducting made of Terylene, with a neoprene coating to make it impermeable, was used to convey the gas or foam to the fire site.

In similar investigations,[7,18] a smaller inert gas generator was constructed which produced approximately 3.300 cu ft/min (1.6 m^3/sec) of the mixture, consisting of 68 percent water vapor, 28 percent nitrogen, and 4 percent carbon dioxide at a temperature of 194°F (90°C). Depending upon the fuel involved, it was reported that the inert gas concentration must reduce the oxygen level to between 9 and 12 percent for effective extinguishment. In addition, a quantity of inert gas equal to twice the building volume involved must be produced within 15 min for successful extinguishment.

Air Agitation for Oil Tank Fire Control

Fuel tanks often are protected by topside foam protection systems or by subsurface foam injection into the fuel itself. Fire in an oil storage tank may, under some conditions, be controlled or extinguished by introducing air under pressure near the bottom of the tank. The principle is founded upon the fact that flammable and combustible liquids require a temperature greater than their flash point temperature to sustain burning. If a tank of oil with a flash point above the actual temperature of the liquid ignites when the surface temperature is raised above the flash point, or the oil has become contaminated with a low-flash-point liquid, the resulting fire may be controlled or extinguished by agitating the oil mass. By agitating the mass, cool oil circulated at a proper rate decreases the temperature of burning oil at the surface by displacement and mixing to a point below its flash point, thus slowing or inhibiting further combustion.

The time element during which such control operations must be pursued actively is critical. If the oil mass heats too quickly, the cooling effect might be inadequate; and if the burning liquid is crude oil, the time before boiling occurs can be shortened considerably. This technique is not considered a standard method of combating oil tank fires. Under most circumstances where fire protection is provided for such storage tanks, foam fire fighting equipment meeting the recommendations contained in NFPA 11, *Low Expansion Foam and Combined Agent Systems*, should be employed.

COMBINED AGENT SYSTEMS

It is common fire fighting practice to use two or more agents simultaneously or in rapid sequence, taking advantage of the best qualities of any two agents in achieving fast fire control and permanent extinguishment. Some common combinations used in manual fire control include water, usually water spray, and foam; carbon dioxide and foam; and certain dry chemicals and foam. Aircraft rescue and fire fighting operations have long employed such combined agent methods, using water spray, carbon dioxide, or dry chemical to secure rapid flame knockdown, plus simultaneous or sequential use of foam to permanently smother the fire. During World War II, the combined use of bulk applications of carbon dioxide from mobile low-pressure carbon dioxide trucks, with simultaneous applications of foam from specialized crash trucks, led to many significant personnel rescues in aircraft fires and achieved quick fire extinguishment or control, as well. This technique, and the combined use of foam-compatible dry chemicals and foam, is still being used. While these techniques do involve the simultaneous and/or sequential use of two agents, each agent system is independent of the other, most often located on separate mobile vehicles.

Recent developments in dual-agent systems combine light water with potassium salt-based dry chemical, or mechanical (air) foam with potassium salt-based dry chemical, providing the foam is compatible with dry chemical. These are systems in the sense that they are designed to provide a balanced discharge of the agents, although the agents themselves are not premixed. The two agents are discharged through independent but twinned nozzles, both of which are independent but under the control of one fire fighter. Some experiments have entrained certain dry chemicals in the water-foam concentrate turret stream with encouraging results.

A recent study[19] has shown that certain salts, such as diammonium hydrogen phosphate and calcium hydrogen carbonate, can be used effectively to reduce the quantity of water required for extinguishment by up to 73 percent. It was found that the time to extinguishment was also significantly reduced on wood crib fires and in full-scale furniture fire tests. Apart from the combined agent systems using foam, other combined agent systems using combinations of halons and water and halons with dry chemical (potassium bicarbonate) have also been tried and found to be effective.[6] This work has been extended more recently,[19] with foams being generated using halons rather than air.

A halon gas is added to the mixture of water and foam agents and distributed by traditional fire fighting jets. Several large-scale tests have been performed using aqueous film-forming foam (AFFF) agent, together with Halon 2420 and Halon 2330, and rapid extinguishment with a relatively small amount of agent has been achieved.

SPECIAL APPLICATIONS

A series of examples from selected industries serves to illustrate how special techniques, combinations of agents, or unusual control mechanisms may be used to overcome specialized fire problems.

Bulk Sulphur Storage

Sulphur is one of industry's most widely used chemicals. It comes in the form of rock, known as brimstone or as a powder. Solid, finely ground sulphur is both a fire and an explosion hazard. Sulphur is unusual in that it has a low melting point of approximately 239°F (115°C) and a low ignition temperature of 374 to 392°F (190 to 200°C). It burns with a pale blue flame to form mainly sulphur dioxide.

Thompson[20] indicates that small fires in bulk sulphur can be extinguished by carefully shoveling more sulphur onto the fire, thus removing the oxygen supply. For larger fires, water is the most effective extinguishing agent, but it must be applied gently in the form of a water fog to avoid raising sulphur dust and creating an explosion hazard.

Microelectronic Fabrication Facility

These fabrication facilities are exceptionally expensive to build and operate and require very extensive cleanroom provisions to maintain low particle counts to avoid product contamination. Even a small fire, then, can cause widespread damage to sensitive microchips and lead to significant business interruption losses.

Much of the manufacturing in these facilities occurs in so-called "wet benches" that handle flammable, corrosive, and toxic chemicals under strong ventilation conditions. Recent experimental work[21] suggests that a halon suppression system, initiated by fast-response infrared flame detectors and backed with fast-response automatic sprinklers, is the best combination to extinguish a fire quickly and prevent contamination of adjoining cleanroom facilities. Further work remains to be done to investigate the use of carbon dioxide or nitrogen.

Anechoic Chambers

The combination of halon and automatic sprinklers is also appropriate for anechoic chambers. These chambers, designed to be free of echoes or reverberations, use geometrically shaped foam in the form of wedges or pyramids to achieve electromagnetic radiation absorption on all internal surfaces. The foam, which is impregnated with carbon to improve its conductivity, represents a major fuel load and, if it is ignited, can lead to a large fire and great damage.

Research[22] has shown that a special telescoping sprinkler system, forming part of a deluge system to minimize accidental water damage, is the most appropriate water-based suppression system. (See Figure 5-22B.) This is supported by a fast-response halon system using cross-zoning of optical and ionization smoke detectors. Given ventilation rates of up to 700 air changes/hour, however, experimental work has shown that a VESDA™-type smoke detection system is perhaps a more appropriate sensing system for anechoic chambers. VESDA™, an acronym for "Very Early Smoke Detection Apparatus," is the generic trade name for a type of smoke detector manufactured by IEI (Aust.) Pty. Ltd. This would support other work[23] that indicates that high-sensitivity-sampling smoke detection systems provide the best form of detection in high airflow situations.

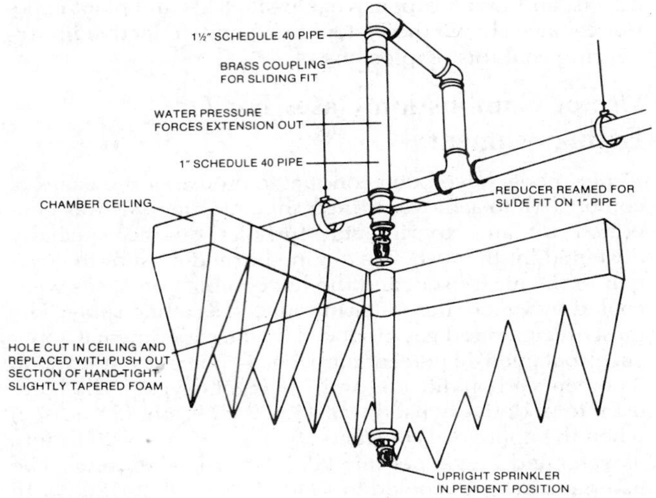

Figure 5-22B. Telescoping drop-down sprinkler.

Filter Plenums and Gloveboxes

In the nuclear industry, the handling of plutonium, uranium, and beryllium represent a hazard that requires special fire protection precautions. Two special risks are gloveboxes, in which nuclear materials are processed, and filter plenums that house the HEPA filters used to prevent loss of nuclear material to the atmosphere.

One approach to this hazard[24] is to use special heat detectors to initiate an automatic deluge and water curtain system. Special spray nozzles are used and hot fire gases are cooled before reaching the combustible HEPA filters. The automatic deluge system is backed by a separate manual deluge system for increased reliability.

A unique feature of the heat detectors used to initiate water deluge is the special heaters surrounding the detector sensors to allow remote testing in gloveboxes. Entry to these gloveboxes, which contain highly radioactive material, is very difficult, so testing by remote activation of heating elements means that routine maintenance and assurance of operation can be checked regularly.

Future of Halon

Chlorofluorocarbons (CFCs), such as halon, have been identified as contributors to ozone depletion in Earth's atmosphere. In 1987, the Montreal Protocol was signed to limit ozone-depleting substances and to set production limits on CFCs, including Halons 1301 and 1211. As a result, the future use of halon as a fire extinguishing agent is in question.

BIBLIOGRAPHY

References Cited

1. Lev. Y., "A Novel Method for Controlling LNG Pool Fires," *Fire Technology*, Vol. 17, No. 4, 1981, pp. 275-284.
2. Lambert, G.M.S., unpublished data, 1989.
3. McCormick, J.W. and Schmitt, C.R., "Extinguishment of Selected Metal Fires Using Carbon Microspheroids," *Fire Technology*, Vol. 10, No. 3 (Aug. 1974), pp. 197-199.
4. Schmitt, C.R., "Carbon Microspheres as Extinguishing Agents for Fissionable Material Fires," *Fire Technology*, Vol. 11, No. 2 (May 1975), pp. 95-98.
5. Geyer, G.B., "The Use of Ground Cover Materials to Suppress Fuel Fires at Airports," *Fire Technology*, Vol. 9, No. 4 (Nov. 1973), pp. 254-262.
6. "Fire Safety Aspects of Polymeric Materials—Volume 10—Mines and Bunkers," *Publication NMAB 318-10*, National Academy of Sciences, Washington, DC, 1980.
7. Bryan, J.L., *Fire Suppression and Detection Systems*, Glencoe Press, Encino, CA, 1982.
8. Sharma, T.P., Badami, G.N., Lal, B.B., and Singh, Jagbir, "A New Particulate Extinguishant for Flammable Liquid Fires," *Fire Safety Science, Proceedings of the Second International Symposium*, Hemisphere Publishing Corporation, New York, 1989, pp. 667-677.
9. NFPA Forest Committee, "Chemicals for Forest Fire Fighting," *Report*, 3rd ed., National Fire Protection Association, Quincy, MA, 1977.
10. NFPA Forest Committee, "Air Operations for Forest, Brush, and Grass Fires," *Report*, rev. ed., National Fire Protection Association, Quincy, MA, 1975.
11. Neill, R.R. and Peterson, H.B., "An Investigation of the Heating and Fire Extinguishment of Deep Frying Fat," *N.R.L. Memorandum Report 2080*, Naval Research Laboratory, Washington, DC, 1969.
12. Drysdale, D.D., *Fire Dynamics*, John Wiley & Sons, Chichester, UK, 1985.
13. Dyer, J.H., Marjoram, M.J., and Simmons, R.F., "The Extinction of Fires in Aircraft Jet Engines—Part III, Extinction of Fires at Low Airflows," *Fire Technology*, Vol. 13, No. 2 (May 1977), pp. 126-130.
14. "Fire Safety Aspects of Polymeric Materials—Volume 6—Aircraft: Civil and Military," *Publication NMAB 318-6*, Appendix C, D, National Academy of Sciences, Washington, DC, 1977.
15. Corlett, R.C., Stone, J.P., and Williams, F.W., "Scale Modeling of Inert Pressurant Distribution," *Fire Technology*, Vol. 16, No. 4 (Nov. 1980), pp. 259-273.
16. *Proceedings of the Fifty-First Annual Meeting of the National Fire Protection Association*, May 26-29, 1947, National Fire Protection Association, Quincy, MA, pp. 119-123.
17. McGuire, J.H., "Large-Scale Use of Inert Gas to Extinguish Building Fires," *Research Paper 246*, National Research Council of Canada, Division of Building Research, Ottawa, Canada, 1964.
18. John, R., "New Additives to Extinguishing Water for Fire Fighting," *New Technology to Reduce Fire Losses and Costs*, Grayson, S.J., Smith, D.A., eds., Elsevier Applied Science Publishers, New York, 1986, pp. 280-287.
19. Thompson, C., "Fire Safety in Bulk Sulphur Handling Locations," *Fire Prevention*, No. 208 (Apr. 1988), pp. 28-31.
20. Fisher, F.L., Williamson, R.B., Toms, G.L., and Crinnion, D.M., "Fire Protection of Flammable Work Stations in the Clean Room Environment of a Microelectronic Fabrication Facility,"*Fire Technology*, Vol. 22, No. 2 (May 1989), pp. 148-165.
21. Kirson, D., "Anechoic Chambers±A Unique Challenge to the Fire Protection Engineer," *Papers of IFPEI-V International Fire Protection Engineering Institute, Ottawa, Vol. 2*, Society of Fire Protection Engineers, Boston, 1989.
22. Johnson, P.F., "Very Early Smoke Detection for Computer and Telecommuications Industries," *Fire Safety Journal*, Vol. 14, Nos. 1 & 2 (July 1988), pp. 13-24.
23. Campbell, D.G., "Fire Protection for Filter Plenums at a Nuclear Facility," *Papers of IFPEI-V International Fire Protection Engineering Institute, Ottawa, Vol. 2*, Society of Fire Protection Engineers, Boston, 1989.

NFPA, Codes, Standards and Recommended Practices

References to the following NPFA codes, standards, and recommended practices will provide further information on special systems and extinguishing techniques discussed in this chapter. (See the latest *NFPA Catalog* for availability of current editions of the following documents.)

NFPA 11, *Low Expansion Foam and Combined Agent Systems*.

NFPA 18, *Wetting Agents*.

NFPA 86, *Ovens and Furnaces*.

Additional Reading

Banerjee, S. P., "Experience of Inert Gas Injection in Combating Fires in Indian Coal Mines," *Proceedings of the 3rd Mine Ventilation Symposium*, Society of Mining Engineers of AIME, 1987, pp. 438-443.

Bannister, W. W., Walker, J. L., and Morehouse, T., "Applications of Amine Gelling Agents in Fire Technology," *Plant/Operation Progress*, Vol. 8, No. 2 (April 1989), pp. 80-81.

Bowman, J. W. and Perkins, R. P., "Preventing Fires with High Temperature Vaporizers," *Plant/Operations Progress*, Vol. 9, No. 1 (Jan. 1990), pp. 39-43.

Breen, D.E., "Interactions in Binary Halon Mixtures Used as Fire Suppressants," *Fire Technology*, Vol. 13, No. 4 (Nov. 1977), pp. 261-265.

Cohen, P., et al., "Trial By Fire, Understanding the Design Requirements for Agents in Complex Environments," *AI Magazine*, Vol. 10, No. 3 (Fall 1989), pp. 32-48.

Garg, P. C., "Development of Nitrogen Infusion Technology for Fighting and Inhibition of Fires," *Journal of Mines, Metals and Fuels*, Vol. 35, No. 8 (Aug. 1987), pp. 368-377, 394.

Lomai, T. and Isei, T., "Underground Fire-Fighting System by a Rapid Evaporation Method of Liquid Nitrogen," *Mining Science and Technology*, Vol. 8, No. 2, 1989, pp. 145-152.

Ramaswamy, A. and Katiyar, P. S., "Experiences with Liquid Nitrogen in Combating Coal Fires Underground," *Journal of Mines, Metals and Fuels*, Vol. 36, No. 9 (Sept. 1988), pp. 415-424.

Simpson, J. M. and Gardener, N. J. L., "Graphite-Based Extinguishants for Liquid Metal Fires," *Proceedings* of the International Conference on Science and Technology of Fast Reactor Safety, Thomas Telford, 1986, pp. 603-606.

"Special Fire Risks Require Special Extinguishing Systems," *National Safety and Health News*, Vol. 134, No. 3 (Sept. 1986), pp. 43-48.

Wrenn, C., "Inerting for Safety," *Plant/Operation Progress*, Vol. 5, No. 4 (Oct. 1986), pp. 225-227.

Zallen, D. M. and Morehouse, E. T., "Fire Extinguishing Agents for Oxygen-Enriched Atmospheres," *Proceedings* of the Third International Symposium on Flammability and Sensitivity of Materials in Oxygen-Enriched Atmospheres, Third Volume, American Society for Materials and Testing, Philadelphia, PA, 1988, pp. 391-412.

SELECTION, OPERATION, DISTRIBUTION, INSPECTION AND MAINTENANCE OF FIRE EXTINGUISHERS

Revised by David P. Demers

Before choosing an extinguisher, it is important to know the nature of the fuels present, who will use the extinguisher, the physical environment in which the extinguisher will be placed, and whether any chemicals present in the area will react adversely with an extinguishing agent. When choosing from among various extinguishers, one should consider whether it is effective on the specific hazards present, whether it is easy to operate, and what maintenance and upkeep it requires.

This chapter specifically discusses these important fire extinguisher concerns within the following topics: matching extinguishers to hazards, available personnel, physical environment, health and operational safety, operation and use, obsolete extinguishers, distribution, inspections, and maintenance.

Related information can be found elsewhere in this section.

MATCHING EXTINGUISHERS TO HAZARDS

By far the most important consideration when selecting extinguishers is the nature of the area to be protected. NFPA 10, *Portable Fire Extinguishers*, classifies fires as either Class A, Class B, Class C, or Class D, according to the fuel involved. Extinguishers are classified for use on one or more of these types of fires.

In addition, the relative hazard in a building varies according to its fire load, or the amount of combustibles it contains. NFPA 10, *Portable Fire Extinguishers*, establishes three types of hazards. A light, or low, hazard exists when there are few combustibles and only small fires need be expected. Light-hazard occupancies include offices, churches, schoolrooms, assembly halls, and so on. An ordinary, or moderate, hazard exists when the amount of combustibles is such that a medium-sized fire may be expected. Examples of ordinary-hazard occupancies are mercantile storage and display areas, auto showrooms, and parking garages. Some offices, schools, and so on may contain a sufficient amount of combustible materials to be classified as ordinary hazard. An extra, or high hazard exists in areas where a severe fire may be expected, such as woodworking areas, aircraft servicing areas, and warehouses with high-piled combustibles.

Hazard type is an important factor when selecting extinguishers. For example, a $2^1/_2$-gal (9.5 L) water extinguisher may only be suitable in low- and moderate-hazard areas. In a high-hazard area, multi-purpose dry chemical extinguishers with ratings of 3-A to 40-A may be required.

Class-A-rated extinguishers are used most often for ordinary building protection. Among the agents classified for Class A use are water, loaded stream, aqueous film-forming foam (AFFF), multi-purpose (ammonium-phosphate-base) dry chemical, and halogenated types. Due to the environmental problems associated with halogenated agents, however, their use is being discouraged except in specific circumstances.

Class-A-rated extinguishers are not the only type needed for building protection. In most areas of a restaurant, for example, the principal combustibles are wood, paper, and fabrics. In the kitchen, however, the essential hazard is cooking grease, which requires a Class-B-rated extinguisher. In hospitals, there is a general need for Class-A-rated extinguishers in rooms, corridors, and offices, but Class-B:C-rated extinguishers should be placed in laboratories, kitchens, generator rooms, and areas where anesthetics are stored or used. In short, the extinguishers in any one area should correspond to the hazards of that area.

Class B fires are fires in flammable liquids. Class-B-rated extinguishing agents include carbon dioxide, dry chemicals, AFFF, and halogenated types. There are three general types of flammable liquids fires: (1) fires in liquids of appreciable depth [deeper than $^1/_4$ in. (6.4 mm)], such as those in industrial dip tanks and quench tanks; (2) spill fires or running fires in liquids of no real depth [$^1/_4$ in. (6.4 mm) or less]; and (3) pressurized flammable liquid or gas fires from damaged vessels or product lines. Each of these fires is very different from the others, and the differences may be complicated further by atmospheric conditions. Portable fire extinguishers should not be relied upon when the surface area of an indoor open tank is in

David P. Demers, P.E., is president of Demers Associates, Inc., fire protection consultants, Lunenburg, MA.

excess of 10 sq ft (1 m^2); fires in such areas give off so much heat and smoke that it is dangerous for anyone to remain in the area.

Pressurized flammable liquids and pressurized gas fires present special hazards. Only dry chemical type extinguishers have proven to be effective. In addition, special nozzles and rates of agent application are required. Extinguishers should therefore be selected on the basis of manufacturers' recommendations. *No* attempt should be made to extinguish these fires unless there is reasonable certainty that the source of fuel can be shut off promptly.

Class-C-rated extinguishers are for use on fires in charged electrical equipment. They should be chosen according to how the electrical equipment is constructed, the degree of agent contamination that can be tolerated, and the nature of other combustibles in the area. Of these, the last is particularly important. For example, a power panel will contain more Class A insulating materials than an oil-filled transformer, which will contain mostly Class B material. The agents classified for Class C use include carbon dioxide, dry chemicals, and the halogenated types.

Class D fires are fires in combustible metals. These require special extinguishing agents, generally known as dry powder.

Once an area has been analyzed for hazards, appropriate extinguishers can be chosen. For the Class A fire, there are three basic types of extinguishers that can be used: water-based extinguishers, multi-purpose (ammonium-phosphate-base) dry chemical extinguishers, or halogenated agent extinguishers. For Class B fires, there are carbon dioxide, dry chemical, halogenated agent, and AFFF extinguishers. (Some small extinguishers are rated less than 5-B and, as indicated by their omission from Table 5-23A, may not be permitted as a required extinguisher.) For Class C fires there are carbon dioxide, dry chemical, or halogenated agent extinguishers. The various types of extinguishing agents for Class D combustible metal fires are discussed separately.

AVAILABLE PERSONNEL—EASE OF USE

Before extinguishers are selected, consideration should be given to who will use them. Evaluation should include the potential user's physical abilities, reactions under stress, and previous training. The more choices the user must make in an emergency, the greater the chance for error. Many firms have standardized their extinguishers so that employees need only learn one set of instructions. In companies employing trained fire brigades, there may be more variation.

An individual's emotional reaction to a fire will be influenced largely by his or her familiarity with the extinguisher, experience in using it or observing its use, and training and self-confidence. Training is, therefore, very important. Many companies have employees practice with extinguishers when the units are scheduled for recharging. Employees should be adequately trained so they will not jeopardize their own safety.

Sometimes, the size or weight of an extinguisher is important. Some extinguisher models have lightweight shells or use agents with more extinguishing capacity per unit of weight. The most common fire extinguisher holds 2½ gal (9.5 L) of water and weighs about 30 lb (13.6 kg). The weight of carbon dioxide and dry chemical extinguishers varies. For example, one manufacturer offers two dry chemical extinguishers with a rating of 40-B:C. The sodium bicarbonate-based model has a 20-lb (9.1 kg) capacity and weighs 27 lb (12.3 kg), but the potassium bicarbonate-based model has a 9-lb (41 kg) capacity and weighs only 14 lb (6.4 kg).

PHYSICAL ENVIRONMENT

Still another factor that influences extinguisher selection is the area in which the extinguishers will be placed. Is the extinguisher affected by extreme temperatures, for example? ANSI standards require evaluation of water-based extinguishers at temperatures between 40 and 120°F (4 and 49°C) and all other types between -40 and 120°F (-40 and 49°C). If extinguishers are installed in areas subject to higher or lower temperatures, they should be listed for those areas or put in an enclosure where the proper temperature is maintained. Some stored-pressure extinguishers for Class B fires use nitrogen rather than carbon dioxide as the pressurizing force. For units that must perform in temperatures as low as -65°F (-54°C), nitrogen pressurization is used.

Other conditions that may affect extinguisher performance are direct sunlight, snow, rain, airborne debris, and corrosive fumes. If extinguishers must be placed outdoors, installing them in cabinets and sheltered areas or placing a protective cover over them will help prevent damage or premature deterioration. (See Figures 5-23A and 5-23B.)

Corrosives can cause extinguishers to fail, and extinguishers capable of withstanding corrosive conditions are listed separately. For example, extinguishers that may be used in salt-air atmospheres appear under the heading "Marine Type, USCG." Where corrosive fumes exist at industrial sites, special analysis should be made before extinguishers are chosen.

Extinguishers may also be affected by the vibration found in places such as a drop forge or hammer mill, trains, vehicles, and power boats. In such cases, they should be of rugged design, mounted securely, and inspected at frequent intervals.

HEALTH AND OPERATIONAL SAFETY CONSIDERATIONS

Potential health hazards should always be considered when selecting extinguishers. Manufacturers normally provide prominent labels of caution on extinguishers that could produce toxic vapors or decomposition vapors. Sometimes, however, the danger resides not in the extinguisher but in the area in which it will be used. Useful safeguards include posting warning signs at the entries to confined areas, providing extinguishers with long-range nozzles, installing special ventilation, or supplying employees in the area with self-contained breathing apparatus.

All water-based extinguishers are rated only for Class A fires, except AFFF models, which are also used on Class B fires. If the nonfoam/water types are used on Class B fires, the fire may flare up, spread, or injure the operator in some way. If water-based extinguishers are used on fires in or near live electrical equipment, the water stream may transmit an electric shock to the operator.

Although carbon dioxide is not itself toxic, it will not support life when used in concentrations high enough to extinguish a fire. If a carbon dioxide extinguisher is used in an unventilated area, it dilutes the oxygen supply, and

TABLE 5-23A. *Characteristics of Extinguishers*

Extinguishing Agent	Method of Operation	Capacity*	Horizontal Range of Stream†	Approximate Time of Discharge	Protection Required Below 40°F (4°C)	UL or ULC Classifications‡
Water/Antifreeze	Stored-Pressure or Cartridge	2½ gal	30–40 ft	1 min	Yes	2-A
	Pump	2½ gal	30–40 ft	1 min	Yes	2-A
	Pump	4 gal	30–40 ft	2 min	Yes	3-A
	Pump	5 gal	30–40 ft	2–3 min	Yes	4-A
Water (Wetting Agent)	Stored-Pressure	1½ gal	20 ft	30 sec	Yes	2-A
	Carbon Dioxide Cylinder	25 gal (wheeled)	35 ft	1½ min	Yes	10-A
	Carbon Dioxide Cylinder	45 gal (wheeled)	35 ft	2 min	Yes	30-A
	Carbon Dioxide Cylinder	60 gal (wheeled)	35 ft	2½ min	Yes	40-A
Loaded Stream	Stored-Pressure or Cartridge	2½ gal	30–40 ft	1 min	No	2 to 3-A:1-B
	Carbon Dioxide Cylinder	33 gal (wheeled)	50 ft	3 min	No	20-A
AFFF	Stored-Pressure	2½ gal	20–25 ft	50 sec	Yes	3-A: 20 to 40-B
	Nitrogen Cylinder	33 gal	30 ft	1 min	Yes	20-A: 160-B
Carbon Dioxide	Self-Expelling	2½ to 5 lb	3–8 ft	8 to 30 sec	No	1 to 5-B:C
	**	10 to 15 lb	3–8 ft	8 to 30 sec	No	2 to 10-B:C
		20 lb	3–8 ft	10 to 30 sec	No	10-B:C
		50 to 100 lb (wheeled)	3–10 ft	10 to 30 sec	No	10 to 20-B:C
Dry Chemical (Sodium Bicarbonate)	Stored-Pressure	1 to 2½ lb	5–8 ft	8 to 12 sec	No	2 to 10-B:C
	Cartridge or Stored-Pressure	2¾ to 5 lb	5–20 ft	8 to 20 sec	No	5 to 20-B:C
	Cartridge or Stored- Pressure	6 to 30 lb	5–20 ft	10 to 25 sec	No	10 to 160-B:C
	Nitrogen Cylinder or Stored-Pressure	75 to 350 lb (wheeled)	15–45 ft	20 to 105 sec	No	40 to 320-B:C
Dry Chemical (Potassium Bicarbonate)	Cartridge or Stored-Pressure	2 to 5 lb	5–12 ft	8 to 10 sec	No	5 to 20-B:C
	Cartridge or Stored-Pressure	5½ to 10 lb	5–20 ft	8 to 20 sec	No	10 to 80-B:C
	Cartridge or Stored-Pressure	16 to 30 lb	10–20 ft	8 to 25 sec	No	40 to 120-B:C
	Cartridge	48 lb	20 ft	30 sec	No	120-B:C
	Nitrogen Cylinder or Stored-Pressure	125 to 315 lb (wheeled)	15–45 ft	30 to 80 sec	No	80 to 640-B:C
Dry Chemical (Potassium Chloride)	Stored-Pressure	2 to 5 lb	5–8 ft	8 to 10 sec	No	5 to 10-B:C
	Stored-Pressure	5 to 9 lb	8–12 ft	10 to 15 sec	No	20 to 40-B:C
	Cartridge or Stored-Pressure	9½ to 20 lb	10–15 ft	15 to 20 sec	No	40 to 60-B:C
	Stored-Pressure	19½ to 30 lb	5–20 ft	10 to 25 sec	No	60 to 80-B:C
	Stored-Pressure	125 to 200 lb	15–45 ft	30 to 40 sec	No	160-B:C

those remaining in the area may become unconscious or even die if they do not receive oxygen. In addition, the thick cloud of condensing water vapor that forms upon discharge may cause persons to become disoriented.

Older carbon dioxide extinguishers may have metal horns that transmit a shock to the user when the horns touch live electrical equipment. These metal horns should be replaced with nonmetallic horns. Occasionally, the operator may receive a shock even when no contact has been made; these result from built-up static electricity and are generally more annoying than hazardous. They are usually caused by the turbulence of the agent discharging through a damaged or defective pickup tube which can be replaced easily.

Dry chemical extinguishers are not considered toxic, but their discharge can be irritating if breathed for a long time. Monoammonium phosphate is the most irritating, followed by potassium-based agents. Sodium bicarbonate is the least irritating. If dry chemicals are discharged in a confined area, they may reduce visibility and cause disorientation. Because dry chemical agents are nonconductors, deposits left on electrical contacts can reduce or negate the ability of the contacts to conduct. They may also clog air conditioning and air cleaning filters if discharged nearby.

TABLE 5-23A. *Characteristics of Extinguishers (cont)*

Extinguishing Agent	Method of Operation	Capacity*	Horizontal Range of Stream†	Approximate Time of Discharge	Protection Required Below 40°F (4°C)	UL or ULC Classifications‡
Dry Chemical (Ammonium Phosphate)	Stored-Pressure	1 to 5 lb	5–12 ft	8 to 10 sec	No	1 to 2-A§ and 2 to 10-B:C
	Stored-Pressure or Cartridge	2½ to 8½ lb	5–12 ft	8 to 15 sec	No	1 to 4-A and 10 to 40-B:C
	Stored-Pressure or Cartridge	9 to 17 lb	5–20 ft	10 to 25 sec	No	2 to 20-A and 10 to 80-B:C
	Stored-Pressure or Cartridge	17 to 30 lb	5–20 ft	10 to 25 sec	No	3 to 20-A and 30 to 120-B:C
	Cartridge	45 lb	20 ft	25 sec	No	20-A:80-B:C
	Nitrogen Cylinder or Stored-Pressure	110 to 315 lb (wheeled)	15–45 ft	30 to 60 sec	No	20 to 40-A and 60 to 320-B:C
Dry Chemical (Foam Compatible)	Cartridge or Stored-Pressure	4¾ to 9 lb	5–20 ft	8 to 10 sec	No	10 to 20-B:C
	Cartridge or Stored-Pressure	9 to 27 lb	5–20 ft	10 to 25 sec	No	20 to 30-B:C
	Cartridge or Stored-Pressure	18 to 30 lb	5–20 ft	10 to 25 sec	No	40 to 60-B:C
	Nitrogen Cylinder or Stored-Pressure	150 to 350 lb (wheeled)	15–45 ft	20 to 150 sec	No	80 to 240-B:C
Dry Chemical (Potassium Chloride)	Cartridge or Stored-Pressure	2½ to 5 lb	5–12 ft	8 to 10 sec	No	10 to 20-B:C
	Cartridge or Stored-Pressure	9½ to 20 lb	5–20 ft	8 to 25 sec	No	40 to 60-B:C
	Cartridge or Stored-Pressure	19½ to 30 lb	5–20 ft	10 to 25 sec	No	60 to 80-B:C
	Stored-Pressure	125 to 200 lb (wheeled)	15–45 ft	30 to 40 sec	No	160-B:C
Dry Chemical (Potassium Bicarbonate Urea Based)	Stored-Pressure	5 to 11 lb	11–22 ft	13 to 18 sec	No	40 to 80-B:C
	Stored-Pressure	9 to 23 lb	15–30 ft	17 to 33 sec	No	60 to 160-B:C
		175 lb (wheeled)	70 ft	62 sec	No	480-B:C
Halon 1301 (Bromotrifluoromethane)	Stored-Pressure	2½ lb	4–6 ft	8 to 10 sec	No	2-B:C
Halon 1211 (Bromochlorodifluoromethane)	Stored-Pressure	1 lb	6–10 ft	8 to 10 sec	No	1-B:C
		2 lb	6–10 ft	8 to 10 sec	No	2-B:C
		2½ lb	6–10 ft	8 to 10 sec	No	5-B:C
		5½ to 9 lb	9–15 ft	8 to 15 sec	No	1-A:10-B:C
		13 to 22 lb	14–16 ft	10 to 18 sec	No	1 to 4-A and 20 to 80-B:C
		150 lb	20–30 ft	30 to 35 sec	No	30-A:160-B:C
Halon 1211/1301 (Bromochlorodifluoromethane/Bromotriluoromethane) Mixtures	Self Expelling	1 to 5 lb	3–12 ft	8 to 10 sec	No	1 to 10-B:C
	Stored-Pressure	9 to 20 lb	10–18 ft	10 to 22 sec	No	1-A and 10-B:C to 4-A and 80-B:C

Notes: * 1 gal = 3.78 L; 1 lb = 0.45 kg. † 1 ft = 0.30 m.

‡ UL and ULC ratings checked as of December 9, 1983. Readers concerned with subsequent ratings should review the pertinent "lists" and "supplements" issued by these laboratories: Underwriters Laboratories Inc., 333 Pfingsten Road, Northbrook, IL 60062, or Underwriters' Laboratories of Canada, 7 Crouse Road, Scarborough, Ont., Canada M1R 3A9.

**Carbon dioxide extinguishers with metallic horns do not carry a "C" classification.

§ Some small extinguishers containing ammonium phosphate base dry chemical do not carry an "A" classification.

N.B.: Vaporizing liquid extinguishers (carbon tetrachloride or chlorobromomethane base) are not recognized in NFPA 10.

N.B.: Soda acid and inverting-type foam extinguishers are no longer acceptable for use. These extinguishers can be extremely dangerous to use due to the explosion hazard.

Multi-purpose dry chemical (monoammonium-phosphate-base) is acidic and, if mixed with even a small amount of water, will corrode some metals unless all agent residues are removed promptly and thoroughly. Finally, the initial discharge of agent from an extinguisher has considerable force. If it is aimed at close range at a small flammable liq-

FIG. 5-23A. An extinguisher mounted on an outside wall, covered with plastic to shield it from substances which would interfere with operation. (Source: The Ansul Company)

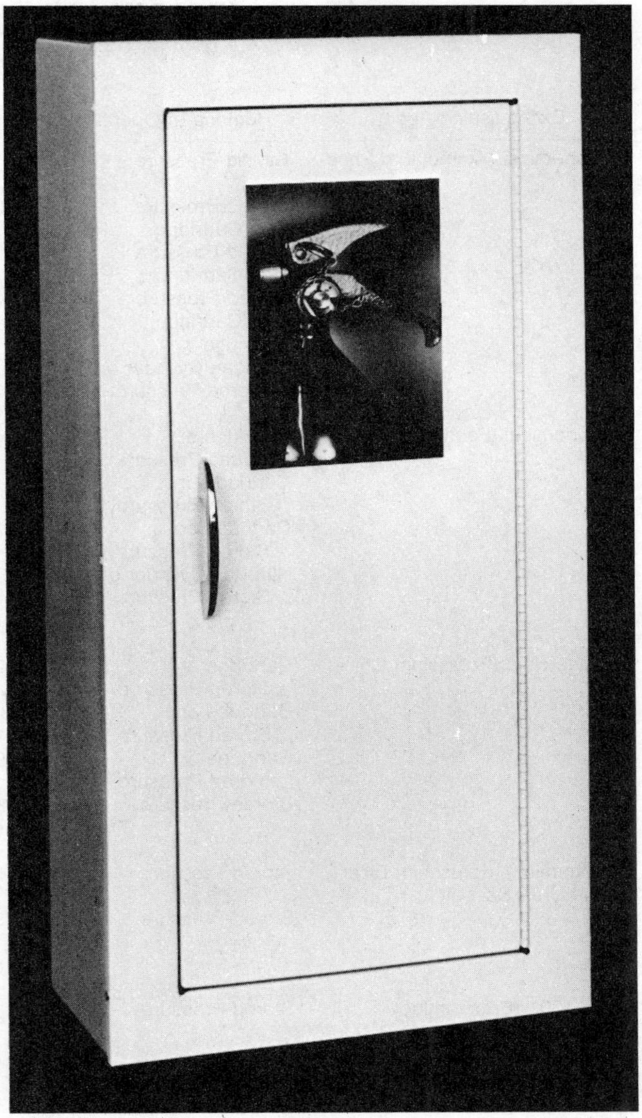

FIG. 5-23B. A surface-mounted extinguisher cabinet with a hinged door. (Source: Larsen's Manufacturing Company)

uid or grease fire, it may cause the fire to spread extensively before it can be brought under control.

Extinguishers containing halogenated agents—that is, Halon 1301, Halon 1211, and Halon 1301/1211 mixtures—present some degree of toxicity under normal operating conditions. However, the decomposition products of these agents can be hazardous. When using these extinguishers in unventilated places such as small rooms, closets, motor vehicles, or other confined spaces, it is best to avoid breathing the vapors or the gases produced by thermal decomposition.

Class D fires involving burning metal chips can be scattered if the full force of a dry powder extinguisher is used at close range. To avoid spreading the fire, the nozzle should be opened slowly at a safe distance.

Virtually every fire produces toxic products of combustion, and some burning materials create highly toxic gases. Until the fire has been extinguished and the area well ventilated, it is important either to stay out of the area or to wear protective breathing apparatus.

OPERATION AND USE

Whether an extinguisher is effective often depends on who is using it. One person may be able to extinguish a fire that someone else, using the same equipment, may not. Many extinguishers discharge their entire contents in 8 to 15 sec, leaving little time for experimentation. Occasionally, improper use of an extinguisher injures the operator and delays extinguishment.

There are several kinds of extinguishers. Because differences exist among extinguishers, it is imperative that people be trained to use them properly. Ideally, this includes the general public. In any case, fire fighters and others responsible for fire protection, such as industrial fire brigades, should be trained thoroughly in the operation and use of extinguishers.

Currently, listed fire extinguishers are classified into five major groups, based on the extinguishing medium each contains. They are water-type, carbon dioxide, halogenated agent, dry chemical, and foam. Dry powder for Class D fires receives special testing and listing based on specific combustible metals. Information about each of these can be found in the following subsections and in Table 5-23A.

In addition, extinguishers that are no longer manufactured may still be found in some areas. Some information on them is provided under the heading "Obsolete Extinguishers."

Water-Based Extinguishers

Water-based extinguishing agents include water, antifreeze, loaded stream, wetting agent, soda-acid, and foam. All except AFFF foam are for use on Class A fires only. Soda-acid and ordinary foam extinguishers are no longer available and are discussed later. Antifreeze, loaded stream, AFFF, and wetting agent all use water as a base to which chemicals are added to improve the extinguisher's performance. Both antifreeze and loaded stream models are specially treated to withstand low temperatures; the additive in loaded stream extinguishers is an alkali metal-salt solution. In wetting agents, a material is added to reduce the surface tension of the water so that it will spread and penetrate better.

Originally, water-based extinguishers were of three basic designs: stored-pressure, pump tank, and inverting. In 1969, however, the manufacture of all inverting extinguishers was discontinued. Consequently, the agents used exclusively in inverting extinguishers, soda-acid and foam, also became obsolete. The two designs that remain, stored-pressure and pump tank, are discussed later.

If ordinary, or nonfoam, water-based extinguishers are used on flammable liquids or electrical fires, they may spread the fire, or injure the operator, or both. After activating an extinguisher, the operator should point the stream at the base of the flames and work from side to side or around the fire. When flames are high, the range of the stream [about 30 ft (9 m)] should be used to best advantage. As the flames diminish, it is possible to move closer and change the solid stream to a spray by holding a fingertip over the end of the nozzle. A spray stream is more effective on burning embers. Deep-seated smoldering or glowing areas should be wetted thoroughly. If necessary, a hand tool should be used to poke apart burning materials to do this.

Stored-pressure: For the capacities, ratings, discharge times, stream range, and temperature requirements of the various stored-pressure water-based extinguishers available, see Table 5-23A. The most common stored-pressure water-based extinguisher contains 2½ gal (9.5 L) and weighs about 30 lb (13.6 kg). It can be operated intermittently, is rechargeable, and has a comparatively long stream range and discharge time. It consists of a single chamber which contains both the agent and expellant gas. The cap, or head assembly, includes a siphon tube, a combination carrying handle/operating lever, a discharge valve, an air pressure valve and gage, a discharge hose, and a nozzle. (See Figure 5-23C.) The extinguisher is pressurized with air or inert gas by means of an automobile-tire-type valve. Charging pressures range from 90 to 125 psi (620 to 862 kPa). A "fill mark" is stamped on many older stored-pressure water-based extinguishers about 6 in. (152.4 mm) from the top; when refilling, this level should never be exceeded. Some models use a special tube device to prevent overfilling.

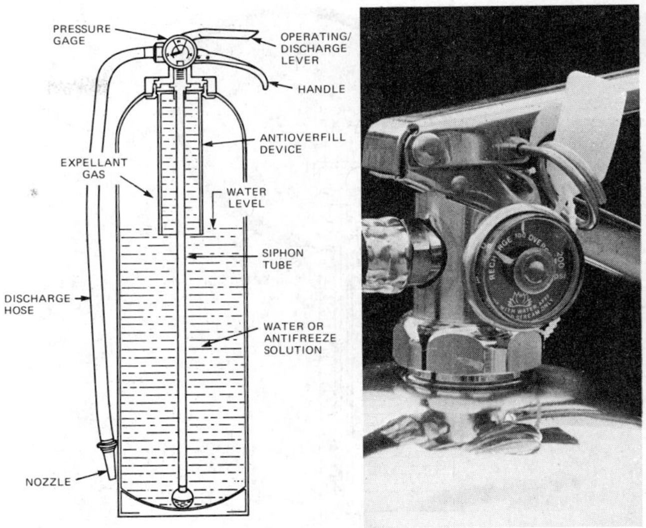

FIG. 5-23C. A stored-pressure water extinguisher with close-up of cap assembly. (Source: Badger-Powhatan)

In most models, the operating lever is locked by a ring pin that prevents accidental discharge. To activate the extinguisher, set it on the ground. Hold the combination handle loosely in one hand and pull out the ring pin or release a small latch with the other hand. Then grab the hose in one hand and squeeze the discharge lever with the other.

Pump tanks: Two different types of pump tanks are available: one is cylindrical, and the other is made to be used as a backpack. The sizes, ratings, discharge times, stream ranges, and weather requirements of the various pump tanks are given in Table 5-23A. The cylindrical model has carrying handles either attached to the container or built into the pump handle, and the water is discharged by a built-in, hand-operated vertical piston pump with an attached short rubber hose. The pump is double-acting and discharges water on both the up and the down strokes. (See Figure 5-23D.) The cylindrical models are available with copper, steel, or plastic shells.

To operate a cylindrical pump tank, place it on the ground and put one foot on the extension bracket at the base to steady the unit. To force water through the hose, pump the handle up and down. Cylindrical pump tanks have two characteristics that may be slight disadvantages: to move the extinguisher, the operator must stop pumping, and the force, range, and duration of the stream are dependent, in part, on the operator.

Cylindrical pump tanks may be filled with either plain water or antifreeze charges recommended by the manufacturer. Common salt or other freezing depressants may corrode the extinguisher or damage the pump assembly. Copper- or plastic-shell models do not corrode as easily as steel, and are recommended for use with antifreeze.

Backpack pump tanks are used chiefly for fighting outdoor brush and wildland fires. As the name implies, they are carried on the operator's back. The most common backpack pump tank holds 5 gal (19 L) and weighs about 50 lb (23 kg) when full. (See Figures 5-23E and 5-23F.) Although listed, backpack pump tanks do not have a designated rating. Generally, the tank is filled with plain water,

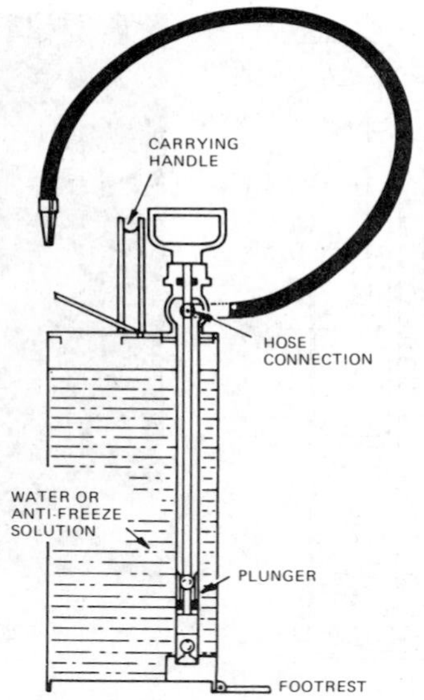

FIG. 5-23D. A pump tank fire extinguisher.

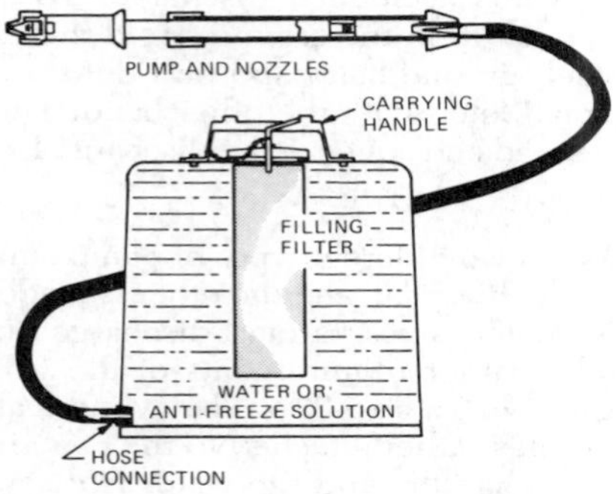

FIG. 5-23E. A backpack pump tank fire extinguisher.

though antifreeze agents, wetting agents, and other special water-based agents may be used. The tank may be made of fiberglass, stainless steel, galvanized steel, or brass, or it may be a flexible water bag. Some models have a large opening with a tight-fitting filter which allows speedy refilling and prevents foreign matter from entering and clogging the pump. This design also permits refilling from nearby sources, such as ponds, lakes, and streams.

The most common backpack pump tank has a trombone-type, double-acting piston pump connected to the tank by a short length of rubber hose. To discharge the device, the operator holds the pump in both hands and moves the piston back and forth. Other models have compression pumps mounted on the right side of the tank. In these, the expellant pressure is built up with about ten strokes of the handle and then maintained by slow, easy pumping. The left-hand controls discharge by means of a lever-operated shutoff nozzle at the end of the hose.

Carbon Dioxide Extinguishers

Carbon dioxide (CO_2) is a compressed gas agent. Though intended for use on Class B and C fires, it may be used on Class A fires until water or some other Class-A-rated agent can be obtained.

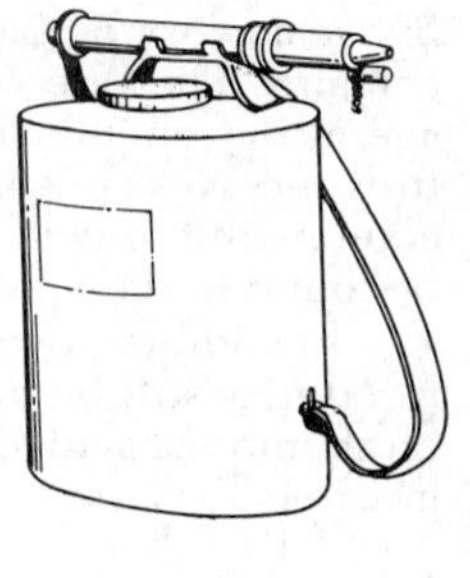

FIG. 5-23F. Backpack pump tank extinguisher with 5-gal (19 L) tank made of fiberglass. Trombone-type pump action is at nozzle.

Carbon dioxide prevents combustion by displacing the oxygen in the air surrounding a fire and by cooling the fuel. Its principal advantage is that it does not leave a residue, a consideration that may be important in laboratories and in areas in which food is prepared or electronic equipment is present. The rapid expansion and pressure reduction of the pressurized liquid carbon dioxide in the cylinder results in the cooling and refrigeration effect. However, carbon dioxide extinguishers have a relatively short range because the agent is expelled in the form of a gas/snow cloud; they are also affected by wind or drafts. If a carbon dioxide extinguisher is used in a confined or unventilated area, precautions should be taken so that people are not overcome from lack of oxygen. For the various sizes, stream ranges, discharge times, temperature requirements, and ratings of carbon dioxide extinguishers available, see Table 5-23A.

In all carbon dioxide extinguishers, the agent is retained as a liquid at 800 to 900 psi (5516 to 6205 kPa) at temperatures below 88°F (31°C), and it is self-expelling. The extinguisher design consists of a pressure cylinder, or shell; a siphon tube and valve for releasing the agent; and a discharge horn or horn-hose combination. The siphon tube extends from the valve almost to the bottom of the shell, so that normally only liquid CO_2 reaches the discharge horn until about 80 percent of the content has been released. The remaining 20 percent enters the siphon tube as a gas. The rapid expansion from liquid to gas when most of the CO_2 is discharged converts about 30 percent of the liquid into a very cold "snow" or "dry ice," which then sublimes into a gas.

To operate a carbon dioxide extinguisher, hold it upright by its carrying handle, remove the locking pin, and squeeze the operating lever. (See Figure 5-23G.) In smaller portable models, the discharge horn often is connected to the valve assembly by a metal tube/swing joint connector, and the models may be operated with one hand. Larger portable models require two hands, and their discharge horns are attached to a length of hose. Wheeled extinguishers have a cylinder valve with a locking ring pin, a long hose of 15 to 40 ft (4 m to 12 m), and a projector that consists of a horn, a long handle, and a control valve. Once the cylinder valve has been opened, the operator controls the discharge with the valve on the projector handle.

Care should be taken not to touch the discharge horn during operation, because it can become extremely cold. If carbon dioxide extinguishers are used in subzero temperatures, the valve must remain open at all times or the discharge may become blocked unless a special low-temperature charge has been added.

Because carbon dioxide extinguishers have a limited range and are affected by draft or wind, they should be applied as close to the base of a fire as possible. Agent

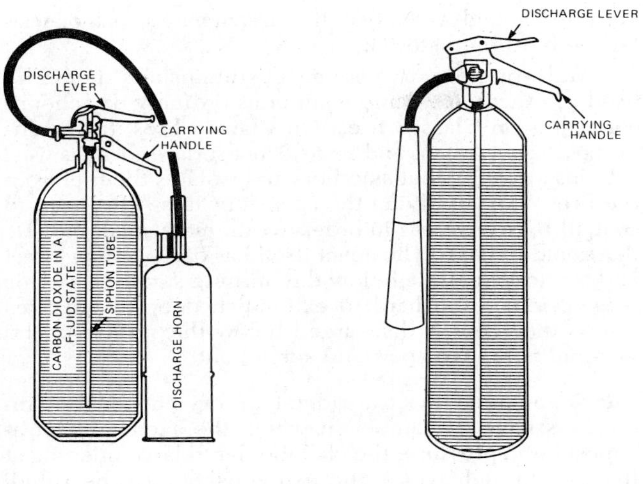

FIG. 5-23G. Carbon dioxide fire extinguisher.

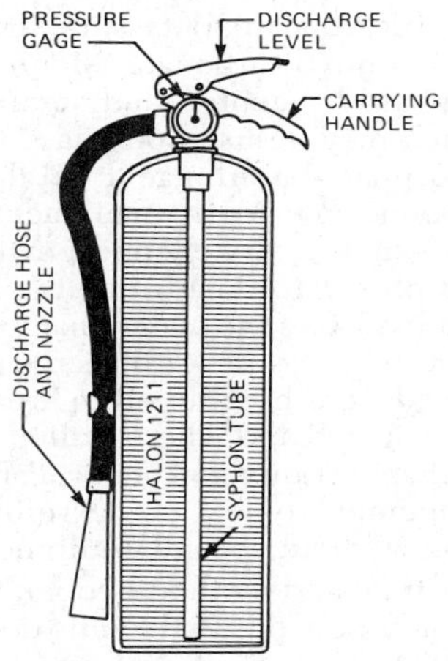

FIG. 5-23H. Halon 1211 stored-pressure fire extinguisher.

should be applied even after the flames have been extinguished to allow time for cooling and to prevent reflash. Due to the relatively short discharge range, carbon dioxide extinguishers are of limited effectiveness on large Class B fires. For flammable liquid fires, the usual method is to begin at the near edge and sweep from side to side toward the back of the fire. However, there is another method called "overhead application." In this method, the discharge horn is pointed downward at an angle of about 45 degrees toward the center of the burning area. Usually, the horn is not moved, and the agent spreads out in all directions. The side-to-side sweeping method may give better results on spill fires, while the overhead method may be best for confined fires.

For fires involving electrical equipment, the discharge should be directed at the source of the flames. It is important to deenergize the equipment as soon as possible to prevent possible reignition.

Halogenated Agent Extinguishers

In general, bromochlorodifluoromethane, or Halon 1211, is similar to carbon dioxide in that it is a "clean agent." (See Figure 5-23H.) Though intended for use mostly on Class B:C fires, Halon 1211 is effective on Class A fires. Sizes of 9-lb (4.1 kg) capacity and greater have Class A ratings. For listed ratings, capacities, discharge times, stream range, and weather requirements for Halon 1211, see Table 5-23A.

Halon 1211 leaves no residue, is virtually noncorrosive and nonabrasive, and is at least twice as effective on Class B fires as carbon dioxide when compared on a weight of agent basis. It also has about twice the range of carbon dioxide. Like carbon dioxide, it needs no cold weather protection. Though Halon 1211 does not have the cooling effect that carbon dioxide has, it is not as severely affected by wind as carbon dioxide, although strong air currents may disperse the agent too rapidly. When Halon 1211 is used on a fire, the decomposition products include hydrogen chloride, hydrogen fluoride, hydrogen bromide, and traces of free halogens. Normally, only small quantities of these chemicals are formed, and, as a warning of their presence, they give off an acrid odor. Although Halon 1211 is retained under pressure in a liquid state [40 psi at 70°F (276 kPa at 21°C)], a booster charge of nitrogen is added to ensure proper operation.

Several manufacturers have produced Halon 1301 extinguishers during the past 30 years in a $2\frac{1}{2}$-lb (1.1 kg) size. (See Figure 5-23I.) These extinguishers are rated only for small Class B:C fires and have a significantly less toxicity hazard. Because of its low vapor pressure, the discharge stream of Halon 1301 is principally an invisible gas, which may complicate effective application.

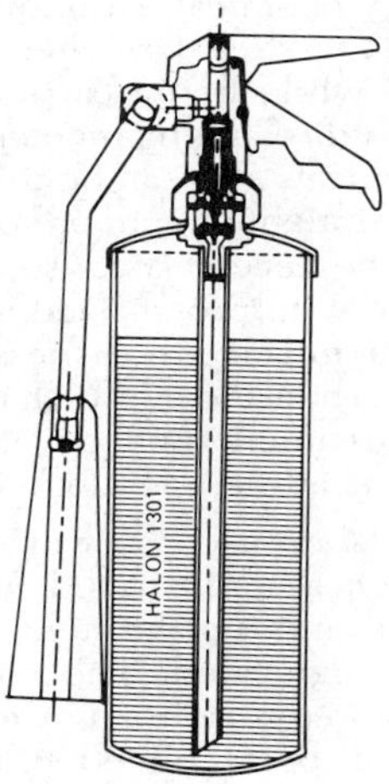

FIG. 5-23I. Halon 1301 fire extinguisher.

Halogenated agent extinguishers are also available containing a blend of Halon 1211 and Halon 1301. Halogenated agent extinguishers should be operated and applied to fires in the same general way that carbon dioxide extinguishers are.

Again, due to environmental problems associated with halogenated agents, their use is being discouraged except in specific circumstances.

Dry Chemical Extinguishers

There are two basic kinds of dry chemical agents: ordinary dry chemicals, which may be used on Class B:C fires and include sodium bicarbonate, potassium bicarbonate (Purple K), urea potassium bicarbonate (Monnex®), and potassium chloride-based agents; and multi-purpose dry chemicals, which may be used on Class A:B:C fires. An ammonium-phosphate-based agent is the only multi-purpose dry chemical currently manufactured. There are also two basic designs of dry chemical extinguishers: one uses a separate pressurized cartridge to expel the agent, and the other pressurizes the agent chamber for the same purpose. The stored-pressure, or rechargeable type, is the most widely used. It is best suited to areas where infrequent use is anticipated and where skilled personnel with professional recharge equipment are available. By contrast, the cartridge-operated type can be refilled quickly in remote locations without special equipment.

The size, rating, and method of operation of any particular extinguisher depends both on its design and on the agent. Table 5-23A gives specific information on the capacities, ratings, discharge times, and stream ranges of the dry chemical extinguishers now available.

In areas where Class A:B:C protection is needed, water-based extinguishers may be omitted if multi-purpose dry chemical extinguishers are installed. However, they are not replacements for water-based extinguishers under all conditions.

When choosing a dry chemical extinguisher for Class C protection, it is important to remember that potassium chloride is more corrosive than the other dry chemicals and that multi-purpose agent (ammonium phosphate) also is corrosive and will be more difficult to remove because it hardens when it cools.

The various dry chemical extinguishers possess certain common characteristics. Dry chemical extinguishers can be discharged while being carried, and all can be briefly stopped from discharging momentarily to conserve the agent. Dry chemicals also can be used simultaneously with water, either straight stream or spray. Special long-range nozzles may be necessary for some very hazardous areas, such as those with pressurized gases and flammable liquids. Dry chemicals are dispersed less easily by wind than either carbon dioxide or halogenated agents, though dry chemicals are most effective during windy conditions if the wind is at the operator's back.

If dry chemicals are used on wet, energized electrical equipment, such as rain-soaked utility poles, high-voltage switch gear, and transformers, electrical leakage problems may be aggravated. The combination of dry chemical with moisture provides an electrical path that can keep insulation from being effective. In such cases, all traces of dry chemical should be removed after the fire has been put out.

Although all dry chemicals are treated for water repellancy, they may harden if exposed to water. It is therefore important to avoid exposing them to any moisture during storage, handling, and recharging. Manufacturers' specifications must be followed carefully.

Ordinary dry chemicals are rated for use on Class B:C fires, but they may be used on Class A fires to knock down flames rapidly until something more suitable can be obtained. When used on flammable liquid fires, the stream should be directed at the base of the flame. Attack the fire near the edge, and move the discharge toward the back of the fire while sweeping the nozzle rapidly from side to side. Do not direct the initial discharge directly at the burning surface at close range [less than 5 to 8 ft (1.5 to 2.4 m)], because the high velocity of the stream may splash or scatter the burning material.

Multi-purpose dry chemical extinguishers should be used in exactly the same manner as ordinary dry chemical agents on Class B fires. On Class A fires, the multi-purpose agent softens and sticks to hot surfaces. In this way, it forms a coating that smothers and isolates the fuel from the fire. When applying the agent to Class A fires, try to coat all burning areas in order to eliminate small embers that could reignite. The agent itself has little cooling effect and cannot penetrate below the burning surface. For this reason, it may be hard to extinguish deep-seated fires unless the agent is discharged below the surface or the material is broken apart and spread out.

Cartridge-operated: Cartridge-type dry chemical extinguishers have a chamber in which the agent is kept at atmospheric pressure; the chamber has a large opening at the top through which the extinguisher may be filled. Attached to the side of the extinguisher, on most models, is a small cartridge of propellant gas, either carbon dioxide or nitrogen, threaded into a puncture valve and gas tube assembly. The agent is discharged through a hose attached to the bottom edge of the shell, and the discharge is controlled by a squeeze grip nozzle at the end of the hose. (See Figure 5-23J.) Cartridge-operated extinguishers should be recharged once they have been pressurized. Even if no agent has been released, the propellant gas can leak away in several hours, leaving a "dead" extinguisher.

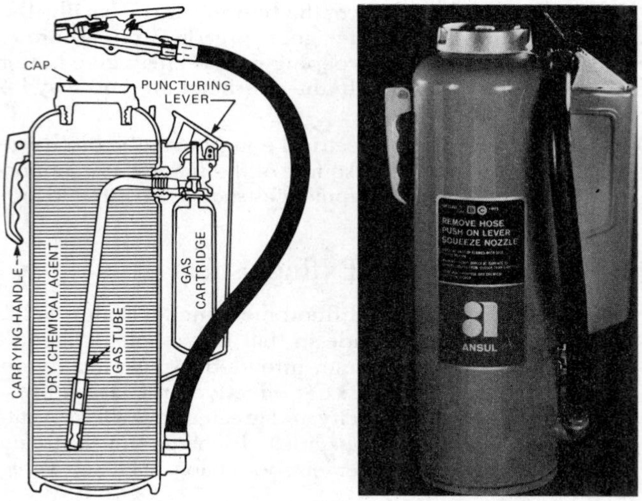

FIG. 5-23J. A cartridge-operated dry chemical fire extinguisher. (Source: The Ansul Company)

To activate a cartridge-operated extinguisher, hold it upright or place it on the ground. Remove the nozzle from its holder, and hold it in one hand while first pushing down the puncture lever before squeezing the nozzle. Pushing the puncture lever releases the propellant from the cartridge and pressurizes the agent in the cylinder. On some models, it may be necessary to remove a locking pin before pushing the puncture lever. This operation requires two hands, one to hold the device and the other to release and direct the discharge. Do not stand directly over the extinguishier when pressurizing it.

Stored-pressure: Dry chemical extinguishers with this expellant method are available in both rechargeable and disposable shell models. Most disposable models have a disposable, factory-sealed cylinder containing agent and propellant gas that is threaded into the valve and nozzle assembly. Some small models are designed so that the entire device can be discarded after use. Once this type of device has been used, it should be replaced, even if only a small amount of agent has been discharged, because the propellant gas will leak, leaving a dead extinguisher.

Rechargeable stored-pressure extinguishers come in two types. In both, the agent and the propellant gas are mixed in the extinguisher shell. When the extinguisher is activated, the agent is forced up the siphon tube, where its release is controlled by the operator. One type of extinguisher has a threaded valve assembly and combination carrying handle/operating lever that screws into an opening on the top of the shell. To activate it, release the locking device and squeeze the operating lever. (See Figure 5-23K.) On smaller sizes of this extinguisher, only one hand is needed to operate the device because the nozzle is part of the valve assembly. Larger sizes require two hands for operation, one to squeeze the lever and carry the device, and the other to direct the agent discharge from the hose.

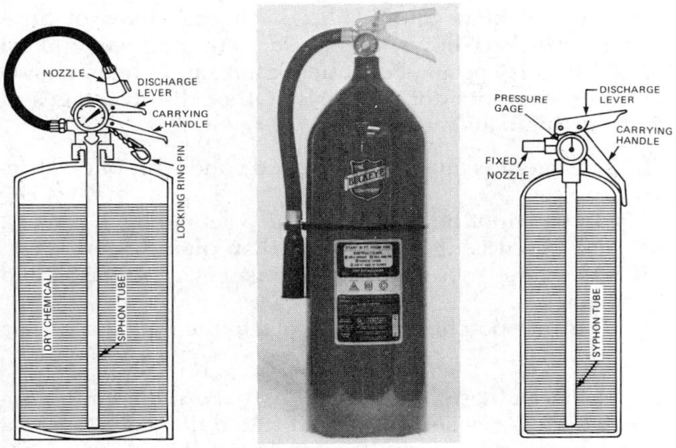

FIG. 5-23K. Stored-pressure dry chemical fire extinguishers. (Photo source: Buckeye Fire Equipment)

The other rechargeable stored-pressure dry chemical extinguisher (pre-1975) has a release lever and a hose attached to the cap assembly that covers the fill opening. The hose has a squeeze-grip nozzle for controlling the discharge. To activate it, pull the ring pin and push down the release lever. The agent will travel down the hose to the nozzle, where its discharge can be controlled by squeezing the nozzle. Two hands are needed to operate this extinguisher, one to carry the extinguisher, and the other to release and aim the discharge stream.

Dry Powder Extinguishers

Dry powder extinguishers are intended for use on Class D fires, which involve combustible metals. The agent, extinguisher, and method of application should be chosen according to manufacturers' recommendations. The agent may be applied to the fire from an extinguisher or with a scoop and shovel, depending on the type of both agent and metal. In any case, the agent should be applied so that it covers the fire and provides a smothering blanket. More agent may be necessary on hot spots. Care should be taken not to scatter the burning material, which should be left undisturbed until it has cooled.

If there is a fire in finely divided combustible metal or combustible metal alloy scrap that is wet, or if such a fire is wetted with water or water-soluble machine lubricants, the metal is likely to burn rapidly and violently. Such fires may become so hot that it is impossible to get close enough to apply extinguishing agent. If burning metal is on a combustible surface, it should be covered with dry powder. Then a 1- or 2-in. (25 or 50 mm) layer of powder should be spread out nearby, and the burning metal shoveled into it. (See Section 5, Chapter 21, "Combustible Metal Agents and Application Techniques.")

One cartridge-operated portable [30 lb (13.6 kg)] dry powder extinguisher currently is available. (See Figure 5-23L.) Wheeled models are available in 150- and 350-lb (68 and 159 kg) sizes. The extinguishing agent is sodium chloride with additives that render it free-flowing. Thermoplastic material also is added to bind the sodium chloride particles into a solid crust when applied to a fire. With the nozzle fully open, the portable model has a range of 6 to 8 ft (1.8 to 2.4 m).

The method of agent application depends on the type, quantity, and physical form of the burning metal. If the fire is very hot, discharge should begin at the maximum range with the nozzle fully open. Once control is established, the nozzle should be partly closed to produce a soft, heavy flow so that complete coverage can be accomplished at close range. More complete details should be obtained from the manufacturer.

In bulk form, dry powder agents are available in 40- or 50-lb (18 or 23 kg) pails and 350-lb (159 kg) drums. The two most common agents are sodium chloride and G-1 powder. The latter consists of graded, granular graphite to which compounds containing phosphorous have been

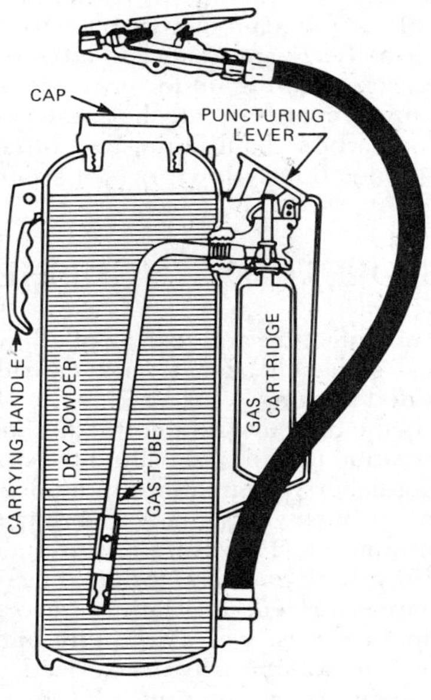

FIG. 5-23L. Dry powder extinguisher.

added. The sodium chloride can be used in an extinguisher or applied by hand. The G-1 agent must be applied by hand. When G-1 is applied to a metal fire, the heat of the fire causes the phosphorous compounds to generate vapors which blanket the fire and prevent air from reaching the burning metal. The graphite, being a good conductor of heat, cools the metal.

Aqueous Film-Forming Foam (AFFF) Extinguishers

This extinguishing agent is an aqueous film-forming surfactant. When added to water, AFFF forms a solution that creates a foam when discharged through an aspirating nozzle. On Class A fires, the agent both cools and penetrates to reduce temperatures below the ignition level. On Class B fires, it acts as a barrier to exclude oxygen from the surface of the fuel.

AFFF currently is available in a 2½-gal (9.5 L) stored-pressure model rated at 3-A:20-B. It discharges its contents in approximately 50 sec and has a range of 20 to 25 ft (6 to 8 m). It should be installed only in areas not subject to temperatures below 40°F (4°C). There is also a 33-gal (125.4 L) unit with a 20A:160-B rating.

This type of extinguisher closely resembles the stored-pressure water extinguisher, except for its special aspirating nozzle. (See Figure 5-23M.) On flammable liquid fires of appreciable depth, the best results are obtained when the discharge is played against the inside of the back wall of the vat or tank just above the burning surface, which should permit the natural spread of the foam back over the burning liquid. If this is not possible, the operator should stand far enough away from the fire to allow the foam to fall lightly on the burning surface instead of splashing it into the burning liquid. Where possible, the operator should walk around the fire while directing the stream to get maximum coverage during discharge. For flammable liquid spill fires, the foam may be flowed over a burning surface by bouncing it off the floor just in front of the burning area. The operator should never turn his or her back on the fire, as unburned fuel may reignite. For fires in ordinary combustibles, the foam may be used to coat the burning surface directly. Foam is not effective on flammable liquids and gases escaping under pressure, nor is it suitable for fires involving ethers, alcohols, esters, acetone, lacquer thinners, carbon disulphide, and other flammable liquids that either break down or penetrate the foam blanket.

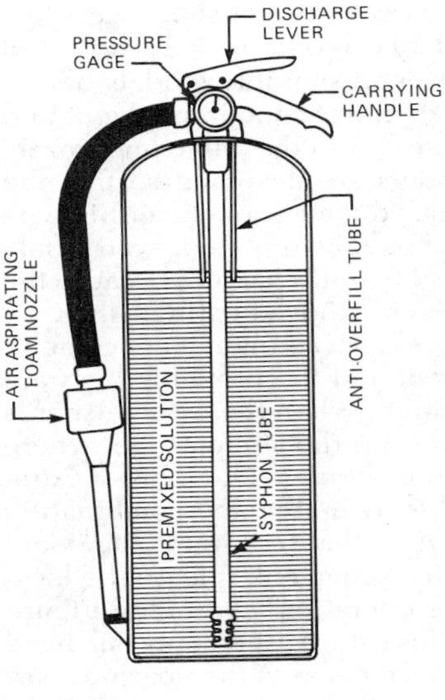

FIG. 5-23M. Aqueous film-forming foam (AFFF) extinguishers. (Photo source: Amerex)

When inverted, normal operating pressures are about 100 psi (690 kPa). Should the discharge elbow or hose become blocked, however, pressures in excess of 300 psi (2069 kPa) may occur. Container failures have been known to injure the operator seriously. Other disadvantages of these extinguishers are:

1. The agent is an extremely good conductor of electricity.
2. They cannot be turned off once actuated.
3. The agent is more corrosive than plain water.
4. They are more costly to inspect, maintain, and recharge.
5. They are potentially dangerous to the operator during use.

For all of these reasons, NFPA 10, *Portable Fire Extinguishers*, was revised in 1978. It stated that extinguishers with copper or brass shells joined by soft solder or rivets could no longer be hydrostatically tested, which would result in their removal from use within five years of the latest hydrostatic test date. Tests showed that the reliability and safety of this type of construction could not be determined by standard hydrostatic test procedures.

Vaporizing liquid extinguishers with CCl_4 (carbon tetrachloride) and CBM (chlorobromomethane) became obsolete in the late 1960s. The toxic properties of these agents expose the operator to unwarranted health hazards, and their use was supplanted by safer, more effective extinguishers. If any extinguishers of this type are found in use, they should be destroyed promptly and replaced with other suitable extinguishers currently available.

OBSOLETE EXTINGUISHERS

In 1969, the manufacture and testing of all inverting-type extinguishers—soda-acid, foam, and cartridge-operated water and loaded stream—was halted in the United States. It was not only the difficult and unorthodox "upside-down" method of actuation that brought about the discontinuance of these extinguishers. Of greater importance was the fact that, after ten to fifteen years, many inverting types tended to fail the minimum test pressure requirements of NFPA 10, *Portable Fire Extinguishers*, (original factory test pressure). When pressurized, the failure record, including hydrostatic test failures, was alarmingly high. Since the inverting types are not normally pressurized, potential failures generally are not evident until the time of operation or hydrostatic testing.

DISTRIBUTION OF FIRE EXTINGUISHERS

No matter how carefully extinguishers are chosen to match the hazards of an area and the ability of the people who will use them, they will not be effective unless they are readily available. Sometimes extinguishers are kept at hand, as in welding operations, but, more often, one has to travel from the fire to the extinguisher and back before beginning to put out the fire. In such cases, travel distance to the nearest extinguisher is very important. Travel distance is the actual distance around partitions, through doorways and aisles, and so on that someone must walk to reach the extinguisher.

When placing extinguishers, select locations that provide uniform distribution, easily accessible and relatively free from temporary blockage, near normal paths of travel, near exits and entrances, free from the potential of physical damage, and readily available.

Mounting Extinguishers

If an extinguisher falls, it may injure someone or be so damaged that it must be replaced. Most extinguishers are mounted on walls or columns by securely fastened hangers so that they are supported adequately. Some extinguishers are mounted in cabinets or wall recesses. When this is the case, the operating instructions should face outward, and the extinguisher should be placed so that it can be removed easily. Cabinets should be kept clean, dry, and ventilated if installed in outdoor locations.

Where extinguishers may become dislodged, brackets specifically designed to cope with this problem are available. In areas where they are subject to physical damage, such as warehouse aisles, protection from impact is important. In large open areas, such as aircraft hangars, extinguishers may be mounted on moveable pedestals or wheeled carts. In order to maintain some pattern of distribution and specify intended placement, locations should be marked on the floor.

NFPA 10, *Portable Fire Extinguishers*, specifies floor clearance and mounting heights, based on extinguisher weight, as follows:

1. Extinguishers with a gross weight not exceeding 40 lb (18 kg) should be installed so that the top of the extinguisher is not more than 5 ft (1.5 m) above the floor.
2. Extinguishers with a gross weight greater than 40 lb (18 kg), except wheeled types, should be installed so that the top of the extinguisher is not more than 3½ ft (1 m) above the floor.
3. In no case can the clearance between the bottom of the extinguisher and the floor be less than 4 in. (100 mm).

When extinguishers are mounted on industrial trucks, vehicles, boats, aircraft, trains, and so on, special mounting brackets, available from the manufacturer, should be used. Although cabinets or lockers are sometimes used, these locations frequently become cluttered with items that hamper quick retrieval. It is also important that the extinguisher be located at a safe distance from the hazard so that it will not become involved in the fire.

Extinguisher Distribution for Class A Combustibles

Table 5-23B is a guide to determining the minimum number and rating of extinguishers for Class A fires needed in any particular area. Sometimes extinguishers with ratings higher than those indicated in Table 5-23A may be necessary because of process hazards, building configuration, and so on, but in no case should the recommended maximum travel distance be exceeded.

The first step when calculating how many Class A extinguishers are needed is to determine whether an occupancy is light-, ordinary-, or extra-hazard, according to NFPA 10, *Portable Fire Extinguishers*. Next, the extinguisher rating should be matched with occupancy hazard to determine the maximum area that an extinguisher can protect. Table 5-23B also specifies the maximum travel distance, or actual walking distance, allowed. For Class A extinguishers, it is 75 ft (23 m). For example, each 2½-gal (9.5 L) stored-pressure water extinguisher rated 2-A will protect an area of 3000 sq ft (279 m^2) in an ordinary-hazard occupancy, but only 2000 sq ft (186 m^2) in an extra-hazard occupancy.

TABLE 5-23B. ***Fire Extinguisher Size and Placement for Class A Hazards***

	Light (Low) Hazard Occupancy	Ordinary (Moderate) Hazard Occupancy	Extra (High) Hazard Occupancy
Minimum rated single extinguisher	2-A	2-A	4-A*
Mazimum floor area per unit of A	3,000 sq ft	1,500 sq ft	1,000 sq ft
Maximum floor area for extinguisher	11,250 sq ft**	11,250 sq ft**	11,250 sq ft**
Maximum travel distance to extinguisher	75 ft	75 ft	75 ft

* Two 2½-gal (9.46-L) water-type extinguishers can be used to fulfill the requirements of one 4-A rated extinguisher.
** See Appendix E-3.3 of NFPA 10, *Portable Fire Extiguishers.*
For SI Units: 1 ft = 0.305 m; 1 sq ft = 0.929 m^2

The figure of 11,250 sq ft (1044 m^2) in Table 5-23B is used instead of 12,000 sq ft (1115 m^2), which would appear to be a normal progressive increment. This is because the largest square inside a circle with a 75-ft (23 m) radius would be 106 by 106 ft (32 m × 32 m), or 11,250 sq ft (1044 m^2). Because buildings are usually rectangular, this is the largest open area one can have and still comply with the 75-ft (23 m) travel distance rule. (See Figure 5-23N for an illustration of this concept.)

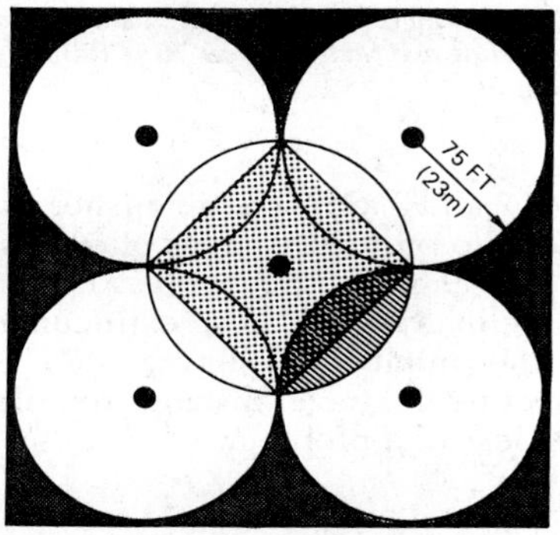

FIG. 5-23N. ***The dotted square shows the maximum area [11,250 sq ft (1044 m2)] that an extinguisher can protect within the limits of a 75-ft (23 m) radius.***

NFPA 10, *Portable Fire Extinguishers*, also provides that up to one-half of the complement of extinguishers for Class A fires, as specified in Table 5-23B, may be replaced by uniformly spaced small-hose [1½ in. (38 mm)] stations.

However, the hose stations and extinguishers should be located so that the hose stations do not replace more than every other extinguisher.

The following examples illustrate the number and placement of extinguishers according to occupancy hazard and extinguisher rating. The sample building is 150 by 450 ft (46 by 137 m), which gives a floor area of 67,500 sq ft (6270 m^2). Although several different ways of placing extinguishers are given, a number of other locations could have been used with similar results.

The first example demonstrates placement at the maximum protection area limits [11,250 ft^2 (1044 m^2)] allowed per extinguisher in NFPA 10, *Portable Fire Extinguishers*, for each class of occupancy. Installing extinguishers with higher ratings will not affect distribution or placement.

Example 1:

$$\frac{67,500}{11,250} = 6 \begin{cases} \text{4-A Extinguishers for light-hazard occupancy} \\ \text{10-A Extinguishers for ordinary-hazard occupancy} \\ \text{20-A Extinguishers for extra-hazard occupancy} \end{cases}$$

This placement along outside walls would not be acceptable because it clearly violates the travel distance rule. (See Figure 5-23O.) Instead, relocation and/or additional extinguishers are needed.

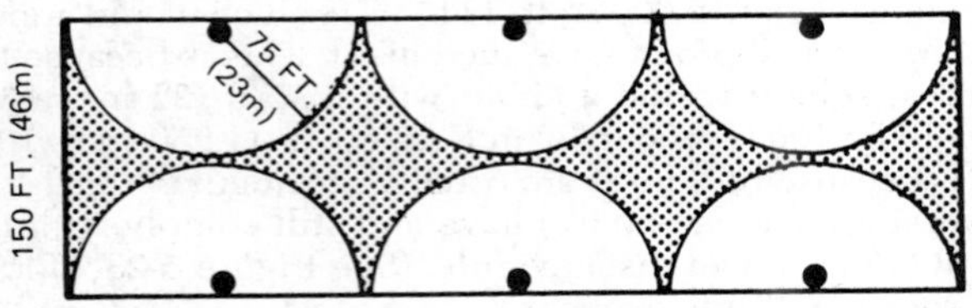

FIG. 5-23O. A diagrammatic representation of extinguishers located along the outside walls of a 150 by 450-ft (46 by 137 m) building. The large dots represent extinguishers. The shaded areas indicate "voids" that are farther than 75 ft (23 m) from the nearest extinguisher.

Examples 2 and 3 are for extinguishers having ratings that correspond to protection areas of 6000 sq ft (557 m^2) and 3000 sq ft (279 m^2), respectively. The examples show only one of the many ways these extinguishers could be placed. As the number of lower-rated extinguishers increases, meeting the travel distance requirement generally becomes less of a problem.

Example 2:

$$\frac{67,500}{6,000} = 12 \begin{cases} \text{2-A Extinguishers for light-hazard occupancy} \\ \text{4-A Extinguishers for ordinary-hazard occupancy} \\ \text{6-A Extinguishers for extra-hazard occupancy} \end{cases}$$

Example 3:

$$\frac{67,500}{3,000} = 24 \begin{cases} \text{1-A Extinguishers for light-hazard occupancy} \\ \text{2-A Extinguishers for ordinary-hazard occupancy} \\ \text{3-A Extinguishers for extra-hazard occupancy} \end{cases}$$

Extinguishers could be mounted on exterior walls or, as shown in Figure 5-23P, on building columns or interior walls, and conform to both distribution and travel distance rules.

The arrangement illustrated in Figure 5-23Q shows extinguishers grouped together on building columns or interior walls in a manner that still conforms to distribution and travel distance rules.

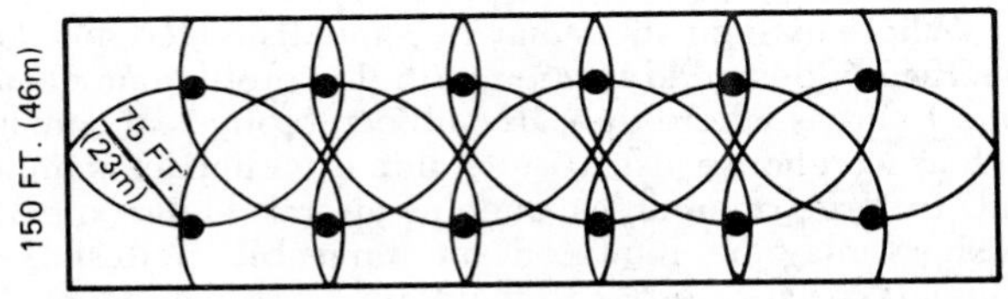

FIG. 5-23P. Requirements for both travel distance and extinguisher distribution are met in this configuration of 12 extinguishers mounted on building columns or interior walls.

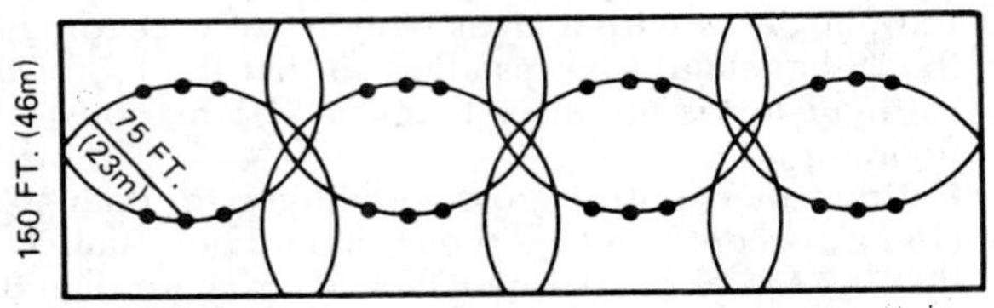

FIG. 5-23Q. Extinguishers grouped together.

Extinguisher Distribution for Class B Combustibles

As noted earlier, Class B fire hazards fall into two distinct categories. The first includes liquids 1/4 in. (6.4 mm) deep or less, and the other includes liquids deeper than 1/4 in. (6.4 mm).

In areas where liquids do not reach an appreciable depth, extinguishers should be provided according to Table 5-23C. The reason the basic maximum travel distance to Class B extinguishers is 50 ft (15 m), as opposed to 75 ft (23 m) for Class A extinguishers, is that flammable liquids fires reach their maximum intensity almost immediately, and thus the extinguisher must be nearer to hand. With lower-rated extinguishers, the travel distance is reduced to 30 ft (9 m).

Even though Table 5-23C specifies maximum travel distances to extinguishers for Class B fires, judgment should be used when actually placing the devices. The closer the extinguisher to the hazard, the better—up to the point at which a fire might damage or obstruct access to, the device. When an entire room is a Class B hazard, such as is the case

TABLE 5-23C. ***Fire Extinguisher Size and Placement for Class B Hazard Excluding Protection of Deep Layer Flammable Liquid Tanks***

Type of Hazard	Basic Minimum Extinguisher Rating	Maximum Travel Distance to Extinguishers ft (m)
Low	5-B	30 (9)
	10-B	50 (15)
Moderate	10-B	30 (9)
	20-B	50 (15)
High	40-B	30 (9)
	80-B	50 (15)

in an auto repair garage, extinguishers should be placed at regular intervals so that the travel distances do not exceed those in Table 5-23C.

When flammable liquids reach an appreciable depth, the extinguisher's rating number, except for foam types, should be at least twice the number of square feet (m^2) of surface area of the largest tank in the area, assuming that other requirements are met. The travel distances specified by Table 5-23C should also be used to locate extinguishers for protection of spot hazards. Sometimes, one extinguisher can be installed to provide protection against several different hazards, provided that travel distances are not exceeded. Where hazards are widely separated and travel distances are exceeded, individual protection should be installed according to the square-foot requirements.

Where there are open process tanks of flammable liquids with surface areas greater than 10 sq ft (1 m^2), complete dependence should not be placed on fire extinguishers. Fires in tanks as large as these rapidly become so large and intense that it is impossible to approach them, and some appropriate fixed protection should be installed. If a fixed protection system suitable for Class B fires is installed, then the extinguisher requirement may be waived for the hazard, or hazards, it protects, though not for the complete structure or any other special hazards in the area. But portable extinguishers are always desirable. They may be useful even when fixed protection systems have been installed, in case a burning tank spills liquid outside the range of the fixed equipment or a fire begins adjacent to a tank rather than in it.

Pressurized flammable liquids and gases are not stored in open containers, and it is not possible to select extinguishers for them according to the square foot requirements. Instead, extinguishers with special nozzles and rates of agent application should be chosen. The manufacturers of these specialized extinguishers usually recommend what equipment they are suited for. In general, however, no attempt to extinguish pressurized fuel fires should be made unless the source of fuel can be shut off promptly because an explosion may occur otherwise. As before, the travel distances to portable extinguishers should not exceed those specified by Table 5-23C.

Because Class B fires become so intense so quickly, the flow rate and the duration of discharge of an agent are very important. For these reasons, NFPA 10, *Portable Fire Extinguishers*, does not permit substituting two or more extinguishers of lower rating for the minimum ratings given in Table 5-23C, except for certain foam extinguishers. The exception permits the substitution because foam progressively "secures" a fire, and the foam from one extinguisher is effective during the time it takes to bring other units into operation. With carbon dioxide and dry chemical extinguishers, however, four extinguishers rated 5-B are not equal to one extinguisher rated 20-B; the larger extinguisher has a higher flow rate in pounds per second and a longer continuous discharge time than the smaller models. Smaller models are appropriate only if access to an area is limited or a trained fire brigade is available to attack a fire simultaneously from several positions.

Wheeled extinguishers with ratings from 20-B to 480-B are available. They are designed chiefly for outdoor fire fighting and should be used only by trained employees. They should be distributed according to the 50-ft (15 m) travel distance rule, though longer travel distances may be authorized by the proper authorities.

Figure 5-23R provides a sample problem for protection by portable extinguishers.

SAMPLE PROBLEM

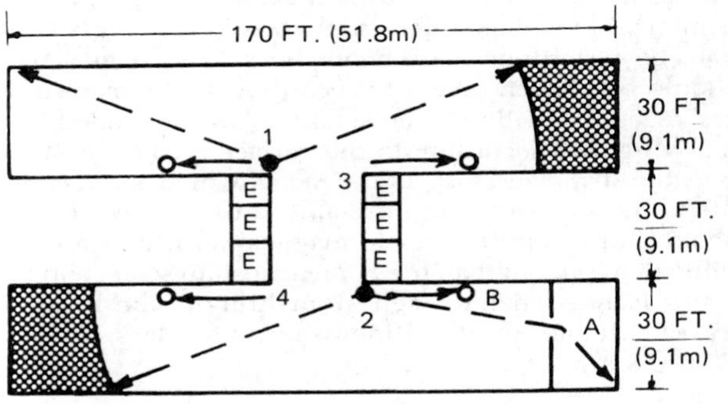

A light-occupancy office building needs to be protected by portable fire extinguishers. The floor area is 11,100 ft² (1031m²) and of unusual design.

The most common extinguisher selection would be 2½ gal (9.5L) stored-water pressure models rated 2-A. According to the requirements, two extinguishers are needed (11,100 divided by 6,000 = 2). Travel distance requirements are 75 ft. (23m) maximum.

The two units are placed at Points 1 and 2, and a check is made on the travel distance requirement. Because of the area's unusual shape, it is found that the shaded areas exceed the 75 ft. (23m) distance. Two additional extinguishers (at Points 3 and 4) are needed. The additional extinguishers afford more flexibility in placement, and alternate locations are indicated. It is important to consider any partitions, walls or other obstructions in determining the travel distance.

As an additional item, consider that Area A contains a small printing and duplicating department that uses flammable liquids. This area is judged to be an ordinary Class B hazard. A 10-B:C or 20-B:C extinguisher should be specified to protect this area.

There are now two alternatives to be considered. First, a fifth extinguisher, either carbon dioxide or ordinary dry-chemical, with a rating of 10-B:C or 20-B:C could be specified. Second, the water extinguisher at Point 2 could be replaced with a multi-purpose dry-chemical extinguisher that has a rating of at least 2-A:10-B:C. It should be located near Point B, keeping in mind the 75 ft. (23m) travel distance for the 2-A protection and the 30 or 50 ft. (9 or 15m) travel distance required for the Class B protection that this extinguisher provides.

***FIG. 5-23R.** Sample problem for protection by portable extinguishers.*

Extinguisher Distribution for Class C Fires

Extinguishers for Class C fires are required wherever there is live electrical equipment. This sort of extinguisher contains a nonconducting agent, usually carbon dioxide, dry chemical, or a halogenated agent.

Once the power to live electrical equipment is cut off, the fire becomes a Class A, Class B, or Class A:B fire, depending on the nature of the burning electrical equipment and the burning material in the vicinity. Extinguishers for Class C fires should be selected according to the size of the electrical equipment; the configuration of the electrical equipment, particularly the enclosures of units, which influence agent distribution; and the range of the extinguisher's stream. At large installations of electrical equipment where continuity of power is critical, fixed fire protection is desirable. But even when fixed fire protection is present, it is recommended that some Class C extinguishers be provided to handle incipient fires.

Class D Extinguisher Distribution

It is particularly important that the proper extinguishers be available for Class D fires. Because the properties of combustible metals differ, even an agent for Class D fires may be hazardous if used on the wrong metal. Agents should be chosen carefully according to the manufacturers' recommendations. The amount of agent needed is normally figured according to the surface area of the metal, plus the shape and form of the metal, which could contribute to the severity of the fire and cause "bake-off" of the agent. For example, fires in magnesium filings are more difficult to put out than fires in magnesium scrap, and more agent is needed for magnesium filings. The maximum travel distance to all extinguishers for Class D fires is 75 ft (23 m).

INSPECTION AND MAINTENANCE OF FIRE EXTINGUISHERS

Once a fire extinguisher has been purchased, it becomes the responsibility of the purchaser or an assigned agent to maintain the device. Adequate maintenance consists of periodically inspecting each extinguisher, recharging each extinguisher following discharge, and performing hydrostatic tests as needed.

A fire equipment servicing agency is usually the most reliable way for the general public to maintain extinguishers, but large industries often train employees to handle this maintenance themselves. Many jurisdictions require service technicians to be licensed.

Inspection

An inspection is a quick check that visually determines whether the fire extinguisher is properly placed and will operate. Its purpose is to give reasonable assurance that the extinguisher is fully charged and will function effectively if needed. An inspection should determine that the extinguisher is in its designated place; is conspicuous; is not blocked in any way; has not been activated and partially or completely emptied; has not been tampered with; and has not sustained any obvious physical damage or been subjected to an environment that could interfere with its operation, such as corrosive fumes. If the extinguisher is equipped with a pressure gage and/or tamper indicators, the inspection should show conditions to be satisfactory. In addition, the maintenance tag can be checked to determine the date of the last thorough maintenance check.

In order to be effective, inspections must be frequent, regular, and thorough. In a small building with few extinguishers, the manager, property owner, or some designated person could check extinguishers at the beginning of each workday. If a building is large enough to employ security guards or watchmen, extinguishers should be inspected at least once during each 8-hr shift. In industrial plants, the plant fire brigade or fire inspector often inspects extinguishers either daily, weekly, or monthly. The maximum time period between inspections is 30 days.

An individual evaluation must be made of each property to determine how frequent inspections should be made. If a particular operation is fire-prone or is crucial to the use of the property, more frequent inspections should be made. For example, if all the products manufactured in a particular industrial plant had to be painted, a fire in the painting room could be disastrous, so inspections should be very frequent.

It is important to consider the nature of the hazards present, which influence the potential use of the equipment; the exposure of the extinguisher to tampering, vandalism, and malicious mischief; extraordinary weather conditions; the likelihood of accidental damage to the equipment; and the possibility of visual or physical obstructions to the accessibility of extinguishers.

Maintenance

Maintenance, as distinguished from inspection, means a complete and thorough examination of each extinguisher. A maintenance check involves examining all its parts, cleaning and replacing any defective parts, and reassembling, recharging, and, where appropriate, pressurize the extinguisher.

Maintenance checks sometimes reveal the need for special testing of extinguisher shells or other components. For example, they may reveal that the extinguisher container should be hydrostatically tested or even replaced.

Maintenance should be performed periodically, but at least once every 12 months, after each use, or when an inspection shows that the need is obvious. If an inspection reveals evidence of serious damage by corrosion, for example, the extinguisher should be subjected to a thorough maintenance check, even though it may have undergone one recently. Similarly, if an inspection shows evidence of tampering, agent leakage, or physical damage, a complete maintenance check should be initiated. NFPA 10, *Portable Fire Extinguishers*, contains specific details related to maintenance.

Tags, seals, and tamper indicators: For many years, extinguisher tags have been used as a convenient means for recording maintenance checks. For routine maintenance, a tied-on tag or pressure-sensitive label is used to record the date and the inspector's initials. Newer technology using bar code readers also can be used. Seals and tamper detectors also should be used; the seal or tamper indicator often consists of a wire, band, plastic insert, or other device that conforms to ANSI standards. Lead and wire seals were used commonly until plastic seals were introduced in 1972. As long as the seal remains intact, one can be reasonably sure that the extinguisher has not been used. However, it is important to note that a stored-pressure extinguisher can develop a leak and lose its pressure even though the tamper indicator remains intact or the pressure gage reads normal.

Maintenance Operations

In any maintenance test of a portable fire extinguisher, there are three basic items that need to be checked: the mechanical parts of the device—that is, the extinguisher shell and other component parts; the amount and condition of the extinguishing agent; and the condition of the means for expelling the agent.

A record of the date of purchase, as well as maintenance dates, should be kept for each extinguisher. A separate record is also desirable and should include the maintenance date and the name of the person or agency performing the maintenance; the date last recharged and the name of the person or agency performing the recharge; the hydrostatic retest data and the name of the person or agency performing the hydrostatic test; description of dents remaining after passing a hydrostatic test; and the date of the six-year maintenance for certain stored-pressure dry chemical and halogenated agent extinguishers.

Individuals who own extinguishers often neglect them because there is no planned periodic follow-up program. It is recommended that owners become familiar with their extinguishers so that they can detect telltale signs which may suggest the need for maintenance. An alternative is to have the dealer from whom the extinguisher was purchased establish an annual follow-up maintenance program.

On properties where extinguishers are maintained by the occupant, a supply of recharging materials should be kept on hand. When recharging extinguishers other than those with plain water, use only those recharging materials specified on the extinguisher's nameplate. Other recharging materials may impair the efficiency of the extinguisher or cause it to malfunction and injure the operator. Special precautions are necessary for certain types of extinguishers, and they are discussed separately in this chapter.

NFPA 10, *Portable Fire Extinguishers*, has an appendix with a checklist of items that require maintenance. One section of the checklist is arranged to pinpoint the mechanical parts common to most extinguishers.

Water-Type Extinguishers

Inspection and maintenance for stored-pressure models is too often thought of as quite simple. Unless the extinguisher has been used or a routine inspection reveals a defect, maintenance is sometimes left until the five-year hydrostatic test is performed. This practice has resulted in many failures and malfunctions. The principal items that need to be checked during an inspection are loose, worn, or damaged hose; a plugged nozzle; a dented shell; a damaged indicator gage; and a damaged or jammed ring pin. Normal maintenance service, as specified in NFPA 10, *Portable Fire Extinguishers*, should be performed annually.

Mechanical pump extinguishers, such as pump tanks and backpacks, are easy to inspect and maintain. The tanks containing the water or antifreeze solution must be checked to ensure they are in good condition, have not been weakened by corrosive action, and do not contain sediment which might block the stream during the pumping operation. If the device has not been used in the last 12 months, the liquid should be removed from the tank and the tank should be flushed, and filled with new liquid. Pumps may require lubrication from time to time. They should be checked annually to ensure that the plungers are in proper condition, that seals and washers have not deteriorated, and that hoses are not clogged. Antifreeze solutions may need to be checked to ensure that they can withstand the temperatures in the area and that they are not contaminated.

Dry Chemical Extinguishers

Dry chemical extinguishers should be inspected monthly, and they should also undergo normal annual maintenance. The quantity of agent for a cartridge-operated model can be checked by weighing or by removing the fill cap and checking it visually. The gas cartridge also may be checked by weighing. On stored-pressure models, the pressure gage will indicate if adequate pressure is maintained, and the agent quantity can be checked by weighing.

Dry chemical extinguishers should be refilled promptly after use, even if they have been discharged only partially. When refilling, extreme caution must be taken to ensure that no water, moisture, or foreign material enters the cylinder. Even though dry chemical agents are treated for moisture repellency, they can eventually harden if moisture is present. When these extinguishers are hydrostatically tested, they must be dried thoroughly so that no trace of water or moisture remains. Before new agent is added, all of the unused agent should be removed by dumping or vacuuming, and any residue should be removed from the hose.

The type of dry chemical used in recharging must be the one recommended by the manufacturer. For example, an extinguisher containing a Class B:C dry chemical (bicarbonate-base or potassium chloride) should not be refilled with a Class A:B:C agent (monoammonium-phosphate-base). Mixing different dry chemical agents can result in malfunction, or damage to the extinguisher, or both. The bicarbonate-based agent is chemically alkaline and will react with the acidic ammonium phosphate. This reaction is aggravated by exposure to heat or the presence of moisture in amounts as small as 0.1 percent. One result is caking of the agent; another possible result is the internal corrosion of the extinguisher. Under certain conditions, the reaction will cause excess pressure to build up within the shell, which may damage or rupture the extinguisher.

Substituting another manufacturer's dry chemical of the same type is not recommended unless it has the same chemical and physical characteristics, or has been tested and found to give equivalent performance. The problems involved in substitution include:

1. An altered flow rate of the dry chemical, which could influence extinguishing efficiency.
2. The amount of agent that could be placed in the extinguisher, which could influence discharge time.
3. Incompatibility of one dry chemical to another, including chemical reactions, caking, and jamming of hose or nozzles. The flow rate can change with the particle size and density of the agent. A discharge nozzle designed to dispense one dry chemical efficiently might well be less efficient for another. An extinguisher designed to hold a given weight of one formula may not hold the same amount of another. Dip tubes, hoses, or valves could become plugged.

Recharge operations for the cartridge-operated models are relatively easy. The rubber sleeves on the gas tube should be checked for cracking or overstretching, and the gasket and gasket seats on the shell and cap should be wiped clean. The cap should be screwed on handtight. When replacing the cartridge, care should be taken that the threads are not dirty, cross-threaded, or otherwise damaged. For stored-pressure models, the entire valve body, stem, and "O" ring should be carefully wiped clean and blown out with dry nitrogen to get rid of all traces of agent residue which might cause a pressure leak.

Nitrogen gas used for pressurizing should be of the standard industrial grade, with a dew point of -60°F (-51.1°C) or lower so that it is free of moisture. Once the extinguisher has been pressurized, it should be given a leak test or allowed to stand for about 12 hr and then checked for leaks before it is returned to service.

Some stored-pressure extinguishers are factory-sealed and are not rechargeable. No effort should be made to recharge these units in the field. Normally, the shell of the extinguisher is discarded following use; only the valve and nozzle assembly are retained. Refill units should be obtained from the manufacturer, and detailed instructions for replacement are included on the extinguisher nameplate.

The general inspection and maintenance procedures for dry powder (Class D) extinguishers are the same as for cartridge-operated dry chemical extinguishers.

Carbon Dioxide Extinguishers

Weighing is the only way to determine whether carbon dioxide extinguishers are fully charged. They should be weighed at least semiannually for loss of weight and inspected for deterioration and/or physical damage. The full and empty weights are stamped on the valve assembly. Any carbon dioxide extinguisher that has a weight loss of 10 percent or more should be recharged and tested for leaks. Recharging is generally done by an extinguisher servicing company. Should on-site recharging be desirable, however, the manufacturer should be contacted for assistance in setting up a recharging station.

Recharging extinguishers with carbon dioxide from dry ice converters is no longer permitted due to the high potential for moisture in the carbon dioxide. The vapor phase of carbon dioxide must not be less than 99.5 percent carbon dioxide. The water content of the liquid phase must not be more than 0.01 percent by weight [-30°F (-34.4°C) dew point]. The oil content of the carbon dioxide must not exceed 10 ppm by weight.

Specific recommendations are given for such recharging in NFPA 10, *Portable Fire Extinguishers*. The required source of carbon dioxide is a low-pressure carbon dioxide supply (300 psi at 0°F or 206.8 kPa at -17.8°C), either directly from the source or through dry cylinders used as intermediaries. It cannot be emphasized too strongly that internal moisture can seriously corrode an extinguisher, and that moisture is most easily introduced into a cylinder either during recharging or following a hydrostatic test.

Halogenated Agent Extinguishers

The general inspection and maintenance procedures for halogenated agent extinguishers are similar to the requirements for other extinguishers. Bromochlorodifluoromethane (Halon 1211) extinguishers are physically similar to stored-pressure dry chemical extinguishers. The specific requirements of each manufacturer should be followed.

HYDROSTATIC TESTING OF EXTINGUISHERS

The purpose of hydrostatic testing of portable fire extinguishers that are subject to internal pressures is to protect against unexpected, in-service failure. Such a failure may be due to undetected internal corrosion caused by moisture in the extinguisher; external corrosion caused by atmospheric humidity or corrosive vapors; damage caused by rough handling, which may or may not be obvious by external inspection; repeated pressurizations; manufacturing flaws in the construction of the extinguisher; improper assembly of valves or safety relief discs; or exposure of the extinguisher to abnormal heat, as during a fire.

TABLE 5-23D. ***Hydrosttic Test Interval for Extinguishers***

Extinguisher Type	Test Interval (Years)
Stored-pressure water and/or antifreeze	5
Wetting agent	5
AFFF (Aqueous Film Forming Foam)	5
Loaded stream	5
Dry chemical with stainless steel shells	5
Carbon dioxide	5
Dry chemical, stored-pressure, with mild steel shells, brazed brass shells, or aluminum shells	12
Dry chemical, cartridge or cylinder operated, with mild steel shells	12
Halogenated agents	12
Dry powder, cartridge or cylinder operated, with mild steel shells	12

NFPA 10, *Portable Fire Extinguishers*, requires that hydrostatic pressure tests be performed on extinguishers according to Table 5-23D. The first hydrostatic retest may be conducted between the fifth and sixth year for those with a designated test interval of five years. However, carbon dioxide types require a strict five-year interval according to federal law. These test intervals, based on experience, have been established in an effort to present general guidance. Hydrostatic tests also should be conducted immediately upon discovery of any mechanical injury or corrosion to the extinguisher shell.

In 1978, NFPA 10, *Portable Fire Extinguishers*, called for the removal from service, by or before 1983, of all riveted and soft-solder copper and brass shell extinguishers of the inverting type. The one exception is stainless steel shells and brass shells that are brazed, as opposed to soft-soldered. Also in 1978, stored-pressure water and/or antifreeze fiberglass shell types were required to be removed from service immediately because they had been recalled by the manufacturer.

In the United States, various U.S. Department of Transportation (DOT) rules apply to specific types of cylinders used for fire extinguishers. Title 49 of the Code of Federal Regulations calls, with some exceptions, for the hydrostatic retesting every five years of compressed-gas cylinders offered for interstate transportation in a charged condition. Paragraph 173.34(e) calls for periodic retesting of DOT compressed-gas cylinders whether or not the cylinders are shipped interstate.

A great many different DOT specification cylinders are used for dry chemical extinguishers, including Types DOT-4B and DOT-4BA. The requirements for these types are peculiar to them.

The U.S. Coast Guard Regulations Title 46, Code of Federal Regulations, Part 147, Paragraph 147.04-1(a)(2) and (3), specifies that compressed-gas cylinders brought aboard a vessel must have been tested hydrostatically within five years. After that, a cylinder continuously installed on board a vessel as part of the vessel's equipment for a period exceeding five years must be removed from the vessel after twelve years have elapsed from the date of previous test and marking. Its contents must be discharged, and the cylinder must be retested and remarked. The Board of Transport Commissioners of Canada has published similar rules covering these same subjects.

The preferred method of hydrostatic testing of compressed-gas cylinders is the water-jacketed, volumetric expansion method recommended in NFPA 10, *Portable Fire Extinguishers*. The guide to follow in conducting this type of test is Pamphlet C-1, "Methods for Hydrostatic Testing of Compressed Gas Cylinders," published by the Compressed Gas Association, Inc. (CGA). For visually evaluating the condition of cylinders made to DOT specifications, CGA's Pamphlet C-6, "Standard Visual Inspection of Compressed Gas Cylinders," is helpful.

Procedures for testing extinguishers other than compressed-gas extinguishers or affixed compressed-gas cylinders are detailed in NFPA 10, *Portable Fire Extinguishers*. Table 5-23E gives the basic data on the hydrostatic test pressure requirements. Figures 5-23S and 5-23T illustrate equipment used in hydrostatic testing work.

TABLE 5-23E. *Hydrostatic Test Pressure Requirements*

Carbon dioxide extinguishers Carbon dioxide and nitrogen cylinders (used with wheeled extinguishers)	5/3 service pressure stamped on cylinder
Carbon dioxide extinguishers with cylinder specification ICC3	3000 psi (20 685 kPa)
All stored-pressure and Bromochlorodifluoromethane (1211)	Factory test pressure not to exceed 2 times the service pressure
Carbon dioxide hose assemblies	1,250 psi (8619 kPa)
Dry chemical and dry powder hose assemblies	300 psi (2068 kPa)

Note: The factory test pressure is the pressure at which the shell was tested at time of manufacture. This pressure is shown on the nameplate.

The service pressure is the normal operating pressure as indicated on the gage and nameplate.

It is not necessary to hydrostatically test certain extinguishers such as pump tanks, backpacks, and similar devices. Factory-sealed, nonrefillable, disposable fire extinguishers cannot be hydrostatically tested. When such extinguishers are damaged, they must be replaced.

Proper hydrostatic testing requires competent personnel and suitable testing equipment and facilities. The preparation for testing and the removal of all traces of water and moisture with special drying equipment after testing are very important and reinforce the recommendation that only those experienced in this type of work should undertake such servicing. The DOT requires that agencies testing carbon dioxide extinguishers hydrostatically be certified by the DOT.

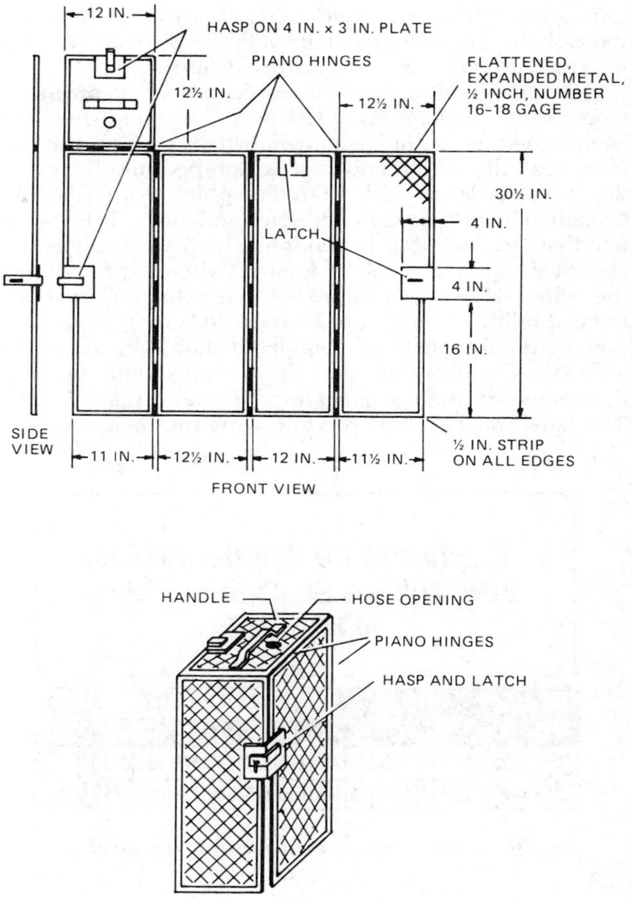

FIG. 5-23S. ***A low-pressure portable hydrostatic test cage used for hydrostatic tests of noncompressed gas extinguishers. Cage is not used for hydrostatic testing of compressed gas extinguishers. Cage should not be anchored to floor during testing. Such cages can be made by any metal fabricator.***

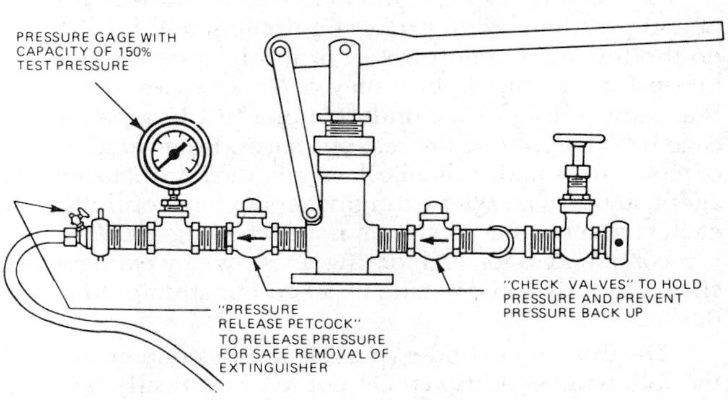

FIG. 5-23T. ***Hydrostatic testing equipment (test pump) for use with other than compressed gas cylinders.***

Extinguisher hoses of certain types also need to be hydrostatically tested, and the details of these tests can be found in NFPA 10, *Portable Fire Extinguishers*.

Because hydrostatic test results are of major importance, they must be recorded on the extinguisher. For compressed-gas cylinders and cartridges passing a hydrostatic test, the month and year is stamped into the cylinder, in accordance with CGA Pamphlet No. C-1 or the Canadian Transport Commission regulations. It is important that the recording, or stamping, be placed only on the shoulder, top head, neck, or footing (when so provided) of the cylinder. For noncompressed-gas extinguisher shells, the test information should be recorded on metal or some equally durable material. The label should be affixed by a heatless process to the shell and should be self-destructive if removal is attempted. (See Figure 5-23U.) The label must include the following information:

FIG. 5-23U. A typical hydrostatic test label.

1. The month and year the test was performed, indicated by a perforation, such as by a hand punch.
2. The test pressure used.
3. The name or initials of the person performing the test, or the name of the agency performing the test.

Above all, remember the following: Allow only competent personnel with proper equipment and facilities to do the testing. Do not use air or gas for pressure testing because a violent rupture may occur in cases of failure. Place any extinguisher undergoing a test in a protective cage before applying the test pressures. Remove all traces of moisture from dry chemical, carbon dioxide, halogenated agent, and dry powder extinguishers before refilling after each test; a heated air stream not exceeding 150°F (65°C) is recommended for such drying. Destroy any extinguisher shell that fails a hydrostatic test—do not attempt to repair it.

Destroy any cylinder or shell if it has one or more of the following conditions. Do not hydrostatically test it:

1. Repairs by soldering, welding, brazing, or use of patching compounds. For welding or brazing on mild steel shells, consult the manufacturer of the extinguisher.
2. Damaged cylinder or shell threads.
3. Pitting caused by corrosion, even under the removable nameplate band assemblies.
4. Burns from a fire.
5. Calcium chloride agent in a stainless steel extinguisher.

EXTINGUISHER MAINTENANCE SERVICES

Fire extinguisher maintenance, particularly hydrostatic testing, is a specialized activity and should be performed by competent, dependable people. Fire extinguishers are provided to protect life and property; this means that there should be no doubt as to their reliability or safe use in an emergency. Extinguisher owners are thus urged to seek out the services of reliable fire extinguisher maintenance firms. Such firms should be able to show proof that they are competent, that their facilities are adequate, and that they are licensed or registered in accordance with any local or federal law.

BIBLIOGRAPHY

NFPA Codes, Standards, and Recommended Practices

Reference to the following NFPA codes, standards, and recommended practices will provide further information on selection, operation, distribution, inspection, and maintenance of fire extinguishers discussed in this chapter. (See the latest *NFPA Catalog* for availability of current editions of the following documents.)

NFPA 10, *Portable Fire Extinguishers*.

NFPA 10L, *Sale or Leasing and Servicing of Portable Fire Extinguishers*.

Additional Reading

"Beware of the Fire Extinguisher Servicing Racket," *Fire Journal*, Vol. 60, No. 3 (May 1966), pp. 22-23.

"Checklist for Fire Extinguisher Applications," *Cat. No. CK 84*, National Association of Fire Equipment Distributors, Chicago, IL, 1984, p. 10.

Fighting Fires with Portable Extinguishers, Video, National Fire Protection Association, Quincy, MA, 1986.

Fire Extinguishers: Fight of Flight?, Video, National Fire Protection Association, Quincy, MA, 1988.

Hock, B. H., "Set Up for Repairs," *Fire Command, Vol. 56, No. 4 (April 1989), pp. 39-40.*

Katzel, J. A., "Selecting, Maintaining and Using Portable Fire Extinguishers," *National Safety News*, Vol. 119, No. 6 (June 1979), pp. 52-58.

Peterson, H. B. and Gipe, R. L., "Discharge Characteristics of Potassium Bicarbonate Dry Chemical Fire Fighting Agents from Cartridge and Stored Pressure Extinguishers," *NRL Report 5853*, U.S. Naval Research Laboratory, Washington, DC, Dec. 13, 1962.

"Portable Extinguishers: Selection, Placement, Use," (for use with NFPA Slide Set No. SL-47), National Fire Protection Association, Quincy, MA, 1979.

Riley, J. F. and Kraus, M. R., "Selecting and Using Wheeled Fire Extinguishers: Training, Inspection, and Maintenance," *Plant Engineering, Vol. 40, No. 22, 1986, pp. 58-60.*

Sayers, D. R., "Halon 1211, Areas of Particular Effectiveness," *Fire Journal*, Vol. 67, No. 6 (Nov. 1973), pp. 14-15.

"Training Your Fire Brigade to Use First Aid Extinguishers," Walter Kidde & Co., Belleville, NJ, 1964.

Tryon, G. H., "Hydrostatic Testing of Fire Extinguishers," *Fire Journal*, Vol. 61, No. 1 (Jan. 1967), pp. 32-35.

Tuve, R. L., "Dry Chemical Fire Extinguishers," *Security World*, July-August 1966.

"When Fire Extinguishers are Dangerous," *Cat. No. DNG-84*, National Association of Fire Equipment Distributors, Chicago, IL, 1984, p. 14.

THE ROLE OF EXTINGUISHERS IN FIRE PROTECTION

Marshall E. Petersen

Virtually all fires are small at first and might be extinguished easily if the proper type and amount of extinguishing agent were applied promptly. Portable fire extinguishers are designed for this purpose, but their successful use depends on the following conditions:

1. The extinguisher must be located properly and be in good working order.
2. The extinguisher must be the proper type for the fire which occurs.
3. The fire must be discovered while still small enough for the extinguisher to be effective.
4. The fire must be discovered by a person ready, willing, and able to use the extinguisher.

Fire extinguishers are the first line of defense against unfriendly fires and should be installed regardless of other fire control measures. However, an alarm should be given and the fire department notified as soon as a fire is discovered. Notification should never be delayed in the hope that the extinguisher will be sufficient.

This chapter extensively discusses the role of portable fire extinguishers. It begins by giving historical background on the development of extinguishers and then discusses their reliability and design safety. Finally, current extinguisher identification and fire extinguishment in the home are detailed.

For further information on allied topics, see Section 5, Chapter 23, "Selection, Operation, Distribution, Inspection, and Maintenance of Fire Extinguishers."

HISTORICAL BACKGROUND

The first real portable fire extinguishers were developed in the late 1800s. They contained glass bottles of acid which was released into a soda solution to produce a mixture with sufficient gas pressure to expel the solution. Cartridge-operated water extinguishers of the inverting type were introduced in the late 1920s. In 1928, a nonfreeze alkali metal-salt solution called "loaded stream" was developed for use in cartridge-operated extinguishers. Stored-pressure water extinguishers were developed in 1959, and, over the next ten years, they gradually replaced cartridge-operated models. In 1969, the manufacture of all inverting extinguishers was discontinued in the United States, and these extinguishers are no longer listed or approved by testing laboratories.

The first foam extinguisher was developed in 1917, and it looked and worked much like the soda-acid extinguisher. The use of foam extinguishers steadily increased over the years until, during the 1950s, dry chemical extinguishers gained widespread acceptance.

In 1976, aqueous film-forming foam (AFFF) extinguishers were introduced. These proved to be a direct replacement for the inverting foam type. The latest addition to water-type extinguishers came in 1988 with the introduction of film-forming fluoroprotein foam (FFFP).

NFPA 10, *Portable Fire Extinguishers*, no longer recognizes inverting types of extinguishers, that is—soda-acid, foam, and cartridge-operated models—as of the next hydrostatic testing due date.

Vaporizing Liquids

Carbon tetrachloride (CCl_4) was one of the first chemicals used in portable fire extinguishers in 1908. However, it was subsequently found that its vapors were toxic, and, when used on a fire, this substance could produce highly toxic hydrogen chloride and phosgene. Slightly less toxic chlorobromomethane (CH_2ClBr) was produced after World War II, when the term "vaporizing liquid" was first used to designate these extinguishers. However, some federal agencies banned vaporizing-liquid extinguishers in the 1950s because they were poisonous. By the mid-1960s, many states, cities, and industrial firms also had banned them. In the late 1960s, listings of vaporizing liquids by testing laboratories were discontinued.

Halogenated Agents

Although vaporizing liquids proved unacceptable, less toxic halogenated hydrocarbon chemicals were used in the form of compressed or liquefied gases. Bromotrifluoromethane,

Marshall E. Petersen, P.E., is president of Marshall Petersen & Co., M. Prospect, IL.

or Halon 1301, was first introduced in 1954 in a high-vapor-pressure compressed-gas extinguisher for use on fires in flammable liquids and live electrical equipment. A medium-vapor-pressure extinguisher using bromochlorodifluoromethane, or Halon 1211, became available in 1973. In 1974, extensive testing was begun on extinguishers containing low-vapor-pressure dibromotetrafluoromethane, or Halon 2402, which is a liquid at room temperature. Its use in portable extinguishers has proven to be impractical due to high costs and potential toxicity problems.

Halon is a chlorofluorocarbon (CFC). CFC emissions have been identified as a major contributor to the decay of the ozone layer in Earth's atmosphere. The Montreal Protocol, signed in 1987, is designed to limit ozone-depleting substances and has set production limits on CFCs, including Halons 1211 and 1301. It is evident that the future of halon as an extinguishing agent is in question, and alternate methods for fire extinguishment should be considered.

Carbon Dioxide

The first carbon dioxide extinguishers were produced during World War I, and, during World War II, they were the leading extinguisher for flammable liquids fires. By 1950, however, dry chemical agents had frequently replaced them as the preferred agent for flammable liquids fires. A further decline in the use of carbon dioxide extinguishers occurred as the popularity of halogenated agent extinguishers increased. With the phase out of halon extinguishers, CO_2 use may increase.

Dry Chemicals

Although the extinguishing ability of sodium bicarbonate was recognized as early as the late 1800s, it was not until 1928 that an effective cartridge-operated dry chemical extinguisher was developed. Research and development produced an improved, finely granulated agent in 1943 and a further improved model in 1947.

As the use of flammable liquids increased, so did the development of effective dry chemical agents. In 1959, a potassium-bicarbonate-based agent called "Purple K," about twice as effective as the ordinary sodium-bicarbonate-based agent, was introduced.

In 1961, manufacturers introduced a new kind of agent called "multi-purpose (ABC) dry chemical." It had the added advantage of being approximately 50 percent more effective than ordinary dry chemical on flammable liquid and electrical fires, and also was capable of extinguishing fires in ordinary combustibles. Originally, diammonium phosphate was used because it was less expensive, but monoammonium phosphate soon became preferred because it is considerably less hygroscopic.

In 1968, an agent with a potassium chloride base, known as "Super K," was introduced. It was approximately 80 percent more effective than ordinary dry chemical, but it was more corrosive and hygroscopic than potassium bicarbonate. A urea-potassium-bicarbonate-based agent (potassium carbanate), called "Monnex,"™ was developed in Europe in 1967 and brought to America in 1970. It has been judged at least 2½ times as effective as ordinary dry chemical.

Dry Powder

The increased use of combustible metals, such as magnesium, sodium, and lithium, established the need for special agents to extinguish fires involving them. The designation "dry powder" was specifically chosen to indicate an agent's suitability for use on Class D, or combustible metal fires, while the term "dry chemical" was reserved for agents effective on Class A:B:C or B:C fires. In 1950, dry powder extinguishers using sodium chloride as a base agent were first marketed.

RELIABILITY AND DESIGN SAFETY OF FIRE EXTINGUISHERS

Portable fire extinguishers may remain idle for many years, but they must always be capable of functioning at any time with maximum efficiency and without hazard to the user. Although most extinguishers are pressure vessels, they may rupture if not properly designed, constructed, and maintained. The initial responsibility for safe extinguishers belongs to the manufacturer, who is subject to the design standards, testing, inspection, labeling procedures, and follow-up program of responsible fire testing laboratories. But the owner is responsible for maintaining an extinguisher once it is in service, and may retain the services of a qualified service company.

NFPA 10

NFPA 10, *Portable Fire Extinguishers*, contains requirements for the selection, installation, inspection, maintenance, and testing of extinguishers. It has been widely adopted by property owners, sales/servicing agencies, and enforcing officials.

The first edition of this standard was published in 1921 from data assembled by the NFPA Committee on Field Practices, the predecessor of the present committee. This standard is reviewed continuously, and revised editions are published every few years. Starting with the 1978 edition, more detailed information, with specific examples, was added to give guidance on selection and distribution.

Extinguisher Testing, Labeling, and Inspection

In North America, manufacturers have traditionally submitted their extinguishers to Underwriters Laboratories Inc. (UL), Underwriters Laboratories of Canada (ULC), and Factory Mutual Research Corporation (FMRC) for evaluation. Both UL and ULC have their own standards for construction, testing, and rating of extinguishers.

To assist purchasers of extinguishers in the United States and Canada, UL, ULC, and FMRC authorize manufacturers to affix a label to extinguishers that have been constructed and evaluated according to their standards. (See Figure 5-24A.) UL and ULC also require periodic examinations and tests of samples of extinguishers taken from a manufacturer's current production and/or stock. NFPA standards call for the use of listed or approved extinguishers, and most responsible authorities and property owners rely on this requirement.

Typically, extinguishers manufactured in the United States have been both listed by UL and approved by FMRC. The combined effect of the standards of these two testing agencies resulted in a quality and reliability consistent with the objectives of NFPA 10, *Portable Fire Extinguishers*.

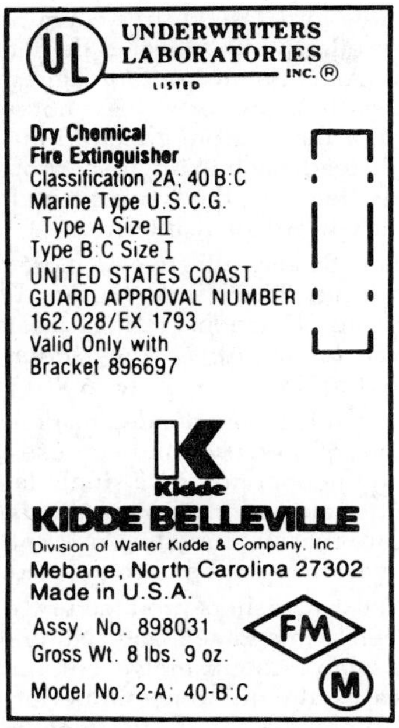

FIG. 5-24A. A close-up of an extinguisher label, showing approvals from both Underwriters Laboratories Inc. (UL) (top) and Factory Mutual Research Corp. (FMRC) (bottom right.)

In recent years, other testing organizations have begun to evaluate portable fire extinguishers. In an effort to establish uniformity and maintain the high levels of quality and reliability that have been achieved, the NFPA Extinguisher Committee incorporated specific standards that must be used by any organization evaluating extinguisher products. In addition to a specific standard for each type of fire extinguisher, the American National Standards Institute (ANSI) also publishes a standard that requires a "third-party certification program." The following U.S. and Canadian standards are included in the requirements of NFPA 10, *Portable Fire Extinguishers*.

Fire Test Standards

ANSI/UL 711, *Rating and Testing of Fire Extinguishers*.

CAN 4-S508-M83.

Performance Standards*

Carbon dioxide (CO_2) types: ANSI/UL 154, CAN 4-S503-M83.

Dry chemical types: ANSI/UL 299, ULC-S504.

Water types: ANSI/UL 626, CAN 4-S507-M83.

Halogenated agent types: ANSI/UL 1093, ULC-S512.

Foam types: ANSI/UL 8.

Factory follow-up on third-party certified portable fire extinguishers: ANSI/UL 1803.

*ANSI-American National Standards Institute, Inc.; UL-Underwriters Laboratories Inc.; ULC-Underwriters Laboratories of Canada; and CAN-Standards Council of Canada.

According to NFPA 10, *Portable Fire Extinguishers*, extinguishers manufactured after January 1, 1986 must have the identification of the listing and labeling organization, the fire test, and the performance standard that the extinguisher meets or exceeds clearly marked on each extinguisher.

Substandard Extinguishers

Extinguishers are designed for use in emergencies, and it is vital that they operate effectively. Only extinguishers that are now tested in accordance with ANSI standards should be purchased, because otherwise it is difficult to know whether an extinguisher is reliable and effective. An inadequate extinguisher gives its owner a false sense of security.

Some common types of untested extinguishers are aerosol cans, "glass bulb grenades," and dry chemical "shaker units." Their instructions may claim that they can be used on all types of fires, both indoors and outdoors. However, they are unlikely to list the exact composition and amount of extinguishing agent. Even if unlisted extinguishers do contain recognized extinguishing agents, one cannot assume that they are as safe and effective as those tested in accordance with ANSI standards.

RELATION OF EXTINGUISHERS TO CLASSES OF FIRES

Because various extinguishing agents are not uniformly effective on different fires, NFPA 10, *Portable Fire Extinguisher*, classifies fires into the following four types:

Class A: Fires in ordinary combustible materials, such as wood, cloth, paper, rubber, and many plastics, that require the heat-absorbing, cooling effects of water or water solutions, the coating effects of certain dry chemicals that retard combustion, or the interruption of the combustion chain reaction by dry chemical or halogenated agents.

Class B: Fires in flammable or combustible liquids, flammable gases, greases, and similar materials that must be put out by excluding air (oxygen), by inhibiting the release of combustible vapors with AFFF or FFFP agents, or by interrupting the combustion chain reaction.

Class C: Fires in live electrical equipment. The operator's safety requires the use of electrically nonconductive extinguishing agents, such as dry chemical or halon. When electrical equipment is deenergized, extinguishers for Class A or B fires may be used.

Class D: Fires in certain combustible metals, such as magnesium, titanium, zirconium, sodium, and potassium, that require a heat-absorbing extinguishing medium that does not react with the burning metals.

Some portable extinguishers will put out only one class of fire, and some are suitable for two or three, but none is suitable for all four. Most extinguishers are labeled so that users may quickly identify the class of fire for which they may be used. This classification is contained in NFPA 10, *Portable Fire Extinguishers*, and it gives the applicable picture symbol or symbols. Color coding also is used. (See Figures 5-24B and 5-24C.) The NFPA classification is required on the extinguisher label in accordance with ANSI standards.

Rating numerals also are used on the labels of extinguishers for Class A and Class B fires. The rating numeral gives the relative extinguishing effectiveness of the extinguisher. For example, an extinguisher rated 4-A, 20-B:C

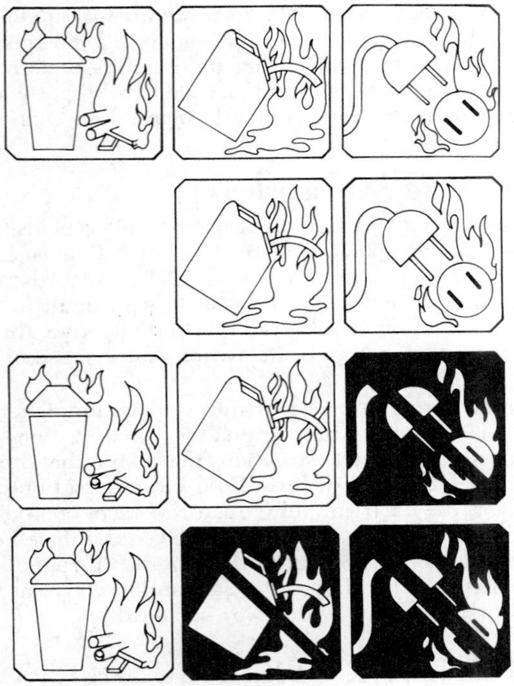

FIG. 5-24B. ***These pictographs are designed so that the extinguisher's proper use may be determined at a glance. When an application is prohibited, the background is black and the slash is bright red. Otherwise, the background is light blue. The top row of symbols indicates an extinguisher for Class A:B:C fires; the second row indicates an extinguisher for Class B:C fires; the third row indicates an extinguisher for Class A:B fires; and the bottom row indicates an extinguisher for Class A fires.***

FIG. 5-24C. ***These are extinguisher markings that can be used until conversion to pictographs is complete. Color coding is part of the identification system, and the triangle (Class A) is colored green, the square (Class B) red, the circle (Class C) blue, and the five-pointed star (Class D) yellow.***

indicates that it should extinguish approximately twice as much Class A fire as a 2-A-rated extinguisher, that it should extinguish considerably more Class B fire than a 1-B-rated extinguisher, and that it is suitable for use on energized electrical equipment.

Extinguishers rated for Class B fires have numeral ratings, based on the relative quantity of burning flammable liquid in a flat pan that can be extinguished during a laboratory test. Again, an extinguisher rated 20-B can put out much more fire than one rated 5-B.

No rating numerals are used for extinguishers labeled for Class C fires. Since electrical equipment has either ordinary combustibles or flammable liquids, or both, as part of its construction, an extinguisher for Class C fires should be chosen according to the nature of the combustibles in the immediate area.

Extinguishers for Class D fires contain different dry powders that are effective on fires in different kinds of combustible metals. An extinguisher for magnesium fires may not work on a sodium fire, or at least not with the same effectiveness. For that reason, general numerical ratings are not used. Instead, each extinguisher for Class D fires has a nameplate detailing the type of metal in which the particular agent will extinguish a fire.

Extinguishers that are effective on more than one class of fire have multiple "letter" and "numeral-letter" classifications and ratings. Fractional ratings are not recognized in NFPA 10, *Portable Fire Extinguishers*, and are not included in the requirements of the ANSI standards.

The most recently recommended marking system combines pictographs of both uses and non-uses, which could be hazardous to the operator, on a single label. (See Figure 5-24B.) Letter-shaped symbol markings, as shown in Figure 5-24C, are recommended for use until full conversion to the newer pictographs is completed.

Sometimes extinguishers produced by different manufacturers or even by the same manufacturer have the same quantity of the same extinguishing agent, but different ratings. In such cases, the difference in performance is usually due to differences of design, including rates of discharge, nozzle design, discharge patterns, and so on.

IDENTIFICATION OF EXTINGUISHERS

Clearly marked extinguishers and extinguisher locations are of the utmost importance. In an emergency, it is essential that extinguishers be located quickly and used while the fire is still small.

The rating class and numeral of an extinguisher should be visible so that the proper unit can be selected for the particular fire at hand. Manufacturers are required to provide permanently attached markings that describe not only the type and rating but also the way the unit is operated. ANSI standards specify general requirements for the form of the operating instructions that must be placed on the front of the extinguisher. (See Figures 5-24D and 5-24E.) Maintenance and other information can only be included on a rear label. A stenciled inventory number on extinguishers and mountings also may aid in inventory and maintenance record-keeping.

If the pictograph marking system is used, the operating instructions must be visible from the front of the extinguisher as it hangs. If class and rating markings are applied to wall panels in the vicinity of extinguishers, they should be easily legible at a distance of 15 ft (4.5 m).

The locations of wall- or column-mounted extinguishers can easily be marked by painting a red rectangle or band about 8 to 10 ft (2.4 to 3.0 m) above them. (See Figure 5-24F.) It is also good practice to paint the background on which it is mounted red.

If separate extinguishers for different classes of fire are mounted at the same location, extra attention should be given to distinguishing between them. Where extinguishers may easily be blocked by storage or equipment, barriers or floor markings can be employed. If the problem persists, it may be more practical to find another location.

Extinguishers installed in recessed cabinets or wall recesses generally are more difficult to find unless clearly marked. Where possible, the cabinet frame or wall recess should be painted red. When such installations are in long halls or corridors, however, they may still be very difficult

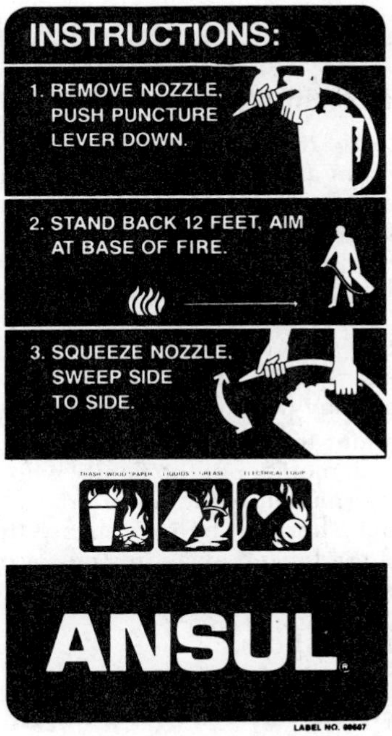

FIG. 5-24D. Example of the type of instruction/identification label required by ANSI standards for cartridge-operated dry chemical extinguishers. (Source: ANSUL)

FIG. 5-24E. Example of the type of instruction/identification label required by ANSI standards for stored-pressure water extinguishers. (Source: AMEREX)

FIG. 5-24F. An extinguisher marker. It should be placed so that it is clearly visible from a distance. (Source: The Badger Company)

to find unless a sign is mounted perpendicular to the cabinet wall at a height of about 8 ft (2.4 m).

In many public and commercial buildings, extinguisher locations are camouflaged for aesthetic reasons or installed in hidden areas, such as closets or stairwells. Unless one knows where to look or happens to see a small sign on a door, these extinguishers are of little value in an emergency.

FIRE EXTINGUISHMENT IN THE HOME

The cardinal rules to follow when a fire occurs in the home are: make sure that everyone gets out of the house before the exits become blocked by heat or smoke; be certain that the fire department is called immediately; and, if the fire is small, try to control or extinguish it. To achieve the last, every home should have readily available, easy-to-use fire fighting equipment. Listed or approved portable fire extinguishers are the most reliable first defense against fire. In addition, a garden hose may be useful.

Selection of Extinguishers

Since most dwelling fires are Class A fires, the most practical and economical extinguishing agent is water. Although stored-pressure water extinguishers or pump tanks may be used, they are selected infrequently because they are large, unattractive, heavy, expensive, and limited to Class A fires. Small, efficient, ABC-type dry chemical extinguishers are ideally suited for use on most small fires that may occur in the home. Of these, the most readily available are stored-pressure models in capacities ranging from 1 to 5 lb (0.5 to 2.3 kg). The most popular size contains about 2½ lb (1.1 kg) of agent, and both refillable and disposable models are sold. (See Figure 5-24G.) Many home owners prefer the disposable type because they can keep a replacement on hand. The disposable type also requires less maintenance. Currently, these small extinguishers can be purchased with ordinary, or bicarbonate-base, agent or multi-purpose agent. It is important to note that the multi-purpose agent can cause corrosion and may seriously damage stoves, heaters, appliances, and vehicles unless all the agent deposits are removed promptly and thoroughly after extinguishment. The 5-lb (2.3 kg) and larger sizes of ordinary and multi-purpose dry chemical extinguishers also can be obtained in cartridge-operated models.

In general, dry chemical extinguishers will provide adequate protection for small Class B fires involving grease or cooking oils in the kitchen, paints and solvents in the basement or utility area, and oils or gasoline in the garage or outdoors. However, it is important to stand back at least 6 ft (2 m) when discharging the extinguisher, or the grease, oil, or gasoline may splash and cause the fire to spread. When multi-purpose extinguishers are used on fires of ordinary combustibles, the small sizes will be of limited value. The larger sizes, which are given higher ratings by the testing laboratories, are more suitable. Multi-purpose dry chemicals are surface-coating agents. Even though extinguishers of this type may rapidly extinguish the flames in combustible materials, it is important that the deep-seated burning embers, especially those in furniture cushions, pillows, or bedding, be thoroughly wetted with water.

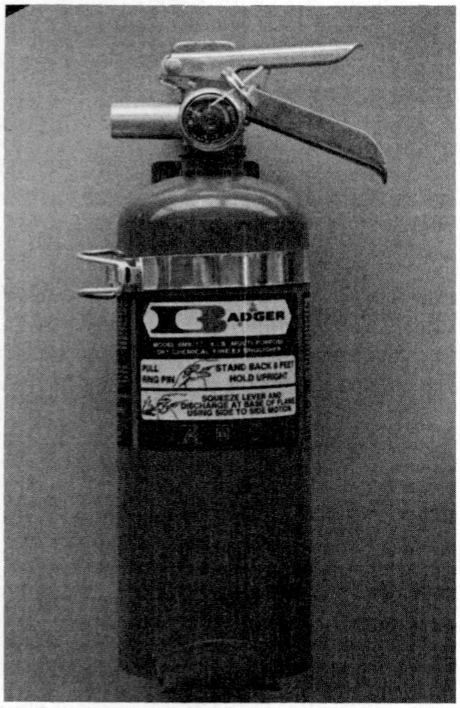

FIG. 5-24G. A small, dry chemical fire extinguisher suitable for home protection. (Source: The Badger Company)

It is also essential that, once the extinguisher has been used, it be refilled or replaced as soon as possible. Even if only a short burst of agent is released, the extinguisher will probably lose the rest of its pressure very shortly.

Possibly the best approach to home fire extinguishment is to provide fire extinguishers, such as ordinary or dry chemical, for Class B:C protection and the means for rapid flame "knock-down" of Class A fires. A water extinguisher or permanently connected hose should then be used for final extinguishment of the Class A fire. (See the subsection on garden hose in the home later in this chapter.)

Homeowners who have extensive home workshops, gasoline-powered equipment, and so on should consider installing additional, conveniently located fire extinguishers to control any fire that might occur in such areas or equipment. A logical choice would be a dry chemical extinguisher with a capacity of 5 lb (2.3 kg) or greater.

Although more expensive, extinguishers containing halogenated agents—Halon 1211 and/or Halon 1301—are also suitable for home fire protection. Small sizes containing 2 to 2½ lb (0.9 to 1.1 kg) are well-suited for small Class B:C fires. For Class A fires, it is recommended that extinguishers of at least 9 lb (4.1 kg) be selected. One advantage of the halogenated agents is that they do not leave residue and are not corrosive. As previously indicated, however, halon extinguishers are being phased out due to environmental concerns.

For private automobiles, a multi-purpose dry chemical extinguisher is effective on engine fires and any electrical fires that also include Class A insulating materials. For small trucks, NFPA committees have recommended extinguishers in the 5- to 20-B:C range, depending on the type of vehicle. Due to the corrosive characteristics of multi-purpose dry chemical, it is important to promptly and thoroughly clean all agent deposits off metal surfaces.

Location of Extinguishers

Experience clearly indicates that most dwelling fires start in the living room and kitchen. Thus, at least one extinguisher should be located where it can be reached quickly from both of these rooms. It is best to locate each extinguisher near the path of exit travel so that if the fire cannot be controlled readily with the device, a quick escape can be made. In bedrooms, the extinguisher should be located in a handy closet or cabinet. In basements, the head of the basement stairs is preferred, except when a basement workshop may dictate otherwise.

It is important that the location of each extinguisher be known to each member of the family who is able to use the device. A permanently mounted bracket on which to hang the extinguisher will help to ensure that it remains in place and is not tucked away in a closet or some other place that is difficult to reach.

Use of Extinguishers

The mere presence of an extinguisher in the home is not worthwhile unless the homeowner is willing to learn how to use the device properly, instruct family members who may have to use it, and maintain and recharge it according to the manufacturer's instructions. The manufacturer of listed extinguishers is required to provide an instruction manual with each unit. This manual contains instructions and cautions for the installation, operation, inspection, and maintenance of the extinguisher. For safety and to obtain the maximum benefit of having a fire extinguisher, the manual should be studied carefully, kept in a safe place, and reviewed periodically.

It is important that homeowners understand that extinguishers of the sizes discussed here have a discharge time of only 8 to 15 sec. In actual use, no time can be wasted determining the best way to use the device. Operating instructions are given on each listed or approved extinguisher, and most of them are easily understood. When possible, families should practice using extinguishers in a safe outdoor location. Instructions on using fire extinguishers also may be obtained from local fire department personnel.

Maintenance of Extinguishers

Maintenance requirements vary for each extinguisher, and the information is given on each device. Most small, modern extinguishers have a pressure gage that should be checked on a regular basis. To be sure that the device can be readily removed from its bracket and is in good physical condition, the extinguisher also should be lifted from its bracket occasionally and handled. The family should periodically review how each extinguisher should be operated and used.

Garden Hose in the Home

An ordinary garden hose of high quality, connected to a domestic water system, is an effective and inexpensive means for combatting fires in ordinary combustible materials. (See Figure 5-24H.) With a special adaptor, it can be connected either to the cold water supply pipe for kitchen, bathroom, or utility sinks, or near the entry point to the hot-water heater. Because of its central location, the bathroom is generally an ideal place. In large multi-level homes, it may be advantageous to have several hose installations. The hose can be coiled up and placed on a shelf under the sink, or the pipe connection can be extended through a wall into an adjoining closet or stairway where the hose can be hung on a bracket. A concealed location can be built into a wall and covered with a hinge-mounted picture. The special hose reels available for garden use are also ideal for indoor installation. Any lightweight plastic hose with at least ½-in. (13 mm) inside diameter would be a good choice. However, it should be equipped with an adjustable squeeze-grip nozzle and should be long enough to reach all intended areas. Such a hand hose, though small, can be very effective, provided it remains connected, is checked periodically for deterioration, and is reserved for use in fires only.

FIG. 5-24H. A garden hose connected to an ordinary domestic water supply and stored beneath a bathroom sink. To operate, the lever must be pushed to "open" and the nozzle of the hose squeezed.

If the homeowner decides to install a hose, he or she also may decide to forego the Class A capability of the multi-purpose agent and purchase an extinguisher with the more powerful potassium-based, or "Purple K," Class B:C agents.

BIBLIOGRAPHY

NFPA Codes, Standards, and Recommended Practices

Reference to the following NFPA codes, standards, and recommended practices will provide further information on the role of extinguishers in fire protection discussed in this chapter. (See the latest *NFPA Catalog* for availability of current editions of the following documents.)

NFPA 10, *Portable Fire Extinguishers.*

NFPA 10L, *Sale or Leasing and Servicing of Portable Fire Extinguishers.*

Additional Reading

"A Computerized Study of Fire Extinguisher Effectiveness," National Association of Fire Equipment Distributors, Chicago, IL, 1979, p. 11.

"Carbon Tetrachloride," *Fire Journal*, Vol. 65, No. 3 (May 1971), p. 19.

"Fire Extinguishers," *Consumer Reports*, Vol. 44, No. 10 (Oct. 1979), pp. 607-609.

"How Useful are Portable Fire Extinguishes," *Fire Prevention*, No. 227, March 1990, pp. 16-17.

James, D., "Fire Extinguishers," *Fire Prevention Handbook*, Butterworths, Boston, 1986, pp. 36-65.

Kokkala, M. A., "Extinguishment of Compartment Fires Using Portable Chemical Extinguishers and Water," *Fire Safety Journal*, Vol. 11, No. 3, 1986, pp. 201-210.

"Portable Fire Extinguishers," *Handbook of Industrial Loss Prevention*, Factory Mutual Engineering Corp., McGraw-Hill, NY, 1967.

Underwriters Laboratories Inc., Safety Standards:

UL 154, Carbon Dioxide Fire Extinguishers.

UL 299, Dry Chemical Fire Extinguishers.

UL 626, 2½-Gallon Stored Pressure, Water-Type Fire Extinguishers.

UL 711, Rating and Fire Testing of Fire Extinguishers.

UL 715, 2½-Gallon Cartridge-Operated, Water-Type Fire Extinguishers.

Bulletin of Research No. 54, July 1963, "The Compatibility Relationship Between Mechanical Foam and Dry Chemical Fire Extinguishing Agents", Underwriters Laboratories Inc., July 1963.

CONFINING FIRES

Throughout the *Fire Protection Handbook*, it has been emphasized that firesafety must be addressed through systematic analysis of all elements and their relationships to each other. Nowhere is this more essential—or unavoidable—than in the decisions that dictate the strength, location, and other features of the barriers, surfaces, and spaces in a property. Confining fires, and all that deceptively simple term implies, is the subject of this section.

"Effective, firesafe design begins with conscious analysis and decision-making early in the design process," says Chapter 1, which provides the fundamentals of building and site layout. Particular attention is given to the exterior, both in terms of fire department access and in terms of exposure hazards. Moving inside, Chapters 2 and 3 address building construction. The basic assemblies and systems—columns, walls, partitions, floors, trusses, ceilings, roofs—are each described in terms of function and major alternatives. Chapter 5 then expands on a related topic, briefly introduced in Chapter 3: the means of assuring the building's structural integrity under fire conditions. This essential step of protecting the building features that protect the building and its occupants involve test procedures and methods for calculating the fire conditions to design against and relating those conditions to measurable fire performance properties of the building features. After a fire occurs, building integrity must be carefully evaluated as well, which is examined in Chapter 13. Chapters 4 and 6 then provide similar detail to Chapter 5 but on interior finish and interior barriers, respectively. These first six chapters thus cover all the fixed passive features for fire confinement in a building.

Chapters 7 and 8 address air and smoke movement. Chapter 7 describes the physics of air and smoke movement in buildings, including special phenomena such as cold smoke, stack effects, and wind velocity. Techniques of smoke management are also described, which leads to the discussion of venting practices in Chapter 8. Chapter 16 examines air conditioning and ventilating systems as equipment, including a brief discussion of active smoke control methods, and air moving equipment is discussed in Chapter 19.

Structural aspects of some specific classes of structures are discussed in Chapter 9, which addresses one- and two-family dwellings, and 10, which covers special structures, including towers, tunnels, bridges, tents, grandstands, and piers.

Chapters 11 and 12 provide a shift in perspective. Chapter 11 discusses building construction as it affects the environment in which fire fighters will fight fires. The author ties these considerations back to guidelines for prefire inspection and planning, to further reduce hazards and surprises. Chapter 12 then reviews the body of building and fire codes and standards as the principal American mechanism for controlling fire-related characteristics of built environments.

The remaining chapters address particular operations and systems. Chapter 14 reviews the hazards of construction, demolition, alteration, and other similar construction operations, because fire may not wait until the building is built or rebuilt. Chapter 15 covers various building services—environmental services such as climate control, piped services, electrical and electronic services, and transportation and conveyance—while Chapter 17 adds other services, such as plumbing, chutes, and shafts. Chapter 18 reviews special systems for explosion damage control.

Also look for these: Other chapters that emphasize concepts of system design include Chapters 1 through 3 of Section 1, Chapters 1 and 2 of Section 3, Chapters 1 and 2 of Section 7, and Chapter 10 of Section 8. With calculation and test methods essential to every facet of design for fire confinement, all of Section 10 will be of use. And for still more detailed treatment of these topics, most chapters of *The SFPE Handbook for Fire Protection Engineering* will be relevant.

BUILDING AND SITE PLANNING FOR FIRESAFETY

Revised by Clifford S. Harvey

Effective, firesafe design begins with conscious analysis and decision-making early in the design process. This broad overall approach includes consideration of both interior building functions and layout, as well as exterior site planning. This chapter will present some broad guidelines to be considered by building designers in analyzing fire protection measures that must be provided for a firesafe environment for structures and their sites. Detailed information of the various aspects of firesafe site planning and building design can be found elsewhere in this handbook, particularly in the other chapters in this section.

To effectively incorporate the building's fire defenses into the design, the firesafety objectives must first be identified. Section 1, Chapter 3, "Systems Concepts for Building Firesafety," briefly discusses a systematic approach to assessment of firesafety objectives. Decisions must then be made regarding the means to achieve the objectives. The firesafety concepts tree in Section 1, Chapter 3 can be used to obtain an overall perspective of the firesafety system. Venting in conjunction with sprinkler protection continues as a subject of some controversy and is discussed in greater detail in Chapter 8 of this section.

Concepts of egress design, an extremely important part of the design process, are discussed in Section 7, Chapter 2, "Concepts of Egress Design." That chapter, based on NFPA 101®, *Life Safety Code*®, describes the elements that must be considered when designing adequate egress in buildings for life safety from fire.

BUILDING INTERIOR DESIGN CONSIDERATIONS

The architectural design of a building has a significant influence on its firesafety capabilities. Interior layout, circulation patterns, interior finish materials, and building services are all important factors in firesafety. Manual suppression of fires, particularly by fire department operations, is another important consideration. The building design and location on the lot relative to access roads significantly influence the efficiency of fire department operations. Consequently, manual suppression activities should be considered during all phases of architectural design.

A concept of creating firesafety involves the philosophy that the building itself must be designed to either assist the manual suppression of fire or be self-protecting from fire spread. Design features should consider the local fire fighting resources that are available. The fire service cannot and should not be expected to provide complete protection for building occupants and property; it must be assisted by both active and passive building fire defenses, to provide reasonable safety from the effects of fire.

Interior Layout

During a fire the occupants of the entire building are exposed to two types of danger: (1) exposure to flame and hot products of combustion, the danger of which rapidly decreases as the distance from the fire increases; and (2) smoke and toxic gases, which presents a different type of hazard. The greatest number of fire deaths result from these latter products of combustion, and the danger is present at considerable distances from the location of the fire.

Most fires, even relatively minor ones, produce large quantities of smoke and gases. These products can obscure vision and irritate the eyes to the extent that visibility is reduced to practically zero. Even occupants familiar with their surroundings often experience great difficulty in locating means of egress. This problem is compounded for transients and occasional visitors to the building.

Architectural layout and normal circulation patterns are important elements in emergency evacuation. For example, many large office buildings are a maze of offices, storage areas, and meeting rooms. Even under normal conditions, a visitor can become confused and have difficulty exiting the building. Clearly marked emergency travel routes can enhance life safety features in all buildings.

The building height is also related to the interior layout and firesafety. Under optimum conditions, modern fire department aerial equipment reaches only to approximately

Clifford S. Harvey is president of Fire Mark Limited, in Boulder, CO, and is the chief fire marshal for that community.

the seventh floor of a building. Occupants above the seventh floor cannot be evacuated by exterior aerial equipment. Consequently, interior layout becomes more significant to occupant evacuation and protection and to fire department operations.

BUILDING DESIGN AND FIRE DEPARTMENT OPERATIONS

From the beginning of the construction project, the building designer should consult fire department personnel about fire suppression operations in a building. Such consultation is particularly important in the design phase of a building project. In this way, the designer can incorporate features into the building that will aid, rather than hinder, fire suppression and emergency operations.

Briefly, the operations may be broadly grouped as rescue, fire control, and property conservation. The first priority of any fire fighting operation is rescue, which is defined as the removal of trapped and injured occupants and the search of all areas to ensure that all occupants are out of the building. The larger the building, the greater the number of fire fighting personnel that must be committed to the rescue operation. In some cases, simultaneous fire suppression operations will be necessary to complete the rescue operation.

Accessibility for Fire Fighting

Building design features are important factors in the spread of fire and the ease of suppression. One of the most important design features involves access to the fire. This includes access to the exterior and interior of the building by fire fighters and their equipment.

Access to the building itself requires roads or fire lanes that are designed to withstand the weight of the heaviest apparatus owned by the municipality in which the building is located. These access lanes must be designed to allow fire equipment to get close enough to all sides of the building for rescue and fire suppression functions. These access lanes must be of sufficient width to ensure they will not be obstructed when needed. Street or road widths should not be less than 28 ft (8.5 m) curb face to curb face in low-density residential areas and should be much wider in commercial and industrial areas. Secondary access and emergency fire lanes should be readily visible and at least 16 ft (4.9 m) wide [20 ft (6.1 m) wide at buildings], with adequate turning radii at each corner or turn. Accepted standards dictate a 22-ft (6.7 m) inside turning radius and a 45-ft (13.7 m) outside turning radius, but larger equipment may need even greater radii.

Access to the interior of a building can be greatly hampered where large areas exist and where buildings have blank walls, false facades, solar screens, or signs covering a high percentage of exterior walls. Obstacles that prevent ventilation allow smoke to accumulate and obscure fire fighters' vision. Lack of adequate interior access can also delay or prevent fire department rescue of trapped occupants or initiation of fire suppression efforts.

Windowless buildings and basements present unique fire fighting problems. The lack of natural ventilation facilities, such as windows, contributes to the buildup of dense smoke and intense heat, which hampers fire fighting operations.

Spaces in which adequate fire fighting access and operations are restricted because of architectural, engineering, or functional barriers should be provided with automatic extinguishing systems. A complete automatic sprinkler system is probably the best solution to this problem. Other methods can be incorporated in appropriate design situations, such as access panels in interior walls and floors, fixed nozzles in floors with fire department connections, automatic smoke venting, and pressurization of certain building areas, although none of these items can take the place of, or be considered equivalent to, a complete automatic sprinkler system.

Ventilation

Ventilation is an important fire fighting operation. It involves the removal of smoke, gases, and heat from building spaces. Ventilation of building spaces performs the following important functions:

1. Protection of life by removing or diverting toxic gases and smoke from locations where building occupants must find temporary refuge.
2. Improvement of the environment in the vicinity of the fire by removal of smoke and heat. This enables fire fighters to advance close to the fire and extinguish it with a minimum of time, water, and damage.
3. Control of the spread or direction of fire by setting up air currents that cause the fire to move in a desired direction. In this way, occupants or valuable property can be more readily protected.
4. Provision of a release for unburned, combustible gases before they develop a flammable mixture, thus avoiding a backdraft or smoke explosion.

The building designer should be conscious of these important fire ventilation functions and provide effective means of facilitating venting practices whenever possible. This may involve access panels, moveable windows, skylights, or other means of readily opening spacing in case of a fire emergency. Emergency controls on mechanical equipment may also be an effective means of accomplishing fire ventilation. Each building has unique features, and, consequently, a unique solution should be incorporated into each design. NFPA 204M, *Smoke and Heat Venting*, should be consulted for additional information on venting.

Water Supply and Use

Water is the principal agent used to extinguish building fires. Although other agents may occasionally be employed (e.g., carbon dioxide, dry chemical, foams and surfactants, and halons), water remains the primary extinguishing agent of the fire service. Consequently, the building designer should anticipate the needs of both the fire department and automatic extinguishing systems and provide an adequate supply of water at adequate residual pressure.

Water is normally supplied to the building site by mains that are part of the municipal water distribution system. Few cities can supply a sufficient amount of water at required pressures to every part of the city. Consequently, water supplied to hydrants, standpipes, or sprinklers may need to be boosted by pumps located on fire department apparatus or in the buildings themselves.

Careful attention must be given to water supply, distribution, and pressure for emergency fire conditions. High-rise buildings are particularly sensitive because of the higher water pressures required due to the building height. Large-area buildings must also be given careful attention as to the water supply needs.

Fire conditions that require operation of a large number of sprinklers or use of a large number of hose streams can reduce pressure in sprinkler and standpipe systems to the point where residual pressures in the distribution system are adversely affected. Fire department connections for sprinkler and standpipe systems, so the fire department can augment system pressure, are therefore important components of the building fire defenses. The building designer must carefully consider installation details of fire department connections to ensure they will be easily located, readily accessible, and properly marked. Locations for the connections should always be approved by the local fire department.

Water removal: Water-tight floors are important in this respect. Salvage efforts can be greatly affected by the integrity of the floors. Of greater importance is the number and location of floor drains. If interior drains and/or scuppers are available, salvage teams can remove water effectively with a minimum of damage.

BUILDING DESIGN AND FIRE SUPPRESSION

The building designer has a significant influence on the relative ease and effectiveness of fire suppression operations. Not only is it important to incorporate the needs of the fire service into the functional layout of the building and its services, but also to properly plan for automatic fire detection and extinguishing capabilities.

Compartmentation

Fire fighting efficiency decreases rapidly as the fire propagates vertically. Fires on two or more floors are extremely difficult to control and extinguish by manual fire fighting methods. Building designs that utilize unprotected vertical openings, such as open stairwells, curtain wall construction not sealed at each floor, poke-through assemblies, and air-handling ductwork (without dampers), provide avenues for vertical fire spread. It is more difficult to isolate a space effectively in modern construction than it was in pre-World War II construction, yet isolation can be accomplished if attention is paid to the details of design and construction.

Detection, Alarm, and Communications

Time is the most significant factor concerning fire control. The time for fire control includes several distinct segments, including fire detection, occupant notification, fire department notification, fire department response, fire situation assessment, suppression activities, and overhaul operations. In the early development stages of a fire, a matter of minutes is a significant factor both in life safety and in manual fire extinguishment capabilities. Consequently, effective fire detection becomes a vital element in firesafety. After a fire or smoke detector is activated, appropriate action must be initiated. This may involve alarm, communications, fire suppression, or a combination of these activities. An alarm may alert building occupants to the existence of a fire, but what action should then be taken? Evacuation is the normal procedure in smaller buildings. High-rise buildings, on the other hand, cannot reasonably be totally evacuated without allowing for a greater period of time. Consequently, zoned evacuation and/or safe areas of refuge should be provided within the building, and instructions should be given to building occupants concerning the appropriate course of action.

Communications are vital in occupant safety and fire control. Communications help warn occupants, provide instructions for action, alert the fire department early about the existence and location of a fire, and can assist the fire department in manual fire suppression. Too often, fire department notification has been delayed because occupants were under the mistaken impression that a local fire alarm system notified the fire department.

Automatic Fire Suppression

For more than a century, automatic sprinklers have been the most important single system for automatic control of fires in buildings. Many desirable aesthetic and functional features of buildings that might offer some concern for firesafety can be protected by the installation of a properly designed sprinkler system. NFPA currently has no record of a multiple fatality in a fully sprinklered building where the sprinkler system was properly designed, properly installed, and operational at the time of the fire.

Among the advantages of automatic sprinklers is that they operate directly over a fire and are not affected by smoke, toxic gases, or reduced visibility. In addition, much less water is used because only those sprinklers fused by the heat of the fire operate, particularly if the building is compartmented. Other automatic extinguishing systems (carbon dioxide, dry chemical, halon agents, high-expansion foam) also provide protection in certain portions of buildings or types of occupancies for which they are particularly suited.

Another advantage that fully sprinklered properties may offer is the reduction in number of fire department equipment access lanes, because these access lanes (necessary for rescue and fire fighting operations) are historically and statistically not as necessary for fully sprinklered properties.

SITE PLANNING

The architect must utilize a given site in designing the building and adapt the functional and engineering considerations to the particular site conditions that are present. In a similar manner, the architect should consider site features in arriving at decisions on fire protection. A particular set of site characteristics may significantly influence the type of building fire defenses incorporated by the design team. Among the more significant features are traffic and transportation conditions, fire department access, and water supply. Water supply was discussed briefly earlier in this chapter. A few additional considerations are given here.

Traffic and Transportation

Time is a vital factor in fire control. The response time of the fire department can be a major component of the overall time for fire control. Fire apparatus must respond to a location via streets at all times of the day. Depending upon traffic conditions, apparatus can be seriously delayed in responding to some locations.

It may or may not be helpful to consider limited access highways for fire department response. Highways may attract motorists, thus improving traffic conditions on other city streets. On the other hand, the limited access highway may divide a community into sections. Means of travel to locations intermediate to the access points can be delayed. This can have a significant effect on response times and must be considered by the design team in selecting the appropriate fire defenses for the building. Lengthy response times may dictate greater built-in fire protection capability.

Fire Department Access

Ideal exterior accessibility occurs where a building can be approached by fire department apparatus from all sides. This, unfortunately, is not often possible. In congested areas, only the sides of buildings facing streets may be accessible. In other areas, topography or other obstacles can prevent effective use of apparatus in combatting the fire.

Some shopping centers and buildings that are located some distance from the street make the approach of apparatus difficult. If obstructions or topography prevent apparatus from being located close enough to the building for effective use, such equipment as aerial ladders, elevating platforms, and water tower apparatus are rendered useless. Valuable manpower must be expended to carry ground ladders or hand carry hose lines long distances.

The matter of access to buildings has become far more complicated in recent years. The building designer must consider this important aspect in the planning stage. Inadequate attention to site details can place the building in an unnecessarily vulnerable position. If its fire defenses are compromised by preventing adequate fire department access, more complete internal protection in the building itself must make up the difference. If fire department access is limited or nonexistent, complete automatic sprinkler protection should be provided throughout the structure.

Location of Hydrants

An adequate water supply delivered with the necessary pressure is important to control a fire. In many new developments, such as shopping centers, apartments, and housing projects, inadequate attention is given to the number and location of hydrants. There are situations that present extremely difficult fire fighting problems where water mains are so small and hydrants are so poorly spaced that adequate water to control a fire is unavailable. The building designer must consider these conditions when planning for the fire defenses.

EXPOSURE PROTECTION

A fire in one building creates an external fire hazard to neighboring structures by exposing them to heat by radiation and convection, as well as to the danger of flying brands from the fire. Any or all of these sources of heat transfer may be sufficient to cause an ignition in the exposed structure or its contents. This part of the chapter describes a method for evaluating exposure severity, and suggests methods for protecting buildings from exterior fire exposures. These methods are aimed at protecting combustibles within, and on the exterior of, an exposed building. NFPA 80A, *Protection from Exposure Fires*, is a source for further information on exposure protection.

Factors Influencing Severity of Exposure

When discussing protection from exposure fires, there are two conditions to be considered: (1) exposure to horizontal radiation, and (2) exposure to flames issuing from the roof or top of a burning building in cases where the exposed building is greater in height than the burning building. Radiation exposure can result from an interior fire where the radiation passes through windows and other exterior wall openings. It can also result from the flames issuing from the windows of the burning building or from flames of the burning facade itself. (See Figures 6-1A, 6-1B, and 6-1C.)

FIG. 6-1A. The Burlington Building (right), Chicago, March 15, 1922. Fire in a group of brick, wood-joisted buildings (left) spread across the 80-ft (24 m) street to ignite the upper seven floors of the 15-story office building, which was of fire-resistive construction but lacked exposure protection for street-front windows. Wind carried hot gases against the Burlington Building. Updraft due to convection made exposure most severe above the level of exposing buildings.

FIG. 6-1B. Typical ignition of wood-frame dwelling by heat radiated from an exposure fire. Distances of 10 to 20 ft (3 to 6 m) between frame buildings, as commonly specified by building codes, do not eliminate exposure hazard, but usually provide space for fire department operations.

A number of factors significantly influence the danger and intensity of exposing fires to neighboring exposed structures. Among the more important parameters is the

FIG. 6-1C. Fire starting in Wellesley, MA (left), ignited a building in Newton (right) by radiated heat across the Charles River, a 100-ft (30 m) distance, against the wind. The river prevented access for fire department operations to protect the exposure.

severity of the exposing fire (total energy of the fire) itself. It involves both the temperatures developed within the exposing fire and the duration of burning. NFPA 80A, *Protection from Exposure Fires,* describes three levels of exposure severity as light, moderate, or severe. The classifications are based on: (1) the average combustible load per unit of floor area, and (2) the characteristics of an average flame spread rating of the interior wall and ceiling finishes. Tables 6-1A and 6-1B serve as a guide in assessing severity on the basis of these properties. The more severe of the two classifications should govern when using these tables.

TABLE 6-1A. ***Classification of Exposure Severity Based on Fire Loading****

Classification of Severity	Fire Loading in Lbs/Sq Ft (kg/m²) of Floor Area	
Light	0–7†	(0–34)
Moderate	7–15	(34–73)
Severe	15–up	(73–up)

† Excluding any appreciable quantities of rapidly burning materials such as certain foamed plastics, excelsior, or flammable liquids. Where these materials are found in substantial quantities, the severity should be classed as moderate or severe.

* Source: NFPA 80A, *Protection from Exposure Fires.*

TABLE 6-1B. ***Classification of Exposure Severity Based on Flame Spread of Interior Finish****

Classification of Severity	Average Flame Spread Rating of Interior Wall and Ceiling Finish
Light	0–25
Moderate	26–75
Severe	75–up

NOTE: Where only a portion of the exposing building has combustible interior finish (i.e., some rooms only, ceiling only, some walls only, etc.), this factor is considered in judging severity classification in as much as it reduces the average flame spread rating.

* Source: NFPA 80A, *Protection from Exposure Fires.*

The duration of the exposing fire and the total heat produced by the fire are related to the guide in Table 6-1A. The speed of fire buildup is influenced by both the nature of the combustibles and by the combustibility of the interior walls and ceiling finish. Table 6-1B relates the flame spread classification with severity.

Besides the temperature and duration of the exposing fire, other variables influence the severity of exposure on buildings. Some of these variables include the following:

1. Exposing fire
   a. Type of construction of exterior walls and roofs.
   b. Width of exposing fire.
   c. Height of exposing fire.
   d. Percent of openings in exposing wall area. Exterior walls that are combustible or that do not have sufficient resistance to contain the fire should be treated as having 100 percent openings.
   e. Ventilation characteristics of the burning room.
   f. The fuel dispersion, or surface-to-volume ratio of the fuel.
   g. The size, geometry, and surface-to-volume ratio of the room involved.
   h. The thermal properties, conductivity, specific heat, and density of the interior finish.
   i. Whether or not the exposing building is fully sprinklered.
2. Exposed building
   a. Type of construction of exterior walls and roofs.
   b. Orientation and surface area of exposed exterior walls.
   c. Percent of openings in exterior wall area.
   d. Protection of openings.
   e. Exposure of interior finish and combustibles to the radiation, convection, and flying brands of the exposing fire.
   f. Thermal properties, conductivity, specific heat, density, and fuel dispersion of the interior finish materials and the building contents.
   g. Whether or not the exposed building is fully sprinklered.
3. Site and protection features
   a. Separation distance between exposing and exposed building.
   b. Shielding effect of intervening noncombustible construction.
   c. Wind direction and velocity.
   d. Air temperature and humidity.
   e. Accessibility for fire fighting operations.
   f. Extent and character of fire department operations.
   g. Built-in fire protection features.

Design Guidelines for Exposure Protection

When analyzing or designing a building for exposure protection, two situations are considered. The first occurs where the exposing building is equal or greater in height than the exposed building. In this case, only the thermal radiation from walls or wall openings is considered. The second case arises when the exposing building is shorter than the exposed building.

The criteria for protection is based on the separation distance between the exposing and the exposed buildings for these two cases. Tables 6-1C and 6-1D provide guidelines for determining separation distances that should protect exposed structures from fire spread. They are based on the condition that separation distances are great enough that ignition of the exposed building or its contents is unlikely, assuming that no means of protection are installed in connection with either building.

TABLE 6-1C. ***Guide Numbers for Minimum Separation Distances****

Severity			Width/Height or Height/Width Ratio																
Light	Moderate	Severe	1.0	1.3	1.6	2.0	2.5	3.2	4	5	6	8	10	13	16	20	25	32	40
Percent Openings			Guide Number (Multiply by Lesser Dimension, Add 5 Feet, to Get Building-To-Building Separation)																
20	10	5	0.36	0.40	0.44	0.46	0.48	0.49	0.50	0.51	0.51	0.51	0.51	0.51	0.51	0.51	0.51	0.51	0.51
30	15	7.5	0.60	0.66	0.73	0.79	0.84	0.88	0.90	0.92	0.93	0.94	0.94	0.95	0.95	0.95	0.95	0.95	0.95
40	20	10	0.76	0.85	0.94	1.02	1.10	1.17	1.23	1.27	1.30	1.32	1.33	1.33	1.34	1.34	1.34	1.34	1.34
50	25	12.5	0.90	1.00	1.11	1.22	1.33	1.42	1.51	1.58	1.63	1.66	1.69	1.70	1.71	1.71	1.71	1.71	1.71
60	30	15	1.02	1.14	1.26	1.39	1.52	1.64	1.76	1.85	1.93	1.99	2.03	2.05	2.07	2.08	2.08	2.08	2.08
80	40	20	1.22	1.37	1.52	1.68	1.85	2.02	2.18	2.34	2.48	2.59	2.67	2.73	2.77	2.79	2.80	2.81	2.81
100	50	25	1.39	1.56	1.74	1.93	2.13	2.34	2.55	2.76	2.95	3.12	3.26	3.36	3.43	3.48	3.51	3.52	3.53
***	60	30	1.55	1.73	1.94	2.15	2.38	2.63	2.88	3.13	3.37	3.60	3.79	3.95	4.07	4.15	4.20	4.22	4.24
***	80	40	1.82	2.04	2.28	2.54	2.82	3.12	3.44	3.77	4.11	4.43	4.74	5.01	5.24	5.41	5.52	5.60	5.64
***	100	50	2.05	2.30	2.57	2.87	3.20	3.55	3.93	4.33	4.74	5.16	5.56	5.95	6.29	6.56	6.77	6.92	7.01
***	***	60	2.26	2.54	2.84	3.17	3.54	3.93	4.36	4.82	5.30	5.80	6.30	6.78	7.23	7.63	7.94	8.18	8.34
***	***	80	2.63	2.95	3.31	3.70	4.13	4.61	5.12	5.68	6.28	6.91	7.57	8.24	8.89	9.51	10.05	10.50	10.84
***	***	100	2.96	3.32	3.72	4.16	4.65	5.19	5.78	6.43	7.13	7.88	8.67	9.50	10.33	11.15	11.91	12.59	13.15

*Source: NFPA 80A, *Protection from Exposure Fires.*

TABLE 6-1D. ***Separation Distance Based on Building Height****

Number of Stories Likely to Contribute to Flaming Through the Roof	Horizontal Separation Distance or Height of Protection Above Exposing Fire.—Ft (m)
1	25 (7.6)
2	32 (9.8)
3	40 (12.2)
4	47 (14.3)

* Source: NFPA 80A, *Protection from Exposure Fires.*

In Table 6-1C, the parameters include severity classification (described in Tables 6-1A and 6-1B), width and height of exposing fire, and percent of openings in exposing wall area. The definitions of the terms are as follows.

Width of exposing fire (w): The length in feet or meters of the exposing wall between interior fire separations or between exterior end walls where no fire separations exist. Fire separations, such as fire partitions or fire walls, should have sufficient resistance to contain the expected fire.

Height of exposing fire (h): The height in feet or meters of the number of stories involved in the exposing fire, considering such factors as building construction, closure of vertical openings, and fire resistance of floors. The relevant fire separations must have sufficient fire resistance to contain the expected fire.

Percent of openings in exposing wall area: This is the percentage of the exposing wall that consists of doors, windows, or other openings within the assumed height and width of the exposing fire. Walls without the ability to withstand fire penetration for the expected duration of the fire should be treated as having 100 percent openings.

In using Table 6-1C, for example, assume that a building has a moderate severity [7 to 15 lbs per sq ft (34 to 73 kg/m^2) of fire load]. Assume further that the width and height of exposing fire is 100 ft (30 m) and 50 ft (15 m), respectively, and that 60 percent of the exposed wall area is open. Using a width to height ratio of 100/50 (30/15) = 2.0, a moderate severity, and 60 percent openings, a guide number of 2.15 is obtained from Table 6-1C. This indicates that the minimum separation an unprotected building should have from an exposing fire in the building described should be 2.15 multiplied by the smaller dimension plus 5 ft (1.5 m).*

Naturally, site conditions and economic constraints preclude the opportunity of providing most buildings with the calculated separation distance. When this occurs, the separation may be reduced by protecting the structure. Some of the means of protecting buildings from exposure fires, and thus reducing the desirable separation distance, are:

1. Complete automatic sprinkler protection.
2. Blank walls of noncombustible materials.
3. Barrier walls (self-supporting) between building and exposure. (See Figure 6-1D.)
4. Extension of exterior masonry walls to form parapets or wings.
5. Automatic outside water curtains for combustible walls.
6. Elimination of openings by filling them with equivalent construction.
7. Glass block panels in openings.
8. Wired glass in steel sash (fixed or automatic closing) in openings, coupled with automatic or deluge sprinklers outside over openings. (See Figure 6-1E.)
9. Automatic (rolling steel) fire shutters on openings.
10. Automatic fire doors on door openings.
11. Automatic fire dampers on wall openings.

The application of the means of protection described previously will enable the separation distance to be reduced. Guidelines for the distance reduction are given in Table 6-1E.

It should be noted that none of these measures is necessary, or even desirable, when both the exposing and exposed properties are provided with a complete fire sprinkler system.

*The 5 ft (1.5 m) is added to the computed values of separation distance partly to account for the horizontal projection of flames from windows and partly to guard against the risk of ignition by direct flame impingement where small separations are involved.

FIG. 6-1D. Above are two types of free-standing fire walls. At left is a brick fire wall reinforced with concrete abutments to make it free-standing. At right is a reinforced concrete fire wall which protected the dwelling from a fire in an adjacent lumberyard.

FIG. 6-1E. This wired-glass window in a metal frame, though cracked by intense heat of an exposure fire, remained in place and combined with an open sprinkler to prevent fire from entering the building. Note the open sprinkler at top outside the window.

TABLE 6-1E. ***Adjustments for Reducing Separation Distances****

Means of Protection	Separation Distance Adjustment
Frame or Combustible Exterior Wall:	
1. Replace with blank fire-resistive wall (3 hr minimum)	Reduce to 0 ft (mm)
2. Install automatic deluge water curtain over entire wall with no windows or with wired-glass windows closed by ¾-hr protection	Reduce to 5 ft (1.5 m)
3. Install automatic deluge water curtain over entire wall with ordinary glass windows	Reduce by 50 percent
Noncombustible Exposed Exterior Wall (Fire Resistance Less Than 3 Hrs):	
1. Replace wall with blank fire-resistive wall (3 hr minimum)	Reduce to 0 ft (m)
2. Close all wall openings with material equivalent to wall, or with ¾-hr protection and eliminate combustible projections	Reduce by 50 percent
3. Install automatic deluge water curtain over entire wall with no windows or with glass windows or with windows closed by ¾- hr protection	Reduce to 5 ft (1.5 m)
4. Install automatic deluge water curtain on all wall openings equipped with ordinary glass and on combustible projections	Reduce by 50 percent
Veneered Exposed Exterior Wall (Combustible Construction Covered by a Minimum of 4 in. of Masonry):	
1. Replace wall with blank fire-resistive wall (3 hr minimum)	Reduce to 0 ft (m)
2. Close all wall openings with ¾-hr protection and eliminate combustible projections	Reduce by 50 percent
3. Close all wall openings with material equivalent to wall construction and eliminate combustible projections	Reduce to 5 ft (1.5 m)
4. Install automatic deluge water curtain over windows equipped with wired glass or over ¾-hr closed openings and on combustible projections	Reduce to 5 ft (1.5 m)
5. Install automatic deluge water curtain over windows equipped with ordinary glass and on combustible projections	Reduce by 50 percent
Fire-Resistive Exposed Exterior Wall (Minimum 3 hr Rating):	
1. Close all openings with material equivalent to wall or protect all wall openings with 3-hr protection	Reduce to 0 ft (m)
2. Protect all openings with 1½-hr protection	Reduce by 75 percent (maximum required = 10 ft (2.1 m)
3. Protect all wall openings with ¾-hr protection	Reduce by 50 percent (maximum required = 20 ft (6.1 m)

TABLE 6-1E. ***(Continued) Adjustments for Reducing Separation Distances****

Means of Protection	Separation Distance Adjustment
4. Install automatic deluge water curtain on all wall openings with wired glass or with ¾- or 1½-hr protection	Reduce to 5 ft (1.5 m)
5. Install automatic deluge water curtain on all wall openings equipped with ordinary glass	Reduce by 50 percent

Source: NFPA 80A, *Protection from Exposure Fires.*
SI units: 1 ft = 0.3048 m.

BIBLIOGRAPHY

NFPA Codes, Standards, and Recommended Practices

Reference to the following NFPA codes, standards, and recommended practices will provide further information on building and site planning for firesafety in this chapter. (See the latest *NFPA Catalog* for availability of current editions of the following documents.)

NFPA 80A, *Protection from Exposure Fires.*

NFPA *101, Life Safety Code.*

NFPA 204M, *Smoke and Heat Venting.*

NFPA 1231, *Water Supplies for Suburban and Rural Fire Fighting.*

Additional Reading

Anchor, R. D., Malhotra, H. L., and Purkiss, J. A., eds., *Proceedings* of the International Conference on Design of Structures Against Fire, Elsevier, New York, 1986.

Brannigan, F. L., *Building Construction for the Fire Service*, National Fire Protection Association, Quincy, MA, 1982.

Breen, D. E., "Improved Life Safety Through More Reliable Smoke Detection Systems," *Proceedings* from the Conference on New Technology to Reduce Fire Losses and Costs, Elsevier, New York, 1986, pp. 227-234.

Clark, W. E., *Fire Fighting Principles and Practices*, Donnelly Publishing Corporation, New York, 1974.

Fried, E., *Fireground Tactics*, H. M. Ginn Corporation, Chicago, IL, 1972.

Gilardi, S. A., "Planning for Fire Safety," *Construction Specifier*, Vol. 41, No. 4 (Apr. 1988), pp. 33-34.

Glon, P. L., "Building Safety—A New Educational Approach," *Building Standards*, Vol. 56, No. 2, 1987, pp. 20-21.

Harvey, C. S., "A Flexible Approach to Fire-Code Compliance," *Architectural Record*, Vol. 176, No. 12 (Oct. 1988), pp. 130-135.

Law, M., "Heat Radiation from Fires and Building Separation," Technical Paper No. 5, Joint Fire Research Organization, Borehamwood, Hertfordshire, England, 1963.

Lie, T. T., "Safety Factors the Fire Loads," *Canadian Journal of Civil Engineering*, Vol. 6, 1979, p. 617.

McGuire, J. H., "Spatial Separation of Buildings," *Fire Technology*, Vol. 1, No. 4 (Nov. 1965), pp. 278-287.

Morris, J., "Life Safety and Sprinkler Protection," *Fire Prevention*, No. 209 (May 1988), pp. 18-21.

Nakamura, H., "Investment Model of Fire Protection Equipment for Office Building," *Proceedings* of the First International Sym posium on Fire Safety Science, Hemisphere, Washington, DC, 1986, pp. 1019-1028.

Nelson, H. E., "Jefferson National Memorial Historical Site Analysis of Impact of Fire Safety," *NBSIR 84-2897*, National Bureau of Standards, Gaithersburg, MD, March 1985.

Ow, C. S. and Thin, C. C., "Upgrading Fire Protection in Existing Buildings," *Fire International*, Vol. 12, No. 112 (Aug.-Sept. 1988), pp. 39-40.

Shorter, G. W., *et al*, "The St. Lawrence Burns," *NFPA Quarterly*, Vol. 53, No. 4 (Apr. 1960), National Fire Protection Association, Quincy, MA, pp. 300-316.

Thomas, P. H., "The Size of Flames from Natural Fires," Ninth Symposium on Combustion, Academic Press, 1963, pp. 844-859.

Williams-Leir, G., "Approximations of Spatial Separation," *Fire Technology*, Vol. 2, No. 2 (May 1966), pp. 136-145.

CLASSIFICATION OF BUILDING CONSTRUCTION

Revised by Richard G. Gewain and David C. Jeans

A well-established means of codifying fire protection and firesafety requirements for buildings is to classify them by types of construction, based upon the materials used for the structural elements, and the degree of fire resistance afforded by each element.

In early codes, only two classifications of construction were identified: (1) "fireproof," and (2) "nonfireproof." The term "fireproof" was replaced by the term "fire resistive," since it was recognized that no material or building is totally fireproof, and that the building contents can produce a significant fire without involving the structure. It is possible, however, to design buildings that will resist a fire without suffering serious structural damage. Optimum fire-resistive design, balanced against anticipated fire severity, is the objective of structural fire protection requirements in modern codes.

Several distinct types of construction that use combustible framing were originally classified based on the materials—masonry or wood—used in the exterior wall construction and the type and size of the framing members, i.e., heavy timber *versus* conventional framing. As fire-resistance ratings for construction assemblies were recognized in building codes, subclassifications of building types were added for both noncombustible and combustible types of construction, based on the degree of fire resistance provided.

Code regulations governing the size, area, and height of buildings and their allowable uses are usually predicated on the relative fire load represented by the occupancy and the construction materials used in the building.

This chapter identifies the basic types of building construction that are recognized in NFPA 220, *Types of Building Construction*, and in the model building codes. It also recognizes the current classification system of building construction equated with the traditional descriptive terms used to identify building types, e.g., "fire resistive," "noncombustible," "ordinary," "frame," etc., that no longer are prime references to construction types.

Richard G. Gewain is director of Fire Research for American Iron and Steel Institute (AISI); David C. Jeans is director of Codes and Standards for AISI.

CONSTRUCTION CLASSIFICATIONS

The construction types presently identified in NFPA 220, *Types of Building Construction*, as well as in the three model building codes, i.e., UBC (Uniform Building Code); BNBC (BOCA National Building Code); and SBC (Standard Building Code), fall into ten classifications in NFPA 220 and the BNBC. The UBC and SBC have nine types of construction. All classifications, however, are derived from five fundamental construction types: (1) fire resistive, (2) noncombustible, (3) ordinary (exterior protected), (4) heavy timber, and (5) wood frame. These descriptive names are now being discontinued because they no longer define the construction types as precisely as needed. The names are helpful, however, in tracing the development of building types.

Although the fire-resistive construction types differ in detail from code to code, the three model building codes and NFPA 220, *Types of Building Construction*, all define subtypes of fire-resistive construction, using as a basis the amount of fire resistance (2, 3, or 4 hr) required for the structural members.

Where the interior structural members and floors are of noncombustible materials with fire-resistance ratings of 1 hr or less, the type of construction is generally identified as noncombustible. Most codes subdivide the noncombustible classification into two types: (1) protected, and (2) unprotected.

NFPA 220, *Types of Building Construction*, and the three model building codes employ three broad classifications for combustible types of construction: (1) exterior protected ordinary, (2) heavy timber, and (3) wood frame. Exterior protected ordinary and wood frame each include two subtypes, i.e., protected and unprotected. They are almost identical in most respects, except for their exterior wall requirements. Heavy timber construction is unique because it is identified by detailed requirements relating mainly to the size of structural members and their connections. Properties, such as combustibility or fire resistance, are not specifically included in the requirements for heavy timber construction, except that exterior walls are required to be of noncombustible construction.

TABLE 6-2A. ***Types of Construction and Their Firesafety Characteristics, National Building Code of Canada****

Basic Type of Construction	Group	SubTypes	Characteristics (under fire load conditions)
Combustible construction	I	Wood frame Wood post and beam Plank Plastic Other unprotected combustible	Fuel contributing and unstable
		Heavy timber construction and other protected combustible construction	Fuel contributing but partially stable to the degree of fire resistance
Noncombustible construction	II	Unprotected steel construction Ordinary prestressed concrete Thin unprotected reinforced masonry Other unprotected noncombustible construction	Nonfuel contributing but unstable
	III	Steel construction with fire resistance Masonry with fire resistance Reinforced concrete with fire resistance	Nonfuel contributing and stable to the degree of fire resistance

* Table reproduced from "Steel and Fire Safety as required in the National Building Code of Canada—1975," R. V. Hebert, Canadian Steel Industries Construction Council.

Canadian Classifications

Construction type classification in building codes is more of a convenience than a necessity. The National Building Code of Canada (NBCC) does not classify buildings in the traditional manner as do United States codes, but rather specifies fire-resistive requirements for the structural components of a building, depending upon its occupancy and its story height and floor area. In this code, two basic types of construction, i.e., combustible and noncombustible, are recognized. These are further subdivided by the characteristics of the materials used in construction under fire conditions, as shown in Table 6-2A.

New York City Building Code Classifications

The New York City Building Code divides construction types into two groups, i.e., (1) noncombustible, and (2) combustible; each of these, in turn, is divided into five types. These subdivisions are distinguished by the fire resistance required for the interior structural members and for the exterior walls.

BCMC (Board for the Coordinating of the Model Codes)

To achieve better uniformity in building codes, the Model Codes Standardization Council (MCSC), predecessor to the Board for the Coordinating of the Model Codes (BCMC), established a committee in 1972 to study the classifications and fire resistance requirements for types of construction used in the model building codes and to develop recommendations for the model code organizations.

As a result of its comparative study, the BCMC proposed that the basic types of construction now recognized in the codes be continued but that they be reordered to some degree and be divided into two groups: (1) noncombustible, and (2) combustible. It was also proposed that the identifying names for types of construction, such as "fireproof," "ordinary," "heavy timber," etc., be dropped because current design methods and architecture no longer follow the concepts in vogue when the named building types were established. The classifications proposed are shown in Table 6-2B. (These are the classifications recognized in the current edition of NFPA 220, *Types of Building Construction*.)

TABLE 6-2B. ***Model Codes Standardization Council Recommended Types of Construction***

	Noncombustible	
Type I (433) Type I (332)	Type II (222) Type II (111) Type II (000)	
	Combustible	
Type III (211) Type III (200)	Type IV (2HH)	Type V (111) Type V (000)

The MCSC also concluded that to rationally compare the various types of construction, a notational system was needed to identify the fire resistance required for three basic elements of the building. These elements are: (1) the exterior wall, (2) the primary structural frame, and (3) the floor construction. A three-digit notation was developed, as follows:

1. *First digit*—Hourly fire resistance requirement for exterior-bearing wall fronting on a street or lot line.
2. *Second digit*—Hourly fire resistance requirement for structural frame or columns and girders supporting loads from more than one floor.
3. *Third digit*—Hourly fire resistance requirement for floor construction.

For heavy timber construction, the notation "H" and not a digit was used for the structural frame and floor construction designations.

Thus, for example, a "322" building would have 3-hr fire-resistant exterior bearing walls, a 3-hr fire-resistant structural frame, and 2-hr fire-resistant floor construction, and would correspond to the NFPA 220, *Types of Building Construction*, Type I (322) building, the Basic Building Code Type IB building, the Uniform Building Code Type I FR (fire resistive) building, and the Standard Building Code Type II building.

TABLE 6-2C. *A Comparison of Construction Types (Based on the MCSC National System)*

NFPA 220	I (443)	I (332)	II (222)	II (111)	II (000)	III (211)	III (200)	IV (2HH)	V (111)	V (000)
UBC	—	I FR	II FR	II-1 hr	II N	III-1 hr	III N	IV HT	V 1-hr	V-N
BNBC	1A	1B	2A	2B	2C	3A	3B	4	5A	5B
SBC	I	II	—	IV 1-hr	IV unp	V 1-hr	V unp	III	VI 1-hr	VI unp
BBC	1A	1B	2A	2B	2C	3B	3C	3A	4A	4B

A comparison of types of construction, based on the MCSC notational system, as found in NFPA 220, *Types of Building Construction*, and the current editions of four model building codes, is shown in Table 6-2C.

A standard nomenclature was also developed for identifying and defining the structural elements in buildings as they relate to fire resistance. For example, it was found in reviewing various codes and fire protection standards that floor construction was referred to by such terms as "floors," "floor assemblies," "floor and ceiling assemblies," and "floor deck construction." If codes agree, for example, that "floor construction" includes the floor deck and all beams, joists, and other structural elements directly supporting the loads from the floor, as recommended by MCSC, then some misinterpretation of a code's intent would be avoided.

CLASSIFICATION OF BUILDING TYPES

Following the completion of these recommendations in 1974, the model code organizations and NFPA adopted a number of changes to their requirements for types of construction to agree with the MCSC classifications. However, it was recognized that some conflicts among the model codes still remained. In 1975, therefore, the BCMC established a committee to develop more detailed recommendations for types of construction.

In 1980 the committee's recommended definitions of types of construction and fire resistance requirements were finalized. The requirements are based on five basic types of construction. Two are identified as noncombustible construction and three as combustible construction types. Table 6-2D gives the fire resistance requirements for the structural frame, interior bearing walls, floor construction, and roof construction of the five basic types of construction.

The term "structural frame," as used in the table, refers to the columns and the girders, beams, trusses, and spandrels having direct connections to the columns, and all other members that are essential to the stability of the building as a whole. The members of floor or roof panels that have no connection to the columns are considered part of the floor or roof construction and are not classified as a part of the structural frame.

Type I Construction

Type I construction (formerly referred to as fire resistive) is construction in which the structural members are noncombustible and have a fire resistance as specified in Table 6-2D. This classification is divided into two subtypes, i.e., Type I (443) and Type I (322). The basic difference between the subtypes is in the level of fire resistance specified for the structural frame.

For both subtypes, the required fire resistance of those portions of the structural frame and bearing walls supporting roof loads only may be reduced by one hour.

The fire resistance requirements for Type I (433 and 322) construction were selected because they provide reasonable firesafety for the structure for occupancies with moderate- and low-combustible contents. In occupancies with higher fire loads and hazardous uses, fire resistance may be supplemented by additional protection, usually including an automatic fire extinguishing system. Even in occupancies with moderate fire loads, such as in mercantile and in some factory industrial and storage uses, supplementary firesafety precautions are required. These include restrictions on the building size or requirements for automatic fire extinguishing equipment.

In Type I construction, only noncombustible materials are permitted for the structural elements of the building. This is an accepted regulation that appears in practically every modern building code. Obviously, if combustible structural materials were allowed in noncombustible building types, the whole concept of their allowable use (height and area) would become meaningless. However, for practical reasons, the use of some combustible materials in Type I and Type II buildings are permitted for other than structural components. Roof coverings, some types of insulating materials, and limited amounts of wood for interior finish and flooring have been traditionally recognized as not adding significantly to the fire hazard or fire load if these materials are properly regulated and qualified by fire tests.

Some codes have attempted to regulate combustible materials by using a definition of noncombustible materials which includes two or three alternatives that allow for the acceptance of materials having relatively low fuel content and surface burning characteristics. The purpose of this definition was to recognize certain materials or nonhomogenous assemblies containing limited amounts of combustible, such as gypsum wallboard which, although covered with paper, is used as a fire-resistive material. These alternate definitions include limits on surface flame spread rating and on the heat content—the latter being 3500 Btu per lb (8050 J/kg), somewhat less than one-half that of untreated wood.

Rather than complicate the definition for the accomodation of certain materials, a more fundamental approach is to define limited uses and combustibility characteristics of materials that may be acceptable in buildings of noncombustible construction. This approach is followed in the NBCC and by the BCMC committee in its recommendations for the allowable kinds and extent of use of combustible material in noncombustible buildings.

TABLE 6-2D. ***Fire Resistance Requirements for Type I Through Type V Construction (NFPA 220, Types of Building Construction)***

	Type I		Type II			Type III		Type IV	Type V	
	443	332	222	111	000	211	200	2HH	111	000
EXTERIOR BEARING WALLS—										
Supporting more than one floor, columns or other bearing walls	4	3	2	1	0[1]	2	2	2	1	0[1]
Supporting one floor only	4	3	2	1	0[1]	2	2	2	1	0[1]
Supporting a roof only	4	3	1	1	0[1]	2	2	2	1	0[1]
INTERIOR BEARING WALLS—										
Supporting more than one floor, columns or other bearing walls	4	3	2	1	0	1	0	2	1	0
Supporting one floor only	3	2	2	1	0	1	0	1	1	0
Supporting a roof only	3	2	1	1	0	1	0	1	1	0
COLUMNS—										
Supporting more than one floor, bearing walls or other columns	4	3	2	1	0	1	0	H[2]	1	0
Supporting one floor only	3	2	2	1	0	1	0	H[2]	1	0
Supporting a roof only	3	2	1	1	0	1	0	H[2]	1	0
BEAMS, GIRDERS, TRUSSES & ARCHES—										
Supporting more than one floor, bearing walls or columns	4	3	2	1	0	1	0	H[2]	1	0
Supporting one floor only	3	2	2	1	0	1	0	H[2]	1	0
Supporting a roof only	3	2	1	1	0	1	0	H[2]	1	0
FLOOR CONSTRUCTION	3	2	2	1	0	1	0	H[2]	1	0
ROOF CONSTRUCTION	2	1½	1	1	0	1	0	H[2]	1	0
EXTERIOR NONBEARING WALLS	0[1]	0[1]	0[1]	0[1]	0[1]	0[1]	0[1]	0[1]	0[1]	0[1]

Those members listed that are permitted to be of approved combustible material.

[1] Requirements for fire resistance of exterior walls, the provision of spandrel wall sections, and the limitation or protection of wall openings are not related to construction type. They need to be specified in other standards and codes, where appropriate, and may be required in addition to the requirements of this Standard for the construction type.

[2] "H" indicates heavy timber members; see text for requirements.

Type II Construction

Type II construction (formerly referred to as noncombustible) is a construction type in which the structural elements are entirely of noncombustible or limited combustible materials permitted by the code and protected to have some degree of fire resistance, either 2 hr [Type II (222)], 1 hr [Type II (111)], or completely unprotected except for exterior walls in Type II (000) construction.

The fire resistance required in Type II (222 or 111) construction will afford adequate firesafety for residential, educational, institutional, business, and assembly occupancies, without supplementary restrictions. Height limits, however, are commonly prescribed for this type of construction. When used for other occupancies involving a greater fire loading, additional firesafety precautions are usually required, such as more stringent area limitations and automatic fire extinguishing equipment. In occupancies with low-combustible contents, the absence of fuel in noncombustible construction not only helps prevent the spread of fire but also reduces potential risk of a fire starting within the structure itself.

The noncombustible feature is valuable because it prevents fire from spreading through concealed spaces or involving the structure itself. Because of this attribute, a fire in a building of noncombustible construction can be controlled more readily. (See Figure 6-2A.)

Type III Construction

Type III construction (formerly referred to as exterior protected combustible or ordinary construction) is a construction type in which all or part of the interior structural elements may be of combustible materials or any other material permitted by the particular building code being applied. The exterior walls are required to be of noncombustible or limited noncombustible materials acceptable to the code and have a degree of fire resistance depending upon the horizontal separation and the fire load. Type III construction is further divided into protected and unprotected subtypes. Protected construction, Type III (211), has a 1-hr fire resistance for the floors and structural elements. Type III (200) construction has no fire resistance for the floors or structural elements. Whether or not fire resistance is provided, it is essential that all concealed spaces be properly firestopped in buildings of combustible construction. This must be done with care in all furred spaces, partitions, ceiling spaces, and attics. Codes are very specific as to the materials to be used for firestopping and the locations where firestopping is required. To be effective, firestopping must completely close off and subdivide the combustible construction into limited areas, thereby restricting the spread of fire and hot gases and allowing additional time for detection and evacuation of the building or area involved.

The 1-hr fire resistance provided in Type III (211) construction offers a measure of safety for fire fighting and evacuation before the construction itself becomes involved. It has been well established, however, that combustible parts of any fire-rated assembly will be burning actively before the end of the rated time period. For this reason, that portion of the fire load represented by combustible structure must be considered as part of the total potential fire load, whether or not the construction is protected.

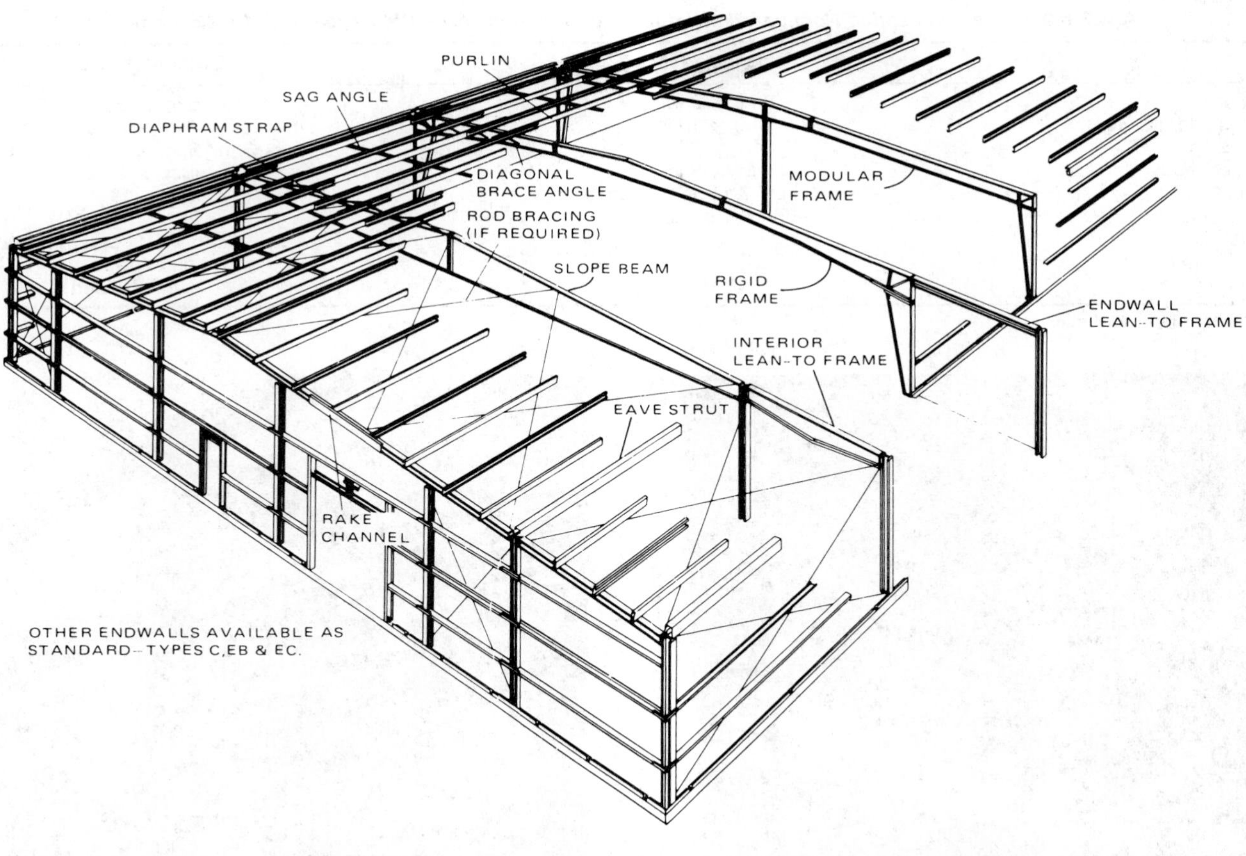

FIG. 6-2A. The framing system of a representative building of Type II (noncombustible) construction. Shown is preengineered pitched roof and lean-to-framing with structural elements of unprotected steel. Requirements for exterior walls of Type II construction are specified by the applicable building code or standard that is used by the authority having jurisdiction.

Type IV Construction

Type IV construction (formerly referred to as heavy timber) is a construction type in which structural members, i.e., columns, beams, arches, floors, and roofs, are basically of unprotected wood (solid or laminated) with large cross-sectional areas. No concealed spaces are permitted in the floors and roofs or other structural members, with minor exceptions. NFPA 220, *Types of Building Construction*, and most model building codes are specific in the minimum dimensions permitted for the various wood structural members (Table 6-2E) and minimum fire-resistive ratings required for interior columns, arches, beams, girders, and trusses of materials other than wood that may be permitted as acceptable alternatives to wood members.

Walls, both interior and exterior, including structural members framed into them, can be of noncombustible or limited combustible materials acceptable to the code being applied. Brick and stone were the traditional materials used in early heavy timber, or "mill" construction.

During a fire, heavy timber construction resists failure longer than a conventional wood frame structure because the structural members are larger, have a smaller surface to mass ratio, and take longer to burn. As the wood member burns, a layer of char develops which acts like insulation and slows down the rate of burning. The large wood members, therefore, can continue to carry their structural loads due to the mass of unburned wood.

Heavy timber construction is more properly considered as a building system, not just a construction type using large-size framing members. It was developed during the mid 1800s by insurance interests for the purpose of reducing fire losses in the many textile factories, paper mills, and storage buildings in the New England states. Through the intelligent use of combustible materials of sufficient mass, the absence of concealed spaces, and by paying attention to details to avoid sharp corners and ignitable projections, the chance of rapid spread of fire are lessened and the probability of serious structural damage is reduced.

Examples of heavy timber construction are shown in Figures 6-2B and 6-2C.

Type V Construction

Type V construction (formerly referred to as wood frame) is a type of construction in which the structural members are entirely of wood or any other material permitted by the code being applied. (See Figure 6-2D.) Depending upon the exterior horizontal separation, the exterior walls may or may not be required to be fire resistive.

Type V construction is probably more vulnerable to fire, both internally and externally, than any other building type. Accordingly, it is essential that greater attention be given to the details of construction of this basically light wood frame building. Firestopping in exterior and interior walls at ceiling and floor levels, in furred spaces, and other

TABLE 6-2E. ***Recommended Nominal Dimensional Requirements for BCMC Type IV (2HH) Construction***

	Supporting Floors	Supporting Roofs
Columns	8 in. × 8 in.	6 in. × 8 in.
Beams and girders	6 in. × 10 in.	4 in. × 6 in.
Arches	8 in. × 8 in.	6 in. × 8 in., 6 in. × 6 in., 4 in. × 6 in.
Trusses	8 in. × 8 in.	4 in. × 6 in.
Floors	3 in. T & G or 4 in. on edge w/1 in. flooring	
Roofs		2 in. T & G or 3 in. on edge or 1⅛ in. plywood

SI units: 1 in. = 25.4 mm.

FIG. 6-2B. Elements of a building of Type IV (heavy timber) construction. Note the large size of the columns and beams and the absence of concealed spaces. The exterior wall at far left is of lightweight corrugated steel.

FIG. 6-2C. A variation of Type IV (heavy timber) construction. Shown are haunched arches made of laminated wood (gluelaminated construction). Beams are anchored to the arches by steel hangers.

concealed spaces can retard the spread of fire and hot gases in these vulnerable areas.Type V construction is subdivided into two subtypes, i.e., Type V (111) construction, which has 1-hr fire resistance throughout, including the exterior walls, and Type V (000) construction, which has no fire protection or fire resistance requirements, except for the exterior walls when horizontal separation is less than 10 ft (3 m).

Mixed Types of Construction

Where two or more types of construction are used in the same building, it is generally recognized that the requirements for occupancy or height and area would apply for the least fire-resistive type of construction. However, in cases where each building type is separated by adequate fire walls or area separation walls having appropriate fire resistance, each portion may be considered as a separate building.

Another general limitation included in some codes prohibits construction types of lesser fire resistance to support construction types having higher required fire resistance. In the event of a fire, the risks of a major structural collapse are generally too great to permit this type of design. This limitation does not necessarily apply where construction supports nonbearing separating partitions, that provide protection for exit corridors or tenant spaces.

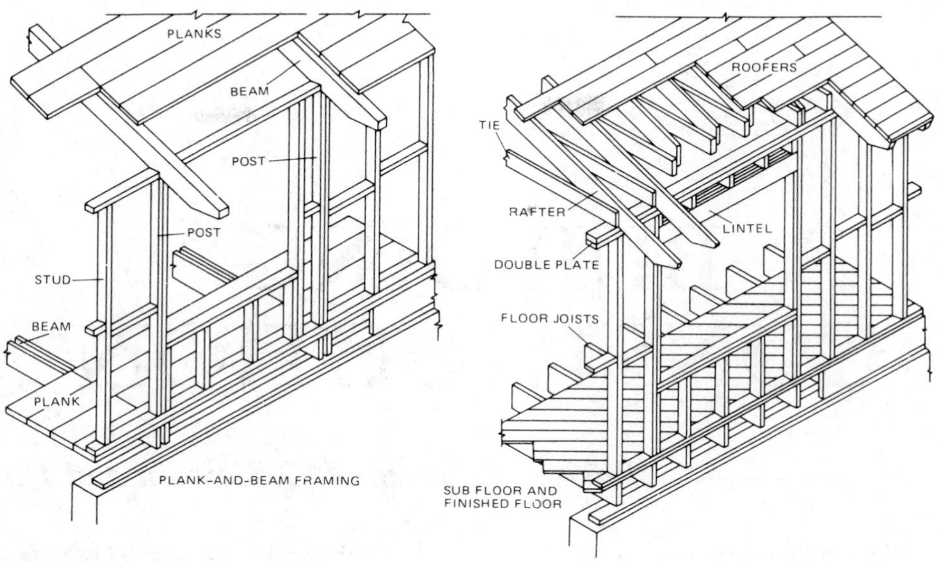

FIG. 6-2D. Two variations on basic Type V (wood frame) construction. At left is plank and beam framing in which a few large members replace many small members used in typical wood framing. At right is conventional wood framing (western or platform construction). Firestopping is essential in concealed spaces. (For details see Chapter 3, "Building Construction," in this section.)

BIBLIOGRAPHY

NFPA Codes, Standards, and Recommended Practices

Reference to the following NFPA codes, standards, and recommended practices will provide further information on classification of building construction discussed in this chapter. (See the latest *NFPA Catalog* for availability of current editions of the following documents.)

NFPA 203M, *Roof Coverings and Roof Deck Construction.*

NFPA 220, *Types of Building Construction.*

NFPA 251, *Fire Tests of Building Construction and Materials.*

NFPA 255, *Surface Burning Characteristics of Building Materials.*

NFPA 256, *Fire Tests of Roof Coverings.*

NFPA 258, *Determining Smoke Generation of Solid Materials.*

NFPA 259, *Potential Heat of Building Materials.*

Additional Readings

American Society for Testing and Materials, *Standard Test of Materials in a Vertical Tube Furnace at 750°C,* (ASTM E136-79), Philadelphia, PA, 1979.

ASTM, *Standard Test Method for Surface Burning Characteristics of Building Materials,* (ASTM E84-80), Philadelphia, PA, 1980.

Bletzacker, R. W., *et al.*, "Fire Resistance of Construction Assemblies," EES0245, Dec. 1969, Engineering Experiment Station, Ohio State University, Columbus, OH.

Brannigan, F. L., *Building Construction for the Fire Service,* National Fire Protection Association, Quincy, MA, 1982.

Fire Resistance Ratings, American Insurance Services Group, New York, NY, 1985.

Siegel, L. G., "The Severity of Fires in Steel Frame Buildings," *AISC Engineering Journal*, Vol. 4, No. 4., Oct. 1967, pp. 137-142.

BUILDING CONSTRUCTION

Revised by Richard G. Gewain and David C. Jeans

This chapter briefly outlines building construction. It identifies the more common construction assemblies that are used or have been used in building construction in the United States, but is by no means exhaustive. It provides basic information on how structural elements of a building relate to one another, and methods by which the final construction is intended to resist the effects of fire. Refer to architectural or engineering design books for more comprehensive information.

TABLE 6-3A. *Structural Elements of a Building*

Load bearing elements	Nonload bearing elements
Compressive stress	Curtain or panel walls
columns	partitions
Walls, exterior or interior	ceilings
Flexurally stressed	
Beams, girders, trusses	
floors, roofs	

FIRE PROTECTION OF BUILDING ELEMENTS

Fire protection of building elements is provided for two reasons. The first is to prevent the spread of fire within or into the building during a protracted or uncontrolled fire exposure, and the second is to ensure that even under that exposure, the building frame or elements of that frame will not collapse. Such collapse or even the threat of collapse will render fire fighting measures less effective than they might be otherwise.

There are two groups of building elements: (1) load bearing, and (2) nonload bearing. Load-bearing elements are those that support loads other than their own weight. Nonload-bearing elements support only their own weight. Removal of nonload-bearing elements would have no effect on the structural behavior of the building as a whole. Table 6-3A lists the structural elements that are common to most buildings, separated into these two general categories.

Building codes provide requirements for both structural loads and superimposed live loads. The code requirements are such that building "failures" are rare. Structural failures are generally the result of application of unanticipated loadings. In a fire situation, "loads" are induced by heat which may cause thermal stresses. These stresses may be increased if the members are in any way restrained against expansion. Also, heat may cause a loss of strength if not actual consumption of the member. While restraint in some designs may offset any loss in strength, there is the increased likelihood of collapse in the event of a protracted fire. Almost by definition, properly designed and constructed fire-resistive assemblies will retain adequate strength during fire exposure and continue to resist collapse.

Columns

Columns serve to carry building loads to the foundation where the loads are distributed to the supporting ground or rock. The material of the column is established by the type of construction—steel or reinforced concrete if noncombustible, or wood, including heavy timber designs, if combustible. In a fire situation, interior columns are the most severely exposed of any structural members, as they may be enveloped in fire on all sides. Exterior columns may not be as severely exposed, and, in some designs, the exposure may be minimized by shielding the column by structurally independent nonload-bearing shields.

Functions of Walls

Building walls may serve one or more functions and they may be either bearing or nonbearing, and exterior or interior. The following brief definitions describe the general functions that walls may serve.

Bearing wall: A wall that supports vertical loads in addition to its own weight.

Curtain wall: An exterior wall supported by the structural frame of the building. Also called a panel wall.

Richard G. Gewain is director of Fire Research for American Iron and Steel Institute (AISI); David C. Jeans is director of Codes and Standards for AISI.

Enclosure wall: An interior wall that separates a vertical opening for a stairway, elevator, duct space, etc., that connects two or more floors.

Exterior wall: A wall that forms a boundary to a building and is usually exposed to the weather.

Fire partition: An interior wall that serves to restrict the spread of fire, but does not qualify as a fire wall.

Fire wall: A wall of sufficient durability and stability to withstand the effects of the most severe anticipated fire exposure. Openings in the wall, if allowed, must be protected.

Parapet wall: A portion of an exterior, fire, or party wall that extends above the roof line.

Nonbearing wall: A wall that supports only its own weight.

Partition: An interior wall, not more than one story in height, that separates two areas in the same building but is not intended to serve as a fire barrier.

Party wall: A wall that lies on a common lot line for two buildings and is common to both buildings. Most of these walls may be constructed in a wide range of materials or assemblies.

Cavity wall: A wall of two parallel wythes (vertical wall of bricks) with an air space between them. The wythes are connected by metal ties.

Faced wall: A wall comprised of two different masonry materials; one, the facing wythe; the other, the backup wythe, which are bonded together to act as a single unit.

Hollow wall: A wall of two parallel wythes, with an air space between them, but without ties to hold the wythes together.

Sandwich wall: A nonbearing wall whose outer faces enclose an insulating core material.

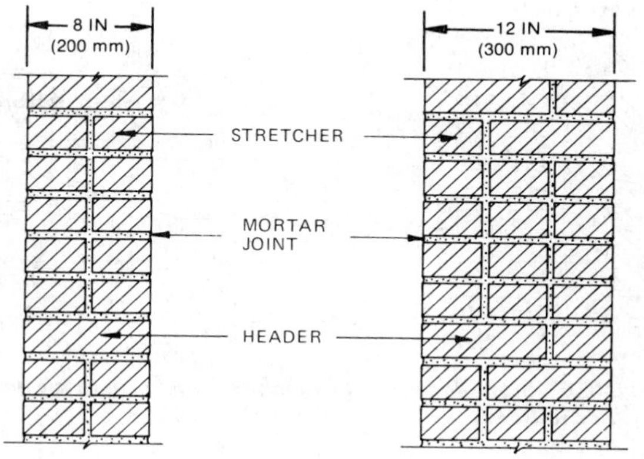

FIG. 6-3A. Typical types of wall and partition assemblies showing an 8-in. (200 mm) brick bearing wall and a 12-in. (300 mm) brick bearing wall.

EXTERIOR WALLS

The primary function of all exterior walls is to protect the inside of the building from the elements, such as heat and cold, water, wind, and windblown dust and dirt. In addition, some exterior walls may support floor and roof framing systems and may include portions that support girders or beams.

The fire resistance required for exterior walls is determined not only by the type of construction, but also by the distance the wall is set back from a lot line or an exposing structure. The greater that distance, the less severe the exposure and hence the less fire resistance that would be needed.

Load-Bearing Exterior Walls

Load-bearing exterior walls are generally constructed of masonry units, such as stone, brick, concrete block, or a combination of these materials. Brick veneer is sometimes

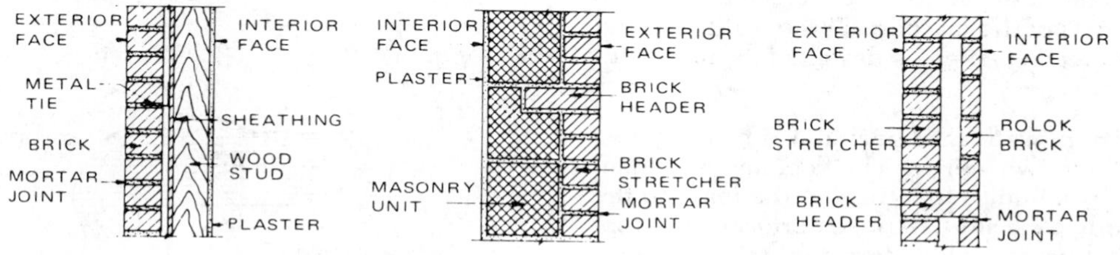

FIG. 6-3B. Typical types of wall assemblies showing (left to right) an exterior brick veneer on wood-frame wall, a 12-in. (300 mm) exterior faced or veneered wall, and an 8-in. (200 mm) exterior hollow Rolok Bak brick wall.

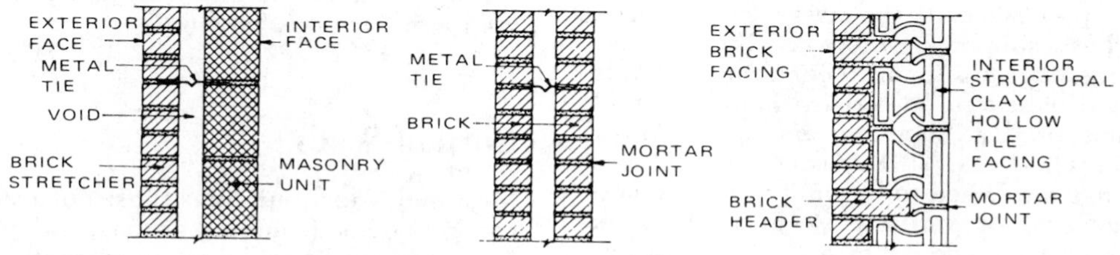

FIG. 6-3C. Typical types of wall assemblies showing (left to right) two examples of exterior nonbearing cavity walls and a 12-in. (300 mm) exterior bearing wall.

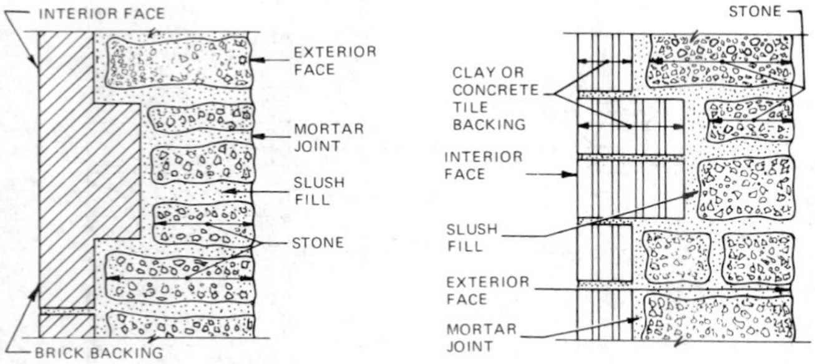

FIG. 6-3D. ***Stone-faced wall assemblies, one with brick backing, the other with tile.***

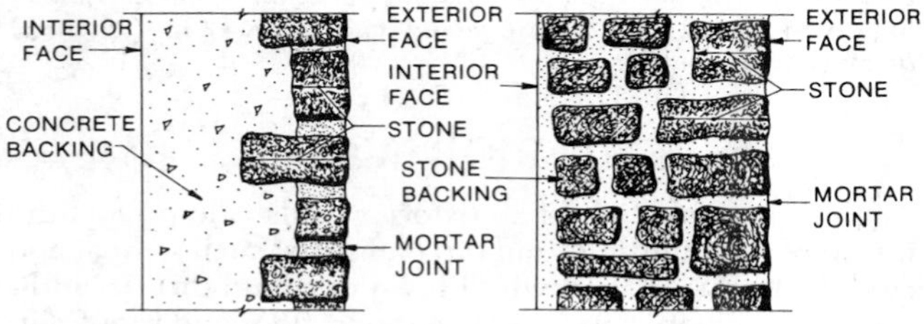

FIG. 6-3E. ***At left, a wall of concrete backing and stone face; at right, a solid stone wall.***

used as a facing in wood-frame construction. In this case, the wood studs support the applied loads, while the veneer provides an attractive, useful exterior surface. Veneers are also used as the exterior face of cavity walls. These latter types are useful only in buildings of very limited height. Figures 6-3A, 6-3B, 6-3C, 6-3D, and 6-3E illustrate some common forms of exterior wall construction.

Exterior walls can also be constructed of reinforced concrete which is either poured in place or precast. Masonry veneers are often used as the exposed surface of reinforced concrete walls. The brick veneer is tied to the concrete by metal ties fastened to the concrete and set into the bed mortar joints of the masonry. If the walls are load bearing, the reinforced concrete is designed to support all of the applied loads.

Exterior masonry walls may be nonload bearing, i.e., supporting only their own weight. The floor and roof framing is supported by columns that transfer the loads to the foundation. Usually each story of the exterior wall is supported on spandrel beams, which frame into the columns.

Some of the structural difficulties experienced with masonry walls in fires are illustrated in Figure 6-3F.

Openings, such as doors and windows, in masonry walls must have supports to carry the masonry units above the openings. These supports, called lintels, are short beams over the openings to support the masonry. Lintels can be constructed of several materials, including steel angles, steel beams, precast concrete beams, and stone or brick arches. Figures 6-3G and 6-3H illustrate several types of lintels. Openings may need to be limited in size and number when the exterior wall is close to the lot line. Openings that are protected do not have fire resistance as such, but can impede the spread of fire even though they have little resistance to the transmission of heat.

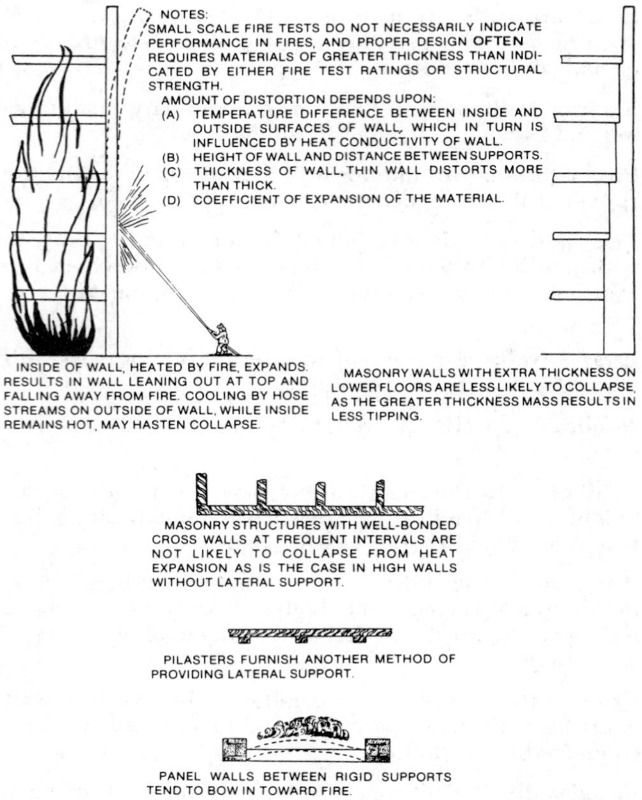

FIG. 6-3F. ***Heat expansion effects on ordinary masonry walls.***

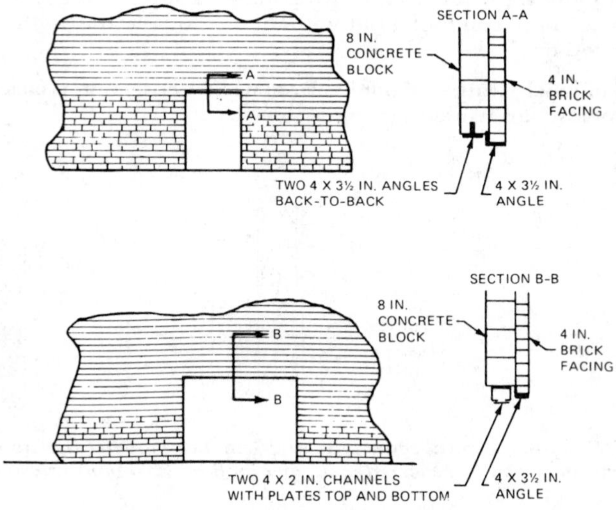

FIG. 6-3G. ***Lintels formed from steel angles and channels in brick-faced, concrete block walls.***

Curtain Walls

Most multi-story buildings consist of a steel or reinforced-concrete frame (columns, girders, and beams). The building envelope may be enclosed with nonbearing walls supported at each level. These walls are often identified as either curtain or panel walls.

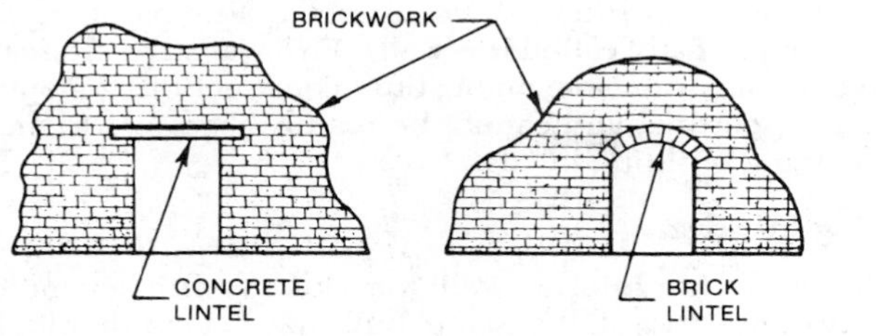

FIG. 6-3H. Use of concrete and brick lintels in masonry walls.

Many materials and types of construction are used for curtain walls. Aluminum and stainless steel curtain walls are, by far, the most common, but copper and copper alloys, carbon steel, galvanized metals, porcelain enamel finish, concrete, glass, and plastics are also used. Large window areas are common in this type of wall. Figure 6-3I shows an example of contemporary curtain wall construction.

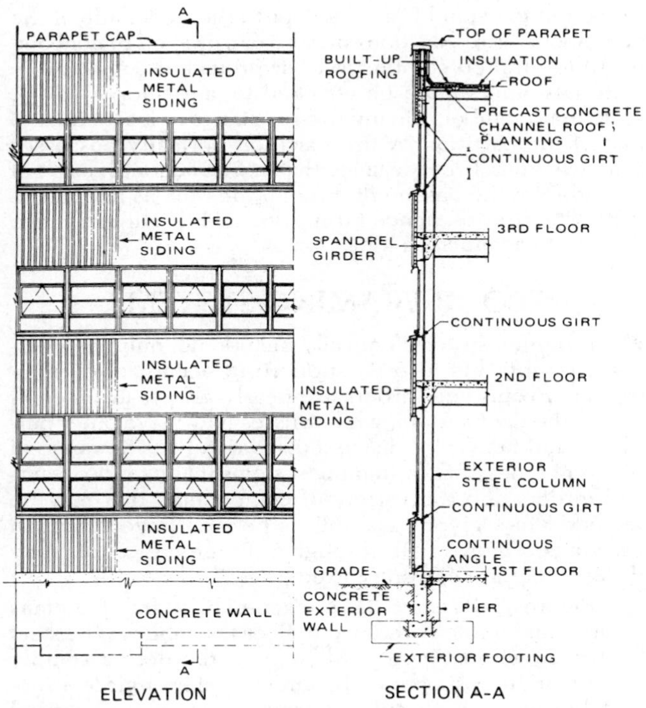

FIG. 6-3I. Elevation of typical bay of steel frame curtain wall construction.

A complete curtain wall assembly may consist of a panel with finished outside and inside surfaces, insulation, and means of attachment to the building frame. However, this type is not used as frequently as is a metal or glass skin assembly reinforced by conventional construction.

Curtain walls are required to have fire-resistance ratings up to 2 hr, depending upon the separation distance between the wall and a lot line or exposing structure. Secure fastening of curtain walls is important for many reasons, including stability during fire exposure. Curtain walls are generally bolted to clips attached to the columns, spandrel, or floor slab. There is usually a space between the outer end of the floor slab and the inside face of the curtain wall. Unless adequately firestopped, this space may act as a route for vertical fire spread for the entire height of a building.

Parapet Walls

A parapet wall is an extension of the wall construction above the roof line. The parapet on a fire wall prevents a fire from spreading across the roof over the fire wall. Where walls extend only a few inches above the roof, ignition of an adjoining roof may occur, depending upon wind direction and velocity and the character of the roof covering. Factory Mutual Research Corporation (FMRC), for example, specifies a parapet height of 30 in. (762 mm). Greater heights may be necessary for safety in some cases, as in walls over 50 or 60 ft (15 or 18 m) in length. Many building codes permit lesser heights, and in large sections of the country, 18-in. (457 mm) parapets are considered standard. The higher the parapet, the greater the degree of safety, but considerations of expense and appearance dictate practical compromises.

Fire may also extend around the ends of fire walls where the exterior walls of the building on both sides of the fire wall are combustible. There are two methods of minimizing this danger: (1) extend the fire wall several feet out beyond the wall of the building, or (2) provide a "T" section at the end of the wall. Where combustible roofs or cornices project beyond the walls of the building, fire walls should be extended to form a break in such combustible construction, as shown in Figure 6-3J. Many otherwise effective fire walls have failed, because wood platforms or projecting canopies along the sides of buildings have spread fire from one fire area to another.

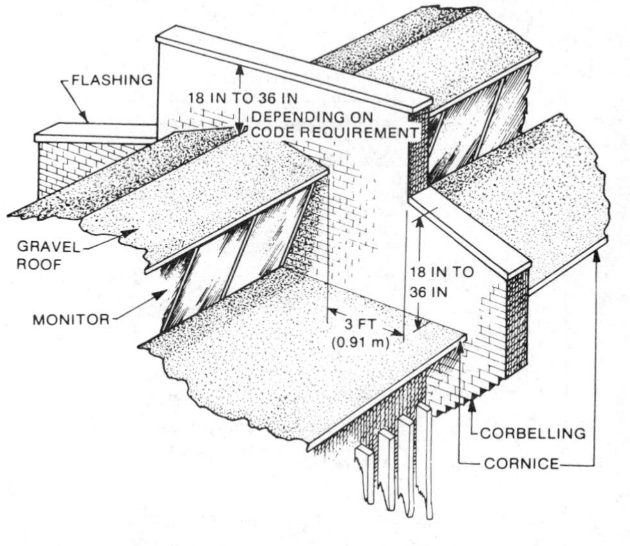

FIG. 6-3J. Fire wall installation on building with combustible roof and monitor.

INTERIOR WALLS AND PARTITIONS

Interior walls and partitions used for building corridors or rooms may be either bearing or nonbearing. Bearing partitions are common in the older, wall-bearing construction systems and are also employed with industrialized building systems, particularly those of precast concrete. Newer construction tends to use nonbearing partitions.

The need for open space flexibility in modern construction has led to floor and interior partition design that allows nonbearing partitions to be installed at any location. These moveable partitions are often made of steel studs and gypsum board, and they may be installed, then dismantled, and reinstalled at another location when an occupancy needs change. Normally, moveable partitions extend only from the floor to the underside of the ceiling.

Interior partitions, particularly nonload-bearing partitions, can be installed with a number of other different materials. Wood stud and gypsum board or plaster is another very common type of partition. Partitions constructed of masonry units, such as concrete block, structural clay tile, terra cotta, and gypsum block, are common in a wide variety of buildings and are more permanent. Figure 6-3K shows typical partition constructions.

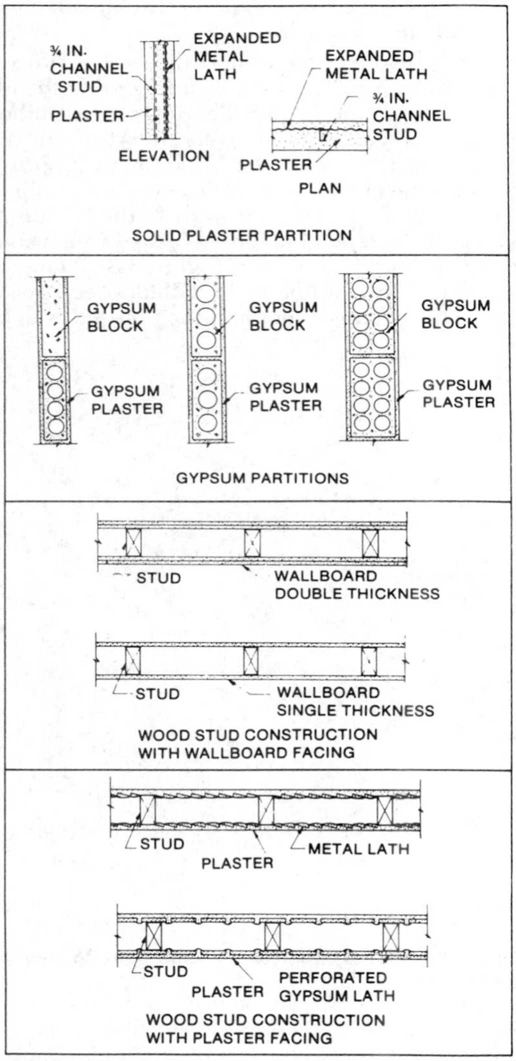

FIG. 6-3K. Typical interior wall and partition constructions.

Properly designed interior partitions can act as barriers to the spread of fire. To protect certain areas more completely than would be possible with ordinary partitions, fire walls and fire partitions are constructed. Fire partitions are often incorrectly called fire walls. Fire walls are fire resistive, of superior noncombustible construction, generally self-supporting, and cannot be readily modified to meet changing building needs.

Fire Walls

Fire walls are interior walls providing a fire separation between areas of the same building. They should be designed to maintain structural integrity, even in cases of complete collapse of the structure on either side of the fire wall. To withstand heat expansion effects, they are commonly made thicker than would be required by normal fire-resistance ratings. Also, they may be buttressed by cross walls or pilasters if of considerable height or length. In fire-resistive buildings, structure-supported fire division walls may be used, provided the structure has equal or greater fire resistance than that of the wall.

Fire Partitions

Usually, a fire partition subdivides a floor or an area and is erected to extend from the floor to the underside of the floor above. Fire partitions may be constructed of noncombustible, limited combustible, or protected combustible materials, and should be attached to, and supported by, structural members having fire resistance at least equal to that of the partition. A fire partition normally possesses somewhat less fire resistance than a fire wall and does not extend from the basement through the roof, as does a fire wall. The fire-resistance ratings for such partitions range from ½ to as much as 4 hr.

FLOOR FRAMING SYSTEMS

Floor framing systems typically include not only the flooring assembly but also its supporting beams, girders, or trusses. Beams and girders are nearly always an integral part of the floor system, while trusses may serve other purposes (and hence are discussed separately). The range of different types of floor framing systems that include beams and girders and the variety of components that may be included in a given assembly is best portrayed through drawings. Figures 6-3L through 6-3V are typical of many designs that are currently used.

Figures 6-3L and 6-3M are generalized framing plans for steel and reinforced-concrete floor assemblies. The steel beams shown in Figure 6-3L support the floor assembly and are, in turn, supported by girders. Interior girders support beams on both sides. Girders are often concealed within partitions where their depth is not apparent, and they can directly support the weight of partitions in the space above. The girders frame into steel columns. Figure 6-3M illustrates a slab beam girder column system cast monolithically (no joints) of reinforced concrete. The functions of the various components are the same as those described for the steel frame.

The floor slab supported by the steel beams shown in Figure 6-3L need not be of reinforced concrete. Alternative types of deck are the composite decks shown in Figures 6-3N, 6-3O, and 6-3P. This type of floor system offers many construction advantages. The metal deck acts as a form for the concrete that remains in place after curing. In addition, the cellular panels can be used for building service raceways where desired. A feature of this floor system is that the steel deck also acts as the tensile reinforcement of the concrete floor slab.

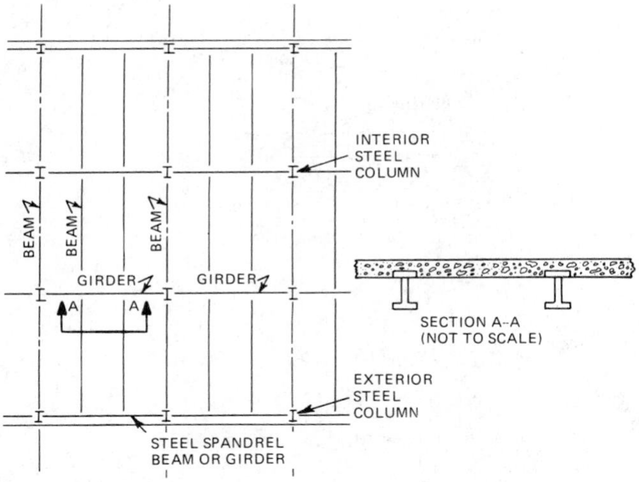

FIG. 6-3L. ***Portion of floor plan of steel frame structure.***

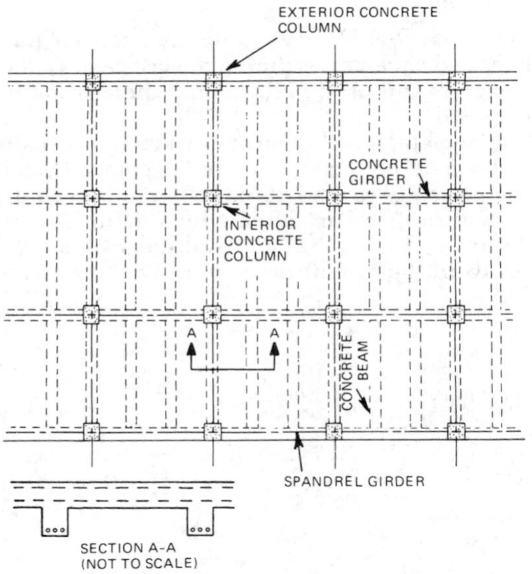

FIG. 6-3M. ***Portion of floor plan of concrete beam and girder construction.***

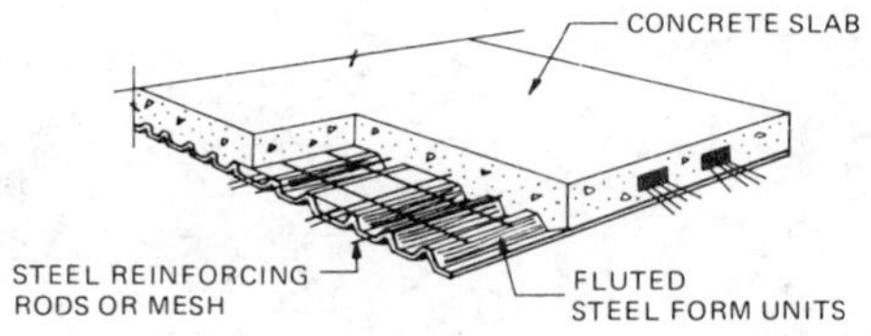

FIG. 6-3N. ***Example of concrete floor construction showing composite floor assembly.***

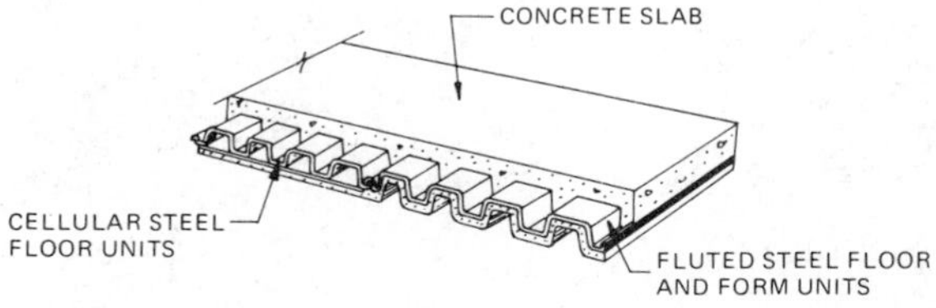

FIG. 6-3O. ***Example of concrete floor construction showing light gage cellular floor panels alternated with light gage steel forms.***

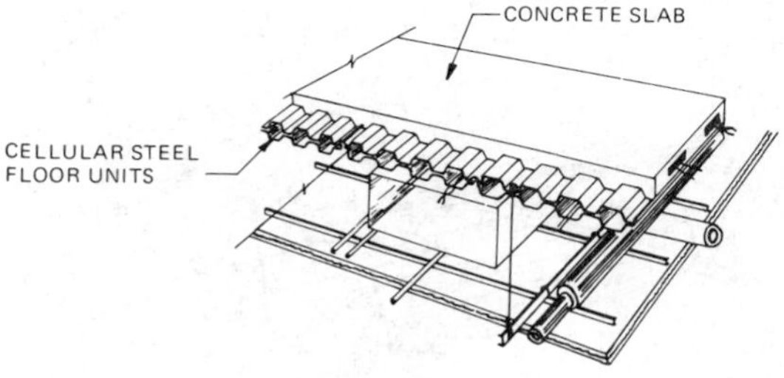

FIG. 6-3P. ***Example of a concrete floor poured over light gage cellular floor panels. The cellular panels can carry all three basic building services — power, telephone, and data transmission lines.***

Another floor deck modification is to replace the reinforced-concrete floor slab with a precast concrete system. Figure 6-3Q illustrates three common precast concrete floor slabs. The precast concrete planks generally have voids through their length which reduce the weight of the planks and act as building service raceways. The planks may be supported by either steel beams or reinforced concrete beams.

Open-web joists, which are lightweight prefabricated trusses, may replace steel beams as the intermediate flexural framing and are a very common type of construction both for floors and roofs. The spacing of floor joists is approximately 2 ft (0.61 m), and generally about 4 ft (1.22 m) for roof joists. Figure 6-3R illustrates this type of construction.

Because the spacing of the joists is so close, the floor slab can be thinner and still support the same load. Corrugated steel forms with 2½ in. (64 mm) of concrete as a wearing surface is a typical design. The corrugated deck acts as a form for the concrete and contributes to the support of live loads. Lightweight concrete is often used in place of normal-weight concrete to reduce the dead load.

Similarly, the reinforced concrete beams shown in Figure 6-3M may be spaced more closely together, permitting both a thinner floor slab and smaller beams. This type of construction is generally called a ribbed reinforced-concrete system or a concrete joist system. The ribbed system can be either cast in place or precast. Figure 6-3S illustrates the concrete joist floor, while Figure 6-3DD illustrates two of the more common forms of ribbed precast systems. In each illustration, the ribs are the intermediate flexural framing.

The two-way flat slab is an increasingly popular floor system. Two-way reinforced-concrete slabs, used since the turn of the century, include reinforcement placed in two directions. The slab performs the functions of deck, intermediate flexural framing, and primary flexural framing. The underside of the slab may be either flat or ribbed in two directions. Figures 6-3T and 6-3U illustrate two different forms of this type construction.

Wood floor systems can be designed to perform the same functions as the basic model in Figure 6-3L. If the reinforced-concrete deck were replaced by heavy wood planking 2 in. (51 mm) or more in thickness, and the steel beams, girders, and columns with large wood members with a minimum dimension of 6 in. (152 mm), the basic form would be that of mill construction. This construction,

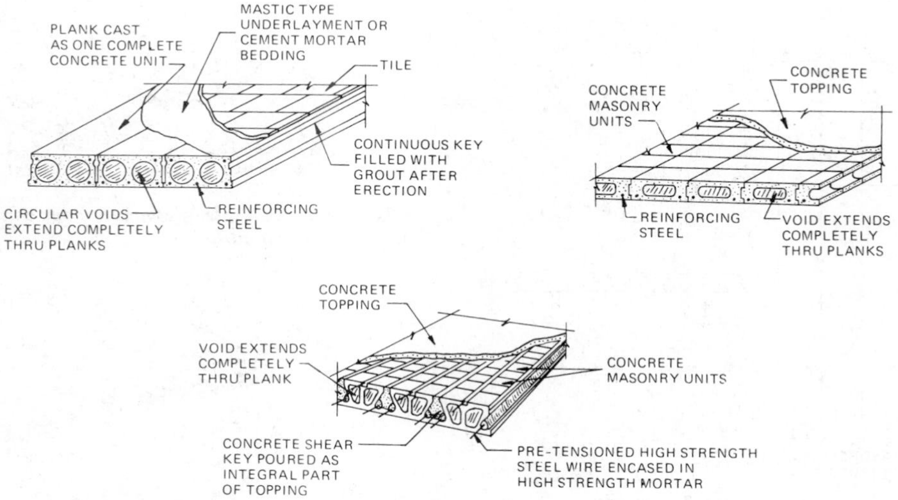

FIG. 6-3Q. Three examples of precast concrete floor slab construction.

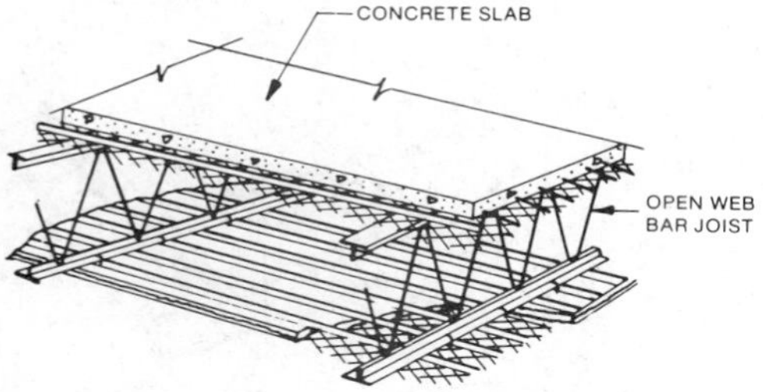

FIG. 6-3R. Example of concrete floor construction showing open-web steel joist.

shown in Figure 6-3V, was quite common for industrial buildings and warehouses during the last century. The general design is still used in locations where wood has aesthetic appeal.

Lightweight, wood-frame construction is usually used in buildings of limited size. Floor joists in such construction are normally spaced 16 in. (406 mm) on center, and the vertical supports are often 2 by 4 in. (51 by 102 mm) or 2 by 6 in. (51 by 152 mm) wall-bearing studs, again spaced 16 in. (406 mm) on center. The stud walls may

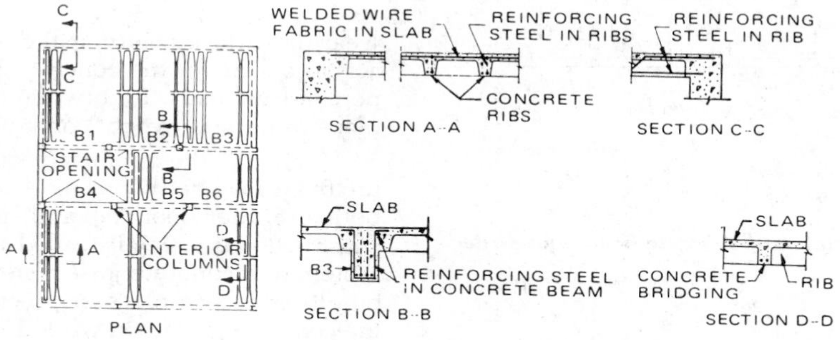

FIG. 6-3S. Partial plan of a concrete joist floor with four sectional views.

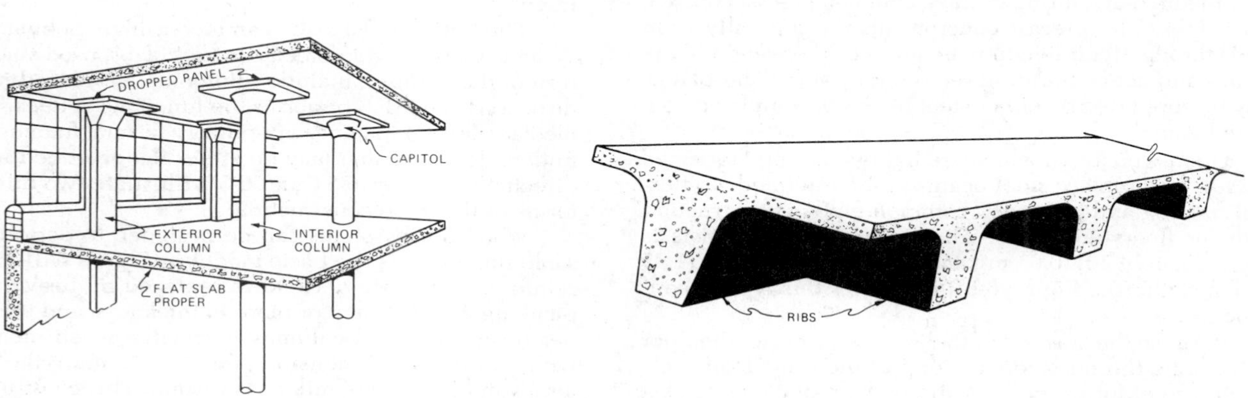

FIG. 6-3T. Two types of two-way flat slabs: flat underside and two-way ribbed underside.

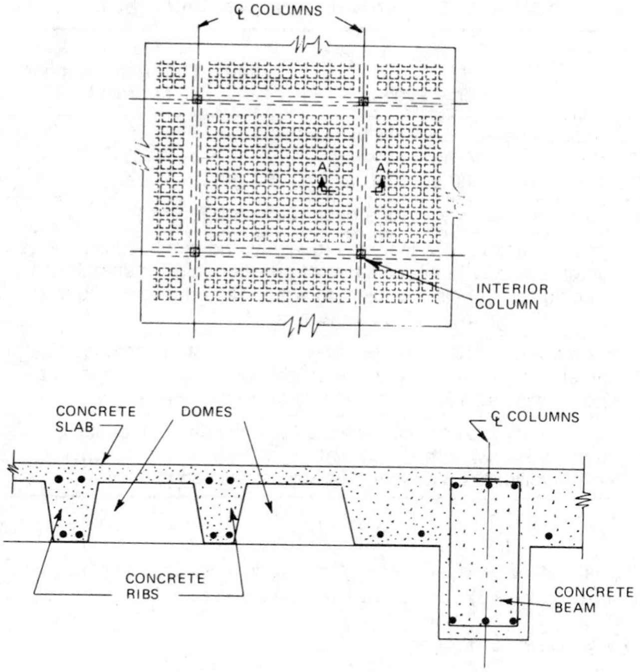

FIG. 6-3U. Partial typical interior two-way ribbed floor slab with section view A-A.

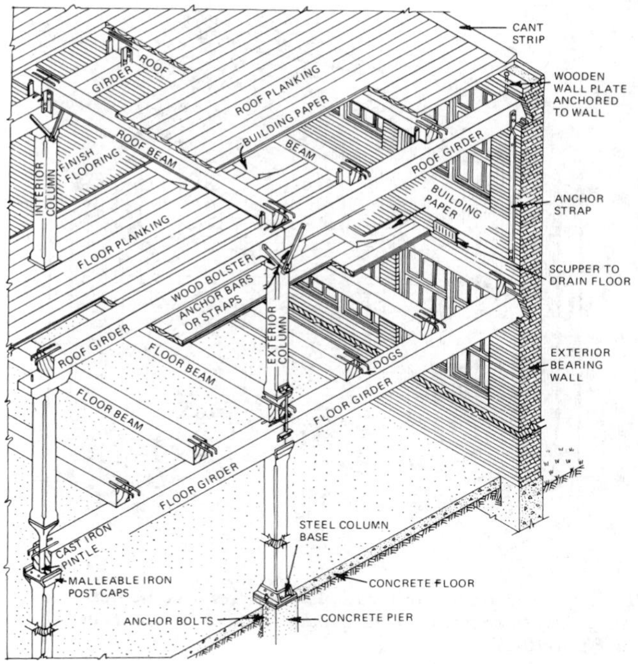

FIG. 6-3W. Example of wood-frame platform construction common to dwellings. Structural members are identified.

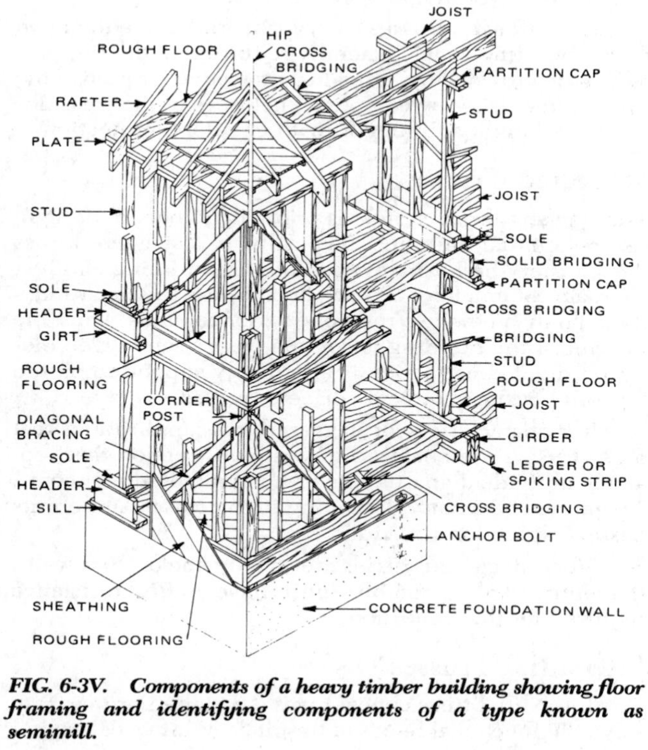

FIG. 6-3V. Components of a heavy timber building showing floor framing and identifying components of a type known as semimill.

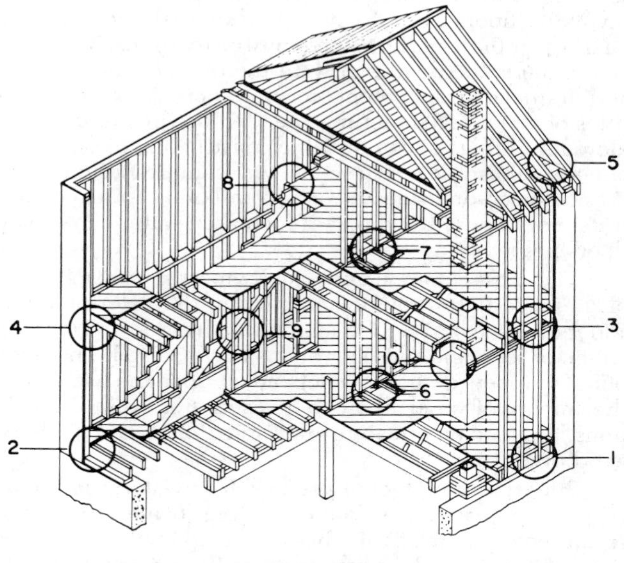

FIG. 6-3X. Example of wood balloon frame construction showing points to be firestopped. Expanded views of points are shown in Figure 6-3Z.

extend only from floor to floor in platform framing (Figure 6-3W), or they may be extended continuously for two or three floors, a type of framing identified as balloon construction. (See Figure 6-3X.)

Wood-frame construction has little fire resistance because flames and hot gases can penetrate into the spaces between the joists or the studs. Firestopping must be installed at critical locations throughout the building to prevent the rapid vertical and horizontal spread of fire. Firestops are normally made of wood blocks or noncombustible material. Figures 6-3X and 6-3Y illustrate critical locations for firestopping in balloon frame and in platform frame construction; Figure 6-3Z shows the firestopping for these constructions in greater detail.

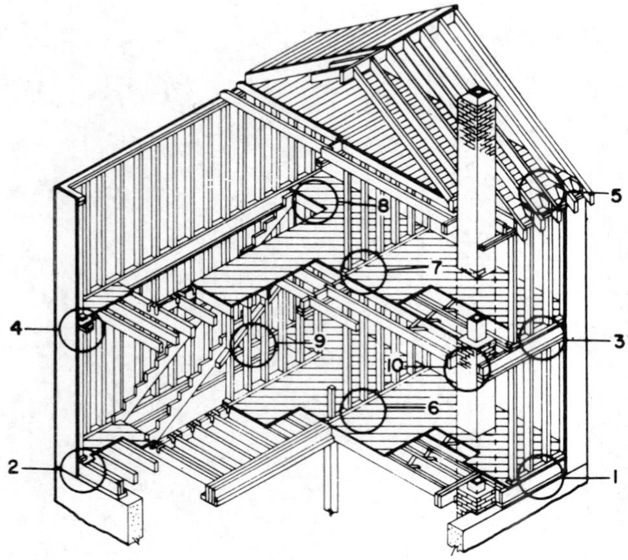

FIG. 6-3Y. Example of wood platform frame construction showing points to be firestopped. Expanded views of points are shown in Figure 6-3Z.

Watertightness and Drainage of Floors

In addition to the effectiveness of floor framing systems as barriers to fire spread, there is another consideration involving floors in multi-story buildings that can have a bearing on their performance in fire situations. This consideration is the degree of watertightness of construction and drainage arrangements for the floors. Massive quantities of water are sometimes needed on fires in unsprinklered buildings of combustible construction or buildings of noncombustible construction with significant fuel loads. Without good drainage and/or waterproofing arrangements, water could pose the threat of increased water damage on floors below.

The most common and usually most satisfactory type of drainage is to provide scuppers in the exterior walls. Floor drains connected to ample size headers or a combination of scuppers and floor drains may be used. The number of scuppers or drains is dependent upon the hazard and the amount of water likely to be used. For average conditions, the recommendations in Table 6-3B are considered good practice.

Waterproofing techniques, such as waterproof membranes, hot mastics, asphalt emulsions, cementitious surfacings, etc., are available that can be applied to the floors depending upon the basic type of floor construction in question. The intent of these applications is to provide a watertight barrier on the floor itself which extends up 4 to 6 in. (50 to 150 mm) at walls and columns. Water impounded by these protective measures must be carried off before its weight becomes a loading threat to the building.

Guidance on the cost/benefits of providing waterproofing or drainage systems in buildings is contained in a Factory Mutual Research Corporation data sheet.[1]

TRUSSES

Where large areas must be column free or where special occupancy requirements may warrant, trusses may be used for purposes other than roof support. Three such applications are identified as: (1) transfer trusses, (2) staggered trusses, and (3) interstitial trusses.

TABLE 6-3B. *Sizes for Scuppers and Drains*

Floor Areas	No. of 4-in. (102 mm) scuppers or drains
For floor areas 500 sq ft (46 m^2) or less	2
For floor areas 750 sq ft (70 m2)	3
For floor areas 1000 sq ft (93 m^2)	4
Additional scuppers for areas over 1000 sq ft (93 m^2):	
For extra hazard occupancies (quantity and combustibility of contents is very high), or floors of questionable watertightness, or contents especially subject to water damage—one scupper for each additional 500 sq ft (46 m^2).	
For moderate hazard occupancies (quantity and combustibility of contents is moderate) with watertight floors—one scupper for each additional 1000 sq ft (93 m^2) or fraction thereof.	
For ordinary hazard occupancies (quantity and combustibility of contents is low) with strictly watertight floors—one scupper for each additional 2000 sq ft (186 m^2) or fraction thereof.	

Transfer Trusses

Load transfer trusses create a clear space on a lower floor by directly supporting the loads from columns above the truss or, at times, from tension members below. This design allows large, column-free areas for auditoriums, ballrooms, etc., at any level in a high-rise building.

Since transfer trusses carry loads from more than two floors, building codes generally require that the fire protection be provided by individual protection for each of the truss elements, or by complete enclosure of the truss (for its entire height and length) with envelope protection.

Staggered Trusses

The staggered truss system is primarily intended for high-rise residential buildings. Typically, in a staggered truss design, story-high trusses span the full building width at alternate column lines on each floor. These trusses are supported only on the two rows of exterior columns. Thus, the interior of the building is column free; at any given elevation, floor construction is alternately supported on the top and bottom chords of adjacent trusses.

It is characteristic of staggered truss applications that these trusses are enclosed in wall construction that separates individual apartments or hotel/motel guest rooms. There may be a control opening in the truss that permits passage space for a corridor.

Since staggered trusses are usually enclosed in walls, the entire wall assembly must have a fire resistance required for this condition.

Interstitial Trusses

The interstitial truss concept was developed primarily to solve the functional needs of hospitals. While steel trusses in interstitial framing systems are quite deep [on the order of 8 ft (2.5 m) in height], they do not extend from floor to floor as do staggered trusses. The top chords support the floor above, while the bottom chords support a suspended ceiling system and a walking surface for maintenance purposes. As such, interstitial trusses are analogous to very deep open-web steel joists.

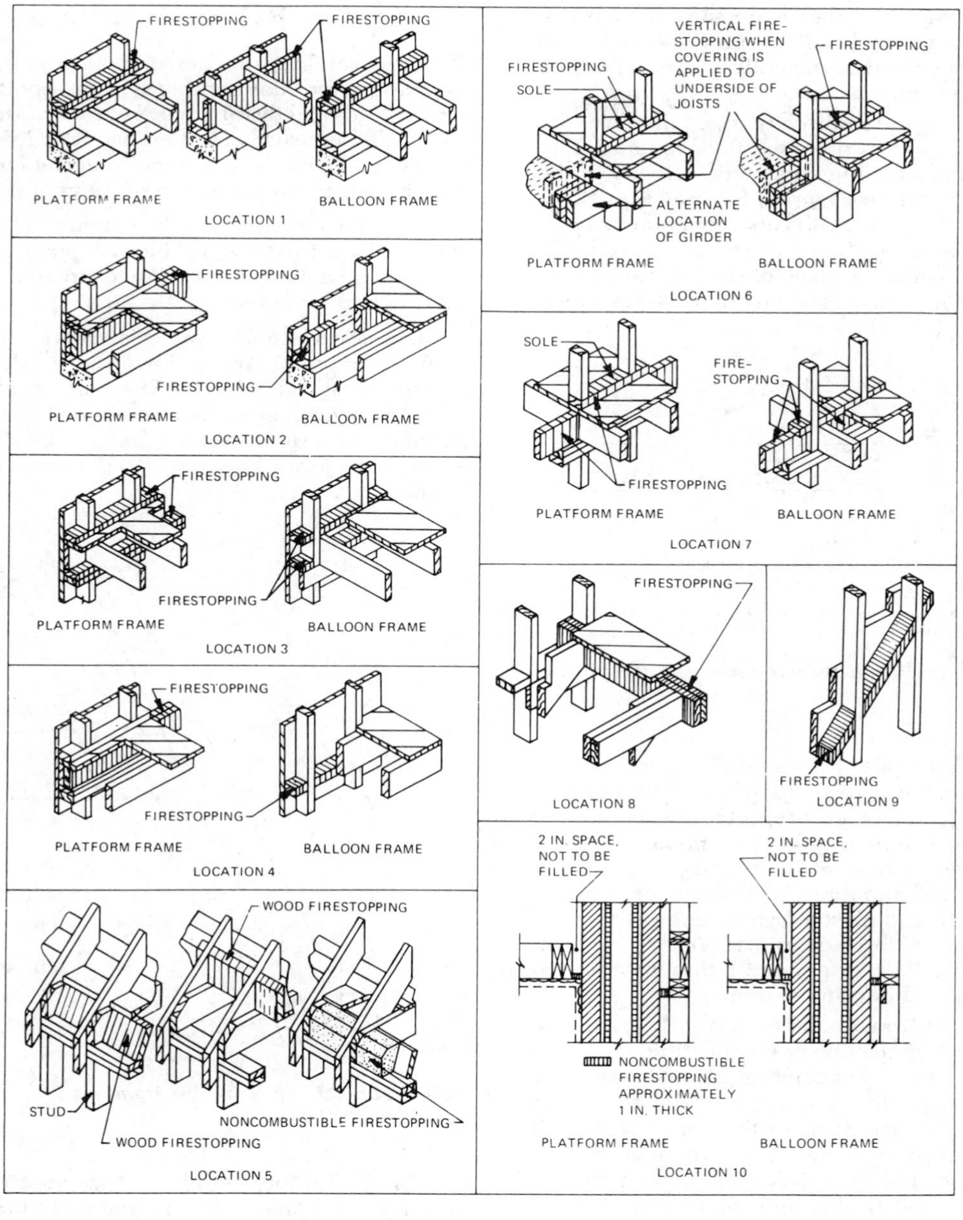

FIG. 6-3Z. Details of the application of firestopping to platform and balloon framing. Location numbers coincide with locations circled in Figures 6-3X and 6-3Y.

The interstitial space thus created provides a convenient location for the complex mechanical and electrical systems that are necessary components of a modern hospital. Direct access for maintenance, renovation, and replacement of the various system components within these interfloor spaces is provided without significant interference with normal operations.

Since each interstitial truss supports only one floor, all three conventional fire protection methods for trusses are permitted by the model building codes. However, because of practical considerations, individual protection of each truss element or ceiling membrane protection are the methods most widely used.

FLOOR/CEILING ASSEMBLIES

Ceiling components are important elements in the performance of a fire-resistive floor/ceiling assembly. In the event of fire within a room, the ceiling acts as a barrier to protect the structural framing above it. The degree of protection, of course, depends upon the type of material, its installation, and its completeness. Combustible ceilings or ceilings that do not remain in place when subjected to the pressures and temperatures of a fire do not provide a significant degree of protection.

It is important to note that the membrane ceiling is one part of the floor/ceiling assembly. The entire assembly, acting together, provides the designated fire resistance. The ceiling itself has no fire resistance.

Ceilings may be applied directly to, or they may be suspended from, the underside of the floor framing. Figure 6-3DD illustrates a ceiling connected directly to the floor framing system, while Figure 6-3P shows a ceiling suspended from the floor slab. It is also common to apply a fire-protective material, such as a plaster or sprayed mixture, directly to the bottom surface of the floor slab. Figure 6-3AA illustrates a floor slab with plaster applied directly to the steel floor deck.

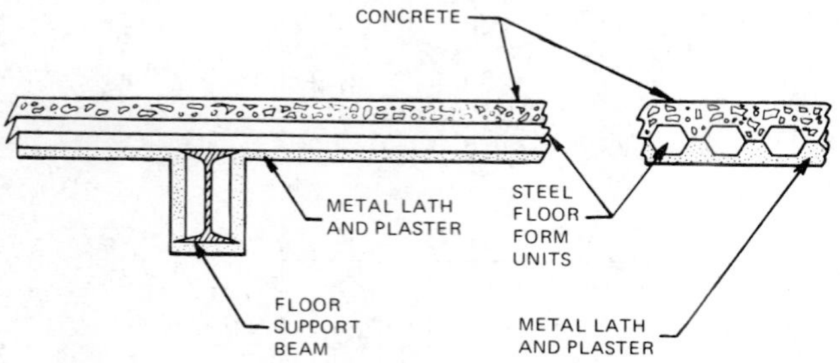

*FIG. 6-3AA. **Plaster applied directly to underside of floor slab construction.***

There are several types of suspended membrane ceilings in common use. One type consists of a lay-in system in which the ceiling panels are supported by an exposed metal grid. Another common type of membrane has the metal grid concealed by recesses in the edges of the ceiling panels. Suspended membrane ceilings may also consist of traditional lath and plaster or permanently secured gypsum wallboard with finished joints. Both of these latter systems can be either suspended below or attached directly to the basic subflooring system.

In the variety of arrangements currently used, the space above the ceiling may be of combustible construction and may also contain other combustible materials, such as duct insulation, wire insulation, and vapor seals. Air-handling systems may use ducts or the void space itself (plenum) as a means of supplying, exhausting, or recirculating air; but associated materials must meet stringent requirements for combustibility and smoke evolution.

The material used for the membrane ceiling is important. Gypsum plaster and lath were a common construction of early membranes. Today special mineral tile formulations are generally used for acoustical panel systems that will not warp during fire exposure. The support framing is designed to accommodate thermal expansion with a minimum of distortion, so that the ceiling panels stay in place.

If lighting fixtures and duct openings are included in membrane ceilings that are part of fire-rated assemblies, they both must be of suitable design, properly spaced, and often require shielding to reduce heat transmission into the ceiling space. Fire test performance is based on specific lighting fixtures and spacing, so indiscriminate substitution of lighting fixtures can cause premature failure. If air duct openings are installed in a membrane-type ceiling, they should be suitably protected or dampered, as determined by a fire test on the ceiling assembly that incorporates the air-handling components.

ROOF FRAMING

The design and construction of roof framing follow the general pattern for floor framing systems—both must support vertical loads and distribute these loads to walls or columns. Roof loads are usually smaller than floor loads. In addition, architectural considerations may demand longer spans than floor framing, and the shape of the roof need not be flat.

The roof covering may be supported by steel or wood joists or by a truss where a longer span is needed. Roof trusses can be made to conform to any roof shape, whether flat, pitched, or curved.

Open-web steel or wood joists are often used in flat roof construction. An open-web joist is merely a lightweight, parallel chord truss. They are usually spaced about 4 ft (1.22 m) on center. This close spacing avoids the necessity of purlins, since the roof deck can be designed to span between the joists. Figure 6-3BB illustrates this type of roof framing.

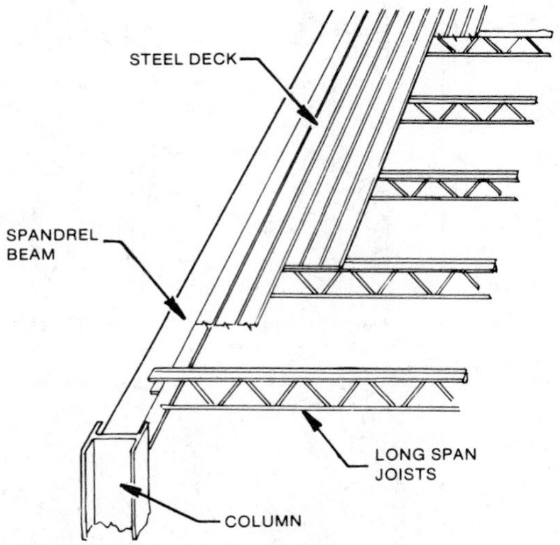

*FIG. 6-3BB. **Long-span joist framing.***

In single-story buildings that require a large open space, rigid frames are sometimes used both as columns and roof supports. The portion spanning the roof is rigidly connected to columns on opposite sides of the building to form a single member. The frame itself may provide for a sloping roof. Figure 6-3CC shows a rigid frame structure.

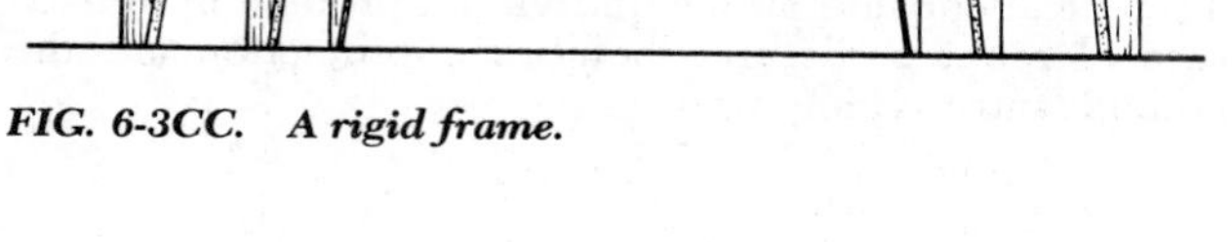

*FIG. 6-3CC. **A rigid frame.***

Flat slab and ribbed concrete slab systems may be used for roof construction in those buildings in which that is the predominant type of framing. Other systems utilizing long-span prestressed concrete double-tee or channel sections are also common. These units serve both as support and as the deck. (See Figure 6-3DD.)

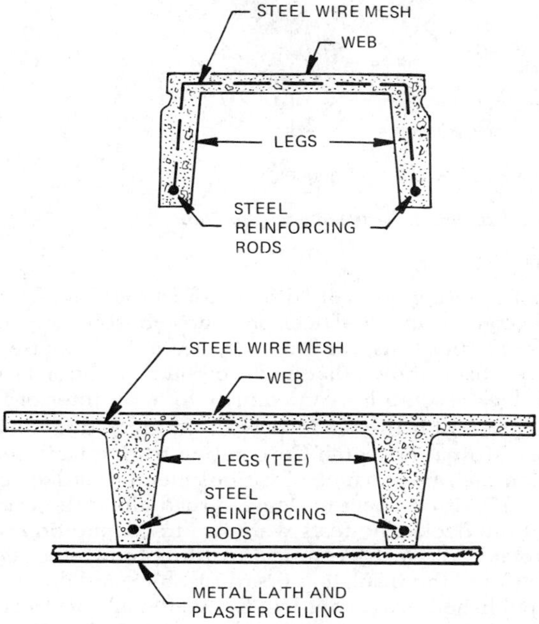

FIG. 6-3DD. Sections through channel and double-tee concrete slabs. The slab at bottom shows a metal lath and plaster ceiling attached directly to the ribs of the slab.

Roof decks may also consist of precast reinforced-concrete planks fastened to the structural steel supports by galvanized metal clips, as shown in Figure 6-3EE. These planks are manufactured in three general shapes: (1) square edge, (2) channel slab, and (3) tongue and groove. To reduce weight they may be fabricated with aerated concrete using lightweight aggregates.

ROOF COVERINGS

In resistance to ignition and burning, roof coverings range from combustible wood shingles with no fire-retardant treatment to built-up or prepared coverings that are effective against severe external fire exposure. Insofar as well-designed roof coverings can protect buildings from exposure fires, the likelihood of fire spread from one building to another can be reduced considerably.

Fire-Retardant Roof Coverings

Definitions of three classes of roof covering that include criteria for resistance to ignition have been prepared by Underwriters Laboratories Inc. (UL). The test standard for roof coverings is NFPA 256, *Fire Tests of Roof Coverings* (also known as ASTM E-108). The three classes are:

Class A coverings: Include roof coverings that are effective against severe fire exposures. These coverings are not readily flammable, do not carry or communicate fire, afford a fairly high degree of fire protection to the roof deck, do not slip from position, possess no flying brand hazard, and do not require frequent repairs to maintain their fire-retardant properties.

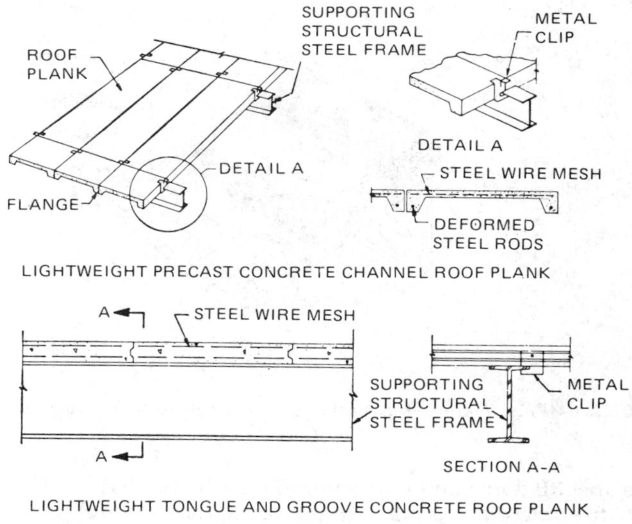

FIG. 6-3EE. Lightweight precast concrete planks.

Class B coverings: Include roof coverings that are effective against moderate fire exposures. These coverings are not readily flammable, do not readily carry or communicate fire, afford a moderate degree of fire protection to the roof deck, do not slip from position, and possess no flying brand hazard; however, they may require repairs to maintain their fire-retardant properties.

Class C coverings: Include roof coverings that are effective against light fire exposure. These coverings are not readily flammable, do not readily carry or communicate fire, afford at least a slight degree of fire protection to the roof decks, do not slip from position, and possess no flying brand hazard; however, they require repairs or renewals to maintain their fire-retardant properties.

Building codes commonly require Class A or B coverings within the fire limits of cities or wherever fire-resistive construction is required. Class C roofing is appropriate for other buildings. Many cities specify Class C as the minimum standard for roofing.

Fire testing laboratories classify metal deck roof assemblies by type of construction.[2] These classifications are discussed later in this chapter.

Built-up and Prepared Coverings

Fire-retardant roof coverings fall within one of two groups. One is the built-up covering which, as the name implies, consists of several layers of materials applied or "built up" on the roof decks according to specifications. What is known as a "tar and gravel" roof is actually a built-up roof covering consisting of several layers of roofing felts and insulating panels or sheets bonded together by hot or cold cements and topped with roofing gravel. (See Figure 6-3FF.)

The second group (prepared coverings) includes fire-retardant shingles and sheet coverings, which can be applied only to roof decks capable of receiving and retaining nails and which are sloped sufficiently to permit drainage. In some instances, however, the slope must not exceed

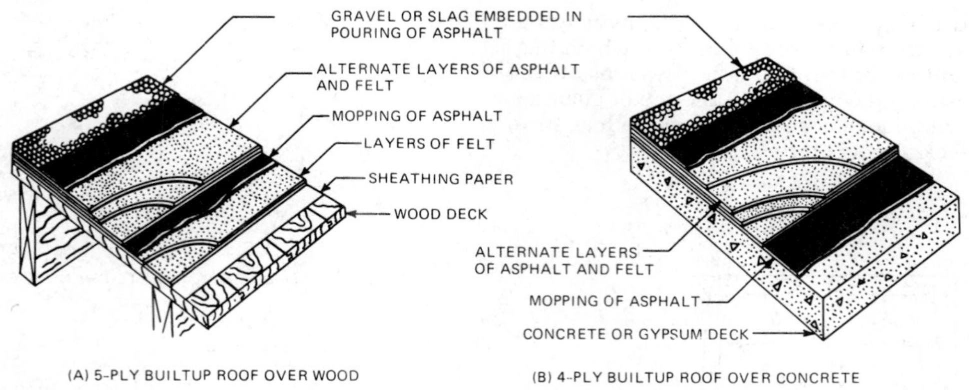

FIG. 6-3FF. Typical built-up roof coverings with hot asphalt mopping or coal tar pitch between each two layers.

a specified maximum in order to qualify for Class A, B, or C fire-retardant rating. Asphalt organic felt shingles, i.e., "composition" roofs, are a common example of prepared roof coverings and are frequently used on dwellings. (See Figure 6-3GG.)

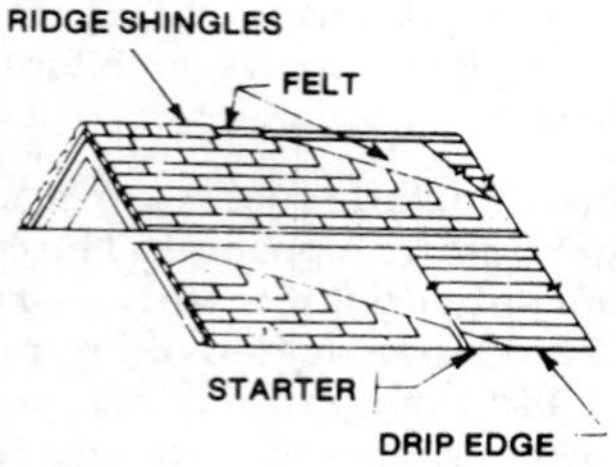

FIG. 6-3GG. Installation of a typical prepared roof covering.

Prepared roof coverings also include such noncombustible coverings as brick, concrete, tile, and slate. Tables 6-3C and 6-3D list various types of prepared and built-up roof coverings and their fire-retardant classifications. Any roof covering can be used for a less severe exposure than the one for which it is listed.

In addition to the built-up roof coverings described in Table 6-3D, there are several other types consisting of asbestos, combinations of asbestos and rag felt, glass fiber, aluminum, and tile applied in a special manner with special listed proprietary cements that are listed by testing laboratories.

Roof Deck Insulations and Vapor Barriers

Since the 1953 General Motors fire at Livonia, MI, major attention has been paid to the combustibility of insulated metal roof decks. In that fire, the asphalt mopping in the felt vapor barrier beneath the insulation on the 1,502,500 sq ft (139,582 m^2), flat, steel-deck roof melted and vaporized. Asphalt vapor under pressure entered the building through the joints in the steel deck and burned inside. As a result of this and similar fires, research was conducted to find a solution to the problem. The significant findings are summarized in the following paragraphs.

The combustibility of a roof was historically determined by the physical characteristics of the roof deck and its supporting structure, with no consideration given to the combustibility of the roof insulation and covering. Thus, combustible fiberboard insulation and asphalt-impregnated felt roof covering normally did not affect the classification of a noncombustible roof deck on noncombustible supports. Large-scale fire tests, confirmed by actual fire experience, however, have shown that under certain conditions some metal deck assemblies can contribute to an interior fire.

A series of full-scale tests were conducted in 1955 at Factory Mutual Research Corporation testing facilities to compare the performance of various metal roof deck constructions with respect to flame spread along the underside of the deck. The tests were run in cooperation with the Metal Roof Deck Technical Institute (now Steel Deck Institute) and the Insulation Board Institute, and the results were published in a pamphlet.[2] Conventional construction, with the insulation fastened to the metal deck with complete moppings of asphalt or with vapor barriers using complete asphalt moppings above and below one or more plies of felt, was shown to contribute significant amounts of fuel when exposed to the heat of an intensive interior fire below the deck. (See Figure 6-3HH.) The asphalt was vaporized by the heat of the fire below, and unable to escape upward through the roof covering, was forced down through the joints in the deck, when it ignited and contributed to the spread of fire under the roof deck.

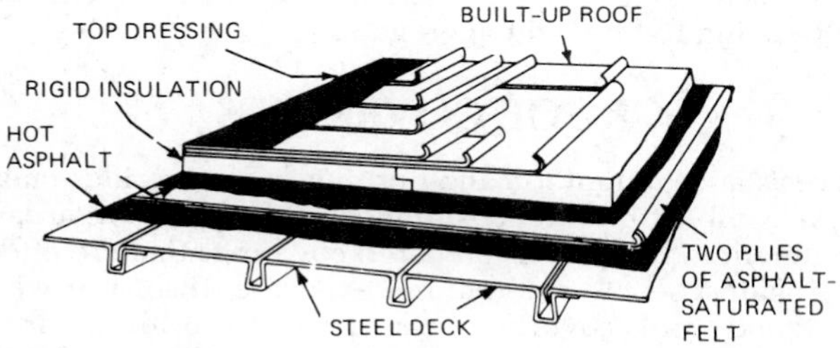

FIG. 6-3HH. Typical built-up roof covering with a combustible vapor barrier adhered to the roof deck and to roof insulation by a combustible adhesive.

Recognized fire testing laboratories now list metal roof deck construction and components that will not contribute significantly to an interior fire and that meet certain performance standards. A typical built-up roof covering of this construction is shown in Figure 6-3II.

Metal roof deck constructions use both combustible and noncombustible insulation fastened with noncombustible adhesives or mechanical fasteners to the upper surface of the deck. Asphalt can also be used as the adhesive

TABLE 6-3C. ***Typical Prepared Roof Coverings*†***

Description	Minimum Incline In. to Ft	CLASS A	CLASS B	CLASS C
Brick Concrete Tile Slate		Brick, $2\frac{1}{4}$ in. thick. Reinforced portland cement, 1 in. thick. Concrete or clay floor or deck tile, 1 in. thick. Flat or French type clay or concrete tile, $\frac{3}{8}$ in. thick with $1\frac{1}{2}$ in. or more end lap and head lock, spacing body of tile $\frac{1}{2}$ in. or more above roof sheathing, with underlay of one layer of Type 15 asphalt-saturated asbestos felt or one layer of Type 30 or two layers of Type 15 asphalt-saturated organic felt. Clay or concrete roof tile, Spanish or Mission pattern, $\frac{7}{16}$ in. thick, 3 in. end lap, same underlay as above. Slate, $\frac{3}{16}$ in. thick, laid American method.		
Metal Roofing	12	Sheet roofing of 16 oz copper or of 30-gage steel or iron protected against corrosion. Limited to noncombustible roof decks or noncombustible roof supports when no separate roof deck is provided.	Sheet roofing of 16 oz copper or of 30-gage steel or iron protected against corrosion or shingle-pattern roofings with underlay of one layer of Type 15 saturated asbestos-felt, or one layer of Type 30 or two layers of Type 15 asphalt-saturated organic felt.	Sheet roofing of 16 oz copper or of 30 gage steel or iron, protected against corrosion, or shingle-pattern roofings, either without underlay or with underlay of rosin-sized paper.
				Zinc sheets or shingle roofings with an underlay of one layer of Type 30 or two layers of Type 15 asphalt-saturated organic-felt or one layer of 14 lb unsaturated or one layer of Type 15 asphalt-saturated asbestos felt.
Cement-Asbestos Shingles	Exceeding 4	Laid to provide two or more thickness over one layer of Type 15 asphalt-saturated asbestos felt.	Laid to provide one or more thicknesses over one layer of Type 15 asphalt-saturated asbestos felt.	

TABLE 6-3C. ***Typical Prepared Roof Coverings (Cont.)*†***

Description	Minimum Incline In. to Ft	CLASS A	CLASS B	CLASS C
Asphalt-Asbestos Felt Sheet Coverings	Not Exceeding 12	Factory-assembled sheets of 4-ply asphalt and asbestos material.	Factory-assembled sheets of 3-ply asphalt and asbes tos material or sheet coverings of single thickness with a grit surface.	Single thickness smooth surfaced.
Asphalt-Asbestos Felt Shingle Coverings	Exceeding 4		Asphalt-asbestos felt grit surfaced.	
Organic-Felt (previously referred to as rag felt) Sheet Coverings	Exceeding 4			Sheet coverings of asphalt organic felt either grit surfaced or alumi num surfaced.
Organic-Felt (previously referred to as rag felt) Shingle Covering, with special coating	Sufficient to permit drainage	Grit surfaced, two or more thicknesses.	Grit surfaced, two or more thick-nesses.	
Organic-Felt (previously referred to as rag felt) Shingle Coverings	Sufficient to permit drainage	Grit surfaced, two or more thicknesses.	Grit surfaced, two or more thick-nesses.	Grit surfaced shingles, one or more thicknesses.
Asphalt Glass Fiber Mat Shingle Coverings	Sufficient to permit drainage	Grit surfaced, two or more thicknesses.	Grit surfaced, one or more thick-nesses.	Grit surfaced shingles, one or more thicknesses.
Asphalt Glass Mat Sheet Covering	Sufficient to permit drainage			Grit surfaced.
Fire-retardant treated red cedar wood shingles and shakes	Sufficient to permit drainage			Treated shingles or shakes, one or more thicknesses; shakes require at least one layer of Type 15 felt underlayment.

* Prepared roof coverings as classified as applied over square-edge wood sheathing of 1-in. nominal thickness, or the equivalent, unless otherwise specified. See footnote (built-up roof coverings) to Table 6-3D. Laid in accordance with instruction sheets accompanying package. Limited to decks capable of receiving and retaining nails.

Where organic-felt is indicated, asbestos felt of equivalent weight can be substituted.

By end lap is meant the overlapping length of the two units, one place over the other. Head lap in shingle-type roofs is the distance a shingle in any course overlaps a shingle in the second course below it. However, with shingles laid by the Dutch-lap method, where no shingle overlaps a shingle in the second course below, the head lap is taken as the distance a shingle overlaps one in the next course below.

Prepared roofings are labeled by Underwriters' Laboratories to indicate the classification when applied in accordance with direction for application included in package.

† 1 in. = 25.4 mm; 1 oz = 29 mL; 1 ft = 0.3 m.; 1 lb = 0.45 kg

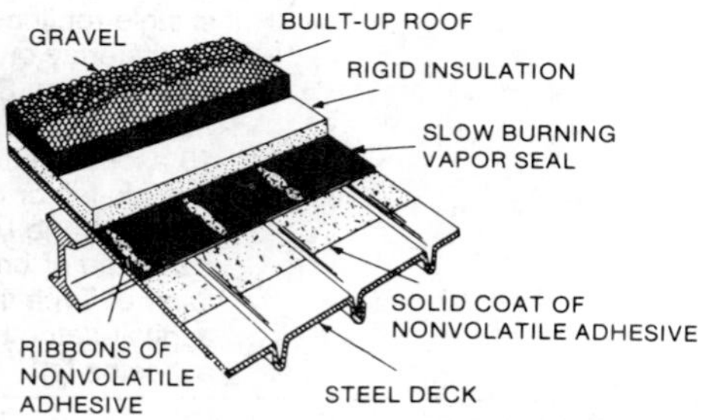

FIG. 6-3II. Typical built-up roof covering with a slow-burning vapor seal adhered to the roof deck and to the insulation by a nonvolatile adhesive.

if applied in strips (strip mopping), and if the total amount used between the deck and the insulation does not exceed 12 to 15 lb per 100 sq ft (5.4 to 6.8 kg/9.3 m^2) of roof area.

There is no restriction on the use of asphalt in conventional built-up roofing used above the insulation. When a vapor seal is used between the deck and the insulation, a listed, noncombustible, or slow-burning material is recommended, fastened to the deck and insulation with a noncombustible adhesive or strip mopping. Testing laboratories list various manufacturers of acceptable vapor seals and adhesives. A roof cover with a slow-burning vapor seal is shown in Figure 6-3II.

Factory Mutual Research Corporation divides metal deck roof assemblies into two classes. Class I construction is any insulated metal roof deck construction having a special vapor barrier (if any is used) and an adhesive that will not contribute significantly to an interior fire and that will meet or equal Factory Mutual performance standards. Class II construction is any insulated metal roof deck construction using asphalt in sufficient quantity to provide adequate adhesion for wind resistance, with or without felts between

TABLE 6-3D. ***Built-up Roof Coverings*†***

Description	Minimum Incline In. to Ft	CLASS A	CLASS B	CLASS C
Asphalt organic-felt, bonded with asphalt and surfaced with 400 lb of roofing gravel or crushed stone, or 300 lb of crushed slag per 100 sq ft of roof surface, on coating of hot mopping asphalt.	3	4 (plain) or 5 (perforated) layers of Type 15 felt. 1 layer of Type 30 felt and 2 layers of Type 15 felt 1 layer of Type 15 felt and 2 layers of Type 15 or 30 cap or base sheets. 3 layers of Type 15 or 30 cap or base sheets. 3 layers of Type 15 felt. Limited to noncombustible decks.	4 layers of perforaated Type 15 felt. 3 layers of Type 15 felt. 2 layers of Type 15 or 30 cap or base sheets.	
Tar-asbestos-felt or organic-felt bonded with tar and surfaced with 400 lb of roofing gravel or crushed stone, or 300 lb of crushed slag per 100 sq ft of roof surface on a coating of hot mopping tar.	3	4 layers of 14 lb asbestos-felt or Type 15 organic-felt. 3 layers of 14 lb asbestos-felt or Type 15 organic-felt.	3 layers of Type 14 lb asbestos-felt or Type 15 organic-felt.	
Steep tar organic-felt	5	4 layers of Type 15 tar-saturated organic-felt, bonded with steep coal-tar pitch, surfaced with 275 lb of ⅝ in. crushed slag per 100 sq ft of roof surface on steep coal-tar pitch.		
Asphalt organic-felt, plain or perforated, bonded and surfaced with a cold application coating.	12			3 layers of Type 15 felt. 1 layer of Type 30 felt and 1 layer of Type 15 felt. 2 layers of Type 15 or 30 cap or base sheets. 2 layers of Type 15 felt and 1 layer or Type 15 or 30 cap or base sheets.

* Built-up roof coverings are classified as applied over square-edge wood sheathing of 1 in. nominal thickness, or the equivalent, unless otherwise specified. From the standpoint of relative effectiveness of the different types of wood roof sheathing, the tongue-and-groove boards and 3⁄4 in. moisture-resistant plywood give better results in the brand and flame tests than square-edge sheathing with boards spaced about 1⁄4 in. apart. For classifications based on square-edge sheathing, tongue-and-groove or plywood sheathing can be substituted. Square-edge sheathing boards should be butted together as closely as possible. Reference to 1⁄4 in. spacing is to indicate fire test procedure intended to simulate actual conditions after shrinkage of boards due to age or other reasons.

The minimum weight of cementing material between separate layers of felt is considered to be 25 lb per 100 sq ft of roof surface.

Types 15 and 30 felts are defined as saturated felts weighing a minimum of 14 lb and 28 lb per 100 sq ft of the finished materials, respectively. Where saturated felts are referred to by weight, the weight is minimum and is expressed in pounds per 100 sq ft of the finished material.

Materials intended for built-up roof coverings are labeled by Underwriters' Laboratories. The classifications indicated are of generally accepted combinations.

† 1 in. = 25.4 mm; 1 ft = 0.3 m

the insulation and the deck, and regardless of the type of insulation used. This class of construction does not meet Factory Mutual standards and can provide fuel that will contribute significantly to an interior fire. Constructions that are found acceptable are listed by Factory Mutual.[3]

Wood Shingles

Untreated wood shingles may be readily ignited by small sparks from chimneys or exposure fires, by radiated heat, or by burning brands. Burning shingles themselves also produce brands, which may be carried by the wind to start other fires. Age and low humidity increase the susceptibility of wood-shingled roofs to ignition.

Treatment of wood shingles with fire-retardant coatings has been proposed at various times but has not proved practical to date. Ordinary flame-resistant treatments lose their effectiveness with continued exposure to the weather. Wood shingles impregnated with a fire-retardant solution are more durable. Shingles of this type have been tested and carry a Class C rating.

Untreated wood shingle roofs are prohibited by law in the congested sections of practically all large cities, and a very large number of cities and towns prohibit their use altogether within municipal limits.

Because of the somewhat greater susceptibility of nonsealing asphalt shingles to windstorm damage, wood shingles have been more widely used than asphalt shingles in certain areas, particularly areas subject to high winds. However, where a recently developed self-sealing type of asphalt shingle with good fire resistance has been used, the incidence of windstorm damage has been materially reduced.

BIBLIOGRAPHY

References Cited

1. "Protection Against Liquid Damage," Loss Prevention Data Sheet 1-24, Factory Mutual Research Corp., Norwood, MA, 1983.
2. "Insulated Metal Roof Deck Fire Tests," Factory Mutual Research Corp., Norwood, MA, 1955.
3. "Insulated Steel Deck," Loss Prevention Data Sheet 1-28, Factory Mutual Research Corp., Norwood, MA, 1983.

NFPA Codes, Standards, and Recommended Practices

Reference to the following NFPA codes, standards, and recommended practices will provide further information on building construction systems discussed in this chapter. (See the latest *NFPA Catalog* for availability of the current edition of the following document.)

NFPA 256, *Fire Tests of Roof Coverings*.

Additional Readings

Anchor, R. D., *et al.*, *Design of Structures Against Fire*, Elsevier, New York, NY, 1986.

Bescher, R. H., "A New Class C Treatment for Wooden Shingles and Shakes," *Fire Journal*, Vol. 61, No. 5, Sept., 1967, pp. 52-56.

Brannigan, F. L., "Are Wood Trusses Good for Your Health," *Fire Engineering*, Vol. 141, No. 6, 1988, pp. 73-80.

Brannigan, F. L., "Beware the Truss," *Fire Engineering*, Vol. 138, No. 7, 1985, p. 30.

Brannigan, F.L., *Building Construction for the Fire Service*, National Fire Protection Association, Quincy, MA, 1982.

Brannigan, F. L., "Ceiling Suspended Loads," *Fire Engineering*, Vol. 14, No. 3, 1987, p. 30.

Brannigan, F. L., "Know Your Roof," *Fire Engineering*, Vol. 139, No. 9, 1986, pp. 44-51.

Brannigan, F. L., "The Ties That Bind," *Fire Engineering*, Vol. 142, No. 6, 1989, pp. 57-61.

Carling, O., "Fire Resistance of Joint Details in Loadbearing Timber Construction, A Literature Survey," Research Report No.18, Building Research Association of New Zealand, 1989.

Corbett, G. P., "Lightweight Wood Truss Floor Construction: A Fire Lesson," *Fire Engineering*, Vol. 141, No. 7, 1988, pp. 41-47.

Coursey, R., "Do Roof Fire Tests Assure Performance," *Plant Engineering*, Apr. 14, 1988, pp. 54-57.

Day, T., "Roofs and Fire," *Fire Prevention*, No. 201, Jul.-Aug. 1987, pp. 18-23.

Fire Resistance Design Manual, 12th ed., Gypsum Association, Evanston, IL, 1988.

Fire Retardant Chemicals Association, *Fire Safety Problems Leading to Current Needs and Future Opportunities*, Technomic, Lancaster, PA, 1989.

Harlow, T. D., "New Roofs Over Old," *Fire Engineering*, Vol. 140, No. 11, 1987, p. 51.

Howell, I. D., "Examination of Various Passive Fireproofing Materials in the Laboratory," *Proceedings* from the Conference on Offshore Passive Fire Protection, Plastics and Rubber Inst., London, England, 1987, pp. 1-21.

Kirby, B. R., "Recent Developments and Applications in Structural Fire Engineering Design — A Review," *Fire Safety Journal*, Vol. 11, No. 3, 1986, pp. 141-180.

Lawson, J. R., "Fire Performance of Interstitial Space Construction System," NBSIR 85-3158, May 1985, Center for Fire Research, Gaithersberg, MD.

Mittendorf, J., "Joist-Rafter *Versus* Lightweight Truss," *Fire Engineering*, Vol. 141, No. 7, 1988, pp. 48-50.

Odeen, K., "Fire Spread Along Roofs—Some Experimental Studies," *Proceedings* of the First International Symposium on Fire Safety Science, Hemisphere, 1986, pp. 829-837.

Peterson, C. E., "Construction Helps Limit High-Rise Fire," *Fire Command*, Vol. 56, No. 2, Feb. 1989, pp. 20-24.

Rogowski, B. F. W., "Investigating the Contribution to Fire Growth of Combustible Materials Used in Building Components," *Proceedings* of the Conference on New Technology to Reduce Fire Losses and Costs, Elsevier, 1986, pp. 88-105.

Sutherland, R. J. M., "Design of Structures Against Fire: Some Practical Constructional Issues," *Proceedings* of the International Conference on the Design of Structures Against Fire, Elsevier, 1986, pp. 177-187.

UL, *Building Materials Directory and Annual Supplement*, Underwriters Laboratories Inc., Northbrook, IL. (Directory published annually in January; supplement annually in July.)

Williams, R. J., "Timber—Its Role in Aesthetic Fire Protection," *Fire Surveyor*, Vol. 18, No. 5, Oct. 1989, pp. 25-27.

Woolhead, F., "Fire Test Report: Insulated Metal Roof Decks," *Fire Surveyor*, Vol. 19, No. 1, Feb. 1990, pp. 25-29.

Yuill, C. H., "Floor Coverings: What is the Hazard?," *Fire Journal*, Vol. 61, No. 1, Jan. 1967, pp. 11-19.

INTERIOR FINISH

Revised by Norman DeHaan

Traditional fire hazard study of buildings has evaluated three principal elements: the fire resistance of the structure, the contents or process enclosed by the structure, and the characteristics of the interior finish of the structure. This chapter discusses the characteristics of interior finishes as a single or traditional element described by building codes. The role of interior finish combustion is presently being reconsidered by the fire science community and NFPA *101*®, *Life Safety Code*®, due to the implementation of computer modeling of building fires. In addition, fire research and consensus standards-writing organizations have developed a number of new fire property test methods which interface with the computer fire model simulations. At this writing, building codes do not reflect the above trend in fire evaluation techniques, and, therefore, the new fire property test methods are not required.

This chapter discusses materials commonly used for wall and ceiling finishes, such as wood, plaster, wallboard, acoustical tile, insulating materials, and decorative materials inside buildings. It also discusses interior floor finishes. The chapter defines interior finishes, the role of interior finishes, the methods of application, and fire tests used to evaluate interior finishes as they relate to current fire codes.

DEFINITION OF INTERIOR FINISH AND INTERIOR FLOOR FINISH

Interior finish is traditionally considered to consist of those materials or combinations of materials that form the exposed interior surfaces of walls and ceilings in a building. Interior floor finishes are considered to mean the exposed floor surfaces of buildings, and include floor coverings such as carpets and floor tiles that may be applied over, or in lieu of, a finish floor. The term "interior lining" is used by the international fire community to define interior finish and the role of the interior surface areas in the development of fire growth in the room of fire origin. The term "interior lining" is gaining wider acceptance in North America and may replace the term "interior finish" in the near future.

Variations of the basic definition of interior finish are found in some building regulations where counter tops, built-in cabinets, and even doors are included as interior finish. Many codes, such as NFPA *101*, *Life Safety Code*, and NFPA 101M, *Alternative Approaches to Life Safety*, exclude trim and incidental finish from the requirements for wall and ceiling finish. Less rigid requirements are set for trim of a type acceptable to the code in question if they comprise less than 10 percent of the aggregate wall and ceiling area.

Free-hanging draperies that cover most or all of a wall surface have on occasion been subject to the requirements for interior finish, as have framed, flexible, or folding, door assemblies. The normal tests for interior finish combustibility do not accurately predict fire behavior in these cases. Such materials are more properly tested according to NFPA 701, *Fire Tests for Flame-Resistant Textiles and Films*. However, when applied to a solid backing, such as gypsum wallboard, drapery material can be considered as interior finish and tested accordingly.

Many local building regulations have been expanded to include provisions that regulate floorings and floor coverings, either by including them as interior finish or by requiring that they meet other criteria based on testing in accordance with one or more test methods.

NFPA *101*, *Life Safety Code*, does not consider floorings and floor coverings to be interior wall and ceiling finish but regards them as "interior floor finish." Where the authority having jurisdiction determines that the material used poses an unusual hazard, or where the *Life Safety Code* specifically has requirements, floorings and floor coverings are required, where so specified, to comply with special "interior floor finish" provisions. These provisions are based on NFPA 253, *Critical Radiant Flux of Floor Covering Systems Using a Radiant Heat Energy Source*. Another test method used by some jurisdictions to regulate floorings and floor coverings is the "chamber test" developed by Underwriters Laboratories Inc. Further, under the Flammable Fabrics Act, the U.S. Department

Norman DeHaan, FASID and AIA (deceased), was president of Norman DeHaan Associates, Architects and Interior Designers, Chicago, IL.

of Commerce now regulates rugs and carpets for U.S. consumption and for hospitals. Some states also regulate the use of systems office furnishings if the movable partitions exceed a specified height. To meet these criteria, the Business and Institutional Furniture Manufacturers Association (BIFMA) established voluntary flammability test criteria for their members' products. Determination of hazard under the Flammable Fabrics Act is based on the methanamine "pill" test.

TYPES OF INTERIOR FINISH

The types of interior finish materials are numerous and include such commonly used materials as plaster, gypsum wallboard, wood, plywood paneling, fibrous ceiling tiles, plastics, and a variety of wall coverings. Collectively, these finishes serve several functions—aesthetic, acoustical, and insulating, as well as protecting against wear and abrasion. Ordinary paint, wallpaper, or other similar wall coverings that are no thicker than 1/28 in. (0.9 mm) are not generally included as interior finish, except where they are deemed to be a hazard by the authority having jurisdiction. Chicago, IL, and Boston, MA, for example, establish stringent wall covering criteria in areas of public assembly, in fire exit stairs and passageways, and in lobby egress areas.

The development of certain types of cellular plastics in board, poured-in-place, and sprayed-on form has provided lightweight materials with exceptional thermal insulation. The incorporation of fire retardants into some cellular plastic products makes it possible for them to meet building code requirements for interior finishes. As a result, cellular plastics, particularly the sprayed-on type, have been widely used as exposed insulation. Rapid fire spread in several widely publicized fires involving exposed cellular polyurethane and polystyrene materials has led to federal action and industry recommendations for protection of such surfaces against ignition and fire spread.[1,2] NFPA 101, *Life Safety Code*, states that cellular or foamed plastic materials must not be used as interior finish unless actual fire tests substantiate, on a reasonable basis, their combustibility characteristics for the intended use. NFPA 101 also states that cellular or foamed plastics may be used as trim when they do not exceed 10 percent of the wall or ceiling area, their density is not less than 20 lb/cu ft (32 kg/m^3), they are at least ½ in. (13 mm) thick and 4 in. (101 mm) wide, and they comply with Class A or B flame spread rating without the smoke rating requirement.

THE ROLE OF INTERIOR FINISH IN FIRES

Most building fires begin when decorative materials, furnishings, or waste accumulations ignite or when electrical systems or mechanical devices fail. Interior finishes are not usually the first items ignited, except when ignition occurs by overheated electrical circuits, careless use of plumbers' torches, or direct impingement of flame from some other source, such as a candle or a match. Once a fire has started and intensified, however, the interior finish can become involved and contribute extensively to the spread of fire.

The combustibility of the interior finish is particularly significant. Combustible interior finish in an enclosure can greatly reduce the rate of heat release necessary for flashover and can reduce the preburn time before flashover. Full-scale room and building fire tests have shown that flashover is caused by thermal radiation feedback from the ceiling and upper walls which have been heated by the fire. This radiation feedback gradually heats the contents of the fire area. When all the combustibles in the space have become heated to their ignition temperatures, simultaneous ignition occurs. Interior finish plays an important role in the occurrence of flashover—an interior finish that absorbs heat readily and holds it as an insulator would might reduce the time to flashover. If the finish material is combustible, it will be a source of fuel for the fire. Considering the nature of thermal radiation, the size and shape of the space in which the fire occurs becomes a critical factor.[3] Recently, the term "flameover" was coined to denote the rapid spread of flame over one or more surfaces. This reaction was observed in corridor tests conducted by the National Bureau of Standards which is now known as the National Institute of Standards and Technology.[4]

Once a room fire reaches the stage of full involvement, or flashover, and the openings to adjoining spaces allow heat, smoke, and combustion gases to escape, combustible interior finish of any kind or quantity becomes a significant factor in the spread of fire to other areas. Several full-scale fire tests have demonstrated that heat, smoke, and noxious combustion gases from burning furnishings may pose a greater threat to the life safety of persons unable to evacuate the room of fire origin than do those from interior finishes.[5,6] Because the life safety of others in the building and potential property damage are important considerations, however, the nature of the interior finish in and beyond the room of origin is a serious and legitimate concern.

Interior finish relates to a fire in four ways. It can affect the rate of fire buildup to flashover conditions, contribute to fire extension by flame spread over its surface, add to the intensity of a fire by contributing additional fuel, and produce smoke and toxic gases that can contribute to life hazard and property damage.[7] An interior finish that would provide the ultimate safety would be made of a relatively dense and noncombustible material that would be a good conductor of heat, would not speed up flashover, would not add fuel to the fire, would provide no path for surface flame spread, and would produce little or no smoke or toxic gases. Materials that exhibit high rates of flame spread, contribute substantial quantities of fuel to a fire, or produce hazardous quantities of smoke or toxic gases would be undesirable.

The effort to develop controls on the use of interior finish began in earnest in 1946 when three hotel fires—the Winecoff in Atlanta, GA; the LaSalle in Chicago, IL; and the Canfield in Dubuque, IA—took the lives of 199 persons. Each of these fires involved delayed discovery, open stairways, and combustible interior finish. Interior finish materials continue to be a serious life safety factor, as many recent fires indicate. For example, interior finishes contributed to the Beverly Hills Supper Club fire at Southgate, KY, on May 28, 1988, in which 164 persons died.[8]

METHODS OF APPLICATION

The method of applying an interior finish can have a serious effect on its behavior when the finish is exposed to fire. For this reason, the manufacturer's specifications for application should be strictly followed. Special attention must be paid to the size and spacing of nails or similar fasteners, the type and application of adhesives, and the number of coats and the application rate of fire-retardant coatings. Application details are equally important in repair or replacement of interior finishes. Any new material used in retrofit should meet current code requirements. Substandard application and substitution of "equivalent" materials without supporting test data have delayed the occupancy of many new buildings.

The substrate material to which surface finishes are attached should be considered. A thin combustible finish applied to a noncombustible substrate may present little hazard. The same finish material on a combustible backing, however, presents considerably greater hazards. In the former situation, the substrate will not ignite and will absorb heat during the early stages of fire development. In the latter case, both the surface finish and the backing material become involved.

The adhesive used is also a factor in the fire behavior of interior finishes. Adhesives that soften at moderate temperatures will allow wall or ceiling finishes to drop or peel away during the growth stage of a fire. This not only increases the susceptibility of the surface material to ignition but it also exposes the substrate material, which, if combustible, adds fuel to the fire. Some building codes specify that wall and ceiling finishes should not become detached when exposed to elevated temperatures of 200 to 300°F (93 to 149°C) for a specified time interval, usually 30 min. Unfortunately, no standard test method has yet been developed for this purpose.

Most building regulations state that a combustible material in sheets less than 1/28 in. (0.9 mm) thick, applied to backings, shall not be subject to the requirements for interior finishes. This exception has been shown by test to be valid for the paper surface on gypsum wallboard and for ordinary paint. This, of course, assumes proper application procedures. Where successive coats have been applied, the fire hazard can be greatly magnified.

Some building regulations further require that combustible interior finish materials of other than the most restrictive class, less than 1/4 in. (6.3 mm) thick and intended to be applied directly to studs or joists, shall be applied over substrate of a noncombustible material. This requirement followed upon several rapidly burning residential fires where thin combustible paneling that was applied directly to the framing provided fuel for the fire.

The use of sprayed-on materials for interior finishes has proliferated. Some of these materials are coatings that are inherently resistant to attack by fire. Other materials, however, especially the sprayed-on cellular or foamed plastics used for insulation or decorative effects, are not resistive to attack by fire. This is particularly true of some cellular plastic formulations. However, their use may be permitted if the fire behavior can be substantiated under actual fire conditions or if the cellular or foamed plastic meets the minimum density, specific installation limitations, and interior finish classification of the building codes.

FIRE TESTS FOR INTERIOR FINISHES

The nature of materials and the fire environment vary so widely that development of a fire test becomes highly complex. Three factors must be taken into account in the development process:

1. The start and growth of fire in a building affected by the ignition source, space geometry, ventilation, and by the nature, amount, and location of other processes and materials in the building.
2. The changing condition during a fire, such as oxygen concentration, rate of heat release, and protection systems.
3. Variations in form, composition, density, and application of the materials present.

With these variables in mind, the difficulty in designing a test that will provide a basis for predicting performance under fire exposure becomes obvious. Equally obvious is the impracticality of designing tests to represent all fire conditions. A test designed to represent a "typical" fire or to expose materials to one set of "stand test" conditions may not provide a reliable basis for predicting "real life" performance of all materials tested. Thus, there is a constant search for improved test methods with a numerical range of results and for an adequate array of tests to describe suitably the behavior of the various materials available.

The Steiner Tunnel Test

The 25-ft (7.62 m) Steiner tunnel test, also known as ASTM E84, NFPA 255, and UL 723, was developed by A. J. Steiner at Underwriters Laboratories Inc. (UL).[9] After the fatal hotel fires of 1946 mentioned earlier, the need for a method of controlling interior finishes was recognized and the use of the tunnel test proposed. The method was adopted by the American Society for Testing and Materials (ASTM) as a tentative standard in 1950 and as an official standard in 1958. NFPA adopted the test method tentatively in 1953 and officially in 1958 as NFPA 255, *Surface Burning Characteristics of Buildings Materials*.

Figures 6-4A and 6-4B show the general appearance and basic dimensions of the tunnel test apparatus. A detailed description can be found in NFPA 255, *Surface Burning Characteristics of Building Materials*. Briefly, a 20-in.-by 25-ft (508 mm by 7.62 m) specimen is placed face down on a ledge in the top of the furnace. A gas burner is ignited and flame travel over the bottom face of the test specimen is observed through sealed windows on one side of the tunnel, forming the basis of the rating for flame spread. Temperature and smoke density are also recorded, and these figures can provide a basis for calculating the fuel contributed by the specimen and the smoke developed. All three measurements are relative to asbestos cement board, which is arbitrarily assigned a O rating, and to red oak flooring, which is arbitrarily assigned a rating of 100. Provision may be made for measuring and analying combustion gases. A relationship does not necessarily exist between the flame spread, smoke development, and fuel contribution ratings obtained by this test method.

The tunnel test was designed to provide a moderately severe exposure of approximately 1600°F (900°C) in the area of flame impingement under controlled conditions. The specimen size is scaled sufficiently large to simulate the effect of joints, the lack of uniformity within the material, and the synergistic reaction of composite surface finishes. The draft, fuel input, and flame size are varied to provide a wide range of numerical results.

At least fifteen interior finish test tunnels are known to be in use in the U.S. and Canada. While several are reserved for product development purposes by individual companies, the majority are available for product acceptance testing.

Application of Tunnel Test Results

A considerable degree of uniformity exists in the application of tunnel test results with regard to flame-spread ratings. Smoke-developed ratings are used more extensively

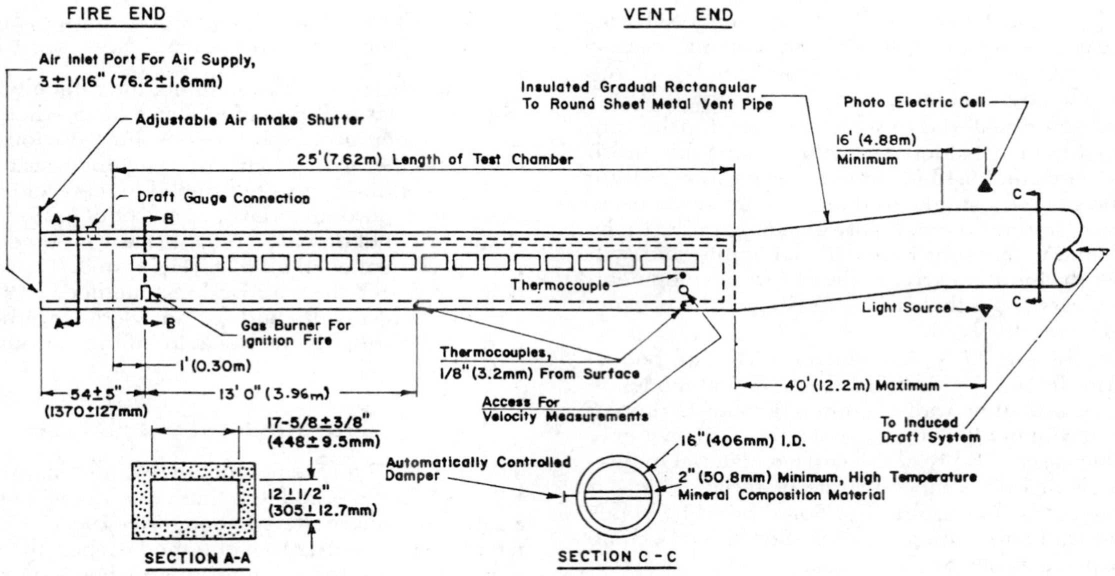

FIG. 6-4A. A schematic diagram of the Steiner tunnel test apparatus used for the fire hazard classification of building materials.

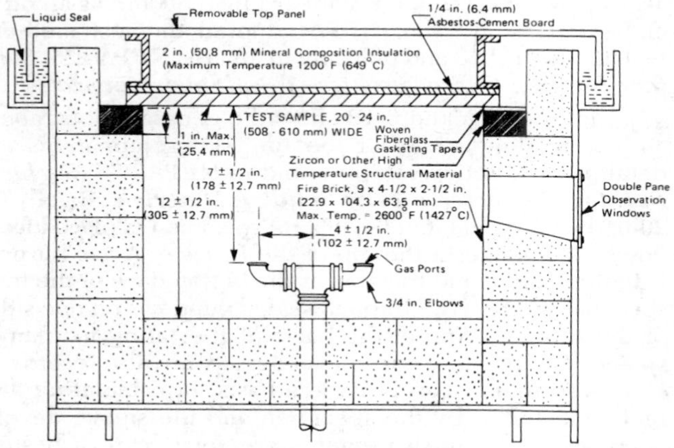

FIG. 6-4B. A cross-sectional view of the Steiner Tunnel Test apparatus.

today, but with less uniformity. Fuel-contributed factors have been applied only in a few scattered instances. Most building regulations base requirements for interior wall and ceiling finish on tunnel test results.

Recognizing that variations exist, NFPA *101, Life Safety Code*, treats the classification of new interior finish materials as follows:

Classification	Flame Spread	Smoke Developed
A	0-25	0-450
B	26-75	0-450
C	76-200	0-450

In some building regulations, vertical exit enclosures are most severely restricted with a requirement, for flame-spread rating not exceeding 25 (Class A), up to a flame spread rating of 75 (Class B) in horizontal exit enclosures. The limits on interior wall and ceiling finishes set forth in the 1991 edition of NFPA 101, *Life Safety Code*, are given in Table 6-4A, which also includes requirements for interior floor finishes based on two classification, Class I and II. These classifications are used to evaluate floor covering materials in the critical radiant flux test, described in NFPA 253, *Critical Radiant Flux of Floor Covering Systems Using a Radiant Heat Energy Source.*.

The performance of materials in the tunnel test depends upon the quality and composition of the material tested, as well as its application or use. Generally, the higher the numerical rating, the greater the flammability hazard. When automatic fire suppression, such as automatic sprinklers, is provided, NFPA *101, Life Safety Code*, allows interior finish materials to drop one class in certain occupancies. If the code requires a Class A interior finish and automatic sprinklers are installed, for example then a Class B interior finish may be used.

Eight-Foot Tunnel Furnace

Many attempts have been made to develop a smaller-scale test that can be used by manufacturers and testing laboratories in place of the 25-ft (7.62 m) tunnel furnace. The advantages of such a facility are obvious—less space required for the equipment, smaller specimens needed, and lower costs.

Such an effort was undertaken in 1951 at the Forest Products Laboratory. Initially, a tunnel was built following the plan of the 25-ft (7.62 m) tunnel, but reduced in scale.[10] The reduction in scale, however, lengthened the tongues of flame from burning specimens and made visual measurement of the flame front difficult. A new approach was devised and a test apparatus developed that was quite different from the 25-ft (7.62 m) tunnel furnace. The test method for using this apparatus was tentatively adopted by ASTM in 1965 and officially adopted for research and development in 1968.[11]

In this test, a 13¾-in.-by-8-ft. (0.35 by 2.44 m) specimen is supported at a 30-degree angle from the horizontal by a perforated panel of 12-gage stainless steel. This panel separates the upper part of the test apparatus from the combustion chamber. A burner at one end of the combustion chamber provides the proper ratio of gas to air to

TABLE 6-4A. ***Life Safety Code Requirements for Interior Finish***

Occupancy	Exits	Access to Exits	Other Spaces
Assembly—New*			
Class A or B	A	A or B	A or B
Class C	A	A or B	A, B, or C
Assembly—Existing*			
Class A or B	A	A or B	A or B
Class C	A	A or B	A, B, or C
Educational—New*	A	A or B	A or B C on low partitions**
Educational—Existing*	A	A or B	A, B, or C
Day-Care Centers—New	A I or II	A I or II	A or B
Day-Care Centers—Existing	A or B	A or B	A or B
Group Day-Care Homes–New	A or B	A, or B	A, B, or C
Group Day-Care Homes–Existing	A or B	A, B, or C	A, B, or C
Family Day-Care Homes	A or B	A, B, or C	A, B, or C
Health Care—New (A.S. Mandatory)	A or B	A or B C lower portion of corridor wall**	A C in small individual rooms**
Health Care—Existing	A or B	A or B	A or B
Detention & Correctional—New	A* I	A* I	A, B, or C
Detention & Correctional—Existing	A or B* I or II	A or B* I or II	A, B, or C
Residential, Hotels & Dormitories—New	A I or II	A or B I or II	A, B, or C
Residential, Hotels & Dormitories—Existing	A or B I or II†	A or B I or II†	A, B, or C
Residential, Apartment Buildings—New	A I or II**	A or B I or II**	A, B, or C
Residential, Apartment Buildings—Existing	A or B I or II†	A or B I or II†	A, B, or C
Residential, Board and Care‡	See *Life Safety Code*, Chapters 22 and 23		
Residential, 1- and 2-family, Lodging or Rooming Houses	A, B, or C	A, B, or C	A, B, or C
Mercantile—New*	A or B	A or B	A or B
Mercantile—Existing Class A or B*	A or B	A or B	ceilings—A or B existing on walls —A, B, or C
Mercantile—Existing Class C*	A, B, or C	A, B, or C	A, B, or C
Office—New	A or B I or II	A or B I or II	A, B, or C
Office–Existing	A or B	A or B	A, B, or C
Industrial	A or B	A, B, or C	A, B, or C
Storage	A or B	A, B, or C	A, B, or C
Unusual Structures	A or B	A, B, or C	A, B, or C

* Interior wall and ceiling finish in corridors, exits, and any space not separated from the corridors and exits by a partition capable or retarding the passage of smoke shall meet this interior finish classification.

** Refer to the *Life Safety Code* for details.

A.S. Automatic Sprinklers

N.R. Not Regulated

† Previous installed floor coverings may be continued in use, subject to the approval of the authority having jurisdiction.

‡ See Chapter 21 of NFPA 101.

Notes:

Class A interior wall and ceiling finish—flame spread 0-25, smoke developed 0-450.

Class B interior wall and ceiling finish—flame spread 26-75, smoke developed 0-450.

Class C interior wall and ceiling finish—flame spread 76-200, smoke developed 0-450.

Class I Interior Floor Finish—minimum 0.45 watt per sq cm.

Class II Interior Floor Finish—mimimum 0.22 watt per sq cm.

Automatic Sprinklers—where a complete standard system of automatic sprinklers is installed, interior finish with flame spread rating not over Class C may be used in any location where Class B is normally specified and with rating of Class B in any location where Class A is normally specified; similarly, Class II interior floor finish may be used in any location where Class I is normally specified and no critical radiant flux rating is required where Class II is normally specified.

Exposed portions of structural members complying with the requirements for heavy timber construction may be permitted.

produce a blue flame at approximately 3400 Btu per min (959.76W). Open-view ports on one side of the furnace also allow air to be drawn across the specimen and into a full-length stack by a self-induced draft. As in the 25-ft (7.62 m) tunnel test, asbestos cement board and red oak flooring are the materials used as comparison standards and assigned flame-spread ratings of 0 and 100, respectively.

Several manufacturers have built this test apparatus for product development purposes, and some authorities accept these results in lieu of other test data. Good correlations with the large tunnel test apparatus have been obtained for many materials. Some manufacturers have also constructed scale models of the 25-ft (7.62 m) test apparatus with good results reported for specific products.

The Radiant Panel Test

While the Forest Products Laboratory developed the 8-ft (2.44 m) tunnel furnace, the National Bureau of Standards (NBS) developed the radiant panel test apparatus. This used a much smaller test specimen of 6 by 18 in. (152 by 457 mm) and measured the hazard in terms of both flame spread and rate of heat release after ignition. The test method was adopted as a tentative standard by ASTM in 1960 and as a full standard for research and development purposes in 1967.[12]

In this test, the specimen is positioned at an angle of 30 degrees to the horizontal in front of a gas-fired, porous refractory vertical panel. The specimen slants toward the radiant panel at the top and a small pilot flame at that location ignites flammable gases developing from the surface of the specimen. Air is drawn over the surface of the specimen at a controlled rate by a fan in the hood under which the equipment is located. The rate of flame travel from the top of the specimen to the bottom is noted, as are temperatures that develop in the stack. The amount of smoke generated can be measured by weighing deposits on a filter located in the stack. The test is continued for 15 min or until surface flaming reaches the lower edge of the specimen.

This test apparatus is available commercially and is used in many research, commercial, and industrial laboratories. The numerical results are on a scale similar to that of the 25-ft (7.62 m) and 8-ft (2.44 m) furnaces. In several jurisdictions, radiant panel test results are acceptable in lieu of 25-ft (7.62 m) tunnel test results.

In this test, as with the 8-ft (2.44 m) tunnel test, the airflow is against or across the direction of flame travel. This provides a clear definition of the interfacial burning. With the 25-ft (7.62 m) furnace, the flame travel and airflow coincide, and with some materials, the flame front may be several feet in front of the interfacial burning. (See Figure 6-4C.)

The Corner Test

Seeking a more realistic assessment of the hazard of interior finishes, several laboratories conducted simulated room corner tests some 30 years ago. These usually comprised an 8-ft (2.44 m) high corner construction with 2- to 4-ft. (0.1 to 1.22 m) wing walls. A simulated ceiling of the same material was provided. A wood crib placed in the corner at floor level was used for ignition. The degree of flame spread and the rate and amount of smoke developed were the primary observations.

Interest in the rapidity of flame spread across the surface of what was considered low-flame-spread cellular plastics in actual fires revived the use of the corner test. Much larger scale corner tests have been conducted by Factory Mutual Research Corporation (FMRC) and Underwriters Laboratories Inc. Corners up to 25 ft (7.62 m) high with wing walls up to 50 ft (15.4 m) long have been used to determine the burning characteristics of these cellular plastics and the effectiveness of protective measures, such as automatic sprinkler protection or thermal barrier.[13] Results have reinforced the premise that fire hazard cannot be fully judged on the basis of any single fire test method.[14] (See Figure 6-4D.)

Work continues on the development of a small-scale test that will correlate with the large-scale corner test. One such effort consisted of a 24-ft (7.31 m) inverted tunnel furnace. Known as the Factory Mutual wall-ceiling channel test, it is still in the development stage. It is anticipated that this test method will eventually replace the more expensive full-scale corner test.[14]

Small-Scale Tests

Many small-scale "bench" tests are used in industry for research and development and quality control purposes. Use of such tests for promotional purposes was curtailed following action by the Federal Trade Commission (FTC) in 1973. in fact, the FTC findings included some of the larger tests as well, further emphasizing the probability that no single test would predict the reaction of materials when exposed to fire under the wide range of possible uses.

Many of the smaller tests relate to specific types of materials, such as wood or plastics. The SS-A-118b federal specification test for flammability of ceiling tiles and the ASTM C209 inclined panel test for cellulosic fiber insulation board generally have been replaced by the 25-ft (7.62 m) tunnel furnace test. Both tests are still used to some extent in their respective industries.

Following is a list of small-scale fire tests relating to the flammability of building materials that are primarily useful for product development and experimental laboratory work:

1. Combustible Properties of Treated Wood by the Crib Test, ASTM E 160-50.
2. Combustible Properties of Treated Wood by the Fire Tube Apparatus, ASTM E 69-50.
3. Determining Material Ignition and Flame Spread Properties, ASTM E 1321-90.
4. Fire Retardancy of Paints (Cabinet Method), ASTM D 1360-58.
5. Flammability of Plastics 0.050 in. and under in Thickness, ASTM D 568-77.
6. Flammability of Rigid Plastics over 0.050 in Thickness, ASTM D 635-77.
7. Flammability of Flexible Thin Plastic Sheeting, ASTM D 1433-77.
8. Incandescence Resistance of Rigid Plastics, ASTM D 757-77.
9. Flammability of Treated Paper and Paperboard, ASTM D 777-74.
10. Flammability of Rigid Cellular Plastics, ASTM D 3014-76.
11. Flammability of Plastics using the Oxygen Index Method, ASTM D 2863-77.
12. Flammability of Finished Textile Floor Covering Materials, ASTM D 2859-76.
13. Heat and Visible Smoke Release Rates for Materials and Products, ASTM E 906-83.
14. Heat and Visible Smoke Release Rates for Materials and Products Using and Oxygen Consumption Colorimeter, ASTM E 1354-90.

Two tests for surface flammability are also sometimes encountered in addition to the above. Both use a sample of the material to be tested that is approximately 4 by 24

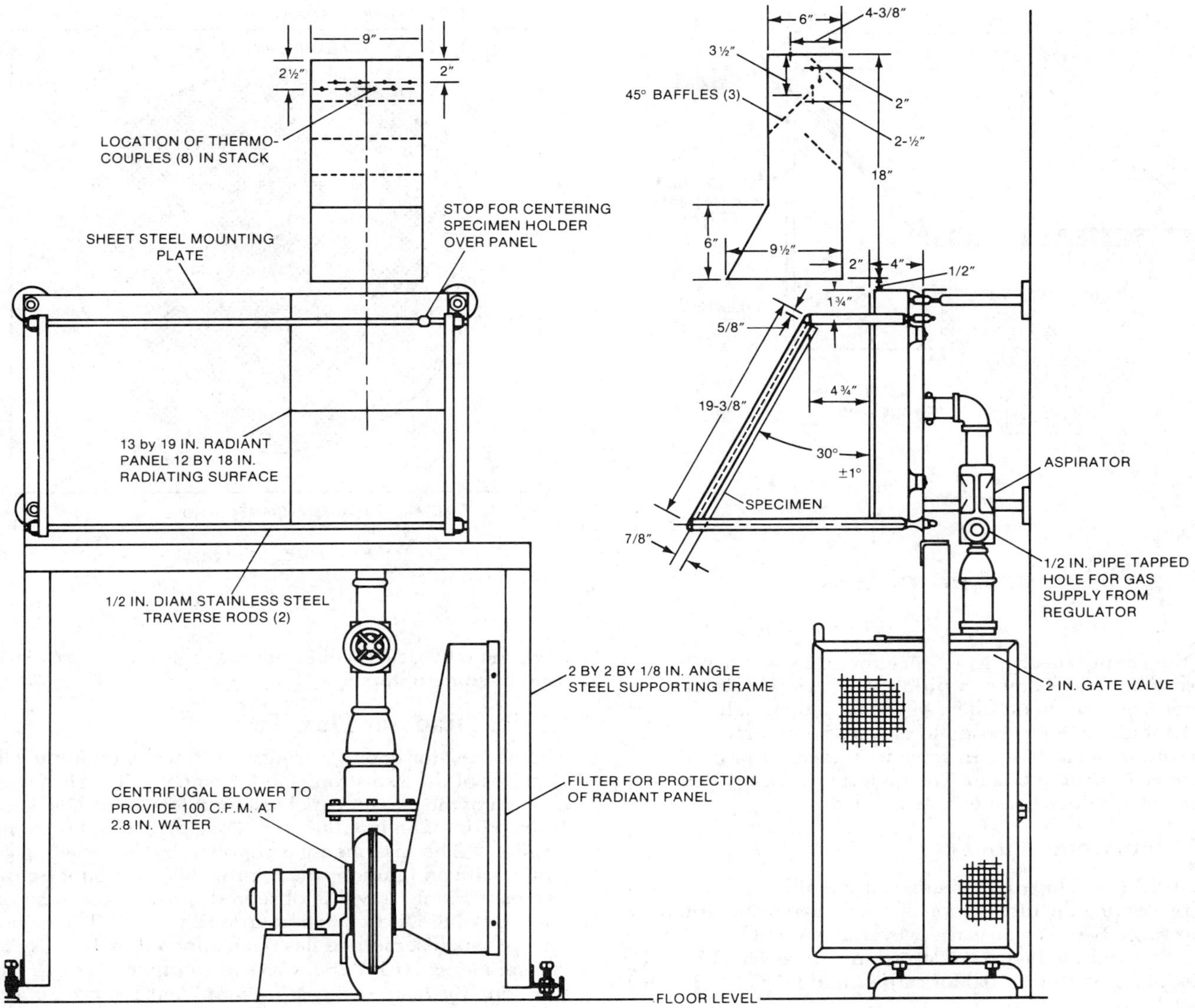

FIG. 6-4C. Diagram of the raidant panel tests.

in. (102 by 610 mm) in size, placed face down in an inclined position with a small heat source applied at the lower end.[15,16]

Smoke Density Chamber

A "bench test" is available for assisting in research, development, and production quality control regarding the smoke generation characteristics of materials. Described in NFPA 258, *Determining Smoke Generation of Solid Materials*, it measures the total smoke generated in a chamber from test specimens of solid materials and assemblies through 1 in. (25.4 mm) thick. Despite the specific intent of NFPA 258 to limit the test procedure to use as a research and development tool, some jurisdictions erroneously require it as the basis for accepting smoke development characteristics of some materials.

FIRE TESTS FOR INTERIOR FLOOR FINISHES

Fire tests for interior finishes were developed primarily with wall and ceiling finishes in mind, long before carpeting became popular as an interior floor finish in institutional, commercial, and other occupancies in which there are high human occupancy loads. Official attention was directed toward a possible hazard with soft floor coverings in 1960 and 1961 as a result of a series of small fires in the Washington, DC, area.[17] A well-publicized dwelling fire on the west coast in 1967, followed by the Harmer House Nursing Home fire in Ohio in 1970, focused attention on the problem, although carpets were a contributing, rather than a causative, factor in these incidents.[18,19]

In 1965, the Public Health Service of the U.S. Department of Health, Education and Welfare issued a directive calling for flame-spread limits on floor coverings in federally aided hospitals, citing the 25-ft (7.62 m) tunnel test

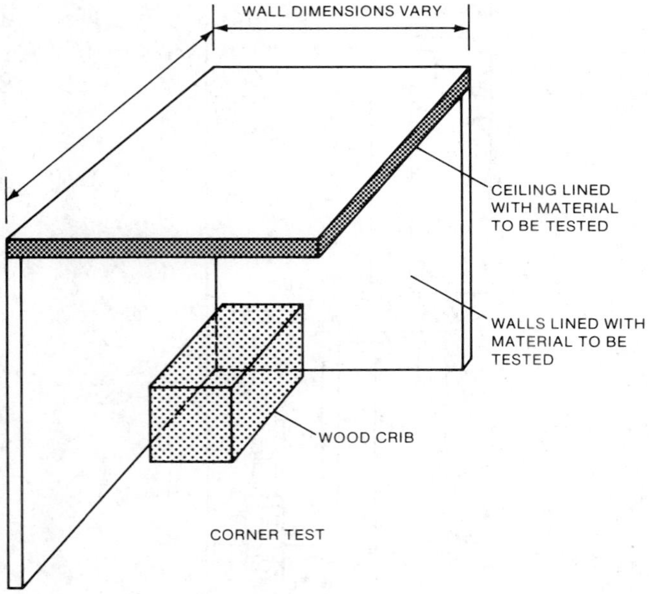

FIG. 6-4D. Corner test.

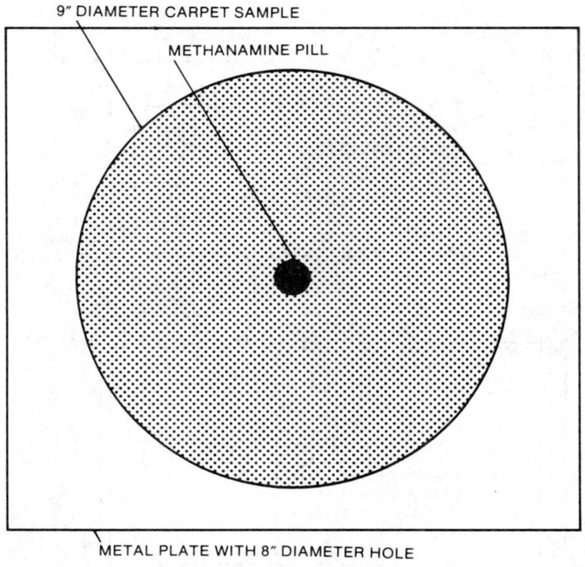

FIG. 6-4E. Pill test.

as the control mechanism. Since the test specimen in this test is held face down, a problem developed for carpets made with synthetic fibers of the type that melt, drip, or delaminate when exposed to elevated temperatures. The mounting of carpets with separate underlays or parts also posed a difficult problem. Thus, a test specifically designed for interior floor finishes was needed.

Methanamine Pill Test

The NBS developed the methanamine pill test as a means of preventing the distribution of highly flammable soft floor coverings. Based on an earlier government purchasing specification, this method was adopted in 1970 as DOC FF-1-70 (Federal Register 1970a) for carpets and DOC FF-2-70 for rugs.[20,21]

In this test, eight 9-in. (229 mm) square sections of a carpet are over-heated to drive off excess moisture, brought to room temperature in a desiccator, and tested. Each specimen, in turn, is placed on the bottom of a 1-ft (0.30 m) enclosed cube, which is open at the top, and held in place by a 9-in. (229 mm) square metal plate having an 8-in. (203 mm) circular cutout. The methanamine tablet is placed at the center of the circle and lighted. The specimen fails if the flame advances at any point to within 1 in. (25.4 mm) of the metal ring in the hold-down plate. At least seven of the eight specimens must pass the test to meet the established criteria. All carpet made in the U.S. for hospital use must pass this test. (See Figure 6-4E.)

Floor Covering Chamber Test

In 1969, UL started work on a new test for floor coverings with the test specimens mounted in a floor position.[22] The program was sponsored by the U.S. Public Health Service and resulted in what is known as UL-992, the floor covering chamber test. In essence, it is an 8-ft (2.44 m) version of the 25-ft (7.62 m) tunnel furnace, with the test specimen mounted on the floor of the tunnel and with appropriate modifications in heat input, burner design, airflow, and other test specifications. This test is not as widely used as some others.

Critical Radiant Flux Test

Another test for floor coverings was developed in the laboratories of the Armstrong Cork Company. This is a modification of the radiant panel test for interior finishes with a 10-by-42-in. (254 by 1066 mm) specimen in a horizontal position.[23] Thermal energy is supplied by the radiating gas panel, with an ignition source provided by a pilot light at one end. Flame travel is observed through a window in one side of the test chamber. (See Fig. 6-4F.) The critical radiant flux test method has been adopted by both NFPA and ASTM as NFPA 253, *Critical Radiant Flux of Floor Covering Systems Using a Radiant Heat Energy Source*.

This test method simulates conditions that have been observed and defined in large-scale corridor experiments. Both the NFPA and the ASTM test methods indicate that the method is intended for evaluating floor coverings installed in building corridors having little or no combustible wall or ceiling finish. Corridors with combustible wall and ceiling finishes would be expected to be a greater potential fire hazard. Experimental results suggest that floor coverings would contribute much less to fire spread than wall or ceiling finish in the initial growth and spread of corridor fires.[24]

NFPA *101*, *Life Safety Code*, classifies interior floor finishes in accordance with the critical radiant flux test method. Specifically, floor finishes are grouped into two classes. They are:

Class I: A minimum critical radiant flux of 0.43 Btu per sq ft per sec (0.45 W/cm^2).

Class II: A minimum critical radiant flux of 0.19 Btu per sq ft per sec (0.22 W/cm^2).

See Table 6-4A for assignment of the two classes of floor finishes to the various occupancies identified in NFPA *101*, *Life Safety Code*. An advantage of the relatively simple and inexpensive radiant flux test method is that some manufacturers are printing test results on their samples,

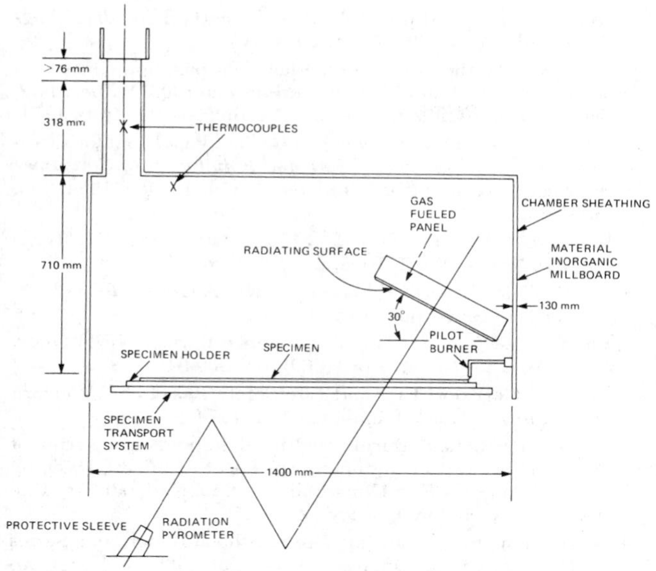

FIG. 6-4F. Flooring radiant panel tester schematic-side elevation.

including test results for various installation methods, such as pads and glue down.

While the radiant flux test method is widely used for flammability, some local jurisdictions establish additional criteria for permissible floor finishes based on a test for smoke generation. The test in NFPA 258, *Determining Smoke Generation of Solid Materials*, is the test used. Conceived as a laboratory test method, this test provides a procedure for measuring the total smoke generated in a chamber from a specimen of solid materials and assemblies, and uses a photometric system to measure the optical density of the smoke.

FULL-SCALE TESTS

Many large-scale fire tests have been conducted using existing buildings slated for demolition or available for other reasons. When carefully planned, such tests can, and have, added significantly to knowledge about the growth and spread of fire in buildings.

One of the first of these tests was conducted in Great Britain in 1949 under the auspices of the Fire Research Station.[25] Two two-story dwellings were used, one with cellulose fiber insulation board lining and the other with plasterboard over fiberboard. One test in each house, both with real or simulated furnishings, was conducted with bedroom doors open. The other test was conducted with the doors closed. With both types of lining, temperatures in the living room where the fire was started became intolerable within a few minutes. As in many other tests and actual fires, the value of the closed door also was clearly demonstrated in minimizing the life hazard in bedrooms.

In 1958, the Division of Building Research of the National Research Council of Canada conducted a series of full-scale tests known as the "St. Lawrence Burns" in six dwellings and two larger buildings.[26] Again, the one objective was to study fire spread as it would affect the life safety of the occupants of the second-floor bedroom behind open and closed doors. All dwellings became "smoke logged" within 6 min of the ignition of the wood cribs, regardless of the type of interior finish. Temperatures and gaseous combustion products developed much faster in the dwellings with combustible finishes and in those tests in which the bedroom doors were open.

Many large buildings scheduled for demolition were partially burned under the auspices of the IIT Research Institute. In these, and in extensive room/corridor tests, much information was developed relative to fire spread, flashover phenomena, and factors affecting life safety in fires.

The Office of the State Fire Marshal in California sponsored a series of tests in unused buildings at Camp Parks. The objective was to develop criteria for egress facilities, particularly corridors. The final report, published in 1974, includes a discussion of the reaction and interaction of wall, ceiling, and floor finishes.[27] Precedent for the full-scale corridor burns had been established earlier in 1959 and 1960 by the City of Los Angeles Fire Department. Final reports on the Los Angeles tests were published in two volumes by NFPA.[28,29]

Furnished room burnout and corridor tests conducted at the Forest Products Laboratories of the U.S. Department of Agriculture compared the relative importance of room furnishings versus room finishes.[5] The conclusion that lethal levels of combustion products developed from burning furnishings before the wall finishes were seriously involved was supported by later work at Southwest Research Institute.[6] These and other studies recognize that, once a fire is well established, it is highly probable that all combustibles in the room will become involved. It is also recognized that early detection, containment, and extinguishment in the room of fire origin is important, not only for early evacuation from the fire area, but also for the safety of persons elsewhere in the building and for the protection of the building itself.

In 1979-80, the U.S. Fire Administration sponsored a series of 75 tests to evaluate the performance of residential sprinklers in single-family and mobile homes. These tests showed the rapid buildup of heat and toxic gases that was possible with ordinary-hazard furnishings, particularly when the fire was ignited in the corner of the room or near curtains. There was a significant difference in the levels of combustion products and the times to reach those levels between fires in noncombustible interior finish and combustible interior finish.[30]

Room fire tests were commonly used in the 1980s for research purposes to evaluate interior finishes, wallcoverings, and room furnishings. To help make sense of the proliferation of testing procedures, ASTM E 603, *Standard Guide to Room Fire Experiments,* was developed. This guide provides information on how room fire tests can be implemented and what combustion parameters are measured. Testing instrumentation may include, but is not limited to, oxygen, carbon dioxide, carbon monoxide and other gas measurements; rate of heat release; heat flux; flame spread; temperature; air velocity profiles; mass loss rates; and smoke optical densities.

In 1986, researchers at the University of California-Berkeley Fire Research Laboratory showed that wallcoverings, with ASTM E84 (NFPA 255) ratings as low as 15, produced flashovers in full-scale room tests.[31] Consequently, the full-scale room tests provided a better indication of the hazard presented by these particular wallcoverings than did the bench-scale test method. A future response by the building code organizations to this issue may require the use of full-scale room burn tests for some types of interior finishes. The fire science community is attempting to address this problem by developing bench-scale test methods that provide good correlation with full-scale fire test behavior.

BIBLIOGRAPHY

References Cited

1. "Disclosure Requirements and Prohibitions Concerning the Flammability of Plastics," Federal Trade Commission, Washington, DC, Aug. 1974.
2. "Fire Safety Guidelines for Use of Rigid Urethane Foam Insulation in Building Construction," *Urethane Safety Group Bulletin,* The Society of Plastics Industry, Inc., New York, NY, May 1974.
3. Waterman, T. E., "Room Flashover—Model Studies," *Fire Technology,* Vol. 8, No. 4 (Nov. 1972), pp. 316-325.
4. "NBS Corridor Fire Tests: Energy and Radiation Models," *NBS Technical Note 794,* National Bureau of Standards, Washington, DC, Oct. 1973.
5. Bruce, H. D., "Experimental Dwelling Room Fires," *Report No. 1941,* U.S. Department of Agriculture, Forest Products Laboratory, Madison, WI, Apr. 1959.
6. Pryor, A. J., "Full-Scale Fire Tests of Interior Wall Finish Assemblies," *Fire Journal*, Vol. 63, No. 2 (Mar. 1969), pp. 14-20.
7. Christian, W. J., "The Effect of Structural Characteristics on Dwelling Fire Fatalities," *Fire Journal*, Vol. 68, No. 1 (Jan. 1974), pp. 22-28.
8. "Reconstruction of a Tragedy: Beverly Hills Supper Club," National Fire Protection Association, Quincy, MA, 1978.
9. Wilson, J. A., "Surface Flammability of Materials: A Survey of Test Methods and Comparison of Results," *ASTM STP No. 301,* American Society for Testing and Materials, Philadelphia, PA, 1961.
10. Peters, C. C. and Eichner, H. W., "Surface Flammability as Determined by the FPL 8-ft Tunnel Method," *FPL Report No. 2257,* Forest Products Laboratory, Madison, WI, Nov. 1962.
11. "Standard Method of Test for Surface Flammability Using and 8-ft (2.44 m) Tunnel Furnace," *ASTM E 286-69,* American Society for Testing and Materials, Philadelphia, PA, 1969.
12. "Standard Test Method for Surface Flammability of Materials Using a Radiant Heat Energy Source," *ASTM E 162-67,* American Society for Testing and Materials, Philadelphia, PA, 1967.
13. Christian, W. J. and Waterman, J. E., "Fire Behavior of Interior Finish Materials," *Fire Technology*, Vol. 6, No. 3 (Aug. 1970), pp. 165-178.
14. Maroni, W. F., "Large-Scale Fire Tests of Rigid Cellular Plastic Wall and Roof Insulations," *Fire Journal*, Vol. 67, No. 6 (Nov. 1973), pp. 24-30.
15. Vandersall, H. L., "The Use of a Small Flame Tunnel for Evaluating Fire Hazard," *Journal of Paint Technology,* Vol. 39, No. 511, 1967, pp. 494-500.
16. Levy, M. M., "A Simplified Method for Determining Flame Spread," *Fire Technology*, Vol. 3, No. 1 (Feb. 1967), pp. 38-46.
17. Yuill, C. H., "Floor Coverings: What is the Hazard," *Fire Journal*, Vol. 61, No. 1 (Jan. 1967), pp. 11-19.
18. "Fire in Acrylic Carpeting," *Fire Journal*, Vol. 62, No. 2 (May 1968), pp. 13-14.
19. Sears, A. B., Jr., "Nursing Home Fire, Marietta, Ohio," *Fire Journal*, Vol. 64, No. 2 (May 1970), pp. 5-9.
20. "Carpets and Rugs—Notice of Standard," *Federal Register*, Vol. 35, No. 74 (Apr. 16, 1970).
21. "Small Carpets and Rugs—Notice of Standard," *Federal Register*, Vol. 35, No. 251 (Dec. 29, 1970).
22. "Standard Method of Test for Flame Propagation Classification of Flooring and Floor Covering Material," *Subject 992,* Underwriters Laboratories Inc., Northbrook, IL, Feb. 1971.
23. Hartzel, L. G., "Development of a Radiant Panel Test for Flooring Materials," *Journal of Fire and Flammability/Consumer Product Flammability Supplement*, Vol. 1 (Dec. 1974), pp. 305-353.
24. McGuire, J. H., "The Spread of Fire in Corridors," *Fire Technology*, Vol. 4, No. 2, 1968, pp. 103-108.
25. "British Fire Tests of Fiberboard," *NFPA Quarterly*, Vol. 45, No. 3 (Jan. 1952), pp. 218-224.
26. Shorter, G. W. *et al*, "The St. Lawrence Burns," *NFPA Quarterly*, Vol. 53, No. 4. (Apr. 1960), pp. 300-316.
27. "Project Corridor: Fire and Life Safety Research," Western *Fire Journal*, North Highlands, CA, 1974.
28. "Operation School Burning: Official Report on a Series of School Fire Tests Conducted April 16 to June 30, 1959, by the Los Angeles Fire Department," 1959, National Fire Protection Association, Quincy, MA, 1959.
29. "Operation School Burning, No. 2: Official Report on a Series of Fire Tests in an Open Stairway, Multi-Story School Conducted June 30, 1960 to July 30, 1960, and February 6, 1961 by the Los Angeles Fire Department," National Fire Protection Association, Quincy, MA, 1961.
30. Cote, A. E., and Moore, D. "Field Test and Evaluation of Residential Sprinkler Systems," National Fire Protection Association, Quincy, MA, 1981.
31. Fisher, F. L., MacCracken, W., Williamson, R. B., "Room Fire Experiments of Textile Wall Coverings, A Final Report of All Materials Tested Between March 1985 and January 1986," ES-7853, *Service to Industry Report No. 86-2,* Fire Research Laboratory, 1986.

References

"New Fire Research Building," *Dimensions,* Vol. 58, No. 6 (June 1974), pp. 123-124.

Shorter, G. W., *et al*, "SLRP Analysis of Recommended Protection for Foamed-Plastic Wall-Ceiling Building Insulations," *Fire Journal*, Vol. 68, No. 5 (Sept. 1974), pp. 51-55.

NFPA Codes, Standards, and Recommended Practices

Reference to the following NFPA codes, standards, and recommended practices will provide further information on interior finish in this chapter. (See the latest *NFPA Catalog* for availability of current editions of the following documents.)

NFPA *101, Life Safety Code.*

NFPA 253, *Critical Radiant Flux of Floor Covering Systems Using a Radiant Heat Energy Source.*

NFPA 255, *Surface Burning Characteristics of Building Materials.*

NFPA 258, *Determining Smoke Generation of Solid Materials.*

NFPA 701, *Fire Tests for Flame-Resistant Textiles and Films.*

Additional Readings

Alderson, S. and Bredan, L., "Evaluation of the Fire Performance of Carpet Underlayments," *NBSIR 76-1018*, National Bureau of Standards, Gaithersburg, M.D., Sept. 1976.

America Burning: The Report of the National Commission on Fire Prevention and Control, Superintendent of Documents, U.S. Government Printing Office, Washington, DC, 1973.

Babrauskas, V., "Estimating Room Flashover Potential," *Fire Technology*, Vol. 16, No. 2 (May 1980), pp. 94-104.

Benjamin, I. A. and Davis, S., "Flammability Testing for Carpet," *NBSIR 78-1436*, National Bureau of Standards, Gaithersburg, MD, Apr. 1978.

Brannigan, F. L., "Flame Spread Can Be Accelerated by Interior Finishes," *Fire Engineering*, Vol. 138, No. 4 (1985), pp. 36-37.

Castino, G. T., *et al.*, "Flammability Studies of Cellular Plastics and Other Building Materials Used for Interior Finish," *UL Report*, Underwriters Laboratories, Inc., Northbrook, IL, 1975.

Davis, S., Lawson, J. R., and Parker, W. J., "Examination of the Variability of the ASTM E 648 Standard with Respect to Carpets," *NISTIR 89-4191*, Oct. 1989, National Bureau of Standards, Gaithersburg, MD.

Day, T., "Surface Coatings: Will Time Affect Their Performance?" *Fire Prevention* No. 222, Sept. 1989, pp. 40-41.

Den Braven, K., "Radiative Ignition of Some Typical Floor Covering Materials," *NBSIR 75-967*, National Bureau of Standards, Gaithersburg, MD, Dec. 1975.

D'Souza, M. V. and McGuire, J. H., "ASTM E84 and the Flammability of Foamed Thermosetting Plastics," *Fire Technology*, Vol. 13, No. 2 (May 1977), pp. 85-94.

Denyes, W. and Quintiere, J., "Experimental and Analytical Studies of Floor Covering Flammability with a Model Corridor," *Journal of Fire and Flammability/Consumer Products Flammability Supplement*, Vol. 1 (Mar. 1974), pp. 32-109.

Fang, J. B., "Fire Buildup in a Room and the Role of Interior Finish Materials," *Technical Note 879*, National Bureau of Standards, Washington, DC, 1975.

Fire Safety Progress in Regulations, Technology, and New Products, Technomic Publishing Co., Lancaster, PA., 1987.

Fung, F. C. W., *et al.*, "The NBS Program on Corridor Fires," *Fire Journal*, Vol. 67, No. 3 (May 1973), pp. 41-48.

Groah, W. J., "The ASTM Tunnel Test: What It Is and How It Works," *The Building Official and Code Administrator*, Vol. 8, No. 6 (June 1974), pp. 4-6.

Harkleroad, M. F., "Fire Properties Database for Textile Wall Coverings," *NISTIR 89-4065*, March 1989, Center for Fire Research, Gaithersburg, MD.

Harmathy, T. Z., "A New Look at Compartment Fires, Part I and Part II," *Fire Technology*, Vol. 8, No. 3 (Aug. 1972), pp. 196-217, 326-351.

Hartzell, L. G., "Development of a Radiant Panel Text for Flooring Materials," *NBSIR 74-495*, National Bureau of Standards, Gaithersburg, MD, May 1974.

Klitgaard, P. S. and Williamson, R. B., "The Impact of Content on Building Fires," *Journal of Fire and Flammability/Consumer Product Flammability Supplement*, Vol. 2 (Mar. 1975), pp. 84-113.

Lee, B. T., "Quarter-Scale Room-Fire Tests of Interior Finishes," *Fire and Materials*, Vol. 9, No. 4, 1985, pp. 185-191.

Lieberman, P. and Bell, D., "Smoke and Fire Propagation in Compartment Spaces," *Fire Technology*, Vol. 9, No. 2 (May 1973), pp. 91-100.

Magnusson, S. E. and Sundstrom, B., "Modeling of Room Fire Growth—Combustible Lining Materials," Report LUTVDG/(TVBB-3019), Lund Institute of Technology, Lund, Sweden, 1984.

Magnusson, S. E. and Thelandersson, S., "A Discussion of Compartment Fires," Fire Technology, Vol. 10, No. 3 (Aug. 1974), pp. 228-246.

McGuire, J. H. and D'Souza, M. V., "The E162 Radiant Panel Flammability Test and Foamed Plastics," *Fire Technology*, Vol 15, No. 2 (May 1979), pp. 102-106.

Moulen, A. W., *et al.*, "The Early Fire Behavior of Combustible Wall Lining Materials," *Fire and Materials*, Vol. 4, No. 4, 1980, p. 165.

Parker, W. J., "An Investigation of Fire Environment in the ASTM E84 Tunnel Test," *NBS Technical Note 945*, National Bureau of Standards, Gaithersburg, MD, Aug. 1977.

Pryor, A. J., "Full-Scale Fire Tests of Interior Wall Finish Assemblies," *Fire Journal*, Vol. 63, No. 2 (Mar. 1979).

Quintiere, J. G., "A Characterization and Analysis of NBS Corridor Fire Experiments in Order to Evaluate the Behavior and Performance of Floor Covering Materials," *NBSIR 75-691*, National Bureau of Standards, Gaithersburg, MD, June 1975.

Quintiere, J. G., "Some Factors Influencing Fire Spread Over Room Linings and in the ASTM E-84 Tunnel Test," *Fire and Materials*, Vol. 9, No. 2, 1985.

Quintiere, J. G., and Bromberg, K., "Calculations of Radiant Heat Flux in the Proposed Floor Covering Flame Spread Test Apparatus," *NBSIR 75-706*, National Bureau of Standards, Gaithersburg, MD, Dec. 1975.

Rose, A., "Some Aspects of Carpet Flammability Testing," DBR, *Paper No. 712*, National Research Council of Canada.

Schaffer, E. L. and Eickner, H. W., "Corridor Wall Linings—Effect on Fire Performance," *Fire Technology*, Vol. 1, No. 4 (Nov. 1965), pp. 243-255.

Sherad, S. E., *ed.*, *Interior Finish and Fire Spread*, National Fire Protection Association, Quincy, MA, 1977.

"Space Age Contribution to Residential Fire Safety," *Fire Journal*, Vol. 68, No. 2 (Mar. 1974), pp. 18-25.

Teller, H., "The Red Carpet Treatment," *UL Lab Data*, Underwriters Laboratories, Northbrook, IL, Winter 1976.

Thomas, P. H., "Old and New Look at Compartment Fires," *Fire Technology*, Vol. 11, No. 1 (Feb. 1975), pp. 42-47.

Thomm, E. C., "Effect of Carpet Variables on the Methanamine Pill Test," *Journal of Fire and Flammability*, Vol. 4 (July 1973), pp. 197-209.

Tu, K., and Davis, S., "Flame Spread of Carpet Systems Involved in Room Fires," *NBSIR 76-1013*, National Bureau of Standards, Gaithersburg, MD, June 1976.

Waksman, D. and Ferguson, J. B., "Fire Tests of Building Interior Covering Systems," *Fire Technology*, Vol. 10, No. 3 (Aug. 1974), pp 221-220.

Waterman, T. E., "Room Flashover—Model Studies," *Fire Technology*, Vol. 8, No. 4 (Nov. 1972), pp. 316-325.

Williams-Lier, G., "The Steiner Tunnel Index as a Measure of Flame Spread Rate," *Fire Technology*, Vol. 14, No. 3 (Aug. 1978), pp. 223-225.

Williamson, R. B. and Baron, F. M., "A Corner Fire Test to Simulate Residential Fires," *Journal of Fire and Flammability*, Vol. 4 (Apr. 1973), pp. 99-105.

Yuill, C. H., "Flame Spread Tests in a Large Tunnel Furnace," *ASTM STP No. 344*, American Society for Testing Materials, Philadelphia, PA, 1962, pp. 3-17.

STRUCTURAL INTEGRITY DURING FIRE

Revised by Robert W. Fitzgerald, Ph.D.

The selection of building materials and the design of the details of construction have always played an important role in building firesafety. Two of the important structural fire considerations are the ability of the structural frame to avoid collapse and the ability of the barriers to prevent ignition and resulting flame spread into adjacent spaces.

Three approaches to structural frame and barrier design for fire-resistance are in use or under development today. They include:

1. Standard fire-resistance testing combined with building code requirements;
2. Analytical calculations to determine the resistance to a standard fire test exposure as a substitute for laboratory testing; and
3. Analytical structural fire engineering design methods based on real fire exposure characteristics.

The traditional method of treating the structural aspects of fire protection is through building code requirements. Codes require structural frames and barrier assemblies to be selected on their ability to pass a laboratory fire-resistance test.

Chapter 2 of this section describes the classification of buildings with regard to fire-resistance requirements. This approach has the principal advantage of being easy to administer from a code enforcement viewpoint. It has a major disadvantage of being unable to predict accurately the field performance of a structural frame or barrier. In other words, code compliance alone is not sufficient to ensure performance success of the barriers or structural frame in an actual fire. Studies that correlate building code requirements and fire test results with field performance have not been made.

Although the fire-resistance test can be criticized for its shortcomings, it is the only method universally accepted in building codes today. The first part of this chapter describes the fire-resistance test procedures common in building construction today. Later parts of the chapter discuss methods of calculating fire-endurance (resistance) ratings and the behavior of building materials at elevated temperatures. The chapter concludes with a brief discussion of some of the more advanced approaches to designing for structural integrity in a fire.

Dr. Fitzgerald is professor of fire protection and civil engineering at Worcester Polytechnic Institute, Worcester, MA.

FIRE-RESISTANCE TESTING AND STRUCTURAL ASSEMBLIES

The fire endurance of the beams, girders, and columns that comprise the structural frame and the endurance of the walls, partitions, floor/ceiling assemblies, and roof/ceiling assemblies that serve as barriers to flame movement have been a historical basis for classifying buildings and rating frame and barrier capabilities. This part of the chapter will describe the history and procedure for fire testing, as well as discuss the interpretation of laboratory fire tests. In addition, structural behavior of frames and barriers is described.

History of Fire-Resistance Tests

One review of fire test methods for building constructions refers to tests on metal and masonry conducted in Germany as early as 1884-1886.[1] The first large-scale fire tests in this country are reported to have been conducted on masonry arches in Denver, CO, in 1890. These were followed by tests in New York City in 1896.

Efforts to establish an acceptable test procedure were initiated by Professor Ira H. Woolson of Columbia University and Rudolph P. Miller, chief engineer, Building Bureau, New York City. Preliminary tests by the Bureau, "necessitated by the rapid development of the skyscraper," led to the development of a test furnace (using railroad ties as fuel). This provided a means of establishing hourly ratings for floor constructions.

After the Baltimore, MD, conflagration of 1905, the American Society for Testing Materials [now the American Society for Testing and Materials (ASTM)] established a committee to standardize the test method, with Prof. Woolson as chairman and Mr. Miller as secretary. A test method for floor constructions was proposed in 1906 and adopted by ASTM in 1907. A procedure for testing wall and partition constructions was proposed in 1908 and adopted in 1909.[2]

These standards were presented to the NFPA Committee on Fire-Resistive Construction for consideration in 1914. In 1916, a joint committee composed of representatives from eleven engineering societies, including NFPA, was organized to revise and update the standard. This was done, and the revised standard test method controlled by a standard time-temperature curve was adopted subsequently by NFPA, ASTM, and the American Engineering Committee [now the American National Standards Institute (ANSI)]. The standard was adopted by NFPA as a tentative standard in 1917 and advanced to official standard status in 1918. Time-temperature curves and testing procedures developed in other countries follow the same general pattern, with minor differences.

Fire Test Procedure

Fire test procedures usually require that columns, floors, partitions, walls, and other structural elements be loaded in a manner calculated to develop, as nearly as practicable, the theoretical working stresses expected in the design. Separate test procedures are provided for load-bearing and nonload-bearing constructions and for constructions involving restrained and unrestrained beams and girders.

The Appendix to NFPA 251, *Fire Tests of Building Construction and Materials*, contains detailed specifications for test procedures, a guide to the determination of restraint required, if any, and a suggested report form. The standard specifies in detail the preparation and conditioning of the test specimens.

Acceptance criteria are specific for the construction or element tested and on predetermined conditions of test (load or no load-restrained or unrestrained). The criteria may include:

1. Failure to support load.
2. Temperature increase on the unexposed surface 250°F (121° C) above ambient.
3. Passage of heat or flame sufficient to ignite cotton waste.
4. Excess temperature (as specified) on steel members.
5. Failure under hose streams (walls and partitions).

The end restraint conditions during the fire test influence significantly the test results and, consequently, the ratings. Appendix E of NFPA 251, *Fire Tests of Building Construction and Materials*, defines a restrained condition as one in which expansion at the supports of a load-carrying element is prevented during the test. This usually provides some unknown degree of rotational restraint at the ends of the element in addition to prestressing some parts of the assembly. An unrestrained condition is one in which the load-carrying element is free to expand and rotate at its supports.

One justification for incorporating two differing conditions of end restraint is to simulate simple (statically determinate) and continuous (statically indeterminate) constructions. Figure 6-5A illustrates simple and continuous construction. In general, continuous construction is inherently stronger than simple construction. It is possible to calculate the increase in load-carrying capacity of structural members. However, the amount of increased strength in an indeterminate structure can be quite variable, depending on the type of construction materials used, the location of structural members within the structure, the degree of indeterminacy, the loading conditions, and the details of construction.

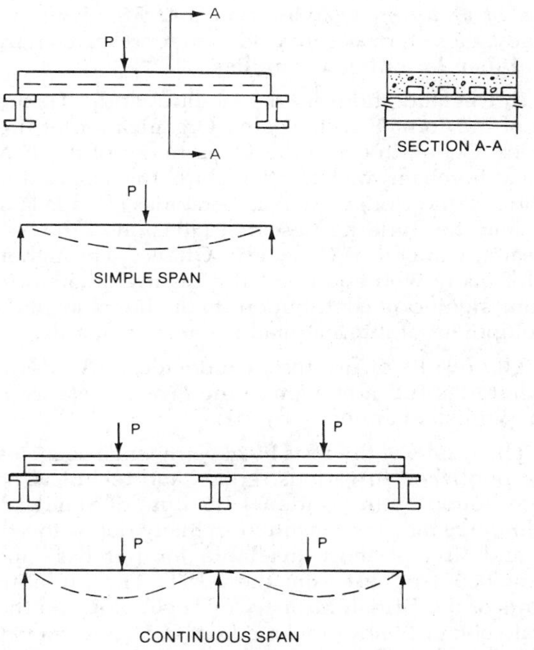

FIG. 6-5A. ***Influence of structural continuity on collapse mechanisms.***

Test results based on the two conditions of support (restrained and unrestrained) were introduced in 1970. The degree of restraint for structural members and assemblies tested and accepted for building construction prior to 1970 is unknown.

Fire-Resistance Ratings

The fire resistance (also described as the fire endurance) is the time duration the member or assembly withstood the fire test without failure. While the actual time is recorded to the nearest integral minute, fire-resistance ratings are given in standard intervals. The usual fire-resistance ratings for all types of members, structural assemblies, doors, and windows are 15 min, 30 min, 45 min, 1 hr, $1\frac{1}{2}$ hr, 2 hr, 3 hr, and 4 hr. Therefore, a 1-hr rating indicates that the assembly withstood the standard test for 1 hr or longer. A 2-hr rating indicates that the assembly withstood the standard test for longer than 2 hrs without failure by any one of the failure criteria listed in the fire test protocol.

The principal agencies in the United States that test assemblies of building construction materials for fire resistance are Underwriters Laboratories Inc. (UL) and the National Institute of Standards and Technology (NIST) previously, the National Bureau of Standards (NBS). There are a number of other agencies that have furnaces or equipment for fire tests of various special assemblies. These include the Factory Mutual Research Corporation in Norwood, MA; the Forest Products Laboratory at Madison, WI; the Engineering Experiment Station at Ohio State University, Columbus; University of California at Berkeley; the Portland Cement Association, Skokie, IL; Armstrong Cork Co., Lancaster, PA; the Corbetta Construction Company at College Point, Queens, NY; and the National Gypsum Co., Buffalo, NY. Some of these test furnaces may not conform to the specifications described in NFPA 251, *Fire*

Tests of Building Construction and Materials. Consequently, those furnaces may be used for research purposes, rather than for rating assemblies.

In England, there are the facilities at the Testing Station of the Joint Fire Research Organization of the Fire Offices' Committee and the Department of the Environment at Borehamwood, Hertfordshire. In Canada, there are facilities at the Underwriters Laboratories of Canada in Toronto and the Building Research Division of the National Research Council of Canada in Ottawa. Throughout the world, many well-equipped fire testing laboratories are making significant contributions to the literature and to the development of international fire test standards.

The results of fire tests conducted by Underwriters Laboratories Inc. are given in the *Fire-Resistance Directory*, published annually by UL.

The results of fire tests by governmental agencies have been published in various reports and technical papers. Those issued by the National Institute of Standards and Technology may be consulted in many depository libraries, and lists of those available for purchase may be obtained on request from the NIST. The bulletins and reports of the British Ministry of Technology on the subject are obtainable by purchase from H.M. Stationery Office or the British Information Services, New York, NY.

The Factory Mutual Research Corporation publishes annually in its *Approval Guide* illustrations of building assemblies that have met the test requirements for various fire-resistance hourly ratings.

Various building codes, which specify fire resistance in terms of fire test results, may include tabulations of construction forms that will be accepted as meeting code requirements for specific fire-resistance ratings. Such tables are usually based upon fire test data, but some include ratings determined on a judgmental basis or estimated from limited test data.

Not listed are the many useful data sheets and summary tables published by trade associations of the building materials manufacturers. These sources are not cited because they are so numerous and because the information published either pertains to the products of a specific manufacturer or consists of tabulated ratings for a single type of construction material.

As indicated above, the number of test facilities in use today and the variety of technical papers, reports, compilations, etc., reporting on test results that are available would make it almost impossible to tabulate systematically in a single source the data on all the various assemblies that have been subjected to tests. Users of this handbook are urged to consult the fire-resistance index ratings listing and reports mentioned above for the specifics on design specifications for assemblies that have been tested and for which fire-resistance ratings have been assigned.

As a matter of information and to illustrate the scope of testing activities, tabular compilations of test results or representative assemblies will be found later in this chapter. They are included in this handbook to help give an understanding of basic requirements for test specimens and how the results of tests are recorded. In addition, the information contained in the tables can be useful in identifying, within reasonable limits, the fire-resistance capabilities of assemblies as they are found in the field and for which precise data on their fire resistance are not available or are no longer available. The tables are not presented as references for design but to familiarize handbook users with the type of test information that is available.

Variation In Test Results

It should be recognized clearly that the fire-resistance rating is the time the member or assembly withstood a standard laboratory fire test. It is not necessarily the time duration the assembly will perform without failure under actual fire conditions. For example, a 2-hr. assembly may withstand failure in a standard fire test for greater than 2 hrs. Under actual field conditions, that same assembly may fail in a considerably shorter or a considerably longer time duration. One of the major misconceptions in fire protection is the belief that an assembly rating indicates the time that the assembly will survive an actual fire.

The fact that test-time duration and field performance may be vastly different is not intended to demonstrate that fire-resistance ratings do not have value or purpose. Over the years this procedure has resulted in improved fire resistance of code-complying buildings. However, one must understand the limitations of the procedure so that unthinking reliance is not placed on the construction.

The standard fire test attempts to provide a relative measure of fire performance of comparable assemblies under specified fire exposure conditions. It does not consider its suitability for use after the fire. Many effects from fire tests are observed indirectly, if at all. For example, the temperature gradient through a wall or floor slab results in internal strains and deflections. The strains may cause spalling or other disruptions, and distortions may be severe enough to crack floor slabs and walls, sometimes leading to collapse. The greater the area exposed, the more serious are the results of unequal expansion. General deterioration of the test specimen is not considered, except when it has been involved in the failure of the test specimen.

While the test standard specifies the preparation and conditioning of specimens, there are many opportunities for differences between a test specimen and an actual structural element in a building. The test specimen may be superior in both materials and workmanship to those found in a building; the test specimen is usually smaller than the construction it represents. Restraints to thermal expansion may be of different magnitudes, therefore, discretion in the interpretation of fire test results is in order.

Differences in the results of fire tests on apparently equal test specimens of building constructions arise from many factors, such as undetermined differences in the quality of materials, workmanship, moisture content, and test procedures. The standard method of test requires that materials in the specimen and the workmanship to be representative of those in actual buildings. Considerable variation in field practice can occur.

The test method permits the intensity of the fire exposure to deviate as much as 10 percent (formerly 15 percent) from that prescribed as standard and requires adjustment in the reported results to correct for such deviations only for tests of $1/2$-hr. duration or greater. The effects of several of the variables encountered in fire testing procedures are found in the technical reports listed in the bibliography at the end of the chapter.

The character and proportions of aggregates and binders have an important influence on the results of fire-resistance tests. For example, gypsum plaster with lightweight aggregates, mixed with from 2 to 3 cu. ft. (0.057 to 0.085m^3) to each 100 lb. (45 kg) of gypsum, has been shown by test to provide fire resistance from 10 to 70 percent greater than equal thicknesses of sanded gypsum plaster. The use of such aggregate in specific constructions should be adopted only after consulting the lists of ratings based on tests in which these aggregates have been used.

Vermiculite aggregate plaster, if too wet when applied, may be subject to shrinkage cracks. Such cracks, if they develop, are likely to occur within a short time. Some expanded perlite aggregates tend to absorb atmospheric moisture and may show destructive expansion after a few years. There may be considerable variation in this effect, as perlite is a natural volcanic glass or rock from many sources and varies in composition.

Finishing lime produced from dolomite contains magnesium oxide. That which is designated as "normal" finishing hydrate may not be sufficiently hydrated, and sometimes subsequent gradual hydration results in destructive expansion. Plasters containing such lime are subject to rapid destruction in the event of fire. This difficulty is avoided with lime hydrated under high temperature and pressure and known as "special" or "autoclaved" lime.

So-called stabilized gypsum plaster containing a small percentage of the normal hydrated lime may similarly be subject to deterioration with age and, in tests, may not provide the fire resistance to be expected from such constructions.

The effects mentioned are not such as to preclude the use of these materials where long life is not a factor or where adequate guarantees are provided. They are merely illustrations of the variability in test results that can occur as a result of differences in materials.

Although standard fire tests are made on fairly large specimens representative of building constructions or assemblies, they do not necessarily produce heat-expansion effects similar to those of fires in buildings having larger wall or floor areas. It may be necessary to specify thickness of construction or lateral support, in addition to rated fire resistance, to guard against the adverse effects of heat expansion or temperature gradients.

In addition to the material variation noted, construction differences may be even more significant. For example, a test does not provide full information on performance of assemblies constructed with components or lengths other than those tested. Performance is often reduced when the spans are increased. Also, great care must be exercised in approving "or equal" clauses in construction specifications. Often, substitutions in materials are approved for components that have not been listed with the assembly.

The standard test does not incorporate information regarding the effect on fire endurance of conventional openings in the assembly, such as electrical receptacle outlets, pipe chases, etc. Poke-through construction for electrical services or piping often is not patched properly. Transfer grilles, windows, and other penetrations are often incorporated into barriers without considering their impact on the fire resistance.

The factors noted above, in addition to the many deviations to plans and specifications during and after construction, significantly affect the fire-resistance ratings of members and assemblies. Often the code calls for, and the architect may think he or she is providing, a specified fire resistance, only to have that resistance reduced because of inattention to penetrations and important details of construction.

Structural Frame Systems

The fire-resistance rating of structural framing members, such as beams, girders, and columns, may be achieved in several ways. Generally, the members are protected by encasing them in a material sufficiently inert to prevent excessive thermal penetration or by providing a membrane protection that delays thermal penetration to the members.

The general behavior of reinforced concrete, structural steel, and barrier assemblies are described in the following paragraphs. Illustrative fire-resistance ratings are shown in tabular material later in this chapter.

Reinforced Concrete Systems

Reinforced concrete construction has had a good record with regard to structural collapse. Because concrete has a low thermal conductivity and a low thermal capacity, it provides an effective cover for reinforcing steel. For example, Figure 6-5B shows the temperature gradient in a 6-in. (152 mm) slab after a 2-hr. fire exposure. Although undoubtedly the moisture in the concrete greatly influences the values, the significant feature is the fact that the temperatures vary considerably throughout the thickness, even after a considerable time exposure.

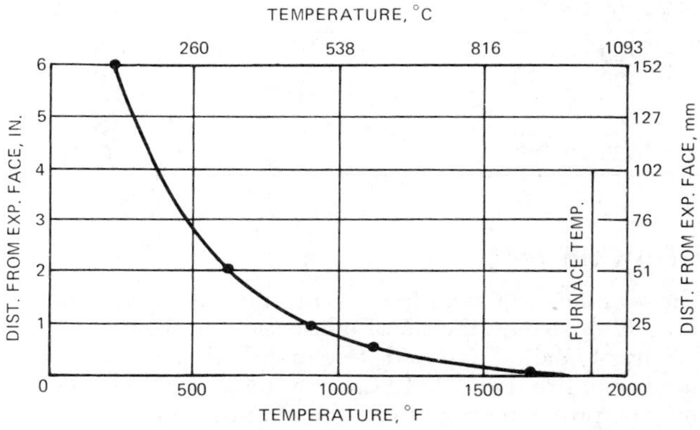

FIG. 6-5B. Thermal gradient in a 6-in. slab after 2-hr fire exposure.[3] SI units: 1 in. = 25.4 mm; °C = 5/9 (°F -32).

This feature provides some insight into one reason that reinforced-concrete systems usually perform comparatively well during fire exposure. Consider, for example, a continuous, monolithic reinforced-concrete beam or slab, as shown in Figure 6-5C. Considering the temperature gradient of Figure 6-5B, it will take some time before the tension steel at midspan is affected. Even after it reaches its yield value, the negative steel over the supports has not been seriously affected because of the insulating effect of the concrete and the moisture.

Continuous construction of this type has inherent capabilities far greater than statically determinate (simple) construction. Considerable stress redistribution can take place before collapse will occur. It takes time before excessive rotation will develop at all the necessary locations, causing structural collapse of the member. Although the member is weakened by the fire, structural stability against collapse will remain for a considerable period of time.

The level of stress in a reinforced-concrete member exposed to the elevated temperatures of a fire has a significant influence on its endurance. Table 6-5A illustrates

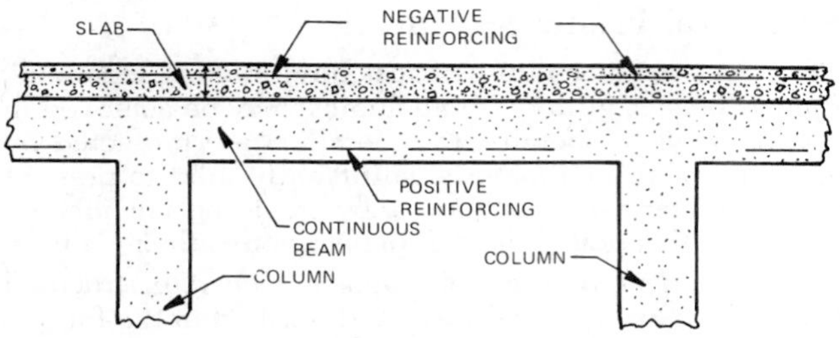

FIG. 6-5C. Monolithic reinforced-concrete beam and slab.

the effects of stress level on the fire resistance of reinforced-concrete columns. The columns used for these tests were 15 by 15 in. (0.38 by 0.38 cm) containing four number-nine reinforcing bars.[4] It can be seen that the magnitude of stress during a fire causes significant reductions in capacity. This is attributed primarily to the reduction in the mechanical properties of steel and concrete at elevated temperatures.

TABLE 6-5A. ***The Influence of Stress on the Fire-Resistance of Concrete Columns***

Applied Load, % Design Load	Fire Resistance, Minutes
150	68
100	124
75	198
50	248
30	358

Steel Construction

The popularity of steel-frame building construction is due to its high strength, ease of fabrication, and assured uniformity of quality. Exposed structural steel, however, is vulnerable to fire damage. In order to have fire resistance, it must be protected from high temperatures encountered in fires.

Protection for steel beams, girders, and columns, such as encasements of concrete, clay, tile, or gypsum blocks, have been generally superseded by plastered or sprayed-on applications applied either to a furred plaster base, such as expanded metal lath, or to the surface of the member to be protected. The applications may be conventional plasters of portland or gypsum cements combined with appropriate aggregates, or one of the many combinations of mineral fibers with binders. Currently, gypsum board encasement is a popular technique for protecting steel structural elements.

Barrier Systems

Exterior walls, interior partitions, floors, and floor/ceiling assemblies are components that define the architectural layout of rooms in a building. In the normal functional use of a building, these components are used to provide privacy, security, protection from the elements, and noise control. They also provide fire protection by delaying or preventing flames from moving from one room to an adjacent room.

The effectiveness of a barrier in preventing flames from moving from one room to another depends upon the fuel load in the room, the fire-resistant construction of the barrier, the applied loading on the barrier, the construction features, and the effect of openings and penetrations in the barrier. The most common cause of fire movement from one room to an adjacent room is through unprotected openings in barriers. Often, code requirements and expensive constructions are rendered ineffective because of lack of attention to the details of opening protection.

Building codes through construction classifications identify the fire-endurance requirements of barriers. In addition, special locations, such as around vertical shafts, are required to provide specific resistances.

Fire-resistance ratings are determined by subjecting the barrier assembly to a standard fire test, as described in NFPA 251, *Fire Tests of Building Construction and Materials*. The length of time the assembly withstands the laboratory fire without failure describes the fire endurance. Fire resistance is the endurance time rounded down to the standard durations. Both combustible and noncombustible barriers can obtain fire-resistance ratings in the standard fire test.

The cautions expressed earlier in this chapter with regard to the interpretation of the fire-resistance time durations also apply here. That is, the time durations reflect laboratory times and are not necessarily the values to be expected in a real fire. For example, one should not expect a 2-hr. barrier assembly to withstand an actual building fire for 2 hrs. Failure could occur earlier or later, depending upon construction details.

Floor/Ceiling Assemblies

The fire resistance of floor/ceiling assemblies is important in the prevention of flame movement vertically from floor to floor. Fire-resistance durations from the standard fire test are determined from unpenetrated assemblies. The anticipated fire resistance may be reduced greatly or destroyed completely in building construction when holes and poke-throughs are not protected adequately or when details do not conform to the tested assembly. Attention to details is important.

The method of attaching ceilings is a major factor in determining the fire resistance of floors. For example, the nailing of plaster bases of gypsum lath, metal lath, or gypsum wallboards to the soffits of wood joists is often critical. The longer thinner nails, particularly those with cement coatings, conduct less heat to char the wood surrounding them than do the common types of wire nails. Similarly, the integrity of suspended ceilings must be maintained to reduce the likelihood of premature failure on some assemblies. Details, such as attention to expansion of the supporting framework, are essential to preventing premature ceiling failures.

Self-tapping screws, made particularly for the attachment of gypsum boards, offer greater holding power and less damage to the core materials than do nails. Such screws can be used to attach wallboards to either wood or cold-rolled channels, without previous drilling.

Consideration must also be given to the character of the plaster base with respect to loosening of plaster mixes from the base on application of heat sufficient to char combustible surfaces. The use of wire or better yet, wire fabric, to reinforce the plaster mixes applied to such plaster bases ensures increased fire resistance. Clearances for longitudinal expansion of metal furring members are required to prevent damage from buckling. The tendency of certain plaster bases and plaster mixes to expand or contract with changes in atmospheric humidity should also be given consideration where resultant cracking might affect the fire resistance of structures incorporating such plaster.

Suspended ceilings with openings for air diffusers and light troughs should be designed so that such openings are not points of vulnerability to fire. Continuous construction above recesses for lighting fixtures and properly designed self-closing dampers for air ducts provide protection.

Roof/Ceiling Assemblies

Roof/ceiling assemblies are tested and rated in a manner similar to the floor/ceiling assemblies. The results are generally comparable. However, it should be noted that roof assemblies often have a given thickness of insulation in place at the test. If additional thicknesses of insulation are desired, the fire-resistance rating may be reduced.

Walls and Partitions

The fire resistance of walls and partitions will delay or prevent flames from moving horizontally from one room to an adjacent room. These assemblies are also tested in accordance with NFPA 251, *Fire Tests of Building Construction and Materials*. The cautions expressed earlier in this section concerning the relationship between test duration and actual fire performance also apply to these constructions. Walls and partitions are particularly vulnerable to the effects of horizontal communication mechanisms. The fire resistance can be almost completely destroyed by ineffective opening protection for doors, windows, grilles, ducts, and other openings in these barriers.

The fire-resistance ratings are obtained for unpenetrated constructions. When openings are made for doors, windows, transfer grilles, pipe chases, etc., the fire resistance is reduced or destroyed. If the fire resistance of a barrier is important to the fire protection design of the building, attention must be given to the details of design for all openings.

Many fire tests are stopped arbitrarily before an endpoint criterion has been attained. In some cases, the indications are that, had the test been continued, the construction would have qualified for a high fire-resistance rating than that assigned to it.

TABLE 6-5B. ***Reinforced-Concrete Beams and Girders of Medium Size***

Concrete Grade*	Protective Cover of Reinforcement, Inches	Fire-Resistance Rating† Hours,
1	¾	1
	1	2
	1¼	3
	1½	4
2	¾	½–1‡
	1	1–2‡
	1½	2–3‡
	2	2–4‡

* For lightweight concrete having an oven-dried density of 110 pcf or less, the cover shown for Concrete Grade 1 may be reduced 25 percent.

† May be increased if some bars are better protected by being away from corners or in an upper layer or if beam is large. Should be decreased if beam is small.

‡ Variable depending on spalling characteristics of aggregate. The use of mesh to hold cover in place will give ratings about as high as for concrete of Grade 1.

SI units: 1 in. = 25.4 mm.

ILLUSTRATIVE FIRE-RESISTANCE RATINGS FOR STRUCTURAL FRAME AND BARRIER CONSTRUCTIONS

Fire-resistance testing has produced a large amount of experimental data. To illustrate the effect of materials and constructions on the fire-resistance rating of assemblies and structural members, several graphs and tables have been included. These graphs and tables can be used both to give guidance on the needs to achieve fire-resistance ratings and to provide a basis for judgmental interpretations of the fire resistance of construction encountered in field evaluations.

Reinforced-Concrete Members

The details of construction and the kind of aggregates affect the fire resistance of concrete structures.

TABLE 6-5C. ***Prestressed Concrete Girders, Beams, Joists, and Slabs (Grade I Concrete)***

Type of Unit	Condition of Restraint	Cross-Sectional Area, Sq In.†	Cover in Inches for Fire Rating Shown*			
			1 Hr	2 Hr	3 Hr	4 Hr
Girders, beams and joists	Unrestrained	40 to 150	2	2.5	—	—
		150 to 300	1.5	2.5	3.5‡	—
		Over 300	1.5	2.25	3‡	4‡
	Axially restrained	40 to 150	1.5	2	—	—
		150 to 300	1	1.5	2	—
		Over 300	1	1.5	1.5	2
Slabs, solid or covered, with flat undersurface	Unrestrained		1	1.5	2	2.5
	Biaxial restraint		0.75	1.25	1.5	2

* Cover for an individual steel tendon is measured to the nearest exposed surface. For several tendons in the same member having different concrete covers, the minimum cover may be reduced slightly. The covers shown may be reduced 25 percent for lightweight concrete having an oven-dried density of 110 pcf or less. For Grade 2 concrete, the cover may need to be increased.

† In computing the cross-sectional area of joists, the area of the flange shall be added to the area of the stem, but the total width of the flange so used shall not exceed three times the width of the stem.

‡ Provide against spalling of the cover by means of a light, 2-in., U-shaped mesh, covered about 1 in.

Note: Data in this table are based on 67 Standard ASTM fire tests.

SI units: 1 in. = 25.4 mm.

TABLE 6-5D. ***Fire-Resistance of Reinforced Concrete Columns****

Column				Concrete			Reinforcement							
	Section		Load	Aggregates		Mix	Vertical			Lateral		Concrete Cover	Fire-Resistance	
No.	In.	Area Sq In.	in 1000 Lbs	Fine	Coarse	Cement Fine Coarse	Number	Bar Size No.	Sq In.	Diam In.	Spacing In.	Thickness In.	Hr	Min
70	16 × 16	256	101	Fox River sand	Chicago limestone	1:2:4	4	9	4.00	¼	12	2¼	8 (13+	40 —)
71	16 × 16	256	101	Long Island sand	New York trap rock	1:2:4	4	9	4.00	¼	12	2¼	7	22
72	17 dia	227	107.5	Fox River sand	Chicago limestone	1:2:4	6	9	6.00	¼	12	2½	8 (12+	04 —)
73	17 dia	227	107.5	Long Island sand	New York trap rock	1:2:4	6	9	6.00	¼	12	2½	7	57
74	17 dia	227	129	Fox River sand	Chicago limestone	1:2:4	6	6	2.64	¼	1½	2¼	8 (13+	06 —)
75	17 dia	227	129	Long Island sand	New York trap rock	1:2:4	6	6	2.64	¼	1½	2¼	8	02
25	16 × 16	256	92	Pittsburgh sand	Pittsburgh gravel	1:2:4	4	8	3.16	¼	12	1½	4 (6	— 30)
44	16 × 16	256	92	Long Island sand	Pure quartz gravel	1:2:4	4	8	3.16	¼	12	1½	4 (6	— —)
51	16 × 16	256	92	Pittsburgh sand	Blast furnace slag	1:2:4	4	8	3.16	¼	12	1½	4 (8	— —)
56	16 × 16	256	92	Pittsburgh sand	New Jersey trap rock	1:2:4	4	8	3.16	½	12	1½	4 (7	— —)
7	18 dia	254	99.75	Pittsburgh sand	Pittsburgh gravel	1:2:4	8	6	3.52	¼	12	1½	5 (6	— —)
2	18 dia	254	141	Pittsburgh sand	Pittsburgh gravel	1:2:4	8	6	3.52	3⁄16	2	1½	4	—
48	18 dia	254	141	Pittsburgh sand	Blast furnace slag	1:2:4	8	6	3.52	3⁄16	2	1½	4 (10+	— —)
85	18 dia	254	141	Elgin, Ill. sand	Elgin, Ill. gravel	1:2:4	8	6	3.52	3⁄16	2	1½	4 (12+	— —)
12	18 dia	254	81	Pittsburgh sand	Pittsburgh gravel	1:2:4	None	—	—	—	—	—	4	—
33	12 dia	113	51	Pittsburgh sand	Pittsburgh gravel	1:2:4	4	5	1.24	¼	2⅛	1½	Avg. of 2 3	—

* Columns Nos. 70 to 75 tested at UL. Test No. 70 of the group was stopped at 8 hr 40 min, others at failure or at 8 hr, and all loaded to failure at end of fire exposure (NBS Tech. Paper 184). All other columns tested at NBS Laboratory at Pittsburgh, PA. The fire endurance test of Col. No. 7 stopped at 5 hr, all others of series stopped at 4 hr. Figures in parentheses are estimates of fire resistance if tests had continued to failure (NBS Tech. Paper 272).
SI units: 1 in = 25.4 mm; 1 lb = 0.45 kg.

The fire-resistance ratings for reinforced concrete beams are given in Table 6-5B and for prestressed concrete girders, beams, joists, and slabs in Table 6-5C. As the cold-drawn, high-strength steel tendons used in prestressed concrete are more adversely affected by high temperatures than normal reinforcement steel, these tendons require a thicker protective cover than is required in conventional reinforced concrete. The fire resistance of reinforced concrete columns is shown in Table 6-5D.

Structural Steel Members

Fire protection generally is provided for structural steel by encasing the members in concrete, lath and plaster, gypsum boards, or sprayed fibers. A second common method of providing fire resistance is by installing a membrane barrier to delay or prevent the heat from raising the temperature of the steel to the critical temperatures. Table 6-5E gives minimum thicknesses of portland cement encasement for steel beams, while Tables 6-5F and 6-5G illustrate the influence on the fire resistance of columns for various methods of encasement. Figures 6-5D and 6-5E illustrate different methods of encasement for steel columns. Figure 6-5F provides a means to estimate the necessary encasing requirements for steel columns.

Floor/Ceiling Assemblies

Fire resistance for floor/ceiling assemblies of reinforced concrete, structural steel, and wood can be achieved in several ways. For example, Figure 6-5G illustrates the influence of floor thickness and aggregate type on the fire resistance of reinforced-concrete slabs, while Table 6-5H shows the fire-resistance for several types of concrete floor

TABLE 6-5E. *Concrete Protection for Steel Beams*
(All reentrant portions filled)

Fire-Resistance Rating		Thickness of Concrete Protection, Inches							
		Grade 1 Size of Member (flange width)				Grade 2 Size of Member (flange width)			
Hr	Min	2 to 3¾ in.	4 to 5¾ in.	6 to 7¾ in.	8 in. and over	2 to 3¾ in.	4 to 5¾ in.	6 to 7¾ in.	8 in. and over
4	—	4	3¼	2½	2	4¾	3¾	3	2½
3	—	3½	2½	2	1½	4	3	2½	2
2	—	2½	2	1½	1	3	2½	1¾	1¼
1	30	2	1½	1	1	2½	1¾	1¼	1
1	—	1½	1	1	1	1¾	1¼	1	1

Note: Protective concrete having thickness one-fourth of flange width or less shall have steel wire reinforcement spaced not more than four times the thickness of the concrete covering the flange.
SI units: 1 in. 25.4 mm.

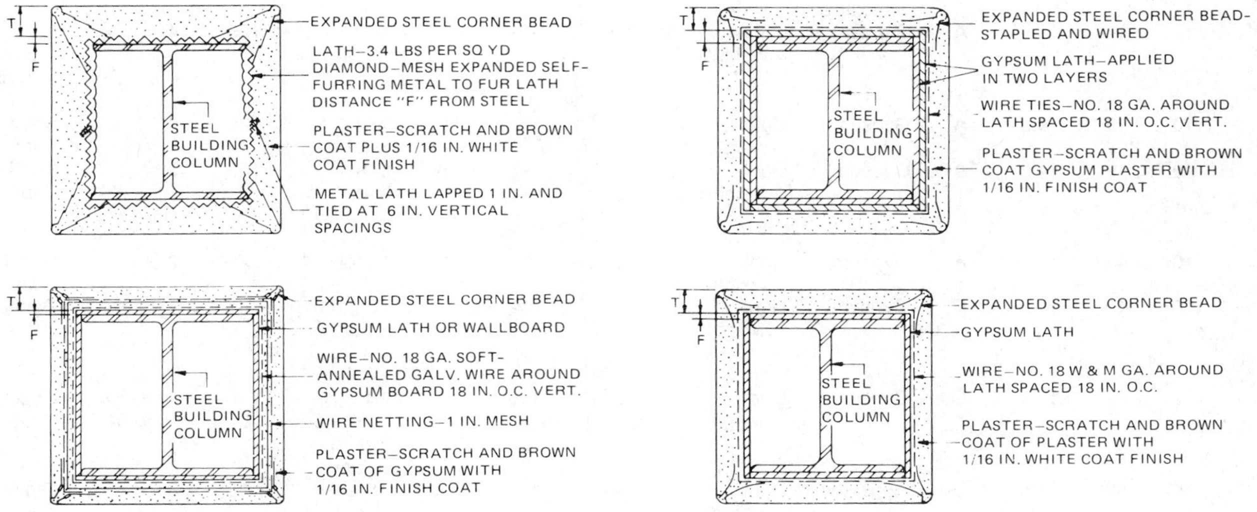

FIG. 6-5D. Typical steel column protection of lath and plaster assemblies.

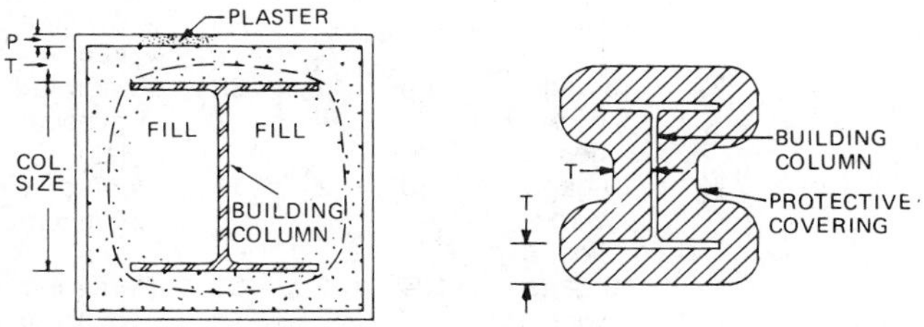

FIG. 6-5E. Typical steel column protections of concrete, masonry, or sprayed fibers.

constructions. Table 6-5I shows the test results for structural steel joist floor and roof constructions, and Table 6-5J provides some data on the fire resistance of steel-formed concrete floor systems. Illustrative fire-resistance ratings for wood floors are provided in Tables 6-5K and 6-5L.

Walls and Partitions

Walls and partitions are commonly constructed of masonry, wood, or metal studs faced with fire-resistant materials. Table 6-5M gives the fire resistance of load-bearing brick or clay tile walls. Figure 6-5H shows a graph that allows the fire resistance of burned clay brick walls to be estimated. Tables 6-5N and 6-5O provide fire-resistance ratings for wood stud walls, while Figure 6-5I gives the fire resistance of stud walls faced with common construction materials and can be used to estimate quickly and conveniently. Table 6-5P and Figure 6-5J are very useful descriptions of the fire resistance of solid, non-load-bearing partition materials.

CALCULATING FIRE ENDURANCE

The traditional approach to structural fire protection is to specify in the building code the fire-endurance ratings for identified construction classifications. Structural members and assemblies are subjected to the standard fire test (NFPA 251) to establish individual fire-endurance ratings.

During the past three decades, a substantial amount of research has been conducted on structural behavior in fires. Computer models of compartment fire behavior, heat transfer, and structural performance at elevated temperatures have been developed. These models utilize basic research on mechanical and thermal properties of materials at elevated temperatures, as well as experimental validation of the computer models. These studies have

TABLE 6-5F. ***Fire Resistance of Steel Columns with Lath and Plaster Protective Coverings***

Metal Column				Protective Covering							Total Area of Materials	Fire-Resistance Rating		
				Type of Covering				Thickness ††	Furring ††					
					Plaster									
Type of Section	Size In.	Wt per Lin Ft Lb	Area of Metal Sq In.	Design	Type	Aggregate	Mix, Volumes	In.	In.	Bond of Covering	Sq In.	Hr	Min	Notes
H	6	44	13	—	Portland cement & lime	Sand	1:1/10:2½	⅞	1	Metal lath	40	—	45	Metal lath furred out
H	6	31	9	—	Two thicknesses of above	Sand	1:1/10:2½	⅞ + ⅞	1 & 1	Metal lath	80	1	30	Metal lath furred out
H	10	49	14.5	A	Gypsum-cement mixture	Lightweight*	Mill mix	1¾	⅜	Wire fabric	125	3	25	
H	10	49	14.5	A	Gypsum	Lightweight*	Mill mix	1 ⅞	⅝	Metal lath	125	4	—	½-in. channel behind lath
H	10	49	14.5	A	Gypsum	Lightweight*	1½:2 1½:3	1¾	⅜	Metal lath	125	4	—	Self-furring lath
H	10	49	14.5	A	Gypsum	Lightweight*	1½:2 1½:3	1⅜	⅜	Metal lath furred out	102	3	—	Self-furring lath
H	10	49	14.5	A	Gypsum	Lightweight*	1½:2 1½:3	1	⅜	Metal lath	78	2	—	Self-furring lath
H	10	49	14.5	B	Gypsum	Lightweight*	½:3½ ½:4	2⅛	½	18-gage wire & wire fabric	145	4	—	Gypsum
H	10	49	14.5	C	Gypsum	Lightweight*	1½:2 1½:3	1½	1	18-gage wire & wire fabric	140	4 to 15 4 to 40		Gypsum lath
H	10	49	14.5	B	Gypsum	Lightweight*	1½:2½	1½	½	18-gage wire & wire fabric	110	3	40	Gypsum lath
H	10	49	14.5	D	Gypsum	Lightweight*	1:2½	½	⅜	18-gage wire ties	53	1	20	Perforated gypsum lath
H	10	49	14.5	D	Gypsum	Lightweight*	1:2½	⅝	⅜	18-gage wire ties	60	1	30	Perforated gypsum lath
H	10	49	14.5	D	Gypsum	Lightweight*	1½:2 1½:3	1	⅜	18-gage wire ties	80	2	15	Perforated gypsum lath
H	10	49	14.5	D	Gypsum	Lightweight*	1½:2 1½:3	1½	⅜	18-gage wire ties	104	2	30	Perforated gypsum lath
O	7	51	15.5	—	Portland cement & lime	Sand	1:1/10:2½	1¼	⅞	⅞-in. rib lath	70	2	45	Metal lath on cast column

* Lightweight aggregate can be either perlite or vermiculite.
† Dimensions as shown in Figure 6-5D.
SI units: 1 in. = 25.4 mm; 1 lb = 0.43 kg.

TABLE 6-5G. ***Fire Resistance of Steel Columns Encased with Concrete, Masonry, or Sprayed Fibers***

Steel Column			Protective Covering									
Type of Section	Size In.	Wt per Lin Ft Lb	Design	Type of Covering	Thickness Outside Steel t‖ In.	Re-entrant Portion Filled	Plaster Thickness In.	Section Area of Solid Material Sq In.	Bond of Covering	Fire-Resistance Rating Hr	Fire-Resistance Rating Min	Notes
H	8	34		None	0	No	0	8	—	—	10	Bare column
H	6	20	E	Siliceous gravel concrete, 1:2½:3½ mix	2	Yes	0	100	8-gage wire spiral 8-in. pitch	3	30	NBS test
Plate & angle	6	34	E	Traprock or cinder concrete, 1:6 mix*	2	Yes	0	130	6-gage wire spiral	3	45	UL test
H	8	34	E	Limestone concrete, 1:6 mix*	2	Yes	0	144	6-gage wire spiral	6	30	UL test
H	8	34	E	Limestone concrete, 1:6 mix*	4	Yes	0	256	6-gage wire spiral	7	30	UL test
H	8	34	E	Traprock, granite, cinders, 1:6 mix*	4	Yes	0	256	6-gage wire spiral	7	—	UL test
Plate & angle	6	34	E	Gypsum concrete†	2	Yes	½	114	4-in. mesh fabric	6	30	NBS test gypsum plaster
Plate & angle	6	34	E	Gypsum block	2	No	½	107	1 by ⅛-in. O clamps	4	—	NBS test gypsum plaster
Plate & angle	6	34	E	Cinder block	3¾	Yes	¾	240	Block bond	7	—	NBS test gypsum plaster
H	8	34	E	Common brick	4¼	Yes	0	270	Brick bond	7	—	UL test
H	8	34	E	Semi-fireclay hollow tile	2	No	0	96	Wire ties	1	30	UL test
H	8	34	E	Semi-fireclay hollow tile	4	No	0	158	Wire ties	1	30	UL test
H	10	49	F	Sprayed mineral fiber‡	2¼	Yes	—	164	No special adhesive	5	—	
H	10	49	F	Sprayed mineral fiber‡	3⅜	Yes	—	238	Special adhesive	5	—	
H	8	28	F	Sprayed mineral fiber‡	2	Yes	—	44	Special adhesive	5	—	
I	8	28	F	Sprayed asbestos fiber‡	2	Yes	—	38	No special adhesive	3	—	
	8	35	E	Sprayed asbestos fiber‡	1	Yes	—	90	No special adhesive	2	—	
	8	35	E	Sprayed asbestos fiber‡	1¾	Yes	—	98	No special adhesive	4	—	
	8	35	E	Sprayed asbestos fiber‡	1⅞	Yes	—	120	No special adhesive	4	—	
I	8	28	F	Sprayed asbestos fiber‡	1½	Yes	—	28	No special adhesive	2	—	UL test
O	7.6	24		None (Bare steel pipes filled with concrete)§	0	Yes	0	46	—	—	35	UL test

* Concrete mix—1 part cement to 6 parts total aggregate including sand and coarse aggregate.
† Gypsum concrete—7 parts gypsum stucco to 1 part wood shavings, by weight.
‡ Mineral fibers, with bonding agent as required, sprayed on to all surfaces of column shaft to thicknesses indicated. (Thickness different on account of characteristics of fiber and binder.)
§ Concrete-filled columns require vent holes to prevent explosion in the event of fire.
‖ Dimensions as shown in Fig. 6-5E.
SI units: 1 in. = 25.4 mm; 1 lb = 0.45 kg.

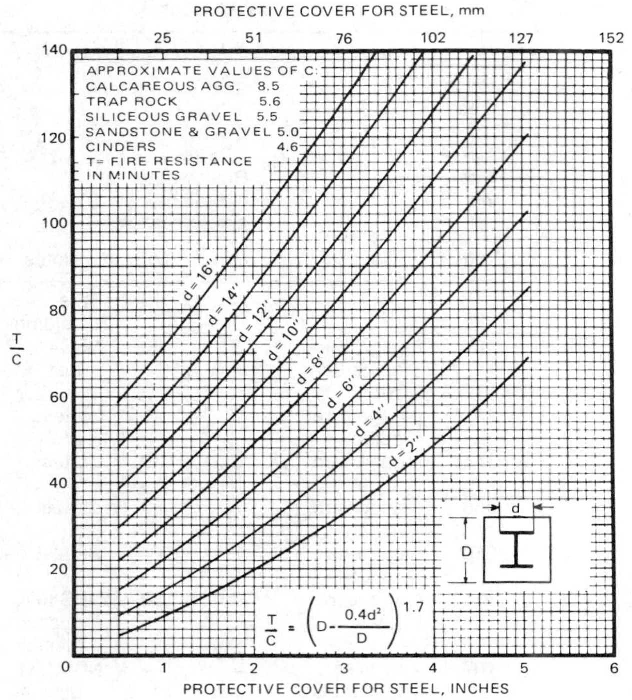

FIG. 6-5F. Encasing requirements of steel columns and other free-standing steel members.

resulted in more realistic predictions of structural behavior in fires than has been possible with the traditional code and standard fire test procedures of the past.

Calculation methods offer advantages in economy and better predictability over the traditional test approach. The calculation methods may be grouped into two categories: 1) calculation of the fire endurance that would have been obtained in the standard fire test, and 2) calculation of structural or thermal performance in an actual building fire compartment.

Building code requirements specify fire endurance as reflected by the standard fire test. Consequently, it has been more productive to develop methods to calculate the fire endurance that would have been obtained in the standard fire test. Illustrative equations and graphs for this type of evaluation are given below. A brief description of procedures to calculate performance in actual building fires is given at the end of this chapter.

Equivalent Fire Endurance

Fire testing has been ongoing for many years, yielding a large amount of data and experience. The procedures described below reflect the type of methods that will enable equivalent fire resistance to be calculated. It should be noted that many of these calculation methods are obtained from test data. Consequently, one should be cautious when applying these methods to materials that have not been used in the tests that were the basis for the calculation procedures. For example, the data for structural steel has been based on testing of A-7 or A-36 structural steel. In recent years, high-strength steels have become more popular. The mechanical properties of high-strength steels at both normal and elevated temperatures are different than those of A-7 and A-36 steel. Consequently, for fire-resistance calculations, when the term structural steel is used in this section, A-7 and A-36 steels are intended.

The fire endurance of structural steel beams and columns can be improved by insulating the members. Equation 1 calculates the fire endurance of steel beams and columns protected by light insulation.[5,6] The members may be protected by boxing the slope or by a contour protection. The equation is:

$$R = \left(C_1 \frac{M}{D} + C_2\right) l \qquad [1]$$

where

R = fire endurance in minutes

M = mass of the member in lb/ft

D = heated perimeter in inches

I = thickness of protection in inches

C_1, C_2 = *constants that are empirically derived for the insulating units.*

In SI units:

$$R = \left(0.672 C_1 \frac{M}{D} + 0.039 C_2\right) l \qquad [1m]$$

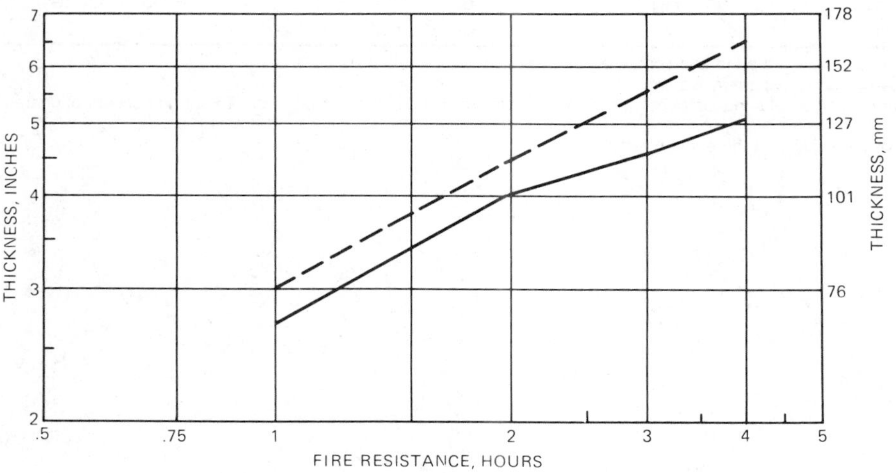

***FIG. 6-5G.** Fire-resistance ratings of reinforced concrete floors of varying thicknesses. The dotted line represents concrete floors made with regular aggregates, and the solid line represents lightweight concretes.*

TABLE 6-5H. ***Concrete Floor Constructions***

Materials	Fire-Resistance Rating Hr	Min
Reinforced Concrete (Free or partly restrained, 1500-2500 psi)		

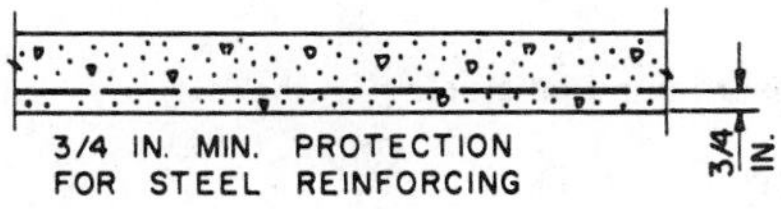

Materials	Hr	Min
3 in. thick	—	45
4 in. thick	1	15
6 in. thick, 1-in. minimum protection for steel	2	—
Reinforced Concrete on Precast Joists		

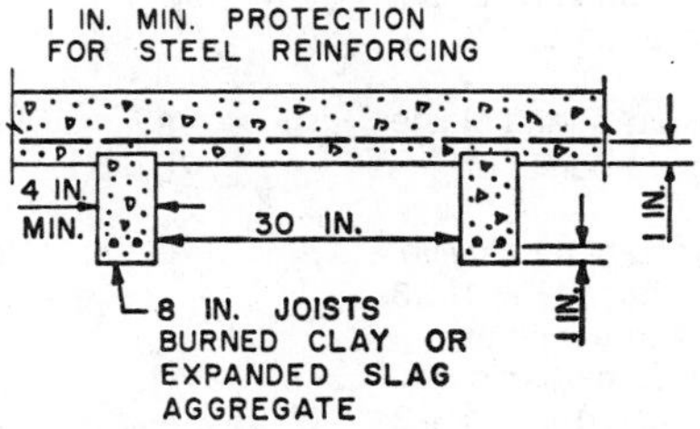

Materials	Hr	Min
Reinforced concrete, 1:3½:4, 3 in. thick, no ceiling—	45	
Reinforced concrete, 1:3½:4, 3 in. thick, ceiling of gypsum wallboard ½-in. thick, nailed to wood, strips wired to joists	1	—
Combination of Tile and Concrete Floors		

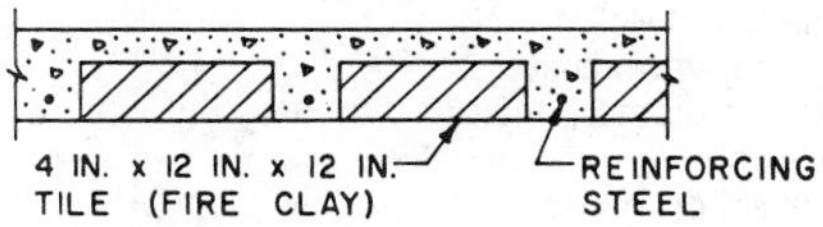

Materials	Hr	Min
Concrete 2 in. or 1½ in. thick, and fire clay tile 6 in. or 4 in. thick, no ceiling finish	1	—
Concrete 1½ in. thick, and tile 4 in. thick with gypsum-sand plaster ceiling finish, 1:3 mix, ⅝ in. thick	1	30
Concrete 2 in. thick, and fire clay tile 6 in. thick with gypsum plaster ceiling finish, 1:3 mix, ⅝ in. thick	2	—
Concrete 2½ in. thick, limestone aggregate 4 in. thick, expanded slag concrete tile	3	—
Reinforced Concrete Ribbed Slab		

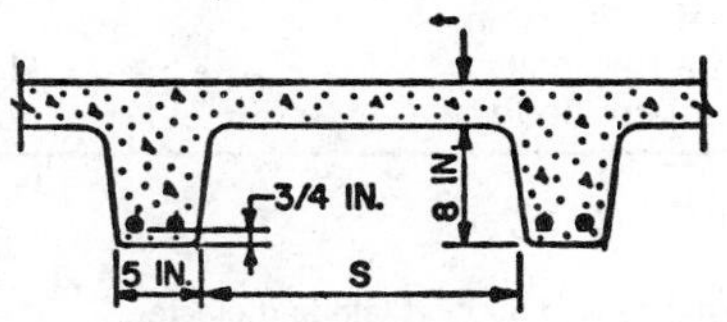

Materials	Hr	Min
Concrete, ribbed slab, limestone aggregate, t = 1½ in. S = 20 in.	—	20
Concrete, ribbed slab, limestone aggregate, t = 2½ in., S = 20 in.	—	45
Same with metal lath and ⅞-in. gypsum-sand plaster ceiling, 1:2, 1:3 mix	2	30
Concrete, ribbed slab, limestone aggregate, t = 3 in. S = 30 in.	1	—

SI units: 1 in. = 25.4 mm; 1 psi = 6.89 kPa.

where

R = fire endurance in minutes

M = mass of the member in kg/m

D = heated perimeter in mm

I = thickness of protection in mm

C_1, C_2 = *empirical constants, the same as used for U.S. customary units.*

For insulating materials, such as mineral fibers, vermiculite, and perlite, having densities (r), in the range of 20 to 50 lb per cu ft (32 to 80 kg/m³), the factors C_1 *and* C_2 *are:*

$C_1 = 1{,}200/r$, *and* $C_2 = 30$.

For insulating materials of the same range of densities, but incorporating cement pastes or gypsum, the factors C_1 *and* C_2 *are:*

$C_1 = 1{,}200/r$, *and* $C_2 = 72$.

Heavy unprotected steel columns are capable of exhibiting some significant fire resistance. Equations (2), (3), (2m), and (3m) can be used to predict the fire resistance of unprotected steel columns.[5]

$$R = 10.3\left(\frac{M}{D}\right)^{0.7} \quad \text{for} \quad \frac{M}{D} < 10 \qquad [2]$$

$$R = 8.3\left(\frac{M}{D}\right)^{0.8} \quad \text{for} \quad \frac{M}{D} > 10 \qquad [3]$$

where

R = fire endurance in minutes

M = mass of the member in lb/ft

D = heated perimeter in inches

In SI units:

$$R = 75.1\left(\frac{M}{D}\right)^{0.7} \quad \text{for} \quad \frac{M}{D} < 171 \qquad [2m]$$

$$R = 60.5\left(\frac{M}{D}\right)^{0.7} \quad \text{for} \quad \frac{M}{D} > 171 \qquad [3m]$$

where

R = fire endurance in minutes

M = mass of the member in kg/m

D = heated perimeter in mm

Thermal and mechanical properties vary for all materials with the temperature of the material. Because the heat transmission through concrete is quite slow, the variability of properties throughout the member is quite nonuniform. As a result, the behavior of reinforced concrete in fire is very complex. Nevertheless, equations have been developed to predict the fire endurance of reinforced concrete columns. Equation (4) illustrates this type of calculation.

$$R = \frac{t}{4f} - 1 \qquad [4]$$

where

R = fire endurance in hours

TABLE 6-51. ***Steel Joist Floor or Roof Constructions***

Joists		Floor Slab	Thickness	Flurring	Ceiling Kind	Thickness	Fire-Resistance Rating	
Type	Depth In.		In.			In.	Hr	Min
I or S*	8	T & G wood flooring on 2- by 2-in. wood strips	25/32	3.4-lb metal lath	Gypsum—sand plaster	3/4	—	45†
I or S*	8	T & G wood flooring on 2- by 2-in. wood strips	1 5/8	3.4-lb metal lath	Gypsum-sand plaster	3/4	1†	—
I or S*	8	Reinforced concrete, precast concrete, or gypsum planks	2	3.4-lb metal lath	Gypsum—sand or portland cement-sand plater	3/4	1	—
S	8	Reinforced concrete or precast gypsum tile	2 1/4	3.4-lb metal lath	Gypsum—sand plaster, 1:2; 1:3 mix	3/4	2	—
S	10	Reinforced concrete or reinforced gypsum tile or planks	2	3.4-lb metal lath	Neat†† gypsum, or gypsum-vermiculite plaster, 1:2; 1:3	1 3/4	2	30
S	10	Reinforced concrete	2 1/2	3.4-lb metal lath	Gypsum—sand plaster	7/8	2	30
		Reinforced concrete	2 1/2	3.4-lb metal lath	Gypsum-perlite of gypsum-vermiculite plaster, 1 1/2:2; 1 1/2:3	3/4	3	—
S	8	Reinforced concrete perlite, or vermiculite aggregate	2 1/2	3.4-lb metal lath	Gypsum-perlite or gypsum-vermiculite plaster, 1 1/2:2; 1 1/2:3	3/4	3	—
S	10	Reinforced concrete, 1:2:4 gravel aggregate	2 1/2	3-lb metal lath	Gypsum-vermiculite or gypsum-perlite plaster, 1 1/2:2; 1 1/2:3	1	4	—
S	10	Reinforced concrete, 1:2:4 gravel aggregate	2	Gypsum lath‡	Gypsum-perlite or gypsum-vermiculite plaster, 1 1/2:2 1/2	5/8	1	—
S	10	Reinforced concrete, 1:2:4 gravel aggregate	2	Gypsum & wires§	Gypsum-perlite or gypsum-vermiculite plaster, 1 1/2:2 1/2	1/2	2	—
S	10	Reinforced concrete, 1:2:4 gravel aggregate	2	Gypsum‖	Gypsum-vermiculite or perlite plaster, 1 1/2:2; 1 1/2:3	1	4	—
S	10	Reinforced concrete, 1:2:3.4 gravel	2 1/2	Gypsum & wires§	Sprayed-on mineral fiber	3/4	3	—
S	10	Reinforced concrete, 1:2.5:3.5 gravel	2	Special Z section#	Special acoustical tiles (see UL list)	5/8	2	—
S	12	Reinforced concrete, gravel aggregate	2	Nailing channels 16 in. o.c.	Type X** wallboard	5/8	1	30
S	12	Reinforced concrete, 1:3:3 2/3 gravel aggregate	2	2 3/4 × 7/8 in. 26-gage channels 14 in. o.c.	Type X** wallboard applied with No. 6 by 1-in. wallboard screws	5/8	1	30
S	10	Reinforced concrete, 1:2:4 gravel aggregate	2	25-gage nailing channels 16 in. o.c.	Gypsum wallboard applied with 1 1/4-in. long barbed nails 3/8-in. diam. head	5/8	1	—

* I-beam or open web type joists.
† Combustible construction.
‡ All gypsum lath 3/8-in. perforated type.
§ Gypsum lath and No. 20-gage wires attached to nailing channels. Wires attached diagonally to reinforce and support lath and plaster.
‖ One-in. hexagonal mesh wire fabric to reinforce plaster and hold up lath and plater.
Special No. 25 gage galvanized steel Z runners 12 in. o.c.
** Type X gypsum wallboard designates gypsum wallboard with a specially formulated core which provides greater fire resistance than regular gypsum wallboard of the same thickness.
†† Unsanded wood-fiber plaster.
SI units: 1 = 25.4 mm; 1 lb = 0.45 kg.

TABLE 6-5J. ***Floors of Concrete on Steel Floor and Form Units***
(Plaster or Sprayed on Fire Protective Covering)

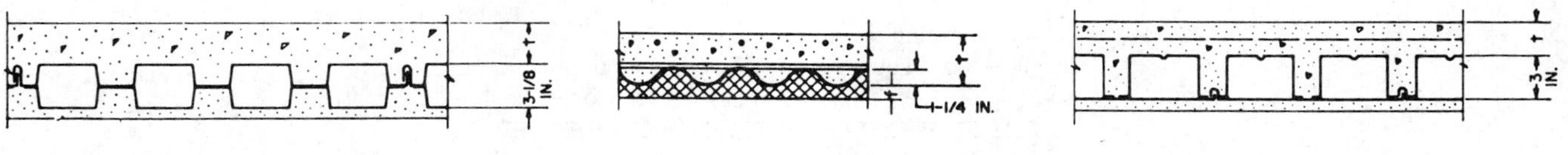

Type A Type B Type C

Type of Floor Unit	Thickness of Floor In.	Furring	Protective Covering Material	Application	Thickness In.	Fire-Resistance Rating Hr	Min
A	5⅝	None	Mineral fibers applied to floor units	Sprayed	½ to 2	5	—
C	5½	None	Same	Sprayed	1½	5	—
A	5⅝	None	Vermiculite or perlite acoustical plastic	Sprayed	1 1/16 to 3 1/16	4	—
B	4½	None	Same	Sprayed	4	—	
B	4½	See Footnote*	Gypsum-vermiculite or perlite plaster	Troweled or Sprayed	⅜ to 1⅝	4	—
C	4	None	Mineral fiber applied to floor units	Sprayed	¾	3	—
A	5⅝	None	Vermiculite acoustical plastic, cellular floor units	Sprayed	½ to 2	2	—
B	5¼	None	None†	—	—	2	—
B	4¼	None	None‡	—	—	1	—
A	8	See Footnote§	Gypsum-vermiculite or perlite plaster, 100 lb gypsum to 2 cu ft for scratch coat and 3 cu ft for browncoat plaster, white finish 1/16 in.	Troweled	⅜	4	—
A	8	See Footnote§	Same	Troweled	1	5	—
A	6⅝	See Footnote‖	Acoustical tiles, T & G edges with saw kerfs	Sheet metal clips	¾	4	4

* Expanded metal lath tack welded or tied to bottom of corrugated steel floor units.
† Floor slab, limestone concrete, 5¼ in. thick.
‡ Floor slab, limestone concrete, 4¼ in. thick.
§ 24-gage, 3.4-lb, ⅜-in. mesh expanded metal lath suspended 2½ to 7½ in. below floor units.
‖ Special furring system to which acoustical tiles are clipped 10¾ in. below floor units.
SI units: 1 in. = 25.4 mm.

t= minimum dimension of the column in inches

f = a factor that considers overdesign, effective length, and percent of steel (Table 6-5Q provides values for f).

In SI units:

$$R = \frac{t}{101.6f} - 1 \qquad [4m]$$

where

R = fire endurance in hours

t= minimum dimensions of the column in mm

f = the same factor from Table 6-5Q.

Equation (5) has been developed for the fire resistance of normal-weight concrete slabs.[7,8]

$$R = 0.031\rho^{1.2}L^{1.85} \qquad [5]$$

where

R = fire resistance in hours

ρ = concrete density in lb/cu ft

L = slab thickness in feet.

In SI units:

$$R = 0.010\rho^{1.2}L^{1.85} \qquad [5m]$$

where

R = fire resistance in minutes

ρ = concrete density in kg/m^3

L = slab thickness in meters (m)

When timber members are tested, they burn. As burning continues, a char layer is formed on the exposed surfaces. This char layer reduces the useable strength of the timber members. The time duration that elapses before the member reaches its critical failure load is the fire endurance.

The fire endurance for wood beams is calculated by determining the breaking strength of the uncharred residual cross section. The time to reach a critical depth may be calculated from the following equations.

$$t_c = (D - d)/\beta \qquad [6]$$

$$t_c = (D - d)/2\beta \qquad [7]$$

TABLE 6-5K. ***Wood Joist Floors with Plaster Ceilings (Combustible)***

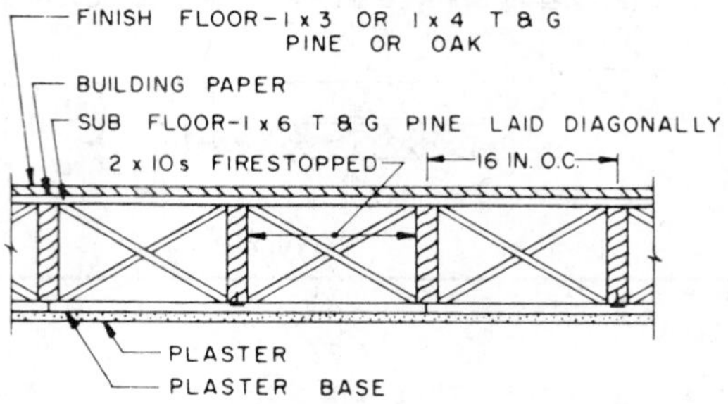

Plaster Base		Nails				Plaster						
	Thick-ness in inches or wt. per sq yd	Size or Length		Head Diam	Spac-ing				Thick-ness	Ceiling Thick-ness	Fire-Resistance Rating	
Type		Inches	Gage	Inches	Inches	Type	Aggregate	Mix	Inches	Inches	Hr	Min
Wood lath	⅜	3d	15	11/64	1⅞	Lime	Sand	1:4½	⅝	1	—	30
Wood lath	⅜	3d	15	11/64	1⅞	Gypsum	Sand	1:2 / 1:3	⅞	—	35	
Gypsum, perforated	⅜	1⅛	13	5/16	3½	Gypsum	Sand	1:2	½	⅞	—	30
Gypsum, perforated	⅜	1⅛	13	⅜	3½	Gypsum	Sand	1:2	½	⅞	—	45
Gypsum, perforated	⅜*	1¾	12	½	3½	Gypsum	Sand	1:2	½	⅞	1	—
Gypsum, plain	⅜†	5d / 8d	13 / 12½	5/16 / 5/16	3½ / 8	Gypsum	Vermiculite or perlite	1½:2½	½	⅞	1	40
Gypsum, perforated	⅜	4d	—	—	3½	Gypsum	Vermiculite or perlite	1½:2½	½	⅞	1	—
Metal lath	3.4 lb	6d / 1¼	11½ / 11	¼ / ⅜	6 / 6	Gypsum	Sand	1:2 / 1:3	¾	¾	—	45
Metal lath	3.4 lb	1½	11	5/16	6	Gypsum	Sand	1:2 / 1:3	¾	¾	1	—
Metal lath	3.0 lb	8d	11½	¼	6‡	Gypsum	Sand	1:2 / 1:3	¾	¾	1	15
Metal lath	3.4 lb	1½	11½	7/16	5	Portland cement§	Sand	1:2 / 1:3	¾	¾	1	—
Metal lath	3.4 lb	1½	11	7/16	5½	Gypsum	Vermiculite or perlite	1½:2 / 1⅓:3	¾	¾	1	30

* Three-in.-wide strips of metal lath with two 1¾-in. 12-gage ½-in. head barbed roofing nails in each joist covering joints of lath to reinforce plaster.
† Plaster reinforced with 1-in. hexagonal mesh wire fabric (1 lb/sq yd) nailed to joists with 8d 2¾-in.-long cement-coated nails spaced 8 in. on centers at each joist.
‡ Additional support for metal lath by ties of 18-gage wire spaced 27 by 32 in. and nailed 2 in. up on sides of joists.
§ Three-lb asbestos fiber and 15-lb hydrated lime per bag of cement added.
SI units: 1 in. = 25.4 mm.

where

t_c = *fire endurance time in minutes*

D = original depth of the beam in inches (mm)

d = critical residual depth of the beam in inches (mm)

β = charring rate for wood in inches (mm). [An average charring rate for wood is 1/40 in. (0.6 mm) per min.]

The critical residual depth, d, can be obtained from Figures 6-5K and 6-5L. The family of curves shows ratios of allowable bending strength (Y) to ultimate bending strength (a) for the beam.

STRUCTURAL MATERIALS AT ELEVATED TEMPERATURES

All structural materials used in building construction are adversely affected by the elevated temperatures caused by fire. The degree and significance of this adverse behavior depends primarily on the function of the elements and on the degree of protection afforded. The mechanical properties of strength and stiffness decrease as the temperature rises. Other adverse behavior, such as excessive expansion and accelerated creep, also develops with increasing temperatures. In general, however, the design parameters that are of concern at normal temperatures are the same parameters that are of concern at elevated temperatures.

Structural Steel

Steel is the backbone of modern building design. Whether it acts as the reinforcement for concrete or the skeleton framework for buildings, it constitutes the major load-carrying material in modern building construction. From the designer's viewpoint, steel possesses many qualities, such as high strength and good ductility, which will make it an ideal structural material. However, steel, like all other materials, is adversely affected by fire.

TABLE 6-5L. ***Wood Joist Floors with Wallboard Ceilings (Combustible)***

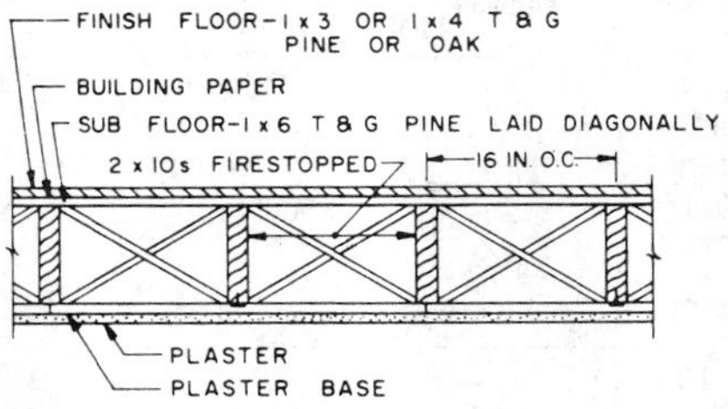

Wallboard Type	Wallboard Thickness Inches	Wallboard Core Materials	Nails Type	Nails Size	Nails Gage	Nails Length Inches	Nails Spacing Inches	Fire-Resistance Rating Hr	Fire-Resistance Rating Min
Gypsum	⅝	Type "X"* special fire-retardant gypsum	Cement-coated wire	6d	13	1⅞	6	1	—
Gypsum	½	Type "X"* special fire-retardant gypsum	Cement-coated wire	5d	13½	1⅝	6	—	45
Gypsum	⅜	Type "X"* special fire-retardant gypsum	Cement-coated wire	4d	14	1⅜	6	—	30
Two thicknesses of gypsum	½ + ½	Gypsum	Box wire	5d(1) 6d(2)	14 10¼	1¾ 2½	18 6	1†	—
Two thicknesses of gypsum	⅜ + ½	Gypsum	Plasterboard cement-coated	1½ in. 6d	13 13	1½ 1⅞	7 6	—	40
Two thicknesses of gypsum	½ + ⅜	Gypsum	Plasterboard cement-coated	1½ in. 6d	13 13	1½ 1⅞	7 6	—	35
Two thicknesses of gypsum‡	⅜ + ⅜	Gypsum	Box	4½d(1) 4½d(2)	— —	1½ 1½	6 6	—	35
Gypsum	½	Gypsum	Box	4½d	15	1½	6	—	25
Gypsum§	⅜	Gypsum	Box	4½d	15	1½	6	—	25
None‖	—	—	—	—	—	—	—	—	14
Acoustical Tile	⅝	12- by 12-in. mineral fiber tiles mounted on special channels						1	—

* Type X gypsum wallboard designates gypsum wallboard with a specially formulated core which provides greater fire resistance than regular gypsum wallboard of the same thickness.
† 1-in. hexagonal mesh 20-gage wire fabric between wallboards nailed with 8d nails 8 in. o.c.
‡ NBS test on floor 4½ by 9 ft; joints of wallboard staggered, but no tape and joint finisher.
§ NBS test; bottom of ceiling covered with 14-lb asbestos paper applied with paperhanger's paste and casein paint.
‖ NBS test on 2 specimens of open-joist floors, each 4½ by 9 ft; fire endurance 15 min and 12 min.
Note: for other similar constructions, see UL *Building Materials List.*
SI units = 1 in. = 25.4 mm.

Steel is noncombustible and does not contribute fuel to afire. In the past, these properties have sometimes provided a false sense of security with regard to its durability in a fire because they overshadow the fact that steel loses strength when subjected to temperatures easily attained in a fire. The relative seriousness of the problem depends on several factors, such as the function of the steel element, its level of stress, the support conditions, its surface area and thickness, and the temperature within the steel itself. This temperature can be quite different from the ambient temperature in the compartment.

From a structural viewpoint, the yield stress of steel is the significant parameter in establishing load-carrying capacity. The tensile stress strain diagram for A-36 steel at various temperatures in shown in Figure 6-5M. It can be seen that both the yield strength and the modulus of elasticity decreases with increasing temperatures. Figure 6-5N shows the ratios of modulus of elasticity and yield stress for A-36 steel at various temperatures. As can be seen, both values decrease with an increase in temperature.

This reduction in strength, combined with the reduction in the modulus of elasticity, causes compression members to be more sensitive to higher temperatures than tensile or flexural members. Figure 6-5O shows the influence of temperature on the critical stress of compression members of A-36 steel.

It should be recognized that the temperature considered for stress limitations is the temperature within the steel, and not the ambient temperature. Because steel has a high thermal conductivity it can transfer heat away from a localized heat source rather quickly. This property, in conjunction with its thermal capacity, enables steel to act as a heat sink. When the steel has an opportunity to transfer heat to cooler regions, it can take a relatively long time for a member to reach its critical value. On the other hand, an extensive fire that distributes heat simultaneously over a greater area reduces this time considerably.

TABLE 6-5M. ***Load-Bearing Brick and Clay Tile Walls***

Material	Wall Thickness (Inches)	Solid Content of Walls (Percent)	Hollow Units: Number of Cells in Wall Thickness	Hollow Units: Thickness of Shells of Unit (Inches)	Combustible Members Framed 4 in. into Wall: No Plaster	Combustible Members Framed 4 in. into Wall: Plaster on Two Sides	No Combustible Members Framed into Wall: No Plaster	No Combustible Members Framed into Wall: Plaster on Two Sides
Brick,	12	90 to 100	—	—	8	9	10	12
clay or shale	10*	72	2-in. cavity	—	2	2½	5	7
	8	90 to 100	—	—	2	2½	5	7
	4†	90 to 100	—	—	—	—	1	1½
Load-Bearing	12	45	3	0.7	2½	3½	3	6
Hollow Tile (not	12‡	48	4	⅝	2½	4	5	7½
partition tile)	10*	36	2 + 2-in. cavity	—	—	1¼	—	4
	8	48	3 or 4	—	1	1¾	2½	3½
	8	40	2	—	¾	1½	2	3
	6†	40	2	⅝	—	—	¾	1½

* Cavity wall with metal ties across cavity.
† Nonload-bearing wall restrained on all edges.
‡ Two units, 8 by 12 by 12-in. 6-cell and 3¾ by 12 by 12-in. 3-cell tiles, in wall thickness.
SI units = 1 in. = 25.4 mm.

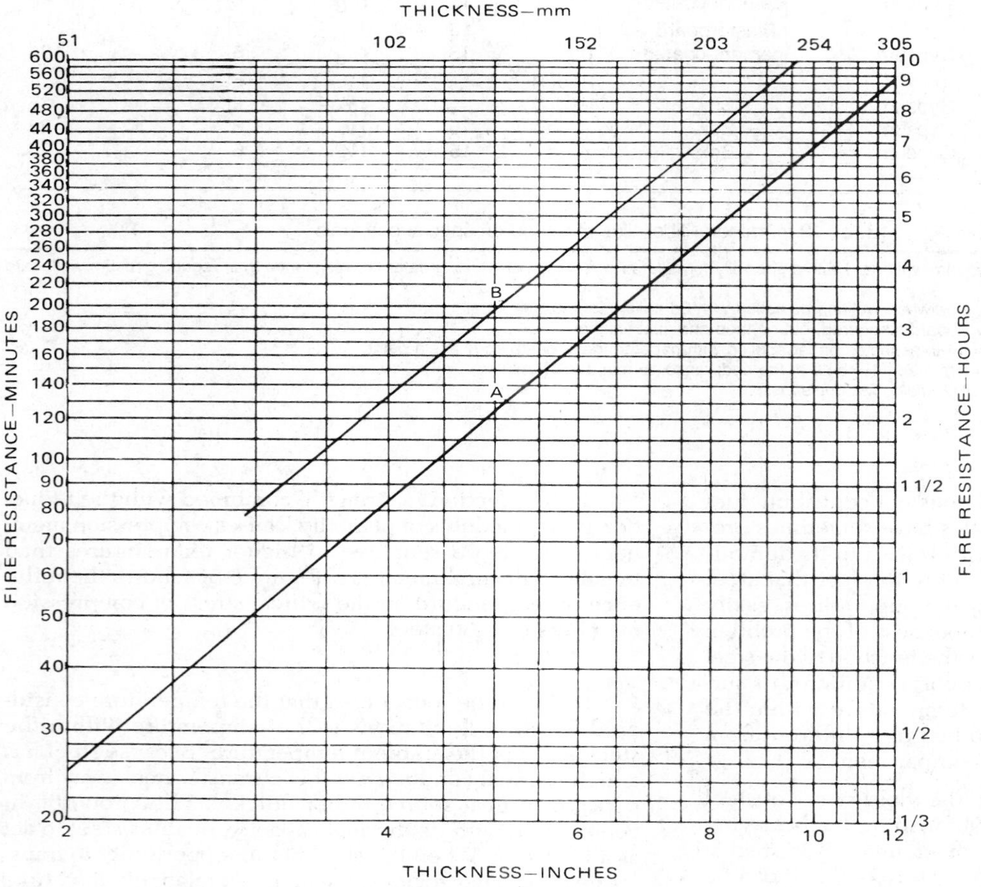

FIG. 6-5H. Fire resistance of burned clay brick walls: A, unplastered; B, plastered both sides.

TABLE 6-5N. *Wood Stud Walls and Partitions (Combustible)*

(Bearing and nonbearing: 2- by 4-in. studs spaced 16 in. on centers, fire stopped)

Material	Fire-Resistance Rating: Partition Hollow Hr	Partition Hollow Min	Partition Filled with Mineral Wool† Hr	Partition Filled with Mineral Wool† Min
Plasterless Types of Construction				
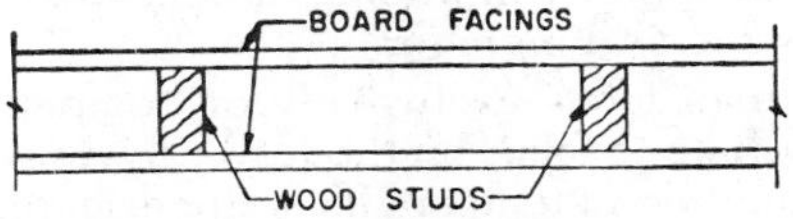				
The following are applied to both sides of studs:				
Sheathing boards (tongue-and-groove) 3/4 in. thick	—	20	—	35
Gypsum wallboard, 3/8 in. thick	—	25	—	—
Gypsum wallboard, 1/2 in. thick (nonload-bearing only for mineral wool filled)	—	40	1	—
Gypsum wallboard, 3/8 in. thick, in two layers each face	1	—	—	—
Gypsum wallboard, 1/2 in. thick, in two layers each face	1	30	—	—
Gypsum wallboard, 1/2 in. thick, Type X*, one layer each face	—	45	—	—
Gypsum wallboard, 5/8 in. thick, Type X*, one layer each face	1	—	—	—
Gypsum wallboard, 5/8 in. thick, Type X*, on fire retardant wood fibreboard, 1/2 in. thick	1	—	—	—
Fir plywood, 1/4 in. thick	—	10	—	—
Fir plywood, 3/8 in. thick	—	15	—	—
Plasterless Types of Construction				
Fir plywood, 1/2 in. thick	—	20	—	—
Fir plywood, 5/8 in. thick	—	25	—	—
Cement-asbestos board, 3/16 in. thick	—	10	—	40
Cement-asbestos board, 3/16 in. thick, on gypsum wallboard, 3/8 in. thick	1	—	—	—
Cement-asbestos board, 3/16 in. thick, on gypsum wallboard, 1/2 in. thick	1	25	—	—
Plaster and Lath Construction				
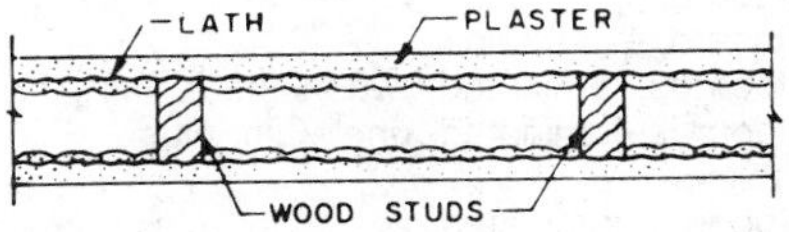				
The following are applied to both sides of studs:‡				
Gypsum-sand plaster, 1:2, 1:3, 1/2 in. thick on wood lath	—	30	1	—
Lime-sand plaster, 1:5, 1:7.5, 1/2 in. thick on wood lath	—	30	—	45
Gypsum-sand plaster, 1:2, 1:2, 1/2 in. thick on 3/8 in. perforated gypsum lath	1	—	—	—
Gypsum-sand plaster, 1:2, 1:2, 3/4 in. thick on metal lath	1	—	1	30
Gypsum lath, 1/2 in. thick, Type X*, and 1/8 in. gypsum-sand plaster, each face	1	—	—	—
Gypsum wallboard, 1/2 in. thick, Type X*, and 1/16 in. gypsum plaster, each face	1	—	—	—
Portland cement-lime-sand plaster, 1:1/30:2, 1:1/30:3 and asbestos-fiber plaster, 7/8 in. thick on metal lath	1	—	—	—
Gypsum-vermiculite, or perlite plaster, 100 lb gypsum to 2 1/2 cu ft aggregate, 1/2 in. thick on 3/8 in. perforated gypsum lath	1	—	—	—
Gypsum perlite plaster, 1:2, 3/4 in. thick on metal lath	1	—	—	—
Exterior Bearing Wall				
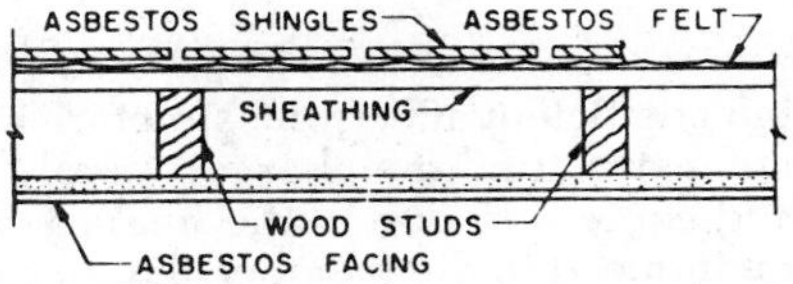				
Outside: Cement-asbestos shingles, 5/32 in. thick, on layer of asbestos felt on wood sheathing, 3/4 in. thick, on wood studs. Inside: Cement-asbestos facing, 1/8 in. thick on fiberboard, 7/16 in. thick	—	30	—	—
Outside: Gypsum sheathing, 1/2 in. thick. Inside 1:2 gypsum-sand plaster, 1/2 in. thick on 3/8 in. perforated gypsum lath	1	30	—	—

* See footnote ‡ to Table 5-8S.
† Mineral wool fill requires some degree of anchorage so as to be held in place after partition facing has been burned away.
‡ See Table 5-8Q for one side ratings.
SI units: 1 in. = 25.4 mm; 1 lb = 0.45 kg; 1 cu ft = 0.09 m^3.

Related to this thermal activity is the effect of mass and surface area of structural steel members. Heavy, thick sections have a far greater resistance to the effects of building fires than do lighter ones. Unprotected lightweight sections, such as those found in trusses and open-web joists, can collapse after 5 or 10 min of exposure.

Another property of steel that has an effect upon its performance at elevated temperatures is its coefficient of expansion. The linear coefficient of expansion of steel at temperatures up to 1100°F (600°C) is given as:

$$\alpha = 0.0000061 + 0.0000000022\ \Delta t$$

where

α = the coefficient of expansion

Δt = temperature change in degrees Fahrenheit

In SI units:

$$\alpha = 6.1 \times 10^{-6} + 3.96 \times 10^{-9}\ \Delta t$$

where

α = coefficient of expansion

Δt = temperature change in degrees Celsius

TABLE 6-5O. *Various Finishes Over Wood Framing, One Side (Combustible) with Exposure on Finish Side*
(See Table 6-5L for 2-side ratings)

Material	Fire-Resistance Rating* Min
Fiberboard, ½ in. thick	5
Fiberboard, flameproofed, ½ in. thick	10
Fiberboard, ½ in. thick, with ½ in. 1:2, 1:2 gypsum-sand plaster	15
Gypsum wallboard, ⅜ in. thick	10
Gypsum wallboard, ½ in. thick	15
Gypsum wallboard, ⅝ in. thick	20
Gypsum wallboards, laminated, two ⅜ in.	28
Gypsum wallboards, laminated, one ⅜ in. plus one ½ in. thick	37
Gypsum wallboards, laminated, two ½ in. thick	47
Gypsum wallboards, laminated, two ⅝ in. thick	60
Gypsum lath, plain or indented, ⅜ in. thick, with ½ in. 1:2, 1:2 gypsum-sand plaster	20
Gypsum lath, perforated, ⅜ in. thick, with ½ in. 1:2, 1:2 gypsum-sand plaster	30
Gypsum-sand plaster, 1:2, 1:3, ½ in. thick, on wood lath	15
Lime-sand plaster, 1:5, 1:7.5, ½ in. thick, on wood lath	15
Gypsum-sand plaster, 1:2, 1:2, ¾ in. thick, on metal lath (no paper backing)	15
Neat gypsum plaster, ¾ in. thick on metal lath (no paper backing)†	30
Neat gypsum plaster, 1 in. thick, on metal lath (no paper backing)†	35
Lime-sand plaster, 1:5, 1:7.5, ¾ in. thick, on metal lath (no paper backing)	10
Portland cement plaster, ¾ in. thick, on metal lath (no paper backing)	10
Gypsum-sand plaster, 1:2, 1:3, ¾ in. thick, on paper-backed metal lath	20

* From National Bureau of Standards BMS-92.
† Unsanded wood-fiber plaster.
SI units: 1 in. = 25.4 mm.

This high coefficient affects the structure in two ways. If the ends of a structural member are axially restrained, the attempted expansion due to the heat causes thermal stresses to be induced in the member. These stresses combine with those of the normal loading, causing more rapid collapse. If the structural member is nor axially restrained, the increased stresses described do not occur; instead, movement takes place. This movement causes the ends of steel columns to be moved laterally, producing an eccentrically loaded column. In other cases, walls can be moved to the point of collapse by expansion of beams. This creates an extremely hazardous condition both for the building itself and for the fire fighters.

To illustrate the magnitude of movement, consider a 50-ft. (15.24 m) long steel beam that is heated uniformly over its length from 72°F to 972°F (22.2° to 522°C). The average value for alpha is 0.0000073, and the increase in length, delta, becomes approximately,

$$\delta = \alpha \angle \Delta t = (7.3 \times 10^{-6})(50 \times 12)(900);$$

Thus $\delta = 3.9$ in.

In NFPA 251, *Fire Tests of Building Construction and Materials*, alternate tests may be used to evaluate protection of steel beams and columns. These alternate tests evaluate the thermal protection of the insulating materials by measuring the temperature in the steel for the standard time-temperature exposure. In these alternate tests, failure occurs when the average temperature reaches 1000°F (538°F). Often, this temperature, or a temperature of 1100°F (593°C) is perceived as the critical temperature for structural steel. While numbers such as these are useful in a conceptual sense, they should not be taken literally.

If critical temperature for structural steel is intended to describe the steel temperature at which collapse is impending, these temperatures in the range of 1000°F (538°C) or 1100°F (593°C) may be viewed as a reasonable approximation. The actual temperatures at which collapse is impending can differ from these values, depending upon the load and support conditions, dimensions, and geometry of the structural member.

Rather than focus exclusively on temperature, it is more appropriate to focus on the load-carrying capacity of a member at different temperatures. For example, one may question, what is the load-carrying capacity of the structural member when the temperature reached F? The related question may then be asked, what is the likelihood that the steel temperature will reach this value in a room fire? Modern calculation methods enable both of these questions to be addressed with a reasonable degree of confidence, although not yet as a simple, routine evaluation.

Fire Protection of Structural Steel

Because unprotected structural steel loses its strength at high temperatures, it must be protected from exposure to the heat produced by building fires. This protection, often referred to as "fireproofing," insulates the steel from the heat. The more common methods of insulating steel are encasement of the member, application of a surface treatment, or installation of a suspended ceiling as part of a floor-ceiling assembly capable of providing fire resistance. Additional methods, such as sheet steel membrane shields around members and box columns filled with liquid, have been introduced.

Over the years, encasement of the structural steel member has been a very common and a very satisfactory method if insulating steel to increase its fire resistance. In floor systems of reinforced concrete slabs supported by structural steel beams, the encasement can be placed monolithically with the floor. Figure 6-5P illustrates an old technique of encasement. The major disadvantage of this procedure is the cost, which is related both to the added formwork and concrete and to the increased weight of the supporting members due to the added dead load. To reduce the cost of encasement, systems utilizing lath and plaster or gypsum boards, or spray-on mineral fibers have been developed, as shown in Figures 6-5Q and 6-5R.

Because of labor costs and the weight increases of the encasement method, surface treatments applied directly to the member are quite popular. Sprayed-on mineral fiber coatings are widely used for protecting structural steel. While the protection is excellent if applied correctly, it can easily be scraped off the member during construction or renovations. Consequently, sprayed-on mineral fiber coatings are suspect in their effectiveness over long-term use.

Cementitious materials also have been used as sprayed-on coverings. During a fire, however, they can spall. Adhesion problems have also been experienced with this type of sprayed-on coating. Thus, effective application, complete coverage, and long-term maintenance are attributes that must be evaluated in considering sprayed-on applications.

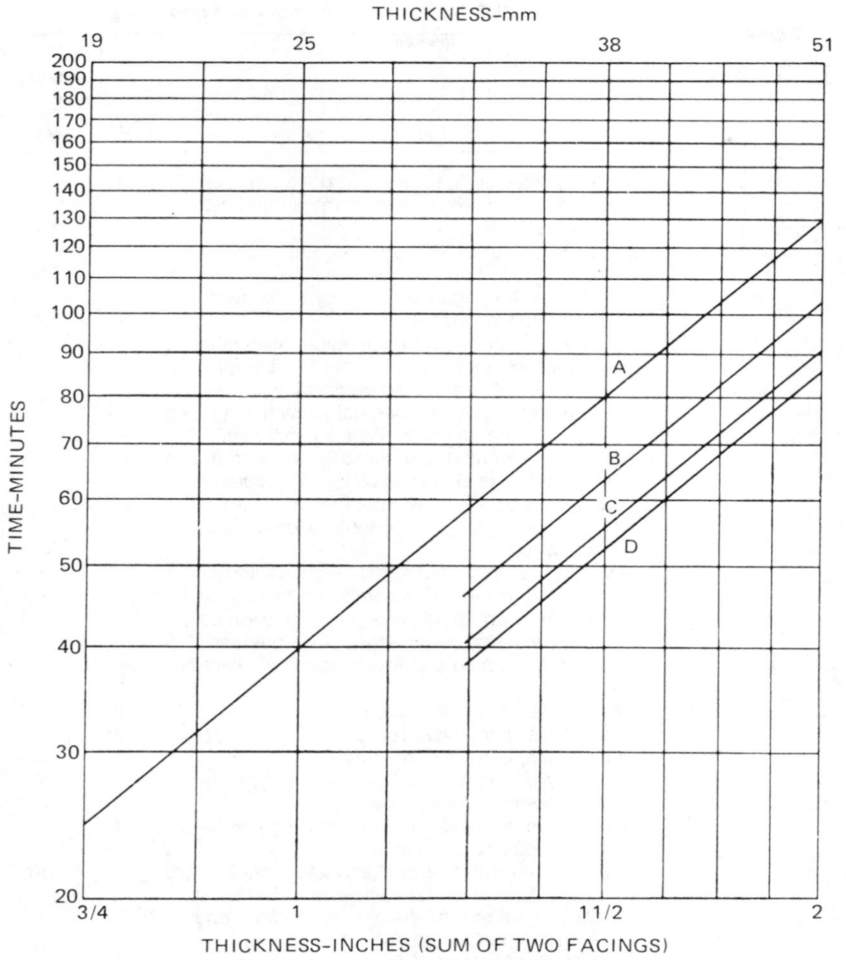

FIG. 6-51. Fire resistance of wood or metal stud partitions faced with gypsum wallboards or gypsum plaster on metal lath: A, Type X gypsum wallboards or wood fiber gypsum plaster; B, 1:1 gypsum-sand plaster; C, 1:2 gypsum-sand plaster; and D, 1:2 and 1:3 gypsum-sand plaster.

Intumescent paints and coatings have been utilized to increase the fire endurance of structural steel. These coatings intumese, or swell, when heated, thus forming an insulation around the steel. They are primarily used for nonexposed steel subject to elevated temperatures, as prolonged exposure to flame can destroy the char coating.

Suspended ceilings consisting of lath and plaster, gypsum panels, or acoustical tile supported on a grid system as part of a floor-ceiling assembly are a popular method of fireproofing. The grid system can be suspended from wire hangers or it can be attached directly to the bottom chord of joists or to the bottom flange of beams. Sometimes ceiling tiles are either mechanically fastened or fitted into splines to prevent the pressures that occur in building fires from lifting them out of place.

The overall effectiveness of this type of barrier protection, often called membrane protection, is questionable. This is due to experiences where a lack of control during construction resulted in improper installation procedures, such as inattention to expansion control in the suspension system. In addition, maintenance of ductwork and fixtures in the plenum area is frequently done by personnel who are not aware of the importance of the integrity of the ceiling to the fire-protection system. Removed tiles are not replaced in a manner that will ensure their integrity during a building fire. Consequently the unprotected steel in the plenum area is exposed to fire and hot gases, which reduce its strength.

Water-filled columns have received attention for their fire-resistive capabilities. During a fire, heat is transferred away from the location of exposure by convection currents set up in the liquid. Consequently, the heat is transferred before it has an opportunity to raise the temperature of the unprotected steel to its critical value. Although the principle of operation is valid and a few tests have been performed, this type of construction has never been exposed to an actual building fire.

Structural steel members can also be protected by sheet steel membrane shields. The sheet steel holds inexpensive insulation materials in place, thus providing a greater fire resistance. In addition, polished sheet steel has been used in tests to protect spandrel girders. The shield reflects radiated heat and protects the load-carrying spandrel.

Reinforced Concrete

Concrete is often used as a protective covering for other materials. Consequently, reinforced-concrete buildings give a sense of fire security. However, concrete as a material also is adversely affected by the heat of a fire. Although collapse of reinforced concrete structures is comparatively rare, loss in strength, spalling, and other deleterious effects do occur.

When the temperature of a reinforced-concrete member is raised, the member loses strength. The amount of

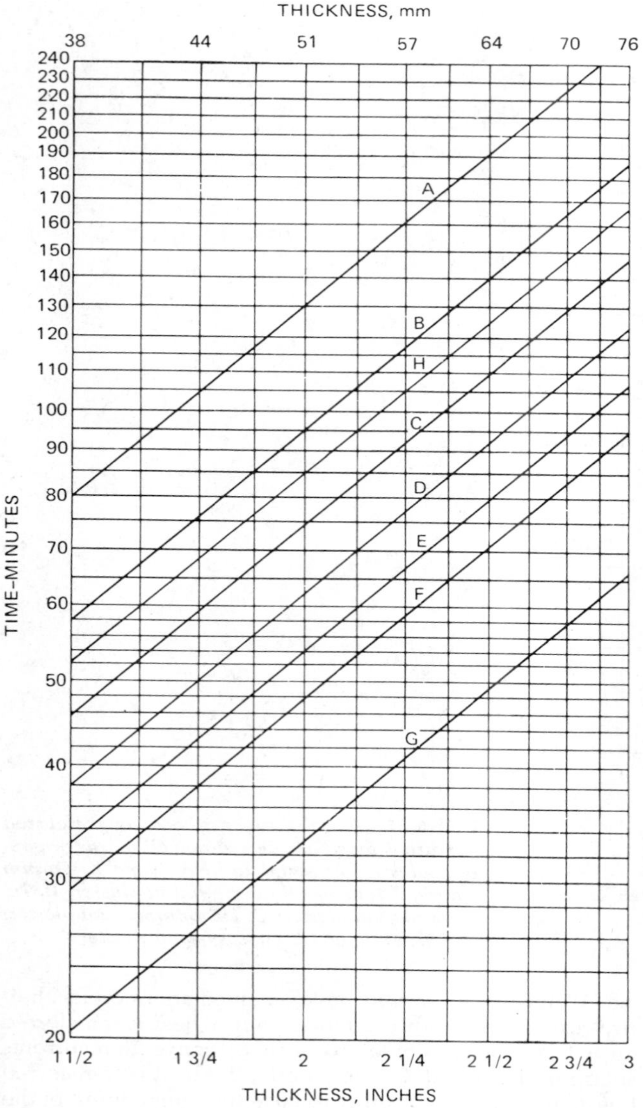

FIG. 6-5J. Fire resistance of solid partitions of metal lath and plaster: A, wood fiber gypsum; B, 1:1/2 gypsum-sand; C, 1:1 gypsum-sand; D, 1:1 1/2 gypsum-sand; E, 1:2 gypsum-sand; F, 1:2 and 1:3 gypsum-sand; G, 1:2 and 1:3 portland cement + 0.2 lime to cement.

TABLE 6-5P. *Solid Partitions: Nonbearing*

Materials	Fire-Resistance Rating Hr	Fire-Resistance Rating Min
Sheathing planks (tongue-and-groove), in 2 layers, each 3/4 in. thick (1 in. nominal) and with joints staggered	—	15*
Same, with layer of 30-lb asbestos felt between planks	—	25*
Planking, pine (tongue-and-groove), 2 in. thick (nominal), wet vertically	—	12*
Wallboard, 3/8-in. gypsum, full height facings on two thicknesses 1/2-in. coreboard, full height, cemented with staggered vertical joints to form 1 3/4-in. thick partition, external joints finish taped	1	—
Wallboard, 5/8-in. gypsum, Type X‡, full height facings, cemented and nailed or screwed to ribs made of two thicknesses of 1/2 -in. gypsum board 3 1/2 or 6 1/2 in. wide and 1- by 1 5/8-in. wood runners top and bottom, external joints finish taped	1	—
Wallboard, 1/2-in. gypsum, full height, nailed and cemented to 1-in.-thick coreboard factory laminated from two 1/2-in. thick by 24-in.-wide coreboards with staggered edges, external joints staggered, butted and finish taped with joint finisher	2	—
Gypsum tile, 3 in. thick, cored	2	—
Gypsum tile, 4 in. thick, cored	2	—
Gypsum tile, 3 in solid, no cores	3	—
Gypsum tile, 3 in. cored, 1/2-in. of 1:3 gypsum-sand plaster on each side	3	—
Gypsum tile, 4 in. cored, 1/2-in. of 1:3 gypsum-sand plaster on each side	4	—
Gypsum-vermiculite or perlite plaster, 1 1/2:2, 1 1/2:3 by vol., 3/4-in. thick on each side of 1/2-in. gypsum lath, vertical full height, tied to floor and ceiling runners, no studs	1	30
Gypsum-sand plaster, 1:2, 1:3 by wt, 3/4 in. thick on each side of 1/2-in. gypsum lath vertical full height, tied to floor and ceiling runners, no studs	1	—
Partition tile, burned clay, 4 in. thick, 1 cell in thickness	—	10†
Cinder block, 4 in. thick, solid	1†	—
Cinder block, 6 in. thick, 1 cell in thickness	1	15†
Calcareous gravel concrete tile, 4 in. thick, 65 percent solid	—	45‡
Calcareous gravel concrete tile, 8 in. thick, 55 percent solid	2	30

* Combustible.

† When plastered on both sides with 1/2-in. 1:3 gypsum-sand plaster, the tile partition described has 45-min fire resistance and the cinder block and 4-in. concrete tile assemblies described have 2-hr fire resistance.

‡ Type X gypsum wallboard designates gypsum wallboard with a specially formulated core which provides greater fire resistance than regular gypsum wallboard of the same thickness.

SI units: 1 in. = 25.4 mm; 1 lb. = 0.45 kg.

strength reduction is influenced by a number of factors. Among the more significant from a structural viewpoint are the type of aggregate, moisture content, type of loading, and level of stress during the fire exposure.

One of the more significant factors in determining the change in strength and the thermal characteristics of concrete is the type of aggregate. Aggregate types can vary widely in various sections of the country. Consequently, numerical values of strength properties are related to a percentage of the original strength, rather than a specific stress value. The qualitative behavior of concrete is generally accurate, however.

Lightweight concrete performs better at elevated temperatures than does normal-weight concrete. Not only does it retain more of its strength during heat buildup, it also has a lower coefficient of thermal conductivity. Concrete using aggregates or vermiculite or perlite is particularly good at protecting structural steel from a heated environment.

Figures 6-5S and 6-5T illustrate the effect of aggregates on the fire resistance of reinforced-concrete slabs. The lightweight aggregates, such as expanded shale and expanded slag, have considerably more fire endurance than do normal-weight concretes made from carbonate and siliceous aggregates.

TABLE 6-5Q. ***Values for f***

Overdesign factor	Effective length, kL (kL_{max} = 12 ft)	Effective length, kL 12 ft < kL < 24 ft	
		$p \leq 0.03$ $t \leq 12$ in.	All other cases
1.00	1.0	1.2	1.0
1.25	0.9	1.1	0.9
1.50	0.8	1.0	0.8

SI units: 1 ft. = 0.30 m; 1 in. = 25.4 mm.

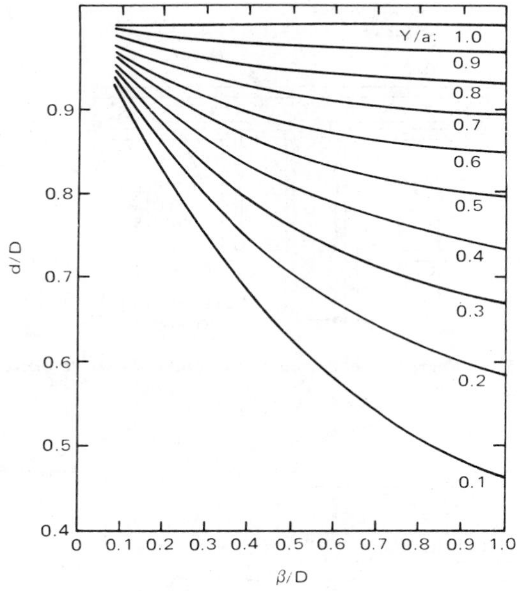

FIG. 6-5K. Critical depth of solid timber beams of rectangular cross section exposed on three sides to fire.[9]

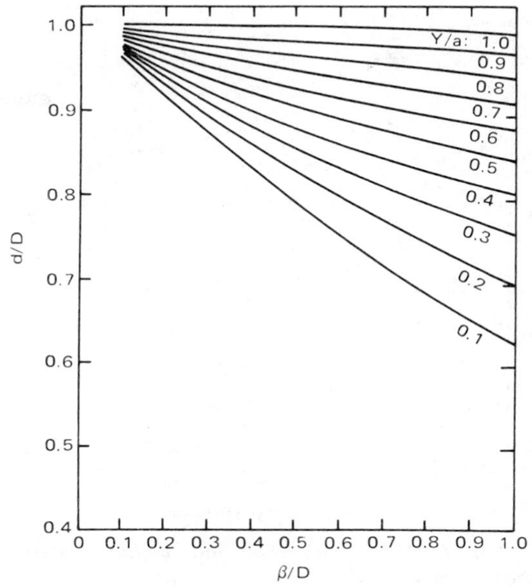

FIG. 6-5L. Critical depth of solid timber beams of rectangular cross section exposed on four sides to fire.[9]

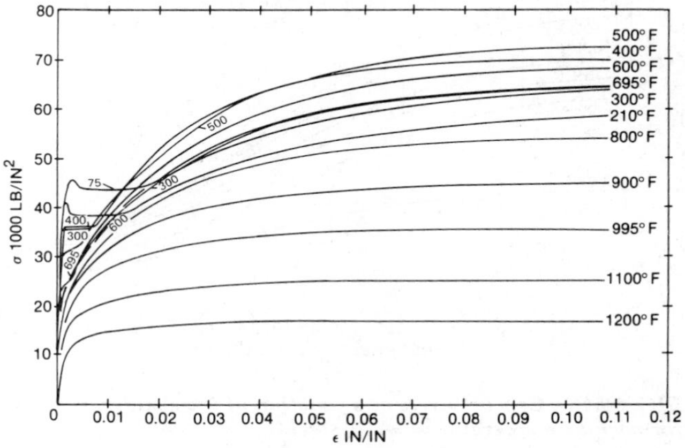

FIG. 6-5M. Stress-strain curves for an ASTM A-36 steel.[10]

The moisture content of concrete has a significant influence of its thermal performance. A considerable quantity of the heat energy of a fire is expended in vaporizing the absorbed and capillary moisture in concrete. In the case of horizontal members, the water vapor is driven upward and maintains a temperature at the top of the member of 212°F (100°C) until the water has been driven off. This increases the fire endurance, as it keeps the temperature on the unexposed side below that defined as the failure temperature. The voids caused by the evaporation of water contribute to shrinkage and a decrease in concrete strength.

The mechanical properties of concrete are significantly reduced at elevated temperatures. Figure 6-5U shows the effect on the compressive strength and modulus of elasticity by increasing the temperature. There is some question about whether concrete completely regains its strength after exposure to high temperatures.

Prestressed Concrete

The factors that are significant in the behavior of prestressed concrete are similar to those that affect reinforced concrete. In addition to the influences of moisture content and aggregate, the higher strength concrete and the function and type of steel used for prestressing are important considerations.

The concrete used for prestressed concrete is of a higher strength than that used in ordinary reinforced-concrete construction. The overall fire resistance of this concrete is somewhat better than the lower strength concrete. The heat transmission is about the same for the two systems. However, there is a somewhat greater tendency for prestressed concrete to spall, thus exposing the prestressing steel.

The greatest problem of prestressed concrete subjected to elevated temperatures involves the prestressing steel. The fact the the steel is put under high initial stress, coupled with the fact that the reinforcing wires are high-carbon, cold-drawn, rather than low-carbon, hot-rolled steel, is the root of the problem. Normal prestressing losses due to deformation and creep are considered in prestressed concrete design. At elevated temperatures these losses are accelerated. Creep in the steel increases, and the modulus of elasticity of the prestressing wires is reduced by 20 percent when the temperature reaches 600°F (316°C). These losses reduce the carrying capacity of the member.

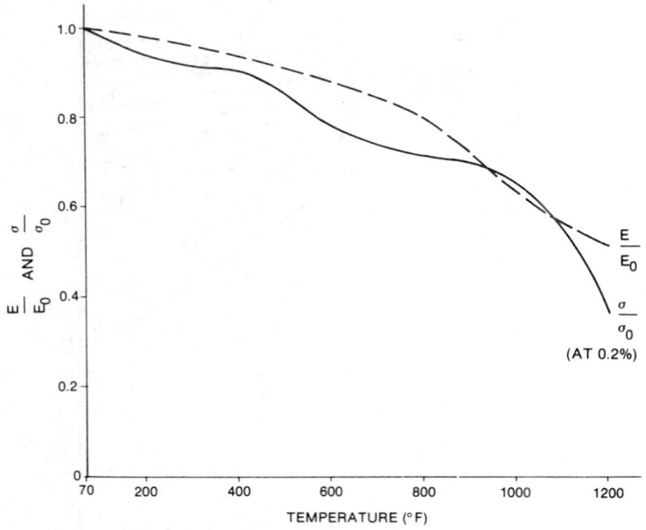

FIG. 6-5N. Ratio of modulus and yield strength with temperature—A-36 steel.[11]

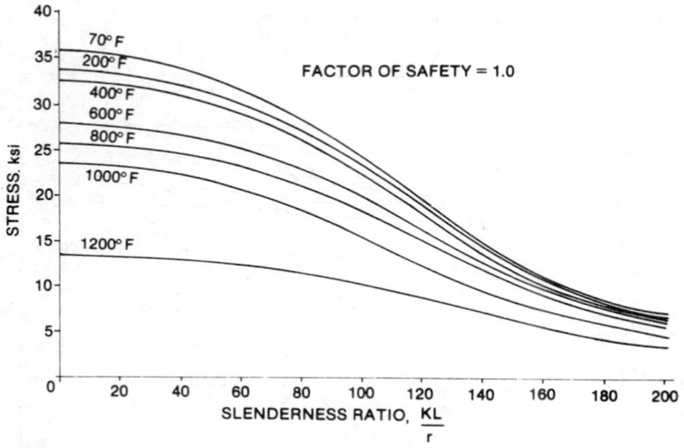

FIG. 6-5O. Critical stress as a function of the slenderness ratio for various temperatures—A-36 steel.[11]

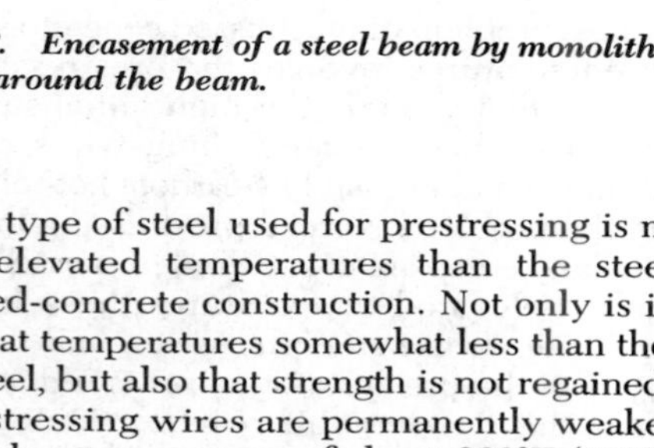

FIG. 6-5P. Encasement of a steel beam by monolithic casting of concrete around the beam.

The type of steel used for prestressing is more sensitive to elevated temperatures than the steel used in reinforced-concrete construction. Not only is its strength reduced at temperatures somewhat less than those for hot-rolled steel, but also that strength is not regained after cooling. Prestressing wires are permanently weakened when they reach a temperature of about 800°F (427°C).

FIG. 6-5Q. Spray-on fireproofing.[12]

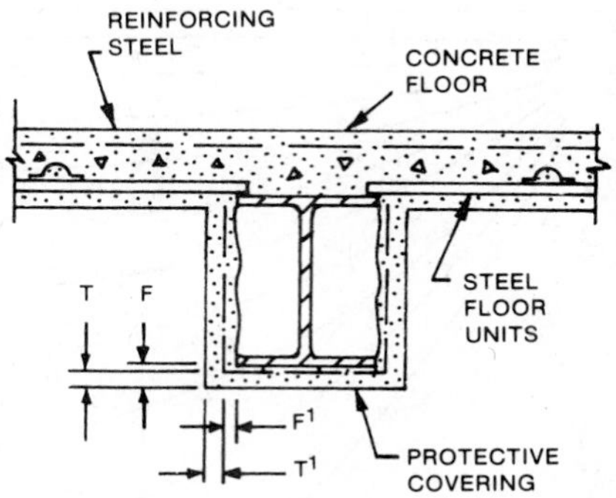

FIG. 6-5R. Furred steel beams with noncombustible protective coverings.

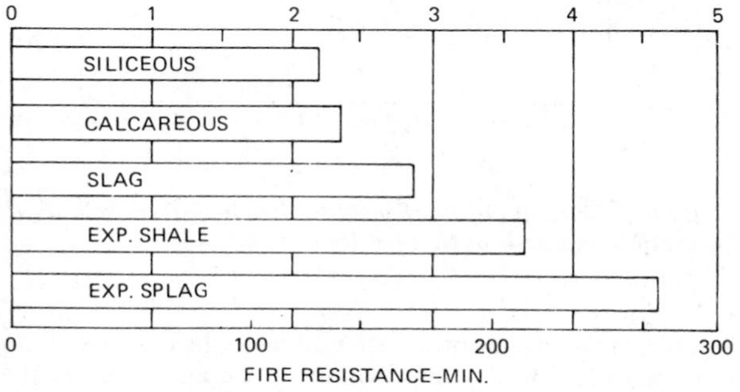

FIG. 6-5S. Effect of various types of aggregate on the fire endurance of 4¾-in. (121 mm) slabs.[3]

Wood

Depending on its form, wood may or may not provide reasonable structural integrity in a fire. The important factors that influence fire endurance are the physical size and the moisture content of the members. Fire-retardant treatments may be used to delay ignition and retard combustion, this providing time for extinguishing procedures. However, all wood will burn.

The burning of wood produces a charcoal on the surface at an average rate or about 1/40 in. per min (0.6 mm/min). This charcoal provides a protective coating that insulates the unburned wood and isolates it from the flame, thus retarding pyrolysis. Therefore, thicker members provide much more structural integrity over the period of fire exposure than do thin ones.

Heavy timber construction has proved to be an excellent form of construction. It maintains its integrity during a fire for a relatively long time, providing an opportunity

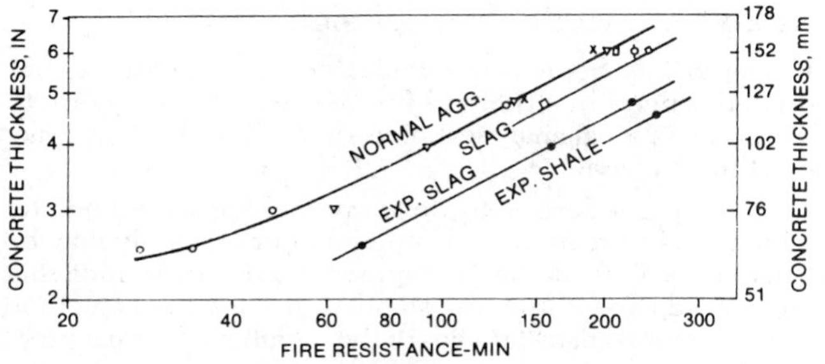

FIG. 6-5T. Relationship of slab thickness and type of aggregate to fire endurance.[3]

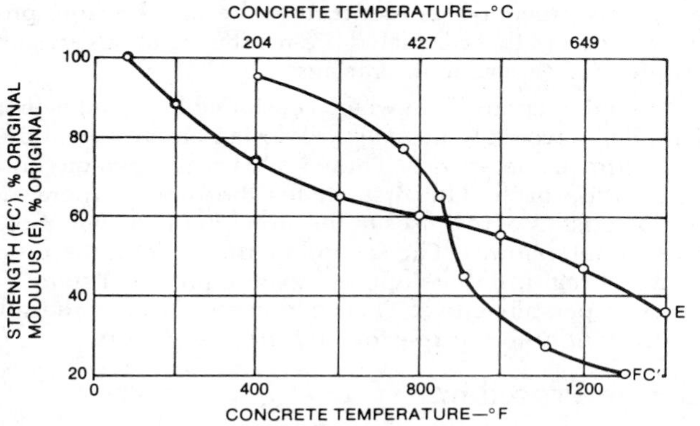

FIG. 6-5U. Effect of temperature on modulus of elasticity and compressive strength. The curves are taken from two differing specimens.[3]

for extinguishment. When the fire is extinguished relatively soon, much of the original strength of the members is retained and reconstruction is possible.

Glued laminated frames, arches, and beams have become increasingly popular. These members also provide reserve strength during a fire, and, if the layer is not deep, the char may be removed by sandblasting to restore the aesthetic appearance.

Wood-frame construction utilizes structural members considerably smaller than mill construction. The exposed area is greater, and the fire resistance considerable reduced. When this type of construction is exposed to a fire, it offers relatively little structural integrity. Therefore, protective surfaces, such as gypsum wall-board or plaster, are important to provide fire endurance.

FIRE BEHAVIOR OF OTHER BUILDING MATERIALS

Many materials other than steel, concrete, and wood are commonly used in modern building construction. They frequently made up a large volume and/or surface area of the structure. Nonbearing partitions, insulation, building services, and finish materials are all important parts of building construction. Some of the nonstructural, thermally inert materials are used as fireproofing. Others may contribute significant fuel to a potential fire.

Glass

Glass is utilized in three common ways in building construction. The most obvious is glazing for windows and doors. In this capacity the glass has little resistance to fire. It quickly cracks because of the temperature difference between the surfaces. Double glazing does not provide much improvement. Wire-reinforced glass is an improvement, as it provides somewhat greater integrity in a fire if it is properly installed. However, no glazing should be relied upon to remain intact in a fire.

A second common use of glass in buildings is in fiberglass insulation. The fiberglass does not burn and is an excellent insulator. The fiberglass is often coated with a resin binder, however, which is combustible and which can spread flames, although relatively slowly.

A third form in which glass is found in buildings is as reinforcement for fiberglass-reinforced plastic building products. The products include translucent window panels, siding, and prefabricated bathroom units. They have distinct advantages of economy and aesthetic appeal. The fiberglass acts as reinforcement for a thermo-setting resin, usually a polyester. The resin, combustible even with fire retardants incorporated in the composition, frequently comprises 50 percent or more of the material. While the fiberglass itself is noncombustible, the products are quite combustible.

Gypsum

Gypsum products, such as plaster and plaster board, are excellent fire protection materials. The gypsum has a high proportion of chemically combined water. Evaporation of this water requires a great deal of heat energy, making gypsum an excellent, inexpensive, fire-retardant building material.

Lightweight Concrete

Lightweight concrete, made with noncombustible aggregates, resists high temperatures extremely well without degradation. Vermiculite and perlite are the most common types of light concrete used for this purpose. Vermiculite is an inert aggregate made from weathered mica. The mica is crushed and roasted, which causes it to expand to form pellet-like aggregates. Perlite is a volcanic rock which is crushed and heat treated. The heat treatment causes the rock to expand in volume. During the process, water vapor is absorbed by the rock particles, and the perlite takes the form of glasslike, cellular-structured particles.

Asbestos

Asbestos is a mineral fiber that historically has been used in several forms in building construction. When it is used with a cementitious binder and sprayed onto structural members, it forms an excellent fireproofing agent. However, the asbestos fibers are a health hazard, and they can be easily scraped off the members; therefore, its use has been significantly curtailed in recent years.

Asbestos is combined with portland cement to make asbestos cement products. Although these products are noncombustible, they often shatter during the temperature buildup of a fire, thus reducing their effectiveness. However, asbestos also is combined with materials other than portland cement to form products such as asbestos insulation board and asbestos wood. These products behave quite well in fires, providing a great deal of fire resistance and protection.

Masonry

Brick, tile, and concrete masonry products behave well when subjected to the elevated temperatures of a fire. Hollow concrete blocks may crack from the heat, but they generally retain their integrity. Brick can withstand high temperatures without severe damage.

Plastics

There is a wide range of plastic products used by the building industry. They provide numerous aesthetic, physical, and economic advantages in building applications. Their major disadvantage is that all plastics are combustible. Although there are certain treatments that increase ignition temperatures or inhibit flame spread, there is no known additive that will make them noncombustible.

CONTEMPORARY TRENDS IN STRUCTURAL FIRE PROTECTION

There is an increased interest internationally in the development of more rational methods of structural fire design. These methods attempt to establish a theoretical base for the design of structural members and assemblies that will predict their actual fire performance more accurately than present methods. This section briefly addresses some of these modern trends.

Usual Structural Design Procedures for Fire Conditions

The standard fire-resistance test, combined with building code requirements that specify fire-endurance ratings for structural frames and barrier assemblies, is the usual basis for structural fire design throughout the world today. The building code identifies building-construction classifications based on materials and fire-endurance requirements for barriers and structural framing members. The code relates these construction classifications with use groups, the building height and area, and adjustments for fire-protection features. These code requirements for fire resistance are the subjective judgments of the code-writing groups.

The numbers and assemblies are laboratory tested in accordance with a standard fire test. This test is the equivalent to NFPA 251, *Fire Tests of Building Construction and Materials*, for the jurisdiction served by the code. An acceptable design occurs when the test results exceed the code requirements.

Although this procedure is common throughout the industrial world today, its validity is subject to increasing doubts. The fire test itself is being severely criticized. In addition to the concerns identified earlier in this chapter, considerable variation can occur for the same assembly when it is tested in different laboratories. The relationship between test results and field performance is unknown. The code requirements have a weak technical base. The procedure, however, is relatively easy to administer from a regulatory viewpoint, and many other code requirements can be related to the form of construction anticipated by the fire-resistance ratings.

Analytical Methods of Design

Research has been conducted along two different, but related aspects of structural fire design.[13] Both attempt to substitute rational analytical procedures for predicting structural fire behavior.

One procedure is to develop analytical methods by which the fire resistance of a member or assembly may be calculated. This method computes the fire resistance that one would expect from the standard fire test. This method uses structural characteristics of the members, thermal properties of the materials, heat-transfer characteristics of the assembly, mechanical properties of structural materials and compartment, and design service loads. This method enables the important considerations of structural restraint to be taken into account more easily than the standard fire test. This procedure is identical to the usual design procedure, except that calculated fire-resistance ratings are substituted for experimental ratings.

Another approach in which considerable research effort has been devoted is an analytical design based on real fire-exposure characteristics. There are basically two methods in this approach. The first relates the time-temperature characteristics of real fires to the structural behavior at elevated temperatures. The second method relates the properties of real fire development to an equivalent standard time-temperature curve. This method relates a theoretically equivalent time to experimental fire test results.

Design Procedure

The Swedish Institute of Steel Construction publishes a design manual, entitled *Fire Engineering Design of Steel Structures*.[14] A building designer has the option of designing the structural system in accordance with the traditional code or by the procedures described in the manual.

The manual describes a rational fire-engineering design process for steel structures on the basis of performance requirements. The manual consists of four parts. The first part is a relatively detailed description of fire energy impacts and structural behavior at elevated temperatures. This part provides the foundation for the design procedures.

The second part presents the detailed design procedure. Design charts and curves which provide the numerical base are provided. Worked examples comprise the third part, and an alternate design method based on the concept of equivalent fire duration is given in the fourth.

The American Iron and Steel Institute publishes *Fire-Safe Structural Steel, A Design Guide*,[15] for exterior structural members. Exterior members, of course, cannot be tested in the standard laboratory test. The guide provides a design procedure by which interior members can be designed for fire conditions. The design guide presents step-by-step procedures to arrive at a design.

The basis for this design guide is *Design Guide for Fire Safety of Bare Exterior Structural Steel*.[16] Part One of the AISI guide presents the theory and validation of the method, while Part Two review the state of the art of relevant research programs conducted during the past 20 years.

The Portland Cement Association has published a procedure to analytically determine the fire resistance of prestressed concrete structures. This method is described in *PCI Design for Fire Resistance of Precast Prestressed Concrete*.[17] The method calculates fire resistance by obtaining temperatures at various locations for the various standard fire-test times, using tables and diagrams based on test results. This information is then used to compute a fire-resistance value.

BIBLIOGRAPHY

References Cited

1. Clay, W., "Standard Fire Tests," *Proceedings* of the 13th Annual Meeting of the Building Officials' Conference of America, Chicago, IL, 1927, pp. 74–88.
2. Shaub, H., "Early History of Fire Endurance Testing in the United States," *ASTM Special Technical Publication 301*, American Society for Testing and Materials, Philadelphia, PA, 1961, pp. 1–9.
3. Benjamin, I. A., "Fire Resistance of Reinforced Concrete," *Symposium* on Fire Resistance of Concrete, American Concrete Institute, Detroit, MI, 1961, pp. 29 and 31.
4. "Fire Tests of Columns Protected with Gypsum," NBS *Research Paper No. 563*, National Bureau of Standards, Washington, DC, 1961.
5. Lie, T. T. and Stanzak, W. W., "Fire Resistance of Protected Steel Columns," *Engineering Journal*, Vol. 10, No. 3, 1973.
6. *Designing Fire Protection for Steel Columns*, American Iron and Steel Institute, Washington, DC.
7. Harmathy, T. Z., "Thermal Performance of Concrete Masonry Walls and Fire," *Special Technical Publication 464*, American Society for Testing and Materials, Philadelphia, PA, 1970.
8. Allen, L. W. and Harmathy, T. Z., "Fire Endurance of Selected Concrete Masonry Units," *Journal of the ACI*, Vol. 69, 1972.
9. Schaffer, E. W., "State of Structural Timber Fire Endurance," *Wood and Fiber*, Vol. 9, No. 2, 1977.
10. Harmathy, T. Z. and Stanzak, T. T., "Elevated-Temperature Tensile and Creep Properties of Some Structural and Prestressing Steels," *ASTM Special Technical Publication 464*, American Society for Testing and Materials, Philadelphia, PA, 1969, pp. 186–208.
11. DeFalco, F. D., "An Investigation of Modern Structural Steels at Fire Temperatures," Ph.D. Thesis, University of Connecticut, Storrs, CT, 1974.
12. Przetak, L., *Standard Details for Fire-Resistive Building Construction*, McGraw-Hill, NY, 1974.
13. Pettersson, O., "Structural Fire Protection," *Fire and Materials*, Vol. 4, No. 1, 1980.
14. Pettersson, O., Magnusson, S. E., *et al.*, "Fire Engineering Design of Steel Structures," *Publication 50*, Swedish Institute of Steel Construction, Stockholm, Sweden, 1976.
15. *Firesafe Structural Steel, A Design Guide*, American Iron and Steel Institute, NY, 1979.
16. Law, M., *Design Guide for Fire Safety of Bare Exterior Structural Steel*, Ove Arup & Partners, London, England, 1977.
17. Gustaferro, A. H. and Martin, L. D., *PCI Design for Resistance of Precast Prestressed Concrete*, Prestressed Concrete Institute, Chicago, IL, 1977.

Reference

Stanzak, W. W. and Lie, T. T., "Fire Resistance of Unprotected Steel Columns," *Journal of the Structural Division*, Vol. 99, No. ST5, 1973.

NFPA Codes, Standards, and Recommended Practices

Reference to the following NFPA codes, standards, and recommended practices will provide further information on structural integrity during fire discussed in this chapter. (See the latest *NFPA Catalog* for availability of current editions of the following documents.)

NFPA 251, *Fire Tests of Building Construction and Materials.*

NFPA 252, *Fire Tests of Door Assemblies.*

NFPA 257, *Fire Tests of Window Assemblies.*

Additional Reading

Barnett, J. R., "Uses and Limitations of Computer Models in Structural Fire Protection Engineering Applications," *Fire Safety Journal*, Vol. 9, Nos. 1-2, 1985, pp. 137–146.

Brannigan, F. L., *Building Construction for the Fire Service*, National Fire Protection Association, Quincy, MA, 1982.

Bresler, B., "Analytical Prediction of Structural Response to Fire," *Fire Safety Journal*, Vol. 9, 1985, pp. 103–117.

Byrne, S. M., "Fire Resistance of Load-Bearing Masonry Walls," *Fire Technology*, Vol. 15, No. 3 (Aug. 1979), pp. 180–188.

Carling, O., "Fire Resistance of Joint Details in Loadbearing Timber Construction, A Liturature Survey," *Research Report No. 18*, Building Research Association of New Zealand, 1989.

Cooke, G. M. E., "An Introduction to the Mechanical Properties of Structural Steel at Elevated Temperatures," *Fire Safety Journal*, Vol. 13, No. 1 (1988), pp. 45–54.

"Design of Buildings for Fire Safety," *ASTM Special Technical Pub. 685*, American Society for Testing and Materials, Philadelphia, PA, 1979.

ECCS European, *European Recommendations for the Fire Safety of Steel Structures*, Elsevier, NY 1983.

Fleischmann, C., "Analytical Methods of Determining Fire Resistance of Concrete Members," *SFPE Handbook of Fire Protection Engineering*, NFPA, Quincy, MA, 1988.

Gamble, W. L., "Predicting Protected Steel Member Fire Endurance Using Spread-Sheet Programs," *Fire Technology*, Vol. 25, No. 3 (1989), pp. 256-273.

Gehri, E., "The Fire Resistance of Steel Structures," *Fire Technology*, Vol. 21, No. 1 (Feb. 1985), pp. 22–33.

Harmathy, T. Z., "Thermal Performance of Concrete Masonry Walls in Fire," *ASTM Special Technical Pub. 464*, American Society for Testing and Materials, Philadelphia, PA, 1970, pp. 209–243.

Harmathy, T. Z., Sultan, M. A., and MacLaurin, J. W., "Comparison of Severity of Exposure in ASTM E119 and ISO 834 Fire Resistance Tests," *Journal of Testing and Evaluation*, Vol. 15, No. 6 (Nov. 1987), pp. 371-375.

Howe, S., "Glass and Glazing Systems," *Fire Surveyor*, Vol. 18, No. 4 (Aug. 1989), pp. 12-16.

Jeanes, D. C., "Developing Design Concepts for Structural Fire Endurance Using Computer Models," *Proceedings* of the International Conference on the Design of Structures Against Fire, Elsevier, 1986, pp. 127–153.

Jeanes, D. C., "Predicting Temperature Rise in Fire Protected Structural Steel Beams," *SFPE TR 84-1*, Society of Fire Protection Engineers, Boston, MA, 1984.

Kirby, B. R., "Recent Developments and Application in Structural Fire Engineering Design," *Fire Safety Journal*, Vol. 11, No. 3 (1986), pp. 141-180.

Lie, T. T., *Fire and Buildings, Applied Science*, London, England, 1972.

Lie, T. T., "Calculating Resistance to Fire," *Canadian Building Digest 204*, Division of Building Research, National Research Council, Ottawa, Canada, May 1979.

Lie, T. T. and Williams-Leir, G., "Factors Affecting Temperature of Fire-Exposed Concrete Slabs," *Fire and Materials*, Vol. 3, No. 2 (June 1979), pp. 74–79.

Lyon, D. E., *et al.*, "Evaluation of Strength Properties of Fire-Retarded Treated Wood Using the 1983 National Forest Products Association Protocol," *Forest Products Journal*, Vol. 38, No. 6 (1988), pp. 13–18.

Melinek, S. J., "Prediction of the Fire Resistance of Insulated Steel," *Fire Safety Journal*, Vol. 14, No. 3 (1989), pp. 127–134.

Milke, J., "Analytical Methods for Determining Fire Resistance of Steel Members," *SFPE Handbook of Fire Protection Engineering*, NFPA, Quincy, MA, 1988.

Milke, J. E., "Overview of Existing Analytical Methods for the Determination of Fire Resistance," *Fire Technology*, Vol. 21, No. 1 (Feb. 1985), pp. 59–65.

Odeen, K., "The Fire Resistance of Wood Structures," *Fire Technology*, Vol. 21, No. 1 (Feb. 1985), pp. 34–40.

Pattersson, O., "Practical Need of Scientific Material Modes for Structural Fire Design — General Review," *Fire Safety Journal*, Vol. 13, No. 1 (1988), pp. 1–8.

Petterson, O., Magnusson, S. E., and Thor, J., "Fire Engineering Design of Steel Structures," *Bulletin* 52, Lund Institute of Technology and Swedish Institute of Steel Construction, Lund, Sweden, 1976.

Prendergast, E. J., "Fire Breaks Down Concrete," *Fire Engineering*, Vol. 142, No. 9 (Sept. 1989), pp. 32–36.

Purkiss, J. A., "Developments in the Fire Safety Design of Structural Steelwork," *Journal of Constructional Steel Research*, Vol. 11, No. 3 (1988), pp. 149–173.

Routley, J. G., "How Wood Trusses Perform During a Real Fire," *Fire Journal*, Vol. 83, No. 1 (1989), pp. 49–53.

Rudolph, K., *et al.*, "Principles for Calculation of Load-Bearing and Deformation Behaviour of Composite Structural Elements Under Fire Action," *Proceedings* of the First International Symposium on Fire Safety Science, Hemisphere, 1986, pp. 301–310.

Schaffer, E. L., "How Well Do Wood Trusses Really Perform During A Fire," *Fire Journal*, Vol. 88, No. 2 (1988), p. 57.

Schleich, J. B. and Mathieu, J., "Metallic Structure Subjected to Localized Fire," *Cahiers d'Informations Techniques-Revue de Metallurgie*, Vol. 86, No. 5 (May 1989), pp. 429–438.

Schneider, U., "Concrete at High Temperatures—A General Review," *Fire Safety Journal*, Vol. 13, No. 1 (1988), pp. 55–68.

Smith, C. I., "Structural Fire Engineering Design," *Structural Engineering*, Vol. 65A, No. 2 (1987), pp.T 51–55.

White, R. H., "Analytical Methods for Determining Fire Resistance of Timber Members," *SFPE Handbook of Fire Protection Engineering*, NFPA, Quincy, MA, 1988.

CONFINEMENT OF FIRE IN BUILDINGS

Revised by John A. Campbell

People and property not directly exposed to a fire can be protected by confining heat and smoke to the area of origin until the fire either is extinguished or burns itself out. People can also be protected by delaying the spread of fire and smoke until the occupants can be relocated to a place of safety.

This chapter discusses barriers that are intended to limit the spread of fire. Smoke movement in buildings is discussed in Chapter 7, "Smoke Movement in Buildings," and smoke and heat venting in Chapter 8, "Venting Practices," both in this section. The same barriers used to prevent the spread of fire will almost always be the bulwark of systems designed to prevent the spread of smoke. To be contained, a fire must be bounded by barriers that limit the transmission of heat and hot gases. Such barriers must maintain their continuity and stability under the thermal and physical forces of a fire and during the structural distortions and collapse that sometimes occur within the fire area.

The fire resistance required of a barrier depends upon its intended purpose and on the expected severity of the fire to which it may be exposed. In most cases, the temperature history of the fire provides an approximate but adequate description of fire severity. If the purpose of the barrier is to limit probable fire size independent of any fire suppression actions, the barrier must then withstand the maximum expected fire that would occur during a burnout of combustibles inside the fire zone. However, if the purpose of the barrier is to contain the fire until occupants are evacuated and the fire department gains access, the time necessary for these actions determines the time that the barrier must hold back the fire, unless the fire is expected largely to burn itself out first.

Properly designed and constructed barriers that satisfy fire endurance test criteria are assigned a fire-resistance rating that is measured in hours or fractions thereof. Any breach or unprotected opening in a fire barrier will negate its fire-resistance rating and may indeed contribute to rapid fire spread through the barrier.

John A. Campbell, P.E., is a principal of Varley-Campbell & Associates, Oak Brook, IL.

FIRE SEVERITY

The fire severity to which a barrier can be exposed is related to the intensity of a fully developed fire in the space adjacent to the fire barrier. For a room fire, a fully developed fire would be a post-flashover fire; however, in large open volumes such as those found in many industrial plants, a fully developed fire may occur in one area without flashover of the entire volume. It is the fully developed fire that first imposes extensive thermal and physical stresses on fire barriers. The initial possibility of barrier penetration occurs prior to full development. A typical developing fire is characterized by a flame front moving over a surface and/or flames localized to a stationary source. Although such a fire does not massively attack fire barriers, it can spread through faults or openings in the barrier and cause local destruction of barrier fire resistance.

A growing fire may or may not continue to flashover or become a fully developed area-wide fire. Unless it reaches these stages, it is unlikely to threaten fire-resistive barriers except through unprotected openings or serious defects in the barrier system.

Flashover of an enclosure is likely to occur if the temperature of the upper gas layer reaches approximately 1100°F (600°C). Full-scale fire experiments and energy balance analysis of room fires have shown that the temperature of this upper gas layer depends upon the heat released by the burning fire, ventilation of the enclosure, dimensions of the enclosure, and the type of material lining the enclosure.[1] These factors also are interdependent with each other to some degree. The larger the enclosure, the higher the heat release necessary to produce the upper gas temperature needed for flashover. Conversely, the greater the combustibility of the enclosure lining, the smaller the fire needed to produce flashover. The combustibility of the lining, or interior finish, is particularly significant. Combustible interior finish in an enclosure can greatly reduce the rate of heat release necessary for flashover as well as reduce the preburn time before flashover. A practical difficulty in estimating the likelihood of room flashover is in determining a value for the heat-release rate possible from the room contents. Typical heat-release rates from some common furnishings have been summarized from full-scale experimental data.[2] These data can be used in calculating the likelihood of flashover in a particular room.

The intensity and duration of a fully developed fire depend upon the quantity of combustibles available, their burning rates, and the air available for combustion. Fire intensity will also be somewhat lower when walls and ceilings absorb significant amounts of energy rather than act primarily as insulation or radiation barriers.

The burning rate of a fully developed fire involving a specific material or grouping of similar materials is determined either by: (1) the fuel surface area available to participate in the combustion reaction, or (2) the amount of oxygen available for combustion. These are referred to as fuel-surface controlled and ventilation-controlled combustion, respectively. The maximum rate of heat transfer into fire separation barriers occurs at the point where the ventilation is just sufficient so that combustion is controlled at the fuel surface.[3] At higher ventilation rates, more heat is removed from the fire by the excess air. At lower ventilation rates, the combustion heat-release rate is less, and more unburned pyrolysis products and fuel particles are vented outside the fire area.

The possibility of failure of fire separation barriers can exist long after the fully developed fire begins to decay. However, in many real fire situations, this threat is mitigated by fire suppression activities. The decay in air temperature in a fire room has been reported as 27 to 36°F (15 to 20°C) per minute after fully developed fires of 10 to 15 min duration. Other data indicates a decay rate of 18°F (10°C) per minute for fully developed fires under 1 hr duration and about 13°F (7.2°C) per minute for longer duration fires.[4] Cooling can be even slower in large debris piles. Fire endurance testing in the U.S. does not simulate a fire decay period, although the decay period is simulated by some European and proposed U.S. testing.

Poorly ventilated fires that are encountered in spaces such as basements, ship holds, or enclosed interior rooms often produce sufficient heat over a long period of time to penetrate separation barriers. These fires typically start with flaming combustion and, as the air in the space is consumed, revert to a state of mixed smoldering and glowing combustion with isolated or intermittent flaming. However, at present there is no adequate experimental data or theoretical approach capable of reliably estimating the effect of these fires on fire-resistive barriers.

Standard Time-Temperature Curve

Fire-resistive barriers are evaluated in a testing furnace by exposure to a fire whose severity follows a time-varying temperature curve known as the standard time-temperature curve. The specified time-temperature history is tabulated in NFPA 251, *Fire Tests of Building Construction and Materials*, and illustrated in Figure 6-6A. The standard time-temperature curve was adopted by the American Society for Testing and Materials (ASTM) in 1918 and has been the basis of almost all fire-resistance testing ever since.

Following adoption of the curve, the National Bureau of Standards (NBS) conducted a number of full-scale fire tests to determine how actual building fires compared with the temperatures represented on the curve.[5,6] The tests included two actual buildings that were allowed to burn to destruction and a series of fires in fire-resistive test buildings containing contents representative of office, record room, and household occupancies. The principal variable

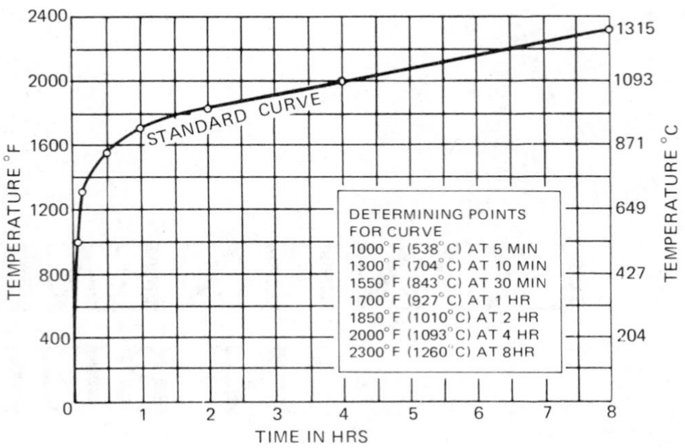

FIG. 6-6A. The standard time-temperature curve.

considered in these occupancy fire tests was the amount of combustible materials present, which is defined as the fire load. Although the ventilation in the test buildings was not reported, the windows were equipped with steel shutters that could be adjusted to control ventilation and maximize fire severity. The quantitative importance of ventilation on fire severity was not identified until more than twenty-five years after these tests. These tests conducted by the NBS provided quantitative data on the temperature history of fires that was representative of various occupancies and fire load at that period of time. Fire load was expressed as the weight of ordinary combustibles in the room divided by the floor area of the room. Loading is the average amount of ordinary combustible material per square foot (m^2) of floor area. The temperature history of the fully developed fires in the three test occupancies was approximately bounded by the standard time-temperature curve.

The NBS developed the concept of equivalent fire severity to define the severity of actual fires that had various temperature histories. This concept states that the area above a baseline under the time-temperature curve of a test fire, which is expressed in degree hours, is an approximate representation of the severity of a fire involving ordinary combustibles. The baseline used represents the temperature the materials can be exposed to without impairing their fire-resistive capabilities. Two fires with differing temperature histories are considered to have equivalent severity when the areas under their time-temperature curves are similar. This concept permitted comparison of any fire test data to the standard time-temperature curve by relating the area under the test curve to the area under the standard curve.

FIRE LOAD

The original concepts of fire severity and fire load are very important even though they are technically obsolete. These concepts are the basis for many of the fire-resistance requirements of building codes and for government agencies. In many cases, this original fire severity/fire load relationship was more severe than is indicated by more accurate analysis. Such results are conservative since the resultant error is on the safe side.

Analysis of NBS tests developed an approximate relationship between fire loading and an exposure to a fire severity equivalent to the standard time-temperature curve.

The weight per square foot (m^2) of ordinary combustibles (wood, paper, and similar materials with a heat of combustion of 7000 to 8000 Btu per lb [16 282 to 18 608 J/kg]) was related to hourly fire severity, as described in Table 6-6A.

TABLE 6-6A. ***Estimated Fire Severity for Offices and Light Commercial Occupancies***

Data applying to fire-resistive buildings with combustible furniture and shelving

Combustible Content Total, including finish, floor, and trim psf	Heat Potential Assumed* Btu per sq ft†	Equivalent Fire Severity Approximately equivalent to that of test under standard curve for the following periods:
5	40,000	30 min
10	80,000	1 hr
15	120,000	1½ hrs
20	160,000	2 hrs
30	240,000	3 hrs
40	320,000	4½ hrs
50	380,000	7 hrs
60	432,000	8 hrs
70	500,000	9 hrs

* Heat of combustion of contents taken at 8,000 Btu per lb up to 40 psf; 7,600 Btu per lb for 50 lb, and 7,200 Btu for 60 lb and more to allow for relatively greater proportion of paper. The weights contemplated by the tables are those of ordinary combustible materials, such as wood, paper, or textiles.
† SI units: 1 psf = 4.9 kg/m^2; 1 Btu/ft^2 = 1.14 J/m^2

The fire severity/fire load relationship was the first method developed to predict the severity of a fire that would be anticipated in various occupancies. It was used to determine resistance required of fire barriers as well as structural components. Although the technique has its limitations, the fire severity/fire load relationship still provides an approximate but conservative estimate of the probable maximum fire severity in residential, institutional, and some commercial occupancies. Fire load should not be used as an approximate indicator of fire severity with combustibles having a high heat-release rate and when fire conditions can produce temperatures significantly higher or lower than the standard time-temperature curve.

Fire load is a measure of the maximum heat that would be released if all the combustibles in a given fire area burned. Maximum heat release is the product of the weight of each combustible multiplied by its heat of combustion. In a typical building, the fire load includes combustible contents, interior finish, floor finish, and structural elements. Fire load is commonly expressed in terms of the average fire load, which is the equivalent combustible weight divided by the fire area in square feet (m^2).

Equivalent combustible weight is defined as the weight of ordinary combustibles having a heat of combustion of 8000 Btu per lb (18 608 J/kg) that would release the same total heat as the combustibles in the space. For example, the equivalent weight of 10 lb per sq ft (48.8 kg/m^2) of a plastic with a heat of combustion of 12,000 Btu per lb (27 912 J/kg) would be:

10 lb per sq ft × 12,000 Btu per lb = 120,000 Btu per sq ft

120,000 Btu per sq ft ÷ 8,000 Btu per lb ordinary combustibles = 15 lb per sq ft

Technically accurate methods for relating fire severity, fire load, and fire resistance requirements are complex but can be advantageously used in important specific applications. Such methods require consideration of parameters other than the fuel load, such as ventilation, type of enclosure walls, and ceiling. These methods are complex and currently too difficult for general use in design or selection of barrier fire resistance.

Occupancy Fire Load

A number of surveys have identified the fire loads found in various occupancies.[3,7,8] (See Tables 6-6B, 6-6C, and 6-6D, and Figure 6-6B.)

Data from some fire-load surveys as well as the inherent nature of combustible contents likely to be encountered suggests that the dispersion of fire load within a certain class of rooms can be approximated by either a normal or moderately skewed frequency distribution curve. (See Fig. 6-6C.) The standard deviation, included in Tables 6-6B and 6-6C, can be used to determine the probability that a particular fire-load value will not be exceeded in a class of rooms. A fire load that is one standard deviation above the mean value of a normal distribution curve would represent an upper boundary for 84.13 percent of the fire loads in rooms of that class. Two standard deviations above the mean would bound 97.73 percent of the fire loads in that class of rooms, and three standard deviations, 99.86 percent of the fire loads. Thus, if a fire barrier were to be

TABLE 6-6B. ***Characteristics of Fire Loads in Office Buildings***

	Government Buildings			Private Buildings		
	No. of Rooms Sampled	Total Fire Load, psf		No. of Rooms Sampled	Total Fire Load, psf	
Room Use		Mean	Std. Dev.		Mean	Std. Dev.
General	342	7.3	4.4	479	7.7	4.3
Clerical	77	5.8	5.2	146	6.8	4.0
Lobby	15	2.6	1.4	45	5.0	4.2
Conference	39	4.2	6.1	57	5.9	4.6
File	10	17.9	11.9	20	16.2	12.9
Storage	35	11.7	19.2	77	13.2	11.7
Library	2	30.2	7.8	10	23.6	10.8

Notes: Fire in steel enclosures. Weight of combustibles was converted to an equivalent weight of combustibles having a heat of combustion of 8,000 Btu/lb.
SI units: 1 psf = 4.88 kg/m^2

TABLE 6-6C. ***Samples of Typical Fire Loads***

Type of Room	Contents Fire Load psf	Standard Deviation psf
Living room	3.9	1.13
Family room	2.7	.65
Bedroom	4.3	1.15
Dining room	3.6	1.02
Kitchen	3.2	.77
Hospital patient room	1.2	.36
Nursing home patient room	2.6	.62

SI units: 1 psf = 4.68 kg/m^2

TABLE 6-6D. ***Fire Severity Expected by Occupancy****

Temperature Curve A (Slight)
Well-arranged office, metal furniture, noncombustible building.
Welding areas containing slight combustibles.
Noncombustible power house.
Noncombustible buildings, slight amount of combustible occupancy.

Temperature Curve B (Moderate)
Cotton and waste paper storage (baled) and well-arranged, noncombustible building.
Paper-making processes, noncombustible building.
Noncombustible institutional buildings with combustible occupancy.

Temperature Curve C (Moderately Severe)
Well-arranged combustible storage, e.g., wooden patterns, noncombustible buildings.
Machine shop having noncombustible floors.

Temperature Curve D (Severe)
Manufacturing areas, combustible products, noncombustible building.
Congested combustible storage areas, noncombustible building.

Temperature Curve E (Standard Fire Exposure—Severe)
Flammable liquids.
Woodworking areas.
Office, combustible furniture and buildings.
Paper working, printing, etc.
Furniture manufacturing and finishing.
Machine shop having combustible floors.

* See Figure 6-6B for the temperature curves identified in this table.

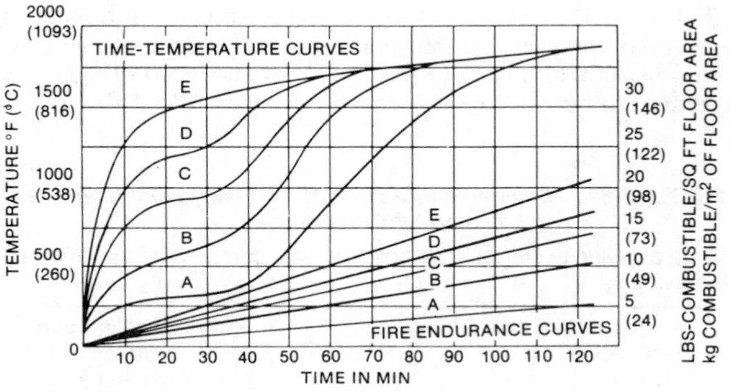

FIG. 6-6B. Possible classification of building contents for fire severity and duration. The straight lines indicate the length of fire endurance based upon amounts of combustibles involved. The curved lines indicate the severity expected for the various occupancies. (See Table 6-6D.) There is no direct relationship between the straight and curved lines, but, for example, 10 lb of combustible per sq ft (48.8 kg/m²) will produce a 90-min fire in a C occupancy, and a fire severity following the time-temperature curve C might be expected.

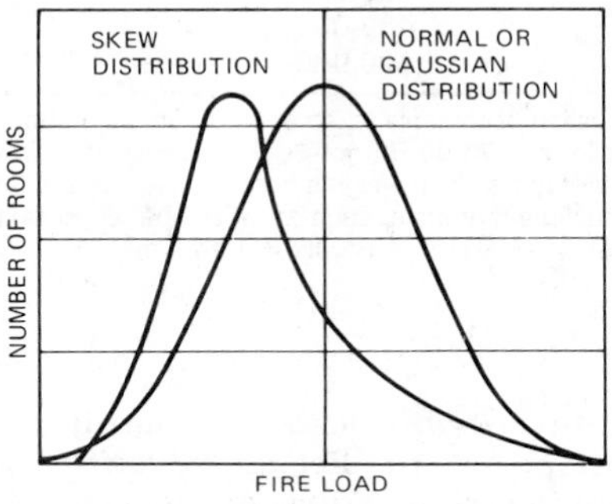

FIG. 6-6C. Expected distributions of sample fire loads.

designed on the basis of two standard deviations above the mean, there would be a 97.73 percent probability that this fire load would not be exceeded in a similar room.

The above percentages are exact only if the distribution of fire loads is perfectly normal. If the distribution is more accurately defined by a moderately skewed curve, the percentages only represent close approximations.

Derated Fire Loads

Ordinary combustibles that are completely or largely enclosed in steel containers will not burn completely during a room fire and therefore will not contribute a full 8000 Btu per lb (18 608 J/kg) to the fire load. The General Services Administration has developed guidelines for determining a derated fire load for office buildings, which can be applied to other occupancies having similar classes of combustibles.[10] The total contents fire load is divided into three categories: (1) weight of materials completely enclosed in containers, such as steel desks or file cabinets, W_E; (2) weight of materials enclosed on five sides, such as in a steel bookcase, W_{PE}; and (3) weight of free combustibles, W_{FE}.

Completely enclosed combustibles will be heated by the room fire and pyrolyze; and the escaping pyrolysis products will burn. Therefore, the heat that the enclosed combustibles release depends upon the extent to which they are pyrolyzed. This is related to the intensity and duration of the room fire, which in turn is related to the total combustibles in the room. The extent to which the enclosed contents are derated is determined by considering the ratio of the total weight of enclosed combustibles, W_E, to the total weight of all combustibles in the room, F_T. Thus:

$$F_T = W_E + W_{PE} + W_F$$

A derating factor is assigned to W_E, as tabulated below:

Ratio W_E/F_T	Derating Factor, K
under 0.5	0.4
0.5 to 0.8	0.2
over 0.8	0.1

Ordinary combustibles enclosed on five sides by steel, such as in a bookcase, are derated to 75 percent of their weight.

The total derated fire load is given by:

$$F_{DR} = K \times W_E + 0.75\ W_{PE} + W_F$$

The specific fire load is then computed by dividing by the floor area.

This derating procedure can be applied if other than ordinary combustibles are included in the fire load. The total weight of other combustibles must be expressed in terms of an equivalent weight of ordinary combustibles that would release the same total heat in burning. This is accomplished by multiplying the weight of the other combustibles by the ratio of their heat of combustion in Btu per lb, to 8000 Btu per lb (18 608 J/kg), the heat of combustion of ordinary combustibles.

British Fire-Loading Studies

The British have attained a similar objective by grading building occupancies according to hazard. Three classifications—low, moderate, and high fire loads—are defined in terms of Btu per sq ft (J/m^2) as follows.

Occupancies of low fire load: The fire load of an occupancy is described as low if it does not exceed an average of 100,000 Btu per sq ft (114 000 J/m^2) of net floor area of any compartment, nor an average of 200,000 Btu per sq ft (228 000 J/m^2) in limited isolated areas, provided that storage of combustible material necessary to the occupancy may be allowed to a limited extent if separated from the remainder and enclosed by appropriate-grade fire-resistive construction. Examples of occupancies of normal low fire load are offices, restaurants, hotels, hospitals, schools, museums, and institutional and administrative buildings.

Occupancies of moderate fire load: The fire load of an occupancy is described as moderate if it exceeds an average of 100,000 Btu per sq ft (114 000 J/m^2) of net floor area of any compartment but does not exceed an average of 200,000 Btu per sq ft (228 000 J/m^2), nor an average of 400,000 Btu per sq ft (456 000 J/m^2) in limited isolated areas, provided that storage of combustible material necessary to the occupancy may be allowed to a limited extent, if separated from the remainder and enclosed by fire-resistive construction of an appropriate grade. Examples of occupancies of normal moderate fire load are retail shops, factories, and workshops.

Occupancies of high fire load: The fire load of an occupancy is described as high if it exceeds an average of 200,000 Btu per sq ft (228 000 J/m^2) of net floor area but does not exceed an average of 400,000 Btu per sq ft (456 000 J/m^2) of net floor area, nor an average of 800,000 Btu per sq ft (912 000 J/m^2) in limited isolated areas. Examples of occupancies with normal high fire load are warehouses and other buildings used for the bulk storage of commodities of a recognized nonhazardous nature.

The low fire load grading of occupancies used by the British is approximately equivalent to the classification of occupancy represented by the temperature curve *A*; moderate fire load grading by temperature curves *B*, *C*, and *D*; and the high fire load grading by temperature curve *E* in Figure 6-6B.

EFFECT OF VENTILATION

The burning rate of fully developed fires may depend upon the available fuel surface area or on the air available for combustion. When ample air is available, the burning rate of a fire depends upon the exposed surface area and on the properties of the combustible itself. Fully developed fires involving ordinary residential furnishings burn at a rate (*R*) that can be approximated by the equation:

$$R = 0.09\ A_f \quad \text{(lbs per min)}$$

where A_f is the exposed fuel surface in sq ft (m^2).[10]

For the general case, the equation becomes:

$$R = W_f\ A_f$$

where W_f = surface rate of burning of the fuel, lb per sq ft (kg/m^2) of exposed surface per minute.

Typical furniture found in homes and offices has a surface-area-to-weight ratio between 0.55 and 0.90 lb/sq ft (0.113 and 0.185 kg/m^2).[11] Loose combustibles, cellular material, hanging clothes, etc., have much higher surface-to-weight ratios and can produce rapidly developing fires. Packed solid material or heavy furniture items have lower surface-to-weight ratios and are associated with more slowly developing fires of longer duration.

When a fire cannot get sufficient air to maintain the burning rate associated with fuel-surface-controlled combustion, it will burn at a ventilation-controlled rate. The burning rate for fully developed fires in ordinary combustibles to which air is supplied through broken windows or a doorway is approximated by:

$$R = 0.62\ A_o\ H_o^{1/2} \quad \text{(lb per min)}$$

where A_o = the opening area in sq ft (m^2) and H_o = the height of the opening in ft (m).[12]

Airflow into the fire, through a single opening, has been found to be approximately equal to:

$$\dot{m} \simeq 5.06\ C_D\ A_o\ H_o^{1/2} \quad \text{(lb per min)}$$

where C_D = the orifice coefficient, normally about 0.5 to 0.7.[13]

When there are multiple openings or a window wall, the flow is less than predicted by the area, and a C_D of about 0.35 is recommended.

The maximum fire intensity, from the standpoint of rate of heat input into barriers, occurs at a ventilation rate just sufficient to sustain a surface burning fire. This can be expressed as:

$$W_f A_f = 5.06\ C_D\ W_a\ A_o\ H_o^{1/2}$$

where W_a = the weight of fuel each lb (kg) of air will burn completely. Typical values of W_a are presented in Table 6-6E.[13]

TABLE 6-6E. ***Fuel Consumed by One Pound of Air at a Stoichiometric Fuel/Air Ratio***

Combustible	lb fuel/lb air	g fuel/kg air
Wood	0.175	175
Polyethylene	0.069	69
Polystryene	0.076	76
Polyurethane	0.135	135
Benzene	0.076	76
Methane	0.060	60

The preceding relationships assume that wind is not a factor in ventilation. In addition, if the ventilating opening is an interior door, such as from a corridor, adequate combustion air must be available for the fire.

Considerable ventilating area is required for a fully developed fire to burn at a fuel-surface-controlled rate. For example, over one-fourth of the wall area would have to be open in a 20-by-20 ft room (6.1 by 6.1 m) with an 8-ft (2.4-m) ceiling and an exposed combustible surface of 800 sq ft (74.3 m^2) of ordinary combustibles. Many, if not most, building fires will be ventilation controlled at least during the period of time in which containment is a consideration. A fully developed fire can change from ventilation-controlled to fuel-surface-controlled as ventilation changes (such as when windows break out).

FIRE MODELING

A number of mathematical models have been developed to calculate the temperature history of fully developed room fires as a function of ventilation, fuel, and the walls and ceiling of the room.[3,4,11,13,14] Calculations also yield the temperature rise on the unexposed wall and ceiling surfaces. Models that cover the developing and spreading fire are available for operation on mainframe[15] and on personal computers.[16,17,18] It is possible to calculate temperature rise in a barrier under fire exposure, although this technique has not been used in lieu of testing. Temperature rise is only one of the ways a fire barrier can fail. Mathematically modeling other failures can be difficult with many common constructions. In determining fire severity, this technique represents an improvement over the single-parameter fire load concept; however, it also is an approximation and has definite limitations. A major disadvantage of these models is their complexity and specificity. At the present time, it would not be practical generally to use calculated fire severity for fire barrier design even if it were permitted by codes. However, calculations can be used for specific applications as long as the user recognizes their capabilities and limitations. In addition, qualitative relationships identified by these analyses can provide guidance in the design of fire barriers and assist in comparing advantages of containment and suppression protection.

The principal assumption that must be made in mathematical fire history models is that the temperature is uniform in the fire room. The turbulence associated with a post-flashover fire is assumed to mix the hot gases so that no appreciable temperature gradients exist. In fire models, this assumption is used to calculate mass airflow into the room, heat transfer from the room to walls and ceiling, and pyrolysis of the fuel. This assumption is an approximation, because temperature differences of between 250 and 500°F (139 and 278°C) have been measured within a room during post-flashover fires; larger differences could be encountered in larger compartments.[19,20,21]

The maximum intensity of post-flashover room fires occurs when the ventilation is just sufficient to permit fuel-surface-controlled combustion.[3] At either higher or lower ventilation levels, the maximum fire temperature is lower.[4] At higher ventilation levels, the fire duration will be shorter, and at lower levels, it will be longer. The ventilation necessary to sustain fuel-surface-limited combustion will depend upon the combustibles in the room, their exposed surface area, surface burning rate, and the amount of air each lb (kg) of fuel requires for combustion. More ventilation would be needed to sustain fuel-surface-controlled combustion if a room contains blocks of foam rubber than if it contains an equivalent fire load of ordinary furnishings. The effect ventilation area has on the temperature of a fully developed room fire is qualitatively shown in Figure 6-6D.

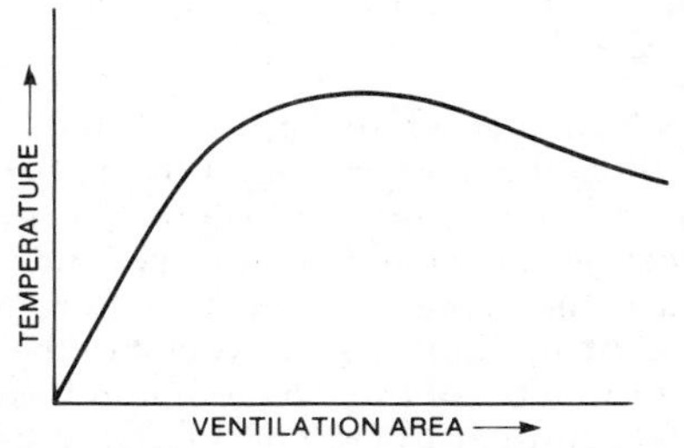

FIG. 6-6D. Typical fully developed fire temperature-ventilation

The majority of experimental fires, which form the basis for the previously described relationships, have emphasized one-room fires, fuel consisting of either ordinary household and business furnishings or wood cribs, fuel loads under 10 lb per sq ft (48.8 kg/m^2), and at least a level of ventilation provided by an open door or large window representing 10 to 15 percent of the room area. The results of these fires have shown the following:

1. Fire room temperatures may rise much faster than the standard time-temperature curve, remain above the curve for a period of time, and then drop below it.
2. Within a normal ventilation range of about 10 to 15 percent of room area on the low end and 25 to 30 percent on the high end, the maximum fire temperature depends primarily upon fire load, which, in turn, is related to the exposed fuel surface area.
3. Ordinary combustible materials with a very high exposed fuel surface area of 8 sq ft per sq ft (0.74 m^2/m^2) of floor area can result in maximum fire room temperatures over 2000°F (1093°C). Maximum fire temperatures involving ordinary furnishings generally ranged between 1400 and 1800°F (760 to 982°C).

Temperature histories of some typical small room fires in which ventilation was provided by an open corridor door are illustrated in Figure 6-6E. Higher temperatures associated with the large fuel surface areas of wood cribs are shown in Figure 6-6F; the fuel surface area was about 1000 sq ft (93 m^2) for the 10 lb per sq ft (48.8 kg/m^2) fire loading.

FIRE SPREAD

Fire spread rarely occurs by heat transfer through, or structural failure of, walls and floor-ceiling assemblies. The common mode of fire spread in a compartmented building is through open doors, unenclosed stairways and shafts, unprotected penetrations of fire barriers, and nonfire-stopped combustible concealed spaces. Even in buildings of combustible construction, the common gypsum board or lath-on-plaster protecting wood stud walls or wood joist floors provides 25 to 30 min of resistance to a fully developed fire, as determined by a standard fire test.[23] When such barriers are properly constructed and maintained and have protected openings, they will normally contain fires

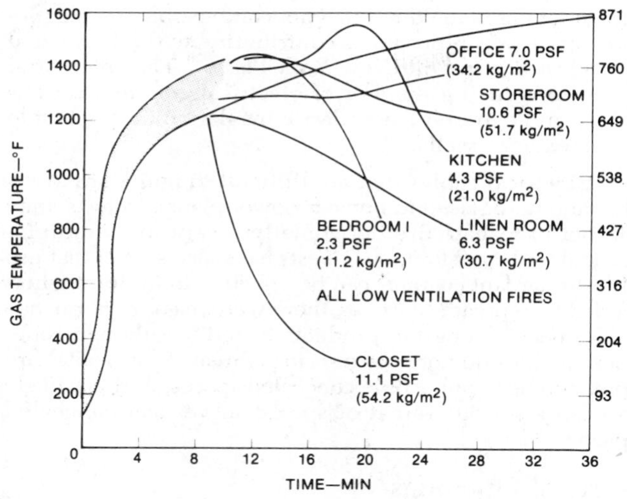

FIG. 6-6E. Gas temperature at ceiling of burning room.[21]

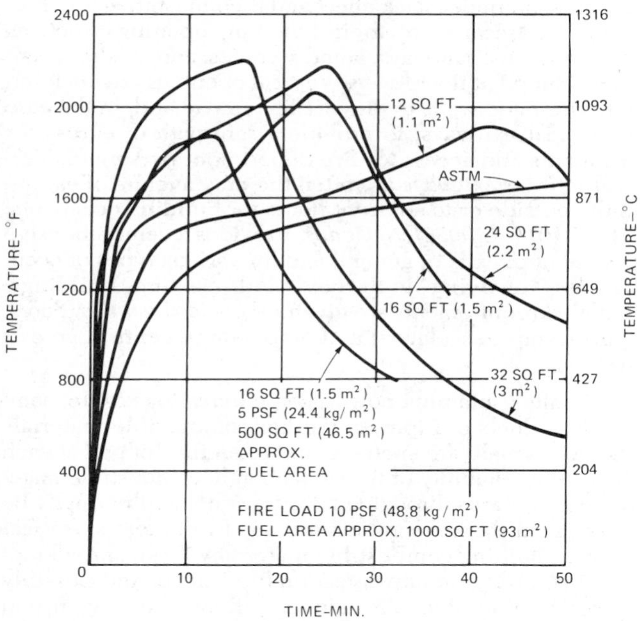

FIG. 6-6F. Effect of window area on average fire room temperature.[22]

of maximum expected severity in light-hazard occupancies. However, no fire barrier will reliably protect against fire spread if it is not properly constructed and maintained, and openings in the barrier are not protected.

Although typical wall and floor-ceiling constructions generally have adequate inherent fire resistance in light-hazard occupancies, there are practical advantages in requiring rated fire-resistive assemblies in new construction. Materials and construction methods required for fire-rated assemblies provide quality controls not found in typical construction.

Fire can spread horizontally and vertically beyond the room or area of origin and through compartments or spaces that do not contain combustibles. Heated unburned pyrolysis products from the fire will mix with fresh air and burn as they flow outward. This results in extended flame movement under noncombustible ceilings, up exterior walls, and through noncombustible vertical openings. This is a common way fire spreads down corridors and up open stairways and shafts. Similar phenomena have been observed in flame spread underneath the ceiling in industrial and storage buildings. Combustible interior finish in corridors and vertical openings, which by itself may be incapable of propagating flames, will be heated and may produce pyrolysis products. These products add to those from the main fire, and increase the intensity and length of flames.

Once a room fire becomes fully developed, fire can spread very quickly to adjacent rooms in the absence of any fire separation barriers. When a building contains similar size rooms, the total volume of the rooms involved in fully developed fires tends to increase at an exponential rate.[24] This is illustrated in Figure 6-6G, which shows the form of percentage increase in total fire volume based on the initial room volume as a function of time after the initial room flashed over.

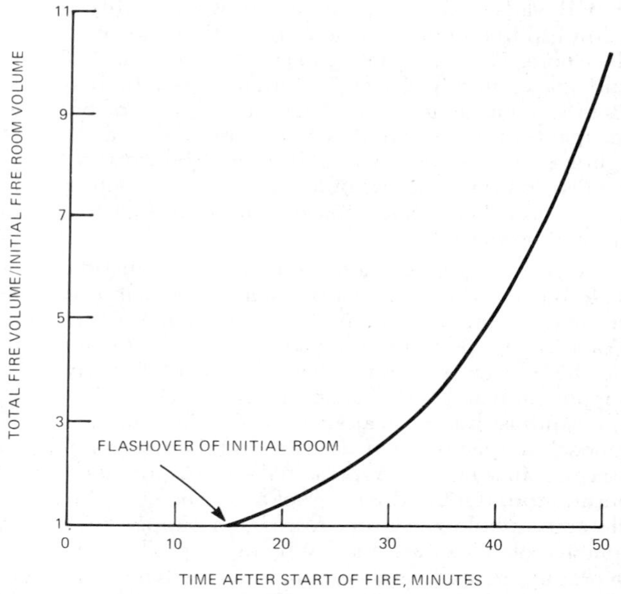

FIG. 6-6G. Exponential fire volume increase for a room flashover time of 15 min.

Floor-to-floor fire spread along the outside of a building is not a common occurrence, but it can and does occur, such as in the Hilton Hotel fire in Las Vegas, NV, in 1980. Glass panes normally break when heated to 550 to 600°F (288 to 316°C), although some breakage may occur at lower temperatures.[25] The hazard is greater in high-rise buildings because of fire fighting difficulties and because there are more floors to which fire can spread. Wide spandrels and projections, such as balconies, will reduce the risk of, although not necessarily prevent, external fire spread.

Whether a barrier will or will not contain a fire can be considered as a probability and reliability problem that parallels reliability problems encountered in the operation of electronic, electrical, and mechanical equipment. Using this analogy, barrier failures can be considered to fall into one of three categories: (1) early failures, (2) random failures, and (3) degradation failures. Early failures would be the result of occurrences such as a door not closing or an opening not being protected. Random failures would be the result of faults in materials or construction, a fire of unexpected severity, or design weaknesses not identified by standard testing methods. Random failure probabilities follow an exponential law and would predominate until barrier thermal degradation became a factor. Degradation failures would be similar to wearout failures encountered in electronic, electrical, and mechanical equipment. A probability of a wearout failure follows a normal or Gaussian distribution law, and the probability of barrier degradation failures should be similarly distributed. This technique of considering the three categories of barrier failure probability permits a more realistic comparison to be made between compartmentation and other protective measures. It is also apparent from this analogy that a barrier having a certain fire-resistive rating is not necessarily twice as reliable as one having one-half that rating.

Concealed Spaces

Buildings may contain a wide variety of concealed spaces behind walls, above suspended ceilings, in utility chases, behind soffits, under computer room floors, in attics, and elsewhere. The spaces range in size from 1⅝-in. (41.3-mm) stud spaces to 8-ft (2.4-m) and higher interstitial spaces. Fires in concealed spaces burn out of sight of building occupants, and detection is frequently delayed. Manual fighting of concealed-space fires can be very difficult because of limited accessibility and inherent venting problems. Vertical concealed spaces can act as flues to spread fire and hot gases.

Fire development and spread in combustible concealed spaces is a classic cause of large losses in fires. The fire may originate in, or spread into, a combustible concealed space and burn for a long time, spreading throughout the concealed volume. The disastrous Beverly Hills Supper Club and MGM Grand Hotel fires both originated in a combustible concealed space.[26,27] Fires in horizontal concealed spaces, such as cock lofts, attics, interstitial spaces, soffits, etc., have spread undetected until they either burned through the floor or roof above or caused parts of the ceiling below to drop. A fresh air supply, preheated combustible materials, and hot pyrolysis products combine to produce a rapidly developing fire, which may break out of the concealed space over a wide area. Vertical fire spread inside walls and chases can spread fire between floors and into attic spaces where it mushrooms out horizontally. The rapid vertical spread of fire was quantitatively demonstrated during several full-scale fire tests in wood-frame housing in the Bushwick section of Brooklyn, NY. In one test, temperatures in excess of 1500°F (816°C) were recorded at the top of a 32-ft (9.75-m) shaft one minute after a fire was started at the bottom.[28]

Fire spread through noncombustible concealed spaces is rarely a hazard unless the space contains combustible materials. Interstitial ceiling spaces frequently contain thermal insulation, communications cable, plastic pipe, etc. If thermal insulation is combustible, fire spread can be similar to that in combustible concealed spaces. Isolated combustible items are not likely to propagate fire horizontally; however, they may when grouped together. For example, grouped cables in trays spread a fire, relatively slowly, in the Browns Ferry Generating Station fire, although the cables had passed a single cable flame progagation test.[29] Movement of flame through a noncombustible ceiling plenum space was reported as contributing to the horizontal spread of fire in One New York Plaza.[30] The interstitial space contained a number of electrical communications cables and exposed foam-plastic insulation on the inside of the exterior walls.

Electrical cables that are difficult to ignite are available and being used in nuclear power plants. In tests, they did not propagate fire horizontally except in a multiple-stacked tray configuration.[31] Tests have also shown that use of fire-retardant coatings can be effective in inhibiting horizontal fire spread; however, there were major performance differences among the products tested.[32] Although some combustibles do not pose a serious threat of horizontal fire spread in noncombustible concealed spaces, they are likely to pose a serious threat of spread in vertical concealed spaces.

Vertical Openings

Unprotected vertical openings have been responsible for many large loss-of-life fires. These openings can act as a chimney—smoke, hot gases, and burning pyrolysis products flow up under stack effect and then mushroom out horizontally. Because of their function, openings such as elevator shafts, stairways, laundry chutes, and air shafts cannot be cut off at floor levels. Vertical openings are enclosed with fire-rated walls to prevent fire spread and, in the case of vertical exitways, to provide a safe path of egress for occupants and access for fire department personnel. Vertical interior exitways are often the only avenue of escape to the outside or to adjacent floors for building occupants. NFPA 101®, *Life Safety Code®*, provides a comprehensive treatment of exits in general and for various types of occupancies involving both new and existing buildings. Detailed requirements are given for enclosing walls, doors, stairs, ramps, escalators, and other components of an exit system.

Shafts containing power, communications cable, combustible ducts or pipes, and other combustible materials should normally be enclosed and often firestopped at each floor. The reliability of the protection of combustible material penetrations through enclosure walls will normally be lower than for noncombustibles. If fire enters a vertical shaft containing combustible materials, it can spread rapidly upward, generate considerable smoke, and possibly spread to other floors. An eleventh-floor storeroom fire in the World Trade Center, New York City, spread into a telephone closet through a louvered door.[33] The closets on each floor were connected through an unfirestopped hole in the slab to the closet on the floor above, up to the forty-first story of the structure. The fire ignited electrical wiring and plywood mounting boards and then spread up and down grouped cables that penetrated each floor. The fire spread up to the sixteenth and down to the tenth floor before it could be controlled.

Room or Suite Compartmentation

The goals of compartmentation in confining a fire to the room or suite of rooms of origin are generally the following:

1. Segregate a space with a higher level of fire hazard than the surrounding area. This is commonly found around rooms or suites used for storage, trash, flammable liquids, furnaces, laboratories, maintenance, painting, etc.

2. Minimize risk of loss to an occupant of one space as a result of a fire in space controlled by another. This is commonly found by separating apartments, office suites, motel/hotel rooms, row houses, etc., from each other.

An added benefit is that compartmentation also limits the size of the fire, which limits the amount of smoke that will be generated and facilitates fire suppression.

Properly designed and installed compartmentation has been successful in limiting many fires to the unit of origin. In a number of high-rise fires, occupants who were unable to escape safely through corridors were able to "sit out" a major fire in an apartment adjacent to theirs.[34] The most common cause of "failure" of this level of compartmentation has been a door that did not have a closer or was left open. Failures due to construction deficiencies are most commonly reported in buildings of combustible construction.

When a single room is compartmented, there may be insufficient ventilation for a fire to develop fully unless a window is open or happens to break.

Compartmentation is also used to protect locations of high value or critical operations from a fire in the surrounding area. Computer rooms, some control rooms, vaults, records storage, etc., are often protected from a fire involving the rest of the building.

Protection of Corridors

Fire-resistive corridor partitions may be required: (1) to protect the means of access to an exit for sufficient time to permit occupant evacuation, or (2) to provide a protected means of access to the fire for fire department personnel. In addition, when used in conjunction with room-to-room or suite-to-suite fire-resistive separation, the corridor wall forms an element in preventing fire spread.

Corridor partitions typically are required to have a 1-hr fire-resistance rating, and codes may require the partition to extend from the floor to the underside of the floor above. Either automatic or self-closers are generally required on doors opening into the corridor. Since smoke entering the corridor is a significant problem, as the corridor provides access to the exits, automatic door closers, if used, are generally actuated by smoke detectors. Additional information on corridor doors can be found later in this chapter where protection for openings is discussed.

Building Separation

Walls separating two buildings or dividing a building into separate fire areas limit the maximum probable property loss and also can divide one building into what is legally two or more buildings to comply with the height and area limits of building codes. Stability becomes a very important consideration in this class of wall. Although all fire separation walls must maintain their stability under fire exposure for their rated duration, walls separating buildings or dividing a building into two fire areas must maintain stability during a complete burnout on either side, which is often accompanied by structural collapse.

If at least one of the buildings has a fire-resistive frame—such as reinforced concrete or protected steel—panel walls built in along a column line can provide fire separation. The frame must have sufficient resistance to withstand a fire of the maximum expected severity for that building. Care must be taken so that the floor construction will not adversely affect stability of the wall under fire exposure. In buildings of Type V (wood frame), Type IV (heavy timber), or Type III (ordinary) construction, the combustible framing members can be tied into the fire wall so that they are self-releasing in case of collapse. The wall then remains supported by the framing on the unexposed side. The use of self-releasing framing has been generally successful in combustible construction but has questionable reliability in steel-framed buildings. Caution must be exercised in the design of these fire walls because some methods of framing combustible members into the wall will lower its fire resistance.

Freestanding fire walls are most commonly used in one- or two-story industrial and storage buildings of unprotected steel-frame construction. The maximum height is generally limited by economic considerations. A freestanding fire wall is entirely self-supporting under vertical loads and is not directly connected to the building framing. The adjacent building framing can provide support under horizontal loading. During a fire the wall must be capable of acting as a cantilever to withstand all horizontal forces directed toward the fire side. Freestanding fire walls should be designed to withstand at least a 5 lb per sq ft (20 kg/m^2) uniform lateral loading without any support from the framing on either side.[35]

Tension stress in mortar joints limits the height of unreinforced 12-in. (0.3-m) concrete block walls to 15 ft (4.6 m). Higher walls either require massive construction, which is rarely practical, or reinforcement. A common reinforcement technique is installation of vertical steel bars, anchored to the foundation within hollow masonry units. Reinforced pilasters can also be built into the wall at periodic points along the perimeter. A typical freestanding fire wall is illustrated in Figure 6-6H.

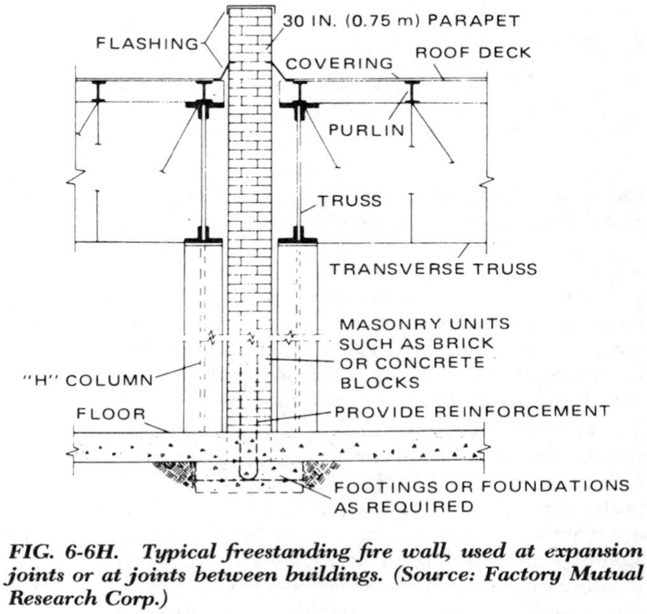

FIG. 6-6H. Typical freestanding fire wall, used at expansion joints or at joints between buildings. (Source: Factory Mutual Research Corp.)

Freestanding fire walls have very definite limitations under horizontal forces, which may preclude or restrict their use. They are particularly vulnerable to collapse under seismic loads and wind forces received by exterior walls.

Additional support must be provided if the walls are temporarily used as an exterior wall or become an exterior wall as a result of a fire. Piping, conveyors, and similar items whose collapse in a fire will exert a horizontal pull should not pass through freestanding fire walls.

Fire walls in steel-frame buildings may be tied into the building structure so the forces of collapse on one side are resisted by the framing on the other side. The wall may be built along a column line and the columns and horizontal framing tied into the wall. The columns and framing in the wall line must be protected so that they have the same fire resistance as the wall. The walls have to be located in the framing so that the strength of framing on one side will be capable of withstanding the pull of collapsing framing on the other side. The construction of a typical tied fire wall is shown in Figure 6-6I.

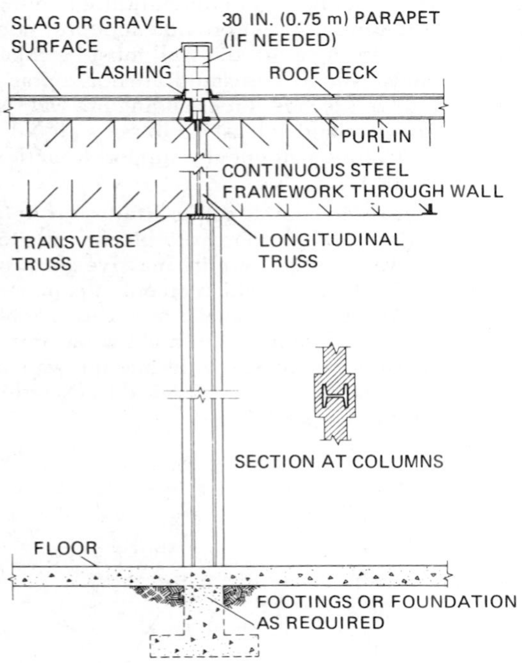

FIG. 6-6I. Typical tied fire wall, used with continuous building framework. (Source: Factory Mutual Research Corp.)

Fire separation between buildings can also be provided by two blank exterior walls of adequate fire resistance and located very close together. Each wall is tied to the frame in its building; collapse of the frame pulls the wall in, leaving the other wall to resist the fire.

Pipes, conveyors, cable trays, and similar through-penetrations of fire walls can present special problems in seismic areas. The need for mobility may conflict with opening protection criteria. The complexity of the problem depends upon whether the systems are to be designed to protect against only one hazard at a time (fire or earthquake) or whether the simultaneous or consecutive occurrence of earthquake and fire should be considered in protection.

Fire Plumes above Roofs

The configuration factor for plume/roof relationships can be calculated using the formula found in a reference.[36] The effect of wind velocity, which deflects the fire plume, must be accounted for in calculation of the configuration factor. At high winds a fire plume can be deflected so it is almost horizontal above a burning roof. However, in high winds, a fire plume also tends to break up and is expected to be cooled by excess air. The angle of the fire plume selected is a matter of professional judgment; use of 45 degrees is considered reasonable by some engineers.

If the roof surface is combustible, the value of the incident thermal radiation calculated will indicate whether ignition of the roof is expected. If the surface is noncombustible or resistive to ignition by radiant heat, it is then necessary to calculate the temperature of the combustible subsurface material to which heat will be transferred from the surface. This is an unsteady-state heat transfer problem readily solved by standard numerical procedures.

A simple example of the calculation of incident thermal radiation can be used to illustrate the method of analysis. For the example, consider a 12-ft-high (3.7 m) and 60-ft-wide (18.3 m) frame building with a wood-surfaced roof. The building is subdivided by a masonry fire wall with a 3-ft (0.91-m) parapet. (See Figure 6-6J.) The expected height of flames above the roof would be about 1.4 times the height of the building, or approximately 17 ft (5.2 m).[37] Assuming a flame temperature of 1400°F (760°C), the thermal radiation from the fire plume would be about 5.8 Btu per sq ft per sec (6.6 W/m^2). In a moderate wind, a fire plume deflection of 45 degrees is possible. The maximum configuration factor would be about 0.3 and the incident radiation on the wood roof surface about 1.75 Btu per sq ft per sec (2 W/m^2).

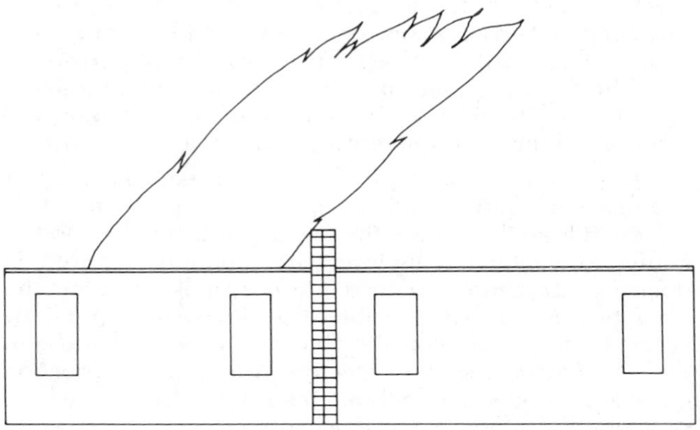

FIG. 6-6J. A fire plume exposing a wood roof over a parapeted fire wall.

At an incident radiation of 1.1 Btu per sq ft per sec (1.25 W/m^2), a wood roof can be sufficiently heated so that a small burning brand will ignite it;[38] this is referred to as pilot ignition. Since in the example the incident thermal radiation is well above that required for pilot ignition, flame spread over this fire wall is to be expected if the wind deflects the fire plume toward the exposed roof.

Fire walls must extend through and above a combustible roof to reduce the risk of fire spread over the top of the wall. Codes and standards typically call for fire walls to have a parapet 18 to 36 in. (0.46 to 0.9 m) above a combustible roof. The parapet minimizes the risk of direct flame spread over the fire wall and reduces the risk of fire spread by radiant heat from flames above the roof. The risk of direct flame spread over an 18- to 36-in. high (0.46 to

0.9 m) parapet is very low. However, risk of fire spread by radiant heat depends upon the combustibility of the roof surface, the height of the parapet, the dimensions of the fire plume through the roof of the fire zone, the wind velocity, and, if the roof covering is resistive to ignition by radiant heat, its insulating properties and the duration of the exposing fire. If a roof surface is combustible, the risk of fire spread by radiant heat past a parapet can be quite high.

The threat of fire spread by radiant heat over a parapet can be calculated using the thermal radiation values identified in Appendix A of NFPA 80A, *Protection from Exposure Fires*, and fire plume dimensions.[37] Standard heat transfer procedures can then be applied, using the formula:

$$I_o = SxT^4x\phi$$

where:
I_o = unit incident ratiation
S = Stefan-Boltzman constant
T = absolute temperature
ϕ = configutation factor or view factor

This formula can be used with either customary American or SI units, as long as the units are consistent.

Structural Stability of Fire Walls

Fire-rated wall requirements may be intended to ensure structural stability rather than to provide a fire barrier. In many cases, for example, hourly rated exterior bearing walls are permitted to have unlimited unprotected window areas; therefore, it is obvious that the rating refers to structural stability rather than provision of a fire barrier. Required fire ratings of interior bearing walls may or may not be intended to provide a fire barrier. Interior bearing walls with an hourly rating for fire separation do require protection of all openings; however, interior bearing walls that have an hourly rating only for structural stability purposes would not need opening protection. Caution must be exercised in selecting the proper hourly rating for interior bearing walls intended for structural stability only. A barrier separation wall is exposed to fire on only one side, whereas an interior bearing wall that would be providing only structural stability could be exposed to fire on both sides. The same hourly rating wall will not provide the same protection in both cases.

Fire-resistive walls of a high hourly rating are occasionally improperly specified to separate areas for protection against an explosion hazard rather than a long-duration fire. The fire resistance of a wall has no relationship to its ability to withstand explosion forces. A wall with a 1-hr rating may withstand explosion overpressures better than a 4-hr wall; no conventional wall will remain in place unless the explosion pressure is limited by venting or suppression.

PROTECTION OF OPENINGS

The protection for openings in a fire-rated wall generally has less resistance to fire spread than is provided by the wall. This is allowable because: (1) easily ignited combustibles are not normally found against doors and other opening protection constructions, and (2) fire suppression forces can usually extinguish small localized fires that may spread past the wall. However, because openings do reduce the effectiveness of a fire barrier, fire doors generally cannot occupy more than 25 percent of the perimeter of any fire separation wall.

Factors that reduce the fire resistance of opening protection as compared to resistance of walls include the following:

1. There is no maximum temperature rise limitation on the unexposed sides of most types of fire doors. The unexposed side of steel doors may actually glow red during fire testing. When there is a limit to or listing of a temperature rise on a fire door, it applies only to the temperature rise during the initial 30 min of the fire test. (Temperature rise limits are often specified in building codes for doors on exit stair enclosures.) Fire doors also buckle during fire tests and are permitted to move out of their frames in a direction perpendicular to the plane of the door as much as 2⅞ in. (72 mm). Some flaming is also permitted on unexposed sides of fire doors during the test procedures.
2. Requirements for the protection of duct penetrations place no limit on the temperature rise on the duct itself on the unexposed side of the wall.
3. Piping, cable trays, and conduit can penetrate fire walls and, although the opening must be firestopped, the temperature rise on the metal penetration itself would normally be above the 250°F (139°C) average or 325°F (161°C) single-point temperature-rise limits required of the wall.
4. The standard fire test furnace is operated at a negative pressure so that air flows in around protected openings rather than outward. In a real fire there may be a higher pressure on the fire side that is more likely to force flame through indirect paths or firestopped openings.
5. Wired-glass vision panels may transmit heat by both conduction and radiation, without any restrictions.

Thermally induced distortions of between 4 and 5 in. (102 and 127 mm) were observed in some foreign tests of swinging steel fire doors.[39] Considerably smaller distortions were noted with wood and insulated metal swinging doors. However, wood doors were noted as being more likely to fail by localized carbonation at hinges, locks, and knobs. Rolling steel fire doors generally do not deform appreciably during a fire. Large distortions of some rated fire doors, both wood and metal, were also reported in "Project Corridor," a series of fire tests conducted by the California State Fire Marshal in a simulated light-hazard occupancy.[40] In some countries, extensible bolts and latches are added to swinging steel fire doors so that the door is held in the frame at five or six points. Distortions of this type of door were reported to be under 1 in. (2.54 mm) during a standard fire test.[39]

Fire doors, windows, and shutters are the most widely used and accepted means of protecting openings in fire-resistive walls. Suitability of these closures is determined through tests by recognized testing laboratories, and doors not tested cannot be relied upon for effective protection. Fire door assemblies for the protection of openings depend upon the use of labeled fire doors and frames (where frames are required) and listed or labeled hardware. Hardware for fire doors is referred to as builders hardware (which includes fire exit hardware) and fire door hardware. The doors are tested as they are installed in the field, that is, with the frame, hardware, wired-glass panels, and other accessories necessary to complete the installation.

Classification of Openings and Doors

Fire doors may be classified by an hourly rating designation, an alphabetical letter designation, or a combination of these. Current practice is to use the hourly rating designation; formerly, the alphabetical letter designation was used. Appendix F of NFPA 80, *Fire Doors and Windows*, refers to openings as *A*, *B*, *C*, *D*, and *E*, in accordance with the character and location of the wall. The alphabetical classification of the opening does not apply to the closure; however, in actual practice, the distinction between opening classification and door classification was rarely maintained. A 3-hr door for use in a Class A opening was commonly called a Class A door.

Building codes and NFPA 80, *Fire Doors and Windows*, commonly specify a door by its fire-protection rating instead of by the classification of opening to be protected. Fire doors are now available with ½-hr and ⅓-hr ratings, which do not fall within the specified protection criteria for the classes of opening. The following paragraphs summarize current applications of doors, windows, and shutters for openings in fire-resistive walls.

Three-hour fire doors: Openings in walls separating buildings or dividing a building into different fire areas are generally protected by 3-hr fire doors. However, many codes only require 3-hr doors in separation walls required to have a fire resistance of 3 hrs or more. In addition, some authorities require two 3-hr fire doors, one on each side of the opening, whenever a wall is required to have a fire resistance of 4 hrs.

One and one-half-hour fire doors: Openings in 2-hr enclosures of vertical openings in buildings are protected by 1½-hr fire doors. Many codes also permit the use of 1½-hr fire doors to protect openings in walls separating buildings or dividing buildings into different fire areas when the wall is only required to have a fire resistance of 2 hrs. One and one-half-hour fire doors are used in walls required to have a 2-hr fire resistance to enclose hazardous areas.

One and one-half-hour fire doors and shutters: Openings in exterior walls that can be subjected to severe fire exposure from outside the building are protected by 1½-hr fire doors and shutters.

One-hour fire doors: Openings in 1-hr enclosures of vertical openings in buildings, such as stairs and shafts, are protected by 1-hr fire doors.

Three-quarter-hour fire doors: Openings in room partitions and walls around some hazardous areas are protected by ¾-hr fire doors. Sometimes they are also permitted in partitions that subdivide floors of a building. Although ¾-hr fire-rated doors are for use in 1-hr corridor partitions, many codes permit installation of other types of doors, such as ½- or ⅓-hr fire-rated or 1¾-in. (445-mm) solid-bonded wood-core doors. Either automatic or self-closers are generally required on corridor doors. Since smoke control is also necessary to protect a corridor as an access to an exit, automatic closers are generally actuated by smoke detectors.

Three-quarter-hour fire doors and shutters: Openings in exterior walls subject to a moderate or light fire exposure from outside the building are protected by ¾-hr fire doors and shutters.

Three-quarter-hour fire windows: Openings in corridor or room partitions or in exterior walls subject to a moderate or light external fire exposure can be protected by ¾-hr fire windows.

One-half-hour (30-min) and one-third-hour (20-min) fire doors: Doors with these ratings are for use where smoke control is a primary consideration. They are also used for the protection of openings in partitions between a habitable room and a corridor when the wall is constructed to have a fire-resistance rating of not more than 1 hr or across corridors where a smoke partition is required. Some codes permit the use of 1¾-in. (445-mm) solid-bonded wood-core doors in corridor, room, and smoke-stop partitions that are required to have a fire resistance of not more than 1 hr. These doors cannot be used for corridor doors to hazardous areas or to protect openings in enclosures of vertical openings in buildings.

Types of Doors

There are several types of construction for fire doors. They are:

Composite doors: These are of the flush design and consist of a manufactured core material with chemically impregnated wood-edge banding and untreated wood-face veneers or laminated plastic faces, or surrounded by and encased in steel.

Hollow metal doors: These are of formed steel of the flush and paneled designs of No. 20-gage or heavier steel.

Metalclad (Kalamein®) doors: These are of flush and paneled design consisting of metal-covered wood cores or stiles and rails and insulated panels covered with steel of No. 24 gage or lighter.

Sheet-metal doors: These are of formed No. 22-gage or lighter steel and of the corrugated, flush, and paneled designs.

Rolling steel doors: These are of the interlocking steel-slat design or plate-steel construction.

Tin-clad doors: These are of two- or three-ply wood-core construction, covered with No. 30-gage galvanized steel or terneplate [maximum size 14 by 20 in. ([0.35 by 0.50 m]); or No. 24-gage galvanized steel sheets not more than 48 in. (1.2 m) wide.

Curtain-type doors: These consist of interlocking steel blades or a continuous formed spring steel curtain in a steel frame.

Wood-core doors: These doors consist of wood, hardboard, or plastic-faced sheets bonded to a wood block or wood particleboard core material with untreated wood edges.

Unrated Door Protection

The fire resistance of existing doors can be improved by coating the doors with an intumescent paint, although no formal fire-resistance rating for such a door has been established. This method is not commonly accepted in the U.S., although it has been used in England. Intumescent paint is listed for reducing flame spread, not for improving fire resistance. However, tests conducted by the NBS showed that a single layer of intumescent paint, 7 to 8 mil (0.18 to 0.20 mm) thick, significantly delayed char penetration into a soft wood joist.[41] Ordinary wood-panel doors, in which both door and frame were coated with two layers of intumescent paint, withstood fully developed room fires similarly to 1¾-in. thick (44.5 mm) solid-core wood doors in simulated nursing home room fires.[19] In another test, a wood-panel door was protected with gypsum board on the thin panel and intumescent paint on the remainder of the wood. This upgraded door withstood a standard fire test, modified to simulate the positive pressure of a room fire, longer than a 20-min-rated fire door.[42] However, there is no fire-protection rating assigned to any upgraded fire doors; it is entirely up to the authority having jurisdiction whether or not this is acceptable for improving the fire-safety in existing buildings.

Wired Glass

Wired glass is used as vision panels in fire doors, for exterior windows subject to moderate fire exposure, and in 1-hr-rated corridor walls. In addition, it is frequently used in smoke-stop barriers and to enclose open stairways in older buildings. Such panels are not allowed in doors having a fire-protection rating of 3 hrs or in doors having a 1½-hr fire-protection rating for use in severe exterior fire exposure locations. Vision panels are limited to 100 sq in. (0.065 m^2) in 1½-hr-rated doors (except as noted previously) and to 1296 sq in. (0.84 m^2) with a maximum dimension of 54 in. (1.37 m) in ¾-hr-rated doors. However, the total maximum area of glass per door leaf is simply limited to the maximum area tested.

Wired glass is a glass sheet containing an imbedded net of steel that helps distribute heat, lowers thermal stresses, and increases the strength of the assembly. When exposed to a fire, the glass starts cracking after a minute or two but does not open up. The glass begins to weaken when heated to about 1470°F (799°C) and gradually starts to soften. At about 1600°F (871°C) it deforms so badly that it will drop out.[39] Its normal 45-min fire-resistance rating corresponds to 1638°F (892°C) on the standard time-temperature curve. In actual fires, the endurance of wired glass is temperature-dependent; if it is never heated above the temperature at which it weakens, it could remain in place for an extended period of time.

Wired-glass panels differ from a solid wall primarily in the transmission of radiant heat. Conductive heat transmission is also increased, but high conductive heat transmission is also found in door hardware, frames, etc. The intensity of radiant heat, I, to which a combustible or person would be exposed through a wired-glass panel from a fully developed room fire, is given by:

$$I = k\phi \, I_o$$

where I is the transmissivity of the window, k is the configuration factor, and I_o is the radiant intensity of the exposing fire.

This equation may be used for conventional or SI units, as long as their use is consistent.

A radiant intensity of 5 Btu per sq ft per sec (5.7 W/m^2) has been measured for a room fire involving ordinary residential furnishings with average ventilation, such as an open door.[43] Measurements of well-ventilated fires in light-hazard occupancies indicate a peak radiant intensity of 7.4 Btu per sq ft per sec (8.4 W/m^2).[28] Transmissivity of glass windows is reported to range from 0.4 to 0.6.[38] The configuration factor, ϕ, can be determined from any specific situation from graphs found in most heat-transfer texts.

If wood on the unexposed side of the wired glass is exposed to a radiant intensity above 3 Btu per sq ft per sec (3.4 W/m^2), auto-ignition may occur. Most synthetic materials will require a higher level of radiant heat intensity for auto-ignition.

When wired-glass panels are installed in walls on a dead-end corridor or other location in which building occupants have no alternate escape path, the heat radiated through the glass may prevent escape. If persons moving past the glass absorb sufficient heat to cause severe pain, their ability to escape could be impaired. The human threshold of severe pain for exposure to radiant heat depends upon both the intensity and the time over which it is received. Experimental data that has defined this limit[44] can be approximated by the equation:

$$Q_{max} \simeq 2.3\, t^{0.25} \quad t \leq 45 \text{ s}$$

where Q_{max} is the total heat absorbed by the skin in Btu per sq ft (W/m^2) over t seconds at the threshold of severe pain. As a person moves past the wired-glass panel, the view factor, ϕ, will change. The absorbed heat can be calculated by determining ϕ for a number of points along the person's path, and using a stepwise integration over the time required to move past each point. The normal walking speed used in exit calculations is 3.5 ft per sec (1.07 m/sec).[9] If the total heat absorbed exceeds the limits in the equation, the escape of occupants past the wired-glass panels may be impaired.

Glazing materials other than wired glass now qualify for fire-resistance ratings. A few manufacturers have produced clear, transparent vision panels, most often of glass/plastic sandwich construction that offers resistance to fire. Those that have passed the necessary fire tests can be used instead of wired glass.

Firestopping

The term *firestopping* is used to describe both barriers to restrict the spread of fire in concealed spaces and materials used to fill gaps around penetrations in walls and ceilings.

In wood-frame construction, the normal firestop inside walls and ceiling spaces is a 2-in.-thick (50.8 mm) (nominal) piece of lumber. However, for other applications, firestopping should normally be noncombustible and have a sufficiently high melting point so that it will remain in place under fire exposure. Gypsum board, sheet metal, plaster, brick, cement grout, mineral fiber insulation, asbestos cement board, and ceramic fiber boards are all examples of commonly used firestopping. Firestop protection for penetrations of fire-rated walls and floors by noncombustible pipe, tube, and conduit has commonly been provided by filling the annular space around the penetrant with a noncombustible material, such as cement grout, mineral wool, cement plaster, etc. This type of firestopping has performed effectively in actual fires. However, lack of firestopping[27,30] or improperly protected openings, such as the combustible foam plastic used at Brown's Ferry Nuclear Plant[45], have been responsible for a number of serious fire losses.

Considerable attention and research has been directed toward wall and floor penetrations by plastic drain, waste, and vent (DWV) pipes.[46,47,48,49] Full-scale tests have shown that the integrity of a 2-hr fire-resistive chase enclosure could be maintained by encasing the pipe in an 18-in.

(0.46-m) steel sleeve and penetrating the chase at a 45-degree downward angle. These results were applicable to 3-in. (76-mm) laterals of both DVC and ABS DWV pipe. Unless otherwise tested and approved, chases should be firestopped at each floor. In many buildings, much of the plumbing is installed in wall cavities. Use of plastic DWV pipe inside fire-resistive wall assemblies has been extensively tested, and a number of methods of protection that will not compromise the fire resistance or create a risk of vertical fire spread have been identified.

Cable-tray penetrations present another challenge; the size of the penetrant is large and contains a mixture of combustible and noncombustible material. Research and development programs were sponsored by the Nuclear Regulatory Commission on firestops for use in nuclear power plants. The results of these programs, plus work by suppliers, led to new firestopping products.

Recent editions of some building codes now require approved and tested firestops wherever conduit, pipe, cables, or other utilities pass through fire-rated—and sometimes nonfire-rated—walls, floors and ceilings. These firestops can be qualified under either ASTM E-814 or under a fire exposure corresponding to ASTM E-119. The test furnace must be operated at a specified positive pressure, such as 0.01 or 0.03 in. of water column. Currently, neither of these tests evaluate smoke spread.

There are two types of tested firestop protection: (1) through-penetration firestop devices, and (2) through-penetration firestop systems. The firestop devices are manufactured products used primarily for protecting cable and poke-through penetrations. Through-penetration firestop systems are field-erected constructions for protecting penetrations of floors or walls by conduit, pipe, duct, cable, cable trays, etc. The basic standard used to investigate these firestops is Underwriters Laboratories Test Standard UL 1479, which is based on ASTM E-814.

ASTM E-814 was developed for evaluating firestops that are installed to prevent spread of fire through an opening where cable trays, pipe, conduits, ducts, etc., pass through a wall or floor. This standard was first published in 1981. The ASTM E-814 test has many similarities to ASTM E-119, but it can be conducted on a much smaller scale and at a documented positive pressure. In addition, all test items are subject to a hose stream test similar to that required for some constructions tested under ASTM E-119. ASTM E-119 requires testing of at least a 100-sq-ft (9-m^2) sample of a wall and a 180-sq-ft (16.2-m^2) sample of a floor. A wall or floor sample less than 9 sq ft (0.81 m^2) can be used in ASTM E-814. The ASTM E-814 furnace is heated to follow the temperature history of ASTM E-119.

Two types of hourly time ratings are established for a tested firestop: *F* and *T*. The conditions for these ratings are broader. The F rating is a measure of the ability of the firestop system to maintain its physical integrity under the fire exposure and hose stream tests and to prevent occurrence or passage of flame on the unexposed surface. The T rating is intended to measure whether combustible materials on the unexposed side of a fire barrier would be ignited by conduction of heat through the firestop material or along the penetrating conduit, pipe, etc. The same maximum temperature limit is used in the ASTM E-814 test as in the E-119 test. The hourly F or T rating is the duration of the fire test that the through-penetration firestop system passed.

The T rating achieved can be less than the F rating; there is nothing similar to this in the ASTM E-119 test. If the temperature limit is reached before the completion of a successful test for an F rating, the T rating will be based on the time at which the temperature limit was reached. However, the F rating assigned would be the total hourly duration of the successful test. Building codes that require firestop systems tested under ASTM E-814 differ as to if and when a T rating is necessary.

There are many types of listed through-penetration firestop system constructions, ranging from relatively simple to complex arrangements. A typical through-penetration firestop system requires installation of both a form and a fill material. The form material is generally a ceramic fiber mat; a hole is cut in it the size of the penetrating conduit (or pipe) and the form is slipped over the conduit into the opening in the wall or floor. The form material serves to place and restrain the fill material that is installed in the annular space around the conduit to a specified thickness. Fill materials include one- and two-part foams, silicone elastomers, proprietary caulking and grouting materials, specific proprietary cementitious mixtures, etc.

Some through-penetration firestop systems also require use of an additional filling material, such as ceramic fibers, and some only require a single material, such as a proprietary caulk or grout. There are a number of through-penetration firestop systems that are much more complex and require additional features, such as sleeves, special supports to retain the system in the opening, and insulation on the conduit or pipe extending out from the surface of the floor or wall.

Some of these systems permit penetrating items to be easily removed or replaced. This facilitates future additions of pipe, tube, or cable through the penetration opening. However, restoration of the integrity of the original firestop may or may not be possible under the conditions of the system's listing by a testing laboratory. Any additions or changes that require removal and restoration of a through-penetration firestop system have to be tightly controlled so that: (1) the restoration is performed in an approved manner; (2) the allowable number of penetrating items is not exceeded; (3) only permitted penetrants are installed; and (4) adequate clearances are maintained among penetrating items and between penetrating items and the sides of the opening.

Some designs for curtain walls, particularly in high-rise buildings, offer the danger of vertical spread of fire behind the curtain walls for the entire height of the building. This can occur when the panels of a curtain wall do not rest tightly for their full length on a floor slab. Rather, there is a continuous relieving angle attachment between the panels and the floor slab, creating vertical flue spaces between the panels and the end of the floor slab. Where firestopping is not inherent in the design, it is necessary to fill this space with appropriate firestopping materials. This arrangement is generally less satisfactory because of the tendency for both expansion and contraction of the exterior wall and the liklihood of maintenance operations causing unplanned openings through and around the firestopping.

Atria

Atria, which are becoming more common in many new buildings, depart from the traditional compartmentation concept of fire containment by enclosing all vertical openings. Alternative arrangements must be provided in atrium buildings to achieve the same level of protection found in buildings using the traditional compartmentation concept. The occupancy should be one in which a rapidly spreading fire would not be encountered, and all occupants should be expected to be aware of any hazard before they are endangered, and in time to move to a place of safety if necessary.

Fire protection in atrium buildings is generally provided by a combination of methods, such as compartmentation, ventilation, automatic suppression, and contents and material control. NFPA 101, *Life Safety Code*, requires atria in new construction to be separated from adjacent spaces by fire barriers having at least a 1-hr fire-resistance rating. However, as many as three levels of a building may open directly to the atrium without the need for a fire-resistive barrier. As an alternative where 1-hr barriers are normally required, glass walls may be used, provided there are sprinklers spaced 6 ft (1.8 m) apart not more than 1 ft (0.3 m) from the glass along both sides of the glass wall. The sprinklers must be located to ensure that the glass surface is wet when the sprinklers operate. Sprinklers are not required on the atrium side of the glass wall if there is no walkway or other floor area on that side above the main floor level.

Large-volume atria will dilute fire gases and, with proper ventilation, direct their flow safely to the outside. Small atria may not have the capacity to dilute fire gases, although if they are properly designed and ventilated, fire gases can be channeled to the outside and the risk of horizontal fire spread minimized.

BIBLIOGRAPHY

References Cited

1. McCaffrey, B. J., *et al.*, "Estimating Room Temperatures and the Likelihood of Flashover Using Fire Data Correlations," *Fire Technology*, Vol. 17, No. 2, 1981, pp. 98-119.
2. Quintiere, J. G., "A Simple Correlation for Predicting Temperature in a Room Fire," *NBSIR 832712*, U.S. Department of Commerce, National Bureau of Standards, Gaithersburg, MD, 1983.
3. Berry, D. L., and Minor, E. E, "Nuclear Power Plant Fire Protection—Fire Hazards Analysis (Subsystems Study Task 4)," *Report NUREG/CR-0654, SAND 79-0324*, Sandia National Laboratories, Albuquerque, NM, 1979.
4. Lie, T. T., "Characteristic Temperature Curves for Various Fire Severities," *Fire Technology*, Vol. 10, No. 4, 1974, pp. 315-326.
5. Ingberg, S. H., "Fire Tests of Office Occupancies," *NFPA Quarterly*, Vol. 20, No. 3, 1927, pp. 243-252.
6. Ingberg, S. H., "Tests of the Severity of Building Fires," *NFPA Quarterly*, Vol. 22, No. 1, 1928, pp. 43-61.
7. Culver, C. G., "Characteristics of Fire Loads in Office Buildings," *Fire Technology*, Vol. 14, No. 1, 1978, pp. 51-60.
8. Campbell, J. A., "Fire Safety Systems Analysis Data Base," reported at NFPA Fall Meeting, Montreal, Quebec, Canada, 1978.
9. "Handbook, Building Firesafety Criteria," *PBS P5920.9, Change 6*, General Services Administration, Washington, DC, 1977.
10. Waterman, T. E., *et al.*, "Prediction of Fire Damage to Installations and Built-up Areas from Nuclear Weapons," *Final Report—Phase III, Experimental Studies, Appendices A-G*, Contract No. DCA-8, National Military Command System Support Center, Washington, DC, 1964.
11. Harmathy, T. Z., "Design of Buildings for Fire Safety—Part I," *Fire Technology*, Vol. 12, No. 2, 1976, pp. 95-108.
12. Heselden, A. J. M., *et al.*, "Burning Rate of Ventilation-Controlled Fires in Compartments," *Fire Technology*, Vol. 6, No. 2, 1970, pp. 123-125.
13. Babrauskas, V. and Williamson, R. B., "Post-Flashover Compartment Fires," *Report UCB FRG 75-1*, Fire Research Group, University of California, Berkeley, CA, 1975.
14. Kawagoe, K., "Estimation of Fire Temperature-Time Curve in Rooms," *Building Research Paper No. 29*, Ministry of Construction, Japanese Government, Tokyo, Japan, 1967.
15. Mitler, H. E. and Emmons, H. W., "Documentation for the Fifth Harvard Computer Fire Code," *Home Fire Project Technology Report No. 45*, Harvard University, Cambridge, MA, 1981.
16. Bukowski, R. B., Peacock, R. D., Jones, W. W., and Forney, C. L., "Technical Reference Guide for the HAZARD I Fire Hazard Assessment Method," *Handbook 146, Vol. II*, National Institute of Standards Technology, Gaithersburg, MD, 1989.
17. Davis, W. D. and Cooper, L. Y., "Estimating the Environment and the Response of Sprinkler Links in Compartment Fires with Draft Curtains and Fusible-Link-Actuated Ceiling Vents—*Part II: User Guide for the Computer Code LAVENT,*" *NISTIR 89-4122*, National Institute of Standards and Technology, Gaithersburg, MD, 1989.
18. Mitler, H. E. and Rockett, J. A., "User's Guide to FIRST, A Comprehensive Single-Room Fire Model," *NBSIR 87-3595*, National Bureau of Standards, Gaithersburg, MD, Sept. 1987.
19. "Fire Tests in a Nursing Home Patient Room," *Report HEW*, Contract HSA 105-74-116, American Health Care Association, Washington, DC, 1975.
20. Zinn, B.T., *et al.*, "Fire Spread and Smoke Control in High-Rise Fires," *Fire Technology*, Vol. 10, No. 1, 1974, pp. 35-53.
21. Christian, W. J. and Waterman, T. E., "Characteristics of Full-Scale Fires in Various Occupancies," *Fire Technology*, Vol. 7, No. 3, pp. 204-218.
22. "Fire Severity at the Exterior of a Burning Building," *Report 67NK5227A*, American Iron and Steel Institute, Washington, DC, 1975.
23. "Fire Resistance Ratings of Less Than One Hour," National Board of Fire Underwriters, New York, NY, 1956.
24. Waterman, T. E., "Experimental Structural Fires," *Report J6269*, Contract DAHC 20-72-C-0290, DCPA Work Unit 2562B, 1974, IIT Research Institute, Chicago, IL, 1974.
25. Roytman, M. Y., *Principles of Fire Safety Standards for Building Construction*, Construction Literature Publishing House, Moscow, USSR, 1969; *TT-71-58002*, National Bureau of Standards, Amerind Publishing Co., PVT Ltd., New Delhi, India, 1975.
26. Best, R. L., "Tragedy in Kentucky," *Fire Journal*, Vol. 72, No. 1 (Jan. 1978), pp. 18-35.
27. Best, R. L. and Demers, D. P., "Fire at the MGM Grand," *Fire Journal*, Vol. 76, No. 1 (Jan. 1982), pp. 19-37.
28. DeCicco, P. R., "What to Do with Existing Row-Frame Residential Buildings," *Fire Journal*, Vol. 70, No. 6, 1976, pp. 23-31.
29. "Recommendations Related to Brown's Ferry Fire," *NUREG-0050*, Special Review Group, U.S. Nuclear Regulatory Commission, Washington, DC, 1976.
30. Powers, W. R., "One New York Plaza Fire," New York Board of Fire Underwriters, New York, NY, 1970.
31. Kamerus, L. J., "A Preliminary Report on Fire Protection Research Program (July 6, 1977 Test)," *SAND 77-1424*, Sandia National Laboratories, Albuquerque, NM, 1977.
32. Kamerus, L. J., "A Preliminary Report on Fire Protection Research Program Fire Barriers and Fire Retardant Coating Tests," *NUREG CR-0381, SAND 78-1456*, Sandia National Laboratories, Albuquerque, NM, 1978.
33. Lathrop, J. K., "World Trade Center Fire," *Fire Journal*, Vol. 69, No. 4 (July 1975), pp. 19-21.
34. Watrous, L. D., "Fire in a High-Rise Apartment Building, Hawthorne House, Chicago," *Fire Journal*, Vol. 63, No. 3 (May 1969), pp. 5-11.
35. "MFL Fire Walls: Barriers against Destruction," *Factory Mutual Record*, Factory Mutual Research Corp., Norwood, MA, 1982, p. 13.

36. Hamilton, D. C. and Morgan, W. R., "Radiant-Interchange Configuration Factors," *Technical Note 2836*, National Advisory Committee for Aeronautics, 1952.

37. Pingree, D., "Looking at Fire Hazards: The Height of Flames above a Roof," *Fire Journal*, Vol. 62, No. 3 (May 1968), pp. 24-27, 32.

38. Law, M., "Heat Radiation from Fires and Building Separation," *Technical Paper No. 5*, Joint Fire Research Organization, Her Majesty's Stationery Office, London, England, 1963.

39. Bushev, V. P., *et al.*, *Fire Resistance of Buildings*, Construction Literature Publishers, Moscow, USSR, 1970; *IT 73-52030*, National Bureau of Standards, Amerind Publishing Co., PVT Ltd., New Delhi, India, 1978.

40. Reagan, R., *et al.*, "Project Corridor, Fire and Life Safety Research," *Western Fire Journal*, Bellflower, CA, 1974.

41. "A Compendium of Fire Testing," Feedback, Operation Breakthrough, Vol. 5, *HUD-PDR-28-3*, U.S. Department of Housing and Urban Development, Washington, DC, 1976.

42. Fisher, F. L., *et al.*, "A Study of Potential Post-Flashover Fires in Wheeler Hall and the Results from a Full-Scale Fire Test of a Modified Wheeler Hall Door Assembly," *Report UCX 77-3*, Fire Research Laboratory, University of California, Berkeley, CA, 1977.

43. Battelle Columbus Laboratories, "Space Age Contribution to Residential Fire Safety," *Fire Journal*, Vol. 68, No. 2 (Mar. 1974), pp. 18-25.

44. Beuttner, K., "Effects of Extreme Heat on Man, III: Surface Temperature, Pain, and Heat Conductivity of Living Skin in Experiments with Radiant Heat," *Project 21-26-002, Report No. 3*, USAF School of Aviation Medicine, 1951.

45. Hanauer, S. H., Collins, H. E., Levine, S., Minners, W., Moore, V. A., Panciera, V. W., and Sayfirt, K. V., "Recommendations Related to Brown's Ferry Fire," Report by Special Review Group, *NUREG-0050*, U. S. Nuclear Regulatory Commission, Washington, DC, Feb. 1976.

46. Attwood, P. C., "Penetration of Fire Partitions by Plastic Pipe," *Fire Technology*, Vol. 16, No. 1, 1980, pp. 37-62.

47. Benjamin, I. A. and Parker, W. J., "Fire Spread Potential of ABS Plastic Plumbing," *Fire Technology*, Vol. 8, No. 2, 1972, pp. 104-119.

48. McGuire, J. H., "Penetration of Fire Partitions by Plastic DWV Pipe," *Fire Technology*, Vol. 9, No. 1, 1973, pp. 5-14.

49. Williamson, R. B., "Installing ABS and PVC Drain, Waste, and Vent Systems in Fire-Resistant Buildings," *Fire Journal*, Vol. 73, No. 2 (Mar. 1979), pp. 36-45.

NFPA Codes, Standards, and Recommended Practices

Reference to the following NFPA codes, standards, and recommended practices will provide further information on the methods for confinement of fire in buildings discussed in this chapter. (See the latest *NFPA Catalog* for availability of current editions of the following documents.)

NFPA 80, *Fire Doors and Windows*.

NFPA 80A, *Protection from Exposure Fires*.

NFPA 101, *Life Safety Code*.

NFPA 251, *Fire Tests of Building Construction and Materials*.

References

Alpert, R. L. and Ward, E. J., "Evaluation of Unsprinklered Fire Hazards," *Fire Safety Journal*, 1982, pp. 7, 127.

Babrauskas, V., and Walton, W. D., "A Simplified Characterization for Upholstered Furniture Heat Release Rates," *Fire Safety Journal*, Vol. 11, 1986, pp. 181-192.

Babrauskas, V., "Fire Tests and Hazard Analysis of Upholstered Chairs," *Fire Journal*, Vol. 74, No. 2 (Mar. 1980), pp. 35-39.

Cooper, L. Y., "Estimating the Environment and the Response of Sprinkler Links in Compartment Fires with Draft Curtains and Fusible Link-Actuated Ceiling Vents—Part I: Theory," *NBSIR 88-3734*, National Bureau of Standards, Gaithersburg, MD, Apr. 1988.

Davis, S., "Assessment of Fire Hazards from Furniture," International Fire, Security, and Safety Conference, London, England, Apr. 24-28, 1978.

Harmathy, T. Z., "A New Look at Compartment Fires—Parts I and II," *Fire Technology*, Vol. 8, Nos. 3 and 4, 1972.

Lathrop, J. K., *et al.*, "In Osceola a Matter of Contents—Hospital Fire Kills Seven," *Fire Journal*, Vol. 69, No. 3, 1975, pp. 20-29.

Lee, B. T., "Heat Release Rate Characteristics of Some Combustible Fuel Sources in Nuclear Power Plants," *NBSIR 85-3195*, National Bureau of Standards, Washington, DC, 1985.

Quintiere, J. G., "Growth of Fire in Building Compartments." Fire Standards and Safety, *ASTM STP 614, ed.*, A. F. Robertson, American Society of Testing Materials, 1977, pp. 131-167.

Sharry, J. A., "Another Pennsylvania Nursing Home Fire, Wayne, Pennsylvania," *Fire Journal*, Vol. 68, No. 3 (May 1974), pp. 11-14.

Vodvarka, F. J. and Waterman, T. E., "Fire Behavior, Ignition to Flashover," *Final Report*, Task 2-C, OCD-PS-64-50, OCD Work Unit 2536-C, IIT Research Institute, Chicago, IL, 1965.

Additional Readings

Babrauskas, V., "Estimating Room Flashover Potential," *Fire Technology*, Vol. 16, No. 2 (May 1980), pp. 94-104.

Beason, D., "Fire Endurance of Sprinklered Glass Walls," *Fire Journal*, Vol. 80, No. 4 (July 1986), p. 43.

Belles, D. W. and Beitel, J. J., "Preventing Vertical Fire Spread in Aluminum Curtain Walls," *Building Standards*, Vol. 57, No. 1, 1988, pp. 10-16.

Birmingham, J. A., "Firestops Protect Property—and Lives," *Fire Journal*, Vol. 80, No. 2 (Mar. 1986), p. 41.

Brady, B., "Closing the Doors on Fire," *Fire Prevention*, No. 220 (June 1989), pp. 20-24.

Choi, K. K., "Fire Stops for Plastic Pipe," *Fire Technology*, Vol. 23, No. 4, 1987, pp. 267-279.

Chow, W. K., "Smoke Movement and Design of Smoke Control in Atrium Buildings," *International Journal for Housing Science and Its Applications*, Vol. 13, No. 4, 1989, pp. 307-322.

Chow, W. K., "Sprinklers in Atrium Buildings," *Hong Kong Engineer*, Vol. 16, No. 9 (Sept. 1988), p. 41, 43.

Cooper, L. Y., "Convective Heat Transfer to Ceilings Above Enclosure Fires," in *Proceedings* of 19th Symposium (International) on Combustion, Combustion Institute, 1982, pp. 933-939.

Degenkolb, J. G., "Atriums," *BOCA Magazine*, Vol. 17, No. 6 (Dec. 1983).

Degenkolb, J. G., "Field Test of an Atrium Exhaust System," *Building Standards*, Vol. 57, No. 2, 1988, pp. 18-19.

Ferguson, A., "New Standards for Atrium Building," *Fire Prevention* (London), No. 184, Nov. 1985.

Finnimore, B., "Need for Atria Fire Codes," *Fire Prevention*, No. 205 (Dec. 1987), pp. 30-33.

"Fire-Rated Hollow Metal Doors and Frames," National Association of Architectural Metal Manufacturers, 1983.

Fire Resistance Design Manual, 12th ed., Gypsum Association, Evanston, IL, 1988.

"Fire Wall Design," *Sentinel*, Vol. 36, No. 6 (Nov.-Dec. 1980), pp. 14-15.

Ford, N. J., "Safety: Smoke and Fire Curtains," *H&V Engineer*, Vol. 16, No. 683, pp. 7-8.

Gross, D., "Data Sources for Parameters Used in Predictive Modeling of Fire Growth and Smoke Spread," *NBSIR 85-3223*, National Bureau of Standards, Gaithersburg, MD, 1985.

Harmathy, T. Z., "The Fire Resistance Test and Its Relation to Real World Fires," *Fire and Materials*, Vol. 5, 1981, p. 112.

Harmathy, T. Z. and Oleszkiewicz, I., "Fire Drainage System," *Fire Technology*, Vol. 23, No. 1, 1987, pp. 26-48.

Irwin, W. T., "Duct Penetrations of One-Hour Fire Resistance Rated Nonload-bearing Walls/Partitions," *ASHRAE Transactions*, Vol. 92, 1986, pp. 556-565.

Lawson, J. R., "Fire Performance of Interstitial Space Construction System," *NBSIR 85-3158*, National Bureau of Standards, Gaithersburg, MD, May 1985.

Lorigheed, G. D. and Richardson, J. K., "Sprinklers in Combustible Concealed Spaces," *Journal of Fire Protection Engineering*, Vol. 1, No. 2, 1989, pp. 49-62.

Morehart, J. L., "Sprinklers in the NIH Atrium: How Did They React during the Fire Last May?" *Fire Journal*, Vol. 83, No. 1 (Jan.-Feb. 1989), pp. 57-57.

Parry, L., "Fire Resisting Timber Doorsets," *Fire Surveyor*, Vol. 18, No. 6 (Dec. 1989), pp. 18-21.

Quintiere, J., "The Spread of Fire from a Compartment—A Review," *ASTM STP 685*, American Society for Testing and Materials, Philadelphia, PA, 1980.

Richardson, J. K. and Oleszkiewicz, I., "Fire Tests on Window Assenblies Protected by Automatic Sprinklers," *Fire Technology*, Vol. 23, No. 2, 1987, pp. 115-132.

Rockett, J. A., "Data for Room Fire Models," *Comb. Sci. & Technology*, Vol. 40, 1984, p. 137.

Schwartz, J. K., Jensen, R. H., and Antell, J., "Role of Dampers in a Total Fire Protection System Analysis," *ASHRAE Transactions*, Vol. 92, 1986, pp. 566-576.

Semple, J. B. and Bruce, D. O., "Review of Current Fire Damper Requirements in NFPA Standard 90A and Model Codes," *ASHRAE Transactions*, Vol. 92, 1986, pp. 541-549.

Sinclair, J., "Selecting the Correct Door Control," *Fire Prevention*, No. 205 (Dec. 1987), pp. 38-41.

Smith, T. and Post, H., "Fire Safety in Atrium Buildings," *Buildings*, Vol. 77, No. 5 (May 1983).

Tanaka, T., "A Model of Multiroom Fire Spread," *NBSIR 83-2718*, National Bureau of Standards, Gaithersburg, MD, 1983.

Waters, R. A., "Stansted Terminal Building and Early Atrium Studies," *Journal of Fire Protection Engineering*, Vol. 1, No. 2, 1989, pp. 63-76.

SMOKE MOVEMENT IN BUILDINGS

Revised by John H. Klote and Harold E. "Bud" Nelson

Smoke and fire gases, inherent in all accidental fires, are dangerous products of combustion that have critical influences on life safety, property protection, and fire suppression practices in buildings. In some fires, the volume of smoke is so great that it may fill an entire building and obscure visibility at the street level to such an extent that it is difficult to identify the fire-involved building. In other incidents, the volume of smoke generated may be considerably less, although the danger to life is not necessarily diminished because of the presence of other airborne products of combustion.

This chapter gives information on the techniques used to evaluate the physical characteristics of smoke movement through both short and tall buildings as a basis for designing smoke-control systems. It also covers the approaches that can be used to test the effectiveness of designed smoke-control systems in the absence of actual performance tests involving test fires.

For more information on controlling the hazards of smoke, see the following chapters in this section: Chapter 8, "Venting Practices," and Chapter 16, "Air Conditioning and Ventilating Systems." Also see Section 10, Chapter 11, "Simplified Calculations for Enclosure Fires."

This chapter provides general background, a discussion of relationships, and selected equations useful in understanding smoke movement and smoke management in buildings. Of necessity, the information is not sufficient for detailed design analysis, but design information is available from a number of sources. The 1983 manual by Klote and Fothergill[1] was the first publication to provide a consolidation and systematic presentation of data and calculations necessary for the design systems to manage smoke movement by pressurization. Specific design information was provided for pressurized stairwells and zoned smoke-control systems. The manual also provided general information about smoke movement in buildings. The smoke-control chapter of the 1988 *SFPE Handbook*[2] summarizes much of the general information from Klote and Fothergill. NFPA 92A, *Smoke Control Systems*, was first published in 1988 and provides additional recommendations for stairwell pressurization systems and zoned smoke-control systems, including suggested levels of pressurization for such systems in sprinklered and unsprinklered buildings. The NFPA Smoke Management System Committee has prepared a technical guide for the design of smoke management for atria, shopping malls, and other large spaces. This document—NFPA 92B, *Smoke Management Systems in Malls, Atria, and Large Areas*—became available in early 1991.

John H. Klote, Ph.D., P.E., is the leader of the Building Fire Physics Group at the Building and Fire Research Laboratory, NIST. He is a member of SFPE, the NFPA Air Conditioning Committee, and the NFPA Smoke Management Systems Committee. Mr. Klote is also chairperson of the ASHRAE Fire and Smoke Control Committee. Harold E. Nelson, P.E., is a senior research fire protection engineer at the Building and Fire Research Laboratory, National Institute of Standards and Technology (NIST), Gaithersburg, MD. He is also a Fellow and past president of the Society of Fire Protection Engineers (SFPE).

CLASSIFICATION OF SMOKE ZONES

As a fire burns, it:

1. Generates heat.
2. Changes major portions of the burning material or fuel from its original chemical composition to one or more other compounds, such as carbon dioxide, carbon monoxide, water, and/or other compounds.
3. Often, due to less than 100 percent combustion efficiency, transports a portion of the fuel as soot or other material that may or may not have undergone a chemical change.

A major portion of the heat generated as a fuel burns remains in the mass of products liberated by the fire. This mass expands, is lighter than the surrounding air, and rises as a plume. The rising plume is turbulent and, because of this, entrains large quantities of air from the surrounding atmosphere into the rising gases. This entrainment:

1. Increases the total mass and volume of the plume.
2. Cools the plume by mixing the cool entrained air with the rising hot gases. Normally, the rising plume is hotter at its center and cooler toward the edges where cooler air is entrained.
3. Dilutes the concentration of fire products in the plume.

Smoke, as discussed in this chapter, is therefore defined as a mixture of hot vapors and gases produced by the combustion process along with unburned decomposition and condensation matter and the quantity of air that is entrained or otherwise mixed into the mass.

For the purposes of describing smoke movement in buildings, the treatment of smoke movement is divided into two general areas: the hot smoke zone and the cool smoke zone.

Hot Smoke Zone

This zone includes those areas in a building where the temperature of the smoke is high enough so that the natural buoyancy of the body of smoke tends to lift the smoke toward the ceiling while clean, or at least less polluted, air is drawn in through the lower portion of the space. Normally, this condition exists in the room of fire origin. Depending upon the level of energy produced by the fire and the size of connecting openings, such as open doors, hot smoke zones can readily exist in adjacent rooms or corridors. Industrial and warehouse smoke and heat venting, atria smoke removal, and the movement of smoke in corridors open to spaces that have flashed over, all involve a hot smoke zone where the smoke is lifted and driven by the buoyant forces produced by the fire.

Cool Smoke Zone

This zone includes those areas in a building where mixing and other forms of heat transfer have reduced the effect of the driving force of the fire to the point at which buoyant lift in the smoke body is a minor factor. In these areas, the movement of smoke is primarily controlled by other forces, such as wind and stack effects, and the mechanical heat, ventilating, air conditioning, or other air-movement systems. In these areas, the movement of smoke is essentially the same as the movement of any other pollutant.

SMOKE MOVEMENT IN THE HOT SMOKE ZONE

The volume of combustion products entrained in a rising plume in the hot smoke zone is relatively small, compared with the volume of air in the total mixture. Consequently, the smoke produced by a fire will approximate the volume of air drawn into the rising plume. Figure 6-7A illustrates the process.

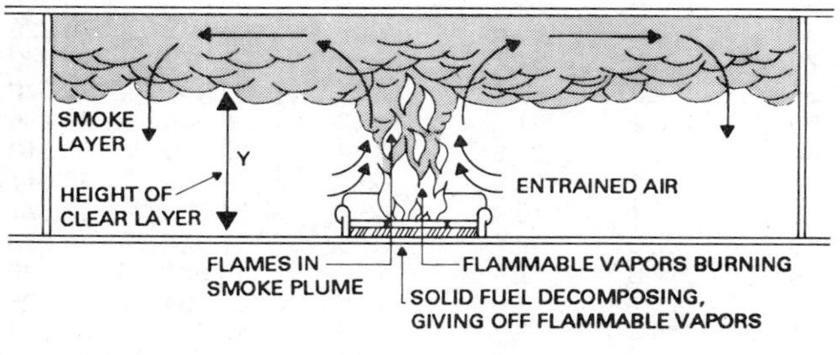

FIG. 6-7A. The production of smoke from a fire.

In situations in which the height of the plume, as measured from the top of the fire to the level of the smoke layer, is more than about twice the height of the solid body of flame, it is reasonable to estimate the amount of smoke using developed formulas.[3,4]

In general, the equations given in this chapter for conditions in the hot smoke zone should be used where the fire is small compared to the height of the space involved. For locations where this is not true, the equations in Section 10, Chapter 11, "Hand Calculations for Enclosure Fires," are more appropriate.

The following equations were derived from research conducted at the British Fire Research Station more than 25 years ago. This work showed that the amount of smoke could be reasonably estimated solely as a function of the height of the fire plume over a "virtual fire source." The research indicated that the virtual source for a free-burning fire having a circular shape would be approximately 0.15 diameters below the burning surface.

The mass of gas drawn into the fire can be estimated as:

$$M = 0.096\, P q_o Y^{3/2} (g\, T_o/T)^{1/2}$$

where:

M = rate of smoke production (kg/s)
P = perimeter of the fire (m)
q_o = density of ambient air (kg/m^3)
Y = distance from floor to bottom of smoke layer (m)
g = acceleration due to gravity (m/s^2)
T_o = absolute temperature of the ambient air (K)
T = absolute temperature of the flames of the smoke plume (K)

Typical numerical values of the parameters are:

q_o = 1.22 kg/m^3 @ 17°C
T_o = 290 K
T = 1100 K
g = 9.81 m/s^2

Using these values, the rate of smoke production becomes:

$$M = 0.188\, P y^{3/2}$$

The simple expression $M = 0.188\, Py$ includes a series of assumptions, the most important of which are:

1. The tip of the flame is a significant distance below the bottom of the smoke layer. The formula, while useful, is much less accurate in spaces with a low ceiling relative to the height of the fire involved.
2. The fire bed itself covers an area whose length and width are reasonably approximate to each other. The original formula is based on the assumption of a circular fire. The degree of error in the formula increases as the relationship of length to width increases.

Flame Height

A reasonable estimate of flame height[5] can be obtained from the expression:

$$H_f = 0.011\, (k\dot{Q})^{0.4}$$

where:

H_f = flame height (m)
k = wall effect factor. The value of k to be used is:
  k = 1 when there are no nearby walls
  k = 2 when the fuel package is near a wall
  k = 4 when the fuel package is in a corner
$\dot{Q}$ = fuel heat release rate (watts)

The results of this equation are shown graphically in Figure 6-7B.

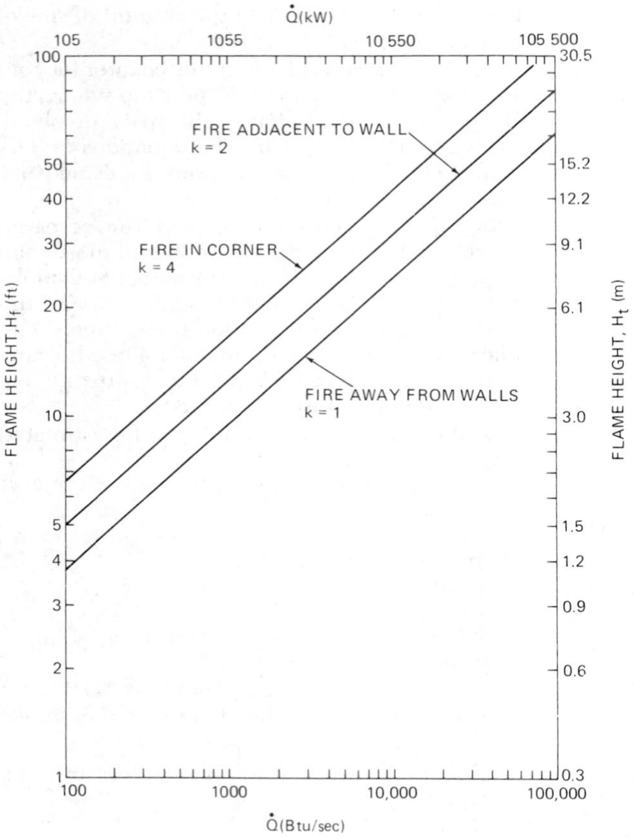

FIG. 6-7B. Flame height versus fire heat release rate.

Plume Gas Temperature

Detailed engineering equations for properties of fire plumes have been presented.[6] In simpler terms, however,[5] an empirical estimate plume temperature is provided at a given point above the fuel as:

$$\Delta T = \frac{0.22\ (k\dot{Q})^{2/3}}{H^{5/3}}$$

where:

ΔT = maximum temperature increase (°C) above ambient (room) temperature
$\dot{Q}$ = total heat release rate (W)
k = wall factor. The value of k is:
k = 1 when there are no nearby walls
k = 2 when the fuel package is near a wall
k = 4 when the fuel package is in a corner
H = distance (m) above the top of the fuel package (for a pool of flammable liquid, such as gasoline or heptane. H is the distance above the fuel surface minus one pool diameter)

Smoke production is, therefore, dependent upon the perimeter of the fire and the effective height of the gas column above it. As the fire continues to burn, the rate of smoke production will vary as the distance *y* changes. Figure 6-7C illustrates this variability.

The mass rate of smoke production, *M*, can be converted into a volumetric rate of production by dividing the

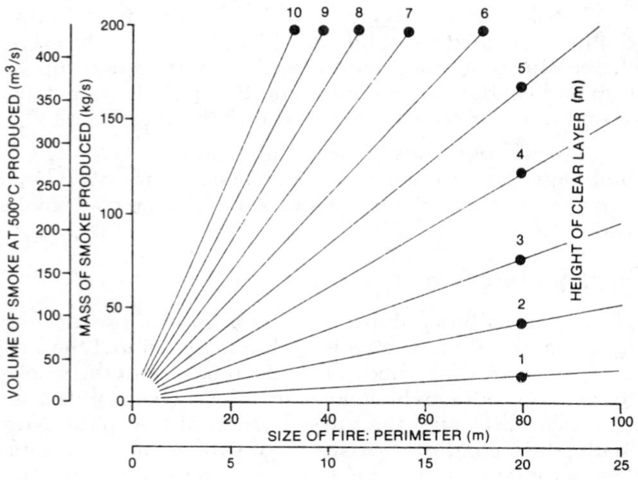

FIG. 6-7C. Rate of smoke production as a fire continues to burn.

expression above by the density of the air (as smoke) at T°C. This factor becomes 1.22 [290/(T+273)] kg/m^3. Table 6-7A illustrates the relationship between mass rates and volumetric rates of flow.

Where the hot gas flows through an opening of relatively small size and is either entirely above the smoke layer or the portion of interface is small compared to the full size of the opening—for example, the space between a door frame and the vertical side of a closed smoke barrier door—it is possible to use adaptations of Bernouli's equation to estimate the smoke movement. The basic formulas have been assembled[7] and adapted to the following statement.[8]

TABLE 6-7A. *Conversion of Mass Rates of Flow of Smoke into Volume Rates of Flow*

Mass rate of flow		Volume rates of flow			
		m^3/sec		ft^3/min	
kg/sec	lb/sec	at 20°C	at 500°C	at 20°C	at 500°C
200	440.8	164.9	436.9	346 928	925 354
100	220.4	81.9	218.5	173 464	462 783
90	198.4	73.8	196.6	156 308	416 399
80	176.6	65.6	174.8	138 941	370 226
70	154.3	57.4	152.9	121 573	323 842
60	132.2	49.2	131.1	104 205	277 670
50	110.2	41.0	109.2	86 838	231 286
40	88.2	32.8	87.4	69 470	185 113
30	66.1	24.6	65.4	52 103	138 517
20	44.1	16.4	43.7	34 735	92 557
10	22.0	8.2	21.8	17 346	46 278
9	19.8	7.4	19.7	15 631	41 640
8	17.7	6.6	17.5	13 894	37 023
7	15.4	5.7	15.3	12 157	32 384
6	13.2	4.9	13.1	10 420	27 767
5	11.0	4.1	10.9	8 684	23 128
4	8.8	3.3	8.7	6 947	18 511
3	6.6	2.5	6.5	5 210	13 852
2	4.4	1.6	4.4	3 473	9 256
1	2.2	0.8	2.2	1 735	4 628

$$f = C_d\, A\, (2\, gh)^{1/2}\, (T_s/T_a - 1)^{1/2}$$

where:

f = flow (m^3/s)
C_d = flow coefficient (typical value of 0.60 to 0.70)
A = area of opening (m^2)
g = gravitational constant (9.8 m/s^2)
h = height above neutral plane (m)
T_a = ambient temperature (K)
T_s = smoke temperature (K)

In conventional units, the formula is:

$$f = 7214A \left(\frac{1}{T_a} - \frac{1}{T_s} \right)^{1/2} (h)^{1/2} \left(\frac{T_s}{530} \right)^{1/2}$$

$$\Delta P = 7.64 \left(\frac{1}{T_a} - \frac{1}{T_s} \right) h$$

where:

f = flow (ft^3/min)
A = area of opening (ft^2)
T_a = ambient temperature (°R)
T_s = smoke temperature (°R)
ΔP = pressure difference (in. of water)
h = height above neutral plane (ft)

Figure 6-7D shows typical results from this formula in conventional units.

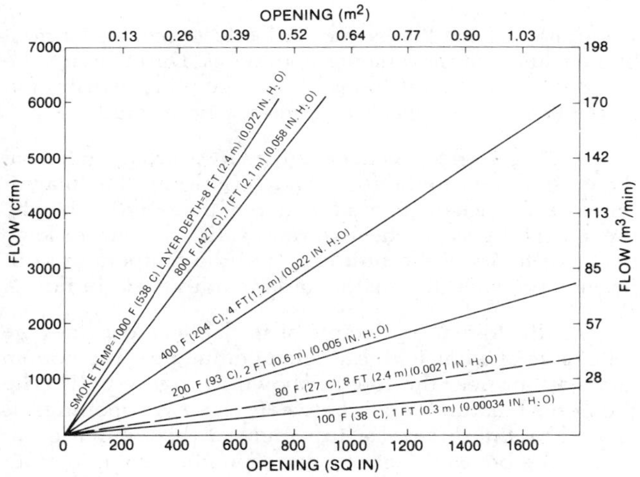

FIG. 6-7D. Volume of smoke flow through an opening.

NFPA 92B, *Smoke Management Systems in Malls, Atria, and Large Areas*, was recently introduced. This guide provides detailed equations and procedures for appraising the management of smoke in atria. Figure 6-7E provides a general estimate of the effect exhaust from an atrium has on the level and temperature of various-sized fires within it. In all cases, this figure assumes a steady-state fire within the atrium.[9]

Procedure for fan selection: The fan's size, temperature rating, and means of operation is determined using Figure 6-7E by the following procedure:

1. *Acceptable smoke level*. Determine the lowest acceptable level of smoke accumulation. This is the highest level in which sleeping accommodations are permitted. The vertical distance between head level, which is approximately 5 ft (1.5 m) above the floor, and the floor level of the lowest floor in the atrium is the value Z_{clear} to be used in Figure 6-7E for determining the required rate of volume of smoke removal. If sleeping accommodations are only permitted on the lowest floor, then Z_{clear} = 10 ft (3 m).
2. *Characteristic fuel*. Determine the steady rate of convected energy, Q_c, passing into the smoke layer. In Figure 6-7E, curves are plotted that relate to the steady rate of convected energy of the fire which would threaten the atrium space in units of Btu/s. The upper sketch in the figure is meant to indicate that the curves are useful for describing conditions related to combustibles burning on the atrium floor or on any balcony open to the atrium. The lower sketch indicates that the curves are also relevant when combustibles burn in rooms that enter into the atrium.
3. *Exhaust fan rate*. From Figure 6-7E, determine the exhaust fan capacity needed to extract smoke at the rate that will keep the smoke level at Z_{clear}. This rate is found in the base line of the figure and corresponds to the level of Z_{clear} on the vertical axis, as determined by the solid line characterizing the maximum anticipated steady rate of convected energy—that is, the largest anticipated fire—in the atrium. This is the minimum exhaust capacity of the fan.
4. *Intake air*. Provide intake air openings that will be present or automatically activated at the time of emergency smoke removal. These are to be located at or near the lowest floor involved to allow for air intake at the rate vented by the fan. The openings provided must be large enough so that losses at the intake do not significantly reduce the fan exhaust capacity. Standard air-handling design criteria are used in making this calculation.
5. *Fan temperature rate*. Determine the potential temperature of gases that the fan may be required to handle. To do this, identify the highest floor of the atrium where balcony combustibles or potentially hazardous room fires are to be found. Determine the distance from the elevation of this floor to the centerline of the fan or fan ports if the fan is in a dock or similar arrangement. Determine the intersection of the new Z_{clear} value with the appropriate ventilation rate curve (solid line) for the maximum rate of convected energy at that higher level. Estimate the temperature rise by interpolating between the constant temperature rise curves (dashed) on Figure 6-7E. Provide all elements of the exhaust system that are to be above the applicable smoke level with the capacity to effectively operate at the indicated increase of temperature.
6. *Operation of exhaust system*. Design the emergency exhaust system for direct manual operation and to initiate automatically when smoke is detected, when the manual fire alarm system operates, or when the sprinklers operate for any of the spaces exposing the atrium. The automatic exhaust system should be able to be started manually at both the main desk or control location and at another remote location.

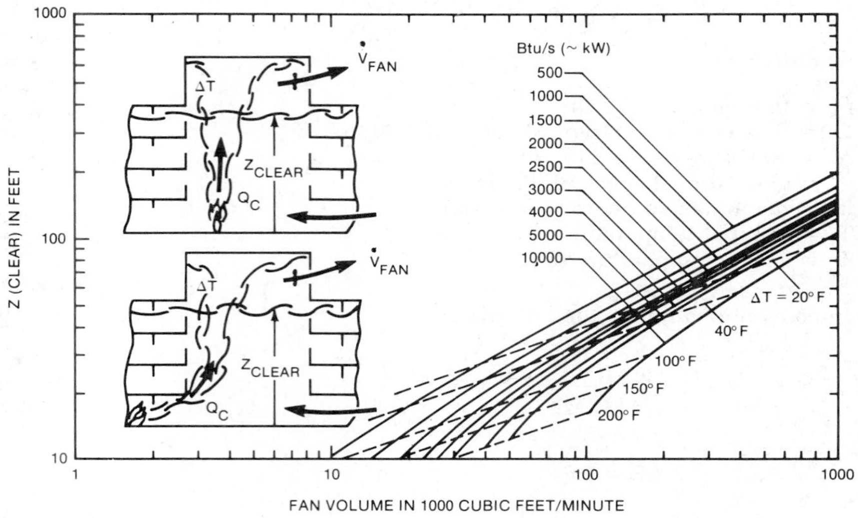

FIG. 6-7E. Estimates of effective exhaust from an atrium.

SMOKE MOVEMENT IN COLD SMOKE ZONES

As smoke is transmitted from the area of fire origin, it is cooled by entrainment of air; by the transfer of heat from the smoke body to building materials, primarily those in the walls and ceilings; and, as the smoke cools, by radiant energy losses. When smoke from a fire flows through a relatively small crack, the entrainment of cool air on the unexposed side tends to cool the smoke very quickly. When the leakage is through larger openings, there may be less entrainment relative to the mass of smoke movement at such junctures and, therefore, cooling will be slower. Once the smoke has cooled to a significant degree, however, it is transported in the same manner as any other pollutant, and the primary moving forces are those presented by the stack effect, the wind effect, and mechanical air movement systems.

When hot smoke is transported from one area of a building to another through a confined passageway, such as a duct, shaft, or stairwell, there will be little or no cooling due to entrainment. In such cases, cooling will be limited to heat lost by conduction from the moving smoke to the shaft material. Often, this loss is modest, and hot smoke can be transported significant distances with only minor cooling by such confined passageways.

SMOKE MOVEMENT IN TALL BUILDINGS

Smoke can behave very differently in tall buildings than in low buildings. In the lower buildings, the influences of the fire, such as heat, convective movement, and fire pressures, are the major factors that cause smoke movement. Smoke removal and venting practices reflect this behavior. In tall buildings, these same factors are complicated by the stack effect, which is the vertical natural air movement through the building caused by the differences in temperatures and densities between the inside and outside air. This stack effect can become an important factor in smoke movement and in building design features used to combat that movement.

The predominant factors that cause smoke movement in tall buildings are the stack effect, the influence of external wind forces, and the forced air movement within the building. The following text describes the theoretical natural air movement, which is affected by the first two factors. Forced air movement caused by the building air-handling equipment is presented elsewhere in this Handbook, but it should be noted that air movement can be influenced significantly by the mechanical systems of the building. Many design solutions to the problem of tenability use emergency operation of the mechanical systems.

Stack Effect

Under normal conditions, the stack effect accounts for most of the natural air movement in buildings. During a fire, the stack effect is often responsible for the wide distribution of smoke and toxic gases in high-rise buildings.

The stack effect is characterized by a strong draft from the ground floor to the roof of a tall building. The magnitude of this stack effect is a function of the building height, the air-tightness of the exterior walls, the air leakage between floors of the building, and the temperature difference between the inside and outside of the building.

To illustrate the principle of stack effect, consider the schematic of a box with a single opening near the bottom and another near the top, as shown in Figure 6-7F. The theoretical natural draft between the two openings is caused by the difference in weight of the column of air within the box and that of a corresponding column of air of equal dimensions outside the box. The magnitude of the theoretical natural draft may be computed using the following formula:

$$D_t = 2.96HB_o p \left(\frac{1}{T_o} - \frac{1}{T_i}\right)$$

where:

D_t = theoretical draft in inches of water
H = vertical distance between the inlet and the outlet in feet
B_o = barometric pressure in inches of mercury
T_o = temperature of outside air in degrees Rankine
p = density of air at 0°F and 1 atmosphere pressure in pounds per cubic foot

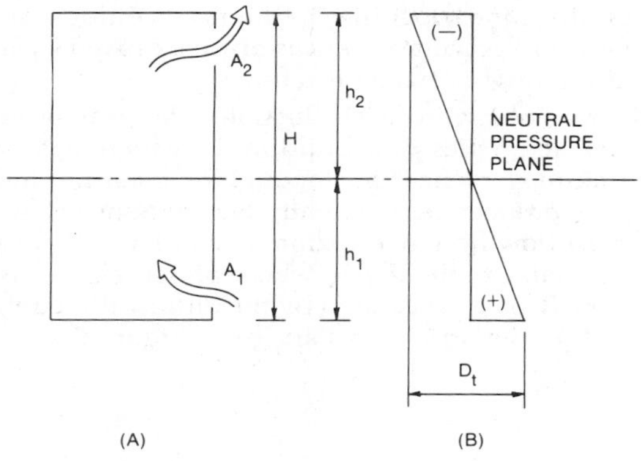

FIG. 6-7F. Air movements caused by pressure (a) and location of neutral pressure plane (b) in a structure without horizontal barriers and with the two openings shown.

Assuming values of B_o = 29.9 in. and p = 0.0862 pcf, this expression reduces to

$$D_i = 7.63H\left(\frac{1}{T_o} - \frac{1}{T_i}\right)$$

Vertical air movement in a building is caused by this natural draft or stack effect. The magnitude of the stack effect depends on the difference between the inside and outside temperatures and on the vertical distance between openings. If the inside and outside temperatures are equal ($T_i = T_o$), no natural air movement takes place. When $T_o \leq T_i$, the air moves vertically upward, with the lower opening acting as the inlet and the upper opening as the outlet. A reverse stack effect occurs when $T \geq T_i$. In this case, the upper opening is the inlet and the lower opening becomes the outlet.

Part (b) of Figure 6-7F illustrates the pressures that cause these movements. If it is assumed in this figure that $T_o \leq T_i$, the exterior pressure will be greater than the interior pressure at the lower opening. This is a positive pressure which forces outside air into the building at that location. The outside pressure at the upper opening is lower than the inside pressure, which creates a negative pressure at that location which forces the inside air outside. The pressure distribution between these two locations is assumed to be linear.

If an opening were present in the exterior wall in a region of positive pressure, air would flow into the building. An opening in a region of negative pressure would cause air to flow out of the building. The neutral pressure plane indicates where inside and outside pressures are equal. If there were an opening at this level, air would move neither inward nor outward. The location of the neutral pressure plane in a structure without horizontal barriers and with the two openings shown in Figure 6-7F can be determined from the following relationship:

$$\frac{h_1}{h_2} = \frac{A_2^2 T_o}{A_1^2 T_i}$$

where:

h_1 and h_2 represent the distances from the neutral pressure plane to the lower and upper openings respectively

A_1 and A_2 represent the cross-sectional areas of the lower and upper openings respectively

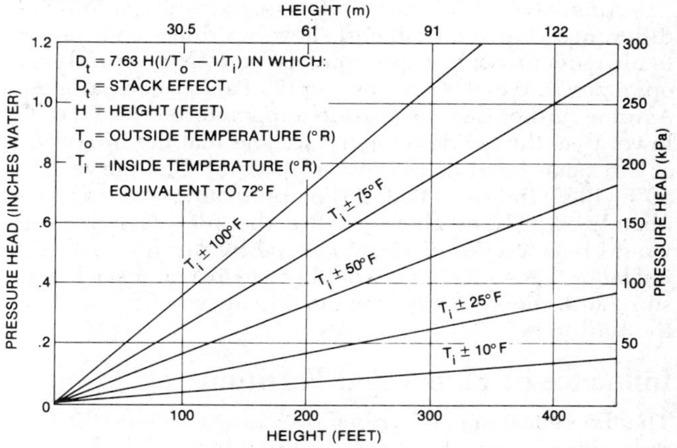

FIG. 6-7G. Stack effect due to height and temperature difference [°C = (°F-32)×5/9].

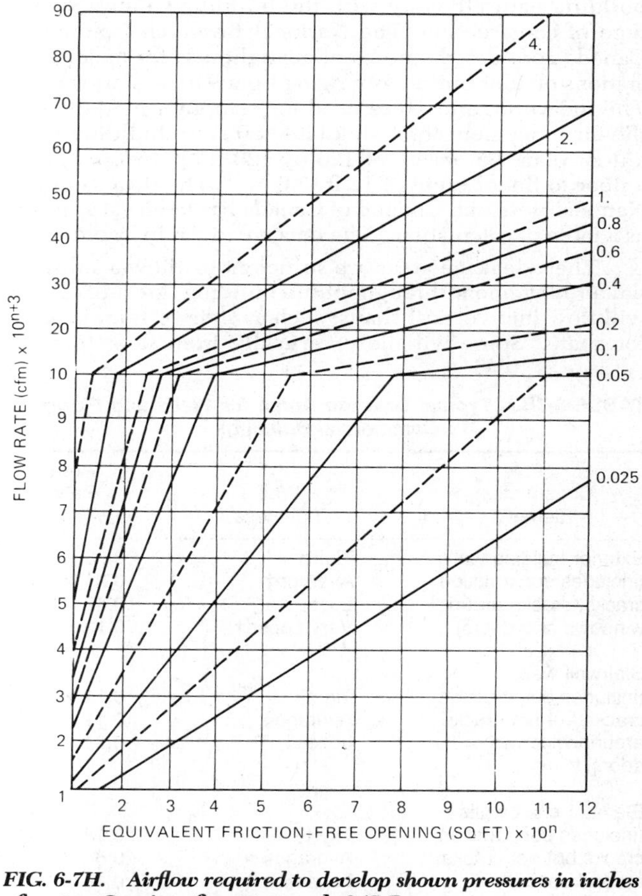

FIG. 6-7H. Airflow required to develop shown pressures in inches of water. One in. of water equals 249 Pa.

T_i and T_o represent the absolute temperatures of the air inside and outside the building respectively

The magnitude of the pressures created by the stack effect are described by the equation $d_i = 7.63H\left(\frac{1}{T_o} - \frac{1}{T_i}\right)$.

An analysis of Figure 6-7G illustrates the significant differences between tall and short buildings with regard to air movement. For example, assume that a fire develops a pressure of 0.06 in. of water (25 Pa) in a compartment. Assume further that the outside temperature is 50°F (10°C) lower than the inside temperature and that the fire occurs at the same level as the lower opening. The curve $T_i \pm$ 50°F (10°C) indicates that, if the upper outlet were approximately 40 ft (12 m) above the fire, the inlet stack pressure would balance the pressure caused by the fire. A building taller that 40 ft (12 m) would create a greater stack pressure, and, theoretically, the outside air would move into the building.

Influence of Floors and Partitions

The theoretical draft described by Figure 6-7F and the final reduced equation above are modified in real buildings by the presence of floors and partitions. These barriers impede the free movement of air, although a significant flow can take place through openings in the assemblies.

The magnitude and location of the leakage areas in a building naturally vary with the building's function and type of construction. The National Research Council of Canada conducted studies of air-tightness for major separations on four buildings ranging from 9 to 44 stories high. The measurements were used for computer modeling of the air movement for a simulated 20-story building with a floor plan dimension of 120 by 120 ft (36 by 36 m) and a floor to floor height of 12 ft (3.6 m).[10] The data from the National Research Council of Canada has been established as a table of calculation.[7] The data are given in Table 6-7B.

These leakage areas are sufficient to allow a substantial air movement throughout the building. Most of the air will flow into vertical shafts, such as stairwells and elevator shafts. Some will flow vertically from floor to floor through the minor openings in the floor-ceiling assembly. This floor-to-floor movement is always caused by a pressure differential between the floors.

Part (a) of Figure 6-7I illustrates the pressure difference characteristics of a building in which stack action causes air movement. The slopes of the pressure lines represent differences between any two regions at the same height. Airflow from one region to another will always be in the direction of the region whose pressure curve is more to the left. This is illustrated by the airflow directions represented by the arrows in Part (b) of Figure 6-7I.

TABLE 6-7B. *Typical Leakage Areas for Walls and Floors of Commercial Buildings*

Construction Element	Wall Tightness	Area Ratio A/Aw*
Exterior building walls (includes construction cracks, cracks around windows and doors)	Tight†	0.70×10^{-4}
	Average†	0.21×10^{-3}
	Loose†	0.42×10^{-3}
	Very Loose‡	0.13×10^{-2}
Stairwell walls (includes construction cracks but not cracks around windows or doors)	Tight§	0.14×10^{-4}
	Average§	0.11×10^{-3}
	Loose§	0.35×10^{-3}
Elevator shaft walls (includes construction cracks but not cracks around doors)	Tight§	0.18×10^{-3}
	Average§	0.84×10^{-3}
	Loose§	0.18×10^{-2}
		A/AF
Floors (includes construction cracks and cracks around penetrations)	Average#	0.52×10^{-4}

* A = leakage area; Aw = wall area; and A_F = floor area.
† Tamura and Shaw 1976.
‡ Tamura and Wilson 1966.
§ Tamura and Shaw 1976.
\# Tamura and Shaw 1978.

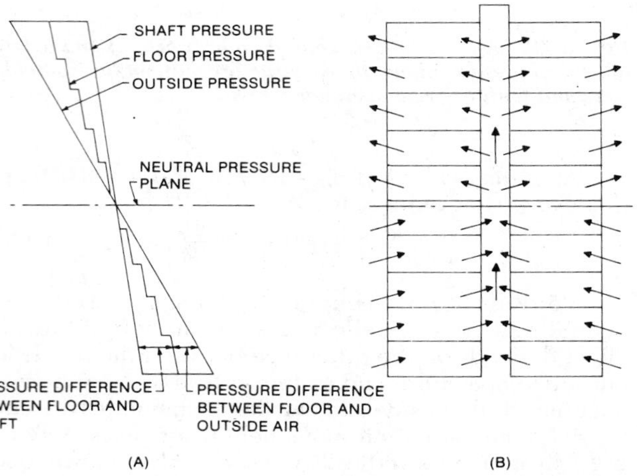

FIG 6-7I. The pressure difference characteristics of a building in which stack action causes air movement.

Wind Effects

Wind action is another important feature in the movement of smoke. Again, tall and short buildings behave somewhat differently in this regard. Figure 6-7J illustrates the air pressure distribution along the four sides and the roof of a building. The plan view of the pressures shows that the windward wall is subjected to an inward pressure, while the leeward wall and the two side walls have an outward pressure, or suction. The flat roof has an upward pressure, with the maximum amount occurring at the windward edge.

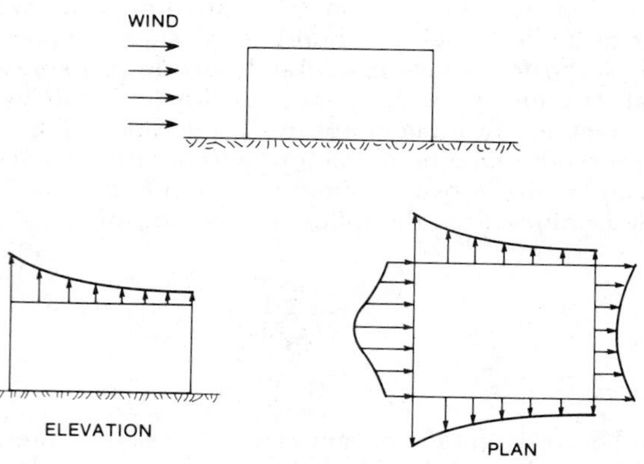

FIG. 6-7J. The air pressure distribution along the four sides and the roof of a building.

These pressures are caused by the movement of a mass of air around and over the structure. A short, wide building will cause the major volume of air to move over the roof, with correspondingly less air movement around the sides. A tall, narrow building, on the other hand, will cause the major volume of air to follow the path of least resistance around the building, with less movement over the top. The velocities of these movements are the primary cause of the amount and directions of the pressures on the building.

Wind velocities and direction vary over any face of a building. The most important effects are:

1. *Wind velocity:* The higher the wind velocity, the greater the effects of the following two influences.
2. *Ground effect:* Unless influenced by unusual arrangements of structures or terrain, the friction and turbulence that occur as air moves over the ground results in the lowest velocity at ground level and increases with increases in height.
3. *Structures:* Buildings and other man-made or natural features, such as trees, can produce localized effects that can increase, decrease, or alter the direction of wind forces.

The effect of wind pressures and suctions modifies the natural air movement within a building. For example, the negative pressure on the roof of a tall building can have an aspirating effect on a vertical shaft opened at the roof level. This can cause the observed draft to exceed the theoretical draft shown in Figure 6-7K.

Horizontal pressures and suctions cause the neutral planes in exterior walls to move. Positive wind pressure would tend to raise the neutral pressure plane, while negative pressure will lower it. Figure 6-7K illustrates the influence of wind action on air movement in a building.

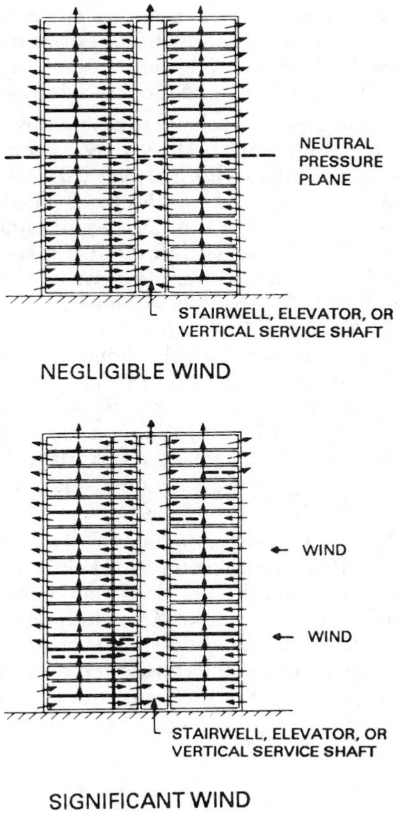

FIG. 6-7K. Influence of wind action on air movement in a building. Note how the neutral pressure plane changes location throughout the building in the presence of significant wind.

SMOKE MANAGEMENT

The term "smoke management," as used in this section, includes all methods that can be used alone or in combination to modify smoke movement for the benefit of occupants or fire fighters or to reduce property damage. The mechanisms of compartmentation, dilution, air flow, pressurization, and buoyancy are used by themselves or in combination to manage smoke conditions in fires. These mechanisms are discussed below.

Compartmentation

Barriers with sufficient fire endurance to remain effective throughout a fire exposure have a long history of providing protection against fire spread. In such fire compartmentation, the walls, partitions, floors, doors, and other barriers provide some level of smoke protection to spaces remote from the fire. This section discusses the use of passive compartmentation, while the use of compartmentation in conjunction with pressurization is discussed later. Many codes, such as NFPA 101®, *Life Safety Code*®, provide specific criteria for the construction of smoke barriers, including doors and smoke dampers in these barriers. The extent to which smoke leaks through such barriers depends on the size and shape of the leakage paths in the barriers and on the pressure differences across the paths.

There is no formalized analytical method for determining the rate of smoke leakage through barriers and the resulting levels of hazard in areas to be protected. However, emerging fire and smoke transport models can address the smoke leakage through barriers. A first-order approximation of the leakage can be made using the equation for flow through an opening, typical leakage areas listed in Table 6-7B, estimates of the dimensions of paths such as gaps around doors, and the procedures for estimating effective flow areas. More accurate calculations await better data and improved calculation procedures. Full appraisal of the impact of such leakage requires knowledge of the smoke toxicity or an assumed design value of acceptable smoke concentration in protected spaces. A formalized approach to smoke compartmentation should include development of appropriate methods of acceptance testing and routine testing. More effort is needed to increase understanding of the passive capabilities of barriers in order to maximize the usefulness of this oldest and most fundamental method of smoke management.

Dilution

Dilution of smoke is sometimes referred to as smoke purging, smoke removal, smoke exhaust, or smoke extraction. Dilution can be used to maintain an acceptable smoke concentration in a compartment subject to smoke infiltration from an adjacent space. This can be effective if the rate of smoke leakage is small compared to either the total volume of the safeguarded space or the rate of purging air supplied to and removed from the space. Dilution also can be beneficial to the fire service for removing smoke after a fire has been extinguished. Sometimes, when doors are opened, smoke will flow into areas intended to be protected. Ideally, doors will only be open for short periods during evacuation. Smoke that has entered spaces remote from the fire can be purged by supplying outside air to dilute the smoke.

Many people have unrealistic expectations about what dilution can accomplish in the fire space. There is no theoretical or experimental evidence that using a building's heating, ventilation, and air conditioning (HVAC) system for smoke dilution will result in any significant improvement in tenable conditions within the fire space. It is well known that HVAC systems promote a considerable degree of air mixing within the spaces they serve. Because of this and the fact that building fires can produce very large quantities of smoke, it is generally believed that dilution of smoke by a HVAC system in the fire space will not result in any practical improvement in the tenable conditions of that space. Thus, smoke purging systems intended to improve hazard conditions within a fire space or in spaces connected to a fire space by large openings should not be used.

The following is a simple analysis of smoke dilution for spaces in which there is no fire. At time zero ($t = 0$), a compartment is contaminated with some concentration of smoke, and no further smoke flows into or is generated within the compartment. In addition, the contaminant is considered uniformly distributed throughout the space. The concentration of contaminant in the space can be expressed as:

$$a = \frac{1}{t} \log_e \left(\frac{C_o}{C} \right)$$

$$t = \frac{1}{a} \log_e \left(\frac{C_o}{C} \right)$$

where:

C_o = initial concentration of contaminant
C = concentration of contaminant at time, t
a = dilution rate in number of air changes per min
t = time after smoke stops entering space or time after which smoke production has stopped, in min
e = constant approximately 2.178

The concentrations C_o *and* C must be expressed in the same units, and they can be any units appropriate for the particular contaminant being considered. McGuire, Tamura, and Wilson[11] evaluated the maximum levels of smoke obscuration from a number of fire tests and a number of proposed criteria for tolerable levels of smoke obscuration. Based on this evaluation, they stated that the maximum levels of smoke obscuration are greater by a factor of 100 than those relating to the limit of tolerance. Thus, they indicate that an area can be considered "reasonably safe" with respect to smoke obscuration if its atmosphere will not be contaminated to an extent greater than 1 percent by the atmosphere prevailing in the immediate fire area. It is obvious that such dilution would also reduce the concentrations of toxic smoke components. Toxicity is a more complicated problem, and no parallel statement has been made regarding dilution needed to obtain a safe atmosphere with respect to toxic gases.

In reality, it is impossible to ensure that the concentration of the contaminant is uniform throughout the compartment. Because of the buoyancy, it is likely that higher concentrations would tend to be near the ceiling. Therefore, an exhaust inlet located near the ceiling and a supply outlet located near the floor would probably dilute smoke even faster than indicated by the above equations. Caution should be exercised in locating the supply and exhaust points to prevent the supply air from blowing into the exhaust inlet and thus short circuiting the dilution operation.

Example A: Smoke purging after the fire is extinguished.

1. After the fire department puts out a fire, they want to clear the smoke quickly so that an inspection can be made to determine if the fire is completely out. If the smoke HVAC system is capable of a dilution rate of six air changes per hour, how long will it take to reduce the smoke concentration to 1 percent of the initial value?

The dilution rate, a, is 0.1 changes per min, and C_o/C is 100.

$$t = \frac{1}{0.1} \log_e (100) = 46 \text{ min to purge smoke to 1 percent of initial value}$$

Considering the fire department's desire to inspect the area quickly, such a long purging time will probably be excessive.

2. If the fire department wants the space to be purged in 10 min, what dilution rate is needed?

The dilution time, t, is 10 min, and C_o/C is 100.

$$a = \frac{1}{10} \log_e (100) = 0.46 \text{ changes per minute (28 changes per hour}$$

Pressurization

Systems using pressurization produced by mechanical fans are referred to as smoke-control systems in NFPA 92A, *Smoke Control Systems*. Pressurization results in airflows of high velocity in the small gaps around closed doors and in construction cracks, thereby preventing smoke backflows through these openings. The pressurization systems most commonly used are pressurized stairwells and zoned smoke control. Elevator smoke control is less common.

Many pressurized stairwells are designed and built with the goal of providing a tenable environment within the escape route in the event of a building fire. It is obvious that a pressurized stairwell can meet its objectives, even if a small amount of smoke infiltrates the stairwell. The three major design concerns with pressurized stairwells are:

1. Nonuniform pressure differences that occur over the stairwell height.
2. Large pressure fluctuations caused by doors being opened and closed.
3. The location of supply air inlets and fans.

At first, it might appear that the pressure differences from the stairwell to the building would be essentially the same over the height of the stairwell. Unfortunately, this is not the case. For a building without vertical leakage through floors or shafts other than the stairwell, the pressure profile is linear. Of course, this leakage characteristic is not representative of many buildings. However, this case is useful because it has been analytically solved, and it represents a worst case. The analysis has been addressed.

It is a worst-case scenario in that its minimum pressure difference is less than that for other, more realistic leakage configurations and its maximum pressure difference is greater than that for other leakage configurations. Computer analysis can be performed to include the effects of more complicated building leakage arrangements.

When a door is opened in a pressurized stairwell, the pressure difference across the remaining closed doors can drop dramatically. The two classes of design concepts that have been used to deal with this problem are over-pressure relief and feedback control. An over-pressure relief system that has gained attention as being simple and cost-effective is the "Canadian System." The essential features of this system are that air is supplied by one or more fans at relatively constant flow rates, and the ground-floor exterior stairwell door opens automatically when the system activates. This system eliminates the source of the most severe pressure fluctuations—the opening and closing of the exterior door.

There is concern about locating supply air inlets near the exterior ground-floor doors of the stairwell. If a supply inlet is located near this door, it is possible that much of the supply air will flow directly through the exterior doorway when it is opened, thus effectively reducing stairwell pressurization. It is believed that locating inlets only one floor away from exterior doors eliminates this potential.

In the late 1960s, the concept of the "pressure sandwich" evolved. This consisted of exhausting the fire floor and pressurizing surrounding floors to limit smoke movement to the fire floor. The pressure sandwich concept has evolved into today's zoned smoke-control systems. According to the concept of zoned smoke control, a building can be divided into a number of smoke zones, each separated from the others by partitions and floors. A smoke control zone can consist of one floor or more than one floor, or a floor can consist of more than one smoke zone. In the event of fire, pressure differences and air flows produced by mechanical fans can be used to restrict smoke spread to the zone in which the fire began, or the smoke zone. The concentration of smoke in this zone may render it untenable. Accordingly, in zoned smoke control systems, building occupants should evacuate the zone in which the fire occurs as soon as possible after the fire has been detected.

Air Flow

Air flow has been used extensively to manage smoke from fires in subway, railroad, and highway tunnels. Large flow rates of air are needed to control smoke flow, and these flow rates can supply additional oxygen to the fire. Because of the need for complex controls, air flow is not used as extensively in buildings. The control problem consists of having very small flows when a door is closed, and then having those flows increase significantly when that door opens.

Thomas[12] determined that air flow in a corridor in which there is a fire can almost totally prevent smoke from flowing upstream of the fire. As illustrated in Figure 6-7J, the smoke forms a surface that slopes into the direction of the oncoming air flow. Molecular diffusion is believed to result in the transfer of trace amounts of smoke, producing no hazard upstream, just the odor of smoke. There is a minimum velocity below which smoke will flow upstream, and Thomas[12] developed the following empirical relation for this critical velocity. This relation, evaluated at air density of 0.081 lb/ft^3 and temperature of 81°F (27°C) is:

$$V_k = 5.68 \left(\frac{E}{W}\right)$$

where:

V_2 = critical air velocity to prevent smoke backflow, ft/min
E = energy release rate into corridor, Btu/hr
W = corridor width, ft.

This relation can be used when the fire is located in the corridor or when the smoke enters the corridor through an open doorway, an air transfer grill, or some other opening. The critical velocities calculated are approximate, because only an approximate value of k was used. However, the critical velocities from this relation are indicative of the kind of air velocities required to prevent smoke backflow from fires of different sizes.

Example B: Rough estimates of air flow for a doorway.

1. Thomas[12] indicated that his relationship for critical velocity can be used to obtain a rough estimate for doorways. A room fully involved in fire could have an energy release rate on the order of 8x10^6 Btu/hr. What estimate of critical velocity is obtained from the Thomas[12] equation for a door 3 ft (0.9 m) wide?

$$V_k = 5.68\ (8\text{x}10^6/3)^{1/3} = 800 \text{ ft/min}$$

If the door has an area of 20 sq ft, this would amount to a flow of 1600 cu ft/min.

2. Consideration of a smaller fire, such as a wastebasket fire, may be appropriate for many situations. What flow rate does the Thomas[12] relation indicate is needed to prevent backflow for the above door? A wastebasket fire has an energy release rate near 0.5x10^6 Btu/hr.

$$V_k = 5.68\ (0.5\text{x}10^6/3)^{1/3} = 300 \text{ ft/min}$$

For a door area of 20 sq ft, this would amount to a flow of 6000 cu ft/min.

Buoyancy

Buoyancy of hot combustion gases is employed in both fan-powered and non-powered venting systems. Such fan-powered venting for large spaces is commonly employed for atria and covered shopping malls. Design analysis of these systems for malls is treated in NFPA 92B, *Smoke Management Systems in Malls, Atria, and Large Areas*. There is concern that the sprinkler flow will cool the smoke, thus reducing its buoyancy and the system's effectiveness. There is no question that sprinkler flow does cool smoke, but it is unknown to what extent the cooling reduces the effectiveness of fan-powered venting. Further research is needed in this area, but the existing information can be used to develop new design information for fan-powered venting systems.

BIBLIOGRAPHY

References Cited

1. Klote, J. H. and Fothergill, J. W., *Design of Smoke-Control Systems for Buildings*, American Society of Heating, Refrigerating, and Air-Conditioning Engineers, Atlanta, GA, 1983.
2. DiNemno, Philip, J., *ed.*, *SFPE Handbook of Fire Protection Engineering*, National Fire Protection Association, Quincy, MA, 1988.
3. Thomas, P. H., *et al.*, "Investigations into the Flow of Hot Gases in Roof Venting," *Fire Research Technical Paper No. 7*, Joint Fire Research Organization, London, England, 1963.

4. Butcher, E. G. and Parnell, A. C., *Smoke Control in Fire Safety Design*, E. and F. N. Spon, London, England, 1979.

5. Alpert, R. L. and Ward, E. J. "Evaluating Unsprinklered Fire Hazards," *SFPE Technology Report 83-2*, Society of Fire Protection Engineers, Boston, MA, 1983.

6. Heskestad, G., "Engineering Relations for Fire Plumes," *SFPE Technology Report 82-8*, Society of Fire Protection Engineers, Boston, MA, 1982.

7. Klote, J. H. and Fothergill, J. W., "Design of Smoke Control Systems for Buildings," *National Bureau of Standards Handbook 141*, National Bureau of Standards, Washington, DC, 1983.

8. Nelson, H. E., "Emerging Engineering Methods Applied to Fire Safety Design," *General Proceedings*, Research and Design 85: Architectural Applications of Design and Technology Research, American Institute of Architects Foundation, Washington, DC, 1985.

9. Cooper, L. Y., "An Interior Buoyant Smoke Control Approach (for Atrium-Like Arrangements)," Appendix B of *NBSIR 84-2896*, National Institute of Standards and Technology, Gaithersburg, MD, 1984.

10. Tamura, G. T., "Computer Analysis of Smoke Movement in Tall Buildings," *Annual Meeting*, American Society of Heating, Refrigerating and Air Conditioning Engineers, June 1969.

11. McGuire, J. H., Tamura, G. T., and Wilson, A. G., "Factors in Controlling Smoke in High Buildings," *Symposium* on Fire Hazards in Buildings, ASHRAE Semiannual Meeting in San Francisco, CA, 1970, pp. 8-13.

12. Thomas, P. H., "Movement of Smoke in Horizontal Corridors Against an Air Flow," *Institute of Fire Engineers Quarterly*, 30 (77), (1970), pp. 45-53.

References

Cooper, L. Y., "The Development of Hazardous Conditions in Enclosures with Growing Fires," *NBSIR 82-2622*, National Bureau of Standards, Washington, DC, 1982.

Tamura, G. T. and Shaw, C. Y., "Studies on Exterior Wall Air Tightness and Air Infiltration of Tall Buildings," *Transactions*, American Society of Heating, Refrigerating, and Air Conditioning Engineers, Vol. 82, Part 1, 1976, pp. 122-134.

Tamura, G. T. and Shaw, C. Y., "Air Leakage Data for the Design of Elevator and Stair Shaft Pressurization Systems," *Transactions*, American Society of Heating, Refrigerating and Air Conditioning Engineers, Vol. 83, Part II, 1976, pp. 179-190.

Tamura, G. T. and Shaw, C. Y., "Experimental Studies of Mechanical Venting for Smoke Control in Tall Office Buildings," *Transactions*, American Society of Heating, Refrigerating and Air Conditioning Engineers, Vol. 86, Part I, 1978, pp. 54-71.

Tamura, G. T. and Wilson, A. G., "Pressure Differences for a Nine-Story Building as a Result of Chimney Effect and Ventilation System Operations," *Transactions*, American Society of Heating, Refrigerating and Air Conditioning Engineers, Vol. 72, Part I, 1966, pp. 180-189.

Tamura, G. T. and Wilson, A. G., "Pressure Differences Caused by Chimney Effect in Three-Story-High Buildings," *Transactions*, American Society of Heating, Refrigerating and Air Conditioning Engineers, Vol. 73, Part II, 1967.

NFPA Codes, Standards, and Recommended Practices

Reference to the following NFPA codes, standards, and recommended practices will provide further information on smoke movement in buildings discussed in this chapter. (See the latest *NFPA Catalog* for availability of current editions of the following documents.)

NFPA 92A, *Smoke Control Systems*.

NFPA 92B, *Smoke Management Systems in Malls, Atria, and Large Areas*.

NFPA 101, *Life Safety Code*.

NFPA 204M, *Smoke and Heat Venting*.

NFPA 258, *Determining Smoke Generation of Solid Materials*.

Additional Readings

Bengston, S. and Hagglund, B., "A Smoke-Filling Simulation Model and Its Engineering Applications," *Fire Technology*, Vol. 22, No. 2 (1986), pp. 92-103.

Bodart, X., "Validation of Network Models for Smoke Control Analysis," *ASHRAE Transactions*, Vol. 91, No. 2B (1985), pp. 1134-1145.

Chow, W. K., "Smoke Movement and Design of Smoke Control in Atrium Buildings," *International Journal for Housing Science and Its Application*, Vol. 13, No. 4 (1989), pp. 307-322.

Christian, W. J. and Waterman, T. E., "Characteristics of Full-Scale Fires in Various Occupancies," *Fire Technology*, Vol. 7, No. 3 (Aug. 1971), pp. 205-218.

Cole, J., "Smoke Movement in Single Story Buildings," *Fire Surveyor*, Vol. 18, No. 1 (Feb. 1989), pp. 25-32.

Cooper, L. Y., "Compartment Fire-Generated Environment and Smoke Filling," *SFPE Handbook of Fire Protection Engineering*, NFPA, Quincy, MA, 1988.

Cooper, L. Y., "The Need and Availability of Test Methods for Measuring the Smoke Leakage Characteristics of Door Assemblies," *NBSIR 84-2876*, National Bureau of Standards, Washington, DC, 1984.

Cresci, R. J., "Smoke and Fire Control in High-Rise Office Buildings—Part II; Analysis of Stair Pressurization Systems," *Symposium* on Experience and Applications on Smoke and Fire Control, ASHRAE Annual Meeting, Atlanta, GA, 1973, pp. 16-23.

Dias, C., "Stairwell Pressurization in a High-Rise Commercial Building," *ASHRAE Journal*, Vol. 20, No. 7 (July 1978), pp. 24-26.

Evers, E. and Waterhouse, A., "A Computer Model for Analyzing Smoke Movement in Buildings," *BRECP 69/78*, Building Research Establishment, Borehamwood, Hertfordshire, England, Nov. 1978.

Ford, N. J., "Safety: Smoke and Fire Curtains," *H&V Engineer*, Vol. 16, No. 683, pp. 7-8.

Gross, D., "A Review of Measurements, Calculations and Specifications of Air Leakage through Interior Door Assemblies," *NBSIR 81-2214*, National Bureau of Standards, Washington, DC, Feb. 1981.

Gross, D., "Estimating Air Leakage Through Doors for Smoke Control," *Fire Technology*, Vol. 26, No. 1 (Feb. 1990), pp. 75-81.

Hansell, G. O. and Morgan, H. P., "Fire Sizes in Hotel Bedrooms—Implications for Smoke Control Design," Fire Safety Journal, Vol. 8 No. 3 (1985), pp. 177-186.

Heselden, A. J. M., "Studies of Smoke Movement and Control at the Fire Research Station," CIB Symposium on Control of Smoke Movement in Building Fires, Fire Research Station, Garston Watford, UK, Vol. 1, 1976, pp. 185-198.

Heselden, A. J. M., "Studies of Fire and Smoke Behavior Relevant to Tunnels," *BRECP*, Building Research Establishment, Borehamwood, Hertfordshire, England, Nov. 1978.

Heselden, A. J. M. and Baldwin R., "The Movement and Control of Smoke and Escape Routes in Buildings," *BRECP*, Building Research Establishment, Borehamwood, Hertfordshire, England.

Heselden, A. J. M. and Baldwin, R., "The Movement and Control of Smoke on Escape Routes in Buildings," *Fire Technology*, Vol. 14, No. 3 (Aug. 1978), pp. 206-222.

Heskestad, G., "Note on Maximum Rise of Fire Plumes in Temperature—Stratified Ambients," *Fire Safety Journal*, Vol. 15, No. 4 (1989), pp. 271-276.

Heskestad, G., "Smoke Movement and Venting," *Fire Safety Journal*, Vol. 11, Nos. 1 & 2 (1986), pp. 77-83.

Heskestad, G. and Hill, J. P., "Propogation of Fire Smoke in a Corridor," *Proceedings* of the 1987 ASME-JSME Conference, Vol. 1, ASME, 1987.

Hinkley, P. L., "A Preliminary Note on the Movement of Smoke in an Enclosed Shopping Mall," *Fire Research Note 806*, Fire Research Station, Borehamwood, Hertfordshire, England, Mar. 1970.

Isner, M. S., "Smoky Fire Kills Four in New York High-Rise," *Fire Journal*, Vol. 82, No. 5 (1988).

Jones, W. W., "A Model for the Transport of Fire, Smoke and Toxic Gases (FAST)," *NBSIR 84-2934*, National Bureau of Standards, Gaithersburg, MD, 1984.

Jones, W. W. and Quintiere, J. G., "Prediction of Corridor Smoke Filling by Zone Models," *Combustion Science and Technology*, Vol. 35, Nos. 5 and 6, 1984, pp. 239-253.

Klote, J. H., "An Overview of Smoke Control Technology," *NBSIR 87-3626*, (Sept. 1987), Center for Fire Research, Gaithersberg, MD.

Klote, J. H., "Computer Modeling for Smoke Control Design," *Fire Safety Journal*, Vol. 9, No. 2 (1986), pp. 181-188.

Klote, J. H., "Considerations of Stack Effect in Buildings," *NBSIR 89-4035*, (May 1989), Center for Fire Research, Gaithersberg, MD.

Klote, J. H., "Smoke Control," *SFPE Handbook of Fire Protection Engineering*, NFPA, Quincy, MA, 1988.

Klote, J. H., "Smoke Control by Stairwell Pressurization," Center for Fire Research, National Bureau of Standards, Washington, DC, 1980.

Klote, J. H., "Smoke Control for Elevators," *ASHRAE Journal*, Vol. 26, No. 4 (Apr. 1984), pp. 23-33.

Klote, J. H., "Smoke Movement through a Suspended Ceiling System," *NBSIR 81-2444*, National Bureau of Standards, Washington, DC, 1982.

Klote, J. H., "Elevators as a Means of Fire Escape," *NBSIR 82-2507*, National Bureau of Standards, Washington, DC, May 1982.

Klote, J. H. "Field Tests of the Smoke Control System at the Bay Pines VA Hospital," *ASHRAE Transactions*, Vol. 91, Part Ib, 1985, pp. 802-819.

Klote, J. H., "Fire Safety Inspection and Testing of Air Moving Systems," National Bureau of Standards, Gaithersburg, MD, *NBSIR 87-3660*, 1987.

Klote, J. H., "An Analysis of the Influence of Piston Effect on Elevator Smoke Control," National Bureau of Standards, Gaithersburg, MD, *NBSIR 88-3751*, 1988.

Klote, J. H. and Bodart, X., "Validation of Network Models for Smoke Control Analysis," *ASHRAE Transactions*, Vol. 91, Part 2b, 1985, pp. 1134-1145.

Klote, J. H. and Budnick, E. K., "The Capabilities of Smoke Control: Fundamentals and Zone Smoke Control," *Journal of Fire Protection Engineering*, Vol. 1, No. 1 (1989), pp. 1-10.

Klote J. H. and Fothergill, J. W., *Design of Smoke Control Systems for Buildings*, American Society of Heating, Refrigerating and Air Conditioning Engineers, Atlanta, GA, 1983.

Klote, J. H. and Tamura, G. T., "Elevator Piston Effect and the Smoke Problem," *Fire Safety Journal*, Vol. 11, No. 3, (1986), pp. 227-233.

Klote, J. H. and Tamura, G. T., "Smoke Control and Fire Evacuation by Elevators," *ASHRAE Transactions*, Vol. 92, Part 1a, 1986, pp. 231-245.

Klote, J. H. and Tamura, G. T., "Experiments of Piston Effect on Elevator Smoke Control," *ASHRAE Transactions*, Vol. 93, Part 2a, 1987, pp. 2217-2228.

Klote, J. H. and Tamura, G. T., "Smoke Control and Fire Evacuation by Elevators," *ASHRAE Transactions*, Vol. 92, Part 1a, 1986, pp. 231-245.

Lieberman, P. and Bell, D., "Smoke and Fire Propogation in Compartment Spaces," *Fire Technology*, Vol. 9, No. 2 (May 1973), pp. 91-100.

Ling, W. C. T. and Williamson R. B., "Use of Probabilistic Networks for Analysis of Smoke Spread and Egress of People in Buildings," *Proceedings* of the First International Symposium for Fire Safety Science, Hemisphere, NY, (1986), pp. 953-962.

Marchant, E. W., "Effect of Wind on Smoke Movement and Smoke Control Systems," *Fire Safety Journal*, Vol. 7, No. 1, (1984), pp. 55-63.

Marshall, N. R., "The Behavior of Hot Gases Flowing within a Staircase," *Fire Safety Journal*, Vol. 9, No. 3, (1987), pp. 245-255.

Marshall, N. R. "Air Entrainment into Smoke and Hot Gases in Open Shafts," *Fire Safety Journal*, Vol. 10, No. 1, (1986), pp. 37-46.

Matsushita. T., Fukai, H., and Terai, T., "Calculation of Smoke Movement in Building in Case of a Fire," *Proceedings* of the First International Symposium for Fire Safety Science, Hemisphere, NY, (1986), pp. 1123-1132.

McGuire, J. H., "Control of Smoke in Buildings," *Fire Technology*, Vol. 3, No. 4 (Nov. 1967), pp. 281-290.

McGuire, J. H. and Tamura, G. T., "Simple Analysis of Smoke Flow Problems in High Buildings," *Fire Technolgy*, Vol. 11, No. 1 (Feb. 1975), pp. 15-27.

Morgan, H. P. and Hansell, G. O., "Atrium Buildings: Calculating Smoke Flows in Atria for Smoke-Control Design," *Fire Safety Journal*, Vol. 12, (1987), pp. 9-36.

Morgan, H. P. and Hansell, G. O., "Fire Sizes and Sprinkler Effectiveness in Offices: Implications for Smoke Control Design," *Fire Safety Journal*, Vol. 8, No. 3 (1985), pp. 187-198.

Morgan, H. P. and Marshall, N. R., "Smoke Hazards in Covered, Multi-Level Shopping Malls: An Experimentally Based Theory for Smoke Protection," Building Research Establishment, Borehamwood, Hertfordshire, England, May 1975.

Morgan, H. P. and Marshall, N. R., "Smoke Hazards in Covered, Multi-Level Shopping Malls: A Method of Extracting Smoke from Each Level Separately," Building Research Establishment, Borehamwood, Hertfordshire, England, Jan. 1978.

Morgan, H. P. and Marshall, N. R., "Depth of Void-Edge Screens in Shopping Malls," *Fire Engineers Journal*, Vol. 48, No. 152 (1989), pp. 7-9.

Morgan, H. P., *et al.*, "Smoke Hazards in Covered Multi-Level Shopping Malls: Smoke Studies Using a Model 2-Story Mall," Building Research Establishment, Borehamwood, Hertfordshire, England, June 1976.

Phillips, A. M., "Canada's Fire Research Facility," *Fire Journal*, Vol. 78, No. 2 (Mar. 1984), pp. 46-48.

Said, M. N. A., "A Review of Smoke Control Models," *ASHRAE Journal*, Vol. 30, No. 4, (1988), pp. 36.

Savilonis, B. and Richards, R., "Survey and Evaluation of Existing Smoke Movement Models," *Fire Safety Journal*, Vol. 13, Nos. 2 & 3 (1988), pp. 87-98.

Schulte, R. C., "Smoke Control State-of-the-Art," *Consulting Engineer*, Vol. 64, No. 5 (1985), pp. 44-48.

Sugawa, O., *et al.*, "Full Scale Test of Smoke Leakage from Doors of a Highrise Apartment," *Proceedings* of the First International Symposium on Fire Safety Science, Hemisphere, 1986, pp. 891-900.

Tamura, G. T. and Klote, J. H., "Experimental Fire Tower Studies on Elevators: Pressurization Systems for Smoke Control," *Elevator World*, Vol. 37, No. 6 (1989) pp. 80-89.

Tamura, G. T. and Klote, J. H., "Experimental Fire Tower Studies on Elevator Pressurization Systems for Smoke Control," *ASHRAE Transactions* Vol. 93, Part II, 1987, pp. 2235-2257.

Thomas, P. H., "Movement of Smoke in Horizontal Corridors Against an Air Flow," *Institute of Fire Engineers Quarterly*, Vol. 30, No. 77, (1970), pp. 45-53.

Thomas, P. H., "Designing Stair Pressurization Systems," *Fire Safety Journal*, Vol. 12, No. 3, (1987), pp. 191-204.

Thornberry, R. P., "Designing Stair Pressurization Systems," *TR 82-4*, Society of Fire Protection Engineers, Boston, MA, 1982.

Wakamatsu, R., "Calculation Methods for Predicting Smoke Movement in Buildings and Designing Smoke Control Systems, Fire Standards and Safety," *ASTM STP-614*, A. F. Robertson, *ed.*, American Society for Testing and Materials, Philadelphia, PA, 1977, pp. 168-193.

VENTING PRACTICES

Gunnar Heskestad

The importance of the buoyant properties of heat and smoke was realized at an early date, as evidenced by an NFPA standard adopted in 1903 that called for smoke vents over theater stages and in the ceilings of theater auditoriums. However, until the advent of effective artificial lighting, buildings were generally small enough so that windows provided adequate smoke venting, other than venting of fire through the roof.

The main body of this chapter covers venting practices as they would be applied to nonsprinklered buildings, following the recommendations of NFPA 204M, *Smoke and Heat Venting*. An addendum at the conclusion of the chapter (in which the several different approaches are incorporated) discusses the current state of the technology involving the sprinkler/vent issue.

HISTORICAL BACKGROUND

Large undivided floor areas present extremely difficult fire fighting problems, since fire fighters must enter these areas to fight fires in central portions of the building. If fire fighters are unable to enter because of the accumulation of heat and smoke, fire fighting efforts may be reduced to ineffective application of hose streams to perimeter areas while fire consumes the interior. (See Figure 6-8A.)

Great impetus to the subject of smoke and heat venting was provided by the General Motors fire at Livonia, MI, in 1953, when fire spread horizontally under an unvented metal roof, with 34 acres of undivided area. Fire protection engineers were in general agreement that this fire could have been greatly reduced if there had been effective roof venting. The General Motors fire led to a new approach to the subject by the NFPA Committee on Building Construction, which prepared NFPA 204M, *Smoke and Heat Venting*, adopted by NFPA in May 1961. In 1968, the venting guide was expanded to include a new section on inspection and maintenance.

Gunnar Heskestad, Ph.D., is principal research scientist in the Research Division, Factory Mutual Research Corporation, Norwood, MA.

A reconfirmation action failed in 1975, as concerns had surfaced over use of NFPA 204M, *Smoke and Heat Venting*, in conjunction with automatically sprinklered buildings. Because of this controversy, work on a revision of NFPA 204M continued at a slow pace, but concluded with the 1982 edition.

The 1982 edition of NFPA 204M distinguishes between unsprinklered and sprinklered buildings. The unsprinklered part is considered to represent a major advance in engineered smoke and heat venting. The sprinklered part, limited to a single chapter (Chapter 6), does not recognize that venting is necessarily desirable in a sprinklered building and does not offer a design basis, pending the resolution of some technical questions.

No changes were made for the 1985 edition of NFPA 204M, except for a limited revision of Chapter 6 dealing with venting of sprinklered buildings. Reference is made to new test data on deploying vents in a test building with automatic sprinklers. However, the new data did not permit conclusions to be developed whether sprinkler control was impaired or enhanced by the presence of automatic roof vents of typical spacing and area.

The technical questions that remain unresolved in application of venting to sprinklered buildings are related to: (1) the effects of sprinkler discharge on venting effectiveness, and (2) the effects of fresh air introduced into the building on the burning process and the water demand of the sprinkler system. Sprinkler discharge will cool the fire gases, perhaps to the extent that the vent discharge is reduced, hence reducing venting effectiveness. Additionally, the sprinkler sprays will entrain ambient smoke and air, transporting smoke to the floor level and possibly drawing gas from the vent exhaust wherever nozzles are located close to vents, further reducing venting effectiveness. Unless the building is very large, fresh air flowing into the building and replacing smoke escaping through the vents will increase the oxygen concentration in the fire space. The increased oxygen concentrations may cause a more vigorous fire than would otherwise exist, with the possible outcome of an increased number of operating sprinklers, in some cases overtaxing the water supply. Against these possible adverse effects must be balanced the likelihood that some improvement in visibility for fire fighting will result

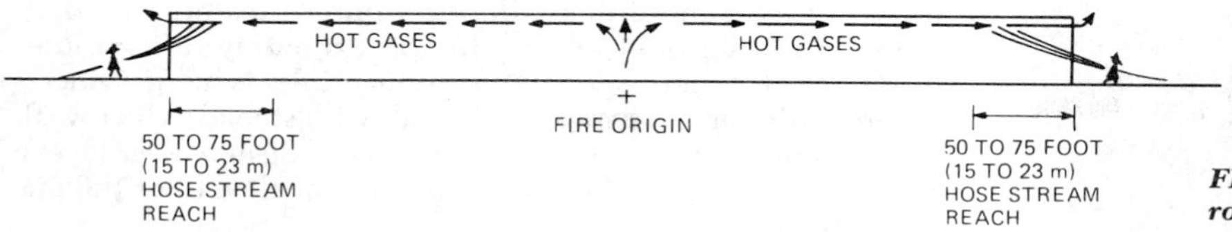

FIG. 6-8A. ***Behavior of hot gases under a flat-roofed building.***

in many cases, and the possibility that the number of operating sprinklers may sometimes be reduced because of the cooling effect of vent flows. There are, as yet, no universally accepted conclusions from either fire experience or research.

Essential features specified in NFPA 204M, *Smoke and Heat Venting*, include roof vents operated by fusible links, with curtain boards to confine heat and prevent lateral fire spread, as well as openings for fresh air makeup at low levels. (See Figure 6-8B.) Two general classes of fires are considered: (1) limited growth fires, which are not expected to grow past a predictable maximum size, and (2) continuous growth fires, which can be expected to grow indefinitely until intervention by fire fighters. Mechanical exhaust at ceiling apertures is treated as an option to natural ventilation at roof vents. The provisions of NFPA 204M may be applied to one-story buildings or to the top story of multiple-story buildings. With mechanical exhaust, lower stories of multiple-story buildings can also be vented.

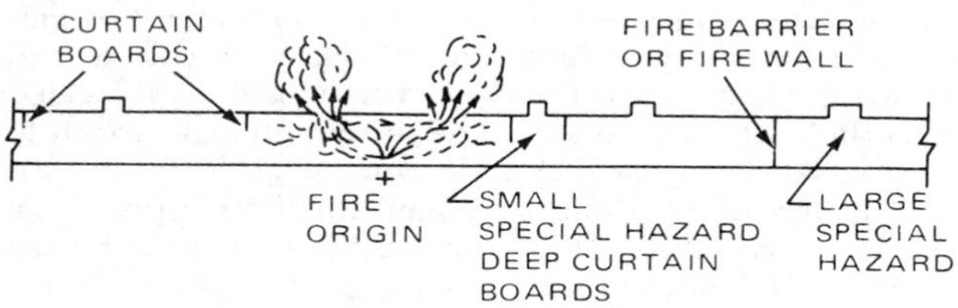

FIG. 6-8B. ***Behavior of combustion products under vented and curtained roof.***

INDUSTRIAL BUILDING VENTILATION

Although any opening in a roof will reduce some heat and smoke, building designers and fire protection engineers cannot rely on casual inclusion of skylights, windows, or monitors as adequate means of venting. Standards now exist (from Factory Mutual Research Corp., Underwriters Laboratories Inc., etc.) that include design criteria and test procedures for unit vents and also call for simulated fire tests as well as engineering analysis.

Unit Vents

Unit vents are relatively small, usually 16 to 100 sq ft (1.49 to 9.29 m^2) in area. Automatic unit vents are of two types, based on manner of operation—fusible link or drop-out plastic. (See Figure 6-8C.) The former type consists of a metal housing with lids that depend upon a temperature-rated fusible link to trip the lid mechanism, but alternative modes of operation (by heat, smoke, etc.) are possible. The latter type depends upon a temperature-sensitive, transparent or translucent, thermoplastic dome that deforms from its setting and falls out of the roof. Vents designed for manual operation are constructed with metal lids to resist elevated fire temperatures and may be opened from

FIG. 6-8C. ***Building with roof vents.***

the floor with wires and cables. These units can also be modified for automatic operation.

Vents may be a single unit, in which the entire unit opens fully with a single sensor, or multiple units in rows, clusters, groups, or other arrays that will satisfy the venting requirements for the specific hazard.

Mechanical roof ventilators actuated by fire conditions are possible alternatives to roof vents based on natural ventilation, especially in lower stories of multiple-story buildings. These ventilators must be capable of functioning under expected high-temperature fire conditions.

Curtain Boards

In large-area buildings, unless vented areas are subdivided by means of walls or partitions, curtain boards are important for prompt and positive actuation of vents because they bank up heat in the curtained area. They also limit the spread of heat and smoke beneath the ceiling during the design duration of the venting system. Curtain boards can be made from any substantial noncombustible material that will resist the passage of smoke.

The depth of curtain boards would normally be selected to correspond with the design depth of the smoke layer. However, the depth should not be less than 20 percent of the ceiling height to prevent spillage of smoke under the curtain where depth and ceiling height are referenced to the center of the lowest roof vent. It would rarely be desirable to have the curtain extend below 10 ft (3 m) from the floor. Around special hazards, the curtain should preferably extend down to this limit. (See Fig. 6-8D.)

The distance between curtain boards should not exceed eight times the ceiling height to ensure that vents remote from the fire will be effective within the curtained compartment. Smaller curtained areas may be desirable where occupancies are particularly vulnerable to damage. However, it is important that the distance between curtain boards not be less than two times the ceiling height, unless the curtain boards extend down to a depth of at least 40 percent of the ceiling height. The increased curtain depth

FIG. 6-8D. Deep curtain board around a special hazard. Equipped with proper venting, a noncombustible curtain board extending down from a ceiling around special hazards will prevent smoke and heat from mushrooming throughout the facility. A curtain board for a heat-treating department is shown.

is needed for these small curtain spacings to prevent significant spillage of fire gases underneath the curtain because of the close proximity of the fire.

Dimensioning and Spacing of Vents

When the area of an individual vent becomes sufficiently large, there is a possibility that a core of clear air from beneath the smoke layer will be included in the exhaust from the vent, which reduces the effectiveness of the vent. To prevent inclusion of clear air, the area of a unit vent or cluster of vents should not exceed $2d^2$, where d is the design depth of the smoke layer or curtain board. In the case of a row of unit vents or a monitor vent, the width of the row or monitor should not exceed d.

A large number of small vents on close spacing is preferable to a small number of large vents on wide spacing. This ensures early operation of the first vents in a fire, reducing the likelihood of initial smoke excursions beyond the curtained area above the fire. In no case should the vent spacing in a rectangular matrix exceed $2H$, where H is the ceiling height measured from the floor to ceiling for flat roofs, and from the floor to the center of the vent for sloped roofs. Alternatively, in a nonrectangular vent matrix or plan, the distance between any point on the floor and the nearest vent should not exceed $2.8H$ (the diagonal of a square whose side is $2H$).

The total vent area for each curtained compartment under the ceiling depends upon the severity of the expected fire and is discussed later in this chapter.

Fresh Air Makeup

Openings must be provided at or near floor level to allow the introduction of makeup air. This is critical in today's tightly constructed and insulated buildings. The total area of these openings must normally be at least as great as the installed vent area for each curtained compartment; otherwise, the inlets will effectively throttle the vent flow. If doors and windows below the designed smoke layer cannot meet the total required inlet area, special air inlet provisions are necessary.

It is essential that a dependable means be provided for admitting inlet air within approximately one minute after the first vent opens. If prompt air inlet is not provided, the entire building may quickly fill with smoke, which will clear only slowly at lower levels (in the design clear layer) in response to the fully developed vent flow after the air inlets have been actuated.

Fire Characterization*

Each curtained compartment, or the ceiling area of buildings requiring no curtain boards, must be furnished with a total installed vent area (or exhaust capacity in case of mechanical ventilation) sufficient to vent fires of the expected severity. In addition to the expected fire severity, the installed vent area (or exhaust capacity) will depend upon the depth of the curtain boards or design depth of the smoke layer. Furthermore, unless the occupancy or hazard is such that the expected fire will peak or level off at a predictable maximum size, the installed vent area (or exhaust capacity) will also depend upon the minimum clear visibility design time as measured from the time the vents first operate.

The fire severity is expressed differently according to the class of the fire, which for purposes of calculating vent areas is classified as either a limited-growth or a continuous-growth fire.

Limited-growth fires: These are fires that are not expected to grow past a predictable maximum size in terms of heat-release rate, expressed in Btu per sec or watts. Special-hazard fires can be assigned to this class; so can fires in occupancies with concentrations of combustibles separated by sufficiently wide aisles. The minimum aisle width to prevent lateral spread (by radiation), W_{min}, [1] can be estimated from an equation for radiant flux from a fire and a (conservatively low) value for the ignition flux of most materials (1.8 Btu per sq ft per sec or 20.4 kW/m^2):

$$W_{min}(\text{ft}) = 0.14\,[Q\ (\text{Btu/sec})]^{1/2} \qquad (1)$$

For example, if the predicted maximum fire size is 30,000 Btu/sec (31.6 MW), the aisle width should be at least 24 ft (7.3 m). Table 6-8A contains examples of heat-release data, expressed as Btu per sq ft per sec (W/m^2) of floor area. To obtain heat release in Btu per sec (watts), a number in the table is multiplied by the floor area underneath the combustible.

Continuous growth fires: These are fires that can be expected to grow indefinitely until intervention by fire fighters. (See Figure 6-8E.) Starting after an incubation period, the heat-release rate of these fires grows continuously, proportional to the square of time. The growth time of a given fire is defined as the interval of time between the effective ignition time and the time when the fire

* The theory and application of venting outlined in this chapter is presented in U.S. customary units. These units reflect the system used in the original research and are consistent with the design recommendations and background materials contained in NFPA 204M, *Smoke and Heat Venting*. For those more familiar with S.I. units, quantities such as curtain board depth (in meters) and heat release rate (in kW) should be converted to the appropriate conventional units (feet and Btu/sec, respectively), using the conversion factors given at the end of this footnote and at various points throughout the text. After conversion, design data should be inserted in unit-dependent formulas to calculate vent areas and mass flow rates. As in the NFPA 204M, 1 ft = 0.305 m, 1 Btu/sec = 1.054 kW.

TABLE 6-8A. *Limited Growth Fires*
Heat-release rate per unit floor area of fully involved combustibles, assuming 100 percent combustion efficiency. (PE = polyethylene; PS = polystyrene; PVC = polyvinyl chloride; PP = polypropylene; PU = polyurethane; FRP = Fiberglass-Reinforced Polyester)

	Btu/sec/ft2 of Floor Area
1. Wood pallets, stack 1½ ft high (6–12% moisture)	120
2. Wood pallets, stack 5 ft high (6–12% moisture)	340
3. Wood pallets, stack 10 ft high (6–12% moisture)	600
4. Wood pallets, stack 15 ft high (6–12% moisture)	900
5. Mail bags, filled, stored 5 ft high	35
6. Cartons, compartmented, stacked 15 ft high	200
7. PE letter trays, filled, stacked 5 ft high on cart	750
8. PE trash barrels in cartons, stacked 15 ft high	260
9. FRP shower stalls in cartons, stacked 15 ft high	110
10. PE bottles packed in Item 6	550
11. PE bottles in cartons, stacked 15 ft high	170
12. PU insulation board, rigid foam, stacked 15 ft high	170
13. PS jars packed in Item 6	1300
14. PS tubs nested in cartons, stacked 14 ft high	450
15. PS toy parts in cartons, stacked 15 ft high	180
16. PS insulation board, rigid foam, stacked 14 ft high	280
17. PVC bottles packed in Item 6	300
18. PP tubs packed in Item 6	380
19. PP and PE film in rolls, stacked 14 ft high	540
20. Methyl alcohol	65
21. Gasoline	200
22. Kerosene	200
23. Diesel oil	170

SI units: 1 ft = 0.31 m; 1 ft^2 = .093 m^2; 1 Btu = 1.054 kW.

reaches an intermediate energy release rate of 1000 Btu per sec (1054 kW). (Any reference heat-release rate could have been chosen with a corresponding change in the growth time. The rate 1000 Btu per sec [1054 kW] was chosen for convenience.) Table 6-8B contains examples of growth times for continuous-growth fires.

INSTALLED VENT AREA

Limited-Growth Fires

Using theory for air entrainment in fire plumes and gas flow through roof vents, required vent areas can be calculated. The results are presented in Figure 6-8F as recommended vent area per curtained compartment (in sq ft) versus expected maximum heat-release rate (in Btu per sec) of the combustibles underneath the curtained compartment. Several ceiling heights in the range 15 ft to 60 ft (4.6 m to 18.3 m) are represented. The figure pertains to a curtain depth (or design smoke layer depth) that is 20 percent of the ceiling height. It is assumed that the fire is located on the floor, a conservative assumption since the lower the fire source, the greater the air entrainment rate from the clear layer and the required vent area. Moreover, an aerodynamic discharge coefficient of 0.6 has been assumed,

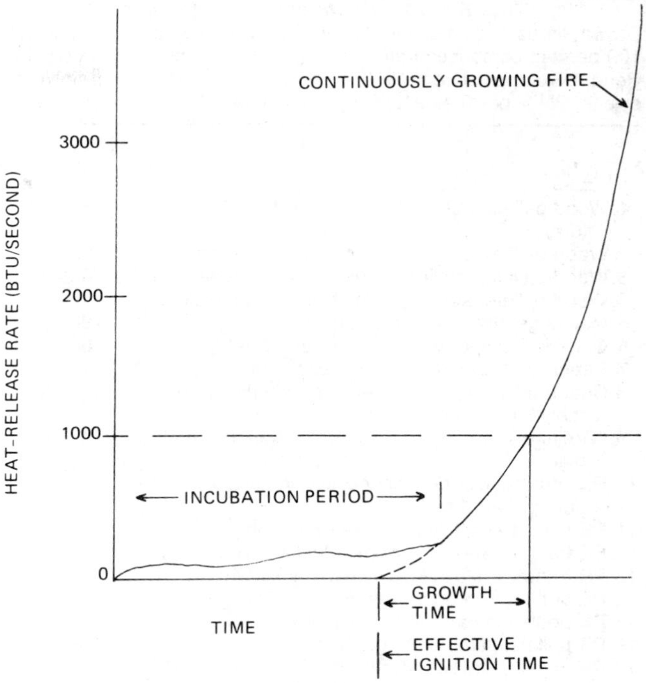

FIG. 6-8E. Conceptual illustration of continuous fire growth.

which is normal for commercial unit vents. If the discharge coefficient is different from 0.6, the recommended vent areas need to be multiplied by the ratio of 0.6 to the actual discharge coefficient.

For each ceiling height in Figure 6-8F, the respective curve begins at a heat-release rate where vents operated by fusible links rated at 100°F (37.8°C) to 220°F (104°C) above ambient are first expected to operate promptly. Furthermore, for each ceiling height, the respective curve terminates near a heat-release rate, $Q_{feasible}$, beyond which the feasibility of roof venting, using the present approach, might be questioned. $Q_{feasible}$ can be estimated from the equation:

$$Q_{feasible}\ (\text{Btu/sec}) = 1130\ (H - d)^{5/2} \qquad (2)$$

where H is the ceiling height and d is the curtain depth ([0.2H]) in this case). At $Q_{feasible}$, the fire may become controlled by the ventilation rate allowed by the roof vents. Ventilation-controlled fires do not support a clear layer. Venting at heat-release rates greater than $Q_{feasible}$ to maintain a clear layer would require larger vent areas than indicated in Figure 6-8F.

Along the dashed segments of the curves in Figure 6-8F, gas temperatures in excess of 1000°F (538°C) may be reached; unprotected structural steel may begin to lose strength and the possibility of flashover exists within the curtained area. The lowest rate of heat release at which this may occur, Q_{1000}, has been estimated from the equation

$$Q_{1000}\ (\text{Btu/sec}) = 69\ (H - d)^{5/2} \qquad (3)$$

where, in the case of Figure 6-8F, $d = 0.2H$.

For curtain depths greater than 20 percent of the ceiling height, the vent areas read from Figure 6-8F may be multiplied by the factors indicated in Table 6-8C. New values for $Q_{feasible}$ and Q_{1000} can be calculated using Equations

TABLE 6-8B. *Continuous Growth Fires*
Growth times of developing fires in various combustibles, assuming 100 percent combustion efficiency. (Pe = polyester; PE = polyethylene; PS = polystyrene; PVC = polyvinyl chloride; PP = polypropylene; PU = polyurethane; FRP = Fiberglass-Reinforced Polyester)

	Growth Time (sec)
1. Wood pallets, stack 1½ ft high (6–12% moisture)	160–320
2. Wood pallets, stack 5 ft high (6–12% moisture)	95–190
3. Wood pallets, stack 10 ft high (6–12% moisture)	80–120
4. Wood pallets, stack 16 ft high (6–12% moisture)	75–120
5. Mail bags, filled, stored 5 ft high	190
6. Cartons, compartmented, stacked 15 ft high	60
7. Paper, vertical rolls, stacked 20 ft high	17–27
8. Cotton (also Pe, Pe/Cot Acrylic/Nylon/Pe), garments in 12 ft high rack	22–43
9. "Ordinary combustibles" rack storage, 15–30 ft high	40–270
10. Paper products, densely packed in cartons, rack storage, 20 ft high	470
11. PE letter trays, filled, stacked 5 ft high on cart	190
12. PE trash barrels in cartons, stacked 15 ft high	55
13. FRP shower stalls in cartons, stacked 15 ft high	85
14. PE bottles packed in Item 6	85
15. PE bottles in cartons, stacked 15 ft high	75
16. PE pallets, stack 3 ft high	150
17. PE pallets, stacks 6–8 ft high	32–56
18. PU mattress, single, horizontal	120
19. PU insulation board, rigid foam, stacked 15 ft high	8
20. PS jars packed in Item 6	55
21. PS tubs nested in cartons, stacked 14 ft high	110
22. PS toy parts in cartons, stacked 15 ft high	120
23. PS insulation board, rigid foam, stacked 14 ft high	7
24. PVC bottles packed in Item 6	9
25. PP tubs packed in Item 6	10
26. PP and PE film in rolls, stacked 14 ft high	40
27. Distilled spirits in barrels, stacked 20 ft high	25–40

SI unit: 1 ft = 0.31 m.

2 and 3, respectively, by inserting the appropriate values of H and d.

Continuous-Growth Fires

Required vent areas for each curtained compartment for fires in this class depend upon ceiling height (H), growth time, spacing of curtain boards (S_c), vent spacing, and means of vent actuation. They also depend upon the desired minimum clear visibility time from the time the first vents operate. The minimum clear visibility design time will facilitate such activities as locating the fire, appraising the severity and extent of the fire, evacuating the building, and making an informed decision on deployment of personnel and equipment to be used for fire fighting.

Table 6-8D lists recommended vent areas per curtained compartment for (1) the minimum recommended curtain depth of 20 percent of ceiling height, and (2) vents spaced at no more than one-half of the curtain board spacing. For other than square curtains, the spacing S_c is interpreted as the largest spacing defined by the curtained area. The tabulated areas are approximate, pertaining to vents that are operated by heat-responsive devices of an average thermal inertia, or response-time index (RTI), of 520 (ft · sec)$^{1/2}$[287 (m · sec)$^{1/2}$] and rated between 100°F (38°C) and 220°F (104°C) above ambient temperature.[2] Each entry in the table gives the range of vent areas in 1000 sq ft (92.9 m^2) associated with the selected range of temperature ratings. Entries boxed in are not possible (since the vent areas exceed the largest possible curtained area of S_c x S_c); however, these entries may be needed for curtain depths greater than 20 percent of ceiling height as treated in a later paragraph. Where values are not given, heat-release rates are greater than Q_{feasible}, as given in Equation 2; the vent area associated with Q_{feasible} is A_{feasible}, which has been calculated from:

$$A_{\text{feasible}}\ (\text{ft}^2) = 8.5\ (H - d)^{5/2}/d^{1/2} \qquad (4)$$

where, in the case of Table 6-8D, $d = 0.2H$. Entries in parentheses in the table correspond to levels of heat release greater than Q_{1000}, as given in Equation 3; the vent area associated with Q_{1000} is A_{1000}, which has been calculated from:

$$A_{1000}\ (\text{ft}^2) = 1.6\ (H - d)^{5/2}/d^{1/2} \qquad (5)$$

where, in the case of Table 6-8D, $d = 0.2H$.

To illustrate the use of Table 6-8D, consider an installation with heat-responsive devices rated approximately 100°F (38°C) above ambient, a ceiling height of 20 ft (6.1 m), a growth time of approximately 150 sec, a (square) curtain spacing of 80 ft or 24.4 m ($S_c = 4 \times H$), a curtain depth of 4 ft or 1.2 m (4/20 = 20 percent of ceiling height), and a minimum clear visibility time of 10 min. In Table 6-8D, the lower limit 100°F (38°C) of the appropriate entry indicates a vent area per curtained compartment of 0.64 x 1000 = 640 sq ft (59.5 m^2) for this case.

The recommended vent area for each curtained compartment is reduced if larger curtain depths than minimum (20 percent of ceiling height) are installed. The reduced areas are calculated by multiplying the values listed in Table 6-8D by the appropriate multiplication factor listed in Table 6-8C. To determine if Notes 4 or 6 from Table 6-8D apply to the newly derived values for vent area, the value of A_{feasible} associated with Q_{feasible} is calculated from Equation 4, and the value of A_{1000} associated with Q_{1000} is calculated from Equation 5. Note 4 applies if a vent area is larger than A_{feasible}, and Note 6 applies if a vent area is larger than A_{1000}.

Vent areas for each curtained compartment should be distributed among individual vents within the constraints discussed in the subsection, "Dimensioning and Spacing of Vents," of this chapter. In some cases, the calculated number of vents may be so large that the vent spacing will be considerably smaller than the design spacing for vents assumed in Table 6-8D (½ S_c). The closer vent spacing implies earlier operation of the first vents than is the case for the designs of Table 6-8D. Earlier operation, such as

TABLE 6-8C. *Multiplication Factors for Vent Areas in Figure 6-8F for Curtain Depths other than 20 Percent of Ceiling Height*

Curtain Depth in Percent of Ceiling Height	Multiplication Factor
30	0.71
40	0.53
50	0.40
60	0.29
70	0.20
80	0.13

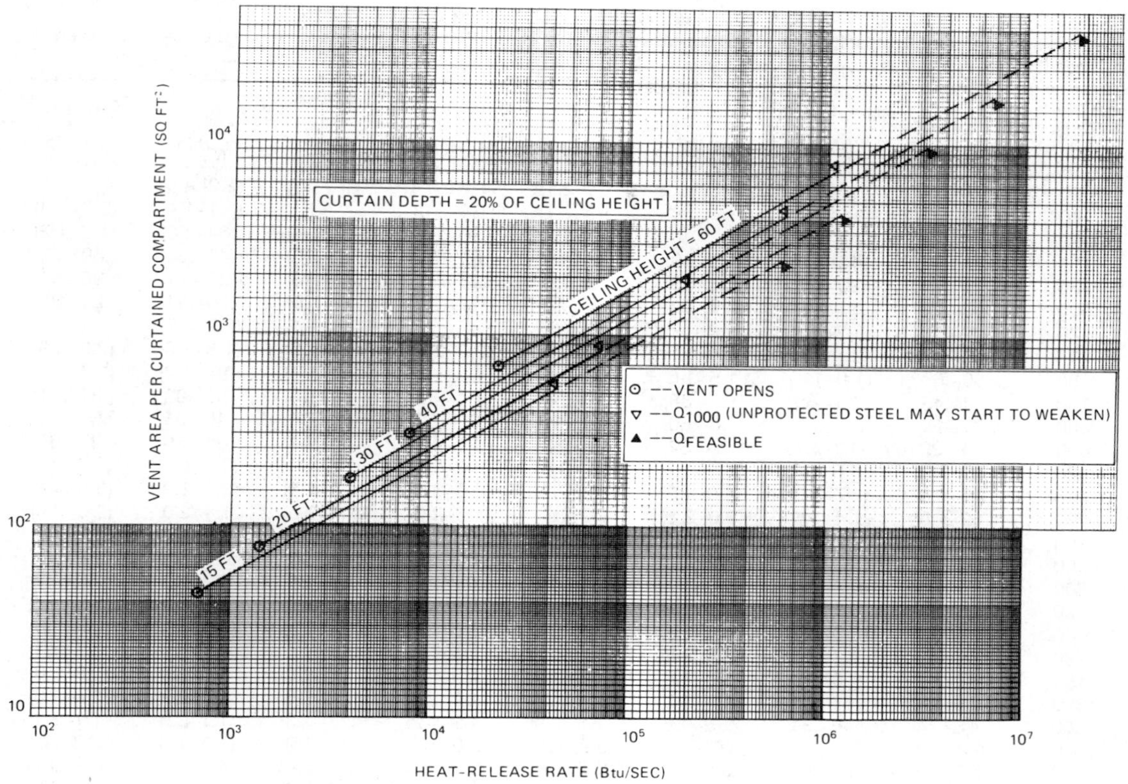

FIG. 6-8F. Limited fire growth; recommended vent areas for each curtained compartment for various maximum heat-release rates (Btu per sec or kW/sec).

that provided by an auxiliary fire detection system, would provide extra clear visibility times beyond the values of 5, 10, and 15 minutes selected in Table 6-8D. The extra time available with vents spaced at less than ½ S_c may be considered to represent a safety factor.

Selection of Design Basis

The vent area in a curtained compartment need not exceed the vent area recommended for the largest limited-growth fire predicted for combustibles beneath the curtained area. Using sufficiently small concentrations of combustibles and minimum aisle widths according to Equation 6-8A, it may be possible to satisfy the venting needs using smaller vent areas than required by a continuous-growth fire vent design. For example, in the illustration discussed previously for the use of Table 6-8D, the continuous-growth fire vent design for a growth time of 150 sec led to a required vent area for each curtained compartment of 640 sq ft (59.5 m²). A limited-growth fire vent design for a 50 sq ft (4.7 m²) floor area concentration at 200 Btu per sec per sq ft (2271 kW/m²) (if that is the heat-release rate per unit floor area of the combustible considered) involves a total heat-release rate per fuel concentration of 10,000 Btu per sec (10,540 kW) and a minimum aisle width of 14 ft (4.3 m), according to Equation 1. For the relevant vent parameters of a ceiling height of 20 ft (16.1 m), curtain depth at 20 percent of ceiling height, heat-release rate is 10,000 Btu per sec (10,540 kW). Figure 6-8F indicates a vent area per curtained compartment of 250 sq ft (23.2 m²), which is considerably smaller than the 640 sq ft (59.5 m²) vent area according to the design for continuous-growth fire. Of course, the combustible and floor area concentrations must be carefully controlled when limited-growth fire vent designs are selected. Furthermore, designs incorporating heat-release rates greater than Q_{1000} are risky, since the fire may flashover to all the combustibles under the curtained area. Such designs should be based on the potential heat-release rate of all the combustibles under the curtained area and should not be attempted at all if the resulting heat-release rate approaches Q_{feasible}. For continuous-growth fires, designs giving vent areas greater than A_{1000} cannot be recommended because of the flashover potential.

Mechanical Ventilators

For mechanical venting systems capable of functioning under the expected fire exposure, recommended exhaust capacities per curtained compartments are obtained by simple conversion from the recommended vent areas per curtained compartment. The conversion depends upon the depth of the curtain board or the design depth of the smoke layer, according to Table 6-8E.

ELEMENTS OF VENTING THEORY

To stop the descent of a smoke layer, the mass flow rate of hot gas out of the vents, $\dot{m}_v$ must match the mass injection rate of gas by the fire plume at the interface with the smoke layer, $\dot{m}_p$. (See Figure 6-8G.) Therefore, expressions are needed for the vent flow and for the plume flow.

TABLE 6-8D. *Vent Areas for Curtained Compartments*

Vent Area (in 1000 ft^2) per Curtained Compartment for Heat-Responsive Device Operated Vents With Various Curtain Board Spacings (S_c) and Minimum Clear-Visibility Design Times (5, 10 or 15 minutes).

Ceiling Height, H	Growth Time (Sec)	$S_c = 2 \times H$			$S_c = 4 \times H$			Sc = 8 × H		
		5 min	10 min	15 min	5 min	10 min	15 min	5 min	10 min	15 min
15 ft	20				(1.9–2.1)			(2.2–2.5)		
	40	.87–.97			(.98–1.1)	(1.8–2.0)		(1.1–1.4)	(2.0–2.3)	
	80	(.44–.52)	(.82–.90)		(.52–.64)	(.90–1.0)	(1.3–1.4)	(.64–.83)	(1.0–1.2)	(1.5–1.7)
	150	.25–.32	(.43–.50)	(.63–.70)	.31–.41	(.50–.60)	(.70–.80)	(.41–.58)	(.60–.77)	(.81–.98)
	300	.15–.20	.23–.29	.32–.38	.20–.28	.28–.36	.37–.46	.27–.41	.36–.51	(.46–.61)
	600	.10–.14	.13–.18	.17–.23	.13–.21	.17–.25	.21–.29	.20–.34	.24–.38	.29–.43
20	20	2.2–7.3			(2.5–2.7)			(2.7–3.2)		
	40	(1.1–1.2)	2.1–2.2		(1.2–1.5)	(2.2–2.5)	(3.3–3.6)	(1.5–1.8)	(2.5–2.9)	(3.6–4.0)
	80	.56–.68	(1.0–1.1)	1.5–1.6	.68–.86	(1.1–1.3)	(1.6–1.8)	(.87–1.2)	(1.3–1.6)	(1.8–2.1)
	150	.34–.43	.55–.65	(.77–.88)	.43–.58	.64–.80	(.88–1.0)	.58–.83	(.80–1.1)	(1.0–1.3)
	300	.21–.29	.30–.39	.40–.50	.28–.41	.38–.52	.48–.63	.40–.65	.51–.76	.62–.88
	600	.14–.22	.19–.27	.23–.32	.20–.33	.25–.38	.30–.44	.32–.56	.37–.61	.42–.67
30	20	(2.9–3.2)	5.6–6.0		(3.2–3.8)	(6.0–6.6)		(3.8–4.6)	(6.7–7.6)	
	40	1.5–1.8	(2.7–3.0)	4.0–4.3	(1.8–2.2)	(3.0–3.4)	(4.3–4.8)	(2.2–2.9)	(3.5–4.2)	(4.8–5.6)
	80	.82–1.0	1.4–1.6	(2.0–2.2)	1.0–1.4	1.6–2.0	(2.2–2.6)	1.4–2.0	(2.0–2.6)	(2.6–3.2)
	150	.51–.71	.78–.99	1.1–1.3	.68–.99	.96–1.3	1.3–1.6	.97–1.5	1.3–1.8	(1.6–2.2)
	300	.34–.53	.47–.66	.59–.80	.48–.77	.61–.91	.74–1.1	.74–1.3	.88–1.4	1.0–1.6
	600	.26–.44	.32–.50	.38–.57	.38–.67	.44–.74	.50–.81	.62–1.2	.69–1.2	.76–1.3
40	20	(3.6–4.1)	6.7–7.3	10–11	(4.1–4.9)	(7.4–8.2)	(11–12)	(5.0–6.3)	(8.3–9.7)	(12–13)
	40	1.9–2.3	(3.3–3.8)	(4.8–5.3)	2.3–3.0	(3.8–4.5)	(5.3–6.1)	(3.0–4.1)	(4.5–5.6)	(6.1–7.3)
	80	1.1–1.5	1.7–2.1	2.4–2.8	1.4–2.0	2.1–2.7	2.8–3.4	2.0–3.0	2.7–3.7	(3.4–4.5)
	150	.72–1.1	1.0–1.4	1.4–1.8	.98–1.5	1.3–1.9	1.7–2.2	1.5–2.4	1.8–2.8	2.2–3.2
	300	.51–.84	.66–1.0	.81–1.2	.74–1.3	.89–1.4	1.1–1.6	1.2–2.2	1.4–2.3	1.5–2.5
	600	.41–.74	.48–.81	.55–.89	.61–1.1	.69–1.2	.77–1.3	1.1–2.0	1.1–2.1	1.2–2.2
60	20	4.9–5.9	(8.9–10)	(13–14)	5.9–7.4	(10–12)	(14–16)	(7.5–10)	(12–14)	(16–19)
	40	2.8–3.6	4.6–5.5	6.5–7.4	3.5–4.8	5.4–6.7	(7.3–8.8)	4.8–7.0	(6.7–9.1)	(8.7–11)
	80	1.7–2.5	2.5–3.4	3.4–4.3	2.3–3.5	3.2–4.4	4.1–5.4	3.4–5.6	4.3–6.6	5.2–7.6
	150	1.2–2.0	1.6–2.4	2.1–2.9	1.7–2.9	2.2–3.4	2.6–3.9	2.8–4.9	3.2–5.4	3.7–5.9
	300	.95–1.7	1.2–1.9	1.3–2.1	1.4–2.6	1.6–2.8	1.8–3.1	2.4–4.6	2.6–4.8	2.9–5.1
	600	.82–1.6	.92–1.7	1.0–1.8	1.3–2.4	1.4–2.6	1.5–2.7	2.2–4.4	2.3–4.5	2.5–4.6

For SI Units: 1 ft = .3048 m; 1 ft^2 = 0.093 m^2.

Notes:

1. Vents are assumed to be spaced at one-half of the curtain board spacing.
2. Curtain depth assumed at 20 percent of ceiling height.
3. Each entry is the vent-area range (in 1000 ft^2) associated with heat-responsive devices rated between 100°F and 220°F (38°C and 104°C) above ambient temperature.
4. No Entries: Heat-release rates greater than Q feasible.
5. Entries Boxed-In: Not possible, but needed for curtain depths greater than 20 percent.
6. Entries in Parentheses: Correspond to levels of heat release greater than Q_{1000}.

TABLE 6-8E. *Conversion from Vent Area of Gravity Vents to Equivalent Mechanical Exhaust Capacity*

Curtain Depth (ft)*	Mechanical Exhaust Capacity Per Unit Area of Gravity Vent (SCFM/ft^2)†
6	354
8	409
10	457
12	501
16	578
20	647
24	708

SCFM = Standard Cubic Feet per Minute (Standard Temperature and Pressure)

* 1 ft = 0.3 m

† 1 ft^2 = 0.028 m^3

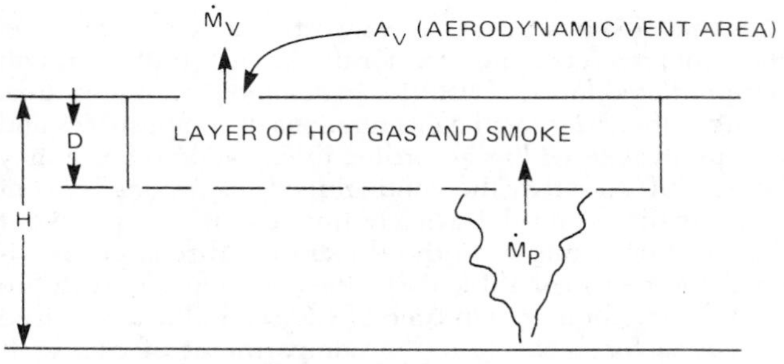

FIG. 6-8G. A schematic of a venting system.

Vent Flow

The vent flow can be calculated from the following equation:[3,4]

$$\dot{m}_v = (2\rho_o^2 g)^{1/2}\left[\frac{T_o\,(T - T_o)}{T^2}\right]^{1/2} A_v d^{1/2} \qquad (6)$$

where $\dot{m}_v$ is the mass flow rate through the vent (lb per sec or kg/sec); ρ_o is the density of the ambient air (lb per cu ft or kg/m^3); g is the acceleration of gravity (ft/sec^2 or m/sec^2); T_o is the ambient temperature (°R or K); T is the smoke layer temperature (°R or K); A_v is the aerodynamic vent area (sq ft or m^2); and d is the depth of the smoke layer (ft or m), generally interpreted as the height of the center of the vent above the smoke interface.

The aerodynamic vent area, A_v, is always smaller than the geometric vent area. For simple apertures, A_v may be taken as 0.6 times the geometric through-flow area.

The temperature function $\left[\frac{T_o (T - T_o)}{T^2}\right]^{1/2}$ can be approximated at 0.50 for smoke layer temperatures in the range of 275 to 1400°F (135 to 760°C), which covers most vent applications. Then Equation 6 becomes simply

$$\dot{m}_v = (\rho_o^2 g/2)^{1/2} A_v d^{1/2} \quad (7)$$

To prevent air from the clear layer below from being entrained in the vent exhaust, it has been proposed that the area of the vent not exceed $2d^2$.[5] If the vent is long and narrow, an analogous requirement would be that the width of the vent not exceed d.

Plume Flow

The mass flow rate injected into the smoke layer by the fire plume is practically equal to the air entrainment rate of the plume from the clear layer; the contribution of the fire source itself is small in comparison. Before the 1982 revision of NFPA 204M, *Smoke and Heat Venting*, an entrainment theory[6] was already in existence. However, that theory was considered somewhat unwieldy for the format of NFPA 204M and an alternative, more adaptable, and probably more accurate theory was developed in the Appendix of 204M.

The plume flow, m_p, from the new theory is calculated according to either of two equations, depending upon whether the convective heat-release rate of the fire is larger or smaller than a critical value, Q_c, defined as (fire assumed to be located on floor of building):

$$Q_c \text{ (Btu/sec)} = 11.3\,(H - d)^{1/2} \quad (8)$$

(where H and d are in ft)

The plume flow equations are:

For $Q \leq Q_c$

$$\dot{m}_p \text{ (lb/s)} = 0.022\, Q^{1/3} (H - d)^{5/3} [1 + 0.19\, Q^{2/3}/(H - d)^{5/3}] \quad (9)$$

For $Q > Q_c$

$$\dot{m}_p \text{ (lb/s)} = 0.097\,(H - d)^{5/2} (Q/Q_c)^{3/5} \quad (10)$$

where Q and Q_c are Btu/sec and H and d are in ft.

Required Vent Area

For $Q \leq Q_c$, where Q_c is given by Equation 8, the expression for $\dot{m}_p$ in Equation 9 is set equal to the expression for m_v in Equation 7 and solved for A_v, the aerodynamic vent area. For $Q > Q_c$, the expression for $\dot{m}_p$ in Equation 10 is set equal to the expression for $\dot{m}_v$ in Equation 7 and solved for A_v.

The resulting relations for A_v can be greatly simplified whenever Q/Q_c is larger than approximately 0.2, which is nearly always the case in vent design. Then the two expressions for A_v can be consolidated into a single relation with the aid of Equation 8, valid for heat-release rates both smaller and larger than Q_c:

$$A_v \text{ (ft}^2) = 0.075\, Q^{3/5} \frac{H - d}{d^{1/2}} \quad (11)$$

where Q is in Btu per sec, and H and d are in ft.

For fires growing with the second power of time (continuous-growth fires), Equation 11 can be written:

$$A_v \text{ (ft}^2) = 4.8\,[(t_d + t_r)/t_g]^{6/5} (H - d)/d^{1/2} \quad (12)$$

where H and d are in ft; t_d is the detection time, or the time the first vents operate; t_r is the additional, clear visibility time; and t_g is the growth time defined in the subsection "Fire Characterization."

These are the basic relations used for calculating vent areas in the 1982 edition of NFPA 204M, *Smoke and Heat Venting*, with adjustments for a discharge coefficient of 0.6 (aerodynamic vent areas, A_v, divided by 0.6). In Equation 12, the detection time, t_d, was taken as the time of operation of the first vent in a square matrix (farthest possible vent from the fire location). The vents were assumed to be actuated by heat-responsive devices of various temperature ratings above the ambient temperature. Link actuation times (t_d) were calculated from a thermal response equation for heat-responsive devices derived previously,[7] together with generalized data on gas temperatures and velocities under extensive flat ceilings.[8,9] The RTI value of the heat-responsive device was taken as 520 (ft·sec)$^{1/2}$ [287(m·sec)$^{1/2}$], which is considered to be a conservatively high value for heat-responsive devices listed by testing laboratories.

Limiting Heat-Release Rates

Q_{1000} was defined in conjunction with Equation 3 as the heat-release rate at which gas temperatures in excess of 1000°F (538°C) may be reached with possible weakening of structural steel and potentials for flashover within the curtained areas. The expression for Q_{1000} was derived first using Equation 10, with substitution for Q_c from Equation 8, to obtain $\dot{m}_p$ expressed as:

$$\dot{m}_p \text{ (lb/sec)} = 0.0226\,(H - d) Q^{3/5} \quad (13)$$

where Q is in Btu/sec, and H and d are in ft.

The average temperature rise in the smoke layer, ΔT_s (°F), follows from:

$$\dot{m}_p\, c_p\, \Delta T = Q \quad (14)$$

where c_p [Btu per lb per °F or J/(kg)/K] is the specific heat of air and where it has been assumed that no heat is lost to the ceiling and walls. With substitution of Equation 13 for $\dot{m}_p$, c_p = 0.24 Btu per lb per °F [1004 (J/kg)/K] and ΔT = 1000°F (555°C) in Equation 14, the resulting expression can be solved for Q to give Equation 3. Of course, the result is quite conservative, since a significant heat loss may occur to the ceiling and the walls of the curtained compartment.

$Q_{feasible}$ was described in conjunction with Equation 2 as a heat-release rate beyond which the feasibility of roof venting, using the present approach, might be questioned because of the onset of ventilation control of the burning process. Experience has indicated that ventilation-controlled fires do not support a clear layer as, for example, in the case of the typical, flashed-over room fire. According to experiments on wood crib fires in enclosures, vented through doors or windows,[10] ventilation control appears to set in when the so-called "ventilation parameter," $A_w \sqrt{h_w}$, in ratio to the mass burning rate, R, is less than 266 ft$^{5/2}$ per lb per sec), where A_w is the window (or door) area, and h_w is the window (or door) height. Generalized to any combustible, the limiting ratio might be expressed as $A_w \sqrt{h_w}$, in ratio to the stoichiometric air requirement associated with the mass burning rate, Rr, where r is the stoichiometric mass ratio, air to combustible (assumed at 5.5 for wood). Now, the ventilation parameter, $A_w \sqrt{h_w}$, is proportioned to the mass flow rate of air through a window or door opening, $\dot{m}_v$.[11]

$$\dot{m}_v \text{ (lb/sec)} = 0.064\, A_w \sqrt{h_w} \quad (15)$$

(A_w in ft^2, h_w in ft).

The limiting condition for ventilation control can, therefore, be expressed in terms of the mass venting rate of air in ratio to the stoichiometric air requirement, $\dot{m}_v/Rr$, which turns out to be approximately 3. Using the fact that Rr can be written $Q/(H_c/r)$, where Q is the heat-release rate and H_c is the heat of combustion, the limiting mass rate ratio can be converted to a limiting heat-release rate:

$$Q = \frac{1}{3}\ \dot{m}_v\ (H_c/r) \qquad (16)$$

In application to roof vents, $\dot{m}_v$ can be expressed as in Equation 7. Furthermore, H_c/r is quite constant among common combustibles. Substituting Equation 7 and taking H_c/r = 1328 Btu per lb (3086 kJ/kg), Equation 16 becomes:

$$Q\ (\text{Btu/sec}) = 133\ A_v d^{1/2} \qquad (17)$$

where A_v is in sq ft, and d is in ft.

In the venting approach used in NFPA 204M, *Smoke and Heat Venting*, the vent area A_v is given by Equation 11, which, divided by 0.6 to convert to geometric vent area and then substituted in Equation 17, gives a relation that can be solved for Q. The result is the expression for the limiting heat-release rate, Q_{feasible}, in Equation 2.

BIBLIOGRAPHY

References Cited

1. Alpert, R. L. and Ward, E. J., "Evaluation of Unsprinklered Fire Hazards," *Fire Safety Journal*, Vol. 7, 1984, pp. 127-143.
2. Heskestad, G. and Smith, H. F., "Plunge Test for Determination of Sprinkler Sensitivity," *Technical Report FMRC 3A1E2.RR*, Factory Mutual Research Corporation, Norwood, MA, 1980.
3. Thomas, P. H., *et al.*, "Investigations into the Flow of Hot Gases in Roof Venting," *Fire Research Technical Paper No. 7*, Department of Scientific and Industrial Research and Fire Offices' Committee, Joint Fire Research Organization. Her Majesty's Stationery Office, London, England, 1963.
4. Thomas, P. H. and Hinkley, P. L., "Design of Roof-Venting Systems for Single-Story Buildings," *Fire Research Technical Paper No. 10*, Department of Scientific and Industrial Research and Fire Offices' Committee, Joint Fire Research Organization, Her Majesty's Stationery Office, London, England, 1964.
5. Thomas, P. H. and Hinkley, P. L., "Design of Roof-Venting Systems."
6. Thomas, P. H., *et al.*, "Investigations into the Flow of Hot Gases."
7. Heskestad, G. and Smith, H. F., "Investigation of a New Sprinkler Sensitivity Approval Test: The Plunge Test," *Technical Report FMRC 22485*, Factory Mutual Research Corporation. Norwood, MA, 1976.
8. Heskestad, G., "Similarity Relations for the Initial Convective Flow Generated by Fire," *Paper No. 72-WA/HT-17*, American Society of Mechanical Engineers, New York, NY, 1972.
9. Heskestad, G. and Delichatsios, M. A., "The Initial Convective Flow in Fire" *Seventeenth Symposium (International) on Combustion*, The Combustion Institute, Pittsburgh, PA, pp. 1113-1123, 1979.
10. Croce, P. A., "Modeling of Vented Enclosure Fires, Part I: Quasi-Steady Wood-Crib Source Fire," *Technical Report FMRC 7A0R5.GU*, Factory Mutual Research Corporation, Norwood, MA, 1978.
11. Harmathy, T. Z., "Ventilation of Full-Developed Compartment Fires," *Combustion and Flame*, Vol. 37, 1980, pp. 25-39.

NFPA Codes, Standards, and Recommended Practices

Reference to the following NFPA codes, standards, and recommended practices will provide further information on venting practices discussed in this chapter. (See the latest *NFPA Catalog* for availability of current editions of the following documents.)

NFPA 204M, *Smoke and Heat Venting*.

Additional Readings

Butcher, E. G. and Parnell, A. C., *Smoke Control in Fire Safety Design*, E. & F. N. Spon Ltd., London, England, 1979; also National Fire Protection Association, Quincy, MA.

Carlson, G. and Orton, C., *ed.*, *Fire Ventilation Practices*, 6th ed., International Fire Service Training Association, Oklahoma State University, Stillwater, OK, 1981.

Davis, W. D. and Cooper, L. Y., "Estimating the Environment and the Response of Sprinkler Links in Compartment Fires with Draft Curtains and Fusible-Link-Activated Ceiling Vents, Part I," *NBSIR 88-3734*, Center for Fire Research, Gaithersburg, MD, Apr. 1988.

Davis, W. D. and Cooper, L. Y., "Estimating the Environment and Response of Sprinkler Links in Compartment Fires with Draft Curtains and Fusible-Link-Activated Ceiling Vents, Part 2: User Guide for the Computer Code LAVENT," *NISTIR 89-4122*, National Institute for Standards and Technology, Gaithersburg, MD, Aug. 1989.

Degenkolb, J. G., "Field Test of an Atrium Exhaust System," *Building Standards*, Vol. 57, No. 2, 1988, pp. 18-19.

Edwards, J., "Theatre Fires—The Importance of Smoke Ventilation," *Fire Prevention*, No. 198, Apr. 1987, pp. 37-38.

Edwards, J., "Vents and Sprinklers—Controversy Resolved," *Fire Prevention*, No. 211, July/Aug. 1988, pp. 39-42.

Heskestad, G., "Model Study of Automatic Smoke and Heat Vent Performance in Sprinklered Fires," *Technical Report RC74-T-29*, Factory Mutual Research Corporation, Norwood, MA, Sept. 1974.

Heskestad, G., "More on Fire Venting Tests," Letter to Editor, *Fire Journal*, Vol. 78, No. 5, Sept. 1984, pp. 6-84.

Heskestad, G., "Smoke Movement and Venting," *Fire Safety Journal*, Vol. 11, Nos. 1 and 2, 1986, pp. 77-83.

Hinkley, P. L., "Case for Combining Venting and Sprinkler Systems," *Fire Engineers Journal*, Vol. 47, No. 145, June 1987, pp. 17-22.

Hinkley, P. L., "The Effect of Smoke Venting on the Operation of Sprinklers Subsequent to the First," *Fire Safety Journal*, Vol. 14, No. 4, 1989, pp. 221-240.

Hinkley, P. L., "Rates of Production of Hot Gases in Roof Venting Experiments," *Fire Safety Journal*, Vol. 11, No. 1, 1986, pp. 57-65.

Hinkley, P. L., "Smoke and Heat Venting," *SFPE Handbook of Fire Protection Engineering*, National Fire Protection Association, Quincy, MA, 1988.

Hopkinson, J., "Venting a Smoky Fire in a Hotel Stairway," *Fire Safety Journal*, Vol. 10, No. 1, 1986, pp. 11-18.

Hughes, L. D., "Positive-Pressure Ventilation in a Test Setting," *Fire Engineering*, Vol. 142, No. 12, Dec. 1989, pp. 56-59.

Kandola, B., "Effects of Atmospheric Wind on Flows through Natural Convection Roof Vents," *Fire Technology*, Vol. 26, No. 2, May 1990, pp. 106-120.

Klote, J. H. and Cooper, L. Y., "Model of a Simple Fan-Resistance Ventilation System and Its Application to Fire Modeling," *NIST 89-4141*, National Institute for Standards and Technology, Gaithersburg, MD, Sept. 1989.

Langdon-Thomas, G. J. and Hinkley, P. L., "Fire Venting—Small-Story Industrial Buildings," *Fire Note No. 5*, Ministry of Technology, Industrial and Fire Offices Committee, Joint Fire Research Organization, Her Majesty's Stationery Office, London, England, 1965.

Lathrop, J. K., "Atrium Fire Proves Difficult to Ventilate," *Fire Journal*, Vol. 73, No. 1, 1979.

Lyons, R. J., "Automatic Heat and Smoke Venting," Progessive Architecture, Apr. 1972.

Miller, E. E., "Position Paper to 204 Subcommittee," *Fire Venting of Sprinklered Property*, National Fire Protection Association, Quincy, MA.

Morgan, H. P., "Roof Venting—Similarities between Large and Small-Scale Calculations," *Fire Prevention*, No. 198, Apr. 1987, pp. 32-33.

Poole, G. A., "Contribution of Emergency Vent Design to Loss Prevention in Process Plants," *Fire Prevention*, No. 197, Mar. 1987, pp. 28-31.

Searle, B., "Efficient Smoke Extraction: Saving Lives and Money," *Civil Engineering* (London), July-Aug.1988, pp. 16-17.

Shea, L. E., "Flammable Vapor Exhaust Systems," *Building Standards*, Vol. 56, No. 1, 1987, pp. 4-8.

Skelton, R. E., "A Remotely Controlled Fire-Venting System in a Shopping Complex," *Fire Journal*, Vol. 72, No. 1, Jan. 1978, p. 76.

Swift, I., "NFPA 68 Guide for Venting of Deflagrations: What's New and How It Affects You," *Proceedings* of the American Institute of Chemical Engineers National Meeting, AIChE, 1988, p. 30.

Talbert, J. H., "Smoke and Heat Venting for Sprinklered Buildings: A Different Perspective," *Fire Journal*, Vol. 81, No. 3, 1987, p. 26.

Teter, W. J., "A Blow to a Killer," *Industrial Fire World*, Vol. 3, No. 4, Aug. 1987, pp. 12-14.

Tewarson, A., "Fire Ventilation," *Combustion and Flame*, Vol. 53, Nos. 1-3, Nov. 1983, pp. 123-134.

Tewarson, A. and Steciak, J., *Fire Ventilation*, Elsevier, New York, NY, 1983.

"Venting Plus Sprinklers—The Case Against," *Fire International*, Vol. 10, No. 101, 1986, pp. 31-32, 34.

Waterman, T. E., "Fire Venting of Sprinklered Buildings," *Fire Journal*, Vol. 78, No. 2, Mar. 1984, pp. 30-39, 86.

Waterman, T. E., *et al.*, "Fire Venting of Sprinklered Buildings," *IITRI Project J08385* for Fire Venting Research Committee, IIT Research Institute, Chicago, IL, July 1982.

ADDENDUM

AUTOMATIC HEAT AND SMOKE VENTING IN SPRINKLERED BUILDINGS

This addendum supplements the venting practices in this chapter as written by Dr. Heskestad. It presents in summary the various views on the controversial and unresolved subject of automatic venting in sprinklered buildings. The history of research testing on the subject is traced. Contributors include Ernest E. Miller, Thomas E. Waterman, and Edward J. Ward.*

* Ernest E. Miller is an executive engineer with Industrial Risk Insurers (IRI). Thomas E. Waterman is director of research for the Institute for Advanced Safety Study and, while employed by the IIT Research Institute, conducted the IITRI test series of 1980–1981. Edward J. Ward is vice president of Manufacturing, Service, and Research and Development of MicroFridge Incorporated, and was employed by Factory Mutual Research Corporation at the time he contributed his views. In this revision, Dr. Heskestad has deleted one entry from Table 6-8G, one of Mr. Ward's contributions, following discovery that the entry (Test 73) involved in-rack sprinklers; associated text has been revised for consistency.

The Different Views

There has been controversy for approximately two decades over automatic venting for sprinklered buildings.

Proponents of automatic venting in sprinklered buildings claim that venting will aid manual fire fighting by delaying loss of visibility, reduce the risk of structural failure by venting gases with dangerously high temperatures, vent the equivalent of an unsprinklered fire if the installed sprinklers are defeated by human failure or mechanical damage, and substitute for manual roof venting by fire service personnel.

Opponents believe that, in some cases, venting may even be detrimental because it draws in fresh makeup air, keeping oxygen levels higher than they would be otherwise, causing more vigorous combustion with an increase in fuel consumption, and potential for loss of sprinkler control. They also believe sprinkler discharge will cool the fire gases, perhaps to the extent that the vent discharge is reduced, hence reducing venting effectiveness. Further, the sprinkler sprays will entrain ambient smoke and air, transporting smoke to the floor level and possibly drawing gas from the vent exhaust wherever sprinklers are located close to vents and further reducing venting effectiveness. Additionally, opponents see little, if any, evidence from research testing of the benefit to fire control obtained from the use of vents in a sprinklered building, and believe that the high cost of installation does not justify their use.

Sprinkler/Vent Research

Research testing on the subject includes:

1. **Large scale tests:** In 1956 Factory Mutual Research Corporation (FMRC) ran a series of large-scale tests from which it concluded that the effects of venting in sprinklered buildings are different from unsprinklered buildings. The research project[1] was conducted in a 120-by-60-ft (36.6-by-18.3-m) test building equipped with 5-ft (1.5-m) draft curtains and vent areas ranging up to 32 sq ft (3 m^2) within a curtained area of 2280 sq ft (212 m^2). This is a vent ratio of about 1:70—that is, 1 sq ft (0.09 m^2) of vent area for every 70 sq ft (6.5 m^2) of floor area. A 5-gal-per-min (18.9 L/min) gasoline spray fire was used as the exposure, and protection consisted of 160°F (71°C) automatic sprinklers installed on a 10-by-10-ft (3-by-3-m) spacing.

The tests in the series were conducted using various combinations of vents, draft curtains, and sprinklers. Six of these were sprinklered tests. (See Table 6-8F.)

TABLE 6-8F. *FMRC Test Results*

Test No.	Curtain ft (m)	Vent ft^2 (m^2)	Sprinkler Discharge gpm (L/min)	Number of Sprinklers Operated
1	None	None	15 (57)	48
2	None	32 (3)	15 (57)	44
3	5 (1.5)	32 (3)	15 (57)	24
4	5 (1.5)	16 (3)	15 (57)	24
5	5 (1.5)	None	15 (57)	28
6	5 (1.5)	None	25 (95)	15

Comparison of average temperatures indicates that vents contributed significantly to temperature reductions in the unsprinklered tests in the series; however, they were of marginal value in the sprinklered tests. The greatest reduction in sprinkler operation was attributed to increased sprinkler discharge.

2. **FMRC model study:** In the early 1970s, a FMRC study was conducted.[2] The objective was to investigate experimentally the performance of automatic heat and smoke vents in sprinklered fires in one-story buildings, principally in terms of sprinkler water demand, but also in terms of visibility conditions and fuel consumption. The study was performed at FMRC's Norwood, MA, laboratory and involved a 1:12.5 scale model of FMRC's fire test facility at West Gloucester, RI. Automatic, individually fused vents on 50-ft (15.2-m) spacing were employed, often in combination with a draft curtain encompassing a 10,000-sq-ft (929-m^2) curtained area.

Of primary interest were venting installations conforming to recommendations of standards-setting groups that were state-of-the-art at the time. For a fire in cellulosic material that opened about fifty 212°F (100°C) sprinklers at a density of 0.27 gpm per sq ft (11 [L/min]/m^2), distributed vents alone (without draft curtains) had no effect on the water demand, but delayed loss in visibility from 13.1 to 15.7 min and increased fuel consumption by 31 percent. Vents and draft curtains caused a 35 percent increase in water demand relative to the unvented fire, delayed loss in visibility from 13.1 to 20.2 minutes, and increased fuel consumption by 66 percent.

Favorable effects of venting were observed for a series of large, heptane fires that opened an average of one hundred twelve sprinklers at 0.27 gpm per sq ft (11 [L/min]/m^2). Vents alone reduced the water demand by 8 percent and markedly improved visibility conditions; vents and draft curtains reduced the water demand by 18 percent, but did not improve visibility conditions as much as without draft curtains.

The test results were based on ignition points that were equidistant from the four nearest vents in the vent matrix. Experiments with ignition directly under a vent indicated that some reduction in water demand could be expected for fires that opened fifty sprinklers or less. It was concluded, however, that for randomly started fires, less than about 13 percent of the fires would benefit, respective to water demand, from closeness to a nearby vent.

Critics counter that the 0.08-scale-model experiments, although carefully designed and executed, incorporated numerous uncertainties. Of particular concern was modeling of a full-scale fuel bed (rack storage configuration), by using ½-in. (12.7-mm) thick triwall cardboard. Some ten years later, the modeling of room fire development has proceeded to an advanced state in all respects, except for the burning fuel; both analytical and experimental models address only the simplest of fuel configurations. Yet the model study assumed that both flame spread and burning rate of the fuel bed were modeled under conditions of depleted oxygen and impacting water droplets.

The FMRC model study was also criticized because of the configuration of the water discharge devices that were used. The study pioneered the use of nondescript miniature nozzles (representing sprinklers) arranged to be operated in small open-head deluge systems of groups of five to eleven nozzles controlled by individual sensors. Critics claim this arrangement magnified the known imprecision in measuring comparative sprinkler performance. It required multiplying the normal spread experienced in full-scale sprinkler operation by a variable factor of 5 to 11. Due to the small deluge systems, which operated as groups, sprinkler skipping occurred in units of 5 or more open nozzles, rather than the skipping of individual sprinklers as would be customary in full-scale fire research.

Lastly, the critics agreed that, although up to three times as much combustible material was consumed in the vented tests as compared to the unvented tests, the implication of detriment was improper. They claimed the explanation for the increased fuel consumption in the vented tests lies in the customary manner of conducting fire tests involving sprinklers. The test fires are allowed to continue far beyond sprinkler control to give the fires every opportunity to escape. During the additional minutes of these tests, the oxygen reduction in the unvented tests limited the fuel consumption, whereas oxygen remained abundant in the vented tests and resulted in greater fuel consumption. Since sprinkler-controlled fires continue to smolder and burn, it was felt that the reported increased fuel consumption was attributable to more complete burning of the rubble and did not represent increased fire damage. Had the fires spread to involve a significantly larger area, additional sprinklers would have operated.

3. **Other FMRC large-scale testing:** More than eighty full-scale rack storage tests were conducted between 1968 and 1975. Only three tests employed perimeter ventilation (not to be confused with roof venting directly over a fire) and only one of these three (No. 72) was identical to two other tests (Nos. 65 and 66), except for the ventilation variable. Results of these tests are given in Table 6-8G.

TABLE 6-8G. ***Rack Storage Tests***

Test No.	Ventilated	Number of Ceiling Sprinklers Operated
65	No	45
66	No	48
72	Yes	92

Comparing Test Nos. 65 and 66 to Test No. 72, researchers discovered that venting caused a dramatic detriment to the performance of the sprinklers. However, it is pointed out that Test No. 72 had a significantly different initial fire growth behavior compared to the other tests, which may have affected the outcome. FMRC's position on the effects of ventilation in these tests is that they are not conclusive.

Venting proponents argue that, although the influence of venting was inconclusive because the perimeter windows were too remote, the ventilated tests maintained visibility for 48:40 and 33:00 (minutes:seconds), as compared to 10:30 and 18:00 for the unventilated tests.

Venting opponents claim the effect of ventilation on fire control was best demonstrated during FMRC's large-scale fire testing of rubber tires in 1970. This test was made to evaluate sprinkler protection for automobile tires stored in portable steel racks. Storage was located in a single pile 35 ft by 50 ft by 18 ft (11 m by 15 m by 5.4 m) high. Protection consisted of 286°F (141°C), ½-in. (12.7-mm) sprinklers, spaced 50 sq ft (4.6 m^2), each with a controlled discharge of 0.6 gal per min per sq ft (24.4 [L/min]/m²). There was no ventilation at the start of the test.

The fire was started at the base of a rack. The first sprinkler operated 2 min and 15 sec after ignition. By 8 min and 20 sec, forty-three sprinklers had operated and controlled the fire. Only one additional sprinkler operated at 28 min. The fire remained under control until 60 min into the test, when all doors and windows were opened to ventilate the building and sprinklers were left on. The fire then began to spread and grow in intensity. At 117 min, when it was apparent that sprinklers were failing to control the fire, all doors and windows were closed. A total of ninety-five sprinklers operated, and water was discharged for over 5 hr. Only the ninety-fifth sprinkler operated after doors and windows were closed, and that was at 118 min, 1 min after closure.

Critics reappraised the ventilated rubber tire fire test[3] and contended that the loss of initial sprinkler control was not due to remote window ventilation, as reported. Ceiling temperature gradients revealed that during the hour delay before hose extinguishment of the sprinkler-controlled fire was attempted, the fire had burrowed to the other end of the pile where sprinklers were not operating and had erupted with great intensity. The tightly stacked tires, stored on tread, formed horizontal tunnels that offered avenues of fire spread that were sheltered from sprinkler discharge.

4. **IITRI full-scale venting research testing:** In 1977, the IITRI (IIT Research Institute) was commissioned by the intra-industry Fire Venting Research Committee to review past research and fire experience related to vent/sprinkler interactions in large-area single-story structures. Based on IITRI's review and other considerations, the committee ultimately funded some forty-five large-scale segment experiments in 1980–1981.[4] The experiments were conducted in a 75-by-25-by-17-ft high (23-by-7.6-by-5.2-m) portion of IITRI's fire laboratory. Fires were placed in a corner to represent one-quarter of a larger fire in the center of a 150-by-50-ft (46-by-15.2-m) room. To simulate the test area as part of an even larger area, two garage doors on the wall farthest from the fire were partially opened to represent a draft curtain. The area beyond the curtains was also enclosed by vertical air stacks to minimize extraneous wind effects.

To allow variations in vent area, two pairs of automatic roof vents were installed in the laboratory roof. A diagonal sprinkler pattern was chosen to eliminate aisles between sprinklers that were located between the test fires and the vents. Experiments were conducted using propane diffusion burners or stacked pallets as the fuel source. For each fuel source, fire size and sprinkler water supply pressure were varied until a condition of "marginal" sprinkler control was achieved. Then, vent areas were varied to assess effects of venting on sprinkler performance (number of operating sprinklers and temperature levels at various locations). The laboratory size and excessive recirculation of smoke due to the substitution of vertical stacks for added rooms precluded useful measures of smoke obscuration.

Propane-source fires produced results suggesting a slight reduction in water demand for vented fires when either 165 or 286°F (74 or 141°C) sprinklers were employed (vents were operated either with 165°F [74°C] links or by simulated smoke detector or waterflow switch actuation).

All pallet fire experiments employed 165°F (74°C) sprinklers and the same vent arrangement previously described. These experiments demonstrated that, under marginal sprinkler protection, the configuration of the test facility was extremely sensitive to variations in fire intensity from any cause. Once this possibility appeared, a final series of ten "replicate" experiments was conducted, alternating between vented and unvented configurations. These experiments proved to produce widely varying results, apparently independent of the presence of automatic venting. The number of operating sprinklers varied from seven to twenty-two per test, and the pattern of sprinkler operating times appeared unrelated to the time that vents opened. Other measured factors (temperature, O_2) varied in the same way. Although the number of operating sprinklers varied widely in these experiments with marginal sprinkler control, a total of eighty-four sprinklers operated in the five unvented tests, eighty-five in the five vented tests. Earlier tests at higher water supply pressures produced good replication, independent of venting.

On the basis of the IITRI experiments, the test sponsors concluded that automatic roof venting did not detract from current state-of-the-art automatic sprinkler performance. Likewise, no particularly significant benefit to sprinkler performance was noted. Thus, it was suggested that the role of automatic vents, if used in sprinklered properties, will be to:

1. Vent unsprinklered fires, if installed sprinklers are defeated by human failure or mechanical damage, and
2. Substitute for manual roof venting upon arrival of fire service personnel.

Primarily on the basis of the first listed application, the researchers recommended that, where they are used for sprinklered properties, the design and installation of automatic roof vents for unsprinklered properties follow guidance provided by NFPA 204M, *Smoke and Heat Venting*, until further research, testing, or experience suggests more beneficial alternate configurations.

Critics of the IITRI research effort do not agree that the experimental results support the main conclusion of the investigation, which is that automatic roof vents do not impair sprinkler control of fires capable of growth.[5]

The critics also claim that the finding that automatic roof vents do not impair the ability of 165°F (74°C) sprinklers to control fires capable of growth contradicts the studies described above, which have indicated that the increased availability of oxygen associated with open vents may lead to increased fire intensity (of fires capable of growth), water demand, and consumption of combustibles.

The critics concluded that the reported results do not justify the overall conclusions and recommendations of the IITRI researchers. Their critique suggested the investigation suffered from a number of defects: (1) situations claimed to be unvented were not; (2) one of the most important principles of venting was violated (i.e., the provision of adequate openings for inlet air); and (3) inadequate control was exercised over the experimental conditions to the extent that major variations observed in fire behavior could not be attributed to the parameter under study.

Conclusions

The proponents of automatic venting in a sprinklered building cite the IITRI research work as substantiation of the merit of vents in sprinklered buildings. On the basis of this data, they believe that automatic roof venting can provide two major contributions to 165°F (74°C) sprinkler-protected (large one-story) properties:

1. Perform as vents in unsprinklered properties should installed sprinklers be defeated by human failure or mechanical damage.
2. Substitute for manual roof venting upon arrival of the fire services.

The opponents of automatic venting in a sprinklered building believe that the high installation cost of vents is difficult to justify when one considers the limited benefits and possible detriment. They are not cost-effective because it is unlikely that a large loss will be averted solely due to the presence of vents when automatic sprinkler protection is inadequate or impaired.

Venting may or may not be detrimental, depending upon many factors, such as the location of the fire origin in relation to the location of vents. More often than not, vents will increase the water demand.[2] Even when automatic vents result in some improvement, the improvement is not required for sprinklers to gain control. Vents can also create conditions that will inhibit or prevent sprinkler control.[5]

Installing automatic vents in unsprinklered buildings is acceptable. It would certainly be more beneficial to the building owner, however, to install sprinklers rather than vents to obtain active rather than passive fire control.

Installing manual vents in a sprinklered building is also acceptable, if desired by the building owner. These vents can be used during manual overhaul or at locations that would be expected to produce dense smoke. However, a similar effect can be achieved by venting through windows, by fire fighters cutting holes in the roof, or by ventilation equipment or smoke exhausters.

Through NFPA's consensus-making standards process, NFPA members agreed to the following statements for the 1985 edition of NFPA 204M, *Smoke and Heat Venting*:

Paragraph 6-3: "A series of tests was conducted to increase the understanding of the role of automatic roof vents simultaneously employed with automatic sprinklers [Section 6-5(c)]. The data submitted did not permit consensus to be developed as to whether sprinkler control was impaired or enhanced by the presence of automatic (roof) vents of typical spacing and area."

Paragraph 6-4: "While the use of automatic venting in sprinklered buildings is still under review, the designer is encouraged to use the available tools and data referenced in this document for solving problems peculiar to a particular type of hazard control."

Even though the issue was raised twenty years ago, proponents maintain venting critics have been unable to cite a single fire in which automatic venting was blamed for loss of fire control by sprinklers. Thus, to proponents it is paradoxical that fire research, which is typically motivated only by adverse fire experience, should be the sole basis of suspecting venting to be a detriment. They urge that serious students of venting should obtain and carefully examine this research and compare it with related research, both direct and indirect.

Additional research and testing will be needed before definitively establishing the benefits and detriments of automatic venting in a sprinklered building.

BIBLIOGRAPHY

References Cited

1. FMRC, "Heat Vents and Fire Curtains, Effect on Operation of Sprinklers and Visibility," Factory Mutual Research Corporation, Norwood, MA, 1956.
2. Heskestad, G., "Model Study of Automatic Smoke and Heat Vent Performance in Sprinklered Fires," *Technical Report FMRC No. 21933 RC74-T-29*, Factory Mutual Research Corporation, Norwood, MA, 1974.
3. Miller, E. E., "Reappraisal of Ventilated Rubber Tire Fire Tests," *Fire Venting Mini-Study No. 8*, Industrial Risk Insurers, Chicago, IL, 1982.
4. Waterman, T. E., "Fire Venting of Sprinklered Buildings," *Fire Journal*, Vol. 78, No. 2, Mar. 1984, pp. 30-39, 86. (Also see "Letters to the Editor," *Fire Journal*, Vol. 78, No. 5, Sept. 1984, p. 6.)
5. Heskestad, G., "Review of 'Fire Venting of Sprinklered Buildings by T. E. Waterman, *et al.*,' " Interoffice Correspondence to E. J. Ward," Factory Mutual Research Corporation, Norwood, MA, 1983. (Also see "Letters to the Editor," *Fire Journal*, Vol. 78, No. 5, Sept. 1985, p. 6.)

Additional Reading

Miller, E. E., "A Position Paper to NFPA 204 Subcommittee: F-ire Venting of Sprinklered Properties," Improved Risk Insurers, Chicago, IL, 1980.

STRUCTURAL FIRESAFETY: ONE- AND TWO-FAMILY DWELLINGS

Revised by Peter H. Billing

It has been estimated that approximately 80 percent of the population of the United States reside in one- and two-family dwellings. In order to relate to the high losses, i.e., deaths, injuries, and property, that occur in one- and two-family residential structures, it is desirable to look closely at the various design considerations and field practices that are an integral part of such residential construction.

This chapter is confined to a discussion of the structural elements of one- and two-family dwellings as they affect the firesafety of the structure. It does not cover the influence of interior finish or heat conservation measures, the hazards of building facilities (heating and electrical installations), or the role of detection and extinguishing systems as life safety features. These subjects are included in other chapters of the handbook; see Section 2, Chapter 3, "Electrical Systems and Appliances"; Section 2, Chapter 4, "Heating Systems and Appliances"; Section 3, Chapter 14, "Energy Conservation in Buildings"; Section 4, Chapter 4, "Household Warning Systems"; Section 5, Chapter 13, "Residential Quick-Response Sprinkler Systems"; and Section 6, Chapter 4, "Interior Finish."

CONVENTIONAL TYPES OF CONSTRUCTION

This part of the chapter addresses the various types of construction used in the design and erection of both conventional and manufactured one- and two-family dwellings (including mobile homes). Specific requirements are dictated by local building codes and, in the case of mobile homes, by federal regulation. In general, most one- and two-family residential buildings erected are of Type V (frame) or Type III (ordinary) construction as defined in NFPA 220, *Types of Building Construction*. There are, of course, exceptions where some dwellings may be erected of Type II (noncombustible) or Type I (fire resistive), and possibly of Type IV (heavy timber) construction.

Type V (Frame) Construction

The principal categories of Type V (frame) construction are: (1) plank and beam, (2) balloon, (3) platform or western, (4) braced, and (5) veneer (a combination of one of the previous four with a facing wythe of brick, concrete masonry units, or stone on the exterior walls). The buildings may be constructed with either basements, cellars, crawl spaces, or slab on grade. Geographical peculiarities or the needs of the owner generally dictate which foundation type is used. Where basements, cellars, or crawl spaces are provided, they play a definite role insofar as residential firesafety is concerned, since in these areas, heating, air conditioning, and water heater equipment are usually installed. These areas are also used for storage by the building's occupants. Roof framing may be either of the rafter or trussed type. Where trusses are used, interior bearing partitions may not be required.

Plank and beam framing: In plank and beam framing, a few large members replace the many small wood members used in typical wood framing, i.e., large dimensional beams more widely spaced (4 by 10 in. or 6 by 12 in.* on 4- or 6-ft† centers) replace the standard floor and/or roof framing of smaller dimensioned members (2 by 8 in.* or 2 by 10 in.* joists or rafters on 16-in.* centers). The decking for floors and roofs is planking in minimal thicknesses of 2 in.* or more as opposed to 1/2-, 5/8-, or 3/4-in.* plywood sheeting. Instead of 2 by 4 in.* bearing partitions supporting the floor or roof joist or rafter systems, the beams are supported by posts. Plank and beam framing results in a saving in the number of members and allows for more rapid site assembly.

Balloon, platform or western, and braced framing: The basic difference among balloon, platform or western, and braced framing is in the manner in which the floor, roof, and bearing partitions are supported and/or erected.

In platform or western framing, stud-bearing partitions are set on soles that are set on top of the joists, with the joists bearing on sills at the foundation level and girts at intermediate levels.

Peter H. Billing is senior district manager, National Forest Products Association, Washington, DC.

*Nominal sizes; for comparison 1 in. = 25.4 mm.

†Nominal dimensions; for comparison 1 ft = 0.3 m.

In both balloon and braced framing, the stud-bearing partitions are set on sills at the foundation level. In balloon framing, the studs in exterior-bearing partitions extend for two stories, with the joists supported by 1 by 6 in.* ledger strips or ribbon boards at the intermediate level. In braced framing, the bearing partition extends for one story only with joists at the second level of bearing partitions bearing on 4 by 6 in.* girts. In both framing types, the interior bearing partitions are erected in one-story heights.

The use of wood foundation walls has been recently introduced as an alternate construction procedure; and crawl spaces have been utilized as return air plenums for a number of years.

The exterior wall finish of buildings of frame construction, except masonry veneer, generally consists of stucco, wood, or plastic siding, or metal siding having either plastic coating, baked enamel coating, or, in the case of aluminum, an anodized finish.

Masonry veneer exteriors utilize one of the wood framing systems, with the addition of a wythe of masonry secured by metal ties to the wood frame exterior walls. Usually an insulating board of some type is provided between the studs and the masonry. Although the exterior exposed surfaces are masonry, veneer construction is considered a combustible frame construction because the load-bearing members are wood.

Type III (Ordinary) Construction

The significant difference between Type III (ordinary) and Type V (frame) construction lies mostly with the construction of the exterior walls. While in frame construction the load-bearing components of the walls are wood, in ordinary construction the exterior walls are masonry or other noncombustible materials. The interior partitions, floor, and roof framing systems are of wood and, in general, utilize either the platform or braced framing methods previously described.

Manufactured Housing

During the period 1968 to 1977, a total of 3,884,380 mobile homes were manufactured in the United States, and an additional 2,823,772 manufactured homes were produced and shipped from 1978 through 1988.[1,2] While many of these homes were put into service as construction offices, banking-type occupancies, and other nonresidential occupancies, the great majority were utilized as dwelling units.

As more and more manufactured housing units were put into service, the fire service became increasingly aware that although the fire incident rate for manufactured housing was approximately the same as for conventional dwellings, the injury and life hazard and the extent of property damages were three to five times greater.[3] While most fires in conventional dwellings are initially localized and small in size, the design characteristics inherent in manufactured housing, such as fire load density, room geometry, and combustible finishes, may provide the potential for rapid flame development, resulting in higher temperatures and smoke and toxic gas generation in a relatively short time.[4]

Four major components or subassemblies—the chassis, floor system, wall system, and roof system—comprise the structural systems of the manufactured house, which, in essence, is designed specifically to meet the requirements of an efficient assembly-line production.

The chassis is the structural base of the mobile home, receiving all vertical loads from the walls and floor and transferring them to a substructure of either the wheel assembly (when the home is in transit) or to a foundation (when the home is finally erected at a permanent site). The chassis generally consists of two longitudinal steel beams, braced by steel cross members. Steel outriggers cantilevered from the outsides of the main beams bring the width of the chassis to the approximate overall width of the superstructure. The running gear used when the unit is in transit is also considered part of the chassis.

The floor system consists of its framing members, generally conventional 2 by 6 in.* or 2 by 8 in.* wood joists, with plywood decking glued and nailed to the joists, glass fiber insulation blankets installed between the joists, and an asphalt-impregnated insulation board sealing the bottom of the floor system. Duct work and piping are installed longitudinally within the floor system, often requiring the cutting of the joists. The floor finish is generally carpeting or resilient flooring, such as linoleum or tile.

The wall systems, utilizing the stressed-skin principle, consist of an interior skin of plywood that is glued and nailed to wood studs, and an exterior skin of aluminum siding. The actual sizing of members is dictated by the structural loads. Insulation batts are installed in the stud spaces.

The roof system consists of either the framed wood roof rafter and ceiling joist system or a wood truss system. Roof decking is generally a rigid insulation board attached to the top of the roof rafters or trusses. Finished roofing is galvanized steel or aluminum decking. The ceiling is either acoustical planks or gypsum wallboard attached directly to the bottom of the ceiling joists or the bottom chords of the trusses. Insulation blankets provide the roof insulation.

Steel tie plates reinforce connections between wall and floor systems; diagonal steel strapping binds the floors, walls, and roof into a complete unit.

CONSTRUCTION CONSIDERATIONS FOR FIRESAFETY

Of all the occupancy use group classifications regulated by building codes, one- and two-family dwellings are the least regulated insofar as firesafety and life safety are concerned. With the exception of fire resistance ratings for exterior walls, which depends upon location of the wall with regard to separation distance from property lines or other buildings on the same lot and upon the separation between garages and habitable space, building codes do not mandate fire resistance ratings for building elements.

The minimum property standards (MPS) for one- and two-family dwellings promulgated by the U.S. Department of Housing and Urban Development (HUD) established specific fire-resistance ratings for bearing walls and partitions, separations between garage and habitable space, and for all floor/ceiling assemblies. These regulations, however, were applicable only to those buildings for which Federal Housing Authority (FHA) or Veterans Administration (VA) loan assistance was provided. Even the interior finish requirements of the building codes and the MPS,

*Nominal sizes; for comparison 1 in. = 25.4 mm.

*Nominal sizes; for comparison 1 in. = 25.4 mm.

as related to one- and two-family dwellings, are less restrictive than for other occupancy classifications. Thus, the one occupancy that is the source of the greatest number of fire deaths and injuries in the U.S., an estimated 3545 civilian deaths and 15,225 civilian injuries in 1989 alone,[5] is probably the least regulated.

On November 1, 1985, HUD, as part of the administration's efforts to deregulate, abolished the MPS in favor of recognizing the model building codes and local code enforcement.

In response to the disproportionate fatality, injury, and property damage rate for conventional construction/manufactured housing, in 1976 HUD promulgated the "Mobile Home Construction and Safety Standards," later termed the "Manufactured Home Construction and Safety Standard," which was based on NFPA 501B, *Mobile Homes*, which has since been withdrawn. These standards have been amended several times to strengthen requirements for interior finish and firestopping, and to identify acceptance criteria limiting the use of materials that generate smoke and gases more toxic than those produced by untreated wood.[6] The number of deaths resulting from fires in manufactured housing decreased by one-third from 1977 to 1980. Although the fatality rate per hundred fires for manufactured housing is still slightly more than twice that for conventional dwellings, there is evidence that the HUD standards are making an impact on this statistic.[7]

Since the majority of one- and two-family dwellings are erected of frame or ordinary construction, the physical nature of these types of construction suggest the addition of certain built-in features that will inhibit rapid fire spread. The large concentrations of combustible materials in the structural framework of these construction types, compounded by voids in concealed spaces connected to other voids, are basic conditions that contribute to the propagation and migration of fire throughout the structure. These conditions are addressed in the various building regulations used in this country. These regulations are clear in their requirements for the installation of draft stops and firestopping.

Each of the three model building codes [8,9,10] and the *CABO One- and Two-Family Dwelling Code*[11] contain firestopping and draftstopping criteria to reduce the spread of fire through concealed horizontal and vertical spaces. These code requirements identify particular locations where firestops and draftstops are required to be installed. The junction points at walls and floors and ceilings require firestops. Draftstops are required within all open web-floor systems to reduce the size of the concealed spaces.

Figures 6-3X and 6-3Y in Section 6, Chapter 3 of this handbook illustrate the points to be firestopped in balloon and platform framing respectively. Figure 6-3Z provides expanded views of the points of firestopping.

One key to structural firesafety is to confine the fire to the area of origin, i.e., compartmentalize the structure so as to preclude the extension of the fire to areas adjacent to the room or area of origin. This is not easily achievable in the typical one- and two-family dwelling where the structural elements are not required to provide any specific fire rating, and rooms are accessible through non-rated doors.

Unrated gypsum wallboard, the material most commonly used as partition, wall, and ceiling material in the housing industry, affords a definite degree of fire protection when unpenetrated or when its penetrations are properly firestopped. But, since fire resistance ratings are not generally mandated for one- and two-family dwellings, the inspection of the installation of this material is not required, and unprotected penetrations are made for heating ducts, electrical wiring and appurtenances, and plumbing. To compound the problem, even though required firestopping is installed, it may be removed, cut, or drilled to permit installation of electrical, plumbing, and mechanical work. *Building Construction for the Fire Service*[12] addresses wood frame and ordinary construction in depth, pointing out both their attributes and problems regarding firesafety. The U.S. Army Corps of Engineers has a technical manual that further addresses firestopping of penetrations of fire-resistance rated assemblies.[13]

Studies of fires in residential buildings of frame or ordinary construction reveal a number of built-in contributing factors to the spread of fire:[14]

1. The use of non-rated soffit materials, both combustible and noncombustible, and the use of soffit or eave vents can allow fires that break through an exterior wall opening to spread into the attic or roof space by the flue action of the attic or roof ventilation system. (See Figure 6-9A.)

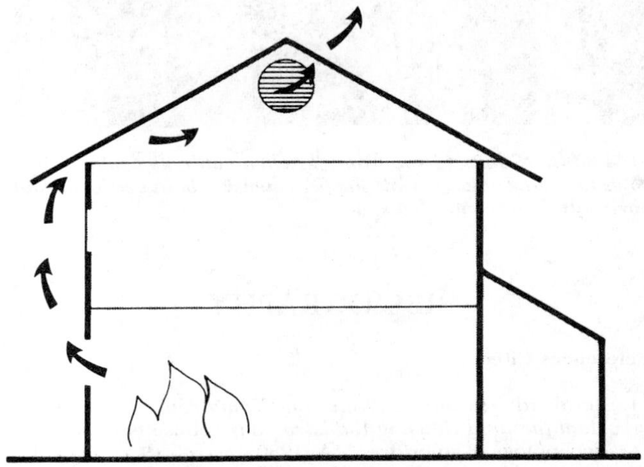

FIG. 6-9A. Attic vents under the eaves have serious potential for outside extension of fire into the attic space.[12]

2. Mansard roofs extending below the top-story windows with the windows recessed. The soffit extending from the face of the window to the edge of the roof is typical of non-rated materials. In addition, the wall construction is not extended in back of the plane of the mansard roof, thus providing an interconnected void. A fire breaking through the window impinges on this soffit, burning through in a relatively short time and involving the attic and roof spaces.
3. Unfirestopped penetrations of the gypsum wallboard partitions by plumbing, mechanical, and electrical work.
4. The widespread use of wood-trussed roof and floor framing precludes the need for the interior bearing partitions normally required where solid sawn joists and rafters are provided. Regulations typically require joists to be doubled under interior bearing partitions running parallel to joists, and bridging to be installed under partitions running perpendicular to joists. This results in a minimum amount of firestopping of joist

spaces. The current model building codes compensate for this by requiring draftstopping of the trussed floor systems to reduce the spread of fire.

5. Installing cabinets and other fixtures directly to stud framing, without an intervening protective diaphragm, presents a situation where the only firestops between a room fire and the concealed stud spaces are the materials that constitute the bottoms and backs of the cabinets or fixtures. (See Figure 6-9B.) This same practice exists in the installation of bathtubs or shower stalls.

FIG. 6-9B. Soffits (arrow) over kitchen cabinets connect wall voids to ceiling voids, permitting fire extension both vertically and horizontally in concealed spaces.[12]

BIBLIOGRAPHY

References Cited

1. Bernhardt, Arthur D., *Building Tomorrow: The Mobile/Manufactured Housing Industry*, Massachusetts Institute of Technology, Cambridge, MA, 1980.
2. MHI, "Quick Facts About the Manufactured Housing Industry," Manufactured Housing Institute, Arlington, VA, July 1989.
3. Schaennon, P. S. and Herrin, C. L., *Evaluation of Mobile Home Fire Safety*, Tri Data, Arlington, VA, 1982.
4. Budnick, E. K. and Klein, D. P., "Mobile Home Fire Studies: Summary and Recommendations," NBSIR 70-1720, 1979, Center for Fire Research, National Bureau of Standards, Washington, DC.
5. Karter, M. J., Jr. "Fire Loss in the United States in 1989," *Fire Journal*, Vol. 84, No. 5 (Sept.-Oct. 1990), pp. 56-67.
6. HUD, "Manufactured Home Construction and Safety Standards," 1984, U.S. Department of Housing and Urban Development, (rev. Oct. 1984), Washington, DC.
7. Gates, Howard, *Fire Risk in Manufactured Houses—An Update*, Manufactured Housing Institute, Arlington, VA, 1983.
8. BOCA, *National Building Code*, Building Officials and Code Administrators International, Country Club Hills, IL, 1990.
9. ICBO, *Uniform Building Code*, International Conference of Building Officials, Inc., Whittier, CA, 1991.
10. SBCCI, *Standard Building Code*, Southern Building Code Congress International, Inc., Birmingham, AL, 1991.
11. CABO, *CABO One- and Two-Family Dwelling Code* —1989, Council of American Building Officials, Falls Church, VA, 1989.
12. Brannigan, Francis, L., *Building Construction for the Fire Service*, National Fire Protection Association, Quincy, MA, 1982.
13. USACE, "Firestopping," TM-5-812-2, 1985, U.S. Army Corps of Engineers.
14. Vogel, B. M., "A Study of Fire Spread in Multi-Family Residences: The Causes—The Remedies," NBSIR 76-1194, 1977, Center for Fire Research, National Bureau of Standards, Washington, DC.

Reference

HUD, "Minimum Property Standards for One- and Two-Family Dwellings," U.S. Department of Housing and Urban Development, Washington, DC.

NFPA Codes, Standards, and Recommended Practices

Reference to the following NFPA codes, standards, and recommended practices will provide further information on structural firesafety for one- and two-family dwellings discussed in this chapter. (See the latest *NFPA Catalog* for availability of current editions of the following documents.)

NFPA 220, *Types of Building Construction*.

Additional Readings

Brannigan, F. L., "A Field Study of Non-Fire-Resistive Multiple Dwelling Fires," NBS Special Pub. 411, Nov. 1974, National Bureau of Standards, Gaithersburg, MD, pp. 178-194.

DeCicco, P. R., "Fire Hardening of Old Residential Buildings in High-Risk Urban Communities," SFPE TR 80-5, Society of Fire Protection Engineers, Boston, MA, 1980.

Fang, J. B., "Fire Endurance Tests of Selected Residential Floor Construction," NBSIR 82-2488, Apr. 1982, National Bureau of Standards, Gaithersburg, MD.

Fang, J. B., "Fire Performance of Selected Residential Floor Constructions Under Room Burnout Conditions," NBSIR 80-2134, Dec. 1980, National Bureau of Standards, Gaithersburg, MD.

Hare, C. W., "Protecting Residential Construction," *Fire Engineering*, Vol. 140, No. 12, 1987, pp. 38-40.

Issen, Lionel A., "Fire Endurance Tests of Residential Walls Containing Branch Circuit Wiring—Preliminary Findings," NBSIR 78-1415, Feb. 1978, National Bureau of Standards, Gaithersburg, MD.

King, J. A., "Thatched Roofs—Fire Hazards Precautions," *Fire Prevention*, No. 218, Apr. 1989, pp. 29-31.

SPECIAL STRUCTURES

Revised by John G. Degenkolb

Special structures are designed for specific purposes that are different from the typical day-to-day uses of most structures. Examples of special structures are towers, tunnels, underground buildings, bomb shelters, highway and railroad bridges, grandstands, tents, membrane structures, signs, mechanical parking garages, marine terminals, piers and structures surrounded by water used for other-than-vessel mooring or cargo handling, and air-tight structures. Because these structures represent unusual uses or solutions to design problems, they also present unusual or special fire protection design problems.

Additional relevant information can be found in Section 3, Chapter 4, "Fibers and Textiles"; Section 7, Chapter 2, "Concepts of Egress Design"; Section 6, Chapter 1, "Building and Site Planning for Building Firesafety"; Section 8, Chapter 11, "Assembly Occupancies"; Section 8, Chapter 27, "Occupancies in Unusual Structures"; Section 8, Chapter 36, "Fixed Guideway Transportation Systems"; and Section 5, Chapter 22, "Special Systems and Extinguishing Techniques."

TOWERS

The major fire problems with towers are the difficulty of extinguishing fires that may occur high in the tower; limited means of egress for occupants of lookout, air traffic control, and observation towers, which prompts the use of noncombustible materials throughout and good fire prevention practices; and vulnerability to exposure fires. When towers are built of unprotected steel or wood, a ground fire can cause ignition or structural failure, or both. Towers are frequently appended or attached to other structures of lower height. In such cases, egress from the tower should be directly outside where possible. If this is not feasible, the building exits should be designed so that occupants of the tower may also use them.

Apart from fire damage, but extremely important from a life safety standpoint, is the possibility of windstorm damage to towers. The Federal Aviation Agency (FAA) has been active in developing building code requirements for the towers they occupy.

Water Cooling Towers

Functionally, a water cooling tower is designed to transfer heat from water to air. This is accomplished by passing the water in small particles through the air, where heat is removed from the water partly by an exchange of latent heat, or the heat required to pass from liquid to a gas due to the evaporation of some of the water particles, and partly by a transfer of sensible heat, or the heat required to change the temperature. Figure 6-10A shows a cross section of a typical mechanical-induced draft water cooling tower and some of its significant parts.

Water cooling towers may be all metal, metal-frame with wood or plastic fillers and wood or plastic draft eliminators, all wood, or ceramic construction. Some towers have a noncombustible exterior covering. Wood, generally redwood, is used in cooling tower construction primarily because of its durability, its lack of corrosion problems, and the relatively low cost of both original and replacement materials.

Water cooling towers are of atmospheric and mechanical draft types. Mechanical draft towers are of two general types: forced and induced draft. They may be further classified as counterflow and crossflow.

Contrary to popular belief, records indicate that approximately two-thirds of the water cooling tower fires studied occurred while the tower was in operation. Despite their appearance, towers do have some relatively dry areas even when operating, particularly the induced-draft types.

The majority of cooling tower fires are ignited by outside sources. The most common of these sources are sparks from welding and cutting, either on the tower or on adjacent structures, or sparks from trash fires, incinerators, chimneys, and industrial stacks. Other causes include carelessly discarded smoking materials, lightning, and exposure fires. Another problem is the windblown leaves and trash that collect around towers and are easily ignited.

Fires caused by tower equipment may be the result of mechanical failures in gear reduction boxes and bearings, misaligned fan blades, or metal fatigue, which can

John G. Degenkolb is a fire protection engineer and code consultant in Carson City, NV.

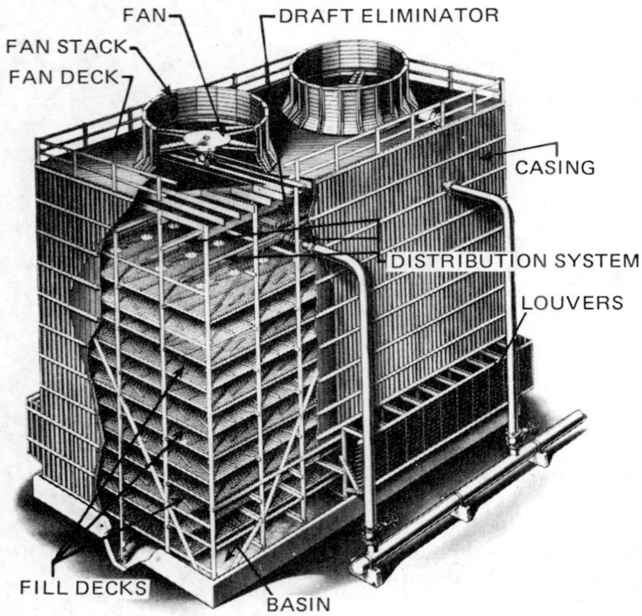

FIG. 6-10A. A typical mechanical, induced-draft, counterflow water cooling tower. Water is pumped to the distribution system where it is cascaded over the fill decks and collected in the basin at the base of the tower. The fan draws air in through the louvers and the casing of the tower. Draft eliminators minimize the loss of water through the fan stacks.

result in localized heating. Electrical breakdowns in motors, short circuits in wiring, and other electrical faults also account for many cooling tower fires.

The construction of the water cooling tower is a primary factor in reducing the possible fire hazard. Small towers or those whose main structure does not exceed 2000 cu ft (57 m^3) in volume are generally completely noncombustible and therefore are seldom a problem. Larger towers, however, generally contain considerable amounts of combustible materials. In addition, towers on roofs may be inaccessible to automotive fire fighting equipment. Those in yards may require fencing and weed control or protection to prevent exposure damage to or from an adjacent building.

Once the degree of hazard has been determined, any one or a combination of the following protection measures may be considered when dealing with essentially combustible towers:

1. Adequate separation from exposures.
2. Noncombustible exterior coverings.
3. Division of areas by fire partitions between cells.
4. Automatic fire protection systems such as deluge systems or dry- or wet-pipe automatic sprinkler systems. The latter should be used in warm climates only.
5. Automatic water spray systems for the exterior of the tower only.
6. Hydrants and standpipes.
7. Lightning protection.

The key element in fire protection is to provide a combination of prudent, engineered tower design with sufficient consideration given to automatic extinguishment and good preventive maintenance. This is all directed at ensuring that the fan deck, fan, and related motor and drive can survive the effects of a fire intact. This is recommended for two reasons:

1. The entire tower is considerably damaged when the fan deck collapses during a fire, dropping its heavy equipment down through the structure.
2. The tower's downtime is considerably reduced when only the louvers and fill deck material need to be replaced. This is critical since downtime on a cooling tower may cause downtime on a key income-producing manufacturing process.

Cooling towers, like other outside structures, must be designed and constructed to prevent damage from windstorms. Care also should be taken that the towers are not under, or adjacent to, high-voltage wires or transformers.

Fire prevention also involves a regular maintenance program. Scheduled maintenance of mechanical parts for overheating, excessive wear, inadequate lubrication, and so on is an essential part of this program. Preventing fires and fire damage in water cooling towers is covered in detail in NFPA 214, *Water Cooling Towers*.

Television, Microwave, and Radio Transmitting Towers

The electronic equipment in television and radio transmitting towers is frequently at such heights that fire fighting from the ground is impossible. In such situations, an automatic carbon dioxide, halon, or dry chemical extinguishing system, with an interlock to cut off power to the electronic equipment, should be considered. In any case, it is good practice to have a means of shutting off the power to the tower from the ground.

Microwave towers, frequently located in remote areas, sometimes have equipment buildings near their bases for relays, standby generators, and batteries. These buildings should be constructed of noncombustible materials, be protected by automatic detection and extinguishing systems, and be able to alarm to a base station.

Airport and Railroad Control Towers

Airport and some railroad control towers present special fire problems because of the expensive, complicated electrical and electronic equipment normally installed in them. Automatic fire extinguishing equipment is usually justified by the importance of the tower equipment.

In recent years, the FAA has proposed amendments for building codes to establish basic guidelines for aviation control towers with regard to height and area limitations, limitation on activities, and so on. Wood-frame buildings, whether protected or not, are unacceptable. While one means of egress, an enclosed stairway, is acceptable, the stairway may be located in a common shaft enclosure with the elevator hoistway provided they are separated from each other by an unpierced fire wall and access to one is well separated from the other. Smoke detection is required for the occupied level. Standby power, independent of that needed for aircraft control purposes, is required for towers over 65 ft (19.8 m) high. Such towers need not be accessible to the handicapped.[1]

Forest Fire and Other Observation Towers

Forest fire and other observation towers should be of noncombustible construction throughout, not only because of the possibility of ignition of the base from a ground fire, but also to avert any fire in the upper structure of the tower. The problem of fire protection in these towers is especially important since they normally are occupied by observation personnel and are remote from fire suppression facilities.

UNDERGROUND BUILDINGS

The inaccessibility of underground structures results in some unique fire problems. Primary among these are the diffuculty of venting smoke and gases from fires and the difficulty in fire fighting and evacuating occupants. The inaccessibility of underground structures eliminates any thought of partial fire protection, which might suffice in an aboveground building that depends on the public fire service. Protecting occupants and property in underground structures prompts maximum utilization of good fire protection.

The solution to these fundamental problems has only recently been introduced into building codes and standards. Building code requirements, as well as in NFPA 101®, *Life Safety Code®*, are now beginning to include regulations for underground buildings. The underground buildings currently regulated are those having an occupied level more than 30 ft (9.1 m) below grade. Generally, they must be provided with automatic sprinkler protection, and each level that is larger than a certain area must be divided into not less than two compartments so that egress can be made from an endangered area to a safe area on the same level. To ensure that the two levels are well separated from each other, each section must be air conditioned separately. Emergency power, mechanical means for evacuating the building, and smoke management are other basic requirements for underground building protection.

The Council of American Building Official's (CABO) code arm, the Board for the Coordination of Model Codes, completed a study of requirements for underground buildings and submitted certain proposals for the consideration of the membership. Among the proposed requirements are recommendations that a building with a level more than 60 feet (18 m) below the lowest level of exit discharge be divided into at least two compartments of approximately equal size. When elevators are provided, each compartment must have direct access to an elevator through a fire-resistive lobby. When compartmentation is required, a smoke management system is also required. There are other recommendations, but these are the most significant beyond the current requirements.

Many of these protective measures are also applicable to windowless buildings, since the only advantage such buildings have over underground buildings is that direct access to the outside can be provided. Windowless buildings provide the same problems of venting, fire fighting, and rescue as underground buildings. These measures are not intended to be all-inclusive nor to eliminate the usual fire protection considerations typical of buildings.

Means of egress from underground buildings are provided for in NFPA 101, *Life Safety Code.* Those recommendations take into consideration the panic that may result when there is no direct access to the outside and no windows to permit fire department rescue and ventilation.

Automatic sprinklers must be installed in all underground and windowless buildings even if construction is noncombustible, because of combustible contents and concealed spaces. Underground mines and caverns that are being converted for use as buildings without the incorporation of specific building construction are considered to be of a basic noncombustible construction.

When possible, venting facilities must be provided to exhaust smoke and fire gases from the buildings. Storage buildings may require extensive venting facilities, while buildings with low fire loading, noncombustible construction, and automatic sprinkler protection may be cleared of smoke through the ventilation system which provides for normal changes of air.

Emergency lighting for safe evacuation is required since artificial light is necessary in underground or windowless buildings.

The use of combustible construction and other-than-Class A interior finish should be prohibited. Foam plastics should never be left exposed but should be protected by a thermal barrier acceptable to the authority having jurisdiction, unless significant fire test results show that the thermal barrier is not needed.

Compartmentalization by fire barriers will help limit the extent and severity of a fire and provide areas of refuge for occupants.

Manual fire fighting equipment, such as standpipe and hose systems and portable fire extinguishers, can provide quick extinguishment of fires when handled by trained personnel who may discover a fire in its incipient stage.

Drainage of water from sprinkler discharge or from hose streams can be a serious problem in underground structures and, therefore, requires early planning. If drainage is required for reasons other than fire protection, it may be possible to use one drainage system for all purposes, provided it is designed to handle the expected maximum flow.

TUNNELS

Tunnels for automotive and tracked vehicles, such as trains and subways, present fire problems similar to those of underground buildings, except that the cargo of the vehicles using the tunnels may present any number of hazards. The transportation of certain cargoes, such as high explosives, through tunnels by automotive vehicles is prohibited in some cities. Some juristictions also prohibit vehicles with LP-Gas on board, including RVs, from using tunnels.

Because gasoline is commonly involved in vehicle fires, handling the hazard of gasoline spill fires is a typical consideration in providing fire protection for tunnels. Another primary consideration is a means for giving a fire alarm in a tunnel. This may be satisfied by fire alarm boxes or telephone stations spaced at intervals along the tunnel. This alarm system can also be tied into the traffic control system so that incoming traffic can be stopped.

Automatic sprinklers provide good tunnel protection. In addition, an adequate water supply with hose connections should be provided on both sides of the tunnel. Supplemental portable fire extinguishers for handling small fires can be installed in wall cabinets for use by attendants and motorists.

NFPA 130, *Fixed Guideway Transit Systems*, provides information on firesafety for subways, trains, and so on. NFPA 130 also provides guidelines for the vehicles themselves and for passenger stations.

Fire apparatus equipped to pull disabled vehicles from tunnels, to combat vehicle fires, and to extricate accident victims should be stationed within a reasonable distance of each end of tunnels. Personnel assigned to such locations should have special training and specialized equipment for these situations.

As with underground buildings, ventilation in tunnels is important to dissipate smoke and fire gases. An existing mechanical ventilation system may be satisfactory for emergency use if it can handle the volume required to exhaust smoke and fire gases. Low points in the tunnel should have suitable drainage to handle flammable liquid spills and the water used for extinguishment.

Pedestrian Tunnels

Pedestrian tunnels, normally used to enter and leave buildings, terminals, subway stations, and so on primarily involve safety to life. These tunnels are commonly used to satisfy exit requirements for large industrial and commercial facilities. Detailed requirements for such tunnels are contained in NFPA 101, *Life Safety Code.*

BOMB SHELTERS

Shelters designed to protect people from the effects of bombing, especially nuclear bombs, are underground structures and, therefore, are subject to the same general fire protection factors as other undergound structures.

Areas of refuge designated as bomb shelters in buildings may be considered temporary expedients. Nevertheless, they should be chosen with care, taking into account alternate means of egress, noncombustible construction, sprinklered areas, and proximity to gas mains, water pipes, and other building services that may be damaged by explosion or by fires resulting from a bombing. Such factors could either help protect or unnecessarily expose people seeking refuge. Storage of emergency supplies should be carefully planned to avoid the problem of exposed combustibles.

BRIDGES

Highway Bridges

Highway bridges are continually exposed to accidents that may cause direct damage from impact or, occasionally, fires that may follow that impact. When flammable cargoes are involved, either on the roadway or on adjacent lands or water, there is a potential for a serious fire. The record reveals remarkably few incidents that warrant special fire protection to the structures themselves, however, considering the hundreds of thousands of bridges in service. Fire-resistive or noncombustible construction and the means to transmit emergency alarms on longer structures generally suffice. Established response to accidents should include fire fighting capability.

Fire alarm boxes or telephones spaced along a bridge provide a means of notifying the fire department or bridge attendants of an emergency. As in tunnels, this system can be tied into a traffic control system to stop traffic from driving onto the bridge and to alert vehicles already on the bridge.

Bridges in critical seismic areas may require special anchoring to ensure continued use in times of severe earthquake activity.

Since fire fighting is a necessity on bridges, an adequate water supply from standpipes is good practice, preferably on both sides of the bridge or, on long bridges, at intervals along the length.

The location of apparatus to combat a bridge fire can be a problem if the bridge is located in a rural area. Apparatus should be stationed as near the bridge as is practical. In addition to carrying fire fighting equipment, this apparatus should be designed to move disabled vehicles and should carry the equipment needed for rescue.

Railroad Bridges

Railroad bridges are a fire problem because so many of them are constructed of wood, which may have been treated with a flammable wood preservative. In addition, many railroad bridges are located in remote areas and, if ignited, are generally a complete loss.

There are two kinds of wood bridges and trestles: open deck and ballast deck. The fire potential is considerably more severe in open-deck design.

Wooden railroad bridges are ignited by such sources as the friction sparks and hot metal particles generated when brakes on heavily loaded freight trains are applied on steep downgrades and by burning waste from overheated journal boxes. Exposure fires from burning grass and brush around supporting piles are another hazard. (See Figure 6-10B.)

FIG. 6-10B. ***Fire fighters were forced to pull hose lines on hand cars across thousands of feet of track to fight a fire in this wooden trestle in a remote area of Long Island, NY. Water around the trestle was too shallow for fire boats. High winds drove the fire rapidly through the trestle and destroyed about 2500 ft (762 m) of the structure. (Source: United Press International)***

Some satisfactory fire-retardant treatments are being used successfully on timbers for bridges, but wooden bridges, even when treated, should not be considered an adequate substitute for fire-resistive or noncombustible bridges. Material treated with a fire retardant may lose its fire retardancy over time, depending upon the environment to which it is exposed.

Fighting railroad bridge fires presents many problems, particularly in areas where bridges are inaccessible to organized fire fighting facilities. One method of providing minimal fire extinguishing capacity is to provide water casks at the approaches to bridges or at intervals along their length for use by train crews. Some railroads keep a magazine of explosives nearby to blow fire breaks in bridges if necessary. In other instances, pre-emergency planning calls for tearing down sections of platform-type bridges to stop the spread of fire.

Monorail Bridges

A fire involving an elevated monorail train demonstrated the problem of evacuating passengers and the difficulties of fire suppression. Passengers were able to get on to the roof of the fire-involved car because of the presence and assistance of two off-duty fire fighters.

PLACES OF OUTDOOR ASSEMBLY

Places of outdoor assembly include amusement parks, athletic fields and stadiums, grandstands, tents, and similar places where crowds gather to watch an event or take part in recreational activities. The frequency of fires in these places, and the possibility of loss of life from fire and panic in any place where crowds congregate, reinforces the need for providing adequate and accessible ways of escape and for providing good construction features that reduce the probability of fire spread. NFPA 102, *Assembly Seating, Tents, and Air-Supported Structures*, provides recommendations on reasonable measures to prevent loss of life in these structures, as does NFPA 101, Life Safety Code.

The primary consideration in these places is to provide an escape route from a fire area to a place of refuge or to the outside. This escape may have to be made through gates in a fence, from a grandstand, out of a tent, or from any confinement that restricts the passage of masses of people. Providing sufficient exit width to accommodate the occupant load of the area is the recommended method of ensuring adequate egress capacity. Exit width is determined by dividing the floor or ground area by an occupant load or by counting the number of actual seats. This assumes that the occupant load will not be allowed to be exceeded and that the exits will be within a specified maximum travel distance from all the occupants of the area. It also assumes that the access to the exits will be unobstructed. The area of refuge for occupants may be an open space that is well separated from the danger area. Access to the place of assembly for fire apparatus and other emergency vehicles is also necessary.

Exit requirements for open-air grandstands and other places of outdoor assembly are less stringent than for places of indoor assembly, because a build up of hazardous smoke is not as much of a problem. Placing a complete roof over a place of assembly may serve to confine smoke, and may increase the panic hazard, thereby calling for more exits for quicker evacuation. In some of the new installations, however, grandstands within such large structures have such tremendous quantities of air that heavy concentrations of smoke are unlikely. Such exceptionally large structures containing grandstands are the subject of major revisions proposed for NFPA 101 and NFPA 102. The concept of smoke protected assembly seating, taken from NFPA 102, *Assembly Seating, Tents, and Air-Supported Structures*, has been introduced into NFPA 101, *Life Safety Code*, thereby allowing them to be roughly equivalent to outdoor assembly.

Construction is the second consideration in a place of outdoor assembly. The temporary or portable nature of the structures generally used in such places and the false sense of complacency that may exist due to the open or partially open nature of the structures, whether fixed or portable, may result in construction weaknesses that accelerate fire spread.

Other typical features include temporary wiring; inadequate maintenance and poor housekeeping, particularly when exhibitions involving displays are present; use of considerable combustible materials, including decorations and flammable liquids; and the general lack of proper fire prevention practices.

A good supply of portable fire extinguishers as well as a reliable method of quickly communicating with the closest fire department and other appropriate emergency organizations are necessary for fire protection in places of outdoor assembly.

Tents

Tents became a major concern to fire protection authorities following the disastrous circus fire in Hartford, CT, on July 6, 1944, in which 168 lives were lost. This fire clearly demonstrated the need for flame-retardant materials for tents in places of outdoor assembly. Flame-resistant materials are now generally required for all tents. Decorative materials used in tents are generally required to be flame retardant. The use of open-flame and heating devices is closely regulated or prohibited.

Tents are combustible, even when made of flame-resistant material, and it is good practice to limit their number and size in a location and to keep them separated from each other and from other structures. The area around tents must be kept free of combustible material, including vegetation. Combustible material used inside a tent should be kept to a minimum, and smoking in tents occupied by the public should be prohibited.

Grandstands

Grandstands are typical examples of structures found in places of outdoor and indoor assembly and of structures that constitute a safety problem. These structures must have adequate aisles, the proper distance between rows of seats, strong guard railings, and other exit features to ensure rapid and orderly evacuation to areas of safety. Without these features, panic could develop during an emergency. (See Figure 6-10C.) Grandstands should also be designed to withstand predetermined deadweight and live loads, as well as anticipated wind loads.

Since many grandstands are constructed entirely or partially of wood, basic fire protection principles of division of areas and separation from exposures apply. Long, combustible grandstands must be divided by fire partitions, or they may be built in smaller sections with adequate spaces between the sections.

Frequently, the space underneath a grandstand is used to store materials and for concession booths, and it becomes littered with refuse. This space should be kept clear of such activities. Refuse under the grandstand was a major factor in the Bradford, England, Soccer Stadium fire on May 11, 1985, which claimed 54 lives. NFPA 101, *Life Safety Code*, is considering new provisions affecting crowd management

FIG. 6-10C. More than 5000 people escaped without serious injury when a fire occurred in this wooden grandstand in Louisville, KY, in the early 1950s. The evacuation was not orderly, and several occupants received minor bruises in their haste to escape. A cigarette is believed to have fallen through a crack into a concealed space below the wooden flooring, where it ignited debris. (Source: Wide World Photos)

as a result of another such disaster, the April 1989 Shaffield, England, fire in which 94 persons died.

Amusement Park Structures

Structures supporting amusement rides are generally built of wood, and contain considerable electrical wiring, gear boxes for pulleys, and similar-friction producing machinery. They are usually poorly maintained, as well. Life safety is the primary consideration in evaluating these structures, so adequate and accessible means of escape in an emergency is vitally important. Fire prevention, noncombustible construction, exposure hazards, maintenance, and housekeeping are other factors to be considered.

Recent disasters in amusement park structures have disclosed weaknesses in modern code requirements. There are structures other than the so-called "rides" such as the merry-go-round, roller coaster, and ferris wheel. Some are for amusement purposes, and some are even educational in nature. Others simulate a bobsled run, for example, or a car travelling through a building. Still others operate in semidarkness, such as mystery houses or haunted castles.

Since most of these structures are windowless—or at least the public spaces are without windows—they should be required to have automatic sprinkler systems using the newly developed quick response sprinklers. Egress provisions almost necessarily are not standard and some innovations are needed to meet the intent of NFPA 101, *Life Safety Code,* and the model building codes. Of primary importance is emergency lighting and good illumination and marking of paths of egress travel. Sprinkler protection is probably the most important requirement in an amusement structure, whether it is a permanent structure or one made up of semi-permanent trucks or trailers.

A fire in a "haunted castle" attraction made up of interconnected commercial trailers claimed eight lives in a Jackson Township, NJ, amusement park on May 11, 1984. Major factors contributing to the loss of life were lack of properly designed fixed detection and suppression systems, ignition of synthetic foam material from which fire spread to other combustible contents and interior finish, and the difficulty occupants had in trying to escape along a convoluted smoke-filled path.

MEMBRANE STRUCTURES

NFPA 102, *Assembly Seating, Tents, and Air-Supported Structures,* is not applicable solely to places of assembly. The term "membrane" replaces "air-supported" because it better reflects all the various types of structures, not just those supported by air and those in which the occupants are in a pressurized atmosphere. Some structures are of the air-inflated type, where the air pressure is within a series of tubes which then form the structure and keep it upright. In this case, the occupants are not within a pressurized atmosphere. Also included are cable-supported membrane structures, such as some newer sports stadiums, where the roof is supported by cables, and air pressure may or may not be provided. In other types of structures, the membrane is tensioned, and weather protection is usually provided without enclosing walls. Finally, there are the framework-type structures in which the membrane is stretched over the frame to form enclosing walls and a roof.

By definition, a membrane is a thin, flexible, water-impervious material capable of being supported by an air pressure of 1.5 in. (3.7 Pa) of water column. The membrane may be of very thin metal or glass fiber coated with a fluorocarbon and is considered to be noncombustible or limited combustible. Others are of a glass, nylon, or similar fibrous material coated with vinyl or silicone. These are considered to be combustible structures, even though they are flame-resistant when treated in accordance with NFPA 701, *Fire Tests for Flame-Resistant Textiles and Films.*

An air-supported structure is a "balloon-like" shelter constructed of flexible, coated fabrics supported and stabilized against wind loads by a small amount of internal pressure, usually 1 to 1.5 in. of water pressure (2.5 to 3.7 Pa), supplied by continuously operated centrifugal fans. (See Figure 6-10D.) There are no beams, columns, girders, or other structural members involved. Variations on the air-supported structure include structures with an air-inflated, double-walled roof and side panels and combination structures that are rib-supported but air-supported in heavy wind.

A plastic-coated synthetic fiber is used in air-supported structures. The synthetic fiber will not absorb flame-resistive solutions, but the plastic coating can contain flame retardants. If the fan serving an air-supported structure fails or if a hole is made in the fabric, by heat from an exposure fire, for example, it takes a relatively long time for the structure to deflate. The normal opening and closing of doors will not affect the structure. In fact, breather holes are provided in the skin for air changes.

PIERS AND WATER-SURROUNDED STRUCTURES

When piers or related structures surrounded by water are used for places of amusement, for restaurants, or for passenger terminals, they fall out of the normal use category—

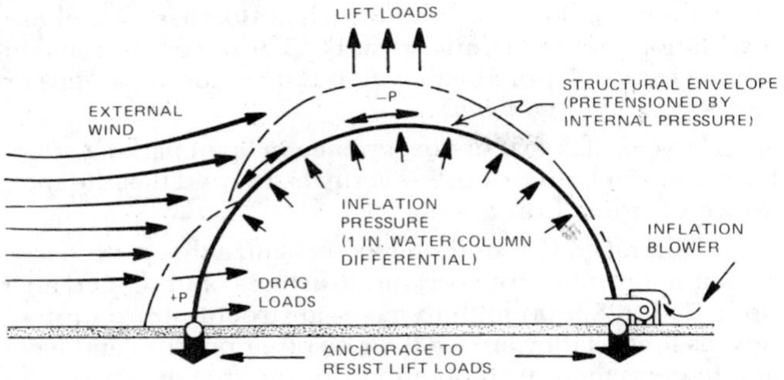

FIG. 6-10D. The aerodynamic and inflation loading of a typical single-walled, air-supported structure.

that is, mooring of vessels and handling of cargo—and fall into the special structure category. The question of life safety is of primary concern, since these structures, which may contain large numbers of people, may have limited egress facilities due to their location or arrangement on the water.

For piers falling outside the normal use category and extending more than 150 ft (45.7 m) from the shore, the following recommendations are made. The critera arise from the recognized maximum travel distance requirement found in NFPA 101, *Life Safety Code*. These design approaches are considered equivalent:

1. The pier may be arranged to have two separate ways of travel to shore, as by two well-separated walkways or independent structures.
2. The pier deck may be designed to be of open, fire-resistive construction, resting on noncombustible supports.
3. If combustible construction is used for the pier deck, superstructure, and/or substructure, they should be protected by an automatic sprinkler system.
4. If a pier is completely open and unobstructed and is more than 500 ft, it may be considered generally safe if the minimum width is not less than 50 ft (15.2 m) wide. If a pier is open and unobstructed and longer than 500 ft (152.4 m), a 10:1 ratio must be maintained for the relationship of length to width.

Regardless of whether the four items above are applicable, individually or jointly, to a particular pier, the minimum requirements of NFPA 101, *Life Safety Code*, apply concurrently for providing means of egress. These requirements cover the number, arrangement, location, and protection of means of egress for the type of occupancy involved, plus related questions of hardware, construction, and interior finish for the means of egress. Further guidance for piers is given in NFPA 307, *Marine Terminals, Piers, and Wharves*.

When a building or structure, such as a typical lighthouse, or an oil-drilling platform and related housing facilities, is completely surrounded by water, several considerations must be given to life safety from fire. Either sufficient outside ground area, such as an island, is needed for refuge, or a fire-resistive platform must be constructed for this purpose. This must be coupled with a communications system and a means of transportation for evacuating the occupants from the refuge area. Such transportation will be limited to either boat or helicopter, due to the obvious nature and location of these special structures. However, such a system of refuge, communication, and rescue is only as good as the planning and availability of the transportation on a standby basis. Delays imposed by poor planning or by intolerable weather conditions can lead to disaster. Thus, such factors must be considered before an emergency, not after.

Permanently Moored Vessels

Where a sizable vessel is permanently moored and used as a restaurant, hotel, museum, or convention center, it is, for all practical purposes, similar to any permanently constructed building occupied for those purposes.

Because the vessels were not built as "buildings," but under completely different standards, it is almost impossible to try to make them comply literally with the requirements of NFPA 101, *Life Safety Code*, or the model building codes. Passageways are not as wide as would be required for exit access corridors. Doors are smaller than those found in conventional buildings. The rise and run of stairs, originally known as "ladders," probably do not conform with stair requirements in buildings. As the tide rises and falls, the land connection changes in slope. So, if the vessel is to be accepted for use as other than a ship, some concessions are usually made. A prime means for accepting nonconforming construction details is to require sprinkler protection for the vessel, to limit the occupant load, to require strict compliance with interior finish requirements, and so on. Generally, the power plant for the vessel is inactivated and shore power is substituted after the operating machinery and fuel have been removed.

AIR-RIGHT STRUCTURES

The economics of purchasing choice urban space, preparing the site, demolishing existing structures, and solving the complex problem of foundation design and caisson construction, all without adversely affecting surrounding structures or exceeding stringently applied cost limitations, has led to the development of a structure that either totally or partially solves many of those problems—the air-right structure. (See Fig. 6-10E.)

FIG. 6-10E. An air-right hotel and office building shown spanning an expressway and a two-track railroad right-of-way.

The air-right structure is generally a facility built over existing rail lines, highways, or even other buildings. From a firesafety standpoint, its design is not unlike that which would exist if it were isolated on its own site, with one key exception. The air-right structure is more likely to be adversely affected by an exposing event on or in the facility above which it is erected. This is due to the fact that the exposure is in the vertical plane, which is ideal for the heat transfer process to take place. Thus, normal good fire-safety design practice must be followed and allowances must be made for potentially severe fire exposure from the facility the air-right structure straddles.

Much of the previous discussion of tunnels and bridges would apply to the air-right structure. Normal design guidance is found elsewhere in this handbook and in the NFPA codes, based on the occupancy of the structure. However, NFPA 220, *Types of Building Construction*, should be emphasized in the selection of basic building types, which should be chosen on the basis of the hazards involved and the exposures encountered.

OTHER SPECIAL STRUCTURES

Signs

In general, outside signs on buildings are not a very serious fire problem because of the limited amount of combustibles involved and because of their location. However, certain types of signs, such as those illuminated by neon tubing, may cause fires because of the wiring and transformers connected to them.

An outside sign may suffer considerable damage from wind and may expose other properties to damage if torn loose by wind. If a sign is of such size, construction, and location as to be considered a fire hazard, it should be protected like any other structure; for example, automatic sprinklers may be installed.

A combustible sign attached to the exterior and covering a large percentage of one side of a fire-resistive or noncombustible building may significantly change the fire-safety considerations of the building. This is a fire exposure problem not generally contemplated in building design. A large sign can also be hazardous to fire fighters if it falls during fire fighting operations. For these reasons, some building codes limit the size and construction type of combustible signs that can be installed on buildings.

Mechanical Parking Garages

At one time, parking garages that permitted drivers to drive their own vehicles to a parking stall were required to meet fire-resistive constrictions far in excess of the fire severity that could exist. Despite the presence of gasoline and combustible tires, the fire load and hazard from private automobiles is very low. Where these structures have permanently open exterior walls that can dissipate smoke and hot gases, the likelihood of a serious fire is extremely low.

Many tests here and abroad have demonstrated the validity of these conclusions. One such test was conducted in 1972 by the American Iron and Steel Institute (AISI) in a multi-story open parking structure with exposed steel structural members.[2] Three automobiles parked next to each other, each with a fuel tank containing 10 gal (38 L) of gasoline, were used as the test ignition and fuel source. The center car was gutted 48 min. after crumpled newspapers in its rear seat were ignited. The contents of its fuel tank were spilled or consumed, but the fire did not spread to the adjacent cars, and the overhead structural steel was essentially unaffected. The temperature of the steel remained far below critical levels throughout the test. A similar test conducted by the British at Boreham Wood fire test station yielded similar results.[3] These conclusions do not necessarily apply to aboveground enclosed garages or to underground garages.

Surveys of actual fire experience in open parking structures confirm both that fire severity is low and that the incidence of fire is infrequent.

Building code requirements recognize this pattern and permit noncombustible parking structures of unlimited area up to 75 ft (22.9 m) high to have no structural fire protection, as long as they are used for no other purpose and have ample permanent wall openings for the free dissipation of smoke and gases.

BIBLIOGRAPHY

References Cited

1. *Uniform Building Code*, International Conference of Building Officials, Whittier, CA, 1988.
2. Gewain, R. G., "Fire Experience and Fire Tests in Automobile Parking Structures," *Fire Journal*, Vol. 67, No. 4, (Jul. 1973).
3. Butcher, E. G., *et al.*, "Fire and Car-Park Buildings," *Fire Note No. 10*, Ministry of Technology and Fire Offices' Committee/ Joint Fire Research Organization, London, England, 1968.

NFPA Codes, Standards, and Recommended Practices

Reference to the following NFPA codes, standards, and recommended practices will provide further information on special structures. (See the latest *NFPA Catalog* for availability of current editions of the following documents.)

NFPA 101, *Life Safety Code.*

NFPA 102, *Assembly Seating, Tents, and Air-Supported Structures.*

NFPA 130, *Fixed Guideway Transit Systems.*

NFPA 214, *Water-Cooling Towers.*

NFPA 220, *Types of Building Construction.*

NFPA 307, *Marine Terminals, Piers, and Wharves.*

NFPA 502, *Recommended Practice on Fire Protection for Limited Access Highways, Tunnels, Bridges, Elevated Roadways, and Air Right Structures.*

NFPA 701, *Fur Tests for Flame-Resistent Textiles and Films.*

Additional Readings

"Automobile Parking Structures," *A Building Code Modernization Bulletin*, 2nd ed., American Iron and Steel Institute, New York, 1971.

Ayres, D. J., "Treatment of Shallow Underground Fires," *Proceedings* of the Symposium on Failures in Earthworks, Thomas Telford, London, England, 1986, pp. 470-472.

Bament, A. E., "Fire Protection in Underground Structures," *Fire Journal*, Vol. 69, No. 1 (Jan. 1975), p. 40.

Bond, H., "Underground Buildings," *Fire Journal*, Vol. 59, No. 4 (July 1965), pp. 52-55.

Burton, R. C., *et al.*, "Automatic Fire Detection Underground," *Colliery Guardian*, Vol. 235, No. 5, 1987, pp. 166, 168.

Corbin, E. and Sale, J. W., "Fire Protection at the Grand Coulee Hydro Project," *Proceedings* of the International Conference on Hydropower: Waterpower '87, ASCE, New York, 1988, pp. 2091-2099.

Haerter, A., "Ventilation: Fighting Fires in Road Tunnels," *Tunnels and Tunnelling*, Vol. 20, No. 4, 1988, pp. 55-58.

Harris, Dr. L. M., "Survey of Fire Experience in Automobile Parking Structures in the United States and Canada," Marketing Research Associates, Jan. 1972.

Iida, T., Kobayashi, S., and Kenmochi, T., "Facilities of the Seikan Tunnel," *Japanese Railway Engineering*, No. 106 (June 1988), pp. 12-16.

Irvison, J. and Newberry, R., "Fire and Life Safety in Air-Supported Domes," *Fire Engineering*, Vol. 138, No. 5 (May 1985), pp. 66.69.

Luzik, S. J., "Protection of Aluminum Overcast Construction Against Fire," *Fire Technology*, Vol. 24, No. 3, 1988, pp. 227-244.

Stevens, R. E., "Air-Supported Structures," *Fire Journal*, Vol. 59, No. 10 (Sept. 1965), pp. 42-44.

Stevens, R. E., "Water Cooling Towers Will Burn," *NFPA Quarterly*, Vol. 50, No. 9 (Oct. 1956), pp. 97-105.

Thomas, P. H., "On the Upward Movement of Smoke and Related Shopping Mall Fires," *Fire Safety Journal*, Vol. 12, No. 3, 1987, pp. 191-204.

Wintworth, G., "Channel Tunnel—Vital Need to Design a Safe System," *Fire Engineers Journal*, Vol. 47, No. 145, 1987, pp. 5-12.

Woods, D. K., "BP's Use and Experience of Passive Fire Protection Offshore," *Proceedings* of the Conference on Offshore Passive Fire Protection, Plastics and Rubber Institute, London, England, 1987, pp. 1-23.

Zhao, Y., Yang, G., and Wang, X., "Investigation of the Dynamic Process in the Ventilation Network During Underground Fire," *Archiwum Gornictwa*, Vol. 34, No. 3, 1989, pp. 503-515.

BUILDING CONSTRUCTION CONCERNS OF FIRE DEPARTMENTS

Francis L. "Frank" Brannigan

Because building construction materials and methods play such an important role in fires, fire department interest in building construction may be broader than that of many other users of the handbook. The principal areas of building construction which concern the fire service include:

- Review and approval of plans for fire protection features in new construction. This is often done in cooperation with the building department.
- Code maintenance, such as the Uniform Fire Code. This code is maintained by the Western Fire Chiefs Association, a division of the International Association of Fire Chiefs (IAFC).
- Inspections to check on the reliability of building and fire code-specified fire protection features. This includes passive protection, such as fire walls, and active protection, such as the fire doors which protect openings in fire walls.
- Knowledge of building construction for investigating the origin and extension of serious fires.

Fire departments fight fires in many kinds of buildings from those under construction to those built hundreds of years ago. Some of the construction methods used are long forgotten, but the hazards they present still exist. For example, the reader could search many books in vain for a reference to tile arch floors. (See Figure 6-11A.) Yet there are thousands of them in existence, and they present a specific hazard for fire fighters.

Finally, the building on fire is the fire fighter's enemy. A load of furniture burning in an open field is only a minor problem. The same furniture fire on the fiftieth floor of a high rise presents a major problem for the fire department.

Other Relevant Sections and Chapters

This Handbook is a formidable document. Its size can be intimidating. But it also serves as a valuable source of information on a wide variety of fire protection topics. There are a number of sections and chapters which deal with many important aspects of building construction. Fire officers should be aware of their content, and be familiar with material which pertains to their own local situation. Relevant material should be used in in-service training programs.

FIG. 6-11A. Hollow tile floors should not be cut. The arch may collapse.

Relevant Handbook chapters include all the other chapters in Section 6, as well as Section 1, Chapter 2 Fundamentals of Firesafe Building Design; Section 8, Chapter 19 One and Two Family Dwellings; Section 9, Chapter 7 Fire Prevention and Code Enforcement; and Section 9, Chapter 14 Identification of the Hazards of Materials.

This chapter concentrates on building construction and fire suppression. Specifically, this chapter looks at construction concerns and deficiencies which affect the fire service.

While the following material contains some of the principal characteristics of buildings relevant to manual fire suppression, it is by no means a complete discussion.

Principles of Construction

The fire officer should understand the principles of construction for a number of reasons. Fire investigation, build

Francis L. "Frank" Brannigan, SFPE, is a fire protection consultant based in Port Republic, MD and a well know champion of fire fighter safety. He is the author of NFPA's *Building Construction for the Fire Service*.

ing inspection, and plan review are reasons that are covered in other chapters of this Handbook. For the purpose of this chapter there are two main reasons. First, errors in understanding of basic building concepts or mistakes in use of terminology may cause the knowledgeable listener to discount what a fire officer may say. Fire fighters may be considered ignorant of building construction and their words may go unheeded. Unfortunately, this discounting can be a handy reason when the listener would prefer not to hear what is being said. Furthermore, in court testimony, a testifying fire officer might be completely discredited by an opposing attorney.

Second, twenty four hours a day, seven days a week, the force of gravity attempts to pull a building down. By a construction system, the builder defeats, for a time, the force of gravity. A fire of sufficient intensity will accelerate the process and cause the building to fail in whole or in part. This is critical information to the fire service.

Some types of construction, and some specific structural elements, are more likely to fail in a fire than others. If fire fighters are in, on, or adjacent to the structure when it fails, injury or death may result. Difficult and dangerous rescue efforts may be required. Literally only seconds may elapse between the time it is recognized that fire fighters should evacuate a structure, and failure of the structure.

Fire departments should have a readily recognized signal which means immediate evacuation. Multiple, short, air horn blasts are used by some departments. Evacuation drills should be carried out regularly to overcome the reluctance of fire fighters to abandon equipment and withdraw. The proudest ships in the navy conduct regular "Abandon Ship" drills.

Failure on the part of command officers to understand the principles of construction and its repercussions has cost injuries and deaths. Take for example, a cantilever beam which can be compared to a seesaw. It is supported in position by connections in the interior of a building. (See Figure 6-11B.) If these connections fail because of fire, the extended portion of the beam, and whatever it supports will fall. In lieu of a cantilever, a suspended beam may be used. (See Figure 6-11C.) To the building designer there is little difference in whether the reaction goes downward through a column, or upward through a tension member to the wall. However, if the connection fails, the suspended beam becomes an unsupported cantilever and will fall.

***FIG. 6-11B.** Fire in an apartment floor could destroy one end of these cantilevered wooden I beams, collapsing the balcony.*

***FIG. 6-11C.** This heavy beam suspended on a steel rod, supports the mezzanine of a library.*

Other Hazards

The building being attacked by fire presents other serious hazards to fire fighters. Fire can hide in void spaces, with little or no evidence and burst out unexpectedly and increase in intensity when a nearby breach admits oxygen. Buildings of otherwise non-combustible or fire-resistive construction may have extensive, hazardous interior finish of floors, walls and ceilings.

Fire fighters may be inadequately trained in these or other hazards. When live fire training is conducted in most typical training school structures, the hazards of collapse, hidden fire and highly combustible interior finish are absent. There have been serious accidents during live fire training in abandoned buildings when these hazards were present. One alternative is adequate classroom instruction, followed by preplanning for the hazards of individual major buildings and general building construction.

Contents

The problems of structure fires cannot be isolated from contents. Most building fires originate in contents. High heat-release fires in contents can destroy non-combustible structures and damage fire resistive structures. The hazard of today's fast burning, high rate-of-heat-release contents is a major problem.

In 1975, the Society of Fire Protection Engineers warned, "A high rate of fire development can create a condition that may tax or overpower traditional fire defenses. Defenses of the past, both passive and active (evacuation, alarm, ventilation, and manual fire control), have not been designed by engineer or code, to anticipate this hazard. This is primarily a furnishings problem. Many occupancies (residences, office buildings, theaters, hospitals) are being affected."[1]

Fire Resistance

All structures have some resistance to fire-caused collapse. This can informally be described an *inherent* fire resistance, as distinguished from *legal* or code-specified. The inherent fire resistance of one structure may be absent in another, similar structure. Direct experience with this fire resistance, whether personal or organizational, is not transferable from one structure to another. To put this simply, *"What You Know, May Not Be So."*

By experience the fire service has developed some understanding of and criteria for inherent fire resistance. In fact there are many estimates as to how long fire fighters can safely stay inside a structure on fire. Unfortunately this is imprecise. Many times fire fighters risk life and limb without knowing the degree of risk involved. Generally accepted indications of imminent collapse—softening, water flowing between bricks, smoke pushing from mortar joints, strange noises—are grossly inadequate, even for older buildings. If they are relied on to protect fire fighters from collapse in today's different, lighter buildings, disasters will certainly result.

Building Codes and Building Construction Classification

Building codes classify buildings as to their fire resistance. Here the subject is discussed following the traditional five fundamental construction types.

- Wood Frame
- Heavy Timber
- Ordinary
- Non Combustible
- Fire Resistive

Wood Frame Structures

The most prevalent construction material in the United States and Canada is wood. Wood can carry structural loads such as columns and beams. In older buildings there are huge quantities of non-structural wood used as lath to support plaster. Wood is also used for decoration and interior trim. A wooden interior in a restaurant in a high-rise building provided such a fierce fire that the fire department was unable to reach three trapped civilians, who finally jumped to their deaths.

For over 150 years attempts have been made to render wood fireproof or non-combustible. None have worked. Wood can be surface-treated to render it ignition-resistant or reduce its surface flame spread. One method is to paint wood with an intumescent coating, which swells up like a marshmallow when heated and retards ignition. One problem in using this method to reduce the hazard of installed wood paneling is its untreated reverse side.

Wood can be rendered fire retardant by drawing out the sap and moisture and replacing it with chemicals. Some codes will accept such wood as non-combustible, although this is a misnomer. Fire retardant treated wood is just that—fire retardant. It is still combustible.

In recent years, the excess wood in wooden structural members has been reduced. This excess wood had provided some inherent fire resistance due to its additional mass. Using sawn or laminated two by four lumber or flakeboard in wooden I beams has reduced the mass of these wooden beams. These lighter beams can be expected to fail earlier in a fire, because as soon as the web starts to burn, the strength of the beam is lost.

In the construction of wood frame row type dwellings, no fire protection provision is resisted more than parapetting fire walls to separate the units. Parapetted fire walls present a special problem to the builder because they require skilled craftsmen to flash the wall properly to prevent leaks. It is much easier to place shingles on a flat unbroken roof.

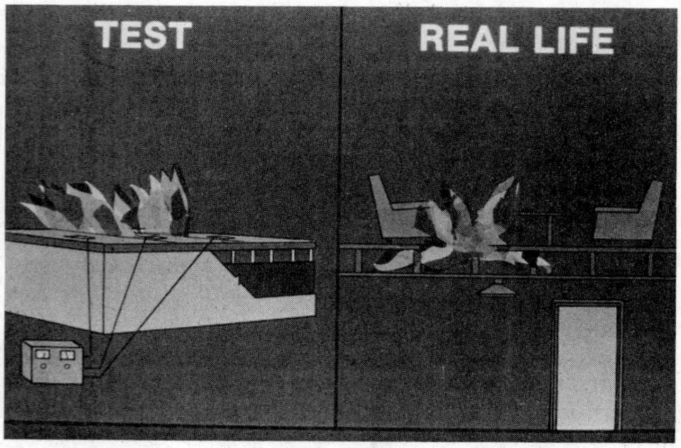

FIG. 6-11D. In ASTM E 119 fire attacks the floor only from below. Real fires are different.

Some years ago the practice of laying a four-foot sheet of ignition-resistant plywood on each side of a fire wall which did not penetrate the roof was adopted in lieu of parapetting. The treated plywood is supported on untreated lightweight, wood trusses, subject to early failure. It is now known that plywood, laid over the top of masonry firewalls, will delaminate and or raise up and pass fire over the top of the wall. Furthermore, plywood over a rough cut, concrete block fire wall is difficult to seal against the passage of fire, smoke and hot gases.

Recently a special problem has come to light regarding the use of fire retardant treated plywood for roof sheathing. At least some fire retarding chemicals react when heated by the sun and weaken plywood to the point where it is subject to failure under very light loads. This presents another special hazard to firefighters operating on plywood roofs.

Another method of protecting wood from fire is found in floor and ceiling assemblies and wall sections which combine wood framing with gypsum board membranes. A number of such floor and ceiling assembles have received fire resistance ratings of one hour or more after being subjected to the NFPA 251/ASTM E 119 test ("Test Methods for Fire Tests of Building Construction and Materials"). One problem is that this fire resistance test was developed for floors of homogeneous, non-combustible materials, which were essentially the same from top down and bottom up. The one-way test in which the fire is applied from the bottom does not adequately determine fire resistance in today's fires where severe temperatures develop at floor level quite early in the fire. (See Figure 6-11D.)

The difficulty with fire fighters accepting the 1-hour resistance rating as indicating a degree of safety, is even more serious in the case of lightweight gusset-plate trusses. When solid wood floor joists are used, each joist can act as a fire stop, thus slowing the progress of the fire through the floor construction. In the case of a truss, the entire floor void, and its air supply, is available to the fire as soon as fire enters the void. The lightweight members of the truss are of small kindling-like dimensions. The voids can extend over sizable area.

Firestopping is difficult to install and may be ineffective in preventing the extension of fire to adjacent truss voids. Early collapse of a structure in which fire has possession of the truss voids in inevitable. A three-story trussed floor apartment house in San Antonio, Texas collapsed moments after fire fighters evacuated the building. The fire started when a flammable liquid, accidently spilled on a floor, leaked down into the truss void and was accidentally ignited.[2]

Trusses can extend out past the exterior wall of the building to form the platforms of the stairway structure. A piece of gypsum board, plywood, or flakeboard is often used as firestopping to separate the floor void from the balcony void. (See Figure 6-11E.) There are no data indicating that such firestopping is adequate, particularly when it is often penetrated such as for utilities. In such a structure, any fire in the floor void would likely extend to the stair platform void, leading to early collapse of the stairway which is the exit for the occupants and a principal avenue for attack by the fire fighter.[3]

Heavy Timber

Heavy timbers are slower to ignite than lighter wood members. This has lead to the term slow burning being applied to buildings of masonry exterior walls and timber interiors. Such a building is expected to retain its structural stability for a long time when subjected to a fire. Unfortunately, the slow burning characteristic sometimes becomes long burning. There is no merit to slow burning once the fire department can no longer remain in the building and must operate defensively.

The original concept of heavy timber construction, or mill construction, employed timber columns. Where the column intersected the floor girder, it should have been replaced by a solid cast iron pintle, which passes through a hole in the girder. (A girder is any beam which supports other beams.) The small cross section of the pintle would cause it to be protected by the mass of wood girder. This procedure was ignored in many buildings. Some heavy timber buildings have cast iron columns which will fail early in a fire. Where these columns pass through the floor girder, there is no reduction in size of the column. As a result, two "half moons" of the timber rest on a shelf protruding from the column. Failure of the shelf, or the loss of a small amount of wood around this column, will cause the floor to fall.

FIG. 6-11E. Truss floors provide a huge void. The fire or draft stopping in this truss floor is a sheet of gypsum board. One section is missing.

FIG. 6-11F. Many churches are of plank on laminated wood beam or arch construction.

Rehabilitated buildings often are fitted with unprotected steel columns, which may fail early in a fire. Sometimes, lally columns, (steel columns filled with concrete) are used. In the 19th century these lally columns were often cast iron and were drilled to release the steam from the concrete. Current columns often are not drilled and could explode when heated. Because of the steam generated when the concrete core is heated and releases water.

Heavy timber, slow burning, or mill construction buildings should be carefully examined for these potentially disastrous weaknesses, which make invalid the assumption that the building will retain its stability for any appreciable time.

Plank and beam construction is sometimes called western framing. The typical 16 inch spacing of floor beams may be considered too box like and unattractive. Except in the roughest construction, a ceiling is installed to hide floor or roof beams. One take-off from heavy timber construction provides residences, churches and other public buildings with an aesthetically pleasing interior by eliminating the ceiling, and exposing the wood structure. Heavy beams, widely spaced, are spanned with heavy tongue and grooved planks instead of floor boards. The wood surface is planed smooth. Often a clear lacquer is used as a finish. This has the excellent advantage of eliminating void spaces. However, fire may spread rapidly over these wood surfaces.

The hazard to the plank-on-beam roof of a building can be reduced if there are no flammable subsidiary structures such as an office to provide the kindling to ignite the structure. Such spaces should be fire-resistive enclosures, or completely sprinklered. (See Figure 6-11F.)

Long heavy timbers are often in short supply or are not available. It is common practice to splice timbers to attain the proper length. Laminated arches are commonly shipped in sections to be field spliced. A properly-designed spliced timber will carry its load adequately in normal use, but may fail disastrously in a fire. The arches of a Florida Jai-Lai Fronton were of spliced laminated timbers. Though the timbers were burned only moderately, the arches fell apart because the heated metal of the splice connections simply burned away the wood to which they were attached.

Ordinary Construction

Ordinary construction is the term applied to buildings of usually combustible interior with masonry exterior walls.

FIG. 6-11G. A wood beam is laid in this brick wall to level the floor joists.

Originally, such buildings had brick or stone exterior walls and wood floors. The brick or stone walls were often required by law to limit fire spread from building-to-building in cities. In most building codes, the area of the city required to have construction which limits fire spread is defined by the "fire limits." This requirement started with the building code for the City of Washington, signed by President Washington. It has been generally quite effective. During urban strife in 1969, many fires in Washington, D.C. were unattended by the fire department. Nevertheless, there was no significant extension from one brick building to another. However, the buildings involved were only two or three stores high.

In more recent times, in addition to brick and stone construction, exterior masonry construction may use brick and clay tile composite, brick and block composite, cast-in-place concrete, concrete block, hollow clay tile, and adobe.

Brick is attractive, but expensive. Many buildings which appear to be of brick construction are actually a single layer of brick veneer on the face of a wooden building. Brick veneer can be applied to any surface. Brick or stone veneer is often used to rehabilitate an old building. Imitation stone veneer is made of concrete cast in molds.

Brick veneer is totally dependent on the basic structure of the building for stability. If the supporting structure is damaged, the veneer may fall down. A veneer building is not a masonry building. It should be described by its basic construction type, for example wood frame, steel, or concrete. It is common practice to have some solid masonry and some veneer in the same building. For example, one wall may be solid masonry and another wall may be veneer. The same may be the case with multiple stories. Lower stories could be solid masonry and upper stories, veneer.

In the past it was possible to recognize brick masonry from veneer, because in solid masonry some brick courses were turned to show the ends (headers), while the others were laid lengthwise (stretchers). The development of the masonry wire truss has made it possible to lay all the bricks as stretchers, so the difference is no longer obvious.

Collapse of masonry walls has killed hundreds of fire fighters. In one building fire, an interior floor collapse brought down a brick veneer wall and killed a fire lieutenant. Observers reported that the wall was obviously bowed before the collapse. There are a number of deficiencies or indications of brick wall failure. Some are more recognizable than others.

- Many brick walls are not totally brick. It was common practice to insert wooden lintels over windows and doors. In many buildings, wooden beams were laid in the wall to provide a level surface for floor beams. When this wood burns out, a collapse is certain. This can be determined only by competent prefire analysis. (See Figure 6-11G.)
- Water-soluble sand-lime mortar was universally used until 1880, and partially used thereafter for many years. It is still used today in the rehabilitation of older brick work. It can be washed out by hose streams. The loss of mortar to water leaks has caused some collapses when there was no fire.
- While lightweight steel bar joists will fail early in a fire, first they will elongate. Elongating steel has pushed down many masonry walls.
- Collapse of wood floors was early recognized as a hazard to the masonry in which the floor beams were imbedded. Collapse of floors has precipitated many wall collapses. The beams may act as a lever pulling down the brick wall.

In some areas builders corbelled out a ledge. The beams were set on the ledge, so that when they fell, the wall was undisturbed. In other cases, a fire cut was required on wood beams. In these a 45 degree cut was made on the end of the beam, so that the top was shorter that the bottom. Thus the beam could fall out of the wall without disturbing the brickwork. Since wood is removed, the fire cut beam will likely collapse earlier than a beam solidly set into the wall. Another method uses beam boxes which are cast iron boxes laid in the brick wall to accommodate a girder. When the girder falls, the box remains in place and the wall is not affected.

- The impact load of debris from a wall collapse has collapsed adjacent buildings, with loss of fire fighters' lives.
- Unreinforced masonry buildings are liable to collapse in earthquakes.
- Old masonry buildings have been renovated for other uses. Many have included the conversion of old downtown residences into commercial buildings. In many cases, the floor loads from files, safes and merchandise are much greater than previously existed. This can place additional stress on the floor construction as well as the supporting wall construction.
- Some older masonry buildings were built with interior walls of balloon frame construction. (See Figure 6-3Z.) Fire in such a wall spreads freely from floor to floor and into the floor voids. The wall is structural and its damage can precipitate an interior collapse.
- More substantial buildings were built with interior masonry structural walls. Since the practical span of wood beams was only about 25 feet there were many small interior rooms. In many cases, walls have been removed to enlarge the interior space. The heavy masonry above was supported on a steel beam which in turn was supported by cast iron columns, usually unconnected to the beam. (See Figure 6-11H.) The connection is vulnerable to any lateral thrust. Such an arrangement provided the larger space needed for

***FIG. 6-11H.** The collapse of the Vendome Hotel cost nine Boston fire fighters their lives.*

a coffee shop, in the century old Vendome Hotel in Boston. Nine fire fighters died in 1972 when the beam-column arrangement failed.[4]

Girders typically are not strongly attached to columns. They rest on a shelf and are attached to one another, across the column, by oversize staples known as dog irons. Thus, floor sections can release without affecting the wall or other parts of the floor. Such a floor is more likely to collapse earlier, than one in which the girders are tied tightly to the columns.

Beyond these indications, there are other dangers associated with the building construction that the fire service needs to be concerned with. There are some widely accepted beliefs regarding construction-related issues which are open to question. Some of these beliefs may prove fatal to fire fighters or others at the fire scene.

One rule of thumb attempts to specify how far out a wall would fall depending on its height. This rule is of doubtful validity. Even if true for most of the wall, bricks and timbers can land much further out than anticipated.

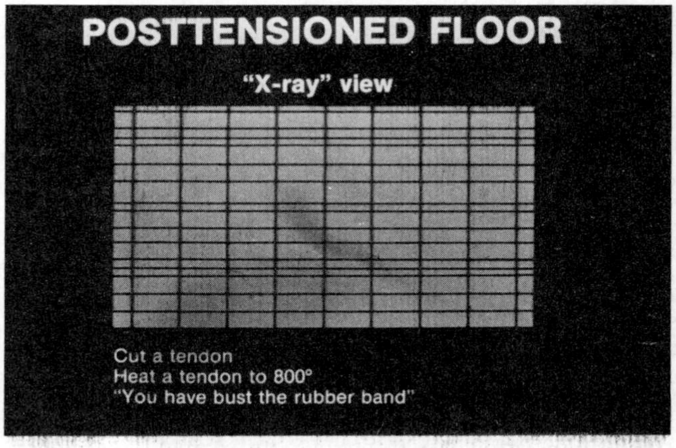

***FIG. 6-11I.** The Post Tensioned concrete building is a different building forever.*

Collapse of masonry walls is sometimes attributed to contraction caused by cold water hitting hot bricks. This is unproven. The greatest amount of water thrown in a defensive attack is directed through windows, not onto a wall. Considering the low heat transmission rate of brickwork, it is likely that the brick is at best only slightly cooled by the water.

Many older buildings have an outer layer of finished brick, which is not necessarily a veneer. A hose stream hitting such a wall can get behind the finished brick, tear the bricks off the surface, and convert bricks into missiles.

The interior of ordinary buildings is almost completely of combustible construction. Where steel is used it is often left unprotected or enclosed in combustible voids which provide no protection from heat. The fire department may be completely unaware of the hazard of the hidden steel. Another major hazard of the voids which has been noted is the potential for hidden fires.

Alterations of the interior may leave hazardous floor conditions. When a stairway is relocated, the former opening is rarely restored to a strength equal to the original floor. This may present a weak floor through which fire fighters may fall.

Non Combustible Construction

Non combustible construction is a building code term which unfortunately may not be literally true. Fire departments should be aware of what the local code permits under this heading. It is possible that substantial combustible components such as a wooden balcony or roof, or a combustible metal deck roof be included in a non-combustible building. The fact that a material is non-combustible is not necessarily significant in reducing the fire loss, or in reducing hazards to fire fighters. The two common materials of non-combustible construction are steel and concrete.

Steel is an extremely strong material. Heavy loads can be carried on very light structural steel elements. Because of the small mass of the steel, all but very heavy members are readily heated to the elongation temperature. Steel beams will elongate 9 inches in 100 feet at about 1000 degrees F. This can be sufficient to push out wall panels and cause toppling. Elongating steel has pushed down many walls in this fashion. At slightly higher temperatures steel reaches its collapse range. Collapse of steel roofs which are carrying the sprinkler piping have caused very early sprinkler system failures, resulting in massive destruction in several warehouse fires, when the sprinkler system was inadequate for the hazard involved.

As steel trusses are heated, connecting ties can transmit undesigned torsional load to other trusses. This may result in failure of trusses away from the fire area.

Height of the steel above the floor is no guarantee of stability during a fire, if there is a significant fire load. Tests at UL after the devastating 1967 McCormack Place Exhibition Hall Fire in Chicago, showed that failure temperatures were reached in steel 30 feet above the floor a few minutes after the fire started.

Steel being heated by the fire should be cooled by hose streams if a safe operating position is available. If the steel is elongating, it will retract to its original length when cooled. If it has started to fail, it will be frozen in the shape it had reached. Contrary to a once prevalent myth, the water does not cause the distortion of the steel.

Extreme caution should be the rule at any fire where unprotected steel is being heated. The potential consequences are not always evident. Preplanning should be thorough, and limits should be set on fire fighting procedures to ensure safety of personnel.

Concrete is strong in compression, but weak in tension. Plain concrete, usually found in the form of concrete blocks, is used for compressive loads. Reinforced concrete is a composite material. Steel is incorporated into the concrete to provide the tensile strength. By definition, a composite material is one in which both elements must act together to carry the load. A failure of the bond between the steel and concrete destroys the composite nature and strength of the structural element.

Unlike steel protected from fire by an insulating covering, concrete can be inherently fire resistive. The resistance to fire is accomplished by the nature and thickness of the concrete itself. However, it is impossible to distinguish fire resistive concrete from that which is merely non-combustible by simply looking at the concrete member.

Non-fire resistive concrete has no specific fire resistance requirement and can fail early in a fire, even when exposed to only modest heat. No valid assumptions can be made as to when fire-exposed, non-fire resistive concrete will fail. If the building is of monolithic construction, however, the load may be redistributed throughout the building, and a general collapse is unlikely. However, local collapse may cause injuries from falling concrete or from fire fighters falling through holes.

Precast concrete tilt slab buildings are now commonly used for warehouses and factories. Many of them are several stories high to accommodate high stack storage. The integrity of the roof is vital to the tilt slab building.

The roof may be carried on several types of beams. Most common are wood, steel bar joists, and concrete pre-tensioned TEE beams. Because heavy wooden beams burn slowly, total roof failure is delayed. However, falling roof boards may be a hazard.

Concrete TEE beams would not generally be rated fire resistive unless the building was required to be fire resistive. If the concrete below the bottom tendon spalls off, the cold drawn tendon, which typically fails at 800 degrees F, is exposed to the fire, and the beam is subject to failure.

Massive reinforced concrete, fire resistive multi-story buildings have a good fire record. However, there have been cases of serious destruction, usually during long duration, high intensity fires. A recent fire in a concrete building loaded with tires caused heavy damage.[5] A long burning fire in the top floor of the Military Records Center near St. Louis, Missouri caused considerable elongation of the roof, which resulted in columns being torn off either the roof or the floor. After the fire, the top floor was removed.[6]

Massive concrete is a substantial heat sink. The heat that is stored in the concrete is not available to extend the fire. However, the retained heat in the concrete may cause serious health hazards to fire fighters during operations and overhauling. Personnel should be monitored and regular reliefs provided. Fire fighters required regular relief in the Los Angeles Library fire due to the retained heat.

Finished, post-tensioned concrete buildings cannot be distinguished by appearance from conventional reinforced concrete buildings. They are very different with respect to fire operations. It is not safe to drill through a post-tensioned floor to attack a stubborn fire on a floor below. The drill might cut a tendon and cause collapse. A hole alongside a tendon might permit the tendon to heat to failure. To cut large holes with jackhammers, as was required in the library fire, would be extremely hazardous in a post-tensioned building.[7] (See Figure 6-11I.)

When concrete buildings are under construction, massive loads are supported on temporary forms which are either combustible, of, if made of steel or aluminum, subject to fire-caused failure. A massive failure of forms which drops one floor on another is almost certain to cause progressive collapse of several floors, possibly all the way to the ground. Fire in such forms is a serious concern and might well justify keeping fire fighters entirely out of the potential collapse zone.

In such cases the command decision process might be the opposite of the traditional method. Traditionally, fire fighters rush into the structure, and withdraw only when it is determined that the structure is unsafe. In the case of fire in concrete forms, which support thousands of pounds of concrete, it may be advisable to stay out until a decision can be made as to whether it is safe to enter the structure, or even be near it.

In Fairfax county, Virginia in 1973, workers were prematurely ordered to remove shores supporting the 23rd floor. The floor collapsed causing the progressive collapse of the floors below, all the way to the ground. Had the shoring burned, the result would have been the same.

The situation in the case of post-tensioned concrete construction is even more serious than for conventional reinforced concrete. Until the tendons are tensioned, and the cables are stretched the entire weight of the concrete, even hardened and dry to the touch, is supported on the concrete forms. If the forms burn, the entire floor or floors dependent on it will fall, possibly precipitating a total collapse. A 14-story post-tensioned concrete structure under construction is Cleveland, Ohio in 1974 totally collapsed when fire attacked the forms. The fire chief, aware of the hazard, had kept the fire fighters out of the collapse area.[8]

Fire Resistive Construction

The major components of fire resistive buildings are required to be similar to building components which have been subjected to the NFPA 251 Standard Method For Fire Tests of Building Construction and Materials (ASTM E 119 Fire Resistance Test). Test results are stated in the time to the last full hour (or half hour) the assembly withstood the assault of the test fire. Thus a column might be rated as having "One Hour Fire Resistance" or a floor-ceiling assembly as having "Two Hour Fire Resistance."

There may be no specific relationship between the time given in the rating and the time to failure of the structure in a real fire, however. There are many variables that affect the time a structural element can withstand fire exposure. The limit of confidence that one can have is more nearly that a four hour fire resistive building is more fire resistive than a two hour fire resistive building. Or, that a one hour fire resistive building is less fire resistive than a two hour fire resistive building.

Fire resistive buildings fall generally into three classes, corresponding roughly to the time they were built.

- During the period 1880 to 1920 emphasis was on the building itself. Floors were of tile arch with or without protection of the steel beams. Vertical opening protection was not even considered. Fire resistance consisted of whatever the architect thought proper as there were few requirements for fire resistance in the building codes. There are many such buildings still in use.
- From 1920 to 1945 many building components were rated fire resistive in accordance with the ASTM E 119 test standard. Steel frames were fireproofed with concrete. Floors were cast-in-place concrete. Stairways and elevators were generally enclosed. Fire and occupant loads were low because of limited floor areas due to need for natural light and air. Many exit stairs were designed to provide an atmospheric break between the floor and the stairway thus providing exits which did not become smoke polluted. Sprinklers were generally not provided, except for such buildings as the headquarters of the National Board of Fire Underwriters, and high rise factory buildings in New York City as a result of laws passed in the wake of the Triangle Shirtwaist fire. Only a few cities had high rise buildings of this type. The Empire State building represents the zenith of this type of fire resistive construction.
- From 1945 to present many changes have occurred in building construction techniques. Air conditioning and fluorescent lighting have made extensive floor areas possible. The increase in height and floor area has permitted a huge increase in occupants. Timely evacuation is difficult. Air conditioning often requires non-operable windows. Building height can increase the stack effect which can become a serious factor in smoke movement.

Areas of Concern

The following areas of concern for the fire service were drawn from reports of serious fires in fire resistive buildings. There are no minor deficiencies in buildings being attacked by fire. Any single deficiency may contribute to loss of life, or the destruction of the building.

Alarms and staff training: Building staff should be properly trained. A common and, at times, fatal error is for a security guard or maintenance personnel to go to the floor from which the fire alarm has been received—thus walking right into the fire. The lone fatality in the spectacular 1988 First Interstate Bank Fire in Los Angeles was the maintenance person who went to the fire floor to investigate.

Sometimes personnel are temporary employees who have not had adequate instruction in their duties and responsibilities. Fire department personnel should inspect buildings during the night shift and question employees as to the actions they would take in the event of a fire alarm, or for reported smoke.

Building staff have reset alarms to prevent the alarms from being transmitted to the fire department. This was a factor in a 12-fatality fire in the Westchase Hilton Hotel in Houston, Texas in 1982.[9] Delayed alarms are often due to a mistaken management perception that the arrival of the fire department is bad publicity. A policy of charging for false alarms should be carefully monitored to determine if it results in non transmission of alarms.

Preplanning: A thorough study of a target building should be made before the action preplan is developed. This fire department preplanning should study each building as an individual problem. Problems and or deficiencies in areas noted below may be present in buildings. Most were factors in serious fires. Some problems or deficiencies not listed here will no doubt be listed in the next edition, after being found significant at a serious fire or disaster.

Automatic sprinklers: Full automatic sprinkler protection, properly maintained is a proven fire protection measure which can provide reasonable assurance of occupant and building fire safety. However, far too often sprinklers are inoperable. The fire department should carefully monitor the maintenance and shutdown of the sprinkler system. The history of serious fires in sprinklered buildings is replete with examples of disasters which occurred when the sprinklers were cut off. Special precautions and watch service should be required during periods of sprinkler impairment.

In many cases building codes permit alternatives from code provisions if sprinklers are installed. If the sprinklers are turned off when the building is occupied, it is probably in serious violation of the code provisions.

Water supply: The water supply system should be carefully checked for possible failures. "What happens if?" questions should be developed, asked, and answered.

Examples of water supply problems include water supply pumping system disconnections. At the time of the First Interstate Fire this was the case. Also, falling glass may cut lines supplying standpipes. Improperly marked standpipe connections has also been a major factor at fires.

Compartmentation and structural integrity: A fire resistive building is generally designed to provide for compartmentation and structural integrity in a fire. Unfortunately, the design may have been flawed, or the construction faulty. Changes after the building was occupied may compromise the value of the compartmentation or structural integrity.

- Early fire resistive design did not include compartmentation. It was believed to be sufficient that the building was "fireproof." Several disastrous fires in fire resistive buildings proved the concept faulty, and compartmentation became required. Many early fire resistive buildings are still undivided and allow the passage of smoke and toxic gases throughout the structure.
- Floors are penetrated for wiring and other services. Often the openings are not properly protected to restrict the passage of heat and smoke.
- The reliability of horizontal compartmentation separating floors into fire areas or smoke compartments must be questioned. The wall may remain intact but there may be utility openings through the walls which are not properly sealed.
- Fire barrier doors into stairways and between fire areas are required to have door closers and latches. These are often removed or doors are blocked open for convenience. This problem occurred at a high rise apartment house which had both interior stairway doors propped open. A fast spreading fire erupted which filled the stairs with heat and smoke. Four occupants died. It took almost 200 fire fighters to subdue the fire and to evacuate the tenants. [10]

Door closers with fusible links can be purchased so that the door could remain open, but when the link fuses due to heat from the fire the door will close. Such fusible links are not sensitive to smoke and toxic gases. Another method is to release or close doors upon operation of smoke detectors.

Structural Integrity: The structural integrity of a building may depend on how the fire resistance was achieved.

- Buildings with tile arch floors often do not provide protection for the steel beams. In later buildings, skewback tiles were provided to protect the steel.
- Steel floor and ceiling assemblies using suspended ceilings are common. Unfortunately, ceiling tiles are easily removed and integrity is hard to maintain. The ceiling voids can pass smoke and fire.
- Permitting steel columns to be unprotected in the plenum space is particularly dangerous. A single failure of the ceiling membrane would subject the column to fire temperatures. The heating of only a short length of a column to failure temperature could have costly, or even catastrophic effects on the building.[11]
- Spray on fireproofing used asbestos fibers for many years. The health hazard of asbestos fibers now requires its removal. A most important question is what if anything is done to fire-protect the steel when the asbestos fire proofing is removed.

Flame Spread: Fire departments should be aware of the presence of combustible interior finish such as plywood and combustible acoustical tile in buildings. Older acoustical tile was made of compressed wood fibers and will burn furiously. It is usually installed on wood stringers, which enables burning on both sides of the tile. If it is applied with glue, the adhesive can add to the rate of burning very significantly. This was discovered in the investigation of the Hartford Hospital Fire in 1961 in which 16 died. The combustible tile was glued to a suspended gypsum board ceiling, surface-treated with a flame retardant. When tested it was learned that the adhesive caused a very rapid flame spread. When new tile is installed, it will probably be required to meet flame spread requirements. However, there is often no requirement that the old tile be removed. Fire may develop on the old combustible tile in the concealed space above the new tile ceiling.

Construction in Occupied Buildings: Buildings are often partially occupied before construction is finished. Many major remodeling projects are carried on in occupied buildings. The fire department should be aware of any such construction. Special permits should be required for any construction after the Certificate of Occupancy is issued.

A typical construction fire in such a building is a serious threat to the safety of all the occupants. At least two very serious fires have occurred.

Light Weight Construction: The almost complete change from sawn lumber to gusset plate wood trusses and wooden I-beams has profoundly changed the fire suppression environment. Tactics learned, and experience gained, on sawn joist and rafter buildings is not transferrable to truss buildings. The truss floor introduces a new hazard, the floor void, in which deadly explosive carbon monoxide gas can accumulate. (See Fig. 6-11J.)

FIG. 6-11J. Much recent construction is of light weight floor and roof trusses. Experience in fires in solid sawn construction is not transferrable.

Vacant Buildings: Baltimore, Philadelphia, Lynn (MA), Minneapolis, Indianapolis, and Montreal are some of the cities which have suffered recent massive downtown fires in old, combustible, interior masonry buildings which were being remodeled. The buildings were often undivided, and sprinkler systems had been removed. In these cases, the fire was in possession of the building on fire department arrival. Multi-million dollar damages were sustained in nearby structures. Many valuable assets and plans for downtown rehabilitation went up in smoke. In the Minneapolis fire, floors six through sixteen of an adjacent fire resistive high rise office building were gutted by an exposure fire in a department store being demolished. The loss was almost $100,000,000.[12]

The identical problem is presented by similar huge structures, not planned for rehabilitation but simply vacant because of economic changes. Sprinklers are often cut off to prevent freezing and the structures are an open invitation to arson.

Summary

This chapter presents only the highlights of the problems which buildings present to the fire suppression forces. Further detailed information can be found in many other materials such as those listed in additional readings. Needless to say knowledge and experience with building construction methods and materials can go a long way to improving fire department safety and efficiency.

BIBLIOGRAPHY

References

1. *Hazard Alert Bulletin*, Society of Fire Protection Engineers, 75-2, April, 1975, Boston, MA.
2. Corbett, G., Light Weight Wood Truss Floor Construction, A Fire Lesson, *Fire Engineering*, July 1988.
3. Brannigan, F. Are Wood Trusses Good For Your Health?, *Fire Engineering*, June 1988. See also Routley, J.G., How Wood Trusses Perform During a Real Fire, *Fire Journal*, January 1989.
4. Collapse of Hotel Vendome, Boston, MA, *Fire Journal*, January 1973.
5. Stronach, I., $100,000,000 Blaze Thwarts Montreal Firefighters, *Firehouse*, June 1987.
6. Sharry, J., Culver, P., Crist, R., Hillerson, J., Military Records Center Fire, *Fire Journal*, Vol. 68, No. 3 (May 1974).
7. Isner, M., Investigation Report Central Library Fire Los Angeles, CA, April 28, 1986, NFPA, Quincy, MA 02269.
8. Brannigan, F., Wooden Structure High In the Sky, *Fire Engineering*, April 1987.
9. Twelve Die in fire at Westchase Hilton Hotel, Houston, TX, *Fire Journal*, January 1983, p. 11.
10. Isner, M., Investigation Report Apartment High Rise Fire, Manhattan, New York, January 11, 1988, NFPA, Quincy, MA 02269. See also DeVita, A., and Dunn, V., Fatal Fire on E. 50 St., WNYF First Issue, 1988 New York Fire Department, Fire Academy, Randalls Island, NY 10035.
11. *Fire Protection Through Modern Building Codes*, 5th ed, American Iron and Steel Institute, Washington, DC, p. 126.
12. Best, J., Demolition Exposure Fire, *Fire Journal*, July 1983.

NFPA Codes, Standards Recommended Practices and Manuals. (See the latest NFPA Codes and Standards. Catalog for availability of current editions of the following documents)

NFPA 13, *Installation of Sprinkler Systems*

NFPA 220, *Standard on Types of Building Construction*

NFPA 241, *Standard for Safeguarding Construction, Alteration and Demolition Operations*

NFPA 251, *Standard Methods of Fire Tests of Building Construction and Materials*

NFPA 252, *Standard Methods of Fire Test of Door Assemblies*

NFPA 255, *Surface Burning Characteristics of Building Materials*.

Additional Readings

Brannigan, F. L., *Building Construction For The Fire Service*, 2 ed, National Fire Protection Association, Quincy, MA, 1982.

Dunn, V., *Collapse of Burning Buildings*, Fire Engineering, New York, 1988.

O'Hagen J., *High Rise Fire and Life Safety*, Fire Engineering, New York, 1989.

BUILDING AND FIRE CODES AND STANDARDS

Revised by Arthur E. Cote

Throughout history there have been building regulations for preventing fire and restricting its spread. Over the years these regulations have evolved into the codes and standards developed by committees concerned with fire protection. In many cases, a particular code dealing with a hazard of paramount importance may be enacted into law.

THE HISTORY AND DEVELOPMENT OF FIRE PROTECTION REGULATIONS

King Hammurabi, the famous law-making Babylonian ruler who reigned from approximately 1955 to 1913 B.C., is probably best remembered for the *Code of Hammurabi*, a statute primarily based on retaliation. The following decree is from the *Code of Hammurabi*:

> In the case of collapse of a defective building, the architect is to be put to death if the owner is killed by accident; and the architect's son if the son of the owner loses his life.

Today, society no longer endorses Hammurabi's ancient law of retaliation but seeks, rather, to prevent accidents and loss of life and property. From these objectives have evolved the rules and regulations that represent today's building codes and current standards for fire prevention, fire protection, and fire suppression.

Early Building and Fire Laws

The earliest recorded building laws apparently were concerned with the prevention of collapse. During the rapid growth of the Roman Empire under the reigns of Julius and Augustus Caesar, the city of Rome became the site of a large number of hastily constructed apartment buildings—many of which were erected to considerable heights. Because building collapse due to structural failure was frequent, laws were passed that limited the heights of buildings—first to 70 ft (21.3 m) and then to 60 ft (18.2 m).

Later in history there evolved many building regulations for preventing fire and restricting its spread. In London, during the 14th century, an ordinance was issued requiring that chimneys be built of tile, stone, or plaster; the ordinance prohibited the use of wood for this purpose. Among the first building ordinances of New York City was a similar provision, and among the first legislative acts of Boston was one requiring that dwellings be constructed of brick or stone and roofed with slate or tile (rather than being built of wood and having thatched roofs with wood chimneys covered with mud and clay similar to those to which the early settlers had been accustomed in Europe). Obviously, the intention of these building ordinances was to restrict the spread of fire from building to building in order to prevent conflagrations. As an inducement for helping to prevent fires, a fine of ten shillings was imposed on any householders who had chimney fires. This encouraged the citizenry to keep its chimneys free from soot and creosote. Thus was the first fire code in America established and enforced.

In colonial America, the need for laws that offered protection from the ravages of fire developed simultaneously with the growth of the colonies. The laws outlined the fire protection responsibilities of both homeowners and authorities. Some of these new laws were planned to punish people who put themselves and others at risk of fire. For example, in Boston no person was allowed to build a fire within "three rods" of any building, or in ships that were docked in Boston Harbor. It was illegal to carry "burning brands" for lighting fires except in covered containers, and arson was punishable by death. Regardless of such precautions, in Boston and in other emerging communities, fires were everyday occurrences. Therefore, it became necessary to enact more laws with which to govern building construction and to make further provisions for public fire protection. There emerged a growing body of rules and regulations concerning fire prevention, protection, and control. From these small beginnings, various codes and types of codes have evolved in this country, ranging from the most meager of ordinances to comprehensive handbooks and volumes of codes and standards on building construction and firesafety.

Development of Building and Fire Codes

The rapid growth of early American cities inspired much speculative building, and the structures usually were built

Arthur E. Cote, P.E., is assistant vice president and chief engineer at NFPA.

close to one another. Construction often was started before adequate building codes had been enacted. For example, the year before the great Chicago fire of 1871, Lloyd's of London stopped writing policies in Chicago because of the haphazard manner in which construction was proceeding. Other insurance companies had difficulty selling policies at the high rates they had to charge. Despite these excessively high rates, many insurance companies suffered great losses when fire spread out of control.

The National Board of Fire Underwiters [NBFU; now the American Insurance Association (AIA)], organized in 1866, realized that the adjustment and standardization of rates were merely temporary solutions to a serious technical problem. This group began to emphasize safe building construction, control of fire hazards, and improvements in both water supplies and fire departments. As a result, the new tall buildings constructed of concrete and steel conformed to specifications that helped limit the risk of fire. These buildings were called Class A buildings. In 1905 the National Board of Fire Underwriters published the first edition of its *Recommended Building Code* [later the *National Building Code* (NBC)]. This was a first and very useful attempt to show the way to uniformity.

In San Francisco in 1906, although there were some new Class A concrete and steel buildings in the downtown section, most of the city consisted of fire-prone wood shacks. Concerned with such conditions, the National Board of Fire Underwriters wrote that "San Francisco has violated all underwriting traditions and precedents by not burning up."

On April 18 of that same year, the city of San Francisco experienced a conflagration—started by an earthquake—that killed 452 people and destroyed some 28,000 buildings. Although the contents of many of the new Class A buildings were destroyed in the San Francisco Fire, most of the walls, frames, and floors remained intact and could be renovated. (See Figure 6-12A.)

Following analysis of the fire damage caused by the San Francisco disaster and other major fires, the National Board of Fire Underwriters became convinced of the need for more comprehensive standards and codes relating to the design, construction, and maintenance of buildings. With this increasing recognition of the importance of fire protection came more knowledge about the subject. Engineers started to accumulate information about fire hazards in building construction and in manufacturing processes, and much of this information became the basis for the early standards and codes.

Most chapters in this section of the handbook have a bearing on the provisions of building codes and their enforcement. Of particular interest would be "Classification of Building Construction," which contains information on the various types of construction and how they are classified in building codes as a basis for fire protection requirements.

BUILDING CODE DEFINED

A building code is a law that sets forth minimum requirements for design and construction of buildings and structures. These minimum requirements, established to protect the health and safety of society, generally represent a compromise between optimum safety and economic feasibility. Although builders and building owners often establish their own requirements, the minimum code requirements of a jurisdiction must be met. Features covered include structural design, fire protection, means of egress, light, sanitation, and interior finish.[1]

There are two types of building codes. Specification codes spell out in detail what materials can be used, the building size, and how components should be assembled. Performance codes detail the objective to be met and establish criteria for determining if the objective has been reached; thus, the designer and builder are free to select construction methods and materials as long as it can be shown that the performance criteria can be met. Performance-oriented building codes still embody a fair amount of specification-type requirements, but provisions exist for substitution of alternate methods and materials ("trade offs"), if they can be proved adequate.

FIG. 6-12A. A great earthquake and ensuing conflagration devastated San Francisco in 1906. As many as 452 people were killed, and 28,000 buildings were damaged or destroyed. Total financial loss was $350 million.

BUILDING CODES AND FIRE PROTECTION

The requirements contained in building codes are generally based upon the known properties of materials, the hazards presented by various occupancies, and the lessons learned from previous experiences, such as fire and natural disasters.[1] The promulgation of modern building codes in the U.S. began with the disastrous conflagrations and earthquakes that occurred at the turn of the century.

For a number of years, building codes dealt mainly with structural safety under fire or earthquake conditions. Since then, codes have grown into documents prescribing minimum requirements for structural stability, fire resistance, means of egress, sanitation, lighting, ventilation, and built-in safety equipment. More than 50 percent of a modern building code usually refers in some way or another to fire protection.

Building codes usually establish fire limits or fire districts in certain areas of a municipality. Only specific types of construction are allowed within the fire limits. Such a restriction is said to reduce the conflagration potential of the more densely populated areas. Use of a given type of building construction alone, however, is not necessarily a deterrent to conflagration. Outside the fire limits, the restriction of certain construction types is relaxed, due to such factors as decreased building density (i.e., increased spacing between buildings). Unfortunately, as areas outside the fire limits are developed, building density increases and the fire limits frequently must be extended. In addition, without construction restrictions, areas outside the fire limits invite the erection of large buildings despite public protection that is weak or lacking.

Another example of the impact of building codes on fire protection and prevention is the establishment of height and area criteria. The criteria establish height and area of a particular building, based on its intended use. These requirements have varied considerably from one area to the next; there is no nationally recognized standard for setting height and area limitations. However, the Board for the Coordination of Model Codes (BCMC) has developed standardized height and area limitations for use in each of the model building codes. The types of building construction are important factors in establishing height and area limitations.

Other requirements found in building codes that directly relate to fire protection include: (1) enclosure of vertical openings such as stair shafts, elevator shafts, and pipe chases; (2) provision of exits for evacuation of occupants; (3) requirements for flame spread of interior finish; and (4) provisions for automatic fire suppression systems. Exit requirements found in most building codes are based on specifications in NFPA 101®, *Life Safety Code*®.

Inasmuch as a building code is actually a law, many state and local jurisdictions write their own codes. Because of the complexities of modern building code development, several organizations develop model building codes for use by jurisdictions which can then adopt the model codes into law.

Relationship Between Building and Fire Codes

It often is difficult to differentiate between items that should go into a fire prevention code and those best included in a building code. Generally, whatever requirements deal specifically with construction of a building are part of a building code administered by the building department. A fire prevention code, on the other hand, includes information on fire hazards in a building, and usually is regulated by the fire official. Requirements for exits and fire extinguishing equipment generally are found in building codes, while the maintenance of such items is covered in fire prevention codes.

MODEL BUILDING CODE ORGANIZATIONS

With the exception of the independent operations of some of the largest cities, the business of building code development in the U.S. is mainly in the hands of three model building code organizations; they are: International Conference of Building Officials (ICBO), Southern Building Code Congress International (SBCCI), and Building Officials and Code Administrators (BOCA). The primary objectives of these organizations is to provide standardization of construction regulations and enforcement of these regulations. Each organization and its model codes are discussed in the following paragraphs.

ICBO (International Conference of Building Officials)

ICBO first published the *Uniform Building Code (UBC)* in 1927. The UBC is principally used in the western U.S., but has been adopted in municipalities as far east as Michigan.

In addition to publishing the building code, the Conference also publishes a *Mechanical and Plumbing Code*, in association with the International Association of Plumbing and Mechanical Officials (IAPMO), and a *Fire Prevention Code*, in association with the Western Fire Chiefs Association.

The Conference maintains a staff of architects and engineers in Whittier, CA, which provides governmental bodies with technical assistance in the administration and enforcement of the ICBO codes.

SBCCI (Southern Building Code Congress International)

The SBCCI was organized in 1940 and first published the *Southern Standard Building Code* in 1945. Now called the *Standard Building Code (SBC)*, this code is used principally throughout the southern portion of the U.S.

Like ICBO, SBCCI also publishes mechanical, plumbing, fire prevention, and gas codes to be used in conjunction with the *SBC*. SBCCI maintains a technical staff headquartered in Birmingham, AL.

BOCA (Building Officials and Code Administrators)

As the Building Officials Conference of America, BOCA published the first edition of the *Basic/Building Code (BBC)* in 1950. Since that time, the organization has changed its name to Building Officials and Code Administrators, International. For a period of time, the *BBC* was called the *Basic/National Building Code*, but is now published as the *National Building Code*. It is principally used in the midwest and northeast portions of the U.S.

Like the other code groups, BOCA also publishes mechanical, plumbing, and fire prevention codes. BOCA maintains a technical staff in Country Club Hills, IL.

Other Code Producers

There are two other organizations that have been directly involved in the development of either a model building code or a model life safety code.

AIA (American Insurance Association): As previously noted, the National Board of Fire Underwriters (NBFU), now the American Insurance Association (AIA), first published the *National Building Code (NBC)* in 1905. The code was used as a model for adoption by cities, as well as a basis to evaluate the building regulations of towns and cities for town grading purposes. The code was periodically reviewed by the NBFU staff, revised as necessary, and republished. The last code revision was the 1976 edition. Since then, the AIA has discontinued updating and publishing the *National Building Code*, and Building Officials and Code Administrators (BOCA) has acquired the right to use the title *"National Building Code."* The AIA also published a fire prevention code, most recently published in 1976, but has also discontinued the updating and publishing of this document.

NFPA (National Fire Protection Association): NFPA does not publish a model building code *per se*; however, NFPA 101, *Life Safety Code*, establishes minimum requirements necessary for providing a reasonable degree of safety from fire. The *Life Safety Code* addresses those construction, protection, and occupancy features necessary to minimize danger to life from fire, smoke, fumes, or panic. It also identifies the minimum criteria for design of egress facilities to permit prompt escape of occupants from buildings or, where perferable, evacuation into safe areas within buildings. The *Life Safety Code* does not attempt to address those general fire prevention or building construction features that normally are functions of fire prevention and building codes. The NFPA Committee on Safety to Life was founded in 1913 and initially developed a number of pamphlets on exits from various occupancies. The first edition of the NFPA *Building Exits Code* (later the *Life Safety Code*), developed by the Safety to Life Committee, was published in 1927.

NFPA 101, *Life Safety Code*, is one of more than 270 codes, standards, recommended practices, manuals, guides, and model laws developed and published by NFPA. The complete compendium of these documents, which encompass the entire scope of fire protection and prevention, practices, and safeguards, comprises the NFPA *National Fire Codes® (NFC)*. Included within the *NFC* are a number of individual firesafety codes, e.g., NFPA 70, *National Electrical Code®*, one of the most widely adopted codes in the U.S.; NFPA 30, *Flammable and Combustible Liquids Code*; and NFPA 54, *National Fuel Gas Code*—just to name a few. NFPA also has developed its own *Fire Prevention Code*, NFPA 1, which also is included in the *National Fire Codes*.

NFPA standards and codes are developed by more than 200 NFPA technical committees, each representing a balance of affected interests. More than 5,000 individuals serve on the NFPA committees, all on a voluntary, unpaid basis. Committees operate according to a detailed *Regulations Governing Committee Projects* and are administered by a Standards Council which reports to the NFPA's Board of Directors.

Built into the standards development and adoption process is the publication of calls for proposals to amend existing documents, or to shape the content of new documents. Only after a public review and comment cycle has been completed is the final committee report brought before the NFPA membership for action. This democratic legislative procedure allows proponents and opponents to be heard freely. Once adopted by the NFPA membership at either the NFPA Annual or Fall meeting, and issued by the NFPA Standards Council, the documents are published and made available for voluntary adoption. Many of these documents are referenced by the model building codes.

Code Adoption and Use

It must be recognized that model building codes are only representations of possible regulations, and they do not actually become law until enacted by state and municipal legislatures. The general areas of model building code adoption and use can be seen in Figure 6-12B.

BUILDING CODE DEVELOPMENT

The operations of model code organizations are based on the input of affected interest groups. Any individual or interested organization can provide input to the model building code organizations. Participation is voluntary, but it is essential that the total involvement be representative of a viable cross section of the building community, including trade associations and manufacturers; engineers, architects, and code consultants; federal agencies; fire service representatives; and building officials. This input is the means by which the model codes are continually amended to reflect technological progress. It is also the way by which new concepts, materials, and systems of construction, and new research and test findings are incorporated into the model building codes. In the model building code adoption process, only the building official gets a final vote on the acceptance of code changes.

Model building codes are revised annually. Revised editions are published at three-year intervals, with annual supplements in the interim years.

TOWARD UNIFORMITY OF BUILDING CODES

Although model codes originally were known as regional codes, boundary lines for their adoption are much less significant today. In fact, much effort has been expended toward the elimination of differences among the model building codes. The Joint Committee on Building Codes, composed of representatives of the organizations sponsoring the model codes and others concerned with the development of codes and standards, was formed in 1949 to work toward uniformity among the codes. The Joint Committee later became the Model Code Standardization Council and then the Board for the Coordination of Model Codes (BCMC). Representatives of BOCA, ICBO, SBCCI, and NFPA now participate in BCMC. The purpose of this committee is to develop uniform code language to be included in each of the model building codes and NFPA 101, *Life Safety Code*. Proposals resulting from BCMC are processed in accordance with the code change procedures of each code organization.

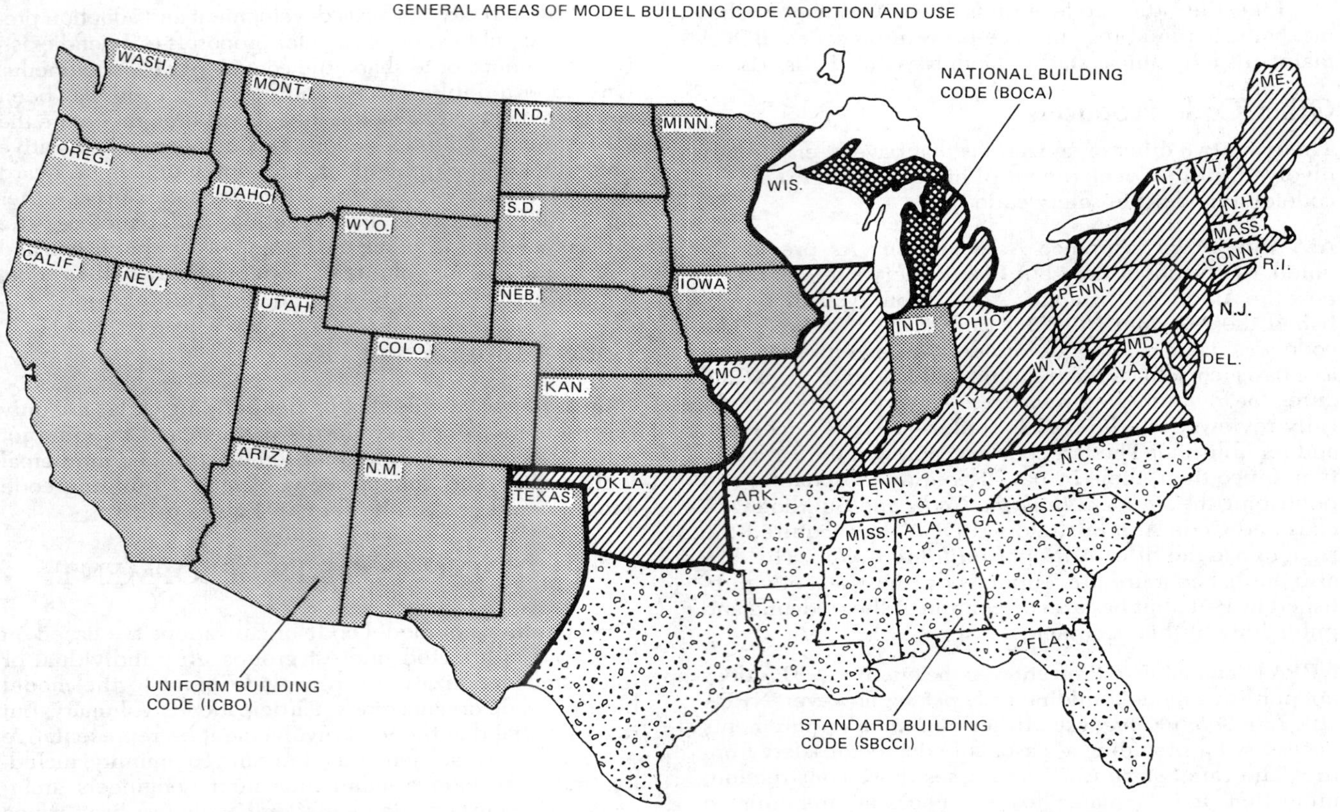

FIG. 6-12B. General areas of model building code adoption and use.

OTHER CODE-RELATED ORGANIZATIONS

Other organizations involved in codes- and standards-related issues include the following.

NCSBCS (National Conference of States on Building Codes and Standards)

NCSBCS is a nonprofit corporation founded in 1967 as a result of Congressional interest in reform of building codes. It attempts to foster increased interstate cooperation in the area of building codes and standards and coordinates intergovernmental code administration reforms. NCSBCS is an executive-branch organization of the National Governors Association and includes as members governor-appointed representatives of each state and territorial government. It has a working relationship with the National Conference of State Legislatures and the Council of State Community Affairs Agencies.

CABO (Council of American Building Officials)

The Council of American Building Officials (CABO) is an organization formed by the three major model code groups, i.e., ICBO, SBCCI, and BOCA, in 1972. (The AIA is not a member of this organization.) CABO was formed to represent the model building code process on a national level and to promote the model code process. One of the committees formed by CABO is the BCMC (Board for the Coordination of the Model Codes).

Two of the major accomplishments of CABO have been: (1) to organize the National Research Board, and (2) publish the *One- and Two-Family Dwelling Code*. The National Research Board coordinates the research and evaluation programs of the three model code groups (i.e., ICBO, SBCCI, and BOCA) to eliminate the need for a manufacturer working with three different organizations. The *One- and Two-Family Dwelling Code* contains regulations for detached housing that meet the requirements of the three model codes.

Association of Major City Building Officials

The Association of Major City Building Officials was formed in 1974. This group recognizes code problems that are peculiar to large cities, defines problem areas, and seeks solutions.

NIBS (National Institute of Building Sciences)

NIBS was authorized by Congress in 1974, under Public Law 93-383, as a nongovernmental, nonprofit organization governed by a 21-member board of directors. Fifteen of the board members are elected and six are appointed by the President of the United States, with the advice and consent of the U.S. Senate. The Institute is a core organization that serves primarily as an investigative body, offering its findings and recommendations to government and to responsible private-sector organizations for voluntary implementation. It carries out its mandated mission essentially by identifying and investigating national problems confronting the building community, and proposing courses of action to bring about solutions to the problems. NIBS activities are board-based and center around regulatory concerns, technology for the built environment, and distribution of technical and other useful information. In establishing the objectives, powers, and structure of NIBS, Congress also outlined certain functions relating to building regulations in four general areas. These are:

1. Development, promulgation, and maintenance of nationally recognized performance criteria, standards, and other technical provisions for maintenance of life, safety, health, and public welfare that are suitable for adoption by building-regulating jurisdictions and agencies. This also includes test methods and other evaluative techniques relating to building systems, subsystems, components, products, and materials, with due regard for consumer interests.
2. Evaluation and prequalification of existing and new building technology.
3. Conduct of needed investigations.
4. Assembly, storage, and dissemination of technical data and other related information.

Working under its very broad mandate, NIBS has established a Consultative Council, with membership available to representatives of all appropriate private trade, professional, and labor organizations; private and public standards, codes, and testing bodies; public regulatory agencies; and consumer groups. The Council's purpose is to ensure a direct line of communication between such groups and the Institute and to serve as a vehicle for representative hearings on matters before the Institute.

WOBO (World Organization of Building Officials)

WOBO was founded in 1984, with the primary objective of advancing education through worldwide dissemination of knowledge in building science, technology, and construction. WOBO was established because of increased participation of nations in the global marketplace; the rapid development of new international building technologies and products; and development of international standards that now make it impossible for building officials to confine their concern to activities within their own national boundaries.

ENFORCEMENT OF CODES AND STANDARDS

Today the life and property of every citizen is safeguarded to at least some extent by fire legislation enacted by the Congress of the United States, state legislatures, city councils, town meetings, and many other jurisdictions and levels of government. The implementation and enforcement of this legislation is in the hands of administrative agencies of government, such as federal departments and agencies, state fire marshal offices and other appropriate state agencies, and local fire departments, building departments, electrical inspectors, etc.

In this country's earlier days, the protection of citizens from fire was solely the concern of the local community. Present-day fire fighting is carried on by local fire departments. While most communities have had some type of building code since the beginning of the 20th century, they did not have fire prevention codes until more recently.

With the need for more detailed, comprehensive standards and codes relating to the construction, design, and maintenance of buildings came the knowledge that regulations based on such codes certainly could prevent most fires and reduce losses in the fires that did occur.

Regulations relating to firesafety are determined and enforced by different levels of government. While some functions overlap, federal and state laws generally govern those areas that cannot be regulated at the local level.

Federal Firesafety Regulations

There is a substantial amount of federal regulation pertaining to firesafety. Under the Consitution, Congress has the power to regulate interstate commerce; this power has been interpreted to permit Congress to pass laws authorizing various federal departments and agencies to adopt and enforce regulations to protect the public from fire hazards.

Any federal department or agency can promulgate firesafety regulations only if authority to do so is granted by a specific act of Congress. These regulations have the force of law, and violations can result in legal action. In general, such federal laws can be enacted to provide: (1) that all state laws on the same subject are superseded by the federal law, (2) that state laws not conflicting with the federal law remain valid, or (3) that any state law will prevail if it is more stringent than the federal law. Among the federal agencies that have the authority to promulgate firesafety regulations are the Occupational Safety and Health Administration (OSHA), the Department of Health and Human Services (HHS), and the Consumer Product Safety Commission (CPSC).

FIRESAFETY REGULATIONS OF STATE AND LOCAL GOVERNMENT

Within the scope of the police power of state government is the regulation of building construction for the health and safety of the public—a power usually delegated to local governments of the state.

Building code requirements usually apply to new construction or to major alterations to buildings. Retroactive application of code requirements is very rare. Building code applicability usually ends with the issuance of an occupancy permit. The basic premise that fire legislation should regulate for the safety of current occupants and for current risk is not generally the province of building codes once a structure is occupied. Then, after-occupancy fire codes or fire prevention codes apply. Also, this usually is the point at which the authority of the building official ends and the fire official begins.

This division of authority, however, does not preclude interaction between the two officials during both a building's development and its subsequent use. In practice, many jurisdictions assign responsibilities to building and/or fire officials in both building and fire code application. The division of authority varies considerably among communities.

In most states, the principal fire official is the state fire marshal. For the most part, the state fire marshal is the statutory official charged by law with responsibility for the administration and enforcement of state laws relating to safety to life and property from fire. Usually the state fire marshal also has the power to investigate fires and to suppress arson.

The manner in which each state handles the promulgation of building and fire regulations varies widely. In some states, each local government may have its own code, while in others the local authority has the option of adopting the state building code. In still others, the state code establishes the minimum below which the local regulations cannot go. Finally, in some states the local government has no choice and must adopt the state code.

These situations have resulted in a plethora of different local building and fire codes. Some of the local governments adopt one or more of the model codes or codes based upon the model codes. Others draft their own local codes. This lack of uniformity has been criticized by materials producers, building designers, builders, and others, and some years ago prompted the appointment of federal commissions to study the situation and make recommendations to the administration.[2,3,4]

The legal procedure for adopting codes and standards into law can also vary from one enforcing jurisdiction to another. Usually, the simplest and best way is to adopt by reference. This method, applicable to public authorities as well as to private entities, requires that the text of the law or rule cite the standard by its title and give adequate publishing information to permit its exact identification. The standard itself is not reprinted in the law. All deletions, additions, or changes made by the adopting authority are noted separately in the text of the law. Adoption of a current edition of a standard obviates outdated editions maintained as law until a new law referencing a new edition is adopted.

Where local laws do not permit adoption by reference, a standard can be adopted by transcription. This requires that the text of the adopted standard be transcribed into the law. Existing material can be deleted and new material added only if such material does not change the meaning or intent of the existing or remaining material. Under adoption by transcription, the standard cannot be rewritten, although changes can be made for administrative provisions. Because the text of the standard is transcribed into the law, due notice of the copyright of the standard's developer is required. As a result, most code groups copyright their standards to prevent misuse and unlawful use.

THE ROLE OF STANDARDS IN BUILDING CODES

Many requirements found in building codes are excerpts from, or based on, the standards published by nationally recognized organizations. The most extensive use of the standards is their adoption into building codes by reference, thus keeping the building codes to a workable size and eliminating much duplication of effort. Such standards are also used by specification writers in the design stage of a building to provide guidelines for the bidders and contractors.

Numerous NFPA standards are referenced by the model building codes and, thus, obtain legal status where these model codes are adopted. Notable examples of such referenced NFPA standards are those that deal with electrical systems, extinguishing systems, flammable liquids, hazardous processes, combustible dusts, liquefied petroleum gas, and fire tests.

Two of the model building codes—BOCA and SBCCI—contain appendices that list standards published by many organizations, including standards-making organizations, professional engineering societies, building materials trade associations, federal agencies, and testing agencies. The appendices are prefaced with a statement indicating that the standards are to be used where required by the provisions of the code or where referenced by the code.

The other model code organization—ICBO—publishes a book of standards to accompany its code. Some of the standards in the book have been written by ICBO; others are standards of other organizations adapted for ICBO use. These organizations can be divided into four principal groups:

1. Organizations structured to deal exclusively with the preparation, publication, and distribution of a wide variety of specifications intended for voluntary use in the private and public sectors.

As an example, the American Society for Testing and Materials (ASTM), a private-sector organization, falls into this category. In the public sector, the Standards Development Services Section of the National Bureau of Standards and the U.S. Department of Commerce have similar functions.

2. Professional societies and technical organizations that deal with design standards for construction and equipment. The American Concrete Institute (ACI), the American Society of Mechanical Engineers (ASME), and the American Society of Heating, Refrigeration, and Air Conditioning Engineers (ASHRAE) are examples in this category of activity.

Prominent standards developed by these organizations include ACI 318, *Building Code Requirements for Reinforced Concrete*; the boiler and pressure vessel specifications by ASME; and the ASHRAE Standard 90A, *Energy Conservation in New Building Design*.

3. Industry Associations and Manufacturers, a group that produces proprietary standards for materials and test methods applicable to their particular industry products. Although such specifications are not developed under national consensus proceedings, their broad voluntary use achieves national acceptance.

Three examples of proprietary standards are the American Institute of Steel Construction (AISC) specifications for *Design, Fabrication, and Erection of Structural Steel for Buildings*; the specifications for *Aluminum Siding and High Performance Coatings for Aluminum Siding* by the Architectural Aluminum Manufacturers Association (AAMA); and the American Plywood Association (APA) document *Design and Fabrication Specifications for Plywood Lumber Components*.

4. A mixture of standards-developing organizations that cannot properly be classified in any of the categories described above. For instance, the National Fire Protection Association focuses its standards development program on a singular interest: firesafety. Underwriters Laboratories Inc. (UL), an independent testing and certification organization, develops a variety of standards needed in the conduct of its work. UL specifications become nationally recognized standards and many receive approval as consensus standards through the ANSI process.

Similar to UL is the Factory Mutual Research Corporation (FMRC), which develops safety standards and test methods widely used by insurance and other interests.

Another organization in this category is the National Conference of States on Building Codes and Standards (NCSBCS). This group, whose principal members are state officials, develops certain mobile home standards and also is heavily involved in the development of standards dealing with energy conservation.

NATIONAL STANDARDS

The voluntary standards development system in the United States is unmatched in the world: it is efficient, cost-effective, highly productive, and results in the promulgation of thousands of quality standards each year.

U.S. voluntary standards are developed by a diverse, decentralized network of private-sector entities. Many different organizations are involved in standards work in this country, a feature that is one of the great strengths of the system. It has been reported that, in total, there are approximately 89,000 "standards" in the U.S. But, 50,000 of these "standards" are actually procurement specifications developed and used by government, not true standards, thus leaving about 39,000 voluntary standards developed in the U.S.[5]

It has also been estimated that there may be 600 private organizations that are occasionally involved in standards activities. However, according to R. B. Toth Associates, only "about 270 standards developers have ongoing standardization programs."[5]

Of the 39,000 voluntary standards developed in the U.S., 23,570 are developed by fourteen leading standards-developing organizations.[5]

American National Standards Institute (ANSI)

The significant private-sector standards development system in the U.S. is largely self-regulated, with oversight and coordination provided by ANSI, a federation of U.S. standards developers that was founded in 1918.

Approximately 250 of the 270 active standards developers, including 12 of the 14 major developers of U.S. standards, are members of ANSI.[5] ANSI is able to fulfill its coordinating role for the voluntary standards system in the United States because of the support it receives from those actively involved in standards work.

ANSI coordinates and harmonizes private-sector standards activity in the U.S. In order for a document to be designated an American National Standard, the principles of openess and due process must have been followed in its development, and consensus among those directly and materially affected by the standard must have been achieved. ANSI also represents the U.S. interests in the international standardization activities of the International Organization for Standardization (ISO) and the International Electrotechnical Commission (IEC).

Under ANSI procedures, all American National Standards must be reviewed and reaffirmed, modified, or withdrawn every five years—a requirement that ensures that voluntary standards in this country keep pace with developing technology and innovations. Thus, the voluntary system produces quality standards that do not become outdated.

SAFETY *vs* RISK IN STANDARDS DEVELOPMENT

There are two broad categories of voluntary standards: (1) safety standards, and (2) product standards. Standards are not strictly a matter of science, especially safety standards.

Safety is dependent upon risk, and the degree of safety achieved depends on how much willingness there is to "pay" to eliminate the risk. Total elimination of some risks would be exorbitant, and elimination of all risk is not feasible, even apart from cost. In addition, part of the cost of risk elimination is the reduction of freedom. Many aspects of safety systems or materials standards have this effect, as they come to bear on the human factors in risk elimination.

Assessments of human factors also are needed with respect to calculations of onerousness and cost of use, for if tolerance limits are exceeded, standards will be modified in practice, or ignored. Also, the more onerous and costly compliance becomes, the more carefully critics will examine the "degree of contribution to a safe environment" that the standard will bring about.

Although standards-making does not deal with the "science" of safety, amenable to full laboratory control, an aggregation of subjective factors enters in: social, economic, political, and competitive.

One of the strengths of the voluntary consensus standards development system in the U.S. is that the deliberative committee structure, which is comprised of a balanced representation of all affected interests, including users, consumers, manufacturers, suppliers, distributors, labor, testing laboratories, enforcers, and federal, state and local government officials, can consider all of the diverse factors at hand and develop a consensus on an acceptable level of standardization. It has been observed that "this may be one of the greatest strengths of the present private standards-writing system, insofar as it truly represents variety, and one of the greatest insufficiencies of a governmental system."[6]

BIBLIOGRAPHY

References Cited

1. Sanderson, R. L., *Codes and Code Administration*, Building Officials Conference of America, Inc., Chicago, IL, 1969.
2. "Building the American City," Report of the National Commission on Urban Problems, Superintendent of Documents, U. S. Government Printing Office, Washington, DC, 1968.
3. *Building Codes: A Program for Intergovernmental Reform*, Advisory Commission on Intergovernmental Relations, Superintendent of Documents, U.S. Government Printing Office, Washington, DC, 1966.
4. "Report of the President's Commission on Housing," Superintendent of Documents, U.S. Government Printing Office, Washington, DC, 1982.
5. Peralta, Manuel, "Statement of the American National Standards Institute Concerning International Voluntary Standardization," American National Standards Institute, New York, July 25, 1989.
6. Dixon, Robert G., Jr., *Standards Development in the Private Sector: Thoughts on Interest Representation and Procedural Fairness*, National Fire Protection Association, Quincy, MA, 1978.

NFPA Codes, Standards, and Recommended Practices

Reference to the following NFPA codes, standards, and recommended practices will provide further information on building and fire codes and standards discussed in this chapter. (See the latest *NFPA Catalog* for availability of current editions of the following documents.)

NFPA 80, *Fire Doors and Windows.*
NFPA 80A, *Protection from Exposure Fire.*
NFPA 88A, *Parking Structures.*
NFPA 88B, *Repair Garages.*
NFPA 90A, *Air Conditioning and Ventilating Systems.*
NFPA 90B, *Warm Air Heating and Air Conditioning Systems.*
NFPA 92A, *Mechanical Smoke Control.*
NFPA 92B, *Atrium Smoke Control.*
NFPA 101, *Life Safety Code.*
NFPA 105, *Smoke- and Draft-Control Doors.*
NFPA 203M, *Roof Coverings.*
NFPA 204M, *Smoke and Heat Venting.*
NFPA 220, *Standard Types of Building Construction.*
NFPA 241, *Building Construction and Demolition Operations.*
NFPA 703, *Fire Retardant Treatments of Building Materials.*

Model Building Codes

BOCA, *Basic/National Building Code,* 1990 ed., Building Officials and Code Administrators, International, County Club Hills, IL.

ICBO, *Uniform Building Code,* 1988 ed., International Conference of Building Officials, Whittier, CA.

SBCCI, *Standard Building Code,* 1985 ed., Southern Building Code Congress International, Inc., Birmingham, AL.

Model Fire Prevention Codes

The BOCA National Fire Prevention Code, 1990 ed., Building Officials and Code Administrators, International, Country Club Hills, IL, 1990.

Standard Fire Prevention Code, 1985 ed., Southern Building Code Congress, International, Inc., Birmingham, AL, 1985.

Uniform Fire Code Standards, 1988 ed., International Conference of Building Officials, Whittier, CA, 1988.

Additional Readings

Albert L. Batik, "A Layman's View of the Relationship of Standards to Product Liability," *Standards Engineering,* Dayton, OH, January/February 1990.

ASTM Standards in Building Codes, 27th ed., American Society for Testing and Materials, Philadelphia, PA, 1990.

Baker, D. R., "Meeting High-Rise Requirements for Fire Detection/Alarm/Supression," *Consulting—Specifying Engineer,* Vol. 3, No. 2, Feb. 1988, pp. 56-59.

Baker, D. R., "Performance by Computer Modeling or Prescription by Model Code," *TR 86-5,* Society of Fire Protection Engineers, Boston, MA, 1986.

Bihr, J. E., "Building and Fire Codes: The Regulatory Process, Fire Standards and Safety," *ASTM STP 614,* (A. F. Robertson, ed.), American Society for Testing and Materials, Philadelphia, PA, 1977.

BOCA, *Basic/National Building Code,* 1990, ed., Building Officials and Code Administrators, International Country Club Hills, IL, 1990.

Boring, D. F., *Fire Protection Through Modern Building Codes,* 5th ed., American Iron and Steel Institute, Washington, DC, 1981.

Breitenberg, M. A., *The ABC's of Standards-Related Activities in the United States,* U.S. Department of Commerce, National Bureau of Standards, Gaithersburg, MD, May 1987.

Cooke, P. W., *A Review of U.S. Participation in International Standards Activities,* U.S. Department of Commerce, National Bureau of Standards, Gaithersburg, MD, January 1988.

Cooke, P. W., *A Summary of the New European Community Approach to Standards Development,* U.S. Department of Commerce, National Bureau of Standards, Gaithersburg, MD, August 1988.

Cooke, P. W., *An Update of U.S. Participation in International Standards Activities,* U.S. Department of Commerce, National Institute of Standards and Technology, Gaithersburg, MD, January 1988.

Curless, M., "Codes, Standards and Fire Protection Engineering," *MP 69-1,* National Fire Protection Association, Quincy, MA, 1969.

Deakin, G., "International Standardization of Fire Tests," *Fire Prevention,* No. 198, April 1987, pp. 26-30.

Finnimore, B., "Need for Atria Fire Codes," *Fire Prevention,* No. 205, Dec. 1987, pp. 30-33.

Hansen, A. T., "Applying Building Codes to Existing Buildings," *CBD 230,* Division of Building Research, National Research Council, Ottawa, Canada, Jan. 1984.

Harvey, C. S., "Flexible Approach to Fire-Code Compliance," *Architectural Record,* No. 10, Oct. 1988, pp. 130-135.

Harter, P. J., "Regulatory Use of Standards: The Implications for Standards Writers," *NBS-GCR-79-171,* National Bureau of Standards, Gaithersburg, MD, Nov 1979.

Hosker, H., and Waters, C., "Building Regulations Determined," *Fire Prevention,* No. 224, Nov. 1989, pp. 37-38.

Korman, R., and Post, N. M., "The Code System, It Ain't Pretty- . . . But it Works, Codes, ENR," *Construction Weekly* , June 22, 1989.

Kouba, D., *ed., Code Administration and Enforcement: Trends and Perspectives,* International City Management Association, Washington, DC, 1982.

Lathrop, J. K., *Life Safety Code Handbook,* 4th ed, National Fire Protection Association, Quincy, MA, 1988.

McConnaughey, J. S., "An Economic Analysis of Building Code Impacts: A Suggested Approach," *NBSIR 78-1528,* National Bureau of Standards, Gaithersburg, MD, Oct. 1978.

Oey, K. H., and Passchier, E., "Complying with Practice Codes," *Batiment International/Building Research and Practice,* Vol. 21, No. 1, 1988, pp. 30-36.

Rawie, C. C., "Estimating Benefits and Costs of Building Regulations: A Step by Step Guide," *NBSIR 2223,* National Bureau of Standards, Gaithersburg, MD, 1981.

Robertson, J. C., "Development and Enactment of Fire Safety Codes," *Intoduction to Fire Prevention,* 3rd ed., Macmillan, New York, 1989, pp. 112-132.

Sanderson, R. L., *Readings in Code Administration,* 3 vols., Building Officials and Code Administrators International, Inc., Chicago, IL, 1975.

Sabatini, J., "Ensuring Code Compliance in High-Hazard Buildings," *Plant Engineering,* Vol. 44, No. 9, May 10, 1990, pp. 57-59.

Schirmer, C., "Helping Develop the Codes and Standards," *Fire Journal,* Vol. 84, No. 3, 1990, p. 44.

Smyrl, E. S., "Literature Review: The Building Regulatory System in the United States," *NBS-GCR-80-286,* National Bureau of Standards, Gaithersburg, MD, Oct. 1980.

Standards Activities of Organizations in the United States, National Bureau of Standards, U.S. Dept. of Commerce, Washington, DC, 1984.

Steiner, V. M., "Building Codes - Bane or Blessing?," *Plant Engineering,* July 21, 1988.

Stubbs, M. S., "The Widening Web of Codes and Standards," *AEBO Section Newsletter,* Fall 1988, National Fire Protection Association, Quincy, MA, 1988. (Reprinted from *Doors and Hardware.*)

Sullivan, C. D., *Standards and Standardization: Basic Principles and Applications*, Marcel Dekker, New York, 1983.

Swankin, D. A., *How Due Process in the Development of Voluntary Standards Can Reduce the Risk of Anti-Trust Liability*, U.S. Department of Commerce, National Institute of Standards and Technology, Washington, DC, February 1990.

Terio, C., *Introduction to Building Codes and Standards*, The American Institute of Architects, State Government Affairs, Washington, DC, April 1987.

Todd, N. W., and Ryan, J. D., "Improving Codes by Predicting Product Performance in Real Fires," *Fire Journal*, Vol. 84, No. 2, 1990, p. 64.

Traw, J. S."ICBO Code Interpretation Policy," *Building Standards*, January-February 1990.

Turner, M., "New Code Governing the Means of Escape for Disabled People," *Fire Prevention*, No. 215, Dec. 1988, pp. 36-37.

Use of Building Codes in Federal Agency Construction, Building Research Board, National Research Council, Building Research Board, Commission on Engineering and Technical Systems, Washington, DC 1989.

1987 ASTM Standards in Building Codes, 24th ed., American Society for Testing and Materials, Philadelphia, PA, 1987.

EVALUATING STRUCTURAL DAMAGE

Revised by Herman H. Spaeth

This chapter covers the factors that should be considered in evaluating the integrity of structures for further use and occupancy after exposure to fire. Special attention is directed to the techniques for evaluating the post-fire strengths and weaknesses of the basic building materials, i.e., steel, concrete, masonry, and wood, in structural assemblies.

Other chapters in this section that address structural fire damage are Chapter 2, "Classification of Building Construction"; Chapter 5, "Structural Integrity During Fire"; and Chapter 6, "Confinement of Fire in Buildings."

All structural materials, whether classified as combustible or noncombustible, inherently possess a degree of fire resistance. However, they are adversely affected when exposed to elevated temperatures during a fire. The degree of damage may vary with the basic materials and building configuration. Where there is no visible cosmetic damage to the building after a fire, such as glass breakage, concrete spalling, or slight steel distortion, it is held that there is little chance of serious damage, although this is no guarantee. Current public interest in life safety, legal implications, and the designer's reputation may warrant a careful inspection to verify no further damage occurred due to excessive expansion and instability in unit design.

THE POST-FIRE INSPECTION

Immediately after a fire, several interested groups, such as the fire department, the building inspection department, and insurance interests, will usually insist on a fact-finding inspection. The fire department will be interested in cause of the fire, whether accidental or arson, as well as possible code violations. The building official, also interested in code violation, joins with the insurance concern of property damage, as well as residual structural stability and reusability.

A recent Smithsonian Magazine article references a new engineering discipline, called "building diagnosticians," a field that is slowly but progressively gaining a reputation as viable analytical experts on inherent structural deficiencies, including fire damage.

It is the responsibility of the building department to inspect the damaged structure for evidence of potential collapse. Inspections may be accomplished on a gross basis by inspecting the major load-bearing elements to determine prime weakness. Distorted or partially collapsed bearing walls, columns that are misaligned by heat (to the point where loads are no longer supported axially), partial collapse of critical supports, and unsymmetrical loadings are important aspects of post-fire inspection. Evidence of removal of lateral supports of flexural members, either by the fire or by subsequent clean-up operations, is also of critical concern. Temporary shoring or lateral supports may be required prior to admitting any inspection parties.

Buildings damaged by fire may be classified as dangerous. The International Congress of Building Officials (ICBO) lists 18 classes, the most prominent being that, "whenever the building or structure, exclusive of the foundation, shows 33 percent or more damage or deterioration of its supporting member or members, or 50 percent damage or deterioration of its nonsupporting members, enclosing or outside wall, or coverings, it is within the jurisdiction of the building official to declare a building as dangerous and suggest repair, vacuation, or demolition. Repaired buildings shall comply with current building code or shall be demolished at the option of the building owner."[2]

It should be noted that the building official may, with the approval of ICBO, make slight revisions to the above ruling. Also, costs might well discourage rebuilding. New zoning requirements may also prohibit reconstruction.

If the building is to be renovated, the strength of the structural assemblies that were exposed to the fire must be determined. Assessment of damage will involve both evaluation of the structure as a unit, and evaluation of specific structural members and assemblies. The evaluation should be conducted by a qualified structural engineer, as the influence of distortion and residual stresses may have a significant influence on the load-carrying capacity of the

Herman H. Spaeth was staff supervisor, Codes and Standards, Insurance Services Offices, San Francisco, CA, prior to his retirement in 1984. He is now a fire protection consultant, based in San Francisco.

structure. The engineer should make every effort to obtain original plans and specifications. These may be available at the building inspection department or possibly from the architect. Cooperation with the fire department is essential to establish the path and progress of fire, including the method of extinguishment. It may be possible to establish maximum temperatures reached during the fire by examining debris for melted material and by inspecting structural members for spalling, cracking, discoloration, deflection, etc.

The influence of temperature on the mechanical properties of structural materials raises the question of the "use ability" of the material after is has cooled down to ambient temperature. The evaluation of the structural behavior of steel, concrete, masonry, and wood is described below. A more detailed evaluation procedure and a case study of renovations is given in Chapters 12 and 13 of *A Complete Guide to Fire and Buildings*.[3]

It is important to determine if the fire-resistance rating of specific structural elements or a structural assembly has been reduced to a value less than that required. While a building may remain structurally sound after a fire, i.e., retain its ability to withstand normal loadings, its fire-resistance rating may have been impaired to the extent that occupancy cannot be permitted.

Fire-resistance requirements for different types of building construction are contained in NFPA 220, *Types of Building Construction*. Construction type is indicated by a Roman numeral. The Arabic numerals following the construction type designation indicate the fire-resistance ratings (in hours) of exterior bearing walls, structural frame or columns and girders supporting loads of more than one floor, and floor construction, in that order. In a multi-story structure, for example, fire damage may have been confined to a single story with no reduction in the tensile strength of structural members but with damage to the enclosure or protection of a beam or column. If a Type I (443) structure is required in this example and the fire-resistance rating of a column supporting more than one floor is reduced to less than four hours, the structure can no longer be defined as a Type I (443). Under these conditions, occupancy of any portion of the structure would violate building code requirements.

STEEL

The use of several grades of steel in buildings and bridges is accepted in modern building codes and design standards. Although different grades of steel have a wide range of strengths, tensile and yield strengths of all steel grades are similarly affected by the temperatures that may be expected in fires in buildings.

The behavior of beams or other members subject to bending stresses under fire conditions is complex. In a building fire, the steel temperature may vary considerably over a single cross section, as well as along the length of a structural member. Information relating to the strength properties of steel at elevated temperatures has been derived from the results of tests on small specimens heated so that the entire specimen was at or close to the measured temperature. Conclusions relating to strength characteristics from such small-scale tests may not be applicable to steel structural members. Moreover, plastic action results in the redistribution of stresses in steel members that are loaded close to the design limit. This characteristic permits steel members to sustain loads greater than those calculated to be safe on the base of yield strength alone; therefore, the strength of a given steel member cannot be determined only from isolated temperature data. (See Figure 6-13A.)

FIG. 6-13A. ***Unprotected steel damage on 34th floor of office high rise. Fire load was minimal, the loss extensive.***

In a building fire, parts of the structure may have been exposed to heating followed by abrupt cooling by water from hose streams. This temperature change is usually less severe than what is accepted practice in heat treating of steel during manufacture. Tests performed on structural steel specimens taken from a building that experienced a fire during construction showed no significant loss of either yield or tensile strength. If a steel member shows no distortion due to heat, or if it can be straightened, its physical properties are generally unchanged. Connections between members should be checked, however, for cracks around rivet or bolt holes.

Occasionally, steel exposed to a fire will have a somewhat roughened appearance due to excessive scaling and grain coarsening. The coarsening is caused by exposure of steel to temperatures around 1,600°F (870°C) or higher. The steel will usually have a dark gray color, although other colors may be present if certain chemicals have been involved in the fire. Steel so modified is commonly called "burnt" steel. Members that have become burnt will usually be severely corroded as well, and their suitability for further use is a matter for individual judgment.

Many instances have been reported where straightening of structural steel members distorted due to fire has been both feasible and economical. Following the McChord Air Force Base fire in 1957 near Tacoma, WA, in which two aircraft hangars were seriously damaged, 1,486 structural steel members were either straightened or replaced in the steel frame. Of that number, only 46 members were replaced; the remaining 1,440 members were flame straightened, using welding torches.

The use of cast iron as structural material has all but ceased. Cast-iron buildings, if found, are undoubtedly archaic, historical preservations. Cast iron exposed to temperatures of 800°F (426°C) will deteriorate and fracture if struck with water from a fire hose.

Excluding fire protection features, such as extinguishing systems, low fire loads, compartmentation, etc., damage to structural steel members may be minimized by application of protective coatings that provide a period of fire resistance. Generally, a fiber or cementitious mixture is applied by spray application; however, the adherence and durability of such coatings, even under normal circumstances, has been the subject of some concern. Too often, questionable application resulted in unreliable fire resistance and, subsequently, considerable structural damage. (See Figure 6-13B.)

FIG. 6-13B. Vulnerability of steel in a fire. These large unprotected steel girders were damaged beyond repair.

Sprayed-on protective coverings can be expected to be easily dislodged during fire fighting and overhaul operations. Usually injury of this kind is easily detected, but a complete examination of the structure must be made to determine the extent of damage. Also, before occupancy is permitted, it is imperative to determine that fire damage to a specific section of a building does not impair the integrity of zones of safety, means of egress, and smoke towers, or the operation of fire doors, fire dampers, or other protective devices or systems in areas not damaged by fire.

About 20 years ago several buildings were constructed with hollow exposed steel columns and beams filled with water—apparently an economic endeavor that developed a passing interest. The concept was valid but lacked standard fire tests or actual fire experience. Fire-resistance ratings could revert to unprotected steel in the event of water leakage, improper venting, or damage during an earthquake.

Unfortunately, many architects and design engineers are of the opinion that the standard ASTM E 119 fire-resistance test provides factual data of materials and assemblies under actual fire conditions. At best, it is a destructive comparative test with little relation to actual fire.

Heavy damage to roofs, floors, beams, and trusses has been traced to misinterpreted fire test listings. For fire-resistive purposes, many floor/ceiling and roof/ceiling assemblies are considered as a single fire-resistive element. The ceiling by itself does not provide a specific fire-resistance rating. It should be noted that many floor or roof and ceiling tests provide an assembly rating, as well as a beam rating. Untrained persons have assumed the beam rating as protection afforded by the ceiling. Unfortunately, since the ceiling membrane does not provide a fire-resistance rating, structural components above the ceiling are subject to damage.

CONCRETE

In a fire lasting one to two hours, concrete will be generally only moderately damaged, and so routine cutting and patching procedures will usually be adequate before repairs. In intense and lasting fires, such as those which may occur in large, heavily stocked warehouses and department stores, severe damage to concrete may be expected. In some cases of record, restoration entailed the removal of severely damaged areas and patching in areas less severely damaged. Experienced engineering judgment is required for evaluating the residual strength of those areas that are somewhere between moderately and severely damaged. An example of one approach to the problem of evaluating the residual strength of apparently marginally damaged concrete structural units can be found in the article "Prestressed Concrete Resists Fire."[4]

A waiting period of perhaps several weeks should elapse after the fire has been extinguished before careful study of structural damage is initiated. This delay will allow any damage to the concrete, such as cracking, layering, calcination, and discoloration [a change from the natural gray color to pink or brown is indicative of heating to temperatures in excess of 450°F (232°C)], to become more discernible. The thickness of fire-damaged concrete in structural members can be determined by chipping with a pick or geologist's hammer. Unsound concrete may be colored and will be more or less soft and friable, while sound concrete will give a distinctive ring when struck with a pick or hammer. Cored concrete samples for compressive strength tests and reinforcing steel for tensile strength determinations will enable a closer evaluation of the residual strength of damaged members. Load tests may be applied, but should be conducted only under the supervision of a registered structural engineer.

Two other methods for evaluating fire damage are worthy of mention, but each requires an experienced operator. These make use of the Schmidt hammer and the soniscope. The Schmidt hammer has a spring-loaded plunger, which is caused to strike the test surface by the release of a trigger. The rebound of the plunger is a measure of concrete strength. The rebound numbers should not be considered more than a qualitative evaluation of the concrete strength, as there are several variables other than strength which may affect rebound numbers. The soniscope is an electronic device that has been used to gage the soundness of relatively heavy concrete sections, such as highway pavement slabs, bridge components, and dams. A high-frequency pulse is directed by an electronic sender through the section in question and is picked up by an electronic receiver. The speed at which the pulse travels through the section from sender to receiver, in feet or meters per second, is a gage of the integrity of material in the pulse path. Severe exposure of heavy concrete sections to fire may cause "layering," i.e., partial separation of the outer 1 to 2 in. (25 to 50 mm) of concrete of a building member from the interior mass. Such "layering" can absorb the full energy of the pulse, so interpretative experience is necessary. The device has been successfully used in conjunction with other methods in at least one case to evaluate fire damage.

A complete report dealing with a survey of fire damage to a multi-story reinforced-concrete building and the subsequent repair procedure can be found in the paper "Fire Damage to General Mills Building."[5]

A severe fire occurred in 1951 in an unsprinklered paper warehouse. This fire lasted for more than 44 hours, and it is estimated that heat intensities of more than 1,600°F (870°C) existed for 3 hours or longer. Even after severe fire, the structure was still standing and the concrete floors prevented the spread of fire and major water damage. An inspection of the structure after the fire showed that the concrete roof and columns appeared to have suffered little damage, except that the roof showed deflection up to a maximum of approximately 2½ in. (64 mm) in a 20-ft (6 m) span. When holes were cut through the roof, it was found that the concrete was calcined and had a light brown color in varying depths. This damaged concrete had almost no strength, and began to disintegrate after a period of several weeks. As a result, the portions of the roof slab that showed appreciable amounts of calcine were replaced. Many of the columns required removal of the concrete down to the reinforcing steel spiral, and, in some cases, calcining appeared inside the spiral. In these cases, the entire column was replaced. The column caps were replaced completely if more than one-half of the column showed evidence of calcining. Reinforcing rods showed some reduction in tensile strength but most were salvaged and reused, and downgraded to about three-quarters of their original strength.

In 1982 a fire-damaged rapid transit terminal in Chicago was scheduled for demolition. Due to the inflated cost of rebuilding and time lost, a cost-effective study suggested restoration. The $18.4 million building was restored at a cost of $200,000, and a minimum of time.

If a decision is made to repair the damage, the usual procedure is to shore up the structure, if necessary, and to remove the fire-damaged concrete, using a hammer, chisel, or a lightweight mechanical hammer. (Use of heavy hammers is discouraged, since they might aggravate the damage by inadvertently chipping good concrete.) The steel reinforcements are then cleaned and, if necessary, additional reinforcements are added and, finally, the concrete is built up with Gunite. Durable concrete repairs also have been made with epoxy resins.

The significant difference between conventional reinforced concrete and stressed concrete in fires is the performance of the high-tensile-steel wire or rods used for pre- or post-stressing. Under fire conditions, the stressed steel units are liable to rapid loss of strength at temperatures in excess of 752°F (400°C). A load test is recommended in post-inspection for significant pronounced sag or an indication of excessive temperature in a range where stress loss may have been sufficient to seriously affect the strength.

Tilt-up construction is a popular, simple, and effective type of concrete construction. As the name implies, slabs are precast and lifted into place. Reinforcing steel projecting from adjoining slabs are welded and encased in concrete. Several fires on the West Coast displayed some inherent weaknesses (see Figure 6-13C.) In several cases, reinforcing ties between panels were not welded and, in some cases, joints were grouted with a flexible, combustible mastic instead of concrete. Complete collapse and highly damaged panels precluded any effort of cost-effective repair. To assess blame is rather difficult—possibly the design specifications neglected to state welding, the contractor might have been negligent, or the building inspector was at fault.

FIG. 6-13C. Fire in tilt-up construction. (Source: Oakland, CA, Fire Department).

BRICK

During production, clay bricks are exposed to temperatures in excess of 2,000°F (1093°C), hence their strength is retained in actual fires. Reinforcing steel embedded in the center of a clay brick wall would normally be protected by a minimum of 3 to 4 in. (75 to 100 mm) of brick and not be affected. Spalling should be expected, especially if hot bricks are drenched with water from a fire hose. In most cases, repairs can be made with epoxy cement or Gunite.

WOOD

Wood is one of the oldest and most widely used building materials. Its behavior in fire conditions varies considerably, depending upon the species of wood and the design configuration, i.e., solid sawn lumber, glue laminates, plywood, wood chipboard, etc. The effect of fire on glue laminates may be considered the same as that on solid sawn lumber (heavy timber), assuming that the adhesives used were not affected by heat and that metal plates joining members and their attachment are not damaged. Generally the phenol-resorcinal and melamine adhesives are not affected by heat.

Plywood and chipboard are also dependent upon proper adhesives, the difference being slow burning *versus* a hazardous flash fire caused by delamination.

Redwood, found on the west coast of the U.S., withstands high fire exposures. It is reported that the high resistance is due to the lack of the usual volatile resins and oils found in other woods.

When wood structural members are subjected to fire, the ability to withstand the imposed loads is dependent to a degree upon the remaining undamaged cross-sectional area. The average rate of penetration of char when flame is impinged upon an exposed wood member is approximately 1½ in. (38 mm) per hr. Beyond the char area to a distance not more than ¼ in. (6 mm), the structural properties of wood may be affected by its exposure to high temperatures. The degree of strength loss in this small zone adjacent to the char is not exactly known, but is presumed to be insignificant.

Fire tests made on two solid sawn wood joints, 4 by 14 in. (100 by 350 mm), nominal size, at the Southwest

Research Institute showed that, after 13 min. of fire exposure, 80 percent of the original wood section remained undamaged and available to carry the load.[6] In another test of two 7 by 21 in. (170 by 540 mm) glued laminated beams, after 30 min. fire exposure, 75 percent of the original wood section remained and continued to support the design load.[7]

The previous tests, as well as actual fire experience, substantiate the fact that large-dimension wood members will remain in place under fire conditions and continue to support design loads. It is usually in the larger or heavy timber members that char can be scraped clear and an evaluation made by a qualified engineer or architect to determine the remaining load-supporting capacity of the wood member.

PLASTICS

Plastic construction is limited to small structures, student housing domes, cabins, and radomes. The use of plastics in buildings has steadily increased,[8] as well as the resultant fire load. The Munich Reinsurance Company reported extensive losses due to corrosion from gaseous decomposition of burning plastic. Twelve buildings were listed as having extensive corrosion-damaged structural steel members. In several cases, it was necessary to destroy the buildings. Steel members moderately damaged by corrosion may be sandblasted but it is suggested that a stress analysis be conducted before reparations are started. Damage to reinforcement concrete is more complex, since corrosion, in time, is apt to penetrate to the reinforcing. Preliminary analysis is necessary before power hammers are used to inspect extent of damage to reinforcing steel.

CONSTRUCTION—HIGH-RISE FIRE-RESISTIVE AND REINFORCED-CONCRETE BUILDINGS

A dangerous practice is often found during the course of construction of steel-frame buildings. It is common during the application of fire proofing to structural steel members that the coating on the lower first and second stories is postponed until final stages of construction. The application of fireproofing to these lower floors is often delayed due to the potential damage in these high-traffic areas. These are the heavy-working areas and contain storage of materials and equipment, much of which is highly combustible. (See Figure 6-13D.) A fire at this stage could result in a tragic loss.

Buildings of reinforced concrete depend upon wood shoring supports to retain the shape of the building until final curing time. As above, at this stage of construction the building is highly vulnerable to fire damage. (See Figure 6-13E.)

An extreme example of this problem was demonstrated by the St. Mary Cathedral in San Francisco, CA, built at a cost of $10 million to replace a former church destroyed by fire. The cupola walls extended some 150 ft (45 m) above the ground floor. The supporting scaffolding filled the interior with 1½ million board feet of lumber at a cost of $100,000 dollars. The chief building superintendent, aware of the fire loss potential, ruled that a temporary sprinkler system be installed.

***FIG. 6-13D.** Lower floor used for storage of materials and equipment. The combustible material and density would undoubtedly provide a fire load capable of destroying the building.*

***FIG. 6-13E.** Timber used as shoring and support of reinforced-concrete construction, essentially a forest of wood. A fire before the concrete curing process would result in a total loss.*

BIBLIOGRAPHY

References Cited

1. Larson, Erick, "A New Science Can Diagnose Sick Buildings—Before They Collapse," *Smithsonian Magazine*, May 1988.
2. ICBO, *Uniform Code for the Abatement of Dangerous Buildings,* International Conference of Building Officials, Whittier, CA, 1988.
3. Marchant, E. W., *ed., A Complete Guide to Fire and Buildings*, Barnes and Noble, New York, 1973, p. 268.
4. Zollman, L., and Garavaglin, M. "Prestressed Concrete Resists Fire," *Civil Engineering*, 1960, pp. 36-41.
5. Fruchtbaum, J, "Fire Damage to General Mills Building," *Proceedings* of American Concrete Institute, 1941, Detroit, MI.
6. "Comparative Fire Tests on Wood and Steel Joists," Technical Report No. 3, 1961, National Forest Products Association, Washington, DC.
7. "Comparative Fire Tests of Timber and Steel Beams," Technical Report No. 3, 1961, National Forest Products Association, Washington, DC.
8. Schaden Spiegel, "Losses and Loss Prevention" Apr. 1968, Munich Reinsurance Co., Munich, Germany.

NFPA Codes, Standards, and Recommended Practices

Reference to the following NFPA codes, standards, and recommended practices will provide further information on the processes and protective systems evaluating structural damage discussed in this chapter. (See the latest *NFPA Catalog* for availability of the current edition of the following document.)

NFPA 251, *Fire Tests of Building Construction and Materials.*

Additional Readings

"Assessment of Concrete Structures Damaged by Fire," *Indian Concrete Journal*, Vol. 61, No. 2, 1987, pp. 29-30.

Baldwin, R. & Cooke, G. M. E., "Computing Fire Resistance", *Fireline*, June-July, 1977.

Bresler, B., "Fires - RC, A Computer Program for Fire Response of Structures - Reinforced Concrete Framer," *UCB-FRG-3*, National Science Foundation, Washington, DC, 1974.

Bird, Eric L., "Fire in Buildings", D.Van Nostrand & Co.

"Building Construction & Structural Fire Protection", London, Her Majesty's Stationery Office.

"Building Failures", McGraw Hill Book Co.

Davis, Norman H., Jr., "Burning Characteristics of Building Materials," *Proceedings* of the 20th Annual West Virginia Fire School.

Dill, F. H., "Structural Steel After a Fire," *Proceedings* of AISC, National Engineering Conference, Brown Palace Hotel, Denver, CO, May 5 and 6, 1960.

Egan, M. David, "Concepts in Building Firesafety", Wiley & Sons.

"Failure Lessons in Concrete Construction", Collection of Articles, Concrete Construction Magazine.

Feld, Jacob, "Construction Failure", John Wiley & Sons.

"Fire Damage - Civil Liability," Fire Surveyor, Oct. 1983.

"Fire Warps Dallas Skyscraper Frame", *ENR*, April '53.

"Firemen Fear Floor Collapse," Fire Engineering, Nov. 1958.

Fire Resistance Properties of Various Building Materials, Government Printing Office, Washington, DC, 1909

Gustaferro, A. H., "Experiences form Evaluating Fire-Damaged Concrete Structures," in: *Proceedings* of the International Symposium on Fire Safety of Concrete Structures, ACI Meeting, American Concrete Institute, Detroit, MI, Sept. 1980.

Hammersmith, R. J., "U.S. Experience with Fires in Prestressed Concrete Construction", Prestressed Concrete Institute.

"How Materials Behave in Fire—A Realistic Approach," *Materials* Engineering, Nov. 1976.

Jephcott, Donald, "Repair of Fire Damaged Structures", *Structural Engineer*.

Kramps, N., "Alternative Approach to Fire Damage," *Fire International*, Vol. 11, No. 104, 1987, pp. 66-67.

Kramps, N., "Damage Control - Limiting Secondary Losses after Fire," *Fire Prevention*, No. 2-5, Dec. 1987, pp. 26-29.

Lie, T. T., "Optimum Fire Resistance of Structures," *Proceedings* of the American Society of Civil Engineers, Jan. 1972.

Lie, T. T.,"Fire and Buildings," *Applied Science*, London, England, 1972.

Lin, T. Y., *Reusability of Buildings After a Warfire, T. Y. Lin and Associates.*

Lyons, John W., "Fire", Scientific American.

"Repairs Erase Fire Damage - Chicago Terminal", *ENR*, 12//'82.

Sharry, John A., *et al.*, "Military Personnel Records Center Fire, Overland, Missouri (Part 1)." *Fire Journal*, Vol. 68, No. 3 (May 1974), pp. 509.

Smith, P., "Investigation and Repair of Damage to Concrete Caused by Formwork and Falsework Fire," *Journal of the American Concrete Institute*, Nov. 1963, pp. 1535-1565.

"Take the Surprise Out of Building Collapse," *Fire Engineering*, Jan. 1984.

Voss, W. C., *Fireproof Construction*, D. Von Nostram, New York, 1948.

Walker, Evans, *et al.*, "Military Personnel Records Center Fire, Overland, Missouri (Part 2)." *Fire Journal*, Vol. 68, No. 4, July 1974, pp. 65-70.

FIRE HAZARDS OF CONSTRUCTION, ALTERATIONS, AND BUILDING DEMOLITIONS

Revised by John A. Sharry

Buildings and other structures are more vulnerable to fire when they are under construction, alteration, or demolition, regardless of construction type or construction method, than when completed or demolition is finished. The reason for this is that when they occur, fires are likely to spread more rapidly due to the absence or impairment of fire suppression and detection systems, lack of compartmentation, the presence of heavier concentrations of combustibles than would be expected during normal use, and the fact that fires are often not discovered in their incipient stage. In new construction, fires are likely to cause more severe damage because of lack of all structural members, lack of applied fire-resistive materials, and the open exposed condition of the structure. Thus, fires can cause the destruction of building materials stored on site, lengthy delays in project completion, long-term business interruption (in the case of rehabilitation projects), and, more importantly, the possible loss of life.

Construction operations can be made reasonably safe in new construction, rehabilitation, or demolition with proper planning, proper allowances in job estimates, and proper on-site supervision and control. Although new construction, rehabilitation, and demolition projects differ greatly in the scope of work, they have many firesafety items in common. These common items relate to establishment and maintenance of on-site fire protection, provisions for temporary fire protection, and maintenance of means of escape for workers and others in the building. NFPA 241, *Safeguarding Construction, Alteration, and Demolition Operations*, contains measures that, with prefire planning, will help prevent fire or at least minimize damage when fire occurs.

Guard service on construction operations is recommended during nonworking hours. Patrols should be planned so that no portion of the job site is overlooked. The use of guard clock and time recording systems is recommended to ensure patrols have been made. Guards should be briefed on the fire protection measures available on the job site, on developments during the workday that affect fire hazards and fire protection capabilities, and on emergency procedures. Provision (either a telephone or a fire alarm box) should be made for notifying the fire department in the event of a fire.

NEW CONSTRUCTION

Site Preparation

Site preparation is the first item necessary in any new construction project. This involves the removal of brush, trees, and debris from the site prior to the start of construction. Although such land clearing provides for control of natural cover fuel fires, it mainly provides site accessibility for construction. Today's methods of site preparation differ from the "scorched earth" methods of several years ago in that the preservation of as much natural vegetation as practical is desired. This should present no serious fire problem as long as temporary buildings and materials storage are properly isolated from any natural cover fuel by fire breaks.

Of prime importance in site preparation is the establishment of roadways and the installation of water mains for fire protection. Many jurisdictions now require that permanent all-weather roads and site utilities be provided before construction begins in housing and industrial developments. However, these provisions are not always required for the single building or building complex. In any event, construction site access by temporary or permanent all-weather roadways should be provided, as well as water service for fire protection.

While it is usually more economical to provide permanent water service to serve the construction fire protection needs early in the project, it is sometimes necessary to provide temporary water service in the form of aboveground water mains.

Advance planning can minimize the impact of these requirements by proper construction sequencing and proper site preparation.

John A. Sharry is fire chief of Lawrence Livermore National Laboratory, Livermore, CA.

Temporary Buildings

Temporary buildings are commonly used on construction sites. They provide for the storage of tools and equipment, and serve as temporary offices for the construction management team. The use of mobile structures, such as converted mobile homes, trailers, or manufactured buildings, has largely replaced the construction of temporary buildings.

The hazards are much the same whether a mobile structure or a temporary structure is used. Overloaded temporary wiring, incorrectly installed portable or temporary heating equipment, and inadequate control of open-flame devices are examples of the common hazards. It is also important to recognize the high level of fuel load in the form of construction materials and construction plans, specifications, and other documents. In addition, the use of space (sometimes concealed) beneath these temporary structures for miscellaneous storage can be hazardous depending upon the nature of the materials stored. Such spaces and storage can be subject to vandalism and incendiarism. Vegetation growing on, or left in, these spaces can also create hazards.

The protection of these structures, especially mobile structures, is usually possible by the installation of a residential-type sprinkler system that can be connected to the site water supply. The cost of this protection is low for the mobile structures, since there is only a one-time installation cost and connection costs on the site are minimal.

The exposure protection necessary is often overlooked if several temporary or mobile structures are on the same site. Proper spacing between structures and from the project itself by a minimum of 30 ft (9 m) can significantly reduce this hazard. Often mobile structures can be attached or installed adjacent to each other, creating a larger building with greater hazards than one structure alone.

Loss Prevention During Construction

Normal building operations require considerable amounts of combustible building materials, forms, scaffolding, etc. Water service at the site should be adequate not only for construction needs but also for fire protection needs in view of the amount of combustibles present. In multi-story structures requiring either temporary or permanent standpipes, the standpipe system (or temporary standpipe service) should be put into service as each floor is constructed to provide fire fighting capability. Temporary standpipe service is usually a dry standpipe with proper valves at each floor and a fire department siamese connection easily accessible to fire department pumpers.

Temporary enclosure of buildings is common and should only be done with care. Only flame-resistive tarpaulins or materials of similar fire-retardant characteristics should be used. If temporary enclosure is required, metal or fire-retardant-treated wood forms should be used and the enclosure materials securely fastened or guarded to prevent contact with heaters or other sources of ignition. Fabric or plastic used should be certified to meet the requirements of NFPA 701, *Fire Tests for Flame-Resistant Textiles and Films*. (See Figure 6-14A.)

Concrete should be poured as quickly as possible after combustible forms have been constructed, and the forms removed as soon as possible after the concrete has set properly. During the time the forms are in place, storage and construction operations on that floor should be held to a minimum and ignition sources should be eliminated. Non-combustible forms should be used whenever possible. (See Figure 6-14B.)

FIG. 6-14A. Large sheets of plastic are sometimes used to enclose buildings under construction to confine heat. (Source: Francis L. Brannigan)

FIG. 6-14B. Combustible formwork is a constant source of danger to concrete buildings under construction. Here fire consumes wood formwork for cast-in-place floor and wall panels in a parking garage.

Where "fireproofing" is specified, it should be applied as soon as possible to afford fire protection to beams, columns, and other structural elements early in the construction phase.

Rubbish and trash accumulations can present a serious fire hazard on the construction site. Daily cleanup of scrap lumber, cardboard containers, and other debris removes the hazard and provides a more orderly working environment. Trash containers should be provided on site for proper storage of debris and should be located at a safe distance from the building or protected to prevent undue exposure of the building.

Cutting and welding operations must be controlled carefully, and proper safeguards utilized. Careless use of welding and cutting torches and plumbing torches has caused numerous fires. NFPA 241, *Safeguarding Construction, Alteration, and Demolition Operations*, recommends the use of a permit system for welding operations and specifies controls for safe welding operations. Also important is the guidance given in NFPA 51B, *Cutting and Welding Processes*.

Because they were improperly controlled, salamanders used to provide temporary heat have been responsible for many fires. However, since salamanders are often needed, their use should be continuously supervised and the area cleared of combustible materials.

Flammable liquids present obvious fire protection problems. Small quantities can be safely handled in approved safety containers and should be stored in an isolated location. Bulk quantities of flammable or combustible liquids should be avoided, but if bulk quantities are needed, they should be stored in an approved manner. NFPA 395, *Flammable and Combustible Liquids on Farms and Isolated Construction Projects*, provides guidance on flammable liquids storage on construction sites.

Internal combustion engines for pumps, air compressors, etc., should be placed to avoid exhaust discharge near, or in contact with, combustibles. A minimum of a 6-in. (152 mm) clearance to combustibles should be maintained if the exhausts are piped to the exterior. The engine should be shut down during refueling to prevent flash fires. For safety reasons, electric- or pneumatic-driven equipment, not internal-combustion-engine-driven equipment, should be used in underground or basement locations.

The use of tar kettles should be continuously supervised and only permitted outdoors away from combustibles or on a noncombustible floor or roof in the building. Metal covers should be provided to smother potential fires. Should a fire occur, it is important to remember that water thrown into the tar kettle will cause the tar to froth and may overflow the container. Roofing mops should never be left indoors or near ignition sources or combustible materials. Roofing mops soaked with tar have been known to be susceptible to spontaneous ignition; however, modern roofing materials are less susceptible to this problem. In any case, care should be taken in how mops are stored or discarded.

Permanent Safeguards

In most construction operations, the progress of the work toward completion gradually enhances the safety of the structure. As the need for combustible formwork and scaffolding, materials storage, temporary buildings and trailers, and other inherent hazards diminishes, they should be removed from the site.

Fire fighter access to the structure is important. Installation of permanent stairways and stairway enclosures should be completed as quickly as possible. Fire barriers and other essential features that provide for the confinement of fire should be installed as early as possible. Penetrations of fire-resistive construction made for building services should be sealed immediately after the services are installed. Integrity of all fire cutoffs should be maintained.

Permanent standpipe and hose systems should be installed as construction work progresses. In buildings lacking automatic sprinkler systems, or those in which the installation of tanks and other equipment must wait for the completion of structural elements, standpipe and hose systems may provide the only certain source of water for fire fighting throughout the project. Where automatic sprinkler systems are to be a part of the permanent protection for the building, proper correlation of the work will provide water supplies for the system and prompt installation of sprinklers before significant combustibles are present in the building. Blank gaskets used in flanges to permit sprinkler protection by sections as construction work is completed should be provided with lugs that are painted red or are otherwise clearly marked to ensure removal when the system is extended.

Permanent wiring systems should replace temporary wiring as rapidly as the removal of formwork will permit. Permanent heating plants and temporary nonfired heat exchangers can often be used to supplant the more hazardous salamanders.

Supervision of Fire Protection

All construction, renovation, and demolition projects should have a qualified person in charge of fire protection. This person should be responsible for the maintenance and location of fire protection and suppression equipment, general supervision of safeguards, location of portable heating devices and tar kettles, and the establishment and maintenance of a safe cutting and welding program. On larger projects, this person should also devise a written emergency plan for the project. It may be possible to establish an emergency assistance team from among the craftsmen on the project to take initial actions in emergencies. However, care should be taken to ensure that members of emergency action teams are properly trained for the actions they are expected to perform.

On all projects, but particularly on large construction, renovation, or demolition projects, there are numerous contractors and subcontractors all contributing to the completion of the project. It is important from a project standpoint, as well as a fire protection standpoint, that someone supervise and coordinate the work done by these various contractors. This person is the key in implementing proper attitudes toward safety and fire protection in the normal course of work. Work guidelines and expectations can be clearly spelled out and enforced in this manner.

DEMOLITION OPERATIONS

If not properly controlled, demolition operations can create more serious problems than construction operations. Demolition operations should include precautions to ensure maintenance of fixed fire protection systems for as long as possible. Automatic sprinkler systems should be modified to allow their removal on a floor by floor or area by area basis. The conversion of a wet system to a dry system fed only by a fire department connection is sometimes possible and provides good protection for the building as well as for fire fighting personnel.

Standpipe systems should also be removed floor by floor and should be the last fire protection feature removed. This maintains fire fighting capability to otherwise demolished floors. A wet standpipe can be easily converted to a dry standpipe.

It is common practice to provide chutes for the removal of trash and debris from the upper floors. If chutes are used, they should be erected outside the building. Cutting holes through floors to provide an inside chute should be avoided, since this creates a vertical opening through which fire can spread rapidly from floor to floor.

Figure 6-14C shows the results of a demolition operation that violated these principles. The results were disastrous; not only was the building being demolished destroyed by fire, but the fire spread to four other buildings.[1]

FIG. 6-14C. Fire originating on the top floor quickly spread throughout this partially demolished building and involved four other buildings. The sprinkler system had been shut down about a week before the fire instead of being shut down in stages as demolition progressed. Contrary to good practice, holes had been made in the floors to facilitate the removal of debris.

REHABILITATION PROJECTS

There has been an increase in the rehabilitation of older buildings in recent years. This effort is partly the result of a desire to preserve our national heritage and partly a result of rising construction costs. From a fire protection standpoint, rehabilitation projects can produce firesafe buildings if the extensive compartmentation usually present in older buildings is at least partially preserved.

From a building code standpoint, existing buildings being rehabilitated usually must meet current code requirements for means of egress, fire protection, and light and ventilation.

The use of equivalency concepts to provide the level of safety intended by a particular code is usually possible when it is practically impossible or undesirable to meet the letter of the code. In buildings with historic significance, it is sometimes undesirable to provide all of the code-required safeguards, as these changes may destroy the historic features. In such cases, the safety of the occupants takes precedence, and the proper safeguards must be installed to ensure life safety. While improvement of exits to total code compliance may not be possible, providing other compensating features in the building to control fire and smoke may result in equivalent safety. These compensating features may involve the installation of automatic sprinkler protection, smoke detection systems, and smoke control systems. Whatever equivalency is used should be evaluated carefully to ensure that a comparable level of life safety to that required by the applicable code is being provided.

The U.S. Department of Housing and Urban Development (HUD) has produced guidelines for the rehabilitation of buildings. An interesting feature of these guidelines is a volume that provides fire resistance information on older methods of building construction.[2] This information is extremely valuable when attempting to evaluate the fire resistance ratings for existing building structural systems and fire barriers.

In some rehabilitation projects, the renovations must be made while the building is partially occupied. Special precautions must be taken in these cases. The most important of these is the maintenance of proper exits from the building. Not only must exits be provided for building occupants, but at least one exit must also be provided for building trades workers in the construction areas. The accumulation of trash and other debris must be kept to a minimum, and refuse removed daily.

If fire suppression, detection, or alarm systems are being renovated, their downtime must be kept to a minimum. Proper planning can eliminate unnecessary downtime. Isolation of parts of systems is usually possible to ensure operation in unaffected areas of the building. If it becomes necessary to shut down entire systems, a fire watch should be posted near the main control to restore service in case of fire. Some form of reliable communication should be worked out if the main control is remote from the work area. This precaution is especially important in sprinklered buildings. Removing the entire sprinkler system as part of a rehabilitation project can have disastrous results. (See Figure 6-14D.)

FIG. 6-14D. Remains of the historic Harrison Building in Philadelphia, PA, which was destroyed by fire on May 3, 1984, while the building was undergoing renovation. Although originally equipped with automatic sprinklers and standpipes, the extinguishing systems had been removed from the building as part of the remodeling work. Many openings created by the removal of stairways and elevator shafts from the six floors of the building contributed to the rapid spread of fire.

Means of egress should be readily available to building occupants during normal working hours. Therefore, alterations to means of egress should be accomplished during off hours. In some cases, rerouting of traffic may be a practical alternative. In all cases, exit systems and fire protection systems should be restored at the end of each work day.

In cases where additions to buildings block existing exits, provision must be made for alternate means of egress or for a protected path of travel. The use of combustible materials in temporary exit construction should be avoided.

In any project, whether new construction, rehabilitation, or demolition, the fire department should be kept aware of construction progress. The fire department can thereby provide for command posts and prefire plans and be ready to deal with unusual problems encountered during the course of the project.

BIBLIOGRAPHY

References Cited

1. Sharry, John A., "Group Fire, Indianapolis, Indiana," *Fire Journal*, Vol. 68, No. 4, 1974, pp. 13-16.
2. HUD, "Guideline on Fire Ratings of Archaic Materials and Assemblies," Vol. 8, Rehabilitation Guidelines 1980, U.S. Department of Housing and Urban Development, Washington, DC.

NFPA Codes, Standards, and Recommended Practices

Reference to the following NFPA codes, standards, and recommended practices will provide further information on the fire hazards of construction, alteration, and building demolitions discussed in this chapter. (See the latest *NFPA Catalog* for availability of current editions of the following documents.)

NFPA 13D, *Installation of Sprinkler Systems in One- and Two-Family Dwellings and Mobile Homes*.

NFPA 30, *Flammable and Combustible Liquids Code*.

NFPA 51, *Oxygen-Fuel Gas Systems for Welding, Cutting, and Allied Processes*.

NFPA 51B, *Cutting and Welding Processes*.

NFPA 241, *Safeguarding Construction, Alteration, and Demolition Operations*.

NFPA 395, *Flammable and Combustible Liquids on Farms and Isolated Construction Projects*.

NFPA 495, *Code for the Manufacture, Transportation, Storage, and Use of Explosive Materials*.

NFPA 701, *Fire Tests for Flame-Resistant Textiles and Films*.

Additional Readings

Brannigan, F. L., *Building Construction for the Fire Service*, National Fire Protection Association, Quincy, MA, 1982.

Carney, J. P., "Fire Protection During Construction—A Critical Time," SFPE TR 84-7, Society of Fire Protection Engineers, Boston, MA, 1984.

"Collapse of the Hotel Vendome, Boston, Mass.," *Fire Journal*, Vol. 67, No. 1, Jan. 1973, pp. 33-41.

Herbstman, D., "Fire Protection During Construction," *Fire Journal*, Vol. 64, No. 1, Jan. 1970, pp. 29-32, 89.

Hubitsky, J., "Preventing Fires on Job Sites," *Fire Command*, Vol. 45, No. 7, July 1978.

Johnson, G. L., "Trouble Times Three," *Fire Command*, Dec. 1984, pp. 16-19.

"Materials in Refurbishment—Designing for Fire," *Fire Prevention*, No. 210, June 1988, pp. 21-26.

NFPA, Fire Data Package 19, "Vacant, Abandoned, Under Demolition Buildings," NFPA Fire Analysis—Research Division, National Fire Protection Association, Quincy, MA, 1990.

Ow, C. S. and Thin, C. C., "Upgrading Fire Protection in Existing Buildings," *Fire International*, Vol. 12, No. 112, Aug.-Sept. 1988, pp. 39-40.

Rule, C. H., "Fire Destroys Philadelphia Building under Construction," *Fire Journal*, Vol. 79, No. 3, May 1985, pp. 42-46, 105-111.

Steenbeigen, H. E., "In a Fire, Seconds Count," *Fire Command*, Vol. 56, No. 7, July 1989, pp. 15-17.

HAZARDS OF BUILDING SERVICES

Robert W. Ryan and Mark Chubb

Building services are those systems that connect a building to utilities and public services to provide a livable and functional environment for people and machines. These systems can be classified into four major groups: (1) environmental services, (2) piped services, (3) electrical/electronic services, and (4) transportation and conveyance. These services are commonly referred to as heating, ventilating and air conditioning (HVAC) and temperature control; domestic water and plumbing, sanitary sewer, natural gas service, and air and medical gas services; electric power, light, and communications; and elevators, escalators, conveyors, people movers, mail, laundry, and refuse chutes. To understand how building services may affect fire behavior, and the fire hazards that could result from these systems and their components, a basic knowledge of the individual systems, and their relationship to each other, the structure, and the type of occupancy is needed. In short, not only must one understand how these systems affect the building, but how people will affect the building and these systems.

This chapter presents an overview of building services in the context of fire hazard. Fire hazards in this area include situations where systems, or their components, represent potential heat energy or ignition sources, potential fuels, or potential heat or fuel transport systems. The discussion of hazard is, therefore, organized around a discussion of the role of people in designing, operating, maintaining, and modifying these systems to minimize fire hazards. More detailed information about specific systems can be found in the following chapters: Section 6, Chapter 1, "Building and Site Planning for Firesafety"; Section 6, Chapter 6, "Confinement of Fire in Buildings"; Section 6, Chapter 7, "Smoke Movement in Buildings"; Section 6, Chapter 16, "Air Conditioning and Ventilating Systems"; Section 6, Chapter 17, "Miscellaneous Building Services"; and Section 6, Chapter 19, "Air-Moving Equipment." Related information can be found in: Section 2, Chapter 3, "Electrical Systems and Appliances"; Section 2, Chapter 4, "Heating Systems and Appliances"; Section 2, Chapter 5, "Boiler Furnaces"; Section 2, Chapter 8, "Heat Transfer Systems (Nonwater Media)"; Section 2, Chapter 18, "Refrigeration Systems"; Section 2, Chapter 26, "Storage of Gases"; Section 2, Chapter 31, "Control of Electrostatic Ignition Sources"; Section 2, Chapter 32, "Lightning Protection Systems"; and Section 2, Chapter 33, "Waste Handling Systems and Equipment." The following chapters also relate to this topic: Section 3, Chapter 6, "Medical Gases"; and Section 3, Chapter 14, "Energy Conservation in Buildings." Section 7, Chapter 4, "Building Transportation Systems," addresses issues related to elevators, escalators, lifts, and similar systems. Finally, Section 8, Chapter 31, "Materials Handling Equipment," addresses other conveyance systems. Additional references on these systems, their design, and operation are listed under additional readings at the end of this chapter.

Robert W. Ryan is acting director of, and Mark Chubb is a fire protection specialist in, the Department of Environmental Safety, University of Maryland.

DESIGN

Designing and installing building services to act in harmony with a building's structural system, use, and occupancy is quite a challenge. Architects, engineers, and builders must interpret, and integrate such diverse elements as owners' and end-users' needs, environmental conditions, financial limitations, and the limits of technology when designing buildings and their systems. The elements selected for inclusion in a building's design must ultimately act in harmony with one another to provide a safe, functional, and livable environment.

The state of the art in building services appears to be driving new design approaches. In the past, building services were often seen as "add-ons"— designed to fit physical and structural aspects of the design as they responded to the end-user's needs. Increasingly, technological advances in building services are driving design decisions, thereby creating what can be described as the "intelligent buildings revolution."[1] This trend focuses on the use of advanced technologies to create environments that enhance productivity. These buildings place the emphasis on the comfort of building occupants, environmental quality (particularly indoor air quality), and flexibility in occupancy services, e.g., communications, computing, and clerical support. Perhaps even more important to designers and owners than the quality of the end-result, is the potential energy cost savings, and return on investment gained through increased productivity of employees. This revolution may not necessarily be limited to commercial buildings. The so-called "smart house" describes the residence of tomorrow as a facility that combines modular construction techniques with state-of-the-art telecommunications and microprocessor technology, to produce a safer, more secure, and energy-efficient home.

Another movement influencing building design and building services stresses the benefits of "universal" design. Accessibility advocates suggest that by incorporating building features that benefit the disabled into every design, aesthetic and cost considerations need not be compromised to make a building equally accessible to everyone. By removing the "institutional" feel and "special" label from barrier-free features, the cost of such features can be reduced.[2] The cost of many barrier-free features does not exceed existing, accepted solutions to common design problems. At the same time, incorporating these features into buildings tells occupants, "this building is for everyone."

Authorities having jurisdiction should participate in the decision-making process. Soliciting their input—early and often—in the design and construction process may prove invaluable. It is noted that fire and life safety codes are not specifications, but rather prescribe the minimum acceptable practices for ensuring safety. Economy, efficiency, aesthetics, reliability, and maintainability issues not addressed directly by these regulations are important factors in the selection, operations and maintenance of building services.

While considering each building service and system, and their potential hazards, separately, it is important to note how each system functions as a component of the larger building system. In fact, the sum of a building's individual systems is larger than the whole. Likewise, hazards associated with individual systems may take on a larger dimension when considered in the context of the building as a metasystem. While these individual building systems may represent a heat or energy source, a fuel source, or a fuel or energy transport mechanism, usually the system under consideration fits more than one of these descriptions, as clarified in the following discussion.

Environmental Systems

Environmental systems regulate temperature and air movement in buildings to maintain safe, acclimate, and liveable environments. Typically, this involves moving large quantities of air. Often, this air is also cleaned to remove particulates or other contaminants, exhausted, diluted or exchanged with outside air, heated, cooled, or any combination of these. Air movement incorporates ducts, shafts, plenums, or chases that permit air to move vertically or horizontally, thereby separating "new" air (supply) from "old" air (return).

Several NFPA standards describe construction and installation standards for systems and their components, to minimize the contribution of environmental services to building fire problems. These standards incorporate techniques intended to control fuels by regulating the materials used to build these systems, control heat sources by prohibiting installations in hazardous locations, and limit heat (energy) source, and fuel interactions, by separating and enclosing system elements, and minimizing the transport of products of combustion through the system, among other methods. In some extreme cases, or in lieu of other methods, automatic fire suppression systems are required to control the development, and/or spread, of fires involving these systems.

Heat (energy) sources: Environmental services that heat air always involve a heat or energy source. The type and location of the energy source selected is a function of the local climate, fuel availability, fuel cost, building environment, and its use and occupancy. Under normal, well-planned conditions, this energy source interacts primarily with environmental air only to raise its temperature to a modest, comfortable level. Heated, convected air, then, would only represent a potential ignition source under the most extreme circumstances. Exceptionally few substances ignite under these conditions, and this reaction is usually pyrophoric—related more to the oxygen content of the air than its temperature. However, many substances, unlike air, respond vigorously when they come into direct (radiation or conduction) contact with the energy source itself. Metal flue pipes and ductwork near or in direct contact with combustible structural elements, electric baseboards or gas-fired unit heaters in the vicinity of flammable vapor-air mixtures, or steam radiators in contact with an unprotected human hand, may generate unfortunate results.

The location of the energy source and the type and location of potential fuels, then, must be carefully considered. Fuels present in the immediate environment should always be a prime consideration. Whenever flammable vapor-air mixtures, combustible dusts, or fibers are present, then energy sources capable of igniting them should not be. Designers should specify only indirect heating systems, or direct heating systems designed and approved for hazardous locations, when flammable or explosive gases, vapors, dusts, or fibers are present in the atmosphere. Likewise, combustible building elements should be protected or separated from system components, such as metal ductwork and flue pipes. Many tragic fires have resulted from failure to maintain clearances between building elements and such components.

Fuel sources: Ductwork, duct connectors, duct coverings, linings, vapor barrier facings, tapes, insulating panel core materials, plenums in buildings of other than noncombustible or fire-resistive construction, and cooling towers are among the components of environmental systems that may be combustible themselves. In addition, these systems accumulate combustible materials commonly suspended in air. To minimize the hazards associated with combustible system components, these materials are generally restricted to use where air temperatures do not exceed 250°F (121°C), or extend more than two stories vertically. Combustible materials used to cover or connect ductwork must have a flame-spread rating of less than 25 (when tested in accordance with NFPA 255/ASTM E84), with a smoke-developed rating of less than 50. Likewise, combustible materials may not extend through fire-resistance-rated assemblies, or interfere with the operation of fire dampers or fire doors. Filters are commonly installed in systems to trap combustible matter suspended in air. While filters may, or may not, be combustible, their contents usually are. For this reason, filters must be replaced or removed and cleaned regularly. The use of plenums for purposes unrelated to air movement, such as concealment of piping, wiring, and other building services, must not interfere with their use as a plenum, or increase the fire hazard. Therefore, combustible materials must possess low flame-spread and smoke-developed ratings, and most spaces containing materials of this nature must be draftstopped or protected by automatic sprinklers.

Heat (energy) source-fuel transport: Perhaps the greatest danger associated with building systems is that they are usually hidden from view. Located behind walls, above ceilings, and under floors, building services travel throughout the building to provide and maintain a livable environment. Usually, this involves large concealed spaces, e.g., plenums and shafts to permit the movement of air horizontally and vertically. Recognizing the hazards of moving air, people, and fire in common spaces, some codes and standards, including NFPA 90A, *Installation of Air Conditioning and Ventilating Systems*, have restricted or prohibited the use of means of egress components as return air-plenums.[3] This has forced designers to use other spaces for this purpose. The resulting improvement in life safety may translate into more complex fire problems. Fires in concealed spaces can easily grow and travel undetected for long periods of time. To control these potential avenues of fire and smoke spread, vertical shafts must be segregated from the remainder of the building by fire-resistance-rated construction. Likewise, unsprinklered plenums and horizontal concealed spaces should be draft-stopped into manageable fire areas. Even when concealed spaces are not used for air movement, the ductwork and air-handling equipment is often concealed. These system components can collect and distribute smoke. Installation of fire dampers, smoke leakage-rated dampers, or fire doors where ductwork penetrates fire-resistance-rated assemblies can control this potential avenue of fire spread. Even when an air-handling system serves only a single fire area, use of automatic mechanical system controls may be warranted. Smoke detectors in supply, return, or supply and return air plenums are required by NFPA 90A. However, shutting down fans alone will not control the movement of smoke within a building or fire area. Phenomena, such as stack effect, buoyancy, and wind, affect the spread of smoke through supply and return air ducts, air shafts, plenums, and other building openings.[4]

Piped Services

Piped services collect or distribute fluids, usually liquids or compressed gases, but can also include solid/liquid combinations. Common piped distribution systems include water, fuel gases, fuel oil, compressed air, medical gases, and vacuum and sanitary sewer lines. Hazards associated with these services involve the following: (1) the ability of the piping or conduit to conduct heat or electric current, including static electricity; (2) combustibility of the fluid, the conduit, or both; (3) the ability of the fluid to support combustion; or (4) the ability of the system, or the space in which it is installed, to provide an avenue for fire and smoke spread.

Heat (energy) sources: Piped services transporting steam, hot water, or heated gases can generate sufficient energy to dry nearby combustible structural members or building materials, thereby making them susceptible to ignition. Metallic piping systems are usually good conductors of heat and electricity. For this reason, many piped services associated with indirect heating systems are insulated to prevent heat loss. This may make them good conductive ignition sources when exposed to external fires. Perhaps more dangerous, however, is the likelihood of ignition of flammable contents when metallic piping is not properly grounded during flammable liquid transfer operations. Whenever sections of pipe carrying a flammable product are mechanically and electrically isolated, each individual section must be independently grounded, or bonded, to another grounded section.

Fuel sources—contents: Piped services containing flammable liquids and flammable compressed gases are a widely recognized and well-regulated hazard. NFPA 54, *National Fuel Gas Code*, and NFPA 58, *Storage and Handling of Liquified Petroleum Gases*, regulate storage and distribution of the common fuel gases. Both standards are widely recognized and adopted. NFPA 30, *Flammable and Combustible Liquids Code*, and NFPA 31, *Oil Burning Equipment*, specify requirements related to piped distribution of flammable and combustible liquids for nearly all applications. NFPA 99, *Health Care Facilities*, however, prohibits the piped distribution of flammable anesthetics and other flammable medical gases. The design and planning of piped systems containing flammable compressed gases must consider the demands and location of the equipment supplied. In most cases, cooking, heating, medical, or laboratory equipment is involved. Keeping runs of flammable liquid and compressed gas piping short and direct satisfies the objectives of simplicity and economy, and can contribute to safety, as well. Clearly identifying pipe contents and valves minimizes the likelihood of inadvertent release. Valves critical to isolating or interrupting the flow of gas in the event of inadvertent release should be accessible.

Fuel source—conduit: The widespread use of plastics for distribution and collection piping has focused interest on fire and toxicity hazards of piped services. Interest has been particularly keen in residential occupancies where both the fire death toll is the highest, and use of plastic plumbing and drain, waste, and vent (DWV) piping has been accepted the longest. These products include materials fashioned from acrylonitrile-butadiene-styrene (ABS), polyvinyl chloride (PVC), chlorinated polyvinyl chloride (CPVC), and polybutylene (PB), and are widely used throughout the building industry for domestic water, automatic sprinkler, and DWV among other uses. These services can be subject to failure when exposed to fire, and can become involved themselves. When these services are installed in concealed spaces, particularly plenums, automatic sprinkler protection may not only be advisable, but mandatory if these materials are installed in substantive quantities.

Heat (energy) source—fuel transport: Although fires spreading through piped service conduits themselves may be an infrequent occurrence, structural collapse of these services may permit fire to compromise fire barriers. Like environmental services, piped services travel in concealed spaces, thereby making fire detection and control difficult. Unlike environmental systems, though, some piped service through-penetrations cannot be protected by simple opening protectives such as fire doors and dampers. Concern over the contribution of pipe and wire penetrations in fire-resistance-rated assemblies to the failure of these assemblies to control horizontal and vertical fire spread has led to new requirements for through-penetration firestopping systems.

Twelve of these systems were evaluated, including methods using generic materials and simple mechanical designs, as well as chemical and combination firestop systems, for application in plastic pipe through-penetration situations.[5] (See Figures 6-15A through 6-15E.) Of the systems evaluated, only five demonstrated satisfactory results when tested in accordance with CAN4-S101-M82, *Standard Methods of Fire Endurance Tests of Building Construction and Materials*. Many new systems have entered the market in recent years. Most of these systems are chemical firestops, employing a variety of new materials and technologies to seal the voids around such openings. Intumescent tapes, foams, putties, and caulks, introduced in the 1980s, used independently or in combination with inorganic insulation materials and retaining collars or pipe sleeves, have become popular solutions due to their flexibility and ease of installation. Regardless of the technique employed, through-penetration firestop systems are finding their way into new and amended code requirements referencing ASTM E814, *Test Method for Fire Tests of Through Penetration Firestops*. (See also UL 1479.) These improved methods of protecting openings around pipes are expected to reduce the problem of fire spread and smoke movement between fire areas and in concealed pipe chases and shafts. In addressing the subject of PVC piping and firesafety in detail, it is noted that extensive testing using ASTM E119 (NFPA 251) and ASTM E814 (UL 1479) test methods, suggests, that these piping systems and materials present little threat to the integrity of fire-resistance-rated assemblies when proper construction techniques and through-penetration firestop systems are used.[6]

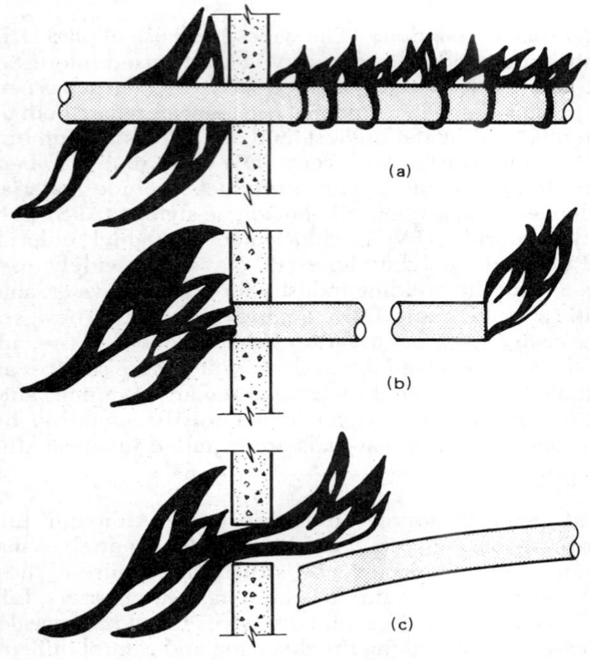

FIG. 6-15A. Fire hazards associated with plastic pipe.

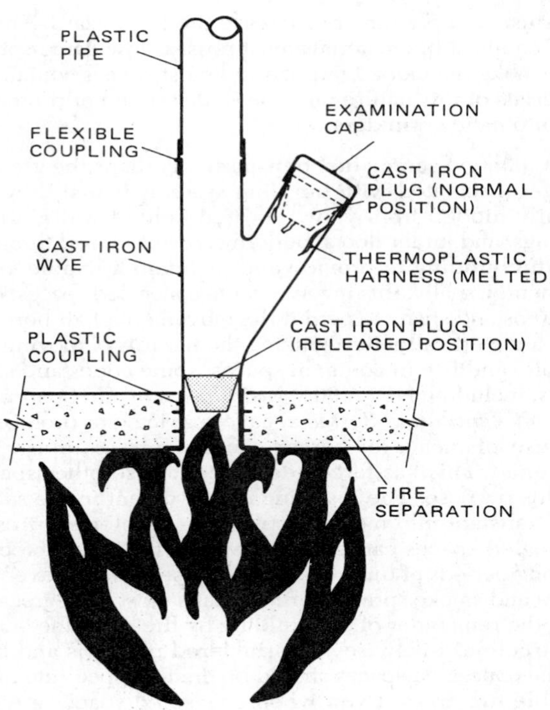

FIG. 6-15B. Gravity-activated mechanical firestop.

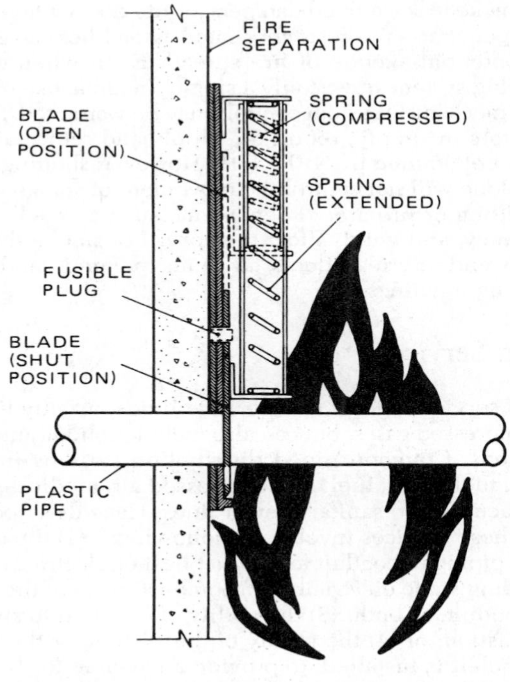

FIG. 6-15C. Spring-activated mechanical firestop.

Electrical Systems

Electrical systems supply electric voltage to power lights, motors, appliances, and other conveniences, or convey signals to controls, or communicate with other people or machines. Electrical conductors and equipment may also be installed to collect and safely dissipate static electricity, radio frequency interference, and other sources of noise. The most widely adopted of all NFPA documents, NFPA 70, *National Electrical Code*, regulates the hazards of electrical devices, equipment, and wiring. NFPA 77, *Static Electricity*, discusses the hazards associated with this

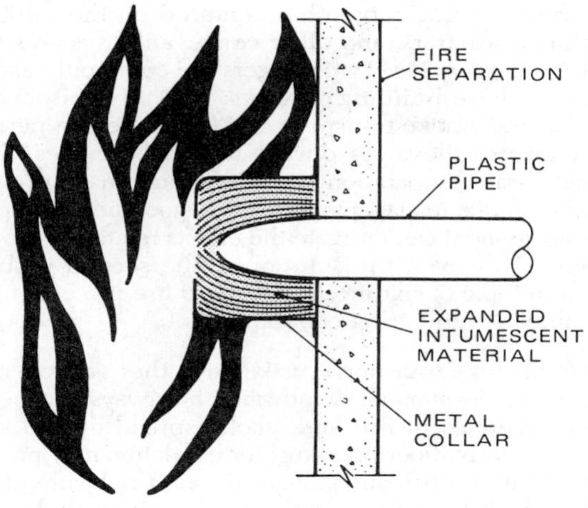

FIG. 6-15D. Intumescent-type chemical firestop.

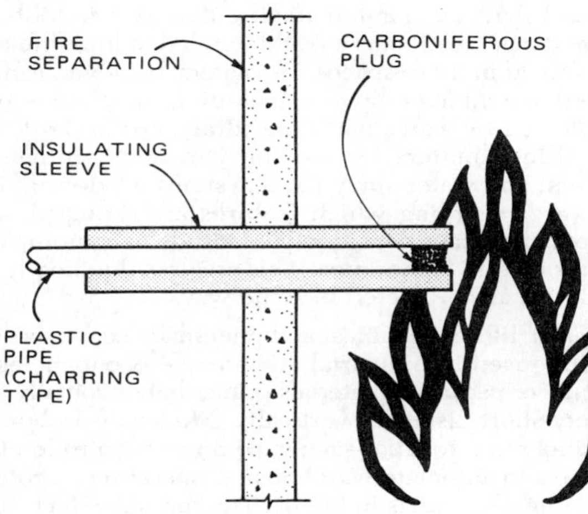

FIG. 6-15E. Protective sleeve for PVC pipe.

energy source, and NFPA 78, *Lightning Protection Code*, addresses the management of this special case of static electricity. The principal fire hazard associated with electrical systems is their potential as an ignition source. Although beyond the scope of this discussion, it is important to note that despite the regulatory environment, resistance heating and electrical arcs incidental to the operation of electrical devices, equipment, and appliances, improper control of static charges, and faulty installation or maintenance are significant causes of accidental fires.

Heat (energy) sources: Proper design of electrical installations must consider the atmosphere involved, the loads connected, the anticipated needs of building service equipment and building occupants, and provision of adequate clearances for maintenance and safety. Many electrical and electronic system components produce concentrated or localized heat loads. The following are listed under this heading: (1) switching devices, including fuses and circuit breakers; (2) distribution equipment, such as transformers, panelboards, switchboards, and motor controls; and (3) utilization equipment and devices, such as lighting, resistance and induction heaters, and motors.[7] Care must be taken to maintain clearances from combustibles. Widespread use of aluminum wiring has raised concerns about the hazards associated with this material and common installation and maintenance practices. Greater care must be exercised with aluminum wiring to ensure proper connections. Damage or poor contact can develop due to formation of corrosion—particularly where copper and aluminum conductors or contacts meet—or "creep" due to cold-flow of the conductors under heavy loads. Arcs from unclassified electrical equipment and static sparks consistently rank among the most common ignition sources when flammable liquids and gases are involved. NFPA 70, *National Electrical Code*, specifies requirements for electrical installations in hazardous locations.

Fuel sources: Like piped services, the use of plastics has been a boon to the electrical service industry. Plastic insulation materials, conduits, and raceways are coming into widespread use. Concern about the contribution of these materials to fire growth and smoke toxicity has been widely debated. As a result, new and amended code requirements regulate the use of wire, cable, and conduit materials with high-flame spread, or smoke-developed ratings. NFPA 262, *Fire and Smoke Characteristics of Wire and Cables* [originally developed and published as UL 910—an adaptation of the NFPA 255, *Surface Burning Characteristics of Building Materials* (ASTM E84) Steiner Tunnel Test] is the most widely recognized test method used to evaluate the fire hazard and smoke production of these materials. However, as yet, no standard screening test has been adopted to evaluate the toxicity of combustion byproducts of these insulation materials. Despite this, the state of New York adopted legislation requiring manufacturers who wish to sell electrical conduit and electrical wire insulation; pipe, duct and thermal insulation; and interior wall, ceiling and floor finishes to submit toxicity data for inclusion in a statewide toxicity databank. Manufacturers submitting data have been required to submit samples of their products to independent testing laboratories for destructive testing, using the University of Pittsburgh toxic potency test method.[8] This pioneering regulatory activity may be expected to spread as concern grows in the private sector over common workplace hazards. Work done by the Center for Fire Research at the National Institute of Standards and Technology evaluated common fire scenarios involving electrical and electronic components. None of these rank among the most common or severe of fire scenarios. However, concern over the toxicity issue has stimulated continuing research efforts related to this question. These efforts focus on developing ways to quantify the hazards associated with toxic products of combustion generated when these materials burn. Table 6-15A illustrates some of these scenarios.

Electric service failures: Since all electrical and electronic components are subject to resistance heating, and will eventually fail, consideration should be given to reducing hazards from such failures. Nearly all building services discussed in this chapter depend on electric service for safe, efficient operation. NFPA 101, *Life Safety Code*, requires emergency power for exit signs and means of egress lighting. NFPA 72, *Protective Signaling Systems*, also requires an emergency power supply for the fire alarm system when required by another code or standard. ASME A17.1, *Safety Code for Elevators and Escalators*, requires at least one car in each bank of elevators to be supplied with emergency power, with a capability available to manually transfer power to other cars in each bank. The arrangement of

TABLE 6-15A. ***Example of Potential Electrical Fire Scenarios That May Produce Smoke Toxicity Hazards9***

Fire Scenario & Electrical/ Electronic Component(s) Involves	Potential Impacts
Electronic component fails and burns	1 to 2 persons in immediate vicinity exposed for several seconds
Switchgear fails and burns	At most, several persons in or near electrical closet /control room exposed for minutes
Larger electrical control(s) or building overloads/heats	Depending on paths for smoke travel, may expose total building population for minutes during escape/evacuation
Wall cavity wiring or receptacle overloads/heats	One or more residents of home may be exposed for minutes
Electrical wiring/tubing in wall cavity involved by room fire	Possible increase in smoke hazard to occupants in adjacent space for minutes during escape
Computer/communications cables in plenum involved by room fire	Possible increase in smoke hazard to perhaps large fraction of building occupants exposed for 5 to 15 minutes or so
Wiring concentrations in electricity/utility tunnels, etc., involved by fire	Exposure of building occupants for duration of event and evacuation process

such systems must minimize the possibility that the emergency power supply will be disabled by a fire, or other emergency, involving the primary power supply. During the One Meridian Plaza Fire in Philadelphia—that burned for nearly 19 hours, killing three fire fighters, and destroying or heavily damaging 8 floors of a 38-story downtown high-rise—separate electric utility supplies from two substations became disabled when the fire entered an unprotected electrical room on the floor of fire origin. Article 700 of NFPA 70, *National Electrical Code*, provides that, when separate electric services are permitted for emergency power by the authority having jurisdiction,

> This service shall be in accordance with Article 230, with separate service drop or lateral, widely separated electrically and physically from the normal service to minimize the possibility of simultaneous interruption of supply.[10]

Elevator operation was consequently disrupted, thereby hampering fire fighting efforts.[11]

Transportation and Conveyance

Transportation and conveyance systems are those systems provided to facilitate the vertical or horizontal movement of people and materials, bulk or packaged. Perhaps no other building service has had as significant an impact on the building environment than the elevator. Without a safe, efficient means of moving people vertically in buildings, the modern urban skyline would look much different than it does today. This innovation has also made even buildings of moderate height more accessible to those with temporary or permanent mobility impairments. Like other building services, great debate has centered on the safety of elevators, escalators, and other conveyance systems during fire emergencies. Two dangers are commonly associated with these building services: (1) their association with fire and smoke transport, and (2) dangers to persons who may use elevators during fire emergencies. Fire-resistance-rated separation assemblies, automatic fire suppression, smoke management systems, good housekeeping, and management can mitigate the effects related to the first problem. However, the solution to the second problem remains a topic of significant debate in fire protection and mechanical engineering communities.

Fire and smoke transport: Like any other vertical communication, elevator and dumbwaiter hoistways may be significant avenues of fire and smoke spread due to stack effect. Similarly, floor openings for escalators may provide an ideal path for fire and smoke spread. Enclosure of elevators and machine rooms with fire-resistance-rated assemblies; self-closing fire doors at lobbies; ventilation or pressurization of elevator hoistways and machine rooms; installation of automatic sprinklers in elevator machine rooms and shafts; and automatic fire detectors in lobbies, shafts, and machine rooms are all intended to limit fire and smoke spread in these spaces. Escalators, however, can be protected in a number of ways, including complete or partial enclosure by walls, partitions, draftstops or draft curtains, rolling shutters, or moving partitions; automatic sprinklers; and water-spray fixed systems. Code requirements vary regarding which features are required, and designers often have considerable latitude to combine different protection techniques. This ensures that nearly all installations are protected in some way.

Cranes, lifts, mechanical and pneumatic conveyors are commonly used in industrial and storage occupancies to move bulk or packaged materials primarily horizontally and relatively short distances vertically. Modern warehouses increasingly turn to labor-saving, computer-controlled lifts and cranes to automate warehousing operations. Protecting horizontal openings in fire barriers through which such devices pass is a significant concern. Means must be provided to permit opening protectives to operate without interference or obstruction from either the stock or the conveyor. Common methods of protecting fire wall openings include providing mechanical or electrical interlocks on conveyors or installing water-spray fixed systems.

People movement: Increased sensitivity and attention to the legitimate needs and rights of people with mobility impairments have led to widespread support and acceptance of barrier-free design. A principal component of this design strategy is the installation of special lifts, and elevators, in multi-story buildings. While barriers to ingress are gradually being eliminated through the integration of barrier-free concepts, a major hurdle remains: barrier-free egress. Once mobility-impaired occupants get into a building, the concern arises as to how they get out when fire occurs. ASME A17.1 provides requirements for automatic and manual recall of elevator cars to the designated floor (usually the level of exit discharge or primary level of fire fighter access) during fire emergencies that may threaten elevator occupants. Phase I fire fighter service is, therefore, initiated only upon activation of automatic detectors (smoke or heat, as required in ASME A17.1) in elevator lobbies, the elevator machine room, or the elevator hoistway itself. This leaves the elevator in service for use by disabled building occupants until safe elevator operation is threatened, or initiation of Phase II service (manual control). However, NFPA 101, *Life Safety Code*, provides that an elevator must not be considered an element of the means of egress, and the model fire prevention codes and ASME A17.1 require the installation of signs at elevator lobbies directing occupants to use stairs, not elevators during fire emergencies.[12] Ensuring a safe environment for all building occupants requires an integrated design approach. Designers and code officials must work together to ensure all building occupants are adequately protected.

To date, when interest in the plight of the disabled has been translated into action, the predominant approach has been to move those persons with mobility impairments to areas of refuge, or "areas of evacuation assistance," to wait for rescuers. In some cases, emergency planning has focused on occupant assistance to persons with disabilities. Meanwhile, persons without mobility impairments are free to climb down the stairs and exit out the doors to safety. As a result of the efforts of life safety experts and design professionals dedicated to barrier-free design and advocacy for persons with disabilities, increased attention is once again focused on this concern. The question arises as to whether elevators and lifts will become accepted components of barrier-free egress systems in the future. While there is no definitive answer, it is certain that as long as tragedies associated with well-intentioned, but poorly reasoned use of elevators during fire emergencies persist, this solution will be resisted by many.

Investigators concluded that the sole fatality in the Los Angeles First Interstate Bank Building fire of 1988 was killed by exposure to fire products when he took an elevator to the floor of fire origin.[13] Preliminary reports from the One Meridian Plaza fire in Philadelphia indicate that a similar tragedy nearly occurred there. Had another building occupant—a guard in the building lobby—not heard the building engineer's call for help over his portable radio and initiated Phase II fire fighter service, the survivor might have been yet another victim of carelessness.[14]

OPERATION AND MAINTENANCE

Fires involving heating systems, appliances, electrical equipment, and other equipment together represent the largest number of fire incidents reported to U.S. fire departments.[15] These systems were not designed to start fires or fail. Design flaws and faulty products are certainly responsible for their share of fires. However, improper operation, maintenance, or alteration of mechanical and electrical systems represent significant causes of accidental fires. Evidence suggests that older structures are more prone to fires than newer ones, and many believe that fires in newer buildings are more severe due to the widespread use of plastics. In view of these points, proper maintenance and conscientious management of building services can significantly reduce the fire threat in both new and older existing buildings.

Building owners, occupants, insurers, and code officials working together can significantly reduce the fire problem due to operational and maintenance problems. An innovative program run by Mead Loss Control Consultants, Inc., of Dayton, OH, regularly surveys risks covered by the Mead Corporation's captive insurance organization for electrical and mechanical hazards using an infrared scanner and videotape equipment. "Hot-spots" detected by the infrared equipment, e.g., worn bearings, faulty transformers, or loose electrical connections, are scheduled for immediate preventive maintenance. Mead's loss control engineers believe this program has contributed significantly to the company's excellent loss history.[16]

Environmental Systems

NFPA 101, *Life Safety Code*, requires periodic tests and maintenance of systems serving as part of engineered smoke management systems to ensure proper operation. However, many environmental systems that are not part of such an emergency system may frequently become neglected. Systems that move air always move anything suspended in the air. This point is illustrated by the dust that can be seen in a beam of light. This dust and dirt is transported and can accumulate in a building and its systems. This accumulation can be to such a degree that one of the principal functions of an environmental system is to control this dust and dirt. Filters used to remove these substances from the air may present potential problems. Grease, HEPA, and other special-purpose filters are particularly susceptible to fire involvement when exposed to external fires. Consequently, NFPA 96, *Removal of Smoke and Grease-Laden Vapors from Commercial Cooking Equipment*, requires an automatic fire extinguishing system in all such installations. NFPA 91, *Blower and Exhaust for Dust, Stock, and Vapor Removal or Conveying*, recommends similar protection, compatible with the hazard involved, in systems used for the removal or control of hazardous vapors or substances. Systems moving ordinary environmental air may also be prone to similar hazards. Fires associated with heating systems consistently rank among the most common causes of fire in the U.S. In 1987, heating systems ranked third among causes associated with residential fire deaths in the United States.[16] These figures include all fires of all types involving heating equipment, and may include a significant number of failures involving fuel gas (piped service) components. Nonetheless, fire fighters who must respond to the spate of smoke scares and chimney fires at the beginning of each heating season, can attest to the results of neglected maintenance.

Periodic maintenance, particularly cleaning and inspecting, will identify and eliminate hazards before they become problems, and extend the life of building environmental system components. Appendix B of NFPA 90A, *Air Conditioning and Ventilating Systems*, describes the elements of an HVAC system maintenance program, including steps for reducing fire hazard potential. Duct and plenum cleaning, filter replacements, bearing inspections, and tests of automatic and manual controls are among the most important elements of these programs. The appendix notes, "Failure to maintain proper conditions of cleanliness in air duct systems and carelessness in connection with repair operations have been important contributing causes of several fires which have involved air conditioning systems."[17] Storage of combustible materials in plenums and near fresh air intakes has also been cited as an important contributor to fires involving HVAC systems. Misalignment of motor bearings causes overheating and belt wear. The heat produced from such motor failures is sufficient to ignite dirt and debris—including grease and lubricants associated with the motor and bearings—in the system ductwork. Flammable or combustible solvents should never be used to clean system ductwork or filters. Great care should be exercised when open-flame devices are used to perform repairs inside ductwork and plenums.

Piped Services

Three fire scenarios dominate incidents involving piped services: (1) ignition of building structure, insulation, dirt, debris, or other nearby combustibles, while using a torch or other heat-producing device for repair; (2) piping leaks caused by defective or damaged system components; and (3) ignition of flammable piping contents when piping or containers are not properly grounded. In the first scenario, the maintenance activity, not the piped service, is responsible for the ignition. Leaks involving noncombustible, oxidizing gases distributed by pipe may be just as dangerous as the flammable compressed gases when ignition sources are present. Flammable liquids especially produce prolific amounts of static electricity. Ignitions during transfer operations remain a significant cause of accidental fires involving flammable liquids.

NFPA 51B, *Cutting and Welding Processes*, describes the precautions that should be taken to prevent ignitions while using open-flame devices. These include operation of such equipment only by trained operators under the direct supervision of competent management, once inspections have determined that combustible materials will not be ignited by conduction, sparks, or slag. Combustibles within 35 ft (11 m) must be removed from the work area, which must then be swept clean. Sprinklers—if installed—must be operational, and portable fire extinguishers or small hoselines must be available nearby. The standard also requires adequate protection for workers, including smocks, aprons, gloves, helmets, faceshields, and goggles, and proper maintenance of equipment. Following the conclusion of welding or cutting operations, a firewatch must be maintained in the area for at least 30 min to detect and extinguish smoldering fires.

Many safeguards are provided to prevent the inadvertent release of piping contents under conditions of normal use and operation. However, despite the mechanical and physical protection provided, gas and liquid leaks involving flammable and oxidizing compounds routinely occur. To prevent and minimize the hazards presented by such events, piping, valves, and system controls should be clearly identified and readily accessible. When a leak occurs, immediate care should be taken to control or eliminate potential ignition sources and disrupt the flow of pipe contents. Fire fighting equipment should be readied for service, or summoned while controlling the release. Often, locating and stopping a release at the source is not practical. In such cases, valves or controls remote from the source may have to be shut, possibly impairing other services.

As noted, flammable liquids produce prolific quantities of static electricity, especially when atmospheric humidity is low. This source of ignition remains one of the principal causes of accidental fires involving flammable liquids. NFPA 77, *Static Electricity*, treats this subject in detail, and NFPA 30, *Flammable and Combustible Liquids Code*, requires the bonding and grounding of flammable and combustible liquid piping systems. NFPA 54, *National Fuel Gas Code*, requires grounding of aboveground natural gas piping, as well. However, neither flammable nor combustible liquid piping nor fuel gas piping should be used as a grounding electrode. Bonding during liquid transfer operations will help ensure that static electricity formed by pouring such liquids is safely dissipated without generating a spark capable of igniting escaping vapors.

Electrical Services

Electrical failures resulting in fires may be attributed to one of two causes: (1) arcing, or (2) overheating. All electrical equipment and devices are subject to wear and deterioration from prolonged use. Heating and arcing caused by normal operation are responsible for much of this wear and tear. While all devices are designed taking these factors into account, it remains the responsibility of the user, or owner, to determine when these conditions have resulted in an unsafe device, equipment, or installation. Additionally, users and owners must take care not to exacerbate these conditions by placing unreasonable demands on electrical installations or modifying conforming installations in a manner that makes them unsafe. Periodic inspection of electrical equipment, devices, and installations from damage, defects, and misuse will help prevent these situations from developing into fires.

The importance of maintaining adequate clearances between combustible and heat-producing electrical equipment and devices, noted previously, deserves further attention. Overheating of electrical devices is generally caused by the inability of equipment or devices to adequately dissipate heat generated during normal operation. All electrical and electronic components are subject to resistance heating to some degree. This heat may be caused by insulation, friction, resistance, or induction. Either excess heat is produced faster than it can be safely dissipated, or heat is trapped by thermally insulating materials. Electrical insulation is designed to limit mechanical damage and prevent arcing, but not to restrict the liberation of heat. Coaker and Hirschler have modeled the insulating effect of combustible dusts, e.g., bagasse, coal dust, and sawdust, on electrical transmission cables and concluded that practically attainable, critical thicknesses of these materials (usually on the order of several centimeters) deposited on cables could produce insulation failures resulting in short circuits, if not ignite the dust itself.[18] The possibility of such failures points up the importance of housekeeping and routine inspections of electrical installations.

The following scenarios are not intended to include all the possible conditions likely to produce a fire, but rather to illustrate some common maintenance and operation failures. Loose connections caused by improper maintenance and normal wear and tear on switches or contacts are significant sources of arcing. Turning switches on and off generates a small arc within the switch enclosure. Each time this arc occurs, a small amount of the material from one contact is deposited on the other, reducing the electrical clearance between the conductive paths. Eventually, this situation will result in a short-circuit if not corrected. Contacts in electrical receptacles may similarly wear out from accumulated wear resulting from inserting and removing plugs or routinely unplugging energized equipment, thereby causing a failure. Likewise, damaged conductors, particularly flexible cords, may be subject to resistance heating and eventual arcing from damage, misuse, or neglect. In fact, misuse of flexible cords remains one of the leading causes of electrical fires. Misaligned bearings in electric motors may result in excessive friction between motor bushings and the motor housing. When the motor seizes up from such damage, often current continues to flow to the equipment until a short-circuit develops, causing the overcurrent protection to trip. However, if sufficient heat is generated before the activation of overcurrent protection, a fire may result. Once again, clearance from combustibles will help avert disaster.

TABLE 6-15B. ***Contributing Factors Involved in Residential Electrical Distribution Systems Fires by Age of Dwelling***[20]

Contributing Factors	Number	Percent	≤10	11–20	21–30	31–40	>40	Unknown
Improper alterations	55	37%	1	2	9	7	29	7
Improper initial installations	30	20	4	4	8	3	7	4
Deterioration due to aging	25	17	2	3	—	5	9	6
Improper use	23	15	1	1	2	5	13	1
Inadequate electrical capacity	22	15	—	—	4	1	16	1
Faulty product	17	11	2	3	2	1	8	1
Unknown	9	6	—	—	—	2	4	3
Total	149	100%	10	13	25	24	86	23

Note: Frequencies add to more than number investigations, since multiple factors were cited in 31 cases.

Transportation and Conveyance Systems

Fortunately, fires associated with the normal operation of elevators are rather infrequent. The most common hazards associated with normal operation of elevators are: (1) housekeeping, (2) repair operations in the elevator hoistway or machine room, and (3) maintenance of motors and equipment. Nearly all elevator hoistways seem to accumulate dirt, trash, and other debris at the bottom. In the case of hydraulic elevators, this may include some accumulation of oil or grease, as well. Obviously, the ignition of such debris can present a serious hazard. All elevators operate on some form of track, or rail, inside the hoistway. Repair or maintenance on this track or rail, using welding or cutting equipment, has been the source of serious fires inside elevator hoistways. One such fire occurred at the U.S. Embassy in Moscow, USSR, in March 1991. Workers using welding and cutting equipment apparently started an accidental fire in the hoistway, thereby heavily damaging the upper floors of the building.[19] Similarly, poorly maintained elevator drive motors may overheat, igniting nearby combustibles. This can include hydraulic fluid in the elevator fluid reservoir.

MODIFICATION AND RENOVATION

Change may be the only constant in the universe. Buildings are rarely built and occupied by a single occupant, or for a single-purpose, through their entire lifespan. Rather, owners and occupants tend to be caretakers of the built environment, moving from one structure to the next, as their needs and capacities change. The hazards associated with renovation of existing systems reflect a combination of the problems commonly associated with original design and inadequate, or improper, maintenance. Additions to existing nonconforming systems should, at the very least, not contribute further to these deficiencies. Rather, whenever possible, the opportunity to correct existing weaknesses—whether a result of technological advances, new regulations, design deficiencies, or poor maintenance—should be advanced. In fact, most building and firesafety codes require the correction of past defects or related deficiencies when modifications are undertaken. Where a new, completely objective systems approach is impractical, unwarranted, or otherwise unsuitable, it remains wise to take the opportunity presented by modifications or renovations to detect and correct maintenance deficiencies or operational inadequacies.

In the context of modifications—substantial changes to original installations—electrical system modifications standout as a source of significant and continuing concern. Nonconforming changes lead causes of electrical fires in a survey conducted by the U.S. Consumer Product Safety Commission (CPSC) in which 149 fires were examined in closer detail. Table 6-15B illustrates the findings of this study.[20]

SUMMARY

Owners, occupants, architects, engineers, builders, fire protection consultants, and authorities having jurisdiction must work together to control and eliminate hazards in the built environment. Controlling and eliminating hazards associated with building services requires recognition of the contribution of these systems to a safe, comfortable, efficient building environment and the hazards associated with the design, operation, maintenance, and modification of these systems. As human needs evolve, thereby placing greater demands on the built environment, the state of the art in buildings services is bound to evolve, too. Fire protection practitioners must keep abreast of these changes to ensure that the needs of safety keep pace with the needs of comfort, efficiency, and economy.

BIBLIOGRAPHY

References Cited

1. Hartman, T., "Intelligent Building Design Demands," *Heating/Piping/Air Conditioning*, Vol. 61, No. 11, Nov. 1989, pp. 67-70.
2. Mace, R. L., "Smart Planning for Accessibility," *Buildings*, Vol. 83, No. 4, Apr. 1989, p. 72.
3. BOCA, *National Building Code 1990*, ICBO *Uniform Building Code, 1988*, SBCCI *Standard Building Code*, 1988.
4. Klote, J. H., "Inspecting and Testing Air Moving Systems for Fire Safety," *Heating/Piping/Air Conditioning*, Vol. 60, No. 4, Apr. 1988, pp. 77-87.

5. Choi, K.K., "Firestops for Plastic Pipe," *Fire Technology*, Vol. 23, No. 4, Nov. 1987, pp. 267-279.
6. Zicherman, J. B., "Is PVC Piping Firesafe," *Fire Journal*, Vol. 84, No. 6, Nov./Dec. 1990, pp. 37-42.
7. Whittington, B. W., "Electrical Installations in Industrial Locations," *Industrial Fire Hazards Handbook*, 3rd ed., Cote, A. E., *ed.*, National Fire Protection Association, Quincy, MA, p. 1104.
8. Teague, P. E., "The Analysis of the Toxicity Problem Continues," *Fire Journal*, Vol. 83, No. 3, pp. 62-64.
9. Snell, J. E., "Measuring Hazards of Products of Combustion from Electrical Systems," *Fire Journal*, Vol. 81, No. 5, Sept./Oct. 1987, p. 108.
10. NFPA 70, *National Electrical Code*, Section 700-12(d), National Fire Protection Association, Quincy, MA, 1991.
11. "Negligence Cited in Lack of Water at Meridian Fire," *Philadelphia Inquirer*, Vol. 323, No. 72, Wed., Mar. 13, 1991, pp. 1A, 14A. (Although the circumstances as of yet are unclear, this or a related emergency power failure also appears to have affected operation of the fire pump.)
12. NFPA 101, *Life Safety Code.* Section 7-4.1, National Fire Protection Association, Quincy, MA, 1991.
13. Klem, T. J., "Los Angeles High-Rise Bank Fire," *Fire Journal*, Vol. 83, No. 3, May/June 1989, pp. 72-91.
14. "Negligence Cited in Lack of Water at Meridian Fire," *Philadelphia Inquirer*, Vol. 323, No. 74, Wed., Mar. 13, 1991, pp. 1A, 14A.
15. United States Fire Administration, *Fire in the United States*, 7th ed., Emmittsburg, MD, Office of Fire Data and Analysis, Aug. 1990.
16. Mead Loss Control, Inc., *Mead Loss Control Engineering Services*, Dayton, OH, The Mead Corp., 1983.
17. NFPA 90A, *Standard for the Installation of Air Conditioning and Ventilating Systems*, Appendix B-1-1, National Fire Protection Association, Quincy, MA, 1989.
18. Coaker, A. W., and Hirschler, M.M., "Effect of Deposition of Combustible Matter onto Electric Power Cables," *Fire Safety Journal*, 16 (6), pp. 459-467.
19. *Washington Post*, Vol. 114, No. 114, Fri., Mar. 29, 1991, p. A1, A13.
20. Smith, L. E., and McCoskrie, D., "What Causes Wiring Fires in Residences?," *Fire Journal*, Vol. 84, No. 1, Jan./Feb. 1990, pp. 18-24, 69.

Reference

ASTM E-814, American Society of Testing and Materials, Philadelphia, PA.

NFPA Codes, Standards, and Recommended Practices

Reference to the following NFPA codes, standards, and recommended practices will provide further information on the safeguards for hazards of building services discussed in this chapter. (See the latest *NFPA Catalog* for availability of current editions of the following documents.)

NFPA 30, *Flammable and Combustible Liquids Code.*

NFPA 31, *Oil Burning Equipment.*

NFPA 51B, *Cutting and Welding Processes.*

NFPA 54, *National Fuel Gas Code.*

NFPA 58, *Storage and Handling of Liquified Petroleum Gases.*

NFPA 70, *National Electrical Code.*

NFPA 77, *Static Electricity.*

NFPA 78, *Lightning Protection Code.*

NFPA 82, *Incinerators, Waste and Linen Handling Systems and Equipment.*

NFPA 90A, *Air Conditioning and Ventilating Systems.*

NFPA 90B, *Warm Air Heating and Air Conditioning Systems.*

NFPA 91, *Blower and Exhaust Systems for Dust, Stock and Vapor Removal or Conveying.*

NFPA 96, *Removal of Smoke and Grease-Laden Vapors from Commercial Cooking Equipment.*

NFPA 99, *Health Care Facilities.*

NFPA 101, *Life Safety Code.*

NFPA, 211, *Chimneys, Fireplaces, Vents, and Solid Fuel Burning Appliances.*

NFPA 214, *Water-Cooling Towers.*

NFPA 251, *Fire Tests of Building Construction and Materials.*

NFPA 255, *Surface Burning Characteristics of Building Materials.*

NFPA 262, *Fire and Smoke Characteristics of Wires and Cables.*

NFPA 550, *Firesafety Concepts Tree*

Additional Readings

Armstrong, J. H., *Maintaining Building Services: A Guide for Managers*, Mitchell, London, England, 1987.

Belles, D. W., "Reducing Fire Hazards with Fire Retardants," *Fire Journal*, Vol. 83, No. 3, May/June 1989, pp. 52-60, 129.

Birmingham, J. A., "Firestops Protect Property—and Lives," *Fire Journal*, Vol. 80, No. 2, Mar./Apr. 1986, pp. 41-44, 63.

Cooper, P., "Heating Tapes and Cables Can Cause Mobile Home Fires," in Letters, *Fire Journal*, Vol. 84, No. 2, Mar./Apr. 1990, p. 9.

Cote, A. E., *ed.*, *Industrial Fire Hazards Handbook,* 3rd ed., National Fire Protection Association, Quincy, MA, NFPA, 1990.

Donoghue, E. A., "Elevators and Sprinklers: The Controversy Continues," in Members' Forum, *Fire Journal*, Vol. 84, No. 2, Mar./Apr. 1990, pp. 15-17.

Donoghue, E. A., "Elevator Code Revisions Protect the Public and Firefighters," in Letters, *Fire Journal*, Vol. 83, No. 6, Nov./Dec. 1989, p. 6.

Doyle, M., "Life Safety and Security Systems Grow in Sophistication," *Building Design and Construction*, Vol. 27, No. 8, Aug. 1986, pp. 108-110.

Earley, M. W., "Minimizing the Hazards of Transformer Fires," *Fire Journal*, Vol. 82, No. 1, Jan./Feb. 1988, pp. 73-74.

Ehrenkrantz, E., *Architectural Systems: Needs, Resources, Design*, McGraw-Hill, New York, 1989.

Franklin, F. F., "A Survey of Electrical Fires," *Fire Journal*, Vol. 78, No. 2, Mar./Apr. 1984, pp. 41-44.

Gibbons, J. A. M., and Stevens, G. C., "Limiting the Corrosion Hazard from Electrical Cables Involved in Fires," *Fire Safety Journal*, 15 (2), 1989, pp. 183-190.

Gray, B. F., *et al*, "Effect of Combustible Matter onto Electric Power Cables," *Fire Safety Journal* 16 (6), 1990, pp. 459-467.

Haines, R. W., *Heating, Ventilation and Air Conditioning Systems Design Handbook*, Tab Professional and Research Books, Blue Ridge Summit, PA, 1988.

Harris, C. M., *Building Utilities and Services Handbook: Planning, Design, and Installation*, McGraw-Hill, New York, 1990.

Harris, R. J., *The Investigation and Control of Gas Explosions in Buildings and Heating Plants*, E. & F. N. Spon Ltd., London, England, 1983.

Hartman, T., "Intelligent Building Design Demands," *Heating/Piping/Air Conditioning*, Vol. 61, No. 11, Nov. 1989, pp. 67-70.

Hicks, H. D., "The Fire Protection Engineer and the Authority Having Jurisdiction," *Building Official and Code Administrator*, Vol. XXIII, No. 6, Nov./Dec. 1989, pp. 28-32.

Isner, M.S., "Five Die in High-Rise Office Building Fire," *Fire Journal*, Vol. 84, 4, July/Aug. 1990, pp. 50-59.

Kaufman, S., "Fire Tests and Fire-Resistant Telecommunications Cables," *Fire Journal*, Vol. 80, No. 6, Nov./Dec. 1986, pp. 33-38.

Klem, T. J., "Los Angeles High-Rise Bank Fire," *Fire Journal*, Vol. 83, No. 3, May/June 1989, pp. 72-91.

Klote, J. H., "A Computer Model of Smoke Movement by Air Conditioning Systems (SMACS)," *Fire Technology*, Vol. 24, No. 4, Nov. 1988, pp. 299-311.

Ley, M., *Grading Methods of Building Fire Safety*, M.S. Thesis, Worcester Polytechnic Institute, Worcester, MA 1987.

Malhotra, H. L., *Fire Safety In Buildings*, Building Research Establishment, Borehamwood, England, 1987.

Murray, R. H., and Lathrop, J. K., "Fire Barrier Penetrations Must Be Firestopped," *Fire Journal*, Vol. 81, No. 6, Nov./Dec. 1987, pp. 66-67.

Olsen, C., "Have Smart Buildings Flunked the Test?," *Building Design and Construction*, Vol. 27, No. 9, Sept. 1986, pp. 72-74.

Pasek, F., "Door Controls Complete Compartmentalization Design," *Building Design and Construction*, Vol. 27, No. 11, Nov. 1986, p. 77.

Plumer, J. A., "We Need Better Lightning Protection," *Fire Journal*, Vol. 81, No. 1, Jan./Feb. 1987, pp. 41-45, 73.

Scurry, P. S. G., "Suggested Topics for Research in Building Services Engineering," *Building Services Engineering Research and Technology*, Vol. 9, No. 2 (1988), pp. 87-88.

Shields, T. J., *Building and Fire*, Wiley, New York, 1987.

Smith, L. E., and McCoskrie, D., "What Causes Wiring Fires in Residences?," *Fire Journal*, Vol. 84, No. 1, Jan./Feb. 1990, pp. 18-24, 69.

Snell, J. E., "Measuring Hazards of Products of Combustion from Electrical Systems," *Fire Journal*, Vol. 81, No. 5, Sept./Oct. 1987, pp. 108-109.

Teague, P. E., "The Analysis of the Toxicity Problem Continues," *Fire Journal*, Vol. 83, No. 3, May/June 1989, pp. 62-64.

Todd, C. S., "Lack of Maintenance Jepardises the Benefits of Active Systems," *Fire Survival*, Vol. 16, 1987, pp. 6-11.

Transue, R. E., "Fire Management in Intelligent Buildings," *Fire Journal*, Vol. 84, No. 2, Mar./Apr. 1990, pp. 74-76.

Zicherman, J. B., "Is PVC Piping Firesafe?," *Fire Journal*, Vol. 84, No. 6, Nov./Dec. 1990, pp. 36-42.

AIR CONDITIONING AND VENTILATING SYSTEMS

Revised by William A. Schmidt

The term "air conditioning" has been defined by the American Society of Heating, Refrigerating, and Air Conditioning Engineers (ASHRAE) as "the process of treating air to simultaneously control its temperature, humidity, cleanliness, and distribution to meet the comfort requirements of the occupants of the conditioned space." Air conditioning and ventilating systems, except for self-contained units, invariably involve the use of ducts for air distribution. The ducts, in turn, present the possibility of spreading fire, fire gases, and smoke throughout the building or area served.

This and other potential hazards of air conditioning and ventilating systems are the subjects of this chapter. Installation and protection of air heating systems are discussed in Section 2, Chapter 4, "Heating Systems and Appliances." Fire confinement, smoke movement, and venting practices are addressed in Section 6, Chapter 6, "Confinement of Fire in Buildings," Chapter 7, "Smoke Movement in Buildings," and Chapter 8, "Venting Practices."

Details on safeguarding against these hazards are presented in NFPA 90A, *Air Conditioning and Ventilating Systems*. The bibliography and additional readings at the end of this chapter contain additional references from which much useful information may be obtained.

SYSTEM TYPES AND OPERATION

The several types of air conditioning systems include: (1) systems in which air is filtered or washed, cooled and dehumidified in summer, and heated and humidified in winter; (2) systems where air is filtered, cooled, and dehumidified; and (3) systems where air is filtered, heated, and humidified. Figure 6-16A depicts a typical arrangement of the various components of a central air conditioning system. A ventilating system simply supplies or removes air by natural or mechanical means to or from a space. The air may or may not be conditioned.

Referring to the typical system depicted in Figure 6-16A, a fresh air intake duct connects directly to the system's return duct. From this point, the mixture of fresh and

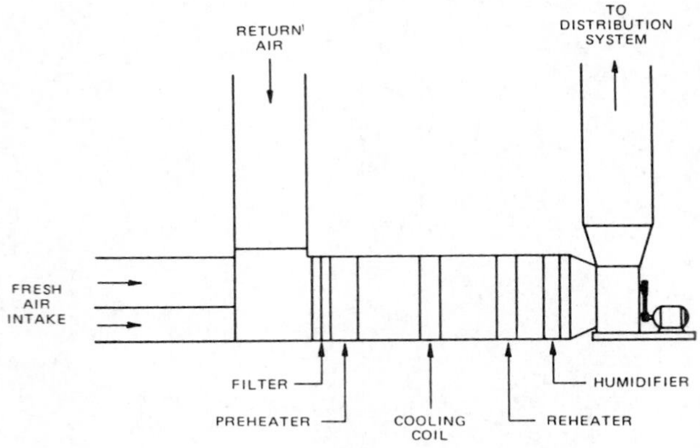

FIG. 6-16A. Typical arrangement of the component parts of a central air conditioning system.

recirculated air passes through the air conditioning equipment. The air is subjected to several operations in this equipment, including filtration or cleaning, heating or cooling, and humidification. The conditioned air is then circulated throughout the area served via the duct system. (See Figure 6-16B.) Those systems that do not recirculate any air take all of their makeup air directly from the outside. A building may contain more than one system, not necessarily of the same type.

LOCATION OF EQUIPMENT

Fans, heaters, filters, and associated equipment that make up a central system air conditioning unit are preferably located in a room separated from the rest of the building area by walls, floor, and floor-ceiling assembly providing a minimum 1-hr fire-resistance rating. This arrangement prevents a fire involving the equipment from immediately spreading to adjacent areas of the building. Such an arrangement also prevents access to the equipment by unauthorized persons. Ideally, service rooms housing air conditioning equipment are protected by automatic sprinklers. At minimum, smoke detectors should be provided

William A. Schmidt, P.E., is a consultant in private practice in Bowie, MD.

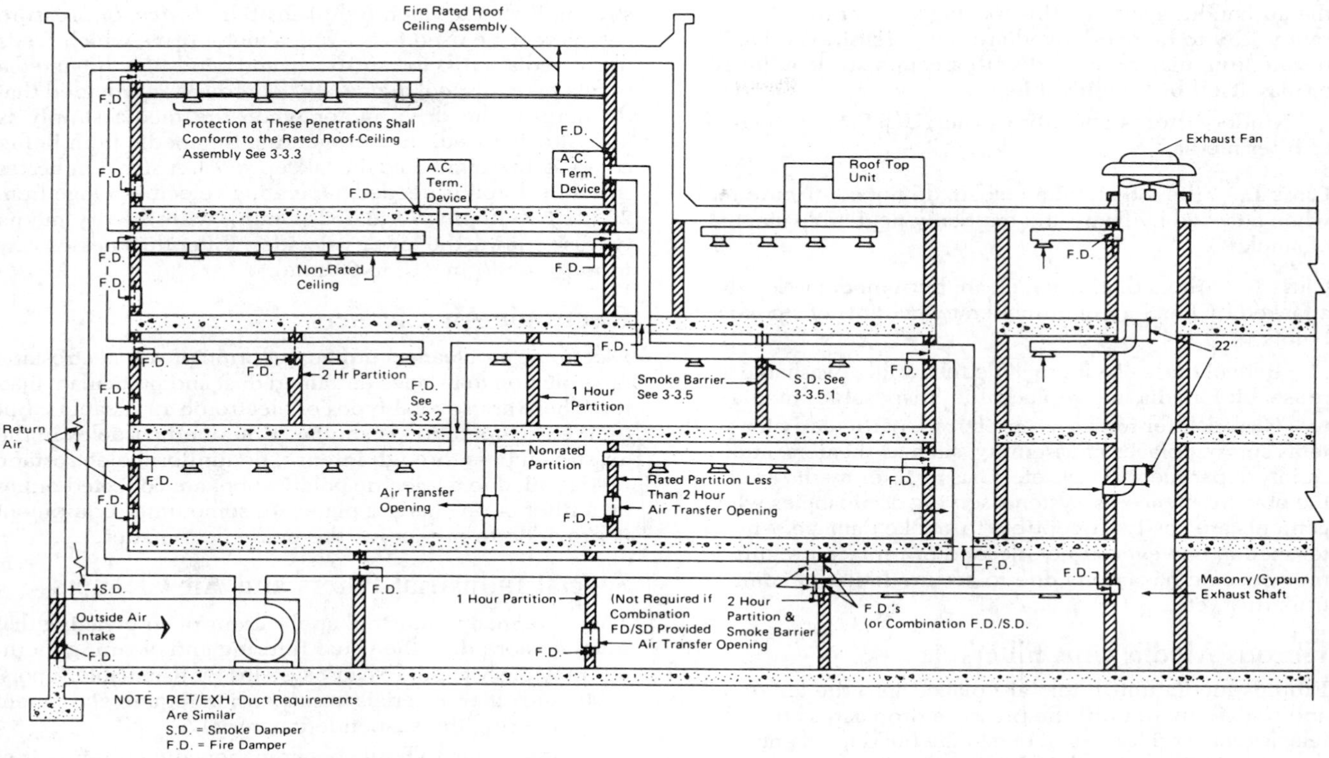

FIG. 6-16B. Typical building duct installation illustrating required protection of walls, ceilings, floors, and shafts.

and arranged to initiate an alarm and shut down the air conditioning system. No combustible storage should be allowed in the equipment room.

FRESH AIR INTAKES

The location selected for the fresh air intakes of a system is critical since fire, fire gases, or smoke originating outside the building can easily be drawn in through these intakes and spread throughout the building. Where such a hazard may exist, protection can be provided by the installation at the intakes of fire dampers or smoke dampers that are controlled by fire and smoke detectors.

When considering the location of exterior fresh air intakes, thought must be given to the possibility of sparks or other products of combustion from an exposing fire chimney, or incinerator stack, being drawn into the system. Consideration should not be limited to adjacent buildings or combustible storage. The possibility of fire from a different section of the same building or an adjoining building exposing the intakes is a factor that must also be considered. Since smoke usually rises, the lower the intakes are installed, the less the possibility of drawing in smoke.

All air intakes must be provided with screens of corrosion-resistant material not larger than ½-in. (13 mm) mesh to prevent material from entering the system. Proper maintenance includes periodic removal of any accumulated rubbish or other waste from the immediate vicinity of the intakes. Some fresh air intakes are fitted with a filter that is subject to the same hazards mentioned later in this chapter under "Air Filters and Cleaners." These filters should be protected and maintained accordingly.

AIR COOLING AND HEATING EQUIPMENT

Air cooling equipment presents two basic classes of hazards: (1) those of the electrical equipment, and (2) those of the particular refrigerant used. Fire experience is generally good where the cooling equipment is properly installed and maintained. Installation of all electrical equipment should follow both the manufacturer's recommendations and NFPA 70, *National Electrical Code®*.

In general, the refrigerant poses a toxicity problem and, in a few cases, a combustibility hazard. Even some of the halogenated hydrocarbon refrigerants used in most systems are slightly flammable. The greatest problem associated with refrigeration units is the explosion hazard due to overpressurization of the refrigerant. Recommendations for the installation of mechanical refrigerating equipment are contained in the ASHRAE "Safety Code for Mechanical Refrigeration."[1]

AIR FILTERS AND CLEANERS

The types of air filters and cleaners used in air conditioning and ventilating systems fall into three general categories: (1) fibrous media unit filters, (2) renewable media filters, and (3) electronic air cleaners. The first two are true filters; the last is a static precipitator. Air filters and cleaners pose a potential hazard due to their function of removing entrained dust and other particulate matter from the air stream. This material builds up on the filter media or precipitator collection plates and, if ignited, may burn, producing large volumes of smoke. The smoke and other combustion gases can be circulated throughout the building by the air handling system, thus posing a direct threat to life safety. Not to be overlooked are the possibilities that filter medium may be coated with a combustible adhesive or may itself be combustible.

Underwriters Laboratories Inc. (UL) lists two classes of filter media:[2]

Class 1: Filters that, when clean, do not contribute fuel when attacked by flame and emit only negligible amounts of smoke.

Class 2: Filters that, when clean, burn moderately when attacked by flame or emit moderate amounts of smoke, or both.

Both of these classes include renewable (washable and reuseable) media and replaceable (disposable) media.

Class 1 filter media are preferred, particularly for systems serving places of assembly, such as theaters, auditoriums, department stores, etc. Class 1 filter media are also the obvious choice for systems serving occupancies whose contents are easily susceptible to smoke damage. Any filter media, however, if not cleaned or replaced regularly, may become hazardous due to accumulation of combustible dust, etc.

Fibrous Media Unit Filters

Fibrous media unit filters are placed into the air stream and remain there until the pressure drop across the filter reaches some critical point, due to the build up of entrained material. At this point, the filter is either removed, cleaned, and reinstalled or simply discarded and replaced with a new filter. Fibrous media unit filters are of either the viscous-impingement type or the dry-media type.

The viscous-impingement type of filter is characterized by flat or pleated panels of relatively coarse fiber mats. Porosity of the panel is high. The fibers are coated with an adhesive that traps any material entrained in the air stream. The mats are ½ to 4 in. (13 to 102 mm) thick, 1 and 2 in. (25 mm and 51 mm) being most common. This type of filter is most effective when air velocity ranges from 400 to 700 ft/min (122 to 213 m/min). Most of these unit filters are ready for replacement when the pressure drop reaches ½ in. of water (124 Pa). The renewable panels must be washed with steam or a hot detergent solution, then recoated with fresh adhesive.

Dry media unit filters are flat or pleated panels of relatively fine fibers, usually ½ to 2 in. (13 to 51 mm) thick. As their name implies, these filters have no adhesive coating. Porosity is not as great as for the viscous-impingement type filter; hence, particulate removal is greater, depending upon fiber size and porosity. These filters are most effective with an air velocity of 90 to 500 ft/min (27 to 152 m/min). Pressure drop may reach as much as 2 in. of water (500 Pa) before replacement is necessary. Disposable dry fibrous media unit filters, particularly of the deep-pleated design, are fast becoming the standard for large central air conditioning systems. The dry media classification of air filters also includes membrane and high-efficiency types which are used to ultraclean air for clean rooms and similar areas.

Renewable Media Filters

Renewable media air filters can more accurately be termed "moving curtain" air filters, since they operate in exactly such a fashion. The medium, whether viscous coated or dry, is supplied on a large roll and extends across the air stream. Either a timer, light-sensitive device, or pressure switch may be used to activate a motor drive which feeds fresh media across the air stream and winds the dirty media onto a takeup spool. Generally, controls are provided that deenergize the drive motor when the media supply is almost exhausted, thus preventing the media from being completely wound onto the takeup spool. A signal indicates that a fresh roll is needed. Operating velocities range from 200 to 500 ft/min (70 to 152 m/min), with the dry media types requiring the lower velocities. Filter thicknesses vary from ½ to 2½ in. (13 to 63 mm).

Electronic Air Cleaners

Electronic air cleaners utilize the principle of electrostatic precipitation to remove entrained dust and particulate matter. There are several types of electronic air cleaners, but their basic operation is similar. Entrained particles in the air stream pass through intense, nonuniform electrostatic fields and, due to electric polarization, are collected either on a filter or on charged plates. In some units, equipment is provided to pre-ionize the particulate matter.

Special Industrial Filters and Air Cleaners

There are many industrial applications of air cleaning that involve more than the usual filtering and cleaning methods previously cited. Exhaust systems for flammable vapors, dusts, and other materials in suspension require equipment for recovering the suspended material.

Air cleaning to limit contamination and pollution is of growing concern to industry and public health authorities. Whatever the reason for specialized air cleaning, and whatever the type of equipment used, the selection and protection of the equipment are of concern as the fire hazards are similar to more common types of air cleaning equipment.

One current industrial application of air filtering is in clean rooms where high-efficiency particulate air (HEPA) filters are used to filter the atmosphere. These filters must pass an operational efficiency test of 99.97 percent efficiency with 0.3 micron particles. The filters are tested and labeled by UL in accordance with UL 586, *Standard for High-Efficiency Particulate Air Filter Units*.[3]

Protection for Air Filters and Cleaners

Fire in the filters or air cleaning equipment can release copious quantities of smoke or fire gases that can be distributed by the air handling equipment throughout the area served. Adequate protection to minimize the possibility of such an occurrence must be designed into and around the air conditioning system.

Some method is necessary to prevent smoke and fire gases from being distributed by the main supply fan to all areas served by the system. To accomplish this, detectors (either heat or smoke, depending on the size of the system) are located in the main supply duct, downstream of the filters or air cleaner, to sense smoke or particles of combustion. The detectors are interlocked so as to immediately shut down the entire air conditioning system upon activation. The detectors also control the operation of smoke dampers located in the main supply and return ducts, thus isolating the entire air conditioning section of the system.

With specific regard to viscous impingement filters, the adhesive used should have a flash point of not less than 325°F (163°C) via the Pensky-Martens closed tester.[4] Also, combustible adhesives should be stored in a safe location, remote from the equipment room housing the air conditioning equipment.

Fire protection should always include facilities for manual fire fighting, usually portable fire extinguishers. Fans, motors, pumps, control circuits, etc., all point to the need for extinguishers suitable for electrical (Class C) fires; however, dry chemical (Class B) extinguishers would be the most suitable for use on filters, especially the viscous-impingement type, since the chemical powder would readily adhere to the coated media.

The operational voltage and amperage of electronic air cleaners is lethal; therefore, interlocks should be provided on every access door and panel so that the equipment is immediately shut down if any one of them is opened. An alarm should also be incorporated into this safety interlock circuit.

DUCTS

Ducts are to an air conditioning or ventilating system what pipes are to a water system—a means of distribution. Unfortunately, in fire situations, the ducts may transport deadly smoke and products of combustion instead of breathable air. If proper design and installation precautions are not taken, smoke, fire gases, heat, and even flame can spread throughout the area served by the duct system. Exit corridors used as plenums, lack of smoke detection activated control equipment in the system, and lack of required fire and smoke dampers in appropriate walls, ceilings, or partitions can lead to tragic situations.

Duct Construction

Ducts may be fabricated of metal, masonry, or other noncombustible material. The thickness of materials used in metal ducts of various sizes and methods of bracing, reinforcing, and hanging are covered in the duct manuals of the Sheet Metal and Air Conditioning Contractors National Association (SMACNA).[5] SMACNA also publishes manuals on the installation of glass fiber ducts.

UL tests and lists duct materials in accordance with UL 181, *Standard for Factory-Made Air Ducts and Connectors*.[6] This standard sets limits on such characteristics as flame spread and flame penetration. Materials are classified as follows:

Class 0: Air ducts and connectors having surface burning characteristics of zero.

Class 1: Air ducts and connectors having a flame spread rating of not over 25, without evidence of continued progressive combustion, and a smoke developed rating of not over 50.

Class 2: Air ducts and connectors having a flame spread rating of not over 50, without evidence of continued progressive combustion, and a smoke developed rating of not over 50 for the inside surface and not over 100 for the outside surface.

In addition to the above, Class 0 and Class 1 materials must pass a 30-min flame penetration test, and Class 2 materials must pass a 15-min flame penetration test.

NFPA 90A, *Air Conditioning and Ventilating Systems*, gives other mandatory provisions for duct linings and coverings, duct tapes, and bands. It also places limitations on the use of flexible duct connectors that must pass through walls, partitions, floors, or ceilings intended to afford fire resistance or smoke control.

NFPA 90A, *Air Conditioning and Ventilating Systems*, recently added a provision where gypsum board may be used for negative pressure or return air ducts, and for shafts subject to specific conditions. Gypsum board shafts must be constructed in accordance with the Gypsum Association fire resistance design manual, be constructed airtight, and must be designed to handle structural and air pressure loadings.

Duct Installation

By their very nature, ducts provide a means for transferring heat, fire gases, and flame, thus resulting in the spread of fire from one area to another. In addition, at some point or another, a duct probably will pass through a wall, partition, floor, or ceiling which is designed specifically to provide fire resistance. Literally, a hole has been poked through a fire-rated design. Theoretically, of course, the duct fills the opening. But if the installation has been made without proper regard for firestopping, this is not valid. Also, under severe fire exposure, the duct will eventually collapse, creating an opening in the fire barrier. An effective method of protecting such penetrations is by the installation of fire dampers.

In the gages commonly used, some sheet metal ducts, if properly hung and adequately firestopped, may protect an opening in a building construction assembly for up to 1 hr. Therefore, ducts passing through fire barriers having a rating of up to 1 hr of fire resistance can possibly present no extraordinary hazard. If the wall, partition, ceiling, or floor is required to have a fire-resistance rating of more than 1 hr, a fire damper is required to properly protect the opening. Where it is necessary for a duct to pierce a fire barrier, an automatic closing fire damper or fire door assembly should be installed at the wall opening. NFPA 90A, *Air Conditioning and Ventilating Systems*, provides comprehensive recommendations and requirements for the location of fire dampers in rated assemblies.

Fire dampers and ceiling dampers are tested and listed for use in air conditioning and ventilating ducts by UL in accordance with UL 555, *Standard for Fire Dampers and Ceiling Dampers*.[7] These dampers include single-blade, multi-blade, and interlocking-blade types, all actuated by fusible links. Most fire dampers are designed for vertical installation although some can be installed horizontally as well.

SMOKE CONTROL—PASSIVE

Both NFPA 101®, *Life Safety Code®*, and NFPA 90A, *Air Conditioning and Ventilating Systems*, recognize two approaches to smoke control: (1) passive, and (2) active. The passive approach recognizes the long-standing compartmentation concept which requires that fans be shut down and fire and smoke dampers in ductwork be closed in fire conditions. The active approach utilizes the building's heating, ventilating, and air conditioning (HVAC) systems to create differential pressures to prevent smoke migration from the fire area, and to exhaust the products of combustion to the outside.

Smoke Dampers

Smoke dampers are required in air conditioning or ventilating ducts that pass through required smoke barrier partitions. NFPA 90A, *Air Conditioning and Ventilating*

Systems, requires smoke dampers to operate automatically upon detection of smoke and must function so that smoke movement through the duct is halted. Basically, they simply interrupt airflow through the duct. NFPA 90A permits the use of fire dampers for smoke control purposes. Obviously, a combination fire and smoke damper must meet the requirements for both. Smoke dampers are tested and classified by UL in accordance with UL 555S, *Standard for Leakage Rated Dampers for Use in Smoke Control Systems*.[8]

Smoke Detectors

Smoke detectors must be installed in all air conditioning or ventilating systems over 15,000 cu ft/min (425 m^3/min) capacity. Further, smoke detectors for use in ducts must include features in their design specifically for this purpose. Smoke detectors may shut down the air conditioning or ventilating system, sound alarms, operate smoke control dampers, activate fire suppression equipment, or initiate active smoke control functions. Preference is for detectors with adjustable sensitivity, thus minimizing false alarms due to incidental dust or other particulate matter.

These smoke detectors are located in the main supply ducts, downstream of air filters or air cleaners, and in the main return ducts prior to exhausting from the building or joining the fresh air intake ducts. Smoke detectors at these locations are primarily intended to prevent smoke circulation throughout the entire area served by shutting down the air handling system. Also they prevent circulation of smoke from a fire in the air filters or air cleaners. Due to dilution effects of air picked up from various branch return ducts, these smoke detectors cannot be expected to reliably provide "early warning" smoke detection. For this reason, additional smoke detectors may be provided, e.g., in the main branch return duct from each floor or major area division. Such detectors could also be tied into a zoned fire alarm system; however, such an arrangement is not a substitute for a smoke detection system for building protection. For guidance on smoke detector location, see NFPA 72E, *Automatic Fire Detectors*.

SMOKE CONTROL—ACTIVE

The preceding material covered passive control of smoke and fire gases—control designed to prevent products of combustion from moving out of the area of its source. It is an inescapable fact that attempts to completely confine smoke and fire gases are seldom successful. Recognizing this, smoke movement in high-rise buildings, and its threat to life safety, has been the object of much investigation. The discussion of modes of smoke movement, their causes and effects are outside the scope of this chapter. However, it is worth noting that high-rise buildings do present several unique problems, e.g., lengthy evacuation time, inability of conventional fire department equipment (aerial ladders, snorkels, and monitor nozzles) to reach upper floors, and the reinforcement of existing upward airflow patterns within the building via vertical shafts (stack effect).

In view of the increasing trend toward high-rise buildings, it becomes attractive to utilize the air conditioning or ventilating system for smoke control and removal in case of fire. Tests have been conducted on the feasibility of pressurizing emergency exit stairwells and elevator shafts to prevent smoke migration from the fire floor to other parts of a building during evacuation.[9,10]

The ASHRAE manual *Design of Smoke Control Systems for Buildings* provides guidelines for designers who wish to provide active smoke control systems for buildings.[11] This information is generally intended to provide systems that exhaust smoke from the immediate fire area, and provide pressurized outside air to adjacent areas, access corridors, and stairwells. It is fully recognized that this approach would apply more to large HVAC units serving individual floors, or large systems with volume control dampers at each floor. For additional guidance, see NFPA 92A, *Smoke Control Systems*, and NFPA 92B, *Smoke Management Systems in Malls, Atria, and Large Areas*.

The smoke control system must maintain safe exit routes with sufficient exiting time for building occupants to either leave or move to designated safe refuge areas.

Exhaust of smoke from the fire area is of primary concern. To replace this exhausted air, the HVAC system should provide 100 percent outside air to adjacent areas, thereby providing a clean atmosphere in exitways through the area immediately above the fire, and preventing smoke from flowing up through any holes in the floor slab and to the area immediately below the fire to provide safe areas for the fire fighters.

It must be fully understood that the smoke control systems mentioned previously are intended to provide a smoke-free means of exiting the building. If a fire gets out of hand, there is danger of ducts burning through and falling from the ceiling, or fans being subjected to intense heat so they may cease to operate. It can then be assumed that initial efforts at extinguishing the fire have failed and that occupants remaining in the building would probably be in serious danger. It is not intended that special electrical generation units, heavy-duty fans, or heavy ductwork would be used.

FANS, CONTROLS, ETC.

The fan unit on an air conditioning system should not in itself present undue hazard if properly installed and firmly supported on a rigid foundation. It should also be readily accessible for cleaning, servicing, and lubrication. Fans should be provided with excess vibration switches, wired to sound an alarm and initiate system shutdown when bearing failure is imminent.

Fan motors installed inside ducts or plenums need protective devices to cut off power before temperatures reach a point where smoke may be generated. Most fractional horsepower motors have over-temperature protective devices. Thermal overload relays are recommended for fan motors of one horsepower or larger.

Electric wiring to all components should follow NFPA 70, *National Electrical Code*. All electrical equipment should be listed by a qualified electrical testing laboratory. Wiring installed in ducts, plenums, and other spaces used for environmental air should meet the requirements of NFPA 262, *Fire and Smoke Characteristics of Electrical Wires and Cables*.

All air conditioning or ventilating systems need manual shutoffs for use in case of fire or other emergency. This shutoff should be well identified and located where it is readily accessible, such as near building exits. In systems of 2,000 to 15,000 cu ft/min (57 to 425 m^3/min) capacity, it is good practice to provide automatic shutoff controls triggered by thermostatic devices in the same locations as recommended for smoke detectors. A setting of 136°F (58°C) for the thermostatic device in the return air stream and a setting of 50°F (10°C) above maximum operational temperature for the device in the supply stream are recommended.

Energy Conservation

Energy conservation practices require a careful evaluation of the design and control of HVAC systems. To reduce electrical costs, fans are turned off during various portions of the day and during unoccupied hours. Without airflow, the duct fire and smoke detectors may not detect fire and thereby will not provide the protection that may be assumed as inherent in HVAC systems. The use of variable volume air systems is increasing as these systems have an overall lower energy use than most other systems. The variation in duct airflow in such systems can create a problem with the sensitivity of the duct-mounted detectors and cause false readings and alarms. Fan cycling and variable volume systems can also cause variations in air pressure relationships of the occupied spaces. An area may have a positive pressure relationship to another area when the fans are operating in one mode, and when the fans are cycled a completely different relationship can occur which can affect the performance of detection and control systems, and calls for careful design evaluation.

UNIT AIR CONDITIONERS

The term "unit air conditioner" may include any factory-produced unit serving one room or area. Such units do not involve the hazard of spreading fire from floor to floor or area to area as do ducted systems. However, if improperly designed, installed, or maintained, they may involve the other hazards associated with larger systems. For example, any window-sill type unit can overheat through failure of its thermal relay. This could lead to ignition of wire insulation or filter media, and the fire could spread to curtains or the wood sash of the window. Defective wiring could lead to the same condition. A common problem involving these units is that they are too frequently plugged into outlets on branch circuits not designed to carry the design load or the circuit is already overloaded. This practice directly violates principles of NFPA 70, *National Electrical Code*.

MAINTENANCE

Maintenance and cleaning are of utmost importance to safe operation of any air conditioning or ventilating system. Filters must be changed or cleaned as frequently as necessary. Ducts, particularly on the return side of the system, are cleaned out periodically to prevent hazardous accumulations of combustible dust and lint. Evidence of any defect of wiring or electrical equipment must be checked out immediately and corrected. Repairs on ducts or equipment casings which require welding or cutting should be protected by complete shutdown of the system and thorough cleaning of the area. If possible, the duct section to be repaired should be isolated from the rest of the system.

Proper maintenance includes periodic testing of all fire protection devices, including fire suppression equipment, smoke control and fire dampers, fire detectors, and alarms, and even vibration switches on fans. A regular testing program should be established. If such testing is outside the function of regular maintenance staff, it should be contracted to an outside agency.

BIBLIOGRAPHY

References Cited

1. ASHRAE, "Safety Code for Mechanical Refrigeration," No. 15-78, American Society of Heating, Refrigerating, and Air Conditioning Engineers, Atlanta, GA.
2. UL 900, *Standard for Performance of Air Filter Units*, Underwriters Laboratories Inc., Northbrook, IL, 1987.
3. UL 586, *Standard for High-Efficiency Particulate Air Filter Units*, Underwriters Laboratories Inc., Northbrook, IL, 1990.
4. ASTM D-93, *Standard Method of Test for Flash Point by Pensky-Martens Closed Tester*, American Society for Testing and Materials, Philadelphia, PA, 1980.
5. SMACNA, *Fibrous Glass Duct Construction*, STD 5th ed., 1985; *Duct Construction Standards*, 1st ed., 1985; Sheet Metal and Air Conditioning Contractors National Association, Inc., Tysons Corner, VA.
6. UL 181, *Standard for Factory-Made Air Ducts and Connectors*, Underwriters Laboratories Inc., Northbrook, IL, 1984.
7. UL 555, *Standard for Fire Dampers and Ceiling Dampers*, Underwriters Laboratories Inc., Northbrook, IL, 1986.
8. UL 555S, *Standard for Leakage Rated Dampers for Use in Smoke Control Systems*, Underwriters Laboratories Inc., Northbrook, IL, 1983.
9. Koplon, N. A., *Report of the Henry Grady Fire Tests*, City of Atlanta Building Department, Atlanta, GA, 1973.
10. McGuire, J. H., and Tamura, G. T., "The Pressurized Building Method of Controlling Smoke in High-Rise Buildings," Technical Paper No. 394 (NRCC 13365), 1973, National Research Council of Canada, Division of Building Research, Ottawa, Ontario, Canada.
11. ASHRAE, *Design of Smoke Control Systems for Buildings*, American Society of Heating, Refrigerating, and Air Conditioning Engineers, Atlanta, GA, 1983.

References

ASHRAE Handbook and Product Directory 1988 Equipment, American Society of Heating, Refrigerating, and Air Conditioning Engineers, Inc., Atlanta, GA.

Gypsum Association Fire Resistance Design Manual, 12th ed., Gypsum Association, Evanston, IL, 1988.

NFPA Codes, Standards, and Recommended Practices

Reference to the following NFPA codes, standards, and recommended practices will provide further information on air conditioning and ventilating systems discussed in this chapter. (See the latest *NFPA Catalog* for availability of current editions of the following documents.)

NFPA 70, *National Electrical Code*.

NFPA 72E, *Automatic Fire Detectors*.

NFPA 80, *Fire Doors and Windows*.

NFPA 90A, *Air Conditioning and Ventilating Systems*.

NFPA 92A, *Smoke Control Systems*.

NFPA 101, *Life Safety Code*.

NFPA 252, *Standard Methods of Fire Tests of Door Assemblies*.

NFPA 262, *Fire and Smoke Characteristics of Electrical Wires and Cables*.

Additional Readings

Associate Committee on the National Building Code, *Measures for Fire Safety in High Buildings*, National Research Council of Canada, Ottawa, Ontario, Canada, 1977.

Butcher, E. G., and Parnell, A. C., *Smoke Control in Fire Safety Design*, E & F. N. Spon Ltd., London, England, 1979.

Coad, W. J., "Safety Factors in HVAC Design," *Heating, Piping, Air Conditioning*, Vol. 57, No. 1, Jan. 1985.

Day, T., "Development of a European Test Method for Fire and Fire/Smoke Dampers," *Fire Prevention*, No. 220, June 1989, pp. 26-28.

"Fire and Smoke Control," *ASHRAE Handbook*, Systems Vol., Chap. 5, 1987.

Gewain, R. G., "Protection of Duct Openings in Two-Hour Fire-Resistant Walls and Partitions," *ASHRAE Journal*, Vol. 32, No. 5, May 1990, p. 16.

Gewain, R. G., "Fire Protection Criteria for Air Ducts," ASHRAE *Transactions* 1986, Vol. 92, 1986, pp. 550-555.

Hinkley, P. L., "Case for Combining Venting and Sprinkler Systems," *Fire Engineers Journal*, Vol. 47, No. 145, June 1987, pp. 17-22.

Irwin, W. T., "Duct Penetrations of One-Hour Fire Resistance Rated Nonloadbearing Walls/Partitions," ASHRAE *Transactions*, Vol. 92, 1986, pp. 556-565.

Kirson, D., "Automatic Sprinklers in Exhaust Systems," *Heating, Piping and Air Conditioning*, Vol. 61, No. 1, Jan. 1989, pp. 163-166.

Klote, J. H., "A Computer Model of Smoke Movement by Air Conditioning Systems (SMACS)," *Fire Technology*, Vol. 24, No. 4, 1988, pp. 299-311.

Klote, J. H., "Fire Safety Inspection and Testing of Air Moving Systems," NBSIR 87-3660, Nov. 1987, Center for Fire Research, Gaithersburg, MD.

Klote, J. H., and Cooper, L. Y., "Model of a Simple Fan-Resistance Ventilation System and Its Application to Fire Modeling," NIST 89-4141, Sept. 1989.

McCarthy, J. H., "Changing Regulations Over Fire Dampers," *Australian Refrigeration, Air Conditioning and Heating*, Vol. 42, No. 12, Dec. 1988, pp. 28-31, 32.

Mountain, S. C., "Safety in Air Conditioning," *H&V Engineer*, Vol. 61, No. 687, p. 22.

Newman, J. S., and Tewarson, A., "Flame Propagation in Ducts," *Combustion and Flame*, Vol. 51, 1983, pp. 347-355.

Perzak, F. J., Lazzara, C. P., and Kubala, T. A., "Fire Tests of Rigid Plastic Ventilation Ducts," Investigation Report 9085, 1987, U.S. Bureau of Mines, Pittsburgh, p. 16.

Reddaway, L. N., and Smith, D. J., "Fire Safety—The Future of Air Conditioning," *Australian Refrigeration, Air Conditioning, and Heating*, Vol. 40, No. 12, 1986, pp. 28-30.

Richards, P. E., "Air Ducts: The Uses and Abuses of Flexible Air Ducts," *Australian Refrigeration, Air Conditioning, and Heating*, Vol. 42, No. 9, 1988, p. 4.

Schwartz, J. K., "The Role of Fire Dampers in a Total Fire Protection System," TR 86-2, 1986, Society of Fire Protection Engineers, Boston, MA.

Schwartz, J. K., Jensen, R. H., and Antell, J., "Role of Dampers in a Total Fire Protection System Analysis," ASHRAE *Transactions*, Vol. 92, 1986, pp. 566-576.

Semple, J. B., and Bruce, D. O., "Review of Current Fire Damper Requirements in NFPA Standard 90A and Model Codes," ASHRAE *Transactions*, Vol. 92, 1986, pp. 541-549.

Wild, J., "Fans for Fire Smoke Venting," *FIre Surveyor*, Vol. 18, No. 2, Apr. 1989, pp. 5-9.

Woods-Ballard, W. R., "HT Series of Smoke Venting Fans," *Fire Surveyor*, Vol. 18, No. 3, June 1989, pp. 11-14.

MISCELLANEOUS BUILDING SERVICES

Robert W. Ryan and Mark Chubb

This chapter contains information about specific building services—those features or systems that, connected to public utilities, create a practical and efficient building environment. This discussion covers hazards associated with systems such as telecommunications equipment and plumbing. Also addressed are utility chases, shafts, and chutes, which are not addressed elsewhere in this section. While these hazards are similar to those related to building services discussed in other chapters, specific examples of fire scenarios are presented to illustrate concerns associated with these systems. Building services hazards generally fall into three categories: (1) a potential fuel, (2) a potential heat (ignition energy) source, or (3) a potential heat-energy or fuel transport mechanism. Telecommunications wiring and equipment, plumbing pipe, and utility shafts, chases, and chutes are no exceptions.

For a better understanding of hazards of building services, in general, consult Section 6, Chapter 15, "Hazards of Building Services." More detailed information about other systems can be found in Section 6, Chapter 1, "Building and Site Planning for Firesafety"; Section 6, Chapter 6, "Confinement of Fire in Buildings"; Section 6, Chapter 16, "Air Conditioning and Ventilating Systems"; and Section 6, Chapter 19, "Air Moving Equipment." The following chapters contain related information: Section 2, Chapter 3, "Electrical Systems and Appliances"; Section 2, Chapter 5, "Boiler Furnaces"; Section 2, Chapter 18, "Refrigeration Systems"; Section 2, Chapter 26, "Storage of Gases"; Section 2, Chapter 31, "Control of Electrostatic Ignition Sources"; Section 2, Chapter 32, "Lightning Protection Systems"; and Section 2, Chapter 33, "Waste Handling Systems and Equipment." Additional references related to these topics may be found at the end of this chapter.

TELECOMMUNICATIONS

Information is power. Access to, and control of, data has become an integral part of competitive forces in the global community. With a telecommunications revolution well underway, the need to access and control information has led to increased dependence upon electronic telecommunication technology. Associated with this technology is an immense amount of wire, cable, and hardware to connect people and machines in an ever-expanding network.

Although technology burnout from rapid change may be the most apparent issue arising out of this "Age of Information," a more insidious challenge exists in the area of fire protection. It is important to consider the following fire protection concerns associated with these changes: (1) wire and cable insulation, and the equipment itself, represent a potential fuel load; (2) installation of telecommunication equipment commonly accompanies large open areas or a reduction in building compartmentation; (3) unsightly communications cable and wire is frequently concealed, and (4) the loss of service from a telecommunications system, in many cases, represents a business's most significant interruption exposure. To reduce the risk associated with the last item—business interruption—adequate, appropriate steps must be taken to manage the hazards associated with the first three.

Hardware and Equipment

Investigations following the First Interstate Bank fire in Los Angeles on May 4, 1988, illustrate some of these points. This fire has been studied in detail. This includes efforts by Nelson, and other researchers at the National Institute of Standards and Technology, Center for Fire Research (NIST/CFR), to model the fire development scenario. Figures 6-17A and 6-17B illustrate the heat release rate (RHR) of a computer workstation. Data about this fuel package was central to the NIST/CFR modeling efforts for the First Interstate fire, and correlated well with available evidence. Using the detailed investigatory record and engineering calculations, Nelson and other NIST/CFR researchers concluded that concentrated groupings of computer workstations, combined with low ceilings, led to flashover conditions.[1] It was suggested that similar circumstances involving fuel and room geometry could lead to similar results. These findings further suggested that traditional assumptions about the light-hazard nature of office environments may need to be reconsidered.

Robert W. Ryan is acting director of, and Mark Chubb is a fire protection specialist in, the Department of Environmental Safety, University of Maryland.

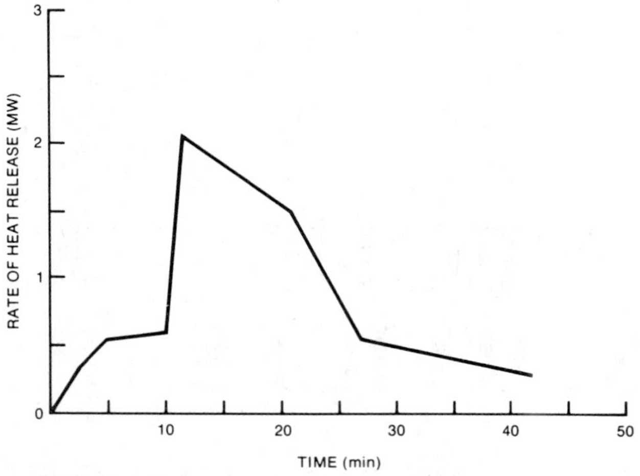

Figure 6-17A. Rate of heat release at a typical work station.

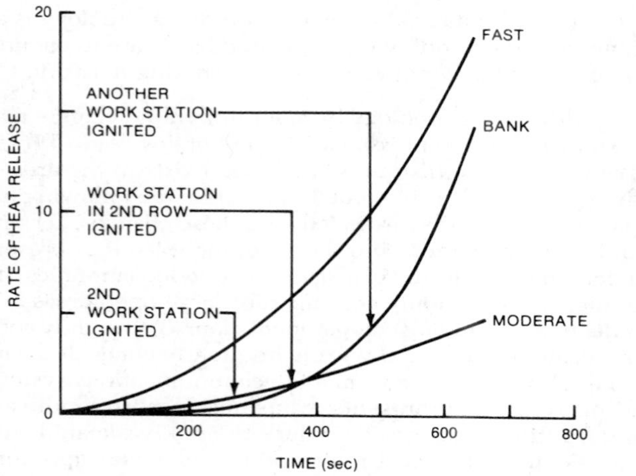

Figure 6-17B. Estimated free-burn rate of heat release of groups of work stations on the 12th floor.

Wire and Cable

In an office, fuel packages represented by workstations and other plastic commodities, including telephones, facsimile machines, and photocopiers, represent a significant fire hazard. The role of wire and cable in significant fires is less conclusive. Certainly, combustible insulation materials can degrade and even burn when subjected to internal heat from overloading or external heat from a fire. Concern about the contribution of combustible insulation materials focuses on two hazards: (1) fuel, and (2) toxicity. As a fuel, wire and cable sheathed in combustible insulations, usually plastic and, in particular, PVC, bundled in risers and cable trays, above ceilings, and in air plenums has been a significant concern. In recent years, however, new requirements mandating use of fire-resistant insulation materials have abated much of the concern about flame spread associated with these materials. Likewise, concern about the smoke produced by insulation materials, especially in supply and return air plenums, has been addressed by new requirements for low-smoke-producing wire and cable products. These changes are intended to supplant concern about PVC insulation. PVC, unlike new insulating materials containing polytetrafluoroethylene (PFTE) and other heat-resistant materials, produces hydrogen chloride when it undergoes pyrolysis. Telecommunications, signaling and control, optical-fiber, and coaxial antenna wires and cables carry little or no current or voltage. Consequently, when properly designed, installed, and maintained, these circuits represent little hazard of self-ignition due to overheating from misuse or damage. This combination of power-limited application and fire-resistant/low-smoke-producing insulation promises to maintain the fire hazard of new wire and cable installations within a manageable and generally acceptable level. (See Table 6-17A.)

TABLE 6-17A. *Cable Markings*

Cable Markings	Type
CL2P	Class 2 plenum cable
CL2R	Class 2 riser cable
CL2	Class 2 cable
CL2X	Class 2 cable, limited use
CL3P	Class 3 plenum cable
CL3R	Class 3 riser cable
CL3	Class 3 cable
CL3X	Class 3 cable, limited use
PLTC	Power-limited tray cable
NPLFP	Nonpower-limited fire protective signaling circuit plenum cable
NPLFR	Nonpower-limited fire protective signaling circuit riser cable
NPLF	Nonpower-limited fire protective signaling circuit cable
FPLP	Power-limited fire protective signaling circuit plenum cable
FPLR	Power-limited fire protective signaling circuit riser cable
FPL	Power-limited fire protective signaling circuit cable
MPP	Multipurpose plenum cable
CMP	Communications plenum cable
MPR	Multipurpose riser cable
CMR	Communications riser cable
MP	Multipurpose cable
CM	Communications cable
CMX	Communications cable, limited use
CMUC	Undercarpet communications cable
CATVP	CATV plenum cable
CATVR	CATV riser cable
CATV	CATV cable
CATVX	CATV cable, limited use

Test Methods

The following test methods are used to determine the fire hazards of wire and cable products used for telecommunications, signaling, and control: (1) NFPA 262, *Fire and Smoke Characteristics of Electrical Wire and Cable*, (2) UL 1581, *Vertical-Tray Flame Test*, and (3) UL 1666, *Standard Test for Flame Propagation Height of Electrical and Optical-Fiber Cable Installed Vertically in Shafts*.

PLUMBING

Plumbing fixtures and piping were not considered to be fire hazards, except during installation, until the widespread use of fiberglass and plastic. Currently, a wide variety of plastics are used for domestic water, sprinkler, industrial process, underground natural gas, and drain, waste, and vent (DWV) piping. Common plastic pipe polymers include: acyrlonitrile-butadiene-styrene (ABS), polyvinyl chloride (PVC or uPVC), chlorinated polyvinyl chloride (CPVC), polybutylene (PB), and polypropylene (PP).

The contribution of these materials to fire hazard has been widely investigated from as early as 1966. Much of the attention has focused on the ability of these materials to propagate fire through fire-resistance-rated assemblies. With the introduction of through-penetration firestop assemblies much of this concern may also be receding. Zicherman, reviewing the history of the plastic pipe debate, summarizes a discussion of the fire hazard of these materials as follows:

> Rarely have products used in fire-resistive construction been subjected to as extensive an evaluation as PVC-based piping products...The results of this testing and evaluation, as well as many years of field use, indicate that properly installed PVC-based products do not constitute a fire hazard in structures.[2]

A 1990 fire in a board and care facility in Bessemer, AL, resulted in six fatalities. This fire initially raised concern about the use of CPVC piping in automatic sprinkler systems. Subsequent investigation by NFPA and the Alabama State Fire Marshals Office indicated that improper design and grossly inadequate water supply to the sprinkler system—*not* the use of CPVC piping—were to blame for this system failure. Experts who conducted the post-incident analysis universally agreed that, even had metallic sprinkler piping been installed, the protection provided would also have been wholly inadequate.

SERVICE CHUTES, CHASES, AND UTILITY SHAFTS

Vertical communications are common in most buildings with stories more than one level above or below grade. These communications perform a variety of functions, including a supply or return air path; a route for piping, wire, or cable; or a means for conveying trash, linen, mail, and other materials from operating areas to service areas. Although these vertical communications are essential, they present a predictable and persistent fire hazard. The fundamental problems in any fire—controlling the travel of smoke, heated gases, and flame—are complicated by such communicating spaces. Preventing vertical spaces from contributing to fire spread requires forethought and planning. Fortunately, concern about the contribution of vertical spaces to the transporting of heat and smoke has prompted considerable research and code attention.

Enclosures

Addressing a fundamental problem, such as controlling the vertical progress of fire and its by-products, relies on a fundamental response, that is, compartmentation. Vertical shafts, chases, and chutes, regardless of their purpose, must be segregated from other spaces by fire-resistance-rated enclosures of appropriate fire endurance. Successfully containing a fire and its by-products requires adequate fire-resistance to protect the area exposed and the structural integrity of the assembly itself in concert with an automatic sprinkler system. Construction of a fire-rated assembly must, therefore, consider the rating required, continuity of the assembly, the structural systems involved, and the function of the spaces on either side of the assembly. NFPA 251, *Fire Tests of Building Construction and Materials* (ASTM E119) provides the standard method of determining the fire endurance of walls, partitions, floor/ceiling assemblies, and roof/ceiling assemblies.

Code requirements: The rating required to protect a vertical shaft from the vertical spread of fire is primarily a function of the hazards involved (i.e., how big a fire is likely to be and where it will occur). These determinations may be rather subjective and/or somewhat variable. Most codes require two-hour fire-resistance-rated enclosures for shafts of more than two stories in height, and one-hour ratings for one or two floors. However, some situations may merit more protection considering the hazards involved.

Continuity: The greatest problem affecting the performance of fire-resistance-rated enclosures may be continuity. Two circumstances repeatedly contribute to failure of fire-resistance-rated enclosures: (1) failure to protect through-penetrations adequately, especially those created after occupancy; and (2) overlooked construction deficiencies. Generic and proprietary through-penetration firestop systems and devices are commercially available. When properly selected and installed, they can provide proven protection where duct work, piping, wire, cable, and other devices or systems must pass through fire-resistance-rated assemblies. These systems or devices may employ heat-passive protection using generic construction materials, such as mortar, grout, and thermal insulation. They may also employ active systems and devices that typically consist of proprietary, heat-actuated chemical and mechanical systems and devices. Mechanical devices in this category include fire dampers and fire doors, as well as guillotine-style and gravity-actuated plug devices for plastic pipe. Chemical systems and devices usually employ intumescent technology to seal irregular openings created around wire, cable, and plastic piping when they collapse or fail during a fire. Construction deficiencies can include inadequate structural fire-resistance supporting rated wall or floor assemblies, non-rated construction materials, substitution of unapproved materials in rated systems and assemblies, and incomplete construction or hidden voids.

Structural considerations: The structural system itself must be a prime consideration when designing fire-rated enclosures. A structure supporting a fire-resistance-rated enclosure must remain capable of supporting the enclosure assembly under fire conditions. If the structure involved supports other building elements, these loads must not compromise the integrity or endurance of the fire-rated enclosure. Too frequently, the fire-resistance-rated assemblies are considered separately from the structural system involved. Passive and active fire protection features, like other building services and systems, are often imposed upon the basic architectural and structural design after the fact. This arrangement can too easily result in construction and maintenance difficulties that will ultimately compromise either passive or active approaches.

Hazards and exposures. The use of the space itself is the last, and perhaps most apparent, factor involved in the selection and construction of a fire-resistance-rated enclosure. It must be determined on which side is the hazard and the exposure. Under most circumstances, concern focuses on controlling fires originating outside the shaft that could void the protection and thus spread vertically through these spaces. However, some vertical spaces, particularly service chutes (e.g., linen, laundry, and trash) are frequently associated with fires originating in them. One such instance of a fire originating in a trash chute occurred March 22, 1987, in the Schomberg Plaza apartment building in the Harlem section of Manhattan. This fire started in trash lodged between the twenty-seventh and twenty-ninth floors and spread to the top of the building resulting in seven deaths. Although automatic sprinklers were installed in the shaft, valves controlling water supply to the compactor and trash chute sprinklers were closed at the time of the fire. In addition, the fire department's board of inquiry concluded that construction openings between the chute and the apartment kitchens, where victims either were found or jumped, contributed to radiant and convected heat transfer, while metal pipe supports and chute anchors contributed through conduction. Clearly, both active and passive systems did not perform as intended. The fire department report examined the reasons for this outcome in considerable detail, and concluded that many factors were involved, including the fire department itself.

SUMMARY

Many lessons have been learned, too often tragically, about the contribution of certain building service components of fire hazard. Recent innovations and research, however, have gone a long way toward reducing the threat presented by many building service materials. Nonetheless, many lessons still remain to be learned. Controlling the selection and distribution of fuels in buildings, separating communicating spaces, and maintaining installed fire protection features, both active and passive, are each essential if building service features are to keep a building safe, as well as comfortable and efficient.

BIBLIOGRAPHY

References Cited

1. Nelson, H. E., "Science in Action: An Engineering View of the Fire at the First Interstate Bank Building," *Fire Journal*, Vol. 83, No. 4, July-Aug. 1989, pp. 28-34.
2. Zicherman, J. B., "Is PVC Piping Firesafe?" *Fire Journal*, Vol. 84, No. 6, Nov.-Dec. 1990, pp. 36-42.

NFPA Codes, Standards, Recommended Practices, and Manuals

Reference to the following NFPA codes, standards, and recommended practices will provide further information on the miscellaneous building services discussed in this chapter. (See the latest *NFPA Catalog* for availability of current editions of the following documents.)

NFPA 13, *Installation of Sprinkler Systems.*

NFPA 54, *National Fuel Gas Code.*

NFPA 58, *Storage and Handling of Liquefied Petroleum Gases.*

NFPA 70, *National Electrical Code®.*

NFPA 72, *Protective Signaling Systems.*

NFPA 80, *Fire Doors and Windows.*

NFPA 82, *Incinerators, Waste, and Linen Handling Systems and Equipment.*

NFPA 90A, *Air Conditioning and Ventilating Systems.*

NFPA 90B, *Warm Air Heating and Air Conditioning Systems.*

NFPA 96, *Removal of Smoke and Grease-Laden Vapors from Commercial Cooking Equipment.*

NFPA 101®, *Life Safety Code®.*

NFPA 211, *Chimneys, Fireplaces, Vents, and Solid-Fuel-Burning Appliances.*

NFPA 251, *Fire Tests of Building Construction and Materials.*

NFPA 252, *Fire Tests of Fire Door Assemblies.*

NFPA 262, *Fire and Smoke Characteristics of Electrical Wires and Cables.*

Additional Readings

Attwood, P. C., "Penetration of Fire Partitions by Plastic Pipe," *Fire Technology*, Vol. 16, No. 1, Jan. 1980, p. 37.

Bellino, R. A., "Developing and Testing High-Performance Multi-Pair Cables," *Connection Technology*, Vol. 5, No. 11, Nov. 1989, pp. 12-15.

Benjamin, I. A., and Parker, W. J., "Fire Spread Potential of ABS Plastic Plumbing," *Fire Technology*, Vol. 8, No. 2, May 1972, pp. 104-119.

Benjamin, I. A., *et al.*, *Fire Endurance of Gypsum Board Walls and Chases Containing Plastics and Metallic Drain, Waste, and Vent Plumbing Systems*, U.S. Government Printing Office, Washington, DC, 1975.

Bimonthly Fire Record, "Electrical Fire Spreads through Store," *Fire Journal*, Vol. 77, No. 2, Mar. 1983, p. 10.

Bimonthly Fire Record, "Group Cable Fire," *Fire Journal*, Vol. 70, No. 6, Nov. 1976, p. 41.

Bimonthly Fire Record, "Mail Room Fire," *Fire Journal*, Vol. 76, No. 2, Mar. 1982, p. 13.

Bimonthly Fire Record, "Outside Trash Chute Fire," *Fire Journal*, Vol. 78, No. 1, Jan. 1984, p. 16.

Bimonthly Fire Record, "Short Circuit Ignites PVC Insulation," *Fire Journal*, Vol. 73, No. 4, July 1979, p. 22.

Bimonthly Fire Record, "Short Circuit Results in Loss over $750,000," *Fire Journal*, Vol. 76, No. 3, May 1982, p. 22.

Bimonthly Fire Record, "Telephone Equipment Destroyed," *Fire Journal*, Vol. 74, No. 2, Mar. 1980, p. 21.

Bimonthly Fire Record, "Welding Spark Ignites Plastic Pipe," *Fire Journal*, Vol. 70, No. 4, Jan. 1976, p. 34.

Boyd, H. D., and Locurto, C. A., "Reliability and Maintainability for Fire Protection Systems," *Proceedings* of the First International Symposium on Fire Safety Science, Hemisphere, Washington, DC, 1986, pp. 963-970.

Braun, E., Shields, J. R., and Harris, R. H.,"Flammability Characteristics of Electrical Cables Using the Cone Calorimeter," *NISTIR 88-4003*, Center for Fire Research, Gaithersburg, MD, Jan. 1989.

Bukowski, R. W., "Toxic Hazard Evaluation of Plenum Cables," *Fire Technology*, Vol. 21, No. 4, 1985, pp. 252-266.

Choi, K. K., "Firestops for Plastic Pipe," *Fire Technology*, Vol. 23, No. 4, Nov. 1987, pp. 267-279.

Church, J. C., *Practical Plumbing Design Guide*, McGraw-Hill New York, NY, 1979.

Clarke, F. B., and Benjamin, I. A., "Overall Safety of Wire and Cable Materials," *Proceedings* of the 34th International Wire and Cable Symposium, U.S. Army, 1985, pp. 241-249.

Crane, *et al.*, *Electrical Insulation Fire Characteristics*, U.S. Dept. of Transportation, Oklahoma City, OK, 1979.

Daly, J. M., "Wire and Cable Revisions in the 1987 NEC," *Record of Conference Papers - 34th Annual Petroleum and Chemical Industry Conference*, IEEE, 1987, pp. 55-61.

Dieter, A., and Graf, R., "Curbing the Threat of Electrical Cables," *Fire International*, Vol. 12, No. 112, 1988, pp. 22-23, 25.

Eiden, A. J., "Designing Cables to Resist Fire," *Plastics and Rubber International*, Vol. 14, No. 4, Aug. 1989, pp. 16-18.

Eiermann, H. W., "Fire Protection for Electrical Cable Installations: The KBS-System," *Proceedings* of Conference on Offshore Passive Fire Protection, Plastics and Rubber Institute, 1987, pp. 1-17.

Ettling, B. V., "Electrical Wiring in Building Fires," *Fire Technology*, Vol. 14, No. 4, Nov. 1978, p. 317.

"Fire Hazard in Cable Runs," *Civil Engineering*, March 1987, pp. 47-48.

Frank, T. E., "Fire and Explosion Control in Bag Filter Dust Collection Systems," *Fire Journal*, Vol. 75, No. 2, Mar. 1981.

Fujimura, S., and Fukuda, T., "Smoke Generating Properties of Cable Materials," *Proceedings* of the 19th Symposium on Electrical Insulating Materials, Institute of Electrical Engineers of Japan, 1986, pp. 289-292.

Glass, R. A., and Rubin, A. I., *Fire Safety for High-Rise Buildings: The Role of Communications*, Center for Building Technology, National Bureau of Standards, Washington, DC, 1979.

Hendricks, V., Pokrywka, J., and Creek, C., "Wired for Disaster, Cableway Improvement Program," *Journal of Ship Production*, Vol. 5, No. 4, Nov. 1989, pp. 245-248.

International Conference on Fire-Resistant Hose, Cables and Belting, Plastics and Rubber Institute, London, England, 1986.

Kaufman, S., "Fire Tests and Fire-Resistant Telecommunications Cables," *Fire Journal*, Vol. 79, No. 6, Nov. 1985, pp. 33-38.

Kaufman, S., "1987 National Electrical Code Requirements for Cable," *Proceedings* of the 35th International Wire and Cable Symposium, U.S. Army Communications-Electronics Command, 1986, pp. 545-553.

Klem, T. J., "Los Angeles High-Rise Bank Fire," *Fire Journal*, Vol. 83, No. 3, March/April 1989, pp. 72-91.

Larina, E. T., *et al.*, "Evaluating the Fire-Safety Characteristics of Electrical Cables," *Soviet Electrical Engineering*, (English translation of *Elektrolekhnika*), Vol. 59, No. 12, 1988, pp. 3-38.

Lathrop, J. K., "Telephone Exchange Fire," *Fire Journal*, Vol. 69, No. 4, July 1975, p. 5.

Lichtenstein, S., "Operation Firestop," *Professional Safety*, Vol. 23, No. 6, June 1978.

McGuire, J. H., "Small-Scale Fire Tests of Walls Penetrated by Telephone Cables," *Fire Technology*, Vol. 11, No. 2, May 1975, p. 21.

McGuire, J. H., "Penetration of Fire Partitions by Plastic DWV Pipe," *Fire Technology*, Vol. 9, No. 1, Feb. 1973, p. 5.

McLaughlin, D. L., "Fire Tests of Fiberglass and PVC Ducts for Minimum Sprinkler Coverage," *Fire Journal*, Vol. 72, No. 2, Mar. 1978, p. 59.

Meshchanov, G. I., *et al.*, "Testing of Electrical Cables Not Spreading Combustion Under Actual Installation Conditions," *Soviet Electrical Engineering*, Vol. 59, No. 12, 1988, pp. 29-32.

National Electrical Manufacturers' Association, "NEMA High Rise Fire Alarm Systems Recommendations for State and Local Codes," Washington, DC, 1983.

National Electrical Manufacturers' Association and The Society of the Plastics Industry, Inc., "Characteristics of Polyvinyl Chloride Conduit, Insulated Wire & Piping in Fire Situations," Washington, DC.

Nemeth, Craig W., "Penetration Sealing with Silicone RTV Foams," *Fire Journal*, Vol. 76, No. 1, Jan. 1982.

Pannkoke, T., "Thermoplastic Piping: An Overview," *Heating/Piping/Air Conditioning*, Vol. 51, No. 4, Apr. 1979.

Peytier, A., "Assessment of Fire Risks Due to Low Voltage, Low Power Cables in Domestic and Office Applications," *Conference Record* of the 1986 IEEE Industry Applications Society Annual Meeting, Papers Presented at the 21st Annual Meeting, IEEE, 1986, pp. 1024-1028.

Philbrick, S. E., "Selecting Cables for Fire-Risk Applications," *Electronics and Power*, Vol. 26, No. 3, Mar. 1980, pp. 232-233.

Plastics and Plastics Products, National Fire Protection Association, Quincy, MA, 1975.

Powers, F. C., ed., "Electric Cables in Trays," *Sentinel*, Vol. 35, No. 4, Aug. 1979, p. 3.

Powers, F. C., ed., "Why Cable Penetrations Need Fire Stops," *Sentinel*, Vol. 35, No. 4, Aug. 1979.

Sawyer, R. G., and Elsner, J. A., "Cable Fire at Browns Ferry Nuclear Plant," *Fire Journal*, Vol. 70, No. 4, July 1976, p. 5.

Schaenman, P., *Schomberg Plaza Fire New York City (Harlem), March 22, 1987*, Major Fire Investigation Project, Report 004, Federal Emergency Management Agency, United States Fire Administration, Emmittsburg, MD, 1987.

Schuman, A. R., "Poke-through Protection," *Fire Technology*, Vol. 11, No. 4, Nov. 1975, p. 294.

Smith, K., "Selecting Cables for Fire Risk Situations in Mines and Other Installations," *Elektron*, Vol. 5, No. 8, Aug. 1988, p. 5.

Stevens, R. E., "Utility Shafts for Piping and Wiring," *Fire Journal*, Vol. 61, No. 4, July 1967, pp. 22-23.

Suzuki, H., *et al.*, "Fire-Resistant Optical Cables with Special Plastic-Coated Fibers," *Polymer Enginering and Science*, Vol. 29, No. 17, 1989, pp. 1182-1185.

Swingler, S. G., Stevens, G. C., and Gibbons, J. A. M., "Small-Scale Assessment of Flame Propagation and Heat Release Rate of Electric Cable Materials," *Proceedings* of the Fifth International Conference on Dielectric Materials, Measurements and Applications, IEE Conference Publication No. 289, IEE, London, England, 1988, pp. 45-50.

Szendzielorz, A., and Spyra, F., "Flammability of Single Cables," *Proceedings* of the 5th BEAMA International Electrical Insulation Conference, Cavanagh Associates, Leatherhead, England, 1986, pp. 107-110.

Taylor, K. T., "Temporarily Disconnected: An Overview of Fire Experience in Telephone Exchanges and Central Offices in the U.S. from 1982 to 1986," *Fire Journal*, Vol. 83, No. 3, May-June 1989, pp. 24-27.

Troxell, G. E., "Fire Tests of Plastic Vents and Drain Pipes," *Fire Journal*, Vol. 60, No. 4, July 1966, pp. 52-57.

UL 1581, *Vertical-Tray Flame Test*, Underwriters Laboratories Inc., Northbrook, IL .

UL 1666, *Standard Test for Flame Propagation Height of Electrical and Optical-Fiber Cable Installed Vertically in Shafts*, Underwriters Laboratories Inc., Northbrook, IL..

Watrous, L. D., "High-Rise Building Fire - Sao Paulo, Brazil," *Fire Journal*, Vol. 66, No. 4, July 1972, p. 107.

Watrous, L. D., "High-Rise Fire in New Orleans," *Fire Journal*, Vol. 67, No. 3, May 1973, p. 9.

Watrous, L. D., "Tae Yon Kak Hotel Fire-Seoul, Korea," *Fire Journal*, Vol. 66, No. 3, May 1972, p.12.

Williamson, R. B., "Installing ABS and PVC Drain, Waste, and Vents Systems in Fire-Resistant Buildings," *Fire Journal*, Vol. 73, No. 2, Mar. 1979, pp. 36-45.

Woolhead, F., "Risk Management: Preventing and Controlling Cable Fires," *Fire Surveyor*, Vol. 18, No. 3, June 1989, pp. 24-28.

Woolhead, F., "The Threat to a Business Due to Fire at Electric Cable Terminations," *Fire Surveyor*, Vol. 19, No. 2, Apr. 1990, pp. 17-19.

EXPLOSION PREVENTION AND PROTECTION

Revised by Joseph A. Senecal

An explosion in an industrial setting is ordinarily the result of the sudden and rapid conversion of chemical energy to thermal energy, usually due to the deflagration of a fuel/oxidant mixture or exothermic decomposition of a chemical substance. Such processes quickly heat the surrounding gas phase to high temperatures. Further, the number of moles of gas contained in the process volume may be increased. The magnitude of the ensuing pressure rise will depend on several factors. If the process enclosure is unable to withstand the mechanical forces due to a large rise in pressure, it will become damaged or rupture, possibly issuing projectiles, flaming matter, unburned dust, mist, or gas to further fuel the flames. A pressure shock is also likely, which may lead to damage at locations removed from the initial event. Personal injuries and fatalities are possible and all too common.

Explosions may also arise by other means. Examples are boiling liquid expanding vapor explosions (BLEVES), runaway chemical reactions, pyrotechnic explosions, and high-explosive detonations. These are, however, outside the scope of this chapter.

Five requirements must be met in order for an explosion to occur. These are:

1. Fuel concentration must be between lower and upper flammability limits.
2. Oxidant must be present above maximum safe concentration.
3. Reactants must be intimately mixed.
4. An ignition source must be present.
5. Confinement of reactants restricts escape of expanding gases and leads to pressure rise.

The combination of 1, 2, and 4 has long been referred to as the fire triangle. It is the intimate mixing of fuel and oxidant, however, which gives rise on ignition to a deflagration, rather than a fire, and high rates of thermal energy release. The degree to which the deflagrating medium is confined will regulate the magnitude of the ultimate pressure rise.

Protection against the effects of industrial explosions may be obtained using two general approaches: (1) prevention, and (2) mitigation. Prevention measures discussed in this chapter relate to the control of ignition sources and reducing the concentrations of oxidants or fuel species in order to prevent formation of combustible mixtures. The methods discussed for mitigating the effects of a deflagration once initiated include pressure containment, deflagration suppression, and deflagration venting.

The prevention and protection measures discussed herein are discussed in depth in NFPA 69, *Explosion Prevention Systems*, and NFPA 68, *Venting of Deflagrations*. The following chapters in this Handbook are also recommended in order to understand more fully the fundamentals of fire and explosion physics, materials flammability, ignition, and extinguishment:

Section 1, Chapter 4, "Chemistry and Physics of Fire"; Section 1, Chapter 5, "Explosions"; Section 1, Chapter 6, "Theory of Fire and Explosion Control"; Section 2, Chapter 31, "Control of Electrostatic Ignition Sources"; Section 3, Chapter 5, "Flammable and Combustible Liquids"; Section 3, Chapter 7, "Gases"; and Section 3, Chapter 12, "Dusts."

In spite of an increased awareness of the potential hazards attendant to the handling of combustible materials, industrial explosions continue to occur at a high frequency. A survey of European data[1] indicated that in the period 1965 to 1980 there were 357 explosions involving dusts alone. Agricultural and wood products accounted for 57 percent of these incidents; plastic, metal, chemical, and coal dusts accounted for the balance. The most frequently involved types of materials processing equipment were silos (20 percent), pulverizers (14 percent), filters (14 percent), conveyors (10 percent), driers (8 percent), mixers (5 percent), furnaces (5 percent), and miscellaneous (24 percent). The most common identifiable ignition source was mechanical sparks at 29 percent of events; 46 percent of ignitions were about equally distributed among causes

Joseph A. Senecal, Ph.D., P.E., M.B.A., is manager of the Combustion Research Center, Fenwal Safety Systems, Inc. He is a member of National Fire Protection Association's Committee 68 on Deflagration Venting and Committee 69 on Explosion Protection Systems; the American Institute of Chemical Engineers (AIChE) 11a Committee on Loss Prevention; and the American Society for Testing and Materials E27 Committee on Hazards of Chemicals.

related to smoldering particles, frictional heating, static electricity, hot surfaces, fires, and auto-ignition. In about 25 percent of the events, the ignition source was not determinable. Thus, it is clear that all types of combustible materials and materials-handling units have been, and continue to be, susceptible to potential explosions, and that nearly every possible ignition source has, in fact, been verified to pose a real threat.

While the theoretical and empirical details are presented at length elsewhere,[2,3,4] it is useful to note here several of the more important issues relating to deflagration development. These are: (1) the physical and chemical properties of materials; (2) the particle size distribution, in the case of dusts or mists; (3) the concentration of combustible material suspended in air or other oxidizing medium; (4) the concentration of oxygen or other oxidizer; (5) the concentration of moisture or other inert materials; (6) the initial turbulence intensity of the fuel-air mixture; (7) the initial temperature and pressure of the combustible mixture; (8) the internal geometry of the process enclosure to include size, shape, and distribution of obstacles to flow; (9) the nature and location of the ignition source; and (10) the size, location, and operating characteristics of pressure-relief openings.

Before proceeding, it is important to understand some terms regarding explosion suppression. The following definitions are from NFPA 69, *Explosion Prevention Systems*.

Deflagration: Propagation of a combustion zone at a velocity that is less than the speed of sound in the unreacted medium. (Note: The speed of sound is approximately 1100 ft per sec (335 m/sec) at sea level.)

Detonation: Propagation of a combustion zone at a velocity that is greater than thespeed of sound in the unreacted medium.

Explosion: Bursting or rupture of a building or a container due to the development of internal pressure.

EXPLOSIVE ENERGY RELEASE

Combustive deflagration or other processes liberating heat or adding large amounts of gas to an enclosed space results in a rise in pressure at a rate dependent on the total energy release rate and the cross-sectional area of openings available through which gas may escape. In the case of a closed-vessel deflagration, the maximum pressure attained may be up to ten times the initial pressure. Enclosures not designed to pressure vessel standards will most likely fail. The severity of the consequences will depend on several factors but is governed in particular by the pressure attained in the enclosure at the failure point. The energy released at the point of vessel rupture is given by.[5]

$$W_e = \frac{P_1 V_1}{(k-1)} \left[1 - (P_2/P_1)^{(k-1)/k}\right] \qquad (1)$$

where

W_e = explosive energy released, J
P_1 = vessel pressure at rupture, Pa
P_2 = ambient pressure, Pa
V = vessel volume, m^3
k = ratio of specific heats of vessel contents at time of failure, Cp/Cv

The energy release computed by Equation 1 may be expressed in terms of the explosive equivalent of a mass of TNT, as follows:

$$M_{TNT} = 2.13 \times 10^{-7}\, W_e \text{ (kg)} \qquad (2)$$

It may be readily shown using Equations 1 and 2 that explosions in average-size process volumes can be equivalent to an alarming quantity of high explosives. For example, a 10 m^3 vessel that ruptures at 100 psig (690 kPa/g) liberates explosive energy equivalent to 5 lb (2.3 kg) of TNT. Such an example helps to give weight to the outcome of an inadequately protected process system that crosses the boundary between a "potential hazard" and an industrial accident.

CONTROL OF IGNITION SOURCES

Deflagrations, and possible resulting explosions, would be impossible if ignition sources could be completely eliminated from process spaces. Procedures used to design, operate, and maintain process systems should consider ignition source prevention. Some of the more common means of ignition control are discussed below.

Open Fires and Hot-Work Permits

Direct-fired equipment should not be located in areas that are, or might become, hazardous by virtue of a combustible atmosphere. If locating such equipment in a nonhazardous area is impractical, then isolation of the fired system from its surroundings may be accomplished by use of vapor-tight enclosures or barriers, with combustion air and fuel piped to the combustion chamber from supplies in safe locations.

In combustion-hazard spaces, there must be strict administrative control of smoking, welding, and electrical work by means of a permit system.

Electrical Equipment

Electrical equipment must be selected and installed in accordance with NFPA 70, *National Electrical Code®*, in order to avoid having such equipment become potential ignition sources.

Ignition by Electrostatic Discharge

The development of electrostatic charges can result from the contact and separation of objects, particularly small particles, if at least one of the objects has a high surface resistivity.[6,7] Thus, particulate matter (and fluids) can become charged during transport due to innumerable contact charge transfers made by particles with duct and container walls, and even with air. Powder charging is particularly prone to occur if the bulk resistivity of the powder is greater than 10^8 ohm-m, a value exceeded by most organic substances.

Electrostatic charges, once accumulated on objects or bulk powders, may discharge in any of several modes, each of which has a different incendiary capability. The energy dissipated on discharge may be as little as a few milliJoules or as much as several Joules. The ignition energy of vapors is usually on the order of 1 mJ, while that of many fine dusts is on the order of 10 to 100 mJ. Thus, ignition of vapors and dust clouds by electrostatic discharge is clearly possible. NFPA 77, *Static Electricity*, should be consulted for guidelines in handling charging materials. In general, process equipment handling dusts should be constructed of materials that are conductive or of low dielectric strength (less than 4 kV). Parts of equipment subject to charge accumulation should be grounded. Also, personnel who handle powder having a minimum ignition energy (MIE) less than that of dusts that are known to be easily ignitable should be grounded. Lycopodium, a naturally occurring spore and common reference material used in dust ignition tests, is considered easily ignitable. Dusts having an MIE lower than that of lycopodium are candidates for conservative grounding practices. (Note: A particular MIE value is not stated below which conservative grounding practices should be observed. This is because several different methods of determining MIE are in use, all of which are probably self-consistent, but which result in widely varying values of MIE for the same test material.) Electrically insulating coatings on process surfaces and conveying ducts should be avoided when handling combustible dusts.

Mechanically Generated Sparks

Mechanical sparks of sufficient temperature and thermal energy content to cause ignition of dust and vapor clouds can readily be generated when a sparking material is struck by a second object at sufficiently high velocity. Pulverizing and grinding equipment must be carefully protected from accidental inclusion of tramp metal or other spark-inducing materials in the feed streams. Magnetic separators are one means of preventing iron and steel objects from entering such equipment.

Hot Surface Ignition

Surface temperatures high enough to ignite layered dusts can result from a number of causes. Inadequately lubricated bearing surfaces or misaligned belts in bucket elevators are examples of potential hot surface ignition sources. Electrical components covered with a thick layer of dust, a good thermal insulator, may overheat to the point of heating the dust covering to smoldering and ignition. The resultant fire may then lead to major damage itself or serve as an ignition source for a combustible atmosphere. It is suspected that many dust-collector explosions originate in a primary dust layer fire started by passage of an incendary ember or spark into the hopper.

Every effort should be made to identify and control potential ignition sources. Doing so will reduce, but not eliminate, the probability of the occurrence of an ignition point. In order to reduce further the possibility of a process deflagration, steps must also be taken to determine and control the concentrations of oxygen and airborne combustibles.

OXIDANT CONCENTRATION REDUCTION

Explosions can be prevented by maintaining the local oxygen (or other oxidant) concentration below that necessary to support combustion at the initial temperatures and pressure of the process. NFPA 69, *Explosion Prevention Systems*, terms this "oxidant concentration reduction." The usual method of oxidant concentration reduction is by purging or inerting the space with a gas that is deficient in oxidant.

Fundamentals of Inerting Systems

The fire and explosion hazard of many materials can be safeguarded during storage and processing operations by the use of a suitable inert gas. This is possible since combustion of most materials will not occur if there is an absence of atmospheric oxygen or if the concentration of atmospheric oxygen is reduced below a certain specific limit.

When inert gas is used as a means of controlling fires and explosions, its principal function is to prevent the formation of explosive vapor-air mixtures, generally in enclosed spaces. Typical examples are its use to inert tanks prior to repair, to empty flammable liquid storage tanks by pressure, to prevent the formation of explosive mixtures in drying ovens, and to blanket flammable products in storage tanks or reaction equipment.

In many cases, dust explosions can be prevented by inert gas. Industries that are faced with the explosion hazard of flour, starch, sugar, coal, plastics, metals, and other combustible dusts have found it practical in some cases to install inert gas protection. Equipment, such as grinders, pulverizers, mixers, conveying systems, classifiers, dust collectors, sacking machines, and the like, can be protected in this manner.

Other applications of inert gas include: (1) use in chemical processes where there is a continuous explosion hazard if oxygen is present; (2) for protection of operations that must be conducted above the ignition temperature of the materials involved; (3) to arrest spontaneous heating of products in storage; and (4) as a means of achieving explosion suppression.

The limitations of inerting methods should be recognized. These include reliability and adequacy of supply, freedom from moisture or any other constituents that could cause contamination or degradation of product, dependability of instrumentation and excess-pressure-relieving devices, and the suitability of the supply system to ensure sufficient quantity under peak demand.

Personnel must be protected by proper respiratory equipment before entering any enclosure where inert gas has been used, and an atmosphere deficient in oxygen may exist. Air-supplied or oxygen-supplied masks should be used. Self-contained breathing apparatus of short duration has been recognized by the U.S. Bureau of Mines for self-rescue. Filter-canister-type masks are inadequate for work involving inert gas because they do not supply any oxygen. The toxicity of certain gases used for inerting must also be recognized.

Basic Installation Criteria

NFPA 69, *Explosion Prevention Systems*, provides a considerable amount of information on inerting materials, methods for installing inerting systems, and oxidant and combustible concentration reduction, including basic design data for the guidance of engineers.

Hazard evaluation: Consideration should be given first to the evaluation of all hazards that are to be protected, to the operating equipment involved, and to any abnormal conditions that might be encountered. Such an overall study is essential in order to plan properly the most practical and reliable installation and distribution system.

The need to provide inert gas protection can influence basic plant layout design. It may be desirable, for example, to locate the gas supply near the operation with the largest demand. Likewise, the type, size, and location of process vessels and storage facilities might be quite different if inert gas protection is to be provided.

Type of inert gas: Although there are a number of inert gases readily available, the two most common are carbon dioxide and nitrogen. Others, such as argon, helium, steam, flue gas, and the halogenated hydrocarbons (halons), may satisfy special needs.

The gas that is most suitable for a specific application will depend on a number of factors. In addition to being inert from a fire and explosion standpoint, the gas must be chemically unreactive with the materials to be protected and free from contaminants. If there is a corrosion problem, or if the gas will come in contact with water-reactive chemicals, control of moisture must be possible and practical.

A sufficient volume of gas must be available at an adequate pressure to satisfy requirements at periods of peak demand. A completely oxygen-free gas may be necessary for process reasons or in order to maintain product quality, though it is not essential for fire protection. However, it is always advisable to maintain as low an oxygen concentration as practicable. The maximum permissible oxygen percentage below which combustion will not be supported varies with the flammable materials involved and the inerting medium. (See Tables 6-18A through 6-18C.)

Quantity requirements: The amount of inert gas required and the rate of application will depend upon: (1) the oxygen concentration that is permissible and the amount of oxygen in the inert gas—if any; (2) the safety margin to be observed; (3) the amount of loss through leakage; (4) atmospheric conditions; (5) operating conditions; (6) size and shape of the equipment to be protected; and (7) the method of application.

METHODS OF INERT GAS APPLICATION

There are two ways of applying inert gas to ensure the formation of a noncombustible atmosphere within an enclosed tank or space. These may be designated as the: (1) batch or fixed volume requirement method, and (2) continuous methods. Each has several modes of application. (See NFPA 69, *Explosion Prevention Systems*.)

Fixed Volume Method

In one variation of this method, the system to be protected is purged and the atmosphere rendered inert by first reducing the pressure and then introducing inert gas. Equipment that normally operates under a vacuum may be inerted for periods of shutdown in this manner. Conversely, inert gas under pressure can be introduced into an enclosure and, after mixing has taken place, the pressure can be reduced to normal by venting the gas to the atmosphere. Several pressurizing cycles may be necessary to reduce the oxygen content sufficiently.

The fixed volume method is useful when containers that are filled with a flammable material are to be emptied and an inert atmosphere provided. In all cases, the design limitations of the equipment must be observed. Enclosures may be purged by displacing or diluting the flammable vapors at substantially atmospheric pressure. One or more vents discharging to a safe location are opened and the inert gas added until the oxygen content, as shown by test, has been reduced to the desired limit.

TABLE 6-18A. ***Maximum Permissible Oxygen Percentage to Prevent Ignition of Flammable Gases and Vapors Using Nitrogen and Carbon Dioxide for Inerting***

	N_2-Air	CO^2-Air
	O_2 Percent Above Which Ignition Can Take Place	O_2 Percent Above Which Ignition Can Take Place
Acetone	13.5	15.5
Benzene (Benzol)	11	14
Butadiene	10	13
Butane	12	14.5
Butene-1	11.5	14
Carbon Disulfide	5	8
Carbon Monoxide	5.5	6
Cyclopropane	11.5	14
Dimethylbutane	12	14.5
Ethane	11	13.5
Ether (Diethyl)	10.5	13
Ethyl Alcohol	10.5	13
Ethylene	10	11.5
Gasoline	11.5	14
Gasoline		
73–100 Octane	12	15
100–130 Octane	12	15
115–145 Octane	12	14.5
Hexane	12	14.5
Hydrogen	5	6
Hydrogen Sulfide	7.5	11.5
Isobutane	12	15
Isopentane	12	14.5
JP-1 Fuel	10.5	14
JP-3 Fuel	12	14
JP-4 Fuel	11.5	14
Kerosene	11	14
Methane	12	14.5
Methyl Alcohol	10	13.5
Natural Gas (Pittsburgh)	12	14
Neopentane	12.5	15
n-Heptane	11.5	14
Pentane	11.5	14.5
Propane	11.5	14
Propylene	11.5	14

Notes:
Data in this table were obtained from publications of the U.S. Bureau of Mines.
Data were determined by laboratory experiments conducted at atmospheric temperature and pressure. Vapor-air inert-gas samples were placed in explosion tubes and exposed to a small electric spark or open flame.
In the absence of reliable data, the U.S. Bureau of Mines or other recognized authority should be consulted.

Continuous Methods

Fixed rate mode: In this method, the inert gas is added continuously in an amount sufficient to supply peak requirements. The quantity required is based on the maximum inbreathing rate under conditions of sudden cooling, such as that caused by rain, plus the maximum product withdrawal.

TABLE 6-18B. *Maximum Permissible Oxygen Concentration to Prevent Ignition of Combustible Dusts Using Carbon Dioxide and Nitrogen for Inerting*

	Oxygen Percent by Volume Above Which Ignition Can Occur	
	Carbon Dioxide-Air	Nitrogen-Air
Aluminum (atomized)	2	7
Antimony	16	—
Dowmetal	0	—
Ferrosilicon	16	17
Ferrotitanium	13	—
Iron, Carbonyl	10	—
Iron, Hydrogen reduced	11	—
Magnesium	0	2
Magnesium-Aluminum	0	5
Manganese	14	—
Silicon	12	11
Thorium	0	2
Thorium Hydride	6	5
Tin	15	—
Titanium	0	4
Titanium Hydride	13	10
Uranium	0	1
Uranium Hydride	0	2
Vanadium	13	—
Zinc	9	9
Zirconium	0	0
Zirconium Hydride	8	8

Notes:

Data in this Table were obtained principally from U.S. Bureau of Mines RI 6543.

In the furnace test dust clouds of Zr, Th, U, and UH_3 also ignited in CO_2. During heating for several minutes, undispersed layers of samples of the following metal powders ignited (glowed) in CO_2: Stamped Al, Mg, ZnMg-Al, Dowmetal, Ti, TiH_2, Zr, ZrH_2, Th, ThH_2, U, and UH_3. Visible burning of dust layers was also observed in N_2 with powders of Mg, Sn, Mg-Al, Dowmetal, Ti, TiH_2, Zr, Th, ThH_2, U and UH_3.

In the absence of reliable data for combustible dusts, the U.S. Bureau of Mines or other recognized authority should be consulted.

Data were obtained by laboratory experiments conducted at atmospheric temperature and pressure. An electric spark was the ignition source.

This method is relatively simple and has the advantage of requiring no mechanical devices, such as regulators or motor valves. The principal disadvantage is wasting inert gas. Since the peak rate is applied continuously, there are vapor losses due to the "sweeping" action of the inert gas passing through the vapor space. An additional objection is the possible plugging by rust, scale, or ice of the orifice plates controlling the flow of inert gas. A personnel hazard also may exist in the immediate area of the vents because of oxygen deficiency. However, where large volumes of inexpensive gas are available, this method may be found most suitable.

Variable rate mode: In this method, the inert gas is admitted to the system being protected on a demand basis. As shown in Figure 6-18A, a low-volume bleed provides for minor pressure changes in the enclosure, while the solenoid valve, which is operated by the pump motor switch, immediately supplies the inert gas flow needed when enclosure contents are being removed. This method has the advantage of reducing vapor losses by maintaining a slightly positive pressure. It is the most efficient procedure, since the gas is introduced primarily as needed.

The variable rate method is recommended for maintaining an inert atmosphere in systems that are subject to a wide variation in inert gas demand.

INERT GASES

The inerting media for fire and explosion prevention purposes must be obtained from a dependable source capable of continuously supplying the amount required to maintain an atmosphere that will not support combustion. Distribution should be in conformance with accepted piping standards, with protection provided against physical damage. Main distribution lines should be located so that exposure to fire is minimized.

Carbon dioxide or nitrogen in cylinders is probably the best source of inert gas for small plants, or where the systems to be protected are of small volume and loss through leakage is relatively small. Under some conditions, commercially available carbon dioxide or nitrogen may be the most practical supply—even for large installations. Carbon dioxide fire extinguishers should not be used.

Where no oxygen can be tolerated, carbon dioxide gas or nitrogen as a source of supply has many advantages. Bonding and grounding are important to prevent any static discharge during inerting.

A common method of obtaining inert gas is by the combustion of hydrocarbons, as from flame-type producers that operate on liquid or gaseous fuels, natural gas, or manufactured gas. Combustive inert gas generations are commercially available. The products of combustion generally contain 9 to 12 percent carbon dioxide, some carbon monoxide, and about 85 percent nitrogen. Oxygen will also be present in inert gas, 2 to 8 percent with fuel oil and usually less than 1 percent with natural gas as the fuel. The composition of the gas produced by the combustion of hydrocarbons varies, depending upon the operation of the combustion equipment. If purified inert gas is necessary, the oxygen and traces of carbon monoxide can be removed in one operation. If the carbon dioxide is also undesirable, it can be removed in a second operation. Coolers and scrubbers are needed with flame-type producers to remove any particles of glowing soot that might be present, and to make certain the combustion products are not hot enough to ignite any vapor mixtures in the equipment being purged. Inert gas produced in this manner may be stored, or piped directly to the point of use. Provision for adequate reserves is important so that continuation of protection can be ensured in case of producer failure.

The products of combustion from process furnaces or boiler furnaces find considerable use where large volumes are needed. The flue gas from power plant stacks will contain from less than 9 percent to about 14 percent carbon dioxide, and usually only a fraction of a percent of carbon monoxide, although the latter may reach several percent depending upon the efficiency of the combustion process. Likewise, it is not unusual for the oxygen content to reach 15 or 16 percent if dampers are not properly adjusted. So-called "blow-off gas" from certain chemical oxidation processes may also be suitable for use in inerting. Purification equipment for these waste gases will vary, depending upon composition and specific needs. A means for removing solid particles from the gas stream must be provided, and there will generally be a scrubber, dryer, some means for removing excess oxygen, and a compressor. The exact order of the units will vary with individual installations.

TABLE 6-18C. ***Maximum Permissible Oxygen Content to Prevent Ignition by Spark of Combustible Dusts Using Carbon Dioxide as the Atmospheric Diluent***

Dust	Maximum Allowable Oxygen Concentration, Percent
Agricultural	
Clover seed	15
Coffee	17
Cornstarch	11
Dextrin	14
Lycopodium	13
Soy flour	15
Starch	12
Sucrose	14
Chemicals	
Ethylene diamine tetra acetic acid	13
Istoic anhydride	13
Methionine	15
Ortazol	19
Phenothiazine	17
Phosphorous pentasulfide	12
Salicylic acid	17
Sodium lingo sulfonate	17
Steric acid and metal stearates	13
Carbonaceous	
Charcoal	17
Coal, bituminious	17
Coal, subbituminous	15
Lignite	15
Metals	
Aluminium	2
Antimony	16
Chromium	14
Iron	10
Magnesium	0
Manganese	14
Silicon	12
Thorium	0
Titanium	0
Uranium	0
Vanadium	14
Zinc	10
Zirconium	0
Miscellaneous	
Cellulose	13
Lactalbumin	13
Paper	13
Pitch	11
Sewage sludge	14
Sulfur	12
Wood flour	16

Dust	Maximum Allowable Oxygen Concentration, Percent
Plastics Ingredients	
Azelaic acid	14
Bisphenol A	12
Casein, rennet	17
Hexamethylenetetramine	14
Isophthalic acid	14
Paraformaldehyde	12
Pentaerythritol	14
Phthalic anhydride	14
Polymer glyoxyl hydrate	12
Terephthalic acid	15
Plastics—Special Resins and Molding Compounds	
Coumarone-indene resin	14
Lignin	17
Phenol, chlorinated	16
Pinewood residue	13
Rosin, DK	14
Rubber, hard	15
Shellac	14
Sodium resinate	14
Plastic—Thermoplastic Resins and Molding Compounds	
Acetal resin	11
Acrylonitrile polymer	13
Butadiene-styrene	13
Carboxymethyl cellulose	16
Cellulose acetate	11
Cellulose triacete	12
Cellulose acetate butyrate	14
Ethyl cellulose	11
Methyl cellulose	13
Methyl methacrylate	11
Nylon polymer	13
Polycarbonate	15
Polyethylene	12
Polystyrene	14
Polyvinyl acetate	17
Polyvinyl butyral	14
Plastic—Thermosetting Resins and Molding Compounds	
Allyl alcohol	13
Dimethyl isophthalate	13
Dimethyl terephthalate	12
Epoxy	12
Melamine formaldehyde	17
Polyethylene terphthalate	13
Urea formaldehyde	16

Notes:

Data in this table are from U.S. Bureau of Mines RI 6543. The data were obtained by laboratory experiments conducted at room temperature and pressure, using a 24-watt continuous spark as the ignition source.

For moderately strong igniting sources, such as a low current electrical arc or a heated motor bearing, the maximum permissible oxygen concentration is 2 percentage points less than the corresponding value for ignition by spark.

For strong igniting sources, such as an open fire, flame or glowing furnace wall, the maximum permissible oxygen concentration is 6 percentage points less than the corresponding value for ignition by spark.

The maximum permissible concentration for ignition by spark, when nitrogen is used as the atmospheric diluent, can be calculated by the "rule of thumb" formula:

$$O_n = 1.3O_c - 6.3$$

where O_n = the maximum permissible oxygen concentration using nitrogen as the atmospheric diluent

O_c = the maximum permissible oxygen concentration using carbon dioxide as the atmospheric diluent.

Research data on the use of dry powders or water as inerting materials and on the effects of inerting on pressure development in a closed vessel are given in U.S. Bureau of Mines RI 6543, 6561 and 6811.

Inert gas can also be obtained by the catalytic oxidation of ammonia with air. This method produces high-purity nitrogen with only traces of carbon dioxide, hydrogen, oxygen, and residual ammonia.

Another means of obtaining inerting media is by the liquefaction of air with subsequent fractionation to produce nitrogen. Package units of various capacities using this method are commercially available.

Distribution piping must be properly sized to deliver the required volume of inert gas at adequate pressure, and it must be constructed of suitable material. Moisture traps and strainers may be necessary. Back-pressure valves are recommended for each branch from the main distribution line to prevent reduction of the pressure in the main below a predetermined set pressure if there is excessive demand in a branch line. Contamination of the entire inert gas system, due to reversal of flow either through loss of inert gas

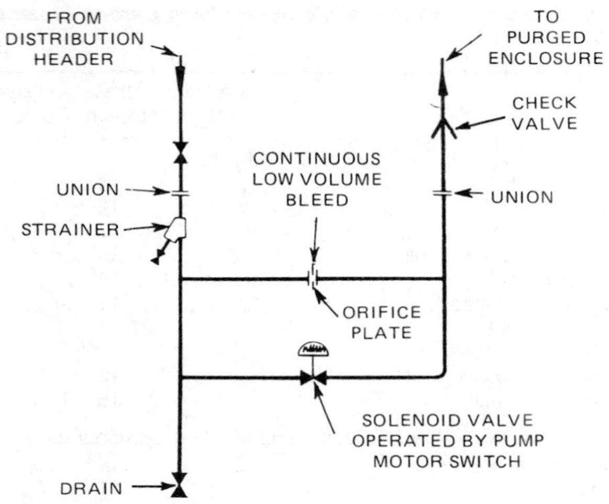

FIG. 6-18A. Schematic sketch showing a method of flow control that can be used with variable rate application.

pressure or by excessive pressure in an inerted unit, may be prevented by installation of check valves. The entire distribution facility should be installed, inspected, and maintained with the same care and attention given to automatic sprinkler systems.

For the special problems of safeguarding aircraft fuel tank atmospheres by the use of inert gas, reference should be made to NFPA 410, *Aircraft Maintenance*.

The inert gases discussed above are all-oxygen deficient and render a space noncombustible by reducing the concentration of oxidant so that the mixture is outside the flammable range. The oxidant-deficient gas used is not always inert. A combustible gas, such as natural gas, is sometimes used in the vapor space of a storage tank to keep the space fuel-rich, or above the flammable limit, making the space oxidant-deficient, from an explosion prevention standpoint.

COMBUSTIBLE CONCENTRATION REDUCTION

Containment of the Fuel

The concept of explosion prevention is usually concerned with a specific finite space. Although it can be open air space in the vicinity of certain process operations, it is usually space enclosed by a building, by tank walls, or by other process equipment. Explosions can be prevented by exclusion of the fuel from spaces where it is not wanted, and by good design and maintenance for secure containment of the fuel within the storage tank, process vessels, cyclones, ducts, conveyors, silos, screens, and hoppers where it is supposed to be kept. Proper containment of the fuel will automatically provide for combustible concentration reduction in other spaces.

A second application of the containment concept that can sometimes be used is containment of the pressures generated by the combustion. This will be discussed later in this chapter in the section "Containment of the Pressure."

Ventilation

General ventilation: Combustible concentration reduction in a given space can sometimes be attained by general ventilation of the space, using clean air to remove dust, gas, or vapor and thus prevent explosions. Properly designed installations may be able to keep the fuel concentration below the lower explosive limit (LEL) at all times.

Even when an abnormal spill raises the fuel concentration to above the LEL, emergency ventilation may be able quickly to reduce the flammable mixture in the ventilated space to a nonflammable condition. This reduces the length of time an explosion potential exists. It also reduces the overall probability of an accident, but does not eliminate the possibility of an accident. If an ignition source is present in the area during the time an explosive mixture exists, a deflagration will result with a high probability of a damaging explosion.

Spot ventilation: Spot ventilation is often used at points of potential leakage to prevent spread of flammables throughout an area. Pick-up velocities, fuel concentrations in ductwork and blowers, safe discharge areas, and air pollution regulations need to be considered in designing ventilation systems. Proper design will provide sufficient airflows to keep fuel concentrations well below the LEL throughout the system under the conditions of the largest anticipated peak load that will be incurred. NFPA 69, *Explosion Prevention Systems*, Appendix A, has useful information and references relative to both general and spot ventilation systems.

Purging

Purging of rooms or enclosures with fuel-free air is a specialized utilization of the ventilation principle to prevent explosions by control of concentration of combustibles. Purging, rather than removing fuel from a space, is usually the reverse process of pressurizing the room or enclosure with clean air to prevent the entry of fuel into the space.

Purging of electrical equipment enclosures is covered in detail in NFPA 496, *Purged and Pressurized Enclosures for Electrical Equipment*. Highlights from that standard are included herein for reference.

Purging Electrical Equipment

In 1967, the first edition of NFPA 496, *Purged and Pressurized Enclosures for Electrical Equipment*, was officially adopted. This standard filled the need for a nationally recognized method of using air (or inert gas) to purge and pressurize electrical equipment enclosures in Class I hazardous (classified) locations so that the atmosphere in the enclosure is nonflammable. In such enclosures, the electrical equipment need not be explosion-proof. For example, in chemical plants it is common practice to install as much of the electrical equipment as possible in an air-pressurized control room. As long as a positive pressure is maintained in the control room with clean air, flammable vapors and gases cannot enter from adjoining Class I hazardous (classified) locations of the plant. Motors, instruments, and control equipment can be located in hazardous locations if the enclosure or case is purged and pressurized, and if the enclosure is designed so that external surface temperatures cannot approach the ignition temperature of the gas or vapor in the Class I hazardous (classified) location in which the enclosed equipment is installed.

Several factors have to be considered when designing a purging and pressurizing system, including a source of clean air, safe discharge of air from the enclosure, purging procedures to be followed before equipment in the enclosure is turned on, and construction of the enclosure. Recommendations on these and other considerations are given in NFPA 496, *Purged and Pressurized Enclosures for Electrical Equipment*, which defines three types of purging with different safeguards for each type. They are as follows.

Type X purging: Type X purging reduces the classification within an enclosure from Division 1 (normally hazardous) to nonhazardous. Because the probability of a hazardous concentration of gas or vapor external to the enclosure is high and the enclosure normally contains a source of ignition, an essential safeguard in Type X purging is the automatic deenergizing of all equipment in the enclosure if purging is interrupted.

Type Y purging: Type Y purging reduces the classification within an enclosure from Division 1 to Division 2 (hazardous only under abnormal conditions). Electrical equipment in the enclosure must be suitable for use in Division 2 hazardous (classified) locations (equipment that does not normally contain a source of ignition). Thus, a hazardous condition will exist in the enclosure only if an electrical equipment failure creates an ignition source within the enclosure at the same time that the purging system fails. In Type Y purging, an automatic warning is given when purging fails, but the electrical equipment within the enclosure is not automatically deenergized.

Type Z purging: Type Z purging reduces the classification within an enclosure from Division 2 to nonhazardous. Since the area surrounding the enclosure is a Division 2 hazardous (classified) location, a hazardous condition will exist within the enclosure only if purging failure occurs simultaneously with some other occurrence that changes the area surrounding the enclosure from a Division 2 to a Division 1 hazardous (classified) location. As in Type Y purging, an automatic warning is required if purging fails so that steps can be taken to reestablish purging, but automatic shutdown of power in the enclosure is not required.

MATERIAL DEFLAGRATION PARAMETER

The rise of pressure in a closed vessel due to the deflagration of a combustible atmosphere within occurs at a rate that is dependent on a number of factors, enumerated earlier. Several of these factors determine the fundamental explosibility of the combustible. For dusts these factors are chemical composition, inert content in the case of dust mixtures, and particle size distribution. Moisture content is not considered in assessing the hazard potential of the base material. A generally accepted measure of the potential severity of a dust cloud deflagration for a particular dust is the explosibility index, K_{st}, defined as follows:

$$K_{st} = (dP/dt)_{max}\, V^{1/3} \qquad (3)$$

where:

V = vessel volume, m^3

$(dP/dt)_{max}$ = maximum rate of pressure rise, MPa/s

The procedure for determining K_{st}* for dusts (K_g for gases) has been standardized and is set forth in ASTM E-1226, *Test Method for Pressure and Rate of Pressure Rise for Combustible Dust*, and is described in Appendix A of NFPA 68, *Venting of Deflagrations*. A simple classification of material explosibility has been defined as follows:

K_{st}[a] MPa – m/s	Explosibility Class
0	St-0 non-explosible
1 to 20	St-1
20 to 30	St-2
30 and up	St-3

DEFLAGRATION SUPPRESSION SYSTEMS

Deflagration suppression systems are active systems that detect combustion processes in their initial stages of development and then rapidly deliver sufficient extinguishing agent to suppress the incipient deflagration. Effective suppression times of 20 to 150 milliseconds (ms) are typical. Suppression is the only explosion mitigation method that stops the advance of the combustion process, thereby eliminating the hazards of high-pressure and high-temperature combustion products. Deflagration suppression systems have been employed in the protection of industrial processes since the early 1950s. Suppression technology has steadily evolved, particularly in the areas of agent type and agent delivery systems. Suppression systems are found in nearly all types of industrial settings where combustion hazards are found.

Fundamentals of Deflagration Suppression

Deflagration suppression systems are routinely employed to protect materials having K_{st} values up to 30 MPa-m/s. However, other factors, such as initial temperature, pressure, and turbulence intensity, may limit the applicability of suppression. Applicability of suppression to systems processing materials having K_{st} values above 30 MPa-m/s has been demonstrated.[8]

An actual pressure-time curve for the deflagration of a propane-butane-air mixture in a 3.8 m^3 vessel is given in Figure 6-18B. While the rate of pressure rise is very rapid in the advanced stages of the event, it is quite slow just after ignition. Provided that detection of the incipient deflagration occurs quickly, there may be sufficient time to deliver extinguishing agent in sufficient quantity to quench the flame ball before it has released enough heat to raise the pressure to the point of damage to the protected system. An important implication of Equation 3 is that the rate of pressure rise obtained for a given combustible increases as the volume of the protected space decreases. Therefore, in protecting very small vessels the suppression system must be very fast. Thus, the three basic elements of an effective deflagration suppression system are: (1) early detection of the incipient deflagration, (2) use of an effective extinguishing agent, and (3) a system capable of a high rate of agent delivery. Deflagration suppression systems are discussed in NFPA 69, *Explosion Prevention Systems*.

---

*K_{st} values have historically been expressed in the units bar-m/s. As the bar is not an SI unit of pressure, K_{st} values are here stated using Pa as the unit of pressure. Conversion of MPa-m/s to bar-m/s is accomplished by multiplying by a factor of 10.

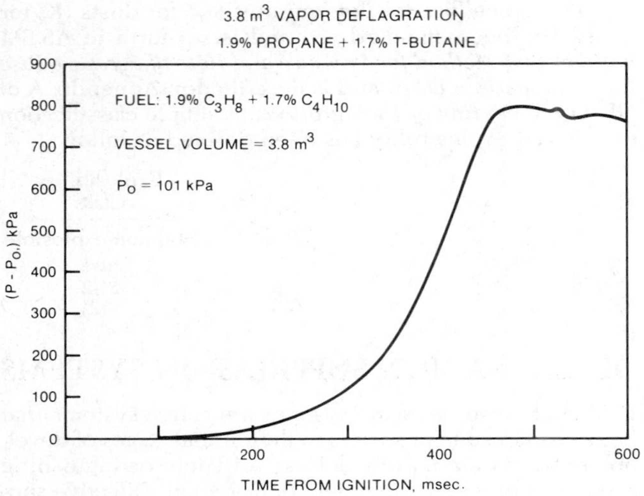

FIG. 6-18B. Closed-vessel deflagration.

Elements of a Suppression System

Detectors: At present three types of deflagration detection devices are used in conjunction with suppression systems: (1) static pressure detectors, (2) rate-of-pressure-rise detectors, and (3) optical flame detectors. (See Figure 6-18C.) Static pressure detectors are high-reliability, fast-response pressure switches. They normally have adjustable closure settings in the range of 0.25 to 5 psig (1.7 to 34 kPa g) or more. The closure pressure is set as low as possible, typically 0.5 to 1.0 psi (3.4 to 6.9 kPa) above the maximum expected operating pressure of the protected space.

Rate-of-pressure-rise detectors are preferred where the process operating pressure is significantly above or below atmospheric pressure. The design of the "rate" detector is such that it will not actuate during normal process pressure fluctuations (e.g., due to closure of a damper or startup of a blower) but will actuate on an incipient deflagration.

Optical flame detectors are used in open environments where pressure detectors would be ineffective. Optical detectors are of the ultraviolet or combination ultraviolet/infrared type and are usually not affected by normal ambient light. Typical applications for optical detectors include solvent storage rooms and areas where aerosol products are manufactured.

Agents: Several extinguishing agents are currently in use. These include the following:

1. Water (with or without freezing-point depressant)
2. Chlorobromomethane (Halon 1011)
3. Bromotrifluoromethane (Halon 1301)
4. Dibromotetrafluoroethane (Halon 2402)
5. Bromochlorodifluoromethane (Halon 1211)
6. Sodium bicarbonate (formulated)
7. Monoammonium phosphate (formulated).

The mechanism by which the agents extinguish a developing flame ball is a combination of thermal quenching and chemical kinetic effects. The choice of agent depends on a number of factors, including: (1) effectiveness, (2) secondary inerting ability, (3) compatibility with process materials, (4) ease of cleanup, (5) residual contamination, and (6) toxicity.

The saturated halogenated agents (Halons 1301, 1211, and 2402) have high atmospheric ozone depletion potentials (ODP) and are subject to regulation as to long-term availability and use taxes. Halon 1011 is not a saturated halocarbon. It has a low ODP and is not subject to regulation. It is also quite toxic and is not suitable for use in occupied spaces. Environmentally acceptable and low-toxicity alternatives to the saturated halocarbons have been proposed for fire protection application. These include bromodifluoromethane, trifluoromethane, and pentafluoroethane. These materials are not expected to be available in commercial quantities until 1992.

Agent delivery systems: Extinguishing agents are stored in, and released from, pressurized containers. The agent may be of any of the types mentioned above. The propellant gas is usually nitrogen at a pressure, depending on the product, of 200 to 880 psig (1.4 to 6 MPa). Rapid discharge of agent is ensured by use of a valve consisting of a metal disk 3 to 5 in (76 to 125 mm) in diameter that is petaled open (opens like a flower) on actuation of an explosive charge. An electric detonator or line-cutting charge causes the disk to open fully in 1 to 2 ms. Extinguishers of this type are referred to as high-rate discharge extinguishers or HRDs. Distribution of the agent is accomplished using a spreader or nozzle that may be fixed in place or that may extend into the protected space on discharge of the agent.

Other components of a deflagration suppression system are the control panel, backup power supply, and dedicated supervised electrical system.

Design of Deflagration Suppression Systems

For the proper application of a deflagration suppression system to a hazardous process or area, the following information is required.

Explosion characteristics: Inasmuch as effective deflagration suppression demands that the entire operating sequence of the suppression system take place during the incipient stage of the deflagration, it is important to know the initial rate of pressure rise that the particular fuel-air system can develop under the conditions that prevail within the protected process. In those cases where optical flame detectors are to be used, the spectral characteristic of the combustion must also be known in order to ensure that it falls within the range of spectral sensitivity of the detector. Finally, it is important to know the chemical nature of the fuel-air mixture in order to select the proper suppressing agent and determine the concentration of that agent required to accomplish effective suppression under process operating conditions.

Ignition: In designing the detection subsystem, it is important to diagnose the nature and location of any possible ignition source. Generally, such sources can be categorized in the following manner:

1. Mechanical
   1.1 Tramp metal
   1.2 Friction
2. Electrical
   2.1 Electrostatic discharge
   2.2 Electrical fault

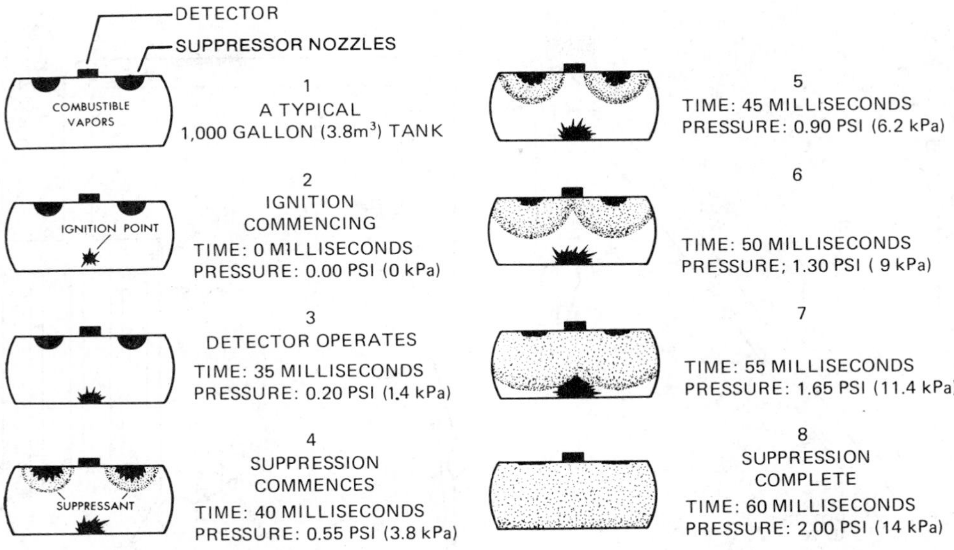

FIG. 6-18C. Schematic diagram of suppression of an explosion in a typical 1000-gal (3.8-m³) tank.

3. Thermal
   3.1 External source
   3.2 Spontaneous

Optimum positioning of the detection equipment depends upon advance knowledge of those locations where ignition is likely to occur. If such sources exist only in one small area, it is possible to provide protection with considerably less equipment than if ignition sources are randomly located. If multiple ignition sources are a possibility, then accelerated rates of pressure rise can be anticipated which will, in turn, put more stringent requirements on the suppression system.

Process variables: The temperature and pressure of a fuel-air mixture prior to ignition will affect the characteristics of the deflagration. It is necessary to have this information in order to determine accurately the factors necessary for system design. These variables will also affect the operation of the equipment, and, in cases where exceedingly high temperatures and pressures are encountered, special techniques must be used in order to ensure adequate life service for the equipment.

Structural integrity: A deflagration, to the degree it progresses, and the suppression system discharge combine to elevate momentarily the pressure in the protected space by a small amount. It is necessary, therefore, that the process enclosure be able to withstand the resulting pressure pulse.

For most processes operating at normal pressures and temperatures, the maximum pressure that can be expected during a suppression is a transient pressure peak in the order of 3 psi (20 kPa); therefore, ideally the enclosure should be sufficiently strong to withstand this pressure. Actually, depending on the tightness of the process, this pressure may be dissipated in milliseconds, and ponderous pieces of equipment such as bag collectors—which might not be capable of withstanding steady-state pressures of this value—would nevertheless be unaffected by the momentary peak due to their inertia. In other cases, equipment might undergo some deformation yet remain intact, with the result that a secondary explosion would be avoided.

To illustrate the application of a deflagration suppression system, a typical installation for a grinding plant is shown in Figure 6-18D. In plants such as this, the primary suspect ignition source would be a grinder; therefore, a detector would be located as near to this point as possible to achieve early response of the system. Ignition in the grinder may result in initiation of a dust cloud explosion in that region or it may result only in burning material being carried to the cyclone where a greater percentage of fines are in suspension and where a condition more conducive to development of a dust explosion exists. There is also the possibility of electrostatic discharge, which would constitute a prime ignition source within the cyclone. Therefore, a detector is also located on this piece of equipment, together with high-rate discharge (HRD) extinguishers.

High-rate discharge extinguishers are deployed to provide optimum coverage within the cyclone. An additional container is discharged immediately below the rotary gate valve, which will be deenergized upon actuation of the system but may be sufficiently worn that it does not constitute an effective flame block. Additional high-rate discharge extinguishers are installed on the interconnecting ducting between major pieces of equipment and oriented to discharge in opposition to the direction of normal product flow. Their function is to isolate each piece of equipment by intercepting any flame front that may be propagating from the piece of equipment within which the explosion originated.

This example assumes that the bag collector is located outdoors, which is the recommended practice, and that is suitably vented. Where this is not practicable, explosion suppression would also be applied to the collector hopper with fire detection and suppression in the bag area. Actuation of any detector triggers all high-rate discharge extinguishers connected into that particular system via the suppression system control panel.

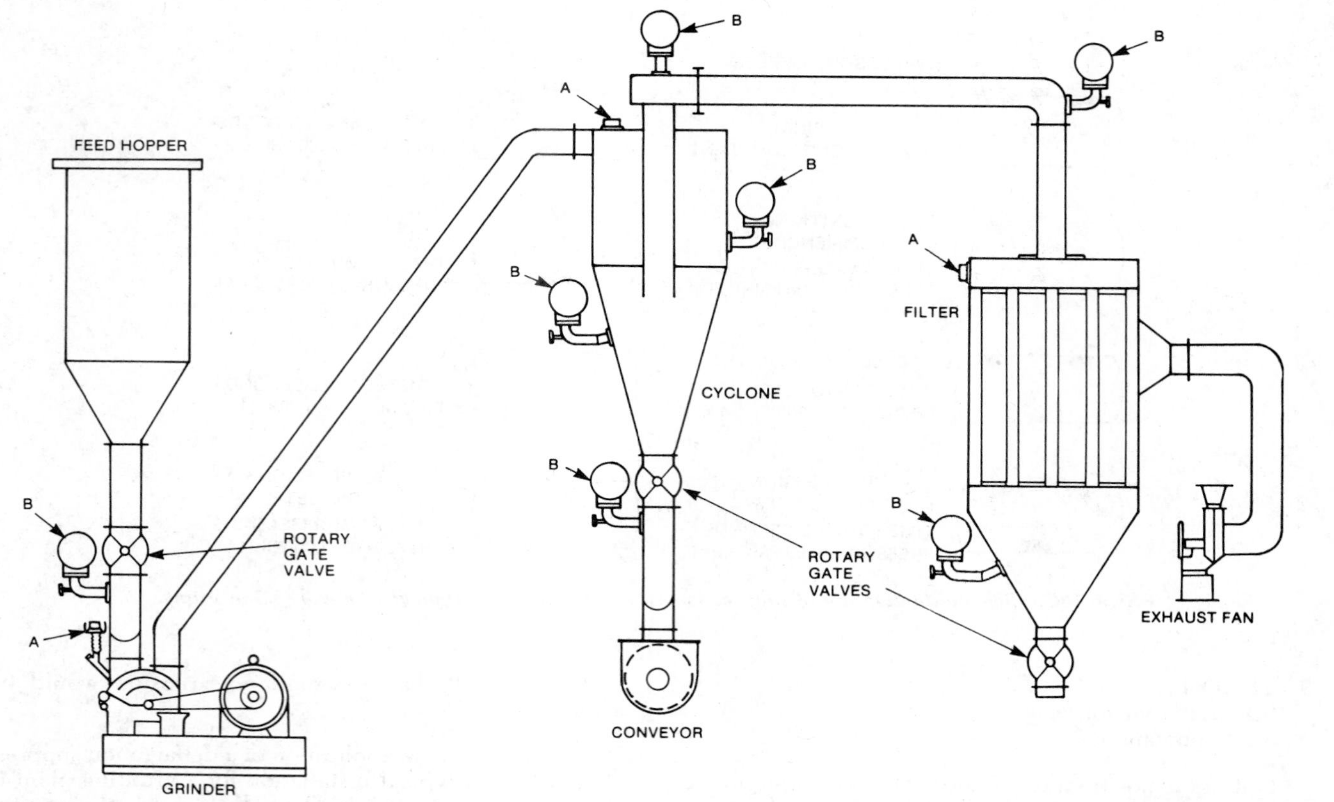

FIG. 6-18D. Explosion protection for a typical grinding plant. The explosion detectors (A) actuate the high-rate discharge extinguishers (B).

Typical equipment applications: Figure 6-18D also illustrates the method of applying a deflagration suppression system to a size-reduction process. In general, the system is applied by determining the most hazardous area in the process and working from this area to other possible hazards in order to ensure that all of these would be successfully suppressed by the equipment. This method has been applied to many other types of industrial processes, such as the following:

Storage tanks. The storage of flammable liquids in many cases presents a severe explosion hazard, and suppression systems have been applied to these tanks to prevent explosions from rupturing and spreading the fire to other tanks in the area.

Coal pulverizing. Bowl mills, ball mills, and other grinding equipment have been protected by this system in order to prevent explosions resulting from the entrance of tramp metal into the grinder, or during startup after a mill trip where glowing particles are suddenly thrown into suspension.

Feed and grain processing: Suppression systems have been applied to elevator bucket legs and milling operations encountered in the feed and grain industry where extreme explosion hazards exist due to the dust that is created.

Plastic grinding: The equipment for grinding plastics is quite similar to that shown in Figure 6-18D and represents an extreme hazard. Several suppression installations have operated successfully and have shown the value of this form of protection.

Those processes and materials where explosion suppression systems have found wide usage are listed in Tables 6-18D and 6-18E. It should be noted that in many instances both flammable vapors and dust (hybrid mixtures) may be present. Such mixtures may present an especially critical hazard since the presence of even small amounts of vapor (e.g., 1 percent or less) can significantly increase the severity of a dust explosion.

TABLE 6-18D. ***Processes Utilizing Explosion Suppression Systems***

Process	System Utilized	
	Dust	Vapor
Size reduction	X	
Dust collection	X	
Solvent recovery		X
Drying	X	X
Conveying		
mechanical	X	
pneumatic	X	X
Spray painting	X	X
Reactors		X
Flaring		X
Storage	X	X

TABLE 6-18E. *Industries Utilizing Explosion Suppression Systems*

Type	System Utilized	
	Dust	Vapor
Plastics	X	X
Forest products	X	
Grain and feed	X	
Pharmaceutical	X	X
Aerosol		X
Waste disposal	X	X
Power generation	X	X
Petroleum		X
Propellant and explosives	X	

CONTAINMENT OF THE PRESSURE

Process Equipment

Maximum pressures from deflagration combustion in a closed vessel reach about 100 to 150 psi (700 to 1000 kPa) when starting from one atmosphere, or about seven to ten times the initial pressure.

Much process equipment, built to withstand full vacuum and/or moderate working pressure, may be found on careful strength analysis to have a bursting strength higher than the maximum expected combustion pressure in the system.

Whereas common practice dictates at least a 4:1 safety factor of bursting pressure over working pressure in a vessel, it is not unusual to consider a potential explosion as a "once in a vessel's lifetime" occurrence and depend on vessel yield strength for pressure containment with very little factor of safety. Such a system would limit explosion damage to the vessel itself, which might stretch or deform under worst conditions. The containment approach avoids vessel rupture with catastrophic damage in the area.

If, in fact, pressure containment is the option selected in designing the process equipment, it is imperative that the potential maximum deflagration pressures be known. Otherwise, the damage could be catastrophic. For example, if the process contains long duct runs or if any of the process equipment has a high length-to-diameter ratio, the seven to ten multiplier no longer applies. In such configurations, it is possible to obtain pressure transients well above ten times the initial pressure. In ducts and pipes, pressure transients as high as thirty times the initial pressure are possible. This is a consequence of flame acceleration and deflagration to detonation transition.

This approach is practiced only for substantially built vessel systems that can withstand that multiple of the pressure at which a confined combustion deflagration might be initiated; it is not applicable to buildings and lightly built equipment, such as normal hoppers, dust collectors, tanks, bins, silos, etc.

DEFLAGRATION VENTING

Deflagration venting is the means of creating an open area in the wall of a process volume in response to a sudden and excessive rise in pressure. Such a newly created open area will limit the buildup of pressure to values sustainable by the equipment without causing damage, provided that the event causing the pressure rise is no more severe than the worst case for which the vent system was designed. Deflagration venting is discussed in detail in NFPA 68, *Venting of Deflagration*. Some of the more essential elements of venting are presented below.

Fundamentals of Deflagration Venting

Deflagration venting may be appropriate on any process volume, including rooms, in which a combustible material may achieve a vapor or disperse particulate cloud concentration above the lower flammable limit. A number of factors must be considered when designing a deflagration vent system:

1. The basic combustibility characteristics of the materials being processed must be understood. Where different materials may be processed in the same equipment, the design must be adequate to the demands of the worst-case material. Uncertainty about the combustibility of a material being processed should be clarified by reference to the literature or by test. In particular, the explosibility parameters of the worst-case material being processed in the volume in question must be known in order to apply the vent design models correctly. The basic explosibility parameters are the maximum deflagration pressure, P_{max}, and the volume-normalized maximum rate of pressure rise, K_{st}. (See Equation 3.) The latter term is also referred to as the explosibility index and is determined by test. It is important that the K_{st} value be determined for the material being processed in the most hazardous form that it could credibly assume in the process. In particular, the properties of the process material in its finest and driest processed forms should be known. The relevance of the K_{st} value to vent design is indicated below.
2. The volume of the protected space bears directly on the vent area required. The relationship of unrestricted vent area required as a function of volume for a variety of dusts with different combustibility characteristics is indicated in Figures 6-18E and 6-18F.
3. The inertia of a vent closure will tend to retard its opening. Thus, it is preferred that vent inertia be kept to a minimum.
4. To relieve the pressure of a deflagration, a vent opens and discharges the pressurized contents of the protected space. The material ejected may include flame, combustion products, and as-yet-unburned material that may ignite on exposure to ambient air. Burning of ejected material will be vigorous due to the high turbulence intensity of the discharged mass. The rapidly discharged mass will also create a pressure front ahead of it that may stir up available combustible matter originally external to the vented equipment, which may, in turn, ignite to cause a secondary deflagration.
5. Vented equipment should be located outdoors, away from occupied spaces. Vent openings, in particular, must be oriented so as not to direct the discharge to a location in which personnel may be working or passing.
6. Excellent housekeeping is necessary around vented equipment to avoid a secondary deflagration or the creation of potential missiles.
7. Vented equipment that must be located indoors may be vented to the outside by means of vent ducts. To keep ducts as short as possible the equipment should be located near an external wall. The use of vent ducts

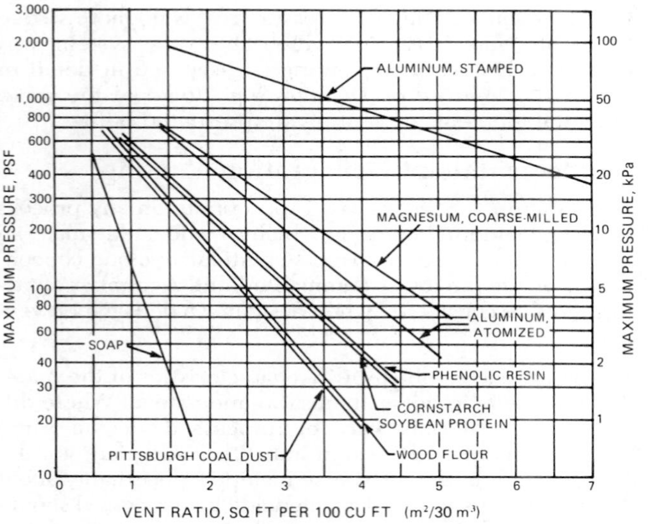

FIG. 6-18E. Effect of unrestricted vents on pressures developed by mild dust explosions. These explosions were produced in a 64 cu ft (1.8 m³) gallery. (Source: Bureau of Mines, U.S. Department of Interior)

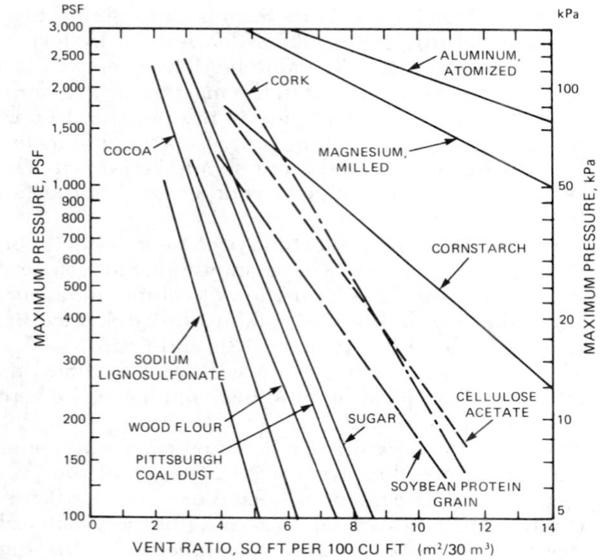

FIG. 6-18F. Effect of unrestricted vents on pressures developed by strong dust explosions. These explosions were produced in a 1 cu ft (.028 m³) gallery. (Source: Bureau of Mines, U.S. Department of Labor)

will necessarily restrict the discharge from the vent to the ambient air, and special considerations are in order.[9]

The design of a deflagration vent, specifically the specification of the total amount of vent area required, is not an exact science. A number of different approaches have been employed, both in the United States and in Europe. It is recommended that the guidelines set forth in NFPA 68, *Venting of Deflagration*, be adhered to for the design of pressure-relief vents. The essential aspects of vent design are summarized below. The reader is referred to NFPA 68 for a more complete discussion.

Design for Low-Strength Enclosures

A low-strength enclosure, for the purposes of deflagration vent design, is one that cannot withstand an internal pressure more than 1.5 psi (10 kPa) above that of the surroundings. In making such a strength assessment, all structural elements must be considered, including walls, ceilings, doors, and windows. The recommended design equation for determining the area of vents for these enclosures is as follows:

$$A_v = CA_s/(P_{red})^{1/2} \qquad (4)$$

where:

A_v = vent area, ft² or m²
C = combustible-dependent constant, see below
A_s = internal surface area of enclosure to include walls, floor, and ceiling, ft² or m²
P_{red} = maximum overpressure tolerable by weakest structural element, psi or kPa

Combustible-Dependent Constants for Equation 4: Low-Strength Enclosures

Combustible	C (psi)$^{1/2}$	C (kPa)$^{1/2}$
Anhydrous ammonia	0.05	0.13
Methane	0.14	0.37
Gases with S_u < 0.6 m/s	0.17	0.45
St-1 dusts	0.10	0.26
St-2 dusts	0.12	0.30
St-3 dusts	0.20	0.51

Note: S_u = fundamental burning velocity. See Table B-1 of NFPA 68 for the S_u of a number of gases.

A single vent should be located near the middle of the longest dimension of an enclosure. Vent design for elongated enclosures, where a single vent must be located at one end, as on a silo, is restricted to cases where the following criterion is met:

$$L_3 < 12\ A/p \qquad (5)$$

where

L_3 = longest dimension of enclosure, ft or m
A = cross-sectional area of enclosure, ft² or m²
P = perimeter of cross-section, ft or m

Where the criterion of Equation 5 cannot be met, reference should be made to the subsection on elongated enclosures later in this chapter. Where multiple vents are used, the required venting area should be developed from the total area of the several smaller vents used. Such vents should be located as evenly as practicable along the longest dimension of the protected space.

The value of reduced pressure used in Equation 4 should not exceed 66 percent of the ultimate strength of a ductile enclosure, and not more than 25 percent of the ultimate strength of a brittle enclosure. In any case, the enclosure strength should exceed the value of P_{red} by at least 0.35 psi (2.4 kPa).

Vents for low-strength enclosures must have low inertia and open at low overpressures. These criteria can be satisfied, provided that the area-average weight of the vent panel assembly does not exceed 2.5 lb/sq ft (12.2 kg/m²) and that the panel releases at an applied pressure differential in the range of 0.14 to 0.21 psi (0.96 to 1.4 kPa).

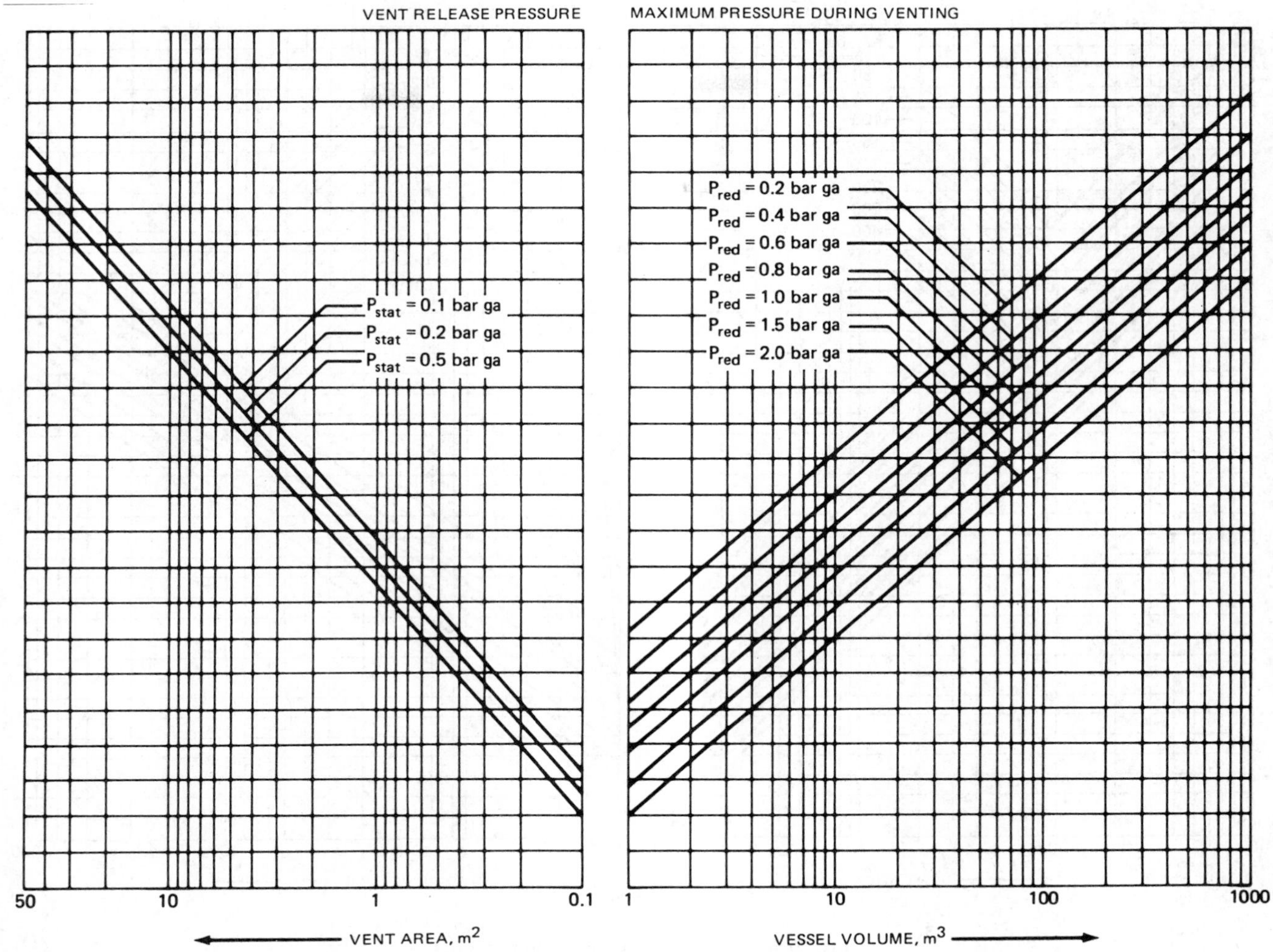

FIG. 6-18G. Venting nomograph for methane.

Design for High-Strength Enclosures

Structures capable of withstanding an internal overpressure of more than 1.5 psi (10 kPa) are considered high-strength enclosures. The pressures developed in vented high-strength enclosures may be considerable, depending on the design employed. The design should be such as to ensure a value of P_{red} that is no more than 66 percent of the expected failure strength of the enclosure. In this regard, bulging of the enclosure walls is not considered failure. The area-average mass of the vent panels should conform to the guidelines given for low-strength enclosures.

Determination of the required vent area for combustible gases or dusts can be made using the nomographs presented in NFPA 68, *Venting of Deflagration*, for the appropriate conditions. Two of these nomographs are reproduced herein. (See Figures 6-18G and 6-18H.)

The nomographs (Figures 6-18G and 6-18H) were developed from a wide range of test data, and are valid when applied to systems that meet all of the following criteria:

1. Initially quiescent gas mixture,
2. No obstructions internal to the enclosure that may enhance turbulence development during deflagration,
3. Ignition energy of no more than 10J,
4. Initial pressure of 1 atm,
5. Enclosure length-to-diameter ratio (L/D) < 5,
6. $1 < V < 1000$ m^3,
7. $20 < P_{red} < 200$ kPa g, and
8. $10 < P_{stat} < 50$ kPa g.

Design for Elongated Enclosures

Deflagration development in ducts or similar elongated enclosures is subject to rapid acceleration, due to the development of turbulence by drag and boundary layer effects. Venting of duct systems is less well understood than venting of more regular enclosures. The following guidelines are recommended:

1. The total vent area at each vent position should at least be equal to the cross-sectional area of the duct.
2. Vents should be located as close as possible to potential ignition sources.

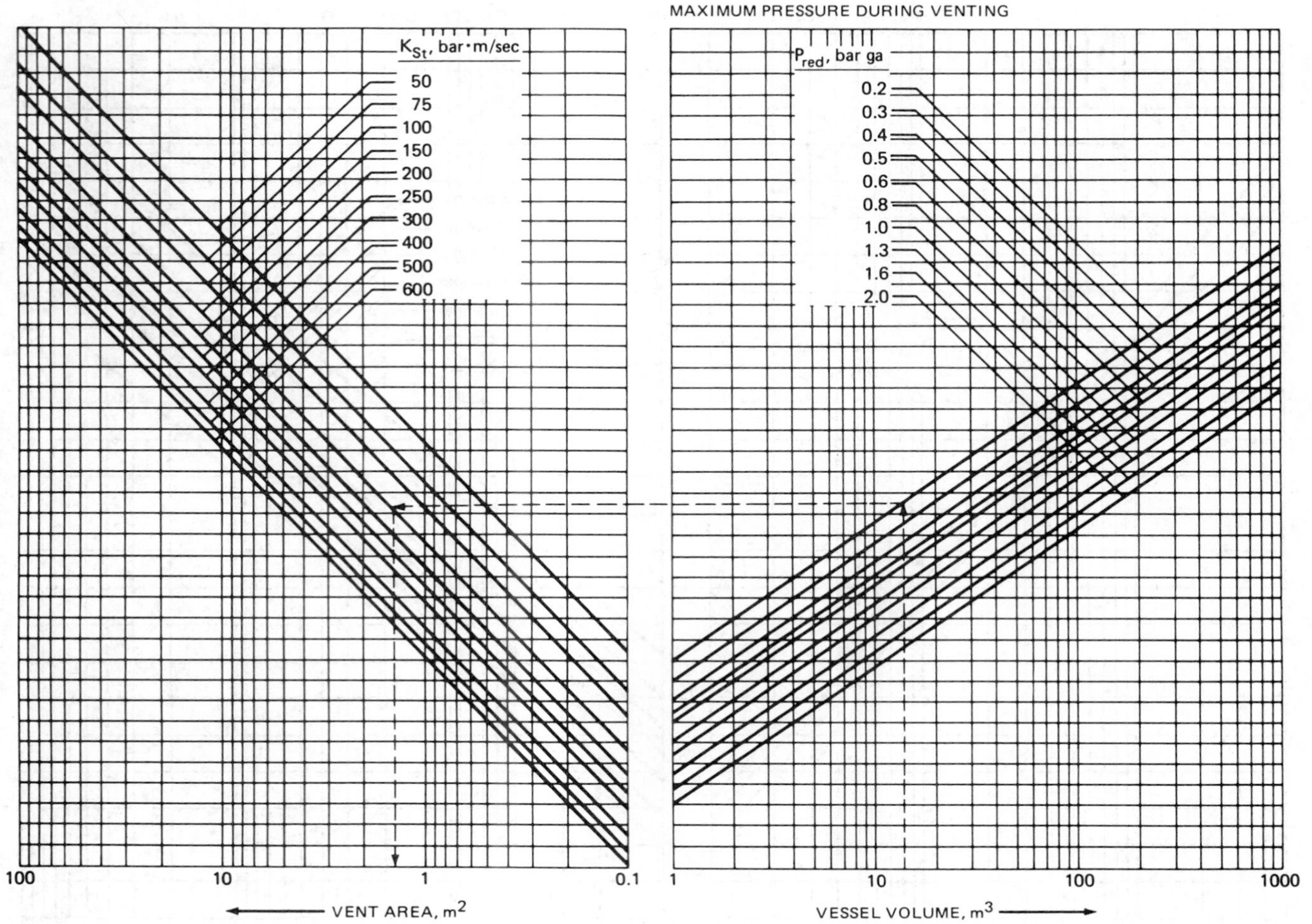

FIG. 6-18H. Venting nomograph for dusts.

3. Ducts containing obstacles should be vented on both sides of the obstacle. Obstacles may be elbows, tees, valves, or any blockage amounting to more than 5 percent of the duct area.
4. When multiple vents are used in long ducts, certain spacing requirements should be followed. See NFPA 68, *Venting of Deflagrations*.

Detonations

The vent design guidelines, as given above, presume that any potential combustion threat develops as a deflagration in which the mass and heat transfer processes are slow relative to the speed of sound. This is to say that it is assumed that the pressure within the protected space is at all times essentially uniform. Under certain conditions, depending on the type and concentration of fuel or system geometry, a relatively slow-moving deflagration wave can accelerate and even undergo transition into a detonation wave. Under such conditions, the enclosure pressure is not uniform. The maximum pressures experienced by the structure can be several times higher than the usual maximum deflagration pressure. Vents cannot be used effectively to protect spaces where detonations have developed. Vents can, however, be used to help prevent the development of deflagrations into detonations in duct systems, for example, if they are designed according to the guidelines given above.

Vent Ducts

The operation of a vent when protecting an enclosure from the rise in pressure due to an explosion will normally result in the discharge of both a flame ball and a pressure wave. The flame ball presents a hazard to personnel and may be the cause of a secondary explosion external to the vented equipment. Thus, vented equipment, where possible, should be located outdoors. Where indoor equipment must be vented, it is recommended that it be located near an outside wall and that the vent be exhausted to the outdoors, using a connecting duct. An example of a ducted vent is shown in Figure 6-18I. Vent ducts should be kept as short as possible and bends in the duct should be avoided. The effect of vent duct length on P_{red} is shown in Fig. 6-18J. The application of vent ducts is discussed in greater detail in reference 9.

Vent Closures

Vent closures may be of several types, including panels, windows, or doors. The total area average mass of the movable portion of a closure should not exceed 2.5 lb/sq ft (12.2 kg/m^2). Panels may tear open or move as a unit due to friction-pin or spring-type fasteners. Closures must be restrained so that they will not become missiles on actuation of the vent. Tethers with shock absorbers are often

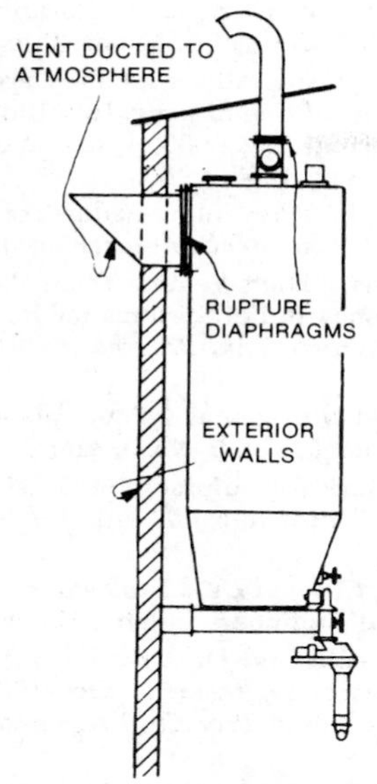

FIG. 6-18I. Dust explosion venting through a duct to the outside for a vessel located indoors.

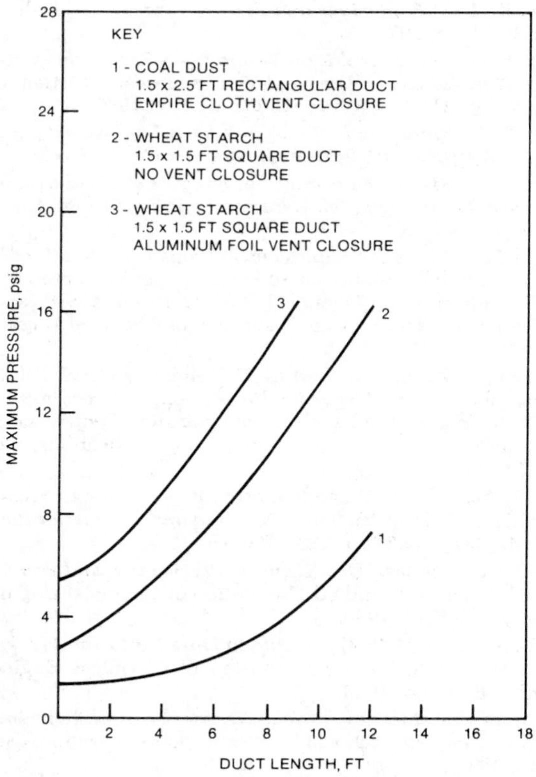

FIG. 6-18J. Effect of duct length on explosion pressure developed in the 64 cu ft (1.8 m3) gallery. (Source: Nagy and Verakis[10])

used to keep released panels from flying away. Vent closures must be protected both from internal process conditions (e.g., corrosive vapors) and ambient conditions (e.g., icing) that may tend to corrode or otherwise impair the condition or operability of the panel.

Inspection and Maintenance

Vent systems should be inspected on a regular basis. Inspections should note not only the condition of the vent unit but also changes in the building structure or occupancy of the vent location. Any change in the latter after the vent is installed may require a redesigned vent system in that area. Inspection procedures should be in writing.

Complete maintenance records should be kept on vent systems. Any deficiencies noted during inspection should be recorded and the corrective action taken. Manufacturers' recommendations on maintenance should be followed.

BIBLIOGRAPHY

References Cited

1. Bartknecht, W., *Dust Explosions: Course, Prevention, Protection*, Springer-Verlag, Berlin, Germany, 1989.
2. Bartknecht, W., *Dust Explosions*, Springer-Verlag, Berlin, Germany, 1989.
3. Bartknecht, W., *Explosions: Course, Prevention, Protection*, Springer-Verlag, Berlin, 1981.
4. Nagy, J., and Verakis, H. C., *Development and Control of Dust Explosions*, Marcel Dekker, Inc., New York, NY, 1983.
5. Glor, M., *Electrostatic Hazards in Powder Handling*, Research Studies Press, Ltd., Letchworth, Hertfordshire, England, 1988.
6. Glor, *Electrostatic Hazards*, Research Studies Press Ltd., Detchworth, Hertfordshire, England, 1988.
7. Crowl, D. A., and Louvar, J. F., *Chemical Process Safety: Fundamentals with Applications*, Prentice-Hall, Englewood Cliffs, NJ, 1990.
8. Senecal, J. A., "Deflagration Suppression of High-K_{st} Dusts," *Plant/Operations Progress*, Vol. 8, No. 3, July 1989, pp. 147-151.
9. Lunn, G. A., *Guide to Dust Explosion Prevention and Protection, Part 3: Venting of Weak Explosions and the Effect of Vent Ducts*, IChemE, Rugby, England, 1988.
10. Nagy and Verakis, *Development and Control of Dust Explosions*, Marcel Dekkar, Inc., New York, 1983.

References

ASTM E 1226, *Test Method for Pressure and Rate of Pressure Rise for Combustible Dust*," American Society for Testing and Materials, New York, NY 1988.

ISO 6184, *Explosion Protection Systems* (4 parts), International Organization for Standardization, Geneva, Switzerland, 1985.

Journal of Physics and Chemistry Reference Data, Vol. 14, Suppl. 1, 1985.

Lewis, B., and von Elbe, G., *Combustion, Flames and Explosions of Gases*, 3rd ed., Academic Press, New York, NY, 1987.

NFPA Codes, Standards, and Recommended Practices

Reference to the following NFPA codes, standards, and recommended practices will provide further information on explosion prevention and protection discussed in this chapter. (See the latest *NFPA Catalog* for availability of current editions of the following documents.)

NFPA 68, *Venting of Deflagrations*.

NFPA 69, *Explosion Prevention Systems*.

NFPA 70, *National Electrical Code*.

NFPA 77, *Static Electricity*.

NFPA 410, *Aircraft Maintenance*.

NFPA 496, *Purged and Pressurized Enclosures for Electrical Equipment*.

Additional Readings

Alexander, J. M., "Managing Fire and Explosion Hazards in Process Plant," *Proceedings* of the 12th Australian Chemical Engineering Conference, Institute of Chemical Engineers, 1984, pp. 371 - 378.

Almgren, L. E., "Designing for Fire and Explosion Safety," *Proceedings* of the National Meeting of the American Institute of Chemical Engineers, American Institute of Chemical Engineers, New York, NY, 1988, p. 10.

Bartknecht, W., "Effectiveness of Explosion Venting as a Protective Measure for Silos," *Plant/Operations Progress*, Vol. 4, No. 1, 1985, pp. 4 - 13.

Bartknecht, W., *Explosions — Course Prevention Protection*, Springer-Verlag, New York, NY, 1981.

Bartknecht, W., "Pressure Venting of Dust Explosions in Large Vessels," *Plant/Operations Progress*, Vol. 5, No. 4, 1986, pp. 196 - 204.

Bodurtha, F., *Industrial Explosion Prevention and Protection*, McGraw Hill, New York, NY, 1980.

Bradley, D., and Mitcheson, A., "The Venting of Gaseous Explosions in Spherical Vessels, I and II," *Combustion and Flame*, Vol. 32, 1978, pp. 221 - 255.

Cartwright, P., "Combating the Problem of Dust Explosions," *Process Engineering*, Vol. 70, No. 2, 1989, pp. 49 - 52.

Coffee, R. D., "Dust Explosions: An Approach to Protection Design," *Fire Technology*, Vol. 4, No. 2, May 1968, pp. 81 - 87.

Cross, J., and Farrer, D., *Dust Explosions*, Plenum, New York, 1982.

Cybulski, W., *Coal Dust Explosions and Their Suppression* (translated from Polish), National Technical Information Service, Springfield, VA, 1981.

Decker, Dick A., "Explosion Venting Guide," *Fire Technology*, Vol. 7, No. 3, Aug. 1971, pp. 219 - 223.

Donat, C., "Release of the Pressure of an Explosion with Rupture Discs and Explosion Valves," paper presented at Achema 73, Frankfurt, West Germany.

Doyle, W. H., "Protection in Depth for Increased Chemical Hazards," *Fire Journal*, Vol. 59, No. 5, Sept. 1965, pp. 5 - 7.

Eckoff, R., *et. al. Dust Explosion Experiments in a Vented 500 ft m^3 Silo*, Christian Michelson Institute, Bergen, Norway, 1982.

"Equipment Survey: Explosion Protection Equipment," *Bulk Solids Handling*, Vol. 8, No. 5, Oct. 1988, pp. 635 - 638.

Fauske, H. K., *et. al.*, "Emergency Relief Vent Sizing for Fire Emergencies Involving Liquid-Filled Atmospheric Storage Vessels," *Plant/Operations Progress*, Vol. 5, No. 4, 1986, pp. 205 - 208.

Field, P., *Dust Explosions, Vol. 4*, Elsevier Scientific Publishing Co., New York, NY, 1982.

Fishkin, C. I., and Smith, R. L., "Handling Flammable Dusts," *Chemical Engineering Progress*, April 1964.

Grabowski, G. J., "Progress in Industrial Explosion Protection Systems," *Fire Journal*, Vol. 62, No. 1, Jan. 1968, pp. 21 - 24.

Grabowski, G. J., "Theoretical and Practical Aspects of Explosion Protection," *Fire Protection Manual for Hydrocarbon Processing Plants*, 3rd ed., Gulf Publishing Co., Houston, TX, 1985.

Hart, R. L., "Formulas for Sizing Explosion Vents," *Plant/Operations Progress*, Vol. 4, No. 1, 1985, pp. 1 - 4.

Heinrich, H. J., "Dimensions of Pressure-Release Openings for the Protection of Plants in the Chemical Industry Which Are Endangered by Explosions," *Chemie, Ingenieu, Technik*, Vol. 38, No. 11, Nov. 1966, pp. 1125 - 1133.

Howard, W. B., *Loss Prevention*, Vol. 6 (a CEP Technical Manual), American Institute of Chemical Engineers, 1972, pp. 68-73.

Howard, W. B., *Tests of Explosion Venting of Buildings Plant/Operations Progress, AIChe, Vol. 1*, Jan. 1982; Vol. 1 corrected, Apr. 1982.

Hub, L., and Jones, J. D., "Early On-Line Detection of Exothermic Reactions," *Plant/Operations Progress*, Vol. 5, No. 4, 1986, pp. 221 - 224.

Jacobson, M., Cooper, A. R., Nagy, J., "Explosibility of Metal Powders," *RI 6516*, USDI Bureau of Mines, Pittsburgh, 1964.

Jenett, E., "Design Considerations for Pressure Relieving Systems," Part I, *Chemical Engineering*, July 1963, p. 125; Part II, *Chemical Engineering*, Aug. 1963, p. 151; and Part III, *Chemical Engineering*, Sept. 1963, p. 83.

Kirby, G., and Sirvek, R., "Preventing Failures of Equipment Subject to Explosions," *Chemical Engineering*, June 23, 1986.

Klein, H. H., "Analysis of Diers Venting Tests: Validation of a Tool for Sizing Emergency Relief Systems for Runaway Chemical Reactions," *Plant/Operations Progress*, Vol. 5, No. 1, 1986, pp. 1 - 10.

Klueg, E. P., "Liquid Nitrogen as a Powerplant Fire Extinguishant," *Fire Technology*, Vol. 5, No. 3, Aug. 1969, pp. 197 - 202.

Le Vine, R. Y., "Electrical Equipment in Outside Chemical and Petroleum Plants," *Fire Journal*, Vol. 59, No. 3, May 1965, pp. 30 - 31.

Lunn, G. A., *Venting Gas and Dust Explosions — A Review*, Institution of Chemical Engineers, Rugby, England, 1984.

Maisey, H. R., "Gaseous and Dust Explosion Venting," Part I, *Chemical and Process Engineering*, Oct. 1965, pp. 526 - 535; Part II, *Chemical and Process Engineering*, Dec. 1965, pp. 662 - 672.

Nagy, J., Dorsett, H. G., and Jacobson, M., "Preventing Ignition of Dust Dispersions by Inerting," *RI 6543*, USDI Bureau of Mines, Pittsburgh, PA, 1964.

Nagy, J., Verakis, H., *Development and Control of Dust Explosions*, Marcel Dekker, Inc., New York, NY, 1983.

Palmer, K., *Dust Explosions and Fires*, Chapman and Hall, London, England, 1973.

Palmer, K. N., "Dust Explosion Venting — a Reassessment of the Data," *Fire Research Note No. 830*, Fire Research Station, Boreham Wood, Hertsfordshire, England, Aug. 1970.

Pineau, J. P., *Suppression of Gas and Dust Explosions*, Cerchar, Verneuil-en-Halatte, France, 1984.

Potter, A. E., "Flame Quenching," in *Progress in Combustion Science and Technology, Vol. 1*, Pergamon Press, Oxford, England, 1960, pp. 145 - 81.

Rasbash, D. J., "Relief of Explosions in Propane/Air Mixtures Moving in a Straight Unobstructed Dust," paper presented at Second Symposium on Chemical Process Hazards with Special Reference to Plant Design, Institution of Chemical Engineers, 1964.

Robertson, J. W., and Woolbert, G. D., "Improved Coal Mill Monitoring for Fire and Explosion Prevention," *Proceedings of the 7th International Coal and Lignite Utilization Conference: Coal Technology '84, Vol.3*, Industrial Publications, 1984, pp. 53 - 62.

Salter, R. L., Fike, L. L., and Hansen, F. A., "How to Size Rupture Discs," *Hydrocarbon Processing and Petroleum Refiner*, Vol. 42, May 1963, pp. 159 - 160.

Schofield, C., *Guide to Dust Explosion Prevention and Protection, Part 1 — Venting*, 2nd ed., Institution of Chemical Engineers, Rugby, England, 1988.

Schofield, C., and Abbot, J. *Guide to Dust Explosion Prevention and Protection*, Part 2, Institution of Chemical Engineers, Rugby, England, 1988.

Schram, P. J., and Earley, M. W., *Electrical Installations in Hazardous Locations*, National Fire Protection Association, Quincy, MA, 1989.

Schwab, R. F., and Othmer, D. F., "Dust Explosions," *Chemical and Processing Engineering*, April 1964.

Senencal, J. A., "Deflagration Suppression of High K_{st} Dust," *Plant/Operation Progress*, Vol. 8, No. 3, July 1989, pp. 147 - 151.

Sestak, E. J., "Venting of Chemical Plant Equipment," *Engineering Bulletin No. N-53*, Factory Insurance Association (now IRI), Hartford, CT, Apr. 1965.

Short, W. A., "Hazardous Locations and Electrical Equipment — Making the Mix Work," *Fire Journal*, Vol. 82, No. 4, 1988, p. 63.

Simmonds, W. A., and Cubbage, P. A., "The Design of Explosion Reliefs for Industrial Drying Ovens," paper presented at Symposium on Chemical Process Hazards with Special Reference to Plant Design, Institution of Chemical Engineers, 1961, pp. 69 - 77.

Sirvek, R., "Dust Explosion Venting for Dusts Pneumatically Conveyed into Vessels," *Plant/Operation Progress*, Vol. 8, No. 3, July 1989, pp. 129 - 140.

Sirvek, R., "New Knowledge about Rotary Air Locks in Preventing Dust Ignition Breakthrough," *Plant/Operation Progress*, Vol. 8, No. 3, July 1989, pp. 165 - 176.

Stretch, K. L., "Part I — The Relief of Gas and Vapor Explosions in Domestic Structures," *Structural Engineer*, Vol. 47, No. 10, Oct. 1969, pp. 408 - 411.

Swift, I., "Design of Deflagration Protection Systems," *Journal of Loss Prevention in the Process Industries*, Vol. 1, 1988, pp. 5 - 15.

Swift, I., "Developments in Explosion Protection," *Plant/Operation Progress*, Vol. 7, No. 3, July 1988, pp. 159 - 167.

Swift, I., and Epstein, M., "Performance of Low-Pressure Explosion Vents," *Plant/Operation Progress*, Vol. 6, No. 2, 1987, pp. 98 - 105.

Tamanini, F., "Turbulance Effects on Dust Explosion Venting," *Plant/Operation Progress*, Vol. 9, No. 1, 1990, pp. 52 - 60.

Tonkin, P. S., and Berlemont, C. F. J., "Dust Explosions in a Large-Scale Cyclone Plant," *Fire Research Note No. 942*, Fire Research Station, Boreham Wood, Hertsfordshire, England, July 1972.

Tuhtar, D., *Fire and Explosion Protection: A System Approach*, Halsted Press, New York, NY, 1989.

Weldon, George E., "Damage-Limiting Construction," *Fire Technology*, Vol. 9, No. 4, Nov. 1973, pp. 263 - 270.

Westerberg, W. C., "Testing Electrical Equipment for Chemical Atmospheres," *Fire Technology*, Vol. 2, No. 3, Aug. 1966, pp. 226 - 233.

Wilson, M. J., "Fast Response Systems for Pyrotechnic Factory," *Fire Engineers Journal*, Vol. 48, No. 149, June 1988, pp. 7 - 8.

Wood, L. E., "Rupture Discs," *Chemical Engineering Progress*, Vol. 61, Feb. 1965, p. 93.

Zalosh, R. G., "Explosion Protection," *in SFPE Handbook of Fire Protection Engineering*, National Fire Protection Association, Quincy, MA, 1988.

AIR-MOVING EQUIPMENT

Revised by Jane I. Lataille

Many industrial and commercial activities and processes require the removal of smoke, fumes, and/or dusts. This necessitates equipment for moving air in and out of the processing area. Both the accumulation and moving of impurities and the substitution of other atmospheres present fire and explosion hazards. Additional information about the elimination of such hazards can be found in Section 3 Chapter 2, "Fire Hazards of Materials: An Overview;" Section 2, Chapter 5, "Industrial and Commercial Heat Utilization Equipment;" Section 2, Chapter 15, "Chemical Processing Equipment;" Section 2, Chapter 20, "Metalworking Processes;" Section 2, Chapter 21, "Woodworking Processes;" Section 2, Chapter 31, "Control of Electrostatic Ignition Sources;" and in Section 2, Chapter 35, "Grinding Processes."

Air-moving equipment (AME) includes all mechanical-draft duct systems, of both the pressure and exhaust types, for removal of dusts, vapors, and waste material, and for the conveying of materials. The hazards of such systems lie in the possibility of igniting flammable materials or vapors by sources such as sparks generated by fans or foreign material, e.g., tramp metal, or by overheated fan bearings. Also, such systems could inadvertently spread fires through the building.

Air-moving systems do, however, play an important role in fire protection. If the materials they remove were allowed to accumulate, the result could be an explosion from vapor-air mixtures, a flash fire due to accumulations of lint or other combustibles, and generally poor housekeeping conditions conducive to fires in general.

Air moving systems usually contain axial flow fans or centrifugal blowers; several different designs of each kind are available. (See Figure 6-19A.) A straight-blade centrifugal fan is suitable for exhausting large particles of materials because it resists clogging and the blades can withstand considerable abrasion. Propeller fans will move large volumes of air, but only against small resistance. Since these fans could not operate efficiently against the friction a duct would introduce, they are not suitable for ducts of any appreciable length.

Jane I. Lataille, P.E., ARM, is senior account consultant with Industrial Risk Insurers, Hartford, CT.

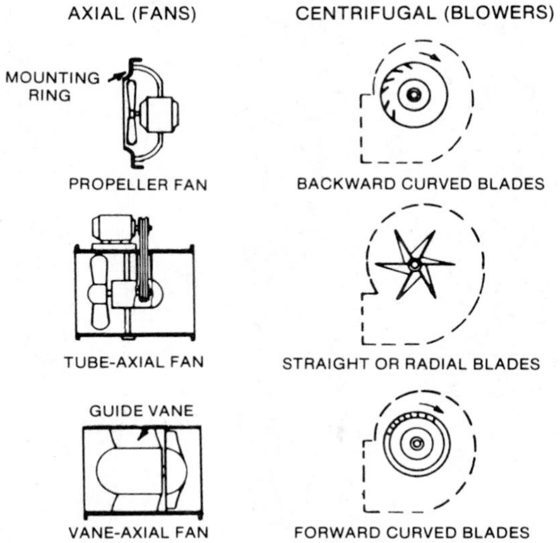

FIG. 6-19A. Fan and blower designs suitable for use in exhaust systems.

To reduce the hazard of fire, fans should be: (1) of noncombustible construction, (2) able to be shut down by remote control in case of fire, (3) accessible for maintenance, and (4) structurally sound enough to resist wear and overcome distortion and misalignment caused by structural weakness or overloading. Fans used for smoke and heat venting should be able to withstand temperatures of 932°F (500°C) for 4 hours. Construction materials for all fans must be appropriate for the intended use. A spark caused by a blade hitting the housing, due to distortion or misalignment, could result in ignition when the exhaust contains flammable solids or vapors. This possibility of friction sparks is minimized if the fan and fan housing are of nonsparking material. Aluminum and magnesium alloys are not compatible with ferrous alloys, which may rust.

Details on the installation of air-moving equipment are given in NFPA 91, *Exhaust Systems for Air Conveying of Materials*, and NFPA 96, *Removal of Smoke and Grease-Laden Vapors from Commercial Cooking Equipment.*

HAZARDS OF SPECIFIC USES

Ventilation of Flammable Vapors

Because flammable vapors ignite easily, precautions must be taken to eliminate ignition sources in ducts that carry them. Using a single system to exhaust flammable vapors and particles from spark-producing processes is obviously dangerous. Similarly, drawing different vapors which individually may not be flammable, but which may be hazardous as a mixture in a single exhaust system, is extremely poor practice. For example, perchloric acid acts as an oxidizing agent at elevated temperatures. If perchloric acid vapors were drawn into a system exhausting organic materials, the combination could cause a fire or explosion.

It is important that vapors be withdrawn from the rooms or equipment in which they are generated and taken directly to the outside of the building or to suitably protected pollution-control equipment. Processes generating flammable vapors are best located along an outside wall of the building to facilitate efficient vapor removal.

When flammable vapors cannot readily be picked up at a specific source, general ventilation through a system of suction ducts with inlets to the room or area may be used. Because suction inlets have minimal directional effect beyond a few inches (1 in. equals 25.4 mm) from the face of the inlet, they should be located so that they produce a sweeping or purging effect that will eliminate pockets in which vapors may accumulate. A make-up air supply, properly located in relation to the point where vapors are generated, and openings for exhaust ducts will aid in the dilution and removal of vapors. The ventilation system should provide sufficient air movement to maintain the vapor concentration below the lower explosive limit in the area where vapors are being liberated. If vapors are toxic, it may be necessary to maintain concentrations well below those required for flammability.

NFPA 86, *Ovens and Furnaces*, gives procedures for calculating the volume of air per minute necessary to dilute flammable vapors below their lower flammable limit.

Where heavier-than-air vapors or mixtures are handled, exhaust openings located near the floor line are generally the most effective. Conversely, for vapors or mixtures lighter than air, exhaust openings located near the top of the room, hood, or enclosure are the most effective. Caution in evaluating the vapor density is necessary where other than normal temperatures and pressures exist.

Fans: All fans should be suitable for moving vapors and air. If the vapor contains a material that could condense and build up on the fan blades, this possibility should be minimized by the selection of a fan with backward curved blades. Both the fan and the fan housing should be of nonferrous construction. The contruction material chosen should not be adversely affected by the vapors handled.

Ducts: Ducts for systems handling flammable vapors need to be structurally capable of withstanding some fire exposure. Where vapors can condense, continuously welded joints in the ducts will prevent leakage.

Since flash fires or explosions can occur in ducts, ductwork should be installed away from combustibles, but where it will be readily accessible. Ducts should never be concealed in a wall or ceiling. Duct systems that exhaust flammable materials should terminate outside in an area where the vapors cannot be ignited and where they will not form deposits, such as overspray residue, on the building or other structures. An enclosure is sometimes used around the discharge end of a duct to prevent deposits on exposed property. These enclosures should be sprinklered.

Frequent cleaning of ducts, filters, and any enclosures will minimize both the intensity of a fire in a duct system and any spontaneous heating of deposits subject to this phenomenon.

Electrical equipment: All equipment that may be exposed to flammable vapors should be governed by NFPA 70, *National Electrical Code®*, for such hazardous locations.

Fire extinguishing equipment: Fixed fire-suppression systems suitable for the flammable material involved, as well as portable fire extinguishers, should be provided. The extinguishing agent should be water, foam dry chemical, or CO_2 as appropriate for the hazard.

Ventilation of Corrosive Vapors and Fumes

If corrosive vapors must be exhausted, the degree of expected corrosion is the governing factor in the construction of the ducts. In some cases, a heavier-gage metal is used, and in others, protective coatings may be sufficient. Occasionally, however, the corrosiveness is so extreme that a special lining is required. Stainless steel has been used very successfully in some cases.

Plastic duct systems are also used, but only if the corrosive vapors are nonflammable and the plastic has a flame-spread rating of 25 or less and a smoke-developed rating of 50 or less, when tested in accordance with NFPA 255, *Surface Burning Characteristics of Building Materials*. Automatic fire protection is also necessary at the hood, canopy, or intake to plastic duct systems. A duct system of plastic materials for a typical industrial exhaust system is shown in Figure 6-19B, and a duct system for a typical laboratory hood exhaust system is shown in Figure 6-19C.

Ventilation of Kitchen Cooking Equipment

Exhaust systems for restaurant equipment are troublesome because grease condenses in the interior of the ducts. Grease accumulations may be ignited by sparks from the stove or, more often, by a small fire on the stove caused by overheated cooking oil or fat in a deep-fat fryer or on a grill. If the duct did not have a grease accumulation, fires on stove tops could often be extinguished before causing appreciable damage. Fires occur frequently in frying because cooking oils and fats are heated to their flash points. Thus, fats and oils can reach their self-ignition temperatures by being accidentally overheated or by being ignited when spilled on the stove top. Details of a typical kitchen range exhaust system are shown in Figure 6-19D.

Fans should be selected according to their ability to exhaust the required quantity of air against all calculated friction losses.

Duct systems: The following should be considered when designing a duct system for commercial cooking equipment.

1. Design the system to minimize grease accumulations, with a minimum air velocity of 1,500 ft/min (457 m/min) through any duct.
2. Arrange ducts with ample clearance from combustible materials to minimize the danger of ignition, in case of fire in the duct.

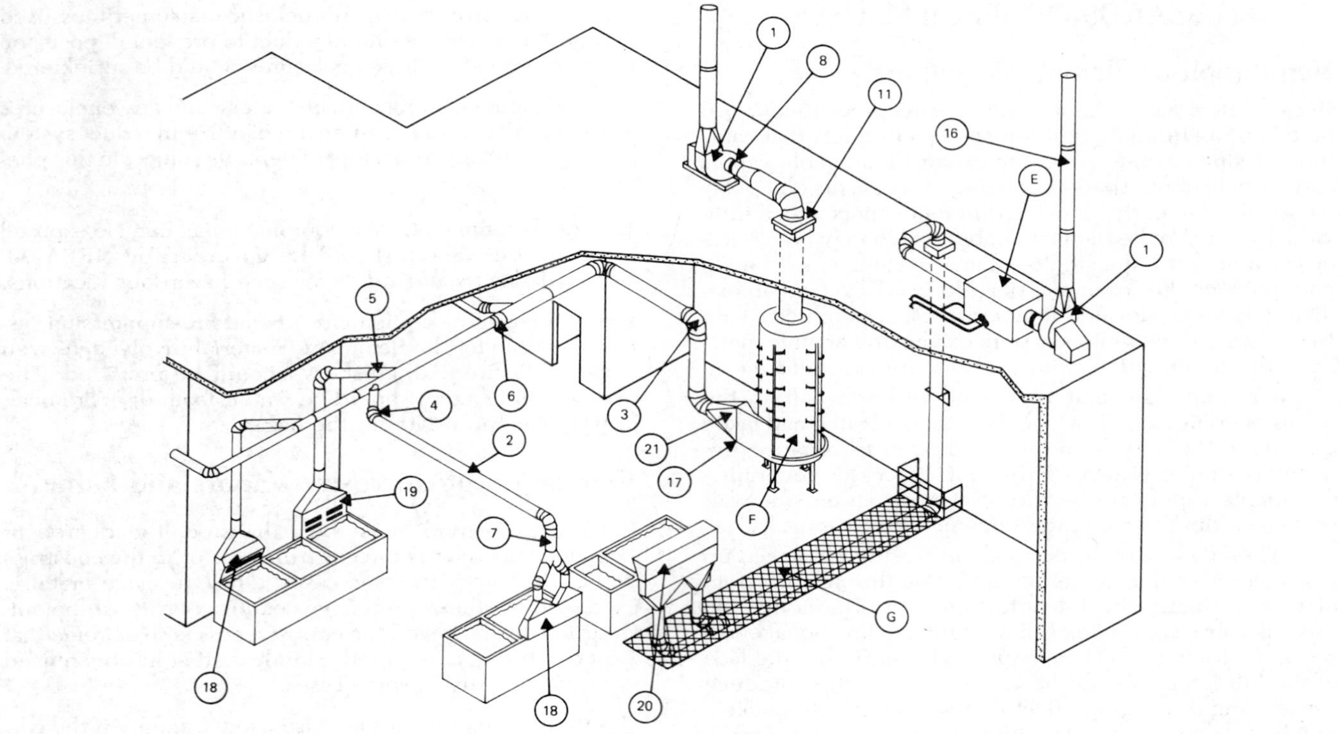

FIG. 6-19B. Exhaust system for one-story building occupied by various type fume hoods with vertical fume scrubber and service trench.

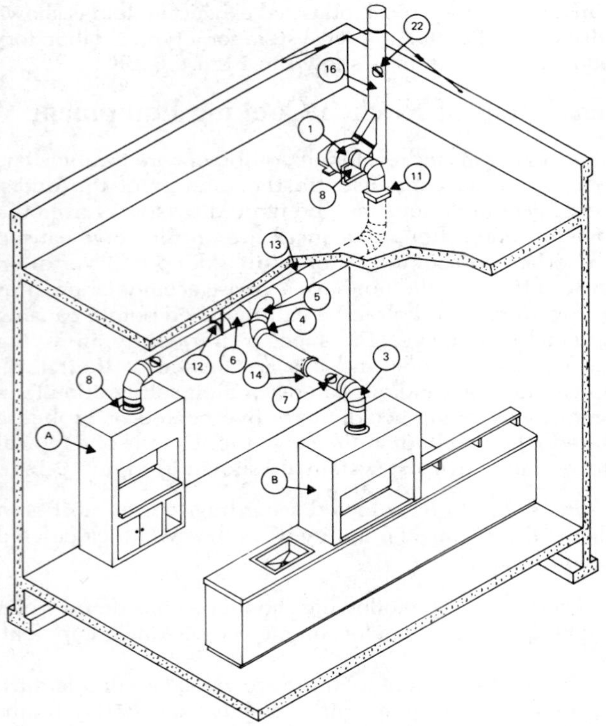

NOMENCLATURE:

I. EQUIPMENT
   - A. CABINET TYPE LABORATORY FUME HOOD
   - B. BENCH TYPE LABORATORY FUME HOOD
   - C. FILTER BOX FOR SPECIAL OR HIGH EFFICIENCY FILTERS
   - D. SHAFT
   - E. HORIZONTAL TYPE FUME SCRUBBER
   - F. VERTICAL TYPE FUME SCRUBBER
   - G. SERVICE PIT OR TRENCH

II. SYSTEM COMPONENTS
   1. AIR MOVING EQUIPMENT (CENTRIFUGAL TYPE EXHAUST FAN)
   2. HORIZONTAL DUCT SECTION
   3. 90 DEGREE ELBOW
   4. ELBOW (LESS THAN 90 DEGREE)
   5. LATERAL ENTRY
   6. TRANSITION
   7. MANUAL BALANCING DAMPER
   8. FLEXIBLE CONNECTION
   9. FIRE DAMPER
   10. ACCESS DOOR
   11. COUNTERFLASHING
   12. DUCT HANGER
   13. CIRCUMFERENTIAL GIRTH JOINT (BUTT WELDED)
   14. BELL END DUCT SEAM
   15. WEATHER CAP
   16. FAN DISCHARGE STACK
   17. FLANGED DUCT CONNECTION
   18. OPEN FACE TANK EXHAUST HOOD (UPDRAFT)
   19. SLOTTED FACE TANK EXHAUST HOOD (UPDRAFT)
   20. OPEN FACE TANK EXHAUST HOOD (DOWNDRAFT)
   21. ROUND TO RECTANGULAR (OR SQUARE) TRANSITIONAL FITTING
   22. GRAVITY OPERATED BACKDRAFT DAMPER

FIG. 6-19C. Rooftop exhaust system for one-story building occupied by a cabinet-type laboratory fume hood and bench-type laboratory fume hood.

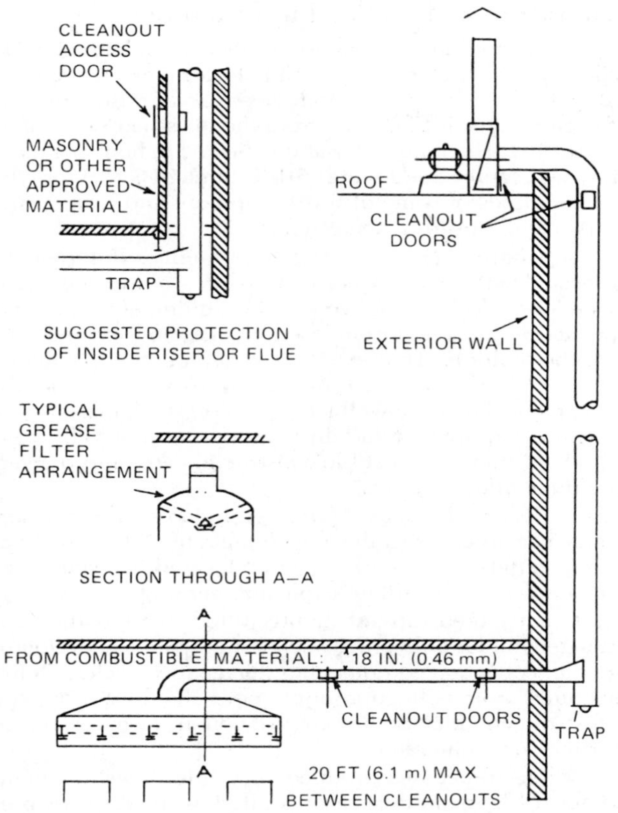

FIG. 6-19D. Typical kitchen range exhaust system arrangement, showing vertical riser outside the building. If necessary to locate riser inside the building, it should be enclosed in a masonry shaft.

3. Use ducts of substantial construction (not lighter than No. 16 Manufacturers Standard Gage steel or No. 18 Manufacturers Standard Gage stainless steel) with all seams and joints having a liquid-tight, continuous external weld.
4. Separate systems to make sure there is no connection with any other ventilating or exhaust system.
5. Lead ducts directly outside the building, without dips or traps, unless automatic grease removers are employed at the dips and traps.
6. Provide openings for inspection and cleaning. Do not install dampers in any duct system, unless required as part of a grease extractor or extinguishing system.

Although clean ducts are essential, cleaning them is likely to be neglected because it is difficult and unpleasant, and can be dangerous if flammable solvents are used. Satisfactory cleaning results have been obtained with a powder compound consisting of one part calcium hydroxide and two parts calcium carbonate. This compound saponifies the grease or oily sludge, thus making it easier to remove and clean. Proper ventilation must be provided and safety precautions taken if cleaning is done inside the duct or fan housings.

Spraying the duct interiors with hydrated lime after cleaning is a fire-prevention method in commercial use. Though this tends to saponify the grease and may facilitate subsequent cleaning, it does not provide any permanent fire protection or flame resistance, for grease eventually coats the compound.

Grease-removal devices: All kitchen exhaust systems require a means for removing grease. These may be grease extractors, grease filters, or other grease removal devices, such as water-wash systems and special fans designed to remove grease vapors effectively and provide a fire barrier. Grease filters, including frames, or other grease-removal devices should be made of noncombustible materials.

Electrical equipment: Manual control of the fan motor should be provided near the motor and also near the hood. In addition, it is desirable to have automatic shutdown of the motor by a heat-sensitive device in the hood close to the outlet.

All electrical equipment that may be exposed to vapors, grease, or heat should be installed in accordance with NFPA 70, *National Electrical Code*, requirements for those conditions. Fixtures should not be installed in ducts or hoods used for removal of cooking smoke or grease-laden vapors or located in the path of travel of such exhaust products unless they are specifically designed and tested for such use. Electrical equipment may be placed outside the path of vapor travel by locating it on the outside of the hood with illumination through tight-fitting glass panels in the hood.

Fire extinguishing equipment: For sizable cooking installations, this equipment may consist of fixed pipe carbon dioxide, dry chemical, wet chemical, foam-water sprinkler, water spray, or sprinkler systems, supplemented by portable alkaline (sodium bicarbonate or potassium bicarbonate) dry-chemical extinguishers.

Acidic base extinguishing agents, such as ammonium-phosphate-based multi-purpose types (ABC rated), impede saponification. Therefore, if the cooking equipment being protected involves exposed liquefied fat or oil in depth, such as deep-fat fryers, extinguishers employing these extinguishing agents are not recommended, as they may interfere with alkaline-based fixed systems.

Where fixed extinguishing systems are installed, they should: (1) be located so that they easily can be manually activated from the path of egress; (2) be arranged for simultaneous automatic operation of all systems in a single hazard area, upon operation of any one system; and (3) automatically shut off all sources of fuel and heat to all equipment protected, upon operation of the system.

Dust Collecting and Stock and Refuse Conveying Systems

These systems consist of suction ducts and inlets, air-moving equipment, feeders, discharge ducts and outlets, collecting equipment, vaults, and other receptacles designed to collect powdered, ground, or finely divided material.

Collecting and conveying systems are often a very important part of the operations of a plant. When the material they handle is a combustible dust, there is danger of a fire or explosion. These factors make it a prime necessity that the design, construction, and operation of the systems conform to recognized standards. The general recommendations given in the first part of this chapter should be observed, as should the following more specific ones.

Fans: Systems conveying combustible dust should be arranged so that the fan is on the clean air side of the collector, so that the system operates under suction, and dust collecting equipment removes the dust before the air stream reaches the fan. This arrangement prevents combustible dust from passing through the fan where it may be ignited. If such an arrangement is not possible and the fan must be located between the dust-producing equipment and the collector, the blades and spider of the fan and the fan housing should be made of nonsparking material, with ample clearance between the blades and the housing. Fan bearings and motors should be outside of casings unless the fan and motor assembly are designed and tested for use in the dust atmosphere present.

Ducts: For conveying dusts or stock, ducts should be constructed of metal. Changes in direction in the duct system should be made with long bends or elbows. This minimizes accumulations of solid particles at the turns.

Following are some general design techniques recommended for ducts conveying dusts and other solid materials:

1. Every duct should be kept open and unobstructed throughout its length.
2. Not more than two branches should connect to any section of the main suction duct.
3. Branch ducts should be connected to the top or side of the main duct at an angle not exceeding 45 degrees, inclined in the direction of air flow.
4. Main suction and discharge ducts should be as short as possible.
5. Flexible duct sections should not restrict airflow and should be as short as possible.
6. Systems handling combustible dusts should, as far as possible, be located outside of the building. Branch ducts from each floor should pass through the wall and discharge into the main duct outside.
7. Additional branch ducts should not be added without redesigning the system. Disconnected or unused portions of the system should not be blanked off without providing orifice plates to maintain required airflow.

Magnetic separators: As with flammable-vapor conveying systems, combustible-dust collecting systems should not be used with processes that may produce sparks. If there is a possibility of particles of ferrous materials ("tramp metal") entering the collecting systems, permanent magnetic separators should be installed at points where ferrous particles may enter. After collection, the dust passes into rooms or bins. These places of collection should be made of noncombustible construction and provided with explosion vents terminating outside of the building.

Explosion prevention: When ignition sources are difficult to control, inerting may be used to create a safe atmosphere within the system, or an explosion suppression system or spark extinguishing system may be used. There are limits to these systems—inerting is generally practical for essentially closed systems, while explosion suppression is limited to those materials and enclosures that can be successfully protected. Efforts to suppress explosions in some materials, e.g., metal dusts, have not been successful. Spark extinguishing systems are suitable for fibers and flyings. Refer to NFPA 69, *Explosion Prevention Systems*, for additional information.

Separating and Collecting Equipment

Separating equipment includes cyclones, condensers, wet-type collectors, cloth screen and stocking arresters, centrifugal collectors, and other devices used for the purpose of separating solid material from the air stream in which it is carried. Then the material is collected in hoppers, bins, silos, and vaults. See Figures 6-19E through 6-19H for typical examples of some of this equipment and how sprinklers may be used in some types.

Separating and collecting equipment is designed to withstand anticipated explosion pressures, allowance being made for explosion relief vents. This equipment should be constructed of steel or enclosed in steel and located outside the building. To prevent the equipment from collapsing (which could result in an explosive dust cloud), equipment should be well supported on steel, masonry, or concrete. Equipment and discharge ducts should be well separated from combustible construction and unprotected openings into buildings.

Collectors that must be located indoors, and that cannot be constructed of sufficient strength to withstand anticipated explosion pressures, can be located in rooms near outside walls to facilitate explosion venting.

Gravity feed through tightly fitted ducts is the best arrangement for delivering stock from separators, cyclones, or other collection equipment to storage receptacles. Delivery ducts from collection equipment should not convey refuse directly into the fireboxes of boilers, furnaces, refuse burners, or incinerators.

Where processes produce very fine dusts or where combustible metal dusts are handled, wet collectors provide efficient dust control. Dust is removed by passing the flow of air through a water curtain and is collected as a sludge submerged in water. Except where combustible metal dusts are collected, these wet collectors generally have no fire or explosion hazards.

Where refuse is to be used as fuel, the discharge system from the storage receptacle or intermediate feed bin to the furnace should be designed to prevent a flashback from the furnace. This may be accomplished by means of a choke feeder or choke conveyor so that a positive cut-off is provided. The installation of a steam spray in the duct to the furnace which blows steam in the direction of the fuel flow is recommended because it provides an added safety factor in preventing a flashback. See Figure 6-19E for a typical installation of this type.

The installation of screw conveyors or rotary feeds at appropriate points in stock or dust conveying systems has been used to good advantage in many plants by providing a "choke," which helps stop the spread of a flash fire. The installation of an explosion vent also relieves the pressure of an explosion and prohibits its progress. This combination has often prevented small fires or explosions from becoming large and disastrous.

High efficiency air filter units: Particulate air filter units are used to remove very fine particulate matter, i.e., to remove not less than 99.97 percent of 0.3-micron diameter particles, from the air of industrial and laboratory exhaust systems.

The Nuclear Regulatory Commission (NRC) requires high-efficiency filters for filtering air exhausted from spaces where radioactive materials are handled. The filter units used are made of a filter medium of glass fiber, or equivalent inorganic material. Although the adhesive used is combustible, it contains a self-extinguishing additive. Fire

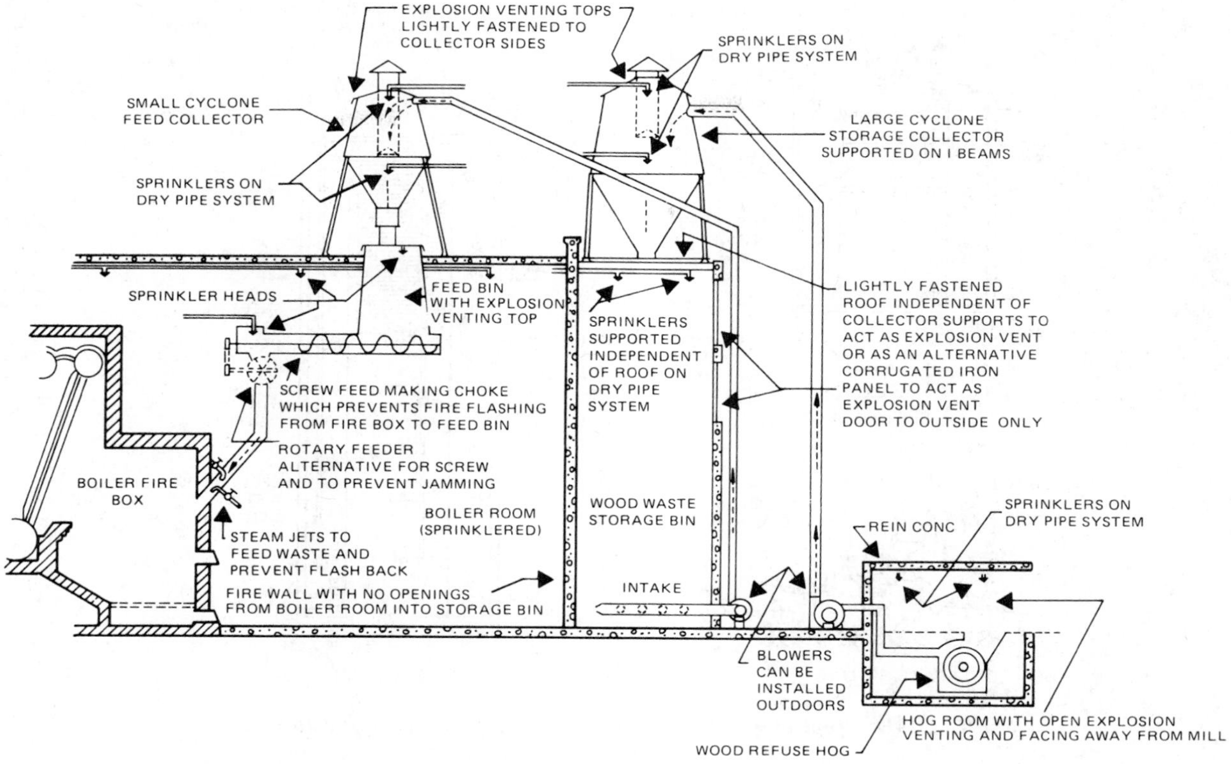

FIG. 6-19E. Suggested arrangement for wood waste firing of boiler to minimize explosion and fire hazard.

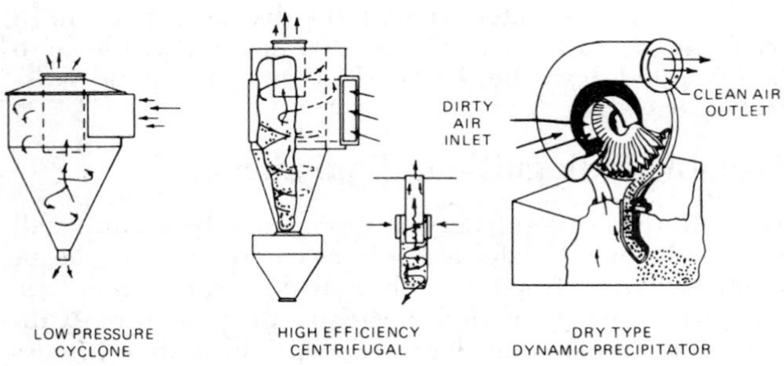

FIG. 6-19F. Examples of typical types of dust collecting equipment.

of sufficient temperature and duration to melt glass fibers can damage the filter at points of contact, but will not stop the exhaust of filtered air through the undamaged area. The NRC regulations generally require large banks of these filters, limit the number in a fire area to 100, and require automatic sprinkler protection.

Fire extinguishing systems: Cloth screen or bag-type dust collectors used for the collection of fine dusts present a special problem because of the use of a combustible fabric even where the dust is noncombustible. Automatic sprinkler protection may be needed where cloth dust collectors are important for continuity of production or where they provide exposure to other property. Figures 6-19G and 6-19H show typical layouts of sprinkler protection for cloth dust collectors.

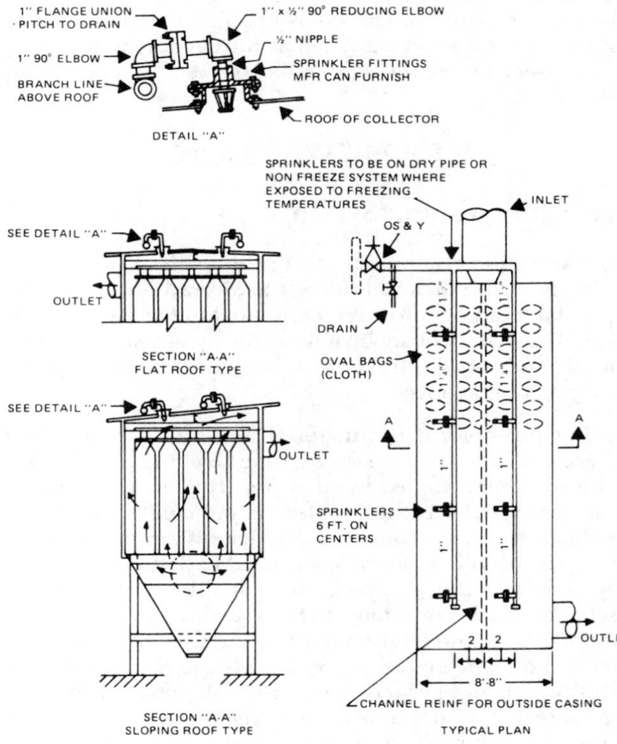

FIG. 6-19G. Typical sprinkler protection for a bag-type dust collector.

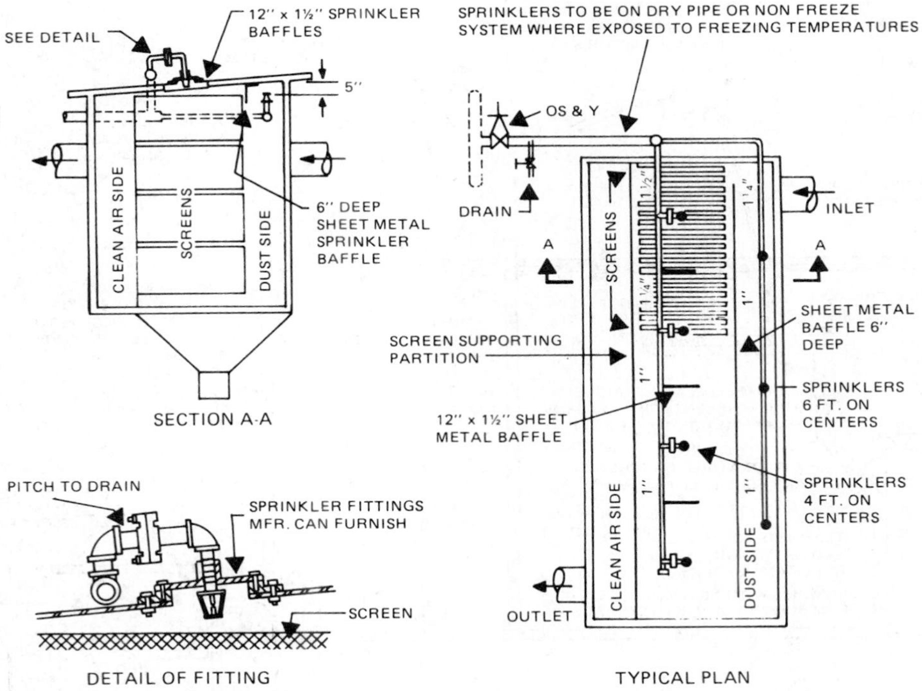

FIG. 6-19H. Typical sprinkler protection for a screen-type dust collector.

Equipment of large volume, such as bins, or dust collectors in which pulverized stock is stored or may accumulate, should be protected by automatic sprinklers. Automatic carbon dioxide, dry chemical, or water spray extinguishing systems can be used effectively in dust collecting systems. Inert gas, such as nitrogen, may be effectively used to create safe atmospheres in conveying systems.

FIRE PROTECTION

Fire Extinguishing Systems

Because of the combustibility of either the ducts themselves, or of the material being transferred through them the installation of automatic extinguishing systems is justified. The systems may be automatically or manually controlled and may utilize any of several appropriate extinguishing agents.

For example, if the material being transported is a flammable vapor or an easily ignited combustible dust, a deluge system actuated by heat-sensitive devices may be most appropriate. If the problem is the combustibility of the duct itself, an automatic sprinkler system may be adequate. In still other systems, a special extinguishing agent may be required or deemed more suitable. Sprinklers and discharge nozzles may have to be coated or covered to protect them from the environment inside the duct; they may have to be inspected on a regular basis and cleaned periodically to avoid serious build up of deposits. Similarly, heat detectors or other types of detectors used to activate the extinguishing system may have to be periodically cleaned of deposits that might hamper their proper operation.

One important problem frequently overlooked is the obstruction of automatic sprinklers or other discharge nozzles by the ductwork. Care should be taken that ductwork does not seriously interfere with the discharge pattern. In many cases, additional sprinklers or nozzles will have to be extended down below the ductwork to provide satisfactory coverage.

Portable Extinguishing Equipment

Portable fire extinguishers of appropriate type and small hose with spray nozzles are helpful where fires may occur in ducts. This is true even where fixed extinguishing systems have been provided. Judicious placement of extinguishers and hoselines with respect to location of access panels will make them more effective.

Explosion Prevention and Venting

Explosion relief vents prevent or minimize damage to duct systems that carry explosive mixtures. The vents should lead by the most direct practical route to the outside of the building. Information in NFPA 68, *Explosion Venting*, will help when designing explosion vents. The use of suppression and inerting systems is limited by the configuration of the equipment and the physical and chemical properties of the material being conveyed. Details concerning these systems are given in NFPA 69, *Explosion Prevention Systems*.

Static Electricity

When flammable vapors, dusts, or other materials pass through a duct, static charges on the duct are generated. If a charge is allowed to accumulate on an electrically insulated portion of a duct system, it could discharge to an adjoining duct section, at a joint for example, and ignite the material being conveyed. For this reason, exhaust systems carrying flammable vapors, dusts, gases, or other materials should be electrically bonded and grounded. Methods of eliminating dangerous static charges are treated in detail in NFPA 77, *Static Electricity*.

Dampers

Whenever ducts penetrate rated walls, floors, or partitions, dampers with equivalent fire-resistance ratings should be provided to preserve the integrity of the fire area. Dampers should also be used to prevent backdrafts in manifolded duct systems to keep undesirable vapors, dusts, or impurities from being sucked upstream of their collection point and being spread. Firestopping spool pieces are available for plastic ductwork. These pieces collapse when warm and block the duct, preventing fire spread.

BIBLIOGRAPHY

NFPA Codes, Standards, and Recommended Practices

Reference to the following NFPA codes, standards, and recommended practices will provide further information on air-moving equipment discussed in this chapter. (See the latest *NFPA Catalog* for availability of current editions of the following documents.)

NFPA 33, *Spray Application Using Flammable And Combustible Materials.*

NFPA 61A, *Prevention of Fire and Dust Explosions in Facilities Manufacturing and Handling Starch.*

NFPA 61B, *Prevention of Fire and Explosions in Grain Elevators and Facilities Handling Bulk Raw Agricultural Commodities.*

NFPA 61C, *Prevention of Fire and Dust Explosions in Feed Mills.*

NFPA 61D, *Prevention of Fire and Dust Explosions in the Milling of Agricultural Commodities for Human Consumption.*

NFPA 65, *Processing and Finishing of Aluminum.*

NFPA 68, *Explosion Venting.*

NFPA 69, *Explosion Prevention Systems.*

NFPA 70, *National Electrical Code.*

NFPA 77, *Static Electricity.*

NFPA 86, *Ovens and Furnaces.*

NFPA 91, *Standard for the Installation of Blower and Exhaust Systems for Dust, Stock, and Vapor Removal or Conveying.*

NFPA 96, *Removal of Smoke and Grease-Laden Vapors from Commercial Cooking Equipment.*

NFPA 255, *Method of Test of Surface Burning Characteristics of Building Materials.*

NFPA 654, *Prevention of Fire and Dust Explosions in the Chemical, Dye, Pharmaceutical, and Plastics Industries.*

Additional Readings

American National Standards Institute Committee on Ventilation, Fundamentals Governing the Design and Operation of Local Exhaust Systems, *ANSI Z9.2-1979*, American National Standards Institute, New York, 1980.

American Society of Heating, Refrigerating and Air Conditioning Engineers Inc., *ASHRAE Handbook and Product Directory—Applications*, New York, 1978.

American Society of Heating, Refrigerating and Air Conditioning Engineers Inc., *ASHRAE Handbook and Product Directory—Fundamentals*, New York, 1981.

American Society of Heating, Refrigerating and Air Conditioning Engineers Inc., *ASHRAE Handbook and Product Directory—Systems*, New York, 1981.

Bartknecht, W., Explosions: Course, Prevention, Protection, Springer-Verlag, New York, 1981.

Burchsted, C. A., "Basic Requirements for HEPA Filters," *Fire Technology*, Vol. 3, No. 4 (Nov. 1967), pp. 271-280.

"Safe and Efficient Plant Operation and Maintenance," *Chemical Engineering Magazine*, McGraw-Hill, New York, 1980.

Committee on Industrial Ventilation, *Industrial Ventilation*, 20th ed, American Conference of Governmental Industrial Hygienists, Lansing, MI. 1988.

Frank, T. E., "Fire and Explosion Control in Bag Filter Dust Collection Systems," *Fire Journal*, Vol. 75, No. 2 (March 1981), pp. 75-80, 94.

Heinsohn, R. J., *Industrial Ventilation*, Wiley & Sons, New York, NY, 1990.

Hutcheon, N. B., "Fire Protection in Air System Installations," *Heating, Piping and Air Conditioning*, Vol. 40, No. 12 (Dec. 1968).

Keigher, Donald J., "Fire Protection Considerations in Clean Room Design and Operations," *Fire Technology*, Vol. 3, No. 4 (Nov. 1967), pp. 261-271.

Levenback, G., "Grease Fires in Kitchens," *Fire Journal*, Vol. 66, No. 4 (July 1972), pp. 69-72.

Roberts, A. F., "Fire in Ducts Under Forced Ventilation Conditions," *Fire Technology*, Vol. 6, No. 1 (Feb. 1970), pp. 13-21.

Schmitt, C. R., "Flammable Solvent Cleaning Operations in a Laminar Flow Clean Room," *Fire Prevention and Suppression*, Hilado, C. J., *ed.*, Technomic, Westport, CT, 1974, pp. 90-96.

Siconolfi, C. A., "Fire Retardancy in Chemical Process Ductwork," *Fire Technology*, Vol. 5. No. 3 (Aug. 1969), pp. 217-224.

Smith, E. E., "Evaluation of the Fire Hazard of Duct Materials," *Fire Technology*, Vol. 9. No. 3 (Aug. 1973), pp. 157-170.

Talbot, G., "Static Electricity," *Fire*, 70(871), 1979, pp. 397-398.

Wrenn, C., "Inerting for Safety," *Plant/Operations Progress*, Vol. 5, No. 4, 1986, pp. 225-227.

EVACUATION OF OCCUPANTS

Most of the fire prevention and protection strategies addressed in the previous section have been tied directly to the timeline of fire growth and development. Whether the system element is fire prevention; control of materials, products, and environments; suppression; or confining fires, the aim is to slow down or stop the fire and its potentially devastating effects. However, life safety also depends on using the extra time provided by a delayed fire to move occupants out of harm's way. Effective evacuation involves understanding and using the latest knowledge regarding human behavior in fires—how people tend to react and how that affects how they can be trained to react—and building design features that can accommodate or shape occupant behavior toward effective action. Section 8 covers these essential bodies of knowledge.

Chapter 1 covers what we know about human behavior and fire. Forget about panic. When the term is used precisely, such behavior very rarely occurs, even in the most severe fire conditions. Chapter 1 also addresses the means by which people investigate "ambiguous threat cues" and decide that there really is a fire—"recognition, validation, definition, evaluation, commitment, and reassessment."

As Chapter 1 says, "Behavior in fires can be understood as a logical attempt to deal with a complex, rapidly changing situation in which minimal information upon which to act is available." The inescapable conclusion is that people need to be given more and better information. Topping the list is the kind of information people acquire when they practice exit drills effectively, which is the subject of Chapter 3.

Chapters 2 and 4 address the design of building features to facilitate evacuation. Chapter 2 provides overall concepts and principles, while Chapter 4 addresses specific building transportation systems, such as elevators and escalators.

Chapter 2 reviews concepts that underlie the provisions of NFPA 101, Life Safety Code. These include the sizes of people and other key factors in flow speed. They also include characteristics of the building that can protect or threaten means of egress, such as interior finish that promotes rapid flame spread. Formulas and models for calculating egress are covered in Chapter 2, as well, which concludes that, "Maintaining the means of egress in safe operating condition at all times is as important to the prevention of loss of life as the proper construction of the building and the elimination of fire hazards."

Also look for these: Chapters 1-15 and 1-16 of *The SFPE Handbook of Fire Protection Engineering* provide more detailed treatment of the science of human behavior in fire and the modeling of people movement. NFPA's

E.D.I.T.H. program (Exit Drills In The Home) remains the best training program for home exit drills, while other well-designed training materials are available from NFPA to design and implement evacuation plans and drills in schools, health care facilities, and other settings. In the *Fire Protection Handbook*, the early chapters of Section 6 will be of interest, because the building design principles for confining fire and for protecting egress routes need to be considered together. Chapter 1 of Section 2 is relevant because the methods of public firesafety education are also essential to teaching people safe ways to respond to fire, particularly prompt, effective evacuation. Chapters 2 and 3 of Section 1 include fundamental concepts that help put evacuation in its firesafety systems context. And special evacuation requirements for specific property-use classes, if needed, are addressed in the appropriate chapters of Section 8.

HUMAN BEHAVIOR AND FIRE

Revised by John L. Bryan

How one reacts during a fire is related to the role assumed, previous experience, education, and personality; the perceived threat of the fire situation; the physical characteristics and means of egress available within the structure; and the actions of others who are sharing the experience. Post-event analysis of behavior has described actions as adaptive or nonadaptive, participative or inhibited, and altruistic or individualistic. Detailed interview and questionnaire studies over 30 years have established that instances of nonadaptive, or panic, type behavior are rare events that occur under specific conditions. Most behavior in fires is determined by information analysis, resulting in cooperative and altruistic actions.

INTRODUCTION

The characteristics of the behavior of people individually and within groups have been determined primarily by research studies in which individuals were interviewed at the time of the fire by fire department personnel.[1, 2] It must be recognized that an individual's behavior in a fire is affected by the variables of the building in which the fire occurs and by the appearance of the fire at the time of detection. For example, the occupants' response will vary if they smell smoke rather than see flames or dark, acrid smoke completely obscuring a corridor. Variables of the fire protection provided for the building also may be critical to the individual's perception of the threat involved. Obviously, the most important individual decisions and behavior in life-threatening situations occur before the arrival of the fire department, in the early stages of the fire. Studies of health care facilities have indicated the importance of this early behavior:

> "In the process of investigating these case studies we have come to believe that the period between detection of the fire and the arrival of the fire department is the most crucial life-saving period in terms of the first compartment (the area in direct contact with the room of origin and the fire)."[3]

John L. Bryan is a professor and chairman of the Department of Fire Protection Engineering, College of Engineering, University of Maryland, College Park, MD.

Thus, the behavior of the individuals intimately involved with the initiation of the fire is critical not only for themselves, but often for the other occupants of the building. It should be recognized that the altruistic behavior observed in most fires with the interaction of the occupants and the fire environment in a deliberate, purposeful manner, appears to be the general mode of reaction. The nonadaptive flight or panic-type of behavioral reaction is apparently an unusual behavior in fires.

Awareness of the Fire

Obviously, the way in which an individual is alerted to the presence of a fire may determine the degree of threat perceived. With vocal alerting systems in buildings, variations in voice quality, pitch, or volume, as well as the content of the message, tend to provide threat cues.[4] Most of the participants in residential occupancy studies were alerted initially to the fire by the odor of smoke. When the two categories "notified by family" and "notified by others" are combined, however, personal notification becomes the most common means of initial perception of fire, as indicated in Table 7-1A.[1] The category of noise includes noise from persons moving downstairs and through corridors, plus miscellaneous noise sources, including the breaking of glass and the arrival of fire apparatus.

TABLE 7-1A. ***Means of Awareness of the Fire Incident (United States population)***

Means of awareness	Participants	Percent
Smelled smoke	148	26.0
Notified by others	121	21.3
Noise	106	18.6
Notified by family	076	13.4
Saw smoke	052	09.1
Saw fire	046	08.1
Explosion	006	01.1
Felt heat	004	00.7
Saw/heard fire department	004	00.7
Electricity went off	004	00.7
Pet	002	00.3
N = 11	569	100.0

Table 7-1B presents a comparison of the means of awareness of the British population[2] and the U.S. population.[1] The number of stimuli was reduced because the British study had fewer categories, and the U.S. population responses have been adapted to the British categories. There was only one significant difference in the means of awareness between the two populations: 15 percent of the British population became aware of the fire upon observing flame, contrasted with 8.1 percent of the U.S. population.

TABLE 7-1B. ***Comparison of the British and United States Populations Relative to Means of Awareness of the Fire Incident***

Means of awareness	British percent	U.S. percent	$P_1 - P_2$	$SE_{P_1} - P_2$§	CR
Flame	15.0	08.1	6.9	1.64	*4.21**
Smoke	34.0	35.1	1.1	2.27	0.48
Noises	09.0	11.2	2.2	1.41	1.56
Shouts & told	33.0	34.7	2.7	2.25	1.20
Alarm	07.0	07.4	0.4	1.23	0.33
Other	02.0	02.8	0.8	0.70	1.14
	2193	569			

* Critical ratio (CR) significant at or above the 1 percent level of confidence.
§ Standard error.

A study of the NFPA-recommended smoke detector noise level of 75 dBA indicates that individuals with hearing impairments, those taking sleeping pills, or those on medication may require a detector noise level exceeding 100 dBA.[5] (See NFPA 74, *Household Fire Warning Equipment.*) Flashing or activated lights are effective fire signals in occupancies populated primarily by hearing-impaired persons.[6] The 1981 edition of NFPA 101®, *Life Safety Code®*, permitted the flashing of exit signs along with activation of an audible fire alarm system for the first time.

A study of 24 male subjects designed to determine whether they were awakened by a smoke detector's audible alarm signal and could identify fire cues found that the subjects slept through the alarm signals at a signal-to-noise ratio of 10 dBA and consistently failed to identify the awakening cue or radiant heat and smoke odor cues as fire warnings.[7] Other researchers have indicated the alarm-signal-to-noise ratio is attenuated by physical surroundings.[8] Thus, a signal passing through a ceiling or wall may be reduced by 40 dBA, while a signal passing through a door may be reduced by 15 dBA. In addition, the signal could be masked by a typical residential air conditioner noise level of 55 dBA.

The recognition of ambiguous threat cues as signaling an emergency may be inhibited by the presence of other people. Experimental studies of the inhibition of adaptive reaction to emergencies[9] led to an experiment involving college students. While the students were completing a written questionnaire, the experimenter would introduce smoke into the room through a small vent in the wall. If the students left the room and reported the smoke, the experiment was terminated. If the students did not report the presence of the smoke within 6 min from the time it was first noticed, the experiment was considered completed. Students alone in the room reported the smoke in 75 percent of the cases. When two passive, noncommittal persons joined each student, only 10 percent of the groups reported the smoke. When the total experimental group consisted of three naive subjects, one individual reported the smoke in only 38 percent of the groups. Of the 24 persons involved in the eight naive-subject groups, only one reported the smoke within the first 4 min of the experiment. In the single-subject situation, 55 percent of the subjects reported the smoke within 2 min and 75 percent in 4 min.

The study reported that noticing the smoke was apparently delayed by the presence of other persons, with the median being 5 sec for single subjects but 20 sec in both of the group conditions. These results undoubtedly reflect the constraints that people accept regarding their behavior in public places. The performance of naive subjects in the passive-confederate situation was reported as follows:

> "The other nine stayed in the waiting room as it filled up with smoke, doggedly working on their questionnaires, and waving the fumes away from their faces. They coughed, rubbed their eyes, and opened the window but did not report the smoke."

It has been suggested that, while trying to interpret the emergency potential of ambiguous threat cues, the individual is influenced by the reactions of others. Should these others remain passive and seem to interpret the situation as a nonemergency, the individual will tend to modify his or her own interpretation according to this inhibiting social influence.[9] This behavioral experiment may help explain the reported tendency of people to disregard threat cues or interpret them as nonthreatening when they occur in places where there are many other people, such as restaurants, motion picture theaters, or department stores. These experimental results may help explain the calls received by fire departments minutes or even hours after an incident is first detected. In the report of the Arundel Park Hall fire,[10] several of the sample population indicated that, when they entered the hall after observing the fire from outside the building, they warned their friends and suggested they leave, but were laughed at, their warnings apparently disregarded.

The processes of social inhibition, diffusion of responsibility, and mimicking were indicated to be primarily responsible for the inhibition of adaptive and assistance behavior in emergencies. The inhibition of behavior in the early stages of a fire, when the cues are relatively ambiguous, may lead to nonadaptive flight behavior because the time available for evacuation has been expended. It is sometimes difficult to get the occupants of a building to evacuate because of social inhibition and diffused responsibility. The tendency to adopt cues for behavior from others is well-documented in fires in restaurants, other public assembly occupancies, and hotels.

DECISION PROCESSES OF THE INDIVIDUAL

Seven processes have been identified that an individual may use in trying to structure and evaluate situational threat cues.[11] Six of these — recognition, validation, definition, evaluation, commitment, and reassessment — are presented in Figure 7-1A. The seventh, the process of a lattice of defense involving the failure of successive defensives and a hierarcy of defenses, has not been identified as an active decision process in fires.

Recognition

The process of recognition occurs when the individual perceives cues that indicate a threatening fire. The cues may

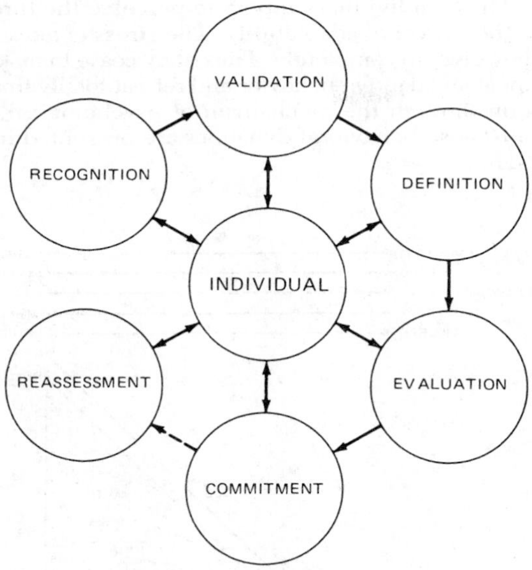

FIG. 7-1A. Decision processes of the individual in a fire.

be very ambiguous and not clearly indicative of a severe fire. However, the clues usually are continuous, with an increasing intensity due to the dynamics of flame, heat, and smoke production. It also was reported that an individual is predisposed to recognize threat cues in terms of the most probable occurrences, usually in relation to past experience and in the form of an optimistic wish. The optimistic wish aspect of the response may be a direct result of the individual's concept of his or her personal invulnerability.

The problem of threat recognition appears to be important for fire protection. The adaptive action involved in the initiation of the fire alarm, the evacuation of building occupants, and the suppression of the fire may be delayed or postponed if individuals do not perceive the cues as indicative of a fire. The ambiguous nature of threat cues indicates that individuals who do not have specialized fire prevention or fire protection education and experience recognize only large amounts of smoke or sudden and threatening flames as indicative of a threatening fire.

Validation

The process of validation consists of attempts by an individual to determine the seriousness of the threat cues, usually by reassurance of the mild nature of the threat and its improbability. When the cues are significantly ambiguous, however, the individual tries to obtain additional information. In other words, the person is aware that something is happening but is not sure exactly what it is. This process of validation may be conducted by questioning other nearby individuals. In studies of the explosion of a fireworks plant in Houston, TX, it was found that, of the 139 persons interviewed, 85 individuals — or 61 percent of the population — obtained information on the source and nature of the explosion and smoke from someone they saw or from someone who telephoned and told them.[12] The presence of others during the threat recognition and validation process was found possibly to inhibit or influence the behavioral responses of the individual.

Definition

The definition process essentially consists of an attempt by the individual to relate the information concerning the threat to some of the variables, such as the qualitative nature of the threat, the magnitude of deprivation of the threat, and the time context. The individual's stress and anxiety appear to be most severe before he or she has determined the situation's structure or meaning, although it is apparent that the situation requires interpretation. The role concept of the individual is one of the critical factors in the situation, relative to the personalization of the threat and the physical environment. The most important physical aspects in the definition process are the generation, intensity, and propagation of the smoke, flames, and thermal exposure.

Evaluation

The process of evaluation may be described as the cognitive and psychological activities required for the individual to respond to the threat. The individual's ability to reduce his or her stress and anxiety levels becomes the essential psychological factor. In the threat situation created by a fire, evaluation is the process involved in the decision to react by fight or flight. With evaluation, an initial decision to make an overt behavioral response is completed. Because of the time context of the generation and propagation of the fire, the mental processes up to and including the process of evaluation may have to be accomplished within several seconds. Variables of the physical environment are an important source of information for individuals involved in formulating adaptation, escape, or defense plans. Additional determinants may be the location of the individual relative to the egress routes, other people, the untenable effects of the fire, and the behavior of other individuals.

During the process of evaluation, an individual may decide to leave the building — flight — or to use a portable fire extinguisher — fight — . During this time, he or she is particularly susceptible to the actions and communications of others. Thus, the individual may mimic the behavioral reactions of observed individuals, resulting in mass adaptive or nonadaptive behavior rather than selective, individualized behavior. The following situation at an auto sales and service agency in 1971 demonstrates what may have been an instance of mimicked behavior becoming normative group behavior:[13]

> "About 10 pm, the fire department received an alarm from a street fire alarm box. When fire fighters arrived, the 150 by 200 ft (46 by 61 m), one- and two-story building of wood frame and hollow block construction was well alight and nearly 300 spectators were watching the fire in 10°F (-12°C) weather. An investigation revealed the fire had been burning for about 90 minutes before the fire department was notified."

In studies of nonadaptive group behavior, the concept that this mode of behavior depends directly on the individual's perception of the reward structure of a situation has been developed.[14] People in a building who are confronted with a fire probably would initially perceive a reward structure that would encourage cooperative and adaptive behavior; in such cases, everyone should be able to reach and proceed through the available exits. However, the reward structure perceived by some individuals more remote from the egress routes could result in competitive behavior. Such individuals would perceive that cooperative behavior would make it impossible for them to reach an exit in time to escape the fire. Once the pattern of competitive behavior is initiated, the behavior pattern of the group may become one of intense, individual competition for the escape routes.

In the evaluation process, an individual's cultural influences and assumption of a particular role may be very important in formulating defense or escape plans. It is believed that an individual playing a familiar role that is also suitable for the threat situation will experience less anxiety, and respond with more adaptive behavior than individuals in unfamiliar roles confronted with an unfamiliar threat.

Commitment

Commitment consists of the mechanisms the individual uses to initiate the behavioral activity required to fulfill the defense plans conceptualized in the evaluation process. This overt response to the threat of fire results in success or failure. If the response fails, the individual immediately becomes involved in the next process of reassessment and commitment. If the action results in success, the anxiety and stress aspects of the situation are reduced and relieved, although the general fire situation may have increased in severity.

Reassessment

The process of reassessment and overcommitment is the most stressful of the individual's processes because his or her previous attempts to adjust to the threat have failed. Thus, more intense effort goes into the behavioral reactions, and the individual tends to become less selective in the choice of response. As successive failures are encountered, the individual becomes more frustrated. The possibility of injury and risk increases with a greater activity level and with less probability of success, as was demonstrated in the Arundel Park Hall fire. There, the number of those who selected windows as a means of escape increased as people became involved in their second escape attempts.[10]

In analyzing the behavior of an individual involved in the processes of recognition, validation, definition, evaluation, commitment, and reassessment, it must be remembered that all of these processes are dynamic. They are constantly being modified in relation to their magnitude, velocity, and intensity. A person's usual psychological and physiological activities probably will be below normal during the recognition process, when he or she is concentrating on perceiving the threat cues. During the process of validation and definition of the threat, adjacent members of the threatened population will communicate overtly. The period of hyperactivity appears to occur initially during the process of commitment and to become intense during the process of reassessment and recommitment. Stress will increase with each successive stage, since the primary motivation of the behavioral activity is stress reduction. The appearance, the proximity, the propagation, the time, and the toxic gases of the fire threat also will tend to predispose the individual to a higher level of behavioral activity, again depending upon the individual's perception of these threat variables. During the process of reassessment and recommitment, the individual's activity level may assume the hyperactive mode of frantic activity, or it may be expressed in the catastrophic state of complete physical immobility with a loss of ability to communicate coherently. These individuals appear to perceive the threat as above their level of adaptability. The stress is too severe, and they give up completely. Thus, they cease to make any attempt at an adaptive behavior and retreat totally from the situation through the mechanism of psychological withdrawal. These behavioral dynamics are presented in Figure 7-1B.

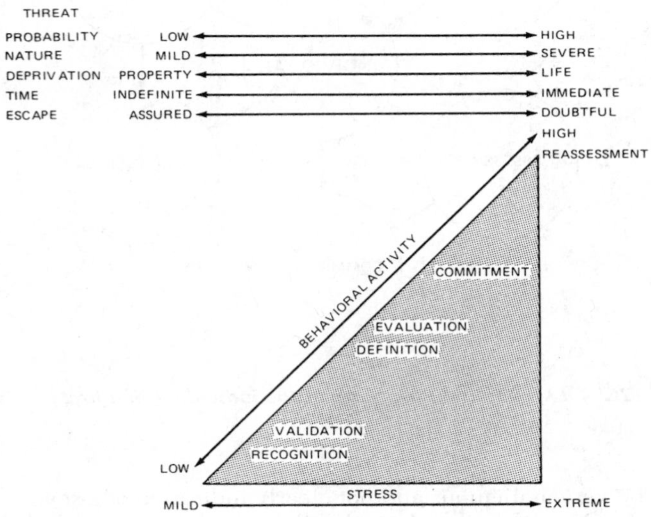

FIG. 7-1B. Dynamics of behavioral activity of the individual.

A conceptual model of the individual's decision processes similar to some of the concepts previously discussed has been developed. Instead of the six processes referenced previously, only three have been used: recognition/interpretation; behavior, with either action or inaction; and the outcome of the action, which involves the evaluation and long-term effect of the behavior.[15] The behavior evaluation is similar to the process of reassessing the decision model. Both the recognition/interpretation concept and the behavior concept involve factors critical to the decision processes. Experience and immediate circumstances all have an impact on the recognition/interpretation concept. It has been emphasized that individuals in a fire may not know right away that they are involved in a fire and may not know where, in relation to their location, the fire is developing or the egress routes in the building are. This conceptual model is presented in Figure 7-1C.

The conceptual model just described has been modified into one involving three phases: the detection of cues, the definition of the situation, and coping behavior. In addition, tentative determinants of the behavior have been developed that increase the probability of detection and of fire suppression.[16] The similarity between the two models can be observed by comparing Figure 7-1C with Figure 7-1D.

BEHAVIOR ACTIONS OF OCCUPANTS

In a study involving 952 fires and 2193 individuals interviewed by fire department personnel at the fire scene in Great Britain, it was found that the most frequent responses to fire involved evacuation of the building, fighting or containing the fire, and alerting other individuals or the fire

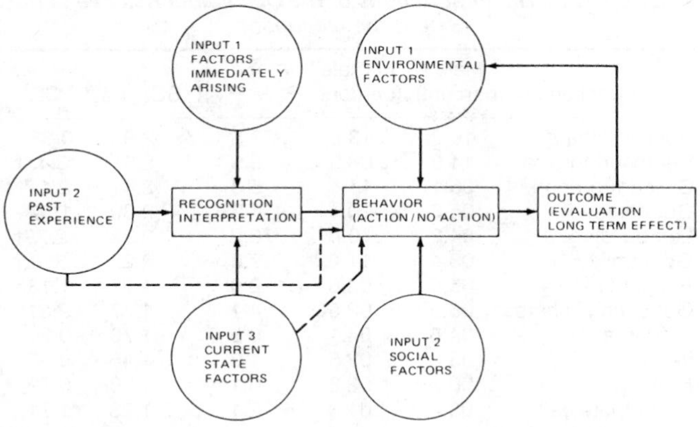

FIG. 7-1C. ***Preliminary heuristic systems model of behavior in fires.***

brigade.[2] The identical type of broad categorization of behavior was found in a similar study, which involved interviewing 584 participants in 335 fire incidents in the U.S. Interviews were conducted by fire department personnel, who used a structured questionnaire at the scene of the fire.[1]

The examination of those initial actions to fire, as found in parallel in the studies of British and U.S. populations, is presented in Table 7-1C. The behavior of the individuals varied by sex, with female and male behavior divided along culturally determined primary group roles. Thus, the males were predominately active in fighting the fire, while the females were predominately concerned with alerting others and helping them leave the building.

It should be noted that there were ten statistically significant differences between the British and the U.S. populations. The U.S. population was predominant in five categories of first actions: "notified others," "got dressed," "got family," "left area," and "entered the building." A greater percentage of the British population engaged in the first actions of "fought fire," "went to fire area," "closed door to fire area," "pulled fire alarm," and "turned off appliances."

The general classification of the three early actions for British and the U.S. populations alike were categorized as "evacuation," "reentry," "fire fighting," "moved through

TABLE 7-1C. ***Comparison of the First Actions of British and U.S. Populations***

Actions	British percent	U.S. percent	$P^1 - P_2$††	$SE_{1_1 - P_2}$§	CR‖
Notified others	8.1	15.0	6.9	1.38	*5.00*†
Searched for fire	12.2	10.1	2.1	1.51	1.39
Called fire dept.	10.1	9.0	1.1	1.40	0.79
Got dressed	2.2	8.1	5.9	0.85	*6.94*†
Left building	8.0	7.6	0.4	1.27	0.31
Got family	5.4	7.6	2.2	1.11	*1.98**
Fought fire	14.9	10.4	4.5	1.63	*2.76*†
Left area	1.8	4.3	2.5	0.70	*3.57*†
Nothing	2.1	2.7	0.6	0.69	0.87
Had others call F.D.	2.8	2.2	0.6	0.76	0.79
Got personal property	1.2	2.1	0.9	0.55	1.64
Went to fire area	5.6	2.1	3.5	1.01	*3.47*†
Removed fuel	1.2	1.7	0.5	0.53	0.94
Enters building	0.1	1.6	1.5	0.30	*5.00*†
Tried to exit	1.6	1.6	0	0	0
Closed door to fire area	3.1	1.0	2.1	0.76	*2.76*†
Pulled fire alarm	2.7	0.9	1.8	0.70	*2.57*
Turned off appliances	4.1	0.9	3.2	0.85	*3.20*†
N = 18	2193	580			

* Critical ratios significant at or above the 5 percent level of confidence.
† Critical ratios significant at or above the 1 percent level of confidence.
†† British percent minus U.S. percent.
§ Standard error.
‖ Critical ratio.

smoke," and "turned back" behavior. The behavioral comparisons of the two populations are presented in Table 7-1D. There was a statistically significant difference in every category except "moved through smoke."

An interesting aspect of the U.S. study involves modifications in the first, second, and third behavioral actions of the participants. Table 7-1E presents the three actions for the sample U.S. population, totaling 584 individuals. The action of "notifying others" accounted for 15 percent of the first actions, but, by the time of the third actions, it accounted for only 5.8 percent. A similar reduction in frequency can be observed with the action of "searching for the fire." There is a reduction in this activity from 10.1 percent as the first action to 0.8 percent as the third action. The behavioral actions of "getting dressed" and "got family" also diminished in frequency with the progression from

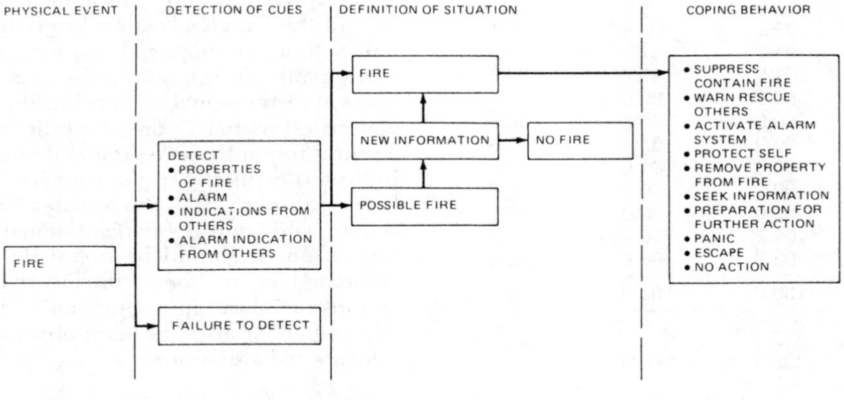

FIG. 7-1D. ***Flow diagram model of human behavior in a fire.***

TABLE 7-1D. ***Comparison of the Behavior of the British and U.S. Populations***

Behavior	British percent	U.S. percent	$P_1 - P_2$†	$SE_{P_1 - P_2}$§	CR‖
Evacuation	54.5	80.0	25.5	2.30	*11.09**
Reentry	43.0	27.9	15.1	2.30	*6.57**
Fire fighting	14.7	22.9	8.2	1.74	*4.71**
Moved through smoke	60.0	62.7	2.7	2.29	1.18
Turned back	26.0	18.3	7.7	2.01	*3.83**
	2193	584			

* Critical Ratios significant at or above the 1 percent level of confidence.
† British percent minus U.S. percent.
§ Standard error.
‖ Critical ratio.

the first to the third action as time passed during the fire. In contrast, an increase in frequency from the first to the third actions may be noted for "called fire department," "left building," and "fought fire."

Behavior According to Sex

The differences between the first actions of the participants according to their sex has been examined. Table 7-1F presents the initial actions of the U.S. study population relative to the sex of the participants.

TABLE 7-1E. ***Summary of the First, Second, and Third Actions of the Occupants***

Actions	1st action (percent)	2nd action (percent)	3rd action (percent)
Notified others	15.0	09.6	05.8
Searched for fire	10.1	02.4	00.8
Called fire department	09.0	14.6	12.7
Got dressed	08.1	01.8	00.3
Left building	07.6	20.9	35.9
Got family	07.6	05.9	01.4
Fought fire	04.6	05.7	11.5
Got extinguisher	04.6	05.3	01.6
Left area	04.3	02.8	01.1
Woke up	03.1	00.0	00.0
Nothing	02.7	00.0	00.0
Had others call F.D.	02.2	04.0	04.1
Got personal property	02.1	03.8	00.8
Went to fire area	02.1	01.0	00.0
Removed fuel	01.7	01.0	01.1
Entered building	01.6	00.8	01.1
Tried to exit	01.6	02.4	00.5
Went to fire alarm	01.6	01.8	01.1
Telephoned others	01.2	00 6	01.1
Tried to extinguish	01.2	01.8	01.9
Closed door to fire area	01.0	00.2	00.3
Pulled fire alarm	00.9	00.6	00.5
Turned off appliances	00.9	00.6	00.3
Checked on pets	00.9	01.4	00.5
Awaited F.D. arrival	00.0	01.0	03.6
Went to balcony	00.2	00.8	02.7
Removed by F.D.	00.0	00.0	01.6
Opened doors/windows	00.2	00.4	01.1
Other	03.9	08.0	06.6
N = 29	100.0	100.0	100.0
Range	0–87	0–106	0–131
Percent of participant population	99.3	86.6	62.9

TABLE 7-1F. ***The First Actions of the Occupants Relative to the Sex of the Occupant***

First action	Male (percent)	Female (percent)	$P_1 - P_2$††	$SE_{P_1 - P_2}$§	CR‖
Notified others	16.3	13.8	2.5	2.98	0.83
Searched for fire	14.9	06.3	8.6	2.51	*3.43†*
Called fire dept.	06.1	11.4	5.3	2.41	*2.19**
Got dressed	05.8	10.1	4.3	2.30	1.87
Left building	04.2	10.4	6.2	2.22	*2.79†*
Got family	03.4	11.0	7.6	2.22	*3.42†*
Fought fire	05.8	03.8	2.0	1.77	1.13
Got extinguishers	06.9	02.8	4.1	1.77	*2.31**
Left area	04.6	04.1	0.5	1.70	0.29
Woke up	03.8	02.5	1.3	1.45	0.90
Nothing	02.7	02.8	0.1	1.38	0.72
Had others call F.D.	03.4	01.3	2.1	1.23	1.71
Got personal property	01.5	02.5	1.0	1.17	0.85
Went to fire area	01.9	02.2	0.3	1.20	0.25
Removed fuel	01.1	02.2	1.1	1.08	1.02
Entered building	02.3	0.09	1.4	1.02	1.37
Tried to exit	01.5	01.6	0.1	1.05	0.09
Went to fire alarm	01.1	0.19	0.8	1.02	0.78
Telephoned others	00.8	01.6	0.8	0.91	0.87
Tried to extinguish	01.9	00.6	1.3	0.91	1.43
Closed door to fire area	00.8	01.3	0.5	0.87	0.57
Pulled fire alarm	01.1	00.6	0.5	0.75	0.66
Turned off appliances	00.8	00.9	0.1	0.79	0.12
Checked on pets	00.8	00.9	0.1	0.79	0.12
Other	06.5	02.5	4.0	1.70	2.35*
N =25	262	318			

* Critical ratios significant at or above the 5 percent level of confidence.
† Critical ratios significant at or above the 1 percent level of confidence.
†† Male percentage minus female percentage.
§ Standard error.
‖ Critical ratio.

There are significant statistical differences between males and females in the categories of "searched for fire," "called fire department," "got family," and "got extinguishers." Male participants were predominant in fire fighting activities. Thus, 14.9 percent of the males "searched for fire," as opposed to 6.3 percent of the females, and 6.9 percent of the males "got extinguishers," as opposed to 2.8 percent of the females. Females differed significantly from males in warning and evacuation activities. Thus, 11.4 percent of the females "called fire department" as their initial action, as opposed to 6.1 percent of the male participants. In relation to the evacuation behavior, 10.4 percent of the females "left building" as the first action, contrasted with 4.2 percent of the male participants. The cultural role influence on female participants is probably indicated explicitly in the concern for other family members — 11 percent of the females "got family" as the first action, while only 3.4 percent of males engaged in this initial action. It should be noted that the male actions of "searched for" or "fought fire" were matched by the female actions of "alarm initiating" and "evaluation behavior."[1] This behavior also has been observed in health care and educational situations.

Behavior in Hotel Fires

The fire protection of high-rise buildings and their occupants was tested severely by the MGM Grand Hotel fire in Clark County, NV, on November 21, 1980,[17] and by the subsequent fire at the Las Vegas Hilton Hotel on February 10, 1981.[18] Both of these hotel fires involved injuries and fatalities among the guests. NFPA conducted an intensive questionnaire study of the guests registered in the MGM Grand Hotel for the evening of November 20-21, 1980.[19]

The MGM Grand Hotel fire was discovered by a hotel employee who entered the unoccupied deli-restaurant located on the casino level of the hotel at approximately 7:10 on the morning of November 21, 1980. As instructed, the hotel telephone operator immediately notified the Clark County Fire Department at approximately 7:18. The telephone operators were forced from their switchboard by the smoke immediately after they had made an announcement over the public address system, at approximately 7:20, to evacuate the casino area. The fire quickly reached flashover in the deli, immediately spread from east to west through the main casino area, and extended out the west portico doors on the casino level immediately following the arrival of the first fire department personnel.

An addition to the hotel was being constructed adjacent to the west end of the building, and construction workers helped warn and evacuate guests and assisted in fire fighting. The heat and smoke rapidly extended from the casino area through the seismic joints, elevator shafts, and stairways throughout the 21 residential floors of the hotel. The heat was intense enough on the 26th, a top floor, to activate automatic sprinklers in the lobby adjacent to the elevator shafts.

Due to the rapid early evacuation of the telephone staff, guests were not alerted by the hotel public address system or the local fire alarm system. Guests warned early in the fire, and those already awake and dressed were able to escape before the smoke became untenable on the upper floors. Guests alerted later remained in their rooms or moved to other rooms, usually with other occupants. The fire itself did not extend above the casino level, with the exception of its extension of a rather minor nature into two guest rooms on the fifth floor. The fire resulted in 85 fatalities and injured 778 guests and 7 hotel employees. Seventy-nine body locations were documented: 18 on the casino level, 25 in guest rooms, 22 in corridors and lobbies, 9 in stairways, and 5 in elevators. The victims were found on the casino level and on the 16th and upper floors, with the majority between the 20th and the 25th floors.

Figure 7-1E is a diagram of the guest floor of the MGM Grand Hotel which was used in the occupant questionnaire study conducted by NFPA.[19] Of the nine victims found in the stairways, two were in Stairway 1 at the extreme south end of the south wing on the 17th floor; six were between the 20th and 23rd floor in Stairway 2 at the central end of the south wing; and one victim was found at the ground-floor level of Stairway 4 at the extreme west end of the west wing. There are various estimates of the number of guests and fire department personnel who suffered injuries at the MGM Grand Hotel fire. Morris indicated that 619 people were taken to hospitals and another 150 were treated at the

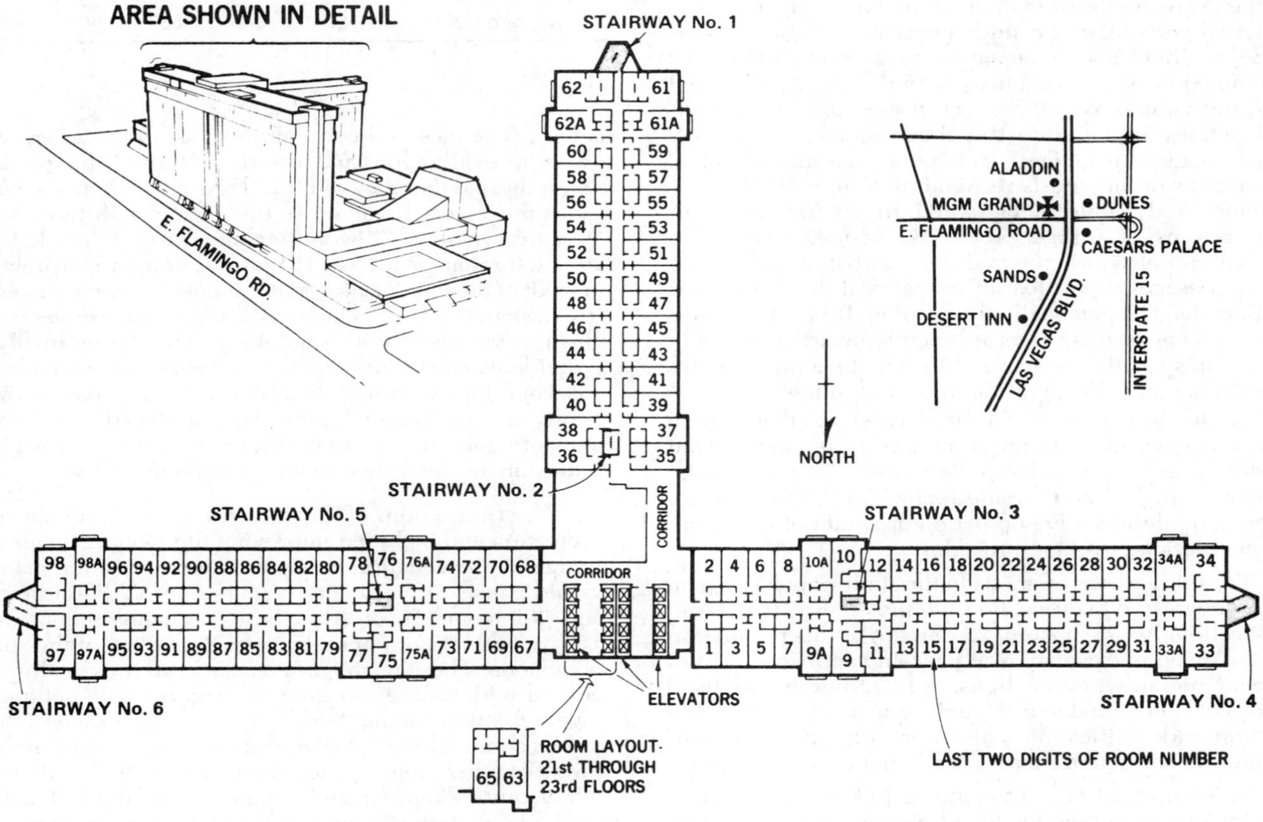

FIG. 7-1E. Residential floor diagram of the MGM Grand Hotel.

Las Vegas Convention Center, where the survivors were transported from the hotel.[20]

The MGM Grand Hotel tragedy was a unique fire, especially from two aspects: it was the second most serious hotel fire in U.S. history, being surpassed only by the Winecoff Hotel fire in Atlanta, GA, on December 7, 1946, which killed 119; and it was the first high-rise fire in the U.S. in which helicopters evacuated large numbers of people. About 300 were evacuated in this manner; the fire department rescued approximately 900 people by other means.

Shortly after the MGM Grand Hotel fire, NFPA prepared a 4-page, 28-item questionnaire that included the floor plan of the guest rooms. A total of 1960 questionnaires were mailed, and 554, or approximately 28 percent, of these were returned. Four hundred fifty-five of the responding individuals indicated a willingness to be interviewed.

The age of the questionnaire population ranged from 20 to 84 years, with an average age of 45. The population consisted of 331 males and 222 females; one respondent did not indicate a sexual classification. One-hundred and three guests indicated that they were alone at the time they became aware of the fire in the hotel. The presence of other people, especially if they belong to the individual's primary group, appears to be a determinant of the response of many individuals in residential fires.

The initial five actions of the 554 guests, as elicited from the NFPA questionnaire study, are presented in Table 7-1G. Notice that the five most frequent first actions were "dressed," "opened door," "notified roommates," "dressed partially," and "looked out window." Guests involved in the first actions were predominately engaged in determining the degree of threat to themselves. Only 7.9, or approximately 8 percent, of the study population began or tried to begin their own evacuation with such actions as "attempted to exit," "went to exit," and "left room." A total of 16 individuals, or 2.9 percent of the population, initiated actions to improve the room as an area of refuge: "wet towels for face" and "put towels around door." The actions of the guests responding to the NFPA questionnaire study could be classified, in general, as evacuation actions or refuge processes. Actions relating to evacuation behavior appeared to be initiated early if the egress passages were clear of smoke or if the smoke was not perceived as personally threatening. If the smoke was heavy, however, the guests apparently decided to stay in their rooms or other rooms and to initiate actions to prevent smoke migration into the rooms of refuge.

Further examination of Table 7-1G shows that the five most popular actions reported by guests as their second actions were "opened door," "dressed," "went to exit," "dressed partially," and "secured valuables." Approximately 19 percent of the study population dressed before initiating evacuation or refuge procedures.

The third actions of guests in the study population generally progressed to evacuation, attempted evacuation, and notification. Approximately 25 percent of this population was involved in evacuation actions, and approximately 10 percent attempted evacuations, as identified by the third actions of "attempted to exit" and "returned to room." The alerting and notification actions are identified as third actions of "notified occupants" and "notified other room."

The fourth actions of the guests in the study population indicate a progression to evacuation, attempted evacuation, and self-protection or room refuge procedural actions. The most frequent fourth action of the guests was "went to exit"; approximately 16 percent of this population indicated that they did this. However, when one combines the guests involved in this action with those who "went down stairs," "went to another exit," "left hotel," and "left room," a total of 151 guests, or approximately 30 percent of the fourth action guest population, were involved in evacuation actions. The process of forming convergence clusters was noted in this hotel fire. This action involved individuals clustering together in rooms they considered areas of refuge with individuals they usually characterized as not knowing before the fire. The fourth actions of "went to other room" and "went to other room/others" are explicit indicators of the formation of convergence clusters.[21]

The fifth actions of the guests were primarily for self-protection and included improving the room as an area of refuge and evacuation behavior. The evacuation actions would consist of: "went up stairs to roof," "left hotel," and "left room." Involved in these evacuation actions were 175 individuals, or approximately 40 percent of the study population. Those unable to evacuate, and thus vitally concerned with refuge procedures, used the fifth actions of "went to other room/others," "wet towels for face," "put towels around door," "broke window," "returned to room," "went to other room," "offered refuge in room," and "went to balcony." Approximately 40 percent of the fifth-action study population was involved in refuge procedures and self-protection actions.

TABLE 7-1G. ***First Five Actions of Guests in the MGM Grand Hotel Fire***

	Percent of Population				
Actions	first	second	third	fourth	fifth
Dressed	16.8	11.6	6.5	—	—
Opened door	15.9	11.7	6.7	3.4	—
Notified roommates	11.6	3.0	—	—	—
Dressed partially	10.1	7.5	4.5	—	—
Looked out window	9.7	5.7	—	—	—
Got out of bed	4.5	—	—	—	—
Left room	4.3	5.4	8.1	2.4	2.0
Attempted to phone	3.4	3.6	—	2.8	—
Went to exit	2.5	10.3	9.5	16.1	6.7
Put towels around door	1.6	2.5	3.0	6.8	7.7
Felt door for heat	1.3	2.3	—	—	—
Wet towels for face	1.3	3.7	6.3	4.6	7.9
Got out of bath	1.1	—	—	—	—
Attempted to exit	1.1	3.0	5.8	4.3	—
Secured valuables	—	6.8	4.3	—	—
Notified other room	—	3.4	2.2	—	—
Returned to room	—	—	3.9	8.4	4.1
Went down stairs	—	—	3.9	5.4	21.3
Left hotel	—	—	3.4	2.6	2.0
Notified occupants	—	—	3.0	—	—
Went to another exit	—	—	—	3.6	4.8
Went to other room	—	—	—	3.6	3.6
Went to other room/ others	—	—	—	3.4	8.7
Looked for exit	—	—	—	2.4	—
Broke window	—	—	—	—	4.3
Offered refuge in room	—	—	—	—	1.8
Went up stairs to roof	—	—	—	—	2.9
Went to balcony	—	—	—	—	1.8
Other	14.8	19.5	28.9	30.2	20.1
Total (percent):	100.0	99.1	96.9	90.6	79.6
No. of guests:	554	549	537	502	441

Convergence Clusters

The phenomenon of convergence cluster formation was first noticed in a study of occupant behavior in a high-rise apartment building fire in 1979.[22] The clusters appear to involve occupants of the building involved in the fire who converged into specific rooms they perceived as areas of refuge. In the MGM Grand Hotel fire, guests tended to select rooms on the north side of the east and west wings and rooms on the east side of the south wing. In addition, guests reported that people had converged in the rooms with balconies and doors leading out to the balconies because of the ventilation, reduced smoke, improved visibility, and communication that the balconies offered. The guests who reported their participation in this behavior either estimated the number of persons in the room or connecting rooms, or they indicated only that "others" or "other persons" were present.

Table 7-1H lists the rooms identified by guests as areas of refuge for numerous persons other than the original occupants. This table also presents estimates of the length of time that the clusters were maintained in the rooms — usually until the individuals were evacuated, or until the occupants were notified by fire or rescue personnel that evacuation was possible. The numbers in the two right-hand columns indicate the total number of persons in the clusters for the total number of rooms identified on the floor. The smallest number of people identified as a cluster was three, and the largest was 35.

TABLE 7-1H. *Summary of Rooms, Time Duration and Number of Guests Reported in Convergence Clusters*

Floor	Room Number(s)	Time (hours)	Persons no.	Persons percent
7	731	0.6	3	0.7
8	827, 840	1.5–1.75	14*	3.3
9	927	2.5	5	1.2
10	1009A, 1025, 1034,1060	1–2	53	12.7
11	1129, 1115	1.5–2	30*	7.2
12	1261, 1225, 1233A	2–3	53	12.7
14	1433A, 1461A, 1451, 1416A	1.5–2	8*	1.9
15	1501, 1533A, 1510	2–3	38*	9.1
16	1643, 1625, 1633, 1629, 1627, 1615	2–3.5	35*	8.4
17	1725, 1775, 1731, 1719, 1762, 1756, 1733A	2–2.5	84	20.1
18	1819, 1802, 1850	2–3	20	4.8
19	1929, 1919, 1962A, 1962, 1964, 1925	2–3.5	13*	3.1
20	2027, 2013, 2030	2.5–3.5	25	6.0
22	2213, 2221,2229	2–3	13	3.1
23	2329, 2314, 2342, 2331,2308, 2340	2.5–3.25	20*	4.8
24	2446	3.5	4	0.9
25	2512, 2509A	3.5	*	0
Total: 17	57		418	100.0
Range 7–25	1–7	0.6–3.5	3–84	0–20.1

* Persons indicated only as "Others."

The greatest number of rooms used by convergence clusters, and thus the largest population participating in convergence clusters, was located on the 17th floor of the hotel. No convergence clusters were identified by guests on the 6th, 21st, or 26th floors. The clusters appear to serve as an anxiety- and tension-reducing mechanism for individuals confronted with a threatening situation. The action of "offered refuge in room," previously identified in the discussion of the fifth actions, is a positive indication of the occurrence of a convergence cluster.

In addition to the detailed human behavior study of the MGM Grand Hotel fire,[23] NFPA conducted a questionnaire study of guests' behavior in the Westchase Hilton Hotel fire in Houston, TX, on March 6, 1982, in which 12 people died.[24]

The classic types of nonadaptive behavior in a fire involve the disregard of adaptive actions that might facilitate the evacuation of others or limit the propagation of smoke, heat, or flame. Nonadaptive behavior ranges from the single act of leaving a room of fire origin without closing the door, thus allowing the fire to spread throughout the structure and endanger the lives of all the occupants, to the more generalized concept of fleeing from a fire without regard for others and perhaps injuring others in what is often termed "panic."

Nonadaptive behavior may be an omission, such as forgetting to close a door, or it may involve an action that, although well-meaning, results in negative consequences. When the results of behavior are extinguishment of the fire and elimination of the threat, the behavior may be said to be adaptive. However, the same behavior may be ineffective because the fire was more severe than was first perceived. In such cases, the time spent trying to extinguish it might have been used more effectively to warn others and to notify the fire department. Thus, some behavior that appears to be nonadaptive really is behavior that would have seemed most adaptive if it had been successful. The injuries people suffer in relation to a fire may be cues to their nonadaptive or risk behavior.

Panic Behavior

One concept always discussed following a fire in which multiple fatalities occur, such as the Beverly Hills Supper Club fire,[25] is panic behavior. One classic definition of panic is:

> A sudden and excessive feeling of alarm or fear, usually affecting a body of persons, originating in some real or supposed danger, vaguely apprehended, and leading to extravagant and injudicious efforts to secure safety.

According to this definition, panic is a flight or fleeing type of behavior that involves extravagant and injudicious effort and is likely not to be limited to a single individual, but to be transmitted to and adopted by a group of people. From simulation experiments, a panic-type of behavior reaction has been defined in the following manner:

> "A fear-induced flight behavior which is nonrational, nonadaptive, and nonsocial, which serves to reduce the escape possibilities of the group as a whole."

The concept of panic is often used to explain the occurrence of multiple fatalities in fires even when there is no physical, social, or psychological evidence showing that competitive, injudicious flight behavior actually took place. The media and public officials often label various types of fire behavior as panic. The evidence accumulated from interviews with participants in the Beverly Hills Supper Club fire, and questionnaires completed by occupants, provided no evidence of the classic group-type of panic behavior with competitive flight for the exits.[26]

It has been said that panic as a concept is primarily a description rather than an explanation of behavior. The concept is used to support the introduction of requirements in fire and building laws or ordinances to provide for the firesafety of occupants. There also has been shown to be a difference between using of the concept to describe other persons' behavior in a fire and the use by someone engaged in the behavior to indicate his or her own state of concern and anxiety.[27] Just because an individual identifies behavior as associated with panic does not necessarily identify the behavior as the classic panic-type response. The outcome of the behavior, as previously discussed, affects its labeling: the behavior of people in a fire is most likely to be misinterpreted when the outcome of the fire has been unfortunate.

The use of the concept of panic must be separated from use of the terms "anxiety" or "fear." The concept of self-destructive or animalistic panic responses to stimuli, such as the presence of smoke, has not been supported by the research on human behavior in fires. As has been pointed out, it is rare to have panic behavior in which the flight is characterized by competition among the participants, with resultant personal injuries.[1,2,4,27,28,29]

In an interview study of 100 participants in single-family dwelling fires, no instances of panic behavior were found. Primarily altruistic, helpful behavior was found instead.[29]

Reentry Behavior

The study of the 1956 Arundel Park Hall fire was the first to document the phenomenon of reentry behavior.[10] Some older codes and regulations affecting design of the means of egress appear to have been based on the assumption that pedestrian traffic only moves away from a fire and away from the area or floor of the building involved. However, the Arundel Park Hall study indicated that approximately one-third of the survivors interviewed had reentered the building.

Thus, it has become apparent that doors, stairways, and corridors often will be subjected to two-way movement of occupants and others. The occupant who, after leaving the building safely, turns around and reenters is often completely aware of the fire in the building and of the specific portions of the building involved in fire and smoke propagation. Table 7-1I presents the number of participants who reentered Arundel Park Hall during the fire, from the interviewed population of 61 persons. Note the reasons for the reentry behavior and the fact that those who reentered were predominately male.

The Arundel Park Hall fire occurred in an assembly occupancy being used for a church-sponsored oyster roast, a family-type affair. Thus, the primary group cultural role of father or husband apparently was a critical variable in the reentry behavior of the population interviewed and may have resulted in the fact that the reentry participants were mostly male. It can reasonably be argued that reentry behavior is not a nonadaptive behavior, since it is often used to assist or rescue persons remaining or believed to be remaining in the building. This type of behavior is often used by parents whose children are missing during a fire. The behavior is often undertaken in a rational, deliberate, and purposeful manner, without the emotional anxiety and self-doubt usually associated with nonadaptive behavior.

TABLE 7-1I. ***Behavior of Occupants who Reentered in the Arundel Park Hall Fire, Relative to Sex, and Reentry Reasons***

Sex	Reentered and left same exit	Reentered and left different exit	Stated reason for reentrance
M	1		Turn off kitchen stoves
M	1	1	Tell people to leave
M	3		To help
M	1		Assist people
M	2	3	Find wife
M	2	2	Assist fire fighting
M & 1 F		5	No stated reason
21 M & 1 F	10	12	

However, reentry behavior has been considered nonadaptive, since people going back into a burning building often hinder the efficient and effective evacuation of others through the same means of egress.

The reasons elicited from participants in reentry behavior in the Project People study[1] in the U.S. are presented in Table 7-1J. It would seem that 162 people from the total study population of 584, or 27.9 percent, engaged in reentry behavior. The most popular reason given was to "fight fire," followed by "obtain personal property," "check on fire," "notify others," "assist fire department," and "retrieve pets." These six reasons accounted for approximately 73 percent of this reentry behavior.

TABLE 7-1J. ***Reasons for Reentry of the Occupants***

Reasons	Participants	Percent
Fight fire	36	22.2
Obtain personal property	28	17.2
Check on fire	18	11.0
Notify others	13	8.0
Assist F.D.	12	7.4
Retrieve pets	12	7.4
Call F.D.	9	5.5
Assist evacuation	4	2.5
Taken to hospital	3	1.8
Turn power back on	2	1.2
Rescue from balcony	1	0.6
Help injured family member	1	0.6
Turned off gas	1	0.6
Open windows	1	0.6
Close door	1	0.6
No apparent danger	1	0.6
Entered non-danger area	1	0.6
Job responsibility	1	0.6
Due to fire	1	0.6
Told to by others	1	0.6
Not reported	16	9.8
N = 21	163	100.0
Range = 1–36	Percent of participant population = 27.9	

Table 7-1K compares the reentry behavior of the British and U.S. study populations. Note that all of the reasons were significantly different, with the exception of the item "save personal effects." The reentry reasons of the U.S. population was predominantly "save personal effects," "call fire department," "rescue pets," "notify others," "assist fire department," and "assist the evacuation." The British population's were predominant "fight fire," "observe fire," "shut doors," "await fire department," and "fire not severe."

TABLE 7-1K. ***Comparison of Reasons for Reentry Behavior of British and U.S. Study Populations***

Reasons	British	U.S.	$P^1 - P_2$††	$SE_{1_1 - P_2}$§	CR‖
Fight fire	36.0	22.2	13.8	4.02	*3.43†*
Observe fire	19.0	11.0	08.0	3.25	*2.46**
Save personal effects	13.0	17.2	04.2	2.91	1.44
Shut doors	10.0	00.6	09.4	2.38	*3.95†*
Await fire department	09.0	00.0	09.0	2.26	*3.98†*
Call fire department	02.0	05.5	03.5	1.32	*2.65†*
Rescue pets	02.0	07.4	05.4	1.40	*3.86†*
Fire not severe	05.0	01.2	03.8	1.74	*2.18**
Notify others	00.0	08.0	08.0	0.92	*8.69†*
Assist fire department	00.0	07.4	07.4	0.88	*8.41†*
Assist evacuation	00.0	02.5	02.5	0.54	*4.63†*
N = 11	943	163			

* Critical ratios significant at or above the 5 percent level of confidence.
† Critical ratios significant at or above the 1 percent level of confidence.
†† British minus U.S. populations.
§ Standard error.
‖ Critical ratio.

Occupant Fire Fighting Behavior

Occupants who engaged in fire fighting behavior were predominately male, and this behavior now appears to be a culturally determined and expected aspect of the male role. However, it should be noted that, in the "Project People"[1] study of 335 U.S. fires, approximately 23 percent of the study population of 584 individuals was involved in occupant fire fighting behavior. Of these, 37.3 percent was female. Of the 134 individuals who participated in fire fighting behavior, 50 were female and 84 male.They ranged from a 7-year-old girl to an 80-year-old man. Distribution of the participants by sex and age is presented in Table 7-1L. Most of those involved in fire fighting behavior, or approximately 30 percent of the fire fighting behavior population, were between 28 and 37 years old.

TABLE 7-1L. ***Age and Sex of the Occupants Engaging in Fire Fighting Behavior***

Sex	Participants	Percent
Male	84	62.7
Female	50	37.3
Total	134	100.0
Age		
07–17	08	05.9
18–27	31	23.1
28–37	41	30.6
38–47	27	20.1
48–57	16	11.9
58–67	02	01.5
68–80	03	02.2
Unknown	06	04.7
Total	134	100.0
Percent of participant population = 22.9		

The statistically significant differences in the behavioral actions of males and females were the actions of "got extinguisher" and "fought fire." (See Table 7-1M.) Approximately 15 percent of the male population reacted by obtaining extinguishers. Similarly, approximately 26 percent of the male population fought the fire when they became aware of it, as contrasted with approximately 10 percent of the female participants. The women predominately notified the fire department: approximately 33 percent of the females, compared with 25 percent of the males, reacted to the fire by notifying the fire department, as indicated in Table 7-1M.

TABLE 7-1M. ***Sexual Differences of the Occupants Engaging in Fire Fighting and Notifying the Fire Department***

Action	Male (percent)	Female (percent)	$P^1 - P_2$††	$SE_{1_1 - P_2}$§	CR‖
Searched for fire	17.2	09.1	08.1	4.23	1.91
Got extinguisher	15.6	06.0	09.6	3.95	*2.43**
Fought fire	25.6	09.7	15.9	4.83	*3.29†*
Removed fuel	03.4	03.1	00.3	2.17	0.14
Tried to extinguish	05.3	02.8	02.5	2.49	1.00
Went to fire area	03.1	02.8	00.3	2.07	0.14
Total	70.2	33.5	36.7	6.01	*6.11†*
N =	184	101			
Called F.D.	25.6	33.0	07.4	5.83	1.27
Had others call F.D.	09.2	07.5	01.7	3.27	0.52
Went to fire alarm	03.8	03.8	0	0	0
Pulled fire alarm	01.9	01.6	00.3	1.65	0.18
Total	40.5	45.9	05.4	6.31	0.85
N =	106	146			

* Critical ratios significant at or above the 5 percent level of confidence.
† Critical ratios significant at or above the 1 percent level of confidence.
†† Male percent minus female percent.
§ Standard error.
‖ Critical ratio.

Occupant fire fighting behavior appears most prevalent in occupancies in which the individuals are emotionally and economically involved — that is, in their homes or where such behavior is an assigned role as a result of training.[30] At some time during the fire, 285 individuals engaged in one of the six actions defined as fire fighting behavior, and 252 individuals participated in one of the four actions defined as notifying the fire department.

In the study of residential fire incidents in Berkeley, CA, 180 persons were involved in extinguishing and fire fighting behavior. This study surveyed a population different from that of Project People, since the 1411 Berkeley households, with 208 fires, included fires not reported to the fire department; these accounted for approximately 80 percent of the total 208 fires. The majority of the unreported fires were extinguished by the occupants alone or with the help of neighbors.[31] Table 7-1N presents the percentage distribution from the study of the individuals responsible for extinguishing the fire. Six percent of these fires self-extinguished, and 52 percent were extinguished by the individual who had started the fire. Thus, it appears that only the fires in the Project People study that were judged uncontrollable by the occupants resulted in notification of the fire department. Similarly, approximately 85 percent of the fires in the National Fire Prevention and Control Administration National Household Survey[32] were not reported to the fire department.

The types of occupancies in which equipment in the occupancy was used to fight the fire are presented in Table 7-1O. The rather high frequency of residential occupancies — 64 percent were either single-family dwellings or apartments — may be a variable of the population of this

TABLE 7-1N. ***Occupants Extinguishing Residential Fires in Berkeley, CA***

Fire Suppressed by	Percent
Person engaged in heat-using activity	52.8
Other member(s) of household	28.3
Friends and neighbors	8.9
Fire department	18.9
Burnout	6.1
Total	115.0
Single individual	80.7
Group effort	19.3
Total	100.0

study,[1] as well as representative of many urban areas where fire problems are essentially residential.

In the Project People study, 107 of the 584 participants did not leave the building voluntarily after becoming aware of the fire. Their reasons for staying in the building are presented in Table 7-1P. Fifty-two of the participants, or approximately 49 percent of the population that stayed in the building, reported that they remained because they wished to engage in fire control or fire fighting activities. The other most frequent reasons were to notify others of the fire or because the occupant's way out of the building was blocked by smoke. It is apparent that approximately 15 percent of the study population voluntarily remained in the fire building.

Occupant's Movement Through Smoke

Often related to fire fighting behavior, and a definite component of evacuation behavior in many fires,[1, 2] is the movement of occupants through smoke. The principal variables influencing an occupant's decision to move through smoke appear to be recognition of the location of the exit and thus of the travel distance, the appearance of the smoke, the smoke density, and the presence or absence of heat.[23, 24]

TABLE 7-1O. ***Distribution of Occupancies in Which Fire Fighting Equipment Was Utilized by Occupants in Fire Fighting Behavior***

Occupancy	Incidents	Percent
Dwelling (1 family)	23	35.9
Apartment (20 units)	18	28.1
Restaurant	3	4.8
Apartment (20 units)	3	4.8
Manufacturing	2	4.8
Hotel and motel	2	3.2
School	3	3.2
Billiard center	1	1.5
City club	1	1.5
Hospital	1	1.5
Dwelling (2 family)	1	1.5
College dormitory	1	1.5
Service station	1	1.5
Office	1	1.5
Photographic laboratory	1	1.5
Other	2	3.2
N = 16	64	100.0
$M = 4.00$ $SE_M = 6.55$	$SD = 6.55$	$SE_{SD} = 1.16$

TABLE 7-1P. ***Reasons Elicited from Occupants for Not Leaving the Fire Building***

Reason	Participants	Percent
Fight fire	52	48.7
Notify others	7	6.5
Blocked by smoke	7	6.5
Blocked by fire	5	4.7
Overcome by smoke	5	4.7
Search for fire	3	2.8
Needed help	2	1.9
Secure property	2	1.9
Afraid of fire spread	2	1.9
No fire in area	1	0.9
Help others	1	0.9
Does not know	1	0.9
No response to F.D.	1	0.9
Home	1	0.9
Return to area	1	0.9
Not reported	16	15.0
N = 15	107	100.0
Range = 1–52	Percent of participant population = 15.6	

To achieve evacuation, occupants have moved through smoke, even for extended distances under conditions of extremely limited visibility at personal risk, and sometimes have been forced to turn back without completing the evacuation.[1, 2, 23, 24]

Table 7-1Q compares the distance moved through smoke for the 1316 persons in the British study and the 322 persons in the U.S. study. Sixty percent of the British study population and 62.7 percent of the Project People participants reported that they moved through smoke. It is thus apparent that building occupants will move through smoke in an evacuation process. An important variable may be the smoke density or the visibility distance of the occupants during the evacuation process.

TABLE 7-1Q. ***Comparison of the Distance Moved Through Smoke for the British and U.S. Populations***

Distance moved (ft)#	British (percent)	U.S. (percent)	$P_1 - P_2$††	$SE_{P_1 - P_2}$§	CR‖
0–2	03.0	02.3	00.7	1.02	00.69
3–6	18.0	08.4	09.6	2.23	*04.30*†
7–12	30.0	17.1	12.9	2.71	*04.76*†
13–30	19.0	45.5	26.5	2.62	*10.11*†
31–36	05.0	02.0	03.0	1.25	*02.40**
37–45	04.0	04.1	00.1	1.19	00.08
46–60	05.0	11.0	06.0	1.47	*04.08*†
60+	15.0	09.6	05.4	2.10	*02.57**
	1316				

* Critical ratios significant at or above the 5 percent level of confidence.
† Critical ratios significant at or above the 1 percent level of confidence.
†† British percent minus U.S. percent.
§ Standard error.
‖ Critical ratio.
\# 1 ft = 0.3 m

Table 7-1R presents the visibility distance of the British and U.S. occupants as they moved through smoke while evacuating a fire building. They reported their movement through smoke under relatively high smoke density conditions, with visibility under 12 ft (3.7 m) for 64 percent

TABLE 7-1R. ***Comparison of the Visibility Distance for the British and U.S. Populations When Moving Through Smoke***

Visibility distance (ft)#	British (percent)	U.S. (percent)	$P_1 - P_2$††	$SE_{1_1 - P_2}$§	CR‖
0–2	12.0	10.2	01.8	1.99	0.90
3–6	25.0	17.2	07.8	2.65	*2.94†*
7–12	27.0	20.2	06.8	2.73	*2.49**
13–30	11.0	31.7	21.7	2.24	*9.69†*
31–36	03.0	02.2	00.8	1.03	0.78
37–45	03.0	03.7	00.7	1.08	0.65
46–60	03.0	07.4	04.4	1.21	*3.64†*
60+	17.0	07.4	09.6	2.24	*42.9†*
	1316	322			

* Critical ratios significant at or above the 5 percent level of confidence.
† Critical ratios significant at or above the 1 percent level of confidence.
†† British percent minus U.S. percent.
§ Standard error.
‖ Critical ratio.
\# 1 ft = 0.3 m

of the British population and for 47.6 percent of the U.S. population.

Visibility distance for both the British and U.S. populations at the time participants were forced to turn back is presented in Table 7-1S. Comparison of Table 7-1S with Table 7-1R reveals that very few participants turned back when they could see more than 31 ft (9.4 m). The greater percentage of participants turned back at the reduced visibility levels. When the visibility distance was below 12 ft (3.7 m) (see Table 7-1S), 91 percent of the British study population and 76.4 percent of the U.S. population turned back.

TABLE 7-1S. ***Comparison of the Visibility Distance for the British and U.S. Populations Relative to the Turn Back Behavior***

Visibility distance (ft)#	British (percent)	U.S. (percent)	$P_1 - P_2$††	$SE_{1_1 - P_2}$§	CR‖
0–2	29.0	31.8	02.8	5.31	0.53
3–6	27.0	22.3	14.7	5.57	*2.64**
7–12	25.0	22.3	02.7	5.02	*0.54*
13–30	06.0	17.6	11.6	3.07	*3.78**
31–36	00.5	01.2	00.7	0.90	0.77
37–45	01.0	0	01.0	1.10	0.91
46–60	00.5	04.7	04.2	1.16	*3.62**
60+	01.0	0	01.0	1.10	*0.91*
	570	85			

* Critical ratios significant at or above the 5 percent level of confidence.
†† British percent minus U.S. percent.
§ Standard error.
‖ Critical ratio.
\# 1 ft = 0.3 m

HANDICAPPED OR IMPAIRED OCCUPANTS

Fire problems involving occupancies designed for permanently or temporarily disabled persons, such as nursing homes and hospitals, appear to be matched on the basis of building design, adequate staff training, and ability to protect the occupants in place until evacuation is possible. An extensive study of human behavior in health care facilities[30] indicated that the nursing staff performed their professional roles toward their patients even where they were at risk.

The few fires studied involving handicapped persons in occupancies other than health care facilities primarily have been in residential occupancies. In two of these cases, handicapped individuals were helped by other occupants to evacuate successfully. One instance involved a wheelchair user[23] and the other a blind person.[33]

Handicapped people may have a variety of limitations that increase their risk in a fire: sensory problems, such as deafness and blindness; mobility problems that may entail the need for a wheelchair; and intellectual problems, such as mental retardation. Many handicapped persons with mobility problems also are concerned about their personal risk in high-rise office and residential buildings where the use of elevators is not allowed in a fire. In such situations, adequate areas of refuge must be provided for handicapped, as well as nonhandicapped, occupants.[34]

A study of a number of evacuation drills in high-rise office buildings in Canada has indicated that approximately 3 percent of the occupants will be unable to use the stairs due to permanent or temporary conditions limiting their mobility.[35] The study population included occupants with heart conditions and individuals recovering from surgery, other illnesses, and accidents.

SUMMARY

Behavior in fires can be understood as a logical attempt to deal with a complex, rapidly changing situation in which minimal information upon which to act is available. It is suggested that the goals of codes should be "reoriented to increase the likelihood of informed decisions being made by people in fires."[36] Examination of behavior in the Beverly Hills Supper Club fire led to the recommendation that "firesafety education should consider and be based on people's erroneous conceptions about distance being related to safety, and the time needed to escape from a fire emergency."[37] More than a decade of detailed systematic research on human behavior in fires has resulted in the following consensus[27] on the behavior of most persons:

> "Despite the highly stressful environment, people generally respond to emergencies in a 'rational,' often altruistic manner, insofar as is possible within the constraints imposed on their knowledge, perceptions, and actions by the effects of the fire. In short, 'instinctive panic' type reactions are not the norm."

The relationship between the physical and social environment in which behavior occurs is complex. The situation is complicated by the individual's perception of ambiguous fire cues, which is primarily influenced by the person's relevant training and previous fire experience, if any. It must be recognized that fire cues are a product of a rapidly changing dynamic process that is constantly altering the decision choices of the building occupant. This decision dilemma has been summarized: "What is an appropriate action at one stage may be quite inappropriate a minute later."

BIBLIOGRAPHY

References Cited

1. Bryan, J. L., *Smoke as a Determinant of Human Behavior in Fire Situations*, Department of Fire Protection Engineering, University of Maryland, College Park, MD, 1977.

2. Wood, P. G., "The Behavior of People in Fires," *Fire Research Note 953*, Building Research Establishment, Fire Research Station, Boreham Wood, Hertfordshire, England, 1972.
3. Lerup, L., *et al.*, "Human Behavior in Institutional Fires and Its Design Complications," *NBS-GCR-77-93*, Center for Fire Research, National Bureau of Standards, Washington, DC, 1978.
4. Keating, J. P. and Loftus, E. F., "The Logic of Fire Escape," *Psychology Today*, 1981, pp. 14-19.
5. Berry, C. H., "Will Your Smoke Detector Wake You?," *Fire Journal*, Vol. 72, No. 4, 1978, pp. 105-108.
6. Cohen, H. C., "Fire Safety for the Hearing Impaired," *Fire Journal*, Vol. 76, No. 1 (Jan. 1982, pp. 70-72.
7. Kahn, M. J., "Human Awakening and Subsequent Identification of Fire-Related Cues," *Fire Technology*, Vol. 20, No. 1, 1984.
8. Nober, E. H., *et al.*, "Waking Effectiveness of Household Smoke and Fire Detector Devices," *Fire Journal*, Vol. 75, No. 4 (Jul. 1981), pp. 86-91, 130.
9. Latane, B. and Darley, J. M., "Group Inhibition of Bystander Intervention in Emergencies," *Journal of Personality and Social Psychology*, Vol. 10, No. 3, 1968, pp. 215-221.
10. Bryan, J. L., *A Study of the Survivors' Reports on the Panic in the Fire at Arundel Park Hall, Brooklyn, Maryland, on January 29, 1956*, Fire Protection Curriculum, University of Maryland, College Park, MD, 1957.
11. Withey, S. B., "Reaction to Uncertain Threat," *Man and Society in Disaster*, Baker, G. W. and Chapman, D. W., eds., Basic Books, New York, 1962.
12. Killian, R. M., *et al.*, "A Study of Response to the Houston, Texas, Fireworks Explosion," Disaster Study No. 2, *Publication 391*, National Academy of Science, Washington, DC, 1956.
13. National Fire Protection Association, "Bimonthly Fire Record," *Fire Journal*, Vol. 65, No. 3 (May 1971), p. 51.
14. Mintz, A., "Nonadaptive Group Behavior," *Journal of Abnormal and Social Psychology*, Vol. 46, 1951, pp. 150-159.
15. Breaux, J., *et al.*, *Psychological Aspects of Behavior of People in Fire Situations*, University of Surrey, Guilford, England, 1976.
16. Bickman, L., *et al.*, "A Model of Human Behavior in a Fire Emergency," *NBS-GCR-78-120*, National Bureau of Standards, Washington, DC, 1977.
17. Best, R. and Demers, D. P., "Fire at the MGM Grand," *Fire Journal*, Vol. 76, No. 1 (Jan. 1982), pp. 19-37.
18. Demers, D. P., "Investigation Report on the Las Vegas Hilton Hotel Fire," *Fire Journal*, Vol. 76, No. 1 (Jan. 1982), pp. 52-57.
19. Bryan, J. L., "Human Behavior in the MGM Grand Hotel Fire," *Fire Journal*, Vol. 76, No. 2 (Mar. 1982), pp. 37-41, 44-48.
20. Morris, G. P., "Preplan Was the Key to MGM Rescue as EMS Helped Thousands of Hotel Fire Victims," *Fire Command*, Vol. 48, No. 6, 1981, pp. 20-21.
21. Bryan, J. L., "Convergence Clusters: A Phenomenon of Human Behavior Seen in Selected High-Rise Building Fires," *Fire Journal*, Vol. 74, No. 6 (Nov. 1985), pp. 27-30, 86-90.
22. Bryan, J. L. and DiNenno, P. J., "An Examination and Analysis of the Dynamics of the Human Behavior in the Fire Incident at the Georgian Towers on January 9, 1979," *NBS-GCR-79-187*, National Bureau of Standards, Washington, DC, 1979.
23. Bryan, J. L., *An Examination and Analysis of the Dynamics of the Human Behavior in the MGM Grand Hotel Fire*, revised edition, National Fire Protection Association, Quincy, MA, 1983.
24. Bryan, J. L., *An Examination and Analysis of the Dynamics of the Human Behavior in the Westchase Hilton Hotel Fire*, National Fire Protection Association, Quincy, MA, 1983.
25. Best, R. L., "Tragedy in Kentucky," *Fire Journal*, Vol. 72, No. 1 (Jan. 1978), pp. 18-35.
26. *Investigative Report to the Governor, Beverly Hills Supper Club Fire*, Kentucky State Police, Frankfort, KY, 1977.
27. Sime, J. D., "The Concept of Panic," *Fire and Human Behavior*, Canter, David, ed., John Wiley & Sons, New York, 1980.
28. Quanrantelli, E. L., *Panic Behavior in Fire Situations: Findings and a Model from the English Language Research Literature*, Disaster Research Center, Ohio State University, Columbus, OH, 1979.
29. Keating, J. P., "The Myth of Panic," *Fire Journal*, Vol. 76, No. 3 (May 1982), pp. 57-61, 147.
30. Bryan, J. L., *et al.*, "The Determination of Behavior Response Patterns in Fire Situations, Project People II, Final Report — Incident Reports, Aug. 1977 to June 1980," *NBS-GCR-80-297*, National Bureau of Standards, Washington, DC, 1980.
31. Crossman, E. R., *et al.*, "FIRRST: A Fire Risk and Readiness Study of Berkeley Households," UCBFRG/WP 75-5, University of California, Berkeley, CA, 1975.
32. *Highlights of the National Household Fire Survey*, National Fire Prevention and Control Administration, United States Fire Administration, Washington, DC, 1976.
33. Bryan, J. L., *et al.*, "An Examination and Analysis of the Dynamics of the Human Behavior in the Fire Incident at the Taylor House on April 11, 1979," *NBS-GCR-80-200*, National Bureau of Standards, Washington, DC, 1979.
34. Levin, B. N. and Nelson, H. E., "Firesafety and Disabled Persons," *Fire Journal*, Vol. 75, No. 5 (Sept. 1981), pp. 35-40.
35. Pauls, J. L., "Movement of People in Building Evacuations," *Human Response to Tall Buildings*, Conway, D. J., ed., Dowden, Hutchinson and Ross, Stroudsburg, PA, 1977.
36. Canter, D., *et al.*, *Human Behavior in Fires*, Department of Psychology, University of Surrey, Guilford, England, 1978.
37. Pauls, J. L. and Jones, B. K., "Research in Human Behavior," *Fire Journal*, Vol. 74, No. 3 (May 1980), pp. 35-41.

References

Bryan, J. L., *Human Behavior Factors and the Fire Occurrence in Buildings*, International Fire Protection Engineering Institute, Department of Fire Protection Engineering, University of Maryland, College Park, MD, 1971.

Paulsen, R. L., "Human Behavior and Fires: An Introduction," *Fire Technology*, Vol. 20, No. 2, 1984, pp. 15-27.

Swartz, J. A., "Human Behavior in the Beverly Hills Fire," *Fire Journal*, Vol. 73, No. 3 (May 1979), pp. 73-74, 108.

NFPA Codes, Standards, and Recommended Practices

Reference to the following NFPA codes, standards, and recommended practices will provide further information on human behavior and fire discussed in this chapter. (See the latest *NFPA Catalog* for availability of current editions of the following documents.)

NFPA 74, *Household Fire Warning Equipment.*

NFPA 101®, *Life Safety Code.*®

Additional Reading

Ballast, D. K., *Egress from Buildings in Emergencies: A Bibliography*, Vance Bibliographies, Monticello, IL, 1988.

Beck, K. H., "A Canonical Correlation of Fire Protective Behaviors and Beliefs," *Fire Technology*, Vol. 25, No. 1 (Feb. 1989), pp. 41-50.

Bodamer, M., "How People Behave in Fires," *Fire Prevention*, No. 224 (Nov. 1989), p. 20, 22-23.

Bryan, J. L., "Behavioral Response to Fire and Smoke," *SFPE Handbook of Fire Protection Engineering*, National Fire Protection Association, Quincy, MA, 1988.

Canter, D., *Fires and Human Behavior*, 2nd ed., Fulton, London, 1988.

Hole, A. R., *Individual Behavior in the Control of Danger*, Elsevier, New York, 1982.

Keating, J. P., "Human Resources During Fire Situations: A Role for Social Engineering," *General Proceedings Research and Design*, American Institute for Architects Foundation, Washington, DC, 1985.

Paulsen, R. L., "Human Behavior and Fires: An Introduction," *Fire Technology*, Vol. 20, pp. 15-27, 1984.

Ramachandian, G., "Human Behaviors in Fires," *Fire Technology*, Vol. 26, No. 2, 1990, pp. 149-155.

CONCEPTS OF EGRESS DESIGN

Revised by John L. Bryan

Means of egress and their design should be based upon an evaluation of a building's total fire protection system and an analysis of the population characteristics and hazards to the occupants of that building. The means of egress design should be treated as an integral part of the total system that provides reasonable safety to life from fire.

This chapter covers the fundamental concepts of good egress design that are the basis for NFPA 101®, *Life Safety Code*®. NFPA 101 governs good practices to provide life safety features that can be designed as integral parts of new and existing buildings and structures to provide reasonable safety to occupants in fires. The components of good means of egress are discussed in some detail, with their functions and relationships in the total concept of proper egress design. Computer modeling and simulation to assist the egress design process also are discussed.

FUNDAMENTALS OF DESIGN

The approach to designing means of egress first requires a familiarity with the reaction of people in fire emergencies. These reactions can differ widely, depending upon the physical and mental capabilities and conditions of building occupants. The psychological and physiological factors affecting the use of exits during emergencies are being identified and measured in research studies.

Patterns of movement of people, singly and in crowded conditions, also must be understood. In buildings used as schools or theaters housing highly mobile occupants, for example, studies have shown certain reproducible flow characteristics from persons exiting the buildings. These predictable flow characteristics have fostered computer simulation and modeling to aid the egress design process. However, no number of practical exit facilities can prevent injury or loss of life if the occupant egress flow is inhibited or prevented by the building itself, by personnel, or by fire and smoke conditions.

Dr. John L. Bryan is professor and chairman, Department of Fire Protection Engineering, at the University of Maryland, College Park, MD.

Human Factors

The design and capacity of passageways, stairways, and other components in the total means of egress are related to the physical dimensions of the human body. The tendency of people to avoid bodily contact with others should be recognized as a major factor in determining the number of persons who will occupy a given space at any given time. Given a choice, people usually automatically establish "territories" to avoid bodily contact with others.

Studies have shown that most adult men measure less than 20.7 in. (520 mm) across at the shoulder, with no allowance for additional thicknesses of clothing.[1] A "body ellipse" concept is used to develop the design of pedestrian systems. The major axis of the body ellipse measures 24 in. (609 mm), whereas the minor axis is considered 18 in. (457 mm). This ellipse equals 2.3 sq ft (0.21 m^2), which is assumed to help determine the maximum practical standing capacity of a space.

The movement of persons results in a swaying action that varies from male to female and, depending upon the type of motion, varies with movement on stairs, on level surfaces, or in dense crowds. Body sway has been observed to range 1½ in. (38 mm) left and right during normal free movement. Where movement is reduced to shuffling in dense crowds and to movement on stairs, a total sway range of almost 4 in. (101 mm) has been observed. In theory, this indicates that a total width of 30 in. (762 mm) would be required to accommodate a single file of pedestrians traveling up or down stairs.[2]

Crowding people into spaces where less than 3 sq ft (0.28 m^2) of space per person is available under nonemergency conditions may create a hazard. When the average area occupied per person is reduced to 2¾ sq ft (0.25 m^2) or less, contact will be unavoidable. Needless to say, under the psychological stresses imposed during a fire, such crowding and contact could contribute to crowd pressures, resulting in injuries. When a queue occurs because of an artificial, temporary situation or because of some permanent design feature, crowd control becomes difficult, and the well-being of individuals is threatened.

Factors Affecting Movement of People

There are several factors that determine how quickly people may pass through the means of egress.

Studies in level walkways have shown that an average walking speed of 250 ft/min (76 m/min) is attained under free-flow conditions, with 25 sq ft (2.3 m^2) of space available per person. Speeds below 145 ft/min (44 m/min) show shuffling, which restricts motion. Figure 7-2A, adapted from *Research Report No. 95* of the London Transport Board,[3] shows the rate of speed reduction for space concentrations of less than 7 sq ft (0.65 m^2) per person. Speeds of less than 145 ft/min (44 m/min) result in shuffling, and, finally, a jam point is reached with one person every 2 sq ft (0.18 m^2). The possibility of a significant nonadaptive behavior exists whenever egress movement is restricted, and the problem becomes urgent under fire exposure conditions, especially when there is more than one person every 3 sq ft (0.28 m^2).

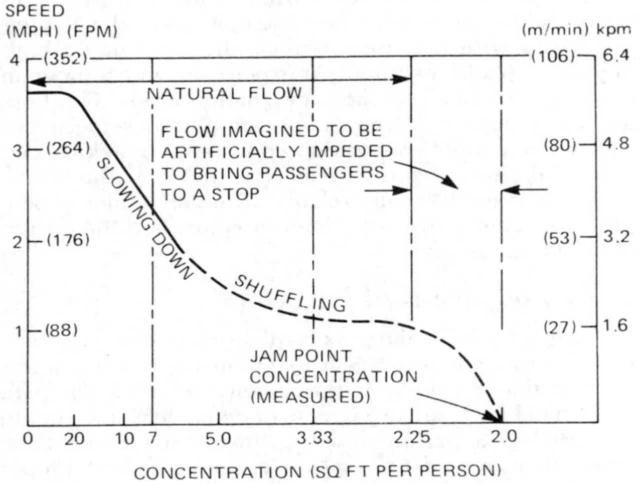

FIG. 7-2A. Speed in level passageways.[3] (SI units: 1 ft/min = 0.305 m/min; 1 sq ft = 0.093 m^2.)

Calculations of flow rates using velocity [ft/min (m/min)] and density [people per sq ft (m^3)] will reveal flow [people per minute per ft (m) of width], which increases as the pedestrian area decreases. The flow increases will continue until forward movement becomes restricted to the point that the flow begins to drop. Interestingly, observations of flow rates in one study noted the same flow rate sometimes occurred even though walking speeds of people were significantly different. Investigation revealed that the rate of decrease in speed, accompanied by an increase in density, results in uniform flow rates over a wide range of conditions.

A study of footways indicates that, for passageways over 4 ft (1.2 m) wide, flow rates are directly proportional to width. The London Transport Board *Research Report No. 95*[3] determined the flow rate in level passages to be 27 persons per min per ft (0.30 m) of width. Travel down stairways was determined at 21 people per min per ft (0.30 m) of width, whereas upward travel was reduced to 19 persons per min per ft (0.30 m) of width. Where the width of a footway is less than 4 ft (1.2 m), the flow rate depends upon the number of possible traffic lanes. Absolute maximum flow rates occur when approximately 3 sq ft (0.28 m) is occupied per person, which is applicable to both level walkways and stairs. In observed and measured evacuations, however, it has been empirically determined that the maximum flow rates down stairs in high-rise buildings occur when from 4 to 5 sq ft of space (0.37 to 0.46 m^2) is occupied per person, as shown in Figure 7-2B.[2] An observation confirmed by two separate studies indicates that, when flow in opposite directions takes place in a passageway up to the point where the two flows are of equal magnitude, there is no significant reduction in total flow below that which would be predicted on the basis of unidirectional flow in the same passageway.

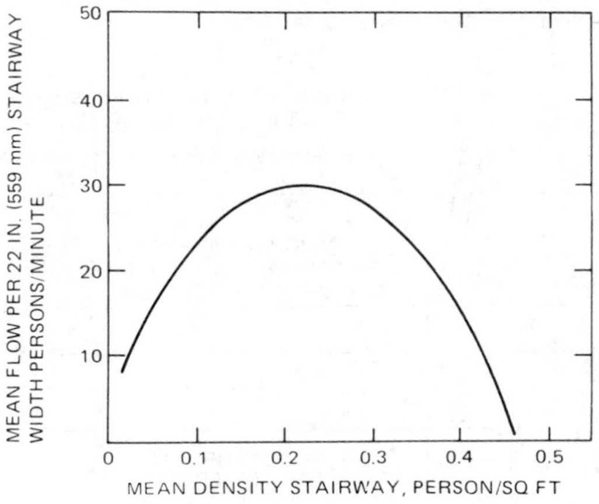

FIG. 7-2B. Effect of density on flow down exit stairways in evacuations of high-rise office buildings.[2] (SI units: 1 sq ft = 0.093 m^2.)

Further, observations of flow rates indicate that flow can be 50 percent greater in short passageways less than 10 ft (3.05 m) long than through a long passageway of the same width. Minor obstructions within a passageway do not appear to have a significant effect on flow. Observations made within a 6-ft (1.82 m) wide passageway indicated no effect on flow rates when a 1-ft (0.45 m) projection was introduced. A 2-ft (0.61 m) projection resulting in a 33 percent reduction in width reduced the flow rate approximately 10 percent. A major obstruction, though, such as that which occurs at a ticket booth or turnstile, may interrupt the movement of people and reduce flow rates.

Corners, bends, and slight grades up to 6 percent are apparently not factors in determining flow rates. A slight reduction in speed does occur, but the flow rate is maintained by an increased concentration of persons.

A center handrail or mullion, which may divide a passageway into narrower sections, can further reduce the capacity of the passageway. In one study, the observed capacity of a 6-ft (1.82 m) wide stairway revealed a reduction from 130 to 105 persons per minute after installation of a center handrail.

Except for the very young and the very old, age does not appear to be a significant factor in determining travel speed. Studies have shown a significant reduction in walking speeds for persons over 65 years of age. Studies have further revealed that a 40 percent increase is possible in the normal walking speed, which tends to discount this factor as a major influence on flow rates.[1]

Methods of Calculating Exit Width

Two major principles are used to determine the necessary exit width. They are based on anticipated population characteristics identified with a specific occupancy.

The Flow Method: This method uses the theory of evacuating a building within a specified maximum period of time. Flow rates have traditionally been set at 60 persons per 22 in. (559 mm) width per min through level passageways and doorways. The flow method may be applied in assembly occupancies, such as theaters, and educational occupancies where people are alert, awake, and assumed to be in good physical condition. Figure 7-2C illustrates the flow time in seconds relative to the effective stair width per person and the units of width.

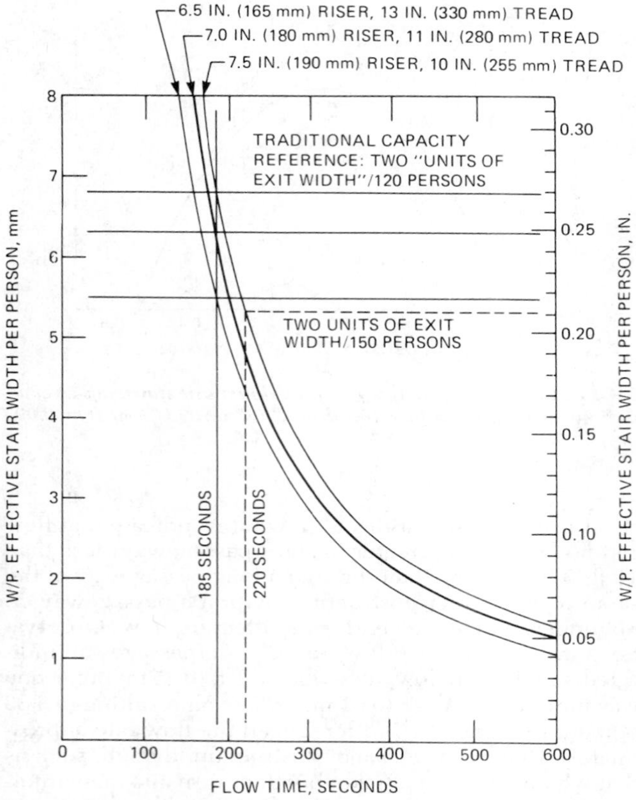

FIG. 7-2C. ***Relationship between effective stair width and units of exit width per person and flow time for three stair geometries.***[4]

Pauls'[4] effective stair width concept advocates the consideration of only the portion of the stair used in effective movement by the occupants, as observed in functional and practice evacuations. This width is established with 6-in. (150 mm) clearance from each side wall of the stair. The effective width concept of exit design is included in NFPA 101M, *Alternative Approaches to Life Safety*.

The Capacity Method: This method is based on the theory that sufficient numbers of stairways should be provided in a building to adequately house all occupants of the building without requiring any movement, or flow, out of the stairways. In theory, assuming a stairwell provides a safe and protected area for all occupants within the protective barrier created by the stairway enclosure, evacuation of the building may then be more leisurely, permitting people to travel at a rate within their physical ability. The capacity method recognizes that evacuation from high-rise buildings is physically very demanding. Further, evacuation of a health care facility is likely to be slow. Thus, design criteria are established to permit holding occupants within exits or areas of refuge.

Application

The capacity and flow methods may both be applied to efficient egress design, depending upon specific circumstances. Where people are expected to be physically or mentally sick, aged, asleep, or incapacitated in any way, evacuation and use of the flow method is unwise. Therefore, the capacity method that provides a place for everyone within an area of refuge is the appropriate method.

There is little time between an alert and the use of an exit in assembly occupancies, and maximum flow rates that cause reductions in the area used by each person may result in reduced traffic flows. On the other hand, the control of children in an educational setting, coupled with their familiarity with the surroundings, their presumed high physical capabilities, and their experience with a program of drills, should allow rapid evacuation times. The flow method appears to have its application in those occupancies where people are considered to be alert, awake, and of normal physical ability. Pauls has reviewed the historical and current literature relative to the principles of people movement, exit width determination, and the design of the means of egress.[5]

Design of Means of Egress

Designing a means of egress involves more than numbers, flow rates, and densities. Safe exit from a building requires a safe path of escape from the fire environment. The path is arranged for ready use in case of emergency and should be sufficient to permit all occupants to reach a safe place before they are endangered by fire, smoke, or heat. Proper exit design permits everyone to leave the fire-endangered areas in the shortest possible time with efficient exit use. If a fire is discovered in its incipient stage and the occupants are alerted promptly, effective evacuation may take place.

Evacuation travel distances are related to the content fire hazard. The higher the hazard, the shorter the travel distance to an exit.

Depending upon the physical environment of the structure, the characteristics of the occupants, and the fire detection and alarm facilities, fire or smoke may prevent the use of one means of egress. Therefore, at least one alternate means of egress remote from the first is essential. Provision of two separate means of egress is a fundamental safeguard, except where a building or room is small and arranged so that a second exit would not provide an appreciable increase in safety. There are no advantages to separate means of egress if there is travel through a common space or use of common structural features that result in the loss of the two distinct and physically separate means of egress.

One example of a "common" structure is a multi-story building where scissors stairs are used. These are two stairs enclosed within a common shaft, separated by a partition common to both stairs. Scissors stairs are sometimes used to provide the required exit capacity while minimizing the loss of valuable floor space. Where a set of scissors stairs is the only means of egress when two remote exits are required, however, the fundamental principle of two separate means of egress design may be violated. If the common partition between the stairs fails, it would result in the simultaneous loss of both exits during a fire, leaving no alternate means of egress. With scissors stairs, the validity of the two separate means of egress, therefore, depends upon the design characteristics and construction of the common partition. (See Figure 7-2D.)

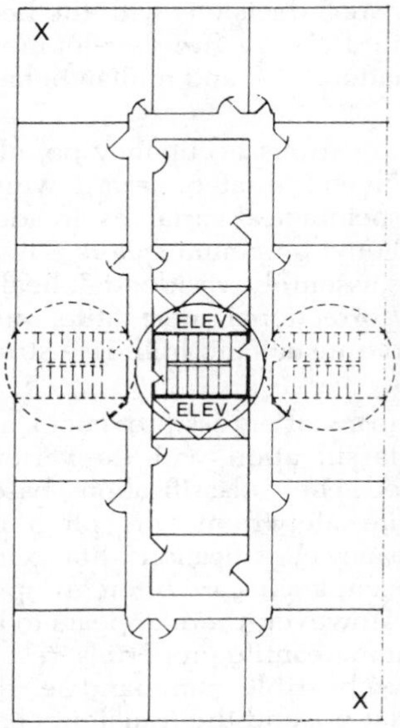

FIG. 7-2D. Advantages and disadvantages of scissors stairs vs. conventional stairs.

In some proposed egress designs, all the exits discharge through a single lobby at street level, even though this procedure results in egress travel through a common space. This design philosophy presumes that the lobby may be considered a safe area for all future egress needs during the life of the building. Where two remote means of egress are required, this type of egress design is unsuitable.

NFPA 101, *Life Safety Code*, limits openings in exit enclosures to those necessary for access to the enclosure from normally occupied spaces and for egress from the enclosure. Penetration of enclosures by ducts or other utilities constitutes a point of weakness and may result in contamination of the enclosure during a fire. Furthermore, it is not good practice to use exit enclosures for any purpose that could interfere with their value as exits. For example, piping for flammable liquids or gases should not be routed through such spaces.

It has been estimated that 12 million people within the U.S. have limited mobility due to physical disabilities. More than 250,000 persons use wheelchairs. Each year, an estimated 100,000 children are added to the total because of birth defects. The removal of handicapped persons is an important consideration in the design of an emergency means of egress from a building. A 32-in. (813 mm) doorway is considered the minimum width to accommodate a person in a wheelchair. Since handicapped employees or visitors may be found in all types of buildings, special life safety considerations are indicated.

LIFE SAFETY CODE

NFPA 101, *Life Safety Code*, introduced in 1927 and revised and reissued in successive editions, is developed by the NFPA Committee on Safety to Life, a representative group dedicated to safety of life from fire. NFPA 101 is primarily concerned with the control of conditions that threaten the lives of individuals in building fires. This objective is different from fire protection provisions in building codes, which are concerned with the preservation of property, in addition to the preservation of life.

Adequate means of egress alone are not a guarantee of life safety from fire. They do not protect an individual whose own carelessness causes a threat to life, such as setting his or her own clothes on fire. Neither do sufficient means of egress alone provide adequate protection in occupancies such as hospitals, nursing homes, prisons, and mental institutions, where occupants are confined or are physically or mentally unable to escape without effective and immediate assistance. NFPA 101, *Life Safety Code*, does recognize such situations and provides life safety measures, including low-flame-spread and reduced-smoke-producing materials for interior finish. In addition, automatic sprinkler and smoke control systems called for by NFPA 101 are designed to restrain the spread of fire and smoke, and thus help to defend the occupants within an area of refuge until they are able to use the exits or until the fire has been extinguished.

In general, saving building occupants from a fire requires the following, all of which are identified in NFPA 101:

1. A sufficient number of properly designed, unobstructed means of egress of adequate capacity and arrangement.
2. The protection of the means of egress against fire, heat, and smoke during the egress time determined by the occupant load, travel distance, and exit capacity.
3. The provision of alternate means of egress for use if one means of egress is blocked by fire, heat, or smoke.
4. The subdivision of areas by proper construction to provide areas of refuge in those occupancies where total evacuation is not a primary consideration.
5. The protection of vertical openings to limit the operation of fire protection equipment to a single floor.
6. The provision of detection or alarm systems to alert occupants and notify the fire department in case of fire.
7. The adequate illumination of the means of egress.
8. The proper marking of the means of egress, and the indication of directions.
9. The protection of equipment or areas of unusual hazard that could produce a fire capable of endangering the egressing occupants.
10. The initiation, organization, and practice of effective drill procedures.
11. The provision of instructional materials and verbal alarm systems in high-density and high-life-hazard occupancies to facilitate adaptive behavior.
12. The use of interior finish materials that prevent a high flame spread or dense smoke production that could endanger egressing occupants.

Figure 7-2E illustrates some of the principles of exit safety.

NFPA 101, *Life Safety Code*, recognizes that full reliance cannot be placed upon any single safeguard, since any single protective feature may not function due to mechanical or human failure. For this reason, redundant safeguards,

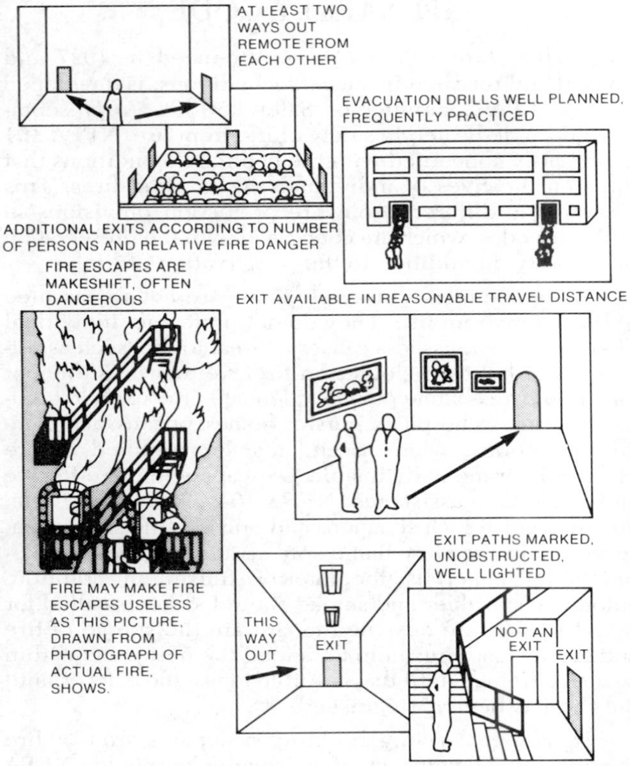

FIG. 7-2E. Principles of exit safety.

any one of which will result in a reasonable level of life safety, should be provided. NFPA 101 also recommends the special protection of hazardous areas and specifies where automatic sprinkler, detection, and other protective systems are required.

NFPA 101, *Life Safety Code*,-is used widely as a guide to good practice and as a basis for local laws or regulations. It differs from building codes since it generally provides little distinction among the different classes of building construction. However, where total evacuation of a building is not practical, due either to the occupant characteristics or the building environment, the construction type becomes an important variable and should be considered.

NFPA 101 also recognizes that all habitable buildings contain sufficient quantities of combustible contents to produce lethal quantities of smoke and heat.[6,7] In addition, casualty studies have established that the toxic properties of smoke are the principle hazard to life,[8] and this hazard is recognized in NFPA 101.

NFPA 101 is intended to be applied to both new and existing buildings and is designed to provide a reasonable level of life safety from fire in both types of buildings. The authority having jurisdiction is given considerable latitude in achieving conformance with existing buildings. Each existing building represents a special situation that requires individual attention for the most effective and economical method of achieving a reasonable level of life safety.

The argument that buildings constructed many years ago according to all the legal requirements are sufficiently safe now should not necessarily be accepted. If the economic cost of reasonable life safety is judged to be prohibitive, the occupancy or the structure should be changed or prohibited because there is no justification for subjecting building occupants to an unreasonable level of peril from a fire.

There may be a variety of differing opinions as to what constitutes reasonable life safety from a fire in any given case. It is not possible to guarantee occupants 100 percent life safety from a fire; beyond certain conditions, a building becomes hazardous to the life safety of the occupants in a fire. How should the authority having jurisdiction establish the minimum conditions? NFPA 101, *Life Safety Code*, provides guidance for such decisions with the help of studies of major-loss-of-life fires, [9,10] fire development research,[7,11] personnel evacuation,[12,13,14] and human behavior.[15,16]

NFPA 101 examines the various occupancy populations according to their perceived life safety hazard, which includes psychological and sociological variables, in addition to the physiological and environmental factors. These occupancy classifications are assembly, residential, health care, educational, detention/correctional, mercantile, business, industrial, storage, and unusual and high-rise structures.

Separate and distinct means of egress provisions are made for each occupancy classification, with the various occupancy subgroups included. These classifications, based on the perceived hazard to life safety from a fire, often differ from building code occupancy classifications. For example, mercantile and office occupancies are often grouped together in building codes. However, there appears to be an increased hazard to life in mercantile properties, resulting from the displays of combustible merchandise, the greater density of the population, and the transient character of most of the occupants. These factors are not usually found in office and educational buildings, which have a relatively low combustibility content, a lower population density, and normally alert occupants who are in the building daily and presumably have the opportunity to familiarize themselves with the means of egress through functional use and evacuation drills.

HAZARDS OF CONTENTS

An evaluation of the hazard of the building contents must take into account the relative probability of the ignition of combustibles, the spread of flames and heat, the probable smoke and gases expected to be generated by the fire, and the possibility of a fire-related explosion or other structural failure endangering occupants. The degree of hazard is usually determined by the flammability or toxicity of the contents and by the processes or operations conducted in the building. Most NFPA 101, *Life Safety Code*, requirements are based on the exposure created by contents with an ordinary hazard. Special requirements for areas with high-hazard contents usually consist of special protection systems, construction isolation of the hazard area, reduced travel distances, and additional means of egress.

Influence of Occupancy

To assist in evaluating the contents hazards, NFPA 101, *Life Safety Code*, establishes three classifications of contents: low-, ordinary-, and high-hazard. They are discussed below.

Low-hazard contents: These are contents of such low combustibility that no self-propagating fire can occur in them. Consequently, the only probable danger requiring the use of emergency exits will be from smoke or from fire from some external source.

Ordinary-hazard contents: These are contents that are liable to burn with moderate rapidity and to give off a considerable volume of smoke. This class includes most buildings and is the basis for the general requirements of NFPA 101.

High-hazard contents: These are contents that are liable to burn with extreme rapidity or from which explosions are to be feared in the event of fire. Examples are occupancies in which flammable liquids or gases are handled, used, or stored; in which combustible dust explosion hazards exist; in which hazardous chemicals or explosives are stored; in which combustible fibers are processed or handled in a manner that produces combustible flyings; and similar situations.

Influence of Building Construction and Design

A building of fire-resistive construction is designed to permit a burnout of contents without structural collapse. Fire-resistive design does not ensure the life safety of the occupants of such buildings.[9,15] However, the ability of a structural frame to maintain building rigidity under fire exposure is important to the maintenance of the fire-resistance protection of exit enclosures. Where a 2-hr fire-rated exit enclosure is required, a fire-resistive structural frame capable of withstanding stresses imposed by fire for a similar period is also necessary. It is inconsistent to provide a 2-hr exit enclosure in a building with a structural frame rated at less than 1 hr, for example, unless special construction precautions are taken to prevent structural failure of the building from adversely affecting the protective construction of the exit enclosures.

The protection of vertical openings is one of the most significant factors in the design of multi-story buildings, from the standpoint of life safety and exit design. Because of the natural tendency of fire to spread upward in a building, careful attention to details of design and construction are required to minimize this effect. One of the greatest hazards to life safety results from fires that start below the occupants and the means of egress, such as in basements or on the level of exit discharge. Similarly, fires in multistory buildings may result in smoke spread into enclosed exits before evacuation.[9,15] Conversely, escape from fires that occur above the occupants is relatively simple, provided sufficient warning is given and adequate means of egress are available.

The influence on the life safety of the occupants by the materials used in building construction depends primarily upon whether the materials will propagate flame, support combustion, or create dense amounts of smoke when exposed to a fire initially involving the building contents. Some materials used as insulation, for example, could contribute to rapid flame development and dense smoke production spread. Masonry walls enclosing a wood-frame interior provide no increased occupant life safety compared with a total wood-frame structure.

Exit requirements are based on buildings of conventional design. Unusual buildings, such as those without windows or those with unopenable windows, call for special consideration. Windows provide a number of advantages in a fire. Persons at openable windows have access to fresh air, can see fire department rescue operations in progress, are able to communicate verbally and visually with rescue personnel, and thus may be less subject to stress and anxiety. Windows provide a means of escape and accessibility to the building by the fire department for rescue and fire fighting. Automatic sprinklers are considered a primary requirement for life safety in windowless buildings, buildings with unopenable windows, and underground structures.

Influence of Interior Finish, Furnishings, and Decorations

The rapid spread of flame over the surface of walls, ceilings, or floor coverings may prevent occupant use of the means of egress. In general, NFPA 101, *Life Safety Code*, limits the flame-spread index classification of interior finish materials on walls and ceilings to a maximum of 200, based on the results of tests conducted in accordance with NFPA 255, *Surface Burning Characteristics of Building Materials*, also known as ASTM E84. Lower ratings are prescribed for the interior finish materials used in exits and in exit accesses. Materials classified as having a lower flame-spread index are also required in certain areas in individual occupancies. A fire-retardant coating may be used on existing interior finish materials to reduce the rate of flame spread. In areas protected with automatic sprinklers, the use of materials with higher flame-spread index classifications sometimes is permitted. Table 7-2A summarizes the interior finish requirements contained in NFPA 101 for the various occupancy classifications.

The flame spread of floor coverings is evaluated by NFPA 101, *Life Safety Code*, through the use of NFPA 253, *Critical Radiant Flux of Floor Covering Systems Using A Radiant Heat Energy Source*, also known as ASTM E648. Two classes of floor coverings are established: Class I finishes, with a minimum critical radiant flux of 0.45 W/cm^2; and Class II finishes, with a minimum critical radiant flux of 0.22 W/cm^2.

Furnishings and decorations—particularly furnishings—play an increasingly important role in loss of life by fire. Decorations can be treated with a flame retardant. Furnishings, on the other hand, are difficult to control and regulate as a fire hazard, since they are not attached to, or part of, the building construction or of the interior finish materials. Furnishings are moved, refurbished, and replaced. However, there are now test procedures for measuring the combustibility of upholstered furniture and its susceptibility to ignition.[17] Two NFPA standards address furniture combustibility: NFPA 260, *Cigarette Ignition Resistance of Components of Upholstered Furniture*, and NFPA 261, *Resistance of Mock-Up Upholstered Furniture Material Assemblies to Ignition by Smoldering Cigarettes*. The "Operating Features" chapter of NFPA 101-1991 specifies that all new upholstered furniture introduced into health care occupancies must meet the requirements of NFPA 260, with a char length under 1.5 inches (3.8 cm). The U.S. Consumer Products Safety Commission (CPSC) also has a standard for evaluating the ignitibility of mattresses.[18]

The use of some materials in furnishings results in fuels that are easily ignited—by a match, for example—and capable of rapid fire development with accompanying dense amounts of smoke. Some incidents especially illustrate this—for example, a fire principally involving plastic seating in the BOAC Passenger Terminal at New York's Kennedy Airport in August 1970[6], a New York office building fire in August 1970 in which two persons died[11]; and

TABLE 7-2A. ***Summary of Life Safety Code Requirements for Interior Finish***

Occupancy	Exits	Access to Exits	Other Spaces
Assembly—New			
Class A or B	A	A or B	A or B
Class C	A	A or B	A, B, or C
Assembly—Existing			
Class A or B	A	A or B	A or B
Class C	A	A or B	A, B, or C
Educational—New	A	A or B	A or B C on low partitions
Educational—Existing	A	A or B	A, B, or C
Day-Care Centers—New	A	A	A or B
	I or II	I or II	Not Required
Day-Care Centers—Existing	A or B	A or B	A or B
Group Day-Care Homes—New	A or B	A or B	A, B, or C
Group Day-Care—Existing	A or B	A, B, or C	A, B, or C
Family Day-Care Homes	A or B	A, B, or C	A, B, or C
Health Care—New—Automatic sprinklers mandatory	A or B	A or B C lower portion of corridor wall	A or B C in small individual rooms
Health Care—Existing	A or B	A or B	A or B
Detention & Correctional—New	A	A	A, B, or C
	I	I	Not Required
Detention & Correctional—Existing	A or B*	A or B	A, B, or C
	I or II	I or II	Not Required
Residential, Hotels & Dormitories—New	A	A or B	A, B, or C
	I or II	I or II	Not Required
Residential, Hotels & Dormitories—Existing	A or B	A or B	A, B, or C
	I or II	I or II	Not Required
Residential, Apartment Buildings—New	A	A or B	A, B, or C
	I or II	I or II	Not Required
Residential, Apartment Buildings—Existing	A or B	A or B	A, B, or C
	I or II	I or II	Not Required
Residential, 1- and 2-family, Lodging or Rooming Houses	A, B, or C	A, B, or C	A, B, or C
Residential, Board and Care—See Chapters 22 and 23 of NFPA *101*			
Mercantile—New	A or B	A or B	A or B
Mercantile—Existing Class A or B	A or B	A or B	ceilings—A or B existing on walls—A, B, or C
Mercantile—Existing Class C	A, B, or C	A, B, or C	A, B, or C
Office—New	A or B	A or B	A, B, or C
	I or II	I or II	Not Required
Office—Existing	A or B	A or B	A, B, or C
Industrial	A or B	A, B, or C	A, B, or C
Storage	A or B	A, B, or C	A, B, or C
Unusual Structures	A or B	A, B, or C	A, B, or C

a fire in December 1974 at the Sac-Osage Hospital in Osceola, MO, which resulted in the death of eight persons.[7] In the hospital incident, the fire was confined to a single patient room and principally involved two plastic mattresses and two chairs with foam cushions. The fire produced heavy quantities of black smoke before it was discovered.

Influence of Psychological and Physiological Factors on Egress

The psychological and physiological conditions of the occupant population must be considered, in addition to the physical configuration factors of the building, in planning means of egress. Studies indicate people usually behave adaptively and often altrustically in the stress of a fire.[16,19] A heterogeneous collection of persons under the influence of alcohol or drugs, as may be present in a place of public assembly, poses the greatest probability of nonadaptive group behavior, with a competitive flight, panic-type behavior the likely result. Historically, this type of nonadaptive behavior has been documented, although studies indicate that the phenonomenon is rare and depends upon unique, predetermined conditions involving both the population and the physical environment of the structure.[16,19,20]

In some cases, evacuation procedures and the creation of areas of refuge within high-rise buildings encourages occupant movement upward within the building. The effectiveness of this concept has not been completely validated in actual fires. Because of the orientation of some people toward total evacuation and escape from the building, it is possible that they may attempt to evacuate a building in the conventional "down and out" approach despite instruction to the contrary.[19]

The evacuation procedures in federal high-rise office buildings, as directed by vocal alarm systems, have continually obtained the selective movement of personnel in both upward and downward directions.[12] In both of the serious high-rise office building fires in Sao Paulo, Brazil, the occupants moved upward to the roof when their downward movement was inhibited by smoke and heat.[9] In the MGM Grand Hotel fire in Las Vegas, NV, in November 1980, there also was upward movement to areas of refuge in the stairways to the roof and to rooms on upper floors when downward travel was made untenable by smoke and heat.[10,16]

All exits need to be conspicuously marked, since people are likely to be unfamiliar with the various exits from an area under fire conditions and thus to neglect alternate means of egress. It is also important that the means of egress from a building be used as a matter of daily routine, so the occupants will be familiar with their location and operation. NFPA 101, *Life Safety Code*, requires that the main exit of assembly occupancies, which also serves as the entrance, be sized to handle at least one-half of the total occupant load of the building.

There are three critical parameters in the effective use of the zoned evacuation of personnel to areas of refuge within a building.[21] They are proper construction to provide compartmented areas that are protected from the effects of fire and smoke; an effective verbal alarm system giving clear and comprehensive instructions, with provision for originating on-scene instructions from the fire department[12]; and effective evacuation drills to familiarize the occupants with the way the system functions.

It has been advocated that occupants in fire-resistive, compartmented buildings used as hotels, motels, apartments, condominiums, dormitories, hospitals, and other health care facilities should stay in their rooms rather than evacuate, since the rooms are the most adequate area of refuge.[22] This method has not been adopted by NFPA 101, *Life Safety Code*, nor by the model building codes.

Influence of Fire Protection Equipment

It is unsuitable to rely on manual or automatic fire extinguishing systems in place of adequate means of egress, since fire extinguishing systems are subject to both human and mechanical failure. In addition, building areas may become untenable for human occupancy before the fire extinguishing systems are effective. Under no condition can manual or automatic fire suppression be accepted as a substitute for the provision and maintainance of proper means of egress.

Where a complete standard system is installed, automatic sprinklers are sufficiently reliable to have a major influence on life safety. In addition to providing an automatic alarm of fire, they quickly discharge water on the fire before smoke has spread dangerously. While automatic sprinklers should never be used in place of adequate means of egress, they are recognized in various ways by NFPA 101, *Life Safety Code*. When total automatic sprinklers are provided, NFPA *101* permits increased travel distance to exits, the use of interior finish of greater combustibility, and, in health care occupancies, the use of combustible construction in situations where it would otherwise be prohibited. Sprinklers are particularly valuable in dealing with travel distance problems in existing buildings.

Automatic fire detection, or fire alarm, systems are valuable in notifying building occupants of a fire so they may evacuate promptly. Automatic fire detection systems only provide a warning of fire and do nothing themselves to suppress or limit the spread of fire and smoke. An automatic fire detection system is not a substitute for adequate means of egress.

DEFINITION OF THE TERM "EXIT"

NFPA 101, *Life Safety Code*, includes the term "exit" in an overall definition of means of egress. A means of egress is a continuous path of travel from any point in a building or structure to the open air outside at ground level. Egress consists of three separate and distinct parts: the exit access, the exit, and the exit discharge.

An exit access is defined as that portion of a means of egress which leads to the entrance to an exit.

An exit is that portion of a means of egress that is separated from the area of the building from which escape is to be made by walls, floors, doors, or other means that provide the protected path necessary for the occupants to proceed with reasonable safety to the exterior of the building. An exit may comprise vertical and horizontal means of travel, such as doorways, stairways, ramps, corridors, and passageways.

Exit discharge is that portion of a means of egress between the termination of the exit and a public way.

Figure 7-2F illustrates the relationship among these three parts of an exit in a building.

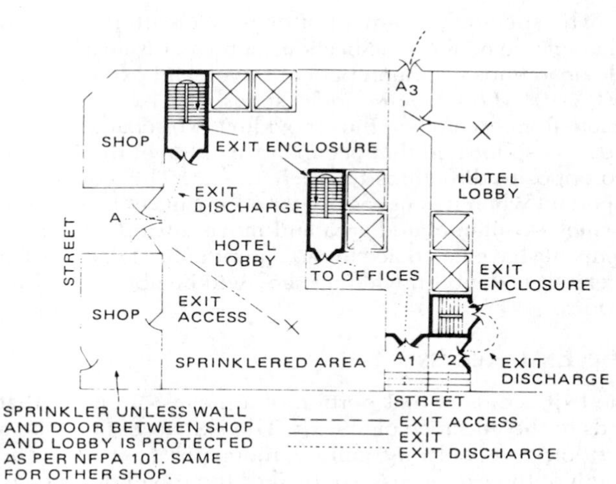

FIG. 7-2F. Examples of exit discharge. To the occupant of the building at the discharge level, the doors at A, A_1, A_2, and A_3 are exits, and the path denoted by dashes is the exit access. To the person emerging from the exit enclosure, the same doors and the paths denoted by dotted lines are the exit discharge.

The types of permissible exits are doors leading directly outside or through a protected passageway to the outside, smokeproof towers, interior and outside stairs, ramps, escalators in existing buildings, and moving walkways. Elevators are not accepted as exits. See Figures 7-2G and 7-2H for illustrations of some common types of exit arrangements.

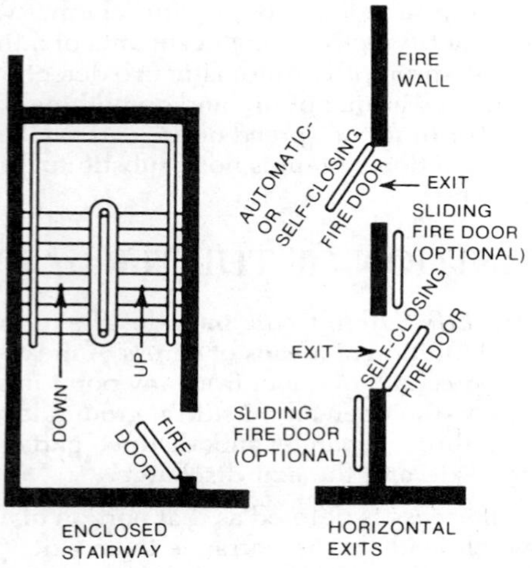

FIG. 7-2G. Plan views of types of exits. Stair enclosure prevents a fire on any floor from trapping the persons above. A smokeproof tower is better, as it opens to the air at each floor, largely preventing the chance of smoke in stairway. A horizontal exit provides a quick refuge and lessens the need for a hasty flight down stairs. Horizontal sliding fire doors and swinging doors may be arranged to close automatically in case of fire when open. Swinging doors also may be self-closing.

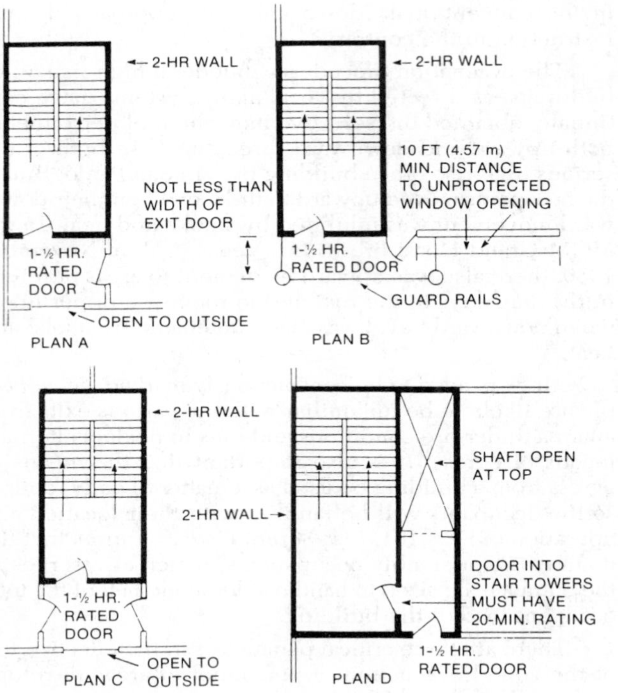

FIG. 7-2H. Four variations of smokeproof towers. Plan A has a vestibute opening from a corridor. Plan B shows an entrance by way of an outside balcony. Plan C could provide a stair tower entrance common to two areas. In Plan D, smoke and gases entering the vestibule would be exhausted by a natural or induced draft in the open air shaft. In each case, a double entrance to the stair tower with at least one side open or vented is characteristic of this type of construction. Pressurization of the stair tower in the event of fire provides an attractive alternate for tall buildings and is a means of eliminating the entrance vestibule. NFPA 101 requires complete supervised sprinkler protection of the building with stair pressurization.

Exits are measured in inches (mm) of egress width. The studies of an occupant's movements on stairs during both staged and normal evacuations led to advocacy of the concept of a 30-in. (762 mm) width for an exit unit.[2,13,14]

The specific placement of exits is a matter of design judgment, given the specifications of travel distance, allowable dead ends, common path of travel, and exit capacity. NFPA 101, *Life Safety Code*, states that exits must be remote from each other, thus providing two separate means of egress so located that occupants can travel in either of two opposite directions to reach an exit. This concept is important when it is necessary for occupants to leave a fire or smoke-contaminated area and move toward an exit. If occupants have no choice but to enter the fire area to reach an exit, it is doubtful whether they will be able or willing to do so.

The Exit Access

The exit access is that portion of a means of egress that leads to the entrance of an exit. The exit access may be a corridor, aisle, balcony, gallery, room, porch, or roof. The length of the exit access establishes the travel distance to an exit, an extremely important feature of a means of egress, since an occupant might be exposed to fire or smoke during the time it takes to reach an exit. The average recommended maximum travel distance is 200 ft (61 m), but this distance varies with the occupancy, depending upon the fire hazard and the physical ability and alertness of the occupants. (See Table 7-2B.) The travel distance must be measured from the most remote point in a room or floor area to an exit.

In most cases, the travel distance can be increased up to 50 percent if the building is completely protected with a standard supervised automatic sprinkler system.

A dead end is an extension of a corridor or aisle beyond an exit or an access to exits that forms a pocket in which occupants may be trapped. Since there is only one direction of travel to an exit from a dead end, a fire in a dead end between the exit and an occupant prevents the occupant from reaching the exit. Another problem with dead ends is that, while traveling toward an exit in a smoke-filled atmosphere, an occupant may pass by the exit and be trapped in the dead end. In good egress designs, dead-end corridors are not used. However, NFPA 101 permits dead ends in most occupancies, within reasonable limits. Two dead-end corridors are illustrated in Figure 7-2I.

The width of an exit access should be at least sufficient for the number of persons it must accommodate. In some occupancies, the width of the access is governed by the character of activity in the occupancy. One example is a new hospital, where patients will be moved in beds. The corridors in the patient areas of the hospital must be 8 ft. (2.4 m) wide to allow for a bed to be wheeled out of a room and turned 90 degrees.

A fundamental principle of exit access is the provision of a free and unobstructed way to the exits. If the access passes through a room that can be locked or through an area containing a fire hazard more severe than is typical of the occupancy, the principles of free and unobstructed exit access are violated.

TABLE 7-2B. *Exit Travel Distance and Dead-End Limits (By Occupancy)*

Type of Occupancy	Dead-End Limit (ft)	Travel Limit to an Exit	
		Unsprinklered (ft)	Sprinklered (ft)
Assembly			
New	20[a] (6.1 m)	150 (45 m)	200 (60 m)
Existing	20[a] (6.1 m)	150 (45 m)	200 (60 m)
Educational			
New	20 (6.1 m)	150 (45 m)	200 (60 m)
Existing	20 (6.1 m)	150 (45 m)	200 (60 m)
New Day-Care Center	20 (6.1 m)	150[c] (45 m)	200[c] (60 m)
Existing Day-Care Center	20 (6.1 m)	150[c] (45 m)	200[c] (60 m)
Health Care			
New	30 (9.1 m)	N.A.[b]	200[c] (60 m)
Existing	N.R.[b]	150[c] (45 m)	200[c] (60 m)
New Ambulatory Center	20[d] (6.1 m)	150[c] (45 m)	200[c] (60 m)
Existing Ambulatory Center	50 (15 m)	150[c] (45 m)	200[c] (60 m)
Detention and Correction			
New			
Use Conditions			
II, III, IV	50 (15 m)	150[c] (45 m)	200[c] (60 m)
V	20 (6.1 m)	150[c] (45 m)	200[c] (60 m)
Existing			
Use Conditions			
II, III, IV, V	N.R.[b]	150[c] (45 m)	200[c] (60 m)
Residential			
A. Hotels and Dormitories			
New	35[d] (10.7 m)	100[e] (30 m)	200[e] (60 m)
Existing	50 (15 m)	100[e] (30 m)	200[e] (60 m)
B. Apartments			
New	35[d] (10.7 m)	100[f] (30 m)	200[f] (60 m)
Existing	50 (15 m)	100[f] (30 m)	200[f] (60 m)
C. Board and Care	[g]	[g]	[g]
D. Lodging or Rooming Houses, 1- and 2-Family Dwellings	N.R.[b]	N.R.[b]	N.R.[b]
Mercantile			
Class A, B and C			
New	20[d] (6.1 m)	100 (30 m)	200 (60 m)
Existing	50 (15 m)	150 (45 m)	200 (60 m)
Open Air	0	N.R.[b]	N.R.[b]
Covered Mall			
New	20[d] (6.1 m)	100 (30 m)	400[h] (120 m)
Existing	50 (15 m)	150 (45 m)	400[h] (120 m)
Business			
New	20[d] (6.1 m)	200 (60 m)	300 (91 m)
Existing	50 (15 m)	200 (60 m)	300 (91 m)
Industrial			
General	50 (15 m)	200 (60 m)	200[i] (75 m)
Special Purpose (Low or Ordinary Hazard)	50 (15 m)	300 (91 m)	400 (122 m)
High Hazard	0	75 (23 m)	75 (23 m)
Open Structures	N.R.[b]	N.R.[b]	N.R.[b]

Note: The following Chapter references are to NFPA *101, Life Safety Code*, 1991 edition.
[a] See Chapters 8 and 9 for aisles and mezzanines.
[b] No requirement or not applicable.
[c] This dimension is for total travel distance, for travel distance within the room, and from the room exit access door to the exit. See the appropriate occupancy chapter.
[d] In sprinklered facilities 50 ft (15 m).
[e] This dimension is from the room exit access door to the exit. See Chapters 16 and 17 for exceptions and limitations within the room/suite.
[f] This dimension is from the room exit access door to the exit. See Chapters 18 and 19 for exceptions and limitations within the room/suite.
[g] See Chapters 22 and 23.
[h] See Chapters 24 and 25 for exceptions and special considerations.
[i] See Chapter 28 for special considerations.
[j] See Chapters 28 and 29 for special requirements.

TABLE 7-2B. (continued)

Type of Occupancy	Dead-End Limit (ft)	Travel Limit to an Exit: Unsprinklered (ft)	Sprinklered (ft)
Storage			
Low Hazard	N.R.[b]	N.R.[b]	N.R.[b]
Ordinary Hazard	50[j] (15 m)	200 (60 m)	400 (122 m)
High Hazard	0	75 ((23 m)	100 (30 m)
Parking Garages, Open	50 (15 m)	200 (60 m)	300 (91 m)
Parking Garages, Enclosed	50 (15 m)	150 (45 m)	200 (60 m)
Aircraft Hangars, Ground Floor	50[j] (15 m)	Varies[j]	Varies[j]
Aircraft Hangars, Mezzanine Floor	50[j] (15 m)	75 (23 m)	75 (23 m)
Grain Elevators	[j]	200[j] (60 m)	400[j] (122 m)
Miscellaneous Occupanices, Towers, Piers, and Water Surrounded Structures, Vehicles, and Vessels, and Emergency Shelters	50 (15 m)	100 (30 m)	150 (45 m)

Note: The Following Chapter references are to NFPA *101, Life Safety Code*, 1991 edition.
[a] See Chapters 8 and 9 for aisles and mezzanines.
[b] No requirement or not applicable.
[c] This dimension is for total travel distance, for travel distance within the room, and from the room exit access door to the exit. See the appropriate occupancy chapter.
[d] In sprinklered facilities 50 ft (15 m).
[e] This dimension is from the room exit access door to the exit. See Chapters 16 and 17 for exceptions and limitations within the room/suite.
[f] This dimension is from the room exit access door to the exit. See Chapters 18 and 19 for exceptions and limitations within the room/suite.
[g] See Chapters 22 and 23.
[h] See Chapters 24 and 25 for exceptions and special considerations.
[i] See Chapter 28 for special considerations.
[j] See Chapters 28 and 29 for special requirements.

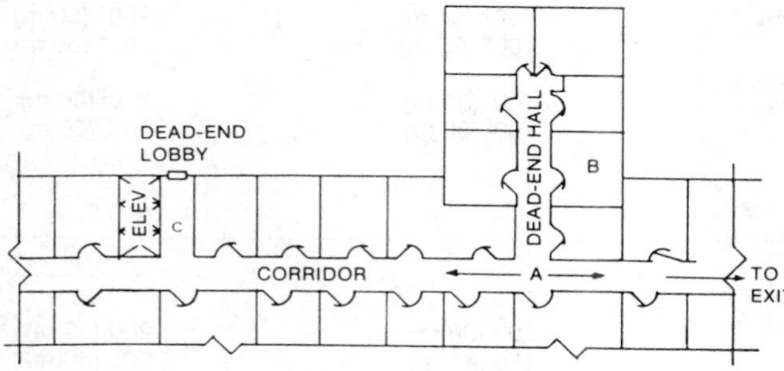

FIG. 7-21. Examples of two types of dead-end corridors.

The floor of an exit access should be level. If this is not possible, small differences in elevation may be overcome by a ramp and large differences by stairs. Where only one or two steps are necessary to overcome differences in level in an exit access, a ramp is preferred, because people may trip in a crowded corridor and fall on the stairs if they do not see the steps or notice that those in front of them have stepped up.

The Exit Discharge

Ideally, all exits in a building should discharge directly to the outside or through a fire-resistive passageway to the outside of the building. NFPA 101, *Life Safety Code*, permits a maximum of 50 percent of the exit stairs in most occupancies to discharge onto the street floor. The obvious disadvantage of this arrangement is that, if a fire occurs on the street-level floor, it is possible for people using the exit stairs discharging to that floor to be discharged into the fire area. If any exits discharge to the street floor, NFPA 101 therefore requires that such exits discharge to a free and unobstructed way to the outside of the building, that the entire street floor be protected by automatic sprinklers, and that the street floor be separated from any floors below by construction having a 2-hr fire-resistance rating.

Discharging an exit to the outside is not necessarily discharging to a safe place. If the exit discharges into a courtyard, an exit passageway must be provided from the courtyard through the building so that the occupants can get away from the building. If the exit discharges into a fenced yard, the occupants must be able to get out of the yard to get away from the building. If the exit discharges into an alley, the alley must be of sufficient width to accommodate the capacity of all the exits discharging into it, and any openings in the building walls bordering the alley should be protected to prevent fire exposure to the occupants proceeding through the alley.

When exit stairs from floors above the street floor continue on to floors below the street floor, occupants evacuating the building may miss the exit discharge door to the street level, continue down the stairway, and enter a floor below the level of exit discharge. Therefore, NFPA 101, *Life Safety Code*, requires a physical barrier at the street floor landing to prevent evacuees from passing the level of exit discharge.

CAPACITY OF EXITS

The capacity of exits is calculated using a capacity factor provided in NFPA 101, *Life Safety Code*. This capacity factor is given as inches per person and varies with the occupancy. (See Table 7-2C.) The total exit capacity for each component of the means of egress, such as doors, stairs, ramps, corridors, and so on, is calculated based on its clear width. For example, one 34-in. clear-width door in an office occupancy would have an exit capacity of 170 persons (34 in. ÷ 0.2 in./person = 170 persons). The reason for

TABLE 7-2C. ***Summary of NFPA 101, Life Safety Code,*** **Provisions for Occupant Load and Exit Capacity**

Occupancy	Occupant Load Sq. ft (m^2) per Person	Level Components (Doors, Corridors, Horizontal Exits)	Capacity of Exits (Inches Per Person) Class A Ramps and Class B Ramps in Descent	Class B Ramps-Ascent	Stairs
Assembly					
Less concentrated use without fixed seating	15 Net (1.4)	0.2	0.2	0.22	0.3
Concentrated use without fixed seating	7 Net (.65)	0.2	0.2	0.22	0.3
Fixed seating	Actual Number of Seats	0.2	0.2	0.22	0.3
Educational					
Class rooms	20 Net (1.9)	0.2	0.2	0.22	0.3
Shops & vocational	50 Net (4.6)	0.2	0.2	0.22	0.3
Care Centers	35 Net (3.3)	0.2	0.2	0.22	0.3
Health Care		<u>NAS</u> / <u>AS</u>	<u>NAS</u> / <u>AS</u>	<u>NAS</u> / <u>AS</u>	<u>NAS</u> / <u>AS</u>
Sleeping departments	120 Gross (11.1)	0.7 / 0.5	0.7 / 0.5	1.0 / 0.6	1.0 / 0.6
Treatment departments	240 Gross (22.3)	0.7 / 0.5	0.7 / 0.5	1.0 / 0.6	1.0 / 0.6
Residential	200 Gross (18.6)	0.2	0.2	0.22	0.3
Board & Care					
Mercantile	200 Gross (18.6)	0.2	0.2	0.22	0.3
Street floor and sales basement	30 Gross (3.7)	0.2	0.2	0.22	0.3
Multiple street floors—each	40 Gross (3.7)	0.2	0.2	0.22	0.3
Other Floors	60 Gross (5.6)	0.2	0.2	0.22	0.3
Storage—shipping	300 Gross (27.9)	0.2	0.2	0.22	0.3
Malls	See Code	0.2	0.2	0.22	0.3
Business	100 Gross (9.3)	0.2	0.2	0.22	0.3
Industrial	100 Gross (9.3)	0.2	0.2	0.22	0.3
Detention & Correctional	120 Gross (11.1)	0.2	0.2	0.22	0.3

these variations in exit capacity factors is to establish a consistent total evacuation time in different occupancies, based on the physical ability, mental alertness, age, and sociological roles of the occupants. In occupancies where people sleep or are housed for care, the time taken to reach exits will be greater than in some other occupancies, so the exits must be sufficiently wide to allow nonambulatory occupants to egress and to prevent any waiting to get into the exit. It can be expected that people in an assembly occupancy will move rapidly to the exits and reach them at about the same time, which requires them to wait before entering the exit. This expected queuing time is reduced by an NFPA 101 provision that requires the main exit in assembly occupancies to provide at least 50 percent of the total required exit capacity and by the provision of a total capacity for all exits of 100 percent of the occupant load.

The capacity of exits is used to establish a consistency of evacuation time on the basis of the rate of travel through a door of 60 persons per min and down a stairway of 45 persons per min per 22 in. (558.8 mm) of exit width, respectively. These figures were established by evacuation counts conducted primarily in federal office buildings.[23] More recent studies of evacuations in high-rise office buildings indicate peak flows of 30 persons per min and mean flows of 24 persons per min per 22 in. (558.8 mm) of exit width down stairways.[2,13,14]

Occupant Load

Occupant load, or the number of people to be expected in a building at any time for whom exits must be provided, is determined by dividing the gross area of the building or the net area of a specific portion of the building by the area in sq ft (m^2) projected for each person. The amount of floor area projected for each person varies with the occupancy. (See Table 7-2C.) These figures are based on actual counts of people in buildings and on reviews of architectural plans. In some situations, the maximum number of people in a building above the occupant load can be determined at the design stage, in which case this number should be used in the design of the exits. A typical example is an assembly occupancy in which fixed seating is installed. Counting the number of seats provided, and calculating the standing or waiting areas by the occupant load factor, would obviously give a more accurate figure than multiplying a sq-ft (m^2) per-person figure by the net floor area.

Computing Required Exit Width

To compute the minimum required exit widths from the individual floors of a building, it is necessary to calculate the floor area, either net or gross, whichever is applicable; determine from NFPA 101, *Life Safety Code*, the estimated number of sq ft (m^2) per person, or occupant load factor; divide the number of sq ft (m^2) per person (occupant load factor) into the floor area to determine the minimum number of people for whom exits must be provided for that floor; measure the clear width of each component in the means of egress; determine the capacity factor from NFPA 101 for each exit component for the appropriate occupancy; divide the clear width of each exit component by the capacity factor to determine the exit capacity for each component; determine the most restrictive component in each exit; determine the total exit capacity for the floor; and ensure that the total exit capacity equals or exceeds the total occupant load.

In multi-story buildings, the exit capacity for each floor is calculated separately. In other words, the capacity of the stairs need only be wide enough to serve each floor, but it must not be less that the minimum width required by NFPA 101. It must be noted, also, that the required egress capacity cannot be decreased in the direction of egress travel.

Street-floor exits may require special treatment, depending upon the occupancy. Some occupancies require that street-floor exits be sized to handle not only the occupant load of the street floor but also a percentage of the occupant load of the exits discharging to the street floor from floors above and below. In addition, in those occupancies where floors above and/or below the street floor are permitted to have unenclosed stairs and escalators connecting them with the street floor, the exits must be sufficient to provide simultaneously for all the occupants of all communicating levels and areas. In other words, all communicating levels in the same fire area are considered a single floor area for the purposes of determining the required exit capacity. This identical, single fire area factor can have a considerable effect on the sizing of the street-floor exits.

Should two or more exits converge into a common exit, the common exit should never be narrower than the sum of the width of the exits converging into it.

Generally, the minimum number of exits is two. In certain limited situations, however, one exit may be permitted in some occupancies if there is a very low occupant load, low fire hazard, and a limited travel distance.

Dynamic Evaluation of Exit Design

Exit design may be evaluated on a dynamic basis using calculated evacuation times. Dynamic evaluation allows for the establishment of goals in terms of evacuation times and certain other key criteria.

For example, the U.S General Services Administration (GSA) has established a goal-oriented system approach to building firesafety that uses specific sets of goals for normal federal office operations.[14] The established goals are:

1. All occupants exposed to the fire environment must be able to evacuate to a safe area within 90 sec of alarm.
2. A portion of this time, not to exceed approximately 15 sec, can be involved in traveling in a direction toward the fire, such as in a dead-end corridor.
3. All occupants must reach an area of refuge within 5 min of downward vertical travel or within 1 min of upward vertical movement.

Further criteria established by the GSA for evaluation uses 3.5 ft/sec (1.07 m/sec) as the rate of horizontal movement. The exit flow rate for level travel is calculated at 60 persons per min per 24 in. (610 mm) width, 45 persons per min per 24 in. (610 mm) width down stairs, and 40 persons per min per 24 in. (610 mm) width up stairs.

Fatigue is judged to become important after 5 min of travel in a downward direction or 1 min of travel in an upward direction. Thus, fatigue becomes a "human factor" consideration affecting design.

The time to exit a building can be calculated using information and formulas contained in studies produced by the London Transport Board and the National Research Council of Canada.[25,26]

Calculations are possible based on the number of persons discharged per 22 in. (558.8 mm) of exit width per min. The calculated evacuation time reflects:

1. The time required to fill the stairs with people.
2. The time during which additional persons can enter the stairs from the upper floors.
3. The time required for all persons remaining in the stairs to discharge to the outside.

The following calculation method results in the time for complete evacuation, based upon the sum of the three preceding intervals.

$$T = \frac{N + n}{r \times u}$$

where:

T = the time in minutes required for complete evacuation by stairs.

N = the number of persons in the building above the first floor.

n = the number of persons who can stand on the stairs at 3 sq ft (0.28 m^2) per person or the number of persons on the floor, whichever is fewer.

r = the rate of discharge of the stairs in persons per 22 in. (558.8 mm) exit width per min. (See Table 7-2D.)

u = the number of 22 in. (558.8 mm) of stair width.

This calculation method assumes occupants will be uniformly distributed over the entire floor area. If all occupants were located 100 ft (30.5 m) from the stairs, however, additional time would be required. In fact, an additional ½ min evacuation time would be added to the total.

Further, it is necessary to determine the time required for the person located at the most remote point of the floor under consideration to reach the stairs or exit. If the travel time for this person exceeds the time calculated for all persons to egress by stairs or other exits, this additional time interval becomes a factor in the total evacuation time of the building.

TABLE 7-2D. *Relationship Between Concentration of People on Stairs and Forward Movement*[26]

Concentration of People on Stairs sq ft (m^2) per person	Forward Movement, ft per min (m/mm)	Resultant Discharge from Stairs, persons 22 in. (558.8 mm) of exit width per min
2 (0.19)	0 (0.00)	0
2.5 (0.23)	53 (15.2)	39
3.0 (0.28)	75 (22.9)	45
3.5 (0.33)	82 (25.0)	43
4.0 (0.37)	94 (28.6)	43
4.5 (0.42)	106 (32.3)	43
5.0 (0.46)	117 (35.7)	43
5.5 (0.51)	129 (39.3)	43
6.0 (0.56)	139 (42.4)	43
6.5 (0.60)	143 (43.6)	40
7.0 (0.65)	147 (44.8)	39
7.5 (0.70)	150 (45.7)	37
8.0 (0.74)	152 (46.3)	35
8.5 (0.80)	154 (46.9)	33
9.0 (0.84)	156 (47.5)	31
9.5 (0.88)	157 (47.8)	30
10.0 (0.93)	158 (48.2)	29
11.0 (1.02)	158 (48.2)	26
12.0 (1.11)	158 (48.2)	24
13.0 (1.21)	158 (48.2)	22
14.0 (1.30)	158 (48.2)	21
15.0 (1.39)	158 (48.2)	19

The method of calculation described previously provides guidance in terms of the minimum time necessary for evacuating a building under normal considerations. It is obvious that the loss of an exit stair due to fire or smoke contamination, artificial obstructions to exit paths, or the like, could seriously affect evacuation times. In earlier discussions, it was noted that, when densities result in less than 7 to 8 sq ft (0.65 to 0.74 m^2) of space per person, forward motion is significantly slowed, as indicated in Table 7-2D.

Table 7-2E records the calculated evacuation times and provides a comparison to actual evacuation times measured as a result of drills conducted during nonemergencies.[27] As noted in Table 7-2E, the actual recorded evacuation times exceeded the calculated times. Similar results have been found using differing formulas for these buildings.[28]

Evacuation times[26,28] have been compared with other data[29] for both observed and predicted total evacuation times for tall buildings, as presented in Figure 7-2J. Pauls' data[29] is based on measurements obtained from 29 evacuation drills, primarily in office buildings ranging from 8 to 21 stories high. Pauls[29] observed evacuation times varying from approximately 10 sec per story for buildings with small populations to approximately 20 sec per story for buildings with large populations. The evacuation equations indicated in Figure 7-2J were developed from these observed evacuation times. The first equation,

$$T = 0.70 + 0.0133p$$

is to be applied for the prediction of evacuation times in buildings with large populations exceeding 800 persons per meter of effective stair width. T is the minimum time, in minutes, to complete an uncontrolled total evacuation by stairs, and p is the actual evacuation population per meter of effective stair width, measured immediately above the discharge level of the stair.

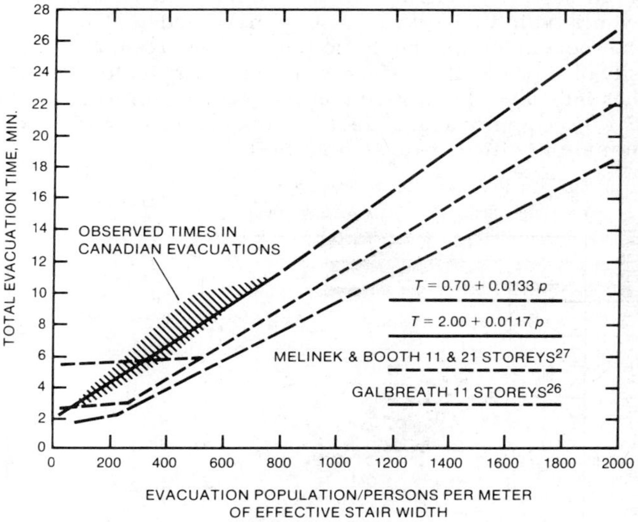

*Fig. 7-2J. **Predicted and observed total evacuation times for tall office buildings.***[29]

TABLE 7-2E. *Time of Evacuation for Certain Existing Office Buildings*[26]

Building No.	Height in Stories	Area of Exit Stairs per Floor, sq ft (m^2)	Width of Exit Stairs, Unit Exit Width	Average Number of Occupants per Floor at Time of Survey	Evacuation Time Calculated by Formula, min	Evacuation Time in Practice Drill, min	Maximum No. of Occupants per Floor By NBC Provisions
1	7	857 (79.6)	10	61	2.1	4½	600
2	7	636 (59.1)	8	108	2.1	5	480
3	9	692 (64.3)	8	133	3.6	4½	480
4	9	408 (37.9)	4	111	6.0	5½	300
5	11	346 (32.1)	4	110	6.7	6½	240
6	11	150 (13.9)	4	100	5.8	7½	240
7	12	314 (29.2)	4	67	4.3	9	240
8	13	319 (29.6)	6	38	1.8	4	360
9	18	260 (24.2)	4	50	5.2	7½	240
10	22	160 (14.9)	2	80	20.0	incomplete	180

It should be recognized that the definition of the "effective stair width," as used by Pauls, is defined in the following manner:[29]

> This empirically based model describes flow as a linear function of a stair's effective width—the width remaining once the edge effects are deducted (6 inches or 150 mm from each wall boundary and 3.5 inches or 90 mm from each handrail centerline). It takes into account the propensity of people to sway laterally—especially when walking slowly in a crowd—and therefore to arrange themselves in a staggered traditional unit-width model based on presumed static dimensions of people's shoulders.
>
> The second equation in Figure 72-J,
>
> $$T = 2.00 + 0.0117p$$
>
> is to be applied when the population per meter of effective stair width is less than 800 persons.

Pauls[29] has also examined the relationship between the speed or velocity of evacuation and the density on the stairs during the uncontrolled total evacuation, as indicated in Figure 7-2K. It should be remembered this movement would be in the vertical, downward direction. The vertical movement appears to be the most effective at a density of approximately 0.9 persons per square meter. Pauls[29] has indicated that a speed on the stairs of approximately 2.1 ft/sec approximates the traveling of 8 to 12 stories per minute in office or residential buildings.

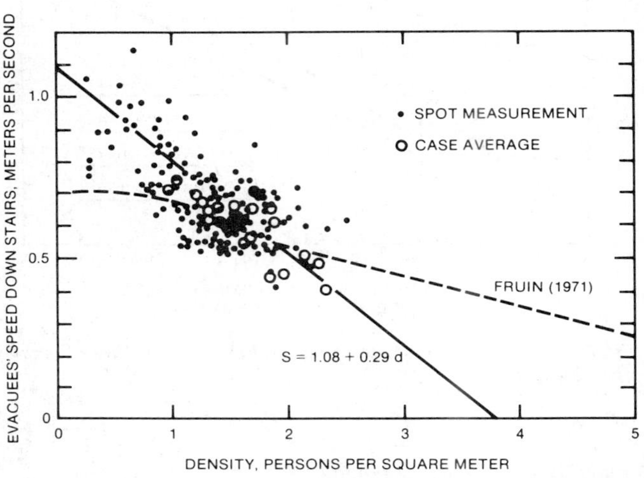

*Fig. 7-2K. **Relation between speed and density on stairs in uncontrolled total evacuations.***[29]

Kendik[30] has examined the evacuation flow relative to the flow density for the various means of egress components, as determined by normal evacuation procedures. This data for doors, corridors, and stairs in both the ascent and descent modes is presented in Figure 7-2L.

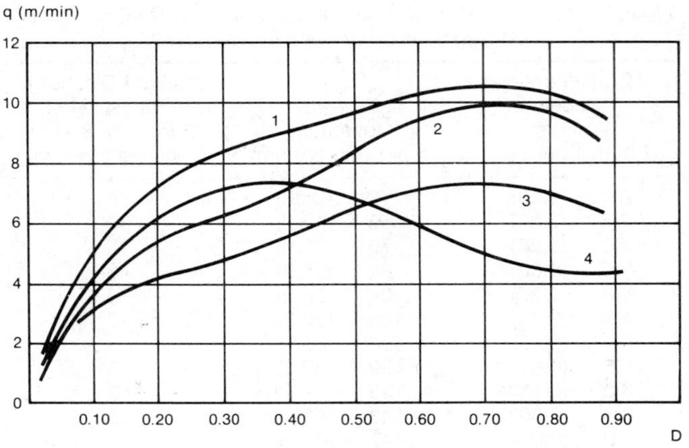

*Fig. 7-2L. **Illustration of specific flow pertinent to the flow density for different kinds of escape routes under normal environmental conditions: (1) doorways, (2) horizontal routes, (3) stairs (upwards), and (4) stairs (downwards).***[30]

COMPUTER SIMULATION AND MODELING OF EGRESS DESIGN

Computer simulation and modeling have become important tools in designing adequate means of egress under a variety of occupancy and structural conditions. The following paragraphs summarize activity to date in applying simulation and modeling techniques to solving egress design problems.

In one study of the critical variables for firesafety in relation to buildings used to house the elderly, the problem of fire development and evacuation as a time-structured problem was considered.[31] This study analyzed the variables related to the occurrence and spread of fire relative to the population in terms of their ability to attain an area of refuge from the effects of the fire. The study established the variables for the fire on a continuum of a "critical time," and the parameters for the survival of the occupants on a continuum of a "reaction time."

The definition adopted for critical time is the elapsed time from the start of the fire to the attainment of intolerable levels. The definition for reaction time is reported as the amount of time used by the occupant to react to the fire and to achieve safety by evacuating the fire area or by obtaining a place of refuge from the effects of the fire. Thus, within the framework of these definitions, both the parameters of the problem of the human behavior factors involved in a fire in a building and the variables of the problem are considered.

This conceptualization of a critical time for fire development within a building and of the reaction time required for occupants to perceive and respond to the fire threat, either by evacuation or movement to an area of refuge, has been studied thoroughly. It has resulted in multiple computer models of this essential egress behavior since Caravaty and Haviland's study in 1967.[31]

A computer model that simulates the movement of people during evacuation through the floor of fire origin has been developed.[32] A Markov-based model focused on the movement of people through a fire floor from the time of alarm until their safe exit or until they became casualties of the fire. Six variables affecting their movement have been identified:

1. Objective location of the threatening stimuli in time and space.
2. Occupants' prior knowledge of effective egress routes.
3. Occupants' perception of the location and severity of the threat.

4. Occupants' perception of available alternatives.
5. Occupants' threat-reducing experiences prior to the current movement decision.
6. The interjection of sudden interpretations to the occupants' goal-directed behavior.

Stahl has indicated that his decade of effort in modeling the movement of occupants has resulted in an improved computer model and an appreciation of the value of simulation in egress design.[33,34] Simulation modeling may be appropriate for problems that would otherwise require costly, time-consuming, and tedious manual effort; that cannot be solved through experimentation because of high costs or unacceptable risks to human participants; and for which past experience, intuition, or available data do not provide the proper insight. Figure 7-2M compares data developed on the effect of the variation in occupant density upon walking speed in two computer simulation programs and data compiled from two actual pedestrian movement studies.

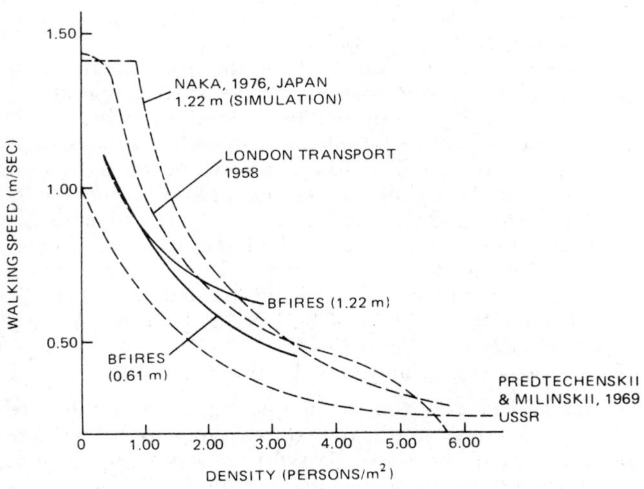

FIG. 7-2M. A comparison of the effect of a variation in the density of occupants upon walking speed from simulations and studies. The NAKA and BFIRES curves are based on computer simulations. The London Transport and the Predtechenskii & Milinski curves are based on actual pedestrian movement studies. The curves indicate that computer simulation data lies within trends established by real-world observation.

A modeling technique has been developed that would appear to have potential for comparing the evacuation behavior of occupants assisted by trained personnel with evacuation without assistance.[35] This model determines the escape potential from an area of a building based on a deterministic approach with a computer algorithm, and it evaluates the effects of fire growth and smoke movement on occupants as they try to egress. Occupant evacuation is simulated with evaluation of the effects of the egress design, the density of the occupants in the means of egress, the congestion at door or other restrictions, and the effects of the combustion products on occupants.

The basic components of the original Building Firesafety Model have been applied to the specific problem of the evacuation of board and care homes during a fire.[36] This simulation model has added an evaluation of the residents' physical and mental characteristics that affect evacuation. These characteristics are movement variables or impairments and stress behavior, including resistance to assistance, mobility, the need for assistance, and the residents' responsiveness. In addition to residents' characteristics, this model evaluates the staff characteristics that are critical to providing the required assistance for effective evacuation. Simulations with this model have indicated that residents should be located on the ground floor near exits. The quickest egress routes should be identified. With increased staff/resident ratios, rescuing those farthest away first can reduce evacuation time.

The development and the current applications of the building fire simulation model (BFSM) and its five submodels have been reviewed. The applications are the parameter simulation conversion logic, the fire development model, the combustion products model, the escape routing model, and the estimated escape time escape routing model.[37] The relationship of these submodels is illustrated in Figure 7-2N.

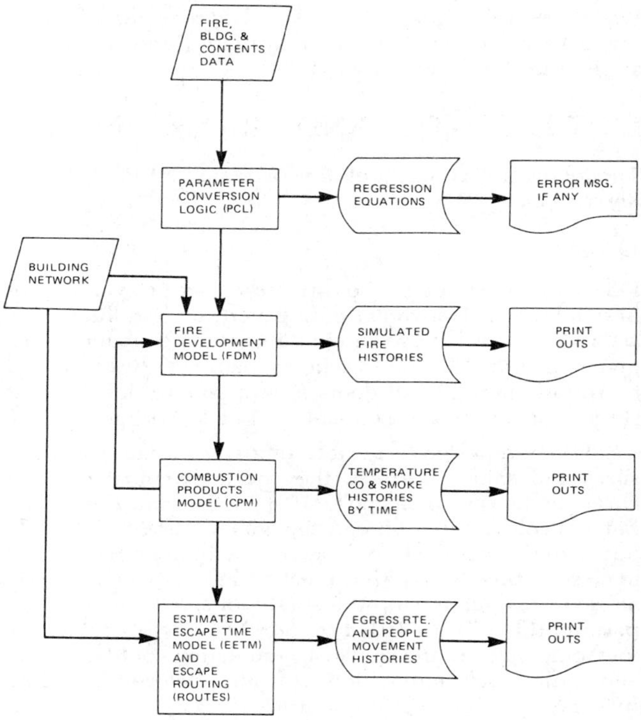

FIG. 7-2N. The building fire simulation model design with the submodels relationship.[37]

The concepts of critical time and reaction time as originally formulated by Caravaty and Haviland[31] have been adapted into a determination of the available safe egress time (ASET) model.[38] This model is a mathematical procedure for simulating of the conditions that develop between the time of fire ignition and the onset of untenable conditions for human occupancy. Cooper's[38] model thus addresses the fire development and combustion products submodels of the BFSM.

A simulation model has been developed to evaluate the evacuation plans and procedures within a specific building.[38] This model requires input data on the physical dimensions of the building areas, the means of egress, and the specified evacuation routes with the number and location of the occupants. The model provides an estimated average evacuation time and an estimated total evacuation time.

Building network evacuation models similar to the model of O'Leary and Gratz[39] have been developed which evaluate the egress environment within the building and the characteristics of the population relative to density and location.[40] The model predicts evacuation flows and times, and it identifies queueing problems. The model has been validated with evacuation data from high-rise federal office buildings and college dormitories.

An analytical queing network model (QNM) has also been developed to be used in the analysis of a building design relative to the suitability of the egress system.[41] This model provides estimates of the evacuation times, the average queue lengths along egress routes, potential impairments, and total egress probability.

The improvement and use of computer models for evacuation analysis have been examined and reviewed by Watts.[42] Network, queuing, and simulation models of building evacuations are currently available and are being applied in the design process.

EXIT FACILITIES AND ARRANGEMENTS

The following exit facilities are covered in NFPA 101, *Life Safety Code*.

Doors

Doors should swing in the direction of exit travel, except in small rooms. Horizontal sliding, vertical, or rolling doors are recognized for use in exits in some occupancies. In places of assembly and in schools, panic hardware should be installed on all exit doors equipped with latches that serve rooms with an occupant load of 100 or more.

Where doors protect exit facilities, as in stairway enclosures and smoke barriers, they normally must be kept closed to the spread of smoke. If open, they must be closed immediately in case of fire. Although ordinary, fusible-link-operated devices to close doors in case of fire are designed to close in time to stop the spread of fire, they do not operate soon enough to stop the spread of smoke and are not permitted by NFPA 101, *Life Safety Code*. At relatively low temperatures, the smoke accumulation could continue and could reach untenable levels long before the fusible link melted, allowing the door to close.

Sometimes, people keep self-closing doors open with hooks or with wedges under the door. Doors also can be blocked open to provide ventilation, for the convenience of building maintenance personnel, or to avoid the accident hazard of swinging doors. The following measures have been provided in the NFPA 101, *Life Safety Code*, to alleviate this undesirable situation:

1. Use of smokeproof towers that protect against smoke, even if the doors are open.
2. Doors that are normally closed can be equipped to open electrically or pneumatically when a person approaches the door.
3. Doors that normally are closed can be opened and held open manually by monitors, as in schools.
4. Doors that are normally kept open can be equipped with door closers and automatic hold-open devices that release the door and allow them to close when an automatic sprinkler system, the fire alarm system, an automatic fire detection system, and smoke or other products of combustion detection devices operate.

Qualifications and limitations are applicable to each of these measures. One is that, in the event of electrical failure, the door must close and remain closed unless it is opened manually for escape purposes.

Another major maintenance difficulty with exit doors is the exterior door that is locked to prevent unauthorized access or for other reasons. NFPA 101, *Life Safety Code*, specifies that, when the building is occupied, all doors must be kept unlocked from the side from which egress is made.

NFPA 101, *Life Safety Code*, allows a delayed releasing device on exterior exit doors, provided this is permitted by the requirements of the occupancy in question. Where the devices are allowed, the following provisions apply:

1. The building must be protected throughout by an approved and supervised automatic fire detection system or automatic sprinkler system.
2. The release devices are installed only in low- or ordinary-hazard areas.
3. The devices must unlock when the fire detection system, alarm, or automatic sprinkler system operates.
4. The devices must unlock upon loss of power.
5. The devices must initiate an irreversible process that will free the latch within 15 sec whenever a force of not more than 15 lb (6.8 kg) is applied to the releasing device, and the door must not relock automatically. Operation of the releasing device must actuate a signal near the door.
6. A sign must be placed adjacent to the door that reads: PUSH UNTIL ALARM SOUNDS. DOOR CAN BE OPENED IN 15 SECONDS!
7. Emergency lighting must be provided at the door.

Locks on a door that let people exit but not enter are satisfactory, but even this type of lock may not be satisfactory for security purposes. Possible measures to prevent unauthorized use of exit doors include:

1. An automatic alarm that rings when the door is opened.
2. Visual supervision such as wired-glass panels, closed-circuit television, and mirrors, which may be used where appropriate.
3. Automatic photographic devices to provide pictures of users.

So-called exit locks, with a break-glass unit actuated by striking a handle with the hand, are not permitted by NFPA 101, *Life Safety Code*, unless installed in conjunction with panic bars. Otherwise, they do not comply with the NFPA 101 provision that reads: "A latch or other fastening device on an exit door shall be provided with a knob, handle, panic bar, or other simple device, the method of operation of which is obvious, even in darkness."

Other types of break-glass locks and electrical controls for releasing exits from a central point are not permitted by NFPA 101, *Life Safety Code*. The exception is an occupancy where controls may be necessary, as in health care, educational, and detention and correctional occupancies.

A single door in a doorway should not be less than 32 in. (813 mm) wide in new buildings and 28 in. (711 mm) in existing buildings. Doors in the required means of egress are limited to a maximum width of 48 in. (1.2 m). To prevent tripping, the floor on both sides of the door should have the same elevation for the full swing of the door.

Panic Hardware

Exit doors in assembly and educational occupancies, such as schools or movie theaters, normally are equipped with panic hardware. Basically, panic hardware devices are designed to facilitate the release of the latching device on the door when a pressure not to exceed 15 lb (6.8 kg) is applied in the direction of exit travel. Such releasing devices are bars or panels extending not less than one-half of the width of the door and placed at a height not less than 30 in. (762 mm) or more than 44 in. (1.1 m) above the floor.

Panic hardware that has been tested and listed for use on fire-protection-rated doors is termed "fire exit hardware." If panic hardware is needed on fire-protection-rated doors, fire exit hardware only is to be used.

Panic hardware is available for use on single and double doors, with variations for rim-mounted hardware and mortise or vertical rod devices.

Horizontal Exits

A horizontal exit is a means of egress from one building to an area of refuge in another building on approximately the same level, or a means of egress through a fire barrier or partition to an area of refuge at approximately the same level in the same building that affords safety from fire and smoke. With a horizontal exit, it is obvious that space must be provided in the area or building of refuge for the people entering the refuge area. NFPA 101, *Life Safety Code* recommends 3 sq ft (0.28 m^2) of space per person, with the exception of health care occupancies, where 6 to 30 sq ft (0.56 to 2.79 m^2) of space is recommended. Horizontal exits cannot comprise more than one-half the total required exit capacity, except in health care facilities, where horizontal exits may comprise two-thirds of the total required exit capacity, and in detention and correctional facilities, where horizontal exits can comprise 100 percent of the total exit capacity. Horizontal exits have been applied universally in health care facilities where the evacuation of patients over stairs is slower and more difficult than taking them through a horizontal exit to a safe area of refuge. A horizontal exit arrangement within a single building and between two buildings is illustrated in Figure 7-2O.

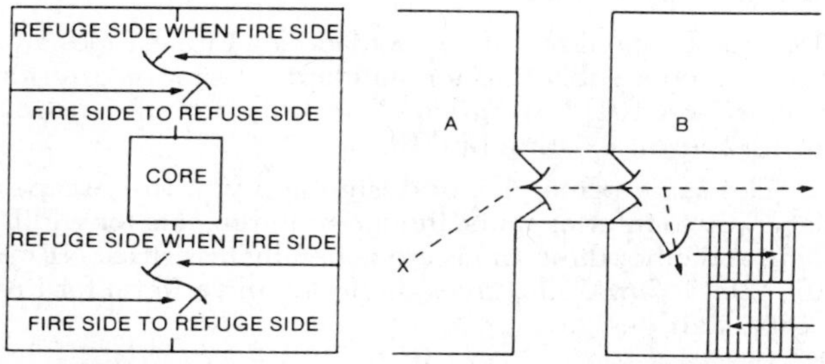

TWO-WAY HORIZONTAL EXIT IN AN OPEN-PLAN BUILDING. SELF-CLOSING FIRE DOORS REQUIRED IN FIRE SEPARATION.

ONE-WAY HORIZONTAL EXIT FROM BUILDING A TO BUILDING B. SELF-CLOSING OR AUTOMATIC-CLOSING FIRE DOORS AND PROTECTED PASSAGE REQUIRED.

FIG. 7-2O. Types of horizontal exits.

A swinging door in a fire wall provides a horizontal exit in one direction only. Two openings, each with a door swinging in the direction of exit travel or sliding doors, are needed to provide horizontal exits from both sides of the wall. Where property protection requires fire doors on both sides of the wall, a normally open, automatic, fusible-link-operated, horizontally sliding fire door may be used on one side, with a swinging fire door on the other.

Stairs

Exit stairs are arranged to minimize the danger of falling, because one person falling on a stairway may result in the complete blockage of an exit. Stairs must be wide enough for two persons to descend side by side, thus maintaining a reasonable rate of evacuation, even though aged or infirmed persons may slow the travel on one side. There must be no decrease in the width of the stair along the path of travel, since this may create congestion.

Steep stairs are dangerous. Stair treads must be wide enough to give good footing. NFPA 101, *Life Safety Code*, specifies a minimum 11-in. (279 mm) tread and a maximum 7-in. (178 mm) riser. Landings should be provided to break up any excessively long individual flight. Continuous railings are now recommended for both sides of the stairs. New stairs more than 60 in. (150 cm) wide should have one or more center rails.

Two classes of stairs are permitted in NFPA 101, *Life Safety Code*, for existing buildings, with a single class of stairs for new stairs. There are Class A and Class B stairs for existing buildings. The requirements for each class are given in Table 7-2F.

Stairways may be inside the building where the NFPA 101, *Life Safety Code*, generally specifies protective enclosures. They also may be outside if they comply with the requirements for exterior stairs, and are arranged so that persons with a fear of heights will not be reluctant to use them, they are not exposed to fire conditions originating in the building, and, where necessary, are shielded from snow and ice. Exterior stairs should not be confused with fire escape stairs. (See Fig. 7-2P.)

Construction details of stair enclosures involve the principles of limiting fire and smoke spread. Doors on openings from each story are essential to prevent the stairway from serving as a flue. In general, stairway enclosures should include not only the stairs, but also the path of travel from the bottom of the stairs to the exit discharge, so that occupants have a protected, enclosed passageway all the way out of the building. The stair enclosure should be of 1-hr noncombustible construction when connecting three or fewer floors and of 2-hr noncombustible construction when connecting four or more floors.

Smokeproof Towers

Smokeproof towers provide the highest protected type of stair enclosure recommended by NFPA 101, *Life Safety Code.* Access to the stair tower is only by balconies open to the outside air, vented vestibules, or mechanically pressurized vestibules, so that smoke, heat, and flame will not spread readily into the tower even if the doors are accidentally left open. (See Figure 7-2H.)

Ramps

Ramps, enclosed and otherwise and arranged like stairways, are sometimes used instead of stairways where there are large crowds and to provide both access and egress for nonambulatory persons. To be considered safe, exits ramps must have a very gradual slope.

TABLE 7-2F. *Requirements for New and Existing Building Stairs*

	New Stairs	Existing Stairs: Class A	Existing Stairs: Class B
Minimum width clear of all obstructions except projections not exceeding 3½ in. (0.89 mm) at and below handrail height on each side	44 in. (1.12 m) 36 in. (0.91 m) where total occupant load of all floors served by stairways is less than 50.	44 in. (1.12 m) 36 in. (0.91 m), where total occupant load of all floors served by stairways is less than 50.	44 in. (1.12 m) 36 in. (0.91 m)
Maximum height of risers	7 in. (178 mm)	7½ in. (191 mm)	8 in. (203 mm)
Minimum height of risers	4 in. (102 mm)	10 in. (244 mm)	9 in. (229 mm)
Minimum tread depth	11 in. (279 mm)		
Winders	See 5-2.2.2.5.*	See 5-2.2.2.5.*	See 5-2.2.2.5.*
Minimum headroom	6 ft 8 in. (2.03 m)	6 ft 8 in. (2.03 m)	6 ft 8 in. (2.03 m)
Maximum height between landings	12 ft (3.7 m)	12 ft (3.7 m)	12 ft (3.7 m)
Minimum dimension of landings in direction of travel	Stairways and intermediate landings shall continue with no decrease in width along the direction of exit travel. In new buildings every landing shall have a dimension, measured in direction of travel, equal to the width of the stair. Such dimension need not exceed 4 ft (1.22 m) when the stair has a straight run.		
Doors opening immediately on stairs, without landing at least width of door	No	No	No

* See NFPA *101, Life Safety Code.*

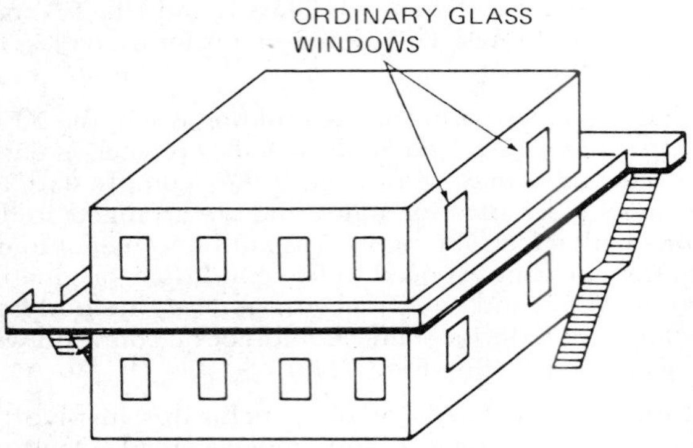

***FIG. 7-2P.** An example of using outside stairs to provide direct exits to the outside for all rooms in a multi-story building. There are no interior corridors through which smoke and flame could spread. This method has application in many types of occupancies, such as schools, motels, small professional buildings, and so on. Note that there are two means of egress, remote from each other, from the second-story balcony.*

Exit Passageways

A hallway, corridor, passage, tunnel, or underfloor or overhead passageway may be designated an exit passageway, providing it is separated and arranged according to the requirements for exits.

The use of a hallway or corridor as an exit passageway introduces some unique considerations. The use of these spaces for purposes other than exiting may violate fundamental design considerations. In an industrial situation, for example, the use of a gasoline-powered fork-lift in a corridor designated as an exit passageway would violate the principles of exit design. NFPA 101, *Life Safety Code*, specifies that an exit enclosure should not be used for any purpose which could interfere with its value as an exit and specifically prohibits piping for flammable liquids and gases. Furthermore, penetration of the enclosure by ducts and other utilities may violate the protective enclosure.

Each opening in an exit enclosure introduces a point of weakness that could allow fire contaminants to spread into the exit and prevent its use. The typical corridor used as an exit with numerous door openings could result in fire contamination of the enclosure if a door fails to close and latch. The door openings in exit enclosures should be limited to those necessary for access to the enclosure from normally occupied spaces. Therefore, doors and other openings to spaces such as boiler rooms, storage spaces, trash rooms, and maintenance closets are not allowed into an exit passageway.

An exit passageway should not be confused with an exit access corridor. Exit access corridors do not have the construction protection requirements of exit passageways, since they provide access to an exit rather than being an extension and component of the exit.

Fire Escape Stairs

Fire escapes should be stairs, not ladders. Fire escapes are, at best, a poor substitute for standard interior or exterior stairs. NFPA 101, *Life Safety Code*, only permits existing fire escapes in existing buildings.

The same principles of design apply to fire escapes that apply to interior stairs, though requirements for width, pitch, and other dimensions are generally less strict. NFPA 101, *Life Safety Code*, gives the following criteria for fire escape stair design.

Fire escape stairs ideally extend to the street or to ground level. When sidewalks would be obstructed by permanent stairs, swinging stair sections designed to swing down under the weight of a person may be used for the lowest flight of the fire escape stairs. The area below the swinging section must be kept unobstructed so the swinging section can reach the ground. A counterweight of the type that balances on a pivot should be provided for swinging stairs; cables should not be used. Fire escapes that end on balconies above the ground level and provide no way to reach the ground, except by portable ladders or jumping, are unsafe.

Many persons with a fear of high places are reluctant to use fire escapes. As far as possible, design should provide a sense of security, as well as suitable railings and other details actually needed for safety. Fire escapes must be well-anchored to building walls and kept painted to prevent rust.

Preferred access to fire escapes is through doors leading from the main building area or from corridors, never through rooms that may have locked doors except where every room or apartment has separate access to a fire escape. Although preferred access to fire escapes is by doors, windows may be used, in which case sills should not be too high above the floor. Windows should be of ample size, and, if insect screens are installed, they should be of a type that can be opened or removed quickly and easily. Decorative grilles or security bars should not be installed over windows that provide access to fire escapes.

In some situations, fire escapes have created a severe fire exposure to people when flames came out windows beneath them. The best location for fire escapes is on exterior masonry walls without exposing windows, with access to fire escape balconies by exterior fire doors. Where window openings expose fire escapes, fixed wired-glass in metal sashes should be used. Where there is a complete standard automatic sprinkler system in the building, the fire exposure hazard to personnel on fire escapes is minimized.

In northern climates, outside fire escapes may be obstructed by snow and ice.

Escalators, Moving Walkways, and Elevators

Escalators may be recognized as exits in existing buildings, if they have enclosures similar to exit stairs and meet the requirements for stairs as to tread width and riser height. However, they are seldom installed in such a way that they would qualify as exits, and it is common to find escalator installations with unprotected floor openings. Escalators are not recognized as an acceptable component in a means of egress in new construction.

Moving walkways also may be used as means of egress if they conform to the general requirements for ramps, if inclined, and for passageways, if level.

Elevators are not recognized as exits.

Ropes and Ladders

Ropes and ladders generally are not recognized in codes as a substitute for standard exits from a building. This is proper since there is no excuse for permitting their use except possibly in existing one- and two-family dwellings where it is economically impractical to add a secondary means of escape. In this case, a suitable rope or chain ladder or a folding metal ladder may be suitable. However, the homeowner should recognize that aged, infirmed, very young, and physically handicapped persons cannot use ladders and that, if the ladder passes near or over a window in a lower floor, flames from the window can prevent the use of the ladder.

Windows

Windows are not exits. They may be used as access to fire escapes in existing buildings if they meet certain criteria concerning the size of window opening and the height of the sill from the floor. Windows may be considered a means of escape from certain residential occupancies.

Windows are required in school rooms subject to student occupancy, unless the building is equipped with a standard automatic sprinkler system, and in bedrooms in one- and two-family dwellings that do not have two separate means of escape. These windows are for rescue and ventilation and must meet the criteria for size of opening, method of operation, and height from the floor. NFPA 101, *Life Safety Code*, also requires operable bedroom windows in hospitals, nursing homes, and limited care facilities to vent products of combustion and to provide fresh air to the occupants.

EXIT LIGHTING AND SIGNS

Exit Lighting

In buildings where artificial lighting is provided for normal use, exit lighting and the illumination of the means of egress is required to ensure that occupants can evacuate the building quickly. The intensity of the illumination of the means of egress should be not less than 1 foot candle (10.77 lu/m^2) measured at the floor. It is desirable that such floor illumination be provided by lights recessed in the wall and located approximately 1 ft (305 mm) above the floor because such lights are then unlikely to be obscured by the smoke that might occur during a fire. In auditoriums and other places of public assembly where motion pictures or other projections are shown, NFPA 101, *Life Safety Code*, permits a reduction in this illumination for the period of the projection to values of not less than $^1/_5$ footcandle (2.2 lu/m^2).

Emergency Lighting

NFPA 101, *Life Safety Code* requires emergency power for illuminating the means of egress in some occupancies. For example, emergency lighting is required in places of assembly; in certain types of educational buildings; in health care facilities; in residential buildings with more than 25 rooms, such as hotels, or living units, such as apartments; in dormitories; in Class A and B mercantiles; in business buildings subject to occupancy by more than two stories, more than 100 persons above or below grade, or more than 1000 persons; in parking garages; and in underground or windowless structures subject to occupancy by more than 100 persons.

Well-designed emergency lighting using a source of power independent from the normal building service automatically provides the necessary illumination in the event of an interruption of power to normal lighting. The failure of the public utility or other outside electric power supply, the opening of a circuit breaker or fuse, or any manual act, including accidental opening of a switch controlling normal lighting facilities, should result in the automatic operation of the emergency lighting system.

Reliability of the exit illumination is most important. NFPA 70, *National Electrical Code®*, details requirements for the installation of emergency lighting equipment. Battery-operated electric lights and portable lights normally are not used for primary exit illumination, but they may be used as an emergency source under the restrictions imposed by NFPA 101, *Life Safety Code*. Luminescent, fluorescent, or other reflective materials are not a substitute for required illumination, since they are not sufficiently intense to justify recognition as exit floor illumination.

Where electric battery-operated emergency lights are used, suitable facilities are needed to keep the batteries properly charged. Automobile-type lead storage batteries are not suitable because of their relatively short life when not subject to frequent recharge. Likewise, dry batteries have a limited life, and there is a danger that they may not be replaced when they have deteriorated.

If normal building lighting fails, well-arranged emergency lighting provides necessary exit floor illumination automatically, with no appreciable interruption of illumination during the changeover. Where a generator is provided, a delay of up to ten sec is considered tolerable. The normal procedure is to provide such emergency lighting for a minimum period of $1\frac{1}{2}$ hr. Most health care occupancies have self-contained electric generating plants for emergency power supplies, not only for exit lighting but also for use in the event of failure of the public utility. Where such emergency electric facilities are provided, they may supply power for emergency exit lighting, as well as other critical areas of such buildings.

Exit Signs

All required exits and access ways must be identified by readily visible signs where the exit or the way to reach it is not immediately visible to the occupants. Directional "EXIT" signs are required in locations where the direction of travel to the nearest exit is not immediately apparent. The character of the occupancy will determine the actual need for such signs. In places of assembly, hotels, department stores, and other buildings with transient populations, the need for signs will be greater than in a building with permanent or semi-permanent populations. Even in permanent residential-occupancy buildings, signs are needed to identify exit facilities, such as stairs, that are not used regularly during the normal occupancy of the building. It is just as important that doors, passageways, or stairs that are not exits but are so located or arranged that they may be mistaken for exits be identified by signs with the words "NO EXIT."

Signs should be so located and of such size, color, and design as to be readily visible. Care should be taken not to locate decorations, furnishings, or other building equipment so as to obscure the visibility of these signs. NFPA 101, *Life Safety Code*, does not make any specific requirement for sign color but requires that signs be of a distinctive color. Some building codes do specify exit sign color. NFPA 101, *Life Safety Code*, specifies the size of the sign and the dimensions of the letters. NFPA 101 also specifies the levels of illumination for both externally and internally illuminated signs.

Improvement in the physical marking of exits in an office occupancy with point-source, red or green strobe lights has been suggested. Placing corridor illumination on the walls close to the floor to provide effective illumination under smoke conditions, as is the practice in Japan, is a technique worthy of research.[43]

ALARM SYSTEMS

Fire alarm systems to alert occupants to leave the building are normally operated manually. The alarm-sounding devices themselves should be distinctive in pitch and tone quality from all other sounding devices, and the use of these devices should be restricted to evacuation notification. Vocal alarm systems have been developed and installed in some high-rise buildings.[11] NFPA 101, *Life Safety Code*, mandates voice alarm and communication systems in high-rise buildings. It is, of course, very important that all alarm system devices be distributed throughout a building so as to be heard effectively in every room above all other sounds. Visual, as well as audible, alarm devices are sometimes used in buildings. NFPA 101 permits flashing the exit signs with the activation of the fire alarm system.

The proper maintenance of alarm systems is most important. Alarm systems should be supervised by a responsible person who will make the proper tests at specified intervals and will take charge of all alterations and additions to the systems.

FIRE EXIT DRILLS

Fire exit drills are essential in schools and are desirable in every type of occupancy to ensure familiarity with the exits and their operation. In occupancies such as hospitals, nursing homes, hotels, and department stores, drills are usually limited to employee participation, without alarming patients, guests, or customers. Drills should be planned to get everyone out of the building or to an area of refuge in an orderly manner, as promptly as possible. Fire fighting is always secondary to life safety, and, in general, fire fighting operations should not be started until the evacuation is completed, except in cases where trained fire departments conduct rescue and fire fighting operations simultaneously.

Drills should be held at least once a month or more often, but not at regularly scheduled periods. Drills should occur on all shifts in an occupancy operated 24 hours a day. They should be conducted without warning and should simulate typical fire conditions for the occupancy.

School fire exit drills are an exercise in discipline, not speed, though reasonably prompt evacuation of a building is important. Students and staff should not be permitted to stop to put on coats. No individuals should be permitted to remain in the building, and nobody should be excused from participating in the drill. The drill should include a roll call by class at designated assembly areas outside the building to make sure that no one has been left behind.

There also should be an established routine for a complete check of the entire building, including toilets, to make sure that no one has been left behind. All exits should be used in drills, but routes should be varied from drill to drill. Occasional drills should be held that simulate conditions of an exit blocked by fire or smoke. All drills should simulate the fire department notification procedure. For a more detailed discussing of fire exit drills, see Chapter 3 of this section.

MAINTENANCE OF THE MEANS OF EGRESS

The provision of a standard means of egress with adequate capacity does not guarantee the safety of the occupants in the event of an evacuation of any building. Means of egress that were not properly maintained have been responsible for loss of life in a number of fires. Property managers usually assign definite responsibility for maintenance of mechanical and electrical equipment but fail to do the same for the means of egress. As a result, it is all too common for inspection authorities to find otherwise safe stairways used as storage for materials during peak sales or manufacturing periods. In apartment buildings, rubbish, baby carriages, and other obstructions are sometimes allowed to collect in stairway enclosures. Exit doors are often found locked or the hardware in need of repair. Doors blocked open or removed from openings into stairway enclosures are certain to permit rapid spread of smoke or hot gases throughout the building. Loose handrails and loose or slippery stair treads offer the dangerous probability that persons evacuating a building will fall in the path of others seeking escape. Maintaining the means of egress in safe operating condition at all times is as important to the prevention of loss of life as the proper construction of the building and the elimination of fire hazards.

Bibliography

References Cited

1. Fruin, J. J., *Pedestrian Planning and Design*, Metropolitan Association of Urban Designers and Environmental Planners, Inc., New York, 1977.
2. Pauls, J. L., "Movement of People in Building Evacuations." *Human Response to Tall Buildings*, Dowden Hutchinson and Ross, Inc., Stroudsburg, PA, 1977.
3. "Second Report of the Operational Research Team on the Capacity of Footways," *Research Report No. 95*, London Transport Board, London, England, 1958.
4. Pauls, J. L., "Calculating Evacuation Times for Tall Buildings," *Fire Safety Journal*, Dec. 1987, pp. 213-236.
5. Pauls, J. L., "The Movement of People in Buildings and Design Solutions for Means of Egress," *Fire Technology*, Vol. 20, No. 1 (Feb. 1984), pp. 27-47.
6. Abbott, J. C., "Fire Involving Upholstery Materials," *Fire Journal*, Vol. 65, No. 4 (July 1971), p. 88.
7. Lathrop, J. K., *et al.*, "In Osceola: A Matter of Contents," *Fire Journal*, Vol. 69, No. 3 (May 1975), pp. 20-26.
8. Karter, M. J., Jr. and Gancarski, J. L., "Fire Loss in the United States During 1983," *Fire Journal*, Vol. 78, No. 5 (Sept. 1984), pp. 48-51, 54-61.
9. Sharry, J. A., "South America Burning," *Fire Journal*, Vol. 68, No. 4 (July 1974), pp. 23-33.
10. Best, R., and Demers, D. P., "Fire at the MGM Grand," *Fire Journal*, Vol. 76, No. 1 (Jan. 1982), pp. 19-37.
11. Powers, W. R., "New York Office Building Fire," *Fire Journal*, Vol. 65, No. 1 (Jan. 1971), pp. 18-23, 87.
12. Keating, J. P., *et al.*, *An Evaluation of the Federal High Rise Emergency Evacuation Procedures*, University of Washington, Department of Psychology, Seattle, WA, 1978.
13. Pauls, J. L., "Evacuation and Other Fire Safety Measures in High-Rise Buildings," *Research Paper No. 648*, National Research Council of Canada, Division of Building Research, Ottawa, Canada, 1975.
14. Pauls, J. L., "Management and Movement of Building Occupants in Emergencies," *Research Paper No. 788*, National Research Council of Canada, Division of Building Research, Ottawa, Canada, 1978.
15. Phillips, A. W., "You and the High-Rise Building Fire," *Technology Report 74-1*, Society of Fire Protection Engineers, Boston, MA, 1974.
16. Bryan, J. L., "Human Behavior in the MGM Grand Hotel Fire," *Fire Journal*, Vol. 76, No. 2 (Mar. 1982), pp. 37-41, 44-48.
17. Krasny, John F., *et al.*, "Development of a Candidate Test Method for the Measurement of the Propensity of Cigarettes to Cause Smoldering Ignition of Upholstered Furniture and Mattresses," *NBSIR 81-2363*, Center for Fire Research, National Bureau of Standards, Washington, DC, 1981.
18. CFR Part 1623, *Standard for the Flammability of Mattresses and Mattress Pads*, FF-4-72, 40 FR 59940, U.S. Consumer Product Safety Commission, Washington, DC, 1972.
19. Keating, J. P. and Loftus, E. F., "The Logic of Fire Escape," *Psychology Today*, June 1981, pp. 14-19.
20. Keating, J. P., "The Myth of Panic," *Fire Journal*, Vol. 76, No. 3 (May 1982), pp. 57-61, 147.
21. Sharry, J. A., "Real-World Problems with Zoned Evacuation," *Fire Journal*, Vol. 77, No. 2 (Mar. 1983), pp. 32-33, 55.
22. Macdonald, J. N., *Non-Evacuation in Compartmented Fire-Resistive Buildings Can Save Lives and Makes Sense*, 88th NFPA Annual Meeting, New Orleans, LA, May 23, 1984.
23. "Design and Construction of Building Exits," *Miscellaneous Publication M51*, National Bureau of Standards, Washington, DC, 1935, pp. 30-37. (Out of print.)
24. "Fire Protection Safety and Health," *PBS P5900.2A*, General Services Administration, Washington, DC, 1985.
25. Ministry of Works, Part III, "Personal Safety and Fire Grading of Buildings," *Post-War Building Studies No. 29*, Joint Committee on Fire Grading of Buildings, Her Majesty's Stationary Office, London, England, 1952.
26. Galbreath, M., "Time of Evacuation by Stairs in High Buildings," *Ontario Fire Marshal*, Vol. 5, No. 2 (First Quarter), 1969.
27. Galbreath, M., "A Survey of Exit Facilities of High Office Buildings," *Building Research Note 64*, Division of Building Research, National Research Council, Ottawa, Canada, 1968.
28. Melinek, S. J. and Booth, S., "An Analysis of Evacuation Times and the Movement of Crowds in Buildings," *CP 96175*, Building Research Establishment, Fire Research Station, Borehamwood, England, 1975.
29. Pauls, J. L., "Calculating Evacuation Times for Tall Buildings," *Fire Safety Journal*, Dec. 1987.
30. Kendik, E., "Designing Escape Routes in Buildings," *Fire Technology*, Nov. 1986, Vol. 23, No. 4 pp. 272-294.
31. Caravaty, R. D. and Haviland, D. S., "*Life Safety From Fire, A Guide for Housing the Elderly*," Architectural Standards Division, Federal Housing Administration, Washington, DC, 1967.
32. Stahl, F. I., "Simulating Human Behavior in High-Rise Building Fires: Modeling Occupant Movement Through a Fire Floor from Initial Alert to Safety Egress," *NBS-GCR-77-92*, Center for Fire Research, National Bureau of Standards, Washington, DC, 1975.
33. Stahl, F. I., "B Fires II: A Behavior-Based Computer Simulation of Emergency Egress During Fires," *Fire Technology*, Vol. 18, No. 1 (Feb 1982), pp. 49-65.
34. Stahl, F. I., "B Fires II: A Behavior-Based Computer Simulation of Emergency Egress During Fires," *Fire Technology*, Vol. 18, No. 2 (May 1982), p. 63.
35. Berlin, G., N. "A Simulation Model for Assessing Building Fire Safety," *Fire Technology*, Vol. 18, No. 1 (Feb. 1982), pp. 66-75.
36. Berlin, G. N., *et al.*, "Modeling Emergency Evacuation from Group Homes," *Fire Technology*, Vol. 1 (Feb. 1982), pp. 38-48, Vol. 18, No. 1.
37. Fahy, R., "Building Fire Simulation Model," *Fire Journal*, Vol. 77, No. 4 (July 1983), pp. 93-95, 102-105.
38. Cooper, L. Y., "A Mathematical Model for Estimating Available Safety Egress Time in Fires," *Fire and Materials*, Vol. 6, Nos. 3 & 4 (Sept./Dec. 1982), pp. 135-144.
39. O'Leary, T. J., and Gratz, J. M., "An Analysis of Fire Evacuation Procedures Using Simulation," *Fire Journal*, Vol. 76, No. 3 (May 1982), pp. 119-121.
40. Chalmet, L. G., *et al.*, "Network Models for Building Evacuation," *Fire Technology*, Vol. 18, No. 1 (Feb. 1982), pp. 90-113.
41. Smith, J. M., "An Analytical Queing Network Computer Program for the Optimal Egress Problem," *Fire Technology*, Vol. 18, No. 1 (Feb. 1982), pp. 18-33.
42. Watts, J. M., "Computer Models for Evacuation Analysis," *Fire Safety Journal*, Dec. 1987, pp. 237-245.

43. Cohn, B. M., *Study of Human Engineering Considerations in Emergency Exiting from Secure Spaces*, Gage-Babcock & Association, Inc., Chicago, IL, 1978.

NFPA Codes, Standards, and Recommended Practices

Reference to the following NFPA codes, standards, and recommended practices will provide further information on concepts of egress design discussed in this chapter. (See the latest *NFPA Catalog* for availability of current editions of the following documents.)

NFPA 13, *Installation of Sprinkler Systems.*

NFPA 70, *National Electrical Code.*®

NFPA 101®, *Life Safety Code.*®

NFPA 101M, *Alternative Approaches to Life Safety.*

NFPA 253, *Critical Radiant Flux of Floor Covering Systems Using a Radiant Heat Energy Source.*

NFPA 255, *Surface Burning Characteristics of Materials.*

NFPA 260, *Cigarette Ignition Resistance of Components of Upholstered Furniture.*

NFPA 261, *Resistance of Mock-Up Upholstered Furniture Material Assemblies to Ignition by Smoldering Cigarettes.*

Additional Readings

Ballast, D. K., *Egress from Buildings in Emergencies: A Bibliography*, Vance Bibliographies, Monticello, IL., 1988.

Behrens, J. F., "Handrails," *Fire Journal*, Vol. 77, No. 3 (May 1983), pp. 14, 132.

Behrens, J. F., "Horizontal Exits," *Fire Journal*, Vol. 77, No. 2 (Mar. 1983), pp. 30-31.

Behrens, J. F., "Protection From Hazards," *Fire Journal*, Vol. 77, No. 6 (Nov. 1983), pp. 5-6.

Bryan, J. L., *An Examination and Analysis of the Dynamics of the Human Behavior in the MGM Grand Hotel Fire*, rev. ed., National Fire Protection Association, Quincy, MA, Apr. 1983.

Bryan, J. L, *An Examination and Analysis of the Dynamics of the Human Behavior in the Westchase Hilton Hotel Fire*, National Fire Protection Association, Quincy, MA, Mar. 28, 1983.

Bryan, J. L., "Behavioral Response to Fire and Smoke," *SFPE Handbook of Fire Protection Engineering*, National Fire Protection Association, Quincy, MA., 1988.

Bryan, J. L., "Convergence Clusters: A Phenomenon of Human Behavior Seen in Selected High-Rise Building Fires," *Fire Journal*, Vol. 79, No. 6 (Nov. 1985), pp. 27-30, 86-90.

Bryan, J. L., *Smoke as a Determinant of Human Behavior in Fire Situations*, (Project People), Department of Fire Protection Engineering, University of Maryland, College Park, MD, June 30, 1977.

Canter, D., *Fires and Human Behavior*, 2nd. ed., Fulton, London, 1988.

Chalmet, L. G., *et al.*, "Network Models for Building Evacuation," *Management Science*, Vol. 28, No. 1 (Jan. 1982), pp. 86-105.

Cooper, L. Y., "A Concept for Estimating Available Safe Egress Time in Fires," *Fire Safety Journal*, Vol. 5, 1983, p. 135.

Francis, R. L., "A Simple Graphical Procedure to Estimate the Minimum Time to Evacuate a Building," *SFPE TR 79-S*, Society of Fire Protection Engineers, Boston, MA, 1979.

Francis, R. L., "Network Models of Building Evacuation: Development of Software Systems," *NBS-GCR-85-489*, National Bureau of Standards, Gaithersburg, MD, March 1985.

Fruin, J. J., *Pedestrian Planning and Design*, rev. ed., *Elevator World*, Mobile, AL, 1987.

Jones, B. K. and Hewitt, J. A., "Leadership and Group Formation in High-Rise Building Evacuations," *Proceedings* of the First International Symposium on Fire Safety Science, Hemisphere, 1986, pp. 513-522.

Kendik, E., "Assessment of Escape Routes in Buildings and Design Method for Calculating Pedestrian Movement," *TR 85-4*, Society of Fire Protection Engineers, Boston, MA, 1985.

Kendik, E., "Methods of Design of Means of Egress: Towards a Quantitative Comparison of National Code Requirements," *Proceedings* of the First International Symposium of Fire Safety Science, Hemisphere, Washington, D.C., 1986.

Kisko, T. M. and Francis, R. L., "EVACNET+, A Computer Program to Determine Optimal Building Evacuation Plans," *Fire Safety Journal*, Vol. 9, No. 2, 1985, pp. 211-220.

Kisko, T. M. and Francis, R. L., "Network Models of Building Evacuation: Development of Software Systems," *NBS-GCR-85-489*, National Bureau of Standards, Gaithersburg, MD, 1985.

Kisko, T. M. and Francis, R. L., "Network Models of Building Evacuation: Development of Software Systems," *NBS-GCR-84-457*, National Bureau of Standards, Gaithersburg, MD, 1984.

Klevan, J. B., "Modeling of Available Egress Time from Assembly Spaces or Estimating the Advance of the Fire Threat," *SFPE TR 82-2*, Society of Fire Protection Engineers, Boston, MA, 1982.

Klote, J. H., "Elevators as a Means of Fire Escape," *NBSIR 82-2507*, National Bureau of Standards, Gaithersburg, MD, May 1982.

Lathrop, J. K., *ed., Life Safety Code Handbook*, 4th ed., National Fire Protection Association, Quincy, MA, 1988.

Ling, W. C. T. and Williamson, R. B., "Use of Probabilistic Networks for Analysis of Smoke Spread and Egress of people in Buildings," *Proceedings* of the 1st International Symposium for Fire Safety Science, Hemisphere, New York, 1986, pp. 953-962.

Maclennan, H. A., "Towards an Integrated Egress/Evacuation Model Using an Open Systems Approach," *Proceedings* of the First International Symposium on Fire Safety Science, Hemisphere, 1986, pp. 581-590.

Nelson, H. E. and MacLennan, H. A., "Emergency Movement," *SFPE Handbook for Fire Protection Association*, National Fire Protection Association, Quincy, MA., 1988.

Ouellette, M. J., "Exit Signs in Smoke: Design Parameters for Greater Visibility," *Lighting Research and Technology*, Vol. 20, No. 4, 1988, pp. 155-160.

Ozel, F., *Way Finding and Route Selection in Fires*, School of Architecture, New Jersey Institute of Technology, Newark, 1986.

Pauls, J., "Calculating Evacuation Times for Tall Buildings," *Fire Safety Journal*, Vol. 12, No. 3, 1987, pp. 213-236.

Pauls J., "Development of Knowledge About Means of Egress," *Fire Technology*, Vol. 20, No. 2, 1984, pp. 28-40.

Pauls, J., "Movement of People," *SFPE Handbook of Fire Protection Engineering*, National Fire Protection Association, Quincy, MA., 1988.

Predtechenskii, V. M. and Milinskii, A. I., *Planning for Foot Traffic Flow in Buildings*, Amerind Publishing Co., New Delhi, India, 1978.

Ruskouski, C., "The New Emergency Lighting Technology," *Fire Journal*, Vol. 84, No. 1 (Jan.-Feb. 1990), p. 48.

Sime, J. D., "Perceived Time Available: the Margn of Safety in Fires," *Proceedings* of the First International Symposium on Fire Safety Science, Hemisphere, 1986, pp. 561-570.

Stevens, R. E., "Scissors Stairs as Exits," *Fire Journal*, Vol. 59, No. 1 (Jan. 1965), p. 40.

Stevens, R. E., "Smokeproof Towers," *Fire Journal*, Vol. 60, No. 1 (Jan. 1966), pp. 54-55.

Stevens, R. E., "What is an Exit?" *Fire Journal*, Vol. 59, No. 6 (Nov. 1965), pp. 44-45.

Takahashi, K. and Tanaka, T., "An Evacuation model for the Use in Fire Safety Designing of Buildings," 9th Joint Panel Meeting of the UJNR Panel on Fire Research and Safety, *NBSIR 88-3753*, National Bureau of Standards, Gaithersburg, MD, April 1988.

Templer, J., *Stair, Shape and Human Movement*, University Microfilms, Ann Arbor, MI, 1977.

Turner, M., "New Code Governing the Means of Escape for Disabled People," *Fire Prevention*, No. 215 (Dec. 1988), pp. 36-37.

Van Bogaert, A. F., "Evacuating Schools on Fire," *Proceedings* of the First International Symposium on Fire Safety Science, Hemisphere, 1986, pp. 551-560.

Watts, C., "Emergency Lighting: Designing to Meet the Legal Standard," *Fire Surveyor*, Vol. 18, No. 2 (April 1989), pp. 23-28.

Webber, G. and Hallman, P., "Photoluminescence for Aiding Escape," *Fire Surveyor*, Vol. 17, No. 6 (Dec. 1988), pp. 17-29.

Weinroth, J., "An Adabtable Microcomputer Model for Evacuation Management," *Fire Technology*, Vol. 25, No. 4, 1989, pp. 291-307.

TRAFFIC AND EXIT DRILLS

Revised by John L. Bryan

Traffic and exit drills are important components of effective firesafety. During a fire or an emergency, fire fighters, police, fire brigade staff, industry management personnel, and other people who perform essential duties must be able to move to locations where they are needed and where they can perform their necessary functions. In addition, in fire or emergency situations, it is usually necessary to quickly and efficiently evacuate building occupants.

To achieve evacuation it is necessary to devise and implement plans and practices that move people to safe areas in or outside the building of fire origin and provide access for various emergency personnel. Implicit in such plans and practices is the need for pedestrian and vehicular traffic control. Even well-drilled people are likely to be anxious and behave impulsively in times of real emergency, unless guided and directed. Without direction and control, evacuees may actually hamper or nullify safety procedures.

This chapter examines traffic control and exit drills, with special emphasis on health care facilities. Additional helpful information on traffic and exit drills can be found in Section 7, Chapter 2, "Concepts of Egress Design."

TRAFFIC CONTROL

Emergency traffic control can be divided into two categories: (1) external, e.g., on public streets and highways, and (2) internal, e.g., inside private property. Both external and internal traffic control can be made more effective with careful preparation.

External Traffic

The traffic direction on public streets and highways is usually the responsibility of the local law enforcement agency. Occasionally, however, a facility may employ private security personnel or guards to help ensure the safety of employees and property. This should be done only after consultation with, and authorization by, the appropriate law enforcement officials.

Regardless of who is responsible for external traffic control on public streets and highways, employees in the fire-risk prevention and control management program of the facility must be able to reach the location of their assignment.

Many large companies provide members of their emergency control forces with identification approved by both the local law enforcement agency and the Civil Defense authorities. This identification allows passage through roadblocks into emergency or disaster areas, and it may also be used to gain emergency admittance to restricted areas inside the facility. With external vehicle and pedestrian traffic control for safety, external traffic planning should include primary and alternate approach routes for fire equipment and other emergency vehicles.

NFPA 601, *Guard Service in Fire Loss Prevention*, and NFPA 601A, *Guard Operations in Fire Loss Prevention*, provide information on guard service and operations that may be involved in traffic firesafety management for facilities.

Internal Traffic

Most police departments will not enter private property to control traffic, unless prior arrangements have been made to do so. Generally, if there is a private security force, traffic control for both general and emergency movement is usually part of their responsibility. If there is no security force, company personnel should be assigned and trained to control both pedestrian and vehicular traffic.

One person should be assigned to the entrance designated for use by fire department and other emergency control forces to direct them to the fire scene. In a large facility, it may be advisable to have an employee accompany incoming emergency forces to the specific area and building involved.

Personnel should also be assigned and trained to control access to the emergency scene, and admit only identified emergency personnel. This precaution will prevent unnecessary exposure to personnel and will minimize general confusion.

Dr. John L. Bryan is professor and chairman, Department of Fire Protection Engineering, University of Maryland, College Park, MD.

Planning and preparing before emergencies occur should not be limited to traffic control. If the facility has underpasses, overpasses, tunnels, or overhead piping across access drives, the fire department should be invited to bring in its largest piece of fire apparatus to ensure that there is adequate clearance through the facility.

FIRE EXIT DRILLS

Well-marked exits do not ensure life safety during a fire. Exit drills are necessary so that occupants will know how to make an efficient and orderly escape according to NFPA *101,® Life Safety Code,®* which contains detailed information on exit drills in individual occupancies. Exit drills are required in schools, board and care facilities, and health care facilities, and are common in industries with high hazards. Employee training and drills are required in assembly, hotel, mercantile, and large business occupancies. Some form of exit drill should be conducted wherever or whenever possible, to avoid confusion and ensure the evacuation of all occupants during a fire.[1] Personnel should be assigned to check exits for availability, to search for stragglers, to count occupants once they are outside the fire area, and to control reentry into the building before it is safe. (See Figure 7-3A.)

***FIG. 7-3A.** Orderly evacuation of school building during fire exit drills.*

This reentry behavior for rescue purposes of persons involved in fire incidents should be noted. In a study of 335 fire incidents involving 584 persons, it was found that 163 persons, approximately 28 percent of the study population, reentered the fire buildings following evacuation.[2] Approximately 10.5 percent of those persons who reentered the buildings did so to alert or assist other persons.

Determining when and what area to evacuate is probably the most important decision in a fire emergency. Any area at all affected by heat, flame, or smoke should be evacuated; in case of doubt, the entire building should be evacuated.

The fire loss prevention and control management staff are responsible for planning exit drills. Plans should be discussed with both middle and line management to ensure understanding and cooperation. If there is no fire loss prevention and control manager, the plant, facility, or building manager should assume this responsibility or assign it to a staff member.

All employees should recognize the evacuation signal and know the exit route they are to follow.[3] Upon hearing the signal, they should shut off equipment and report to a predetermined assembly point. Primary and alternate routes should be established, and all employees should be trained to use either route.[1,4]

The problem with audible evacuation signals is the conditioning of the population within the occupancy to ignore the signal due to numerous false alarms. An investigation of an apartment building fire found that the alarm system actuation to initiate evacuation behavior was ignored by many of the building occupants due to the conditioning effect of numerous prior false alarms: 44 percent of the building occupants believed the alarm signal was a false alarm.[5]

When employees are assembled, the manager or supervisor of each area should account for all personnel. Missing employees should be immediately reported to the fire loss prevention and control manager and responding fire department personnel so that search and rescue efforts can be initiated. Only trained fire fighting search and rescue personnel with adequate protective equipment should be permitted to reenter an evacuated area.

After each exit drill, a meeting of the responsible managers should be held to evaluate the success of the drill and to solve any problems that may have arisen.

One significant improvement to the traditional concept of fire drills in educational occupancies was suggested by a study of fire drills conducted in such occupancies.[6] The concept of smoke drills has been established, whereby the occupants are instructed to move through the simulated smoke areas in a crouched position. Students have transferred the smoke drill concept to fire incidents in residential occupancies, with effective results. Obviously, the utilization of smoke drill training may be effective in a fire incident and should be used where applicable.

The timing of drills depends upon the nature of the operation in the facility. Generally, drills conducted a few minutes before the lunch break have been found to minimize loss of time and production. The frequency of drills should be determined by the degree of hazard present and by the complexity of shutdown or evacuation procedures.

If a facility does not maintain a security organization that is responsible for daily inspection of emergency exits and designated evacuation routes, one employee in each area should be assigned this task. Maintenance of doors, panic hardware, exit lights, and emergency illumination should be given high priority, and repairs must be made without delay.

Research has found that for multi-storied office buildings, a trained group of floor wardens is the most effective means of monitoring the evacuation of occupants.[1] Adequate training for floor wardens or other personnel is necessary, and must be specifically developed to include the procedures of the emergency evacuation plan for the facility.

The lecture method has been used to convey the essential features of the emergency plan to employees in health care facilities.[4] However, it was also found that the emergency plan in the facility studied was too general and ambiguous.

The most serious problem with using building monitors is the turnover of personnel due to employee transfers, reassignments, or resignations. Effective evacuation planning and preparation should assign specific responsibilities to staff positions (rather than individuals) within an organization. This ensures a continuity of performance despite personnel changes.

A content and time evaluation of fire drill behavior by staff in six nursing homes concluded that a training program of the most modest type can produce changes in both knowledge and behavior of evacuation and fire emergency procedures.[7] A total of 339 nursing home staff participated in the study that matched a group of 37 persons receiving the training with a control group of 49 persons not receiving the training. The high rate of personnel turnover, which appears to be rather typical in nursing home facilities, was noted. Following the presentation of the training program, staff members were evaluated on a written knowledge test, and their behavior was observed during the conduct of a drill of the emergency plan.

The evacuation signal should be familiar to all employees. Vocal alarm systems (VAS)[1,3] reduce the need for employee perception and recognition of a signal, since the system provides vocal communication to the areas designated for evacuation. NFPA *101*, *Life Safety Code*, first recommended the use of the VAS in assembly occupancies, in 1981. An evaluation of VAS systems in nine buildings found that familiarization with the system or initial activation did not significantly affect the egress behavior of populations.[1] In addition, the investigation determined the evacuation drills were valuable because they gave floor or area wardens an opportunity to rehearse their procedures.

The use of an alerting tone in the frequency range of 2,000 to 4,000 Hz for the VAS is recommended prior to the verbal announcement, which should be specific for the audience and the facility.[1,8]

Health Care Facilities Drills

Fire drills in health care institutions are usually conducted as a part of the orientation program for new employees. Later, the drills are supplemented with in-service training for the staff personnel, including the emergency procedures. Fire drills in many facilities are conducted once a month on each shift. The training for the drills typically involves instruction and practice for the staff personnel in the various means of moving nonambulatory patients, the procedures for alerting the facility staff, and the method of notifying the fire department. Many facilities have fire departments provide training once or twice a year in the operation of portable fire extinguishers. Some fire departments actually provide staff personnel with experience in the operation of extinguishers on external fires.

However, most health care facilities prefer to train their personnel. Most adopt the philosophy that it is the staff's responsibility to ensure the safe evacuation of patients initially to an area of refuge, and then to the exterior if necessary. The control of the fire is limited to preventing the spread of heat and smoke by the closing of doors. Doors are closed to protect the occupants and to inhibit or restrict the propagation of the smoke and heat throughout the facility. Staff personnel have effectively accomplished evacuations of numerous patients under fire conditions, or have protected the patients in their rooms by closing doors.[9]

Thus, the evacuation process may be considered in four sequential phases: (1) the personnel supply phase, (2) the patient preparation phase, (3) the patient removal phase, and (4) the rest and recovery phase.[10] This approach focuses on the occupants in the fire-threatened area and the patients in or adjacent to the fire area. Removing immediately threatened patients, and closing doors to the room of fire origin and to adjacent patient rooms, would be compatible with this four-phase approach to evacuation.

A detailed report on the fire evacuation organization, training, and drills involved in a 502-bed acute-care teaching hospital with 2,500 employees has been published.[11]

NFPA *101*, *Life Safety Code*, included a new chapter devoted to the fire protection and life safety requirements for board and care facilities, in 1985. That chapter requires the evaluation and classification of the population of the facility, according to their evacuation capability.

Evaluating Fire Drill Plans

The ultimate evaluation of fire drill and emergency plans has two factors: (1) the performance of the occupants in a fire incident, and (2) the effectiveness of the behaviors used in accordance with the fire drills or the fire emergency plan. In a World Trade Center fire incident report,[12] building occupants tended to attempt to verify their beliefs about the threat of fire by physical clues, primarily smoke in the occupants' area. The report also indicated public address messages were not sufficient to alleviate spontaneous evacuations when occupants saw smoke on their floor. Further, occupant evacuation was reported (9th through 22nd floors) due to the perception and concern that a valid fire threat existed. In actuality, the fire did not require such an extensive evacuation.

Successful evacuation of personnel from the two floors above and below a fire in a 28-story high-rise college dormitory has been reported.[13]

To allow free evacuation flow of the occupants down the stairways, and allow fire department personnel to move up the stairs, stairs have been marked for occupant and fire department movement. The fire department movement stair has a red circle on the door, 6 in. (152 mm) in diameter, and is also utilized for ventilation. The occupant stair is marked with a 6-in. (152-mm) green circle. The safe evacuation of a high-rise hotel fire, with 190 guests, had 110 guests assisted by the fire department. The success of the evacuation was made possible by the hotel employees' fire safety education and practice of evacuation procedures.[14]

BIBLIOGRAPHY

References Cited

1. Keating, John P., *et al.*, "An Evaluation of the Federal High-Rise Emergency Evacuation Procedures," 1978, Department of Psychology, University of Washington, Seattle, WA.
2. Bryan, John L., "Smoke as a Determinant of Human Behavior in Fire Situations (Project People)," 1977, Department of Fire Protection Engineering, University of Maryland, College Park, MD.
3. Keating, John P. and Loftus, Elizabeth F., "Vocal Emergency Alarms in Hospitals and Nursing Facilities: Practice and Potential," NBS-GCR-77-102, 1977, Center for Fire Research, Gaithersburg, MD.
4. Herz, E., *et al.*, "The Impact of Fire Emergency Training on Knowledge of Appropriate Behavior in Fires," NBS-GCR-78-137, 1978, Center for Fire Research, Gaithersburg, MD.
5. Scanlon, Joseph, "Human Behavior in a Fatal Apartment Fire—Research Problems and Findings," 1978, Emergency Communications Research Unit, Carleton University, Ottawa, Canada.

6. Phillips, Anne W, *To Keep Them Safe*, National Smoke, Fire and Burn Institute, Inc., Brookline, MA, 1979.
7. Bickman, L. E., *et al.*, "An Evaluation of Planning and Training for Fire Safety in Health Care Facilities—Phase Two," NBS-GCR-79-179, 1979, Center for Fire Research, Gaithersburg, MD.
8. Shavit, Gideon, "Evacuation: Testing the Effect of Voice-Message Formats," *ASHRAE Journal*, 1978, pp. 38-41.
9. Bryan, John L. and DiNenno, Philip J., "Human Behavior in a Nursing Home Fire," *Fire Journal*, Vol. 73, No, 3, 1980, pp. 82-87, 126-127, 141-143.
10. Archea, John, "The Evacuation of Non-Ambulatory Patients from Hospital and Nursing Home Fires: A Framework for a Model," NBSIR 79-1906, 1979, Center for Fire Research, Gaithersburg, MD.
11. Elliott, Shirley and Scheidt, James, "Hospital and Fire Department Unite to Design New Code Red Program," *Fire Journal*, Vol. 73, No. 4, 1983, pp 47-54.
12. Lathrop, James K., "Two Fires Demonstrate Evacuation Problems in High-Rise Buildings," *Fire Journal*, Vol. 70, No. 1, 1976, pp. 65-70.
13. Nygren, Ronald G., "Alarm Signaling and Evacuation in a High-Rise University Resident Hall," *Fire Journal*, Vol. 66, No. 2, 1972, pp. 5-6, 11.
14. Timoney, Tom, "Howard Johnson's Hotel Fire, Orlando, Florida," *Fire Journal*, Vol 78, N0. 5, 1984, pp. 37-45, 88.

References

Holton, David, 1981, "Boarding Homes—The New Residential Fire Problem?," *Fire Journal*, Vol. 74, No. 2, pp. 53-56.

NFPA Codes, Standards, and Recommended Practices

Reference to the following NFPA codes, standards, and recommended practices will provide further information on traffic and exit drills discussed in this chapter. (See the latest *NFPA Catalog* for availability of current editions of the following documents.)

NFPA 72, *Protective Signaling Systems.*

NFPA *101, Life Safety Code.*

NFPA 601, *Guard Service in Fire Loss Prevention.*

NFPA 601A, *Guard Operations in Fire Loss Prevention.*

Additional Reading

Ballast, D. K., *Egress from Buildings in Emergencies: A Bibliography*, Vance Bibliographies, Monticello, IL, 1988.

Cooper, L. Y., and Stroup, D. W., "ASET: A Computer Program for Calculating Available Safe Egress Time," *Fire Safety Journal*, Vol. 9, 1985, p. 29.

Kisko, T. M., and Francis, R. L., "Evacnet+: A Computer Program to Determine Optimal Building Evacuation Plans," *Fire Safety Journal*, Vol. 9, 1985, p. 211.

Magawa, M., Kose, S., and Moushita, Y., "Movement of People on Stairs During a Fire Evacuation Drill—Japanese Experience in a High-Rise Office Building," *Proceedings* of the First International Symposium on Fire Safety Science, Hemisphere Publishing Corp., Washington, DC, 1986.

Nelson, H. E., "Emergency Movement," *SFPE Handbook of Fire Protection Engineering*, National Fire Protection Association, Quincy, MA, 1988.

Pauls, J., "Calculating Evacuation Times for Tall Buildings," *Fire Safety Journal*, Vol. 12, 1987, p. 213.

Pauls, J., "Movement of People," *SFPE Handbook of Fire Protection Engineering*, National Fire Protection Association, Quincy, MA, 1988.

Robertson, J. C., "Instilling Proper Public Fire Reaction," *Intoduction to Fire Prevention*, 3rd ed., Macmillan, New York, 1989, pp. 219-248.

Tong, D., and Carter, D., "The Decision to Evacuate: A Study of the Motivations Which Contribute to Evacuation in the Event of a Fire," *Fire Safety Journal*, Vol. 9, 1985, p. 257.

Watts, J. M., "Computer Models for Evacuation Analysis," *Fire Safety Journal*, Vol. 12, 1987, p. 237.

BUILDING TRANSPORTATION SYSTEMS

Edward A. Donoghue

Because of their impact on firesafety, building transportation systems must be considered during the design stage and should be integrated with the total building fire protection system. The hazards associated with these systems must be included in any prefire planning and fire protection survey.

Building transportation systems, such as elevators and escalators, make high-rise buildings feasible. While it is unrealistic for megastructures to function without elevators, elevator hoistways can contribute to the spread of smoke and/or fire. On the other hand, an elevator is a necessary tool for fire fighting operations in high-rise buildings.

The discussion of elevators, dumbwaiters, escalators, and moving walks contained in this chapter is intended to complement NFPA *101*®, *Life Safety Code*®, requirements that equipment for elevators and so on be installed in accordance with ASME A17.1, *Safety Code for Elevators and Escalators.*[1] *The three model building codes—National Building Code* (BOCA), *Standard Building Code* (SBCC), and *Uniform Building Code* (ICBO)—also refer to ASME A17.1.[1]

See Section 8, Chapter 31, "Materials Handling Equipment," for other-than-freight elevators and dumbwaiters. Section 6, Chapter 6, "Confinement of Fire in Buildings," and Section 6, Chapter 7, "Smoke Movement in Buildings," are pertinent to the subject matter of this chapter and they should be reviewed for a more comprehensive view of the fire problems associated with building transportation systems.

ELEVATORS

An elevator can be defined as a hoisting and lowering mechanism equipped with a car or a platform that moves in guide rails and serves two or more landings.[1] The two major types of elevators, classified by their driving means, are electric and hydraulic.

Edward A. Donoghue, CPCA, is president of Edward A. Donoghue Associates, Inc., code and safety consultants, Salem, NY.

Electric Elevators

In an electric elevator, the power source is an electric motor. The most common electric elevator is the electric traction elevator that employs a grooved traction drive sheave, over which pass the suspension ropes that are attached to the car and counterweight. (See Figure 7-4A.) This arrangement is very simple and safe, allowing its use in buildings of any height.

Another type of electric elevator is the winding drum machine, found on many older elevators. These elevators employ a winding drum to which the suspension ropes are attached and onto which they wind. Counterweight ropes also may be fastened to, and wind onto, the drum. Not all winding drum machines have counterweights, while other designs have a car counterweight and/or a drum counterweight. This roping arrangement does not permit a loss of traction which is possible with an electric-traction type. It is possible for either the elevator or counterweight to be pulled dangerously into the overhead structure.

Hydraulic Elevators

Hydraulic elevators are powered by a hydraulic plunger or piston. (See Figure 7-4B.) This is referred to as a direct plunger hydraulic elevator. The rise, or travel, of a hydraulic elevator is limited to the length of its piston, usually six floors or less.

Another type of hydraulic elevator is the roped hydraulic. These elevators have their plunger, or piston, connected to the car with wire ropes or indirectly coupled to the car by means of wire ropes or sheaves.

Classification of Elevators by Use

Elevators are classified according to use as either passenger or freight elevators. A passenger elevator is used primarily to carry persons other than an operator and those persons necessary for loading and unloading. A freight elevator is used for freight; only the operator and the persons necessary for unloading and loading the freight are permitted to ride it. Service elevator is another term used to describe elevators. A service elevator is classified officially as a passenger elevator that has also been designed to carry freight.

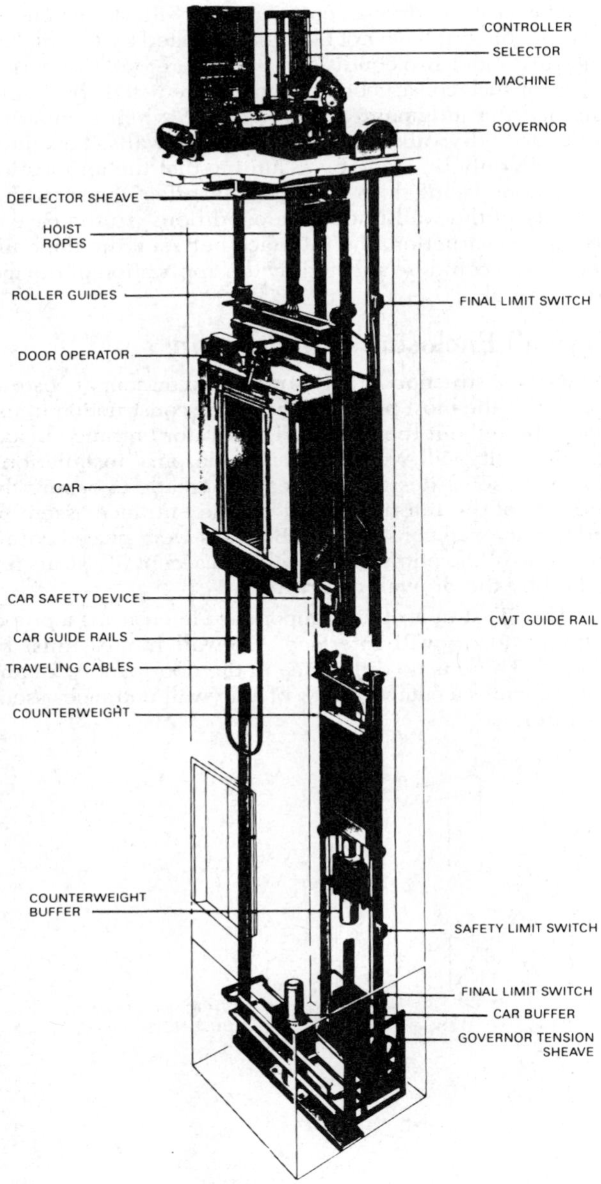

FIG. 7-4A. ***Electric traction elevator. (Source: National Elevator Industry, Inc.)***

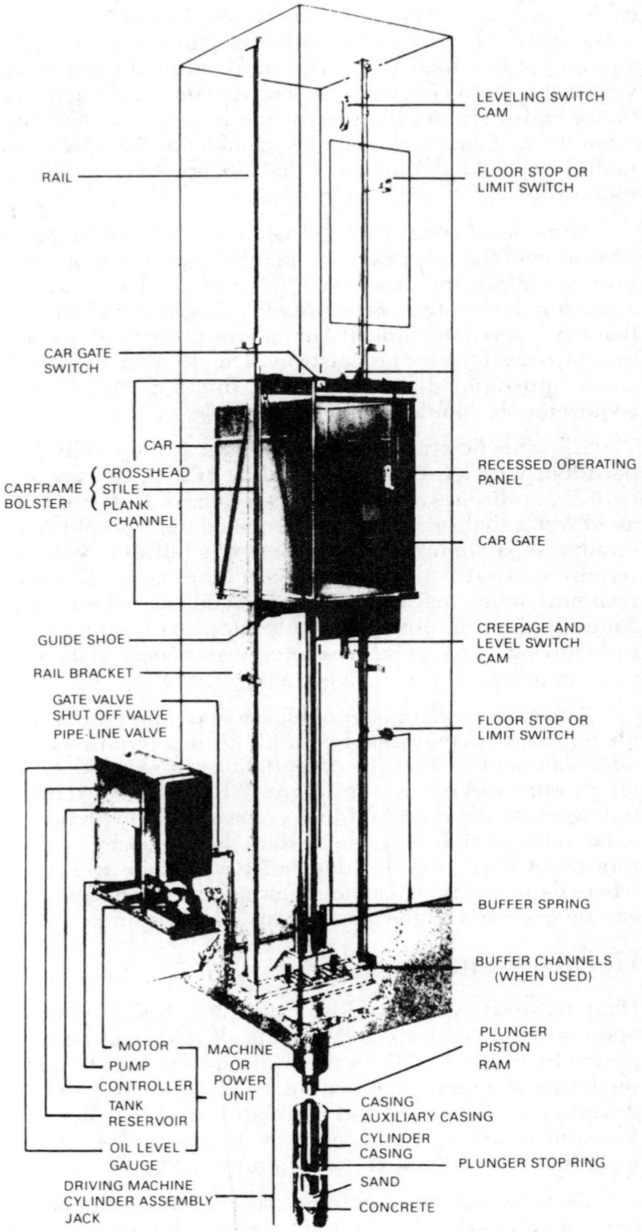

FIG. 7-4B. ***Hydraulic elevator. (Source: National Elevator Industry, Inc.)***

HOISTWAY CONSTRUCTION

Elevators travel in a vertical space or opening, called a hoistway or shaft, that extends from the pit floor of a building to the floor, or roof, above. ASME A17.1[1] requires that hoistway construction conform to the applicable building code or, in the absence of a local code, to provisions of one of the three model codes.

Although elevators have made high-rise buildings practical, they have also contributed to dangerous and complicated firesafety problems. Hot smoke and gases from fire, if allowed to accumulate at the top of the elevator hoistway, will result in mushroom fires at the upper floors served by the elevator. This is possible because an enclosed elevator hoistway acts as a chimney or flue due to the stack effect. This generally results in the movement of smoke and combustion products from lower to upper levels of the building.

The stack effect may also have an adverse effect on elevator door closing, even under normal conditions. Pressure differentials must be taken into account to regulate door closing operations safely.

All of the model building codes require venting of elevator hoistways. Most require venting of the hoistway foı elevators serving three or more stories. Some local codes permit venting through the machine room, with mechanical or natural venting from the machine room to the outside. Other codes prohibit this practice and require that cable slots and other openings between the machine room and hoistway be sleeved from the machine room floor to a point not less than 12 in. (305 mm) below the hoistway vent to inhibit the passage of smoke into the machine room. Other codes restrict the size of the opening in machine room floors. Some codes allow sprinklers in the hoistways in fully sprinkled buildings that do not have sleeping rooms, in lieu of hoistway venting.

Some local codes prohibit venting, and require pressurization of the hoistway to a specified minimum positive pressure above the pressure of the elevator lobby. When a pressurized hoistway is provided, it should contain a vent that can open automatically in case of power failure or a buildup of smoke in the hoistway. Due to numerous variances and rapid developments in this area, local code requirements should be checked.

Elevator hoistway enclosure walls are normally fire partitions with a fire-resistance rating of 2 hr. In some situations, no fire-resistive rating is required. For example, an elevator that serves only open balconies without penetrating separate fire-resistive areas of a building will not require a fire-resistive hoistway. In other cases, the fire-resistance rating may only be required on one or two walls. An example is an observation elevator that permits exterior viewing by passengers, where the entrances to the elevator penetrate fire-resistive walls.

The maximum number of elevators permitted in a single hoistway is controlled by building code requirements, which attempt to limit the potential of a fire knocking out all elevator service in a structure. Where there are three or fewer elevators in a building, codes generally permit all to be in the same hoistway enclosure. Four elevators would require at least two separate hoistway enclosures, and, where there are more than four elevators, no more than four can be enclosed in the same hoistway enclosure.

Hoistway Entrances

If the hoistway wall is load-bearing, the hoistway entrance operating mechanisms and locking devices can be supported by the walls. When the walls are not load-bearing, the hoistway entrance operating mechanisms and locking devices must be supported by other building structures. Elevator entrance frames are not designed to carry the weight of the wall above, so a lintel must be provided.

Elevator hoistway entrance assemblies customarily have been rated at 1½-hr, but they may be rated at 1-hr or ¾-hr. They are usually designated as assemblies for Class B openings which are openings to enclosures for vertical communication through buildings. A labeled entrance ensures that the hoistway entrance door assembly can meet the firesafety requirements specified by building codes and NFPA 80, *Fire Doors and Windows*. The label is visible from the hoistway. Arrangements must be made with the elevator company to view the label safely from the top of the car.

Passenger elevator doors installed in masonry walls are designed to perform under fire exposure conditions similarly to those with frames in drywall, providing the doors overlap the masonry opening the same distance as an assembly incorporating a frame. When this requirement is met, the frames, if supplied, are not required to be labeled. Masonry-type walls are generally considered to consist of brick, concrete block, or reinforced concrete construction. All three materials are fire-resistive.

Masonry and drywall constructions with stone veneers are available but have not been investigated by testing laboratories under fire conditions, and, therefore, the performance of such construction cannot be predicted absolutely. Engineering judgment can be applied when comparing stone-faced drywalls with solid-masonry walls. This judgment can only be made by assuming that the application of the stone facing does not adversely affect the structural integrity of the wall under fire conditions. In the case of drywall construction, the interface between the door and steel frame could be affected by the application of the facing material.

Drywall Enclosure Construction

Drywall construction largely supplanted masonry construction and is the most prevalent hoistway construction in use today throughout the U.S. Early elevator entrance installations in drywall were similar to masonry installations. However, some design changes were made to ensure the integrity of the interface between the entrance assembly and the dry wall construction. Brackets were placed within the frame of the entrance assembly to accept "J" struts furnished by the drywall contractor.

The "J" strut is of vital importance in ensuring a proper entrance to drywall interface. Drywall frames must be labeled. There is no difference in the door panels. Figure 7-4C provides a cutaway view of a drywall entrance assembly interface.

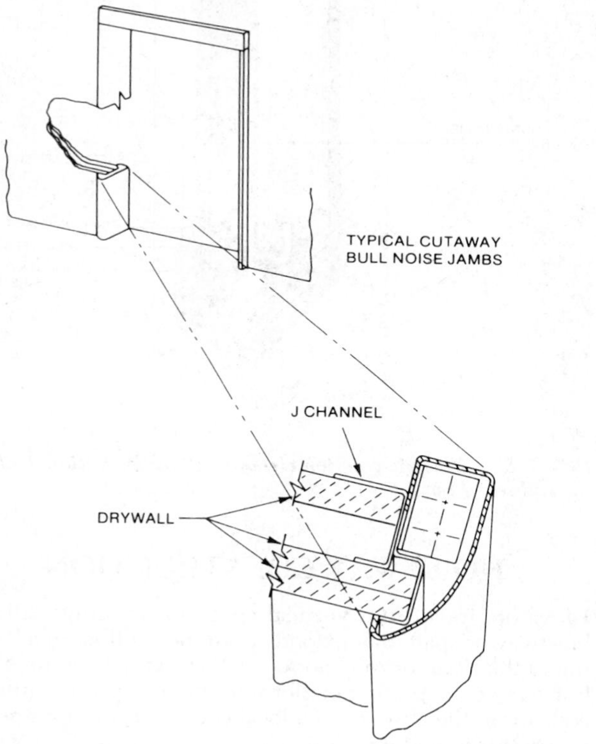

FIG. 7-4C. Details of the interface between drywall construction and bull-nose door jamb of an elevator entrance.[1]

Based upon a review of past fire performance data of masonry and drywall elevator door entrances, a listing agency determined that, in general, the drywall entrance assembly was more critical with respect to fire performance. As a result of the performance of drywall entrance assemblies, the listing agency could establish coverage for the same assemblies in masonry construction.

The classification marking, or label, on passenger elevator doors covers the design and construction of the door panels only. In addition to the door panels, fire-door frames for drywall must contain a marking label. Beginning in 1985, ASME A17.1[1] required all passenger elevator door frames in drywalls to be labeled.

The hardware also must be listed for a completely listed entrance assembly. Passenger elevator door hardware consists of a header; track hangers; pendant bolts; floor sill with guides, sill support plates, and brackets; retaining angles; and closure assemblies. Each component must be labeled individually. For hardware packaged and shipped as a single unit, ASME A17.1[1] permits one label for all components.

Door Gasketing Materials

Listing agencies have classified gasketing materials for use on elevator fire door and frame assemblies. The individual gasketing materials currently are investigated for use on particular frame or door types and for specific fire duration periods. The basic standards used to investigate gasketing materials are Underwriters Laboratories Inc. standards *Fire Test of Door Assemblies*,[2] and *Standard for Air Leakage Tests of Door Assemblies*.[3] Additional information can be found in NFPA 105, *Smoke-Control Door Assemblies*. However, the tests do not evaluate the potential adverse effect on door operation.

Fire departments consider in-car elevator operation crucial in a high-rise fire. The question arises as to whether melting gasket material will collect in the door tracks, rollers, and other parts of the equipment, thus affecting elevator door operation. The kinetic energy and door closing forces of power-operated doors are regulated for passenger safety by ASME A17.1.[1] During the last few inches of door travel, the closing speed must be reduced. If deposits of gasketing material were to collect in the door tracks, the doors might be unable to move past the deposits, thus preventing complete closure. Friction from the gasketing material also may prevent complete closure. As a result, the elevator would be immobilized, and the elevator hoistway would be exposed to smoke, hot gases, and fire. Another question is what effect this seal will have on doors arranged to close automatically if the car leaves the landing zone for any reason.[4]

Although enclosing elevator lobbies with smoke and draft control doors is perhaps not as aesthetic as the architect and building owner would prefer, it is the most practical substitute for smoke seals on elevator entrances, as a means of controlling the movement of smoke into the elevator hoistway. An enclosed lobby also could serve as an area of refuge for the handicapped in a fire and as a safe staging area for fire fighting.

Machine Room Construction

When a fire-resistive hoistway is required for electric elevators, the machine room must be constructed of equally fire-resistive material. When a nonfire-resistive hoistway is constructed for an electric elevator or for a hydraulic elevator, and when the building code permits, the machine room enclosure must be of noncombustible material extending to a height of not less than 6 ft (1.83 m). Machine rooms are to be kept closed and locked, and they should be restricted to authorized personnel familiar with the precautions that are necessary around moving elevator machinery. Machine room floors should be kept free of oil and grease. Material not necessary for the maintenance or operation of the elevator should not be stored in the machine room. Flammable liquids with flash points of less than 110°F (43°C), should not be kept in the machine room. An extinguisher for use on Class C (electrical) fires is required by ASME A17.1[1] in all electrical machine spaces, and should be located convenient to the access door.

Machine rooms that are not located at the top of hoistways should not contain equipment that is not essential to the operation of the elevator, because a fire that starts in a basement machine room has a clear unobstructed path to the hoistway. A machine room located above the hoistway may be in a room with other equipment essential to the operation of the building, provided the elevator equipment is separated from the other equipment by at least a 6-ft (1.83 m) high metal grill or solid partition.

Sprinklers in Hoistways and Machine Rooms

Provisions are outlined in NFPA 13, *Installation of Sprinkler Systems*, for sprinklers installed in elevator hoistways and machine rooms. Sprinklers are not required by ASME A17.1,[1] but, when installed, sprinklers must meet requirements of this code in addition to those of NFPA 13. Before the installation of sprinklers in spaces containing elevator control equipment is considered, certain potential problems should be analyzed. One should consider whether any discharge of water on the control equipment may adversely affect the safe operation of the elevator and note the effect of water on safety circuits. Water has been known to short out the safety circuits and allow an elevator to run with an open car or hoistway door. In addition, wet brakes may be unable to stop and hold an elevator.

ASME A17.1[1] requires that, before a sprinkler in the machine room or hoistway is discharged, the main line power source to the elevator be disconnected. In a fire, the sequence of events would probably be as follows: a smoke detector in the machine room, hoistway, or elevator lobby would recall the elevator; the main line power would automatically be disconnected; and the sprinkler would discharge.

Even if the smoke detector is not activated, or if all elevators have not been returned to the lobby, it is considered safer to stop the car and contain the passengers than to allow continued operation with the discharging sprinkler. Fire fighters should be aware that, if fire is in the elevator machine room, the elevators powered from that room will not be available for their use.[5]

Other requirements in ASME A17.1[1] pertain to the location of sprinkler piping and valving. Sprinkler activation by a smoke detector also is prohibited. NFPA *101*, *Life Safety Code*, requires sprinklers in the top of all shafts to meet the specifications of NFPA 13, *Installation of Sprinkler Systems*.

Elevator Car Construction

ASME A17.1[1] requires that all material exposed to the car interior and the hoistway be metal or glass, or have a flame spread rating of 0 to 75 and smoke development rating of 0 to 450. The materials must be tested in their end-use configuration. Padded protective linings for temporary use in passenger cars during the handling of freight also must meet these criteria.

The smoke development rating for materials in cars is equal to NFPA *101, Life Safety Code*, requirements for an exit passageway in a fire-resistive building. Smoke development characteristics of materials may be more crucial than flame spread, as passengers enclosed in a confined box may not be able to escape rapidly.

Napped, tufted, woven, looped, and similar materials must be subjected to a vertical burn test as specified by ASME A17.1.[1] This test is based on the applicable portions of *FAA Regulation 25.853*, in addition to the flame spread and smoke development test (ASTM E84) and NFPA 255, *Surface Burning Characteristics of Building Materials*. Such material, located on elevator car walls, is extremely susceptible to accidental ignition. Tufted material, such as carpeting, may accumulate dust, which could increase the possibility of ignition and flame spread.

Floor covering, underlayment, and adhesive are required to have a critical radiant flux of not less than 0.45 W/cm^2, as measured by the ASTM E648 test[6] and NFPA 253, *Critical Radiant Flux of Floor Covering Systems Using Radiant Heat Energy Source*. The level of critical radiant flux acceptable for floor systems in elevator cars is based on the assumption that the occupants of an elevator may not be able to escape rapidly. The flux level equals the requirements recommended for health care facilities.

Handrails, operating devices, ventilating devices, signal fixtures, audio and visual communications devices, and their housings are not required to meet any of the above criteria, as they contribute little to the fire load in relation to the overall elevator car assembly.

Handicapped Considerations

Two national standards address handicapped requirements for elevators. These are the *Minimum Passenger Elevator Requirements for the Handicapped*[7] and *The American National Standard Specification for Making Buildings and Facilities Accessible to and Usable by Physically Handicapped People*.[8] Both standards require all passenger elevators to be made accessible to the handicapped. Planned and practiced procedures are needed to evacuate the handicapped in a fire.

Emergency Lighting, Alarm, and Communications

ASME A17.1[1] requires emergency lighting on all elevators. The power source must originate on the elevator to ensure that passengers are not thrust into total darkness if building power fails. The building emergency power source is not a recognized alternative to this requirement, since this source generally would not respond to a branch circuit failure and usually is activated only upon loss of the power supply. Moreover, it would rely on the elevator's traveling cables to supply lighting power, which would be useless if the lighting problem was in the traveling cables.

All elevators must have an audible signaling device, alarm, and a means of two-way conversation to an accessible point outside the hoistway. (See Figure 7-4D for a diagrammatic description of these requirements.) The two-way communications system does not have to have a means of activation from within the car. Most communications systems, excluding telephones, are activated in the main lobby or building emergency control center.

In addition to these requirements, the three model building codes require all elevators in high-rise buildings to have a communication system from the elevator lobby, car, and machine rooms to the building's central control station.

ELEVATORS IN FIRE EMERGENCIES

High-rise buildings present new and different problems to fire suppression forces, including the use of elevators during emergencies. Elevators are unsafe in a fire for several reasons. First, persons may push a corridor button and have to wait for an elevator that may never respond, losing valuable escape time. Second, elevators do not prioritize car and corridor calls, and one of the calls may be at the fire floor. Third, elevators cannot start until the car and hoistway doors are closed, and panic could lead to overcrowding of an elevator and the blockage of the doors, which would thus prevent closing. And, finally, the power can fail during a fire at any time, thus leading to entrapment.

The elevator can be delivered to the fire floor when an elevator passenger presses the car button for the fire floor; when one or both of the corridor call buttons is pushed on the fire floor; when heat melts or deforms the corridor pushbutton or its wiring at the fire floor; and when the elevator functions normally at the fire floor, as in high or low call reversal.

ASME A17.1[1] recognizes all the aforementioned unsafe conditions and mandates elevator recall, more commonly referred to as Phase I, Fire Fighters' Service.

Phase I Operations

Phase I is the automatic or manual return, or recall, of elevators to a designated level or recall floor. Phase I also ensures that an elevator is not available to the general public during a fire. The provision that allows fire fighting personnel to operate the elevator from within the car on emergency in car operation is commonly referred to as Phase II.

The "designated level" is defined as the main floor or some other level that best serves the needs of emergency personnel for fire fighting or rescue purposes.[1] A three-position—on, off, bypass—key-operated switch in the designated-level lobby can be used by emergency personnel to control each single elevator or a group of elevators. Another two-position—on, off—key-operated switch may be provided in the building's central control station. In the on position, the switch instructs all elevators, thus controlled, to return nonstop to the recall floor, disregarding all activated call buttons.

Hoistway doors on the recall floor should remain open. Upon arrival, fire fighters have little time to learn whether all the elevators are present. Open hoistway doors will reveal those elevators that have been recalled, as well as those that have to be located to ensure that no passengers are trapped. Position indicators that can help emergency personnel locate errant elevators are required to remain operative during emergencies.

The hoistway door opens at the designated level and also will admit air to the hoistway. If the fire is on a floor below the neutral pressure plane, the additional air will

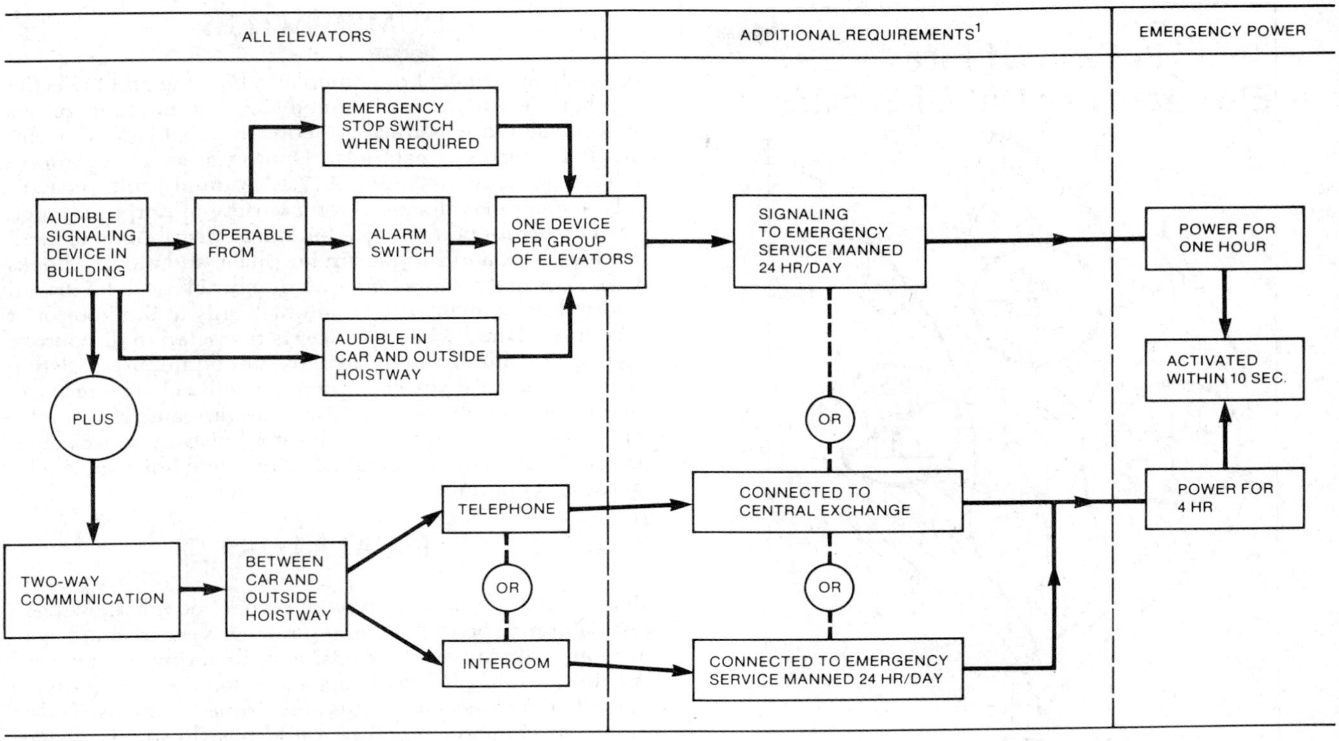

NOTE:
(1) IN A BUILDING IN WHICH A BUILDING ATTENDANT, BUILDING EMPLOYEE, OR WATCHMAN IS NOT CONTINUOUSLY AVAILABLE TO TAKE ACTION WHEN AN EMERGENCY SIGNAL IS OPERATED.

FIG. 7-4D. Emergency elevator signaling device requirements.[1]

reduce the amount of smoke that can enter the hoistway from the fire floor, a beneficial side effect. If the fire is above the neutral pressure plane, there will be an increased flow of air from the hoistway to the floor, which is also beneficial.

Visual and audible signals alert passengers in an automatically operated elevator to an emergency and can help minimize any apprehension that the passengers have as the elevator returns to the recall floor. In an attendant-operated elevator, this signal alerts the attendant to the emergency so that he or she can return the car immediately to the recall floor.

More recent elevator recall systems combine a key-operated switch with an automatic smoke detection system, using detectors at each floor lobby. Elevators are recalled, either manually or automatically, to the main floor, or alternate floor if the fire is on the main floor, depending upon which mode initially operates.

To advise the public that elevators may not be available during a fire, the pictograph in Figure 7-4E should be posted above all elevator hall call buttons. Some jurisdictions may require different wording and pictographs, but the message is similar.

Phase II Operations

Phase II fire fighter operations are for the benefit of fire fighters who must have the elevators for their own use. It is standard operating procedure for fire fighters to use elevators not only to carry equipment for fire fighting or evacuation purposes, but also to deliver fire personnel to nonfire floors.

The current ASME A17.1[1] calls for Phase II operation whenever Phase I operation is required. The rule considers the need for fire fighters to evacuate the handicapped and disabled persons during an emergency. This code also has standardized the operation procedures, regardless of the elevator manufacturer.

The required switch keys for Phase I and Phase II operation must be the same to ensure a speedy response to an emergency. The use of lock boxes to hold Phase I and Phase II keys is preferred over the use of a jurisdiction-wide uniform key, as the lock box method provides greater assurance that the keys are restricted. The uniform key method has resulted in disruption of normal elevator service, as there is no means of controlling the distribution of elevator keys.

Operating procedures must be incorporated with, or be adjacent to, the Phase I and Phase II key-operated switches to provide emergency personnel quick access to instructions during an emergency.

ASME A17.1[1] does not require standby power for elevators. This requirement is found normally in the building code. However, the safety code does require that elevator operation be the same when standby power is supplied as it is when normal power is supplied.

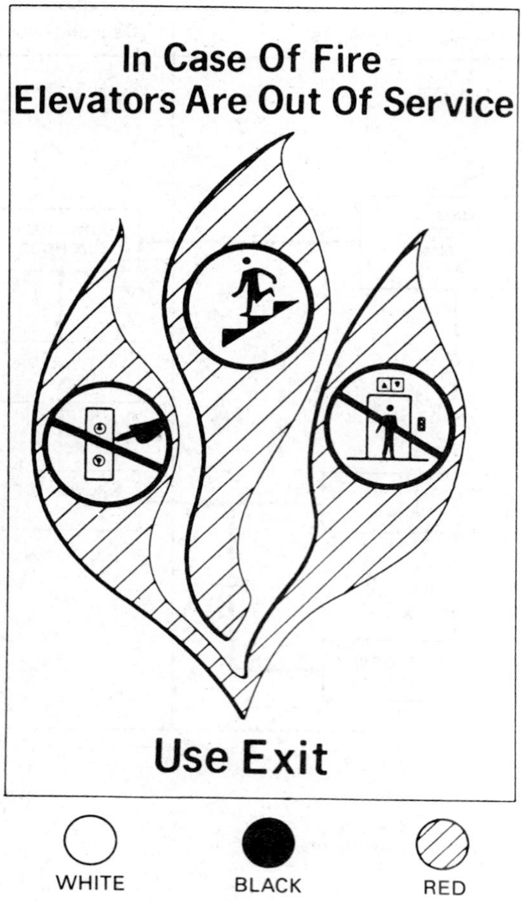

FIG. 7-4E. An example of a pictographic warning message for elevator use.[1]

Additional information on using fire fighters' service can be found in NFPA's *Handling Elevator Emergencies*[9] and the slide training package, *Using Elevators in High-Rise Fire Fighting*.[10]

Evacuation from a Stalled Elevator

Any evacuation of passengers from a stalled elevator car should be performed by trained elevator personnel. Their expertise will ensure that the evacuation is carried out in a manner that is safe for both the passengers and the rescue party. However, waiting for trained elevator personnel may be impossible in a life-threatening emergency. Under such conditions, passenger evacuation must be performed by carefully selected and trained personnel. Planned and practiced procedures are needed to ensure the safety of the rescued passengers and the members of the rescue party. Any rescue party should be cautioned never to try moving an elevator from the machine room. This should only be attempted by trained elevator personnel.

Three available references on evacuation procedures are the ASME *Guide for Emergency Evacuation of Passengers from Stalled Elevator Cars*,[11] NFPA's *Handling Elevator Emergencies*,[9] and NFPA's slide training package, *Elevator Emergency Evacuation Procedures*.[12]

DUMBWAITERS

A dumbwaiter may be defined as a hoisting and lowering mechanism with a car of limited size that moves in guides in a substantially vertical direction and that is used exclusively for carrying materials.[1] Dumbwaiters must conform to requirements in ASME A17.1.[1] A dumbwaiter is actually a small elevator used for a variety of purposes, such as mail distribution in office buildings; distribution of medication, food, and supplies in hospitals; and moving books from floor to floor in a library. A dumbwaiter can be loaded and unloaded manually or automatically at the floor or at a counter. Dumbwaiter car size is restricted to discourage riding. As dumbwaiters usually penetrate fire-resistive floors, their hoistway construction is critical. The requirements for a dumbwaiter hoistway are the same as those for an elevator. The section on elevator hoistway construction earlier in this chapter details fire-resistive hoistway enclosures and entrances.

ESCALATORS

The escalator is another type of vertical people mover. An escalator may be defined as a power-driven, inclined, continuous stairway used for raising or lowering passengers.[1] In the early days, escalators were found principally in department stores and in bus and airline terminals. Today, they are common in office buildings, hospitals, banks, sports arenas, and other locations where many people must be moved quickly from one floor to another.

NFPA *101*, *Life Safety Code*, requires that escalator floor openings be enclosed or protected, as required for other vertical openings. In completely sprinklered buildings, escalators need not be enclosed if they are protected by alternate means.

The sprinkler draft curtain method is detailed in NFPA 13, *Installation of Sprinkler Systems*, and consists of surrounding the escalator opening with an 18-in. (457 mm) deep draft stop located on the underside of the floor to which the escalator ascends. A row of automatic sprinklers located outside the draft stop surrounds the escalator well. A typical installation is shown in Figure 7-4F.

Two methods recognized in previous editions of NFPA *101*, *Life Safety Code*, and found in existing buildings, are as follows.

Sprinkler Vent Method

An automatic fire or smoke detection system, an automatic exhaust system, and an automatic water curtain are combined in this method. When a detector senses a fire, the automatic damper opens, thereby venting smoke and gases. Replacement air is drawn through the outdoor air intake above the escalator opening. To control smoke, an exhaust rate of about 60 air changes per hour is required. The sprinkler curtain provides a thermal barrier. A typical installation is shown in Figure 7-4G.

Spray Nozzle Method

This method combines an automatic fire or smoke detection system and a system of high-velocity water spray nozzles. There must be enough spray nozzles with discharge angles such that the escalator opening between the top of

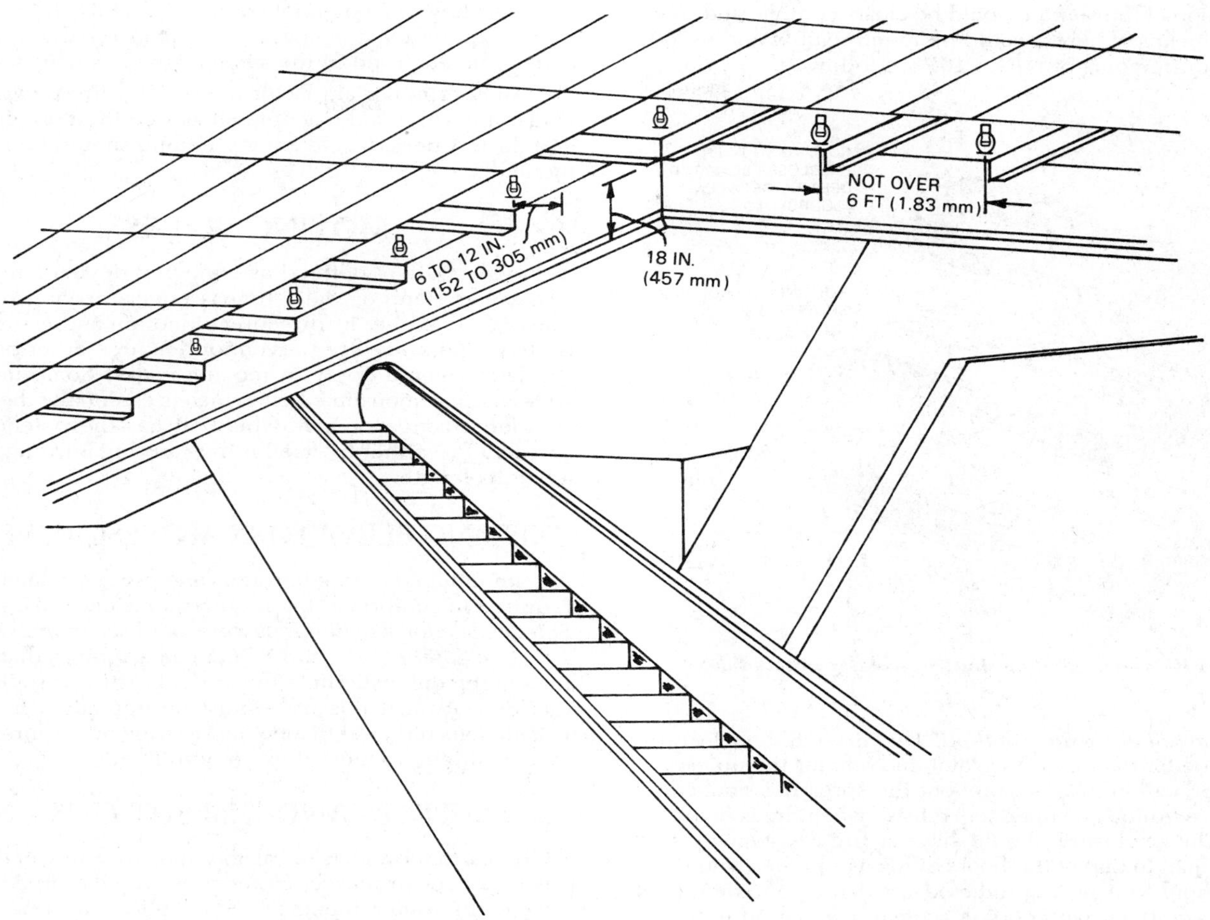

FIG. 7-4F. Sprinklers around an escalator.

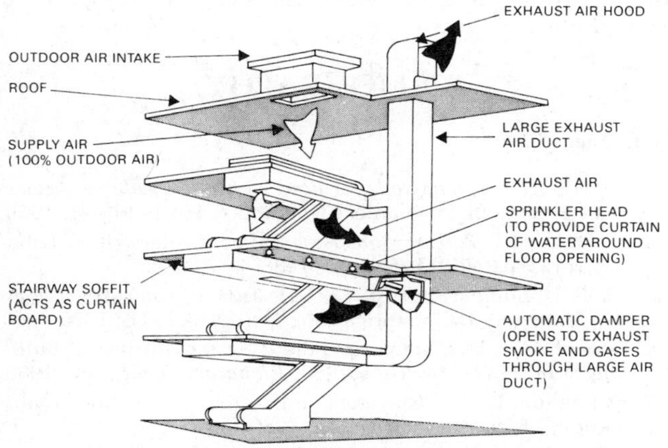

FIG. 7-4G. Sprinkler vent method installation.

the wellway housing and the treadway will be completely filled with a dense water spray on operation of the system.

The two methods of enclosing the escalator opening, used in both new and existing buildings, are:

1. *Rolling shutter method.* In this method, escalators above the street floor may be protected by automatic self-closing rolling shutters that completely enclose the top of the escalator wellway. To avoid injury, the escalator must be stopped automatically before the shutter begins to close. The shutter should close slowly and have a pressure-sensitive leading edge that will stop the shutter upon contact. A typical installation is shown in Figure 7-4H.

Rolling steel shutters are not recommended at the tops of escalators or between basements and street floors, even though the stairways are not required exits under the provisions of NFPA *101*, *Life Safety Code*. In an emergency, persons seeking egress from basements served by escalators could be trapped by fully closed rolling shutters at the street level, even though other means of egress are available to them. It also has been observed that quite a different psychological reaction is exhibited by those confronted with a closed shutter above their heads, as they try to climb to safety from a basement, than is seen in those faced with a closed shutter at an exit on the same level as the floor they are trying to leave. In the latter case, the operation of the shutter would be clearly visible, and some other means of egress could be found readily and used if the requirements of NFPA 101 are followed.

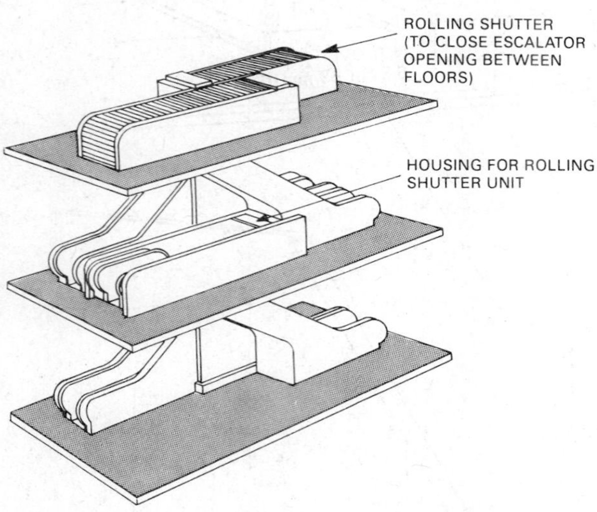

FIG. 7-4H. Rolling shutter escalator installation.

2. *Partial enclosure method.* Two fire-rated enclosures, one for the down escalator and one for the up escalator, can be used to prevent the spread of smoke and fire. Automatic fire doors release when fire is detected. The enclosure should have a fire-resistance rating equal to that of the floor/ceiling assemblies, and there should be no unprotected escalator penetrations of more than two floors. A typical installation is shown in Figure 7-4I.

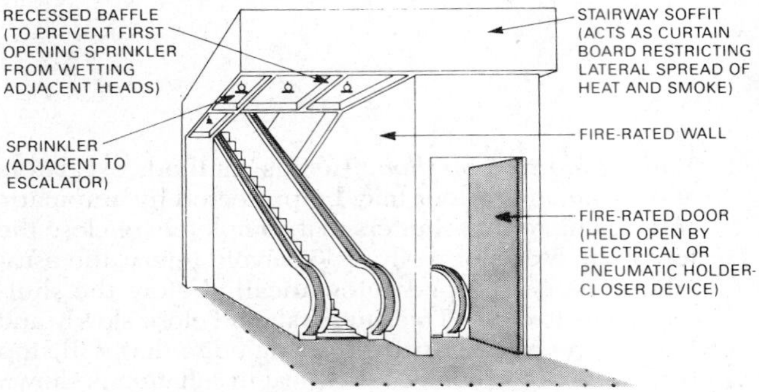

FIG. 7-4I. Partial enclosure escalator installation.

In new buildings, escalators cannot be used as a means of egress. Modern escalator design requires the removal of steps for normal maintenance, thus rendering the escalator unusable. A stopped escalator also presents a tripping hazard, at the floor entrance and exit, due to the nonuniform riser height of the first and last few steps. In some existing buildings, escalators are part of the means of egress. These escalators should be arranged to operate only in the direction of egress, or they should be stopped during a fire. Where the evacuation plan calls for the use of escalators, efficient crowd control is required to avoid serious crowding and potential panic. NFPA *101, Life Safety Code*, requires the openings for escalators used as required exits to be enclosed in the same manner as exit stairs.

Another important factor in escalator fire prevention is keeping truss and machine areas free from oil, grease, and dust. A periodic cleaning schedule should be implemented.

MOVING WALKS

A moving walk is defined as a moving device on which passengers stand or walk. Its passenger-carrying surface remains parallel to its direction of motion and is uninterrupted. The same fire prevention features described for escalators would apply to moving walks. Some moving walks use a combustible belt, which is essentially the same as a large conveyor belt. This belt has the potential to spread a fire either by itself or by carrying burning items along its length.

EXISTING ELEVATORS AND ESCALATORS

At a minimum, existing elevators and escalators should be required to conform to the requirements of ASME A17.3, *Safety Code for Existing Elevators and Escalators.*[13] NFPA *101, Life Safety Code*, and BOCA codes require that existing equipment conform to this code. Existing installations that do not meet this code must be upgraded. Existing installations required to meet more stringent requirements must continue to meet those requirements.

TESTS AND INSPECTIONS

Elevators, dumbwaiters, escalators, moving walks, and other passenger conveyance equipment that are required to conform to the requirements of ASME A17.1[1] must be tested and inspected periodically. ASME A17.2, *Inspectors' Manual for Elevators and Escalators*[14] should be used as a guide for these inspections. The quality of the inspections depends upon the competence of the inspector. ASME QEI1, *Standard for the Qualification of Elevator Inspectors*[15] is intended to establish uniform criteria for this purpose and to serve as a guideline on which certification is based by detailing the expertise necessary to perform inspections.

BIBLIOGRAPHY

References Cited

1. ASME A17.1, *Safety Code for Elevators and Escalators*, American Society of Mechanical Engineers, Fairfield, NJ, 1990.
2. UL 10B, *Fire Test of Door Assemblies*, Underwriters Laboratories Inc., Northbrook, IL, 1988.
3. UL 1784, *Standard for Air Leakage Tests of Door Assemblies*, Underwriters Laboratories Inc., Northbrook, IL, 1990.
4. Donoghue, E. A., "Smoke and the Elevator Hoistway," *Building Standards*, May/June 1983; *Elevator World*, May 1983.
5. Donoghue, E. A., "Elevators and Water—A Volatile Combination," *Elevator World*, Aug. 1989.
6. ASTM E648, *Test for Critical Radiant Flux of Floor Covering Systems*, American Society of Testing and Materials, New York, 1988.
7. *Minimum Passenger Elevator Requirements for the Handicapped*, National Elevator Industry, Inc., Fort Lee, NJ, 1985.
8. ANSI A117.1, *American National Standard for Buildings and Facilities Providing Accessability and Unability for Physically*

Handicapped People, American National Standards Institute, New York, 1986.

9. *Handling Elevator Emergencies*, National Fire Protection Association, Quincy, MA, 1979.
10. *Using Elevators in High-Rise Fire Fighting* (slide training package), National Fire Protection Association, Quincy, MA, 1982.
11. ASME A17.4, *Guide for Emergency Evacuation of Passengers from Stalled Elevator Cars*, American Society of Mechanical Engineers, Fairfield, NJ, 1986.
12. *Elevator Emergency Evacuation Procedures* (slide training package), National Fire Protection Association, Quincy, MA, 1979.
13. ASME A17.3, *Safety Code for Existing Elevators and Escalators*, American Society of Mechanical Engineers, Fairfield, NJ, 1990.
14. ASME A17.2, *Inspectors' Manual for Elevators and Escalators*, American Society of Mechanical Engineers, Fairfield, NJ, 1988.
15. ASME/QEI 1-1990, *Qualifications of Elevator Inspectors*, American Society of Mechanical Engineers, Fairfield, NJ, 1990.

NFPA Codes, Standards, and Recommended Practices

Reference to the following NFPA codes, standards, and recommended practices will provide further information on building transportation systems discussed in this chapter. (See the latest *NFPA Catalog* for availability of current editions of the following documents.

NFPA 13, *Installation of Sprinkler Systems*.

NFPA 70, *National Electrical Code*.

NFPA 80, *Fire Doors and Windows*.

NFPA *101*, *Life Safety Code*.

NFPA 105, *Smoke-Control Door Assemblies*.

NFPA 253, *Critical Radiant Flux of Floor Covering Systems Using Radiant Heat Energy Source*.

NFPA 255, *Surface Burning Characteristics of Building Materials*.

Additional Reading

ASTM E84, *Standard Test Method for Surface Burning Characteristics of Building Materials*, American Society for Testing and Materials, Philadelphia, PA, 1989.

National Building Code, Building Officials and Code Administrators International, Homewood, IL, 1990.

Donoghue, E. A., *Handbook A17.1 Safety Code for Elevators and Escalators*, American Society of Mechanical Engineers, Fairfield, NJ, 1990.

Elevator World, Published monthly by Elevator World, Inc., Mobile, AL.

Uniform Building Code, International Conference of Building Officials, Whittier, CA, 1988.

Klote, J. H., *Smoke Control for Elevators*, U.S. Department of Commerce, National Bureau of Standards, Washington, DC.

Klote, J. H., "Smoke Control for Elevators," *ASHRAE Journal*, Vol. 26, No. 4, 1984, pp. 23-33.

Klote, J. H. and Tamura, G., "Smoke Control and Fire Evacuation by Elevators," *ASHRAE Transactions*, Vol. 92, No. 1A, 1986, pp. 231-245.

Pedestrian Planning and Design, Elevator World, Inc., Mobile, AL.

Standard Building Code, Southern Building Code Congress International, Birmingham, AL, 1988.

Sumka, E., "Presently, Elevators Are Not Safe in Fire Emergencies," *Elevator World*, Vol. 36, No. 11, 1988, p. 5.

State Elevator Code Authority Directory, Edward A. Donoghue Associates, Inc., Salem, NY.

Strakosch, G., *Vertical Transportation, Elevators, and Escalators*, John Wiley and Sons, New York, 1983.

Tamura, G. T. and Klote, J. H., "Experimental Fire Tower Studies of Elevator Pressurization Systems for Smoke Control," *Elevator World*, Vol. 37, No. 6, 1989, pp. 80-89.

USG Cavity Shaft Wall Systems, United Gypsum Company, Chicago, IL.

Vertical Transportation Standards, National Elevator Industry, Inc., Fort Lee, NJ, 1983.

SYSTEMS APPROACHES TO PROPERTY CLASSES

Sections 2-7 presented specific firesafety elements—fire prevention and fire protection—arrayed along the timeline of fire development and building and occupant response. For the most part, these elements were presented in a general form that made them applicable to all kinds of properties. But as Section 1 stated, firesafety requires a systems design, which means that the special characteristics of the specific property or application must be addressed in the design. Every place has its own needs, and every class of properties has some needs that are different from the general needs of all properties.

Section 8 therefore combines all the chapters that address special requirements of particular property-use classes or particular areas, processes, or activities, not limited to their role as sources of fire ignition. Section 8 also includes some cross-cutting systems issues that do not fit neatly into the timeline of fire development.

Chapters 1-8 cover occupancies where there are special concerns for property protection. Chapters 1-3 cover several process fire hazards—wastewater treatment, solvent extraction, and food processing. Other process fire hazards are included in Section 2 on fire prevention; the decision on where to place these chapters was made based on the relative emphasis on fire prevention vs. other hazard mitigation strategies. Chapters 4-8 cover several special considerations that arise with storage properties.

Chapter 9 covers environmental issues in fire protection. This is a classic instance where new knowledge and new concerns have forced the fire community to consider the whole subject of fire in a larger systems context. As Chapter 9 says, "Almost all human activity can harm the environment...More often than not, efforts made to protect the environment from those activities have raised new fire protection concerns. Likewise, many fire protection measures have added to environmental problems. Therefore, whenever attempts are made to reduce pollution or to protect a structure or a process from fire, the interrelationship between fire protection and the environment must be considered."

Chapter 10 provides concepts for systems thinking with respect to life safety in buildings. It amplifies and complements some of the concepts in Section 1 and provides a basis for defining and analyzing the special firesafety needs of specific buildings in a manner that will be consistent across diverse property types.

Chapters 11-25 and 27 cover the different types of buildings, grouped in chapters whose sequencing largely follows the sequencing of groups in NFPA 901, *Uniform Coding for Fire Protection*, the basis of fire incident report coding in the United States. From the large seating requirements of assembly occupancies in Chapter 11, to the special needs and limitations of the typical occupants of educational and health care facilities in Chapters 12-13, to the restricted movement allowed in detention facilities in Chapter 14, to the limited control possible in homes and the related problems found in other residential properties in Chapters 15-20, to the myriad special hazards of commercial and industrial properties in Chapters 21-24, each of these chapters defines the fire problem in a major property-use class and identifies the keys to firesafety appropriate to the special needs of that class. Chapter 25, on nuclear facilities, and Chapter 27, on miscellaneous "unusual" problems in structures, complete this group.

Chapters 28-31 cover topics described in previous editions of the *Fire Protection Handbook* as "special fire protection problems." They are typically problems associated with relatively new and exotic technologies. These include computers and other sensitive electronic equipment (Chapter 28), laboratories using chemicals (Chapter 29), and telecommunications equipment (Chapter 30). Conveyors, cranes, and other materials handling equipment are covered in Chapter 31.

Chapters 26 and 32-37 cover properties that are not buildings. These include mines (Chapter 26), wildlands (Chapter 32), aircraft (Chapter 33), road vehicles (Chapter 34), rail vehicles (Chapters 35-36), and watercraft (Chapter 37).

Also look for these: It is inherent in this section that most chapters will lead back to related material in all the previous sections and often to the models in Section 10 as well. The *Life Safety Code Handbook* and the *Industrial Fire Hazards Handbook* are essential references for additional detail on fire protection for specific property-use classes. Nearly all the chapters in Section 8 leads naturally into one or the other of these books.

PROTECTION OF WASTEWATER TREATMENT PLANTS

James F. Wheeler

This chapter discusses wastewater treatment processes, process equipment, and their fire and explosion hazards. Traditionally, wastewater treatment process equipment is classified according to the various unit operations being performed. The basic unit processes fall into three categories: (1) collection and pumping, (2) liquid treatment systems, and (3) solid treatment systems. In general, the highest risks of fire and explosion are associated with collection and pumping operations and in the early stages of liquid and solids processing. Specific unit processes to consider are pumping station wet wells that handle raw sewage or unstabilized solids, preliminary screening and grit removal processes, primary sedimentation, anaerobic digestion, scum collecting processes, and fuel and chemical handling and storage areas. To provide the necessary processing there is a considerable variety of makes and models of equipment. Consequently, the fire and explosion hazards associated with wastewater treatment processes is much too broad a subject to be examined in a single chapter. Therefore, some basic principles of risk evaluation, mitigation, and fire protection that can be applied generally to individual unit processes and equipment will be discussed.

The collection and concentration of the liquid wastes from a community, known as wastewater, creates a disposal problem that demands a solution for the protection of the health and comfort of the public. The series of closed conduits (pipes) conveying liquid wastes in a municipality is commonly called a sewer system. Among the first historical traces of wastewater collection is the sewer arch at Nippur, India, which was probably constructed about 3950 BC. Although there are other examples of ancient sewers, the development of the modern wastewater collection system did not begin in the United States until 1805, with the construction of the first large sewer in New York City.[1]

With the collection of wastewater comes the requirements to provide treatment. The aim of all methods of wastewater treatment has so far been to produce an effluent which could be disposed of without nuisance and to protect human health. It is evident that modern cities and present-day metropolitan centers could not exist as they do without the protection of health and the conveniences that are afforded by comprehensive collection systems and sophisticated treatment facilities. Today, in the U.S., there are over 15,000 municipal wastewater treatment facilities, serving nearly 176 million people, and treating approximately 30 trillion gallons of wastewater per day. (See Figure 8-1A.) There are also thousands of industries and businesses that provide their own wastewater treatment services. In addition, there are millions of people, mostly living in rural areas, that are still served by individual on-site treatment units, such as septic tanks and small aerobic package plants.[2] As development expands into these rural areas, and as the on-site septic systems begin to fail and pollute the ground water supplies, new collector sewers must be constructed and larger more complex treatment plants will be required.

Wastewater treatment covers any artificial processes that remove or alter the objectionable constituents to make it less offensive or dangerous. Early treatment plants included anaerobic lagoons or cesspools, which provided barely primary treatment, and treatment simply by dilution. Modern wastewater treatment began in the United States in 1886 with the introduction of the intermittent sand filter. The wastewater treatment industry grew rapidly during the early 1900s with the development of aerobic processes, such as the trickling filter and activated sludge treatment.[1]

In addition to conventional pollutants, such as biochemical oxygen demand (BOD) and suspended solids (SS), today's wastewater industry must be prepared to treat hazardous and toxic industrial waste or explosive and flammable materials which may be illegally or accidentally discharged to the sewer system. The treatment of this waste involves highly specialized knowledge of the design, construction, maintenance, and operation of sophisticated equipment and processes. Wastewater treatment is a viable and growing industry which is ever-changing as demands for better removal of toxics and hazardous materials increase and more sophisticated and complex chemical and biological processes evolve.

James F. Wheeler, P.E., is an environmental engineer for the U.S. Environmental Protection Agency, Washington, DC.

FIG. 8-1A. Aerial view of a modern waste water treatment plant.

OPERATIONS AND EQUIPMENT

The treatment of wastewater can be broken down into three major components: collection and pumping systems, liquid treatment systems, and solids treatment systems. Each component utilizes different types of processes and equipment. Each component also has specific hazards associated with its particular function.

Collection and Pumping Systems

The function of the collection system is to gather the wastewater from houses, factories, or other sources and transport the wastewater to a central facility for processing. Where the terrain is flat the collection system may consist solely of gravity piping; however, in most areas the collection system requires pumping. Although there are many different kinds of collection systems, the sanitary sewer and the combined sewer are the most common. The sanitary sewer carries wastewater from individual homes and excludes storm water, surface water, and ground water. Sanitary sewers also collect wastewater from industrial and commercial businesses in the service area. Combined sewers carry domestic wastewater as well as storm water and industrial wastewater. Although today only separate sanitary sewers are being constructed, there are many older cities that still have thousands of miles of large combined sewers.

Sanitary sewers are generally smaller than combined sewers. Sanitary sewers with diameters of 8 in. to 48 in. (0.2 to 1.2 m) are common. Combined sewers generally are very large, often 20 ft (6 m) in diameter or larger. These collection systems also include other appurtenances, such as manholes, valve boxes, catch basins, curb inlets, and a variety of other structures. Combined sewers may also have regulators or diversion structures that allow overflow directly to rivers or streams during major storm events.

Pumping wastewater has long been a problem because of the fibrous and stringy material in the wastewater. Rotary and reciprocating pumps are generally not suited for wastewater pumping, unless the wastewater has been treated to remove solids. Even many of the centrifugal pumps used for pumping wastewater experience problems with handling the solids. Today, most wastewater is pumped using solids-handling centrifugal pumps with single-suction volutes.[3] These pumps have impellers with only two vanes, thus creating large passageways. These centrifugal pumps can also be equipped with bladeless impellers for pumping unscreened wastewater and sludge. Pneumatic ejectors have also been used successfully for handling small volumes of unscreened wastewater.

Most pumping stations have two parts, a dry well and a wet well. The wet well receives and temporarily stores wastewater. Wet wells often contain screens that remove large solids which could damage the pumps. Wet wells may also contain mechanical equipment, fans, lights, etc. However, most electrical equipment, including motors, pumps, and switches, are placed in the dry well. Most pumping stations have both above- and below-ground structures, although some smaller stations are placed entirely underground.

Most stations have a number of pumping units with various capacities designed to handle changes in flow rates. The pumps are generally driven with electric motors which can be mounted either vertically or horizontally. The vertical arrangement has the advantage of permitting the motor to be placed above the pump, which safeguards it against damage by flooding. Today, many pump stations use submersible pumps. These pumps are located in the wet well and can be equipped with quick disconnects so the pumping units can be removed from the wet well for servicing. A flat efficiency curve is desirable for sewage pumps, since the head against which the pumps must work is variable. Because of the special non-clog impellers used in sewage pumps, the efficiencies are not as high as those of water pumps. Since dependability is more important than efficiency with most wastewater pumping applications, slow-speed operation is desirable because of the increased equipment life.

Where interruption of the source of electric power is possible, an auxiliary source of power is often required. In larger stations, gasoline or natural gas engines are provided. The engines are directly connected to the pump shaft by means of a right-angled gear drive unit so that either the engine or electric motor can be used by operating a clutch. Some of these gas engines are duel-fuel compatible and can use either natural gas or methane gas produced at the treatment plant by anaerobic digestion of sewage sludge.

Liquid Treatment Systems

The function of the liquid treatment processes is to remove the objectionable constituents from the wastewater so that the treated water can be returned to the environment without being offensive or dangerous to public health. The principal components of liquid treatment are: preliminary treatment, primary treatment, secondary treatment, tertiary treatment, and disinfection. A typical schematic flow and process diagram for wastewater treatment is shown in Figure 8-1A.[4]

Preliminary treatment comprises the conditioning of wastewater as it enters the treatment plant. Preliminary treatment removes materials that might be harmful to or may adversely affect the operation of the treatment plant or process equipment. Such material may include lumber, cardboard, rags, stones, sand, plastic, and grit. Methods and

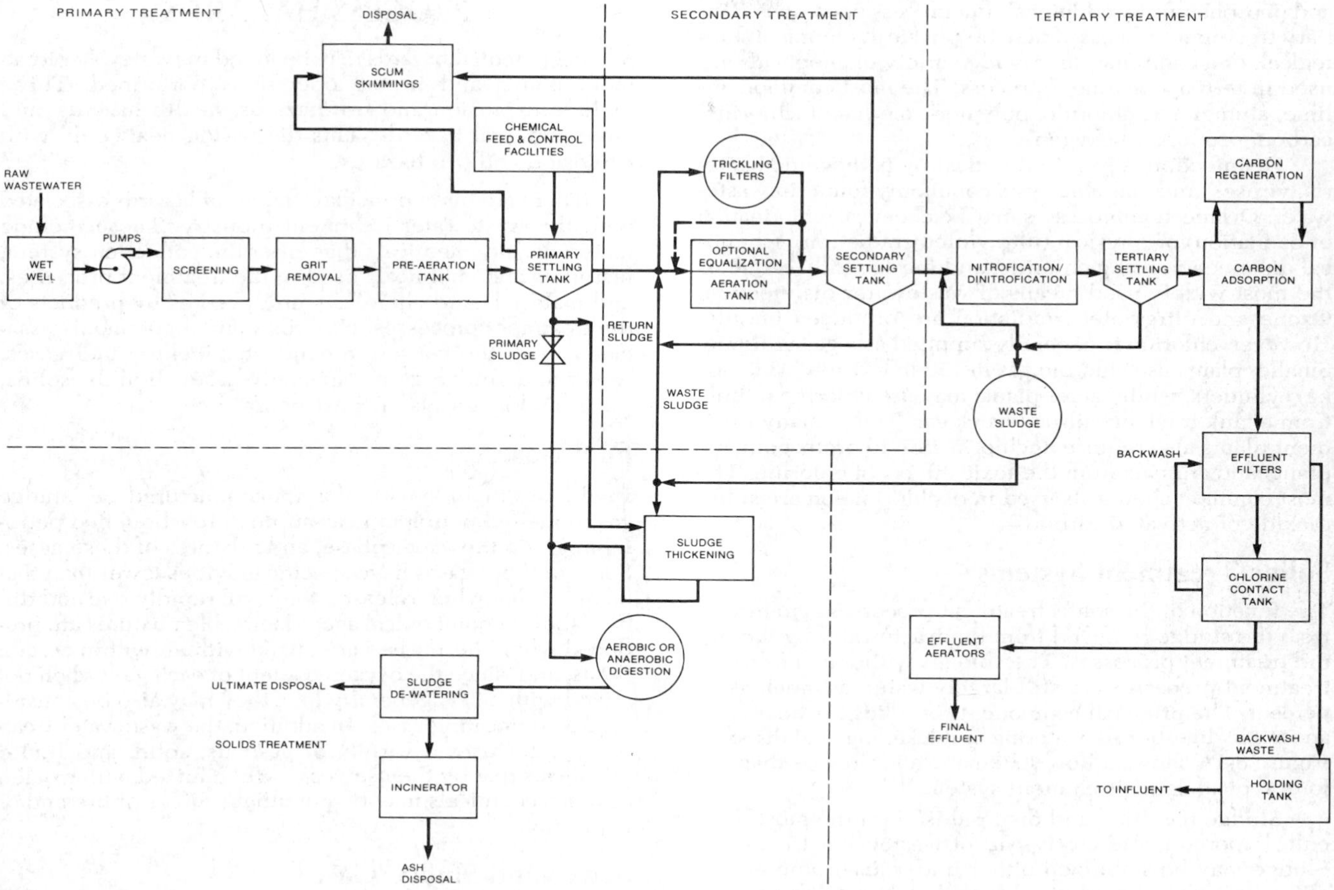

FIG. 8-1B. Typical schematic flow and process diagram.[4]

equipment used to remove these materials include comminutors, mechanically or manually cleaned bar racks, and bar screens. Particularly, in combined sewers, grit and sand washed into the collection system can damage mechanical equipment and adversely affect downstream units, such as sedimentation tanks and digesters. Grit is generally removed by gravity or in aerated grit chambers.

Primary treatment is first-stage sedimentation, which removes settleable suspended solids, and floating material such as grease and scum from the wastewater. Well-operated primary treatment facilities may remove as much as 60 percent of the influent-suspended solids and 30 percent of the influent biochemical oxygen demand. However, primary treatment does not remove colloidal or dissolved solids. In some treatment plants, chemicals, such as lime, alum, or ferric chloride, are added to increase the colloidal solids removal.

Secondary treatment is intended to reduce the concentrations of the remaining suspended solids and the dissolved and colloidal organic matter in the wastewater. Such material is not removed to any significant degree in primary treatment. A wastewater treatment plant having secondary treatment following primary treatment commonly can achieve removal of 85 percent of the influent-suspended solids and biochemical oxygen demand of the raw wastewater. Secondary treatment processes may be either biological or physical-chemical.

Most municipal secondary treatment processes are biological. These processes may be classified as fixed film or suspended growth. Fixed film processes include trickling filters, bio-towers, and rotating biological contactors (RBC). Suspended growth processes include aerobic ponds, oxidation ditches, and a variety of air- and oxygen-activated sludge systems. In each process, a mixed population of microorganisms is established in the presence of oxygen. These microorganisms metabolize the dissolved organic matter in the wastewater and form a biological mass. The effluent from fixed film or suspended growth processes contains suspensions of biological solids. These solids are removed from the treated wastewater in a secondary sedimentation tank for further processing.

In a small number of cases physical-chemical treatment is used in place of, or in combination with, biological unit processes. Physical-chemical processes can include chemical coagulation, precipitation, and filtration to remove suspended matter, and activated carbon absorption to remove soluble organics. In addition to lime, alum, and ferric chloride, a variety of anionic and cationic polymers are also used to enhance settling in the physical-chemical process.

Tertiary treatment is used, as required, to reduce the concentration of inorganic and organic constituents below the concentrations achievable through secondary treatment. Tertiary treatment also includes the removal of nitrogen and phosphorous by additional unit process operations. Tertiary treatment processes may be physical, chemical, biological, or a combination. A wide variety of chemicals are used in tertiary treatment process. The most common are lime, alum, ferric chloride, polymers, methanol, chlorine, carbon, ozone, and oxygen.

Disinfection is required to destroy pathogenic bacteria, viruses, and amoebic cysts commonly found in wastewater. Disinfection processes may be chemical (chlorination or ozonation) or physical (ultraviolet irradiation). Chemical disinfection using chlorine, and infrequently ozone, is the most widely used means of wastewater disinfection. Ozone and ultraviolet irradiation are produced on site. However, chlorine is generally supplied as a gas or liquid. Smaller plants use chlorine gas in 150-lb to 1-ton (23 to 907 kg) cylinders, while larger plants may use chlorine in bulk from a tank truck or railroad truck car. Today many treatment plants also require dechlorination to protect aquatic plants and animals from the toxic effects of chlorine. The most common chemicals used in dechlorination are sulfur dioxide or activated carbon.

Solids Treatment Systems

The function of the solids treatment processes is to further treat the sludge removed from the wastewater by the liquid treatment processes. The sludges withdrawn from the treatment processes are still largely water, as much as 97 percent. The principal components of solids treatment are: anaerobic digestion, dewatering or thickening, and disposal. Figure 8-1A shows a flow schematic and process diagram for a typical solids treatment system.[4]

Sludge handling and disposal is often the most difficult, important, and costly part of wastewater treatment. Sludge may be stabilized either under anaerobic or aerobic conditions. Anaerobic sludge digestion takes place in the absence of free oxygen. The solid end product of anaerobic digestion is relatively nonputrescible and inoffensive. The off-gas produced in anaerobic sludge digestion contains about 65 percent methane and may be collected and used as fuel.

Both anaerobic and aerobic digestion result in a reduction in the total volume and weight of the excess organic matter. It is often desirable, before final disposal, to reduce further the volume and weight of sludge and to change it from a liquid that is more than 95 percent water to a semisolid form. This dewatering may be accomplished by using drying beds, vacuum filters, centrifuges, filter presses, or mechanical gravity units. The dewatering operation often is enhanced by chemically conditioning the sludge with lime or polymers before dewatering. The conditioning may include a thickening step which could use gravity or air flotation. Thermal conditioning may also be used to prepare sludge for dewatering.

In smaller plants much of the dewatered and stabilized sludge is trucked to sanitary landfills. Municipal sludge, however, contains essential plant nutrients and useful trace elements. Some treatment plants take advantage of these nutrients and apply the sludge to the land. The sludge can be composted and used as a soil conditioner, or the sludge can be applied as a liquid fertilizer. For larger plants, or where land is not available, sludge is often incinerated. The two most common types of incineration systems are the multiple-hearth furnace and the fluid-bed incinerator. The exhaust gas from the incinerator must be treated carefully to avoid air pollution. The incinerator ash can also be toxic and requires special handling and disposal.

PROCESS HAZARDS

Several potential hazards may be found in wastewater treatment plants and in the operations performed. These include explosion and fire hazards, health hazards, and environmental hazards. This discussion deals only with explosion and fire hazards.

There are three principal sources of hazards associated with the wastewater treatment industry. These include materials and chemicals that enter the collection system, materials and chemicals used in the treatment processes, and materials and chemicals produced as by-products of the treatment processes. Hazards sources commonly associated with the wastewater industry include fuel gases, sewer and sludge gases, specialty gases, liquids, solids, dusts, and materials of construction.

Fuel Gases

Fuel gases include natural gas, manufactured gas, sludge gas, liquefied petroleum gas-air mixtures, liquefied petroleum gas in the vapor phase, and mixtures of these gases. Some of these gases have specific gravities lower than that of air, so that when released they will rapidly rise and diffuse above a point of leakage. Flammable mixtures are produced when these gases are mixed with air within certain limits, and, since the oxygen content of each gas (when not mixed with air) is generally low, they may also be considered as suffocating gases. In addition, the wastewater treatment plant uses a variety of gaseous, solid, and liquid chemicals that by themselves or when mixed with oxygen or other chemicals may be potential sources of fire and/or explosion.

Sewer and Sludge Gases

Sewer and sludge gases are flammable gases resulting from the fermentation or decomposition of organic matter. Explosive conditions (especially concerning the anaerobic digestion process) may result when these gases are mixed with air within certain limits.

Specialty Gases

Specialty gases utilized for (1) laboratory analysis and instrumentation calibration, e.g., hydrogen, methane, etc.; (2) wastewater treatment plant unit processes, e.g., chlorine, ozone, etc.; and (3) welding operations, e.g., acetylene, oxygen, etc., may provide flammable and/or explosive conditions when either acting alone or mixed with other chemicals.

Liquids

Disposal of liquid waste chemical products gathered through the collection system and discharged into the wastewater treatment plants may be potential sources or contributing causes of fire and/or explosive conditions. Hydrocarbon liquids, such as gasoline, kerosene, oils, and other solvents, either discharged to drains or used for various applications at wastewater treatment plants may also provide fire and/or explosion hazards at certain locations.

Combustible Solids and Dusts

Solids, such as granulated or powdered activated carbon, and other combustible dust by-products produced by various wastewater treatment processes, may be combustible or cause potential fire and/or explosive conditions.

Materials of Construction

Some materials of construction used in wastewater treatment plants, such as (1) plastic, (2) fiberglass-reinforced plastics (FRP), (3) paints and coatings, (4) insulating materials, and (5) furnishings, may either be combustible or limited combustible under certain conditions. Some of these materials can present a considerable fuel load, if ignited.

Sources of Ignition

In addition to a combustible or flammable fuel source, there must also be a source of ignition to cause a fire or explosion to take place. The potential ignition of flammable gases, liquids, and solids (including dusts) that may be found at a wastewater treatment plant is limited by certain fundamental conditions. Gases and generated vapors must be mixed with air or oxygen to form a flammable mixture, and provided heat of sufficient intensity for ignition. Ignition may result from one or more of the following causes: open flames and hot surfaces, electrical arcs, sparks, or chemical reaction.

Open flames and hot surfaces: These are potential means of ignition and may be encountered during operations and repairs or with malfunctioning equipment and appliances. Sources of ignition can include welding equipment, boilers, incinerators, kerosene-type lanterns, internal combustion engines, and smoking by humans.

Electrical arcs and sparks: Sustained arcing faults can cause extensive damage to electrical switchgear and motor control centers. This can provide sufficient heat to ignite flammable gases or vapors present or generated as a result of the arc, e.g., pyrolysis of insulating material.

Sparks generated by (1) defective/worn electrical and mechanical equipment, (2) activities performed by personnel, and (3) static electricity may be a source of ignition for gases or flammable vapors.

Chemical reaction: Fire and explosion may result due to the chemical reaction of substances that are (1) introduced by the wastewater treatment plant influent, (2) used for laboratory analyses, (3) required in various unit processes, and (4) produced as by-products. Chemical reactions can cause hazardous conditions that range in severity from the generation of flames, e.g., spontaneous combustion, to explosions.

Many collection systems collect not only wastewater but a variety of hazardous materials and chemicals. Materials and chemicals that enter the collection system are the most numerous type of in-plant hazards, are the least controllable, and, therefore, probably present the most risk of fire and explosion.

Some industries discharge combustible or explosive products, such as alcohol, industrial solvents, hexane, and other liquids and gases. Sewers also collect natural gas or gasoline from leaking pipelines or underground storage tanks. Combined sewers are particularly dangerous because they collect hazardous liquids and gases from spills on the highway, and fire departments often wash flammable hydrocarbons from traffic accidents into the combined sewer. There is also always the possibility of illegal discharge of explosive or flammable material into the sewer system.

Pumping stations that handle raw wastewater are subject to the same hazards as the collection system. When confined in a wet well, many hydrocarbons float on the surface of the wastewater, and many gases are lighter than air and diffuse rapidly through the structure. Other liquid treatment processes, such as screening equipment and grit chambers that are housed in buildings or in below-grade pits, are often subject to the same fire and explosion hazards as the pumping station wet well. Unit processes, such as primary sedimentation, are generally open and allow lighter gases to escape but may collect and concentrate floating flammable liquids. Secondary and tertiary sedimentation tanks and aeration tanks not preceded by primary sedimentation may also collect and concentrate floating flammable liquids.

Liquid treatment processes are not only subject to the hazardous materials and chemicals in the incoming wastewater, but they are subject to a variety of chemicals used as additives in treating the wastewater. Some of these materials are flammable or explosive, some are nonflammable but accelerate combustion, and some are not hazardous by themselves but react with other materials or chemicals. Gases commonly used in wastewater treatment and their physical properties are shown in Table 8-1A and their uses described below.[4]

Natural gas and gasoline are used as vehicle fuels, to heat buildings and unit processes, to provide hot water for personnel and cleaning operations, and for engine-driven pumps or generators. Methanol is used as a carbon source in denitrification processes. Oxygen is used in certain types of biological processes, such as oxygen-activated sludge. Chlorine and ozone are used for disinfection, and sulfur dioxide is used in dechlorination processes. Lime, alum, ferric chloride, and polymers are used in sedimentation processes; and granulated and powdered carbon are used in some activated sludge processes or in carbon columns to remove organic compounds.

Solids treatment processes not only use gases and chemicals, but some processes also produce explosive or flammable materials or gases. Although there are several anaerobic processes that produce sludge gas, the principal gas-producing unit process is anaerobic digestion. When organic matter is decomposed in the absence of oxygen, a sludge gas is produced. This sludge gas is approximately 65 percent methane. This gas is often used in large plants as a fuel source. When sludge decomposes in sewers, wet wells, pits, or other tanks it can produce a form of sludge gas sometimes called sewer gas. Although never used as a fuel source, sewer gas can contain up to 5 percent methane and can reach explosive limits if confined in improperly ventilated spaces.[3]

As with liquid treatment processes, natural gas is used to heat solids treatment unit processes, such as anaerobic digesters and other heat treatment processes. Natural gas is also used as a fuel in sludge incinerators. Ammonia is used as a nutrient in some activated sludge processes, and is a by-product of air-stripping processes, and some composting and sludge dewatering processes. Chlorine and ozone are used in sludge stabilization processes. Hydrogen sulfide is found in sewer gas and sludge gas, and is a by-product of some sludge stabilization and dewatering processes. Nitrogen is used as a medium to transport very dry organic material in certain sludge dehydration processes and is a by-product of on-site oxygen generation processes. Oxygen is used in some sludge stabilization processes and in reaeration processes.

There are, of course, many other chemicals, fuels, and materials used in or around the wastewater treatment plant that might present a fire or explosion hazard, if not handled properly. These chemicals and gases include solvents,

TABLE 8-1A ***Gases Commonly Found in Wastewater Treatment Plants***[4]

Name/Chemical Formula	Explosive Limits (% vol) LEL	UEL	Density[a] Heavier/ Lighter than Air	Sources
Ammonia (NH_3)	16	25	L	—Storage tank leaks
Chlorine[b] (Cl_2)	Nonflammable		H	—Disinfection processes —Storage leaks
Gasoline (C_5H_{12}–C_9H_{20})	1.3	7	H	—Storage tank —Tank truck spills
Hydrogen Sulfide (H_2S)	4.3	46	H	—Sewer gas —Sludge gas
Natural Gas (fuel gas)	3.1	15	L	—Gas piping leaks
Nitrogen (N_2)	Nonflammable		L	—Storge tanks —Oxygen generation processes —Dentrification processes
Oxygen[b] (O_2)	Nonflammable		L	—Generation of oxygen on site —Activated sludge processes —Storage tanks —Sludge processes
Ozone[b] (O_3)	Nonflammable		H	—Disinfection processes —On-site generation processes
Sewer Gas[c]	5.3	19.3	L	—Sewer systems
Sludge Gas[d]	5	15	L	—Sludge digestion processes
Sulfur Dioxide (SO_2)	Nonflammable		H	—Dechlorination processes —Storage tanks

NOTE a: This table lists the physical properties at standard temperature and pressure. Due to actual field conditions, these gases may disperse and may be present throughout the structure.
NOTE b: These gases accelerate combustion.
NOTE c: Contains approximately 70 percent carbon dioxide, 5 percent methane, and 25 percent other gases. (Source: USEPA.)
NOTE d: Contains approximately 65 percent methane, 30 percent carbon dioxide, and 5 percent other gases. (Source: USEPA.)

oxidizing materials, hydrogen, acetylene, kerosene, oils, and a variety of specialty gases used in laboratory analyses and instrumentation calibration. The handling of these gases and chemicals is beyond the scope of this chapter, but they are covered in other NFPA documents.

FIRE AND EXPLOSION MITIGATION

General Practice

The principal control procedures used to minimize potential fire and explosion incidents at wastewater treatment plants include: (1) hazard evaluation, (2) process and equipment controls, (3) ventilation, (4) materials of construction, and (5) education. These control procedures also include the proper electrical classification of hazardous locations, and the proper selection, installation, and operation of electrical equipment, motors, and devices that are suitable for these locations. Effective control procedures cannot be implemented and enforced without the complete cooperation of the public, private, and government sectors with plant management and personnel, in comprehensive safety programs.

Hazard Evaluation

A hazard evaluation should be initiated early in the design process and the hazard prevention and protection recommendations integrated into plant process specification or design considerations. The evaluation should be reviewed and updated periodically as conditions at the plant change. All wastewater processes should be given some kind of hazard evaluation before plants are built and whenever significant changes are made. Some evaluations can be quite informal, while others are highly structured with complete documentation and attempts at quantification of hazard inherent in the operation.

The first and most important consideration is the identification of potential hazards. The potential hazard associated with the raw wastewater entering the plant, the materials used in the treatment processes, and materials produced by the treatment processes must be completely understood and evaluated. The effect of temperature and pressure outside of normal ranges must be studied. The possibility of creating a hazardous by-product and gradually increasing its concentration in a closed system must be considered. In other words, there must be complete hazard identification for all aspects of the treatment. With this information, the potential severity of the process hazards can be determined. Then the means to control the anticipated hazards can be identified. The most important aspect of hazard analysis is complete, comprehensive hazard recognition.[5]

Risk Evaluation

Risk evaluation takes into account the likelihood of the hazard resulting in a fire or explosion. Numerical quantification of the risk requires estimation of failure rates of equipment and people. A judgment must be made of the necessary degree of maintenance of all important equipment and instruments, as well as the degree of training and judgment required of operators.

Risk control demands that wastewater treatment processes and equipment be well designed and well maintained to minimize the potential for the occurrence of leaks and spills. Redundant instrumentation, emergency controls, and fail-safe design are some of the tools of risk control. Venting and pressure-relief systems are essential for the preservation of process equipment. Damage-limiting construction should be used where processes are housed in a structure. Equipment and piping should be well supported to prevent vibrations that could cause leaks.

Control of Fire and Explosions

The three basic ways to control explosions and fire are: (1) to remove the fuel or explosive material, (2) to remove oxygen required for combustion, or (3) to remove the source of ignition. In most wastewater treatment plants it is difficult to control the fuel or oxygen sources, therefore, controlling the source of ignition is most practical. Each part of the system, whether collection, liquid treatment, solids treatment, or fuel and chemical handling, has different potential sources of ignition to be considered. In general, the potential for ignition within the collection system is restricted to those sites where personnel entry is possible. Therefore, manholes and pumping stations are likely to present the greatest concern. The introduction of ignition sources at these sites must be limited to those occasions following due life-safety procedural mandates and always with adequate ventilation. In the event that a foreign combustible material enters the sewer system, removal by vacuum or coverage with foam may be necessary.

The potential for ignition within the liquid stream of a treatment plant is restricted to flammable materials entering the early stages of treatment and to flammable gases generated as by-products of wastewater decomposition in nonflowing or septic portions of the liquid stream. Introduction of ignition sources into these areas should be limited, and adequate ventilation should always be provided.

Conditions in the solids treatment stream are often similar to liquid treatment processes. The potential for ignition within the solids treatment process is restricted to floating flammable materials skimmed from tanks and to flammable gases generated as by-products of anaerobic decomposition of sewage solids. Introduction of ignition sources into these areas should be limited, and adequate ventilation should always be provided.

Fuel and chemical handling and storage areas, including laboratories, require special consideration. In general, the potential for ignition is restricted to reactive or flammable chemicals, liquid fuels, flammable natural fuel gases, and fuels generated as by-products for use in various unit processes. Introduction of ignition sources into these areas should be limited, and adequate ventilation should always be provided. Chemicals and fuels should always be stored in accordance with safety codes and the manufacturer's instructions. Reactive chemicals should always be stored separately.

Ventilation

Mitigation of explosions and fire hazards is best achieved by copious flushing with fresh air, i.e., ventilation. Ventilation rates for enclosed spaces containing wastewater exposed to the atmosphere should be based upon the calculated vaporization rate of the most volatile liquid anticipated to be present in the wastewater. In considering ventilation requirements, the designer should base calculations upon the surface area of channels, tanks, or other vessels containing wastewater exposed to the atmosphere; the temperature of the wastewater; the ambient air temperature; and the vaporization rate of the volatile liquid. Allowances should be made for vaporization rate of the liquid from the free water surface in connecting sewers within a reasonable distance from the structure, turbulence that may accelerate vaporization of the volatile liquid, inefficiency of the ventilation system in purging the enclosures, and any other factors that the designer could reasonably expect to affect the rate of release of the flammable vapor to the structure. Table 8-1B presents typical ventilation rates for various areas in the wastewater treatment plants. Ventilation rates should conform to Table 8-1B or be based on actual calculations, whichever is greater.

TABLE 8-1B. ***Minimum Ventilation Rates***[4]

Description	Ventilation Rate
Wet wells, screen rooms, and other enclosed spaces with wastewater exposed to atmosphere.[a]	12 air changes/hour[b]
Rooms or spaces intended for storage or conveyance of wastewater solids.	12 air changes/hour
Equipment rooms, tunnels, and other below-grade spaces.	
With gas piping and/or flammable gas equipment handling.[a]	12 air changes/hour or 74 fpm velocity in tunnels or galleries
Without gas piping.	6 air changes/hour or 37 fpm velocity in tunnels or galleries

NOTE a: Combustible-gas detection equipment recommended.
NOTE b: Consideration should be given to higher ventilation rates when the collection system serves a significant industrial area or is a combined system.

Materials of Construction

Materials of construction can be divided into three basic categories: (1) combustible, (2) noncombustible, and (3) limited combustible. These terms are defined in NFPA 220, *Standard Types of Building Construction*. Construction materials being considered for wastewater treatment plants should be selected based upon the fire hazard and fire risk evaluation. The proper application of construction materials will not prevent explosion or fire hazards. The proper application may, however, reduce or eliminate effects of fire or explosion by maintaining structural integrity, controlling flamespread and smoke generation, preventing the release of toxic products of combustion, and maintaining serviceability and operation of the facility.

Materials of construction meeting the definition for noncombustible should be used in all building or unit processes that are considered *critical* to the integrity of the treatment plant (e.g., raw wastewater pumping station), and that, if out of service for even a few hours, could permanently or unacceptably damage the environment or endanger public health by allowing the release of raw wastewater or sludge. All buildings should be constructed in accordance with all national and local fire codes.

Materials of construction meeting the definition for noncombustible or limited combustible should be used in building or unit processes that are considered *important* to the integrity of the treatment plant (e.g., biological treatment), and that, if out of service for short periods of time, would not permanently or unacceptably damage the environment or endanger public health, but would become critical if continued out of service for several days.

Any appropriate materials of construction can be used in other areas of the treatment plant, where being out of service for longer periods of time (a week or more) would not permanently or unacceptably damage the environment or endanger public health.

For separate sanitary sewers serving residential areas, where there is limited possibility that significant quantities of flammable or hazardous materials will enter the system, all appropriate material may be considered. For sanitary sewers that may handle flammable or hazardous materials and for all combined sewers, only materials meeting the definition of noncombustible or limited combustible should be used.

Structures entered by personnel that handle raw or partially treated wastewater should be constructed only of materials meeting the definition of noncombustible or limited combustible. When combustible materials and coatings are used, consideration should be given to flamespread rates, smoke generation, and release of toxics during fire events.

Noncombustible materials should be used for air-supply and exhaust systems. However, when combustible or limited combustible materials are used to control corrosion, approved smoke dampers and fire dampers should be installed. Separate smoke ventilation systems are preferred; however, smoke venting can be integrated into normal ventilation systems using automatic or manually positioned dampers and motor speed control.

Cellular or foamed plastic materials should not be used as interior finish. Roof coverings should be Class A. Materials of construction and interior finishes should provide a maximum degree of fire resistance, with a minimum flamespread rate and smoke generation for a particular application.

Plastic or fiberglass-reinforced plastic products are often used as materials of construction in unit processes, such as rotating biological contactors (RBC), bio-towers, trickling filters, inclined plate (tube) settlers, ventilation ducts, and other equipment which may be subject to corrosion. Under normal operating conditions, these plastic or fiberglass-reinforced plastic materials may be submerged; however, during maintenance or repair they may become exposed. Extreme care should be taken with open flame, such as cutting torches, during any maintenance or repair operations, because exposed plastic or fiberglass-reinforced plastic materials may present a considerable fuel load, if ignited.

Education

Another important and often overlooked mitigation measure is education. In-house training programs, such as plant emergency organizations (PEO) and housekeeping/maintenance, for all employees should be established that will provide information to (1) understand, (2) identify, (3) prevent, and (4) handle hazardous sources or situations relating to potential fire, explosion, and toxicity problems. Close liaison should be implemented between the local fire department (including other authorized emergency personnel) and wastewater treatment plant safety personnel so that mutually approved emergency procedures (including familiarity of the plant) can be established.

FIRE PROTECTION MEASURES

Wastewater treatment plants receive flammable and combustible liquids and gases in three ways: (1) through the collection system, (2) through introduction into the treatment processes, or (3) as by-products of the processes. In spite of the considerable care taken in the design and operation, fires and explosions do occur, and fire protection and suppression equipment is necessary. Generally, the fire protection and suppression measures used in the wastewater treatment industry include: (1) automatic sprinkler systems, (2) chemical suppression systems, (3) standpipes and hydrants, (4) portable fire extinguishers, and (5) special fire protection measures.

Automatic Sprinkler Systems

Automatic sprinkler systems should be installed where appropriate in buildings or structures located at a wastewater treatment plant. The fire hazard evaluation should include detailed hazard classifications, with system density and rates of application sufficient to suppress any anticipated fire. In certain areas of the wastewater treatment plant, such as chemical storage areas, underground tunnels or structures, or areas where electrical hazard is the principal concern, the use of other appropriate fire protection measures should be considered and carefully evaluated.

Chemical Suppression Systems

Foam, halon, and dry chemical systems should be installed or used where appropriate in buildings or structures located at a wastewater treatment plant. Foam systems are most effective for wet wells, grit and screening processes, primary clarifiers, and pits and tanks where floating flammable liquid may collect on the surface. Halon systems are generally used where computer equipment is located. Dry chemical extinguishing systems should be considered in chemical storage areas, underground tunnels or structures, or where electrical hazard is the principal concern and where water damage would seriously impair the integrity of the treatment plant.

Standpipes and Hydrants

Standpipes, hose streams, and hydrants should be provided where appropriate in buildings or structures located at a wastewater treatment plant. Water supplies should be capable of delivering the total demand of sprinklers, hose streams, and foam systems. In areas where there is no public water supply or where the public water supply is inadequate, treatment plant effluent can be used for fire protection, i.e., if all contaminents have been eliminated. In treatment plants with both a public water supply and a plant water system, the plant water system can be used as the principal source of water for the fire protection system, or it can be used as a backup to the public water supply system.

When the plant water system is used as the principal source for fire protection, the system must be capable of providing an adequate quantity and pressure and have sufficient standby capacity to meet all fire waterflow requirements. If the plant water system is used as a backup to the public water supply, the system should provide easy access and connection for pumper equipment. Where dual-hydrant systems are used, cross connections (where allowed) between the public water supply and the plant water system must be installed in accordance with local requirements. When fire pumps are the sole source of supply used in the plant water system, multiple pumps with sufficient capacity to meet fire flow requirements with the largest pump out of service should be provided. Pumps should be automatic starting with manual shutdown and should not be subject to common failure of either electrical or mechanical equipment.

Portable Fire Extinguishers

Portable fire extinguishers should be provided in buildings where appropriate. In some areas of the treatment plant, such as basements, underground pipe galleries connecting buildings, and other areas which are not occupied continuously, existing codes and standards may not be appropriate. In these cases, the authority having jurisdiction should consider local optional requirements for portable fire extinguishers, depending on frequency of occupancy, intended use and equipment contained in the space, and hazard potential for fire and/or explosion.

Special Fire Protection Measures

Some wastewater treatment plants and processes have unique problems that require special fire protection considerations. For example, fire protection measures during construction at both new and existing wastewater facilities should consider safety to life, protection of property, and potential for delays in construction, as well as plant or unit process startup. Lightning protection should be provided for those structures having a risk index (R) of four or greater, according to NFPA 78, *Lightning Protection Code*, Appendix I. In addition, arrangements should be made to permit rapid entry into the plant by the municipal fire department, police department, or other authorized personnel in case of fire or other emergency. The plant emergency organization (PEO), where provided, should be properly instructed and trained in the use of all fire protection equipment located at the treatment plant.

Early detection and reporting of fires and explosions is also important in protecting the integrity of the buildings and unit processes. Protective measures that will detect flame, heat, or smoke should be selected and installed where needed. The location of the proper types of detection equipment, e.g., smoke, heat, flame, etc., is a function of the hazard severity or electrical classification. Where appropriate, central station, local protective auxiliary, remote station, or proprietary sprinkler waterflow alarms should be provided.

BIBLIOGRAPHY

References Cited

1. Babbitt, Harold E., *Sewerage and Sewage Treatment*, 7th ed., John Wiley & Sons, Inc., New York, 1956, pp. 1-5.
2. "1988 Needs Survey Report to Congress," EPA 430/9-89-001, Feb. 1989, U.S. Environmental Protection Agency, Office of Municipal Pollution Control, Washington, DC.
3. Steel, Ernest W., *Water Supply and Sewerage*, 4th ed., McGraw-Hill, New York, 1960, pp. 396-402.
4. NFPA 820, *Recommended Practice for Fire Protection in Wastewater Treatment Plants*, National Fire Protection Association, Quincy, MA.
5. Miller, Russell L., "Chemical Processes," *Industrial Fire Hazards Handbook*, 2nd ed., National Fire Protection Association, Quincy, MA, 1984.

NFPA Codes, Standards, and Recommended Practices

Reference to the following NFPA codes, standards, and recommended practices will provide further information on the processes and safeguards for wastewater treatment operations. (See the latest *NFPA Catalog* for availability of current editions of the following documents.)

NFPA 1, *Fire Prevention Code*.
NFPA 10, *Portable Fire Extinguishers*.
NFPA 11, *Low Expansion Foam and Combined Agent Systems*.
NFPA 11A, *Medium and High Expansion Foam Systems*.
NFPA 11C, *Mobile Foam Apparatus*.
NFPA 12, *Carbon Dioxide Extinguishing Systems*.
NFPA 12A, *Halon 1301 Fire Extinguishing Systems*.
NFPA 12B, *Halon 1211 Fire Extinguishing Systems*.
NFPA 14, *Standpipe and Hose Systems*.
NFPA 15, *Water Spray Fixed Systems for Fire Protection*.
NFPA 17, *Dry Chemical Extinguishing Systems*.
NFPA 20, *Installation of Centrifugal Fire Pumps*.
NFPA 22, *Water Tanks for Private Fire Protection*.
NFPA 24, *Installation of Private Fire Service Mains*.
NFPA 30, *Flammable and Combustible Liquids Code*.
NFPA 31, *Installation of Oil Burning Equipment*.
NFPA 37, *Stationary Combustion Engines and Gas Turbines*.
NFPA 43A, *Storage of Liquid and Solid Oxidizing Materials*.
NFPA 43C, *Storage of Gaseous Oxidizing Materials*.
NFPA 45, *Fire Protection for Laboratories Using Chemicals*.
NFPA 49, *Hazardous Chemicals Data*.
NFPA 50, *Bulk Oxygen Systems at Consumer Sites*.
NFPA 51, *Oxygen-Fuel Gas Systems for Welding, Cutting, and Allied Processes*.
NFPA 51B, *Cutting and Welding Processes*.
NFPA 53M, *Fire Hazards in Oxygen-Enriched Atmospheres*.
NFPA 54, *National Fuel Gas Code*.
NFPA 58, *Storage and Handling of Liquefied Petroleum Gases*.
NFPA 59A, *Production, Storage, and Handling of Liquefied Natural Gas (LNG)*.
NFPA 61A, *Prevention of Fire and Dust Explosions in Facilities Manufacturing and Handling Starch*.
NFPA 68, *Explosion Venting*.
NFPA 69, *Explosion Prevention Systems*.
NFPA 70, *National Electrical Code®*.
NFPA 70B, *Electrical Equipment Maintenance*.
NFPA 70E, *Electrical Safety Requirements for Employee Workplaces*.
NFPA 71, *Installation, Maintenance, and Use of Signaling Systems for Central Station Service*.
NFPA 72A, *Installation, Maintenance, and Use of Local Protective Signaling Systems*.
NFPA 72B, *Installation, Maintenance, and Use of Auxiliary Protective Signaling Systems*.
NFPA 72C, *Installation, Maintenance, and Use of Remote Station Protective Signaling Systems*.
NFPA 72D, *Installation, Maintenance, and Use of Proprietary Protective Signaling Systems*.
NFPA 72E, *Automatic Fire Detectors*.
NFPA 77, *Static Electricity*.
NFPA 78, *Lightning Protection Code*.
NFPA 80, *Fire Doors and Windows*.
NFPA 82, *Incinerators, Waste and Linen Handling Systems and Equipment*.
NFPA 85A, *Prevention of Furnace Explosions in Fuel-Oil and Natural Gas-Fired Single Burner Boiler-Furnaces*.
NFPA 85B, *Prevention of Furnace Explosions in Natural Gas-Fired Multiple Boiler-Furnaces*.

NFPA 85D, *Prevention of Furnace Explosions in Fuel Oil-Fired Multiple Burner Boiler-Furnaces.*

NFPA 85F, *Installation and Operation of Pulverized Fuel Systems.*

NFPA 90A, *Installation of Air Conditioning and Ventilating Systems.*

NFPA 91, *Blower and Exhaust Systems for Dust, Stock, and Vapor Removal or Conveying.*

NFPA 101®, *Life Safety Code®.*

NFPA 204M, *Smoke and Heat Venting.*

NFPA 220, *Types of Building Construction.*

NFPA 231, *General Storage.*

NFPA 241, *Safeguarding Building Construction and Demolition Operations.*

NFPA 251, *Methods of Fire Tests of Building Construction and Materials.*

NFPA 253, *Standard Method of Test for Critical Radiant Flux of Floor Covering Systems Using a Radiant Heat Energy Source.*

NFPA 255, *Method of Test of Surface Burning Characteristics of Building Materials.*

NFPA 256, *Methods of Fire Tests of Roof Coverings.*

NFPA 259, *Standard Test Method for Potential Heat of Building Materials.*

NFPA 321, *Basic Classification of Flammable and Combustible Liquids.*

NFPA 327, *Cleaning or Safeguarding Small Tanks and Containers.*

NFPA 328, *Flammable and Combustible Liquids and Gases in Manholes, Sewers, and Similar Underground Structures.*

NFPA 329, *Underground Leakage of Flammable and Combustible Liquids.*

NFPA 395, *Storage of Flammable and Combustible Liquids on Farms and Isolated Construction Projects.*

NFPA 491M, *Manual of Hazardous Chemical Reactions.*

NFPA 496, *Purged and Pressurized Enclosures for Electrical Equipment.*

NFPA 600, *Private Fire Brigades.*

NFPA 602, *Guard Operations in Fire Loss Prevention.*

NFPA 1231, *Water Supplies for Suburban and Rural Fire Fighting.*

Additional Reading

ASTM E136, *Standard Test Method for Behavior of Materials in a Vertical Tube Furnace at 1382°F (750°C), American Society for Testing and Materials, Philadelphia, PA.*

ASTM E814, *Standard Method of Fire Tests of Through-Penetration Fire Stops*, American Society for Testing and Materials, Philadelphia, PA.

Chlorine Manual, 5th ed., Chlorine Institute, Washington, DC, 1986.

40 CFR761.30, July 1989, Code of Federal Regulations, Office of the Federal Register, National Archives and Records Administration, U.S. Government Printing Office, Washington, DC.

Gold, *Fire Brigade Training Manual*, National Fire Protection Association, Quincy, MA, 1983.

OSHA 1910.156, July 1989, Code of Federal Regulations, Office of the Federal Register, National Archives and Records Administration, U.S. Government Printing Office, Washington, DC.

SOLVENT EXTRACTION

Revised by C. Louis Kingsbaker

Seeds that contain approximately 20 percent oil by weight, such as soybeans, are usually extracted directly. Seeds containing more than 20 percent oil usually are prepared by prepressing to reduce their oil content to 10 to 20 percent. Facilities employing this step are called prepress solvent extraction plants. Some of the major oilseeds processed by this procedure are cottonseed, rapeseed, flaxseed, corngerm, sunflower, safflower, peanuts, and copra.

Additional information relevant to the solvent extraction process can be found in: Section 2, Chapter 28; "Storage and Handling of Grain Mill Products," Section 3, Chapter 5, "Flammable and Combustible Liquids;" Section 3, Chapter 12, "Dusts;" and Section 9, Chapter 17, "Hazardous Waste Control."

THE SOLVENT EXTRACTION PROCESS

Solvents Used

Hexane is the solvent exclusively used in oilseed extraction because it is relatively easy to desolventize from meal and oil products, making them nontoxic; it is essentially immiscible with water; and it can be produced from petroleum at a relatively low cost. Its major disadvantage, i.e., the danger of fire and/or explosion, is overcome by careful design, construction, and operation of the solvent extraction plant.

Other flammable solvents, such as mixtures of aromatic hydrocarbons, are used for extracting lignite, Douglas fir bark, and other special raw materials whose end products are not used by humans for internal consumption.

Description of the Process

Unit operations for extraction of all oilseeds are similar, and usually the same equipment can handle the flakes or cakes from these materials. (See Figure 8-2A.)

For safe storage, oilseeds are brought into the processing plant, checked for moisture content, and dried in a flue gas dryer to about 10 or 11 percent moisture content by weight. To eliminate fire hazards in both the dryer and in the preparation step of the extraction process, the seeds are cleaned to remove trash, dirt, and foreign material before they are dried.

The solvent extraction process is continuous. The rate is usually controlled by measuring at the weigh scale and adjusting the cracking mill feed rolls. The cracking mill splits the hulls and breaks the seeds. Hulls are removed by screens and aspiration. The seeds are flaked between rollers after passing through a rotary steam tube conditioner. Here they are heated to temperatures between 140 and 165°F (60 and 74°C) and the moisture content is adjusted to between 10 and 10½ percent.

Hot flakes are delivered to the extractor, which is usually of the continuous percolation type. The liquid solvent enters above the flake bed and drains or percolates through the bed to a compartment below the flakes to be recycled by a pump to another stage of the extractor. Most percolation extractors have six or more extraction stages.

There are many types of percolation extractors, some of which are the vertical basket, rotary, perforated belt, and rectangular loop extractors. (See Figure 8-2B.) Fresh, recovered hexane solvent, heated to about 140°F (60°C), contacts flakes near the discharge end of the extractor to remove the remaining oil from the flakes. This solvent, which now contains some oil, is pumped from stage to stage in a direction counter to the flow of flakes, becoming richer in oil with each successive stage. The oil extracted from the flakes and mixed with hexane usually has a concentration of 25 percent when it exits the extractor. The amount of hexane solvent added to the extractor is one weight part of solvent to one weight part of flake. This is defined as solvent ratio and ranges from 0.85 to 1.1. The extractor normally operates at 140°F (60°C) and at either atmospheric pressure or a slight vacuum of ½ in. water gage (124 Pa). Variable-speed drive is provided to control the extractor speed for changes of plant rate and also bed height.

After the flakes move beyond the solvent addition point, time is provided for hexane to drain. Extracted and drained flakes are conveyed to a desolventizer-toaster (D-T) in which the solvent is stripped from the flakes with open or sparge steam. Toasting is accomplished by contact with a series of trays heated indirectly by high-pressure steam.

C. Louis Kingsbaker is president of C. L. Kingsbaker, Inc., consultants to the oilseed industry.

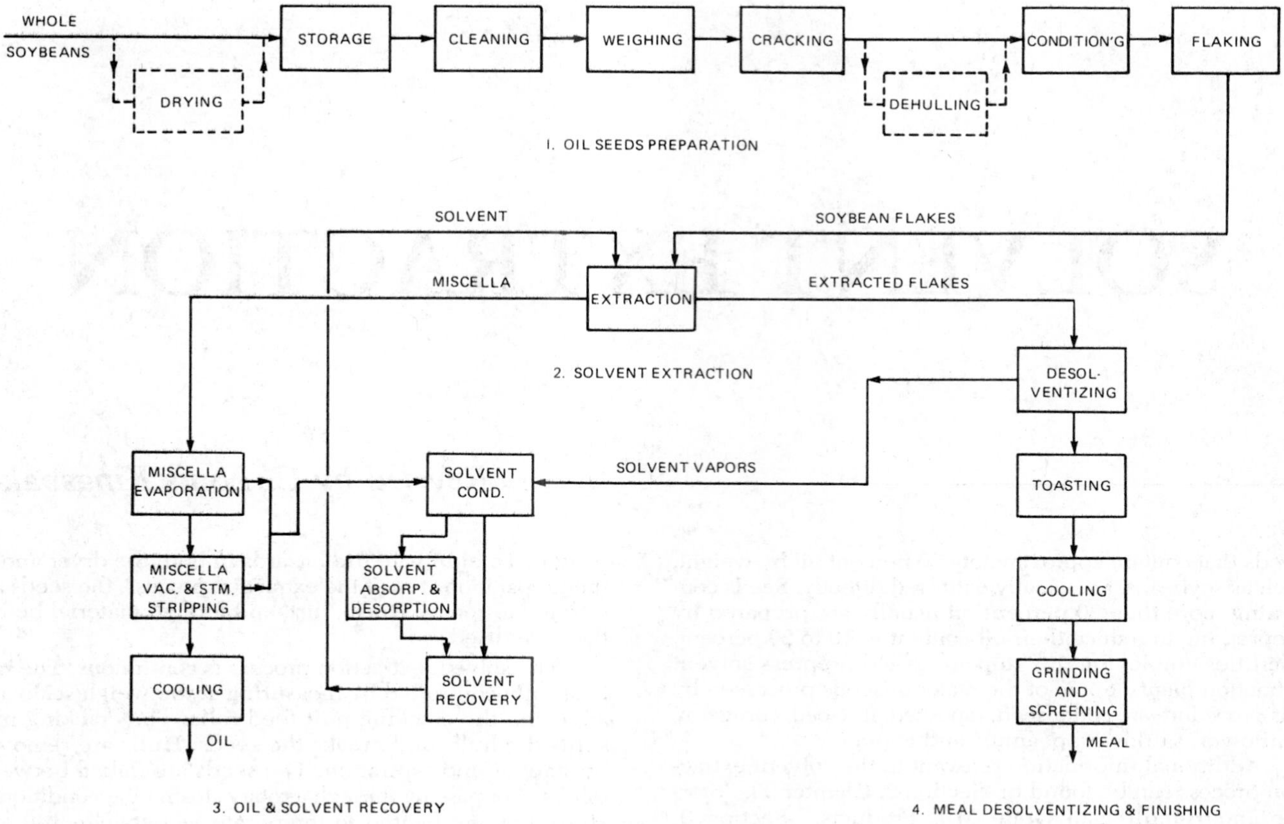

FIG. 8-2A. Flow diagram of the soybean solvent extraction process.

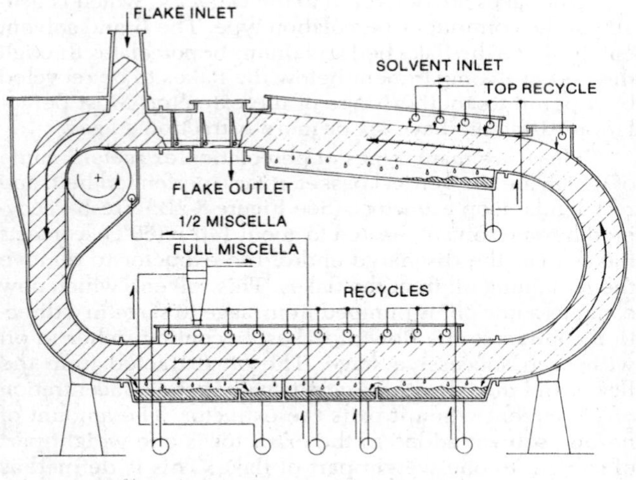

FIG. 8-2B. Rectangular loop extractor.

FIG. 8-2C. Typical desolventizer-toaster (with six trays) used for processing soybeans.

The desolventizer-toaster is a vertical, cylindrical unit consisting of multiple trays or decks. (See Figure 8-2C.) The flakes drop from tray to tray. Solvent is removed by open steam in the top three trays. The steam condenses in the flakes, raising the flake moisture content. Toasting or cooking in the bottom trays reduces the moisture content, cooks the flakes to the desired color, and destroys enzymes that are injurious to animals.

Usually about 15 percent excess sparge steam is used in the desolventizing step. The top of the desolventizer-toaster unit has a normal operating temperature of about 167°F (75°C). The flake outlet temperature from the bottom of this unit must be at least 221°F (105°C). Lower flake outlet temperatures indicate that not all solvent has been removed, which could present a potential safety hazard. The operating pressure at the top of the desolventizer-toaster should be lower than the pressure in the extractor. This will prevent steam vapor from flowing back to the extractor and stop the flow of solvent vapor downward through the desolventizer-toaster unit. Solvent and excess sparge steam vapors leaving the top of the desolventizer-toaster unit are scrubbed with liquid hexane to remove fines, condensed, and the solvent then reused in the extraction step.

From the toaster, the flakes move to a rotary steam tube dryer. After they are dried to 12 percent or less moisture content, and cooled to between 115 and 120°F (46 and 49°C), the flakes are conveyed to the meal finishing system for sizing.

Oil is removed from the solvent in three stages, by two long-tube rising film evaporators and a stripping column. The first-stage evaporator operates at a vacuum of about 15 in. of mercury (51 kPa) on the tube side and uses the vapors from the desolventizer-toaster to provide the heat. Miscella from the first-stage evaporator has an oil concentration of about 50 to 60 percent. The second-stage evaporator operates at atmospheric pressure, using low-pressure steam in the shell side. Final removal of solvent from the 92 percent miscella out of the second-stage evaporator is carried out in a stripping column operating under vacuum ranging from 22 to 27 in. (74 to 91 kPa) of mercury at a temperature of 210 to 240°F (99 to 115°C) and using open or sparge steam at the bottom of the column. The vacuum dries or removes water from the oil, and the sparge steam strips out the final traces of hexane solvent.

All the solvent is condensed and returned to the solvent separator along with solvent from the flake-desolventizing step. The solvent separator is designed with a 15-min. holding interval to allow water condensed in the process to separate from the solvent. The water flows from the separator to a wastewater evaporator, where it is heated to at least 200°F (93°C) with open steam to remove any entrained solvent, before leaving the plant for a wastewater trap and finally to a sewer. The separated solvent is returned to the extractor for reuse.

A low-temperature alarm that sounds at 180°F (82°C) is required by NFPA 36, *Solvent Extraction Plants*, in plants to warn of possible carryover of hexane solvent in process wastewater entering public sewer systems. There was no such alarm at a soybean plant in Louisville, KY, when a massive quantity of hexane entered the sewers in 1981 and blew up six miles (10 km) of the sewer system.

The extractor and all other tanks and condensers in the process are vented to a separate header and into a vent recovery system. This system, which uses an edible mineral oil to absorb vent gases, consists of two columns filled with ceramic packing. One column absorbs hexane solvent vapors with a flow of cool mineral oil counter to the flow of vapor. The other column is used to strip the absorbed hexane solvent vapors from the mineral oil with open steam. A condensing system is provided to condense these vapors. The mineral oil is recirculated continuously for reuse. A blower is provided on top of the mineral oil absorber to remove the nonabsorbed water and air vapors that discharge into the atmosphere through a flame arrestor.

Efficiency of the Process

Most designers of solvent extraction facilities make efficiency guarantees for the process. The guarantees are important not only for the profitability of the process, but also for the safety of plant operation. Exceeding these guarantees indicates that there are potential safety problems, and steps must be taken to correct them. The guarantees given here are typical for the soybean processing industry and will not vary considerably when other oilseeds are processed. In a process having a capacity that can be measured in U.S. tons per 24-hr day, the following conditions can be expected:

1. Solvent loss of 0.15 percent by weight of beans processed or 0.55 U.S. gal per U.S. ton of beans (2.29 liters per metric ton).
2. Residual oil content of flakes from extractor of 0.5 percent by weight, corrected to 12 percent water by weight on a solvent-free basis.
3. Crude oil 0.15 percent of total moisture and volatiles by weight that will not flash at 300°F (150°C) in a closed-cup flash tester.
4. Soybean flakes from a meal cooler will not exceed a 0.15 pH rise in urease enzyme activity, measured by the Caskey-Knapp method.

HAZARDS OF SOLVENT EXTRACTION

The principal hazards in solvent extraction operations are the highly flammable solvents used in the process and combustible dusts associated with the storage and handling of oilseeds. Sources of ignition include arcing electrical equipment, static electricity, and open flame. Ignition can occur during regular operations, maintenance operations, or an emergency. Attempts to operate a facility beyond its design capacity can introduce hazards of abnormal operation.

Normal Operations

Solvent loss: In order to prevent fires, it is necessary to keep solvent liquid or vapor from leaving the extraction plant and controlled areas. Hexane solvent vapor is about three times heavier than air and, if not dispersed, could possibly enter areas where a source of ignition is present. In order to be ignitable, the vapor concentration in air must be within its flammable limits—1.2 to 6.9 percent by volume.

Solvent loss in an extraction plant is a key indicator to possible hazards during normal operation. A solvent loss of 0.15 percent by weight of the material processed is considered within the bounds of efficient operation. If the loss exceeds 0.30 percent, reasons for the increase must be found and corrective action taken. Table 8-2A shows the five sources of solvent loss from the extraction process and the percentage of loss attributed to each.

TABLE 8-2A. ***Sources of Solvent Loss from the Solvent Extraction Process***

Source	Loss (% by weight)
Flakes from D-T unit	0.04
Leaks	0.04
Vent gas from vent system	0.04
Oil from oil stripper	0.02
Effluent from process waste water	0.01
Total	0.15

It is of primary importance to prevent flammable solvents from leaving the extraction building and entering the preparation building. This can happen if solvent remains in the flakes after they have been removed from the desolventizer-toaster and sent to the preparation building to be ground, sized, and finished. Because the equipment in this building is not of explosionproof design, ignition could occur with disastrous results.

A simple check is to use a "pop" test on a sample from the desolventizer-toaster unit. The flakes are held in a quart (L) size can for 15 min. The can then is removed from the controlled area. As the lid is slowly opened, a match at least 8 in. (0.2 m) long is inserted into the can. If there is no flash, the solvent in the flakes is less than 0.04 percent and can be considered safe.

Whenever a transfer of flammable solvents takes place, immediate precautions must be initiated to protect the building until the solvent-laden material is removed.

Startup, shutdown, and purging: The startup or shutdown of an extraction plant introduces a transient hazard. The equipment, especially the extractor, is full of air before startup. As hexane solvent is added, the concentration of solvent vapor in the atmosphere passes through the flammable range of 1.2 to 6.9 percent by volume. Two methods are available to eliminate any possibility of ignition caused by static electricity when using hot liquid to purge the extractor of air. One method is to design the plant so hot vapors from the second-stage evaporator can flow into the extractor to rapidly heat it to 104°F (40°C) and thus replace the air. The advantage of this procedure is to shorten extractor heatup time, which usually takes about 4 hrs, to about ½ hr. Stage pumps are not started until the extractor is hot. The second method is to replace the extractor air with carbon dioxide or nitrogen gas before adding hot liquid hexane to the extractor.

Vaporproof slide gates located upstream and downstream of the extractor are closed during the warmup to prevent flow of hexane solvent vapors back to the preparation building.

A normal or controlled shutdown is accomplished by emptying the extraction plant of all oilseed flakes and hexane liquid and purging the empty extractor or desolventizer-toaster unit with air until the unit is cooled. Steam purging is used if normal maintenance is required inside the extractor.

If welding is necessary in the extraction area, personnel must take the following precautions:

1. Empty all solids and liquids.
2. Store hexane from the plant in solvent tanks isolated from the plant.
3. Steam the purge extractor, desolventizer-toaster unit, and all equipment containing hexane or miscella.
4. Fill all vessels with water.
5. Seal off flake connections from the extractor and desolventizer-toaster unit to the preparation building using water.
6. Use a portable gas analyzer to locate possible flammable mixtures.

Inert gas is satisfactory for purging an empty extractor before normal startup procedures. Inert gas can also be used for purging during normal shutdown, but steam purging is a surer method than inert gas purging for removing solvent vapor.

Abnormal Operations

Emergency breakdowns: The most serious hazard in the operation of a solvent extraction plant is an emergency breakdown in the extractor when it is full of solvent-laden flakes and cannot be emptied. Quite often the problem can neither be determined nor corrected without someone having to enter the unit.

The unit should be cooled for at least three hours, during which time a plan for correcting the problem should be devised. Then the unit should be purged with air. Steam purging is impractical and inert gas purging does not ensure a nonflammable mixture. Persons entering the unit must wear air masks and be under constant observation. Ignition sources should be eliminated, since flammable mixtures may be present.

If a desolventizer-toaster unit fails under load, the danger is that the flakes in the cooking trays may overheat and cause a fire. It is important to quickly turn off the heating system in the cooking trays when such a failure occurs. Normally, sparge or open steam can be added to the desolventizer-toaster unit for several hours to desolventize the flakes. The doors on each tray are then opened one by one and the contents carefully raked out until the unit is empty and the problem corrected.

Failures: There should be a sufficient supply of emergency cooling water to operate the condensers long enough for a safe shutdown. If cooling water fails, the process must be stopped, the steam shut off, and the vapor slide gates closed. Similar steps should be taken in the event of steam or electrical failures.

System overloads: Often a solvent extraction plant capacity is increased above its design rating. This situation can create a hazard because normally there is insufficient solvent condensing capacity to recover the solvent. This results in higher vent pressures, with the inherent danger that solvent vapors may be forced into the atmosphere or carried out with the flakes to form flammable mixtures.

FIRE PROTECTION

Fire protection for solvent extraction plants involves building construction and services, plant layout, fire protection equipment and systems, and safe operating procedures. Detailed guidance can be found in NFPA 36, *Solvent Extraction Plants*, and in other related standards, guides, and recommended practices listed at the end of this chapter.

Layout and Construction

Structural elements of solvent extraction plants should be laid out so that separation distances are adequate to isolate or dissipate flammable concentrations of solvent vapor from ignition sources. (See Figure 8-2D.)

The extraction and preparation buildings should be of fire-resistive or noncombustible construction and equipped with some form of explosion relief. It is important that electrical wiring and equipment be suitable for use in the presence of flammable vapors. All vessels, pipes, tubes, and hoses containing or carrying flammable solvent should be electrically bonded together and grounded to prevent the buildup of a static charge. Portable flammable gas detectors should be available for monitoring the atmosphere.

For a process involving combustible dust, electrical wiring and equipment should be suitable, a dust collecting system should be provided, and protection against static electricity discharges should be installed.

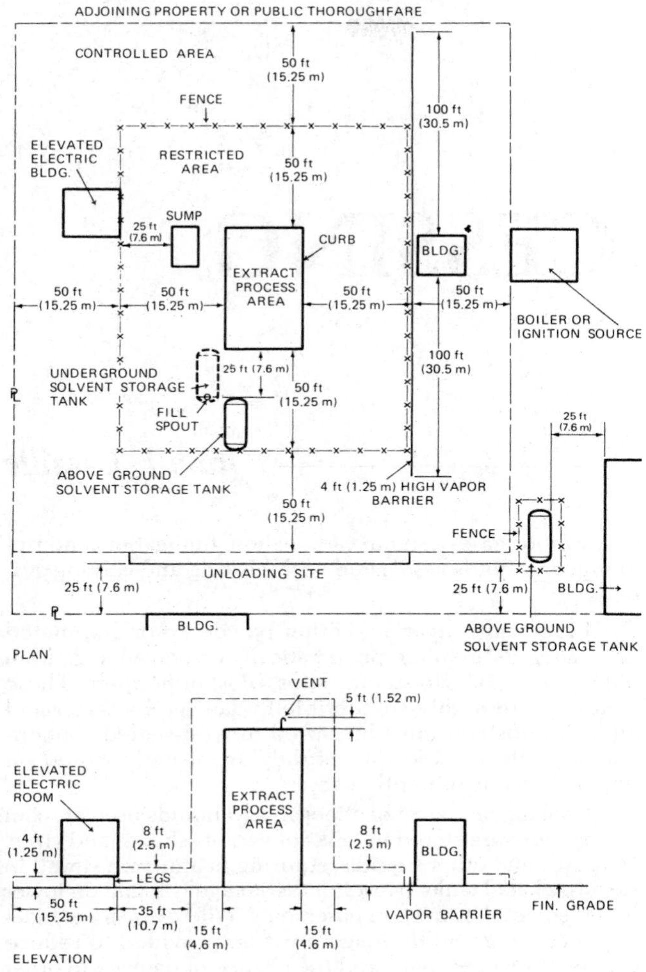

FIG. 8-2D. ***A typical distance diagram.***

Fire Protection Equipment

Water spray, deluge, or foam-water systems—singly or in combination—are suitable for use in the extractor building. Automatic sprinkler systems are appropriate for use in the preparation building. The solvent unloading and storage area may be adequately protected by portable fire extinguishers of the proper types and sizes, if the area is isolated from exposure hazards.

Portable fire extinguishers should be strategically located. The facility may also have standpipe and hose systems equipped with combination nozzles. A system of yard hydrants is an essential part of the protection. Finally, the available water supply must be adequate to meet the needs of the fixed protection and yard hydrant systems.

Policies and Procedures

It is imperative that solvent extraction equipment be operated in a manner prescribed by the manufacturer and that no attempt be made to bypass or defeat safety devices and systems. Company policy should limit the output demanded of the extraction plant so that its design capacity is not overtaxed. Policy should also provide for shutdown in the event of excessive solvent loss and for regular maintenance and cleaning operations. If solvent loss increases from 0.15 to 0.30 percent or 1 gal per ton (4.2 liters per metric ton) of material processed, an abnormal hazard exists and preventive action must be taken.

Fire prevention is a key factor in any fire protection program. This should include the conspicuous posting of safety rules and emergency procedures throughout the plant, a safety education program for new employees, the appointment of a plant emergency organization, and a compulsory monthly safety program. A safety system audit program must be implemented to regularly check the workability of all safety devices and controls.

If a fire should occur, appropriate action would be to activate fire extinguishing systems (if they are not automatically controlled), activate the plant interlock system to shut down all solids-conveying equipment in the plant, turn off the main steam valve to the extraction plant, leave the area, and notify the fire department.

BIBLIOGRAPHY

NFPA Codes, Standards, and Recommended Practices

Reference to the following NFPA codes, standards, and recommended practices will provide further information on the safeguards for solvent extraction discussed in this chapter. (See the latest *NFPA Catalog* for availability of current editions of the following documents.)

NFPA 10, *Portable Fire Extinguishers.*

NFPA 13, *Installation of Sprinkler Systems.*

NFPA 14, *Standpipe and Hose Systems.*

NFPA 15, *Water Spray Fixed Systems for Fire Protection.*

NFPA 16, *Deluge Foam-Water Sprinkler and Spray Systems.*

NFPA 24, *Installation of Private Fire Service Mains.*

NFPA 30, *Flammable and Combustible Liquids Code.*

NFPA 36, *Solvent Extraction Plants.*

NFPA 61B, *Prevention of Fires and Explosions in Grain Elevators and Facilities Handling Bulk Raw Agricultural Commodities.*

NFPA 61C, *Prevention of Fire and Dust Explosion in Feed Mills.*

NFPA 68, *Explosion Venting.*

NFPA 70, *National Electrical Code®.*

NFPA 91, *Blower and Exhaust Systems for Dust, Stock and Vapor Removal or Conveying.*

NFPA 385, *Tank Vehicles for Flammable and Combustible Liquids.*

NFPA 496, *Purged and Pressurized Enclosures for Electrical Equipment.*

Additional Reading

Collings, A. J., and Luxon, S. G., *Safe Use of Solvents*, Academic Press Inc., NY, 1982.

"Hazard and Hazard Prevention in Solvent Evaporating Ovens," *Fire Prevention*, (127), 1978, pp. 22-25.

Marcus, Y., ed., *Solvent Extraction Reviews*, Vol. 1, Marcel Dekker, Inc., NY, 1973.

Sawyer, W., "Relationship of Flash Points of Solvents, Resin Solutions, and Paints," *Journal of Coatings Technology*, 49 (627), pp. 52-55.

Tess, R. W., ed., *Solvents Theory and Practice*, American Chemical Society, Washington, DC, 1973.

Welker, J. R., Martinseen, W. E., and Johnson, D. W., "Effectiveness of Fire Control Agents for Hexane Fires," *Fire Technology*, Vol. 22, No. 3, 1986, pp. 329-340.

FOOD PROCESSING

Jane I. Lataille

The food processing industry is especially sensitive to damage from fire, smoke, heat, or water due to their contaminating aspects. Food contamination is the outstanding loss potential common to all food processing and handling facilities. Loss situations that cause relatively minor damage in other industries can cause extremely high amounts of damage to food items, since health authorities often condemn items exposed to smoke, heat, or water, even when there is no visible damage.

This chapter discusses the causes of fire losses in the food processing industry, primarily those losses associated with combustible dusts, flammable and combustible liquids, conveyors, refrigeration systems, fuel-fired equipment, and general storage. After a discussion of the raw materials that undergo food processing, the fire hazards of process equipment, gases, liquids, combustible dusts, conveyors, and storage are discussed. Finally, the safeguards are presented, including firesafe construction, sprinkler systems, and fixed extinguishing systems.

For the hazards associated with electrical control systems, see Section 2, Chapter 3, "Electrical Systems and Appliances." Section 2, Chapter 25, "Storage of Flammable and Combustible Liquids" and Section 2, Chapter 26, "Storage of Gases." These chapters provide respectively, in-depth discussions of the storage practices and hazards of flammable and combustible liquids and gases. For a discussion of the hazards of aerosol food production, see Section 2, Chapter 23, "Aerosol Charging Operations."

RAW MATERIALS

Fruits, vegetables, grains, beef, poultry, fish, and milk are common raw materials in the food processing industry. Other materials are powders, such as flour, salt, sugar, cornstarch, and cocoa; liquids, such as water, oil, alcohol, molasses, and vinegar; and miscellaneous items, such as butter, chocolate, flavorings, colorings, chemicals, and spices. In addition to product ingredients, there are cooking oils and fats; various gases used in carbonation, fumigation, and ripening; and fluids associated with heating and cooling systems.

Flour, salt, sugar, and other powdered or granulated raw materials are often pneumatically conveyed, e.g., from railroad cars, or into storage silos, bins, or hoppers. These materials are highly susceptible to damage by water and other liquids and must be stored in well-sealed containers. In multiple-story plants they are usually stored on upper floors or in penthouses.

Cooking oils, alcohol, vinegar, and liquids used at room temperature are stored in tanks of various shapes and sizes. Molasses and other liquids requiring heating are stored in steam-jacketed tanks. Most liquids storage is found on lower floors, sometimes even in basements. Wherever stored, adequate curbing and drainage must be provided to reduce existing loss potentials, and the chance of damage to other materials, equipment, storage, and the building itself. Generally, storage in basements is not advisable, due to the chance of flooding from surface-water runoff, water-main breaks, spills from upper floors, reduced fire department accessibility, and the difficulty of venting heat and smoke.

PROCESSES

Dairy Production

The dairy industry depends heavily upon refrigeration. Dairy products must be kept within specified temperature ranges or they may be declared unfit for use. The consequences of lost refrigeration capability are therefore important considerations in planning and protecting refrigeration systems.

In pasturization, milk is heated to kill bacteria and other microorganisms. It then must be cooled within a specified amount of time and kept within acceptable temperature ranges. Milk is also homogenized, or mixed, to give it a uniform consistency. Other dairy products are cream, skim milk, butter, cream cheese, dips, ice cream, buttermilk, yogurt, and cheese. These products also must be kept within specified temperature ranges for acceptable quality.

Jane I. Lataille, P.E., is senior account consultant with Industrial Risk Insurers, Hartford, CT.

Manufacture of Convenience Foods

Another facet of the food industry is manufacture of convenience food. Examples of convenience products are instant soup, powdered milk, instant coffee, egg and meat substitutes, powdered drinks, instant potatoes, and instant rice. The advantages of these products include economy, ease of preparation, and long shelf life.

The processes most often used in producing convenience foods are flash drying and flash freezing. During these processes, food products are converted into their desired forms by rapid exposure to extreme heat or extreme cold. Some products also contain various chemicals and additives for preservation, texture or flavor improvement, coloring, and moisture control.

Preserving

Since most crops can only be grown during limited times, it is necessary to preserve them to achieve year-round availability. Meat, poultry, and fish also are preserved. Canning, freezing, and pickling are common means of food preservation. In both canning and freezing, the food is usually cooked in steam-jacketed vessels. Salt and vinegar are the primary materials used for pickling.

Baking

Continuous fuel-fired ovens are representative of food baking process equipment. The fuel, number of burners, number of zones, temperature, and amount of ventilation will vary for this equipment. Occasionally, electric ovens are used. Baked products include bread, pastry, pies, cakes, cookies, and crackers. In pie and pastry making, fruit must be prepared and cooked before baking. Some ovens are arranged to spray vegetable oil into pans before baking or onto the product during baking.

Candy Making

Most candy making involves cooking or heating, e.g., melting chocolate to pour into molds and cooking flavored sugar mixtures to make hard candy. Process equipment is likely to include kettles, ovens, and cooling tunnels. Many candies are covered with coatings, such as chocolate, icings, fruit mixtures, and glazes. The coatings are either melted and mixed or carried in a solvent.

Meat Processing

In processing, meat is cleaned and cut into desired sections. Meat preservation consists mainly of drying, salting (soaking in brine), and smoking. The smoking is performed in smoke chambers. Any other processing is usually done by plants that use meat in their products, such as those making soups, stews, hash, canned meat, meat rolls, or even pet foods.

Distribution Warehousing

Some food facilities simply store large quantities of many different food products for distribution to grocery stores. As with non-food warehousing facilities, some grocery warehouses are equipped with automatic retrieval systems (automated warehousing). Automatic retrieval systems usually allow the storage of products at a greater density than conventional racks. This increases fuel loading, lessens access to stock, and increases the amount of food exposed to contamination from a single loss. Many other locations may depend on grocery warehouses for food products; consequently, loss prevention is very important for these warehouses.

Miscellaneous Processes

Other food processes, such as frying, do not fall into the previous categories. Frying processes include the making of potato chips, corn chips, french fries, onion rings, cheese curls, pork rinds, and other snacks. Fryers using hot fat or oil are used to make these products. Nondairy beverages, such as carbonated beverages, fruit drinks and juices, beer, and liquors, represent use of other miscellaneous processes.

THE FIRE HAZARDS

Process Equipment

Refrigeration equipment within the food processing industry presents hazards which are inherent to compressed gases, potential vapor release, moving mechanical parts, and electrical control systems. Ammonia refrigerant is volatile and toxic. (See Figure 8-3A.) Freon is less volatile, but is still considered toxic. Both can contaminate food and otherwise damage equipment and stock. Refer to Section 2, Chapter 18, "Refrigeration Systems" for more information. Vessels for cooking or melting are usually heated with electricity or steam. Their fire hazards are usually limited to those of electrical systems and overheating. Boilers that produce the steam for these vessels present the same fire and explosion hazards as those associated with fuel-fired equipment.

*FIG. 8-3A. **Result of an anhydrous ammonia explosion in Houston, TX, on December 11, 1983. (Source: Houston Fire Department)***

Baking ovens also present fuel firing hazards. In addition, ovens have interior moving parts and fixed ductwork which become coated with oils and can be involved in a fire. Electrically heated ovens sometimes contain concealed oil-filled transformers which are a concern. Another feature of ovens that requires attention is the presence of combustible insulation. The primary hazards introduced by cooling tunnels are combustible construction and/or insulation. (See Figure 8-3B.) Fryers and associated ductwork involve the heating of a combustible liquid. The degree of hazard increases as the temperature approaches the flash point of the liquid.

Another characteristic of food processing equipment which contributes to its loss potential is a high level of automation. Process equipment is often custom-made and can take a long time to replace. It can also be so much more

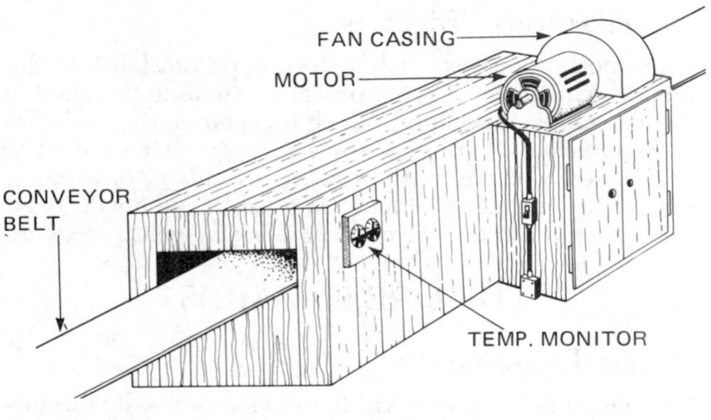

FIG. 8-3B. Cooling tunnels are sometimes made of wood.

efficient than other production methods that lost business cannot be made up if the equipment is out of service. For this reason, highly automated processes should be reviewed for duplication, alternate production methods, and outside assistance. Where they exist, duplicate equipment lines should be separated so they will not be exposed to the same potential loss incident.

Gases and Liquids

Some gases used in the food industry are hazardous. Cocoa and other powdered products are treated with gaseous fumigants which, depending upon their composition, could be flammable. Ethylene oxide is a flammable gas used to ripen fruit which has been shipped "green" to distribution centers. Whenever gases are used, their physical characteristics should be checked.

Combustible and flammable liquids are commonly found in food processing plants. Combustible liquids used include lubricating oils, cooking oils, certain alcoholic beverages, and solvent-based extracts. Alcohol, high-proof alcoholic beverages, and solvents are the most commonly used flammable liquids. In the candy industry, ether is used to dissolve the coating that makes jelly beans shiny. In many types of plants, alcohol is used to dissolve dried, crushed materials, or liquids, to make flavorings and colorings. One example of this is the production of vanilla extract. Waxes, which are liquids when heated, also are used in food plants.

Combustible Dusts

Dust hazards are not unusual in the food processing industry. Under the right conditions, any organic dust can explode. Among the many potentially explosive dusts are those from sugar, flour, grains, starches, and cocoa. Since the explosibility of a dust depends partly upon its fineness, the finer dusts, e.g., confectioners' sugar and cornstarch, present the most severe explosion potential.

Conveyors

Conveyors, which can be used anywhere in a process from raw material transfer to processing, packaging, and storage, pose many hazards. Their drives can jam, misalign, or overheat, and cause friction which can lead to fires. The conveyors themselves can be a means of spreading fire from one area to another; so may the openings made in the walls they pass through. Many belt conveyors have combustible belts. Rubber or plastic belts produce large quantities of smoke when they burn, resulting in a high potential for contamination. Chain conveyors can carry plastic pans. Wide conveyors shield the areas below from ceiling sprinkler protection. Finally, conveyors are part of highly automated systems that cannot function without them.

Storage

Raw materials and food products are stored in various ways. Bins and tanks are often used for powders and liquids. Packaged products are commonly stored on pallets or in racks 80 ft (24.4 m) high or more, including automatic retrieval systems. (See Figure 8-3C.) Since wood, cardboard, and plastics are used to package food products, the combustible loading in storage areas can become very high.

FIG. 8-3C. Erecting storage racks in a grocery warehouse. (Source: Giant Food)

Some food products, such as vegetable oil spray, are stored in aerosol cans. Under pressure, aerosol propellants can rocket cans during a fire so the fire spreads beyond control. Necessarily, the storage of this type of product must be carefully planned.

THE SAFEGUARDS

Construction Considerations

Since food products have a high susceptibility to smoke contamination, noncombustible construction of buildings is preferred. Fire cutoffs should be provided to separate manufacturing and warehousing areas, to separate duplicate production lines, and to isolate fuel-fired equipment, refrigeration systems, and storage of more hazardous materials such as flammable liquids, paper, cardboard, plastics, pallets, and aerosols. Fire cutoffs need to be preserved

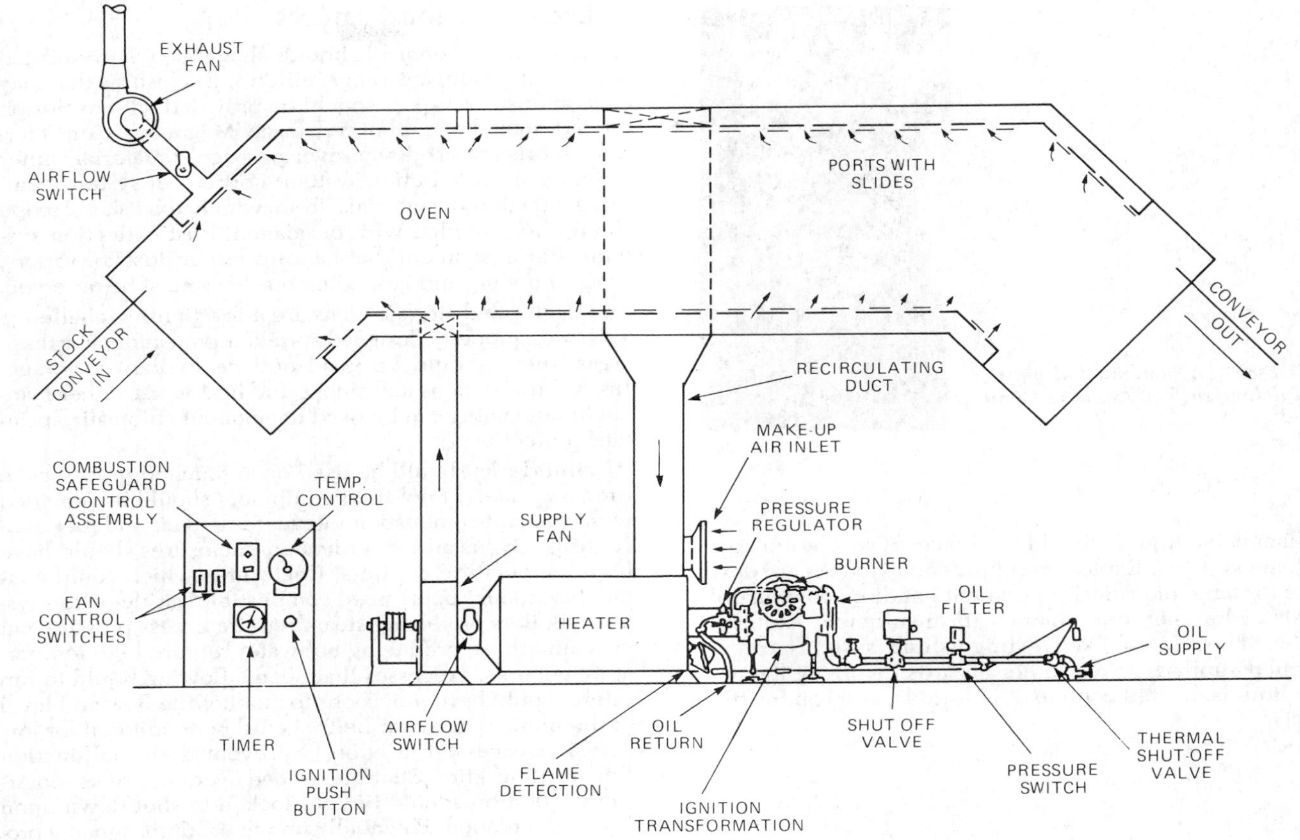

FIG. 8-3D. Conveyor-type oven with the controls labeled. (Source: Industrial Risk Insurers)

where conveyors pass through them. To do this, conveyor lines are specially designed to break open at, or hinge away from, the point at which a fire door or shutter closes. The use of water spray systems is sometimes proposed as an alternative to cutoffs. This is less desirable because water spray by itself cannot prevent the radiation of heat through an opening. Water spray systems also depend upon a water supply and therefore are subject to impairments.

Heating and cooling requirements in the food processing industry call for the widespread use of insulating materials in buildings and process equipment. Noncombustible insulation should be chosen whenever possible. When combustible insulation is used, it should have a low flame spread, as well as low fuel-contributed and low smoke-developed ratings established by a testing laboratory. Combustible insulation should also be protected by sprinklers and thermal barriers, such as gypsum or dry wall. Process equipment should be noncombustible.

Sprinkler Systems

The various combustible materials commonly encountered in the food processing industry suggest the provision of appropriately designed sprinkler protection in all buildings. Sprinklers also should be provided for high storage racks; for process enclosures handling (or built of) combustible materials; under obstructions over 4 ft (1.22 m) wide, such as conveyor belts; and in coolers, freezers, and heating enclosures. Where wood cooling tunnels or other combustible equipment are used, sprinklers should be provided. Hose connections supplied from sprinkler systems should be provided in storage areas and wherever large amounts of combustibles may be present. Water supplies should be sufficient to supply the largest sprinkler demand area plus hose streams for the amount of time prescribed by the hazard in the protected area under consideration.

Despite low temperatures, it is possible for fires to occur within freezers. Providing sprinkler protection in them, however, requires special design. The usual wet-pipe sprinkler system is replaced by a combination dry-pipe valve and deluge valve. (See Figure 8-3E.) This system reduces the chance of water damage to a minimum by requiring two means of detection before the system operates.

Hose connections are more complicated to install in freezers. They must be kept drained and contain a way to both release the air in the sprinkler piping and open the deluge valve. Maintenance of these complex systems is difficult due to the subfreezing temperatures.

Fixed Extinguishing Systems

A fixed extinguishing system is the most effective protection for some hazards found in the food processing industry. Deep-fat fryers and their associated ductwork can be protected with carbon dioxide, or dry or wet chemical extinguishing systems. (See Figure 8-3F.) Large outside tanks

FIG 8-3E. A combined dry-pipe and deluge system. (Source: Giant Food)

of flammable liquids should be protected with water spray or foam systems. Explosion suppression systems are desirable for large or critical equipment handling combustible dusts or for such equipment with insufficient explosion relief. The use of fixed extinguishing systems can be applied similarly to any other hazards involving flammable liquids, heated combustible liquids, and combustible dusts.

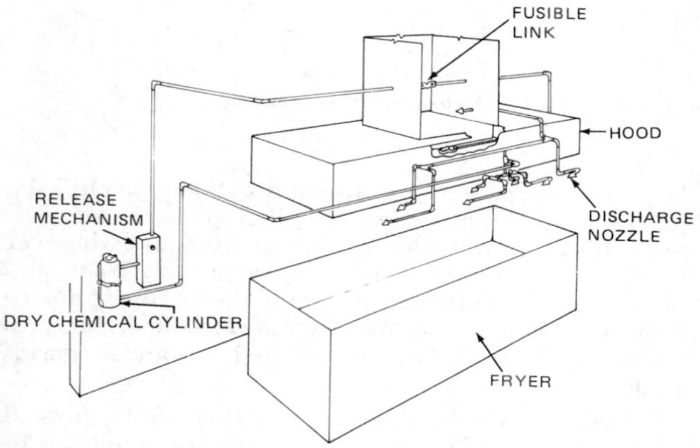

FIG. 8-3F. Layout of a wet chemical extinguishing system for a fat fryer. (Reprinted with permission of Wormald U.S., Inc.)

Electrical Equipment

Electrical equipment in food processing plants should be suitable for the location in which it is installed. (See NFPA 70, *National Electrical Code*.) A review should be made of possible vapors or dusts which could be present in each area. Where liquids such as alcohol may be present, electrical equipment suitable for Class I, Group D locations is recommended. Where ether is used, the electrical classification is Class I, Group C. Ethylene oxide requires the use of Class I, Group B equipment. Class II, Group G locations are those where nonconductive dusts are likely to be present.

Other Protection Features

Areas handling flammable liquids should be well ventilated to prevent significant vapor buildup. Enclosures that may contain dusts or vapors should be provided with explosion relief designed to minimize damage. Magnets to extract ferrous debris are used wherever powdered materials enter a storage or distribution system. Portions of systems handling powdered materials from which dust can escape should be provided with permanent dust collection systems. For equipment that handles either dusts or vapors, proper bonding and grounding practices must be observed.

High-piled storage areas are a fire fighting challenge even with properly designed sprinkler protection. For these areas, there should be good outside hydrant coverage. Inside hose stations and smoke and heat vents, either manual or automatic, can be used to augment automatic sprinkler protection.

Interlocks should be used on automated processes to run them safely. Fuel-fired equipment should be provided with standard combustion safeguards and air and fuel train controls. Ovens and other heated enclosures should have high temperature cut outs. Enclosures which could contain hazardous vapors need combustible-gas detection systems. Boilers producing steam require excess pressure cut outs, and those producing hot water require high temperature cut outs. Processes that need a flowing liquid to run safely should have provisions to monitor the flow and level of the liquid. Conveyor belts should be monitored for low speed or excessive friction to prevent their malfunction from causing a fire. Continuous-feed ovens or dryers requiring ventilation should be interlocked to shut down upon loss of ventilation. Potentially unsafe conditions in any process should be monitored and interlocked to avoid hazardous conditions.

BIBLIOGRAPHY

NFPA Codes, Standards, and Recommended Practices

Reference to the following NFPA codes, standards, and recommended practices will provide further information on the safeguards for food processing discussed in this chapter. (See the latest *NFPA Catalog* for availability of current editions of the following documents.)

NFPA 10, *Portable Fire Extinguishers*.

NFPA 11, *Low Expansion Foam and Combined Agent Systems*.

NFPA 11A, *Medium and High Expansion Foam Systems*.

NFPA 12, *Carbon Dioxide Extinguishing Systems*.

NFPA 12A, *Halon 1301 Fire Extinguishing Systems*.

NFPA 12B, *Halon 1211 Fire Extinguishing Systems*.

NFPA 13, *Installation of Sprinkler Systems*.

NFPA 14, *Standpipe and Hose Systems*.

NFPA 15, *Water Spray Fixed Systems for Fire Protection*.

NFPA 16A, *Installation of Closed-Head Foam-Water Sprinkler Systems*.

NFPA 30, *Flammable and Combustible Liquids Code*.

NFPA 34, *Dipping and Coating Processes Using Flammable or Combustible Liquids*.

NFPA 49, *Hazardous Chemicals Data*.

NFPA 61A, *Prevention of Fire and Dust Explosions in Facilities Manufacturing and Handling Starch*.

NFPA 61B, *Prevention of Fires and Explosions in Grain Elevators and Facilities Handling Bulk Raw Agricultural Commodities*.

NFPA 61C, *Prevention of Fire and Dust Explosions in Feed Mills*.

NFPA 61D, *Prevention of Fire and Dust Explosions in the Milling of Agricultural Commodities for Human Consumption.*

NFPA 68, *Explosion Venting.*

NFPA 69, *Explosion Prevention Systems.*

NFPA 70, *National Electrical Code.*

NFPA 77, *Static Electricity.*

NFPA 85A, *Prevention of Furnace Explosions in Fuel-Oil and Natural Gas-Fired Single Burner Boiler-Furnaces.*

NFPA 85C, *Prevention of Furnace Explosions/Implosions in Multiple Burner Boiler-Furnaces.*

NFPA 86, *Ovens and Furnaces.*

NFPA 96, *Removal of Smoke and Grease-Laden Vapors from Commercial Cooking Equipment.*

NFPA 204M, *Smoke and Heat Venting.*

NFPA 231, *General Storage.*

NFPA 231C, *Rack Storage of Materials.*

NFPA 321, *Basic Classification of Flammable and Combustible Liquids.*

NFPA 325M, *Fire Hazard Properties of Flammable Liquids, Gases, and Volatile Solids.*

NFPA 493, *Intrinsically Safe Apparatus in Division I Hazardous Locations.*

NFPA 496, *Purged and Pressurized Enclosures for Electrical Equipment.*

NFPA 497A, *Classification of Class I Hazardous Locations for Electrical Installations in Chemical Plants.*

NFPA 497M, *Classification of Gases, Vapors and Dusts for Electrical Equipment in Hazardous (Classified) Locations.*

NFPA 650, *Pneumatic Conveying Systems for Handling Combustible Materials.*

Additional Reading

Cote, A.E., ed., *Industrial Fire Hazards Handbook*, 3rd ed., National Fire Protection Association, Quincy, MA, 1990.

Factory Mutual Engineering Corp., "Industrial Ovens and Dryers," *Loss Prevention Data* 6-9, Oct. 1977.

Factory Mutual Engineering Corp., "Mechanical Refrigeration," *Loss Prevention Data* 7-13, Oct. 1975.

Factory Mutual Engineering Corp., "Grain Storage and Milling," *Loss Prevention Data* 7-75, Feb. 1982.

Factory Mutual Engineering Corp., "Refrigerated Storage," *Loss Prevention Data* 8-29, May 1976.

Food Processing and Packaging Equipment, 19th ed., Business Trend Analysts, Dix Hill, NY.

Heldman, D. R., and Singh, R. P., *Food Process Engineering*, AVI Publishing Co., Inc., Westport, CT, 1981.

Linko, P., ed., *Food Processing Systems*, (Vol. 1), Elsevier Science Publishing Co., Inc., NY, 1980.

"Moving Fire: Fire Hazards of Belt Conveyors," *Record*, Vol. 54, No. 6, 1977, pp. 18-21.

Schwartzberg, H. G., and Lund, D., *Food Process Engineering*, American Institute of Chemical Engineers, NY, 1982.

Strouppe, D. E. "Ammonia Contamination: An Avoidable Loss," *Locomotive*, Vol. 66, No. 5, Spring 1989.

WAREHOUSE PRE-FIRE PLANNING AND FIRE FIGHTING OPERATIONS

Larry Davis and Jeffrey Moore

While properly designed automatic sprinkler systems can be expected to control a fire in a warehouse, effectively trained and equipped fire suppression forces will be required to effect final extinguishment. These fire suppression forces may be members of an industrial fire brigade, a full-time industrial fire department, the public fire department, or any combination of these forces.

This chapter discusses the necessity of developing an effective pre-fire plan for a warehouse and the problems that will be faced by fire fighters responding to a warehouse fire. Specifically, the chapter is concerned with the type of information that must be gathered in order to develop a pre-fire plan and the operational problems that will be faced by fire suppression forces.

The specific problems associated with the overall protection of warehouses and storage occupancies are covered in Section 8, Chapter 23, "Industrial Occupancies;" and Section 8, Chapter 24, "Storage Occupancies."

WAREHOUSE FIRE FIGHTING PROBLEMS

According to statistics compiled by the three major industrial fire insurance carriers, a fire occurs in a warehouse or storage facility every 22 hours. Once every 11 days, one such fire results in a loss of more than $500,000. Warehouse fires occur more frequently than one might expect, and fires of major proportions are becoming more common.

Warehouses represent a unique fire challenge to both fixed fire suppression systems and the manual fire fighting forces that are called upon to deal with a fire. Modern warehouses and storage occupancies are especially subject to rapidly developing fires of great intensity, because complex configuration of storage and building layout are usually conducive to rapid fire spread, presenting numerous obstacles to manual fire suppression efforts. The only proven method of controlling a warehouse fire is with properly designed and maintained automatic sprinkler systems. If sprinkler protection is not provided, the likelihood of controlling a fire in a warehouse is minimal, at best.

Since automatic sprinkler protection is the most effective method of successfully controlling a warehouse fire, all fire fighting operations should be geared toward the total support of the sprinkler system. This support not only increases the likelihood of fire control, but also maximizes fire fighter safety because it is unnecessary for fire fighters to be exposed to the hazards of an interior fire attack.

It is essential to recognize the significant difference between *control* of a fire and *extinguishment* of a fire in a warehouse. A fire is said to be under control when enough sprinklers have operated to stop the spread of the fire by prewetting fuel ahead of the fire. It also denotes that temperatures within the building have been reduced to a point where the structure is no longer in danger of collapse. Typical warehouse sprinkler designs anticipate the operation of 2000 to 5000 sq ft (186 to 465 m^2) of sprinkler coverage before the fire is controlled. At this time, although the fire may be under control it is a long way from being extinguished. Whereas it may require only a few minutes for the sprinklers to control the fire, it may require several hours or even days to actually extinguish the fire. It is important to realize that a warehouse fire is an emergency of major proportions and will require a planning effort and emergency response of equal magnitude to both control and eventually extinguish it.

Once effective support for the sprinklers has been established, the fire emergency can be considered stabilized, providing sufficient time to carefully organize a safe and successful fire suppression operation. In addition, the time that sprinklers buy helps maximize safety and operational effectiveness—hurried fire fighting operations are not only disorganized, but are also usually unsafe and rarely effective.

The overall success of a warehouse fire fighting operation is determined long before the first smoke is visible—in fact, it is determined before actual ignition occurs. The success of the operation is determined during the development of the warehouse pre-fire plan.

Larry Davis has been involved in industrial and municipal fire protection for over 20 years. He is currently senior loss prevention training consultant for Industrial Risk Insurers, Hartford, CT. Jeffrey Moore has been involved in industrial and municipal fire protection for over 15 years. He is currently fire protection engineer for Wright-Patterson Air Force Base, near Dayton, OH.

The pre-fire plan must be a cooperative effort among the building owner, plant emergency teams, and the public fire department that will be responding to the facility. Other agencies may also be able to provide valuable input during the development of the pre-fire plan. Such agencies may include the plant security forces, plant engineering staff, public utility companies, and the insurance carrier.

WAREHOUSE FIRE PROTECTION ELEMENTS

Before the pre-fire planning begins, all parties involved must understand some basic information about warehouses and what happens when a warehouse fire occurs. There are many factors concerning warehouse fires that must be addressed.

Sprinklers

A sprinklered warehouse or storage area can be subject to a catastrophic fire. When sprinklers are properly designed for the occupancy, they can be expected to control a fire until the arrival of the fire department. If they are not properly designed, however, they will not control the fire. In fact, it is quite probable that the fire will be far beyond control by the time the fire department arrives. An inadequately designed sprinkler system cannot hold a fire in check, and manual fire suppression efforts cannot be expected to make up for an inadequately designed sprinkler system.

Many people, including building owners, fire fighters, and some insurance companies, are under the false impression that a building equipped with automatic sprinklers is "safe" from a major fire. Nothing could be further from the truth. Sprinklered buildings burn down every day for a variety of reasons. The fire challenge presented by high piling in a warehouse or by materials with a high rate of heat release may be far beyond the capabilities of the sprinkler system. This can easily occur as the type, amount, and arrangement of the storage in a warehouse changes over time.

The sprinklers may also be compromised by an impairment. Many fires have occurred while sprinklers were turned off for repairs. An even more dangerous situation can occur when the sprinklers are unknowingly impaired due to poor maintenance. Without careful inspection of systems by trained personnel, such impairments may not be discovered until after a fire has destroyed the facility.

Fire Protection Deficiencies

Many building owners do not recognize the protection deficiencies in their warehouse. They are often distracted by the business situation at hand. For example, if the sprinkler protection in the warehouse is compromised because of excessive storage heights, the owner may be busy worrying about the large amount of inventory on hand. If business is very good and large amounts of inventory are moving through the warehouse, the owner may be concentrating all of his/her attention on the good business climate, instead of protecting the warehouse.

Building owners often assume that if a problem exists in their warehouse the public fire department will point it out. The reality is that, while the fire department may have a general idea of the type and arrangement of storage in a particular warehouse, they seldom have the personnel or time to keep track of all changes that occur. In some instances, the storage in a warehouse may change significantly from month to month, or even from one week to the next. Few fire departments have the resources required to fully analyze the protection in a warehouse, to determine the capabilities of the sprinkler system, or to recognize how changes in the storage will affect the ability of the sprinklers to control a fire. As a result, critical protection deficiencies that can spell disaster during a fire may go unrecognized.

Fire Protection Recommendations

As the hazards within a warehouse increase, an insurance carrier may recommend upgrading the fixed fire protection systems. Unfortunately, however, building owners are not usually well-versed in fire protection, and, as a result, they often see the recommendations of insurance carriers as luxuries which are not absolutely necessary. This can result in inadequate fire protection, including deficient automatic sprinkler design.

Insurance

Insurance does not guarantee that a building is properly protected. However, insurance companies do have several means of protecting themselves financially if they are insuring a poor risk. These include: (1) charging very high insurance rates for the property, (2) the use of very high deductibles (which can exceed several million dollars), (3) purchasing reinsurance on the property, and (4) providing only limited amounts of insurance for the property.

Storage

Sprinkler designs are based on open aisles that act as fire breaks and permit sprinkler discharge to fall between what is burning and what is not burning. When storage is present in the aisles (even one pallet load), it simply forms a bridge of fuel which enables the fire to extend across the aisle space more quickly.

Also, storage heights must not be increased beyond the design of the sprinkler system, because not only does it increase the fuel load, but it can also block sprinkler efficiency.

High-hazard commodities: Anything that increases the hazard of the storage requires a corresponding increase in the level of protection. There are no proven rules for determining how much of a higher hazard material may be introduced before the sprinkler protection will be compromised. In some cases, such as those involving flammable liquids or aerosols, less than one pallet load is more than enough to burn a warehouse to the ground. In other cases, such as when expanded foam plastics are used as packing materials inside cartons, the increase in hazard may not be readily apparent. If there is any question as to the hazard level of the storage, fire protection should be designed or reinforced to provide for the most hazardous commodity.

Fire Brigades

Sprinkler systems and fire brigades have two different purposes. The sprinklers are needed to control the fire, while the fire brigade is needed to ensure the completion of critical functions, such as the operation of fire pumps, securing utilities, assisting the public fire department, and conducting salvage operations.

Public Fire Departments

On arrival, the fire department will be most concerned with the safety of the building occupants and the fire fighters themselves. The next priority is to ensure that the fire does not spread to any neighboring structures. The last priority is to protect the property itself. If the fire can be extinguished with the resources available, and without undue risk to fire fighting personnel, an attempt will be made. However, in some cases, it is in the best interest of the public not to extinguish the fire, such as when hazardous materials are involved and water runoff from such fire suppression operations will result in environmental damage.

Public fire departments have an obligation to develop pre-fire plans for the target hazards within their jurisdictions. However, if the plans are to be effective, building owners must actively participate in their development. The building owner should provide the fire department with building plans, design specifications for the fire protection systems, and information on the special hazards within the facility. The building owner may need to contact other resources, such as corporate fire protection officials or a consulting fire protection engineer, to analyze the protection features in the warehouse if such information is not available. Building owners may also call on the engineering staff of their insurance carrier. Major industrial property insurers normally have detailed information on the protection features of the facilities they insure and can answer specific questions about the capabilities and limitations of the fire protection systems. Insurance companies cannot usually release information directly to the municipal fire department without the building owner's consent. However, the fire department, the building owner, and the insurance carrier can convene to discuss specific fire protection concerns.

DEVELOPING A PRE-FIRE PLAN

The pre-fire planning process begins with a tour of the warehouse. Arrangements should be made with the building owner to have someone with a working knowledge of the facility and its operations available to accompany the fire department representatives on the tour. Plans and diagrams of the facility showing the building layout, construction, storage configurations, and the design of the fire protection systems and equipment should be provided for examination prior to the tour.

The purpose of the tour is to gather information which will be used to help the fire department predict the type of fire that can be anticipated and the possible complications that may be encountered during fire suppression operations. The information gathered should include at least the following:

- The size and construction characteristics of the building must be evaluated to determine the probable effect of a fire. For example, a building with a roof supported on lightweight steel bar joists or trusses can be expected to fail early during a serious fire.
- Firewalls, fire barriers, and fire doors that separate the storage area from the surrounding operations should be located and checked for proper operation. They must be relied upon to operate properly during an emergency to check the spread of the fire.
- The commodities stored within the warehouse must be determined. Knowledge of their burning characteristics is essential. For example, aerosol products, flammable liquids, or similar materials may out-strip the capabilities of the sprinkler system.
- The method of packaging materials in the warehouse must be determined. For example, cardboard cartons can be expected to collapse into the aisle quickly, and materials stored strapped onto pallets with plastic straps can be expected to melt quickly.
- Method of storage, e.g., racks, solid piles on the floor, or palletized, must be determined.
- Normal and maximum levels of storage in the building must be evaluated. Stock levels must be assessed as to relative stablity from season to season. Pre-fire plans should be based on the worst case (e.g., plan for a worst-case fire in a department store warehouse to occur in September or October when it is likely to be filled to capacity with holiday-sale merchandise.)
- Determine the type and design of the automatic sprinkler systems. It is very important to obtain complete information on the capability of the sprinkler systems so they can be compared to the hazards posed by the storage in the warehouse. If the sprinkler design is inadequate for the type and arrangement of storage, fire control is unlikely.
- Determine the minimum flow and pressure required to supply sprinkler systems. The water supply demands for the sprinklers must be known in order to evaluate the adequacy of the available water supplies. If the water supply is inadequate, the sprinklers will not perform as designed. Current water supply test results should be available or tests should be conducted to obtain current information.
- Type and number of water supplies available for fire protection should be determined. Information should be obtained on how to start fire pumps so that they may be started manually by fire fighters, if necessary.
- Location of public hydrants and fire department sprinkler connections must be known. It is important that fire apparatus not steal water from the sprinkler systems by connecting to yard hydrants. The location of suitable public hydrants and static water sources to supply fire apparatus must be located and evaluated.
- Arrangement of interior standpipes and hose connections must be determined. Are they fed from overhead sprinklers or can they remain in service with the sprinklers shut off? All hose connections must have the same hose threads as the public fire department.
- Type, capacity, and method of operation of any automatic or manual heat and smoke venting facilities must be assessed. How can exhaust fans be activated? How is the power supply to the fans arranged? Will power be lost when electric power for the warehouse is shut down during an emergency?
- Determine main and alternate means of access to the warehouse. What security features will make access more difficult? Are there normally security guards or guard dogs in the warehouse during off hours?
- Determine what type of training is provided for the plant emergency organization. Also assess how many members will be available during a fire, and what procedures are followed in the event of a fire.
- Assess what types of manual fire suppression equipment are available to the plant emergency organization, and whether this equipment can be utilized by the public fire department.

Assess the general storage practices within the building. Are piles neat and orderly, or are they sloppy and in disarray, indicating poor housekeeping practices that are conducive to rapid fire spread?

Investigate any storage in the aisles. Even so-called "temporary" storage will block access to the aisles in an emergency and can cause rapid bridging of a fire across an aisle.

Determine what materials-handling equipment will be available during overhaul operations to move stock out of the building. Will employees be available to operate the equipment or must fire fighters be trained in the use of the equipment?

Once this basic information has been gathered, the development of the actual pre-fire plan can begin. The plan, of course, should be developed in conjunction with the building owner so that everyone knows specific responsibilities during an emergency.

The building owner should establish and enforce basic fire prevention programs for the warehouse. These should include, but are not limited to, smoking regulations, hot-work control, safe refueling practices for material handling equipment, and the identification and elimination of other sources of fire. Employees and the plant emergency organization should be instructed in the procedures for reporting a fire, making sure that employees are evacuated, checking sprinkler control valves to ensure they are open, and closing fire doors to prevent the spread of a fire.

FIRE FIGHTING OPERATIONS

Strategic Considerations

The strategy employed in fighting structure fires is to confine the fire to the smallest possible area until arrival of the first fire department unit. In most cases, this consists of confining the fire to the room or compartment of origin. Even in large commercial buildings, fire fighters can usually depend on at least some degree of compartmentation being available to at least slow the spread and intensity of a fire. In cases where the compartmentation works as intended, the fires are "simple" room-and-contents fires.

Unfortunately, such compartmentation is often missing in a modern warehouse. Warehouses with several hundred thousand sq ft (100,000 sq ft equals 9290 m^2) of floor area under a single roof with few, if any, fire walls or fire barriers are not uncommon. It is in the best interest of material handling to maintain this space as free of obstructions as possible. This provides for maximum flexibility in the use of various storage configurations and material handling equipment. Fire walls and fire barriers, if provided, are often compromised by conveyor openings, drive-through doors, and holes for utilities to pass through. These openings may or may not be properly protected with firestopping or automatic closing fire doors.

In some cases, water spray systems are provided in an attempt to protect openings in fire walls or fire barriers. Although such systems may have some value in preventing small fires from passing through the opening, they are no substitute for automatic closing fire doors. Fire doors provide a physical barrier that is not dependent on the operation of sprinklers or any other system. Water spray systems, on the other hand, are dependent on the operation of sprinklers and the maintenance of an effective water supply, both of which are commonly compromised when a major fire causes collapse of portions of the roof and the subsequent rupture of sprinkler piping.

The size-up of a warehouse fire can, and most likely will, be very difficult. A serious fire may be burning in a large-volume warehouse, and yet very little smoke may be visible from the outside. Smoke showing from the exterior of the building may provide no indication of the location of the fire within. Since most warehouses have few if any windows, there may be no easy method of determining the size, location, or current status of the fire. This makes it all the more important to have an up-to-date pre-fire plan that details the conditions inside the warehouse.

Sprinkler System Support

Fire tests and past history have shown that the best way of controlling a warehouse fire is with automatic sprinklers. If the fire cannot be controlled by the sprinkler system it is probably uncontrollable. Sprinklers begin fighting the fire before the arrival of the fire department, discharge water directly into the fire area, and are unaffected by poor visibility, heat, and toxic gases. The best course of action is to support the operation of the sprinkler system by pumping into the fire department sprinkler connection at full capacity. The higher the pressure available to the sprinkler system, the more water is discharged from the operating sprinklers, and the better chance of controlling the fire. Once support for the sprinklers has been established, the fire ground commander will have time to conduct a careful size-up to determine the best use of the resources available to contain the situation.

Support of sprinklers means that the fire department must not only pump into the fire department sprinkler connections to ensure that proper pressures are maintained within the system, but steps must also be taken to ensure that water for manual fire suppression operations is not taken from the sprinklers or that sprinklers are robbed of water by apparatus connecting to yard hydrant systems. In some cases, where water supplies were marginal, fire departments have taken water from the system and caused pressure within the sprinkler system to drop to critically low levels. Fire fighters should also understand that, while a flow of 1000 gpm (63 L/s) may be a high rate of flow for many types of fires, the sprinkler system in a warehouse may require from 1500 to over 3000 gpm (95 to 190 L/s) to operate effectively.

Arriving fire companies may be faced with a number of different situations that hinge mostly on the degree of effectiveness of the automatic sprinkler system. Possible conditions on arrival include:

No sprinklers provided: If automatic sprinklers have not been provided in the warehouse and the fire has developed beyond the incipient stage, control of the fire will be very difficult. Saving anything in the compartment of origin is unlikely and efforts should be directed toward preventing the spread of fire beyond the compartment currently involved. This can be accomplished by closing fire doors, using hose lines to prevent the spread of fire through unprotected openings in fire walls and fire barriers, and using master streams through doorways to contain the fire. Entry into the fire area will be extremely dangerous due to the speed with which the fire spreads and the probability of early structural collapse. A good water supply should be secured as soon as possible to supply the large-caliber hose streams that will be required to control the fire and protect exposures.

Sprinklers provided but not operating: If sprinklers are provided but are not yet operating when fire companies arrive, one of two situations has occurred. First, it is possible that the fire has not yet grown large enough to fuse any sprinkler heads. If this is the case, hose lines can be advanced into the area to control the fire. The second reason that sprinklers may not be operating is because of an impairment to the sprinkler system. One or more valves may be closed for maintenance or repair. It is also not unusual for someone to intentionally close the sprinkler valves in incendiary-related incidents. Personnel should always be assigned to check sprinkler control valves and water supplies to ensure they are in service. At least one engine company should be assigned to support the sprinkler systems by pumping into the sprinkler connection which may be arranged to by-pass the closed valve.

Sprinklers operating and controlling the fire: If on arrival sprinklers are operating and appear to be controlling the fire, a first arriving engine company should be assigned to pump into the sprinkler connection. Increasing the pressure available to the sprinklers will result in quicker, more effective fire control. Once the sprinklers have controlled the fire there will be time to plan the operations needed to effect final extinguishment, overhaul, and salvage.

Sprinklers operating, but not controlling the fire: If the sprinklers are not controlling the fire on arrival, the pressure in the sprinkler system must be increased immediately by connecting to and pumping into the sprinkler connection. There will be very little time to establish support for the sprinklers before the sprinkler systems are overwhelmed. If only one sprinkler connection is available, it should be used to maximum advantage by connecting multiple lines to it. Additional water can be supplied to the sprinkler systems by pumping *into* wall hydrants or private yard hydrants, if they are available.

Hazards Posed by Stock

Personnel operating at a warehouse fire must be familiar with the specific hazards of the stock in the warehouse. Materials, such as flammable liquids, flammable aerosols, and toxic chemicals, pose obvious hazards. The hazards of other materials are often overlooked. For example, baled materials, such as scrap paper or paper pulp, can be deadly. These materials absorb water from fire suppression operations and can collapse on fire fighters operating inside the building. Another hazard of materials as they absorb water is that they may expand when wetted. If materials, such as paper pulp, are packed into a building against masonry walls, it is possible that as the material expands it may push walls outward, causing a localized or total collapse of the structure. Such possibilities must always be considered when pre-fire plans are developed.

Material stored in cardboard cartons will also collapse as the cartons are wetted and weaken. In fact, in most cases collapse of a pile is considered an advantage from a fire control standpoint because it will expose the fire in the interior of the pile to discharge from the sprinkler system. Fire fighters should understand that fire protection engineers may desire a pile in a warehouse to collapse in order to facilitate fire control.

An example of the hazards of collapsing stock occurred in Idaho where three members of an industrial fire department and two other employees were killed during a fire in a sprinklered paper warehouse in March 1980. The noncombustible storage building was 46 ft by 72 ft (14 by 23 m) and fully protected by automatic sprinklers. It was part of a paper mill and was used to store baled scrap paper for recycling to a height of about 15 ft (4.6 m). A fire started by welding and grinding operations was discovered by an employee, and the plant fire department was notified. Arriving fire fighters found the building heavily charged with smoke and sprinklers operating at the ceiling. They entered the building with hose lines to find the seat of the fire. One crew of fire fighters was only 10 to 12 ft (3 to 3.7 m) into the building when bales of paper collapsed on top of them and trapped two of the fire fighters. Other fire fighters and employees outside the building rushed in to assist the trapped fire fighters. A second collapse trapped seven of the would-be rescuers. By the time the incident was over, two employees and three fire fighters were dead due to the collapsing bales. All of the victims died of suffocation. Seven other fire brigade members were injured in the incident. The NFPA investigative report on the incident said, "This fire clearly illustrates the hazard to fire fighters of the collapse of storage materials which expand with the absorption of water. The hazard is particularly acute in sprinklered warehouses and must be considered in the pre-fire plans of fire departments that protect plants or storage facilities involving such commodities."[1]

Personnel must also be aware of the potential of stock collapsing from racks in a warehouse. In many cases, racks may be over 30 ft (9.1 m) high. In some cases, there are warehouses in use today with storage heights that exceed 100 ft (30.5 m). Any burning stock falling from such heights could easily be fatal to anyone unfortunate enough to be working in the aisles. Regardless of the type of stock, the storage arrangement, or the design of the fire protection systems, fire fighters should always be alert to the probability of collapsing stock and protect themselves accordingly.

Visibility

Visibility inside a warehouse during a fire incident will usually be limited. Most warehouses are built with limited access and few windows. Natural lighting may be nonexistent, resulting in poor visibility, especially if electric power is cut to the building as is often the case when a fire occurs. When smoke fills the building, visibility will be reduced even further.

As sprinklers operate in the fire area, the thermal layers normally present in a fire will be disrupted, just as they are when a hose line is discharged into an enclosed area. Contrary to what some people believe, sprinklers will not "drive" smoke to the floor, but as they operate and steam is formed, it tends to cool the atmosphere in the fire area. And as every fire fighter knows, cool, damp smoke is difficult to vent. However, one should never shut the sprinklers off in an attempt to improve visibility.

Ventilation

Ventilation is important at a warehouse fire, as any other structure fire. Fire fighters may be aided by automatic smoke and heat vents installed in the building, or by mechanical smoke exhaust systems. If some type of heat and smoke venting facilities has not been provided, ventilation may have to be accomplished by the more traditional methods, such as opening the roof. Cross-ventilation may be accomplished by opening overhead doors or breaking eave-line windows, if they are available.

It is important that fire fighting personnel not be committed to the roof of a steel-frame building unless the sprinklers have positively controlled the fire. If the fire is not under control, the lightweight steel structural members will quickly fail, causing collapse of the roof. Personnel should also never be committed to the roof of a wood-truss-supported structure. Wood-truss buildings collapse quickly and without warning during a fire. Many fire fighters have been killed in incidents involving the collapse of both wood- and steel-truss-supported structures.

Charged hose lines should be available before venting is accomplished, as ventilation, although necessary to improve visibility, may result in an increase in fire intensity. As mentioned during the discussion of visibility, if the sprinklers are operating properly, steam will be formed in the fire area, the smoke will become saturated with steam, and it will be difficult to move. Cross-ventilation may be the best method of clearing the building.

Fire Fighter Orientation

Warehouses are big places. Aisles and storage pile arrangements can become confusing. If fire fighting personnel are not careful, they can easily become disoriented and lost in the building, especially when visibility is limited. Two fire fighters in Arizona nearly died in a warehouse fire after they left the hose line to crawl farther into the building. After entering the building, they found that sprinklers were controlling the fire and the building was relatively cool. However, it was heavily charged with smoke. They advanced a hose line as far into the building as it would reach and still could not locate the seat of the fire. They left the hose line to advance farther into the building. They became disoriented in the smoke-filled building and were unable to escape before their air supply was exhausted. Luckily both fire fighters survived after being rescued by other companies, but the result could have been much different. Personnel operating inside a warehouse should always maintain contact with a hose line or a life line that can be followed outside to safety.

Logistics

The logistics of a warehouse fire fighting operation must not be underestimated. Even under ideal circumstances it will require a large number of personnel and supplies to successfully fight a fire. The physical demands on fire fighters due to the shear size of the building will require regular rotation of personnel out of the fire area for rest and rehabilitation. Pre-fire plans should contain provisions for assembling a large pool of trained personnel to assist in fire fighting operations.

Other supplies that will be required include air cylinders. Most self-contained breathing apparatus (SCBA) have only a 30-min. rating and will probably last only half that long during strenuous fire fighting operations. If fire fighters must walk 300 ft (91.4 m) into the building to get to the actual fire area, they may only be able to spend 5 to 7 min. fighting the fire before they have to exit the building to replenish their air supply. It is not unlikely that well over 100 cylinders of air would be required at an average fire.

Materials-handling equipment for moving stock during overhaul and salvage operations must also be available as well as qualified personnel who can operate it under emergency conditions. This may require that the operators be trained in the use of self-contained breathing apparatus so they can assist with overhaul operations.

Fire Control Priorities

After life safety has been ensured, the primary problem confronting the fire department on arrival at a warehouse fire will be to control the fire. Establishing control simply means preventing the fire from spreading any farther. Assuming that sprinklers are operating, water damage should not be a concern until the fire has been extinguished. Anything that is going to get wet was probably already wet before the fire department arrived.

It is not uncommon for building owners or tenants to be screaming about the water flowing into the building, and fire fighters may feel pressured to shut off the sprinklers to prevent further water damage. Such pressure must be ignored. Many buildings have burned to the ground because someone shut off the sprinklers in an attempt to minimize water damage. It should be remembered that the only fire in which there is no water damage is a total loss.

Overhaul

As effective as sprinklers are in controlling a fire in a warehouse, final extinguishment will have to be accomplished manually. This means that personnel must break open smoldering pallets, extinguish residual fire inside the loads, and then remove them from the warehouse. If possible, this should be accomplished under the protection of the operating sprinklers. At the very least, multiple-charged hose lines must be available in the area.

Overhaul of a warehouse fire can present several challenges, especially if rack storage is involved. For example, how will fire fighters and hose lines reach the 30-ft (9.1 m) or the 80-ft (24.4 m) level in a high rack storage area for final extinguishment and overhaul? Such problems must be addressed in the pre-fire plan and should be practiced during drills at the site.

Rekindling

It is not uncommon for a fire to rekindle during overhaul operations as cartons of stock are broken open. If the sprinklers are shut down, someone with a radio should be stationed at the sprinkler control valve(s) to quickly open it in the event of a rekindle. Fire fighters have been killed after a fire rekindled during overhaul and spread so quickly that they were unable to escape.

In general, the following are basic rules for shutting down the sprinkler system:

- Do not shut the sprinklers off until it has been positively determined that the fire is extinguished. If there is any doubt, the sprinklers should remain in operation.
- Charged hose lines should be available in the fire area(s) before the sprinklers are shut down.
- Station someone at the sprinkler control valve(s) with a radio to reopen the valve(s) in the event of a rekindle.
- Restore the sprinkler system to full operation as soon as possible.

Limitations of Manual Fire Suppression

The best method of protecting a warehouse is to install a properly designed automatic sprinkler system and maintain it in proper working order. If sprinklers are not provided or they are not in service due to poor maintenance, the chances of saving a warehouse involved in a fire are very slim. Personnel should not be committed to dangerous positions in an attempt to control an uncontrollable fire. The best equipped fire department can never make up for the lack of an effective sprinkler system.

SUMMARY

A fire in a warehouse is a very serious occurrence. Only through the provision of a properly designed automatic sprinkler system can the fire be controlled. Once control has been established, the difficult task of overhauling and extinguishing the fire falls on the manual fire suppression forces of the plant emergency organization and the municipal fire department. The effectiveness of their actions will be largely dependent on the thoroughness of the pre-fire planning efforts conducted in cooperation with the warehouse owner.

BIBLIOGRAPHY

Reference Cited

1. Best, R. L., "Storage Collapse Kills Five," *Fire Command*, Nov. 1980.

References

Ad Hoc Committee for Emergency Operations in High Rack Storage, *Emergency Operations in High Rack Storage*, 1982. (Now available from International Fire Service Training Association, Stillwater, OK.)

Barritt, J. S., "Fire Fighting Tactics for Racked Storage," *Fire Journal*, Vol. 67, No. 6, Nov. 1973.

Barritt, J. S., "Fire Protection and Today's Warehouses," *The Sentinel*, First Quarter 1988.

Best, Richard, "Firefighter Killed in Warehouse Fire," *Fire Command*, June 1980.

Brannigan, Francis L., "High-Rack Storage," *Fire Engineering*, May 1986.

Factory Insurance Association, *Recommended Good Practice for Protection of High Piled Stock*, Factory Insurance Association (now Industrial Risk Insurers), Hartford, 1971.

Factory Mutual Research Corporation, "Stored Plastics: The High-Challenge Risk," *Record*, Vol. 51, No. 6, Nov.-Dec. 1974.

Fields, Terry, "Warehouses: A Case for Control," *Fire Prevention*, Dec. 1988.

Moore, Jeffrey, "Firefighter Safety During Warehouse Fire Fighting Operations," *The Voice*, April 1989.

Pedrotti, Dean R., "Firefighters Down!," *Firehouse*, Jan. 1986.

NFPA Codes, Standards, and Recommended Practices

Reference to the following NFPA codes, standards, and recommended practices will provide further information on the hazards, protection, and emergency operations in warehouses and storage occupancies discussed in this chapter. (See the latest *NFPA Catalog* for availability of current editions of the following documents.)

NFPA 13E, *Fire Department Operations in Properties Protected by Sprinkler and Standpipe Systems*.

NFPA 231, *General Storage*.

NFPA 231C, *Rack Storage of Materials*.

NFPA 231D, *Storage of Rubber Tires*.

NFPA 231E, *Storage of Baled Cotton*.

NFPA 231F, *Storage of Roll Paper*.

Additional Reading

Brunacini, Alan V., *Fire Command*, National Fire Protection Association, Quincy, MA, 1985.

Cox, David, A New Look at Pre-Fire Planning, Fire Engineering, May 1985.

Davis, Larry, and Moore, Jeffrey, *Industrial Fire Control Concepts*, International Society of Fire Service Instructors, Ashland, MA, 1988.

Edwards, Richard J., "Industry/FD Cooperation Produce Improved Operations," *Fire Engineering*, May 1986.

Factory Mutual Research Corporation, Warehouse Storage, *Record*, Winter 1983.

Factory Mutual Research Corporation, *Warehouse Storage: Old Problems and New Challenges*, Factory Mutual Research Corp., Norwood, MA, 1986.

Industrial Risk Insurers, *Overview*, IRI, Hartford, CT, 1986.

Jenaway, William E., *Pre-Emergency Planning*, International Society of Fire Service Instructors, Ashland, MA, 1986.

GENERAL INDOOR STORAGE

Revised by Martin M. Brown

This chapter covers the storage of a broad range of combustible commodities. For the purpose of this review, a commodity is defined as a combination of a product and any packing material, container, and storage aids, such as pallets. Information on the storage of specific materials that may present an explosion or fire hazard can be found throughout this handbook. Additional information on storage can be found in the following chapters: "Flammable and Combustible Liquids," "Gases," "Chemicals," "Explosives and Blasting Agents," and "Dusts."

FIRE PROTECTION PRINCIPLES

The storage of goods does not generally involve a high ignition fire risk. However, when warehouse fires do occur, special difficulties often are encountered in controlling and extinguishing them. Automatic sprinkler protection is the practical and preferred means of fire protection, supplemented by manual fire fighting. However, because storage conditions can be unfavorable, sprinkler systems may sometimes perform less than satisfactorily. This possibility exists even with complete area coverage and all sprinkler valves fully open.

Modern warehousing has introduced a variety of fast-burning substances. For economic reasons, there usually is maximum utilization of warehouse space by high piling with minimum aisle distances between piles, large undivided fire areas, and sometimes enormous values of materials in a single fire area. Spaces inside storage configurations provide, to a greater or lesser extent, opportunity for fire to spread beyond the reach of water discharged from sprinklers.

Because of these warehouse realities, experience with automatic sprinklers has in recent years shown the need for great care in the design of the systems, and in maintaining the conditions upon which the design was based. As a result of continuing full-scale applied research fire testing, primarily at Factory Mutual Research Corporation (FMRC) facilities, and the analysis of fire loss experience, principles and practices of good protection have been derived. To a great extent, they comprise the body of standards that are referenced in this chapter.

COMMODITY CLASSIFICATION

Two conditions determine the probable degree of fire intensity and the difficulty facing automatic sprinkler operation. The first is the nature of goods that are stored, i.e., the commodity classification. The other, covered in the next part of this chapter, is the arrangement of the storage.

For general varieties of stored goods, NFPA 231, *General Storage*, and NFPA 231C, *Rack Storage of Materials*, define commodity classifications relative to their heat of combustion, rate of heat release, and rate of flame spread. For guidance in applying fire protection requirements, general goods are divided into Classes I, II, III, and IV, which may include plastics as part of an item. For plastics *per se*, there are additional groupings: A, B, and C.

General Commodity Classifications

Class I: These commodities essentially are noncombustible products arranged on combustible pallets, in ordinary corrugated cartons with or without single-thickness dividers, or in ordinary paper wrappings with or without pallets. Such products may have a negligible amount of plastic trim, such as knobs or handles.

Class II: These commodities are Class I products placed in slatted wood crates, solid wood boxes, multiple-thickness paperboard cartons, or equivalent combustible packaging material with or without pallets. In rack storage, only wooden pallets are contemplated.

Class III: These commodities are wood, paper, natural fiber cloth, or Group C plastics with or without pallets. In rack storage, only wooden pallets are contemplated. The products may contain a limited amount of Group A or B plastics. (See the following section on "Plastics.") A metal bicycle with plastic handles, pedals, tires, and seat or a wooden dresser with plastic drawer glides, handles, and trim are examples of a commodity with a limited amount of plastic.

Martin M. Brown, P.E., is a fire protection consultant, based in White Plains, NY.

Class IV: These commodities are Class I, II, or III products containing an appreciable amount of Group A plastics in corrugated cartons and Class I, II, and III products in ordinary corrugated cartons, with Group A plastic packaging with or without pallets. In rack storage, only wooden pallets are contemplated. Group B plastics and free-flowing Group A plastics are also included in this class. An example of packing material is a foamed (expanded) plastic cocoon which would hold a typewriter in an ordinary corrugated carton.

In rack storage, a distinction is also made, within these four classes, between encapsulated and nonencapsulated loads, the former being pallet loads tightly enclosed on top and sides by a film of plastic, such as polyethylene. This causes increased difficulty for sprinklers, but encapsulated loads can be altered to the nonencapsulated status by removing the film from the top.

Plastics

In general, the combustion of a plastic produces about twice the amount of heat per unit of weight as cellulosic materials (wood, paper, cotton cloth). In the four commodity classes, the references to plastics are divided into three groups, designated A, B, and C, which also may be stored independently of Classes I, II, III, and IV. Group A includes the fastest-burning types and Group C the slowest.

Plastics Classification

Group A:

ABS (acrylonitrile-butadiene-styrene copolymer)
Acrylic (polymethyl methacrylate)
Acetal (polyformaldehyde)
Butyl rubber
EPDM (ethylene-propylene rubber)
FRP (fiberglass-reinforced polyester)
Natural rubber (if expanded)
Nitrile rubber (acrylonitrile-butadiene rubber)
PET (thermoplastic polyester)
Polybutadiene
Polycarbonate
Polyester elastomer
Polyethylene
Polypropylene
Polystyrene
Polyurethane
PVC (polyvinyl chloride—highly plasticized, e.g., coated fabric, unsupported film)
SAN (styrene acrylonitrile)
SBR (styrene—butadiene rubber)

Group B:

Cellulosics (cellulose acetate, cellulose acetate butyrate, ethyl cellulose)
Chloroprene rubber
Fluoroplastics (ECTFE—ethylene-chlorotrifluorethylene copolymer, ETFE—ethylene-tetrafluoroethylene copolymer, FEP—fluorinated ethylene-propylene copolymer)
Natural rubber (not expanded)
Nylon (nylon 6, nylon 6/6)
Silicone rubber

Group C:

Fluoroplastics (PCTFE—polychlorotrifluoroethylene, PTFE—polytetrafluoroethylene)
Melamine (melamine formaldehyde)
Phenolic
PVC (polyvinyl chloride—rigid or lightly plasticized, e.g., pipe, pipe fittings)
PVDC (polyvinylidene chloride)
PVF (polyvinyl fluoride)
PVDF (polyvinylidene fluoride)
Urea (urea formaldehyde)

NOTE: These categories are based on unmodified plastic materials. The use of flame-retarding modifiers or a different physical form of the material, e.g., shredded, may change the classification.

When assigning a class number to a general commodity, or a group letter to an essentially plastic commodity, the deciding factor is generally the most hazardous category present in an appreciable amount. If Group A plastic cushioning in a Class IV commodity carton is judged to be of such volume as to dominate the fire behavior of the stored item, the commodity as a whole will fall into Group A plastics and should be protected accordingly. There are two exceptions: (1) if there are multiple layers of corrugation or equivalent outer material that would significantly delay fire involvement of the Group A plastic, or (2) if the amount and arrangement of the Group A plastic within an ordinary carton would not be expected to significantly increase the fire hazard. Frequently, it is better to assign a next-higher class than is present if there is any probability of its being introduced later. The difference in protection cost at the outset would be relatively small.

The classifications already mentioned are for high piled storage, which is over 12 ft (3.65 m) high and typical of modern warehouse practice. When storage is located in stockrooms, multistory buildings, and freight transfer sheds having only low piled goods, it can be classified as Ordinary Hazard-Group 2, or Ordinary Hazard-Group 3, according to NFPA 13, *Installation of Sprinkler Systems*. Typical of Ordinary Hazard-Group 2 would be cold storage warehouses, library stack rooms, and tobacco products storerooms. Typical of Ordinary Hazard-Group 3 would be those having moderate to higher combustibility of content, such as paper, household furniture, whiskey in bottles, and general storage items. The protection requirements in NFPA 13 would apply.

Empty Pallets

Idle pallet storage introduces a severe fire condition that is incidental to most storage practices. Pallets are not classified in the commodity categories listed above because the hazard can be controlled by strictly limiting pile heights or keeping the idle pallets out of the building. When stored indoors, wooden and certain solid plastic pallets should be protected as shown in Table 8-5A, unless kept no higher than 6 ft (1.8 m) and in a small area (four-stack) in detached piles. Idle combustible pallets should not be stored in racks.

Plastic pallets other than the type shown in Table 8-5A should be piled no higher than 4 ft (1.2 m) and be in no more than two stack groups, each at least 8 ft (2.4 m) away from other pallets or 25 ft (7.6 m) from stored commodities. Otherwise, they are placed outdoors or in cutoff rooms with extra-hazard fire protection.

TABLE 8-5A. ***Protection for Indoor Storage of Wood Idle Pallets or Nonexpanded Polyethylene Solid Deck Idle Pallets***

Height of Pallet Storage		Sprinkler Density Requirements		Area of Sprinkler Demand in sq ft and (m2)			
feet	meters	gpm/sq ft	(L/mm)/m^2	286°F	(141°C)	165°F	(74°C)
Up to 6	Up to 1.8	0.20	8.1	2,000	(186)	3,000	(279)
6 to 8	1.8 to 2.4	0.30	12.2	2,500	(232)	4,000	(372)
8 to 12	2.4 to 3.6	0.60	24.4	3,500	(325)	6,000	(557)
12 to 20	3.6 to 6.1	0.60	24.4	4,500	(413)	—	—

TABLE 8-5B. ***Minimum Distances from Pallet to Wall in Outdoor Storage***

Wall Construction		Minimum Distance (m) of Wall from Storage of		
Wall Type	Openings	Under 50 Pallets	50 to 200 Pallets	Over 200 Pallets
Masonry	None	0	0	0
	Wired glass with outside sprinklers One Hour Doors	0	10 ft (3 m)	20 ft (6.1 m)
	Wired or Plain glass with outside sprinklers ¾ Hour Doors	10 ft (3 m)	20 ft (6.1 m)	30 ft (9.1 m)
Wood or Metal with outside sprinklers				
Wood, Metal, or Other		20 ft (6.1 m)	30 ft (9.1 m)	50 ft (15.2 m)

NOTE 1: Fire-resistive protection comparable to that of the wall should also be provided for combustible eave lines, vent openings, etc.
NOTE 2: When pallets are stored close to a building, the height of storage should be restricted to prevent burning pallets from falling on the building.
NOTE 3: Manual outside open sprinklers are generally not a reliable means of protection unless property is attended at all times by plant emergency personnel.
NOTE 4: Open sprinklers controlled by a deluge valve are preferred.

All types of pallets stored outdoors should be kept a sufficient distance from a building, using distances as in Table 8-5B as a guide.

Flammable Aerosols

Flammable liquids in small pressurized spray cans, such as hair sprays and paints, have demonstrated a shocking ability to explode from internal pressure when heated in a fire, creating fireballs and often rocketing projectiles that leave a trail of burning liquid. Any appreciable storage of these aerosol cans has the potential to spread fire grossly, overtaxing sprinkler systems. While technically a flammable liquid problem, these products normally are included in many general product warehouses, such as grocery, hardware, and department store warehouses.

For information on sprinkler protection requirements, see the chapter entitled "Aerosol Charging Operations."

STORAGE ARRANGEMENT

From a fire suppression viewpoint, storage arrangements include bulk storage, solid piling, palletized pile storage, and rack storage. Bins and narrow shelves also are of importance, but they usually are employed in stockrooms holding moderate quantities of items for direct use. The basic differences among the four categories that affect the fire behavior and difficulty of fire control are in the horizontal and vertical air spaces, or "flues," created by the storage configurations.

Bulk Storage

Bulk storage consists of piles of unpackaged materials in a loose, free-flowing condition, such as powder, granules, pellets, or flakes, or original items, such as peanuts. The materials will be found in silos, bins, tanks, or in large piles on the floors of storage buildings.

Conveyor equipment, such as belt conveyors, air-fluidizing ducts, and bucket conveyors ("legs"), agitate the material during certain stages of its movement. If it is prone to developing airborne dust, a combustible material presents an explosion hazard, notably in grain storage facilities. Conveyor belts are generally combustible and, together with the commodity, can burn in inaccessible places, such as high above the floor or in tunnels. Automatic sprinklers frequently are needed in the housings around conveying equipment.

Fires in large piles tend to burrow down and require prolonged soaking to be reached. Spontaneous ignition fires may start inside of piles, and may be difficult to locate if internal heating has not been monitored continually by heat sensors immersed in the pile.

Solid Piling

Solid piling consists of cartons, boxes, bales, bags, etc., in direct contact with each other. Air spaces, or flues, exist only where there is imperfect contact, or where a pile is close to but not touching another pile. Stacking is done by hand or by lift trucks using side clamps or the usual prongs in the absence of pallets, when bales or other packages can be pried up from below without serious damage. (See Figure 8-5A.)

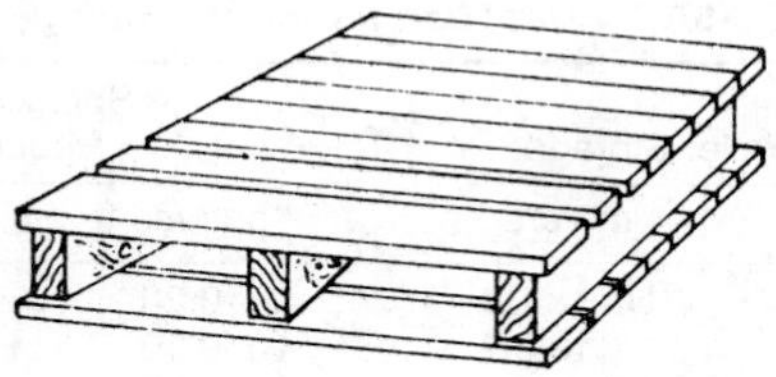

FIG. 8-5B. Conventional wooden pallet.

FIG. 8-5A. A type of solid piling in which spaces are left between cartons to accommodate lift-truck prongs. Wide aisles give the lift truck plenty of room to maneuver. The dark pipes at the ceiling are sprinkler lines.

Compared with palletized and rack storage, solid piling gives fire the least opportunity to develop, and gives water application the greatest chance to be effective. Still, where outer surfaces possess rapid flame spread properties, high piling starting at about 15 ft (4.6 m) can present a severe hazard. Movement of stock during a fire to get at the burning interior is more difficult.

Solid piling of general classes of goods up to 12 ft (3.7 m) high requires sprinkler protection complying with the NFPA 13 sprinkler standards. (See bibliography.) However, NFPA 231, *General Storage*, gives protection requirements for plastics more than 5 ft (1.5 m) high and for other piling up to 30 ft (9 m) high.

Palletized Storage

Palletized storage consists of unit loads mounted on pallets. The load usually is an approximate cube, about 3 to 4 ft (0.9 to 1.2 m) in height, consisting of a single package or block of packages presenting a top surface that can sustain the weight of additional pallet loads without crushing the packages or forming an unstable pile. Each pallet is approximately 4 in. (102 mm) high and usually composed of wood, although some are made of metal, plastic, expanded plastic, or cardboard. (See Figure 8-5B.) The pallet accepts the prongs of a forklift truck, and can be an integral part of a sizable shipping container. The height of palletized storage, usually 30 ft (9.1 m), is limited by the stackability of the packaged goods.

Horizontal air spaces, formed by the pallets themselves, significantly assist the spread of fire within the pile, because they are out of reach of water from sprinklers. The air spaces usually are continuous in one direction for the entire width of a pile.

Sprinkler system requirements for palletized storage up to 12 ft (3.7 m) high are contained in NFPA 13, *Installation of Sprinkler Systems*. However, NFPA 231, *General Storage*, gives the requirements for plastics over 5 ft (1.5 m) high and for other goods with heights above 12 ft (3.7 m).

Rack Storage

A storage rack consists of a structural framework into which are placed unit loads, generally on pallets. (See Figures 8-5C, 8-5D, and 8-5E.) The height of storage racks potentially is limited only by the vertical reach of the materials-handling machinery which, like the racks themselves, can be designed for great heights. While most racks are 20 to 25 ft (6.1 to 7.6 m) high, an appreciable number are higher. (See Figure 8-5F.) In fully automated warehouses, racks are sometimes as high as 100 ft (30 m) or more.

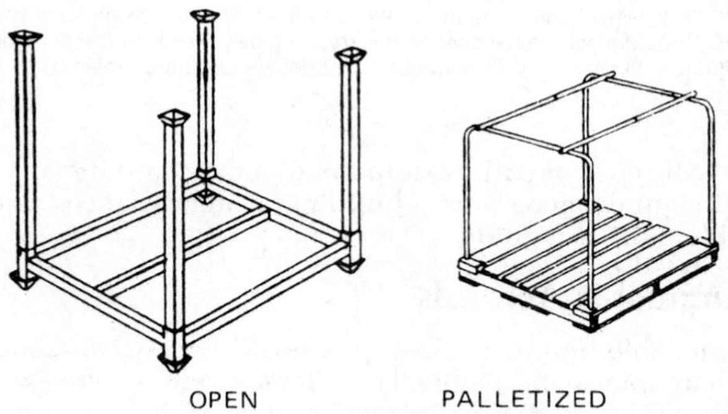

FIG. 8-5C. Two types of portable storage racks.

There are numerous variations to open-single and double-row racks. (See Figures 8-5G, 8-5H, and 8-5I.) Portable racks approximate pallets, except that the upper pallet does not rest on the storage below, but leaves an air space between them.

Automated materials-handling machinery for high racks can operate in narrow aisles, such as those 4 ft (1.2 m) wide, across which fire can readily jump. In racks, horizontal air spaces about 1 ft (0.3 m) deep under each tier of supports provide clearance for handling. Since racks are seldom completely filled, the random vacancies also contribute to the air spaces. Vertical flues exist at upright rack members and between unit loads. They allow upward fire spread, but make possible some sprinkler water penetration into the usually open-style racks.

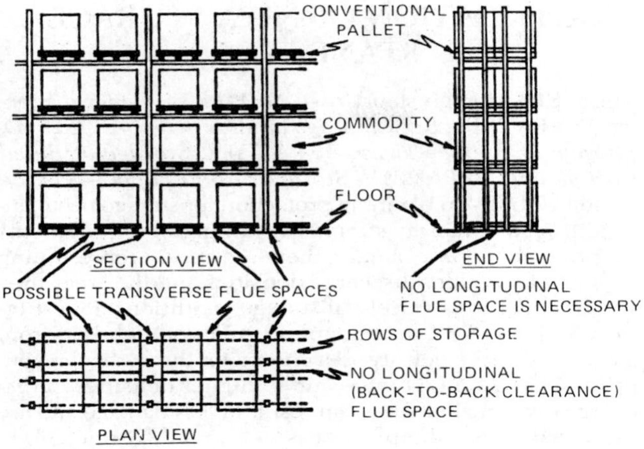

FIG. 8-5D. A typical double-row (back-to-back) storage rack arrangement.

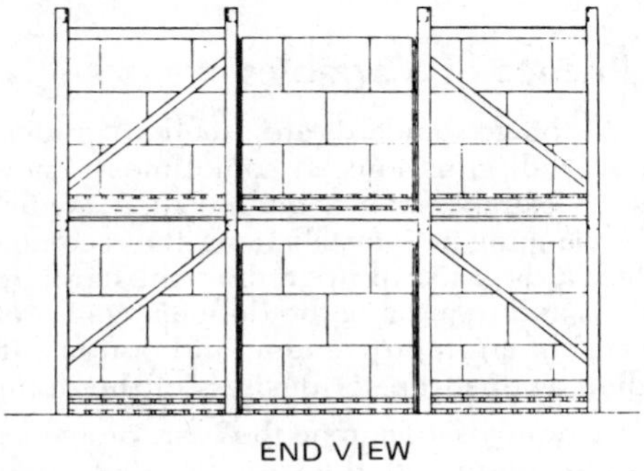

FIG. 8-5E. A multiple-row, drive-in storage rack that is two or more pallets deep. "T" indicates transverse flue spaces. Fork-lift trucks drive into the rack to deposit and withdraw loads in the depth of the rack.

In high automated rack storage fires, even if the damage to contents is not severe, rack storage is vulnerable to the effects of distortion by heat because materials-handling mechanisms must be accurately aligned to function. Such damage could lead to the impairment of the entire warehouse operation.

Fortunately, racks are a semipermanent type of installation which can support sprinkler piping. Otherwise, a combination of horizontal air spaces sheltered from over

FIG. 8-5F. Fifty-three-ft (16 m) high storage racks with narrow aisle. Stacker machine will ride on floor rail, guided from the top. (Source: Unarco Materials Storage)

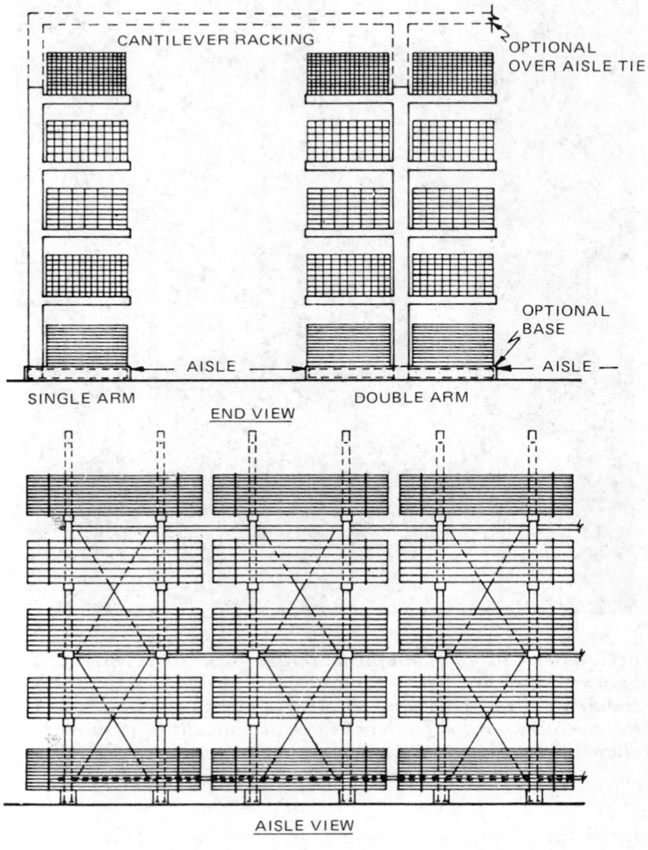

FIG. 8-5G. A cantilever storage rack.

FIG. 8-5H. (Top) Nontypical storage racks with three pallets between uprights, hence three transverse flues. (Source: Clark Industrial Truck Division.) (Bottom) Drive-in-type multiple-row storage racks. Frozen foods are Class I commodities. (Source: Merchants Refrigerating Co.)

head sprinkler water discharge, great height, and narrow aisles would pose an impossible problem for a conventional sprinkler system installed at ceiling level.

APPLICATION OF NFPA STORAGE STANDARDS

The NFPA storage standards—NFPA 231, *General Storage*; NFPA 231C, *Rack Storage of Materials*; NFPA 231D, *Storage of Rubber Tires*; NFPA 231E, *Storage of Baled Cotton*; and NFPA 231F, *Storage of Roll Paper*—provide some flexibility in planning protection for storage occupancies instead of merely stipulating minimum requirements for protection. For example, there are curves representing a range of sprinkler discharge densities and the areas they would cover for a variety of storage conditions. (See Figures 8-5J and 8-5K for examples.) Any point chosen from a curve gives the density area criteria for the particular conditions represented by the curve; higher densities of discharge over smaller areas can result in less damage and are preferred. Often the planner is not bound by one curve, but can alter conditions so that a more favorable curve can be used.

Other choices are available, including different in-rack sprinkler arrangements for rack storage more than 25 ft (7.6 m) high.

The Influence of Variables

The NFPA storage standards are excellent guides, but they do not cover all situations. It sometimes is necessary to improvise by extrapolation or interpolation. While intended mostly for planning new installations, the recommendations in the standards assist in upgrading substandard existing installations and in judging the deficiency of protection so that the cost of an improvement (and options, if any) can be weighed against the seriousness of the deficiency.

Before improvisation upon the basic protection requirements can be attempted, the variables that can be considered must be understood. Armed with an appreciation of these conditions, the designer can employ effectively the evaluation of existing protection and improvisation in original planning or upgrading of protection. The following variables influence experienced judgment in using the standards and, in fact, play a major role in the requirements of the standards.

Variable No. 1—storage height: Other than the fire properties of the commodities themselves, probably no other condition has a more profound influence on the progress of fire in a storage occupancy and on the difficulty of fire control than storage height. In rack storage tests, fire intensity varied with the square of the storage height. For example (without in-rack sprinklers), a 10-percent increase in rack storage height from 20 to 22 ft (6.1 to 6.7 m) requires a 35-percent increase in sprinkler discharge density. (See Figures 8-5L and 8-5M.)

Although increasing height increases fire intensity, all heights up to 15 ft (4.6 m) in solid piles or 12 ft (3.7 m) in palletized and rack storage are treated the same. That is, palletized storage 5 ft (1.5 m) high requires the same level of sprinkler discharge as that required for storage 12 ft (3.7 m) high, except for plastics. This illustrates the principle that a safer condition must sometimes be grouped with the more hazardous condition to allow for the effects of future changes that may influence the degree of hazard.

Effective protection may decline seriously in a high-ceiling area when the occupant uses less than the full height available when calculating the sprinkler system density/area design. For example, in a 30-ft (9 m) high area,

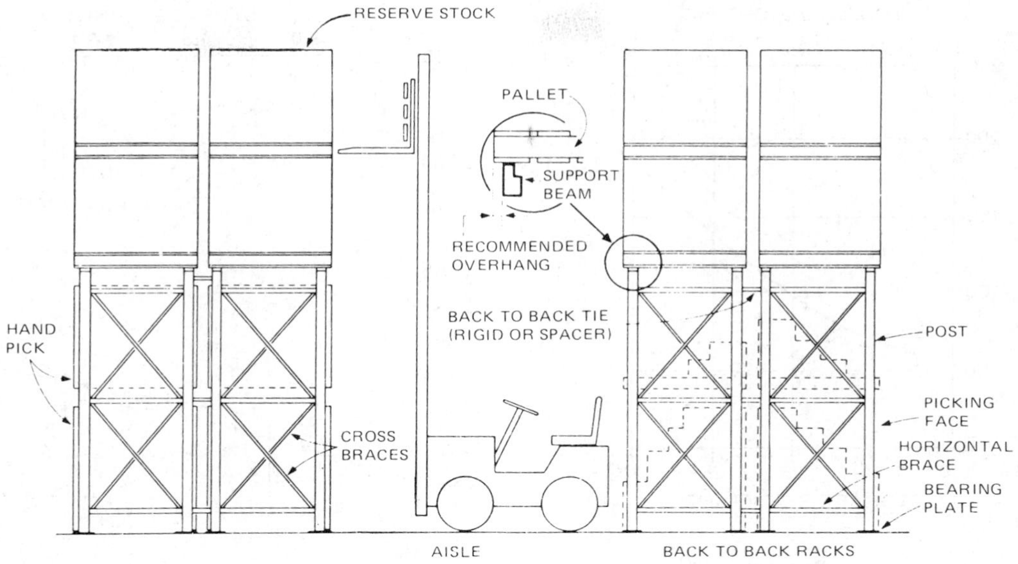

FIG. 8-5I. Common arrangement of double-row storage racks with palletized storage atop. (Source: Unarco Materials Storage)

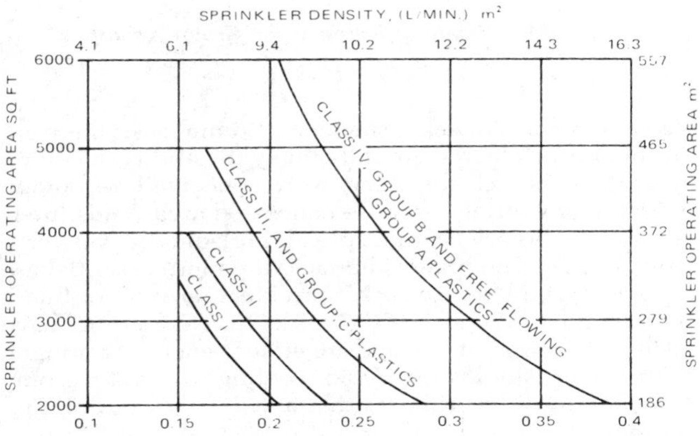

FIG. 8-5J. Wet-pipe sprinkler system design curves for 20-ft (6.1 m) high storage and 165°F (74°C) sprinklers. For 286°F (140°C) sprinklers, reduce the sprinkler operating area 40 percent, but to not less than 2000 sq ft (186 m²).

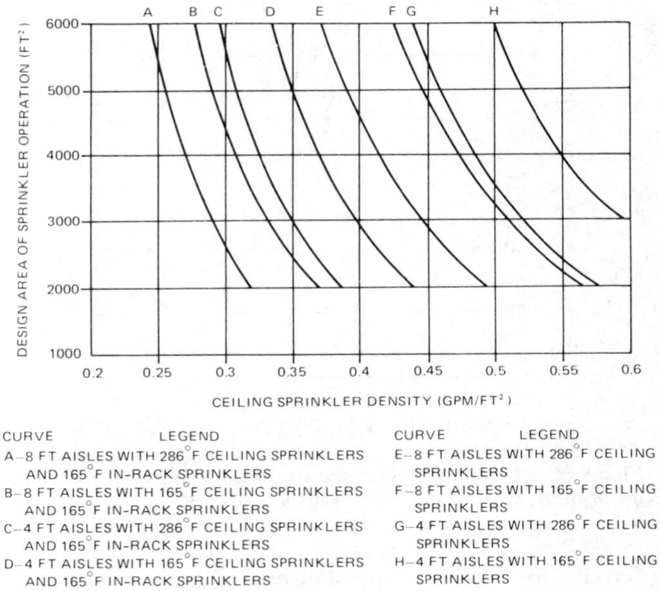

FIG. 8-5K. Typical sprinkler system design curves for rack storage of materials. These curves apply to systems protecting 12-ft to 20-ft (3.6 to 6.1 m) high double-row racks holding Class IV non-encapsulated commodities on conventional pallets. Other curves govern other storage conditions and configurations, as covered in the NFPA storage standards. [1 ft = 0.31 m; 1 sq ft = 0.093 m²; 1 gpm/ft² = 40.75 (L/min)/m²; 5/9 (°F–32) = °C.]

a sprinkler system design for storage up to 15 ft (4.5 m) high can provide protection that becomes grossly inadequate when a new occupant stores goods up to 25 ft (7.6 m) high. Because occupancy conditions can change, it is safe practice at the outset to use the maximum height available for storage as a design parameter. Of course, with permanent racks, the building height can be disregarded. (*Exception*: See Variable No. 5.) As height for racks more than 25 ft (7.6 m) high increases, there is no change in the ceiling sprinkler requirements, because fire control for all but the highest storage is essentially by in-rack sprinklers. In such high rack storage, ceiling sprinklers primarily protect the ceiling structure and only the top portion of the storage.

Variable No. 2—aisle width: Wide aisles help to get water on the fire, retard transfer of fire from one pile to another, and permit access for fire fighting and salvage operations. For rack storage up to 25 ft (7.6 m) high, aisle width is a factor in determining sprinkler density for aisle widths of 4 and 8 ft (1.2 and 2.4 m). For aisle widths between 4 and 8 ft (1.2 and 2.4 m), a direct linear interpolation between curves can be made. (See Figure 8-5K.)

When space permits, it is desirable for aisle widths to be at least one-half the pile height to restrict fire jumping across aisles. Palletized storage piles should not be more than 50 ft (15.2 m) wide between major aisles, so that small hose streams can penetrate 25 ft (7.6 m) to the center of a pile. Although NFPA 231, *General Storage*, does not give

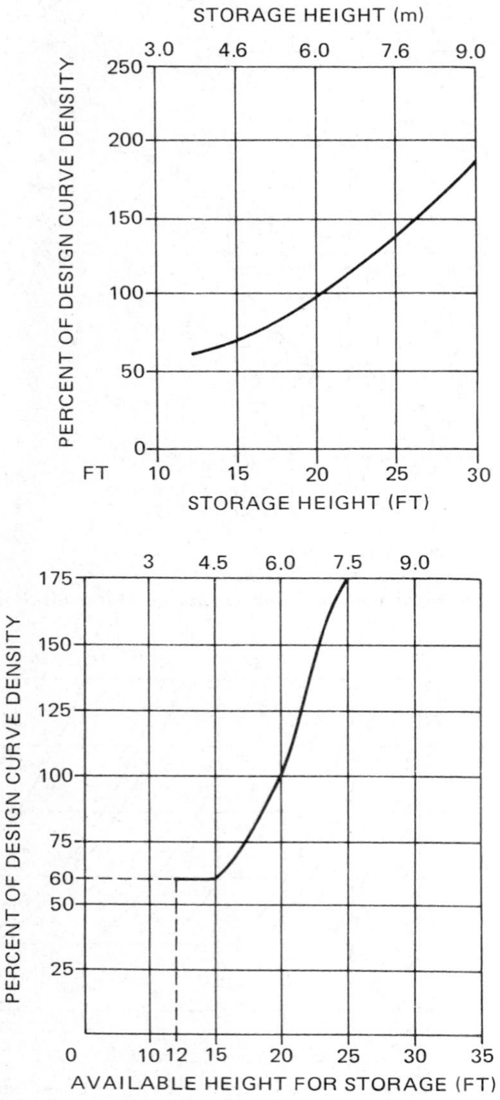

FIG. 8-5L. Ceiling sprinkler density versus storage height curves for both piled (top) and rack (bottom) storage.

"credit" for wide or frequent aisles, the presence of aisles is assumed, and the more and wider the better. Fortunately, aisles usually are necessary for efficient operation in conventional warehouses, with 8-ft (2.4 m) width the normal minimum for maneuvering a lift truck. Where there are frequent aisles, approximately every 10 ft (3.04 m), it is generally agreed that a somewhat lower ceiling sprinkler density is needed over solid or palletized storage than indicated in NFPA 231.

Double-row rack storage needs aisles 4 ft (1.2 m) or more in width to achieve the protection intended by NFPA 231C, *Rack Storage of Materials*. Should the aisles be, for instance, 3½ ft (1.07 m) wide or narrower, the storage would have to be classified as "multiple-row racks," requiring a higher ceiling sprinkler density. For example, storage in the aisles in a huge automotive parts warehouse converted it from a double-row rack configuration to multiple-row racks, thereby making the designed sprinkler coverage inadequate in a disastrous fire.

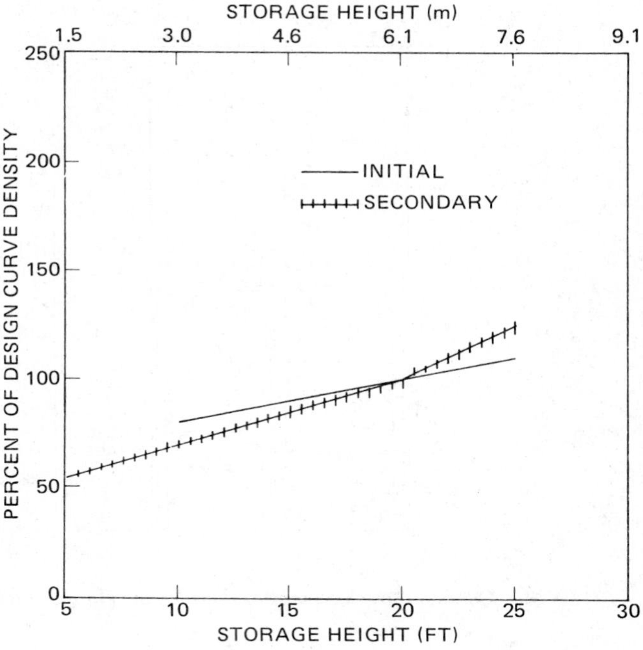

FIG. 8-5M. Height adjustment for Group A plastics.

Variable No. 3—in-rack sprinklers: Within racks, there are sizable unsprinklered areas that defy the ability of ceiling sprinklers. In-rack sprinklers were conceived to provide a degree of wetting for those concealed areas, thus interrupting the otherwise free spread, horizontally and vertically, of fire. The higher the rack, the more essential are in-rack sprinklers. In-rack sprinklers are of ordinary temperature—130 to 170°F (54.4 to 76.7°C)—rating, have ½-in. (12.7 mm) orifices, and are either pendent or upright, with water shields to avoid cooling by water spray from any in-rack sprinklers that may be above. (See Figure 8-5N.)

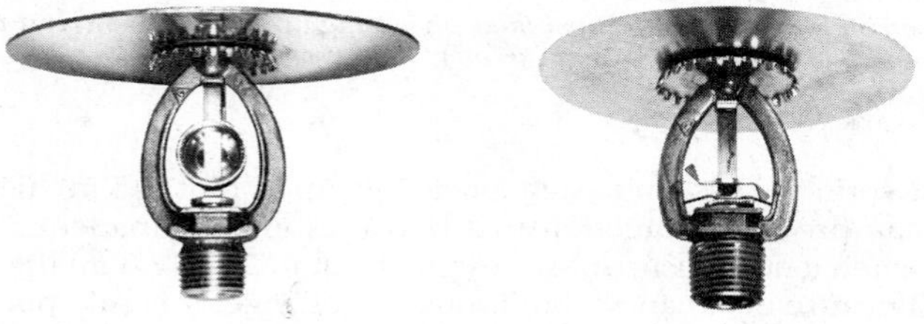

FIG. 8-5N. Typical in-rack sprinklers: upright standard response (left) and upright fast response (right). Pendent sprinklers can be field-equipped with water shields. The fast-response type is appropriate for protection under open-gridded catwalks between racks, shelves, or bins. (Source: Grinnell Fire Protection Systems Co., Inc.)

For rack storage containing solid or slatted shelves greater than 12 ft (3.7 m) high, sprinklers are needed beneath each shelf, unless transverse flue spaces at least 6 in. (152 mm) wide are maintained. [An exception is single-row racks up to 25 ft (7.6 m) in height.] Otherwise, the rules for open racks apply.

In-rack sprinklers are not needed if an automatic high-expansion foam system is used in conjunction with the ceiling sprinklers. Nor are they needed if early suppression/fast response (ESFR) sprinklers are installed. ESFR sprinklers provide faster and better water penetration from ceiling sprinklers in certain moderate-height rack storage situations. The ESFR sprinkler, which has a more sensitive operating element and an extra-large orifice, will produce large flows of water that can quickly pierce the fast-rising plume of hot fire gases while the fire is still small, an advantage in certain problem cases. (See Variable No. 11—sprinkler orifice size.)

Storage up to 25 ft (7.6 m): For rack storage arrangements without solid shelves up to 20 ft (6.1 m) high, in-rack sprinklers are optional for most conditions, but their presence appreciably reduces the ceiling sprinkler density requirement. If in-rack sprinklers are installed at only one level, they are located at the tier level nearest to one-half to two-thirds of the storage height and are arranged longitudinally in the center of the rack. They become practical when storage height is at least 15 ft (4.6 m).

For the higher range of storage heights under 25 ft (7.6 m), one level of in-rack sprinklers is usually mandatory in double-row racks and in multiple-row racks. However, two levels are needed when Class IV storage is more than 20 ft (6.1 m) high.

Sometimes racks are introduced into an existing building having an ordinary-hazard ceiling sprinkler system. Installing one or more levels of in-rack sprinklers may relieve the necessity of upgrading the ceiling sprinkler system.

The recently developed and commercially available ESFR sprinklers have great ability to penetrate racks. Under favorable conditions, such sprinklers at the ceiling level thus can relieve the need for in-rack sprinklers. (See Variable No. 12—sprinkler response time.)

Storage over 25 ft (7.6 m): Ceiling sprinkler discharge can effectively wet exposed storage at the aisles only for the upper 15 ft (4.6 m) or so of the rack. Thus, for rack storage more than 25 ft (7.6 m) high, the lower faces of the rack are protected by "face" sprinklers. They are like other in-rack sprinklers, but are located at transverse flues and positioned within 18 in. (0.46 m) of the aisle. They protect against vertical spread of fire over the face of the storage and assist in controlling fire in the racks. Various arrangements of face sprinklers and centrally located in-rack sprinklers have been devised, including the use of horizontal barriers. (See Figure 8-50 for examples of arrangements for Class I, II, and III commodities.) The arrangements prescribed can be repeated indefinitely as pile height increases.

Horizontal barriers are solid barriers, such as sheet metal or wallboard, which cover the entire length and width of the rack, including all flue spaces. Their effect, when equipped with in-rack sprinkler coverage below, is to reduce the number of centrally located in-rack sprinklers needed. The barriers have the same restrictive effect on vertical fire spread as a full complement of face and central in-rack sprinklers at the same level.

Variable No. 4—temperature rating of ceiling sprinklers: In storage occupancies of low height, ordinary-temperature [135 to 170°F (57 to 76°C)] sprinklers generally are used, subject to higher temperature ratings for high ambient temperature conditions.* Some engineers recommend intermediate- [175 to 225°F (79 to 107°C)] or high-temperature [250 to 300°F (121 to 149°C)] sprinklers to reduce the number of sprinklers operating unnecessarily beyond the actual fire when the commodity may be expected to produce a rapid rate of heat release, which is often the case.

In high palletized or solid-piled storage, or in rack storage up to 25 ft (7.6 m), high-temperature sprinklers can reduce a sprinkler operating area by 40 percent, as compared with ordinary- or intermediate-temperature sprinklers. Somewhat surprisingly, the situation is reversed for rack storage over 25 ft (7.6 m). In a series of fire tests, in-rack sprinklers operated before ceiling sprinklers, indicating that in the over-25-ft (7.6 m) racks, in-rack sprinklers convert what normally would be a rapidly developing fire, from the standpoint of ceiling sprinklers, to a slower developing fire with a lesser degree of heat release. This result differed from tests involving storage 20 ft (6.1 m) high. In those tests, ceiling sprinklers operated before the in-rack sprinklers. In rack storage, over 25-ft (7.6 m) high, therefore, ordinary-temperature ceiling sprinklers are preferred, as they require a distinctly lower density than high-temperature ceiling sprinklers. For example, with Class IV

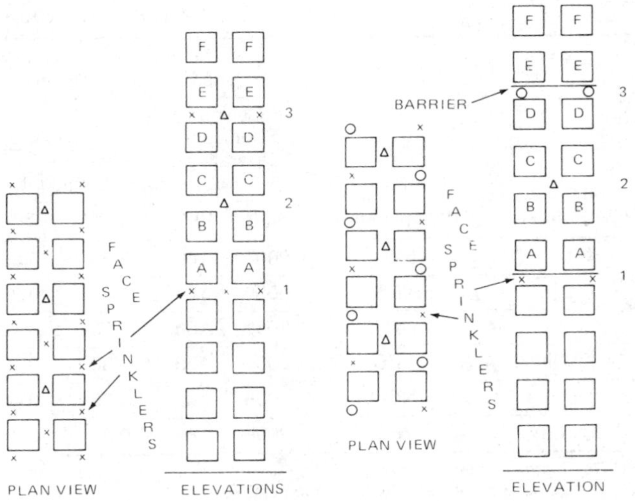

NOTES:
1. SPRINKLERS LABELED 1 REQUIRED WHEN LOADS LABELED A OR B REPRESENT TOP OF STORAGE.
2. SPRINKLERS LABELED 1 AND 2 REQUIRED WHEN LOADS LABELED C OR D REPRESENT TOP OF STORAGE.
3. SPRINKLERS LABELED 1 AND 3 REQUIRED WHEN LOADS LABELED E OR F REPRESENT TOP OF STORAGE.
4. FOR STORAGE HIGHER THAN REPRESENTED BY LOADS LABELED F, THE CYCLE DEFINED BY NOTES 2 AND 3 IS REPEATED, WITH STAGGER AS INDICATED.

FIG. 8-50. In-rack sprinkler arrangement for Class I, II, or III commodities, with height of storage more than 25 ft (7.6 m). Note how the presence of horizontal barriers within the racks (right) reduces the number of in-rack sprinklers required (left). The symbols O, D, or X indicate sprinklers installed in a vertical or horizontal alternating or "staggered" arrangement on the sprinkler piping.

*Automatic sprinklers have six different temperature ratings: (1) ordinary, 135 to 170°F (57 to 76°C); (2) intermediate, 175 to 225°F (79 to 107°C); (3) high, 250 to 300°F (121 to 149°C); (4) extra high, 325 to 375°F (163 to 190°C); (5) very extra high, 400 to 475°F (204 to 246°C); and (6) ultra high, 500 to 575°F (260 to 301°C).

TABLE 8-5C. ***Storage Over 25 ft (7.6 m) High***

		Double-Row Racks Without Solid Shelves, Aisles Wider Than 4 ft (1.2 m)						Multiple-Row Racks					
		Ceiling Sprinklers Operating Area		Ceiling Sprinkler Density				Ceiling Sprinklers Operating Area		Ceiling Sprinkler Density			
				gpm/sq ft		(L/min)/m²				gpm/sq ft		(L/min)/m²	
Commodity Class	Encapsulated	sq ft	m²	165°F	286°F	74°C	141°C	sq ft	m²	165°F	286°F	74°C	141°C
	NO	2000	186	0.25	0.35	10.2	14.3	2000	279	0.25	0.35	10.2	14.3
I	YES	2000	186	0.25	0.35	10.2	14.3	2000	279	0.31	0.44	12.6	17.9
	NO	2000	186	0.30	0.40	12.2	16.3	2000	279	0.30	0.40	12.2	16.3
I, II, III*	YES	2000	186	0.30	0.40	12.2	16.3	2000	279	0.37	0.50	15.0	20.4
	NO	2000	186	0.35	0.45	14.3	18.3	2000	279	0.35	0.45	14.3	18.3
I, II, III, IV†	YES	2000	186	0.35	0.45	14.3	18.3	2000	279	0.44	0.56	17.9	22.8

* Good in rack sprinkler arrangement.
† Not as good in rack sprinkler arrangement.

commodities, a density of 0.35 gpm per sq ft [14.3(L/min)/m²] is required for ordinary-temperature sprinklers versus 0.45 gpm per sq ft [18.3(L/min)/m²] for the high-temperature type. (See Table 8-5C.)

Variable No. 5—clearance below sprinklers: Although a minimum clearance of 18 in. (0.46 m) is required below sprinkler deflectors to allow a good spread of water discharge, there is a limit to how much clearance is desirable over high-piled or rack storage. This problem must be addressed in the case of some Group A plastics. Beyond approximately 4½ ft (1.37 m), the finer droplets tend to remain suspended in the air or to be carried away laterally by the updraft of flames and hot gases. Thus, there are two conflicting variables: (1) under a given roof height, higher storage creates a more severe fire potential, while (2) lower storage creates greater difficulty for sprinklers if the clearance starts to exceed 4½ ft (1.37 m). The two variables may not exactly neutralize each other, so the designer needs to explore the worst condition of variable storage, including a sloping roof. The NFPA storage standards reduce the design criteria to within the acceptable limits where lesser clearances are provided. (See Figure 8-5P.)

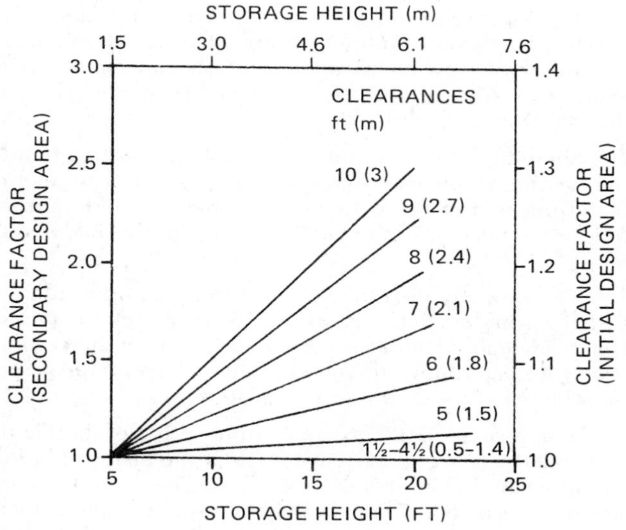

FIG. 8-5P. Clearance adjustment for piled Group A plastics.

Variable No. 6—dry-pipe versus wet-pipe sprinkler systems*: Where dry-pipe systems are used, the delay in water discharge from the earliest operating ceiling sprinklers will allow heat to spread and open a larger number of sprinklers beyond the immediate fire than would be the case with a wet-pipe system. To compensate for this, the design area of sprinkler operation is usually increased by 30 percent for dry-pipe systems. The density should be selected so that the design area, after the 30-percent increase, does not exceed the upper area limit given in the design curve, such as the curves in Figure 8-5K.

Variable No. 7—pile stability: Instability of piles often is undesirable, since it fosters collapse into the aisles, provides a bridge for fire to cross over, impedes fire fighting operations, and possibly endangers building walls. However, tests show that in some cases, sprinklers are more effective after some collapse, spillage of contents, or leaning of stacks across flue spaces has taken place. Evidently, a collapse in these situations chokes off of the upward flow of fire in flue spaces and exposes some otherwise concealed fire to the water from sprinklers.

Under fire conditions, pile stability is difficult to anticipate, but some guidelines are available. Compartmented cartons containing stiff cardboard dividers were found to be stable under test fire conditions, while noncompartmented cartons tended to be unstable. Storage on pallets within height limits suitable for the commodity to withstand compressive forces, and items held in place by materials which do not deform readily under fire conditions, are both examples of stable storage. If there are leaning stacks, crushed bottom cartons, or reliance on combustible bands for stability, pile instability under fire conditions can be predicted.

*In a wet-pipe sprinkler system, the piping to which the automatic sprinklers are attached contains water under pressure at all times. In a dry-pipe system, the piping contains air or nitrogen under pressure. When a sprinkler operates, the pressure is reduced, a dry-pipe valve is opened, and water enters the piping to flow out of any opened sprinklers.

The sometimes beneficial effects of pile collapse should not, generally, lead one to purposely plan for it. Racks, in particular, should have adequate cross bracing, anchorage at floors, and tight connections, as rack collapses tend to be chain reactions.

Variable No. 8—encapsulation: Encapulation is a packaging method in which a thin plastic sheet, such as polyethylene, completely encloses the sides and top of a pallet load containing a commodity package or packages. The plastic covering apparently keeps some of the water from reaching fire that has penetrated a pallet load from below, which is likely to happen in rack storage. Tests show that, where there is uncapsulation, a higher ceiling sprinkler density is needed for rack storage at all heights, even with in-rack sprinklers. The adverse effect of encapsulation has not yet been noted appreciably in palletized storage pile tests. Standards require no difference in the ceiling sprinkler density, with or without encapsulation, in nonrack storage. To convert an encapsulated pallet load to a nonencapsulated load, only the top covering portion of plastic needs to be removed.

Variable No. 9—smoke venting: Smoke removal is important to manual fire fighting and overhaul. Ideally, ventilation operations in a well-protected warehouse should be deferred until automatic sprinkler operation has reduced all temperatures in the building to ambient, which should occur within 30 min of ignition. However, this is often difficult advice for fire fighters who have learned that ideal results are not always attained. To merely pump into the sprinkler system and stand by, waiting for the building to cool down, represents an uncertain situation for the fire department. Hence, fire fighters likely will most make ventilating holes in the roof and enter the building to put small or large hose streams on the fire.

Automatic roof vents: Fire protection engineers still are debating the value of automatic roof vents in sprinklered buildings which, when actuated by temperature, will open and allow smoke and hot gases to escape near the seat of the fire. Tests show they are quite effective in unsprinklered buildings. NFPA 204M, *Smoke and Heat Venting*, provides guidance. On the other hand, the operation of automatic sprinklers tends to interrupt the operation of the vents and to spoil the stack effect that causes the hot smoke to escape. In fact, the initial effect of sprinkler operation often is to beat down smoke, obscuring vision within the building.

Because the fire tests upon which NFPA storage standards are based did not employ smoke venting, they do not require smoke removal facilities. However, the standards do comment that venting through eaveline windows, doors, monitors, or gravity or mechanical exhaust systems is essential to smoke removal after the fire is controlled.

Variable No. 10—high-expansion foam: While automatic high-expansion foam extinguishing systems can be an independent means of fire suppression, there is a reluctance to use them as the sole means of automatic fire control. They are expensive; complicated relative to sprinkler systems; do not protect the roof structure until foam reaches that level; involve the entire contents of a protected area regardless of how small the fire may be; and present a problem of foam residue removal after discharge. However, they have found acceptance when used with automatic sprinklers for certain high-challenge storage occupancies, such as storage facilities for rubber tires, roll paper, and exposed plastics, where excessive foam contact with the stored matter is not a serious problem.

A high-expansion foam system uses a series of foam-makers at ceiling level. When actuated by the fire detection system throughout the area, the foam system causes a spray of water mixed with special foam concentrate in each foam-maker to strike a screen while a fan blows through it. Many bubbles of uniform size are produced, which cascade down into, and gradually fill, the warehouse area. The foam has an expansion ratio of up to 1000: 1, flashes to steam on contact with burning material, and engulfs other material, keeping it from burning. Building doors automatically close when the system is actuated. NFPA 11A, *Medium and High Expansion Foam Systems*, contains the requirements for installing these systems.

When high-expansion foam systems are used in combination with ceiling sprinkler systems in general storage facilities, the sprinkler discharge density may be reduced to one-half the density specified otherwise, but not less than 0.15 gpm per sq ft [6.1 (L/min)/m^2] for Class I through IV solid-piled or palletized commodities, including idle pallets or plastics, and not less than 0.24 gpm per sq ft [9.8 (L/min)/m^2] for rubber tire storage, or 0.25 gpm per sq ft [10.2 (L/min)/m^2] for roll paper storage. In rack storage, in-rack sprinklers are not required when high-expansion foam is installed, and ceiling density can be reduced to 0.2 gpm per sq ft [8.1 (L/min)/m^2] for Class I, II, and III commodities, and to 0.25 gpm per sq ft [10.2 (L/min)/m^2] for Class IV commodities.

Variable No. 11—sprinkler orifice size: Theoretically, any required sprinkler discharge density can be achieved with any size automatic sprinkler that normally is used [½-in. (12.7 mm) or larger orifice] by coordinating the sprinkler spacing and pressure available at the sprinkler. In piping system design, however, a larger-than-½-in. (12.7 mm) orifice can be beneficial when the higher values of density are needed. For densities of 0.40 gpm per sq ft [16.3 (L/min)/m^2] and higher, for example, better results are obtained with large-orifice—$^{17}/_{32}$ in. (13.5 mm)—sprinklers and 70- to 100-sq ft (6.5 to 9.3 m^2) spacing, than with ½-in. (12.7 mm) orifice sprinklers at 50-sq ft (4.6 m^2) spacing. Substituting the $^{17}/_{32}$ in. (13.5 mm) for a ½-in. (12.7 mm) sprinkler results in a delivery of 40 percent more water under the same pressure, with less of the weakly penetrating fine spray.

The NFPA storage standards (see Bibliography) indicate preferences for sprinkler orifice sizes as follows:

NFPA 231—½ in. (12.7 mm) implied, with economy dictating $^{17}/_{32}$ in. (13.5 mm) for higher densities. This standard also allows for large-drop sprinklers [0.64 in. (16.25 mm)] for the various types of commodities in various configurations. (See Chapter 8 of NFPA 231.) ESFR sprinklers [¾ in. (1.75 cm)] are allowed for plastics storage. (See Chapter 9 of NFPA 231.)

NFPA 231C—Densities and areas of discharge are based on tests using ½ in. (12.7 mm) and $^{17}/_{32}$ in. (13.5 mm). If large-drop sprinklers with 0.64-in. (16.25 mm) orifice are used, numbers of operating sprinklers with minimum sprinkler operating pressure are specified instead of densities and areas. (See Table 8-5D.) The advantage of large-drop sprinklers is primarily in their use for Group A plastics.

NFPA 231D—½ in. (12.7 mm) or $^{17}/_{32}$ in. (13.5 mm) implied.

NFPA 231E—½ in. (12.7 mm) or $^{17}/_{32}$ in. (13.5 mm) implied.

NFPA 231F—$^{17}/_{32}$ in. (13.5 mm) required for new installations.

TABLE 8-5D. ***Pressure and Number of Design Sprinklers for Various Hazards (Large-Drop Sprinklers)***

	Number Design Sprinklers			Sprinkler Temperature Rating
Minimum Operating Pressure (Note 1)	@ 25 psi	@ 50 psi	@ 75 psi	
Hazard (Note 2)				
Double-Row Rack Storage with minimum 5.5 ft aisle width (Note 4) having:				
Class I and II commodities up to 25 ft with maximum 5 ft clearance to ceiling	20	Note 3	Note 3	High
Class I, II, and III commodities up to 20 ft with maximum 10 ft clearance to ceiling	15	Note 3	Note 3	High
Class IV commodities up to 20 ft with maximum 10 ft clearance to ceiling	Does Not Apply	20	15	High
Non-expanded Group A plastics in corrugated cartons up to 20 ft, with maximum 10 ft clearance to ceiling	Does Not Apply	30	20	High
Non-expanded Group A plastics in corrugated cartons up to 20 ft, with maximum 10 ft clearance to ceiling	Does Not Apply	20	Note 3	Ordinary
Non-expanded Group A plastics in corrugated cartons up to 20 ft, with maximum 5 ft clearance to ceiling	Does Not Apply	15	Note 3	High

Notes:

1. Open wood joist construction: Testing with open wood joist construction showed that each joist channel should be fully fire-stopped to its full depth at intervals not exceeding 20 ft. In unfirestopped open wood joist construction, or if firestops are installed at intervals exceeding 20 ft, the minimum operating pressures should be increased by 40 percent.

2. Building steel required no special protection for the occupancies listed. Protection requirements are based on rack storage with no solid shelves or slave pallets.

3. The higher pressure will successfully control the fire, but the required number of design sprinklers should not be reduced from that required for the lower pressure.

4. In addition to the transverse flue spaces required by NFPA 231C, *Rack Storage of Materials*, minimum 6 in. longitudinal flue spaces were maintained.

For SI Units: 1 ft = 0.305 m; 1 in. = 25.4 mm; 1 psi = 6.895 kPa.

Variable No. 12—sprinkler response time: The sensitivity of a conventional automatic sprinkler to ambient heat varies somewhat with sprinkler height above the fire, closeness to the ceiling, individual design, horizontal air currents, etc. Nevertheless, sprinkler response time has not been considered in sprinkler system design until recently.

In the late 1970s, it became necessary to require greater heat sensitivity for residential sprinklers, and faster response is now an integral feature of the early suppression/fast response (ESFR) sprinkler, a major advance in sprinkler technology for high-challenge storage. The ESFR sprinkler has a large orifice [3/4 in. (1.75 cm)], which permits a large quantity of water to be delivered to the fire surface at an early stage of the fire because it responds earlier than conventional sprinklers. This phenomenon is extremely critical with ESFR sprinklers and to a lesser extent with large-drop sprinklers. Tests show that certain high-challenge storage fires can be suppressed more quickly by such ceiling sprinklers, and, in some instances, they can relieve the need for in-rack sprinklers. A minimum operating pressure of 50 psi (3.4 bars) to the twelve most hydraulically remote sprinklers is required. The physical arrangements for this application are limited; hence, NFPA 13, *Installation of Sprinkler Systems*; NFPA 231, *General Storage*; and NFPA 231C, *Rack Storage of Materials*, should be followed carefully with respect to the ESFR sprinkler. (See Variables No. 3 and No. 11.)

Variables—Summary

Requirements have been cited from various NFPA storage standards merely to illustrate some of the statements included under "The Influence of Variables" and to show

how they enter into warehouse fire suppression system design. With an understanding of the variables, one can pursue in detail the standards themselves, containing comprehensive requirements, graphs, tables, and explanatory indices.

FIRE PROTECTION FOR WAREHOUSES

While automatic sprinklers are considered the main line of fire defense in storage occupancies, they are not the only needed method of protection. Hose systems, portable extinguishers, and manual fire fighting operations also have a role in protecting storage occupancies, and each is discussed in the following pages.

Automatic Sprinkler Systems

For warehouse ceiling sprinkler systems, the most important design consideration is, of course, a required "sprinkler discharge density" at a corresponding "design area of sprinkler operation." (See Figures 8-5J and 8-5K.)

The NFPA storage standards provide charts containing curves from which a density/area point can be selected. For piled Group A plastics, however, two points are selected from a curve. (See Figure 8-5Q.) One is for the "initial density," the other for the "secondary density," when the storage is in solid piles or palletized piles. The initial density is appreciably higher, but only discharges over a smaller area, as would be expected when the first few sprinklers are operating directly over the fire.

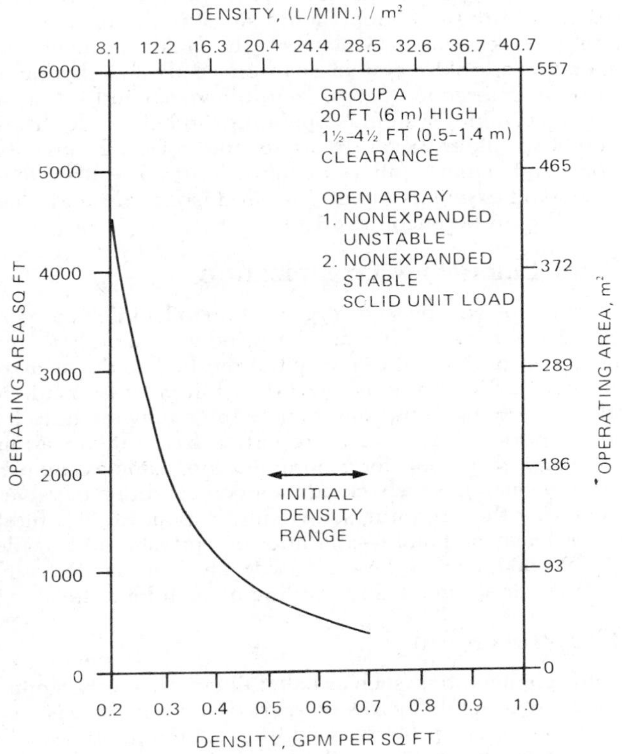

***FIG. 8-5Q.** An example of a density/area curve indicating initial and secondary densities for piled group A plastics.*

For rack storage of plastics, density/area curves are not used; rather, specific density/areas are stipulated for particular conditions. Deviations from the conditions require well-considered deviations from the stipulations. (See Table 8-5E.)

TABLE 8-5E. ***Group A Plastics in Cartons in Single-and Double Row- Racks with 8-ft Aisles, Height of Storage Up Through 25 Ft – 165°F Sprinklers***

	Ceiling	In-Rack
Storage Height (ft)/ Clearance (ft)	Density (gpm/ft^2 Area of Application (ft^2)	Sprinklers Needed (Note 2)
15/3	0.45/2000 0.30/2000	None One Level
15/10	0.60/3000 0.30/2000	None One Level
20/3	0.60/3000 0.45/2000	None One Level
20/10 or 25/3	0.45/2000 0.30/2000	One Level Two Levels
25/10	0.30/2000 (Note 3)	Two Levels

NOTES

1. For 4-ft aisles a density of 0.60 gpm/ft^2 area of application of 1500 ft^2 should be used. For aisle widths between 4 ft and 8 ft, a direct linear interpolation may be made between densities and areas of application.

2. Based on use of 1/2-in. or 17/32-in. orifice sprinklers at 15 psi operating pressure. Sprinklers spaced in the longitudinal flue or an 8-ft spacing with 6-in. clearance between the top of stock and the sprinkler deflector.

3. Based on maximum of 5 ft of storage above the top level of in-rack sprinklers. For storage greater than 5 ft up to maximum of 10 ft, increase density to 0.45 gpm/ft^2.

For SI Units: 1 in = 25.4 mm; 1 ft =.305 m; 1 psi = 6.895 kPa; 1 gpm = 3.785 L/min; 1 gpm/ft^{2}4 L/min/m^2.

Water Supply

The fire service water supply at a warehouse must satisfy design requirements for ceiling sprinklers, in-rack sprinklers (if any), hydrants, and standpipe and hose systems for indoor use. An adequate water supply will have the capacity to supply these protective system components and still have enough pressure in the mains to guarantee sufficient operating pressure at the sprinklers.

Multiplying the needed ceiling sprinkler density by the design area of the sprinkler operation produces a flow requirement in gpm (L/min) to which approximately 10 percent is added to compensate for unavoidable pressure inequalities in the sprinkler system. This is also referred to as the "hydraulic gain" of the system. To the ceiling sprinkler demand is added the in-rack sprinkler demand, if any, based upon operation of a number of the most hydraulically remote in-rack sprinklers. That number depends upon the number of sprinkler levels and the class of commodity involved.

After adding ceiling and in-rack sprinkler water demands, another 500 gpm (1894 L/min) is added for large and small hose streams, without altering the residual pressure requirement, under the assumption that they will be used concurrently with sprinkler system operation.

The total water supply estimate can be expressed as a flow rate at a corresponding minimum residual pressure. That pressure is affected by the sprinkler system piping design, but, in general, at least 30- to 50-psi (207 to 345 kPa) pressure is needed at the ceiling level distribution point or top of the riser. When greater pressure is available, more economic system design is possible, although it is undesirable for standard orifice sprinklers to have more than 60 psi (414 kPa) at the remote end sprinkler, as it is believed that using ½-in. (12.7 mm) sprinkler orifices causes excessive ineffective ultrafine spray in the system discharge.

The water supply has to be available for a sufficient time (usually two hours) for full fire control by sprinklers, any necessary manual fire fighting, and mop-up operations. The reliability requirement for a water supply at a high-value warehouse, for example, can lead to a need for a multiple supply, i.e., a good fire pump-suction tank private supply may back up an adequate public supply, or there may be two similar private supplies. Such redundancy is based on good judgment; obviously, it is not prudent for a $50-million warehouse to depend entirely upon a connection to a single city water main, no matter how powerful that supply, because there is a possibility that it would be out of service for some time.

The layout of yard mains, tanks, pump houses, power supply to pumps, hydrants, and valves warrants qualified fire protection engineering attention in the planning stage. In correcting an existing water supply deficiency, alternate methods can be considered, and the variables discussed earlier in this chapter offer such alternatives. Adding a booster fire pump may be an economical alternative when many sprinkler systems on the property need, and will benefit from, the higher pressure. On the other hand, if just one sprinkler system out of many is deficient, it may be more economical to (1) upgrade the piping layout only in that system, (2) replace ceiling sprinklers for that system with ones of a different temperature rating, (3) install in-rack sprinklers in that area, (4) lower pile heights in that area (not a good long-range solution), or (5) use a combination of methods.

Large and Small Hose

Warehouses of moderate area close to city hydrants present no special fire suppression problem. But when the smaller dimension of a warehouse exceeds about 200 ft (61 m), hose lays from public hydrants to the far side of the building can be difficult. Private hydrants then become important around the perimeter, with access doors to the warehouse near them. Private hydrant spacing of 250 ft (76 m) is common for such situations. Guidance on the number and location of hydrants can be found in NFPA 24, *Installation of Private Fire Service Mains*. Indoor small hose is recommended in high piled or rack storage buildings for use by occupants on incipient fires. Their relatively good reach and long-lasting supply make them more effective than portable fire extinguishers on high storage fires, but extinguishers are also needed.

Portable Fire Extinguishers

NFPA 10, *Portable Fire Extinguishers*, provides guidance in selecting types and sizes of fire extinguishers and locating them properly. But one caution is in order: There is a tendency to provide dry chemical (ABC-type) fire extinguishers everywhere because they are all-purpose units. Such extinguishers have a limited range, or reach, and time of discharge. For example, the 20-lb (1 kg) ABC dry chemical unit, which is about as heavy an extinguisher as can be handled by the average person, has a maximum effective horizontal range of approximately 20 ft (6.1 m) and discharges within 25 sec. A 2½-gal (9.5 L) water-type unit lasts for one minute with an effective range of up to 40 ft (12.2 m), providing a distinct advantage in most warehousing situations, assuming Class BC and its units (for flammable liquid and electrical fires) are provided where needed.

Fire Fighting

Even with adequate fire control by sprinklers or other mechanical means, final manual extinguishment of storage fires is not always simple. At this stage, sprinklers have already done the work of reaching, surrounding, and generally controlling the fire, making it safer for occupants to evacuate. But as the burning continues, fire fighers must cope with the volume of smoke being generated. Sprinkler discharge tends to decrease visibility by the presence of the downpour and by the smoke it drives down from the ceiling. (See Variable No. 9—smoke venting.) In the past, some ill-advised fire officers, upon arrival at the scene, ordered sprinklers shut off to assist in getting at the seat of the fire. Fortunately, the necessity of working with sprinklers operating is now the recognized, standard fireground procedure.

Other manual fire extinguishing problems involve getting at residual fire in the upper reaches of high racks, gaining access through aisles blocked by collapsed storage, and removing from the building burning items, such as fiber bales or rubber tires, that cannot be fully extinguished while in the original, still-smoldering pile. A well-planned system of fire protection should simplify the manual fire fighting tasks. Automatic alarms to the fire department from operating sprinkler systems, as well as adequate hydrants, 24-hour emergency access, audible/visual indication of which sprinkler system is operating, and clear identification of sprinkler valves, hydrants, interior small-hose stations, and siamese pumper connections, all contribute to successful extinguishment. Pre-fire inspections and planning should be encouraged.

Plant Emergency Organization

A warehouse needs some organization to handle emergencies. Even if a small building's procedure is merely to designate an individual to notify the public fire department and use a fire extinguisher, a decision must be made to identify the individual and to determine how the tasks are to be performed. Larger properties frequently warrant in-plant assignments for communication, using extinguishers and small hose, checking the open condition of valves, operating the fire pumps, advising responding fire fighters, salvage, and more—all duties of a private fire brigade. (NFPA 600, *Private Fire Brigades*, gives guidance on the organization, duties, and training of such brigades.)

Fire Prevention

Some commodities, such as baled fibers, are easily ignited, sometimes merely by friction sparks. Goods in cartons need a substantial or prolonged ignition source, unless inadequate housekeeping permits scrap materials to accumulate where they can easily be ignited and act as kindling for the stored items.

The more common causes of fires in storage are smoking, electrical causes, industrial trucks (gasoline, LP-Gas, diesel, or electrical power), and sparks from flame cutting and welding. Steel racks preferably are bolted together rather than welded; this avoids flame cutting during possible future disassembly. Cutting and welding sparks tend to start fires out of range of convenient portable fire fighting equipment.

Arson fires pose a special problem and are combatted by superior automatic sprinkler protection and appropriate security measures.

SPECIAL OCCUPANCIES

A number of commodities have been studied separately because of the fire properties associated with their physical form and method of storage. In addition to the brief descriptions of their fire characteristics, which follow, a sampling of sprinkler system density requirements for 15-ft (4.6 m) high storage is shown in Table 8-5F.

Rubber Tires

Fires in rubber tires are infrequent, but they are very hot and smoky, and are difficult to control and extinguish. High sprinkler densities are needed to tame the fire and protect the building. (See NFPA 231D, *Storage of Rubber Tires*.)

Tires are piled solid, in compact portable racks referred to as pallets, and in racks. (See Figures 8-5R and 8-5S.) Since a tire is not packaged, it contributes its own circular air space to the storage, and this forms considerable horizontal or vertical flues. The interiors of tire carcasses can flame vigorously, mostly out of reach of water from sprinklers. Final extinguishment involves the laborious application of water to individual tires, usually by removing them from the building.

In combination with sprinklers, high-expansion foam is very effective on rubber tires, and causes minimal water damage or contamination. To obtain full penetration to the inner reaches of the tires, it is advisable to allow an additional hour of foam soaking after the sprinklers are shut off to maintain the foam level.

Roll Paper

Roll paper is stored on its side or, more commonly, on end. It might be assumed that the latter arrangement would permit easier paths for sprinkler water to penetrate the vertical air spaces and slow the fire, but experience with roll paper has shown otherwise.

TABLE 8-5F. ***Protection for Various Specific Materials Stored 15 ft (4.6 m) High***

	Sprinkler System Density		Temperature Rating of Head in °F‡	Additional gpm for Hose Streams§	Duration of Flow (hrs)	Area Adjustment for Dry Pipe	Reference Standard	Remarks
	gpm/ft²*	Area ft²†						
Rubber Tires								
Palletized & Fixed	0.48	3550	165	750	3	30%	NFPA 231D	
Rack Storage with Pallets	0.48	2100	286	750	3	30%	NFPA 231D	
Fixed Rack Storage without Pallets or Shelves	0.60	5000	286	750	3	30%	NFPA 231D	Water supply to meet both requirements
	0.90	3000	286	750	3	30%		
Baled Combustible Fibers	0.15	6000	212	500	4	None	FM 8-7	
Hanging Garments	0.60	3000	165	250	1	Avoid DP	FM 8-18	Max. 3 ft. (1.5 m) below sprinklers
Roll Paper								
Rolls on End, Close Spaced	0.30	2000	286	500	2	30%	NFPA 231F	Max. 5 ft (1.5 m) below sprinklers
Banded Rolls, 4 in. (100 mm), or more apart; heavy wt. paper	0.30	2500	286	500	2	30%	NFPA 231F	" "
Banded Rolls, 4 in. (100 mm), or more apart; med. wt. paper	0.45	2500	286	500	2	30%	NFPA 231F	" "
" "	0.60	2300	286	500	4–6	About 75%	FM 8-21	
Baled Waste Paper	0.20	3200	160	500–1000	4–6	35%	FM 8-22	Water supply
Baled Waste Paper	0.20	2700	212–286	500–1000	4–6	40%	FM 8-22	from curves
Carpets								
Cubicle Racks	0.25	3000	286	500	2	None	FM 8-30	
Baled Wool	0.15	2500	212	500	4	None	FM 8-7	
Baled Cotton	0.25	3000	165	500	2	30%	NFPA 231E	Water supply
Rack Storage	0.33	3000	165	500	2	30%	NFPA 231E	from curves
Wood Pallets	0.60	4500	286	500	2	None	NFPA 231	

Note: Full requirements are in the referenced NFPA standards. Above data is abstracted from the standards for comparison purposes. * 1 gpm/ft² = 40.746 (L/min)/m²; † 1 ft² = 0.093 m²; ‡ 5/9 (°F−32) = °C; § 1 gpm = 3.78 L/min.

FIG. 8-5R. On-tread storage of tires in open, portable racks. (Source: Goodyear)

FIG. 8-5S. On-site storage of rubber tires in palletized racks. (Source: Goodyear)

In storage on end, peeling or delamination during a fire is a major problem which can be abated somewhat by metal banding, steel baling wire applied tightly by hand, fire-retardant-treated tight paper wrappers covering ends as well as sides, or close spacing between columns of rolls. Effective close spacing would occur where stacks or columns are less than 4 in. (101 mm) apart.

NFPA 231F, *Storage of Roll Paper*, prescribes sprinkler density area requirements according to the arrangement of the rolls, whether they are banded or unbanded, the height of the piles, and the weight of the paper, i.e., heavy-, medium-, or light-weight. Light-weight paper and tissue are not covered, however.

Carpet Storage

Rugs or carpeting in rolls are generally stored in racks that accommodate 12- to 15-ft (3.7 to 4.6 m) long rolls. Therefore, racks are at least that deep and sometimes placed back to back, forming a total width of 24 to 30 ft (7.3 to 9.1 m) between aisles. Of course, small carpet pieces and rolls may be placed in cartons and stored in regular solid or palletized piles or conventional racks.

Long carpet rolls would deflect if not supported along their length, so, solid or slatted shelves are used in the wide racks. An exception would be for carpets individually encased in strong paperboard tubes that have sufficient bending strength to be supported in open-style racks without shelving. Note that in-rack sprinklers are needed under each solid or slatted shelf in racks, unless there are transverse flue spaces at least 6 in. (152 mm) wide. (See Variable No. 3—in-rack sprinklers.) With carpet racks having as many as 10 tiers, the number of sprinklers and the amount of piping for in-rack sprinklers can be prohibitive. Therefore, protection focuses on providing a minimum 2-in. (51 mm) wide transverse flue at all vertical supports, which are normally 10 to 12 ft (3 to 3.7 m) apart, and providing a level of in-rack sprinklers, including face sprinklers for the wider racks, about every third tier for storage over 12 ft (3.7 m) high. Tiers vary in height from 24 to 40 in. (0.61 to 1 m), so the sprinkler is installed in a tight area. (See Figure 8-5T.) Some engineers recommend vertical transverse barriers at every third set of vertical supports instead of relying upon 2-in. (51 mm) wide transverse flues.

With back-to-back racks, a 12-in. (0.3 m) space should be provided between vertical members, creating a longitudinal flue. If rolls tend to project into this space, toe plates or other means can be fastened to the racks to stop the rolls physically at the rear face. Fire does not tend to spread rapidly in normal carpet rolls along the length of the rack unless there is a large quantity of carpet with attached expanded (foam) rubber backing. Nevertheless, since the racks often extend for several hundred feet (100 ft = 30.5 m), a valuable restriction to fire spread is to provide clear spaces 8 ft (2.4 m) wide about 100 ft (30.5 m) apart along the length of the rack. This serves as an assist to in-rack sprinklers, or as a fire-stop where no in-rack sprinklers are used, usually for storage under 12 ft (3.7 m) high.

Carpet padding: Padding or backing, usually made of expanded plastic, expanded rubber, or jute, generally is stored in carpet warehouses. These materials burn much faster than the carpeting *per se* and should be segregated for special arrangement and protection. Ceiling sprinkler

FIG. 8-5T. Racks for the storage of carpeting on slatted shelves. The closeness of the tiers to each other, plus the depth of the tiers, complicates problems of providing in-rack sprinkler protection. (Source: Clark Industrial Truck Div.)

density that is adequate for the warehouse as a whole probably will not be adequate for the padding unless the storage is kept low, such as less than 5 ft (1.5 m) for expanded rubber or plastic.

Baled Fibers

The main hazard of baled cotton and other fibers of vegetable origin comes from the surfaces of the bales that have a multitude of exposed minute fibers. Fire flashes quickly over these vertical surfaces, as well as over any loose particles on the floor or lint on overhead piping and structure. Fire on one side of an automatic-closing fire door can progress through the open doorway on loose floor scraps before the door can close automatically. Housekeeping, therefore, is especially important.

Fire also tends to penetrate between and into bales, requiring removal of burning bales from the building for extinguishment. Considerable smoke is emitted and complicates fire fighting. Certain fibers, such as jute, are likely to swell when wet, so they should be piled with regard to stability in a fire and with proper clearance from walls.

NFPA 231E, *Storage of Baled Cotton*, limits the height of tiered or rack storage to 15 ft (4.6 m) and pile sizes to 700 bales, with a 12-ft (3.7 m) main aisle and 4-ft (1.2 m) cross aisles, in maximum fire divisions of 10,000 bales; the standard calls for large operating areas for sprinklers. (See Factory Mutual Research Corporation Loss Prevention Data Sheet 8-7, which covers baled combustible fibers generally, including wool which burns much slower than most other fibers.)

Ordinary dry chemical (BC-type) fire extinguishers are very effective in knocking down surface fires on bales. However, they should be backed up by water spray from small hose or garden hose, or by water-type extinguishers equipped with spray nozzle attachments to extinguish smaller fires that may have penetrated into the bales. Preferable, "wet water," a chemical agent additive that increases water's penetrating and spreading ability, should be used.

Baled Wastes

Paper: Like baled fibers, baled wastepaper is stored in solid piles into which fire tends to burrow. When paper is finely shredded, fire can flash over the surface of the bales, as it does with baled fiber. Wastepaper becomes mushy and difficult to handle when wet; in fact, the integrity of the bales slowly disappears as the hose stream application progresses, making removal of burning bales difficult. Smoke can also be a troublesome problem. Baled paper sometimes is stored at great heights because of its low unit value, but fire protection standards do not apply to storage over 30 ft (9.1 m) high, except in racks.

Pesticides

Pesticides are not only poisonous to insects and small animals, but are harmful, even fatal, to humans when ingested or breathed as products of combustion. They are stored as solutions in flammable or combustible liquids, as powders or granules in combustible packages, or as compressed gases for fumigation. Special attention must be given to the personnel hazard, in addition to the commodity's combustibility. Pesticide fires can endanger persons fighting the fire or standing nearby, and the poisonous runoff from fire fighting can pollute water or soil in the area.

Automatic sprinkler protection is advisable, but provision should be made for safe accumulation and disposal of the water runoff. Fire fighting strategy should include plans to use protective clothing and respiratory equipment, spray nozzles rather than straight streams to reduce water runoff, and specialized medical back-up services, and to avoid container breakup and pesticide dispersal.

NFPA 43D, *Pesticides in Portable Containers*, gives general requirements for both inside and outside storage of pesticides.

SPECIAL STORAGE FACILITIES

Piers and Wharves

Warehouses often form the superstructure of piers and wharves. They may be referred to as "sheds," which, on piers, can project great distances over the water. They have the same general characteristics as other warehouses, but with more fire protection and suppression problems. Among these problems are reduced accessibility for land-based fire department vehicles; the frequently combustible nature of the substructure, which can be exposed to floating burning debris or flammable liquids; the danger of water supply mains freezing; and the hazard of ships colliding with the pier. On the favorable side, commodities tend to be low piled because of the temporary, transfer nature of the storage, i.e., ship-to-shore or *vice versa*.

At the Luckenbach Pier in Brooklyn, NY, on December 3, 1956, a fire and explosion in stored Cordeau detonant fuse for explosives killed ten people and caused $7.6 million in damage. It illustrated the need for better limitations on hazardous materials, in this case contiguous with ordinary combustibles.

NFPA 87, *Standard for the Construction and Protection of Piers and Wharves*, requires a water supply for both hose streams and sprinkler systems to be available for at least 4 hrs—about double the usual duration. To protect the underside of a combustible substructure, sprinklers should be either standard pendent sprinklers in the upright position, or old-style sprinklers in the upright position, to wet the undersurface of the substructure.

It is desirable to limit the area between transverse fire walls in a pier, making these walls continuous with substructure fire walls, which, in turn, should extend to low water. The walls should be spaced not more than 450 ft (137 m) apart. Below a combustible substructure, transverse firestops should be spaced not more than 150 ft (45 m) apart.

Storage Garages

Motor vehicles, including automobiles and trucks in "dead storage," are housed in storage garages or outdoors. Because of their generally fast-burning upholstery and gasoline or diesel-oil content, fires in individual vehicles can be severe, but the overall building fire loading is moderate, evidently because the considerable amount of metal in the vehicles absorbs heat, and the average weight of combustibles per sq ft (m^2) is not high.

According to NFPA 88A, *Parking Structures*, storage garages and enclosed parking structures (not open-air parking structures) need automatic sprinkler protection if they are located in basements, in buildings more than 50 ft (15.2 m) high having combustible roof/floor assemblies, or inside or below a building used for another purpose, typically high-rise apartments, hotels, or offices. In the last case, an alternative to sprinklers is a supervised smoke detection system used together with a mechanical ventilating system capable of exhausting smoke. Dispensing of flammable liquid fuels from underground tanks sometimes is a feature inside such garages, but the pumps should be at street level within 50 ft (15 m) of a vehicle exit or entrance. (See NFPA 30, *Flammable and Combustible Liquids Code*.) Many municipal building codes require automatic sprinkler protection in noncombustible and fire-resistive public parking garages that exceed certain areas and/or heights, so applicable codes should be consulted.

Refrigerated Storage

Coolers and freezer storage buildings are primarily for foodstuffs, although certain antibiotics, pharmaceuticals, and unstable chemicals also are kept under refrigeration. To date, fire loss experience in refrigerated warehouses has been good during normal occupancy. It is during construction or temporary shutdown for repair that some devastating fires have occurred, usually caused by cutting and welding operations. The housekeeping in these structures generally is excellent, and smoking is mostly nonexistent because smoke odor clings to frozen packages. Nevertheless, the potential for large loss is present in the containers, pallets, dunnage, waxy paper containers, and electrical equipment.

Insulation at walls and ceilings can spread fire quickly. Present practice involves prefabricated sandwich panels with insulation cores, lining sheets of expanded polystyrene, or foamed-in-place expanded polyurethane. Older warehouses, and some newer ones, use cork or other cellulose-type insulation, or noncombustible insulation, such as fibrous glass or expanded glass block. When an expanded plastic lining is used, it should be covered with an approved thermal barrier, such as cement plaster on lath, gypsum plaster wallboard, fire-retardant plywood, or an approved fire-resistive inorganic spray material, a few of which are now listed for this purpose by Underwriters Laboratories Inc. (UL) and the Factory Mutual Research Corporation. When a non-plastic combustible lining is used, it too should be covered by a thermal barrier if the occupancy does not require sprinklers.

The same sprinkler system design used for nonrefrigerated buildings is appropriate for this occupancy, except that it must be designed so as not to freeze. The commodity hazard classification generally is lowered in freezer areas because of ice in the packages.

Isolated Storage Buildings

Some high-value warehouses are needed for only a few years, such as those in construction projects in remote areas. At times, such a warehouse can contain quite a bit of electrical and electronic equipment, wire, cables, fixtures, pipe fittings, etc. There are also experimental or mining sites that may have a large warehouse. These remote areas are often without public water mains or fire departments, making adequate private protection more costly. Several factors have to be weighed, such as the criticality of the building to the project and the time needed to replace vital contents. Standards and building codes do not apply rigidly in these situations. Suitable decisions could be to separate unprotected warehousing into small units, to provide fully adequate private protection, or to compromise and use protective systems with a limited water supply. Any compromised physical protection should be accompanied by increased vigilance regarding guard service, housekeeping, maintenance, and smoking control.

Underground Storage

Large underground warehouses can be a boon to energy conservation, as rock caverns have a nearly constant temperature. In the U. S., some caverns have been used for compressed gas storage and some old mines for records storage.[1] Caves have been developed for warehousing and include automatic sprinkler protection.

In general, the problems of underground structures include exits, venting of smoke and heat, and access for fire fighting. Automatic sprinkler protection can be installed under constructed floors and ceilings and is vital to protect combustible storage and associated personnel.

Air-Supported Structures

For warehousing in temporary or remote locations, such as at construction sites, or as a low-cost adjunct to more permanent conventional types of buildings, air-supported structures of considerable size are sometimes used, based on the convenience and economics of the risk involved. (See Figures 8-5U and 8-5V.) These structures consist of a plastic-coated fabric envelope which resembles a balloon and is kept rigid by low positive air pressure within. When used for warehousing, such as palletized or rack storage, the structure may be equipped with loading dock arrangements, such as air locks with electric roll-up doors. Structures less than 150 ft (46 m) in width or diameter should comply with NFPA 102, *Assembly Seating, Tents, and Membrane Structures*, which deals with wind resistance, strength, load distribution, and pressurization of air-supported structures. There is a trend toward using a cable harness net system to encapsulate the envelope in all directions, thus increasing the structure's stability during wind load.[2]

These structures do not support overhead piping or wiring, and so are unable to satisfy the usual need for automatic fire control systems. Therefore, they are not suitable for long-term combustible storage of high value or high hazard. When there are compelling reasons to use these structures, it is preferable to have a number of separate smaller units rather than one large structure.

FIG. 8-5U. A typical air-supported structure that is suitable for warehousing purposes. (Source: Air-Tech Industries, Inc.)

FIG. 8-5V. Interior of a 100- by 300-ft (30 by 91 m) air-supported warehouse, showing rack storage. (Source: Air-Tech Industries, Inc.)

CONSTRUCTION

Any important building, warehouse or otherwise, merits durable construction that resists wind and snow loads. Many construction types meeting these criteria are combustible or vulnerable to fire temperatures, but automatic sprinklers are virtually always needed to protect the storage contents and compensate for these hazards.

Buildings used for both manufacturing and warehousing should have a good barrier wall, preferably a true fire wall, between these components because the greater activity (hazard) in the former can expose the high values of the latter to the damaging effects of a fire. Incidental adjoining areas, such as boiler, machinery, or service rooms, should be separated by fire partitions.

Steel columns within storage racks over 15 ft (4.6 m) high in which there are no in-rack enclosed sprinklers need to be "fireproofed," protected by one or two sidewall sprinklers, or under high-density ceiling sprinkler discharge, in accordance with NFPA 231C, *Rack Storage of Materials*.

BIBLIOGRAPHY

References Cited

1. Holdcraft, R. L., "Fire Protection Criteria for Caves," *Fire Journal*, Vol. 79, No. 3 (May-June 1985), pp. 35-37, 121.
2. Air Structures Institute, "Air Structures Design and Standards Manual," *ASI-77*, Air Structures Institute, St. Paul, MN, 1977.

NFPA Codes, Standards, and Recommended Practices

Reference to the following NFPA codes, standards, and recommended practices will provide further information on general indoor storage discussed in this chapter. (See the latest *NFPA Catalog* for availability of current editions of the following documents.)

NFPA 10, *Portable Fire Extinguishers*.
NFPA 11A, *Medium and High Expansion Foam Systems*.
NFPA 13, *Installation of Sprinkler Systems*.
NFPA 13A, *Inspection, Testing, and Maintenance of Sprinkler Systems*.
NFPA 14, *Standpipe and Hose Systems*.
NFPA 24, *Installation of Private Fire Service Mains*.
NFPA 30, *Flammable and Combustible Liquids Code*.
NFPA 30B, *Aerosol Products*.
NFPA 43D, *Pesticides in Portable Containers*.
NFPA 51B, *Cutting and Welding Processes*.
NFPA 71, *Installation, Maintenance, and Use of Signaling Systems for Central Station Service*.
NFPA 72A, *Installation, Maintenance, and Use of Local Protective Signaling Systems*.
NFPA 72B, *Installation, Maintenance, and Use of Auxiliary Protective Signaling Systems*.
NFPA 72C, *Installation, Maintenance, and Use of Remote Station Protective Signaling Systems*.
NFPA 72D, *Installation, Maintenance, and Use of Proprietary Protective Signaling Systems*.
NFPA 72E, *Automatic Fire Detectors*.
NFPA 87, *Standard for the Construction and Protection of Piers and Wharves*.
NFPA 88A, *Parking Structures*.
NFPA 102, *Assembly Seating, Tents, and Membrane Structures*.
NFPA 204M, *Smoke and Heat Venting*.
NFPA 231, *General Storage*.
NFPA 231C, *Rack Storage of Materials*.
NFPA 231D, *Storage of Rubber Tires*.
NFPA 231E, *Storage of Baled Cotton*.
NFPA 231F, *Storage of Roll Paper*.
NFPA 505, *Powered Industrial Trucks, Including Type Designations, Areas of Use, Maintenance, and Operation*.
NFPA 600, *Private Fire Brigades*.
NFPA 601, *Guard Service in Fire Loss Prevention*.
NFPA 602, *Guard Operations in Fire Loss Prevention*.

Additional Reading

Andrews, C. L., "Rebuilding a Warehouse Complex," *Fire Prevention*, No. 204 (Nov. 1987) pp. 31-32.
"Baled Fiber Storage," *Loss Prevention Data,* Factory Mutual Research Corp., Norwood, MA, 1974.
Before the Fire—Fire Prevention Strageties for Storage Occupancies, NFPA Ad Hoc Task Force, 1987.
Best, R., "$100 Million Fire in K-Mart Distribution Center," *Fire Journal*, Vol. 77, No. 2 (Mar. 1983), pp. 36-42.
Brannigan, F. L., "High Rack Storage," *Fire Engineering*, Vol. 139, No. 5, 1986, p. 32.

Clarke, G., "The Idle Pallet Fire Problem," *Fire Journal*, Vol. 66, No. 4 (July 1972), pp. 98-101.

Corbett, G. P., "$100-Million Warehouse Fire," *Fire Engineering*, Vol. 138, No. 6, 1985, p. 36.

Deacon, F. C., "Designing Fire Protection to Limit Monetary Loss," *SFPE TR 80-2*, Society of Fire Protection Engineers, Boston, MA, 1980.

"Designing to Limit Loss in High-Rise Rack Warehouses," *Kemper Group Report*, Vol. 10, No. 3 (Sept. 1981), pp. 2-9.

Field, P. and Murrell, J., "The Fire Hazard and Protection of Bin Storage," *Fire Surveyor*, Vol. 17, No. 6 (Dec. 1988), pp. 5-15.

Fields, T., "Warehouses: A Case Study for Control," *Fire Prevention*, No. 215 (Dec. 1988), pp. 24-29.

"Fire and Safety Arrangements in a Warehouse Complex," *Fire Prevention*, No. 199 (May 1987), pp. 21-22, 24-27.

Goring, G., "Sprinkler Protection for Storage Risks," *Fire Protection*, Vol. 8, No. 2 (June 1981), pp. 20-25.

Harrington, J. L. and Hopkinson, R. B., *Rack Storage Protection*, Worcester Polytechnic Institute, Worcester, MA, 1977.

Johnson, R. S., "How to Protect Roll-Paper Storage from Costly Fires," *Inland Printer/American Lithographer*, Mar. 1968.

Khan, M., "Evaluation of Fire Behavior of Packaging Materials," *FMRC RC87-TP-7*, presented at Defense Fire Protecton Association Symposium, 1987.

Lee, J. L., "The Effect of Different Storage Configurations on Required Delivered Density," *FMRC J.I. OMOER.RA*, April 1986

Lee, J. L.,"The Effect of Paper Construction and Polyethylene Coating on the Flammability and Extinguishability of Roll Paper Products," *FMRC JI ONOE9.RA*, July 1986.

Lee, J. L., "Extinguishment of Rack Storage Fires of Corrugated Cartons Using Water," *Proceedings* of the First International Symposium on Fire Safety Science, Hemisphere, Washington DC, 1986, pp. 1177-1186.

Linville, J. L., ed., "Industrial Storage Practices," *Industrial Fire Hazards Handbook*, 3rd ed., National Fire Protection Association, Quincy, MA. 1990.

Murrell, J. V. and Field, P., "Sprinkler Protection of Past Pallet Storage in High Rocks," *Fire Surveyor*, Vol. 19, No. 1 (Feb. 1990), pp. 16-20.

Patterson, C. B., "Powered Industrial Trucks: Appraising Their In-Plant Fire Safety," *Fire Journal*, Vol. 66, No. 5 (Sept. 1972), pp. 103-104.

"Roll Paper Storage," *Loss Prevention Data Sheet 8-21*, Factory Mutual Engineering Corp., Norwood, MA.

Schirmer, C. W., "Meeting the High-Piled Storage Challenge with Standards," *Fire Journal*, Vol. 65, No. 6 (Nov. 1971), pp. 61-66.

"Solid, Palletized, and Rack Storage of Plastics," *Loss Prevention Data Sheet 8-9*, Factory Mutual Engineering Corp., Norwood, MA.

"Storage of Baled Waste Paper," *Loss Prevention Data*, Factory Mutual Research Corp., Norwood, MA, 1977.

"Stored Plastics—The New High Challenge Risk," *P7422*, Factory Mutual Engineering Corp., Norwood, MA.

"Warehouse Storage: Large-Scale Solutions for Large-Scale Problems," *P8324*, Factory Mutual Engineering Corp., Norwood, MA.

Young, R. A. and Nash, P., "The Fire Protection of Modern High Bay Storages," *Fire Prevention Science and Technology*, No. 18 (Dec. 1977) pp. 4-13.

Woolhead, F. E., "Meeting the Challenge of Fires in Warehouses," *Fire International*, Vol. 10, No. 101, 1986, pp. 23-25.

COLD STORAGE WAREHOUSES

Revised by Robert M. Hodnett

Cold storage warehouses are used primarily for extended storage of food products at temperatures that prevent or retard spoilage. Products, such as pharmaceuticals, antibiotics, and unstable chemicals, may also require refrigerated storage.

Additional information on warehouses can be found in Section 8, Chapter 4, "Warehouse Pre-Planning and Fire Fighting Operations."

Depending upon the products or processes, warehouse temperatures range from –35°F (–37.2°C) for initial freezing up to 65°F (18.3°C). Despite low temperatures, cold storage warehouses are not immune to fire hazards. In fact, the low temperatures present unusual fire prevention and control problems which may be aggravated when warehouses are located away from municipal water distribution systems. Combustible materials in such warehouses include cork or expanded plastic insulation; wood dunnage, pallets, boxes, and baskets; fiberboard containers; paper and cloth wrapping; plastic containers and boxes; and grease-impregnated materials. These present the potential for large monetary losses. Fire frequency, however, is relatively low in cold storage warehouses. About half the fires that do occur originate outside the refrigerated areas, damaging unprotected combustible insulation, structural components, and electrical equipment.

CONSTRUCTION OF COLD STORAGE WAREHOUSES

Refrigerated warehouses may be of combustible or noncombustible construction, or a combination of both. The current trend is to build larger and higher buildings in which automated storage racks are structural units supporting the walls and roof of the building. Such construction is acceptable if the rack structure will adequately support wind and snow loads. Although the structural materials themselves are noncombustible, such buildings must be adequately sprinklered to protect both the structure and the stored material. When large amounts of cork and/or foam insulation are ignited, they can burn out of control, generating temperatures high enough to distort steel and cause the structure to collapse.

Polyurethane foam, either in sheets or foamed-in-place, and polystyrene foam are two common insulation materials. When used in walls or ceilings, these materials should be protected by an approved thermal barrier or by a ½-in. (12.7 mm) coat of cement plaster on metal lath attached to the building framing. For polystyrene, the barrier also may be either ½-in. (12.7 mm) Type X gypsum wallboard or ¾-in. (19 mm) fire-retardant plywood supported by studs or furring attached to the framing. These thermal barriers are required to be coated with a United States Department of Agriculture (USDA) approved washable finish to meet sanitary standards. If used in the floor, the insulation should be covered with concrete and the joint between floor and wall provided with a cove or curb. Automatic sprinklers should be provided below suspended ceilings, and the space above the ceiling should be protected against fire spread and sprinklered if it is combustible.

Refrigerant Gases

Refrigerant gases present two basic hazards: toxicity and flammability. Sprinklers are very effective because the spray dilutes, disperses, and cools the escaping gases.

STORAGE ARRANGEMENTS

As in other warehouses, storage arrangements in refrigerated warehouses can be bulk, solid piling, palletized, or rack type, with bulk storage minimally used. One exception to this arrangement is the hook storage of meat and poultry products awaiting further processing. This storage method presents minimal fire hazard due to the low temperature and absence of combustible packaging.

Of the three commonly used storage arrangements, solid piling presents the least opportunity for fire development. In this arrangement, cartons, bales, and other packages are in direct contact with each other. Air spaces, or

Robert M. Hodnett is a consultant in fire protection systems, based in South Kingstown, RI. He was staff liaison to the NFPA Water Extinguishing Systems Committees prior to his retirement from NFPA in 1984.

flues, exist only where there is imperfect contact. Palletized storage is limited in height by the ability of the palletized package to sustain the weight of additional packages. The construction of pallets, which are usually made of wood, provides horizontal flues that are usually out of reach of sprinklers. Rack storage is virtually unlimited in height. Vertical flues exist in rack storage at the vertical members and between unit loads. Like palletized storage, rack storage also has horizontal flues.

HOUSEKEEPING PRACTICES

Housekeeping in refrigerated warehouses is usually excellent due to the possibilities of contamination. As a result, fire loss is low during normal occupancy. It usually is during shutdown for repairs or during construction that a large fire loss occurs, most commonly from such hazardous operations as cutting or welding. Short circuits in electrical components which sometimes are damaged by materials-handling equipment account for many fires in refrigerated warehouses.

FIRE PROTECTION

A cold storage warehouse should be protected by an adequate sprinkler system. Even though the occupancy might not require sprinkler protection, sprinklers should be installed to protect the insulation and the structure. Room-flooding carbon dioxide or high-expansion foam systems are not acceptable alternatives to automatic sprinklers. In chill rooms and coolers, sprinkler systems of the electrically operated preaction type are preferred to dry pipe systems. In freezers or holding rooms, systems should combine deluge and dry pipe features; such a system is shown in

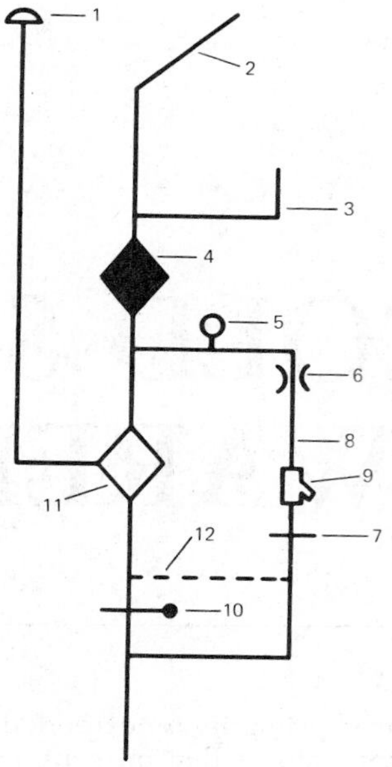

1. HEAT-ACTUATED DEVICE
2. TO SPRINKLERS
3. TO AIR SUPPLY
4. DRY PIPE VALVE
5. PRESSURE GAGE
6. 1/8 IN. (3 mm) BRASS RESTRICTING ORIFICE
7. VALVE, NORMALLY OPEN
8. 1/2 IN. (12.7 mm) BRASS PIPE
9. STRAINER
10. MAIN WATER SUPPLY VALVE
11. DELUGE VALVE
12. ALTERNATE CONNECTION TO MAIN WATER SUPPLY

FIG. 8-6A. Piping to chamber between deluge valve and dry pipe valve.

Figure 8-6A. In this system, water pressure under the dry pipe valve is maintained through a ⅛-in. (3.2 mm) orifice in a bypass. The main water supply is held back by a deluge valve electrically actuated by a separate fire detection system.

1. 0.125 IN. (3.2 mm) RESTRICTOR ORIFICE
2. STRAINER
3. FLOW TEST VALVE*
4. PRIMING PIPE
5. PRIMING WATER VALVE*
6. CHECK VALVE
7. DRIP CHECK
8. DRIP CUP
9. ALARM TEST VALVE
10. SYSTEM DRAIN VALVE*
11. MAIN WATER SUPPLY VALVE
12. 1/2 IN. (12.7 mm) THERMOSTATIC RELEASE PIPING
13. ALARM SWITCH
14. EMERGENCY TRIP VALVE
15. DIAPHRAGM BY PASS VALVE
16. PILOT OPERATED RELIEF VALVE
17. MODEL "C" THERMOSTATIC RELEASE
18. AIR BYPASS VALVE*
19. AIR PRESSURE MAINTENANCE DEVICE
20. 1/32 IN. (0.8 mm) RESTRICTION PLUG
21. LOW AIR PRESSURE SWITCH
22. CIRCLE SEAL CHECK
23. NITROGEN CYLINDER & REGULATOR
24. 0.046 IN. (1.2 mm) RESTRICTOR ORIFICE
25. AIR COMPRESSOR
26. SPRINKLER SYSTEM CHECK VALVE
27. DELUGE VALVE

*VALVES ARE NORMALLY CLOSED

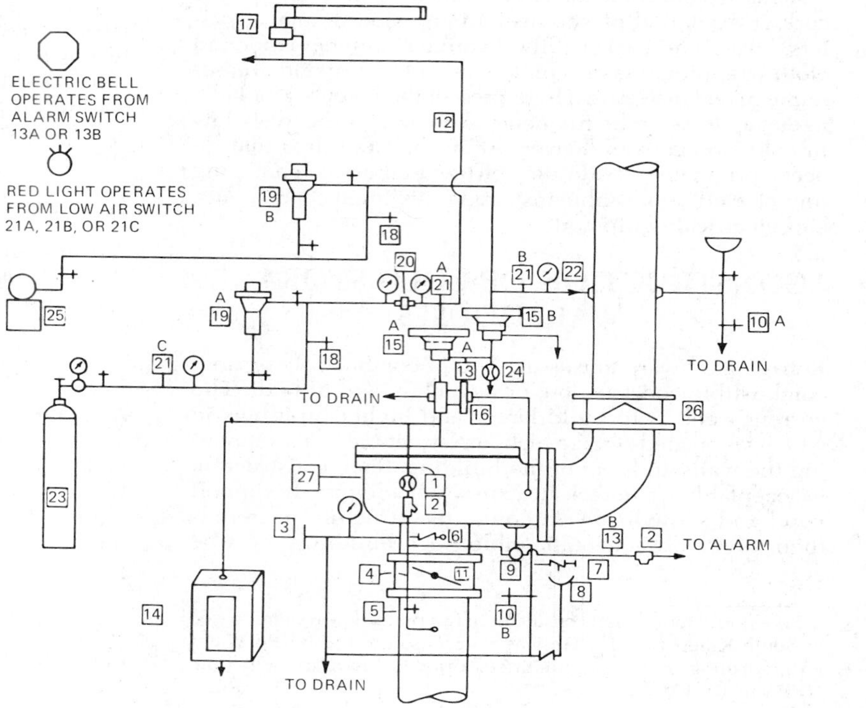

FIG. 8-6B. Pneumatic dual-release automatic water control valve.

Where high racks are used for storage, it is necessary to use in-rack sprinklers designed to reach spaces that cannot be reached by overhead sprinklers. Some storage racks have tubular uprights capable of carrying water which may be incorporated into the sprinkler system if the tube wall has sufficient strength to withstand 700 psi (4827 kPa) water pressure or four times the expected water pressure, whichever is greater. It is also necessary that provisions be made for thawing and draining after system activation.

All sprinklers in refrigerated warehouses should be pressurized and equipped as described in NFPA 13, *Installation of Sprinkler Systems*. They should be designed so that the systems can be easily inspected, and disassembled for removal of ice plugs.

The combination dry pipe deluge system shown in Figure 8-6A will help to avoid ice formation due to accidental tripping of dry valves. When this combination is used:

1. The dry system should be manifolded to the deluge valve.
2. The protected area should not exceed 40,000 sq ft (3716 m^2).
3. The distance between valves should be as short as possible.
4. The chamber between deluge and dry pipe valves should be pressurized from the supply side of the deluge valve.
5. An approved ball drip valve should be installed on the dry pipe valve.

Properly located heat detecting devices should be provided in the protected area to automatically operate the deluge valve. A deluge valve having electrical actuation is preferred.

An acceptable alternate to the deluge valve/dry pipe valve combination is shown in Figure 8-6B. Approved equipment should be used throughout and all electrical equipment should be compatible. The piping to the heat-actuated devices should be supervised. The control piping should be arranged so both loss of sprinkler piping air pressure and operation of a heat-actuated device occur before the deluge valve release mechanism operates.

BIBLIOGRAPHY

NFPA Codes, Standards, and Recommended Practices

Reference to the following NFPA codes, standards, and recommended practices will provide further information on cold storage warehouses discussed in this chapter. (See the latest *NFPA Catalog* for availability of current editions of the following documents.)

NFPA 13, *Installation of Sprinkler Systems*.

Additional Reading

Factory Mutual Engineering Corporation, "Refrigerated Warehouses," *Loss Prevention Data Sheet* 8-29, Factory Mutual System, Norwood, MA, May 1976.

Klem, T. J., "Explosion in Cold Storage Kills Fire Fighter," *Fire Journal*, Vol. 79, No. 2, Mar. 1985, p. 43.

Linville, J. L. ed., *Industrial Fire Hazards Handbook*, 3rd ed., National Fire Protection Association, Quincy, MA, 1990.

Safety Code for Mechanical Refrigeration, ANSI/ASHRAE 15-1978, ASHRAE, New York, 1978.

OUTDOOR STORAGE PRACTICES

Revised by Martin M. Brown

Truly adequate engineered fire protection is extremely difficult to achieve for outdoor storage, as it is with indoor unsprinklered storage. However, depending upon its hazard, monetary value, area, or a combination of these, a degree of protective safeguards and installations should be provided that is justified by these features. Thus, for small amounts of incidental and transitory outdoor storage, appropriate protection might consist merely of good security fencing and outdoor lighting. On the other hand, elaborate safeguards are warranted for very large, high-value storage yards.

Good general practices, developed from fire experience, for sizeable storage areas are outlined in this chapter, with references to certain types of storage that have received special study. (See NFPA 231, *General Storage*.)

Additional information on storage practices can be found in Section 8, Chapter 5, "General Indoor Storage;" Section 5, Chapter 3, "Water Supply Requirements for Fire Protection;" Section 2, Chapter 14, "Welding and Cutting;" and Section 2, Chapter 29, "Storage and Handling of Solid Fuels."

CHOOSING THE SITE

Size

The area should be of sufficient size to hold the quantity of stored material, with allowance for spacing between piles and possible future expansion. Where adequate area is not available, additional sites should be found. Congestion is a major cause of fire spread.

Terrain

The ground should be level, if at all possible. Sloping terrain may make piles unstable and present a serious hazard to fire fighters. Refuse areas, sawdust-filled land, swampy ground, or areas prone to underground fires are examples of unsuitable terrain.

Martin M. Brown is a fire protection consultant, based in White Plains, NY.

Exposure

Adequate clearances to adjacent properties should be maintained to minimize mutual fire exposure. Zoning regulations often specify clear distances to a property line. If no such regulations exist, the nature of future development on adjacent property should be considered, for it may reduce the size of the storage area.

Other exposure considerations include features that offer protection from grass, brush, or forest fires, and protection from potential ignition sources, such as sparks given off by railroad rolling equipment, incinerator stacks, electrical transformers on poles, lighted cigarettes flicked from nearby cars, etc.

Fire Protection

The manner in which outdoor storage is arranged (including the size of the piles, and the clearances required from adjacent piles, buildings, and property boundary lines) should be influenced by the protection that is available. The local fire protection capabilities, such as the public water supply and its record of reliability, the fire flow available, the type of fire department available and the distance it must travel to the site, and the means available for notifying the fire department of a fire, in particular should be evaluated before choosing a site.

Floods and Windstorms

Areas subject to flooding or windstorms are to be avoided. Windstorms are a particular problem in some coastal areas. Fires occurring during high winds will present an exposure problem against which protection is almost impossible. Burning materials and brands will be carried over considerable distances, even though the fire may be confined to a relatively small area.

PREPARING THE SITE

Clearing the Site

Vegetation should be cleared away so that it cannot dry out and become fuel for ignition or fire spread. The site should be leveled as nearly as possible and then paved. If the entire yard is not to be surfaced, care should be taken to ensure that fire apparatus can easily maneuver throughout the yard. This requires properly developed roadways capable of supporting heavy trucks. Proper drainage of the site is essential.

Many paved outdoor storage yards have painted lines to show aisles and roadways, as well as the location of yard hydrants, extinguishers, water buckets, and hose houses.

Layout of the Site

A definite plan for the site is advisable. The plan should detail where specific materials are to be piled, the proper separation between piles, and the access to all areas of the site, including fences and their gates.

The density of the packed materials makes a tremendous difference in the way they burn. Lumber stacked in solid, orderly piles perhaps not over 20 ft (6 m) high does not present the same problem as lumber stored in "stickered" piles. In the latter case, fire can spread more rapidly because of the air spaces in the piles. Pulpwood is sometimes stored in piles 200 ft (61 m) in diameter and 100 ft (30 m) high; these piles contain air spaces and pockets, made by the rough and varied shape of the logs, which accelerate burning.

Some materials burn quickly and produce a great deal of heat. Baled cotton, hay, lumber, packing materials, pallets, plywood, pulpwood, and rubber are examples of such materials, and considerable clearance is required between and around these piles. Aisle widths equal to the height of the pile are desirable for hazardous commodities.

Both the yard itself and the piles within the yard must be easily accessible to fire fighters. Storage close to railroad spurs often hinders access due to boxcars and other railroad equipment left standing on the tracks. Driveways at least 15 ft (4.5 m) in width permit fire equipment to reach all portions of the storage area. Aisles of 10 ft (3 m) or more reduce the danger of fire spread from pile to pile. For unusually large storage yards or moderate-size yards with valuable commodities, main aisles or firebreaks can subdivide the storage in much the same way that fire walls do indoors. Aisle widths will depend upon the commodity, how it is stored, height of piles, normal and abnormal wind conditions, fire fighting forces and equipment, and other factors.

In some cases, packaging and palletizing affect storage methods, particularly if materials are irregularly shaped or small. If the pallets themselves are combustible, they may present an added hazard. Some materials are packed in heavy crates. Usually, this does not present an increased hazard except after severe weathering or where handling has caused breakage or splintering. Tarpaulins and other weather-resistant materials used to cover stock should be of fire-retardant-treated material.

A pile that is stable under normal conditions may present a severe hazard in a fire. It is wise to anticipate the effects of fire and water on the stability of piles when planning their sizes and configurations. Collapsing piles may cause severe fire spread and hamper fire fighting, particularly if there is danger from flying brands.

Areas used to service and maintain equipment should be designated and properly marked or cordoned off. If flammable liquid fuel is used, it should be stored in an underground tank, if possible. If this is not practical, fuel storage tanks should be located so spills will not flow under or around the storage, and conversely, so that a fire in a storage area will not expose a tank of flammable or combustible liquid.

Installation of Fire Protection

Adequate fire protection must be provided while the site is being prepared. Depending upon the size and location of the site, it may be necessary to install private water mains and hydrants throughout the yard.

In planning for hydrants and yard mains, the water supply, whether from public mains or a private source, should be able to furnish the needed fire flow in gallons or liters per minute.

Based upon accumulated fire experience, the Insurance Services Office (ISO) has developed formulas to calculate fire flow for a particular large unsprinklered building, based on the area, combustibility of stored goods, and a construction factor that, of course, would not apply to outdoor storage. It is important to realize that fire flows needed for hose stream protection of indoor unsprinklered storage, as well as outdoor storage, are far greater than those for a well-designed automatic sprinkler system plus concurrent hose streams. Also, these larger flows will not necessarily minimize the fire damage as well as the lower flows utilized in sprinklered buildings, but they represent reasonable protection.

Table 8-7A contains calculated fire flows for hose stream protection of outdoor storage (assuming early detection, adequate hydrant availability, and access).

The four occupancy classes are defined as follows:

1. *Limited combustible*: Low combustibility with limited concentrations of combustible material.
2. Combustible: Moderate combustibility.
3. *Free burning*: Examples include cotton bales, furniture stock, wood, and wood products.
4. *Rapid burning*: Commodities which either (a) burn with great intensity, (b) spontaneously ignite and are difficult to extinguish, or (c) give off flammable vapors or dusts at ordinary temperatures.

A minimum level of manual fire suppression equipment would be to have rated, properly marked portable fire extinguishers (usually the nonfreezing water type) placed so that the travel distance to the nearest unit is 75 ft (23 m) or less. If the site is active and people are usually present, fully equipped hose houses should be provided and personnel trained to use them in a fire incident.

A means for notifying the fire department is essential. A system that sends a signal directly to the fire department is best, but, at minimum, a telephone should be accessible.

Security Measures

Trespassing, vandalism, and theft are problems in many outdoor storage yards. Protection from children (who like to play in yards and are sometimes responsible for setting fires) and vagrants seeking shelter frequently make fencing and lighting a requirement. A fence, however, must not prevent ready access to the yard by the fire department. The fire department should be consulted about incorporating remote gates into the fencing so additional access can be provided under serious fire conditions.

TABLE 8-7A. ***Fire Flow for Hose Stream Protection of Outdoor Storage****

Area		Limited Combustible		Combustible		Free Burning		Rapid Burning	
sq ft	m^2	gpm	L/min	gpm	L/min	gpm	L/min	gpm	L/min
10,000	929	1,500	5678	1,750	6624	2,000	7571	2,250	8517
20,000	1848	2,000	7571	2,500	9464	3,000	11356	4,000	15142
50,000	4645	3,500	13429	4,000	15142	4,500	17034	6,000	22712
100,000	9290	5,000	18927	5,500	20820	6,500	24606	8,000	30283
200,000	18580	6,750	25551	8,000	30282	9,250	35015	10,000	37854

* Adapted from ISO formulas. Assumes early detection, adequate hydrants, and access.

Security guards are very effective in the protection of outdoor storage yards. NFPA 601, *Guard Service in Fire Loss Prevention*, covers the selection, the duties, and the instruction and training of such personnel.

UTILIZING THE SITE

Management

When a yard is selected and laid out, the amount of material it is designed to accommodate is also established. These quantities should not be exceeded since excess material may reduce firesafety. The material and other fire prevention and protection features, including disposal of waste materials, should be monitored by frequent periodic inspections.

In general, the attitude of management toward fire protection in the yard provides an example that employees are likely to follow.

Fire Protection and Prevention

All fire protection equipment, including hydrants, fire pumps, fire extinguishers, and any suppression, detection, or alarm systems on the storage site, should be properly maintained and tested.

All materials-handling equipment personnel at the site need to carry a portable fire extinguisher suitable for any fire, i.e., Class ABC.

The location of all hydrants, hose houses, portable extinguishers, alarm boxes, and other fire protection equipment should be properly marked. Elevated signs are preferable. Arrows and signs painted on the pavement are the minimum markings required.

If material to be torch cut or welded cannot be moved from the storage yard to a remote location, the work should be done only after adequate precautions are taken. (See NFPA 51B, *Cutting and Welding Processes*.)

Depending upon the nature of the material stored, smoking should be prohibited or restricted to specific areas only. In either case, adequate signs should be displayed and the regulations strictly enforced.

A private fire brigade of employees provides at least initial fire fighting. If there are enough employees to organize a fire brigade, the level of organization, training, and equipment provided normally will be governed by the availability and ability of a public fire department. The larger the storage yard and the more valuable its contents, the greater the need for a private fire brigade. NFPA 600, *Private Fire Brigades*, gives helpful information on this subject.

Perhaps the most important duty of a brigade or security guard is to immediately notify the fire department of any fire. The fire department should be called even if brigades can handle the emergency without outside help. In too many cases, notifying the public fire department has been delayed because brigades or security guards unsuccessfully attempted to control fires, resulting in higher losses than necessary.

Maintenance and Housekeeping

Repairs to fencing, lighting, and the yard surface should be made promptly and materials-handling equipment should be kept in good condition. Suitable safeguards should be provided to minimize the hazard of sparks from equipment, such as refuse burners, boiler stacks, vehicle exhausts, and locomotives.

Good housekeeping also includes controlling weeds and vegetation. Weeds, grass, and other vegetation should be sprayed with an acceptable herbicide or ground sterilizer, or grubbed out. Dead weeds should be removed after destruction, but weed burners should not be used in the removal.

In many instances, scrap lumber, broken pallets and broken containers, bales, or pieces of material stored on the site are discarded into the clear space around the yard. Daily checks should be made for such discarded materials; where found, they should be properly removed. Care should be taken that wind-blown debris and other combustible materials do not accumulate under piles of materials.

If a pile of material falls into an aisle or clear space, the stock should be repiled immediately.

OUTDOOR STORAGE OF SPECIFIC MATERIALS

Discussions of safe storage practices for a few common materials follow. As a source for good practices, see referenced NFPA publications and industry or insurance company standards. Many times, the guidelines for inside storage of a commodity are a good starting point for devising guidelines for outdoor storage.

Wood and Wood Products

Most wood and wood products are stored outdoors. Because wood is moved from the forests only at certain times of the year, large quantities of logs are stored at sawmills, paper mills, and pulp mills. Large circular piles with logs dumped on the top of the pile are called stacked piles. Logs stacked in parallel form, like matches in a box, are called ranked piles. Stacked piles are usually much larger in size, with the height of the pile often approaching 100 ft (30.5 m).

Ranked piles are usually 10 to 15 ft (3 to 5 m) high. Because maintaining separation and aisles is much easier in ranked piles, fire protection is much easier in ranked than in stacked piles. (See Figure 8-7A.)

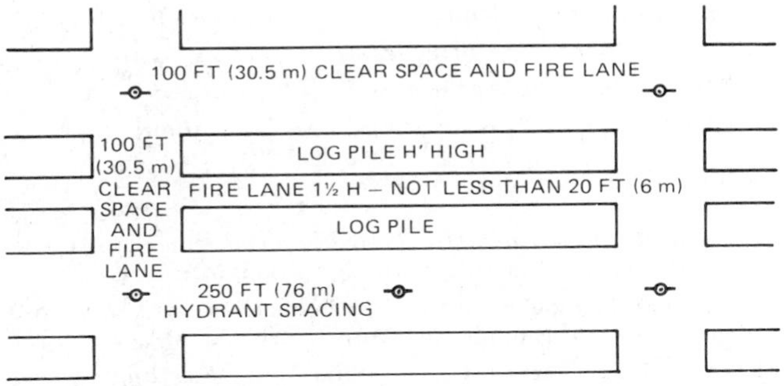

FIG. 8-7A. A good layout for ranked piles of logs in a storage yard.

Large quantities of water are needed to cope with log yard fires. The total volume required may be many thousands of gallons or liters per minute if many portable turrets and monitor nozzles [each discharging about 1,000 gpm (3785 L/min)] are operated simultaneously. A looped underground fire main system with hydrants spaced through the yard is good practice. Monitor nozzles on towers have been common in log yards, especially with high stacked piles. In large stacked piles, burrowing fires are difficult to extinguish even after the surface burning is under control. NFPA 46, *Storage of Forest Products*, provides additional guidelines for the storage of logs.

Chip storage has replaced log storage at many pulp and paper mills. Two completely different types of fires occur in chip piles: surface fires and internal fires. NFPA 46, *Storage of Forest Products*, provides guidelines for fire protection of chips. The amount of water needed to control a chip pile fire will vary substantially, depending upon the size of the pile. Weather conditions, operating methods, geographic location, the type of wood chip, and the degree to which wetting may be employed are all factors influencing fire conditions. Experience indicates that exposure to long periods of hot, dry weather with no regular surface wetting creates conditions under which fast-spreading surface fires can occur; and they often require many hose streams.

Likewise, the frequency of pile turnover and operating methods affect the prospects for serious internal fires. Piles built using methods that allow a concentration of fines, and piles stored for long periods of time with no turnover, are subject to internal heating which, if undetected, can create intense internal fires.

Sawdust storage is not common now but once was prevalent at sawmills. Fires in sawdust are not especially serious, but they can smolder and smoke unless the piles are broken open and the fire is completely extinguished.

Lumber storage is quite common in urban areas, particularly in built-up neighborhoods. Local ordinances generally prohibit storage of any appreciable quantity in zoned areas, but many lumberyards originally located in unzoned areas now border heavily developed areas. The exposure of stored wood to adjoining areas is a major consideration. Adequate aisles and good housekeeping, along with proper procedures for controlling ignition sources, such as salamanders, smoking, etc., will reduce the fire hazard considerably. Large quantities of water are needed to bring a lumberyard fire under control once it has gained headway. Flying brands can spread the fire thoughout the yard and into adjoining areas readily, particularly under windy conditions. NFPA 46, *Storage of Forest Products*, provides guidelines for the safe storage of lumber.

Paper and Paper Products

Some paper and paper products are stored outdoors, but most are stored indoors to protect them from rain and wind. Roll paper is normally stored in large rolls weighing 2 tons (1814 kg) or more. Because the paper is tightly wound, it is very difficult to ignite; however, roll paper stored outdoors is more vulnerable to ignition. Once ignited, fire in roll paper stored outside is difficult to extinguish with manual fire fighting methods.

Baled wastepaper does not produce as intense a fire as does roll paper, but instead tends to produce burrowing fires. Fire in baled wastepaper is difficult to extinguish and generates heavy smoke, which inhibits manual fire fighting. Broken bales are difficult to handle after wetting. Usually a motorized vehicle with a shovel is needed to move the debris to complete extinguishment. Spontaneous ignition is common in wastepaper if foreign materials subject to spontaneous heating become trapped in bales. Fire protection for wastepaper storage is generally the same as for other outdoor storage.

Rubber

Rubber tires: Tire storage presents a severe hazard. Tires burn rapidly, emitting intense heat and large quantities of dense smoke which hamper manual fire fighting. Large quantities of water at high pressures are usually needed, because control is difficult due to the shielded nature of fire within a tire casing. Narrow piles with good aisles are best for outdoor storage.

Baled crude rubber: Bales are often stored outdoors. Factory Mutual Research Corporation (FMRC) recommends that individual piles be limited to 100 tons (90 720 kg) with a minimum of 30 ft (9 m), but preferably 50 ft (15 m), between piles.[1] Piles should be grouped to a maximum of 1,000 tons (90 7200 kg) with 100-ft (30 m) aisles separating them. It is important that burlap used to wrap the bales not be contaminated with oil; if oil gets into a tightly packed pile, spontaneous heating may result.

Baled Combustible Fibers

Although storing baled combustible fibers outdoors is not good practice, much of this material, such as baled cotton in transit from the gin to a warehouse, is temporarily stored outdoors. FMRC recommends that piles be limited to 500 bales per pile with a minimum of 30-ft (9 m), and preferably 50-ft (15 m), clear space between individual piles, from an exterior fence, or from buildings.[2] Piles of uncleaned baled flax straw should be limited to 300 tons (272 160 kg) and a height of 20 ft (6 m), and should be located 200 ft (60 m) from buildings and 100 ft (30 m) from each other or potential ignition sources. Storing bales of combustible fibers off the ground on pallets provides ventilation and prevents excessive damage from ground moisture. Covering the tops and sides of all piles with a securely fastened tarpaulin of fire-retardant material protects them from the weather and mildew.

Coal

The main problem with coal storage is that bituminous coal tends to heat spontaneously. Anthracite coal is not subject to spontaneous heating. Freshly mined coal, however, is more susceptible because it absorbs oxygen more rapidly. Moisture and coal dust also make coal more susceptible to spontaneous ignition.

BIBLIOGRAPHY

References Cited

1. Factory Mutual Research Corporation, "Storage of Baled Crude Rubber," *Loss Prevention Data Sheet 8-1*, Factory Mutual Research Corp., Norwood, MA.
2. Factory Mutual Research Corporation, "Baled Fiber Storage," *Loss Prevention Data Sheet 8-7*, Factory Mutual Research Corp., Norwood, MA.

NFPA Codes, Standards, and Recommended Practices

Reference to the following NFPA codes, standards, and recommended practices will provide further information on outdoor storage practices discussed in this chapter. (See the latest *NFPA Catalog* for availability of current editions of the following documents.)

NFPA 10, *Portable Fire Extinguishers.*

NFPA 24, *Installation of Private Fire Service Mains.*

NFPA 46, *Storage of Forest Products.*

NFPA 51B, *Cutting and Welding Processes.*

NFPA 80A, *Protection from Exposure Fires.*

NFPA 231, *General Storage.*

NFPA 505, *Powered Industrial Trucks, Including Type Designations, Areas of Use, Maintenance, and Operation.*

NFPA 600, *Private Fire Brigades.*

NFPA 601, *Guard Service in Fire Loss Prevention.*

NFPA 601A, *Guard Service in Fire Loss Prevention.*

Additional Reading

"Coal and Coal Storage," *Loss Prevention Data Sheet*, 8-10, Factory Mutual Engineering Corp., Norwood, MA, Aug. 1975.

"General Storage Safeguards," *Loss Prevention Data Sheet*, 8-0, Factory Mutual Engineering Corp., Norwood, MA, Mar. 1977.

Howard, H. A., "Tires Burning by the Acre," *Fire Engineering*, Vol. 141, No. 6, 1988, pp. 22-34.

"Outdoor Storage of Wood Chips," *Loss Prevention Data Sheet*, 8-27, Factory Mutual Engineering Corp., Norwood, MA, Dec. 1980.

"Roll Paper Storage," *Loss Prevention Data Sheet*, 8-21, Factory Mutual Engineering Corp., Norwood, MA, Mar. 1978.

"Sawmills and Lumber Yards," *Loss Prevention Data Sheet*, 7-25, Factory Mutual Engineering Corp., Norwood, MA, July 1979.

LIBRARY AND MUSEUM COLLECTIONS

Revised by Stephen E. Bush

From a fire protection viewpoint, libraries and museums are storage facilities providing the special environment needed to house and preserve cultural and technological heritage so as to provide each succeeding generation access to these resources. The materials stored in these occupancies involve extraordinarily high fuel loads, or high value collections—some are irreplaceable—or both. While it might appear that libraries and museums are quite dissimilar, most museums contain libraries, and many libraries feature exhibits of art or artifacts. The chief differences are in the value, density, and replaceability of the collections; the concentration of combustibles; and the degree of public access.

However, there is a tendency to underrate the fire risk of these occupancies because of the low fuel loads normally housed in public areas such as library reading rooms and museum exhibit galleries. These areas generally have high housekeeping standards, they are overseen by staff or security guards, and smoking is either controlled or prohibited. Despite their low apparent risk, library reading rooms and museum exhibit galleries have suffered costly fires.

Non-public areas, such as bookstack, storage, and work areas, present an even greater hazard. Here, the fuel loads are much higher, and housekeeping and smoking are more difficult to control.

The potential hazard is illustrated by a reading of museum and library fire experience as presented by the NFPA Technical Committee on Protection of Cultural Resources: Libraries, Museums, Places of Worship, and Historic Structures, in NFPA 910, *Recommended Practice for the Protection of Libraries and Library Collections*, NFPA 911, *Recommended Practice for the Protection of Museums and Museum Collections*, and others.[1,2] Recent fires described in NFPA 910 and 911 that are worthy of special attention include the disastrous fire losses in the Los Angeles Central Public Library (two in 1986 and one in 1988), the Louisiana State Museum in New Orleans in 1988, and the Library of the USSR Academy of Sciences in Leningrad, Russia, in 1988.

Stephen E. Bush, CSP, ASSE, is chief of safety services for the Library of Congress, Washington, DC.

Loss Potential

Some museum curators, librarians, and archivists believe that water is a greater hazard to their collections than fire. As a result, they place emphasis upon fire prevention almost exclusively and limit fire protection to installation of automatic early warning detection systems. However, despite effective fire prevention, fires do occur (See Table 8-8A.)

TABLE 8-8A. ***Fires in Libraries and Museums*, by Year 1980-88 Structure Fires Reported to U.S. Fire Departments***

Year	Fires	Civilian Injuries	Direct Property Damage (in Millions)
1980	484	0	$3.05
1981	386	0	$1.32
1982	381	0	$14.40
1983	266	0	$4.39
1984	355	10	$4.92
1985	384	0	$9.72
1986	343	7	$44.90
1987	279	2	$15.76
1988	236	0	$0.84
Average	346	2	$11.03

* Refers to whole buildings, not library or museum room, and includes art galleries, planetariums, and aquariums.
Note: There were no estimated deaths in any year.

Arson dominates as a cuase of fires in libraries (see Table 8-8B), particularly for property damage. It has been cited as the cause of 80 percent of significant fires in libraries, [30] including the disastrous Los Angeles Central Public Library fire in 1986. It was also the second most frequent cause of fires in museums during the period 1980 through 1988 (see Table 8-8C). But arson is difficult if not impossible to prevent.

Where there is early detection and quick action to stop fire growth, a large loss can be prevented. Note however, that 70 percent of all library fires occur between the hours of 9 p.m. and 9 a.m. when libraries are least likely to be

TABLE 8-8B. ***Fires in Libraries*, by Major Cause Annual Average by 1980–88 Structure Fires Reported to U.S. Fire Departments***

Major Cause	Fires	Civilian Injuries	Direct Property Damage (in Millions)
Incendiary or suspicious causes	98	0**	$6.25
Electrical distribution system	47	0	$0.37
Other equipment	17	0	$0.00**
Smoking material	15	0**	$0.11
Open flame	13	0	$0.01
Heating equipment	12	0**	$0.23
Appliance, tool, or air conditioning	9	0**	$0.05
Cooking equipment	6	0	$0.01
Child playing	6	0	$0.00**
Natural causes	4	0	$0.01
Other heat source	2	0	$0.00**
Exposure (to other hostile fire)	2	0	$0.09
Unknown	13	0	$1.74
Total	244	1	$8.88

* Refers to whole building, not library room.
** Rounds to zero but is not zero.
Note: There were no estimated deaths. Sums may not equal totals because of rounding error.

TABLE 8-8C. ***Fires in Museums*, by Major Cause Annual Average by 1980–88 Structure Fires Reported to U.S. Fire Departments***

Major Cause	Fires	Civilian Injuries	Direct Property Damage (in Millions)
Electrical distribution system	22	0	$0.92
Incendiary or suspicious causes	20	0	$0.83
Other equipment	9	0	$0.10
Open flame	8	0**	$0.01
Smoking material	8	0	$0.01
Heating equipment	7	0**	$0.00**
Cooking equipment	6	0	$0.03
Exposure (to other hostile fire)	4	0	$0.07
Natural causes	3	0	$0.04
Appliance, tool, or air conditioning	3	1	$0.00**
Child playing	1	0	$0.00
Other heat source	0**	0	$0.00
Unknown	9	0	$0.14
Total	102	1	$2.15

* Refers to whole building, not museum room, and includes art galleries, aquariums, and planetariums.
** Rounds to zero but is not zero.
Note: There were no estimated deaths. Sums may not equal totals because of rounding error.

occupied and an additional 18 percent start between 5 p.m. and 9 p.m.[3] Therefore, the library or museum that is totally dependent upon fire prevention and manual extinguishment has accepted a serious risk of total loss when prevention fails. This is the most significant lesson to be derived from the study of fire experience in libraries and museums. The common element in the large-loss fires is the absence of automatic suppression systems to prevent small fires from becoming larger.

The 1986 fire in the Central Library of the Los Angeles Public Library System illustrates the point. In this fire an automatic smoke detection system gave early warning to evacuate building occupants, but there was no automatic suppression system to contain the fire while it was small. Total dependence upon fire prevention and on manual extinguishment leaves a museum or library vulnerable to large, even catastrophic, losses.

FIRE PREVENTION PRINCIPLES

Fire prevention is the cultural institution's first line of defense against fire. It consists of controlling ignition sources and the supply of fuel to keep them separated.

Ignition Control

Ignition control involves recognizing all sources of heat generation that could cause ignition in combustibles and isolating these sources from the fuel.

Arson: The single most important source of ignition for destructive fires in libraries and, to a somewhat lesser degree, museums is arson. Arson accounted for 70 percent of the average annual property damage costs due to fires in libraries during the years 1980 through 1988 and it accounted for 40 percent of these losses in museums during the same period (see Table 8-8B and 8-8C). For purposes of fire prevention management, the fire setter is an unpredictable variable who can negate any fire prevention program.

While it may be impossible to prevent all deliberately set fires, the fire prevention program must address ways to reduce or deter incendiarism. Fundamental security measures and procedures include:

1. Uniformed guards on station and patrolling well planned and monitored routes.
2. Surveillance of all areas at irregular intervals.
3. Windows and doors secured with proper locking devices. Panic hardware on emergency exit doors allow doors to be opened from the inside while remaining locked from the outside.
4. Windows and doors equipped to provide an alarm upon any unauthorized opening—whether by an intruder from outside or by a thief, vandal, or other miscreant opening the portal from within. In some communities, such alarms may be connected directly to the police or fire department, or to a central station.
5. Closed circuit surveillance by a television system can be extremely useful in maintaining surveillance of exhibit areas, print rooms, and other collection study facilities, as well as emergency exits. In addition, the cameras provide a psychological deterrent to potential miscreants.
6. Thorough security and safety procedures at closing time.
7. Adequate exterior lighting and fences. Where not provided by public utilities, lighting should be added at all concealed approaches to the building.
8. Regular and close inspection of ash trays, waste receptacles, soiled linen hampers, electric heating appliances, and other places that breed fire. Although not a check against incendiarism alone, this routine can uncover hazards that could involve incendiarism, such as a filled wastebasket hiding a time-delay igniter.

9. Either eliminate book drops used for after-hours return at libraries, or isolate them from the building by physical separation or by fire protective design. Book drops have been used by arsonists to inflict significant fire losses on libraries.[4]

Electrical system: The electrical distribution system—the wiring, associated equipment, lighting fixtures, sign, and lamps—is the second leading cause of fires in libraries and the leading cause in museums, accounting for nearly half the property damage in museums during 1983-87.

When installed in accordance with the requirements of NFPA 70, *National Electrical Code®*, wiring is provided with overcurrent protection to open the circuit if the current reaches a value that will cause an excessive or dangerous temperature in the conductor or conductor insulation. Nevertheless, there are conditions under which overloaded or partially grounded wiring may heat up sufficiently to ignite combustibles without blowing fuses or tripping circuit breakers.[5] This is what happens when circuits that have been subjected to flooding[6], are dried inadequately and tested or when the current path is altered in any other way that obviates the protection of a properly sized fuse or circuit breaker.[7] Therefore, an effective preventive maintenance program for the building's electrical distribution system is essential to the fire prevention program.

Existing building wiring systems may be inadequate to meet the need for electric outlets created by the proliferation of information processing equipment such as computer terminals, word processors, microcomputers or PCs, minicomputers, and peripheral accessories, and of telefacsimile, or "fax," machines and photocopy machines. The use of extension cords as a substitute for fixed wiring is not an acceptable practice as extension cords are subject to mechanical damage and can be easily overloaded. Where permitted, extension cords must be protected from mechanical damage and must never be concealed under carpets.[8] In addition, they should have a circuit breaker in the multiple outlet assembly at the output end to provide overcurrent protection for the extension cord.

Incandescent lamps near, or in contact with, combustible materials may ignite them. Surface temperatures on a bulb can vary widely and can be within the range of the ignition temperature of paper. The much cooler surface temperatures of fluorescent lamps do not present the ignition hazards of incandescent bulbs. However, ballasts in fluorescent light fixtures can be potential sources of ignition, particularly when mounted in heat-entrapping installations. A potentially severe fire hazard is presented when they are mounted flush against combustible, low density, cellulose fiberboard and materials of similar combustibility.

Heating equipment: The malfunction or misuse of heating equipment is an important potential cause of fires. Boilers and furnaces of central heating systems should be isolated in a fire-resistant enclosure, either separate from or attached to the library or museum. Unit space heaters and portable heaters should not be used in combustible collection storage areas.

Because cellulosic materials may ignite at temperatures far below their usual ignition temperatures after extended exposure to relatively moderate heat, combustibles such as paper, wood, and textiles should be kept away from steam or other heat, piping and ducts.

Electrical appliances: If not prohibited entirely, space heaters, hot plates, microwave ovens, coffee makers, and other small appliances should be regulated rigidly and monitored closely. Where permitted, each appliance should be:

1. Listed by an independent testing laboratory.
2. Placed on a noncombustible base.
3. Located so there is adequate separation from combustible materials.
4. Located where air circulation will prevent heat buildup.

The use of extension cords to connect heating devices to electric outlets should also be prohibited. Security guards should be furnished with a list showing the location of each heating appliance, and they should check each appliance during their rounds to ensure it is in the "off" position when not in use or attended. This check is especially important when the facility is closed.

Smoking: Smoking should be permitted only in places, such as administrative offices, staff rest areas, and designated visitor lounges, where firesafe practices can be monitored and controlled. It is recognized that a total ban on smoking may result in surreptitious smoking in unsupervised locations, thus actually increasing the risk of fire from careless smoking practices.

Open flame devices: Open flames used in building repairs, laboratory operations, or the interpretation of historic environments are severe ignition hazards, as are hot metal sparks or slag from welding and cutting. Use of open flame devices should require the written approval of a responsible management official. Before signing such an authorization, the official should evaluate the risk to life safety and collection materials, and should prescribe protective measures to be included as conditions of the authorization. Management conditions for authorization should include, as a minimum:

1. Removing exhibit or collection materials a safe distance from the ignition source.
2. Requiring a fire watch of one or more persons with appropriate fire extinguishing equipment through all periods of hazardous activity and beyond any interruption or termination of activity long enough to ensure the discovery of any incipient fire. A minimum of 30 min is desirable when welding and cutting torches have been used.

Fuel Control

Fuel control must consider all combustible contents, including the collection and its ancillary records, as well as furniture, interior finish, packaging materials, and flammable liquids. Control measures include the arrangement of storage to limit fire spread and to provide separation of fuel from ignition sources. Much of this can be accomplished through fire-safe housekeeping practices.

Flammable liquid storage and handling: Flammable liquids permitted inside a library or museum should be contained in safety cans. The quantity permitted outside of storage areas should be limited to the amount required during an 8-hr shift. Special attention to adequate ventilation and elimination of ignition sources is required.

Spontaneous heating: Oil- or solvent-soaked cloths and rags from oil-based paint can heat spontaneously. After use, such cloths and rags should be placed immediately in a metal can with a tight-fitting metal top, pending their prompt removal.

Fuel geometry and overcrowding: The combustible materials contained in a library or museum may be seen to be arranged in fuel packages—exhibit cases, bookstacks, desks, tables, chairs, and so on—that also may be covered with an additional complement of loose paper or other combustibles. Through the use of distance and low-flame-spread-rated interior finish materials, such as carpet, wallcoverings, and draperies, these fuel packages should be arranged to minimize the risk of fire spreading from one package to another. However, when interior finish materials with high flame-spread rates, such as fiberboard and some carpets, are permitted, especially in the vertical plane, the principle of separation of fuel packages by distance is negated.

For example, flame spread in low-density cellulosic fiberboard and acoustic ceiling tile can be as fast as, or faster than, people can run. Although this life safety problem was demonstrated in building test fires in 1959, these materials can be found in libraries and museums across North America.[9] Where it still exists, it should be treated with intumescent, i.e., fire retardant, paint and maintained as prescribed by the manufacturer pending removal. Carpet may present a similar hazard when used in exhibits or applied to wall surfaces, unless specifically tested to establish an acceptable flame-spread rating for mounting in the vertical plane.

Space limitations resulting from the growth of collections and staff can result in overcrowding, thereby reducing the space between fuel packages and increasing the risk that a fire will grow by igniting adjacent fuel packages rather than burning itself out. Therefore, periods of overcrowding require compensating emphasis on other elements of the fire prevention program, especially control of ignition sources.

FIRE PROTECTION

Since fire prevention efforts can lessen, but not eliminate, the possibility of fire in a museum or library, knowledge of the options available to limit fire spread is essential. Local fire and building codes provide minimum requirements for the survival of the building and for the life safety of its occupants. However, sole reliance on code provisions may not adequately provide for the preservation of building contents, especially high-value collections. Additional fire protection features to protect the contents of the building may be needed over and above the minimum requirements imposed by local codes.

The Systems Approach to Firesafety

The systems approach to firesafety is a useful management tool for selecting the level of fire protection that should contain fire loss within "acceptable" limits. This approach uses decision tree analysis and other systems techniques to establish the maximum acceptable fire loss and to create a fire control system designed to confine a fire loss within acceptable limits.

Each institution must develop its own firesafety system objectives based on levels of protection appropriate to the value of its collections, the life safety of its patrons and staff, and its obligation for continuity of service to the community or the public. The firesafety objectives adopted by the Library of Congress in Washington, DC, may provide a useful point of reference.[10] The General Firesafety Objectives and Critical Space Objectives, shown graphically in Figure 8-8A, are similar to those originally adopted by the U.S. General Services Administration (GSA) for federal office buildings nationwide.[11] This graph, showing the firesafety objectives for Library of Congress buildings, represents the desired minimum probability of success in limiting the growth of a fire from its start to full building involvement. Adoption of acceptable limits of fire loss should, of course, reconcile the cost of the fire defense system to achieve them with the resources available to the institution.

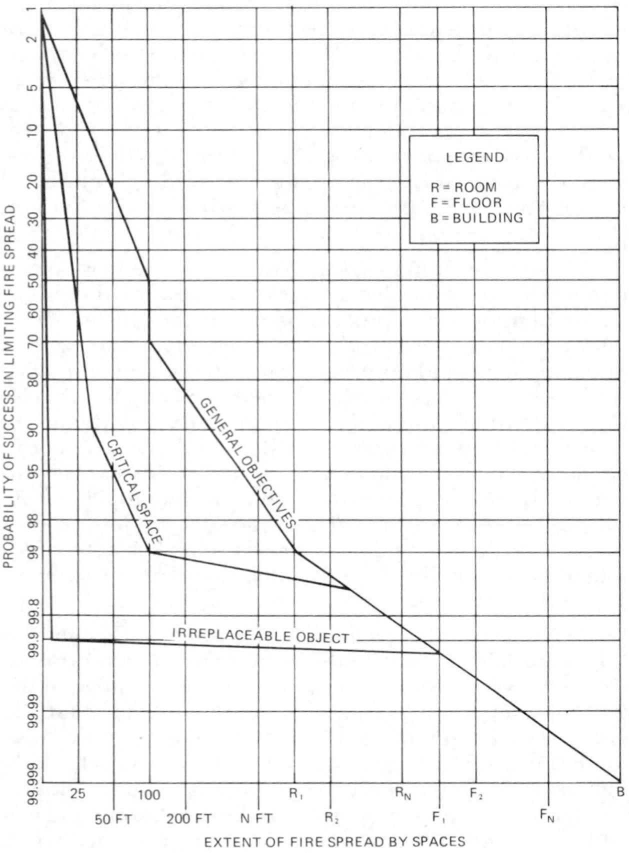

Fig. 8-8A. Firesafety objectives.

Designing the Firesafety System

Depending upon the collection values to be protected and the values and characteristics of the building that houses them, including the fuel loading, the fire protection system designed to achieve an institution's firesafety objectives should provide for detection, alarm, and communication; manual extinguishment; automatic sprinklers; protection of special hazards; and other elements of the firesafety system involving construction considerations that are essential for life safety and protection of collections.

Detection, alarm, and communication: An early warning fire detection and alarm system should be installed throughout a library or museum building, using smoke detectors in all exhibit galleries, reading rooms, and collection storage areas and smoke, heat or flame detectors in other parts of the building. In addition to sounding an alarm throughout the building, the system should be connected directly to a central station or to the local fire department. A public address system should also be considered, especially in very large facilities, to provide voice emergency instructions and information to minimize the risk of panic in public assembly areas, such as exhibit galleries and reading rooms.

An automatic sprinkler system also can provide the alarm when the first sprinkler opens and water begins to flow in the system. However, this detection occurs at a later stage of fire development—that is, when the fire reaches the size of a person.

A complete early warning detection and alarm system alerts the occupants in time for orderly evacuation and facilitates prompt response by the fire service. It also provides an opportunity for trained building occupants to extinguish the fire before automatic suppression equipment is activated or the fire service arrives. (Types of fire detection and alarm systems are described in Section 4 of this handbook.)

An early warning system should be designed by a qualified fire protection specialist to ensure complete coverage of the building and minimum risk of false alarms. This involves proper selection of fire detectors, alarm signals, and supervisory circuits, as well as compliance with all applicable codes and standards.

After the installation and acceptance tests have been completed, a regular test and maintenance program should be established. This is very important since testing is the only way to determine that no part of the detection and alarm system has failed.[12] Furthermore, since the sensitivity of smoke detectors can change with the accumulation of dust and dirt, periodic inspection and cleaning is needed to keep the detector from false alarming or going to sleep.

Manual extinguishment: Portable extinguishers in the hands of trained users constitute an institution's first line of fire attack. In order to prevent the use of the wrong class of extinguisher on a particular fire, some institutions provide only multi-purpose portable extinguishers. These should be located appropriately, and inspected and maintained regularly, so they will be fully charged and operational whenever needed.

Occupant-use standpipe hose lines require specific hands-on training and drill to avoid personal injury and unnecessary property damage. Hose lines must be inspected at least annually and should be service-tested where doubtful conditions are identified.

Unfortunately, because of the failure to train occupants in the proper use of fire hose and to inspect and test it when required, municipal fire departments have arrived at the fire scene to find the occupant hose used ineffectively and/or dangerously, if at all. In such cases, the occupant hose lines must be disconnected before the larger fire hose can be connected to the standpipes. Many fire departments regard this unwarranted delay as too great a risk and so recommend that occupant-use fire hose be removed in existing occupancies and not provided in new occupancies.

Manual extinguishment is provided by the fire department, as well as by occupants, especially in buildings without automatic sprinkler systems.

If fire has entered the free-burning phase, the extent of fire damage will increase exponentially with the seconds that pass between the time the alarm is received and the time trained response personnel begin fighting the fire.[13] Fire protection that fails to provide automatic suppression capability and depends entirely upon manual extinguishment risks disaster when human response is too late or is unavailable.

Automatic Sprinklers: Lack of an automatic suppression system is the foremost contributing factor to large-loss fires in museums and libraries. Sprinkler systems are the single most reliable and effective means for minimizing the risk of large-loss fires in these cultural heritage institutions.[13] A recent Factory Mutual Research Corp. study revealed that the average dollar loss in fires with adequate sprinkler protection was $126,000 (loss amounts indexed to 1988 dollars) in the five-year period 1984 through 1988. By contrast, the average dollar loss in fires in which there was no adequate sprinkler protection during the same period was $732,600, or 5.8 times the average with adequate sprinkler protection. For this study, fires with adequate sprinkler protection were those in which sprinklers were in service, in which there were no sprinkler system or water supply deficiencies, and, in which no additional sprinklers were needed.[17] (See Fig. 8-8B.)

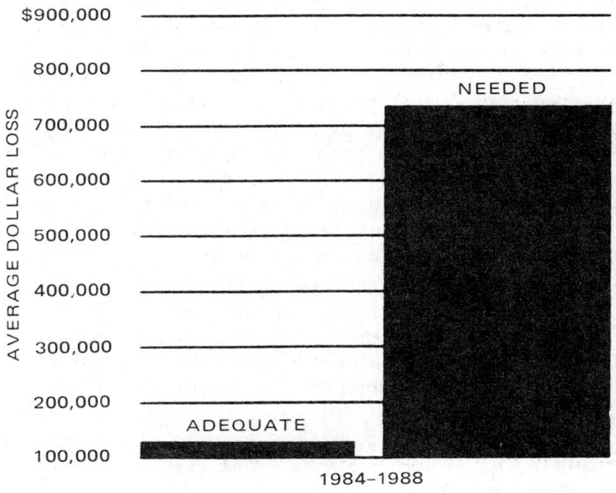

Fig. 8-8B. Sprinklers adequate vs. sprinklers needed. (Courtesy Factory Mutual Engineering Record)

For many years, library and museum conservators typically have opposed automatic water sprinkler protection. Fear of water damage, even more than fire damage, is reflected in library and museum planning references.[14,15,16] Libraries and museums have experienced water damage to their collections from flooding associated with problems other than fire, such as roof leaks, storm damage, plumbing problems, rivers overflowing, and so on.

Furthermore, flooding is not unusual when fire department hose lines are used to fight fires. However, unnecessary water damage seldom occurs in facilities completely protected by well designed and maintained automatic sprinkler systems. On the basis of loss data from actual fires in libraries, museums, and historical sites, most heavy water damage resulted not from sprinklers, which place small amounts of water directly on a fire, but from fire department hose lines, which can drench an entire area.[17]

Accidental flooding due to defects in sprinklers, water control devices, piping, or associated equipment has been rare. Based on sprinkler leakage loss reports, the probability that a defective sprinkler may open accidentally is less than one in a million per year.

Automatic sprinklers actually minimize the potential for water damage. Fire is stopped by the timely release of 20 to 25 gpm (76 to 95 L/min) in a spray pattern from a sprinkler, in contrast to the 150 to 250 gpm (568 to 946 L/min) of pressurized water from each firefighter's hose stream sweeping materials from shelves and displays into a disorganized mass on a flooded floor. Prospects of salvaging wet materials that have remained in place under the relatively gentle action of the sprinklers are infinitely better than they are for materials knocked to the floor, then soaked and possibly trampled upon.

There are alternatives to the standard wet-pipe sprinkler system that minimize water damage after the fire has been extinguished, such as on/off sprinklers and automatic recycling systems. Further information is provided in NFPA 910, *Protection of Libraries and Library Collections*, Sec. 7-2.1. Another alternative, the pre-action sprinkler system, has been designed primarily for applications such as libraries and museums where there may be a fear of water damage to collections from damaged sprinkler heads or broken piping. The pre-action sprinkler system piping is dry until the water supply valve is opened by a signal from an automatic fire detection system. However, failure of the fire detection system would prevent operation of the pre-action sprinkler system, except by manual operation of the water supply valve, and thus represents a failure mode that reduces the reliability of this system compared with wet-pipe systems. Furthermore, the pre-action system requires a significantly higher level of regular maintenance involving additional potential failure modes that further reduce its reliability relative to wet-pipe systems.

In retrofitted sprinkler installations for library or museum collection areas, preventing leakage can pose a problem when the system is initially charged with water. One solution, used by the Office of the Architect of the U.S. Capitol in the installation of wet-pipe sprinkler systems in Library of Congress bookstacks, is to require pneumatic testing of each system before proceeding with the normally required hydrostatic testing.

Collection items especially vulnerable to water damage are best stored in cabinets, manuscript boxes, or other appropriate containers that will shield them from water spray in the event of sprinkler discharge.[8]

Since about 1970, a growing number of new and existing libraries and museums have installed automatic sprinkler systems to achieve firesafety objectives and to keep fire risk within manageable and insurable limits. The resulting reduction in insurance premiums usually enables the sprinkler system to "pay back" its installation cost.[18]

Protection of Special Hazards: Areas housing high-value collections or equipment identified as essential for continuity of operations may require a higher level of fire protection than can be provided by the combination of a smoke detection system with an automatic sprinkler system to minimize damage or interruption of service within acceptable limits. The firesafety systems analysis the cultural institution performs to define acceptable loss limits and firesafety objectives should also use NFPA 550, *Firesafety Concepts Tree*, to identify fire protection strategies and special fire protection systems and technologies to achieve these higher levels of protection within the limits of affordability.[19] Particular attention should be given to passive fire protection utilizing special fire- and water-resistant vaults, cabinets, manuscript boxes, and other containers to protect high-value collection items.

Unless it can at least match the reliability and maintainability of the automatic sprinkler system, the special system* installed for this purpose should be in combination with, and not a substitute for, the sprinkler system. The installation cost of a special system to augment a standard automatic sprinkler system should be justified on the basis of the extraordinary value and/or irreplaceability of the collections or because it is required for continuity of operations that cannot accept any down-time such as in the control room for the facility fire protection/security systems and building utilities. The justification should demonstrate a need for a very high probability of success in confining fire growth to an area significantly smaller than would be possible using standard automatic sprinklers alone—for example, less than 100 sq ft or 9.3 m^2.

Halon 1301 often has been used for special fire protection systems where the values to be protected can justify the additional cost. It can be used in normally occupied areas, has a rapid extinguishing action on the flaming portion of fires, leaves no residue, and is not known to harm objects chemically or physically. However, while its toxicity is low in concentrations less than ten percent, inhalation hazards are associated with its decomposition products. Safety precautions for the design and operation of these fixed total flooding systems are provided in NFPA 12A, *Halon 1301 Fire Extinguishing Agent Systems*, and should be followed. Its limitations as well as advantages for application in cultural heritage institutions also are discussed in NFPA 910, *Protection of Libraries and Library Collections*, and 911, *Protection of Museums and Museum Collections*.

During the 1980s, halon fire suppressants, along with chloroflurocarbons (CFCs), were linked with the depletion of stratospheric ozone.[20] By international agreement, their manufacture will be curtailed and possibly eliminated before the end of the century. The Halons Technical Options Committee Report states that "social benefit and human safety considerations are considered to be the only justifications to offset the environmental risk associated with halon use.[21]" A matrix approach has been developed for use in making the determination of essential uses for Halon 1301 in cultural heritage institutions.[22]

Research efforts to develop an environmentally acceptable substitute for Halon 1301 are in progress. Because of the uncertainty future availability of Halon 1301, museums and libraries should consider carefully other quick action systems using an agent other than water, as well as the recently developed quick response sprinklers.

*Among the various special fire suppression systems, carbon dioxide total flooding systems are not generally recommended for normally occupied areas, and Halon 1211 total flooding systems are prohibited in such areas. Both of these gaseous agents can create an atmosphere immediately hazardous to life when used in enclosed areas.

Other special hazards: While the same firesafety principles are applicable to the requirements of museum and library collections, several activities common to museums and some libraries require special attention. These are:

1. Storage of art and other valuable objects.
2. Packing and unpacking traveling exhibits.
3. Storage of shipping crates and packing materials.
4. Cleaning and restoration.
5. Construction and renovation of displays.

Areas where these activities take place should be isolated and sprinklered.

CONSTRUCTION CONSIDERATIONS

Intrinsic design features of library and museum buildings should include firesafety aspects of site planning, fire-resistant construction and interior finish, smoke control, water supply for fire protection, and special requirements for underground structures. Topics deserving special attention in this chapter are compartmentation, means of egress, lighting, and gallery flexibility.

Compartmentation

A well-protected building is subdivided into compartments where walls provide barriers to the spread of fire. Compartments should be as small as possible, and the walls should be designed to resist the estimated fire duration, based on maximum fuel loads in the compartments.

As smoke is damaging to collections and harmful to occupants, fire walls also should confine smoke to the compartment of fire origin. Fire doors protecting openings in these walls must be controlled by automatic door closers but may be held open by electromagnetic devices installed in compliance with NFPA 101, *Life Safety Code*, to automatically release and close the door upon a signal from the fire detection systems. Fusible link assemblies have been used to hold doors open with automatic door closers. They are not acceptable for this purpose as they depend upon heat, rather than smoke or other fire detection system signals, to release the door closer.

Where small fire compartments would restrict flexible use of space, the installation of automatic sprinkler systems permits larger compartment areas and compensates for heavy fuel loads in storage areas, including bookstacks.

High-hazard areas where quantities of combustible material are in use, or stored, should be separated by fire walls from the exhibition galleries, reading rooms, other public areas, and from collection storage areas. Hazardous materials such as flammable liquids, including some paints, should be housed, when possible, in a structure separated from the museum or library building. These high-hazard areas include carpenter shops; display or exhibit preparation shops; research, restoration, and conservation laboratories; paint rooms; packing rooms and restaurant kitchens, among other places. Fire walls protecting these facilities should be designed to endure fires in the maximum fuel loads they will enclose, rather than the minimum required by building codes.

Means of Egress

It is common for library and museum security arrangements to require that all departing occupants be channeled through one or two entry/departure points that can be closely monitored. Unfortunately, this often means that other doors required by NFPA 101, *Life Safety Code*, for exit access or egress are locked. This problem most commonly occurs in museums and libraries with valuable collections and in libraries with heavily utilized reference collections, such as those in colleges and universities. Use of electromagnetic and electromechanical door locking systems and devices is gaining acceptance as a way to resolve this conflict between life safety and security. Such systems should include fail-safe features designed to provide a level of life safety equivalent to that required by NFPA 101. The *Life Safety Code* provides for delayed release locks under strict limitations in assembly occupancies that are protected throughout by automatic sprinklers, or fire detectors. Also see NFPA 910, *Protection of Libraries and Library Collections*, and NFPA 911, *Protection of Museums and Museum Collections*.

Attendance in exhibit galleries and reading rooms will vary with the popularity of the exhibit and the season of the year. During periods of high attendance, museums and libraries must exercise control to ensure exit capacity is not exceeded. Emergency planning and organization is a prime responsibility of library and museum management to provide leadership by their staff for support of handicapped persons and to ensure that required areas are vacated by all occupants when evacuation is ordered. As mentioned previously in this chapter, the use of voice communications should be considered for larger libraries and museums with high attendance and complex egress paths. Voice communications facilitate coordination and calm the fears and anxieties of occupants during evacuations.

Lighting

Art museums typically make use of as much natural light as possible. This often leads to installation of glass roofs, light-diffusing glass ceilings, and window walls, all of which increase the museum's vulnerability to exposure fire. Conversely, to protect their collections from ultraviolet radiation and achieve complete light control, some museums eliminate most wall and roof openings. Complex wiring systems requiring unusually heavy electrical loads may be needed to compensate for the absence of natural light. Museums also need numerous electrical outlets in floors, walls, and ceilings to provide flexibility for frequent changes in exhibits and to avoid dangerous use of extension cords.

Gallery Flexibility

Movable walls, temporary furring, and lightweight partitions facilitate rearranging exhibit space and change exhibits. However, such features should not be allowed to impede the movement of occupants in case of an emergency or to increase fire hazard by adding to the fuel load.

FIRE EMERGENCY MANAGEMENT

Management of a library or museum fire involves decisions and actions that must be taken to mitigate the consequences before, during, and immediately following the incident. Effective management includes continuous monitoring to ensure that fire protection systems and features are always in operational readiness and are never degraded or defeated by space changes or other building modifications.

A viable fire emergency contingency plan should provide for pre-emergency training of a fire brigade in evacuation, fire fighting, and salvage operations. In addition to life safety considerations, emphasis should be placed on the need to minimize water damage and to protect or remove endangered high-value collections. Pre-fire planning also must provide for the security of valuable collection materials after they have been removed from the building.

SALVAGE

Through the use of freeze/vacuum drying techniques, library preservation specialists have been increasingly successful in salvaging water-soaked library, archival, and other collection materials. However, water is only one of the hazards to which collections are vulnerable during a fire. Others include smoke, acids contained in combustion products, and chemical agents that may be used in fighting the fire, hazards perhaps more dangerous to museum collections than water.

Museum Salvage

With much higher values per item and fewer items than libraries, museums must concentrate salvage efforts upon removing endangered collections from the fire area to a safe location as quickly and carefully as possible. Conservation-oriented fire fighting strategies and techniques enhance salvage efforts and minimize collection losses.

Winterthur Museum in Wilmington, DE, has developed appropriate fire fighting techniques adaptable to other museums and libraries.[23] Fire fighting efforts are divided into three phases that function concurrently and are directed by the fire marshal and staff. These are collection protection and salvage operations, led by the housekeeping supervisor and staff; security for collections removed from the fire area, which is the responsibility of the security supervisor and staff; and overall coordination, provided by the building superintendent or a designee.

Library Salvage

The degree of success and expense in salvage of water-soaked library collections depends upon advance planning and the amount of wetting suffered by the materials. Freeze/vacuum drying has been very effective in removing water and smoke odors, while the use of a sterilizing agent, ethylene oxide, during the process arrests the growth of mold. Freeze/vacuum drying cannot, however, restore physical damage inflicted by hose streams, trampling, and/or mishandling.

Before the Fire

Planning for salvage efforts before a fire must include identification of the following:

1. Collection values. This facilitates decisions under emergency conditions as to which items or collections are to be saved first.
2. Preservation specialists in salvage operations to provide guidance when needed.
3. Short-notice sources of salvage materials, equipment, and facilities.
4. Organized and trained employees who will be needed in the salvage effort during and after the fire.

During the Fire

1. Remove endangered high-value collections.
2. Use tarpaulins or plastic sheeting to protect from water materials that remain in or near the fire area, but are not directly involved in the fire.

After the Fire

1. Obtain guidance from a preservation specialist experienced in salvage.
2. Wrap and freeze damaged articles.
3. Determine appropriate restoration procedures.

Much less salvage work should be needed in facilities protected by automatic sprinklers. Water absorption is minimized when materials are left on the shelf undisturbed by the gentler action of automatic sprinklers, as opposed to the more forceful action of hose streams. An automatic sprinkler system also greatly reduces the quantity of materials requiring salvage by limiting the size of the fire area to that covered by the operation of one or just a few sprinklers.[24]

FIRESAFETY IMPLICATIONS OF NEW DEVELOPMENTS

Automation of Library Catalogs

Automation may lead to replacement of traditional card catalogs. As this occurs, continuity of public service increasingly depends upon the computer and necessitates a high level of fire protection to ensure continuity of operation. Duplicates of magnetic media containing a library's computer based catalog should be maintained in a safe, remote location.

Bookstacks

Multi-tier bookstacks: Modeled after bookstacks developed for the Library of Congress in 1893, this type of shelving has been used for several decades in many libraries. (See Fig. 8-8C.) Typically, decks or tiers are supported by unprotected iron or steel columns and beams at intervals of 7 ft (2.14 m). Vertical openings between decks (See "Deck Slit" in Figure 8-8D) permit heating of bookstack areas by convection of air currents. Under fire conditions, these same openings function as flues to accelerate vertical fire spread to the tiers above.

Smoke barriers should be installed in these vertical openings, or deck slits, to facilitate smoke detection on the tier or deck of fire origin. This had not been done when the smoke detection system was installed in the multi-tier bookstack of the Los Angeles Central Public Library because a ducted ventilation system had not been installed for their bookstacks. When the arsonist set the fire on the fifth tier, the first detectors to annunciate were on the sixth tier, one tier above the tier of fire origin. This resulted in a delay in finding the fire, and occupants lost the opportunity to stop the fire with portable extinguishers while it was small, with catastrophic results.[25] It took nearly 350 fire fighters and over 70 pieces of fire apparatus 7.5 hours to extinguish the ensuing inferno.[26]

Modern versions of these systems are still sold, but without vertical openings in the modules. (See Figure 8-8E.) However, the unprotected steel support structure remains vulnerable to collapse in a fire. Cast iron and steel

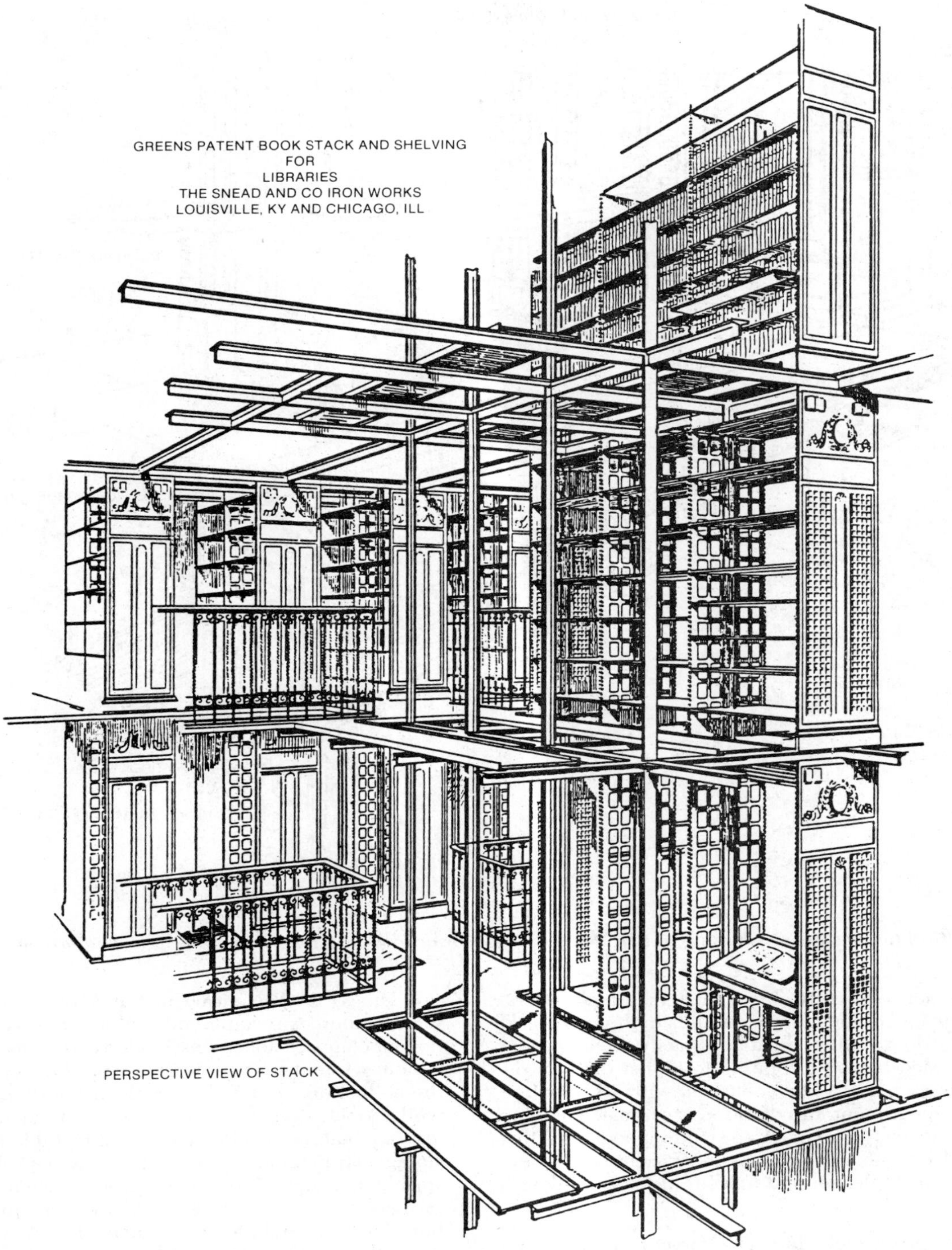

Fig. 8-8C. Multi-tier bookstack—as installed in the Library of Congress, circa 1897.

structural members lose strength at the high temperatures encountered in fires and may collapse. For this reason, the fire service may not be able to enter a multi-tier bookstack for manual fire suppression. This is also applicable to any variation on this bookstack design that uses exposed steel structural elements. Therefore, since it may be impossible for the fire service to provide manual fire suppression in bookstacks of this or similar design, it is essential that they be equipped with automatic fire suppression systems to defend against fire.

In new library construction, multi-tier bookstacks are being replaced by free-standing bookstack ranges installed on structural fire-resistant floors.

The difference in fuel load between multi-tier stacks and free-standing stacks is substantial. All levels in a multi-tier system are usually considered as one fire compartment,

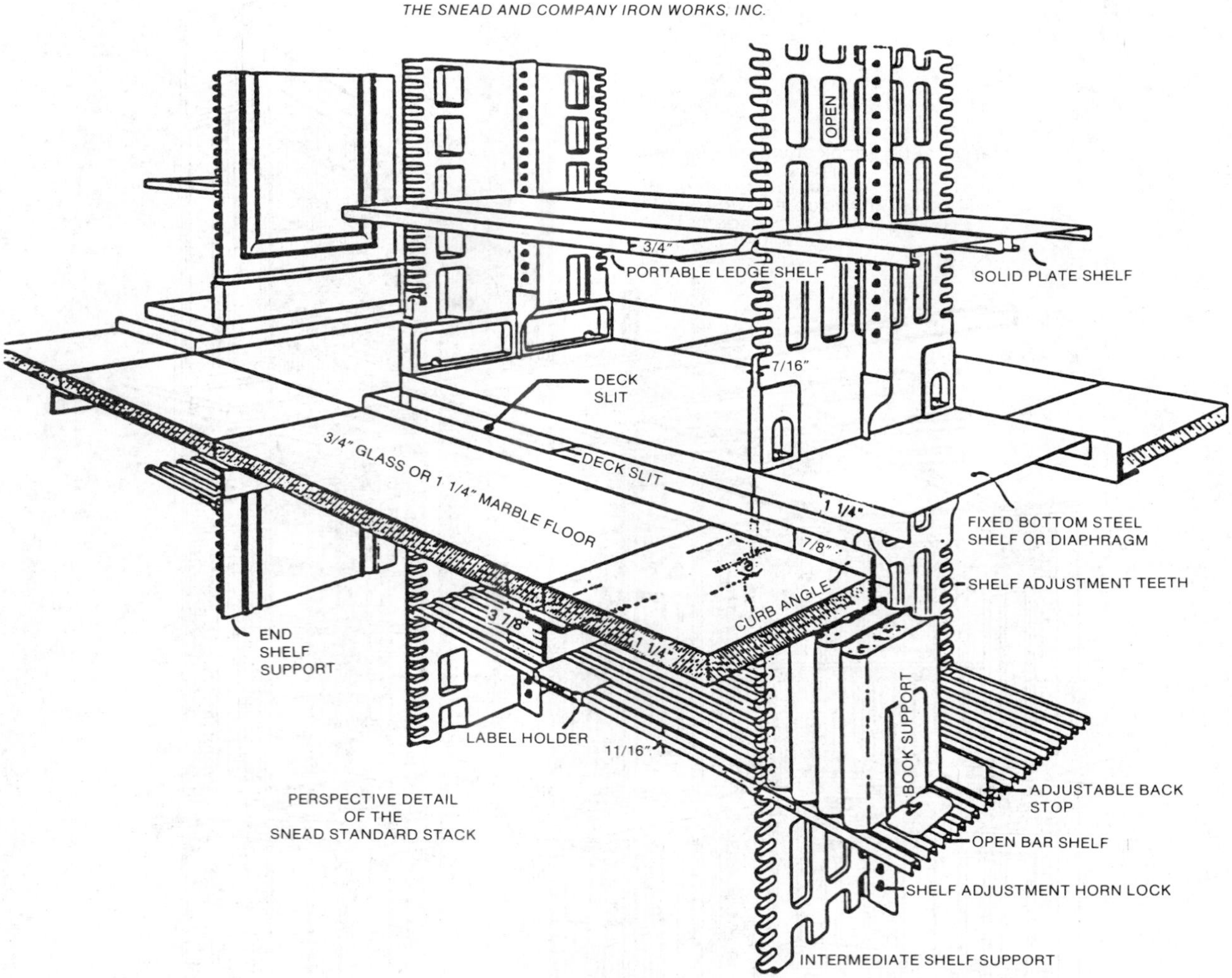

***Fig. 8-8D.** Multi-tier bookstack—showing section through deck flooring, deck slit, fixed bottom shelf, and adjustable shelves.*

due to the absence of vertical fire barriers between tiers. Fire loads depend on the number of tiers in the bookstack. With shelf loading at 70 percent of capacity, the expected fire load in each tier would be 55 to 65 psf (268 to 317 kg/m^2). Thus, in a multi-tier bookstack with 10 tiers in a single fire compartment, fire duration is estimated at 70 to 85 hours. Conversely, fire in a free-standing bookstack that is seven shelves high and set on a fire resistant floor would be limited to a single tier and to a fire duration of 7 to 8 hours.

Compact storage or track files: The practice of mounting bookstack shelving units, or ranges, on carriages that roll on tracks is becoming a common feature in new library and museum construction and in renovations. This space-saving bookstack system design employs one moving aisle to serve several bookstack ranges. The track systems are modular, with two or more mobile ranges between two fixed-end ranges in each module. (See Figure 8-8F.) This compact storage method can result in a fire load in excess of 120 psf (586 kg/m^2) and a fire duration that might exceed 15 hours, more than enough to challenge the most fire-resistant barriers and construction prescribed by building and fire codes.

The NFPA Technical Committee on Protection of Cultural Resources recommends automatic sprinkler protection for compact storage installations. To install this storage system without such protection would not only endanger the collections, but might result in building collapse, as well. Conclusions from an independent analysis[27] of fire tests evaluating the effectiveness of sprinklers on compact storage arrangements[28] indicate a high probability that sprinklers installed over a compact storage module would prevent a fire originating in the module from damaging building structural elements outside the module. Furthermore, there is a good probability that sprinklers would prevent fire spread across 4-ft (1.22 m) aisles between compact storage modules and would be effective in preventing fire spread between back-to-back shelves of adjacent modules when each shelf is backed by a sheet metal panel with a 1-in. (25 mm) air space between adjacent panels. Thus, tests indicate that automatic sprinklers can be expected to limit fire development to that portion of the module of fire origin between the fixed-end range and the open aisle. However, total loss of contents within that portion of the storage module is possible. (See Figure 8-8C.)

FIG. 8-8E. A modern multi-tier installation.

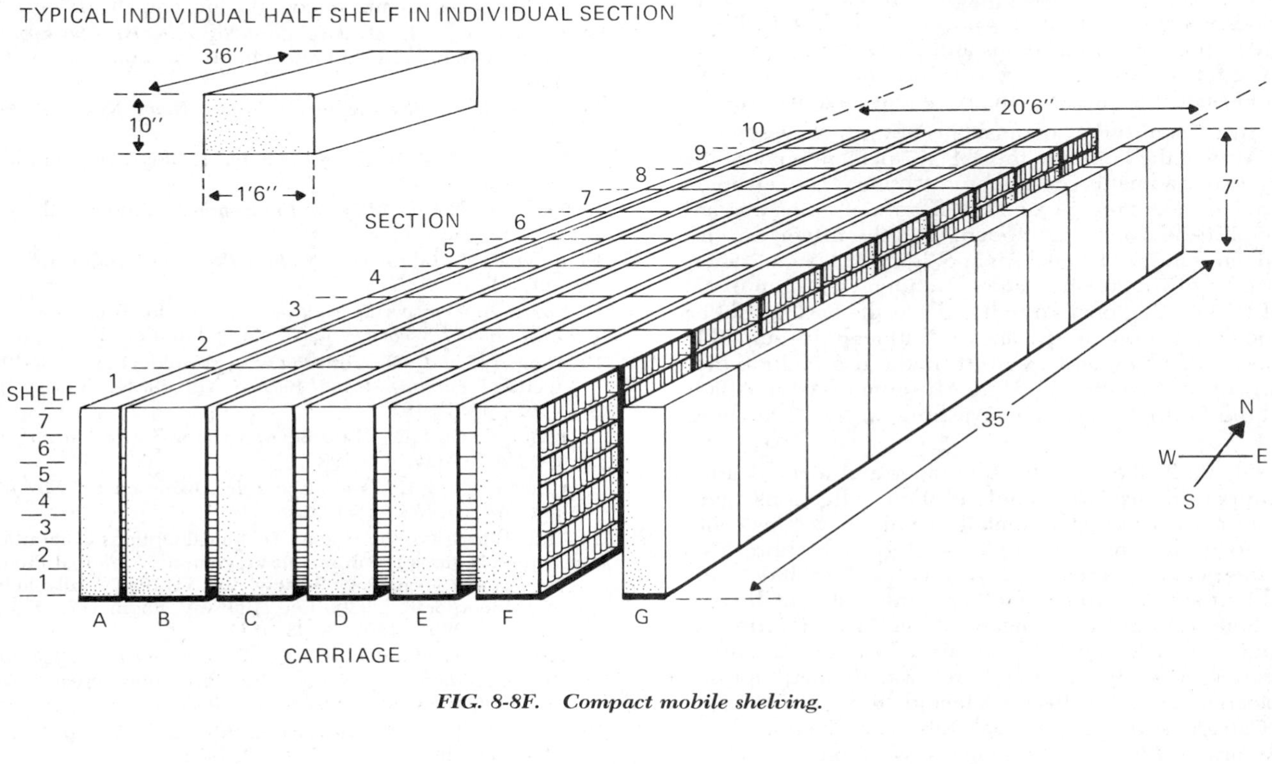

FIG. 8-8F. Compact mobile shelving.

Loss of contents within the module of fire origin can be minimized by careful attention to the following considerations in designing the compact storage system:

1. More efficient use of space results in greater density or concentration of values. That is, it increases the number of items subject to fire damage per unit volume of storage space. This risk should be considered in determining the maximum number of ranges to be included in each module.
2. Existing automatic fire detection and fire suppression systems may have to be modified, and Halon 1301 may be ineffective.
3. Compact storage modules may conceal the origin of smoke, thereby compounding the difficulty in locating and extinguishing a fire.
4. Compact storage modules prevent penetration of water from hose streams for fire extinguishment and delay detection by entrapping smoke and heat. Consider designing the system so that ranges can be parked with a five inch (12.7 cm) gap between them during inactive storage periods. This arrangement was tested with satisfactory results by Underwriters Laboratories for the U.S. National Archives and Records Administration using "quick response" sprinkler heads. Loss was limited to 10 cu ft (0.28 cu m) of paper records and 3 cu ft (0.08 cu m) of computer records.[31]
5. Bookstack ranges may be moved electrically or manually. In compact storage systems that are moved electrically, the electric motor in each bookstack range is a potential ignition source.

FIRE PROTECTION DECISIONS

The elapsed time between the discovery of a fire and the beginning of effective manual suppression easily can be too long to prevent unacceptable loss, especially during periods when the building is unoccupied. Faced with this reality, directors of museums and libraries and their governing bodies are deciding to incorporate automatic fire suppression systems as primary defense against fire loss.

In a recent survey of museums of various sizes, including thirty of the largest in the U.S., 77 percent reported that they use automatic sprinkler protection.[13] Nevertheless, there has been great progress. A list of museums that have made this decision might begin with the fifteen Smithsonian museums: National Air and Space Museum, National Museum of American History, National Museum of Natural History, National Portrait Gallery, the Sackler Gallery, National Museum of African Art, National Museum of the American Indian, and so on. It might also include the J. Paul Getty Museum, the High Museum of Art in Atlanta, and the Phillips Gallery in Washington, D.C., to name a few.

Similarly, the list of libraries, large and small, that have equipped themselves to defend their collections against fire loss by installing automatic sprinkler systems continues to grow. Some examples include city libraries in Atlanta; Dallas; Houston; Los Angeles; Portland, Maine; and Portland, Oregon, as well as many academic libraries, the State Library of Michigan, and national libraries from Saudi Arabia to the U.S. Library of Congress. National libraries currently planning to retrofit automatic sprinkler protection for their collections include the National Library of Canada and the National Library of Scotland. The new British Library at St. Pancras, with four floors below grade level, 180 miles (300 km) of shelving, 864,000 sq ft (80,000 m^2), and plans for later expansion to 2,160,000 sq ft (200,000 m^2) will be added to the list when it opens in 1993.[29]

Guidance for the procurement, installation, testing and maintenance of fire protection systems is provided in NFPA 910, *Protection of Libraries and Library Collections*, and 911, *Protection of Museums and Museum Collections*, as well as in other chapters of this handbook.

BIBLIOGRAPHY

References Cited

1. Morris, J., *Managing the Library Fire Risk*, 2nd ed., University of California, Berkeley, CA, 1979.
2. Johnson, E. M., *ed.*, *Protecting the Library and Its Resources*, American Library Association, Chicago, IL, 1963.
3. Harvey, B., "Fire Hazards in Libraries: Part I—Clearing the Smoke," *Library Security Newsletter*, Vol. 1, No. 1 (Jan. 1975).
4. Morris, J., "Is Your Library Safe from Fire?," *American School and University*, Apr. 1980. p. 61.
5. McElroy, F. E., *ed.*, *Accident Prevention Manual for Industrial Operations*, 7th ed., National Safety Council, Chicago, IL, 1974.
6. Factory Mutual Research Corp., *Handbook of Industrial Loss Prevention*., 2nd ed., McGraw-Hill, Inc., NY, 1967.
7. McKinnon, G. P., *ed.*, *Industrial Fire Hazards Handbook*, 1st ed., National Fire Protection Association, Boston, MA, 1979.
8. Johnson, E. V. and Horgan, J. C., *Museum Collection Storage*, United Nations Educational Scientific and Cultural Organization, Paris, France, 1979.
9. *Operation School Burning No. 1*, Los Angeles Fire Department, National Fire Protection Association, Quincy, MA, 1959.
10. Firepro, Inc. *Fire Defense Alternatives: Library of Congress*. Unpublished report, 1977.
11. *Building Firesafety Criteria*, PBS P5920.9, Appendix D, General Services Administration, Washington, DC, 1979.
12. Zimmerman, C. E., *ed.*, *Fire Alarm Signaling Handbook*, NFPA SPP 82, National Fire Protection Association, Quincy, MA, 1987.
13. Wilson, J. A., "Fire Fighters", *Museum News*, Nov./Dec. 1989, pp. 68-72.
14. Myller, R., *The Design of the Small Public Library*, Bowker, NY, 1966.
15. Thomson, G., *The Museum Environment*, Butterworths, London, England, 1978.
16. Brawne, M., *Libraries: Architecture and Equipment*, Praeger, NY, 1970.
17. Kirsch, A., "Preserving Today's Treasures for Tomorrow." *Factory Mutual Record*, Vol. 67, No. 1 (Jan./Feb. 1990), pp. 4-8.
18. Thomas, S., *ed.*, "Retrofitting with Sprinklers for Added Protection." *Factory Mutual Record*, Vol. 59, No. 3 (May-June 1982), pp. 13-19.
19. Grant, C. C., P.E., "Life Beyond Halon." *Fire Journal*, Vol. 84, No. 3 (May/June 1990).
20. Grant, C. C., P.E., "Halons and the Ozone Layer" *Fire Journal, Vol. 83, No. 5 (Sept./Oct. 1989)*.
21. "Final Report of the Halons Technical Options Committee," United Nations Environment Programme, Montreal Protocol Assessment Technology Review, Aug. 11, 1989. Available from ICF Incorporated, 9300 Lee Highway, Room 1171, Fairfax, VA, USA 22031-1207, $6.03 USD.
22. DiNenno, P. J. and Taylor, G. M., *Best and Essential Halon Use, A Methodology*, National Fire Protection Research Foundation, Quincy, MA., December 1989.
23. Fennelly, L. J., *ed.*, *Museum, Archive and Library Security*, Butterworths, London, England, 1983.

24. Fuhlrott, R., and Dewey, M., *Library Interior Layout and Design*, Saur, Munich, Germany, 1982.
25. Morris, J., "Fire Protection for the Library," *The Construction Specifier*, October 1989.
26. Isner, M. S., "Fire in Los Angeles Central Library Causes $22 Million Loss." *Fire Journal*, Vol. 81, No. 5 (March/April 1987).
27. Cutler, H. R. *Engineering Analysis of Compact Storage Fire Tests*, Library of Congress, Washington, DC, 1979.
28. Chicarello, P.J., *et al.*, *Fire Tests in Mobile Storage Systems for Archival Storage*, General Services Administration, Washington, DC, 1978.
29. Cartwright, N.K., "Fire Protection at the New British Library." *Fire Prevention 203*, October 1987.
30. Morris, J., *The Library Disaster Preparedness Handbook*, American Library Association, Chicago and London, 1986.
31. Underwriters Laborartories, Inc., "Report on Archives II Mobile High Density Shelving Fire Protection System." A copy of this report, dated November 30, 1989, is available from the National Archives and Records Administration (NAFS), Washington, D.C. 20408.

References

NFPA Codes, Standards, and Recommended Practices

NFPA codes, standards, and recommended practices will provide further information on library and museum collections discussed in this chapter. (See the latest *NFPA Catalog* for availability of the current editions of the following documents.)

NFPA 11, *Low-Expansion Foam and Combined Agent Systems*.
NFPA 12, *Carbon Dioxide Extinguishing Systems*.
NFPA 12A, *Halon 1301 Fire Extinguishing Agent Systems*.
NFPA 13, *Installation of Sprinkler Systems*.
NFPA 14, *Installation of Standpipe and Hose Systems*.
NFPA 70, *National Electrical Code*.
NFPA 101, *Safety to Life from Fire in Buildings and Structures*.
NFPA 232, *Protection of Records*.
NFPA 232AM, *Fire Protection for Archives and Record Centers*.
NFPA 550, *Firesafety Concepts Tree*.
NFPA 910, *Protection of Libraries and Library Collections*.
NFPA 911, *Protection of Museums and Museum Collections*.

Additional Reading

Burgess, D. "The Library Has Blown Up!" *Library Journal*, Oct. 1, 1989.

Cotton, P. E., "Fire Tests of Library Bookstacks," *NFPA Quarterly*, Vol. 53, No. 4 (April 1960), pp. 288-295.

DeCandido, G. A., "Special Report: Fire at the USSR Academy of Sciences Library," *Library Journal*, June 15, 1988.

Egan, M. D., *Concepts in Building Firesafety*, reprint R. Krieger, Malabar, FL, 1986, p. 28.

Factory Mutual System, "Protection Against Incendiary Fires," Factory Mutual Research Corp., 1985.

"Fire Security Problems: Prevention and Cures," *Library Journal*, Dec. 1, 1975, pp. 2203-2204.

Fisher, W. R., "Protect Our Treasures from Threat of Fire," *Professional Safety*, Vol. 25, No. 2 (Feb. 1980), pp. 21-24.

Facility Standards for Public Building Service, PBS P 3430.1A, General Services Administration, Washington, DC, 1989.

Kallenbach, W., *et al.*, *Fire Protection in Historical Buildings and Museums*, Arbeitsgruppe...e.v., Hamburg, Germany, 1980 (in German).

Lerup, L., *et al.*, *Learning From Fire: A Fire Protection Primer for Architects*, National Fire Prevention and Control Administration, Washington, DC, 1977.

Maddox, J., "Norwood Book Burning," *Wilson Library Journal*, Vol. 34, (Feb. 1960), pp. 412-414.

Morris, J., "Restoring Water-logged Books," *Cleaning and Restoration*, Nov. 1989.

Morris, J., "Mopping Up After Library Fires," *Fire Prevention*, No. 220, (June 1989), pp. 33-35.

Morris, J., "Protecting the Library from Fire," *Fire Journal*, Vol. 80, No. 2, 1986, p. 35.

Nelson, H. E., "Jefferson National Memorial Historical Site Analysis of Impact of Fire Safety," *NBSIR 84-2897*, March 1985, National Bureau of Standards, Gaithersburg, MD.

Schaefer, G. L., "Fire!," *Library Journal*, Vol. 85, (Feb. 1, 1960), pp. 504-505.

Schell, H. B., "Cornell Starts a Fire," *Library Journal*, Vol. 85, (Oct. 1, 1960), pp. 3398-3399.

Sellers, D. Y. and Strassberg, R., "Anatomy of a Library Emergency," *Library Journal*, (Oct. 1, 1973), pp. 2824-2827.

Solomon, R. E., *ed.*, *Automatic Sprinkler Systems Handbook*, 4th ed., National Fire Protection Association, Quincy, MA, 1989.

Swayne, L., H., "Fire Protection at the National Archives Building, Washington, DC," *Fire Journal*, Vol. 69, No. 1, Jan. 1975, pp. 65-67.

Tillotson, R. G., *Museum Security*, International Council of Museums, Paris, France, 1977, p. 46.

Tweedie, A. T., "Freeze-Dried Books," *Library Journal*, Jan. 15, 1974, p. 82.

Waters, P., *Procedures for Salvage of Water-Damaged Library Materials*, Library of Congress, Washington, DC, 1975.

Wilson, R., "The L-Curve: Evaluating Fire Protection Tradeoffs," *Specifying Engineer*, (May 1977), pp. 110-113.

ENVIRONMENTAL ISSUES IN FIRE PROTECTION

Jane I. Lataille

Almost all human activity can harm the environment. Manufacturing products, storing and using chemicals, burning fuel, or discarding wastes can cause pollution. More often than not, efforts made to protect the environment from these activities have raised new fire protection concerns. Likewise, many fire protection measures have added to environmental problems. Therefore, whenever attempts are made to reduce pollution or to protect a structure or a process from fire, the interrelationship between fire protection and the environment must be considered.

This chapter presents an overview of the environmental issues related to fire protection. It is not an exhaustive review of environmental incidents that have affected fire protection engineering. For more specific information, see the bibliography at the end of this chapter.

The first part of this chapter—Pollution Control—describes fire protection concerns introduced by pollution control measures. The second part of this chapter—Fire Protection Systems—describes environmental problems that are related to fire protection systems and methods. The last part of this chapter explores the impact these interrelationships have on fire protection engineers.

POLLUTION CONTROL

Pollution may be classified as air, water, land, thermal, or noise pollution. Air, water, and land pollution generally imply pollution by substances. Thermal pollution is most often associated with water, and noise pollution with air. Efforts to control any type of pollution may raise fire protection concerns.

Air Pollution

Vapors: One way to control air pollution is to collect vapors from vapor-producing processes. Collected vapors are then converted, incinerated, or recycled (recovered). Each of these three options for treating vapors needs protection.

Jane I. Lataille, P.E., ARM, is senior account consultant with Industrial Risk Insurers, Hartford, CT.

Catalytic conversion can involve enclosed vessels, high temperatures, and fluidized beds. The hazards needing protection include heated combustible materials, fuel-fired equipment, and the presence of ignitable vapors in enclosed spaces. Process monitoring and control are also important to safe operation.

Incineration is done in flare stacks, in fuel-fired equipment designed primarily for incineration, or in fuel-fired equipment designed for some other purpose and modified to burn waste liquids or vapors. Incineration by flare often is used with emergency venting systems to burn off emergency discharges. It also is used when the non-emergency venting of vapors is not frequent enough to warrant their recovery. A flare stack is just a tall stack into which vapors are piped to be burned in a pilot flame at the top of the stack. The flame normally is monitored with a closed-circuit television camera or with thermal sensors. Stacks also must be monitored for safe air flows and oxygen levels so the stack gas mixture does not become explosive.

Besides the protective measures normally taken for fuel-fired equipment, incineration requires proper design of burners and combustion safeguard logic to account for the different physical and chemical properties of the materials to be burned. Sometimes, this design includes the ability to switch from fuel to fuel or to burn different fuels simultaneously.

Solvent recovery systems reduce pollution, as well as recycle solvents. Recycling is now more common because laws require collection of vapors that were previously released to the atmosphere. Most solvent recovery systems have vapor collection ductwork, condensers, and liquid storage tanks. Activated carbon recovery systems absorb solvent that is then collected by steaming it out of the carbon. In some cases, collected solvent must be filtered, scrubbed, or distilled before it can be reused. Often, both "clean" and "dirty" solvent storage tanks are needed in a solvent recovery system. Each tank, piece of equipment, and process involving a solvent requires proper fire protection.

Plastic ductwork often is used to collect vapors that corrode metal. The interior of this ductwork is a combustible concealed space that requires sprinkler protection. In addition, burning plastics emit dense, acidic smoke, so fire response must include actions that minimize corrosion of exposed equipment.

Particles: Process-generated particles, such as dust, ash, or fibers, must be removed from the air to keep it clean. Such particles are removed with dry or wet dust collectors, or with electrostatic precipitators. Particle collection equipment can involve combustible dusts, heat- and friction-producing mechanical equipment, combustible filters, combustible collection bags, transformers, and other electrical equipment—all of which require protection.

General building ventilation systems use filters to remove particles from both fresh and recirculated air. If the filters burn, a ventilation system can spread smoke throughout a building. Since ventilation systems are enclosed, fires in them are difficult to locate and extinguish. Therefore, ventilation system filters should always be noncombustible, with the lowest possible smoke-generation ratings. Ventilation systems also can be arranged to exhaust those portions of a building in which smoke has been detected and to pressurize adjacent areas simultaneously to prevent smoke leakage into them.

An extreme case of controlling air quality is seen in today's cleanrooms. The massive amounts of filters used in cleanroom air-handling systems make fire protection crucial. Although the filters may be noncombustible, the materials the filters collect can burn, causing damage to expensive cleanroom equipment and materials. Products of combustion from coated wiring and other plastics materials also can do extensive damage when circulated through the cleanroom air-handling system. Carefully designed air-handling systems with fast smoke detection and flexible air control are necessary parts of the fire protection design.

Fluorocarbons: It is now believed that the ozone level in Earth's upper atmosphere is depleted when normally stable fluorocarbon molecules are broken down by ultraviolet radiation. Fluorine atoms thus freed from the fluorocarbon molecules then combine with single oxygen atoms from oxygen molecules that also have been broken down by ultraviolet radiation. These single oxygen atoms would normally combine with oxygen molecules to make ozone if the fluorine atoms were not present. Bromine and chlorine have the same effect.

As early as the 1970s, it was suspected that fluorocarbons had detrimental effects on the environment. International action to study these effects took place during the early 1980s and led to the Vienna Convention of 1985, when 27 countries signed an agreement to protect the ozone layer. Research continued, and in 1987, the Montreal Protocol was signed. This protocol froze the production of most fluorocarbons to 1986 levels by July 1989. It also called for further cuts in 1993 and 1998.

After the protocol was enacted, scientists determined that the ozone-depletion problem was even more serious than previously thought. So, the protocol was revised in June 1990 to mandate *no* fluorocarbon production by the year 2000.

Fluorocarbons are used as refrigerants and propellants. To safeguard the environment, these fluorocarbons are being replaced by much more hazardous materials, such as hydrocarbons, alcohol, or ammonia. Use of the replacement substances creates new fire protection problems.

Water Pollution

The cleanliness of Earth's water is maintained by treating it with various types of chemicals. These chemicals can neutralize the water, react with harmful substances to inert them, or cause contaminants to settle out of the water. Fire protection must be considered when storing and using treatment chemicals that are hazardous.

Sometimes, pollutants removed from the water are hazardous. A good example of this is oil spilled into the ocean by a tanker. Appropriate fire protection measures must be taken during collection and storage of such materials. Mixed pollutants may have to be separated further after removal because they may have different disposal requirements. Separation and other treatment equipment must be designed and arranged to handle the materials safely.

The need to clean up the Earth's water affects more than the water being treated. Chemicals that were once allowed to be dumped into rivers and streams must now be collected and stored. Fire protection measures appropriate for storage and handling of hazardous materials must then be taken for these chemicals.

Land Pollution

Waste disposal is increasing due to the rising world population and industrial growth. Dumps and landfills are ravaging the land and contaminating groundwater that serves as the source of public water supplies. Recycling helps restore the land, but recycling systems often mean more fire protection concerns.

Recycling is an industry of its own, with many plants that do nothing else. These plants need basic fire protection and risk management programs, just as any other industry does. They must also deal with the hazards unique to their recycling processes.

Plastics recycling involves grinding, melting, and extruding processes, as well as warehousing. Due to the burning characteristics of plastics, fire protection systems for their storage and handling must be designed carefully. Process equipment must be designed with due regard for the capacity of plastics to hold static charges.

A fast-emerging recycling industry is the so-called "trash to cash" business. In this industry, municipal waste is collected, separated, shredded, and burned to generate electric power. The hazards inherent in the generation of electrical power must be protected, as well as those unique to the storage of large amounts of combustible waste inside buildings and to the processing and burning of this waste. Unique protection problems include the large distance between the combustible waste and roof sprinklers, due to the need for large cranes or other materials-handling systems, and the special design of systems that safely burn waste with varying chemical content.

Other materials now commonly recycled are glass, metal, paper, and wood. In each case, protection must be provided for the buildings, materials, and processes associated with recycling of materials that used to be buried in the land and forgotten.

Another strategy to eliminate sources of land pollution is to replace underground liquids storage tanks, especially those for gasoline and oil, with aboveground tanks. This strategy reverses the 1960s policy of burying tanks to reduce their fire protection problems, except that now, there are even more problems.

To contain leaks from aboveground tanks, they are provided with dikes sized to hold the contents of the largest tank within the dike. To keep spills from seeping into the ground, the surfaces of diked areas must be nonporous, or, if there is a spill, the ground must be dug up and tested. Contaminated ground must then be removed and treated as hazardous waste.

Rainwater that collects in the dike must be tested before it can be released. If there are any contaminants, the water must be treated as hazardous waste. While this treatment greatly reduces the chance of pollution, it increases the amount of fire protection needed.

If underground tanks are necessary, they must be designed to minimize the potential for leakage. Design features include proper preparation of the tank bed, anchoring the tank, careful backfilling, using double walls on the tank, leak detection, groundwater monitoring, and liquid level alarms. As an option to double walls, fiberglass tanks or tanks of other nonmetallic materials may be used. These tanks require especially careful installation.

Thermal and Noise Pollution

Concern for the environment rests mainly with the addition of physical pollutants to the air, water, and land. However, the need to control heat and sound also has had an effect on the fire protection engineer.

Even pure water should not be dumped into a stream if it will raise the temperature of the stream enough to affect its ecology. Elevated water temperatures can cause excessive algae growth and can be harmful to fish and other water life.

Cooling towers reprocess cooling water to help alleviate thermal pollution of waterways and to help preserve Earth's water. Because cooling towers are often of combustible construction or have combustible fill, they need fire protection systems.

Heat preservation is good for global ecology. It is also economical because fuel and fuel-burning equipment are expensive to buy and maintain. Insulating is a common way to preserve heat, but it introduces fire protection concerns, in that many of the materials with good insulating properties are combustible and can emit toxic and acidic products of combustion when burning. The problem increases when such insulation is installed inside nonaccessible spaces, such as closed-off attics and crawl spaces.

Noise control requires careful design and placement of process equipment, as well as the use of soundproofing. Soundproofing materials introduce the same concerns that insulating materials do. They may be combustible, they may release toxic and acidic products of combustion when burning, and they may be installed in inaccessible places, such as inside air-handling ducts or process equipment.

FIRE PROTECTION SYSTEMS

All fire protection system extinguishing agents can affect the environment. Of primary concern are halons. Like refrigerants and propellants, fire protection halons are fluorocarbons. The relationship between the fire protection halons and depletion of the ozone layer has drawn much attention. The most damaging halon is considered to be Halon 1301, which is the most common fluorocarbon used for fire protection. While much attention is focused on halons, however, fire protection engineers must be aware of other sources of potential harm to the environment.

Halons and the Ozone Layer

Research has found that Halon 1301 has the highest ozone-depletion potential of all the fluorocarbons, at least ten times higher than the four most common fluorocarbon refrigerants. As a result, the fire protection community has had to move quickly to work out ways of acceptably controlling loss potential while minimizing the use of this previously well-accepted extinguishing agent.

Full-flooding halon acceptance tests are now often replaced with pressure and puff tests to prove the integrity of the piping and with door fan tests to prove room tightness. These alternative methods eliminate the dumping of halon into the environment from extinguishing systems testing. Halon release can be reduced further by carefully designing detection systems to suit the occupancies they protect, and by periodically inspecting, testing, and maintaining halon systems so that inadvertent discharge does not occur. Recovery of halon discharged from cylinders during hydrostatic testing is another way to reduce the amount of halon released into the environment. (See Figure 8-9A.)

FIG. 8-9A. ***A Halon 1301 storage container. (Source: IRI and Fenwal)***

Using Halon 1301 in new systems must be evaluated carefully. Many occupancies that can be protected with halon systems also can be protected with sprinklers, and detectors can supplement the sprinklers for early warning. Underfloor areas can be protected with carbon dioxide extinguishing systems, as can the insides of important electronic equipment.

Halon 1301 substitutes are being developed. They are halons, too, but they have much lower ozone-depletion potentials than Halon 1301. Pentafluoroethane, with no ozone-depletion potential, and dichlorotrifluoromethane, with an ozone-depletion potential of 0.02, are two such compounds. In accordance with the latest Montreal Protocol, however, these substitutes cannot be made after the year 2000.

Other Special Extinguishing Agents

Any substance that gets into the ground can contaminate groundwater. These substances include agents used in special extinguishing systems, such as dry and wet chemicals, fire protection foams, and the antifreezes sometimes added to wet-pipe sprinkler systems. It is becoming more common to enclose or dike areas protected with these agents so that they may be cleaned up after discharge. Sometimes, areas protected with these agents are drained to a suitably sized holding tank for later disposal. (See Figure 8-9B.)

FIG. 8-9B. Foam storage tank. (Source: IRI and Rockwood)

One of the early fire protection agents was carbon tetrachloride. This liquid, a precursor of the halogens, was known to be an effective extinguishing agent. It was either put into pressurized containers with sprinkler-like operating mechanisms at the bottom, or it was sealed into glass bulbs for throwing at a fire manually. (See Figure 8-9C.) These containers or bulbs were once commonly placed in unsprinklered dead records storage rooms and in other small rooms. Carbon tetrachloride is no longer used because of its high toxicity. It has been replaced with alternate extinguishing agents, all of which must now be reviewed for their effects on the environment.

Carbon dioxide is a nontoxic, relatively inert gas that is found naturally in the atmosphere. It extinguishes fire by displacing the oxygen required for combustion and, therefore, poses a suffocation hazard. Careful system design with appropriate safety interlocks is used to mitigate this danger to people. Otherwise, carbon dioxide has been an ideal extinguishing agent for protecting many hazards. However, the warming of the Earth through the greenhouse effect is thought to be aggravated by excessive carbon dioxide. So now, even the use of this agent must be considered carefully.

Fire Protection Water

With most extinguishing agents posing some sort of environmental threat, an obvious solution is to use water-based extinguishing systems , such as sprinklers, water spray, deluge, and so on, wherever water is a suitable extinguishing agent. However, even this presents environmental concerns. In fact, it is likely that discharge from water-based systems will be one of the biggest fire protection concerns of the coming decade.

FIG. 8-9C. Old-style carbon tetrachloride extinguisher. (Source: IRI)

When a sprinkler system operates, the water flows over whatever is burning and over anything else that is in the area of the sprinkler discharge. The water then collects and flows even farther, carrying potential contaminants, which seep into the ground unless the protected area has been designed to contain the sprinkler discharge.

There have been many incidents in which sprinkler discharge has carried hazardous materials and posed a contamination hazard to drinking water. In a May 1987 paint plant fire in Dayton, OH, sprinkler discharge spread flammable liquids near potable water sources.

There have also been incidents in which fire protection discharge contributed to air pollution. In these cases, chlorine gas was released from stored swimming pool chemicals when they were wetted by sprinklers. Two well-known incidents of this type occurred in June 1988 in Springfield, MA, and in August 1988 in Glendale, AZ. The effects of fire protection discharge must therefore be considered in the design of a protected facility and its site.

Even if a facility existed that had no possible contaminants, the sprinkler system fed by a public water supply could still pose an environmental threat—that is, contamination of the public water supply through backflow. Pollutants can pass from the sprinkler system to the water supply through the normal backflow permitted by check valves. The pollutants come from the water pumped into the sprinkler system through the fire department connection. This water could be contaminated if a fire department used a nonpotable auxiliary source, such as a pond, or if the water in the fire department tankers was treated with anticorrosion chemicals.

To keep sprinkler system water from contaminating public water supplies, many states and municipalities have passed laws pertaining to the arrangement of sprinkler systems. Some do not permit connections to the public supply if the fire protection system includes a suction or gravity

FIG. 8-9D. Reduced-pressure principle backflow preventer. (Source: IRI and Cla Val)

tank. Others do not permit booster pumps. Antifreeze systems may not be allowed. In some cases, systems with tanks or pumps may be connected to the public water supply if double check valves are used.

A requirement that is becoming more common for sprinkler systems is the installation of a reduced-pressure-principle backflow preventer wherever the potential for contamination of the public water supply exists. (See Figure 8-9D.) Interpretation of where a potential for contamination exists is often left to a state or municipality. Examples of the potential for contamination are the presence of a fire department connection on a sprinkler system, the proximity of a nonpotable suction source, or the addition of anticorrosion chemicals to fire department tanker water.

The reduced-pressure principle backflow preventer uses two check valves, two taps for pressure sensing, and a diaphragm-operated dump valve. The dump valve releases pressure in the backflow preventer's zone of reduced pressure, which prevents backflow whenever the first check valve is closing. Although reduced pressure principle backflow preventers prevent backflow better than double check valves, they have many disadvantages, including high cost and excessive friction loss. Backflow preventers also can rob water from the sprinkler system, if the dump valve fails to close when it should. (See Figure 8-9E.)

Manual fire fighting efforts introduce the same environment-contaminating potential that automatic fire protection systems do. Any water used to extinguish a fire can carry hazardous materials that had been in the area of the fire. These materials can seep into the groundwater. Therefore, even unprotected facilities need careful site layout.

Fire Protection Measures

Many measures have been taken for protection from fire beyond those for installation of automatic extinguishing systems. Not surprisingly, these, too, are a source of environmental concern.

PCBs (polychlorinated biphenyl) were used to replace most transformer dielectric fluids due to their low fire and explosion hazard compared with the formerly used combustible oils. Unfortunately, it was later learned that the stability that made PCBs safe from a fire protection standpoint also caused serious pollution problems—that is, PCBs are poisons that do not break down. PCB and PCB-contaminated transformers now must be retrofitted or replaced. PCBs also are found in capacitors, large circuit breakers (usually over 1000 volts), and isolating switches.

Structural steel members of buildings or process structures often are fireproofed to withstand the heat of possible fires. The materials used in fireproofing formulations can be hazardous to the environment. Asbestos is a primary example of such a material. Application of spray-on fireproofing can result in overspray. After application, any fireproofing can crumble when fire protection hose streams are applied. Therefore, fireproofing materials must be reviewed for their contamination potential.

Fire-retardant chemicals are used to reduce the flame-spread of plastics, wood, and other materials. When a treated product is used outside, the fire-retardant chemi-

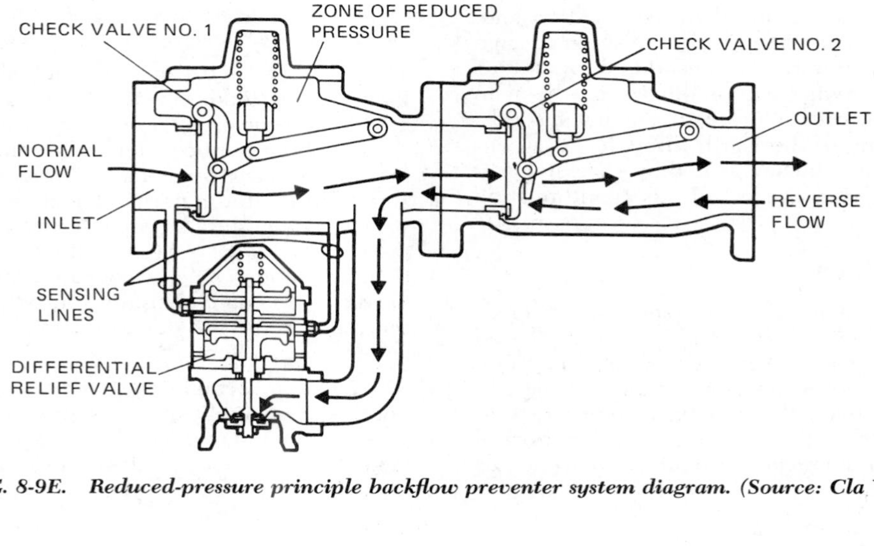

FIG. 8-9E. Reduced-pressure principle backflow preventer system diagram. (Source: Cla Val)

cals can leach due to harsh weather and get into the soil. Both inside and out, these chemicals escape into the air. Like all chemicals, the fire retardants must be reviewed for their potential to contaminate the environment, both before their use and after they have become part of the finished product.

To keep the bottom of a steel suction tank from rusting, a specified thickness of the sand under the tank is saturated with No. 2 fuel oil. This practice, required by NFPA 22, *Water Tanks for Private Fire Protection*, must now be reviewed and environmentally acceptable alternatives must be developed.

CONCLUSIONS

Recently, the PCB, landfill, ozone, and oil spill problems have focused more attention on the environment. So, too, have incidents of groundwater contamination by fire protection discharge. Many new laws have been passed to protect and preserve the environment, and there are more to come. Every fire protection engineer must be aware of these laws and must apply them properly when designing and installing fire protection systems.

Among the fire protection engineer's present and future concerns are the following:

1. Backflow preventers may have to be installed. Sprinkler system hydraulics must then take backflow preventer friction loss into account. Testing and maintenance of backflow preventers will have to be added to fire protection equipment inspection programs. Where the preventers are not used, careful analysis of the potential for contamination will have to be made.
2. The use of halon systems must be reviewed very carefully. All other options for extinguishing agents and types of protective systems must be considered. Emergency operating procedures and disaster recovery plans must be developed and tested. A thorough business interruption analysis is necessary to develop emergency plans and to specify the appropriate protection.
3. Underground tanks must be designed and installed carefully. Proper tank bed preparation, tank anchoring, and backfilling are critical. Double-walled tanks with leak detection between the walls often are required. The quality of groundwater around the tank must be monitored. Aboveground tanks will be more common, and fire protection engineers will have to decide where to install such tanks on crowded sites and how to protect the tanks and their exposures.
4. For every fire protection system installed, consideration must be given to how the discharge from that fire protection system will be contained, handled, and disposed of. If fire protection discharge is found to have contaminants, the discharge must be handled as hazardous waste.
5. Any places on a site where rainwater collects, such as sumps, catch tanks, and dikes, will have to be monitored for the presence of contaminants, and, if any are found, this water must be treated as hazardous waste.
6. Increased storage of hazardous chemicals will be more common. Every environmentally hazardous substance used in manufacturing facilities will have to be recovered to comply with the new laws. Fire protection engineers will have to decide where to place that storage and how to protect it.

Fire protection engineers have begun to plan fire protection systems with concern for the environment, but there is still much to be done. The fire protection discipline must be coordinated with the civil, structural, mechanical, and electrical disciplines to ensure a total facility design that preserves the environment while allowing the most economical and effective fire protection possible. High cost and much effort will be involved, but this is necessary because an environment safe from fire and explosion is of little value if one cannot live in it in good health.

BIBLIOGRAPHY

References

Air quality:

ASME Research Committee on Industrial and Municipal Waste, "Rotary Kiln Incinerators: The Right Regime," *Mechanical Engineering*, Sept. 1989, pp. 78-81.

Gordon, V. R. and Holness, P. E , "Human Comfort and Indoor Air Quality," *Heating/Piping/Air Conditioning*, Feb. 1990, pp. 43-52.

McKee, B. A., "Yearning to Breath Free," *Nation's Business*, Feb. 1990, pp. 46-47.

Backflow prevention:

AWWA, "Recommended Practice for Backflow Prevention and Cross-Connection Control", *AWWA M14*, American Water Workes Association, Denver CO, 1980.

Backflow Protection for Fire Sprinkler Systems, National Fire Sprinkler Association, Inc., Patterson, NY, 1988.

"Protecting Drinking Water Systems from Backflow," *Consulting-Specifying Engineer*, Nov. 1989, p. 64."Recommended Practice for Backflow Prevention and Cross-Connection Control," *AWWA M14*, American Water Works Association, Denver, CO, 1980.

Fire retardants:

"Fire-Resistant Plywood--Hot Topic for Builders," *Engineering News Record,* Nov. 30, 1989, p. 17.

Fluorocarbons:

"An Inside Look at How CFCs Affect Your Life," *ASHRAE Journal*, Nov. 1989, p. 42.

Anderson, S. O., "Halons and the Stratospheric Ozone Issue," *Fire Journal*, Vol. 81, No. 3 (May/June 1987), p. 56.

Chines, S. A., "Halon, Ozone, and the Environment," *The Sentinel*, Third Quarter 1989, p. 3.

"Controlling Fire Protection Halon Emissions," *Fire Technology,* Feb. 1988, p. 70.

"Final Report of the Halon-Technical Options Committee of the United Nations Environmental Programme," *Montreal Protocol Assessment Technology Review*, Aug. 11, 1989. (Available from ICF Inc., 9300 Lee Highway, Room 1171, Fairfax, VA, 22031-1207.)

Gallup, J. G., P. E., "Ozone Fears Limit Halon Use," *Plant Engineering*, Sept. 6, 1990, pp. 92-93.

Grant, C. C., "Controlling Fire Protection Halon Emissions," *Fire Technology*, Feb. 1988, pp. 70-78.

Grant, C. C., "Fire Protection Halons and the Environment," *Fire Technology*, Feb. 1988, pp. 63-64.

Grant, C. C., "Halons and the Ozone Layer: An Overview," *Fire Journal*, Vol. 83, No. 5 (Sept./Oct. 1989), p. 59.

Grant, C. C., "Life Beyond Halon," *Fire Journal*, Vol. , No. 3 (May/June 1990), pp. 52-59.

Mauzerall, D. L., "Protecting the Ozone Layer: Phasing out Halon by 2000," *Fire Journal*, Vol. 84, No. 5 (Sept./Oct. 1990), pp. 22-31.

Nadel, B., "Ozone-Friendly Cooling," *Popular Science*, July 1990, pp. 57-59.

Stamm, R. H., "The CFC Problem: Bigger than You Think," *Heating/Piping/Air Conditioning*, April 1989, p. 51.

Stoecker, W. F., "Opportunities for Ammonia Refrigeration," *Heating/Piping/Air Conditioning*, Sept. 1989, pp. 93-108.

Stouppe, D. E., "Taxes Help the Ozone Layer," *The Locomotive*, Vol. 67, No. 1 (Spring 1990), pp. 11-13.

Willey, A. E., "Conference on Halons and the Environment Held in Switzerland," *Fire Journal*, Vol. 82, No. 6 (Nov./Dec. 1988), p. 47.

Zurer, P., "Fate of CFC Alternatives Remains Up in the Air," *C&EN*, July 16, 1990, pp. 5-6.

PCBs:

McPartland, B. J., "PCBs...Time is Running Out," *Electrical Construction and Maintenance*, Sept. 1988, p. 62.

"PCBs and PCB-Containing Equipment—Disposal and Treatment Options," *Environmental Contractor Magazine*, Nov. 1989, p. 73.

Spills and fire protection discharge:

Constantine, P., "Lining up Against Oil," *Civil Engineering*, Jan. 1990, p. 70.

"Foam-Water Sprinkler Protection for Flammable Liquids," *Plant Operations Progress*, Oct. 1989, p. 218.

"Guidelines for Safe Handling and Storage of Calcium Hypochlorite and Chlorinated Isocyanurate Pool Chemicals," Monsanto-Olin-PPG (St. Louis, MO; Cheshire, CT; Pittsburgh, PA), 1989.

Isner, M. S., "$49 Million Loss in Sherwin-Williams Warehouse Fire," *Fire Journal*, Vol. 83, No. 2 (Mar./Apr. 1989), p. 65.

Isner, M. S., *Flammable Liquids Warehouse Fire, Dayton, Ohio, May 27, 1987*, Investigation Report, National Fire Protection Association, Quincy, MA, 1987.

PVI Industries, "HVAC Technology Speeds Alaskan Oil Cleanup," *Engineered Systems*, Jan./Feb. 1990, pp. 26-32.

Underground tanks:

Donovan, B. C., and O'Connor, P., "Underground Storage Tank Update," *Plant Engineering*, June 22, 1989, p. 60.

EPA—LUST, *Locating Underground Storage Tanks*, U.S. Environmental Protection Agency, Office of Underground Storage Tanks, Washington, DC, 1985. (Video.)

Gellop, J. G., "Ozone Fears Limit Halon Use," *Plant Engineering*, Sept. 6, 1990, pp. 92-93.

"Government Regs Froce Loss Prevention Changes," *Sentinel*, Vol. 47, No. 4, pp. 3-7.

Gross, R. A., "Preventing Contamination of the Earth," *The Sentinel*, Third Quarter 1989, p. 8.

Hazardous Waste: A Guide to RCRA Requirements, National Fire Protection Association, Quincy, MA, 1986.

Hazardous Waste: From Cradle to Grave, (Video, 40 min.), Distributed by National Fire Protection Association, Quincy MA, 1986.

Hazardous Waste: Small Quantities, Big Challenges, (Video, 27 min.), Distributed by National Fire Protection Association, Quincy, MA, 1985.

Henry, M. F., "Update on the Underground Leakage Problem," *Fire Journal*, Vol. 80, No. 1 (Jan. 1986), pp. 26-27 and 86.

Smalley, J. C., "Underground Storage Tanks: Rest in Peace," *Fire Command*, Mar. 1986, pp. 40-42.

Underground Storage Tanks: A Guide to Installation, National Fire Protection Association, Quincy, MA, 1988.

Underground Storage Tanks: A Question of When, (Video, 37 min.), Distributed by National Fire Protection Association, Quincy, MA, 1988.

Underground Storage Tanks: Close to Home, (Video, 9 min.), Distributed by National Fire Protection Association, Quincy, MA, 1988.

Underground Storage Tanks: In Your Own Backyard, (Video, 26 min.), Distributed by National Fire Protection Association, Quincy, MA, 1988.

Underground Storage Tanks: Rest in Peace, (Video, 30 min.), Distributed by National Fire Protection Association, Quincy, MA, 1986.

NFPA Codes, Standards, and Recommended Practices

Reference to the following NFPA codes, standards, and recommended practices will provide further information on environmental issues in fire protection discussed in this chapter. (See the latest *NFPA Catalog* for availability of current editions of the following documents.)

NFPA 11, *Low-Expansion Foam and Combined Agent Systems.*

NFPA 11A, *Medium- and High-Expansion Foam Systems.*

NFPA 12, *Carbon Dioxide Extinguishing Systems.*

NFPA 12A, *Halon 1301 Fire Extinguishing Systems.*

NFPA 13, *Installation of Sprinkler Systems.*

NFPA 15, *Water Spray Fixed Systems for Fire Protection.*

NFPA 16, *Deluge Foam-Water Sprinkler and Spray Systems.*

NFPA 17, *Dry Chemical Extinguishing Systems.*

NFPA 17A, *Wet Chemical Extinguishing Systems.*

NFPA 20, *Installation of Centrifugal Fire Pumps.*

NFPA 22, *Water Tanks for Private Fire Protection.*

NFPA 24, *Installation of Private Fire Service Mains.*

NFPA 30, *Flammable and Combustible Liquids Code.*

NFPA 33, *Spray Application Using Flammable and Combustible Materials.*

NFPA 34, *Dipping and Coating Processes Using Flammable or Combustible Liquids.*

NFPA 43A, *Storage of Liquid and Solid Oxidizing Materials.*

NFPA 43B, *Storage of Organic Peroxide Formulations.*

NFPA 43C, *Storage of Gaseous Oxidizing Materials.*

NFPA 43D, *Storage of Pesticides in Portable Containers.*

NFPA 45, *Fire Protection for Laboratories Using Chemicals.*

NFPA 54, *National Fuel Gas Code.*

NFPA 58, *Storage and Handling of Liquefied Petroleum Gases.*

NFPA 75, *Protection of Electronic Computer/Data Processing Equipment.*

NFPA 231, *General Storage.*

NFPA 231C, *Rack Storage of Materials.*

NFPA 231D, *Storage of Rubber Tires.*

NFPA 231E, *Storage of Baled Cotton.*

NFPA 231F, *Storage of Roll Paper.*

NFPA 232, *Protection of Records.*

NFPA 329, *Underground Leakage of Flammable and Combustible Liquids.*

NFPA 471, *Responding to Hazardous Materials Incidents.*

NFPA 703, *Fire-Retardant Impregnated Wood and Fire-Retardant Coatings for Building Materials.*

NFPA 850, *Fire Protection for Fossil-Fueled Steam Electric Generating Plants.*

ASSESSING LIFE SAFETY IN BUILDINGS

Revised by John M. Watts, Jr.

Assessment of life safety is the process of estimating the quality of security against fire and its effects. There is no well-defined method of assessing life safety from fire in buildings. Life safety is a concept, and no formula can identify or guarantee that a building is safe from fire. First of all, assessment requires an understanding of the fundamentals of the life safety concept. Then an evaluation can be made of the parameters that create hazards to life and those that tend to offset or control a portion of the life hazard. A wide variety of tools has been devised to relate these parameters so as to assess life safety in buildings.

Every general type of firesafety practice and fire protection strategy discussed in this handbook may be applicable to life safety in buildings. Specific additional information that can be helpful in a life safety assessment can be found in Section 1, Chapter 1, "America's Fire Problem and Fire Protection"; Section 1, Chapter 2, "Fundamentals of Firesafe Building Design"; Section 1, Chapter 3, "Systems Concepts for Building Firesafety"; Section 3, Chapter 1, "Combustion Products and Their Effects on Life Safety"; Section 7, Chapter 1, "Human Behavior and Fire"; Section 7, Chapter 2, "Concepts of Egress Design"; and Section 10, "Information and Analysis for Fire Protection."

LIFE SAFETY CONCEPTS

Concern for life safety implies avoiding exposure to harmful levels of products of combustion. This goal is usually achieved by controlling the fire process or by separating endangered individuals from the harmful effects of fire by time, distance, or shielding. Thus, life safety is accomplished if endangered individuals can move away from potential danger or if harmful effects of fire can be delayed indefinitely from reaching people in the building.

Details of the fire's development, along with characteristics of exposed occupants, determine the magnitude of the hazard. In addition, specific safety measures may be employed to reduce the hazard. Understanding the interrelationships of these components is the first step in assessing life safety from fire in buildings.

The Importance of Time

As a fire develops over time, smoke and heat buildup to create an environment that is hazardous to life. The rate at which the environment will deteriorate is difficult to predict, since a great many variables are involved. Figure 8-10A is a generalization of the way life hazard increases over time. At ignition (lower left corner), the environment is normal. Most fires develop slowly, so the initial hazard is small. Eventually, fire intensity will increase more rapidly, building up the level of dangerous products of combustion.

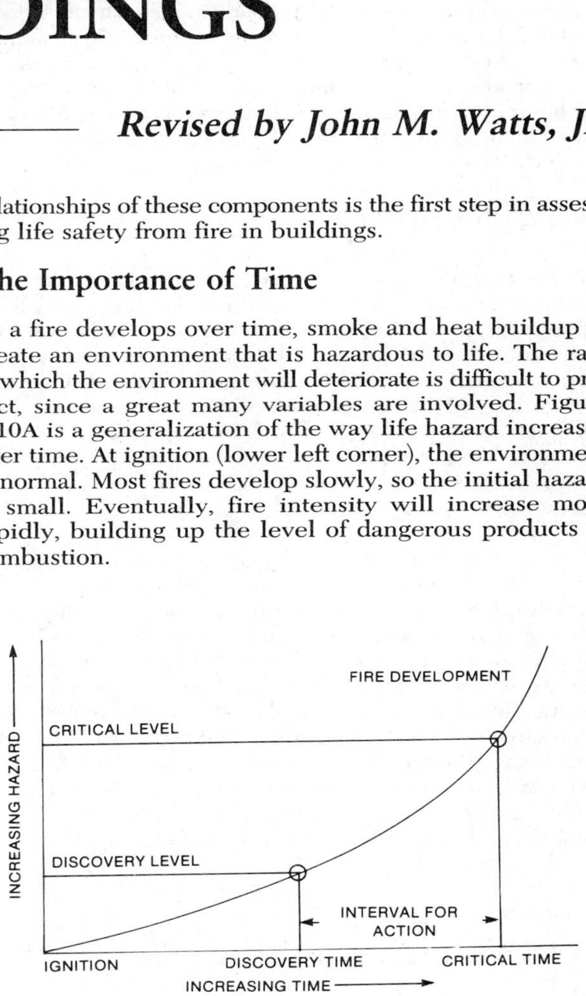

FIG. 8-10A. Representative rate of deterioration of the environment as a fire progresses.

At some level of accumulation of the products of combustion, the fire will be discovered by automatic fire detectors or by personal detection, i.e., smell or sight. The level of hazard at which discovery occurs corresponds, in Figure 8-10A, to a specific time in the course of the fire, the discovery time. The onset of lethal or incapacitating

John M. Watts, Ph.D., is Director of the Fire Safety Institute, a not-for-profit information, research, and educational corporation, located in Middlebury, VT. He also serves as editor of NFPA's quarterly technical journal, *Fire Technology*.

conditions (critical time) typically occurs later, either a short time later or after a period sufficient to permit meaningful actions.

Fire Hazard

The critical time will depend on the interaction of three sets of conditions: elevated environmental temperatures, toxic conditions resulting from pyrolysis or combustion products, and pre-existing or current psycho-physiological attributes of the occupants. Elevated temperatures can cause burns or heat stress ranging from trivial to lethal. Specific chemical pyrolysis or combustion products, decreased oxygen concentration, or particulate smoke can cause toxic effects. The clinical consequences of these physical conditions also will reflect the psycho-physiological conditions of the occupants. For example, pre-existing heart disease has been established as a contributory factor in fire deaths. Assessment of the variable interactions of these three sets of conditions is, obviously, extremely complicated.

Interval for Action

The interval between discovery and criticality is the time available to undertake action to prevent occupants from being exposed to the critical hazard level. This action may take various forms, such as activation of automatic equipment, evacuation of occupants, or both. From examination of Figure 8-10A, lowering the level where discovery occurs will increase the interval of time available for action. On the other hand occupants with greater susceptibility and, hence, a lower personal critical level, will have less time to react.

Fire growth and hazard do not always develop at the same rate. If conditions are insufficient to sustain a fast-spreading fire, the rate of deterioration of the environment is reduced, resulting in a decreased slope of the fire development curve. For example, curve B in Figure 8-10B represents a slower-developing fire than curve A, with a resultant increase in the interval of time available for action. Alternatively, curve C might represent the effect of an automatic extinguishing system used alone or in combination with a smoke control system. Activated after fire detection, the system maintains the atmosphere below the critical level for an indefinite period of time.

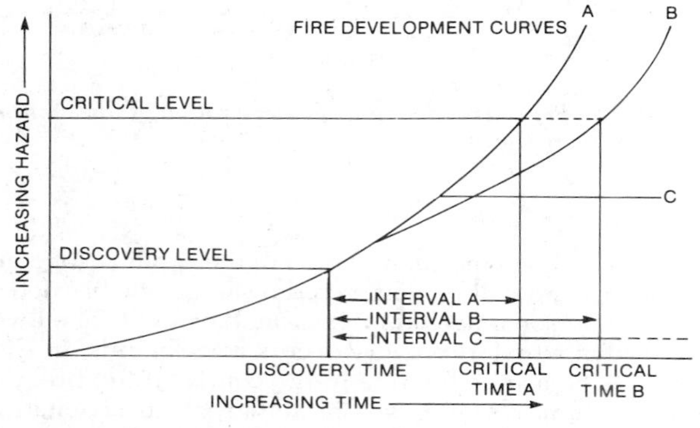

FIG. 8-10B. Difference in deterioration rates between a faster-developing and a slower-developing fire.

CHARACTERISTICS OF OCCUPANTS

The most difficult component of life safety to evaluate is the population at risk—that is, the occupants of the building. This difficulty is due to wide variations among building occupants. It is necessary to assess their susceptibility to fire and fire products and their ability to undertake and follow through with procedures necessary for their safety, or their anticipated response to a fire. Indications of these qualities may be found in physical and mental characteristics of the occupants, individually and as a group. Important population parameters are age, mobility, awareness, knowledge, density, and discipline.

Age

Age is the most easily identifiable characteristic of an exposed occupant, and it may directly affect other important characteristics, such as mobility, awareness, knowledge, and discipline. Variation of life risk with age is indicated by statistics that show that the very young and the very old suffer higher fatality rates from fire.

Mobility

Mobility is, for most people, a function of age; the very young and very old are less mobile. However, there are many other classes of immobile persons or of those with limited mobility. Disabled persons are present in more and more locations as accessibility to public facilities increases. Thus, it is necessary to consider the limitations of people with handicaps in assessment of the life risk. In occupancies such as hospitals, many people are temporarily incapacitated and can be relocated only with assistance. In still other occupancies, such as psychiatric institutions or prisons, individuals of average agility may be restrained or incarcerated. Therefore, lack of mobility is not necessarily tied to age or physical capability.

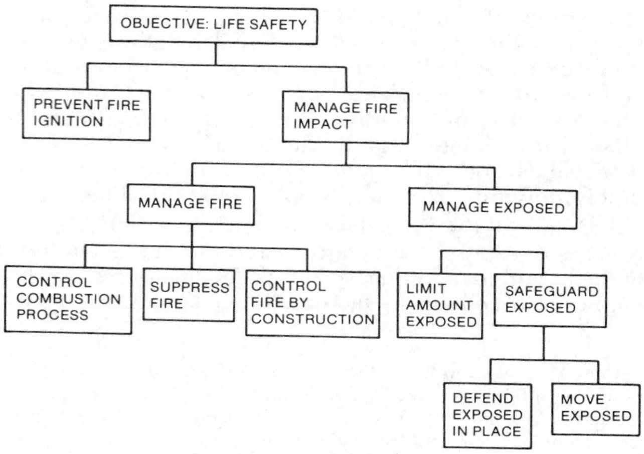

FIG. 8-10C. Simplified portion of the firesafety concepts tree.

Awareness

Awareness is another characteristic that may be affected by age, as well as by other conditions. A major factor is whether occupants are awake and alert, as they are in offices, or asleep, as they may be in residential occupancies. In addition, limited awareness may be found among those persons to whom drugs have been administered. The influence of alcohol and narcotics is a contributing factor in a significant number of fire deaths.[1,2] Most institutional occupancies contain individuals with varying degrees of awareness and a range of decision-making capabilities.

Knowledge

Knowledge is perhaps a limited term for the comprehensive concept of self-preservation, which includes such factors as instinct. Some of these characteristics are discernible, if not measurable. Training and drills may increase the level of the occupants' self-preservation knowledge. This can be extended to include societal self-preservation, whereby certain individuals are trained, or react spontaneously, to assist others. A less direct aspect of knowledge involves occupants' familiarity with the premises. Regular occupants of a building are likely to know the exits better than transient visitors.

Density

Population density, or the number of persons in a given area, is important to the magnitude of risk and to the safe relocation of occupants. The greater the number of people in a given area, the greater the potential loss of life. Studies have shown the relationship of occupant density to speed of movement.[3,4] Phenomena such as formation of arches of people, which obstruct passage through a doorway, are dependent upon occupant density.

Discipline

Like density, discipline is characteristic of occupants as a group more than as individuals. Controllability is evidenced in occupancies such as schools and certain industries. In general, people regularly exposed to disciplinary control and training are apt to respond to authority in a fire with less likelihood of endangering behavior.

LIFE SAFETY STRATEGIES

Ideally, building design considers the risk factors associated with occupants and fire, and it includes safety features to mitigate the risks. The discussion in this chapter is intended as a synthesis of the various safety measures that may be applied to reduce the danger of fire to occupants. Major categories of safety strategies have been identified by NFPA 550, *Firesafety Concepts Tree*, as "prevent fire," "manage fire," and "manage exposed" (occupants). A simplified portion of the firesafety concepts tree showing the relationships of these strategies is presented as Figure 8-10C.

Fire Prevention

No harm can come from fire if no fire takes place. Fire prevention, therefore, has the potential to eliminate the need for other firesafety measures. However, no fire prevention strategy is ever totally effective, so it is not prudent to rely on fire prevention alone.

Fire prevention considerations relate to heat energy sources, fuels, and the mechanisms by which they are brought together. For example, major potential ignition energy sources, such as electrical power, can be controlled largely through regulation, such as by following the requirements of NFPA 70, *National Electrical Code®*. In addition, some fuels, such as flammable liquids and interior finish, also may be addressed by codes and standards. However, not all energy sources nor all fuels can be regulated. This is also true of people, the primary casual factor of ignition.

Assessment of the probability of fire occurrence involves analysis of ignition potential, especially in relation to the activities of building occupants, and of factors that will decrease the likelihood of ignition.

Fire Management

Since it is impossible to avoid all ignitions, managing fires that occur also is important. The strategies of fire management may be seen as reducing the slope of the fire development curves portrayed in Figures 8-10A and 8-10B. These approaches strive to control the rate of production of smoke and heat through altering fuel and/or the environment, control the combustion process by manual or automatic suppression, and control the products of combustion through venting and/or containment.

Objectives of the "manage fire" strategy are to reduce risks associated with fire growth and to reduce fire and smoke spread. Together, these reductions diminish the impact of a fire on building occupants.

Occupant Management

This life safety strategy is the most complex, dealing with the risk factors of both fire and people. Occupant management involves undertaking emergency action appropriate to the expected fire development and to characteristics of the occupants.

To initiate occupant management action, there first must be detection and alerting activities. These functions may be performed by automatic equipment. Actions for managing exposed persons involve evacuation, refuge, or rescue. Evacuation is the most common approach where occupants are alert and mobile. In other cases, areas of refuge from fire and smoke within a building are employed, along with movement assisted by emergency personnel.

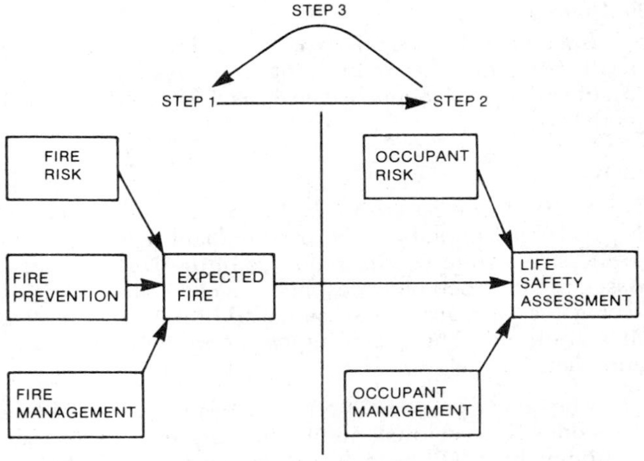

FIG. 8-10D. General approach to assessing life safety in buildings.

RISK PARAMETERS	RISK FACTOR VALUES					
1. PATIENT MOBILITY (M)	MOBILITY STATUS	MOBILE	LIMITED MOBILITY	NOT MOBILE	NOT MOVABLE	
	RISK FACTOR	1.0	1.6	3.2	4.5	
2. PATIENT DENSITY (D)	PATIENT	1-5	6-10	11-30	>30	
	RISK FACTOR	1.0	1.2	1.5	2.0	
3. ZONE LOCATION (L)	FLOOR	1ST	2ND OR 3RD	4TH TO 6TH	7TH AND ABOVE	BASEMENTS
	RISK FACTOR	1.1	1.2	1.4	1.6	1.6
4. RATIO OF PATIENTS TO ATTENDANTS (T)	PATIENTS / ATTENDANT	1-2 / 1	3-5 / 1	6-10 / 1	>10 / 1	ONE OR MORE / NONE†
	RISK FACTOR	1.0	1.1	1.2	1.5	4.0
5. PATIENT AVERAGE AGE (A)	AGE	UNDER 65 YEARS AND OVER 1 YEAR	65 YEARS & OVER 1 YEAR & YOUNGER			
	RISK FACTOR	1.0	1.2			

†RISK FACTOR OF 4.0 IS CHARGED TO ANY ZONE THAT HOUSES PATIENTS WITHOUT ANY STAFF IN IMMEDIATE ATTENDANCE

(Dated 1/88, 1988 *Life Safety Code*)

FIG. 8-10E. Occupancy risk parameter factors for firesafety evaluation of health care occupancies.

Emergency egress systems should be assessed in terms of their adequacy and reliability. Adequacy refers to structural components that determine the capacity to evacuate part or all of a building within a safe time span. Reliability considers how efficiently the egress capacity will be used. Factors of reliability include alerting messages and instructions, signage and emergency lighting, and protection of egress routes from fire, smoke, and toxic gases.

LIFE SAFETY ASSESSMENT TOOLS

The components of a generalized approach to assessment of life safety from fire in buildings are shown in Figure 8-10D. The first step in this approach is analysis of the fire hazard and of the safety measures corresponding to fire prevention and fire management. This analysis should yield a concept of the expected fire in the building. The second step is consideration of this expected fire in conjunction with occupant risk factors and management of exposed occupants. The life safety assessment is then evaluated; if found lacking, step three is a return to the beginning to consider enhanced firesafety strategies. Thus, assessing life safety in buildings is an iterative process of matching risk and safety factors.

Specific techniques that can be used in an assessment of life safety from fire in buildings include codes, scenarios, life safety evaluation, exit analysis, FSES and computer models.

Codes

NFPA 101,® *Life Safety Code,*® in particular, and building codes in general are the predominant overall guides to life safety from fire in buildings in the United States. Assessments based on codes focus on code compliance as surrogates for a direct assessment of life safety from fire in a building. There are important limitations to this approach:

1. The stated purpose of NFPA 101 and most building codes is to establish minimum requirements for public welfare. Other tools are required where a higher degree of life safety is desired for altruistic or liability reasons.
2. While NFPA 101 and the building codes contain a provision on equivalency concepts to foster a performance approach to fire protection, practical means of establishing equivalent safety to life are not usually specified in the codes.
3. In situations where several buildings are under one ownership or authority, it may be of interest to identify the "worst" life safety risks. Some form of numeric rating schedule or other risk-ranking technique is necessary in this case.
4. NFPA 101 identifies circumstances under which a life safety evaluation is required.

Scenarios

Fire scenarios are particularly useful in assessing life safety in buildings. Construction of a fire scenario begins with identification of a particular situation that corresponds to the behavior of fire and occupants within a building. Historical fire experience is a valuable tool in developing scenarios, but its suitability will be affected by the structure of available data bases. Fire death scenarios devised to help guide national fire research strategy are described by Clarke and Ottoson.[5]

By considering various fire scenarios, it often is possible to identify and evaluate the potential for life loss. Although they are subjective assessment tools, scenarios can be based on the collective judgment of several experts. Plausible fire scenarios are an input to most of the other approaches to life safety assessment described below.

Life Safety Evaluation

NFPA 101, *Life Safety Code*, defines a life safety evaluation as a written review dealing with the adequacy of life safety features relative to fire and other perils. The review should be done by a qualified person or persons acceptable to the authority having jurisdiction. The evaluation will include documentation confirming that products of combustion produced by all probable scenarios will not endanger occupants using the means of egress in the facility. Moreover, it should establish that means of egress, together with facility management, will be adequate to cope with scenarios where an egress route is blocked for some reason.

In addition to making realistic assumptions about the capabilities of persons in the facility—for example, an assembled crowd including many disabled persons and/or persons unfamiliar with the building—the life safety evaluation should include a factor of safety of at least 2.0 in all calculations relating hazard development time and required egress time. This takes into account the possibility that half of the egress routes may not be usable in an emergency.

Topics to be considered in preparing a life safety evaluation include, but are not limited to, human behavior, exit system, building construction, contents and finishes, fire detection, emergency notification, smoke management, fire suppression systems, and emergency preparedness management.

Exit Analysis

Exit analysis is an important component of a life safety evaluation, as well as a tool for other forms of life safety assessment. The analysis uses anthropometric and biokinetic data on occupants, together with hydraulic flow analogies or other models, to calculate the time required to evacuate

PARAMETERS	PARAMETERS VALUES						
1. CONSTRUCTION	COMBUSTIBLE TYPES III, IV AND V				NON-COMBUSTIBLE TYPES I AND II		
FLOOR OF ZONE	000 (U)	111	200 (U)	211 + 2HH	000 (U)	111	222, 332, 443
FIRST	−2	0	−2	0	0	2	2
SECOND	−7	−2	−4	−2	−2	2	4
THIRD	−9	−7	−9	−7	−7	2	4
4TH & ABOVE	−13	−7	−13	−7	−9	−7	4
2. INTERIOR FINISH (Corridors & Exits)	CLASS C	CLASS B	CLASS A				
	−5 (0)[f]	0(3)[f]	3				
3. INTERIOR FINISH (Rooms)	CLASS C	CLASS B	CLASS A				
	−3(1)[f]	1(3)[f]	3				
4. CORRIDOR PARTITIONS/WALLS	NONE OR INCOMPLETE	<1/3 HR.	≥1/3<1.0 HR.	≥1.0 HR.			
	−10 (0)[a]	0	1 (0)[a]	2 (0)[a]			
5. DOORS TO CORRIDOR	NO DOOR	<20 MIN. FPR	≥20 MIN. FPR	≥20 MIN. FPR & AUTO CLOS.			
	−10	0	1 (0)[d]	2 (0)[d]			
6. ZONE DIMENSIONS	DEAD END			NO DEAD ENDS >30' & ZONE LENGTH IS:			
	> 100'	50'–100'	30'–50'	>150'	100'–150'	<100'	
	−6 (0)[b]	−4 (0)[b]	−2 (0)[b]	−2	0	1	
7. VERTICAL OPENINGS	OPEN 4 OR MORE FLOORS	OPEN 2 OR 3 FLOORS	ENCLOSED WITH INDICATED FIRE RESIST. <1 HR.	≥1 HR.<2 HR.	≥2 HR.		
	−14	−10	0	2 (0)[e]	3 (0)[e]		
8. HAZARDOUS AREAS	DOUBLE DEFICIENCY IN ZONE	DOUBLE DEFICIENCY OUTSIDE ZONE	SINGLE DEFICIENCY IN ZONE	SINGLE DEFICIENCY IN ADJACENT ZONE	NO DEFICIENCIES		
	−11	−5	−6	−2	0		
9. SMOKE CONTROL	NO CONTROL	SMOKE BARRIER SERVES ZONE	MECH. ASSISTED SYSTEMS BY ZONE				
	−5 (0)[c]	0	3				
10. EMERGENCY MOVEMENT ROUTES	<2 ROUTES	MULTIPLE ROUTES DEFICIENT	W/O HORIZONTAL EXIT(S)	HORIZONTAL EXIT(S)	DIRECT EXIT(S)		
	−8	−2	0	1	5		
11. MANUAL FIRE ALARM	NO MANUAL FIRE ALARM		MANUAL FIRE ALARM W/O F.D. CONN.	W/F.D. CONN.			
	−4		1	2			
12. SMOKE DETECTION & ALARM	NONE	CORRIDOR ONLY	ROOMS ONLY	CORRIDOR & HABIT. SPACE	TOTAL SPACE IN ZONE		
	0	2	3	4	5		
13. AUTOMATIC SPRINKLERS	NONE	CORRIDOR & HABIT. SPACE	ENTIRE BUILDING				
	0	8	10				

NOTE: [a]Use (0) when item 5 is −10.
[b]Use (0) when item 10 is −8.
[c]Use (0) on floor with less than 31 patients (existing buildings only).
[d]Use (0) when item 4 is −10.
[e]Use (0) when item 1 is based on first floor zone or on an unprotected type of construction (columns marked "U").
[f]Use (0) if the area of Class B or C interior finish in the corridor and exit or room is protected by automatic sprinklers and item 13 is 0

Conversion: ft X 3048 = m.

(Dated 1/88, 1988 *Life Safety Code*)

FIG. 8-10F. Safety parameter values for firesafety evaluation of health care occupancies.

a building or space. The result can be compared to a calculated time for deterioration of the environment. Some basic engineering approaches to exit analysis have been developed and are presented elsewhere.[4,6,7,8] Computer optimization and simulation techniques also have been applied to exit analysis.[9] It is critical that results of exit analysis calculations, whether manual or computer, be examined with respect to the vagaries in human behavior which accompany an emergency. These concepts are discussed by Bryan in this handbook and elsewhere.[10]

FSES

Most of NFPA 101M, *Alternative Approaches to Life Safety*, deals with firesafety evaluation systems (FSES). The FSES is a rating schedule approach to determining equivalencies to NFPA 101, *Life Safety Code*, for certain occupancies. The technique was developed at the Center for Fire Research, National Bureau of Standards (now the Building and Fire Research Laboratory, National Institute of Standards and Technology) in cooperation with the U.S.

Department of Health and Human Services in the late 1970s.[11,12] The FSES originally was created to provide a uniform method of evaluating health care facilities and to identify firesafety measures that would provide a level of firesafety equivalent to NFPA 101.

Occupant Risk: Unlike NFPA 101, *Life Safety Code*, the FSES begins with a determination of relative risk derived from occupant characteristics. Variations of selected characteristics are assigned relative weights, as shown in Figure 8-10E, for health care occupancies. The values in this figure were determined from the experienced judgment of a group of fire professionals. Occupancy risk is then calculated as the product of the risk factor values appropriate for the particular occupancy.

Safety parameters: The calculated risk must be offset by safety features. Thirteen possible safety parameters are considered. These parameters and their respective ranges of values for health care occupancies are shown in Figure 8-10F. The values in the table are based on opinions of the same panel of experts.

Safety strategies: An important concept of the FSES is redundancy through the simultaneous use of alternative safety strategies. Fire safety strategies considered in the FSES are containment, extinguishment, and people movement. Figure 8-10G indicates the expert panel's opinion of which safety parameters apply to each strategy. Values for a particular occupancy are selected from Figure 8-10F and entered in the appropriate places on Figure 8-10G. They are then added up for each column. The resulting sums are compared to predetermined minimum values and to the occupancy risk previously calculated.

Computer Models

SAFETY PARAMETERS	CONTAINMENT SAFETY (S_1)	EXTINGUISHMENT SAFETY (S_2)	PEOPLE MOVEMENT SAFETY (S_3)	GENERAL SAFETY (S_G)
1. CONSTRUCTION				
2. INTERIOR FINISH (Corr. & Exit)				
3. INTERIOR FINISH (Rooms)				
4. CORRIDOR PARTITIONS/WALLS				
5. DOORS TO CORRIDOR				
6. ZONE DIMENSIONS				
7. VERTICAL OPENINGS				
8. HAZARDOUS AREAS				
9. SMOKE CONTROL				
10. EMERGENCY MOVEMENT ROUTES				
11. MANUAL FIRE ALARM				
12. SMOKE DETECTION & ALARM				
13. AUTOMATIC SPRINKLERS			÷ 2 =	
TOTAL VALUE	S_1 =	S_2 =	S_3 =	S_G =

(Dated 1 88. 1988 *Life Safety Code*)

FIG. 8-10G. Individual safety evaluations for firesafety evaluation of health care occupancies.

As described elsewhere in this handbook, computer models are developing rapidly, concurrent with the available technical knowledge and hardware. Applications in life safety assessment include models of fire development in enclosures, such as ASET-B,[13] and models of the evacuation process.[9] There are also primitive simulation models that combine these two concepts.[14,15] Computer modeling for life safety assessment in buildings will probably improve in the near future.

BIBLIOGRAPHY

References Cited

1. Halpin, B. M., *et al.*, "A Fire Fatality Study," *Fire Journal*, Vol. 69, No. 3 (May 1975).
2. Karter, M. J., Jr. and Miller, A. L., "Patterns of Fire Casualties in Home Fires by Age and Sex, 1983-1987," Fire Analysis and Research Division, National Fire Protection Association, Quincy, MA, Feb. 1990.
3. Peschl, I.A.S.Z., "Passage Capacity of Door Openings in Panic Situations," *Bouw*, Vol. 2, No. 9 (Jan. 1971).
4. Pauls, J., "Movement of People," Section 1, Chapter 15, *SFPE Handbook of Fire Protection Engineering*, Philip J. DiNenno, *ed.*, National Fire Protection Association, Quincy, MA, 1988, pp. 1-246 to 1-268.
5. Clarke, F. B., III and Ottoson, J., "Fire Death Scenarios and Firesafety Planning", *Fire Journal*, Vol. 70, No. 3 (May 1976).
6. Kendik, E., "Designing Escape Routes in Buildings," *Fire Technology*, Vol. 22, No. 4 (Nov. 1986), pp. 272-294.
7. Nelson, H. E., and MacLennan, H. A., "Emergency Movement," Section 2, Chapter 6, *SFPE Handbook of Fire Protection Engineering*, Philip J. DiNenno, *ed.*, National Fire Protection Association, Quincy, MA, 1988, pp. 2-106 to 2-115.
8. Pauls, J. L. and Fruin, J. J., *People Movement in Buildings and Public Places: Design, Management, and Safety for Individuals and Crowds*, Butterworths, Stoneham, MA, 1991.
9. Watts, J. M., Jr., "Computer Models for Evacuation Analysis," *Fire Safety Journal*, Vol. 12, 1987, pp. 237-245.
10. Bryan, J. L., "Behavioral Response to Fire and Smoke", Section 1, Chapter 16, *SFPE Handbook of Fire Protection Engineering*, Philip J. DiNenno, *ed.*, National Fire Protection Association, Quincy MA, 1988, pp. 1-269 to 1-285.
11. Benjamin, I. A., "A Firesafety Evaluation System for Health Care Facilities," *Fire Journal*, Vol. 73, No. 2 (Mar. 1979).
12. Nelson, H.F. and Shibe, A.J., "A System for Firesafety Evaluation of Health Care Facilities," *NBSIR 78-1555*, National Bureau of Standards, Washington, DC, Nov. 1978.
13. Walton, D., "ASET-B, A Room Fire Program for Personal Computers," *Fire Technology*, Vol. 21, No. 4 (Nov. 1985), pp. 293-309.
14. Fahy, R., "Building Fire Simulation Model", *Fire Journal*, Vol. 77, No. 4 (Jul. 1983), pp. 93-95, 102-105.
15. Peacock, R. D. and Bukowski, R. W., "A Prototype Methodology for Fire Hazard Analysis," *Fire Technology*, Vol. 26, No. 1 (Feb. 1990), pp. 15-40.

NFPA Codes, Standards, and Recommended Practices

Reference to the following NFPA codes, standards, and recommended practices will provide further information on assessing life safety in buildings discussed in this chapter. (See the latest *NFPA Catalog* for availability of current editions of the following documents.)

NFPA 70, *National Electrical Code.*®

NFPA *101,*® *Life Safety Code.*®

NFPA 101M, *Alternative Approaches to Life Safety.*

NFPA 550, *Firesafety Concepts Tree.*

Additional Reading

Berl, W. G., "Protecting the Public from Fires," *John Hopkins APL Technical Digest,* Vol. 8, No. 1, 1987, pp. 148-151.

Clarke, F. B. and Birky, M. M., "Fire Safety in Dwellings and Public Buildings," *Bulletin of the New York Academy of Medicine*, Vol. 57, No. 10 (Dec. 1981), pp. 1047-1060.

Committe on Fire Toxicology, *Fire and Smoke: Understanding the Hazards*, National Academy Press, Washington, DC, 1986.

Lathrop, J. K., *ed., Life Safety Code Handbook*, 4th ed., National Fire Protection Association, Quincy, MA, 1988.

Lerup, L., *et al., Learning from Fire: A Fire Protection Primer for Architects*, University of California, Berkeley, CA, 1977.

Lyons, J., *Fire*, Scientific American, NY, 1985.

Nelson, H. E., "Conceps for Life Safety Analysis," *Fire Safety Journal*, Vol. 12, No. 3, 1987, pp. 167-178.

Peters, G. A., "Why Only a Fool Relies on Safety Standards," *Hazard Prevention*, Vol. 14, No. 2 (Nov./Dec. 1977).

Rasbash, D. J., "The Definition and Evaluation of Fire Safety," *Fire Prevention Science and Technology*, No. 16 (Mar. 1977).

Shields, T.J. and Silcock, G.W.H. *Buildings and Fire*, Longman, Esses, UK, 1987.

Society of Fire Protection Engineers, "Quantitative Methods for Life Safety Analysis", *Proceedings* of Symposium, College Park, MD, March 5-7, 1986.

Takahashi, J. Tanaka, T., and Kose, S., "An Evacuation Model for Use in Fire Safety Design of Buildings", Fire Safety Science, *Proceedings* of the Second International Symposium, Hemisphere, NY, 1989, p. 551-560.

Watts, J. M., Jr., "Fire Risk Rating Schedules", *ASTM Symposium* on Fire Hazard and Fire Risk Assessment, San Antonio, TX, December 3, 1990.

ASSEMBLY OCCUPANCIES

Revised by John A. Sharry

Assembly occupancies generally can be defined as structures in which groups of people gather for purposes such as deliberation, worship, or entertainment. Examples of assembly occupancies are large meeting rooms, restaurants, nightclubs, dance halls, bars, cocktail lounges, auditoriums with fixed or loose chair seating, libraries, concert halls, theaters, cinemas, multi-purpose rooms, exhibition halls, convention centers, sports arenas, field houses, and passenger terminals for air or surface transportation.

Because this type of occupancy is concerned with the safety and hazards of large numbers of people gathered in one place, an established minimum number of occupants must be reached before one of the above examples constitutes an assembly occupancy. Although this minimum can vary, most building codes and NFPA 101®, *Life Safety Code*®, set it at 50. Occupancies with similar uses but occupant loads below 50 are classified as other occupancy categories, usually business.

OCCUPANCY CHARACTERISTICS

Inasmuch as a public assembly occupancy involves the safety of a large group of people, the density of the occupant population presents the major safety problem. No other occupancy experiences occupant loads of such density. It is not uncommon for occupant densities in public assembly occupancies to approach one person per 5 sq ft (0.46 m^2) or greater.

This density produces problems in the physical movement and behavior of the occupants, the capacity of the exits, the maintenance of adequate aisles of proper width, and the method of alerting occupants in case of emergency. Assembly occupancies are usually inhabited by persons who do not use the building frequently and, therefore, are not familiar with the location of exits, exit paths, or other safeguards that may be present. In addition, many assembly occupancies, such as theaters, concert halls, nightclubs, lounges, and some restaurants, are used in conditions of near-total darkness.

All these factors—high occupant density, unfamiliarity with the building, and darkness—are common to the many and varied forms of assembly occupancies. Provisions must be made to deal with all of these factors to avoid panic when an emergency occurs.

SPECIAL CONSIDERATIONS

Restaurants and Nightclubs

Both restaurants and nightclubs share common problems, the most prevalent of which is aisles that provide inadequate access to exits. There is a tendency in these assemblies to add tables in an effort to increase profits. While the resultant crowding is simply uncomfortable under normal conditions, it can be disastrous in an emergency.

Proper aisles must be maintained to facilitate exiting. Aisles should be wide enough to accommodate the movement of people, taking into consideration the position of chairs during normal use and during emergencies. Responsible restaurateurs have found that proper aisle widths actually improve profits by making patrons feel more comfortable and making table service easier and more efficient. Nightclubs, on the other hand, generally do not value ease and efficiency in table service because there is less need for service in nightclubs than in restaurants. To improve the profit of their admission fees, nightclubs tend to squeeze as many people into the building as possible, especially when dinner service is not offered. Certain techniques, such as using small, round tables rather than larger, square tables, help achieve maximum patron capacity.

In both restaurants and nightclubs, the decor can be elaborate and thematic. Unless it is properly designed, decor can obstruct or obscure exits, exit markings, emergency lighting, automatic suppression systems, and other safety features.

Methods of alerting patrons to an emergency and methods of notifying the fire department are common problems in these occupancies. Restaurants and nightclubs are reluctant to notify patrons of an emergency before the last possible minute because it destroys the "ambience" of the facility, may result in lost revenue from patrons who have

John A. Sharry is the fire chief at Lawrence Livermore National Laboratory in Livermore, CA.

not settled their bills, and purportedly, gives the establishment a bad reputation.

This reluctance results in delayed notification and shortens the available evacuation time in case of a real emergency. Restaurants and nightclubs are also reluctant to notify the fire department for the same reasons, which results in delayed fire department response.

Fixed Seating

Added to the common problems of adequacy of exits, exit marking, emergency illumination, and notification of patrons in an emergency are special problems related to seating. Occupancies that use fixed seating present the usual, as well as some unique, problems.

Fixed seating arrangements put a large number of people into a confined environment where there is a limited ability to move. People must move within a row before they can reach an aisle, and the aisle then limits their movement in reaching an exit. The design of the seating in these occupancies is critical to ensuring the rapid egress of all occupants in a fire.

Before 1988, fixed seating was broken into two types: "continental" and "normal." Normal seating involves a limited number of seats, usually a maximum of 14 or 15, between aisles; limited length of dead-end rows; and use of mid-aisles and cross-aisles to ensure rapid exiting. (See Figure 8-11A.) The spacing of the seats to provide adequate width between rows is important for ease of movement. In general, 12 in. (305 mm) of clear space for movement between rows is considered the minimum. (See Figure 8-11B.) The aisles must be wide enough to accommodate the influx of patrons as they leave their rows and enter the aisles. The proper aisle width must continue toward the exit. If cross aisles are used, they must be wide enough to accommodate the flow of people from tributary aisles and to permit movement to the exits. Finally, the exits must be sized properly to accommodate the flow of people from the cross aisles and their tributary aisles. Dead-end aisles should be limited in length or avoided altogether.

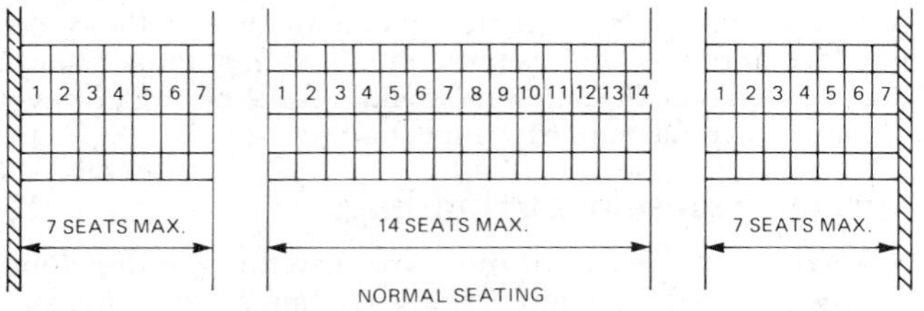

FIG. 8-11A. Arrangement of seats and aisles in an assembly occupancy with normal seating.

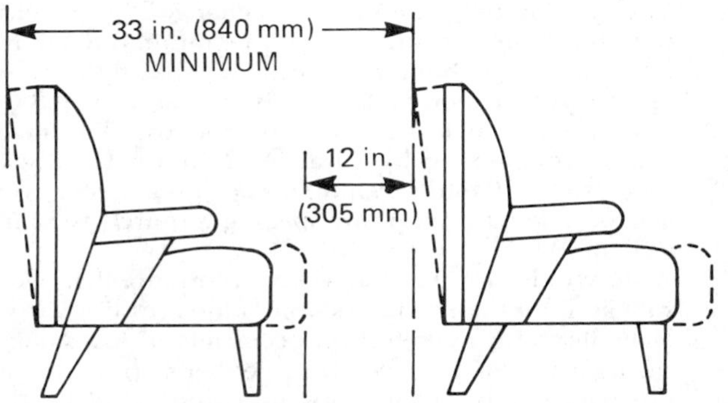

FIG. 8-11B. Correct measurement of minimum spacing between rows of seats without self-rising seats.

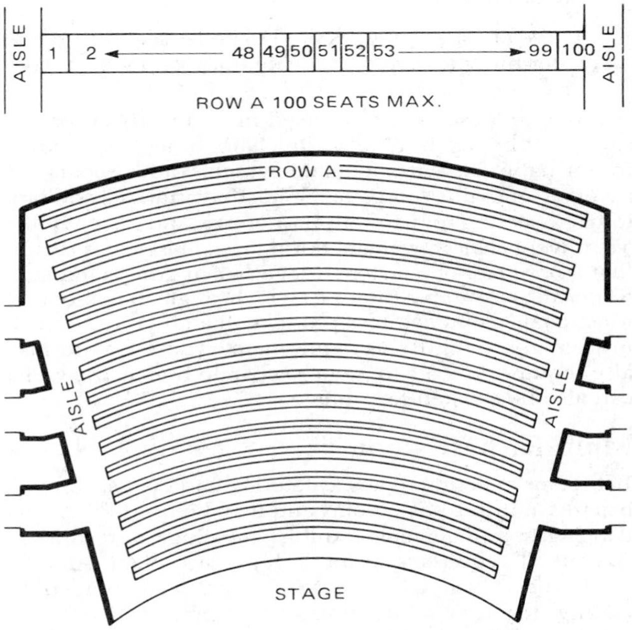

FIG. 8-11C. Arrangement of seats and aisles with continental seating. One hundred seats is the maximum number for one row. The frequency of the exits from side aisles is also depicted in the theater arrangement.

Continental seating is characterized by long rows of chairs discharging into side aisles which, in turn, discharge directly to the exits. Mid- and cross-aisles are not used. (See Figure 8-11C.) Although most codes limit rows to 100 seats each, they are usually functionally limited to fewer seats by the available sight lines. Because the flow of people is less complicated than it is in normal seating, and because row spacing is greater, the rows themselves function as mini-aisles. This results in efficient people movement and superior evacuation times compared with those for normal seating. Continental seating also has the advantage of greater patron comfort and more seats in the prime viewing areas, due to the increased row spacing and longer row length.

In 1988, NFPA 101, *Life Safety Code*, was the first model code to adopt new requirements for seating in new construction. These new requirements recognize the advantages of continental seating and apply those concepts to all seating. Rather than dividing seating into two categories, the 1988 *Life Safety Code* established one set of requirements for all seating. Briefly, these new requirements can be summarized as follows:

1. All seating arrangements are permitted to extend to 100 seats per row. The old limit on the number of seats between aisles and the limit on the number of seats being served by an aisle on one side only were eliminated.

2. The spacing between rows was changed by increasing the aisle spacing above the minimum 12 in. (305 mm). (See Figure 8-11B.) The spacing of rows served by aisles on both sides is increased by 0.3 in. (8 mm) for each seat over fourteen across. The spacing of rows served by an aisle on one side only is increased by 0.6 in. (15 mm) for each seat over seven across. The maximum row spacing required is 22 in. (560 mm).
3. Aisle widths are determined by a formula that takes into account the fire protection of the building, especially its ability to protect the occupants against smoke; the geometry of the aisle, that is, either steps or ramps; the riser height of the steps in a stepped aisle; the availability of handrails; the slope of the ramp in ramped aisles; and an assumed flow pattern of the occupants.
4. The requirements for cross-aisles and mid-aisles were eliminated.

These changes have resulted in better seating arrangements for life safety, audience site lines, and viewer comfort.

Where loose chairs are used in lieu of fixed seating, care must be taken to keep the chairs from being moved into a haphazard arrangement which could impair exit access. Generally, loose chairs must be arranged similarly to fixed seating to maintain proper row and aisle widths. To prevent chair movement during use, most codes require that loose chairs be fastened together in groups too large to permit easy repositioning, which might block egress. Most chair manufacturers produce chairs with interlocking features to fulfill this requirement. These features usually require no tools to join or separate the chairs, which can also be stacked for storage.

Multi-Purpose Rooms

Ballrooms, meeting rooms, cafeterias, and gymnasiums are usually multipurpose rooms and may be used for dining, dancing, sporting events, exhibits, meetings, or receptions. In general, requirements for each use are contained in the local codes. Overall, the key to occupant safety is adequate exiting, together with automatic suppression systems if exhibit hall fuel loading is expected.

Where large areas are subdivided by movable walls or partitions, each subdivision must provide proper exit accesses and exits, a factor frequently overlooked by those planning such facilities. Care must be taken to ensure that proper exiting is designed into the arrangement.

Exhibit Halls

Exhibit halls are large assembly areas that are really multipurpose in nature. Special diligence regarding control of display and chair arrangement must be exercised to ensure unimpeded egress and to maintain the proper travel distances to exits. It is recommended that trade shows or exhibitions be required to submit layouts for displays and seating in advance so that they may be approved before the use date.

Exhibit halls can have very large fire loads unless provisions are made for properly storing the packing materials needed to transport the displays and for the surplus quantities of literature. The importance of this cannot be overemphasized, since failure to remove this heavy fuel load to proper storage areas can result in large fires that spread rapidly. The McCormick Place fire of January 1967, in Chicago, IL, is an example of the fire potential of this occupancy.

Recent trends in exhibit booth design are toward larger and multi-level booths. Special attention must be paid to the travel distance to the aisle within an exhibit booth or display; it is recommended that this distance be limited to 50 ft (15 m). Multi-level exhibit booths present problems in both egress and fire protection. This type of booth, as well as large exhibit booths with ceilings, can shield the booth contents from the building sprinkler system. In those cases, consideration should be given to providing sprinkler protection for the booth itself. In all cases, booths should be constructed of noncombustible, limited combustible, or fire-retardant-treated materials. NFPA 101, *Life Safety Code*, contains special requirements for exhibit halls.

Because of the fuel load and the large number of occupants, moderate- and larger-size exhibit halls should be provided with an automatic fire suppression system.

Sports Arenas

Sports arenas and field houses usually have fixed seating for large numbers of spectators, as well as a large area. More than 10,000 people at one time is not uncommon in such occupancies. Here, occupant density presents the major problem to life safety from fire. Proper aisles and travel distances are difficult to maintain, unless care is taken in the planning stage. On the positive side, these occupancies usually involve very large open areas, permitting smoke to be diluted in the early stages of a fire, and smoke control measures can keep these facilities reasonably safe for egress. If they are used for exhibitions, the special considerations for exhibit halls must also be followed.

Passenger Terminals

Passenger terminals require special consideration for fire-safety because only general rules can be written for their regulation. Dense populations are localized, especially at departure and arrival gates. However, most terminals have large, open areas with significant fuel loads; this can lead to large losses if a fire is not extinguished in its incipient stage. As in most assembly occupancies, the occupants of passenger terminals are generally unfamiliar with the building, its exit routes, and its protection features. Proper marking of exits and exit routes and maintenance of proper travel distances are particularly important.

Special Amusement Buildings

Special amusement buildings are structures, either temporary, permanent, or mobile, that contain a conveying system or walking space to permit the viewing of a display for the purposes of amusement. These structures are of particular concern because the egress path is not readily apparent due to low lighting levels, visual or audio distractions, and intentionally confounded paths of travel. In addition, the amusement display usually involves a large amount of combustibles. The "Haunted Castle" fire at the Great Adventure Amusement Park in Jackson Township, NJ, on May 11, 1984, is an example of all of the above concerns. Eight teenagers, ranging in age from 15 to 19 years, died in that fire.

Special amusement buildings require unique protection provisions. Consideration should be given to automatic sprinkler protection, special controls that will increase lighting levels and turn off confusing or confounding sounds and visual displays when smoke is detected, the strategic placement of exit signs, and control of interior finish materials. NFPA 101, *Life Safety Code*, contains special provisions for special amusement buildings that involve all the above considerations.

OCCUPANCY HAZARDS

Cooking and Open Flames

Cooking is associated with the use of many assembly occupancies. The hazard of cooking in the traditional kitchen can be handled by automatic extinguishing systems and proper vapor removal, as outlined in NFPA 96, *Removal of Smoke and Grease-Laden Vapors from Commercial Cooking Equipment*. The widespread use of "display cooking" presents new problems in vapor removal and in protecting the cooking surfaces and humans in case of fire. However, display cooking on properly designed and fixed equipment can be made reasonably safe with fixed systems, proper aisles, and a trained staff.

The use of open-flame devices in tableside and flambé cooking should be carefully reviewed before it is permitted. Specially designed equipment and a properly trained staff are necessary to ensure safety.

Candles and other open flames require the same degree of awareness as tableside cooking. Several commercial devices are available that make open-flame lighting safe, even in the event of a tipover. Coordination between facility operators and the fire department can help maintain an acceptable level of safety.

Theatrical Stages

Most serious theater fires have begun in the stage area. The 1903 Iroquois Theater fire in Chicago, IL, is probably the most vivid example of a stage fire and its tragic consequences.

Traditional proscenium stages have scenery and lighting "flown" above the stage and scenery on the back and sides of the stage; shops along the back and sides of the stage; and storage, props, trap doors, and stage lifts under the stage floor. The potential for a fire is great with this combination of fuel and potential ignition sources. Since the Iroquois Theater fire, many safeguards have been required to control these hazards. Included among these safeguards are automatic sprinklers at the ceiling level, below the gridiron, in usable spaces under the stage, and in all auxiliary spaces surrounding the stage; ventilation over the stage, operable manually or automatically by fusible links; and an automatic closing safety curtain to cut off the stage from the audience chamber. All of these features are necessary with a full theatrical stage.

Modern stages are generally modified versions of the classic theatrical stage. More scenery is now moved horizontally, eliminating the need for the high scene loft or fly space. Modern stages also tend to be variations of the traditional proscenium stage, thrusting the stage farther out into the audience or having it open to the audience on three sides, as in an arena theater—often called "theater in the round."

Whatever the arrangement of scenery on the stage, scenery-handling equipment and allied shops need to be protected to prevent a large stage fire from threatening the audience, either directly or indirectly.

Projection Booths

Projection booths refer to any booth housing equipment for the transmission of light onto a screen, curtain, or stage. The hazard is not with the projection of motion pictures or slides made on flammable film, as is commonly assumed, but with the mechanism used to project light. Electric arc, zenon, and other light sources generate hazardous gases, dust, or radiation, and can fail with explosive force under certain circumstances. Where these light sources are used, a booth around the projection equipment is required to protect the audience. Proper ventilation also is required. Incandescent light sources do not produce the same hazard and, therefore, need not have the same enclosure.

Modern motion pictures and slides use safety film, which does not introduce the hazards of nitrocellulose found in early movies. Therefore, modern projection rooms are not designed for, and cannot safely project, nonsafety film.

Storage

In this occupancy, as well as many others, fire and life safety problems often arise from improper storage practices. Storage of tables and chairs in exit ways, storage of scenery so it blocks exits, and storage of supplies in aisles and exit paths are all too common in assembly occupancies. In large measure, this problem is related to improper building design. Little consideration is given to storage needs in the design process. It is essential that space be allocated for proper storage of materials, supplies, props, tables, chairs, and other items associated with assembly occupancies to avoid the creation of unnecessary hazards.

LIFE SAFETY CONCEPTS

Construction

Places of assembly have a high occupant density under variable conditions which, to one degree or another, makes alerting and evacuating the occupants more difficult than in other occupancies. Because of this, building construction is an important element in the life safety system.

In general, the building should be constructed to allow the structure to remain intact under fire conditions, and not contribute significantly to the fire development for at least the time necessary for evacuation. Obviously, for a one-story building, this is relatively easy to accomplish when occupant loads are moderate in size (under 1000). But even in a one-story building with proper exits, a large occupant load (over 1000) means higher degrees of structural protection are necessary to ensure everyone's safety.

As building heights increase, the level of construction and protection must increase accordingly to permit large places of assembly at higher stories of a building. NFPA 101, *Life Safety Code*, specifies types of places of assembly that can be located in buildings based on construction, height of the assembly occupancy above the level of exit discharge, and fire protection provided.

Alarm Systems

Prompt notification of occupants that there is an emergency cannot be overemphasized. However, the sounding of a fire alarm without accompanying verbal instructions might introduce the threat of panic. To overcome this possibility, an appropriate alarm system—perhaps using prerecorded messages—can be designed without undue cost or risk to the occupants.

Exit Hardware

Because of the threat of a large group of occupants rushing to an exit, leaning together on the door, and making the use of traditional knob-activated latching devices difficult or impossible, assembly occupancies usually require panic hardware. Security-conscious owners in the past have objected to panic hardware because of the potential for slipping the latch from the outside. However, modern panic hardware designs provide for both life safety and security.

There is no excuse for chained or padlocked doors, given today's availability of the right kind of exit hardware.

Interior Finish

Interior finish is a key element to provide for fire control and life safety. Materials used in an assembly occupancy must limit the rate of flame spread and smoke production. Generally, materials are limited to flame spreads of 75 or less (Class A or B) for all but the smallest assembly uses.

Drapes, hangings, tapestries, and other decorative materials must be fire-retardant if they constitute a significant part of the decor or if they would provide a continuous path for fire travel. Inadvertent ignition of such materials has been responsible for panic in densely occupied spaces, such as the Cocoanut Grove nightclub fire in Boston, MA, in 1942. Proper treatment to make materials fire-retardant is necessary to avoid disaster.

Employee Training

Employees of assembly occupancies are critically important to the life safety of patrons. If the staff is trained properly, they can prevent serious injury or death to many patrons. The Beverly Hills Supper Club fire in 1977 at Southgate, KY, showed the importance of staff assistance in fire survival. Although the building lacked proper exits, staff members saved hundreds of lives by leading patrons to means of escape unknown to the patrons.

It is recommended that management of every assembly occupancy devise an emergency plan in conjunction with the local fire department, deal with the many contingencies associated with fires, and properly train staff members in safe emergency procedures.

Assembly occupancies can be safely occupied when the following conditions are avoided:

1. Overcrowding.
2. Blocked or impaired exits or means of exit access.
3. Chained or locked exits.
4. Storage of combustibles in other-than-proper locations.
5. Improper use or control of open flames.
6. Disregard for fire characteristics of materials and decorations.

BIBLIOGRAPHY

NFPA Codes, Standards, and Recommended Practices

Reference to the following NFPA codes, standards, and recommended practices will provide further information on assembly occupancies discussed in this chapter. (See the latest *NFPA Catalog* for availability of current editions of the following documents.)

NFPA 96, *Removal of Smoke and Grease-Laden Vapors from Commercial Cooking Equipment.*

NFPA 101®, *Life Safety Code.®*

NFPA 101M, *System Approaches to Life Safety.*

Additional Reading

Crossland, J. W., "Fire Precautions in Public Houses and Restaurants," *Fire Surveyor*, Vol. 18, No. 6 (Dec. 1989), pp. 9-16.

Bouchard, J., *Investigation Report, Haunted Castle Amusement Facility Fire, Jackson Township, New Jersey, May 11, 1984*, National Fire Protection Association, 1984.

Edwards, J., "Theatre Fires—The Importance of Smoke Ventilation," *Fire Prevention*, No. 198, Apr. 1987, pp. 37-38.

"Fires in Places of Public Assembly," *Fire International*, Vol. 10, No. 100, 1986, pp. 25-27, 30-31, 34-36.

Klevan, J. B., *Modeling of Available Egress Time from Assembly Spaces or Estimating the Advance of the Fire Threat*, Society of Fire Protection Engineers, Boston, MA, 1982.

Klem, T. J., "56 Die in English Stadium Fire," *Fire Journal*, Vol. 80, No. 3 (May-June 1986), p. 128.

Pauls, J., "Movement of People," *SFPE Handbook of Fire Protection Engineering*, National Fire Protection Association, Quincy, Ma, 1988, pp. 246-268.

Taylor, K. T., "Whats Cooking in Restaurants...Besides the Food," *Fire Journal*, Vol. 83, No. 5 (Sept.-Oct. 1989), p. 72.

EDUCATIONAL OCCUPANCIES

Revised by John A. Sharry

Educational occupancies can be generally defined as structures used for the gathering of six or more persons for purposes of instruction. Examples of educational occupancies include schools, academies, colleges, and universities, as well as nursery schools, day-care centers, kindergartens, and other facilities whose purpose is primarily educational even though the students are of preschool age.

Recent actions by model code groups have defined educational occupancies as places where students are present for instruction for more than 12 hours per week or more than four hours per day through the 12th grade. This definition excludes facilities, such as churches or museums, in which instruction is incidental to some other occupancy; in such cases, the requirements of principal occupancy apply.

OCCUPANCY CHARACTERISTICS

Nature of Occupants

People in educational occupancies vary in their ability to deal with an emergency condition, depending upon their age and mental and physical condition, plus the physical characteristics of the facilities. Generally, regulations concerning schools are based on abilities of children in third through eighth grade, with special provisions being made for younger children. High-school occupants gain an extra degree of safety because the firesafety design is based on capabilities of younger children.

Occupants in the third through eighth grades should be capable of traversing stairs and acting for their own self-preservation if they are led by an adult. Thus, the aim is to provide sufficient exits and egress paths so that the occupants can be led to an area of safety.

Children below the third-grade level require special consideration because of their limited ability to traverse stairs and move quickly in an emergency. There is a potential for younger children to be overrun on stairs by older students. Most codes require that kindergarten and first-grade students be housed on the first or grade-level discharge to facilitate exiting. Second-grade students are usually limited to one level above the first or grade-level discharge, recognizing their improved movement ability.

Design Considerations

Schools having only one story, where each room has a direct exit to the outside, represent the most conservative design for life safety. However, economics often dictate other designs, which can be made safe as well by adhering to certain design principles noted elsewhere in this chapter.

The necessity for accommodating physically and mentally handicapped students within the general school population is a fairly recent development affecting school design. Consideration must be given to access for and egress of these students by providing facilities such as elevators, horizontal exits, and areas of refuge in multiple-story buildings. Provisions must be made for the use of elevators or other special facilities for evacuation of these students.

Flexible and Open Plan Design

Flexible and open plan design concepts sometimes used in schools differ from conventional designs, in that the walls are demountable and easily moved without major construction. The ability to easily rearrange walls to suit changing educational needs is valuable, but proper consideration to firesafety must be included in the planning.

Open plan buildings delineate spaces and corridors by use of movable fixtures and low partitions [usually maximum height of 5 ft (1.5 m)]. While this design provides great flexibility, the firesafety of the building is diminished by omission of features that could confine fire and smoke to a single compartment long enough to permit evacuation. The compensating factor is the ability of occupants to observe the entire area over the low partitions, and presumably detect any fire in its incipient stage. Since occupants are awake and alert, their natural faculties serve as fire and smoke detectors. Early detection should make prompt evacuation and extinguishment possible.

John A. Sharry is the fire chief at Lawrence Livermore National Laboratory in Livermore, CA.

Colleges and Universities

Because educational occupancies have requirements based on the behavior of students in the third through eighth grades, these requirements are not applicable to colleges and universities.

College students are generally presumed to be capable of adult behavior because of their age. Therefore, most codes no longer treat colleges and universities as educational occupancies.

Because college and university buildings are actually combinations of other occupancies, codes now consider the actual use of the space and apply the respective occupancy requirements. For example, classrooms for under 50 occupants are treated as business occupancies, classrooms with an occupant load of 50 or more are considered assembly occupancies, etc. Thus, colleges and universities receive no special fire or life safety treatment because of their diversified educational mission.

Day-Care Facilities

Day-care facilities have traditionally been associated with the care of children, and thus have been considered as an educational occupancy. Recent changes in society and medical science have indicated a need to expand the scope of day-care facilities to also accommodate elderly people. Because many of the physical limitations that apply to children also apply to older adults, this approach seems logical from a fire protection and life safety standpoint. NFPA *101®*, *Life Safety Code®*, provides special requirements for day-care facilities, serving both children and adults.

It should be recognized that some day-care facilities operate twenty-four hours a day to provide care for dependents of people who work at night. These facilities present the greatest hazard because their occupants may be asleep when fire starts. Staff members for day care are required to be awake and alert at all times; however, human nature being what it is, there is the possibility that the staff may be napping when an emergency occurs. Therefore, special provisions are required when day-care facilities operate at night. The capabilities of the staff to perform in case of an emergency must be verified regularly to ensure the safety of the occupants.

OCCUPANCY HAZARDS

Mixed Occupancy

Educational occupancies are generally mixed occupancies, with other facilities, such as assembly occupancies, often occupying the same building.

With mixed occupancies, care must be taken to ensure that the fire and life safety provisions for all occupancies are met. It is important to provide sufficient protection to prevent the educational occupancy from being exposed to the hazards of the other occupancies in the structure.

Hazardous Areas

Areas, such as vocational shops, laboratories, home economics laboratories, kitchens, storage rooms, and stages, must be separated from educational occupancies. Usually, fire-rated walls and doors will provide the necessary degree of protection unless the hazard is severe, in which case automatic suppression systems may also be required.

LIFE SAFETY CONCEPTS

Means of Egress

There is no substitute for properly designed exits, exit access paths, and exit enclosures. Travel distance requirements and dead-end restrictions are especially important in educational occupancies because of the nature of the occupants.

Designs involving circuitous exit access paths should be avoided. Proper exit enclosures are important to prevent contamination by smoke and heat. Multi-story buildings whose dimensions necessitate stairways away from the building periphery require proper enclosure of the exit path to the exterior by the use of exit passageways.

Corridor Protection

In standard double-loaded corridor designs, precautions must be taken to prevent the corridor from becoming untenable. The use of fire-rated corridor construction with proper door controls is necessary to protect this exit access path. Although many codes require self-closing doors in corridors, operational necessities make this impractical in many schools. Therefore, staff training is necessary to ensure the proper closing of doors at appropriate times.

Subdivision of any long corridors for smoke control purposes is desirable. By providing smoke doors at 300-ft (90 m) intervals, corridors can be kept reasonably smoke-free in areas away from the fire origin.

Exit Hardware

Because of the potential for large numbers of occupants using the same exit doors, and to prevent crushing against unopened doors, panic hardware is required in schools of any substantial size. In no case are chains or padlocks permitted on exits when the building is occupied. If such security devices are used during unoccupied times, provisions for their removal must be made to the satisfaction of local authorities.

Alarm Systems

In general, schools require (as a minimum) a manual fire alarm system. Because of vandalism in public schools in recent years, fire alarm systems sometimes have been turned off or otherwise disabled to prevent malicious false alarms from interrupting the learning process. Recent changes in some codes permit the deletion of manual pull stations if two-way communication is maintained in all rooms and if there is a continuously staffed central location where an alarm can be sounded. This allows for an operational fire alarm system without the vandalism problem. NFPA *101*, *Life Safety Code*, permits such an arrangement.

Staff Training

Educational occupancies should develop emergency plans in conjunction with the local fire department. A plan should include emergency actions, position descriptions for key staff, an evacuation plan, and a fire drill procedure and schedule. The plan should be practiced at various times during the year, with fire drills conducted regularly. The staff should be well informed as to their responsibilities and practice the plan to ensure smooth functioning during an emergency.

BIBLIOGRAPHY

NFPA Codes, Standards, and Recommended Practices

Reference to the following NFPA codes, standards, and recommended practices will provide further information on educational occupancies discussed in this chapter. (See the latest *NFPA Catalog* for availability of the current edition of the following document.)

NFPA *101, Life Safety Code.*

Additional Reading

Juillerat, E. E., *Campus Firesafety*, National Fire Protection Association, Quincy, MA, 1977.

Los Angeles Fire Department, *Operation School Burning, No. 12*, Official Report on a Series of School Fire Tests Conducted April 16, 1959 to June 30, 1959, National Fire Protection Association, Quincy, MA, 1961.

Los Angeles Fire Department, *Operation School Burning, No.* 22, Official Report on a Series of Fire Tests in an Open Stairway, Multistory School Conducted June 30, 1960 and Feb. 6, 1961, National Fire Protection Association, Quincy, MA, 1961.

NFPA, Fire Data Package 14, "Schools," Fire Analysis and Research Division, National Fire Protection Association, Quincy, MA.

"A Study of School Fires," National Fire Protection Association, Quincy, MA, 1973.

Taylor, K. T., "Burning Down the School...The Lessons We Don't Learn Can Hurt Us," *Fire Journal*, Vol. 83, No. 3, 1990, p. 60.

Woodall, R. D., "Why Do Fires in School Buildings Cause So Much Damage," *Fire Prevention*, No. 223, Oct. 1989, pp. 19-20.

HEALTH CARE FACILITIES

Revised by Donald W. Belles

Health care facilities are used for the treatment or care of persons suffering from physical or mental illness, disease, or infirmity, and for the care of infants, convalescents, or aged persons. These facilities provide sleeping accommodations for occupants who may be incapable of self-preservation because of physical or mental disability or age. Some buildings that house mentally disabled occupants have security measures that limit freedom of movement.

In recent years, facilities—sometimes called ambulatory surgical care facilities—have been developed to provide medical treatment on an outpatient basis. Although patients might be placed under general anesthesia, they are not housed overnight. Occupants exhibit some of the characteristics of people in business occupancies and some characteristics typical of those in health care facilities.

There is a growing trend among certain agencies toward housing persons with physical, mental, or emotional disabilities in a "deinstitutionalized" residential setting. These facilities are variously referred to as board and care facilities, halfway houses, adult congregate living facilities, and so on. Residents of board and care homes differ greatly in their ability to respond to a fire threat. Only when a facility meets the definition in NFPA 101®, *Life Safety Code®*, of a health care facility should the safeguards appropriate for health care facilities be applied.

Additional information relating to health care facilities can be found in Section 6, Chapter 4, "Interior Finish"; Section 6, Chapter 6, "Confinement of Fire in Buildings"; Section 8, Chapter 14, "Board and Care Facilities"; and Section 8, Chapter 28, "Protection of Electronic Equipment."

OCCUPANCY CHARACTERISTICS

Occupants of health care facilities are generally presumed to be incapable of self-preservation. A significant percentage of occupants in hospitals and nursing homes are incapable of self-evacuation or are ambulatory but incapable of perceiving a fire threat and making a rational choice of response.

There are three types of care in most modern hospitals: ambulatory, general, and intensive care. Given proper directions, and unless smoke or heat is intense, ambulatory patients can make their own way to safety. General care patients may be transported on stretchers or in wheelchairs with some difficulty; horizontal and even some vertical movement is generally possible, although independent evacuation is not. Patients in intensive care are likely to be connected to a variety of life-support devices, making movement for even short distances very difficult and evacuation almost impossible without further endangering such patients' lives.

Occupants of nursing homes vary from geriatric residents who are capable of evacuation with limited assistance to patients requiring close supervision and skilled nursing care. Those requiring skilled nursing care generally will be incapable of responding to the threat of fire. The use of physical restraints and tranquilizing drugs may also prevent a patient from responding to a fire.

The aged present a unique fire problem. There have been fires in which elderly people acted contrary to self-interest, either by resisting rescue efforts and reentering burning buildings or by seeking refuge in their rooms and failing to notify others of a fire. However, the application of health care safeguards should not be made simply on the basis of age, but should be based on the occupants' ability to escape in an emergency.

Because occupants will be incapable of movement or slow to evacuate, a health care facility resembles a ship at sea or a high-rise building: it is better to keep the fire from the patient than to remove the patient from the fire. Thus, occupants must be defended in place. As a result, health care facility design and operation must incorporate methods by which a fire can be detected early, contained, and fought rapidly and successfully. Accomplishing this requires careful planning of the health care facility and of its day-to-day operation.

NFPA 101, *Life Safety Code*, widely used to establish minimum requirements for life safety from fire within health care facilities, sets forth criteria based upon the following general principles:

Donald W. Belles, P.E., is principal, Donald W. Belles and Associates, Inc., fire protection consultants, Madison, TN.

1. Fire-resistive construction.
2. Subdivision of spaces, known as compartmentation.
3. Protection of vertical openings.
4. Provision of adequate means of egress.
5. Provision of exit marking, exit illumination, and emergency power.
6. Limits on the use of interior finish materials.
7. Fire alerting facilities.
8. Smoke control mechanisms.
9. Protection of hazardous areas.
10. Adequate protection of building service equipment.

Total building fire protection for life safety is more necessary in health care facilities than in other occupancies because of the nature of the occupants. At the same time, exits are slightly less important. The first principle of designing a firesafe health care facility must be that safety must not depend wholly upon any single safeguard.

IGNITION SOURCES

Smoking materials, both lighted tobacco products and the implements used to light them, and incendiary and suspicious acts account for 95 percent of the deaths and 64 percent of the injuries in facilities that care for the sick, and for 85 percent of the deaths and 60 percent of the injuries in facilities that care for older adults. These causes totally dominate the ignition side of the life safety problem in these properties, although other causes, notably failures in electrical distribution systems, appliances, and other equipment, are also important in property damage. (See Tables 8-13A through 8-13D.)

Smoking materials and associated lighting implements, in particular, dominate the fire deaths. Lighted tobacco products, matches, and lighters account for 61 percent of the deaths in facilities that care for the sick and 72 percent of the deaths in facilities that care for older adults.

The majority of fatalities in health care fires are so close to the point of origin that their locations are coded as "intimate with ignition." (See Table 8-13E.) Nearly all fatalities that are anywhere in the room in which a fire begins turn out to have been intimate with ignition.

Most intimate-with-ignition fire deaths begin with the victims' clothing or with the mattress, bedding, or upholstered furniture on which they were lying at the time the fire began. Fires such as these typically begin near the upper torso, since the materials ignited are near the area where the victims dropped a lighted tobacco product or lighting implement. Only a couple of cases in the NFPA's files involve points of origin well away from the victim's upper torso. For example, one victim died in a fire that began when a lamp fell on the bottom of her bed and ignited the sheet.

TABLE 8-13A. ***Causes of Fires and Direct Property Damage in Facilities that Care for the Sick***

Cause	Fires	Property Damage (in Million)
Smoking material	1,800 (30.2%)	$0.4 (7.3%)
Incendiary or suspicious causes	800 (13.2)	1.8 (30.0)
Other equipment	700 (11.8)	1.0 (16.5)
Telephone, computer, x-ray or other electronic equipment	100 (1.8)	0.3 (4.3)
Separate motors or generators	100 (1.8)	0.1 (1.5)
Incinerators	100 (1.1)	0.0 (0.3)
Appliances, tools, or air conditioning	700 (11.3)	0.6 (11.0)
Dryers	300 (4.6)	0.3 (5.5)
Unclassified appliances	100 (1.0)	0.1 (1.2)
Room air conditioners	100 (1.0)	0.0 (0.3)
Central air-conditioning equipment	100 (1.0)	0.0 (0.2)
Cooking equipment	700 (11.1)	0.2 (3.9)
Stoves	300 (4.2)	0.1 (0.2)
Portable cooking or warming units	200 (2.7)	0.0 (0.3)
Ovens	100 (1.8)	0.0 (0.2)
Electrical distribution	500 (8.9)	1.3 (21.3)
Lighting fixtures, ballasts, or signs	200 (2.9)	0.4 (7.3)
Fixed wiring	100 (1.4)	0.3 (4.3)
Transformers	100 (1.0)	0.3 (4.5)
Open flame, embers, or torches	500 (7.9)	0.2 (3.4)
Torches	200 (3.7)	0.2 (2.6)
Matches	100 (2.0)	0.0 (0.3)
Other known cause	300 (5.5)	0.4 (6.5)
Total*	6,100 (100%)	$5.8 (100%)

*Totals may not equal sums do to rounding.
Source: 1983-87 NFIRS and NFPA Survey. Unknown-cause fires are allocated proportionally.

TABLE 8-13B. ***Causes of Civilian Deaths and Injuries in Facilities that Care for the Sick***

Cause	Civilian Deaths	Civilian Injuries
Smoking materials	4 (36.8%)	38 (21.9%)
Incendiary or suspicious causes	3 (34.2)	47 (26.9%)
Open flame, embers, or torches	2 (23.7)	38 (21.5)
Lighters	1 (14.2)	11 (6.4)
Matches	1 (9.5)	15 (8.3)
Electrical distribution	1 (5.3)	0 (5.2)
Overcurrent protection devices	1 (5.3)	3 (1.8)
Other equipment	0 (0.0)	25 (14.3)
Appliances, tools, or air conditioning	0 (0.0)	7 (4.0)
Other known cause	0 (0.0)	11 ((6.1)
Total*	10 (100%)	175 (100%)

*Totals may not equal sums due to rounding.
Source: 1983-87 NFIRS and NRPA Survey. Unknown-cause fires are allocated proportionally.

FIRE LOADS

Studies show relatively low fuel loads within most spaces in health care facilities. Fire duration varies from approximately 20 min for patient areas to several hours, depending upon the space involved.

A study by the National Bureau of Standards (NBS) conducted in 1942 involving three hospitals reveals an average fuel load of 5.7 lb per sq ft (27.8 kg/m^2).[1] Fuel loads for typical spaces are indicated in Table 8-13F. A more recent study of fuel loads in a U.S. Navy hospital confirmed the relatively low fuel loads for general hospital areas but indicates that higher fuel loads may be anticipated in some spaces such as medical libraries, X-ray file rooms, linen storage, and general storage rooms. Further, the increased use of disposables and modern medical record storage practices are likely to result in fuel loads exceeding average. These areas may contain fuel loads sufficient for fires from 1 to 3 hr duration. However, such spaces represent a small percentage of the total floor area.

Doctor office areas have been identified as an intermediate fuel load space having combustibles in sufficient quantity to produce fires of 30 to 90 min duration.

TABLE 8-13C. ***Causes of Fires and Direct Property Damage in Facilities that Care for Older Adults***

Cause	Fires	Property Damage (in Millions)
Appliances, tools, air conditioning	1,100 (27.2%)	$0.6 (16.0%)
Dryers	700 (17.9)	0.3 (9.1)
Room air conditioners	100 (1.5)	0.0 (0.5)
Washing machines	100 (1.5)	0.0 (0.2)
Unclassified appliances	100 (1.3)	0.0 (0.4)
Smoking materials	700 (10.0)	0.6 (15.7)
Cooking equipment	500 (13.5)	0.1 (3.9)
Stoves	300 (7.6)	0.1 (2.9)
Ovens	100 (2.4)	0.0 (0.2)
Portable cooking or warming units	100 (2.2)	0.0 (0.7)
Electrical distribution	400 (10.2)	0.5 (13.7)
Lighting fixtures, ballasts, or signs	100 (3.2)	0.0 (0.4)
Fixed wiring	100 (1.7)	0.1 (3.5)
Cords or plugs	100 (1.4)	0.2 (4.4)
Heating equipment	300 (8.6)	0.1 (3.9)
Fixed area heaters	100 (3.5)	0.0 (1.2)
Central heating units	100 (2.5)	0.0 (1.4)
Other equipment	300 (7.5)	0.2 (5.3)
Incendiary or suspicious causes	300 (6.8)	1.1 (27.7)
Other known cause	300 (7.1)	0.5 (13.8)
Total*	3,900 (100%)	$3.8 (100%)

*Totals may not equal sums due to rounding.
Source: 1983-87 NFIRS and NFPA Survey. Unknown-cause fires are allocated proportionally.

TABLE 8-13D. ***Causes of Civilian Deaths and Injuries in Facilities that Care for Older Adults***

Cause	Civilian Deaths	Civilian Injuries
Smoking materials	10 (58.6%)	53 (27.4%)
Open flame, embers, or torches	2 (13.8)	30 (15.8)
Matches	2 (10.3)	8 (4.4)
Lighters	1 (3.4)	20 (10.2)
Incendiary or suspicious cause	2 (12.1)	32 (16.7)
Appliances, tools, or air conditioning	1 (5.2)	32 (16.6)
Refrigerators or freezers	1 (3.4)	5 (2.5)
Cooking equipment	1 (3.4)	16 (8.2)
Stoves	1 (3.4)	11 (5.6)
Electical distribution	1 (3.4)	11 (5.9)
Lamp or light bulb	1 (3.4)	2 (0.8)
Child playing	1 (3.4)	1 (0.4)
Other known cause	0 (0.0)	18 (9.1)
Total*	17 (100%)	193 (100%)

*Totals may not equal sums due to rounding.
Source: 1983-87 NFIRS and NFPA Survey. Unknown-cause fires are allocated proportionally.

A major portion of the floor area of health care facilities is used for patient sleeping or treatment rooms. Fuel loads for such spaces are low. For example, fuel loads in nursing homes have been estimated at 2.5 to 3 lb per sq ft (9.72 to 14.64 kg/m^2).[2] NBS surveys indicate that fuel loads for hospital patient rooms approximate 4 lb per sq ft (19.52 kg/m^2) and that the combustible load in patient sleeping areas ranges from approximately 3 to 4.5 lb per sq ft (14.64 to 22.96 kg/m^2). A study of a Navy hospital indicates fuel loads for sleeping rooms average 1 lb per sq ft (4.88 kg/m^2) or less. Assuming standard time/temperature conditions, fire duration for patient areas and a majority of other occupied spaces would be less than 30 min.

Disposables

The use of combustible disposable equipment and supplies is on the increase for a variety of reasons, including the hazards of cross infection, personnel shortages, and possible financial savings. Disposables include bedding, gowns, gloves, drapes, collection bags, tubing, dishes, glasses, syringes, needles, and many diagnostic and therapeutic instruments. All such items require packaging, which adds to the combustible load both before and after use. Bulk purchasing is economical, but it sometimes results in an overflow of combustibles into areas that are not designed or protected for such use.

Data Processing and Medical Records

Data processing centers are becoming increasingly important within health care facilities. Used to satisfy general business needs as well as to store patient records, the centers contain quantities of combustibles. These combustibles could expose high-value equipment, could result in loss of vital records, and could produce a fire that threatens occupants outside the data processing areas. Special protection should be considered for data processing centers.

Health care facilities generate and store files in considerable quantity. Files stored in closed steel cabinets do not represent any significant increase in hazard over that typical of most areas. However, files stored on open shelving create a serious fire hazard. Open-file storage should be treated as a severe hazard and should be separated by fire-rated construction and protected by automatic sprinklers.

FIRE SEVERITY

Determining relative fire hazard involves considerations beyond total fuel loads. The arrangement of combustibles, their chemical makeup, and their physical state are all factors to be evaluated, in addition to room geometry, ventilation rates, fire compartment size, and fire protection facilities. Generally, the faster a fire develops, the greater the threat. Multiple-death fires nearly always result from fires that quickly develop to large size, reaching full room involvement or flashover.

Although the total fuel load in patient rooms remains low, the nature of the combustibles is changing. The introduction of foam plastic decubitus pads, upholstered furniture, and polyurethane foam mattresses may not affect the

TABLE 8-13E. ***Locations of Victims of Fatal Health Care Facility Fires***

Property Class	Intimate with Ignition	Same Room as Fire but Not Intimate	Not Same Room as Fire
Facilities that care for the sick	77%	3%	20%
Hospitals	79	0	21
Other or unknown type	50	50	0
Facilities that care for older adults	49	15	35
With nursing staff	52	12	36
Other or unknown type	36	29	36
All facilities combined 58%	11%	31%	

Source: 1983-87 NFIRS and NFPA survey.

TABLE 8-13F. ***Fuel Loads in Typical Health Care Facilities***

	Average Combustible Contents (psf)		
Location	Movable Property	Exposed Woodwork and Floors*	Total
Rooms (single)	0.5	3.2	3.7
Corridors	0	2.6	2.6
Waiting rooms	1.7	1.5	3.2
Janitors' closets and supplies	3.1	3.4	6.5
Doctors' offices	5.7	2.9	8.6
Nurses' offices and rooms	3.1	1.9	5.0
Nurses' infirmary	0.8	2.2	3.0
Diet kitchens and dining rooms	1.2	2.4	3.6
Laundries	4.4	0.6	5.0
Laundries and clothes storage	12.5	0.6	13.1
Dormitories	0.8	2.0	2.8
Pharmacy, dispensary, and stores	5.8	1.9	7.7
Lockers, toilets, and barber shops	0.2	1.2	1.4
Approximate average for entire usable floor area of three hospital buildings surveyed			5.7**

* Combustible floor finish, where present, was 1/4 in. linoleum; it was assumed to be the equivalent of 1 lb of combustible material, such as wood, per ft2 of floor area (4.88 kg/m^2). Doors, windows, trim, mouldings, baseboards, etc., are included.

** This approximate average weight was computed from Table 16 on page 25 of the Bureau Report BMS 92. The value is somewhat high because the highest weight in each bracket of combustible contents was used in figuring it, i.e., in the bracket "0 to 4.9 lb/ft^2 (23.9 kg/m^2)," the value 4.9 lb (2.22 kg) was applied to the indicated area, etc.

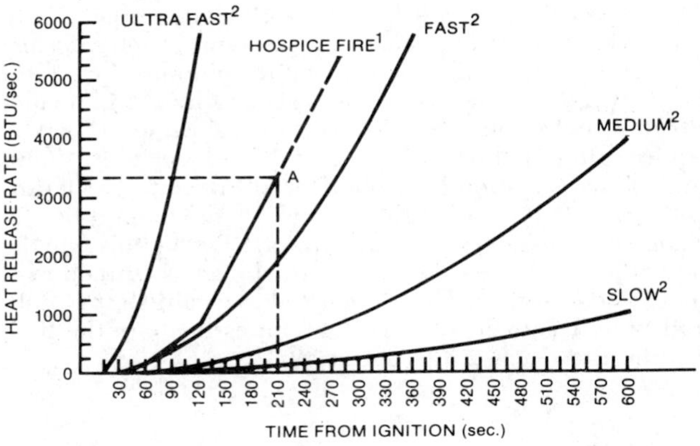

1—FROM NFPA STUDY OF THE HOSPICE FIRE, SOUTHFIELD, MICHIGAN, DECEMBER 1985 AND CFR/NBS COMPUTER FIRE MODEL ANALYSIS.
2, 3, 4—FROM NFPA 72E, APPENDIX C.
A—ROOM FLASHOVER

FIG. 8-13A. ***Comparison of the hospice fire to NFPA 72E Appendix C growth curves.***

length of time a fire will burn, but such items have affected the rate of fire growth. These types of products have caused fire to grow to a large size quickly.

Fires that reach flashover will produce acutely lethal atmospheres generating thousands of cubic feet of smoke per minute (1,000 cu ft per min equals 28 m^3/min). Such fires threaten fire-rated barriers and produce enough energy to drive smoke to remote areas. A fire that grows to full room size in a health care facility represents an unacceptable level of risk; there is a high likelihood that such a fire will result in injuries or fatalities. Therefore, every effort should be made to recognize and eliminate fuel arrangements that might produce such fires.

Fire tests and actual fire experience have shown that certain common arrangements and types of fuels in patient rooms create especially hazardous situations because they are able to produce large fires in short periods of time. In January 1976, for example, multiple-death fires in both the Wincrest and Cermak House nursing homes involved wooden wardrobes.[3,4] Tests have shown that combustible wardrobe fires can result in acutely hazardous environments in as little as 120 sec.[5] Full-scale tests conducted by the National Bureau of Standards [now the National Institute of Standards and Technology (NIST)] following the Sac-Osage Hospital fire, which involved a styrene butadiene rubber mattress, resulted in full room involvement approximately 7½ min after open-flame ignition of bedding.[6]

A 1989 fire in a Norfolk nursing home resulting in 12 deaths originated in a foam plastic decubitus pad on a mattress in a patient sleeping room. The fire grew to flashover in less than 5 min.[7] A 1985 fire in a Michigan hospice initially involved an upholstered chair. The fire caused eight deaths.[8] Analysis of this fire established that flashover could have occurred in the room of origin in under 4 min. See Figure 8-13A for documentation of the analysis for the hospice fire.

Any combination of finishes, combustible building materials, or contents and furnishings that could result in full room involvement or flashover in 5 min or less represents a severe fire hazard in a health care facility. Such spaces should always be protected by automatic sprinklers and separated by fire-rated construction.

Computer fire models developed at NIST have been used to establish the rate of heat release required to produce flashover in a typical patient sleeping room. Under the "worst" circumstances—where the room door is partially open—a 1-MW fire can cause flashover. When the room door is fully open, approximately a 2-MW fire is necessary to cause flashover. The Appendix of 1991, NFPA 101, *Life Safety Code*, suggests that upholstered furniture, mattresses, and wardrobes be constructed to produce a maximum rate of heat release of 500 kW. Such a limit would require two objects to burn simultaneously with their peak rates overlapping to cause flashover in a patient room under "worst-case" conditions. It also has been determined that hazard thresholds are exceeded, and patients must be removed from sleeping rooms when a fire grows beyond 250 kW in size.

It is a well-established fact that furnishings are frequently major contributors to fire growth. Recent developments make it possible to determine whether furnishings in a given environment are capable of producing sufficient energy to cause full room involvement.

A simplified equation estimating the rate of heat release required for flashover to occur in a room[9] is given by the expression:

$$Q \geq 750\, A \sqrt{h}$$

where Q is the rate of heat release (kW), A is the ventilation opening area in sq ft (m^2), and h is its height in ft (m).

Once the heat release rate required to produce flashover is known for a typical room geometry, such information can be compared to actual heat release rates for typical furnishings, as determined by tests conducted in a calorimeter such as the NIST furniture calorimeter[10] or by Underwriters Laboratories Inc. (UL) Subject 1056, "Outline of Investigation for Upholstered Furniture." Figures 8-13B and 8-13C are idealized curves developed by the National Bureau of Standards (now NIST) that illustrate the rate of heat release for typical furnishings as a function of time. Such information can be used to establish the probability of flashover; it also allows an estimate of the time required to reach critical fire size.

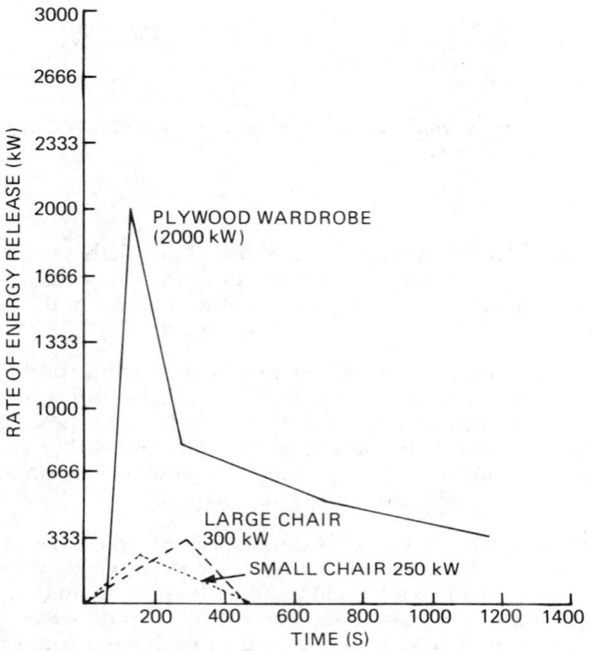

FIG. 8-13B. Heat release rates for miscellaneous furniture.

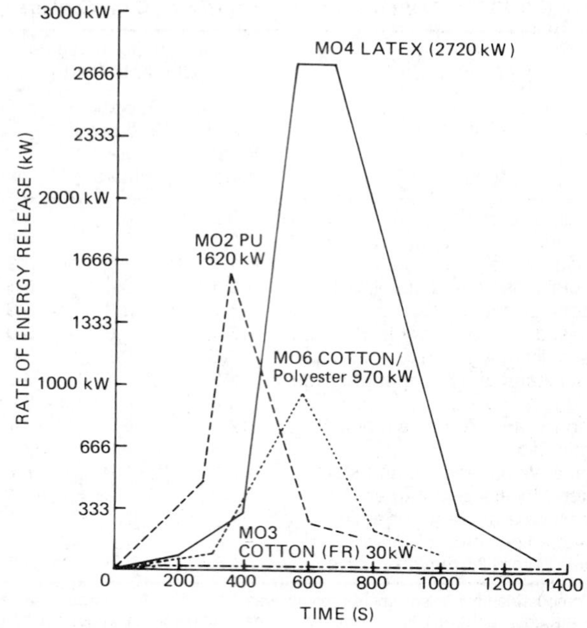

FIG. 8-13C. Heat release rates for beds.

Interior Finish

A successful fire protection strategy requires fires to remain small. Any large fire in a confined space creates a potentially lethal atmosphere. The initial growth of a fire may be affected significantly by the interior finish of walls, ceilings, and floors. Interior finishes, therefore, deserve special attention. Combustible interior finishes, such as low-density fiberboard ceilings and plastic floor coverings, have been found to be significant factors in multiple-death fires.[11,12] Combustible wall and ceiling finishes can act as a fuse, causing a fire to spread to objects remote from the fire origin. Alternatively, wall and ceiling finishes provide a large continuous surface over which fire may spread. Thus, an interior finish may, by its release of energy, cause a fire that would otherwise have remained small to become large.

The relative hazard of an interior finish is usually determined by a test conducted in accordance with NFPA 255, *Surface Burning Characteristics of Building Materials*, commonly called the tunnel test.

Interior finish on walls and ceilings within the means of egress and any room should be limited to Class A materials, which have a flame-spread rating of 25 or less. Class B materials, or those with a flame-spread rating of 25 to 75, are considered tolerable, but they should be limited to small rooms. Full-scale experiments show that automatic sprinklers can limit fire growth in rooms with Class C wall and Class D ceiling finishes.[2,5] Accordingly, in buildings with automatic sprinkler protection, it has been judged acceptable practice to allow the use of materials having higher flame spread classifications than would otherwise be permitted. For example, Class B materials are sometimes used where Class A is normally specified, and Class C materials where Class B is normally required.

Further, it has been shown that the performance of interior finishes also is related to location.[13] Finishes on the upper portions of walls and ceilings contribute more significantly to flame propagation than finishes on the floor or on the lower half of a wall. Therefore, where finishes are limited to the lower half of a wall and are less than 4 ft (1.2 m) above floor level, materials having a higher flame-spread rating than would otherwise be allowed might be used without significantly affecting fire growth. For example, where Class A materials are judged necessary, a Class B material might be allowed on the lower portion of a wall.

In the past, floor finish materials were excluded from the requirements for interior finishes. This was based on favorable experience and on the assumption that limited exposure would exist at the floor level during an actual fire. However, a fire on January 9, 1970 in the Harmer House Convalescent Home in Marietta, OH, caused a significant change in this attitude.[12] Thirty-two persons died in this fire in which carpeting with foam-rubber backing was judged to have played a significant role.

Interior floor finishes in the corridors of nonsprinklered health care facilities should be limited to Class I materials, or those with a minimum critical radiant flux of 0.45 W/cm^2. Where automatic sprinklers are provided, interior floor finishes need not be regulated beyond the federal flammability standard.

BUILDING CONSTRUCTION

Because occupants of health care facilities must be defended in place, construction becomes an important factor, especially in multi-story buildings. Buildings preferably should be constructed of a noncombustible material that can resist the effects of fire and maintain structural integrity.

Buildings of two or more stories should be constructed of noncombustible materials, with major structural members having at least 2-hr fire resistance. Materials that either burn or support combustion, although less desirable, are considered acceptable if special precautions are taken. An automatic sprinkler system is an essential part of the total fire defense system for such buildings.

Any evaluation of building materials should include consideration of their smoke-generating capabilities. In addition, plastic construction materials, which are becoming more common, sometimes are capable of generating large quantities of smoke.

Subdivision of Building Spaces

Separation of patient sleeping rooms: Because it may not be possible to remove occupants during a fire, sleeping rooms sometimes must serve as temporary areas of refuge. Therefore, sleeping rooms should be isolated from all other building spaces by fire-rated construction. Partitions should be continuous from the floor slab to the floor or roof above through any concealed spaces, such as those above suspended ceilings. If the building is protected by sprinklers, NFPA 101, *Life Safety Code*, allows these walls to be nonrated, provided the walls resist the passage of smoke, and they are permitted to terminate at the ceiling, provided the ceiling resists the passage of smoke. (See Figure 8-13D for typical floor plan for a health care facility.)

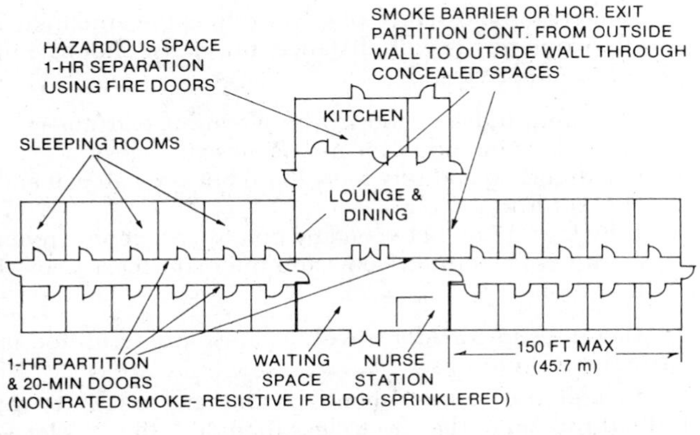

FIG. 8-13D. ***Typical floor plan for a health care facility.***

Considerable controversy exists as to whether patient room doors should be equipped with self-closing or automatic closing devices. One school of thought attributes fatal fires, such as those which occurred at the Harmer House Convalescent Home, the Sac-Osage Hospital, the Willow Point Nursing Home,[14] and the Extendicare Skilled Nursing Facility,[15] to the fact that the door to the room of origin remained open during the fire. The open door allowed fire effects to spread to the corridor and adjacent rooms. Proponents of door closers argue that these devices would have closed the door to the room of origin and would have confined the fire, thereby preventing many of the fatalities.

Opponents of door closers argue that functional considerations require patient room doors to be open most of the time. Further, they note that, except for a few isolated instances, trained staff have been able to close the door to the room of origin manually during the many fires that occur annually in health care facilities. In addition, it might be noted that the majority of fire deaths in health care facilities involve persons who are at the point of fire origin. Door closers, which cause the doors to patient rooms to close at the start of a fire, could decrease the occupants' chances of survival in the room of origin. Closed doors also increase the time required to find the fire and, in the interim, can prevent any dilution of smoke. For these reasons, consideration should be given to providing smoke detectors within patient rooms whose doors are equipped with closers.

Automatic sprinkler systems respond automatically to limit fire size. NFPA 101, *Life Safety Code*, now requires all new health care facilities to be protected by automatic sprinklers. Fast-response sprinklers should be used in compartments containing sleeping rooms. (See NFPA 101, Section 12-3.5.) Where such protection is provided, partitions separating spaces occupied by patients need not be fire-rated, but they should resist the passage of smoke. Partitions may be terminated at suspended ceilings, and glass may be used in corridor doors and partitions without limit as to size or type. Transfer grills should not be used within such doors or partitions.

Any penetration of 1-hr partitions by building service equipment should be protected in order to maintain the 1-hr fire-rated separation. All spaces around piping and ducts should be sealed tightly with a noncombustible material having adequate fire resistance and capable of retarding smoke transfer.

The effect of duct penetrations on 1-hr partitions should be carefully evaluated. Considerations should include the effect of metallic *versus* nonmetallic ducts, the location of openings, the purpose of the duct system, the direction of airflow, interconnected spaces, control features, and the general arrangement of the air-handling system. Steel ducts with a limited number of relatively small openings may not need to be protected. Where flexible or nonmetallic ducts are employed, consideration should be given to protecting the duct penetration with a fire damper.

Smoke barriers: Every floor used by inpatients should be subdivided into at least two compartments by 1-hr partitions capable of retarding smoke. A horizontal exit, when constructed to satisfy the additional criteria imposed upon construction of smokestop barriers, is a desirable alternative to a smokestop partition. To minimize the number of occupants exposed to a single fire, the building should be subdivided into smoke compartments.

Protection of Vertical Openings

Fire and fire-produced contaminants tend to spread vertically within a building. Special effort is required to prevent fire on one level from threatening the occupants above; this is especially important in health care facilities.

All shafts should be enclosed with materials that provide a minimum 2-hr fire resistance. Openings in shaft walls should be limited to only those necessary, and any such opening should be protected.

When designing partitions to enclose vertical shafts, consideration should be given to the varying durability of materials. In spaces where partitions may be subject to mechanical injury, materials used to provide floor-to-floor separation should be able to resist damage in order to maintain the required fire resistance.

Exit Design

Exits in health care facilities should be limited to doors leading directly to the outside of the building, interior stairs and smokeproof towers, ramps, horizontal exits, outside stairs, and exit passageways.

Vertical evacuation of occupants within a health care facility is, at best, difficult and time-consuming. Therefore, horizontal movement of patients is of primary importance.

Horizontal passageways and doors opening into corridors and rooms used for sleeping or treatment should be wide enough to allow the horizontal movement of occupants, even those in beds. Relocation of patients is a slow process, even under favorable staff-to-patient ratios. Because of the time required to move patients, exit access routes should be protected against fire effects. Spaces open to the corridor should not be used for patient sleeping or treatment rooms, nor should hazardous contents or activities be permitted within them. Such spaces preferably should be arranged to allow direct visual supervision by the staff and should be equipped with electrically supervised smoke detectors that, if activated, will sound the building fire alarm.

All other spaces containing combustible materials that could prevent use of exit access corridors should be isolated by fire-resistive partitions. For example, lounges are typically equipped with combustible furnishings, and any electrical devices, such as lamps and television sets, and smoking in lounges can increase the possibility of ignition. Lounge spaces should therefore be separated by fire-rated construction.

Horizontal exits: Horizontal exits are common in health care facilities. Partitions used as horizontal exits and smoke barriers should provide the fire resistance required for exits and, in addition, should satisfy the criteria for smoke barriers. If possible, door openings should be limited to corridors, lobbies, or public spaces. The most desirable arrangement of mechanical systems is one in which the partitions forming the horizontal exit are not penetrated. If penetration by utilities or piping occurs, the space around the piping should be filled tightly with noncombustible materials. If ducts penetrate partitions, fire dampers that close if smoke detectors within the duct activate should be provided.

Since a horizontal exit implies that occupants will be transferred from one side of a partition to the other, adequate space must be available to "store" occupants after movement. At least 30 net sq ft (2.79 m^2) per patient should be available on each side of the horizontal exit, allowing for the total number of patients in adjoining compartments.

Interior stairs: Exit stairs should be designed to satisfy the criteria for interior stairs. Stairs should be enclosed with fire-resistive materials, with stair openings limited to those necessary for access and discharge purposes. Stairs must be protected properly from the effects of fire.

Exit Features

Life safety from fire in health care facilities relies upon a "defend in place" principle. Horizontal exits or smoke barriers are required to subdivide each story of a health care facility to provide an area of refuge on each floor.

The original concept for the design of exits for health care facilities was derived from studies conducted in the early part of this century. A philosophy evolved of using exit stair enclosures as areas of refuge. Exit capacity for health care facilities was set conservatively to offset slow rates of travel and to create space within exit enclosures for "storing" patients on litters and in wheelchairs.

Exit design concepts have changed over the years. For example, NFPA 101, *Life Safety Code*, approaches life safety from fire in health care facilities using a "defend in place" principle. Means for horizontal evacuation are provided for each story, using either a smoke barrier or a horizontal exit. Each story is subdivided by a barrier to provide an area of refuge for patients without traversing stairs. Furthermore, it is common—indeed, it is required in the 1991 *Life Safety Code*—to install automatic sprinklers throughout all new health care facilities. Automatic sprinklers will limit fire size and will complement the "defend-in-place" strategy currently in use.

Exit capacity in nonsprinklered health care facilities is set at 0.6 in. (15.24 mm) per person for travel over stairs, while the capacity through doors and level passageways is calculated at 0.5 in. (12.7 m) per person. Where automatic sprinklers are provided throughout a building, exit capacity is increased to 0.3 in. (7.62 mm) per person for travel over stairs and 0.2 in. (5.08 mm) per person for travel over level passageways.

Capacity is calculated using a "flow rate" principle. Flow rates assumed are for able-bodied persons because it is presumed that evacuation over stairs will involve only staff, visitors, and ambulatory patients. Nonambulatory occupants will be expected to remain in the building under the "defend-in-place" concept, with those patients on the floor of fire origin being moved horizontally to an area of refuge.

Limits on the distance of travel reflect the anticipated slow movement. Travel distance normally should not exceed the following:

1. One hundred feet (30 m) between an exit and any room door intended for use as an exit access.
2. One hundred and fifty feet (46 m) between an exit and any point in a room.
3. Fifty feet (15 m) between any point in a sleeping room or suite of sleeping rooms and the exit access door of that room.

Increases in corridor travel distance are permitted in sprinklered buildings.

In addition, facilities should be arranged to limit travel in the direction of the fire to less than 30 ft (9 m). Elevators are not usually counted as required exits because they possess numerous shortcomings that may prevent their use during a fire. In the case of critically ill patients, patients in body casts or balkan frames, and others who would be difficult to move, however, elevators provide the only practical method of evacuation from the upper stories of the facility. If separate banks of elevators are located in separate smoke compartments, and if the staff are well trained, it may be possible to devise a plan in which it will be safe to use elevators during fires.

Exit Marking and Exit Illumination

All exits should be identified by readily visible signs. Where access to exits is not immediately visible, access routes also should be marked.

Illumination of the entire means of egress must be continuous whenever the building is occupied. In some cases, normal street lighting is adequate for illumination of exit discharge. However, consideration should be given to the conditions that would result from a power failure.

Emergency power also is required to illuminate the means of egress and exit marking. In hospitals, this power should be supplied by the life safety branch of the hospitals' essential electrical system. Luminescent, fluorescent, or reflective material should not be substituted for required lighting.

Emergency power supplies should maintain illumination automatically in the event of a power failure, without any appreciable interruption during the changeover from normal to emergency power. Where a generator is provided, the delay should not be more than 10 sec, per NFPA 99, *Health Care Facilities*. Where emergency power is supplied by a central system with an engine-driven generator, the design should minimize the possibility of any single emergency simultaneously interrupting both normal and emergency power supplies. The switch(es) that transfers power from normal to emergency circuits is one place at which normal and emergency circuits are required to merge. If this switch(es) is exposed to fire, it could simultaneously interrupt power to both normal and emergency circuits. To minimize this possibility, the generator and its attendant fuel hazards should be separated from the remainder of the building by 1-hr fire-rated partitions. Similarly, the transfer switch and other electrical distribution panels and switch gear should be separated from the generator, as well as from the remainder of the building.

Fire Alarms

Every building should be equipped with an electrically supervised, manually operated fire alarm system. When actuated, the system should sound alarms that can be heard above ambient noise levels throughout the facility. The fire alarm should also be transmitted automatically to the fire department. Any fire detection or fire suppression system that activates should automatically activate the building alarm system.

Alarm systems, including detection devices, should be provided with an emergency power supply and should be designed according to NFPA 72, *Protective Signaling Systems*.

Any alarm that is activated should provide automatically, without delay, a general alarm. Presignal systems are not considered suitable for health care occupancies. Zoned systems with a coded signal have certain desirable characteristics and should be considered for use.

FIRE SUPPRESSION EQUIPMENT

Many authorities believe the most practical and reliable approach to life safety in health care facilities is to use automatic fire suppression—in particular, automatic sprinkler systems. Although persons in the area of origin may still be seriously threatened, those in adjoining spaces—and, in a number of cases, in the same room—are protected.[2,5,7,16] NFPA 101, *Life Safety Code*, now requires all new health care facilities to be protected by automatic sprinklers.

The ability of automatic sprinklers to provide a survivable environment for building occupants has been debated at length. Full-scale tests have shown that standard sprinklers can extinguish many fires while maintaining a survivable atmosphere outside the room of fire origin.[2,5] In addition, sprinklers have been shown to be effective in limiting carbon monoxide to nonlethal levels outside the room. Tests have also shown that privacy curtains may interfere with sprinkler discharge. To obtain full sprinkler effectiveness, the influence of any building design feature or furnishing that would impair sprinkler discharge should be evaluated carefully.

The quick-response or fast-response sprinkler has been shown in most instances to maintain a survivable atmosphere within the room of fire origin. Recent full-scale tests at NIST have documented this performance.[17]

Where fire defenses are to be based upon automatic sprinkler systems, the use of fast-response sprinklers should be considered for the entire building. As a minimum, fast-response sprinklers should be used throughout compartments having sleeping rooms. This is now required for new health care facilities by NFPA 101, *Life Safety Code*.

Automatic sprinklers should adhere to NFPA 13, *Installation of Sprinkler Systems*. Operation of the sprinklers should sound the building fire alarm automatically. The sprinkler system and components should be supervised electrically to ensure reliable operation; this should include gate valve tamper switches with a local alarm at a constantly attended location when the valve is closed. If a single water supply is provided by a connection for city mains, a low-pressure monitor should be included. If pressure tanks are the primary source of water, air pressure, water level, and temperature also should be supervised. If fire pumps are provided to boost system pressure, electrical supervision should monitor loss of pump power, pump running indication, low system pressure, and low pump suction pressure.

Portable fire extinguishers should be placed in all buildings in conjunction with small hose lines, as they may provide an opportunity to control a fire during its early stages. In all cases, however, the fire department should be notified before or at the same time that occupants are attempting to fight the fire. Delayed alarms have allowed fires to grow to large scale which, in turn, threatens occupants prior to fire department notification and arrival.

Smoke Control

Every patient sleeping room should be provided with an outside window or door that can be opened from the inside. This will allow venting of products of combustion if there is a fire. It may also provide fresh air to patients forced to remain in their rooms during a fire.

A specially designed smoke control and exhaust system can be a desirable alternate to the outside window. Special forced-air systems or, in some cases, the adaptation of conventional building air-handling systems can permit venting of products of combustion early in the fire. Such systems also may make it possible to create a pressure differential across physical barriers, such as floors or partitions, and prevent smoke transfer. The effectiveness of fire partitions is often improved significantly by the use of such systems.

Where adaptation of the building air-handling system is contemplated for smoke removal, the design should be as suggested in NFPA 92A, *Recommended Practice for*

Smoke Control Systems. Consideration should be given to alternate power supplies and electrical supervision of critical system components.

PROTECTION OF HAZARDOUS AREAS

Areas with contents more hazardous than those normally found in health care facilities should be arranged to minimize the exposure to occupants if there is a fire. Hazardous areas, such as boiler and heater rooms, laundries, kitchens, and repair shops, should be separated by 1-hr fire-rated construction, with openings protected by fire doors. As an alternative, the area should be protected by automatic sprinklers and, if the hazard is judged severe, 1-hr separation should also be provided. Typical spaces requiring both separation and sprinklers are soiled linen rooms; paint shops; and rooms or areas, including repair shops and trash collection rooms, used to store combustibles, supplies, and equipment in hazardous quantities.

Laboratories that contain quantities of flammable, combustible, or hazardous materials should be protected and separated from other building spaces. Pertinent information is found in NFPA 30, *Flammable and Combustible Liquids Code*, which is applicable to repair shops as well as laboratories, and in Chapter 10 of NFPA 99, *Health Care Facilities*.

Cooking equipment should be arranged and protected in accordance with NFPA 96, *Removal of Smoke and Grease-Laden Vapors from Commercial Cooking Equipment*.

Nitrous oxide and oxygen are usually piped through hospital spaces from a central distribution point. Although these gases will not burn, they do significantly accelerate combustion. Special precautions are necessary and are detailed in NFPA 50, *Bulk Oxygen Systems at Consumer Sites*, and in NFPA 99, *Health Care Facilities*.

Building Service Equipment

Building service equipment should be installed and maintained in accordance with appropriate NFPA standards. Special consideration should be given to the design and installation of heating and air conditioning systems. Because rubbish chutes have been an important factor in a number of fires,[11] due regard should be given the design of rubbish and linen chutes, including pneumatic systems.

Portable heating devices are unsafe in patient-occupied portions of health care facilities. All heating devices should be designed and installed to prevent ignition of combustible materials. Approved suspended unit heaters may be used, except in means of egress and patient sleeping areas, if they are high enough to be out of the reach of persons using the area.

Combustion and ventilation air for boilers, incinerators, or heater rooms should be taken directly from, and discharged directly to, the outside of the buildings.

OPERATING FEATURES

Many fires in health care facilities are caused by careless smokers. Adoption and enforcement of suitable smoking regulations is essential.[8] Smoking should be prohibited in any room, ward, or compartment where flammable liquids, combustible gases, or oxygen is being used or stored, and such areas should be posted with suitable signs. Smoking by patients who are under sedation or who are not considered responsible should be prohibited. Metal containers with self-closing covers should be available for disposal of smoking materials in all areas where smoking is allowed.

A very interesting debate is emerging on the most effective way to control smoking by patients. Should there be a total ban on smoking? A requirement for supervision? Or isolation of smoking to certain designated areas?

Those who do not favor a total ban can argue that such a policy cannot truly eliminate patient smoking but can only drive it underground, where concealed smoking may involve more hazardous behavior than open smoking. Those who do not favor supervision can argue that health care providers will be so uncomfortable in this role that they will tend to perform it badly or erratically, if at all. Those who do not favor the use of designated areas may be concerned about the hazards of fires starting in those rooms.

Window draperies and curtains should be made of noncombustible material or material that has been rendered and maintained flame retardant. These window hangings should be capable of passing both the large- and small-scale tests required by NFPA 701, *Fire Tests for Flame-Resistant Textiles and Films*. Furnishings, decorations, and other objects should not obstruct exits or exit access routes. Combustible decorations should be prohibited.

Exits and mechanical devices provided to control or limit fire should be maintained to ensure reliable operation. Inspections and tests should be performed, as required, to verify satisfactory performance.

In facilities with locked exits, adequate staff with keys should always be present to release occupants and direct them away from the fire area to a place of safety during an emergency.

Care should be exercised during construction and repair operations to ensure that such activities do not reduce life safety.

Adequate preventive maintenance for mechanical systems, including tests and periodic inspections, are necessary to ensure their reliability.

EMERGENCY PLANNING

Every health care facility must have a fire and evacuation plan, including a disaster plan with which all personnel must be familiar. NFPA 99, *Health Care Facilities*, provides guidance for both internal and external disasters that affect health care facilities. In addition, personnel should be trained to use fire extinguishers and hose cabinet lines. They must also know how to sound an alarm, move or evacuate patients, and contain the fire.

Each facility should have a safety officer whose prime responsibility is to recognize hazards, act as the liaison with the fire service, and arrange for training personnel. While the training of hospital personnel is straightforward and can be accomplished on the job, orienting members of the fire service to hospital problems is more difficult.

Copies of the fire and evacuation plan should be available to all personnel. The plan should contain specific instructions for key—that is, supervisory—personnel if there is a fire. A copy of the plan also should be posted for reference. All employees should have periodic training to ensure readiness.

Emergency drills should include transmission of a fire alarm signal and simulation of emergency conditions insofar as possible without jeopardizing the occupants. Drills should be conducted at least quarterly on each shift, with at least 12 drills held every year. The drills should be varied to test the alertness of all shifts and, if possible, should be unannounced. Use of the building alarm during drills also verifies that it is operating normally.

The fire and evacuation plan should include the following fundamentals:

1. Training personnel in use of the alarm and alarm equipment.
2. Transmission of alarm to the fire department.
3. Details of the fire location.
4. Evacuation practices for all areas.
5. Preparation of building spaces for evacuation.
6. Fire extinguishment.

Emphasis during drills should be placed on immediate notification of the fire department; many fires have spread because of delayed alarms.

BIBLIOGRAPHY

References Cited

1. "Building Materials & Structures," *Report BMS 92*, National Bureau of Standards, Washington, DC, 1942.
2. "Full-Scale Fire Tests in a Nursing Home Patient Room," *Report 7463*, U. S. Department of Health, Education and Welfare. HEW Contract HSA 105-74-116, Prepared by American Health Care Association, 1975.
3. Best, R., "The Wincrest Nursing Home Fire," *Fire Journal*, Vol. 70, No. 5 (Sept. 1976).
4. Best, R., "The Cermak House Fire," *Fire Journal*, Vol. 70, No. 5 (Sept. 1976).
5. O'Neill, J. G., *et al.*, "Full-Scale Fire Tests with Automatic Sprinklers in a Patient Room, Phase II," *NBSIR 80-2097*, 1980, National Bureau of Standards, Gaithersburg, MD, 1980.
6. Lathrop, J. K., *et al.*, "In Osceola, A Matter of Contents," *Fire Journal*, Vol. 69, No. 3 (May 1975).
7. Hall, J. R., Jr, "The Elderly, the Sick, and Health Care Facilities," *Fire Journal*, Vol. 84, No. 4 (July/August 1990).
8. NFPA Fire Analysis Division, "Fatal Fire Risks and Hazards in Health Care Facilities," *Fire Journal*, Vol. 81, No. 5 (Sept./Oct. 1987).
9. Babrauskas, V., "Estimating Room Flashover Potential," *Fire Technology*, May 1980.
10. Babrauskas, V., *et al.*, "Upholstered Furniture Heat Release Rates Measured with a Furniture Calorimeter," *NBSIR 82-2604*, National Bureau of Standards, Washington, DC, 1982.
11. Juillerat, E. E., Jr., "The Hartford Hospital Fire," *NFPA Quarterly*, Vol. 55, No. 3, 1962, pp. 295-303.
12. Sears, A. B., Jr., "Nursing Home Fire, Marietta, OH," *Fire Journal*, Vol. 64, No. 3 (May 1970).
13. Christian, W. J., and Waterman, T. E., "Flame Spread in Corridors: Effects of Location and Area of Wall Finish," *Fire Journal*, Vol. 65, No. 4 (July 1971).
14. Lathrop, J. K., "Nursing Home Fire Causes Two Deaths," *Fire Journal*, Vol. 72, No. 2 (Mar. 1978).
15. Demers, D. P., "25 Die in Nursing Home," *Fire Journal*, Vol. 75, No. 1 (Jan. 1981).
16. Boettcher, E. N., M.D. "Hospital Fire Defense: People and Sprinklers," *Fire Journal*, Vol. 61, No. 4 (July 1967), pp. 93-96.
17. Notarianni, K. A., "Five Small Flaming Fire Tests in a Simulated Hospital Patient Room Protected by Automatic Fire Sprinklers," *Report* of Test FR-3982, National Institute of Standards and Technology, Gaithersburg, MD, Oct. 31, 1990.

Reference

UL Subject 1056, "Outline of Investigation for Upholstered Furniture," Underwriters Laboratories Inc., Northbrook, IL.

NFPA Codes, Standards, and Recommended Practices

Reference to the following NFPA codes, standards, and recommended practices will provide further information on health care facilities discussed in this chapter. (See the latest *NFPA Catalog* for availability of current editions of the following documents.)

NFPA 13, *Installation of Sprinkler Systems.*

NFPA 30, *Flammable and Combustible Liquids Code.*

NFPA 50, *Bulk Oxygen Systems at Consumer Sites.*

NFPA 72, *Protective Signaling Systems.*

NFPA 72E, *Automatic Fire Detectors.*

NFPA 90A, *Air Conditioning and Ventilating Systems.*

NFPA 92A, *Recommended Practice for Smoke Control Systems.*

NFPA 96, *Removal of Smoke and Grease-Laden Vapors from Commercial Cooking Equipment.*

NFPA 99, *Health Care Facilities.*

NFPA 101, *Life Safety Code.*

NFPA 255, *Surface Burning Characteristics of Building Materials.*

NFPA 701, *Fire Tests for Flame-Resistant Textiles and Films.*

Additional Reading

Archea, J., "The Evacuation of Non-Ambulatory Patients from Hospital and Nursing Home Fires: A Framework for a Model," *NBSIR 79-1906*, National Bureau of Standards, Gaithersburg, MD, Nov. 1979.

Bell, L.R., "200 Patients Evacuated in Hospital Fire," *Fire Journal*, Vol. 79, No. 4 (July 1985), pp. 55-63.

Bickman, L., *et al.*, "An Evaluation of Planning and Training for Fire Safety in Health Care Facilities—Phase Two," *NBS-GCR-79-179*, National Bureau of Standards, Gaithersburg, MD, Jan. 1979.

Chapman, R.E., "A Cost-Conscious Guide to Fire Safety in Health Care Facilities," *NBSIR 82-2600*, National Bureau of Standards, Gaithersburg, MD, 1982.

Chapman, R.E., "Assessing the Costs of Fire Protection in Health Care Facilities," *Fire Safety Journal*, Vol. 9, No. 2, 1985, pp. 221-231.

Chapman, R. E., *et al.*, "User's Manual for the Fire Safety Evaluation System Cost Minimizer Computer Program," *NBSIR 83-2797*, National Bureau of Standards, Gaithersburg, MD, 1983.

Chapman, R. E., *et al.*, "Economic Aspects of Fire Safety in Health Care Facilities: Guidelines for Cost Effective Retrofits," *NBSIR 79-1902*, National Bureau of Standards, Gaithersburg, MD, Nov. 1979.

Fire Protection for Hospitals, P8404, Factory Mutual System, Norwood, MA.

Firesafety in Hospitals—Employee's Workbook, National Fire Protection Association, Quincy, MA, 1977.

Firesafety Evaluation System for Health Care Facilities—Student Manual, Office of Planning and Education, U.S. Federal Emergency Management Agency, U.S. Fire Administration, Washington, DC, 1980.

"Firesafety Evaluation of Health Care Facilities," *NBSIR 78-1555*, National Bureau of Standards, Gaithersburg, MD, Nov. 1978.

Hall, J.R., "A Brief Look at Fire Experience in Health Care Facilities," *Fire Journal*, Vol. 80, No. 6 (Nov 1986), p. 51.

Hospital Hazardous Materials, ECRI, Plymouth Meeting, PA, 1987.

Klein, B. R., *ed.*, *Health Care Facilities Handbook*, 2nd ed, National Fire Protection Association, Quincy, MA, 1987.

Klote, J.H., "Smoke Control at Veterans Administration Hospitals," *NBSIR 85-3297*, National Bureau of Standards, Gaithersburg, MD, Jan. 1986.

Krueger, L. J. and Patton, R. M., "More Fire Safety Can Cost Less," Hospitals, Vol. 51 (Feb. 1, 1977), pp. 127-132.

Marchant, E.W., "Hospitals 88," *Fire Technology*, Vol. 24, No. 4, 1988, pp. 369-373.

Marchant, E.W., "Hospital Safety," *Fire Prevention*, No. 213 (Oct. 1988), pp. 27-30.

Meland, O. and Sharet, E., "Smoke Control in Hospitals," *Fire Technology*, Vol. 22, No. 1, 1986, pp. 33-44.

O'Neill, J. G., "Fast Response Sprinklers in Patient Rooms," *Fire Technology*, Vol. 17, No. 4 (Nov. 1981), pp. 254-274.

O'Neill, J. G., *et al.*, "Full-Scale Fire Tests With Automatic Sprinklers in a Patient Room. Phase III," *NBSIR 80-2097*, National Bureau of Standards, Gaithersburg, MD, July 1980.

Palmer, K., "Fire Protection on Health Care Premises," *Fire Prevention*, No. 209 (May 1988), pp. 27-31.

Sprague, J. G., "A Common Sense Approach Needed in Dealing with Safety," *Hospitals*, Vol. 51 (Feb. 1, 1977), pp. 67-75.

Stolland, P., "The Development of a Points Scheme to Assess Fire Safety in Hospitals," *Fire Safety Journal*, Vol. 7, 1984, pp. 145-153.

Sugunendran, S., "New Developments in Hospital Fire Safety," *Fire Prevention*, No. 204 (Nov. 1987), pp. 33-34.

Todd, C., "Fire Saftey in Health Care Premises," *Fire Surveyor*, Vol. 18, No. 1 (Feb. 1989), pp.33-40.

BOARD AND CARE FACILITIES

Revised by William E. Koffel

The residential board and care home, although it has been with us for more than a century, has become an American phenomenon of the 1970s and 1980s. It is estimated that there are more than 300,000 board and care facilities in the United States and that they may house up to 2 million persons. These numbers are guesses because, in many states, such facilities are unregulated and, indeed, unidentified.

The reasons for the growth of this occupancy are numerous. The population of state hospitals was reduced by two-thirds, or nearly 300,000 patients, in the ten-year period from 1969 to 1979. Social, judicial, economic, and therapeutic pressures to remove patients from the restrictive environment of psychiatric hospitals, nursing homes, state schools and other institutional settings helped create a need for board and care facilities. This occupancy provides the deinstitutionalized person with a place to live in a more normal setting, and furnishes the support services the resident needs to cope with the requirements of daily life.

Today's older adults—those over age 65—often live alone, even past the point where they can care for all their own needs. They might need someone to look after their nutrition, personal hygiene, and so on.

Alcohol and drug rehabilitation programs often use the halfway house concept, in which the individual is somewhat sheltered from the pressures of being returned too soon and too quickly to the general population for independent living.

Shelters for battered persons, unwed mothers, and homeless children also became more common in the 1980s.

The fire experience in this type of facility was striking during 1979-1981 and remains a concern today. (See Table 8-14A.) During the first two weeks of April 1979, fires in three board and care homes resulted in 45 fatalities. Many of the multiple-death fires in Table 8-14A resulted in fatalities to over half of the residents, and it is not unusual for these largest fires to totally destroy the facility. At the same time, these fires have been rarer and smaller in the past couple of years; none since June 1986 have made the list in Table 8-14A. This is a hopeful development.

This chapter will examine what makes this occupancy so susceptible to fire and what has to be done if the fire record is to be improved.

DEFINITION

A residential board and care facility is defined in NFPA 101®, *Life Safety Code*®, as a residence which always provides shelter and overnight accommodations, often provides meals, and, as distinct from an ordinary boarding house, provides the residents with some form of personal care. In the fire incident data bases, a board and care facility is defined by the needs of its occupants. It is important to keep these two definitions in mind, because there is no guarantee that the needs of the occupants will match the care provided by the facility. In particular, the care needs of occupants that qualify a property as a board and care facility for fire reporting purposes will often be greater than the care delivered by a facility legitimately constituted as a board and care facility under NFPA 101, *Life Safety Code*.

The NFPA 101, *Life Safety Code*, definition could easily describe a hospital or a nursing home. The primary difference is in the definition of personal care. The care given in a hospital or a nursing home is certainly personal, but its primary purpose is to provide for the medical needs of the patient. In the board and care home, the care provided is not medical in nature, nor is it a type that requires the services of doctors and nurses. It is generally a kind of assistance that can be rendered by laypersons who help the residents cope with the rigors of daily living. This care might include looking after the residents' personal hygiene, cleaning their living quarters, helping those who are physically handicapped to move around, preparing meals, looking after the residents' financial matters, seeing that appointments are kept, and numerous other tasks.

As this discussion implies, NFPA 101, *Life Safety Code*, seeks to identify distinct populations in terms of needed levels of care, and then define distinct categories of facilities that are constituted to provide the level of care needed by some group of potential tenants. A separate

William E. Koffel, P.E., is president, Koffel Associates, Inc., Ellicott City, MD.

TABLE 8-14A. *Board and Care Home Fires Causing Four or More Deaths (1971–1989)**

Date	Occupancy	Civilians Killed
1/73	Rest Home, Pleasantville, NJ	10
3/77	Family Care Home, Dexter, NY	4
2/78	Rooming House, Nashville, TN	4
5/78	Halfway House for State Hospital, Athens, TX	4
7/78	Rooming House, Ashburg Park, NJ	
4/79	Wayside Inn Boarding House, Farmington, MO	25
4/79	Halfway House, Washington, DC	10
4/79	Foster Home, Connellsvile, PA	10
11/79	Coats Boarding Home, Pioneer, OH	14
7/80	Brinkley Inn Boarding Home, Bradley Beach, NJ	24
11/80	Foster Home, Detroit, MI	5
1/81	Beachview Rest Home, Keansburg, NJ	31
2/81	Boarding Home for Elderly, Point Pleasant Beach, NJ	4
12/81	Boarding House for Outpatients, Patchogue, NY	4
10/82	Domicilary Care Home, Pittsburgh, PA	5
2/83	Group Home, Eau Claire, WI	6
3/83	Foster Care House, Gladstone, MI	5
4/83	Community Home, Worcester, MA	7
8/83	Boarding House, Lawrenceville, GA	8
12/83	Group Home for Mentally Retarded, Cincinnati, OH	6
11/84	Board and Care Facility, Lexington, KY	5
5/86	Residential Facility for Metally Impaired, Jacksonville, IL	4
6/86	Boarding House, Detroit, MI	4
6/86	Halfway House, Detroit, MI	4

*The classification as a board and care home is based on the needs of the occupants, specifically the presence of tenants who were over age 65 or had chronic mental illness. The classification is not based on the level of care the facility offered or the level of care it claimed to offer.

Specific facility names are given for only the four largest and best-known incidents.

problem which must be solved, is making sure that tenants are not put in facilities that cannot or will not serve all their needs. That problem, implicit in most of the fires in Table 8-14A, is one for enforcement authorities and is probably the most important key to firesafety for all populations needing care.

Although there are thought to be more than 300,000 board and care homes in the U.S., few such facilities call themselves by that name. Some of the facilities that fit into the definition of this occupancy are:

1. Group homes for mentally retarded persons.
2. Group homes for released psychiatric patients.
3. Rest homes for the aged.
4. Foster care homes.
5. County poor houses.
6. Orphanages.
7. Shelters for battered persons.
8. Shelters for unwed mothers.
9. Halfway houses for rehabilitated alcoholics.
10. Halfway houses for rehabilitated drug abusers.
11. Halfway houses for prison parolees.
12. Shelters for runaways.
13. Rescue missions with overnight accommodations.

Whatever the name, these facilities are all tied together by a common thread: the facility provides its residents with more than just food and shelter. The residents usually are furnished some form of assistance, support, or care that is not of a medical nature.

OCCUPANCY CHARACTERISTICS

Characteristics of Buildings

A board and care facility falls into the ordinary-hazard category by the traditional methods of evaluation under NFPA 101, *Life Safety Code*. There are rarely any massive concentrations of combustible materials and usually no use of flammable liquids or gases. There are no processes to pose "special hazards." Ignition sources are typical of those found in residential occupancies, and fuel loads are generally light. The most significant fire threat in this occupancy is the enormous potential for loss of life.

The buildings that house residential board and care facilities cover a wide range of structural characteristics. They range from single-family dwellings, in which a family takes in a few boarders, to high-rise, reinforced-concrete apartment buildings for the elderly operated by religious organizations, to commercial rest homes built for the purpose. Construction is likely to be of practically any type.

Characteristics of Residents

A description of the characteristics of the "typical" resident of a board and care facility is just as elusive as a description of a "typical" construction type. Residents of board and care homes do not fit into a stereotype—they may be children or elderly, physically impaired or physically sound, mentally handicapped or brilliant. They may be capable of self-preservation or totally dependent upon others to provide for their safety. There is no one description that fits the residents of all board and care homes.

The variations that exist in the buildings and the range of capability of residents in these facilities pose the most significant challenge to fire protection professionals.

FIRE PROBLEMS

The problems of board and care facilities generally fall into two categories: structural and behavioral.

Structural Problems

It is probable that the vast majority of the estimated 300,000 board and care facilities are single-family dwellings or single-family dwellings to which space has been added to accommodate a number of boarders. Consequently, it is probable that the vast majority of facilities are in structures built to standards intended for the housing of a "normal" family with normal abilities to detect, respond to, and escape from a fire.

Building construction: Most facilities are believed to be housed in one-, two-, and three-story wood-frame structures. In older buildings, balloon construction and structural members, exposed by deteriorating plaster, are common structural hazards. Under the best of circumstances, wood-frame construction can offer some measure of protection, but fire endurance is limited and the combustible structure can eventually contribute fuel to a fire.

Exit facilities: Generally, there is only a single route that occupants can use from any given room to get to safety outdoors. This escape route frequently consists of a single unenclosed stairway that might take the escaping residents through the area of the house which is on fire. Often, the only alternative escape route is through a window, which in the case of a three-story building, may be more than 20 ft (6 m) above the ground. Typical of single-family dwellings, exit doors often are equipped with locking devices which impede egress, particularly for those who are either unfamiliar with the locks or incapable of operating them.

Compartmentation: Separation of rooms from corridors and rooms from each other is either nonexistent or of construction which provides little or no resistance to the passage of fire and smoke. Consequently, a fire in any room can quickly fill the entire building with smoke and toxic combustion products, limiting visibility and making the environment intolerable for human survival.

Vertical openings: As with many multi-story dwellings, the stairway, which also serves as the primary means of escape, is not enclosed. The stairs are usually open to the corridor on the upper floors and the living spaces on the first floor. The spread of fire and smoke from one floor to the next can occur very rapidly.

Interior finishes: Frequently, walls and ceilings are finished with paneling and acoustical ceiling tiles without any thought to the combustibility of these materials. The facility owner, trying to improve the environment in which the residents live by providing attractive decor, may be placing them in jeopardy without knowing it.

Highly flammable wall paneling and ceiling tiles contribute to rapid horizontal and vertical fire spread and are frequently a major factor contributing to flashover. Often, they also contribute to the speed with which exit pathways become unusable.

Electrical wiring and appliances: Wiring is generally typical of that found in single-family dwellings. In older buildings, circuits may be inadequate in number and capacity, insulation may be old and deteriorating, fuses may be of the wrong sizes for the circuits they protect, and wiring modifications are likely to have been made by unqualified people. Use of extension cords, portable heaters, and other residential-type electrical appliances contribute to the risk of fire.

Furnishings: The fire hazard posed by furniture and furnishings varies widely. Practically all such products contribute fuel to a fire, with some, of course, being worse than others. There are generally no regulations governing the kinds of furnishings that can be used in a board and care facility. Use of furniture that burns fiercely or gives off inordinately large quantities of thick smoke or toxic combustion products is a major hazard. Often, the residents are permitted to bring an unlimited quantity of their personal furnishings into the facility.

Behavioral Problems

Much of the concern over life safety in board and care facilities arises out of the fact that they house a number of people who, in many cases, have diminished physical and/or mental capacity. Although this is not true in all facilities, or for all residents of a given facility, the very fact that impaired people are residents of a facility that provides them with assistance in coping with daily life suggests that they may have problems fending for themselves.

Behavioral problems generally fall into two categories: evacuation capability and safety consciousness.

Evacuation capability: Because the populations that can be housed in board and care facilities differ widely, a broad statement describing the evacuation capability in all such facilities cannot be made.

In the case of homes for the elderly, some residents may be slow and unsteady, and be unable to manage stairs, to see well, or to remember the procedures to be followed in a fire. Some may be so feeble that they cannot be evacuated without much assistance.

In a group home for high-functioning mentally retarded persons, evacuation capability could be comparable to that expected of a group of unimpaired teenagers.

Residents of some facilities may be physically handicapped to such an extent that self-evacuation is not possible.

Evacuation capability can be affected by the facility's staff. In a facility housing deaf residents, for example, the presence of one staff member who can awaken and alert the residents to the emergency might be sufficient to normalize the evacuation capability of the group. In facilities housing more debilitated handicapped persons, a large staff might still be incapable of effecting a prompt evacuation.

Safety consciousness: One of the factors that makes this occupancy highly prone to fires is that the residents often are unaware of or unconcerned about the dangers of their actions. In many of the small facilities, even the management personnel have little awareness of good life safety and fire prevention practices and procedures. Careless smoking habits, improper use of portable heating units, and improper use of electrical extension cords and appliances are fairly common hazards in many of these facilities. In addition, some residents of board and care facilities have been known to set fires intentionally.

FIRE PROTECTION STRATEGIES

The systems approach to firesafety in correctional facilities can be modified to apply to board and care facilities, as well. (See Section 8, Chapter 15, "Detention and Correctional Facilities.") With respect to life safety, the fire problems in board and care facilities can be addressed by ignition control, fuel control, occupant protection, detection and suppression activities, and planning and training operations.

Ignition Control

Many fatal fires in board and care facilities are started by smoking materials. Each facility should have a smoking policy that addresses such issues as where smoking is permitted and the proper disposal of smoking materials. Clearly, the policy should attempt to prevent ignitions that are caused by occupants falling asleep while smoking or improperly disposing of smoking materials. Proper ash receptacles should be provided in areas where smoking is permitted. For those facilities that permit smoking, designated smoking areas that are usually supervised or in which an occupant is rarely alone have worked well.

Other ignition sources, such as heat-producing appliances, portable heating devices, and electrical equipment, should be controlled and maintained properly. The use of such equipment should be limited to those who are capable of operating the appliance properly or to those who are being trained under supervision. Adequate electrical outlets should be provided to eliminate the use of extension cords.

Fuel Control

In many board and care facilities, the residents are permitted to bring their own furnishings into their sleeping rooms. Most of these furnishings have not been subjected to any type of test that would indicate their ease of ignition or heat-release rates. Where furnishings can be controlled, consideration should be given to items that are resistant to ignition by both cigarettes and small flames. Furnishings also should be evaluated to determine their heat-release rates. Tests of chairs commonly used in board and care facilities have resulted in heat-release rates that are capable of producing flashover in a typical sleeping room without ignition of any other item.

If furnishings cannot be controlled, other protection features, such as early detection, suppression, and compartmentation, should be evaluated to ensure that an acceptable level of protection is provided.

Other fuel sources, such as interior finish materials, also should be evaluated with respect to their potential to spread fire. Interior finish materials have been identified as a major contributing factor in many of the multiple-death fires in board and care facilities.

Occupant Protection

Setting minimum criteria for the protection of life from fire in this broad occupancy type is not a simple matter. As indicated, this is not a homogeneous occupancy. What is minimum protection in one facility may be overprotection or inadequate protection in another. In few, if any, other property classes is it so difficult to ensure over time that the tenants in residence require all the care and fire protection provided by the facility, but no more. However, it will always be appropriate to require a certain level of protection for the occupants, particularly for those who are not intimate with the fire from its onset.

Perhaps the evacuation capability of the residents is the most significant factor in determining the fire protection features needed to achieve an acceptable level of life safety in a given board and care home. In a facility that houses a group with a fairly normal ability to respond to a fire, relatively little protection may be needed. In buildings housing people who can respond to an emergency, but who do so slowly, a protection system that provides them a little extra time to react and evacuate may be adequate. For groups that cannot be expected to evacuate to safety unaided, a defend-in-place protection system may be needed.

One might suspect that, over a period of time, all facilities may house residents who are incapable of evacuation, so that protection for the worst situation should be provided. This approach is valid in the instance of homes for the aged, where deteriorating physical and mental conditions are predictable. However, there are many types of board and care facilities that, because of their size and the nature of the services they provide, never deal with people who are incapable of self-preservation. Such facilities should not be required to provide the same degree of built-in fire protection as those which house less capable populations. Therefore, it is reasonable to establish fire protection criteria based upon the evacuation capability of the residents of the facility. More or less built-in protection would be required, depending upon the residents' ability to fend for themselves.

For a population with relatively normal evacuation capability, the most basic system of protection consists of:

1. Controls to prevent ignition.
2. Prompt detection.
3. Means to alert the residents to the existence of a fire.
4. At least two routes by which to escape from the endangered area.
5. Prohibition of the use of highly flammable interior finish materials. (This limits the rate of fire spread and minimizes the risk of flashover.)
6. Some form of enclosure of vertical openings. (This limits the vertical spread of fire and smoke.)

For a population that is able to evacuate, but does so slowly or with difficulty, a reasonable system of protection would include all the items listed above, plus:

1. Tighter controls to prevent ignition.
2. Early detection.
3. Exits that are easier to use than those that might be adequate for a more capable population.
4. Tighter controls on the flammability of interior finishes.
5. Inclusion of a degree of fire endurance to maintain building integrity during a longer evacuation period.
6. Inclusion of a degree of compartmentation to confine the fire and smoke, thus keeping the exit pathways usable during the longer evacuation period.
7. Greater resistance to the vertical spread of fire and smoke.

For a population that is not capable of evacuation, a defend-in-place protection concept would include all the features listed above, plus:

1. Sufficient structural fire endurance to allow the building and the internal compartmentation to outlast the fire.
2. A means of automatically suppressing the fire before it becomes a serious threat to the structure and the compartmentation.
3. Controls on fuels, such as furnishings.

These protective concepts are the same as those used in various other occupancies in which people sleep overnight. For a detailed set of criteria for life safety in this occupancy, see Chapters 22 and 23 of NFPA 101, *Life Safety Code*.

Detection and Suppression Activities

The means by which ignition controls and fuel controls are implemented, as well as the occupant's evacuation capability, are critical factors in determining the appropriate level of detection and suppression necessary. In sleeping areas, residential sprinklers should be considered as a means of increasing life safety. In accordance with NFPA 101, *Life Safety Code*, either an NFPA 13D, 13R, or 13 system may be used in board and care facilities, depending on the size of the facility and the evacuation capability of the occupants. With respect to NFPA 13D, it should be recognized that the water supply duration need only be 10 minutes, and the domestic water demand is not necessarily included. With respect to NFPA 13D and 13R, it should be recognized that sprinklers may be omitted from certain areas such as small closets, bathrooms, attics and other areas in which the data indicate that fatal fires rarely originate. A system installed in accordance with NFPA 13 will result in sprinklers installed throughout the building. While NFPA 13 does not mandate residential sprinklers, it certainly permits residential sprinklers. (See bibliography for NFPA titles.)

In addition to the desired level of protection, insurance carriers and applicable codes should be consulted before selecting detection and suppression systems. The preventive maintenance requirements of each type of system should also be considered during the selection and design process.

Planning and Training Operations

The facility management should ensure that an emergency plan is developed that covers various emergencies or disasters, including fires. The plan should be realistic and capable of being implemented with the minimum resources that may be available, typically during the night. The plan should be coordinated with the local fire department to ensure that their expectations and the expectations of the facility are consistent. Periodically during the year, the plan should be re-evaluated with an exercise that tests its various aspects.

Depending on the residents' capabilities, they should participate in the training and drills. As discussed above, the residents need to be familiar and comfortable with the various egress paths available to them. Local fire departments, fire training schools, and fire marshal offices may have personnel and audio-visual materials that can assist in the training of staff and residents.

BIBLIOGRAPHY

NFPA Codes, Standards, and Recommended Practices

Reference to the following NFPA codes, standards, and recommended practices will provide further information on board and care facilities discussed in this chapter. (See the latest *NFPA Catalog* for availability of current editions of the following documents.)

NFPA 13, *Installation of Sprinkler Systems.*

NFPA 13D, *Installation of Sprinkler Systems in One- and Two-Family Dwellings and Mobile Homes.*

NFPA 13R, *Installation of Sprinkler Systems in Residential Occupancies Up to Four Stories in Height.*

NFPA 101®, *Life Safety Code®.*

NFPA 101M, *Alternative Approaches to Life Safety.*

Additional Reading

Alvord, D. M., "The Escape and Rescue Model—A Simulation Model for the Emergency Evacuation of Board and Care Homes," *NBS-GCR-83-453,* National Bureau of Standards, Gaithersburg, MD, Dec. 1983.

Berlin, G. N., *et al.*, "Modeling Emergency Evacuation from Group Homes," *Fire Technology,* Vol. 18, No. 1, (Feb. 1982), pp. 38-48.

Blye, P. and Yess, J. R., *Fire Safety in Boarding Homes: A Self-Study Guide for Owners and Operators,* National Fire Protection Association, Quincy, MA, 1985.

Blye, P. and Yess, J. P., "Firesafety in Elderly Housing," *Fire Journal, Vol. 81, No. 6, (1987), pp. 28-30, 75-76.*

"Board and Care Homes: A Study of Federal and State Actions to Safeguard the Health and Safety of Board and Care Home Residents," U.S. Department of Health and Human Services, Washington, DC, 1982.

Cote, R. and Timoney, T., "Boarding House Fire Causes Fifteen Deaths," *Fire Journal,* Vol. 79, No. 1, (Jan. 1985), pp. 44-48, 50-54.

Groner, N. E., "A Matter of Time—A Comprehensive Guide to Fire Emergency Planning for Board and Care Homes," *NBS-GCR-82-408,* National Bureau of Standards, Gaithersburg, MD, Nov. 1982.

Groner, N. E., *Fire Safety In Board and Care Homes,* Project SHARE, Rockville, MD, 1986.

Isner, M. S. and Smith, R., "Fire in Boarding Home: A Success Story," *Fire Journal,* Vol. 80, No. 2 (Mar. 1986), p.75.

Lathrop, J. K., *ed., Life Safety Code Handbook,* 5th ed, National Fire Protection Association, Quincy, MA, 1991.

Levin, B. M. *ed.*, "Fire and Life Safety for the Handicapped," *NBS-STP-585,* National Bureau of Standards, Gaithersburg, MD, July 1980.

Levin, B. M. and Nelson, H. E., "Firesafety and Disabled Persons," *Fire Journal,* Vol. 75, No. 5 (Sept. 1981), pp. 35-40.

Nelson, H. E., *et al.*, "A Fire Safety Evaluation System for Board and Care Homes," *NBSIR 83-2659,* National Bureau of Standards, Gaithersburg, MD, Mar. 1983.

Pearson, R. G. and Joost, M. G., "Egress Behavior Response Times of Handicapped and Elderly Subject to Simulated Residential Fire Situation," *NBS-GCR-83-429,* National Bureau of Standards, Gaithersburg, MD, 1983.

Waller, M. B. and Vreeland, R. G., "Report of a Conference on Fire Emergency Plans in Group Homes for the Developmentally Disabled," *NBS-GCR-81-315,* National Bureau of Standards, Gaithersburg, MD, Mar. 1981.

DETENTION AND CORRECTIONAL FACILITIES

Wayne G. Carson

Detention and correctional occupancies include buildings and facilities in which persons are restrained by locks not under their control. Such occupancies include adult correctional institutions, adult local detention facilities, adult community residential centers, juvenile detention facilities, juvenile training schools, juvenile community residential centers, adult and juvenile work camps, and adult and juvenile substance abuse centers. Some mental hospitals and nursing homes may have similar security provisions, but this chapter addresses only facilities where controlled movements are not based entirely on health care considerations. Security is a major operational consideration in these facilities and must be included in the fire protection design process.

Large correctional facilities may contain other occupancies, including industrial occupancies, such as vocational shops; business occupancies, such as classrooms and offices; assembly occupancies, such as dining halls, auditoriums, and gymnasiums; and storage occupancies, such as warehouses. The principal concern of Chapters 14 and 15 of NFPA 101®, *Life Safety Code®*, is the residential portion of correctional facilities. Except for the locking of doors, other uses within the detentional and correctional occupancy must comply with the appropriate occupancy chapter of NFPA 101. If locking these occupancies is required, Chapters 14 and 15 of NFPA 101 should be reviewed for guidance. The other occupancies are discussed elsewhere in this section.

Additional information relevant to firesafety in correctional institutions can be found in Section 1, Chapter 3, "Systems Concepts for Building Firesafety;" Section 6, Chapter 4, "Interior Finish;" Section 6, Chapter 7, "Smoke Movement in Buildings;" and the Portable Fire Extinguisher chapters in Section 5.

OCCUPANCY CHARACTERISTICS

The major difference between a detention and correctional occupancy and other residential occupancies is that the occupants are not capable of significant self-preservation actions until someone on the staff unlocks the doors. However, the occupants are capable of such actions when the doors are unlocked.

The degree of locking can have a significant impact on the risk to the occupants. For example, a facility with only two locks that can be remotely released to allow the occupants out of the building into a controlled exercise yard generally would present less risk to the occupants than one that required 15 locks to be unlocked manually with 10 different keys.

The protection provided generally depends on the degree of locking. Five types of restraint or locking systems are generally found in detention and correctional occupancies. These different locking conditions, referred to as "use conditions" by NFPA 101, *Life Safety Code*, are illustrated in Figure 8-15A and defined as follows.

Use Condition I—Free Egress

Free movement is allowed from sleeping areas and other spaces where access or occupancy is permitted to the exterior through means of egress meeting the requirements of NFPA 101, *Life Safety Code.* For example, work release centers, where the doors are not locked, would be considered Use Condition I. Use Condition I is not considered detention and correction facilities, and is addressed in other residential chapters of the code.

Use Condition II—Zoned Egress

Free movement is allowed from sleeping areas and any other occupied smoke compartments to other smoke compartments.

Use Condition III—Zoned Impeded Egress

Free movement is allowed within individual smoke compartments—for example within a residential unit composed of individual sleeping rooms and within group activity space—with egress from that smoke compartment to another smoke compartment provided by the remote-control unlocking of doors.

Wayne G. Carson, P.E., is principal of Carson Associates, Inc., Fire Protection Consultants, Warrenton, VA.

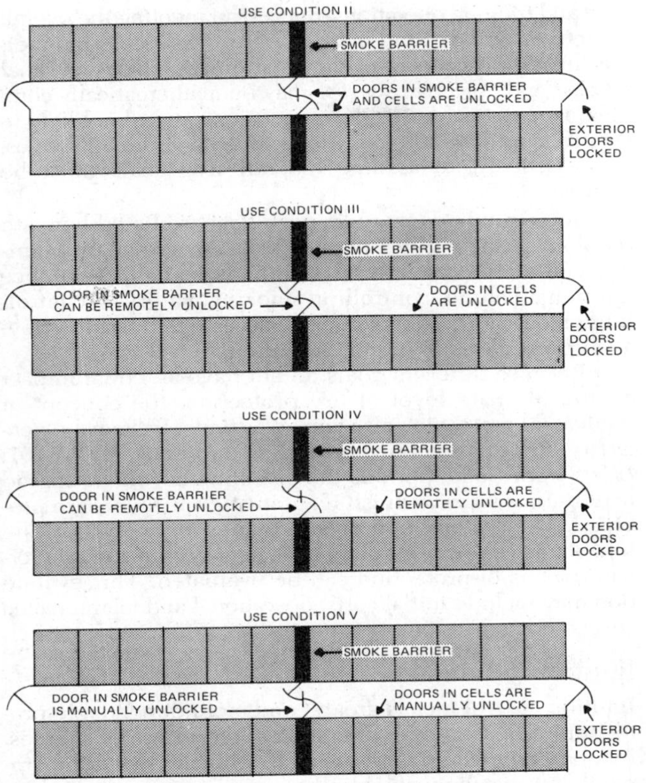

FIG. 8-15A. Classes of restraint, use conditions II, III, IV, and V.

Use Condition IV—Impeded Egress

Free movement is restricted from an occupied space. Remote-control release is provided to permit movement from all sleeping rooms, activity spaces, and other occupied areas within the smoke compartment to other smoke compartment(s).

Use Condition V—Contained

Free movement is restricted from an occupied space. Staff-controlled manual release at each door is provided to permit movement from all sleeping rooms, activity spaces, and other occupied areas within the smoke compartment to other smoke compartments.

THE FIRE PROBLEM

The fire problem in correctional facilities is statistically analyzed by NFPA each year.[1] An expanded version of this analysis which appears in Table 8-15A, identifies the significant common characteristics of correctional facility fires and groups them into several categories.

Most fires in detention and correctional facilities are incendiary or suspicious in nature. Motives may include:

1. Increased chances of escape.
2. Malicious damage as a protest against conditions.
3. Show of force during a riot.
4. Suicide attempt.

In nearly all of the intentionally set fires for which the ignition source could be identified, the source was a match, smoking materials, or a cigarette lighter. These are the ignition sources most readily available to inmates.

TABLE 8-15A. ***Patterns of Fires in Prisons and Jails, 1984–1988***

Category	Fires per Year	
Major Cause		
Incendiary or suspicious causes	2,200	(71.3%)
Smoke materials (i.e., lighted tobacco products)	300	(8.0%)
Open flame, embers, or torches	100	(4.8%)
Matches	100	(2.3%)
Appliances, tooks, or air conditioning	100	(4.4%)
Dryers	100	(2.4%)
Electrical distribution system	100	(3.0%)
Cooking equipment	100	(2.6%)
Other equipment	100	(2.4%)
Heating equipment	100	(1.7%)
Natural causes	0	(0.8%)
Other heat source	0	(0.4%)
Exposure (to other hostile fire)	0	(0.3%)
Child playing	0	(0.1%)
Total	3,100	(100.0%)
Leading Areas of Fire Origin		
Cell or other bedroom	1,900	(61.6%)
Hallway in corridor	200	(4.8%)
Laundry room	100	(4.0%)
Kitchen	100	(3.5%)
Bathroom or locker room	100	(2.2%)
Leading Areas First Ignited		
Mattress or bedding	1,100	(35.9%)
Trash	500	(16.9%)
Paper	200	(7.9%)
Clothing not on a person	200	(6.3%)
Wire or cable insulation	100	(3.3%)
Linen other than bedding	100	(3.0%)

Source: 1984–88 NFIRS, NFPA Survey

Fires are expressed to the nearest hundred, property damage to the nearest hundred thousand dollars. Property damage figures have not been adjusted for inflation. Percentages are calculated on the actual estimates, so two figures with the same rounded-off estimates may have different percentages.

The 12 major cause categories are based on a hierarchy developed by the U.S. Fire Administration. Sums may not equal totals because of rounding errors.

The typical correctional facility fire is incendiary in origin, starts in a cell, and involves bedding, trash or papers, or clothing or other soft goods. A serious fire would generate intense heat and dense smoke, and quickly spread to corridors and adjoining areas, significantly hampering the safe evacuation of the inmates and the staff.

THE SYSTEMS APPROACH TO FIRESAFETY IN CORRECTIONAL FACILITIES

In dealing with the firesafety problem in correctional facilities, two concerns need to be addressed continually: security for the public and safety from fire for the inmates. The systems approach to firesafety helps to achieve these two objectives through a systematic analysis of each problem area and application of available technologies. Firesafety should be an integrated subsystem of building design, construction, and operation. This method of designing firesafety is known as the systems approach or systems concept of firesafe building design. (See Section 1, Chapter 3, "Systems Concepts for Building Firesafey.") A system organizes interacting components in such a way that, working together, they can perform a predetermined function or reach a specified objective. The use of the systems approach first requires that firesafety goals be clearly identified. These goals should describe the amount of protection a building should provide its occupants, contents, and operations, and the methods used to achieve these goals should work collectively to reach and maintain a prescribed level of firesafety. These goals should be quantified wherever possible.

The systems approach can be illustrated by the simplified firesafety system for correctional facilities. (See Figure 8-15B.) As shown by the box at the top of the diagram, the four objectives of the simplified firesafety system are:

Life safety: The protection of life is paramount in any fire. Occupants can be protected by providing a safe area of refuge from the fire within the building or by providing a safe and readily available path of travel to the outside.

Property protection: The protection of property is also of concern, particularly with today's higher replacement costs. Some areas may be considered more important than others—for example, a control room *versus* a storage room—and therefore require more protection.

Limited downtime: This involves providing protection to limit fire damage so an area can be returned quickly to use. For example, the loss of a storage area may not seriously affect the prison's operation, as trailers or other temporary storage units can be obtained quickly. However, loss of the kitchen could seriously affect a prison's operation.

Security: The primary function of a correctional facility is to maintain a secure perimeter. Firesafety must be compatible with this function.

These objectives are achieved through a series of goals: (1) ignition control, (2) fuel control, (3) occupant protection, (4) detection and suppression activities, and (5) planning and training operations. Success in meeting the overall objectives will depend on the degree of success in meeting these five goals, and the relationships between goal success and objective success may be mathematically complex. In practical terms, however, no one goal is likely to be sufficient by itself to achieve success of the objectives, so it is safest to assume that all five goals must be addressed.

Some methods to attain each goal are listed beneath the goal as shown by Figure 8-15B. For the goal of ignition control, for example, the methods available to reduce ignitions include: controlling smoking materials, controlling electrical ignition sources, and using alternate grievance procedures to reduce intentionally set fires.

Because different goals do not have an equal impact on the ultimate level of fire protection, the concept of equivalent protection, also known as tradeoffs, may be necessary. For example, under certain conditions, NFPA 101, *Life Safety Code*, permits the use of higher flame spread materials as interior finish if automatic sprinklers are provided. The systems approach provides for analysis of the interacting components of the firesafety system so that alternate means of protection can be evaluated. This evaluation may include initial costs, operational and maintenance costs, and impact on operations.

Ignition Control

Ignition control means greater and more dependable protection of heat sources and separation from fuel sources. In a property where most fires are deliberately set, this primarily means eliminating unnecessary heat sources. Unfortunately, total ignition control is nearly impossible to establish and may therefore be the least effective fire defense measure. Sources of ignition are nearly always available because cigarettes and matches are, in most cases, available to inmates, and electrical appliances are sometimes allowed in cells. However, an effort must be made to control unwanted or unnecessary ignition sources. The

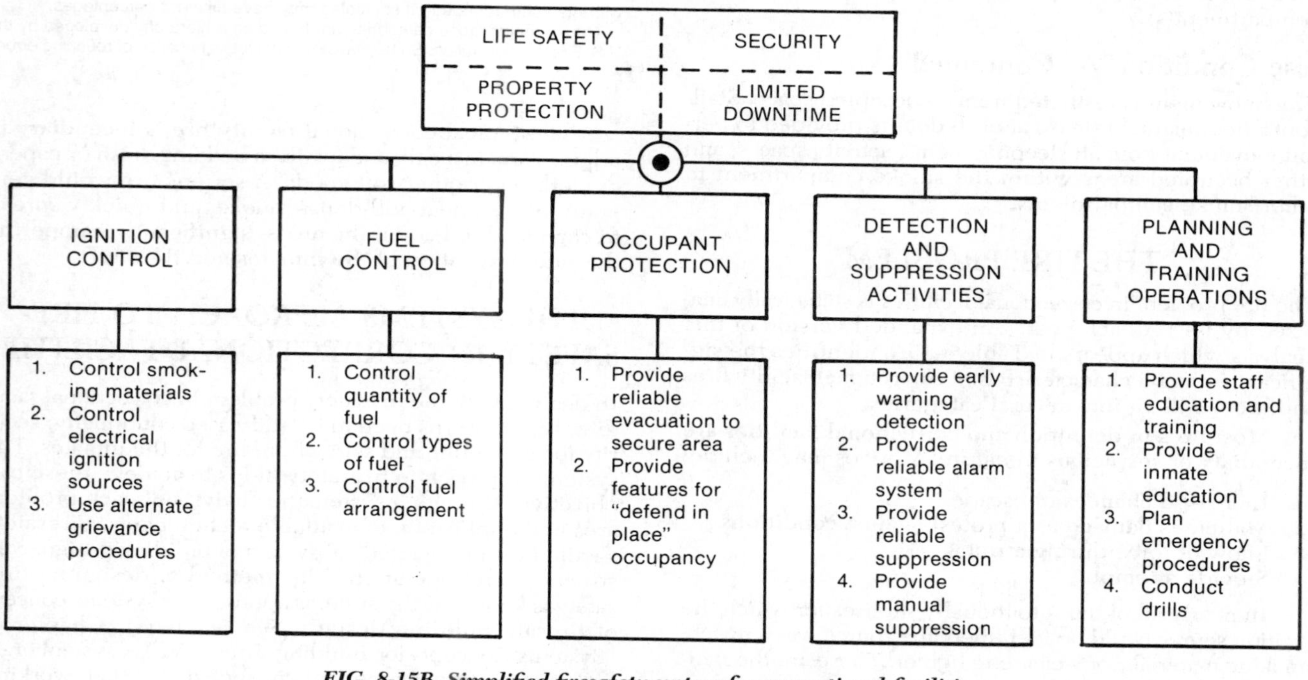

FIG. 8-15B. Simplified firesafety system for correctional facilities.

types of lighters or matches can be specified, and the overall use of electrical power must be carefully supervised. The number and type of heat-producing appliances, such as toasters, hot plates, and space heaters, must be controlled by the facility administrator to prevent overloading circuits. If electrical devices are allowed in the cell adequate electrical outlets should be provided to discourage the use of extension cords.

Fuel Control

Fuel control means controlling the type, arrangement, and burning characteristics of potential fuels. These fuels may include the building structural system, interior finish materials, and combustible contents, such as furnishings and inmates' personal property. Assuming that heat sources will be available, the likelihood of fire and the rate of growth in hazard if a fire occurs can be controlled by limiting the type, quantity, and arrangement of the fuels available. Limiting the speed at which fire develops and spreads reduces its impact on life safety. Slow-burning fires give people and suppression equipment time to react.

However, fast fires—those with a rapid rate of smoke development, flame spread, and production of toxic gases—have been significant factors in fire deaths in correctional facilities. Ordinary combustible materials, such as low-density fiberboard ceilings, thin plywood paneling, and some plastics used in furnishings and interior finish, can contribute to fast fire development.

Achieving the goal of fuel control means keeping fuel quantity at a minimum, controlling the type of fuel, eliminating those fuels that are easy to ignite or result in fast fires, and separating fuels from readily available ignition sources. One part of fuel control is to govern furnishings, such as mattresses. Since mattresses and bedding are the fuel sources most readily available to inmates, they are the ones most frequently involved in fires. Certain types of polyurethane foam mattresses have been a significant fuel source in many prison fires because they typically result in fast fire development, high heat release, and heavy smoke production.

Mattresses can be made to resist ignition from cigarettes, which is a low-heat ignition source. The federal "Flammability Standard for Mattresses"[2] requires that mattresses resist ignition by cigarettes placed at 18 specified locations. This test does not include sheets or blankets on the mattress and does not indicate the resistance to ignition from open flames or the intensity of the resulting fire. A series of tests of mattresses by the U.S. Department of Agriculture[3] concluded that "the data show that mattresses containing polyurethane foam easily comply with the FF4-72 standard[2] where cigarettes are the igniting source; however, such mattresses present a significant hazard where the igniting source is an open flame. Mattresses containing 100 percent polyurethane foam usually burn vigorously until little char remains. Burning in such cases is accompanied by the release of copious amounts of black smoke."

In 1977, the National Bureau of Standards (NBS) conducted fire tests of mattresses and issued a report[4] which categorized mattresses into four groups in order of safety, as follows.

Group A: Mattresses that did not exceed any of the tenability criteria for the duration of the 30-min test. This group included two treated, cotton-batting mattresses.

Group B: Mattresses that only exceeded the smoke obscuration criterion. Two neoprene mattresses were in this category.

Group C: Mattresses that exceeded all tenability criteria, but did not cause full room involvement. This group included three polyurethane foam-core mattresses and one of mixed fiber construction. The best-performing polyurethane mattress was of the type associated with a multiple-life-loss prison fire.

Group D: Mattresses that exceeded all criteria. Included were one styrene-butadiene latex foam core and one polyurethane foam-core mattress. The latex mattress was of the type associated with a multiple-life-loss fire in a health care institution.

These tests indicate that the best mattresses for use in correctional facilities are those with padding material of cotton treated with boric acid. Mattresses of cotton treated with boric acid pass FF4-72 and perform well when exposed to open-flame ignition sources. Such mattresses will burn, but at a much slower rate than urethane foam mattresses.[5] Some promising new materials are entering the market for mattress padding, including treated neoprene. Since there is no national standard for open-flame ignition testing of mattresses, however, each jurisdiction must evaluate new mattress materials carefully and thoroughly.

Inmate possessions and furnishing in the cell must be controlled in order to limit the size of fire that can be expected. Books, clothing, and other combustible personal property allowed in cells should be stored in closable metal lockers or fire-resistant containers. Combustible decorations should be prohibited unless they have been treated with flame retardants. Draperies, curtains, or other decorative and acoustical materials should be noncombustible or rendered and maintained flame-resistant according to NFPA 701, *Fire Tests for Flame-Resistant Textiles and Films.*

Interior finish has been a major factor in several prison fires that resulted in multiple deaths. Interior finish materials contribute fuel to a fire, they may accelerate room flashover, and they can result in rapid fire spread. Materials that have high flame spread rates would contribute substantial quantities of fuel to a fire, or produce hazardous concentrations of smoke or noxious gases should not be used. This includes plastic wall finish material, fiberboard, thin paneling, and untreated plywood. (See Table 8-15B.) Interior finish alternatives with good fire characteristics include paneling treated to provide Class A interior finish with a flame spread of 25 or less, painted steel, gypsum board, or masonry block.

Occupant Protection

Occupant protection means providing life safety to building occupants in case of fire. This may be accomplished either by evacuating them to a secure area or by defending them in place. This goal is the most controversial in the firesafety system for correctional facilities because "evacuation" is often interpreted by administrators and staff to mean "escape." While this is not a valid assumption, means of egress does directly affect security.

With reference to the evacuation of inmates, most detention and correctional facilities can be grouped into two general types, based on their physical arrangement. In the first group are larger institutions that have an inner secure area such as an outdoor ball field or courtyard. It

TABLE 8-15B. ***Flame Spread of Some Building Materials****

Material	Flame Spread
Ceilings	
Glass-fiber sound-absorbing blankets	15 to 30
Mineral-fiber sound-absorbing panels	10 to 25
Shredded wood fiberboard (treated)	20 to 25
Sprayed cellulose fibers (treated)	20
Walls	
Aluminum (with baked enamel finish on one side)	5 to 10
Asbestos cement board	0
Brick or concrete block	0
Cork	175
Gypsum board (with paper surface on both sides)	10 to 25
Northern Pine (treated)	20
Southern Pine (untreated)	130 to 190
Plywood paneling (untreated)	75 to 275
Plywood paneling (treated)	10 to 25
Red Oak (untreated)	100
Red Oak (treated)	35 to 50
Floors	
Carpeting	10 to 600
Concrete	0
Linoleum	190 to 300
Vinyl asbestos tile	10 to 50

* For a comprehensive list of flame spread and smoke developed ratings for proprietary materials, see the current edition of *Building Materials Directory* published by Underwriters Laboratories Inc.

is possible to evacuate inmates rapidly from the fire area to this area of refuge and still maintain security. In the second category are the smaller city or county facilities where there is no separate, secure outdoor area of refuge. In these facilities, in which there are no enclosed courtyards or other areas into which to evacuate inmates and still maintain security, it becomes necessary to defend the inmates in place from fire.

A defend-in-place occupancy is a workable and accepted means of providing firesafety for building occupants and is commonly used to protect persons in hospitals and nursing homes. The technology exists to defend inmates in place so that only a few cells need to be evacuated—possibly only the cell of fire origin. A defend-in-place occupancy, as well as an occupancy using evacuation to a secure area of refuge, needs a reliable means of egress. Although means for defending the occupants in place are provided, it is always considered necessary to provide reliable exits. According to NFPA 101, *Life Safety Code*, this means that two distinct paths of travel must be provided from each cellblock or area. The exits should be remote from each other so that a single fire cannot readily block both. In addition, travel distances must not exceed those specified by NFPA 101; the normal distance recommended is 150 ft (45 m), but the length can vary depending upon the protection provided. The travel distance can be increased up to 50 percent if the building is sprinklered. The exit access needs to be free and unobstructed, and it should not be circuitous or require travel through several rooms, long corridors, or many stairs. An exit access that requires travel through a room or an area containing a fire hazard higher than usual for the occupancy violates the principles of safe egress. Dead-end corridors are not good practice because a fire in a dead end between an exit and an occupant can prevent the occupant from reaching the exit. Exitways need to be illuminated continuously, and emergency lighting must be provided. Exits and the paths to them should be clearly marked. However, NFPA 101 permits the elimination of exit signs in inmate housing areas where no visitors are permitted. The rationale for this is that the inmates cannot leave until someone unlocks the doors and that the inmates are generally familiar with the door locations.

Compartmentation is an important aspect of occupant protection, whether inmates are evacuated or defended in place. The walls, ceilings, and floors of fire compartment boundaries must be fire-resistant. Openings must be protected with self-closing, fire-rated doors. The degree of fire protection these elements provide depends on the degree of hazard the occupancy presents, or its fuel loading; the type of building construction—for example, fire resistive *vs.* combustible and the function served, such as a load-bearing or nonload-bearing wall.

Controlling smoke means controlling the type and quantity of materials used in the building construction and building contents, and providing a means of restricting smoke movement within the building. Dilution, which is reducing smoke concentration by introducing massive quantities of uncontaminated air into a building, is not always satisfactory when used alone, since smoke may be generated in such quantities that adequate dilution may not be obtained. Prudent use and placement of automatically opening vents can provide some relief from smoke and the products of combustion in small, one-story buildings. However, the confinement of smoke can best be achieved by providing a physical barrier, such as a wall with self-closing doors and dampers that restricts smoke movement, and by using a pressure differential across the physical barrier to prevent smoke from entering the non-fire area. The building's heating, ventilating, and air-conditioning (HVAC) system can be designed to provide this pressurization. Physical barriers alone usually are not effective in controlling smoke movement because they have many penetrations, and the fire, the building HVAC, and/or the weather conditions create uncontrolled pressures. NFPA 92A, *Smoke Control Systems*, provides information on the design and installation of smoke control systems.

Since the primary objective of detention and correction facilities is security, reliable locking systems are essential. However, problems with locking systems have played a major role in many correctional fire tragedies. Therefore, whatever their type, locking systems must function reliably in emergencies, whether a facility is designed to evacuate its inmates or to defend them in place. Individual key locks have proven to be the most unreliable for several reasons, including the time required to unlock each door, the loss of keys during an emergency, key breakage during an emergency, heat and smoke prohibiting entry into the cell block, and confusion due to the number of keys required.

Detection and Suppression Activities

Detection and suppression activities deal directly with the fire—detecting its presence, sounding an alarm to alert occupants, and inhibiting fire growth by active fire suppression. To achieve this goal, the following must be provided: an early warning fire detection system, a reliable alarm system, and a reliable fire suppression system.

There are three separate phases of detection and suppression activities, each of which can be performed automatically or manually. (See Table 8-15C.) Automatic and manual systems can also be combined. For example, detection can be provided by smoke detectors installed throughout the facility with manual fire fighting by fire brigade personnel using a standpipe hose. However, any system requiring manual intervention requires that someone make a decision and requires time for human action. The human element is generally the most unreliable part of a firesafety system.

TABLE 8-15C. ***Stages of Detection and Suppression***

Stage	Manual	Automatic
Detection	Inmate or guard detects fire	Sprinklers detect fire
Alarm	Guard verbally transmits information to other guards	Activates water flow switch
Suppression	Guards use extinguishers to suppress fire	Sprinklers begin extinguishment immediately

The effectiveness of fire detection and suppression systems depends on the rate of the fire growth and the time from ignition until detection and, eventually, suppression activities are begun. If the fuel is capable of producing a fast fire, as it is in padded cells, the extinguishing agent, usually water, must be applied to the fire very quickly after ignition. This is very difficult to do with manual fire suppression even if early warning fire detection, such as automatic smoke detectors, is available. Automatic sprinklers provide the most reliable method of fire detection and suppression and they need no human intervention. With an automatic sprinkler system, the extinguishment phase begins almost simultaneously with detection and alarm, a response difficult to achieve with manual suppression.

Sprinklers have been, and are being, installed quite successfully in detention and correctional facilities throughout the U.S. and Canada. Sprinklers control fire development, thereby reducing the production of heat and smoke. They also give fire service personnel a better opportunity to begin rescue and extinguishment operations. Automatic sprinklers can reduce property loss and limit downtime. In addition, they offer several economic advantages: insurance premiums may be reduced with the installation of sprinkler protection; many building codes offer tradeoffs when sprinklers are used, thereby reducing building costs; and sprinklers can be installed at a discount in correctional facilities by inmates under the supervision of a qualified fire protection engineer. Sprinklers may also result in fewer persons being evacuated, reduce the burden for manual fire fighting, and, in effect, increase security.

Smoke detectors are required in the sleeping areas of detention and correctional occupancies by NFPA 101, *Life Safety Code*. However, smoke detectors often are not connected to sound the building alarms automatically nor to cause the transmission of the alarm to the fire department automatically. Smoke detectors are sensitive devices and may be prone to needless or nonfire emergency alarms. Therefore, they may alarm at a constantly attended location, such as a Control Room. A manual fire alarm system is also required. NFPA 101 does permit the manual stations to be locked, provided the staff has the keys. In addition, the alarm systems should be connected directly to the local fire department. Manual suppression ability should include portable fire extinguishers of the proper type and number, readily accessible fire hose stations for use by correctional officers, and a means to stretch fire hoses through double security gates, or sallyports, so the gates can be closed and security maintained. All automatic detection and suppression systems and manual equipment need to be inspected and tested regularly.

Planning and Training Operations

Planning and training means conducting training activities among inmates and staff and planning emergency operating procedures. To achieve this goal, the following methods are used: staff education and training, inmate education, planning emergency procedures, and conducting drills. Planning and training require little capital investment in equipment, but they can make a big difference in reducing the impact of a potentially disastrous fire, especially in a system where fire defenses are marginal. In addition, planning and training are important to maintain a high level of security during a fire.

Because firesafety should be everyone's concern, both staff and inmates should be involved in a firesafety program. Each shift should practice the fire emergency plan at least quarterly, and new employees should be briefed routinely on the fire emergency plan. Inmates should be instructed in emergency procedures. Safety information may also be included in an inmate information booklet.

The firesafety program should be designed to meet the needs of the facility; the size and age of the buildings and the security classification of the facility, as well as its proximity to municipal fire departments, should be considered. All programs should include a short description of the background and evolution of the problem; how to recognize, prevent, and reduce fire hazards; information on the fire protection technology available for application at the facility; hands-on training for staff and inmate fire brigades; emergency operating procedures; and identification of potential problems that affect firesafety.

Fire brigades should be equipped and trained to deal effectively with a fire emergency. Brigade responsibility and functions will vary with the size of the facility and the size and location of the nearest fire department, but they should include calling the fire department, safeguarding lives, providing manual suppression to control the fire until the fire department arrives, and protecting equipment. In large facilities, personnel should be organized into separate fire fighting teams assigned to predetermined areas.

Each building in a correctional facility should have a written fire emergency plan detailing staff action during a fire emergency. The plan provides a guide for evaluating the particular problems and coordinating the response of the fire brigade, fire department, staff, and inmates. Emergency plans should be simple yet comprehensive, specific, flexible, and workable. Preparing the plan can be accomplished in five steps:

1. Define the potential fire protection problems in the particular correctional facility.
2. Set objectives for what can be accomplished with the plan in an emergency.
3. Determine the facility's capability for controlling an emergency.
4. Define the roles of the responding agencies, especially the fire department and fire brigade.
5. Put the information in written form.

The local fire department should be involved in formulating the fire emergency plan and briefed on building conditions, contents, and fire fighting equipment within the complex. Fire departments with correctional facilities within their jurisdictions should have their own pre-fire plans for each building.

BIBLIOGRAPHY

References Cited

1. Hall, John R., Jr., *The U.S. Fire Problem Overview Report Through 1988*, NFPA Fire Analysis and Research Division, Quincy, MA, 1989.
2. "Flammability Standard for Mattresses," *FF4-72*, June 1973, U.S. Department of Commerce, Washington D.C.
3. "Resistance of Mattresses Containing Boric Acid Treated Cotton Batting to Open Flame Ignition," *Journal of Consumer Product Flammability*, Vol. 4 (June 1977), pp. 169-188.
4. "Combustion of Mattresses Exposed to Flaming Ignition Sources/Part I—Full-Scale Tests and Hazard Analysis," *NBSIR-77-1290*, National Bureau of Standards, Washington, DC, 1977.
5. "Firesafety Bulletin on Penal Institutions," National Fire Protection Association, Quincy, MA, 1977.

NFPA Codes, Standards, and Recommended Practices

Reference to the following NFPA codes, standards, and recommended practices will provide further information on detention and correctional facilities discussed in this chapter. (See the latest *NFPA Catalog* for availability of current editions of the following documents.)

NFPA 13, *Installation of Sprinkler Systems.*

NFPA 72, *Protective Signaling Systems.*

NFPA 72E, *Automatic Fire Detectors.*

NFPA 90A, *Air Conditioning and Ventilating Systems.*

NFPA 92A, *Smoke Control Systems.*

NFPA 101®, *Life Safety Code.®*

NFPA 251, *Fire Tests of Building Construction and Materials.*

NFPA 255, *Surface Burning Characteristics of Building Materials.*

NFPA 701, *Fire Tests for Flame-Resistant Textiles and Films.*

Additional Reading

Best, R., "The Seminole County Jail Fire," *Fire Journal*, Vol. 70, No. 1 (Jan. 1976), pp. 5-10.

Demers, D. P., "Penal Institutions: Firesafety Versus Security," *Fire Journal*, Vol. 73, No. 2 (Mar. 1979), pp. 60-62

Demers, D. P., "Fire in Prisons—42 Die in Maury County, TN, Jail; 21 Die in Saint John, NB, Detention Center; 5 Die in FCI, Danbury," *Fire Journal*, Vol. 72, No. 2 (Mar. 1978), pp. 29-42.

DiMeo, M., "Fire in Pennsylvania Prison," *Fire Journal*, Vol. 70, No. 3 (May 1976), pp. 70-75.

Federal Bureau of Prisons, "Board of Inquiry into the Danbury Fire," U.S. Department of Justice, Washington, DC, July 7, 1977.

Hartson, C. and Rickey, G., "Ohio's Institutional Firesafety Program," *Fire Command*, Vol. 46, No. 3 (Mar. 1979), pp. 34-35.

Knoepfler, N. B., *et al.*, "Mattresses that Resist Open-Flame Ignition," *Fire Journal*, Vol. 72, No. 3 (May 1978), pp. 36-40.

Lathrop, J. K., "No Freedom for John—2 Die in Youth Correctional Center, Cranston, RI," *Fire Journal*, Vol. 69, No. 3 (May 1975), pp. 16-17.

Lee, B. T., "Effect of Ventilation on the Rates of Heat, Smoke, and Carbon Monoxide Production in a Typical Jail Cell Fire," *NBSIR 82-2469*, National Bureau of Standards, Gaithersburg, MD, Mar. 1982.

"A Study of Penal Institution Fires," National Fire Protection Association, Quincy, MA, 1977.

National Institute of Corrections, *Fire Safety in Correctional Facilities*, available from N.I.C., U.S. Department of Justice, Washington, DC, 1980.

Nelson, H. E. and Shibe, A. J. "The Development of a Fire Evaluation System for Detention and Correctional Occupancies," *NBSIR 84-2976*, National Bureau of Standards, Gaithersburg, MD, 1984.

Occupational Safety and Health Administration, (OSHA) *Code of Federal Regulations* Part 29, Section 1910.156 Fire Brigades.

Scala, J. C., *Fire Safety in Correctional Institutions*, National Fire Protection Association, Quincy, MA, 1981.

"Seven Die in Gas Explosion at a Penitentiary Farm Building," *Fire Journal*, Vol. 73, No. 3 (May 1979), pp. 25-28.

Tuck, C. A., *Analysis of Three Multiple-Fatality Penal Institution Fires*, National Fire Protection Association, Quincy, MA, 1978.

HOTELS

James R. Bell

Hotels are buildings or groups of buildings under the same management, in which there are more than 16 sleeping accommodations primarily used by transients who are lodged, with or without meals, for a period of less than 30 days. These facilities may be designated as hotels, inns, clubs, motels, guest quarters, suite hotels, or by other names. So-called apartment hotels also are classified as hotels, because they are subject to transient occupancies like those of hotels.

OCCUPANCY CHARACTERISTICS

These facilities are unique in that they almost always combine several different occupancies under one roof. In addition to sleeping quarters, which are residential occupancies, hotels usually provide space for assembly occupancies such as ballrooms, meeting rooms, exhibition halls, and restaurants; or mercantile occupancies such as, shopping areas, gift shops, and other retail areas; and offices and commercial establishments, or business occupancies.

Larger hotels in major cities may have several floors available for sale as condominium apartments. Many large hotels also contain industrial-type laundries and dry cleaning facilities, as well as kitchens, which use large broilers, ovens, and deep-fat fryers.

Larger-scale hotel building configurations often have atria two or three stories high and sometimes up to sixty stories high, which are often the focal point of building design. Atrium areas themselves may include several occupancies or mixed functions associated with the operation of the hotel.

Some structures also may include parking facilities which may be open, enclosed, above- or below-ground, and often directly beneath or adjacent to the hotel itself. These arrangements may require special types of fire protection, and the building codes may require fire separations.

Since hotel guests are transients, special consideration must be given to the potential threat to their life safety from fire. For example, the occupants of the residential portion of a hotel would be sleeping in unfamiliar surroundings and could possibly become disoriented when trying to evacuate under conditions of heavy smoke. Likewise, those persons in the various ballrooms, lounges, and restaurants could become disoriented due to low-level lighting, crowd size, and unfamiliarity with evacuation routes.

Furthermore, it is not unusual to find the residential portion of a hotel full at the same time the banquet halls, ballrooms, lounges, and restaurants are operating at capacity. This situation could tax the egress facilities of a hotel and present a logistical problem for fire fighters trying to locate and extinguish a fire, while simultaneously attempting rescue and evacuation. Added to this are the inherent problems in evacuating high-rise buildings with their sealed windows, their inaccessibility to fire department ladders, and the potential smoke problems in corridors and stairwells.

CONSTRUCTION FEATURES

Current model building codes address these problems through the application of construction requirements, protection of means of egress, fire suppression, local and area fire detection and notification, and other features designed to limit the effects of fire within a building. In recent years, the installation of sprinkler protection throughout all portions of hotel buildings, regardless of their height, has become a general requirement in most building codes. In addition, some model building codes, and many local ordinances, require that the sprinklers in hotel guestrooms, suites, or other portions of the building be fast response or residential-type sprinklers that will stop a fire while still small.[1] Thus, the possibility of a large fire and the production of smoke is held to a minimum.

Of particular importance for the protection of hotels four stories or fewer in height is the recent development of *NFPA 13R, Standard for the Installation of Sprinkler Systems in Residential Occupancies up to Four Stories in Height,* which provides design and installation requirements of sprinkler systems for small residential occupancies.

James R. Bell is fire protection specialist for the Marriott Corporation, based in Washington, DC.

Corridor compartmentation, pressurized or smokeproof stairways, smoke barriers, and enclosed elevator lobbies are some of the features used to prevent the propagation of smoke within the means of egress. Automatic shutdown of air circulation or the activation of smoke evacuation equipment and stairwells pressurization by smoke detectors or sprinkler waterflow are also used to ensure safe use of the means of egress by guests.

In addition to building code requirements, the potential fire and life safety problems that facilities of this type present are addressed in the various occupancy sections of NFPA 101®, *Life Safety Code*®. For example, ballrooms, restaurants, lounges, and exhibition halls are dealt with in the chapter of NFPA 101 that addresses assembly occupancies, whereas the portion of the hotel providing sleeping rooms is dealt with in the residential chapters of the *Code*. NFPA 101 does not generally require occupancy separation, however, the model building codes may require separations between different occupancy classification. This fire barrier essentially separates the occupancies into different buildings. This occupancy separation applies unless one use is considered incidental or the uses are intermingled. In the latter case, the more restrictive of the life safety requirements of the occupancies involved apply.

LIFE SAFETY FEATURES

NFPA 101, *Life Safety Code,* provides guidelines for minimum standards regarding various life safety features in the building(s), such as those set forth below.

Means of Egress

This section deals with the type, capacity, number, arrangement, illumination, marking, and measurement of travel distances to exits. These provisions greatly enhance the chance for a safe means of egress from the building in emergencies. Because the risk to life safety is viewed as different in unsprinklered and sprinklered hotels, factors such as common paths of travel, dead-end corridors, travel distance from guestroom doors to the nearest exit, and travel distances within a room or suite may be increased if sprinklers are provided.

Protection

Enclosures of vertical openings, such as stairways, elevator shafts, and atria, are required by this section of NFPA 101, *Life Safety Code,* to impede the spread of smoke and heat within the building. Hazardous areas such as employee locker rooms, gift and retail shops, laundries, storage rooms, trash rooms, and similar areas require separation by one-hour-rated separation walls and/or sprinkler protection, depending on the severity of the hazard. This section also deals with protection from other potential hazards, such as boilers, transformers, and other service equipment subject to explosion.

Interior Wall, Ceiling, and Floor Finish

Due to the flammability and toxicity of modern-day fabrics and interior finish materials on walls and ceilings, flame spread and smoke production in these materials are regulated in exit enclosures, corridors, lobbies, and all other spaces. Requirements for floor finish in corridors and exits are also addressed.

Detection and Alarm Systems

Because hotels are occupied by persons who are normally expected to be asleep as part of the standard conditions of occupancy and who are unfamiliar with the building, provisions outlined in NFPA 101, *Life Safety Code,* require early warning or notification of occupants and annunciation of fire alarm signals. This section outlines requirements for the initiation of alarms from manual fire alarm stations, automatic sprinkler systems, and any required automatic detection systems. In high-rise buildings, notification of occupants is required to be through a voice/alarm system operated from a central fire command room. A single-station smoke detector(s) installed in each guestroom, each sleeping room, and each living area within a guestroom or suite is required to alert the occupants of that room or suite, but it is not usually connected to the building fire alarm system.

Extinguishment Requirements

NFPA 101, *Life Safety Code* requires that approved automatic sprinkler protection be installed in all new hotels, except non-high-rise buildings that have guestroom doors that open directly to the outside at ground level or have exterior exit accesses arranged in accordance with the *Code*. The sprinkler systems in buildings up to, and including, four stories may be installed according to NFPA 13R, *Standard for the Installation of Sprinkler Systems in Residential Occupancies up to Four Stories in Height.*

NFPA 101 also requires that all existing high-rise hotels be sprinklered, unless the exceptions for exterior exit access, arranged in accordance with Chapter 5, of NFPA 101 are met.

Corridor Walls and Doors

Another provision of NFPA 101 requires rated corridor walls and self-closing doors in guestroom areas. (See Figures 8-16A and 8-16B.) Not only are door-closing mechanisms among the most effective life safety features of the *Code*, but they are also among the least expensive to install and maintain. Several recent multiple-death hotel fires have illustrated the importance of self-closing doors.[2,3]

In most cases, fire and smoke can be contained in the room of origin as long as the door remains closed. This is especially true in sprinklered rooms. Tests in San Francisco, indicated that fast-acting sprinklers are not only effective in suppressing fire and minimizing smoke in guest

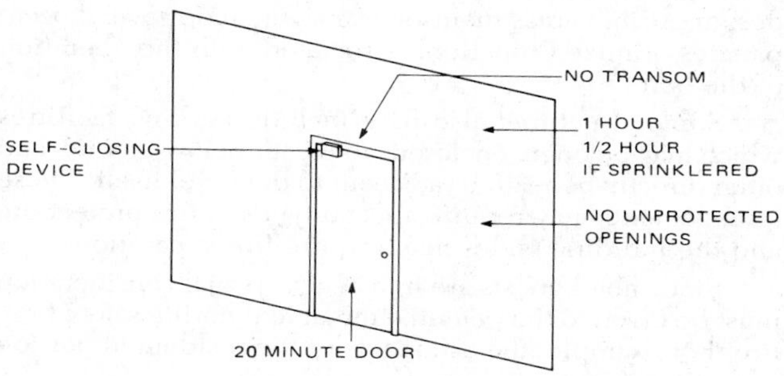

FIG. 8-16A. ***Provisions for the protection of guest rooms (corridors) in new hotels. The need for the self-closing, 20-min door cannot be overemphasized. There are no exceptions or options to the self-closing door.***

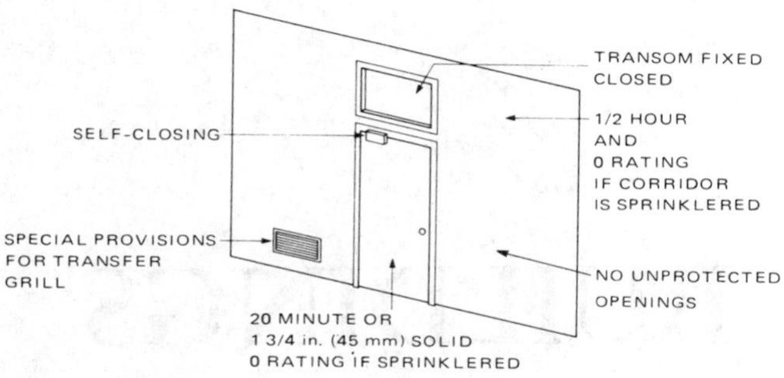

FIG. 8-16B. ***Provisions for protection of guest rooms (corridors) in existing hotels. The need for the self-closing door cannot be overemphasized. There are no exceptions or options to the self-closing device. Although no rating is required when sprinkler protection is provided, the wall must be substantial and must resist the passage of smoke.***

rooms, but they will, in conjunction with door closers, contain smoke and heat in the room of origin, leaving the egress corridors tenable.

Staff Training

Even though these built-in life safety features are paramount in the maintenance of a firesafe hotel, a well-trained emergency organization is of equal importance. The emergency organization consists of on-duty employees who are trained to conduct fire prevention inspections and tests of life safety systems on a regular basis. In addition, they should hold should regularly scheduled fire and disaster drills. In the event of an emergency, their responsibilities may include notifying the fire department, incipient-stage fire suppression, evacuation, and sprinkler/fire pump monitoring, as well as salvage and overhaul after extinguishment. Organization members should also be trained in first aid and certified to perform emergency medical treatment, such as cardiopulmonary resuscitation (CPR).[4]

An effective emergency organization, along with automatic sprinklers, compartmentation, effective egress design, and detection and alarm systems, will provide hotel guests with a degree of protection that will greatly increase the probability that the hotel in which they sleep will be safe from fire.

BIBLIOGRAPHY

References Cited

1. *The Uniform Building Code,* International Conference of Building Officials, Whittier, CA, 1988.
2. Klem, T. J. and Best, R. L., "Four Hotel Fires: Lessons Learned," *Fire Journal,* Vol. 76, No. 6, (Nov. 1982), p. 72.
3. Klem, T. J., "Investigation Report on the Dupont Plaza Hotel Fire," *Fire Journal,* Vol. 8, No. 3, (May-June 1987).
4. *Hotel Fire Emergency Organization,* Marriott Corporation, Washington, DC.

References

The BOCA Basic/National Building Code, Building Officials and Code Administrators International, Inc., Country Club Hills, IL, 1990.

Standard Building Code, Southern Building Code Congress, Inc., Birmingham, AL, 1990.

NFPA Codes, Standards, and Recommended Practices

Reference to the following NFPA codes, standards, and recommended practices will provide further information on hotels discussed in this chapter. (See the latest *NFPA Catalog* for availability of current editions of the following documents.)

NFPA 13, *Installation of Sprinkler Systems.*

NFPA 13R, *Standard for the Installation of Sprinkler Systems in Residential Occupancies up to Four Stories in Height.*

NFPA *101*®, *Life Safety Code*®.

Additional Reading

Bell, *et al.*, "Investigation Report on the Westchase Hilton Hotel Fire," National Fire Protection Association, Quincy, MA, 1982.

Best, R. and Demers, D., "Investigation Report on the MGM Grand Hotel Fire," National Fire Protection Association, Quincy, MA, 1982.

Bill, R. G., "A Life Safety Team: Smoke Detectors and Sprinklers in Hotels," *Fire Journal,* Vol. 83, No. 3 (May-June 1990), p. 28.

Bill, R. G. and Kung, H. C., "Evaluation of an Extended Coverage Sidewall Sprinkler and Smoke Detector in a Hotel Occupancy," *Journal of Fire Protection Engineering,* Vol. 1, No. 3, 1989.

Bryan, J. J., *An Examination and Analysis of the Dynamics of the Human Behavior in the MGM Grand Hotel Fire,* Revised ed., National Fire Protection Association, Quincy, MA, 1983.

Coakley, D., *et al., The Day the MGM Grand Hotel Burned,* Lyle Stuart, 1982.

Cote, R. M., *et al.,* "Investigation Report of the Ramada Inn Central Fire," National Fire Protection Association, 1984.

Daly, T. G., "Hotel Firesafety--An Update," *Fire Journal,* Vol. 79, No. 1 (Jan. 1985), pp. 56-58.

Hotel Fires: Behind the Headlines, National Fire Protection Association, Quincy, MA, 1982.

Klem, T. J., "Ninety-Seven Die in Arson Fire at Dupont Plaza Hotel," *Fire Journal,* Vol. 81, No. 3 (May-June 1987).

"Operation Life Safety," The Operation San Francisco Smoke/Sprinkler Test, International Association of Fire Chiefs, Washington, DC, 1984.

Rule, C. H., "Increase Fire Safety in Hotel/Motel Guest Rooms," *Fire Engineering,* Vol. 138, No. 12, 1985, pp. 40-43.

Rutes, W. A. and Penner, R. H., *Hotel Planning and Design,* Whitney Library of Design, Watson-Guptill Publications, 1985.

Schaenman, P. S. and Daly, T. G., "The Facts about Fire Protection in the Lodging Industry," *Fire Journal,* Vol. 83, No. 1 (Jan.-Feb. 1989), pp. 23-26.

Thomas, J., "Dupont Plaza...MGM Grand: Could They Happen Again," *Fire Journal,* Vol. 82, No. 3 (May-June 1988).

Zeiss, W. E., *Active Fire Protection Concepts for Hotels,* Cerberus A. G., Switzerland, 1985.

APARTMENT BUILDINGS

Kenneth Bush

Apartment buildings are identified as those structures containing three or more living units with independent cooking and bathroom facilities, whether designated as apartment houses, tenements, condominiums, or garden apartments. Apartments differ from multi-unit residential occupancies that are not considered homes (such as hotels and boarding homes), by the provision of individual cooking facilities, the number of sleeping rooms, and the less transient nature of the occupants.

The adequate protection of residential buildings and their occupants from the effects of fire has historically been a major concern to fire protection professionals. This job is made more complex by the construction of multiple dwelling units. Such construction not only adds building size and numbers of occupants, but also adds to major complexity due to building design, construction, and fire protection features.

OCCUPANCY CHARACTERISTICS

In 1987, 26.7 percent of all occupied year-round housing units were in structures with two or more housing units—that is, in duplexes or apartments. (Duplexes cannot be isolated in these statistics.) The breakdown by size was 10.4 percent of housing units in structures with 2 to 4 units, 5.0 percent in structures with 5 to 9 units, 4.3 percent in structures with 10 to 19 units, 3.2 percent in structures with 20 to 49 units, and 3.7 percent in structures with 50 or more units. In 1987 alone, 345,600 new apartment units were completed, and 66 percent of these were rented within three months. Not all apartments are renter-occupied, however. In structures with two or more units, 86.5 percent of the units were renter-occupied. The percentage was over 90 percent for structures with 5 to 49 units but only 80.2 percent for structures with 2 to 4 units and 83.8 percent for structures with 50 or more units.[1]

U.S. homes dominate U.S. fire losses, and apartments share in that dominance. In 1989, apartments in buildings with three or more units experienced 96,000 structure fires reported to U.S. fire departments; these resulted in 790 civilian deaths, 5050 civilian injuries, and $541 million in direct property damage. The 790 civilian fire deaths represented 18 percent of all fire deaths in homes. By comparison, 27 percent of catastrophic fire deaths in homes in 1989—those involving at least five deaths per fire—were in structures with three or more housing units.

Comparisons of fire risk between apartments and one- and two-family dwellings, including manufactured homes, are difficult because statistics on duplexes are grouped with apartments for housing units and with single-family properties for fire experience. In addition, structures with one- to two-apartments over a business are grouped with apartments for fire experience but not for housing units. The rough estimates that are possible suggest little or no difference in fire risk. In 1987, as noted, just under 27 percent of housing units were in structures with two or more units. After making rough adjustments for the category problems noted above, it appears that 24 to 25 percent of 1987 homes fires and 25 to 26 percent of 1987 home fire deaths were in structures with two or more housing units. These differences are not significant in view of the rough quality of the estimates.

OCCUPANCY HAZARDS

The occupancy hazards of apartment buildings include all the risk factors that may arise in particular segments of the population. Pre-schoolers and older adults, if present, have a higher risk of dying in fires because of the mental or physical limitations associated with their age. Older children and younger adults may be of risk if they are physically or mentally handicapped, or as a result of drug or alcohol abuse. And fatal fires are more common at night, when people are asleep.

The pattern of causes for fatal apartment fires is different in many ways from the pattern for one- and two-family dwellings. Because apartment buildings are more likely to use central systems and professional supervision and maintenance for their equipment, most equipment-related causes rank much lower for apartment buildings than they do for one- and two-family dwellings. For example, using 1983-87 structure fire deaths, heating equipment

Kenneth Bush is fire protection engineer, Maryland State Fire Marshal's Office.

ranked sixth, with 5.3 percent of civilian fire deaths in apartments, compared to second and 19.5 percent in one- and two-family dwellings. Electrical distribution equipment ranked fifth, with 5.5 percent of civilian fire deaths in apartments, compared to fourth and 10.6 percent in one- and two-family dwellings. By contrast, smoking, incendiarism, and child fireplay ranked first, second, and third, respectively, for apartments, with a combined 68.7 percent of fire deaths, compared to 46.3 percent for one- and two-family dwellings.

Smoke detectors have been a great success in apartment buildings, as well as in private homes. Use of detectors continues to grow, but more slowly since 1982. In 1989, 85 percent of all homes had at least one smoke detector, and there was evidence that their use in apartments was much higher still, probably because state and local laws requiring detectors often have stronger requirements for apartments. However, NFPA studies indicates that roughly one-third of apartment detectors are not operational, the same share as for one- and two-family dwellings.

Once a potentially serious fire has started, apartment buildings can pose special problems to fire department suppression forces.

The variety of these types of residences, as well as the architectural desire to make buildings aesthetically pleasing yet functional, creates an interesting combination of fire protection demands. In many cases, building designs, space considerations, and parking arrangements create major access problems, particularly for fire fighting apparatus. (See Figure 8-17A.) Frequently, long hose lays and blocked roadway accesses create new problems to fire fighting operations in addition to existing problems, such as weather, personnel deficiencies, and hampered water supplies. (See Figure 8-17B.) Architectural designs may use false partitioning and veneered construction, giving an unrealistic impression of the type and magnitude of the actual building construction. (See Figure 8-17C.) Although NFPA 101®, *Life Safety Code*®, makes no special requirements for the construction of these buildings, many such requirements are found and enforced through the model building codes, as well as through many of the local codes and ordinances currently in effect.

An additional problem arises in the location and combination of apartments with other occupancy types, particularly these above and behind mercantile and business occupancies. (See Figure 8-17D.) Where multiple occupancy classes occur in the same building and are so intermingled that separate safeguards are impractical, means of egress facilities, construction, protection, and other safeguards must comply with the most restrictive life safety requirements for the occupancies involved.

LIFE SAFETY CONCEPTS

The residential fire death problem is very complex, and several strategies must be presented to help solve it. The installation and proper maintenance of smoke detectors in sleeping areas provide an effective, low-cost, and widely available method of early warning so that evacuation, containment, and suppression can be initiated during the incipient stages of a fire.

The general public must be taught to protect themselves and others occupying the residential unit from fire through the safe use and installation of alternative heating devices, the proper storage and handling of flammable liquids, and the identification and correction of home fire hazards. In addition, stringent flammability standards for upholstered furniture, such as those previously issued by the U.S. Consumer Product Safety Commission (CPSC) for children's sleepwear and mattresses, will provide long-term firesafety benefits. Specially designed systems that are effective in terms of life safety should be installed to provide a high level of protection to occupants, particularly where large numbers of persons are present, such as in a high-rise apartment building, or where the occupants' ability to escape is hampered, such as in apartments for the elderly.

Although such firesafety precautions are not always practical, particularly within an individual dwelling unit, a more concentrated effort must be made to confine the fire and its effects to a well-defined, limited area of the structure. This task is accomplished through the adoption of accepted firesafety codes, such as NFPA 101, *Life Safety Code*. Since many current laws and regulations prevent fire inspection authorities from entering individual living units, adequate fire protection features must be designed and constructed during the initial phases of the project. The regulation of interior furnishings provides only a partial

FIG. 8-17A. Many apartment building designs and parking arrangements create major access problems and hinder fire fighting operations. (Photo courtesy of Stephen C. Leahy.)

FIG. 8-17B. The location and lack of access routes for many new apartment buildings create major fire apparatus placement and fire fighting operation problems.

FIG. 8-17C. Architectural designs often use false partitioning and veneered construction, creating an unrealistic impression of the building.

FIG. 8-17D. Additional firesafety problems arise in the location and combination of apartments with other occupancy types, particularly above and behind stores and businesses. (Photo courtesy of Stephen C. Leahy.)

solution to the firesafety problem, although such consumer items are generally in use for many years before they are replaced. Futhermore the individual habits and attitudes of building occupants can never be regulated or otherwise altered.

Because apartment buildings, and residential occupancies in general, present such a diversified collection of building size, configuration, and resident population, many of the regulatory codes pay particular attention to construction designs and fire protection features. NFPA 101, *Life Safety Code*, covers the presence of hazards such as cooking and heating equipment, as well as the degrees of familiarity of the occupant with his/her living space. NFPA 101 requires most new apartment buildings to be protected by sprinklers. However, where each apartment has a door directly to the outside at ground level, such as in townhouse-style apartments, sprinkler protection is not required. NFPA 101 has a unique method of regulating the construction and design of existing apartment buildings based upon the type and extent of automatic fire detection and/or fire suppression equipment provided. Recognizing equivalency provisions found elsewhere in NFPA 101, the residential subcommittee established four equivalent schemes to provide a high degree of flexibility. These designs are considered equal in providing a minimum level of life safety for apartments. Some systems have additional protective capability, permitting higher building heights and larger building areas.

This overall approach provides one of the first system design attempts to be codified. Whereas a total system would have many design approaches, this is a more limited system, in that only four different approaches are available. Yet an evaluator can identify an appropriate method from the four approaches based on the building size, height, and arrangement. This allows the person evaluating the existing building to formulate a safety approach that best fits the building, rather than fitting the building to a single codified design criterion.

Under the special definitions found in Chapter 4 of NFPA 101, *Life Safety Code*, the contents of living units in residential occupancies fall into the ordinary-hazard classification. Characteristics of these hazards include moderately rapid burning and considerable smoke generation. (See Figure 8-17E.) Under normal conditions, no unduly dangerous exposure should develop during the period necessary to escape from the fire area. Generally, this classification represents conditions found in most buildings. Even with the introduction of plastics, foamed materials and other combustible materials in furnishings, the amount and configuration of such materials present a lower degree of hazard than in other occupancies where they may be sold, stored, or displayed. NFPA 13, *Installation of Sprinkler Systems*, would classify the contents of apartment buildings as "light" for the design of extinguishing systems. This difference in classifications is based on the threat to life safety assumed in the ordinary classification *versus* that assumed where the extinguishing capability of the automatic sprinkler system results in the light-hazard classification.

In designing the number and types of exits required for apartment buildings, NFPA 101, *Life Safety Code*, determines the occupant load on the basis of one person per 200 sq ft (18.6 m^2) of gross floor area, or the maximum probable population of any room or section under consideration, whichever is greater. There are many buildings, such as dormitories, that may produce a greater occupant load. However, even though some portions of these buildings are densely populated, the building as a whole may not necessarily exceed one person per 200 sq ft (18.6 m^2) of gross area, owing to the space taken for toilet facilities, hallways, closets, and living rooms. These requirements do not preclude the need for providing adequate exit capacities from concentrated use and sleeping areas based on the maximum probable population, rather than on the design figure. The capacities of required exits are as specified in NFPA 101.

FIG. 8-17E. Apartment buildings are classified as ordinary-hazard occupancies which include moderately rapid burning of building contents and considerable smoke generation. (Photo courtesy of Stephen C. Leahy.)

Although seemingly contrary to the basic code requirements of two distinct, remote means of egress from all locations, several exceptions to this rule are found within the requirements for apartment occupancies. While the traditional interior exit corridor arrangement commonly found in larger apartment buildings and condominiums requires two remote exits, several other options in apartment building configurations permit other arrangements. The common townhouse arrangement, which provides an exit directly to the street or yard at ground level or by way of an outside or enclosed stairway serving that apartment only, permits the front door to be the only required exit. Therefore, a rear door, which is often provided, would not be required and could be a sliding door to a porch or patio.

Another exception is a basic design approach for garden apartments where the apartment entrances are enclosed around a single protected stairway. This single stairway usually is open to the exterior or is glass-enclosed. It must be separated from the building by construction of at least 1-hr fire-resistance rating. The doors should be treated similarly. Interestingly, the basic design of a typical garden-style apartment has influenced other chapters of NFPA 101, *Life Safety Code*. Previous editions of NFPA 101 have required that all exit stairways continuing beyond the floor of discharge be interrupted at that level by partitions, doors, or other effective means to make clear the direction of egress to the street. However, an exception to this requirement allows these stairways to continue one-half story beyond the level of discharge without such physical interruption. This is a typical exit arrangement found in garden-style apartments that have apartments or service areas on the ground-floor or terrace level. Based on this exception, stairways serving these levels need not be interrupted at the floor of exit discharge for firesafety reasons.

In addition to the number and types of required exits, the arrangement and travel distance to these exits are regulated by the general requirements of Chapter 5 of NFPA 101, *Life Safety Code*, with due consideration to the levels of fire protection features within the building. As in other occupancies, all exits must terminate directly at a public way or at an approved exit discharge, unless certain additional protection features, such as automatic sprinkler protection and vestibule separation and/or enclosures, are provided in accordance with Section 5-7 of NFPA 101 to permit 50 percent of the required exit capacity to discharge through areas on the level of discharge.

Appropriate illumination must be provided for public spaces, hallways, stairways, and other means of egress. Emergency lighting is required for apartment buildings that have more than 12 living units or are more than three stories high, except in buildings where every living unit has a direct exit to the outside at grade, such as in townhouses. Approved exit signs are required in all apartment buildings with more than one required exit. However, discretion must be used in placing such signs where exits are obvious, or all occupants are familiar with the building.

Because a higher degree of transient occupancy in some apartments is a definite possibility, special exiting considerations are made within the individual living units, in addition to those found in the public access spaces. All individual living units with two or more rooms must comply with the minimum provisions for operable exterior openings to be used as a secondary means of escape, or with the specialized separation or protection requirements of Chapter 21 of NFPA 101, *Life Safety Code*. Not only must these openings be of a minimum size, but they also must be accessible and easy to operate. In addition, every dwelling unit that is greater than 2000 sq ft (180 m^2) or that has a travel distance to the primary means of escape greater than 75 ft (22.5 m) must have two primary means of escape remote from each other, or it must be protected by approved supervised automatic sprinkler protection. Special multi-level units such as penthouses are permitted to have regular, curved, or spiral stairways that connect to one level above or below the entrance to the apartment.

Additional requirements prohibit any door in an apartment building, including individual unit doors, from being locked against egress while the building is occupied. This means that a door may be locked so that it can be opened from within the building but not from the outside. Ordinarily, dead bolts, double-cylinder locks, and chain locks would not meet these provisions. Several tragic multiple-death fires have occurred because a key could not be found to unlock the door or the chain was not removed.

In apartment buildings, the protection of vertical openings, such as stairways, elevator shafts, and atria, follows the requirements found in NFPA 101, *Life Safety Code*. (See Figure 8-17F.) Smokeproof towers are required in existing high-rise apartment buildings except those that are totally sprinklered. This limits the possibility of smoke contamination of exits and ensures a safe, protected means of egress. The protection from hazards, as well as the classification of interior finishes, is also based upon the levels of fire detection and/or protection within the building.

Perhaps the best form of fire protection in a residential occupancy is early warning. All living units in an apartment building must have approved automatic smoke detection. These detectors are usually located in hallways that have access to the sleeping areas. In multiple-level units, a detector also should be located at the tops of stairways. Detection systems must be installed in accordance with basic engineering practices. Special consideration should be given to room configuration, and air movement, stagnant air pockets that would reduce detector efficiency, and to cooking areas, fireplaces, or other normally smoke-producing appliances that would cause an excess of nuisance alarms. All detectors required for installation in multiple-dwelling units must be powered by house current. In addition, where a single apartment needs more

FIG. 8-17F. The vertical spread of fire and other products of combustion is of primary concern to most firesafety codes. Photo courtesy of S. R. Spicer).

than one detector, the detectors must be connected.electrically inter Note that this type of detection system is required in addition to the requirements for any other detection or suppression system.

Manual fire alarm systems are required in apartment buildings according to the size and height of the building and the evacuation capabilities of the occupants. As building designs become higher and more complex, additional special features are required, such as annunciator panels, voice communications systems, and automatic transmission of building fire alarms. Voice communications systems often are used as part of a multi-faceted system that allows the fire department to contact building occupants during a fire.

As mentioned before, NFPA 101, *Life Safety Code*, requires almost all new apartment buildings to be protected by automatic sprinklers. In existing apartment buildings, the extent of automatic sprinkler protection is again governed by the size and height of the building, as well as by the four protection options discussed in Chapter 19 of NFPA 101. Although not required by NFPA 101, the use of residential or quick-response sprinklers is encouraged for new installations of sprinkler systems in dwelling units, apartments, and guest rooms. The increased technology, cost effectiveness, and appearance of these systems have provided numerous additional incentives for choosing this protection option.

NFPA 101 requires portable fire extinguishers to be located in hazardous areas only, not throughout the entire building. Many building owners place these extinguishers in the individual living units, under the direct responsibility of the occupant.

The design, installation, and maintenance of all such fire detection and protection systems are based on referenced fire protection standards, as well as on sound engineering judgment. For occupancies four stories or fewer, see NFPA 13R, *Installation of Sprinkler Systems in Residential Occupancies Up to Four Stories in Height.*

When fires cannot be confined to the area of origin, the means of egress must be sufficiently protected to allow all building occupants enough time for safe evacuation. This basic concern for providing safety for the occupant in a room during a fire lead to a minimum corridor wall construction to keep fire in a corridor from entering a room or to keep fire in a room from entering the corridor. Doors protecting openings in these enclosures must provide a level of protection commensurate with the expected fuel load in the room and with the fire resistance of the corridor wall construction. Fuel-load studies conducted by the National Bureau of Standards (now the National Institute of Standards and Technology) have shown that residential occupancies will have fuel loads in the 20- to 30-min range. Contrary to the general rule for door assembly considerations, the requirements for doors in residential occupancies apply to the leaf only, with a 1¾-in. (45 mm) solid, bonded, wood-core door considered equivalent to a door with a 20-min fire protection rating. The door rating requirement establishes a minimum quality of construction, and does not require a complete listed fire door assembly. However, the requirement that doors between apartments and corridors be self-closing will definitely lead to a significant reduction in fatalities. Studies have shown that, in some cases, fire spread has been due mainly to the door being left open as the occupant flees the fire. In other cases, people have died after opening the door to a fully involved room, or after causing a room to become fully involved by opening a door and introducing oxygen to the fire. Under both circumstances, a door equipped with spring-loaded hinges or a door closer would have prevented smoke or fire from spreading down the corridor and exposing other occupants.

During a fire, the evacuation of all residents from a large apartment building is an inefficient, time-consuming process. This problem is compounded by the introduction of larger and taller structures, complex and intricate building designs, and a larger population of residents who are incapable of rapid evacuation, especially by stairways. Realistically, the most expedient movement of a sizable number of residents is horizontally. The introduction of required smoke barriers and horizontal exits serves three purposes fundamental to the protection of building occupants by limiting the spread of fire and fire-produced contaminants, limiting the number of occupants exposed to a single fire, and providing for horizontal evacuation by creating an area of refuge on the same level.

Areas of refuge are required in apartment buildings, based on the height and area of the building and on the separation distance of the exit stairways. Since the majority of apartment residents are assumed to be capable of vertical evacuation using stairways, the location of stairways provides both the required area of refuge as well as the required means of egress. Where travel time to stairways is increased due to excessive horizontal distances and/or where a majority of residents have reduced mobility, specialized areas are required on the same floor level. It is important to remember that the requirement for smoke barriers and horizontal exits also is dependent upon the fire protection features of the building, as well as the building configuration and height, and the anticipated mobility of its occupants.

Typically, all building service equipment and utilities in apartment buildings are required to be designed and installed in accordance with sound engineering practices and all applicable NFPA standards. The use of a public corridor as part of the supply, return, or exhaust air system is not permitted. In fact, these corridors must be pressurized against the movement of smoke in certain apartment building designs. The standard requirements for the reliability of the means of egress, fire retardancy for interior furnishings and decorations, and the proper maintenance and testing of fire protection equipment also apply equally to apartment occupancies.

Each living unit must be given emergency instructions on a yearly basis, indicating the location of alarms, exiting paths, and actions to be taken in response to a fire in the living unit and in response to the sounding of an alarm. However, other operating features, such as specialized firesafety training and fire exit drills, have been deleted due to the nontransient nature of most building occupants.

As is clearly evident from the statistical data previously cited, the fire problem in apartment buildings and in residential occupancies as a whole is complex, significant, and not easily solved. The increasing demand for adequate, yet low cost, functional, and aesthetically pleasing housing has led to an increasing demand for adequate, safe, and economical fire protection. The problem intensifies with the demand for higher and larger building with a higher density of occupants and with the demand for more personal services for building occupants. Although the solution to these fire problems undoubtedly will require much future study, the obvious short-term solution of effective code formulation, adoption, and enforcement is the immediate responsibility of every firesafety professional.

BIBLIOGRAPHY

Reference Cited

1. U.S. Bureau of the Census, *Statistical Abstract of the United States: 1990*, 110th ed., Washington, DC, 1990.

Reference

Karter, M., J., Jr., "Fire Loss in the United States During 1989," *Fire Journal*, Vol. 84, No. 5 (Sept./Oct. 1990), pp. 56-67.

NFPA Codes, Standards, and Recommended Practices

Reference to the following NFPA codes, standards, and recommended practices will provide further information on apartment buildings discussed in this chapter. (See the latest *NFPA Catalog* for availability of current editions of the following documents.)

NFPA 13, *Installation of Sprinkler Systems*.

NFPA 13R, *Installation of Sprinkler Systems in Residential Occupancies Up to Four Stories in Height*.

NFPA 101®, *Life Safety Code®*.

Additional Reading

(Note: All the major causes of fires in apartment buildings and the use of smoke detectors are addressed in annual statistical reports from NFPA's Fire Analysis & Research Division.)

Alvard, D. M., "The Fire Emergency Evacuation Simulation for Multifamily Buildings," *NBS-GCR-84-483*, National Bureau of Standards, Gaithersburg, MD, Dec. 1984.

Berl, W. G. and Halpin, B. M., "Human Fatalities From Unwanted Fires," *Fire Journal*, Vol. 73, No. 5 (Sept. 1979), p. 105.

Blye, P. and Yess, J. P., "Firesafety in Elderly Housing," *Fire Journal*, Vol. 81, No. 6 (Nov. 1987), p. 28.

Derry, L., "Fatal Fires In America: How They Happen, Where They Happen, How To Stop Them," *Fire Journal*, Vol. 72, No. 5 (Sept. 1979), p. 67.

Fire In The United States, 4th ed., Federal Emergency Management Agency, Washington, DC, 1982, pp. 25-27.

"Fire Safety in Multi-Family Housing," U.S. Congressional Hearing, Subcommittee on Science, Research and Technology, July 18, 1988.

Jones, J. C., "1982 Multiple-Death Fires In The United States," *Fire Journal*, Vol. 77, No. 4 (July 1983), p. 10.

Karter, M. J., Jr., "Fire Loss in the United States in 1988," *Fire Journal*, Vol. 83, No. 5 (Sept. 1989).

Lathrop, J. K., *ed., Life Safety Code Handbook*, 4th ed., National Fire Protection Association, Quincy, MA, 1988.

Public Health Service: Vital Statistics of the United States, 1978, National Vital Statistics Division, National Center for Health Services, U.S. Government Printing Office, 1978.

Salamone, R., "Retrofitting High-Rise Dorms with Alarm and Detection Systems," *Fire Journal*, Vol. 84, No. 1 (Jan./Feb. 1990), p. 37.

LODGING OR ROOMING HOUSES

Revised by Alfred J. Longhitano and Mario A. Antonetti

Lodging or rooming houses include buildings in which separate sleeping rooms are rented and sleeping accommodations are provided for 16 or fewer persons on either a transient or a permanent basis with or without meals, but without separate cooking facilities for individual occupants. One- and two-family dwellings in which a room or rooms are rented to no more than three persons are not considered lodging or rooming houses. Facilities with sleeping accommodations for more than 16 persons are immediately classified as hotel; while those with individual cooking facilities are immediately classified as apartment buildings.

The occupants of a lodging or roomimg house must be capable of self-preservation. The presence of four or more occupants who are incapable of self-preservation would immediately reclassify the facility as a health care, or possibly a board-and-care, facility.

Based on these restrictions, the classification "lodging or rooming house" is effectively limited to facilities providing sleeping accommodations for 4 to 16 persons, capable of self-preservation without separate cooking facilities.

OCCUPANCY CHARACTERISTICS

The 1970s and 1980s created at least two entirely new markets that have spurred a growth in the number and nature of lodging and rooming houses which were once considered a budget-conscious alternative to expensive hotels. First, landmark court decisions required that psychiatric patients capable of living in a less restrictive environment than the psychiatrict hospital be released to live in the general population. Many of these de-institutionalized people, preferring not to assume all the responsibilities of independent apartment living, meal preparation, and the like, have chosen to live in rooming houses. The second phenomenon affecting the growth of rooming houses is the increasing popularity of the bed-and-breakfast and country inns as alternative travel accommodations.

Very few new buildings are being classified as lodging or rooming houses. Most are existing facilities in converted dwellings, motels, or small apartment houses. Mixed occupancies generally are not encountered, except in cases where mercantiles are located on the lower floor or floors and sleeping rooms are located above. Such an arrangement is not permitted by code unless the dwelling occupancy and exits are separated from the mercantile occupancy by construction with a fire-resistance rating of at least one hour and the mercantile occupancy is protected by automatic sprinklers.

Lodging or rooming houses can be in buildings of any construction type permitted by local building codes. NFPA 101, *Life Safety Code,*® does not identify any minimum construction requirements. Because most lodging or rooming houses are located in converted dwellings or share space with mercantile operations, construction is generally limited to Type III or V, as defined by NFPA 220, *Types of Building Construction*.

Fuel loading is generally considered light, while the hazard of the contents is considered "ordinary," a trait consistent with most residential occupancies. Unfortunately, extremely fast-spreading fires where detection is delayed are not uncommon in this type of occupancy, based on construction characteristics and interior features as noted below.

Occupancy Conversion or Remodeling

In conversion or remodeling, existing wall and ceiling finishes are removed, exposing combustible structural components. Concealed combustible spaces may be created by installating drop ceilings and new wall finishes and these concealed combustible spaces permit rapid fire development and spread, while limiting accessibility for fire fighting. The wall and ceiling finishes, although limited to Class A, B, or C, typically exceed this limitation and significantly affect fire spread and smoke generation characteristics.

Lack of Firestopping

As a result of building codes or their enforcement at the time of construction, many older buildings lack firestopping.

Alfred J. Longhitano, P.E., is a principal with Gage-Babcock & Associates, Inc., Mount Kisco, NY. Mario A. Antonetti, P.E., is supervisory engineer and secretary of Gage-Babcock & Associates, Inc., Mount Kisco, NY.

Unprotected Vertical Openings

Unprotected vertical openings are not limited to stairs. They include shafts, ducts, heat grates, or simply old floor openings that were never covered. Some vertical openings are more than three stories high and each represents a path for fire and smoke movement, which may compromise an exit that is considered protected.

Building Services

In lodging or rooming houses, building services generally are limited to taking care of the electrical systems, heating, and possibly air conditioning. Primary consideration should be given to the proper maintenance of heating equipment and to the prevention of electrical circuit overloading. Some tenants may be permanent, so consideration should be given to tenant spaces to prevent tenants from overloading receptacles or misusing extension cords.

Storage Areas for Personal Belongings

Storage areas are a common problem with apartments, one that is occasionally encountered in lodging or rooming houses, as well. Storage areas normally are located in basements, under stairs, and in rooms off egress corridors, and, while they are commonly readily accessible, they present a serious hazard.

Supplemental Heating Devices

Inadequate heating can lead to the use of supplemental heating devices, such as portable electric, gas, and kerosene space heaters. Each represents a specific hazard and has its own accompanying set of controls. For example, one specific code requirement prohibits installing a stove or heater where its malfunction would block escape in case of fire.

LIFE SAFETY CONSIDERATIONS

Due to the limited number of sleeping accommodations and the lack of separate cooking facilities for individual occupants, lodging or rooming houses are viewed, from a life safety standpoint, as falling somewhere above one- and two-family dwellings and below dormitories, hotels, and apartment buildings. NFPA *101*®, *Life Safety Code*,® requirements for this occupancy center on the four key elements essential to life safety.

Means of Escape

For life safety purposes, safe egress from the building is always of paramount concern. In lodging or rooming houses, the egress system consists of a "means of escape" which, by definition, is a way out of a building or structure that does not conform to the strict definition of means of egress but does provide an alternate way out. This term, separate and distinct from means of egress, accepts a reduced level of egress for this specific occupancy in relation to all other occupancy classes, but maintains a higher level of egress than required in one- and two-family dwellings.

Sleeping rooms above and below the level of exit discharge are required to have two separate means of escape, one of which should be either an enclosed interior stairway, an exterior stairway, or a horizontal exit. Fire escapes are acceptable for existing buildings only. This primary means of escape must provide a safe path of travel from the building, one that does not expose the occupants to an unprotected vertical opening, except in completely sprinklered buildings three stories or less in height. (See Figures 8-18A, 8-18B, and 8-18C.)

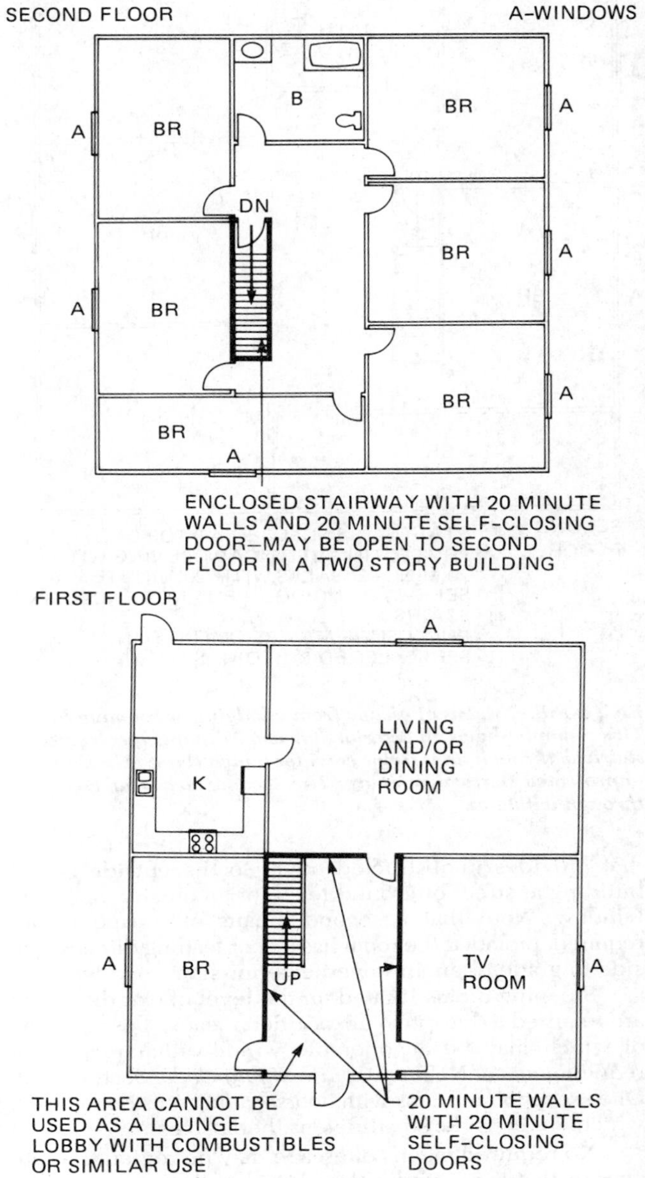

FIG. 8-18A. Means of escape from a lodging or rooming house. This example shows an enclosed interior stairway which discharges directly outside. Access to the interior stairway is by an interior corridor which is not exposed to an unprotected vertical opening. The second means of escape could be through windows. The enclosure at the bottom of the stairway can be done several ways; this is only one example.

The specified means of escape need not meet the requirements of Chapter 5 of NFPA 101, *Life Safety Code*, with the exception of width, stair riser, and tread. Details about the second means of escape are provided in Section 21-2 of NFPA 101, and include either a door or stairway

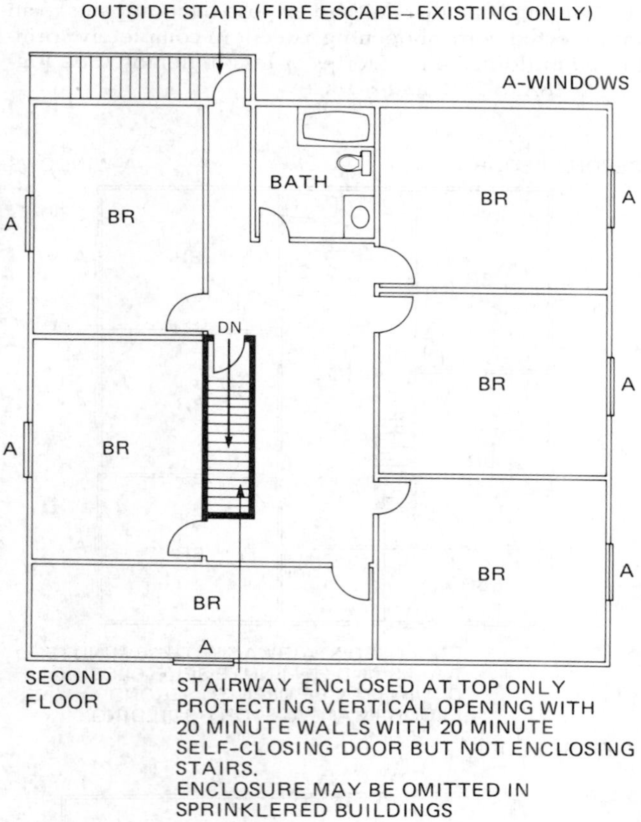

***FIG. 8-18B.** Means of escape from a lodging or rooming house. This example shows an exterior stairway. Tenants reach exterior stairway through an interior corridor which is not exposed to an unprotected vertical opening. The second means of escape is through windows.*

that provides unobstructed travel to the outside of the building at street or ground level, or an outside operable window. Note that a second means of escape is not required, provided the room has a door leading directly outside to grade or an approved exterior stair.

Sleeping rooms located on the level of exit discharge are required to have two unspecified means of escape, one of which may be an operable window that meets the requirements of NFPA 101, *Life Safety Code*, Section 21-2. One exception is rooms with doors leading outside to grade, which are considered sufficient themselves.

No required means of escape may be routed through an area that is not under the control of the occupant who is leaving the building. Nor may it be routed through a door that may be locked.

DETECTION AND ALARM SYSTEMS

Detection and alarm systems in residential occupancies play a critical role in the early warning and evacuation of occupants. A manual fire alarm system installed in accordance with NFPA 72, *Protective Signaling Systems*, is required in all cases, except buildings that have approved smoke detection or sprinkler systems.

Smoke detectors installed in accordance with NFPA 74, *Household Fire Warning Equipment* and powered by the house electrical service are required on each floor,

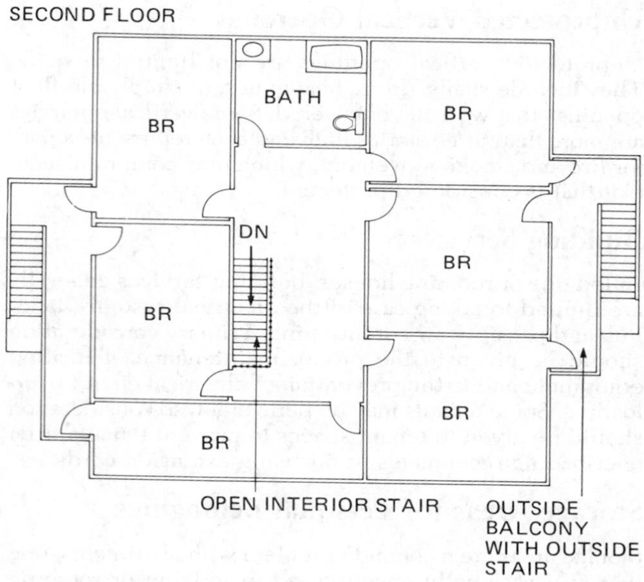

***FIG. 8-18C.** Means of escape from a lodging or rooming house. This example shows an outside stairway with exterior exit access. Access is not through the interior corridor, which is exposed by the open stairway. The second means of escape is through the open interior stairway.*

including basements but excluding crawl spaces and unfinished attics. When activated, the detectors should initiate an alarm audible in all sleeping areas. This requirement is generally satisfied by interconnecting detectors with the manual fire alarm system.

In addition to smoke detectors in the corridors on each level, a single-station smoke detector powered by the building electrical system is required in each sleeping room to alert the occupant to a fire or smoke in the room.

Past performance of alarm systems in alerting building occupants, particularly in residential occupancies, has generally been less than satisfactory. It is critical that the manual fire alarm system will be audible in all sleeping rooms.

SEPARATION OF SLEEPING ROOMS

Rooming houses are required to be compartmented to restrict the spread of smoke. Specifically, sleeping rooms must be separated from corridors by smoke-resistant walls and doors. This feature helps to prevent smoke from compromising the egress corridors in case of a fire in a room; if the corridor does become smoke-logged before all occupants can escape, it provides a limited period of refuge from the fire within the room until the occupants can be rescued or alternate escape strategies can be developed.

AUTOMATIC SPRINKLER PROTECTION

NFPA 101, *Life Safety Code*, requires most new lodging and rooming houses to be protected by automatic sprinklers. Exceptions to other requirements can be made if sprinklers have been installed.

BIBLIOGRAPHY

NFPA Codes, Standards, and Recommended Practices

Reference to the following NFPA codes, standards, and recommended practices will provide further information on lodging or rooming houses discussed in this chapter. (See the latest *NFPA Catalog* for availability of current editions of the following documents.)

NFPA 72, *Protective Signaling Systems*.

NFPA 74, *Household Fire Warning Equipment*.

NFPA 101®, *Life Safety Code*.®

NFPA 220, *Types of Building Construction*.

Additional Reading

Crossland, J. W., "Fire Precautions in Public Homes and Restaurants," *Fire Surveyor*, Vol. 18, No. 6 (Dec. 1989) pp. 9-16.

Haley, G., "Lodging or Rooming Houses," *Conducting Fire Inspections*, 2nd ed., National Fire Protection Association, Quincy, MA, 1989.

Lathrop, J. K., ed., *Life Safety Code Handbook*, 4th ed., National Fire Protection Association, Quincy, MA, 1988.

ONE- AND TWO-FAMILY DWELLINGS

Harry L. Bradley

One- and two-family dwellings are defined as residential structures in which not more than two families reside. These dwelling units may be attached or detached from one another, and typical styles include detached single-family dwellings, townhouses, and duplexes. There are many different designs, such as the one-story ranch, two-story colonial, split level, and three-level townhouse. Wood frame and masonry are the most common construction types.

In 1987, 67.5 percent of all year-round occupied housing units were single-family detached or attached units, and another 5.8 percent were mobile homes or trailers.[1] Two-family houses were not tabulated separately, but housing units in buildings with two to four housing units accounted for another 10.4 percent of the total. Therefore, one- and two-family housing accounts for somewhere between three-fourths and five-sixths of all housing in the United States.

Each year, the majority of *all* U.S. fire deaths occur in one- and two-family dwellings. In 1989, for example, 65.5 percent or 3,545 deaths[2], occurred in such dwellings. Thus, it is important to consider every element of firesafety for its potential value in this setting.

NFPA 101®, *Life Safety Code*®, includes requirements for one- and two-family dwellings. In particular, NFPA 101 addrresses the need for two means of egress from every room for occupant evacuation; the selection of interior finish materials to prevent rapid early fire growth and spread and to protect occupant evacuation routes; and smoke detectors to provide detection and alarm. Additional information on smoke detectors can be found in Section 4, Chapter 4, "Household Warning Systems." The emerging fire protection strategy of sprinklers for the home is addressed in Section 5, Chapter 13, "Residential Quick-Response Sprinklers."

The philosophy of life safety and fire protection for one- and two-family dwellings is based on evacuation of the building in the event of a fire. The defend-in-place concept in other types of occupancies, which relies on fixed fire protection systems and fire-resistant construction, does not lend itself to one- and two-family dwellings. To allow residents time to evacuate, they must be alerted to a fire that has been detected at the incipient stage, they must know what action to take, and they must have adequate means of escape.

Early detection can be accomplished by proper installation and use of residential-type smoke detectors. NFPA 74, *Household Fire Warning Equipment*, recommends smoke detectors be provided on each level of the dwelling.

Once the occupants have been alerted, they must take prompt action to evacuate. A written fire plan should be made for each dwelling, showing two means of escape from every room, especially the bedrooms, and this plan should be practiced by the entire family. Programs such as NFPA's "EDITH" (Exit Drills in the Home) shows how to write and practice a home fire plan.

Adequate means of escape from each room should be provided in accordance with the requirements of NFPA 101, *Life Safety Code*. Two means of escape are required from each room. One must be a door or stairway, and the second way must be an operable window. (See Figures 8-19A and 8-19B.)

Residential-type automatic sprinkler systems provide a high degree of protection for one- and two-family dwellings. These relatively new types of automatic systems are not widely installed at present, but the technology is gaining in acceptance and use.

FIRE AND LIFE SAFETY HAZARDS

Many other fire protection strategies are under discussion, but they have not yet been reduced to codes or regulations. These address the contribution of various types of contents, furnishings, and construction elements to fire growth; smoke and gas generation; and confinement after a fire begins.

Most fire fatalities in one- and two-family dwellings are a result of toxic gases, not burns, and most victims die in a room that is not the room or area of fire origin. In other words, they die as a result of a fire that grew large enough to spread beyond the room in which it began. In most fatal

Harry L. Bradley, P.E., is fire protection engineer, State Fire Marshal's Office, Baltimore, MD.

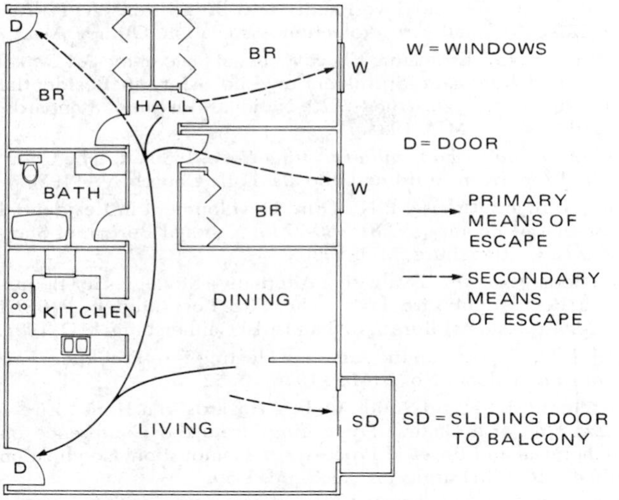

FIG. 8-19A. Means of escape from a three-bedroom single-family home. The bedroom in the upper left has no window, but it has a door directly to the outside. The alternate means of escape from the other bedrooms is through windows and must comply with the requirements of NFPA 101, Life Safety Code.

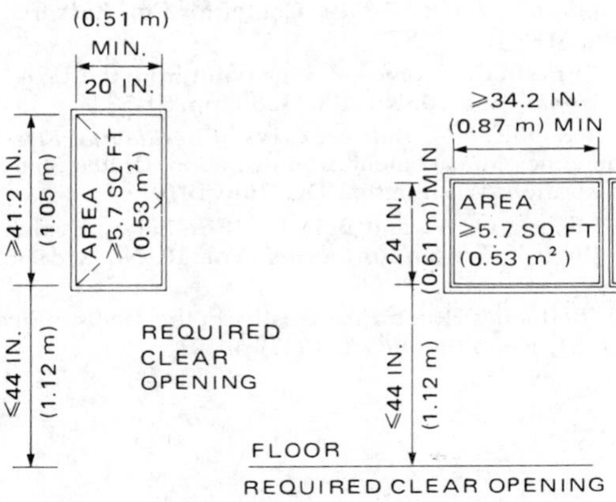

FIG. 8-19B. Minimum size and dimensions of outside windows used as a second means of escape.

fires in dwellings, duplexes, and mobile homes, the fire has spread to the contents, furnishings, finishes, and building elements, so the physics and chemistry of fire development can be quite complex. Prevention or action early in the fire is needed to control the development of these lethal conditions.

Prevention of Fire Ignition

Fatal fires in one- and two-family dwellings are so numerous that nearly every imaginable cause may be worthy of attention. The leading cause of fire deaths in one- and two-family homes is smoking materials, or lighted tobacco products, which were responsible for 980 civilian deaths a year in 1983-87, or one-fourth of all fire deaths.[3] (All statistics are based on a hierarchical sorting procedure developed by the U.S. Fire Administration and include a proportional allocation of fires of unknown causes. Higher estimates are obtained if the causes are considered individually outside the hierarchy.) Fatal smoking-material fires usually involve the ignition of upholstered furniture, mattresses, or bedding, which also rank highest as combustible items first ignited in fires. Fires begun by people smoking in bed are less common than those that start in living rooms, family rooms, and dens, and it is not unusual for a fire to smolder for hours before it progresses to open burning. This is why many of these fatal fires occur at night when everyone is asleep.

The second-ranking cause of fire deaths in one- and two-family homes is heating equipment, which is responsible for 720 deaths a year. Heating eqiipment is also the leading cause of fires: 154,000 fires a year. Most of these fires and fire deaths are caused by portable or area heating devices or associated chimneys and connectors, or hot water heaters and furnaces or their associated ducts and pipes. Each portable or area unit has its own rules for safe installation, maintenance, and use. Solid-fuel appliances, in particular, are covered by NFPA 211, *Chimneys, Fireplaces, Vents, and Solid Fuel Burning Appliances*. Adequate clearance to combustibles, whether fixed, such as walls and structural members, or moveable, such as furniture, bedding, and clothing, is a common problem for all types of portable and area heating equipment. Safe fueling practices are especially important for liquid-fueled units, as is adequate venting for gas-fueled units and regular inspection and cleaning for solid-fueled units.

Arson and suspected arson rank third in fire deaths in one- and two-family dwellings, at 460 per year, and first or second in direct property damage, at $526 million per year in 1983-87. Incendiary and suspicious fires have been declining for the past decade, however. Juvenile firesetters account for two of every five arson arrestees overall and are the largest single part of the problem.

Electrical distribution system components rank fourth as a cause of fire deaths, resulting in 390 facilities per year. Many people mistakenly believe that electrical system fires represent a larger share of fires, but the widespread and long-term use of the *National Electrical Code*® has reduced them to a lower-order problem, usually involving some kind of failure to observe the *Code*. Electrical system fires can take many forms. Damaged components, such as frayed cords, broken switches, or plugs; by-passed protection systems, such as oversized fuses or pennies in place of fuses; overloaded cords, circuits, or outlets; and cords run through traffic areas or pinned by furniture, are all potential problems. Repairs and modifications should always be performed by knowledgeable, experienced people in strict accordance with applicable codes.

Cooking equipment ranks fifth as a cause of fire deaths, resulting in 290 per year but first in fire injuries at nearly 3000 per year. Such equipment also accounts for a majority of unreported fires, that results in tens of thousands of injuries. Unattended cooking is a principal cause. Others include combustibles, such as rags, pot holders, or bags, placed too close to heat; failure to clean stove tops and ovens; and overhanging curtains, drapes, or clothing.

The sixth leading cause of fire deaths in the United States is children playing with fire, usually with matches or lighters. This type of fire resulted in 280 deaths a year. Children playing with fire also is the leading cause of fire deaths for children under age 6, and has been one of the few causes of fire deaths to increase in recent years. Children must be monitored closely and taught at an early age that matches and lighters are tools for adults, not toys. Matches and lighters must be kept out of reach and out of sight of young children.

Of the appliances and heat sources not already mentioned, clothes dryers, irons, electric blankets, and hot embers and ashes stand out. Each causes at least 1 percent of fires in one- and two-family dwellings. Care is needed in installing and using or handling all potential heat sources.

BIBLIOGRAPHY

References Cited

1. *Statistical Abstract of the United States 1990*, 110th ed., U.S. Department of Commerce, Washington, DC, Jan. 1990.
2. Karter, Michael J., Jr., "Fire Loss in the United States During 1989," *Fire Journal*, Vol. 84, No. 5 (Sept./Oct. 1990), pp. 56-67.
3. Hall, John R., Jr., *The U.S. Fire Problem Overview Report Through 1988*, Fire Analysis & Research Division, National Fire Protection Association, Quincy, MA, Nov. 1989.

NFPA Codes, Standards, and Recommended Practices

Reference to the following NFPA codes, standards, and recommended practices will provide further information on one- and two-family dwellings discussed in this chapter. (See the latest *NFPA Catalog* for availability of current editions of the following documents.)

NFPA 13D, *Installation of Sprinkler Systems in One- and Two-Family Dwellings and Mobile Homes*.

NFPA 70, *National Electrical Code*.®

NFPA 74, *Household Fire Warning Equipment*.

NFPA *101*®, *Life Safety Code*.®

NFPA 211, *Chimneys, Fireplaces, Vents, and Solid Fuel Burning Appliances*.

Additional Reading

"A Study of Fatal Residential Fires," National Fire Protection Association, Quincy, MA.

"A Study of One- and Two-Family Dwelling Fires," *NFPA No. FR75-1*, National Fire Protection Association, Quincy, MA.

Budnick, E. K., "Estimating Effectiveness of State-of-the-Art Detectors and Automatic Sprinklers on Life Safety in Residential Occupancies," *NBSIR 84-2819*, National Bureau of Standards, Gaithersburg, MD, 1984.

CABO One and Two Family Dwelling Code, 1989 ed., The Council of American Building Officials, Falls Church, VA, 1989.

Fang, J. B. and Breese, J. N., "Fire Development in Residential Basement Rooms," *NBSIR 80-2120*, National Bureau of Standards, Gaithersburg, MD, 1980.

Gomberg, A., *et al.*, "Evaluating Alternative Strategies for Reducing Residential Fire Loss—The Fire Loss Model," *NBSIR 82-2551*, National Bureau of Standards, Gaithersburg, MD, 1982.

Hall, J. R., "Update on the Auxiliary Heating Fire Problem," *Fire Journal*, Vol. 80, No. 2 (Mar. 1986), p. 52.

Hirschler, M. M. and Smith, G. F., "Hazards in a House Fire—Example of a Chair," *Proceedings* from the Conference on Chemical and Physical Processes in Combustion, Combustion Institute, Pittsburgh, PA, 1985, pp. 1-59.

"Home Safe Home," *P7838*, Factory Mutual Research Corp., Norwood, MA.

Issen, L. A., "Single-Family Residential Fire and Live Loads Survey," *NBSIR 80-2155*, National Bureau of Standards, Gaithersburg, MD, 1980.

Levin, B. M., "EXITT—A Simulation Model of Occupant Decisions and Actions in Residential Fires: Users Guide and Program Description," *NBSIR 87-3591*, Center for Fire Research, Gaithersburg, MD, July 1987.

Mischutin, V., "Fire in the Home—A Viewpoint from the USA," *Fire International*, Vol. 10, No. 100, 1986, pp. 51-53.

Munson, M. J. and Ohls, J. C., *Indirect Costs of Residential Fires*, Federal Emergency Management Administration, United States Fire Administration, Washington, DC, July 1979.

Shields, T. J., Silcock, G. W., and Bell, Y., "Fire Safety Evaluation of Dwellings," *Fire Safety Journal*, Vol. 10, No. 1, 1986, pp. 29-36.

Willey, A. E., "Reducing Home Fire Deaths in the 1990s," *Fire Journal*, Vol. 81, No. 5 (Sept./Oct. 1987) p. 121.

MANUFACTURED HOUSING AND RECREATIONAL VEHICLES

Revised by Travis Pitts

This chapter covers manufactured housing and recreational vehicles, including their associated regulations, utility systems, fire loss history, and firesafety requirements.

MANUFACTURED (MOBILE) HOMES

Amendments made in 1983 to the National Manufactured Housing Construction and Safety Standards Act of 1974 changed the definition of mobile homes from "mobile" to "manufactured." Manufactured housing is not to be confused with modular or factory-built housing.

Manufactured homes are factory-assembled structures that are transportable in one or more sections. They are usually 8 ft (2.5 m) or more wide and 32 to 80 ft (10 to 24 m) long. Each is built on a permanent chassis and is designed to be used as a dwelling when placed on stabilizing devices (which may be piers and footings rather than permanent foundations) and connected to the required utilities. Due to the increasing cost of conventional housing and the improved quality of manufactured homes, these homes become the choice of residence for nearly a quarter of a million families each year.

Construction, or the body and frame design; plumbing systems; heating, cooling and fuel burning systems; and electrical systems are built to a special standard because of the uniqueness of a transportable home. NFPA 501B, *Mobile Homes* (or ANSI A119.1), had been the guiding document for construction of mobile homes since 1968. Almost all states adopted the NFPA/ANSI standard for mobile homes, and concerned federal agencies, such as the Federal Housing Administration and the Veterans Administration, used it in connection with the purchases of mobile homes under loan programs they administered.

However, both the mobile home industry and the federal government were concerned about the lack of uniform enforcement of NFPA 501B among the states, counties, and cities. To ensure a safe, low-cost form of housing of uniform quality throughout the U.S., Congress passed the National Manufactured Housing (formerly Mobile Home) Construction and Safety Standards Act of 1974 (Title VI of the Housing and Community Development Act of 1974). It established the U.S. Department of Housing and Urban Development (HUD) as the sole source of standards governing the construction of these homes in the U.S., and gave HUD the authority to establish the procedural and enforcement regulations necessary to ensure that makers of mobile homes met the construction standards.

The Act was fully implemented in mid-1976, when the National Conference of States on Building Codes and Standards (NCSBCS) was named by HUD as the contract agent for ensuring the uniform enforcement of the HUD version of NFPA 501B, *Mobile Homes*. To date, approximately 3.5 million mobile homes have been built under the 1974 Act, adding to the estimated existing mobile home stock of 4.3 million built before mid-1976.[1,2] The infusion of "safer" new mobile homes into the U.S. housing stock has had a dramatic effect on life safety and fire incidents in mobile homes built after 1976.

During 1980 through 1987, mobile homes built before 1976 averaged 2.3 deaths per 100 fires.[3] Mobile homes built after 1976 to the federal standard averaged 0.6 deaths per 100 fires, or nearly three-fourths less. Similarly, the injury rate per 100 fires in pre-1976 homes averaged 4.4 compared to an injury rate of 2.9 per 100 fires in post-1976 homes, a one-third reduction in the injury rate. Despite these large differences and the steady shift toward post-1976 units in the manufactured home inventory, the total number of fire deaths and injuries in manufactured homes showed no steady improvement in the 1980s, at least through 1988. It is not clear why this is the case.

This dramatic difference in the injury and death rates is directly attributable to HUD uniformly applying an updated version of NFPA 501B, *Mobile Homes,* as the core document for the portion of the HUD standard that applies to firesafety. The most important element in reducing death rate appears to be the mandatory smoke detector provision. Pre-1976 manufactured homes that are retrofitted with detectors also show dramatically lower death rates per 100 fires. It is distressing, therefore, that nearly half the fires reported in post-1976 manufactured homes occurred in homes that had no detector, indicating a high rate of removal of detectors by owners.

Travis Pitts is deputy director of the Department of Housing and Community Development, Sacramento, CA.

Some of the other pertinent features of the HUD standard (CFR 24, Part 3280) that have produced this positive effect on firesafety are discussed in the following paragraphs.

The HUD standard requires that interior finish be regulated for flame spread characteristics, and, in certain areas of the home, for combustibility. Firestopping is required in concealed wall and partition spaces. At least two exterior doors are required, and they must be arranged to provide a means of unobstructed travel to the outside. The width of doors is specified, as is the ability to operate locking mechanisms from the inside to facilitate egress. Every room designed expressly for sleeping purposes, unless it has a door to the outside, is required to have at least one outside window large enough to permit emergency egress, and the window must be openable without the use of special tools.

Utilities

Where LP-Gas is used for heating or cooking, the LP-Gas containers are limited in size, number, and location. They must be mounted on the A-frame of the mobile home or in a vented compartment that is vaportight to the inside of the mobile home and accessible only from the outside. Requirements are included to ensure that the mounting of the containers is secure so they will not jar loose, slip, or rotate while the home is in transit. Special provisions are included to protect shutoff valves on containers while the mobile home is in transit or storage. LP-Gas regulators must be connected directly to the container shutoff valves or mounted on adjacent support brackets connected by a listed high-pressure connector to the valve. LP-Gas safety relief devices are required, and the discharge from these devices is regulated as to proximity to any opening in the mobile home. Allowable pressures of gas piping systems are also regulated, as are piping materials, routing, sizing, anchoring, and the provision of shutoff valves. Appliance connectors cannot run through walls, floors, ceilings, or partitions, and the manufacturer must perform specific gas piping leakage tests before delivering the mobile home.

Where oil is used as the heating fuel, there are specific requirements for oil tanks, fill and vent pipes, liquid-level gages, and shutoff valves. Materials for oil piping systems are specified as to size, type of joints, couplings, grading, hangers, and tests for leakage.

One of the unique features of the HUD standard concerns the installation of heat-producing appliances. Especially noteworthy is the requirement that all fuel-burning appliances except ranges, ovens, illuminating appliances, clothes dryers, solid-fuel-burning fireplaces, and solid-fuel-burning fireplace stoves be installed to provide for complete separation of the combustion system from the interior atmosphere of the mobile home. Combustion air inlets and flue gas outlets must be listed or certified as components of the appliance. The required separation may be obtained by installing direct vent systems (sealed combustion systems) or by installing the appliance within an enclosure so its appliance combustion and venting systems are separated from the interior atmosphere of the mobile home.

No forced-air appliance, nor its air return system, can allow the creation of a negative pressure which will affect either its combustion air supply or that of any other appliance, nor can they act to mix products of combustion with circulating air. Other requirements for heat-producing appliances include special provisions relating to solid fuel burning fireplaces or fireplace stoves. The size and air-tightness of circulating-air duct materials are specified, and the design and combustibility of duct materials are regulated. Special provisions are included for registers and grills, and there are additional special requirements for the use of ducts in expandable or multiple transportable section connections.

The HUD standard also specifies the maximum construction requirement, thickness, and gage of the metal ventilating hood to be installed over a kitchen range. In addition, the HUD standard limits the flame spread of the wall finish and the cabinet finish in the immediate vicinity of the kitchen range. This combination of requirements effectively negates or minimizes the direct exposure of the wall surface and the cabinet surface nearest the kitchen range in the event of a cooking-surface fire. Fire experience statistics show that these provisions produce smaller cooking and heating fires in post-1976 manufactured homes and that a much smaller share of such fires spread beyond their room of origin than they do in pre-1976 units.The HUD standard includes specific requirements for electrical installations. It concentrates on those provisions that differ from provisions applicable to all buildings under NFPA 70, *National Electrical Code.®* Both documents are coordinated. Some of the special features relate to the compactness of mobile homes, to the fact that they are factory-assembled, to the lighter construction techniques commonly used, to the under-chassis wiring requirements, to the wiring of expandable and dual units, to the need for outdoor outlets, to the need for bonding of sometimes extensive amounts of noncurrent-carrying metal parts, and to the grounding of services and appliances.

HUD issued the first update to its standard in 1985. Due to the standard's success in the area of firesafety, HUD "fine tuned" the standard in lieu of making wholesale changes. HUD lowered the maximum height above the floor of the egress window latch from 60 to 54 in. (1.5 to 1.4 m). More importantly, HUD issued a stricter limit on ceiling interior finish flame spread—to a maximum rating of 75—and expanded its criteria on kitchen cabinet protection. Other minor changes, included a further clarification of firestopping construction techniques in concealed wall, ceiling, and floor construction; the recognition of 5/16-in. (8 mm) thick gypsum board as firestopping material; and a clarification of smoke detector placement instructions.[4]

It should be noted that manufactured homes have increased in width and length from a minimum of 8 by 32 ft (2.5 by 10 m) to as much as 14 by 80 ft (4 by 24 m) and that some units are designed so that they can be joined at the site to form "double wides" or even "triple wides," thus becoming sizable homes. Some manufactured homes have been for employed unintended uses, such as multi-family occupancies, dormitories, and multi-story structures. Basic manufactured homes also are used as temporary banks or offices, as field offices at construction sites, and for many other purposes. Manufactured homes basically are not designed for such uses, and special attention must be paid to firesafety where they are so utilized.

NFPA 501A, *Manufactured Home Installations, Sites, and Communities*, should be consulted for firesafety at the installation site.

RECREATIONAL VEHICLES

Recreational vehicles are primarily designed as temporary living quarters for recreational camping or travel. They either have their own motive power or are mounted on or drawn by another vehicle. The basic vehicles are the travel trailer, the camping trailer, the truck camper, van conversions, and the motor home. Together, they account for about 5000 fires a year reported to fire departments in the U.S. There are several variations on these recreational vehicles, and new equipment is being developed constantly.

In general, the automotive features of recreational vehicles are covered by federal motor vehicle safety standards. However, the federal standards do not apply currently to plumbing, heating, and electrical systems in recreational vehicles. Nor do they apply, except in multi-purpose passenger vehicles such as van conversions and motor homes, to materials of construction for interior walls, partitions, ceilings, exit facilities, and fire protection. NFPA 501C, *Recreational Vehicles* (or ANSI A119.2), concentrates on plumbing, heating, electrical, and firesafety and life safety considerations. NFPA 501C's requirements for the installation of fuel-burning appliances provide for complete separation of the combustion system from the interior atmosphere. This applies to all types of fuel-burning appliances used in recreational vehicles, except ranges, ovens, and illuminating appliances. Attention is likewise given to the ventilation and combustion air systems, clearances between heat-producing appliances and adjacent surfaces, circulating-air system ducts and their sizing, duct supports, registers, and grills.

Electrical systems are also covered in NFPA 501C, *Recreational Vehicles*, as well as in Article 551 of NFPA 70, *National Electrical Code*. The bulk of the provisions relate to the electrical equipment and materials required in a recreational vehicle for connection to a wiring system nominally rated 115 V (two wires with ground) or a wiring system nominally rated $^{115}/_{230}$ V (three wires with ground). Other special requirements cover low-voltage systems other than circuit supply lines subject to federal or state regulations, combination electrical systems for connection to a battery or to a direct current supply that may also be connected to a 115-V source, and generator installations.

Fire and life safety requirements in NFPA 501C, *Recreational Vehicles*, cover interior walls, partitions and ceilings, and exit facilities, and stipulate that each recreational vehicle equipped with fuel-burning appliances or an internal combustion engine must have a listed portable fire extinguisher with a specified minimum rating.

To facilitate proper use of recreational vehicles, another standard, NFPA 501D, *Recreational Vehicle Parks and Campgrounds* (or ANSI A119.4), has been developed. The intent of this standard is to provide minimum construction requirements for parks designed primarily for use by owners of recreational vehicles. It devotes attention to park design and construction, recreational vehicle stand construction, environmental health and sanitation, fuel gas systems, storage of flammable and combustible liquids, electrical systems, and firesafety.

BIBLIOGRAPHY

References Cited

1. Budnick, E. K. and Klein, D. P., "Mobile Home Fire Studies, Summary and Recommendations," *NBSIR 79-1720*, National Bureau of Standards, Gaithersburg, MD, 1979.
2. Klem, T. J., "Interim Report: The Mobile Home Fire Problem in the United States," National Fire Prevention and Control Administration (now U.S. Fire Administration), Washington, DC, 1978.
3. Hall, J. R., Jr., "Mobile Home Fires in the U.S., 1980-1987," NFPA Fire Analysis and Research Division, Quincy, MA, May 1990.
4. *Memorandum*: "HUD Standards on Formaldehyde, Firesafety, and Ventilation," Manufactured Housing Institute, Arlington, VA, 1984.

NFPA Codes, Standards, and Recommended Practices

Reference to the following NFPA codes, standards, and recommended practices will provide further information on manufactured housing and recreational vehicles discussed in this chapter. (See the latest *NFPA Catalog* for availability of current editions of the following documents.)

NFPA 70, *National Electrical Code.®*

NFPA 501A, *Manufactured Home Installations, Sites, and Communities.*

NFPA 501B, *Mobile Homes.*

NFPA 501C, *Recreational Vehicles.*

NFPA 501D, *Recreational Vehicle Parks and Campgrounds.*

Additional Reading

Budnick, E. K., "Estimating Effectiveness of State-of-the-Art Detectors and Automatic Sprinklers on Life Safety in Residential Occupancies," *NBSIR 84-2819*, National Bureau of Standards, Gaithersburg, MD, 1984.

Budnick, E. K. *et al.*, "Mobile Home Living Room, Fire Studies: The Role of Interior Finish," *NBSIR 78-1530*, National Bureau of Standards, Gaithersburg, MD, 1978.

Budnick, E. K. and Klein, D. P., "Mobile Home Bedroom Fire Studies: Summary and Recommendations," *NBSIR 79-1720*, National Bureau of Standards, Gaithersburg, MD, 1978.

Budnick, E. K., "Fire Spread Along a Mobile Home Corridor," *NBSIR 76-1021*, National Bureau of Standards, Gaithersburg, MD, 1976.

Fact Sheet No. 39: "Mobile Homes," U.S. Consumer Products Safety Commission, Washington, DC.

"Fire Performance Evaluation of the Federal Mobile Home Construction and Safety, Standard," U.S. Department of Housing and Urban Development, Washington, DC, 1980.

Frieborne, W., "Evaluation of Manufactured Home Fire Safety: 1981-83"; U.S. Department of Housing and Urban Development, Washington, DC, Feb. 1987.

Gause, W. P., "Mobile Home Flammability," *Journal of Products Liability*, Vol. 3, 1979, pp. 85-106.

Gomberg, A., *et al.*, "Evaluating Alternative Strategies for Reducing Residential Fire Loss — The Fire Loss Model," *NBSIR 82-2551*, National Bureau of Standards, Gaithersburg, MD, 1982.

Gustin, B., "Mobil Home Fires," *Fire Engineering*, Vol. 142, No. 3, 1989, p. 58.

Herrin, C. L. and Schaenman, P. S., "Data Base for Evaluation of Mobile Home Fire Safety — 1979-1980," National Bureau of Standards, Gaithersburg, MD, 1982.

Klein, D. P., "Characteristics of Incidental Fires in the Living Room of a Mobile Home," *NBSIR 78-1522*, National Bureau of Standards, Gaithersburg, MD, 1978.

Mischutin, V., "Fire in the Home—A Viewpoint from the USA," *Fire International*, Vol. 10, No. 100, 1986, pp. 51-53.

NFPA Fire Analysis Division, "Manufactured Home Fires, 1984-85: Final Report," *Report* to NAHB National Research Center for U.S. Department of Housing and Urban Development, Jan. 1988.

NFPA Fire Analysis and Research Division, "1986-87 Manufactured Home Fires: Final Report," *Report* to NAHB National Research Center for U.S. Department of Housing and Urban Development, Dec. 1989.

Schaenman, P. S. and Herrin, C. L., "Evaluation of Mobile Home Fire Safety: 1979-1980," *Report* prepared for the Department of Housing and Urban Development by Tri Data, Arlington, VA, Mar. 1982.

Willey, A. E., "Reducing Home Fire Deaths in the 1990's," *Fire Journal*, Vol. 81, No. 5 (Sept. - Oct. 1987), pp. 12-13.

MERCANTILE OCCUPANCIES

William Hiotaky

Mercantile occupancies are those facilities in which a wide variety of goods and services are displayed and sold. Examples of such goods and services include clothing and footwear; jewelry; beauty, health, and fitness equipment; home furnishings, gifts, and luggage; books, cards, and stationery; music, electronic equipment, and photography supplies; sport specialties; toys, hobbies, and pets; drugs, varieties, and tobacco; food and food specialties; and hardware.

Mercantile occupancies' contents are classified in NFPA 101®, *Life Safety Code*®, as ordinary hazard, notwithstanding the wide variety of goods with varied degrees of combustibility that might, on occasion, suggest a higher or lower classification. On balance, the ordinary hazard classification is an appropriate designation, assuming that, in those instances where a limited higher hazard is present, adequate steps are taken to address that particular circumstance.

The variety of facilities in which any or all of the aforementioned goods and services can be found is within the experience of the general public. Basically, mercantile facilities can be differentiated as follows:

1. Individual stores with a single category of merchandise, such as specialty shops and supermarkets.
2. Individual stores with multiple categories of merchandise, such as department stores with or without ancillary nonmercantile uses such as restaurants or administration offices.
3. Shopping centers that are some combination of the above types, in addition to multiple ancillary or accessory nonmercantile uses such as restaurants and theaters.

Since there are many instances when a mercantile use may be the ancillary or accessory use in connection with a totally different occupancy classification, this chapter covers only those instances where mercantile is the primary occupancy classification.

William Hiotaky, AIA, is group executive vice president of The Taubman Company, Inc., based in Bloomfield Hills, MI.

SINGLE-TYPE MERCHANDISE STORES

The single category of merchandise retail stores, or Type I stores, comprises the greatest variety of stores, with respect to range of floor area and diversity of merchandise. For example, jewelry stores, tobacco stores, and gift shops are typically at the lower end of the scale in terms of floor area, whereas furniture stores, supermarkets, and sporting goods stores are usually at the higher end. The floor area can range from a couple of hundred square feet (200 sq ft equals 18.6 m^2) to 30,000 or 40,000 sq ft (2800 or 3700 m^2).

Smaller Type I Stores

In the past, smaller Type I shops were constructed principally in cities and towns, along business thoroughfares, next to each other, often with basements for stock, and sometimes with an office or residential use immediately above. Many such stores still exist today, especially in the older business sections of cities; they are sometimes referred to as "ma-and-pa" stores because the proprietors often live in the residential units directly above them. However, this type of store is slowly fading out of existence.

Because of more restrictive zoning regulations, Type I stores now are being constructed without other occupancies above them, unless the mercantile occupancy serves an ancillary or accessory use, such as retail shops in a hotel lobby. In addition, basement space, even for stock space, is being phased out, since stock space on the same level as the sales area is more efficient and functional.

Originally, smaller Type I stores were constructed primarily of wood or masonry bearing walls with wood joists, floors, and roofs. The subsequent establishment of fire districts in urban areas, plus the adoption of more stringent building code requirements, led to the widespread use in the construction of Type I stores of noncombustible materials, such as masonry walls, either load-bearing or non-load-bearing; steel joists; concrete floors; and metal roof decks.

Until recently, smaller Type I stores were almost never sprinklered. Nor were larger Type I stores. NFPA 101, *Life Safety Code*, currently requires sprinkler protection based on height and area and, in certain instances, if the stores are located below the level of exit discharge.

Larger Type I Stores

Larger Type I stores or chain stores, such as supermarkets and discount drug stores, did not become prominent until the mid-to-late 1940s. In many areas, they replaced the neighborhood grocer and corner druggist, who could not compete with the high-volume chains.

Larger Type I stores that are approximately 30,000 to 40,000 sq ft (2800 to 3700 m^2) in area are usually one story higher with a possible mezzanine for management offices, and are of noncombustible unprotected construction. Until recently, they were not required to be sprinklered.

These Type I stores are generally free-standing buildings, unless they are part of a shopping center complex, and may have relatively large contiguous parking areas surrounding them.

Larger Type I stores usually are divided into at least two principal areas: the stock space or back of the house employee area, and the sales space or customer area. The apportionment of areas is approximately one-quarter to one-third stock and two-thirds to three-quarters sales. The larger Type I stores may include nonmercantile accessory uses, such as management offices, that comprise a small area in relation to the sales and stock spaces. From a retailer's point of view, the distinction between retail stock space and storage space is important. Employees enter the retail stock areas frequently during the day to bring merchandise onto the sales floor. In this sense, the stock space is essentially an extension of the sales space, except that the occupant load is considerably less. Stock space is not generally open to the public, except as an alternate exit access route in case of fire. Storage areas, on the other hand, are less frequently accessed because goods are set aside in such areas for extended periods of time. In the retailing industry, storage areas serving or supporting mercantile occupancies are almost always in separate locations and are essentially distribution warehouses.

Occupant Load—Type I Stores

The occupant load consists of customers and sales employees. In smaller Type I stores, sales employees double as stock employees; larger Type I stores have a separate workforce employed exclusively in the stock area.

The occupant load will vary with the seasons of the year, generally being higher before school begins; before Thanksgiving, Christmas, and Easter; and during occasional clearance sales. NFPA 101, *Life Safety Code*, has taken these primary merchandising seasons into account in establishing the occupant load factor for calculating exiting requirements; this seems to work reasonably well.

Fire Load—Type I Stores

As in most other occupancies, contents represent the major potential hazard in Type I stores. Case histories and statistical evidence have proven that sprinklers remain the most effective means of combating fires in mercantile occupancies. In terms of life safety, the issue of cost-benefit in installing sprinklers is appropriately addressed by NFPA 101, *Life Safety Code*, requirements for sprinklers based on height and area limits. These requirements obviate the need for sprinklers in small shops unless, of course, these small shops are accessory uses to an occupancy requiring sprinklers.

MULTIPLE-TYPE MERCHANDISE STORES

The multiple-category-type merchandise store, such as a department store, is known as a Type II store and is almost as common as the smaller Type I stores.

This type of store is generally from one to three or four stories in height and can vary in area from 50,000 to 250,000 sq ft (4645 to 23 225 m^2).

Earlier Type II stores, and particularly department stores, were constructed exclusively in business/retail districts in cities. The stores were several stories high, either of exterior masonry wall-bearing construction with wood joists and floors, or of reinforced concrete, and they had no sprinkler protection. More recently, however, many department stores have been constructed of unprotected structural steel and are fully sprinklered.

As the name implies, department stores are divided into departments or sections that carry different kinds of merchandise, with or without the use of partition walls. The departments are laid out in a particular way to influence customer movement patterns vertically and horizontally through the store according to a preconceived merchandising plan.

The vertical movement in multistory Type II stores is more effectively accomplished by means of escalators and stairs in open wells in highly visible and accessible areas of the store.

While basements were at one time quite common in Type II stores for use as either sales or stock areas, this practice generally is no longer followed because basement space is not as desirable as the same area constructed at or above ground level.

Unlike the vast majority of Type I stores, where the stock space is located in the rear of the store, stock space in Type II stores is often distributed on all four sides of the store. These areas are staffed strictly by stock personnel, as opposed to smaller Type I stores where sales personnel often double as stock help.

Another example of a Type II store is the discount store, which grew out of the well-known "five-and-dime" variety store. It is usually one story high and laid out in a manner similar to a retail food supermarket, with shopping cart self-service and checkout counters. Merchandise in such stores generally is not as expensive or of the same quality as that sold in department stores. However, the same sectionalization of merchandise occurs as in a department store.

Accessory Occupancies

To round out the full range of goods and services a customer needs and expects, certain accessory or ancillary occupancies, in addition to administrative office areas, are often included in Type II stores. Examples of such occupancies are restaurants, beauty shops, travel agencies, and optometry services. Restaurants and, more particularly, the food preparation areas of restaurants, warrant special attention because of their potential life safety hazard.

Occupant Load—Type II Stores

As in Type I stores, the occupant load at Type II stores consists of the general public, or customers, and sales and stock employees. The occupant load will vary somewhat more dramatically with the primary shopping seasons in Type II stores than in Type I stores. This is especially true during the Thanksgiving/Christmas season when temporary employees are likely to be hired to supplement the permanent workforce, and a heavier volume of customer traffic that can be expected.

Fire Load—Type II Stores

Contents represent the major potential hazard, as in Type I stores. Efforts to control the potential hazard in Type II stores, such as department stores, are somewhat more complicated, because the fire load can vary greatly from one department to another and from floor to floor within the same store. Moreover, accessory occupancies have their own special fire loads that must be considered in determining firesafety measures in these stores.

THE COVERED MALL SHOPPING CENTER

A covered mall, herein referred to as a Type III store, is commonly defined as a covered or roofed interior area used as a pedestrian way, which connects buildings or portions of a building housing a single and/or multiple tenants. The covered mall shopping center became very popular in a relatively short period of time, and, today, most large shopping centers either planned or under construction are of this type. In addition, many covered malls are now being built in urban areas in conjunction with parking decks, office buildings, hotels, recreational facilities, and public or private transit systems.

Design of Covered Mall Shopping Centers

The covered mall shopping center is generally designed as one building composed of from one to six or seven sizeable department stores and numerous smaller, specialty stores, all of which are interconnected by a covered, climate-controlled public pedestrian way. The complex may also include other ancillary occupancies, such as movie theaters, bowling lanes, ice arenas, project management offices, and other customer service areas with access from the mall.

The mall may be designed as a single- or multi-level structure, depending upon such factors as topography, the size of the land parcel, and the number and size of the department stores and retail shops. The vast majority of malls in the United States have either one or two levels, with an occasional partial mezzanine.

When a mall has two levels, the parking lot surrounding the building usually is shaped to provide grade access to each level of the department stores and the small shops. This equalizes customer flow so that one level has no advantage over the other as far as sales exposure is concerned. The two-level shopping center is distinguished from the two-story shopping center in this important respect. (See Figure 8-21A.) When they are part of a two-level covered mall shopping center, department stores are designed and merchandised in a similar manner.

The covered mall proper is designed primarily to serve the requirements for occupant egress, maximization of tenant sales, and promotional activities. The storefronts along the pedestrian "public street" of the mall are usually designed to encourage unrestricted customer flow and traffic control from the mall to the individual shops, as well as to the department stores. This system of customer traffic flow and traffic control is the essence of the merchandising concept behind covered mall shopping centers.

Swing doors, whether glass or solid, not only make it less easy to exit, but they also promote what is referred to in the retail industry as "threshold resistance"—that is, the reluctance of customers to push, pull, or slide doors to gain access. The storefront closures ideally suited to the requirements for flow and for maintaining security are those that can be fully recessed, such as rolling overhead grilles, side-coiling grilles, and horizontal sliding doors. Since the ambient temperature in the mall is the same as it is in the tenant space, the storefront closure need only satisfy a security requirement when the store is unoccupied.

Occupant Allowance Requirements

Many covered mall shopping centers are constructed by a "fast track" construction procedure, so the ultimate ratio of sales space to storage space for tenant stores is not known at the time construction begins. In simple terms, fast tracking is a phased construction procedure that allows construction to proceed upon completion of the construction documents for any given phase of the work. Hence, a projection must be made concerning occupant load so the required units of exit width can be determined well in advance of negotiations with prospective tenants.

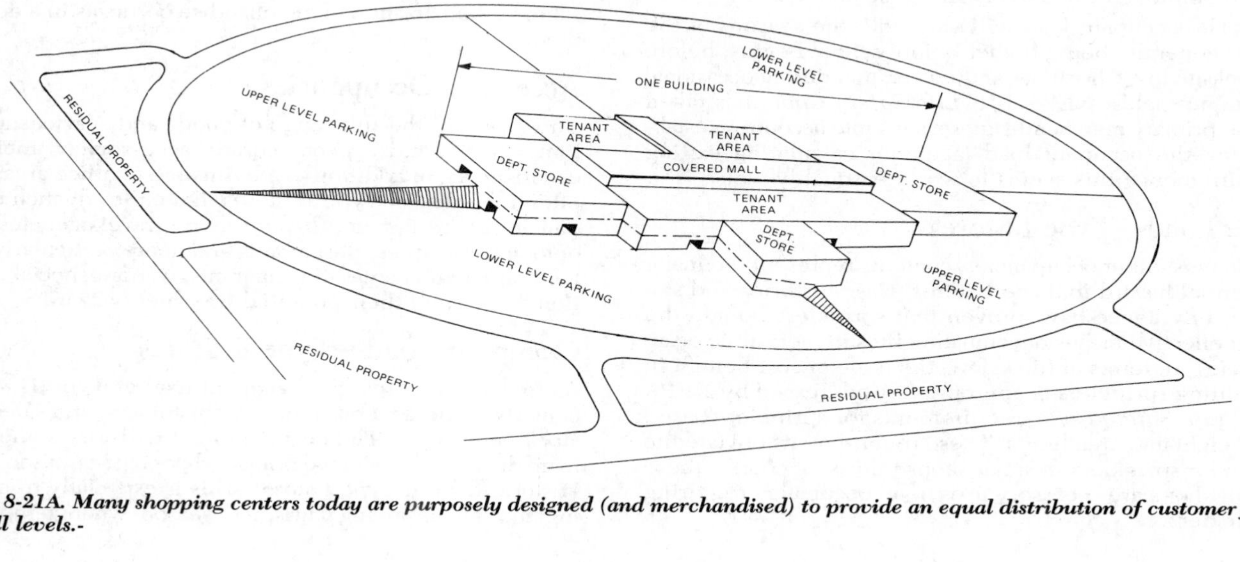

FIG. 8-21A. Many shopping centers today are purposely designed (and merchandised) to provide an equal distribution of customer flow on all levels.-

Many model codes, including NFPA 101, *Life Safety Code*, require that the occupant load for Type I and Type II stores be calculated on the basis of a factor of one occupant per 30 sq ft (2.8 m^2) of street floor area and basement sales areas, if planned, plus a factor of one occupant per 60 sq ft (5.6 m^2) of other upper sales floors. The occupant load for stock or storage space that is not open to the public is calculated on the basis of a factor of one occupant per 100 to 300 sq ft (9.3 to 27.9 m^2), depending upon the particular code being used. Whether the covered mall proper is assigned an occupant load depends on its designed function.

The Covered Mall Proper—A Systems Approach

In addition to the typical one-level design, the covered mall may be designed as a multi-level space serving multi-level tenant areas and department stores. Although the vast majority of suburban shopping centers built in the U.S. are either one- or two-level centers, with the occasional introduction of a partial mezzanine level, multi-level shopping centers are becoming more commonplace in urban areas as a result of urban redevelopment programs and the diminishing number of appropriately sized suburban sites.

In most cases, two-level covered malls are designed for visual intercommunication of the levels by means of openings in the floor of the upper level. Wherever practicable, visual intercommunication between the levels is important in maximizing exposure of storefronts and merchandise to customer traffic. The floor areas between openings in the upper level serve as bridges that promote cross-mall shopping convenience for the customer. (See Figures 8-21B and 8-21C.)

At the time construction is started, not everything about the shopping center is known, even to the developer. For example, the final architectural treatment of the exterior and interior spaces may be determined only to a point where the structural elements can be designed. The location of tenant demising walls may be unknown, since lease negotiations with prospective tenants may not begin until the superstructure has been erected. Mechanical, electrical, and fire protection systems are designed for main distribution only, with branch distribution added to the construction documents when the tenant space is defined by lease agreement.

The covered mall proper may contain other amenities for sales promotion and customer service and convenience, such as seating areas, art objects, planting areas, pools, specialty retail kiosks, directories, openings in upper levels of multi-level structures, and areas designed for periodic promotional activities. Care must be exercised in the location of these amenities so they do not interfere with, nor encroach upon, required exit access.

Basically, the covered mall may be considered in either of two ways: as a way of exit access from the connected buildings, or as a pedestrian way permitting an increase in the distance of travel from each of the tenant stores to a mall exit.

In the first instance, the entire complex is treated as one building or one compartmented retail facility, where the covered mall is treated simply as an extension of the sales space. In terms of exit access, the covered mall is considered an aisle common to the various tenant stores that joins the exit access aisles of the tenant stores to mall exits. This treatment, in terms of NFPA 101, *Life Safety Code*, leads to the strict application of all design factors as though

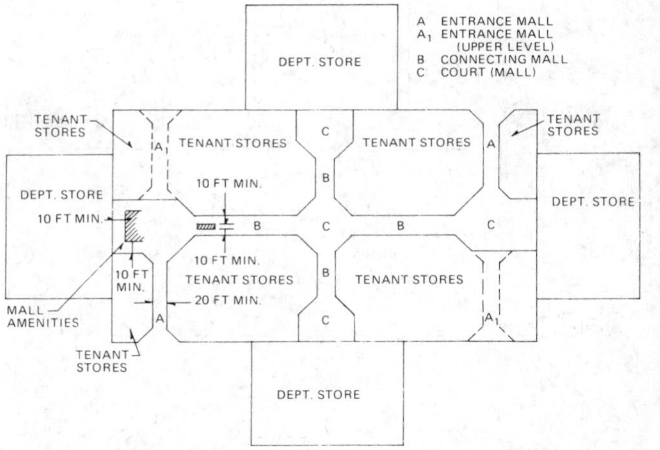

FIG. 8-21B. Typical two-level shopping center (lower level).

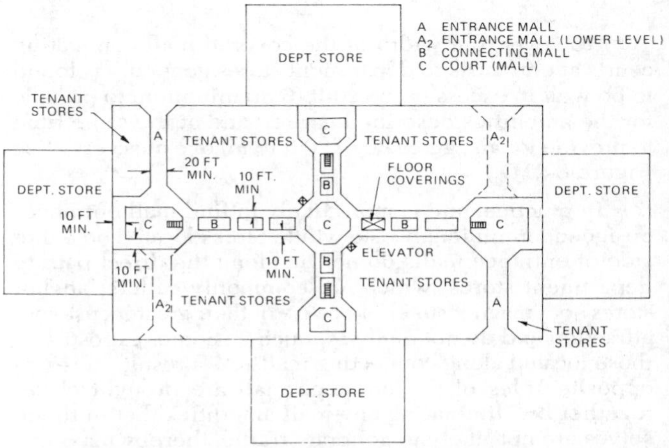

FIG. 8-21C. Typical two-level shopping center (upper level).

the shopping center were a Type II store or department store.

In the second instance, a systems approach is employed where the mall is considered to offer a higher degree of life safety if certain minimum conditions of the system are met. The covered mall should be of at least sufficient clear width to accommodate egress requirements for mercantile buildings, but in no case should it be less than 20 ft (6 m) wide in its narrowest dimension.The minimum width dimension of 20 ft (6 m) is particularly significant in terms of exit access and should not be construed as a requirement to provide minimum separation between storefronts on opposite sides of the covered mall.

The need for separation in a covered mall shopping center that is protected by an automatic sprinkler system is not substantiated by the history of recorded accounts of exposure fires involving mercantile and various other types of occupancies.

The excellent performance of automatic sprinklers in connection with exposure fires, as documented in *Fire: Automatic Sprinklers Performance in Australia and New Zealand*,[1] together with the sprinkler performance data compiled by NFPA, mitigates almost any reasonable doubt regarding an additional requirement for separation over and above the minimum 20-ft (6 m) width requirement for exit access.

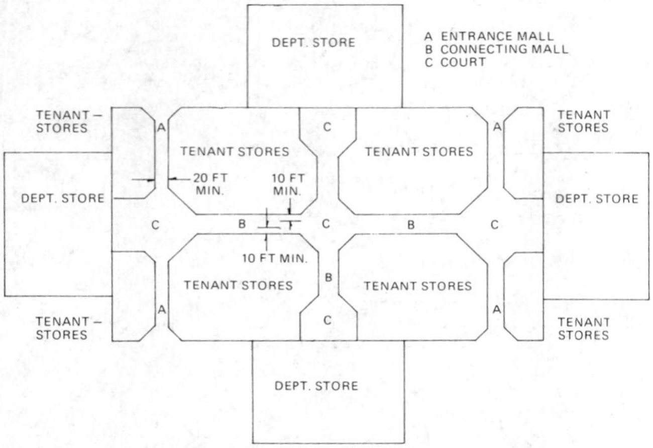

FIG. 8-21D. Typical one-level shopping center.

However, the width of the covered mall connecting courts at entrances to department stores generally is found to be well in excess of the 20-ft (6 m) minimum to provide for the amenities described earlier, and at the same time to provide for an aggregate of 20 ft (6 m) of exit access. (See Figure 8-21D.)

In practice, one is more likely to find mall entrances designed for minimum aisle width. Stores located on either side of entrance malls do not lie along the direct path to department stores, which are commonly called "anchor stores" or "magnet stores" because of their greater customer attraction and do not enjoy as much customer exposure as those located along connecting malls. As a result, stores on opposite sides of the entrance mall are brought closer together by eliminating any mall amenities that in themselves are not likely to generate traffic, thereby maximizing convenient cross-mall customer shopping. The minimum mall width of 20 ft (6 m) is entirely compatible with this merchandising concept and does not impose an unreasonable burden on developers or merchants. This minimum width requirement has been applied successfully in shopping centers throughout the U.S.

The covered mall should have an unobstructed exit access of not less than 10 ft (3 m) in clear width on each side of the mall floor area, parallel and adjacent to the mall storefront. Such exit access should lead to an exit having a minimum of three units of exit width. The purpose of the requirement of 10 ft (3 m) of clear exit access is to provide a higher degree of safety in the covered mall commensurate with its use as a continuation of exit access from the tenant stores. Safe, continuous, and unobstructed exit access from each tenant store is provided, while the owner's merchandising and operational requirements for the mall amenities are recognized.

The minimum requirement of 10 ft (3 m) of clear exit access parallel and adjacent to the mall storefronts relates directly to the minimum mall width of 20 ft (6 m). None of the mall amenities mentioned earlier should encroach on this minimum dimension of 10 ft (3 m). The net effect of this requirement is to preclude the installation of mall amenities in areas of the covered mall that are the minimum 20 ft (6 m) in width. In terms of life safety, this requirement has proven thus far to be reasonable and workable in practice and has the added advantage of not being unduly restrictive or burdensome to developers.

Occupant Load of Covered Mall Shopping Centers

The units of exit width from the covered mall need only satisfy the calculated occupant load based on all of the connected tenant occupancies. It is not necessary to provide units of exit width from the covered mall commensurate with the minimum mall width, which would necessarily result in wall-to-wall doors, unless the calculation of the occupant load, together with the number and location of mall exits, so dictates.

The occupant load factor used in determining exits for the mall proper varies with the aggregate area of the connected, or Type I, stores. This sliding scale of occupant load factors is based on empirical data which indicate that, when shopping centers of a certain aggregate area are doubled in size, the resultant occupant load, although increased, does not double. In other words, the relationship between an increase in the size of a shopping center and the increase in the occupant load is not linear but parabolic, as shown in Figure 8-21E.

Sprinkler Protection

The covered mall and all its connected buildings should be provided with an electrically supervised automatic sprinkler system throughout. It is generally accepted that this is the single most effective way to protect life and property from fire. Sprinkler performance data give rise to objective scrutiny of long-standing, accepted code requirements. For example, accounts of sprinkler performance published recently have brought into question whether steel structural members need to be fireproofed at current established levels when the building is protected by a supervised sprinkler system.

Considerable data attesting to the effectiveness of sprinkler systems would strongly suggest that—at least, in the context of one- and two-level covered mall shopping centers—current levels of fire resistance of steel structural members may not be fully justified in cost-benefit terms when the building is protected by an electrically supervised sprinkler system. Another example is the imposition of additional building code restrictions on buildings in fire districts even when such buildings are protected by sprinkler systems.

Originally, fire districts were established to prevent, or at least minimize, the possibility of conflagration primarily in older or more highly congested urban areas. This resulted in the placement of added restrictions on building area, height, separation, and construction type, without due regard for the effectiveness of sprinkler systems. Model codes have recognized this problem by eliminating many of the unwarranted fire district restrictions.

Horizontal Separation of Type I Stores

Walls dividing stores from each other should extend, to the extent practicable, from the floor to the underside of the roof deck or floor deck above. No separation is required between a store and the covered mall. The purpose of this requirement is to confine fire and smoke spread to the place of origin by inhibiting the passage of fire and smoke through ceilings and over the tops of tenant demising walls into adjacent occupancies. However, the engineering of a smoke control system may require openings in tenant partitions above the ceilings to effectively prevent the accumulation of smoke. Model codes call for such walls to be

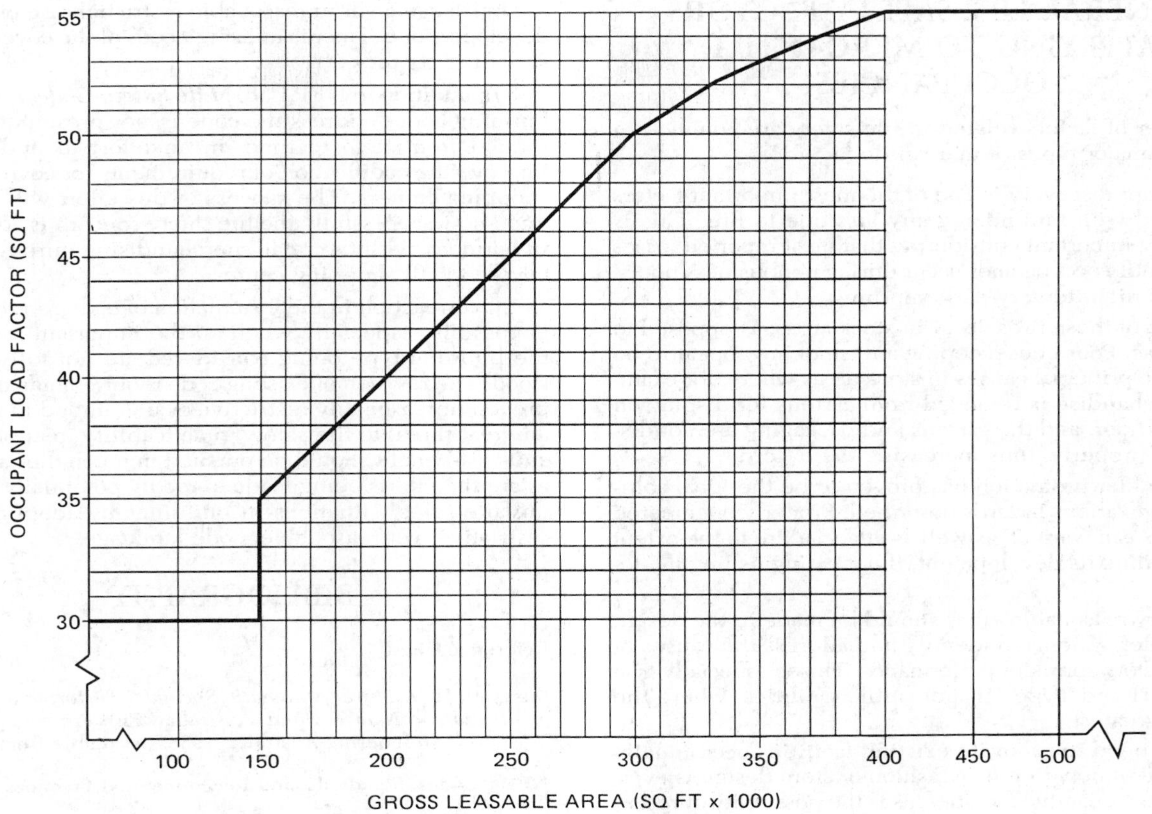

FIG. 8-21E. Relationship of an increase in the size of a covered mall to an increase in the occupant load.

constructed of noncombustible materials; in practice, tenant demising walls are usually constructed of metal studs and drywall.

In effect, tenant demising walls represent a degree of compartmentation to the extent that no separation is provided at the storefront. A requirement for separation at the storefront would defeat the merchandising purpose of the covered mall, which is to optimize unrestricted customer flow between the covered mall and the tenant store. This form of compartmentation, in concert with an electrically supervised automatic sprinkler system, makes the need for any additional fire wall building code requirements highly questionable. Accounts of fires in shopping centers where this configuration was evident tend to support the theory that any additional fire wall requirement is unnecessary and, in fact, burdensome from an operational standpoint in the leasing and subsequent releasing of shopping centers where maximum flexibility to rearrange space is important to the continued success of the shopping center.

Smoke Control

The covered mall should be provided with an effective smoke control system. Under fire conditions, and due to the open storefront configuration, any buildup of smoke in a tenant store could find its way quickly into the covered mall. Effective smoke control in the covered mall proper is essential in order to ensure the mall's continuous use as a smoke-free primary way of exit access.

Sectionalized proprietary heating, ventilation, and air-conditioning (HVAC) system service for multiple tenants, as opposed to a separate system for each tenant, is being used with increasing frequency to maximize efficiency and control and to minimize energy consumption.

An added benefit of such systems is the ability to use them effectively for smoke control in the event of a fire in any given tenant space. Thus, the products of combustion can be confined to the area of origin, with the help of the sprinkler system, and subsequently discharged to the exterior.

This may mean modifying a requirement for fire dampers in walls above ceilings between tenant spaces, in order not to negate the smoke-removal mode within any given sectionalized area.

General Requirements

In addition to the foregoing, certain conditions of exiting should be present in all covered malls. These conditions of exiting are as follows:

1. Every floor and every store of a covered mall, except those less than 50 ft (15 m) deep, should have no fewer than two exits located remotely from each other.
2. No fewer than one-half the required exit widths for each store more than 3000 sq ft (279 m^2) in area connected to a covered mall should lead directly outside without passing through the mall.
3. Every covered mall should have unobstructed exit access parallel and adjacent to the connected buildings. This exit access should extend to each mall exit.
4. Exits from the covered mall should be arranged so that the length of travel from any mall store entrance to an exit is no more than 200 ft (61 m).

GENERAL LIFE SAFETY FACTORS APPLYING TO MERCANTILE OCCUPANCIES

A number of factors related to life safety are common to all three major types of mercantile facilities.

Prompt discovery is one of the most important factors associated with minimizing any loss due to fire. This is especially important considering that most reported losses in mercantile occupancies occur during nonbusiness hours, from late night to very early morning.

Most of these fires occur in stock areas, as opposed to sales areas. Poor housekeeping and smoking appear to be two of the principal causes in stock areas where, for example, merchandise is removed from cartons for display on the sales floor, and the cartons and packaging are not disposed of properly, thus increasing the hazard.

Sprinkler protection has proven to be the ideal solution to the various hazards described. Properly engineered sprinklers can warn of, as well as attack, a fire to the extent of controlling its development, if not extinguishing it altogether.

Every reasonable effort should be made in the design of sprinkler systems to identify and address the causes of unsatisfactory sprinkler performance. This is especially true in Type II and Type III mercantile facilities, where the need is greatest.

The need to renovate existing facilities occasionally as a result of new trends in fashion or store design is ever-present in mercantile facilities, as is the possibility of reconstructing existing facilities due to the releasing of space, especially in shopping centers. Extra care should be taken to mitigate the potential problem of fire during these times, since the reconstruction and renovation processes are very likely to increase the hazard.

Certain accessory uses, such as food preparation areas in restaurants, often found in Type II and Type III facilities and more particularly in department stores and shopping centers, warrant special attention since they are very often the place of fire origin—much more so than a public eating space. Such areas should be segregated with appropriate construction, if not sprinklered, and appropriate fire suppression devices should be installed in food preparation equipment.

CONCLUSION

An important purpose of the foregoing discussion on the nature of the mercantile occupancy is to form a basis for consideration or reconsideration of code requirements that allow the mercantile use to function optimally and yet provide for a reasonable degree of life safety for the occupants of the facility.

All of the requirement-related items discussed in this chapter have been applied practically in many stores and covered mall shopping centers throughout the U.S., and they have answered the need for life safety without imposing burdensome or unreasonable restrictions on either the developers or the merchandising needs of the covered mall shopping centers.

In addition to NFPA 101, *Life Safety Code*, the model building codes address the code issues presented in this section from time to time, in an effort to update and improve the codification of requirements for covered mall shopping centers. The success of this effort will depend upon how successfully the life safety concern is addressed in harmony with the retail merchandising purpose of the covered mall shopping center.

Overreaction in the formulation of code requirements is possible, especially when all the important aspects of the building type being considered are not fully understood. The revision of existing code requirements that have proven unreasonably restrictive or unfounded in terms of any real threat to life safety, practicability in application, and cost-benefit should be pursued in much the same way as are the efforts being made to rectify potentially dangerous life safety situations in buildings by adopting more restrictive, yet reasonable, code language.

BIBLIOGRAPHY

Reference Cited

Marryatt, H. W., *Fire: Automatic Sprinkler Performance in Australia and New Zealand*, Australian Fire Protection Association, Melbourne, Australia, 1988. (Available from NFPA.)

NFPA Codes, Standards, and Recommended Practices

Reference to the following NFPA codes, standards, and recommended practices will provide further information on mercantile occupancies discussed in this chapter. (See the latest *NFPA Catalog* for availability of current editions of the following documents.)

NFPA 101, *Life Safety Code®*.

NFPA 220, *Standard Types of Building Construction.*

Additional Reading

Gardner, J. P., "Unsprinklered Shopping Centers: Smoke Ventilation," *Fire Surveyor*, Vol. 17, No. 6 (Dec. 1988), pp. 44-47.

Law, M., "A Note on Smoke Plumes from Fires in Multi-Level Shopping Malls," *Fire Safety Journal*, Vol. 10, No. 3, 1986, pp. 197-202.

Morgan, H. P. and Marshall, N. R., "Depth of Void-Edge Screens in Shopping Malls," *Fire Engineers Journal*, Vol. 48, No. 152, 1989, pp. 7-9.

Platt, S., "Life Safety in Covered Shopping Complexes, Part 2: Means of Escape and Alarms," *Fire Surveyor*, Vol. 17, No. 1 (Feb. 1988), pp. 4-8.

Platt, S., "Life Safety in Covered Shopping Complexes, Part 3: Exits," *Fire Surveyor*, Vol. 17, No. 3 (June 1988), pp. 24-29.

Platt, S., "Life Safety in Covered Shopping Complexes, Part 4: Public Areas," *Fire Surveyor*, Vol. 17, No. 5 (Oct. 1988), pp. 20-25.

Thomas, P. H., "On the Upward Movement of Smoke and Related Shopping Mall Problems," *Fire Safety Journal*, Vol. 12, No. 3, 1987, pp. 191-203.

BUSINESS OCCUPANCIES

Donald G. Bathurst

As the services side of the economy continues to grow, more and more of us have become part of the many industries that deal in information. Recordkeeping, data processing, and information management are central to businesses that are physically located in office buildings, and office buildings are the prototype for the class of properties defined as business occupancies in NFPA *101*®, *Life Safety Code*®.

More than half, or roughly 6000, of the fires that occur each year in business occupancies occur specifically in general business offices. Other large shares of the business occupancy fire problem include college classroom and administrative buildings, medical offices, and bank buildings. Other examples of this occupancy class include city or town halls, courthouses, laboratories not involving hazardous chemicals, and ambulatory outpatient clinics. In each of these properties, the building's distinctive fuel load is dominated by information storage.

This chapter aims to describe the potential effects that a fire in a business occupancy has on the people in the building. The business occupancy has long been considered a low-hazard occupancy and, therefore, not worthy of serious protection consideration. However, this is not the case, as will be shown. Building construction, occupancy characteristics, potential fire scenarios, means of egress, effects of sprinklers, and special cases of existing buildings will each be examined.

Rather than recite requirements available for reference in codes and standards, this chapter approaches the subject of protecting life in a business occupancy from a more philosophical standpoint. The reader is challenged to look deeper than the codes and to observe, measure, and understand the impact that building and occupancy conditions actually have on the persons in them.

To be aware of the concept of risk is to begin to understand the fire problem. The business occupancy is certainly of a lower hazard class than many industrial or hazardous materials handling operations. But when more people occupy a single building than reside in a small town, as is often the case in the modern high-rise, the magnitude of the challenge faced in protecting the building, its contents and, most important, its occupants is realized.

Additional information on determining necessary levels of protection can be found in Section 1, Chapter 3, "Systems Concepts for Building Firesafety," and in Section 10, "Information and Analysis for Fire Protection," as well as in the referenced and suggested reading material. More information on firesafe building design can be found in Section 1, Chapter 2, "Fundamentals of Firesafe Building Design." Information on interior finish can be found in Section 6, Chapter 4, "Interior Finish."

BUILDING CONSTRUCTION

Construction Type

Business occupancies can be found in a variety of building types. While a two- or three-story noncombustible structure or a fire-resistant high rise may be most familiar, many business occupancies are housed in ordinary, frame, and even heavy timber buildings.

Each construction type affects the business occupancy differently because fires can behave differently in each. This discussion and the examples used will be confined to noncombustible and fire-resistive construction because it is the most prevalent. The reader is cautioned to understand that, in other construction types, the availability of fuel from the structure itself increases fire severity and, therefore, decreases potential structural integrity.

In noncombustible construction, construction materials will not burn, thereby providing a measure of increased safety to the occupants. In reviewing the life safety needs of a business occupancy in a building of noncombustible construction, the designer or reviewing official can be primarily concerned with fuel load from the furnishings and interior finish, and with the means of egress. While the potential fire's effect on the structure also must be assessed, this is usually simpler to do than it is in the case of combustible construction materials.

Donald G. Bathurst is chief of fire protection engineering of the U.S. General Services Administration, Washington, DC.

Fire-resistive structures are similar to noncombustible structures except that the material or combinations of materials used inherently resist failure due to fire or to the passage of fire.

These added protections help ensure sufficient time for persons to egress and/or receive other help.

Interior Finish

Interior finish comprises the various aesthetic treatments to the structure that make it more comfortable to work in and more pleasing to the eye. Interior finish is considered to be the materials used to cover walls, ceilings, and floors, such as paint, wall paper, vinyl wallcovering, paneling, acoustic panels, hardwood floors, vinyl tile, terrazzo, and carpet. Each behaves differently in a fire, and various combinations can make for an interesting analysis.

The main fire performance measure of an interior finish is flame spread. This is the ability of the material to propagate a flame front across its surface. Wall and ceiling materials are ranked by relative ratings from a standard 100 given for a specially prepared sample of red oak. Floor finishes are rated by the amount of heat energy imparted to the surface from an external source that is necessary to sustain combustion; this is called critical radiant flux. The better the flame-spread characteristics—that is, the lower the rating for wall and ceiling material or the higher the critical radiant flux—the more protection can be assumed for occupants.

It is important to note that flame-spread ratings are based on tests of materials under controlled conditions and with specific backing materials. A wallcovering mounted on gypsum wallboard would be expected to perform differently than a wallcovering installed over brick or block.

A most important point that is often overlooked is that interior finish materials are also fuels. When materials are relatively thin—two coats of paint or one layer of vinyl wallcovering, for example—the additional fuel may be insignificant. But when several layers of wallcovering, carpet, floor coverings, or other materials are present, the hazard and risk changes are dramatic. It should not be assumed that a low flame-spread rating alone will result in a significant risk reduction. It is important to understand the impact this additional fuel has on the entire environment.

Furnishings and Contents

Furnishings and contents make up the bulk of the potential fuel load in a business occupancy. Furnishings, for the purpose of this discussion, include desks, chairs, sofas, files, office supplies, and paper.

Over the past several years, there have been many changes in the furnishings put into buildings. At one time, desks and chairs were routinely made of wood. Then metal became popular. Now, any combination of wood, metal, thermoplastics, and foamed plastics can be found.

Business occupancies are considered lower hazard than industrial or other occupancies handling hazardous materials. However, some of this perception is a matter of confusing familiarity with safety. The *quantity* (in lbs/sq ft) of fuel load in business occupancies can be a source of significant hazard, even if there is nothing unusually hazardous about the materials involved. In addition, some of the materials may have burning characteristics—such as peak intensity of heat when fully involved in fire—that are comparable to some hazardous materials.

The designer and reviewing official must be aware of the characteristics of the materials in a building, such as the construction materials, the interior finish materials, and the furnishing materials. Each provides a degree of protection and a degree of hazard, and their combined effect influences risk. Without understanding the potential fire in a business occupancy, one cannot begin to understand its potential affect on people.

OCCUPANCY CHARACTERISTICS

Business occupants are generally characterized as awake, alert, and familiar with their surroundings. While this is true of most offices, designers and reviewing officials must assess the actual characteristics for a particular business occupancy, such as a doctor's office or an outpatient clinic, in which a minority of the occupants would be familiar with the surroundings. In business occupancies, generalities do not always apply.

Support services often are found within business occupancies. Each provides a challenge in the analysis of potential fire impact because these service areas present their own special hazards. Examples include cafeterias, auditoriums, print shops, storage areas, parking facilities, small retail outlets, and banks or credit unions. These are usually areas where people gather during certain times, often in large concentrations relative to the general occupant load for the entire building. Many of these service areas increase the potential for fire ignition because of their operation; one example is a cafeteria kitchen.

Another service area growing in business occupancies is the child care center. With more families having both parents working, employer-provided child care is becoming more common. This poses a special concern due to the ages of these occupants, their lack of familiarity with their surroundings, and the fact that they will be sleeping in the space from time to time. Special protection must be considered for child care centers, including smoke detection, sprinkler protection, fire-resistive enclosures, location at grade level with direct access to the outside, and sufficient adult supervision per child.

Another growing segment of the population in business occupancies is the disabled. Persons with disabilities have proven to be contributing members of the work force, and their numbers in the workplace are increasing. Disabilities cover a wide range, including sight, hearing, and mobility impairments. There also are many persons with hidden disabilities, such as those with heart disease. A disability also can be temporary or transient, such as pregnancy or a broken leg. Designers and reviewing officials must consider the presence of disabled persons, known or hidden, when evaluating a life safety system for a business occupancy.

While persons in a business occupancy are usually awake and alert, they differ considerably in their responsiveness. The actual conditions of occupancy must be reviewed in detail. Only when one understands who is being protected can one decide how to protect them from potential fire.

POTENTIAL FIRE SCENARIOS

Firesafety design for a particular property must begin with a consideration of the characteristics of the most likely fires and the most serious fire the occupancy might encounter.

This may be done by defining potential fire scenarios to use as a basis for analysis.

Fuels for a fire are readily available. They include furnishings, paper, books, and other office supplies. But the significant contribution to fire severity that interior finish materials can provide must not be forgotten. The wide use of plastics also must be realized as a factor in the potential fuel load in a business occupancy. This includes furnishings and a variety of office equipment. Even the structure itself can provide fuel for fire, especially if it is of ordinary or wood-frame construction.

The transient fuels in a burning building represent a significant and often overlooked fuel load. These fuels, which include furniture and carpet deliveries, mail operations, and trash disposal, often expose the egress system, so special care should be taken to identify them.

The leading accidental sources of heat for ignition include electrical distribution systems, portable and area heating equipment, other appliances, torch and other maintenance operations, matches and lighters, and smoking materials. The design professional and reviewing official must know where potential ignition sources are and where they expose potential fuels.

The leading cause of fire in business occupancies is not accidental, however. Arson prevention is partly a matter of understanding the business and those who might wish to harm it, such as competitors, disgruntled employees, angry customers, or economically strapped owners. But arson typically occurs as a result of less obvious motives, such as emotional disturbance, so it is important to emphasize security controls and arrangements, such as housekeeping, that will reduce the range of attractive and easy targets for potential arsonists. Also, the importance of arson underscores the limits of fire prevention as a strategy, so post-ignition fire protection provisions will be needed, too.

The value at risk from a fire in a business occupancy can easily be underestimated. With the increase in regular use of computers, telefacsimile machines, and similar equipment, and with the divestiture of the Bell System leading to the purchase of telephone systems for offices and buildings, the value of an average workstation has grown appreciably over the past ten years. The value of loss of business and other interruption costs, including the occupancy of temporary space and reduced productivity in employees during space restoration, also must be considered.

The designer and reviewing official must look carefully at the business occupancy for available fuels and potential ignition sources. The impact of fire on the occupancy and occupants can then be modeled, using computer models and other engineering tools to translate the occupancy's physical and occupant characteristics into a timeline of fire development and its effects on people and property.

MEANS OF EGRESS

In analyzing the potential fire scenario and choosing strategies to deal with the results of the analysis, it is useful to think in terms of major groups of fire protection provisions, of which means of egress will be the first discussed here. Before the means of egress needs can be assessed, however, an objective must first be established: every occupant should be able to reach a safe location from anywhere in the building without incurring serious harm from fire along the way.

For a long time, this objective was fulfilled by evacuating building occupants when fire was discovered. As buildings get larger and taller, this is not always practical or possible. Some high-rise buildings have populations the size of a small town, and total evacuation may take hours. Nor does it make practical sense to move people on the 40th floor of a building when a small trash fire is on the first floor.

Where total evacuation can be accomplished, it is desired. However, the designer and reviewing official must be aware of conditions that warrant a staged or delayed evacuation, or relocation within the building. In any event, the objective of keeping people in a tenable environment must control all actions.

One method of establishing an acceptable level of protection for persons from fire is the application of NFPA 101, *Life Safety Code*. NFPA 101 provides guidance for occupancy loads, arrangement of exits, capacity of exits, and exit travel distances, as well as guidance for doors, stairs, and interior finish materials. NFPA 101 recognizes differences in existing buildings and new construction, and it provides different guidance for each. In fact, all codes and standards have equivalency clauses so as not to exclude sound engineering approaches that accomplish the same or similar results. The reviewing official must be aware of the application of these equivalency clauses.

Total Evacuation

If a building is small, total evacuation is preferred. In this case, persons should be able to leave the building before conditions in any part of it become untenable. Fire growth, heat rise, and the production of toxic combustion products must be estimated. Then the time needed to evacuate the building must be estimated. The difference in the evacuation time and the time to untenable conditions is the time allowed for fire detection, notification of occupants, and occupant reaction.

The alarm system, either manual or automatic, must be chosen based on the time available to notify occupants. In most business occupancies, a manual alarm system is sufficient, but the designer and reviewing official must be aware of conditions that warrant the use of an automatic detection and alarm system. In cases where automatic sprinkler protection is provided, the designer should take advantage of its presence and use it as an alarm-initiating device.

Alternatives to Total Evacuation

In very large or very tall buildings, total evacuation is neither practical nor possible, but the need to protect the occupants is similar to that of smaller buildings. It is important to ensure that persons can get to an area of relative safety before conditions become untenable.

Relocation: Fire conditions and necessary egress time must be estimated. The area of relative safety must then be chosen. This may be a trial-and-error design process because estimated fire conditions and the structure's ability to resist fire will have an impact on where safer areas will most likely be. Furthermore, persons must be able to reach those areas in a reasonable time. Typically, one or two floor levels above or below the fire floor are considered sufficient in a high-rise building. The designer and reviewing official are cautioned not to take these suggestions, or others in codes and standards, blindly. A measure of the actual expected conditions must be taken before a plan for protection can be devised.

Other egress or occupant protection strategies are similar to relocation and include defend in place, staged evacuation, and use of horizontal exits.

Defend in place: Defend-in-place strategies are generally used in health care occupancies where there is a supervisory staff and persons cannot be readily moved. While not a preferred method for business occupancies, its existence must be noted and understood.

Staged evacuation: Staged evacuation can take several forms. One is staged total evacuation where the fire floor occupants are notified, and, after a determined time period, other occupants are notified. This allows those on the fire floor the first opportunity to escape. Persons in areas farther from the fire start to evacuate a bit later.

Another method of staged evacuation is the use of "hardened" areas in which persons may seek temporary refuge until they are able to egress. These staging areas pose several questions:

1. How should the area be hardened? Research at the National Institute of Standards and Technology (NIST), sponsored by the General Services Administration (GSA), has shown that fire resistance is not enough. Ventilation and pressurization are critical to maintaining a tenable environment when the area is exposed to post-flashover conditions.
2. How many people will use the area? These areas have been suggested for use by the disabled. With the population of disabled growing in business occupancies, no good rule of thumb exists for sizing these areas.
3. How will people use these areas? Practice is the only answer. If provided, these areas must be addressed in the fire evacuation plan for the building. This would suggest that these staging areas have only limited impact on persons who are not familiar with the building.
4. How will persons eventually leave the building? These areas must not be considered as a place to wait out a complete fire. Persons generally must leave the fire floor. These areas, if provided, should be adjacent to stairs or elevators so that fire department personnel or building fire wardens can assist persons in these areas to other areas of relative safety.

The use of this type of staging area takes much planning, practice, maintenance, and coordination. Unfortunately, it is of little benefit to persons unfamiliar with the building and its features. Therefore, a preferred method would be to establish a way to protect the occupants with little or no special instructions.

Horizontal exit: Another method of staged evacuation is through horizontal exits. Horizontal exits can be provided by subdividing a building with fire-resistive walls or partions. Persons passing through doors in these walls move to an area of relative safety. In some cases, the horizontal exit alone may provide enough egress protection. In others, the horizontal exit may be used to provide enough protection to stage occupants, thereby allowing more time for total evacuation or assisted evacuation, as in the case of persons with disabilities. Special instructions or drills are not necessary in the use of a horizontal exit.

In either relocation or staged evacuation, fire control is important. To ensure the success of the egress or occupant protection strategy, fire growth and combustion products must be held to a minimum. This can be done in several ways. Fuel can be limited, room geometry can be controlled, and ventilation of fire areas can be limited. The most efficient method of controlling fire growth and smoke production is through the use of automatic sprinklers. Therefore, where occupant relocation or staging is an intended strategy, the building should be protected with automatic sprinklers, although individual conditions will dictate the actual protection necessary.

EXIT LIGHTING

The means of egress should be continuously illuminated by a reliable lighting system. This usually means spacing lighting fixtures and providing primary and emergency power to ensure a lighting level of at least 1 footcandle (101 lux), measured at the floor level.

Emergency power can be provided in many ways: batteries, inverters, generators, separate building substations with automatic transfer switches, and power distribution system network grids. The concept behind emergency power for egress lighting is to ensure that the exit path is illuminated if a fire in the building disrupts the primary power source. Because a complete power failure at the utility would rarely occur at the same time a fire in the building would, it is sufficient to have only one of the recommended emergency power sources.

AUTOMATIC SPRINKLERS

As discussed, automatic sprinkler protection can increase the level of firesafety in a business occupancy. From the life safety standpoint, sprinklers limit fire growth and the production of smoke, thereby increasing the time available for persons to egress. If designed to do so, automatic sprinklers can even keep conditions in close proximity to the fire in a tenable range.

Another reason sprinklers should be considered is property and mission protection. Fire department suppression capabilities are limited. Even the best department can only be expected to have a suppression capability of about 5000 sq ft (464.5 m^2). If fire fighters must rescue occupants, their capability decreases. As property values and mission criticality increases, this is a potential exposure that the typical business cannot afford.

While the hazard of a business occupancy is relatively low, the risk can be considerable when multiplied with the size, value, and occupant load.

Sprinkler protection automatically detects a fire and starts suppression actions, providing additional time for occupants to exit. The sprinkler system can even notify the occupants of the fire. Sprinklers also limit fire and water damage, thereby decreasing business interruption. With new technologies, such as quick-response sprinklers, now available for business occupancies, these occupant protection factors and property protection features are likely to increase.

Retrofitting sprinkler systems is becoming easier with the use of plastic pipe and new sprinkler technology, such as quick-response sprinklers. In addition, sprinklers can be safely installed in buildings with sprayed-on asbestos containing fireproofing through a process of local encapsulation and control. See the references for the chapter on this subject for more information.

EXISTING BUILDINGS

Business occupancies in existing buildings pose several concerns from a life safety standpoint. Many do not meet the requirements of codes, standards, or design practices for new construction. The question should not be, "Do they comply?" Rather, we should ask, "Is the occupant protection objective fulfilled?" In this case, occupant protection should be no different than that previously discussed. The objective is to get people to an area of relative safety before conditons become untenable.

The difference in an existing building is that the protection strategy is constrained by the structure that already exists. Several resources can be used to help find solutions to egress problems in existing buildings.

NFPA 101, *Life Safety Code*, has a separate chapter for existing business occupancies. The requirements in that chapter are similar to those for new buildings, but they reflect the necessity of accepting those things that cannot be changed, provided a reasonable degree of safety is present.

Another good reference is NFPA 101M, *Alternative Approaches to Life Safety*. Chapter 7 in NFPA 101M is a firesafety evaluation system (FSES) for business occupancies. This is a numeric method that provides a way of ranking building conditions. The result indicates whether the conditions, as measured by the FSES, provide a level of safety equivalent to NFPA 101, *Life Safety Code*.

Other analytical methods exist that may be beneficial in evaluating the risk to life in an existing business occupancy. These include hand calculations and computer-based predictive fire models. In any event, the process is the same—determine the fire exposure, the time available for safe egress, and the time needed to egress.

A special category of existing buildings must be mentioned: historic or architecturally significant buildings. Society has put an additional constraint on these structures, as to the way alterations must be done. Here, historic preservation and life safety objectives must be carefully outlined and communicated. These objectives are not necessarily at cross purposes. Innovative design techniques and engineered solutions, rather than code compliance, are usually called for. A reference on the process and design tips is included in the list of recommended reading following this chapter.

SUMMARY

Business occupancies are a large segment of the communities protected, and they can be found in a variety of building types. It has been seen how construction type, occupancy characteristics, potential fire scenarios, means of egress, the effect of sprinklers, and existing conditions all affect the ability to protect occupants from the effects of unwanted fire. An objective has been set for protecting these occupants by keeping them in a tenable environment or by allowing them to escape to an area of relative safety before untenable conditions are reached. This area may be outside the building, on another floor, or through a horizontal exit.

Several references can be used to determine what the potential fire exposure will be and the necessary protection strategies. NFPA 101, *Life Safety Code*; the FSES in NFPA 101M, *Alternative Approaches to Life Safety*; and the various calculation methods have been discussed.

The designer and reviewing official must look deeper than codes and standards alone to understand the actual conditions and to measure the exposures. They will then realize that business occupancies may be relatively low hazard but they are not necessarily low risk, and they will be able to recommend ways of fulfilling the objective of protecting occupants.

BIBLIOGRAPHY

References

Madrzykowski, D., "The Hazard of Fire Gas Exposure from Sprinklered Rooms to Corridors and Adjoining Areas," National Institute of Standards and Technology, Gaithersburg, MD, to be published as an NISTIR.

Matthey, R. G., *et al.*, "Procedures for Sprinkler Anchor Installation on Surfaces with Fireproofing Materials," *NBSIR 87-3676*, National Bureau of Standards, Gaithersburg, MD, Feb. 1988.

Nelson, H.E., "FPETOOL: Fire Protection Engineering Tools for Hazard Estimation," NISTIR 4380, National Institute of Standards and Technology, Gaithersburg, MD, October 1990.

Nelson, H.E., "Fireform: A Computerized Collection of Convenient Fire Safety Calculations," *NBSIR 86-3308*, National Bureau of Standards, Gaithersburg, MD, Apr. 1986.

"Report from the 1987 Workshop on Analytical Methods for Designing Buildings for Fire Safety, " National Research Council.

"Retrofitting Firesafety Features to Historic Buildings," Advisory Council on Historic Preservation, Washington, DC, Aug. 1989.

Stroup, D. and Madrzykowski, D., "Conditions in Quarters and Adjoining Areas Exposed to Post-Flashover Room Fires," National Institute of Standards and Technology, Gaithersburg, MD, 1991.

NFPA Codes, Standards, and Recommended Practices

Reference to the following NFPA codes, standards, and recommended practices will provide further information on business occupancies discussed in this chapter. (See the latest *NFPA Catalog* for availability of current editions of the following documents.

NFPA *101*, *Life Safety Code*.

NFPA 101M, *Alternative Approaches to Life Safety*.

Additional Reading

Culver, C. G., "Characteristics of Fire Loads in Office Buildings," *Fire Technology*, Vol. 14, No. 1, 1978, pp. 51-60.

Drysdale, D., *An Introduction to Fire Dynamics*, John Wiley and Sons, New York, 1985.

"New Approaches to Evaluating Firesafety in Buildings," *Proceedings* of a Conference, National Research Council, Report Number 5, 1980.

"Public Buildings Service International Conference on Firesafety in Highrise Buildings," General Services Administration, 1971.

Rowe, W. D., *An Anatomy of Risk*, John Wiley and Sons, New York, 1977.

Taylor, K. T., "Office Building Fires... A Case for Automatic Fire Protection," *Fire Journal*, Vol. 84, No. 1 (Jan./Feb. 1990), p. 52.

Walton, W. D. and Budnick, E. K., "Quick-Response Sprinklers in Office Configurations: Fire Test Results," *NBSIR 88-3695*, National Bureau of Standards, Gaithersburg, MD, Jan. 1988.

Walton, W. D., "Suppression of Wood Crib Fires with Sprinkler Sprays: Test Results," NBSIR 88-3696, National Bureau of Standards, Gaithersburg, MD, Jan. 1988.

INDUSTRIAL OCCUPANCIES

Carol A. Caldwell

Industrial occupancies encompass a broad spectrum of purposes. Some employ many people to work in a single building. Other facilities house large items of equipment but have very few employees. Industrial occupancies are generally subdivided into two categories: general-purpose industrial, which covers low- and moderate-hazard facilities, and high-hazard facilities. Examples of industrial occupancies include factories, laboratories, power plants, refineries, and laundries.

This chapter discusses the life-loss history of industrial occupancies; general risk assessment; occupancy and occupant characteristics; fire protection features available; NFPA 101®, *Life Safety Code*®; criteria, and pre-fire planning.

Additional information relevant to the life safety of industrial occupancies can be found in Section 2, Chapter 31, "Control of Electrostatic Ignition Sources"; Section 6, Chapter 4, "Interior Finish"; Section 6, Chapter 6, "Confinement of Fire in Buildings"; and Section 8, Chapter 27, "Occupancies in Unusual Structures." Chapter 1 of this section also lists many other references that provide more detailed information. Explosion suppression devices are covered in Chapter 18, "Special Systems for Explosion Damage Control."

LOSS HISTORY

The potential for loss of life from fire in an industrial occupancy is related to the fire hazard risk of the industrial operation or process within that occupancy. In 1983-87, 12.9 percent of non-residential fires occurred in industrial occupancies, as did 19.9 percent of associated civilian deaths and 23.8 percent of associated civilian injuries.

The causes of fatal fires in industrial properties are quite varied, reflecting the many different kinds of equipment used in industry that can be heat sources. (See Table 8-23A.) Torches and heating equipment are leading common hazards.

Carol A. Caldwell, P.E., is a fire protection engineer at Sandia National Laboratories, Livermore, CA.

In addition, most industrial fire fatalities for which the victim's location was known and specified involve victims in the room of fire origin, often very close to the fire. The implied rapid onset of fire injury is especially pronounced for multiple-death fires, those in which three or more people die.

Most deaths in multiple-death fires in these occupancies are the result of flash fires involving highly combustible contents or explosions involving combustible dusts, flammable liquids, or gases. In the 1980s, explosions in a coal mine, a fireworks manufacturing plant, and an oil refinery accounted for the largest losses of life.

HAZARD ASSESSMENT

To provide adequate life safety for an industrial occupancy, the relative degree of fire and life safety risk must be evaluated. Since the industrial classification is so broad, the hazards involved vary greatly. The first concern is the amount of time available for evacuation. This is affected by both the contents of the building and the construction materials of the building itself if it contributes to the fire during occupant evacuation. Examples of items to consider are interior finish, rate of fire spread, burn rate, toxic fume evolvement, potential ignition sources, fuel load, and smoke generated. Once employees have been evacuated, the problem becomes one of property protection.

Many resources exist to aid in hazard assessment. Examples include talking to plant operators, reviewing building blueprints, and so on. The NFPA codes contain valuable information on the various hazards. Insurance companies and records of previous fires also provide useful information. Section 8, Chapter 10, describes methods for assessing life safety from fire in buildings, including exit analysis, available safe egress time (ASET), and scenarios.

Since explosions are probably the most destructive industrial accidents in terms of life loss and property loss, they require special attention. Flammable dust, vapor, mist, or gas can present an explosion hazard. A carefully designed system is needed to ensure life safety from explosive forces. Two primary approaches to the problem exist:

TABLE 8-23A. Causes of Civilian Deaths and Injuries, Industry and Manufacturing Fires, 1983–87 Annual Average, Unknown-Cause Fires Allocated Proportionally

Cause	Civilian Deaths	Civilian Injuries
Other equipment	13 (26.6%)	385 (43.2%)
Chemical process equipment	2 (4.5%)	55 (6.1%)
Painting equipment	2 (3.2%)	16 (1.7%)
Vehicles	2 (3.2%)	11 (1.3%)
Furnaces, ovens, or kilns	1 (2.6%)	41 (4.5%)
Unclassified special equipment	1 (1.3%)	29 (3.2%)
Heat-treating equipment	1 (1.3%)	28 (3.0%)
Unclassified process equipment	1 (1.3%)	24 (2.6%)
Waste recovery equipment	1 (1.3%)	6 (0.7%)
Unknown-type special equipment	1 (1.3%)	6 (0.6%)
Open flame, embers, or torches	7 (14.3%)	137 (15.1%)
Torches	6 (12.3%)	105 (11.6%)
Lighters	1 (1.3%)	6 (0.6%)
Other heat source	7 (13.6%)	30 (3.3%)
Heating equipment	5 (11.0%)	77 (8.5%)
Fixed area heaters	3 (6.5%)	32 (3.5%)
Heat transfer systems	2 (3.2%)	3 (0.3%)
Portable heaters	1 (1.3%)	12 (1.4%)
Electrical distribution	4 (7.8%)	85 (9.4%)
Unknown type	2 (4.5%)	4 (0.4%)
Overcurrent protection devices	1 (1.9%)	37 (4.0%)
Transformers	1 (1.3%)	7 (0.8%)
Natural causes	3 (6.5%)	90 (9.9%)
Static discharges	2 (3.9%)	27 (2.9%)
Spontaneous ignitions or chemical reactions	1 (2.6%)	56 (6.2%)
Smoking materials	3 (5.8%)	15 (1.7%)
Incendiary or suspicious causes	3 (5.2%)	22 (2.4%)
Cooking equipment	2 (3.9%)	16 (1.8%)
Appliances, tools, or air conditioning	2 (3.2%)	35 (3.9%)
Hand tools	1 (1.3%)	12 (1.4%)
Exposure (to other hostile fire)	1 (1.9%)	6 (0.7%)
Child playing	0 (0.0%)	1 (0.1%)
Total	49 (100.0%)	907 (100.0%)

Source: 1983–87 NFIRS, NFPA Survey.
Civilian deaths and injuries are expressed to the nearest one. Percentages are calculated on the actual estimates, which include fractions of a casualty per year, so two figures with the same rounded-off estimates may have different percentages.
The 12 major-cause categories are based on a hierarchy developed by the U.S. Fire Administration. Sums may not equal totals because of rounding errors.

prevent the explosion—obviously the best choice—and control the damage from the explosion. Specialized equipment designed to detect, suppress, and control the damage from explosions is available. NFPA 69, *Explosion Prevention Systems*, provides additional information.

OCCUPANCY CHARACTERISTICS

Construction requirements for industrial occupancies are not given in NFPA 101, *Life Safety Code*. Due to the varying types of industrial occupancies, many different types of construction are used. Smaller facilities might be nonrated wood, corresponding to Type V in NFPA 220, *Types of Building Construction*, while larger buildings might be of fire-resistive construction, Type I. Additionally, buildings can range from totally enclosed high-rises to open structures providing equipment protection from weather. This decision is generally based on local building codes for the type of use, rather than on life safety concerns.

OCCUPANT CHARACTERISTICS

In general, occupants of an industrial facility are able-bodied adults. Statistically the least likely to be victims of fire, they are ambulatory and capable of responding quickly to a fire. These occupants should be familiar with facility hazards and exit locations. The likelihood also exists that employees in an industrial setting have received some emergency training. As density of the occupant load can vary significantly, it must be considered in exit system design. Facilities employing many physically and mentally handicapped people require supplemental pre-fire planning to ensure safe evacuation.

FIRE PROTECTION FEATURES

The primary life safety feature of an industrial occupancy is an automatic sprinkler system. Originally a property protection feature, it has proven effective in preventing loss of life. Automatic sprinklers control the spread of fire, thereby allowing employees sufficient time to evacuate the building. In addition, the sprinkler system water flow alarm can alert building occupants of the fire, also increasing their time to react. To be effective, a system must be operable. Programs must be in place to provide for inspection of control valves to ensure they are open, and for maintenance of associated trim for alarm piping, dry-pipe valves, and preaction and deluge systems. For preaction and deluge systems, the associated detection systems must also be operational.

NFPA 101

Classification of Occupancy

In order to design the appropriate exit system for an industrial occupancy, the life safety hazard classification per NFPA 101, *Life Safety Code*, must be established. The three basic classifications include general industrial, special purpose industrial, and high hazard.

General-purpose occupancy: General-purpose occupancies involve low- and ordinary-hazard manufacturing operations occurring in any type of building, be it single-story, multi-story, or multiple tenant. These occupancies normally have a higher density of employees than the other classifications. Examples are a laundry or an auto assembly plant having low- or moderate-hazard operations.

Special-purpose occupancy: Special-purpose occupancies also involve low- and ordinary-hazard manufacturing operations. They are characterized by low employee density, with most of the floor area occupied by equipment. An example is a structure built to protect large processing equipment from weather, where people associated with the process are located in a separate control room, thereby reducing employee exposure to fire. These occupancies have slightly different exit requirements that are generally more lenient, such as an increase in the travel distance allowed. Also, exits are designed for the actual number of employees in the structure, rather than the calculated occupant load. A telephone switch building or a turbine generator building at a power plant meet the definition of low or moderate hazard and very reduced number of occupants.

High-hazard occupancy: A high-hazard occupancy differs from low- and ordinary-hazard occupancies by the materials used and the potential results and byproducts of the use. High-hazard occupancies include structures in which there are processes involving highly combustible, highly flammable, or explosive materials, or structures in which materials are likely to burn with extreme rapidity or to produce poisonous fumes or gases. Also included are industrial facilities in which flammable liquids are routinely handled, used, or stored in large quantities or those in which explosive dusts from grain, wood, flour, plastic, aluminum, magnesium, or other explosive-dust-generating materials are produced. Plants such as a grain handling facility or a gasoline refinery are examples of high-hazard industrial occupancies.

Structures with adequately protected, incidental high-hazard uses do not have to be classified as high-hazard facilities. Such structures may include such things as a small flammable liquid storage room designed to NFPA 101, *Life Safety Code*, and NFPA 30, *Flammable and Combustible Liquids Code*. Restricted use of flammable liquids do not require a high-hazard classification. An example is a metalworking plant, normally classified as low-hazard, that has a flammable solvent dip tank coater. While adequate means of egress away from the coater are required, the classification is not changed to high-hazard.

The classification of the life safety hazard of an occupancy must be carefully considered. The goal is to evaluate the hazard of the contents, process, and other factors affecting fire development that impact the time available for occupants to evacuate. Many resources are available to assist in the determination. Review of pertinent NFPA literature, including the codes and this handbook, is helpful. Officials in other jurisdictions with similar occupancies and plant operators can provide additional valuable information.

Means of Egress Design Requirements

Designing the exit system for a building requires consideration of many factors. Some of these involve distance requirements, such as travel distance, common path of travel, and dead ends. (See Figure 8-23A.) These distances vary based on the life safety hazard classification and the absence or presence of automatic sprinklers. Exit distance limitations are shown in Table 8-23B. To use some of the greater distances, special requirements are involved, such as application to one-story buildings only, with automatic sprinklers mandatory and smoke and heat venting. High-hazard occupancies are very restrictive on distances allowed, with no dead ends or common paths of travel permitted. Generally, two exits are required from every story or section. However, NFPA 101, *Life Safety Code*, provides the exceptions to this requirement. By careful design, the listed requirements can be met. The addition of exit tunnels or overhead passageways, or the use of horizontal exits can aid in meeting required distances.

Emergency Lighting

Due to the potential hazards of an industrial occupancy, adequate lighting of the means of egress is critical. Under normal conditions, illumination is required for the means of egress. If the building is occupied only during daylight hours, and skylights and windows are arranged to provide the required level of illumination, then electrical lighting is not required. During a power failure, emergency lighting is required for the means of egress. No appreciable delay is permitted when changing from one energy source to another. Emergency lighting is designed to operate for 1½ hr to allow occupants to evacuate and search and rescue to be performed as necessary. Emergency lighting is not designed to provide illumination for emergency repairs or shutdown of equipment. Again, if adequate exterior light is available from skylights and windows and the facility is occupied only during daylight hours, then supplemental

TABLE 8-23B. ***Exit Distance Limitations***

Industrial Occupancy	Travel Distance: Unsprinklered (ft)	Travel Distance: Sprinklered (ft)	Travel Distance: Special (ft)	Dead End (ft)	Common Path of Travel (ft)
General Purpose	200 (60 m)	250 (75 m)	400 (122 m)*	50 (15 m)	50 (15 m)
Special Purpose	300 (91 m)	400 (122 m)	—	50 (15 m)	50 (15 m)
High Hazard	75 (23 m)	75 (23 m)	—	0	0

* Special requirements in NFPA 101 for this travel distance in general purpose industrial occupancies.

emergency lighting is not required. In special-purpose occupancies in areas not subject to routine personnel use, lighting the means of egress is not required.

Fire Alarm Systems

Due to the size and complexity of most industrial facilities, a fire alarm system is a valuable tool for life safety. It can alert designated personnel, such as an industrial fire brigade, to a fire and allow for prompt response to evacuate occupants, fight the fire, shutdown equipment, and other actions, as required. NFPA 101, *Life Safety Code*, requires a fire alarm system for most industrial occupancies. Exceptions are based on occupant load, where total capacity is less than 100 persons and fewer than 25 persons are located above or below the level of exit discharge. In low- and ordinary-hazard industrial occupancies, the fire alarm must sound an audible alarm at a continuously attended location to initiate emergency action. At high-hazard industrial occupancies, in addition to the above, the fire alarm must initiate an occupant evacuation signal. In these occupancies, early notification can be critical to life safety.

PRE-FIRE PLANNING

Pre-fire planning is essential for both life safety and property protection. In general, occupants of industrial facilities are physically capable of responding to a fire. The emergency plan should include a method of alerting employees, of establishing evacuation routes and outside assembly areas, and of posting this information. Training in the use of fire extinguishers for incipient fires must be provided if employees are expected to use them. Designated employees need to be trained to check that fire protection equipment is operating as designed—for example, that sprinkler valves are open. The responding fire department should be made familiar with the facility, and an employee should be selected as their contact. Hazardous materials should be identified and their location noted on a building plan. Provisions should also be made to locate and evacuate any physically handicapped employees. The pre-fire plan should be evaluated routinely through simulated fire exercises. Such exercises are critical to identify deficiencies in the plan.

If there are actual fire brigades at the site, they must be adequately trained. Training should include brigade organization and responsibility, the basics of fire behavior, special on-site fire and health hazards, and hands-on training with the fire equipment they are expected to use. Available equipment might include fire extinguishers, standpipes, hoses, and hydrants. Appropriate use of this equipment on incipient fires has contributed to a major reduction in fire loss and loss of life in industrial occupancies. Restricting the spread of fire reduces the threat to life.

SUMMARY

Industrial occupancies can pose severe threats to life safety and must be adequately evaluated to determine the potential fire hazard. Building design must allow occupants time to evacuate to prevent loss of life. This chapter briefly summarized the industrial life-loss-per-fire records, characteristics of industrial facilities, fire protection features, and means of egress criteria based on NFPA 101, *Life Safety Code*.

BIBLIOGRAPHY

NFPA Codes, Standards, and Recommended Practices

References to the following NFPA codes, standards, and recommended practices will provide further information on the industrial occupancies discussed in this chapter. (See the latest *NFPA Catalog* for availability of current editions of the following documents.

NFPA 30, *Flammable and Combustible Liquids Code*.

NFPA 69, *Explosion Prevention Systems*.

NFPA 101,® *Life Safety Code*.®

NFPA 220, *Types of Building Construction*.

NFPA 600, *Industrial Fire Brigades*.

References

Hall, J. R., Jr., "Selections from the U.S. Fire Problem Overview Report Through 1988—Leading Causes and Other Patterns and Trends, Industrial and Manufacturing Facilities," National Fire Protection Association, Quincy, MA, 1989.

Fire Protection Guide to Hazardous Materials, 9th ed. National Fire Protection Association, Quincy, MA., 1986.

Additional Readings

Adolphs, W., "Fire Protection Covering the Risks Occurring in Industrial Plants," *Proceedings* of the Conference on New Technology to Reduce Fire Losses and Costs, Elsivier, 1986, pp. 329-331.

Davis, L. and Moore, J., *Industrial Fire Control Concepts*, International Society of Fire Service Instructors, Ashland, MA, 1988.

Fender, B. G., "Fighting Fires in High Rise Industrial Buildings," *Fire International*, Vol. 12, No. 109 (Feb.-Mar.1988), pp. 25-27.

Fire Inspectors Guide to NFPA 1031, National Fire Protection Association, Quincy, MA., 1983.

Fowell, A. G., "Industrial Fire Suppression," *NBSIR 86-3360*, NBS Workshop on Fire Protection Technology, April 1986.

Gold, D. T., *Fire Brigade Training Manual*, National Fire Protection Association, Quincy, MA, 1982.

Industrial Fire Hazards, 3rd ed., National Fire Protection Association, Quincy, MA, 1990.

King, P. W. and Magid, J., *Industrial Hazard and Safety Handbook*, 3rd rev., Butterworths, Boston, MA., 1982.

Linville, J. L., *ed.*, *Industrial Fire Hazards Handbook*, 3rd ed., National Fire Protection Association, Quincy, MA, 1990.

Miller, C., "Early Suppression-Fast Response Sprinklers: A New Level of Industrial Fire Protection," *National Engineer*, Vol. 93, No. 9 (Sept. 1989), pp. 18-19.

Nolan, P. F. and Bradley, C. W. J., "A Simple Technique for the Optimization of Lay-Out and Location for Chemical Plant Safety," *Plant/Operation Progress*, Vol. 6, No. 1 (Jan. 1987), pp. 57-61.

"Protecting Hazardous Locations From Fire Disasters," *Consulting Specifying Engineer*, Vol. 2, No. 3, 1987, pp. 104-108.

Sax, N. I. and Lewis, R. J., *Dangerous Properties of Industrial Materials*, Van Nostrand Reinhold, New York, 1989.

Schram, P. J. and Earley, M. W., *Electrical Installations in Hazardous Locations*, National Fire Protection Association, Quincy, MA, 1989.

Vervalin, C. H., *Fire Protection Manual for Hydrocarbon Processing Plants*, 3rd. ed., Gulf Publishing Co., Houstin, TX, 1985.

Woodward, C. D., "The Industrial Fire Problem," *Fire Safety Journal*, Vol. 15, No. 5, 1989, pp. 348-366.

Woodward, D., "The Industrial Fire Problem-Part I," *Fire Prevention*, No. 218 (April 1989), pp. 24-28.

Woodward, D., "The Industrial Fire Problem-Part II," *Fire Prevention*, No. 219 (May 1989), pp. 28-33.

STORAGE OCCUPANCIES

Bruce W. Hisley

This chapter discusses fire hazards and fire protection factors that apply to storage occupancies, including the assessment of life safety risk within such occupancies. Also discussed are occupancy characteristics and hazards associated with storage occupancies as related to contents and their arrangement, as well as operational hazards and fire prevention practices, life safety considerations, building construction, fire protection systems, and uses requiring special considerations.

For additional information see Section 2, Chapter 28, "Storage and Handing of Grain Mill Products"; Section 4, Chapter 2, "Protective Signaling Systems"; Section 4, Chapter 3, "Water Flow Alarms and Sprinkler System Supervision"; Section 4, Chapter 7, "Fire Guard Services and Fire Protection Surveillance"; Section 5, Chapter 3, "Water Supply Requirements for Fire Protection"; Section 5, Chapter 10, "Theory of Automatic Sprinkler Extinguishment"; Section 5, Chapter 11, "Water Supplies for Sprinkler Systems"; Section 5, Chapter 12, "Automatic Sprinkles;" Section 5, Chapter 16, "Care and Maintenance of Water-Based Extinguishing Systems"; Section 5, Chapter 23, "Selection, Operation, Distribution, Inspection, and Maintenance of Fire Extinguishers"; Section 8, Chapter 4 "Warehouse Pre-Planning and Fire Fighting Operations"; Section 8, Chapter 5, "General Indoor Storage"; and Section 8, Chapter 10, "Assessing Fire Safety in Buildings."

OCCUPANCY CHARACTERISTICS

Storage occupancies are buildings or structures used to store or shelter goods, merchandise, products, vehicles, or animals. Storage facilities can be separate and distinct facilities or part of a multiple-use occupancy. "In no other area does one occupancy present such a wide range of hazards, particularly as facilities are increasing in size and contain an increasing variety of products."[1] According to Factory Mutual Research Corporation (FMRC), examples of storage occupancies are warehouses, freight terminals, parking garages, aircraft hangars, grain elevators, barns, and stables.

Storage occupancies are unique in that they can be classified as low-, ordinary-, or high-hazard, or as a combination of these where mixed commodities are stored together and not effectively separated. Factors that will affect the hazard classification are the burning characteristic of the material stored, the combustibility of packaging, the method of storage and packaging, and the quantity stored. Modern developments in material handling have brought rapid change to storage occupancies, including high-rack storage areas that can reach heights of 50 to 100 ft (15 to 30 m).

Computer-controlled stacker cranes are now being used to move and place commodities in rack storage areas. Super, regional distribution warehouses that cover several acres under one roof and may contain two- or three-level mezzanines are now being developed. Storage occupancies usually have a small number of people in relation to total floor area. Work patterns usually require employees to move through the structure using industrial trucks. In totally computer-controlled warehouses, there are even fewer occupants, which can complicate the means of egress design.

Mini-storage complexes now being developed consist of several small rental spaces ranging from 40 to 400 sq ft (8 to 80 m^2) in one building. These complexes are unique in that there is very little control over the type and amount of hazardous materials that may be stored in a given rental area because they are accessible to the renter on a 24-hour basis. The rental spaces usually are not separated from each other by fire-resistance-rated walls, and may consist of 50 or more rental spaces in a building.

Storage occupancies can consist of raw materials, finished products, or goods in an intermediate stage of production. These materials can be found in bulk storage, solid piling, palletized storage, and rack storage arrangements. Bins and narrow shelves are also used, usually in stockrooms, and hold only small amounts of materials for immediate use. The main difference among these storage arrangements that has an effect on fire behavior and control is the nature of horizontal and vertical air spaces or

Mr. Hisley is a Fire Service Management Specialist, Educational Operations Division, National Fire Academy, National Emergency Training Center, Emmitsburg, MD. He was division chief, Fire Prevention Bureau of the Anne Arundel County Fire Department, MD, before joining the Academy staff.

"flues" that storage configurations create. Parking garages, grain elevators, and aircraft hangars have other unique special problems caused by the nature of the operations performed in them. These problems will be addressed later in this chapter.

HAZARDS ASSOCIATED WITH OCCUPANCY

Contents

It is not unusual to find large, densely stored quantities of inherently combustible materials, such as textiles, stored in combustible packing materials, such as wood, plastic, and cardboard. Highly flammable materials and gases also may be contained in the materials in storage. Increasing amounts of plastics are now being used as part of the product as well as the packaging. In determining the hazard classification of contents, consideration should be given to the product, product container, and packaging materials used. Fire behavior will depend upon the ease of ignition, rate of fire spread, and rate of heat release of the commodity as it is stored.

Commodities are often complex items whose fuel content, arrangement, shape, and form affect their performance in a fire. A packaged commodity must be considered as a whole, since that is the way it burns. For example, bottled beer in itself would be considered a low hazard, but when it is stored in cardboard or wood containers, it becomes an ordinary hazard. Washing machines have very few combustible components in their assembly. If they are packaged in cardboard boxes and surrounded with plastic packing, however, the commodity can burn rapidly and produce large amounts of smoke. Stored commodities are divided into general burning hazard classifications, based upon the fire behavior of the typical items in each classification as defined in NFPA 231, *General Storage*.

In storage areas where mixed items are stored, the hazard classification should be based upon the most severe hazard category. This type of condition is common in hardware or automotive parts warehouses. High-hazard materials or materials that require special consideration can sometimes be separated to keep them from influencing the overall hazard classification. Examples of these materials are rubber tires, plastic products, combustible fibers, paper and paper products, hanging garments, carpeting, pesticides, flammable liquids and gases, and reactive chemicals. The requirements of NFPA 231D, *Storage of Rubber Tires*; NFPA 231E, *Storage of Baled Cotton*; and NFPA 231F, *Storage of Roll Paper*, should be considered.

Aerosol cans that contain flammable products stored at high pressure present a very high hazard risk. When ignited, they can explode to produce fireballs and can rocket throughout a given area to start multiple fires. The bulk storage of these containers should meet the requirements of NFPA 30B, *Aerosol Products*.

Arrangement of Contents

The arrangement of the materials being stored has a major impact on fire spread. Fire behavior will depend upon the height of storage, aisle widths, and whether storage is in bulk, solid piles, or palletized piles. Fire development will depend upon the combustible surfaces of the stored goods and the horizontal and vertical flue spaces between the surface of the materials stored. Where combustible fibers are stored, a fast-travelling surface fire is possible if the fiber bales have multiple exposed fibers.

Fire usually spreads in a fan-shaped pattern, as fire at the base preheats the material, above which then ignites and burns. As the height of the storage increases, the effect on fire growth can be expected to intensify as the fire moves rapidly upward. Aisles that are at least 8 ft (2.5 m) wide are needed to help restrict the spread of fire across an aisle. The presence of horizontal air spaces formed by the pallets in palletized storage can cause fast-spreading fires. Rapid fire spread can also be expected in rack storage areas due to the height of the racks and the narrow width of the aisles that are usually present when automatic materials-handling equipment is used.

OPERATIONAL HAZARDS AND FIRE PREVENTION PRACTICES

Storage occupancies can consist of large floor spaces on several levels occupied by only a few personnel. Because of this factor, fires often go undetected for an extended period of time after they start, particularly in spaces that are not protected by automatic fire detection or suppression systems.

Common hazards and fire causes that are generally associated with storage occupancies are careless disposal of smoking materials, poor housekeeping practices, packing and unpacking of goods, storage of idle pallets, sparks from cutting and welding, ignition from industrial trucks or other mobile equipment, piling of storage close to heating units or electrical appliances, and incendiarism. Specially designed materials-handling systems may also present unique hazards.

Smoking

Smoking should be controlled at all times. The control of smoking requires a sincere effort by management to enforce observance of permissible and prohibited smoking areas for employees and outside visitors. Smoking should be confined to specific areas set aside from storage that are kept clean and provided with adequate disposal containers.

Housekeeping Practices

The importance of good housekeeping cannot be overstressed. The packing or unpacking of goods usually requires or results in the presence of quantities of loose combustibles, such as foamed polystryene beads, cocoons of foamed plastic, shredded paper, excelsior, and straw. Other combustibles, such as baled fibers and detached labels or tags, can act as kindling to ignite stored materials.

Packing and Unpacking Operations

Areas where packing and unpacking, sorting, repairing, refinishing, painting, and general maintenance take place often invite the accumulation of combustible materials. Such areas are comparable to an industrial occupancy. It is a good practice either to locate this type of operation away from the storage area or to provide a fire-resistance-rated separation.

Storage of Idle Pallets

Piles of wooden pallets introduce a severe fire hazard incidental to many storage occupancies. With age, these pallets can be ignited easily by a small ignition source. Even in sprinkler-protected areas, the undersides of the pallets provide dry areas on which a fire can grow and expand. The process of fire jumping to other pallets continues until the fire spreads through the top of the stack. With the strong updraft of flame, very little water from an ordinary-hazard sprinkler system can reach the seat of the fire. Pallets should be stored in accordance with NFPA 231, *General Storage*. Plastic pallets and shipping containers often present similar hazards.

Welding and Cutting Operations

Precautions should be taken at all times during welding and cutting operations. Such operations should not begin until all combustible materials have been removed from the affected area or covered with a fire-retardant cover. Portable fire extinguishers or small hoselines should be made ready before the operation begins. A fire watch should be present at all times during the operation and for at least 30 minutes after the operation has been completed. Consideration should be given to the use of mechanical fastening devices and saws when repairing or replacing steel racks to avoid cutting or welding. All cutting and welding should be conducted in accordance with NFPA 51B, *Cutting and Welding Processes*.

Industrial (Forklift) Trucks

Several large-loss fires have been ignited by industrial forklift equipment. Hazards associated with the use of industrial trucks are found in refueling operations, maintenance, and storage (when not in use). The type of industrial truck being used should be approved for use within the building for the hazardous material being stored. NFPA 505, *Powered Industrial Trucks*, designates the type of truck that can be used in hazardous areas. All refueling operations should be conducted outside the building. Fuel for the trucks must be stored and handled properly. Areas that are used for maintenance and battery recharging for electrical trucks should be separated from storage areas.

Heat Equipment and Electrical Appliances

Material should be stored so that adequate clearance is maintained from heating air ducts, unit heaters, duct furnaces, flue pipes, radiant space heaters, lighting fixtures, electrical appliances, and other heat-producing equipment. Special care is needed when using temporary or portable heating appliances.

LIFE SAFETY CONSIDERATIONS

Storage occupancies are often vulnerable to incendiary acts because they present an available fuel supply and a large potential loss, and they often allow an arsonist to enter and start a fire without being detected. Even where security personnel are present, a fire may be ignited in a location that is out of their sight and grow to major proportions before it is detected.

In storage occupancies, the potential loss of life is dependent upon the fire hazard of the material in storage and the special characteristics of the storage building. Fire spread in high-piled or rack storage can be expected to be rapid with some types of materials. In single-story buildings where high ceilings are present, the smoke and heat produced by a fire will have a place to accumulate before the means of egress becomes obscured or impassable. In buildings with low ceilings, the opposite will occur. Where multiple-level, open-grating-floor-type mezzanines are used, smoke and heat from fires below can be expected to block a means of egress readily.

Particular attention to the means of egress and exit locations is required. In older, multiple-floor warehouses, unprotected vertical openings for freight elevators and other materials-handling systems are common. These can allow rapid spread of smoke and heat to the upper floors.

Factors that will affect life safety in storage occupancies are the stored commodity, which consists of the product, the packing and the container; the fire behavior of the commodity, which is based on the ease of ignition, rate of fire spread, and rate of heat release; the storage arrangement, which includes height of storage and aisle widths; the maximum single fire area; smoke and heat venting; exterior fire fighting access; and the form of the stored material.

NFPA 101®, *Life Safety Code*®, addresses life safety from fire and similar emergencies and covers features necessary to minimize danger to life from fire, smoke, fumes, and panic. NFPA 101 also deals with egress and other considerations that are essential to life safety. The minimum requirements of NFPA 101 should be followed in storage occupancies.

Storage occupancies can be classified as low-, ordinary-, or high-hazard, or as a combination where mixed commodities are stored together, and noticeable differences exist among the life safety requirements for the different hazard classifications in NFPA 101, *Life Safety Code*. Where these different hazards exist in the same structure and cannot be effectively fire separated, the requirements for the most hazardous classification must apply. Sound judgment must be used when determining the hazard classification. NFPA 101 uses the ordinary-hazard classification as the basis for general requirements, and most storage occupancies will fall into this classification. Only a very few will fall into the low or high classification. NFPA 101 recognizes storage occupancies that might contain low-hazard content. However, the type of building construction should be considered when classifying a structure as low-hazard. Combustible building materials will influence the spread and development of fire in the building or structure, especially where combustible concealed spaces are present.

Special concern for the stability of the storage arrangement is required when high-piled storage is present. High-piled storage can collapse during the early stages of fire development, due either to inherent instabilities or to excessive height and weight, which crushes the lower units. Pile collapse may block egress travel routes from the structure.

Exit Design

The means of egress in storage occupancies are arranged like those in other occupancies. The chief difference is that fewer exits are required in storage occupancies. The required exits are based only on travel distance to reach an exit and on the minimum number of exits required from a given area. Unlike other occupancies, there is no occupancy load factor to consider. In storage occupancies, only a small number of people will usually occupy the structure at any one time. Work patterns usually require employees to move throughout the structure, which can complicate the egress design for life safety. Every type of storage occupancy that is classified as ordinary or high-hazard must have access to at least two separate means of egress as remote from each other as practicable. These two means of egress should be available from all parts and all levels of the occupancy, and must be within the travel distances specified by NFPA 101, *Life Safety Code*. Exits must be arranged so that they can be reached by different paths of travel from different directions, although a dead end or common path of travel is allowed in ordinary-hazard occupancies. Low-hazard occupancies require only a single means of egress, with no limitation on travel distance to reach an exit. In areas or occupancies that contain high-hazard contents, occupants must be able to travel at least two separate routes remote from each other to reach an exit. In these areas, special consideration is needed to make sure that no dead-end aisles are present.

Exit doors must be kept unlocked from the egress side of the door when the occupancy is occupied by employees. In low- and ordinary-hazard occupancies, special listed locking devices are allowed if the structure is protected throughout by an approved automatic fire detection or supervised sprinkler system. Exit doors from high-hazard areas should swing in the direction of exit travel and be equipped with panic hardware. Due to the continual movements of stock within a storage occupancy, special attention is needed to keep required means of egress aisles and exit doors from being blocked.

Exit Identification

The means of egress and exit location have to be identified by signs that are readily visible from all directions of exit access. Exit identification can be a problem in high-stocked storage areas, so other measures, such as painting exit travel paths on the floor, may be needed. Adequate illumination for the means of egress is necessary, especially in windowless buildings that lack any opening for natural light. Buildings that are occupied at night or lack openings for natural lighting should be equipped with emergency lighting. This will provide illumination for required egress stairs, aisles, corridors, ramps, and passageways that lead to an exit.

Vertical Openings

Vertical openings are permitted in low- or ordinary-hazard storage occupancies, provided that they do not extend more than three floors, that the building is protected throughout by an automatic sprinkler system, and that the openings do not serve as required exits. Exits from all floor levels must be protected in accordance with NFPA 101, *Life Safety Code*.

Fire Alarm Systems

Due to the large open floor areas and few employees who may be working in many different parts of a storage building, a fire alarm system should be considered to alert all occupants and allow for timely exiting and initiation of some type of emergency action. If the occupancy has a trained fire brigade or an emergency pre-fire plan, there should be a means of notifying people in all areas of the building so that the emergency plan can be initiated. Because of the low risk of fire, occupancies with low-hazard contents are not required to have an alarm system. NFPA 101, *Life Safety Code* does require a fire alarm system in ordinary- and high-hazard-content occupancies that are not protected by an automatic sprinkler system and that have a total floor area exceeding 100,000 sq ft (9290 m^2). In buildings equipped with a fire alarm system, provisions must be made so that the alarm system, when activated, will sound an alarm in a continuously attended location for the purposes of initiating emergency actions.

BUILDING CONSTRUCTION AFFECTING HAZARDOUS CONDITIONS

Storage occupancies can be located in any type of construction. In addition, storage is found in mixed-use structures, because storage space is needed in all types of occupancies. Most construction types are suitable for storage. However, combustible construction adds to the fire loading and can create combustible concealed space that contributes to fire spread.

The combustibility, flame spread rate, smoke production, heat release potential, and structural stability of materials used in building construction should all be considered. One must consider the type of covering used on steel deck roofs, plastic panels used for insulation within wall panels and roofing, and the flame spread rating of the vapor barrier for exposed interior insulation. Certain expanded plastic insulation core panel walls should be used only in buildings with automatic sprinkler protection and when covered with fire-resistive members. In newer buildings, lightweight steel and wood truss construction is now commonly used and may be susceptible to early structural collapse. In some buildings with rack systems, the structural framework of the racks themselves supports the exterior walls and roof of the building.

It is not uncommon to find buildings up to 100 ft (30 m) high used for rack storage. Rack systems that are fully automated may have narrow aisle widths of 4 ft (1.2 m) between the racks. Even in buildings protected by automatic sprinkler systems, it may be difficult to provide complete fire extinguishment within the racks.

Fire involving the upper portions of high-rack storage can present unusual problems and severe risks to fire fighters. Access to the upper portion for complete extinguishment and overhaul is very limited. The use of ground ladders inside buildings is extremely difficult and dangerous and is limited to 35 ft (10.5 m) at most. The heat produced by the fire may cause structural failure of the rack system or collapse of the stored material into the aisle space. When falling material blocks the aisle, access to the fire area is even more difficult.

Buildings or structures with limited exterior access for fire fighting and rescue operations can pose a serious life safety hazard. This type of design can cause large areas to become lethal fire environments.

The installation of heat and smoke vents in storage occupancies should be considered. Some storage occupancies are extremely large with very few windows or doors that can be used to remove smoke and heat. In buildings without automatic sprinkler protection, venting can reduce the horizontal spread of smoke and heat along the ceiling, which can aid in the evacuation of the building. In buildings protected by automatic sprinkler systems, venting can aid in smoke removal, which, in turn, can aid fire fighting operations and possible rescue. Smoke and heat venting facilities, as well as automatic sprinkler protection, are essential for life safety in windowless buildings and underground structures.

Special mechanical ventilation systems should be considered for large-area storage occupancies to remove smoke and products of combustion. The ventilation of large-area structures can be particularly difficult when automatic sprinkler systems have controlled a fire and cooled the atmosphere. Several deaths have occurred when fire fighters became lost in the zero-visibility condition created by "cold smoke" and have run out of air. Persons without respiratory protection may easily be overcome by products of combustion when trapped in the building, and unnecessary smoke damage may result if effective ventilation is not provided.

FIRE PROTECTION SYSTEMS

While automatic sprinklers are considered the main line of fire defense in storage occupancies, they are by no means the only method of protection. Standpipe hose systems, high-expansion foam systems, portable fire extinguishers, manual fire fighting operations, and alarm systems also have a role in protecting storage occupancies.

Goods stored to great heights, mechanical stacking equipment, and narrow aisles are highly conducive to vertical fire spread. Even with automatic sprinkler protection, these types of storage arrangements can pose a challenge for control.

Automatic Sprinklers

Automatic sprinklers are particularly effective for life safety because they warn of the existence of fire and, at the same time, apply water to the burning area. Properly installed and maintained sprinklers provide a highly effective safeguard against the loss of life and property.

Automatic sprinkler systems are usually required by the model building codes or locally adopted codes when the storage occupancy is classified as a high-hazard occupancy. Some codes require sprinkler protection when materials are stored in racks and high piles more than 12 ft (3.6 m) high. The model building codes usually allow storage buildings to be constructed with unlimited floor area when they are protected by sprinkler systems and are not used for high-hazard storage.

Disastrous fires have occurred in sprinklered warehouses where combustible materials have been stored to heights over 50 ft (15 m). It is important that the systems be designed so that they are compatible with the commodity stored and with the storage heights. A major factor in several large fire losses in storage occupancies has been the overtaxing of the automatic sprinkler system, which was not designed for the type of material stored or for the type of storage arrangement. It is important to keep detailed records to determine what type of hazard is located in the storage occupancy. Records indicating the type of material stored, pile arrangement, storage methods, and height of storage should be maintained. Automatic sprinkler systems should be designed and installed in accordance with NFPA 13, *Installation of Sprinkler Systems*; NFPA 231, *General Storage*; and NFPA 231C, *Rack Storage of Materials*.

Fire Alarm Systems

Fire alarm systems are of the utmost importance in warning occupants of fire, especially in storage areas that contain only a few employees working on a large floor area and in multiple-story buildings. Alarm systems should have sounding devices that are distinctive from other sounds, and these devices should be distributed in such a way that they may be heard in every room or area of a building. It is important to keep the alarm pull stations clear of any storage and to mark them well for easy identification.

Standpipe Hose Systems

Standpipe hose systems should be installed in storage occupancies that contain rack or high-piled storage. Connections for $1\frac{1}{2}$-in. (1 in. equals 24.4 mm) hoselines should be provided for initial fire fighting and mop-up operations. The standpipe hose connections should be used only by fire department personnel or by members of a properly trained and equipped industrial fire brigade. Connections should be so located that all portions of the area can be reached. Providing hose connections for high-rack systems requires special consideration. In addition to the normal floor-level connections, additional connections may be needed at different heights to enable the hoselines to reach all areas.

Fire Extinguishers

All employees should be familiar with the location and use of the fire extinguishers that are provided in the occupancy. The training of employees should stress the importance of sounding an alarm and notifying the fire department as soon as a fire is discovered.

The extinguishers should be kept in readily visible locations where storage will not prevent access at any time. All employees should be familiar with the operation of the extinguishers that are provided. (See NFPA 10, *Portable Fire Extinguishers*.)

USES REQUIRING SPECIAL CONSIDERATIONS

Parking Garages

Parking garages require special consideration in that the method of operation and use will affect the degree of life safety requirements. There are two types of parking garages: those in which vehicles are parked exclusively by attendants or by mechanical means, and those in which the customers themselves park the vehicles. NFPA 101, *Life Safety Code*, addresses the exiting requirements of garages in which the customer parks the vehicle and can occupy all parts of the garage.

Occupancy characteristics: Parking garages can be on several levels above or below grade and of the enclosed or open type. A garage is considered open when at least 25 percent of the total enclosing walls are open to the atmosphere on two sides of each level.

Parking garages are often found in conjunction with other uses, such as hotels, apartments, and office buildings. When garages are used for both parking and repairs, the repair area should be separated from the parking area and treated as an industrial occupancy.

Hazards associated with garages: Motor vehicles generally contain fast-burning fuels, including gasoline, diesel fuel, or LP-Gas. Major parts of newer-model vehicles are made of plastic. These vehicles can create severe fires that produce large amounts of smoke. In some cases, gasoline is dispensed in garages. NFPA 30A, *Automotive and Marine Service Station Code*, and NFPA 88A, *Parking Structures*, list requirements for this type of operation. In addition, NFPA 101, *Life Safety Code*, has special life safety requirements when gasoline is dispensed inside. Garages used for vehicle storage are classified as ordinary life safety hazards.

Parking garages are usually only occupied by a few persons at any one time. However, structures that are located near large public assembly complexes, such as civic centers or theaters, can be occupied by a large number of persons at one time after a show or event has ended. During this time, several hundred people will be moving throughout the structure, either going to their vehicles or waiting in the vehicles to exit the parking garage.

Life safety considerations: To ensure life safety conditions in a garage, every floor level must have access to at least two separate exits, arranged so that the path of travel is in two different directions. Vehicle ramps can serve as a means of exit under special conditions. The travel distance allowed to reach an exit depends upon whether the building is open or enclosed and whether the garage is protected by automatic sprinklers.

Special consideration must be given to the location of gasoline pumps to avoid trapping occupants if there is a fire or explosion at the pumps. Travel in any direction must lead to an outside exit at the same level or to properly arranged exit stairs. Where parking areas are located below the gasoline dispensing pumps, each floor must have direct access to the outside. This arrangement eliminates the possibility that gasoline vapors will accumulate in the enclosed exit stairs.

The means of egress to exits should be provided with illumination and emergency lighting when the garage is used at night or does not provide natural lighting from windows or other openings during the daytime. Most people using a parking garage are unfamiliar with the location of exits. Exits and access to the exits should be marked and identified.

Enclosed parking garages are required to have a fire alarm system when the total aggregate floor area exceeds 100,000 sq ft (9290 m^2) and is not protected by automatic sprinkler systems. In general, automatic sprinkler protection is required if the garage is enclosed and located below grade and if the building is over 50 ft (15 m) high with a combustible roof or floor assembly, or if the garage is located inside or below buildings used for other occupancies.

Grain and Other Bulk Storage Elevators

These structures are used to move, store, and process grain, such as wheat, corn, oats, soy beans, and sunflower seeds. (See Figure 8-24A). During the handling of the commodity, some dust is generated due to kernel breakage and so on, making the grain stream susceptible to fire and explosion. Commodities are stored in bulk form in concrete and steel silos, wooden bins, and steel tanks. Dust explosions are the primary hazard in the grain industry. NFPA 61B, *Grain Elevators and Facilities Handling Bulk Raw Agricultural Commodities*, lists fire protection and safety requirements for the installation and operation of grain elevators.

Structures of this type are unique and particularly dangerous, posing a serious life safety hazard for all occupants. The hazards of both fire and explosion need special consideration. Past fire experience has shown that grain elevators account for the major portion of life loss in storage occupancies. In most instances, they store and handle materials that create highly combustible dust. In many past dust explosions, the primary and only means of exiting from the upper parts of an elevator have been damaged or destroyed, trapping the workers on top of the structure.

Life safety considerations addressed in NFPA 101, *Life Safety Code*, are based on the occurrence of fires, not on the possibility of a grain dust explosion. Basic life safety requirements require that at least two means of egress be available and located as remotely as possible from each other. These means of egress should be available from all working areas and from the headhouse, which is located on top of the storage structure. All working areas should have access to at least one stairway that leads to an exit discharge point at ground level. This stairway should be constructed within a dust- and fire-resistive-rated enclosure.

In addition to the stairway, an alternate means of escape is required for life safety. This secondary means should provide a continuous path to the ground from the top of the elevator structure, but it need not meet all the provisions for a means of egress. This secondary escape can consist of exterior stairs or basket-type ladders accessible from all working levels of the headhouse. This means of escape will provide passage to the ground or to the top of adjoining structures.

An exterior stair or basket-type ladder should be provided from the top of storage structures such as silos, conveyors, galleries, and gantries. This secondary escape should be located at the opposite end of the structure from the headhouse.

Most grain elevators have underground passages beneath the silos for conveyors. These spaces should have at least two means of egress so located that no dead-end condition is present. One of the means of egress can be a ladder or other escape method that leads to a window, hatch, or panel that can be opened readily to allow escape.

Aircraft Hangers

An aircraft hangar is a large structure built to provide weather protection and shop space for aircraft during maintenance and storage. Since it is impractical to remove all fuel from a craft before moving it into a hangar, large quantities of flammable liquids are always possible inside a hangar. Fire during maintenance and servicing creates the greatest exposure to personnel in the hangar and endangers aircraft that may be valued in the millions of dollars. Many maintenance procedures use highly flammable solvents and sometimes unstable toxic chemicals. Special precautions for ventilation and control of ignition sources are needed.

Aircraft hangars provide a particular challenge when designing adequate exits for life safety. The large open area needed for aircraft, especially jumbo jets, requires extended travel distances to reach exits. This problem is compounded by the presence of flammable and combustible liquids. Exit locations must be located at intervals not to exceed 150 ft (46 m) along all exterior walls of the hangar. Each part of the hangar or servicing area must have access to at least two exit locations. If approved interior horizontal exits (2-hr fire walls) are provided, then exit locations along the wall must be provided at intervals not to exceed 100 ft (30 m). Since a large hangar door cannot be left open in poor weather, small access doors can be installed in the large hangar doors. To use additional space, mezzanine floors can be constructed in the hangar. Exiting from these levels should be arranged so that an exit can be reached

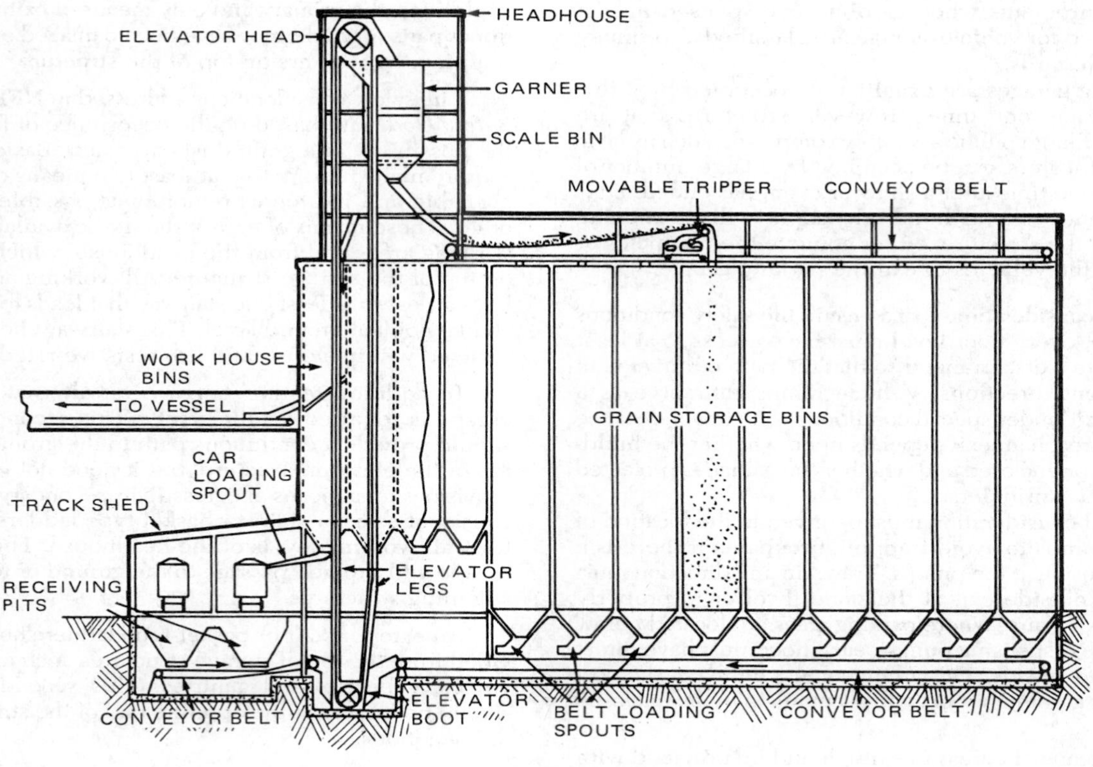

FIG. 8-24A. Cutaway view of a grain elevator.

within a maximum travel distance of 75 ft (23 m). These exits must lead directly to an approved enclosed stairway that discharges directly to the outside, to another cutoff fire-separated area, or to outside stairs.

Because hangars encompass such large areas, several hazard classifications can be found in the structures at one time. In those areas that are classified as high-hazard or where a high-hazard operation is being conducted, exits must be available and located where no dead-end conditions are present. For life safety purposes, a fire alarm system is required in hangars that are not protected by automatic sprinkler systems and that exceed 100,000 sq ft (9290 m^2) in total floor area. For additional requirements related to the construction and protection of aircraft hangers from fire, refer to NFPA 309, *Aircraft Hangars*.

BIBLIOGRAPHY

References Cited

1. *Record*, Factory Mutual Research Corporation, Norwood, MA, July/August 1982.

NFPA, Codes, Standards and Recommended Practices

Reference to the following codes, standards, and recommended practices will provide further information on storage occupancies discussed in this chapter. (See the latest *NFPA Catalog* for availability of current editions of the following documents.)

NFPA 10, *Portable Fire Extinguishers*.
NFPA 13, *Installation of Sprinkler Systems*.
NFPA 30, *Flammable and Combustible Liquids Code*.
NFPA 30A, *Automotive and Marine Service Station Codes*.
NFPA 30B, *Aerosol Products*.
NFPA 51B, *Cutting and Welding Processes*.
NFPA 61B, *Grain Elevators and Facilities Handling Bulk Raw Agricultural Commodities*.
NFPA 88A, *Parking Structures*.
NFPA 101,® *Life Safety Code*.®
NFPA 231, *General Storage*.
NFPA 231C, *Rack Storage of Materials*.
NFPA 231D, *Storage of Rubber Tires*.
NFPA 231E, *Storage of Baled Cottons*.
NFPA 231F, *Storage of Roll Papers*.
NFPA 409, *Aircraft Hangers*.
NFPA 505, *Powered Industrial Trucks*.

Additional Readings

Before the Fire—Fire Prevention Strategies for Storage Occupancies, NFPA Ad Hoc Task Force, National Fire Protection Association, Quincy, MA, 1987.

Cote, A. E., *ed.*, *Industrial Fire Hazards Handbook*, 2nd ed., National Fire Protection Association, Quincy, MA, 1985.

European Insurance Commission, Fire Commission, Sub-Committee 42P, *Notes on the Recommendation Concerning Fire Protection in Warehouse Stocking Dangerous Materials*, Zurich, Switzerland, 1988.

Factory Mutual Engineering Corp, *Loss Prevention Data 8-0*, March 1977.

Fields, T., "Warehouses: A Case Study for Control," *Fire Prevention*, No. 215 (Dec. 1988), pp. 24-29.

Isner, M. S., "49 Million Loss in Sherwin-Williams Warehouse Fire," *Fire Journal*, Vol. 82, No. 2 (March/April 1988).

Cote, A.E., *ed.*, *Industrial Fire Hazards Handbook*, 3rd ed., National Fire Protection Association, Quincy, MA 1990.

Moulton, G. A., *ed.*, *Conducting Fire Inspections—A Guidebook for Field Use*, National Fire Protection Association, Quincy, MA, 1982.

Tuck, C.A. Jr., *ed.*, *NFPA Inspection Manual*, 5th ed., National Fire Protection Association, Quincy, MA, 1982.

United National Environment Programme, "Storage of Hazardous Materials—A Technical Guide for Safety Warehousing of Hazardous Materials, " 3rd Draft Prepared by UNEP/IPO Secretariat, Paris, France, Jan. 1989.

Woolhead, F., "The Warehouse Fire Threat to Profits and Prospects," *Fire Surveyor*, Vol. 17, No. 5 (Oct. 1988), pp. 13-15.

NUCLEAR FACILITIES

Revised by George Weldon

In general, radioactive substances and operations involving radioactive materials or devices and equipment which present radiation hazards have the same fire and explosion features as similar materials and operations without radiation hazards. However, due to the hazard to personnel and the possibility of long-term contamination of property from exposure to sudden accidental escape of radioactive substances, the subject of protection from radiation hazards deserves special consideration, especially the procedures that must be followed during emergencies.

NUCLEAR REACTORS

A nuclear reactor is a device or assembly for initiating and maintaining a controlled nuclear chain reaction in a fissionable fuel (uranium or plutonium). Nuclear reactors are used to produce energy, to study the fission process, or to produce radioactive materials within the reactor or in a material exposed by the reactor's radiation or radioactive particles. Basically, nuclear reactors may be divided into two categories: (1) nuclear power reactors of large size, up to 3,500 MW (megawatts thermal) or 1,100 MW(e) (megawatts electrical), and (2) research reactors that operate at power levels from a few watts to many megawatts. In 1988 there were over 100 operating or near-operating nuclear power reactors and many additional nuclear power reactors with construction permits in the United States alone. Construction of many others has been delayed—some indefinitely. Dozens of research reactors are now operating, but, in general, the number of research reactors is not increasing.

Nuclear reactors that include a containment vessel, generating equipment, and heat-removal equipment can be as large as the largest fossil-fueled electrical generating plants. Most research reactors, however, are so small that they may occupy only one small corner of a room in a typical laboratory building at a research facility or college campus. Therefore, the magnitude of hazard presented by each kind of reactor varies considerably.

George Weldon, P.E., is engineering manager for the MAERP Reinsurance Association, Chicago, IL.

Various national and international groups have addressed the need for fire protection requirements for nuclear power reactors and research reactors. These groups include the National Fire Protection Association (NFPA), the American Nuclear Society, the American National Standards Institute (ANSI), the United States Nuclear Regulatory Commission (NRC), the MAERP Reinsurance Association, and the American Nuclear Insurers. (See bibliography at the end of this chapter.)

The "defense-in-depth" philosophy, which calls for the provisions that follow, is applicable to both power and research reactors. Those provisions are:

1. Fire prevention.
2. Quick detection and suppression of fires that occur.
3. Designing the plant to limit the consequences of fire.

Heat Removal

All nuclear reactors, even very low-power training or research reactors, produce heat while operating. This heat either must be dissipated or used, depending upon the amount produced and the purpose for which the reactor is intended.

Reactor Control

Reactor control systems and safety systems are of utmost importance. The control system design is fitted to the technical characteristics of the reactor and is capable of producing power changes at acceptable rates. The control system design also makes it possible to produce and maintain the desired power level within the reactor in such a way that excessive temperatures are avoided. The safety system, which is an addition to the control system, is adapted to the characteristics of the reactor in the instrument and control system. It responds to signals from the instruments by automatic operation, in order to prevent operational variables from exceeding safe limits. On appropriate signals, the safety system warns of incipient performance changes and, if necessary, shuts down the reactor.

A reactor becomes "critical" when the total rate of production of neutrons, under control conditions, is such that self-sustaining reactions occur. Control methods must be rapid and sensitive, and protected from fire. Since the control system is vital to the adequate functioning and safe operation of the reactor, the protection of the control room, cableways, emergency power supply, and electrically or hydraulically operated equipment is of prime importance. Protection for these areas should be fully consistent with that used in computer rooms containing vital records.

Construction Problems

Fire records indicate that one of the more vulnerable periods for fire damage in the lifetime of a large reactor system, such as found in nuclear power plants, exists during the construction stage. (See Figure 8-25A.) Because the construction of such a plant usually requires many years, the construction hazards acquire a nearly permanent status and should be considered as if they were to be permanent.

FIG. 8-25A. Nuclear facilities are most vulnerable to fire damage during construction, a period of several years, and thus require a good construction firesafety program.

Power reactors present unique fire protection problems during construction, since they require a containment vessel as a final protection system. Construction techniques require the containment structure to be built early during the project. This means that much of the subsequent reactor construction takes place inside a large vessel that has limited exits for evacuation and limited fire fighting access. In addition, the vessel confines smoke and other products of combustion, which greatly increases the difficulties of evacuation and manual fire fighting. A good construction firesafety program should ensure that all penetrations of the containment vessel suitable for evacuation remain open and usable during the period that other construction is taking place within the vessel.

Due to the limited access for fire fighting and the lack of normal venting possibilities for smoke and gases, it is imperative to severely limit all combustible materials needed for construction. Metal formwork, scaffolding, platforms, stairways, etc., are preferable to wood. The use of wood should be limited to those species that are appropriately treated to reduce inherent combustibility and flame-spread ratings.

Installation of utilities and equipment in the containment vessel requires special care so a low level of combustibles is maintained. Since reactor equipment must meet very high levels of quality assurance, reactor equipment that has been subjected to fire and smoke damage is much more likely to require replacement than similarly exposed equipment in normal industrial installations. Special efforts are necessary to reduce the usual accumulation of packing cases, cartons, insulation, etc., to an acceptable level. This may take the form of conducting all uncrating operations outside the containment vessel, and providing special handling devices to transport unpackaged items into the vessel.

Research Reactors

In general, these may present particular problems due to their location in existing buildings (which are sometimes of combustible construction), and the use of much combustible loading in the form of paraffin shielding, wall finishes, and instrumentation. Combustibles should be eliminated wherever possible. For example, water can be used in place of paraffin. Where combustibles cannot be eliminated, automatic sprinkler protection should be provided. Supervision of construction/operating personnel is especially important because a number of different operating groups may be involved with a single reactor.

RADIATION MACHINES

Radiation machines include mechanical and electrical devices that produce or make use of subatomic particles or electromagnetic radiation, or both. X-ray machines are used in radiography, therapeutic treatment, and in studies of the behavior of radiation and its effect upon materials. Particle accelerators, while a source of radiation, are primarily devices for imparting extremely high energies to subatomic particles which enter and alter atomic nuclei, thereby providing the means for developing basic information concerning the structure and behavior of matter. Gamma ray sources in the form of radioactive isotopes are employed in radiography equipment. This equipment may produce intense radiation. The use of isotopes as a source of radiation is not discussed in this chapter.

X-Ray Machines

Except for the radiation hazard while in use, the hazards of X-ray machines are mainly the hazards of high potential and high energy electrical equipment. When shut down, there is seldom any appreciable residual radiation to interfere with fire fighting or salvage operations. Although no flammable gases or hazardous amounts of flammable liquids are ordinarily needed to operate X-ray machines, they are frequently encountered in studies of the effects of radiation on a wide variety of substances.

Particle Accelerators

Particle accelerators include Van de Graaff generators, linear accelerators, cyclotrons, synchrotrons, betatrons, or bevatrons. The machines are used, as the name implies, to accelerate various charged atomic particles to tremendous speeds and, consequently, to high energy levels. Particle accelerators furnish scientists with atomic particles, in the form of a beam, which may be utilized for fundamental studies of atomic structure. In addition, accelerators furnish high-energy radiation which may be utilized for radiography, therapy, or chemical processing.

Particle accelerators emit appreciable radiation only while in operation. Attempts to extinguish a fire in the immediate vicinity of the machine should be delayed until the machine's power supply can be disconnected.

Certain "target" materials become radioactive when bombarded by atomic particles, and for this reason monitoring equipment should be used during fire fighting operations to estimate the radiation hazard. The usual hazard presented by particle accelerators is largely that of electrical equipment. There are, however, some important exceptions. Some installations use such hazardous materials as liquid hydrogen or other flammable materials in considerable quantities. Large amounts of paraffin are used for neutron shielding purposes. Another factor is the possible presence of combustible oils used for insulating and cooling.

Industrial applications for particle accelerators include chemical activation, acceleration of polymerization in plastics production, and the sterilization and preservation of packaged drugs and sutures. The general fire protection and prevention measures for these machines should include the use of noncombustible or limited combustible (Type I or Type II) construction housing, noncombustible or slow-burning wiring and interior finishing, and the elimination of as much other combustible material as possible. (See NFPA 220, *Standard Types of Building Construction.*) Automatic sprinkler protection should be provided in areas containing hazardous amounts of combustible material or equipment. Special fire protection should be provided for any high-voltage electrical equipment.

FACILITIES HANDLING RADIOACTIVE MATERIALS

The type of equipment used to process radioactive materials depends not only upon the work to be performed, but also upon the degree of hazard associated with the material and the process it is to undergo. Materials with low levels of radioactivity and with little or no inherent fire or explosion hazards require less protective equipment than others. For purposes of personnel protection, the amount and kind of shielding required will depend upon the types of radiation emitted, as well as the activity involved. In addition, the chemical and physical nature of the radioactive materials will dictate the degree of containment necessary, as well as the construction materials necessary in the containment system. All equipment to be used for handling and processing radioactive materials should be designed to minimize fire and explosion potentials, as well as to protect personnel against harmful radiation exposure and prevent damage to property by contamination. There are many types of equipment and systems for handling radioactive materials, but most can be classified as either benches, hoods, glove boxes, or hot cells.

Benches

Benches are used generally for handling relatively small amounts of alpha- or beta-emitting materials requiring little or no shielding when handled with gloved hands or tongs. No special ventilation for the bench is provided in most instances, and its use is thereby restricted to materials that will not easily become airborne.

Benches should be of noncombustible construction with a nonporous continuous working surface which can be decontaminated easily. Usually, one or two layers of blotting paper on the bench top to absorb small spills will not increase materially the fire hazard.

Hoods

Hoods, sometimes referred to as "fume hoods," are similar to benches except for the addition of an enclosure and exhaust system for removing vapors. The nature of the operations conducted within the hood may require a filter system to prevent the spread of radioactive materials. Filters with a low degree of combustibility are desirable.

Glove Boxes

The term "glove box" refers to a system designed to contain materials, generally alpha radiation emitters, which present little or no external radiation hazard but which can present a serious problem if they become airborne. Glove boxes may be large and used in a wide variety of operations involving flammable liquids and gases, combustible solids, and toxic materials. The sides are fitted with long rubberlike gloves which permit manual operations to be conducted without personal contact with the hazardous materials. Special ventilation and fire protection systems are usually necessary. (See Figure 8-25B.)

FIG. 8-25B. A typical glove box showing gloves extending from the ports in the viewing window at left. Note the portable fire extinguisher adapted for discharge into the box through a fixed piping arrangement.

Hot Cells

A hot cell is a heavily shielded enclosure in which gamma-emitting radioactive materials can be handled by persons using remote manipulators while viewing the operation through shielded windows or periscopes. Hot cells are constructed preferably of noncombustible materials and contain the minimum amount of combustibles consistent with operational requirements.

In addition to all of the fire and explosion hazards of glove boxes, hot cells also present increased damage potential due to the nature of the high gamma ray producing materials used. The safeguards recommended for glove boxes apply equally to hot cells. Where very high gamma radiation levels are encountered, consideration must also be given to the possible failure of containers as a result of radiation damage.

RADIATION EXPOSURE

Radiation Injury

How radiation actually damages living cells is not exactly known. Unfortunately, the human body has no defense mechanism against radiation; nor can nuclear radiation be detected by any of the five senses. Thus, it is possible for an individual to receive a severe exposure to radiation without knowing it. This danger requires that some form of instrumentation be used to detect radioactivity.

The amount of injury to a person from radiation varies with the type of radiation, how much of the body has been exposed, and whether it is a one-time exposure or an accumulation of exposures to small amounts of radiation. Injuries from excessive exposures may not become apparent for days, weeks, months, or years.

Radiation experts report that, similar to many potentially hazardous materials, any exposure to radiation, either external or internal, has some element of risk, which may be too low to be measurable. Certain exposures are believed to be of reasonable risk balanced against the benefits from any activity using radiation exposure, such as medical and dental uses of radiation. Since the human race has evolved on a planet which has always been radioactive from the naturally occurring radioisotopes in the air, soil, and water, it is probable that a low "background" radiation is tolerable. The controversy on radiation exposure concerns the additional amounts that may be tolerated by humans. Standards have been set with the objective of lowering risks to the best practicable levels.

OCCUPATIONAL EXPOSURE FROM RADIATION IN AIR AND WATER

Radiological authorities having jurisdiction have set extremely low limits on concentrations of radioisotopes in air and water, based on quantities which may be inhaled or ingested. Complete treatment of the subject would require consideration of maximum permissible concentrations in both air and water, but the problem of airborne concentrations is of particular concern in fire situations, as fire fighters and other emergency personnel may be confronted with such material in the fumes, dust, smoke, and gases liberated by a fire in which radioactive materials are involved.

A hard-and-fast rule should be mandated that self-contained breathing apparatus (SCBA) is to be used whenever exposure to airborne radiation is a possibility. Maximum permissible concentrations (MPC) of various radioisotopes in air and water are commonly stated as limits intended to apply to persons who are continuously exposed to the concentrations named. Consequently, the concentrations are far below the exposures which could be tolerated for infrequent exposure, as would most often be the case with fire fighters or emergency workers.

Apparatus is available for taking a sample of an atmosphere. The number of radioactive emissions in the air can be counted with an appropriate counting instrument. From these counts, the extent to which the particular atmosphere is contaminated can be determined. (See Figure 8-25C.)

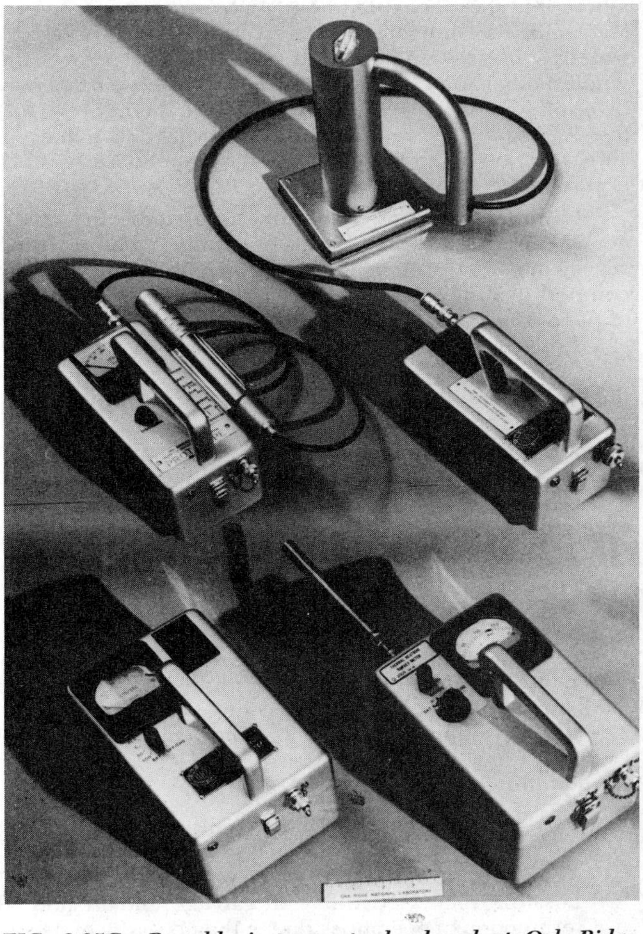

FIG. 8-25C. Portable instruments developed at Oak Ridge National Laboratory for measuring radioactive emissions. The meters are for fast neutrons (bottom row at left), thermal neutrons (bottom row at right), beta-gamma (top row left), and for alpha particles (top row right), with an alpha scintillation detector at the top of the picture.

Any space normally occupied by persons not primarily engaged in radiation work should not be subjected to unreasonable radiation levels; also a person outside the installation should not be subjected to excessive radiation level exposure through contact with radioactive waste or by other means. Air should be monitored continuously for the presence of radiation from fixed sources or from airborne radioactive matter. In emergencies, alarms should sound, and radiation levels be recorded by available commercial instruments.

Fire Department Radiation Exposures

Emergency exposures are usually allowed to exceed those tolerable to persons who work continuously with radioactive materials. In an emergency case, such as a necessary rescue operation, it is considered acceptable for the exposure to be raised, within limits, for single doses. The National Council on Radiation Protection and Measurement has recommended that in a life-saving action, such as search for and removal of injured persons or for entry to prevent conditions that would injure or kill numerous persons, the planned dose to the whole body should not exceed 100 rems. During less stressful circumstances, where it is still desirable to enter a hazardous area to protect facilities, eliminate further escape of effluents, or control fires, it is recommended that the planned dose to the whole body should not exceed 25 rems. These rules may be applied to the fire fighter for a single emergency; further exposure is not recommended. Internal radiation exposure may be guarded against by adequate respiratory equipment.

External exposure at the time of a single fire emergency can be judged by the use of commercial radiation survey meters which measure radiation in roentgens or by counted disintegration rates, or by the close observation of the dosimeter indicators carried by individuals. Pocket-sized dose rate alarms, which can be carried on the person, are also available. These give an audible signal dependent upon the radiation intensity. Film badges do not provide immediate information.

A rescue procedure that would combine external and internal radiation exposure is usually not attempted. Self-contained breathing apparatus should be used when instruments indicate the presence of any airborne radiation.

FIRE PROTECTION

As noted previously, substances and operations involving radioactive substances or devices presenting radiation hazards have the same fire and explosion features as those of similar materials and operations without radiation hazards. The loss caused by fire, explosion, and accident is affected by the presence of radiation or of radioactive substances in the following ways:

1. Possible interference with manual fire fighting due to the presence of harmful radiation or possible criticality of radiation levels.
2. Possible increased delay in salvage and in normal resumption of operations due to the necessity of decontamination of buildings, equipment, or materials.

Contamination of Property

Entire buildings, land, and important equipment can be rendered unusable for long periods of time because of severe radioactive contamination from the accidental escape of radioactive substances.

Radiological contamination may not stay in one area—it can sift through openings or ventilating systems in the form of dust or vapor, and spread the radioactive material throughout a structure. Careless movement of persons through a contaminated area could also spread contamination to an uncontaminated area.

Once a surface has become contaminated, a decision must be made as to how the particular contaminating material is to be removed, if this is possible. Vacuum cleaning can sometimes be used to remove radioactive dust from building surfaces. If vacuum cleaning is used, however, absolute filters must be used on the exhaust. Hosing with water can be used on some surfaces. Cleaning with soap and detergents is often a hand operation which must be carried out with continuous checks on the amount of exposure that may be tolerated by the persons doing the cleaning. Sand or vacuum blasting can be used on some surfaces, and paint may cover alpha contamination.

Plant Fire Protection Organization

In properties where atomic energy is a factor, an in-plant fire protection force is recommended. In nuclear reactors, and many other such plants, 24-hr/day routines must be maintained for handling fires and emergencies.

Plan for Handling Fires

In plants involving a nuclear reactor, radiation machines, and in other facilities handling radioactive materials, the problems affecting decisions on how best to deal with a fire or other emergency are not those types of problems that can be solved by simply calling the public fire department. As many decisions as possible must be made with respect to the types of fire or emergency to be expected—and these decisions must be made well in advance. The particular fire fighting and personnel safety measures to be taken may involve shutting down or isolating parts of the plant or individual equipment items. The areas where special procedures are necessary must be identified, and the procedures for these special areas thoroughly understood by all plant/facility personnel.

Fire emergency arrangements should include provisions for prompt notification of the plant emergency organization and public fire department, usually through a public fire alarm signal box. However, the plant fire protection department must preplan fire fighting operations with the local fire department so that the local department will be properly coordinated with the plant's own emergency plans. Emergency planning should include measures to prevent the spread of contamination and to promptly decontaminate the area in case of accidental release of radioactive substances.

Fire fighters and other emergency personnel operating in areas where radiation exposure is a danger must be fully trained and provided with suitable protective clothing. Respiratory protective equipment is a must, and competent radiological advisors, equipped with instruments for measuring area and local exposure, are necessary to guide emergency personnel. Dosimeters or other instruments for recording each individual's accumulated radiation exposure are helpful.

A nuclear reactor site must have a generous water supply to facilitate fire control and decontamination operations. Facilities must also be prearranged for safe disposal or storage of water that may be contaminated. The use of noncombustible materials for reactor buildings and equipment will help to avoid complications of fire hazards. For example, all finish materials used for decorative, acoustical, or insulation purposes should be both noncombustible and easy to decontaminate.

The hazard of a reactor structure exposing other buildings to radiation is prevented by appropriate distance separation or fire barriers. To prevent exposure to the reactor, it is always appropriate to separate shops and service spaces from the reactor equipment and structure itself. Wiring ducts in floors introduce an opportunity for the spread of fire or of contaminated liquid or gas from one space to another. Good duct seals separate one space from another. Subassembly or other operations in the preparation of fuel elements for reactors is carried on in work areas separated from the reactor in such a way that fire cannot reach the reactor space.

Equipment for Fighting Fires

Automatic sprinkler systems or specially designed piped water spray systems are the first choice for fire protection in any location where fires may occur in nuclear reactor plants, properties housing radiation machines, and facilities handling radioactive materials. Sprinklers can operate with full effectiveness under radiation or contamination conditions that would make approach by fire fighters impossible.

In spaces where water used in fire fighting would be subject to possible contamination, the collection and disposal of this water must be provided for in the local facilities; this means the facilities should have waterproofed floors and controlled floor drainage. Substantial capacity of such drainage systems would be required if hose streams and manual fire fighting were necessary. By contrast, sprinklers or a specially designed spray system would require relatively modest amounts of water for fire fighting.

If a fire occurs in a containment vessel during construction, the difficulties of access and visability warrant the provision of temporary fixed automatic extinguishing systems when combustibles cannot be effectively controlled. Temporary interior hose stations and an ample supply of portable extinguishing equipment should be within easy reach in all portions of the vessel. Because of the smoke confinement potential, only very fast manual response may be effective, hence the available manual fire fighting equipment should be in excess of normal construction practice to ensure the earliest response.

Incompatible Materials

Careful design analysis is required to reduce the fire protection problems inherent in the use of materials that are incompatible in fire situations. As an example, the contemplated use of liquid metal as a reactor coolant/moderator requires special extinguishing systems not compatible with water; in fact, the possibility of a water-liquid metal reaction may justify the exclusion of water systems from the area. If such a decision is made, however, it imposes severe limitations on the presence of flammable oils, plastics, foam insulations, and other materials that generally require copious quantities of water for fire extinguishment. Where such mixed hazards exist, it is imperative that careful consideration be given to the potentials for a failure in one system to cause a failure in the incompatible system. In such cases, either protection systems must be provided that can ensure the extinguishment of fire in either system before it can cause a rupture of the other system, or a single protection system (such as inerting) must be developed that is adequate for either hazard. The difficulties inherent in such problems warrant the most thorough hazards analysis at the earliest design stages.

BIBLIOGRAPHY

NFPA Codes, Standards, and Recommended Practices

Reference to the following NFPA codes, standards, and recommended practices will provide further information on the safeguards for nuclear facilities discussed in this chapter. (See the latest *NFPA Catalog* for availability of current editions of the following documents.)

NFPA 10, *Portable Fire Extinguishers.*

NFPA 72E, *Automatic Fire Detectors.*

NFPA 220, *Standard Types of Building Construction.*

NFPA 255, *Method of Test of Surface Burning Characteristics of Building Materials.*

NFPA 259, *Standard Test Method for Potential Heat of Building Materials.*

NFPA 480, *Storage, Handling, and Processing of Magnesium.*

NFPA 481, *Production, Processing, Handling, and Storage of Titanium.*

NFPA 482, *Production, Processing, Handling, and Storage of Zirconium.*

NFPA 801, *Facilities Handling Radioactive Materials.*

NFPA 802, *Nuclear Research Reactors.*

NFPA 803, *Fire Protection for Light Water Nuclear Power Plants.*

Additional Readings

Apostolakis, G., "Some Probabilistic Aspects of Fire Risk Analysis for Nuclear Power Plants," *Proceedings* of the First International Symposium for Fire Safety Science, Hemisphere, 1986, pp. 1039-1046.

Brandsjo, K., "Being There: A Firsthand Account of the Nuclear Accident at Chernobyl," *Fire Journal*, Vol. 82, No. 5, 1988, p. 67.

Chavez, J., "An Experimental Investigation of Internally Ignited Fires in Nuclear Power Plant Control Cabinets, Part I," NUREG/CR-4527/1 of 2, April 1987, Sandia National Labs, Albuquerque, NM.

Clarke, M. C., and Kememy, L. G., "Proposal for the Handling of Out of Control Supercritical Nuclear Reactors," *Chemical Engineering in Australia*, Vol. 12, No. 1, 1987, pp. 11-13.

Green, B. J., "Protection in a Nuclear Research Establishment," *Fire International*, Vol. 11, No. 105, 1987, pp. 24-26, 29.

Hosser, D., and Sprey, W., "A Probabilistic Method for Optimization of Fire Safety in Nuclear Power Plants," *Proceedings* of the First International Symposium for Fire Safety Science, Hemisphere, Washington DC, 1986, pp. 1047-1056.

Hosser, D., and Sprey, W., "Fire Hazard Analysis for Nuclear Power Plants," *Transactions* of the 8th International Conference on Structural Mechanics in Reactor Technology, Vol. M1-M2, North-Holland, 1985, pp. 385-390.

Kench, R. L., "Fire Safety in Atomic Power Plants," *Fire Prevention*, No. 207, 1988, pp. 32-37.

Kench, R. L., "Fire Safety in Nuclear Power Stations," *Fire Prevention*, No. 206, 1988, pp. 18-22.

Lalloo, R., "Fire Service Involvment with Nuclear Reactors," *Fire Engineers Journal*, Vol. 49, No. 154, Sept. 1989, pp. 17-21.

Lee, B. T., "Heat Release Charecteristics of Some Combustible Fuel Sources in Nuclear Power Plants," NBSIR 85-3195, 1985, Center for Fire Research, Gaithersberg, MD.

Mowrer, D. S., "Summary of Fire Protection Audits in Twenty Nuclear Power Plants," *Nuclear Plant Journal*, Vol. 7, No. 5, Sep.-Oct. 1989, pp. 82-84.

Nuclear Safety, (bimonthly), U.S. Government Printing Office, Washington, DC.

Purington, R. G., and Patterson, H. W., *Handling Radiation Emergencies*, NFPA, 1977.

Regan, J. D., "Design for Fire Protection," *Nuclear Engineering*, Vol. 28, No. 1, 1987, pp. 5-9.

Scotford, G. B, "For Protection for the Nuclear Industry," *Nuclear Engineer*, Vol. 27, No. 4, 1986, pp. 106-111.

Scotford, G. B., "Particular Problems for the Fire Service in the Nuclear Industry," *Fire Engineers Journal*, Vol. 46, No. 142, 1986, pp. 8-9.

Sedge, L. A., and Lakey, J. R. A., "Fire Training, Drills and Exercises in the Nuclear Industry," *Nuclear Engineering*, Vol. 28, No. 1, 1987, pp. 16-20.

Siu, N., and Apstolakis, G., "Methodology For Analyzing The Detection and Suppression of Fires in Nuclear Power Plants," *Nuclear Science and Engineering*, Vol. 94, No. 3, Nov., 1986, pp. 213-226.

Standards of the U.S. Nuclear Regulatory Commission, Code of Federal Regulations, Part 20, Chapter 1, Title 10, U.S. Government Printing Office, Washington, DC.

Vecchio, F. J., and Sato, J. A., "Drop, Fire and Thermal Testing of a Concrete Nuclear Fuel Container," *ACI Structural Journal*, Vol. 85, No. 4, Jul.-Aug. 1988, pp. 374-383.

MINING METHODS AND EQUIPMENT

William H. Pomroy

Mining is an industrial activity characterized by inherent and significant fire and explosion risks. At the turn of the century, mine fires and explosions resulted in loss of life and property damage on a scale unmatched in other industrial sectors. However, marked progress has been achieved in controlling these hazards, as evidenced by the decline in mine fires and explosions reported in recent years. The purpose of this chapter is to describe basic mining methods and equipment, fire and explosion hazards, and safeguards involved in the mining of coal, metal and nonmetal ores, sand and gravel, and stone.

Additional information relevant to mining processes and hazards can be found in the following chapters: Section 1, Chapter 5, "Explosions"; Section 2, Chapter 9, "Explosives and Blasting Agents"; Section 3, Chapter 12, "Dusts"; Section 2, Chapter 9, "Fluid Power Systems"; Section 2, Chapter 25, "Storage of Flammable and Combustible Liquids"; and Section 4, Chapter 6, "Gas and Vapor Testing."

Mining can be grouped into two broad categories: surface mining and underground mining. Surface mining requires the removal of the overlying dirt and rock strata, or overburden, before the desired minerals are excavated. Underground mining is practiced where the overburden thickness precludes surface mining. It permits the selective extraction of desired minerals, with minimal disturbance to the overlying strata.

The economics of large-scale production and mechanization strongly favor surface mining. Over 95 percent of all mine production is accomplished by surface methods.[1]

SURFACE MINING METHODS

Numerous surface mining methods have evolved in response to varying surface and subsurface geological conditions and in response to innovations in mining equipment.

Methods of surface coal mining, or strip mining, include area strip mining and various forms of contour mining.[2,3] Area strip mining is practiced where the terrain is relatively flat, and the coal seams are of moderate thickness [3 to 30 ft (0.9 to 9 m)]. It begins with the removal of overburden from above the coal seam in a roughly linear strip usually 100 to 170 ft (30 to 52 m) wide and up to several miles long. Overburden depths of 60 to 120 ft (18 to 37 m) are common. As coal is uncovered, it is loaded into trucks for haulage to storage or processing facilities. When an entire strip has been mined, the process is repeated, with the overburden above the adjoining strip of coal cast onto spoil piles in the cut previously mined. (See Figure 8-26A.) Specialized mining systems resembling metal and nonmetal open pit methods have been developed for multiple, steeply pitched, and/or thick seams.

Contour strip mining is most common where flat-lying coal seams occur in rolling or mountainous terrain. In contour mining, an initial cut is established along a hillside at the point where the coal seam outcrops, or is exposed. Successive cuts then are made into the hillside until an economic stripping limit is reached. Mining proceeds laterally along the hillside, following the outcrop. Contour mining follows the same drill-blast-strip-load-haul cycle as area strip mining, but the equipment employed is generally much smaller.

Most surface metal and nonmetal mining is by the open pit or open cast method.[4] The overburden is first stripped to expose the top of the ore body; stripping and mining then proceed concurrently. The pit expands in depth and area until an economic pit limit is reached. (See Figure 8-26B.) Pit geometries vary, owing to the irregular shape and orientation of ore bodies, but dimensions of ½ mile (0.8 km) to several miles across and 100 to over 1000 ft (30 to 305 m) deep are common.

Specialized mining systems have been developed for certain metal and nonmetal ore deposits. Examples include dragline stripping and hydraulic removal of phosphates, placer mining, and dredging of alluvial beach sands, gold, and tin. Sand and gravel generally are mined from shallow pits and small surface excavations, or with draglines and dredges from natural or artificial ponds.

William H. Pomroy is group supervisor, Mine Fire Safety Group, Twin Cities Research Center, Bureau of Mines, U.S. Department of the Interior.

FIG. 8-26A. Area strip mining.

FIG. 8-26B. Open pit mine.

Crushed stone and dimension stone are mined from rock quarries. Stone for crushed aggregate generally is mined by conventional open pit methods. Dimension stone is removed in large blocks using wire saws, channeling machines, or similar means.

Other than maintenance facilities, few fixed structures are involved in the surface mining process. Rather, surface mining is performed outdoors by specialized mobile and portable mining equipment. The major equipment types and their primary functions include blasthole drills to drill holes for explosives; stripping machines, such as draglines, stripping shovels, and bucketwheel excavators, for overburden removal; loading equipment, such as shovels, wheeled loaders, and hydraulic excavators, for loading overburden, coal, or ore at the working face; and haulage trucks, trains, or conveyors to transport materials from the working face to storage or processing facilities.[5]

A wide variety of miscellaneous equipment is required to support the mining process. This equipment includes scrapers, explosives haulers, dozers, graders, water trucks, pumps, power substations, generators, crushers, cranes, backhoes, and maintenance and utility vehicles.

UNDERGROUND MINING METHODS

Access to underground mine workings from the surface is by shaft, slope, or adit. A shaft is a vertical or nearly vertical opening, usually equipped with hoisting facilities for transporting personnel, supplies, and/or mined products. A slope — also called an incline or decline — is an inclined opening that may be designed to accommodate a belt conveyor for materials haulage, a hoist for personnel and supplies, or diesel trackless haulage. An adit mine, or drift mine, is entered through a horizontal opening in a hillside. An individual mine may employ any or all of these means of access, depending upon the depth and orientation of the coal seam or ore body and the requirements of the mine production system.

Where a single, uniform, relatively flat-lying coal seam or ore body is worked, the entire mine is generally confined to a single working level. Where multiple, irregularly shaped, and/or steeply inclined coal seams or ore bodies are worked, mining may be spread over many levels. Large mines may comprise hundreds of miles of drifts or entries, which are horizontal openings in metal or coal mines, respectively, on many levels and interconnected with shafts; slopes; raises, which are vertical openings between levels; and ramps, inclined openings between levels.

The predominant constraint influencing the selection of an underground mining method is the amount of support required to prevent the unwanted failure of the roof and/or walls. Factors related to this constraint are the physical character, size, shape, orientation, and depth of the coal seam or ore body, and the characteristics of the surrounding and overlying strata. In addition, planned production capacity and the presence of water, methane, rock temperatures, radon, or other environmental factors may be important considerations in selecting a mining method.

Operating practices vary widely, since nearly infinite variability exists among these factors from deposit to deposit and even within a single mine. However, the broad spectrum of underground mining methods can be effectively subdivided into three generic classifications. These are: (1) methods that produce openings that are naturally supporting or that require minimal artificial support, (2) methods that provide for substantial artificial support of the roof, and (3) caving methods, where failure of the roof is integral to the mining process.

With few exceptions, coal mining systems are profoundly different from noncoal mining systems, and they are treated separately in the following sections. Where similarities do exist, they are limited to the softer, bedded nonmetallics, such as potash, salt, and trona, which are amenable to coal mining systems and equipment.

Underground Coal Mining

The two basic coal mining methods are room-and-pillar, which produces openings that are naturally supporting, and longwall, which requires substantial artificial support.[2] As

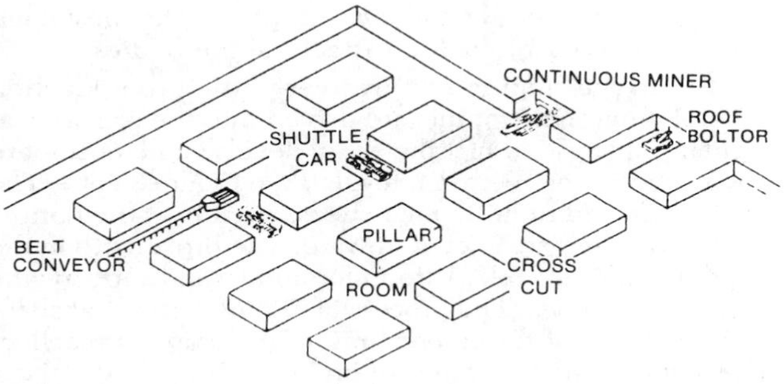

FIG. 8-26C. Room-and-pillar coal mining.

the name implies, room-and-pillar mining involves the extraction of coal in a regular pattern of rooms separated by pillars of in-place coal to support the roof. (See Figure 8-26C.)

Two systems are used for room-and-pillar coal mining: conventional and continuous. In conventional mining, the coal is extracted in a sequence of operations, and specialized equipment is required to execute each step. Using a cutting machine resembling a large chain saw, a slot is cut into the coal face the entire width of the room along the floor, center, or roof line. Next, a drill is used to bore holes for explosives in the coal face. Coal broken by the explosives is gathered by a loading machine, which either feeds a self-propelled shuttle car or may be loaded and hauled by a self-propelled scoop. In either case, the coal is discharged onto a conveyor belt or into rail cars for transport to the surface or to hoisting facilities.

In continuous mining, a single machine called a "continuous miner" is used to mechanically cut the coal from the face and load the broken coal into a shuttle car.

After each drill-blast-load cycle in conventional mining, or each machine advance in continuous mining, the mining equipment is withdrawn, and the roof is secured by a machine called a "roof bolter." Holes are drilled into the roof, and long bolts are inserted and anchored to strengthen the roof span and prevent roof failure.

Longwall mining involves the extraction of coal in a nearly continuous operation using a specialized and integrated mining and roof support system. (See Figure 8-26D.) Using standard room-and-pillar techniques, longwall panels 300 to 1000 ft (90 to 305 m) wide by 3000 to 6000 ft (915 to 1830 m) long are prepared. Each panel is mined in linear slices at full seam height by a mechanical cutting machine or plow that is drawn back and forth across the short face. As the coal is cut, it is forced onto a chain conveyor that extends the entire length of the face. The roof immediately adjacent to the face is supported by large, self-advancing hydraulic jack units. As the roof support line advances with the coal face, the roof behind it is permitted to cave.

Most coal mining equipment is electrically powered. Undercutting machines, drills, loading machines, continuous miners, shuttle cars, scoops, and roof bolters are generally supplied with power through a trailing cable. Belt conveyors generally are wired directly to a permanent or semipermanent power center, as is longwall equipment. Self-propelled rail-mounted equipment generally is supplied with power from an overhead trolley wire. Battery-powered scoops, personnel transports and utility vehicles are also common. Some mobile haulage equipment, notably scoops, load-haul-dump (LHD) vehicles (low-profile front-end loaders or scoop tram), and rail locomotives, can be diesel-powered. Though diesel usage is growing, it is not yet extensive in underground coal mining.

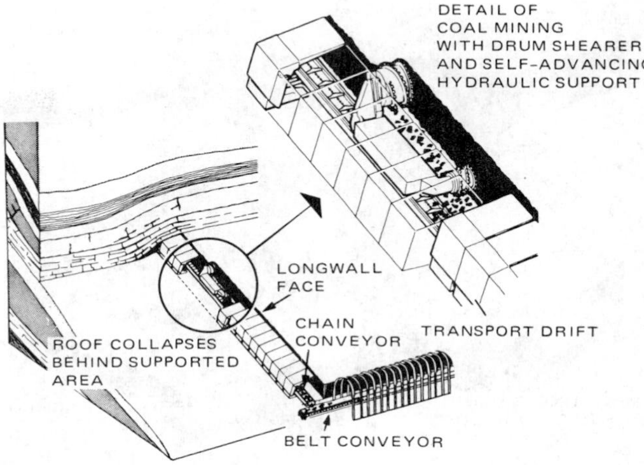

FIG. 8-26D. Longwall coal mining. (Source: Atlas Copco)

Numerous ancillary operations must be coordinated with the mining process. The main haulage network, whether rail or belt, must function smoothly to prevent materials-handling bottlenecks from interfering with production. The roof in active areas is constantly monitored for failures or signs of impending failure. In heavily traveled areas, such as main haulageways and important ventilation routes, heavy timbers or steel arches often are installed to help support the roof. Water supply, power distribution, and ventilation systems require periodic attention, and equipment and facilities inspection, maintenance, and repair are continuous. Dust control also receives high priority, both to protect the miners' health and to prevent explosive conditions.

Underground Metal and Nonmetal Mining

Underground metal and nonmetal mining methods are more diverse than underground coal mining methods because there is greater variability in the physical character, size, shape, and orientation of metal and nonmetal ore bodies than there is in most coal seams.[6, 7] Room-and-pillar and sublevel stoping methods are used where minimal artificial roof support is required in the extraction areas. Shrinkage stoping and cut-and-fill are used where the roof and walls in the extraction areas require substantial support. The two most common caving methods are sublevel caving and block caving.

The room-and-pillar method is used for relatively flat-lying deposits of moderate thickness with a competent roof. With the exception of the softer, bedded nonmetallics, metal and nonmetal mining is generally characterized by larger openings than those found in typical room-and-pillar coal operations, permitting the use of larger, more productive mining equipment. (See Figure 8-26E.)

Sublevel stoping, used in vertical or nearly vertical ore bodies of highly competent rock, requires considerable pre-mine development to prepare the ore body for production mining.

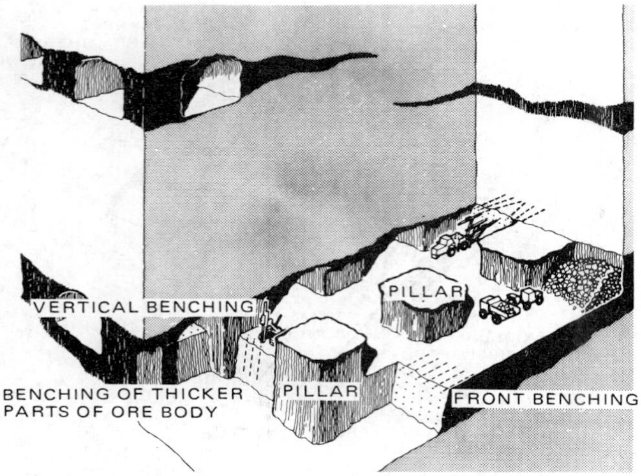

FIG. 8-26E. Room-and-pillar metal and nonmetal mining. (Source: Atlas Copco)

Sublevel drifts along the longitudinal centerline of the ore body are driven in a vertical column between the main levels of the mine. (See Figure 8-26F.) On the main haulage levels, drawpoints perpendicular to the sublevel drifts are driven into the ore body. A complete radial pattern of blastholes or parallel rows of vertical blastholes then are drilled at regular intervals along the entire length of each sublevel drift. Each ring or row of holes is loaded individually with explosives and blasted. Every blast results in a vertical slice of ore falling to the bottom of the open cavity, or stope, where it is loaded out through the drawpoints.

If the ore or surrounding rock is too weak or the rock pressures too great, open stopes are not feasible. Such ore bodies require artificial support of the stopes during mining. Shrinkage stoping and cut-and-fill are the most common methods employed to extract the ore bodies.

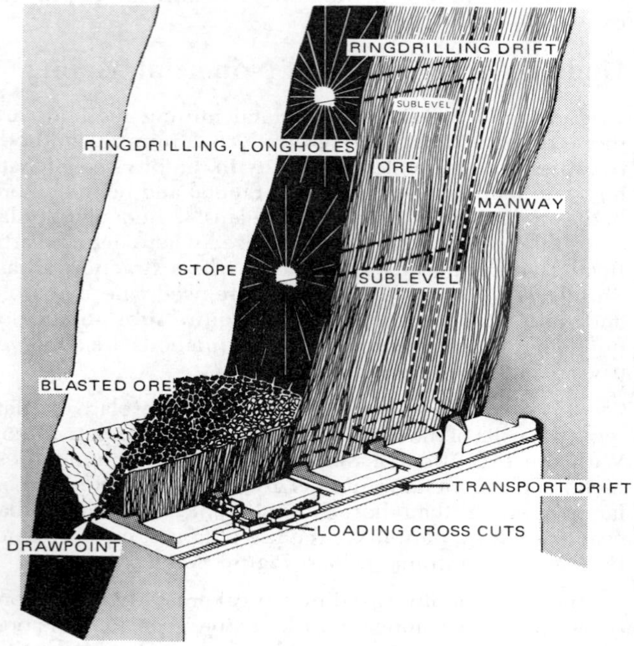

FIG. 8-26F. Sublevel stoping. (Source: Atlas Copco)

Shrinkage stoping requires very little preproduction development. Drawpoints are driven into the ore body at regular intervals along the main levels, and raises are driven into the ore between levels. (See Figure 8-26G.) The ore is extracted in horizontal slices, starting at the bottom of the stope and advancing upward. The broken ore in the stope provides a work platform for miners and supports the walls of the stopes. The process of mining horizontal slices is repeated until the upper limit of the stope is reached. The stope is then emptied of ore.

Preproduction development for cut-and-fill mining is similar to that for shrinkage stoping, except that only one or two drawpoints are required. (See Figure 8-26H.) Mining is similar as well, with the ore body mined in horizontal slices from bottom to top. However, the stope is emptied of broken ore after each slice, or cut, and the stope is filled with waste material before mining resumes. The fill provides a work platform for miners and supports the stope walls. Ore is removed from the stope through timber or steel ore chutes embedded in the fill.

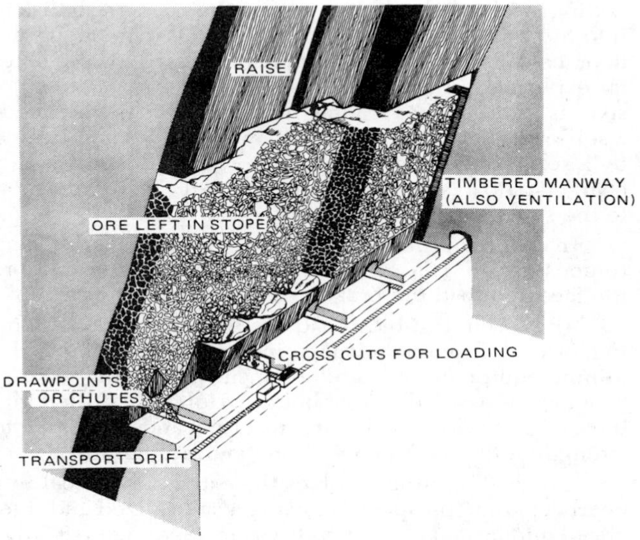

Fig. 8-26G. Shrinkage stoping. (Source: Atlas Copco)

Caving systems are characterized by a high degree of mechanization, high production capacity, and low production costs. In sublevel caving, preproduction development is similar to sublevel stoping, with sublevel drifts driven into the ore at 30- to 50-ft (9 to 15 m) intervals. (See Figure 8-26I.) Drawpoints on the main levels are not required, however, because the ore is retrieved through the sublevel drifts. Fan-shaped blasthole patterns are drilled upward at regular intervals along the entire length of each sublevel drift. The drill fans are blasted individually, with the broken ore caving into the sublevel drifts. LHDs are used to load the ore and transport it to the ore pass system.

The principle of block-cave mining is the natural fracturing and caving of ore that has been undercut over a large area. A minimum of drilling and blasting during the ore extraction phase is required, because the ore fractures itself as a result of gravity acting on the undercut rock masses.

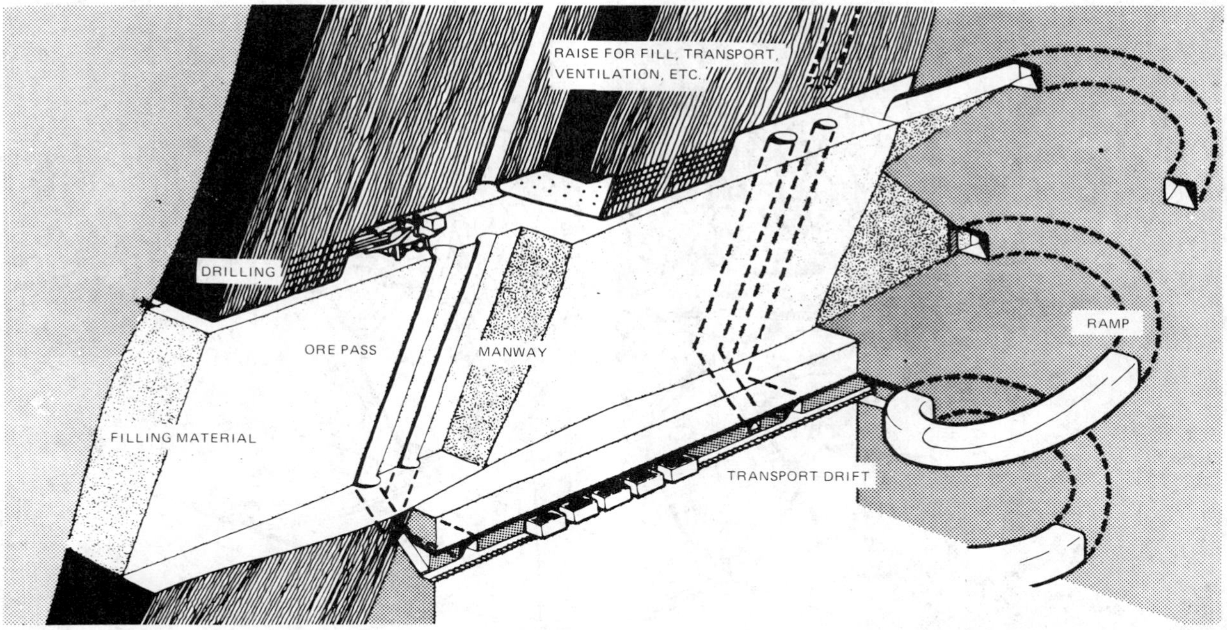

FIG. 8-26H. Cut-and-fill mining. (Source: Atlas Copco)

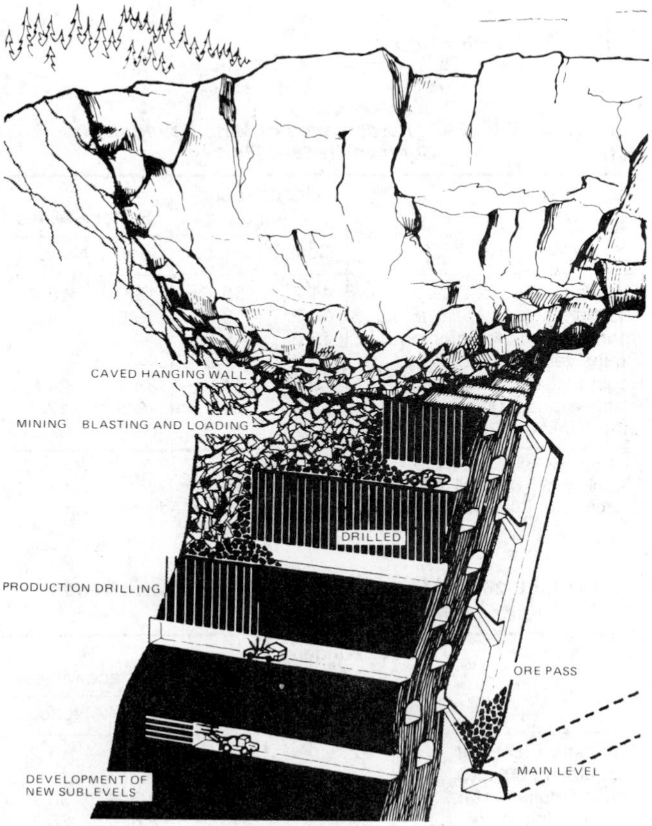

FIG. 8-26I. Sublevel caving. (Source: Atlas Copco)

Preproduction development is undertaken in five steps. (See Figure 8-26J.) First, a network of haulageways is developed beneath the ore horizon. Next, finger raises are driven up to a set of grizzly drifts. From the grizzly drifts, a second set of finger raises is driven, gradually widening to form funnels at the undercut level. Finally, the entire ore block is undercut.

The weight of the overlying ore and overburden creates enormous stresses in the ore at the bottom of the block, causing it to fracture and cave into the funnels.

A wide variety of equipment is used in underground metal and nonmetal mining. Where space permits, drilling is performed with mobile "drill jumbos" fitted with two or more rock drills. Diesel-powered LHDs are used to load and haul broken ore from the drawpoint or working face. Where space is limited, drilling is performed with small, portable, manually operated rock drills. Broken ore is loaded out by small pneumatic loading machines or by a scraper blade suspended on a cable between a hoist and a pulley, which gathers ore as it is dragged over a pile. Main haulage usually is completed by conveyor belt, rail, or haulage truck.

As with underground coal mining, the ore extraction process is supported by a vast array of ancillary operations. These operations include mining, mine development, and the maintenance of haulage equipment, which is performed at most mines in large, underground shops. Mines relying on diesel equipment also must have facilities in which to store and/or transfer diesel fuel. In addition, power distribution, ventilation, hoisting, roof control, and dewatering equipment require frequent inspection, maintenance, and repair.

THE FIRE AND EXPLOSION HAZARDS

Fires and explosions pose a constant threat to the safety of miners and to the productive capacity of mines. Mine fires and explosions historically have ranked among the

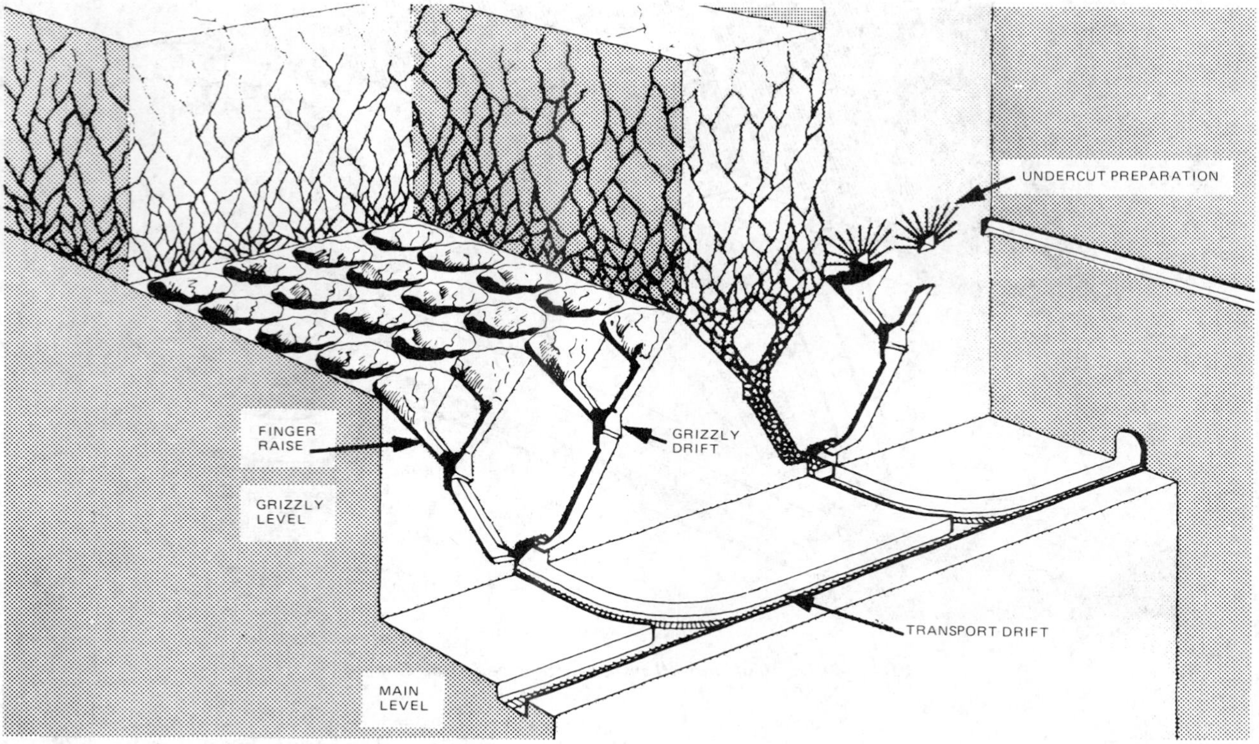

FIG. 8-26J. Block caving. (Source: Atlas Copco)

most devastating industrial disasters, with over 10,000 miners killed in coal mine explosions alone from 1880 to 1940.[8] The federal government agencies responsible for mine regulation maintain one of the best specialized data bases on fire and explosion incidents in any area of American society. That data base is used throughout this section.

Although more recent advances in mining and safety technology have reduced losses to a tiny fraction of their former levels, fires and explosions continue to occur, challenging the best efforts of mine safety, production, and engineering personnel to minimize losses. The major fire and explosion hazards in mining are discussed in the following subsections.

Mine Fire Hazards

During the 1960s and 1970s, about 50 fires per year were reported to federal mine safety authorities. Nonreportable fires, defined as those lasting less than 30 min and not resulting in an injury, were estimated at another 200 per year. In the mid-1970s, a steady decline in fire frequency was observed, probably due to the adoption of improved mining and safety technology, such as roof bolts for roof support, ac-powered face equipment in coal mines, and so on. Reported fires now average less than 20 per year.[9,10,11,12,13] This downward trend has begun to level off.

During 1968 to 1984, mine fires resulted in over 180 fatalities. Although about one-half of the fires occurred in surface mines, over 90 percent of the fatalities occurred in underground mines, where smoke and toxic fire gases are the primary life safety hazards. The major ignition sources, equipment, and burning substances involved in mine fires from 1968 through 1984 are listed in Tables 8-26A, 8-26B, and 8-26C, respectively.

TABLE 8-26A. ***Percentages of Mine Fire Ignition Sources (1968–1984)†***

	Underground Mines		Surface Mines	
	Coal	Noncoal	Coal*	Noncoal
Electrical	41.7	35.7	19.0	16.2
Friction	10.2	8.9	9.5	4.7
Spontaneous Combustion	12.2	8.3	—	—
Explosives	0.6	1.8	—	—
Engine Heat	0.3	14.9	38.1	24.6
Welding and Cutting	11.9	13.7	9.5	17.3
Other/Unknown	22.7	16.7	23.9	37.2

* Data for 1968–1979 only.
† Totals may not equal 100% due to rounding error.
Source: U.S. Bureau of Mines, Mine Safety and Health Administration.

TABLE 8-26B. ***Percentages of Equipment Involved in Mine Fires (1968–1984)†***

	Underground Mines		Surface Mines	
	Coal	Noncoal	Coal*	Noncoal
Stationary Electrical Equipment	22.6	14.9	23.9	5.2
Mobile Equipment	34.5	32.7	42.7	30.9
None or Unknown	30.1	38.1	6.8	38.7
Other Equipment	12.8	14.3	26.6	25.1

* Data for 1968–1979 only.
† Totals may not equal 100% due to rounding error.
Source: U.S. Bureau of Mines, Mine Safety and Health Administration.

TABLE 8-26C. ***Percentages of Burning Substances Involved in Mine Fires (1968–1984)†***

	Underground Mines		Surface Mines	
	Coal	Noncoal	Coal*	Noncoal
Electrical Insulation	25.2	19.6	23.8	8.6
Timber	7.5	25.7	—	—
Coal and Combustible Ore	31.6	1.7	—	—
Rubber	13.6	11.7	14.3	9.0
Explosives	0.3	0.4	—	—
Flammable and Combustible Liquids	13.9	22.6	60.9	42.5
Other/Unknown	7.8	18.3	1.0	35.7

* Data for 1968–1979 only.
† Totals may not equal 100% due to rounding error.
Source: U.S. Bureau of Mines, Mine Safety and Health Administration.

The largest category of fires in underground mines are those of electrical origin. During the 1960s and 1970s, about 40 percent of underground coal mine electrical fires involved face equipment powered through a trailing cable, and about half of those fires were caused by faults in the cable. Face equipment fires have been significantly reduced in recent years by the conversion from dc to ac power.

More fires start on mobile equipment than on any other equipment type. Such fires may be ignited by electrical faults, frictional heating or sparks, or hot engine surfaces. Combustible liquids, such as hydraulic fluids, diesel fuel, and lubricants, constitute the greatest hazard. However, wiring hoses, tires, and combustible refuse also are contributing hazards.

Fires on board large, surface-mining mobile equipment are also a serious hazard. (See Figure 8-26K.) Fires on diesel-powered equipment typically involve leaking high-pressure hydraulic lines, which spray a heated mist of highly combustible liquid onto an ignition source, such as a hot exhaust manifold or turbocharger. On shovels, blasthole drills, and draglines, faults in electrical equipment are the most frequent cause of fires.

FIG. 8-26K. Haulage truck fire.

Welding and cutting operations are also a leading cause of fires in mines and have been increasing in frequency in recent years. Welding and cutting operations are the primary cause of shaft fires in both coal and noncoal underground mines. The potential seriousness of shaft fires cannot be overemphasized, because fresh air to underground workings and safe mine evacuation may be impaired by a fire in a shaft.

Exothermic oxidation reactions occur in both coal and metal sulfide ores. When the heat generated by these reactions is not dissipated, the temperature of the rock mass or pile increases. If temperatures become high enough, rapid combustion of coal, sulfide minerals, and other combustibles can result.[14] Although spontaneous ignition fires occur relatively infrequently, they are generally quite disruptive to mine operations and difficult to extinguish. Spontaneous ignition fires often occur in remote, abandoned sectors of the mine where fire fighting access is difficult. Half of underground coal mine fires lasting more than 24 hours and 57 percent of noncoal fires lasting more than 24 hours are caused by spontaneous ignition.

Heat generated by friction between conveyor belt and conveyor drives or idlers were a leading cause of fires in underground coal mines until about 1970, when requirements for sequence and slippage switches became effective. Other frictional heat sources include overheated rubber tires and parking brakes on mobile equipment that are engaged during vehicle operation.

For many years, timbering was the most common means of providing both temporary and permanent support of underground openings. The extensive use of timber resulted in a large number of timber fires. Before 1967, over half of all underground metal and nonmetal mine fires involved timber. In recent years, the use of roof bolts has reduced significantly the need for timber underground. But older mines contain large amounts of timber from previous years, and timber still is used in varying amounts at most mines to supplement other means of roof control.

About one fire in fifteen in underground coal mines and one fire in four in underground noncoal mines involve timber. However, timber fires tend to constitute a greater overall hazard than these figures indicate, because timber fires spread more rapidly, burn longer, and are more difficult to extinguish than fires involving most other extraneous combustible materials. In underground noncoal mines, over 75 percent of the fires lasting longer than 24 hours involve burning wood.

The ultimate objective of underground coal mine fire protection efforts is to prevent the ignition of the coal. Equipment fires are generally limited by the amount of combustible material present. Once coal is ignited, however, the entire mine represents the available fuel supply. Over one-third of fires that involve coal as a burning substance last longer than 24 hours, with the average duration of 6 days.[10] Failure to extinguish a fire while it is developing results in a 50-percent chance that it will take more than 8 hours to bring it under control, and a 5-percent chance that part or all of the mine will be sealed.[15]

The storage, handling, and use of flammable and combustible liquids pose fire hazards for all sectors of the mining industry. In surface mines, flammable and combustible liquids are involved in more fires than any other combustible material. Most of these fires occur in mobile equipment. Hydraulic fluid at elevated temperature and pressure is a primary hazard.

In underground noncoal mines, the storage of flammable and combustible liquids is an important concern. Many mines store large quantities — up to 30,000 gal (113 m^3)

— of flammable and combustible liquids underground. The potential seriousness of a fire in an underground flammable and combustible liquid storage area has prompted extreme care in the design of the storage areas, plus the implementation and strict enforcement of safe operating procedures. As a result, few fires have been reported in such storage areas.

Mine Explosion Hazards

Over 100 mine explosions have occurred since 1968, most in underground coal mines, resulting in the deaths of nearly 200 miners.[16] Practically all coal mine explosions start with an ignition of methane. If the explosion propagates more than a few hundred feet, however, coal dust becomes the most important fuel source. In underground coal mines, methane explosions outnumber coal dust explosions by about six to one. Along with methane explosions in mines are methane ignitions, or explosions that do not result in fatalities, injuries, or damage to mine workings or equipment. Methane ignitions outnumber methane explosions by about seven to one.[8]

The high frequency of methane explosions and ignitions can be attributed to the small amount of methane necessary to produce an explosive mixture in air and to the low energy required to ignite a methane-air mixture. The lower explosive limit (LEL) for methane in air is 5 percent. As little as 0.3 millijoule of electrical energy can ignite methane under the proper conditions. This is the equivalent to $1/50$ of the static electricity accumulated by the average person walking across a carpeted floor on a dry day.

The LEL for a suspension of high-volatile bituminous coal dust in air is 0.05 oz per cu ft (0.28 g/m^3). The presence of methane in the atmosphere increases the hazard by producing a linear reduction in the LEL for coal dust. In the absence of methane, coal dust can be ignited by electrical or frictional sparks or by explosives, but the energy required for ignition is much higher if methane is not present. Coal dust explosions are generally triggered by methane ignitions. The flame provides the necessary ignition source, and the shock wave causes settled coal dust to become suspended in air.

The destructive potential of ignitions and explosions results from the high-temperature flame fronts and the static and dynamic pressures produced. Flame temperatures of 3600°F (1982°C) and static pressures in excess of 50 psig (345 kPa) are possible. Dynamic, or "wind" pressure is directional and depends upon the air velocity produced by the explosion, which, in turn, depends upon the static pressure.

Ignition sources of recent mine explosions and methane ignitions are shown in Table 8-26D.

Frictional sparking between rock surfaces and cutting bits, continuous miners, roof bolters, undercutters, face drills, and longwall equipment causes over 80 percent of the ignitions and explosions in underground coal mines. Other common sources of frictional sparking are drill steel striking machine frames, sandstone hitting sandstone or other hard rock during a roof failure, and mobile vehicle brake linings.[8]

Welding and cutting operations are the second leading cause of mine explosions and ignitions. In underground coal mines, the trend since 1970 has been toward increasing numbers of explosions and ignitions caused by welding and cutting operations.

TABLE 8-26D. ***Ignition Sources of Mine Explosions and Methane Ignitions (1970–1977)***

	Coal Mines			Noncoal Mines
	Underground		Surface	
	Explosions	Ignitions		
Friction	32	285	0	0
Welding	3	24	18	
Electric arc	7	13	10	26
Smoking	6	2	3	4
Open flame	0	0	1	10
Battery	2	1	0	1
Lightning	0	2	1	0
Explosives	4	8	2	0
Safety lamp	2	0	0	0
Other	0	0	5	0
Total	56	335	40	23

Source: U.S. Bureau of Mines, Mine Safety and Health Administration.

About 5 percent of underground coal mine ignitions and explosions result from electric arcs.[8] This figure is surprisingly low in view of the extensive use of electrical equipment in underground coal mine face areas and the low electrical energies required to ignite methane.

THE SAFEGUARDS

Fire and explosion safety in the mining industry is based on the general principles of fire and explosion prevention, early fire detection and warning, fire suppression, limiting fire propagation, and providing for miner safety during a fire. Implementation of these general principles is discussed in the following sections.

Mandatory regulations addressing fire protection for both surface and underground mines have been promulgated by most states and by the federal government.[17] In addition, many NFPA codes, standards, recommended practices, and guides are applicable to mining operations and may have been adopted by authorities having jurisdiction. The following should therefore be used for informational purposes only.

Fire Prevention

Fire prevention practices fall into three categories: limiting fuel sources, limiting ignition sources, and limiting fuel and ignition source contact.

Limiting fuel sources: Where there is sufficient frequency and/or severity of fires involving certain combustible materials, and where suitable and less hazardous substitutes for those materials are available, use of the less hazardous materials is preferred, or, in some cases, mandated by law. Examples of less hazardous materials include fire-resistive hydraulic fluids, conveyor belting, hydraulic hoses, and ventilation tubing, all of which are required in underground mines under certain conditions.[18] Even more basic is good housekeeping to prevent unsafe accumulations of trash, oily rags, coal dust, and other combustible materials.

Limiting ignition sources: Sources of fire that are not essential to the mining process can be banned altogether. Examples are prohibitions on open fires and on smoking in underground coal mines, and in certain areas of underground noncoal and surface mines. Means to prevent unwanted buildup of heat, such as the use of slippage and sequence switches on conveyors and of thermal cutouts on electric motors, are also common.

Limiting fuel and ignition source contact: Many combustible materials and potential ignition sources are essential to mining operations. Firesafety in these instances depends upon preventing contact between the ignition source and the fuel source. Certain precautions are observed during welding and cutting operations. When welding cannot be performed in firesafe enclosures, areas are wet down, and, if practical, nearby combustibles are covered with fire-resistive materials or relocated. Fire extinguishers must be readily available and a fire watch posted for as long as necessary to guard against smoldering fires. On mobile equipment, the hydraulic fluid, fuel, and lubricant lines can be rerouted away from hot surfaces, electrical equipment, and other possible ignition sources. Spray shields also can be installed to deflect sprays of combustible liquid from a broken fluid line away from a potential ignition source. Areas with a high loading of combustible materials, both underground and surface, such as timber storage areas, explosives magazines, flammable and combustible liquid storage areas, and shops, can be designed to minimize possible ignition sources. Potential sources of ignition, such as power substations, battery chargers, and electric motors, can be kept clear of extraneous combustible material.

Explosion Prevention

Explosion prevention practices fall into the same three categories as those for fire prevention: limiting fuel sources, limiting ignition sources, and limiting fuel and ignition source contact.

Limiting fuel sources: Coal dust and methane are the primary fuels involved in underground coal mine explosions. Methane also may be present in noncoal mines.[19] Although every attempt is made to minimize the generation of coal dust in mining processes, the tiny amount of dust sufficient to propagate a coal dust explosion will be present and is unavoidable. Indeed, a layer of dust on the floor just 0.005 in. (0.012 mm) thick, if suspended in air, will propagate an explosion; less is necessary if methane is present. When bituminous coal dust is properly mixed with an inert material, such as pulverized limestone, dolomite, or gypsum (rock dust), however, the resulting mixtures will not propagate an explosion.[8]

Methane is treated in two ways. Most commonly, it is diluted by ventilation air and exhausted from the mine. However, "degassification" in advance of mining may be practiced where unusually high levels of methane are encountered.[20, 21]

Limiting ignition sources: Every effort is made to eliminate extraneous ignition sources from the mining environment. Smoking is prohibited in coal mines, and electrical equipment operating where methane may be present must be "permissible" or "intrinsically" safe. Permissible electrical equipment is equipment that has been tested by the federal government and whose design, materials of construction, and installation will not cause a mine fire or explosion. Use of explosionproof enclosures, specially designed plugs and receptacles, automatic circuit-interrupting devices, and voltage limitations are typical. Intrinsically safe equipment is equipment that has been tested by the federal government and is incapable, under normal or abnormal conditions, of releasing sufficient electrical or thermal energy to ignite an explosive gas mixture. Some success has been achieved in reducing frictional sparking at the face by using slower bit rotation, novel bit designs and bit materials, and specially engineered water sprays.[22,23,24] Explosives and diesel-powered equipment must also be permissible.

Limiting fuel and ignition source contact: Because of geologic nonuniformity, varying mining rates, atmospheric pressure, and other factors, the liberation of methane into mine ventilation air from the workings is not uniform. In addition, methane and ventilation air may not mix completely and may form explosive pockets or layers, even though the average methane concentration is below the LEL. Thus, dilution and drainage of methane cannot be relied upon to produce nonexplosive atmospheres. A great deal of effort has been devoted to developing safer procedures for ventilating active coal mine working areas, both longwall and room-and-pillar, to minimize the occurrence of localized pockets of explosive methane/air mixtures.[25,26,27] Methane checks are made frequently with handheld and machine-mounted methanometers. If the methane level reaches or exceeds a predetermined point, all electrical equipment is shut down.

Early Fire Detection and Warning

The elapsed time between the onset of a fire and its detection is critical, because fires tend to grow in size and intensity with time. Early fire detection and warning permit the initiation of an emergency plan in the mine (evacuation, fire fighting, etc.) while the fire is still small or, ideally, while it is still in the incipient stage. Over 70 percent of fires detected within 15 minutes cause only light damage to a mine.[11] Advanced fire detection and warning systems using sensitive heat, flame, smoke, and gas analyzers provide the most rapid and reliable indication of fire.[28,29,30,31]

Thermal fire detection systems are commonly installed over conveyor belts, belt drives and takeups, and other unattended equipment. In localized, high-hazard areas, such as flammable and combustible liquids storage areas, refueling areas, and shops, faster-acting fire detection devices may be appropriate. Optical flame detectors, which sense either ultraviolet or infrared radiation emitted by a fire, have been used successfully.

Smoke and/or gas detection is the most cost-effective approach to providing large-area, or even whole-mine, fire detection coverage.[32,33,34,35,36,37,38,39] (See Figure 8-26L.) Instruments sampling the mine ventilation air streams can detect increases in particulates, or smoke, of less than one micrometer (1 μm) in size in concentrations as low as 1 mg/m^3 and of distinguishing diesel smoke from fire smoke.[39] Instrumentation also is available that is capable of detecting very small increases in combustion gases. Carbon monoxide (CO), for example, can be detected reliably at levels as low as 2 parts per million (ppm) with instruments intended for permanent underground installation.

Once a fire has been detected and the responsible mine officials notified, each miner must be warned of the fire. In coal mines, the most common means of fire warning are shutdown of electric power and/or notification by telephone and messengers. In noncoal mines, shutdown of electric power is generally ineffective because so little equipment is powered electrically. Telephone and messengers are used sometimes, but most miners are too remote from telephones and too widely scattered for either of these means to provide a timely warning. Stench warning is the most common method of emergency communication in noncoal underground mines.[40] Wireless radio-frequency communications systems have been used successfully in both coal and noncoal mines.[39]

FIG. 8-26L. ***Fire detection instruments in an underground mine.***

Fire Suppression

The most common types of fire suppression equipment used in underground coal mines are portable hand extinguishers, generally multi-purpose dry chemical; water hoselines and sprinkler systems; rock dust, applied manually or from a rock dusting machine; and foam generators. Fire suppression equipment in noncoal underground mines includes portable hand extinguishers and water hoselines. Fire suppression systems, either manual or automatic, are becoming more common for mobile equipment, combustible liquids storage areas, conveyor belt drives, and electrical installations.[39,41,42,43] (See Figure 8-26M.)

Fire protection requirements for underground coal mines are contained in NFPA 123, *Fire Prevention and Control in Underground Bituminous Coal Mines*. NFPA 122, *Storage of Flammable and Combustible Liquids Within Underground Metal and Non-Metal Mines (Other than Coal)*, covers requirements for the storage of flammable and combustible liquids within underground metal and nonmetal mines. Fire protection requirements for diesel equipment and diesel fuel in coal, metal, and nonmetal underground mines are covered in NFPA 124, *Underground Diesel Mining Equipment*.

Where large areas of coal or timber are burning and fire fighting is complicated by extensive roof falls, ventilation uncertainties, and accumulations of explosive gas, the only practical alternatives are inerting with nitrogen, carbon dioxide, or the combustion products of an inert gas generator; flooding; and/or sealing all or parts of the mine.[15]

All underground miners are trained to use basic fire fighting equipment. However, fires that grow to an advanced stage are fought only by highly trained and specially equipped fire fighting teams.

Mobile equipment is the primary fire hazard in surface mines. Consequently, most surface mining fire suppression equipment is specifically designed for maximum effectiveness on typical mobile equipment fires. Mobile equipment is commonly provided with one or more portable hand extinguishers. Manually or automatically actuated suppression systems may be installed for added

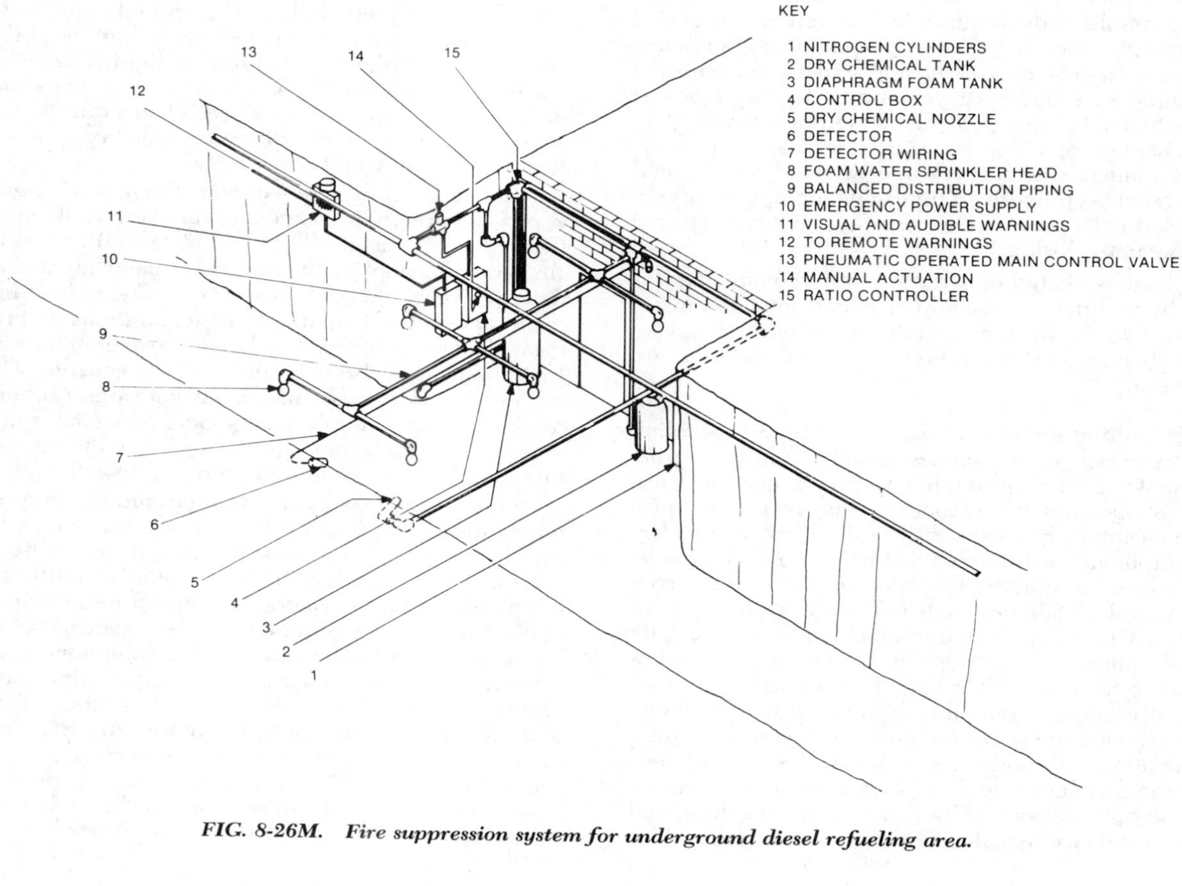

FIG. 8-26M. ***Fire suppression system for underground diesel refueling area.***

protection.[44,45,46,47] Fire protection requirements for such mining equipment are contained in NFPA 121, *Fire Protection for Mobile Surface Mining Equipment.*

Limiting Fire Propagation

Means for confining or limiting the rate of propagation of an underground mine fire can help ensure a safer mine evacuation and lessen the hazards of fire fighting. In undergound coal mines, oil and grease must be stored in closed, fire-resistant containers, and the storage areas must be of fire-resistant construction. Transformer stations, battery-charging stations, substations, shops, and other installations must be housed in fire-resistant areas or in fireproof structures. Unattended electrical equipment must be mounted on a noncombustible surface and separated from the coal or protected by a fire-suppression system. Materials for building bulkheads and seals, including wood, brattice cloth, saws, nails, hammers, plaster or cement, and rock dust, must be readily available to each working section. In underground noncoal mines, oil, grease, and diesel fuel must be stored in tightly sealed containers in fire-resistive areas at safe distances from explosives magazines, electrical installations, and shaft stations. Ventilation-control doors and fire doors are required in certain areas to prevent the spread of fire, smoke, and toxic gas.[48,49]

Providing for Miner Safety During a Fire Emergency

The primary concern during an underground fire is the safety of underground personnel. Because smoke and toxic fire gases represent the greatest threat, the mine ventilation system and its relationship to the various working areas, potential fires, primary and secondary escape routes, refuge chambers, and so on, are critically important. Detailed emergency planning must consider these factors. The use of computer models that simulate mine ventilation systems can be very helpful in developing and optimizing emergency plans and in designating escape routes. Particularly valuable are advanced models that calculate ventilation changes due to a mine fire — heat-induced buoyant forces causing throttling, reversals, and so on — and can track the distribution and concentration of contaminants.[39,50] To ensure smooth implementation of the emergency plan, miners are provided with comprehensive training and annual retraining in emergency procedures. Fire drills, complete with the activation of the mine warning system and the total evacuation of all mine personnel, are performed frequently to reinforce the training and to identify weaknesses in the emergency plan.

Although every attempt is made to avoid such situations, evacuating miners are sometimes required to travel through areas contaminated by smoke and toxic fire gases, so appropriate respiratory protection for all miners is required. In coal mines, self-contained breathing apparatus, supplying a minimum of 1 hr of oxygen, must be provided. In noncoal mines, 1-hr-rated self-rescue devices that convert carbon monoxide to carbon dioxide must be provided.

BIBLIOGRAPHY

References Cited

1. *Mineral Commodity Summaries,* U.S. Bureau of Mines, Washington, DC, 1983.
2. Cassidy, S. M., ed., *Elements of Practical Coal Mining,* Society of Mining Engineers of the American Institute of Mining, Metallurgical, and Petroleum Engineers, Inc., Port City Press, Baltimore, MD, 1983.
3. U.S. Bureau of Mines, "Economic Engineering Analysis of U.S. Surface Coal Mines and Effective Land Reclamation," *BuMines Contract Final Report S0241049,* 1975, Skelly and Loy, Engineers-Consultants.
4. Pfleider, E. P., ed., *Surface Mining,* Society of Mining Engineers of the American Institute of Mining, Metallurgical, and Petroleum Engineers, Inc., Maple Press, York, PA, 1969.
5. Martin, J. W., Martin, T. J., Bennett, T. P., and Martin, K. M., *Surface Mining Equipment,* Martin Consultants Inc., Golden, CO, 1982.
6. Cummins, A. B. and Given, I. A., *eds., Mining Engineering Handbook,* Society of Mining Engineers of the American Institute of Mining, Metallurgical, and Petroleum Engineers, Inc., Port City Press, Baltimore, MD, 1973.
7. Hustrulid, W. A., *Underground Mining Methods Handbook,* Society of Mining Engineers of the American Institute of Mining, Metallurgical, and Petroleum Engineers, Inc., Port City Press, Baltimore, MD, 1982.
8. Nagy, J., "The Explosion Hazard in Mining," *U.S. Mine Safety and Health Administration Informational Report 1119,* Washington, DC, 1981.
9. Baker, R. M., Nagy, J., and McDonald, L. B., "An Annotated Bibliography of Metal and Nonmetal Mine Fire Reports," *Contract Final Report J0295035,* U.S. Bureau of Mines, Washington, DC, 1980.
10. McDonald, L. B. and Baker, R. M., "An Annotated Bibliography of Coal Mine Fire Reports," *Contract Final Report J0275008,* U.S. Bureau of Mines, Washington, DC, 1979.
11. McDonald L. B. and Pomroy, W. H., "A Statistical Analysis of Coal Mine Fire Incidents in the United States from 1950 to 1977," *Information Circular 8830,* U.S. Bureau of Mines, Washington, DC, 1980.
12. Stephan, C. R., "Summary of Underground Coal Mine Fires, Jan. 1, 1978 to July 31, 1986," *Bruceton Safety Technology Center Report No. 06-357-86,* U.S. Mine Safety and Health Administration, Washington, DC, 1986.
13. Butani, S. J. and Pomroy, W. H., "A Statistical Analysis of Metal and Nonmetal Mine Fire Incidents in the United States from 1950 to 1984," *Information Circular 9132,* U.S. Bureau of Mines, Washington, DC, 1987.
14. Ninteman, D. J., "Spontaneous Oxidation and Combustion of Sulfide Ores in Underground Mines," *Information Circular 8775,* U.S. Bureau of Mines, Washington, DC, 1978.
15. Mitchell, D. W. and Burns, F. A., "Interpreting the State of a Mine Fire," *U.S. Mine Safety and Health Administration Informational Report 103,* Washington, DC, 1979.
16. Richmond, J. K., Price, G. C., Sapko, M. J., and Kawenski, E. M., "Historical Summary of Coal Mine Explosions in the United States 1959-81," *Information Circular 8909,* U.S. Bureau of Mines, Washington, DC, 1983.
17. Office of the Federal Register, *Code of Federal Regulations,* Title 30, Mineral Industries, Chapter I, Mine Safety and Health Administration, U.S. Government Printing Office, National Archives and Records Administration, Washington, DC, 1987.
18. "Coal Mine Fire and Explosion Prevention," *Information Circular 8768,* U.S. Bureau of Mines, Washington, DC, 1978.
19. Thimons, E. D., Vinson, R. P., and Kissell, F. N., "Forecasting Methane Hazards in Metal and Nonmetal Mines," *Report of Investigations 8392,* U.S. Bureau of Mines, Washington, DC, 1979.
20. Hartman, H. L., Mutmansky, J. M., and Wang, Y. J., *Mine Ventilation and Air Conditioning,* John Wiley & Sons, NY, 1982.
21. Duel, M. and Kim, A. G., "Methane Control Research: Summary of Results, 1964-1980," *U.S. Bureau of Mines Bulletin 687,* U.S. Bureau of Mines, Washington, DC, 1988.

22. Agbde, R. O., Whitehead, K. L., Mundell, R. L., and Saltsman, R. D., "Frictional Ignition Suppression by the Use of Cutter Drum Mounted Sprays," Bituminous Coal Research Inc. *Contract Final Report J0395040*, U.S. Bureau of Mines, Washington, DC, 1982.

23. Hanson, B. D., "Cutting Parameters Affecting the Ignition Potential of Conical Bits," *BuMines RI 8820*, U.S. Bureau of Mines, Washington, DC, 1983.

24. Roepke, W. W. and Hanson, B. D., "Bit Ignition Potential with Worn Carbide Tips," *TPR 121*, U.S. Bureau of Mines, Washington, DC, 1983.

25. Cecala, A. B., Rajan, S. R., and Jankowski, R. A., "Cut Longwall Ignitions by Lowering Methane Concentrations Around Longwall Shearers," *Coal Age*, Vol. 91, No. 8, 1986, pp. 66-67.

26. Cecala, A. B., Organiscak, J. A., and Jankowski, R. A., "Improving Dust and Methane Control" *Coal Mining*, Vol. 24, No. 10, 1987, pp. 51-52.

27. Divers, E. F. and Volkwein, J. C., "Guidelines for Choosing Face Ventilation Systems," *Coal Mining*, Vol. 24, No. 10, 1987, pp. 46-59.

28. Griffin, R. E., "In-Mine Evaluation of Underground Fire and Smoke Detectors," *Information Circular 8808*, U.S. Bureau of Mines, Washington, DC, 1979.

29. Kacmar, R. M., "Reliability of Computerized Mine-Monitoring Systems," *Information Circular 8882*, U.S. Bureau of Mines, Washington, DC, 1982.

30. Johnson, G. A. and Forshey, D. R., "In-Mine Tests of Mine Shaft Fire and Smoke Protection Systems," *Information Circular 8788*, U.S. Bureau of Mines, Washington, DC, 1978.

31. Welsh, J. H., "Computerized, Remote Monitoring Systems for Underground Coal Mines — Fires and Explosive Atmospheres," *Information Circular 8875*, U.S. Bureau of Mines, Washington, DC, 1982.

32. Hertzberg, M. and Litton, C. D., "Multipoint Detection of Products of Combustion with Tube Bundles," *BuMines RI 8171*, U.S. Bureau of Mines, Washington, DC, 1976.

33. Litton, C. D., "Guidelines for Siting Product-of-Combustion Fire Sensors in Underground Mines," *Information Circular 8919*, U.S. Bureau of Mines, Washington, DC, 1983.

34. Litton, C. D., "Design Criteria for Rapid Response Pneumatic Monitoring Systems," *Information Circular 8912*, U.S. Bureau of Mines, Washington, DC, 1983.

35. Stevens, R. B., "Mine Shaft Fire and Smoke Protection Systems," FMRC Corp. BuMines *Contract Final Report H0242016*, U.S. Bureau of Mines, Washington, DC, 1975.

36. Thomas, E. C., "A Pneumatic Sampling Fire Detection System in an Underground Haulageway," *IEEE Transcript on Industry Applications*, Vol. IA-19, No. 3 (May/June 1983).

37. U.S. Bureau of Mines, "Underground Metal and Nonmetal Mine Fire Protection," *Information Circular 8865*, U.S. Bureau of Mines, Washington, DC, 1981.

38. "Metal Mine Fire Protection Research," *Information Circular 8752*, U.S. Bureau of Mines, Washington, DC, 1977.

39. "Recent Developments in Metal and Nonmetal Mine Fire Protection," *Information Circular 9206*, U.S. Bureau of Mines, Washington, DC, 1988.

40. Pomroy, W. H. and Muldoon, T. L., *A New Stench Gas Fire Warning System*, Mines Accident Prevention Association of Ontario, North Bay Ontario, Canada, 1983.

41. Johnson, G. A., "Automatic Fire Protection for Mobile Underground Mining Equipment," *Information Circular 8954*, U.S. Bureau of Mines, Washington, DC, 1983.

42. "Automatic Fire Protection Systems for Underground Fueling Areas," *U.S. Bureau of Mines Technology News 160*, U.S. Bureau of Mines, Washington, DC, 1982.

43. Pomroy, W. H. and Johnson, G. A., "Improved Fire Protection for Underground Fuel Storage and Fuel Transfer Areas," *Information Circular 9032*, U.S. Bureau of Mines, Washington, DC, 1985.

44. Johnson, G. A. and Forshey, D. R., "Automatic Fire Protection Systems for Large Haulage Vehicles," *Information Circular 8683*, U.S. Bureau of Mines, Washington, DC, 1975.

45. Pomroy, W. H., Goodwin, N., and Lynch, F., "Economic Analysis of Surface Mining Mobile Equipment Fire Protection Systems," *Report of Investigations 8698*, U.S. Bureau of Mines, Washington, DC, 1982.

46. Pomroy, W. H. and Bickel, K. L., "Automatic Fire Protection Systems for Surface Mining Equipment," *Information Circular 8832*, U.S. Bureau of Mines, Washington, DC, 1980.

47. "Dragline Fire Protection," *U.S. Bureau of Mines Technology News 106*, U.S. Bureau of Mines, Washington, DC, 1981.

48. "Improved Fire Doors for Noncoal Underground Mines," *U.S. Bureau of Mines Technology News 188*, U.S. Bureau of Mines, Washington, DC, 1983.

49. Bickel, K. L. and Pomroy, W. H., "Fire Doors for Noncoal Mines," *Information Circular 9165*, U.S. Bureau of Mines, Washington, DC, 1987.

50. Edwards, J. C. and Greuer, R. E., "Real-Time Calculation of Product-of-Combustion Spread in a Multilevel Mine," *Information Circular 8901*, U.S. Bureau of Mines, Washington, DC, 1982.

NFPA Codes, Standards, and Recommended Practices

Reference to the following NFPA codes, standards, and recommended practices will provide further information on mining methods and equipment discussed in this chapter. (See the latest *NFPA Catalog* for availability of current editions of the following documents.)

NFPA 10, *Portable Fire Extinguishers*.

NFPA 11A, *Medium and High Expansion Foam Systems*.

NFPA 12A, *Halon 1301 Fire Extinguishing Systems*.

NFPA 12B, *Halon 1211 Fire Extinguishing Systems*.

NFPA 13, *Installation of Sprinkler Systems*.

NFPA 17, *Dry Chemical Extinguishing Systems*.

NFPA 30, *Flammable and Combustible Liquids Code*.

NFPA 51, *Oxygen-Fuel Gas Systems for Welding, Cutting, and Allied Processes*.

NFPA 51B, *Cutting and Welding Processes*.

NFPA 70®, *National Electrical Code*®.

NFPA 120, *Coal Preparation Plants*.

NFPA 121, *Fire Protection for Mobile Surface Mining Equipment*.

NFPA 122, *Storage of Flammable and Combustible Liquids Within Underground Metal and Non-Metal Mines (Other than Coal)*.

NFPA 123, *Fire Prevention and Control in Underground Bituminous Coal Mines*.

NFPA 124, *Underground Diesel Mining Equipment*.

Additional Reading

Ayres, D. J., "Treatment of Shallow Underground Fires," *Proceedings* of the Symposium on Failures in Earthworks, Thomas Telford, London, 1986, pp. 470-472.

Banerjee, S. C. and Acharya, A. K., "High Expansion Foams--Its Use in Mine Fires," *Journal of Mines, Metals and Fuels*, Vol. 34, No. 10, 1986, pp. 448-451.

Banerjee, S. C., *et al.*, "Approach to Assessing the Status of Sealed-off Fires by Examination of Fire Indices," *Mining Science and Technology*, Vol. 10, No. 1 (Jan. 1990), pp. 37-51.

Bickel, K. L., "Analysis of Fires on Diesel-Powered Mine Equipment," *Proceedings* of the Bureau of Mines Technology Transfer Seminar, Diesels in Underground Mines, U.S. Bureau of Mines, Information Circular 9141, 1987, pp. 9-17.

Burton, R. C., *et al.*, "Automatic Fire Detection Underground," *Colliery Guardian*, Vol. 235, No. 5, 1987, pp. 166, 168.

Chaudhari, P. D., "Reducing the Risk of Accidents in the Mining Industry by Use of Automatic Fire Protection Systems on Mining Equipment," *Journal of Mines, Metals and Fuels*, Vol. 63, No. 9 (Sept. 1988), pp. 442-447.

"Coal Mine Fire and Explosion Prevention," *Proceedings*: U.S. Bureau of Mines Technology Transfer Seminar, U.S. Bureau of Mines, Washington, DC, 1978.

Cheng, L., *et al.*, "Novel Coal-Cutting Bits and Their Wear Resistances, U.S. Bureau of Mines," *Report of Investigations 8791*, Washington, DC, 1983.

Cybulski, W., *Coal Dust Explosions and Their Suppression*, (translated from the Polish), National Technical Information Service, Springfield, VA, 1975.

De Rosa, M. I. and Litton, C. D., "Determining the Relative Toxicity and Smoke Obscuration of Combustion Products of Mine Combustibles," *Report of Investigation No. 9274*, United States Bureau of Mines, Pittsburgh, PA, 1989.

De Rosa, M. I. and Litton, C. D., "Primary Gas Toxicities and Smoke Particle Characteristics During Combustion of Mine Brattices," *Report of Investigations No. 9262*, United States Bureau of Mines, Pittsburgh, PA, 1989.

Engel, W. and Kihl, H., "Flame-Resistant and Non-Noxious HFD Hydraulic Fluids for Mining," *Glueckauf and Translation*, Vol. 123, No. 22 (Nov. 19, 1987), pp. 625-628.

Gall, P., "Safety Research for the Coal Mining Industry Develops Advanced Systems," *Australian Mining*, Vol. 81, No. 6 (June 1989).

Greuer, R. E., "Modeling the Movement of Smoke and the Effect of Ventilation Systems in Mine Shaft Fires," *Fire Safety Journal*, Vol. 9, No. 1, 1985, pp. 81-88.

Hertzberg, M., *A Critique of the Dust Explosibility Index*, U.S. Department of the Interior, Bureau of Mines, Pittsburgh, PA, 1987.

Hertzberg, M., *et al.*, "Inhibition and Extinction of Coal Dust and Methane Explosions," *Report of Investigations 8708*, U.S. Bureau of Mines, Washington, DC, 1982.

Hjelmstad, K. E. and Pomroy, W. H., "Novel Fire Warning System for Underground Mines," *Mining Engineering*, Vol. 42, No. 1 (Jan. 1990), pp. 107-112.

Huntley, D. W., *et al.*, "Underground Coal Mine Fire, Wilberg Mine," I.D. No.42-00080, Emery Mining Corporation, Orangeville, Emery County, Utah, U.S Department of Labor, Mine Safety and Health Administration, 1987.

Kuchta, J. M., *et al.*, "Diagnostics of Sealed Coal Mine Fires," *Report of Investigations 8625*, U.S. Bureau of Mines, Washington, DC, 1982.

Kuchta, J. M., *Investigation of Fire and Explosion Accidents in the Chemical, Mining, and Fuel Related Industries: A Manual*, U.S. Department of Interior, Bureau of Mines, Pittsburgh, PA, 1986.

Kuchta, J. M., Rowe, V. R., and Burgess, D. S., "Spontaneous Combustion Susceptibility of U.S. Coals," *Report of Investigations 8474*, U.S. Bureau of Mines, Washington, DC, 1980.

Liebman, I. and Richmond, J. K., "Suppression of Coal Dust Explosions by Water Barriers in a Conveyor Belt Entry," *Report of Investigations 8538*, U.S. Bureau of Mines, Washington, DC, 1981.

Liebman, I., *et al.*, "Extinguishing Agents for Mine Face Gas Explosions," *Report of Investigations 8294*, U.S. Bureau of Mines, Washington, DC, 1978.

Litton, C. D., "Fire Detectors in Underground Mines," *Information Circular 8786*, U.S. Bureau of Mines, Washington, DC, 1979.

Morris, R. and Badenhorst, G. P., "Analysis of Underground Fires in South African Coal Mines from 1970-1985," *Journal of the Mine Ventilation Society of South Africa*, Vol. 40, No. 10, 1987, pp. 134-139.

Nelson, H. E., "A Qualitative Analysis of the Inherent Fire Safety/Fire Risk in a Coal Mine," *NBSIR 86-3502*, National Bureau of Standards, Gaithersburg, MD, Dec. 1986.

Ng, D. and Lazzara, C. P., "Performance of Concrete Block and Steel Panel Stoppings in a Simulated Mine Fire," *Fire Technology*, Vol. 26, No. 1 (Feb. 1990), pp. 51-76.

Pomroy, W. H., "Spontaneous Combustion Fire Detection for Deep Metal Mines," *Report 9144*, U.S. Bureau of Mines, Minneapolis, MN, 1987.

Ramaswamy, A. and Katiyar, P. S., "Experiences with Liquid Nitrogen in Combating Coal Fires Underground," *Journal of Mines, Metals and Fuels*, Vol. 36, No. 9 (Sept. 1988), pp. 415-424.

Sapko, M. J., "Fire Resistance Test Method for Conveyor Belts," *Report of Investigations 8521*, U.S. Bureau of Mines, Washington, DC, 1981.

Schenkel, W. K., "Flame Resistant Conveyor Belts Reinforced with Kevlar for Underground Coal Mining," *Proceedings* from the International Conference on Fire Resistant Hose, Cables and Belting, Plastics and Rubber Inst., London, 1986, pp. 1-17.

Schibe, J. A., "The Development of a Fire Evaluation System for Underground Coal Mines," *NBSIR 86-3425*, National Bureau of Standards, Gaithersburg, MD, Aug. 1986.

Sinha, A. K., Rajwar, D. P., and Ghosh, A. K., "Underground Fire Hazard Detection through Carbon-Monoxide Monitors," *Journal of Mines, Metals and Fuels*, Vol. 35, No. 8 (Aug. 1987), pp. 365-367.

Stewart, B. A., "Development of a Fire Protection Consensus Standard in the Mining Industry," *Proceedings* of the Earthmoving Industry Conference, SAE, 1987, 5p.

Timko, R. J., Derick, R. L., and Thimons, E. D., "Analysis of a Fire in a Colorado Coal Mine — A Case Study," *Proceedings* of the 3rd Mine Ventilation Symposium, Society of Mining Engineers of AIME, Littleton, CO, 1987, pp. 444-452.

von Velsen-Zerweck, R., "Ways of Improving Fire and Explosion Protection in Underground Coalmining," *Glueckauf and Translation*, Vol. 124, No. 3 (Feb. 4, 1988), p. 76.

Watson, R. W., "Prevention of Frictional Ignition on Longwall Sections," *Journal of Mines, Metals and Fuels*, Vol. 37, No. 6-7 (Jun.-Jul. 1989), pp. 261-265.

Zhao, Y., Yang, G., and Wang, X., "Investigation of the Dynamic Process in the Ventilation Network During Underground Fire," *Archiwum Gornictwa*, Vol. 34, No. 3, 1989, pp. 503-515.

OCCUPANCIES IN SPECIAL STRUCTURES AND HIGH-RISE BUILDINGS

Revised by Roger Boyce, Sr.

This chapter is intended to give a brief overview of the relevant issues and features of fire protection for: (1) special structures and high-rise buildings as addressed in *NFPA 101,® Life Safety Code* Chapter 30, and (2) traditional occupancies that are located in special or unusual structures.

Special structures, as defined in NFPA 101, *Life Safety Code*, include towers, vehicles, vessels, underground structures, windowless structures, water-surrounded structures, open structures, and high-rise buildings. Piers are included in the definition of a special structure, but are subject to the specific requirements of NFPA 307, *Marine Terminals, Piers and Wharves*.

Conventional occupancies are often located in special structures that are not normally designed for that occupancy classification. As a result, the terms "unusual occupancy" and "special structure" could both apply to the same situation. Common examples of unusual occupancies in special structures would be:

1. A restaurant located on top of a tower (assembly occupancy).
2. A specialty retail shop located in a fixed railroad car, boat, or airplane (mercantile occupancy).
3. A residential occupancy located in a lighthouse tower.

In the 1988 edition of NFPA 101, *Life Safety Code*, the title of Chapter 30 was changed from "Chapter 30, Occupancies in Unusual Structures," to "Chapter 30, Special Structures and High-Rise Buildings." This change was intended to reflect the fact that the issue considered in this chapter is the structure, as opposed to its impact upon more traditional occupancies. Chapter 30 defines and places specific requirements upon the listed special structures. The code also recognizes that these structures are sometimes used for unusual purposes and, as a result, may require special considerations. It must be remembered that an "unusual use" of a "special structure" still must meet the requirements that would otherwise apply to that occupancy as regulated by NFPA 101, Chapters 8 through 29, in addition to the "special structure" requirements.

Roger Boyce is president of Systems Approach Ltd., a fire protection consulting company located in Newcastle, DE.

In addition, Chapter 30 of NFPA 101, *Life Safety Code*, covers high-rise buildings. Although these structures are not unusual, they are special due to their height and resulting requirements for fire protection.

Occupancy Characteristics

Occasionally, an owner chooses to locate a place of business in a structure that is not normally used for that traditional line of business. The uniqueness of the structure could be used to attract customers and provide a competitive edge. While perhaps giving an owner a competitive edge, the structure can also create difficult life safety problems not found in more traditional structures.

NFPA 101, *Life Safety Code*, details provisions for each individual occupancy class which provide the minimum code requirements for those occupancies when they are located in special structures. It is important to note that placing an occupancy in a special structure does not justify reducing the minimum code standards for the given occupancy classification. Designers and code officials must ensure that the structure meets the traditional occupancy requirements, as well as the requirements found in NFPA 101.

It is noted that the development of an occupancy in a special structure is limited only by the owner's and designer's imaginations. As a result, it is impossible for a model code such as NFPA 101, *Life Safety Code*, to anticipate precisely all of the conditions and hazards that such a design could create. It is incumbent upon building owners, on designers, and on code officials to include those additional (beyond the code) life safety features that may be deemed necessary due to the uniqueness of the special structure and to the atypical life safety problems that it may create. This can only be done using sound design and engineering judgment, common sense, and cooperation between the designers and code officials.

Ignition Sources

A special structure may cause additional ignition sources to be considered, in addition to those that are normally considered for the occupancy. Once the basic occupancy classification—that is, business, assembly, educational, and so on—has been determined, many of the ignition sources will be typical for that occupancy class. One also must consider the unique features of the structure and determine what additional ignition sources may have to be considered. For example, an assembly occupancy located on top of a tower may be more susceptible to lightning as an ignition source than a traditional structure housing a place of assembly. In this case, the uniqueness of the structure requires extra protection that normally would not be indicated. Utility systems, such as electrical, heating, and cooling, may require special modification to adapt and serve the special structure. This may result in atypical ignition sources.

Fuel Load

Like ignition sources, fuel loads are primarily dependent upon the occupancy classification, as well as the construction classification that is being used in the special structure. A study of the appropriate chapter for the occupancy classification under consideration provides a basic insight into fuel loads that should be anticipated. The fuel load then determines the hazards of contents classification per NFPA 101, Life Safety Code. When considering the fuel load of any structure, one must take into consideration that it is normally the contents, or fuel, in the building that create the fire problem. Typically, the building is a "victim" of the fire, not necessarily the cause of the fire. An exception to this rule is combustible construction with concealed combustible spaces or combustible interior finish, which constitute a fuel load.

The contents should be the primary concern when evaluating the fuel. The following items should be taken into consideration in the evaluation:

1. The amount of fuel, measured in lbs per sq ft (kg/m).
2. Btu output per lb of fuel per sq ft [(W/kg)/m].
3. Rate of heat release.
4. Configuration of fuel.
5. Burning characteristics of the fuel.
6. Amount of fuel per individual fuel station.
7. Configuration of fuel stations.
8. Burning characteristics of fuel stations.

In many cases, the actual fuel loading in a special structure exceeds that of traditional occupancies. In addition, the configuration and combustibility of the fuel load may be atypical and hazardous in itself. One example would be the use for aesthetic purposes of a combustible cellular foam that is not protected with adequate thermal barriers. Excessive untreated wood surfaces and mill work on walls and ceilings are other examples.

Once the fuel and its arrangements have been evaluated, the relationship of the fuel load to the unique features of the special structure must be assessed. It must be ensured that the fuel type and loading is at least consistent with the traditional occupancies, or extra protection may be required. The fuel type and loading must not diminish, or have an impact upon, the following:

1. Fundamental requirements in Chapter 2 of NFPA 101.
2. Egress requirements in Chapter 5 of NFPA 101.
3. Features of fire protection in Chapter 6 of NFPA 101
4. Minimum construction requirements of the occupancy chapters of NFPA 101.

Construction

Special structures can involve any type of construction classification and often include a combination of two or more construction types. Although a facility may be classified as an occupancy in a special structure, this does not minimize the need to conform to the minimum construction classification requirements as specified for that occupancy classification. In addition, many model building codes impose the minimum construction classification fire ratings, height and area limitations.

Because of the problems associated with the structure and its occupancy classifications, it may be desirable to increase the fire-resistive characteristics of the construction classification to compensate for unique hazards that may be created. An example would be increasing the integrity of the egress systems through fire-resistive enclosures or passageways, or requiring additional fire separations and smoke divisions to allow additional time for safe egress.

Many times, the conceptual aesthetic design of an occupancy located within a special structure will overlook even the most basic elements of good fire protection and prevention. Key components commonly overlooked are:

1. Concealed combustible spaces.
2. Protection of vertical openings.
3. Remoteness of exits.
4. Enclosure of exits.
5. Illumination and marking of exits.
6. Controlled interior finishes.
7. Automatic suppression systems.
8. Smoke management systems.
9. Fire alarm and detection systems.
10. Enclosure of hazardous areas.

SPECIFIC SPECIAL STRUCTURES

Towers

Chapter 30 of NFPA 101, *Life Safety Code*, defines a tower as an independent structure or part of a building that is used for signaling or some similar limited purpose. This definition does not include towers used for routine industrial, business, or assembly purposes. When a tower is used for these or other traditional occupancy purposes, it must comply completely with the appropriate occupancy classification and code provisions in NFPA 101 and other applicable codes.

When a tower is being used in accordance with its definition, Chapter 30 of NFPA 101 applies. In this case, the means of egress for a tower is usually a single exit and, in some cases, may be only a ladder. If only one means of egress exists, caution must be taken to ensure that occupants cannot be trapped. A maximum of 25 persons may be on any one floor of a tower with a single exit. A tower should not be used for sleeping or living purposes. Fire-resistive or noncombustible construction should be used, with either Class A or B interior finish.

The amount of combustible materials in, under, or around a tower must be carefully controlled. Combustibles should be totally eliminated except for necessary furniture and operating supplies. Careful judgment should be used in determining what combustible materials to allow in the immediate vicinity of the tower. Similar care should be used in evaluating a tower located near high-hazard occupancies. The tower should be separated by a reasonable distance, especially when it has only a single means of egress.

Towers surrounded by water or offshore structures require special consideration and are strictly controlled by the U.S. Coast Guard. Coast Guard regulations and those of similar regulatory bodies in foreign countries normally take precedence over NFPA 101, *Life Safety Code*, requirements.

In small towers where there will be no more than three occupants at any one time, the exit may be a ladder. Ladders should be arranged according to requirements of ANSI A-14.3, Safety Requirements for Fixed Ladders, and must provide continuous access to grade at all times. In towers with a single exit ladder, vertical openings need not be protected as such a requirement does not significantly increase protection for occupants.

Towers that are occupied on the top floor only often do not need enclosed stairs since the lack of operations at lower levels minimizes fire exposure. Alternatively, fire escape stairs may be used on open structures.

It should be noted that NFPA 101, *Life Safety Code*, requirements for towers anticipate a traditional tower used for signaling or some similar limited purpose. Towers that house assembly, educational, business, or some similar occupancy must comply with both traditional occupancy requirements, as well as special tower requirements.

Windowless Buildings and Underground Structures

The hazards of windowless buildings and underground structures are very similar. (See Figure 8-27A.) Therefore, the same concerns found in underground structures also would be related to the windowless building. The significant difference from the standpoint of NFPA 101, *Life Safety Code*, is that windowless structures are not required to have smoke venting facilities. Obviously, the feasibility of ventilating the structure should be looked at and related to the classification, nature, and character of the occupancy. In the event that the occupancy is of such a character that a significant occupant load could occur therein, then smoke control and smoke venting capabilities will have a serious impact on the evaluation of the level of life safety.

Typically, a good exit system can be provided in a windowless building. Additionally, this type of structure lends itself to the use of exterior access panels for fire department access and emergency use. It is noted that access panels that do not meet the requirements of the means of egress cannot be considered an exit.

Features of a windowless building that make it a special structure follow:

1. Due to the lack of windows, there are fewer points of entry into the building for manual fire suppression forces.
2. Ventilation during emergencies and removal of products of combustion, such as heat and smoke, depend on mechanical systems and door openings. If there are no mechanical systems designed for ventilation and smoke removal, then emergency operations may be hindered or additional damage/down time may occur, as compared to buildings with windows.
3. Natural illumination is limited or nonexistent. This issue has an impact upon egress and emergency operations within the building.
4. Windowless buildings may make the fire department's initial size-up more difficult due to the lack of visibility from the exterior. Many times, size-up will be restrained until an initial interior observation can be made.

A common problem with respect to windowless buildings is the determination as to whether the building does, or does not, have windows. It is unusual to find a building that does not have at least a few windows. It is necessary to review the definition of windowless structures and to understand its intent in order to determine whether or not the structure meets the definition of windowless.

The definition from NFPA 101, *Life Safety Code*, is divided into two parts that address two considerations. The first part is, "A building lacking any means for direct access to the outside." This portion of the definition looks at the ability to egress the building, which usually is not a problem unless the designer intentionally deleted exits along the exterior of the building. Exits are often deleted for access control and security purposes. While security and access control are obviously important, they cannot be allowed to interfere with a minimum level of life safety in a building.

The second portion of the definition addresses, "Outside openings for ventilation or rescue through windows." The problem thus becomes, "How many windows or open-

Fig. 8-27A. A typical windowless structure.

ings must be provided to not consider a building a windowless structure?" This determination must be based on the judgment of the authority having jurisdiction, but the definition does give some insight into the intent of NFPA 101, *Life Safety Code*. The 1988 edition of NFPA 101 gives two detailed exceptions when determining whether a structure is windowless. These exceptions address one-story buildings with specific provisions for ventilation and rescue. A review of the definition and exceptions should give reasonable guidance to assess the classification.

Judgment must be exercised in determining whether a building is truly windowless, taking into consideration the nature and character of the occupancy and the actual occupancy classification. For example, a windowless building in a storage occupancy would not be as critical as a windowless building in a place of assembly. One must also keep in mind that an occupancy load of 50 or more will be another major deciding factor.

Underground structures present additional problems not experienced in most other structures. The two primary issues are accessibility or lack of it, and below-grade fires.

As with windowless buildings, it can be difficult to identify and classify underground structures. Many times, the difficulty occurs when a building or structure is constructed on a site with varying grades. This may result in some levels of the building being below grade on one or more sides and at, or above, grade on other sides. One example is a four-story structure built into the side of a steep hill. Although this arrangement creates a building in which more than 50 percent of the total wall surface is below ground, the building is not considered an underground structure because the levels of exit discharge and adequate accessibility are above grade.

NFPA 101, *Life Safety Code*, gives specific guidance in determining when a building is considered an underground structure. The lowest floor used as a level of exit discharge may be considered the demarcation point for above and below grade. This may be true even if much of the wall surface of that floor is below grade. In this specific case, the building levels in question might be considered equivalent to a windowless building versus an underground structure.

From a practical standpoint, a windowless building has similar fire protection problems to an underground structure, but the windowless building can be constructed more easily to meet natural ventilation and rescue accessibility requirements. An underground structure must meet the requirements of a windowless building, and, in addition, some form of smoke management system of a type dependent upon occupant load must be provided. If a windowless building cannot meet the ventilation and rescue requirements, it should be considered equivalent to an underground structure, and the same code requirements should be applied.

Water-Surrounded Structures

This category includes structures fully surrounded by water, including lighthouse and offshore platforms. Occupant loads could vary from a limited number of people in some cases to 200 to 300 persons on offshore oil platforms. A large water-surrounded structure could include areas that contain assembly, industrial, or residential occupancies. Egress from the entire structure is limited because of its location.

Other than the fact that the structure is surrounded by water, traditional occupancy requirements and fire protection features remain the same with respect to the actual occupancy classifications being evaluated. The occupancy should be addressed as if it were not surrounded by water, and the particular circumstances created by the special structure should then be applied. The special structure features should be evaluated as they relate to the occupancy at hand.

Often, the structure is subject to severe environmental conditions, including wind, wave action, and heavy rain. For those reasons, NFPA 101, *Life Safety Code*, excludes water-surrounded structures from its provisions and recommends compliance with U.S. Coast Guard regulations.

Piers

NFPA 307, *Marine Terminals, Piers and Wharves*, includes a definition of a pier. NFPA 307 deals mostly with property conservation features of piers and wharves. Further, it references NFPA 101, *Life Safety Code*, for the applicable occupancy chapter for occupancies built on piers. This would include Chapter 30, "Special Structures and High Rise Buildings," which addresses piers. This section of NFPA 101 specifically addresses egress and the special circumstances for piers, including the fact that the occupancy still must meet the traditional occupancy chapters of NFPA 101.

Open Structures

Open structures are most often found in industrial operations, where the structure would come under the guidelines of an industrial occupancy. (See Figure 8-27B.) It is often difficult to determine whether the occupancy should be classified as general, special purpose, or high-hazard industrial. The hazard classification usually is determined by the classification of the hazards of the contents which can be present. Open-air structures are commonly classified under special-purpose industrial as defined in Chapter 28 of NFPA 101, *Life Safety Code*.

Fig. 8-27B. A typical open industrial structure. This particular building is a solvent extraction plant.

Chapter 28 of NFPA 101, *Life Safety Code*, makes several provisions for special-purpose industrial occupancies. The special-purpose industrial occupancy is characterized by a relatively low density of employee population, where most of an open-air structure is occupied by machinery or equipment. Typically, the open structure facilitates access to the equipment by use of platforms, gratings, stairs, and ladders.

It is sometimes difficult to determine when a structure is open and when it is enclosed. An open structure may include a roof to provide some protection from the elements. Additionally, open structures are provided with partial walls intended to shield the operations from environmental conditions or to segregate the operations. The authority having jurisdiction must determine whether the open-air structure truly meets the definition of an open structure or whether the facility is a building. As a guide, the authority could determine whether the structure would react as an enclosed building in the event of fire.

Within a building, walls acting in conjunction with a roof enclose the combustion process and products of combustion, thereby allowing fire to spread both horizontally and vertically to other areas. The advantage of an open structure is that is allows the products of combustion to vent to the atmosphere, instead of spreading to unaffected areas of the structure. This is dependent upon wind and climatic conditions, in addition to the design of the structure.

If the roof and walls could direct or channel products of combustion to other unaffected portions of the structure, thereby preventing their free venting to the atmosphere, then that portion of the open structure could be considered a building. It is not uncommon to have buildings constructed within the framework of an open structure, resulting in a typical mixed classification.

High-Rise Buildings

NFPA 101, *Life Safety Code*, defines a high-rise building as, "A building more than 75 ft (22.5)m) in height." This definition is consistent with many model building codes, but it should be noted that many different definitions exist in local jurisdictions that use varying height and measurement criteria. These height changes can range from 40 ft (12m) to as high as 150 ft (45m). It is important when designing, inspecting, or reviewing a high-rise building that the local codes be reviewed to determine height and measurement definitions.

Along with the varying heights used to determine the classification of a high-rise, local codes also vary in the method used to measure the height of a building. NFPA 101, *Life Safety Code*, states that, "Building height shall be measured from the lowest level of fire department vehicle access to the floor of the highest occupiable story."

Much emphasis has been placed on defining the characteristics of a high-rise building. The traditional approach has evolved around fire department accessibility with aerial apparatus, with many code definitions predicated on the length of the responding aerial ladder that may be available. Such an approach has several inherent weaknesses that may not serve either the designer or the servicing fire department. Most fire officers recognize that the actual reach of an aerial apparatus is more important than the length of the ladder. The reach depends upon several factors that include the placement of the apparatus and the site/building configuration. Taking these into consideration, many two-story buildings could be considered "high-rise" because they exceed the ability of the aerial device to reach occupied floors and portions of the building. Therefore, the figure of 75 ft, or 40 ft, or any other measurement is a compromise that provides a defined number for the designer and code official.

It is important to review the major issues that make high-rise buildings different from other buildings. Some of the major fire protection factors in high-rise buildings are as follows:

1. Fire department accessibility is a major issue, and it takes several forms, as follows:
   a. The limit of present-day fire apparatus to reach upper floors from the exterior of the building.
   b. The height of the fire and the number of personnel required to deliver adequate types and amounts of equipment to the fire area. Due to the possible height of the fire area, equipment transport and force deployment efforts could exact an exhaustive toll on fire fighting forces before they can even mount a fire attack. This has a significant impact when available fire fighters and equipment are limited. This condition can also occur in a large low-rise building with the same distance problems as a high-rise, although the elevational difference in a high-rise exaggerates the problem.
   c. Inherent delays in deploying equipment and fire fighters can indirectly affect fire growth, thereby resulting in a fire of greater magnitude by the time manual forces are in place to attack.
   d. The height and location of a building further restrict the fire department's ability to approach the area of origin from more advantageous directions. As a result, the fire department may only be able to approach a fire area from below. In many cases where the area of origin has no automatic suppression and compartmentation, the area of origin may not be approachable at all, resulting in a defensive approach that depends upon fuel consumption for control and extinguishment. This approach typically results in a large or unacceptable loss.

2. Egress and people movement systems within a high-rise building also make the building unique. Due to building height, traditional features of life safety, such as means of egress, are limited. Conventional exit systems, such as stair towers, cannot handle the accumulated effect of floor-upon-floor evacuation of occupants into the same exit system at the same time. As a result, evacuation times exceed traditional expectations.

   To mitigate such evacuation issues, other concepts, such as passive and active people movement systems, have evolved. Concepts such as areas of refuge, defend in place, pressurized exits, enclosed/pressurized elevators, increased fire ratings, communication systems, and life support systems all apply when mitigating the egress conditions presented by a high-rise building.

3. The high-rise building often has natural forces affecting fire and smoke movement that are not normally significant in lower buildings. Stack effect and the impact of winds can be very significant, and very different, in high-rise buildings.

   The stack effect is the result of the temperature differential between two areas, which creates a pressure differential that results in natural air movements within a building. In high-rise buildings, this effect is increased due to the height of the building. Many high-rise buildings have a significant stack effect, capable of moving large volumes of heat and smoke uncontrolled through the building.

There are no manual fire fighting techniques know to counter stack effect or to mitigate its effect during a fire. Stack effect cannot be eliminated because the temperature differential and building height exist. As a result, potential stack effect will exist and may vary with climatic conditions. The only thing that can be done to mitigate the potential of stack effect is to design and construct the building to minimize the effect. A thorough review of available resources on the subject will enhance design and construction. Basic concepts include:

a. Air-tight compartmentation from floor to floor and wall to wall. This would involve sealing penetrations and exterior building tightness.
b. Limiting continuous shaft heights. Construction of air-lock vestibules on stairs, elevators, and other vertical shafts.
c. Use of vestibules and gasketing on exterior doors at both the bottom and top of a building.
d. Eliminating naturally ventilated shafts and floors that could contribute to stack effect during a fire. One of the most commonly encountered situations is elevator shafts with normally open vents. These designs should be active so that the venting will terminate during a fire, thus reducing the impact of stack effect.
e. Zone compartmentation and control of mechanical systems, which could contribute to, or be affected by, stack effect.

Winds can have a profound effect upon fire and smoke movement within a building. Wind patterns around high-rise buildings have been the subject of study due to their effect upon structural issues, but very little has been studied with regard to fire protection. In high-rise buildings, winds can vary radically in intensity and direction at different floor levels or sections. It is known that wind velocity and direction can be very different at the street level than they are in the upper sections of the structure, and there is no known method of predicting or preliminarily measuring their effects.

The primary mitigating design approach is to make the exterior walls of a building as tight as possible. This approach is highly dependent upon the design criteria, materials chosen, and integrity of workmanship. The result should be that wind direction and velocity have a reduced impact upon air movement within the structure, thereby allowing conventional smoke management systems to overcome the effects of wind to some degree. It is noted that the degree of the smoke management system's ability to overcome the wind effect is based upon many variables, including system design, system power, tightness of the building, wind velocity, and wind direction.

It is reasonable to assume that, if wind is not taken into consideration in the design and construction of the high-rise building and the exterior of the building is not reasonably tight, any fire may be significantly affected by wind velocity and direction. Wind direction can complicate the accessibility and preferred direction of fire attack and can increase fire and smoke impingement upon areas of refuge, possibly exceeding their design criteria.

4. Due to their nature and design, high-rise buildings significantly increase the occupant, equipment, and material load in a given building. By stacking floor upon floor, the number of occupants and potential fuel load that could be exposed to a given event are increased dramatically when compared to lower-height buildings. This higher density of occupants and fuel load is the result of stacking many floors on the same building foot print. Fire has a natural tendency to move upward, where additional occupants and fuel are stacked.
5. One factor to be considered is the combination of occupancies often located in a single high-rise building. These occupancies range from residential to business, offices, stores, restaurants, and places of assembly, and they often include several levels of underground parking located below the high-rise structure. Many designs include within-the-structure atriums, building interconnections, and public transportation systems such as trains and subway service. Mixing these occupancies and structures complicates the requirements for fire protection, necessitating a sophisticated, and sometimes complex, approach to fire safety.
6. The internal utility services for high-rise buildings typically are arranged to provide for the height of the building. Many high-rise buildings have equipment or mechanical levels servicing every ten, or so, floors. These arrangements can result in multiple levels of fire pumps, additional pressure-reducing devices on sprinkler and standpipe systems, and the host of complex problems that go along with such elaborate arrangements.

Even when HVAC systems are zoned and compartmented, they can share common exhaust shafts and fresh-air intake shafts. These shafts and duct runs often penetrate multiple fire zones and require special attention regarding design and protection. Many high-rise buildings integrate smoke management systems into their conventional HVAC systems. Although this is acceptable, and in many cases preferred, it requires special design considerations, including safe and adequate controls, acceptance testing, and on-going maintenance.

Items 1 through 6 are primary issues that make high-rise buildings different from conventional, lower buildings. As a result, a high-rise building requires different, and additional, design considerations and features when compared to other types of structures. These considerations should not be based only upon the reach of an aerial ladder, but upon the unique features of the particular building and its specific fire protection features.

NFPA 101, *Life Safety Code*, includes specific requirements for high-rise buildings, including automatic sprinkler protection, detection, alarm, communications, emergency power systems, and command stations. Other special features of high-rise buildings, such as atriums and mixed occupancies, also are addressed in NFPA 101.

Summary

Special structures and high-rise buildings are unique with regard to their use, arrangement, fire hazards, and fire protection features. One must always differentiate between a special structure as defined and a special structure being used as a non-traditional occupancy classification.

When evaluating a special structure, many traditional concepts of fire safety, fire protection, and sound engineering judgment apply. In addition, the arrangement of the structure and occupancy may require new approaches to remedy life safety and fire protection problems.

Bibliography

NFPA Codes, Standards, and Recommended Practices

Reference to the following NFPA codes, standards, and recommended practices will provide further information on occupancies in unusual structures. (See the latest *NFPA Catalog* for availability of the current editions of the following documents.)

NFPA 307, *Marine Terminals, Piers and Wharves.*

NFPA 101,® *Life Safety Code.*®

NFPA 92A, *Smoke Control Systems.*

Additional Reading

Bond H, "Underground Buildings," *Fire Journal*, Vol. 59, No. 4 (July 1965), pp. 52-55.

"Fire Hazards of Windowless Buildings," *NFPA Quarterly*, Vol. 58, No. 1 (July 1964), pp. 22-30.

"Occupancies in Unusual Structures." Conduction Fire Inspections "Safety Requirement for Fixed Ladders, "ANSI A14.3 - 1974, American National Standards Institute, NY

"Safety Requirement for Fixed Ladders," *ANSI A14.3*, American National Standards Institute, NY, 1974.

PROTECTION OF ELECTRONIC EQUIPMENT

Revised by Robert J. Pearce

Our society is dependent on computers and other electronic equipment. Computers have become a vital part of government, business, industry, and even personal life. These computers are highly sophisticated and are becoming more complex, faster, and smaller as technology improves. Often, the computer's strategic importance in a business is tied to its uninterrupted use, and, if damaged or destroyed, a vital operation may be totally paralyzed. Many processes such as chemical, petrochemical, basic steel, and pulp and paper are now controlled by computers. Many businesses depend on special sophisticated electronic equipment such as communication systems or test equipment. Electronic laboratory equipment such as production prototypes, simulators, and measuring devices may be vital to a business' development of its products. This type of equipment is more difficult to replace, and its destruction by fire could have immense impact.

Because of the dependence of businesses on computers and other electronic equipment, the importance of fire protection cannot be overemphasized. This should include security measures, as computers are prime targets for both arson and sabotage.

Businesses which are dependent upon computer systems, such as banks and other financial institutions, should have plans to relocate vital computer operations to alternate sites, and should keep back-up copies of vital data in remote locations.

Because of the immense cost of large computer systems, as well as the space considerations, it may not be feasible economically to provide back-up units or even libraries of all records and data at remote locations to ensure continued operation in the event of some catastrophe. If a system is custom-built for its application, the problem of restoration is compounded because there may be no replacement system available. (See Figure 8-28A.)

FIG. 8-28A. Computer room with terminals. (Source: IBM)

Additional information relevant to the protection of computers and electronic equipment from fire may be found in Section 2, Chapter 30, "Storage and Handling of Records;" in Section 4, Chapter 2, "Protective Signaling Systems;" Section 4, Chapter 5, "Automatic Fire Detectors;" and in Section 5, Chapter 22, "Special Systems and Extinguishing Techniques."

PHYSICAL FACILITIES LOCATION AND CONSTRUCTION

Because computers and electronic equipment are valuable, sensitive to damage, and often critical to the ongoing operations of the business or other concern where they are located, major computer systems should be installed in specially designed areas that provide security, fire protection, and a suitable ambient atmosphere. Such installations may be located in computer rooms that are separated adequately from other parts of a building or, in some cases, may be found in separate structures designed for this function. Offices and support areas of light combustible loading and

Robert J. Pearce is Manager, Regional Loss Prevention, for Industrial Risk Insurers, based in San Francisco.

ordinary hazard occupancies, such as light manufacturing, should be separated from computer rooms by walls with 2-hr rating, incorporating listed fire doors, shutters, and dampers in air ducts. Computer rooms should not be located above, below, or adjacent to areas housing hazardous processes unless reliable protective separations are provided. These rooms should be made of noncombustible or fire-resistive construction with noncombustible interior finish.

Most fires damaging computer rooms are not in the equipment itself, but have originated in ordinary combustibles exposing it, either inside or outside of the computer room. Rooms for related necessities, such as programmers, maintenance, paper supplies, and recorded data, should be separated from the computer or electronic equipment room. Only the actual computer and electronic equipment and the necessary auxiliary equipment should be permitted within the room itself.

Small supervisory or operator offices directly related to the electronic equipment operation may be located in the computer room if combustible materials are kept to a minimum. Service transformers, motor generation sets, switchgear, and battery back-up banks should not be permitted in the room. Supplies of paper and repair or service shops should be strictly limited to the minimum needed for efficient operation and preferably located outside the computer room. Paper should be disposed of in waste disposal units designed to snuff out a fire, and trash should be removed each shift.

Records that are generated by the electronic computer systems should be protected according to their importance and difficulty to reproduce. In most cases, the information stored in computer systems or stored as input or output data is more valuable than the computer hardware. It is essential to protect this information and, when the information is extremely critical, to keep back-up copies in a safe, remote location. The information itself may be on magnetic tapes, discs, paper, or a variety of other media that are susceptible to damage from fire, heat, products of combustion, or water. Vital and important records that are irreplacable or very difficult to replace should be stored in a separate room with fire resistance of not less than 2-hr. (see Figure 8-28B.)

FIG. 8-28B. Tape storage room. (Source: IBM)

Mainframe computers are generally installed on raised floor systems which house electrical wiring and serve as air conditioning plenums. The floors, including structural support members, should be concrete, steel, aluminum, resilient tile, or other noncombustible material. Fire wall separations must be maintained under the floor where openings to another area under the floor need to be made. Openings in raised floors for cable penetrations should be kept to a minimum to prevent debris and other combustibles from collecting beneath the floor. Carpeting should be avoided on raised floor systems. The carpet and the adhesives used to attach it to the floor panels could increase the damage to computer equipment if it is involved in a fire. Periodic inspection and maintenance of underfloor space is required to eliminate the accumulation of combustibles. One of the major problems that has been identified with under-floor areas is the accumulation of unused wire and cable as equipment is relocated and updated. This material can add excessive amounts of potential fuel for a fire in the form of wire insulation and connectors. A cable management program should be applied in all underfloor areas.

Equipment and Construction Features

Power, communications, and signal cables, as well as plugs and connectors, should be of a listed type and of a proper size for the application, in accordance with NFPA 70, *National Electrical Code.*® These should be suitable for installation under raised floors. Openings in the floors should be smooth to prevent damage to cables. Power cables should be run in conduit. No splices or connections should be permitted in the wiring under the floor except within listed junction boxes or approved receptacles or connectors, and the number of junction boxes should be kept to a minimum. Cables should be arranged to avoid serious multiple failures because of a fault or overheating in any one conductor.

Large computers and other electronic data processing equipment produce a great deal of heat and require large amounts of air to be passed through the equipment for cooling. Air conditioning systems should be based on the requirements of NFPA 90A, *Installation of Air Conditioning and Ventilating Systems.* Computer rooms should have their own air conditioning system. Air intakes should be located to minimize exposure to flame, smoke, and undesirable fumes. All filters should be Class I (noncombustible). The duct work and its insulation should be noncombustible. The system should be capable of going to 100 percent makeup and exhaust automatically upon detection of smoke, thus avoiding recirculation of the products of combustion.

As technology advances, computers and other electronic systems become denser and more powerful, and, as a result, more heat is generated. When plans are made to upgrade some computer systems, the cooling requirements may need to be changed for safe operation. Many modern systems use coolant media other than air, such as water, freon, and nitrogen cooling. (See Figure 8-28C.)

Most large computer systems rely on uninterruptable power supplies (UPS) for protection from power loss and voltage fluctuations. The UPS is actually a large, rechargeable battery system which is normally "on charge" while it provides the power to the computer system. The UPS has the capacity to keep the system running in the event of a power loss, until regular or emergency power supplies are restored.

FIG. 8-28C. Air conditioning unit. (Source: IBM)

Electrical power supplies and other electrical equipment, such as transformers, motor generators, distribution controls, circuit breakers, and disconnect switches, should be maintained in a separate cutoff room. Where larger battery banks are used, they should be kept in a separate, well-ventilated, detached room. Diesel, light natural or liquid petroleum gas generators for emergency power supplies should be located in separate machinery rooms or outside of buildings. (See Figure 8-28D.)

FIG. 8-28D. Motor-generator used to provide clean power to computer rooms. (Source: IBM)

FIRE PROTECTION

Computers and other electronic equipment are particularly susceptible to damage from fire and the accompanying heat, steam, and smoke. Equipment and data may even be damaged by elevated ambient temperatures. Above 120°F (49°C), permanent damage can begin. At 125°F (52°C), magnetic tapes, floppy disks, and similar material start to lose information. At a sustained ambient temperature of 150°F (66°C), hard disks will be damaged. Equipment components will begin to fail at 174°F (79°C), with major failure of components between 300 and 500°F (149 and 260°C) Damage to microfilm will begin at 225°F (107°C) in the presence of high humidity. Even paper products will be damaged at 350°F (177°C). Finally, between 650 and 750°F (343 and 399°C), polystyrene cases and reels will degrade, producing flammable styrene monomer.

Portable Fire Extinguishers

Computer rooms should be equipped with clean agent Class B:C extinguishers in accordance with NFPA 10, *Standard for Portable Extinguishers*. Dry chemical extinguishers should not be used. If paper and other ordinary combustibles are present, a sufficient number of Class A pressurized water extinguishers should also be provided. Occupants need to be instructed in their use.

Automatic Sprinkler Systems

A fixed automatic sprinkler system should be provided in accordance with NFPA 13, *Installation of Sprinkler Systems*. The sprinkler protection should be provided on a hydraulic design basis arranged as a wet-pipe or pre-action system. The water distribution density should be evaluated for each installation. Few computer installations would meet the definition of light-hazard occupancy, based on the amount of combustibles that are found in the room. Computer facilities with super printers often handle large amounts of paper and could be considered Group III ordinary hazards. Special storage arrangements of media could also affect required sprinkler discharge densities.

Special Extinguishing Systems

When the value and risk of interruption of computer equipment has been deemed critical, total flooding Halon 1301 systems have been installed in many computer rooms. Due to serious environmental concerns involving Halon 1301 and its effect on the ozone layer, however, alternate means of protection should be considered. Halon 1301 systems should be used only where circumstances require that level of protection. Automatic sprinkler protection for the room and protection of the underfloor plenum using CO_2 could satisfy many situations. Alternative agents are expected to be available to replace Halon 1301 for protection of computers and electronic equipment.

Smoke Detectors

Smoke detection devices should be installed at the ceiling level and under raised floor systems. Detection devices installed in under-floor areas should be listed specifically for this application. Airflow characteristics in under-floor plenums make many types of detectors unsuitable. Alarm and detection systems should be designed and installed in accordance with NFPA 72E, *Automatic Fire Detectors*.

Emergency Plans and Procedures

The primary purpose of the emergency plan is to prepare key personnel to initiate actions during and after any emergency. Plans and procedures should be developed by supervisory personnel and reviewed on a regular basis. The plan should incorporate contingency factors for emergencies such as power failures, severe weather conditions, tornados, floods, earthquakes, and so on.

The plan should include actions to safeguard systems from damage and provisions to ensure that back-up copies of program software and data are available in case damage occurs. There should be a contingency plan to relocate operations to another location or to provide alternate means to complete critical functions if a computer center is temporarily out of service or permanently damaged.

Alternate equipment should be available, either from within the organization or from an outside organization if the operation is to continue during the restoration of damaged equipment. A prearranged plan should consider and test compatibility of backup equipment.

The plan should include local emergency personnel such as security and/or local fire response organizations and outside fire departments. The local fire departments should be invited to visit the computer and electronic equipment rooms to familiarize them with the emergency plan. It is important that they be aware of any fixed automatic fire extinguishing systems and know how they operate and what procedures to follow, such as where to enter the building if summoned by a fire alarm signal.

The second part of the plan is an emergency personnel evacuation procedure. The primary purpose of this plan is safety to life of all persons who may be in the computer room or electronic equipment area. The procedure should be posted and updated periodically — every six months —so that all employees and others entering the area know what to do when the alarm signal is sounded. The alarm signal must be audible throughout the entire area, and when it is initiated, all occupants should immediately exit the area and assemble at a predesignated location. The assembly point could be located in a safe, interior part of an adjacent building. The employees should remain in the assembly area until all are accounted for, and they are advised otherwise. Several persons should be assigned to check their areas to make certain all persons have exited. Laboratories, washrooms, storage rooms, and so on should be checked. The plan should include provisions for the handicapped or those who may need physical assistance. A strobe or a visible oscillating light should be provided for people who are unable to hear the alarm.

Emergency lighting also should be provided for the entire interior of the building that houses the computers or electronic equipment and offices. Auxiliary battery lighting packs are permitted.

BIBLIOGRAPHY

NFPA Codes, Standards, Recommended Practices

Reference to the following NFPA codes, standards, and recommended practices will provide further information on protection of computers and electronic equipment discussed in this chapter. (See the latest NFPA Catalog for availability of current editions of the following documents.)

NFPA 10, *Portable Fire Extinguishers.*

NFPA 12, *Carbon Dioxide Extinguishing Systems.*

NFPA 12A, *Halon 1301 Fire Extinguishing Agent Systems.*

NFPA 13, *Installation of Sprinkler Systems.*

NFPA 70, *National Electrical Code.®*

NFPA 71, *Station Signaling Systems for Central Station Service.*

NFPA 72, *Protective Signaling Systems.*

NFPA 72A, *Local Protective Signaling Systems for Guard's Tour, Fire Alarm and Supervisory Service.*

NFPA 72B, *Auxiliary Protective Signaling Systems for Fire Alarm Service.*

NFPA 72C, *Remote Station Protection Signaling Systems.*

NFPA 72D, *Proprietary Protective Signaling Systems.*

NFPA 75, *Electronic Computer/Data Processing Equipment.*

NFPA 80A, *Protection of Buildings from Exterior Fire Exposures.*

NFPA 90A, *Air Heating and Air Conditioning and Ventilating Systems.*

NFPA 92A, *Smoke Control Systems.*

NFPA 232, *Protection of Records.*

NFPA 258, *Determining Smoke Generation of Solid Materials.*

Additional Reading

Adams, W. C., "Computer Room Fires," *Fire Engineering*, Vol. 141, No. 9 (Sept. 1988), p. 12,14,15.

Barry, T. F., "Computer Room Risk Assessment," *Plant/Operation Progress*, Vol. 6, No. 2 (April 1987), pp. 68-72.

"Computer Centers—Measures to Reduce Losses," *Brand Brandweer*, Vol. 1, No. 3, 1977, pp. 53-56.

Davis, R. H., "Fire Protection Systems (for Computers)," *Data Management*, Vol. 14, No. 11, 1976, pp. 11-14.

Eichhorn, R. M. and Pickering, J. J., "Full-Scale Tests to Simulate an Electrical Cable Fire in the Control Room of an Industrial Plant," *Proceedings* of the 34th International Wire and cable symposium, U.S. Army, 1985, pp. 213-219.

"Electronic Computer Systems," *Loss Prevention Data Sheet* 5-32, Factory Mutual Engineering Corporation, Norwood, MA, May 1978.

Factory Mutual Corp., "American Experience in the Fire Protection of Computers," *Fire*, Vol. 7, 1979, pp. 498-499.

Facts About Protecting Electronic Equipment Against Fire, Ansul, Marinette, WI, 1984.

"Halon Prevents Major Central Processing Unit Fires," *Computer Decisions*, Vol. 10, No. 8, 1978, pp. 56, 58.

Hampton, M. and Wilkerson, J. R., "Computer Rooms Require Special M/E Systems," *Consulting Specifying Engineers*, Vol. 1, No. 4, 1987, pp. 82-85, 87-88.

Harrison, G. A. and Lowec, D. G., "Computer Fire and Resultant Circuit Card Fire Tests," *Fire Journal*, Vol. 63, No. 2 (Mar. 1969), p. 5.

Hiles, A., "Testing the Fire Hazards of Computer Tapes," *Fire Prevention*, No. 223 (Oct.1989), pp. 39-42.

Isner, M. S., "Telephone Switching Station Fire Creates Widespread Emergency," *Fire Journal*, Vol. 83, No. 3 (May 1990), p.72.

Jacobson, D. W., "Automatic Sprinkler Protection for Essential Electrical and Electronic Equipment," *Fire Journal*, Vol. 61, No. 1 (Jan. 1967), pp. 48-53.

Johnson, P. F., "Fire Detection in Computer Facilities," *Fire Technology*, Vol. 22, No. 1 (Jan. 1986), pp. 14-32.

Johnson, P. F., "Very Early Smoke Detection for Computer and Telecommunications Industries," *Fire Safety Journal*, Vol. 14, Nos. 1&2, 1988, pp. 13-24.

Keigher, D. J., "Water and Electronics Can Mix," *Fire Journal*, Vol. 62, No. 6 (Nov. 1968), pp. 68-72.

Kuechmann, A. M., "On-Site Fire Protection for Computer Media," *Fire Journal*, Vol. 66, No. 6 (Nov. 1972), pp. 50-51.

Martin, K., "Cable-Fire Tests Under the Raised Floor of Data-Processing Installations," *Proceedings* of the First International Symposium on Fire Safety Science, Hemisphere, 1986, pp. 859-868.

Menkus, B., "Computer-Related Fire Problems Revisited," *Computers and Security*, Vol. 8, No. 7 (Nov. 1989), pp. 581-586.

Menkus, B., "It's Time To Rethink Data Processing Fire Protection," *Computers and Security*, Vol. 8, No. 5 (Aug. 1989), pp 389 - 394.

Osborn, R. W., *ed.*, *Tapping Into the NEC*, National Fire Protection Association, Quincy, MA, 1982.

Perkins, C. and Berenblut, B. J., "Electronic Equipment: What Protection is Required?," *Fire Surveyor*, Vol. 9, No. 5 (Oct. 1980), pp. 28-33.

Philbrick, S. E., "Selecting Cables for Fire-Risk Applications," *Electronics and Power*, Vol. 26, No. 3 (Mar. 1980), pp. 232-233.

"Protecting High-value Computer Systems," *Fire Prevention*, No. 128 (April 1990), pp. 17-20.

Smith, G., "Computer Protection," *Fire Surveyor*, Vol. 18, No. 1 (Feb. 1989), pp. 18-24.

"Standard Practice for the Fire Protection of Essential Electronic Equipment Operations," U.S. Department of Commerce, National Fire Prevention and Control Administration, Washington, DC, Aug. 1978.

Staller, J. J. and Colling, D. A., "The Aftermath of a Computer Fire," *Fire Journal*, Vol. 71, No. 6 (Nov. 1977), pp. 29-33.

"Support for Sprinkler Systems in Controversial Settings," *Fire*, February 1981, pp. 455-456.

Taylor, A. J., "Bringing Fire Protection of Computers Up To Date," *Fire International*, Vol. 12, No. 109, 1988, pp. 43-44.

Taylor, K. T., "Updating the Record on Computer Center Fires," *Fire Journal*, Vol. 83, No. 2 (Mar./Apr. 1989), pp. 31-35.

Taylor, K. T., "Temporarily Disconnected: Fires in Telephone Exchanges and Central Offices from 1982 to 1986," *Fire Journal*, Vol. 83, No. 2 (Mar./Apr. 1989), p. 24.

Williamson, H. V., "New Protection for Electronic Equipment," *Fire Technology*, Vol. 2, No. 4 (Nov. 1966), pp. 279-286.

Woodcock, J., "Current Concepts in Computer Protecton," *Fire Surveyor*, Vol. 18, No. 3 (June 1989), pp. 4-8.

PROTECTION OF LABORATORIES USING CHEMICALS

Revised by Howard F. Kempsell, Sr.

This chapter covers the more common laboratory hazard problems that influence the degree of fire protection that may be required. The basic requirements of laboratory design and construction, together with the fire protection systems and procedures, are essential items to consider. Standard laboratory equipment should be obtained with fire prevention and protection and the reduction of personnel hazards in mind. The storage, handling, use, and disposal of all commonly used laboratory materials, such as flammable and combustible liquids, compressed gases, and biological and radiological materials, must be considered in prevention and protection procedures. These concepts should be of primary consideration to those responsible for laboratory operations in order to minimize losses from fire and/or explosion and to reduce the possibility of injury and life-threatening situations.

This chapter treats the subject of protection for laboratories in a general way. For more information on the hazards of and protection for laboratories, consult the table of contents of this Handbook.

CONSTRUCTION AND DESIGN

The basic modes of construction and design outlined here are suggested as guides only. Specific details of construction and special facets of consideration change routinely with each type of laboratory. NFPA 45, *Fire Protection for Laboratories Using Chemicals,* contains detailed information on classifying laboratory units and work areas based on flammable and combustible liquid content; construction, and the presence of explosion hazards. Other good sources to consult to ensure that all requirements are met are NFPA 99, *Health Care Facilities*, Chapter 10; specialized engineering firms; insurance rating agencies; and the various federal, state, and municipal regulatory agencies.

Howard F. Kempsell, Sr. has served on the Technical Committee for Chemistry Laboratories since 1969 and was its chairman for ten years. Currently, he is a safety and fire protection consultant.

Construction

The construction of laboratories depends on a variety of considerations—the type and quantity of potential hazards involved, the area or location with respect to surrounding activities, and the type of fire protection to be provided. Well-located laboratories are separated from other laboratories and nonlaboratory space by fire-resistive construction. Interior finish used in laboratory construction and the access to exits from them must comply with the requirements of NFPA 101®, *Life Safety Code*®.

Egress

Means of egress requirements for a laboratory building must agree with the exit requirements specified for the particular occupancy and type of building. (See NFPA 101, Life Safety Code.) Most laboratory buildings are constructed to comply with the exit requirements for general-purpose or industrial buildings. Exceptions are laboratory buildings or laboratories located in educational, institutional, or other specialized occupancies. They comply with the exit requirements specified for those particular occupancies.

Two means of access to an exit from a laboratory work area are usually required. These should be located to provide access to exits from all parts of the work area larger than 1000 sq ft (93 m^2) or from a laboratory work area containing large quantities of flammable liquids with an area in excess of 500 sq ft (46 m^2). A second means of egress is also required from a laboratory that has a laboratory hood adjacent to the primary means of egress or from one that contains substantial quantities of compressed gases. Required exit access doors from high-hazard or intermediate-hazard laboratories must swing in the direction of egress. Furniture and laboratory equipment should be arranged so that the means of access to an exit may be reached easily from any point in the laboratory work area without undue obstruction.

Ventilation

Duct systems for laboratory heating and ventilating, including warm air heating systems, general ventilating systems, air cooling systems, and laboratory exhaust and hood systems deserve special attention. NFPA 45, *Fire Protection for Laboratories Using Chemicals*; NFPA 90A, *Air Conditioning and Ventilating Systems*; and NFPA 91, *Exhaust Systems for Air Conveying of Materials*, are good practices to follow.

Air handling systems for laboratories deserve special attention. The fresh air supply system must not draw in flammable or toxic materials or combustion byproducts emitted from the laboratory building itself or other sources, such as vehicle exhaust. Exhaust discharges for laboratories should be located away from all air intakes, including those from other buildings, and high enough above roof level to provide atmospheric dilution. High-velocity discharge also assists in exhaust dilution.

Air handling systems should be balanced to provide a negative pressure with respect to the corridors and surrounding nonlaboratory spaces. An exception is those laboratories housing areas such as clean rooms that preclude a negative pressure in relation to the surrounding space. A slightly positive pressure is required in these areas, and precautions must be taken to prevent the escape of atmospheric contaminants in the laboratory space to surrounding spaces.

Air exhausted from laboratory areas in which highly infectious or radioactive materials are used or handled must pass through high-efficiency filters before being discharged into the atmosphere.

Fume Hoods

Laboratory hoods are the most commonly used means of removing gases, dust, mist, vapors, and fumes from laboratory operations and of preventing toxic exposures and flammable concentrations. To be effective, a laboratory hood and its associated components must confine contaminants within the hood, dilute and remove them through the ductwork, and disperse them so that they do not return to the building through the air supply system. Hood face velocities must be sufficient to ensure the capture of contaminants, especially in the presence of cross drafts. Recommended face velocities are published by the American Conference of Governmental Industrial Hygienists. Laboratory hoods for hazardous operations, such as perchloric acid, radioactive materials, explosion hazards, and so on, require special design and must be constructed of suitable materials that meet rigid criteria. Fume hood controls should be so arranged that shutting off the ventilation in one hood will not reduce the exhaust capacity or create an imbalance for any other hood. All shutoff valves for services should be located outside the hood enclosure in a readily accessible location.

Electrical Equipment

All electrical installations, appliance, and equipment must comply with NFPA 70, *National Electrical Code®*. Circuits should be designed for all electrical equipment that will be installed, and sufficient overcurrent protection devices should be provided. Emergency power for operating exhaust fans, exit lighting, exit signs, evacuation alarms, and other emergency or fire and safety equipment is essential and is also required by the *Occupational Safety and Health Act* (OSHA).

All electrical appliances and equipment should display a listing with, or approval by, a recognized testing laboratory for its intended use, unless the device is one for which test standards have not been established. All electrical appliances and equipment should have an operator's manual, together with a circuit diagram, available for qualified maintenance personnel. It is also important that all portable electrical equipment intended for laboratory use be properly grounded by recognized methods.

Installation of a sufficient number of electrical outlets at convenient locations eliminates the use of extension cords.

Several outlets should be provided with emergency power to prevent loss or interruption of electrical power to critical laboratory equipment or experimentation.

FIRE PROTECTION

All laboratories must have fire protection . As a minimum, they should have portable fire extinguishers appropriate to the hazard, an adequate fire alarm system, and an emergency evacuation plan.

Automatic Fire Extinguishing/Protection Systems

It is common practice to protect laboratories, including associated storage rooms and enclosures, with an automatic sprinkler system designed and installed according to the provisions of NFPA 13, *Installation of Sprinkler Systems*. In some instances, special-hazard laboratories may require automatic detection systems and special extinguishing agents, such as foam, halogenated agents, carbon dioxide, and so on. When such systems are used, they must be installed, inspected, and maintained in accordance with the appropriate NFPA standards. Periodic inspection of the systems ensures that they will activate in an emergency.

The activation of a fire detection system or the discharge of a fire extinguishing system must sound an alarm to ensure prompt response. The alarm system should be arranged to sound alarms both inside the laboratory building and at a constantly attended location, such as a telephone switchboard, communications center, or security office, and the fire department. The alarm system should also be arranged to activate other equipment, such as electromagnetic door closers that effect the fire protection of the facility. The NFPA signaling systems standards give guidance on the various alarm systems and detection equipment that can be used. (See bibliography.)

Standpipe and Hose Systems

Laboratory buildings with two or more stories above or below ground level should be provided with $2^1/_2$ in. (64 mm) hose connections with hose and combination straight stream and fog nozzle. NFPA 14, *Installation of Standpipe and Hose Systems*, is the guide to follow.

Portable Fire Extinguishers

Portable fire extinguishers, suitable to the particular hazards of the laboratory, should be installed and located so that they will be readily available to laboratory personnel. Class A fire extinguishers suitable for fires in ordinary combustible materials, such as wood, paper, and rags, should be provided and supplemented by enough extinguishers suitable for use on Class B (flammable liquid) and Class C (electrical) fires. Special Class D fire extinguishers are needed where the use of metals or metal hydrides indicates a need for them. Multi-purpose extinguishers for use on Class A- B- and C-type fires are frequently the extinguisher of choice due to their versatility and to the ease of giving instructions in their use.

Fire Prevention Procedures

It is essential to develop good procedures for handling laboratory emergencies. These include manual alarm activation, equipment shutdown procedures, evacuation procedures, and provisions for fire-fighting actions. In addition, the following critical areas require special consideration: handling and storage of flammable liquids, handling and storage of other hazardous materials and gases, smoking area controls, electrical hazards, open-flame and spark-producing work, and radiological and biological hazards.

Evacuation plans must be developed and evaluated thoroughly to include all contingencies. Testing the evacuation plan periodically ensures proper and prompt action by all laboratory personnel.

EQUIPMENT

All equipment in a laboratory, whether fixed or portable, and fixed building service equipment must meet specific standards and must be evaluated with respect to safety, fire prevention, and damage. Laboratory and fire brigade personnel must be familiar with all laboratory and building service equipment. Municipal fire department personnel must be made aware of laboratory and building service equipment before they are called upon to handle emergencies in laboratories.

Mechanical

Safe operation of laboratory instruments and equipment depends on purchasing or building apparatus with adequate controls and safeguards, installing the apparatus in safe locations, and using the apparatus within the limitations of the original design or appropriate modifications. Safe design and operation will help to reduce potential fire hazards, unnecessary accidents, and damage or destruction of equipment.

Refrigeration Equipment

Refrigerators and freezers are a valuable asset in most laboratories, but particular care must be taken to ensure their proper use. Ordinary domestic units are completely unsuitable for the storage of flammable liquids. Laboratory-safe or explosion-proof equipment is available from several manufacturers and should be purchased for storage of flammable liquids. For modification of ordinary domestic refrigeration units, see NFPA 45, *Fire Protection for Laboratories Using Chemicals*.

FLAMMABLE AND COMBUSTIBLE LIQUIDS AND HAZARDOUS CHEMICALS

Flammable and Combustible Liquids

Flammable and combustible liquids present a potentially serious fire and explosion hazard in a laboratory. The severity of the hazard from a flammable liquid process or the storage of these materials depends on conditions such as the quantity, volatility, and flammable range of the liquid; whether it is in a closed or open system exposed to air; the method of containment to control leakage or overflow; the location in relation to other equipment and outside ignition sources; the building construction; and the adequacy of fire protection.

Storage and use: Flammable and combustible liquids should be stored in and used from containers of a size and material appropriate to the potential hazard. Refer to NFPA 45, *Fire Protection for Laboratories Using Chemicals*, for specific information on size and type of container. Established laboratory practices are the limiting factors in determining the working quantity of flammable and combustible liquids that are present. All nonworking quantities should be stored in well-constructed storage cabinets or storage rooms. (See NFPA 30, *Flammable and Combustible Liquids Code*, for details of construction.) Laboratory personnel must be thoroughly familiar with the properties and the hazards of flammable and combustible liquids in use.

Handling and transfer: Only trained personnel should be involved in receiving, transporting, unpacking, and dispensing flammable and combustible liquids. These activities should be carried out in locations and in a manner that minimize the risks. Transfer from bulk stock containers to smaller containers must be performed in a separate area outside the building, a laboratory hood, an area with adequate ventilation to prevent the accumulation of flammable vapor, or a separate inside storage area that meets the requirements of NFPA 30, *Flammable and Combustible Liquids Code*.

Disposal: Applicable governmental regulations must be observed in the disposal of waste flammable and combustible liquids. Disposal of these hazardous materials must be accomplished by a disposal specialist who is competent and who knows the basic character and hazards of the waste.

Hazardous Chemicals

Storage and use: Hazardous chemicals must not be brought into a laboratory space unless the design, construction, and fire protection of the receiving, using, and storage facilities are commensurate with the quantities and hazards of the chemicals involved. All laboratory personnel must be aware of the hazards of all chemicals in use. Special storage facilities are needed for materials having unique physical or hazardous properties, such as temperature sensitivity, water reactivity, or explosivity. A reference source of information is NFPA 49, *Hazardous Chemicals Data*.

Disposal: Applicable governmental regulations must be observed in the disposal of waste chemicals. It is preferable to neutralize the hazardous material before disposal. A disposal specialist who is competent and who knows the character and hazards of the waste should be assigned to this activity.

Emergency Showers

Emergency shower installations should be provided for minimizing injury to personnel from clothing fires and other emergencies, such as contact with caustics or cryogenic fluids. Emergency showers supply volumes of water needed for diluting, warming or cooling, flushing chemicals, or extinguishing clothing fires. They should be located outside the laboratory space in conspicuous spots, preferably in usual traffic patterns but not more than 25 ft (8m) from any laboratory entrance. Eye wash fountains are sometimes installed adjacent to emergency showers. Avoid locating showers near electrical apparatus and power outlets. The location of showers should be plainly marked on the floor.

The showers should be tested and flushed, preferably quarterly, to ensure that they are in operating condition.

COMPRESSED OR LIQUEFIED GASES

The use of compressed or liquefied gases in a laboratory presents special problems. Precautions must be based on the particular properties of the materials that are to be used.

Storage, Handling, and Use

Containers designed, constructed, and tested in accordance with U.S. Department of Transportation (DOT) specifications and regulations must be used for storage of compressed or liquefied gases. Compressed gas container storage should be outside and protected from the effects of weather and sun. An alternate location would be in a well-ventilated louvered room equipped with an automatic sprinkler system. (See Compressed Gas Association Pamphlet P-1, *Safe Handling of Compressed Gases in Containers*. Compressed gas cylinders must be secured in position and stored in racks, away from heat or other ignition sources. Flammable gases should be separated from other oxidizing gases by construction that has a fire resistance rating of at least 1 hr. Electrical equipment in flammable gas storage areas must comply with NFPA 70, *National Electrical Code*, provisions for Class I, Division 2 hazardous locations.

Handling and transporting gas cylinders must be consistent with established safety procedures. Compressed gas cylinders must never be used without pressure regulators, and adapters must not be permitted between the cylinder and the regulator.

Piping systems: When laboratory equipment is operated routinely with flammable gases supplied from compressed gas cylinders, the cylinders should be located outside the building and connected to the laboratory equipment by a permanently installed piping system. Pressure-reducing valves should be connected to each cylinder and adjusted to limit pressure in the piping system to the minimum required gas pressure. Pressure regulators must be compatible with the gases for which they are used. Supply and discharge terminals of piping systems should be permanently marked at both ends with the name of the gas to be piped through them. Never use piping systems for gases other than those for which they were designed and identified. Do not attempt to transfer compressed or liquefied gases from one gas container to another.

Additional requirements are covered in NFPA 58, *Storage and Handling of Liquefied Petroleum Gases*.

General Safety Rules

The following general rules for handling compressed or liquefied gas should be observed in a laboratory:

1. Know cylinder contents. It should be labeled.
2. Know properties of contents.
3. Handle cylinders carefully.
4. Store cylinders in a well-ventilated area away from heat.
5. Secure cylinders during use, transit, or storage.
6. Never tamper with valves, safety plugs, or packing nuts.
7. Do not strike an electric arc on cylinders.
8. Do not use cylinders without a regulator.
9. Close cylinder valves when not in use.
10. Never attempt to refill a cylinder.

BIOLOGICAL HAZARDS

Laboratory work done with animals, infectious diseases, or toxic materials presents a variety of safety problems both to laboratory workers and to others whose duties may be required in the laboratory. Fire, explosions, and other accidents present two types of problems: the release of biological hazards, and the hazards encountered by fire fighting personnel entering the space. Laboratory fire brigades and local fire fighting personnel must be educated to the hazards they may encounter in laboratories engaged in biological work. Sufficient protective equipment, breathing apparatus, clothing, gloves, and so on, must be readily available for use by emergency response personnel. Laboratories engaged in this type of work must be identified appropriately, and clear and concise safety instructions must be posted.

RADIATION HAZARDS

Laboratories using radioactive materials present hazards to both laboratory workers and to others required to enter the facility. While rigid safety and health programs have been established for laboratory workers, it is wise to institute a similar program for other personnel, such as fire fighters. Good communication between laboratory radiation safety and health officers and public fire fighting personnel can help keep fire fighters informed of all laboratories actively engaged in radioactive work. Such rapport can be the basis for establishing an educational program planned to cope with disasters and emergencies. See NFPA 801, *Facilities Handling Radioactive Materials*, for further discussion of the hazards and safeguards associated with nuclear reactors, radiation machines, and radioactive materials.

PERSONNEL PROTECTION

Personal protective equipment is essential to a sound safety program in any laboratory. Protective clothing and equipment must be provided where there is a recognized risk of fire or explosion involving the materials that are used in a laboratory. The nature of the equipment necessarily depends upon the particular hazard. The purpose of protective clothing and equipment is to reduce the probability and the severity of injury if an accident occurs.

Protective Clothing

Personal protective clothing must be made available for use by all laboratory personnel and other personnel required to enter laboratory areas where specific protective clothing is required by the nature of the operations. Specific training programs are useful in instructing personnel in the needs and requirements of protective clothing.

Shields and Barriers

The hazards of explosion, rupture of apparatus and systems from overpressure, implosion due to vacuum, sprays or emission of toxic or corrosive materials, or flash ignition of escaping vapors require substantial physical protection for exposed personnel. Analysis of the potential force and characteristics of the type of hazards involved can aid in the selection of effective and economical shields or barriers.

Respiratory Protection

Respirators are essential for the protection of laboratory personnel working directly with or required to enter areas during an emergency where infectious diseases, radioactive materials, harmful dusts, mists, fogs, fumes, sprays, or vapor are present. Respirators or self-contained breathing apparatus (SCBA) that are suitable for the specific problem to be dealt with are necessary. Training in the use of respirator equipment is essential for laboratory personnel.

HAZARD IDENTIFICATION

Signs should be posted at entrances to laboratories, storage areas, and associated facilities warning personnel, especially emergency personnel, of unusual or severe hazards inside that may or may not be directly related to an emergency situation. Included are signs relating to particularly unstable chemicals, radioactive chemicals, pathogenic or infectious materials, water-reactive chemicals, and explosives. NFPA 704, *Identification of the Fire Hazards of Materials*, is a good system to use. Periodic review is necessary to ensure that the particular warning label being displayed properly indicates the nature of the material being used within the identified laboratory area. Severe hazards should be discussed with fire fighting personnel to make certain they know what to anticipate.

The contents of all individual containers within a specific laboratory area must be identified. Unlabeled containers present a serious potential hazard, not only to laboratory workers but also to other personnel required to enter laboratory areas, especially during emergencies.

BIBLIOGRAPHY

NFPA Codes, Standards, and Recommended Practices

Reference to the following NFPA codes, standards, and recommended practices will provide further information on protection for laboratories discussed in this chapter. (See the latest *NFPA Catalog for availability of current editions of the following documents.)*

NFPA 10, *Portable Fire Extinguishers.*

NFPA 11, *Low Expansion Foam and Combined Agent Systems.*

NFPA 11A, *Medium- and High-Expansion Foam Systems.*

NFPA 12, *Carbon Dioxide Extinguishing Systems.*

NFPA 12A, *Halon 1301 Fire Extinguishing Agent Systems.*

NFPA 13, *Installation of Sprinkler Systems.*

NFPA 14, *Installation of Standpipe and Hose Systems.*

NFPA 15, *Water-Spray Fixed Systems for Fire Protection.*

NFPA 30, *Flammable and Combustible Liquids Code.*

NFPA 45, *Fire Protection for Laboratories Using Chemicals.*

NFPA 49, *Hazardous Chemicals Data.*

NFPA 50, *Bulk Oxygen Systems at Consumer Sites.*

NFPA 50A, *Gaseous Hydrogen Systems at Consumer Sites.*

NFPA 50B, *Liquefied Hydrogen Systems at Consumer Sites.*

NFPA 53M, *Fire Hazards in Oxygen-Enriched Atmospheres.*

NFPA 56F, *Non-Flammable Medical Gas Systems.*

NFPA 58, *Storage and Handling of Liquefied Petroleum Gases.*

NFPA 68, *Venting of Deflagrations.*

NFPA 70, *National Electrical Code.®*

NFPA 72, *Protective Signaling Systems*

NFPA 72A, *Local Protective Signaling Systems for Guards' Tour, Fire Alarm and Supervisory Service.*

NFPA 72E, *Automatic Fire Detectors.*

NFPA 77, *Static Electricity.*

NFPA 80, *Fire Doors and Windows.*

NFPA 86, *Ovens and Furnaces.*

NFPA 90A, *Air Conditioning and Ventilating Systems.*

NFPA 91, *Exhaust Systems for Air Conveying of Materials.*

NFPA 99, *Health Care Facilities.*

NFPA 101,® *Life Safety Code.®*

NFPA 220, *Types of Building Construction.*

NFPA 251, *Fire Tests of Building Construction and Materials.*

NFPA 259, *Potential Heat of Building Materials.*

NFPA 321, *Classification of Flammable and Combustible Liquids.*

NFPA 325M, *Fire Hazard Properties of Flammable Liquids, Gases, and Volatile Solids.*

NFPA 491M, *Hazardous Chemical Reactions.*

NFPA 496, *Purged and Pressurized Enclosures for Electrical Equipment.*

NFPA 704, *Identification of the Fire Hazards of Materials.*

NFPA 801, *Facilities Handling Radioactive Materials.*

Additional Reading

American Conference of Governmental Industrial Hygienists, *Threshold Limit Values for Chemical Substances and Physical Agents in the Workroom Environment with Intended changes for 1990-91*, American Conference of Governmental Hygienists, Cincinnati, OH, 1991. (revised annually)

Committee on Industrial Ventilation, *A Manual of Recommended Practice*, American Conference of Governmental Industrial Hygienists, Cincinnati, OH.

ASTM Publications. American Society for Testing and Materials, 1916 Race Street, Philadelphia, PA 19103.

ASTM D 56-1982, *Standard Method of Test for Flash Point by the Tag Closed Tester.*

ASTM D 93-1980, *Standard Method of Test for Flash Point by the Pensky-Martens Closed Tester.*

ASTM D 3278-1982, *Standard Method of Tests for Flash Point for Flash Point of Liquids by Setaflash Closed Tester.*

ASTM D 3828-1981, *Standard Test Methods for Flash Point of Liquids by Setaflash Closed Tester.*

ASTM E 136, *Standard Method of Test for Noncombustibility of Elementary Materials.*

ANSI Publications. American National Standards Institute, 1430 Broadway, New York, NY 10018.

ANSI A13.1-1981, *Standard Scheme for the Identification of Piping Systems.*

ANSI B31.1.0, *Power Piping.*

ANSI B31.2, *Fuel Gas Piping.*

ANSI B31.3, *Petroleum Refinery Piping.*

Other Publications

Benedetti, R. P., *Flammable and Combustible Liquids Code Handbook*, 3rd ed., National Fire Protection Association, Quincy, MA, 1987.

Bon, R. G., Michaelson, G. S., and DeRoos, R. L., *Environmental Health and Safety in Health-Care Facilities*, Macmillan, NY, 1973.

Bond, R. G., Michaelson, G. S., and DeRoos, R. L., *Environmental Health and Safety in Health-Care Facilities*, Macmillan, NY, 1973.

Bretherick, L., *Hazards in the Chemical Laboratory*, 4th ed., Royal Institute of Chemistry, London, 1986.

Christensen, H.E., *ed.*, *The Toxic Substances List*, National Institute for Occupational Safety and Health, Rockville, MD.

DeRoos, J. L., "The Safe Use of Refrigerator and Freezer Appliances for Storage of Flammable Materials," *Fire Journal*, Vol. 67, No. 2 (Mar. 1973), pp. 63-64.

Factory Mutual Engineering Corp., *Laboratory Fires and Explosions*, Loss Prevention Data Sheet 10-19, Factory Mutual System, Norwood, MA.

Fawcett, H. H. and Wood, W. S., *Safety and Accident Prevention in Chemical Operation*, 2nd ed., Wiley, NY, 1982.

Flammability Characteristics of Combustible Gases and Vapors, U.S. Bureau of Mines Bulletin 627, U.S. Bureau of Mines, Pittsburgh, PA, 1965.

Furr, A. K., *ed.*, *CRC Handbook of Laboratory Safety*, 3rd ed., CRC Press, Boca Raton, FL, 1990.

Fuscaldo, A. A., *ed.*, *Laboratory Safety: Theory and Practice*, Academic Press, NY, 1980.

Glove Box Fire Safety, A Guide for Safe Practices in Design, Protection and Operation, FMRC Report TID-24236, Factory Mutual Research Corp, Norwood, MA, 1967.

Green, M. F. and Tark, A., *Laboratory Safety*, Macmillan, NY, 1978.

Guide for Safety in the Chemical Laboratory, 2nd ed., Van Nostrand Reinhold, NY, 1972.

Le, N. B., Santay, A. J., and Jabrenski, J. S., "Laboratory Safety Design Criteria," *Plant/Operation Progress*, Vol. 7, No. 2 (April 1988), pp. 87-94.

Manufacturing Chemists' Association, *Laboratory Waste Disposal Manual*, Washington, DC, 1975.

Matheson Gas Data Book, 4th ed., Matheson Co., East Rutherford, NJ, current edition.

Meidl, J. H., *Flammable Hazardous Materials*, 2nd ed., Glencove Press, Encino, CA, 1978.

Method of Testing Performance of Laboratory Fume Hoods, American Society of Heating, Refrigerating, and Air Conditioning Engineers, Inc., Atlanta, GA.

Miller, B. M., *ed.*, *Laboratory Safety; Principles and Practices*, American Society for Microbiology, Washington, DC, 1986.

Nelson, H.E., *Fire Safety Evaluation System for NASA Office/Laboratory Buildings*, NBSIR 86-3404, National Bureau of Standards, Gaithersburg, MD, Nov. 1986.

Orvos, D.R., "Biohazard," *Fire Engineering*, Vol. 141, No. 4, 1988, p. 49.

Pipitone, D., *ed.*, *Safe Storage of Laboratory Chemicals*, John Wiley, NY, 1984.

Pressure Vessel Code, New York, American Society of Mechanical Engineers, 1980.

Quam, G. N., *Safety Practice for Chemical Laboratories*, Villanova Press, Villanova, PA, 1963.

Safe Handling of Compressed Gases in Container, CGA Pamphlet P-1, New York, Compressed Gas Association.

Sittig, M., *Handbook of Toxic and Hazardous Chemicals*, Noyes, Park Ridge, NJ, 1981.

Sittig, M., *Handbook of Toxic and Hazardous Chemicals and Carcinogens*, 2nd ed., Noyes, Park Ridge, NJ, 1985.

Spindel, W., *Prudent Practices for Handling Hazardous Chemicals in Laboratories*, National Science Foundation, Washington, DC, 1981.

Standard on Laboratory Fume Hoods (LF-10-1980), The Scientific Apparatus Makers Association, Washington, DC.

Standard Specification for Laboratory Fume Hoods, Environmental Protection Agency, Washington, DC.

Threshold Limit Values for Chemical Substances and Physical Agents in the Workroom Environment with Intended Changes for 1973, American Conference of Governmental Hygienists, Cincinnati, OH, 1973.

Walton, W. D., *Quick Response Sprinklers in Chemical Laboratories: Fire Test Results*, NISTIR 89-4200, National Institute of Standards and Technology, Gaithersburg, MD, Nov. 1989.

Welby, P. and Dickinson, K. R., "Monitoring Work Areas for Explosive and Toxic Hazards," *Chemical Engineering*, Vol. 83, No. 22, 1976, pp. 139-145.

TELECOMMUNICATIONS EQUIPMENT FACILITIES

Lawrence A. McKenna, Jr.

This chapter discusses the basic layout and function of the U.S. telecommunications network. Further, it describes the various components of that network and provides guidelines for the provision of fire protection for those components. Both the public telecommunications network and private telecommunications equipment are discussed.

Since Alexander Graham Bell made the first phone call on March 10, 1876, telephones have played an increasingly important role in people's lives. Once an oddity, and then a convenience, the telephone has become a necessity of modern life. Telecommunications, which touches almost every facet of daily life, includes: (1) automatic bank teller machines, (2) credit card validators, (3) electronic funds transfer functions, (4) faxsimile machines, (5) teleconferencing and video-conferencing, and (6) standard telephone service.

This evolution in the uses of telecommunications services has driven the technologies that provide the service to ever-increasing levels of sophistication. This has resulted in three important technological developments currently underway in the industry. First, transmission of signals between points in the network is being converted from analog signaling, which transmits an electrical signal that varies continuously, to digital signaling, which consists of on-and-off pulses of electricity or light.

The second major development is the extensive conversion of main transmission routes to fiber optics. The extension of fiber optic technology to the home is considered to be the next logical step in this development. This would allow a new array of voice, video, data, and other services to be available on demand.

The final development on the telecommunications horizon is the development of advanced radio-based telecommunications systems. This evolution would allow for personal, pocket-sized telephones capable of sending and receiving calls anywhere in the world by satellite.

Lawrence A. McKenna, Jr., is a senior fire protection engineer for AT&T, Basking Ridge, NJ.

THE U.S. TELECOMMUNICATIONS NETWORK

Currently, telecommunications services are provided by approximately 1400 service companies in the U.S. These companies operate networks ranging in size from small rural companies serving up to 2000 customers to large companies operating worldwide networks serving millions of customers. Primary control functions for these networks are located in buildings called central offices (COs). Approximately 20,000 central offices are required to operate the telecommunications network in the U.S. More than 300 of these are over 100,000 sq ft (9,300 m^2) in floor area.

The U.S. telecommunications network can be divided into two segments: (1) the portion provided by local exchange carriers (LECs), or local phone companies; and (2) the portion provided by interexchange carriers (IECs), or long-distance phone companies. The distinction between these two types of phone companies centers around the concept of the local access and transport area (LATA), which was established at the court-ordered divestiture of the Bell System in 1984.

A LATA is a geographic area defining dialing boundaries for local telephone companies (LECs). Often, LATA boundaries coincide with area code boundaries. Under federal regulations, an LEC may serve more than one LATA, but may not provide telecommunications service between LATAs. Service between LATAs is provided by long-distance telephone companies, the IECs. Information regarding the LATA in a specific area can be found in the local telephone directory.

This division results in two separate types of telecommunications networks, as illustrated in Figures 8-30A and 8-30B.

Figure 8-30A is a simplified schematic of the local network, provided by the LEC. In terms taken from sprinkler system design, the local network is a "tree" network. Each customer telephone is connected to one, and only one, central office or exchange. Failure in any of the COs or the cables linking them will isolate all customers or services on one side of the failure from those on the other side.

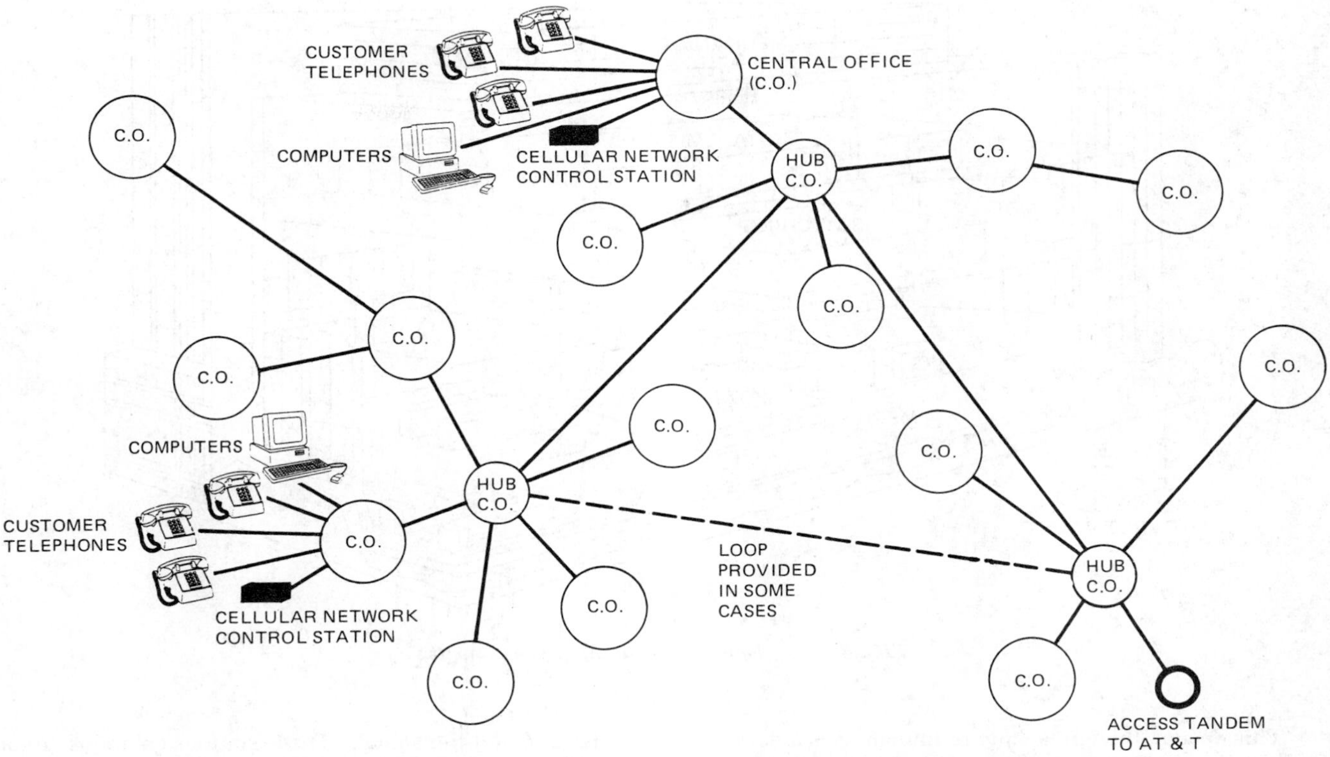

FIG. 8-30A. Local telecommunications network.

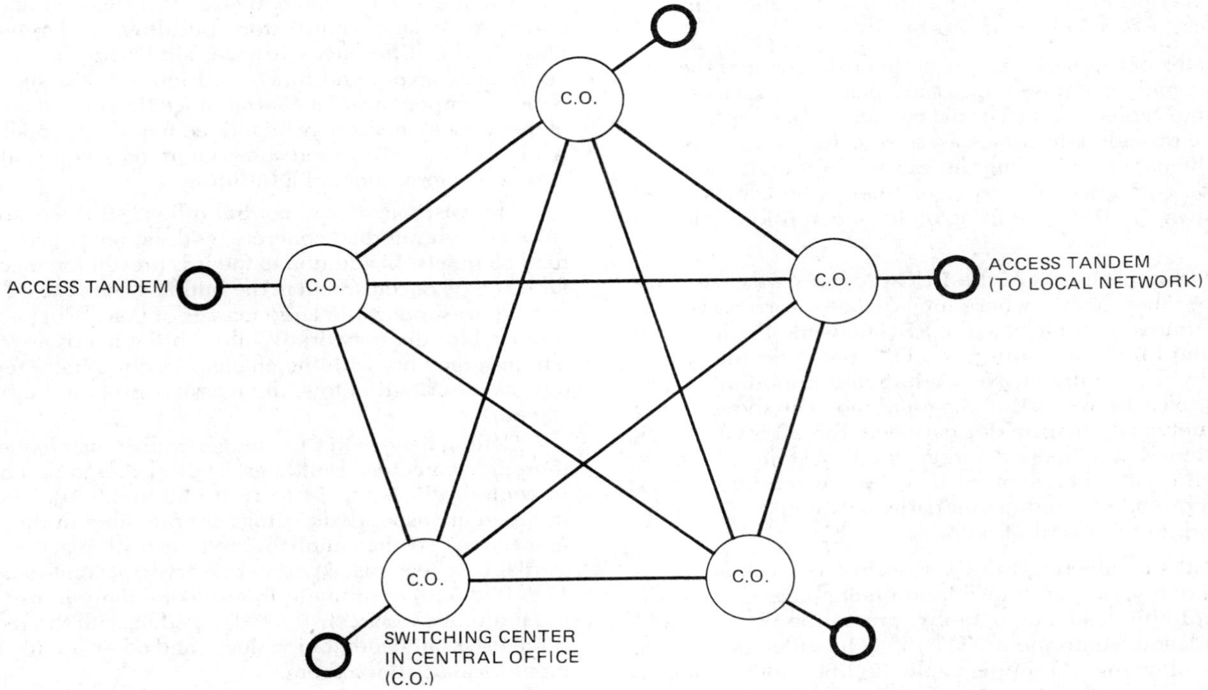

***FIG. 8-30B.** AT&T worldwide intelligent network. Multiple paths between points may be fiber optic cables, copper cables, microwave radio, or satellite radio.*

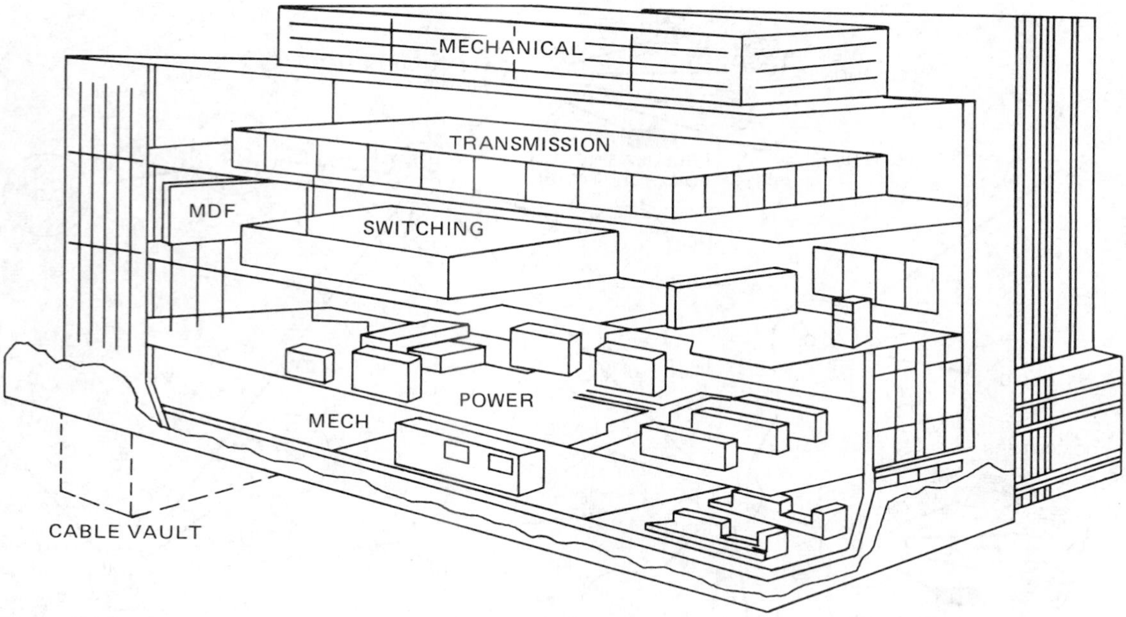

FIG. 8-30C. Typical central office components.

This design, though lacking redundancy, is a deliberate decision made in compliance with the overall network design criteria directed by the FCC, as well as the various state regulatory bodies. The criteria was intended to allow for universal service at a low price, not uninterrupted service. However, a great deal of effort is currently underway to provide redundancies to certain high-traffic routes, such as the links between hub COs. (Customers generally have the option of providing additional redundancies for personal use, at additional cost.)

Paths between the end user, or customer, and the CO are generally composed of twisted-pair copper wires bundled into cables. Radio, coaxial copper, or fiber optic cable may be provided, in some cases, for certain large customers. The paths connecting the various COs to one another may be composed of copper or fiber optic cables, or of microwave radio, depending on local conditions and terrain.

Within each LATA, the LEC provides an access tandem or other facility where long-distance carriers (IECs) are permitted to connect to the LEC network. Figure 8-30B is a simplified diagram of one IEC network, the AT&T Worldwide Intelligent Network. Some important differences exist between this diagram and that showing the LEC network. In sprinkler parlance, the AT&T network is designed as a "looped and gridded" system. There are multiple paths between each of the switching centers, which provide for redundant paths between points in the network in the event of failure.

Paths connecting the COs in this network are composed of a variety of transmission technologies, depending on traffic loads, topography, prevailing weather, and redundancy requirements. They may include one or more of the following: (1) copper cable, (2) fiber optic cable, (3) microwave radio, or (4) satellite radio. Along each of these paths, as well as those in the LEC networks, there are a number of repeater or regeneration stations which amplify and retransmit the signals. These stations compensate for the deterioration of the signals over distance.

THE CENTRAL OFFICE

The nodes in each of these networks are located in buildings called central offices (COs), or telephone exchanges. COs are designed and sized to meet the service needs of the customers. They range in size from small, single-story buildings to large, multi-story buildings in large cities. Despite the differences in size, similarity exists in the equipment layout and function. Figure 8-30C shows the typical components of a central office. In remote areas, all of these components may be located in a single small room, while in large cities each component may require the use of one or more floors of a building.

The vast majority of central office buildings are constructed of reinforced concrete, with rather massive structural elements. In addition to the loss prevention incentives for this type of construction, the buildings need to be strong enough to support the large masses of heavy copper cable required for the network. While cabling needs are diminishing somewhat with the changes in equipment technology, as described below, the massive structural elements remain.

Ceiling heights in COs are generally much higher than those in commercial buildings. Typical slab-to-slab heights in central offices are 14 to 16 ft (4.3 to 4.9 m). Very few dropped or suspended ceilings are provided in the equipment areas so that unobstructed vertical space remains available. Clear space was necessary to accommodate the 11½-ft (3.5 m) equipment frames commonly in use when the buildings were constructed, together with the required cable racks, air conditioning ducts, and other service equipment located above them.

Cables enter and leave most COs through the cable vault, where they are split into smaller, more fire-resistant cables for distribution in the building. The cables then rise through the building to the main distributing frame (MDF) where they are broken down into individual pairs of wire for each circuit, and are cross-connected to cables leading to the switching systems. After switching, the signals are passed to the transmission systems, which multiplex and boost the signals. Once this is accomplished, the signal travels back out of the building through the cable vault on other cables.

Supporting the telecommunications equipment is a variety of standard mechanical and building service systems, in addition to standby generators, battery systems, and associated power control and distribution equipment.

TELECOMMUNICATIONS EQUIPMENT

Description

Telecommunications equipment is fairly standardized in both function and appearance. Three generations of equipment are typically found in COs in the U.S.

The equipment is arranged in parallel rows, or "lineups," of 19 to 26 inches wide (48 to 66 cm). Equipment heights vary from 11½-ft (3.5 m) for the oldest generation (which is being phased out quickly), to 6¾ ft (2.06 m) and 6 ft (1.83 m) for the latest generations of digital electronic equipment. As the height of the equipment decreased to facilitate maintenance operations, its depth increased, from 1 ft (30 cm) to about 24 in.(61 cm).

Earlier generations of equipment were mounted in open frames without enclosures. This allowed easy access for maintenance, and permitted heat dissipation by natural convection. Modern equipment is often enclosed in metal cabinets, much like ordinary computers in appearance. This arrangement, when combined with miniaturization of the equipment and the attendant higher energy densities, requires forced ventilation (internal fans) to dissipate the heat generated during operation.

This provision for heat dissipation is important, since the equipment is sensitive to temperature and humidity changes in the operating environment. While the absolute operating limits are rather wide, rapid changes of either a few degrees of temperature or a few percentage points of humidity can cause serious problems. Consequently, extensive environmental controls are used to ensure that ambient conditions remain within required limits.

Differences from Standard Computers

On first examination, modern digital telecommunications equipment resembles modern computers or data processing equipment. While there are similarities, a number of important differences exist. Some of these differences were deliberately created to reduce the incidence, or the effect, of potential loss-causing events. Other differences, necessary because of various technical requirements, have the opposite effect. Some of these differences present challenges which most traditional loss prevention measures cannot adequately mitigate.

One of the most significant differences is the type of information processing performed. Telecommunications systems are on-line information exchange systems. Customer data is not stored or processed in the telecommunications system; it is merely transferred from point A to point B. In the event of a disruption, all the information that is in transit is lost, and the ability to transmit information ceases. Data cannot be reloaded as long as the disruption continues, and missed opportunities cannot be made up. It is this ability to transmit information in real time that makes telecommunications so important. Many transactions routinely conducted over the network simply cannot wait until later to take place.

In contrast, data processing systems generally process information that has been stored in the system's memory sub-systems. In the event of disruption, the current memory is lost, along with any calculation results that have not been placed in permanent memory. However, all of the stored information remains on the disks or tapes, depending on the storage media. The calculations can usually be reproduced after the cause of the disruption is corrected.

Another important difference between telecommunications equipment and data processing equipment is in the power supplies. Data processing equipment is supplied with ac power to the cabinet. The conversion from ac to dc takes place within the equipment, which generally operates at 5 to 10 volts dc. Telecommunications equipment, on the other hand, is supplied with dc power. The conversion from commercial ac power to dc power takes place outside the equipment, often in a different building compartment. The power plant supplies the equipment with 12, 24, 48, or 130 volts dc, depending on system requirements. Power supply segregation is discussed further, later in this chapter.

Another important difference lies in the redundancies usually provided for telecommunications equipment. In most networks, for instance, all switching and call routing functions are performed by equipment operating in a duplex configuration. This means that each call is handled by two separate processors simultaneously. In the unlikely event that one processor fails, the other will continue to process the call, without interruption to the customer. In fact, the customer will be unaware that such an event has occurred.

The final difference, which has a significant impact on loss prevention, is in the size of the control programs. The programs that control the various networks are among the largest and most complex known. Programs involving millions of lines of program code are not uncommon. Programs of this size naturally require much more time to reload and initialize in the event of a disruption than common data processing programs. This is one reason it can take up to several days to restart an electronic switching system in the event of a power loss. The thermal shock created by suddenly restoring power to the entire system is another.

Telecommunications equipment provided for use on a customer's premises, known as private branch exchange (PBX) equipment, is different in many respects from the equipment used in COs. Major differences that have an impact on a loss prevention program are discussed later in this chapter.

FIRE RECORD

The record of fires in telecommunications facilities and central offices over the past 100 years has been exceptionally good. It is estimated that 109 fires occur annually in approximately 20,000 U.S. telephone exchanges,[1] most being too small to activate detection and suppression systems, reflecting the exceptional efforts in the design and operation of the equipment.[1]

This excellent record is due, in large part, to the exhaustive fire prevention efforts by the industry, described in greater detail later in this chapter. Despite these efforts, three major incidents have occurred. These fires have been very small when compared to major fires in other industries, particularly in terms of equipment or areas damaged, but their impact on the local communities was substantial.

In the most recent incident, the probable cause of the fire in a cable rack was a power cable, possibly damaged during maintenance activities, which shorted to the sheathing of a flexible armored cable and caused the armored cable to overheat and ignite the cable bundle. The principal fire damage was confined to the cable rack. Smoke damage spread throughout the floor and disabled a major switching system. A complete analysis of this incident can be found in the "Hinsdale Central Office Fire Final Report."[2]

FIRE PROTECTION FOR THE PUBLIC NETWORK

A systematic approach is essential in determining proper fire protection measures applicable to telecommunications equipment facilities. (See Section 1, Chapter 3, "Systems Concepts for Building Firesafety.") Such an approach helps clearly define the challenges at hand and provides a framework for identifying all of the elements that have an impact on firesafety. One example of such an approach is the firesafety concepts tree, found in NFPA 550, *Firesafety Concepts Tree*. (See Figure 8-30D.)

Figure 8-30D shows a sample firesafety concepts tree for telecommunications central offices. This tree is modeled after the NFPA firesafety concepts tree and has been customized for this application. The terms listed in the boxes in Figure 8-30D correspond to subtitles in the remainder of this chapter.

In concept, the firesafety objective can be achieved by providing one path through the decision tree. In practice, however, the use of multiple paths provides redundancies that increase confidence in accomplishing the objective. Most U.S. telecommunications providers follow a program that employs many, if not all, of the paths through this tree. A risk management decision to use multiple paths through the tree effectively changes all of the gates in the tree to AND gates. The tree illustrated in Figure 8-30D includes both AND and OR gates for purposes of illustrating the concepts.

Before centering attention wholly on fire protection, it is important to note that fire is just one of the many potential causes of telecommunications service disruption. Some of the techniques employed to mitigate other types of risk have a negative impact on fire risk. This effect can work in the opposite direction, as well.

Firesafety Objectives

At the top of the decision tree are the firesafety objectives to be accomplished through the fire risk management program. In the case of a CO, all telecommunications providers want to minimize service disruptions from any cause. The actual quantification of this goal is influenced by customer demands, as well as by the various regulatory agencies governing telecommunications service providers. In the U.S., the Federal Communications Commission (FCC) and various state regulatory agencies perform this function. (There was an earlier discussion regarding universal service *vs.* uninterrupted service, which has driven the design of the U.S. networks.)

Desired firesafety objectives can be accomplished by preventing ignition from occurring or by managing the fire once ignition has occurred. Considering that ignition prevention is the most desirable scenario in an industry that provides vital services, a look will be taken first at that branch of the tree.

Prevent Ignition

In the context of a CO, ignition prevention can be separated into two areas of concern: (1) those internal to the telecommunications equipment; and (2) those external to the equipment, or in other areas of the building. Modern telecommunications equipment is susceptible to service-

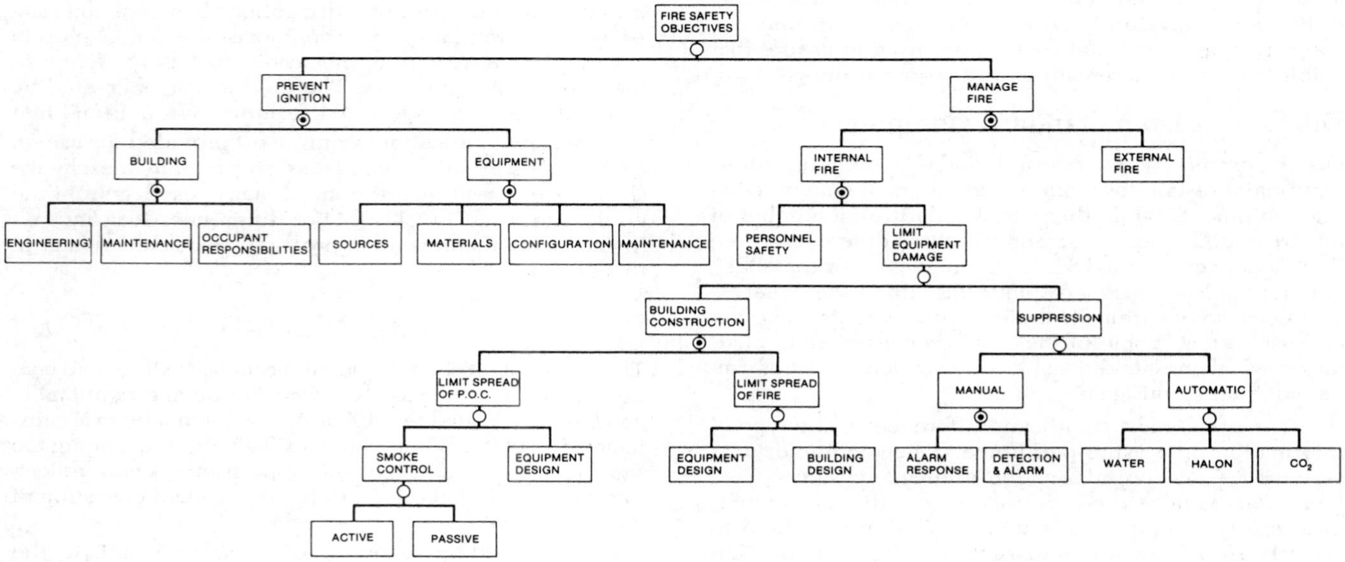

FIG. 8-30D. Firesafety concepts tree for telecommunications central offices.

interrupting damage from the direct insult of a fire, as well as from indirect insults such as smoke. Therefore, prevention of both is necessary to prevent damage to the equipment.

Within the building: Ignition prevention associated with the building, i.e., not in the telecommunications equipment, should be handled in a fairly traditional manner, although a more-rigorous-than-normal implementation is warranted.

Engineering: The building should be engineered and designed as a single-use occupancy for telecommunications equipment. This eliminates the people, ignition sources, and fuel packages typically found in other occupancies. Where this is not possible, substantial fire-rated barriers should be provided to separate the telecommunications equipment from other occupancies and the risks they may pose to service continuity.

Maintenance: Building service equipment, electrical systems, fire protection systems, and other systems in the building should be maintained in a fashion that will reduce or eliminate the chance of ignition.

Occupant responsibilities: All occupants of the building should be thoroughly trained in their responsibilities toward fire prevention and emergency preparedness. This training should include proper procedures for housekeeping, storage of combustibles, and emergency actions. Other chapters of this handbook cover these issues in greater detail. Smoking should be prohibited in all equipment and storage areas, and throughout the building if possible.

Within the equipment: Ignition prevention within the telecommunications equipment is especially important since any established fire in the equipment will result in service disruption. (A fire is generally considered an established fire when it becomes self-sustaining, i.e., when flame height reaches 12 in. (30 cm). In order to prevent ignition within the equipment, four issues are addressed: (1) sources of ignition energy, (2) the selection of materials that would constitute the fuel package for a fire, (3) the configuration of these materials in the equipment, and (4) the maintenance of the equipment.

Sources of ignition energy: All unnecessary sources of ignition energy should be removed from the building. Any necessary sources of ignition energy should be separated from the equipment as much as possible.

A common source of ignition energy is power equipment, such as the rectifiers, transformers, and converters that compose a power supply system. Such devices often can be located remotely from important telecommunications equipment. This physical separation can reduce the risk of fire damage to the more sensitive circuitry in the telecommunications equipment should a fire occur within the power supply.

Materials selection: The selection and configuration of materials used in the manufacture of the telecommunications equipment is essentially controlled in the U.S. by the "Network Equipment — Building System (NEBS) Generic Equipment Requirements."[3] Because this is a proprietary document, efforts are currently underway to produce a more widely applicable standard under the auspices of the American National Standards Institute (ANSI).

Three types of tests are required of telecommunications equipment: (1) flammability tests of components, wiring, and sub-assemblies; (2) equipment flame spread tests; and (3) equipment extinguishability tests.

Individual electronic components must meet the requirements of the International Electrotechnical Commission (IEC) Standard 695-2-2.[4] In this test, the component is exposed by application of a needle-like flame for a period of time determined by the volume of the component. If the component will not ignite, or self-extinguishes within 30 sec after removal of the flame, and if any plastic drippings do not ignite a piece of tissue paper placed 2 in. (5 cm) below the sample location, it passes the test. Structural elements, such as circuit boards, must show evidence of an oxygen index of 28 percent or greater, as determined by ASTM D2863-77.[5] They must also achieve a 94 V-1 or better rating under UL 94.[6]

Other non-metallic parts and components must also meet flammability requirements established by numerous other standard test methods. (See the bibliography at the end of this chapter.)

Materials configuration: Once the individual components are found to satisfy these requirements, the completed assembly is subjected to two large-scale tests:

1. In the equipment assembly flame spread test, a full equipment frame is subjected to a severe fire insult from 8.3 oz. (200 ml) of isopropyl alcohol in a 6-in. (15 cm)-diameter pan, placed 2 in. (5 cm) below the frame so that the flames impinge directly on the polymeric (plastic) components of the equipment. The fire is then permitted to burn until it goes out by itself. If flames spread beyond the frame being tested, the equipment fails the test.
2. In the equipment assembly extinguishability test, the same fire insult is applied to an equipment frame at least 36 in. (91 cm) high. After a 15-min pre-burn, the resulting fire must be capable of being extinguished by a 10B:C-rated CO_2 or Halon 1211 fire extinguisher.

Viewed together, these test requirements serve to assess the ignitability and subsequent flame spread within the equipment. Equipment passing these tests is minimally susceptible to ignition, fire growth, and the subsequent service disruptions.

Equipment maintenance: Once the equipment is designed, manufactured, and installed to meet these exacting requirements, it must be maintained in a manner that eliminates the chance of ignition. Electronic equipment is fairly simple to maintain from a fire prevention perspective. The major maintenance fire hazards are related to the large quantities of cables associated with the equipment.

The majority of cables in a telecommunications facility are low-energy signal cables. There are also a number of higher energy power cables, running between the power equipment and the telecommunications equipment. Although not inherently hazardous, high-energy power cables present a somewhat greater risk of fire, if damaged, than low-energy signal cables.

The continuous upgrades and changes made to CO equipment result in constant additions and frequent abandonment of cables. Unused cables do not present a source of ignition when they are disconnected at both ends. However, they do contribute fuel load for a potential fire, and, in this light, removal of unused cable may be desirable.

Removal creates certain hazards that must be evaluated against the benefits gained. Removal activities, known as cable mining, are inherently hazardous from both fire protection and service continuity perspectives. Damage caused during cable mining operations was identified as a possible cause of the Hinsdale, IL, central office fire.[2]

It is extremely difficult to remove cables from the lower levels of large cable bundles. These operations must be carefully performed by trained technicians to decrease the potential for service interruptions.

Manage the Fire

Despite the best efforts to prevent ignition in the equipment and elsewhere in the building, fire may still occur. Thus, provisions must be made to manage the impact of a fire and its byproducts.

As shown in the firesafety concepts tree in Figure 8-30D, fires outside the building must be managed, as well as those occurring internally.

External fires: External fire exposure should be mitigated in a number of traditional ways. The site for the CO should be carefully selected so that adjacent properties or operations do not constitute a risk to the network equipment. As a minimum, building construction should meet the requirements of NFPA 220, *Types of Building Construction*, for Type II construction. Where necessary, exposure protection systems should be provided.

A prominent example of an exposure protection system can be found in the lack of windows in many CO buildings. This provides protection against exposure fires, as well as protection from sabotage or terrorist activities. The lack of windows does, however, make fire fighter access and ventilation more difficult in the unlikely event of a fire.

Internal fires: The safety of the occupants of a building must come first when managing fire. Strict adherence to NFPA 101®, *Life Safety Code*®, will help ensure this. Once personnel safety is ensured, equipment safety or, more correctly, the limitation of damage to the telecommunications equipment, can be considered.

Limit equipment damage: Equipment damage limitations should include a combination of safeguards built into the building and the telecommunications equipment, as well as actual suppression of the fire.

Telecommunications equipment can suffer damage that affects service from both direct and indirect fire exposure, e.g., from the products of combustion (POC). Both must be managed to achieve the firesafety objective. Both building design/construction and equipment design/construction can be used profitably to limit damage.

Limit smoke (POC) spread: Two broad approaches are useful in limiting damage from smoke. The first is to select materials that minimize smoke generation and to limit materials that generate smoke which is particularly damaging to the equipment. The second approach to limiting smoke damage is to control the smoke that is produced. When selecting materials, the use of polyvinyl chloride (PVC) as an insulation material is of particular interest.

PVC is widely used as insulation on cables and wires in COs. This material has excellent electrical and fire-resistance properties. When PVC burns, however, it releases gaseous hydrogen chloride (HCl), which combines with atmospheric water vapor to form hydrochloric acid. This, in turn, is deposited on, and destructively reacts with, metallic parts of the equipment. This phenomenon has been responsible for serious damage in several fires involving electronic equipment.

A potential solution to this acidic smoke concern involves the use of non-halogenated insulation material, which recently was made available. This material produces no HCl when burning and passes all applicable flammability tests. Although widespread retrofit of this cable into existing COs would pose a large risk of service outages and is not generally recommended, cable with non-halogenated insulation should be used wherever possible in new equipment installations or in modifications to existing equipment.

When considering the control of smoke produced by a fire, both passive and active measures are applicable. Passive smoke control measures are generally adaptations of the measures used to prevent the spread of fire, i.e., fire and smoke barriers. Compartmentation, augmented by fire/smoke dampers in duct penetrations, smoke seals on fire doors, and good firestopping of other penetrations, is widely considered as a successful control measure. Active smoke control measures employ a combination of fans and ducts that pressurize some areas of the building and exhaust others. (See Section 6, Chapter 7, "Smoke Movement in Buildings.")

Limit fire spread: Fire spread should be limited by building construction and by equipment design. Fire spread within equipment should be controlled through the use of the equipment design and material selection criteria. Where equipment that does not meet these criteria is used in the network, it should be isolated from all other equipment with fire-rated barriers. Additional protection may be appropriate for such non-conforming equipment if it presents risks to other equipment or services.

An example of the appropriate use of fire barriers can be found in cable vaults. Cables exposed to the weather or earth are usually insulated with polyethylene plastic which provides protection from these elements. Because polyethylene has rather poor fire-retardant properties, its use inside the CO would increase fire risk. To mitigate this risk, outside cables enter the building in a room with a substantial fire-resistance rating. Inside this vault, the polyethylene outside plant cables are terminated and spliced to cables with acceptable fire-resistance properties. This fire-retardant cable is then used throughout the building.

The vaults also serve as collection areas for any vapors or gases that may enter the building along the path of the buried cable, creating a health or explosion hazard. Appropriate detection and exhaust systems should be provided where such incidents could occur.

Fire detection: Reliable and sufficiently early detection is particularly challenging in modern telecommunications equipment environments. High air flow rates, high ceilings, horizontal air currents, and numerous overhead obstructions combine to present a severe challenge to traditional smoke detection strategies. Air-sampling-type detection systems have the demonstrated capabilities to meet these challenges and should be considered for use in telecommunications facilities.[7,8]

Additional early warning may be obtained through the use of chemical species monitoring of selected spaces. Current COs use large quantities of PVC-insulated cables. PVC releases HCl gas in detectable quantities when heated, and this release begins at temperatures well below PVC's ignition temperature, and before combustion begins. Installation of an HCl detection system could provide detection of an overheated cable before smoke detection systems can activate.[7] Provision of this type of system may be desirable in certain instances.

Fire suppression: Two options are available to accomplish suppression of a fire in a CO: (1) manual action by trained personnel or the public fire service, and (2) automatic suppression systems. When considering a fire originating within the telecommunications equipment, it should be noted that any established fire will result in a failure to meet the firesafety objective. This is the primary reason for the extraordinary efforts in ignition prevention.

Manual fire suppression. Detection systems only signal the presence of fire, thereby alerting personnel who must respond to the fire condition. Employees who are expected to perform fire suppression and related duties must be fully trained in those duties, and training should be demonstrated regularly through exercises and drills.

One of the most important emergency duties is shutting off power. Fires involving any telecommunications equipment will involve energized electrical equipment and/or circuits. The most common extinguishing action for electrical fires is to remove power from the circuit by unplugging the appliance or by throwing the switch or circuit breaker. This is much more difficult in telecommunications facilities.

The power system in telecommunications facilities is designed with multiple redundancies, since a power interruption will disrupt service quickly for an extended period. Typically, standby generators and large battery systems are provided as backups to the commercial power supply. These power systems are designed much like the power supply for an electric fire pump, in that the system is designed to run until total failure. The complexities of these power systems make it difficult to turn the power off to fight a fire. The importance of an easy method to shut off the power was clearly demonstrated in the investigation report on the Hinsdale, IL, CO fire.[2]

While current technology does not facilitate reliable and easy power disconnects for telecommunications equipment, procedures should be developed to guide emergency responders through the power down process. These procedures should clearly identify the steps to be taken to remove power to the various areas within the building, and they should be updated frequently.

Automatic fire suppression. Current model building codes permit the omission of automatic suppression systems in telecommunications equipment areas in COs under a restrictive set of conditions. This exemption is based on the very low probability of ignition, the low fire growth rates, and the excellent fire record of the equipment.

Selecting a suppression system for areas containing telecommunications equipment is difficult, and must be carefully weighed against a clear understanding of loss prevention objectives. The mere presence or functioning of an automatic suppression system will not ensure that the firesafety objectives are met, and such a system should not be substituted for the firesafety measures already described.

Three options are available for automatic suppression systems in electronic equipment areas: (1) halon, (2) CO_2, and (3) automatic sprinklers. Other systems exist, but they have been ruled out for a variety of reasons. Recent environmental considerations have also essentially removed the halon option, and it will not be discussed further in this chapter.

Any automatic suppression system selected for use in a telecommunications facility should meet several criteria. These include: (1) rapid initiation of suppression activity, (2) the capability for sustained application of agent, (3) the ability to control damage to acceptable limits, and (4) permitting safe fire fighter access to the area.

None of the current suppression system options can meet all of these criteria. It is important that the selection and use of any suppression system also include a full analysis of the potential damage the system could cause if it activated during a fire or inadvertently.

CO_2 systems can be designed to activate early enough to limit fire damage, given an appropriate detection system. However, they have several disadvantages which generally preclude their widespread use. It is very difficult to seal such large areas to prevent leakage of the agent and to reliably maintain the seal. Dozens of large cable penetrations through the floor and ceiling are common, and all of them must be tightly sealed. Given the high ceilings commonly used and the location of the major fuel load — the cables — 12 ft (3.7 m) or more above the floor in racks, it becomes apparent that enormous quantities of agent would be necessary. The personnel safety hazards in a large, complex floor area would be substantial.

Other technical difficulties are posed by gaseous suppression agents. When released, compressed gases are very cold and will cause a sudden drop in the temperature of the room. Telecommunications equipment is very sensitive to temperature changes; much of it is limited to a maximum change of 15°F (9°C) per hour. Changes exceeding this can cause substantial damage throughout the affected equipment.

Concurrent with a rapid drop in temperature will be a rapid increase in the relative humidity. Experimental evidence shows that the dew point can be reached quickly, causing condensation to form on many equipment components. This condensation may then create a host of electrical problems and subsequent damage.

Automatic sprinkler systems offer the advantages of sustained suppression capability and better fire fighter access than gaseous suppression systems. Disadvantages include relatively slow activation time and the potential for significant collateral damage to the telecommunications equipment, during both fire-induced and inadvertent system operations. Inadverten operation will cause extensive damage to the equipment and result in an extended period (days or weeks) of service outage.

Measurements taken during equipment assembly flame spread tests show that telecommunications equipment meeting the standards described have a very low rate of heat release and a slow fire growth rate. Tests at a major fire-testing laboratory confirmed that the fire growth is very slow. In those tests, a 165°F (74°C) fast-response sprinkler located directly over the equipment frame where ignition occurred did not activate until 55 min after ignition.

Sprinkler systems are unable to respond to a fire before it grows well beyond the "established burning" phase. They are therefore unable to respond and extinguish a fire before significant equipment damage occurs. Hence, automatic sprinklers in the telecommunications equipment areas will not meet service continuity firesafety objectives.

Collateral damage due to water release in equipment areas will include numerous electrical short circuits, chemical corrosion of circuit paths from entrained contaminants, and serious electrolytic corrosion. While this damage will pale in comparison to the damage from a serious fire, it can be significantly greater than the damage from a small fire. This must be considered carefully when selecting a suppression system for an occupancy with an extremely low rate of fire incidence.

In practical terms, electrolytic corrosion in telecommunications equipment is nearly instantaneous once water is present from any source, including suppression systems, condensation, and leaks. The rate of electrolytic corrosion varies exponentially with the applied voltage. Hence, telecommunications equipment operating at 48 volts will have a corrosion rate when exposed to water many times that of data processing equipment operating at 5 volts.

These effects can be negated if power is removed from the equipment before the agent is applied. If the equipment is deenergized before system activation, aqueous systems would present minimal risk of collateral damage to the equipment. No automatic means of deenergizing the telecommunications equipment would provide the assurances against inadvertent tripping necessary for modern telecommunications networks.

PRIVATE TELECOMMUNICATIONS EQUIPMENT

Equipment provided by public telecommunications companies terminates at a network interface on the customer's property. It is the customer's responsibility to provide all on-site telephone equipment and wiring. This may be accomplished in a variety of ways. Commonly, customers purchase and maintain their own telecommunications system, leasing the equipment from either a phone company or a third-party vendor, or contracting with the local telephone company for a central-office-based service, such as Centrex. Numerous other possibilities exist.

Large commercial or business occupancies typically have large telecommunications systems, many of which are more complex than those provided for most towns. These systems can provide a wide array of voice, data, and video information to the users. Usually, they are controlled by private branch exchange (PBX) equipment located in the building or complex.

At first glance, modern PBX equipment appears to be very similar in design to modern central office equipment. PBX equipment performs many of the same functions as CO equipment does, but only for the building or complex it serves.

From a fire protection viewpoint, three significant differences exist between CO and PBX equipment:

1. The most important difference is that PBX equipment does not have to conform to the very rigorous flammability standards that CO equipment meets. (PBX equipment is listed, and therefore does meet a variety of other tests, including flammability tests, required to achieve that listing.) The implications of this are discussed below.
2. Replacement PBX equipment is more readily available than replacement CO equipment. This allows for more flexibility in risk management decision-making in some instances.
3. PBX systems are usually easier to turn off than the CO equipment. PBX power supplies often have redundancies similar to those the CO has, but the systems are smaller and less complex. In some cases, a switch or circuit breaker is provided that can be used to power down the equipment in the event of an emergency.

Protection Fundamentals

Most of the protection measures indicated for central offices are appropriate for PBX equipment, as well. In general, the PBX should be protected in the same fashion as an important computer room. There are several elements worthy of special note:

1. The equipment should be located in a room separated from the rest of the building by at least a 1-hr-rated fire barrier.
2. Access to the room should be limited to authorized persons.
3. Good fire prevention and housekeeping measures should be in place at all times. Storage of combustible materials in the room should be strictly prohibited.
4. The room should be equipped with a smoke detection system that alarms at a constantly attended location.
5. Power shut-down procedures should be developed and made available for use by responding fire fighters.

Automatic suppression: The exemptions found in the model building codes that allow a central office to omit automatic sprinklers in equipment areas do not apply to PBX equipment or to telephone closets. Those exemptions are based in part on the ignition prevention efforts described earlier in this chapter, and these efforts are not fully utilized in PBX equipment.

If a building is required by code to be equipped with an automatic suppression system, the system should be provided in the PBX room. An appropriate system should be selected with a clear understanding of the risks involved and the advantages that each candidate system can offer. The system may be omitted if a variance or exemption is granted by the local authority having jurisdiction.

SUMMARY

The precautions discussed in this chapter provide a sound, proven basis for fire risk management for telecommunications equipment and services. As with any loss prevention program, the fire risk management program for telecommunications networks and equipment must be ongoing. There will be a great many changes in both the technology employed in the equipment and in the uses of telecommunications services in the near future.

Many of the changes envisioned today will serve to increase redundancy in the networks, thereby decreasing the overall risk. Other changes may increase the net level of risk and present unique new challenges for risk managers. The attendant risks must be evaluated in a systematic manner, so that effective risk reduction measures that truly reduce the overall risk levels can be implemented.

BIBLIOGRAPHY

References Cited

1. Taylor, K. T., "Temporarily Disconnected," *Fire Journal*, Vol. 83, No. 3 (May/June 1989).
2. Forensic Technologies International Corporation, "Hinsdale Central Office Fire Final Report," Joint Report of the Illinois Office of State Fire Marshal and Illinois Commerce Commission, Mar. 1989.
3. "Network Equipment—Building System (NEBS) Generic Equipment Requirements," *TR-EOP-000063*, Issue 3, Bellcore, Morristown, NJ.

4. "Fire Hazard Testing, Part 2: Test Methods, Needle Flame Test," *IEC Standard 695-2-2*, International Electrotechnical Commission, Geneva, Switzerland.

5. ASTM D2863-77, *Standard Method for Measuring the Minimum Oxygen Concentration to Support Candle-like Combustion of Plastics (Oxygen Index)*, American Society for Testing and Materials, Philadelphia, PA.

6. UL 94, *Tests for Flammability of Plastic Materials for Parts in Devices and Appliances*,Underwriters Laboratories Inc., Northbrook, IL.

7. Forssell, E. W. and Budnick, E. K., "*In Situ* Tests of Smoke Detection Systems for Telecommunications Central Office Facilities," American Telephone and Telegraph Company, Basking Ridge, NJ, Oct. 1990.

8. Johnson, P.F., "Fire Detection in Computer Facilities," *Fire Technology*, Vol. 22, No. 1 (Feb. 1986), pp. 14-32.

NFPA Codes, Standards, and Recommended Practices

Reference to the following NFPA codes, standards, and recommended practices will provide further information on protection of telecommunications equipment facilities as discussed in this chapter. (See the latest *NFPA Catalog* for availability of current editions of the following documents.)

NFPA 75, *Electronic Computer/Data Processing Equipment*.

NFPA 220, *Types of Building Construction*.

NFPA 262, *Fire and Smoke Characteristics of Electrical Wires and Cables*.

NFPA 550, *Firesafety Concepts Tree*.

Additional Reading

IEC 332, *Tests on Electric Cables Under Fire Conditions*, International Electrotechnical Commission, Geneva, Switzerland.

IEEE Standard 383, *Type Test of Class IE Electric Cables, Field Splices, and Connections for Nuclear Power Generating Stations*, Institute of Electrical and Electronic Engineers, NY.

"Telephone Central Office Equipment—Ambient Temperature and Humidity Requirements" ANSI T1.304-1989, American National Standards Institute, NY, July 1989.

"Telephone CentralOffices," *Loss Prevention Data Sheet No. 5-14*, Factory Mutual Research Corp., Norwood, MA, Jan. 1985.

UL 510, *Insulating Tape*, Underwriters Laboratories Inc., Northbrook, IL.

UL 910, *Test Method for Fire and Smoke Characteristics of Electrical and Optical Fiber Cables Used in Air Handling Spaces*, Underwriters Laboratories Inc., Northbrook, IL.

UL 1441, *Coated Electrical Sleeving*, Underwriters Laboratories Inc., Northbrook, IL.

UL 1459, *Telephone Equipment*, Underwriters Laboratories Inc., Northbrook, IL.

UL 1581, *Reference Standard for Electrical Wires, Cable, and Flexible Cords*, Underwriters Laboratories Inc., Northbrook, IL.

UL 1666, *Test for Flame Propagation Height of Electrical and Optical Fiber Cables Installed Vertically in Shafts*, Underwriters Laboratories Inc., Northbrook, IL.

UL 1950, *Information Technology Equipment Including Business Equipment*, Underwriters Laboratories Inc., Northbrook, IL.

MATERIALS-HANDLING EQUIPMENT

Revised by Richard Munson

Materials-handling equipment, particularly industrial trucks, mechanical and pneumatic stock conveying systems, and cranes, are essential services in industrial and commercial activity. This chapter describes the basic types of equipment and systems for materials handling that are encountered and discusses the fire and explosion hazards inherent in them. Protection methods are also discussed.

Readers interested in and/or concerned with materials-handling equipment should also consult Section 3, Chapter 12, "Dusts"; Section 3, Chapter 13, "Metals"; Section 2, Chapter 3, "Electrical Systems and Appliances"; Section 2, Chapter 28, "Storage and Handling of Grain Mill Products"; Section 2, Chapter 31, "Control of Electrostatic Ignition Sources"; Section 6, Chapter 18, "Special Systems for Explosion Damage Control"; Section 6, Chapter 19, "Air Moving Equipment"; and Section 5, Chapter 15, "Water Spray Protection."

INDUSTRIAL TRUCKS

Industrial lift trucks are among the most common types of materials-handling equipment. Although they are available in many special designs to suit the many uses and types of load to be handled, the fork and squeeze clamp types are most common. They may be propelled electrically or by diesel, gasoline, or LP-Gas engines. Unless these vehicles are of a type listed by a testing laboratory and are properly maintained and used, they may introduce serious fire dangers. All of the vehicles should be selected, outfitted, maintained, and operated in accordance with the hazards of the locations.

Type Designations and Areas of Use

NFPA 505, *Powered Industrial Trucks*, lists thirteen different type designations of industrial trucks or tractors. These designations are divided into power types: diesel, electric, gasoline, and LP-Gas. In addition, dual-fuel trucks are available. The designation letter reflects the power type, as follows:

1. Type D units are diesel-powered units having minimal acceptable safeguards against inherent fire hazards.
2. Type DS units are diesel-powered units that, in addition to all the requirements for the Type D units, have additional safeguards in the exhaust, fuel, and electrical systems.
3. Type DY units are diesel-powered units that have all the safeguards of the Type DS units and, in addition, do not have any electrical equipment, including ignition. They are also equipped with temperature limitation features.
4. Type E units are electric-powered units having minimum acceptable safeguards against inherent fire and electrical shock hazards.
5. Type ES units are electric-powered units that, in addition to all of the requirements for the Type E units, are provided with additional safeguards to the electrical system to prevent emission of hazardous sparks and to limit surface temperatures.
6. Type EE units are electric-powered units that have, in addition to all of the requirements for Type E and ES units, the electric motors and all other electrical equipment completely enclosed.
7. Type EX units are electric-powered units that differ from the Type E, ES, or EE units in that the electrical fittings and equipment are so designed, constructed, and assembled that the units may be used in atmospheres containing specifically named flammable vapors, dusts, and, under certain conditions, fibers. Type EX units are specifically tested and classified for use in Class I, Group D or in Class II, Group G hazardous locations as defined in NFPA 70, *National Electrical Code®*.
8. Type G units are gasoline-powered units having minimum acceptable safeguards against inherent fire hazards.
9. Type GS units are gasoline-powered units that, in addition to all the requirements for the Type G units, have additional safeguards to the exhaust, fuel, and electrical systems.

Richard Munson is a principal consultant in the Safety and Occupational Health Group of E. I. DuPont de Nemours Company and former chairman of NFPA's Industrial Trucks Technical Committee.

10. Type LP units are liquefied-petroleum-gas-powered units having minimum acceptable safeguards against inherent fire hazards.
11. Type LPS units are liquefied-petroleum-gas-powered units that, in addition to the requirements for the Type LP units, are provided with additional safeguards to the exhaust, fuel, and electrical systems.
12. Type G/LP units operate on either gasoline or liquefied petroleum gas and have minimum acceptable safeguards against inherent fire hazards.
13. Type GS/LPS units operate on either gasoline or liquefied petroleum gas and, in addition to all requirements for the Type G/LP units, are provided with additional safeguards to the exhaust, fuel, and electrical systems.

Industrial trucks of the various types are limited to the locations specified in Table 8-31A. Many fires that began in industrial trucks and spread to involve other property have been the result of operating less-than-minimum-type trucks in hazardous locations.

The greatest potential fire source for gasoline-, diesel-, and LP-Gas-powered trucks is fuel leaks that are ignited by the hot engine, hot muffler, ignition system, other electrical equipment, or other sparks. This danger is somewhat lower for diesel trucks because of the higher flash point of diesel fuel. However, it is especially present in LP-Gas trucks as the vapors are difficult to disperse and tend to gravitate toward lower spots or pits. Care must be exercised with LP-Gas trucks to avoid the high temperatures near ovens, furnaces, and similar sources of heat. Special safeguards in the design of some types of gasoline, diesel, and LP-Gas trucks help to reduce these fire hazards, but the hazards cannot be completely avoided and areas of use should be rigidly limited. (See Table 8-31A.)

To facilitate identification of truck types and their areas of use, a uniform system of marking has been developed and is described in NFPA 505, *Powered Industrial Trucks*. (See Figures 8-31A and 8-31B). Use of these truck and building markers allows easy and quick recognition of a vehicle approved for the location.

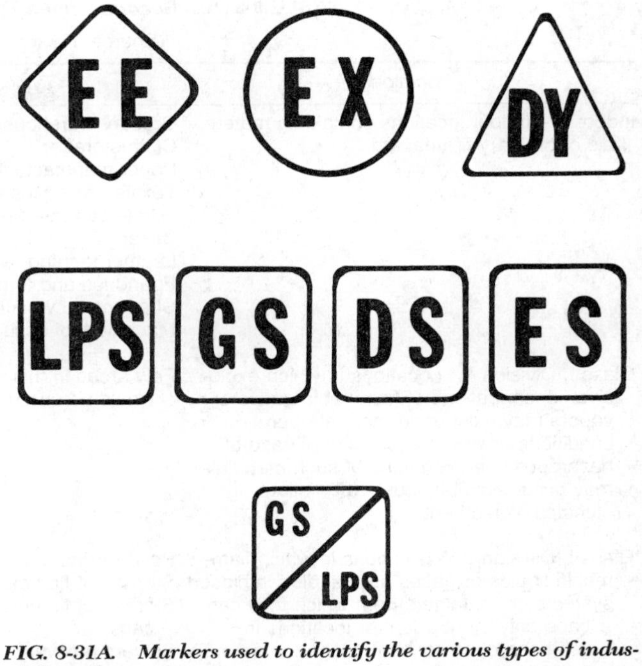

FIG. 8-31A. ***Markers used to identify the various types of industrial trucks.***

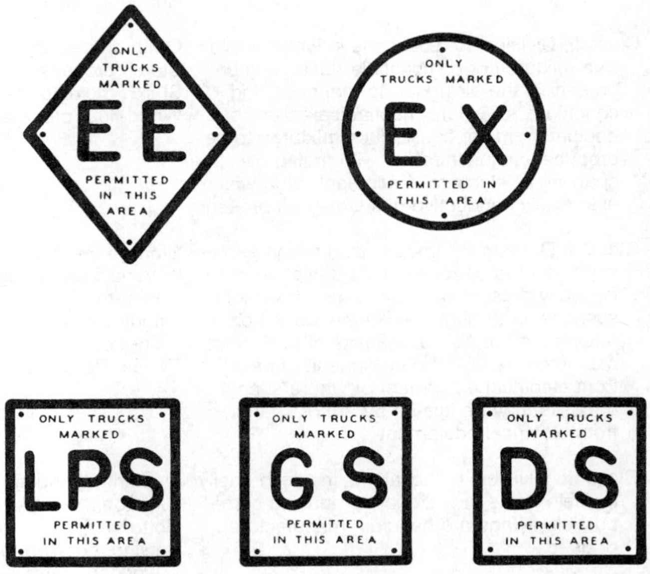

FIG. 8-31B. ***Building signs for posting at entrances to hazardous areas.***

Fire Hazards and Prevention

Careless and uninformed operation of industrial trucks has contributed to much property loss. Collision with sprinkler piping, fire doors, and other fire protection equipment; too-high tiering of rack storage; and the careless handling of loads, such as containers of flammable liquids, have not only contributed directly to fires but have increased fire fighting difficulties. A complete course of instruction for truck operators can reduce the risk of such accidents. Adequate, clear passageways for truck travel and clear warnings of overhead and exposed piping will also reduce the number of incidents. A good source for safe operating rules is ANSI B56.1, *American National Standard Safety Code for Powered Industrial Trucks*.

A large number of fires involving industrial trucks are caused by equipment failure due to inadequate or improper maintenance. A system of regularly scheduled maintenance, based on engine-hour or motor-hour experience, can greatly reduce the incidence of fires of this nature. Trucks are exposed to severe wear and tear, and maintenance programs must be rigidly adhered to. Detecting faulty or damaged fuel connections on gasoline, diesel, and LP-Gas trucks and removing accumulations of grease and dirt requires special attention. Providing portable extinguishers suitable for the hazards presented by the truck and the environment is good practice.

LP-Gas fuel containers require special care to prevent fires. They must not be overfilled. Use a soap solution to check for leaks, never a match or an open flame. Means can be provided in the fuel system to minimize the escape of fuel when removable LP-Gas containers are exchanged—for example, closing the valve on the LP-Gas container and using an approved automatic quick-closing coupling in the fuel line. Removable LP-Gas containers must be securely

TABLE 8-31A. *Recommended Types of Trucks for Various Occupancies*

(Source: Factory Mutual Research Corp.)

Location	Typical occupancies	Types of trucks†‡ approved and listed
Indoor or outdoor locations containing materials of ordinary fire hazard	Grocery warehouse Cloth storage Paper manufacturing and working Textile processes except opening, blending, bale storage, and other Class III locations Bakery Leather tanning Foundries and forge shops Sheet-metal working Machine-tool occupancies	Electrical—Type E Gasoline—Type G Diesel—Type D LP-Gas—Type LP Dual Fuel—Type G-LP
Class I, Division 1.* Locations in which explosive concentrations of flammable gases or vapors may exist under normal operating conditions or where accidental release of hazardous concentrations of such materials may occur simultaneously with failure of electrical equipment	Few areas in this division in which trucks would be used	Electrical—Type EX# Gasoline, diesel, and LP-Gas—not recommended for this service
Class I, Division 2.** Locations in which flammable liquids or gases are handled in closed systems or containers from which they can escape only by accident or locations in which hazardous concentrations are normally prevented by positive mechanical ventilation	Paint mixing, spraying, or dipping Storage of flammable gases in cylinders Storage of flammable liquids in drums or cans Solvent recovery Chemical processes using flammable liquids Paper and cloth coating using flammable solvents in closed equipment Rubber-cement mixing	Electrical—Types EE, EX** Diesel—Type DY** Gasoline, diesel Types D & DS, and LP-Gas—not recommended for this service
Class II, Division 1.* Locations in which explosive mixtures of combustible dusts may be present in the air under normal operating conditions, or where mechanical failure of equipment might cause such mixtures to be produced simultaneously with arcing or sparking of electrical equipment, or in which electrically conductive dusts may be present	Grain processing Starch processing Starch molding (candy plants) Wood-flour processing	Electrical—Type EX§ Diesel—Type DY Gasoline, diesel Types D & DS, and LP-Gas—not recommended for this service
Class II, Division 2.* Locations in which explosive mixtures of combustible dusts are not normally present or likely to be thrown into suspension through the normal operation of equipment but where deposits of such dust may interfere with the dissipation of heat from electrical equipment or where such deposits may be ignited by arc or sparks from electrical equipment	Storage and handling of grain, starch, or wood flour in bags or other closed containers Grinding of plastic molding compounds in tight systems Feed mills with tightly enclosed equipment	Electrical—Types EE, EX, ES‖ Gasoline—Type GS‖ Diesel—Type DY, DS‖ LP-Gas—Type LPS‖
Class III, Division 1.* Locations in which easily ignitible fibers or materials producing combustible flyings are handled, manufactured, or used	Opening, blending, or carding of cotton or cotton mixtures Cotton gins Sawing, shaping, or sanding areas in woodworking plants Preliminary processes in cordage plants	Electrical—Types EE, EX Diesel—Type DY Gasoline, diesel Types D & DS, and LP-Gas—not recommended for this service
Class III, Division 2.* Locations in which easily ignitible fibers are stored or handled (except in process of manufacture)	Storage of textile and cordage fibers Storage of excelsior, Kapok, or Spanish moss	Electrical—Types EE, ES, EX, preferred; E‖ Gasoline—Type GS Diesel—Type DS, DY LP-Gas—Type LPS

NOTES:

* Hazardous location as classified in the *National Electrical Code.*
† Type G (gasoline). Type D (diesel), and Type LP (LP-Gas) trucks are considered to have comparable fire hazard.
‡ Type GS (gasoline), Type DS (diesel), and Type LPS (LP-Gas) trucks are considered to have comparable fire hazard.
§ Acceptable for Groups G, and F, but subject to special investigation.
‖ Acceptable but subject to special investigation.
\# Class I, Division 1, Group D only; no truck should be used in Groups A, B and C.
** Class I, Division 2, Group D only; may be used in Groups A, B and C areas subject to local authority.

mounted to keep them from jarring loose, slipping, or rotating. The safety pressure relief valve opening should always be in contact with the vapor space at the top of the container. When the container is properly installed, an indexing pin and container clamp(s) correctly position the container. It is good practice to examine all LP-Gas containers for defects or damage before refilling.

The number of fires involving battery-powered trucks is comparatively small. Nevertheless, electrical short circuits, hot resistors, arcing and fused contacts, lint accumulations, and exploding batteries have contributed to fire occurrence in electric-powered industrial trucks.

The two types of batteries in common use are lead and nickel-iron. They contain corrosive chemical solutions, either acid or alkali, and therefore present a chemical hazard. On charge, they give off hydrogen and oxygen which, when combined in certain concentrations, can be explosive. Battery-charging installations should be located in areas specifically set aside for that purpose. The facilities should include means for flushing and neutralizing spilled electrolyte; barriers for protecting charging apparatus from damage by trucks; adequate ventilation for dispersal of fumes from gassing batteries; and adequate fire protection. A carboy filler or siphon is used in dispensing acid from carboys. Special care is taken to prevent open flames, sparks, or electric arcs in battery-charging areas. When charging batteries, keep the vent caps in place to avoid electrolyte spray. Care also is taken to ensure that vent caps are functioning. The battery or compartment cover(s) remain open during charging to dissipate heat and gas.

Recharging and Refueling

Refueling and battery-charging operations are performed by trained and designated personnel, and only in specified, well-ventilated areas away from manufacturing and service areas; outdoor refueling is recommended where practicable. Smoking is always prohibited in these areas. Scales for weighing LP-Gas containers should be calibrated to ensure accurate filling.

Trucks using liquid fuels, such as gasoline and diesel fuel, should only be refueled from approved dispensing pumps in safe locations away from sources of heat and ignition. Care must be taken not to spill fuel or overfill the vehicle fuel tank. Approximately 50 percent of the fires involving trucks using liquid fuels are the result of spillage during refueling.

Maintenance and Repair

Trucks are never repaired in Class I, II, and III hazardous locations. Repairs to the fuel and ignition systems of industrial trucks that involve fire hazards should be conducted in locations designated for such repairs. Repairs to the electrical system of battery-powered industrial trucks are performed only after the battery has been disconnected. All parts of any industrial truck that need to be replaced should be replaced only with parts providing the same degree of firesafety as those used in the original design. Water mufflers should be filled daily or as frequently as is necessary to maintain the supply of water at 75 percent of filled capacity or above. Do not operate vehicles whose mufflers, screens or other parts have become clogged. Immediately remove from service any vehicle that emits hazardous sparks or flames from the exhaust system, and do not return it to service until the cause of such sparks and flames has been eliminated. When the temperature of any part of any truck is in excess of its normal operating temperature, a hazardous condition is created, and the vehicle must be removed from service until the cause for such overheating has been eliminated.

It is good practice to keep industrial trucks clean and reasonably free of lint, excess oil, and grease. The conditions under which the truck is operating should govern the frequency of cleaning. Noncombustible agents are preferred for cleaning trucks. Low-flash-point [below 100°F (38°C)] solvents must not be used. Precautions regarding toxicity, ventilation, and fire hazard should correspond to the agent or solvent used. When antifreeze is required in the cooling system, a glycol-based material must be used.

MECHANICAL CONVEYORS AND ELEVATORS

Commonly used equipment in materials handling are mechanical conveyors and elevators that provide an efficient means of transporting bulk and packaged materials. There are many classes and designs of mechanical conveyors. The primary selection considerations are the distance and inclination over which material is to be conveyed; the types of atmosphere and location through which material is to be conveyed; and the lump size, density, flowability, abrasiveness, toxicity, corrosiveness, and so on, of the materials to be conveyed. Dust materials, or dust atmospheres, or both, require equipment that can be enclosed adequately. Screw and "*en masse*" conveyors are limited in the lump size they can handle. Temperatures often rule out belt conveyors; long distances usually require the use of belt conveyors. Substantial vertical lifts are best handled by bucket elevators.

From the point of view of fire protection, the considerations of temperature and dust are the most important. In addition, the protection of openings and the control of static electrical charges are installation factors that must be given careful attention. In the use of belt and other conveyors, two principal hazards should be considered. These are the materials being handled and the belt itself, since both can contribute to fire and to the spread of fire.

Temperature

Screw conveyors, vibrating types, and certain pan conveyors are normally the best choice for handling very hot materials or for use in high-temperature atmospheres. While the upper limit for most belt conveyors is 200°F (93°C), they are normally restricted to less than 150°F (65°C).[1] Experiments by the Bureau of Mines demonstrate that the highest rate of flame propagation occurs with rubber belts but that there is little difference in the ignition characteristics among neoprene, rubber, and polyvinyl chloride. Thus, belt conveyors are not suitable for movement of hot or molten materials and are not used in high-temperature atmospheres.

Fire Protection

Loss experience shows that automatic sprinkler or water spray protection is generally needed for important belt conveyors, particularly if they are enclosed. Controls should be provided to shut down the conveyor when sprinklers operate.

Hose stream protection to reach all portions of the conveyor is also needed. This protection can be provided by 1½-in. (38 mm) hose connections to sprinkler lines or from hydrants.

Dust Control

The most frequently occurring factors in fires involving mechanical conveyors are a dusty material, a dust atmosphere, or the dust inevitably created by the materials-handling process. Dust will almost certainly be produced in any materials-handling system, especially at inlet and discharge points and at the long chutes for free-falling materials.

Dusty material should be fed to belt conveyors through a choke feed to prevent dust clouds. Where dusty conditions prevail, adequate aspiration should be provided to remove dust to collectors in safe locations. If dust clouds cannot be avoided, it is better to use spiral or enclosed conveyors where the escape of dust can be more readily prevented. Conveyor piping should be strong enough to withstand the maximum pressure produced in explosions of the dust involved. Avoid sharp changes in direction wherever possible, and provide vent pipes to outdoors at any necessary changes in direction and at the ends of lines. (This should not be construed as prohibiting the use of explosion-relief vents.)

Screw conveyors should be fully enclosed in tight, noncombustible housings with free-lifting covers at the discharge end and over each shaft coupling. *"En masse"* or drag-type conveyors should be of substantial metal construction designed to prevent the escape of dust. Covers on cleanout, inspection, and other openings should be securely fastened. Conveyors should be designed and constructed to withstand anticipated explosion pressures, considering the pressure release afforded by explosion-relief vents. A choke or seal of proper design or a suppression system should be installed in a conveyor (other than pneumatic conveyors) to prevent the propagation of an explosion from one building to another or from one portion of a building to another separated by a fire wall.

Dust collectors should be located outdoors or in detached rooms with adequate explosion vents for the collectors and the rooms. Where it is necessary to use bag-type collectors, they should be enclosed in a metal housing. A single dust collector should not serve several separate processes. Use individual collectors for progressive stages in any one process. Water spray collectors may be located within buildings, but they are not recommended for certain types of dust.

Static Protection

All parts of the machinery and conveyors should be thoroughly bonded and grounded to minimize static discharges. The chances of generating static electricity are increased when heated or dry materials are conveyed or the conveyor belt is operated in a heated or dry atmosphere.[2] Static electricity can be controlled by using belts made of conductive material, by applying a conductive dressing to the belt surface, or by installing a grounded static collector nearly in contact with the belt just beyond the point where the belt leaves the pulley.[2] Pulleys, guards, and other metal bodies also should be grounded.

Protection of Conveyor Openings

Water spray method: The protection of openings in walls and floors through which conveyors pass presents difficulties in the installation of ordinary forms of closures due to the objects carried through the opening. Where fire doors or shutters are impractical for conveyor openings, a method of protection incorporating the pressure effect and the cooling action of water spray from directed spray nozzles is available. (See Figure 8-31C.) With proper nozzle design and water pressure to provide suitable water velocity and droplet size, the pressure effect from the nozzles will overcome draft due to the temperature difference between one side of the wall and the other and the height of the opening above floor level, unless adverse air currents are prevalent. Since the cooling effect of the spray is directly proportional to the time of exposure of hot gases in the draft to the spray, the effectiveness of the heat absorption may be increased by adding an enclosure to the opening. (See Figure 8-31D.) Figure 8-31E shows the cooling effect of four ½-in. (12.7 mm) nozzles on an 8-by-8-ft (2.4 by 2.4 m) opening with various draft velocities and nozzle pressures in tests conducted by Factory Mutual Research Corporation. The nozzles were discharging water at 28 gpm (106 L/min) each, with an effective angle of about 65 degrees.

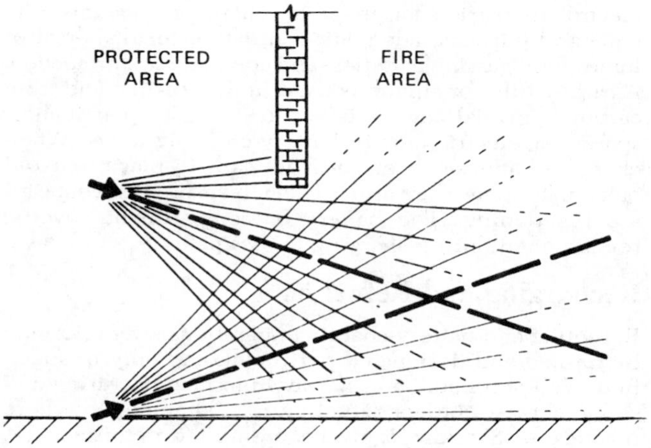

FIG. 8-31C. Spray nozzles protecting a conveyor opening in a fire wall.

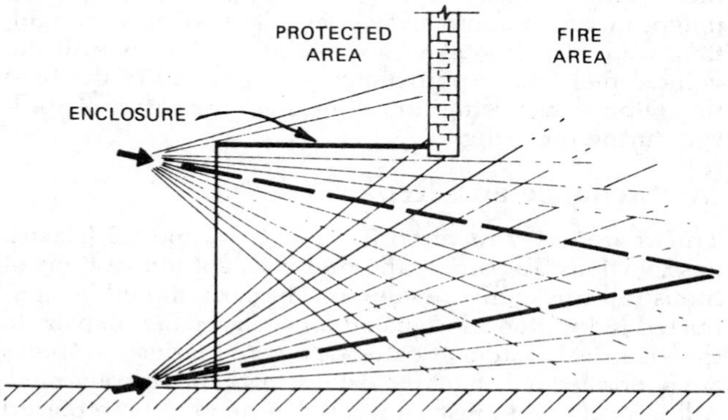

***FIG. 8-31D.** Greater heat absorption is possible by enclosing the opening for a conveyor.*

The Factory Mutual Research Corporation recommendations for installation include the following:

1. Where fire may be expected to originate on either side of the opening, nozzles are installed on both sides. Nozzles are controlled by an automatic valve actuated

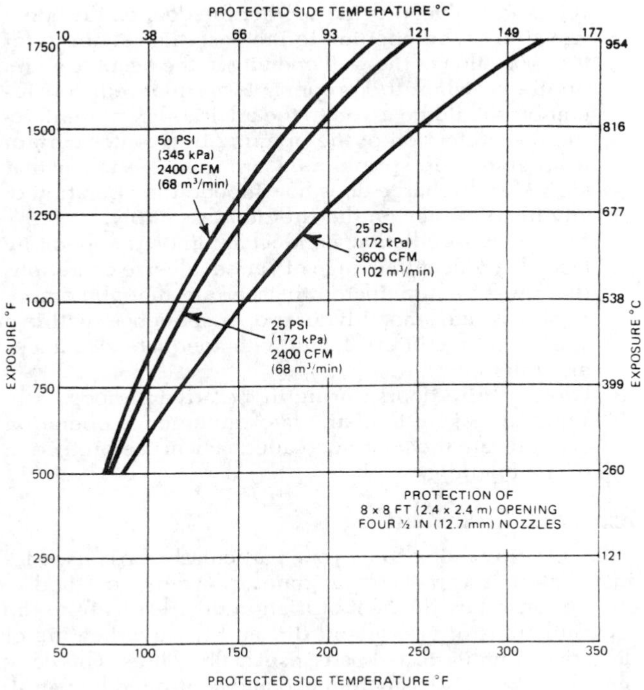

FIG. 8-31E. Exposure temperatures vs. protected side temperatures at various draft velocities and nozzle pressure.

by a heat detector. Four nozzles per side are recommended to give complete coverage of the opening. Water discharge rates between 2 and 4 gpm/sq ft [81 and 163 (L/min)/m^2] or more, depending upon the height of the opening and unfavorable draft effects, are desirable. Nozzles are located at an angle not more than 30 degrees between the centerline of nozzle discharge and a line perpendicular to the plane of the opening. To prevent the nozzle counterdraft from forcing air from the fire area into other areas, all communicating openings to the fire area are protected in a standard manner.

2. Conveyor openings through floors also may be protected by this method, provided an enclosure is constructed around the conveyor from the floor up to, or slightly beyond, the spray nozzles and draft curtains, extending 20 to 30 in. (0.5 to 0.8 m) below and around the floor opening. (See Fig. 8-31F.)

3. The effectiveness of the protection system is, of course, dependent upon rapid detection and appropriate interlocks between the detection system and the machinery.

Fire doors: It is a misconception that conveyorized openings cannot be protected by fire doors. Where possible, of course, conveyor penetration of a fire wall is avoided by rerouting or, as is sometimes feasible with a one-story building, by running the conveyor through the roof, over the fire wall, and down an inverted "V" housing arranged to vent fire readily to the atmosphere. (See Fig. 8-31G.) Any cutout of a labeled fire door done in the field to allow for closure about a conveyor track or other components voids its label, and this practice should be avoided, if possible. Where notching is distinctly advantageous, a certificate may

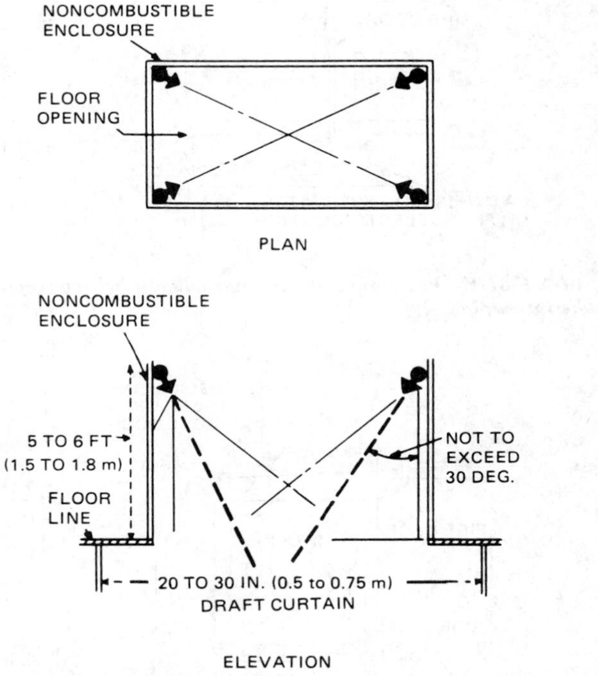

FIG. 8-31F. Spray nozzle protection for floor opening.

be furnished by the testing laboratory affixing the label if it is found by inspection that the notched door is in compliance with the laboratory standards in all other aspects.

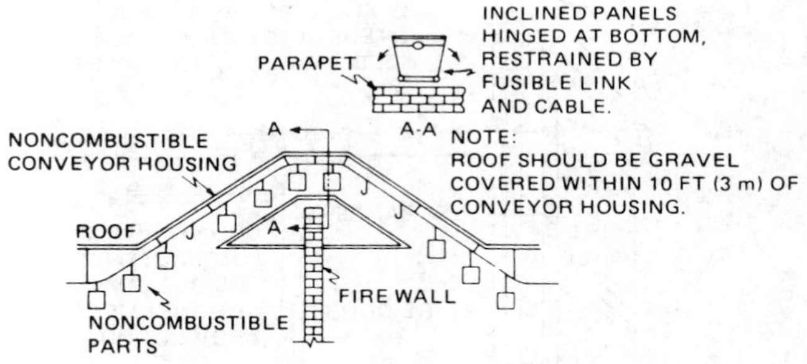

FIG. 8-31G. A conveyor carried over a fire wall.

Figures 8-31H through 8-31J illustrate various conveyor designs and/or programming devices that will minimize or eliminate the threat of obstruction to complete fire door closure by the conveyor or conveyed stock.

The illustrations can only show the basic concepts. Proper performance depends equally on conservative design, good workmanship in installation, operating inspection, and maintenance. Guidelines to observe are:

1. Select a design that is as simple and direct-acting as possible. Emphasis is on "fail safe" operation.
2. Program the sequence of operating steps and interlocks so that obstruction (conveyor, conveyorized material, and so on) to the door closure is positively and permanently—until manually reset—removed from the door's path before the door is released to close.

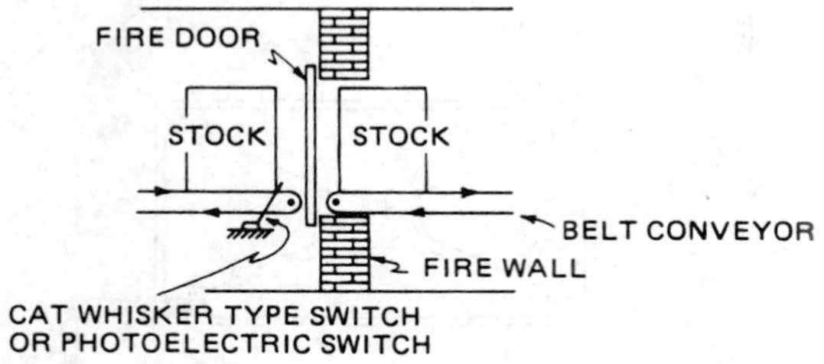

FIG. 8-31H. Protection of openings when a belt conveyor can be interupted.

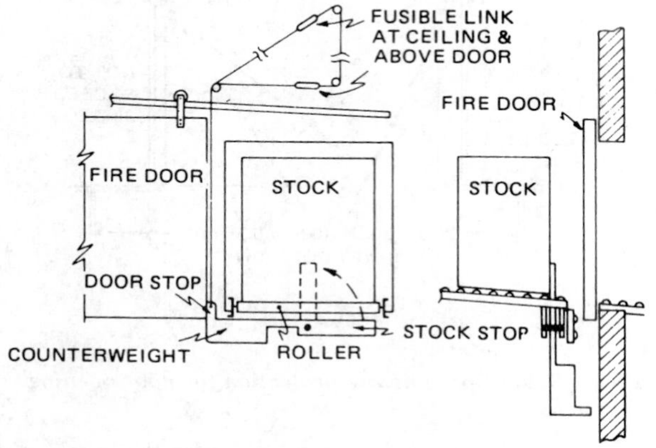

FIG. 8-31I. A method of stopping stock on a gravity roller conveyor.

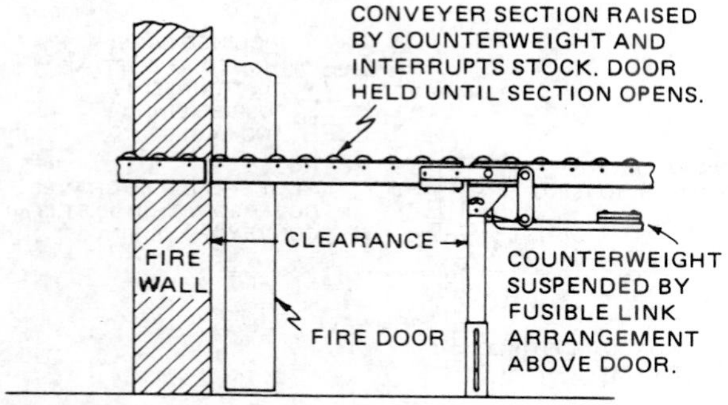

FIG. 8-31J. A counter-weighted, hinged section of a roller conveyor.

3. Design structural and mechanical components, linkages, clearances, and so on in a conservative manner. Counterweights, springs, and other operating forces that are uninterruptable by initial fire stages must have enough reserve strength to handle overload introduced by reasonable anticipated minor changes in configuration and weight of conveyorized material, normal wear, friction, and so on. Major changes will necessitate complete re-engineering to ascertain adequacy of the design, with reinforcement as necessary.
4. Incorporate self-releasing features in the design of conveyor components such as trolley track, chain, and supports.
5. Maintain 3/8-in. (9.5 mm) clearance between the door and the sill.
6. If it is advisable, provide another fire door on the opposite side of the opening to increase the reliability of the protection of the wall opening in the event of a fire. Similarly, when the property is sprinklered, consideration should be given to the advisability of reinforcing the protection of the opening by a water curtain from automatic sprinklers. Care must be taken that sprinkler discharge does not impede the operation of any fusible links on the fire door assembly.
7. Following installation, conduct a number of operating tests that reflect the range of varied adverse conditions that must be anticipated to ascertain that all components operate smoothly, in proper sequence, within a specified time interval, and with adequate clearances and tolerances.
8. Close all fire doors during inoperative periods.
9. Routine closure that simulates emergency operation can indicate the continued adequacy of the protection of the opening.

Friction, Overheating

Many fires involving conveyors, particularly those used for such materials as raw cotton, grains, powders, coal, and so on, are caused by the heat of friction that results from the accumulations of grease and dirt and the overheating of defective or unlubricated parts, especially rollers. This common fire hazard is easily reduced and controlled by patrolling belts, by frequent equipment inspection, and by the removal of dirt and grease buildups.[3] Early replacement of old and worn parts is also important.

Bucket Elevators

These elevators are used in bulk processing plants to convey loads vertically, and they are susceptible to the same fire hazards as the mechanical conveyors. The same precautions need to be taken for temperature, dust control, protection of openings, and elimination of friction and overheating. Elevators are best enclosed in substantial dust-tight casings. These casings should be of noncombustible construction, extend without reduction in size through the roof, and be fitted with light, weatherproof covers designed to lift readily and relieve explosion pressure within.

Elevators should be installed close to an outside wall of the building and be provided with short direct vents through the wall at 20-ft (6 m) intervals on tall elevator legs. Doors should be installed to provide access to head and boot pulleys. All doors in elevator leg casings should be dust-tight. Ample clearance around elevator boots should be provided for cleaning and oiling. Safeguard elevators against overheating or choking by automatic releases actuated by overloading or a reduction in operating speed below normal.

PNEUMATIC CONVEYORS

Pneumatic conveying is a common method of transferring dusts from place to place in a building or from one building to another. This process presents an explosion hazard due to the ease and rapidity by which explosive proportions of dust can be introduced into the air.[2]

Description of Systems

Pneumatic conveying systems consist of an enclosed tubing system in which a material is normally transported by a stream of air with a sufficiently high velocity to keep the conveyed material in motion. Noncombustible gases may be used in place of, or mixed with, air. Such systems are of two principal types, or a combination of the two types, as follows.

Pressure type: Pressure-type systems transport material using air at greater than atmospheric pressure. These systems basically consist of a blower that draws air through a filter, an airlock feeder that introduces materials into the system, tubing or ducts, and a suitable air-material separator.

Suction type: Suction-type systems transport material using air at less than atmospheric pressure. These systems basically consist of a material and air intake, tubing or ducts, a suitable air-material separator, and a suction fan or blower.

See Figure 8-31K for a schematic drawing of a typical combination pressure-type and suction-type system.

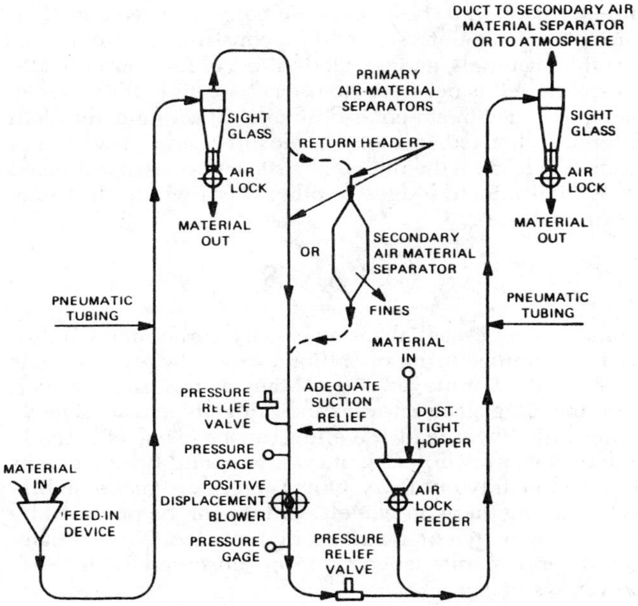

FIG. 8-31K. A typical transfer system of the combination pressure-type and suction-type with a high capacity.

Conveyor Ducts

Conveyor ducts are fabricated with nonferrous, minimum-sparking metal or with nonmagnetic, minimum-sparking stainless steel. They are electrically bonded and grounded. Plastic or other nonconductive liners are not desirable.

Inert Atmospheres

Inert gas should be used in conveying systems wherever the concentration of powder or dust may come within the explosive range. The inert gas, such as nitrogen, argon, or helium with a limiting oxygen concentration based on the explosion characteristics of the particles in the system, is essential for preventing fires and explosions. Basically, it contains insufficient oxygen to permit combustion and no carbon monoxide, and it has a dew point such that no free moisture can condense or accumulate at any point in the system. Further limitations are dictated by the type of material being conveyed and by the character of the inert gas. For example, the inert gas for magnesium dust systems should not contain carbon dioxide. Oxygen limits of 3 to 5 percent have been maintained in aluminum powder systems using a controlled type of flue gas. Other limits are applicable where other inert gases and dusts are present.[4]

A continuous monitor is needed to sound an alarm if the oxygen content of the inert gas is not within the established safe range.

Light metal conveying: Light metal and light metal alloy powders are produced by various mechanical means of particle size degradation. These processes, as well as certain finishing and transporting operations, have a tendency to expose a continuously increasing area of new metal surface. Most metals immediately experience a surface reaction with available atmospheric oxygen, which forms a protective oxide coating that then serves as an impervious layer to inhibit further oxidation. This reaction is exothermic, producing sensible heat. If a fine or thin lightweight particle having a large area of new surface is suddenly exposed to the atmosphere, enough heat will be generated to raise its temperature to the ignition point.

Completely inert gas is not used as an envelope to promote operational safety or for transport of light metal powder in a pneumatic or fluidized transfer device. This would be a very unsafe practice because somewhere in the process of manufacture, packaging, or ultimate use, the powder will eventually be exposed to the atmosphere where the unreacted surfaces will react suddenly with available oxygen to produce enough heat to cause either a fire or an explosion. To provide maximum safety, a means for controlling the oxidation of newly exposed surfaces is provided—as soon as they are exposed—by regulating the oxygen content of the inert gas. Tests conducted by the U.S. Bureau of Mines and others have disclosed that an inert gas as described here is effective for this purpose. This mixture serves to control the rate of oxidation and, at the same time, provides an environment that materially reduces the fire and explosion hazard.

Air Conveying

If the conveying gas is air, as is often practiced in atomizing, the dust-air ratio throughout the conveying system is held below the minimum explosive concentration of the metal dust, as determined by data from the U.S. Bureau of Mines.[4] Although the metal-dust-air suspension may be held below the explosive concentration in the conveying system, the suspension will necessarily pass through the explosive range in the collector at the end of the conveying system unless the dust is collected in a liquid, such as in a spray tower. Such wet collection is not always possible or desirable. Any liquid used must be nonflammable, nonreactive with metal dust, or reactive at a controlled minimum rate under favorably controlled conditions. The liquid remaining in or on the product must be compatible with subsequent processing requirements.

In an air conveying system, any dry collector must be considered an explosion hazard containing a dust-air mixture in the explosive range. It is, therefore, sited in a safe location and is provided with the requisite barricades or other design means of protecting personnel. Construction is of nonferrous, nonsparking metal or of nonmagnetic, nonsparking stainless steel. The entire system, particularly the collector, is thoroughly and completely bonded and grounded. When checked with an ohmmeter, the entire ground system should show less than 5 ohms resistance to ground.

Where the conveying duct is exposed to weather or moisture, it should be moisture-tight, because any moisture entering the system can react with the dust, generating heat and serving as a potential source of ignition.

A minimum conveying velocity is employed throughout the conveying system to prevent the accumulation of dust at any point and to pick up any powder that might drop out during an unscheduled system stoppage.

If the conveying gas is inducted into the system in a relatively warm environment and the ductwork and collectors are relatively cold, the gas temperature may drop below the dew point, causing condensation of moisture. To avoid this, the ducts and collectors are insulated or provided with a heating means.

Relief Vents for Conveyor Ducts

Vents of sufficient area connected to ducts or openings protected with antiflashback swing valves and extending to the outside of the building can provide explosion relief. Care should be taken to limit the inertia of swing valves to the minimum required. Rupture diaphragms can be used in place of swing valves. Wherever damage may result from the rupture of a duct, the duct is designed for an internal working pressure of 100 psi (690 kPa) minimum in case the relief vent fails to offer sufficient pressure relief . Where the duct is so located that no damage will result if it bursts, it may be of very light construction to intentionally fail as an auxiliary vent for the system.

Fan Construction and Arrangement

The blades and housing of fans that are used to move air or inert gas in conveying ducts are constructed of conductive, nonsparking metal, such as bronze, nonsparking stainless steel, or aluminum. In no case should the design be such that the dust is drawn through the fan before entering the final collector. Personnel should not be permitted within 50 ft (15 m) of the fan during operation. This means that the fan and associated equipment are shut down for oiling, inspection, or preventive maintenance. If the area must be approached during operation for a pressure test or other technical reasons, it must only be done under the direct supervision of competent technical personnel and with the knowledge and approval of the operating management. Ultimately, all fans in dust collector systems accumulate enough dust to be a potential hazard; for this reason, it is preferable to locate them outside of all manufacturing buildings.

It is good practice to equip fan bearings with suitable instruments for indicating the temperature. Such instruments are wired with an alarm device to warn of overtemperature.

Sight Glasses

Avoid sight glasses in pneumatic systems whenever possible. If installed, they should be of noncombustible material that is not readily subject to physical damage. The tubing is supported above and below each sight glass so that the sight glass does not carry any of the system weight and is not, in itself, subject to the resulting stresses or strains. The electrical bonding of the system must be continuous around all sight glasses. The strength of the sight glass and its mounting mechanism and its inside diameter are equal to the adjoining tube system. In pressure-type systems, connections between sight glass and tubing are butted squarely and fastened together with rigid, airtight couplings, connectors, or comparable devices. In suction-type systems, connections between the sight glass and tubing are butted squarely and sealed with approved sleeves extending a minimum of 3 in. (76 mm) above and below the sight glass and tubing connections. The sleeves are of a material that has elastic properties that provide an air-tight seal.

Air-Material Separators

Air-material separators are preferably located outside the building and are provided with lightning protection. Material discharge outlets are provided with positive choke devices. The separator is electrically conductive and bonded. Exhaust air is always discharged to the outside, except where provision is made to recirculate transport air directly back into the pneumatic conveying system. The air-material separators should be constructed of noncombustible materials, and the cloth filters of low-hazard materials. Where it is necessary to use combustible filter media, flame-retardant treatment is desirable. In addition, the cloth filters are housed in metal enclosures, and provision is made for cleaning the filters. The separators are constructed so as to eliminate ledges or other areas where dust may accumulate.

CRANES

Cranes are an essential and necessary part of many industrial or manufacturing operations where heavy materials must be lifted or moved about. Many cranes, such as overhead traveling, gantry, tower, and bridge-type cranes, move along rails. Overhead traveling can be used effectively indoors or out, whereas gantry, tower, and bridge cranes are used mainly outdoors. Other cranes are made mobile by mounting them on wheels. Cranes can be powered by electricity or by combustion engine drive. Normal safeguards and maintenance must be observed with these power systems.

Outdoor cranes are susceptible to damage by high winds, unless a positive means of anchorage is provided, in addition to the operating or service brakes. Large cranes that move along rails are generally provided with automatic or manual rail clamps. Other means of anchorage are crane traps, wedges, and cables. Anchorage and support are particularly necessary and advisable when a crane is not in use and unattended.

Crane operators should be thoroughly trained in the proper operation of the equipment, including emergency action that may be necessary in a fire or other hazardous incident. The crane operator's cab should be of noncombustible construction and be provided with an emergency means of egress. It should be kept free of oily waste, rubbish, and other combustibles. All electrical equipment should be in conformance with NFPA 70, *National Electrical Code®*, and should be securely mounted and maintained.

Emergency portable extinguisher protection may be desirable in some operator's cabs. In some large equipment, automatic fixed-piping extinguishing systems may be advisable.

BIBLIOGRAPHY

References Cited

1. Buffington, M. A., "Mechanical Conveyors and Elevators," *Chemical Engineering*, Oct. 13, 1969, pp. 33-49.2.
2. *Handbook of Industrial Loss Prevention*, 2nd ed., McGraw-Hill, New York, 1976.
3. Mitchell, D. W., *et al.*, "Fire Hazard of Conveyor Belts," *RI 7053*, U.S. Bureau of Mines, Washington, DC, 1967.
4. Jacobson, M., Cooper, A. R., and Nagy, J., "Explosibility of Metal Powders," *RI 6516*, U.S. Bureau of Mines, Pittsburgh, PA, 1964.

Reference

Hartmann, I., Nagy, J., and Brown, H. R., "Inflammability and Explosibility of Metal Powders," *RI 3722*, U.S. Bureau of Mines, Pittsburgh, PA, 1943.

NFPA Codes, Standards, and Recommended Practices

Reference to the following NFPA codes, standards, and recommended practices will provide further information on materials-handling equipment discussed in this chapter. (See the latest *NFPA Catalog* for availability of current editions of the following documents.)

NFPA 15, *Water Spray Fixed Systems for Fire Protection*.

NFPA 61B, *Grain Elevators and Facilities Handling Bulk Raw Agricultural Commodities*.

NFPA 70, *National Electrical Code*.®

NFPA 80, *Fire Doors and Windows*.

NFPA 505, *Powered Industrial Trucks*.

NFPA 651, *Aluminum and Magnesium Powder*.

Additional Readings

Anderson, A. E., "Review of Fire Resistant Belting Requirements," *Proceedings* of the International Conference on Fire Resistant Hose, Cables and Belting, Plastics and Rubber Institute, 1986, pp. 1-12.

Block, R. A., *Crane Operation and Preventive Maintenance*, Marine Education Textbooks, Horima, LA, 1983.

"Fire Protection for Belt Conveyors," *FMRC Loss Prevention Data Sheet 7-11*, Factory Mutual Engineering Corporation, Norwood, MA.

International Conference on Fire Resistant Hose, Cables and Belting, Plastics and Rubber Institute, London, 1986.

Johanson, J. R., "Feeding," *Chemical Engineering*, Oct. 13, 1969, pp. 75-83.

Kraus, M. N., "Pneumatic Conveyors," *Chemical Engineering*, Oct. 13, 1969, pp. 59-65.

Kuchta, J. M., Sapko, M. J., and Perzak, F. J., "Improved Fire Resistance Test Method for Belt Materials," *Fire Technology*, Vol. 17, No. 2 (May 1981), pp. 120-130.

"Moving Fire: Fire Hazards of Belt Conveyors," *Record*, Vol. 54, No. 6, 1977, pp. 18-21.

Patterson, C. B., "Looking at Fire Hazards: Powered Industrial Trucks: Appraising Their In-Plant Fire Safety," *Fire Journal*, Vol. 66, No. 5 (Sept. 1972), pp. 103-104.

Sapko, M. J., *et al.*, "Fire Resistance Test Method for Conveyor Belts," *Investigative Report 8521*, U.S. Bureau of Mines, Washington, DC, 1981.

Schenkel, W. K., "Flame-Resistant Conveyor Belts Reinforced with Kevlar for Underground Coal Mining," *Proceedings* from the International Conference on Fire Resistant Hose, Cables and Belting, Plastics and Rubber Inst., London, 1986, pp. 1-17.

Szymanski, J. and Mintz, K. J., "Small-Scale Flame Tests on Fire-Retardant Conveyor Belting," *Journal of Fire Science*, Vol. 4, No. 4 (Jul.-Aug. 1986), pp. 231-236.

WILDLAND FIRE MANAGEMENT

Dan Bailey and Gary Tokle

Each year, on average, 200,000 fires burn over 1.5 million acres (2.2 million hectares) of protected forest, brush, and grass-covered lands in the U.S. and Canada. Protection services cost well over a billion dollars annually, with losses approaching four billion dollars. These costs do not reflect the services of thousands of volunteer fire fighters in both countries, nor the expenses of the many city fire departments that fight fires on wildlands—lands that are essentially undeveloped—within or near their jurisdictions.

Wildfires include any nonprescribed fire burning on wildlands. Most are extinguished while smaller than one acre (0.4 ha) by a few fire fighters working with hand tools or water-handling equipment. Under extremely adverse conditions, however, a fire can spread to well over 100,000 acres (40,000 ha) and require 2000 to 3000 fire fighters and hundreds of mechanized units for several weeks to over a month.

The wildfire problem is highly variable depending on location. This is because:

1. Fire ignition is dependent on natural phenomena, such as lightning or volcanic activity, on human activity, on fuel bed characteristics, on the weather, and on the effectiveness of prevention efforts.
2. Fire behavior—that is, how a fire spreads and how intensely it burns—is dependent on local conditions, such as weather, fuels, and topography.
3. The effectiveness of fire suppression is closely related to accessibility, difficulty of control, and the capability and performance of the local protection agency.
4. Public safety is involved when fires threaten recreation areas, mountain homes, or subdivisions or when smoke obscures visibility along highways or near airports.

The foregoing considerations vary so much by location that each geographical region must deal with a unique set of circumstances. In the Mediterranean climate of southern California, for example, a long, hot summer dries the chaparral, thus preparing it for explosive burning during the gale-force "Santa Ana" winds. Such conditions pose an enormous threat to human life and property. In the humid subtropical climate of the southeastern U.S., early spring and late fall fire seasons threaten extensive forests of pine and hardwood trees. Throughout the boreal forests of central and western Canada, lightning often ignites hundreds of fires during long periods of hot, dry weather, causing extensive damage. Wildfires burning in the tundra of Alaska and northern Canada produce vast ecological effects and, therefore, require special suppression techniques. During droughts, even the marine climate of the Pacific coastal forest, which extends from northern California to Alaska, does not protect these areas from devastating timber fires.

CAUSES OF FIRES

The leading causes of wildfires in the 1.5 billion acres (0.6 billion ha) of protected wildlands of the U.S. are incendiarism, which accounts for about 30 percent of the fires and approximately one-third of the burned-over area. Debris burning accounts for an additional 23 percent of the fires, while careless smoking is credited with causing 8 percent of the fires. Lightning typically accounts for another 8 percent of the fires but for only 20 percent of the burned area. Other prominent causes of fires include equipment use, children playing with matches, campfires, and railroad use.

Approximately 98 percent of these fires are controlled at a size of 100 acres (40 ha) or less. However, the remaining 2 percent of fires result in two-thirds of the total burned-over area. All together, 140,000 wildfires occur each year in the U.S., burning over 2.3 million acres (930,000 ha) of forest, brush, and grass-covered lands.

The relative importance of the fire causes mentioned above varies considerably among the different geographical regions of the country. In terms of the number of fires and burned areas, lightning is the leading cause in the northwestern part of the country, as well as in Arizona and New Mexico. For the entire eastern half of the United States, incendiarism and debris burning are the chief causes. In California, equipment use and incendiarism rank highest, while debris burning and lightning are the main problems in the central Rockies. Alaska's wildfires can be blamed chiefly on debris burning and lightning.

Dan Bailey is zone fire manager for the U.S. Forest Service in Missoula, MT; he also Chairs the NFPA Wildland Fire Management Section. Gary Tokle is senior fire service training and education specialist on the staff of NFPA.

In Canada, approximately 9000 wildfires occur each year, burning over 3.2 million acres (1.3 million ha) of wildlands. About 32 percent of these fires are caused by lightning, although fires started by lightning account for about 86 percent of the burned-over area.

The Role of Lightning

On the large scale, lightning is common: there are eight million cloud-to-ground discharges per day around the globe. While the energy per lightning bolt varies greatly, 250 kilowatt-hours is a good estimate of the average energy discharged in each stroke. Almost 75 percent of a lightning bolt's energy is converted to heat during discharge. This is more than sufficient to ignite most fuels.

There are two types of discharge: cold and hot stroke. Cold strokes exhibit high voltage of short duration, generally with mechanical or explosive effects. Hot strokes discharge a lesser current for a longer duration, thus starting more fires. Approximately 21 percent of all lightning moves from cloud to ground. Of this amount, 20 percent is hot stroke, according to studies in the northern Rockies. Therefore, in the northern Rockies, one stroke in 25 has the electrical characteristics to start a fire, depending on where or what it strikes and on the local weather.

Between 1940 and 1990, a total of 59,518 lightning fires occurred in the national forests of the Southwest; 79,131 in forests of the Rocky Mountains; and 99,689 in forests of California and the Pacific Northwest.

AGENCIES INVOLVED

In the U.S., wildland fire protection is handled by federal, state, county, and in some cases, city agencies, as well as by private corporations and career/volunteer fire departments. The U.S. Forest Service protects about 200 million acres (80 million ha) of national forest and other lands. Approximately 587 million acres (197 million ha) of other federal lands, mostly in the public domain, are protected by the Bureau of Land Management (BLM), the National Park Service (NPS), the U.S. Fish & Wildlife Service, and the Bureau of Indian Affairs. States, local governments, corporations, and career/volunteer fire departments protect about 840 million acres (340 million ha) of the country's essentially undeveloped lands. About 158 million acres (64 million ha), or roughly 9½ percent, of the wildlands in the United States do not qualify for fire protection.

In Canada, wildland fire protection is handled by ten provinces, two territories, and Parks Canada, as well as by private corporations and career volunteer fire departments.

COMPONENTS OF WILDLAND FIRE PROTECTION

Fire prevention, which involves all activities concerned with minimizing the incidence of destructive fires, is a team effort by fire protection agencies and the community. It is accomplished through educating the public and increasing their awareness, regulating the public use of the wildlands, engineering developments, and enforcing fire regulations and laws. Regulating the public use of wildlands limits activities during periods of high fire danger. Such regulation includes area closures, campfire prohibitions, restrictions on burning, equipment operation shutdowns, and the use of spark arrestors on motor-driven equipment. Engineering activities include the reduction of flammable vegetation along roadways and in areas of heavy uses and the modification of vegetation to favor less flammable species. Law enforcement activities are aimed mainly at the prevention of incendiarism, currently the national leading cause of fires.

Fire/Prevention Awareness

Fires caused by people account for the majority of wildfires nationally. Unwanted fires threaten valuable resources, and, for this reason, fire prevention is an on-going job. Fire prevention is one of the most important parts of a fire protection agency's responsibilities. It is the first line of defense against fire. A fire that can be prevented will save lives, resources, and money.

National Fire Prevention Week is the full week — Sunday through Saturday — that includes the date of October 9, the anniversary of the "Great Chicago Fire of 1871" which killed 250 people, left 100,000 homeless, and destroyed 17,430 buildings. Also on this day in Peshtigo, Wisconsin, more than 1500 people died when a wildland fire swept through the town. During this period, national and local programs emphasize the fire prevention message. Fire prevention message are repeated in books, on the radio and television, in public service announcements, on signs and posters, in news articles and brochures, in videos and slide-talks, and by personal contacts.

One of the most effective educational programs in Canada and the U.S. since 1950 has been Smokey the Bear. This program is credited with being a major factor in the prevention of thousands of fires, thereby saving billions of dollars in damages and fire suppression costs. Smokey's message has remained the same, but partnerships have been developed to reach new groups. Such partnerships include the American Cowboy, pro sports figures, and amateur athletes, who have joined with Smokey to get the fire prevention message to the public. Specific prevention programs have been developed by different agencies and areas of the country. The Keep Green Program and the Fire-Safe Program are examples of programs developed to meet regional needs.

Wildland/Urban Interface: The growth of the wildland/urban interface fire problem has focused prevention programs in a new direction. Nationally, the Wildfire Strikes Home campaign has been successful in creating an awareness of the issue. This program has been sponsored by the U.S. Forest Service, the U.S. Department of the Interior, the National Association of State Foresters, the National Fire Protection Association, and the U.S. Fire Administration. Regional and local programs have been developed to meet the different wildland/urban fire needs of each area.For several reasons, the U.S. is experiencing a major population shift from urban to rural living. More and more homes are being built on scenic sites and slopes in forests and other wildlands. The result is that vast areas of North America now contain high-value properties intermingled with highly flammable native vegetation. Fire protection officials report dramatic increases in the loss of homes to fires in these new residential areas. Burned homes are not the only cause for serious concern: according to these officials, major losses of life are not only possible, but inevitable.

The current trend of building homes in areas threatened by wildland fires has introduced new factors that seriously complicate the duties of fire fighters. Both wildland and structural fire fighters have developed time-proven methods for controlling the types of fires expected in their jurisdictions. The efficient, successful methods for protecting a forest's natural resources from fire were not developed with the idea that the forest would include numerous homes. And the methods used to extinguish structure fires are not effective against the power of a wildfire, especially as the fire spreads through areas in which water supplies for fire fighting are limited.

So far, economic constraints have prevented effective cross-training and equipping of all fire fighters to attack these two vastly different types of fire. The areas in which these two types of fires interface can be classified into three general types:

1. *The mixed interface* contains structures scattered throughout rural areas. Usually, there are isolated homes surrounded by areas of undeveloped land. When a fire starts, the individual homes are hard to protect because of the large area that may be burning. While relatively few homes may be at risk, the risk to the individual homes is great.
2. *An occluded interface* is characterized by isolated areas of wildlands, either small or large, within an urban area. An example would be a city park surrounded by homes, where the goal is to preserve some contact with a natural setting. Many homes and other buildings may be at risk, but these relatively small wildland areas are generally less susceptible to uncontrolled raging.
3. *A classic interface* is where homes, especially those crowded onto smaller lots in new subdivisions, press against wildland vegetation along a broad front. These vast wildland areas can propagate a massive flame-front during a wildland fire, causing numerous homes to be at risk from a single fire. Because the built-up quality of the subdivision may give a false sense of security, this is where the greatest loss-of-life is possible.

Fire Detection

Discovering, locating, and reporting fires often is accomplished in wildland areas by lookouts in fire towers and by aircraft patrols. Additionally, thousands of fires are reported annually by travellers, campers, woodcutters, hunters, and others. In the western U.S. and parts of Canada, lightning strikes are routinely detected electronically and their locations plotted by computer. Computer programs have been developed to assess the likelihood of ignition at various locations, as well as the characteristics of the strikes themselves. Automated fixed-point infrared detection systems have been developed but they have yet to be used extensively in North America, although they are used in some European countries.

While fire detection from satellites is technically feasible, the complications of discriminating between legitimate heat sources and incipient fires has not yet allowed the practical use of this technology.

Fire Suppression

Fire suppression includes all work to extinguish or confine a fire, beginning with its discovery. Suppressing or fighting a fire is usually difficult work that is inherently dangerous. However, knowing and applying safety principles and fire fighting tactics serves to increase the safety and effectiveness of operations.

Standard fire fighting orders: A series of standard fire fighting orders provides the basis for safety for those involved in wildland fire management. Every fire fighter must learn these orders and follow each when it applies:

F Fight all fires aggressively, but first provide for safety.
I Initiate all action based on current and expected fire behavior.
R Recognize current weather conditions and obtain forecasts.
E Ensure that instructions are given and understood.

O Obtain current information on fire status.
R Remain in communication with crew members, your supervisor, and adjoining forces.
D Determine safety zones and escape routes.
E Establish lookouts in potentially hazardous situations.
R Retain control at all times.
S Stay alert, keep calm, think clearly, act decisively.

Fire situation hazards:

- Fire not scouted or sized-up.
- Being in areas that fire fighters have not seen before in daylight.
- Safety zones and escape routes not identified.
- Being unfamiliar with weather and local factors influencing fire behavior.
- Being uninformed about strategy, tactics, and hazards.
- Instructions and assignments not clear.
- No communications link with crew members/supervisor.
- Constructing fireline downhill without safe anchor point.
- Building fireline downhill with fire below.
- Attempting frontal assault on fire.
- Unburned fuel between the fire fighter and the fire.
- Not being able to see main fire; not in contact with anyone who can.
- Being on a hillside where rolling material can ignite fuel below.
- Weather getting hotter and drier.
- Wind increasing and or/or changing direction.
- Getting frequent spot fires across the fire line.
- Terrain and fuels making escape to safety zones difficult.
- Taking a nap near the fireline.
- Personal protective equipment not being available or not being used properly.
- Operating unfamiliar equipment.

Four common denominators: Four major common denominators of fire behavior have been noted in fires where a fire fighter has been killed or from which fire fighters narrowly escaped. Such situations often occur:

1. On relatively small or deceptively quiet sectors of large fires.
2. In relatively light fuels, such as grass, herbs, and light brush.
3. When there is an unexpected shift in wind direction or windspeed.
4. When the fire responds to topographic conditions and runs uphill.

These factors should not be considered all-inclusive. For example, a sudden change of wind may change the direction of fire spread, regardless of topography.

Each set of circumstances has the potential for creating a tragedy or near-miss fire. Often, human behavior is the determining factor. Fire fighters who remain calm when the wind direction changes and move back into a burned area will survive. Those who panic and try to outrun a fire under similar conditions may die. The difference between a tragic fire and a near-miss fire may be due to luck, skill, and/or advance planning. In all cases, it is important to be alert and aware of conditions that may signal a sudden change in fire behavior.

In a few words, be alert, watch out for light fuels, wind shifts, steep slopes, and "chimneys."

Those who remain alert and on the lookout for possible trouble have the best chance of survival.

Suppression of Small Fires

Wildland fire management strategies are aimed at prompt, safe, aggressive suppression action of all wildfires. Small fires pose the same kind of suppression problems and require the same kind of practices as larger fires. Effective suppression of small fires involves the following steps: first attack, line location, line construction, burning out, mop-up, patrol, and declaring the fire out.

Suppression strategies range from prompt control at the smallest acreage possible to containment using a combination of fireline and natural or constructed features, to merely ensuring that the fire remains confined to a defined geographical area.

Initial attack: The principles of initial attack include:

- *Sizing up a fire.* Go around the fire as quickly and safely as possible, or inspect it from a vantage point. But do not go around the head of the fire if it is moving rapidly, as entrapment is likely. Size up a fire from a vantage point or from the flanks of the fire.
- *Selecting a point of attack, and making an attack.* The universal rules are to take prompt action on an attack point; to stay with the fire, and take the most effective action possible with the available forces and equipment; to inform the dispatcher of the situation by radio; and to continue to work day or night, if night work can be done safety.
- *Mopping up.* After primary line construction work is completed and a fire is called "controlled," many things remain to be done to make the fireline "safe" and put the fire out. This work is called mop-up. The objective of mop-up is to put out all embers or sparks to prevent them from crossing the fireline. A certain amount of mop-up work is done while building the control line. Mop-up becomes an independent part of fire fighting as soon as the spread of the fire has been stopped and all lines have been completed. Ordinarily, mop-up is composed of two actions: putting the fire out and disposing of fuel, either by burning it to eliminate it or by removing it so it cannot burn.
- *Patrolling.* Patrol is that portion of the mop-up job that consists of moving back and forth over the control line and the edges of burn areas to check for and put out any fire that may burn or blow across the line, and, at the same time, to check for and put out spot fires outside the line.
- *Declaring the fire out.* Before abandoning a fire, and as a follow-up, the incident commander will take steps to ensure that the fire has been extinguished and that any fireline that has been constructed is adequate should a flare-up occur within the fireline.

PRINCIPLES OF COMBUSTION

Fire is a chemical reaction in which energy is produced. When forest material burns, the oxygen in the air combines chemically with wood, pitch, and/or other burnable elements in the fuel. In the forest, several stages in the fire process are normally encountered: first, the igniting spark; then a period of smoldering; and finally, the more rapid combustion of fuels. This process may continue to involve leaping flames, dense smoke, intense heat, loud noises, and occasional explosions. Throughout its life, the action of a fire is governed by certain natural laws or principles of combustion, as they are described below. An understanding of these principles is basic in judging the effect of various environmental factors on fire behavior.

The Fire Triangle*

Three things—heat, oxygen, and fuel—are required in proper combination for ignition and combustion to occur. If any one of the three is absent, or if they are not in proper balance, ignition or combustion will not occur. Variations in balance among heat, oxygen, and fuel govern the violence of a fire, and determine whether the fire will smolder and spread slowly or flame brightly and travel rapidly.

Heat: It is difficult to specify the amount of heat required to ignite forest fuels because of the variation in the nature of the fuels. Vegetative material is high in carbon content and ignites at relatively low temperatures, provided the moisture content is low and the substance is freely exposed to the air. During the forest fire season, a large part of the vegetative matter in a forest—duff, dead limbs, pine needles, tree branches, rotted logs, and so on—is dry enough to be ignited easily. The temperature requirement for ignition of forest fuels varies from approximately 500 to 750°F (260 to 399°C). Many common ignition sources provide the required heat, including a burning match, a glowing cigarette, and a lightning bolt.

Ignition often depends upon the length of time the fuel is exposed to heat. Dry pine needles may be ignited in a few seconds by the heat from a flaming match. Moist pine needles also may be ignited by a match if subjected to the heat for several minutes. When wood fuels are exposed to heat for a long time, the normal ignition temperature may be lowered. Studies have shown that wood exposed to a temperature of 400°F (204°C) for approximately 30 minutes may ignite.

The ease of ignition of forest fuels exposed to heat for a considerable time has an important influence on fire behavior. In a coniferous forest, a hot fire burning in a tangle of downed logs and dry limbs may generate enough

* Although it is recongized that there is a fourth component involved in the combustion process—a chemical chain reaction—for the purposes of this presentation only the components that make up the commonly referred to "fire triangle"—heat, fuel and oxygen—will be addressed. The process of breaking the chemical chain reaction is not normally addressed in relation to wild land fire suppression methods. For a discussion relating to the fire tetrahedron and the chemical chain reaction process, see Section 1, Chapter 4, "Chemistry and Physics of Fire."

heat to make the green tree crowns above the fire easily ignitible. All that is needed to cause the tree crowns to ignite is a flying ember and a gust of wind. Similarly, a fire smoldering in a pile of leaves may generate enough heat to lower the normal ignition temperature of the entire pile. When the leaves are stirred up, the whole pile breaks into flame. The stirring of the pile lets in enough oxygen for the preheated leaves to be ignited easily.

Oxygen: In the forest, there is usually enough oxygen to permit ignition and combustion. However, some of the forest fuels may be arranged so that oxygen is not available in sufficient amount to support a fire. In deep, tightly compacted duff, only the top particles can get enough air to permit a fire to burn. In this situation, a fire will burn from the top down as each layer is exposed to the air. By contrast, in a very loose layer of pine needles, the entire mass is fairly well exposed to air, and consequently, combustion will take place rapidly.

When wind blows on a fire, it usually speeds up the combustion process. Wind forces oxygen around fuel particles where the flow of air normally may be restricted. In addition, wind has a physical reaction on the flames, often bending them into positions that create more favorable situations for the spread of the fire.

Fuel: Under forest conditions, fuel is a major variable in the fire triangle. The fire fighter must become acquainted with the general nature of forest fuels to understand their burning characteristics.

The ease of ignition and rate of combustion of forest fuels depends mainly upon the type of fuel—is it logging slash or dense duff in a green forest? On fuel continuity—is the fuel distributed more-or-less evenly over the area, or is it only present in patches? On moisture content—does it feel damp when touched, or does it crackle and appear very brittle? On fuel temperature—is the fuel exposed to the heat of the sun, or does it lie in cool shade?

Combustion process: When fuels are heated to their ignition temperature, they produce gases which will ignite if combined with oxygen. When a log burns, the flames may appear to be coming directly from the fuel. Actually, the flames come from the ignited fuel gases emerging from the heated log.

In forest fires, the two common stages of combustion are smoldering and flaming. In the smoldering stage, heat is liberated, and a rise in fuel temperature occurs, while flames absent or appear only intermittently. The absence of flames is caused by insufficient oxygen or by moisture in the fuels, which slows the oxidation process.

When a fire is in the flaming stage, all the elements of the fire triangle—that is, heat, oxygen, and fuel—are in proper combination for rapid oxidation to occur.

The flames of very hot fires may be observed intermittently in the smoke at a considerable distance above the fire. This occurs when oxygen is consumed so rapidly near the base of the fire that combustion of the gases is incomplete. As these superheated gases rise, they reach a fresh oxygen supply and break into flames, giving the appearance that the smoke itself is flaming.

Re-ignition of apparently dead fires is an important factor in forest fuels. Although neither flames nor smoke may be observed, a fire can break out again if sufficient heat remains. Re-ignition occurs easily where fuels have been subjected to heat for a considerable length of time. To prevent re-ignition, an experienced fire fighter feels out fuels by hand before leaving the area. If heat continues to be present, the danger of re-ignition exists, and the control job remains incomplete.

Breaking the Fire Triangle

In fire control operations, the objective is to prevent combustion by breaking the fire triangle. If a sufficient volume aof water is applied, the fuel temperature can be lowered below the ignition point. Smothering fires with dirt deprives them of oxygen. Building a line in which all flammable material is removed from the path of the fire prevents further spread by robbing the fire of fuel.

In forest fire fighting, the actual method of suppression is often dictated by the equipment and fire fighters available. The most effective methods for each stage of a suppression operation can be determined by keen observation of the combustion process.

Reducing heat: Water being used to reduce fuel temperatures should be applied directly on the fuels being consumed. A common mistake is to apply water on the flames rather than the fuels. If the liberation of these gases is to be stopped, the fuels themselves must be cooled by the water. While some of the water played on the flames may reach the fuels, a large part will either miss its mark or be lost through vaporization. If water is being used for cooling purposes, the ultimate target is always the fuel.

In a very hot fire accompanied by leaping flames, the nozzle user may not be able to get close enough to the fuels to apply water directly on the trouble spot. In such cases, a fog nozzle should be used to knock down the flames. The water particles help cool the heated gases being liberated by the fuels. Once the flames have been knocked down, the water should be used to thoroughly cool the heated fuels that are generating flammable gases.

Reducing oxygen: Fires burning in forest fuels are difficult to smother completely. Soil thrown on burning forest materials may retard combustion by shielding portions of the fuel surface from the air, but the porous nature of most soils makes it difficult to completely shut off the supply of oxygen in this manner. Throwing dirt on a fire is nevertheless an important means of reducing the rate of combustion, after which the control operation may be continued by attacking one of the other legs of the fire triangle.

In very fine fuels such as dry grass, the oxygen supply may be reduced easily. Fuels of this nature do not retain heat for long periods, and, therefore, combustion normally may be checked by temporarily shielding the fuel surface from the air. Gunnysacks, fire swatters, and shovelfuls of dirt correctly applied are effective implements in smothering grass fires. When larger accumulations of flammable materials, such as dead stems and leaves, lie beneath a stand of grass, the danger of re-ignition exists. The understory material may hold enough heat to cause the fire to reignite once an adequate supply of oxygen becomes available. This danger can be determined by carefully observing the fuel.

Removing fuel: In wildland fire suppression, the removal of fuel from the path of the fire is the most common method of attacking the fire triangle. The fire continues to burn until its fuel is consumed, but it is prevented from spreading any further. A slowly advancing fire burning in sparse ground fuels may be checked simply by constructing a fire line down to mineral soil (soil with little humus or organic matter). A hot or fast-running fire may require several fuel removal operations. Snags of trees or tall brush that could cause spot fires may have to be felled. Thickets of reproduction, or dry brush, may need to be weeded out. Low-hanging limbs may have to be removed to prevent the build-up of a crown fire. Concentrations of limbs and logs may have to be broken up. The objective of these operations is to remove or reduce the flammable substance which could either allow the fire to build in intensity or to continue to spread.

Heat Transfer

The rate and amount of heat transferred influences the rate of spread and the intensity of a fire. Combustion cannot be sustained unless heat continues to be transferred. Heat transfer occurs by three means: radiation, convection, and conduction.

Radiation: In forest fires, radiation is the most significant means of transferring heat from burning fuels to exposed fuels. The location and width of firelines must be governed, in part, by the rate of radiant heat transfer. Potentially hot fires and spots where dangerous flare-ups might occur can often be prevented by breaking up the fuels to reduce the radiant heat transfer between them.

The degree of slope influences the amount of radiant heat transmitted to fuels upslope and downslope of the fire. Most forest fires will burn in the direction of the wind, partly due to the effects of radiant heat. Wind influences radiant heat transfer in two ways: it increases the rate of combustion, thus creating a hotter fire; and it bends the flames, thus decreasing the distance between the heat source and the fuels lying in the path of the fire. The dual effect of the hotter fire and the bent-over flames dries and heats the fuels lying ahead to such an extent that rate or spread may be greatly accelerated.

Often a fire will burn into the wind. This occurs because the wind increases combustion to such a degree that a large amount of radiant heat may be transmitted even to the fuels lying on the upwind side. On the upslope side of a fire, the fuels receive more radiant heat. This is one reason fires often spread more rapidly up steep slopes than on level ground.

Convection: In a forest fire, the fuels lying in the path of convection currents are heated and thus transformed into a more ignitable condition. The hot air mass rising from a surface fire transfers a large amount of heat to the tree crowns, thus bringing them nearer to the ignition temperature.

When fires break out in tree crowns and in other aerial fuels, heat transfer by convection usually is increased. Sparks and burning embers from burning tree crowns and snags also will drop and start new fires in fuels on the ground. As these ground fires gain in intensity, more hot air masses rise through the aerial fuels, and a type of chain reaction may be created. Fire fighters must always be alert to the danger of hot surface fires burning underneath a forest canopy. These surface fires must be cooled promptly, and fuel masses must be broken up to reduce convective heat transfer.

Heat transfer through convection also is increased by wind which moves hot masses of air ahead of the fire. Wind both increases the rate of combustion and accelerates the transport of hot air masses. When driven by wind, the hot convection currents may move closer to the ground fuels and thus create more flammable conditions in the understory vegetation of the forest.

Fuels located above the fire on steep slopes also receive heat by the movement of convection currents up the slope and are thus subjected to an accelerated rate of heating and drying. This is one more reason why fires often burn very rapidly up the sides of steep slopes.

Conduction: Wood is a poor conductor of heat, and the conduction method of heat transfer is relatively minor in evaluating forest fire behavior.

TOPOGRAPHY

Topography provides a useful and easily recognized indicator of fire behavior. Fires often have distinctive behavior characteristics according to aspect, elevation, position on slope, steepness of slope, and shape of the surrounding countryside. These topographic features usually are easy to identify in the field and thus are important factors in the evaluation of fire behavior.

Differences in topography may cause local variations in climate and day-to-day weather conditions. These variations, in turn, influence the character of forest growth and the flammability of fuels. In rough terrain, such as the northern Rocky Mountains, topography has a great influence on fire behavior.

Aspect

Aspect, sometimes referred to as exposure, describes the direction a slope faces. Fire conditions vary greatly according to aspect because different aspects receive varying amounts of sunshine and wind.

In general, southern and southwestern slopes provide favorable conditions for the ignition and spread of fires. Because these slopes receive direct sunshine, the air and fuel temperatures are somewhat higher. This causes snow to melt earlier on southern slopes. For these reasons, vegetation on south-facing slopes is not only sparser, but also drier and more flammable than vegetation on north-facing slopes.

Research has also shown variations in temperature and relative humidity on northern and southern slopes. On south-facing slopes, the average July-August temperature is higher, and the relative humidity is lower. When the combined effects of aspect and elevation are considered, some striking indicators of fire behavior become evident.

Detailed studies of over 21,000 fires by the U.S. Forest Service have shown that more fires occur on southern and southwestern slopes than on any other aspect, and that more fires become large on these aspects. Approximately 31 percent of all fires occur on these two aspects, and 7 percent of the fires originating on south or southwest slopes reach sizes of 10 acres or more. On northern slopes, less than 3 percent of the fires reach these sizes. The large-fire potential is nearly two and a half times greater on southern or southwestern slopes than on northern slopes.

Elevation

In the Rocky Mountains, there is a vertical difference of more than 10,000 ft between the lowest valleys and the highest mountains. At Lewiston, ID, the elevation is only 757 ft above sea level. Along the Continental Divide, there are many peaks over 10,000 ft, and in northwestern Wyoming, some peaks are over 13,000 ft above sea level. Between these extremes of elevation are a variety of weather and fuel conditions that create distinctive fire control problems.

Position of Fire on Slope

Fire behavior at various positions on a slope may be influenced not only by aspect and elevation, but also by the magnitude of the fuel body and by topographic barriers. When a fire starts at the bottom of a slope, an entire mountainside of fuels may lie in its path. Once a fire starting at the base of a slope gains headway, the availability of a continuous fuel body makes a large burn possible.

Steepness of Slope

Other conditions being equal, fires burn more rapidly on steep slopes. In general, as the steepness of the slope increases, the rate of fire spread increases. As explained previously, combustion is accelerated on steep slopes primarily due to increased heat transfer through radiation and convection.

Shape of Country

In rugged, mountainous areas, the shape of the country is of great importance to the fire fighter who must evaluate fire behavior. Narrow canyons, side drainages, sharp ridges, and massive, irregular slopes all have a bearing on the direction of travel, rate of spread, and general behavior of fires.

Experience has shown the following topographic features to be of special importance:

1. *Narrow canyons*. Wind direction normally will follow the direction of the canyon. Wind eddies and strong upslope air movement may be expected at sharp bends in a canyon. Radiant heat transfer from one slope to another is great, and, as a result, fires may spot across the canyon easily. Near the bottom of the canyon, there is a little difference between conditions on various aspects.
2. *Wide canyons*. Prevailing wind direction will not be altered to any great extent by the direction of the canyon. Cross-canyon spotting of fires is not common except in high winds. Strong differences will occur between general fire conditions on northern and southern aspects.
3. *Box canyons*. Fires starting near the base of box canyons will react similarly to a fire in a stove. Air will be drawn in from the canyon bottom, thus creating very strong up-slope drafts. These same conditions may occur at the heads of narrow canyons and at the heads of high mountain valleys.
4. *Ridges*. Fires burning along lateral ridges may change direction when they reach a point where the ridge drops off into a canyon. This change of direction is caused by the flow of air in the canyon. In some cases, a whirling motion by the fire may result from a strong flow of air around the point of a ridge.

FUELS

Keen observation of variations in forest fuels is essential in reliably estimating fire behavior. Fuel is the material of primary concern to fire control agencies. A good fire fighter must be able to evaluate flammability and difficulty of control in the various fuel situations encountered in a forest area.

Flammability Analysis

In a forest, great differences exist in the character of flammable materials. Deep duff, newly fallen dead leaves, clumps of grass, litters of dry twigs and branches, downed logs, low shrubs, green tree branches, hanging moss, snags, and many other types of material are present. Each of these materials has distinctive burning characteristics. The flammability of a particular fuel body is governed by the burning characteristics of individual materials and by the combined effects of the various types of materials present.

Before flammability can be analyzed, the physical characteristics of combustible forest materials must be classified. Such a classification permits the identification of the fuel factors that influence flammability. After the fuel has been classified properly, topographic and weather factors must be considered before the rate of spread and the general behavior of fires in that fuel can be determined.

Because forest fuels are so varied and complex, it is necessary to develop a systematic approach to flammability analysis. First, the fuel body is subdivided into two broad classes, ground fuels and aerial fuels. Then each of these classes is evaluated according to the arrangement, compactness, continuity, volume, and moisture content of the principal materials involved. With practice, this procedure can be performed quickly and easily.

Ground Fuels

Ground fuels include all flammable materials lying on or immediately above the ground or in the ground. The principal materials are duff, tree roots, dead leaves, grass, fine dead wood, downed logs, stumps, large limbs, low brush, and young stands of timbers.

Duff: Duff is composed of partially decayed vegetative matter found on the forest floor. Duff seldom has a major influence on the spread rate of fire as it is typically moist and tightly compressed so that little of its surface is freely exposed to air and its rate of combustion is slow. In forest fires, most of the duff is consumed down to mineral soil. Occasionally, duff contributes to the rate of spread by furnishing a path for the fire to creep along between patches of more flammable material.

The smoldering characteristics of duff fires make them somewhat difficult to control. Firelines must be dug down to mineral soil in duff areas unless the lower layers of duff are too wet or too tightly compressed to burn. Duff fires inside a fireline are best mopped up by turning over the duff with a shovel, loosening the material for better exposure to air, and allowing it to burn out. Water may be used effectively, but great care must be taken to stir the fuel to ensure that all particles are thoroughly soaked. Extinguishing duff fires by smothering them with dirt is very difficult to accomplish.

Roots: Roots are not an important factor in rate of fire spread, as the greatly restricted air supply prevents rapid combustion. However, fires can creep slowly in roots—in fact, some fires have escaped control because a root provided an avenue for the fire to cross the control line. The most flammable roots are the large laterals stemming from dead snags. Root fires are controlled simply by cutting the root where it crosses the fireline. Mop-up of persistent fires may require complete excavation of roots.

Dead leaves: As leaves decay on the ground, they gradually become part of the duff layer. Before this decay takes place, however, leaves are a highly flammable material and should be considered separately in evaluating ground fuels. In northern Rocky Mountain forests, the cover of dead leaves on the ground is composed primarily of needles dropped from coniferous trees. Ponderosa pine needles are the most flammable because their large size and shape lead to a loose arrangement allowing free circulation of air. Smaller needles, such as those from Douglas-fir, are generally less flammable as they are more tightly compacted on the ground.

Needles that are still attached to dead branches are especially flammable because they are exposed freely to air and are not typically in direct contact with the more moist material on the ground. Needles remaining on fallen limbs form highly combustible kindling for larger material. For this reason, logging slash containing dry needles is dangerous fuel.

Many techniques are necessary to control fires for which leaves or needles are the primary fuel. The advance of a fast-running fire may be checked temporarily by smothering it with dirt or by cooling it with water. Only a light cover of dirt thrown with the sweeping motion of a shovel is necessary to slow down a needle fire.

When water is used to check the advance, a spray or fog-type stream is most effective, with the water being aimed at the base and directly in front of the flames. A penetrating straight stream of water is most effective for mopping up a needle fire. Careful stirring of all flammable material is required. A fireline is essential around all fires burning in a continuous cover of needles.

Grass: Grass, weeds, and other small plants are important ground fuels that influence rate of fire spread. The key factor in these fuels is the degree of curing. Succulent green grass acts as a fire barrier. During the course of a normal fire season, however, grass gradually becomes drier and more flammable until the stems and leaves die due to lack of moisture. At this time, the major part of the grass cover becomes highly flammable. Cured grass, if present in large and uniform volume, provides the most flammable ground fuel in the region.

Grass and other small plants occur on the floor of almost all forests. Fire fighters need to observe the volume and continuity of the grass cover. In dense forests where little sunlight reaches the ground, very little grass is found. In more open forests, such as in mature stands of ponderosa pine, there may be a large amount. If there is a more-or-less continuous cover of dry grass on the forest floor, the spread rate of a fire will be governed largely by that cover, rather than by the heavier fuels normally associated with a forest.

The ease with which fires in dry grass can be controlled depends mainly on the volume of grass. When the volume is low, the fire is often cool enough to permit fire fighters to work near the edge of the flame front. When the volume of grass is great, however, the resulting hot fire may prevent work close to the fire front.

In grass fires, smothering with dirt or swatters and cooling with a spray or fog stream of water are effective control methods. Both methods require follow-up to ensure that no hang-over fires remain. Wherever forest material, such as a mat of dead pine needles, twigs, or small limbs, is intermixed with the stand of grass, a fireline dug down to mineral soil is usually required.

Fires in dry grass often have high rates of spread. For this reason, special safety measures need to be observed.

Fine dead wood: Fine dead wood consists of twigs, small limbs, bark, and rotting material. Normally, the fine dead wood classification is confined to material with a diameter of less than 2 in. (50.8mm). These fine dead ground fuels are among the most important of all materials influencing the rate of fire spread and general fire behavior in forest areas. Fine dead wood ignites easily and often provides the main avenue for carrying fire from one area to another. It is the kindling material for larger, heavier fuels.

In areas where a great volume of fine dead wood exists, a fire rapidly develops tremendous heat. The greatest volume of fine dead wood is usually found in areas containing logging slash. Under dry conditions, fires in such areas burn violently, and the strong convection currents created by the intense heat pick up burning embers and throw them out ahead, causing spot fires beyond the main fire front.

In some areas, the occurrence of fine dead wood may be spotty. Troublesome situations may be avoided by breaking up the worst bunches of fine dead wood before a fire reaches them.

Granulated dry rotten wood, while not an especially important factor in the rate of fire spread, is a highly ignitible fuel. Flying embers from the main fire often cause spot fires in rotten wood lying on the ground or in hollow places on old logs or stumps. Fire fighters searching for spot fires should seek out and carefully check these areas.

In most forest fires, the control job must be aimed largely at checking the spread of fires in fine dead wood and in the associated material— that is, duff and leaves— lying underneath. Unless a large volume of dry grass is present, the fine dead wood is the most important fuel and should receive the first and most concentrated attention. If the fire is very hot, the first action may be to smother it with dirt or cool it with water. Final control requires a fireline dug down to mineral soil in nearly all cases.

Downed logs, stumps and large limbs: Heavy fuels, such as downed logs, stumps, and large limbs, require long periods of hot, dry weather before they become highly flammable. When such material reaches a dry state, however, very hot fires may develop. The most dangerous heavy fuels are those containing stringers of dry wood, shaggy bark, or many large checks and cracks. Smooth-surfaced material is less flammable as it dries out more slowly, has little surface exposed to air, and contains less attached kindling fuel. Extremely hot fires may develop in piles of downed logs and large limbs or in crisscrossed windfalls as the various fuel components radiate heat to each other. Individual limbs and logs will not burn very hot unless the fire is supported by large accumulations of fine dead wood.

The control of an advancing fire seldom rests on the fire fighters' ability to suppress the fire in heavy fuels. Usually, fires will not advance from log to log unless finer fuels are present or the area is covered with logs that radiate heat to each other.

Once a fire becomes well established in heavy fuels, complete suppression becomes difficult. A control line around the area is essential. Smothering with dirt or cooling with water is effective, but both these methods require very large volumes of agent. In some cases, it is necessary to allow the fire to burn out until the heat has subsided sufficiently to permit final mop-up operations to take place. When a fire is allowed to burn out in logs containing stringers of bark, a careful lookout must be kept for spot fires caused by embers carried in the strong convection currents. If at all possible, hot fires in such areas should be cooled promptly by any available means.

Low brush and reproduction: Low brush, tree seedlings, and small saplings are classified as ground fuels because they are so closely intermixed with the flammable material on the forest floor. This understory vegetation may either accelerate or slow down the spread rate of a fire. During the early part of a fire season the shade normally provided by understory vegetation prevents other ground fuels from drying out rapidly. As the season progresses, however, continued high air temperature and low relative humidity dry out both the fuel lying on the ground and the understory vegetation. When this happens, most of the low vegetation, particularly small coniferous trees, become fire carriers.

The understory vegetation in a forest often provides a link between ground fuels and aerial fuels. The crowns of small trees may catch fire and, in turn, spread the fire to aerial fuels in the forest canopy. Either thickets of reproduction or dead brush may provide the first means for a surface fire to flare up and spread into the crowns of the overstory trees. In anticipation of this possibility, alert fire fighters break up reproduction thickets and dead brush along the fireline or, wherever possible, locate control lines to prevent fire from spreading into these danger areas. It is not uncommon for fire to creep through ground fuels under low brush or reproduction during periods when there is a low burning index, such as during the night. Heat from the creeping fires dries out the leaves and stems of the low brush and reproduction. Then, on the following day, as the burning index increases, a reburn occurs. Often on the reburn, the dried, low vegetation burns hotly and carries the fire to the aerial fuels, causing a crown fire.

Aerial Fuels

Aerial fuels include all green and dead materials located in the upper forest canopy. The main aerial fuel components are tree branches, crowns, snags, moss, and high brush.

Tree branches and crowns: The live needles of coniferous trees are a highly flammable fuel. Their arrangements on the tree branches allows free circulation of air. In addition, the upper branches of trees are more freely exposed to wind and sun than most ground fuels. These factors, plus the volatile oils and resins in coniferous needles, make tree branches and crowns important components in aerial fuels.

Tree branches and crowns are fuels that can flash quickly with changes in relative humidity. Crown fires seldom occur when relative humidity is high. However, coniferous needles dry out quickly when exposed to hot, dry air. The dryness of needles is influenced by the transpiration process in a tree. When the ground is moist, trees pump a large amount of moisture into the air through the leaves. As the ground becomes drier, the transpiration process slows, and, as a result, leaves and branches become drier and more flammable.

Dead branches on trees are an important aerial fuel. Concentrations of dead branches, such as those found in insect- or disease-killed stands, may cause fire to spread from tree to tree. Concentrations of dead branches on the lower trunks of trees may provide an additional avenue for fires to spread from found fuels into tree crowns. The most flammable dead branches are those still containing needles.

Fires in the upper crowns of trees are extremely difficult to control. The main control method must be aimed at suppressing the fire in ground fuels and preventing the fire from entering the tree crowns. Removal of limbs on the lower trunks of trees is one method of preventing crown fires. Limbs should be removed wherever a concentration of ground fuels makes a crown fire likely.

Snags: Snags, or tree stumps, are one of the most important aerial fuels that influence fire behavior. Studies of nearly 12,000 fires in the national forest of Region 1 have shown that more than 34 percent of the fires started in snags. This high fire-occurrence rate indicates the flammability of snags. Although green trees greatly outnumber snags in most forests, more fires start in snags because they are drier and are arranged for easier ignition.

Snags vary widely in character and, consequently, in their effect on fire behavior. Smooth, solid snags that contain very little bark and few checks or cracks are not highly flammable. On the other hand, broken-topped, shaggy-barked, or partially decayed snags ignite easily and have a major influence on the spread of fires. Burning embers blown from shaggy-barked snags are prolific starters of spot fires. In areas containing large numbers of snags, fire may spread from one trunk to another because of the intense radiation of heat.

Fires in burning snags must be controlled promptly. Wherever possible, the main control effort on the fire must be designed to prevent the blaze from getting into snags. When fires become established in snags, the control method usually requires that the snags be felled. Snag-falling is especially important if shaggy bark is carried from the burning trunk by wind or strong convection currents.

Tree moss: Moss hanging on trees is the lightest and flashiest of all aerial fuels. Moss is important principally because it provides a means of spreading fires from ground fuels to other aerial fuels or from one aerial component to another. Like other light fuels, moss reacts quickly to changes in relative humidity. During dry weather, crown fires may develop easily in heavily moss-covered stands. Methods of controlling moss fires are aimed primarily at breaking up ground fuels to prevent fire from entering the tree crowns through hanging moss. In addition, lower limbs containing tree moss should be removed at all danger spots.

High brush: Crowns of high brush are classified as aerial fuels because they are separated distinctly by distance from ground fuels. In the northern Rocky Mountain region, heavy stands of brush may develop in old burns, and they often form the principal vegetative cover in such areas. Crown fires in brush fuels ordinarily do not occur unless heavy ground fuels are present to develop the required heat. In some brush stands, however, a high proportion of dead stems may create a sufficient volume of fine dead aerial fuels to permit very hot and fast-spreading crown fires. Key factors in evaluating the behavior of fires in high brush are volume, arrangement, the general condition of ground fuels, and the presence of fine dead aerial fuels.

Fuel Conditions

Fuel continuity: Fuel continuity describes the distribution of fuels in a given area. Fuel continuity is an important factor in fire behavior because the distribution of fuels influences the potential area where a fire may spread, as well as the rate of spread. If a dangerous fuel is uniformly distributed over an entire area, a high potential exists for a complete burn to occur at a rapid rate of spread. If the fuel body is broken up by patches of bare ground or much less flammable material, both the potential area of the burn and the rate of fire spread are reduced.

A wide range of fuel continuity conditions is found in most forest areas. For the sake of simplicity in making fire behavior estimates, two broad fuel continuity classes are recognized:

(1) Uniform fuels, which include all fuels distributed continuously over the area being evaluated. Areas containing a network of stringers, or blocks, which connect with each other to provide a continuous path for the spread of fire, are included in this classification.
(2) Patchy fuels, which include all fuels distributed unevenly over the area being evaluated. Definite breaks should be present, such as patches of rocky outcropping or plots where the dominant vegetation is of much lower flammability than the main fuel body.

Volume: As the amount of flammable materials in a given area increases, the amount of heat a fire produces also increases. The hottest fires, as well as those most difficult to control, occur in areas containing the greatest quantity of fuel.

In evaluating fuel volume, the quantity of both small- and large-sized fuel components should be observed. A great volume of small materials, such as fine dead wood, indicates ample kindling for the ignition of other fuels. A great volume of either small- or large-sized material indicates a high potential for a hot fire. Where fires develop in areas containing a great volume of large-sized material, there is intense radiation of heat to fuels lying in the path of the fire.

Fuel compactness: Fuel compactness—that is, the number of individual fuel particles per unit of volume—varies greatly in all kinds of fuel, but it is significant principally in duff and dead leaves lying on the ground. Fires burn rapidly in loosely compacted fuels because more of the individual fuel particles are freely exposed to air.

Moisture content: Two conditions of fuel moisture have major influence on the rating of fuel types. One concerns the greenness, or curing stage, of vegetation. The other relates to the shade and protection furnished by green timber.

In grass fuels, moisture content is a critical factor in determining flammability. Fires spread only at a low rate, or not at all, in grasses that are rank green, but when the same grasses become cured and dry, fires will race through them at an extremely rapid rate. The degree of curing of grass is difficult to evaluate and requires keen observation of the grass stand. For purposes of considering fire behavior, the moisture content of grass can be judged according to the state of curing, as follows:

Green—The condition can be recognized by the green color and the cool, moist feel when crushed in the hand.

Curing—as hot, dry weather prevails, grasses ordinarily progress through a period of gradual curing. This stage is detected by close observation of the individual grass clumps or stems. For cheatgrass, the curing stage is typified by a lavender tinge commonly referred to as "the purple stage." For most other grasses, the curing stage begins when the tips of grass blades become tan or brown, or when individual grass blades take on a cured appearance.

Cured—In the cured stage, grasses are dried completely to a tan or brownish hue, and the stems feel dry or crackly when crushed or rubbed in the hand.

Soils influence curing primarily because of soil moisture relationships. In the deep, moist soils bordering creeks, curing is much slower than in the thin soils on slopes.

Some grasses seldom reach a dangerous cured condition. The shade and protection afforded by timber stands influence fuel type ratings due to the favorable fuel moisture conditions that are created. In a dense forest, ground fuels are protected from the sun and wind. Temperatures and wind velocities are lower so that moisture does not evaporate as rapidly from the dead fuels on the ground. Lower ratings are assigned to fuels situated beneath dense timber canopies.

The moisture content of fuels is influenced also by aspect, altitude, time of year, time of day, and other factors. For the purpose of fuel type classification, these factors are disregarded, and fuel types are classified on the basis of the physical characteristics of the fuels themselves.

SPECIAL FIRE BEHAVIOR FACTORS

Spot Fires

The development of spot fires depends not only upon topographic and weather factors, but also upon the character of fuels in the main fire and fuels beyond the main fire. In the main fire, rotten, shaggy-barked snags, such as broken-topped hemlock snags, and large quantities of ground fuels, such as heavy logging slash, are the fuels most likely to cause spot fires. Spot fires frequently are started by crown fires. Widespread crown fires, with their intense heat and strong convection currents, can throw burning embers far out ahead.

Fuels that are ignited most readily by embers thrown out ahead of the main fire, listed in the order of susceptibility, include:

1. Rotten wood on the ground, on logs, and in snags.
2. Moss and lichens in tree tops.
3. Slash, particularly when compacted in tight piles.
4. Duff.
5. Cured grass.

Spot fires become more frequent and severe with lower fuel moisture and increased wind. On an average dry, late summer afternoon, the smallest sparks quickly ignite rotten wood or tree moss. In compacted slash, in duff, and in cured grass, larger burning embers are required to start spot fires unless sufficient wind exists to fan smoldering material into flames.

Crown Fires

Many forests contain a combination of aerial and ground fuels that favor the development of crown fires. Fuel conditions that influence the probability and character of crown fires include:

1. Volume and arrangement of the timber canopy.
2. Volume and arrangement of fine dry aerial fuels, such as moss and dead twigs.
3. Position of aerial fuels above ground fuels.
4. Character of ground fuels.

In open forests where single trees or small clumps of trees are well isolated from each other, crown fires are usually confined to single trees or to small groups of trees.

Crowning, in such cases, increases rate of spread by intensifying heat and causing spot fires, but it will not result in racing crown fires like those that sometimes occur in dense forests.

When the timber canopy is sufficiently dense and continuous to carry broadcast crown fires, the severity of the crown fire is influenced by the quantity, character, and arrangement of dry fuels in the air and on the ground.

An important consideration in evaluating fuel conditions is the likelihood of reburns in tree crowns over previously burned ground fuels. A combination of fuel, weather, and topographic conditions may confine a fire to ground fuels for a considerable period of time. While the fire is burning on the ground, the aerial fuels may be scorched and singed, and may become critically dry. If conditions change, a crown fire may develop and sweep back over the area. This type of crown fire may develop rapidly and burn more explosively because the aerial fuels have been dried by surface fire.

RESEARCH

Both Canada and the U.S. maintain fire research programs whose ultimate goals are to reduce the loss of life, property, and forest resources from wildfires and to use prescribed fire better to achieve forest and range management objectives at reduced costs.

The Canadian Forestry Services (CFS) of Canada's Department of the Environment is the principal research organization in Canada. Its forest fire research program is centered at the Petawawa National Forestry Institute in Chalk River, Ontario. Fire research work is also carried out at regional forest research centers in Victoria, British Columbia; Edmonton, Alberta; and Sault Ste. Marie, Ontario. These research programs address six major areas:

1. *Fire Behavior*: Fuel moisture physics, fire spread physics, prediction of fire danger by forest type, fire/weather interactions, fire danger rating system, and spatial weather models.
2. *Fire ecology*: Post fire forest regeneration mechanisms, cyclic forest development from fire to fire, predictors of post-fire forest development, and age-class distribution in fire-cycled forests.
3. *Fire suppression*: Performance testing of fire management equipment, air tankers, fire retardants and water additives, aerial ignition devices, backfiring methods, and new suppression methods.
4. *Prescribed fire*: Tree damage and mortality, use of fire for slash removal, seedbed preparation and vegetation control, design of prescriptions for proper burning conditions, and operational techniques.
5. *Economics*: Estimation of values at risk, effect of fire on timber supply, relation between fire management costs and burned area, allowable cut effect, and ultimate impact on the forest economy.
6. *Fire management systems*: Remote sensing applications, computerized systems for integrating weather, fuel type, and terrain into fire spread and growth models, prediction of lightning and human-caused fires, air patrol routing, resource deployment, and fire management strategies.

Current U.S. fire research is being conducted at six forest and range experiment stations. Much of the work is done at forest fire laboratories located in Macon, Georgia; Missoula, Montana; and Riverside, California. Major research projects include:

1. *Fire behavior*: Fundamental studies in fuel chemistry, combustion and ignition processes, firespread mechanisms, time-temperature heat flux interrelationships, and effects of fuel moisture, wind, and slope. Development of systems to aid fire and land managers in dealing with the growth of large fires, fuel consumption and energy release, probability of ignition by lightning, and fire spread in nonuniform fuels.
2. *Fire suppression*: Development of real-time and planning guidelines for individual suppression activities related to primary fuel and fire variables; integration of production rate knowledge into real-time and planning guidelines for fire suppression strategies and tactics; and development of design criteria for chemical formulations and for aerial and ground delivery systems for primary strategies and tactics.
3. *Fire effects, use, and ecology*: Research to determine how, when, and where prescribed fire may be used to improve tree growth, provide better wildlife habitat, reduce fire hazard, and accomplish other forestry goals. Includes studies on soil to ascertain biological responses, impacts on soil, stand structure, and so on.
4. *Fire management planning*: Studies to relate wildland fires and social benefits desired from wildlands; to determine the effectiveness of fire prevention activities; to determine the influence of weather and climate on fire occurrence, control, and effects; and to determine the productivity and effectiveness of air tanker systems.
5. *Other*: Additional research projects involving smoke management for prescribed fires, reducing residues from forestry activities, evaluating the economics of fire protection systems, and aiding managers with systems for applying knowledge gained through research projects.

SUMMARY

The impact of wildland fires continues to become more significant, not only in North America but throughout the world. In 1983, Australia experienced the Ash Wednesday fire that claimed 77 lives, injured more than 3500 people, destroyed more than 2500 homes, and killed more than 300,000 head of domestic livestock. More than 840,000 acres were burned in a single day. In 1985, a series of wildland fires in the United States claimed more than 40 lives and destroyed nearly 2000 structures. In 1987, 193 persons lost their lives and 10,000 homes were destroyed in a devastating fire in China. During 1988, the U.S. experienced the Yellowstone fires and other wildland fires throughout the country. More than $5\frac{1}{2}$ million acres (22 million ha) were burned, destroying more than 409 homes, killing 11 people, and costing nearly three quarters of a billion dollars to fight.

The toll on human life, the financial impact, and the increased value of natural resources make it undesirable to lose thousands of acres of valuable timber, rangeland, and watersheds. Continuing efforts to prepare fire managers and fire fighters to deal with both the beneficial aspects of fire through the use of prescribed fire and the control and extinguishment of unwanted fires is of the utmost importance. In addition, the public must understand its critical role in preventing unwanted fires, and communities must recognize the importance of designing developments that will minimize the threat of fire to real property.

BIBLIOGRAPHY

Additional Readings

Abt, R., Kelly, D., and Kuypers, M., "The Florida Palm Coast Fire: An Analysis of Fire Incidence and Residence Characteristics," *Fire Technology*, Vol. 23, No. 3, 1987, pp. 230-252.

Anderson, H. E., "Forest Fuel Ignitibility," *Fire Technology*, Vol. 6, No. 4 (Nov. 1970), pp. 312-319.

Aubry, Y., "Passive Detection of Forest Fires," *Revue Generale de Thermique*, Vol. 27, No. 317 (May 1988), pp. 313-318.

Bailey, D.W., Wildland Fire Management (Monthly Column), *Fire Command*, 1988-1990.

Bailey, D.W., "Wildland Urban Interface: A National Problem with Local Solutions. "*Presentation* at Interwest Fire Council Meeting, Kamouraska, Quebec, Canada, 1988.

Brabander, O. P., *et al.*, "Investigation of the Conditions of Transition of a Surface Forest Fire to a Crown Fire," *Combustion, Explosion and Shock Waves*, Vol. 24, No. 4 (Jan. 1989), pp. 435-440.

Bratten, F. W. , "Containment Tables for Initial Attack on Forest Fires," *Fire Technology*, Vol. 14, No. 4 (Nov. 1978), pp. 297-303.

Burgan, R. E. and Hartford, R. A., "Computer Mapping of Fire Danger and Fire Locations in the Continental United States," *Journal of Forestry*, Vol. 86, No. 1, 1988, pp. 25-80.

Cappellini, V., Mattii, L., and Mecocci, A., "Intelligent System for Automatic Fire Detection in Forests," *Proceedings* of the Third International Conference on Image Processing and Its Applications, IEE Conference Publication No. 307, Stevenage, England, 1989.

Chandler, C. C., *et al.*, *Fire in Forestry*, John Wiley & Sons Inc., NY, 1983.

Countryman, C.M., "Mass Fire Characteristics in Large-Scale Tests," *Fire Technology*, Vol. 1, No. 4 (Nov. 1965), pp. 303-317.

Davis, J. B., "A New Fire Management Policy on Forest Service Lands," *Fire Technology*, Vol. 15, No. 1 (Feb. 1979), pp. 43-50.

Emori, R. I. and Saito, K., "Model Experiment of Hazardous Forest Fire Whirl," *Fire Technology*, Vol. 18, No. 4 (Nov. 1982), pp. 319-327.

Fahnestock, G. R., "Two Keys for Appraising Forest Fire Fuels," *Forest Service Research Paper PNW-99*, U. S. Department of Agriculture, Washington, DC, 1970.

Fire Information Handbook, British Columbia Ministry of Forests and Lands, Canada, 1897.

Foltz, J. L., "Disposal Respirators for Forest Fire Fighters," *Fire Technology*, Vol. 17, No. 3 (Aug. 1981), pp. 174-176.

Fosberg, M. A., "Prediction of Prepyrolysis Temperature Rise in Dead Forest Fuels," *Fire Technology*, Vol. 9, No. 3 (Aug. 1973), pp. 182-188.

Gardner, P. and Cortner, H. J., "When the Government Steps In," *Fire Journal*, Vol. 82, No. 3 (May/June 1988), p. 32.

Gaylor, H. P., *Wildfires, Prevention and Control*, Robert J. Brady Co., Bowie, MD, 1974.

Greenlee, J. M., "Wildland Fire Modeling and Strategy Assessment," *Fire Technology*, Vol. 18, No. 3 (Aug. 1982), pp. 237-250.

Guth, D., "Organization Meets Wildfire Challenge," *Fire Command*, Vol. 56, No. 1 (June 1989), pp. 19-21.

Guth, R. and Cohen, S. B., *Red Skies of 88: The 1988 Forest Fire Season in the Northern Rockies, the Northern Great Plains and the Greater Yellowstone Area*, Pictoral Histories, Missoula, MT., 1989.

Hamilton, M.P., Salajar, L.A., and Palmer K.E., "Geographic Information Systems: Providing Information for Wildland Fire Planning," *Fire Technology*, Vol. 25, No. 1 (Feb. 1989), pp. 5-23.

Haines, J., "Wildfire: A Global Issue," *Fire Command*, Vol. 57, No. 1 (Jan. 1990), pp. 28-30.

Hirsch, S.N., "Application of Infrared Scanners to Forest Fire Detection," International Workshop Earth Resources Survey Systems, *Proceedings 2*, 1971, pp. 153-169.

Lindquist, J. L., "Building Firelines—How Fast Do Crews Work?" *Fire Technology*, Vol. 6, No. 2 (May 1970), pp. 126-134.

McFadden, J., Clayton, B., and Day, D., "Wildfires Incident Command System," *Fire International*, Vol. 11, No. 104, 1987, pp. 33-35.

Pagni, P. J., "Quantitative Analysis of Prescribed Burning," *Fire Prevention and Suppression*, Hildo, C. J., *ed.*, Technomic, Westport, CT, 1974, pp. 44-61.

Perry, Donald G., "Fire Behavior, Tactics and Command" *Wildland Firefighting*, 1987.

Proceedings of the Symposium on Wildland Fire 2000, USDA Forest Service Gen. Tech. Rep. PSW-101, Pacific Southwest Forest and Range Experiment Station, Forest Service, U.S. Dept. of Agriculture, Berkley, CA, 1987.

Pyne, S. J., *Introduction to Wildland Fire; Fire Management in the United States*, John Wiley & Sons, Inc., NY, 1984.

Pyne, S. J., *Fire in America—A Cultural History of Wildland and Rural Fire*, Princeton University Press, 1989.

Ramsay, G. C., McArther, N.A., and Dowling, V.P., "Preliminary Results from an Examination of House Survival in the 16 February 1983 Bushfires in Australia," *Fire and Materials*, Vol. 11, No. 1 (March 1987), p. 49.

Salisbury, H. E., *The Great Black Dragon Fire: A Chinese Inferno*, Little, Brown, and Company, Boston, MA., 1989.

Schmoldt, D. L., "Knowledge Management: An Application to Wildfire Prevention Planning," *Fire Technology*, Vol. 25, No. 2 (May 1989), pp. 150-164.

Simard, A. J., Blank, R. W., and Hobria, S. L., "Measuring and Interpreting Flame Height in Wildland Fires," *Fire Technology*, Vol. 25, No. 2 (May 1989), pp. 114-133.

Simard, A. J., *et al.*, "Nondirectional Sampling of Wildland Fire Spread," *Fire Technology*, Vol. 18, No. 3 (Aug. 1982), pp. 221-228.

Swinford, R.M., Tokle, G.O., project managers, *building Interagency Cooperation*, National Fire Protection Association, Quincy, MA, 1988.

Ventimiglia, M., "Paradise (Almost) Lost: Pebble Beach Fire," *Fire Engineering*, Vol. 141, No. 5, 1988, p. 18-30.

Webster, Joan, *The Complete Australian Brushfire Book*, Impact Printing Ptg Ltd, Melbourne, Australia, 1986.

"Wildfire: New Challenges, New Innovations," *Fire Command*, Vol. 56, No. 7 (July 1989), pp. 23-28.

Wilson, J. F., "1989: A Minimum Test," *Fire Command*, Vol. 57, No. 1 (Jan. 1990), pp. 16-19.

Wilson R. A. *et al.*, "Airborne Infrared Forest Fire Detection System: Final Report," *Research Paper INT-93* U.S. Department of Agriculture Forest Service, 1971.

AVIATION

Revised by James J. Brenneman

Among the many factors that contribute to aviation firesafety are the requirements that the aircraft be airworthy and firesafe. The hazards of certain maintenance practices must be recognized and proper control measures applied so operating personnel, aircrews, cabin attendants, and ground mechanical and servicing personnel are well trained in normal and emergency conditions.

Airborne and ground navigational aids, weather, air traffic control, proper design of runways with adequate "overrun" areas free of hazardous obstructions, and proper maintenance of this equipment and facilities are of extreme importance; however, they are beyond the scope of this chapter. This chapter discusses only the problem of fire in aircraft in the operational and ground environment modes.

AIRCRAFT FIRESAFETY

Firesafety in aircraft starts on the drawing board, and aeronautical engineers bear the brunt of responsibility for fire prevention and control. Aircraft require large quantities of fuel, lubricating oils, hydraulic fluids, and Class A combustibles, which are in proximity to potential ignition sources such as power plants, auxiliary power units, electrical systems, and heaters. Many aircraft carry oxygen systems (liquefied and gaseous) and some use oxidizers for auxiliary power units or are equipped with small rocket units for additional takeoff thrust. Consequently, aircraft firesafety requires a skillful blending of reasonable safeguards that are lightweight and do not interfere unduly with the use and mission of the particular aircraft.

Although most nations that have a major aircraft production industry also have extensive regulations governing the use and arrangement of the foregoing items, it is extremely important that the designer be thoroughly versed in the letter and intent of these regulations.

Installed fire detection and extinguishing equipment are normally required for those aircraft areas that possess inherent fire hazards and ignition potentials. Other fire prevention techniques used are separations of systems containing flammable fluids from potential ignition sources, compartmentation of fire hazard areas from critical structural components and flight control systems, and judicious use of other materials that are fire and heat resistive or of very low flammability. Firesafety must receive a high priority because aircraft fires in flight present tragic life hazard potentials. Fires following impact accidents—which can result in the loss of many lives—are also an aircraft design concern.

In commercial, light general aviation, and military reciprocating engine aircraft, the lightweight structure needed to allow the aircraft to perform its mission also permits impact energy to be transmitted to the aircraft occupants. Thus, more deaths occur due to impact trauma than fire.

In modern turbine-powered aircraft which operate in a more demanding flight envelope, structures are strengthened by the use of new or heavier gage metals, advanced technology composites, and different design techniques. This aircraft structure absorbs much of the impact energy without transmitting this energy to the occupants. Subsequently, statistics of accidents involving this type of aircraft disclose that the postcrash fire has become the predominant cause of serious injuries or death to the occupants.

As a result of aircraft accident investigations, much research has been conducted, and is still in progress, on methods of minimizing aircraft fatalities. Improved seat belt and buckle design, automatically inflated door-mounted evacuation slides, increased numbers of exits and exit system tests and certifications, pretakeoff safety briefings, and removal of potentially dangerous projecting knobs and other items from seat backs are developments which have greatly enhanced the chances of survival in an aircraft accident.

Many methods are being studied to reduce the postcrash fire hazard. They include, but are not limited to, the following:

1. Segregating flammable-fluid containers and systems from ignition sources.
2. Improving methods of fuel containment.
3. Modifying the physical characteristics of fuel to reduce probability of ignition in ground-impact accidents.

James J. Brenneman, P.E., is the former fire protection engineer for United Airlines, Inc., San Francisco, CA, and is now retired.

4. Reducing the rate of evaporation and the speed of flame spread over the surface of the spilled fuel.
5. Improving the materials used for interior decor, insulation, sound attenuation, and cushioning to reduce ease of ignition, flame spread, smoke, and toxic gas generation.
6. Compartmentation with lightweight fire walls in the occupied portions of the cabin, blind spaces, lavatories, and trash containers.
7. Onboard cabin fire suppression systems using water or a halogenated extinguishing agent.
8. Early warning fire/smoke detection systems in occupied portions of the fuselage.
9. Emergency lighting systems installed in the lower portion of the cabin to enhance evacuation in a smoke-filled environment.
10. Inerting fuel tank vapor space to reduce the possibility of explosion from static electrical discharge and lightning strikes. This can be effective in flight but will do little to contain the postcrash fire, because the inert atmosphere would be lost almost immediately on impact, with the disruption of the tank structure.

Some methods of fuel modification, such as gelling or emulsifying to thicken the fuel, have shown promise; however, they have proved impractical because ground handling of thickened fuel and pumping within the aircraft system created almost insurmountable problems. Fuel modification research, at present, is concentrating on the anti-misting additives. A recent large-scale crash test disclosed that even this technique may have limitations. Since present anti-misting additives must be injected into the fuel at the point of entry into the aircraft, and precise injection ratios are necessary, ground handling of this type fuel is also a problem. In addition, treated fuel is incompatible with untreated fuel; and the fuel reacts with any free water in the fuel or fuel tank sumps to form jellylike lumps.

AIRCRAFT POWER PLANTS

Civil aircraft in the United States are subject to extensive federal regulation through the U.S. Department of Transportation (DOT), Federal Aviation Administration (FAA). The Code of Federal Regulations (CFR), Title 14, "Aeronautics and Space," contains the Federal Air Regulations. Other nations have similar requirements. The following list summarizes the regulations that apply to aircraft power plants:

1. All reciprocating engines, auxiliary power units, fuel-burning heaters, or other combustion devices intended for operation in flight must be separated from the aircraft by fire walls, shrouds, or equivalent means so that no hazardous quantities of air, fluid, or flame can pass from these compartments to other portions of the aircraft. These regulations also apply to the combustion, turbine, and tailpipe sections of turbine engines. The fire walls and shrouds must be made of a material that will withstand heat at least as well as steel. When applied to power plants, the material must perform under the most severe conditions of fire and duration likely to occur in such zones. All openings in fire walls and shrouds must be sealed with close-fitting fire-resistive grommets, bushings, or fittings. In reciprocating engine nacelles, a fire seal or bulkhead is used to isolate the engine power section and exhaust system from the engine accessory section. In addition, a main fire wall segregates the complete engine assembly (power section, exhaust system, and accessory section) from the remainder of the nacelle section and, as applicable, the wheel well. In gas turbines, the fire seal or bulkhead separates the combustion, turbine, and tailpipe section from the compressor and accessory section. An additional main fire wall isolates the engine assembly from the support pylon or remainder of the aircraft, as applicable.
2. The cowling and nacelle skin are designed to prevent fire from circumventing the fire seals and main fire walls.
3. Tanks containing a flammable fluid cannot be located in a fire zone except when it can be proved that construction, connecting lines, controls, and shutoff means provide protection equivalent to segregation. A specified air gap is required between flammable fluid tanks and a fire wall, and materials that can absorb flammable fluids are prohibited from the area of the tank or any other system containing flammable fluids.
4. Emergency fuel shutoffs are required for each engine, auxiliary power unit, or combustion heater. The emergency shutoffs must be fire resistive or located so the operation will not be affected by a fire in any fire zone. Operation of the emergency shutoff must not affect other emergency functions, nor the operation of any other engine.
5. Flammable liquid lines in fire zones must be fire resistive and, where required, flexible. This also applies to drain and vent lines for flammable fluids or vapor.
6. Reciprocating and turbine engine air inlets must be arranged safely to prevent backfire flames from entering the fire zone, and designed so discharge from vents and drains cannot enter the air induction system.
7. Exhaust systems must discharge in a safe manner, not expose any portion of a flammable fluid system, and be provided with heat shields wherever they may impinge on other portions of the aircraft.
8. Drains must be provided for all fire zones, with the discharge arranged so that drained fluids will not be reingested into any portion of the aircraft.

AVIATION FUELS

The fire hazard properties of aviation fuels are identified according to susceptibility or ease of ignition, flash points, flammability limits, distillation range (initial and end boiling point), and electrostatic susceptibility. (Note: Octane rating has no relation to the degree of fire hazard of a fuel.) Table 8-33A summarizes the characteristics of the more common aviation fuels.

Two basic differences which must be considered when evaluating fuel in an operating aircraft and fuel stored in a tank at a refinery or bulk plant are:

1. Because an aircraft travels at different altitudes and through varying ambient temperatures, the conditions of flammability in the tank vapor space can change rapidly. Thus, a fuel type such as Jet A—which is normally too lean in a tank vapor space at sea level with a fuel temperature of 70°F (21°C)—can move into the flammable range as the aircraft gains altitude. Other factors contribute to this change, such as aircraft skin heating from air friction, outgassing of dissolved oxygen, and sloshing of the fuel from air turbulence. Figure 8-33A illustrates changes in the flammability limits of aircraft fuels in the tank vapor space due to altitude and temperature changes.

TABLE 8-33A. ***Summary Data on the Fire Hazard Properties of Aviation Fuels***

	Gasoline	Kerosene Grades	Blends of Gasoline and Kerosene
Characteristics	AVGAS	JET A JET A-1 JP-5, JP-6 JP-8	JET B and JP-4
Freeze Point*	−76°F	−40°F −58°F	−60°F
Vapor Pressure† (Reid-ASTM D323-58)	5.5 to 7.0 psi	0.1 psi	2.0 to 3.0 psi
Flash Point* (By Closed-Cup Method at Sea Level)	−50°F	+95°F to +145°F	−10°F to +30°F
Flash Point* (By Air Saturation Method)	−75°F to −85°F	None	−60°F
Flammability Limits Lower Limit Upper Limit Temp. Range for Flam. Mixtures*	 1.4% 7.6% −50°F to +30°F	 0.74% 5.32% +95°F to +165°F	 1.16% 7.63% −10°F to +100°F
Autoignition Temperature*	+825°F to +960°F	+440°F to +475°F	+470°F to +480°F
Boiling Points* Initial End	 110°F 325°F	 325°F 450°F	 135°F 485°F
Pool Rate of Flame Spread‡§	700–800 fpm	100 fpm (or less)	700–800 fpm

Note: Figures vary for some of these values in different data sources. Those shown herein are average figures based on the latest available information.

* $\frac{5}{9}$ (°F − 32) = °C

† psi = 6.894 kPa

‡ 1 fpm = 0.3 m/min

§ In mist foam, rate of flame spread in all fuels is very rapid.

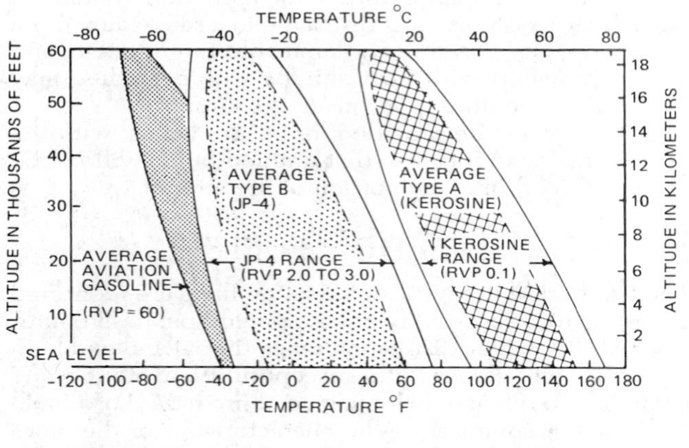

FIG. 8-33A. ***Flammable ranges of aviation gasoline and Jet A (kerosene) and Jet B (JP-4) turbine fuels, showing variations with altitude. According to laboratory studies, some of the sea-level flammable limits shown on this chart for Jet A and Jet B turbine fuel do not agree exactly with Table 8-33A. The test data used to develop this chart were taken from a single source; the table combines and averages data from all available sources.***

2. After an impact when major structural damage occurs to aircraft fuel tanks, the fuel may be released as a mist due to forward momentum, splashing, and wind shearing. Regardless of the type of fuel involved, this mist is easily ignitable from disrupted electrical circuits, hot engine surfaces, or ignition sources on the ground. The resulting fireball then acts as the ignition source for other combustibles in the area, including pools of high flash point Jet A fuel. If anti-misting additives can be successfully developed, they are intended to reduce misting and ease of ignition, or if ignition does occur, to prevent the propagation of flame throughout the mist cloud. In some aircraft accidents where deceleration forces are low, liquid fuel flowing from ruptured fuel tanks or broken fuel lines has been vaporized and ignited by hot engine surfaces, hot brakes, heavy electrical arcs, etc. Thus anti-misting additives solve only a portion of the postcrash fuel spill fire problem.

Relative Safety of Jet Fuels

Jet A (kerosene grade) turbine fuels apparently offer a safety advantage over other types of aviation fuels, especially during fueling operations and aircraft fuel systems maintenance. Studies indicate there is a measurable reduction of the incidence of fire in impact-survivable accidents when the aircraft involved had Jet A fuel in the tanks. However, once ignition occurs, all fuels exhibit similar behavior, and control measures must be instituted in the shortest time possible to prevent injury and fatalities.

In some portions of the world, Jet A (kerosene grade) fuel is not readily available, and Jet B (JP-4) is used. Jet B is easier and more economical to produce. Some nations also have reduced the minimum flash point of Jet A to increase yield of aviation fuel per barrel; the minimum flash point has been in the 80°F (27°C) range. Flash point testing of fuels as delivered from these nations has shown the actual flash point to be above 100°F (38°C). However, if a worldwide fuel shortage develops again, wider use of reduced flash point kerosene (RFK) and Jet B can be expected.

Electrostatic Susceptibility

The degree to which a static charge may be acquired by aviation fuels depends upon many factors: the amount and type of residual impurities, dissolved water, the linear velocity through piping systems, and the types of filters and water separators used. Jet A and Jet B fuels are better static generators than AVGAS. While all fuels generate static charges, the electrical conductivity of the fuel bears a direct relationship to the speed of charge relaxation (dissipation).

Antistatic additives have been developed. However, rather than preventing the formation of static charges, they actually increase fuel conductivity, thus considerably shortening the relaxation time. Antistatic additives increase static charge, since, by their nature, they are an impurity in the fuel. The charge generation is increased as the fuel passes through filter/water separators and other equipment. If an unbonded object is in the vicinity of the charge generation point before the charge has an opportunity to relax, this object can act as a collector and cause a high-energy static discharge.

Although possibly misnamed, antistatic additives have greatly increased the safety of aircraft fueling operations in all but extenuating circumstances (e.g., the unbonded collector in close proximity to the static generation point).

AIRCRAFT FUEL SYSTEMS

Most aircraft make extensive use of the internal wing volume to store fuel. In larger aircraft, the wing structure is sealed and forms the fuel tank. This is commonly called integral tank, or wet wing construction. Older and light aircraft may incorporate a flexible bladder to contain the fuel within the wing structure, using the wing structure only for support. Separate metal tanks or fiber-reinforced nonmetallic tanks are not widely used, and they are mainly located in light aircraft and older transports.

With integral tank construction, and only to a slightly lesser extent with thin-wall bladder tanks, it becomes apparent that disruption of the wing structure by ground impact or other damage will result in the release of fuel and the potential for ignition. This may occur even though occupied portions of the aircraft may be only slightly damaged. Thus, fire becomes the prime threat to the occupants. Figure 8-33B illustrates typical fuel-occupied spaces in a large turbine-powered aircraft.

One solution proposed is the development of crash-resistant fuel tank construction with dry break fittings and automatic fuel shutoffs. While the technology to develop this tank has been highly advanced, it has not been widely adopted due to weight limitations and reduction in volume available for fuel storage in long-range, military, and commercial aircraft.

However, certain helicopters operated by the U.S. Army are equipped with such crashworthy fuel systems. Statistics compiled after this modification disclosed no thermal fatalities or injuries in almost 800 accidents. Identical Army helicopters without the crashworthy system were involved in over 950 accidents, with a resulting 100 thermal injuries and 86 thermal fatalities.

Open-celled foam blocks, cut to fit and placed meticulously in the tank, are used on some military aircraft. While primarily intended for explosion protection after projectile penetration (incendiary bullets, etc.) of the vapor space, they also were tested for improvement of the post-crash fire situation. The tests showed some resulting improvement, but the problems of removal and replacement for tank interior maintenance and loss of available fuel volume have precluded their use in large, long-range, civil, and military aircraft.

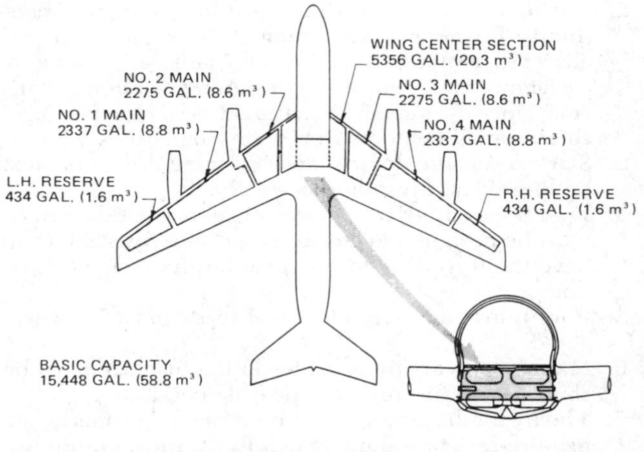

FIG. 8-33B. Arrangement of fuel tanks in a typical turbine-powered air carrier aircraft. The reserve tanks and Nos. 1, 2, 3, and 4 are "integral" tanks in this particular airplane, and the wing center section tank is of the "bladder" type.

Some aircraft equipped with these foam blocks have had internal fuel tank fires. Charred foam, discovered when the tank was opened for inspection and repair, has led to the theory that the foam increased the static charging tendency and/or acted as the unbonded collector. However, the presence of the remaining foam in the tank vapor space prevented further propagation of the fire/explosion.

Many aircraft utilize the wing center section (where it passes through the fuselage) for additional fuel storage. In some aircraft, such as the Boeing 727 and DC-9, this is an integral tank with a bladder liner. Newer aircraft designs utilize a double-wall tank of metal with a honeycomb core. While such tanks are well protected by the center wing section box structure (the heaviest on the aircraft), they directly expose the fuselage interior. To extend normal operating range, some aircraft utilize fuselage fuel tankage of the double-wall type outside of the wing center section box, and thus are deprived of heavy structural protection. As a reasonable compromise, all fuel tanks (at least those within the fuselage) should be of the crash-resistant type with dry break fittings and automatic shutoff valves.

Certain models of existing aircraft contain fuel tanks well forward or aft in the fuselage. Fuel storage in the horizontal stabilizer and vertical fin is being used on certain aircraft to extend range.

OTHER DESIGN CONSIDERATIONS

Several design principles which affect basic aircraft fire-safety and crashworthiness (excluding cabin furnishings and evacuation systems) are mentioned in the Federal Air Regulations and were developed as a result of accident investigations. They include:

1. When the same structure supports fuel tanks and landing gear, shear pins must be incorporated in the landing gear support structure, allowing the gear to be wiped off without applying structural loads to the fuel tanks.

2. The metal aircraft structure must have electrical continuity to prevent accumulation of static electrical charges, particularly in the fuel tank areas. This is extremely important when designing an all-metal aircraft, since the aircraft structure acts as a Faraday Cage, shielding all contents from lightning strikes.
3. Static discharge devices and lightning divertors must be located and installed correctly.
4. Fuel lines supplying rear fuselage-mounted engines must be designed to ensure proper fire resistance and have the flexibility to resist rupture in a crash situation.
5. Fuel lines and main electrical leads must be segregated.
6. Main electrical power cables in the fuselage must be shrouded in fire-resistive flexible conduit.
7. The hydraulic system must be designed properly and use fire-resistive fluids. Such fluids presently in use have autoignition temperatures in excess of 1,000°F (538°C) and are only slightly flammable. (Older types of mineral oil-based hydraulic fluids are still in widespread use, particularly in the military, and have been responsible for many serious fires.)

AIRCRAFT FUSELAGE COMPARTMENTS

The fire reaction of aircraft cabin interior materials, once ignited, can be crucial from a life safety viewpoint and can result in severe structural damage to the aircraft.

Prior to the mid 1940s, there were few, if any, regulations concerning the flammability of cabin furnishings. Old aircraft at air shows and in museums show the wicker chairs, gauze fabric curtains, and other combustibles used. Following World War II, a qualification test was required that involved igniting small horizontally mounted samples by a short exposure to a Bunsen burner flame. If a sample did not continue to burn after removal of the igniting flame, or burned less than a specified distance in the specified time, it was classified as self-extinguishing or slow burning. Although this test procedure was developed for laboratory comparisons, it created a widespread impression in the aviation industry that cabin furnishings were fire resistive.

After several disastrous fires in flight and on the ground, research was initiated to improve the fire-resistive criteria. Various public and private organizations conducted tests that proved the inadequacies of the existing fire-resistance criteria and, further, disclosed the problem of heavy smoke and toxic gas generation.

In the late 1960s and early 1970s, the fire-resistance criteria were upgraded to require a material sample to be self-extinguishing when tested in the vertical position, with exceptions such as floor carpeting. Although aircraft fires have indicated improvement in flame spread of materials qualified by the new vertical burn standards, improvement is still required and the problem of smoke/toxic combustion products remains.

In the mid 1970s, the FAA issued a "notice of proposed rule making" concerning allowable smoke generation and an "advance notice of proposed rule making" concerning toxic gases. After public comment, both these notices were withdrawn temporarily because definitive smoke and toxic gas test procedures had not been developed. (Later, in 1979, the Special Aviation Fire and Explosion Committee was formed. This committee, after more than one year's study, made recommendations concerning fire blocking layers, emergency lighting, smoke detectors, improved cargo liners, flammability standards on interior cabin panels, etc., which served in part as impetus for further study and future implementation of aviation firesafety improvements.)

One airframe manufacturer subsequently developed smoke emission and toxicity standards for aircraft interior furnishings and materials. Whether these standards are adequate in real life remains to be seen. At least one nation, however, has adopted these standards for all its commercial aircraft.

Some causes of aircraft cabin fires are:

1. Ignition source (usually electrical in nature) in the concealed spaces behind the cabin decorative liner. Such a fire can remain undetected for a considerable time and be beyond the control of hand fire extinguishers by the time it is discovered. Figure 8-33C illustrates an electrical failure which caused a disastrous fire.

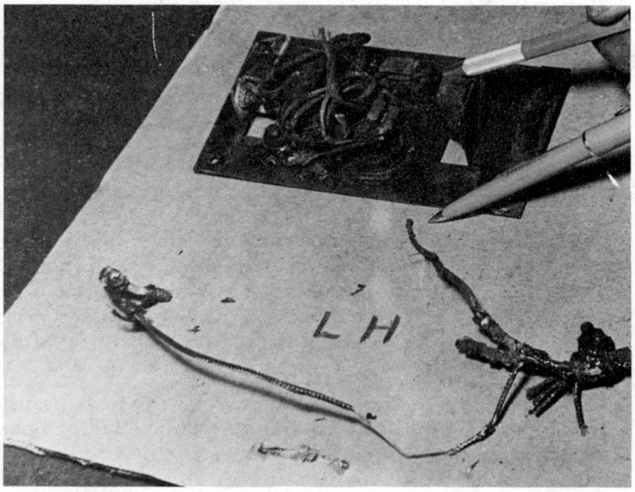

FIG. 8-33C. The shorted wires created a high-resistance ground, which ignited extraneous paper towels. The resultant fire burned in the concealed space for 45 minutes before breaking into the open. (Photograph from author's collection)

2. Ignition of the cabin interior from a postcrash fuel fire or a fire after a fueling operation malfunction. In such a fire, though the interior materials have a certain fire resistance, the heat flux from the exposing fire overwhelms the resistance of the materials.
3. Cigarettes and other carelessly discarded smoking materials on aircraft seats, in trash bins, lavatories, galleys, or receptacles not intended for the purpose.
4. Improper use of flammable liquids during cabin cleaning and refurbishing.

In the late 1970s and early 1980s, researchers developed a method of "fire blocking" aircraft seat cushions, which are usually made of polyurethane foam. This fire blocking layer is inserted between the cushion and decorative upholstery and is intended to delay or prevent the seat cushion involvement in a cabin fire. Under the FAA ruling in 1985 this fire blocking layer became mandatory within a two to three year compliance period.

Fire blocking of seat cushions does reduce the combustibility of the seats. However, unless the fire originates in the seats, fire blocking does not prevent development of serious, often fatal, cabin fires. Flames can propagate fore and/or aft along the ceiling panels, and radiate downward to the seat backs and cushions. By the time the seats become actively involved in the fire, heat and smoke conditions may already be unsurvivable. Figure 8-33D illustrates almost total upper fuselage burnout; seat involvement, however, was moderate. Figure 8-33E is an aircraft totally burned out (no seats were installed at the time of the fire).

***FIG. 8-33D.** Total destruction of the upper portion of the cabin. Seat involvement was moderate and occurred late in the fire. (Photograph from author's collection)*

***FIG. 8-33E.** An electrical spark and use of flammable liquid during maintenance caused this cabin fire. A total burnout occurred with severe damage to the aircraft structure. There were no seats installed in the cabin at the time of the fire. (Photograph from author's collection)*

In addition to the fire blocking, research is continuing toward the development of an improved, fire-resistant aircraft cabin window material to delay or prevent postcrash fire entry into the fuselage via the windows.

Because many aircraft carry supplemental oxygen for the potential failure of cabin pressurization and in portable cylinders for first-aid purposes, in a crash, localized fire intensification can be expected if the oxygen cylinder fuse plug operates due to fire exposure and releases oxygen in the cabin atmosphere.

Cabin fires in flight are infrequent, and usually are discovered and extinguished in their incipient stage. The potential life loss, however, is severe if fire progresses beyond the point of control by hand fire extinguishers. Research is underway for an onboard cabin fire suppression/inerting system utilizing a halogenated extinguishing agent and/or water carried for other purposes. Some corporate aircraft have been equipped with total flooding extinguishing systems utilizing Halon 1301 and such systems are commercially available. FAA research into total flooding on large commercial transports was somewhat inconclusive; however, the primary aim of the project was to delay penetration of a postcrash fire, rather than control or extinguishment of an inflight cabin fire.

Airline operators and governmental regulations routinely prohibit smoking during aircraft takeoff and landing, while a plane is flying in extreme turbulence, or at any other times the command pilot deems that smoking constitutes a hazard to safety. U.S. regulations and those of most other nations prohibit smoking except in a designated section of the aircraft. Smoking in lavatories, galleys, or while standing in an aisle is strictly prohibited.

All aircraft lavatories are required to have smoke detectors. The initial rule utilized domestic-type smoke detectors; although these may be of dubious value in an aircraft environment (since they are not designed, tested, or approved for this purpose), they can serve as an additional deterrent to smoking in the lavatories. Some aircraft operators have reported a good measure of success in this regard. However, missing batteries and false alarms are a problem. (Smoke detectors specifically designed for aircraft lavatories have been developed.)

Trash containers have been redesigned and modified to contain an interior fire, and some aircraft are equipped with a fire suppression system for the trash receptacle. As of 1985, all U.S. aircraft and those registered in most other nations require such a suppression system for lavatory trash containers regardless of container design.

Hazardous Cargoes

Hazardous cargoes occasionally present a problem to aircraft in flight, on the ground, during ground handling, and in a postcrash situation. This is an international problem, since many shipments cross national boundaries. Hazardous cargoes are regulated by many agencies, including the U.S. Department of Transportation, the International Air Transport Association, the International Civil Aviation Organization (an agency of the United Nations), and others.

The regulations cover type of cargo that may be shipped, quantities allowed, method of packaging, and the type of aircraft (passenger, or cargo only) in which this material may be carried. Flight crews must be informed of the presence of hazardous cargoes on the manifest, and in some cases can refuse to carry the material.

If the rules are followed rigidly, there is little hazard to safety of flight or to ground personnel, whether in normal handling or a postcrash situation. The problem arises when the shipper, either in ignorance or in willful contempt of the regulations, misrepresents the contents of the shipment to a carrier, or does not package the material adequately to ensure containment during transit.

After several serious incidents, the regulations were revised and further restrictions were adopted. Better training is now required for each carrier's receiving agents, standard labels have been adopted, and penalties are assessed against shippers who violate the law.

AIRCRAFT FIRE DETECTION AND EXTINGUISHING SYSTEMS

Fire detection and extinguishing systems are required in certain zones of the aircraft, notably the power plant areas. These systems are defined in design regulations of the nation of aircraft origin.

These systems are similar to those used in ground installations, but there are significant differences. In most aircraft installations, the extinguishing system is activated manually by the flight crew. The detection system must be very sensitive, very stable (i.e., free of false alarms), and able to withstand extremes of the environment in which it must function—temperature, vibration, high airflows, and structural flexing. The system must also reset automatically to notify the flight crew when the fire has been extinguished, or when the temperature in the protected zone drops below the set point. System response must be within seconds of the beginning of abnormal conditions.

Extinguishing agent hardware must be lightweight, rugged, and, to overcome the high airflows of flight, be capable of higher rates of agent discharge than would be expected in a similar ground installation.

The most common extinguishing agents used in aircraft are bromotrifluoromethane (Halon 1301) and bromochlorodifluoromethane (Halon 1211). Older aircraft still use carbon dioxide, methyl bromide, and chlorobromomethane. All are effective on flammable liquid and electrical fires.

Cargo Compartment Fire Detection and Extinguishing Systems

Cargo compartments in passenger aircraft often are equipped with fire detection systems. Air starvation is one of the more common techniques used in fire extinguishment in cargo spaces. Upon actuation of fire detection systems, all ventilation to the compartment is sealed off and the fire is allowed to self-extinguish due to lack of oxygen. Fire extinguishing systems usually utilizing Halon 1301 or Halon 1211 are also installed for cargo compartments.

Recent regulations have been adopted to improve the fire resistance and fire penetration capabilities of cargo compartment liners. An upper limit has been placed on the volume of a cargo compartment; above this limit, a fire suppression system must be installed regardless of compartment construction.

AIRCRAFT HAND FIRE EXTINGUISHERS

The FAA requires portable hand fire extinguishers in all air transport category aircraft. In some smaller general aviation aircraft, they are recommended but not required.

NFPA 408, *Aircraft Hand Fire Extinguishers*, requires portable hand fire extinguishers on all aircraft and describes the type, quantity, minimum capacity, installation, location, and spacing for the extinguishers.

While the FAA recognizes carbon dioxide, water, dry chemical, Halon 1211, Halon 1301, and halon combinations, at least two of the extinguishers installed on large transport aircraft must be of the Halon 1211 or combination Halon 1211/1301 type.

NFPA 408, *Aircraft Hand Fire Extinguishers*, no longer recognizes carbon dioxide and dry chemical as suitable for use on aircraft. Carbon dioxide is not recognized as suitable for the following reasons:

1. Ineffectiveness on Class A materials.
2. Chilling effect of solid carbon dioxide (snow) may damage delicate electronic components.
3. Weight of container and agent vs. similar agent capacities of the halon type.

Dry chemical has long been banned from aircraft in NFPA 408, *Aircraft Hand Fire Extinguishers*, for the following reasons:

1. Obscuration of the operator's vision, particularly in confined spaces.
2. Possibility of an insulating chemical layer forming on delicate electrical contacts, which could affect continued safety in flight.
3. Dry chemical can be an irritant to the eyes and mucous membranes even though it is not considered toxic.
4. If not immediately cleaned up, certain types of dry chemical can be highly corrosive to aircraft metals.

Some concern has been expressed over the toxicity of both the halon agents and the products of decomposition in the event of the fire. Figure 8-33F shows the effect of discharging Halon 1211 in a ventilated and unventilated cockpit. These data were generally confirmed by tests conducted by the FAA Technical Center in small aircraft.

The products of halon decompostion are indeed toxic; however, compared to the toxic products of combustion of cabin and flight deck furnishings, the toxicity problem is negligible. (See NFPA 12A, *Halon 1301 Fire Extinguishing Systems*, and NFPA 12B, *Halon 1211 Fire Extinguishing Systems*, and their appendices for a full explanation.)

The addition of a flexible discharge device, as recommended by NFPA 408, *Aircraft Hand Fire Extinguishers*, greatly enhances the capability of the extinguisher to reach hard-to-get areas behind the instrument panels, under seats, etc. The device enables the operator to hold the unit upright during discharge, gaining full use of the agent charge. Figures 8-33G, 8-33H, 8-33I, and 8-33J illustrate some of the advantages of a hose vs. a short nozzle under simulated conditions of use.

MEANS OF EGRESS FROM AIRCRAFT

In aircraft, emergency exit facilities are particularly important because postcrash fire exposure can be severe and the safe evacuation time for the occupants is limited.

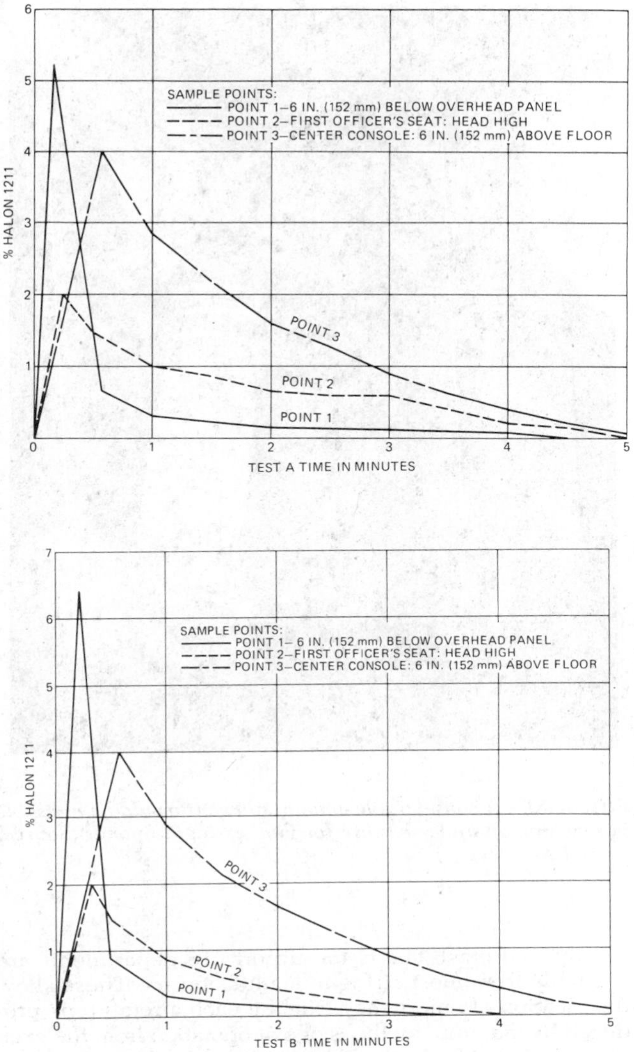

FIG. 8-33F. ***Halon concentration in a B-737 cockpit (240 cu ft or 7 m3) during and after discharge of a 3-lb (1.4 kg) Halon 1211 extinguisher. Altitude sea level, temperature 68°F (20°C), 11.5-second discharge time, cockpit doors and windows closed. Test A, no forced ventilation. Test B, calculated ventilation rate 1.9 air changes per minute, the minimum for this aircraft. (Source: United Airlines)***

U.S. Federal Air Regulations set the number of exits required in transport category aircraft, depending upon passenger capacity. The manufacturer or operator must demonstrate that evacuation of a full load of passengers can be accomplished in 90 sec or less, with half the available exits inoperative. These tests require that the test subjects represent an average passenger load, with certain percentages of able-bodied males and females, elderly, children, and handicapped. The tests are accomplished without normal cabin lighting; emergency lighting, however, is functional. The exits that are to be blocked are not preannounced to the crew or occupants.

While the data obtained are of value, there are some shortcomings in the tests:

1. Smoke, which could obscure emergency lights or exit signs, is not used.

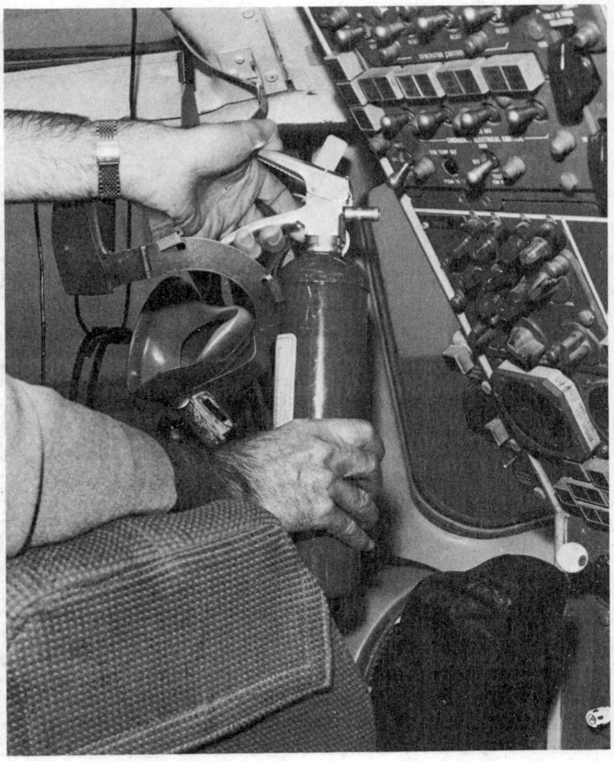

FIG. 8-33G. ***Effective access to space behind instrument panels is limited due to the short discharge device. (Source: United Airlines)***

2. The test subjects know this is an emergency exit certification test and will seek any usable exit. (In real life, most passengers pay little attention to preflight announcements and, consequently, tend to attempt leaving the aircraft by the same door they entered.)
3. Again, many test subjects have taken part in previous demonstrations and, while there is a minimum time limit since last participation, retain a certain knowledge of "what to do in the test."

Escape Systems and Devices

It is acceptable and permissible to utilize the normal entrance and passenger service doors as part of the emergency exit system. If the door is power assisted in its normal mode of operation and operates relatively slowly, it is equipped with a high-speed power assist for the emergency mode.

Each emergency exit with a sill height that exceeds a certain distance above the ground, regardless of landing gear configuration (nose gear collapsed, tail high), is required to have an emergency means of allowing the passengers to reach the ground safely. In recent years, this device has usually been an inflatable slide (which sometimes can double as a life raft). Present regulations require the slide to deploy automatically and inflate within a specified number of seconds from the time the exit opens in the emergency mode. Figure 8-33K shows one type of inflatable escape device.

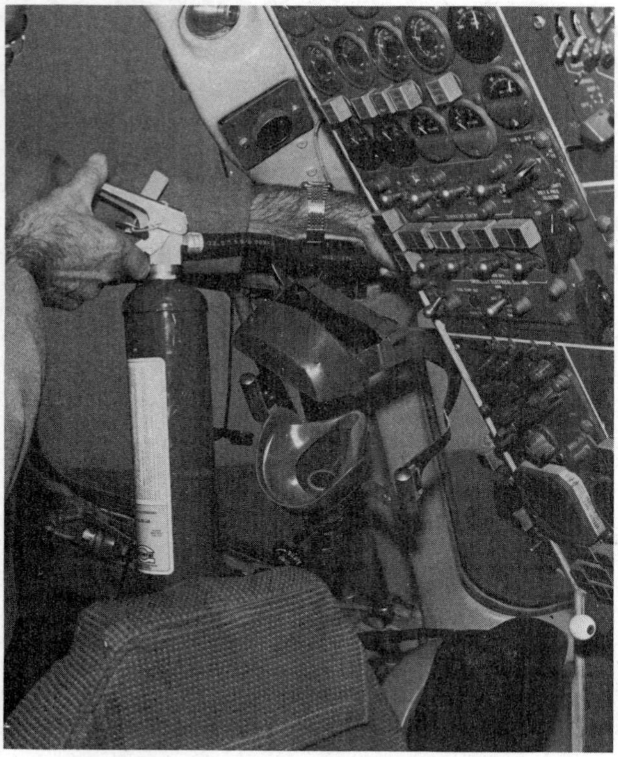

FIG. 8-33H. Improved access to the same space utilizing a short discharge hose. (Source: United Airlines)

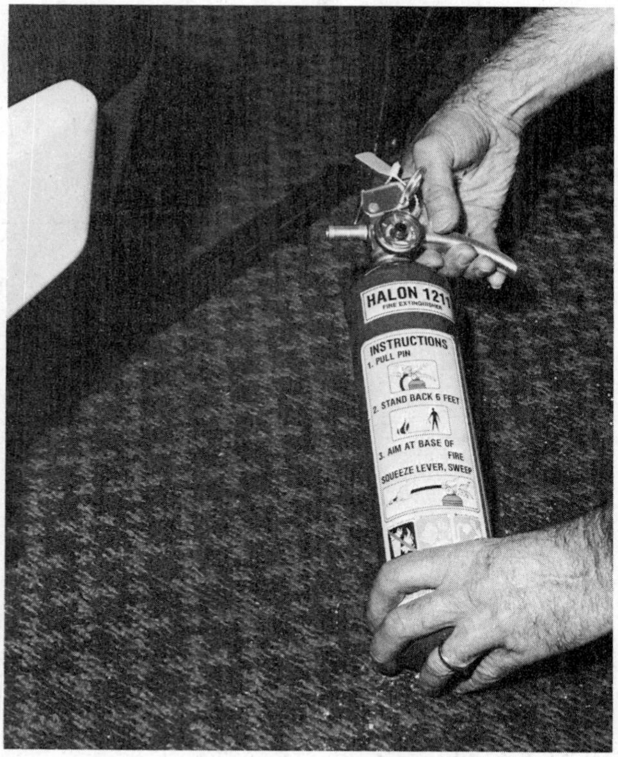

FIG. 8-33I. A considerable amount of agent would be unusable in reaching an underseat fire for final extinguishment. (Source: United Airlines)

The openings designated as emergency exits must be operable from the outside and designed to resist jamming due to fuselage distortion. The slides must deploy properly, regardless of wind direction or other influences.

The fire resistance of the slide material used to be very low, and even slight exposure to flame caused deflation of the slide. However, slide material has now been developed which incorporates a reflective coating, reducing the possibility of damage and deflation caused by radiant heat. At present, not all aircraft have been upgraded with this new material.

In several accidents, obscuration of exit signs and emergency exit lighting by smoke has seriously impeded evacuation of the aircraft. As of 1985, all air transport aircraft are required to have exit signs installed at a lower level and the exit access must be visible from a minimum distance of 35 ft (11 m), assuming a smoke level above the seat back height. In addition, illuminated exit path lights installed in aisle seat armrests or in the floor must be provided.

Research is being conducted to develop an emergency breathing device for cabin crew members which can be donned quickly, does not impair voice communication or hearing, and is independent of the aircraft oxygen system. Similar devices have been proposed for passengers; however, past tests have indicated that the time necessary in donning such a device, among other factors, can best be used in proceeding to an exit.

Research also is being conducted to develop an effective smoke removal system or procedure for inflight cabin fires. If this research is successful, smoke removal may well obviate the need for a special device for passengers.

Special crash charts for airport fire departments are available from most airframe manufacturers. These show the location of emergency exits on each aircraft type produced by that firm, methods of exit operation from the exterior, location of fuel, oil and hydraulic tanks, oxygen storage, and other hazardous areas. Because none of these items is standardized and may differ among aircraft of the same model series, these charts are an invaluable tool for airport crash crews. Many aircraft operators encourage visits by the local fire department for familiarization purposes and, when possible, permit hands-on operation of the exit devices. At certain locations, mockups with qualified instructors are available for use by the fire department.

SPECIAL MILITARY AIRCRAFT HAZARDS

Among the special hazards of military aircraft are ejection seats and canopy ejectors; armaments, consisting of machine guns and automatic rapid-fire cannons, bombs, rockets, nuclear weapons, pyrotechnics, and rocket propellants; and special high-energy fuels.

Information concerning fire and rescue for U.S. military aircraft is available from military aviation installations and is given freely to organized fire departments. Information is only limited on subjects which may be sensitive to national military security. Excerpts appear in NFPA 402M, *Aircraft Rescue and Fire Fighting Operational Procedures*.

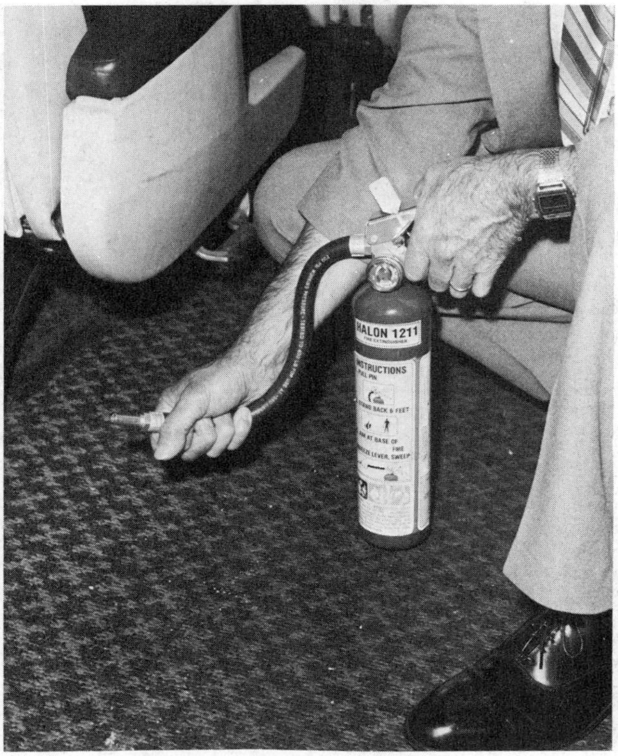

FIG. 8-33J. In the same situation, full use of the contents is obvious. (Source: United Airlines)

FIG. 8-33K. One type of inflatable, overwing ramp/slide escape device used on wide-body aircraft. (Source: United Airlines)

AIRCRAFT RESCUE AND FIRE CONTROL

Two distinct types of ground accidents are part of the flight environment of the aircraft (excluding fires from fueling accidents, malfunction of ground servicing equipment, or fires originating during maintenance procedures).

The first type of ground accident is the high-speed and/or high-angle impact with the ground or other object which results in such structural breakup of the aircraft that survival of the occupants is highly unlikely (i.e., fatalities occur due to impact trauma).

The second accident type involves relatively low speed and/or shallow ground impact angles. In this type of accident, the occupant survival rate can be very high, especially if there is no postcrash fire, or if the fire is controlled quickly in the area immediately surrounding the occupied portion of the aircraft. An impact-survivable accident is illustrated in Figure 8-33L.

FIG. 8-33L. An impact-survivable accident followed by fire. (Photograph from author's collection)

Because fire can be anticipated in almost all abnormal aircraft landings, plus a few incidental hazards such as overheated brakes or undetected fuel leakage, it is imperative that airports maintain an adequate, well-trained, and well-equipped fire department (crash crew) at the airport. At smaller airports, the crew often has correlated duties, such as security, fueling, or maintenance; they also may be volunteer employees of air carriers. However, all crew members must be available immediately at the sounding of an alarm and be transported to the accident scene immediately. At least one operator should be in the crash house or the immediate vicinity to move the provided equipment rapidly to the scene.

Studies by the International Federation of Airline Pilots Association and the U.S. Airline Pilots Association indicate that the largest percentage of survivable accidents occur within a certain area related to the runway centerline and threshold lights. This "critical rescue and fire fighting access area" (CRFFAA) is clearly defined and illustrated in NFPA 402M, *Aircraft Rescue and Fire Fighting Operational Procedures*.

To be effective, the demonstrated response time of the first responding fire fighting vehicle to reach any point on the operational runway must be two minutes or less, and to any point remaining in the CRFFAA, in three minutes or less. These conditions must be met when flight operations are in progress; however, NFPA 402M recognizes that mitigating circumstances can make it impossible to meet these recommended times.

Preplanning for anticipated (amber or red alert) emergency landings is also critically important. Pre-positioning

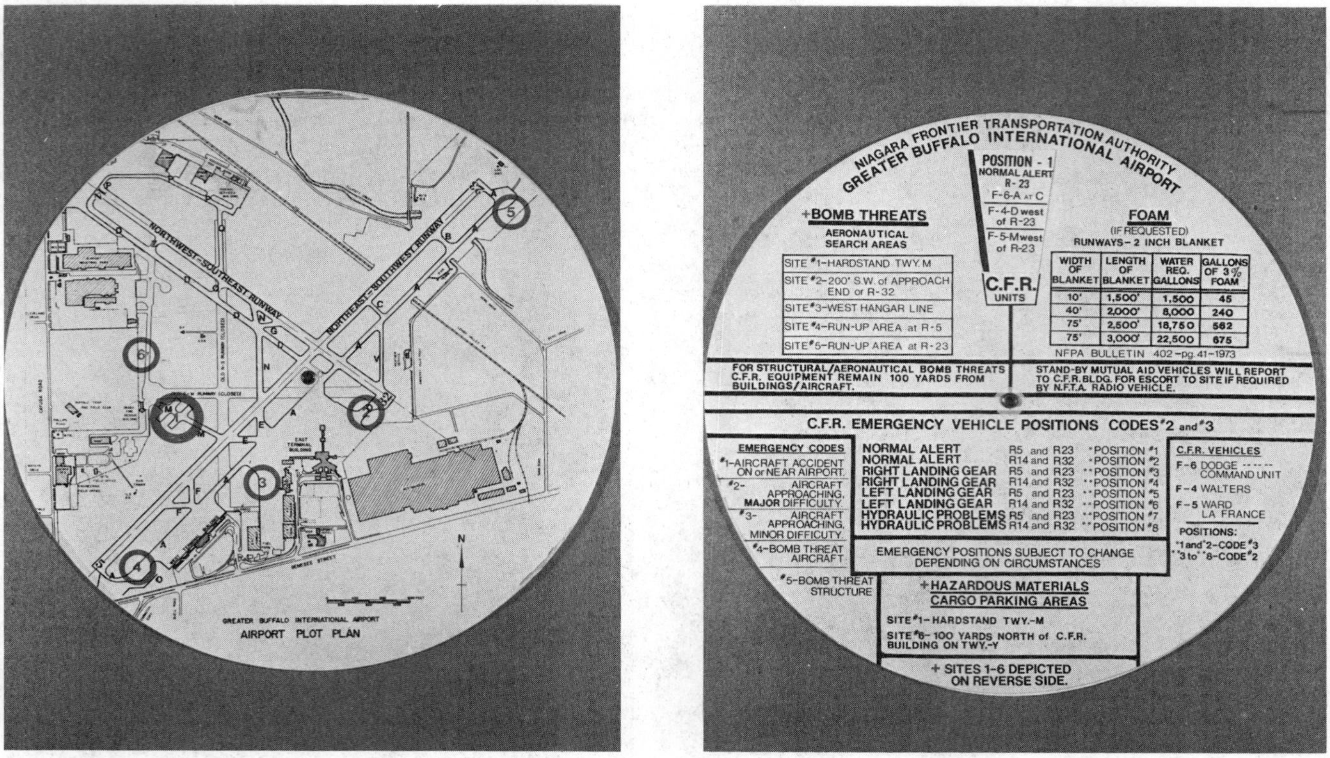

Fig. 8-33M. Left: Airport plot plan indicating preplanned standby position. Right: Rotating the "wheel" gives equipment positions for various types of emergencies for "quick refresher" guidance. (Device from author's collection, courtesy Niagara Frontier Transportation Authority)

of equipment and personnel under these circumstances can greatly reduce response time. Illustrated in Figure 8-33M is but one such device used to pre-position equipment for various emergencies.

The amounts of extinguishing agents needed and the type of specialized equipment required in an accident vary, depending on the types of aircraft that use a particular airport. Persons operating a land-based airport serving any Civil Aeronautics Board Certificated Air Carrier in the U.S. must have an airport operating certificate. Part of the certification requirements concern the provision of a minimum level of fire fighting and rescue equipment, although under certain conditions a waiver may be granted by the FAA. The minimum level of protection required is determined by the airport Index which is based on the frequency and type of aircraft used for air carrier operations. The minimum level was determined, in part, by the use of NFPA standards and private consultant studies; these minimum levels are contained in Part 139 of Title 14 of the Code of Federal Regulations (CFR). In addition, the FAA has published Advisory Circular 150/5210-6B, which gives recommended levels of airport protection which are considerably higher than the minimum levels in Part 139.

Other information on the subject of aircraft fire and rescue protection is published in NFPA 403, *Aircraft Rescue and Fire Fighting Services at Airports and Heliports*, and the International Civil Aviation Organization in Annex 14 (Aerodromes) to the *Convention on Civil Aviation*.

There are interesting similarities of requirements among NFPA, ICAO, and the FAA Advisory Circular 150/5210-6B, as compared to the minimums of CFR Part 139. One major difference among the three is that ICAO and the FAA allow a remission factor so an airport may drop to a lower Index if the number of movements (takeoffs and landings) of the largest aircraft to use the airport is below a certain daily or yearly operational level. NFPA does not recognize the remission factor, requiring protection for the largest aircraft that regularly uses the airport, regardless of operational levels.

Other Considerations for Aircraft Rescue and Fire Control

Aside from provision of fire equipment (and assuming adequate personnel for operation), several other important factors directly affect the success or failure of the airport fire rescue crew mission.

The most important factors are training and physical fitness of the personnel. Training, which includes hands-on operation of the equipment, frequent "hot drills," in which exposure to radiant heat and unexpected windshifts are experienced, and familiarization with the hazards of the aircraft which regularly utilize the airport, is of the utmost importance. All too frequently after an accident, the airport fire department is criticized for slow response, wasting the extinguishing agent in noncritical fire areas, not knowing how to enter aircraft from the outside, positioning equipment under the escape slide, preventing use of the slide, and other errors. Too often, some of this criticism is true and can be traced to a lack of training.

Funds for training materials are frequently cut back or are not available, and drill fires may be so small as to be meaningless. A "hot drill" should present a challenge to the crew and severely test its ability to control or extinguish the fire with available agents or equipment, as illustrated in Figure 8-33N.

FIG. 8-33N. A large-scale "hot drill." (Photograph from author's collection)

A sucessful method of training crash vehicle turret operators is currently in use by a major airport operating authority. A scaled-down version of the fire fighting "package" of a major crash vehicle is mounted on a small truck chassis. A fire scenario, scaled to the capabilities of the simulated CFR vehicle, is used. The prospective turret operator practices using this simulated arrangement until proficient in its use. Comparative tests and cost records over several years have proved the effectiveness of the simulator, as evidenced by the operator graduating to the actual CFR vehicles for the final phase of training.

Some of the more obvious benefits of simulated training are reduced extinguishing agent and fuel costs, less wear-and-tear on the large vehicles, less agent waste when practicing with a high-capacity turret, and less air pollution. Reduced air pollution is of particular importance in large metropolitan areas.

Crews should exercise regularly and be in top physical condition. The sudden physical and mental stresses of a major aircraft accident are demanding, but can be minimized by good physical conditioning and mental alertness. Airport fire fighters should, as a minimum, meet the qualification standards of NFPA 1003, *Airport Fire Fighter Professional Qualifications*.

Another major factor in successful airport fire fighting is the design and operation of the airport fire apparatus. This specialized apparatus must carry all its extinguishing media ready to deliver a massive attack on the postcrash fire. It must have not only the ability to operate on paved surfaces at high speeds, but also be able to negotiate off-pavement terrain at reasonable speeds. Design and performance of the vehicle should be based upon NFPA 414, *Aircraft Rescue and Fire Fighting Vehicles*.

The vehicle crew should be fully trained in the operation of the vehicle off the paved surfaces of the airport. Regular practice is essential because of the skill required to drive safely over soft ground, since it is impossible to design a vehicle that will negotiate all terrain and retain its other necessary attributes. There have been a few incidents when airport fire vehicles stopped short of an accident scene because the operators thought the terrain too difficult; the vehicle might have reached the scene if these drivers had received adequate training. Practice also will disclose airport areas that are impossible to reach by vehicle. Funding for access roads to these areas should be included in airport improvement plans.

The term "rescue," as used in the context of aircraft rescue and fire fighting, means the control of life-threatening fire in the critical area for the time necessary for all physically able aircraft occupants to escape without help, and continuance of that fire control long enough to assist the severely injured or those pinned in the wreckage. To some people, "rescue" infers physically assisting all occupants out of the aircraft. This is certainly possible for small aircraft; however, in a commercial or military aircraft with more than 10 or 12 occupants, such assistance is impossible with the normally available personnel.

AIRPORT AND HELIPORT DESIGN SAFETY

Many factors influence the safety of aircraft operations at airports and heliports: runway lengths and construction, navigational aids, clearances off operational runways below the navigable air space, terrain conditions between runways and taxiways, zoning regulations, and fire protection. Heliports present special problems because they frequently are located in congested areas of cities, on the roofs of buildings, on elevated platforms constructed over piers, or at the water's edge. In view of the fact that heliports and helistops that are not an integral part of a conventional airport have special problems, NFPA has established a separate technical committee to develop special standards or recommended practices for this type of facility or operation.

A number of serious accidents have occurred because of airport hazards, and their seriousness has been increased due to inadequate zoning regulations and insufficient clearance off the operational runways. Airports are frequently surrounded in whole or in part by water; thus the provision of waterborne crash rescue facilities becomes a special problem, unless the U.S. Coast Guard, Navy, or municipal waterborne rescue and fire control equipment is immediately available to perform rescue services if an aircraft ditches in the water.

The areas off the ends of runways have been the scene of a number of accidents and, where dikes or unimproved terrain conditions exist, create special problems. In some cases, blast fences have been erected at the ends of runways to protect adjacent structures or highways, or to reduce the noise factor during takeoff, particularly for turbine-engine aircraft. Under poor visibility conditions, however, accidents have resulted when aircraft have struck these dikes and blast fences.

During airport construction and repair, especially on the movement areas, the presence of construction and resurfacing equipment has been a factor in accidents. Another principal area where accidents frequently occur is in the overrun portions of runways; a number of the most serious accidents have occurred here when aircraft have been unable to brake effectively, running off the runway, have struck airport boundary fences, or have bogged down while traversing unimproved ground surfaces. Unimproved ground surfaces between runways have frequently resulted in aircraft being inaccessible to fire and rescue equipment, especially equipment not specifically designed for off-highway use.

SPECIAL AIRPORT FACILITIES AND INSTALLATIONS

Hangars

An aircraft hangar is simply a large structure built to provide weather protection and shop space during aircraft maintenance and storage. However, special fire protection problems associated with a hangar are due entirely to the nature of its occupancy. Since it is impractical and economically unsound to remove all fuel from an aircraft prior to moving it to a hangar, the potential always exists for having large quantities of flammable liquids, mainly aviation fuel, inside the hangar. Quite often, the aircraft contained within the hangar, particularly larger aircraft, are several times more valuable than the hangar, necessitating some measure of protection for the aircraft as well as the hangar structure.

Past hangar designs concentrated primarily on providing excellent protection for the hangar structure. Protection consisted mainly of water-type sprinkler systems using the extra-hazard pipe schedule, or hydraulically calculated systems, primarily of the deluge type. In certain aircraft hangars, these water-only systems are no longer recognized as viable protection by NFPA 409, *Aircraft Hangars*. With increased value of the aircraft, it is now common practice to utilize foam-water deluge sprinkler systems. Latest designs incorporate foam-producing and oscillating monitor nozzles, in conjunction with all of the previously mentioned systems, to protect the shadow area beneath the wings of large aircraft. (Figure 8-33O illustrates this shadow area.) In nonfire operational tests in actual hangars and large-scale tests conducted by the Factory Mutual Research Corporation, this method indicates that considerable progress has been made in protecting the hangar structure as well as providing increased protection for the aircraft. This is primarily due to more rapid fire control and/or extinguishment.

A different technique has been more recently developed and used, particularly in older hangars being modernized, with the approval of the authority having jurisdiction. In these cases, overhead closed-head-type sprinkler systems hydraulically designed to deliver a specified minimum water density over a specified area are installed as a secondary means of protection for the hangar structure. Some of these systems also have the capability of delivering aqueous film-forming foam (AFFF) solution through standard (nonaspirating) sprinkler heads by utilizing wide-range proportioning devices.

Primary protection for the hangar, and to a certain extent for the aircraft, is provided by oscillating monitors which provide a complete foam blanket on the floor of the entire hangar within 20 to 30 sec of actuation. Small roofed enclosures located within the aircraft work areas are provided with sprinklers capable of delivering AFFF solution. Although standard protein or fluoroprotein concentrates may also be used in this type of system, all work to date has utilized AFFF. (Figures 8-33P and 8-33Q illustrate a test of such a system.)

FIG. 8-33O. A typical wide-body aircraft maintenance and overhaul facility and structure. Foam-water deluge is the primary protection, with fixed-pipe foam-water deluge protection installed beneath the work platforms for the "shadow area." Swing joints and flexible connections are provided to allow limited maintenance structure movement to position the aircraft. Structure above the wing and flexible connectors are for fuel tank ventilation. (Source: United Airlines)

FIG. 8-33P. Test of a low-level foam system in an older, modernized, hangar. This system is designed to cover the entire floor area below the centerline of the aircraft, not just the shadow area. The aircraft is on a hydraulic jack in a normal position for maintenance. Note the dispersed pattern of the foam streams. (Source: United Airlines)

Whether used only for shadow area protection or total floor coverage, foam monitor location, oscillation speed, foam pattern, and barrel centerline height above the floor are critical. Location of the monitors should be such that all areas where coverage is desired can be easily reached. Experience has indicated that, depending upon the arc of coverage, no more than 15 sec should be necessary for a complete cycle. The foam pattern should be dispersed rather than a straight stream to minimize turbulence at the point of stream impact with objects or the floor. Barrel centerline height should be a minimum of 12 ft (4 m) above

FIG. 8-33Q. Test complete. Note the total floor coverage after only 5 min. of operation. System capacity is 20 plus minutes. (Source: United Airlines)

FIG. 8-33R. A foam monitor nozzle. Centerline of this particular nozzle is approximately 12 ft (4 m) above floor level to clear obstructions. (Source: United Airlines)

the floor to extend range and to minimize obstruction by aircraft maintenance equipment, etc. Figure 8-33R illustrates an installation meeting these criteria.

Due to hangar size, or due to multiple aircraft positions, monitor nozzles can be mounted at the bottom of the truss space to provide coverage for these void spaces.

FIG. 8-33S. A monitor nozzle mounted beneath the roofwork to fill void areas unreachable from monitors located near the walls. Centerline of the barrel is approximately 65 ft (20 m) above the floor. Control valves are located at the floor line along the hangar wall. The small-diameter lines illustrated are for testing and exercising the water-powered oscillating mechanism. (Source: United Airlines)

Arrangements should be made to exercise and test the oscillating mechanism from the hangar floor or other easily accessible location. (See Figure 8-33S.)

The principal means of fire detection for hangars has been rate-of-rise devices; however, as hangar roof heights increase [sometimes being as much as 150 ft (46 m) from floor to roof deck], the ability of this type of device to perform in the time required to minimize aircraft damage is becoming suspect. In climates with moderate to severe winter conditions, it is becoming increasingly difficult to maintain stability of such systems (due to the opening and closing of hangar doors and the installation of high-recovery-rate heating systems) and still maintain the sensitivity necessary for rapid fire detection.

Optical-type detectors of ultraviolet or infrared types can be used for high-speed detection of relatively small fires, while being unaffected by rapid temperature changes.

Care must be taken in selecting the type of detector and control devices for optical detection. They must have demonstrated operational integrity, yet not be overly sensitive and subject to false or unwanted operation. Considerable progress has been made recently in developing optical detection systems that automatically ignore or are insensitive to routine aircraft maintenance procedures involving welding, high-intensity lights, boroscopes, radioisotopes, X-ray inspections, etc. Whenever an optical system is installed, its sensitivity to fire should be tested. It is further suggested that a recording device be attached to provide a hard-copy record of what the detectors "see" during routine aircraft maintenance operations. During the initial period after installation (usually 60 to 90 days), the detection systems should be in the "alarm only" mode and a careful record made of the recording device printout. Aircraft maintenance records often can determine what operation affected the optical detectors. Figure 8-33T illustrates a detector test fire during extinguishment.

Floor drainage is another overlooked portion of the hangar fire protection system. The drainage system removes excess fire protection water, and also removes large quantities of the liquid fuel from the fire scene. To prove their

FIG. 8-33T. Extinguishment of a fire following test of the optical detection system. A too "fine" setting of detectors has caused many unwanted operations. In this case, a 20 sq ft (2 m2) circular pan with flame deflector was selected as the minimum size fire which needed to be detected. Actuation occurred in approximately 10 sec. (Source: United Airlines)

efficiency, these systems should be flushed thoroughly with high volumes of water at least annually. Oil/water separators should be maintained meticulously to prevent pollution of lakes and streams, and to reduce hazards in the airport drainage system to which the hangar system may be connected.

Aircraft hangars are divided into Types I, II, or III, which roughly correspond to the types of aircraft housed in them and the anticipated fuel loadings. NFPA 409, *Aircraft Hangars*, defines these types and outlines the requirements for construction, protection, drainage, fire cutoffs, and other provisions for each type of hangar.

Airport Terminal Buildings

Airport terminal buildings include any fully enclosed extensions which function as passenger concourses (sometimes called fingers or piers), and satellite buildings which serve passenger-handling functions. The satellite building may be connected to the main terminal building via tunnels beneath the aircraft operating ramp, or via people-mover transit systems operating on a fixed guideway which may be above or below ground. Terminals also contain airline-related businesses, such as offices, restaurants, and gift shops.

Special attention is given to airport terminal buildings in NFPA 416, *Construction and Protection of Airport Terminal Buildings*, because these buildings have a severe fire exposure potential from immediately adjacent aircraft fueling and servicing operations and the high-occupancy load in terminals.

In recent years, airport security has complicated the fire problems, since preventing access by unauthorized persons to the aircraft operating areas is of prime importance, and directly affects the location and discharge points of the emergency exit facilities.

Aircraft Loading Bridges or Walkways

This equipment is frequently installed at the terminal area for passenger convenience and to protect passengers from the weather while they move from the terminal loading gate area to the aircraft. Loading equipment also increases safety by reducing ramp congestion, and segregating passengers from the aircraft servicing equipment and personnel.

In the event of fire caused by a fueling malfunction or other reason, a loading bridge or walkway can serve as a means of egress from the aircraft to a safe refuge, e.g., the terminal building. Most people have the natural tendency to exit an area (aircraft, building) the same way they entered, and since the emergency situation requiring evacuation may occur before the preflight safety and evacuation briefing, the loading bridge may be the only familiar means of exit to passengers. For this reason, NFPA 417, *Construction and Protection of Aircraft Loading Walkways*, requires 5 min. of safe passage from the aircraft to the terminal. This may be accomplished by construction features, special fire protection, or a combination of both. This safe egress must be provided during severe fire exposure to the bridge.

Doors, if any, at the terminal end of the bridge should be equipped with panic hardware and swing in the direction of travel from the aircraft to the terminal. In no case should the loading bridge be considered part of the terminal exit system, unless a vestibule and stairs conforming to NFPA *101*®, *Life Safety Code*®, are provided at the terminal end, even though there may be auxiliary stairs located near the aircraft end. The auxiliary stairs are strictly for the use of aircraft servicing personnel or the flight crew.

Training of loading bridge operators in positioning of the equipment and obtaining the best possible "seal" with the aircraft in *all* weather conditions is very important. Unless the bridge and closure curtain are properly positioned and utilized, the integrity of the loading bridge as a means of exit from the aircraft is seriously compromised. The operator must be made aware that the closure curtain is a *safety* item and not merely weather protection.

Aircraft Fueling Ramp Drainage

Due to the large amounts of flammable liquids (in the form of fuel) handled on aircraft servicing ramps, special attention must be paid to the drainage system provided to prevent exposing the terminal or aircraft unnecessarily in the event of accidental release. NFPA 415, *Aircraft Fueling Ramp Drainage*, specifies the amount of slope and direction regarding ramp geometry, location of drainage system inlets, water seal traps, and oil/water separators.

Rooftop Heliport Construction and Protection

This is covered in NFPA 418, *Roof-Top Heliport Construction and Protection*, which deals with the special fire problems existing for this type facility. The standard covers landing deck construction, drainage, egress, and fire protection.

AIRCRAFT MAINTENANCE AND SERVICING

Second to the postcrash situation, fire during maintenance and servicing (including fuel servicing) creates the greatest hazard exposure to personnel and property.

In order to keep an aircraft airworthy, every part must be inspected, repaired, or overhauled periodically. The frequency of these procedures will vary; operations may be performed all at once in a single maintenance visit, or as part of a progressive overhaul system where a certain portion of a total overhaul is conducted periodically. In addition, periodic inspections are required between major overhauls to repair minor discrepancies, inspect critical structures, and test various components. Nonroutine maintenance can occur at any time to replace or repair a defective or prematurely failed part.

Many maintenance procedures involve the use of highly flammable solvents, sometimes unstable or toxic chemicals, and personnel entry into integral fuel tanks.

When situations such as these occur, special procedures must be developed to ensure the safety of the operation. It is sometimes possible to pressurize equipment housings with shop air, using appropriate power/pressure interlock to prevent penetration of flammable vapors. Localized ventilation and curtailment of operations utilizing flammable or combustible liquids are also helpful. In any event, each potentially hazardous procedure should be developed or reviewed by a person who is thoroughly familiar with the basics of firesafety and aircraft maintenance requirements and procedures. NFPA 410, *Aircraft Maintenance*, should be used to develop local procedures for the more common hazardous aircraft maintenance operations, such as welding, spray painting, fuel tank ventilation, etc.

[NFPA 70, *National Electrical Code*®, defines certain areas in hangars and around aircraft as Class I, Group D, Division I or II locations. In this age of sophisticated testing using electronics, eddy currents, X rays, etc., it is often impossible to design or obtain equipment listed or approved for these locations. Welding (usually inert gas-shielded arc) is frequently performed on installed engines or aircraft structures.]

Testing of fuel tanks for system leaks is commonly performed in hangars using high flash point Jet A fuel or a special, usually combustible, test fluid. Toward this end, many hangars are provided with a fixed system to board and unload fuel or test fluid. It has also been a practice to park a standard fuel servicing tank truck outside the hangar and run long hoses to the aircraft connection points. This practice is to be discouraged, because the hose is the weak point in any system, and while hoses are necessary for flexible connections, they should be kept as short as possible.

Painting of the interior and exterior of aircraft is also accomplished in hangars. While a few hangars have been constructed specifically for aircraft exterior painting, it is more common to control ignition sources and rely upon the sheer volume of the hangar and natural ventilation to dissipate flammable vapors. Latex interior paints, which contain little if any solvents, are being used for aircraft interiors to permit painting of interior panel partitions and equipment in place rather than to remove it to a standard spray booth. Whenever it is necessary to use flammable paints inside an aircraft, special precautions for ventilation and control of ignition sources must be installed.

Aircraft Fueling

While the potential exists for spills and fires each time an aircraft is fueled, the number of these incidents is rare compared to the total number of aircraft fuelings that take place each day. This excellent safety record is due to the use of NFPA 407, *Aircraft Fuel Servicing*, a document which is accepted worldwide. The standard outlines specific precautions to control the extent of this hazard and gives recommendations on the design of aircraft fueling, hose, and on the design for aircraft fuel servicing tank vehicles, airport fixed fueling systems utilizing fuel hydrants, hydrant vehicles (to connect the fuel hydrant to the aircraft), as well as safety procedures to be followed in the event of an accidental spill. The most common type of spill is at the aircraft tank vent point, when an aircraft internal shutoff valve fails or closes slowly, allowing an overfill condition to develop.

MISCELLANEOUS

Figure 8-33U illustrates hazardous intake and exhaust areas of typical modern aircraft turbine engines. These hazards may be encountered by emergency crews responding to a crash situation when, because of damage, an engine has become uncontrollable, or the flight crew may be unaware of the operation of emergency personnel and equipment in the vicinity.

Walls and glass areas of terminal buildings and other airport structures which may be exposed to a jet blast or explosion will require design for wind loads in excess of that required by building codes for a particular region.

OTHER ORGANIZATIONS IN THE FIELD OF AVIATION FIRESAFETY

Private organizations other than the NFPA working in various fields of aviation firesafety include:

Aerospace Industries Association of America, Inc., 1725 DeSales St., N.W., Washington, DC 20036.

Air Transport Association of America, 1709 New York Ave., N.W., Washington, DC 20006.

Air Transport Section and Aerospace Section of the National Safety Council, 444 North Michigan Ave., Chicago, IL 60611.

National Transportation Safety Board (U.S. Department of Transportation), Washington, DC 20590. The NTSB has responsibility for determining the cause of aircraft accidents, except for certain light-plane accidents. The NTSB also promotes safety through studies in accident prevention and makes safety recommendations to the FAA.

In Canada, the civil aviation fire protection program is coordinated through the Air Services Fire Marshal of the Canada Department of Transport (Ottawa, Ont.), and the military program through the Fire Marshal, Canadian Forces (Ottawa, Ont.).

International aviation organizations also interested in aviation firesafety include:

International Air Transport Association (IATA), P.O. Box 550, Sucuccursale, Place de L'Aviation Internationale, 1000 Sherbrooke St., W., Montreal, Que., Canada H3A 2R2.

International Civil Aviation Organization (ICAO), 1000 Sherbrooke St., W., Montreal, Que., Canada H3A 2R2. (The Chief of Aerodromes, Air Routes, and Ground Aids Division coordinates this program.)

International Federation of Airline Pilots Associations, Office of the Executive Secretary, 1 Hyde Park Place, London W2, England.

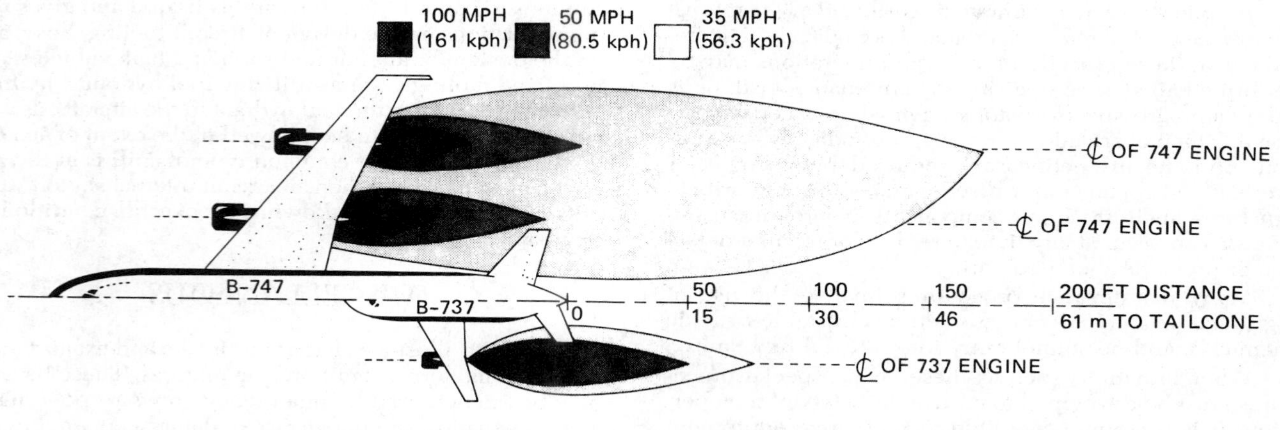

FIG. 8-33U. ***Comparative blast profiles of typical wide-bodied (B-747) and standard-bodied (B-737) jets with engines at "idle" power setting. Blast profile increases with power setting to maximum at take-off thrust. Most authorities agree that a 25-ft (7.6 m) arc area in front of the engine inlet (not shown) should be avoided to prevent ingestion of foreign objects into engine regardless of power setting. (Drawing based on Boeing Commercial Airplane Co. data)***

Airport Operators Council International, 1220 19th St., N.W., Suite 800, Washington, DC 20036.

American Association of Airport Executives, 4224 King St., Alexandria, VA 22302.

Aviation Technical Service Committee of the American Petroleum Institute, 1220 L St., N.W., Washington, DC 20005.

Flight Safety Foundation, Inc., 2200 Wilson Blvd., Suite 500, Arlington, VA 22204.

Society of Automotive Engineers, Inc., 400 Commonwealth Dr., Warrendale, PA 15096.

U.S. government organizations working in various aviation firesafety fields include:

Department of the Air Force (U.S. Department of Defense). The work of the USAF is coordinated through the Headquarters USAF (PREE), The Pentagon, Washington, DC 20330, for operations and administration, and through the Air Force Systems Command (Wright-Patterson Air Force Base, OH 45433) for research in the field.

Department of the Army (U.S. Department of Defense). Army aviation firesafety is coordinated primarily through the U.S. Army Agency for Aviation Safety (Fort Rucker, AL 36360) and the U.S. Army Mobile Equipment Research and Development Center (Fort Belvoir, VA 22060).

Department of the Navy (U.S. Department of Defense). Navy aviation firesafety is coordinated primarily through the Naval Facilities Engineering Command, Washington, DC 20390, and the Naval Research Laboratory, Washington, DC 20390.

Federal Aviation Administration (U.S. Department of Transportation). Several branches of the FAA are concerned directly with aviation firesafety, including the Flight Standards Service and Airport Services, which is headquartered in Washington, DC 20590, and the FAA Technical Center, Atlantic City Airport, NJ 08405.

National Aeronautics and Space Administration, 600 Independence Ave., S.W., Washington, DC 20546, is concerned with space vehicle safety problems, and conducts extensive research into conventional subsonic and supersonic aircraft fire problems, as well.

BIBLIOGRAPHY

NFPA Codes, Standards, and Recommended Practices

Reference to the following NFPA codes, standards, and recommended practices will provide further information on the safeguards for aviation discussed in this chapter. (See the latest *NFPA Catalog* for availability of current editions of the following documents.)

NFPA 12A, *Halon 1301 Fire Extinguishing Systems.*

NFPA 12B, *Halon 1211 Fire Extinguishing Systems.*

NFPA 70, *National Electrical Code.*

NFPA *101, Life Safety Code.*

NFPA 402M, *Aircraft Rescue and Fire Fighting Operational Procedures.*

NFPA 403, *Aircraft Rescue and Fire Fighting Services at Airports and Heliports.*

NFPA 407, *Aircraft Fuel Servicing.*

NFPA 408, *Aircraft Hand Fire Extinguishers.*

NFPA 409, *Aircraft Hangars.*

NFPA 410, *Aircraft Maintenance.*

NFPA 412, *Evaluating Foam Fire Fighting Equipment on Aircraft Rescue and Fire Fighting Vehicles.*

NFPA 414, *Aircraft Rescue and Fire Fighting Vehicles.*

NFPA 415, *Aircraft Fueling Ramp Drainage.*

NFPA 416, *Construction and Protection of Airport Terminal Buildings.*

NFPA 417, *Construction and Protection of Aircraft Loading Walkways.*

NFPA 418, *Roof-Top Heliport Construction and Protection.*

NFPA 419, *Master Planning Airport Water Supply Systems for Fire Protection.*

NFPA 422M, *Aircraft Fire and Explosion Investigators.*

NFPA 424M, *Airport/Community Emergency Planning.*

NFPA 1003, *Airport Fire Fighter Professional Qualifications.*

Additional Reading*

"Aeronautics and Space," *Code of Federal Regulations*, Title 14, Washington, DC (under continuous revision).

Federal Aviation Administration Advisory Circulars, U.S. Department of Transportation, Washington, DC (with the following designations and titles):

Aircraft Fire and Rescue Communications, 150/5210-7B, Apr. 30, 1984.

Aircraft Fire and Rescue Facilities and Extinguishing Agents, -6B, Jan. 25, 1973.

Airport Fire and Rescue Vehicle Specification Guide, 150/5220-14, Mar. 15, 1979.

Airport Operations Manual, 150/5280-1/2, 1981.

Fire and Rescue Service for Certificated Airports, 150/5210-12, Mar. 2, 1972.

Fire Department Responsibility in Protecting Evidence at the Scene of an Aircraft Accident," 520/5200-12A, Apr. 8, 1985.

Fire Fighting Exemptions under the 1976 Amendment to the Federal Aviation Act," 150/5280-3, Feb. 4, 1977.

Fire Prevention During Aircraft Fueling Operations, 150/5230-3, Apr. 8, 1969.

Hand Fire Extinguishers for Use on Aircraft, 20-42C, Mar. 7, 1984.

Heliport Design Guide, 150/5390-1B, Aug. 22, 1977.

Response to Aircraft Emergencies, 150/5210-11, Apr. 15, 1969.

Water Supply Systems for Aircraft Fire and Rescue Protection, 150/5220-4A, Dec. 11, 1985.

Williams, C., and Laughlin, J., eds., *Aircraft Fire Protection and Rescue Procedures*, International Fire Service Training Association, Oklahoma State University, Stillwater, OK, 1978.

Published works, including those of many foreign governments and scientists, are available from the National Technical Information Service, Springfield, VA USA 22161, under the headings "Transportation Safety" and "Air Transportation." In addition, NFPA has, from time to time, published reports of tests, aircraft accidents, etc., which have significant lessons for, or impact upon, the aviation community. The serious researcher, fire investigator, student, or aviation firesafety enthusiast should contact these organizations for an index of materials available.

Anderson, N., "Ultimate in Training Airport Fire-Fighters," *Fire International*, Vol. 11, No. 104, 1987, pp. 59, 62.

Babrauskus, V., "Role of Aircraft Panel Materials in Cabin Fires and Their Properties," DOT/FAA/CT-84/30, June 1985, Department of Transportation.

Everest, J. H., "Trends in Aircraft Fire Safety," *Fire Prevention*, No. 219, May 1989, pp. 18-27.

Farquhar, R. L., and Ball, D. N., "New Systems Make for Safer Aircraft," *Fire International*, Vol. 12, No. 111, 1988, 6p.

Harkleroad, M., "Ignition and Flame Spread of Aircraft Lining Materials," NBSIR 88-3773, May 1988, Center for Fire Research, Gaithersberg, MD.

Hilado, C. J., ed., *Flammability of Aircraft Materials*, Technomic, Lancaster, PA., 1985.

Klam, T. J., and Conroy, M. T., "NFPA Alert Bulletin:The Crash of United Flight 232," *Fire Command*, Vol. 56, No. 10, Oct. 1989, pp. 22-24.

Lodge, J., "Manchester Jet Fire—Remarkable Evidence," *Fire International*, Vol. 13, No. 116, Apr.-May. 1989, pp. 34-35.

Luo, H., "Experimental Investigation of Electrostatic Fire Accidents After Aircraft Landing and Preventive Measures," *Journal of Aircraft*, Vol. 26, No. 5, 1989, pp. 405-409.

Marshall, G., "Fire Hazard in Civil Aviation," *Fire Prevention*, No. 194, Nov. 1986, pp. 22-29.

McCaffrey, B. J., and Rinkinin, W. J., "Fire Environment in Counterflow Ventilation (The In-Flight Cabin Aircraft Fire Problem)," NBSIR 88-3806, June 1988, Center for Fire Research, Gaithersberg, MD.

"NTBS Releases Denver Plane Crash Report," *Fire Command*, Vol. 56, No. 3, March 1989, pp. 12-15.

"Protecting an Airline's Most Valuable Asset," *Fire International*, Vol. 13, No. 114, Dec.-Jan. 1988, 4p.

"Safety from Fire in Aircraft," *Aircraft Engineering*, Vol. 59, No. 3, 1987, pp. 19-20, 22.

Stewart, J. S., "Aircraft Passenger Protection from Smoke and Fire," *Proceedings* of the 24th Annual Symposium of the Survival and Flight Equipment Association, SAFE Association, 1987, pp. 112-116.

Walker, J. L., "Hardened Aircraft Shelter Fire Protection System," *Military Engineer*, Vol. 80, No. 523, Aug. 1988, p. 456.

*To attempt to list all relevant published work in the limited space available is impossible. Continuous research and testing is being conducted throughout the world in aviation firesafety, primarily funded by various governmental agencies. This research, testing, etc., encompasses all aspects of aviation firesafety, emergency evacuation, new concepts and devices in detection and extinguishment, extinguishing agents, etc.

MOTOR VEHICLES

Revised by Neill Darmstadter

Many factors influence motor vehicle firesafety. Among these are vehicle design and construction; materials from which a vehicle is constructed or which are carried by a vehicle, particularly upholstery, plastic, wood, fuel, and hazardous materials cargoes; vehicle maintenance, including safeguards against fire during vehicle repair; vehicle operation, including avoidance of collisions and of other accidents, such as those involving smoking materials; and garaging or storage of vehicles.

The degree of fire hazard depends upon the type of vehicle, such as passenger car, motorcycle, motor home, or tank truck; the use of the vehicle for pleasure driving, commercial service, or off-road use; the climate and environment in which it is used; the age of the vehicle; the condition and maintenance of the vehicle; the material and construction standards to which it is built, particularly the fuel and electrical systems; and the type of fuel used—gasoline, diesel fuel, or propane—and the way it is contained in the vehicle.

Research into the causes of motor vehicle fires has not yet yielded complete or reliable statistics or insights into fire hazards. However, individual crash investigations and collections of crash and other loss data indicate the magnitude of the motor vehicle fire problem and some specific causal factors in motor vehicle fires.

Motor vehicle fires represent about 17 percent of all reported fires, and most vehicle fires result from causes other than crashes. Yet serious injury from vehicle fires occurs overwhelmingly from crash-related fires—fires that occur at a rate of approximately 1 per 1000 crashes.

Property loss from motor vehicle fires probably averages several hundred dollars per incident. However, estimates may be skewed by the nonreporting of minor fires and of fires in uninsured vehicles, as well as by ambiguous reporting on police and fire department forms.

Neill Darmstadter is senior safety engineer, American Trucking Associations, Alexandria, VA. and a member of the NFPA Technical Committee on Motor Vehicle and Highway Fire Protection.

THE NATURE OF VEHICLE FIRES

As with other fires, motor vehicle fires require a flammable substance, an ignition source, and oxygen. Virtually all motor vehicles carry a flammable fuel—gasoline, gasohol, diesel fuel, or another hydrocarbon compound. Vehicle upholstery, insulating and sound-deadening materials, electrical wiring insulation, and plastic body and trim also can fuel a motor vehicle fire. Materials carried as cargo and fare in or on motor vehicles, particularly trucks, also may be flammable.

Ignition sources include electrical short circuits or other electrical malfunctions that cause excessive heating of conductors or components; sparks from an engine ignition system; hot exhaust system components; engine backfire; overheating of tires, brakes, and wheel bearings; friction-generated sparks from a collision or from metal components scraping against the pavement; and careless use of cigarettes and other smoking materials. There is generally sufficient oxygen in the ambient atmosphere for a motor vehicle fire.

Table 8-34A summarizes data from a study of the frequency and area of origin of fires in passenger cars involved in noncollision- and collision-related fires. Table 8-34B summarizes the locations of the origin of fires on trucks, as reported to the Bureau of Motor Carrier Safety (BMCS) of the U.S. Department of Transportation (DOT), reorganized as the Office of Motor Carriers (OMC) in 1986.

Death and injury in motor vehicle fires result from direct exposure to heat and from inhalation of toxic combustion products. In major vehicle crashes involving fire, it may not be possible to determine with certainty whether death resulted from the crash or from the fire. In some cases, injury results from or is exacerbated by the inability of a vehicle's occupant to get out of the burning vehicle—the doors or seats are jammed by a crash, or the occupant is injured or stunned by the crash. In one case, a two-door sedan was driven onto the third rail of an electrified railroad track. The crash forces were not significant enough to cause injury, but the electric current arcing across a short circuit caused by the car body started a fire. The front-seat passengers escaped, but investigators concluded that the three rear seat passengers were trapped in

TABLE 8-34A. ***Passenger Car Fires by Type of Incident and Area of Fire Origin****

	Type of Incident			
	Noncollision		Collision-related	
Area of Fire Origin	Number of Fires	Percent	Number of Fires	Percent
Engine	1,085	59	39	54
Passenger	647	35	3	4
Fuel tank	59	3	24	33
Trunk	31	2	3	4
Tire/brake	29	2	3	4
Total	1,851	100†	72	100†

* Source: "1973 National Survey of Motor Vehicle Fires" commissioned by the Insurance Institute for Highway Safety.

† Column does not add to total due to rounding.

Note: Figures do not include fires of unidentified origin. The 1,923 passenger car fires in which the area of origin was identified comprised 83 percent of the 2,325 passenger car fires surveyed, and 73 percent of the 2,637 total motor vehicle fires surveyed.

TABLE 8-34B. ***Location of Origin of Fire—Property Carriers****

	Moving		Stopped		Total	
Component	No.	Percent	No.	Percent	No.	Percent
Engine	27	5.5	6	8.3	33	4.9
Electrical system	36	7.3	22	12.2	58	8.6
Fuel system**	32	6.4	7	4.0	39	5.7
Service brakes	27	5.5	1	0.6	28	4.1
Parking brakes	3	0.6	0	—	3	0.4
Exhaust system	11	2.2	0	—	11	1.6
Wheel or wheel bearing	26	5.3	3	1.7	29	4.3
Cargo heater	4	0.8	4	2.2	8	1.2
Tires	37	7.5	4	2.2	41	6.1
In cab	10	2.0	13	7.2	23	3.4
Under cab	9	1.8	6	3.3	15	2.2
Around cab	14	2.8	2	1.1	16	2.4
Cargo space	83	16.8	79	43.9	162	24.0
Roof or cargo covering	3	0.6	0	—	3	0.4
Inside mobile home trailer	2	0.4	0	—	2	0.3
Other vehicle or object	90	18.1	20	11.1	110	16.4
Unknown or not reported	81	16.4	13	7.2	94	14.0
	495	100.0	180	100.0	675	100.0

** Broken down as follows:

	Moving		Stopped		Total	
Component	No.	Percent	No.	Percent	No.	Percent
Fuel Tank	19	3.8	3	1.7	22	3.3
Carburetor	2	0.4	1	0.6	3	0.4
Fuel Line	11	2.2	2	1.1	13	1.9
Fuel Pump	0	—	1	0.6	1	0.1

* Source: 1972 Analysis of Accident Reports Involving Fire, U.S. Department of Transportation.

the burning vehicle, probably because they could not locate and operate the latch to push back the front seat.

Hazardous materials in motor vehicles present a particular fire problem. The National Transportation Safety Board (NTSB), the OMC, and NFPA have all carried out a number of detailed accident investigations into such fires. These investigations have led to changes in the regulations for hazardous materials containers and in other aspects of the transportation of such cargoes. Despite such precautions, hazardous materials cargo fires and explosions occur, primarily when vehicles carrying such cargoes are involved in major collisions.

The NTSB has issued a series of reports on accidents in which hazardous materials exploded or burned following a crash. (These and other NTSB reports are available from the National Technical Information Service, Springfield, VA 22161.) As a result of these and other highway crash investigations, the NTSB has made numerous recommendations to the OMC, the Research and Special Programs Administration (RSPA) of DOT, and to other agencies concerning modification and enforcement of the safety and hazardous materials regulations.

FEDERAL MOTOR VEHICLE FIRE STANDARDS

Under the authority of the National Traffic and Motor Vehicle Safety Act of 1966, the National Highway Traffic Safety Administration (NHTSA) of the DOT is authorized to set minimum safety standards applicable to new and used motor vehicles, trailers, and motor vehicle equipment. To date, only two fire-related standards have been issued for new vehicles, and none has been issued for vehicles in use. The NHTSA also has the authority to investigate motor vehicle defects, some of which may present a fire hazard, and to order manufacturers to notify owners and repair the defects.

In 1988 and the first half of 1989, NHTSA issued 303 safety recalls, 60 or 19.8 percent of which involved potential fire hazards. These recalls affected 7.5 million vehicles, 2 million or 27 percent, of which were recalled because of a potential fire hazard.

Federal Motor Vehicle Safety Standard (FMVSS) 301 sets requirements for the fuel system integrity of passenger cars, trucks, buses, and multi-purpose vehicles having a gross vehicle weight rating (GVWR) of 10,000 lb (4536 kg) or less. The standard also applies to school buses of more than 10,000 lb (4536 kg) GVWR using fuel with a boiling point of more than 32°F (0°C).

FMVSS 301 is intended specifically to reduce the fire hazard resulting from fuel leakage in crashes. It was first applied to passenger cars manufactured on and after January 1, 1968. Since that time, the standard has been made increasingly stringent.

Under the present provisions, which became effective on September 1, 1977, all vehicles with a GVWR of 10,000 lbs (4536 kg) or less must pass prescribed front, side, and rear crash barrier tests and a rollover test. Front and rear tests are conducted at impact speeds of 30 mph (48 km/hr), while lateral impact speed is 20 mph (32 km/hr). In the crash barrier tests, fuel leakage cannot exceed 1 oz (28 g) by weight from impact until the vehicle stops moving; 5 oz (142 g) by weight in the 5 min following cessation of motion; or 1 oz (28 g) by weight per min for 25 min.

In the rollover test, the vehicle is turned about its longitudinal axis in 90-degree increments and is held for 5 min in each position. Rotation occurs every 1 to 3 min. Fuel leakage cannot exceed 5 oz (142 g) by weight in the first 5 min of each segment, nor 1 oz (28 g) per min for the remainder of the segment.

The school bus test procedure for buses over 10,000 lb (4536 kg) GVWR uses a special, moving, contoured barrier which strikes the test vehicle at the front, rear, and sides.

No rollover test is prescribed for these buses. Maximum permissible fuel leakage is the same as indicated above for the front, side, and rear barrier crash tests.

The other NHTSA firesafety standard, *Federal Motor Vehicle Safety Standard 302*, sets flammability limits for materials used in the interiors of vehicles in the driver and passenger space. Its requirements are directed at reducing the hazards of interior fires caused by smoking and matches. Vehicle appointments specifically covered by the standard include seat cushions, seat backs, seat belts, headlining, arm rests, trim panels, compartment shelves, head restraints, floor covering, engine compartment covering, padding, and the surface of crash protection components.

The standard specifies a horizontal flame test for all materials and incorporates detailed requirements for the test procedure. Material under test must not burn or transmit a flame across the surface at a rate exceeding 4 in. per min (1.7 mm/s).

OMC, which is a part of the DOT's Federal Highway Administration (FHWA), is another federal agency that administers regulations governing the safe operation of commercial vehicles in interstate or foreign commerce. The agency's regulations affecting vehicle firesafety include standards for electrical wiring, battery installation and protection, exhaust systems, and heating systems—and restrictions on the use of some types of heaters. The standard also prohibits the use of flame-producing emergency warning devices on vehicles transporting certain classes of hazardous materials, and includes special regulations governing the driving and parking of vehicles transporting hazardous materials. The Federal Motor Carrier Safety Regulations are set forth in Title 49, *Code of Federal Regulations*, Parts 390-399.

The federal regulations governing the transportation of hazardous materials, other than the driving and parking rules which are part of the Federal Motor Carrier Safety Regulations, are promulgated by the Office of Hazardous Materials Transportation (OHMT). This agency is part of the DOT's Research and Special Programs Administration. For motor carriers, enforcement of the hazardous materials regulations is handled through OMC.

The hazardous materials regulations cover such matters as the proper preparation of shipping papers to facilitate identification of hazardous materials; marking and labeling hazardous materials packaging; placarding vehicles transporting hazardous materials; regulations applicable to shippers; authorizations of the packaging in which specific materials may be shipped to ensure safety; and standards for packaging, including standards for cargo tanks.

Those provisions of the hazardous materials regulations that deal with the identification of materials are specifically directed to the protection of fire fighters, other emergency service personnel, and the public by warning of the presence of such cargo and by providing information as to the identity of specific materials so that emergency service personnel can take proper action in fire prevention, fire fighting, and cleanup.

New regulations which took effect in 1991 will provide additional assistance to emergency response personnel. These regulations will require shippers to provide a 24-hour emergency telephone contact and will require that emergency information be available at facilities and on board vehicles that handle or transport hazardous materials.

The full text of the federal hazardous materials regulations is contained in Title 49, *Code of Federal Regulations*, Parts 170-189.

Most states have adopted by reference the provisions of the Federal Motor Carrier Safety Regulations and the DOT hazardous materials regulations. A number of other states have regulations that are similar to the federal requirements. As these trends continue, they will foster increasing uniformity of legal requirements.

The National Transportation Safety Board is an independent federal agency that oversees safety for all types of transportation. Probably best known for its investigations of aircraft accidents, the agency also is concerned with fire-related highway accidents. The NTSB is responsible for making recommendations for improved safety, based on its investigations. The majority of its recommendations deal with suggested changes in the regulations and practices of federal and state government agencies, but they may also be directed at others, such as vehicle manufacturers and users.

In Congress, the responsibility for legislation and oversight of transportation rests with the Senate Committee on Commerce Science and Transportation and the House Committee on Public Works and Transportation.) These committees have taken a keen interest in the activities of the federal government in the field of motor vehicle safety. They regularly hold legislative and oversight hearings on the activities of the NHTSA and occasionally on the activities of the OMC and the NTSB. Reports of these hearings are available from the U.S. Superintendent of Documents or from the committees.

DESIGN AND CONSTRUCTION SAFEGUARDS

Many items in the interior of vehicles are flammable, such as upholstery, paneling, trim, carpeting, or floor mats. If ignition occurs from any source and prompt control is not possible, the vehicle can be destroyed.

In large truck bodies and in freight-carrying trailers, wood is used as flooring. It withstands the torsional stresses, impacts, and abrasions encountered in this type of service, and replacement of worn or damaged sections is relatively economical. Wood provides safety benefits because blocking and bracing can be nailed in place to prevent shifting of cargo. It offers a high coefficient of friction for safe forklift operation and a slip-resistant footing for personnel who handle cargo.

Plywood is used for interior lining material in van-bodied trucks and trailers because of its effectiveness in protecting other structural components from damage that may occur during loading, unloading, and transportation of freight. As with wood flooring, the replacement of damaged sections is relatively inexpensive.

Plywood flooring is used in buses for essentially the same reasons. The use of metal flooring would create "tin canning" under torsional stress, and the resulting noise levels would be unacceptable to passengers.

These uses of wood have not created any significant fire hazards. In the forms used, the wood is relatively difficult to ignite and burns slowly. Specific provisions of the Federal Motor Carrier Safety Regulations require that flooring be in good condition. The use of flooring permeated with oil or gasoline is prohibited.

There have been reports of major accidents involving fire in which the presence of wood has been mentioned as a contributing factor. However, these accidents have been so severe that the outcome would appear to be little affected if wood had not been present.

When the cargo must be covered during transportation on flatbed, open-top, and other types of nonenclosed vehicles, the use of tarpaulins is the only practicable means of providing the needed protection. Such tarpaulins normally are not given flame-retardant treatment, but fires rarely start in them.

Vehicle Fuel Tanks and Systems

The location, construction, and security of fuel tanks are important design features for firesafety in motor vehicles. Liquid fuel tanks for general passenger car use are generally of thin-gage steel of various shapes and dimensions, dependent upon other body and chassis characteristics. The vast majority of U.S.-built cars, trucks, and buses have liquid fuel tanks that are located at the rear of the vehicle, frequently in such a position that they are not entirely enclosed in the body. The most severe casualties in terms of loss of life and property occur from fires following rear-end collisions.

The Office of Motor Carriers has developed fuel tank regulations applicable to vehicles operating in interstate or foreign commerce. These regulations closely parallel Underwriters Laboratories (UL) standards referred to elsewhere. In 1973, requirements that previously had been limited to gasoline tanks were extended to include tanks for diesel fuel. This action also required protection for diesel fuel crossover lines located below the bottom of a tank or sump. The DOT regulations include requirements for tank construction and installation and for adequate fillpipe closure. Tanks must pass drop, rupture, vent, and spillage tests. Required safety vent systems must limit pressure rise to 50 psig (345 kPa) in a specified fire test.

Tanks must be marked by a manufacturer's certificate to indicate that they meet DOT-FHWA specifications for sidemounted or nonsidemounted tanks, as applicable.

Efforts have been made to gain DOT approval for plastic fuel tanks for truck service. Despite certain advantages claimed by the manufacturers, doubts about the safety of such tanks in commercial vehicle operations have not been satisfactorily resolved.

Vehicles using flammable compressed gas as a motor fuel must be equipped with fuel systems constructed and installed in accordance with applicable provisions of NFPA 58, *Storage and Handling of Liquefied Petroleum Gases*, or NFPA 52, *Compressed Natural Gas (CNG) Vehicular Fuel Systems*.

Fuel systems must be maintained so they are free of leaks. Fuel tanks must be capped, and connections must be checked regularly. Metal fuel lines are subject to vibration-induced fatigue, and flexible lines may deteriorate due to age. The lines also can be damaged by chafing, cutting, or proximity to hot surfaces. In a gasoline system, flooding of the carburetor due to dirt in the float valve may cause gasoline to overflow onto a hot surface and result in a fire.

These problems are somewhat less critical on diesel-powered vehicles because diesel fuel has a higher flash point. In recent years, however, diesel engines have been designed to operate at higher temperatures to control exhaust emissions. This, in turn, has led to higher temperature of the fuel in the return flow line, thus making the fuel more prone to ignition if the warmed, leaking fuel contacts a hot surface.

NFPA AND RELATED STANDARDS ON MOTOR VEHICLES

Three NFPA standards contain requirements for transportation by truck of specific hazardous materials. NFPA 495, *Manufacture, Transportation, Storage, and Use of Explosive Materials*, details fire and explosion prevention related to the transportation of explosive materials, including driver qualifications, vehicle design, placarding, fire fighting equipment, and vehicle operation. This code is widely used as the basis for state regulations.

Requirements for design and construction of cargo tanks of tank vehicles, for auxiliary equipment, and for operation of tank vehicles are contained in NFPA 385, *Tank Vehicles for Flammable and Combustible Liquids*, and in NFPA 407, *Aircraft Fuel Servicing*. NFPA 407 covers only the special requirements for aircraft fuel servicing tank vehicles and aircraft fuel servicing hydrant vehicles.

NFPA 58, *Storage and Handling of Liquefied Petroleum Gases*, contains requirements for transporting of liquefied petroleum gases, including requirements for transporting portable containers, requirements for cargo tanks, and for parking and garaging vehicles used to carry LP-Gas. NFPA 58 also includes requirements for installing LP-Gas systems in vehicles fueled by LP-Gas. It has been adopted for regulatory purposes by 47 states and by the DOT for vehicles in interstate commerce.

NFPA 52, *Compressed Natural Gas (CNG) Vehicular Fuel Systems*, covers the design and installation of compressed natural gas (CNG) engine fuel systems on vehicles of all types and of their associated fueling systems. NFPA 512, *Truck Fire Protection*, covers property-carrying motor vehicles.

NFPA 58, *Storage and Handling of Liquefied Petroleum Gases*, covers parking and garaging of LP-Gas cargo vehicles. Two other NFPA standards include provisions relating to parking of trucks: NFPA 513, *Motor Freight Terminals*, and NFPA 498, *Explosives in Motor Vehicle Terminals*. Although primarily concerned with fire protection of freight while in a terminal, NFPA 513 contains recommendations for parking vehicles at terminals. Parking vehicles hauling explosives is the subject of NFPA 498. The seriousness of the problem is evidenced by the explosions of parked explosives trucks in Marshall Creek, PA, in 1964 and in Clyde, TX, in 1974. The Pennsylvania incident which involved the accidental detonation of dynamite, other explosives, and blasting caps, killed six persons, injured thirteen and damaged or destroyed $600,000 worth of property: In the Texas incident, an overheated tire on an oil field truck flashed, detonating the explosives on the truck. The accident killed four persons and injured two others.

The dependence of the fire service upon motor vehicles is well recognized, and it is particularly important that fire apparatus be safely constructed. NFPA 1901, *Automotive Fire Apparatus*, and NFPA 414, *Aircraft Rescue and Fire Fighting Vehicles*, detail practices that should be followed on these types of apparatus.

Mobile homes are sometimes classified as "vehicles," but modern practice tends to remove them from this category. For eleven years, NFPA issued NFPA 501B, *Standard on Mobile Homes*, which covered body and frame design and construction, as well as plumbing, heating, and electrical systems for these vehicles. That standard was withdrawn in 1978, and authority for the regulation of mobile homes now rests with the federal government through its *Mobile Home Construction and Safety Standards*, Part 280 of the *Code of Federal Regulations*, Title 24. Most states also have mobile home regulations, some with requirements more stringent than federal regulations.

Recreational vehicles can be divided into four categories: travel trailers, motor homes, camp trailers, and campers. NFPA 501C, *Recreational Vehicles*, covers details of plumbing, heating, and electrical systems for travel trailers, motor homes, truck campers, and camping trailers, and includes life safety and exiting requirements for these vehicles when they are used as temporary living quarters.

Requirements for plumbing are developed by the ANSI A119 Committee, of which the Recreational Vehicle Industry Association is Secretariat. Those requirements are published and distributed under one cover as ANSI A119.2, *Recreational Vehicles*.

Underwriters Laboratories Inc.

Certain over-the-road motor vehicle components and signaling appliances that have special fire hazard significance are tested by Underwriters Laboratories Inc. and listed in *UL's Accident, Automotive, and Burglary Protection Equipment* lists. The specific items listed include:

1. Electrical equipment such as automobile fuses and switches.
2. Fill and vent fittings.
3. Fuel equipment such as backfire deflectors, fuel feed systems, electric gasoline gages, automotive-type LP-Gas accessories, automotive fuel tanks, and tubing.
4. Automotive heaters of the combustion type.
5. LP-Gas automotive vehicles—that is, farm and road tractors incorporating fuel systems designed for use of LP-Gas as engine fuel.
6. Mufflers for automobiles.
7. Signals and signaling appliances, or highway emergency signals.

UL also has its own standard, UL 395, *Standard on Automotive Fuel Tanks*, for liquid fuel tanks mounted outside the frame or in other exposed locations on gasoline- or diesel-powered trucks, tractors, or trailers. It has issued UL 307(a), *Standard on Liquid Fuel-Burning Heating Appliances for Mobile Homes and Recreational Vehicles*, and UL 307(b), *Standard for Gas Burning Heating Appliances for Mobile Homes and Recreational Vehicles*.

Society of Automotive Engineers, Inc.

The Society of Automotive Engineers, Inc. (SAE) is concerned with any vehicle that moves under its own power. SAE has a standardization program covering passenger cars, trucks and buses, farm and earth-moving machinery, marine propulsion units, aircraft, and space vehicles, as well as the materials and components that go into them. Content of the SAE standards is limited to environmental and operating problems with these vehicles. The *SAE Handbook* contains all of the society's surface vehicle documents.

OTHER COOPERATING AGENCIES INTERESTED IN HIGHWAY SAFETY

American Petroleum Institute: Active in the field of truck transportation of petroleum products, API publishes a number of publications of interest and value from the firesafety viewpoint.

American Trucking Association, Inc.: The association reproduces as a tariff the DOT *Regulations Governing the Transportation of Explosives and Other Dangerous Articles by Motor, Rail and Water*, including specifications for shipping containers. This action, similar to that taken by the Association of American Railroads, makes current DOT regulations applicable to participating truck carriers. The association's Safety Department sets trucking industry standards for selection, training, and supervision of employees and develops a variety of materials for the use of trucking companies dealing with general safety and the safe transportation of hazardous materials.

Center for Auto Safety: The center is a consumer advocate organization dedicated to improving the safety and value of automobiles, other motor vehicles, highways, and mobile homes. The center regularly issues reports, books, comments on federal rulemaking, and other materials.

Chemical Manufacturers Association: The association has an active technical service on transportation and packaging. CMA's *Chemical Safety Data Sheets*, with listings available on request, give details on bulk transportation of chemicals. CMA also operates the Chemical Transportation Emergency Center Chemtrec information on hazardous materials involved in emergencies through its WATS line, 1-800-424-9300.

Compressed Gas Association, Inc.: CGA provides technical services on products of interest and concern to its membership.

Consumers Union of U.S., Inc.: A nonprofit consumer information organization with a large technical staff, CU regularly tests automobiles—and occasionally trucks and other motor vehicles—and publishes its findings monthly in *Consumer Reports Magazine*.

Cooperative Hazardous Materials Enforcement and Development: COHMED develops and promotes training programs for personnel responding to hazardous materials emergencies.

Hazardous Materials Advisory Council: The council is concerned with all aspects of hazardous materials transportation as it affects shippers, all modes of transportation, and manufacturers of packagings. It also conducts training in the safe transportation of hazardous materials.

Insurance Institute for Highway Safety: An independent, nonprofit, scientific and educational organization dedicated to reducing the losses resulting from crashes on the nation's highways. The Institute is supported by the American Insurances Service Group, the American Mutual Insurance Alliance, the National Association of Independent Insurers, and several individual insurance companies.

Manufactured Housing Institute: The institute represents mobile home manufacturers east of the Rocky Mountains.

National LP-Gas Association: This association develops LP-Gas standards and provides safety programs for the general public.

National Safety Council: A nonprofit organization dedicated to accident prevention, the council has an extensive program on highway safety geared principally to the motoring public. NSC produces a number of publications on transportation and highway safety.

National Tank Truck Carriers, Inc.: A Conference of the American Trucking Associations, Inc., NTTC helps members, who are operators of tank truck fleets, solve problems associated with safe handling of flammable liquids, gases, and chemicals.

Physicians for Automotive Safety: This organization of medical doctors who are concerned with preventing death and injury in motor vehicle accidents has taken a particular interest in the safety of children in motor vehicles.

Professional Drivers Council: The council is a membership group of truck and bus drivers with an interest in their occupational safety and health.

Recreational Vehicle Institute, Inc.: The institute represents the recreational vehicle industry. Manufacturing members produce travel trailers, truck campers, camping trailers, and motor homes.

The Truck Body and Equipment Association, Inc.: This is a trade association of the manufacturers of truck bodies, suppliers of component parts, and distributors. It has a Fire Apparatus Manufacturers Division, formerly a separate organization known as Fire Apparatus Manufacturers Association. The TBEA represents its members in dealing with the DOT on safety legislation.

Truck Trailer Manufacturers Association: A trade association of manufacturers of truck trailers, it cooperates, through its various committees and representatives, with NFPA, other allied industry associations, and governmental agencies in matters affecting the design and fabrication of tank transports.

Western Manufactured Housing Institute: The institute represents the manufacturers of mobile homes and recreational vehicles whose equipment is made and/or distributed on the West Coast.

PREVENTION OF MOTOR VEHICLE FIRES

Fire prevention in motor vehicles requires the attention of everyone involved. Vehicle designers must be aware of fire hazards in their products. Sources of heat and ignition must be kept away from flammable materials as much as possible. Consideration should be given to the vulnerability of fuel system components, in particular—to their basic integrity, their location away from the perimeter of the vehicle and from crash-collapsible and intrusive parts, and their location away from potentially hot exhaust and electrical components.

Examples of location hazards were found in 1971-1976 Ford Pintos and 1975-1976 Mercury Bobcats. In these cars, the fuel filler neck and the tank could separate in a rear-end collision, resulting in fire. A total 1.4 million of these vehicles were recalled for retrofitting of a longer fuel filler neck and for installation of a protective shield on the front of the fuel tank. Improperly routed fuel lines to the carburetor have been the subject of other recalls because of potential rupture and underhood fires. Other recalls have involved routing fuel close to hot surfaces, which could result in deterioration and rupture; fuel lines subject to physical damage; and potential leakage of oil onto hot surfaces.

Since electrical system failures often cause fires that result in property damage, more attention must be paid to the routing of wiring, aging of insulation and components, and failure modes of components. (That is, do they short circuit or open circuit when they fail?)

To minimize the potential for fuel leakage in any crash, extraneous plumbing and openings should be eliminated in fuel and hazardous liquid and gaseous cargo containers. Necessary plumbing should be designed so it is protected from potential crash damage.

In the construction of vehicles, care must be taken to ensure that the fuel and electrical lines are correctly routed and that connections are secure. In addition, location of sharp or pointed components near fuel or hazardous cargo tanks should be avoided.

The greatest fire hazard during the vehicle repair process is the use of torches, usually in the repair of exhaust systems and crash damage. Some of the items used in vehicle repair are particularly flammable, such as paint, solvents, adhesives, and oily rags. Operating an engine with the carburetor air cleaner removed may result in a fire if the engine backfires through the carburetor.

Care must be taken in the maintenance and rebuilding of damaged vehicles to ensure that their fuel and electrical systems are free of hazards not present in the original vehicle.

Vehicle Electrical Systems

Automotive lighting and accessory circuits are usually 6 or 12 V, but vehicle ignition systems have high voltage, though low amperage. Automobile electrical system firesafety is largely a matter of proper installation, fusing, and maintenance. Important check points include the location and protection afforded the battery; battery cable integrity and protection of exposed battery terminals; adequate flame-retardant insulation on all wiring; proper fusing of normal lighting and accessory circuits; proper support, location, and security of all wiring, with adequate protection by rubber insulating bushings where wiring passes through metal; and good ignition system maintenance.

Fires of electrical origin usually are fed by oily deposits in and around the engine or by combustible materials, such as interior fabric linings and upholstery. In the event of collision or upset, electrical short circuits are apt to occur and may cause fuel vapors to ignite. It is desirable, particularly on buses and trucks, to provide an approved type of manual battery/generator disconnect switch, preferably one incorporating short circuit supervision. However, use of such devices on vehicles is rare.

Miscellaneous Vehicle Hazards

Proper exhaust system installation is important because the hot surfaces of the system may ignite nearby combustible components. Hot carbon particles and hot gases discharged from the exhaust can ignite flammable liquids, grease, or similar exposed materials, such as insulation on electrical wiring.

Catalytic converters in the exhaust systems have been identified as the cause of several wildland fires, when automobiles have been driven through dry grass or vegetation. In one incident, several dozen cars were destroyed at a rural festival, where a grassy area had been designated as a parking lot.

Overuse of vehicle brakes can result in sufficient overheating to cause severe smoldering and sometimes fire. Improper adjustment that prevents the full release of a brake can lead to similar conditions.

The problem of overheating brakes increases with the size and gross weight of the vehicle. On long downgrades, a driver must rely on the braking effect of the engine for the primary control of the vehicle, limiting use of the brakes for slowing for sharp turns or unanticipated, localized, hazardous conditions and for stops. The maximum braking effect of the engine is achieved only in the lower gears of the transmission. Particularly on trucks and buses, it is essential for the driver to get into a low gear at the top of the grade before the speed of the vehicle reaches a point at which downshifting is no longer possible. In recent years, engine braking devices have been used widely on diesel-powered trucks, especially in mountainous regions. Other types of electrically and hydraulically operated retarders are used in special situations.

Another serious common problem arising from overuse of brakes is the buildup of sufficient heat to cause brake fade. When this happens, the brakes become ineffective and a major crash is possible, whether or not fire ensues.

If one tire of a dual-tire installation is run flat or is seriously underinflated, flexing may cause sufficient internal heat to build up to cause ignition. This possibility also exists if tires are seriously overloaded and may be exacerbated by sustained high-speed operation and high ambient temperature. Occasionally, fire results if dual tires are spaced so closely together that they rub or chafe against each other when the vehicle is in motion.

Provisions of the Federal Motor Carrier Safety Regulations for all heating systems used on vehicles in interstate commerce have been upgraded. This has led to a significant reduction in the number of fires caused by combustion heaters on vehicles. The reduction of such fires has also been aided by technological advances in the heaters. The few fires that do occur generally result from unforeseen heater malfunctions, or from a shift in freight that is loaded too close to a heater.

There is no longer any significant use of alcohol-based antifreeze in motor vehicles. Therefore, vehicle fires involving its vapors are seldom a problem.

Farm Tractors and Two-Wheeled Vehicles

Fire dangers inherent in these vehicles arise from the exceptionally close spacing of such components as the fuel tank, carburetor, ignition system, and exhaust pipe; the lack of protection afforded operators by the vehicles' framings; and the severe vibration forces to which the equipment is normally subjected. Vehicles with air-cooled engines are particularly vulnerable; water-cooled engines have lower engine operating temperatures. Particular care is required to avoid fuel system leakage or spillage, especially during fueling, because of the high surface temperatures and the close proximity of exhaust piping. Each fuel system should have some means, readily accessible to the operator, for quickly stopping the flow of fuel to the tank. Sparks to ground from exposed electrical circuit points are also a major ignition hazard, as are oil and grease accumulations.

Use of Fire Extinguishers

Commercial vehicles operating in interstate commerce must be equipped with fire extinguishers to comply with Federal Motor Carrier Safety Regulations. These regulations provide for two minimum levels of protection: a 5-B:C extinguisher is required if the power unit is not transporting hazardous materials in sufficient quantity to require marking or placarding of the vehicle, and a 10-B:C extinguisher is required on a power unit used for transporting hazardous materials.

Many states have similar requirements for commercial vehicles, through adoption of the applicable provisions of the federal regulations or their own regulations. Some state laws require additional or larger extinguishers on tank vehicles transporting flammable liquids or gases, combustible liquids, or Class A and/or Class B explosives.

There are no legal requirements for carrying fire extinguishers in private vehicles, although many people do keep them in vans, motor homes, and mobile homes. As a minimum, the vehicle owner should consider buying a portable extinguisher that can deal with Class B (flammable liquids) and Class C (electrical) fires. Also on the market are extinguishers using multi-purpose agents for use on Class A fires (ordinary combustibles), as well as Class B and C fires. Anyone equipping a vehicle with a fire extinguisher must understand that the best chance for its successful use lies in prompt action while the fire is in its early stages, and proper use to avoid wasting the agent and exhausting the extinguisher's contents prematurely. Additional information on the ratings and use of fire extinguishers is found in NFPA 10, *Portable Fire Extinguishers*.

NFPA 512, *Truck Fire Protection*, references pertinent federal requirements as guidance for truck owners who otherwise may not be subject to regulatory requirements.

Carrying extra gasoline in a can is extremely dangerous because of the possible accumulation of fumes. The hazard is even greater if glass or plastic containers are used, because of the greater likelihood of breakage or leakage.

Smoking by a driver or passengers presents the potential for fire if sparks, hot ashes, or incompletely extinguished matches get into upholstery or other interior materials. Such fires can be extinguished by water or an agent suitable for Class A fires; the burn area then must be watched in case it continues to smolder and eventually rekindles.

While the vehicle is in operation, the driver should be alert for any indication of fire or a fire hazard, such as the smell of something hot, of unusual fumes, or of leaking fuel or lubricant. The driver should check for conditions that can create sufficient heat buildup to cause a fire, such as exhaust leaks and dragging brakes.

In case of an accident, the engines and all electrical accessories of all involved vehicles should be turned off to minimize the danger of fire. At night, headlights can be left on to protect the scene, but persons in the vicinity should be alert for indication of overheated wiring or fire. Smoking and all use of open flames or lights must cease, particularly if leaking fuel is detected. If a travel trailer or motor home is involved, the probable presence of liquefied petroleum gas should be kept in mind, smoking should be prohibited, and open flames and lights should be kept well away from the scene.

When a vehicle fire occurs, the following basic steps should be taken, regardless of the type of vehicle involved:

1. Shut off the engine and all electrical systems that can be reached.
2. Get everyone out of the burning vehicle and well away from it, preferably uphill and upwind. The potential for fire is one justification for quickly moving injured persons from the scene of an accident.
3. Summon the fire department by the best available means.
4. Attempt to fight the fire only if it can be done without endangering anyone's personal safety.

Basic principles to be observed in attempting to fight a vehicle fire with a portable fire extinguisher are:

1. First, see item 4 above. The fire should be fought from the windward side so that wind, if any, will help carry the fire extinguishing agent toward the fire and help blow smoke and flame away from the person attempting extinguishment.
2. The fire extinguisher should be aimed at the base of the flames.
3. If leaking flammable liquid is involved, work toward the source of the leak in putting out the flames. Ultimate control may depend on the ability to shut off leaking fuel at its source.
4. If flammable gas is burning, allow it to continue to burn until the source of any leak is controlled. Otherwise, extinguishing the fire may permit leaking gas to accumulate, with the likelihood of later fire or explosion. If flames are impinging on a flammable gas container, the container should be kept cool to avoid a flame-induced weakening and possible rupture or a BLEVE (boiling liquid expanding vapor explosion). If fire fighting hose streams are not available, RUN. Leave IMMEDIATELY.
5. If no extinguisher is available, throw sand or dirt on a fire to control flames.
6. If stopping to help at the scene of a vehicle fire, park uphill, preferably upwind, and at a safe distance from the burning vehicle.
7. After a fire has been extinguished, do not operate the vehicle until all burned parts are cool and the cause of the fire has been corrected.
8. During an electrical fire, turn off the ignition switch and lights to try to cut off the flow of current and permit faster extinguishment. If tools are available and it can be done safely, the battery should be disconnected.
9. In fighting an underhood fire, use great care in opening the hood to avoid injury in case of a sudden flareup.
10. All extinguishers used should be inspected and recharged without delay.

The following special considerations apply to fires and potential hazards involving commercial vehicles:

1. Any hazardous situation should be evaluated to avoid endangering lives and wasting extinguishing agent.
2. If a vehicular combination unit is involved in a fire, the power unit should be unhooked and moved a safe distance away from the vehicle if it can be done safely.
3. Drivers must be alert for the hard pulling characteristics that may indicate dragging brakes and must readjust the brakes before a fire develops.
4. Drivers should check tire inflation and temperature every 2 hrs or 100 miles (161 km), whichever comes first, and at any other stop. For a vehicle placarded for transportation of hazardous materials, this practice is required by OMC regulations.
5. Drivers should check the rearview mirrors frequently for signs of smoke and must stop and investigate any smoke detected.
6. If a hot or underinflated tire is discovered, it should be moved well away from the vehicle. As an alternative, the driver should remain with the vehicle until the tire is cool to the touch, and then make repairs. If a vehicle is left with a hot tire, the tire may burst into flames and destroy the vehicle and its load. With proper tire-changing equipment and a pair of heavy leather gloves, a driver can remove a hot tire safely if it has not burst into flames.
7. Because a tire fire results from internal heat buildup, portable extinguishers normally cannot do more than control open flames. The cooling effect of large quantities of water is required for extinguishment.
8. If fire is suspected inside a closed van body—usually indicated by smoke seeping out around the doors—the doors should be left closed until fire department assistance is at hand. Should the doors be opened, oxygen reaching the fire may cause a sudden flareup. As long as the doors are closed, the fire can only smolder from lack of oxygen.

In the interest of preventing cargo fires, motor carriers generally prohibit smoking while vehicles are being loaded or unloaded, so sparks or hot ashes will not lodge in the cargo and burst into flame later.

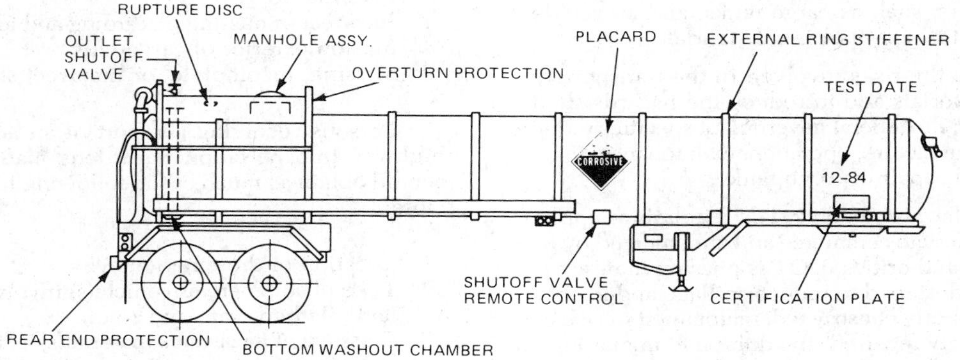

FIG. 8-34A. Corrosive materials cargo tanks must be equipped with an internal shutoff valve if unloaded from the bottom.

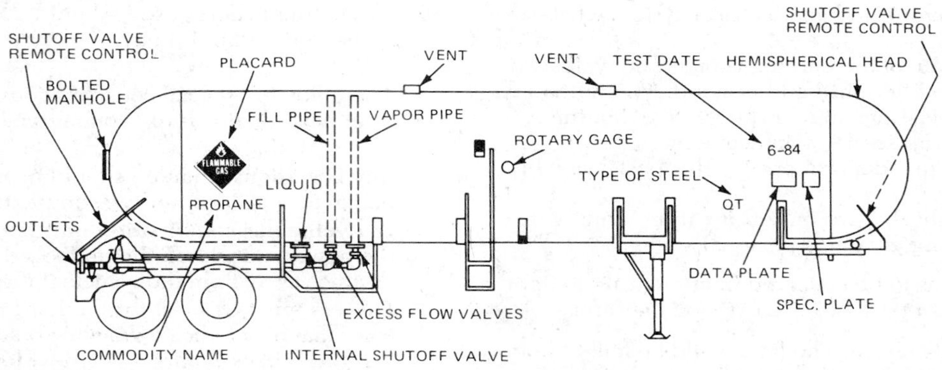

FIG. 8-34B. Compressed gas cargo tanks must be equipped with internal shutoff valves at liquid and vapor discharge openings.

Federal Motor Carrier Safety Regulations prohibit smoking during refueling; while loading, unloading, or transporting explosives, flammable liquids, gases, or solids, or oxidizing materials requiring marking or placarding of the vehicle; and while driving an empty tank vehicle that last contained a flammable liquid or gas and which was required to be marked or placarded.

CARGO TANKS (TANK TRUCKS)

Cargo tanks and portable tanks are large containers for hauling liquid materials in bulk. Cargo tanks are sometimes called tank motor vehicles or tank trucks. Any person offering a hazardous material in a container for transportation must determine that the container used is authorized for the commodity. Specifications for cargo tanks, portable tanks, and all other hazardous materials packagings except rail tank cars are in 49 *CFR*, Part 178. Authorized packagings are listed in 49 *CFR*, Part 173, in the shipper regulations for the particular material, as indicated in columns 5(a) and (b) of 49 *CFR* 172.101. If a container, such as a cargo tank, is supplied by a carrier, the shipper still must determine that the tank supplied is a proper container for the material being offered. The shipper must either examine the manufacturer's specification marking on the tank or obtain papers from the carrier certifying that the tank is proper for the material, per 49 *CFR* Part 173.22.

Cargo tanks are the most common transport vehicles used to move combustible, flammable, and corrosive materials, as well as compressed gases, both flammable and nonflammable. When these hazardous materials are transported in bulk containers, such as cargo tanks, and an accident occurs, the disaster potential is substantial.

To minimize the risks involved in the transportation of hazardous materials and to reduce the hazards should an accident occur, the federal government specifies requirements for the manufacture, operation, maintenance, inspection, testing, and repair of cargo tanks.

The DOT's hazardous materials regulations apply to interstate and intrastate commerce and are enforced by both federal and state authorities. DOT is phasing in new cargo tank regulations designed to reduce spillage and to ensure that tanks are properly constructed, maintained in safe condition, and properly repaired. In addition to upgrading the specifications of certain cargo tanks, the regulations provide for new specification numbers:

Current Specification Number	New Specification Number
MC-306	DOT-406
MC-307	DOT-407
MC-312	DOT-412
MC-331	No Change
MC-338	No Change

The new cargo tank regulations are designated in 49 *CFR*, Part 180.

Accident experience has shown a high incidence of leakage resulting from both contact and noncontact accidents, leading to high cost in terms of personal injury and property damage. Data gathered by the Office of Hazardous Materials Transportation and the Office of Motor Carriers continue to indicate that the major causes of unintentional release of hazardous materials are poor maintenance and deviation from tank specifications.

Potential hazards to fire fighters dealing with cargo tanks transportating hazardous materials are as follows:

1. Multi-purpose tanks holding improper commodities for the specific container.
2. Multi-compartment containers hauling materials in more than one hazard class (corrosive/flammable/poison/oxidizer).
3. Defective or missing safety controls.
4. Release of large quantities of hazardous materials.
5. Increase of potential fires—extra equipment required to fight fires and control spills.
6. Potential for a BLEVE.
7. Incorrect or missing placarding and identification markings on exterior of cargo tank.
8. Missing, incomplete, or incorrect shipping papers.

Persons receiving a report of an actual or potential highway transportation hazardous materials emergency should obtain as much of the following information as possible:

1. Location of the emergency.
2. Type of commercial vehicle(s) involved, such as cargo tank, flatbed, van, and so on.
3. Class(es) of hazardous material(s) as indicated by placards, if visible, including the four-digit identification number, if visible.

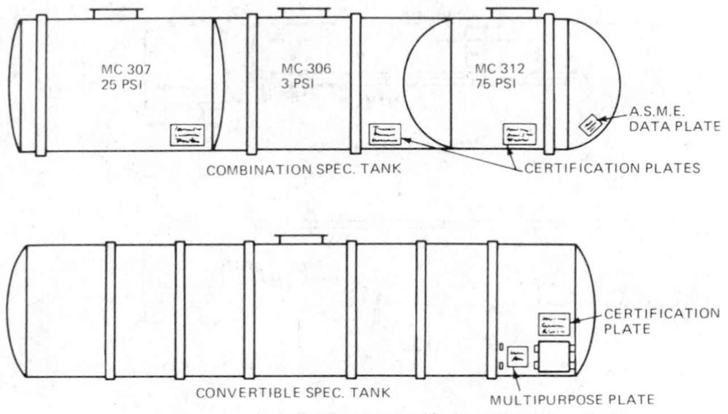

FIG. 8-34C. Profiles of combination (multiple compartment) and convertible (single compartment) cargo tanks.

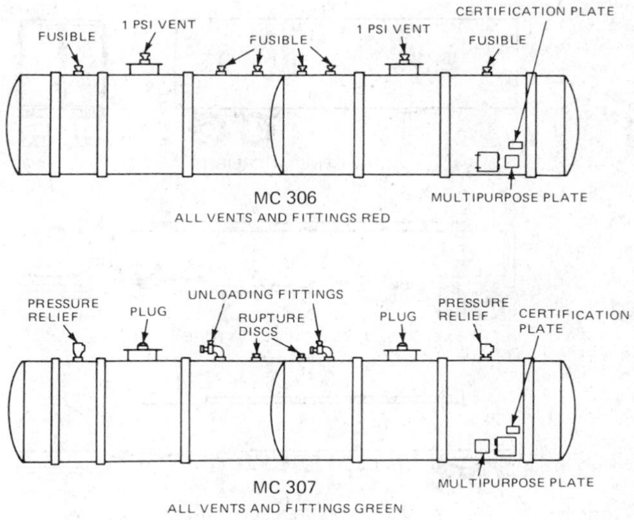

FIG. 8-34D. Profiles of two-compartment convertible cargo tanks.

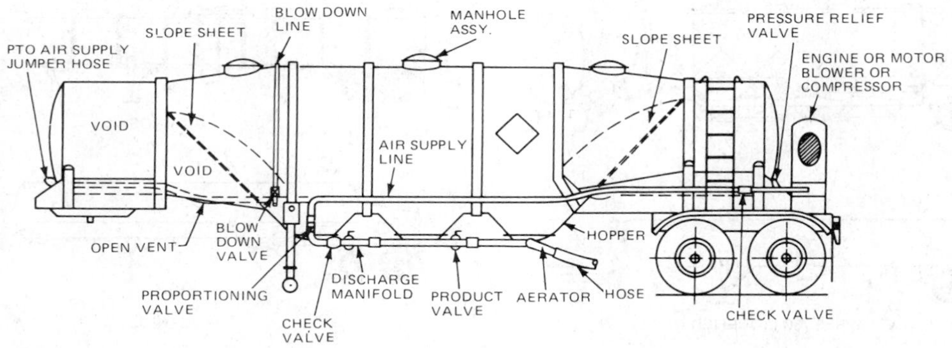

FIG. 8-34E. Profile of a dry bulk cargo tank. Examples of cargo carried are ammonium nitrate, an oxidizer, or corrosive solids. Tanks of similar appearance are also widely used to transport cement and other non-hazardous dry bulk materials.

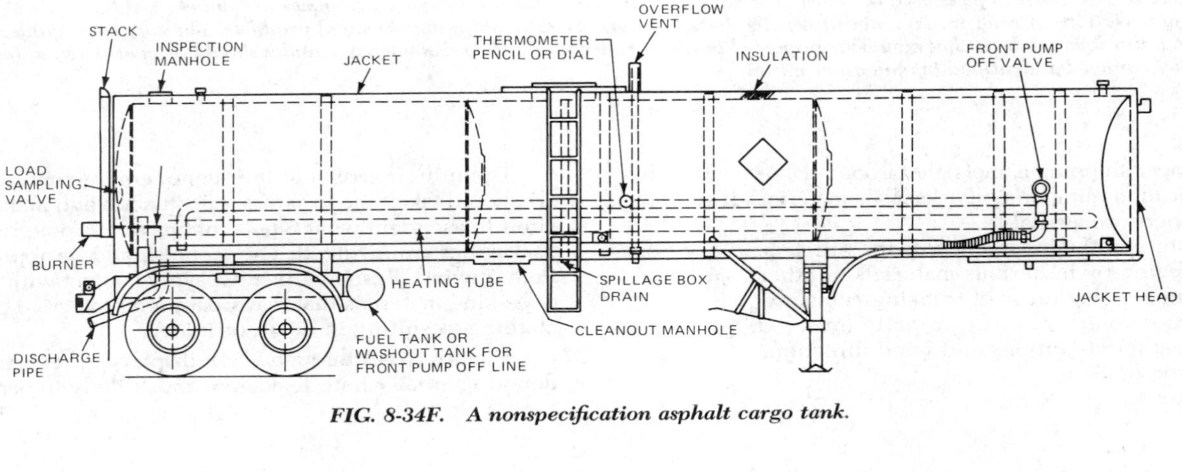

FIG. 8-34F. A nonspecification asphalt cargo tank.

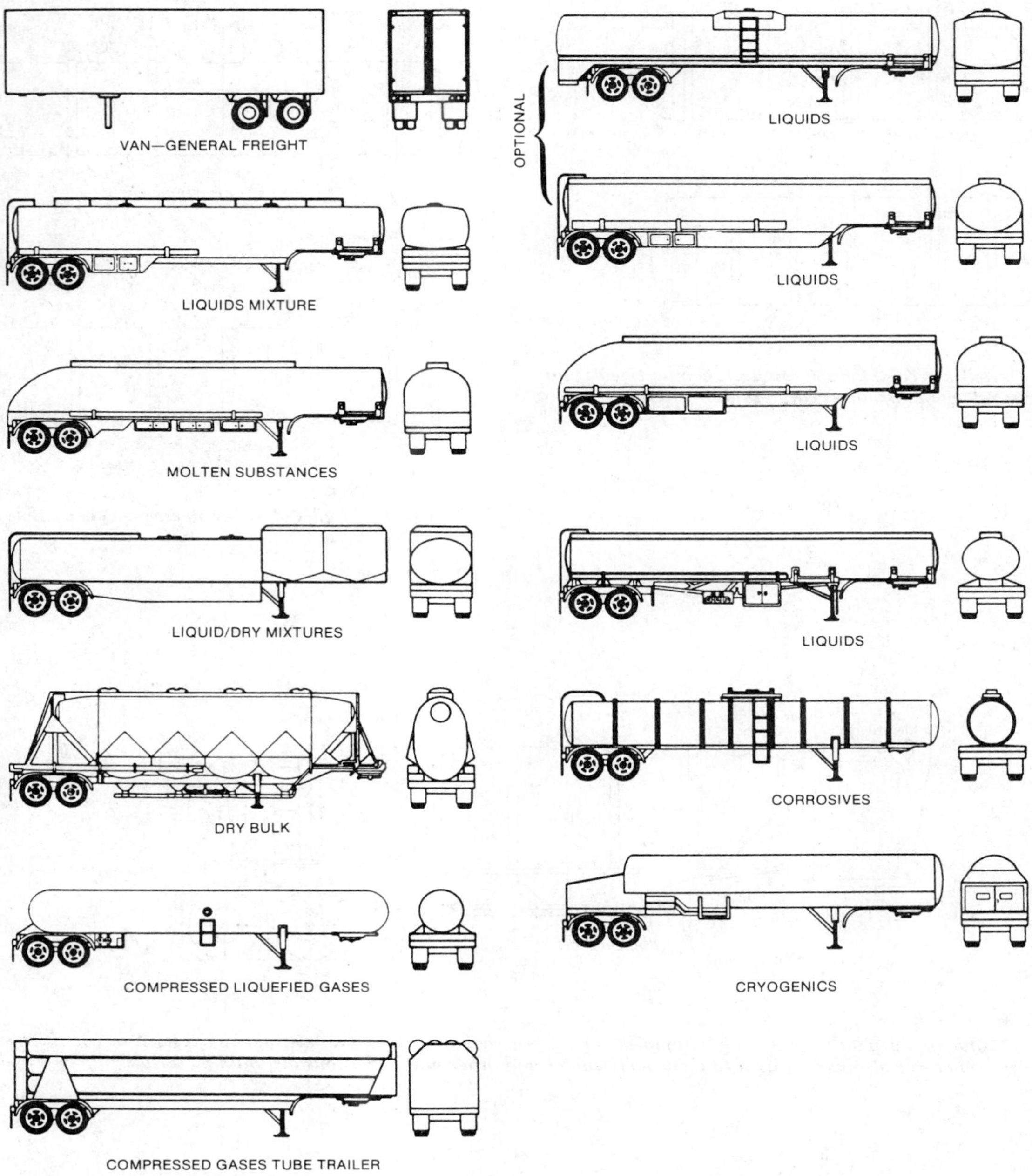

***FIG. 8-34G.** This chart depicts only the most general shapes of road trailers. Emergency response personnel must be aware that there are many variations of road trailers, not illustrated here, that are used for shipping chemical products. The suggested guides are for the most hazardous products that may be transported in these trailer types. The recommended guides should be considered as last resort if product cannot be identified by any other means.*

4. Proper shipping name(s), hazardous class(es), and identification number(s) of hazardous materials, if shipping papers are available.
5. Nature of the emergency. Is it a fire, leakage, persons affected by hazardous materials or other injuries?
6. Name and address of trucking company.
7. Other vehicles and/or property involved.
8. Weather conditions and wind direction.
9. Type of area.

Upon their arrival at the scene, emergency responders should take time to assess the situation and make every effort to ascertain what type(s) of hazardous materials and packagings are involved. The scene should be approached from upwind. Responders must avoid contact with spilled or leaking materials that may penetrate protective or other clothing, resulting in death or injury.

Figures 8-34A through 8-34F display tank construction, denoting areas where leakage is most likely to occur. All

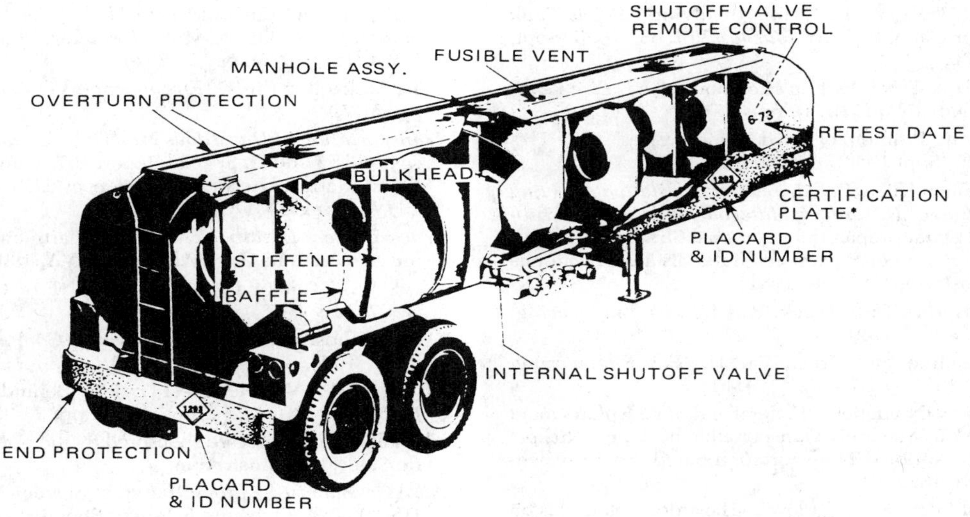

FIG. 8-34H. Cargo tank inspection guide (MC 306).

of these diagrams should be considered as guidelines rather than constants.

Many tank vehicles contain hazardous materials of one or more types. These units, which include farm "nurse" tanks, tank trucks, tank trailers, and railroad tank cars, must all be treated with equal respect. Each emergency must be sized up quickly and individually, taking into consideration the safety of every person at the scene.

BIBLIOGRAPHY

Reference Cited

1. "Safety Recommendation," *H-83-25*, National Transportation Safety Board, Washington, DC, 1983.

NFPA Codes, Standards, and Recommended Practices

Reference to the following NFPA codes, standards, and recommended practices will provide further information on motor vehicles discussed in this chapter. (See the latest *NFPA Catalog* for availability of current editions of the following documents.)

NFPA 10, *Portable Fire Extinguishers*.

NFPA 52, *Compressed Natural Gas (CNG) Vehicular Fuel Systems*.

NFPA 58, *Storage and Handling of Liquefied Petroleum Gases*.

NFPA 385, *Tank Vehicles for Flammable and Combustible Liquids*.

NFPA 407, *Aircraft Fuel Servicing*.

NFPA 414, *Aircraft Rescue and Fire Fighting Vehicles*.

NFPA 495, *Manufacture, Transportation, Storage, and Use of Explosive Materials*.

NFPA 498, *Explosives in Motor Vehicle Terminals*.

NFPA 501C, *Recreational Vehicles*.

NFPA 512, *Truck Fire Protection*.

NFPA 513, *Motor Freight Terminals*.

NFPA 1901, *Automotive Fire Apparatus*.

Additional Readings

Allender, P. J., "Fire Safety Requirements for Public Transport Vehicles," *Proceedings* of the Conference on Flame Retardents '85, Plastics and Rubber Institute, 1985, 27p.

Angelo, P., "Hazardous Cargo!," *Fire Command*, Vol. 41, No. 8 (Aug. 1974), pp. 36-7.

Bomgardner, Paul M., *Handling Hazardous Materials*, Department of Safety, American Trucking Association, Inc., Alexandria, VA, 1991.

"Bulk Tank Truck, Launceston, Tasmania," *Fire Journal*, Vol. 65, No. 2 (Mar. 1971), pp. 22-24.

Cooley, P., *Fires in Motor Vehicle Accidents: An HSRI Special Report*, Highway Safety Research Institute, University of Michigan, Ann Arbor, MI, Apr. 1974.

Cox, G. and Kumar, S., "Numerical Model of Fire in Road Tunnels," *Tunnels and Tunnelling*, Vol. 19, No. 3, 1987, pp. 55-57, 59-60.

Demers, D. P., "Seven Dead in Tank Truck Fire," *Fire Command*, Vol. 45, No. 4 (Apr. 1978), pp. 26-7.

Drivers Guide to Hazardous Materials, Safety Department, American Trucking Association, Inc., Alexandria, VA.

Emergency Response Guide, Research & Special Programs Administration, U.S. Department of Transportation, Washington, D.C.

Facts for Drivers, Safety Department, American Trucking Association, Inc., Alexandria, VA.

Gallagher, G. A. and McCone, S. W., "Lessons in Hazardous Materials Transportation Based on Case Histories," *Plant/Operation Progress*, Vol. 5, No. 3 (July 1986), pp. 186-191.

"Gasoline Tanker Fires Hit Two Communities," *Fire Command*, Vol. 42, No. 11 (Nov. 1975), pp. 19-21.

Hazardous Materials Transportation Accidents, A Compilation of Articles from Fire Journal and Fire Command, National Fire Protection Association, Quincy, MA., 1978.

Hazardous Materials Transportation: Citations from the NTIS Bibliographic Database, National Technical Information Service, Springfield, VA, 1988.

Herman, S. L., *Hazardous Materials Transportation Accidents*, 1st ed., Explosives Research Institute, Scottsdale, AZ, 1982.

Johnson, E. F., "Fire Protection Developments in LNG-Fueled Vehicle Operations," *Fire Journal*, Vol. 66, No. 6 (Nov. 1972), pp. 11-15.

Kaplan, R., O'Day, J., and Filikins, L., *Combination Vehicles:Five Year Accident Experience*, Highway Safety Research Institute, The University of Michigan, Ann Arbor, MI, 1980.

Kletz, T. A., "Transportation of Hazardous Substances: The U.K. Scene," *Plant/Operation Progress*, Vol. 5, No. 3 (July 1986), pp. 160-164.

Kuhner, R. E., "Propane Incident," *Fire Engineering*, Vol. 141, No. 11, 1988, pp. 26-29.

Lathrop, J. K. and Walls, W. L., "Fires Involving LP-Gas Tank Trucks in Repair Garages," *Fire Journal*, Vol. 68, No. 5 (Sept. 1974), pp. 18-20.

McLain, R. F., "Tank Truck Fire in Richmond, VA," *Fire Command*, Vol. 41, No. 4 (Apr. 1974), pp. 70-79.

Moore, G., "Growing Problem of Road Vehicle Fires," *Fire Prevention*, No. 222 (Sept.1989), pp. 29-31.

National Transportation Safety Board, *Federal Legislation Affecting the Transportation of Hazardous Materials with Selected Bibliographies and Data*, prepared for National Strategies Conference on Transportation of Hazardous Materials and Hazardous Wastes, Williamsburg, VA, Feb. 1981.

Noll, G., "The Gasoline Tank Truck: Part I," *Fire Engineering*, Vol. 140, No. 6, 1987, p. 39.

Noll, G., "The Gasoline Tank Truck: Part II," *Fire Engineering*, Vol. 140, No. 7, 1987, p. 37.

"Safety Effectiveness Evaluation—Federal and State Enforcement Efforts in Hazardous Materials Transportation by Truck," *Report NTSB-SEE-81-2*, National Transportation Safety Board, Washington, DC, Feb. 18, 1981.

Schmidt, J. W. and Price, D. L., "Flow of Hazardous Materials on Highways," *Journal of Safety Research*, Vol. 11, No. 3, 1970, pp. 109-114.

"Seven Fire Fighters Injured in LP-Gas Tank 'BLEVE'," *Fire Command*, Vol. 41, No. 8 (Aug. 1974), pp. 34-35.

Sharry, J. A., "Chemical Explosion—Los Angeles, California," *Fire Journal*, Vol. 69, No. 1 (Jan. 1975), pp. 62-63.

Sharry, J. A. and Walls, W. L., "LP-Gas Distribution Plant Fire," *Fire Journal*, Vol. 68, No. 1 (Jan. 1974), pp. 52-57.

Sickles, M. C., "Not Just an Ordinary Accident," *Fire Command*, Vol. 45, No. 6 (June 1978), pp. 30-31.

Stillman, T. G., "Foam Attack on Tank Fire," *Fire Command*, Vol. 38, No. 10 (Oct. 1971), p. 26.

Storrs, C. D. and Lindemann, O. H., "Federal Flammability Standards for Interiors of Motor Vehicles," *Fire Journal*, Vol. 66, No. 4 (July 1972), pp. 24-27, 44.

"The Metro Bus Fires," *Fire Journal*, Vol. 70, No. 2 (Mar. 1976), pp. 61-71.

Transportation of Hazardous Materials: Toward a National Strategy, Vols. I and II, Special Report 197, Transportation Research Board, National Academy of Sciences, National Research Council, Washington, DC, 1983.

Truck Drivers Handbook, Safety Department, American Trucking Associations, Inc., Alexandria, VA, 1990.

Ward, W., "Tanker Fire Contained," *Fire Command*, Vol. 45, No. 7 (July 1978), pp. 28-29.

"Watch Those Gasoline Tanks!," *Fire Command*, Vol. 38, No. 5 (May 1971), p. 23.

Whitaker, E., "Vehicle Fires: Looking Behind the Statistics," *Fire Prevention*, No. 222 (Sept. 1989), pp. 33-38.

The following reports are sponsored by the National Highway Traffic Safety Administration:

An Assessment of Automotive Fuel System Fire Hazards, DOT HS-800 624, Dynamic Science, Phoenix, AZ, Dec. 1971.

Escape Worthiness of Vehicles and Occupant Survival, DOT HS-800 428, University of Oklahoma Research Institute, Norman, OK, Dec. 1970.

Flammability Characteristics of Vehicle Interior Materials, DOT HS-800 205, Engineering Mechanics Division, IIT Research Institute, Chicago, IL, May 1969.

Heavy Truck Fuel System Safety Study, DOT HS 807 484, University of Maryland, College Park, MD, September 1989. Available from National Technical Information Service, Springfield, VA 22161.

Prevention of Electrical Systems Ignition of Automotive Crash Fire, DOT HS-800 392, Dynamic Science, Phoenix, AZ, Mar. 1970.

RAIL TRANSPORTATION SYSTEMS

Revised by Roger K. Fitch and Charles J. Wright

Railroad trains transport billions of dollars worth of merchandise annually. With approximately 181,000 Class I miles (291,229 km) of mainline track operated in freight service in the United States and Canada, the rail network is a vital link in our transportation system. A fire that incapacitates even a portion of the rail system affects much more than transportation.

This chapter identifies the different types of rail rolling equipment used by North American railroads and discusses fire hazards associated with them. Fire problems involving rights of way, specialized railroad facilities, and the hazardous materials transported by rail are also described. It should be noted that the materials on rail tank cars and tank containers came from Union Pacific Railroad publications.

Rapid transit rail systems used to move people in urban environments, also known as mass transit, are covered in Section 8, Chapter 36, "Fixed Guideway Transit Systems." Other helpful information can be found in Section 9, Chapter 16, "Obtaining Technical Assistance in Hazardous Materials Emergencies."

Rail rolling equipment, also called "rolling stock," includes locomotives, freight cars, cabooses, and track work (maintenance of way) equipment.

FIRE LOSS STATISTICS

The fire loss statistics in Tables 8-35A, 8-35B, and 8-35C were abstracted from surveys conducted by the NFPA Rail Transportation System Section's Committee on Statistics, which were based on data from major U.S. and Canadian railroads.

MOTIVE POWER

Fire Protection for Diesel Electric Locomotives

What is generally referred to as a diesel locomotive is actually a diesel electric locomotive. (See Figure 8-35A.) The power is developed by the diesel engine, which drives a main traction generator. The output of this generator is then transmitted to the traction motors, which are mounted in the trucks and geared to the axles and wheels. The traction motors actually drive the locomotive. The numerous support systems of a locomotive include a battery, which provides power to start the diesel engine; an auxiliary direct current generator, which charges the battery and supplies low-voltage direct current for control and lighting circuits; and an auxiliary alternator, mounted integrally with the main traction generator, which furnishes field current for the main alternator and power for the radiator cooling fan motors and for a blower motor which cleans the inertial carbody filters.

Mainline locomotives have a normal service life of more than 15 years. Thousands of units still in service have operated for 20 years or longer and average between 150,000 and 250,000 miles (241,403 and 402,338 km) per year.

The diesel electric locomotive is an enclosed, self-contained piece of equipment. Fire prevention in the engine room is almost exclusively limited to housekeeping and maintenance, which includes stopping and repairing fuel oil, lubricant oil, or exhaust leaks and ensuring that debris and products of leakage do not accumulate. Improved carbody filtration, through the development of self-cleaning inertial-type carbody filters and carbody pressurization has also helped to improve engine room safety in modern diesel electric locomotives.

Other recent improvements have resulted in virtually "fireproof" electrical cabinets on some locomotives. Among these improvements are the use of fire-retardant wire and cable insulation and the practice of ventilating electrical cabinets with filtered air. This prevents flammable gases from collecting and keeps dirt out of the electrical cabinet. Other improvements include better wiring insulation and wiring techniques, increased use of solid-state electronics, increased use of circuit breakers and fuses, and the pressurization of electrical cabinets. Design improvements in direct current traction motors and the advent of the ac/dc traction generator, which replaces the older dc generator, have also reduced fire hazards.

Roger K. Fitch is manager of fire protection for the Union Pacific Railroad Company. Charles J. Wright is manager of hazardous material training for the Union Pacific Railroad Company.

TABLE 8-35A. *Railroad Fire Loss Statistics*

	1987		1988		1989	
	No.	$	No.	$	No.	$
Group 1—Operations & Transportation						
Brake shoe sparks	44	536,457	38	383,473	81	302,053
Collision or derailment	13	618,397	12	1,007,070	15	607,842
Electrical components	21	47,204	56	610,836	59	576,396
Engine exhaust sparks	418	458,894	359	3,001,841	641	3,757,836
Freight car or van heaters	19	169,828	12	34,972	8	49,192
Fusees	4	5,550	10	432,077	7	129,069
Hot journal boxes	3	7,000	3	11,000	4	375,582
Hot lading	7	36,966	5	67,260	13	7,125
Internal combustion engines	5	339,470	14	199,290	6	64,100
Other	576	2,308,564	560	5,936,691	51	356,275
Group 2—Maintenance & Servicing						
Smoking	127	6,022	18	50,079	17	10,931
Electrical	77	558,479	18	2,957,332	23	323,585
Flammable liquids	9	276,160	14	154,500	5	64,664
Fueled heaters and appliances	15	100,300	24	221,715	9	58,518
Open burning on right-of-way	100	76,037	300	298,863	75	119,524
Radiated heat	5	134,770	6	5,800	—	—
Spontaneous ignition	14	16,050	16	154,449	3	75,401
Welding, cutting or brazing	31	368,332	31	150,975	35	300,778
Other	23	44,159	30	402,110	7	221,685
Group 3—Outside Causes						
Exposure fires	20	372,512	254	527,474	18	65,427
Lightning and storms	1	600	5	5,000	5	33,300
Trespassing including arson	152	1,568,763	128	3,487,727	139	2,784,324
Other	180	450,904	174	203,017	30	47,954
Group 4—Cause Undetermined	518	901,677	578	1,154,394	555	2,205,056
Totals	1,741	7,234,329	2,156	15,560,176	1,837	10,560,816

TABLE 8-35B. *Additional Data on Railroad Fire Loss Experience*

	1987	1988	1989
Railroads surveyed	13	13	14
Class I trackage surveyed, miles†	135,327	127,909	131,322
Estimated percentage of total trackage	70.3	70.4	73.5
Total Class I trackage, miles†	192,378	181,639	171,121
Number of fires per mile†	0.012865	0.016857	0.014097
Dollar loss per mile†	$ 53.49	$ 121.66	$ 81.04
Total dollar loss, industrywide (est.)*	$ 10,284,293	$ 22,098,913	$ 14,360,877

* The estimated total dollar loss, industrywide, is a simple ratio of reported loss to the percentage of total Class I trackage reported for the U.S. and Canada. As such, it must be considered an approximation. During the three-year time span shown here, most frequent causes of railroad fires are: "Cause undetermined"; "Trespassers, including Vandalism and Arson"; and "Engine Exhaust Sparks." The latter, after years of supposed decline, again became a leading cause of railroad fires in 1981 when the report form was changed to encourage their reporting. On the other hand, the traditional top fire causes, "brake shoe sparks" and "overheated journals," continue to decline in importance.

† 1 mile = 1.6 km.

TABLE 8-35C. *Major Causes of Railroad Fires**

	1987		1988		1989	
Cause	$ Loss	Freq.	$ Loss	Freq.	$ Loss	Freq.
Trespasser/Arson	1,568,763	(156)	3,487,727	(128)	2,784,322	(139)
Undetermined	901,677	(518)	1,154,394	(518)	2,209,056	(555)
Collision/Derailment	618,397	(13)	1,007,070	(12)	607,842	(15)
Brake shoe sparks	536,457	(7)	383,473	(38)	302,053	(81)
Engine exhaust sparks	458,894	(418)	3,001,841	(359)	1,757,836	(641)
Welding/Cutting	368,332	(31)	150,975	(31)	300,778	(35)

* Compiled by the NFPA Rail Transportation System Section from reports representing about 70 percent of railroad Class I (mainline) track in U.S. and Canada.

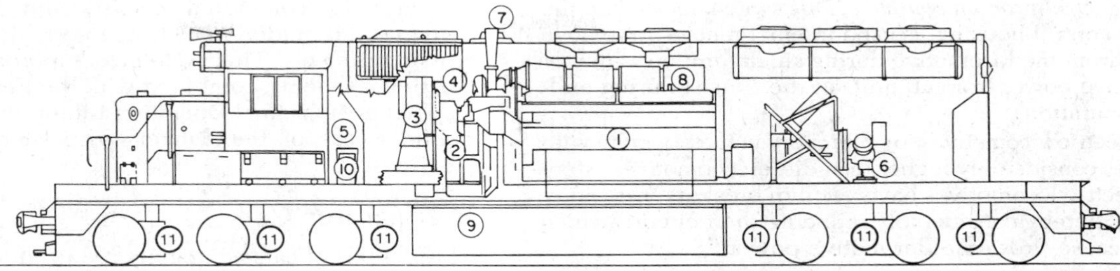

FIG. 8-35A. A diesel electric locomotive showing the location of principal components of the power system: 1, engine; 2, generator-alternator; 3, traction motor-generator blower; 4, auxiliary generator; 5, electrical control cabinet; 6, air compressor; 7, engine exhaust stack; 8, exhaust manifold; 9, fuel tank; 10, electrical cabinet air filter; and 11, traction motor.

Fire protection for diesel locomotives includes the following:

Hot engine protection: To protect against excessive temperatures in the engine cooling system and hot engine oil, devices are installed to prevent the buildup of excessive heat in the engine and supporting systems.

Engine crankcase protection: This device is designed to detect a dangerous buildup of pressure in the engine and to shut down the engine when necessary.

High-voltage ground protection: If a high-voltage fault develops on the locomotive and goes to ground, the ground relay will detect the fault and disconnect the electrical load to the locomotive.

Emergency fuel cutoff switches: In an emergency, the fuel supply to the engine can be stopped by pressing any one of three emergency fuel cutoff buttons. Two buttons are located on the underframe near the fuel filler, one on either side of the locomotive, and a third is found on the engine control panel in the cab.

Main battery knife switch: This large, single-throw knife switch is located in the engine cab at the lower portion of the fuse panel. It connects the battery to the locomotive low-voltage system.

Fire protection equipment: Each diesel electric locomotive is equipped with portable fire extinguisher protection, generally ordinary dry chemical. The quantity and type depends upon the size of the locomotive and its use in yard, local, or mainline service.

Preventive maintenance and inspections: Diesel electric locomotives are inspected, tested, and serviced on a regular schedule, based on lifetime expectancy of component parts, empirical failure data, and Federal Railroad Administration (FRA) regulations.

Fire Protection for Electric Locomotives

Figure 8-35B illustrates the general arrangement of an electric locomotive. This particular unit can deliver 5100 hp (3.8 MW) at the rail and operates on 25,000 or 50,000 V alternating current from an overhead wire.

Because the electric locomotive derives its power from an electrical circuit, it is necessary to deenergize the circuit to extinguish any electrical fire safely.

Emergency stop buttons: These buttons, located one on each side of the locomotive under the operator's cab, can be reached from the ground. Pushing either of the buttons will trip the vacuum circuit breaker on the roofs of all the locomotives in the consist—that is, multiple locomotives in a train—and remove the power.

Manual pantograph grounding switch: Located in the right rear of the locomotive, this switch is used to ground the pantograph before personnel perform maintenance or climb to the roof through the rear hatch. Grounding the pantograph (catenary), which is described in special instructions, will vary depending upon the type of locomotive and the overhead system employed. Fire fighters should obtain this information from railroad officials and include it in prefire plans.

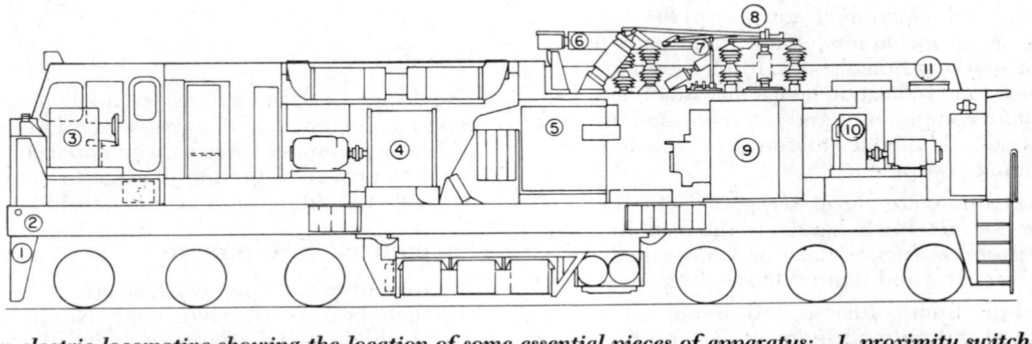

FIG. 8-35B. An electric locomotive showing the location of some essential pieces of apparatus: 1, proximity switch; 2, emergency stop button; 3, operator's console; 4, equipment blower; 5, main rectifier compartment; 6, vacuum circuit breaker; 7, pantograph grounding hook; 8, pantograph (in folded position); 9, transformer; 10, air compressor; and 11, roof hatch.

Emergency shutdown switch: This switch, located on the master control housing, is used in emergencies to remove power from the locomotive during single-unit operation or to remove power from all units of the consist during multiple operation.

Electric locomotives, by their very nature, operate with voltages considerably higher than diesel locomotives. Modern electric locomotives have vacuum breakers that trip in cycles, thereby considerably reducing short circuits which could cause fires on older motive power.

Preventive maintenance: Preventive maintenance is mandatory to preclude downtime caused by fire or equipment failure. Electrical circuits are tested for grounds or other defects when equipment is at major shops or at intervals of no more than three months. All tests and scheduled maintenance are performed in compliance with U.S. Department of Transportation (DOT) rules, as a minimum.

Fire protection equipment: The majority of electric locomotives are equipped with portable dry chemical and/or carbon dioxide fire extinguishing equipment, and, as with diesel locomotives, the number of extinguishers is based on the size of the locomotive and its use.

Safety Precautions

Certain precautions must be observed when boarding an electric locomotive in an emergency:

1. Never enter any high-voltage compartment when the locomotive is energized.
2. Never touch motors, switches, protective barriers, or other electrical apparatus without knowing their exact purpose and function.
3. Never climb on the roof of the locomotive unless the locomotive ground switch is secured and the catenary wire has been deenergized.
4. To protect against serious or fatal personal injury, be sure the pantograph is actually latched down before opening the roof hatch.

FREIGHT CARS AND EQUIPMENT

The major causes of fire in freight equipment, including motive equipment, are collision/derailment, suspected arson, electrical, brake shoe sparks, welding and cutting, hot journals, and heating appliances.

Design and preventive maintenance are the keys to reducing or eliminating fires caused by brake shoe sparks, exhaust sparks, hot journals or "hot boxes," electrical failures, and internal combustion engines. Recent design advances that should lessen the frequency of fires include increased use of turbochargers, spark retention exhaust manifolds, nonsparking brake shoes, roller bearings, heat detectors, sensors and indication lamps that supervise electrical circuits and components, and the increased use and efficiency of trackside devices to detect overheated journals and dragging equipment.

Cotton bales now are shrink-wrapped, which eliminates the need for metal bale bands. In the past, frequent cause of bale fires was friction heat, which resulted when the bale bands moved and ignited loose cotton.

Fire resulting from collisions and derailments are a major concern of the railroad industry. To reduce these incidents, operating rules and safety programs are undergoing major revisions. A program to inventory all grade crossings was completed recently, and the inventory is being used by individual states to establish priorities for crossing projects. This systemized approach to reducing crossing accidents, combined with the Federal Aid Highway Act of 1976 and "Operation Lifesaver," is making the public aware of the dangers associated with railroad crossings.

Refrigerator Cars

Three types of cars commonly are used to transport perishable and semiperishable commodities that require refrigeration, heater service, or protection from the extremes of heat or cold:

1. The standard ice car (RS) is gradually being phased out of service. Few railroads still furnish ice for shipment in such cars. However, the cars may be used to keep commodities from freezing. Portable liquid fuel heaters that burn a mixture of methanol and isopropanol can be installed in the end ice bunkers. Alcohol foam is recommended as an extinguishing agent for these fuels because water may be ineffective.
2. The insulated bunkerless car (RB) is widely used to protect semiperishable commodities such as canned goods, beer, grocery products, and drugs and medicines from extremes of heat and cold. These cars provide no refrigeration, but they can be equipped with portable liquid fuel heaters. The heaters are usually suspended by chains from hooks, four per heater, in the ceiling of the doorway areas. The ceiling above each heater is protected by heat shields.
3. The mechanically refrigerated car (RP) is the most modern and versatile of the freight cars used for perishables. (See Figure 8-35C.) It can provide automatically controlled temperatures from 0 to 70°F (-18 to 21°C). Foamed-in-place polyurethane insulation helps to ensure consistent and dependable car temperatures. A compressor-evaporator is powered by a self-contained diesel-engine generator set located in a separate compartment within the car. The compressor-evaporator also can be powered directly from the alternator output of a diesel electric unit, or from any suitable 220 V standby power supply. The fuel tank for the diesel engine is suspended below the car and normally carries 500 to 550 gal (1.9 to 2.1 m^3) of No. 1 or No. 2 diesel fuel oil. Fire fighting is sometimes complicated by the burning of insulation and by the fact that fire fighters have not learned the location of the diesel engine stop control, which is clearly identified. Fire fighters should wear self-contained breathing apparatus when they enter a burning insulated or refrigerator car.

Box Cars

The design of all box cars is essentially the same; only the capacity and length of the cars vary. Additions, such as special racks, dunnage devices, and nailable steel floors, are made to prevent vibration damage to the contents of the car without adding to the combustibility.

Specialized Equipment

Equipment used to meet special shipping needs includes articulated cars, multi-level and enclosed cars for automobiles, "high cube" (large-capacity) box cars, 100-ton (90 metric tons) capacity covered hoppers, side-loading "all door" box cars, and aerated cars to handle bulk materials

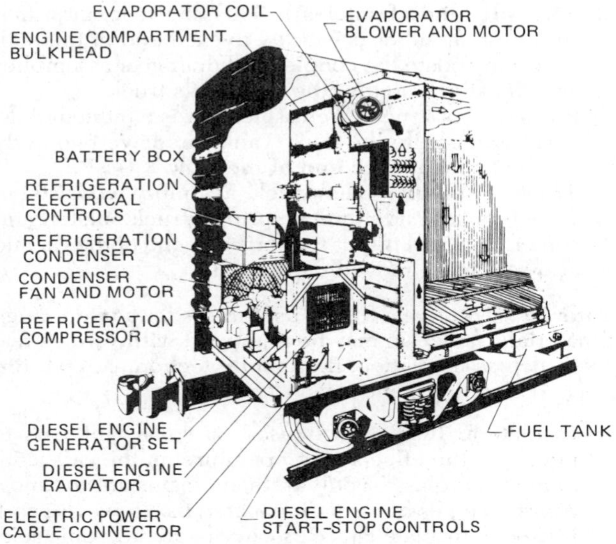

FIG. 8-35C. The engine compartment of a typical mechanically refrigerated car. Note that the start-stop control for the diesel engine is at the lower left, mounted on the side of the car.

that require pneumatic loading and unloading mechanisms to "inhale" cargo at the loading point and "exhale" it at the destination.

Cabooses

The chief fire hazards of cabooses are their combustible furnishings and their heating systems. Most cabooses are heated with oil or coal. Fires start because stoves and stove pipes do not have adequate clearances from combustible materials. Fire protection varies from water extinguishers to portable dry chemical extinguishers, although some carriers have discontinued this protection because of continuing problems with extinguisher theft. Cabooses are becoming less common, as "end of train" electronic devices take over their function.

RAIL TANK CARS

Every year, America's railroads handle a million and a half shipments of hazardous materials. About 72 percent of these materials move in a fleet of more than 200,000 tank cars, most of which are owned by non-railroad companies.

A tank car is a type of bulk packaging in which the tank is an integral part of a rail transport vehicle. Tank cars are used to transport a diverse range of commodities, including hazardous and nonhazardous materials. Tank cars transport a variety of compressed and liquefied gases, liquids, and solids. The number and types of materials transported in a tank car depend on the size, construction, fittings, linings, and other physical features of the tank.

When faced with a tank car problem, an accurate, detailed description of the contents, the condition of the car, and other circumstances relayed to those with the specialized knowledge and skills needed may be the most beneficial contribution an emergency responder can make. The following paragraphs will describe tank car construction and features, tank car markings, types of tank cars, and tank car fittings to help provide that information.

Tank Car Construction and Features

Tank cars generally consist of a single tank mounted on the car structure, although there are exceptions, such as the multi-unit tank car tank commonly known as the "ton container," the high-pressure tube car, and tank cars with multiple compartments. (See Figure 8-35D.)

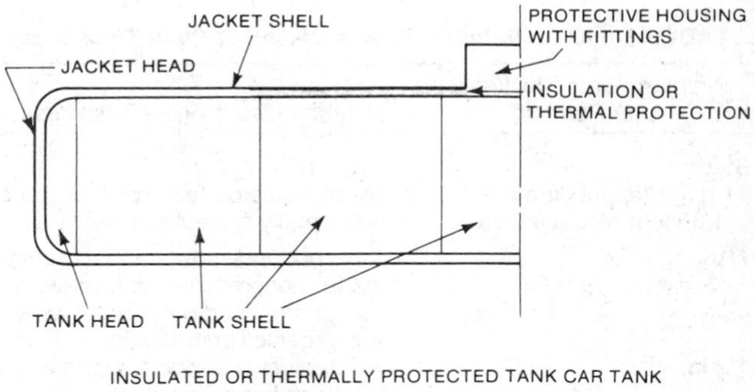

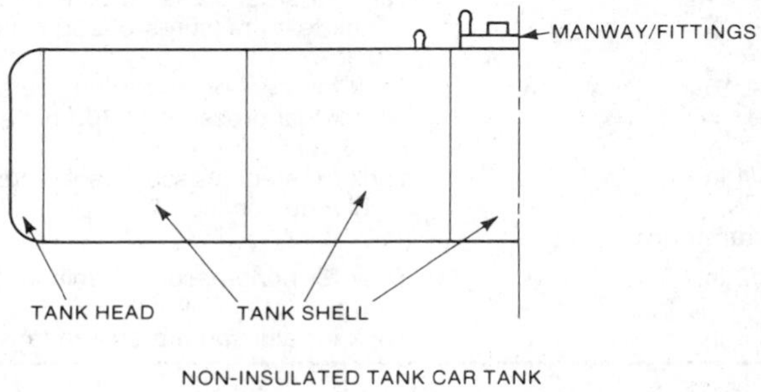

FIG. 8-35D. Tank car tank design and nomenclature.

Tank cars are built to the mechanical standards common to all freight cars. They must also meet the requirements of both the Department of Transportation (DOT) "Hazardous Materials Regulations," 49 CFR Part 179, and the Association of American Railroads' (AAR) "Specifications for Tank Cars." Builders must seek design approval from the AAR Tank Car Committee before building a tank car.

Repairs to tank car tanks requiring welding, riveting, or removal of deformations, alterations, or conversions must be performed only by facilities certified by the AAR, using procedures and materials approved by the AAR Tank Car Committee.

Requirements for Canadian tank cars are found in Transport Canada's "Regulations for the Transportation of Dangerous Commodities by Rail."

Tank car tanks: The tank car tank is made up of a shell closed at the ends by heads. The shell is constructed of two to seven metal plates formed into rings. Heads are made from plates pressed into a flanged-and-dished or an ellipsoidal shape; 2 to 1 ellipsoidal heads are the strongest. The rings and heads are fusion-welded together. In some older nonpressure tank cars, the tank parts are riveted together.

Tank car tanks are heated to 1100°F (593°C) for 1 hr to relieve metal stresses caused by welding. Representative samples are X-rayed to identify possible flaws in the metal or the welds. Finally, they are hydrostatically tested.

Carbon steel is used in over 90 percent of the tank car tanks in use, with aluminum making up most of the remainder. Stainless steel, referred to in the regulations as alloy steel, is used in a smaller number of cars. Nickel or nickel alloy is used for some tanks in acid or food services. The plate thickness of materials used to construct tank car tanks is specified by regulations. (See Table 8-35D.)

TABLE 8-35D. ***Minimum Tank and Jacket Plate Thickness***

Minimum Plate Thickness After Forming	Common Use of Plate Thickness
Steel	
11 gage (approximately 1/8 inch) also aluminum	Jacket of insulated tank cars; or jacket for thermally protected cars.
7/16 in.	Tank for nonpressure tank cars; outer tank for nonpressure tank within a tank; or shell portion of outer tank for cryogenic liquid tank cars.
1/2 in.	Head puncture resistance (head shield); or head portion of outer tank for cryogenic liquid tank cars.
9/16 in.	Tank for steel pressure tank cars with tank test pressures of 200 psi and below.
11/16 in.	Tank for steel pressure tank cars with tank test pressure of 300 psi and greater.
3/4 in.	Tank for steel pressure tank cars in chlorine service.
Aluminum	
1/2 in.	Tank for nonpressure aluminum tank cars.
5/8 in.	Tank for aluminum pressure tank cars.

Notes:

1. If high tensile strength steels are used, the plate thickness for pressure tank car tanks may be reduced, but in no case should that thickness be less than 1/2 in.

2. The plate thickness for nonpressure steel tank cars with expansion domes is a function of where the plate is used in the tank and the diameter of the tank. Thickness ranges from 1/4 to 1/2 in. For tank cars built after 1969, a minimum plate thickness is 7/16 in., except for tank cars with a diameter of 112 to 122 in. where the thickness is 1/2 in.

3. For SI units: 1 in. = 2.54 cm; 1 psi = 6.9 kPa.

The capacities of tank car tanks vary from a few hundred gallons in ton containers to approximately 45,000 gal (170 m^3) in jumbo tank cars. Since 1970, however, the maximum capacity of new DOT-specification tank cars transporting regulated hazardous materials is limited to 34,500 gal (130 m^3), or not more than 263,000 lbs (119,295 kg) gross weight on rail.

Tank car tanks may be divided into as many as six compartments, each of which is a separate tank. Compartments may be of different capacities and may transport different commodities. (See Figure 8-35E.)

Car structure: The completed tank is mounted on a car structure. The car structure consists of body bolsters attached to a framework (either continuous or stub sill). The framework rests on trucks at each end. The structure of the tank car includes the following components:

1. **Continuous underframe:** This one-piece assembly bridges the trucks of a tank car and assumes the draft and buff forces associated with train movement.
2. **Stub sill (underframeless):** This short, longitudinal structural member is welded to each end of the tank to accommodate the coupler and draft gear assemblies and the attachment of the tank to its trucks.
3. **Bolster:** This structural crossmember is mounted transversely to cradle the tank. Tank cars have two body bolsters, one at each end of the tank.
4. **Truck assembly:** The truck assembly consists of wheels, axles, sideframes, springs, truck bolster, and center bowl and pin. It supports one end of the car and allows it to be moved on the rail.

Features: To increase their usefulness for a wide range of materials, tank cars may be equipped with various features, such as insulation, thermal protection, jackets, linings and claddings, and heater coils.

1. **Insulation:** Insulation is used on some tank cars to moderate the effects of temperature on the cars' contents. Fiberglass or polyurethane foams are the most common types of insulating materials. However, cork is used to insulate tank cars carrying hydrocyanic acid. In cars transporting refrigerated liquid gases, perlite is used.
2. **Thermal protection:** Thermal protection, not to be confused with insulation, is used on some tank cars to protect the tank from flame impingement. It is designed to keep tank metal temperatures below 800° F (427° C) for 100 min (pool fire impingement) or 30 min (torch fire impingement). This thermal protection is used primarily on tank cars transporting liquefied flammable gases, and on some non-pressure tank cars, such as the DOT 111J100W4 tank car for ethylene oxide.

   Two types of thermal protection are used:
   a. **Jacketed thermal protection.** Mineral wool or various manmade ceramic fiber blankets held in place by a metal jacket; and
   b. **Sprayed on thermal protection.** A rough-textured coating sprayed onto the tanks or the jacket in some jacketed cars, which protects by expanding on exposure to fire.

3. **Jacket:** Both insulation and jacketed thermal protection are held in place by a jacket, which also keeps out the elements. The jacket is constructed of a minimum of 11-gage (approximately 1/8 in.) steel and serves as a heat-radiation shield. Wood blocks hold the jacket away from the tank.

   Jacketed cars can be recognized by a metal protective cover, or flashing, over the body bolster or tank bands; by the flattened appearance of the ends of the tank car; by flat sections on the sides of the car; or by the rough appearance of visible welds, even lap welds, which are generally thinner than the tank weld.

4. **Linings and claddings:** Some tank cars are lined to protect the tank from the corrosive or reactive effects of the contents or to maintain the purity of the contents.
   a. **Linings**. Materials applied after the tank is constructed. Rubber is the most commonly used lining in hazardous materials service, but glass, lead, nickel, polyurethane, polyvinyl chloride, and stainless steel are also used.
   b. **Claddings**. Materials applied to the tank base metal before the plate is formed. Nickel and stainless steel are used as cladding materials.

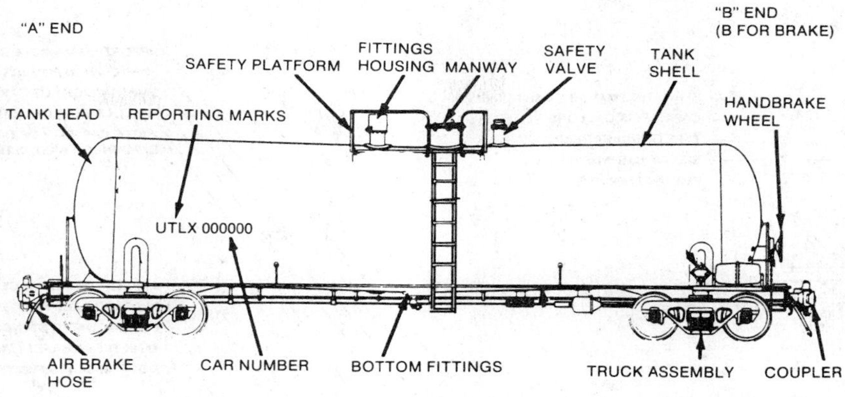

FIG. 8-35E. Diagram of tank car tank with some basic features identified. (Source: Union Tank Car Company)

5. **Heater coils:** Some tank cars are equipped with heater coils, at most 16, either inside the tank or outside. Steam, water, or hot oil from an external source is run through these coils to heat thick or solidified materials such as asphalts, fused solids, heavy fuel oils, phenol, metallic sodium, or petroleum waxes to make them flow more easily when unloading. The outlets and inlets for heater coils have caps, which are in place when the car is loaded so that any damage to the coils will not result in a release of contents. Caps are off when the car is emptied.

Retrofit Programs

Various retrofit programs have been instituted for tank cars, including head puncture resistance, or head shields; thermal protection; top and bottom self couplers; lifting lugs; and bottom protection discontinuity.

Head puncture resistance (head shields): The head shield is applied to the lower portion of both ends or it may cover the entire head to protect the heads against punctures. Some head shields are built into the jacket while others are visible either as "half head" or trapezoidal-shaped plates of steel mounted on both ends of the tank car.

Top and bottom shelf couplers: A top and bottom shelf coupler is a type of coupler with a vertical restraint mechanism, top and bottom, to reduce the potential for coupler disengagement in an accident.

Lifting lugs: The lifting lugs are reinforced lifting points or lifting provisions for uprighting tank cars in derailments.

Bottom discontinuity, or skid, protection: Skid protection is a safety device applied to the bottom of tank cars to protect bottom outlets, washouts, and sumps in a derailment.

Tank Car Markings

Various markings may be found on tank containers, including initials or reporting marks, and a tank number; a specification marking; a DOT exemption marking; and tank and valve test dates. (See Figure 8-35F.)

Initials, or reporting marks, and tank number: Tank cars, like any other freight car, are identified by the car's initials, which are called reporting marks, and number. The initials and number are found on both sides and both ends of a tank car. As one faces the side of the car, the initials and number are found on the left-hand side.

The initials indicate ownership of the car. An "X" as the last initial represents private ownership; that is, the car is not owned by the railroad. The number following the initials identifies the specific car.

Using the car's initials and number, shippers, carriers, and emergency response personnel can identify a tank car's contents with shipping papers or computer data. They can then determine whether the contents are hazardous.

Specification marking: The standards to which a tank car is built are identified by a specification marking. The specification marking is stamped into the head of the tank and stenciled on the sides of the car. As one faces the side of the car, the specification number is to the right opposite the initials and number. Multi-unit tank car tanks, or ton containers, have the specification marking stamped on each tank or on a metal plate attached to the tank. They are not stenciled.

The specification marking consists of a three-letter prefix, followed by a series of numerals and/or letters. Specification markings may be as simple as DOT-103 or as detailed as DOT-111A60ALW1. A specification marking will seldom identify the contents of the car, but it will indicate how the tank was constructed. Specification information can be obtained from the railroad's computer using the car's initials and number. (See Figure 8-35G.)

DOT exemption marking: When exemptions from the regulations for packages, containers, and the preparation and offering of hazardous materials for shipment are made, the outside of each package must be plainly and durably marked "DOT-E," followed by the number assigned, such as DOT-E8623. On portable tanks, cargo tanks, and tank cars, the marking must be in 2-in. (50.8 mm) letters.

Tank and valve test dates: Tank and safety valves, if installed, have varying retest intervals, depending on the specification and/or the age of the car. Retest and test due dates must be marked or stenciled on the tank or on the dataplate. Interior coils are also tested.

Types of Tank Cars

Tank cars are classed according to their construction, features, and fittings. The specification of the tank determines the product it may transport. (See Table 8-35E.)

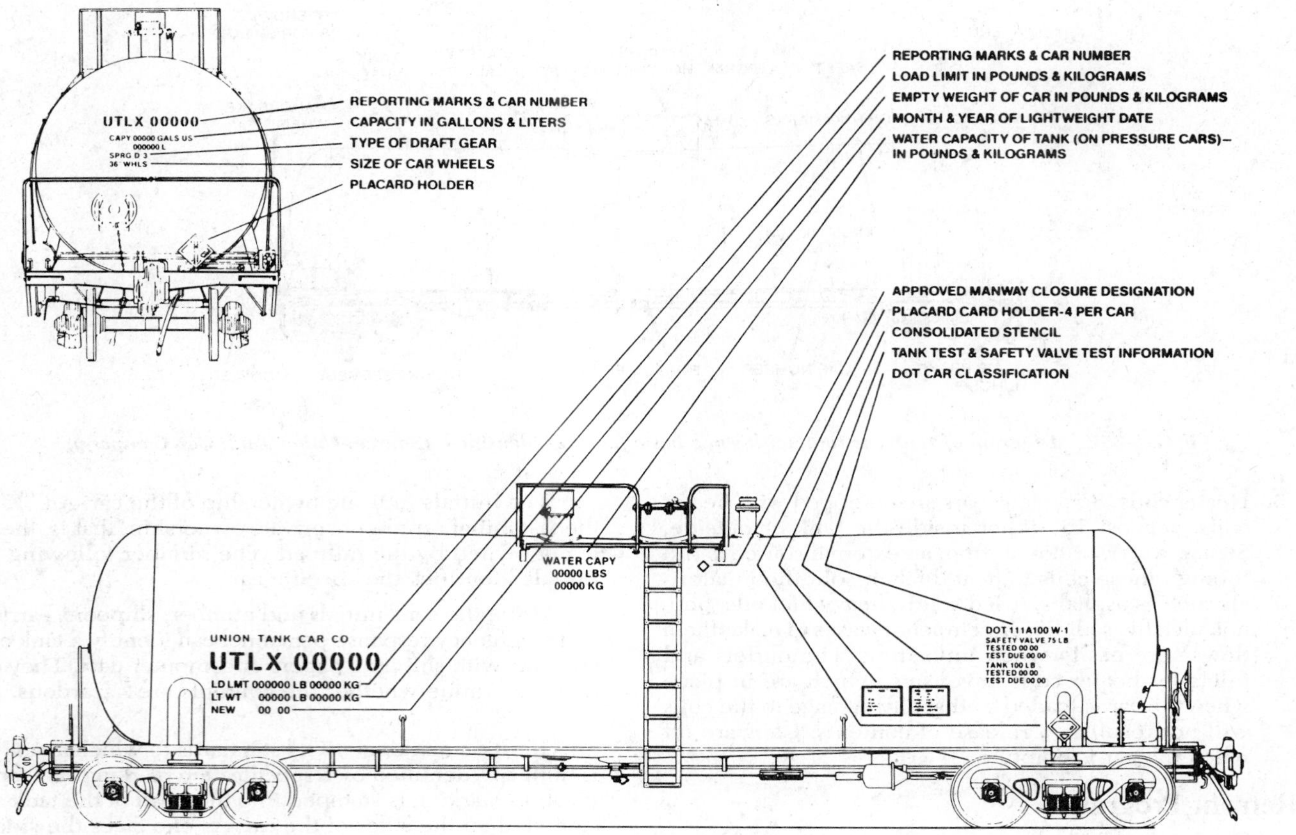

Fig. 8-35F. Diagram of tank car with markings identified. (Source: Union Tank Car Company)

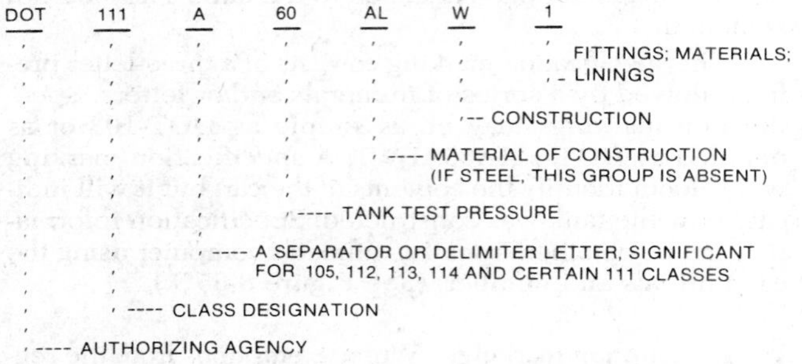

FIG. 8-35G. Explanation of specification marking.

TABLE 8-35E. *Tank Car Classes*

Nonpressure Tank Cars Classes			
DOT-103	DOT-111	AAR-201	AAR-206
DOT-104	DOT-115	AAR-203	AAR-211
Pressure Tank Car Classes			
DOT-105	DOT-112	DOT-114	DOT-120
DOT-109			
Cryogenic Liquid Tank Car Classes			
DOT-113	AAR-204	AAR-204XT	
Miscellaneous Tank Car Classes			
DOT-106	DOT-110	[both multiunit tank car tanks (ton containers)]	
DOT-107	High pressure Tube car		
AAR-207	Pneumatically unloaded hopper car		
AAR-208	Wooden tank car		

Nonpressure tank cars: Nonpressure tank cars, also known as general-service or low-pressure tank cars, transport a wide variety of hazardous and nonhazardous materials at low pressures.

Nonpressure tank cars transport hazardous materials, such as flammable and combustible liquids, flammable solids, oxidizers, organic peroxides, poison B materials, corrosive materials, molten solids, and certain flammable and nonflammable gases. They also transport nonhazardous materials, such as tallow, fruit and vegetable juices, tomato paste, and caramel.

Tank test pressures for nonpressure tank cars range from 35 to 100 psi (251 to 689 kPa). Capacities range from 4000 to 45,000 gal (15 to 170 m^3).

Nonpressure tank car tanks are cylindrical with rounded heads. Newer nonpressure tank cars have at least one manway to allow access to the interior of the car. Some older nonpressure tank cars have at least one expansion dome with a manway. (See Figures 8-35H and 8-35I.) Fittings for loading and unloading, pressure and/or vacuum relief, gaging, and other purposes are visible at the top and/or bottom of the car.

Nonpressure "tank-within-a-tank" tank cars: One nonpressure tank car is built as a tank within a tank. It consists of an inner tank of steel, alloy steel, or aluminum covered with thick insulation and enclosed within an outer

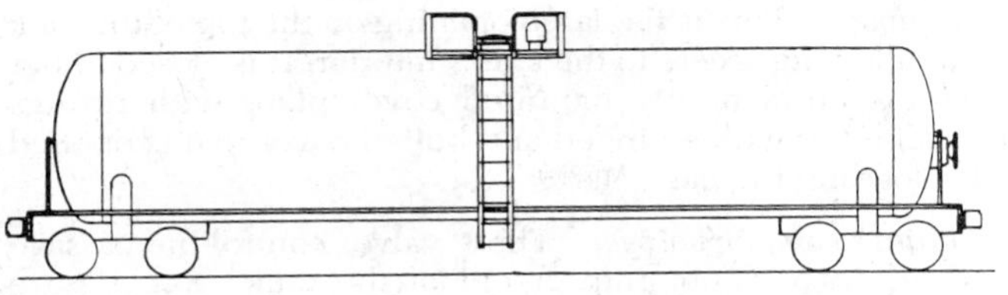

FIG. 8-35H. Diagram of typical nonpressure tank car without an expansion dome. (Source: Union Pacific Railroad.)

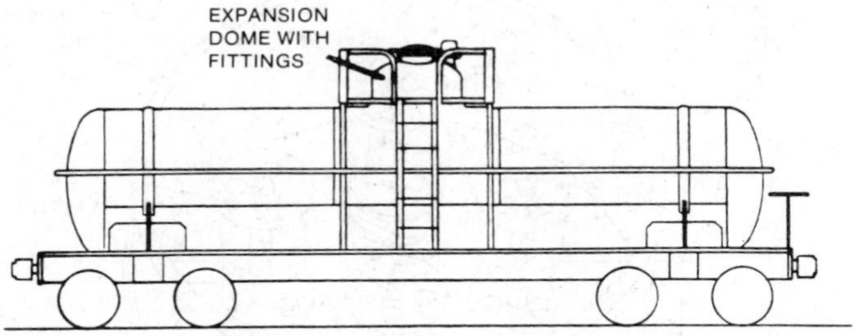

FIG 8-35I. Diagram of a typical nonpressure tank car with an expansion dome. (Source: Union Pacific Railroad.)

tank. This tank car transports temperature-sensitive materials, such as food products.

Tank Train®: The Tank Train® is a series of nonpressure tank cars interconnected with flexible hoses that allow the cars to be the loaded and unloaded from one end. A spring-loaded butterfly valve arrangement on each car is controlled pneumatically from the loading/unloading point. After loading, the hoses are purged of liquid, and the valves are closed automatically, isolating each car.

The Tank Train® transports hazardous and nonhazardous materials, including gasoline, fuel, oil, caustic soda, and pesticides.

Multi-compartmented nonpressure tank cars: Multi-compartmented nonpressure tank cars have up to six compartments. Each compartment is considered a separate tank because of its construction. Compartments may be of different capacities and may contain different materials. Each compartment has its own loading and unloading fittings.

Pressure tank cars: Pressure tank cars typically transport hazardous materials, including flammable, nonflammable, or poisonous gases at higher pressures. However, pressure tank cars can transport other commodities, depending upon the characteristics of the product or the process for loading and unloading the tank. Other products transported in pressure tank cars are ethylene oxide, pyrophoric liquids, sodium metal, motor fuel anti-knock compounds, bromine, anhydrous hydrofluoric acid, and acrolein. (See Figure 8-35J.)

Tank test pressures for these tank cars range from 100 to 600 psi (689 to 4137 kPa). Pressure tank cars range in capacity from 4000 to 45,000 gal (15 to 170 m^3).

Pressure tank cars are cylindrical, noncompartmented steel or aluminum tanks with rounded heads. They are top-loading, with fittings for loading and unloading, pressure, and gaging located inside the protective housing mounted on a manway, of which there is typically one.

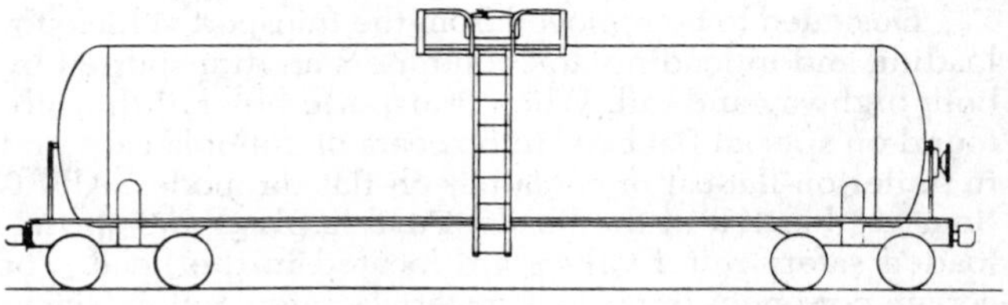

FIG. 8-35J. Diagram of a typical pressure tank car. (Source: Union Pacific Railroad.)

Pressure tank cars may be insulated and/or thermally protected. The top two-thirds of pressure tank cars without insulation and without jacketed thermal protection will be painted white.

Specialized tank cars: In addition to those already described, there are several other types of rail equipment listed under the tank car regulations that do not fit the usual image of a tank car. These include cryogenic tank cars, high-pressure tube cars, multi-unit tank car tanks (ton containers), pneumatically unloaded covered hopper cars, and wood tank cars.

Cryogenic tank cars: Cryogenic tank cars carry low-pressure—usually 25 psig or lower—cold liquids refrigerated to -155°F (-93.5°C) and below. Typical contents of these tanks are argon, ethylene, hydrogen, nitrogen, and oxygen. (See Figure 8-35K.)

FIG. 8-35K. Diagram of typical cryogenic liquid tank car. (Source: Union Pacific Railroad.)

Cryogenic tank car tanks are of the tank-within-a-tank style, with an alloy (stainless or nickel) steel inner tank inside an outer tank. The space between the inner tank and the outer tank is filled with insulation and is under a vacuum. The combination of vacuum and insulation protects the contents for only 30 days, making these shipments time sensitive.

Fittings for loading and unloading, pressure relief, and venting are located in ground-level cabinets at diagonal corners of the car or in the center of one end of the car.

Boxed tank: The few cryogenic tank cars whose tanks are permanently secured within a box car are known as the "XT" boxed tank. Valves and fittings are found inside the doors on both sides.

Multi-unit tank car tanks, or ton containers: Multi-unit tank car tanks, commonly known as ton containers, are cylindrical in shape, with the convex or concave heads welded to the cylinder. The liquid capacity of ton containers ranges from 180 to 320 gal (681 to 1181 L). Tank test pressures range from 500 to 1000 psi (3447 to 6845 kPa). Ton containers transport gases, such as chlorine, anhydrous ammonia, sulfur dioxide, butadiene, refrigerant or dispersant gases, and phosgene.

Designed to be removed from the transport vehicle for loading and unloading, ton containers are transported by both highway and rail. When transported by rail they are found on special flat cars, in box cars or gondola cars, and in trailer-on-flat-car or container-on-flat-car modes. All fittings are located in the heads. Fusible plugs and spring-loaded safety relief valves are located in the head. For certain poisonous or noxious materials, safety relief devices are prohibited.

High-pressure tube cars: The high-pressure tube car is a 40-ft (12 m) box-type, open-frame car. Inside the frame is a visible cluster of 30 seamless steel, uninsulated cylinders, arranged horizontally and permanently attached to the car. Tank test pressures of these tube cars range up to 5000 psi (345 000 kPa). These tube cars transport helium, hydrogen, or oxygen in the gaseous form. (See Figure 8-35L.)

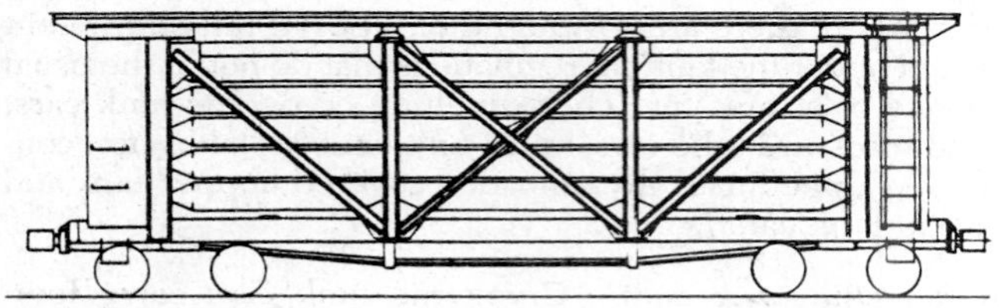

FIG. 8-35L. ***Diagram of a high-pressure tube car. (Source: Union Pacific Railroad.)***

Each end of the tube car is enclosed in a steel case. Loading and unloading fittings and safety devices are located in a walk-in cabinet at one end of the car. Safety relief devices, either safety relief valves or safety vents are found on each cylinder. For cars transporting flammable gases, safety relief devices are equipped with ignition devices to burn off any released material.

Pneumatically unloaded covered hopper cars: The pneumatically unloaded covered hopper car is built to tank car specifications. It is a uncovered hopper car that is unloaded through pressure differential, or pneumatics, by the application of air pressure. Even though the pressure is used only during unloading, tank test pressures for the car range from 20 to 80 psi (138 to 551 kPa). Dry caustic soda is one commodity transported in this type of car.

Wood tank cars: Wooden tank cars are lined, coated, or treated wood-staved, metal-hooped cylindrical tanks used to transport food products, such as vinegar and pickle liquor. The flat heads are rabbeted inside the ends of the tank. The tank has at least one manway and at least one loading and discharge opening in the top of the car. The tank is secured to the underframe by tank bands. No safety relief devices are required.

Tank Car Fittings

Numerous fittings are used on tank cars to allow for loading and unloading and to provide for the safe transportation of the contents. All fittings are not found on all tank cars.

This section addresses tank car fittings for nonpressure and pressure tank cars from a very general standpoint.

Fittings for loading and unloading tank cars: Various fittings are used to load and unload tank cars, including the following.

Manway: This is the large opening on the top of the tank car, allowing access to the tank's interior. It is closed either with a permanently mounted cover plate with fittings attached or with a hinged-and-bolted cover that is opened for loading the car.

Liquid or vapor valves: These valves control the passage of liquid or vapor into or out of the tank. (See Figure 8-35M.)

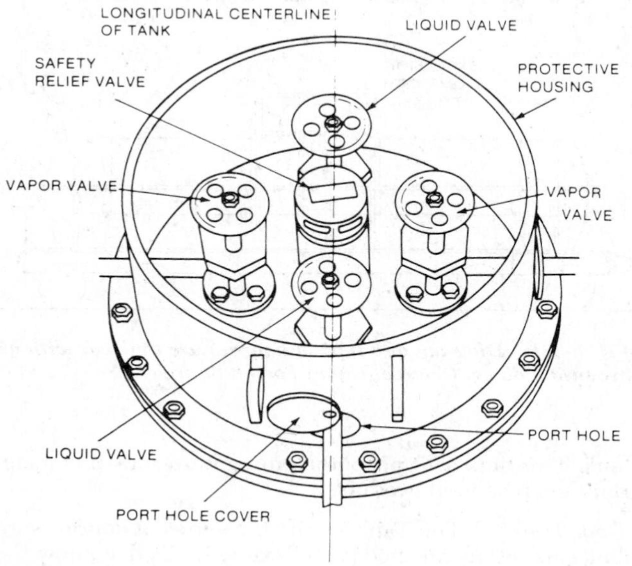

FIG. 8-35M. ***Details of the protective housing, or dome, on a liquid chlorine tank car.***

Liquid valves, usually two, are used to load or unload liquids from tank cars. Unloading occurs as a result of pressure generated by the contents or when the tank is pressurized with air, nitrogen, or other gas. An eduction pipe reaches from the liquid valve to the tank's bottom.

One or two vapor valves are used to remove vapor from the tank or to pressurize the tank. On pressure tank cars, it is called the vapor valve; on nonpressure tank cars, it is called the air inlet or air valve.

(Note: Excess flow valves are found under various fittings. They shut when the flow exceeds a designed amount.)

Bottom outlet valves: These valves are used to unload the tank from the bottom. Examples are a plug-type valve that is operated from the top of the tank, called a "top-operated bottom unloading valve"; a ball-type valve that is either external to or inside the tank and operated from ground level; or a wafersphere, or butterfly valve, mounted outside the tank.

Safety relief devices: These devices are designed to reduce the buildup of excess internal pressure caused by commodity vaporization and expansion.

Safety relief valve: This relief device has an operating part held closed by a single spring or by multiple springs. The device is designed to open and reclose at predetermined pressures. The device can be mounted with the spring inside or outside the tank.

Safety vent: This device uses a frangible disk, called a rupture disk, that seals the vent opening under normal conditions. The disk is designed to rupture at predetermined pressures and, once ruptured, does not reclose. Rupture disks are made of steel; (lead is no longer authorized), plastic, rubber, or a combination of metal, plastic, or rubber. Safety vents are used on certain nonpressure tank cars.

Combination device: This device uses a rupture disk and a breaking pin in combination with a spring operated safety relief valve.

Fusible Plug: This plug functions by melting at a predetermined temperature, creating an opening in the tank.

Fittings for gaging the innage and outage in tank cars: Gaging devices are used to determine the amount of lading in a tank. These devices allow one to measure the amount of liquid in the tank, such as liquefied or cryogenic gases (innage); or the amount of vapor space left in the tank (outage). Gaging devices usually measure outage.

Two types of gaging devices are found:

1. *Open-type gaging devices.* This device ejects liquid once the liquid level reaches the bottom of a fixed- or adjustible-length tube. It reads outage.
2. *Closed-type gaging devices.* This device uses a float, coupled with a magnet on a measuring rod or a dial indicator, to show the liquid level of the commodity.

Another method of determining the amount of lading in a tank car is to insert a measuring pole while using the appropriate innage/outage tables. Outage is also determined by gage bars or "T" bars on most nonpressure cars.

Other fittings: Various other fittings may be found on tank cars.

Sample line: This device is used to obtain a sample of the commodity without opening the tank.

Thermometer well: This closed tube, filled with a permanent-type antifreeze, extends into the tank. By inserting a thermometer into the tube, the temperature of the lading inside may be determined.

Bottom washout. This is a permanently closed opening in the bottom of the tank car that is used only when a tank is cleaned. There is no way to control the lading flow once the closure is removed.

Sump: This is a closed projection in the bottom of the tank which allows the liquid eduction pipe to extend slightly below the bottom of the tank to unload the tank more completely.

Vacuum relief valve: This valve is designed to prevent excessive internal vacuum buildup [greater than 0.75 psig (5.2 kPa) negative pressure in some nonpressure tanks. The vacuum relief valve used during unloading opens to admit air when a vacuum occurs and then recloses after normal conditions have been restored.

INTERMODAL TANK CONTAINERS

In the mid-1960s, intermodal tank containers or, simply, tank containers, were introduced in Europe. Currently, they are used worldwide, and projections indicate that the total number of tank containers may reach 90,000 by the year 2000.

Since the early 1980s, the use of tank containers in North America has increased greatly. Among the factors that account for this increase are improved safety, portability, lower transportation costs, and benefits of a multi-modal transport system.

Advantages over alternate methods of transport, such as drums, tank trucks, and trailers, include a reduction in the amount of handling required, faster transfer at ports and terminals, convenient storage options at the destination, and ready use of conventional container-handling equipment already in place.

Tank containers are built according to many domestic and international standards. They are used to transport a diverse range of commodities, including an increasing number of hazardous materials.

Problems involving tank containers are best handled by giving an accurate, detailed description of the contents, the condition of the tank container, and the circumstances to those with specialized knowledge and skills necessary to help handle the problem.

Tank Container Construction and Features

Tank containers consist of a single, metal tank mounted inside a sturdy, metal supporting frame. This unique frame structure, built to international standards, makes tank containers multi-modal (intermodal). Thus, they are used interchangeably in two or more modes of transport, such as rail, highway, or water. (See Figure 8-35N.) Tank containers may be equipped with a variety of features.

FIG. 8-35N. ***Diagrams of tank containers in various modes of transportation. (Source: Union Pacific Railroad.)***

Tank container tank: The tank container tank is generally built as a cylinder enclosed at the ends by heads. Other tank shapes—rectangular tanks—and configurations—tube modules—exist but they are rare. Tanks with multiple compartments, each built as a separate tank, are also rare. A tank's capacity does not ordinarily exceed 6340 gal (about 24,000 L).

Ninety percent or more of the tanks are built of stainless steel, and the rest are constructed of mild steel. Stainless steel is used because of its resistence to cold temperatures. Aluminum and magnesium alloy tanks are available, but they cannot be used in water transport mode.

Minimum head and shell thickness are measured in terms of "equivalent thickness in mild steel" after forming. For steel tanks, the minimum thickness for nonregulated commodities is 1/4 in. (6.35 mm). For regulated materials, the minimum thickness is 3/8 in. (9.5 mm). For stainless steel tanks, the minimum thickness for nonregulated materials is slightly less than 1/8 in. (3.2 mm). For regulated commodities, the minimum thickness is just under 3/16 in. (4.8 mm).

Most tanks are built according to the pressure-vessel standards of the American Society of Mechanical Engineers (ASME), and the welds are X-rayed. Welds on carbon steel tanks are post-weld heat-treated.

Supporting frame: The supporting frame of a tank container protects the tank and provides for stacking, lifting, and securing the container. It also supports the walkways and ladders. As with other types of freight containers, supporting frames are built to the requirements of the International Standards Organization (ISO) in Switzerland.

The most common size of supporting frame is 20 ft long (6 m), 8 or 8½ ft wide (2.4 or 2.55 m), and from 8 to 9½ ft (2.4 to 2.85 m) high. Except for the Sea-Land Company's half-height tank containers, which are 35 ft (10.5 m) long, very few tanks longer than 20 ft (6 m) are used in the U.S.

There are two basic supporting frame types: the "box type," which encloses the tank in a cage-like framework, and the "beam type," which uses frame structures only at the ends of the tank.

Corner Casting: Supporting frames for all intermodal containers, including tank containers, are built with standard corner fittings, called corner castings. They are used to secure the tank and to lift it with standard container-handling equipment. Corner castings must conform to ISO standards. Cast-iron corner castings are prohibited. In an accident where proper lifting devices are not available, the corner castings may be used to lift or move the tank only after the tank's owner or manufacturer has been consulted.

Features: To increase their use for a wide range of cargos, tank containers may be equipped with various features, such as linings that protect the tank from the lading, refrigeration units, electrical or steam heating, and insulation to maintain the desired temperature of the contents.

Foam, both polyurethane and polystyrene, is the predominant insulating material. However, mineral wool or fiberglass are also used. Insulation, generally 3 to 4 in. (76.2 to 101.6 mm) thick, is always covered with a weathertight jacket. Jackets are made of metal, at least 1/32 in. (1 mm) thick, or of an equivalent thickness of plastic reinforced with either glass or fiber.

Tank Container Markings

Various marking may be found on tank containers, including the tank initials and number, the specification marking, the DOT exemption marking, the AAR 600 marking, the country and size/type markings, the dataplate, and the tank and valve test dates. (See Figure 8-35O).

Tank initials and number: Tank containers must be registered with the International Container Bureau in France. They must be marked with initials , or reporting marks, and with a tank number. The initials indicate the ownership of the tank, and the tank number identifies the specific tank.

The initials and tank number are generally found on the right-hand side of the tank as one faces it from either side, and on both ends. They may be displayed either on the tank itself or on the frame.

With this information, shippers, carriers, and emergency response personnel can identify the tank's contents, using shipping papers or computer data. They can then determine if the contents are hazardous.

Specification marking: The design, construction, and use of tank containers must conform to the strict standards and regulations of many agencies, both in the United States and abroad. Markings on the tank container indicate the standards to which the tank was built.

In the United States, tank containers must meet the design, construction, and safety standards set forth by the DOT. Tanks meeting these standards will have the specification markings, or an exemption number displayed on both sides, generally means the tank's initials and number.

Examples of specification markings are: IM 101, IM 102, Spec. 51, and Spec. 51L.

DOT exemption marking: When exemptions from the regulations governing packages, containers, and the preparation and offering of hazardous materials for shipment are made, the outside of each package must be plainly and durably marked in 2-in. (50.8 mm) letters and numbers—that is, "DOT-E" followed by the number assigned, such as DOT-E8623.

AAR-600 marking: For interchange purposes in rail transportation, tank containers should conform to the requirements of Section 600, "Specification for Acceptability of Tank Containers" of the Association of American Railroad's (AAR) "Specification for Tank Cars." Tanks meeting these requirements will display the AAR 600 markings in 2-in. (50.8 mm) letters on both sides, near the tank's initials and number. The AAR-600 marking indicates tanks that can be used for regulated materials, whereas the AAR-600NR marking indicates tanks that cannot be used for regulated materials.

Country and size type markings: In addition to the initials and number and the specification marking, the tank will also display a country code and a size/type code. The country code of two or three letters indicates the tank's country of registry.

The four-digit size/type code follows the country code. The first two numbers in the code jointly indicate the container's length and height. The second pair of numbers is the type code, which indicates the pressure range of the tank.

Dataplate: For further technical, approval, and operational data, tank containers have dataplates permanently attached to the tank or frame.

Tank and valve test dates: Tanks and safety valves, if installed, must have a retest interval no greater than five years. Retest and test due dates must be marked or stenciled on the tank or on the dataplate.

General Classes of Tank Containers

Tank containers are classed according to the specification of the tank and fittings. The classification of a tank container determines the products that may be carried in that container.

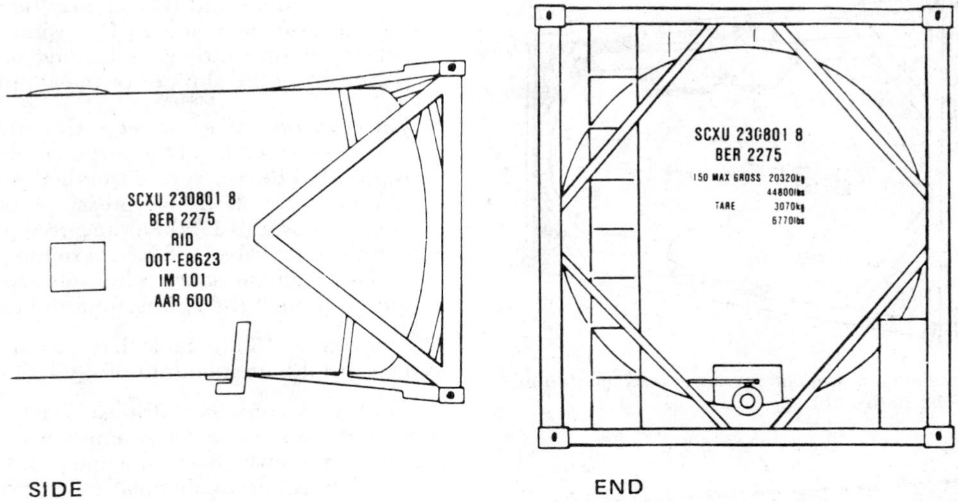

FIG. 8-35O. Typical markings on tank containers.

Nonpressure tank containers: Also called intermodal portable tanks or IM portable tanks, nonpressure tank containers comprise over 90 percent of the total. (See Figure 8-35P.) They usually transport liquid and solid materials at maximum allowable working pressures (MAWP) of up to 100 psig (6890 kPa). Tanks are tested to at least 1.5 times the MAWP. In the U.S., two groups of nonpressure tank containers are common:

1. *IM 101 portable tanks*: These tanks are built to withstand MAWPs of from 25.4 to 100 psig (172 to 6890 kPa). They may transport both nonhazardous and hazardous materials, including toxics, corrosives, and flammables with a flashpoint below 32° F (0° C). Internationally, an IM 101 portable tank is called an IMO type 1 tank container.
2. *IM 102 portable tanks*: These tanks are designed to handle lower MAWP—that is, from 14.5 up to 25.4 psig (103 to 172 kPa). They transport materials such as liquor, alcohols, some corrosives, pesticides, insecticides, resins, industrial solvents, and flammables with flashpoints between 32 and 140°F (0 and 60°C). More often they transport various nonregulated materials, such as food-grade commodities. Internationally, an IM 102 tank is called an IMO type 2 tank container.

Pressure tank containers: Also known as DOT Spec. 51 portable tanks, these containers are less common in transport. They are designed to handle internal pressures ranging from 100 to 500 psig (6890 to 34,450 kPa), and generally transport gases liquefied under pressure, such as LP-Gas and anhydrous ammonia. They may also carry liquids, such as motor fuel anti-knock compound or aluminum alkyls. Internationally, they are called IMO type 5 tank containers. (See Figure 8-35Q.)

Specialized tank containers: In addition to those already described, there are several other variations of tank-type containers. Among them are:

1. *Cryogenic tank containers:* These containers carry refrigerated liquid gases, such as argon, oxygen, and helium, and are build to DOT Spec. 51L standards. Internationally, they are called IMO type 7 tank containers.

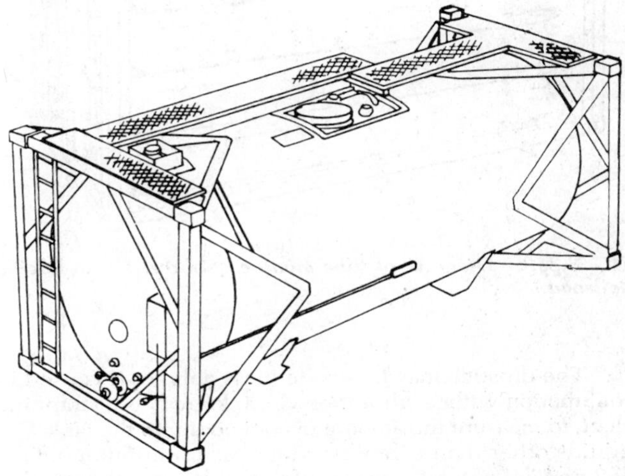

FIG. 8-35P. Illustration of nonpressure tank container. (Source: Union Pacific Railroad.)

2. *Tube modules:* These containers transport gases in high-pressure 3T cylinders tested to 3000 or 5000 psi, permanently mounted within an ISO frame. (See Figure 8-35R.)

Tank Container Fittings

Nonpressure tank container fittings: Nonpressure tanks containers are equipped with various fittings to make them functional and safe.

Spillbox: On nonpressure tanks, the top fittings are surrounded by a spillbox which protects the shell of the tank from any spillage. Any spilled material, as well as rainwater in the spillbox, drains away through an open pipe.

Manhole, cover, and dipstick: The manhole is located on top of the tank at the center. It is secured by six or eight wing nuts on a hinged and bolted lid fitted with a replaceable gasket.

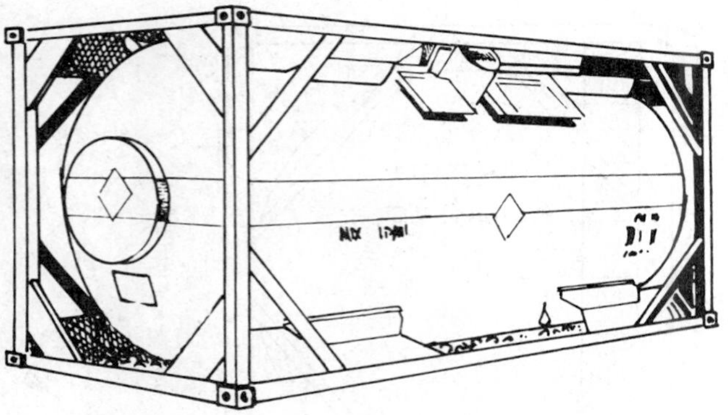

FIG. 8-35Q. Diagram of a typical pressure tank container. (Source: Union Pacific Railroad.)

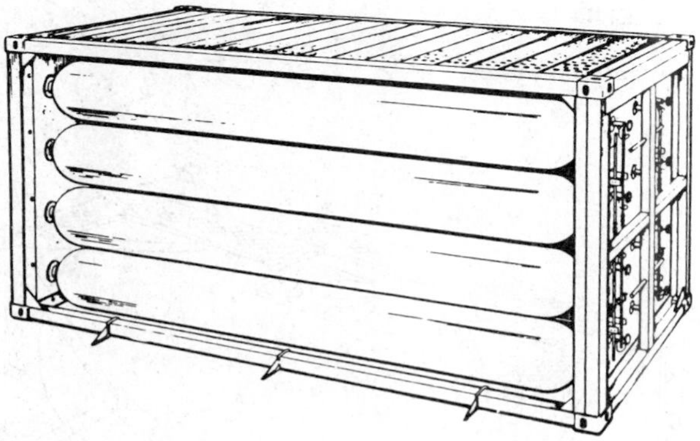

FIG. 8-35R. Diagram of tube module. (Source: Union Pacific Railroad.)

The dipstick may be inside the manhole. It is used in conjunction with a calibration chart, known as a strapping chart, to measure the amount of commodity in the tank. For liquids other than compressed gases, a minimum outage of 2 percent of total capacity of the tank must be provided in rail transportation.

Top-loading valves: Top-loading valves are attached to a removable eduction pipe—dip leg, dip tube, or siphon tube—running into the tank.

Bottom-outlet valves: When tank containers are used for hazardous materials, two externally operated, bottom-outlet valves are required. They are connected in series with a replaceable gasket between them and are located at one end of the tank, the so-called discharge end. A liquid-tight closure on the external valve is also required. It may be a blind flange which is required on international shipments; a screw cap; or a cam-lock cap attached to the external valve. A positive lock is required on the external bottom valve to keep it closed.

In an emergency, the internal valve, or foot valve, can be shut off from a remote location. As one faces the discharge end of the tank, the emergency shutoff will be on the right-hand side near the far end.

Air-line connection. An air-line connection, located on the tank's top, can be used for pressure unloading, vapor return, and blanketing the contents with an inert gas.

On occasion, blind flanges may be found in place of the top-loading valve and air-line connection. In this situation, appropriate fittings for loading and unloading must be provided by the shipper or the supplier of the tank.

Pressure/vacuum relief valves: Generally found in pairs on nonpressure tank containers, a combination pressure/vacuum relief device serves the dual purpose of protecting the tank from both overpressure and from a vacuum of over 0.75 psig (5.175 kPa) negative pressure. In many cases, this relief valve will have a rupture, or bursting, disk located between the safety relief valve spring and the commodity to protect the spring from the commodity.

Thermometer: Some tanks have a built-in thermometer to measure the temperature of the lading.

Pressure tank container fittings: Like nonpressure tank containers, pressure tank containers are equipped with various fittings to make them functional and safe. A wide variety of fitting arrangements exists for pressure tank containers. Pressure intermodal tanks may have fittings on top, at the end, or on the bottom. Generally, the fittings are enclosed with a cover or are recessed to protect them from mechanical damage.

Loading/unloading valves: Liquid and vapor valves are used to fill and empty the tank. The liquid valve reaches into the lading by means of an eduction pipe, which may be fitted with an excess-flow check valve. Vapor valves, which also may have an excess-flow check valve, are used to remove vapor from the tank or to pressurize the tank for unloading.

Safety relief devices: Safety relief valves, mounted on top, protect the tank from overpressure under abnormal conditions. In many cases, a rupture disk is located between the safety relief valve spring and the commodity to protect the spring from the contents.

Gaging devices: Gaging devices may be installed to measure how much liquid is in the tank.

Other fittings: A sample line for sampling the lading and a thermometer well for measuring lading temperature may also be installed.

Tank Car and Intermodal Tank Container Fire Hazards

Fire hazards of tank cars and intermodal tank containers are minimal unless a car is damaged in an accident. If a fire does occur, it is essential to learn the contents of the car or the container before attempting to fight the fire. A tank car or a container exposed to radiant energy from a fire, particularly direct flame impingement, should be approached cautiously. If a commodity absorbs too much heat, vapor pressure will build up and cause the safety valve to operate or the tank to rupture. If any of the commodity is released, personnel should be prepared to deal with corrosive, toxic, or otherwise harmful effects. Direct contact with vapors discharged from tank cars or containers under emergency conditions should be avoided, unless appropriate protective clothing and self-contained breathing apparatus are worn.

PASSENGER EQUIPMENT

Fires involving railroad passenger equipment are relatively uncommon. Modern steel-and-aluminum passenger coaches and diner, mail, express, chair, and sleeping cars do not contain many combustibles. The major cause of fires on passenger trains are careless smoking and electrical faults. In diners, hazards are identical to those inherent in stationary restaurants; namely, grease and exhaust system fires. Air conditioning and heating systems must be safeguarded properly, and preventive maintenance is essential.

Self-propelled electrical passenger equipment, such as that used in Amtrak Metroliner service, has safety emergency cutoffs similar to those on electric locomotives. To deenergize the equipment, it is necessary to lower and ground the pantograph. This can be done automatically by operating the pantograph control in the engineer's compartment or by using the pantograph pole, which is inside a tube mounted horizontally on the side of the car. If the car must be mounted, it is necessary to activate a control on the top at the end of each car labeled "Danger High Voltage—Ground Pantograph Before Going on Roof." Each connected car must be deenergized separately by lowering and grounding its pantograph. It is essential to learn from railroad officials the proper operation of the grounding system and to practice its use before an emergency.

With the pantograph lowered, the battery operating the emergency lights and doors can be disconnected using the battery cutoff switch inside the electrical cabinet.

MISCELLANEOUS RAILROAD FACILITIES

Many railroad facilities are similar to manufacturing facilities, with familiar hazards. However, other facilities are peculiar to the railroad industry, such as diesel locomotive light repair shops, locomotive heavy repair shops, freight car repair shops, paint shops, and locomotive fueling facilities. Hazards associated with a diesel locomotive repair shop include cutting, welding, poor housekeeping, and leakage of fuel.

Fueling facilities need particular protection, not only because of the economic value of the systems, but also because of the value of locomotives and the cost of interruption of service. Fuel pump houses should be of noncombustible construction and, preferably, equipped with automatic fire protection and with light fixtures and devices suitable for hazardous locations. Because leakage is the prime hazard, careful housekeeping and preventive maintenance are essential. Portable and wheeled dry chemical fire extinguishers should be located throughout the fueling area. It is most desirable to have a high-volume water supply nearby.

Other facilities are critical to railroad operation and, if involved in fire, could stop the movement of trains in a given territory. These facilities include computer centers, microwave communications facilities, centralized train control equipment, and the many support elements in classification yards. These facilities should be protected by private detection and protection systems. Typical fire suppression systems range from sprinklers to carbon dioxide and Halon 1301. Adequate water and hydrant systems nearby are essential.

Bridges and Trestles

Prevention is the key to continued operation of these structures. Regular maintenance should be done to provide and maintain a 25- to 50-ft (7.5 to 15 m) clearance between combustible structures and nearby vegetation. Susceptibility to fire damage can be reduced by treating the structure with a fire retardant and by providing of water barrels, fire detection systems, standby pipe and hose systems, and guard service.

At some particularly valuable and critical bridges, fireboats and water buckets that can be attached to helicopters have been provided, and noncombustible bridge segments have been constructed at regular intervals to limit damage should fire occur. Most railroads have been replacing combustible bridges and other track structures with noncombustible construction at every opportunity, thus reducing their exposure to fire-related losses.

Exposures to Freight Equipment

Exposure fires that destroy loaded and unloaded freight equipment reflect the need for close analysis of terminal fire hazards. When classification or switching yards are designed, adequate fire protection, both private and public, should be a prime consideration.

Experience in large yards indicates that lack of nearby fire mains and hydrants is a contributing factor in fire loss. In a major incident, fire fighting activities should be confined to containment and protection of exposed property. A prefire plan should map fire mains and hydrants near the yard, because experience shows that existing protection in the yard may be rendered useless by disaster.

Railroad sidings present a similar exposure hazard, particularly at grain elevators, lumber yards, flammable liquid or LP-Gas unloading facilities, and similar industrial properties.

Self-Propelled Fire Fighting and Derrick Equipment

Most carriers can clear derailments and rerail freight equipment. They use lifting equipment—steam or diesel derricks—ranging from 150 to 250 tons (136 to 227 metric tons). These are mounted on a work train, which also may carry water cars and fire pumps powered by the train air line or powered independently by an internal combustion engine. Fire hoses, nozzles, foam compound, play pipes, and a quantity of extinguishers are usually provided by the carriers for fire fighting.

Work trains have proven most valuable for incidents that occur in remote and inaccessible areas. On occasion, such emergencies have been handled by driving a fire department pumper onto a flat car and taking it to the emergency by train.

Some railroads have self-propelled fire fighting cars that can be used independently of the work train. The availability of such fire fighting equipment, often overlooked in planning, should be considered.

RIGHTS OF WAY

A common, difficult problem is the right-of-way fire, or fire on land adjacent to the roadbed, occasionally spreading off railroad property. Such fires still occur, but their frequency and severity have been reduced by improved railroad equipment, controlled burning, chemical spraying of vegetation, and installation of fire breaks. Cooperation with the U.S. Forest Service has led to development of spark arresters, spark arrester exhaust manifolds, and sparkless brake shoes. Planned vegetation is another solution that can be employed.

Safety

Everyone in the vicinity of a railroad track should assume it is "live" and that a train may appear at any moment. A number of incidents have been recorded in which fire fighting personnel narrowly escaped injury from passing trains whose crews were unaware of their presence. At some fires, hose lines have been laid across a railroad track, only to be cut by a passing train.

In case of fire, communications are essential. Railroad personnel should be notified at the first opportunity and asked to alert train crews to the location of the fire and fire fighting personnel.

TRANSPORTATION OF HAZARDOUS MATERIALS

Rail transportation of hazardous commodities, which annually represents less than 5 percent of the carloads of freight moving over the system, is strictly regulated by the DOT through the Research and Special Programs Administration. These regulations are enforced by the Federal Railroad Administration (FRA). Canadian railroads are similarly regulated by Transport Canada.

When a rail accident involves hazardous materials, the danger is increased. Product spills, fires, and explosions must be confronted by fire, health, safety, and environmental agency personnel.

When accidents, spills, or fire occur in conjunction with the transportation of hazardous materials, the immediate aim of those in charge is to prevent injury and loss of life and then to prevent property and environmental losses as far as practicable. To do this safely and intelligently, it is necessary to know what hazardous materials are involved in the incident.

Upon notification of an accident or other occurrence involving railroad equipment, response personnel should take the following actions:

1. Telephone or otherwise contact the responsible railroad dispatcher. Have this number in advance.
2. Ask the dispatcher what commodities are involved in the accident or fire and the number of cars; where the specific location of the accident is and the best avenues of approach; when the accident occurred; when access will be permitted; and whether evacuation of that area is necessary.
3. Upon arrival at the scene, establish contact with the senior railroad officer or representative before attempting to deal with the emergency.
4. If there is undue risk to life, retreat to a safe distance and remain there until the incident commander determines that it is safe to reenter the area and take action.

It is essential that response personnel know about the presence, type, quantity, and nature of any hazardous materials in any rail accident or fire. This information is available in two forms.

The first means of detecting the presence of a hazardous materials shipment are the placards and hazardous materials identification numbers affixed to both ends and both sides of the railroad vehicle. Placarding alerts personnel to the presence of a hazardous material and identifies its hazard classification. Sometimes, the commodity name is stenciled on the shell of the tank car. Due to the nature of an accident, however, the placard often cannot be read, or it is not prudent to approach the car close enough to read the information. Binoculars are most helpful here.

The second means of identifying the presence or absence of hazardous materials is by referring to the papers carried on the train. By regulation, all cars carrying hazardous materials must be documented by a piece of paper that shows the car number, the names of the shipper and consignee, the name and classification of the commodity(ies), the placard notation, the Standard Transportation Commodity Code (STCC) "49" series of hazardous materials identification numbers, and the amount of material in the freight vehicle. The 24-hr emergency telephone number of the shipper is also included.

The form this information takes will vary depending on the train's nature, as well as the practices of that particular railroad. A local train in the process of delivering cars to local industries and picking up others for later assembly into a train may have a variety of documents including consists or wheel reports, and shipping papers or waybills for the cars being delivered, as well as shipping papers or switch lists for the cars being picked up. A through train generally will have formal documents, usually consists and shipping papers, complete with all required emergency response information for all cars in the order they are arranged in the train.

Within the next few years, through trains on all major and most smaller railroads will be using a new, standardized train consist document. This new document will replace the multiple lists and papers now carried on trains. Much of the present paperwork will be replaced by electronic interchange of shipping information between the shipper, the railroads, and the consignee. The new consist document will list all cars and their contents in the order in which they appear in the train. For each car containing hazardous materials, the consist information will include all the required hazardous materials data and full emergency response information.

Whatever the form, the train's papers will be in the possession of the conductor, who is the person in charge of the train. Although, usually stationed in the caboose, the conductor can also be found in the lead locomotive of trains without cabooses. Emergency responders arriving on the scene of a rail incident should first seek out the conductor and examine all pertinent documents before proceeding with the response.

Technical assistance on hazardous materials identification at the scene is available from CHEMTREC, which can be called toll-free at (800) 424-9300 or at (202) 483-7616 (collect) in Alaska and the District of Columbia.

In Canada and the United States, CHEMTREC will promptly notify the AAR Bureau of Explosives of accidents, fires, or explosions and of leaking, broken containers occurring in connection with the transportation or storage of explosives or other dangerous articles on a carrier's property. Bureau representatives are regularly dispatched to the scene of major emergencies when requested by the railroad involved.

When an incident occurring during transportation involves hazardous materials, carriers must forward a hazardous materials incident report to the DOT Research and Special Programs Administration.

Many carriers prepare guides and recommendations for handling rail emergencies and make them available to fire departments along their rights of way. In addition, the carriers assist the fire service by participating in seminars and providing instructors and training programs at fire department training sessions and fire schools.

Emergency Response Teams

Some carriers have developed emergency response teams that are specially trained to handle emergencies on their lines. Such teams are equipped with special kits and tools to repair leaks and control pollution. This team preparation concept is rapidly spreading throughout the industry.

NFPA Rail Transportation System Section

The NFPA Rail Transportation System Section was organized in 1963 as a membership section of the National Fire Protection Association. It is dedicated to promoting interest in, and improving the methods of, fire prevention and protection in the railroad industry and to encouraging proper safeguards and recommended practices against fire through the interchange of ideas and experience.

The NFPA Rail Transportation System Section's annual meeting is held each May in connection with the NFPA Annual Meeting. This event provides an excellent forum for the exchange of ideas between the fire service and railroad firesafety specialists.

BIBLIOGRAPHY

References

"Hazardous Material Regulations of the Department of Transportation," Bureau of Explosive Tariff No. BOE-6000, Bureau of Explosives, Association of American Railroads, Washington, DC, revised annually and updated quarterly.

GATX Tank Car Manual, 5th ed, General American Transportation Corporation, Chicago, IL, 1985.

General Guide to Tank Container Operation, Sea Containers Group, London, England, 1983.

Inspection, Repair, and Test Requirements for Tank Containers, Sea Container Group, London, England.

Manual of Standards and Recommended Practices, Section C - Part III, Specification for Tank Cars, Operation and Maintenance Department, Association of American Railroads, Washington, DC, 1987.

Maty, A. D., "Guide to the Identification of Tank Cars and Fittings Utilized for the Transportation of Hazardous Materials," 1985, unpublished.

Tank Car Book, Union Tank Car Company, Chicago, IL.

Wright, C. J. and Student, P. J., "Understanding Railroad Tank Cars," *Fire Command*, Vol. 52, Nox. 11 and 12 (Nov. and Dec. 1985).

Wright, C. J. and Hand, W. T., "Intermodal Tank Containers," *Fire Command*, Vol. 55, Nos. 6 and 7 (June and July 1988).

NFPA Codes, Standards, and Recommended Practices

Reference to the following NFPA codes, standards, and recommended practices will provide further information on rail transportation systems discussed in this chapter. (See the latest *NFPA Catalog* for availability of current editions of the following documents.)

NFPA 471, *Responding to Hazardous Materials Incidents*.

Additional Readings

Allender, P. J., "A Survey of the Development of Fire Safety Regulations for Railways," *Fire Safety Journal*, Vol. 8, No. 1, 1984, pp. 15-29.

Allender, P. J., "Combustible Material in Passenger Trains," *Fire Safety Journal*, Vol. 8, No. 1, 1984, pp. 29-38.

Allender, P. J., "Specification of Combustible Materials for Passenger Train Design," *Fire and Materials*, Vol. 8, No. 3 (Sept. 1984), pp. 113-124.

Birk, A. M., *Development and Validation of a Mathematical Model of a Rail Tank-Car Engulfed in Fire*, PhD. thesis, Queens University, Kingston, Canada, 1983.

Brooks, J. L., "Heat Activated Alarm Systems for Railroad Boxcars Carrying Explosives," *TN No. N-1512*, U.S. Navy Civil Engineering Laboratory, Port Hueneme, CA, Dec. 1977.

Bukowski, R. W., "Fire Protection Systems for Rail Transportation of Class A Explosives: Interim Report," *NBSIR 80-2170*, National Bureau of Standards, Gaithersburg, MD, Nov. 1980.

Comptroller General of the U.S., *The Federal Approach to Rail Safety Inspection and Enforcement: Time for Change*, U.S. General Accounting Office, Washington, DC, 1982.

Davis, J. S., "All Aboard: Preplanning for Rail Incidents," *Fire Command*, Vol. 56, No. 5 (May 1989), pp. 32-34.

Dee, A. W., "Fire Protection on Trains," *Proceedings* of the Institution of Mechanical Engineers, Part D: Transport Engineering, Vol. 201, No. 3, 1987, pp. 217-227.

Iida, T., Kobayashi, S., and Kenmochi, T., "Facilities of the Seikan Tunnel," *Japanese Railway Engineering*, No. 106 (June 1988), pp. 12-16.

Jameel, H. M., "Rail Rapid Transit Safety Standards: A Feasibility Study," *Report No. UMTA-CA-MT-82-106*, California Public Utilities Commission, San Francisco, CA, 1982.

"Passenger Fire Safety in Transportation Vehicles," *A. D. Little Report No. C-78203*, U.S. Department of Transportation, Washington, DC, May 1975.

Peacock, R. D. and Braun, E., "Fire Tests of Amtrak Passenger Rail Vehicle Interiors", *NBS Tech Note 1193*, National Bureau of Standards, Gaithersburg, MD, May 1984.

"Recommended Fire Safety Practices for Rail Transit Materials Selection," Urban Mass Transit Administration, U.S. Department of Transportation, *Federal Register*, Vol. 47, No. 228, Nov. 26, 1982, p. 53559.

Smith, D. A. "Some Aspects of Fire Safety Design on Railways," *Fire and Materials*, Vol. 8, No. 1 (Mar. 1984), pp. 6-9.

FIXED GUIDEWAY TRANSIT SYSTEMS

Revised by Lawrence M. Engleman

The environment of a rapid transit system lends itself to some peculiar and difficult firesafety problems. Large numbers of people who move through these subterranean enclosures and elevated structures compound the life safety dangers. Fires within subways have attracted national attention over the years due to the danger facing passengers who must evacuate trains through smoke-filled trackways and other emergency exitways.

Among the causes of fire in a mass transit system are mechanical failure of undercar components, high-energy electrical short circuits, accumulation of combustible debris along the trackways and within vent shafts, accumulation of road film and oils on the underside of revenue vehicles, combustible materials in car components, combustible construction of trainways including crossties, and hazards associated with the human factor, such as carelessness, arson, and pranks.

This chapter covers areas in a rapid transit system requiring special attention, including subways, underground stations, and surface-level and elevated transit systems.

SYSTEM CHARACTERISTICS

Although the most serious threat to transit users from fire is found in subways and underground stations, certain basic considerations must be recognized throughout the transit system.

Traction Power

Traction power, or the electrical energy needed to run the trains, may be carried throughout the system by means of a third rail or overhead wiring and is typically a nominal 750 volts DC. For modern transit systems with traction power provided by a third rail, a coverboard of electrical insulating material is installed throughout the system to prevent people from inadvertently coming in contact with the energized rail. The coverboard should be strong enough to hold a 250-lb (113 kg) weight applied at any point without deflection, and should be supported in such a manner as to allow a fire department ladder to rest against it safely. Warning signs should be affixed, as required, to the top of the coverboard in any area that could be accessible to the public.

Disconnect switches should be located strategically throughout the system so traction power can be cut as quickly as possible under emergency conditions. Otherwise, alternate prompt and reliable means for disconnecting power should be provided.

Access/Egress to Stations

When determining required exit capacity, consideration must be given to future occupancy needs. Once a station has been constructed, it becomes very difficult, if not impossible, to place additional stairs or escalators where they will best serve the public. While it is recognized that complying with required exit width may become a major difficulty to designers, a good source of guidance is NFPA 101®, *Life Safety Code*,® as modified by NFPA 130, *Fixed Guideway Transit Systems*.

To establish required exit widths for any structure, it is first necessary to determine the occupancy classification. For example, the State of California, other jurisdictions, and NFPA 101, *Life Safety Code*, have determined that places where people await transportation should be classified as an assembly occupancy. Effective June 1983, however, NFPA 130, *Fixed Guideway Transit Systems*, established requirements for life and firesafety in transit stations, trainways, vehicles, and outdoor vehicle maintenance areas. The dynamic exiting concept in NFPA 130 determines occupancy based on estimated transit patronage waiting in stations and alighting from trains. The transit stations considered in NFPA 130 are only those accommodating passengers and employees of the fixed guideway system and incidental occupancies. Where large numbers of people other than transit patrons are involved, such as where transit stations are incorporated into shopping malls, sports facilities, or other occupancies, NFPA 101 is used to establish exit requirements.

Since rapid transit systems are designed to move people rapidly, most new systems have installed escalators that operate at the rate of 120 ft/min (37 m/min). Plans are being

Lawrence M. Engleman is director of safety for the Maryland Mass Transit Administration (MTA) in Baltimore, MD.

formulated to increase this speed. Escalators now are designed to be fully reversible, depending upon commute conditions. In many instances, escalators will penetrate two or more floor levels to gain access to the intended platform. This can pose special design problems since many designers prefer to maintain an open environment throughout a station complex. Vertical penetration of more than one floor without enclosures has been accomplished in some rapid transit systems by increasing other fire protection components.

When escalators are designed and accepted as required exits, serious study must be given to their usability in evacuating a station under emergency conditions. For example, provisions must be made to stop all platform-bound escalators so that they can be used as stairs. Consideration also must be given to methods of stopping escalators so as to prevent injury to patrons. One possibility is to notify patrons using a recorded public address announcement, which may be activated through the fire alarm system, stating that the escalator will stop within a specified period. This allows patrons to grasp the handrail and obtain a firm footing or may even alert patrons not to board escalators until they have stopped.

Exit Barriers

Rapid transit stations contain two basic areas to separate those individuals who have paid their fare from those who have not paid. These are commonly referred to as paid areas and free areas. Patrons in the free area are able to move directly to the outside without encountering barriers. Patrons within the paid area must go through fare barriers to gain access to the free area. During an emergency evacuation, either all fare barriers should open automatically, allowing patrons to evacuate the station rapidly, or specially designed access gates should be installed for the same purpose. With increased emphasis being directed to handicapped patrons, access gates become more useful in basic station design.

Procedures and methods that allow operators to quickly control or limit the number of patrons allowed into a station in the event of a delay or a malfunction are most important. A public address system which will notify and advise patrons during an emergency or a malfunction also is considered essential.

Many stations are completely closed off by grills or steel doors when a station is secured after normal revenue hours. The installation of small doors in the grills can provide easy access for fire department personnel, as well as serve as an acceptable means of exit for any employees who may be working in the station.

Emergency Procedures

Due to the variety of hazards involved in a rapid transit system, local fire authorities must establish a direct line of communication with the system's top management. Good inspection techniques must be developed, and coordinated emergency response procedures planned. Access points to all parts of the system must be pinpointed, and engine and truck company response patterns tailored to meet special access problems. Information regarding the system, such as floor plans, electrification, vehicle design, structures, fire protection systems, and communications, is needed to plan emergency procedures properly. A wise course for a fire department is to assign one command officer the responsibility of coordinating all the emergency activities required to protect against fires on rapid transit trains, on the right of way, and adjacent to the right of way.

Communication also must extend in the other direction. Fires and other emergencies in adjacent properties may require modified transit operation. In downtown areas, fire suppression activities in nearby buildings can cause water drainage into subways, or flammable liquid spills can endanger below-grade stations. Elevated structures may block fire department access to adjacent buildings.

The Transit Vehicle

The construction and use of the transit vehicle has become a fire and life safety problem. With a reasonable degree of attention, the other elements of the transit system—guideway, stations, wayside equipment, and maintenance facilities—can be designed with an acceptable level of fire protection. Materials and methods of construction can provide a noncombustible, if not fire-resistive, profile. These elements are static, and many solutions for achieving a degree of fire resistance are already in use in related structures, such as buildings and bridges, and in support subsystems, such as elevators, escalators, and electrical and mechanical systems.

Because of economic and comfort considerations, the modern vehicle has made extensive use of manufactured materials. Included in the vehicle are many attractive and serviceable plastics, such as foams, fibers, and other synthetic materials, that are often quite combustible and may emit toxic products of combustion while burning. These problems are not unique to the fixed guideway transit vehicle. Combustible plastics are used in passenger compartments of other modes of transportation, including aircraft, buses, railroad trains, and the family car. However, the transit vehicle can accommodate several thousand people—far more than even a jumbo jet—and it therefore presents the potential for a great loss of life.

A high level of attention must be focused upon the materials and finishes of every item that goes into each transit vehicle, including insulation for propulsion motors and other electrical wiring. Studies of subway fires have shown the transit vehicle to be the principal source of toxic smoke generated by and fuel contributed to, a fire.

Therefore, the transit vehicle is a primary concern in a fire and life safety program for a transit system. Unfortunately, many of the existing fire test methods used to measure performance of materials in fire test conditions have proven inadequate in predicting actual fire performance. A guideline developed by the Urban Mass Transportation Administration deals with the vehicle fire problem and recommends specific test methods and tests to be used. In addition, some transit systems have been able to use a so-called "Spartan" vehicle using fewer combustible or toxic materials. (See Table 4-2.4 of NFPA 130.)

Considering the above, a complete fire risk assessment for new or renovated transit vehicles should be made, including fire propagation resistance, smoke emission, ease of ignition, and rate of heat and smoke release. The total combustible loading of the vehicles should be limited to as low a value as possible. For example, NFPA 130, *Fixed Guideway Transit System*, advises that the combustible loading of the vehicle above the floor should not exceed 45,000 Btu per sq ft (511 Mj/m^2). Values as low as 30,000 Btu per sq ft (341 Mj/m^2) can be achieved.

Newer individual test methods and the appropriate use of test results are part of an overall firesafety effort. One test detailed in NFPA 253, *Critical Radiant Flux of Floor*

Covering Systems Using a Radiant Heat Energy Source, provides a realistic test to evaluate the flame spread on floor covering systems. Existing tests, such as those in NFPA 255, *Surface Burning Characteristics of Building Materials*; NFPA 251, *Fire Tests of Building Construction and Materials*; NFPA 258, *Determining Smoke Generation of Solid Materials*; ASTM E-162; ASTM E-84; and others also can be used if results are interpreted in relation to the transit environment. More appropriate tests are being developed to better predict the performance of materials when subjected to elevated temperatures, especially with respect to the release of toxic products.

Perhaps one of the least appreciated hazards to life safety is the severity of toxic products of combustion. The difficulties of removing a person from the fire environment, particularly in subways, demands extreme care in evaluating materials and their use in composite assemblies. To date, the use of test results related to smoke development, and generalized statements on avoidance of "recognized" materials generating toxic products of combustion, have been the way to address this problem. The development and use of tests for toxicity of materials during fire exposure remains an unanswered need for transit safety.

SUBWAYS

Fires within the confines of a subway system, especially those in trainways, are among the most difficult to extinguish due to limited room in which fire fighters have to operate. Access points for fire personnel, emergency exit locations for passengers, availability of water supply, and ventilation capabilities are among the fundamentals that must be considered in providing adequate safeguards for passengers and facilities for fire fighters coping with emergencies.

A direct liaison between rapid transit authorities and fire officials is essential to keep emergency forces apprised of current conditions in the underground installations. Floor plans of stations and subways must be reviewed continually. Fire protection included in the original system design may have changed, thus requiring fire fighting plans to be updated.

Ventilation

Ventilation of underground subways is of primary importance. Serious study must be given to the removal of smoke under fire conditions. Exiting schemes also must be developed that will allow passengers to exit rapidly into fresh air. Some rapid transit systems have installed fully reversible fans within vent shafts. These are capable of moving large quantities of air by intake or exhaust, thus permitting smoke to be purged from the subway in a predetermined direction so passengers can be evacuated to the nearest station. Ventilation shafts and fans have been placed at each end of an underground station and, in some instances, between stations. When vertical shafts are included in the ventilation criteria, the possibility of flammable liquid spills entering the shaft at street level must be considered. Shafts should terminate in roadways only when absolutely no other alternative exists; adequate sumps must be developed to retain such spills and be equipped with flammable vapor detectors. Electrical equipment that may be installed within shafts and fan rooms should meet the requirements of local authorities for the expected fire exposure.

Access/Egress

Walkways: Primary consideration must be given to the evacuation of large numbers of passengers to safety if a train is stopped between stations. "Safety" could be a station platform or direct access to the open air through vertical exitways. Many older, existing systems have evacuated passengers by having them climb from the train to the trackway, and then walk between the rails on crossties until they reach a vertical exit or station platform. Modern transit systems prefer to have passengers evacuate the train to a walkway constructed along the side of the trackway opposite the third-rail power source. (See Figure 8-36A.) This allows passengers to step directly from the train to the walkway, thereby keeping passengers off the trackway and allowing specially equipped vehicles to respond to train problems.

When trackways are separated by concrete walls and fire doors, the walkway system also provides easy access to a train on the opposite trackway and an acceptable horizontal exit path that remains relatively free of smoke and heat. Obviously, adequate emergency lighting must be provided to allow safe evacuation.

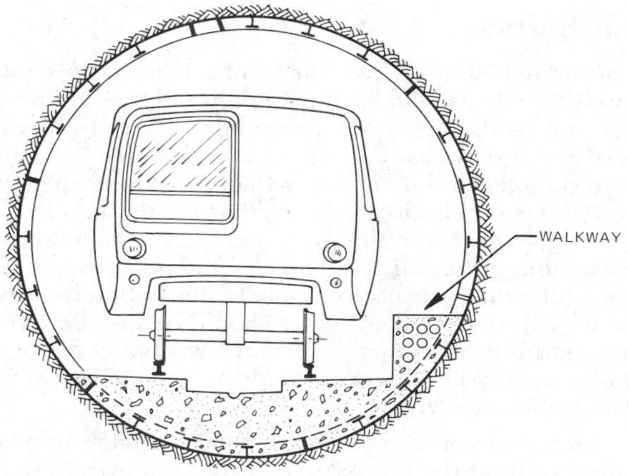

FIG. 8-36A. A sectional view of a single-tube subway tunnel, showing the location of the emergency passenger walkway to the floor of the car.

Tunnel or bore: Many rapid transit systems currently operate underground on trackways that are completely separated from each other by concrete walls and fire doors. (See Figure 8-36B.) As previously mentioned, this concept provides a place of refuge for passengers, as long as adequate train control and planning is practiced. Separation walls should have no less than a 2-hr fire-resistance rating, and openings in them should be protected by $1\frac{1}{2}$-hr fire doors. Cross-passageways should not be more than 800 ft (244 m) apart. Hardware normally used in the installation of fire doors and frames has been found inadequate for the pressures generated by a train moving through the tunnel and for the damp environment found in tunnels. Special study and consideration must be given to the type of door, frame, hinges, locking device, and method of securing the frame to the opening. Sliding fire doors with counterweights require special attention.

Emergency exits: When determining exit requirements from an underground subway system, a number of factors must be considered:

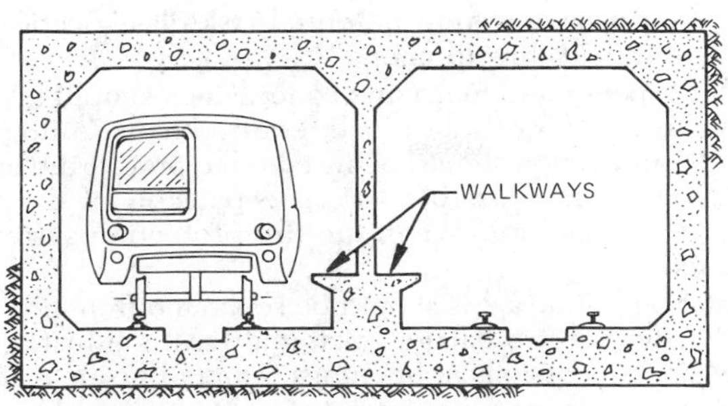

FIG. 8-36B. A sectional view of a subway tunnel having trackways separated from each other by a concrete wall. Openings through the wall, protected by fire doors, can provide an acceptable horizontal exit path from the trackway on which an accident has occurred to the other trackway, which remains relatively free of smoke and heat.

1. Length of train.
2. Depth of trackway below grade.
3. Accessibility to exit at grade.
4. Accessibility to exit at trackway.
5. Time and distance needed for people to exit to surface.
6. Available ventilation and controls.
7. Access to trackway for fire service.

Since unlimited vertical shafts are impractical, NFPA 130, *Fixed Guideway Transit Systems*, allows emergency exit shafts to be placed so that the maximum travel distance does not exceed 1250 ft (381m) in tunnels. The intent and basics of NFPA 101, *Life Safety Code*, as modified by NFPA 130, should be followed as closely as possible in designing the exit stairs. Hatches can be used at the surface, if provisions are made to prevent obstructions that would keep them from opening in an emergency.

Many transit systems have used ventilation shafts as emergency exits by constructing conventional stairways in the shafts. Unless the stairway is completely separated from the vent shaft by 2-hr fire-resistant construction and adequate control of air currents within the bore is maintained, this concept is extremely risky, since smoke and heat may contaminate the vertical exitway.

Under no circumstances should required exitways contain straight, vertical ladders.

Internally illuminated exit signs with two sources of power supply should be installed at the trackway level to direct passengers, and emergency lighting should be provided within the exit enclosure.

Communication

Probably one of the most serious problems encountered during underground emergencies involves communications. Emergency telephones normally are identified throughout the subway system by a distinctive light: most systems designate a blue light for emergency phone locations. Communication from the trackway directly to a central control room is accomplished merely by picking up the instrument. Some systems use the Centrex principle for calls.

Blue light stations identifying the location of emergency telephones also can serve multiple purposes. For example, on the Bay Area Rapid Transit (BART) System headquartered in Oakland, CA, the stations include a third-rail or power-disconnect button, a maintenance jack, a 110-V outlet, and a 20-lb (9 kg) multi-purpose dry chemical extinguisher. The stations are spotted throughout the underground system at 1000-ft (30 m) intervals or in line of sight, whichever is shortest.

Communication through a subway system is sometimes very difficult, particularly radio communication. Many newer subway systems have installed equipment that allows fire department radios to be used in subsurface stations and tunnels. Where this capability does not exist, fire authorities should make every effort to test their communications systems under actual conditions throughout the subway system. Consideration should be given to using hard-wired communication systems which may already exist. Portable radios or emergency phones with a direct line to the central headquarters of the transit system or to train radios are all useful. Every system should have a radio network providing two-way communication connecting personnel on trains and other vehicles anywhere in the system.

Fire Protection in Underground Trainways

One of the principal fire protection devices in fixed guideway transit systems is the standpipe hose system. NFPA 14, *Installation of Standpipe and Hose Systems*, provides good guidance for installations, and Class I or Class III service should be specified.

Standpipes: Standpipes should be located in stations and throughout the underground trainway system. Standpipes in tunnels should be at least 4 in. (101.6 mm) in diameter or sized by hydraulic calculations, and may be of the dry type. Generally speaking, the locations of standpipe outlets are determined by the local fire authorities, with consideration being given to fire department access at tunnel level, available vertical access shafts for emergency forces, availability of street access to the fire department, and siamese connections at grade level.

Some rapid transit systems require that dry standpipe outlets be no more than 200 ft (61 m) apart throughout the underground. Others have determined that maximum separation distances of 300, 400, and 500 ft (91, 122, and 152 m) are acceptable.

Some rapid transit systems place bins or boxes containing 2½-in. (64 mm) hose near dry standpipe outlets and leave the inspection and testing of such hose to rapid transit system personnel. Fire authorities operating under this principle should seriously consider assigning personnel to witness hose inspections and required waterflow testing. In areas where local fire authorities wish to use only their own hose, provisions must be made to transport hose and other equipment to a fire site or to store necessary equipment in tunnels and stations.

Special apparatus: In lieu of the supplying of fire hose required at standpipe stations, some systems have taken innovative measures to ensure that hose is available when needed. BART, for example, with the approval of fire authorities, has removed all fire hose from its subway system with the exception of 1½-in. (38 mm) hose located within stations. In turn, BART has agreed to furnish five fully-equipped, specially-designed fire engines capable of traveling by street or rail to previously designated rendezvous points. The responding fire department would then board the apparatus and go to the fire or emergency location within the underground. Each piece of apparatus includes, as part of its inventory, 1200 ft (366 m) of 2-½ in.

(64 mm) hose and 400 ft (122 m) of 1½-in. (38 mm) hose, as well as nozzles, a portable emergency generator, a power saw, a cutting torch, extension cords, flood lights, demand breathing apparatus, life lines, miscellaneous tools, a high-expansion foam unit and nozzle, a 300-gal (1136 L) water tank, and a small pressure pump.

Fire department operational plans: Fire departments which respond to emergencies in underground systems must be extremely familiar with the layout, access, exit, communications, ventilation, and other special factors which have to be part of an operational plan for both the fire department and the transit system. Such plans must be reviewed and practiced regularly, and all members of the fire department and system employees must be trained to respond appropriately to underground incidents.

Every fire fighter entering an underground system to fight a fire must have self-contained breathing apparatus to meet the requirements of NFPA 1500, *Fire Department Occupational Safety and Health Program*. One of the challenges facing the fire department is how to maintain an adequate supply of replacement air cylinders for members working below grade level. This may require long-duration breathing apparatus and trucks to refill or deliver quantities of SCBA air cylinders.

Fire extinguishers: Fire extinguishers should be placed on board each vehicle. In addition, fire transit extinguishers should be placed near fixed equipment throughout the underground system where ignition sources and/or combustibles exist. Locations should include electrical equipment, sumps, ventilation equipment, and so on. If the blue light or the emergency station is suitably located, one or the other would be a preferred placement for extinguishers. The size and type of the extinguisher to be used is dictated by the size and type of exposure expected.

Drainage: Adequate drainage of water accumulated during a fire requires careful consideration. Fire authorities should be made aware of the underground system's drainage capabilities and recognize that large amounts of water could seriously impair other required rescue operations. When fighting structural fires at street level station entrances or street ventilation grills, fire officers should alert the rapid transit officials that water intrusion into their system may be expected.

Stations

Underground rapid transit stations should be constructed of minimum approved noncombustible materials—that is, Type I, Type II, or combinations thereof—as outlined in NFPA 220, *Types of Building Construction*. Many modern rapid transit systems use reinforced concrete construction for the station's outer shell and protected steel beams, girders, and columns within the shell. This results in a structure with a substantial fire-resistive capability.

Very few fires of major proportions have occurred within stations. A notable exception is the King's Cross Station fire that occurred in London, England, on November 18, 1987. Thirty patrons and one fire fighter were killed in that fire. Many station fires are attributed to poor housekeeping or to electrical fires in escalator machine rooms. The primary fire hazards in underground stations are concessions and trains. Small concessions that sell newspapers and magazines would normally have a low-risk classification, while major concessions, such as restaurants or theaters, would have a high potential risk classification for smoke and heat development.

Newspaper and magazine concessions should be limited in size and must not block required exits. Automatic sprinkler protection should be installed to protect the entire concession area. Possible future expansion of the area should be considered when the fire protection system is designed.

Station public areas should be separated from nontransit areas with a fire barrier having at least a 3-hr fire rating. Major concessions or openings from public areas of the station into existing commercial structures should be protected by fire door assemblies having a 3-hr fire protection rating. Even if the commercial activity and the station are owned by the rapid transit system, good separation between the two areas is needed. Fire barriers can be established by installing fire doors or automatic fire extinguishing systems to prevent fire and smoke spread from the commercial occupancy into the station or from the station into the commercial occupancy. Before any openings into a rapid transit system are made, the existing conditions on both sides of the proposed opening must be reviewed carefully so an effective fire protection plan can be developed.

Protection for Underground Stations

An underground rapid transit station may be compared to a multiple-basement structure, except that a rapid transit station generally has a low fire-loading factor when compared to a commercial basement. Strict application of building or fire code requirements may cause exceptionally high construction costs that are not necessarily justified. If minimal combustible storage or concession areas are involved, large, open public areas may be left with little or no risk of fire involvement. If such is the case, limiting automatic fire protection systems to those areas containing combustibles and designing the systems for possible expansion may have some merit, although the limitations of partial protection must be clearly understood.

Automatic sprinkler systems: All areas in transit stations that are used for concessions, storage, and fare collection, including other similar areas with combustible loadings, as well as the steel truss area of all escalators in a single-entry station should be protected by automatic sprinklers equipped with flow alarms and supervision. Trainways are excluded. NFPA 13, *Installation of Sprinkler Systems*, should be used for guidance. Other approved fire extinguishing systems, such as halon systems in train control rooms, could also be used in lieu of the automatic sprinkler system, but only with the approval of the authority having jurisdiction.

Deluge systems: Since most train fires start in under-car equipment, and train operators are instructed to bring trains with fires onboard to stations for passenger evacuation, if possible, many newer systems have opted for under-car deluge systems. These systems consist of fixed piping connected to a water supply, with open sprinkler heads located between the rails. They are activated manually from the station attendant's booth or at the ends of the platform.

Over-car deluge systems are designed to create a water curtain between a burning train and the platform. They can be activated automatically by heat detectors in the trainway or manually as described above. Examples of both types of deluge installations are found in the Baltimore Metro System.

Emergency communications: Subway stations typically do not have a traditional fire alarm system with pull stations and bells. Instead, the public address system is used to alert and direct passengers in the event of an emergency. Passengers can report emergencies through emergency voice alarm reporting devices located on the platform and throughout the station. Emergency communication systems must conform to NFPA 72A, *Local Protective Signaling Systems for Guards Tour, Fire Alarm, and Supervisory Service.*

Fire detection systems: All nonpublic areas commonly classified as support or ancillary areas, if not protected by an automatic fire suppression system, should be fully protected by a fire detection system conforming to NFPA 72D, *Proprietary Protective Signaling Systems.* Listed smoke detectors are preferable, although rate-of-rise detectors may be used if authorized by the concerned fire authority.

It is good practice to provide supervision for all fire detection and automatic fire suppression systems. Supervisory signals should be received at the system's command center and annunciated by zone at the station agent's booth or kiosk.

Wet standpipes: Where separate standpipe and automatic sprinkler systems are provided, wet standpipes usually are supplied by a piping system that is separate and distinct from that used for automatic sprinkler systems. Fire department siamese connections, properly labeled and installed at grade level, allow the fire department to supply additional water to either system.

Fire hose cabinets may contain 1½-in. (38 mm) and 2½-in. (64 mm) control valves, at the discretion of the local authority having jurisdiction, as recommended in NFPA 14, *Installation of Standpipe and Hose Systems.* A maximum of 100 ft (30 m) of attached 1½-in. (38 mm) hose with nozzle is included in the cabinet. In addition, 2½-in. (64 mm) hose and a spanner wrench may be stored in cabinets for use by the fire department. A suitable fire extinguisher may also be placed in the cabinet. To reduce pilferage of fire equipment, cabinets should be locked and a breakaway glass panel installed to allow ready access under emergency conditions. Some rapid transit systems have installed intrusion alarms, which send a signal to the station agent if a fire hose cabinet has been opened.

SURFACE OR ABOVEGROUND GUIDEWAYS AND STATIONS

Generally fires in transit systems at or above grade are no more difficult to combat than any other type of fire at grade. Primary consideration always must be given to the traction power—even though assurance is given that the power has been shut off, fire department personnel should operate under the assumption that the third rail or overhead wire is still hot.

Although fires in trains on surface track or aerial guideways present a slightly less serious exposure to the public, certain basic considerations, such as means of escape from elevated trainways, must be addressed in design. As in all other configurations of rapid transit, communication is paramount in any emergency operation. The ability to direct emergency forces to the scene of an incident and to place the system in a safe condition for access is necessary for patrons and emergency personnel.

Access to a trainway also may require special provisions. Locating trainways in a joint corridor with a railroad or freeway may limit access for long distances of the trainway. Trainways extending from population centers through undeveloped areas sometimes extend where surface roads and water mains do not exist. Trainways in congested areas, trainways that are elevated to unusual heights, and trainways in other sections not accessible to emergency vehicles, such as elevating platforms or paramedic units, could create other problems. Construction of trainways also may cause problems of fire exposure and access to adjacent structures. For example, an elevated trainway above existing city streets and adjacent to existing buildings may interfere with fire department operations at those buildings.

Similar problems may exist at stations. However, permanent exits provide both patron evacuation and emergency personnel access. Recent systems have incorporated stations in the lower elevations of high-rise buildings or within mall complexes that have divergent occupancies. In these cases, detailed plans for coordination and compatible design are necessary.

Stations that can be considered to be buildings would normally be reviewed through normal code procedures. If a transit system passes through more than one jurisdiction, particularly if different basic codes apply, development of a common set of requirements is desirable to achieve uniformity throughout the system.

The subject of trainways, however, is not usually addressed in most existing building codes. Items that should be considered during a plan review of a guideway would include:

1. Designated mileage markers to provide a response location for fire personnel.
2. Locations where overhead trainways may intersect with known street locations.
3. Access gates allowing patrons to exit the system under fire department direction.
4. Availability of wayside communications allowing the fire department to communicate directly with the system's command center.
5. Locations of substations, switching stations, gap breaker stations, or other major electrical installations of concern to local fire authorities.

BIBLIOGRAPHY

NFPA Codes, Standards, and Recommended Practices

Reference to the following NFPA codes, standards, and recommended practices will provide further information on fixed gateway transit systems discussed in this chapter. (See the latest *NFPA Catalog* for availability of current editions of the following documents.)

NFPA 10, *Portable Fire Extinguishers.*

NFPA 13, *Installation of Sprinkler Systems.*

NFPA 14, *Installation of Standpipe and Hose Systems.*

NFPA 30, *Flammable and Combustible Liquids Code.*

NFPA 72A, *Local Protective Signaling Systems for Guard's Tour, Fire Alarm, and Supervisory Service.*

NFPA 72D, *Proprietary Protective Signaling Systems.*

NFPA 72E, *Standard on Automatic Fire Detectors.*

NFPA 101, *Life Safety Code.®*

NFPA 130, *Fixed Guideway Transit Systems.*

NFPA 220, *Types of Building Construction.*

NFPA 251, *Fire Tests of Building Construction and Materials.*

NFPA 253, *Critical Radiant Flux of Floor Covering Systems Using a Radiant Heat Energy Source.*

NFPA 255, *Surface Burning Characteristics of Building Materials.*

NFPA 258, *Determining Smoke Generation of Solid Materials.*

NFPA 259, *Potential Heat of Building Materials.*

NFPA 1500, *Fire Department Occupational Safety and Health Program.*

ASTM Publications

Available from American Society of Testing Materials, 1916 Race St., Philadelphia, PA.

ASTM E83-81a, *Surface Burning Characteristics of Building Materials.*

ASTM E119-82, *Fire Tests of Building Construction.*

ASTM E136-81, *Standard Method of Test for Noncombustibility of Elementary Materials.*

ASTM C542-78, *Vertical Fire Test Procedures* (FAA-FAR 853).

Additional Readings

Albert, H., "Preventive Fire Protection for Underground Trains Operated by the Hamburger Hochbahn AG," *Fire Safety Journal*, Vol. 8, No. 1, 1984, pp. 63-72.

Allender, P. J., "A Survey of the Development of Fire Safety Regulations for Railways," *Fire Safety Journal*, Vol. 8, No. 1, 1984, pp. 15-29.

Allender, P. J., "Combustible Material in Passenger Trains," *Fire Safety Journal*, Vol. 8, No. 1, 1984, pp. 29-38.

Allender, P. J., "Controling Fire Behavior of Materials on London Underground," *Fire Safety Journal*, Vol. 8, No. 1, 1984, pp. 39-46.

Best, R. L. and Engleman, L. M., "Fact Sheet - King's Cross Station Fire," *Fire Command*, January 1988.

Birky, M. M., *et al.*, "Measurements and Observations of the Toxicological Hazard of Fire in a Metrorail Interior Mock-Up," *NBSIR 75-966*, National Bureau of Standards, Gaithersburg, MD, Feb. 1976.

Braun, E., "A Fire Hazard Evaluation of the Interior of WMATA Metrorail Cars," *NBSIR 75-97*, National Bureau of Standards, Gaithersburg, MD, Dec. 1975.

Braun, E., "Fire Hazard Evaluation of BART Vehicles," *NBSIR 78-1421*, National Bureau of Standards, Gaithersburg, MD, Mar. 1978.

Burnett, J., "Fire Safety Concerns for Rail Rapid Transit Systems," *Fire Safety Journal*, Vol. 8, No. 1, 1984, pp. 3-8.

Cox, G., Chitty R., and Kumar, S., "Fire Modeling and the King's Cross Fire Investigation," *Fire Safety Journal*, 1989, pp. 103-106.

Directory of U.S. Department of Transportation Fire Research (DOT), Report No. DOT-TSC-OST-80-1, Department of Transportation, Washington, DC, 1979.

Electrical Insulation Fire Characteristics, Vol. 1, Flammability Tests, Report No. UMTA-MA-06-0025-79-1, I, Urban Mass Transportation Administration, DOT, Washington, DC, 1979.

Electrical Insulation Fire Characteristics, Vol. 2, Toxicity, Urban Report No. UMTA-MA-06-0025-79-1, II, Urban Mass Transportation Administration, DOT, Washington, DC, 1979.

Engleman, L. M. and Shives, W. J., "Fire Safety Features of the Baltimore Metro," American Public Transit Association Rapid Rail Transit Conference, June 1984.

Fennell, D, *Investigation into the King's Cross Underground Fire*, Her Majesty's Stationary Office, London, November 1988.

"Fire Down Below," *Railway Gazette International*, Vol. 144, No. 1, 1988, pp. 27-28.

Fire Experience and Exposure in Fixed-Guideway Transit Systems, American Iron and Steel Institute, Washington, DC, 1980.

"Fire Safety in Underground Railway Systems," *Fire Surveyor*, Vol. 18, No. 1, (Feb. 1989), pp. 42-43.

Fruin, J. J., *Pedestrian Planning and Design*, rev. ed., Elevator World, Mobile, AL, 1987.

Gooden, W. E. and Troy, J. J., "Metropolitan Atlanta Rapid Transit Authority-Systems Safety, Fire Protection, and Code Documentation for Stations," *Proceedings* Third International System Safety Conference, Washington, DC, Oct. 1977, pp. 517-527.

Gossard, W. H., "Some Major Accident Investigations of Fires In Underground Rail Rapid Transit Systems," *Fire Safety Journal*, Vol. 8, No. 1, 1984, pp. 9-14.

Heffels, P., "Improving Fire Protection in Tunnels for Commuter Rail Traffic," *Tunnelling Underground Space Technology*, Vol. 2, No. 3, 1987, pp. 311-314.

Hill, R. G. and Johnson, G. R., "Fire Detection, Extinguishment, and Material Tests for an Automated Guideway Transit Vehicle," *Report No. FAA-NA-76-52*, Federal Aviation Administration. Available through Natioinal Technical Information Service, Springfield, VA, 1976.

Identification of the Fire Threat in Urban Transit Vehicles, Report No. UMTA-MA-06-0051-80-1, Urban Mass Transportation Administration, Department of Transportation, June 1980.

Jenkins, C. E., "BART Experience with New Seat Materials," *Journal of Consumer Product Flammability*, Vol. 9, No. 1 (Mar. 1982).

Julga, G. "Problems of Operational Planning for Fires Connected with an Underground Rail Transport System—The Hamburg High Speed Railway," *Fire Safety Journal*, Vol. 8, No. 1, 1984, pp. 53-62.

"King's Cross Disaster was Foreseeable in Law," *Fire Prevention*, No. 212, (Sept. 1988), pp. 18-21.

Londregan, R. P., "Life Safety in Underground Rail Systems: The Australian Effort," *SFPE TR 83-3*, Society of Fire Protection Engineers, Boston, MA, 1983.

Metsch, W. W., "Meeting Design Need to Control Subway Environment," *Specifying Engineer*, Mar. 1976, pp.86-91.

Moore, W. L., "Report of the Board of Inquiry on the Fire in the Transbay Tube of the San Francisco Bay Area Rapid Transit District on Jan. 17, 1979," Mar. 5, 1979.

Peacock, R. D., "Fire Safety Guidelines for Vehicles in a Downtown People Mover System," *NBSIR 78-1586*, National Bureau of Standards, Gaithersburg, MD, Jan. 1979.

Peacock, R. D. and Braun, E., "Fire Tests of Amtrak Passenger Rail Vehicle Interiors," *NBS Tech Note 1193*, National Bureau of Standards, Gaithersburg, MD, May 1984.

Rail Transit Committee, *Guidelines For Design of Rapid Transit Facilities*, American Public Transit Association, Washington, DC, 1979.

"Recommended Emergency Preparedness Guidelines for Rapid Transit Systems," *Report Number UMTA-MA-06-0152-85-1*, Urban Mass Transportation Administration, Department of Transportation, Washington, DC, March, 1985.

"Recommended Fire Safety Practices for Rail Transit Materials Selection," Urban Mass Transit Administration, DOT, *Federal Register*, Vol. 47, No. 228, Nov. 26, 1982, p. 53559.

Subway Environmental Design Handbook, Vol. 1, "Principles and Applications," 2nd ed., 1976. Associated Engineers—A Joint Venture, Parsons, Brinckerhoff, Duade, Douglas, Inc., Deleuw, Cather and Company; Kaiser Engineers under the direction of Transit Development Corporation, Inc.

Thomas, A. A., "A Recent Incident on the London Underground," *Fire Safety Journal*, Vol. 8, No. 1, 1984, pp. 47-52.

Troy, J. J., "Fire Protection Provisions for Rapid Transit Systems," *Fire Journal*, Vol. 70, No. 1, (Jan. 1976) pp. 13-17.

Troy, J. J., "Fire Protection for Rapid Transit Systems," *Fire International*, Vol. 5, No. 55, (Mar. 1977).

MARINE

Revised by Marjorie M. Murtagh

According to United States Coast Guard statistics, more than 15 million pleasure and small commercial boats were registered in the United States in 1983. Of that number, 5,569 were involved in accidents that caused the deaths of 1241 persons. A total of 427 of those accidents, in which 12 persons were killed, were due to fire or explosion. The same 5569 boating accidents caused 2913 injuries, 232 of which resulted from fire or explosion. These same accidents resulted in property damage of nearly 16 million dollars.

Marine fire hazards, including those on small pleasure craft, small commercial boats, and commercial vessels, are discussed in this chapter. The first four parts cover pleasure and small commercial craft; large commercial vessels are the subject of the balance of the chapter.

Additional information about extinguishing systems suitable for use on vessels can be found in Section 5, Chapter 17, "Carbon Dioxide and Application Systems"; Section 5, Chapter 18, "Halogenated Agents and Systems"; and Section 5, Chapter 23, "Selection, Operation, Distribution, and Maintenance of Fire Extinguishers."

PLEASURE AND SMALL COMMERCIAL BOAT HULLS

Hulls of pleasure and small commercial boats must be arranged so that all compartments are as accessible as practicable. It must be possible to escape from accommodation spaces going forward or aft. Escape hatches are to be unobstructed and adequate for the designed purpose. Engine compartments should be separated from accommodation spaces by bulkheads and/or barriers that will serve as effective fire barriers and minimize the escape of fire extinguishing media discharged in that space. Congestion of engine compartments is unsafe, since it discourages adequate inspection and maintenance. The addition of auxiliary machinery increases ventilation requirements.

Marjorie M. Murtagh serves as chief of the Fire Protection Section for the United States Coast Guard's Office of Marine Safety, Security and Environmental Protection. Ms. Murtagh heads the delegation for the United States at the International Maritime Organization's Sub-Committee on Fire Protection.

Materials

A wide variety of construction materials, such as aluminum, steel, ferrocement, fiberglass-reinforced plastic, and wood, can be used for the construction of a hull, bulkheads, and superstructures. The choice usually is determined by the hull type, size, intended service, and cost. Where flammable materials, such as wood or fiberglass-reinforced plastic are used, fire-retardant coatings suitable for marine service may be used. In the case of fiberglass materials, fire-retardant resins may also be used. However, fire-retardant resins may reduce the structural strength of the laminate.

Ventilation

Ventilation, which is defined as the positive changing of air by natural or mechanical means within a compartment, may occur by introducing fresh air to dilute any contaminated air or by locally exhausting the contaminated air. Ventilation cannot be relied upon to remove vapors from liquid leakage of gasoline. In fact, in the presence of liquid leakage, ventilation actually may help create an explosive mixture. Natural ventilation only works when there is a wind blowing, and the major factor causing air movement inside the hull is the shape and location of the superstructure or, in the case of runabouts, the position of the windshield.

Liquefied petroleum gas (LP-Gas) and compressed natural gas (CNG) are more likely to jump bulkheads and permeate all spaces in a boat than gasoline is, and they will fill any space in which they are released. CNG can be released with overhead vents but, like LP-Gas, will tend to fill any compartment in which it is released. In boats with diesel engines, the ventilation system, in addition to providing sufficient air for proper engine operation, should be designed to help control compartment temperature.

Lightning Protection

Lightning protection can be provided on a boat if the boat has a mast on which a lightning conductor can be installed. For the most effective protection, the mast should be tall enough that an imaginary line drawn at a 45-degree angle from the tip of a pointed lightning rod at the top of the mast will not intersect any part of the boat. From the pointed lightning rod, a number 6 AWG or 8 AWG copper conductor or an equivalent conductor should be led as straight as possible to a ground plate at least 1 sq ft (0.09 m^2) in area. Large metallic masses near the lightning ground conductor should be connected to the conductor to prevent side flashes.

On a sailboat, all shrouds and stays should be led directly to ground. Some metal-rod-type radio telephone antennas may help, if a suitable lightning arrester or gap is provided at all loading coils. The dc bonding ground system and the ac grounding system are not specifically designed to dissipate lightning currents, but they can help minimize damage from side flashes.

Illustrations of proper lightning protection appear in Figures 8-37A through 8-37D. In the cabin cruiser illustrated in Figure 8-37B, adequate lightning protection is afforded only by the grounded antenna equipped with a lightning arrester or gap on the loading coil.

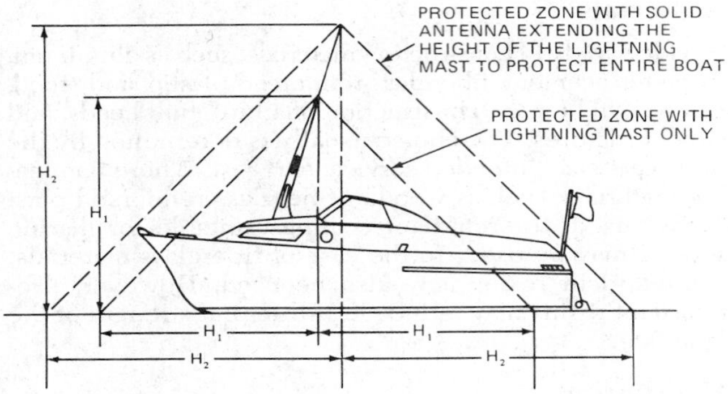

FIG. 8-37A. Proper lightning protection for a boat with a mast not more than 50 ft (15 m) above the water.

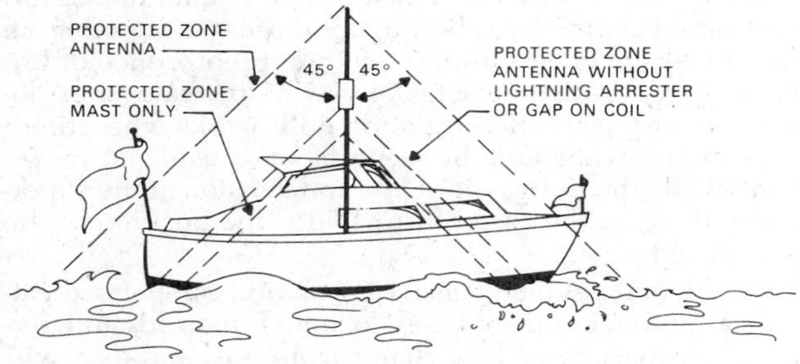

FIG. 8-37B. Diagram of a boat in which the radio antenna is used as part of the lightning protection system.

PLEASURE AND SMALL COMMERCIAL BOAT INSTALLATION AND EQUIPMENT

Engines

Marine gasoline and diesel engines may be cooled directly by sea water, with fresh water, with a heat exchanger, or by air. Liquid-cooled main engines use water-jacketed blocks, heads, and exhaust manifolds, and the cooling water is circulated by an engine drive pump. Fresh-water-cooled gasoline engines operate more efficiently at about 180°F

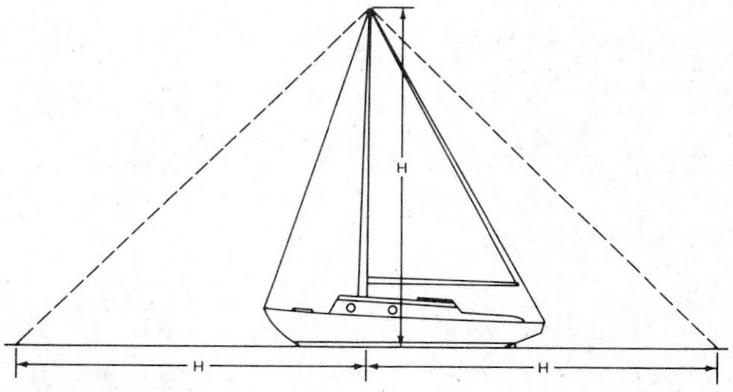

FIG. 8-37C. Proper lightning protection for a small sailboat with a mast not more than 50 ft (15 m) above the water.

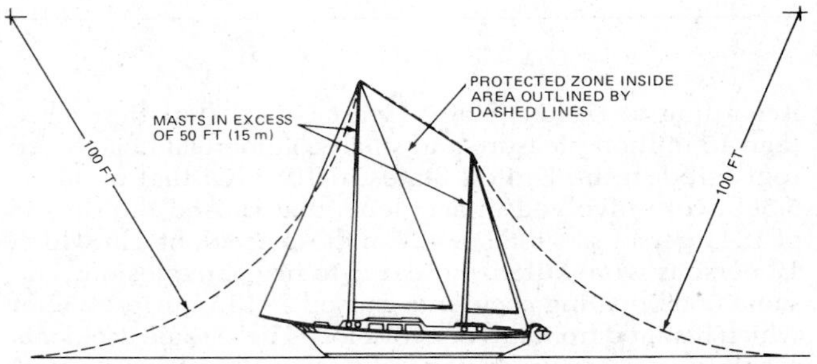

FIG. 8-37D. Proper lightning protection for a boat with masts more than 50 ft (15 m) above the water. Protection is based on a lightning striking distance of 100 ft (30 m).

(82°C), while salt-water engines must operate at a less-efficient 140°F (60°C) to prevent excessive salt precipitation in the block, head, and manifold. For water-cooled engines, gages that indicate cooling water discharge temperature and lubricating oil pressure must be located at the helm position(s). It is recommended that a marine strainer be provided at the raw water intake for direct seawater-cooled engines and engines using heat exchanger cooling systems. Air-cooled engines are not recommended, but, if used in an enclosed space, separate ducts must be provided for engine cooling, and a warning device must be provided to warn of excessive temperatures.

In addition to the engine cooling and ventilation system, the engine space must meet normal engine space ventilation requirements. Updraft and sidedraft carburetors must be equipped with enclosed drip collectors so no liquid fuel escapes to the bilges. The carburetor must have an approved backfire flame arrester. Diaphragm fuel pumps must be designed and installed to prevent the release of fuel to the bilge in case of diaphragm failure. All electrical equipment in the engine space must be ignition-protected. Diesel engines require the use of efficient fuel filters and water separators to prevent damage to the high-pressure fuel injection system.

Fuel Systems

In aircraft and land vehicles, any liquid fuel leakage can be drained by gravity to prevent accumulation; this is not possible in a boat. Because both liquid and fuel vapor will accumulate in a boat, the fuel system must be designed to resist vibration, shock, corrosion, and chemical deterioration. The system also must be kept liquid- and vapor-tight to the hull interior at all times. All parts of the fuel system should be capable of withstanding exposure to free-burning gasoline for at least 2½ minutes without fuel leakage; that fire resistance is not required if the total leakage is less than 5 oz (150 mL) when the fuel line is cut at any point. The fuel system must be electrically bonded to ground, from the fill pipe on deck to the engine, to dissipate static electrical charges.

Diesel fuel systems require the installation of efficient fuel filters and water separators to prevent dirt or water from reaching the high-pressure injector fuel system. Diesel fuel systems have a fuel return line from the engine to the fuel tank which must meet the same requirements as the fuel feed line to the engine. The fuel in the return line is heated and will gradually raise the temperature of the fuel in the tank. Although diesel fuel does not, at normal temperatures, vaporize and create an explosive air-fuel mixture in the way that gasoline does, leaking diesel fuel has a greater tendency to accumulate and create a fire hazard.

Appliances

Open-flame devices are more liable to be misused inadvertently than any other item of boat equipment involving fire risk. It is imperative that such items be designed specifically for marine use and installed to minimize personal and physical hazards. Open-flame devices must be labeled for marine use, and printed instructions for their proper installation, operation, and maintenance must be furnished by the manufacturer. A durable and permanently legible instruction sign covering safe operation and maintenance must be provided. The sign should be installed on, or adjacent to, the appliance where it may be read quickly.

Coal-, charcoal-, and wood-burning stoves should be installed on a hollow tile base or mounted on legs providing a clearance of at least 5 in. (127 mm) to the deck. In addition, the deck must be effectively insulated with a noncombustible material or sheathing.

Continuously burning pilot lights are not permitted on any appliance. Combustion chamber heaters may be used only if the combustion air is completely separated from the atmosphere of the boat.

Liquefied Petroleum Gas and Compressed Natural Gas Systems

In the interest of safety, it is important that the properties of both liquefied petroleum gas (LP-Gas) and compressed natural gas (CNG) be understood. At ambient temperature, petroleum gas can be liquefied and is stored in containers having a rated working pressure of not less than 250 psig (1724 kPa). Natural gas, on the other hand, cannot be liquefied at ambient temperature. In order to package a sufficient usable quantity for the consumer, it is stored at high pressures in cylinders having a rated working pressure of over 2000 psig (13 790 kPa). Both LP-Gas and CNG, being free gases, are miscible in air. If released in an enclosed space, they will diffuse throughout the compartment.

The physical properties of each gas are very different. The hydrocarbon constituents of petroleum gas are heavier than air and, if released from the container, will settle. Natural gas, on the other hand, is lighter than air and will rise if released. If either gas is released in a confined space aboard a vessel, however, this difference is of little comfort, since it is very possible in either case that an explosive mixture could develop, and a source of ignition is all that would be needed to cause an explosion. In recognition of this, NFPA 302, *Pleasure and Commercial Motor Craft,* stipulates that the containers and regulators of either LP-Gas or CNG be located on the open deck, cabin top, outside of cockpits, and so on, and that they be protected by a housing vented to open air near the top and bottom. If construction or design of the motor craft prevents this, then the container and regulator must be mounted in a locker or housing that is vapor-tight to the hull interior and above the waterline in an open cockpit. NFPA 302 also covers the method of venting the locker or housing.

NFPA 302, *Pleasure and Commercial Motor Craft,* further requires that the distribution lines for either system be continuous lengths of tubing, except where a joint is needed to feed each appliance. Lines must be secured against vibration, protected against abrasion whenever they pass through decks or bulkheads, protected from physical damage, and accessible for inspection.

Marine gas-consuming appliances should not use pilot lights, but ovens may have flame control, provided the flame is totally off when the oven control is off. It is recommended that all burners have thermal fuel cutoff devices to prevent gas flow when the flame is extinguished for any reason.

It is important that the gas system be checked for leaks at least twice a month or when the system is serviced or the container changed. NFPA 302, *Pleasure and Commercial Water Craft,* outlines the following procedure to check for leaks:

> "With the appliance valves closed and all other valves open, note pressure on the gage. Close container valve. The pressure should remain constant for at least 10 min. If pressure drops, locate leakage by application of soapy water solution at all connections. Repeat test for each container in multicontainer systems. NEVER USE FLAME TO CHECK FOR LEAKS. NEVER USE SOAP CONTAINING AMMONIA."

If a leak detection device is installed, the above instructions should be modified accordingly.

Electrical Systems

Both low-voltage direct current (dc) electrical systems and 120/230 alternating current (ac) systems should always be of the two-wire type with insulated conductors to and from the source of power and to all accessories.

Direct current electrical systems may be grounded or ungrounded, but ungrounded systems are rarely used. Although an ungrounded system requires that the cranking motor, alternator, and all accessories, including engine accessories, be of the two-wire ungrounded type, such equipment is not readily available. A grounded dc electrical system is actually wired exactly like an ungrounded system except at the engine, where the accessories use the engine block as a common ground. Since the engine is also the common ground point for the entire system, using the engine block as a common ground does not result in any stray current flow from the propeller or shaft connected to that engine. To maintain this condition in twin-screw boats, it is necessary to connect the two engines with a heavy conductor capable of carrying the maximum cranking motor current.

To protect against stray current leakage, grounded dc electrical systems are always connected so the engine block is connected to the battery negative terminal, making the propeller shaft and propellers cathodic if stray current leakage is encountered. If stray current leakage occurs, the underwater parts connected to the cathodic side of the circuit are protected, and the anodic items are subject to accelerated corrosion.

Alternating current electrical systems on a boat may be powered from either a shore power outlet on the dock or by an onboard ac generator. A switch prevents both sources from being used simultaneously. The shore power current-carrying conductors, including the shore-grounded neutral conductor, are never grounded on the boat, but the grounded neutral of the onboard generator may be connected to the boat ground. Only the shore safety grounding wire, which is connected to the noncurrent-carrying parts of the system, is grounded on shore and on the boat. Because of the wet environment, shock hazard is substantially more severe on a boat than on shore. Accordingly, the safety grounding wire is very important, although it can cause accelerated corrosion of any exposed anodic materials, such as aluminum or steel. This problem occurs when the boat is docked at a marina where many boats are connected to the same grounding wire.

Because of interboat corrosion, aluminum, steel, and inboard-outdrive boats with aluminum alloy outdrives must be wired in a special manner to avoid this problem. Such boats must use an isolation transformer to transfer power from the shore to the boat, or a device called an isolator must be installed in series with the grounding wire from shore. The isolation transformer transfers the electrical power, but current-carrying conductors on the boat have no relationship to earth ground. The shore grounding wire is stopped at the transformer core so that no electrical connection exists between the boat with an isolation transformer and any other boat. The isolator will pass alternating electrical current to allow the grounding wire to function as intended as a protection from electrical shock; the isolator also effectively blocks dc galvanic currents from flowing on the same wire. The isolator, therefore, breaks the dc connection between adjacent boats.

Fire Extinguishers

The fire extinguishment potentials of portable fire extinguishers are normally evaluated by testing laboratories. The U.S. Coast Guard also classifies portable fire extinguishers based on the Underwriters Laboratories Inc. (UL) classification of fires, but uses a different method to indicate extinguishment potentials. These designations are shown in Table 8-37A.

PLEASURE AND SMALL COMMERICAL BOAT OPERATIONS

General Maintenance

Operation and maintenance of pleasure and small commercial boats consists mainly of good housekeeping. The boat must be kept "shipshape" at all times. Clean waste and rags should be kept in covered metal containers, and used waste and rags should be kept in separate covered metal containers. Dirty waste and rags should be properly disposed of each time the boat is docked. Flammable paint and varnish removers must be used with caution and only in well-ventilated areas. When repainting interior areas, fire-retardant paint should be used. Unprotected electric lights or open flames should not be taken into areas of possible vapor accumulation, and gasoline or other flammable liquid used for cleaning, including paint brushes, should not be used in such areas. Ventilation ducts and exhaust blowers must be maintained at top efficiency.

Good maintenance and sensible fuel system operation are probably the most important fire prevention duties for a boat owner. Gasoline vapors are heavier than air and will not escape from low-lying cockpits such as bilges or tank bottoms unless drawn or forced out. Atmospheric concentrations of gasoline vapor as low as 1.4 percent and as high as 7.6 percent are flammable. The entire system, including tanks, piping, vent lines, and other accessories, must be checked frequently for leaks or evidence of corrosion. Connections must be kept tight. Fuel carried on board outside of the fixed fuel system should be stored safely and stowed in listed or approved containers or in portable tanks.

Fueling

Utmost care must be exercised during fueling operations. Some general guidelines to be observed during fueling operations are:

1. Fueling should never be undertaken at night, except under well-lighted conditions.
2. Smoking must be forbidden on board and near fueling operations.

TABLE 8-37A. ***Number and Distribution of Fire Extinguishers***

Type of Boat	Class of Extinguishers[1]	Minimum Required	Recommended Locations
Open boats under 16 ft (5 m)	B-I	1	Helmsman's position
Open boats over 16 ft (5 m)	B-I	2	Helmsman's position and passenger space
Boats under 26 ft (8 m)	B-I	2	Helmsman's position and cabin
Boats 26–40 ft (8 to 12 m)	B-I	3	Engine compartment, helmsman's position, and galley[3]
Boats 40–65 ft (12 to 20 m)	B-I	4[2]	Engine compartment, helmsman's position, crew quarters, and galley[3]
Boats 65–75 ft (20 to 23 m)	B-I		Engine compartment, helmsman's position, crew quarters, and galley [3]
Boats 75–100 ft (23 to 30 m)	B-I	6[2]	Engine compartment, helmsman's position, crew quarters, and galley[3]

[1] One of the required extinguishers shall additionally have the capability of extinguishing Class A fires.

[2] If more than three B-I units are recommended, the extinguishing capacity may be made up of a smaller number of larger units, provided each recommended location is protected with an extinguisher readily accessible, e.g., 3 B-II units may be used in lieu of 4, 5, or 6 of the smaller B-I units.

[3] Extinguishers recommended for "engine compartment" should not be located inside such compartment but near an entrance to the compartment unless someone is normally present in the compartment.

3. Before opening tanks, the following precautions should be observed:
   a. All engines, motors, and fans should be shut down.
   b. All open flames should be extinguished.
   c. All ports, windows, doors, and hatches should be closed.
   d. The quantity of fuel to be taken aboard should be determined before the start of the fueling operation.
4. The fuel delivery nozzle should be in contact with the fill pipe before delivery of the fuel is begun. This contact should be continuously maintained until the flow has stopped. There is a serious hazard from static discharge if this rule is not followed.
5. Tanks should not be completely filled. A minimum of 2 percent of the tank space should be allowed for expansion, and this space allowance should be increased to 6 percent or more if the fuel being taken aboard is below 32°F (0°C). To simplify, do not fill the tank full.
6. After the fuel flow has stopped:
   a. The fill cap should be secured tightly.
   b. Any spillage should be wiped up completely and absorbent material disposed of on shore.
   c. Ventilate all spaces and check for gasoline vapors before starting any engines or operating any appliances.

Storage Between Voyages

Before a boat is stored, even for a short period of time, several precautionary actions should be taken. First, a thorough inspection should be made of the entire vessel. All combustible trash and rags should be removed, as well as painting materials and other nonessential flammable liquids. Fuel lines for both engines and appliances should be secured at both ends. Bilges should be inspected and pumped dry. Shaft logs and rudder bearings should be checked and tightened if necessary. All through-hull fitting valves should be closed, except scuppers that permit drainage of rain water. Batteries should be checked and all electrical services, except automatic bilge pumps, secured. When maximum ventilation is necessary, locker doors, drawers, and bilge hatches should be secured in a partially opened position.

NFPA BOATING STANDARDS

Requirements relating to powered boats are contained in NFPA 302, *Pleasure and Commercial Motor Craft*. These requirements are intended to prevent fire and explosion due to fuel leakage. Among the subjects covered are hull arrangement, ventilation and lightning protection; engines and their exhaust systems; fuel systems; cooking, heating, and auxiliary appliances; electrical systems; and fire protection equipment.

Firesafety requirements for areas used for the construction, repair, storage, launching, berthing, or fueling of small craft are contained in NFPA 303, *Marinas and Boatyards*. Among the subjects covered are fire protection, berthing and storage facilities, operational hazards, and electrical wiring and equipment.

OTHER ORGANIZATIONS CONTRIBUTING TO BOATING SAFETY

The American Boat and Yacht Council, Inc.

The Council was established in 1954 so that the knowledge, experience, and skills of technicians in the boating industry could be applied to the development of recommended practices and engineering standards for improving and advancing the safe design, construction, equipage, and maintenance of small craft. A cooperative working relationship exists between the Council and NFPA insofar as fire protection of motor craft is concerned. Consistency of requirements is a mutual goal.

The National Association of Marine Surveyors

This organization includes professional marine surveyors dedicated to dissemination of information concerning current standards, new materials and their application in the marine field, and control of new hazardous materials within the scope of marine surveyors' operations.

Underwriters Laboratories Inc.

Underwriters Laboratories Inc. (UL), founded in 1894, is chartered as a not-for-profit, independent organization and tests products for public safety. It develops product standards, including specific tests to determine that a product is manufactured in accordance with UL requirements. UL also operates laboratories for the examination and testing of devices, systems, and materials in accordance with those requirements. UL standards are intended for use in the investigation of products to determine their relation to life, fire, and casualty hazards and, in some cases, in relation to crime prevention. The UL Marine Department examines and investigates marine products intended for use on commercial vessels, oil-drilling platforms, and pleasure craft. All UL marine standards are designed to indicate compliance with any applicable U.S. Coast Guard regulations. An important factor in UL's listing, classification, or component recognition of products, systems, or materials is that such products are subject to UL's follow-up inspection service at the point of manufacture. This inspection supplements the manufacturer's quality control inspection program and helps determine that the product being manufactured is identical to the product that was tested.

United States Coast Guard

The U.S. Coast Guard publishes regulations for pleasure craft, including fuel and electrical systems requirements. These regulations are found in *33 Code of Federal Regulations 183*.

COMMERCIAL VESSELS

Almost any accident involving a vessel presents either a direct or secondary threat of fire. Collision or stranding can rupture tanks or containers of hazardous materials and provide enough frictional heat to ignite the contents. The same hazards can result from the heavy pounding a ship receives in bad weather. Even the leakage of water into a cargo hold can cause accelerated oxidation and eventual combustion of some organic substances. In discussing marine fire hazards, both the transfer of cargo and the operation of the vessel must be considered, in addition to the traditional fire problems. The latest casualty (1987) statistics for commercial vessels indicate that of 285 ships lost at sea, 39 were the direct result of fire or explosion.

The steadily increasing world population and demands for foreign merchandise have resulted in an ever-increasing volume of commercial water-borne tonnage. Several international conventions relate directly or indirectly to fire protection and prevention aboard commercial vessels; these are concerned with construction, operation, manning, training, and inspection. The U.S. is signatory to many of these conventions, whose key points will be stressed in this section. In addition, several international codes relate to the carriage of hazardous materials. Although they are not conventions, they carry the weight of a convention due to their acceptance by a large number of nations.

In recent years, some land-based concepts have been transferred to the marine environment. Modern cruise ships now incorporate atria in their design, an idea borrowed from hotels, and a major city, responding to a need for more prison space, has built a floating detention facility. These are novel ideas for ships, and the marine regulatory community has had to respond rapidly to allow for their safe development. Fortunately, land-based standards exist, and, although not directly transferrable, they have formed the basis for the latest marine guidance for designing and building these ships. NFPA 101®, *Life Safety Code®*, was used as the basis for the structural fire protection and fire protection system requirements aboard floating detention facilities and provided the basis for new requirements for ships with atria.

MARITIME REGULATIONS AND STANDARDS

The United States is signatory to the Safety of Life at Sea Convention (SOLAS). Foreign and domestic commercial vessels operating on an international voyage must comply with the international requirements contained in SOLAS. Domestic commercial vessels and vessels of foreign countries not signatory to the SOLAS Convention that operate from U.S. ports are regulated by the U.S. Coast Guard for compliance with domestic regulations. The *Code of Federal Regulations*, Titles 33, 46, and 49, specify the design, construction, maintenance, and operational requirements for these ships.

In order to understand the international and domestic fire protection requirements that apply to ships and the philosophy employed in their development, a brief history is helpful.

History

The first international conference to discuss shipboard safety was held in 1914 as a direct result of the sinking of the *Titanic*. Public interest was heightened by that tragedy, and it became apparent that standards had to be developed internationally to ensure safety at sea. Subdivision and lifesaving were the key areas of interest, and no mention was made of fire protection.

In 1929, a second conference was held, and the Convention for the Safety of Life at Sea was prepared. This first SOLAS Convention required the fitting of fire-resisting bulkheads above the weather deck to restrict fire to the zone of origin by dividing the ship into main vertical zones, not to exceed 135 ft (40 m) in length. However, the Convention did not specify by definition or test what a "fire-resisting bulkhead" must be. Then in 1934, the U.S. passenger ship *Morro Castle* burned off the coast of New Jersey, costing 124 people their lives. The U.S. Senate Committee on Commerce created a special Subcommittee on Fireproofing and Fire Prevention to develop recommendations for fire-safety standards aboard ships.

Numerous fire tests conducted aboard a test ship, the *S.S. Nantasket*, ultimately singled out a construction technique that had been recommended by the Marine Section of NFPA. Class A-1 bulkheads were steel lined with asbestos and could resist the spread of fire for 1 hr; Class B Bulkheads were "incombustible" materials (now called noncombustible materials) that could resist the spread of fire for 30 min. The standard fire test, also recommend by the Marine Section of NFPA, was ASTM E-119. The test results were so favorable that the U.S. Senate ratified the 1929 SOLAS Convention and amended the U.S. Code to require that U.S. vessels be constructed similarly.

A third international conference took place in 1948 to upgrade the SOLAS 1929 Convention. The United States proposed the fire protection techniques in the U.S. Code, but the international community could not agree that this should be the only method of construction. Materials were not readily available worldwide, and several nations felt that active fire protection systems were equivalent to passive fire protection.

Three alternate methods of shipboard fire protection were allowed by the SOLAS 1948 Convention. Method I was the "incombustible" U.S. construction technique. Method II was the United Kingdom proposal to require sprinklers with no limitation on combustibles. Method III was the proposal by France to use a limited amount of fire-resistive bulkheads with the addition of fire detection systems. These three methods of construction still remain on ships that were built in accordance with SOLAS 1948 and the subsequent SOLAS 1960 Convention.

In the early 1960s, however, a series of tragic ship fires with multiple loss of life prompted an interest in developing a single standard for new ships and an upgrade in fire protection features for existing ships. The international community agreed to accept only "incombustible" construction as the single method of construction for new ships. They also agreed to require retrofit of some structural fire protection features, such as main vertical zone bulkheads and upgrades to means of escape, on existing ships. These latter requirements put the famous *Queen Mary* out of service as a passenger liner. This latest Convention, SOLAS 1974, went into effect internationally on May 25, 1980. It is still in effect but has been amended several times.

International Maritime Regulations and Standards

The International Maritime Organization (IMO, formerly IMCO), is a specialized agency of the United Nations and addresses matters relating to maritime activities. IMO is the depository of all treaties dealing with commercial vessel safety, and has developed several recommended standards relating to the same subject. A list of these conventions and codes follows, with a brief description of how they relate to fire protection and prevention.

Safety of Life at Sea (SOLAS) '74: Beginning with SOLAS '48, the various International Conventions for the Safety of Life at Sea address, among other things, fire protection aboard merchant vessels. Although all types of vessels are covered, passenger vessels are addressed in greatest detail, including the construction of bulkheads separating the various compartments. With the inclusion of the first and second set of amendments to SOLAS '74, increased emphasis is placed upon cargo ships and tank vessels, especially regarding structural fire protection details.

Under the terms of the Conventions, a certificate attesting to a ship's safety issued by one signatory country is accepted by all other signatory countries. Usually, one of the classification societies will perform the survey associated with issuing the certificate. The certificate ensures a minimum level of safety and permits ships to operate freely from one country to another without risk of discrimination due to their safety features. One fire protection feature of SOLAS '74 is the requirement for an inert gas system for new oil tankers over 100,000 deadweight tons (DWT) (95,256 metric tons) and combination oil/bulk solid carriers over 50,000 DWT (47,628 metric tons).

The current SOLAS treaty, SOLAS '74, was effective internationally on May 25, 1980. Basically, it incorporated resolutions and proposed, but not ratified, amendments that had been developed between 1960 and 1974. Although the amendments to SOLAS '60 never entered into force, the IMO Assembly adopted many of them and recommended that the individual countries incorporate them into their own national maritime safety regulations.

Several changes to SOLAS '74 have been developed since the 1974 treaty was finalized. These have been expressed in the 1978 Protocol Relating to the International Convention for the Safety of Life at Sea-1974, in the 1981 Amendments, and in the 1983 Amendments. The majority of the changes in the 1981 Amendments were in Chapter II-2, which deals with fire protection. There also were significant changes to Chapter III, Lifesaving Appliances in the 1983 Amendments.

The 1978 Protocol: The 1978 Protocol came out of the 1978 Tanker Safety and Pollution Prevention (TSPP) Conference. This conference was a direct result of U.S. initiatives in response to a tragic series of tanker casualties that occurred in 1976-1977 Since the SOLAS '74 treaty had not been ratified at that time, it could not be amended. Therefore, these changes were issued as a Protocol. The 1978 Protocol Relating to the International Convention for the Safety of Life at Sea-1974, came into force May 1, 1981. It mandates steering gear improvements, collision avoidance aids, dual radars, inert gas systems (IGS) for new and existing tank ships down to 20,000 deadweight tons (DWT) (19,000 metric tons), deck foam systems for new tank ships down to 20,000 DWT (19,000 metric tons), and closed ullage systems for all tank ships fitted with IGS. Finally, it requires IGS for tank ships capable of crude oil washing.

The 1981 Amendments: There are two sets of amendments to SOLAS '74. The first, developed between 1974 and 1981 by various IMO subcommittees, came into force September 1, 1984.

The changes to SOLAS contained in the SOLAS '78 Protocol are embodied and partly updated in this first set of amendments. The changes to the fire protection chapter, Chapter II-2, include provisions for halogenated hydrocarbon extinguishing systems and a new Regulation 62 on inert gas systems. The latter regulation was adopted by the eleventh IMO Assembly as a recommendation in 1979. The changes were so extensive that Chapter II-2 was essentially reorganized and rewritten.

The 1983 Amendments: These amendments became effective July 1, 1986. The most important changes concern life saving and the incorporation by reference of the International Bulk Chemical Code and the International Gas Carrier Code into SOLAS. These two codes now become mandatory by the 1983 Amendments.

Convention on Training and Certification of Seafarers, 1978

This convention, commonly referred to as Standards for Training and Watchkeeping (STW), outlines the training required before one can obtain a license. The various types of training needed include fire fighting and fire prevention, as well as familiarity with the cargo systems aboard chemical and gas carriers. Attendance at an approved course or training for an appropriate period under supervised shipboard services is required.

Dangerous Goods Code

As a result of the Safety of Life at Sea Conference of 1960, IMO began work on the development of a code covering the safe transportation by sea of dangerous goods or hazardous materials. Most dangerous goods have as their primary or secondary hazard a potential for fire. If fire is not a hazard, dangerous goods, by their presence, complicate fire fighting and rescue efforts. Today, the *IMO Dangerous Goods Code* is widely recognized by numerous maritime nations and has become the "bible" for seafarers. The *IMO Dangerous Goods Code* is compatible with the method for classifying hazardous materials used by the U.S. for years before the code's development. As a result, the code is recognized as a substitute for the safe carriage of hazardous materials aboard foreign and U.S. vessels while in U.S. waters. The *IMO Dangerous Goods Code* is constantly updated by appropriate IMO committees.

Bulk Chemical Code

As a result of the increased demand for chemicals among industrialized trading nations, the method of shipping chemicals has changed from packages to larger quantities. Standard petroleum tankers were modified and shifted to this trade. Several nations, among them the U.S., became convinced that these modified tankers did not have the necessary safety features for protecting the crew, the port, and the environment against chemicals with properties other than flammability. IMO was petitioned to begin developing a code covering the design, construction, and operation of chemical carriers. On October 12, 1971, IMO adopted a code for bulk chemical carriers which includes special fire protection systems using suppressants other than water that will not react with the chemical cargo, yet will be effective when applied. On September 26, 1977, the U.S. Coast Guard adopted the *IMO Bulk Chemical Code* as part of its regulations. In addition to upgrading the various systems aboard these vessels, the code requires an increased level of stability and cargo containment to protect the cargo and the ship when they are involved in an accident.

The *International Bulk Chemical Code*, which is applicable to new ships, became effective on July 1, 1986. This code, reflecting improvements and previously agreed to amendments to the *Bulk Chemical Code*, became mandatory under the second set of amendments to SOLAS '74.

Liquefied Gas Code

While the *Bulk Chemical Code* was being developed, it became obvious that the code should specifically address the carriage of gases. Gases are transported in other than their natural state, using low temperature, high pressure, or a combination of both. Methane, for example, cannot be liquefied by pressure alone. To transport it economically as a liquid, it must be refrigerated to -162°F (108°C), and very specialized containment systems are needed to maintain that temperature for the long sea voyages involved. Also required are specialized fire fighting systems and techniques to put out any fire that may develop aboard one of these bulk gas vessels. IMO now has two bulk gas codes, one for existing and the other for newly built liquefied bulk gas ships. The U.S. adopted the IMO code for new ships on October 4, 1976. The U.S. Coast Guard requires existing ships to upgrade where the IMO code also requires it, and maintains the existing U.S. standards when they are more strict than the existing IMO code.

As noted above, the *International Gas Code*, which is applicable to new ships, came into force July 1, 1986. This code, containing improvements and previously agreed to amendments to the *Liquefied Gas Code*, became mandatory under the second set of amendments to SOLAS '74.

Domestic Regulations

U.S. Coast Guard regulations covering commercial vessels are contained in the following parts of the *Code of Federal Regulations*:

1. CFR Part 157, *Tank Vessels Carrying Oil in Bulk*.
2. 46 CFR Parts 30-40, *Tank Vessels*.
3. 46 CFR Parts 70-80, *Passenger Vessels*.
4. 46 CFR Parts 90-106, *Cargo and Miscellaneous Vessels*.
5. 46 CFR Parts 107-109, *Mobile Offshore Drilling Units*.
6. 46 CFR Part 146, *Carriage of Military Explosives*.
7. 46 CFR Part 147, *Transportation of Bulk Solids*.
8. 46 CFR Parts 150-153, *Carriage of Chemicals in Tank Vessels and Barges*.
9. 46 CFR Part 154, *Carriage of Liquified Gases*.
10. 46 CFR Parts 160-165, *Specifications*.
11. 46 CFR Parts 166-168, *Nautical Schools*.
12. 46 CFR Parts 175-187, *Small Passenger Vessels (under 100 gross tons)*.
13. 46 CFR Parts 188-196, *Oceanographic Vessels*.
14. 46 CFR Parts 170-189, *Transportation of Hazardous Materials by All Modes Including Water*.

United States Coast Guard

The U.S. Coast Guard (USCG) is the federal agency responsible for enforcing regulations covering the safety of U.S. commercial vessels, both ocean-going and inland. The Coast Guard also has authority over foreign vessels operating into and out of U.S. ports, under the authority of the Ports and Waterways Safety Act as modified by the Tanker Safety Act. The Coast Guard has a comprehensive inspection program for foreign tank vessels directed toward prevention of fires and explosions similar to those that occurred aboard the *S.S. Sansanena* in Los Angeles Harbor on December 17, 1976. The inspections cover the integrity of the various cargo containment and fire fighting systems aboard a tanker. Included in the cargo containment system are the tanks, piping, and venting system that contain the cargo and its vapors. The Coast Guard also inspects foreign vessels to ensure compliance with the various international treaties and standards described earlier. As the enforcement agency for SOLAS '74, the Coast Guard has the authority and responsibility to ensure that U.S. ships and foreign ships visiting U.S. ports comply with the treaty and its amendments.

In most ports, the USCG Captain of the Port (COTP) now heads the Ports Operations Division of the Marine Safety Office (MSO). The COTP is the U.S. Coast Guard official responsible in a port for ensuring that commercial vessels operate, load, and discharge cargo safely, and that they are maintained in accordance with the regulations. The COTP or MSO also is responsible for ensuring that waterfront facilities are maintained and operated in a safe manner, especially regarding fire prevention. Lacking detailed regulations in this area, the COTP or MSO frequently develops local regulations covering waterfront facilities. The COTP or MSO is responsible for the protection of waterfront facilities and is required to have a detailed contingency plan that is to be implemented in the event of a fire involving a vessel or waterfront facility. This officer is also responsible for responding to pollution incidents involving navigable waters and should have a contingency plan covering this type of incident response. Since pollution can involve petroleum products and chemicals, contingency plans for both usually are incorporated into one plan. These plans customarily include the local fire department because the Coast Guard's resources are devoted primarily to fire prevention, limiting its capability to fight fires.

The U.S. Coast Guard Officer in Charge of Marine Inspection (OCMI) is responsible for ensuring that U.S. vessels are built and maintained to existing U.S. regulations, most of which are related to the treaties described previously. In nearly every U.S. port, the functions of both the COTP and OCMI are now combined into one office, that of Commanding Officer of the Marine Safety Office. The COTP functions are handled by the Port Operations Division, and most of the OCMI functions are handled by the Inspection Division.

GENERAL SHIP CONSTRUCTION

Basically, a ship may be considered a huge box girder consisting of the hull plating and the main deck. These parts are, in turn, strengthened by such members as the keel, frames, beams, keelsons, stringers, girders, pillars, lower decks, and transverse bulkheads. To appreciate a ship in its entirety, one must understand the functions of each of its parts.

The keel is primarily the backbone of the ship. It consists of a rigid fabrication of plates and structural shapes which run fore and aft along the centerline of the ship. The stem is connected to the forward end, and at the after end is the stern frame, which supports both the rudder and the propeller.

The frames are the ribs of the ship. Their lower ends are attached at intervals along the keel, and their upper ends are attached through brackets to the beams that support the deck. Internal bracing is provided by keelsons and stringers running fore and aft. The frames determine the form of the ship, and they support and stiffen the shell plating.

The shell plating, necessary for water-tightness, also is one of the principal strength members of the ship. Running continuously from the stem to the stern frame and from the keel to the weather deck, the shell plating forms three sides of the box girder. The plating, aided by the frames, must be able to withstand the exterior water pressure, stress from the buffeting of waves, and rubbing and bumping against docks.

The main deck of the ship forms the fourth side of the girder and, for this reason, must be of strong construction. The plating is connected to beams that extend from side to side across the ship. The deck is strengthened by the doubling of plates in regions weakened by openings, such as hatchways and companionways, and under all deck machinery, chocks, and bits. The deck is supported from below by girders and pillars.

The bottom, sides, and main deck of the ship would not be strong enough to withstand the stresses of an ocean voyage without some internal stiffening. In a cargo vessel, this is provided by the lower decks and the main transverse bulkheads. For tank vessels, stiffening comes from transverse and longitudinal bulkheads that separate the vessel into numerous cargo tanks extending from the keel to the main deck. In the newer tank vessels, including all chemical and gas carriers, double bottoms and sides provide added protection from cargo release should a crack occur in the shell plating.

In addition to furnishing support for the shell and decks, the main transverse bulkheads are made water-tight. Subdividing the vessel into watertight compartments is done to confine water in case of damage. All doors through these bulkheads must be fitted with gaskets to make them water-tight. Doors also must be kept clear at all times so they can be closed instantly. The bulkheads also are fire-resistant and can limit fire spread. This degree of compartmentation can complicate fire fighting efforts, unless fire fighters know how a ship is laid out. In an emergency, the general arrangement plan for the vessel should be examined to locate access and egress routes for fire fighting. Some typical general arrangement plans are shown in Figure 8-37E.

The first bulkhead aft of the stem is known as the collision bulkhead, because its purpose is to limit the flooding that might occur after a collision. No doors or other openings are permitted below the main deck in this bulkhead.

In a cargo vessel, the engine and boiler rooms usually are located amidships. For a tank vessel, the engine room is located in the after section, aft of the cargo tank. Special foundations are necessary to support heavy engines and boilers. In order to provide sufficient headroom for the propelling machinery, it usually is necessary to omit one or more of the decks in this region. To maintain the vessel's strength in the absence of these decks, several extra-heavy web frames and transverse beams are fitted.

The propeller shaft extends through the after holds from the engine to the stern gland. Because the propeller shaft must be accessible at all times for inspection and lubrication, it is enclosed in a narrow tunnel known as the shaft alley. The entrance to the shaft alley from the engine room is closed by a water-tight door, and the sides are of water-tight construction so that a fracture of the tail shaft or similar accident will result in only the tunnel being flooded.

The necessity for good drainage requires special attention in the design and construction of a ship. Free water on the decks, in a hold, or in the bilges is detrimental to the stability of the vessel. Therefore, the drainage system must be as efficient as possible. The decks should be cambered to permit drainage to the scuppers which lead the water either overboard or to the bilges. Sufficient scuppers and suctions must be provided so the drainage will be effective under any condition of list or trim of the ship. Solid bulwarks, where fitted around a deck, should be pierced by large freeing ports to allow any water that is shipped to escape quickly.

Ventilation

The type of ventilation used in a cargo vessel depends upon the nature of the space and the service of the ship. It can be natural, mechanical, or a combination of the two, and may be extended to air heating, cooling, cleaning, humidifying, and dehumidifying. Air movement in natural ventilation systems is created by the difference in density between inside and outside air and depends upon the relative air temperatures. Ventilators dependent upon wind direction and velocity for induction of air currents are used with natural systems. Natural ventilation generally is limited to a few ships, lockers, and storerooms, depending upon their location, and to some dry cargo holds. It also sometimes is used for engine and boiler rooms. In dry cargo holds, ventilation generally is accomplished with vents in the forward end for exhaust, and cowls at the after end for supply. Large ducts are required because of the low velocity necessary for air flow. In a mechanical system, air is moved by various types of fans driven by electric motors. These systems provide positive circulation of air at desired temperature and volume, function regardless of outside

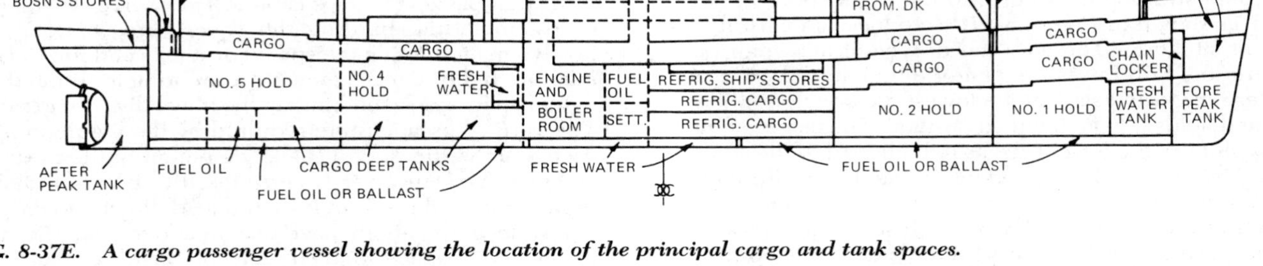

FIG. 8-37E. A cargo passenger vessel showing the location of the principal cargo and tank spaces.

atmospheric conditions, and are easily controlled to meet variations in requirements.

The ventilation for living accommodations on both cargo and tank vessels is by means of forced air through a duct system similar to that used ashore. All the compartments are interconnected through these ducts. A damper is provided in each duct to isolate one compartment from another in order to prevent the spread of fire. The dampers can operate manually or automatically using a fusible link. Cargo tanks on tank vessels are not ventilated, but they use a vent system to allow the tank to relieve excess pressure or to allow air ingress if a vacuum develops. This venting arrangement is explained later under the subsection "Tank Vessels."

Stability

A ship's stability, or the property of a floating body to remain at rest in a stable position, is controlled by the interaction of two opposing forces. The center of gravity (Point G in Figs. 8-37F, 8-37G, and 8-37H) is a point at which the weight of the ship and any other weight aboard is concentrated. It remains in a constant position until the weight distribution aboard the vessel is changed, and it acts with a downward force. The center of buoyancy may be defined as the center of gravity of the body of water displaced by a floating vessel. It is the center of the immersed part of the ship and acts with an upward force, perpendicular to the surface of the water.

When a ship is in a state of vertical equilibrium, as shown in Figure 8-37F, the downward force of gravity (G) and the upward force of buoyancy (B) lie in the same vertical line. When the ship is inclined by some external force, the center of gravity (G) remains in its original position. The center of buoyancy (B), since it is the center of the immersed part of the ship, shifts toward the lower side, as shown in Figure 8-37G. In that situation, the central force of (G) downward, combined with the outer force of (B) upward from the low side, act together to return the vessel to an upright position.

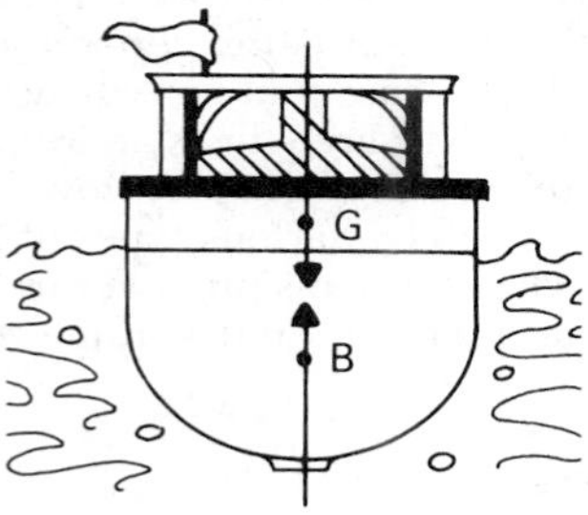

FIG. 8-37F. Ship in a state of vertical equilibrium.

The addition of water into the upper portion of the hull, as shown in Figure 8-37H, produces an entirely different situation. The addition of weight at a high point within the hull raises the center of gravity. The fact that water runs to and stays at the lowest point inclines the vessel and holds it in an inclined position. The center of buoyancy shifts to the lower side, as it did before. If the addition of weight (water) is stopped while the downward force of (G) is inboard—that is, toward the centerline—of the upward force of (B), the vessel will settle in a new stabilized position, inclined toward the side of the additional

FIG. 8-37G. Ship inclined by an external force.

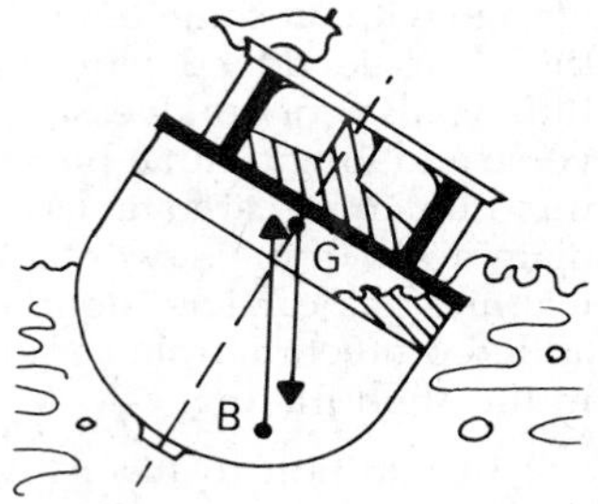

FIG. 8-37H. The effect of adding water (weight) to the upper portion of a ship.

weight. If sufficient water is added to bring the downward force of (G) outside the upward force of (B), as shown in Figure 8-37H, the vessel will continue to roll over and eventually will capsize.

From this explanation of stability, it is easy to see how the addition of water, especially high in the vessel, can dramatically affect the vessel's stability. Whenever a fire is fought on board a vessel, this problem must be recognized. A means of removing the water from a vessel during fire fighting must be established, since there is a limit to how much water can be pumped aboard before the vessel will roll over on its side, as the S.S. *Normandie* did in New York Harbor in 1942. To prevent this from happening, a person who understands the principle of stability should be consulted while a shipboard fire is being fought. Otherwise, the incident could cause loss of life, as well as the loss of a vessel.

Passenger Ships

The most significant influence on designing the internal boundaries, bulkheads, and stairs is the structural fire protection requirements mandated by the international and domestic regulations for passenger ships. Main vertical zones are 1-hr fire protection boundaries placed at approximately 131-ft (40 m) intervals along the length of the ship. They are the foundation on which all structural fire protection for passenger ships is built. They serve several purposes, including limiting the square area of total fire involvement, limiting the spread of smoke and fire to facilitate fire fighting management, accounting for limited fire fighting personnel, and limiting the travel distance to safety. The vertical escape route required by the regulations for each main vertical zone is a key element in the means of escape. The stairtower is considered to be a safe haven from smoke and fire, and it should lead directly to the lifeboats. Recently, efforts have been made to keep the stairtower free of spaces that contain combustibles, but older vessels did not necessarily employ this philosophy. A small fire in a closet could produce enough smoke to block off the vertical escape for an entire main vertical zone. Future efforts are being directed not only to limit the spaces that have access, but to design the ventilation systems to permit smoke control through pressurization of the stairs and perhaps the corridors.

Tank Vessels

Older tank vessels include pump rooms, one forward and one aft, between the last cargo tanks and the engine room. The cargo and ballast pumps are located within the pump room. All cargo and ballast water passes through the pump rooms into and out of the cargo tanks. A pump room can accumulate flammable vapor from any cargo leakage into the bilges from the various piping and valves within the room. For this reason, the room should be well ventilated before anyone enters it, and someone topside should be aware of persons entering a pump room in case they are exposed to an acute concentration of vapors. Tank vessels of newer design, especially the chemical and gas carriers, use deep-well pumps in each cargo tank, thereby eliminating the need for pump rooms.

Each cargo tank on a tank vessel is fitted with a venting system to regulate the pressure within the tank. On crude carriers and petroleum product carriers, each tank is connected to a common venting system. On a chemical or gas carrier, the vents are independent of each other. This arrangement is required to ensure that vapors from different chemicals do not come in contact with each other and to prevent incompatible reactions or contamination.

The venting system contains flame screens or flame arrestors. These devices prevent any flame that develops outside the cargo tank from entering it and causing an explosion, as happened on the *S.S. Sansinena*. In that case, it was theorized that flame entered the cargo tank through a wasted section of the vent piping.

It is extremely important that the various piping systems aboard a tank vessel, including the vent system, be maintained in good condition, and that flame screens be placed over any openings into a cargo tank. During cargo loading or when ballasting a tank that previously contained cargo, copious amounts of flammable vapors are generated. These vapors are vented to the atmosphere to ensure that the cargo tanks are not overpressurized. In the vicinity of a tanker conducting these operations, the air will contain a flammable mixture, especially if low winds are present. Should the flammable mixture be ignited, the flame will be prevented from entering the tank if flame screens or arrestors are in place and all the piping systems that penetrate the cargo tank are intact.

For some toxic chemicals and for all gases, a vapor recovery system is generally employed to return the vapors to shore. With this arrangement, no venting to the atmosphere takes place unless an emergency occurs. The cargo transfer operations and vapor return are balanced to prevent over- or under-pressurizing of the cargo tank. This procedure eliminates the potential flammable atmosphere around the vessel during loading. However, the various piping systems must be intact to prevent a release of any flammable vapors or liquids.

As a result of SOLAS '74 and the TSPP Conference, inert gas systems are now installed aboard tankers. These systems are intended to ensure that the atmosphere within the cargo tanks does not contain a flammable mixture. Without an inert gas system, all openings into a cargo tank must be protected with flame screens or arrestors, and all piping must be in good condition. Otherwise, as discussed previously, a source of ignition can be introduced into the cargo tanks. Experience has shown that precluding entry of all sources of ignition is difficult. Consequently, the trend is toward inerting the cargo tanks whenever they contain hydrocarbon vapors. The inert gas system must be designed, constructed, and operated to render the atmosphere of cargo tanks nonflammable and to keep it that way at all times, except when the tanks are required to be gas-free. The system must be capable of:

1. Inerting empty cargo tanks by reducing the oxygen content of the atmosphere in each tank to a level at which combustion cannot be supported.
2. Maintaining the atmosphere in any part of any cargo tank with an oxygen content not exceeding 8 percent by volume and at a positive pressure at all times in port and at sea, except when it is necessary for such a tank to be gas-free.
3. Eliminating the need for air to enter a tank during normal operations, except when it is necessary for such a tank to be gas-free.
4. Purging empty cargo tanks of hydrocarbon gas so that subsequent gas release operations will at no time create a flammable atmosphere within the tank.

Figure 8-37I is a simplified illustration of tanker operations using inert gas systems. The rule is never to mix both air and hydrocarbons during operation, but to insert inert gas between the air and hydrocarbon phases of the operation. Specific practices for these systems are described in 46 *CFR* 32.53, Regulation 62 of SOLAS '74, which describes international requirements that are very similar to U.S. criteria, and in the *IMO Guidelines for Inert Gas Systems*. Use of inert gas systems enhances tanker safety significantly by greatly reducing the risk of fire and explosion within cargo tanks.

BARGES

Almost any commodity can be shipped by water. The inland waterways industry has developed various types and sizes of barges for the efficient handling of products, ranging from coal in open hopper barges to chemicals and "thermos bottle" barges, and from dredged rock in dump scows to railroad cars on car floats. Barging is the only practical mode of marine transportation to move outside machinery, tanks, kilns, and some space vehicles for long distances.

The most versatile, inexpensive, and common type of barge in the U.S. is the hopper barge. With minor modifications, it can be adapted to transport literally any solid commodity in bulk or package. It is basically a single-skinned, open-top box, the inner shell of which forms a long hopper or cargo hold. The bottom, sides, and ends of the hold are free of appendages. They are generally of welded plate construction, with a double bottom for greater safety. They are braced to resist the heaviest of external blows, as well as to absorb the impact of buckets used in loading and unloading. The covered dry cargo barge is used for bulk loading commodities that need protection from weather. Generally, the only difference between these vessels and open hopper barges is that covered dry cargo barges are equipped with watertight covers over the entire cargo hold.

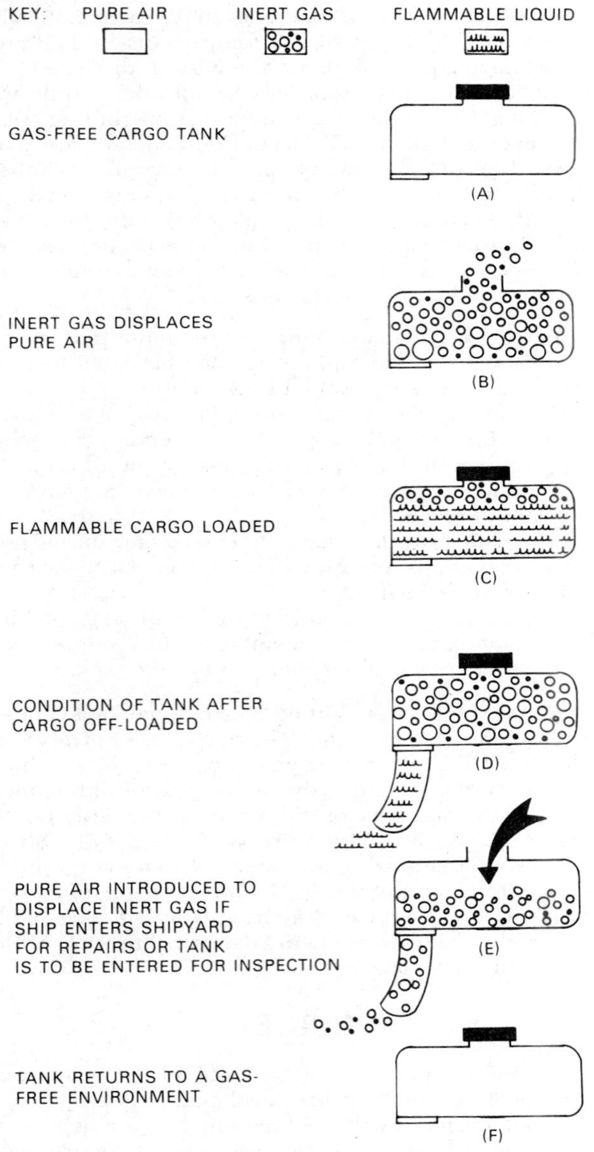

FIG. 8-37I. A tanker inert gas system.

Three basic types of tank barges are used to transport liquid commodities: single-skinned tank barges, double-skinned tank barges, and cylindrical tank barges.

Single-skinned tank barges have bow and stern compartments separated from the midship by transverse collision bulkheads. The entire midship shell of the vessel constitutes the cargo tank. Hydrodynamic considerations require that this huge tank be divided by bulkheads. The usual compartmentation consists of a centerline bulkhead with three transverse bulkheads forming four separate cargo compartments on either side. The entire framing structure is inside the cargo tanks.

Double-skinned tank barges have, as the term implies, an inner and an outer shell. The inner shell forms cargo tanks that are free of appendages and are therefore easier to clean and to line with a protective coating. Poisons and other hazardous liquids require the protection of the void compartments between the outer and inner shells.

Barges with independent cylindrical tanks are used to transport liquids under pressure, or, when pressure is in use, to discharge the cargo. Because of the high efficiency of linings and insulation that can be incorporated, cylindrical tank barges can be used to carry cargoes at or near atmospheric pressures. Cylindrical cargo tanks generally are mounted in the barge hopper and are thus free to expand or contract independently of the entire structure. For this reason, they are preferred for high-temperature cargoes, such as liquid sulphur at 280°F (138°C), or refrigerated cargoes, such as anhydrous ammonia at -28°F (-33.3°C).

All barges carrying hazardous materials are required to have a 2-by-3-ft (0.61 m by 0.91 m) warning sign facing outboard without obstruction, on which is printed "WARNING—DANGEROUS CARGO. NO VISITORS, NO SMOKING, NO OPEN LIGHTS." The sign also must specify the names and locations of all cargoes aboard the vessel. In addition to the warning sign, barges carrying hazardous materials must have an information placard giving details about each of the hazardous cargoes aboard. These placards are required to be displayed in a waterproof container as near to the warning sign as practicable.

Information placards for all hazardous materials in an entire tow must be maintained in the towboat wheelhouse where they are readily accessible to the operator. In case of any problem, the towboat operator on watch should be able to furnish specific details via radio concerning any hazardous cargo in tow.

Tank Cleaning and Gas-Freeing of Cargo Tanks

One of the most hazardous processes in the operation of either tank ships or tank barges is that of tank cleaning and gas-freeing. This procedure is carried out in varying degrees for a change of cargo, on or off charter survey, for periodic U.S. Coast Guard inspection, and for repairs. Although tank ships usually are cleaned and gas-freed at sea and barges are cleaned in port, the procedure used for both is very similar.

The biggest problem in tank cleaning and gas-freeing is the necessity of reducing the flammable vapors in the atmosphere from a point above the upper explosive limit (UEL) to a point below the lower explosive limit (LEL). In other words, the atmosphere of the space must be brought down through the full flammable range of the material of the previous contents. A spark or other source of ignition within the space during the time the atmosphere is within the explosive range can cause an explosion.

The most common and most feared source of ignition during cleaning and gas-freeing operations is a spark caused by static electricity discharge. During washing operations, water mist forming in a tank's atmosphere takes on an electrical charge from the cleaning water jet which penetrates the mist. Should any object not properly bonded to the tank be lowered into the tank space, a static discharge similar to a small lightning bolt could travel from the mist cloud to the ungrounded object.

Another severe fire and explosion hazard is present while a vessel is being repaired. Even though the tanks may have been thoroughly cleaned and gas-freed at sea, there is no guarantee that they will remain in the same condition throughout the duration of repairs. As required by U.S. Coast Guard and Department of Labor regulations, each space is tested and certified to be "safe for hot work" by an NFPA-certificated marine chemist before any hot work can begin. The fact that a cargo tank has been found to be completely safe and has been so certificated by a marine chemist does not necessarily mean that it will remain in that condition. Sun beating down on a tank with a rusty interior can cause the release of sufficient flammable vapors inside the tank to bring the atmosphere from a safe condition to well within the explosive range. Therefore, the marine chemist must not only evaluate the atmospheric condition that exists within the space at the time of the inspection, but must also evaluate any weather conditions and interior vessel conditions that might cause regeneration of the flammable vapors. Where there is any doubt, the marine chemist should recommend that additional precautionary measures be taken by the repairer and should specify the circumstances under which a marine chemist should be recalled for further testing. Timely and regular use of the services of NFPA-certificated marine chemists has helped to virtually eliminate some of the most severe fire and explosion hazards in the marine industry.

SHIPBOARD FIRE EXTINGUISHING EQUIPMENT

Since each ship is different, it follows that fire protection systems will rarely be identical from one ship to another. Under Coast Guard regulations governing U.S. merchant vessels, several alternative fire protection systems may be either permitted or required, depending upon their designed purpose. Foreign vessels are likely to have different systems or arrangements. Similar systems manufactured and installed by competing companies can vary widely. Most fire extinguishing and fire detection equipment for use aboard U.S. vessels is approved by the Coast Guard, as are most structural fire protection materials used on U.S. vessels. Other acceptable fire extinguishing equipment, such as portable fire extinguishers, should be listed and labeled by testing laboratories for marine use.

Firemain System

The firemain system is the line that provides fire fighting and flushing water throughout a ship. It is the backbone of all fire fighting systems aboard ships. The quantity of water available for fire fighting is limited only by the capacity of the fire pumps supplying the system. Most vessels are required to have two fire pumps, with all suction inlets, sources of power, and so on, for each pump located in separate spaces so that one fire will not put both pumps out of operation. An alternative, which must be approved by the Coast Guard, is to install both pumps in the same space and to protect the space with a carbon dioxide extinguishing system. This arrangement is permitted only in unusual circumstances, where separation of pumps would not increase safety, a course usually acceptable for only small vessels. The size of the required pumps depends upon the vessel's size and service, as well as upon the arrangement of the pumps and piping aboard the vessel.

Hydrants on the firemain system are located so that two hose streams may be directed into all portions of the vessel accessible to passengers and crew during navigation. Because one of the streams must flow from a single length of hose, it is essential that the hose be long enough to direct water into all portions of the space, not just long enough to get the nozzle to the door.

International Shore Connection

One particular item of equipment required by SOLAS '74 deserves special mention: the international shore connection. Vessels must be fitted with a special bolted plate that can be attached to the firemain. This fitting is designed to eliminate the possible mismatch of hose threads aboard vessels and in port facilities. Provision of such connections is not mandatory for shore installations, but they can prove invaluable to organizations having marine fire fighting responsibilities.

Carbon Dioxide Systems Aboard Vessels

Carbon dioxide as an extinguishing agent aboard ship has many desirable properties. It will not, of itself, damage cargo or machinery, and it leaves no residue to be cleaned up after a fire. Even if a ship is without power, a carbon dioxide system can deliver the agent to all parts of a space because it is pressurized. Basically, there are two carbon dioxide systems for protecting compartments in a ship: fixed CO_2 systems aboard commercial vessels are classified either as "cargo" systems or "total flooding" systems.

Cargo systems: Fires in Class A materials (ordinary combustibles) carried in cargo holds usually start with smoldering and production of large quantities of smoke. Rapid burning will occur only when sufficient heat has developed to reach the temperature at which solid combustibles give off enough gases to support continued rapid combustion. Until that time, the rate of combustion is relatively slow. After a smoldering fire in a ship's hold is discovered, time to flaming combustion might be at least 20 min, depending upon oxygen available and other circumstances. This would allow time to prepare for fire fighting operations. The cargo hold is sealed and the CO_2 normally is released at a rate of several bottles at a time, so that the oxygen level falls below the rate that will support combustion.

Total Flooding Systems: Fires in machinery and similar spaces are generally Class B (flammable liquids). In this type of fire, heat buildup is rapid. Since the safety of a ship depends to a great extent upon the equipment in the machinery space, it is important to introduce the extinguishing gas quickly. Rapid release of an extinguisher also prevents heat from causing failure of bulkheads, which would make it impossible to maintain a sufficient concentration of carbon dioxide, and it prevents structural members from reaching high temperatures. Quick release of the extinguishing agent also prevents heat updraft from the fire from carrying away the carbon dioxide, and limits the extent of damage to equipment. Discharge of 85 percent of the required quantity of carbon dioxide in these systems should be completed within 2 min; for systems designed to protect roll-on/roll-off cargo spaces, discharging 100 percent of the required quantity within 2 min is required. Slow release, as in the case of the "cargo system," might result in no extinguishment. Two separate and deliberate controls are required to avoid unintentional release of the gas. One releases the minimum required amount of carbon dioxide, and the other operates the stop valve or direction valve.

Liquid cargo tanks aboard cargo and passenger vessels may be protected by a carbon dioxide system that is a modification of the cargo system. A tank system, instead of a steam smothering system or a deck foam system, is most commonly found aboard tank vessels. This system calls for discharge of a specified amount of CO_2 within 5 min. The quantity of CO_2 required to protect a given space is based upon a volume factor of 30 [1 lb CO_2/30 cu ft or 45 kg/m^3]. Operating instructions should state the minimum number of carbon dioxide bottles to be released in relation to the amount of cargo in the tank.

Halon Systems

Bromotrifluoromethane, or Halon 1301, is one of several halogenated hydrocarbon extinguishing agents introduced in recent years. In general, halogenated agents have high extinguishing efficiency per unit weight. This makes them particularly suitable for installations that are weight-critical, such as hydrofoils.

Title 46 of the *Code of Federal Regulations* does not currently contain any provisions for the design or requirements of halon systems aboard commercial vessels. Instead, the approval of these systems is based upon a provision that grants the Commandant of the Coast Guard authority to allow equivalent systems. Halon 1301 is the only halogenated agent that has been found satisfactory for domestic marine use in fixed systems.

It must be demonstrated adequately that a proposed system is equivalent to the existing system required by the regulations before the system can be allowed. Total flooding carbon dioxide fire protection systems are those to which Halon 1301 systems must prove they are equivalent. Therefore, Coast Guard-approved Halon 1301 systems are required by federal law to be designed with an equivalent degree of fire protection capability and reliability. Where basic deviations in design occur due to the use of Halon 1301, specific adaptations to the regulations apply.

The basic design philosophy of CO_2 systems has been retained for halon systems:

1. The protected space must be evacuated before the system is discharged. A predischarge alarm is required.
2. Agent storage containers must be located outside the protected space, except for spaces smaller than 6000 cu ft (170 m^3) and for modular-type halon systems.
3. In order to avoid accidental release, two separate and distinct actions must be performed to discharge the agent.
4. Manual-type release devices are required. Automatic release is permitted only for spaces smaller then 6000 cu ft (170 m^3).
5. Detailed instructions must be provided at the remote release station to explain alternate means of discharging the system.

Coast Guard requirements are divided into two areas: machinery space protection of U.S. flag vessels and fixed systems for pleasure craft. In the first case, the Halon 1301 system has been conceptually approved. Final "type approval" procedures are being developed by the manufacturers, the Coast Guard, and Underwriters Laboratories. Approval is on a ship-by-ship basis. In the second case, the Coast Guard is in the process of developing a standard for systems aboard pleasure craft. A test program has been developed jointly with UL.

Currently, both Halon 1301 and Halon 1211 portable extinguishers are available, and both carry Coast Guard approval for marine use.

Internationally, IMO has developed detailed requirements, compatible with U.S. requirements, for halon systems for machinery spaces, as well as for roll on/roll off vehicle spaces. A halon piping diagram for the engine room of a foreign flag 80,000 DWT tanker appears in Figure 8-37J. The diagram appeared in the May 1984 volume of *Chevron's Safety Bulletin*.

The first set of amendments to the SOLAS '74 Convention permits the installation of, and set out the international requirements for, halon systems on commercial vessels. However, recent events have reversed the trend toward the installation of halon systems in lieu of CO_2 systems. The Second Meeting of the Parties to the Montreal Protocol on Substances that Deplete the Ozone Layer, held in June 1990 in London, adopted amendments to that protocol. The target completion date for the phasing out of halons was set for the year 2000. The Subcommittee on Fire Protection of IMO has been charged with drafting a plan for phasing out halon systems aboard commercial vessels. The draft plan proposes a schedule for compliance by prohibiting new installations after July 1, 1992, prohibiting future testing after January 1, 1992, requesting the listing and registration of halons onboard ships, requiring the phase-out of existing halon systems by January 1, 2000, and investigating and reporting methods of disposal of halon gases. It should be noted that these are currently proposed dates.

Mechanical Foam Systems Aboard Ship

Mechanical foam is produced by introducing foam concentrate in proper proportions into a flowing stream of water and then aspirating it with air. Aboard ship, the foam concentrate is normally introduced through proportioning equipment located near the foam concentrate storage container at a central location on the vessel. The foam solution is pumped through fixed piping to foam nozzles, monitors, and so on in the area to be protected. Air is mixed with the foam solution at the discharge nozzle.

Deck Systems

Deck foam systems are required aboard tank vessels constructed after January 1, 1962. This system is intended to protect any deck area, using a predetermined rate of flow from foam stations—that is, monitors or hose stations—aft of the area to be protected. Piping and foam stations are arranged so that ruptured sections of piping in the path of a fire can be isolated. With this arrangement, it should be possible to fight the fire effectively wherever it occurs by working forward from the after house, assuming machinery, foam pumping, and proportioning equipment are located aft.

The concentrate normally supplied for mechanical foam is suitable for use on most, but not all, flammable liquids carried aboard tankers. For example, it is impossible for foam made from ordinary concentrate to form a blanket on alcohols, esters, ketones, or ethers, commonly called water-soluble or polar solvents. An alcohol-type foam concentrate is available for shipboard fires involving water-soluble flammable liquids. An alternate method of combating alcohol-type fires is the use of water spray to dilute the flammable liquid and cool the surrounding areas. A foam concentrate that is effective on both polar and nonpolar solvents is also available.

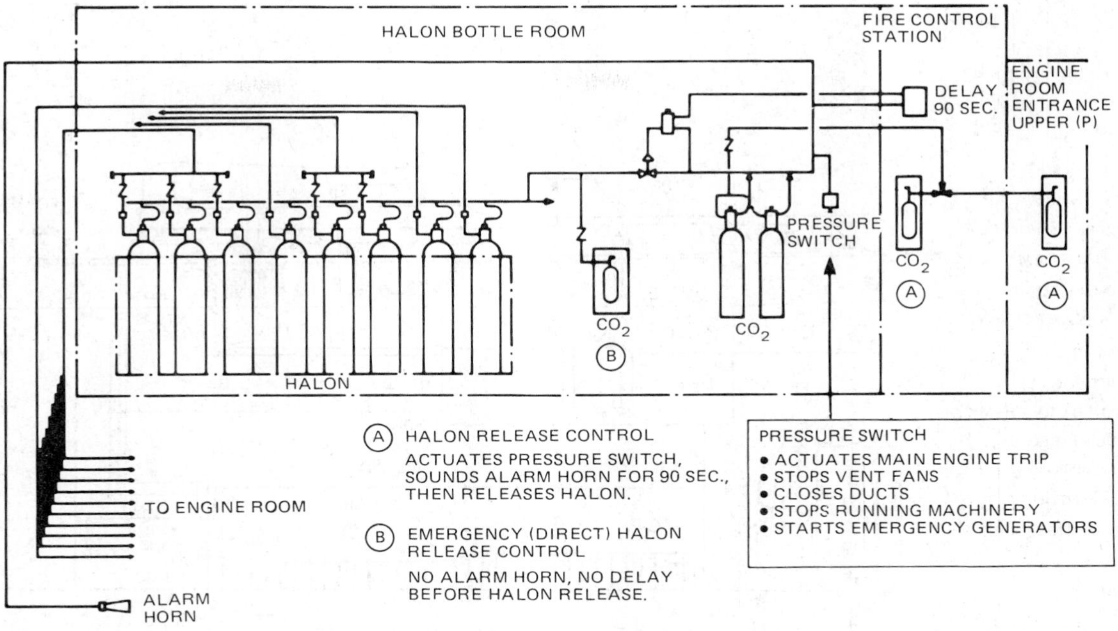

FIG. 8-37J. Halon piping diagram for engine room (System No. 1).

Chemical Carriers

Chemical carriers may be required to have more fire fighting systems than ordinary tank vessels. The systems required for a chemical carrier will be based on the chemical involved; the type of fire protection required is described in 46 *CFR* 153. A foam system will be specified as polar solvent or nonpolar solvent, depending on whether or not the chemical is water-soluble. A water spray system or a dry chemical system also may be required. Each system must be designed to cover each part of the cargo containment system, on the weather deck with exception of the vent riser. The cargo containment system includes the cargo tank, piping system, venting system, and gaging system.

Gas Carriers

Gas carriers are required to have additional fire fighting systems beyond those of an ordinary tank vessel. An exterior water spray system must be installed to protect all exposed cargo tank surfaces, each boundary of an accommodation space or navigational area that faces the cargo area, and the cargo loading and discharge area. The spray system is activated in the event of a fire to cool down and protect these areas. It is not intended to extinguish a liquefied flammable gas fire. On the other hand, a dry chemical system must be installed to protect the cargo area and cargo piping, and to extinguish a liquefied flammable gas fire that might result from a broken cargo handling line or a fire in the vent system. Foam systems are not effective against a liquefied gas fire. If installed, they can only augment, not replace, the systems just described.

Sprinkler Systems

Aboard U.S. vessels, manually operated sprinkler systems are employed only in very limited locations. New SOLAS ship construction primarily depends on structural fire protection, rather than on automatic sprinkler protection. However, installation of a sprinkler system can be offset by a reduction in the degree of insulation required between adjoining spaces.

For installations on vehicular decks, such as aboard ferry vessels, the sprinkler system should be designed to protect the structural integrity of the vessel, confine the fire to the location of origin, and wash flammable liquid spills to a safe location. Installation on vehicular decks is the primary marine use of sprinkler systems in the U.S.

Fire Fighting Plan

All U.S. vessels of 1000 gross tons and over and all vessels subject to SOLAS must permanently display a fire fighting plan or a fire control plan of the ship. Although the primary purpose of the plan is to guide shipboard personnel, it should contain the following information that can greatly assist port fire fighting groups:

1. Fire control stations for each deck.
2. Sections enclosed by fire-resistive divisions.
3. Fire alarms, detection systems, and sprinkler systems.
4. Fire extinguishing appliances.
5. Access to different compartments, decks, and so on.
6. Ventilating systems, including master fan controls, positions of dampers, location of remote controls, and the identification numbers of the ventilating fans serving each section.

Instead of being posted on a plan, the above information can be set forth in a fire fighting booklet. In that case, the booklet is required to be aboard ship at all times.

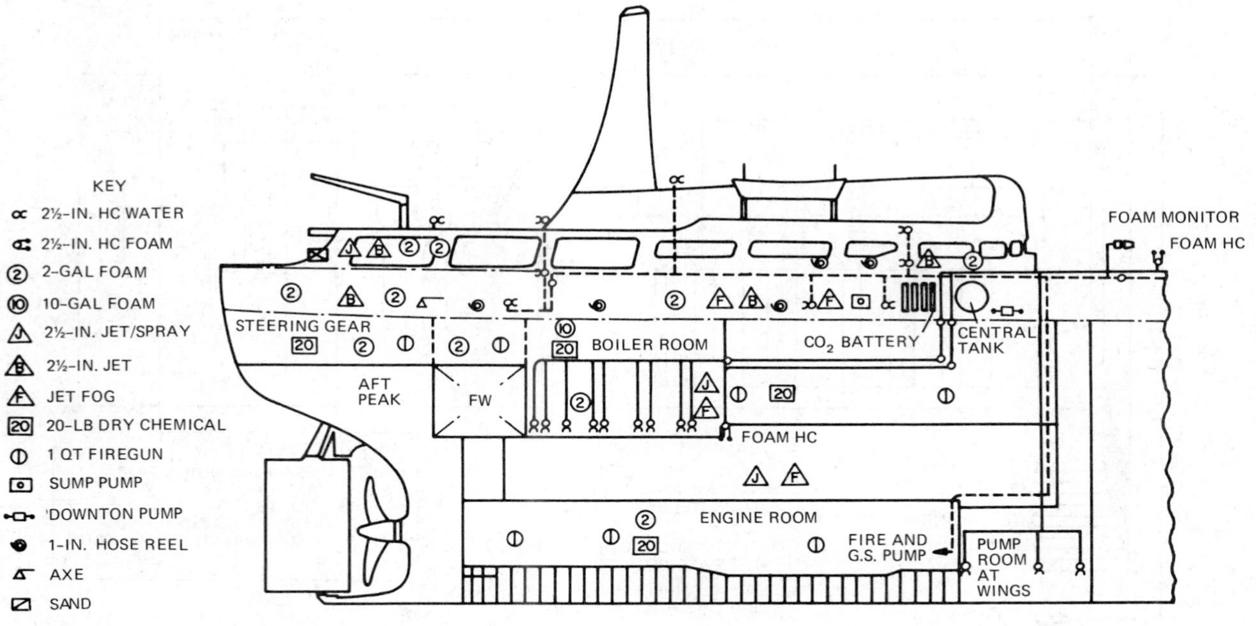

FIG. 8-37K. Fire fighting plan for the aft end of a super tanker.

Whether posted as a fire fighting plan or presented in booklet form, information should also be available on all water-tight compartments, openings therein, means of closure, controls, and arrangements for correcting any list due to flooding.

SOLAS '74 requires a duplicate set of fire control plans to be permanently stowed in a prominently marked, weather-tight enclosure outside the deckhouse for the assistance of shoreside fire fighting personnel. For an illustration of a fire fighting plan for the aft end of a super tanker, see Fig. 8-37K.

Most recently, the international community has agreed upon standard symbols for fire control plans. (See Figure 8-37L.) The majority of these are to be shown in red on the general arrangement plan to highlight their location for shipboard and shoreside fire fighters.

NFPA MARINE STANDARDS

NFPA requirements relating to marine vessels are contained in the following.

NFPA 306, *Control of Gas Hazards on Vessels*. This standard describes the conditions necessary for safety before making repairs on any vessel carrying or having carried, as a fuel or as cargo, combustible or flammable liquids, flammable compressed gases, and chemicals in bulk. It also contains a section on flammable cryogenic liquid carriers.

NFPA 312, *Vessels During Construction, Repair, and Lay-Up*. This standard covers measures for preventing and controlling fires on vessels in the building or repair yard, or on vessels that are laid up. Provisions for each of these circumstances appear separately in the standard.

OTHER ORGANIZATIONS CONTRIBUTING TO MARINE FIRESAFETY

The American Bureau of Shipping

The American Bureau of Shipping (ABS) is the American classification society whose technical committees develop rules for the dimensions and use of materials in the construction and conversion of marine vessels. After a vessel is completed according to the rules and under the constant supervision of an ABS field inspector, it is classed and listed by the bureau as having met all design and structural safety requirements.

The American Petroleum Institute

In the area of marine fire fighting and fire protection, the American Petroleum Institute (API) is active in the development of domestic and international standards, codes, and regulations. Under the policy direction of the API Central Committee on Transportation by Water, most actions are directed by the API Committee on Tank Vessels.

Ad hoc groups are sometimes used for special studies of a nonrepetitive nature.

The Marine Chemist Association, Inc.

This is a professional organization of chemists certificated for marine work by NFPA in accordance with provisions of NFPA 306, *Control of Gas Hazards on Vessels*. The association was established in May 1938 as the Marine Chemists' Subsection of the NFPA Marine Section. After the Marine Section was disbanded, the Marine Chemists organized its present association in 1948.

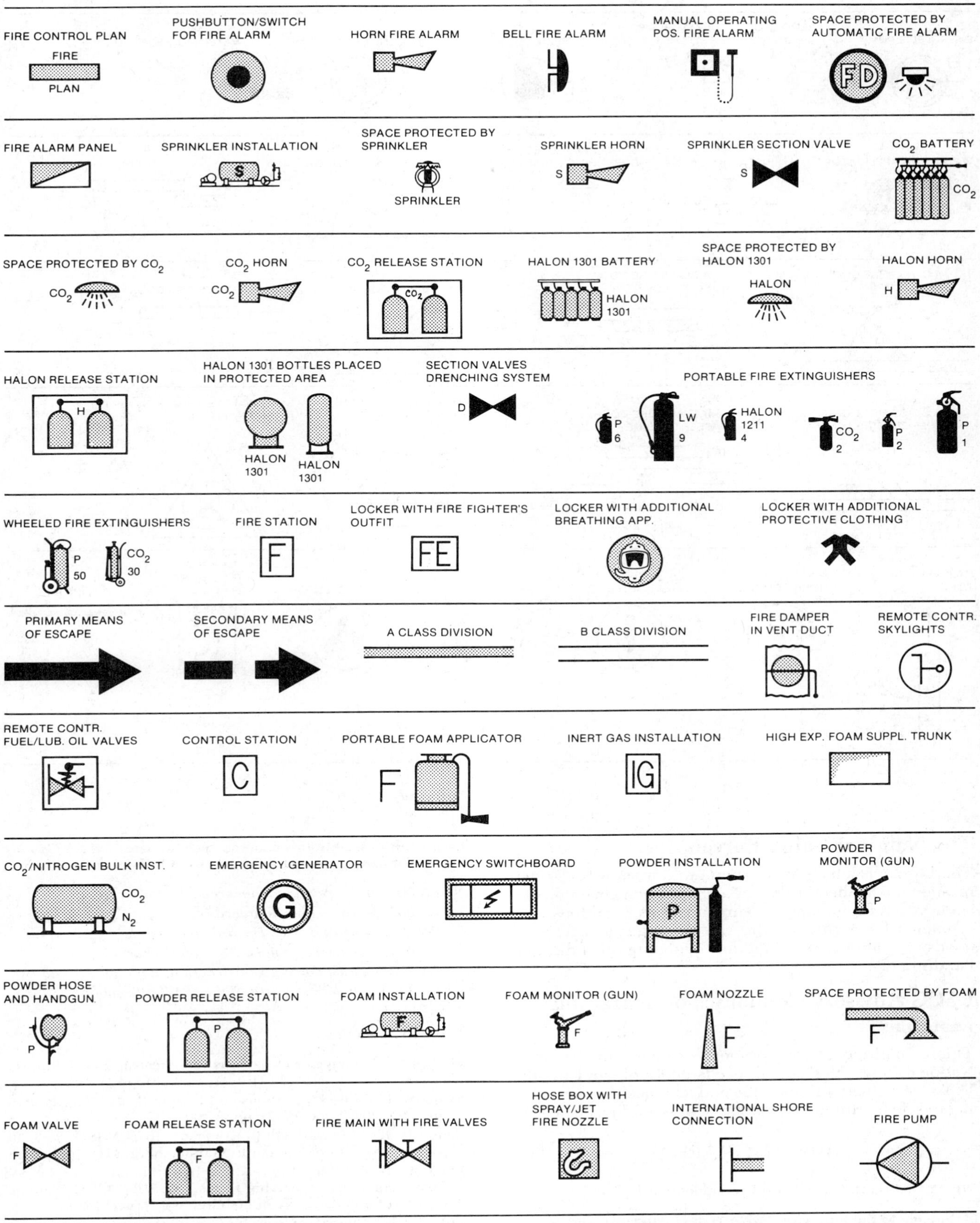

FIG. 8-37L. Symbols for use in accordance with regulation II-2/20 of the 1974 SOLAS Convention as Amended.

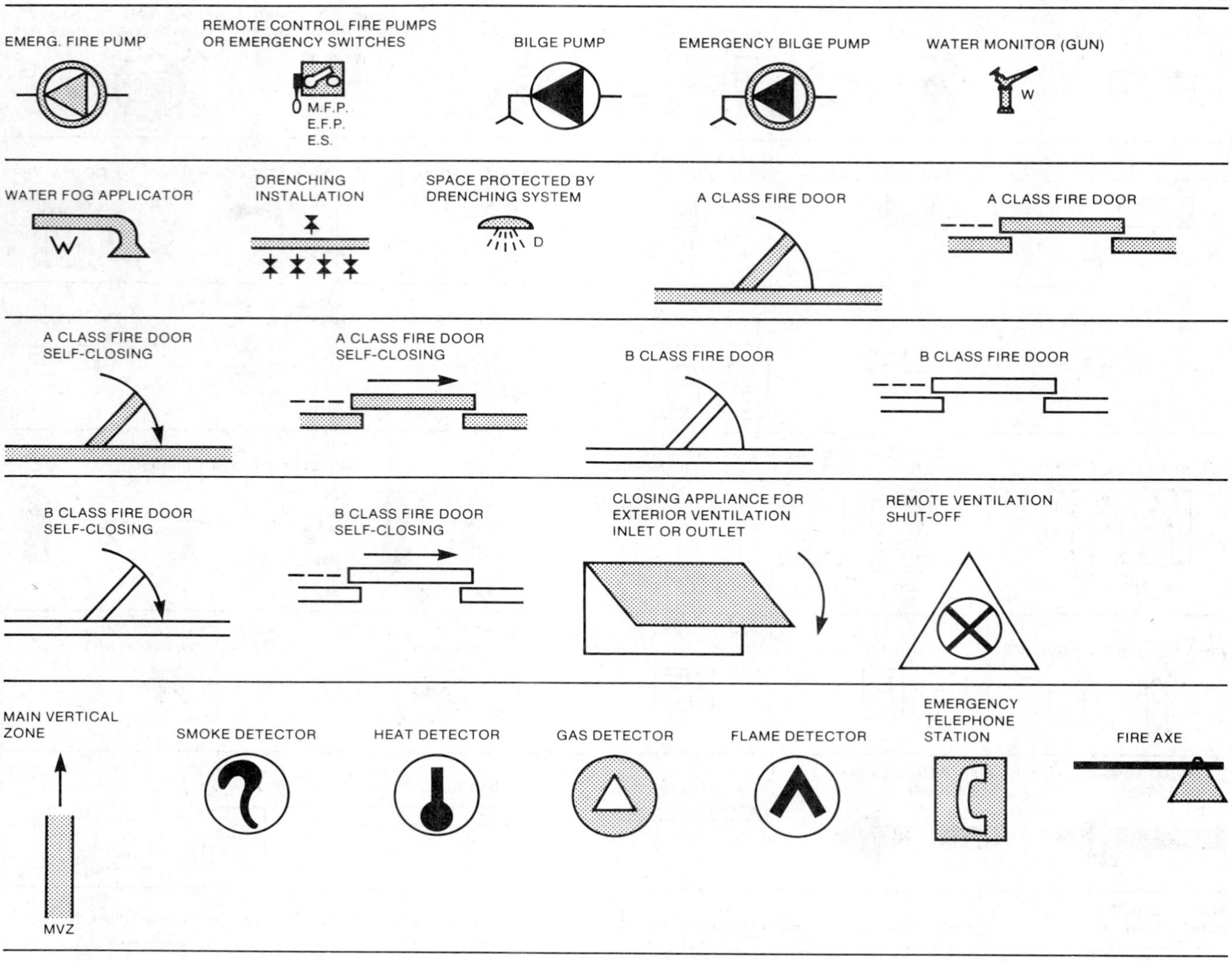

FIG. 8-37L. Continued

The National Cargo Bureau, Inc.

The Bureau is a nationwide, non-profit membership organization established in 1952 as a private, non-governmental agency that formulates recommendations to various governments for regulating the safe stowage of dangerous goods and other cargoes and for regulating related cargo-handling gear.

USCG Advisory Committee on Hazardous Materials

This committee of the National Academy of Sciences, National Research Council, is charged with advising the U.S. Coast Guard on scientific and technical matters relating to safe maritime transportation of hazardous materials.

BIBLIOGRAPHY

NFPA Codes, Standards, and Recommended Practices

Reference to the following NFPA codes, standards, and recommended practices will provide further information on marine fire hazards discussed in this chapter. (See the latest *NFPA Catalog* for availability of current editions of the following documents.)

NFPA 302, *Pleasure and Commercial Motor Craft.*

NFPA 303, *Marinas and Boatyards.*

NFPA 306, *Control of Gas Hazards on Vessels.*

NFPA 307, *Marine Terminals, Piers and Wharves.*

NFPA 312, *Vessels During Construction, Repair, and Lay-Up.*

NFPA 1405, *Land-Based Fire Fighters Who Respond to Marine Vessel Fires.*

Additional Readings

Abell, J. E., "Storage of Dangerous Chemicals in Ships' Stores," *Fire Prevention*, No. 211 (July/Aug. 1988), pp. 33-35.

Ashmore, F., "Fire Precautions on Pleasure Boats," *Fire Prevention*, No. 202 (Sept. 1987), pp. 27-30.

Baum, H. R., "Fire Growth in Combat Ships," *NBSIR 85-3159*, National Bureau of Standards, Gaithersburg, MD, June 1985.

Baum, H. R. and Rockett, J. A., "An Investigation of the Forced Ventilation in Containership Holds," *NBSIR 83-2665*, National Bureau of Standards, Gaithersburg, MD, May 1983.

Beatteay, R. E., *Fire Officer's Guide to Waterfront Fires*, National Fire Protection Association, Quincy, MA, 1975.

Blogg, E. C., "Fire Protection in Modern Merchant Shipping," *Fire International*, Vol. 12, No. 111 (June 7, 1988), pp. 24-25.

Charles, M., "Fresh Look at Ship and Port Fire-Fighting," *Fire International*, Vol. 12, No. 111 (June 7, 1988), pp. 58-59.

Connor, J., *Marine Fire Prevention, Fire Fighting and Fire Safety*, R. J. Brady, Bowie, MD, 1987.

Davies, D., "Naval Fire Protection for the 1990's," *Fire International*, Vol. 11, No. 105, 1987, pp. 39, 42-43.

House, W., Frock, W., and Welch, R. O., *Evaluation of Current Packaging Materials Used Aboard Ship and Recommendations for Reducing Their Flammability and Combustion Toxicity*, Vol. I - Flammability, prepared for Naval Supply Systems Command, U.S. Department of the Navy by Midwest Research Institute, Kansas City, MO, Mar. 1982.

Kerlin, D. J., "A Marine View of Fire Protection," *SFPE TR 82-10*, Society of Fire Protection Engineers, Boston, MA, 1982.

Klote, J. H. and Zile, R. H., "Smoke Movement and Smoke Control on Merchant Ships," *NBSIR 81-2433*, National Bureau of Standards, Gaithersburg, MD, Dec. 1981.

Kristiansen, A., "Reducing Fire Hazards at Sea," *Wire Industry*, Vol. 55, No. 653, 1988, p. 379.

Lee, B. T., "Fire Performance Testing of Bulkhead Insulation Systems for High Strength to Weight Ship Structures," *NBSIR 76-1012*, National Bureau of Standards, Gaithersburg, MD, Aug. 1976.

Lee, B. T. and Parker, W. J., "Fire Buildup in Shipboard Compartments—Characterization of Some Vulnerable Spaces and the States of Prediction Analysis," *NBSIR 79-1714*, National Bureau of Standards, Gaithersburg, MD, May 1979.

Lee, B. T. and Parker, W. J., "Fire Performance Guidelines for Shipboard Interior Finish," *NBSIR 79-1700*, National Bureau of Standards, Gaithersburg, MD, June 1979.

Lee, B. T. and Parker, W. J., "Naval Shipboard Fire Risk Criteria--Berthing Compartment Fire Study and Performance Guidelines," *NBSIR 76-1052*, National Bureau of Standards, Gaithersburg, MD, Sept. 1976.

"Marine Board Reports on Catamaran Fire," *High Speed Surface Craft*, Vol. 27, No. 2 (Mar.-Apr. 1988), pp. 8-9.

Marine Products Directory, Underwriters Laboratories Inc., Northbrook, IL.

Mckenna, P., "Safety Factor in the Transport of Passengers and Goods by Sea," *Fire Engineers Journal*, Vol. 48, No. 149 (June 1988), pp. 9-11.

Murtagh, M.M., "Fire Safety in Passenger Vessel Design," The *Naval Architect*, Royal Institution of Naval Architects, May 1990.

"Navigation and Vessel Inspection Circular 6-72 and 6-72, Change 1," *Guide to Fixed Fire Fighting Equipment Aboard Merchant Vessels*, U.S. Coast Guard, 1972.

"Navigation and Vessel Inspection Circular 6-80," *Guide to Structural Fire Protection Aboard Merchant Vessels*, U.S. Coast Guard, 1980.

"Navigation and Vessel Inspection Circular 2-84," *Amendments* to the 1974 Safety of Life at Sea (SOLAS) Treaty. U.S. Coast Guard, 1984.

Norris, D. A., "Fire Hands on Deck," *Fire Engineering*, Vol. 140, No. 9, 1987, p. 48-50.

Pati, V. B., *et al.*, "Simulation of Intelligent Fire Detection and Alarm System for a Warship," *Defense Science Journal*, Vol. 39, No. 1 (Jan. 1989), pp. 79-94.

Presdee, B., "Computerized Oil Rig Fires Could Save Lives," *Fire International*, Vol. 12, No. 113 (Oct.-Nov. 1988), p. 49, 52-53.

"Proposals to Aid Passenger Survivability," *Marine Engineers Review*, March 1988, pp. 16-17.

Recommended Fire Protection and Fire Prevention Practices for Major Shipyards Engaged in New Vessel Construction, American Hull Insurance Syndicate, NY, May 31, 1977.

Riley, W. M., "Notes on the Preparation of Fire Control Plans," *Marine Technology*, Vol. 25, No. 3, 1988, pp. 205-208.

Rushbrook, F., *Fire Aboard: The Problems of Prevention and Control in Ships, Port Installations and Offshore Structures*, 2nd ed., Heinman, NY, 1979.

Seamon, R. P., "Fire Adrift," *Fire Command*, Vol. 56, No. 4 (April 1989), pp. 26-28.

Ships Firefighting Manual, Marine Publications International, State Mutual Bank, London, England, 1983.

Von Iperen, W., "A Study of Ventilation of Containership Holds for Carriage of Flammable Liquids," (unpublished) Sea-Land Service, Inc., Elizabeth, NJ, June 18, 1979.

Weeks, C. B., "Fire on Board," *Fire Command*, Vol. 56, No. 4 (April 1989), pp. 41-42.

ORGANIZING FOR FIRE PROTECTION

Today's "fire fighter" is part of a broad-spectrum emergency-response team and system. The challenges faced by these men and women are of unprecedented technical complexity. More than $10 billion is spent each year to operate paid local fire departments. The equivalent cost is several times that figure if one includes the costs and paid or donated time of all career and volunteer fire fighters, whether in public or private emergency organizations at the national, state or local level. As the range of emergencies covered by the "fire" service grows, as the sophistication of equipment and methods to do the job increases, as our understanding evolves as to what works and what doesn't work, it is ever more important to refine our set of standards, best practices, and core knowledge to keep pace. This section provides that foundation as it has evolved for the modern fire protection organization.

"Fire fighting continues to be one of the most hazardous occupations in the United States," as Chapter 1 says. Moreover, we have come to realize that many of the leading causes of on-duty fire fighter deaths and injuries—such as heart attacks and vehicle accidents—do not involve questions of fireground equipment and tactics so much as fundamentals of occupational safety and health. Chapter 1 reviews these essentials, with special attention to the central position of NFPA 1500.

Chapters 2 and 3 address major elements of fire protection organizations in industrial and other private-company settings. Chapter 2 describes approaches to fire loss prevention and control through modern engineering methods of hazard and risk identification, analysis and management. Chapter 3 describes the emerging roles of private emergency organizations, a more general and accurate title today than the traditional "industrial fire brigade" and one that reflects the broader charter such groups often have in the 1990s.

Chapters 4-11 then address topics affecting the public fire department. Chapter 4 describes the alternative organizational structures used, tracing the roots of such organizations back to 24 B.C. The linkage between organizational structure and functional assignments is covered as well, as are the newer, nontraditional roles that a modern fire department must also fit onto the organizational chart. With the right structure in place, the next step is resource requirements and specification of procedures, which are among the topics covered in Chapter 5 under administration and management. Then, operational requirements and methods are addressed in Chapter 6. Some specific resource issues are covered in Chapters 9 (apparatus, equipment, clothing) and 10 (training and other facilities). Chapters 7 (fire prevention, code enforcement), 8 (pre-fire planning) and 11 (emergency medical services) review needs and procedures for several of the most important non-suppression activities in emergency departments of the 1990s.

The rest of this section is on hazardous materials, one of the fastest growing and most complex roles faced by the U.S. fire service today. Chapter 12 provides an overview of the fire community's role in this area, where many groups outside the traditional fire community will also be involved. Chapter 13 focuses on identification of specific materials. Hazardous-materials transportation emergencies are addressed in Chapter 14, and in case local knowledge and resources prove insufficient to deal with such emergencies, Chapter 15 describes national networks and sources of technical assistance. Finally, waste control methods are reviewed in Chapters 16-17.

Also look for these: Chapter 1 of Section 1 provides a fair amount of statistical detail on fire-service related topics. Chapter 1 of Section 2 is useful for any fire department planning firesafety education programs. The community infrastructure that supports fire departments is addressed in Chapter 1 of Section 4 (emergency communications systems) and, to a lesser degree, Chapters 2-3 of Section 4 (other detection/alarm systems); and in Chapters 1-7 and 14 of Section 5 (water and all aspects of water-based suppression). Construction, as it relates to the fire service, is addressed in Chapter 11 of Section 6. Chapters 1-3 of Section 10 discuss fire-incident-based information and analysis, most of which occurs in fire departments, while

Chapters 4-5 address uses of data bases and models in the range of decisions fire departments make. Chapters 6-7 of Section 10 provide a broad view of fire hazard assessment and fire risk analysis, which should be compared to the specialized uses of these methods described in Chapters 2 and 6 of this section. Beyond this handbook, many chapters in this section are elaborated in whole books or other training aids, such as *Management in the Fire Service, Building Construction for the Fire Service, Fire Command,* and the many guides to particular fire department operations, particular classes of hazardous materials, or particular fire fighter health and safety programs.

FIRE DEPARTMENT OCCUPATIONAL SAFETY AND HEALTH

William Peterson

NFPA 1500, *Standard on Fire Department Occupational Safety and Health*, was developed by the National Fire Protection Association's Technical Committee on Fire Service Occupational Safety and Health, beginning in late 1984. It was adopted by the membership at the NFPA's 1987 Annual Meeting in Cincinnati, OH, and issued by the NFPA Standards Council on July 17, 1987 with an effective date of August 7, 1987. Developed within the NFPA's concensus standards-making process, NFPA 1500 will give a whole new emphasis and direction to the fire service in the years to come. It is hoped that this new emphasis on fire fighter health and safety will significantly reduce the number of deaths and the severity of injuries experienced in the fire service.

Fire fighting continues to be one of the most hazardous occupations in the United States. Over the past years, well over 100 fire fighter deaths and 100,000 injuries per year have placed fire fighting among those jobs rated highest for occupational death and injury. The losses experienced each year affect career and volunteer fire fighters alike. NFPA 1500 was developed to make fire fighting less dangerous by reducing deaths, injuries, and accidents. The standard also emphasizes the well-being of the fire fighter, especially his or her health and physical fitness.

In order to understand the thrust and direction of NFPA 1500, it is necessary to understand the current situation as it relates to fire fighter death and injury statistics. Each year, the National Fire Protection Association gathers the most complete data available on fire fighter deaths and injuries. By understanding the factors that lead to fire fighter deaths and injuries, it becomes possible to manage the risk of providing fire protection services in a way that reduces the fire fighter's exposure to harm to reasonable levels and provides an acceptable level of occupational safety and health.

In 1989, 116 fire fighters died in the line of duty. This figure marked the second lowest number of fire fighter fatalities since the NFPA began collecting statistics in 1977. Table 9-1A shows the distribution of fire fighter deaths for the years 1978 through 1989.

William Peterson is chief of the Plano Fire Department in Plano, TX.

Table 9-1B shows the distribution of the 116 deaths by type of duty. As in previous years, non-fireground activities accounted for at least half of the deaths in 1989.

TABLE 9-1A. ***Line-of-Duty Fire Fighter Deaths, 1978-1989***

Year	Number of Deaths
1978	169
1979	122
1980	137
1981	135
1982	123
1983	112
1984	119
1985	126
1986	118
1987	130
1988	135
1989	116

TABLE 9-1B. ***Fire Fighter Deaths 1989—ByType of Duty***

Cause	Number of Deaths	Percentage
Fire Fighting	58	50.0
Non-Fire Incident	6	5.2
Responding/ Returning from Alarm	28	24.1
Other On-Duty	12	10.3
Training	12	10.3

Table 9-1C shows the distribution of deaths by cause of fatal injury or illness. The term "cause" refers to the action, lack of action, or circumstances that directly resulted in the fatal injury.

Stress was the major cause of death, resulting in more than half of the fatalities, as in previous years' studies. A significant improvement in this category could be anticipated if fire fighters were in better physical condition and

TABLE 9-1C. *Fire Fighter Deaths 1989—By Cause of Fatal Injury*

Cause	Number of Deaths	Percentage
Stress	64	54.3
Falls	1	0.9
Struck by/Contact with Object	28	24.1
Caught or Trapped	23	19.8

better able to handle the strenuous physical activities associated with emergency operations.

The distribution of deaths by nature of the fatal injury or illness is shown in Table 9-1D. The most frequently reported fatal injury was heart attack (54.3 percent). Of the 64 heart-attack victims, at least 16 were known to have had prior heart problems, usually heart attacks or bypass surgery, and medical documentation showed that 6 others had severe arteriosclerotic heart disease. Four other victims suffered from diabetes, and another was taking medication for blood clotting before the fatal incident. Other major categories of fatal injuries are internal trauma, asphyxiation, and crushing.

TABLE 9-1D. *Fire Fighter Deaths 1989—By Nature of Fatal Injury*

Cause	Number of Deaths	Percentage
Heart Attack	63	54.3
Crushing	8	6.9
Electrocution	3	2.6
Internal Trauma	18	15.5
Drowning	2	1.7
Asphyxiation	11	9.5
Gunshot	2	1.7
Burns	6	5.2
Bleeding	1	0.9
Stroke (CVA)	1	0.9
Pulmonary Embolism	1	0.9

TABLE 9-1E. *1989 Fire Fighter Deaths by Age and Cause of Death*

Age Group	Heart Attacks	Other Trauma	Total Deaths
20 and Under	1	4	5
21–25	0	8	8
26–30	2	8	10
31–35	6	8	14
36–40	4	4	8
41–45	6	8	14
46–50	9	2	11
51–55	10	1	11
56–60	11	5	16
Over 60	14	5	19

The fire fighters who died in the line of duty in 1989 ranged in age from 18 to 75 years. Table 9-1E shows the distribution of fire fighter deaths by age and cause of death. Most years reflect a high proportion of deaths by heart attack for older fire fighters and a low proportion for fire fighters under the age of 35.

Table 9-1F shows the death rates by age categories using estimates of the number of fire fighters in each age group from the NFPA's 1987 profile of fire departments and the fatality data from 1985 to 1989. As the data show, the death rate is lowest for fire fighters aged 20 to 39, slightly above average for fire fighters aged 40 to 49, and significantly higher than average for fire fighters age 50 and over. It is of particular interest to note that only 15 percent of all fire fighters are over age 50, yet that particular age group accounted for more than a third of the deaths from 1985 to 1989.

TABLE 9-1F. *Average Death Rates per 10,000 Fire Fighters, 1985–1989*

Age Group	Deaths per 10,000 Fire Fighters
Under 20	0.92
20–29	0.66
30–39	0.67
40–49	1.30
50–59	2.58
60 and Over	4.70
Overall Average: 1.18 Deaths per 10,000 Fire Fighters	

Note: These figures combine career and volunteer fire fighters. The two groups may have very different age distributions, which are not reflected.

Table 9-1G shows the distribution by fixed property use of the 58 fireground deaths in 1989. It is interesting to note that, while fire fighters respond to non-residential fires far less frequently than to residential fires, the death rate in non-residential properties is much higher. This fact is probably due to the size, complexity, familiarity, and special hazards that exist in these types of occupancies, and to the associated problems encountered during fire-suppression activities.

TABLE 9-1G. *Fireground Deaths in 1989 by Fixed Property Use**

Fixed Property Use	Number of Deaths	Percentage
Residential	22	37.9
Churches	2	3.4
Restaurants	1	1.7
Stores	7	12.1
Storage	7	12.1
Manufacturing	2	3.6
Vacant	5	8.6
Wildland	8	13.8
Street/Highway	4	6.9

* There were 58 fireground deaths in 1989.

Table 9-1H shows the 1984-1988 average fireground death rates for various occupancy types. These rates were calculated using the updated fire fighter fatality data and the estimates of fires from NFPA's annual fire experience surveys.

In the ten-year period from 1980 to 1989, at least 1251 fire fighters died in the line of duty in the United States. Six hundred eighty or 54.4 percent of these were volunteer fire fighters. The remaining 571, or 45.6 percent, were career fire fighters. Statistics from the past three years have shown that career fire fighter fatalities during the decade have dropped as much as 30 percent, while the number of fatalities involving volunteers have increased as much as 30 percent. Volunteer fire fighter fatalities in 1988 and 1989 were the highest in the ten-year period and tend to

TABLE 9-1H. ***Fire Fighter Death Rates on the Fireground, 1984–1989***

Occupancy Type	Deaths per 100,000 Fires
Manufacturing	13.04
Vacant, Special*	18.25
Public Assembly	12.61
Stores and Offices	14.57
Storage	11.48
Educational	5.08
Institutional	1.02
Residential	2.93

* Includes idle buildings, buildings under construction, etc.

indicate that, while being a career fire fighter is safer today than it was ten years ago, a volunteer fire fighter may face the greatest health and safety risks in the fire service today. Table 9-1I compares career fire fighter fatalities to volunteer fire fighter fatalities over the past ten years.

TABLE 9-1I. ***Comparison of Career and Volunteer Fatalities, 1980–1989***

Year	Career	Volunteer
1980	69	68
1981	68	67
1982	53	70
1983	61	51
1984	46	73
1985	61	65
1986	63	55
1987	54	76
1988	48	87
1989	48	68

Based on survey data reported to the NFPA, it is estimated that at least 100,700 injuries were experienced by fire fighters in the line of duty during 1989. While slightly lower than the number experienced in 1987 and 1988, the number of injuries is similar to the levels of injuries experienced between 1983 and 1986. Table 9-1J shows the number of fire fighter injuries between 1983 and 1989 and reveals that reported injuries remained within 3 percent of 100,000 each year during this period. Unlike fire fighter death statistics, there has been no sustained trend in the number of estimated injuries during the past decade.

TABLE 9-1J. ***Number of Fire Fighter Injuries, 1983–1989***

Year	Number of Injuries
1983	103,150
1984	102,300
1985	100,900
1986	94,450
1987	102,600
1988	102,900
1989	100,700

Looking at fire fighter injuries relative to emergency incidents to which the fire service responded, 7.5 injuries per 1000 incidents were experienced in 1989. This figure represents a decrease of 2.1 percent from 1988 and a decrease of 10.7 percent from 1987, and was the lowest rate between 1983 and 1989. Table 9-1K lists the injury rate for this period.

TABLE 9-1K. ***Fire Fighter Injuries per 1,000 Incidents***

Year	Injuries per 1,000 Incidents
1983	9.4
1984	9.3
1985	8.8
1986	8.1
1987	8.4
1988	7.7
1989	7.5

Estimates of fire fighter injuries by the type of duty engaged in at the time of the injury are displayed in Table 9-1L. Types of duty considered by the NFPA study include responding to or returning from an emergency, fireground activities, non-fire emergencies, training, and other on-duty activities.

TABLE 9-1L. ***Number of Fire Fighter Injuries by Type of Duty***

Type of Duty	Number of Injuries
Responding/ Returning	6,000
Fireground	58,250
Nonfire Emergency	12,580
Training	6,010
Other On-Duty	17,860

Table 9-1M shows the estimates of 1989 fire fighter injuries by the nature of injury and the type of duty. The four major types of injuries that occur during fireground operations are strains and sprains; wounds, cuts, bleeding, and bruises; smoke and gas inhalation; and burns. The conscientious use of self-contained breathing apparatus (SCBA) and other articles of fire fighter protective clothing, along with comprehensive training and a fireground incident management system, would have a significant impact on the current injury situation.

If any effort to control injury-causing situations is to be successful, it is important that the causes of the injuries are understood. Table 9-1N takes a closer look at fireground injury causes. As defined here, "cause" refers to the initial circumstance leading to the injury.

Table 9-1O displays the average number of injuries and the injuries requiring hospitalization per department by the population of the protected community during 1988. The average number of injuries per department range from a low of 0.38 for communities that serve a population of less than 2500 to a high of 419.6 for departments that protect a population of half a million to a million persons. Generally, the larger the community, the greater the number of injuries.

The average number of injuries requiring hospitalization ranged from 0.03 for communities with populations of less than 2500 to a high of 19.80 for communities with populations of 500,000 to 999,999. For communities with populations of less than 50,000, less than 1 injury requiring

TABLE 9-1M. ***Fire Fighter Injuries by Nature of Injury and Type of Duty, 1989***

Nature of Injury	Responding to or Returning from an Incident Number	Responding to or Returning from an Incident Percent	Fireground Number	Fireground Percent	Non-Fire Emergency Number	Non-Fire Emergency Percent	Training Number	Training Percent	Other On-Duty Number	Other On-Duty Percent	Total Number
Burns (fire or chemical)	75	1.3	4,815	8.3	155	1.2	415	6.9	325	1.8	5,785
Smoke or gas inhalation	110	1.8	6,205	10.7	215	1.7	140	2.3	135	0.8	6,805
Other respiratory distress	25	0.4	1,015	1.7	270	2.1	95	1.6	255	1.4	1,660
Eye irritation	390	6.5	4,025	6.9	370	2.9	330	5.5	800	4.5	5,915
Wound, cut, bleeding, bruise	1,350	22.5	11,860	20.4	2,600	20.7	1,320	22.0	4,425	24.8	21,555
Dislocation, fracture	315	5.2	1,765	3.0	280	2.2	280	4.7	570	3.2	3,210
Heart attack or stroke	40	0.7	255	0.4	50	0.4	25	0.4	215	1.2	585
Strain, sprain, muscular pain	3,115	51.9	22,360	38.4	6,435	51.2	2,950	49.1	9,020	50.5	43,880
Thermal stress (frostbite, heat exhaustion)	95	1.6	3,040	5.2	110	0.9	230	3.8	85	0.5	3,560
Other	485	8.1	2,910	5.0	2,095	16.7	225	3.7	2,030	11.3	7,745
	6,000		58,250		12,580		6,010		17,860		100,700

Source: NFPA's Survey of Fire Departments for U.S. Fire Experience (1989).
Note: If a fire fighter sustained multiple injuries for the same incident, only the nature of the single most serious injury was tabulated.

TABLE 9-1N. ***Fireground Injury Causes***

Cause of Injury	Number of Injuries	Percentage
Exposure to Fire Products	18,629	18.5
Stepped on/Contact w/ Object	11,178	11.1
Overexertion	20,744	20.6
Fell, Slipped	24,974	24.8
Struck by Object	11,278	11.2
Exposure to Chemicals/ Radiation	3,122	3.1
Extreme Weather	2,719	2.7
Caught/Trapped	1,007	1.0
Other	7,049	7.0

hospitalization was experienced for each population category. Generally, this data seem to indicate that fire fighters are increasingly susceptible to injuries requiring hospitalization as the size of the city increases. Fire fighters should not, however, be lulled into complacency and feel that serious injuries happen only to urban fire fighters. Injuries are a function of many factors, all of which may be present in communities of any size. In fact, the high rate of injuries to fire fighters in communities with populations under 10,000 shows that these departments typically respond to more fires per capita than larger fire departments and thus have a higher hospitalization rate than their urban counterparts.

Table 9-1P shows the average number of fireground injuries per department by the population of the community protected in 1989. These tabulations suggest that the number of fires to which a fire department responds is directly related to the population protected and that the number of fireground injuries incurred by a department is directly related to its exposure to fire—that is, to the number of fires attended by the department.

In order to allow a more direct comparison between fire departments of various sizes, examining the number of injuries per 100 fires attended will reveal whether community size has an effect on the number of fire fighter injuries in a particular community. The number of fireground injuries per 100 fires, shown in column 4 of Table 9-1P, reveals that the overall rate varies very little compared to the average number of injuries. This indicates that the wide range noted in average fireground injuries

TABLE 9-1O. ***Average Number of Fire Fighter Injuries and Injuries Requiring Hospitalization per Department by Population of Community Protected, 1989 For all Types of Duty***

Population of Community Protected	Average Number of Fire Fighter Injuries	Average Number of Injuries Requiring Hospitalization	Number of Injuries Requiring Hospitalization per 100 Injuries
500,000 to 999,000	419.60	19.80	4.72
250,000 to 499,000	138.50	3.22	2.32
100,000 to 249,000	61.64	2.49	4.04
50,000 to 99,000	25.09	1.03	4.11
25,000 to 49,000	10.17	0.49	4.82
10,000 to 24,999	3.87	0.22	5.68
5,000 to 9,999	1.62	0.14	8.64
2,500 to 4,999	1.02	0.11	10.78
Under 2,500	0.38	0.03	7.89

Source: NFPA's Survey of Fire Departments for U.S. Fire Experience (1989).

TABLE 9-1P. ***Average Number of Fires, Fireground Injuries and Injury Rates per Department by Population of Community Protected, 1989***

Population of Community Protected	Average Number of Fires	Average Number of Fire-Ground Injuries	Number of Fire-Ground Injuries per 100 Fires	Number of Fire-Ground Injuries per 100 Fire Fighters
500,000 to 999,000	5,718.0	170.9	3.0	17.1
250,000 to 499,000	2,790.0	91.2	3.3	15.5
100,000 to 249,000	1,178.9	39.3	3.3	14.1
50,000 to 99,000	442.6	13.4	3.0	11.6
25,000 to 49,000	222.4	5.0	2.2	8.9
10,000 to 24,999	117.6	2.2	1.9	5.7
5,000 to 9,999	56.3	1.0	1.8	3.2
2,500 to 4,999	32.9	0.8	2.4	2.9
Under 2,500	14.7	0.3	2.0	1.3

Source: NFPA's Survey of Fire Departments for U.S. Fire Experience (1989).

by population decreases dramatically when the actual fire rate is considered.

Table 9-1Q displays the average number of fires and fireground injuries in 1989 per department by population of community protected and by region of the country. The results for each region indicate that the number of fires to which a fire department responds is directly related to the population protected and that the number of fireground injuries incurred by a fire department is directly related to the number of fires it attends. The Northeast reports a substantially higher number of fireground injuries for all sizes of communities served. Table 9-1Q also shows the number of fireground injuries per 100 fires by population served and by region of the country. These results are consistent with the average fireground injury findings, showing the Northeast as highest for all populations served, except for the two largest population groups for which no sufficient data were available.

As the data reported by the NFPA show, fire fighting operations pose a significant safety hazard and risk to the fire fighter. Because of the nature of the work and the types of hazards encountered on the fireground, it is highly unlikely that all fire fighter injuries can be eliminated. Good risk-management practices and the use of protective clothing and safety equipment can have a positive impact on the current experience. Reducing injuries will ultimately result in reduced suffering, less lost time, and lower medical costs.

Data contained in this section of the document have been obtained for the U.S. fire fighter death and injury reports published by the National Fire Protection Association each year.

NFPA 1500 OVERVIEW

NFPA 1500 was written for the purpose of making the profession less dangerous by reducing the risk of accidents, injuries, and fatalities in the course of conducting emergency operations. NFPA 1500 also is geared toward making fire fighters healthier and more physically able to undertake their duties during their careers and for the remainder of their lives.

The yearly surveys and analyses of fire fighter deaths and injuries clearly show that fire fighters are suffering the consequences of placing their jobs and the welfare of others ahead of their own health and safety. The results of this situation clearly indicate that cancer and heart disease are a major problem for both active and retired fire fighters.

NFPA 1500 was drafted by a cross-section of the fire service. The committee consisted of fire chiefs, company officers, line fire fighters, and union officials representing

TABLE 9-1Q. ***Average Number of Fires and Fireground Injuries per Department and Injuries per 100 Fires by Population of Community Protected and Region, 1989***

Column 1: Average Reported Number of Fires; Column 2: Average Reported Number of Fireground Injuries; Column 3: Number of Fireground Injuries per 100 Fires

Population of Community Protected	Northeast			North-Central			South			West		
	Col. 1	Col. 2	Col. 3	Col. 1	Col. 2	Col. 3	Col. 1	Col. 2	Col. 3	Col. 1	Col. 2	Col. 3
500,000 to 999,000	—	—	—	—	—	—	6,252.2	152.4	2.4	5,272.2	197.0	3.7
250,000 to 499,000	—	—	—	2,973.0	119.8	4.0	2,992.2	77.8	2.6	2,121.3	51.5	2.4
100,000 to 249,999	1,982.5	140.8	7.1	1,246.8	34.0	2.7	1,127.7	22.1	2.0	864.1	20.0	2.3
50,000 to 99,999	630.9	29.5	4.7	388.7	15.6	4.0	486.2	8.3	1.7	356.1	7.2	2.0
25,000 to 49,999	205.9	7.5	3.6	195.3	5.2	2.7	256.2	4.4	1.7	243.8	3.6	1.5
10,000 to 24,999	114.8	3.5	3.0	101.1	2.0	2.0	140.5	1.9	1.4	124.1	1.5	1.2
5,000 to 9,999	52.3	1.5	2.9	51.9	0.9	1.7	61.9	1.0	1.6	64.9	0.8	1.2
2,500 to 4,999	33.9	1.1	3.3	28.0	0.7	2.5	40.0	0.5	1.3	36.5	1.1	3.0
Under 2,500	13.7	0.3	2.2	12.8	0.2	1.6	21.6	0.4	1.9	13.2	0.2	1.5
Overall regional rate			4.8			2.3			1.7			2.1

Source: NFPA's Survey of Fire Departments for U.S. Fire Experience (1989).
* Insufficient data.

both career and volunteer fire departments. Other members of the committee included apparatus and protective-equipment manufacturers, independent experts, and representatives of the United States Fire Administration. Like all NFPA committees, the NFPA 1500 group represented a balanced mixture of interests with diverse views of, and perspectives on, fire fighter safety. However, each member of the committee was committed to improving the health and safety of members of the fire service.

The document was drafted over a period of three-and-one-half years, with input from local fire service members adding to the expertise of the committee members. During the open public comment period, approximately 1200 public comments were received on the proposed standard. Committee review of these public comments resulted in further refinement and improvements for the final draft. With strong support from both the International Association of Fire Chiefs and the International Association of Fire Fighters, the standard was accepted by a near-unanimous vote of the NFPA membership at the 1987 NFPA Annual Meeting.

As an NFPA standard, NFPA 1500 is not a mandatory requirement for any fire service organization until it has been adopted by an authority having appropriate jurisdiction. NFPA develops and publishes standards that express the current thinking of volunteer members on each of more than 200 technical committees. In the case of NFPA 1500, the standard describes the elements of an occupational safety and health program that has been accepted as the minimum level of care that should be provided in the fire service today. All fire departments are being encouraged to comply voluntarily with the standard. As a specific document, NFPA 1500 is also available for legal adoption and enforcement by official entities, such as state and local governments or state occupational safety and health administrations.

Adoption and enforcement procedures vary widely across the country, so it is difficult to predict when and where this standard will become a legally required document. A survey of more than 450 fire departments conducted by the International Association of Fire Chiefs in 1990 indicated that 55 percent of the departments had adopted a plan to implement NFPA 1500. Some states have already begun to adopt health and safety regulations incorporating parts of NFPA 1500 for the fire service. In addition, the newly adopted OSHA/EPA training requirements for hazardous materials response contain some of the requirements of NFPA 1500. One of the basic objectives of NFPA 1500 was to develop a program that would satisfy all of the requirements of the OSHA Fire Brigade Standard and to take those requirements one step further in several important areas. Unlike the OSHA standard, however, NFPA 1500 was written for the fire service, by the fire service.

Establishing a fire service occupational safety and health program can be difficult for a fire department because of the wide variety of issues that need to be addressed. In addition, it may be difficult to deal with program-element costs and with the time and resources required to implement a compliance plan. NFPA 1500 includes a section on implementation that allows for a phased approach which can be tailored to meet the needs and capabilities of a particular fire department. This approach calls for a comprehensive implementation plan and schedule that should be approved by an authority having jurisdiction. This approval should be based on reasonable compliance under anticipated individual circumstances. The development of such a plan will require each fire department to assess its own weaknesses in order to determine what would be required to comply with NFPA 1500. The plan which is then developed must balance the problems that have been identified and the resources available to correct them.

NFPA 1500 addresses fire fighter health and safety as an overall program to create a work environment that will reduce the risk to members of the fire department. The standard considers a department member to be anyone involved in the organization at any level, whether career or volunteer, line or staff. The role of management is to provide as safe a work environment as possible, considering the scope and work of the organization. Management also is required to establish the necessary rules, regulations, and procedures that will allow the program to work effectively.

Every member of the organization has the right to be protected by an effective health and safety program, and the responsibility to comply with the established rules and regulations that structure the program. Organization members also have the right to participate or be represented in the research, development, implementation, and enforcement of the program, since the program is designed for their benefit.

The department is required to identify a safety officer. A companion document, NFPA 1501, *Standard for Fire Department Safety Officer*, describes the role of this person in structuring and implementing the program.

An occupational safety and health committee must be established in the fire department. This committee should be made up of a cross-section of the department and be responsible for reviewing matters that deal with occupational safety and health issues within the department.

A data-collection system must be established to track accidents, injuries, illnesses, and deaths that are or might be job-related. The data-collection system also should contain records of occupational exposure to toxic substances or contagious diseases. Records dealing with personnel training and certification and with the inspection, maintenance, and repair of emergency vehicles and equipment should be maintained.

The standard includes basic training requirements intended to ensure that members are trained adequately to provide for their own safety and that they do not create a hazard to others in the performance of their duties. Members who have not been trained fully must be supervised by qualified, experienced personnel, and their emergency scene duties must be limited to those that fall in the scope of their training and capabilities. If members of the department engage in structural fire fighting, training must be held at least monthly. Any training held in the department must be based on written standard operating procedures. Any training that involves live fire fighting exercises must be conducted in accordance with NFPA 1403, *Standard on Live Fire Training Evolutions in Structures*. Specialized training also must be provided if the department responds to special hazards, such as hazardous materials responses or below-grade and confined-space rescue.

A major requirement in the standard relates to the safe operation of fire apparatus. Riding on tailsteps or in other exposed positions is expressly prohibited. All members must be seated with their seat belts fastened before the fire fighting vehicle begins to move or at any time the vehicle is in motion. As far as the standard is concerned, the only safe way to ride fire apparatus is in a seat, in an enclosed area, with a seat belt fastened. An enclosed area is defined as having three sides and a top. Canopy areas which are open to the rear are acceptable on existing apparatus. However, the new requirements of NFPA 1901 will mandate four-door fully-enclosed cabs on all new fire apparatus.

The standard requires the fire department to specify the number of personnel who may ride on a piece of apparatus, and requires the vendor to provide that number of seats in an enclosed area. The fire department then assumes responsibility for making sure that everyone riding in the vehicle is properly secured in a seat.

The standard also requires fire apparatus and equipment to be inspected periodically and after each use in order to identify unsafe conditions. Any deficiencies found during these inspections must be corrected before the vehicle or piece of equipment is placed back in service.

Hearing protection is required for anyone exposed to vehicle or equipment noise in excess of 90 db, whether they are drivers, passengers, or operators. This may be accomplished by hearing-protection devices, or by insulation, or by a combination of the two.

The fire department is required to provide full protective clothing and self-contained breathing apparatus (SCBA) to all members who will be exposed to the hazards of structural fire fighting. The items provided must comply with appropriate NFPA standards, and the department must ensure that all protective clothing is used properly by all members exposed to those hazards. When the activity is other than structural fire fighting, the department is obligated to provide appropriate protection for the hazards of each particular activity. The standard is explicit in requiring full body protection, including protection for the face and eyes. Full body protection includes coat and pants, not three-quarter-length boots. The use of existing items of protective clothing is restricted only to those that met the respective NFPA standards in effect at the time the item of protective clothing or equipment was bought.

For interior fire fighting, self-contained breathing apparatus must be used, and operations should be conducted in teams of two or more. During interior operations, one member must be assigned to remain outside the area in which respiratory protection is required to be accountable for the interior crews. In imminently hazardous situations, such as hazardous materials incidents or confined-space or below-grade rescues, a safety officer must be assigned, a back-up rescue team must be ready to assist, and qualified emergency medical support personnel must be standing by with medical equipment and transport capability.

The standard requires that operations at the scene of a fire or other emergency be conducted under an incident command system. This incident command system must be based on written procedures that identify roles and responsibilities relating to the safety of emergency operations. This emergency management system requires that the incident commander be responsible for the overall safety of the operation and of all members of the fire department at the scene. The emergency management system should provide for proper supervision for all operations and keep the incident commander aware of the position and function of all units operating on the scene.

The standard limits emergency scene operations to those that can be accomplished safely with available personnel. The standard includes a strong recommendation for a minimum of four fire fighters on each engine and ladder company in order to provide adequate personnel to perform standard functions safely and efficiently.

Fire stations and other fire department facilities also are regulated by NFPA 1500. All fire department facilities are required to meet all legally applicable health, safety, building, and fire codes. Sleeping areas in fire stations must be equipped with smoke detectors, and automatic sprinkler protection is strongly recommended. Mandatory inspections are required at least annually for code compliance and at least monthly to identify health and safety hazards. The standard also requires a 1-hr separation between vehicle storage areas and sleeping areas, and stations must be designed and equipped with devices to ventilate exhaust emissions from apparatus to prevent fire fighters from being exposed to harmful fumes.

The standard addresses both the health and physical fitness of fire fighters, requiring an annual physical examination and a structured physical-fitness program. The established standards for fitness must be job-related and should help members detect and correct problems at an early stage. The fire department is required to establish a health data base for all members that can track exposures and research occupational illnesses in the future, while providing for doctor-patient confidentiality.

A subject of increasing interest in the fire service is the area of exposure to contagious disease, particularly when the fire department is involved with the delivery of emergency medical services. NFPA 1500 treats this as an occupational danger and requires a program to provide state-of-the-art protection for all exposed members.

The final chapter of NFPA 1500 deals with employee assistance programs and recommends an approach that will support the overall wellness of the members of the fire department. This program should deal with substance abuse; stress, including critical incident stress debriefing; smoking cessation; and other personal and family problems. If they are to be accepted and successful, employee assistance programs should be provided by qualified professionals and should protect the confidentiality of those seeking assistance.

NFPA 1500 includes an appendix that contains supporting information and explanations for many of the specific provisions of the standard. A complete set of referenced standards also is included to help the user find complete information on many of the subjects covered by the standard.

IMPLEMENTING NFPA 1500

NFPA 1500, *Standard on Fire Department Occupational Safety and Health*, was written by the Technical Committee on Fire Service Occupational Safety and Health in response to the growing base of knowledge and information on how fire fighters were being injured and killed in the line of duty. NFPA 1500 currently serves as a consensus standard for a fire service occupational safety and health program. As such, any fire service organization can use NFPA 1500 to evaluate the completeness of an existing program or to design and implement a new program where one does not already exist. An occupational safety and health program developed and implemented in compliance with NFPA 1500 is instrumental in securing the highest possible levels of health and safety, given the hazardous nature of fire fighting.

One of the more common questions asked since the development of NFPA 1500 is, "How do we develop an NFPA 1500 compliance plan?" While it may be true that individual elements of an NFPA 1500 compliance plan may vary from fire department to fire department, the process each department goes through during the plan's development will be fairly standard. Itemized here is a suggested methodology for creating a written document that will identify the necessary elements in your fire department's occupational safety and health program. The methodology may, and should, be modified as needed on an individual basis.

Step 1: Obtain a Copy of the Standard

The first step in the process is to obtain a copy of NFPA 1500. The document is available from the National Fire Protection Association, Batterymarch Park, Quincy, Massachusetts 02269. NFPA 1500 also is contained in Volume 8 of the *National Fire Codes*, 1991 edition.

After obtaining a copy of the standard, take the time to read it carefully and get a good feeling for the general requirements listed in the ten chapters. The document also contains two appendices, which may be used to determine the intent and meaning of specific requirements in each of the standard's chapters. The information contained in the appendices is not a requirement of the standard. Appendix material is informative in nature only and may be used by the reader as he or she sees fit.

Step 2: Establish a Project Team

A project team should be established to do all of the work required to develop and implement the program. It is important that the project team represent all areas and ranks within the department for the process to be successful. One of the primary responsibilities of the project team members will be to communicate with all members of the organization about the needs and requirements of fire fighter health and safety issues. For the plan to be effective, all members of the organization should feel that they have the opportunity to become involved in developing the plan. Team members selected or appointed to the team should be good communicators. Good written and verbal communications skills will be an extremely important aspect of the process.

Step 3: Compare NFPA 1500 with Established Practices

The next step is a line-by-line review of the specific requirements of the standard against the department's established current practices and procedures. At this time, the comparison need not be very involved. A check-list of the individual section numbers of the standard with an indication of "yes" or "no" with regard to compliance will provide an initial assessment as to where your organization stands with regard to the standard. At this step, many organizations find that they comply with the standard in more ways than they had previously assumed.

Step 4: Identify Sections Where Compliance Is Met

After completing the initial assessment review, it is necessary to do a more detailed review of the requirements of each section. This step is intended to identify and document whether compliance is either met or exceeded. Each section of the standard, including the specific requirement, should be listed on an individual sheet of paper. Adequate documentation in the form of a written policy, procedure, or practice, should be itemized on the same sheet or attached and made a part of the work records. By the time each section of the standard has been reviewed, adequate material will have been gathered to document compliance with the standard's minimum requirements.

Step 5: Identify Sections Where Compliance Is Needed

The remaining sections of the standard where compliance is still needed occupy the time and efforts of the committee for the next few steps. Each section of the standard in this category should be identified on a separate sheet of paper, as before. The current level of effort in each section should be listed in the event of partial compliance.

Step 6: Identify Available Alternatives or Specific Solutions

A goal should be identified for each section to indicate what is needed in order to comply with each specific requirement identified in Step 5. For example, this goal might indicate that a training program is needed or, perhaps, that only a standard operating procedure is required for compliance. In some instances, a number of alternatives might make compliance with a specific requirement of the standard possible. Each of these alternatives should be identified at this point in the process. If only one alternative exists, it should be identified at this time.

Step 7: Estimate Time and Cost for Each Alternative

Each alternative identified in the previous step should now be examined to determine the time and cost necessary for implementation. Some of the alternatives will probably cost little or nothing. These alternatives will typically be those related to the development of a policy or procedure, and the time required to conduct the training needed to implement the solutions. Some alternatives, particularly those that identify apparatus or equipment that would be required for compliance, may be very costly. Care should be taken to be as accurate as possible in estimating time factors for implementation of the various alternatives identified. Compliance with all of the requirements of NFPA 1500 will probably take far more time than might be expected initially. Even if funding is available for noncompliant requirements, the typical fire department is looking at a time-frame of approximately five years' work to comply fully with the entire standard.

Step 8: Select the Best Alternatives

For those items for which there were a number of possible alternatives, the best alternative should be selected for inclusion in the plan. The choice will depend on the specific situation that exists in each organization. The method chosen by one department might not be appropriate for another.

Step 9: Prepare a Draft Plan

All of the work accomplished up to this point will now be used to write a draft compliance plan. The written plan should include the existing information, practices, and procedures identified in Step 4 that comply with NFPA 1500 and those elements identified in Steps 5 through 8. The draft plan can be organized any way the department may desire. A number of organizations have found it helpful to use the format of NFPA 1500 as a guide for the development of their own compliance plans. At this point, the plan should identify how the organization intends to comply with the requirements of NFPA 1500, and present a timetable for phasing in those elements that will lead to compliance in the future.

Step 10: Legal/Risk-Management Review

While not actually required by NFPA 1500, it is a good idea at this time to ask the department's legal counsel to review the draft document. It is also a good idea to have the authority's risk manager review it. In the past five years, many municipalities and other governmental entities have secured the services of professional risk managers as a means of controlling liability, and this person can be a valuable resource for the department. Feedback and suggestions made by either the legal counsel or the risk manager should be reviewed by the project team. Where appropriate, the draft plan should be changed or modified as a result of this legal or risk-management review.

Step 11: Submit the Draft Plan for Adoption

After the draft plan has been finalized, it should be submitted to the authority having jurisdiction for review and discussion. The authority having jurisdiction in this case might be the fire chief, the mayor or city manager, or the city council, town board, or district trustees, among others. Adequate back-up information should be submitted to identify the need for the program, the goal of achieving specific levels of fire fighter health and safety, and the anticipated benefits that may be expected to accrue to the individual employees, the fire department, and the community at large. The organization should be prepared to answer questions or issues raised in this step. Educating all the parties responsible for the adoption of the plan is crucial to the success of the program.

Step 12: Adopt the Plan

After the concept of the plan has been accepted and approved, the plan should be adopted. This may be accomplished by informal means, such as a cover letter signed by the fire chief, or it may include formal adoption through a statute, law, or ordinance. No matter how the plan is adopted, there should be a commitment to follow through with the programs, practices, and procedures identified in the document.

Step 13: Organize Implementation Teams

After the plan has been adopted, various implementation teams should be established to carry out the specifics of the plan. Each team should be responsible and accountable for implementing specific sections of the plan.

Step 14: Identify Implementation Strategy

For the plan to have a maximum impact on fire fighter health and safety, an overall implementation strategy must be developed. It is likely that simultaneous implementation of a number of elements will be impossible. A common-sense approach should be used in implementing the plan. Each specific element of the plan should be integrated in such a way that full compliance with the standard is ultimately accomplished. The implementation strategy for your department may be different from that of any other organization and should take into consideration specific factors of which only you are aware.

Step 15: Implement the Plan

After the implementation strategy has been established, the plan should be implemented. The implementation should follow the step-by-step sequence identified.

Step 16: Monitor Progress

After implementation, progress should be regularly and periodically assessed. Adjustments to the phasing plan should be made, as necessary, to follow the overall implementation strategy. Any problems should be addressed by the project team. Standard project management practices should be employed to maintain steady progress toward completing implementation.

Step 17: Review and Update the Plan Regularly

The plan should be reviewed periodically to ensure that the information and assumptions that were used to develop it are still valid. New information, fire suppression practices, changes and improvements in technology, and a variety of other factors can have an impact on the validity of any identified health and safety plan. This review will help ensure that the objective you are working toward is still valid when you get there. Specific attention should be given to keeping abreast of the other fire service standards referenced by NFPA 1500 so that the original plan may be modified appropriately during the implementation process.

The implementation of an NFPA 1500 health and safety program is an excellent example of a win-win situation for everyone. The individual fire fighters will benefit from improved levels of health and safety. The fire department will benefit from healthier employees who are better prepared and equipped to carry out their duties. The community will benefit from a better level of service at an efficient cost. While implementation of such a program is neither quick nor necessarily easy, it is one of the most responsible actions that anyone in the fire service today can undertake.

BIBLIOGRAPHY

NFPA Codes, Standards, and Recommended Practices.

Reference to the following NFPA codes, standards, and recommended practices will provide further information about fire fighter injuries and deaths. (See the latest *NFPA Catalog* for availability of the following documents.)

NFPA 472, *Standard for Professional Competence of Responders to Hazardous Materials Incidents.*

NFPA 1001, *Standard on Fire Fighter Professional Qualifications.*

NFPA 1002, *Standard on Fire Apparatus Driver/Operator Professional Qualifications.*

NFPA 1021, *Standard on Fire Officer Professional Qualifications.*

NFPA 1041, *Standard on Fire Service Instructor Professional Qualifications.*

NFPA 1201, *Recommendations for Developing Fire Protection Services for the Public.*

NFPA 1403, *Standard on Live Fire Training Evolutions in Structures.*

NFPA 1404, *Standard for a Fire Department Self-Contained Breathing Apparatus Program.*

NFPA 1500, *Standard on Fire Department Occupational Safety and Health Program.*

NFPA 1501, *Standard for Fire Department Safety Officer.*

NFPA 1561, *Standard on Fire Department Incident Management System.*

NFPA 1581, Standard on Fire Department Infection Control Program

NFPA 1901, *Standard for Pumper Fire Apparatus.*

NFPA 1902, *Standard for Initial Attack Fire Apparatus.*

NFPA 1903, *Standard for Mobile Water Supply Fire Apparatus.*

NFPA 1904, *Standard for Aerial Ladder and Elevating Platform Fire Apparatus.*

NFPA 1911, *Standard for Service Tests of Pumps on Fire Department Appartus.*

NFPA 1914, *Standard for Testing Fire Department Aerial Devices.*

NFPA 1932, *Standard on Use, Maintenance, and Service Testing of Fire Department Ground Ladders.*

NFPA 1962, *Care, Use, and Service Testing of Fire Hose Including Couplings and Nozzles.*

NFPA 1971, *Standard on Protective Clothing for Structural Fire Fighting.*

NFPA 1972, *Standard on Helmets for Structural Fire Fighting.*

NFPA 1973, *Standard on Gloves for Structural Fire Fighting.*

NFPA 1974, *Standard for Protective Footwear for Structural Fire Fighting.*

NFPA 1975, *Standard on Station/Work Uniforms for Fire Fighters.*

NFPA 1981, *Standard on Open-Circuit Self-Contained Breathing Apparatus for Fire Fighters.*

NFPA 1982, *Standard on Personal Alert Safety Systems (PASS) for Fire Fighters.*

NFPA 1983, *Standard on Fire Service Life Safety Rope, Harnesses, and Hardware.*

NFPA 1991, *Standard on Vapor-Protective Suits for Hazardous Chemical Emergencies.*

NFPA 1992, *Standard on Liquid Splash-Protective Suits for Hazardous Chemical Emergencies.*

NFPA 1993, *Standard on Support Function Protective Garments for Hazardous Chemicals Operations.*

Additional Readings

"Practices for Respiratory Protection for the Fire Service," *ANSI Z88.5*, American National Standards Institute, New York, NY, 1981.

"Standard for Respiratory Protection—Respirator Use—Physical Qualifications for Personnel," *ANSI Z88.6*, American National Standards Institute, New York, NY, 1984.

Brunacini, A. V., *Fire Command*, National Fire Protection Association, Quincy, MA, 1985.

Fire Department Safety Officers Reference Guide, National Fire Protection Association, Quincy, MA, 1986.

International Fire Service Training Association, *Firefighter Occupational Safety*, Fire Protection Publications, Stillwater, OK, 1979.

Jacobs, D. T., *Physical Fitness for Public Safety Personnel*, 3rd ed., National Fire Protection Association, Quincy, MA, 1990.

Laughlin, J., *Last Alarm—True Stories of Fire Fighters*, National Fire Protection Association, Quincy, MA, 1986.

Title 29, *Code of Federal Regulations*, Part 1910.133, U.S. Government, Washington, DC, July 1, 1985.

FIRE LOSS PREVENTION AND CONTROL MANAGEMENT

Thomas F. Barry, Richard W. Asa, and Charles H. Moye

Fire loss consequences, which can involve property damage, business interruption, life safety hazards, environmental issues, damage to corporate image, and lack of future profitability, can present a major threat to corporate goals and survival. Recognition of these consequences has prompted the development of a formal management structure for fire loss prevention and control in many corporations, including general fire risk management and loss control strategies, as well as specific provisions for company fire brigades.

FIRE RISK MANAGEMENT

This section describes the general framework of the fire risk management process, represented in Figure 9-2A, which includes hazard identification, quantified risk assessment, and risk management options. Supplementary reading resources that provide detailed discussions of fire risk and decision analysis topics have been added to the bibliography.

Hazard Identification

A fire or explosion hazard can be defined as a characteristic of a system, plant, or process that represents a potential for an unplanned event leading to undesirable losses. The key words in this definition are "undesirable losses." Hazard identification is the process of recognizing hazards that can pose significant undesirable losses. Hazard identification should be a continuous activity in the evaluation of new materials, plant additions, and production modifications, as well as the continuing inspection and evaluation of existing facilities.

Resources such as NFPA's *Industrial Fire Hazards Handbook* describe fire hazards in major industries and special process hazards based on current technology and past loss experience. Where technological changes in materials and processes affect the credibility of past experience, analytical methods can be employed to quantify the hazard potential present.

Methodologies used for hazard identification include the following.

- Engineering checklists;
- Hazard indices;
- Hazard and operability study (HAZOP);
- Preliminary hazard analysis (PHA);
- Failure mode and effect analysis (FMEA);
- Fault tree analysis (FTA);
- Event tree analysis;
- Cause-consequence diagrams; and
- Reliability analysis.

Detailed descriptions of these methodologies is beyond the scope of this chapter. An excellent discussion is found in *Guidelines for Hazard Evaluation Procedures*, available from the American Institute of Chemical Engineers (AIChE).

Risk Assessment

The risk assessment process consists of both identifying risks and estimating the probability and magnitude of potential fire losses. In recent years, there has been an increase in the use of formalized risk assessment methods to support decisions on firesafety issues. Predictive methods that integrate statistical data, deterministic models, and expert opinion increasingly are being used.

The primary steps in fire risk assessment include the following.

1) Identification of the fire events that could lead to significant loss.
2) Quantification of the fire risk—that is, probability of fire event occurrences and loss consequences—for the generated fire loss scenarios.
3) Development and evaluation of alternative fire prevention and/or fire protection strategies (recommendations) to reduce the fire risk.

Thomas F. Barry, P.E., and Richard W. Asa, P.E., are senior fire protection engineers and Charles H. Moye is a fire protection engineering specialist with Professional Loss Control Inc., based in Oak Ridge, TN.

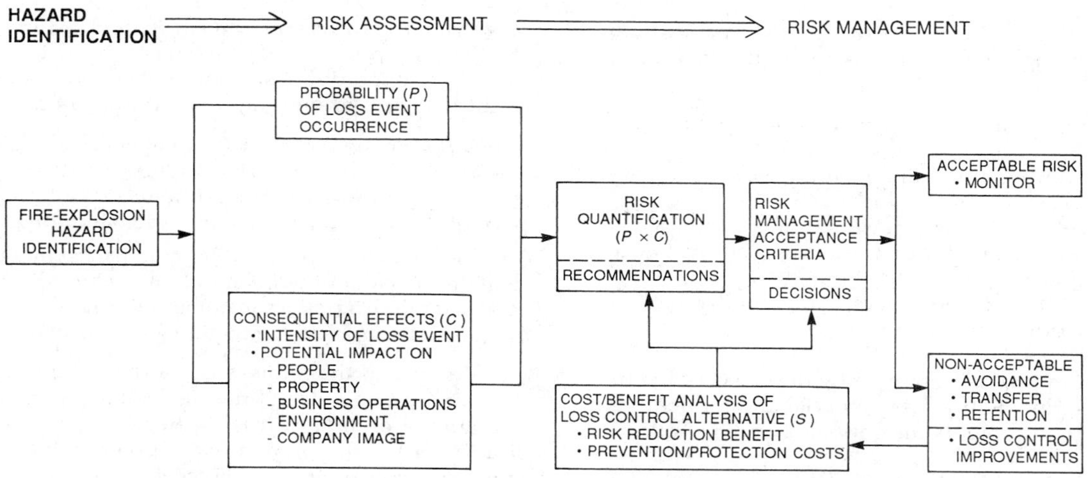

FIG. 9-2A. General framework for industrial fire risk management process.

4) Measurement of the estimated change in fire risk (difference in probability and/or consequences) associated with the alternatives.

One of the most difficult tasks in the risk assessment process is addressing probabilities. Fire risk is the product of the probability of fire occurrence and the loss consequences of the fire. Since these factors will always include a certain amount of subjectivity, there is an element of uncertainty that must be recognized. Approaches for determining the probabilities of values for fire event occurrence are as follows.

Objective estimation: If valid data on loss event frequencies are available and applicable, then probabilities can be extracted from this source. Often objective data sources are scarce. To evaluate the application of historical data, it is necessary to look at the following, both for the source of the data and for the situation under consideration.

- Design standards and quality;
- Inspection methods and quality;
- Maintenance philosophy and quality;
- Operational philosophy and quality; and
- Safety standards and enforcement.

Subjective estimation: If historical data sources are not available for the loss event(s) of interest, probabilities can be evaluated using inferential judgment based on available loss-trending information such as equipment failures, human error, ignition sources, loss control elements, and damageability factors.

Subjective estimation processes should be documented and should involve the best judgment a fire protection expert can make based on knowledge of contributing factors from past fire losses, site-specific evidence of loss control deficiencies, and exposed values.

A very good reference on failure data sources and application precautions is the AIChE's Center for Chemical Process Safety book entitled *Guidelines for Process Equipment Reliability Data.*

The physical intensity of fire-explosion consequences can be quantified in terms of the expected energy released (heat exposure, smoke and/or corrosive gas contamination, explosion blast overpressures, etc.), the area involved, and the duration of the fire. Probabilistic engineering assessment—and, in some situations, deterministic fire-explosion modeling tools—are utilized to aid the evaluation process. The SFPE *Handbook of Fire Protection Engineering* provides information on various analytical techniques that can be used in this evaluation.

Once the intensity and duration of the potential fires have been quantified, then the impact on both direct and indirect loss potential must be assessed. Direct losses include damage to buildings, equipment, and contents. Indirect losses include business interruption, liability for injury or death, environmental contamination, and damage to company image. For most quantification studies, loss potential is expressed in equivalent monetary terms.

The type of risk assessment conducted depends on the significance of the decision, the complexity of the problem, and the time and cost limitations. Routine code-compliance problems can often be handled by simple choices. Complex problems involving new technologies or high-hazard operations require application of more detailed risk assessment and decision analysis methods.

Risk Management

Risk management addresses the value judgments involved in establishing acceptable levels of risk and methods of handling identified risks. The acceptable risk decision-making process is based on specific organizational goals and generally includes (in any order) the following.

- Profit (competitive market position);
- Protection of company assets (major loss exposures);
- Continued company operation (business interruption);
- Continued growth (expansion);
- Humanitarian concerns (employee and public safety);
- Community goodwill (potential embarrassment);
- Legal requirements (liability, building codes, etc.);
- Insurance company requirements; and
- Environmental concerns.

If the risk is acceptable, no immediate action may be necessary, but monitoring for changes that could increase the risk must be done. If the risk is unacceptable, then decisions must be made about how to deal with the risk.

General options available to the risk management decision maker for handling fire risk exposure include the following.

1) Avoiding the risk by nonparticipation in risky operations.
2) Risk transfer by purchasing insurance to cover potential losses.
3) Financing alternate risk transfer arrangements such as captive or corporate funded reserves (self-insurance).
4) Providing loss control improvements.
5) Developing a risk management program that includes a combination of the above.

The fifth option generally provides a cost-effective approach for reducing fire loss potential and reducing the risk funding requirements for options 2 and 3 above.

Once a risk management decision has been made that includes loss control improvements, it may be necessary to conduct a cost/benefit analysis, either formally or informally.

Evaluating the cost of fire prevention and protection alternatives, which includes design, installation, system maintenance, and training expenses, is normally a straightforward process. A good discussion on cost comparison is provided by John Hall in Section 10, Chapter 7 of this Handbook.

Evaluating the benefit or the amount of risk reduction presents a more difficult task. Estimating the degree of risk reduction benefit involves the assessment of reduced probability of fire occurrence and/or reduction of direct and indirect losses.

Current methods for estimating risk reduction for alternative fire prevention and/or protection strategies are primarily subjective, supported by available loss experience and fire protection engineering judgment. Valuable information may be obtained from industry and insurance reports, NFPA's Fire Incident Data Organization (FIDO), the National Fire Incident Reporting System (NFIRS), and internal plant reporting systems. Future development of computer models that integrate deterministic fire hazard modeling, probabilistic models, and risk profile (loss data) information, will provide additional tools for risk assessment studies.

An important part of fire risk reduction is the development, implementation, and monitoring of comprehensive loss control programs. Written documentation should be provided for this program and updated periodically. The fire loss control program should define specific objectives regarding personnel safety (both plant personnel and the general public), property conservation, environmental impact, and minimizing interruption to plant production.

Loss control program documentation should include a thorough description of engineering design, applied engineering standards, and administrative controls for topics such as the following.

Fire prevention: Methods to be employed through design, operational controls, operator training, and maintenance to prevent fires from starting.

Automatic fire detection and suppression: Fixed fire protection systems and equipment installed to rapidly detect, suppress, and control fires that do occur.

Protection for structures and equipment: Fire protection standards for passive and active measures that will be used to protect operations, structures, and equipment in the event that fires are not rapidly extinguished.

Manual protection: Provision of manual fire fighting capabilities as a backup to active and passive fixed protection systems, including fire department pre-fire planning and periodic emergency drills for designated areas.

Indubitably, successful fire risk management is dependent on the commitment and involvement of management in assessing fire risk issues, maintaining loss control programs, and supporting emergency response organizations.

Because of the numerous interfaces between the various engineering disciplines, as well as maintenance and operational programs, it is essential to place the responsibility for the fire protection program with a single individual or small group with direct access to top management. This individual must have sufficient authority to delegate responsibilities affecting plant fire protection across engineering discipline and departmental lines, and even across separate divisions such as Engineering, Plant Services, Utilities, Safety and Loss Control, and Emergency Response.

Only through continual attention to fire risk issues and the utilization of the experience and expertise of fire protection professionals can both the probability and severity of fire risks be decreased.

FIRE LOSS CONTROL

Today, few companies, in the face of severe competition and the high cost of money, could survive a major loss. Over the years, it has become apparent that people can substantially aid in the minimization of losses. It has been statistically demonstrated, by major property insurance companies, that the leading cause, and the factor with the largest effect on the size of a loss by fire/explosion, is what people do or fail to do.

Examples of improper decisions include the following.

1) Failure to inspect, and maintain, fire suppression equipment;
2) Decisions to omit automatic suppression systems;
3) Use of improper building materials; and
4) Violation of safe practices.

Management loss control programs are procedures utilized for the protection of assets from loss due to fire or other causes. This section describes the responsibilities, organization, and content of an effective loss control program.

Management Echelons

The implementation and enforcement of an effective loss control program is dependent on management involvement and support.

Management can be divided into three echelons, each of which makes important contributions to loss prevention and control: 1) executive management—the board of directors and company officers; 2) middle management—facility managers, department heads, and related staff managers; and 3) line management—the supervisors and section chiefs who direct each phase of the operation.

In a relatively small organization, the owner may perform the functions of all three management levels. Although the owner's loss control problems may be fewer, or less complex, than those of the management group in a larger organization, some of the same judgments must be exercised. The owner who tries to be Loss Control Manager may be at a disadvantage, however, because of the lack of specialized training in loss control, and the absence of managers with whom to share expertise and creative ideas regarding a sound loss control program. This need not pose a major obstacle. Expertise is available from professional loss control consultants, insurance companies, and/or fire departments.

Executive management. Members of executive management establish company policy, make major financial decisions, determine the product or service to be provided, and establish production levels. Executive management's primary goal is to guide the organization to produce a profit.

Regardless of insurance coverage, losses to plant property by fire or other causes can disrupt profitability. On the surface, assets diverted to property protection would appear to be a non-productive expenditure. However, after a serious loss, the need for an effective loss prevention/control program becomes apparent. For loss control programs to be effective, they must have complete support from executive management. In addition, once a program has been developed and accepted, executive management must insist on regular updates to monitor progress.

Middle management. Middle management is responsible for the development, implementation, and monitoring of cost-effective loss control programs.

The person with primary responsibility for loss control generally has the title of Loss Control Manager. Depending on the organization, titles assigned to individuals vary, and in some cases, the individual may have several other titles when loss control is not a full-time function. To be effective, the assigned individual must have access to decision makers at the executive management level. Direct access would involve reporting to the officer level (e.g., Vice Presidents of Engineering, Finance, Production, etc.). Indirect access would involve reporting to the Director of Risk Management or other managers with direct access to executive management.

Major responsibilities of the Loss Control Manager include the following.

Overall Supervision. Defining loss control program functions, clarifying responsibilities, and ensuring that all procedures are properly carried out.

Planning. Anticipating hazards, and formulating plans and procedures for fire prevention and overall plant safety.

Education and training. Providing employee training in fire prevention. Making sure that all production processes and operations are carried out safely, and that contractors follow safe procedures according to company regulations.

Assignment. Delegating specific maintenance and emergency duties to employees, including guards, caretakers, patrol officers, and night workers.

Coordination. Maintaining liaison with the following corporate departments and outside organizations.

- With Production and Engineering on new processes or materials that can introduce additional fire hazards within the facility.
- With Plant Engineering and Maintenance for fire protection installations, impaired protection, maintenance of fire protection equipment, and housekeeping.
- With the public fire department and insurance company on plant layout, location and type of hazardous processes, coordination of forces, location and type of fire protection equipment, fire doors, fire walls, defense plans, and main defense lines.

Review. Checking, periodically, the efficiency of the entire loss control program. Reviewing details of the plan with line management. Conducting drills and classes to maintain employee preparedness.

In smaller organizations, the facility manager or his/her appointee must assume these responsibilities.

Line management. Implementation of a loss control program extends beyond the middle management level. Unless the members of line management adequately perform their function, the program cannot produce satisfactory results.

Line managers, those with daily personnel contact, should aid in the information collection that middle managers incorporate into loss control programs. Once programs are implemented, line managers are responsible for regular enforcement of company policy.

FIG. 9-2B. ***Proper training is an important function of many loss control departments.***

With regard to employees, and work areas under his/her supervision, it is the line manager who is responsible for the following.

1) Trains personnel to carry out individual duties in a loss control program.
2) Works with the Loss Control Manager and staff in selecting employees for the private fire brigade or other program assignments.
3) Works with the Loss Control Manager to establish priorities for inspection, testing, and maintenance of fire protection equipment.
4) Inspires employees to develop a fire-conscious attitude and respect for the loss control program.
5) Insists that access to all protection equipment, as well as all means of egress, be kept open.

6) Works closely with the Loss Control Manager and staff to ensure that new equipment or processes are adequately protected before start-up.
7) Reports all occupancy changes that may affect loss control.
8) Works with the Loss Control Manager and staff to ensure that fire exit drills are held regularly.
9) Accounts for each employee, following facility evacuation.
10) Supervises emergency action when a fire or other property-related incident occurs in the absence of members of an established emergency organization.

Program Development and Implementation

Effective loss control programs should be developed with appropriate input from middle managers such as Production, Plant Engineering, and Administration. If the organization has a Loss Control Manager, that person should finalize program structures and review them with other concerned managers for acceptance. Upon middle management acceptance, the programs are sent to executive management for review and approval. In the absence of a Loss Control Manager, the finalization of program development should be assigned to the individual responsible for overall plant engineering. If this manager does not have sufficient expertise in loss control, professional loss control services should be used.

Loss Control Managers should be directly involved in construction project planning. Their responsibilities include:

New construction site evaluation. The Loss Control Manager should determine if the following conditions exist at the site under consideration.

- Adequate water supply to meet fire protection requirements;
- Exposure to flood.
- Exposure conditions involving adjacent facilities;
- Acceptable support forces such as public fire departments, disaster relief, and medical teams; and
- Impediments to quick response by support forces (e.g., lift bridges, railroad crossings, or heavily traveled highways).

Facility and protection systems planning. Loss control factors to be considered during the planning stage are as follows.

- Using fire-resistant materials;
- Limiting the size of fire areas by the use of fire walls, fire doors, etc;
- Segregating unusual concentrations of values (i.e., sensitive equipment and highly hazardous operations);
- Ensuring emergency exits are adequate in number, size, and location;
- Providing physical protection (i.e., automatic sprinklers, hydrants, and standpipes);
- Providing access for fire protection vehicles; and
- Considering design for earthquake, wind, and heavy snow or rain.

Production operations involving new equipment or modifications. Loss control management should participate in process planning, which may require the following.

- Segregation to limit exposure from other operations;
- Special protection/suppression systems;
- Limited access or improved security; and
- Special exit facilities.

Fire protection during facility construction. Loss control management personnel should participate in the following.

- Advising contractor personnel of loss control management policies. (Facility personnel must have authority to enforce compliance);
- Acceptance testing of all fire protection equipment; and
- Monitoring construction for compliance with specifications.

Other duties of the Loss Control Manager include the following.

Communications. Loss control management should assemble, analyze, and submit pertinent reports within a defined reporting structure goals are as follows.

- Furnishing the risk, or insurance, manager with information as required by insurance carriers;
- Providing an escort for insurance company representatives for facility inspections;
- Reviewing loss control recommendations of insurance company representatives or outside consultants;
- Furnishing the insurance manager with economic justification for loss control improvements;
- Reporting impairments of protection systems to the risk or insurance manager; and
- Furnishing the risk or insurance manager with reports of all property loss incidents.

Conducting community relations programs. The Loss Control Manager should assist the facility manager and/or the public relations manager in publicizing the facility's loss control policies to the community and its emergency forces. This type of publicity can help build a favorable company image. The community has an interest in a facility's firesafety planning as it relates to employee safety, to the economic impact of loss of wages due to facility shutdown, and to exposure of other property.

Providing guidance for line management. Property loss control personnel must provide information and guidance to line management for the successful day-to-day implementation of company loss control procedures.

Other critical components of established loss control programs include the following.

- A self-inspection plan and procedure, to include a systematic way to report deficiencies and eliminate hazardous conditions;
- A procedure for proper control of impairments to fire protection systems;
- A "hot work" permit program to control welding and cutting outside of authorized areas, such as a welding department;
- A facility security control program; and
- An emergency organization and contingency plans of actions.

Self-inspection program. Engineered fire protection systems are a vital factor in the reduction of large fire losses at industrial facilities. Statistical studies of suppression by properly designed and maintained fire protection equipment have proven these systems to be effective. Unfortunately, reports of large fire losses stemming from fire protection equipment malfunction continue. Some of the recurring problems include the following.

- Undetected closure of sprinkler system control valves;
- Inoperative fire pumps;
- Empty water supply tanks;
- Malfunctioning special suppression equipment;
- Inoperative fire doors; and
- Inoperative fire detection systems.

Management must take a positive approach in establishing programs for periodic inspection, testing, and maintenance of fire protection equipment. Equally important is management's need for a documented self-inspection program as part of ongoing firesafe plant operation.

Once an adequate program has been established and implemented, inspections must be conducted by individuals knowledgeable in the purpose, operation, and testing of the equipment.

A sample self-inspection form, Table 9-2A, "Self-Inspection Quick Reference Table," was developed by Hartford Steam Boiler Inspection and Insurance Co. to simplify and organize testing of fire protection equipment. Under "Reference" the table lists appropriate NFPA fire codes as of this writing. The recommendations for frequency of inspection should be considered the minimum. Authorities having jurisdiction may require inspection frequencies above the minimum.

To simplify self-inspections, forms appropriate for the occupancy and equipment should be used. Forms should be specific enough to be usable, and comprehensive enough so that no element of prevention or protection is overlooked.

As part of a thorough inspection, regardless of frequency, the occupancy should be inspected for the following.

- Poor housekeeping, waste, and combustible materials accumulations;
- Careless smoking;
- Improperly stored flammable/combustible liquids;
- Blocked electrical switch gear, and storage of combustible material in electrical rooms;
- Improper maintenance of electrical conduits and junction boxes; and
- Abnormal amounts of combustible in-process or finished products in areas where fire protection systems have not been adequately designed for this overload.

Upon the completion of inspections and testing, reports should be forwarded to the facility manager and the Loss Control Manager. For those deficiencies that are severe and could be of imminent danger, the facility manager should be notified immediately and should take immediate action.

Fire protection equipment impairment program. Many large fire losses have been directly attributed to impaired fire protection systems or equipment. Major property insurance companies, during routine facility inspections, continue to find fire protection systems of all types out of service. The need for an effective impairment notification program is evident to eliminate the possibility of undetected shutdown of fire protection systems.

A protection system may become impaired for a number of reasons (e.g. maintenance, renovation, construction, equipment failure, or failure to re-activate the system or device).

Facility managers and Loss Control Managers should be notified immediately of any impairments during normal working hours. During off hours, depending on the seriousness of the impairment, these same individuals may still want to be notified. This procedure should be addressed in detail in the company policy.

Any impairment program requires these basic steps.

1) Assigning responsibility and authority to control the impairment to one individual. This is normally a plant engineer or fire protection safety supervisor. In an emergency, a shift supervisor or fire brigade chief may have the authority to impair a system, but the overall responsibility for the impairment remains with the Loss Control Manager.
2) Educating plant personnel in basic precautions to be taken when a protection system or equipment is impaired. Precautions include:

- Limiting the number, scope, and duration of impairment;
- Supplementing manual fire protection with extra extinguishers;
- Avoiding cutting and welding operations;
- Shutting down any hazardous processes;
- Completing impairment work in a timely manner;
- Restoring protection system upon completion of all work; and
- Verifying, by testing, that the protection system is operational.

The three forms of impairment are concealed, emergency, and planned.

A concealed impairment is an unknown impairment. It occurs when a fire protection system is left out of service or removed from service by an unauthorized person. Concealed impairments are typically discovered during a plant's self-inspection or by a security service.

One example of a concealed impairment is a closed valve that should be open. This can be prevented through a valve supervision program. Depending on specific circumstances, practices for valve supervision include: sealing, locking, and use of protective signaling systems.

Valves are sealed by placing a wire through a movable part of the valve (wheel or shaft nut) and a fixed part of the valve, and then securing the two ends of the wire with a seal. Seals do not prevent the operation of a valve, but are intended to discourage tampering by unauthorized persons. Broken seals indicate that the valve has been operated or tampered with. Any valve with a broken seal should be checked promptly to be certain it is open and then resealed.

Valves are locked in the wide-open position by padlocks, with or without chains or cables, so they cannot be tampered with or operated maliciously. These sturdy securing devices are resistant to breakage or cutting, except by heavy bolt cutters. The distribution of keys is restricted to persons directly responsible for the fire protection system.

TABLE 9-2A. ***Self-Inspection Quick Reference Table***

		HSB Guideline Section				Reference	Plant Inspection Testing Documentation	
		A	B	C	D			
Inspection Item No.	Fire Protection Equipment	Weekly	Monthly	Semiannually	Annually	NFPA's	Written Plant Procedure Established	Person Responsible for Implementation
1	Control valves; includes water supply, sprinkler system, sectional valves	V		S	PO, M	13/26		
2	Fire Pumps	AOP	FPC	S	WF	20		
3	Water Supply Tanks	V		S	WF	22		
4	Public Water	V			WF	13		
5	Special Extinguishing Systems	V		S, AOA, M		12/12A/ 12B/11 11A/16/17		
6	Fire Doors	V			AOD	80		
7	Sprinkler, Water Spray Systems		V, AT, DT	S	DPV, DLV	13/15		
8	Inside Hose, Standpipe Systems		V		M, FHT	14/1962		
9	Fire Hydrants, Monitor Nozzle		V		PO, FHT, M	24/26/1962		
10	Portable Fire Extinguishers		V		M	10		
11	Automatic Detection Systems. Manual Fire Alarm Systems		V, AT	S		71/72E/72H		
12	Mobile Fire Apparatus		V, M			1901/11C		

AOA–Testing of Operation Mechanism
AOD–Automatic Operational Test of Doors
AOP–Automatic Start-up of Pump and Weekly Running
AT–Testing of Local and Remote Alarms
DLV–Deluge Valve Testing
DPV–Dry Pipe Valve Testing
DT–Drain Test
FHT–Fire Hose Testing
FPC–Fire Pump Checklist Form Completed
M–Equipment Maintanence Functions
PO–Physical Operation of Valves—Hydrants
S–Testing of Supervisory Alarms
V–Visual Inspection
WF–Water Flow Testing

* Courtesy of Hartford Steam Boiler Inspection and Insurance Co., Hartford, CT.

Valves can be equipped with a device arranged to transmit a signal electrically whenever the valve is operated. These signals are transmitted to a location on the premises under the control of the plant proprietary system, or to a location remote from the premises under the control of the local fire department or an organization whose function is to furnish such service.

Closed valves and other concealed impairments can be prevented by the following measures.

1) Establishing procedures to be followed during planned or emergency outages.
2) Ensuring that self-inspection programs are performed regularly, promptly, and properly to include testing of alarms and detection devices.

If, during an inspection, a protection system or device is found to be impaired, the conditions should be reported immediately to the Loss Control Manager. This individual should then do the following.

- Restore the fire protection system;.
- Try to determine the reason for the condition; and
- Notify the facility manager of the situation so he can give counsel and guidance. The Loss Control Manager typically is responsible for notifying the insurance company of the impairment, although company procedures differ.

Emergency impairments are caused by unexpected events impairing the normal function of the protection system (e.g., a section of sprinkler piping freezing and bursting).

Emergency situations are normally associated with confusion and a sense of urgency. To eliminate much of the confusion, a written procedure should be in a location available to all personnel.

When handling emergency impairments, the following steps need to be performed.

1) Isolate the area where the situation, or condition, is causing the impairment. If possible, the remaining protection system should be kept in service. This may require temporary connections, or bypasses.
2) Notify the shift supervisor and fire brigade chief that an impairment has occurred.
3) Secure any hazardous production operation in the area where the protection system is impaired.
4) Properly "tag out" the impairment system or equipment. The insurance company will normally supply a facility with the appropriate tags.
5) Start repairs on the impaired system once the area is secured. Work on the impairment should continue until it has been restored to service. Welding or cutting, required for the repair, should be performed in a protected area.
6) Place additional portable extinguishers and/or charged fire hoses in the impaired area, at accessible locations.
7) Notify the public fire department that emergency impairment has occurred and the extent to which the protection system is out of service.
8) Notify the alarm company of the impairment, indicating whether any alarms have been affected.

A planned impairment is a scheduled impairment typically involving improvement or modification to the present system. Such impairment might involve adding a new section of sprinkler piping or changing old sprinkler heads.

Considerations and procedures used for emergency impairments should be followed. However, planned impairments should be organized, thereby reducing the probability of problems and minimizing the time required for the impairment. Contractors should not be allowed to impair a system without authorization from plant personnel. In addition, the contractor should be required to follow the plant's safety rules and requirements to include obtaining special hazard permits and authorization.

Since such impairment work is planned in advance, a schedule can be worked out with the maintenance department and plant operation to ensure the following.

1) Hazardous processes are secured prior to the protection system being out of service.
2) Extra precautions are taken in the area of impairment (e.g., adding extinguishers).
3) Parts and materials are available before work is started.
4) Outside concerns, such as the public fire departments and alarm companies, are notified in advance that the system will be out of service.

When work has been completed, it is important to ensure that fire protection is properly restored. Each step, of the several steps required, should be verified by the individual who authorized the impairment. These steps include the following.

1) Opening all valves that were secured during the impairment and conducting a drain test. (Note: if during the test the pressure drops below normal, the system may have a restricted, or partially closed, valve.)
2) Placing all alarms and/or detection devices back in service.
3) Restoring any fire protection equipment to "automatic" that was either secured or placed in "manual."
4) Verifying that portable extinguishers are in place and fully charged, and hose lines returned to racks or reels.
5) Notifying plant supervisors (shift supervisors and fire brigade chief) that the fire protection system has been restored.
6) Notifying the alarm service, or central stations, that the fire protection has been restored and that alarms will be verified.
7) Notifying the public fire department that the fire protection system has been restored to service and all alarms activated.

Hot work permit program. Fire hazards may occur in the use of both gas and electric welding, and in flame cutting. The majority of fires occur from the use of portable equipment. Outside contractors, performing repair and alteration work, are of particular concern since they are not familiar with buildings or processes, and may not be supervised closely.

Both cutting and welding operations produce dangerous sparks. Sparks from cutting are more hazardous as they are more numerous, and are carried greater distances. Most fires start from drops, or globules, of hot slag. Smoldering fires, not apparent when the work is completed, may later burst into flame when no one is present. Sparks, in the presence of flammable vapors, may start fires immediately.

A written cutting and welding permit should be issued by the fire chief, or other responsible individual, for all cutting and welding operations. Permits should include the following information.

1) Date.
2) Work to be performed.
3) Location of job.
4) Type of immediate fire fighting equipment available, to include noncombustible covers.
5) Fire watch assigned.
6) Inspection of area before commencing work.
7) Authorized signature of individual in charge of the permit system, or approved alternate.
8) Signature of the individual who authorized the job to indicate the area was inspected upon completion of work.

Precautions for cutting and welding should include:

1) Welding or cutting should be prohibited in areas where sprinklers are out of service.
2) Welding or cutting should not be done in a flammable liquids room.
3) Sparks or molten metal will not be permitted to pass through doorways, or cracks or holes in walls and floors.
4) All exposed combustibles should be moved a minimum of 50 ft from cutting and welding operations. Noncombustible curtains must be used between the operation and combustible materials when adequate separation cannot be maintained.
5) Floors should be swept clean. Wooden floors should be wet down or covered with a protective shield, preferably sheet metal.
6) Extinguishers should always be available at all cutting and welding operations. Any extinguishers that are used should be replaced promptly.
7) The immediate areas, and areas on floors above and below, should be inspected for a minimum of thirty minutes after completion of an operation.
8) When oxyacetylene equipment is not in use, the gas should be turned off at the cylinder valve.

Work done by an outside contractor that requires cutting or welding should be closely supervised to comply with the cutting and welding permit system. Approximately one of every three cutting and welding fires reported occurs while outside contractors are engaged in cutting and welding operations.

Facility Security Control Program

It is very important that a facility have a security control program in place. Arson, vandalism, and unsafe practices can be better controlled through improved security.

Emergency Organization

Emergency Organizations (E.O.s) should be formed—and trained—at each facility to provide immediate effective response to any actual, or potential, property damage situation.

The E.O. should be effective during all occupied hours, regardless of staffing, and duties should be detailed in writing and posted in a conspicuous location in all buildings.

The E.O. plan should address fires, explosions, floods, windstorm (tornado and/or hurricane), water/liquid damage, flammable/combustible liquid spills, salvage operations, and cleanup. The primary function of the E.O. is to respond effectively to all emergency situations, including fires.

A detailed discussion of emergency organization is given in Chapter 4 of the NFPA's *Industrial Fire Hazards Handbook*.

PRIVATE FIRE BRIGADES

One of the most important aspects of emergency organization is the creation and training of private fire brigades. The following sections will discuss this issue in detail.

Determining Fire Brigade Options

There are several decisions involved in the determination of brigade organization and training levels. (See Figure 9-2C.) First, there are the motivational factors.

1) Does the plant have a high vulnerability to fire?
2) What are the property damage and business interruption potentials?
3) Would the presence of a fire brigade reduce the plant's vulnerability to losses?
4) Is public fire protection assistance available and is it likely to be effective?
5) How would dependency on fixed automatic protection vs. manual suppression affect insurance premiums?

Next, the potential benefits versus the costs of a fire brigade program should be evaluated:

1) How much is a brigade program going to cost?
2) How much time will employees need to spend training?
3) Who will conduct the training and where will it take place?
4) How will time be scheduled for training all members on all shifts?
5) Will personnel become more aware of fire and its causes and contributing factors making preventing fires more likely?
6) Will fires that are fought by trained industrial fire brigade personnel be fought more safely (OSHA's concern)?
7) Will property loss likely be minimized through prompt action by a trained brigade (the insurer's concern)?

Every plant is obligated to meet OSHA guidelines, and, depending on state and local codes, it may also be obligated to meet fire code requirements. OSHA Subpart L (CFR, Title 29, Subpart L, 1910.155) allows plant management to select the level of plant fire fighting capabilities from five options.

Option 1 is that no employee will fight a fire. This means that upon notification of a fire, all employees will evacuate the facility.

Options 2 through 4 deal with incipient fires. An incipient fire is one that is in the initial or beginning stage and can be controlled or extinguished with portable fire extinguishers, Class II standpipes, or small hose systems without the need for protective clothing or breathing apparatus.

Option 2 is that all employees will be trained (on an annual basis, minimum) to use fire extinguishers to fight incipient fires.

Option 3 is that designated employees will fight incipient fires. This is the same level of training as required in Option 2. However, only specific employees throughout the plant are trained and are expected to respond to incipient fires.

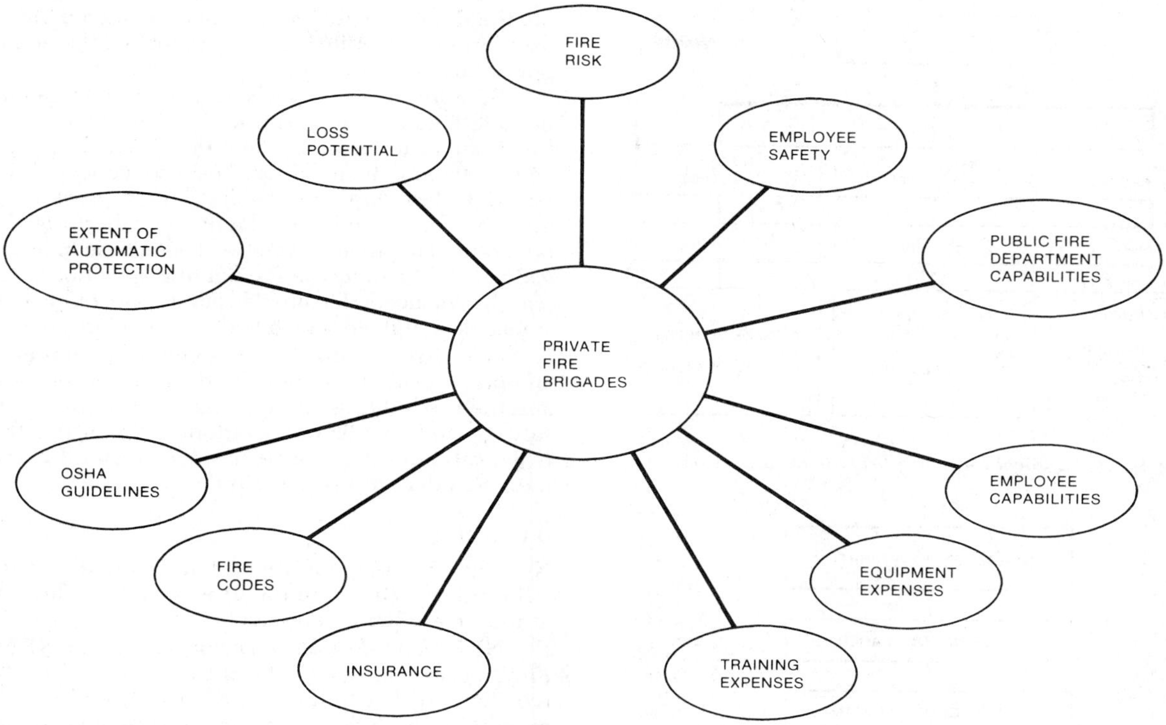

FIG. 9-2C. Issues for fire brigade development.

Option 4 is that the organized fire brigade fights incipient fires. At this level, the management of the plant has written a specific organizational statement regarding the development of a fire brigade. This includes a specific leadership structure, procedures, training, and equipment necessary to perform incipient-level tasks. The organizational statement should be part of the site emergency plan. The brigade leaders must have training exceeding that of the regular brigade member. In addition, special hazards should be addressed in training and procedures for all brigade members. Hands-on training is still required only on an annual basis.

Option 5 is that the organized fire brigade will fight structural fires. This option incorporates the more sophisticated organization of Option 4, but adds more requirements. These include assessment of physical fitness, use of protective clothing and self-contained breathing apparatus (SCBA), quarterly training with hands-on training required annually, and higher levels of overall training and education. (The structural fire brigade should strive to meet the more stringent requirements of NFPA 1500, *Fire Department Occupational Safety and Health Program.)*

Based on the needs assessment of a facility (extent of hazard potential, existing fire prevention and automatic fire protection systems in place, availability and adequacy of public fire department response), management can select the appropriate option. The only considerations for Options 1, 2 and 3 are training and providing extinguishers. Due to the complex considerations involved in Options 4 and 5, the remainder of this chapter will be devoted to them.

Often the type of facility that could benefit from an organized fire brigade does not need a structural fire brigade (Option 5) and would probably find it financially difficult to support one. Yet a team of well-trained individuals equipped to attack incipient fires (Option 4) is relatively easy to develop and maintain. In addition, the incipient fire brigade, due to its proximity to potential fires, its vested interest in the property it is protecting, and its level of training, is an excellent loss control resource. However, many large facilities will need a structural fire brigade to meet their loss control objectives.

Fire Brigade Organization

Based on the size and needs of the brigade, it is important that adequate organization and leadership be established. Titles such as "Chief" and "Captain" are not important but are useful for discussing roles and responsibilities.

Typical fire brigade organizations are shown in Figures 9-2D and 9-2E. The Fire Brigade Chief has overall responsibility for brigade operations. These include training, equipment, procedures, and maintenance of systems and equipment. The Fire Brigade Chief may report to the Plant Emergency Coordinator or may have the dual responsibility of chief and coordinators, depending on the size and needs of the plant. The Fire Brigade Chief should possess qualifications commensurate with the responsibilities of the position.

Assistant Chiefs of the fire brigade are the senior fire officers on each shift and report to the Fire Brigade Chief. In this capacity, they are the primary brigade leaders or incident commanders for the typical brigade response on any shift. Personnel in this position generally have other full-time responsibilities. Under the direction of the Assistant Chief, the Captain directs a fire brigade crew performing tasks such as rescue, fire suppression, salvage, and overhaul. In a small brigade, a leader may combine the duties of several leadership positions.

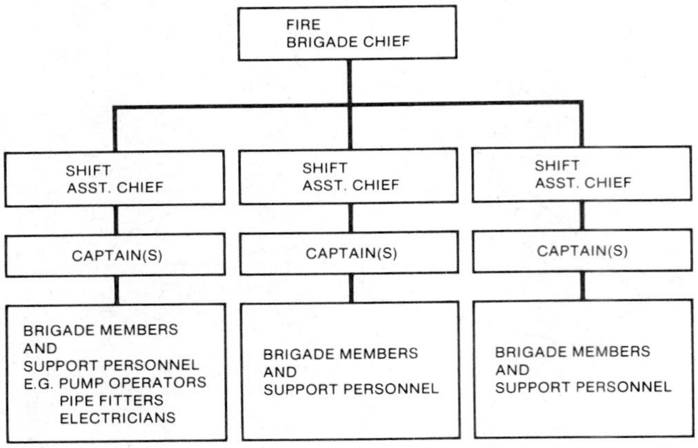

Fig. 9-2D. Typical large fire brigade organization.

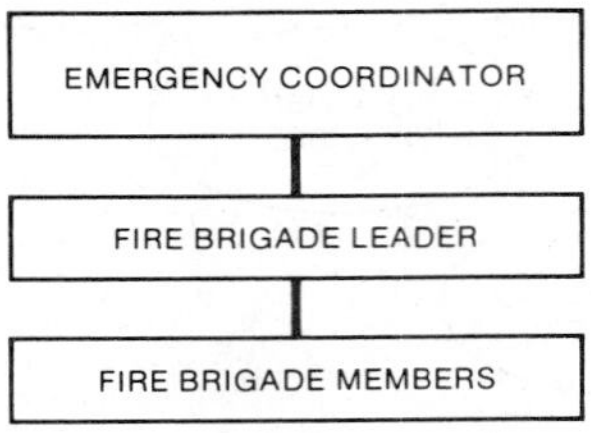

FIG. 9-2E. Typical small fire brigade organization.

Plant personnel who are selected to participate in the fire brigade must have proper physical, mental, and emotional qualifications, in addition to response availability (which is affected by each person's full-time job assignment). The tasks brigade members are expected to perform include regular training, fighting fires, rescue, and any other tasks outlined in the plant's brigade organizational statement.

Based on the occupancy and staffing levels of a particular facility, it may be necessary to include fire brigade support personnel who are not directly involved in fire fighting. For example, an electrician is responsible for isolation of electrical circuits in an area or control of specific equipment that the incident commander has directed him to shut down. The electrician also should ensure that the electrical service to fire protection systems is not inadvertently shut down.

A pipe fitter is an excellent resource for cycling fire protection system valves or operating process control valves that the incident commander has determined should be closed to isolate specific piping. Maintenance personnel might respond as a fire pump operator to ensure that the fire pumps have started or to take any manual actions necessary to ensure their operation. In addition, the operator stands by the pumps to monitor their condition or to take actions as directed to shut down the pumps or return them to regular service (standby or automatic start mode).

Staffing

To determine the number of fire brigade members required, it is necessary to define and document what duties will be performed by the brigade. The brigade's primary responsibilities include controlling and extinguishing the fire, evacuating threatened personnel, minimizing exposures to other areas, and coordinating the efforts of the public fire department.

In order to ensure the safety of brigade members, all fire fighting must be conducted in teams. Since it takes two fire fighters to operate a mobile 1½-in. hose stream of 75 to 100 gpm, the need for a team concept is further reinforced. Unless very extensive fixed fire suppression systems are provided, a minimum of a five-member brigade would be required to provide even two 1½-in. hose lines and a brigade leader to direct the fire fighting operations. Personnel may also be needed to provide additional equipment, set up smoke fans, initiate search and rescue efforts, etc.

Concurrent with the fire fighting operation, efforts should be made to reduce the damage caused by the fire and the fire fighting efforts. This is accomplished through salvage and overhaul operations. Obviously, the more responsibilities the brigade has, the greater the number of members that will be required.

Training

No single item is more important to the effectiveness of a fire brigade than training. It is too late to develop skills at the time of an emergency.

NFPA 600, *Private Fire Brigades*, and NFPA 1500, *Fire Department Occupational Safety and Health Program*, recommend that training sessions be held at least on a monthly basis. This frequency must be considered minimal. The actual training frequency for a specific plant will vary, depending upon the availability and quality of outside fire fighting help, the frequency of actual fires, the number and experience of brigade personnel involved, the type and level of training provided, etc. (OSHA only requires that the brigade receive training "commensurate with their responsibilities.")

Training the brigade can be made easier by making use of agencies and groups such as the local fire department, state or county fire academies, colleges with fire programs, and private interests such as training consultants, the National Fire Protection Association, the International Society of Fire Service Instructors, and the International Fire Service Training Association. Public fire department training grounds are often available in the general area of a plant. These are especially helpful since they are usually arranged to emphasize hands-on training with actual fires. Before engaging in live-fire or hands-on training, NFPA 1403, *Live Fire Training Evolutions in Structures*, should be consulted.

As new personnel are added to the brigade, they should receive an orientation that addresses their responsibilities. This orientation should include classroom training that discusses the theory of fire, plant fire hazards, fixed fire detection systems, fixed fire suppression systems, personal protective equipment with special emphasis on self-contained breathing apparatus (for the structural brigade), and manual fire fighting equipment available to the brigade. Finally, they should receive sufficient practice in actual fire fighting so that some skill is developed. Plant tours are generally needed to show the locations of fire hazards and fire protection equipment.

Fire fighting training should be made as realistic as possible and should simulate the actual fire conditions expected. Too many brigades rely on stereotyped training that consists only of outside oil-pit fires or scrap-wood fires. This approach seldom prepares the brigade for the typical interior fires that will be encountered. For structural brigades, practice with SCBA is especially important, since many plant areas have limited capability for ventilation.

An important part of training is conducting fire drills. Unannounced fire drills should be conducted to check the effectiveness of the brigade response and to identify whether plant pre-fire plans are viable. It is during these drills that areas that are beyond the reach of hose lines or that are inaccessible because of equipment locations, locked doors, or other obstructions will be identified. The pre-fire plans should be revised as needed based on the drill critiques. Drills should be conducted in a realistic manner using charged hose lines where possible. Structural brigades should use protective equipment and SCBA during all drills. Appropriate drills will make responses more automatic under the stress of an actual fire emergency.

The use of computer fire models might be considered as an aid in planning drills. These models can be used to predict likely fire-growth and smoke-spread scenarios. With this information, a more realistic assessment of fire conditions can be made and incorporated into drill scenarios. This same information could be adapted for use in pre-fire plans.

Fire brigade leadership training must be provided to all persons who may direct fire fighting operations. Their leadership abilities will often determine the success or failure of the fire fighting effort. This training should emphasize leadership and fire tactics. The brigade leader should possess a working knowledge of the facility layout, fire hazards, existing protection, and plant operations. All brigade members, but especially brigade leaders, should be trained in the use of an incident command system (ICS) and the supporting principles such as those outlined in the book *Fire Command* by Alan Brunacini.

Pre-Fire Plans

The plant emergency organization should write pre-fire plans for all areas of the plant. The plans should be designed to limit large fires, minimize the threat to employees, and reduce the damage resulting from fires. While the pre-fire plans should be detailed, they must be flexible enough to allow for the diversity of fire problems that will be encountered. It is important that brigade members participate in pre-fire plan development because of the training value. The brigade members will also become more familiar with the plant from a fire protection standpoint.

A pre-fire emergency plan should be developed for each area and should be organized in a form that is useful to the brigade. It should contain, as a minimum, the following information.

1) A review of the facility layout and best access and evacuation routes for each area.
2) A discussion of facility construction features and their probable reaction during a fire incident.
3) An overview of facility operations, equipment, and associated fire hazards.
4) A review of available water supplies, fire pumps, sprinkler control valves, fire department connections, detection, alarms and special suppression equipment.
5) A description of available communications and preestablished plans with the responding public fire department.
6) The requirements for manual fire fighting efforts, including the most appropriate tactics, equipment, and approach to be used by the brigade.
7) Information on ventilation systems that may cause the spread of smoke or may be utilized to prevent smoke spread.
8) An evaluation of chemical hazards and methods to handle spills.
9) The location of flammable liquid and gas system isolation valves and electrical power disconnects.

Fire Fighting Equipment

When fire fighting equipment is mentioned, a fire truck is often initially visualized because it is essential to the operation of public fire departments. Many industries, however, have large quantities of water available at a fairly high water pressure for fire fighting purposes. Since a fire department pumper is used to transport fire fighters and fire equipment and to boost the water pressure, the pumper is seldom needed by the fire brigade. What is needed is a reasonable distribution of yard hydrants and hose houses, even in remote portions of the yard. NFPA 24, *Private Fire Service Mains and their Appurtenances*, lists equipment required for hose houses.

Inside the plant, a well-designed interior standpipe system (NFPA 14) distributes hose stations throughout large industrial buildings. However, if the fire blocks access to one hose station, others usually will not reach the hazard. In addition, safety dictates that a backup hose line be established for the protection of the primary fire attack team(s). For these reasons, some means of easily transporting fire hose should always be provided within the plant. A vehicle or cart may be useful to carry additional equipment, especially to remote areas of the plant site.

Fire fighting and supplementary equipment should be distributed throughout the plant with concentrations at convenient brigade access points. Each structural brigade member must be provided with protective equipment commonly referred to as "turnout" gear, including helmet, coat, boots, trousers, and gloves, as required by OSHA 1910.156. OSHA allows fully extended boots instead of short boots and trousers, but NFPA 1500 requires the use of protective trousers, and therefore, the long boot option is not recommended. NFPA 1500 also requires the use of protective hoods or a combination of helmet earflaps and coat collar to protect the head. Fire brigade members' hands receive a high percentage of injuries, indicating the need for gloves specifically designed for use in fire fighting. Foot and eye injuries are also prevalent. Steel-insole fire boots and fire helmets with eye/face shields will reduce these injuries. Goggles and safety glasses have also been shown to be effective in reducing eye injuries where SCBA is not needed. NFPA standards 1971, 1972, 1973, 1974, 1975, 1981, and 1982 cover protective equipment.

Only those familiar with fighting fires inside buildings can appreciate the amount of smoke, heat, and toxic gases generated during a fire. These fire products necessitate the use of positive pressure self-contained breathing apparatus (SCBA) if the fire has developed beyond the incipient stage. The use of protective clothing and SCBA allows structural fire brigade members to advance safely into a fire area much farther than otherwise would be possible. Because of the limited duration of the air supplied by SCBA during stressful conditions, spare air bottles are necessary.

Specialized equipment may be helpful in conducting fire fighting operations. Items such as high-expansion foam generators, hand-held infrared heat detectors, applicator nozzles, foam nozzles, foam supplies, and eductors may be necessary. The need for special equipment such as this should be identified as a part of the plant fire hazards analysis.

Portable communications equipment must be provided if an efficient and safe fire fighting operation is to be conducted. The brigade leader must have a radio to keep the plant operators and management informed of the situation, to request additional assistance or equipment, and to coordinate the efforts of incoming fire departments. Each fire fighting team should also be provided with radios to facilitate communications with the brigade leader.

Salvage and overhaul equipment will be needed to minimize water, smoke, and fire damage during and after a fire. Salvage equipment should include such items as smoke ejectors (fans with explosion-proof motors) and flexible ducts for smoke removal, floor squeegees, water vacuums, and tarps.

All fire fighting, salvage, and personal protective equipment should be inspected regularly to ensure that it is both available and in good condition. These inspections should be conducted by the brigade members.

Municipal Fire Department Assistance

Regardless of the abilities and resources available to the plant fire brigade, it is a good practice to include the public fire department in fire emergency planning. These personnel may be needed only in the case of a failure of the fixed fire suppression systems or in other unique circumstances, but good emergency planning includes providing for such possibilities. The plant emergency organization should realistically evaluate the local fire department to determine the level of assistance available.

If outside fire departments are to be used, it will be necessary to determine the minimum support they can supply and the response times involved. The number of personnel and response time may vary a great deal in many volunteer departments, depending upon the time of day. The number and type of equipment available to response should also be defined so that pre-fire plans can be developed accordingly.

Another reason for involving the local fire department might be the need for special equipment or capabilities that the plant itself cannot economically provide. These may include the ability to draft water from a static source such as a pond or river. Departments have this basic capability with their pumpers. However, either the plant or the fire department must provide hard suction hose that may not be needed under normal conditions. The pumper must also be provided with adequate access to the water source. Other equipment such as ladders, foam generators, and fire hose should be considered. Compatibility of equipment, such as radio frequencies, air bottles, and hose threads, should be verified. (More than 800 differing hose threads are in use in the United States at the present time.)

It cannot be assumed that the fire fighters from the local department have adequate experience and training in industrial fire fighting. In many cases, local fire department personnel may be most familiar with fighting residential fires with very limited water supplies. Such experience would certainly not provide the average fire fighter with an adequate background for attacking a flammable-liquid fire inside a structure. It must be determined what the local fire department is familiar with the levels of training that are provided for their personnel. It may even be necessary for the plant to supplement the department's training in the fighting of more typical industrial fires such as those involving flammable liquids.

It is important to identify the legal relationships involved if the plant is located outside the formal fire department jurisdiction. Neighboring fire departments are generally pleased to provide assistance in an emergency but may be required by law to leave the plant emergency and respond to a call for services within their jurisdiction.

All public fire department personnel should be given periodic familiarization tours of the plant and should be involved in pre-fire planning. Pre-fire plans made in conjunction with the public fire department should identify personnel assembly points, general fire attack approaches, equipment needs, and personnel requirements. It is especially important that the pre-fire plan clearly define who will direct the combined fire fighting efforts of the brigade and fire department during an emergency. Plans should include a requirement that outside fire department personnel be escorted whenever possible for their safety. Regardless of the amount of time expended by the fire department, they cannot be expected to gain sufficient familiarity with the plant so as to operate safely during an emergency that may generate as much confusion as smoke.

Combined drills should be conducted regularly so that the brigade and fire department can learn to function as a team.

The Fire Brigade and Hazardous Materials Response

Within the last decade, there has been a large amount of legislation regarding the handling of hazardous materials and the response to emergencies involving hazardous materials. The most prevalent of these new laws are 29 CFR 1910.120, Hazardous Waste Operations and Emergency Response, and the Emergency Planning and Community Right-to-Know Act, which is Title III of the Superfund Amendments and Reauthorization Act of 1986 (commonly known as SARA Title III).

Under SARA Title III, Local Emergency Planning Committees (LEPC) were formed to develop pre-emergency plans. The LEPC are composed of officials from fire departments, emergency medical services (EMS), law enforcement agencies, community groups, and emergency management organizations, as well as facility representatives from every plant that falls under the hazardous materials reporting requirements of the new law.

By the end of 1988, each community LEPC was to have completed its emergency plans. These plans are supposed to indicate what agencies will handle the response to any facility for which the plans were developed. In some cases, fire brigades may have the responsibility for response to hazardous materials incidents. If this is the case, the brigade must meet the requirements for a hazardous materials (Hazmat) response team.

The requirements for a Hazmat team include mandatory training, medical surveillance, procurement of necessary equipment, development of standard operating procedures, the use of an Incident Command System, and others as required by OSHA 1910.120. Also, specific personnel decontamination procedures must be in place to ensure Hazmat team members can safely leave a contaminated area.

The complexity of any plant fire brigade's involvement in Hazmat team work will vary according to the chemical hazards encountered, the equipment and training necessary to control expected incidents, the availability of resources from the community, and, specifically, the response that the LEPC has decided is appropriate. This may mean that the plant fire brigade is not involved at all, is involved only as a first responder agency (which is responsible for recognizing that a hazard exists, calling for trained personnel, and securing the area), or is involved as a Hazmat team.

Due to the extensive training time and the cost of equipment, a plant may be financially prohibited from having the fire brigade act as a Hazmat team. Management must also consider costs such as overtime to cover for employees who are in training and not on the job, insurance, medical fees, and "hazardous duty" pay, if provided.

If a fire brigade must function as a Hazmat team, management may consider developing a full-time emergency response organization because of the disruption that the additional extensive training and drill time would cause to work schedules. One type of facility where management might consider this decision is a high-hazard facility where outside assistance might be delayed.

Beyond the legislation, the NFPA has approved two consensus standards regarding response to hazardous materials emergencies and qualifications for the responders. These are NFPA 471, *Recommended Practice for Responding to Hazardous Materials Incidents*, and NFPA 472, *Standard for Professional Competence of Responders to Hazardous Materials Incidents*. These minimum standards provide excellent support in developing Hazmat response programs that will aid in complying with OSHA 1910.120 and SARA Title III.

Conclusion

A fire brigade can make many contributions to plant risk management and loss control. Quick response by a well-trained and organized brigade can minimize loss. The time spent developing the fire brigade and the overall emergency organization will raise the consciousness of the general employee toward firesafety. Moreover, it gives employees the message that management is very concerned about fire protection and employee safety and thus improves employee morale and the efficiency of facility operations.

BIBLIOGRAPHY

NFPA Codes, Standards, Manuals, and Recommended Practices

Reference to the following NFPA codes, standards, manuals, and recommended practices will provide further information on fire loss prevention and control management discussed in this chapter. (See the latest *NFPA Catalog* for availability of current editions of the following documents.)

NFPA 1, *Fire Prevention Code*.

NFPA 10, *Portable Fire Extinguishers*.

NFPA 11, *Low-Expansion Foam and Combined-Agent Systems*.

NFPA 11A, *Medium- and High-Expansion Foam Systems*.

NFPA 11C, *Mobile Foam Apparatus*.

NFPA 12, *Carbon Dioxide Extinguishing Systems*.

NFPA 12A, *Halon 1301 Fire Extinguishing Agent Systems*.

NFPA 12B, *Halon 1211 Fire Extinguishing Systems*.

NFPA 13, *Installation of Sprinkler Systems*.

NFPA 13A, *Inspection, Testing, and Maintenance of Sprinkler Systems*.

NFPA 14, *Installation of Standpipe & Hose Systems*.

NFPA 14A, *Testing, Inspection, and Maintenance of Standpipe and Hose Systems*.

NFPA 15, *Water-Spray Fixed Systems for Fire Protection*.

NFPA 16, *Deluge Foam-Water Sprinkler and Foam-Water Spray Systems*.

NFPA 16A, *Installation of Closed-Head Foam-Water Sprinkler Systems*.

NFPA 17, *Dry Chemical Extinguishing Systems*.

NFPA 20, *Installation of Centrifugal Fire Pumps*.

NFPA 22, *Water Tanks for Private Fire Protection*.

NFPA 24, *Private Fire Service Mains and Their Appurtenances*.

NFPA 26, *Supervision of Valves Controlling Water Supplies for Fire Protection*.

NFPA 51B, *Cutting and Welding Processes*.

NFPA 72, *Protective Signaling Systems*.

NFPA 72E, *Automatic Fire Detectors*.

NFPA 72H, *Local, Auxiliary, Remote Station, and Proprietary Protective Signaling Systems*.

NFPA 80, *Fire Doors and Windows*.

NFPA 471, *Responding to Hazardous Materials Incidents*.

NFPA 472, *Professional Competence of Responders to Hazardous Materials Incidents*.

NFPA 600, *Private Fire Brigades*.

NFPA 601, *Guard Service in Fire Loss Prevention*.

NFPA 602, *Guard Operations in Fire Loss Prevention*.

NFPA 1403, *Live Fire Evolutions for Training Purposes*.

NFPA 1500, *Fire Department Occupational Safety and Health Program*.

NFPA 1901, *Pumper Fire Apparatus*.

NFPA 1962, *Care, Use, and Maintenance of Fire Hose, Including Connections and Nozzles*.

NFPA 1971, *Protective Clothing for Structural Fire Fighting*.

NFPA 1972, *Structural Fire Fighter's Helmets*.

NFPA 1973, *Gloves for Structural Fire Fighting*.

NFPA 1974, *Protective Footwear for Structural Fire Fighting*.

NFPA 1975, *Station/Work Uniforms*.

NFPA 1981, *Open-Circuit SCBA for Fire Fighters*.

NFPA 1982, *Personal Alert Safety System (PASS) for Fire Fighters*.

Additional Readings

Barrell, A. C. and Scott, P. J., "The Regulator Position—United Kingdom and Elsewhere," in *High Risk Safety Technology*, John Wiley & Sons, London, England, 1982.

Bennett, G., "Investigating the Ins and Outs of Fire Prevention," *Control and Instrumentation*, Vol. 12, No. 2, Feb. 1980, p. 59.

Bennett, Gary F., Feates, F. S., and Wilder, Ira, *Hazardous Materials Spills Handbook*, McGraw-Hill, New York, NY, 1982.

Brannigan, F. L., "Fire Loss Management," *Fire Engineering*, Vol. 143, 1989.

Braustowski, T. A., "Risk Assessment in Large Chemical Energy Projects," in *Technological Risk: Proceedings of a Symposium on Risk in New Technologies,* University of Waterloo, Dec. 1981, University of Waterloo Press, Waterloo, Ontario, Canada, 1982.

Brunacini, Alan V., *Fire Command*, National Fire Protection Association, Quincy, MA, 1985.

Bryan, J. L., "Damageability of Buildings, Contents, and Personnel from Exposure to Fire," *Fire Safety Journal*, Vol. 1, Nos. 1 and 2, July-Sept. 1986, pp. 15-31.

Center for Chemical Process Safety, *Guidelines for Chemical Process Quantitative Risk Analysis*, American Institute of Chemical Engineers (AIChE), New York, NY, 1989.

Center for Chemical Process Safety, *Guidelines for Process Equipment Reliability Data, with Data Tables*, AIChE, New York, NY, 1989.

Cooper, D., "Moves Towards Greater Self-Regulation," *Fire Engineers Journal*, Vol. 40, No. 120, Dec. 1980, pp. 33–34.

Cote, A. E., *ed.*, "Industrial Fire Risk Management," in *Industrial Fire Hazards Handbook*, 3rd ed., National Fire Protection Association, Quincy, MA, 1990.

Dittman, C. R., "Selling Management the Best Fire Protection Available," *Professional Safety*, Vol. 33, No. 10, 1988, pp. 21–26.

Dow's Fire and Explosion Index Hazard Classification Guide, 5th ed., American Institute of Chemical Engineers, New York, NY, 1981.

Fire Inspection Management Guidelines, National Fire Protection Association, Quincy, MA, 1982.

"Fire Protection in Refineries," *API Recommended Practice 2001*, 6th ed., American Petroleum Institute, Washington, DC, 1984.

Gold, D. T., "Fire Brigade Training Manual," No. SPP-13A, National Fire Protection Association, Quincy, MA, 1981.

Grayson, S. J. and Smith, D. A., *eds.*, *New Technology to Reduce Fire Losses and Costs*, Elsevier, New York, NY, 1986.

Guidelines for Hazard Evaluation Procedures, American Institute of Chemical Engineers, New York, NY, 1985.

Hall, J. R., "Fire Risk Analysis," *Fire Protection Handbook*, 17th ed., Sec. 10, Chap. 7, National Fire Protection Association, Quincy, MA, 1986.

Handbook of Industrial Loss Prevention, 2nd ed., Factory Mutual Research Corp., Norwood, MA, 1967.

Hawksley, J. L., "Process Safety Management: A. V. K. Approach," *Plant/Operation Progress*, Vol. 7, No. 4, Oct. 1988, pp. 265–269.

Henley, E. J. and Kumamoto, H., *Reliability Engineering and Risk Assessment*, Prentice-Hall, Inc., Englewood Cliffs, NJ, 1981.

Hertz, D. B. and Thomas, H., *Risk Analysis and Its Applications*, John Wiley & Sons, New York, NY, 1984.

Holloway, C. A., *Decision Making under Uncertainty: Models and Choices*, Prentice-Hall, Inc., Englewood Cliffs, NJ, 1979.

Hubitsky, J., "Preventing Fires on Job Sites," *Fire Command*, Vol. 45, No. 7, July 1978, pp. 34–35.

Industrial Fire Hazards Handbook, 3rd ed., Section on Emergency Organizations, National Fire Protection Association, Quincy, MA, 1990.

Industrial Fire Protection, IFSTA, Stillwater, OK, 1982.

Introduction to Fire Protection (a training package), National Fire Protection Association, Quincy, MA, 1982.

Keeney, R. and Raiffa, H., *Decisions with Multiple Objectives: Preferences and Value Tradeoffs*, John Wiley & Sons, New York, NY, 1976.

Kletz, Trevor A., *An Engineer's View of Human Error*, Institution of Chemical Engineers, Warwickshire, England, 1983.

Lauriski, D. D., and Guymon, R. M., "Safety Management: What It Means to Us," *Mining Engineering*, Vol. 41, No. 10, Oct. 1989, pp. 1032–1035.

Lees, F. P., *Loss Prevention in the Process Industries*, Butterworth's, London, England, 1980.

Lecari, Frederick A., *RMPP: Risk Management and Prevention Program Guidance*, California Office of Emergency Services, Hazardous Material Division, Preliminary Advance Copy, June 1989.

McElroy, Frank E., *ed.*, *Accident Prevention Manual for Industrial Operations—Engineering and Technology*, 8th ed., National Safety Council, Chicago, IL, 1980.

Marshall, V. C., *Major Chemical Hazards*, John Wiley & Sons, New York, NY, 1985.

Moulton, G. A., *ed.*, NFPA *Inspection Manual*, National Fire Protection Association, Quincy, MA, 1989.

Mudan, K. and Gustafson, Richard, "Ignition Potential Distribution for Heavy Gas Plumes," in *International Conference on Vapor Cloud Modeling*, AIChE, New York, NY, 1987.

Ozog, Henry and Bendixen, Lisa M., "Hazard Identification and Quantification," *Chemical Engineering Progress*, Vol. 83, No. 4, Apr. 1987, pp. 55-64.

Pessemier, R., *Up in Smoke: A Business Guide to Fire and Life Safety*, Phoenix, Redmond, WA, 1987.

Planner, R. G., *Fire Loss Control*, Marcel Dekker, Inc., New York, NY, 1979. (Available from NFPA.)

Ramachandran, G., "Value of Human Life," SFPE *Handbook of Fire Protection Engineering*, 1st ed., Sec. 4, Chap. 9, National Fire Protection Association, Quincy, MA, 1988.

Ramsey, C. G., Evans, R., and English, M. A., "Siting and Layout of Major Hazardous Installation," in *The Assessment of Major Hazards*, Institution of Chemical Engineers, Pergamon Press, New York, NY, 1982, pp. 335-351.

Rasbash, D. J., "Criteria for Acceptability for Use with Quantitative Approaches to Fire Safety," *Fire Safety Journal*, Vol. 8, 1984-85, pp. 141-158.

Robertson, J. C., *Introduction to Fire Prevention*, Macmillan, New York, NY, 1989.

Rowe, William, *An Anatomy of Risk*, John Wiley & Sons, New York, NY, 1977.

Rutsein, R., and Clarke, M. B. J., "The Probability of Fire in Different Sectors of Industry," *Fire Surveyor*, Vol. 8, No. 1, Feb. 1979, pp. 20-23.

Samson, D., *Managerial Decision Analysis*, Richard D. Irwin, Inc., IL, 1988.

"Self-Fire Inspection: A New Concept in Firesafety," *Fire Chief Magazine*, Vol. 24, No. 5, 1980, pp. 34–35.

SFPE *Handbook of Fire Protection Engineering*, 1st ed., National Fire Protection Association, Quincy, MA, 1988.

Shortreed, John H. and Stewart, Angela, "Risk Assessment and Legislation," *Journal of Hazardous Materials*, Vol. 20, 1988, p. 315-334.

Stephens, H. F., "Fire Strategy for Management," *Fire Prevention*, 133, Nov. 1979, pp. 29–30.

Technica, Ltd., *Techniques for Assessing Industrial Hazards*, World Bank Technical Paper No. 55, World Bank, Washington, DC, 1988.

Thor, J. and Sedin, G., "Principles for Risk Evaluation and Expected Cost to Benefit of Different Fire Protective Measures in Industrial Buildings," *Firesafety Journal*, Vol. 2, No. 3, Mar. 1980, pp. 153–166.

Vervalin, Charles, H., *ed.*, *Fire Protection Manual for Hydrocarbon Processing Plants*, 3rd ed., Vols. 1-2, Gulf Western Publishing Co., Houston, TX, 1985.

Waters, D., "The Fire Protection of Plant and Equipment," *Fire*, Vol. 70, No. 867, 1977, pp. 185–186, 189.

Watts, John M., "Fire Risk Assessment Schedules," SFPE *Handbook of Fire Protection Engineering*, 1st ed., Sec. 4, Chap. 11, National Fire Protection Association, Quincy, MA, 1988.

Withers, John, *"Major Industrial Hazards: Their Appraisal and Control,"* Halsted Press, New York, NY, 1988.

PRIVATE EMERGENCY ORGANIZATIONS

John T. Higgins

Modern commercial facilities require detailed organization to handle the types of emergency situations that may occur. Many facilities think of this only in terms of fire, and feel it is enough to have the local fire department available to come and put out fire. However, today's complicated environment requires much more detailed organization. For example, consider the problems faced by the people in San Francisco during the earthquake in 1989; in Charlotte, NC, during the hurricane in the same year; and in the midwest after the tornado that devastated Xenia, OH; or the problems associated with the bank fire in a high-rise building in Los Angeles; or the K-Mart warehouse fire. This chapter provides guidance on what needs to be done before the emergency occurs and outlines the elements necessary to deal with the emergency.

This chapter assumes that the facility is a commercial establishment that is fairly large and several million dollars in value, and that there are a significant number of employees or visitors on the premises at least part of each day.

Related information can be found in the following: Section 9, Chapter 9, "Pre-Planning;" Section 9, Chapter 4, "Fire Department Organization;" Section 9, Chapter 5, "Fire Department Administration and Management;" and Section 9, Chapter 14, "Identification of the Hazards of Materials."

FACILITY RELATIONS WITH THE PUBLIC FIRE DEPARTMENT

Most commercial facilityemergency situations require the services of the local fire department. The most common reason for calling the fire department usually is to put out a fire that has occurred on the premises. For this reason, it is best for a facility to approach the local fire department in terms of facility emergency organization as it relates to fire.

Public Fire Department Capabilities

Fire departments vary greatly. If the facility in question is in an urban area, the fire department is probably a full-time paid department that is well trained and well equipped. If the facility is in a rural area, the fire department could range from a full-time paid department to a volunteer department with very little equipment or training and with very few people available during the day-time hours. (It should be noted that many volunteer fire departments are excellent, with very modern equipment and well-trained members. Many of these departments have members who work night shifts or are local business people who can respond to fires during the day, as well as at night.)

The facility manager must determine the capabilities of the local fire department in relation to the hazards presented by the commercial facility. For example, if the facility is a high-rise office building, does the local fire department have the training and equipment to handle a fire in that type of facility? Or, in the case of a large warehouse facility, with hazardous materials not only present in the warehouse, but transported into and out of the facility daily, is the local fire department equipped to handle emergencies involving hazardous materials or to fight a fire in a large-volume area?

It is essential that the facility manager (or risk manager, if one exists) and the local fire department discuss the types of hazards present in the facility. This discussion should include a review of the type of fire protection that is provided in the facility, e.g., sprinklers, special-hazard systems, fire alarm systems, etc. A facility tour with the fire department can address their ideas and concerns if a fire or other disaster should occur.

A local fire department may have short-comings. For example, if the facility handles highly flammable materials, does the fire department have enough foam and foam application equipment to deal with any fire that may occur in the facility? If oxygen is used, e.g., in a hospital, does the fire department understand the hazards of this material and how to safely deal with it? Obviously, there are many examples that could be used; however, the point is

John T. Higgins, P.E., is a senior safety specialist in the Corporate Safety and Loss Prevention Department of Dow Corning Corp., Midland, MI.

that each facility must review with the local fire department the specific hazards present on the premises, including fire and safety protection features that can assist in handling an emergency involving specific materials.

As the facility (or risk) manager determines the capabilities of the local fire department, part of the discussion should include how the facility can help the local fire department meet their responsibilities. This could include providing special equipment at the facility and training in how to use the equipment, or actual purchase of equipment for the fire department through a donation or by other means. The bottom line is to ensure that the local fire department can handle any emergency at the facility. If this cannot be done, then consideration must be given to providing and equipping an in-house industrial fire brigade.

Local Laws and the Fire Service

The federal Superfund Amendments and Reauthorization Act (SARA) of 1986 requires each municipality to set up a local emergency planning committee (LEPC). This law also requires that a commercial facility provide to the LEPC material safety data sheets (MSDS) for any chemicals that are used over certain threshold limits and on how much of each material is stored on premises. Information on these limits can be obtained from the U.S. Environmental Protection Agency (EPA). However, just because a facility is not a chemical plant or processor does not mean that it will not come under this act. In many cases, warehouses, hospitals, distributors, and manufacturing facilities will have enough chemicals on hand to justify reporting quantities.

When the local fire department knows what chemicals are present on the premises, where they are located, in what quantities, and what the hazards of these chemicals are (the MSDS will do this), they can respond more efficiently to whatever emergency has occurred, helping to ensure that the emergency is brought under control with a minimum of damage and loss.

Most fire departments have mutual-aid agreements with other fire departments. These agreements should detail who will be in charge at the emergency scene, who will cover if the local fire department has responded to another mutual-aid emergency, and how the local chiefs will communicate at the scene of the emergency.

Local laws or regulations may also detail who will respond to an emergency at the facility.

All of this is important to the facility (or risk) manager. Part of the discussion with the fire chief should include planning for communications between the facility and fire department at the time of the emergency, and how contact will be made with facility management, if the premises is closed when the emergency occurs. This plan should include supervisors from all shifts.

All of this information should be included in the emergency organization plan, which is discussed later in this chapter.

Planning with the Public Fire Department

Most state laws give the chief of the local fire department complete authority at the scene of the emergency to take whatever actions he/she deems appropriate to protect the public and the property of others.

Good pre-emergency planning is vital, and requires cooperation between facility management and the fire officials. This can be done by inviting the fire department officers to visit the facility on a regular basis. Include in these visits a good cross section of the facility management; discussion of the emergency organization (see the following section); a review of the emergency plan (discussed later in this chapter); a review of special hazards on the premises, including where hazardous materials are stored; and a review of the facility's fire protection features. These subjects should be covered over different visits throughout the year. The objective is to have the facility management become familiarized with the fire department officers, and *vice versa*.

The pre-emergency plan should include how the facility will call the fire department. This may be as simple as posting the local emergency number and having the person who recognizes the need for the services of the fire department call them. It may be a procedure where an employee calls a central number at the facility and then that person decides what actions are required and calls the fire department, if needed. The facility may have a fire alarm system activated by either a pull box or by automatic detectors. The system could also be activated by sprinkler flow or some other system. This alarm could go directly to the fire department or could go to a central point at the facility or to a central station which would then make the call to the fire department.

Whatever system is used, an agreement must be made and understood by both the facility management and the fire department as to what actions and response are expected and required by the fire department. Also, facility management should have a plan as to where to meet the responding fire department, including how vital information will be passed on to the senior officer responding. These details must be worked out in advance and put in writing so that everyone understands them. Fire department personnel need to tour the facility on some regular basis so that they are familiar with the layout; the location of equipment, including fire protection equipment; and any hazardous materials that may be present on the premises. They will need to have MSDSs on all chemicals present, and the facility should be prepared to help them assess any chemical involvement at the time of their response.

Evacuation of the employees and visitors from the premises is also very important. This is discussed in detail in the next section. For now, it is important to understand that part of the information that must be relayed to the responding fire department officers is information concerning any missing people, or injuries. If someone is missing, the last known location of that person is also important.

THE EMERGENCY ORGANIZATION

In order to handle an emergency of any magnitude, some pre-planning is necessary and this requires an organization that will be somewhat different from the management team that runs the facility. However, the management team must be an integral part of the emergency organization or team. The three key elements of an emergency organization are: (1) evacuation, (2) managing the emergency, and (3) restoration of the facility.

Evacuation

The most important asset of the facility is the people, not only the employees but any visitors, such as vendors, customers, contractors, truckers, or others, who may be visiting the facility.

It is good practice to have all visitors sign in when entering the facility and include the name of the person they are visiting. In case of an emergency, this sign-in sheet will be invaluable in identifying who was in the facility other than the employees.

An evacuation plan must be put together and people assigned to manage the plan. Key elements of the evacuation plan are as follows.

1. Evacuation routes: Each department or area must plan the route that they will use to leave the building in case of fire. Primary and secondary routes (in case the primary is blocked) must be designated. Maps should be prepared showing the evacuation route, and these maps should be posted where employees and visitors can see them. The evacuation map should also list a primary and secondary accumulation point where occupants should gather to ensure that everyone has been accounted for and to pass on information about the emergency.
2. Monitor duties: Each department should appoint a monitor to be responsible for the evacuation procedures. In addition, at least two alternate monitors should be appointed to take over these responsibilities in the event the first-designated monitor is not available. The names of the monitors should be listed on the evacuation route sheets.

The duties of the monitor should be clearly outlined in the emergency plan. Generally, monitors are responsible for seeing to it that everyone knows about the evacuation and does indeed evacuate, that doors and windows are shut if time allows, and that power and equipment are turned off as needed in case an extended evacuation from the building becomes necessary. These key duties will vary from department to department and must be described in writing and clearly communicated to all.

The monitor is also responsible for getting an accurate count of those evacuating from his/her department and reporting that information to a senior monitor, who is usually the personnel manager (or designee), since that department has a record of the employees in the facility. The senior monitor is then responsible for ensuring that information on whether everyone has escaped the facility is conveyed to the fire department contact and, thus, to the responding local fire department. (See the following subsection.)

3. Employee duties: Duties of individual employees include ensuring that visitors or strangers in their area evacuate with them, and turning off, or shutting down, equipment that cannot be left running for an extended period of time.

The evacuation plan should also include actions to be taken in case of a natural disaster. Obviously, this needs to address the type(s) of natural disaster most likely to occur in the area. Unusual occurances, such as bomb threats, could also be included in this plan.

Finally, the evacuation plan must include what the signal for evacuation will be, and this needs to be well communicated. Normally, this information is included on the evacuation sheet posted in the department. These plans need to be practiced at least annually—that is the only way to ensure that employees will know what to do if a real emergency occurs.

Managing the Emergency

The key to emergency planning is having an organizational team to manage the emergency. The responsibility of the emergency team during the emergency is to attempt to control what is happening within the context of the team's ability. The objectives are to protect the people in the facility, to minimize the loss to the facility, and to reduce the adverse publicity that may occur as part of the emergency. The team must also be prepared to deal with the government agencies that may become involved, responding to them in a way that will minimize any possible fines or future liabilities.

The key team person is usually the facility manager or, in some cases, the risk manager. In all cases, at least two backups must be named. In addition, other management representatives should be available to help. This team should also include: (1) someone from engineering who has plans of the building and knows the location of the mechanical equipment, utilities, roof access, etc.; (2) someone from operations who understands what hazardous materials may be present and where they are, and what other operations were going on that may create a special problem for the fire department; and (3) the senior monitor, as described above.

A spokesperson should be designated to coordinate information. This person will give the fire department whatever information is available upon their arrival and will work with the emergency organization to supply whatever additional information the fire department may need during the course of the emergency.

Media presence can be expected if the emergency is significant and particularly if the facility is the only one of its type involved. Someone should be designated as the contact person for the media. Questions to anticipate are: what happened, who was hurt, what was damaged, what the facility does (i.e., what service is performed or what product is made), number of employees, annual sales, size of facility, etc. Preparation for these questions includes gathering information on the facility (only that which management is willing to give the media) and having it available for use if an emergency does occur. The facility manager, in conjunction with the fire chief, should compile a press release as soon as possible after media arrive and give them pertinent information about the status of the emergency. Also, media will want pictures and, as soon as possible, will want to visit the actual area of the emergency. Decide ahead of time how to handle this; a discussion with the fire department can help ensure that this aspect of the emergency is coordinated properly and without hindrance to any possible investigation.

Another aspect of any emergency is the need to contact appropriate local, state, or federal agencies of the government. Pre-planning should identify in the emergency plan those situations that will require notification of government agencies. (See the section entitled "The Emergency Plan.") Someone should be designated to contact the various agencies as required by law. In turn, expect the agency(s) to send a representative(s) to the scene. The facility contact person should be prepared to meet the government representatives and to respond to their questions and needs. Handling of these government representatives should be planned well in advance so that everyone knows how to respond appropriately. Government agencies may want certain actions to be taken during the course of the emergency. Be prepared to work with the government agency representatives and the fire department to meet these requests.

Restoration of the Facility

The last phase of emergency organization is restoring the facility. Organizing a group to get things cleaned up and the facility back into operation as quickly as possible is essential to restoration. The emergency organization should be concerned with protection of the property. They need to take action quickly to ensure that further damage does not occur, but should preserve the scene long enough for any investigation team or insurance company representatives to make their inspections.

When a fire or damage from a natural disaster occurs, the insurance carrier must be notified as soon as possible. Designate someone in the emergency plan to do this and to handle the insurance claim agent visit.

Pre-planning for restoration is necessary. For example, if the facility operates a large computer system, how critical is it to the operation of the business? If the business cannot operate without the computer, pre-planning needs to include: (1) how to protect the computer during the emergency from water or other problems, such as dirt; (2) how to get the unit back in operation quickly if, for instance, water damage occurs; or (3) where one can locate backup units.

Equipment restoration is possible and plannable. One company had all of their vital records on paper under water in a flood. They immediately contacted a company that freeze-dried the paper and saved the records. A computer facility had hair dryers available and, when the computer got wet in a fire, they put a crew to work immediately to dry the computer with the hair dryers.

Chemicals pose a big problem. Contamination of the environment, whether it is the soil, water, or air, is a big concern of the state and federal waste management groups. Contamination of the ground, local drinking water, or public waterways can be particularly expensive to fix. If chemicals are used at the facility, plans should be made to contain the chemicals during any emergency. This will require pre-planning and appropriate construction to build proper containment facilities. Pre-planning could include the replacement of hazardous chemicals with less hazardous ones, or removal of chemicals that have become obsolete.

When emergencies do occur, they are sometimes accompanied by injuries and death and appropriate actions must be taken. Most likely the fire department will have, or can easily call, an ambulance. However, the emergency team also needs to be concerned with notifying the family of the injured (or deceased), and should provide them with as much information as possible, including financial, insurance, and sick-pay details.

If there is a death or more than five people are hospitalized as a result of an accident, the Occupational Safety and Health Administration (OSHA) must be notified within 24 hours. This will result in an investigation by OSHA.

It will be necessary to preserve the scene so that the physical evidence is present for the OSHA investigation. Pictures will be needed. Plans for who will be the photographer should be made in advance and that person should be called as soon as possible so that the scene can be photographed as soon as the emergency is under control. These pictures will also be a valuable record for the insurance company.

An in-house investigation team must also be appointed as soon as the emergency is under control. The team should be appointed by the facility manager to determine the cause of the accident and the action necessary to prevent the accident from occurring again. Remember that both the insurance company and any government agencies that had to be notified will want to see the results of the in-house investigation and may even want to join the team as part of the investigation. In very bad accidents, it is important to keep the public relations part of the emergency team involved in the investigation process, since further adverse publicity may come out of the investigation.

THE EMERGENCY PLAN

It is necessary that all of the elements that have been discussed in the preceding sections be outlined precisely. This outline is called the facility emergency plan. Each of the different facets of the plan must be coordinated and described in detail. The objective is to protect the facility and its employees, and this can only be done through a well-structured plan.

Start the plan with a description of the purpose. Next, put together an organizational chart showing who the members of the emergency team are and what their individual responsibilities will be. Each team position should have at least two backup individuals, since an emergency can occur when a key person is on vacation or sick.

The emergency plan should include a description of the function of each of the key members of the team and specifics on how the plan should work. Details include reporting of the emergency, signalling evacuation, accounting for people, calling the fire department, etc. Be sure to include expected restoration activities in the plan. Since some sections of the plan may occur simultaneously, make sure that adequate numbers of team members will be present at each phase. Include in the plan descriptions of how the team will handle the press, government reporting and visits, notification of the insurance company, notification of family members in case of injury or death, and chemicals that may have escaped into the environment.

Note that the U.S. EPA, OSHA, and many state governments require specific emergency plans, depending on the type of facility and the chemicals that are handled. In some cases, several of these plans must be prepared to meet the requirements of each of these agencies.

When the plan is complete and thoroughly reviewed by all involved, it should be kept where it can be reviewed frequently and is available in case of an emergency. It should be treated as a "living document," and, annually, at a minimum, should be reviewed to ensure that it reflects the current thinking of the facility management and continues to meet current government laws and insurance company requirements. This review should include the local fire department.

Last, frequent practice of the plan will familiarize the emergency team with all aspects of the plan and will prepare them to react within the context of the plan, whatever the emergency. Quarterly practices should be a minimum. The facility (or risk) manager responsible for the plan should coordinate the simulated emergencies, including at least one annual evacuation. The fire department should be part of these practices whenever possible.

SUMMARY

An emergency can occur at any time, and can become a disaster if the facility does not prepare for it. Comprehensive pre-planning is the key and will pay off in saved lives and reduced property or environmental damage or loss.

BIBLIOGRAPHY

NFPA Codes, Standards, and Recommended Practices

Reference to the following NFPA codes, standards, and recommended practices will provide further information on private emergency organizations discussed in this chapter. (See the latest *NFPA Catalog* for availability of current editions of the following documents.)

NFPA 1, *Fire Prevention Code*.

NFPA 10, *Portable Fire Extinguishers*.

NFPA 13, *Installation of Sprinkler Systems*.

NFPA 14, *Standpipe and Hose Systems*.

NFPA 30, *Flammable and Combustible Liquids Code*.

NFPA *101*®, *Life Safety Code*®.

NFPA 231, *General Storage*.

NFPA 231C, *Rack Storage of Materials*.

NFPA 600, *Private Fire Brigades*.

Additional Reading

Albrecht, A. R., "Handling Spills Involving Hazardous Chemicals Within the Chemical Industry," *Fire Journal*, Vol. 65, No. 3, May 1971, pp. 40-48.

Anderson, N., "Ultimate in Training Airport Fire-Fighters," *Fire International*, Vol. 11, No. 104, 1987, pp. 59, 62.

Barker, J. A., "Training: The Key to Fire Safety," *Fire Prevention*, No. 224, Nov. 1989, pp. 28-30.

Boyle, M. J., "FPA Award Winner Describes CEGB Approach to Fire Safety," *Fire Prevention*, No. 220, June 1989, pp. 28-30.

Davis. L., and Robinson, K., "Trends Affecting Fire Brigades," *Fire Service Today*, Vol. 50, No. 7, July 1983, p. 29.

Dirckze, T., "Evaluation of an Airport Fire Service's Capability," *Fire Engineers Journal*, No. 1, 1989, pp. 10-12

Fire Protection Through Private Enterprise," *Journal of American Insurance*, Vol. 56, No. 2, 1980, pp. 9-12.

Gold, D. T., "A Blueprint for Training a Fire Brigade," *Fire Journal*, Vol. 76, No. 5, Sept. 1982 , p. 61.

Henderson, J. S., "Paper on the Fire Fighting Arrangements for Personnel Involved in the Offshore Oil Industry," *Proceedings* of the Conference on Offshore Passive Fire Protection, Plastics and Rubber Institute, London, 1987, p.2.

James, D., "In-House Fire Teams—Training and Motivation," *Fire Prevention Handbook*, Butterworths, Boston, 1986, pp. 84-95.

James, D., "Training the Workforce," *Fire Prevention Handbook*, Butterworths, Boston, 1986, pp. 84-95.

Lowder, E. J., "A Better Idea for an Industrial Fire Protection Program" *Fire Journal*, Vol. 62, No. 5, Sept. 1968, pp. 10-13.

McKay, J.C., and Mason, B., "Improved Fire Training Facility Plan," *Military Engineer*, Vol. 80, No. 523, 1988, pp. 457-458.

NFPA, *Introduction to Fire Protection* (Training Package), National Fire Protection Association, Quincy, MA, 1982.

Robeson, P., "Industrial Fire Teams in Australia," *Fire Prevention*, No. 216, Jan./Feb. 1989, pp. 32-35.

Robertson, J. C., "Preparing Fire Service Personnel for Fire Prevention Duties," *Introduction to Fire Prevention*, 3rd ed., Macmillan, New York, 1989, pp. 99-111.

Rubin, D. L., "Industrial Fire Brigades: From Planning to Reality," *Fire Journal*, Vol. 78, No. 3, May 1984, pp. 101-104.

Silensky, P., "Monsanto's Meut' Team: Porter with the Public Sector," *Fire Engineering*, Vol. 143, No. 2, 1990, p. 51.

Townley, J. P., et al., "Industrial Fire Protection—1967, *Fire Journal*, Vol. 61, No. 5, Sept. 1967, pp. 12-21.

Vasil, E., "Organizing and Training the Industrial Fire Brigade," *Industrial Fire World*, Vol. 2, No. 3, 1987, pp. 8-11.

Winkworth, G., "Cause for Alarm," *Fire Engineers Journal*, Vol. 48, No. 149, June 1988, pp. 17-18.

Zuccarelli, L. A., "Developing A Performance Based Industrial Fire Brigade Training Program," *Industrial Fire World*, Vol. 2, No. 3, 1987, pp. 17-20.

FIRE DEPARTMENT ORGANIZATION

Revised by Earle G. Roberts

This chapter provides an introductory discussion of the various elements of public fire protection. It starts with a brief historical overview of the beginnings of early fire protection and fire regulations in ancient Rome. Discussions follow on fire-department objectives, fire-service organizations, and fire-department personnel and structures.

Consult the remaining chapters in this section for detailed discussions of other aspects of public fire protection. Administration and management, operations, prevention, and arson investigation are described in the following four chapters, while the final three chapters detail facilities and apparatus, planning, and fire department decision-making.

Today, there are approximately 30,000 fire departments in the United States and there are many types of public fire department organizations as well. Public fire protection is normally (although not necessarily) a function of local government (i.e., a town, city, municipality, county, or organized fire district.) State, provincial, or federal properties may also have organized fire departments to protect properties. Likewise, large industries will often provide organized private fire departments at their industrial complexes. The organization and objectives of public fire departments vary according to resources available, and range from simple to complex.

EARLY FIRE PROTECTION AND FIRE REGULATIONS

Generally, public fire departments evolved from the level of community effort to professional organizations in five basic steps.

1. The establishment of night-watch services.
2. The drafting of fire-prevention regulations and the appointment of fire-protection officers.
3. The organization of societies to salvage building contents from loss by fire.
4. The formation of voluntary fire-fighting companies.
5. The appointment of fire-fighting officers and personnel.

Possibly the first organized fire protection occurred when Augustus became ruler of Rome in 24 B.C. A "vigil," or watch service, was created, and regulations for checking and preventing fires were issued. Night patroling and night-watch forces were the principal services, and some of the vigils had duties more like those of police or soldiers than fire fighters. It is clear from the history of that period, however, that fires were a major problem and that the vigils were provided with fire-fighting tools and equipment (buckets, axes, etc.).

One of the earliest recorded fire-protection regulations dates back to A.D. 872 in Oxford, England, when a curfew was adopted requiring hearth fires to be extinguished at a fixed hour. Later, William the Conqueror established a general curfew law in England, enforced to prevent both fires and revolt.

Fire Brigades in Great Britain

Until 1830, Great Britain did not provide statutory authority to units of local government for night or other watch services with fire apparatus. *The History of the British Fire Service*[1] mentions only two cases where this subject was introduced in England before the establishment of civil police forces. One was during the English Civil War in 1643 when a company of fifty women was organized to patrol the town of Nottingham at night.

The second involved the organization of private fire-fighting forces. Fire insurance brigades were formed in England primarily as a result of the Great Fire of London in 1666. These brigades were formed by the insurance companies without statutory authority or obligations and the insurance-company offices, not the government authorities, decided where the brigades would be located. In London, the insurance-office fire brigades were consolidated into the London Fire Engine Establishment in 1833, which was taken over by the Metropolitan Fire Brigade in 1865.

It was not until Edinburgh's 1824 Fire Brigade Establishment that public fire services began to develop modern standards of operation. A surveyor named James

---

Mr. Roberts is Fire Chief for Madison, WI, and Chairman, NFPA 1201, *Developing Fire Protection Services for the Public.*

Braidwood was appointed chief of the brigade. He selected eighty part-time aides between the ages of seventeen and twenty-five, and required regular drills and night training. Braidwood wrote the first comprehensive handbook on fire department operation in 1830. His handbook included some three hundred ninety-six standards and explained, for the first time, the kind of service a good fire department should perform.

Fire Protection in Early America

Following a disastrous Boston, Massachusetts, fire in 1631, the first fire ordinance in the new world was adopted. The ordinance prohibited thatched roofs and wooden chimneys, and was enforced by the colonial city's board of selectmen. In 1648, New Amsterdam appointed five municipal "fire wardens" with fire-prevention responsibilities; this event is often considered to be the origin of the first public fire department in North America.

In Boston, after a 1679 conflagration destroyed 155 principal buildings and a number of ships, laws were adopted requiring stone or brick walls for buildings and slate or "tyle" roofs for houses. That fire also led to the establishment of the first paid municipal fire department in North America, if not in the world. Boston imported a fire engine from England and employed twelve fire fighters and a fire chief. From the start, Massachusetts used paid municipal fire fighters on an on-call basis, as contrasted with the unpaid volunteer fire companies that were later organized in other colonies.

Colonial communities required each householder to keep two fire buckets and, when the church bells rang an alarm, to report to the scene of a fire to form lines for passing water from wells or springs. As late as 1810, Boston citizens were subject to a ten-dollar fine for failure to respond to alarms with their buckets. When hand-pump fire engines were obtained, teams were organized to operate them. The laws in a number of states still impose penalties on citizens who refuse to assist in fighting fires upon orders from fire officers.

Fire wardens were appointed in Boston in 1711. With the members of their staffs, fire wardens responded to fires and supervised citizen bucket-brigades. By 1715, Boston had six fire companies with engines.

Mutual Fire Societies: The first of a number of mutual fire societies was formed in Boston in 1718 when some of the more affluent citizens organized to assist each other in salvaging goods from fires in their homes or business. Each person's equipment comprised a bag in which to collect valuables, a screwdriver, and a bed key to help disassemble and remove beds from burning buildings. About a century later, these mutual fire societies became inactive when fire insurance became available to the more prosperous citizens. The mutual fire societies were forerunners of the salvage corps.

Salvage Corps: After the principal cities of the U.S. organized paid fire departments equipped with steam engines around 1850, insurance interests formed salvage corps to reduce water damage at fires. Gradually, improved fire-fighting procedures and the increased expense of operation led to the disbandment of salvage corps. Today, public fire departments handle salvage operations at fires.

The Growth of Paid Departments: Lack of discipline of volunteer fire fighters, coupled with their resistance to the introduction of steam-pump engines, led to the organization of paid fire departments. Following serious disorders at fires, a paid fire department with horse-drawn steam pumpers was placed in service in Cincinnati, Ohio, on April 1, 1853. In 1855, two steamers were delivered to New York City, but the volunteer fire fighters would not use them. Ten years later the "Metropolitan Fire Department," using steamers, replaced New York's volunteer force.

Duty Systems and Training

Until World War I, paid members of fire departments worked a continuous-duty system, with limited off-duty time. By World War II, most paid fire departments had adopted some form of the two-platoon system, which allowed additional days off and reduced the average number of hours worked per week. The hours worked per week have continued to decline, although in most cities fire fighters work more hours per week than workers in other municipal employment or private industry. Although many fire fighters continue to work twenty-four-hour duty shifts, 1975 federal legislation has had a significant impact on the working hours of fire fighters.

In 1889, the Boston Fire Department established the first drill school where basic training and uniform company drills were performed. Today most departments provide some degree of training for personnel.

In 1914, New York City established a Fire College for advanced officer training. During that same year, the first state fire school was organized in North Carolina. In 1925, Illinois and Iowa started state fire schools for the training of volunteer fire fighters, and by 1950 most states were providing systematic fire-service training. In 1937, Oklahoma A&M College (now Oklahoma State University) initiated a two-year (later four-year) college program in fire protection. The initial objective of the Oklahoma program was to provide trained individuals for the fire service. However, the emphasis was later shifted to the industrial and insurance aspects of fire protection. Currently, approximately two hundred to two hundred fifty institutions in the U.S. offer two-year programs in fire-protection education. One four-year program (offered by the University of Maryland) offers a full curriculum in fire-protection engineering. Several colleges offer four-year programs of study leading to degrees in fire technology or fire-service management, and one (Worcester Polytechnic Institute in Massachusetts) offers a Masters degree in fire-protection engineering.

FIRE SERVICE ORGANIZATIONS

Most public fire-service organizations in the states and provinces of North America are usually established by local agencies of government, or special local agencies that provide fire protection. Normally, local government is responsible for providing adequate fire protection, and the framework within which the protection operates.

Types of Organizations

The types of public fire-protection organizations vary widely. One of the most common types is the *public fire department*, a department of municipal government, with the head of the department directly responsible to the chief administrative officer of the municipality. Most large municipalities, as well as numerous small communities, operate with this type of organization.

Less common is a *fire bureau*, which is usually a division of a department of public safety. In this type of organization, the public-safety-department head must divide his or her time between several important functions, including police and fire service.

The *county fire department* has gained considerable acceptance in many areas. With this type of organization, numerous small suburban municipalities can enjoy the benefits of a large, professionally administered public fire department with staff and service facilities that, ordinarily, few small communities could afford individually. Frequently, this department begins with a county fire-prevention office and a fire-communications system. The smaller (often volunteer) departments initially remain autonomous for fire-suppression purposes, but gradually more functions, including suppression, are assumed by the county organization.

Another type of public fire-service organization is the *fire district*, which is organized under provisions of state or provincial law. It is, in effect, a separate unit of government, having its own governing body composed of commissioners or trustees, and is commonly supported by a tax levied through the district. Usually it is organized following a favorable vote of the property owners in the proposed district. The fire district may include portions of one or more townships or other governmental subdivisions. Its fire force is frequently termed a "fire department," although in many cases it is the only department operated by that unit of government.

A fifth common type of fire protection authority is the *fire-protection district*, which in some states is a legally established, tax-supported unit that contracts for fire protection from a nearby fire department or even from a voluntary fire association. This type of organization provides the equivalent of municipal fire protection for rural or suburban areas that might find it difficult to maintain their own experienced and effective fire-fighting forces. The fire-protection district often provides a source of extra income and special rural fire apparatus for the small municipal fire departments that contract to supply fire protection.

An early type of public fire service organization is the *volunteer fire company* or *association* that raises its own funds by public activities and subscriptions, frequently with contributions of funds or equipment from interested units of government. Many voluntary fire associations maintain excellent equipment and stations, and also serve as centers for various community activities. Often, volunteer organizations prefer to retain their independence from government, especially when purchasing equipment, although in some instances the activities of independent fire organizations are coordinated through special associations and governmental advisory boards.

FIRE DEPARTMENT PERSONNEL

It is estimated that there are at least two-hundred-thousand career fire-fighting personnel and more than a million on-call or volunteer personnel serving in the U.S. The chief distinction between career and on-call or volunteer personnel is that career personnel are assigned regular periods of duty and are compensated on a regular basis. On-call or volunteer personnel are not normally required to be available except for meetings, training sessions, and fires, and may or may not receive compensation for their services.

While most cities and towns of appreciable size employ only career personnel, some cities use auxiliary personnel to supplement their regular forces. Other cities and towns may use combinations of career, on-call, or volunteer personnel. Some communities maintaining their own fire departments may have a career fire chief, officers, and apparatus operators, but rely upon on-call or volunteer personnel to provide the staffing balance necessary for efficient fire-fighting operations. Other communities may use career personnel only during normal daytime working hours and rely upon on-call or volunteer personnel during the night.

The combination of personnel used—career, on-call, or volunteer—is strictly a matter of choice by the community: what might work well for one community might not work well for another. A number of important factors can influence the type of personnel used within a fire department. These factors are: (1) the financial resources of the community, (2) the availability of on-call or volunteer personnel, (3) the frequency of fire incidents, (4) the range of services expected from the department, and (5) the type of department preferred by the community.

Frequently the financial resources of many smaller communities will dictate that the department be composed entirely of volunteer personnel. Since salaries normally consume a large percentage of a fire department budget, available finances may be sufficient only to purchase and maintain apparatus and equipment. Other communities with adequate financial resources may or may not elect to implement a full career service. This decision may be based on one or a combination of the important factors described below.

On-Call or Volunteer Personnel

In some cases where a community wants or needs fire protection, there may not be a sufficient number of persons willing or able to serve in a volunteer capacity. This requires that the community finance the operation of a fire department staffed either fully or partially by career personnel. A situation of this type is probably most evident in the rapidly growing suburban communities surrounding major metropolitan areas. Originally, these outlying areas were composed of small communities that provided a climate suitable for volunteer departments. As times changed, however, these communities experienced rapid growth rates in population, housing, and ancillary services. Demands for fire-protection services grew accordingly. The original corps of volunteers found themselves unable to meet the increased demand or to recruit new members since many residents in these areas commute out of the community on normal workdays and are unavailable for fire department participation. Therefore, many of these once-volunteer fire departments have added the services of career personnel.

Effect of Frequency of Incidents on Personnel Selection

The frequency with which a fire-fighting department responds to incidents will determine the type of personnel chosen to staff the department. Large, congested areas, especially those that are heavily commercial or industrial, are likely to produce an increased need for fire department service compared to more sparsely settled, largely residential areas. A department that responds to a large number of incidents each year will tend to inhibit a full volunteer operation unless the department has a large membership and the workload can be apportioned to reduce the commitment required of each individual. There are no set figures on the number of incidents that require the use of career personnel. The determination must be made locally, based on the ability of the department to perform at a level acceptable to the community supporting the service. It is reasonable to assume that when the number of incidents increases beyond the level that the volunteers are capable of handling, the members will request a change in department staffing.

Type of Department Personnel Preferred by the Community

Communities often have preferences for the type of staff members they wish to have serve in their fire departments. The preference may be based on one or several of the previous factors or on entirely different considerations. In some instances, the volunteer fire department serves as a focal point of community activity, and the community is satisfied with the level of service provided by volunteer staff. The community itself must ultimately decide on the type of personnel to be used within the department.

There are many fire departments—career, combination, and volunteer—that provide an acceptable level of service to their respective communities. The success of their operations is not dependent upon whether the personnel are paid or unpaid, but upon their individual and collective ability to perform and to accomplish departmental objectives. There are no simple guidelines that set forth the requirements as to the type of personnel to be used for fire department operations. The decision is one that must be made at the local level following a careful analysis of all pertinent factors.

EXPANDED ROLE OF THE FIRE SERVICE

In recent years, the role of the fire service in many communities has expanded far beyond fire suppression. Citizens are dependent on the fire department to ensure their protection against the dangers of fire, panic, explosion, other hazardous conditions, and any emergency events that may occur in the community.

Fire Prevention

Fire prevention and code enforcement is one of the major areas of responsibility for the fire service.

The local fire department should initiate the adoption of a complete local fire code. Most fire departments adopt one of the model codes that are developed by private code-and-standard-development organizations. Model codes may be amended to adjust for local concerns and needs. The fire department should work closely with the local legal authority to develop adoptive ordinance for the code.

In the past, most fire-prevention activities were limited to a small nucleus of full-time specialists who might be civilian or uniformed personnel. While it is still necessary to maintain full-time fire-prevention personnel, the responsibilities of the fire department are greater than can be performed by specialists.

Fire-suppression personnel have been increasingly active in inspections and code enforcement. With proper training and support, suppression personnel are effective in performing code-enforcement inspections. It is imperative that all fire department personnel recognize that firesafety education and prevention are a major part of the fire fighter's responsibilities.

Fire Investigation

There is increased emphasis in the area of fire investigation. Fire investigations identify factors useful in lessening the number and severity of fires that may occur in the future. Information gained through investigations is a valuable tool in developing an effective fire-prevention program including needed code revisions, public-education programs, and planning for future fire-protection needs. A thorough fire investigation of all incendiary or suspicious fires is a powerful deterrent to the crime of arson.

Community Education

Fire-community education has been part of the fire service for many years. However, it has only recently become focused and emerged as a major component in fire protection. The National Fire Protection Association (NFPA) "Learn Not To Burn"® program is one component that has been successful in reaching and educating elementary-school children on firesafety issues.

Incident Command

Vastly improved incident-command systems have been developed and are in use throughout the country. Incident-command systems form the basic structure of operations regardless of scale. An effective system should be designed to manage emergency incidents of various types including structural fires, wildland fires, hazardous-materials incidents, medical operations, and any other major emergencies.

Emergency Medical Services Delivery

Many fire departments are involved in the delivery of emergency medical services (EMS) in addition to the departments' other responsibilities. In most cases, EMS activity exceeds the workload from fire or other types of emergencies.

The emergency-medical-services delivery system may be solely the responsibility of the fire department, from first responder providing basic life support to advanced life support (paramedic-level care) including transport.

Other emergency medical systems may include a combination of both public and private organizations cooperating to respond to medical incidents.

Hazardous Materials

Significant risks have been apparent in communities regarding the storage, use, transportation, and disposal of hazardous materials and hazardous waste. In many cases, the fire department is the lead agency in responding to hazardous-materials incidents and protecting the community from such risks.

The fire department should have direct involvement as either a lead or participating agency in the process of gathering and organizing information, identifying risk, and planning for hazardous-materials emergencies, and in the regulation of the storage, use, transportation, and disposal of hazardous materials and hazardous wastes. The role of the fire department will vary depending on the local and regional determinations.

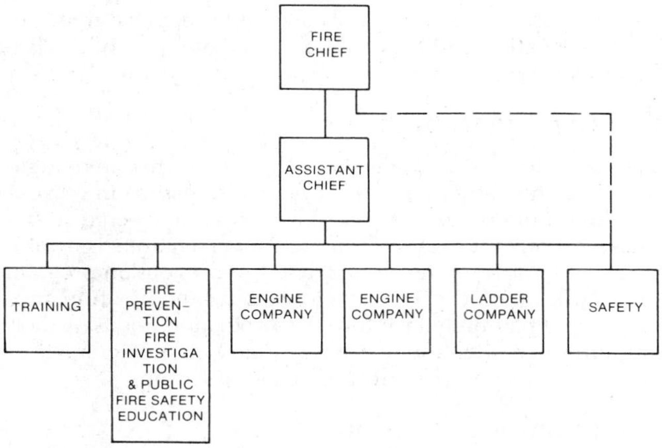

FIG. 9-4A. Typical organizational structure of a small fire department.

Mutual Aid or Automatic Aid

Every fire department today should have mutual-aid or automatic-aid contracts with adjoining departments. These reciprocal agreements provide communities with the ability to share their personnel and equipment to provide sufficient resources to handle major emergencies in a timely and cost-effective manner.

Improved Management Systems

There are a number of systems that have been developed to improve management decision-making through teamwork and closer working relationships. Traditionally these systems have been developed for use by the private sector. However, their application has been found to be relevant in improving the management of fire departments. Several systems have been developed, some of which are organizational development, quality circles, quality- and productivity-improvement programs, and management by objective.

The purpose of these systems is to improve the quality of service delivered, to improve productivity, to increase cost-effectiveness, and to give management clearly stated goals and measurable objectives. This is accomplished by increasing the participation of the managers and workers in the organization's decision-making. The major benefits shared by all these systems are an improved management team, increased employee input, improved employee morale, and a better quality of service delivery utilizing available services.

Every fire department should have a mission statement regarding the scope of services it provides to its jurisdiction. In addition, goals should be established for the department. Each level of the department should also have measurable objectives.

Management Information Systems

Increased emphasis is placed on the use of management-information systems to provide data that can be analyzed in order to improve decision-making. It has been especially effective in the areas of the fire-protection system, the emergency-medical-services delivery system, personnel, and fiscal management.

There are some systems that collect data regionally and nationally on fires, hazardous materials, fire prevention, service-delivery systems, community education, etc. All this information is easily available for use by individual departments.

Occupational Safety and Health

In the past, it was accepted that the fire service continued to have high numbers of employee deaths and injuries. The adoption in 1987 of NFPA 1500, *Fire Department Safety and Health Programs*, focused on methods to improve the health and safety of fire fighters. As these standards gain acceptance and are implemented, fire fighters should enjoy improved health, and the national rate of deaths and injuries in the fire service should decrease.

FIRE DEPARTMENT STRUCTURE

Fire departments, like other organizations, comprise people working together in a coordinated effort to achieve a common set of objectives. For a department to function effectively, it must have an organizational plan that shows the relationship between the operating divisions and the total organization. An organizational plan does not preclude the necessity for active leadership; it merely provides the means by which the organization can be managed effectively. Organizational charts with typical structures of small, medium, and large fire departments are shown in Figures 9-4A, 9-4B, and 9-4C.

Principles of Organization

There has been much written on organization and organizational principles. Although it is impossible to list all of these principles, several that are generally applicable to fire department organizations are briefly described herein.

One of the most basic organizational principles is that work should be divided among the individuals and operating units according to a plan. The plan should be based on the individual functions that must be performed such as fire prevention, training, communications, etc.

The next principle is that as a department increases in size and complexity, the need for coordination also increases. Small departments are simple organizations that allow frequent personal contact among individuals; thus there is less need for extensive formal coordination. However, as departments increase in size and complexity, they require more extensive coordination of the operating units in order to achieve their objectives.

Line Functions

Line functions in fire departments normally refer to those activities directly involved with fire-suppression operations. Fire-suppression officers are primarily considered to be line officers. This does not mean, however, that they do not have other functions. As these officers are promoted within the department, their line responsibilities may be divided equally with staff responsibilities. At the highest officer levels within the department, line responsibilities diminish while staff responsibilities increase.

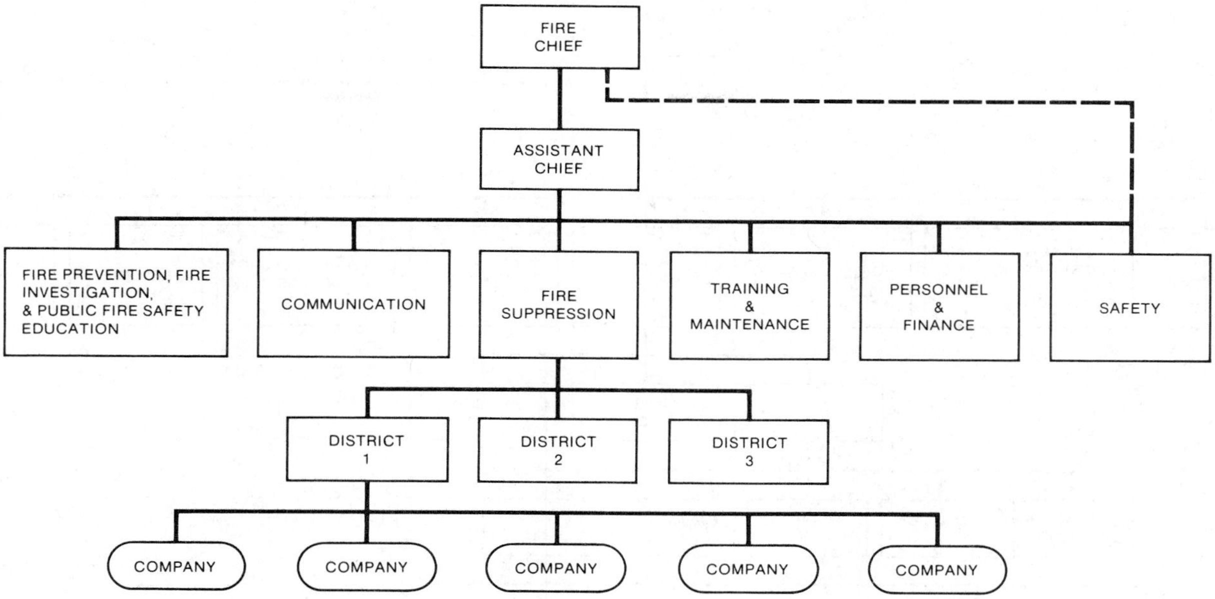

FIG. 9-4B. Typical organizational structure of a medium-size fire department.

Staff Functions

Staff functions are those activities that do not involve dealing with day-to-day emergency incidents such as fire suppression, emergency-medical service, and various hazardous conditions or hazardous materials spills. Briefly, these staff functions include the following activities:

Fire Prevention: The inspection of all properties for compliance with codes and ordinances; the operation of a public education program; and the investigation of fires to determine the reasons that fires start and spread.

Training: Training of all personnel in their job skills; administering continuing education programs in special subject areas; administering the fire department safety program; and organizing and administering pre-fire planning.

Maintenance: The maintenance of apparatus, equipment, and physical facilities; recommendation of replacement programs for apparatus and equipment; and the development of specifications for the purchase of apparatus and equipment.

Communications: Providing and maintaining adequate facilities for the receipt of alarms from the public; and communication with fire companies both in quarters and, by radio, in the field. Communications functions also include developing and maintaining dispatch policy and response requirements.

Research and Planning: Creating the new knowledge that the fire department needs to provide better service; forecasting long-range department goals; and performing the types of analyses necessary for other department functions to assess program effectiveness.

Community Relations: Maintaining contact with the public and the news media to tell the fire department story.

Financial Management: Preparing a budget; monitoring expenses (and income if appropriate) against the budget; planning for capital expenditures; and supervising the purchase and inventory of needed materials.

Personnel Management: Supervising the recruitment, selection, and promotion of personnel; administering the retirement system and the benefits program; and supervising the administration of discipline within the department.

Fire Protection Engineering: Reviewing plans for new construction, major renovation, or installation of fire-protection systems; developing proposals for code changes; and assisting in the technical aspects of code enforcement and fire investigations as necessary.

In large fire departments, a staff officer is normally assigned to supervise each of the above functions. Such officers are not normally involved in line functions. The number of personnel assigned to a staff officer will vary with the size of the department and the importance ascribed to the function by the chief and the community. In small departments, line officers may also be assigned staff functions or a single officer may supervise more than one staff function. In the smallest of departments, the fire chief or assistant may directly assume many of the functions.

All of these functions are important to the operation of a fire department. Therefore it is critical within each organization that the person who is to be responsible for a given function be aware of the responsibility; all persons within the organization should know who has responsibility for each function as well. Without definite assignments, confusion will arise, important tasks may not get accomplished, and the efforts of personnel within the department will not be utilized in the most effective manner.

Organizational Plans

The manner in which fire departments are organized depends on the size of the department and the scope of its operations. Organizational plans are designed to show

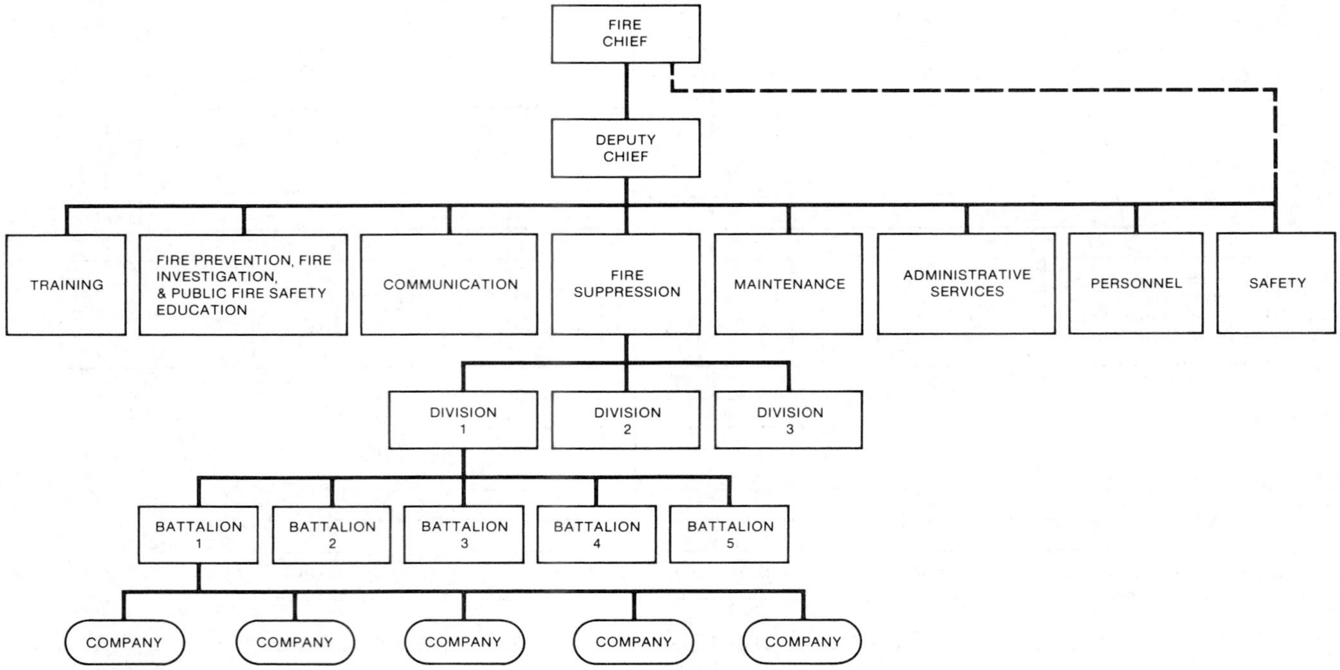

FIG. 9-4C. Typical organizational structure of a large fire department.

the relationship of each operating division to the total organization. Some departments find projected plans useful for budgetary and planning purposes. It is essential that each fire department have an organizational plan that reflects the current status of the department since a good plan is essentially a blueprint of the organization.

A list of responsibilities or a job description for each position should accompany the organizational plan. In small departments, a single individual may have responsibility for more than one function. For example, a single officer may be responsible for both training and maintenance. This should be detailed in the job description.

The organization chart should show how the various functions that may demand time and support from other personnel or groups will be coordinated within the fire department. Both the personnel within the ranks of the fire department and the public need to see a clear coordinated effort of providing fire protection to the community.

Rules and Regulations

As with any organization, rules and regulations are needed to govern operations. This is especially true in the fire service due to the hazardous nature of much of the activity, and the need for clear understanding of expected performance.

Every fire department should have a set of rules and regulations that outline performance expectations for its members, the standard operating procedures for the department, and disciplinary action that can be taken against personnel who do not follow the regulations. These rules and regulations can be, and often are, supplemented by orders from the fire chief who may add to or clarify the rules or change them for a special event or specific purpose. Both the rules and regulations and subsequent orders from the chief should be written and distributed in such a manner as to ensure all persons are made aware of them.

BIBLIOGRAPHY

References Cited

1. Blackstone, G. V., "The Insurance Fire Brigades," in *History of the British Fire Service*, Routledge & Kegan, London, England, 1957.

NFPA Codes, Standards, Recommended Practices, and Manuals. (See the latest *NFPA Catalog* for availability of current editions of the following documents.)

NFPA 1001, *Standard for Fire Fighter Professional Qualifications*.

NFPA 1002, *Standard for Fire Apparatus Driver/Operator Professional Qualifications*.

NFPA 1021, *Standard for Fire Officer Professional Qualifications*.

NFPA 1031, *Standard for Professional Qualifications for Fire Inspector, Fire Investigator, and Fire Prevention Education Officer*.

NFPA 1041, *Standard for Fire Service Instructor Professional Qualifications*.

NFPA 1201, *Recommendations for the Organization for Fire Services*.

NFPA 1202, *Recommendations for Organization of a Fire Department*.

NFPA 1221, *Standard for the Installation, Maintenance, and Use of Public Fire Service Communication Systems*.

NFPA 1500, *Standard for Occupational Safety and Health Programs*.

NFPA 1501, *Standard for Fire Department Safety Officer*.

Additional Readings

Ahlbrandt, R. S., *Municipal Fire Protection Services: Comparison of Alternative Organizational Forms*, Sage Publications, Beverly Hills, CA, 1973.

Bryan, J. L. and Picard, R. C., *eds.*, *Managing Fire Services*, International Fire Services, International City Management Association, Washington, DC, 1979.

Campbell, J. A., *The Small Business Firm as Provider of Fire Department and Emergency Medical Services in American Communities*, Gage-Babcock and Associates, Elmhurst, IL, 1981.

Caplow, T., *Managing an Organization*, 2nd ed., Holt, Rinehart and Winston, NY, 1983.

Carter, H. R., *Management in the Fire Service*, 2nd ed., National Fire Protection Association, Quincy, MA, 1989.

Caulfield, H. J., "The Fire Service Organization," *Fire Engineering*, Vol. 139, No. 7, 1986, pp. 40-46.

Child, J., *Organization: A Guide to Problems and Practice*, Harper and Row, New York, NY, 1984.

Coleman, R. J., *Management of Fire Service Operations*, Bretton, North Scituate, MA, 1978.

Coleman, R. J. and Granito, J. A., *eds.*, *Managing Fire Services*, 2nd ed., International City Management Association, Washington, DC, 1988.

Didactic Systems, Inc., *Management in the Fire Service*, National Fire Protection Association, Quincy, MA, 1977.

DiNenno, P. J., "Private Contract Fire Protection: An Alternative Management System," *The International Fire Chief*, Jan. 1981, pp. 12-14.

Earnest, E., *The Volunteer Fire Company*, Stein and Day, Briarcliff Manor, NY, 1983.

"Fire Protection through Private Enterprise," *Journal of American Insurance*, Vol. 56, No. 2, 1980, pp. 9-12.

Fowell, A. J., "Fire Organization in the United States," NBS Workshop on Fire Protection Technology, *NBSIR 86-3360*, Center for Fire Research, Gaithersburg, MD, Apr. 1986.

Granito, A. R., *Fire Officers' Guide to Company Leadership and Operations*, National Fire Protection Association, Quincy, MA, 1975.

Hall, J. R., *et al.*, *Fire Code Inspections and Fire Prevention: What Methods Lend to Success*, National Fire Protection Association, Quincy, MA, 1979.

Hickey, H. E., *Public Firesafety Organization: A Systems Approach*, National Fire Protection Association, Quincy, MA, 1973.

Holzman, Robert S., *The Romance of Firefighting*, Harper and Brothers, New York, NY, 1956.

Mali, P. W., *How to Manage by Objectives; A Short Course for Managers*, Anacom, NY, 1975.

Morrisey, G. L., *Management by Objectives and Results in the Public Sector*, Addison-Wesley, Reading, MA, 1976.

Office of the Oklahoma State Fire Marshal and Mission Research Corporation, *Basic Guide for Fire Prevention and Control Master Planning*, United States Fire Administration, Emmitsburg, MD, 1978.

Phelps, B. W. and McDonald, E. J., "Command or Combat ?," *Fire Engineering*, Vol. 138, No. 5, 1985, pp. 44-50.

Research Triangle Institute, *Evaluating the Organization of Service Delivery: Fire Phase I and IIA*, Prepared for National Science Foundation, Research Applied to National Needs, Washington, DC, 1978.

Research Triangle Institute, International City Management Association, National Fire Protection Association, *Municipal Fire Service Workbook*, Prepared for National Science Foundation, Research Applied to National Needs, Washington, DC, 1977.

Robertson, J. C., "Organization and Administration of Municipal Fire Prevention Efforts," in *Introduction to Fire Prevention*, 3rd ed., Macmillan, New York, 1989, pp. 76-98.

Schaenman, P. S., *et al.*, *Procedures for Improving the Measurement of Local Fire Protection Effectiveness*, National Fire Protection Association, Quincy, MA, 1977.

Small Community Fire Departments: Organization and Operation, National Fire Protection Association, Quincy, MA, 1982.

The Fire Safety and Disaster Preparedness Task Group, *Criteria for Master Planning and Resource Allocation*, Public Technology, Inc., Washington, DC, 1978.

The Fire Safety and Disaster Preparedness Task Group, *Urban Guide for Fire Prevention and Control Master Planning*, United States Fire Administration, Washington, DC, 1977.

Thomas, P., *Management by Objectives: A Handbook for Governmental Managers and Supervisors*, Masterco Press, Ann Arbor, MI, 1978.

FIRE DEPARTMENT ADMINISTRATION AND MANAGEMENT

Revised by William Peterson

The fire service has many unique management needs. It requires a distinct team spirit, stern discipline for concerted and instant reaction to a wide variety of emergencies; a high quality of leadership from its officers, continuous training, an extremely wide range of technical competence, a labor/employer relationship not comparable to that of other occupations, and an ability to deal with the public during minor and major crises. The fire service is not profit-oriented, and it has an obscure productivity pattern. It is a major consumer of tax dollars, uses costly equipment, is heavily dependent upon personnel, and currently has no satisfactory means of measuring the effectiveness of its operation relative to cost. Despite the complexity of these needs, the fire service has generally performed well for many years.

Almost all fire departments were administered by clearly defined organizational structures long before systems techniques were applied to industry and business. A system of task allocation to engine and ladder crews was developed, whereby each person on the apparatus performed certain functions in sequence so the team operated as a coordinated unit, without duplication of effort. Step-by-step functions were determined many years ago in processes that are now termed "human engineering" and "human factors application."

FUNCTION OF MANAGEMENT

The operation of a fire department is normally a function of local government—in the case of a fire district, possibly the only function—which supports the service and is responsible for the level of service rendered. As with any governmental or business operation, this involves three major areas of responsibility: fiscal management, personnel management, and productivity.

In general, fiscal management practices follow those used by the government agency supporting the department. These practices involve budgeting, cost accounting, personnel costs including payroll, and purchasing or procurement costs. The degree to which these factors are a direct responsibility of fire department management varies, depending upon the practices of local government.

Fire departments use personnel with specialized skills who are organized into various operational and staff units. Fire department management is involved to some degree in the recruitment, selection, and promotion of personnel to fill various positions in the organization. Largely, these matters are governed by local and/or state law; by personnel agencies, including civil service authorities; and by the direct decisions of the governmental agency operating the fire department. The assignment of available personnel to positions provided in the budgeted organizational structure and the supervision of personnel performance are normally the direct responsibility of the fire department management, although certain assignments are frequently governed by work contract agreements.

Effectiveness in the fire service is the most difficult ingredient for management to measure. The basic objective of the fire service is the protection of life and property. Modern fire-service practice involves two major activities: controlling hazards to minimize fire losses and to prevent fires, and dealing with actual fires and emergencies to minimize suffering and losses. It is difficult to assess the number of fires and the amount of suffering fire department activities have prevented. However, experience demonstrates that a lack of effective fire prevention and control measures invites disaster. Likewise, the fact that most fires are suppressed with minimum losses and injuries does not indicate conclusively that an adequate level of fire department service has been provided. Experience shows that major fires and emergencies often arise from a combination of circumstances that are beyond the immediate control of fire department management, but which must be dealt with effectively to protect the public.

It is imperative that fire department management maintain reasonable standards of organization based upon local and national fire loss experience. Fire department management is responsible for maintaining highly trained and efficient operational units to perform assigned tasks in both the prevention and suppression of fires.

In addition to their strictly fire oriented activities, many modern fire departments also provide emergency medical services. These services range from responding as "first

Mr. Peterson is fire chief of Plano, TX.

responders" to assist ambulance crews to actually providing engine/ladder companies and paramedic ambulance service. Fire departments involved in this aspect of public safety have seen significant increases in the use of personnel and equipment and in public support in the community.

The hazardous materials response team is another emerging area for fire department participation. With the ever-increasing problems involved in handling hazardous materials, fire departments increasingly are being asked to step in and take over such incidents.

PERSONNEL

The fire department is typically becoming more involved in recruiting efforts to fill vacancies in its ranks. The most common arrangement is to conduct recruiting efforts jointly with the local government personnel agency. Because of their make-up, most fire districts and volunteer departments recruit their own members exclusively.

It is the responsibility of fire department management to notify the personnel agency of existing vacancies in the organization and to request the number of persons needed to fill these vacancies. In connection with recruitment, fire department management has three responsibilities. The first is to recommend appropriate recruitment standards to the personnel agency. The second is to provide the basic training necessary for the new recruits so they can perform their assigned duties properly. The third is to certify, after providing the basic training, that the new members are ready for appointment as permanent fire fighters or, where individuals prove unable to perform satisfactorily, to recommend that their services be terminated before permanent appointment.

Selection of personnel must meet local, state, and federal standards. U.S. courts have ruled that there must be no discrimination in hiring practices. Some rulings prohibit residency requirements for recruits, although fire department rules of employment may stipulate that, because of the emergency nature of the work, employees must reside within a reasonable distance of the community. One court decision has ruled out examinations that require a knowledge of fire department practices and equipment before appointment and in-service probationary training. Many states have adopted, or are in the process of adopting, minimum fire fighter qualifications standards. Selection practices are a sensitive issue, and knowledgeable counsel should be sought to keep all activities on a sound legal foundation.

In most jurisdictions, applications for employment as a fire fighter are obtained from municipal personnel or a civil service agency. In at least two states, recruitment is handled by a state civil service commission. In either system, the fire department is furnished with a certified list of persons eligible for probationary appointment. Age requirements for entry-level appointments vary from a minimum of 18 years to a maximum of 36 years of age.

For obvious reasons, it is imperative that all fire service personnel be fully qualified and capable of efficiently performing the wide range of services necessary to protect life and property. Many states have enacted legislation establishing commissions on fire fighter standards that require that all personnel employed by fire departments satisfactorily complete required basic training before they are given permanent employment.

In 1971, the Joint Council of National Fire Service Organizations (JCNFSO) created the National Professional Qualifications Board for the Fire Service (NPQB) to facilitate the development of nationally applicable performance standards for various levels of the uniformed fire service. On December 14, 1972, the Board established four technical committees to develop those standards using the NFPA standards-making system. The initial committees addressed the career areas of fire fighter, fire officer, fire service instructor, and fire inspector and investigator.

The original concept of the professional qualification standards, as directed by the JCNFSO and NPQB, was to develop an interrelated set of performance standards specifically for the fire service. The various levels of achievement in the standards were to build upon each other within a strictly defined career ladder. In the late 1980s, the standards were revised to recognize that the documents should stand on their own merits in terms of job-performance requirements for a given field. Accordingly, the strict career-ladder concept was abandoned, except for the progression from fire fighter to fire officer. Thus, the later revisions facilitated the use of the documents by other than the uniformed fire services.

In 1986, the NPQB also directed the Technical Committee on Fire Inspector, Fire Investigator, and Public Fire Educator Professional Qualifications to develop individual documents for each job.

In 1990, the NFPA assumed the total responsibility for the appointment of professional qualifications committees and the development of the professional qualifications standards. The NFPA Standards Council appointed the Correlating Committee for Professional Qualifications Standards in 1990 and assumed the responsibility for coordinating the requirements of all of the professional qualifications documents. The chair of each technical committee sits on this committee.

Currently, technical committees are working on the following projects:

NFPA 1000, *Certification and Accreditation of Fire Service Professional Qualifications Programs*.

NFPA 1001, *Fire Fighter Professional Qualifications*.

NFPA 1002, *Fire Apparatus Driver/Operator*.

NFPA 1003, *Airport Fire Fighter Professional Qualifications*.

NFPA 1031, *Fire Officer Professional Qualifications*.

NFPA 1033, *Fire Investigator Professional Qualifications*.

NFPA 1035, *Public Fire Educator Professional Qualifications*.

NFPA 1041, *Fire Service Instructor Professional Qualifications*.

NFPA 1051, *Wildland Management Personnel Professional Qualifications*.

Each of these standards defines the levels of progression within the specified job. The job-performance requirements defined for each level of progression are considered the minimum requirements for individuals at each level.

The intent of the committees is to develop clear and concise job-performance requirements that can be used to determine whether individuals possess the skills and knowledge necessary to perform the related duties and tasks of the job. These job-performance requirements can be used by any fire department in any city, town, or private fire service organization throughout North America.

Under the new leadership of the National Board on Fire Service Professional Qualifications, the NPQB has assumed the role of third-party accreditor of fire-service certification programs and developer of a national registry of those certified. Certification in the fire service is based primarily upon the NFPA professional qualifications standards. The Fire Service Accreditation Congress at Oklahoma State University has also been established as an accreditation agency for the fire service.

The establishment of standards and testing procedures does not in itself ensure that all personnel will achieve the required level of competency; NFPA 1001 is a professional qualifications standard, not a training standard. Training programs are necessary to prepare members of the fire service to acquire the skills and knowledge necessary to meet the job-performance requirements set forth for each grade. However, training should not be random. It should be organized to prepare trainees to meet the specified levels of performance demonstrated by the performance testing described in NFPA 1001.

The U.S. Supreme Court decisions based upon constitutional prohibition of sex discrimination in employment have enabled women to apply for jobs as fire fighters. In connection with both racial and sexual discrimination, courts have ruled that height and weight requirements are discriminatory, both racially and sexually, but candidates may be required to demonstrate their ability to perform the required duties.

Fire fighting requires physical strength, and fire fighters depend on each other in fire-suppression and rescue operations. If there is a great disparity in strength and endurance between crew members, an unreasonable burden is placed on those with the most strength and stamina. This is dangerous not only to the fire fighter, but to the public, as well. Currently, a new standard for medical and physical-fitness requirements for fire fighters is being developed.

In some jurisdictions, the services of the fire department training division may be used to test recruits and to conduct promotional examinations. In such cases, recognized standards such as NFPA 1001 should be followed carefully so that the results will not be subject to valid charges of discrimination and so that qualifications essential to the work will be tested adequately.

Promotion Practices

In the vast majority of fire departments, various officer ranks are filled by personnel serving in the next lower rank or ranks, although more fire departments are recognizing the potential benefits of allowing lateral entry, transfers, and promotions of well-qualified personnel from other areas and departments. Promotion procedures are designed to take into account technical qualifications for the particular rank and fire department experience. It is essential that examination procedures in the civil service be fully competitive and nondiscriminatory.

In general, promotion procedures are administered by personnel departments or by state or local civil service authorities who usually take the advice of persons who are experienced and knowledgeable about the particular job classification. Such advisors include fire chiefs, fire fighter organizations, and technical consultants. Normally, such advice includes guidance as to the relative weight to be given to experience and to the results of written examinations covering the technical qualifications of the position. In some systems, performance ratings are included, but these tend to introduce discrimination even if such discrimination is quite unintentional. Some supervisors tend to be much more demanding than others when rating performance, and their subordinates often have less favorable performance grades than other employees, who may actually be less qualified. For this reason, subjective performance ratings should be used sparingly in the promotion process. If performance has not been satisfactory, the matter should be dealt with before the promotion process.

Some promotion processes include an oral interview. Again, this can easily become a vehicle for discrimination on the basis of race, color, or mannerisms, and few such oral interviews are scientifically designed or professionally administered. Too often, they have been used by an administration to select and reward its friends. Therefore, increasing emphasis is being given to written examinations that test technical knowledge.

In recent years, some fire departments have relied upon assessment centers as a means of selecting candidates for promotion. Assessment centers have been used for quite some time by industry. The assessment center requires a candidate to demonstrate certain abilities through the use of problem-solving exercises, role playing, and other simulated exercises. Each candidate is observed by a trained assessment team and scored according to performance. Some feel that the assessment center is the most realistic means of determining a candidate's suitability for a particular position.

NFPA 1021, *Standard for Fire Officer Professional Qualifications*, specifies the levels of performance for fire officers. NFPA 1021, written in performance terms, requires an individual to demonstrate competence by knowledge and performance. More fire departments are including educational requirements, such as community college fire science certificates for alls officers or bachelors degrees for chief officers. It is not uncommon to find fire departments that seek individuals with graduate-level degrees in public administration/management for the position of fire chief.

The fire department administration, as an arm of the municipal administration, has an important role to play in the promotion process. First, it must advise the personnel agency of the qualifications required in any job or rank to be filled, where such qualifications have not been previously established. Second, when a list of successful candidates is received from the personnel agency, the administration should advise the promoting authority of the promotions to be made. Usual practice is to fill vacancies from the top of the promotion list, except where the head of the fire department specifies in writing valid reasons for rejecting an individual. Such reasons might be a record of serious disciplinary problems, including disobedience of written orders; frequent bad judgment when performing assigned duties; a record of conflicts with other employees; or other major personality problems. While such problems might not be serious enough to warrant dismissal from the current job, they do indicate that the particular candidate, though technically qualified, would be less preferable than another candidate on the list. Personnel records should be available to substantiate any such reasons for rejection.

Personnel Records

A complete personnel record must be maintained for each member of the fire department. Such records cover all the pertinent facts of each member's fire service career, from probationary appointment through retirement, and include the original application for employment or a copy, all assignments, transfers, promotions, commendations, and records of disciplinary action. Duty records must be carefully maintained. The record should also include information on any special skills an individual possesses that may be useful to the department, as well as the individual's educational background, including any courses that might be of value to the department.

In addition to the general record of an individual's service, a training file should be maintained, as covered in NFPA 1401, *Recommended Practice for Fire Protection Training Reports and Records*. This will show training periods and subjects in which the individual has received instruction, such as apparatus operation, first aid, emergency medical service, and fire inspection. A medical history must be kept for each member, showing absences due to sickness and service-connected injuries. A new addition to the individual file is a record of exposure to hazardous materials and infectious diseases. This provides an historical record of the fire fighter's exposure to toxic materials or to infectious communicable diseases during his or her employment, as well as any appropriate inoculations he or she has received.

Fire Fighter Health and Safety

Fire fighting has been recognized for many years as one of the most dangerous professions. Between 1978 and 1988, an average of 128 fire fighters lost their lives and more than 100,000 were injured yearly. In response to this unenviable record, NFPA 1500, *Standard on Fire Department Occupational Safety and Health*, was established to guide fire departments in the development of fire service health and safety programs. The standard is aimed at making the fire service less dangerous by reducing the risk of accident, injury, and death during line-of-duty activities and by making fire fighters healthier and more physically fit for their current activities.

NFPA 1500 addresses the elements of an occupational safety and health program that has been accepted as the minimum level which today's fire departments should provide. NFPA 1500 was developed by the fire service, for the fire service, and parallels the requirements of the federal OSHA fire brigade standard developed for private-sector fire suppression organizations.

NFPA 1500 addresses health and safety as an overall program to reduce the risks to members of the fire department. The standard applies to all members of the department and specifically identifies management as a provider of as safe a work environment as possible, given the hazardous nature of the work. Fire service management therefore has an important role in leading and directing the establishment of rules, regulations, and procedures geared toward the operation of an effective health and safety program.

Entering into a new program such as this can be a difficult process, since a fire department may have to address a variety of issues with various costs and degrees of difficulty. Implementing a health and safety program is best accomplished on a phased basis that allows for the specific needs and capabilities of a particular fire department. The development of this comprehensive implementation plan will require each fire department to assess its own strengths and weaknesses, and to determine what would be required to meet the intent of the standard. Major elements of this implementation plan should include vehicles and equipment, training and education requirements, protective clothing and protective equipment, incident command procedures, facility safety, health and fitness standards, and employee assistance programs.

STAFFING PRACTICES

Staffing levels for fire departments vary considerably and are influenced by such things as the population protected, population density, fire fighters work hours per week, response distances, and fire fighter safety. Generally, fire departments use a three- or four-person platoon system that will accommodate a 56- to 42-hr work week, respectively. A four-platoon system requires about 25 percent more personnel than a three-platoon system. Staffing levels for major metropolitan cities in the U.S. range from one to three fire fighters per thousand population, with an average of 1.5 per thousand. Cities in the Northeast generally have a higher staffing ratio than cities in the South and West. Communities must assess their needs to determine the level of staffing that meets their requirements. However, it has been demonstrated that when staffing falls below four fire fighters per company, critical fireground operations are not carried out when needed. Tests conducted in 1984 with the Dallas, TX, Fire Department indicated that staffing below a crew size of four can overtax the operating force and lead to higher losses.

One study of 25 fire departments working a 42-hr work week in major metropolitan areas showed a median strength of 3.0 fire fighters per thousand population. This provides an average of twelve officers and personnel on duty for a population of 20,000.

Fire departments operating emergency medical service and rescue squads need additional personnel to maintain basic fire company strength. In some smaller communities, the staffing ratio per population protected may be relatively high because of the need for sufficient on-duty personnel for effective initial attack and rescue operations. This is especially true in "bedroom communities," where call personnel are not readily available during the work day and where there are high-value properties to be protected, which may be more significant than population ratios in determining the number of fire fighters to be provided.

Likewise, fire departments in many core cities protect more lives and property than population figures reflect. A city of 80,000 may be the business center for an area of 500,000 persons and house a high percentage of the low-income groups. The number of high-rise and large-area structures to be protected and the frequency of alarms for fires and emergencies should be considered in determining on-duty fire department staffing.

Some very large fire departments may operate with a lower relative strength per 1,000 population than those in cities of a more average size because, with high population densities, these departments have sufficient companies to provide needed coverage while handling working fires. For example, a large-city fire department may operate one engine company per 15,000 to 20,000 population and still have a large number of well-distributed fire companies, whereas a city of 30,000 could not be properly protected with only two engine companies.

Mutual aid plays an important role in providing additional resources. Almost all jurisdictions rely to some extent on mutual aid from surrounding areas to provide fire fighting resources on a routine or major-emergency basis. Some departments use automatic mutual aid on initial response. Even large cities are making increased use of both regularly assigned and automatic mutual aid. Often, this is practical because companies from neighboring fire departments may be much nearer to a fire than some of the local fire companies.

It is frequently impossible for small cities to fully staff all of the fire companies they need to handle working fires throughout the community. In many cases, the population density and the values protected per square mile are relatively low. In such communities, some engine companies may respond with only three persons on duty, and ladder trucks with only two. Such low levels of staffing should be backed up promptly to ensure adequate personnel by off-shift or call personnel or by multiple-alarm response. Combination fire departments that use a mix of career and either paid on-call or volunteer fire fighters are found throughout the U.S. In some cases, additional apparatus may be assigned to respond, offsetting deficient company strength. In communities with large geographic areas and relatively low concentrations of value, this may be an acceptable arrangement. In general, however, each engine company should have a minimum of four fire fighters on duty, including an officer, where there is no assigned off-shift or call personnel on first alarms.

Staffing Career Fire Departments

The current approach of fire departments is to determine the essential positions in the fire fighting force that must be covered 24 hours a day and 365 days a year, and the total number of duty tours involved. With 24-hr shifts, there is one duty tour per position per day. With 10- to 14-hr or similar tours of duty, there are 2 per day, or 730 per year.

Say that a community has determined that a minimum of 58 officers and fire fighters of various rank should be on duty at all times. With a standard, 42-hr, nominal, average work week, including day and night shifts, each shift or group is on duty 182.5 times during a 365-day year. With 58 persons on duty, this requires 42,340 individual tours of duty per year. A review of fire department records indicates that, with vacations, sick and injured leave, and other contractual absences, the individual members of the fire fighting force average not 182.5 but 146.5 tours of duty per year. The required 42,340 tours of duty, divided by 146.5 tours worked per person, shows that, rather than 232 officers and fire fighters, 289 members, or 72 per platoon, are actually needed to cover the normal anticipated absences. Even when vacations are carefully scheduled so that only one person from each shift of each company is absent at any given time, there may be times off-duty personnel have to be used on an overtime basis due to sickness or injury. This is less expensive than carrying more relief fire fighters on the roster than are required to maintain normal minimum coverage. Overtime will be required when members are called back for major fires and emergencies, so budget allowances should be made for such eventualities.

This example is based upon a minimum effective staffing of eight engine and four ladder companies, grouped in two fire districts and commanded by an on-duty chief with aides. The minimum staffing for all companies is four persons on duty, including the company officer. Five fire fighters are maintained with two ladder companies in districts of high life-hazard and more-than-average fire duty. To distribute the needed relief personnel, the platoon roster for each company carries one additional fire fighter above the minimum that must be maintained, and one relief officer is assigned to each district headquarters.

In a number of fire departments, the minimum levels are not absolute. When there is an unusual amount of absence, stations housing more than one company may be allowed to operate one person below the normal minimum rather than pay overtime, unless the company minimum strength is specified by contract or city ordinance.

In general, a nominal 42-hr work week requires not four but five persons per position. Thus, a twenty-person company is needed to maintain an average of four on duty. Because this does not allow two members to be away from their shifts at one time, overtime or personnel swaps between companies may occasionally be needed.

With a fire department operating on the three-platoon system with 24-hr duty tours, each platoon covers 122 tours in 366 days (a leap year). It requires 21,208 tours to have 58 officers and fire fighters on duty. The records in this example indicate that the average member works 98 tours per year. Thus, 21,208 divided by 98 requires 216 fire fighters, or 72 for each of the three platoons. With a 53-hr maximum work week permitted under federal labor law, however, each member working more than 53 hours in each 28-day work period would exceed the allowable maximum by 3 hours and would be eligible for extra compensation, except possibly when the work cycle is broken by absences.

Where minimum company strength of five persons is desired for a 42-hr work week, most fire companies have 24 persons assigned to the four duty shifts, and 28 assigned for approximately every fourth company. In some fire departments where more vacations are scheduled in the summer months, a four-person minimum may be maintained in the summer and a five-person minimum maintained in the winter. However, most fire departments prefer to maintain minimum staffing year round rather than attempt to adjust for seasonal trends. If additional personnel are needed during severe winter storms, they are provided on a temporary overtime basis and are paid from the overtime account, but this does not add too significantly to the annual personnel budget account.

It was customary in the past to allow 10 percent for absences from assigned shifts due to vacations and sickness. Now, the figure commonly is 20 percent or more. Vacations have been increased, and work contracts provide for various other compensated absences from duty. An important factor may be an increase in injured leave resulting from reduced on-duty staffing per company. With the reduction in work hours, many jurisdictions have reduced the number of fire companies and the number of on-duty fire fighters per company. In some cases, individuals on duty are exposed to much more potential injury than they were when there were more fire companies with full crews. The injury potential is increased further if chief officers are slow in calling additional fire companies to working fires. Accordingly, in fire departments where minimum company staffing has been reduced below four persons, operating procedures should require that additional resources be ordered to incidents to provide the personnel necessary to match the size of the emergency.

Minimum staffing: During recent years, an increasing number of fire departments have established minimum staffing levels for each fire company or each duty shift. It is a policy in many fire departments not to operate engine or ladder companies with fewer than four fire fighters, including an officer, on duty. In some cases, because of the workload and the population and values protected per company, the minimum is five persons on duty per company. Where a company member is sick or injured while another member is on vacation and no on-duty fire fighter is available to cover the absence, it is the department's policy to employ an off-duty member of the company on an overtime basis to maintain the essential minimum strength.

Mandatory minimum staffing levels for fire companies are advantageous to the public and to personnel. Decisions by labor boards and at least one court have found that minimum staffing agreements or ordinances are reasonable requirements for the protection of the public and personnel. A number of small fire departments that do not attempt to maintain minimum on-duty company strength have established a minimum for the duty shift while employing off-duty personnel to maintain the predetermined minimum effective strength. Such a plan should account for apparatus that must be operated from the several fire stations before off-shift or call fire fighters can arrive to assist.

Even though labor laws or contract requirements may require payment of overtime, managers often find it more economical to use personnel on overtime to cover duty absences that exceed the average allowed in the organization staffing tables, rather than to maintain additional personnel on each fire company duty shift to cover abnormal amounts of absence. In the past, however, there was no allowance in the staffing tables of many fire departments to cover scheduled absences, and fire companies were allowed to run shorthanded, thus seriously compromising their operating efficiency. In a number of cases, departments also failed to allow for the usual amount of sickness and injury. Calculations for the number of personnel needed should also include members on terminal leave and new recruits assigned to basic training. Otherwise, overtime costs may exceed the cost of having the needed number of members per shift.

Work schedules: The work weeks of career fire fighters average 40 to 56 hours. Most fire departments working an average of more than 50 hours per week use a 24-hr tour of duty. Most fire departments working 48 hrs per week or less have day and night shifts, and the most popular is a 10-hr day shift and 14-hr night shift. Where the law states that anyone working more than 40 hrs per week will be paid overtime, many fire departments work a 42-hr four-platoon schedule by paying two hours of overtime. Often, this is considerably less expensive than hiring additional personnel, and better teamwork is maintained by keeping crews together on a regular four-shift basis.

Occasionally, municipal administrators who are not knowledgeable about fire department operations have suggested that fire fighters be assigned to an 8-hr-day/40-hr-week work schedule similar to police schedules. This has not proven to be practical or desirable. On-duty police staffing properly varies with the time of day and day of the week as required by needs for traffic control, patrolling, details, and so on. Fire fighting is a team effort, and the team includes platoon chief officers, company officers, apparatus operators, and fire fighters working together on a regular basis. Serious fires occur at any hour of the day or night and on any day of the week. Thus, the constant and uniform staffing provided by the three- or four-platoon systems is essential. These are readily scheduled in seven 24-hr or or fourteen 10- and 14-hr tours of duty per week on either the 42-hr or 56-hr average work week. This may include a 40-hr pay week or a 54-hr or 56-hr pay week with 2 hours of overtime. When the 168-hr calendar week is divided by 8-hr tours, this requires 21 work shifts that cannot be scheduled on a uniform basis with even platoons. In most instances, where the 8-hr schedule has been proposed, it has appeared only as a bargaining chip to counter employee demands for better compensation. Invariably, it has been rejected. In the entire U.S., there are only a few fire departments using an 8-hr work shift.

Given a choice between 24-hr shifts and increasing staffing by 40 percent or reducing staffing or resources by 40 percent to accommodate 8-hr work shifts, most municipal fire departments have not seriously considered 8-hr work shifts. As the fire service becomes more adept at computerized analysis of emergency incidents and develops a good base of 5 to 10 years of response data, it is very likely that a staffing arrangement similar to police staffing will be used in the future.

The requirement for overtime has resulted in improved mutual-aid arrangements because on-duty companies from nearby departments can respond much faster than off-shift local personnel, thus keeping overtime costs down. However, many small fire departments rely heavily upon off-duty response on an overtime basis. Usually, a minimum of 2 and often 4 hours overtime pay is guaranteed for each response. Where alarms for structural fires are infrequent, it may be much more economical for a small municipality to contract for overtime response than to provide full on-duty fire company staffing around the clock.

Manning Combination and Volunteer Fire Departments

Part of the population of both Canada and the U.S. lives in communities that cannot support a career or even a combination career/on-call fire department. Therefore, volunteer fire departments are essential. At the last count, approximately 10 percent of the fire departments in the U.S. served communities with populations of 10,000 or more; approximately 18 percent protected communities with populations from 2,500 to 10,000; and more than 72 percent served communities with populations of less than 2500, or served the fire protection needs of rural areas.

Small community fire departments are often staffed almost entirely by volunteers. Even if a town of 2500 inhabitants had as many as three career fire fighters per 1000 population, which is considerably above the average, there would be only two members on each duty shift, so a full-paid fire department would not be feasible unless there were a substantial tax base to support it.

In most small communities, volunteer fire departments are operated on a "neighbor help neighbor" basis in which fire department members—except possibly fire station custodians and sometimes a few career fire fighters on duty—receive no compensation other than possibly some reimbursement for personal expenses and uniforms. To replace this free community labor with minimum staffing by fully salaried personnel would involve an added tax burden on the local population. Various states have recognized the contribution made by their volunteer fire fighters by enacting protective legislation and providing statewide training programs, facilities, and retirement systems.

When they receive an alarm, members of most volunteer fire departments report to assigned fire stations from which they respond with apparatus. To provide a minimum effective working crew, many such fire departments require that the first piece of apparatus not respond with fewer than three members. Volunteer fire companies should respond to an alarm with a minimum of four members.

Fire department administrators should periodically review response records to determine that enough active fire company members are available to respond at all times. Where necessary, administrators should recruit and train additional personnel to provide the required minimum response. All essential staff positions in a well-organized all-volunteer fire department are covered by assigned volunteer officers. In many jurisdictions, however, career fire prevention training and communication functions are provided by the county or by other units of government.

Where a community can afford on-duty career fire fighters, response to alarms is faster, and efficiency is increased. The on-duty fire fighters take the apparatus to the fire, and the volunteers notified by radio go directly to the fire, thus saving about 3 min in arrival time on the average. The apparatus operator normally is in charge of the apparatus and of the fire station, but volunteer officers may direct the fire fighting. One difficulty with this arrangement is that there are few, if any, opportunities for advancement for career personnel.

With the increasing legal and technical responsibilities of the fire chief as the principal fire protection officer of a community, the chief should be appointed on the basis of qualifications and experience. Communities should consider adopting NFPA standards for fire officers as a minimum requirement.

An arrangement that works quite successfully is to have the first responding pumper staffed by a career officer, apparatus operator, and, where staffing permits, an additional fire fighter. This force is supplemented by additional personnel assigned to respond on call. The second-due engine may be staffed by volunteers or paid call personnel, or it may have a career apparatus operator to take the apparatus to the fire, where it is joined by the volunteer or paid call fire fighters. The ladder truck has a career apparatus operator assigned, but is staffed at the fire by volunteer or paid call fire fighters. This arrangement permits a reasonably effective initial fire attack, quickly backed by volunteer or paid call members. In all cases, there should be just one fire department in any jurisdiction, operating under a clearly defined and unified chain of command.

In a number of combination fire departments, the career fire fighters have complained about being commanded by volunteer officers whom they felt lacked the needed experience and qualifications. All fire officers, whether elected or appointed, should meet the appropriate NFPA qualifications for their rank. Countless volunteer officers have met the technical standards for their duties. When a career apparatus operator is assigned to operate volunteer fire company apparatus, he or she should work under the orders of the volunteer officer of that company on the fireground. It is important that administrators make clear the respective roles and duties of all members, career and volunteer.

Call Fire Fighters

Many fire departments in small communities employ fire fighters who have no regular duty shift in the stations, but are paid by the hour or by the incident for response to alarms and drills. In some cases, such members are loosely termed "volunteers," but, under federal labor and local fire department rules, they are considered paid employees of the fire department and, as such, are subject to the requirements of federal wage and hour regulations. The paid on-call members may also be employed by other municipal agencies, in which case the time they spend on fire department duty may affect their overtime status. In most cases, call fire fighters are local businessmen and tradesmen who are willing to be part-time fire fighters. Call fire fighters are expected to meet the same standards of performance as career members of the same rank, but they may not be assigned as apparatus operators where there are sufficient career operators on shift duty.

Various methods are used to determine compensation for paid call fire fighters. In many departments, they receive the same hourly wage for the rank they hold as do employees who work regular duty shifts. Time is based upon attendance at fires and training sessions, with a minimum hourly rate specified for response to alarms. Often, upon reaching mandatory retirement age, they also receive a pro-rated pension based on their years of service and hours of duty as call fire fighters.

Another method of compensation is a fixed annual salary, based on rank, from which deductions are made for excessive numbers of unexcused failures to respond with their assigned companies. Many fire chiefs arrange to excuse members known to be at their regular employment, except in the case of multiple-alarm fires. Chiefs should have the authority to dismiss members who frequently fail to respond to fires and assigned training sessions.

Still another method of compensation is to make an annual appropriation for call fire service based upon past experience, designed to approximate the hourly wage rate for fire fighters. This is divided on a regular basis among the call members as determined by individual attendance at fires and training sessions, so that members responding most faithfully receive the largest compensation. A fire department should pay for members' insurance, workmen's compensation, and all protective equipment.

It is important that accurate individual service records be kept in the personnel files of all fire fighters, both career and volunteer. Response and attendance records are also essential for all members. Members who are habitually late in arriving should be replaced. Volunteer members should be furnished with night turnout suits so that they will lose no time in getting dressed to respond.

In a number of cases, senior fire fighters who cannot respond regularly to first alarms are assigned to operate reserve apparatus or to pilot mutual-aid fire companies when serious fires occur. Other senior call members may be assigned to cover the alarm desk when all of the paid apparatus operators are out of quarters.

Keeping accurate response records for all fire fighters has enabled many fire chiefs to hire additional career personnel. In numerous cases, municipal officials have believed that because they had the names of several hundred volunteers on the roster, the fire department had ample strength. This has often resulted in serious delays and in the extension of fires that should have been readily controlled. Where such situations persist, additional career personnel may be required.

BUDGETING

Fire department budgets are generally prepared and submitted by the fire chief to the elected body that administers the city or district operations. The type of budget used and the manner in which projections are submitted will vary, depending upon the jurisdiction. The personnel costs are generally the most significant costs for most municipal fire departments, accounting for approximately 90 percent of the total expenditures of a fully paid fire department. Personnel costs of combination fire departments will total approximately 40 to 60 percent of their overall budgets.

It is critical for fire department managers to understand thoroughly their jurisdiction's budgeting system. Inadequately prepared budgets can lead to serious monetary problems at the end of the fiscal year. In order to assure smooth operations, all costs must be estimated realistically and expenditures monitored on a regular basis. An effort should be made to develop a long-range plan that will project capital replacement costs for items such as staff vehicles, fire apparatus, fire stations, and other major pieces of equipment.

Fire apparatus costs normally run from 1 to 2 percent of payroll costs. Some fire departments include an apparatus replacement allowance in their budgets, but this item is regularly cut, with the result that apparatus replacement may be included in a capital expenditures budget. While this reduces the fire department annual budget, it ultimately results in higher taxes due to interest costs. However, such decisions are generally made above the level of the fire department administration. New fire stations usually are included in a capital improvement budget separate from the fire department budget.

Pension payments to retirees are usually paid out of a separate municipal account and may amount to 33 to 40 percent of a fire department's budget.

In large fire departments, there may be separate budget accounts for staff divisions such as fire prevention, maintenance, training, and signal or alarm systems, although the latter may be handled by a different municipal department. Expenditures are charged against specific items in the line budget, and the remaining balance is shown after each expense deduction. Usually, the department head or staff division superintendents have the authority to make emergency transfers of funds between line categories. Transfers between major categories can be made only when authorized by the municipal management, finance officer, or other governing body.

Fire department administrators are required to submit their budget estimates by a specified time for the coming fiscal year. Usually, the budgets are submitted to a finance officer or finance committee, and department heads are then asked to justify specific items. Although the salary total is likely to be governed by contract with the employees, estimates must be included covering all ranks and overtime costs. Quite often, the actual salary scale is not negotiated before the budget is submitted, but municipal administrators commonly make a percentage allowance for increases they hope will be accepted in negotiations. After a departmental budget has been approved by the city administration, it must be approved by the city or town council. In some municipalities, it must be approved by town meeting. With some municipal charters, the council can reduce, but not increase, the budget. This is to guard against political pressure on the administration. Once approved, the budget takes effect at the beginning of the fiscal year. If not approved in time, it is customary to permit expenditures at the same rate as those made the previous year.

As indicated, all expenditures must be made against specified items in the budget. Normally, there is a set amount above which expenses cannot be incurred without competitive bidding under purchasing department procedures.

PLANNING AND RESEARCH

Planning

Planning for the future needs of a fire department is the most important job of fire department managers. Without adequate planning, an administrator will find he or she is handling one crisis after another and can never seem to get ahead. Long-range planning has often been neglected by fire department managers, but with budget constraints today, it is absolutely essential that this be done. The U.S. Fire Administration (USFA) has developed a master planning process, available to local communities, that outlines the steps a community may take to determine long-range goals for its fire department and explains how these goals can be achieved. The NFPA Technical Support Program will assist local governments in developing a master planning process.

All departments, small or large, need to develop long-range plans. These plans need to be flexible and continually updated to reflect changes in the local community, as well as developments within the fire service.

Research

In the fire service, the term "research" is commonly heard, yet few fire departments are staffed or financed to support any significant research activity. Limitation in research is due largely to the fact that most fire departments are relatively small organizations that do not have sufficient personnel to meet their on-going fire protection obligations. True research into efficient equipment design is generally beyond the ability of most fire departments. The same is true even for the majority of fire equipment suppliers because this is a relatively small-volume, competitive business with little profit margin for research and development. In recent years, a major part of the engineering effort of fire apparatus builders has been devoted to meeting the increasingly demanding vehicle safety standards of the U.S. Department of Transportation (DOT). Some improvements have been made in various features of fire apparatus design, but not on a uniform or planned research basis.

One area in which fire department research can readily show returns is in fire record analysis, using programs such as the UFIRS (Uniform Fire Incident Reporting System), which was developed by NFPA in cooperation with a selected group of fire departments. Properly applied fire prevention efforts can be directed against the hazards shown to be most dangerous and significant at any given period, and results of these programs can be analyzed effectively.

Research has been used in a number of instances to help determine the optimum locations for fire stations. However, a principal difficulty is that all areas of a community must be covered within reasonable response distances. Considerable judgment and experience are required when considering such variables as population densities, valuations at risk, fire frequency and severity, and the number of fire companies required in a given area to apply the required water flow and maintain coverage during fires. These requirements may be at variance with any optimum location for a given fire station. A number of research studies have placed considerable emphasis upon the arrival time of the nearest fire company, rather than the total fire protection requirements of the area. Arrival times may be less significant than time required for actually getting to work at a fire, particularly in large high-rise structures or shopping centers.

Fortunately, the fire service is not without competent research resources. NFPA conducts research designed to help fire departments directly. The International Association of Fire Fighters (IAFF) Research Department is available on request to assist its local affiliates with problems. And the USFA conducts research relating to fire service needs.

MANAGEMENT RECORDS AND REPORTS

A records system should be provided to supply the fire chief and other administrative officers with data indicating the effectiveness of the department in preventing and fighting fires, insofar as practicable, to facilitate management of the department. It is essential to maintain complete records of all fires and inspections. The records system should provide data on fire department activities that should be made available by city officials and the public. The fire chief should specify the records to be kept and methods of gathering data. A records retention and disposal system should be employed. All records should be examined in light of their usefulness, since old records that are no longer needed often accummulate.

PUBLIC INFORMATION AND COMMUNITY RELATIONS

As a public agency supported by public funds, the fire department needs public support. The public's understanding and cooperation is required to make fire prevention programs fully effective and to enable the fire department to deal effectively within the political environment of its particular community. Without community support, it can be difficult for the department to obtain the needed funds to operate at the required level. Accordingly, public-information and community-relations programs are an important fire department management activity.

In a good public-information program, it is important to develop and to maintain procedures that keep the public informed of important developments and newsworthy items regarding all types of departmental activities and programs. Press releases should be prepared properly and issued on all programs and items of general interest. Relations with the news media should be cordial, and the fire department should cooperate fully with representatives of the media. This is not always easy, because hundreds of suburban fire departments are located in communities that depend largely upon a metropolitan press, and items that might be of interest to local citizens may not be newsworthy for the entire region. However, there are usually local weekly papers or local-area editions of metropolitan papers that do have local correspondents who can be kept informed of fire department activities. The amount of publicity fire departments get seems to vary greatly among geographic areas. In some areas, citizens are traditionally interested and involved in local governments and in their fire departments, while in other areas, fire departments are not considered to be newsworthy. In the latter case, greater efforts must be made to get fire-related information to the public. In general, communities whose citizens regularly participate in town affairs seem to give fire departments better support. Communities with substantial numbers of low-income residents subject to fire dangers often are most concerned with the adequacy of fire department services.

Normally, public-information programs are of direct concern to the head of the fire department, who makes many personal contacts, often holds memberships in various civic groups in the community, and often knows reporters and editors personally. It is important that news personnel be given information promptly, while it is still timely, when emergencies occur. Most fire departments specify that only the officer in charge at a fire or emergency should give out information. This is to avoid conflicting and inaccurate statements that may be misleading or may compromise the results of subsequent or on-going fire investigations.

Some large fire departments have a designated public-information officer who is assigned to give the press all possible cooperation and information. In smaller fire departments, this function is usually one of the duties performed by the fire chief or, where fires are under investigation, by the fire marshal.

Community relations should be a year-round activity and should embrace various seasonal fire prevention programs, such as Fire Prevention Week, clean-up week, Christmas-tree safety programs, education programs in the proper care and use of wood stoves, and so on. Often, both the fire prevention bureau staffs and the training division staffs are used for such activities. In some fire departments, the community-relations program is coordinated by the fire prevention bureau as a part of its public-education program.

INTERGOVERNMENTAL RELATIONS

Fire departments are but one agency of local government, and much of their success depends upon their cooperative working relationships with other local, state, and federal agencies. Some of the more important intergovernmental contacts are discussed below.

Building Department

The proper construction and arrangement of buildings is essential to a sound fire protection program. The building department of a community is a key component in ensuring quality control in building construction and compliance with the fire protection features of local building codes.

State laws and local ordinances or agreements between fire and building departments increasingly require that the head of the fire department give written approval of specified fire protection features before building permits can be issued. Close cooperation also is needed between these departments to control serious fire hazards that commonly are present while buildings are under construction, before the required fire-resistance or protection features have been installed. In small communities, the fire chief generally must handle this assignment, but in many fire departments, it is one of the responsibilities delegated to the fire prevention bureau.

Law Enforcement

Cooperation between the fire department and law enforcement officials is essential. Regular law enforcement response to fire alarms is necessary to control traffic and crowds. It is also important for fire and law enforcement agencies to develop coordinated plans in the event of an incident that requires the evacuation or closure of areas. Law enforcement and fire officials must also develop working relationships to deal with fire investigations. In many areas, a combination of fire/law enforcement fire investigations teams have been developed. In these cases, both agencies work together and bring their special expertise to a coordinated effort in cases where arson is suspected.

Water Department

Adequate water supplies, including hydrant service, are essential for fire fighting and are the responsibility of the water department. A knowledgeable fire officer should be assigned as liaison with the water authority. All too often, water authorities have little knowledge of the water-flow requirements of the fire department for various areas and types of property. Thousands of fire hydrants have been set improperly because water crews did not understand the proper location and setting of hydrants required for efficient fire fighting. In some communities, the fire department is responsible, by ordinance, for determining the location and setting of hydrants.

It is important that all hydrants be serviced regularly and after each use, especially in cold weather. The fire department should report all hydrants it has used in a particular incident to the water department promptly. Alert fire departments maintain a list of hydrants in each fire company inspection district, with flow data on each hydrant. Hydrants should be properly marked for flows and painted for nighttime visibility.

Public Education

In the realm of firesafety education, the local public and private school systems, the parks and recreation department, and the public library system can augment and support the local fire department's educational activities. If public firesafety educational activities are to be successful, the local fire department must be able to serve as a focal point for other community resources and be able to build partnerships across a wide variety of public and private organizations.

Personnel Department

Members of career fire departments are public employees, and, as such, their recruitment and promotion may involve cooperation with the personnel agency, which, in some jurisdictions, is responsible for conducting entrance and promotional examinations. A fire department officer should be assigned as liaison with the personnel office.

Finance Department

Fire departments need to work closely with finance officials when developing and administering budgets. Budgeting is generally very complex, and it is important that fire officials prepare budget documents correctly. After budgets have been prepared and adopted, it is necessary to ensure that proper records of expenditures are maintained and that spending is kept within the adopted budget. Although some fire departments may have a finance officer, liaison with the finance department may be handled by designated staff officers.

Purchasing

All purchases exceeding stipulated amounts must be made according to specifications, usually with competitive bidding by the purchasing department. Close liaison is necessary to assure that specifications are drawn properly to meet fire department needs and that, when bids are opened, any proposals that deviate from specifications are rejected. This liaison may be handled directly by a staff officer.

Data Processing

Increasingly, fire departments are using electronic data-processing for keeping fire records and payroll records and for statistical analysis. Each fire department should have persons knowledgeable in data processing. It may be desirable to appoint one officer to coordinate this activity, but fire departments commonly have an administrative committee that includes representatives of plans and research, where provided; administration; fire prevention; and fire suppression. This same committee may also be involved in long-range planning for the department.

Planning

Fire departments, particularly those in rapidly growing areas, should maintain a close working relationship with local and regional planning groups. These agencies can provide valuable information on growth patterns that will affect the resources of the department. The plans, studies, and reports prepared by the planning agencies can be used to determine whether more personnel, equipment, or station facilities are needed.

PROCUREMENT OF EQUIPMENT AND SUPPLIES

In most municipalities, fire department equipment and supplies are procured through purchasing departments. Items that are common to all departments may be requisitioned from the purchasing agency and charged to the appropriate fire department account. Where items are of a specialized nature, such as fire apparatus or fire-fighting tools and equipment, purchasing specifications must be prepared by the fire department, approved by the purchasing department, and advertised for bids. In preparing specifications for such items as fire apparatus and fire hose, current NFPA standards should be followed.

The fire chief, with advice from the apparatus and equipment superintendent, should determine whether proposals submitted by bidders meet specifications. In many jurisdictions, the law requires that a contract be awarded to the lowest responsible bidder. However, bidders frequently take exception to various details in the specifications or offer substitutes. This requires that a fire chief determine whether such proposals meet the intent of the specifications. If they do not, the bids should be rejected. But if the proposals conform to the specifications and are within the appropriation or budget item, the contract should be awarded. Upon delivery, new equipment should be tested in accordance with the provisions of NFPA standards.

When emergency purchases must be made, it is customary to require bids from several suppliers. If the amount involved is small and funds are available in the appropriate budget item, the fire chief can authorize the expenditure. If funds are not available in the fire department budget, authorization and funds must be obtained from the municipal management or finance officer.

RESOURCE ALLOCATION AND USE

The principal resource of a fire department is its highly trained personnel. The vast majority of personnel are assigned to the fire fighting division, and possibly 2 to 3 percent of the personnel are assigned full-time to the fire prevention bureau. Thus, for most effective resource allocation, maximum use must be made of the fire fighting personnel through careful time-utilization schedules, assigning appropriate allocations of work periods to apparatus and equipment maintenance, fire service training, and scheduled inspections. Such programs require close coordination between the chiefs of the fire fighting, training, and fire prevention bureaus or divisions. In well-managed fire departments, most of the routine fire prevention inspections are conducted by fire companies in their assigned inspection districts. Time-utilization studies in some fire departments have shown that undue amounts of time are wasted on common janitorial duties that could be done more cheaply under contract or by less skilled labor. In many cases, only the fire chief is available on a regular basis to handle all staff duties, so many of the management functions outlined in this context tend to be neglected. Personnel are not fully used when they are not given management responsibilities for the various programs in the fire department.

In the past, many fire chiefs had no training or experience in staff and business management, and did not know how to delegate responsibility. Changes in attitudes, plus newly acquired management skills, are rapidly compensating for past deficiencies, and many fire chiefs have acquired the management skills necessary to manage a complex organization. Considering that 20 percent or more of all fire department personnel are officers, there should be ample, technically qualified managerial help available, even in a small fire department.

BIBLIOGRAPHY

NFPA Codes, Standards, and Recommended Practices

Reference to the following NFPA codes, standards, and recommended practices will provide further information about fire department administration and management. (See the latest *NFPA Catalog* for availability of current editions of the following documents.)

NFPA 901, *Uniform Coding for Fire Protection.*

NFPA 902M, *Fire Reporting Field Incident Manual.*

NFPA 903M, *Fire Reporting Property Survey Manual.*

NFPA 1001, *Fire Fighter Professional Qualifications.*

NFPA 1002, *Fire Apparatus Driver/Operator Professional Qualifications.*

NFPA 1003, *Airport Fire Fighter Professional Qualifications.*

NFPA 1021, *Fire Officer Professional Qualifications.*

NFPA 1031, *Professional Qualifications for Fire Inspector.*

NFPA 1033, *Professional Qualifications for Fire Investigator.*

NFPA 1035, *Professional Qualifications for Public Fire Educator.*

NFPA 1041, *Professional Qualifications for Fire Service Instructors.*

NFPA 1201, *Developing Fire Protection Services for the Public.*

NFPA 1202, *Organization of a Fire Department.*

NFPA 1401, *Training Reports and Records.*

NFPA 1500, *Fire Department Occupational Safety and Health Program.*

Additional Readings

Anderson, D. L., *ed.*, *Municipal Public Relations*, International City Management Association, Washington, DC, 1966.

Aronson, J. R. and Schwartz, E., *eds.*, *Management Policies in Local Government Finance*, 3rd ed., International City Management Association, Washington, DC, 1987.

Bahme, C. W., *Fireman's Law Book*, 14th ed., National Fire Protection Association, Quincy, MA, 1967.

Beck, A. D., Jr. and Hillmar, E.D., *A Practical Approach to Organization Development through MBO-Selected Readings*, Addison-Wesley Publishing Co., Reading, MA, 1972.

Bennis, W. G., *Changing Organizations*, McGraw-Hill, Inc., New-York, 1966.

Berlin, G. N., "Expert System for Fire Emergency Management," *Proceedings* of a Symposium on Theory and Application of Expert Systems and Emergency Management Operations, National Bureau of Standards, Special Publication 717, Gaithersburg, MD, 1986, pp. 158-182.

Berry, D. J., *Fire Litigation Handbook*, National Fire Protection Association, Quincy, MA, 1984.

Bormann, E. G., *et al.*, *Interpersonal Communications in the Modern Organization*, 2nd ed., Prentice-Hall Publishers, Englewood Cliffs, NJ, 1982.

Brown, F. G. and Murphy, T. P., *eds.*, *Emerging Patterns in Urban Administration*, Lexington Books, Lexington, MA, 1970.

Bryan, J. L. and Picard, R. C., *eds.*, *Managing Fire Services*, International City Management Association, Washington, DC, 1979.

Callahan, T., *Fire Service and the Law*, 2nd. ed., National Fire Protection Association, Quincy, MA, 1987.

Caplow, A., *How to Run Any Organization: A Manual of Practical Sociology*, Dryden Press, Hinsdale, IL, 1977.

Carter, H. R., *Management in the Fire Service*, 2nd ed., National Fire Protection Association, Quincy, MA, 1989.

Casey, J. F., *ed.*, *The Fire Chief's Handbook*, 4th ed., Fire Engineering Book Service, New York, 1987.

Caulfield, H. J., *Winning the Fire Service Leadership Game*, Fire Engineering, New York, 1985.

Chaiken, J. M., *et al.*, *Fire Department Deployment Analysis*, The Rand Fire Project, New York, 1979.

Child, J., *Organization: A Guide for Managers and Administrators*, 2nd ed., Paul Chapman, 1988.

Chiesa, A. M., "Identifying the Emergency Management Profession," *Special Libraries*, Vol. 78, No. 2, 1987, pp. 88-92.

Clark, R.T., "Compulsory Arbitration in Public Employment," Public Employee Relations Library, No. 37, Public Personnel Association, Chicago, IL, 1963.

Coe, C. K., *Cost-Cutting Guide for Volunteer Fire Departments*, Institute of Government, University of Georgia, Athens, GA, 1982.

Coe, C. K., *et al.*, *Changing Local Government Fire Rates: The Costs and Benefits*, Institute of Government, University of Georgia, Athens, GA, 1979.

Coleman, R. J., *Management of Fire Service Operations*, Duxbury Press, North Scituate, MA, 1978.

Coleman, R. J. and Granito, J. A., *Managing Fire Services*, 2nd. ed., International City Management Association, Washington, DC, 1988.

Coleman, R. J., *Opportunities in Fire Protection Services*, VGM Carder Horizons, Lincolnwood, IL, 1990.

Cook, J. L., "Initiating Change," *Fire Engineering*, Vol. 143, No. 8, 1989, pp. 74.

Cutlip, S. M. and Center, A. H., *Effective Public Relations*, 6th ed., Prentice-Hall Publishers, Englewood Cliffs, NJ, 1985.

Czamanski, D. Z., *The Cost of Prevention Services: The Case of Fire Departments*, D. C. Heath & Company, Lexington, MA, 1975.

Davis, P. O., *The Firefighter's Survival Manual—A Guide to Physical Fitness*, National Fire Protection Association, Quincy, MA, 1983.

Drucker, P. F., *The Effective Executive*, Harper and Row Publishers, New York, 1985.

Drucker, P.F., *Managing in Turbulent Times*, Harper and Row Publishers, New York, 1985.

Erven, L. W., *Managing Fire Services Study Guide*, Davis Publishers, Santa Cruz, CA, 1980.

Favreau, D. F., *Fire Service Management*, Reuben Donnelley Corp., New York, 1969.

Fire Department Personnel Management Handbook: Managing the Entry of Women and Minorities, Federal Emergency Management Agency, U.S. Fire Administration, Washington, DC, 1979.

Fire Labor Relations, International City Management Association, Washington, DC, 1983.

Fire Officer's Guide to NFPA 1021, National Fire Protection Association, Quincy, MA, 1983.

Fire Personnel Practices, International City Management Association, Washington, DC, 1983.

Fire Protection Administration for Small Communities and Fire Protection Districts, International Fire Service Training Association, Oklahoma State University, Stillwater, OK, 1980.

Fordyce, J. K. and Weil, R., *Managing with People: A Manager's Handbook of Organization Development Methods*, Addison-Wesley Publishing Co., Reading, MA, 1971.

Fyffe, D. E. and Rardin, R. L., "An Evaluation of Policy-Related Research in Fire Protection Service Management," Georgia Institute of Technology, School of Industrial and Systems Engineering, Atlanta, GA, 1974.

Getz, M., *The Economics of Urban Fire Departments*, Johns Hopkins University Press, Baltimore, MD, 1979.

Gibson, R. B., "A Common Ground," *Fire Command*, Vol. 56, No. 8 (Aug. 1989), pp. 33-35.

Goldback, G., "Leadership: A Review of Literature," *Fire Engineering*, Vol. 142, No. 3, 1989, pp. 101-106, 108-111.

Guide to Firefighter Qualifications Training Programs, National Fire Protection Association, Quincy, MA, 1978.

Hatry, H. P., *et al.*, "How Effective Are Your Community Services? Procedures for Monitoring the Effectiveness of Municipal Services," The Urban Institute and International City Management Association, Washington, DC, 1977.

Hatry, H. and Cotton, J., "Program Planning for State, County, City," George Washington University, State-Local Finances Project, Washington, DC, 1967.

Havlick, J. R. and Bodnar, E. B., "Centralized Municipal Communications Center," *Management Information Service Report No. 262*, International City Management Association, Washington, DC, Nov. 1975.

Heisel, W.D., *et al.*, *Line-Staff Relationships in Employee Training*, International City Management Association, Chicago, IL, 1967.

Hickey, H. E., *A Minimum Statistical Data Base for Statewide Public Fire Department Management Information Systems*, Johns Hopkins University, Silver Spring, MD, June 1972.

Hickey, H. E., *Successful Public Relations*, National Fire Protection Association, Quincy, MA, 1974.

Hoetmer, G. J., "Police, Fire and Refuse Collection and Disposal Departments: Personnel, Compensation and Expenditures," International City Management Association, Washington, DC, Aug. 1982.

Hughes, C. L., *Goal Setting: Key to Individual and Organizational Effectiveness*, American Management Association, NY, 1973.

Jenaway, W. F., "Personnel Management in the Volunteer Fire Service," *Fire Command*, Vol. 45, No. 8 (Aug. 1978).

Kimball, W.Y., *Fire Attack 1 and Fire Attack 2*, (video recording), National Fire Protection Association, Quincy, MA, 1987.

Koontz, H. O., *Appraising Managers as Managers*, McGraw-Hill, Inc., NY, 1971.

Kraemer, K.L., *Policy Analysis in Local Government: A Systems Approach to Decision-Making*, International City Management Association, Washington, DC, 1973.

Kraemer, K. L., *et al.*, *The Integrated Municipal Information System: The Use of the Computer in Local Government*, Praeger Publishers, NY, 1974.

La Patra, J. W., *Applying the Systems Approach to Urban Development*, Dowden, Hutchinson & Ross, Inc., Stroudsburg, PA, 1973.

Lawson, B. D., "Fire Management in a Climate of Change," *Proceedings* from 1988 Northwest Fire Council Annual Meeting, Victoria, British Columbia, 1988.

Lee, R. D., Jr. and Johnson, R. W., *Public Budgeting Systems*, 2nd ed., University Park Press, Baltimore, MD, 1977.

Managing People: Fire Service Personnel Strategies, National Fire Protection Association, Quincy, MA, 1984.

McGregor, D., *The Professional Manager*, McGraw-Hill, Inc., New York, 1967.

Miller, E. C., *Objectives and Standards: An Approach to Planning and Control*, American Management Association, New York, 1966.

Morgan, J. S., *Practical Guide to Conference Leadership*, McGraw-Hill, Inc., New York, 1966.

National Fire Safety and Research Office, *A Basic Guide for Fire Prevention and Control Master Planning*, National Fire Prevention and Control Administration, Washington, DC, 1977.

Nigro, F. A., *Management Employee Relations in the Public Service*, Public Personnel Association, Chicago, IL, 1969.

Odiorne, G. S., *Management by Objectives: A System of Managerial Leadership*, Pitman Publishing Corp., New York, 1965.

Page, J. O., *Effective Company Command for Company Officers in the Professional Fire Service*, Borden Publishing Company, Alhambra, CA, 1973.

Parker, J. K., *Introduction to Systems Analysis, Management Information Service Reports*, No. 298, International City Management Association, Washington, DC, 1968.

Research Triangle Institute, *et al.*, *Research Applied to National Needs*, prepared for the National Science Foundation, U.S. Government Printing Office, Washington, DC, 1977.

Robertson, J. C., "Organization and Administration of Municipal Fire Prevention Efforts," *Introduction to Fire Prevention*, 3rd ed., Macmillan, New York, 1989, pp. 76-98.

Rosenbauer, D. L., *Introduction to Fire Protection Law*, National Fire Protection Association, Quincy, MA, 1978.

Sagoria, Sam, *ed.*, *Public Workers and Public Unions*, Prentice-Hall, Inc., Englewood Cliffs, NJ, 1972.

Sasso, C. O., *Coping with Public Employee Strikes: A Guide for Public Officials*, Public Personnel Association, Chicago, IL, 1970.

Smalley, J. C., *Funding Sources for Fire Departments*, National Fire Protection Association, Quincy, MA, 1983.

Snook, J. W. and Olsen, D. C., *Recruiting, Training and Maintaining Volunteer Firefighters*, 2nd ed., Management Development Institute, Lake Oswego, OR, 1989.

Starrett, P. F., *Mass Communications for Local Officials*, Arizona State University, Institute of Public Administration, Tempe, AZ, 1970.

Stern, J. L., *et al.*, *Final-Offer Arbitration: The Effects on Public Safety Employee Bargaining*, D. C. Heath & Company, Lexington, MA, 1975.

Stieber, J.,, *Public Employee Unionism: Structure, Growth*, Policy, Brookings Institution, Washington, DC, 1973.

Stoner, J. A. F., *Management*, 4th ed., Prentice-Hall, Englewood Cliffs, NJ, 1989.

Terry, G. R., *Principles of Management*, 6th ed., Richard D. Irwin, Inc., Homewood, IL, 1972.

Tien, J. M. and Chiu, S.S., "Impact Analysis of Some Cost Reduction Options for a Metropolitan Fire Department," *Fire Technology*, Vol. 21, No. 1 (Feb. 1985), pp. 5-21.

"Training and Education in the Fire Services," *Proceedings* of a Symposium Conducted by the Committee on Fire Research, National Research Council, National Academy of Sciences, Washington, DC, April 8-9, 1970.

Urban Guide for Fire Prevention and Control Master Planning, National Fire Prevention and Control Administration, Washington, DC, 1977.

Vance, J. E., *Information Communication Handbook: Policies for Working with the Media for Public Officials*, Citizens, Business and Community Groups, published by the author, St. Paul, MN, 1973.

Vougioukles, C. L., *Management of the Entry of Women in the Fire Service: A Directory of Resources*, International Association of Fire Fighters, Washington, DC, 1981.

Webb, W. C., *The Volunteer Fire Service: A Management Perspective*, International City Management Association, Washington, DC, 1974.

Webber, R. A., *Management: Basic Elements of Managing Organizations*, 3rd ed., Richard D. Irwin, Inc., Homewood, IL, 1985.

Wellington, H. H. and Winter, R. K., Jr., *The Unions and the Cities*, reprint, Brookings Institution, Washington, DC, 1989.

FIRE DEPARTMENT OPERATIONS

Revised by J. Gordon Routley

The great majority of public fire departments are structured around the primary mission of fire suppression. This role reflects a realistic appraisal of the fire-risk profile in most communities, which requires that a combat force be ready to respond, in order to control and extinguish fires. In many cases this role has been extended to include the delivery of additional emergency services in a variety of situations that present an immediate threat to lives and property in the community. While the fire service may place an emphasis on fire prevention, public education, risk reduction, and hazard-abatement programs, their ability to respond to and control fires is an overriding operational priority.

Fire suppression is generally organized around a system of decentralized fire stations, providing the fire service with the ability to respond quickly with personnel and equipment to control and extinguish fires. This organization may be staffed by career, part-time, or volunteer personnel; may reflect a variety of characteristics derived from local needs, structure, and tradition; and may be involved in the delivery of other emergency and non-emergency services. The ability to respond to the life-safety and property-protection needs of the local community is the common denominator in fire department emergency operations.

This chapter discusses various basic components of fire department operations that are structured around the emergency response and fire suppression system. It illustrates the typical fire department organization and shows how the fire suppression mission relates to the total organization.

ORGANIZATION FOR FIRE SUPPRESSION

The dominant factor in the structure of most fire departments is the mission of fire suppression. The complexity of the organization is directly related to the size of the department. Many small fire departments operate under the direct supervision of a local fire chief. In larger departments, companies are organized into battalions or districts under the supervision of intermediate-level command officers. (See Fig. 9-6A.)

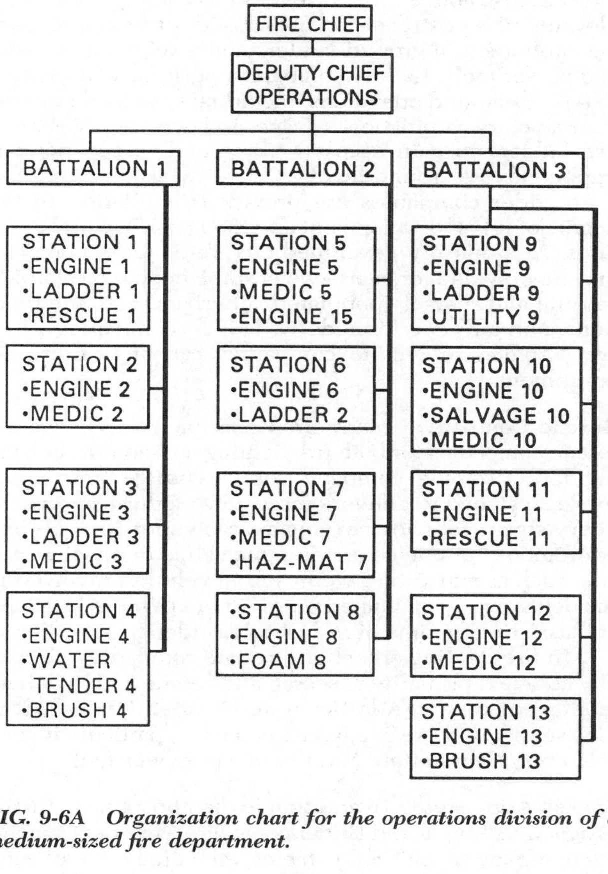

***FIG. 9-6A** Organization chart for the operations division of a medium-sized fire department.*

The company is the basic tactical unit of the fire department. A company is a complement of personnel operating one or more pieces of apparatus under the supervision of a company officer. Several companies may operate

J. Gordon Routley is a fire protection consultant based in Phoenix, AZ. He was previously chief of the Shreveport, LA, Fire Department and assistant to the chief of the Phoenix Fire Department.

from a single fire station. A number of different types of companies are used, depending on local needs. Engine and ladder companies are the most numerous, although a variety of others often are provided to perform combined or specialized functions. These include rescue squads and companies that operate special tactical or support-function apparatus. Some fire departments organize a number of companies operating from the same station as task forces.

Engine Company: The most common type of company in a fire department is normally the engine company. The basic unit of apparatus is the pumper, which carries hose, nozzles, an on-board water tank, and a pump. The engine company's basic role in tactical operations is to deliver water through hose lines to control fires. Most engine companies carry additional equipment to provide medical, rescue, and other emergency services. In most cases, at least one engine company is based at each fire station to respond quickly and to begin fire control operations at a fire scene. The engine company is considered the basic unit of a fire department and is supplemented by other types of companies.

Ladder Company: The basic ladder company apparatus is an aerial ladder or elevating platform device, which provides access above ground level or to rooftops or directs elevated master streams on fires. Ladder trucks also carry a complement of ground ladders and a selection of hand and power tools. Ladder companies perform a supporting role in fireground operations, including search and rescue, forcible entry, ventilation, salvage, and overhaul. They also use ladders to gain access to fires and rescue persons trapped above ground level.

Ladder companies are provided in relation to the degree of urban development and the need for aerial apparatus. In a densely developed city, one ladder company may be provided for every two or three engine companies. In rural and sparsely populated suburban areas, the functions normally performed by ladder companies often are assigned to engine companies carrying additional equipment.

Rescue Company: Many fire departments use separate rescue companies for both fire fighting and non-fire-related incidents. Rescue company vehicles range from small trucks designed to deliver emergency medical services to heavy squad vehicles carrying a large variety of tools and equipment. Rescue companies specialize in physical rescue, such as extricating victims from vehicles involved in accidents, removing injured persons from perilous locations, and assisting victims of industrial accidents.

In fire fighting operations, rescue companies are usually assigned primarily to search and rescue and to deliver medical treatment. Additional duties often involve activities similar to those of a ladder company, particularly forcible entry, ventilation, and the use of power tools.

Special Apparatus: In addition to the apparatus normally assigned to engine and ladder companies, fire departments often employ specialized vehicles, including off-road vehicles for brush fires, water tenders, hose wagons, foam pumpers, hazardous materials units, lighting trucks, breathing-air-supply trucks, and command vehicles. These may be organized as individual companies, or they may be assigned to regular companies.

Some fire departments operate special companies with additional personnel. These companies are often referred to as "manpower squads" and operate vehicles designed to carry a minimum of equipment beyond the protective clothing and breathing apparatus used by the crew.

Fire apparatus may be purchased with a variety of options and configurations to suit the needs of a particular community or fire department. These options include aerial devices, water towers, and foam systems on engine-company apparatus; high-volume pumps on ladder trucks; remote-control nozzles; and large electrical generators and air-supply systems.

There is an increasing tendency to purchase apparatus with multiple capabilities and to equip companies to perform the functions of two or more types of companies.

The National Fire Protection Association publishes a series of standards for the design and construction of fire apparatus. Refer to Section 9, Chapter 9, "Fire Department Apparatus and Equipment," for a detailed discussion of fire apparatus.

Personnel Requirements

Effective fireground operations are highly dependent upon the individual and collective capabilities of the companies responding to an incident. The apparatus assigned to a company basically defines the role that that company will be expected to assume in a fire fighting operation. In order to operate effectively, each company must have skilled and trained personnel who can perform basic functions in a standard manner. An untrained, unskilled, or understaffed crew will not perform effectively, regardless of the apparatus and equipment provided.

The National Fire Protection Association has developed a series of professional qualifications standards for fire fighters, company and command officers, and other positions in the fire service. These standards establish physical and medical requirements, as well as education, training, and performance levels that are recommended for adoption by fire departments and other agencies.

The size of the crew assigned to a company is a local decision and varies with the fire risk in a particular area, the number and types of companies that can respond to incidents, and the economic status of the organization. While engine and ladder companies with five or six crew members are considered desirable in highly urban areas, many fire departments work very effectively with crews of four on each apparatus.The appendix of NFPA 1500, *Standard for Fire Department Occupational Safety and Health Program*, recommends at least four crew members for interior structural fire fighting, on the basis of safety and efficiency.

FIREGROUND OPERATIONS

Incident Management

During fire suppression operations, a fire department uses its resources to combat a fire. The success of a fire fighting operation depends upon a fire department's ability to use the available resources to protect lives and property effectively and efficiently. The incident commander is responsible for managing the available personnel and equipment to achieve maximum results, depending upon the situation, the associated conditions, and the resources available. The same principles apply to other types of incidents that the department may be expected to handle, including medical, rescue, and hazardous materials situations.

An incident commander is responsible for directing and controlling operations at every incident. From the arrival of the first unit at the fire scene, one identified person should be in command, with the responsibility and authority to direct all phases of the operation. The officer in charge of the first-arriving company assumes the role of incident commander until relieved by an officer of higher rank. In complex situations, command may be transferred one or more times, as higher ranking chief officers arrive and assume command.

Many incidents are routinely handled by a single company, with the company officer functioning as incident commander. The officer in charge of the first-arriving company should automatically assume command of an incident, following an established standard operating procedure.

The first-arriving officer may remain in command of the incident, particularly if only one or two companies are used. When the incident requires a larger commitment of resources, a chief officer should respond and assume command. A battalion or district chief will usually take over incidents involving three or more companies.

Higher-level command officers usually will respond to and assume command of multiple-alarm incidents. The incident organization is subdivided according to a standard incident management system to maintain a functional span of control at each level. NFPA 1561, *Standard for Fire Department Incident Management Systems*, defines the basic requirements for an incident management system. The Incident Command System (ICS) taught by the National Fire Academy is a model for managing emergency incidents.

Command Responsibilities

The incident commander has the overall responsibility to manage operations at the scene of an incident. Intermediate levels of command report to the incident commander and are responsible for certain sectors, or geographical portions, of the operation or for supervising particular functions. These officers coordinate the operations of a group of companies.

A major incident may require a fairly complex command staff with a number of officers reporting to the incident commander. Several officers may be assigned to directly support the incident commander, at a command post, providing information or further subdividing the span of control into manageable units.

Standard operating procedures are an important aspect of incident management. Every fire department should have a set of procedures that outlines the basic operating principles to be employed in any situation, from the simplest to the most complex. The procedures should be flexible enough to allow fire fighters to react to different situations, and they should be incremental to permit adjustment to the scale of the incident. Standard operating procedures provide a menu of basic functions that can be employed as needed and establish consistent approaches to fire control.

The incident commander must use strategy and tactics to manage a fire suppression or similar incident. The incident commander is responsible for strategic decision-making and for translating strategic goals into tactical objectives and task assignments. (See Fig. 9-6B.)

Strategy: Strategy involves the development of a basic plan to deal with a situation most effectively. The plan must identify major goals and prioritize objectives. Strategic decisions are based upon an evaluation of the situation, the risk potential, and the available resources.

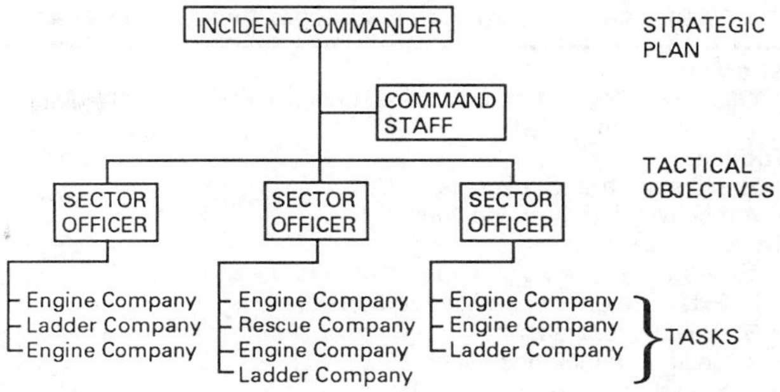

FIG. 9-6B. A common type of fireground organization. The incident commander develops a strategic plan and assigns tactical objectives to the sector officers. The sector officers assign companies to perform specific tasks, in order to accomplish the tactical objectives.

Strategic decisions identify the priorities for committing resources to various tactical positions and activities, based on standard approaches and prevailing conditions. The generally accepted priorities for strategic decisions are rescue, fire control, and property conservation. The strategic plan identifies where and when the forces will attempt to control the fire and how their activities will be combined and prioritized.

The strategic options available to the incident commander involve some very important, basic decisions. The most fundamental is the choice between offensive and defensive modes of operation, based on the available resources and the risk to personnel. For offensive operations, companies extend hose lines into the interior of an involved fire area and extinguish the fire where they find it. In defensive operations, heavy streams are applied from the exterior to confine or control a fire, conceding the loss of the involved area. Offensive and defensive modes of operation must not be mixed in the same place at the same time, so the incident commander must identify what can and cannot feasibly be saved without undue risk to personnel.

Tactics: Tactics are the methods the incident commander uses to implement the strategic plan. The tactical objectives define specific functions that are assigned to groups of companies operating under sector officers. The achievement of these objectives contributes to the strategic goals and must be compatible with the overall strategic plan.

Tactical activities are based on three distinct phases or priorities. The first is to provide for the safety of the public by extending search-and-rescue efforts to all areas where potential victims may be located. The second priority is to control the fire, and the third is to conserve property. Fireground tactics usually involve a mixture of tasks performed under the supervision and coordination of sector officers.

Tasks: The translation of tactical objectives to tasks results in assignments to individual companies. A company generally undertakes one or two specific tasks at any particular time, which must be coordinated and combined to achieve tactical objectives.

TABLE 9-6A. ***Example of Strategic Decision- Making***

Strategy
Offensive—Protect occupants and control fire in the area involved on arrival.
Tactics:
Rapid search and rescue.
Attack with interior hose lines.
Tasks:
1. Search and rescue in immediate fire area.
2. Extend interior hose lines to attack fire.
3. Provide ventilation.
4. Back up attack hose lines.
5. Search and rescue floor above fire.
6. Protect property.

Tactical Functions

Several tactical functions may be employed at each fire and may be carried out simultaneously during multi-company operations. Every company must be trained to carry out all basic functions and to contribute to any or all tactical objectives.

Search and rescue: Rescue is the first and most important consideration at any fire and, until it has been completed, may preclude any fire control efforts. The incident commander may have to initiate fire control activities to protect the rescue operation or to keep the fire away from potential victims. Rescue operations may require only one or two companies, or they may require resources beyond the capabilities of the entire first-alarm assignment. All involved or threatened occupancies should be searched thoroughly for occupants by companies specifically assigned to this task. Every company must be prepared to perform search and rescue as a first priority. Rescue operations may be compounded by the time of the incident, the occupancy, and the height and construction of the structure. Rescue is the only acceptable reason for exposing fire fighters to otherwise unnecessary risks.

Exposure protection: The second fire suppression priority is to control the fire. This begins with confinement of the fire to the property initially involved. The most basic goal of fire departments, with respect to property, is to protect the the community from large-loss fires extending beyond the property involved on arrival. Failure to protect exposed structures adequately may allow a fire to extend beyond the building of fire origin. The problem of exposure protection may be compounded by closely spaced buildings, combustible construction, the type of occupancy, the lack of fire department access to the fire, and the lack of fire department resources. Exposure protection is a vital and necessary tactical consideration and should be the major objective in defensive fire control situations. When the magnitude of a fire requires all of the available fire control forces to be committed to exposure protection, the strategy is considered totally defensive.

Confinement: The confinement of a fire to its area of origin is often a complex problem. Fire control is achieved when the fire is successfully confined to a manageable area. All avenues of possible fire travel must be secured. The concept of surrounding the fire is necessary for successful confinement. Additional factors that influence the success or failure of confinement operations are the type of fuel involved, the location of the fire, building construction features, the presence of built-in fire suppression systems, and the availability of fire department resources. Confinement of a fire may involve offensive or defensive strategies, or a combination of the two options.

Extinguishment: Offensive fire control strategies are aimed at controlling and extinguishing the fire where it is encountered by attack forces. Successful offensive operations are regulated by the type of fuel involved, the location of the fire and degree of involvement, and the ability of fire control forces to apply sufficient extinguishing agents directly on the fire. In some instances, the use of special extinguishing agents may be required.

In defensive operations, final extinguishment may be achieved only when the fire burns down to a size that can be extinguished by the fire department. Defensive tactics depend upon the department's ability to apply a large volume of water or other agents on the fire to confine and eventually extinguish it.

Ventilation: Ventilation operations are the planned and systematic removal of heat, smoke, and fire gases from the structure. In some cases, it may be necessary to initiate ventilation with rescue in order to protect occupants from combustion products and heat and to provide visibility and tenability during rescue operations. Ventilation is also necessary during confinement and extinguishment to limit fire spread, to aid in locating the fire, and to provide safer working conditions for fire suppression personnel, as well as to reduce overall damage to the structure and its contents.

Ventilation often involves roof-top operations to allow trapped heat and gases to escape from the interior of a building. Positive-pressure ventilation is based on forcing heat and products of combustion out of an involved area by introducing volumes of cool fresh air in coordination with attacking hose lines.

Property conservation: Salvage operations are conducted by fire suppression personnel to conserve property by minimizing damage to the structure and contents due to heat, smoke, and water. This involves, in part, covering contents and removing excess water. Salvage is an integral part of tactical operations and should commence as soon as possible to prevent additional damage to the structure and its contents.

Overhaul: Overhaul operations are required to extinguish the fire completely, make the structure safe, and aid in determining the fire ignition sequence. Overhaul may involve only a few personnel for a short period of time, or it may involve large numbers of personnel over an extended period. Extensive overhaul may require special pieces of equipment in addition to those normally provided by the fire department. It is important that extensive overhaul not be started before a thorough investigation has been conducted to determine the cause of the fire. Once the investigation is complete, overhaul should continue to ensure that the premises are left as safe as possible and that all fires have been extinguished.

Fire Fighting Safety

Fire fighting is considered to be one of the most dangerous occupations in North America, but it is possible and essential to improve the safety of fire department operations. Safety should be a primary concern for all personnel, from the incident commander to the individual fire fighter.

All fire fighters must be provided with complete turnout clothing and protective equipment, including self-contained breathing apparatus, which comply with the appropriate NFPA standards. Regulations requiring the use of the proper protective equipment in every situation must be implemented and enforced. All fire departments should implement a complete safety program, including a physical fitness program, health monitoring and medical supervision, the provision and use of protective equipment, ongoing training, and the management of situations that present an unusual hazard to personnel. A comprehensive breathing apparatus program for all fires is an essential element of a succesful fire department safety program.

Safety must be a primary concern of the incident commander at all times. In complex situations, safety officers should be assigned specifically to monitor conditions and advise the incident commander and sector officers of hazardous conditions and safety concerns. Sector officers must be particularly concerned with the safety of personnel under their direction. Every tactical option must be evaluated in terms of its risk to fire fighters.

RISK ANALYSIS

Fire risk analysis is an essential step in determining the level of resources appropriate for a particular community. A detailed knowledge of the potential fire problem in a fire department's service area is necessary in planning resource deployment and responses and in locating facilities. This risk analysis should be conducted systematically throughout the service area to determine an appropriate level of fire suppression resources that will provide adequate public protection. The community's fire suppression capability should be directly related to its level of fire risk.

To ascertain risk potential, it is essential to gain an in-depth understanding of the dynamics and behavior of fire, building construction, human factors, and the properties and hazards of materials.

Assessment of fire hazards, together with a technical knowledge of fire, provides an understanding of the risk potential that can take some of the uncertainty out of fire suppression activities and fireground decision-making.

This information is also critical when a fire officer is called upon to make rapid, often irrevocable decisions affecting the commitment of personnel and apparatus at the fire scene. The fire officer must appreciate the way fire can be expected to behave in any given situation.

This analytical approach can be expanded and used to plan resources and response levels for almost any risk and for preparing action plans. It also can be used to develop training exercises to prepare officers and officer candidates to think in terms of a systematic assessment for fireground decision-making.

The following factors should be considered in determining risk potential for a particular location:

Life risk: How many occupants are present? Are they likely to be active, physically capable, and able to help themselves, or are they likely to be infirm, aged, bedridden, handicapped, or otherwise unable to take any action towards rescuing themselves? Are the occupants likely to be asleep and, therefore, more prone to being trapped? Does the building provide early-warning, fire suppression systems, and adequate exits, or are the occupants highly dependent upon the fire department to be found and rescued?

Contents: Does the building have a high fire load? Are the contents highly flammable, producing rapid fire spread and high heat-release rates? Are they liable to explode, produce dense smoke, or give off highly toxic products of combustion? Are the contents extremely valuable or highly susceptible to heat, smoke, or water damage?

Construction: Is the construction fire-resistive and likely to maintain structural integrity, or is it unprotected and likely to fail early in the fire? Are the interior finishes liable to cause rapid flame spread and extension of fire? Is the building compartmented with fire walls and doors, or are there openings in floors, walls, ducts, and shafts that will allow a fire to spread? Is the building old, or has it been remodeled with possible resultant weaknesses? Are there very large structures or groups of buildings that present a situation in which an established fire is virtually impossible to control? Are there unsprinklered high-rise buildings that present an excessive demand for personnel and equipment to support above-ground fire suppression operations?

Built-in protection: Have automatic sprinklers been installed to control the growth and spread of fire? Are there fire doors, compartments, or other fire protection arrangements that would help to confine a fire?

Time: Are occupants alert, and would they discover a fire soon after its inception? Are occupants asleep, or is no one present to call the fire department? Is there a smoke- or fire-detection system? Is the system connected to the fire department or to a central station system? What is the response time from the nearest fire station? Are there railroad crossings, heavy traffic patterns, or other restrictions on the speed of fire department response? Are there any other factors that would delay discovery, alarm, or response?

Suppression resources: Are water or other extinguishing agents available? Is special apparatus required? Will entry or access be a problem? Will there be rescue problems? Will there be a need for long-duration breathing apparatus? Are there any other factors affecting the fire department response or action? Are adequate fire suppression resources available, including mutual aid and reserve personnel and equipment? Are additional resources that are beyond the capability of the fire department needed?

In addition to structural fires, fire departments must be prepared to face a wide variety of incidents, including fires in outside storage, brush and wildlands, transportation systems, and industrial installations. Most fire departments also are responsible for hazardous materials incidents and for rescuing persons trapped by floods, vehicle accidents, building collapses, cave-ins, and numerous other situations. Many fire departments also have assumed a major role in the delivery of emergency medical services, which often involves more emergency activity than fire suppression.

The fire department has become an all-purpose emergency service and requires a diversified array of equipment and training to fulfill this diversified mission. Many of the standard procedures and much of the equipment used for structural fire fighting are transferable to these additional roles, but additional specialized equipment and methods often are needed to deal with the identifiable risks and hazards in a community. Preparedness is an important element of fire department planning.

Transportation incidents

All public fire departments need to be as well prepared for transportation incidents as they are for structure fires. These incidents may range from automobile fires to aircraft accidents or train derailments, and they may occur anywhere at any time. Planning is essential for large-scale incidents such as those involving mass-transit systems, airports, and railways.

Fires and accidents that occur on bridges, on freeways, on railroads, in tunnels, on mass transit systems, and at other locations must be a part of every fire department's planning process since these incidents combine difficult access, limited water supplies, and special requirements for rescue and fire suppression. These situations may require specialized apparatus, equipment, training, and procedures so personnel can deal effectively with the variety of problems that can occur. Incidents ranging from a gasoline tanker burning on a bridge to a subway train collision and fire in a tunnel must be considered, and effective plans must be in place to deal with them. Some of the most disastrous fires have occurred where unanticipated events and circumstances exceeded the capabilities of the emergency response organizations.

Large quantities of flammable liquids and other hazardous materials are constantly in transit by road and rail. Any incident involving trucks or freight trains should be considered a potential hazardous materials incident. Personnel must be familiar with labeling and placarding systems for hazardous materials, with the use of cargo manifests and waybills to identify cargos, and with resources such as CHEMTREC, a 24-hour emergency service provided by the Chemical Manufacturers Association through their toll-free telephone number (1-800-424-9300).

Air: Aircraft crashes that occur on or off airfields often present a major fire and rescue problem. For effective rescue, fire department action must be rapid and effective. Many public fire departments also provide aircraft rescue and fire fighting (ARFF) protection at airports. There are several good sources of information on dealing with aircraft accidents. (Consult the bibliography at the end of this chapter.)

Marine: Water-borne vessels range from small pleasure boats to barges, cargo carriers, warships, cruise ships, and supertankers. Vessel categories present differing problems that require a thorough knowledge of ship construction, design, stability, and the special techniques of shipboard fire fighting.

In the case of cargo ships, the nature of the cargo may vary from inert materials to general combustibles and highly flammable and explosive materials. As with any other transportation fire, restraint is required until positive identification is made of the materials involved. Materials can be identified from the ship's manifest, which is usually available from the ship's master.

Fire departments with port facilities should be trained in fighting shipboard and waterfront fires. Marine fires may require the use of fireboats and often cannot be handled in the same manner as shore fires.

Some basic factors to consider when fighting marine fires are the stability of the vessel, which may be affected by the application of water; ventilation; water pollution and the possible obstruction of waterways or port facilities should the vessel capsize or sink; the ability to deal with fire away from wharfside; maximum use of a ship's built-in extinguishing systems; and fire-spread through vessel bulkheads. The fire department also has to interact with port authorities, the U.S. Coast Guard, and the master of the vessel concerned. The often unclear divisions of authority and responsibility should be clarified before an incident occurs.

Pipelines: Underground pipelines carry highly flammable products at high pressures through many populated areas. The risk involved in a rupture of one of these lines may be extremely critical. Fire departments should be aware of the locations of underground pipelines and the products they carry, and they should know how to shut down the pipelines in an emergency.

Mutual Aid and Major Emergencies

The possibility of fires and disasters that overwhelm the local emergency forces must always be considered. For this reason, most fire departments traditionally have rendered mutual assistance to other departments in times of need. Mutual-aid plans establish procedures for requesting and dispatching help between fire departments so that each party will know what is expected. Mutual-aid plans may include immediate joint response of several fire departments to high-risk properties; joint response to alarms adjacent to the boundaries between fire department areas (automatic aid); coverage of vacant territories by outside departments when the resources of the local department are engaged; provision of additional units to assist at major fires that may be too large for the local department to handle; and provision of specialized types of fire fighting equipment not available locally in adequate quantity for the particular incident. Mutual-aid plans also should include provisions for incident management, standard operating procedures, interdepartmental communications, common terminology, maps, adaptors, and other considerations that directly affect the ability of departments to operate effectively together.

Command responsibility, jurisdictional questions, insurance coverage, and legal constraints should be covered in written agreements, supported by enabling legislation, to establish mutual-aid systems properly for the participating departments.

Some jurisdictions have extended the mutual-aid concept to multi-jurisdictional agreements in which fire department resources are pooled or merged into an integrated system with standardized training procedures and communications. These networks may include shared facilities, joint purchases of specialized apparatus and equipment, and a coordinated approach to long-range planning.

True mutual aid is a relationship in which each member is prepared to assist the parties of the agreement. Most larger fire departments are willing to assist smaller jurisdictions when major incidents occur that obviously exceed local capabilities. In many places, communities or individual properties known to be deficient in fire fighting resources contract in advance to pay another jurisdiction for certain fire fighting assistance. These programs are known as outside aid programs. In some instances, the contract covers basic first-alarm response; in other cases, additional assistance is provided for fighting major fires. In the cases of both mutual aid and outside aid, definite agreements should be made in advance according to the legal requirements governing fire department operations outside normal jurisdictional areas.

It should be recognized that some existing mutual-aid agreements contain deficiencies. Each local department may have different operating methods and types of equipment, so that maximum coordination may be hampered. The parties to the plan may choose to render assistance only to the extent that they feel they can do so without seriously reducing local protection, although the better regional plans provide for maintaining coverage for all districts dispatching apparatus. Coverage weaknesses should be identified and corrected in advance.

Experience with natural disasters and large-scale incidents has focused attention upon the importance of plans and organizational procedures for systematically mobilizing fire forces. Some states and provinces have established large-area disaster plans involving all emergency services, coordinated under standard incident management systems. For successful disaster operations, it is imperative that such plans integrate with the normal organizational and command procedures used by fire departments. These large-scale mutual-aid networks form a natural basis for smaller-scale, more routine mutual-assistance plans.

NONEMERGENCY ACTIVITIES

Most fire companies are involved in a variety of nonemergency activities during the time that is available between emergencies. Emergencies usually occupy less than 10 percent of the hours that personnel are on duty, and a substantial part of the remaining time can be used productively to prepare for emergencies and to reduce fire risk in the community through fire prevention and public education programs.

Pre-fire planning: Pre-fire planning should involve all fire suppression personnel on a continuing basis. Pre-fire plans should complement standard operating procedures by familiarizing personnel with complex occupancies and special risks. Pre-fire plan information should be documented in a standard format to help the incident commander manage any situation that could occur at the fire location. Plans should be sufficiently flexible to allow for varying conditions and should use the framework of standard operating procedures. Plans that are excessively rigid or complex may handicap an operation more than benefit it.

The following steps are part of the pre-fire planning process:

1. *Information gathering:* Pertinent information such as building construction features, occupancy, exposures, utility disconnects, fire hydrant locations, water main sizes, and so on, that might significantly affect fire fighting operations must be collected at the selected site.
2. *Information analysis:* The information gathered must be analyzed for what is pertinent and vital to fire suppression operations, so that a plan can be documented in a format that can be used on the fireground. A pre-fire plan usually includes a site plan or map; floor plans and diagrams identifying pertinent features, hazards, and fire control equipment; and additional text outlining special problems, specific tactics, hazardous contents, and information on parties responsible for specific areas.
3. *Information dissemination:* Pre-fire plans should be assembled and distributed in a standard format for easy use on the fire ground. Plans may be maintained on paper and carried in fire apparatus, microfilmed and used with viewers in command vehicles, or stored in computer systems accessed by mobile data terminals.
4. *Class review and drill:* Any company that might be involved at a location for which a pre-fire plan has been developed should review the plan on a regular schedule. If possible, periodic drills and familiarization tours with all the companies involved should be scheduled on the property.

Pre-fire plans are desirable for all target hazards, for special risks, and for large complexes. Standard operating procedures are usually sufficient for single-family dwellings and smaller occupancies. Pre-fire planning is a necessary adjunct to tactical operations and should aid in efficient operations, reduce fire losses, and help provide an optimum level of fire protection.

Fire prevention: The participation of fire suppression personnel in fire prevention and public education activities should be as important as their participation in fire suppression operations. Fire department resources are generally deployed throughout the protected area to provide rapid emergency response; those companies usually spend only a small percentage of their time actually fighting fires. Fire departments committed to a comprehensive fire prevention and inspection program use fire suppression personnel on a regular basis for routine inspections in their first-due response areas. They also use full-time fire prevention personnel for follow-up inspections, legal-enforcement actions, and special technical inspections. The involvement of fire suppression personnel in fire prevention and public education activities is a good use of resources because it decreases the risk of fire and familiarizes personnel with occupancies in their response areas.

Training: It is essential that a portion of a fire-suppression force's duty time be devoted to training. Training activities provide the opportunity to develop the skills and knowledge necessary to implement tactical operations. The elements of a good training program are discussed in detail later in this chapter.

COMMUNICATIONS

An effective communications system is a key factor in fire department operations. The communications system is responsible for receiving notification of emergencies from the public; alerting and dispatching personnel and equipment; coordinating the activities of the units engaged in emergency incidents; and providing non-emergency communications for coordinating fire department units.

Receiving Alarms

Most alarms are received from the public over the public telephone system or the municipal alarm systems. In many areas, combined emergency service answering centers receive telephone calls for police, fire, and emergency medical services through a 911 emergency number, while the fire departments in other jurisdictions receive calls at a separate communications office. Enhanced 911 telephone systems are able to identify automatically the telephone number and location from which the call originates. Small departments with low activity levels may receive alarms through a variety of systems that provide 24-hr coverage.

As a result of high false alarm rates, many cities have removed municipal alarm systems or converted from telegraph to systems providing voice contact between the dispatcher and the caller. The majority of fire alarms in most areas are received from private and public telephones.

For more information, see NFPA 1221, *Standard for the Installation, Maintenance and Use of Public Fire Service Communication Systems*. Additional information is provided in Section 4, Chapter 1, "Fire Department Emergency Communications System," of this book.

The communications center should provide recording equipment for all telephone lines and radio channels to provide immediate playback capability to verify information and to provide a complete record of all activity. In addition to telephones and municipal alarm systems, many fire departments receive automatic fire alarms from systems installed in buildings connected to the fire department directly or through a private alarm company.

Dispatch Procedures

The second phase of fire department communications is alerting and dispatching personnel and equipment to an incident. The complexity of this phase varies with the size and population of the area served and the number of units under the control of the alarm center.

The dispatcher must identify the units that are to respond to an incident based on the geographic location and the type of situation indicated. The selection criteria for response units must be determined in advance, based on distance from, or response time to, the reported location. The type and number of units due to respond to each type of incident should also be determined in advance, based on risk criteria and unit capabilities.

The dispatcher must know the status of each unit in the system and be able to contact immediately all units that are available to respond to an incident. If regularly assigned units are engaged at another incident or are otherwise unavailable, the system should identify the next units to substitute. This information is also needed if the dispatched units request additional assistance or sound a multiple alarm. Many fire departments and regional systems have installed computer-aided dispatch systems (CADS) that combine the complex set of information required to manage these functions with the speed necessary for emergency dispatch. Smaller systems often rely on printed "running cards," or policies to provide the dispatcher with response information for each zone.

The units assigned to respond to an incident may be alerted by radio, microwave, telephone, telegraph, or other wired systems. In some areas, individual pagers, outside sirens, or horns are used to alert volunteer or call personnel. Most departments use a voice message from the dispatcher to the responding unit, which may be carried over the radio or wired circuits to the fire station. There should be at least two separate means of communication between the alarm center and each fire station for back-up in case of equipment failure. In addition to voice messages, some fire departments use printers or telegraph systems to back up the vocal message. Units out of quarters are normally alerted by radio.

Radio Communications

Every fire department vehicle should be equipped with two-way radios. Units responding to or engaged at incidents should be in radio contact with other units and with the alarm center. For larger departments, this may require several radio channels to provide sufficient communications capacity. The alarm center must be able to contact responding units to provide additional information or directions while en route to an incident, while units at the scene must be able to request or return additional resources. The incident commander should be able to contact the alarm center at all times, providing progress reports, advising on the need for assistance, or releasing units from the scene. A fireground channel should provide communications between the incident commander and the units operating at the scene.

Each company officer and sector officer should have a portable two-way radio on a fireground channel.

Units released from an incident by the incident commander should advise the alarm center when they are available to respond to other incidents.

The radio system is essential to maintain radio communications with units that are engaged in activities out of quarters. Fire departments have increased their dependency on radio communications as they have become more mobile and active, with units spending less time in quarters. The radio system must reach units in every geographical area of a jurisdiction and provide sufficient capacity and channels to handle the volume of communications a major emergency generates. Regional mutual-aid channels are essential to coordinate activities involving units from multiple jurisdictions.

Staffing

Fire communication centers require trained operators who are familiar with fire department operations and equipment. In very small communities, the fire department telephone number may be arranged to ring in a number of locations where appropriate action can be taken to dispatch fire apparatus. Dispatching may also be handled by the police department, a town office, or other locations that provide 24-hr coverage. Increasingly, small fire departments are being served by regional fire communication centers, which can be properly equipped and staffed.

Larger communities and regional communication centers require trained, capable personnel to be on duty at all times. The number of personnel on duty depends upon the workload. There must be enough operators on duty to handle the volume of communications required by busy activity periods and working incidents. Major emergencies and high-activity situations may necessitate calling in off-duty personnel or additional trained dispatchers.

System maintenance and repair personnel should be on-duty or on-call at all times. All equipment must be maintained properly and tested for maximum reliability, and back-up equipment or systems should be provided in the event that any key component fails. Every fire department should have a back-up facility to which basic communication capability can be transferred if a critical situation makes the primary center unusable.

Information Retrieval and Storage

The communication center should have immediate access to essential information that may be needed in dispatching assistance to fires and emergencies. The data files must include a complete geofile index of all streets, intersections, and related numbering systems in the area. The geofile should also include all target hazards such as schools, hospitals, and major buildings. The system must allow the dispatcher to determine the appropriate response zone and map location for any reported emergency so that the proper units can be dispatched. Maintaining and updating these files is an important on-going function, whether the information is kept in hard-copy form on cards or index systems or in a computer system. The same approach is necessary to keep pre-fire plan information and maps up to date in the communication center, as well as on responding fire apparatus.

Additional information that should be included in the communications center data files includes telephone numbers for responsible parties for major buildings and businesses, utility companies, and other agencies to contact during fires, as well as a variety of other individuals who may have to be notified of, or asked to respond to, certain incidents.

Electronic data processing equipment speeds information retrieval and makes it possible to store and retrieve considerably more data than are available quickly by more conventional means. Computer-aided dispatch systems automate many or all of the dispatch- and information-management functions, including the provision of specific data on individual occupancies. Information available on a particular location may include data on building arrangements, construction, hazards, code-inspection access, water supplies, and even prior fire experience. The system may provide for direct transmission of this information to terminals in responding vehicles or for storage in portable computers or microfiche systems carried in command vehicles.

Station/Personnel Alerting Systems

Some fire departments maintain a 24-hr watch at a console or control room in each fire station. The person on watch is responsible for receiving dispatch messages and controlling alerting devices within the station. Controls for lights, electrically operated doors, traffic-control devices, and similar equipment are usually located at the watch desk. Instead of maintaining a watch in each station, other fire departments control some or all of these devices from the communication center. Radio signals or hard-wired circuits may be used to control equipment from a remote location.

Where stations are staffed entirely by volunteer or on-call personnel, the communication center may alert personnel by activating sirens or horns or by tone activation of radio pagers carried by personnel or kept in their homes.

MAINTENANCE OF FIRE DEPARTMENT EQUIPMENT

The maintenance of fire department apparatus and equipment at peak operating efficiency is a primary fire department responsibility. The safety of the public and of fire department personnel, as well as fire fighting efficiency, depend considerably upon the effectiveness of the maintenance program. When properly cared for, fire apparatus can give years of reliable service. Each fire department needs a clearly established policy concerning maintenance responsibilities and routines to avoid possible equipment failure during operation.

Every fire department should assign an officer the responsibility for apparatus and equipment. This may be a part-time job in small fire departments. This officer should be responsible for the condition, status, and department needs for both apparatus and equipment and should help prepare specifications in accordance with accepted standards for the procurement of new items.

Complete records should be maintained for every piece of apparatus and equipment, showing all repairs and service performed. Service tests of pumping engines should be conducted annually, and test records should be maintained and compared with original equipment performance. Service tests and structural examinations also should be conducted regularly on ground ladders, aerial ladders, elevating platforms, and other equipment. Tests should be conducted in accordance with NFPA 1931, *Standard on Service Tests for Fire Department Ground Ladders*, and NFPA 1904, *Standard for Testing Fire Department Aerial Ladders and Elevating Platforms*.

A preventive maintenance program should be set up for fire apparatus and equipment, with all minor repairs made promptly. Since fire apparatus is subject to frequent starts and relatively high-speed operation with cold engines, this approach becomes critical to maintaining dependable apparatus.

Much routine apparatus maintenance is the responsibility of the assigned apparatus operators under the direction of company officers. This maintenance should be carried out on a daily and weekly basis following a set checklist. Among the things for which apparatus operators are responsible are keeping the fuel tank full, checking the engine oil level, checking the batteries, maintaining tire pressure at the specified level, maintaining the water level in the radiator, keeping the apparatus water tanks full, and checking all lights. All items needing repair should be reported immediately and the work completed without avoidable delay. Frequently used parts should be in stock or readily available, and the maintenance or service manuals delivered with each piece of apparatus should be followed.

Apparatus taken out of service for repairs or maintenance should be replaced by reliable, properly equipped reserve apparatus. Every fire department should have at least one reserve pumping engine in good, usable condition. Some fire departments have a reserve fleet ranging from 25 to 33 percent of their first-line equipment, including reserve ladder trucks, rescue trucks, and ambulances. This reserve apparatus also may be placed in service by off-shift personnel for major fires or during periods of peak activity.

Minor equipment and power tools also need routine maintenance and servicing. All equipment should be inspected periodically and repaired or replaced as needed.

Every fire department should have a repair and servicing facility to care for its apparatus and equipment. This shop should have the necessary work benches, ample power outlets, and jacks and hoists to handle heavy equipment. The shop should meet all fire-protection standards for a repair garage, and areas used for painting should be properly protected. A shop facility should include an equipment repair section and a section or area where fire hose and couplings can be repaired properly. In some cases, pump-testing equipment is provided at the shop; in others, these facilities are located at the fire department training center.

Many fire departments employ mechanics to maintain and service apparatus and to respond to fires to oversee the mechanical equipment operation and to perform emergency repairs. Many departments also have maintenance personnel on 24-hr call. Some small fire departments without full-time maintenance personnel have one or more fire fighters who fill in as part-time mechanics in addition to their fire fighter duties.

In some communities, apparatus repair is assigned to a municipal service garage. This arrangement may be satisfactory if a regular fire apparatus repair and service section is provided and staffed by persons qualified for the specialized nature of the work and available on a 24-hr basis. Often, general mechanics do not have the necessary skills to carry out a proper fire department maintenance program, and fire apparatus may receive a low priority in a municipal repair garage. In some cases, it is advisable to send apparatus to the manufacturer for major repairs or to be rebuilt.

TRAINING

The level of performance demonstrated by a fire department is usually a good indication of the type, quantity, and quality of the training provided. In addition to departmental training programs, most states provide some type of fire service training that, depending upon the state, ranges from basic fire fighter training to fire department management programs.

Large city and county fire departments usually have their own training facilities and full-time training staffs. In these larger departments, training takes several forms, starting with continuing in-service training conducted daily by company officers. This may be supplemented by scheduled programs on various subjects at a fire training center and by specialized training for drivers, apparatus operators, and other personnel. Additional officer training may be conducted monthly or annually at a fire college or a staff-and-command school. New fire fighters normally undergo an intensive recruit training class before they are assigned to regular duty. Recruit training normally requires two to three months of full-time participation.

Training Objectives

The goal of any fire department training program should be to teach each person in the department to operate at acceptable performance levels for his or her rank and assignment. Ideally, training courses should have their own instructional objectives, a list of enabling objectives showing how the instructional objectives can be reached, and stated methods that explain how anticipated or desired behavioral changes can be measured.

State Fire Training Programs

Many state fire training programs operate under the umbrella of an educational agency within the state—usually vocational or occupational education—or under the auspices of a state university or college. In other cases, the director of fire training operates under the state fire marshal's office. In Delaware, for example, the state fire training program operates under a commission appointed by, and reporting directly to, the governor.

Some state fire training directors have no full-time instructors, while others have a small cadre of full-time senior instructors or supervisors who, in addition to their teaching functions, may be responsible for assigning and supervising part-time field instructors, developing instructional outlines, developing and producing audio-visual training aids and props, and monitoring the records required for a state program. State programs also may train recruit fire fighters for small departments. Additionally, state programs provide training for specialists within the service, conduct seminars on material of current interest and importance, and serve as a valuable informational reference.

National Fire Academy

The National Fire Academy (NFA) is a center for fire-protection-related education, information, and expertise, aimed at improving the professional development of fire service personnel and allied professionals. The academy offers a wide variety of courses, including incident management, fire technology, and fire prevention. These courses are delivered through an on-campus program and an extensive outreach program.

The NFA's resident-student program consists of courses conducted at the National Emergency Training Center (NETC) in Emmitsburg, MD. Students, mainly from the fire service, attend these courses at minimal cost through a stipend program that covers the costs of tuition, travel, and accommodations in campus dormitories. Most of the individual courses last for two weeks and are linked so students can either advance through various levels in a particular subject or develop management expertise in a variety of subjects.

The outreach program provides short-term courses, generally two days long, to students all over the U.S. These courses are coordinated through state and local training agencies and are concentrated on weekends to allow maximum participation from both career and volunteer fire service personnel. These courses are designed to be transferred to state and local delivery systems for wider distribution through an increasing network of instructors.

The National Fire Academy's full-time professional faculty and staff is supplemented by a large network of adjunct faculty members who teach courses in their particular areas of expertise. Both resident and adjunct faculty include individuals from the fire service and other backgrounds. The main campus provides classroom space, laboratories, educational resources, and living quarters for several hundred students.

The Open Learning Fire Service Program is an additional aspect of the National Fire Academy educational system. Through a network of accredited colleges and universities, this program coordinates independent-study programs for fire service personnel. Students may earn degrees through these educational institutions by combining a series of upper-division fire-related courses with credits in related subjects. The open learning concept provides a high degree of flexibility for individual students taking correspondence courses and seminars, and it provides them with opportunities to transfer credits earned at other educational institutions.

Fire Service Organization Training Activities

Several fire service organizations sponsor conferences and seminars as a part of an annual meeting or as separate courses on materials of current importance. Examples of these organizations include the National Fire Protection Association (NFPA), the International Society of Fire Service Instructors (ISFSI), the International Association of Fire Chiefs (IAFC), and local and state fire service organizations. Numerous training manuals are published by the International Fire Service Training Association (IFSTA).

Utility Company and Private Agency Training Programs

At the local and regional levels, training programs are available from major utility companies; state agencies, such as those concerned with forestry, public safety, and civil defense; and private agencies that interact in various ways with the fire service.

College Training Programs

There are hundreds of college fire science programs in the U.S., most offered by community and junior colleges on either a full- or part-time basis. In most cases, an associate degree is awarded upon successful completion of the program, and some institutions award certificates for partial completion. A few four-year degree programs that emphasize fire service management are also offered. Masters' programs are offered by the University of Maryland and Worcester Polytechnic Institute in Massachusetts.

College fire science programs usually are designed to supplement, though not replace, the training provided by fire departments and state training agencies. The curriculum design for many such programs emphasizes the arts and sciences, with special courses in fire protection subjects that are beyond the scope of basic fire training programs. A majority of programs emphasize supervisory and management skills along with fire science.

Certification Standards

In an effort to lend uniformity to fire service training, the National Professional Qualifications Board for the Fire Service has developed a set of standards based on performance objectives. The standards, developed through NFPA, are as follows:

NFPA 1001, *Standard for Fire Fighter Professional Qualifications*.

NFPA 1002, *Standard for Fire Apparatus Driver/Operator Professional Qualifications*.

NFPA 1003, *Standard for Airport Fire Fighter Professional Qualifications*.

NFPA 1004, *Standard on Fire Fighter Medical Technicians Professional Qualifications*.

NFPA 1021, *Standard for Fire Officer Professional Qualifications*.

NFPA 1031, *Standard for Professional Qualifications for Fire Inspector, Fire Investigator, and Fire Prevention Education Officer*.

NFPA 1041, *Standard for Fire Service Instructor Professional Qualifications*.

These standards are being applied by several states and municipalities. Some states offer formal certification. The certification program may be mandatory or voluntary, depending upon the authority having jurisdiction over the process, and may provide for certification in a number of areas and levels. Formal certification provides a standard of preparation and performance for various positions and may be applied to hiring, promoting, retaining, and transferring personnel.

Training Records and Reports

Recent court decisions regarding job-related examinations have placed additional importance on training records and personnel evaluations. Training records and reports are particularly important at the entry or recruit level. Training records should be clear and concise and should document a fire fighter's advancement in the department. The content of training records and reports is particularly important when personnel are evaluated for pay increases and promotions. In larger departments, training records may be integrated into a larger management information system along with other personnel and management data.

EMERGENCY MEDICAL SERVICE

Emergency medical service (EMS) has become an important function of many fire departments. While many fire departments have operated ambulance services for decades, the major growth in this area has occurred since 1970, stimulated by higher standards for patient care, training, and equipment. Increased interest from the public, the medical community, and local government in emergency medical service delivery has prompted many fire departments to increase their participation in EMS, and the quality of EMS delivery consequently has improved greatly.

The addition of EMS delivery to a fire department is a natural extension of responsibilities and often can increase organizational productivity without compromising fire protection. Fire service personnel are already oriented toward delivering emergency service and assisting citizens. Fire stations are decentralized to provide rapid response to all areas, while fire communications systems are designed to receive emergency requests from the public and dispatch assistance without delay, both of which are required to provide effective EMS delivery.

The frequency of emergency medical service calls in a community generally outnumbers fire alarms by two to one. Although responding to EMS calls places an increased workload on fire fighting companies, it has proven very efficient in many jurisdictions. Providing basic EMS equipment on engine and ladder companies, with EMT-certified fire fighters, allows these units to respond to most life-threatening situations. First-responders and EMTs are generally backed up by paramedic personnel responding on ambulances or rescue vehicles. In some fire departments, all personnel are trained and certified at the EMT level, and dual-role paramedics are assigned to engine and ladder companies.

There is some concern that increased commitment to emergency medical service will have a detrimental effect on the fire department's ability to provide effective fire suppression. This has not proven to be a problem in most cases, although fire department administrators must be constantly aware of this possible conflict. In extremely busy areas, it may be necessary to provide fire protection and EMS with separate resources.

HAZARDOUS MATERIALS

For many years, fire departments have responded to incidents involving hazardous materials as an unofficial extension of their responsibilities for life safety and property protection. Fire departments could provide the personnel protective equipment and breathing apparatus that was necessary to deal with hazardous material leaks and spills. In recent years, hazardous materials, including prevention of spills, regulation, and incident response, have become a major responsibility for many fire departments.

Every fire fighter should be able to recognize a hazardous materials incident and to take actions that will reduce the immediate risk to the public and to emergency personnel. Many fire departments have chosen to provide hazardous materials response teams, using personnel with advanced training and specialized equipment to evaluate hazardous materials incidents and to take action to control leaks and spills. (Refer to Section 9, Chapters 2, 14, and 15 for additional information on hazardous materials incidents.)

BIBLIOGRAPHY

NFPA Codes, Standards, and Recommended Practices.

Reference to the following NFPA codes, standards, and recommended practices will provide further information about fire department operations. (See the latest *NFPA Catalog* for availability of current editions of the following documents.)

NFPA 295, *Standard for Wildfire Control.*

NFPA 402M, *Manual for Aircraft Rescue and Fire Fighting Operational Procedures.*

NFPA 403, *Recommended Practice for Aircraft Rescue and Fire Fighting Services at Airports and Heliports.*

NFPA 704, *Standard System for the Identification of the Fire Hazards of Materials.*

NFPA 901, *Uniform Coding for Fire Protection.*

NFPA 1001, *Standard for Fire Fighter Professional Qualifications.*

NFPA 1002, *Standard for Fire Apparatus Driver/Operator Professional Qualifications.*

NFPA 1003, *Standard for Airport Fire Fighter Professional Qualifications.*

NFPA 1004, *Standard on Fire Fighter Medical Technicians Professional Qualifications.*

NFPA 1021, *Standard for Fire Officer Professional Qualifications.*

NFPA 1031, *Standard for Professional Qualifications for Fire Inspector, Fire Investigator, and Fire Prevention Education Officer.*

NFPA 1041, *Standard for Fire Service Instructor Professional Qualifications.*

NFPA 1201, *Recommendations for Developing Fire Protection Services for the Public.*

NFPA 1221, *Standard for the Installation, Maintenance, and Use of Public Fire Service Communications Systems.*

NFPA 1401, *Recommended Proactice for Fire Protection Training Reports and Records.*

NFPA 1403, *Standard on Live Fire Training Evolutions in Structures.*

NFPA 1404, *Standard for a Fire Department Self-Contained Breathing Apparatus Program.*

NFPA 1410, *A Training Standard on Initial Fire Attack.*

NFPA 1500, *Standard for Fire Department Safety and Health Program.*

NFPA 1501, *Standard for Fire Department Safety Officer.*

NFPA 1561, *Standard for Fire Department Incident Management System.*

NFPA 1904, *Standard for Testing Fire Department Aerial Ladders and Elevating Platforms.*

NFPA 1901, *Standard for Pumper Fire Apparatus.*

NFPA 1902, *Standard for Initial Attack Fire Apparatus.*

NFPA 1903, *Standard for Mobile Water Supplies.*

NFPA 1911,*Standard on Service Tests of Pumps on Fire Department Apparatus.*

NFPA 1914, *Standard for Testing Fire Department Aerial Devices.*

NFPA 1921, *Standard for Fire Department Portable Pumping Units.*

NFPA 1931, *Standard on Design, and Design Verification Tests for Fire Department Ground Ladders.*

NFPA 1932, *Standard on Service Tests for Fire Department Ground Ladders.*

NFPA 1961, *Standard for Fire Hose.*

NFPA 1962, *Standard for the Care, Use, and Maintenance of Fire Hose, Including Connections and Nozzles.*

NFPA 1963, *Standard for Screw Threads and Gaskets for Fire Hose Connections.*

NFPA 1964, *Standard on Spray Nozzles (Shutoff and Tip).*

NFPA 1971, *Standard on Protective Clothing for Structural Fire Fighting.*

NFPA 1972, *Standard on Structural Fire Fighters' Helmets.*

NFPA 1973, *Standard on Gloves for Structural Fire Fighters.*

NFPA 1974, *Standard on Protective Footwear for Structural Fire Fighting.*

NFPA 1975, *Standard on Station/Work Uniforms.*

NFPA 1981, *Standard on Self-Contained Breathing Apparatus for Fire Fighters.*

NFPA 1982, *Standard on Personal Alert Safety Systems (PASS) for Fire Fighters.*

NFPA 1983, *Standard on Fire Service Life Safety Rope, Harness, and Hardware.*

NFPA 1991, *Standard on Vapor-Protective Suits for Hazardous Chemical Emergencies.*

NFPA 1992, *Standard on Liquid Splash Protective Suits for Hazardous Chemical Emergencies.*

NFPA 1993, *Standard on Support Function Protective Garments for Hazardous Chemical Operations.*

Additional Readings

Air Operations for Forest, Brush and Grass Fires, National Fire Protection Association, Quincy, MA, 1986.

Bachtler, J. R., *Fire Instructors Training Guide*, 2nd ed., Fire Engineering, New York, 1989.

Bahme, C. W., *ed., Fire Officer's Guide to Extinguishing Systems*, 4th rev., National Fire Protection Association, Quincy, MA, 1977.

Barker, J. A., "Training: The Key to Fire Safety," *Fire Prevention*, No. 224 (Nov. 1989), pp. 28-30.

Bennett, J., "High Rise: Be Ready to Fight the Battle," *Fire Engineering*, Vol. 141, No. 8 (Aug. 1988), p. 4.

Brannigan, F. L., *Building Construction for the Fire Service*, 2nd ed., National Fire Protection Association, Quincy, MA, 1983.

Brunacini, A. V., *Fire Command*, National Fire Protection Association, Quincy, MA, 1985.

Building Construction for Fire Suppression Forces, National Fire Academy, Emmitsburg, MD, 1986.

Callahan, T., *Fire Service and the Law*, 2nd ed., National Fire Protection Association, Quincy, MA, 1987.

Carter, H. R., *Management in the Fire Service*, 2nd ed., National Fire Protection Association, Quincy, MA, 1989.

Casper, D. E., *Trends in Urban Fire Fighting: Periodical Literature, 1980-1984*, Vance Bibliographies, Monticello, IL, 1985.

Clarke, W. E., *Fire Fighting Principles and Practices*, Fire Engineering Book Service, New York, 1974.

Coggan, R. S., "Taking Command to the Maximum," *Fire Command*, Vol. 56, No. 8 (Aug. 1989), pp. 23-29.

Cooney, B., "Fire Service Response to Chemical Incidents," *Fire International*, Vol. 11, No. 104, 1987, pp. 39, 42-43.

Davis, P. O. and Daston, C. O., "Physiological Aspects of Fire Fighting," *Fire Technology*, Vol. 23, No. 4, 1987, pp. 280-291.

Delesderrier, J. M., "New Methods and Means of Fire-Fighting —How to Make Fire-Fighting More Scientific," *Proceedings* of the Conference on New Technology to Reduce Fire Losses and Costs, Elsivier, 1986, pp. 272-275.

Dunn, V., "Safe Firefighting Practices," *Fire Engineering*, Vol. 143, No. 1, 1990, p. 37.

Ennis, A. M., "Getting Water to Rural Fires," *Fire Engineering*, July 1970.

Erven, L. W., *Fire Chief's Handbook Study Guide*, Davis Pub., Santa Cruz, CA, 1979.

Fire/Emergency Services Sourcebook, Specialized Publication Services, New York, 1989.

Fire Protection Guide on Hazardous Materials, 9th ed., National Fire Protection Association, Quincy, MA, 1986.

Fire Service Directory of Training and Information, Specialized Publication Services, New York, 1989.

Gaines, G. A., *Firefighting Operations in Garden Apartments and Townhouses*, R. J. Brady, Bowie, MD, 1978.

Grant, R. W., *Public Fire Safety Inspections*, National Fire Protection Association, Quincy, MA, 1967.

Haurum, G., "Standards of Fire Cover," *Fire Safety Journal*, Vol. 8, No. 3, 1985, pp. 239-245.

Jacobs, D. T., *Physical Fitness and the Public Safety*, 3rd ed., National Fire Protection Association, Quincy, MA, 1989.

Lalloo, R., "Fire Service Involvment with Nuclear Reactors," *Fire Engineers Journal*, Vol. 49, No. 154 (Sept.1989), pp. 17-21.

Larkin, S. R., "Training for Success," *Fire Command*, Vol. 56, No. 8 (Aug. 1989), p. 38.

Lesak, D. M., "Operational Decision Making," *Fire Engineering*, Vol. 142, No. 6, 1989, pp. 63-65, 68-69.

Louhevaara, V., Sjoblom, T, and Venalainen, J. M., "Physiological Strain in Actual Fire Fighting Tasks," *Proceedings* of the 24th Annual Symposium of the Survival and Flight Equipment Association, SAFE, Van Nuys, CA, 1987, pp. 229-231.

McDonald, B. R., "Training for Chemical Emergencies," *Fire Command*, Vol. 56, No. 3 (March 1989), pp. 30-35.

McKay, J. C. and Mason, B., "Improved Fire Training Facility Plan," *Military Engineer*, Vol. 80, No. 523, 1988, pp. 457-458.

Mendes, R. F., *Fighting High-Rise Building Fires: Tactics and Logistics*, National Fire Protection Association, Quincy, MA, 1975.

Moulton, G. A., *ed., NFPA Inspection Manual*, 5th ed., National Fire Protection Association, Quincy, MA, 1983.

Murry, L. S., "Training for the Year 2000," *Fire Command*, Vol. 56, No. 3 (March 1989), pp. 16-18.

Obermayer, R., "Risk/Benefit Analysis on the Fireground," *Fire Engineering*, Vol. 142, No. 3, 1989, pp. 67-69.

Page, J. O., *Emergency Medical Services*, National Fire Protection Association, Quincy, MA, 1978.

Richman, H., *Engine Company Fireground Operations*, 2nd ed., National Fire Protection Association, Quincy, MA, 1986.

Robertson, J. C., "Preparing Fire Service Personnel for Fire Prevention Duties," *Intoduction to Fire Prevention*, 3rd ed., Macmillan, New York, 1989, pp. 99-111.

Soros, C. C., and Lyons, P. R., *Safety in the Fire Service*, National Fire Protection Association, Quincy, MA, 1979.

Storey, T. G., "FOCUS: A Computer Simulation Model for Fire Control Planning." *Fire Technology*, Vol. 8, No. 2 (May 1972), pp. 91-103.

Swift, I., "NFPA 68 Guide for Venting of Deflagrations: What's New and How It Affects You," *Proceedings* of the American Institute of Chemical Engineers National Meeting, AIChE, 1988, p. 30.

Tobey, S., "Hazardous Materials Training, Michigan-Style," *Fire Engineering*, Vol. 143, No. 4, 1990, p. 89.

Tobin, E. T., Davis, J. B., and Mandt, C., "Automated Forest Fire Dispatching — A Progress Report," *Fire Technology*, Vol. 5, No. 2 (May 1969), pp. 122-129.

Walsh, C. V. and Marks, L., *Firefighting Strategy and Leadership*, McGraw-Hill, New York, 1976.

Williams, L. and Carter, F. A., "Fight or Flight," *Fire Engineering*, Vol. 140, No. 4, 1987, pp. 17-23.

Willis, B. N., "The Backbone of the Bureau," *Fire Command*, Vol. 57, No. 3 (March 1990), pp. 12-15.

The following additional readings are published by the International Fire Service Training Association, Oklahoma State University:

Essentials of Fire Fighting

Forcible Entry

Fire Fighter Study Guide

Ground Ladder Practices

Public Fire Education

Fire Hose Practices

Salvage and Overhaul Practices

Fire Stream Practices

Fire Apparatus Practices

Fire Ventilation Practices

Fire Service Rescue and Protective Breathing Practices

Fire Service First Aid Practices

Fire Prevention and Inspection Practices

Fire Service Practices for Volunteer Fire Departments

Fire Service Orientation and Indoctrination

Fire Service Training Programs

Photography for the Fire Service

Water Supplies for Fire Protection

Firefighter Safety

Aircraft Fire Protection and Rescue Procedures

Ground Cover Fire Fighting Practices

The Fire Department Officer

Fire Department Facilities, Planning, and Procedures

Fire Service Instructor Training

Leadership in the Fire Service

IFSTA Source Material Reference Guide

FIRE PREVENTION AND CODE ENFORCEMENT

Revised by Robert B. "Skip" Smith

Fire prevention includes all fire service activity that decreases the incidence of uncontrolled fire. Usually, fire prevention methods used by the fire service focus on inspection, which includes engineering and code enforcement, public firesafety education, and fire investigation.

Inspection, including enforcement, is the legal means of discovering and correcting deficiencies that pose a threat to life and property from fire. Enforcement is implemented when other methods fail. Education informs and instructs the general public about the dangers of fire and about firesafe behavior. Fire investigation aids fire prevention efforts by indicating problem areas that may require corrective educational efforts, inspection emphasis, or legislation. Good engineering practices, including plans review—another fire prevention method—can provide built-in safeguards that help prevent fires from starting and limit the spread of fire should it occur.

In the United States, the full value of fire prevention was not realized until fire departments and agencies began to compile meaningful information concerning the causes and circumstances of fires. Such information highlighted problem areas and led progressive departments to initiate more effective fire prevention efforts. The results of fire prevention efforts are borne out statistically, every year confirming the effectiveness of fire prevention programs. Fire prevention, as the most important priority in cutting fire losses, received an endorsement in 1973, when the National Commission on Fire Prevention and Control published the results of its in-depth study on the fire problem in America. In its report *America Burning*, the commission emphasized the necessity of increased fire prevention activities to reduce fire. It was the commission's position that increasing emphasis on fire prevention would measurably affect the U.S. fire loss picture. Statistics validate this position for areas in which fire prevention activities have been implemented.

FIRE PREVENTION PERSONNEL

Effective fire prevention depends on a personnel network technically capable and motivated to enforce fire codes, educate the general public, and investigate fire causes. This network of people is usually organized at the state, county, and/or local level.

State and Provincial Fire Marshal/Commissioner

Most states have offices to oversee certain phases of fire protection. (See Table 9-7A.) The state's chief fire protection administrator usually is called the state fire marshal. The organization of state fire marshal offices differs from state to state. (See Table 9-7B.) Most fire marshals receive their authority from the state legislature and are answerable to the governor, a high state officer, or a fire commission. In some states, the fire marshal's office may be a division of the state insurance department, state police, department of public safety, commerce department, or other state agency. Some offices are organized as separate state agencies.

State fire marshals' offices normally function in areas beyond the scope of municipal, county, or fire-district organizations. Depending upon the authority outlined in enabling legislation or administrative regulations, state fire-marshal offices may have combination responsibilities in the following areas: code enforcement, fire prevention inspections, plans review, fire and arson investigation, fire-data collection and analysis, fire service training, public fire education, fire legislation development, explosives and other hazardous materials regulation, manufactured-housing regulations, mobile-home regulations, electrical inspections, and state agency and public fire protection consulting.

State fire marshals may share responsibility with local fire officials, or each may have specifically defined areas of concern. Local fire protection officials sometimes are granted the authority to act as agents for the state in stipulated areas of inspection, enforcement, and investigation.

At the national level in Canada, the Dominion Fire Commissioner is responsible for firesafety enforcement in all nonmilitary government properties and for gathering national fire statistics. The Canadian Forces Fire Marshal

Mr. Smith is the former executive secretary of the Fire Marshals Association of North America.

TABLE 9-7A. *Functions of the State Fire Marshal's Office*

STATE	Code Enforcement	Fire & Arson Investigation	Plans Review	Fire Prevention Inspections	Fire Data Collection	Fire Data Analysis	Fire Service Training	Public Fire Education	Fire Legislation Development	Manufactured Housing Regulations	Mobile Home Regulations	Electrical Inspections	Boiler Inspections	Distribution of Funds to Fire Dept.
Alabama	X	X	X	X	X	X	X	X				X		
Alaska	X	X	X	X	X	X	X	X	X					
Arizona	X	X	X	X	X		X	X	X					
Arkansas	X	X	X	X			X	X	X					
California	X	X	X	X	X	X	X	X	X					
Colorado										X				
Connecticut	X	X	X	X	X	X	X	X	X				X	
Delaware	X	X	X	X	X	X			X					
Florida	X	X	X	X	X	X	X	X	X	X	X	X	X	
Georgia	X	X	X	X				X			X	X		
Hawaii*			NONE											
Idaho	X	X		X	X	X			X	X				
Illinois	X	X	X	X	X	X	X	X	X				X	
Indiana	X	X	X	X	X	X	X	X	X					
Iowa	X	X	X	X	X	X		X	X	X	X			
Kansas	X	X	X	X	X	X		X	X					
Kentucky	X	X	X	X	X	X	X	X	X	X	X	X	X	X
Louisiana	X	X	X	X	X	X		X	X	X	X	X	X	
Maine	X	X	X	X	X	X		X	X					
Maryland	X	X	X	X	X	X		X	X			X		
Massachusetts	X	X	X	X	X	X		X	X					
Michigan	X	X	X	X	X	X	X	X	X					
Minnesota	X	X	X	X	X	X	X	X	X					
Mississippi	X	X		X	X	X	X			X	X			
Missouri		X	X	X	X	X	X		X				X	
Montana	X	X	X	X	X	X		X	X					
Nebraska	X	X	X	X	X	X		X	X					
Nevada	X	X	X	X			X	X	X			X		
New Hampshire†	X	X	X	X	X	X		X	X			X		
New Jersey	X			X	X	X	X	X	X					X
New Mexico	X	X		X	X	X	X	X	X					X
New York	X	X	X	X	X	X	X	X	X					X
North Carolina	X		X		X	X	X	X	X	X	X	X		
North Dakota	X	X	X	X	X	X	X	X	X					
Ohio	X	X	X	X	X	X	X	X	X					
Oklahoma	X	X	X	X	X	X		X	X					
Oregon	X	X	X	X	X	X	X	X	X					
Pennsylvania	X	X	X		X									
Rhode Island	X	X	X	X	X	X	X	X	X					
South Carolina	X	X	X	X		X	X	X	X			X		X
South Dakota	X	X	X	X	X	X	X	X	X				X	X
Tennessee	X	X	X	X	X	X		X	X	X	X	X		
Texas	X	X	X	X	X	X		X						
Utah	X	X	X	X	X	X	X	X	X					
Vermont‡	X	X	X	X	X	X		X	X		X	X	X	
Virginia	X		X	X										
Washington	X	X	X		X	X		X	X					
West Virginia	X	X	X	X	X	X	X	X	X		X	X		X
Wisconsin#		X												
Wyoming	X	X	X	X	X	X	X	X	X			X		

Footnotes:

* Hawaii: State fire marshal's office disbanded April 1979; all functions transferred to county fire marshals' offices.

† New Hampshire: Division of fire service created July 1, 1989.

‡Vermont: Department of Labor and Industry—fire prevention division.

\# Wisconsin: Fire and arson investigation is a function of fire marshal. Department of Justice; other functions Chief of Fire Protection, Department of Industry, Labor, and Human Relations.

TABLE 9-7B. *State Fire Marshal Organizational Patterns*

Under Department of Insurance	
	Alabama
	Florida
	Idaho
	Mississippi
	New Mexico
	North Carolina
	Tennessee
	Texas
	Washington
Under Department of Public Safety	
	Alaska
	Colorado
	Connecticut
	Iowa
	Louisiana
	Maine
	Maryland
	Massachusetts
	Minnesota
	Missouri
	New Hampshire
	Utah
Under a Separate Government Department	
	California
	Illinois
	Indiana
	Montana (Justice–Attorney General)
	Kansas
	Nebraska
	Nevada
	Oklahoma (Separate Agency)
	Oregon
	South Carolina
	Wisconsin–Fire Investigation (Justice–Attorney General)
	Wyoming
Under a Regulatory Agency	
	Arizona
	Kentucky
	New Jersey
	South Dakota
	Vermont
	Virginia
Under State Police	
	Arkansas
	Michigan
	Pennsylvania
Under Cabinet Level Official	
	Georgia (Controller General)
	New York (Secretary of State)
	North Dakota (Attorney General)
	Ohio (Director of Commerce)
	Rhode Island (Governor's Office)
Under State Fire Commission	
	Delaware
	West Virginia

oversees properties of the armed forces, where fire protection facilities include a number of operating fire departments.

In Canada, each of the provinces has a provincial fire commissioner or fire marshal, while the two territories have territorial fire marshals. In most cases, the provincial/territorial fire officer has a wide variety of responsibilities, including code enforcement, fire service training, operation of fire reporting systems, and fire investigation, as well as support of local fire departments. The Association of Canadian Fire Marshals and Fire Commissioners consists of the previously mentioned dominion and armed-forces fire officials, plus each provincial and territorial fire commissioner or fire marshal. The association exerts a major influence on firesafety policy in Canada.

Chief of Fire Prevention or Local Fire Marshal

Because of the importance of fire prevention activities, certain members of the department should specialize in fire prevention functions. Staff size of a fire prevention division, bureau, or fire marshal's office will depend upon the community's needs and the department size. The division may be divided into specialized subsections addressing administration; fire prevention, code inspections, and enforcement; engineering; public education; and investigation. (See Table 9-7C.) These subsections are headed by subordinate officers.

The fire prevention division personnel should consist of those department members best qualified for this work. In addition, qualified technical specialists should be available when possible—the department's overall effectiveness depends upon the technical skills the fire prevention personnel possess.

The laws of the state, county, municipality, or fire district often delegate responsibility and authority for fire prevention to the fire chief or fire department head, who may then delegate this authority to an individual or division, depending upon the size of the department. In some states, the local fire marshal's authority and area of enforcement responsibility is derived from state laws, independent of or in addition to the powers and duties of the fire department chief.

The fire chief may directly supervise fire prevention activities in smaller departments. In larger departments, the division head should be a high-ranking chief officer, functioning as a staff officer to the fire chief. The chief officer for the fire prevention activities may be described as fire marshal, chief of the fire prevention division, or chief fire inspector.

Fire Inspector or Fire Prevention Officer

Fire inspectors or fire prevention officers should be selected for these tasks based on their technical training, expertise, and their ability to motivate people. Individuals in this position are responsible for conducting fire inspections and also may be responsible for division duties, including fire investigations, public education, or plans review, among others.

An inspector conducting an inspection should be able to convince property owners or occupants to maintain firesafe conditions. The inspector who relies only on police power cannot accomplish as much as the inspector who relies on salesmanship. Strict enforcement of the fire law of the jurisdiction is necessary to achieve compliance and to assure firesafe conditions in the community.

Plans Review Specialist

The review of plans and specifications is a code-enforcement process intended to ensure compliance with the fire protection and life-safety provisions of the building code, as well as the fire prevention code. Individuals in plans review must be technically proficient in both the intent and the letter of the applicable codes. The fire department's plans-review specialist examines site plans, building and fire protection system plans, and specifications and may prepare recommendations or consult with

TABLE 9-7C. ***Sample Organization of Local Fire Prevention Functions in the Fire Marshal's Office***

	Administraton	Fire Prevention, Code Inspections, and Enforcement	Construction Plans and Specification Review	Public Fire Education	Fire Investigation	Research, Statistics, and Evaluation
Personnel:	Fire Marshal Secretarial Staff Clerical Staff	Fire Inspector Fire Officer Fire Company Personnel	Fire Protection Officer Fire Protection Engineer Plans Review Specialist	Public Fire Education Officer Fire Officer Fire Inspector Fire Fighter	Fire Records Specialist Programmers Statisticians	
Functions and Activities:	Overall Supervision Policy Determination Authority Having Jurisdiction Coordination Office Planning Agency Liaison Budget Support	Inspections Permits Violations Summons Court Cases Complaints Night Inspections Red Tags Hazardous Materials	Plans Review Specification Review Consultations On-Site Inspections Certificate of Occupancy Sign-Off Systems Testing Condemnations Use Permits Liaison with: Public Works Building Electrical Mechanical Zoning Housing	Fire Prevention Behavior Education Fire Safety Behavior Education Special Groups Seasonal Programs Juvenile Fire Setters Special Programs Sprinkler Detection EDITH Clean-up Etc.	Fire Cause Determination Fire Investigation Arrest Case Preparation Courtroom Testimony New Products Evaluation New Methods, Approaches, and Alternatives Liaison with: Prosecutor Arson Task Force Local, State, Federal Investigative/ Police Agencies Insurance Interests	Property Files Violation Status Reports: Monthly Quarterly Annual by Special Fire Experience Statistics

individuals involved in building construction, remodeling, or renovations. The plans-review specialist shall regularly interact with other public safety officials and agencies at the local, state, and federal level, including building public works, zoning, health, and others, to ensure the construction of firesafe, code-conforming buildings.

Fire Protection Engineer

Due to the complexity and magnitude of fire protection problems, the services of fire protection engineers (FPEs) can be beneficial. Fire protection engineers may be employed on a consulting basis or as full-time staff engineers. The staff fire protection engineer contributes a high level of technical ability to the plans review process, interpretations, consultations, and the preparation of recommendations for a broad range of fire protection problems. The fire protection engineer's credentials, based on professional training, are recognized by architects, builders, and other professionals involved in the building process.

Fire Prevention Education Officer

The public fire protection education officer creates public awareness of fire as a personal, family, business, and community concern, and then strives to motivate the general public to do something about fire risks, based on proper firesafe behavior. The personnel selected for this function should be knowledgeable in a wide area of fire technology and be able to develop and present effective fire prevention and firesafety programs. This job requires someone with the imagination, creativity, motivation, communication skills, and adaptability needed to develop and convey firesafety programs to all segments of the community.

Depending upon the size of the department and the type of fire prevention and firesafety program it undertakes, all levels of fire department personnel can and should participate in presenting the firesafety and prevention message to the community. Non-uniformed personnel, senior citizens, and citizens with education backgrounds also are being used successfully by the fire department in this area of fire prevention.

Fire Investigators

Fire cause determination and subsequent investigation can be the responsibility of the fire department or of outside agencies. When a fire department is responsible, fire cause detection and investigation may be assigned to the fire chief, fire marshal, battalion chiefs, company officers, fire inspectors, or other personnel specially trained as fire investigators.

Investigative personnel should be perceptive, inquisitive, and thorough in determining facts and conducting an investigation. Investigation experience should be supported by training in areas such as chemistry, criminal law, forensics, and criminal investigation. An increasing number of progressive departments have fire investigation personnel trained in appropriate fields of criminal justice and provided with police powers.

National Professional Qualifications

Professional Qualifications Standards for fire service career positions are the responsibility of the Professional Qualifications Correlating Committee. Three of the ten standards are of particular interest to the fire prevention community. An interest in the field should include a review of the latest editions of NFPA 1031, *Standard for Professional*

Qualifications for Fire Inspector; NFPA 1033, *Standard for Professional Qualifications for Fire Investigator*; NFPA 1035, *Standard for Professional Qualifications for Public Fire Educator*.

Certification to the career levels defined in these Standards is accomplished by agencies based on third party accreditation. Accreditation for the fire service is currently available through the National Professional Qualifications Board of the National Board on Fire Service Professional Qualifications (NBFSPQ) and the Fire Service Accreditation Congress of Oklahoma State University.

Programs such as the NFPA Fire Inspector Certification Program for fire inspector certification to levels I and II are available on a National level with Accreditation from the Professional Qualifications Board.

FIRE PREVENTION INSPECTIONS

Fire prevention inspections are conducted by state or local fire department personnel in compliance with laws and ordinances which usually require specific fire inspections. Occupancies normally inspected include places of public assembly, educational, institutional, residential (except the interiors of dwellings), mercantile, business, industrial, manufacturing, storage, and special-hazards structures. In addition to such mandatory inspections, the fire department also may conduct voluntary fire inspections, such as home firesafety surveys.

The organization and operation of fire prevention inspection programs varies. Inspections required under the fire prevention code traditionally have been conducted by personnel from the fire prevention division. However, this responsibility is being shared increasingly with fire company personnel. The department's training program must train all its members in fire prevention.

Fire Prevention Inspection Objectives

Inspections conducted as part of code enforcement help to ensure reasonable life-safety conditions within a structure. The condition of exits, interior finish, operation of exit doors, emergency lighting, exit signs, and all fire doors should be inspected. Inspection of exiting facilities should include inspection of the exit discharge area.

Inspections, which are intended to prevent fires from occurring, are effective because the inspector identifies fire hazards that could cause a fire, allow a fire to develop, or allow a fire to spread. In addition to locating and correcting potential fire causes, the fire inspector should check any accumulation of combustible trash and debris, storage practices, maintenance procedures, and safe operation of building utilities.

Inspections determine the proper installation, operation, and maintenance of fire protection features, systems, and appliances within the building. The inspection process should ascertain whether each fire protection system is tested regularly by the fire department or by others.

Fire detection equipment, alarms, annunciation and notification systems, sprinkler-valve operation, supervisory switches, and fire pumps all should be tested regularly as part of the overall inspection process. Other fire protection features, including standpipes and fire escapes, should be tested or closely examined to detect possible malfunctions due to deterioration from weather and corrosion. Portable fire extinguishers should be checked as to proper type, placement, maintenance, testing, and distribution in the structure.

Technical information on a building and its processes should be recorded during the inspection. When used in pre-fire planning, such information can be valuable to the fire department in case of a fire at the property. The type of construction, vertical openings, utility type and placement, fire protection systems, fire department access, tenancy, hazardous materials, or special life-hazard conditions are the kinds of information that should also be noted during inspections and used to develop fire fighting plans.

Inspections provide an opportunity to educate the owners or occupants of a building about firesafe behavior and the need for adequate fire- and life-safety conditions in the areas under their control. "Selling" fire prevention is the key to success in obtaining code compliance, and how fire prevention is "sold" should be an important consideration in training programs for inspection personnel. When inspection programs are properly designed and put into practice, inspectors may achieve more through public education and persuasion than through exercising their enforcement authority. The persuasive effect of the inspector's presence, coupled with the inspector's ability to spot and directly see that hazards are corrected, enhances the effectiveness of the inspection program.

Fire Company Inspections

In many communities, in-service fire suppression personnel conduct most or all regular inspections. Company fire inspection procedures may include conducting building surveys, correcting common problems concerning life-safety conditions, locating and correcting fire hazards, and testing fire protection systems. Inspections also may include checking use and storage of hazardous materials, which may require issuing a hazardous-use permit. The inspection process helps familiarize fire company personnel with individual buildings and locations in their jurisdiction at which they may have to fight fires or perform other emergency duties.

Company inspections usually are conducted in the fire company's first-due area. Inspections and reinspections may be scheduled by the company officer, by the battalion or district officer, or by the fire prevention bureau, according to requirements of the fire prevention code or the department. Before fire fighters perform inspections, they should receive proper training and be qualified and authorized to conduct inspections as fire prevention officers.

The inspection may uncover some situations that are easy to correct or others that require more technical skill. In either case, follow-up responsibilities should be assigned to the fire companies, fire company officers, and district chiefs according to the department's resources. The fire prevention division may help to obtain compliance by building owners after violations are located by fire companies, so it is essential for fire prevention personnel to coordinate their activities closely with those of fire company personnel.

Fire Prevention Division Inspections

In some departments, inspection personnel from the fire prevention division are solely responsible for conducting fire-prevention inspections. The objectives of their inspections, like those of the general inspections performed by fire companies, are to assure compliance with applicable fire codes to locate conditions that may cause a fire or endanger life and property. Each inspection must be thorough. The owner or occupants of the property being inspected must be notified when unsafe conditions are found. Inspections usually are required by law in order to locate any violations and to see that they are corrected. Legal direction is available in such situations if necessary. To perform such work competently, the inspector should have appropriate technical education, specialized training, and experience.

While fire companies perform some or all regular inspections, fire prevention division personnel may be concerned with the initial inspection, follow-up inspections, or enforcement actions necessary to correct fire code violations. Fire prevention division personnel may perform inspections associated with the issuance of permits as required by the fire-prevention code and may be concerned with buildings and premises that require a high level of code application. The inspector may need to confer with the property management or with fire department officers to prepare comprehensive reports, recommendations, or orders.

Both fire company and fire prevention division inspections may reveal conditions hazardous to the health and safety of owners, occupants, and the general public. Even when these hazardous situations are not specifically covered in the fire laws, such conditions must be brought to the attention of the owners or occupants; other inspection authorities should be so notified for the record. This mutual assistance in the inspection of buildings or premises can greatly enhance the level of life safety for the general public. Close cooperation among responsible inspection authorities should be encouraged and, where possible, recognized in municipal ordinances or interdepartmental administrative agreements.

Night inspections of public assembly and business occupancies should be part of routine inspection procedures to assure compliance with occupancy load requirements and to demonstrate that the means of egress are in good operating order.

Inspections based on citizen complaints should be conducted by the fire prevention division in a timely manner. An informed and interested public can be an important asset in uncovering unsafe conditions that might develop after routine inspections are conducted.

Dwelling Inspection Process

Approximately 80 percent of lives lost to fire occur in one- and two-family dwellings. Residential inspections traditionally have not been mandatory because of unfounded concerns associated with the rights of citizens to ensure the sanctity of their homes. For years, however, many fire departments have inspected dwellings on a voluntary, by-invitation, or planned basis and have been successful in reducing the residential fire-loss experience. Inspections of this nature, whether conducted by career or volunteer fire department personnel, should be supported by a strong publicity program. Adequate training must be provided for all personnel involved. Voluntary inspections can be conducted either as a separate part of the fire inspection program or as part of fire prevention programs that include occupant fire escape planning and such practices as Operation EDITH (the acronym for Exit Drills In The Home), smoke detector or residential sprinkler drives, spring cleanup, burn prevention programs, heating firesafety, and so on.

CODE ENFORCEMENT

Fire Prevention Codes

The fire laws of the state, county, fire district, or community delegate general responsibility and authority to the fire officials involved in fire prevention activities. A fire prevention code adopted into law that outlines specific fire prevention requirements and enforcement procedures is essential for an effective fire prevention program.

State law or local ordinances may outline how a fire prevention code is written or adopted. The fire prevention official may have authority to write a local fire prevention code or to adopt a nationally developed code by reference. Using a model fire prevention code is preferable to using one that has been developed locally. Nationally developed consensus codes are based on a broad spectrum of accepted fire prevention experience and may prevent a fire prevention official from being accused of developing a fire code that is too stringent or is biased.

There are additional advantages to adopting a model fire-prevention code. A model code provides a document that may be recognized as authoritative by architects, engineers, and builders who already are familiar with code requirements; provides an interpretation process by which the local official may determine the intent of the code-developing body should a question arise; and allows for periodic revision to reflect new technology and current thinking.

Several organizations publish model fire prevention codes that jurisdictions may adopt by reference for enforcement use. NFPA publishes NFPA 1, *Fire Prevention Code*, which incorporates many NFPA standards by reference. Each of the three major model building code organizations also has developed its own model fire prevention code, which correlates with other codes in its series, such as model building and mechanical codes. Building Officials and Code Administrators International (BOCA) publishes the *BOCA National Fire Prevention Code*; the International Conference of Building Officials (ICBO), in conjunction with the Western Fire Chiefs Association, publishes the *Uniform Fire Code*; and the Southern Building Code Congress International (SBCCI), with assistance from divisions of the International Association of Five Chiefs, publishes the *Standard Fire Prevention Code*. Each code references codes, standards, and other official NFPA documents. These documents are found in the volumes of the NFPA *National Fire Codes* published yearly and considered to be the most authoritative set of firesafety regulations in the U.S.

Code Administration

Most fire prevention codes specify similar enforcement procedures and contain similar requirements. A typical fire prevention code contains an administrative section that establishes the legal framework and organization for the fire prevention program. This section usually outlines the code's applicability to occupancy types and specifies whether it applies to new or existing buildings, or both.

The code may define the enforcement authority of the fire prevention official and assistants, including lawful right of entry for inspections, the right to issue orders to correct hazardous conditions within a building, and the right to order evacuation of an unsafe building or premises. The code may further assign duties that require the investigation of fires and the maintenance of fire records. Permit requirements, conditions, and procedures to issue notices of violation may be included.

The administrative section should be written in such a way as to provide the fire prevention official with as broad a scope of authority as possible. This facilitates enforcement of the fire prevention code, other county or city ordinances, and state laws that pertain to the firesafety of buildings and premises, as well as to the control of hazardous materials within the jurisdiction. This section also may outline the owner's or occupant's responsibility for properly maintaining a structure and its fire protection features.

Subsequent code sections may define important code-related terminology, outline general fire precautions, and establish the proper installation, operation, testing, and maintenance procedures for fire protection systems and appliances within a building. Final sections of the code may outline the use and maintenance of specific types of equipment, processes, and occupancies, or they may describe handling requirements for various types of hazardous or explosive materials. Appendices may reference supplemental standards or other helpful data in the administration or application of the fire prevention code.

Under the fire-prevention code or other ordinances of the jurisdiction, a Fire Prevention Code Appeals Board or similar body may be empowered to hear appeals of orders made by the fire official under the fire-prevention code. This board should consist of technically knowledgeable and unbiased members of the community.

Enforcement Procedures

The fire prevention process includes a number of enforcement procedures used to establish compliance with the fire code. They are described in the following paragraphs.

Permits: The permit is an official document issued by the fire prevention division to authorize the performance of a specific activity. Permits are issued in the name of the fire official for the use, handling, storage, manufacturing, occupancy, or control of specific hazardous operations and conditions. The permit should be issued only if the condition meets code requirements.

The permit process provides the fire prevention official with information on what, where, how, or when specific hazards are being installed, stored, or used within the jurisdiction. The process allows cross-checking with building, zoning, public health, or other departments' requirements for the use outlined on the permit. Further, it allows the fire official to review and approve devices, safeguards, and procedures that may be needed to assure the safe use of hazardous materials or operations. The lack of a required permit or failure to meet permit requirements constitutes a misdemeanor in legal terms and is grounds for stopping an operation in, or use of, a structure.

The permit is the property of the issuing agency, not the permit holder. A license or permit authorizes, by law, the right of entry for inspection purposes to ensure compliance with the permit requirements. If an inspector operating under a fire code permit is refused entrance to perform a regulatory inspection, this refusal constitutes grounds to halt operation in, or use of, the structure involved.

Permits usually are issued for the place, process, and operator and are nontransferable so that the notification function of the permit process is maintained.

Certificates: A certificate, which is a written document issued by the authority of the fire official to any person or business, grants permission to conduct or engage in any operation or act for which certification is required. Depending upon the needs of a jurisdiction, certificates of approval may be required before smoke or heat detectors, fire extinguishers, fireproofing materials, or other fire protection devices are offered for sale to the general public. This procedure is designed to ensure that only those fire protection appliances that will function in a satisfactory manner are offered for sale to the public.

Certificates of fitness are issued to individuals or businesses with demonstrated proficiency in skills, training, and testing in areas that affect firesafety. This includes pyrotechnics and persons who handle explosives; persons who install fire protection equipment and systems, including sprinklers; and persons who maintain fire extinguishers and fire-detection systems. Certification requirements may include a financial bond or liability insurance where conduct of the regulated activity is inherently hazardous.

Licenses: A license is a permission granted by a competent authority to individuals about to engage in a business, occupation, or other lawful activity. Licenses are issued to provide knowledge of specific business locations, ensure compliance with particular standards, and add a source of revenue to the community. The fire prevention division may issue some licenses directly and may be involved in the check-off process for licenses issued by other municipal departments.

Enforcement Notices

When violations of the fire laws or ordinances are discovered during regular or spot inspections, the violations must be called to the attention of the owner or occupants. When the situation is not corrected during the inspection or is a recurring uncorrected violation, several types of enforcement procedures may be available to the fire inspection officer.

Warnings or notices of violation: The inspection official may issue these notices to the owner or occupant, stating that a specific violation of fire regulations and/or a fire-prevention code has been identified during the inspection. Using discretion and judgment, the fire official may designate an appropriate period of time for correction of the violation cited. Recommendations for correction of the violation also may be noted on the form. The owner or occupant must sign the form and keep a copy of the document. Reinspection after the allotted time is essential to ensure that the correction has been made. If it has not, further legal action should be taken.

Red tag or condemnation notices: These notices usually are attached to appliances, systems, or equipment that would be unsafe and dangerous if allowed to remain in operation. The red-tag process requires that a competent service technician repair or replace the item befor the tag can be removed and the equipment returned to operation. This process also may require that the fire official inspect the completed work before granting approval to resume the operation of the equipment in question.

Citations or summonses: Violation of the fire prevention code requirements or other fire regulations usually are considered misdemeanors. An authorized fire official may issue a citation or summons to an individual who is in violation of the law. These documents constitute a notice for the violator to appear before the appropriate court.

Warrants: A warrant is an order issued by a magistrate or agent of the court that directs a law officer to arrest a violator of the law and bring the violator before the court to respond to the charges specified in the document. Arrest warrants usually are issued in felony cases. The person requesting the warrant must provide factual information to the magistrate or court officer issuing the warrant, showing the existence of sufficient "probable cause" of a violation of a law.

When authorized by state law or local ordinances, fire marshals, fire investigators, and other fire officials may be empowered to issue summonses, serve warrants, and make arrests. Police or peace officer training, in accordance with the standards of the state, is required by most states before a fire official may serve warrants and make arrests for felony violations of state laws.

Where violations represent a clear hazard to life or property, it may be necessary for the fire official to take immediate action to correct unsafe conditions. Entrance into private property, shutdown of an operation, evacuation of a building, or withdrawal of permits are actions that the fire official may find necessary to ensure the public safety. These powers may be explicitly stated or implied in discretionary powers and "duty to act" requirements of appointing laws or ordinances. In all cases, actions must be based on clearly demonstrable threats to public safety, showing that delay would provide an unreasonable danger to residents, occupants, guests, or the public and that this judgment is based on accepted standards or concepts of safety.

RECORD-KEEPING

Keeping records and files on all actions taken by the fire prevention division or the fire marshal's office is an essential part of code enforcement and administration. All instruments and records of code enforcement, all documents relating to inspections, violation notices, summonses, plans review comments and approvals, fire reports, investigations, permits issued, certificates issued, and so on are to be handled as legal documents. Well-organized and well-maintained inspection files and building records are essential foundations for enforcement actions. Complete and accurate records also are needed to measure fire department effectiveness in accomplishing fire prevention goals and to provide department management with information for budgetary and administrative purposes.

For each inspected property, a file should be maintained that summarizes information about the inspected premises and contains copies of all inspection reports. Records and reports of fire prevention activities should be clear, concise, and complete. Every time an inspector or fire prevention officer inspects a location, information about that location should be included in a record or a report. The occupancy file of each building visited should include a complete history of the building site; building plans and specifications, where possible; fire protection system plans; information on and permits issued for the use, storage, and handling of hazardous materials; correspondence; inspection reports; and records of fires at that location.

Files are needed for properties where a certificate of occupancy, a license, or a permit has been issued. Files also should be maintained on properties with automatic sprinklers, standpipe systems, private hydrants, or other private means of fire protection. A special notation or key should identify any system or equipment that is legally required. With a well-maintained system of files, established data need not be recompiled for each inspection. Inspection work planning is expedited, and time is used more effectively in the field for the inspection itself.

Computer Applications

In recent years, computer technology has helped fire-prevention officials handle record-keeping and manage fire prevention programs. Many communities have found their records are more accurate and complete when computers are used for processing, organizing, or managing a great deal of the information associated with the overall fire prevention activity. Fire prevention reporting systems should be designed to collect, store, and process data and to schedule periodic activities according to local policy. For example, all data, including occupancy description, activity, and violations, are collected on a standard form during an inspection. After the inspection, forms are completed and processed according to local needs. This data, to be useful, must be collected and maintained in a uniform and consistent manner. NFPA 901, *Uniform Coding for Fire Protection*, provides a basis for systematic information-gathering.

Computers can produce management reports related to inspection activity and to fire prevention personnel resource allocation. In addition, separate master file listings can be provided of occupancies currently under inspection and all occupancies to be inspected. Inspection forms or schedule sheets can be printed to show when periodic inspections are required and indicate violations to be checked for correction during follow-up inspections. These management reports should document:

1. The occupancy inspected, locating the time of day and the date, and the name of the inspector;
2. The code violations that have been corrected, filed by type, number, and kind of occupancy;
3. How the fire department used its resources to accomplish fire prevention program objectives.

These systems save the inspector time and provide data in a form useful for decision- making by operational management. Because they contain a current inventory of occupancies, the systems can provide information for fire protection fiscal and long-range master planning.

PLANS REVIEW PRACTICES

Traditionally, the building department has been active in the design, construction, and final occupancy inspection of the building. The fire department's role traditionally has begun when the building has been occupied and has concerned the maintenance of life safety conditions and fire-protection systems, as well as firesafe storage and handling of contents.

Today, a progressive department's role in the building construction process is changing. An increasingly important and practical fire prevention function involves the participation of the fire marshal or a designated representative in the review of building plans and specifications and in the construction process. In most cases, plans review is conducted in cooperation with the local building, zoning, and public works departments or with state agencies that may have this review authority.

The review of building plans and specifications provides the fire service with its best opportunity to see that fire protection standards are met before construction is completed and the building is occupied. The type and depth of the review process depend upon the community's needs and the functions of other local departments or state agencies with review authority.

Whenever possible, fire officials should participate in pre-construction conferences; address questions relating to fire protection features in the planned building, to the building code, or to fire prevention code requirements; and comment during the plans review process. If questions and issues concerning the effect of construction on firesafety are discussed at this time with the architect, engineers, contractors, and other code officials, misunderstandings and conflicts that could arise during the construction or final finish phase can be prevented. The fire official can emphasize firesafety code requirements and coordinate responsibilities with other code enforcement officials. Design professionals and contractors benefit from this procedure as well, because problems that otherwise would cost them time and money are eliminated before construction begins.

Site plan reviews: The site-plan review provides the fire official with the first look at new construction and at additions to existing buildings. The site plan provides an overview of the intended construction in relation to existing conditions and includes information such as building placement, exposures, size, type of construction, occupancy, water supply from both public and private mains, hydrant placement, and access. The site plan also may provide information about existing conditions that must be modified, such as abandoned flammable liquid tanks or pipelines in the area. The contour of the land may be significant. The current and projected uses of adjoining properties, including zoning, also should be reviewed at this time.

Preliminary building plans: The review of preliminary building plans gives the fire official an opportunity to comment on those features of the building that significantly affect life safety and protection of the building from fire. The depth and scope of the review and comments will depend upon local conditions.

The provision for required fire protection systems is a primary concern in plans review. Because an estimated 75 percent of the building code may relate directly to provision for life safety in case of a fire within the building, the review may include, among other items, the type of occupancy, allowable areas and heights, fire separations, fire resistance of construction, interior finish, occupancy loading, number and location of exitways, protection of vertical openings, and special hazards.

Final building plans and specifications: When the final building plans are submitted, they should include modifications required by the review official and agreed to by the design professional submitting the plans. Plans may be approved if they agree with the applicable code requirements. A building permit can then be issued, and construction may begin.

Plans review and approval must be followed by on-site inspections to ensure that the fire protection features and systems are constructed and installed as planned and approved. All deviations from the approved plans should be documented. All agreements reached on-site or by telephone should be documented for all parties in follow-up correspondence or file memos. This correspondence and a copy of the approved plans should be retained in an organized filing system or on microfilm or microfiche so a permanent record of building construction is available for future reference.

As practical, building construction information should be provided to the fire companies responsible for fire suppression and fire inspection of the building. Information provided in all of the plans discussed in this section can aid in pre-fire planning for fire operations.

Certificates of occupancy: If the fire marshal's office is not the primary issuing agency for occupancy certificates, then either the fire marshal's office or the fire prevention division should be involved in the final inspection process. Each agency should certify the building before the certificate of occupancy is issued. This certificate indicates that all requirements under the building and other applicable codes have been met and that the building is safe and habitable. All fire protection systems should be tested and placed in service before occupancy is allowed. The building should not be occupied until inspection agencies have approved it. This final review helps to ensure the life safety of the occupants and to verify that any required corrections have been made before occupancy.

CONSULTATION

The public looks to the fire service for answers and advice concerning fire problems. Due to its unique ability to provide this information, the fire department should offer consulting services to the community. Fire prevention officers must be able to explain fire codes, fire-related sections of building codes, and the application of specific standards to design professionals, contractors, and members of the building trades. Consultation also should be available directly to property owners, managers, occupants, and members of the general public, who may not be as familiar with fire problems and their solutions.

To maximize this service, the fire department should inform and instruct citizens about the best ways to deal with fire hazards. When the fire prevention division receives frequent calls about the same problem, it may wish to develop standard recommendations for that problem. The fire department should maintain a library of up-to-date reference materials. In addition, the chief and other officers should be acquainted with individuals outside the fire department who have specialized knowledge or experience and who could act as resource persons. These and other consulting services usually are based in the fire-prevention division or the fire marshal's office.

FIRE INVESTIGATION

The thorough investigation of fires is an integral part of the fire department's commitment to public safety. Fire investigation includes two areas: fire cause determination, and investigation of criminal actions which may have contributed to a fire.

Fire cause determination is of major importance to a fire prevention program. Analysis of the causes of fires in a community is the basis for establishing fire prevention-program priorities and providing firesafety information to the public. Maximum utilization of resources must be based on firm information about the local fire problem. As information is accumulated from fire investigations, data becomes available on which to base corrective programs. Over time, this data will indicate trends in the area's fire problem, and a fire prevention program designed to tackle priority areas can be implemented.

If it is determined that a fire is caused by arson or other unlawful burning of property, a full criminal investigation should be conducted. Other fires for which a cause cannot be readily determined, including those classified as suspicious or undetermined, should also be investigated. Assertive fire investigations by skilled, trained specialists can deter arsonists.

In communities and states where fire service investigators have police powers, personnel may conduct an investigation to the point of arrest and incarceration of perpetrators. Where fire department personnel do not have police powers, fire cause determination must be made by the fire department, with the follow-up investigation conducted by the police, sheriff, state police, or investigators from the state fire marshal's office.

PUBLIC FIRE EDUCATION

Firesafety education is an increasingly valuable area of public fire protection. This function has undergone rapid change and growth, focusing increasingly on the importance of prevention in public fire protection management.

Public firesafety education has two facets: fire prevention education and fire reaction education. Both facets are necessary in order to change fundamentally the way the general public views fire, and to encourage people to act in a firesafe manner. The public needs to be motivated and instructed in actions that minimize the dangerous effects of a fire, should one occur. The basic method of instruction is changing from "preaching" to "teaching." Information is best presented in short, interesting, even humorous messages that require thought and that place responsibility for action on the recipients. Recipients relate most effectively to the firesafety message when it is presented in a dramatic context. Cultural and language factors should be considered when firesafety messages are prepared for communication throughout the community.

National firesafety campaigns can be matched to local efforts. NFPA's Learn Not to Burn® effort is one such national campaign, with messages designed to supplement, but not supplant, local fire prevention education programs. NFPA has many public firesafety materials and programs designed for general public use and for specific groups and firesafety concerns. Community programs can be developed using the Learn Not to Burn theme and applying it to priority local fire problems.

Community awareness and participation at the grassroots level are the keys to encouraging people to adopt firesafe behaviors. Civic and service clubs, youth and fraternal organizations, neighborhood action groups, the business community, schools, and other groups are contributing to the growth of firesafety education. Highly effective programs in such areas as escape planning, smoke detector installation, fire hazard inspections, burn prevention, juvenile firesetting problems, firesafety for babysitters, and firesafety for the elderly have been conducted by community groups in conjunction with local fire prevention personnel.

Thousands of teachers are giving classroom instruction on firesafe behaviors. NFPA developed the Learn Not to Burn Curriculum® to assist in this effort. The curriculum, designed to teach twenty-two basic firesafety and fire prevention behaviors, presents comprehensive teaching strategies for teachers and fire departments to convey key lifesafety messages to children from kindergarten through the eighth grade. Because the curriculum is designed to integrate easily into existing school subjects, it does not represent an additional course for instructors.

The Public Education Office of the U.S. Fire Administration (USFA) has helped communities and states develop comprehensive public fire education programs by providing funding, technical support, and regional and national workshops to facilitate the exchange of information. State exchange and resource centers for public firesafety education material also have been established through the efforts of the Public Education Office. These efforts have greatly increased the amount of information exchanged among fire educators and encouraged the growth of their educational programs.

Many fire departments and fire prevention divisions have appointed full-time firesafety education officers. As more people have assumed these positions, the level of talent and professionalism of firesafety educators has increased. Many fire departments no longer require that firesafety education officers be trained fire fighters; rather, these departments recognize the value of hiring educators with teaching experience and skills to develop and present educational programs geared to all ages and groups.

Groups with Special Information Needs

Groups with information needs similar to those of the general public, but different enough to require specialized programs include, among others, educational, industrial, institutional, high-rise, civic, service, elderly, professional, handicapped, and commercial groups. Many innovative ways are used to reach such groups with firesafety information.

Seasonal Activities

Informative educational programs of interest to the general public often are built around the four seasons of the year. Public education programs include National Fire Prevention Week, which is always the week that includes the date of October 9, and Operation EDITH. Many topical and effective materials are available from NFPA for use in public education programs, including some featuring Sparky the fire dog, symbol of personal and property firesafety.

BIBLIOGRAPHY

NFPA codes, standards, and recommended practices.

Reference to the following NFPA codes, standards, and recommended practices will provide further information about fire prevention and code enforcement. (See the latest *NFPA catalog* for availability of the current editions of the following documents.

NFPA 1, *Fire Prevention Code.*

NFPA 1031, *Professional Qualifications for Fire Inspector, Fire Investigator, and Fire Prevention Education Officer.*

NFPA 1202, *Recommendations for Organization of a Fire Department.*

NFPA 1301, *Guide to Public Fire Prevention Criteria.*

Additional Readings

Adams, R. C., *ed.*, Firesafety Educator's Handbook, National Fire Protection Association, Quincy, MA, 1983.

Bare, W. K., *Fundamentals of Fire Prevention*, Wiley and Sons, New York, 1977.

Berry, D. J., *Fire Litigation Handbook*, National Fire Protection Association, Quincy, MA, 1984.

Bugbee, P. and Cote, A., *Principles of Fire Protection*, 2nd ed., National Fire Protection Association, Quincy, MA, 1988.

Building Officials and Code Administrators International, Inc., *The BOCA Basic/National Fire Prevention Code*, Country Club Hills, IL, 1990.

Building Officials and Code Administrators International, Inc., *Legal Aspects of Code Administration*, Country Club Hills, IL, 1984.

Callahan, T. W., *Fire Service and the Law*, 2nd ed., National Fire Protection Association, Quincy, MA, 1987.

Clet, V. H., *Fire-Related Codes, Laws, and Ordinances*, Glencoe Press, Encino, CA, 1978.

Clyde, J. E., *Construction Inspection*, Wiley and Son, New York, 1983.

Coffee, C. W., "Consolidated Fire and Building Department Enforcement—A Success Story," *Building Standards*, Vol. 55, No. 5 (Sept.-Oct. 1986), pp. 24-27.

Coggan, R. S., "The Standards Crunch: A Fire Services Dilemma," *Fire Engineering*, Vol. 142, No. 5, 1989, pp. 38-39.

Coleman, R. J. and Granito, J. A., *eds.*, *Managing Fire Services*, 2nd ed., International City Management Association, Washington, DC, 1988.

Computers in Code Administration, Building Officials and Code Administrators International, Country Club Hills, IL., 1987.

Directory of State Building Codes and Regulations, 4th ed., National Conference of States on Building Codes and Standards, Herndon, VA, 1987.

Fire and Emergency Resource Directory, National Fire Protection Association, Quincy, MA, 1984.

Fire Inspection Management Guidelines, National Fire Protection Association, Quincy, MA, 1982. (See especially Guideline No. 11, "Resource Directory," for extensive bibliographic material on fire prevention and code enforcement.)

Fire Marshals Association of North America, *National Conference of State Fire Marshals Report*, National Fire Protection Association, Quincy, MA, 1985.

Hall, J. R. Jr., *et al.*, *Fire Code Inspections and Fire Prevention: What Methods Lead to Success*?, National Fire Protection Association, Quincy, MA, 1979.

Harvey, C. S., "Flexible Approach to Fire-Code Compliance," *Architectural Record*, No. 10 (Oct. 1988), pp. 130-135.

International Fire Service Training Association, *Fire Prevention and Inspection Practices*, IFSTA 110, Oklahoma State University, Stillwater, OK, 1974.

Lucht, D. A., *Fire Prevention Planning and Leadership for Small Communities*, National Fire Protection Association, Quincy, MA, 1980.

Morse, H. N., *Legal Insight*, 2nd ed., National Fire Protection Association, Quincy, MA, 1975.

Moulton, G. A., *ed.*, *NFPA Inspection Manual*, 6th ed., National Fire Protection Association, Inc., Quincy, MA, 1989.

Moulton, G. A., *ed.*, *NFPA Conducting Fire Inspections: A Guidebook for Field Use*, 2nd ed., National Fire Protection Association, Quincy, MA, 1989.

National Commission on Fire Prevention and Control, *America Burning, The Report of the National Commission on Fire Prevention and Control*, U.S. Government Printing Office, Washington, DC, 1973.

Oey, K. H. and Passchier, E., "Complying with Practice Codes," *Batiment International / Building Research and Practice*, Vol. 21, No. 1, 1988, pp. 30-36.

Public Fire Education, IFSTA 606, Oklahoma State University, Stillwater, OK, 1979.

Public Fire Education Planning, United States Fire Administration, U.S. Government Printing Office, Washington, DC, 1979.

Robertson, J. C., "Development and Enactment of Fire Safety Codes," *Introduction to Fire Prevention*, 3rd ed., Macmillan, NY, 1989, pp. 112-132.

Robertson, J. C., "Enforcement of Fire Safety Codes," *Introduction to Fire Prevention*, 3rd ed., Macmillan, NY, 1989, pp. 133-153.

Robertson, J. C., "Fire Prevention Responsibilities of the Public Sector," *Introduction to Fire Prevention*, 3rd ed., Macmillan, NY, 1989, pp. 39-75.

Robertson, J. C., *Introduction to Fire Prevention*, 3rd ed., MacMillan, NY, 1989.

Rosenbauer, D. L., *Introduction to Fire Protection Law*, National Fire Protection Association, Quincy, MA, 1978.

Schaenman, P. S., *et al.*, *Procedures for Improving the Measurement of Local Fire Protection Effectiveness*, National Fire Protection Association, Quincy, MA, 1977.

Small Community Fire Departments: Organization and Operation, National Fire Protection Association, Quincy, MA, 1982.

Standard Fire Prevention Code, Southern Building Code Congress International Inc., Birmingham, AL, 1988.

Uniform Fire Code, International Conference of Building Officials, Whittier, CA, 1988.

Young, K. R., "Excuses, Excuses: Fire Investigations," *Fire Engineering*, Vol. 141, No. 6, 1988, pp. 34-51.

Organization/Agency Information and Program Sources

Building Officials and Code Administrators International Inc. (BOCA), Country Club Hills, IL.

Conference of States on Building Codes and Standards, Herndon, VA.

International Conference of Building Officials (ICBO), Whittier, CA.

International Fire Chiefs Association (IAFC), Washington, DC.

International Fire Service Training Association (IFSTA), Oklahoma State University, Stillwater, OK.

United States Fire Administration, Emmitsburg, MD.

National Fire Academy, Emmitsburg, MD.

National Institute of Standards and Technology, Center for Fire Research, Washington, DC.

Southern Building Code Congress International Inc. (SBCCI), Birmingham, AL.

PRE-FIRE PLANNING FOR INDUSTRIAL EMERGENCIES

Edward Plaugher and Edward Burns

Pre-incident planning can provide valuable information about a structure that can improve the ability of the emergency services personnel to respond effectively to a fire in that structure. Pre-incident planning addresses vital fire protection concerns, such as structure layout, including access systems; contents; construction details; and types and locations of built-in fire protection systems. It includes all data that can have an impact on decisions or actions taken during an emergency. Pre-incident planning is a joint venture between the emergency services and the property management team.

Potential problems must be analyzed before fire service personnel can determine the strategy necessary to control a fire. Input and staff development by the property management team is essential for effective control of an emergency. Assigning a representive or representive team to develop the plan with the emergency service is recommended. Reviewing and updating the plan on a regular basis reinforces its value.

The industrial team should be the key or lead organizer in the review cycle and, as such, initiate reviews or address the concerns of the local emergency team. Emergency plans and drills are also essential to evaluate the need for review and to update the documents generated by both the facility and the available emergency service.

Planning for industrial fires increases the confidence and ability of fire service personnel, both municipal fire fighters and industrial fire brigades, to deal with most situations. More important, it increases the potential for rescuing lives and saving property.

A pre-fire planning session with industrial and fire department personnel is vital. Fire fighters who are familiar with a facility's fire protection features save valuable time when locating sprinkler control valves and fire department pumper connections. In addition, an awareness of a facility's contents increases the fire service personnel's ability to fight a fire effectively and safely.

Edward Plaugher is deputy chief of the Fairfax County Fire and Rescue Department, Fairfax, VA. He also serves as a member of NFPA's Technical Committee on Fire Inspector and Investigator Professional Qualifications. Edward Burns is a retired assistant chief of the Los Angeles City Fire Department.

Pre-incident information is not restricted to building components. It includes recorded data and personal knowledge of a wide range of factors and conditions that may be relevant to the emergency.

PRE-FIRE PLANNING ELEMENTS

A pre-fire planning session provides the fire department and industry staff an opportunity to exchange critical information and to coordinate necessary actions in the event of a fire. It is essential that this information be obtained before an emergency occurs. During the emergency, time is limited, and access to vital information usually is impossible. Some issues raised in the section will have more of an impact on, or apply more to, one group than the other. However, both groups should clearly understand their mutual and individual responsibilities.

Knowledge of factors and conditions that may affect a fire enables the industry and municipal command officers to make intelligent fire behavior predictions and reliable estimates of the resources they will need to control the situation. Accurately predicting fire behavior helps to ensure safe and effective tactical operations.

Six categories of pre-incident information are significant in the control of a fire:

1. Occupancy, or type of building construction, and contents.
2. On-site fire protection features, including water supply sources.
3. Environmental factors.
4. Area knowledge, including access.
5. Interagency assistance.
6. Plan forms and storage of information.

Each major industrial facility must develop an emergency operations plan in which it specifies the actions to be taken in the event of an emergency. A review of the emergency operations plan by the fire department can provide valuable insight into the actions to be coordinated by both plant personnel and the fire department. Incorporating the emergency operations plan into fire department documents is beneficial in case the plant personnel assigned certain responsibilities are unable to perform their critical duties.

Occupancy

Occupancy type, building construction and layout, and contents are among the most important elements in pre-fire planning. The facility's insurance plan if one is available—that is, if the structure is a highly protected risk (HPR)—may be a good source for this information. It should provide details on building construction and occupancy, sprinkler system control valve(s), and other valuable information on fire protection systems. Requesting the assistance of the insurance carrier is recommended during the development and updating of the plan. The insurance representative should be directly involved in reviewing recommended procedures for property conservation and salvage procedures.

Occupancy type: The type of occupancy is important in establishing incident priorities and tactical operations. Consider the difference between a commercial or industrial metal fabricating facility and a furniture refinishing operation facility. The furniture shop will probably pose a much greater difficulty in anticipating fire behavior, related control operations, and safety considerations because of its increased fire load, including wood, fabric, plastics, and flammable liquids such as varnish and wood strippers. Another example is a two-story convalescent home compared to an apartment building of the same height. While life safety is a major concern in both situations, evacuation problems are much more severe in a convalescent home filled with aged and/or non-ambulatory people.

Building construction: Construction features, such as structural framing systems, materials, and the interior and exterior finishes, can be key factors in the rate and extent of fire spread within a building. Awareness of these features by the fire service, the industrial fire brigades, and the facility management is important in estimating the potential problem and ultimately confining the fire to a limited area.

The fire conditions in a building of fire-resistive construction will be markedly different from those in a building constructed entirely of combustible materials. Fire development, intensity, and spread can be far better controlled in structures of fire-resistive construction.

Another critical factor is the physical layout of a building, including its compartmentation and vertical openings. Large, open areas without firestops or fire protection devices create conditions that can spread fire quickly, thereby increasing the fire's size and intensity until it becomes extremely difficult to control. Unprotected, vertical openings in a building compound fire problems by allowing fire, smoke, and toxic gases to travel upward in an unrestricted manner. Awareness of the locations of these vertical openings enables both municipal fire fighters and fire brigade members to place protective hose lines in positions that can restrict the spread of fire and the products of combustion.

Improper roof construction and covering materials can have an impact on ventilation operations, can create exposure problems, and, most important, increase the dangers to fire fighting personnel. The decision to place fire service personnel on a building roof during a fire should be governed by advance knowledge of the particular roof construction. Some roofs, such as those with the panelized designs used on many commercial buildings, may appear very sturdy. During a fire, however, they are extremely dangerous and may fail partially or completely.

The location of a building's entrances and exits, interior hallways, stairs, or other travel paths can be extremely valuable information in developing strategy or directing rescue, fire control, or other tactical operations. Familiarity with building access is often key to directing fire attack efforts that will confine the fire to the involved area, rather than driving it into uninvolved portions of the structure.

False ceilings and common attics can aid fire spread within a building and impair the ability of fire fighting personnel to control the fire. These construction features can create safety hazards by permitting fires to burn undetected in areas that are not readily visible. Awareness of these structural features allows fire fighters to prevent or reduce fire spread in them.

Contents: It is essential to know what is involved during a fire. This can only be done if one has detailed knowledge of the contents of the burning building. Since type of information is often impossible to obtain once a fire starts, knowing it beforehand can be vital in ensuring a successful control operation. Building contents definitely affect fire development, extinguishing methods, and other tactical considerations, such as fire fighter safety. Although some buildings, such as warehouses, are subject to periodic changes in what they contain, most industrial, commercial, and residential occupancies remain fairly constant in terms of contents.

Special attention should be paid to occupancies with unusual contents, such as hazardous or toxic materials or flammable liquids and gases. Facility contents that cause the most concern are plastics, aerosols, compressed gases, explosives, flammable liquids, combustible dusts, and corrosive materials.

Since materials react to fire in different ways, appropriate fire fighting techniques must be addressed in advance. For example, burning plastics cause fires to develop extremely high temperatures, possess a very high burning rate, and give off dense smoke. Because of these unique burning characteristics, plastics require special fire fighting techniques.

Facility management should advise fire brigade and fire department personnel of any valuable documents, materials, or equipment that may need to be salvaged immediately.

On-Site Fire Protection Features

Knowledge of fire protection features in a building, knowing how the equipment functions and what actions are necessary to activate, terminate, or supplement fire operations with these systems, is essential to pre-fire planning. Fire doors, fire sprinklers, and other special control or extinguishing systems play a major role in controlling a fire. In addition, the proper extinguishing agents needed for the various materials contained in the facility must be reviewed before a fire strikes, and an effective strategy must be determined for the unique problems these materials may present.

Pre-incident planning must determine whether a building is sprinklered and, if so, to what extent. Familiarity with the sprinkler system design is also critical in determining whether the protection is adequate for the occupancy.

Recent experience has demonstrated that fully sprinklered storage facilities need special consideration during pre-incident planning. NFPA 231, *General Storage*, and NFPA 231C, *Rack Storage of Materials*, provide established guidelines for the adequate protection of stored goods.

Failure by facility management to maintain high levels of on-site fire protection burdens all emergency responders with additional risk. Mutual understanding of the fire protection issues, problems, and responsibilities must be an active part of pre-incident planning. Information on insurance plans for HPR property can be provided by facility staff.

During pre-fire planning, it is important to understand what changes in conditions or facility use have occurred since the installation of the sprinkler system. Changes in layout, materials, or handling processes, such as additional packaging systems, that were not anticipated during the design of the sprinkler system may indicate inadequate protection for the facility.

Other on-site fire fighting features, such as standpipe systems, are invaluable. It is essential that fire control personnel are provided with the location(s) of supply inlets that will allow them to supplement standpipe and sprinkler systems.

Utility controls: Knowing where utility shutoffs for electricity, gas, and water are located can minimize property loss. Failure to terminate utility services during a fire is often responsible for unnecessary injuries and damage to the structure or contents beyond that associated with the actual fire.

Sprinkler control valves: The location of the sprinkler control valves, and the building areas they protect, must be ascertained. Facility management should post signs that will help fire fighters locate these valves upon arrival. Knowing where control valves are located is essential, because checking to make sure they are open is one of the first actions the fire brigade or the fire department should take when it arrives at a fire scene. If the valves are shut, the sprinklers are essentially inoperative. Unfortunately, shut-valve fires are an all-too-common occurrence. Facility management must be informed that sprinkler control valves are not to be closed until the fire has been completely extinguished. Prematurely closing the valves allows the fire to accelerate and may cause many sprinklers to open. When the valves are eventually reopened, the water supply may be overtaxed because so many sprinklers have operated.

Water supply sources: Because water is the most effective, economical and commonly available agent for extinguishing fires, it is imperative that fire command officers and key plant personnel be as familiar as possible with its availability at the facility site before they respond to a fire. The reliability of the water supply is a key pre-incident factor. Whatever the source, it must always be capable of providing an adequate water supply and sustaining the supply during the required operational period. When considering the reliability of a water supply source, special concern should be given to systems and equipment that are not tested regularly and maintained by fire department and/or the fire brigade.

Inability to deliver effective fire attack streams due to inadequate water supplies most often results in defensive operations, causing needless property loss and safety concerns.

The exact location of fire hydrants and the amount of water available from the hydrants and the water mains are critical pre-incident information. Where hydrant systems and water mains are not available, pre-incident plans must determine the alternative resources required to deliver sufficient water to the fire scene by fire attack vehicles, water tenders, or tankers. All water supply systems must be tested on a scheduled basis and maintained to increase the reliability of the system.

Built-in systems: While fire hydrants connected to public water supply systems are the most common source of water for fire control operations, there are areas where they are not available. In these cases, built-in fire fighting systems, such as water supply tanks, are vital. Pre-incident plans should include the design capacity and operational features of these systems, as they do any other water supply source.

Water damage is a major concern to the facility emergency team. In addition, runoff of hazardous waste from fire fighting activity must be considered during plan development in some occupancies. In some cases, diking can be used to mitigate environmental damage.

Environmental Factors

There are a number of ways that environmental conditions, such as temperature, humidity, and wind, affect fire behavior and fire control operations. Thus, pre-incident planning must consider environmental factors before a fire. Such planning also aids strategic and tactical responses to general environmental conditions in an area, thereby increasing fire fighting effectiveness in the structure.

Environmental conditions can increase fire severity, depending on the length of time they have prevailed before the fire. High temperatures and low humidity will affect almost all combustible materials by removing moisture from them and lowering the temperature at which they will ignite. These conditions may also intensify the manner in which materials will burn and the fire spread. Static electricity must be considered as a viable ignition source and must be controlled during an emergency.

Humidity: Low humidity can increase fire intensity by causing unusual dryness, and spread fire more rapidly than usual humidity conditions. High humidity and temperature inversion affect smoke rise. Under such conditions, smoke may remain at ground level, thereby obscuring visibility and making it extremely difficult to ventilate a building.

Wind: No other environmental factor has a more profound effect on fire behavior than wind. As a general rule, the greater the wind velocity, the more problems created during a fire. Combating fires during high winds requires command officers to develop a specific fire strategy or direct tactical operations. Wind can cause fire to spread within a structure through open or failed doors or windows. High winds can also be a major factor in creating exposure fires in adjacent buildings. Further, wind can cause spot fires at a considerable distance from the main fire area. In addition, high winds can adversely affect hose streams directed at a fire during an exterior operation, either by dispersing the streams or by directing them from their intended target.

Ventilation operations are dependent upon wind direction. For example, smoke removal by opening windows and doors may be ineffective if wind is blowing directly into them and holding the smoke inside. Rooftop ventilation requires knowledge of wind direction to ensure that personnel performing ventilation operations are kept away from smoke and other products of combustion.

High winds may also create additional safety hazards for emergency response personnel. Raising ladders or operating fire streams from ladders or rooftops can be more precarious than usual whenever high winds are present.

Area Knowledge

Pre-fire planning requires a general knowledge of the immediate facility area. Familiarity with nearby types of construction and occupancies helps to identify critical concerns before an emergency. Area contents may influence exposure, fire behavior, and control problems. Decisions and precautions in the overall fire protection operational plan are based on materials present in the area.

Access: Familiarity with local streets and roads in the emergency plan area can provide the best access route to the fire's location. Plans can also provide alternative ways to reach the fire area should normal travel paths become blocked or congested, due to temporary obstructions at railway crossings, bridges, or roads. Knowledge of secondary means of access to a particular building or location is critical, since physical obstructions can often delay or prevent personnel from reaching a fire. Alternative approaches for responding units allow for the most effective placement of additional apparatus. An awareness of narrow streets in the area can also prevent mistakes when accessing the fire site.

During pre-incident planning, it is important to determine which units will respond and from what direction they will come. This can help create safety awareness at those intersections that responding fire apparatus may cross. Assignments for fire companies based on probable order of arrival and approach direction to the scene can increase fire fighting effectiveness.

Interagency Assistance

During many fires, fire personnel are assisted by other agencies and industrial facilities capable of providing the support functions necessary to control the fire. Interagency and outside assistance can be vital to the outcome of emergency control operations and may take different forms, depending on the size and complexity of the incident. This assistance may include traffic control by local law enforcement, mutual aid from another jurisdiction, or the use of specialized resources such as fire fighting foam stored at another industrial or storage facility to deal with an unusual problem. Agreements to use these resources efficiently must be established during the planning phase, not left until a fire is in progress.

Pre-fire planning should take into consideration those agencies and resources available to provide support. It is essential to ascertain the proper method for requesting assistance, as well as the probable response times. In the case of mutual aid from other fire departments, it is important to know what type of company and how many personnel can be expected to respond.

A municipal agency can usually provide a variety of support functions, including utility services control for electrical, gas, and water systems. In many cases, they can also furnish other useful materials, such as sawdust, sand, safety barricades, and so on. Specialized equipment such as tractors, bulldozers, and water tenders are also often available from local public or private agencies.

Because the amount and type of interagency assistance will vary in different areas, pre-plans should identify what is available, establish procedures for requesting needed interagency assistance in a timely manner, and fully utilize these valuable resources to help ensure successful control operations.

Plan Forms and Storage of Information

Although pre-fire plan incident inspection programs are not the same everywhere, they usually include similar information requirements intended to provide response personnel with knowledge that will be useful if a fire occurs.

Most of the specific items of pre-incident information are usually covered during pre-fire plan inspections and recorded on a form, along with other items of critical information. This form provides an effective means of recording information before a fire and is useful as a checklist or a ready reference source for review or for use at the scene of a fire. (See Figures 9-8A and 9-8B.)

Pre-fire plan forms can be referred to by the industrial fire brigade and municipal fire fighters while responding to an emergency, and they are, of course, an invaluable aid at an incident. Back-up copies of the plan should be available to the plant management team at the command post to assist in the emergency. Location of critical valves and pump controls must be easily identified on the plans, as must all external considerations, such as water supplies and drainage control systems.

The value of pre-incident information and planning increases with the size and complexity of the building in which the fire occurs. For this reason, it is imperative that formal pre-fire planning be conducted on major facilities at least, and that the information be made available at the scene of the incident.

BUILDING SURVEY FORM

ADDRESS: ______________________ **DATE:** ______________________

BUILDING NAME: **OCCUPANCY:**

EMERGENCY PHONE NO: ____________ NAME & ADDRESS: ______________________

OWNER OR AGENT: ______________________

OCCUPANT: ______________________

SPRINKLER: (SIAMESE) ______________________

(HOSE THREAD SIZE) ______________________

GENERAL CONTENTS: ______________________

SPECIAL HAZARDS: ______________________

ENTRY HAZARDS: ______________________

MAIN ELECTRIC SWITCH: ____________ GAS SHUTOFF: ____________

FUEL OIL SHUTOFF: ____________ WATER SHUTOFF: ____________

A.C. MAIN SWITCH: ______________________

FIRE ALARM (TYPE): ____________ AGENT: ____________

TYPE OF SPACE HEATING: ______________________

STRUCTURAL INFORMATION OF BUILDING

HEIGHT AND NUMBER OF FLOORS: ________ TYPE OF EXTERIOR WALLS: ____________

FLOOR CONSTRUCTION: ______________________

ROOF CONSTRUCTION: ____________ INTERIOR FINISH: ____________

TYPE OF WINDOWS: ______________________

FIRE DOORS: ______________________

NO. OF STAIRWAYS: N ________ S ________ E ________ W ________ CENTER ________

VERTICAL & HORIZONTAL OPENINGS: ______________________

____

EXPOSURES: N ________ S ________ E ________ W ________ CENTER ________

____

BEST MEANS OF ENTRY: ______________________

ADDITIONAL INFORMATION: ______________________

____

SIGNATURE OF INSPECTION OFFICER: ______________________

STATION AND BATTALION: ______________________

FSA 130
(12/89)

FIG. 9-8A. Pre-incident planning form (front).

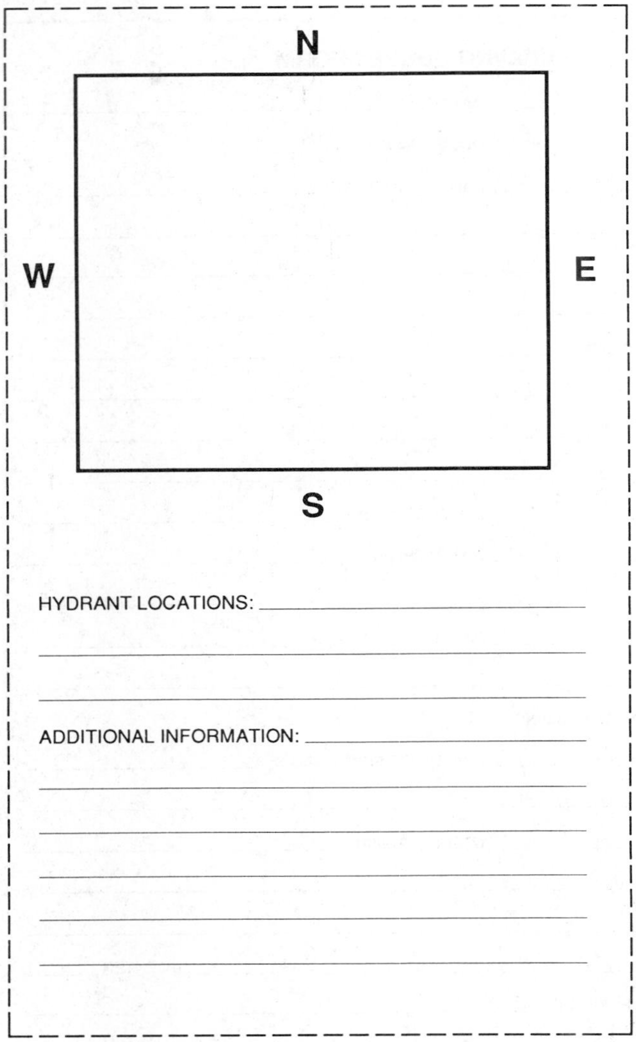

FIG. 9-8B. Pre-incident planning form (back).

BIBLIOGRAPHY

References

Brannigan, F. L., *Building Construction for the Fire Service*, 2nd ed., National Fire Protection Association, Quincy, MA, 1982.

Carter, H. R., and Rausch, E., "Loss Prevention Activities — Pre-Fire Planning and Related Functions," *Management in the Fire Service*, 2nd ed., National Fire Protection Association, Quincy, MA, 1989, pp. 202-233.

National Fire Academy, "Preparing for Incident Command," *Module 3*, pp. 3.3-3.9.

Volk, E., "Pre-Fire Planning: The Rewards are Mutual," *Record*, Vol. 66, No. 2 (Mar. 1989), pp. 11-15.

NFPA Codes, Standards, and Recommended Practices

Reference to the following NFPA codes, standards, and recommended practices will provide further information on pre-fire planning for industrial emergencies discussed in this chapter. (See the latest *NFPA Catalog* for availability of current editions of the following documents.)

NFPA 13, *Installation of Sprinkler Systems*.

NFPA 231, *General Storage*.

NFPA 231C, *Rack Storage of Materials*.

FIRE DEPARTMENT APPARATUS, EQUIPMENT, AND PROTECTIVE CLOTHING

Revised by A. K. Rosenhan

APPARATUS

The tools of the fire department for providing fire suppression and emergency services are apparatus and the equipment they carry. Without the proper tools and the knowledge of how to use those tools correctly, a fire department cannot do its job effectively. This section contains information on the standards used and procurement policies that should be followed in specifying and acquiring apparatus and equipment.

The basic fire apparatus in North America is a diesel- or gasoline-engine-driven vehicle that carries a rather extensive assortment of tools and equipment for fighting fires. Such equipment may include a pump, hose, water tank, aerial ladder or elevated platform, ground ladders, and various portable tools and appliances. The amount and capacities of the various fire fighting components carried vary in accordance with the intended service of the particular vehicle.

For pumping operations and fire attack, the size of the pump and the amount of water, hose, and equipment carried will vary with the type of service the fire department provides and the nature of the community it protects, be it predominantly urban, suburban, or rural. The fire apparatus standards set 750 gpm as the smallest fire pump, but pumps of 1000, 1250, or 1500 gpm (3785, 4732, or 5678 L/min) capacity are popular for general municipal service.

Many fire departments supplement units equipped primarily for pumping and fire attack with other vehicles that provide a large variety of tools and equipment for support functions. These tools include ground ladders, forcible-entry tools, generators, lights, and rescue equipment. Such units are variously termed rescue, squad, or utility vehicles.

About one-third of the work at an average fire involves the use of tools and equipment in duties classed as rescue or ladder-company work. Apparatus suitably equipped for such service should be available at all structural fires and at major emergencies, such as significant highway accidents. While pumping engines may carry considerable equipment, the larger aerial-ladder and elevating-platform apparatus commonly transport additional equipment for forcible entry, cutting, and extrication. This type of apparatus provides vehicle supported, power-operated equipment for access to areas above the normal reach of ground ladders, and effective elevated stream service.

In rural districts and in the outlying districts of cities where hydrant distribution is not complete, supplemental water-transport apparatus, defined as "mobile water supply apparatus," is common. Such apparatus has large water tanks with quick-fill and -dump connections, and they may have a permanently installed pump.

A wide combination of fire fighting equipment is often provided on a single fire apparatus. Besides combinations of water pump, hose, and water tank, commonly termed a "triple combination," it is not uncommon to provide a booster pump and small-stream equipment on aerial-ladder or elevating-platform apparatus or a water tower on a pumping engine. When fire apparatus is equipped with long ground ladders and other usual ladder-company equipment, in addition to the usual pumping engine equipment, the apparatus is referred to as a "quadruple combination," or "quad." If a power-operated aerial ladder or elevating platform is added, such apparatus is termed a "quint." However, operating efficiency and capability tends to decrease if too many functions are to be performed by one piece of apparatus. And, if one feature of the apparatus requires repair, the entire apparatus must be taken out of service.

Increasingly, apparatus is being designed to improve its functional performance. Initial fire-attack capability for pumpers not only includes a variety of pre-connected hose lines but frequently also includes pre-connected master-stream capability or elevated-stream equipment. Pumpers are often built with considerable compartment space for emergency service and medical equipment and may serve as combination rescue pumpers.

NFPA has promulgated four standards for the design of fire apparatus. These are NFPA 1901, *Standard for Pumper Fire Apparatus*; NFPA 1902, *Standard for Initial Attack Fire Apparatus*; NFPA 1903, *Standard for Mobile Water Supply Fire Apparatus*; and NFPA 1904, *Standard for Aerial Ladder and Elevating Platform Fire Apparatus.*

A.K. Rosenhan is president of A. K. Rosenhan Consulting Engineers, Ltd., in Mississippi State, MS.

NFPA 1901 deals with the design, performance, functions, and components of pumper fire apparatus. Pumpers are defined as vehicles designed for sustained pumping operations during structural fire fighting and for supporting associated fire department operations. The standard requires a pump of at least 750 gpm capacity, a water tank of 500 gallons, storage for both supply hose and pre-connected fire fighting hose lines and miscellaneous equipment. One chapter deals with various auxiliary systems that are often installed on pumpers. These include an auxiliary pump, a 120/240-volt electrical system, a foam system, a booster reel, and a water tower.

NFPA 1902 deals with the design, performance, functions, and components of an initial-attack fire apparatus. These are defined as vehicles designed for making the initial fire suppression attack on structural, vehicular, or vegetation fires and for supporting associated fire department operations. The standard requires a pump of between 250 and 700 gpm capacity, a water tank of at least 200 gallons, storage for a small amount of supply hose, pre-connected fire fighting hose lines, and limited equipment. As in NFPA 1901, one chapter of NFPA 1902 deals with various auxiliary systems that are often installed on these vehicles, which include an auxiliary pump, a 120/240-volt electrical system, a foam system, and a booster reel.

NFPA 1903 deals with the design, performance, functions, and components of a mobile water-supply vehicle. These are defined as vehicles designed to transport water to the scene of an emergency to be applied there by other vehicles or pumping equipment. The standard requires a water tank of at least 1000 gallons with quick-fill and -dump capability, as well as limited hose and equipment to support the pickup and dumping of the water. The standard provides requirements if a pump is installed or if a 120/240-volt electrical system is installed.

NFPA 1904 deals with the design, performance, functions, and components of an aerial-ladder or elevating-platform fire apparatus. These are defined as vehicles designed to provide elevated fire fighting and rescue capability. The standard requires a power-operated, self-supporting aerial device capable of attaining an elevation of at least 50 ft. Aerial ladders are required to support at least 250 lbs at the tip in any position in which they can be placed. The elevated platform must be able to support at least 750 lbs in any position in which it can be placed. The standard provides requirements if a pump is installed. One chapter deals with various auxiliary systems that are often installed on these vehicles, including an auxiliary pump, a 120/240-volt electrical system, a foam system, and a booster reel.

All four documents define performance requirements for the apparatus and define tests to measure this performance. In the appendix of each document, there are explanations of the requirements and details, as well as work sheets, to assist in the purchase of the apparatus.

Persons buying the apparatus must specify the options that make it suitable for local needs. For example, requirements for fighting large brush fires in southern California are quite different from those for fighting fires in below-zero weather in northern Minnesota. The standard provides for standardization of many items for which uniform performance, measurable by tests, is desirable, but it allows the necessary flexibility to meet local needs that could not be supplied by one assembly-line production. Such differences include rated pump capacity, water-tank capacity, length of aerial ladders, height of elevating platforms, and many other important design features.

Besides the functional characteristics of a piece of fire apparatus, considerable thought should be given to personnel safety and operations. The design of the vehicle's driving compartment and riding spaces, and the location of various components should be studied carefully. Only fully enclosed driving and crew compartments with sufficient seating for all fire fighters who are expected to ride on the apparatus should be specified. Fire fighters should never be allowed to ride standing up or in exposed positions on the rear or sides of the apparatus. The use of seat belts must be mandatory in all cases.

The pump operator's panel may be positioned to the side, to the rear, or in a top midships position. The position of valve controls and other control equipment will affect the overall efficient and safe operation of the apparatus. The better the operator's view, the more effective he or she can be. Care should also be taken to design the operator's position so that he or she can safely operate all controls without having to straddle hose lines.

Engines in Fire Apparatus

Engines may be either diesel or gasoline types, but there are few gasoline engines capable of supplying sufficient power for modern apparatus. The engine size and horsepower must be chosen to correspond with the conditions of service and apparatus design. All apparatus must have enough power to move it over the road network on which it is expected to operate. Road tests are conducted with apparatus fully loaded with hose, water, ground ladders, the applicable personnel weight, and an equipment allowance weight. From a standing start, through the gears, the vehicle must attain a true speed of 35 mph (56 km/h) within 25 sec. The vehicle must also accelerate from 15 to 35 mph (24 to 56 km/h) in 30 sec without the operator moving the gear selector. This demonstrates that the vehicle has the necessary pick up to operate safely and efficiently in traffic. The vehicle must attain a top speed of at least 50 mph (80 km/h) and must be able to maintain a speed of at least 20 mph (32 km/h) on any grade up to and including 6 percent. While these tests demonstrate the power needed to negotiate the grades found in most communities, any special requirements needed to climb very steep grades should be specified, and the finished apparatus should be tested to those requirements.

Carrying capacity is one of the most important, but least understood, features of a vehicle. The gross axle weight rating (GAWR) and gross vehicle weight rating (GVWR) of the apparatus must be adequate to carry the weight of the fully equipped and staffed vehicle. This includes 200 lbs (76 kg) per person personnel weight, a full water tank, the specified hose load, ground ladders, and a miscellaneous equipment allowance.

One of the critical factors is the size of the water tank. Water weighs about 8⅓ lbs per U.S. gallon (1 kg/L). A value of 10 lbs (4.54 kg) per gallon is often used when estimating the weight of a full water tank, making a full 500-gallon (1892 L) tank 2½ tons (2.27 metric tons). Larger tanks mean heavier vehicles which may have limited mobility on rural roads and bridges. The efficiency of mobile water-supply apparatus, in transporting water to a fire, depends upon the vehicle's over-the-road mobility. Any apparatus that weights too much for local operating conditions severly limits the capabilities of the fire department.

Too many fire departments seriously overload apparatus by adding more equipment than the vehicle was designed to carry. The fire apparatus standards specify minimum equipment allowances of 2000 lb (909 kg) for pumpers, up to 2000 lbs (907 kg) for initial attack vehicles depending upon their size, 1000 lbs (454 kg) for mobile water supply apparatus, and 2500 lbs (1136 kg) for aerial-ladder and elevating-platform fire apparatus. Part of the purchase process should be to ensure that sufficient additional allowance is provided when needed.

GAWR is the value specified by the vehicle manufacturer as the loaded weight on a single-axle system, and GCWR (gross combination weight rating) is the value specified by the manufacturer as the loaded weight of a combination vehicle, such as a tractor-trailer unit. GVWR is the value specified by the manufacturer as the loaded weight of a single vehicle, and is the sum of the weights of the chassis, body, cab, equipment, water, fuel, crew, and all other loads. A number of components that affect the GVWR, such as the springs or suspension system, the rated axle capacity, the rated tire loading, and the weight distribution between the front and rear axles. All chassis are designed with a "rated GVWR," or maximum total weight, that should not be exceeded by the apparatus manufacturer or by the fire department after the vehicle has been placed in service.

The improper distribution of weight between the front and rear wheels can make a vehicle difficult to control and may require tires of different sizes to carry the load. Overloading of the vehicle not only affects the handling characteristics but will result in increased maintenance problems with transmissions, clutches, the drive-train, and brakes, as well as suspension systems and tires.

Compliance with Federal Standards

The federal government has promulgated motor vehicle safety standards that are applicable to all vehicles, including fire apparatus. This legislation is enforced by the U.S. Department of Transportation (DOT). It is unlawful to sell a vehicle that is not in compliance with the current federal standards. Manufacturers should not build fire apparatus that does not conform to these standards. Because fire apparatus is complex and often requires considerable lead time between the signing of a contract and delivery, the federal regulations provide that the standards in effect at the time the contract is signed shall be those complied with, provided the apparatus is delivered within two years.

Additional requirements are placed on the apparatus and engine manufacturers by the Clean Air Act, which is enforced by the Environmental Protection Agency (EPA). Engines cannot be modified once approved by the EPA. These standards have resulted in some downgrading in engine performance, often resulting in the need to use larger engines than previously employed to obtain the same performance. Likewise, more frequent maintenance checks are often required due to the pollution-control equipment now required.

Electrical Power for Apparatus

Sufficient electrical capacity for the vehicle and its components is a major requirement for fire apparatus. Electricity is essential to start the apparatus reliably under all temperature and weather conditions. Emergency warning lights and sirens impose a heavy electrical demand, with vehicle lighting and communication equipment as an added load. Electric rewind hose reels, pump controls, scene lighting, and electrically operated tools can all impose additional loads. Much of the equipment must perform when the apparatus is idling at a fire or other emergency and the engine is not producing maximum output from the alternator.

Batteries, which are an integral part of the electrical system, must be a minimum of 1000 cold-cranking amps (CCA) and of the high-cycle type. However, the batteries should not be expected to carry the electrical load when the engine is idling as many of the electronic components on modern apparatus will not function properly if the voltage drops by 10 percent or more. It is also critical to provide a means for keeping the batteries charged while the apparatus is in the station. This can be done with an onboard battery conditioner or charger or with a polarized plug for connection to an external charger.

Pumps for Fire Apparatus

A fire pump is defined as a pump of at least 750 gpm at 150 psi net pump pressure. It must be capable of pumping 70 percent of its capacity at 200 psi net pump pressure and 50 percent of its capacity at 250 psi net pump pressure. Pumps larger than 750 gpm are rated in 250-gpm (947-L) increments —for example, at 1000, 1250, 1500 gpm and so on (3785, 4732, 5678 L/min, respectively). When new, fire pumps are certified by tests witnessed by an independent third party. The certification test includes, among other things, a test at draft during which the pump must deliver its rated capacity for 2 hr at 150 psi (1034 kPa) net pump pressure, followed by two half-hour periods during which 70 percent of rated capacity is delivered at 200 psi (1379 kPa) net pump pressure and 50 percent of rated capacity at 250 psi (1724 kPa) net pump pressure. The apparatus must also perform a 10-min overload test, discharging rated pump capacity at 165 psi (1138 kPa) net pump presure to demonstrate reserve engine power.

An attack pump is defined as a pump of at least 250 gpm but not more than 700 gpm at 150 psi net pump pressure. Like fire pumps, they must be capable of pumping 70 percent of their capacity at 200 psi net pump pressure and 50 percent of their capacity at 250 psi net pump pressure. Typically, attack pumps are not designed for long-duration pumping, although they must meet a 50-min pump test and can be designed for longer operation. Attack pumps are typically certified by the apparatus manufacturer, and the tests are not witnessed by an independent third party.

A third type of pump, designated as a transfer pump, is used to assist in filling or dumping water tanks on fire apparatus. These pumps have a minimum rated capacity of 250 gpm at 50 psi and are typically used with mobile water-supply apparatus.

The design requirements for fire and attack pumps include the ability to develop 22 in. of mercury vacuum at 2000 feet of elevation and the ability to deliver rated capacity at up to ten feet of lift through twenty feet of suction hose. Where a pump on a piece of apparatus is expected to perform at an altitude above 2000 ft (610 m), the purchaser must advise the apparatus manufacturer of the altitude and advise whether a 10-ft (3 m) lift-suction capability is required, so that the proper engine and pump can be provided.

The pump and the attached piping and valves are designed for 500 psi hydrostatic pressure. Depending upon the size of the pump, one or two large suction intakes and at least one auxiliary gated suction intake is required. This auxiliary intake is normally a 2½-in. (65 mm) intake and is provided so an additional water-supply line can be taken into the pump without shutting down. It is also a means of connecting a supply line in mutual-aid operations if hose connections for the large intake are not compatible. As the large suction intake provides the least restriction, normal supply to the pump should be through that intake, whether directly or through a suction siamese.

Discharge piping from the pump feeds a variety of outlets and, in some cases, may feed a master stream device directly. Fire pumps are required to have two 2½-in. (65 mm) discharge outlets and enough additional outlets to allow the capacity of the pump to be discharged. If the apparatus is equipped with an aerial device with a pre-piped waterway, the pump must be piped directly to the waterway.

To control the development of water hammer in the pump and hose lines, any 3-in. (76 mm) or larger valve should be designed to restrict changing the position of the flow-regulating element from full close to full open, or vice versa, in less than 3 sec. The pump should be further protected by a permanently installed intake pressure-relief system which is 2½ in. (65 mm) or larger and discharges directly to the atmosphere. The surplus-water-discharge location should be away from the pump operator's position and terminate in a male fitting so hose can be attached to carry any water away from the apparatus.

The pressure on the discharge side of the pump must also be controlled, either through an automatic relief valve or a pressure regulator that controls the speed of the pump. The device should limit the pressure rise upon activation to a maximum of 30 psi (207 kPa) and be capable of operating over a range of 90 to 300 psig (620 to 2070 kPa) discharge pressure.

Generally, a fire pump is powered by the vehicle engine through a transfer case that redirects power from the rear wheels to the pump itself. Power is transferred with the vehicle in a stationary position and only after a parking brake has been set. An interlock should be provided to ensure that the engine speed cannot be advanced until the parking brake is set, the transfer is complete, and the chassis transmission is either in neutral or in the correct gear for pumping. Otherwise, the apparatus may move when the engine speed is advanced.

On smaller pumps, the power is often transferred to the pump through a power takeoff (PTO) device. In some designs, the pump is mounted at the front of the chassis where it is driven through a clutch arrangement from the front of the engine.

Hose Carrying Capability

The amount of hose carried should be sufficient to suport the function of the apparatus. Operations involving pumpers typically need the most hose, and pumpers should carry a minimum of 1200 ft (366 m) of 2½-in. (65 mm) or larger hose and 400 ft (122 m) of 1½-in. (38 mm), 1¾-in. (44 mm), or 2-in. (51 mm) hose. However, many fire departments carry a minimum of 2000 ft (610 m) of 2½-in. (65 mm) or larger hose, and 800 to 1000 ft (244 to 305 m) of 1½-in. (38 mm), 1¾-in. (44 mm), or 2-in. (51 mm) hose on their pumpers to permit more versatile use of the apparatus.

Increasingly, fire departments are using hose of diameters larger than the nominal 2½-in. (65 mm) size. While larger diameter hose costs more, it may actually be more economical, since multiple smaller hose lines would be required to meet the increased carrying capacity through one large-diameter line. A standard hose body for pumpers has at least 55 cu ft (1.56 m^3) of space and is designed to provide a split hose load if desired. By splitting a hose load into two bed sections, either one long lay or a shorter-double hose line can be made quickly, saving considerably on the time and personnel needed to establish flows approaching the capacity of the pumper. Where larger diameter hose is to be used, a larger hose storage area may be needed.

With larger capacity pumps now commonplace, additional hose capacity is required to move larger volumes of water. A convenient way to relate needed hose capacity to pumper discharge capability is based on the relative water-carrying capacity of various sizes of hose at normal operating pressures, as follows: 250 gpm (946 L/min) for 2½-in. (65 mm) hose; 350 gpm (1325 L/min) for 3-in. (76 mm) hose; 500 gpm (1893 L/min) for 3½-in. (89 mm) hose; 750 gpm (2839 L/min) for 4-in. (100 mm) hose; and 1300 gpm (4921 L/min) for 5-in. (125 mm) hose. Thus, moving 500 gpm (1893 L/min) 1000 ft (305 m) requires 2000 feet (610 m) of 2½-in. (65 mm) hose or 1000 feet (305 m) of 3½-in. (89 mm) hose. In short lines, some increases in flow may be obtained by higher discharge pressures, but in longer hose lines, increased flow will be minimal.

Auxiliary Pumps

Some fire apparatus will have a separate pump for small-volume/high-pressure operations. Other designs use a third stage in the main pump to develop the higher pressures. If an auxiliary pump is provided and is interconnected with a fire or attack pump, suitable valving and controls should be provided to preclude the introduction of higher pressures into piping and fire hoses not designed for the pressure.

Auxiliary pumps used predominantly for fighting grass fires and other small fires usually have a capacity of up to 100 gpm (379 L/min) at pressures not exceeding 250 psi (1724 kPa). Often, pumps used on grass fires are designed to operate when the apparatus is in motion. Some vehicles will have separate engines to drive the pump so "pump and roll" operations may be accomplished without mechanical complexity. Likewise, the use of skid-mounted, self-contained fire fighting packages, complete with pump and engine, water tank, hose, and equipment, allows any vehicle to transport the unit.

Water Tanks

The majority of fire apparatus equipped with pumps are also equipped with water tanks. The tank supplies water to the pump for initial hose streams before water from hydrants or suction sources is available. Pumpers carry a minimum of 500 gallons (1893 L) of water, initial attack vehicles carry a minimum of 200 gallons (760 L), and mobile water-supply vehicles carry a minimum of 1000 gallons (3785 L). Water tanks supplied on aerial apparatus should hold a minimum of 150 (568 L) gallons.

All water tanks should be constructed of noncorrosive material or materials that are protected against corrosion and deterioration. They should also be equipped with a water-level indicator visible at the pump operator's position. One or more sumps with a 3-in. (76-mm) or larger removable pipe plug should be provided so that debris in the tank can be cleaned out.

All tanks must have baffles to minimize water surging when the vehicle is in motion. The dimension of any spaces in the tank, either transverse or longitudinal, should not exceed 48 in. (1220 mm) nor be less than 23 in. (584 mm). The baffle arrangement should allow an adequate flow rate from the tank to the pump, which is typically tested to 80 percent of the tank capacity.

The tank fill opening should be at least 20 sq in. (12900 mm^2) and vents/overflows at least 12 sq in. (7742 mm^2). The venting must be matched to the maximum fill and discharge rate so as not to overpressure the tank. The overflow outlet should direct any water behind the rear axle so as not to interfere with rear-tire traction.

Tanks that hold more than 1000 gal (3785 L) should have a single outlet capable of allowing water to be dumped from the tank at an average rate of 1000 gpm (3785 L/min). Likewise, a single external fill connection should be provided that permits a minimum filling rate of 1000 gpm (3785 L/min) from sources outside to the unit.

Aerial Ladders

Aerial ladders have been used by fire departments for more than a century to gain access to the upper floors and roofs of buildings. The first aerials were manually operated before spring-assist and air hoists were introduced. Current aerial ladders are steel or aluminum truss construction with hydraulic hoists and ladder controls.

Common sizes of aerial ladders are 75, 85, 100, 110, and 135 ft (22.8, 25.9, 30.5, 33.5, and 41.1 m). The rated height of an aerial is measured by a plumb line from the top ladder rung to the ground with the ladder fully extended at its maximum elevation. These ladders can be mounted on a single-chassis vehicle or a tractor-drawn vehicle. The rear-mount aerial ladder has become common. This arrangement places the turntable over the rear wheels, with the ladder extending forward when bedded, which results in shorter overall vehicle lengths. In some cases, a shorter aerial ladder mounted on a pumper chassis provides a useful combination of devices for fire attack.

Aerial ladders must have a minimum width of 18 in. (457 mm) at the narrowest point of the ladder. Rungs must be spaced on 14-in. (356-mm) centers, and the top rails along the sides must be at least 12 in. (305 mm) high. The ladder must support 250 lbs (114 kg) at the tip of the fly section with the ladder fully extended in a horizontal position without water in any permanently piped water system. It must support the same weight at the tip of the fly section with the ladder at 45 degrees with water flowing.

Aerial ladders may be equipped with a fixed waterway to the tip of the fly section or some other section. Where such a waterway is provided, it should be capable of flowing 1000 gpm at 100 psi nozzle pressure through a 45-degree, side-to-side range of motions and through an arc of 135 degrees from a line parallel to the ladder and downward. Often, the monitor and nozzle on these systems are controlled remotely by electric wires or radio control. The friction loss in the water system between the base of the swivel and the monitor outlet should not exceed 100 psi (690 kPa) with 1000 gpm (3785 L/min) flowing and the water system at full extension.

When the aerial ladder is not equipped with a prepiped water way, a detachable ladder pipe provides elevated fire-stream service. When supplied by 3-in. (76 mm) hose up the ladder, 600 gpm (2271 L/min) is the practical maximum which can be supplied in normal fireground operations. The ladder pipe is provided with 1¼-, 1⅜-, and 1½-in. (32, 35, and 38 mm) tips and with a 500-gpm (1893 L/min) spray nozzle.

The aerial ladder must be stable when a load one-and-a-half times the rated capacity is suspended from its tip while the aerial ladder is in its least stable position and the vehicle on which the ladder is mounted is on a firm, level surface with the stabilizers extended to a firm footing. The aerial ladder must also be stable when a load one-and-a-third times the rated capacity is suspended from its tip when the vehicle on which it is mounted is placed on a firm surface that slopes downward at five degrees in the direction most likely to cause it to overturn. Again, the stabilizers are extended to a firm footing. The stability of the apparatus is checked during the certification tests, and the vehicle cannot show any signs of instability during these tests.

Elevating Platforms

Elevating platforms are of three principal designs. In one, the platform is mounted on an articulated boom that travels in the arc desired by the operator. In the second, the platform is mounted on an extendable or telescopic boom, in much the same fashion as an aerial ladder. In the third design, the platform is mounted on booms that are both articulated and telescopic.

Platforms are available with booms designed for elevations from approximately 75 ft to more than 200 ft (23 m to 61 m). The rated height of an elevating platform is measured by a plumb line from the top rail of the platform to the ground, with the platform raised to its maximum elevation. In selecting an elevating platform, it is important to know its reach and elevation capabilities under operating conditions. The articulated-boom design provides its maximum horizontal reach at approximately half of its maximum elevation. The extendable telescopic boom of the same nominal length generally permits somewhat greater horizontal reach at higher and lower elevations. The telescopic boom often has an extending ladder attached to it, which provides access to and from the platform while it is elevated.

All designs provide stable platforms with controls located both on the platform and at ground level. The ground-level controls must be able to override the platform controls so an operator on the ground can move the platform away from danger if the platform operator is in trouble.

An elevating platform should be able to carry a load of at least 750 lbs (340 kg) in all operating positions without the water system charged. Units of 110 ft or less should be able to reach their maximum elevation and extension and to rotate 90 degrees within 150 seconds. An advantage of an elevating platform in operation is that the platform can be moved quickly from window to window for fire fighting or rescue purposes.

Platforms are designed to provide elevated fire streams. The platform turret or turrets must be able to rotate through at least 45 degrees up, down, and to each side. The mobility of the platform permits the operator to change the turret location quickly, as desired. The apparatus must be designed so that, regardless of the position of the platform and the direction of the stream, the equipment can be operated safely while discharging 1000 gpm (3785 L/min) at 100 psi (690 kPa) nozzle pressure. The friction loss in the water system between the base of the swivel and the monitor outlet should not exceed 100 psi (690 kPa) with 1000 gpm (3785 L/min) flowing and the water system at full extension.

The stability requirements described above for aerial ladders also apply to elevating platforms. In addition, there are requirements in NFPA 1904 for the hydraulic system, for the structure, and for quality control during manufacture which apply to both aerial ladders and elevating platforms.

Water Towers

The success of elevating platforms on the fireground during the 1960s was a prelude to the use of hydraulically operated water towers designed to apply large flows on a fire from effective heights and positions. Such water towers have proven very useful and have been widely accepted in both large and small communities as an important addition to the attack capabilities of a pumper. Water towers are designed to discharge 1000 gpm (3785 L/min) or more at 100 psi nozzle pressure in either a straight stream or a spray pattern and to move the boom and the nozzle both horizontally and vertically under the control of the operator for the best application of water on the fire.

Like elevating platforms, water towers may be of either articulated or telescopic boom design. Heights typically range from 50 to 75 ft (15.2 to 22.9 m). The telescopic type may be equipped with a ladder extending the full length of the boom. In those cases, the ladder should meet the same requirements as an aerial ladder.

Because water towers are typically installed on pumpers, the requirements are covered in NFPA 1901. The tower is mounted on a turntable or pedestal to permit it to rotate 360 degrees in either direction and rotate with the nozzle operating at rated capacity. All controls are typically grouped at the pump operator's position so the operator has full control of the pressure, volume, and stream pattern and position.

The stability requirements described for aerial ladders also apply to water towers. There are also requirements for the hydraulic system, the structure, and quality control during manufacture in NFPA 1901 similar to the requirements in NFPA 1904 for aerial ladders and elevating platforms.

Foam-Proportioning Equipment

Where the potential for encountering serious flammable-liquid fires is present, many fire departments provide on the apparatus various types of foam-making equipment or other agents that are more effective than plain water. Built-in proportioners and foam tanks are often specified for new pumpers. In other cases, foam-making nozzles, portable foam- making equipment, and foam supplies are carried on the apparatus. Foams are available not only to seal off the surface of flammable liquid fires and smother the fire, but foams for class-A fires are becoming particularly popular for wildland-fire suppression application. Special foams are also available for certain types of polar solvent/alcohol and unusual liquid fires.

Portable Pumps

In selecting portable pumps, fire departments should be careful to choose models that will give the needed flow characteristics at a safe, continuous engine speed. Portable pumps for fire department service are covered in NFPA 1921, *Standard for Fire Department Portable Pumping Units*.

Portable pumps for fire department service are of the centrifugal type. They are grouped in categories based upon the pressure-volume characteristics that make them suitable for various classes of work. Small streams at high pressure are intended mainly for grass and brush fire operations. Pumps delivering relatively large volumes at low pressures can supply pumps on fire apparatus where the water supply is beyond the reach of suction hose or refilling water tanks. These pumps also may be used as de-watering pumps.

Communication Equipment

Effective communications is essential for any fire department operation. Every fire department vehicle should be equipped with a two-way radio that operates on all frequencies used for dispatch and fireground communication. It is highly desirable to provide a radio speaker and microphone at the apparatus-operator's position so messages can be heard above the usual noise on the fireground. In addition, each vehicle, as well as chief officers' vehicles, should carry portable radios for effective fireground communications.

Vehicles also may be equipped to send and receive hard-copy messages or to receive visual displays of information, including maps and fire-hazard data that may be transmitted from the communication center. Cellular telephones are also becoming extremely popular in chief's vehicles to provide communication directly with parties outside the fire department radio network.

Specialized Apparatus

There is a wide diversity of fire apparatus designed for special types of service. These units should be designed with the rigors of fire duty in mind and should conform to the general requirements outlined in the fire apparatus standards.

Many fire departments operate a vehicle to support rescue services carrying equipment that deals with everything from emergency medical service to vehicle extrication to building collapse. The larger of these vehicles are typically equipped with a large 120/240-volt electric generator, hydraulic rescue tools, and a wide variety of hand tools, power tools, and devices for jacking, shoring, cutting, and breaching. This emergency equipment typically supplements that carried on pumpers and ladder trucks. Many rescue vehicles have fully enclosed bodies to provide places for personnel to ride, to provide shelter for emergency medical treatment, and to provide an environment for incident-scene rehabilitation during inclement weather.

Fire departments are equipping vehicles to support hazardous-materials operations. The size and amount of equipment on these vehicles will vary with the role that the fire department sees for itself in such operations. Typically, these vehicles carry a library of materials to assist in identifying a hazardous material, tools and equipment for shutting valves or stopping leaks, materials for diking or absorbing spills, and special drums for recovering leaking drums. Specialized clothing to protect the fire fighters while they are working in the contaminated area is also carried.

A SCBA (self-contained breathing apparatus) service unit is designed to field service SCBAs and recharge depleted air cylinders on the fireground. These vehicles may carry numerous extra SCBA cylinders for merely exchanging cylinders, several large air cylinders arranged to allow for refilling of SCBA cylinders in the field, and both large cylinders and a high-pressure air compressor for filling SCBA cylinders in the field. Small fire departments may not need a separate vehicle, but every fire department should be able to or provide full SCBA tanks in the field.

Some fire departments find it advantageous to have separate vehicles with large generators to provide 120/240-volt electricity. These units may have a generator of 15,000 W or larger. The generator may be driven by its own engine; hydraulically, with the hydraulic pump driven by the vehicle engine; or directly from a power take off (PTO) on the vehicle's transmission. These units typically carry floodlights, electric cord and adapters, and various power tools.

It is important that any electrical wiring or equipment on an emergency vehicle be properly installed and grounded. This equipment is typically used under conditions of extreme wetness, where failure to properly install and maintain the electrical integrity of the wiring and equipment will result in injury or death to persons using the equipment.

Another specialized vehicle is the wildland fire apparatus. Generally, these are smaller vehicles, frequently equipped with all-wheel drive, a small water tank, forestry hose, a small-volume/high-pressure pump, a number of portable water extinguishers, and various hand tools for fighting wildland fires. Larger vehicles may have a 500-gpm (1893-L/min) front-mounted or PTO pump and a 500-gal (1893-L) or larger water tank to support initial fire attack on all types of fires, whether wildland, vehicular, or structural.

Chief Officers' Vehicles

Many fire departments find it essential to provide transportation for staff and command officers. In the larger fire departments, sizeable fleets of automobiles are maintained. Automobile transportation is necessary for chief officers, fire prevention officers and inspectors, training officers, communications officers, fire investigators, and others. Some fire departments pay a mileage allowance for the use of private cars. This is not a good arrangement, especially where response to emergencies may be involved, as private vehicles are not properly equipped with warning lights and sirens or otherwise properly marked. They also may not be properly insured for that type of service.

All fire department vehicles, including automobiles, that respond to fires and emergencies must be equipped with warning lights, sirens, and radio communication facilities with the emergency networks, including mutual-aid frequencies, on which the department operates. The vehicles should be clearly identified as fire department vehicles. They should carry protective clothing and equipment for the officers and their aides, as well as portable fire extinguishers, first-aid equipment, and hand lights. If the vehicle is being used by command officers, it should also carry directories containing pre-fire plans on properties in the area served, water distribution plans, and reference books on hazardous materials.

Many fire departments provide their command officers with station wagons or similar style vehicles in which the necessary equipment is mounted for ready access.

Fireboats

Fireboats are available in various sizes and types, in accordance with local needs, and vary from large tugs to fast, jet-propelled fire and rescue craft. They may be operated by fire departments or port authorities. U.S. Navy and Coast Guard vessels also are equipped to provide fire fighting service.

Fireboats are principally used to protect vessels in the harbor; protect piers, pier sheds, and cargoes along the waterfront; protect yachts and houseboats in basins and marinas; assist in marine rescue from all types of water accidents; and serve as pumping stations to provide large flows at fires within reach of hose lines supplied by the boats. Fireboats also may provide a valuable emergency source of water for fire protection should an earthquake or other accident interrupt the normal supply. Some fire departments operate hose trucks or "fireboat tenders" that carry large-diameter hose to allow fireboat pumping capacity to be used at shore fires along the waterfront.

The size, type, pumping capacity, and equipment carried by fireboats will depend upon the type of service expected of the vessels. Fireboats must carry much of the same equipment as pumpers, ladder trucks, and rescue vehicles on land. They need foam-making equipment and may carry quantities of special extinguishing agents. Fireboats need radar, as well as radio communication, for safe operation under all weather conditions and, at times, in heavy smoke. Self-contained breathing apparatus is essential for fireboat crews.

Pumping capacity for individual fireboats varies from 500 gpm (1893 L/min) for very small craft to 10,000 gpm (37,854 L/min) or more for larger vessels. Pumping capacity is rated at 150 psi (1034 kPa) discharge pressure, as with pumpers. Some small jet-powered fireboats rely upon their jet pumps to supply water for fire fighting. These pumps may develop substantial volumes at pressures adequate to supply turret nozzles attached to the pump, but it may be difficult to provide the necessary pressure to supply the hose streams to fight ship fires or fires ashore, unless additional pumps are provided to meet standard pressure requirements.

Airport Crash Trucks

Specialized apparatus is required for aircraft rescue and fire fighting service at airports. In many cities, such equipment is part of the municipal fire department. In others, it is maintained and operated by an airport authority. NFPA 414, *Standard for Aircraft Rescue and Fire Fighting Vehicles*, covers the design and performance requirements for aircraft rescue and fire fighting vehicles equipped for rescuing occupants and combating fires in aircraft at or near an airport.

NFPA 414 covers three types of vehicles: major fire fighting vehicles, Rapid Intervention Vehicles (RIV), and combined-agent vehicles. RIVs are intended to reach the emergency site quickly so rescue operations can be started before the major vehicles arrive. Airport crash apparatus should include a small rescue vehicle, which can also serve as a command car, and a nurse tanker carrying additional water and extinguishing agents where needed. Crash trucks can be modified to fight fires in hangars and other airport structures, but this should not detract from the primary function of these vehicles.

Because of off-highway performance needs, the vehicle weight of crash trucks should be distributed equally over all wheels. These vehicles need greater axle and chassis clearances than standard fire apparatus, as well as high acceleration characteristics. Positive drive to each wheel is required to negotiate soft ground, snow, and ice. The positive drive can be provided by torque proportioning, or no spin differentials, or by other automatic devices that ensure that each wheel, rather than the axle, is driven independently.

EQUIPMENT CARRIED ON APPARATUS

Apparatus must be equipped with the tools necessary to accomplish fireground operations. The NFPA fire apparatus standards include listings of equipment and appliances needed with various types of fire apparatus.

When developing specifications for fire apparatus, the fire department must evaluate its operation and determine how the apparatus will be used in its operation and what equipment will be necessary to support its operation.

Most fire apparatus carry some hose. Pumpers typically carry the most hose, as the operational purpose of a pumper is to establish a continuous water supply and apply water on the fire. Use of larger-diameter supply hose [(4 in. (100-mm) and 5 in. (125 mm)] for pumping apparatus is becoming more common, and the length to be carried will depend on such things as hydrant spacing and distances to water supply points. Attack hose in 1½-, 1¾-, or 2-in. (38-, 44-, or 51-mm) diameters is common for handheld hose lines for interior attack, and 2½-in (65-mm) diameter hose lines are common when larger flows are required during exterior attack or to protect exposures. A variety of nozzles that will produce both spray and straight streams should be carried for the various sizes of hose.

Fire department ground ladders are an important tool for rescuing persons and gaining access to buildings for fire fighting purposes. Ladders may be constructed of wood, aluminum, or fiberglass. All ground ladders used in the fire service should be designed and built to conform to NFPA 1931, *Standard on Design of and Design Verification Tests for Fire Department Ground Ladders*.

Loads that fire ladders are designed to support vary according to the type of ladder. Extension ladders, single ladders, and roof ladders built since 1984 are designed for 750 lbs (340 kg) maximum load, while folding and pompier ladders are designed for 300 lbs (136 kg) maximum load. Load limitations are based on the use of the ladder supported at the top end against a building, and with the ladder set at a 75½-degree angle. This angle is measured from the horizontal, with the ladder in the raised position. At angles smaller than this, the ladder may be unable to support the design load.

While the apparatus standards list the minimum requirements for ground ladders on each type of vehicle, careful consideration should be given to the ladder needs of the area served. Manually raised extension ladders more than 40 ft (12 m) long are generally not required, because aerial ladders and elevating platforms provide adequate emergency access to upper floors and roofs. If congested conditions prohibit the placement of aerial apparatus to provide effective aerial service, however, additional or longer ground ladders should be provided. It must be recognized that additional personnel are required to raise longer ladders and that the space available for ladders on some vehicles is limited.

Besides hose, nozzles, and ground ladders, fire fighters need a wide variety of other equipment to perform their jobs. This includes cutting tools for forcing entry and ventilating smoke from a building, smoke ejectors for ventilation, salvage covers for protecting unburned contents, and a variety of fittings for use with hose lines. The complement of equipment carried will vary from department to department based on the needs and operations of the companies. It is critical that sufficient space and carrying weight be allotted for the equipment when the apparatus is designed so the equipment does not cause the apparatus to become overweight.

APPARATUS PROCUREMENT POLICIES

The responsibility for procurement of fire apparatus and equipment should rest with the agency operating the fire department, whether a municipality, a fire district, or private industry. In some cases, procurement is a cooperative measure in which a larger unit of government contributes to the cost of providing fire apparatus for fire departments serving its territory. In a few cases, state governments contribute to local fire apparatus costs. In some areas, several fire departments have banded together to generate standard apparatus specifications to buy apparatus in quantity and realize significant cost savings. Various fire department groups also cooperate in volume purchases of hose and other equipment.

When the fire department is an agency of municipal government, it is the responsibility of the latter to provide for all public fire fighting equipment. Providing the necessary monies is the responsibility of the appropriate fiscal authorities, but the actual selection of the equipment should be the responsibility of the fire department management. The chief administrative officer of the fire department, aided by a staff of technical specialists, including a master mechanic, should keep the municipal administrator informed of the age and condition of department equipment and should prepare specifications consistent with applicable national standards for items that need to be replaced. In autonomous volunteer fire departments, there may be a purchasing committee appointed to procure apparatus. In municipalities, the actual purchase is usually handled by a municipal purchasing department. The purchasing department should not try to tell the fire department what type of fire apparatus it should use, but should see that required procurement procedures, such as open competitive bidding, are followed.

The appendices of the fire apparatus standards contain helpful suggestions covering the purchase of fire apparatus, including developing specifications, reviewing proposals, dealing with manufacturers, and acceptance of the completed apparatus.

In general, the purchase and replacement costs of fire apparatus should be a regular item of the fire department capital budget. In most cases, except for accidents, the requirements can be planned and funded on a long-range basis. Systematic apparatus replacement provides the fire department with reliable apparatus at all times. Improvements in fire apparatus design can be introduced, maintenance costs become more favorable, operating efficiency increases, and equipment remains reliable.

Lease or lease/purchase of fire apparatus can be an alternative to outright purchase. Income tax benefits and depreciation accrue to the actual, commercial owner of the apparatus, while the fire department, which is tax exempt realizes savings in overall life-cycle cost. In addition, the department does not have to expend a large purchase price at one time, but can spread the cost of apparatus over several years. Further, there is no capital tied up in the event the department wishes to trade, exchange, or dispose of the apparatus. Closed and open-ended leases are available, and the finance department of the municipality should evaluate these alternatives carefully. In a smaller or volunteer department, a local banker can advise the purchasers of the advantages of a lease versus a purchase arrangement.

Any lease or lease/purchase contract should clearly spell out who is responsible for maintenance, repairs, and liability. Likewise, the conditions under which the arrangement may be terminated, by either party, should be stated clearly.

The normal life expectancy for first-line fire apparatus will vary from city to city, depending upon the amount of use the equipment receives and the adequacy of the maintenance program. In general, a ten- to fifteen-year life expectancy is considered normal for first-line pumping engines. First-line ladder trucks should have a normal life expectancy of at least fifteen years. In fire departments where ladder trucks make substantially fewer responses to alarms than engines, a planned first-line service of twenty years may be warranted for ladder trucks. Some smaller fire departments that have infrequent alarms operate pumping engines up to twenty years with reasonable efficiency, although obsolescence will make older apparatus less desirable even if it is mechanically functional. In some types of service, including areas of high fire frequency, a limit of ten years may be reasonable for first-line service. The older apparatus may be maintained as part of the reserve fleet as long as it is in good condition, but in almost no case should the fire department rely on any apparatus more than twenty-five years old.

Acceptance Tests

Acceptance tests are designed to demonstrate that apparatus will perform as specified in the purchase contract. Tests should be performed within ten days of delivery and before the apparatus is accepted. The tests should be conducted by the manufacturer's representative in the presence of such persons the purchaser may have designated in the delivery requirements. Normally, the fire chief or a designated representative is the acceptance authority, exercising this authority following satisfactory completion of tests and inspections to ensure compliance with the purchase specifications.

The acceptance-test requirements for fire apparatus and its various components should be detailed in the purchase specifications, and should be based on the manufacturer's certification tests and any additional tests the fire department desires to ensure that the apparatus performs to specification. The acceptance tests should always be conducted in the community so that any problems that developed during the delivery of the apparatus will be detected.

If the apparatus is equipped with a pump, a test plate is required at the pump-operator's position that gives the rated discharge and pressures, together with engine speed determined by the manufacturer's certification test for the unit. The no-load governed speed of the engine, as stated on a certified brake horsepower curve, is also given. Tests are conducted to see that the water tank has the minimum capacity specified and can flow the specified rate to the pump.

Aerial devices are inspected and tested in accordance with the requirements in NFPA 1914, *Standard for Testing Fire Department Aerial Devices*, as part of the certification tests.

In addition, the stability of the aerial device is tested with the aerial device on a level surface and then on a firm surface sloping downward at five degrees in the direction most likely to cause it to overturn. The vehicle cannot show any signs of instability during these tests.

If the aerial device is equipped with a pre-piped waterway, the system is flow-tested to determine whether the water system can flow 1000 gpm (3785 L/min) at 100 psi (690 kPa) nozzle pressure with the aerial device fully elevated and extended. If there is a fire pump on the vehicle, the test is conducted using that fire pump, and the intake pressure to the fire pump cannot exceed 20 psi (138 kPa).

MAINTENANCE OF APPARATUS AND EQUIPMENT

Equally important to the procurement of proper fire apparatus and equipment is its maintenance. A regular maintenance program should be set up to ensure that all apparatus and equipment is serviced and tested in accordance with the manufacturers' recommendations. The program should define the roles and responsibilities for the maintenance.

Service Tests of Pumps

All pumps should undergo service tests at least annually and after any major repairs. These tests demonstrate that the pump/engine combination is capable of meeting the performance requirements of the original certification or acceptance tests. Records of service tests are important evidence of proper apparatus maintenance.

NFPA 1911, *Standard for Service Tests of Pumps on Fire Department Apparatus*, outlines the procedures for the service test. The test should cover the following items:

1. A test pumping from draft for 20 min at 100 percent of rated capacity, at 150 psi (1039 kPa) net pump pressure; 10 min at 70 percent of rated capacity at 200 psi (1379 kPa) net pump pressure; and 10 min at 50 percent of rated capacity at 250 psi (1724 kPa) net pump pressure.
2. An engine speed test to determine if the engine is capable of reaching its no-load governed speed.
3. A vacuum test to ensure that the pump and the attached piping are still tight.
4. A pressure-control test to ensure that the pressure-control device can control the discharge within the specified limits.
5. A check of the accuracy of the gages and flow meters.

The purpose of the test is to ensure that the pump is generally in good condition, that the pump casing and various fittings are tight, and that the transfer valve is operating properly, if the pump is a series parallel type. If rated capacity cannot be obtained at 150 psi (1034 kPa) and the pump is not cavitating, or it appears that the pump, engine, pump accessories, or other parts of the power train and pumping equipment are not in good condition, the apparatus manufacturer, an authorized representative, or a competent mechanic should be contacted for advice so the condition can be corrected.

Service Tests of Aerial Devices

Aerial devices also need to be service-tested periodically. These devices develop problems not only from use at fires but also from responding to and returning from alarms. NFPA 1914, *Standard for Testing Fire Department Aerial Devices*, requires a yearly inspection of the aerial device, and of the pre-piped water system, if so equipped, and a test of their operation. The standard requires additional non-destructive tests at intervals not exceeding five years that check structural components for hardness, welds for cracks or discontinuities, and bolts and pins for wear or internal flaws. The full testing should be done any time the aerial device has had major repairs to ensure that it can be returned to service.

The annual inspection and tests can normally be conducted by a qualified fire department mechanic. The more complex non-destructive tests require an expertise that may be beyond the abilities of fire department personnel. The qualifications of the inspection personnel and the test protocols they must use are outlined in the standard, and only persons meeting those qualifications and having the proper equipment should attempt to do the non-destructive testing.

Ground Ladder Service Testing

NFPA 1932, *Standard on Use, Maintenance, and Service Testing of Fire Department Ground Ladders*, calls for service testing all ladders at least annually and at any time the ladder is suspected of being unsafe. The tests are designed to show that the ladder is safe for continued use under the conditions for which it was originally designed. The service-test procedures must be carefully observed to ensure that the ladder is not damaged. Ladders also should be inspected visually as outlined in NFPA 1932 to detect loose rungs, loose belts and rivets, weld defects, cracks, splintering, breaks, discoloration, and other signs of possible weakness that might warrant testing to determine whether the ladder is safe to use or needs repair.

HOSE, COUPLINGS, AND NOZZLES

Fire hose is the vital link between the water supply and the nozzles used to project streams on a fire. Hose must be rugged, dependable, and capable of carrying water under substantial pressures, yet flexible and sufficiently easy to handle. Fire department management should be concerned with selecting the proper grades and types of hose and with maintenance to ensure maximum useful life. These two factors are covered in detail in NFPA 1961, *Standard for Fire Hose*, and NFPA 1962, *Care, Use, and Service Testing of Fire Hose Including Couplings and Nozzles*. Aside from unavoidable mechanical injury at fires, a hose's dependability and length of life rest on three factors: the quality and suitability of the hose purchased, the care with which it is handled at fires, and the maintenance and care the hose receives.

Types of Fire Hose

Fire hose is manufactured for at least four uses. These include fire attack by fire department personnel (attack hose), relaying water through large-diameter hose from a source to the fire (large-diameter supply hose), occupant use in buildings from standpipe systems (rack-and-reel hose), and fire department use in wildland fires (forestry hose). Each of these types has its own minimum requirements for strength.

Attack hose is designed for a minimum service test pressure of 300 psi (2070 kPa) to meet a normal highest operating pressure of 275 psi (1895 kPa). If a higher working or operating pressure is needed, the purchaser needs to specify a higher service-test pressure.

Large-diameter supply hose has a minimum size of 3½ in. (89 mm) and a minimum design service-test pressure of 200 psi (1380 kPa) to meet a 185 psi (1275 kPa) normal highest operating pressure.

Forestry hose is only available in 1-in. (25 mm) and 1½-in. (38 mm) sizes and has a minimum design service-test pressure of 300 psi (2070 kPa) to meet a 250 psi (1723 kPa) normal highest operating pressure.

Rack-and-reel hose has a minimum size of 1½ in. (38 mm) and a minimum design service-test pressure of 150 psi (1034 kPa) to meet a 135 psi (930 kPa) normal highest operating pressure.

All hose must meet a proof-test pressure—formerly an acceptance-test pressure—of twice its service-test pressure, a burst-test pressure of three times its service-test pressure, and a kink-test pressure of one-and-a-half times the service-test pressure.

NFPA 1961 provides requirements for the hose jacket, the lining and the lining adhesion, any covering and its adhesion, the tensile strength of the hose, the ultimate elongation of the hose, and cold resistance. Tests are outlined to verify these requirements. Another section defines how the hose must be marked.

Care, Maintenance, and Testing of Fire Hose

To be reliable, fire hose should always be cared for properly. It should not be used for anything but training or fire fighting service, except in emergencies. Burst hose at a fire may seriously injure fire fighters and other persons, and may mean a loss of time in bringing a fire under control. NFPA 1962 and the manufacturer's instructions should form the basis of a hose care and maintenance program.

Hose carried on fire apparatus should be loaded to reduce edge wear and loaded so that air can circulate around it. The hose compartments should be protected by waterproof covers to keep the hose dry and to protect the hose from the direct rays of the sun when fire apparatus is out of quarters during inspection and training periods.

Hose installed at yard hydrants at industrial plants should be kept in well-ventilated hose houses in such a way that air can circulate and excessive heat can be avoided.

To prevent damage and permanent set to the rubber tube, hose should be removed from the apparatus or hose house at least quarterly and reloaded so the folds are in a different position. Whether hose jackets are of cotton or synthetic construction, the hose should be cleaned and dried after use to remove possible abrasive or contaminating material and to protect the hose compartment of the apparatus against rust or water damage.

When used for fighting fires, fire hose is subject to severe strains, pressure surges, and mechanical injury. Care should be taken to lay hose so that injury will not result from contact with sharp or rough objects. Vehicles should not be driven over hose lines. Where it is necessary for fire department vehicles to cross, hose bridges should be used where possible. When it is necessary to hoist hose lines, hose rollers can make the task easier and prevent mechanical injury. Hose lines extended up ladders should be supported by hose-rope tools placed to take the strain off couplings.

Pressure surges are a principal cause of damage to fire hose. Shutoff nozzles should be opened and closed slowly because sudden closure of nozzles can cause severe pressure surges, or water hammer, that can be extremely damaging to both hose and pumping apparatus. Pressure-relief devices on pumping engines should always be used to control sudden increases in pressure.

In cold climates, care should be taken to prevent water from freezing in the hose. Once water has been turned on, some should be left running through the hose because moving water does not freeze readily. Sharp bends should be avoided in any frozen hose. Care must be used in chopping hose free from ice after a fire so as not to cut the hose. The ice should then be allowed to melt off the hose, and any hose that has been frozen should be service tested before being placed back in service.

Care must also be taken to avoid burning the hose at forest and grass fires. As fire is knocked down and the nozzle is advanced, the hose may come in contact with hot spots or embers.

When hose has been returned to quarters it should be laid out where it can be swept and washed as needed to remove grime and contaminants. Hose should be thoroughly dried after cleaning. Hanging in hose towers or laying on racks are common methods for drying hose. However, drying cabinets, which circulate heated air around the hose, are also used.

Good hose records are necessary to keep accurate data on hose performance. Records for hose on racks, on reels, or in hose houses or similar enclosures may be kept at the hose location or at a central location on the premises where the hose is located. Fire department records should include a complete record of all hose. Upon delivery and acceptance, each length of hose should be given an identification number. This is used to record its history throughout its service life, including all testing and repairs, and ultimately the reason it was condemned and removed from service.

All fire hose, except rack-and-reel hose, should be tested at least annually and after repairs, or at any time it has had hard usage and its condition is suspect. NFPA 1962 includes required service-test procedures and a typical annual hose-test record form. The standard also specifies service-test pressures for hose manufactured before July 1987. Hose manufactured after that date has the service-test pressure stenciled on it.

Hose stored on a rack or reel should be examined carefully at least once a year. This annual physical inspection consists of a visual examination to see that the hose has not been vandalized, that the couplings and nozzle are attached and free of debris, and that there is no evidence of mildew, rot, chemicals, vermin, or abrasion. Racked hose should be reracked with the folds in a different location. Five years after the date of purchase and every three years thereafter, the hose should be service-tested, as it should be any time the condition of the hose is questionable.

Fire Hose Connections

NFPA 1963, *Standard for Screw Threads and Gaskets for Fire Hose Connections*, covers ten sizes of threaded connections, from 3/4 to 6 in. (19 to 152 mm), used in fire protection. The standard gives the dimensions for screw-thread connections, gages, gaskets, and gasket seats, as well as the size of the threaded connections. These standards apply to fire-hose couplings, suction-hose couplings, relay-supply-hose couplings, fire pump suction, discharge valves, fire hydrants, nozzles, adapters, reducers, caps, plugs, wyes, siamese connections, standpipe connections, sprinkler connections, and all other hose fittings, connections, and appliances that connect to fire pumps, hose, and hydrants.

These threaded connections are defined as the American National Fire Hose Connection Screw Thread, abbreviated throughout NFPA 1963 as NH and also known as NST and NS. Each of the ten standard sizes is designated by specifying in sequence the nominal size of the connection, the number of threads per inch, and the thread symbol as follows:

0.75-8	NH	3.5-6 NH
1-8	NH	4.0-4 NH
1.5-9	NH	4.5-4 NH
2.5-7.5	NH	5.0-4 NH
3-6	NH	6.0-4 NH

The need for standard fire service connections is most apparent during mutual aid operations. When hose couplings, nozzles, and other equipment do not conform to standards, it becomes necessary to use adapters, thus complicating fire fighting operations.

Nozzles

Nozzles used in the fire service are of either the spray or solid-stream design. A spray nozzle typically can produce a straight stream, although that stream does not have the same characteristics as a stream from a solid-bore nozzle. Nozzles for 1-, 1½-, 1¾-, and 2-in. hose (25, 38, 44, and 51 mm), are typically spray nozzles. Nozzles for 2½-in. (65 mm) hand lines and for master stream devices may be of the spray or solid-stream design. All nozzles should be equipped with shutoff valves, either as an integral part of the nozzle or as an attached item.

Fire department nozzles for 1½-in. (38-mm) hose normally are designed to discharge approximately 95 to 125 gpm (360 to 473 L/min). Nozzles for 1¾- and 2-in. (44-and 51-mm) hose normally are designed to discharge approximately 125 to 200 gpm (473 to 757 L/min). Nozzles for 1-in. (25 mm) hose generally discharge in the 20 to 30 gpm (76 to 114 L/min) range. A standard hose stream from a 2½-in. (65-mm) hose with a 1⅛-in. (29-mm) smoothbore tip is 250 gpm (946 L/min) at 50 psi (345 kPa) nozzle pressure.

Solid-bore nozzles have a straight open tip that generally is attached to some type of stream shaper. These nozzles are designed to hold the solid stream together as water is thrown a considerable distance. The design of the nozzles provides a gentle taper from the diameter of the inside of the hose to the diameter of the tip to reduce the turbulence that causes a stream to breakup.

Requirements for spray nozzles are covered in NFPA 1964, *Standard for Spray Nozzles (Shutoff and Tip)*. There are essentially three general types of spray nozzles.

The basic spray nozzle is an adjustable-pattern spray nozzle in which the rated flow is delivered at a designated nozzle pressure and nozzle setting. Due to its basic design, the flow (gpm) will vary as the pattern is changed from a straight stream through a wide spray pattern. This is caused by the orifice size changing to affect pattern adjustment.

The constant-gallonage spray nozzle is an adjustable-pattern spray nozzle in which the flow is delivered at a designated nozzle pressure. At the rated pressure, the nozzle will deliver a constant gallonage from straight-stream through a wide-spray pattern. This is done by maintaining a constant orifice size during flow-pattern adjustment. These nozzles are popular because the friction-loss characteristics in the hose and the nozzle pressures remain constant regardless of the selected orifice setting.

A constant-pressure (automatic) spray nozzle is an adjustable-pattern nozzle in which the pressure remains constant through a range of flows. The constant pressure provides the velocity for an effective stream-reach at various flow rates, which is accomplished by means of a pressure-activated, self-adjusting orifice baffle. These nozzles can produce streams whose discharge varies considerably but whose visual characteristics and stream reach remain the same. Do not to be mislead by a good-looking stream that lacks the adequate flow for proper fire attack. Remember the volume of water, not pressure alone, extinguishes fire.

There are other nozzles available for special purposes. These include nozzles used in the aspiration and delivery of foaming agents, very-high-pressure spray nozzles that are designed to deliver small flows at pressures in the 400 to 800 psi (2756 to 5516 kPa) range, and spray nozzles used on standpipe hose for first-aid fire protection.

PROTECTIVE EQUIPMENT FOR FIRE FIGHTERS

Each year, fire fighters are injured and some die because they do not have protective clothing and equipment or do not use it properly. No equipment can guarantee a fire fighter's safety, but full protective clothing and self-contained breathing apparatus (SCBA) offer fire fighters a better chance to carry out their duties effectively without suffering injury or death. The safety odds are further improved if that equipment is carefully selected, properly maintained, and used at all appropriate times.

Although the initial cost of good protective clothing may seem high, it is small compared to the expense of hospitalization or the cost of replacing an injured fire fighter. Recruitment and training expenses, medical expenses, disability payments, and early retirements are costly. The loss of a volunteer fire fighter disrupts a community's fire service effort, to say nothing of its economic impact on his or her family.

The protective equipment that fire fighters wear while combating structural fires must be viewed as a system. That system must include a helmet, a protective coat and protective trousers, gloves, footwear, SCBA, and PASS (personal alert safety systems). Together, these can protect fire fighters from toxic fumes and gases, heat, moisture, puncture, impact, and other adverse environmental conditions.

Special situations may call for specialized protective clothing. Approach and proximity garments protect against radiant heat while near a fire and are often used by airport fire fighters. The U.S. Forest Service has special lightweight clothing for wear by wildland fire fighters which provides limited protection to the wearer.

Various types of special protective clothing are available for hazardous-materials incidents, but these must be chosen for protection from a specific exposure. Specific decontamination or disposal procedures must be followed for the chemical to which the garment was exposed. These garments are not designed as protective clothing for fire fighting applications.

Protective clothing should be sized properly for the individual wearer, allowing the person to perform his or her duties without unnecessary hindrance. Most important, its use should be mandated and supported by the fire department and all of its members. NFPA 1500, *Standard on Fire Department Occupational Safety and Health Program*, outlines the type of equipment that must be used for personal protection during fire fighting operations. A complete ensemble of protective clothing and equipment must be provided for each fire fighter working in a hazardous area.

Helmets

A fire fighter's helmet should meet the minimum performance requirements of NFPA 1972, *Standard on Helmets for Structural Fire Fighting*, for exposure to convected and radiated heat; resistance to flame; resistance to penetration; resistance to top, front, side, and back impact; and insulation from electrical shock. A fire fighter's helmet should have flame-resistive flaps that protect the ears and the neck; the flaps are intended to be worn in the full down position during all fireground operations. A retention system must provide a secure fit. The helmet should be waterproof and divert falling liquids and debris, but it should not hinder the use of SCBA. It should also have an attached protective face shield. The helmet shell, suspension system, and an energy-absorbing liner are designed to protect the head from impact and penetration.

An important interface item between the helmet and the coat is a lightweight fabric protective hood such as those worn by race-car drivers. These hoods are made from a flame-resistive fabric and should meet the applicable requirements of NFPA 1971, *Standard on Protective Clothing for Structural Fire Fighting*. The hood is worn over the head and neck and under the coat and helmet, protecting the head, forehead, neck, and throat.

Face shields provide partial eye and face protection from heat, sparks, liquids, and flying debris. The SCBA face piece will also provide protection from these hazards. The face shield does not replace primary eye protection when such is required. Although the polycarbonate-type face shields are susceptible to scratching, replacement face shields are inexpensive and should be used when the scratching interferes with vision.

Coats and Trousers

NFPA 1971, *Standard on Protective Clothing for Structural Fire Fighting*, covers minimum requirements for fire fighters' protective coats and trousers and outlines a layered composite protection system. The outer layer of the composite is the shell. The shell of both coat and trousers must be made of a flame-resistive fabric that will not be destroyed through charring, separating, or melting when exposed to 500°F (260°C) in a forced-air laboratory oven for a 5-min period. The outer shell may be of a light color for better visibility. The coat must have a minimum of 325 sq in. (2097 cm^2) fluorescent/retroflective area, and the trousers must have a minimum of 80 sq in. (520 cm^2) fluorescent/retroflective area.

The second layer is the moisture barrier, which prevents moisture from penetrating through to the wearer. The third layer is a thermal barrier that provides insulation from radiant, conducted, and convective heat. In cold weather, an additional flame resistive, snap-in winter liner may help to provide warmth.

The moisture barrier and thermal barrier are attached at the neck or waist. The shell of the coat and trousers must never be worn without the thermal barrier on the moisture barrier because the garment would offer little, if any, protection against conducted, convected, and radiated heat. Since fire fighters normally work in a high-temperature environment, protection from heat transfer is critical.

The collar of the protective coat should have a throat enclosure that will protect the neck. The collar should be worn up and closed during all fireground operations. The coat should have a flap closure in front to protect against heat, steam, and water.

The length of the turnout coat is particularly important. It must overlap protective trousers enough to protect the wearer adequately in any working position such as kneeling or crawling. Coats worn without protective trousers do not provide adequate torso and leg protection. Protective coats and trousers must be worn as an ensemble for a more complete system of protection.

Station/work uniforms should be made of flame-resistive fabrics that meet the requirements of NFPA 1975, *Standard on Station/Work Uniforms for Fire Fighters*. Station uniforms made of synthetic fabrics that melt and drip, such as many "wash and wear" fabrics, should be avoided. Volunteers should pay attention to the street clothes they wear under their protective clothing or don flame-resistive jump suits or coveralls before they put on their coats and trousers.

Footwear

NFPA 1974, *Standard for Protective Footwear for Structural Fire Fighting*, defines the requirements for footwear used in structural fire fighting operations. This footwear must resist heat, puncture, impact, and water. Good fit is important because it will lessen foot and leg fatigue and can prevent blisters. It should have ladder shanks that spread weight across the sole to provide comfort while working from ladders. Safety toe-caps can protect toes from heavy impact even when the outer shell of the footwear is damaged. Shin padding will help to prevent lower leg injury. Thermal insulation and pull loops should be standard in any fire fighting boot.

Gloves

Hand protection is essential for fire fighters. NFPA 1973, *Standard on Gloves for Structural Fire Fighting*, covers hand protection by gloves and provides performance criteria for heat and flame resistance, cut and puncture resistance, water penetration, dexterity, and sizing. Gloves come in many fabrics and styles.

Self-Contained Breathing Apparatus

NFPA 1981, *Standard on Open-Circuit Self-Contained Breathing Apparatus for Fire Fighters*, sets forth the minimum requirements for the design, performance, and testing of open-circuit self-contained breathing apparatus used in rescue, fire fighting, and other hazardous duties. SCBA must first be certified by the National Institute for Occupational Safety and Health and the Mine Safety and Health Administration (NIOSH/MSHA) as "positive pressure" before it can be tested to the requirements of NFPA 1981. NFPA standards and OSHA regulations specify that only positive-pressure SCBA with a rated service life of at least 30 min can be used by the fire service.

Open-circuit positive-pressure apparatus is designed so the pressure inside the facepiece, relative to the immediate environment, is positive during both inhalation and exhalation. The older-style, demand-type apparatus in which the pressure inside the facepiece, relative to the immediate environment, is positive during exhalation and negative during inhalation should not be used in structural fire fighting, as inward leakage could occur because of improper facepiece fit.

In closed-circuit breathing apparatus, the wearer rebreathes the exhalation in after the carbon dioxide has been effectively removed and a suitable oxygen concentration restored. Closed-circuit breathing apparatus must be NIOSH/MSHA certified with a rated service life of at least 30 min and operate only in a positive-pressure mode.

Self-contained breathing apparatus (SCBA) for fire service use must have a minimum rated service life of 30 min. Certification from NIOSH/MSHA for the duration of use is based on tests conducted by NIOSH at 40 L/min. In NFPA 1981, open-circuit SCBA is tested with a breathing machine at a use rate of 103 ± 3 L/min and must be able to function in the positive-pressure mode without going negative. Closed-circuit SCBA is tested for service life by subjects who wear the apparatus and perform prescribed activity, because the service life of such apparatus is based on metabolic use of oxygen, and no mechanical test is currently available that can simulate this type of use.

Because work performed by the user may be more or less strenuous than the work level of the test procedure, the actual service life of the SCBA is affected. During heavy exertion, the service life may be reduced as much as 50 percent.

The service duration of each unit will depend on such factors as:

1. The degree of physical activity by the user.
2. The physical condition of the user.
3. The emotional condition of the user, such as stress or excitement, which may increase the user's breathing rate.
4. The degree of training or experience the user has had with such equipment.
5. Whether the cylinder is fully charged at the beginning of use.
6. The possible presence of carbon dioxide (CO_2) in the compressed air supply at levels greater than the 0.4 percent found in normal air.
7. Atmospheric pressure. For example, was it used in a pressurized tunnel or caisson? At two atmospheres, the duration will be half as long as the rated service life; at three atmospheres, the duration will be one-third as long as the rated service life.
8. Condition of the breathing apparatus.

Fire departments must not use SCBA with less than 30 min-rated service life for entry into hazardous atmospheres because fire fighters can get into dangerous positions without sufficient time to conduct operations or escape safely. SCBA with a rated service life of less than 30 min is not approved for entry protection for fire fighters.

The closed-circuit SCBA used by fire departments is an oxygen-rebreathing type. This SCBA has a cylinder that supplies oxygen to the wearer through a pressure-reducing valve, or regulator, and a container of chemicals to remove carbon dioxide from the exhaled air. In this apparatus, the cylinder valve opens to supply oxygen to a breathing chamber. When the user inhales, air flows from the breathing chamber through an inhalation hose to the facepiece. Exhaled air passes through an exhalation hose to a carbon-dioxide absorber, where CO_2 is removed, and the air then enters the breathing chamber, where it is enriched by fresh oxygen and then rebreathed.

Breathing-Air Quality

Air supplies for SCBA should be at least Class D breathing air, as specified by the Compressed Gas Association (CGA) in ANSI/CGA G-7.1, *Commodity Specification for Air*. Class D breathing air has less than twenty parts per million (ppm) of carbon monoxide. The water-vapor level of the air supply should be 25 ppm or less.

Fire departments should check the quality of breathing air at least every three months, whether or not they fill their own cylinders. Air samples can be tested by a public-health laboratory equipped for such tests or by a private testing laboratory.

Cylinders for SCBA may be made of steel, of aluminum, or of an aluminum shell with fiberglass wrapping. NIOSH/MSHA requires the maximum weight of the SCBA not exceed 35 lb (15.9 kg), so light-weight cylinders help reduce overall weight. Air tanks used with SCBA should be inspected periodically for external damage and must be recertified periodically through an independent pressure test.

Other Protective Equipment

Fire fighters engaged in ladder work should use life-safety harnesses that meet the requirements of Class I harnesses as defined in NFPA 1983, *Standard on Fire Service Life Safety Rope, Harness, and Hardware*. These harnesses are worn over the protective coat and provide a sturdy, quick-connect clamp to prevent fire fighters from falling.

Personal alert safety systems (PASS) sound an audible alarm for help if the wearer is unable to do so. PASS monitor fire fighter motion and signal an audible alarm when motion is undetected for more than 30 sec. The fire fighter can also actuate the audible alarm if he or she needs assistance. NFPA 1982, *Standard on Personal Alert Safety Systems (PASS) for Fire Fighters*, is the standard covering the design and testing of PASS devices. PASS should be worn by fire fighters whenever they operate in any hazardous area.

Rope used to raise or lower persons is termed life-safety rope and is covered by NFPA 1983, *Standard on Fire Service Life Safety Rope, Harness, and Hardware*. The standard provides design, construction, and testing criteria for the rope and for the associated harnesses and hardware used for rescue operations. Rope is classified as one-person or two-person.

Significant strides have been made in the development of protective clothing for use in the fire service. All members of the fire service who engage in emergency operations should be equipped with and use complete protective clothing and SCBA that meet current minimum standards at all appropriate times on the fireground or emergency scene.

BIBLIOGRAPHY

NFPA Codes, Standards, and Recommended Practices.

Reference to the following NFPA codes, standards, and recommended practices will provide further information about fire department apparatus, equipment, and protective clothing. (See the latest NFPA *Catalog* for availability of current editions of the following documents.)

NFPA 414, *Standard for Aircraft Rescue and Fire Fighting Vehicles*.

NFPA 1500, *Standard on Fire Department Occupational Safety and Health Program*.

NFPA 1901, *Standard for Pumper Fire Apparatus*.

NFPA 1902, *Standard for Initial Attack Fire Apparatus*.

NFPA 1903, *Standard for Mobile Water Supply Fire Apparatus*.

NFPA 1904, *Standard for Aerial Ladder and Elevating Platform Fire Apparatus*.

NFPA 1911, *Standard for Service Tests of Pumps on Fire Department Apparatus*.

NFPA 1914, *Standard for Testing Fire Department Aerial Devices*.

NFPA 1921, *Standard for Fire Department Portable Pumping Units*.

NFPA 1931, *Standard on Design of and Design Verification Tests for Fire Department Ground Ladders*.

NFPA 1932, *Standard on Use, Maintenance, and Service Testing of Fire Department Ground Ladders*.

NFPA 1961, *Standard on Fire Hose*.

NFPA 1962, *Standard for the Care, Use, and Service Testing of Fire Hose, Including Couplings and Nozzles*.

NFPA 1963, *Standard for Screw Threads and Gaskets for Fire Hose Connections*.

NFPA 1964, *Standard for Spray Nozzles (Shutoff and Tip)*.

NFPA 1971, *Standard on Protective Clothing for Structural Fire Fighting*.

NFPA 1972, *Standard on Helmets for Structural Fire Fighting*.

NFPA 1973, *Standard on Gloves for Structural Fire Fighting*.

NFPA 1974, *Standard on Protective Footwear for Structural Fire Fighting*.

NFPA 1975, *Standard on Station/Work Uniforms for Fire Fighters*.

NFPA 1981, *Standard on Open-Circuit Self-Contained Breathing Apparatus for Fire Fighters*.

NFPA 1982, *Standard on Personal Alert Safety Systems (PASS) for Fire Fighters*.

NFPA 1983, *Standard on Fire Service Life Safety Rope, Harness, and Hardware*.

Additional Readings

Arthur D. Little, Inc., *Guidelines for the Selection of Chemical Protective Clothing*, prepared for U. S. Environmental Protection Agency, Los Alamos National Laboratory, Los Alamos, NM, March 1983.

Bailey, M., "Insulated Boots-Field and Laboratory Evaluation," *Fire Technology*, Vol. 15, No. 4 (Nov. 1979), pp. 283-290.

Brunacini, A. V., *Fire Command*, National Fire Protection Association, Quincy, MA, 1985.

Crouch, K. G., "Fire Fighter's SCBA: Belt Radiant Heat Resistance," *Fire Technology*, Vol. 17, No. 1 (Feb. 1981), pp. 39-53.

Davis, L., *Rural Firefighting Operations*, 2 Vols., International Society of Fire Service Instructors, Ashland, MA, 1985-1986.

Fire Department Aerial Apparatus, International Fire Service Training Association, Oklahoma State University, Stillwater, OK, 1991.

Fire Department Pumping Apparatus, International Fire Service Training Association, Oklahoma State University, Stillwater, OK, 1989.

Fire Service Ground Ladder Practices, International Fire Service Training Association, Oklahoma State University, Stillwater, OK, 1984.

Foltz, J. L., "Disposable Respirators for Forest Fire Fighters," *Fire Technology*, Vol. 17, No. 3 (Aug. 1981), pp. 174-176.

Hose Practices, International Fire Service Training Association, Oklahoma State University, Stillwater, OK, 1988.

Mission Research Corporation, *Guide for Preparing Fire Pumper Apparatus Specifications; Part 1: Executive Summary*, FA-29-1, prepared for the Federal Emergency Management Agency, U.S. Fire Administration, Washington, DC, 1980.

Perkins, R. M., "Insulative Values of Single-Layer Fabrics for Thermal Protective Clothing," *Textile Research Journal*, Vol. 49, No. 4, 1979, pp. 202-212.

Saunders, P. B. and Ku, R., "Sequencing the Purchase and Retirement of Fire Engines," *NBS Special Pub. 411*, U.S. National Bureau of Standards, Gaithersburg, MD, Nov. 1974, pp. 201-214.

SCBA: A Fire Service Guide to the Selection, Use and Care of Self-Contained Breathing Apparatus, National Fire Protection Association, Quincy, MA, 1981.

Self-Contained Breathing Apparatus, International Fire Service Training Association, Oklahoma State University, Stillwater, OK, 1982.

Veghte, J. H., *Design Criteria for Fire Fighter's Protective Clothing, Janesville Apparel*, Dayton, OH, 1981.

Worsham, J. P., *Rural Fire Protection: A Selected Bibliography*, Vance Bibliographies, Monticello, IL, Aug. 1978.

FIRE DEPARTMENT FACILITIES AND FIRE TRAINING FACILITIES

by Emmanuel Mesagna, R.A., and John Baroni

Over the past decade, fire station planning for location and design has become increasingly sophisticated and complex. With the use of computer programs and computer model studies, travel-time analysis and fire station site evaluation has allowed the fire service to become more precise in its decision-making procedures. Years of study and experience have made it apparent that by planning a fire station properly, a safer and quicker turnout can be made. This is accomplished primarily by arranging traffic-flow patterns within the fire house to be as direct as possible. The integration of the "primary adjacency" concept for planning the fire station will decrease turnout time considerably by grouping the fire-fighting personnel in the highest activity areas of the fire station, making them readily available when the alarm comes in. Turnout time, along with dispatching time and travel time, are three of the key elements in the successful containment of fire.

The improvements in fire station planning have led to a total upgrading of human comforts, with great emphasis on physical fitness. These improvements include well-planned kitchens, air conditioning, better lighting, well-planned toilet/shower facilities and dormitory spaces, acoustical improvements, safety features in building planning, and the integration of small, gymnasium-like areas into the fire-station plan for physical-fitness purposes.

Determining the Fire Station Location

Determining the location for a fire department facility is an important decision. Many aspects of initial investment, annual operating costs, practicality, and public reaction and support come into play, as does the most important aspect of location, providing the best possible fire protection to the area. The area to be protected by the proposed fire station is the most important factor in determining fire station location. Some areas in the community, such as those containing primarily business, industrial, mercantile, institutional, and multifamily residential occupancies, will present higher risk potentials than do others.

In some instances, it may be undesirable to locate a fire station in a high-risk area. In such cases, the fire station should be within a reasonable response distance to the perimeter of the area. Distribution of fire stations within a jurisdiction should provide a concentration of companies for response into high-risk areas without depleting other areas of the community should a second or major fire occur. In areas characterized by equal risk throughout, such as residential areas, fire stations should have equal response time from all parts of the area.

Where fire stations are staffed by volunteer fire fighters, consideration must be given to locating them in or near areas where the volunteers live and work to facilitate quick response to a fire. Where the lack of fire fighting personnel is a problem, there has been a trend to provide housing for fire fighters in order to entice people to join the volunteer fire departments. Garden-apartment housing has been provided near the fire station to cut down on the turnout time.

Topographical features of a community may also affect fire station locations and the total number of stations required. Natural and artificial barriers that divide communities, such as rivers, mountains, limited-access highways, and railroads, may limit response routes and make additional fire stations necessary. Heavily traveled and one-way streets are undesirable for fire station locations because of access problems and limited response routes. When a fire station is located near a community boundary, its response area is reduced although this may still be desirable if the community is anticipating annexation. If it is anticipated that communities or governmental entities will be establishing mutual-aid areas, an overall plan for fire department facilities will provide enhanced protection with a minimum of investment. Coordination with community or regional planning agencies can provide valuable information on growth potential and land use when planning new fire station locations or cooperative fire response operations.

Fire department records can also provide valuable information for plotting fire station locations. Fire experience may indicate specific areas in which there are high rates of incidence. Response times may also prove useful. Although computers are currently used in some communities to aid in plotting fire station locations, this is not the

---

Mr. Mesagna is the principal of Fire Service Buildings Design Consultants, Architects and Engineers, Syosset, NY and formerly chief architect of the FDNY. Mr. Baroni is capital projects coordinator for Training at the Fire Service Academy, Nassau County, NY.

answer for all communities, since a valid data base must be established before computer use can be meaningful.

Several computer program packages that can be used to analyze fire department run records, response times, fire incident locations, and so on are readily available, but they can be expensive and complicated to use, and may not satisfy all local needs. A common-sense approach involving imput from fire officials, city architect and engineers, insurance-rating officials, and citizens will prove effective.

Concept Planning for the Fire Station and Plan Types

Turnout time is the key element in fire station planning. When planning a fire station, the most important feature is to group various functional spaces adjacent to each other so that the movements fire fighters must make to respond from the fire station during turnout are minimized.

The one-story fire station has a series of plan types that can be categorized in the following manner. (See Fig. 9-10A and Fig. 9-10B.)

One-way straddle of the apparatus area: All of the support functions for this plan, which appears as type A in Figure 9-10A, are located to the left or right of the apparatus area. This plan is the least desirable because it has the longest travel distances to reach the apparatus area and, therefore, adds to the turnout time of the fire company. By its nature, this plan type creates a circulation pattern that can be eliminated in other plan types. In other plan types, supporting areas respond directly onto the apparatus area.

Two-way, "U" wrap-around of apparatus area: This plan, which appears as type B in Figure 9-10A, is the most desirable in fire station planning for minimizing the turnout time. Using the same gross area for the standard two-company unit, it places all areas at the shortest possible distance from the responding apparatus. Another key element in this type of planning concept is that it separates the noisy areas of the fire station from the quiet areas by the natural separation of the apparatus area.

Two-way straddle of the apparatus area: This plan, which appears as type C in Figure 9-10A, is the second-most desirable for minimizing turnout time. The plan clearly separates the noisy areas of a fire station from the quiet areas

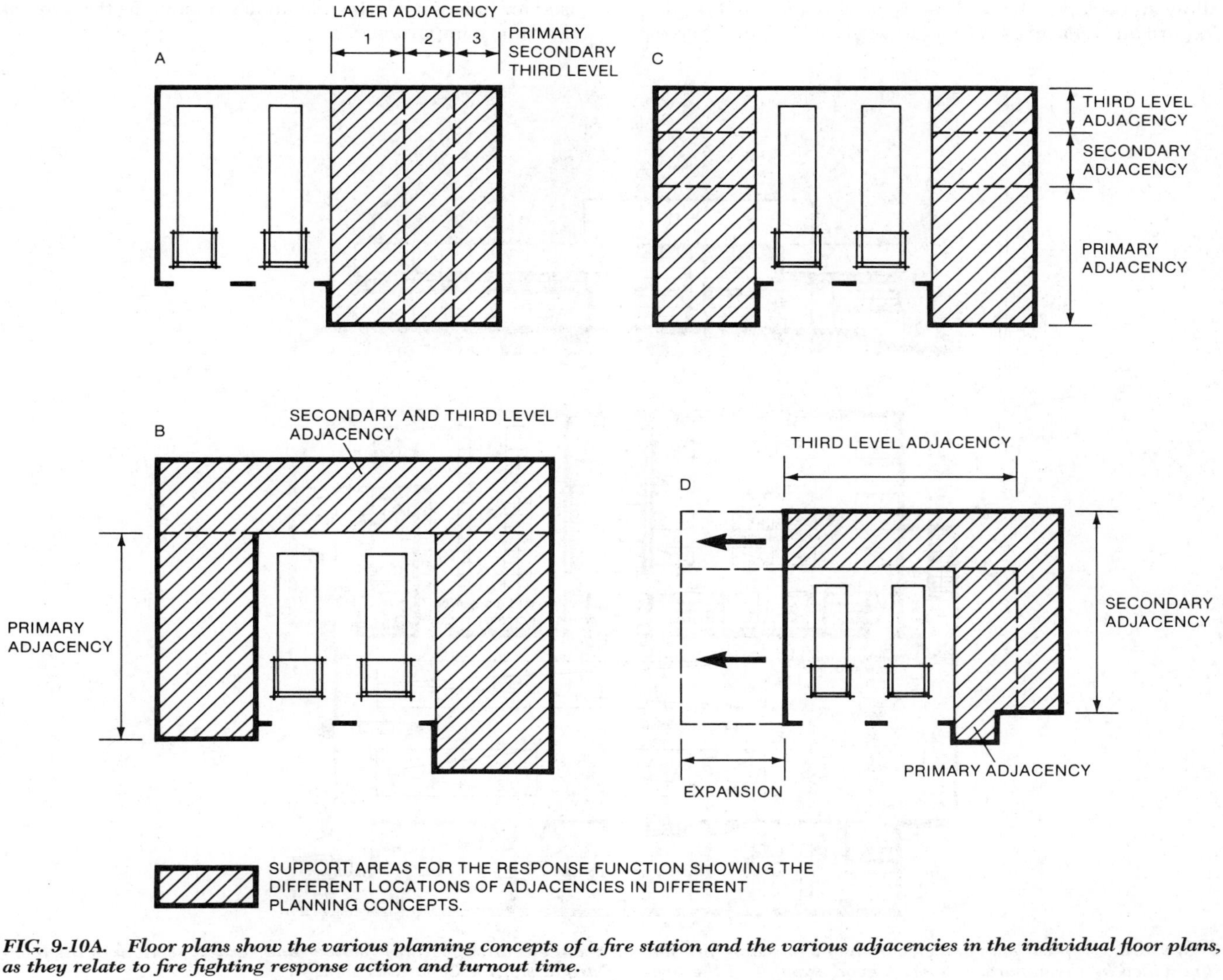

FIG. 9-10A. Floor plans show the various planning concepts of a fire station and the various adjacencies in the individual floor plans, as they relate to fire fighting response action and turnout time.

and may create circulation patterns in the support areas by not taking advantage of the back of the fire station for support-area use.

This plan type is the same for the two-story fire station with the quiet volume stacked over the apparatus area. (See Figs. 9-10B and 9-10C).

"L" wraparound of the apparatus area: This plan, which is type D in Figure 9-10A, is unique in that the "L" arrangement allows for a natural progression of the primary adjacency areas through the third-level adjacency areas as the "L" wraps around the apparatus area from the leg of the "L" to the toe. The key turnout spaces are replaced in normal sequence by virtue of this form. One advantage of this plan type is the flexibility for expansion along the apparatus area and along the toe of the "L." This plan type is the third-most desirable, with the advantage of potential for expansion.

Adjacency Relationships for Space Planning of a Fire Station

The key concept in planning a fire station for the shortest turnout time possible is the development of an adjacency planning concept. The main purpose of this concept is to allow an in-depth study of the spaces in a fire station that require an "adjacency rating" to verify where the greatest amounts of activity occur. These "activity locations" will then be joined in such a manner that a minimum amount of grouping time is required for the fire fighting personnel to respond to the fire. This grouping time is extremely valuable to the response action. At this time, the company officers decide on the shortest route to the fire and develop a response strategy that takes into account any problems at the fire site which may come out of the computer in the dispatching center.

Primary adjacency: Spaces in this category must be directly connected physically to each other or the apparatus area, which is the key turnout location in the response action.

Examples of primary adjacent spaces include dispatcher, radio room, and housewatch areas; the lobby, administrative offices; the kitchen; recreation, gym and training areas; the lounge; classrooms with accommodations for television and videotape teaching; basic toilet facilities close to high-use areas; the dormitory; and the turnout gear storage area, which can be a third-level adjacency according to the response strategy.

Secondary adjacency: Spaces in this category must be placed midway in the fire station plan because they are used for functions during day-to-day operations that are not of primary importance.

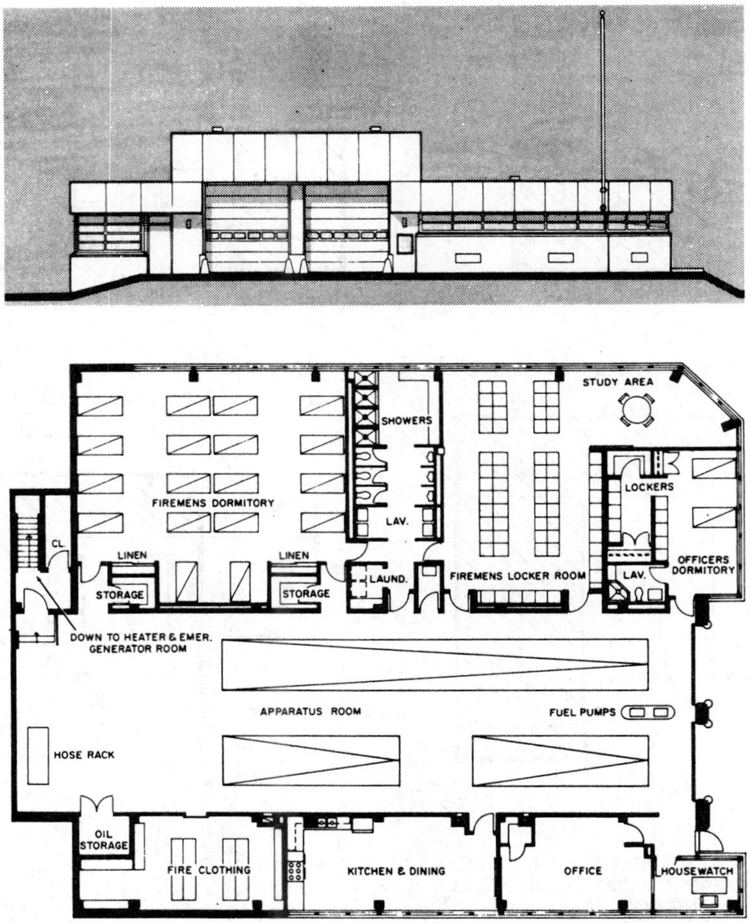

FIG. 9-10B. Typical plan and elevation of a one-story fire station. Front elevation features "active" and "quiet" sections of the facility divided by the apparatus floor. A good example of the two-way straddle of the apparatus area.

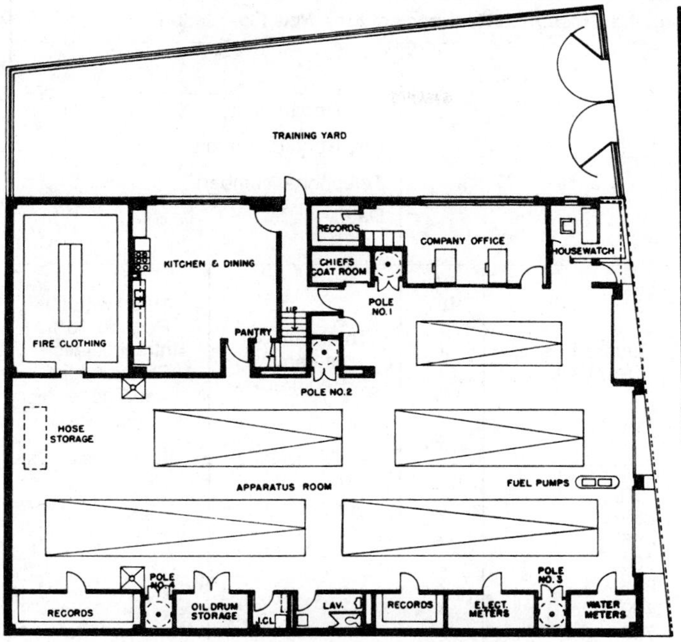

FIRST-FLOOR PLAN OF THE TWO-STORY FIREHOUSE.

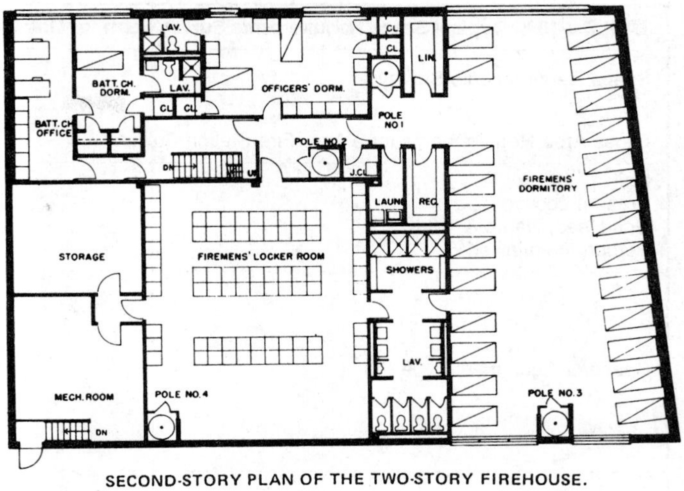

SECOND-STORY PLAN OF THE TWO-STORY FIREHOUSE.

FRONT ELEVATION OF THE FIREHOUSE.

FIG. 9-10C. Typical plans and elevation of a two-story fire station. This is a good example of a two-way straddle of the apparatus area with the "quiet" section stacked over the apparatus area.

Examples of secondary adjacency spaces include general shop storage and repair areas; clean-up areas; and hose storage and drying areas.

Third-level adjacency: Spaces in this category are the least used in a fire station and have no direct day-to-day operational relationship to the primary and secondary adjacency spaces.

Examples of third-level adjacency spaces include apparatus parts storage areas; the boiler plant; the utilities and the emergency generator area; the locker room; miscellaneous storage areas; administrative areas that are not related to the response; conference rooms and other public areas; major toilet and shower rooms; the laundry room; and any other area that houses a function not directly related to the response.

Adjacency levels must be ascertained through in-depth interviews with fire department administrators and may change accordingly.

Space Planning Analysis to Obtain the Gross Area Requirements for the Fire Station

Before site selection, it is essential that an architect/space-planning analyst be retained to ascertain the gross area requirements for the fire station. (See Table 9-10D.) A space-planning analyst is a new breed of expert whose main responsibility is to arrive at the most efficient total gross space required for the building. High building costs have necessitated the use of a space-planning analyst to arrive at the least gross area the building may have and still function with maximum efficiency.

The space-planning analyst will make in-depth studies of equipment, personnel, utility needs, and circulation and arrive at the optimum gross-area requirements for the building. Before planning a fire station, it is essential that all equipment and personnel needs be clearly delineated in numbers and size so that proper circulation allowances

TABLE 9-10A Typical Space Requirements Survey Form for Obtaining the Gross Area Requirement for a New Fire Station

Space Requirements Survey

Gross Area Requirements for a New Fire Station Building

Unit:
Present Location:
Unit Head, Name & Title:
Person Interviewed:

Fire Department:
Key Contact Person:
Telephone Number:
Date:

Space or Equipment Type (**)		Square Feet Per Unit	Multiply	Total Number of Items Required	Areas with (*) Require 15% Intracirculation Factor Added to These Figures
Ladder—Tiller Operated	53′	1,150	X		
Ladder—Tower	39′	885	X		
Ladder—Rear Mount	36′	885	X		
Pumper—Standard	26′	760	X		
Pumper—Squirt	39′	885	X		
Rescue Truck	29′	700	X		
Airport Crash Truck	30′	720	X		
Ambulance	20′	630	X		
Brush Fire Unit	20′	540	X		
Light Truck	26′	650	X		
Communication Vehicle	25′	630	X		
Specialty Van	25′	630	X		
Chief's Car	25′	500	X		
Hose Storage Rack		100	X		
Hose Dryer Unit—Electric		60	X		
Hose Washer Unit		100	X		
Turnout Gear Storage		10 sq. ft. per person	X		
Communications Console Unit	Standard 3′ × 8′	200	—		*
Standard Desk Area		90	X		*
Legal File		10	X		*
Table	36″ × 60″	60	X		*
Shelving Unit	36″ W × 12″ D	12	X		*
Side Chair		10	X		*
Teleprinter, Computerized Response		10	X		*
Kitchen Area, Food Preparation—14′ Counter Service Length, Sink, Dishwasher, Range and Work Counter		120	—		*
For Number of Persons:	6	120	—		*
	8	160	—		*
	10	200	—		*
	12	240	—		*
	14	280	—		*
	16	320	—		*
	18	360	—		*
Conference Rooms Seating For:	6	100	—		*
	12	200	—		*
	15	300	—		*
	20	375	—		*
Size of conference rooms to vary in accordance with seating configurations and space needs.					
Physical Fitness Area		600			*
Amphitheater for Teaching Purposes		600			*

Space or Equipment Type (**)	Square Feet Per Unit	Multiply	Total Number of Items Required	Areas with (*) Require 15% Intracirculation Factor Added to These Figures
Toilet Facilities (per Unit)				
Water Closet	27	X		*
Urinal	8	X		*
Lavatory	16	X		*
Shower Area with Bench	27	X		*
Clothes Washer	24	X		*
Clothes Dryer	24	X		*
Slop Sink—Storage Area	40	X		*
Vehicle Maintenance Area	100	X		*
Locker Room Area 2′ × 2′ Locker Unit	15	X		*
Dormitory Area 3′ × 7′ Bunk Size	100	X		*
Linen Storage Room	80	—		*
Generator Room	200	—		*
General Storage—Per Floor	200	—		*
Boiler Room	360	—		*
Electrical Room	50	—		*
Water Meter Room	50	—		*
			SUB-TOTAL	SQ FT
BUILDING CORE (Intercirculation Factor) Primary Circulation, Enclosing Walls, Interior Walls, Stairs, Flues, Vents, Stacks, Pipe Shafts, Vertical Ducts and Other Space Consuming Items through floors.	25% of net areas above (sub-total) is the space required for the Building Core ________ Sq Ft			
			BUILDING CORE	SQ FT
GROSS AREA REQUIREMENT				SQ FT

(**) It should be noted that this space survey could not possibly cover each and every piece of apparatus/equipment on the market. Therefore, each piece of apparatus/equipment should be studied for size and adjusted accordingly if the length which is the governing factor does not appear in this table.

One of the key variables in preparing this survey format for apparatus is the clearances and space needs around the apparatus and should be adjusted accordingly to suit your requirements.

can be made for the proper functioning of the fire station. These, in turn, will give the gross area requirements. As part of his or her study, the space-planning analyst will examine ways in which space needs may be maximized or minimized and the ultimate advantage and disadvantage of each as they relate to the function of the building.

Building and site relationship: Three major considerations related to the building and site are the building setback, the training area requirements, and the on-site parking needed for fire fighting personnel. The minimum setback is 50 feet, although it should ideally be 65 feet to accommodate the largest piece of apparatus in the fire service. This will give optimum visibility for apparatus leaving the fire station. The turning radius of fire fighting apparatus should be studied in depth to ensure the proper distance from the face of the fire station to the far curb. This distance must be large enough to make turning the vehicle as simple as possible. The apron shall have the smallest possible slope to drain water and may include a hot-water underground piping system or an electrical cable de-icing system in certain climates to clear it for response. All building sites require an open area to one side so that fire fighters can train with the largest piece of apparatus available to the unit. A parking area that can accommodate all personnel on duty at any one time is absolutely necessary, plus a minimum of 50 percent more as extra space for administrative personnel. Beyond this point, the parking requirement is a subjective judgment that may include spaces for public and social functions. Parking is to be located next to the dispatcher-radio room-housewatch area, which should have visual control of the activity in the parking area.

The station's main street must be wide enough to accommodate the apparatus with the largest turning radius. It is also essential that traffic controls be installed at the extreme ends of the front property line to stop traffic during a response.

The building should be oriented in such a way as to eliminate the possibility that an apparatus will emerge from the station directly into a low-sun orientation. This will minimize the vision problem that arises from the quick transition from basic darkness to brightness and will reduce the accident potential.

Wherever possible, additional land should be allocated to the site so that a drive-through apparatus area arrangement can be integrated into the floor plan. The drive-through method of returning from a response creates less disruption in the street and reduces the potential for accidents when the apparatus backs up.

SPACE COMPONENTS IN FIRE STATION PLANNING

Dispatcher-Radio Room-Housewatch Area

This key communication area is being formed as an independent operating space, completely sound-controlled for optimum hearing ability. It must be completely air-conditioned and have an unobstructed view of the quarters and the street.

Glass areas in the front of the housewatch are arranged in such a manner that 180 degrees of visibility in front of the fire station is possible. The alarm-lights button at the fire communications console is not limited to activating the alarm lights as in the past. It also activates the apparatus fume-exhaust system and a series of floodlights mounted on the front of the building. These lights illuminate the apron and street for a safer response. An adjustable timer turns off the floodlights and the fume-exhaust system after the overhead doors have been shut electrically. The floodlights can be activated manually through an override switch by the housewatcher in other than response situations.

Control Functions of the Dispatcher-Housewatch Area

This key communication area is also the center of all the electronic switching devices that control the security and functions of the fire station. These functions include gasoline and diesel pump operation; manual operation of the floodlights mounted on the front of the building; operation of the security lights surrounding problem areas of the building; manual control of fume-exhaust system; operation of the alarm lights for various parts of the building during a response; and daily-use light controls; and a three-button control switch for the overhead doors.

In addition, the housewatch area should have a complete intercom system for immediate verbal communication to all areas of the fire station.

Management adjacency: Because the dispatcher-radio room-housewatch area and the company offices are adjacent, they enjoy excellent audible communication. Both areas also face the apparatus-storage area and have glass walls, allowing for visual control of the apparatus floor. This adjacency of space is ideal for all aspects of communication and decision-making during initial turnout action.

The Apparatus Storage Area

This is the heart of every fire station. Its location, shape, flexibility, size, layout, and column-free approach will provide for easy, quick access from all areas of the fire station. These factors will provide the fire fighting units with a good functional design for response purposes. The integration of large areas such as the apparatus area and hose-storage area into one large, open apparatus area, and the elimination of turnout gear storage from the apparatus area allow for "clear space" mobility. The single open space now offers greater flexibility for apparatus storage and may also function as a training area and a storage area for spare or down apparatus.

Diesel exhaust fumes contain certain particulates that contain significant quantities of polycyclic aromatic hydrocarbons and vapors that contain benzene, toluene, and xylene. These pollutants put the fire fighter at risk when fire apparatus is operated indoors. They are small and remain suspended in the atmosphere for long periods of time, so it is likely that they will be inhaled. This indicates the need for a strong mechanical engineering solution for dilution and ventilation. Although each fire station requires its own individualized plan for solving the exhaust problem, many precautions can be taken to eliminate or limit the problem. The following concepts would substantially cut down on the exposure to fume/exhaust contamination.

Engineering Calculation to Design and Apparatus Room-Fume Exhaust System

Apparatus storage areas are now being equipped with sophisticated fume-exhaust systems. The fume-exhaust system is activated by the alarm-lights button located on the fire communication console unit. The fume-exhaust system is based on the volume in cubic feet of the area to be exhausted. It is suggested that all apparatus rooms be exhausted when the fire apparatus are operating so that there are twelve air changes per hour or one full exhaust evacuation of the contaminated air every 5 min. The following engineering formula should be used in calculating the size of the ventilating fans, which may be located on either the side of the building or apparatus room.

CFM Fan Required = air changes per hour × volume of the apparatus room/60 min

Choose any combination of ventilators that will handle the required cubic feet per minute (CFM) with an 0.25 static pressure, and the required twelve air changes per hour will occur.

The American Conference of Governmental Industrial Hygienists has prepared an *Industrial Ventilation Manual* with specific recommendations for ventilating garages.

The installation of a timer will automatically shut the system down after a set time lapse. Provisions must be made for the manual control, or override switch, of the fume-exhaust system when companies are not in a response action. A study of fume-exhaust pipe locations on the apparatus has allowed intake grilles at optimum locations for greatest exhaust pull. The goal is to eliminate as much exhaust gas on the apparatus floor as possible. When the apparatus returns to quarters, a manual switch operation can be used and the fumes can be exhausted as long as required to create a pollution-free environment for the fire fighters.

Positive Ventilation "Air Seal" Between Fire Station Spaces

Seal off all passageways between the fire station and the living quarters with an airlock arrangement between the apparatus room and other parts of the fire station. If living quarters or offices are directly adjacent to the apparatus floor, make sure that the passage doors and windows have a good seal to prevent the passage of diesel fumes, or construct an "air seal corridor" between the various fire station spaces, with positive exhaust-ventilation within the air seal to prevent exhaust from seeping into other areas of the station.

Gravity Held Exhaust Ports to Dilute Contaminated Air

Provide and install gravity-held louvers at key locations on the outside walls which will open up and allow fresh air to enter the building when the exhaust system ventilators are turned on. This will help dilute the concentration of exhaust in the apparatus room.

Direct-Connection Fume Exhaust System

One of the best solutions for the elimination of exhaust fumes in the apparatus room is to install a direct-connection fume exhaust system, which includes a ventilation fan on the roof tied into flexible exhaust tubing on a hanging-loop system, which is in turn connected to the apparatus tailpipe. The flexible tubing is disconnected when the apparatus is outside the building on the fire station ramp. The flexible tubing is stored on rings on a tension wire at the ceiling and can be moved freely on this wire. This system, which requires that the flexible tubing be walked outside the fire station, where it is removed and brought back inside, is probably the best available to prevent the direct contamination of the fire station.

Vehicle Maintenance

Insuring that apparatus is properly maintained can reduce dangerous emissions to a minimum. Fuel-injector adjustments can reduce carbon monoxide and particulate matter by increasing fuel combustion efficiency.

It is recommended that all apparatus storage areas use single apparatus doors approximately 12 ft wide by 14 ft high. Wide, single-opening apparatus doors are not recommended because they may become frozen closed if the mechanized door operation breaks down. This will put the responding apparatus out of service and increase the response time of first-due apparatus. A pair of doors is more functional in that a breakdown in one door allows the responding apparatus to maneuver through the other, thus reducing the turnout problem.

It is essential to include a totalizer on all apparatus doors so that tension springs may be replaced on a preventive maintenance schedule. The standardization of the door-opening size will simplify the storage of spare parts for repair purposes and minimize the inventory.

It is recommended that all overhead doors be opened with electrical operators to decrease the turnout time. Electrical operators should have the capability of manual operation in case the motorized equipment breaks down. It is essential that the overhead-door-operating equipment be put on the emergency generator in case of electrical failure.

The controls that open the overhead door of the apparatus room have to be designed so that they do not become safety problems. The three-button control feature should have momentary-pressure "UP" and "STOP" buttons and a constant-pressure "DOWN" button. This insures that there will always be a person at the door when it is going down to ensure that the apparatus has already passed through and that personnel are not standing in the opening. When remote door operators are used, they should be adjusted to set in motion the "UP" and "STOP" action only. All "DOWN" activity should be set in motion only by the constant-pressure "DOWN" button. The "DOWN" button should never be located remotely from the overhead door.

Throughout the fire service, the hose tower is being eliminated in the operation of a fire station. With the use of sophisticated hose-drying equipment and of polyester hose, the hose tower is being phased out, and the space allocated for the hose tower is being made into storage rooms.

Turnout Gear Storage

A well-planned fire station should have facilities for storing helmets, coats, and boots, as well as accommodations for washing and drying them and a floor-drain system. The turnout-gear storage areas may be secured with a pull-down, see-through mesh gate and locking device to secure the area while the company is out of quarters.

As part of the equipment for this area be an electric heater for drying the gear and an exhaust fan to clear the humidity out of the area should be included. The wall and ceiling finishes in this area are critical and should include maintenance-free finishes such as permanently glazed surfaces.

Slide Pole and Enclosures

There is a movement in the fire service to eliminate the slide pole as a means of movement from the upper floors of a fire station. Stairways are favored, and there is a trend toward one-story stations wherever the land-value permits. Slide poles have led to serious injuries and have allowed exhaust fumes from the fire fighting apparatus to travel throughout the station. Even when enclosures were installed on the various levels of the station, malfunctioning doors allowed exhaust fumes to travel between floors.

Classroom/TV Amphitheater for Training Purposes

In the future, more and more classroom training will take place in the fire station using closed-circuit television and videotapes. A sophisticated space is required for this purpose to create a positive environment for learning. The space will require complete acoustical treatment, theater-type viewing chairs, a sloped floor for viewing purposes, and desk-top writing surfaces.

Kitchen/Dining Room/Recreation Area

The kitchen/dining room area should be planned to reduce maintenance and operate efficiently. Each component should be commercial-grade and stainless steel. Large appliances include a large refrigerator and a heavy-duty, six-burner, commercial-type range with a grill unit. The facility should also incorporate a stainless steel range hood with removable and washable stainless steel filters. The ceilings should be made of washable acoustical tile, and the floor and wall finished in a ceramic or quarry tile. These materials eliminate maintenance except for simple cleaning.

Dormitory/Locker Room

New planning concepts arrange the dormitory and locker rooms so that they straddle the toilet/shower and laundry areas. This isolates the noisy locker room from the quiet dormitory area. In cases where the dormitory faces onto traffic, it is best not to provide any windows on the dormitory walls facing the street. This will give maximum sound isolation and privacy for this area of the fire station.

Chief's Quarters

The design concept for fire chiefs' quarters has been refined to combine privacy and the need for efficient response in the event of an alarm. The chief's car and turnout-gear storage closet can be located at the foot of the stair or corridor on the apparatus-floor level, and the chief's office and dormitory can have direct access to a response vehicle. In the typical two-story fire station illustrated in Fig. 9-10C, the chief's quarters are located at the head of the stairs on the second floor, and he or she can go directly into a suite of rooms from the stairway. This eliminates many unnecessary steps by giving the chief direct access to a vehicle. This will eliminate circulation patterns that, in the past, carried the responding chief through the company locker room and dormitory. There is a continuity of function between the areas in which the chief's car is parked and the turnout gear is stored, the stairway, and his or her office and dormitory that indicates a minimum circulation pattern.

Physical Fitness Area

Perhaps the newest space to be included in fire station planning is the physical fitness area for weight control and cardiovascular fitness. It is important that a consultant be hired to advise on the kinds of equipment to be included in this area. It is also important that the fitness center be large enough to provide sufficient space around the equipment for safe use. Included in the physical fitness area are a shower room, locker space, a sauna, a steam room, and toilet facilities. In terms of other areas of the station, this area should be placed in the third-level adjacency areas, with its own private entrance off a main corridor so that it does not interfere with response.

THE ADVANTAGES OF A ONE-STORY FIRE STATION

There is a national movement to eliminate the two-story design concept for fire stations. There are three major arguments in favor of the one-story fire station. First, injuries to members of the responding fire companies resulting from the use of stairs and slide poles will be eliminated. Second, the physical exertion required in the constant up and down activity of a high-activity fire-fighting unit will be eliminated. And third, it is apparent that the most economical solution to fire station design is the one-story fire station.

Construction of a single-story fire station costs an average of 20 percent less than construction of a two-story facility. This is often a positive trade-off when land costs and building costs are compared. Although high one-time land costs have been an obstacle to many communities accepting the one-story fire station design, the determining factors in the decision should be the efficiency of response and the reduction of maintenance and operational burdens. A long-term savings in maintenance and operation can far exceed the original cost of the land. In addition, the value of the land can always be recouped by selling the air rights over the property for future development or for additional floor area to adjacent parcels, as allowed by zoning regulations.

TRAINING FACILITIES

Several considerations for the training of fire service personnel must be addressed before developing or upgrading a training site. Will the area be used for entry-level training or in-service training, or to enhance the proficiency of personnel? It is important that the training site meets the objectives and goals the fire service or local authority has set.

Entry-level students require training in the use of fire service tools and equipment. Areas where hand tools can be used, such as a forcible-entry training area, should be provided so that students can develop their ability and skills. Simple training aids, such as railroad ties placed together on the ground, will serve to develop chopping ability with an ax. Building a section of pitched roof a few feet off the ground can provide mock-up that will allow a fire fighter to maintain proficiency in roof ventilation. Plywood supported a few inches above railroad ties can be used to train with power saws. Training facilities need not be costly or formal to be effective. A simple area as just described will help increase the efficiency and competence of the fire fighter.

Ingenuity and creativity, coupled with budgeting, can sometimes yield a suitable training mock-up that will motivate the fire fighter to learn. Fire fighters learn bestby doing, so the environment in which they train is important.

Location

It is essential to select the best possible training site while taking into account many—though not necessarily equally weighted—factors. The site should be remote from the local community but central to the training jurisdiction it will serve. The site should be secluded because it will produce both noise and smoke. The local community may see the site as a nuisance, requiring the fire service to provide fencing or trees to decrease its negative impact.

Size

If multiple training evolutions are to be run simultaneously, there must be space between training areas so that the evolutions will not distract fire fighters in adjoining areas. Safety may be compromised if training activities are placed too close together. The training site should always have room to grow as needs become apparent and money becomes available.

Topography

Flat land is usually the best, with a pitch at one end for drainage. Roadways must be able to support the heavy equipment used by the fire service. This shows a need for a soil-stability study to determine the compaction of the ground. It can be costly to erect such a building on filled land.

Environmental factors

Today's environmental laws can be the biggest challenge in building a fire service training site. An environmental impact study will have to take into consideration, but not be limited to, smoke production which could contaminate the air, and runoff water, which could contaminate the groundwater. Flammable or combustible liquid training requires an oil/water separation process before runoff can be discharged to the ground or into local sewage systems. Flammable or combustible liquid storage may have to meet a local standard to safeguard the environment. In some cases, the fire service may be exempt from these environmental protection laws, but the fire service plays the role of environmental protector when it responds to hazardous materials incidents, so it should police itself.

Water supply

A good water supply and delivery system is an absolute necessity for the training site. If the existing municipal system can deliver the gallons per minute (gpm) needed to maintain adequate fire fighting operations, it is the least expensive way to maintain both pressure and gpm. Water that does not come from a municipal system may not be up to drinking standards. If a fire pumper is needed to boost the pressure for a hydrant system, it may be necessary to install tanks from which to draft or in which to store fire fighting water. A pumping station can be used in place of a fire pumper, and fire pumps can be electric or diesel. It is important to select a water supply system that will meet training needs in a manner that is cost-effective and safe for the student fire fighter.

Winter or freezing conditions must be addressed for both the water supply system and the drainage system.

Electricity

The power supply to the training site must be engineered not only on needs, but on what is available. Will training take place when it is dark? How much power will be needed to run fire pumps or environmental recovery systems? The power demand of these things and of the building itself must be addressed at the training site, so that the power demand does not exceed the supply. If emergency power is called for, will it be available in adequate quantity to keep the training operations safe?

Design Features

The type of curriculum that is planned for the training site dictates the depth of the support services. Will classrooms be sized to hold entry-level fire fighting classes or just in-service company training? Restrooms and locker rooms must be provided for students. Are there showers for both male and female fire fighters? If the training site serves a region, rather than a local community, dormitory facilities may be required. Storage rooms must have adequate space for the tools and appliances used by students, and an apparatus room may be used for training during inclement weather as well as for vehicle storage. Self-contained breathing apparatus (SCBA) and portable extinguishers have special needs when they are serviced at the training site. An area for records and office staff is best placed remote from the training activity, but on the training site. This area can also house a library and research materials for both instructors and students. A media center is essential because audiovisual training aids are an essential part of modern fire training.

A display area must be set up to help the student understand more clearly items that may be difficult or dangerous to handle in the field. Local industry or utility companies may wish to donate these items, so that fire fighters can better handle emergencies involving their products. Hazardous materials training is best done with training aids that duplicate the circumstances responding personnel will encounter.

Injuries do occur in training, so a first-aid station is essential. It must be able to handle both minor injuries and situations requiring advanced life-support.

Personnel who staff the training site will have some of the same needs as the students. Restrooms, dining facilities, and parking areas may be shared.

The entire training site must be easy to maintain. Restoring areas quickly so that the next assigned class can be held is an important consideration. No matter how meaningful or productive the training facility, budget constraints and maintenance costs may force limited use. If this happens, the fire service suffers along with the community. When the site is not in use, some type of security should be in place to prevent vandalism, since fire training sites sometimes serve as attractive and convenient dump sites.

Designing the Facility

A design team of fire-service personnel experienced in training and curriculum objectives should develop the first plan for the training area. Architects and engineers can then be added to the team to start making the plan into a workable document. However, the fire service must take a leading role, mainly because of the unique nature of the site.

It is important to follow a thorough procedure for determining the space requirements of the various buildings needed for training functions. (See Table 9-10A.) This process should include fire service training professionals, as well as architects. The architect's initial role is to interview key training personnel in depth to compile a full list of potential training evolutions and exercises, which will fully describe the individual building functions. The architect then interprets the input from the training experts to design a building or buildings that best suit their training needs. The architect can also develop the size, shape, and complexity of the individual buildings to establish the gross square footage to help determine the building costs.

Each building is developed as a "stripped building" with a certain level of "burning use," which is directly related to cost and must be established early in the interview process. It is important to indicate all the improvements that must be added to the stripped building to accommodate the fire training evolutions. This process is necessary to estimate the cost of the individual buildings properly, since each is unique. Some examples of improvements that are typically added to a stripped building include sprinkler systems, standpipe systems, steel shutters, special lighting, special training openings, ventilation openings, special interior configurations, roof openings, store fronts, security gates, built-in training items, cocklofts, full-height fire walls, and special remote gas-detection systems.

Determining the possible configuration of the building is essential in developing the cost of the stripped building because the complexity of construction severely affects construction costs. "Pin-wheeled" shaped buildings are much more costly than square buildings.

Each building should be assigned a number and a proprietary name that best describes its function. The following descriptions are based on plans for a full-featured modern fire training facility.

COMMERCIAL/INDUSTRIAL BUILDINGS

This high-heat training building should take the shape of an "L," with the long leg of "L" containing the industrial building training function. The building's interior height should be 15 to 18 feet. The bottom of the "L" should contain a two-story "taxpayer" -type building with typical storefront widths along its frontage. A railroad track and loading dock can be added to the building design. The roof of the building can include an opening to simulate a roof burn-through for practice in fighting an interior fire from a tower ladder.

All fire fighting water should be drained from the fire training building through wall scuppers or internal corner catch basin gratings that collect water on each floor and then drain it to the first floor; where it goes out of the building through wall scuppers. Any internal drainage through a piping system will be detrimental to the use of the building.

The building should provide for a long hose stretch. Long aisle spaces simulate industrial characteristics, and a concrete sidewalk should surround the entire building. Interior walls and ceilings should be fire-proofed with gunite or marinite panels. The building complex could have a parapet wall 3 feet high surrounding the entire roof. The building should not contain any lighting or mechanical equipment.

The cellar should have a second means of egress with a remote stairway leading to the outside. The cellar area should be subdivided into two fire rooms off a corridor from the cellar stair. There should be two sidewalk hatches exiting from each of the fire rooms in the cellar.

Industrial Facility

In the industrial part of the building, there should be door openings, window openings, skylights, and roof hatches typical in sidewalk cellar-door construction. The stairway that goes to the second floor should run under an open stair that leads into the cellar, with the base of cellar stairs left open. Stairs that lead to the cellar shall be enclosed and have a door at the top.

A sprinkler two-zoned system should be installed in the industrial building and the lower half of the taxpayer building. The industrial part of the building should also have a canopy over the platform on the part of the building with the railroad-siding.

Taxpayer Facility

The taxpayer building may have a horizontal cockloft arrangement that students can examine to see how detrimental it is to the fire security of buildings arranged in a row. Further, the taxpayer building should have a full-height, through-the-roof firewall for training and for teaching construction principles, such as how a firewall stops the horizontal movement of fire.

The taxpayer part of the building should have various types of storefronts and include the security gates that are typical in a commercial area. A stairway to the second floor can be installed in the taxpayer building to simulate access to a residential area above it. This part of the building should also have a full fire escape with a dropped ladder.

Possible simulations

Possible fire fighting situations and fire conditions that can be simulated for training purposes in such a building include an exterior fire involving a boxcar at the loading dock; an interior industrial building fire with a long hose stretch; heavy forcible entry conditions; an exterior fire on the platform to prevent fire from getting into the building; a loading dock fire involving garbage in a dumpster; and a long hose stretch in a railroad flat configuration, using the second floor of the taxpayer building.

TOWER BUILDINGS

The ideal tower building for training should be at least five stories high have a long horizontal dimension, as well. It will simulate a high-rise building so that fire fighters can practice vertical movements of hose lines, but it will also be suitable for training in the horizontal hose stretch with multiple obstacles.

The tower building should include fire corridors on all floors along which are arranged various room configurations as training obstacles. A fire escape should be installed on the face of the building with a ladder extending to the roof over the parapet wall. All windows in the tower building should have steel shutters, and a roof hatch should be provided to demonstrate roof ventilation.

Fire fighting water shall be drained to the outside through wall scuppers or internal corner basin gratings.

The interior walls and ceilings of the tower building should be fireproofed with gunite or marinite installation, and the interior should be outfitted with electrical wiring and lighting. It is also a good idea to design moveable steel-plate partitions or dividers into the tower building interior so that facility operators can change the configuration of the interior spaces on all floors.

Possible Simulations

Possible fire fighting situations that can be simulated in such a building include fire search along a protected corridor with multiple rooms off it and use of a standpipe system in a fire tower stair, preparing for a long hose stretch. The addition of a second enclosed fire stair can offer a unique facility for simulating situations in which multiple fire companies are working at the same scene. The second fire stair allows fire fighters to practice a multiple hose-line attack from two vertical fire stairs from two fire exposures.

The tower building allows students to participate in fire operations that require stretching hose lines up open and enclosed fire stairs and fire escapes to upper floors, and operating off standpipes and aerial apparatus. Trainees may also participate in truck company operations, including ventilation practices and search-and-rescue operations for multiple dwellings, exterior ladder work, and practical application of self-contained breathing apparatus under actual fire conditions.

A complete standpipe cabinet and accessories distributed by different manufacturers should be installed on all floors. This will acquaint fire fighters with the different standpipe units used in buildings.

GARDEN-APARTMENT BUILDINGS

A "garden-apartment"-style building is a valuable addition to a fire training facility because this type of housing may increase as high land costs force developers to build higher-density housing developments.

FIG. 9-10D. Training tower.

Garden-apartment buildings offer fire fighters the opportunity to simulate low-rise fire fighting situations where small buildings provide a narrow environment for moving through the fire.

The garden-apartment complex should take the shape of an "L", with one leg designed as a garden-apartment complex and the other as a two-story, single-family dwelling. The purpose of the "L" arrangement is to create the courtyard typical of a garden-apartment complex, with all the associated obstacles such as planters, benches, chain barriers, and trees. The "L" shape also allows for co-mingling of the two buildings for integrated fire fighting activities.

The garden-apartment training facility should be built on an elongated plan so that long hose stretches are possible and so that intricate search operations may be simulated in a complex, multiple-room environment. All ceiling heights should residential heights—8 ft, 6 in. The garden-apartment building should be two stories high with typical, narrow winding stairs to the second floor.

A typical air shaft with typical air-shaft windows such as those often found in a tenement building should be integrated into the garden-apartment complex floor plan. At the roof level, the air shaft should terminate in a parapet wall surrounding the opening. The open shaft should have a security grating stretched across to ensure safety during operations and night activities. Wherever training openings appear in the buildings, they shall be guarded from below with rigid grills that can carry the weight of a human body.

Each apartment in the garden-apartment complex should have an individual balcony that does not combine with the adjacent units. All windows in the garden-apartment complex should be 2 ft 6 in. wide by 4 ft 6 in. high and should be pure openings with steel shutters that swing inward.

All interior portions of the garden-apartment complex shall be constructed with adjustable screw- expanding jacks and steel plates to simulate an apartment layout that can be varied to initiate the various problems encountered in fire fighting in this type of building.

A trench should be cut between residential and the garden-apartment buildings to demonstrate the passage of fire between building masses. A safety grid should be installed under the trench cut.

Typical roof types should be provided in this facility, offering the fire fighter the greatest obstacles and learning experiences. The height of the roof edge of the dwelling above grade level should be designed to accommodate a 24-ft ladder.

In the single-family-dwelling part of the building, a typical peaked roof should be installed with one face having a maximum 11-ft slope. A metal scuttle mounted on metal hinges should be installed in the roof to ventilate the attic.

The garden-apartment complex should also have a fake mansard front, applied to the parapet of a load-bearing wall, with a long drop down onto the flat roof of the building. Part of the mansard construction should be exposed to demonstrate the potential for fire travel horizontally through the construction. A removable skylight over the interior stair should be provided for ventilation and for the training related to this particular problem.

Possible Simulations

Additional features for possible simulations and demonstrations include center hall entry confronting a winding stair; a pull-down stair from the ceiling of the second floor to simulate an attic fire with sole access through such a stair; access to the roof of the garden apartment through an interior closet; a skylight over the entry stair that leads

FIG. 9-10E. Burn building.

into the individual apartments of the garden apartment building; a sprinkler in the garden apartment over the main entry stair; and a scuttle-hatch arrangement above the main entry stair in the garden apartment.

THE STORAGE AND RESCUE TRAINING FACILITY

This building should include weatherproof indoor storage space for training with apparatus and secure storage for fire fighting equipment. It is also designed for vehicle-extrication training and includes a training tower for ground-ladder operations and rope exercises with a safety net.

The indoor storage area should be subdivided so that there is one storage area for each outside training area. The facility should also include three tool storage spaces with overhead doors. In the middle of the building, there should be an open-air courtyard staging area for lectures and demonstrations. Each exterior vehicle extrication area should be separated by an 8-ft masonry-block wall for visual and acoustical privacy.

This building may also contain facilities for storing self-contained breathing apparatus and air-recharging compressors.

It should be emphasized that the four-story rescue tower incorporated into this building is not a fire building. However, it should include an active roof training area and windows on each floor, with one window on each wall incorporating a railed balcony. A safety net structure should be attached to the face of the tower with a ship's ladder, railings, and a catwalk on all three sides.

Interior tower stairs should extend all the way to the roof and open onto the roof through a bulkhead. Realistic elements such as chimneys, bulkheads, and open stairs with railings should be built into the roof training area to facilitate rope ties for rescue and general rope work. In addition to interior lighting and electrical outlets on each story, the interior of the tower facility should also be outfitted with furniture, radiators, and piping to facilitate rope work.

PROPANE TRAINING

Training fire service personnel in extinguishing propane fires requires an area dedicated to propane leak and fire simulations. Propane should be stored safely in a 6000-gal propane tank in an adjunct support area that would also include a 15-foot-high elevated observation platform. A 10- by 10-ft enclosure atop the observation tower should house the switching gear that controls the supply of propane during training.

The training area itself should serve as an actual fireground for training and demonstrations. One area would consist of a patio-type barbecue situated at the corner of two reinforced concrete walls erected on a reinforced slab. An expendable residential-type wood-frame exterior wall should be added in front of the concrete wall. A similar arrangement can be constructed with the barbecue in front of a straight, expendable, wood-frame wall backed by a straight, reinforced-concrete wall.

A larger component of the propane training area should consist of a loading dock on which propane tanks are stored. The loading dock should be built of reinforced concrete and simulated in full detail, with a typical metal building facade that is expendable attached to a permanent reinforced-concrete wall.

In yet another part of the propane training area, a large, isolated propane tank situated on a reinforced-concrete slab can be used to simulate a leaking tank or a propane tank fire.

All areas in the propane training area should have separate power posts protected by ground fault interrupters for local electrical use and lighting.

TUNNEL AND MANHOLE RESCUE OPERATION AREA

This part of the fire training facility is designed for exercises in underground fire fighting and for rescue operations in tunnels and manholes. The components of this training site include two manhole enclosures of the standard design found in the fire service jurisdiction connected by a 50-ft length of 48-in. concrete pipe. The manhole enclosures should be partially buried but have exposed access holes for safety purposes during training, as well as emergency lighting operated from a remote switch.

Fire fighting water should be drained into a catch basin through a 36-in. concrete pipe attached at a ninety degree angle to the main connecting pipe.

FORCIBLE ENTRY DISPLAY AREA

It is important that fire fighters be familiar with a wide variety of doors and security hardware so that they can enter a building rapidly during an emergency, even if it is locked. This area of the fire training facility should be for demonstration purposes only. Doors displayed for training and teaching examples are not destroyed during training sessions.

Several types of doors should be installed for demonstration and inspection, including vertical overhead doors; glass stile doors; revolving doors; elevator doors; garage doors; double doors of the type commonly found in auditoriums; and security gates.

OPEN FIRE PIT AREA

This area of the facility is designed to offer training in fighting open flammable liquid fires. The simulated fireground should include six fire pits: two ground-level pits, two below-grade pits, and two ground-level pits dedicated to airplane fire simulations.

All the pits should be built on substantial foundations supported for zero settlement and be made of heavy steel with sloped bottoms for proper drainage. For the airplane fire pits, airplane mock-ups should be fabricated from corrugated culvert pipe.

CELLAR/BASEMENT MOCK-UP BUILDING

As a safety feature, the basement fire simulation facility should be a two-story building entirely above ground so as to allow for rapid ventilation of the fire area. The building should be designed to withstand high heat. The basement floor should be rectangular and divided at the midpoint by a 40-ft-long, 48-in.-wide central hall with an open-riser metal-grate stairway enclosed on the upper level and completely open at the basement level. There should be exits at both ends of the hallway. This building can include moveable partitions so that the floor plans of both stories can be changed to simulate various fire fighting situations.

The upper level of the basement building should be surrounded by a steel-grating deck. Attached to this deck should be two ship's ladders to ground level and one gooseneck ladder to the roof. Also attached to the deck should be two stand pipe connections, one on each of the exit-door sides of the building. These standpipes are to be supplied with water from a fire pumper through a siamese connection.

The floor slab of the second story should incorporate four 9-by-9-in. holes for demonstrating the use of a distribution pipe in fighting basement fires. A similar hole should be installed in the second-story grate. All such openings should be fitted with covers for safety when they are not in use.

Fully removable metal roof-scuttles should be installed, one above the stair and the other above one of the rooms, to demonstrate proper ventilation techniques.

The upper story of this building should be outfitted with normal-sized steel shutters on all walls. The lower level should have oversized steel shutters for quick ventilation.

BIBLIOGRAPHY

NFPA Codes, Standards, and Recommended Practices

Reference to the following codes, standards, and recommended practices will provide further information about fire department facilities and fire training facilities. (See the latest *NFPA Catalog* for availability of the current edition of the following document.)

NFPA 1402, *Building Fire Service Training Centers*

Additional Readings

"Apparatus for the Long Haul," *Fire Command*, Vol. 57, No. 1, Jan. 1990, p. 36.

"Apparatus Overview," *Fire Command*, Vol. 56, No. 2, Feb. 1989, pp. 33-40.

"A stitch in Time...Selecting the Right Protective Clothing," *Fire Command*, Vol. 56, No. 4, April 1989, pp. 29-38.

"A Survey of Hoses and Nozzles," *Fire Command*, Vol. 56, No. 10, Oct. 1989, pp. 25-30.

Arthur D. Little, Inc., *Guidelines for the Selection of Chemical Protective Clothing*, prepared for U. S. Environmental Protection Agency, Los Alamos National Laboratory, Los Alamos, NM, Mar. 1983.

Bailey, M., "Insulated Boots—Field and Laboratory Evaluation," *Fire Technology*, Vol. 15, No. 4, Nov. 1979, pp. 283-290.

Bradley, M., "Heavy Foam Cover," *Fire Engineering*, Vol. 140, No. 6, 1987, p. 52.

Brunacini, A. V., *Fire Command*, National Fire Protection Association, Quincy, MA, 1985.

Corbett, G. P., "Connected: Fire Department Connection...," *Fire Engineering*, Vol. 141, No. 1, 1988, p. 40.

Crouch, K. G., "Fire Fighter's SCBA: Belt Radiant Heat Resistance," *Fire Technology*, Vol. 17, No. 1, Feb. 1981, pp. 39-53.

Evans, C. W., "Review of Fire Resistant Hose Requirements," *Proceedings* of the International Conference on Fire Resistant Hose, Cables and Belting, Plastics and Rubber Institute, London, England, 1986.

Fire Apparatus Practices, International Fire Service Training Association, Oklahoma State University, Stillwater, OK, 1980.

Foltz, J. L., "Disposable Respirators for Forest Fire Fighters," *Fire Technology*, Vol. 17, No. 3, Aug. 1981, pp. 174-176.

Lewis, R. J., "Fire Station Location Studies Using a Microcomputer," TR 86-1, Society of Fire Protection Engineers, Boston, MA, 1986.

Mahoney, G., "Introduction to Fire Department Apparatus and Equipment," *Fire Engineering*, New York, 1987.

Mission Research Corporation, "Guide for Preparing Fire Pumper Apparatus Specifications; Part 1: Executive Summary," FA-29-1, prepared for the Federal Emergency Management Agency, U.S. Fire Administration, Washington, DC, 1980.

Nussbickel, P., "The Fire Hydrant," *Fire Engineering*, Vol. 142, No. 1, 1989, pp. 41-46.

Perkins, R. M., "Insulative Values of Single-Layer Fabrics for Thermal Protective Clothing," *Textile Research Journal*, Vol. 49, No. 4, 1979, pp. 202-212.

"Protective Clothing: Options for the 90's," *Fire Command*, Vol. 57, No. 4, April 1990, p. 31.

Reilly, J. M. and Mirchandani, P. B., "Development and Application of a Fire Station Placement Model," *Fire Technology*, Vol. 21, No. 3, 1985, pp. 181-198.Rucky, F. P., "Remotely Controlled Robotic Vehicle for Fire Fighting," *Proceedings* of the IEEE International Symposium on Intelligent Control, IEEE, New York, 1987, pp. 239-245.

Saunders, P. B. and Ku, R., "Sequencing the Purchase and Retirement of Fire Engines," NBS Special Pub. 411, U.S. National Bureau of Standards, Gaithersburg, MD, Nov. 1974, pp. 201-214.

SCBA: A Fire Service Guide to the Selection, Use and Care of Self-Contained Breathing Apparatus, National Fire Protection Association, Quincy, MA, 1981.

Schwope, A. D., *et al.*, Guidelines for the Selection of Chemical Protective Clothing. Volume 1: Field Guide.

Solomon, S. S., "Fire Apparatus Color: Tradition vs. Safety," *Industrial Fire World*, Vol. 3, No. 5, Oct. 1988, pp. 8-11.

Szmanski, D. J. and Stacy, J. W., "Lesson Plan: Computer-Aided Dispatch System," *Fire Engineering*, Vol. 141, No. 7, 1988, pp. 32-35.Thomas, M., "Recent Research on Fire Extinction and Fire-Fighting Equipment," *Fire Engineers Journal*, Vol. 47, No. 144, 1987, pp. 6-7, 10.

Thrasher, C. L., "SCBA Cylinder Failure", *Fire Engineering* , Vol. 141, No. 12, 1988, pp. 52-54, 56-60.

"Tools of the Rescue Trade," *Fire Command*, Vol. 56, No. 5, May 1989, pp. 39-44.

Tucker, D. J., "SCBA Management," *Fire Engineering*, Vol. 141, No. 12, 1988, pp. 46-47, 50-51.

Veghte, J. H., Design Criteria for Fire Fighter's Protective Clothing, 2nd ed., Janesville Apparel, Dayton, OH, 1988.

Yasukawa, M. K. and Gagliardi, F. M., "Estimated Apparatus Speeds by Street Type in Chicago, Illinois," *Fire Technology*, Vol. 24, No. 4, 1988, pp. 291-298.

Worsham, J. P., *Rural Fire Protection: A Selected Bibliography*, Vance Bibliographies, Monticello, IL, Aug. 1978.

EMERGENCY MEDICAL SERVICES

James O. Page

Since the late 1960s, emergency medical services (EMS) have become an integral part of fire service operations in approximately 75 percent of all U.S. fire departments. Today, two-thirds or more of all alarms commonly received by the typical fire department are requests for emergency medical care. Conservative estimates are that fire service personnel provide emergency medical care to more than 15 million persons annually in the United States.

Many factors have contributed to this trend. Federal and state legislation have produced more stringent training and equipment requirements for EMS providers. In many locales, the traditional ambulance services (operated by funeral homes, hospitals, or private ambulance companies) abandoned this activity when faced with the training and equipment mandates. Frequently, by choice or mandate of elected officials, fire departments assumed responsibility for the service.

An EMS system generally can be defined as a coordinated arrangement of public safety and medical resources to provide the victim of a sudden and unexpected illness or injury with the greatest potential for survival and recovery. The use of fire department and other public safety resources in commencing rescue and medical care in the field, at the earliest possible time, has been shown to improve the statistical chance of recovery from life-threatening medical emergencies.

EMS PERSONNEL

There are various categories of prehospital emergency care personnel within the EMS system.

First Responder

These individuals are members or employees of a public safety agency and have taken a first responder course, or an advanced first aid and CPR (cardiopulmonary resuscitation) course, or have been trained as EMTs (emergency medical technicians); they also serve on an emergency unit that normally is dispatched first and/or is the first emergency unit to arrive at the scene of reported medical emergencies.

EMT (Emergency Medical Technician)

These are individuals who have been trained and certified in one or more categories of prehospital life support and patient transportation. Among the 50 states there are many official types of EMT training and certification. Generally, however, EMT refers to a basic life-support technician, trained in a program consisting of 80 to 100 hours of instruction and observation. "EMT-Intermediate" generally refers to an EMT who has received additional training and certification to provide certain limited advanced life-support functions. This category also includes "EMT-D" (EMT-defibrillation), which is an individual who has been trained to recognize certain cardiac abnormalities and is able to treat them with electrical defibrillation. At present, an "EMT-P" (EMT-paramedic) is the most thoroughly trained of the EMTs. In keeping with that training, most EMT-Ps are authorized to provide advanced life-support services to patients while operating under medical control from their program's medical director. (See Figure 9-11A.)

ROLES AND RESPONSIBILITIES

Published medical reports during the 1970s clearly showed that trained first responders could have a very positive effect on several types of life-threatening illnesses or injuries. First responders, trained in basic life support, could maintain a patient's circulatory and neurological status while advanced life-support personnel (paramedics) responded from longer distances. Due to the availability and placement of fire company personnel throughout many communities, the fire service has been selected by medical and elected officials to serve in the first responder role.

Some of the fire service movement into EMS has been a matter of replicating successful programs from other locales. This change in the traditional fire service role has coincided with changes in the fire protection environment.

James O. Page is publisher of JEMS (Journal of Emergency Medical Services), Carlsbad, CA. He retired in 1989 as fire chief, City of Monterey Park, CA.

FIG. 9-11A. Paramedics initially treat victim at the fire scene. (Source: Engine & Ladder Company Operations)

Urban renewal projects eliminated entire blocks of fire-prone occupancies in cities throughout the country. Improved fire and building codes and stricter enforcement have reduced the number and seriousness of building fires in most areas. Faster, more mobile fire apparatus, lighter and more versatile fire fighting tools and equipment, universal emergency telephone numbers, and improved training of fire fighters all have changed the nature of fire protection in most communities.

ECONOMIC IMPLICATIONS

At the same time, national and international economics have affected municipal governments. Budgets for fire protection are under intense cutback pressure, while costs for fire protection have greatly increased. Reductions in fire company personnel have been common, along with demands for increased productivity in the fire department.

In many cases, the fire service evolution into EMS has been beneficial both for the fire service and for the public. The ever-growing public demand for prehospital emergency care and transportation coincided with efforts to balance municipal budgets by trimming fire department staffing. Overwhelming public support for the fire department's EMS activities in many cases offset the budget cutting and, in essence, preserved fire fighter positions.

THE IMPACT OF EMS ON A FIRE DEPARTMENT

Despite the obvious benefits, the widespread expansion of fire departments into EMS has not been without problems. From the beginning, opinion has been divided as to whether fire departments should participate in medical aid services. Conflicts within fire departments have been common, as have conflicts between fire departments and other organizations or agencies vying for the opportunity to perform EMS roles.

Compared to the single-function fire service, involvement in EMS requires a fire department to interact with numerous unrelated people and institutions in the community. The success of a fire department's EMS program often is determined by the department's ability to meet the expectations of the medical, hospital, and health planning entities. The sheer volume of EMS calls, the demands placed on fire department EMS personnel, the life and death nature of medical aid, and the medical/legal environment result in major management challenges.

THE COMPETITIVE ENVIRONMENT

A new wave of competition for the right to provide prehospital EMS services is developing in many areas. Sophistication and improved management in the private ambulance sector will produce pressure on fire service EMS programs and local elected officials. Large private companies are becoming increasingly aggressive in their efforts to sell local governments on the concept of "privatization." Where fire departments fail to meet the management challenges of EMS, there is the potential that their EMS activity will be transferred to another provider.

IMPROVEMENTS, CHANGES, AND EVOLUTION

While techniques and procedures for prehospital patient care are generally standardized throughout the U.S., improvements and innovations threaten to make those standards obsolete. Procedures that once were considered advanced life support increasingly are being adopted by basic life-support EMS services: for example, application of pneumatic antishock garments, and use of adjunctive ventilation devices. This constant evolution imposes upon the fire department a responsibility to keep up with the state of the art and to provide for continual training in standard as well as new techniques.

Many fire departments have accepted a first responder role—providing basic life support with engine company personnel trained as EMTs. This is a valuable adjunct to the EMS system and in many cases can have a positive effect on medical outcomes. But even this role is likely to change in the next few years. In a few locales, first responders have already been equipped with cardiac defibrillators and have been trained to function as EMT-Ds.

A pilot study, using fire department personnel in several communities of Washington State, demonstrated that the EMT-D concept can save a significant percentage of cardiac arrest patients. Although not permitted to administer medications or use adjunctive ventilation devices, EMT-D personnel are trained to recognize certain lethal cardiac arrhythmias and apply electrical countershock (defibrillation).

Among the requirements for implementing the EMT-D concept are appointment of a physician medical director, voice and ECG tape recording of all calls, and frequent retraining and retesting of all EMT-D personnel. Despite these requirements, this new level of service has been widely adopted by fire departments throughout the U.S.

A BETTER FIRE SERVICE

Controversy is likely to continue over EMS in the fire service. Regardless, this expansion of traditional fire department services already has had major impact on the fire service nationally. It has forced participating departments to relate to other professions and disciplines and has altered the public's view of the fire service. It has created complex management challenges for fire service administrators. In the final analysis, this introduction of expanded roles and services probably has enhanced the typical fire department's ability to protect the community from fire and other emergencies.

LEGISLATION AFFECTING EMS

Federal legislation governing the delivery of emergency medical services, and providing for funding grants, was rescinded by the Omnibus Act of 1981. Block grants to the states were intended to replace some of the EMS funding that was deleted by the Omnibus Act. However, internal competition for health care funds in most states has further diminished federal funds for EMS.

Most states have increased expenditures to their state EMS agencies. However, availability of those funds to individual EMS providers, and the process for application, varies greatly among the states. Similarly, state laws regarding training, licensure, continuing education, equipment, and authorized emergency procedures vary widely.

Research of individual state EMS laws and regulations is necessary to ensure compliance. Copies of applicable laws and regulations are available from state EMS agencies, which are most often a division or branch of the state health department.

BIBLIOGRAPHY

Additional Readings

Bergeron, J. D., *First Responder*, 2nd ed., Prentice Hall, Englewood Cliffs, NJ, 1987.

Coleman, R. and Granito, J., eds., "Managing Emergency Medical and Rescue Services," *Managing Fire Services*, 2nd ed., International City Management Association, Washington, DC, 1988.

Committee on Trauma, American College of Surgeons, "Essential Equipment for Ambulances," *Bulletin of the American College of Surgeons*, Sept. 1977.

Grant, H. and Murray, R., *Emergency Care*, 5th ed., Brady, Englewood Cliffs, NJ, 1990.

Lodge, D. W., *Handbook of Emergency Care Procedures*, Prentice Hall, Englewood Cliffs, NJ, 1988.

Page, J. O. and Smith, B. H., "Fire Service/EMS Program Management Guide," Federal Emergency Management Agency, Washington, DC, 1981.

Page, J. O., *The Paramedics*, Backdraft Publications, 1979.

Page, J. O., *Emergency Medical Services*, 2nd ed., National Fire Protection Association, Quincy, MA, 1978.

Smith, R. E., "Rx for Health," *Fire Command*, Vol. 56, No. 2, pp. 30–32, Feb. 1989.

Stutz, D. R., *Hazardous Materials Injuries: A Handbook for Pre-Hospital Care*, 2nd ed., Bradford Communications, Beltsville, MD, 1988.

Wiltse, O., "Patient Assessment," *Fire Engineering*, Vol. 140, No. 11, p. 38, 1987.

THE ROLE OF THE FIRE PROTECTION COMMUNITY IN MANAGEMENT OF HAZARDOUS SUBSTANCES

Philip Blye and Paul Bacon

Hazardous substances are commonplace in today's civilization. Every day, in cities and towns throughout the nation, thousands of dangerous or potentially dangerous substances are used, manufactured, processed, stored, transported, or disposed of properly and safely. Our society has used these hazardous substances to create a better standard of living than our ancestors ever thought possible. We have learned to create, contain, and harness the power of thousands of these substances for our benefit. Usually, hazardous substances generate a problem for our communities only when they are released as the result of an accident or through neglect of their containment system.

Fire-service personnel face new challenges with respect to an ever-expanding use and development of a broad range of substances by industry. This chapter will present information on means by which the fire-protection community can manage that potential threat—by gaining knowledge of hazardous substances that exist in the area; by enforcement of legislation, regulations and codes that ensure hazardous-substance safety; through emergency-response planning; and by training in the mitigation of hazardous-substance incidents. The use of hazardous substances on a day-to-day basis will surely not end in our lifetime, but the potential threat that they pose can be diminished through their proper management.

Legislation to guarantee the proper management and containment of hazardous substances can help secure the protection of the public and our environment. Laws have been passed regulating the transportation and storage of hazardous chemicals and wastes. Other laws in place are aimed at managing containment systems, such as underground tanks, requiring their removal and/or monitoring to ensure against leakage. And still other laws have been enacted requiring communities and owners or operators of facilities to plan for incidents involving the release of hazardous substances, and to train those emergency-response personnel who would be expected to respond to such incidents. The fire-protection community must learn and take full advantage of all federal, state, and local hazardous-substance legislation and regulations. NFPA codes, standards, recommended practices, and manuals should be consulted and/or implemented by fire-service personnel to assist them in ensuring that proper precautions and safe management techniques are being followed by industry and/or transportation officials in dealing with hazardous substances. NFPA publications that can be consulted include, but are not limited to:

NFPA 30, *Flammable and Combustible Liquids Code*.

NFPA 30B, *Manufacture and Storage of Aerosol Products*.

NFPA 32, *Dry Cleaning Plants*.

NFPA 33, *Spray Application Using Flammable and Combustible Materials*.

NFPA 34, *Dipping and Coating Processes Using Flammable and Combustible Liquids*.

NFPA 35, *Manufacture of Organic Coatings*.

NFPA 36, *Solvent Extraction Plants*.

NFPA 43A, *Storage of Liquid and Solid Oxidizers*.

NFPA 43B, *Storage of Organic Peroxide Formulations*.

NFPA 43C, *Storage of Gaseous Oxidizing Materials*.

NFPA 43D, *Storage of Pesticides in Portable Containers*.

NFPA 45, *Fire Protection for Laboratories Using Chemicals*.

NFPA 49, *Hazardous Chemicals Data*.

NFPA 50, *Bulk Oxygen Systems at Consumer Sites*.

NFPA 50A, *Gaseous Hydrogen Systems at Consumer Sites*.

NFPA 50B, *Liquified Hydrogen Systems at Consumer Sites*.

NFPA 51, *Oxygen-Fuel Gas Systems for Welding, Cutting and Allied Processes*.

NFPA 51A, *Acetylene Cylinder Charging Plants*.

NFPA 53M, *Fire Hazards in Oxygen-Enriched Atmospheres*.

NFPA 54, *National Fuel Gas Code*.

Philip Blye is chairperson of the Department of Fire Science Technology at Massasoit Community College, Brockton, MA. He is also a captain in the Easton, MA, fire department. Paul Bacon is a senior training specialist with Metcalf & Eddy, based in Wakefield, MA, and a member of the Northboro, MA, fire department.

NFPA 58, *Storage and Handling of Liquified Petroleum Gases.*

NFPA 59, *Storage and Handling of Liquified Petroleum Gases at Utility Gas Plants.*

NFPA 59A, *Production, Storage and Handling of Liquified Natural Gases.*

NFPA 68, *Deflagration Venting.*

NFPA 69, *Explosion Prevention Systems.*

NFPA 70, *National Electrical Code®.*

NFPA 72E, *Automatic Fire Detectors.*

NFPA 77, *Static Electricity.*

NFPA 78, *Lightning Protection Code.*

NFPA 79, *Electrical Standard for Industrial Machinery.*

NFPA 86, *Ovens and Furnaces.*

NFPA 86C, *Industrial Furnaces Using a Special Processing Atmosphere.*

NFPA 86D, *Industrial Furnaces Using Vacuum as an Atmosphere.*

NFPA 91, *Blower and Exhaust Systems for Dust, Stock and Vapor Removal or Conveying.*

NFPA *101,® Life Safety Code®.*

NFPA 110, *Emergency and Standby Power Systems.*

NFPA 231, *General Storage.*

NFPA 231C, *Rack Storage of Materials.*

NFPA 306, *Control of Gas Hazards On Vessels.*

NFPA 321, *Basic Classification of Flammable and Combustible Liquids.*

NFPA 325M, *Fire Hazard Properties of Flammable Liquids, Gases, and Volatile Solids.*

NFPA 327, *Cleaning or Safeguarding Small Tanks and Containers.*

NFPA 328, *Flammable and Combustible Liquids and Gases in Manholes, Sewers, and Similar Underground Structures.*

NFPA 329, *Underground Leakage of Flammable and Combustible Liquids.*

NFPA 385, *Tank Vehicles for Flammable and Combustible Liquids.*

NFPA 386, *Portable Shipping Tanks for Flammable and Combustible Liquids.*

NFPA 471, *Responding to Hazardous Materials Incidents.*

NFPA 472, *Professional Competence of Responders to Hazardous Materials Incidents.*

NFPA 490, *Storage and Handling of Ammonium Nitrate.*

NFPA 491M, *Hazardous Chemical Reactions.*

NFPA 495, *Explosive Materials Code.*

NFPA 496, *Purged and Pressurized Enclosures for Electrical Equipment.*

NFPA 497A, *Classification of Class I Hazardous Locations for Electrical Installations in Chemical Plants.*

NFPA 497M, *Classification of Gases, Vapors and Dusts for Electrical Equipment in Hazardous (Classified) Locations.*

NFPA 498, *Explosives in Motor Vehicle Terminals.*

NFPA 600, *Private Fire Brigades.*

NFPA 650, *Pneumatic Conveying Systems for Handling Combustible Materials.*

NFPA 651, *Manufacture of Aluminum and Magnesium Powder.*

NFPA 654, *Prevention of Fire and Dust Explosions in the Chemical, Dye, Pharmaceutical and Plastics Industries.*

NFPA 655, *Sulfur Fires and Explosions.*

NFPA 704, *Identification of the Fire Hazards of Materials.*

NFPA 801, *Facilities Handling Radioactive Materials.*

NFPA 802, *Nuclear Research Reactors.*

NFPA 803, *Light Water Nuclear Power Plants.*

NFPA 820, *Fire Protection in Wastewater Treatment Plants.*

NFPA 1124, *Manufacture, Transportation and Storage of Fireworks.*

NFPA 1991, *Standard on Vapor Protective Suits for Hazardous Chemical Emergencies.*

NFPA 1992, *Standard on Liquid Splash Protective Suits for Hazardous Chemical Emergencies.*

NFPA 1993, *Standard on Support Function Protective Garments for Hazardous Chemical Operations.*

Fire Protection Handbook; various chapters.

Industrial Fire Hazards Handbook.

SFPE Handbook of Fire Protection Engineering.

NFPA Inspection Manual.

Conducting Fire Inspections, A Guidebook for Field Use.

Fire Protection Systems: Inspection, Test, and Maintenance Manual.

Electrical Installations in Hazardous Locations.

(Please note that the legislation, regulations, and corresponding definitions covered in this chapter have been abridged. For more detailed and specific information concerning these laws or any other hazardous materials regulations, consult a copy of the actual law or regulation.)

HAZARDOUS SUBSTANCES: FEDERAL DEFINITIONS

Hazardous materials, hazardous substances, hazardous waste, extremely hazardous substances, toxic chemicals, hazardous chemicals, and dangerous goods—the terms are often used interchangeably, but each term relates to a specific law or regulation, and was coined by an agency of the United States Government, such as the Department of Transportation (DOT), Environmental Protection Agency (EPA), the Occupational Safety and Health Administration (OSHA), or by Transport Canada (TC), the Canadian counterpart to the U.S. DOT, to describe certain substances that may cause harm to the public, the environment, or destroy property during an uncontrolled release. These hazardous substances are listed, and their importation, manufacture, storage, use, transportation, or disposal is regulated to some degree by the applicable governmental agency.

The most commonly used term to describe these substances is "hazardous materials." That term and its definition are from the United States Department of Transportation (DOT), and, in part, it states the following:

Hazardous material: A substance or material, in a quantity or form, which may pose an unreasonable risk to health and safety or property when transported in commerce.

The Environmental Protection Agency (EPA) uses a number of terms and definitions to describe such substances, including the following.

Hazardous substance: Any material that when discharged into the environment may be harmful to the public health or welfare of the United States.

Hazardous waste: any material that presents an actual or potential danger to human health and safety or to other living organisms in the environment. The criteria used by the EPA for judging a hazardous waste are: (1) ignitability, (2) reactivity, (3) corrosivity, and (4) toxicity.

Extremely hazardous substance: One of approximately 360 chemicals determined by the EPA to be extremely hazardous to a community during an emergency spill or release as a result of their toxicity and physical or chemical properties. Industries using chemicals in quantities appearing on this EPA list are required under the Superfund Amendments and Reauthorization Act of 1986 (SARA) to conform with reporting requirements.

Toxic chemical: A chemical that is toxic, a suspected carcinogen, or capable of having a significant adverse effect on the environment. There are approximately 300 toxic chemicals and 20 chemical categories listed by EPA under Section 313 in Title III of SARA.

The Occupational Safety and Health Administration (OSHA) uses the following term and description to cover all substances regulated by both the DOT and EPA.

Hazardous chemical: Any chemical in the workplace that may be a physical hazard or a health hazard to employees if exposed. Examples of a "physical hazard" are combustible liquids, compressed gases, explosives, flammables, organic peroxides, oxidizers, pyrophorics, unstables (reactives), or water-reactives. "Health hazard" means a mixture of chemicals or a pathogen for which there is statistically significant evidence, based on at least one study conducted in accordance with established scientific principles, that acute or chronic health effects may occur in exposed employees. The term "health hazard" includes chemicals that are carcinogens, toxic or highly toxic agents, reproductive toxins, irritants, corrosives, sensitizers, hepotoxins, nephrotoxins, neurotoxins, agents that act on the hematopoietic system, and agents that damage the lungs, skin, eyes, or mucous membranes.

Transport Canada uses the following term and definition.

Dangerous Goods: Any product, substance, or organism included by its nature or by regulation in any of the nine United Nations classifications of hazardous materials.

FEDERAL LEGISLATION

The most significant piece of national hazardous-materials legislation in recent years, with direct impact on local communities, emergency responders, and the fire service, has been the passage by Congress of Public Law 99-499, the Superfund Amendments and Reauthorization Act of 1986 (SARA). SARA, along with other federal, state, and local laws, regulations, and ordinances, provides the basis for identifying hazardous substances that may result in exposure to emergency responders or the general public. Two portions of that October 17, 1986 law, Title III and Title I, are of primary concern to the fire-protection community. Title III calls for the active involvement of the fire service in community-wide emergency planning for hazardous-materials incidents, through participation in a local emergency planning committee (LEPC). Emergency planning must also include provisions for hazardous-materials emergency training for personnel responding to incidents, such as fire fighters. In addition, Title III calls for information on specific chemicals at facilities within the local fire department's jurisdiction to be submitted to them by the facility in the forms of material-safety data sheets (MSDS), lists of MSDS chemicals, and chemical-inventory forms. Under other provisions of Title III, fire departments can access an EPA database, via computer telecommunications, to check on annual toxic-chemical releases within their response districts.

Portions of Title I of SARA (Section 126) address the safety of workers engaged in five areas of hazardous waste site operations: (1) cleanup operations at uncontrolled hazardous-waste sites required by a federal, state, or local government agency; (2) corrective actions involving cleanup operations at sites covered by the Resource Conservation and Recovery Act of 1976 (RCRA); (3) voluntary cleanup operations at uncontrolled hazardous-waste sites; (4) hazardous waste operations at RCRA treatment, storage, and disposal (TSD) facilities; and (5) emergency-response operations for releases of, or substantial threats of releases of, hazardous substances without regard to the location of the hazard. This last area is of particular concern to the fire service. Its impact will be discussed later in this chapter. Title I also established certain grant programs , including the Hazardous Materials Training Grant, which funds training programs for first responders.

Superfund Amendments and Reauthorization Act of 1986 (SARA) — TITLE III

Title III of the law, known as the Emergency Planning and Right-To-Know Act, established requirements for federal, state, and local governments, and industrial facilities regarding emergency planning for spills or other releases, and community right-to-know reporting on hazardous and toxic chemicals.

The Emergency Planning and Right-To-Know Act of 1986 covers four major areas that will provide the fire service and communities with a broad perspective on the chemical hazards within the local area, and those at individual facilities:

Section 301-303: Emergency planning;

Section 304: Emergency release notification;

Sections 311, 312: Community right-to-know reporting requirements; and

Section 313: Toxic chemical release inventory.

Emergency Planning

In order to help local communities protect public health and safety as well as the environment from chemical hazards specific to their regions, Section 301-303 of the act required the governor of each state to appoint a State Emergency Response Commission (SERC) that, in turn, was required to designate local emergency-planning districts and appoint a Local Emergency Planning Committee (LEPC) for each district. Membership in the LEPC was to include elected state and local officials; members of fire, police, civil defense, and public health organizations; environmental, hospital, and transportation officials; and representatives of industry, business, the community, and the media.

The primary responsibility of the LEPC was to develop a comprehensive emergency-response plan by October 17, 1988, and submit it to the SERC. After being reviewed by the SERC, the plan was returned to the LEPC with approval or recommendations for revision. This emergency-response plan is required to be revised and updated annually. The plan must include the following:

- The identification of specific sites and transportation corridors in which extremely hazardous materials are stored, used, or transported
- Emergency-response procedures
- Designation of a community coordinator and facility coordinator to implement the emergency plan
- Emergency notification procedures
- Procedures for determining the occurrence of a chemical release and the probable area and population that will be affected
- Description of community and industrial emergency-response equipment and resources, and the identity of personnel responsible for them
- Evacuation plans
- Description and schedule of a chemical emergency-response training program
- Method and schedule for conducting emergency-response plan exercises

Emergency Release Notification

Section 304 requires facility owners or operators to give immediate notification to the community emergency coordinator of the LEPC, and to the state emergency-response commission (SERC), of any release of a listed hazardous substance or its vapor that will extend beyond the facility's property and possibly endanger the general public. "Facility" means any building, structure, installation, equipment, pipe or pipeline (including any pipe into a sewer or publicly owned treatment works), well, pit, pond, lagoon, impoundment, ditch, storage container, motor vehicle, rolling stock, or aircraft, or any site or area where a hazardous substance has been deposited, stored, disposed of, or placed, or otherwise come to be located; this, however, does not include any consumer product use or any waterborne vessel.

Releases that result only in exposure to persons solely within the site on which the facility is located are not required to be reported to the LEPC or SERC, but may require the owner or operator to notify the National Response Center under Section 103(a) of the Comprehensive Environmental Response, Compensation, and Liability Act of 1980 (CERCLA). Hazardous substances that are subjected to these reporting requirements can be found on a list of approximately 360 extremely hazardous substances that has been published by the United States Environmental Protection Agency (EPA) in the Federal Register (40 CFR 355) or on a list of approximately 725 substances subject to emergency notification requirements under CERCLA, Section 103(a)(40 CFR 302.4). There are additions and deletions to these lists on a periodic basis, and some of the substances can be found on both lists.

Initial emergency notification of a release by the owner or operator can be made by telephone, radio, or in person. To the extent it is known at the time of the notice, and as long as it does not result in a delay in responding to the emergency, the notification must include the following information:

1. The involved substance or substances names or identity;
2. An indication of whether the substance or substances are on the extremely hazardous list;
3. An estimate of the quantity of the substance or substances released into the environment;
4. The time and duration of the release;
5. The medium or media (air, land, water), into which the release occurred;
6. Any known or anticipated acute or chronic health risks associated with the emergency, and, if necessary, advice regarding medical attention for exposed individuals;
7. Proper precautions to take as a result of the release, such as evacuation; and
8. The name and telephone number of the person or persons to be contacted for further information.

As soon as possible after a release that requires notice, the owner or operator must provide a written follow-up emergency notice. As more information becomes available the owner or operator must update the information originally required and include additional information with respect to the following:

1. Actions taken in responding to and containing the release;
2. Any known or anticipated acute or chronic health risks associated with the release; and
3. Where appropriate, advice regarding medical attention necessary for exposed individuals.

Notification of releases of hazardous substances during transportation, or during storage relating to the transportation of such substances, must be reported by dialing 911 or, in the absence of a 911 emergency telephone number, by calling the operator.

Community Right-To-Know Reporting Requirements

Section 311 states that the owner or operator of a facility that is required to prepare or have available a material safety data sheet (MSDS) for each hazardous chemical covered under the Occupational Safety and Health Act of 1970 (and any regulations promulgated under that act) submit a MSDS to each of the following:

1. The local emergency planning committee;
2. The state emergency-response commission; and
3. The fire department with jurisdiction over the facility.

If the hazardous chemical is a mixture, the owner or operator of the facility can fulfill the requirements of this section by submitting a MSDS for, or identifying on a list, each element or compound in the mixture that is a hazardous chemical. The owner or operator may also submit a MSDS for, or identify on a list, the mixture itself.

In lieu of an MSDS, the owner or operator may submit a list of the hazardous chemicals grouped in categories of health and physical hazards according to OSHA, or in terms

TABLE 9-12A. Chemical Lists Associated With Emergency Planning/Community Right-to-Know

List	Section	Purpose
List of Extremely Hazardous Substances (360 Substances) (40 CFR 355)	§302: Emergency Planning §304: Emergency Notification §311/312: Material Safety Data Sheets and Emergency Inventory	■ Facilities with more than threshold planning quantities of these substances must notify the SERC and LEPC. ■ Initial focus for preparation of emergency plans by local emergency planning committees. ■ Certain releases of these substances in excess of the reportable quantity (RQ) trigger section 304 notification to SERC and LEPC. ■ Separate and lower thresholds are established for these substances of concern for the MSDS and Tier I/II reporting requirements.
Substances requiring notification under Section 103(a) of CERCLA (724 Substances) (40 CFR 302.4)	§304: Emergency Notification	■ Certain releases of these substances in excess of the RQ trigger section 304 notification to SERC *and* LEPC as well as section 103(a) requirement for National Response Center notification.
Hazardous Chemicals considered physical or health hazards under OSHAs Hazard Communication Standard (29 CFR 1910, 1200) (This is a performance standard; there is nic list of chemicals.)	§304: Emergency Notification §311: Material Safety Data Sheets §312: Emergency and Hazardous Chemical Inventory	■ Identifies facilities subject to emergency notification requirements. ■ MSDS or list of MSDS chemicals provided by covered facilities to SERC, LEPC and local fire departments. ■ Tier I/II emergency and hazardous chemical inventory forms must be provided by facilities to SERC, LEPC and local fire departments.
Toxic Chemicals (332 chemical/chemical categories) (40 CFR 372)	§313: Toxic Chemical Release Reporting	■ These chemicals are reported on an emissions inventory to inform government officials and the public about the release of toxic chemicals into the environment.

of groups of hazardous chemicals that present similar hazards in an emergency as designated by the EPA Administrator. The list of hazardous chemicals must include: (1) the chemical name or common name of each substance as provided on the MSDS, and (2) any hazardous component of each substance as provided on the MSDS.

A material safety data sheet or revised list must be provided when new hazardous chemicals become present at a facility in quantities at or above established threshold levels. Upon request by the local emergency-planning committee, an owner or operator who submits a list of chemicals must provide the appropriate MSDS for any chemical on that list. If requested by any member of the general public, the local emergency-planning committee must make available to that person a material safety data sheet for any hazardous chemicals required to be submitted to them. This information may be given at a location designated by the LEPC during normal working hours.

Within three months following the discovery by an owner or operator of significant new information concerning an aspect of a hazardous chemical for which an MSDS sheet was previously submitted to the LEPC, a revised MSDS must be provided to the LEPC.

Section 312 stipulates that owners or operators of a facility that are required to prepare or have available a material safety data sheet (MSDS) for each hazardous chemical covered under the Occupational Safety and Health Act of 1970 (and any regulations promulgated under that act), prepare and submit an emergency and hazardous-chemical inventory form to the local emergency planning committee, the state emergency response commission, and the fire department with jurisdiction over the facility.

The inventory form must include all hazardous chemicals above specified thresholds that were present at the facility at any time during the previous calendar year. The EPA has established threshold quantities for hazardous chemicals covered by this section. If the quantities of hazardous chemicals are below that set forth by EPA, a report is not required. Current threshold quantities are as follows:

1. For extremely hazardous substances: 500 lbs. or the threshold planning quantity, whichever is lower.
2. For all other hazardous chemicals, 0 lbs. (*Note*, an EPA final rule establishing final thresholds is expected in the near future; the zero threshold will be revised pending further study.)

Facilities may file either a Tier I or Tier II inventory form. Tier I reporting requires owners or operators to submit the following aggregate information for each of the hazard categories set forth under OSHA regulations—fire, sudden release of pressure, reactivity, acute health hazard, chronic health hazard.

1. An estimate (in ranges) of the maximum amount of hazardous chemicals in each category present at the facility at any time during the preceding calendar year;
2. An estimate (in ranges) of the average daily amount of hazardous chemicals in each category present at the facility at any time during the preceding calendar year; and
3. The general location of hazardous chemicals in each category.

The EPA administrator may modify the OSHA categories of health and physical hazards by requiring information to be reported in terms of groups of hazardous chemicals that present similar hazards in an emergency, or require reporting on individual hazardous chemicals of special concern to emergency-response personnel. Tier I inventory forms are required to be submitted on or before March 1 of each year and contain data with respect to the preceding calendar year.

Tier II inventory reporting forms are required if requested by a state emergency-response commission, a local emergency-planning committee, or a fire department with jurisdiction over the facility. If an owner or operator of a facility files a Tier II inventory form, a Tier I form is not required as long as the same deadlines are followed. The public may also request Tier II information from the LEPC or SERC. Tier II information must include the following:

1. The chemical name or common name of each chemical as provided on the MSDS;
2. An estimate (in ranges) of the maximum amount of hazardous chemicals present at the facility at any time during the preceding calendar year;
3. An estimate (in ranges) of the average daily amount of hazardous chemicals present at the facility at any time during the preceding calendar year;
4. A brief description of the manner of storage of the hazardous chemical;
5. The location at the facility of the hazardous chemical; and
6. An indication of whether the owner elects to withhold location information of a specific hazardous chemical from disclosure to the public.

Upon request by a fire department with jurisdiction over the facility to an owner or operator of a facility that files an inventory form under Section 312, the owner or operator must allow the fire department to conduct an on-site inspection of the facility and must provide to the fire department specific location information on hazardous chemicals at the facility. (See Figure 9-12A.)

Toxic Chemical Release Inventory

Section 313 requires owners or operators of certain facilities to file an annual Toxic Chemical Release Inventory Form (Form R) with the EPA and to those officials designated by the governor of the state, on or before July 1 of each year. A release is defined as any spilling, leaking, pumping, pouring, emitting, emptying, discharging, injecting, escaping, leaching, dumping, or disposing into the environment (including the abandonment or discarding of barrels, containers, and other closed receptacles) of any toxic chemical. Section 313 applies to facilities that have 10 or more full-time employees, fall under the Standard Industrial Classification (SIC) codes 20-39, and that manufactured, processed, or otherwise used a listed toxic chemical in excess of specified threshold quantities during the previous calendar year. The threshold quantity is 25,000 lbs per year for toxic chemical manufacturing or processing. The threshold quantity with respect to use at a facility is 10,000 lbs of toxic chemical per year. The initial List of Toxic Chemicals subject to the provisions of Section 313 were published in August 1986 for the Senate Committee on Environment and Public Works. Through rulemaking, the EPA has modified this list to date by adding nine chemicals and delisting six. Chemicals may be added to the list if there is sufficient evidence to establish any one of the following:

FIG. 9-12A. ***Facility owners or operators must provide the fire department with specific information on hazardous-materials location and allow on-site inspections under Section 312 of SARA Title III.***

1. The chemical is known to cause or can reasonably be anticipated to cause significant adverse acute human health effects at concentration levels that are reasonably likely to exist beyond facility site boundaries as a result of continuous, or frequently recurring, releases;
2. The chemical is known to cause, or can reasonably be anticipated to cause, cancer or teratogenic effects, or serious or irreversible reproductive dysfunction, neurological disorders, heritable genetic mutations, or other chronic health effects in humans; or
3. The chemical is known to cause, or can reasonably be anticipated to cause, because of its toxicity, its toxicity and persistence in the environment, or its toxicity to bio-accumulate in the environment, a significant adverse effect on the environment of sufficient seriousness, in the opinion of the EPA, to warrant reporting under this section.

A chemical may be deleted by the EPA if the agency determines there is not sufficient evidence to establish any of the criteria described above. The governor of a state, or any member of the general public, may petition the EPA to add or delete a chemical from the list, based on that criteria.

The information required by EPA on the Toxic Chemical Release Form includes the following:

1. The name, location of, and principal business activities at the facility;
2. A certification of the report's accuracy and completeness signed by a senior official with management responsibility; and
3. Off-site locations to which the toxic chemicals are transferred in wastes.

Further, for each listed toxic chemical known to be present at the facility, the Toxic Chemical Release Form must include the following:

1. The chemical's or mixture of chemical's identity (unless it is claimed a trade secret);
2. Whether the chemical is manufactured, processed, or otherwise used, and its general categories of use;
3. An estimate of the maximum amount (in ranges) of the toxic chemicals in each category present at the facility at any time during the preceding calendar year;
4. The quantity of chemical being released annually into the environment, including both accidental spills and routine emissions. Separate estimates must be provided for releases to air, land, and water;
5. Waste treatment or disposal methods employed and treatment method efficiency; and
6. Optional information on waste minimization.

The EPA has established and maintains a national toxic-chemical inventory database (TRI database) on the information submitted. The computer database is accessible by the public and government officials via computer telecommunications, and is intended to help answer questions about toxic chemical releases in their community. The EPA is using the data to target problem pollution areas and as a screening tool for the development of regulations, guidelines, and standards. Researchers from the government or universities conducting environmental analysis can also access the data.

SARA – Title I

Under Title I, Section 126 of SARA, Congress required the Secretary of Labor, through the Occupational Safety and Health Administration (OSHA), to promulgate standards for the health and safety of employees engaged in hazardous-waste operations and emergency response. Those regulations, 29 CFR Part 1910.120, were published in the Federal Register on March 6, 1989, and became effective on March 6, 1990. Paragraph (f) of Section 126 required that the U. S. Environmental Protection Agency (EPA) provide those state and local government workers who are not covered by the protections of approved OSHA state plans, with protection that is identical to that provided under the Federal OSHA standard. Those EPA regulations, 40 CFR part 311, reference OSHA 1910.120, and were published in the Federal Register on June 23, 1989. They became effective on September 23, 1989, for non-emergency responders, and on March 6, 1990, for emergency-response personnel.

Paragraph (q), "Emergency Response to Hazardous Substance Release," is the section of 1910.120 with the most bearing on the fire service. This paragraph covers those employees who are engaged in emergency response, no matter where it occurs. (There are some exceptions, and the actual regulations should be consulted for further detail.) "Emergency response" or "responding to emergencies" means a response effort by employees from outside the immediate release area or by other designated responders (*e.g.*, mutual-aid groups, local fire departments, etc.) to an occurrence that results, or is likely to result, in an uncontrolled release of a hazardous substance. Responses to incidental releases of hazardous substances where the substance can be absorbed, neutralized, or otherwise controlled at the time of release by employees in the immediate release area, or by maintenance personnel, or to releases of hazardous substances where there is no potential safety or health hazard (*e.g.*, fire, explosion, or chemical exposure) are not considered to be emergency responses.

Employer Responsibilities

Employers of emergency response personnel (*e.g.*, communities or their political subdivisions) are required to develop and implement an emergency response plan to handle anticipated emergencies prior to the commencement of emergency-response operations. The plan must be in writing and available for inspection and copying by employees, their representatives, and OSHA personnel. Employers who evacuate their employees from the danger area when an emergency occurs, and who do not permit any of their employees to assist in handling the emergency, are exempted from the requirements of this paragraph if they provide an emergency action plan as per other portions of the regulation.

Emergency-response organizations may use the local emergency-response plan or the state emergency-response plan or both, as part of their emergency-response plan to avoid duplication. Those items of the emergency-response plan that are being properly addressed by the SARA Title III plans may be substituted into their emergency plan or otherwise kept together for the employer and employee's use.

The emergency response plan must address, as a minimum, the following to the extent that they are not addressed elsewhere:

1. Pre-emergency planning and coordination with outside parties;
2. Personnel roles, lines of authority, training, and communication;
3. Emergency recognition and prevention;
4. Safe distances and places of refuge;
5. Site security and control;
6. Evacuation routes and procedures;
7. Decontamination;
8. Emergency medical treatment and first-aid;
9. Emergency alerting and response procedures;
10. Critique response and follow-up; and
11. Personal protective equipment (PPE) and emergency equipment.

Employees also are required to develop and implement procedures for management and control of emergency-response activities by means of an Incident Command System (ICS). The senior emergency-response official responding to an emergency must become the individual in charge of a site-specific ICS. All emergency responders and their communications must be coordinated and controlled through the individual in charge of the ICS. This Incident Commander (IC) is to be assisted by the senior official present from each agency and employer present at the scene. The "senior official" at an emergency-response incident is the most senior official on the site who has the responsibility for controlling the operations at the site. Initially, it is the senior officer in the first piece of responding emergency apparatus to arrive on the incident scene. (See Figure 9-12B.) As more senior officers arrive (e.g., battalion chief, fire chief, state law enforcement official, site coordinator, etc.) the position is passed up the line of authority which had been previously established.

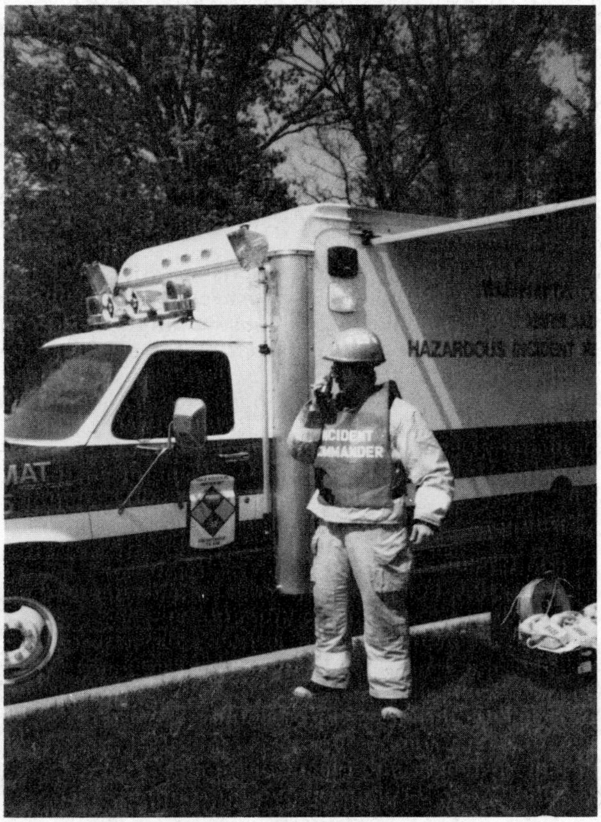

FIG. 9-12B. The first-arriving senior officer at the scene of the emergency should assume the position of Incident Commander and institute the Incident Command System.

The Incident Commander must identify, to the extent possible, all hazardous substances or conditions present and must address, as appropriate, site analysis, use of engineering controls, maximum exposure limits, hazardous-substance handling procedures, and use of any new technologies. Based on those hazardous substances and/or conditions present, the IC must implement appropriate emergency operations, and ensure that the personal protective equipment worn is appropriate for the hazards to be encountered, especially when worn while performing fire-fighting operations beyond the incipient stage for any incident.

The Incident Commander must make certain that employees engaged in emergency response and who are exposed to hazardous substances presenting an inhalation hazard or potential inhalation hazard wear positive-pressure self-contained breathing apparatus (SCBA) while engaged in emergency-response mitigation. The SCBA must be worn until such time that the IC determines, through the use of air monitoring, that a decreased level of respiratory protection will not result in hazardous exposures. When deemed necessary for meeting the tasks at hand, approved self-contained compressed-air breathing apparatus may be used with approved cylinders from other approved self-contained compressed-air breathing apparatus provided that such cylinders are of the same capacity and pressure rating. All compressed-air cylinders used with self-contained breathing apparatus must meet U.S. Department of Transportation and National Institute for Occupational Safety and Health criteria.

The number of emergency-response personnel in those areas of potential or actual exposure to incident or site hazards at the emergency site must be limited by the Incident Commander to those who are actively performing emergency operations. All operations in hazardous areas must be performed using the buddy system in groups of two or more. "Buddy system" means a system of organizing employees into work groups in such a manner that each employee of the work group is designated to be observed by at least one other employee in the work group. The purpose of the buddy system is to provide rapid assistance in the event of an emergency.

Back-up personnel with equipment must be positioned in a standby mode ready to provide assistance or rescue to the entry crew. Advanced first-aid support personnel, as a minimum, must also stand by with medical equipment and transportation capability.

The IC must designate a safety officer, who is knowledgeable in the operations being implemented at the emergency-response site, with specific responsibility to identify and evaluate the hazards and to provide direction with respect to the safety of operations for the emergency at hand. When activities are judged by this safety official to be an Immediately Dangerous to Life or Health (IDLH) condition and/or involve an imminent danger condition, the safety officer must have the authority to alter, suspend, or terminate those activities. "IDLH" or "Immediately Dangerous to Life or Health" means an atmospheric concentration of any toxic, corrosive or asphyxiant substance that poses an immediate threat to life or would cause irreversible or delayed adverse health effects or would interfere with an individual's ability to escape from a dangerous atmosphere. The safety officer will immediately inform the Incident Commander of any actions needed to be taken to correct these hazards at the emergency scene. After emergency operations have been terminated, the individual in charge of the ICS must implement appropriate decontamination procedures to remove any hazardous substances from employees and their equipment to the extent necessary to preclude the occurrence of foreseeable adverse health effects.

Skilled support personnel should be provided with an initial briefing at the hazardous-emergency site prior to their participation in any response. "Skilled personnel" is defined as those employees, not necessarily an employer's own, who may be skilled in the operation of certain equipment, such as mechanized earth-moving or digging equipment or crane or hoisting equipment, and who are needed temporarily to perform immediate emergency-support work that cannot reasonably be performed in a timely fashion by an employer's own employees. They are not required to meet the training requirements for other emergency-response personnel covered in OSHA 1910.120, paragraph (q), but must be instructed during the initial briefing in the wearing of appropriate personal protective equipment, in the chemical hazards involved, and in what duties are to be performed. All other appropriate safety and health precautions provided to emergency responders must be used to ensure the safety and health of these personnel.

Specialist employees should be provided training or demonstrate competency in the area of their specialization annually. "Specialist employees" are defined as employees who, in the course of their regular job duties, work with and are trained in the hazards of specific hazardous substances, and who will be called upon to provide technical advice or assistance at a hazardous-substance release incident to the individual in charge.

Training Requirements

OSHA 1910.120, paragraph (q) also lists requirements for training of the emergency-response organization, based on various levels of involvement. Title III emergency-planning requirements concerning the training of emergency-response personnel were developed prior to OSHA 1910.120 regulations, and programs formulated by LEPCs may not specifically fulfill OSHA training programs and schedules. Paragraph (q) states that each responder must be trained in the duties and functions to be performed by that responder at a hazardous-materials incident. NFPA 472, *Standard for Professional Competence of Responders to Hazardous Materials Incidents*, further defines and details the educational and training requirements outlined by 1910.120.

Skill and knowledge levels required for all new responders (i.e., those hired after the effective date of 1910.120) must be conveyed to them through training before they are permitted to take part in actual emergency operations on an incident. Training for employees who participate, or are expected to participate, in emergency response, must be in accordance with these levels.

First responders awareness level: First responders at the awareness level are individuals who are likely to witness or discover a hazardous-substance release and who have been trained to initiate an emergency-response sequence by notifying the proper authorities of the release. They would take no further action beyond notifying the authorities of the release. First responders at the awareness level must have sufficient training or have had sufficient experience to demonstrate objectively their competency in the following areas:

1. An understanding of what hazardous substances are, and the risks associated with them in an incident;
2. An understanding of the potential outcomes associated with an emergency created when hazardous substances are present;
3. The ability to recognize the presence of hazardous substances in an emergency;
4. The ability to identify the hazardous substances, if possible;
5. An understanding of the role of the first responder awareness individual in the employer's emergency response plan, including site security and control;
6. An understanding of the U.S. Department of Transportation's Emergency Response Guidebook; and
7. The ability to realize the need for additional resources, and to make appropriate notifications to the communications center.

First responders operation level: First responders at the operations level are individuals who respond to releases or potential releases of hazardous substances as part of the initial response to the site for the purpose of protecting nearby persons, property, or the environment from the effects of the release. They are trained to respond in a defensive fashion without actually trying to stop the release. Their function is to contain the release from a safe distance, keep it from spreading, and prevent exposures. In addition to those competencies listed for the awareness level, the employer must also certify that first responders at the operational level have received at least eight hours of training or have had sufficient experience to demonstrate objectively competency in the following areas:

1. Knowledge of basic hazard and risk-assessment techniques;
2. Knowledge of selecting and using proper personal protective equipment provided to the first responder operational level;
3. Understanding basic hazardous-materials terms;
4. Knowledge of performing basic control, containment, and/or confinement operations within the capabilities of the resources and personal protective equipment available with their unit;
5. Knowledge of implementing basic decontamination procedures; and
6. Understanding the relevant standard operating procedures and termination procedures.

FIG. 9-12C. Hazardous-materials technicians have been trained to work in close proximity to the point of release of a hazardous substance, and may become actively involved in its control and mitigation.

Hazardous-materials technician: Hazardous-materials technicians are individuals who respond to releases or potential releases for the purpose of stopping the release. They assume a more aggressive role than a first responder at the operations level in that they will approach the point of release in order to plug, patch, or otherwise stop the release of a hazardous substance. (See Figure 9-12C.) In addition to those competencies listed for the first responder operations level, the employer must also certify that hazardous-materials technicians have received at least twenty-four hours of training and have competency in the following areas:

1. Knowledge of implementing the employer's emergency-response plan;

2. Knowledge of the classification, identification, and verification of known and unknown materials by using field-survey instruments and equipment;
3. Being able to function within an assigned role in the Incident Command System;
4. Knowledge of selecting and using the proper specialized chemical personal protective equipment provided to the hazardous materials technician;
5. Understanding hazard and risk-assessment techniques;
6. Being able to perform advance control, containment, and/or confinement operations within the capabilities of the resources and personal protective equipment available with the unit;
7. Understanding and implementing decontamination procedures;
8. Understanding termination procedures; and
9. Understanding basic chemical and toxicological terminology and behavior.

Hazardous-materials specialist: Hazardous-materials specialists are individuals who respond with and provide support to hazardous-materials technicians. Their duties parallel those of the hazardous-materials technician, but require more directed or specific knowledge of the various substances they may be called upon to contain. The hazardous-materials specialist also acts, as the site liaison with federal, state, local, and other government authorities in regard to site activities. The employer must certify that hazardous materials specialists have received at least twenty-four hours of training equal to the technician level, and in addition have competency in the following areas:

1. Knowledge of implementing the local emergency-response plan;
2. Understanding classification, identification, and verification of known and unknown materials by using advanced survey instruments and equipment;
3. Knowledge of the state emergency-response plan;
4. Being able to select and use proper specialized chemical personal protective equipment provided to the hazardous materials specialist;
5. Understanding in-depth hazard and risk techniques;
6. Being able to perform specialized control, containment, and/or confinement operations within the capabilities of the resources and personal protective equipment available;
7. Being able to determine and implement decontamination procedures;
8. Having the ability to develop a site safety and control plan; and
9. Understanding chemical, radiological, and toxicological terminology and behavior.

On-scene incident commander: Incident commanders, who will assume control of the incident scene beyond the first responder awareness level, must receive at least twenty-four hours of training equal to the first responder operations level and in, addition, the employer must certify that the incident commander also have competency in the following areas:

1. Knowledge of and the ability to implement the employer's incident-command system;
2. Knowledge of how to implement the employer's emergency-response plan;
3. Knowledge and understanding of the hazards and risks associated with employees working in chemical-protective clothing;
4. Knowledge of how to implement the local emergency-response plan;
5. Knowledge of the state emergency-response plan and of the federal regional response team;
6. Knowledge and understanding of the importance of decontamination procedures.

Personnel who teach any of the above training subjects must have satisfactorily completed a training course for instructing the subjects they are expected to teach, such as the courses offered by the U.S. National Fire Academy, or must have the training and/or academic credentials and instructional experience necessary to demonstrate competent instructional skills and good command of the subject matter of the courses they are to teach. Annual refresher training is mandatory for all five levels of responders. The refresher training must be of sufficient content and duration to maintain the responders competencies. As an alternative to the training, the regulations allow responders to demonstrate competency annually for those levels in which they have been trained. A statement of the training or competency must be made, and if a statement of competency is made, the employer must keep a record of the methodology used to demonstrate such competency.

Medical Surveillance and Consultation

Members of an organized and designated hazardous-materials response (HAZMAT) team, and hazardous-materials specialists, must receive a baseline physical examination and be provided with medical surveillance as required. The frequency of medical examinations and consultations must be made available by the employer to each HAZMAT team member on the following schedules:

1. Prior to assignment to the team;
2. At least once every twelve months for each employee covered unless the attending physician believes a longer interval (not greater than biannually) is appropriate;
3. At termination of employment or reassignment to an area where the employee would not be covered if the employee has not had an examination within the past six months;
4. As soon as possible upon notification by an employee that the employee has developed signs or symptoms indicating possible overexposure to hazardous substances or health hazards, or that the employee has been injured or exposed above the permissible exposure limits or published exposure levels in an emergency situation. The term "health hazard" also includes stress due to the temperature extremes. Further definition of the terms used as above can be found in Appendix A of 29 CFR 1910.1200, OSHA Hazard Communication Standard. "Permissible exposure limit" means the exposure, inhalation, or dermal permissible exposure limit specified in 29 CFR Part 1910, Subparts G and Z. "Published exposure level" means the exposure limits published in *NIOSH Recommendations for Occupational Health Standards*, dated 1986, incorporated by reference, or if none is specified, the exposure limits published in the standard specified by the American Conference of Governmental Industrial Hygienists in their publication *Threshold Limit Values and Biological Exposure Indices for 1987-88*, dated 1987, incorporated by reference; and

5. At more frequent times, if the examining physician determines that an increased frequency of examination is medically necessary.

Any emergency responders who exhibit signs or symptoms that may have resulted from exposure to hazardous substances during the course of an emergency incident, either immediately or subsequently, must be provided with medical consultations. This includes those responders who may have been injured, received a health impairment, developed signs or symptoms that may have resulted from exposure to hazardous substances resulting from an emergency incident, or exposed during an emergency incident to hazardous substances at concentrations above the permissible exposure limits or the published exposure levels without the necessary personal protective equipment being used. The medical examination and/or consultation should take place as soon as possible following the emergency incident or development of signs or symptoms, and at additional times, if the examining physician determines that the follow-up examinations or consultations are medically necessary. All medical examinations or consultations must be performed by or under the supervision of a licensed physician, preferably one knowledgeable in occupational medicine.

The content of medical examinations and consultations must include a medical and work history (or updated history if one is in the employee's file) with special emphasis on symptoms related to the handling of hazardous substances and health hazards, and to fitness of duty including the ability to wear any required PPE under conditions (i.e., temperature extremes) that may be expected at an emergency incident. The employer must provide the attending physician with one copy of OSHA Standard 1910.120 and its appendices. In addition, the physician must be provided with the following information for each employee:

1. A description of the employee's duties as they relate to the employee's exposures;
2. The employee's exposure levels or anticipated exposure levels;
3. A description of any personal protective equipment used or to be used;
4. Information from previous medical examinations of the employee which is not readily available to the examining physician; and
5. Any information required by other OSHA standards.

The employer must obtain and furnish the employee with a copy of a written opinion from the attending physician as to whether the employee has any detected medical conditions that would place the employee at increased risk of material impairment of the employee's health from work in hazardous-waste operations or emergency response, or from respirator use. Any recommended limitations upon the employee's assigned work, and results of the medical examination and tests (if requested by the employee), must also be furnished. A statement that the employee has been informed by the physician of the results of the medical examination and any medical conditions that require further examination or treatment should be recorded. The written opinion obtained by the employer must not reveal specific findings or diagnosis unrelated to occupational exposures.

An accurate record of the medical surveillance required must be retained for the period specified and meet the criteria of OSHA 29 CFR 1910.20. The required record must include at least the following information:

1. The name and Social Security number of employee;
2. Physician's written opinions, recommended limitations, and results of examinations and tests;
3. Any medical complaints from the employee related to exposure to hazardous substances; and
4. A copy of the information provided to the examining physician by the employer, with the exception of the standard and its appendices.

Chemical Protective Clothing

Chemical protective clothing and equipment to be used by organized and designated HAZMAT team members, or to be used by hazardous-materials specialists, must be selected and used to ensure that it will protect them from the hazards and potential hazards they are likely to encounter, as identified during site characterization and analysis. (See Figure 9-12D.) A "hazardous-materials response (HAZMAT) team" is defined as an organized group of employees designated by the employer, who are expected to handle and control actual or potential leaks or spills of hazardous substances requiring possible close approach to the substance. The team members perform responses to releases or potential releases of hazardous substances for the purpose of control or stabilization of the incident. A HAZMAT team is not a fire brigade nor is a typical fire brigade a HAZMAT team. A HAZMAT team, however, may be a separate component of a fire brigade or fire department.

FIG. 9-12D. ***The personal protective equipment selected and used must protect emergency workers from the hazards or potential hazards they are likely to encounter during a hazardous materials incident.***

Personal protective equipment (PPE) is divided into four categories, Levels A, B, C, and D, based on the degree of protection afforded. Level A clothing is required when the greatest amount of protection for the eyes, respiratory system, and skin is needed. Level B requires the highest degree of respiratory protection but a lesser level of skin protection. Level C clothing is used when the concentration and type of airborne substance has been identified and criteria for using air-purifying respirators are met. Level D, generally a work uniform, affords minimal protection and is used against nuisance contamination. Whenever site conditions are unknown, entry should be made in the highest level of PPE protection.

Personal protective equipment selection must be based on an evaluation of the performance characteristics of the PPE relative to the requirements and limitations of the site, the task-specific conditions and duration, and the hazards and potential hazards identified at the site. Positive pressure self-contained breathing apparatus, or positive pressure air-line respirators equipped with an escape air supply, must be used when chemical exposure levels present will create a substantial possibility of immediate death, immediate serious illness or injury, or impair the ability to escape. Totally-encapsulating chemical protective suits (Level A) must be used in conditions where skin absorption of a hazardous substance may result in the same conditions. "Totally encapsulating chemical protective suit" (TECP suit) means a full-body garment constructed of protective clothing materials. A TECP suit covers the wearer's torso, head, arms, legs and respirator. It may cover the wearer's hands and feet with tightly attached gloves and boots; it completely encloses the wearer and respirator by itself or in combination with the wearer's gloves and boots. Totally encapsulating chemical protective suits must be capable of maintaining positive air pressure so as to prevent inward test gas leakage of more than 0.5 percent.

The selection of PPE level may be upgraded or downgraded depending upon site conditions. The level of protection afforded by PPE must be increased when additional information on site conditions indicates that increased protection is necessary to reduce employee exposures to below permissible exposure limits and published exposure levels for hazardous substances and health hazards. The level of employee protection provided may be decreased when additional information or site conditions show that decreased protection will not result in hazardous exposures to employees.

A written personal protective equipment program must be established. The PPE program must address the following elements:

1. PPE selection based upon site hazards;
2. PPE use and limitations of the equipment;
3. Work mission duration;
4. PPE maintenance and storage;
5. PPE contamination and disposal;
6. PPE training and proper fitting;
7. PPE donning and doffing procedures;
8. PPE inspection procedures prior to, during, and after use;
9. Evaluation of the effectiveness of the PPE program; and
10. Limitations during temperature extremes, heat stress, and other appropriate medical considerations.

When elements, such as donning and doffing procedures, are provided by the manufacturer of a piece of equipment and are attached to the plan, they need not be rewritten into the plan as long as they adequately address the procedure or element.

Post-Emergency Response Operations

"Post-emergency response" describes that portion of an emergency response performed after the immediate threat of a release has been stabilized or eliminated, and clean-up operations at the site have begun. "Clean-up operation" means an operation where hazardous substances are removed, contained, incinerated, neutralized, stabilized, cleared-up, or in any other manner processed or handled with the ultimate goal of making the site safer for people or the environment. If it is determined that it is necessary to remove hazardous substances, health hazards, and materials contaminated with them (such as contaminated soil or other elements of the natural environment) from the site of the incident, the employer conducting the clean-up must comply with one of the following:

1. Meet all the requirements of OSHA 1910.120, paragraphs (b) through (o); and
2. Where the cleanup is done on plant property using plant or workplace employees, such employees must have completed certain training requirements as described in OSHA regulations and other appropriate safety and health training made necessary by the tasks to be performed, such as use of personal protective equipment and decontamination procedures.

All equipment to be used in the performance of clean-up work must be in serviceable condition and must be inspected prior to use. If post-emergency response is performed by an employer's own employees who were part of the initial emergency response, it is considered to be part of the initial response and not post-emergency response. However, if a group of an employer's own employees, separate from the group providing initial response, performs the clean-up operation, then the separate group of employees would be considered to be performing post-emergency response and subject to the above requirements.

Hazard Communications Standard

Another federal regulation with bearing on the fire-protection community is the Hazard Communications Standard (HCS). Issued on November 25, 1983, by the Occupational Safety and Health Administration, it became effective in November of 1985 for chemical manufacturers, importers, and distributors. All other employers were required to be in compliance by May 25, 1986. It is commonly called the "Right to Know" law (OSHA 1910.1200). The purpose of the regulation is to ensure that the hazards of all chemicals produced or imported by chemical manufacturers or importers are evaluated, and that information concerning their hazards is transmitted to effected employers and employees in the manufacturing sector. The regulation calls for container labeling and other forms of warning, the development of material-safety data sheets, and employee training on those chemical hazards faced on the job. It states, in part, that workers have a right to know the following:

1. The names of chemicals in their work area;
2. The physical or health hazards produced by those substances;
3. Any measures required to protect against those hazards; and
4. The location and availability of the employer's written hazardous-communication program, including the required list of hazardous chemicals and material safety data sheets (MSDS).

In-plant containers of hazardous chemicals must be labeled, tagged, or marked with the identity of the material, appropriate hazard warnings, and the name and address of the chemical manufacturer, importer, or other responsible party. The identity may be a common or trade name or a chemical name. The hazard warning is a brief statement of the hazardous effects of the chemical. In addition, the label may provide the following:

1. An emergency phone number for the manufacturer of the chemical;
2. A signal word such as "danger," "warning," or "caution";
3. Precautionary measures, including basic protective clothing, equipment, and procedures that are recommended when working with the chemical;
4. First-aid instructions;
5. Proper handling and storage instructions; and
6. Special instructions concerning children.

Chemical manufacturers or importers and owners or operators of facilities using chemicals designated by OSHA's Hazard Communications Standard are also required to develop or obtain and distribute current Material Safety Data Sheets (MSDS) for each chemical and hazardous product produced, imported, stored, or used. Although OSHA has developed a model (OSHA form 174), there is no specific MSDS form required by the regulations. Many differing forms are used, but the type of information included on each form has been standardized. The MSDS must be in English.

There are nine separate sections covering all that is known by the manufacturer of the material: chemical identity, hazardous ingredients, physical or chemical characteristics, fire and explosion hazard data, reactivity details, health-hazard information, precautions for safe handling, use of the material, and any control measures to be taken.

Section One of the MSDS identifies the manufacturer of the substance, the manufacturer's address, a phone number to call in the event of an emergency as well as for general information, the date, and by whom the MSDS was prepared. The MSDS is required to be updated within three months if significant details regarding the hazards of a chemical are discovered, or new ways to protect against the hazard are found. At the top of Section One will be the name of the chemical as it appears on its label.

Section Two of the MSDS shows the substance's chemical and common names, chemical abstract service (CAS) number, and any components that present a physical hazard to workers. The percentage of each regulated toxic or hazardous ingredient within the product, provided the ingredient constitutes one percent or more of the product, must appear. If an ingredient is a carcinogen or an extraordinarily hazardous substance, and composes at least one part per million (1 ppm) of the mixture, it must be listed. Worker exposure limits to the chemical, such as the permissible exposure limit set by OSHA, the threshold limit value set by the American Conference of Government Industrial Hygienists, and other safe-exposure limits also will appear in this section. The only time the identity of a chemical will not be listed is when it is a trade secret, but the hazardous properties and effects of the chemical will be disclosed on the MSDS. Additional information on the chemical identity of the "secret ingredient" must be disclosed by the company in the event of a medical emergency or a written request made by an employee, her/his representative, or a health professional for one of seven medical or occupational health reasons. A written agreement of confidentiality about the identity of the material can be required.

Section Three provides information about the material's chemical and physical properties, such as its boiling and melting point, vapor pressure, evaporation rate, vapor density, specific gravity, and water solubility. There is also an area that may include information on the material's appearance and odor under normal conditions.

Fire and explosion hazard data is covered in Section Four—including flash point and flammable range of the chemical. This section also includes information on unusual fire and explosion hazards as well as special fire-fighting procedures and appropriate extinguishing agents.

Section Five covers the reactive properties of the substance, including the material's stability, conditions to avoid, its incompatibility with other materials, any hazardous decomposition or by-products, and if the material tends toward polymerization.

The health-hazards section, Section Six, provides information on a chemical's potential route of entry into the body; its acute or chronic health effects; any existing medical conditions that might be aggravated by exposure; descriptions in lay terms of specific health risks posed by the toxic or hazardous substance including but not limited to carcinogenic, mutagenic, tetratogenic, or neurotoxic effects; signs and symptoms of, and appropriate emergency treatment required for overexposure at hazardous levels.

Section Seven lists safe handling practices and precautions for the chemical's use, including information on spills, leaks, or releases; proper waste-disposal methods; safe methods of storage and handling; and any other precautions relevant to the substance.

Protective equipment that may be required when handling the chemical is also listed in Section Seven, including type of respirator, gloves, eye protection, and protective clothing. Also included is information on work and hygiene practices. The section may also explain any type of ventilation required to minimize overexposure.

The same amount of information may not be found on every MSDS, but everything that is known about a particular substance, its hazards, and the procedures that can be followed to avoid injury or illness when encountering the material can be found. As mentioned earlier, federal laws require that an MSDS be distributed by owners and operators of facilities to both employees working with the substances as well as to state emergency-response commissions, local emergency-planning committees, and the local fire department. The information gathered from the MSDS by these organizations will help in developing comprehensive emergency response plans.

Employee training must include methods and observations that may be used to detect the presence or release of a hazardous chemical in the work area (such as monitoring conducted by the employer, continuous monitoring devices, visual appearance, or odor of hazardous chemicals when released). Physical and health hazards of the chemicals used and measures that the employees can take to protect themselves from these hazards must be covered, as well as specific procedures the employer has implemented to protect employees from exposure to hazard.

Resource Conservation and Recovery Act

Several laws enacted by Congress and state legislatures were written specifically to protect public health and the environment from accidents or negligence dealing with hazardous wastes. In 1976, Congress passed major legislation establishing a uniform national policy for hazardous and solid waste disposal. This act is called the Resource Conservation and Recovery Act (RCRA). Under this act, the Environmental Protection Agency (EPA) is authorized to devise management plans for the safe disposal of hazardous wastes and the recovery of energy from solid waste. In addition, EPA, under RCRA, can regulate the treatment, storage, transport, and disposal of hazardous wastes. Any industry generating more than a minimum amount of hazardous waste must follow federal guidelines for storage, transportation, and disposal. A "cradle to grave" bookkeeping and reporting system is mandated by this legislation. Regulations of both the Department of Transportation (DOT) and the Environmental Protection Agency (EPA) govern the transportation of hazardous wastes. A Hazardous Waste Manifest system, among other things, ensures that the material is properly identified, states the place of origin and destination for treatment, storage, or disposal; classifies the waste; provides the quantity and flashpoint of the substance; and gives special handling instructions. Each shipper handling a hazardous-waste cargo must sign the manifest certifying acceptance.

Comprehensive guidelines have been established by EPA for tracking the movement, treatment, storage and disposal of these waste products. Among the provisions of the guidelines are the following:

1. Identification and listing of materials classified as hazardous waste;
2. A system of recordkeeping and labeling;
3. Procedures for providing correct information regarding hazardous-waste contents to and by persons transporting, storing, or disposing of this waste;
4. A manifest and permit system regulating the transport of wastes to authorized sites;
5. Requirements that transporters of hazardous wastes properly label hazardous-waste shipments and carry them only to treatment, storage or disposal sites licensed under RCRA;
6. Requirements that operators of TSD facilities maintain records and comply with the manifest system. Only EPA- approved methods of treatment, storage, and disposal can be used as indicated in the permit issued by EPA;
7. A mandate for producers and site operators to develop contingency plans in the event of a hazardous-waste emergency. These plans must be the result of consultations with local fire, police, and hospital officials. These organizations must be included as part of the local response team. Contingency plans provide detailed information such as the industrial-site plan, the on-scene coordinator's phone number, and types of hazards present; and
8. Encouragement for states to develop and manage their own hazardous-waste programs consistent with RCRA guidelines. In the absence of a state plan, RCRA authorizes EPA to impose a federal plan for the state.

RCRA also requires hazardous-waste generators to do the following:

1. Consult the list of hazardous and toxic organic and inorganic compounds published by the EPA to determine if a chemical waste is hazardous;
2. Subject all unlisted wastes to chemical analysis to determine if they possess any of the hazardous-waste characteristics established in the regulations;
3. Declare a waste hazardous (based on knowledge of the material or processes used in its production);
4. Obtain an EPA identification number by filing with the EPA's Regional Administrator. Fire officials and local emergency-planning committees can obtain a list of hazardous-waste generators in their area by contacting their EPA regional office. This list is updated on a regular basis and will provide the name and address of the facility, its EPA identification number, and its hazardous-waste generator classification. Hazardous-waste generators are classified in one of three categories, as follows:

- Large Quantity Generator (LQG), is one who generates more than 1000 kg (2200 lbs) of hazardous waste in a month. Once the first 1000 kg has been accumulated, the waste must be shipped within 90 days. There is no limit to the amount which can be accumulated.
- Small Quantity Generator (SQG), is one who generates less than 1000 kg (2200 lbs) of hazardous waste in a month and or less than 1 kg of acutely hazardous waste as listed by the EPA.
- Very Small Quantity Generator (VSQG), is one which generates less than 100 kg (220 lbs) of hazardous waste in a month and no acutely hazardous waste;
- Apply for a facility permit if waste is accumulated on the generator's site for more than 90 days. The waste is considered to be stored at the site when it remains on the generator's property for more than 90 days. If this condition continues, the generator must secure a facility permit for storage of hazardous wastes under section 3005 of the Resource Conservation and Recovery Act (RCRA);
- Treat, store, or dispose of hazardous wastes on site subject to requirements under RCRA Sections 3004 and 3005; and
- Transport hazardous wastes to other locations for use, storage, treatment, or disposal in properly labeled approved containers, and prepare a Hazardous Waste Manifest.

The Hazardous and Solid Waste Amendments of 1984 passed into law on November 8, 1984, modified waste-management practices and strengthened RCRA, by:

1. Establishing tighter requirements for hazardous-waste land disposal;
2. Regulating underground storage tanks for new or waste products under RCRA;
3. Bringing small-quantity generators—those generating between 100 and 1000 kg of hazardous waste per month—under RCRA's authority;
4. Giving the authority to order corrective action at RCRA regulated facilities to the EPA;
5. Setting forth "minimum technological standards" such as double liners, two-leachate collection systems, and groundwater monitoring for new land-disposal facilities, as well as requiring interim-status facilities to either be retrofitted or stop receiving, storing, or treating hazardous waste; and
6. Establishing new requirements for delisting hazardous wastes.

Comprehensive Environmental Response Compensation and Liability Act

In 1980, Congress passed the Comprehensive Environmental Response, Compensation and Liability Act (CERCLA) and established a fund of $1.6 billion called the "Superfund" (PL 96-510) to be administered by the EPA. Under this legislation, the EPA is authorized to inventory all uncontrolled hazardous-waste sites in the nation. If the substances at these sites pose an immediate danger to public health and/or the environment, and those responsible for the contamination cannot be identified or cannot pay for the clean up, the EPA can use the Superfund to clean up chemical spills or toxic wastes.

Toxic Substances Control Act (TOSCA)

The Toxic Substances Control Act (TOSCA), passed by congress in 1976, establishes regulations with respect to the inventory and testing of all chemical substances manufactured or processed in the United States. This act once again makes EPA the central implementation arm of the federal government. TOSCA authorizes EPA to do the following:

1. Develop a uniform listing of all chemical substances;
2. Establish a testing procedure for chemicals already in use and any one of approximately 1000 new chemicals developed each year;
3. Determine if these chemicals present an unreasonable risk to the public's health or the environment;
4. Prohibit or limit the manufacture, processing, use, application, and concentration of such chemicals; and
5. Recall or seize by civil action, hazardous substances that are determined to be imminently harmful to the public's health or the environment.

Federal Water Pollution Control Act

In 1970, the Federal Water Pollution Control Act (PL 92-500) was amended in Section 311 to include Oil and Hazardous Spills. Through this legislation both the EPA and the U.S. Coast Guard are mandated to regulate spills of oil and/or other hazardous substances that threaten coastal waters and inland waterways.

STATE LEGISLATION

Legislation for the control of hazardous substances and wastes varies from state to state. Emergency responders should check with state departments of health, environment, transportation, and public safety to obtain exact details on state laws, regulations, codes, ordinances, or statutes pertaining to hazardous substances and wastes. To regulate hazardous substances and wastes, states must institute a regulatory program equivalent to federal legislation and have adequate means of enforcement.

CONTINGENCY PLANNING

Once the information gathered through legislative, regulative, and other means has been analyzed, a written contingency plan should be formulated in order to manage the problems that may be faced by emergency responders to a hazardous substance incident. A contingency plan should establish an organization for responding to incidents, identify critical personnel, list available resources, and any provisions for obtaining additional assistance. A well written plan will provide the direction needed to reduce the risk to health and safety of emergency responders and the public by establishing, in advance, procedures for their protection.

Hazardous-materials incidents will vary from site to site and day to day because of the diverse factors that can be encountered, such as type of material involved, cause of release, population exposed, surrounding terrain, and weather conditions. Every hazardous materials incident is unique, therefore a multi-hazard, flexible plan must be developed to organize and implement a system of operation. Flexibility allows for modifications of the planas needed in order to respond to the unexpected situations that can be created by the release of a hazardous chemical. A well-written plan will acknowledge that adaptations may be necessary, and will provide the structure fordoing so.

In general, an emergency-response contingency plan should include the following sections:

1. A table of contents that will make each section of the plan easy to locate;
2. A statement of purpose which makes a clear and well defined statement of when and how the plan is to be used;
3. A statement of legal authority and responsibility that details those sections of federal, state, and local legislation delegating authority to responders;
4. A concept of operations statement that explains what the plan is expected to accomplish;
5. A statement showing the relationship to other plans in order to eliminate confusion. The plan should be integrated or coordinated with any other existing emergency plans;
6. Instructions on plan use and distribution which includes a list of facilities and transportation routes covered by the plan. The plan should be made available for review by the general public, and should be distributed to all community agencies (See Figure 9-12E);

FIG. 9-12E. The emergency-response contingency plan should include a list of the routes by which hazardous materials are transported through the community.

7. Organizational roles and responsibilities listing those agencies and organizations, and their respective responsibilities, that will be expected to be involved

in pre-response, response, and post-response activities in the particular community;

8. Emergency assistance telephone roster is a list that should include 24-hour telephone numbers and contact names (including alternates) for community-response and support agencies, technical personnel, CHEMTREC, National Response Center, and other public- and private-sector support groups. During the planning process, one person should be delegated to keep the list up to date by verifying the contact persons and phone numbers every six months;
9. Warning systems and emergency public notification should detail notification and communication systems for alerting the general public as well as any essential information known, such as health hazards, precautions for personal protection, evacuation routes and shelters, and medical-care locations;
10. Response functions should include the method for initial notification of all local, state and federal emergency-response agencies, and respective telephone numbers. Direction and control of the emergency should be delegated to an Incident Commander through a pre-described Incident Command System. A chain of command should appear in the plan;
11. Safety of emergency-response personnel—this section should have a statement concerning scene safety for all responders, and this authority should be delegated to a site Safety Officer, whose duty must be to oversee the entire operation from a safety aspect, from initial arrival through decontamination and clean up operations.
12. Communication among responders should include details on the availability of radio frequencies, telephones and messenger systems;
13. Resource management should list resources needed, where they are located or can be obtained, and provisions for funding;
14. Ongoing incident assessment of the situation must be addressed in the plan. The monitoring of the size, concentration, and movement of the released hazardous substance should be delegated to an individual, most often designated as a Science Officer in the ICS;
15. References should include laboratory, consultant, and other technical support as well as provisions for an on-scene technical library;
16. Health and medical services should describe how emergency medical services can be alerted;
17. Personal protection of citizens should include detailed procedures for evacuation, design of evacuation routes and other public protection strategies;
18. Public information and community relations should describe methods to educate the public about safety procedures before an emergency as well as inform them of events during an incident. One person should be designated as the public-information officer;
19. Human services are the activities of public-service agencies.
20. Containment and cleanup techniques and resources for release containment, cleanup, and disposal should be documented;
21. Documentation and investigative follow-up lists those individuals who are required to file reports for further review and cost recovery;
22. Procedures for testing and updating the plan—plan evaluation procedures by means of tabletop or full-scale exercise should be provided for this section. Provisions for periodic updates of the plan must also be recognized and a record of amendments kept;

FIG. 9-12F. ***An analysis of hazardous substances present within a facility should include facility layout and location, operational hazards, equipment design, operator practices and training, and the properties of the materials, as well as the possibility of the facility being affected by emergencies at neighboring sites.***

23. Hazards analysis (summary)—a site specific analysis of hazardous substances present within the community, the possibility of their accidental release and of populations involved should be addressed in this section. Information should include: hazardous properties of all materials, facility layout and location, physical operation hazards, equipment design, operator practices and training, as well as the possibility of the facility being affected by emergencies at neighboring sites (See Figure 9-12F);
24. Incident information summary—a format and/or checklist should be developed for recording all information initially available on a specific incident; and
25. Glossary—should include meanings of all abbreviations, acronyms and definitions of terms.

RESPONDER ROLES AND RESPONSIBILITIES

In order to manage and direct various emergency operations during a hazardous-materials incident, the personnel of each response or support agency identified in the community's contingency plan must have an understanding of their particular responsibilities and functions within that plan. To ensure the health and safety of those at the scene as well as of the public, a set of standard operating procedures should be followed by each agency. Standard operating procedures are previously defined duties or tasks assigned to be performed by certain individuals, teams, units, task forces, etc., within an agency. Each agency's standard operating procedures should be in writing, be distributed, and understood by all those involved.

The agencies, functions, and responsibilities outlined in the next section represent those that might be needed for a major response effort. Agencies and/or duties might be added, deleted or revised to fit a particular incident. Emergency agencies are generally the public safety forces such as fire or police departments or private industrial brigades that are first on the scene of an incident and are actively involved in its mitigation. Support agencies are those agencies or organizations that assist emergency agencies with technical advice and information, specialized equipment, additional supplies, or aid in evacuation of the public.

Local Government Emergency Agencies

Fire service: The first arriving senior fire official at the scene should radio an initial report, assume command of the incident, establish a command post, if applicable, consult with facility or transportation personnel for incident and product information, and implement an Incident Command System. Acting as Incident Commander, an assessment should be made of all information available, along with initial response actions taken by both facility or transportation personnel and emergency responders. After an initial survey of the scene and adjacent area has been made, the IC should classify the incident according to level of response and communicate such to the dispatch center. If conditions dictate, implementation of the community's contingency plan should take place and dispatch should notify all required agencies. Any required evacuation of immediately exposed areas should begin, and any additional expertise required to mitigate the incident, such as a HAZMAT team, should be requested. Efforts to protect life and property from further harm, such as the evacuation of the surrounding area, rescue of injured or trapped persons, hazardous-materials containment or control activities, and extinguishment of any fires, will have to be addressed. The establishment of hot, warm, and cold zones (exclusion, contamination reduction, and support zones) to control unauthorized entry must be made. The IC must coordinate all incident activities, and cooperate with other participating agencies or departments. Other fire-service duties will include working with the media through the Public Information Officer (the person designated by the Incident Commander whose responsibility is to relay all pertinent information about the emergency to the media) and the documentation of the incident for any future legal course of action.

Hazardous materials team: Working as a branch under the operations section of ICS, the hazardous-materials team functions through a HAZMAT team leader responsible for the tactical operations involving the hazardous material. (See Figure 9-12G.) The hazardous-materials team may be a division of the local fire service, a county, a regional mutual-aid or state team, or a team from private industry. The HAZMAT team leader should be positioned in the vicinity of the command post in order to update the IC of any changes or problems. Personnel reporting to the HAZMAT team leader should include the following.

Safety Officer. A person positioned in the warm zone in a location where observation of hot-zone operations can take place. The Safety Officer is designated the responsibility to oversee the safety of HAZMAT team personnel and all operations. If an unsafe condition exists or has been observed to take place, the Safety Officer has the authority to cease all hot-zone operations and order the team to return to the warm zone. The Safety Officer must also do the following:

1. See that the correct PPE has been selected and donned by the entry team;
2. Ensure that an equal number of back-up personnel are ready to enter the hot zone in the event of an emergency involving the entry team;
3. See that an adequately staffed decontamination corridor has been established with personnel in the proper level of protective clothing, that proper decontamination methods have been determined, and that equipment has been readied before the entry team proceeds into the hot zone.
4. Require that prior to entry, the entry-team leader has reviewed emergency procedures with all entry team members, such as hand signals, SCBA malfunction, PPE failure, and decontamination procedures, as well as the operations that are to be performed by the team, such as leak control, diking, valve shut-down, etc.
5. Ensure that all support personnel in the warm zone are wearing the correct level of PPE;

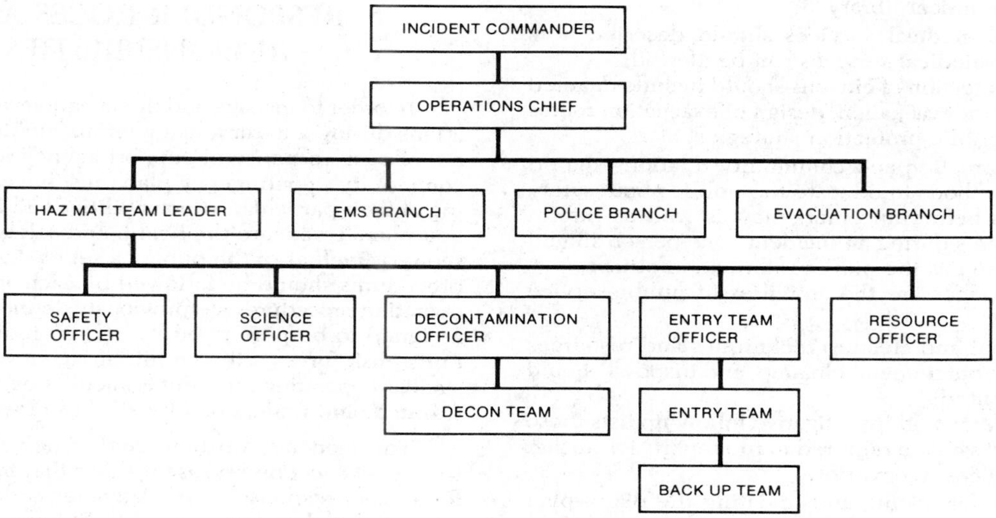

FIG. 9-12G. Typical Incident Command structure for a hazardous-material emergency.

6. See that all equipment to be used is in good condition; and
7. Maintain communications with the HAZMAT team leader.

Science Officer. A person designated the responsibility of gathering and supplying all known information about the hazardous materials involved to the HAZMAT team leader. The Science Officer should be positioned in the cold zone with the hazardous-materials library and/or computer. Duties of a Science Officer include the following:

1. Determine the nature and location of the incident;
2. Research all data about the hazardous material(s) involved, using at least three books in the HAZMAT library or by computer. When looking up this information, use the worst-case data if the information is conflicting;
3. Contact the shipper, manufacturer, or consignee, if possible, for further information;
4. Obtain evacuation distances and evaluate wind speed and direction;
5. Program a projected plume of the chemical using the HAZMAT computer;
6. Relay all pertinent information to each sector officer;
7. Advise the entry team of the protective clothing to be used;
8. Relay any signs and symptoms of exposure and recommended medical treatment to the entry team and the Emergency Medical Services (EMS) Officer;
9. Relay all decontamination methods and solutions; and
10. Advise on the need for obtaining additional personnel.

Decontamination Officer. A person designated as responsible for coordinating safe and acceptable methods of decontamination of all personnel, equipment, and supplies that enter the hot zone. The Decontamination Officer should be located in the warm zone decontamination corridor. The Decontamination Officer's functions include the following.

1. Selecting the location of the decontamination corridor, preferably, upwind and up terrain;
2. Selecting a decontamination team whose responsibility will be the actual decontamination of personnel, tools, and equipment;
3. Setting up the decontamination corridor with appropriate barriers such as tape or pylons, plastic sheeting, basins and tubs, brushes, hand sprayers, hoses, water supply, and ready-made decontamination solution;
4. Selecting, with input from the Science Officer, of decontamination methods and solutions;
5. Assuming responsibility for the detoxification of all personnel, salvageable equipment, and supplies;
6. Isolating of equipment or supplies that cannot be decontaminated;
7. Containing all decontamination solution runoff, such as contaminated water;
8. Assuming responsibility to ensure that the decontamination team thoroughly decontaminate themselves and bag all PPE, equipment, and supplies for further decontamination or disposal.

Entry Team Officer. A person designated the responsibility of directing entry-team operations within the hot zone. The Entry Team Officer's duties include the following:

1. Conducting a team briefing prior to entry, including the review of all known information on the hazard, wind direction and speed, safety precautions, and a potential plan of attack;
2. Determining and obtaining the proper protective clothing and ensuring that it is donned correctly;
3. Documenting the type of SCBA being used and the length of time it should last;
4. Making sure that the back-up team is suited up and ready to enter in the event of an emergency involving the primary entry team;
5. Rescue and delivery of any injured persons to the decontamination corridor;
6. Retrieving and relaying all possible information about the emergency by surveying the scene;
7. Observing and documenting information on the physical layout of the incident site, such as locations of sewers or storm drains, topography, access and egress routes, water supplies, and utilities;
8. Documenting the number, type and condition of containers, identification numbers, etc.;
9. Noting any heavy equipment or vehicles in the area;
10. Documenting of property damage or environmental contamination;
11. Anticipating any tools that may be needed for the mission;
12. Devising methods to control the situation such as minor leak control; and
13. Making sure that every team member exits through the decontamination corridor.

Resource Officer. A person designated the responsibility to supply all equipment that will be needed by the HAZMAT team during the emergency. The Resource Officer should be stationed at the HAZMAT vehicle near the command post area in the cold zone and communicate any special equipment needs to the Logistics Officer. The Resource Officer's functions include the following:

1. Distributing and documenting of all supplies, tools, protective clothing, and other equipment used at the incident;
2. Obtaining and having ready any type of equipment that is needed;
3. Obtaining the correct type and amount of PPE and having it ready for the entry, back-up, and decontamination teams;
4. Obtaining any supplies, tools, PPE or other equipment that may be needed for the incident that was not foreseen prior to the initial entry;
5. Contacting the Logistics Officer about any needed equipment, tools, or PPE that is not readily available to the HAZMAT team, advising of such equipment and the amount needed;
6. Assigning additional personnel as needed;
7. Documenting whether the supplies, tools, PPE, or other equipment have been properly decontaminated and placed back in service, and that the items that were not able to be decontaminated have been disposed of;
8. Conducting an inventory on all supplies, tools, PPE, and other equipment, at the conclusion of the incident; and
9. Forwarding a copy of the inventory to the HAZMAT team leader.

Law enforcement: Law enforcement personnel are likely to be the first emergency agency representatives at the scene of an incident involving a hazardous substance, arriving before fire or other emergency services. The arriving police officer's initial decisions can greatly affect the lives and safety of a vast number of people. Because of this potential, hazardous-materials training for law enforcement personnel should be to the first responder awareness level, at a minimum. The duties and functions of law enforcement personnel include the following:

1. Initial identification and reporting of any information found at the scene;
2. Implementing and assisting in the evacuation of affected or potentially unsafe areas;
3. Maintaining order in and around the emergency area;
4. Safeguarding of the evacuated property to prevent looting;
5. Controlling site access and managing general site security by sealing off the area;
6. Maintaining access and egress to the area for necessary vehicles;
7. Removing any impediments, such as disabled vehicles;
8. Creating road blocks, controlling and re-routing traffic;
9. Identifying any fatalities and investigating the cause;
10. Investigating if a crime has been committed, interrogating witnesses, and searching for and safeguarding any evidence;
11. Providing communications assistance;
12. Cooperating with participating departments and agencies; and
13. Preparing proper records and reports.

Emergency medical service: Emergency medical service (EMS) personnel may be required to provide medical treatment at a hazardous-material incident as well as transport victims to advanced health-care facilities. EMS will be responsible for caring for and providing emergency life support to injured victims who may have been exposed to toxic products. Prior training for medical personnel on hazardous-materials-incident response is a must. EMS personnel can be expected to perform triage and provide treatment to victims in both warm and cold zones.

Some HAZMAT teams will designate a Medical Officer. The Medical Officer should be positioned at the clean end of the decontamination corridor near the entry team staging area. The Medical Officer's duties and functions include the following:

1. Monitoring and documenting all entry-team member's names, job assignments, vital signs (e.g., blood pressure, pulse, body temperature, and respiration);
2. Ensuring that all entry-team members are prehydrated before and rehydrated after entering into the hot zone;
3. Monitoring of vital signs of all decontamination-team personnel before and after decontamination is complete;
4. Assigning additional medical personnel as needed;
5. Determining the signs and symptoms of exposure if the hazardous materials have been identified;
6. Coordinating and working with all emergency medical units at the scene;
7. Removing from duty any team member the Medical Officer believes for medical reasons is unfit for the assignment;
8. Seeing that any team member that needs medical attention be transported to a medical facility;
9. Evaluating and treating any victims involved in the incident once they have been decontaminated; and
10. Notifying the receiving medical facility as soon as possible that a victim or team member who has been contaminated is being transported to their facility.

Emergency management director: The Emergency Management Director may assist in evacuation and relocation of citizens, manage the community's emergency-operations center, recommend that a disaster declaration be issued, function as the public-information officer, and provide communications assistance.

Local emergency planning committee: The LEPC will be able to provide further details on fixed locations and major transportation routes as well as insight on the community's emergency plan.

Surrounding communities: Surrounding communities may be called upon to provide fire, police, and EMS mutual-aid personnel, and equipment and supplies. In addition, surrounding communities may become relocation sites for evacuees. The Incident Commander may designate a Staging Officer to stage all incoming community and mutual-aid units in a safe area, well away from the incident. The Staging Officer will then deploy the units as requested by the IC.

County Government Emergency Agencies

In some areas of the United States, government services are provided on a county-wide basis. Instead of a local fire department or police department, these will be a county fire service or county sheriff's department. The roles and responsibilities mentioned under local government for both emergency operations and support operations will be the same or similar for county organizations.

State Government Emergency Agencies

Public safety agencies: State public safety agencies may include state police, registry police, and the State Fire Marshal's Office. Police units may assist in evacuation, re-routing of traffic, and scene control. Any or all of these agencies may be summoned to investigate the incident and determine the cause.

Regional hazardous materials response teams: Some states have developed regional or district hazardous-materials response teams of fire personnel from the fire services within that region, or, in some cases, by the state police. Their functions would be the same as those listed for local hazardous-materials teams.

National Guard troops: The National Guard or State Militia may be called to provide assistance and vehicles for evacuation. They may also patrol and provide security in evacuated neighborhoods or at the incident site.

Federal Government Emergency Agencies

Coast Guard: During an emergency, the Coast Guard, through the National Response Center, can provide computer-based information on a large number of chemical substances. The Coast Guard can also supply technical advice, spill-control equipment, and personnel to mitigate large spills that threaten or have entered navigatible waterways.

Local Government Support Agencies

Mayor, town manager, or other chief elected official: The mayor's duties can include motivating emergency planners and the inspection and evaluation of any resulting contingency plans. The mayor, with input from other officials, establishes policy and recommends appropriate funding for emergency and support operations. During an incident, the mayor should monitor the emergency plan's performance. Acting as scene coordinator, the mayor must encourage community, county, state, and federal cooperation. The mayor may arrange for response from outside agencies, provide for additional personnel and resources, and act as a liaison to the governor. Mayoral duties may also include the setting up of an emergency operations center and shelters for those evacuated. The mayor may also be responsible for the release of information concerning emergency activities at the incident to the public, through the news media. When necessary, the mayor can officially declare a public emergency and/or issue the "all clear."

Public health department or community environmental officer: The public health department may be summoned to monitor the air, water runoff, and soil for possible contamination. If the hazardous material was a gas or vapor that has a vapor density heavier than that of air, the interior of any buildings or low areas surrounding the scene will also have to be monitored. After the emergency has been terminated, public health officials should arrange health-care follow-up for those exposed to hazardous materials.

Public works department: Highway, water, sewage and engineering departments may be called upon to provide technical assistance, personnel, as well as sand and gravel for diverting, damming, diking, or retaining operations. Immediate emergency support work, such as the temporary operation of certain mechanized equipment, i.e., earthmoving, digging or hoisting equipment, may be requested of these personnel. Prior to becoming involved as "skilled personnel" in the actual mitigation of the incident, federal law (OSHA 1910.120) requires that such support personnel be briefed in the chemical hazards involved, in the duties to be performed and in use of personal protective equipment and appropriate breathing apparatus. Any safety or health precautions provided to other emergency responders must be used to assure the safety and health of these personnel.

Legal department: The affected community's legal department should be called upon to provide advice on a course of legal action to ensure site cleanup and reimbursement of all expended funds. Federal law and many state laws require the spiller of the product to bear all costs associated with mitigation and restoration. Accurate recordkeeping of all expenses incurred by agencies involved in the incident is critical to reimbursement.

Education department: Local school buildings may have been designated by the LEPC (of which the education department is required to be a member) as shelter locations for evacuees. School-department staff may also be requested to provide food for the evacuees. In some instances, members of the science department may be called upon to provide technical assistance.

Medical examiner: Depending on state, county, or local laws, the medical examiner will have to be called on to determine the cause of death for any fatalities that occur as a result of the incident. As a "skilled person," the medical examiner will also have to be briefed as to scene conditions.

State Government Support Agencies

Environmental agency: State environmental agencies may be called upon to provide technical personnel who may be able to recommend procedures that could lessenthe impact of a hazardous-materials release on the environment. State environmental agency roles may also include laboratory services, assistance in locating hazardous waste cleanup contractors, and information on expense reimbursement.

Emergency management agency: State emergency management agencies may be called on to assist with technical personnel, emergency operations, and evacuation problems.

Public health agency: State public-health organizations may be summoned to assist local public-health officers in monitoring and assessing damage to the public's health and the environment. They may also provide technical advice to emergency-response personnel.

Federal Government Support Agencies

Depending on the magnitude of the incident, federal agencies that may respond can include the Environmental Protection Agency, providing an On-Scene Coordinator who can summon a Regional Response Team and/or Coast Guard response. The National Weather Service may be contacted by the Incident Commander or the On-Scene Coordinator to obtain up-to-the-minute area weather conditions. If the incident involves a mode of transportation, investigative involvement by the Department of Transportation and National Transportation Safety Board may be required. The nature of the materials involved or released may require Department of Defense, Department of Energy, or the Health and Human Service's Agency for Toxic Substances and Disease Registry response. If the incident involves injuries to workers at the scene, the Occupational Safety and Health Administration may respond to determine if those injuries occurred as a result of a safety violation. The Federal Emergency Management Agency may also respond to provide technical advice and to investigate and document the incident in order to disseminate information and lessons learned nationally.

Fixed-Facilities or Transportation Company Officials (Rail, Highway, Water, Air, Pipeline)

Facility emergency coordinator: The facility's designated emergency coordinator should be the primary contact for the Incident Commander and/or other emergency responders. This emergency coordinator will probably have clearly defined authority and responsibility to manage and direct facility-response operations, including the authority to expend funds to mitigate the incident. The facility emergency coordinator will be able to provide technical assistance and information on the hazardous material involved, as well as details, maps, and blueprints of the facility. Specialized equipment, materials, resources and personnel may also be available through the facility emergency coordinator.

Facility emergency response team, facility fire brigade, facility security force: A facility emergency-response team, fire brigade, or security force may be able to provide expert advice on the product or products involved. They may be trained for hot-zone entry and assist responders with containment, cleanup, salvage, and possible neutralization of the product. Facility emergency-response teams can aid in the development of plans to plug, repair, or isolate damaged containment vessels or pipelines. They can also arrange for the transfer of any remaining product. A facility emergency-response team may include engineering or maintenance personnel who can ensure the continuity of water supplies, fire-protection equipment, and fire-pump operations. They can also maintain or discontinue electrical power or other utilities. Specialists in potential environmental damage, materials sampling, monitoring-equipment operation, decontamination, or particular hazards associated with the facility (e.g., biological or radiological hazards) may be a part of the team. Facility security forces can also assist in site evacuation and preservation.

Transportation officials: Initial transportation personnel on hand at a emergency may be limited to the vehicle driver, a railroad, or ship's crew. A vehicle driver should have a shipping paper, straight bill of lading, or uniform hazardous-waste manifest listing the material(s) being carried. The driver, if able to, can contact the shipper and provide additional information on the product. If a van truck is involved, overpack recovery drums for leaking containers may be on board. A forklift for handling packaged goods may also be present. If a tank truck is involved, the shipper should be contacted as soon as possible to transfer the bulk product. Some trucking companies will have specially equipped teams to assist and advise the Incident Commander.

At a railroad incident, the train's engineer or conductor will have a waybill, consist (wheel report), switch list (when train is being made up in rail yard), or uniform hazardous-waste manifest that will describe the products being hauled. The railroad or shipper(s) of the tank cars involved may also have specially equipped teams to provide assistance. Most railroads have heavy equipment to handle rail cars and clear track right-of-ways.

During an incident involving a ship or barge, a dangerous-cargo manifest, describing the materials present, and their location, will usually be found in the possession of the captain or first officer. The ship or barge may have a supply of containment booms, and the crew may be able to assist in their deployment.

Private Agencies

CHEMTREC: The Chemical Transportation Emergency Center (CHEMTREC) is a 24-hour-a-day public service, established by the Chemical Manufacturers Association (CMA) to provide specific information to emergency responders on how to handle a spill, leak, fire, or exposure to hazardous materials involved at an incident. CHEMTREC will also immediately notify the shipper(s) and/or manufacturer(s) of the material(s) so they can provide the Incident Commander with additional information. Responsibility for further guidance, including the dispatch of personnel and specially equipped teams to the scene, then passes to the shipper.

Public utilities: electric, gas, telephone, sewer, or waste-water treatment facilities: Public utilities will play an early and on-going role during a hazardous-materials incident. Electrical generating firms may be summoned to cut the power supply or restore power to a site. Gas companies can shut off the gas supply, monitor for leaks in the area, and prior to the restoration of gas service, assure the re-lighting of home appliance pilots in the effected area. Through pre-arrangement, telephone companies may be contacted to provide mobile telecommunications at an incident scene. Sewer or waste-water treatment facilities may be called upon to isolate any drainage or sewer lines that flow from the site. If the hazardous material has already entered the system, waste-water treatment operators should be advised of its nature and properties as soon as possible.

Hospitals, health-care facilities: Arrangement for the treatment of contaminated or injured persons from the scene of a hazardous-materials incident should be worked out with local hospitals or health-care facilities as part of the community's contingency plan. Advanced-care medical personnel should be briefed on all known information concerning the hazardous materials and circumstances surrounding the incident. This will enable them to prepare themselves and the facility, as well as gain insight on the nature of possible injuries to those persons being received.

Red Cross, Salvation Army, and other service or religious groups: Service and religious groups can be called upon to provide food, shelter, and clothing for incident evacuees. They also may provide food-support services to emergency responders at the scene.

Media (television, radio, newspaper): The electronic media (television, radio) can be used by the Incident Commander to communicate emergency messages to the public in order to direct their actions as to evacuation. The IC, through the Public Information Officer (PIO), can use the media to report events and update any progress to the community. Media broadcasts and articles on the incident can also provide the basis for a later critique of the incident and the community's contingency plan.

Local general contractors, construction companies, building supply firms: Through pre-arrangements made during the contingency-planning process, general contractors, construction companies, and building-supply firms in the area may extend assistance to emergency responders in the form of personnel, various heavy construction equipment, sand and gravel, plywood, and other building materials.

Environmental cleanup contractors: Once the emergency has passed, cleanup of any released hazardous materials is usually carried out by licensed environmental cleanup contractors. They will have response teams trained in controlling the further spread and restoration of the site's environment. The contractor may also be licensed and equipped to haul hazardous wastes to a treatment, storage, or disposal facility.

Salvage contractors: Private salvage contractors may be hired by the facility or transportation vehicle's owners to recover any salvageable equipment. These contractors may be equipped with air-lift bags, large cranes, side-boom dozers or other heavy wrecking equipment designed to handle large apparatus or machinery safely.

Insurance companies: The insurance company for the facility or transportation company involved in the hazardous-materials incident should be notified by the owner or operator as soon as time and events permit. Emergency-response services will want to bill for recovery of any expenditures associated with the incident. The insurance company may send an adjuster to the scene and authorize funding for site cleanup and restoration.

TRAINING AND NFPA 472

When all the legislation and regulations that federal, state, and local governments have passed to manage hazardous substances fail, and there is a release, emergency responders must fall back on their training and education. The training of emergency responders is thought to be so important by Congress that, in Public Law 99-499, they directed OSHA and the EPA to create regulations on the matter. NFPA 472, *Standard for Professional Competence of Responders to Hazardous Materials Incidents,* corresponds to those requirements and response levels found in OSHA 1910.120 paragraph (q) and EPA 40 CFR part 311.

OSHA 1910.120 specifies a certain number of training hours, needed for each level of response. NFPA 472, *Standard for Professional Competence of Responders to Hazardous Materials Incidents*, does not specify hourly training, but instead identifies minimum levels of ability for responders. It defines and describes four levels of knowledge and skills needed by emergency workers in order to respond to a hazardous-materials incident without regard to location, and with minimal risk to responder's health and safety and to the health and safety of others. The four levels found in NFPA 472 are: (1) First Responder Awareness, (2) First Responder Operational, (3) Hazardous Materials Technician, and (4) Hazardous Materials Specialist.

NFPA 472, *Standard for Professional Competence of Responders to Hazardous Materials Incidents,* divides First Responders into two levels of competency: (1) first-responder awareness, and (2) first responder operational. Awareness-level competency is to be attained by persons, such as police officers, whose normal duties may result in their being first on the scene of a hazardous-materials incident. Awareness-level personnel are not expected to take any actions other than recognizing that a hazard exists, calling for trained personnel, and securing the endangered area. Operational-level competency is to be attained by those persons, such as firefighters and rescue personnel whose duties and functions include responding to hazardous materials incidents to mitigate the effects of a release without actually trying to stop the release. Operations-level personnel must meet the requirements for awareness level. They are not expected to use specialized chemical protective clothing or special control equipment.

Technician-level competencies specify those abilities needed to safely stop a hazardous-materials release. Technicians must meet all requirements for first-responder awareness and operational levels as well as meet OSHA/EPA training requirements as found in 1910.120. A medical-surveillance program requiring a medical examination upon assignment, and at least annually thereafter, is also a part of the 1910.120 provisions. Response-team technicians must also be examined upon report of symptoms of hazardous-materials exposure and upon termination from the team. Specialist-level personnel may respond with and provide technical support to first responders and technicians at more complicated hazardous-materials incidents. They generally have a more detailed knowledge of various substances than do technicians and may also act as a liaison between the IC and government agencies concerning scene activities. Hazardous Materials Specialists must meet the competencies required for first-responder awareness/operational and technician levels in addition to those stipulated in NFPA 472 for the Specialist level. They must also meet the OSHA/EPA training and the medical-surveillance program requirements.

All hazardous-materials responders are required by OSHA and EPA to receive annual training to maintain their competency level or be able to demonstrate competency in those areas at least yearly. Semi-annual or annual scenarios or mock incidents are an excellent way for response-team managers to gauge or review the competency levels of emergency workers. Critiques of these scenarios by all involved can help point out successes, failures, and the need for additional training or equipment.

HAZARDOUS WASTE EMERGENCY PREVENTION

Prior to 1970, the American public was generally unaware of the dangers involved with the transport, storage, and disposal of hazardous wastes. The careless disposal of what was merely considered to be trash eventually found its way into the environment—polluting water supplies, air, and soil. On occasion, it was encountered by fire fighters called to extinguish exploding barrels of unknown liquids at both legitimate and clandestine chemical-disposal facilities. Prior to federal, state, and local regulations, hazardous wastes could be deposited in general landfills, a hole in the ground, or body of unprotected water. Dumping sites for industrial byproducts could remain undetected for years, only to be discovered when their presence became an immediate danger to the public health. (See Figure 9-12H.)

FIG. 9-12H. ***Illegal and abandoned dump sites can pose a serious threat. Hazardous wastes may remain contained for years, and then disperse into the environment without warning.***

It is still possible for emergency-response personnel to encounter in their own community, an old chemical-disposal site where corroding drums leak unidentified materials into the ground, where multi-gallon hazardous-waste lagoons contain dangerous solids or liquids, or a small unlabeled hazardous-waste barrel stored in an inconspicuous corner of an out building. Incidents involving illegal hazardous wastes are complicated by the poor identification of storage sites, improper or absent labeling of containers, and illegal disposal. Apart from the ever-present risks due to fire from these dangerous substances, emergency personnel responding to an incident can unknowingly endanger their health by merely exposing themselves to these materials. It is possible that such exposures could cause chemical burns, asphyxiation, poisoning, or injury from explosion. In addition, more long-term, but delayed effects, could result in respiratory disease, cancer, and kidney or liver failure.

Prior to emergency workers responding to an incident involving known or unknown hazardous wastes, they must plan. The following list suggests ways in which local emergency response personnel can plan for such incidents:

1. Develop a working knowledge of applicable state and federal regulations governing the generation, storage, transportation and disposal of hazardous wastes.
2. Form a working relationship with state and regional hazardous-waste coordinators. Record for immediate use all telephone numbers of municipal, county, state and federal emergency response agencies.
3. Survey, inventory, and inspect all manufacturers, businesses, educational institutions and health-care providers that manufacture, import, use, store, transport, treat, or dispose of hazardous materials. Remember that even small businesses may generate, store, and dispose of hazardous materials. One area that must be included in the survey is the local municipal or private contractor's landfill. Many landfills have become ecological "time bombs" due to the hazardous wastes that have been dumped there in pre-regulation days.
4. Review old municipal records to uncover and locate areas of past chemical activity. Companies that have long gone out of business may have left a deadly legacy.
5. Assist industries regulated by the Resource and Conservation Recovery Act (RCRA) in the development of their plans for handling chemical emergencies. EPA regulations specifically provide for emergency-responder participation in such industrial contingency plans. Copies of these plans should be kept on file with the local fire department.
6. If a facility does not fall within the scope of RCRA regulations, diplomatically request information about the presence of hazardous materials and where they are located.
7. Know what types of hazardous wastes are likely to be generated in and/or transported in and through your community, by what routes, and the likely disposal areas. Develop procedures and obtain equipment needed to protect against the specific hazard each substance may present.
8. Consult your community's contingency plan to define what the roles and responsibilities of local fire, police, emergency medical services, or hospital emergency personnel will be during a hazardous-waste incident. Conduct a hazardous-waste emergency drill to ensure that all agencies know their assignments and how to execute them properly.
9. Develop a comprehensive hazardous-materials and hazardous-waste training program for all emergency responders. Include sessions designed to familiarize emergency personnel with the operational features of specially designed hazardous-waste transport vehicles or other bulk containers. A lesson on appropriate DOT and EPA hazard identification markings and manifests for hazardous-waste shipments, along with procedures to be followed during a hazardous-waste incident, should also be included in the training.

IMMEDIATE RESPONSE GUIDELINES

Planning and training go hand in hand. The best plan in the world will not be sufficient if the persons implementing the plan are not trained in its execution. Familiarization with and rehearsal of the plan is crucial to its successful implementation, but even the best plans and training may not cover novel emergency events. There are, however, certain basic safety precautions that can be taken to protect both the lives of first responders and the community. Actions for first responders to take in situations involving an unknown hazardous material or hazardous wastes include the following:

1. Observation of the scene from a safe distance, up-wind and up-hill;
2. Establishment of a command post and implementation of the Incident Command System;
3. Immediate evacuation of the incident site and surrounding area, if required;
4. Establishment of hot, warm, and cold zones of operation;
5. Identification of the hazardous substance as soon as possible using any DOT or EPA markings, labels, numbers, etc., on the containment vessel;
6. Location of the facility manager or safety officer at a fixed facility to obtain first-hand knowledge of what substances might be involved. The facility may have an emergency-response team that can provide assistance or equipment such as specialized instruments that can be used to detect and track the spread of the release;
7. In a highway transportation incident, consult with the driver or search the cab of the vehicle, if possible, to locate the bill of lading or hazardous-waste manifest. Establish contact with the shipper as soon as possible, to determine the safest mitigation method;
8. If approach must be made, wear the appropriate personal protective equipment. If the material is still an unknown, wear the highest level of PPE available. Use caution, some hazardous wastes may penetrate even the best of protective outerwear;
9. During an approach, the entry team must work in pairs, watching their buddy for signs of possible exposure such as giddiness, fatigue, or abnormal behavior. Make sure a back-up team is standing by in the event of a problem involving the initial entry team;
10. Arrange for the removal and decontamination of any victims, emergency personnel, and equipment; and
11. Arrange for site cleanup once the incident has been stabilized.

BIBLIOGRAPHY

References

"EPA Form R and Instructions, Toxic Release Inventory Reporting Form," Jan. 1988, U.S. Environmental Protection Agency, Washington DC.

EPA Title III List of Lists, Consolidated List of Chemicals Subject to Reporting Under the Emergency Planning and Community Right-to-Know Act, EPA 560/4-90-011, Jan. 1990, United States Environmental Protection Agency, Washington, DC.

"Hazardous Materials Emergency Planning Guide," NRT-1, Mar., 1987, National Response Team of the National Oil and Hazardous Substances Contingency Plan, G-WER/12, 2100 2nd Street SW, Washington DC.

Henry, Martin F., *ed.*, *Hazardous Materials Response Handbook*, National Fire Protection Association, Quincy, MA, 1989.

It's Not Over in October!, A Guide for Local Emergency Planning Committees Implementing the Emergency Planning and Community Right-to Know Act, (SARA Title III), U.S. Government Printing Office, Washington DC,1988.

NFPA 472, *Standard for Professional Competence of Responders to Hazardous Materials Incidents*, National Fire Protection Association, Quincy, MA, 1989.

Part III Department of Labor, Occupational Safety and Health Administration, 29 CFR Part 1910, Hazardous Waste Operations and Emergency Response; Final Rule, Federal Register Vol. 54, No. 42, Monday, Mar. 6, 1989, Rules and Regulations.

Part IV Department of Labor, Occupational Safety and Health Administration, 29 CFR Part 1910, Hazardous Waste Operations and Emergency Response; Final Rule; Corrections, Federal Register Vol. 55, No. 72, Friday, Apr. 13, 1990, Rules and Regulations.

Part IV Department of Labor, Occupational Safety and Health Administration, 29 CFR Part 1910, Hazardous Communication; Final Rule; Federal Register Vol. 48, No. 228, Friday, November 25, 1983, Rules and Regulations.

Part IV Environmental Protection Agency, 40 CFR Part 311, Worker Protection Standards for Hazardous Waste Operations and Emergency Response; Final Rule, Federal Register, Vol. 54, No. 120, Friday, June 23, 1989, Rules and Regulations.

Public Law 99-499 — October 17, 1986, Superfund Amendments and Reauthorization Act of 1986, Sections 300-330.

"The Emergency Planning and Community Right-to-Know Act, Section 313 Release Reporting Requirements," Dec. 1988, U.S. Environmental Protection Agency, Washington DC.

"SARA Title III Fact Sheet: Emergency Planning and Community Right-to-Know," Feb., 1990, U.S. Environmental Protection Agency, Washington DC.

Additional Readings

Albrecht, A. R., "Handling Spills Involving Hazardous Chemicals within the Chemical Industry," *Fire Journal*, Vol., 65, No. 3, May 1971, pp. 40-48.

Alexander, G., "Regional Teamwork," *Fire Command*, Vol. 57, No. 5, Jan. 1990, pp. 20-23.

Cooney, B., "Fire Service Response to Chemical Incidents," *Fire International*, Vol. 11, No. 104, 1987, pp. 39, 42-43.

Davis, D., "Planning for Incidents Involving Hazardous Materials," *Fire Prevention*, No. 218, Apr. 1989, pp. 19-22.

"Dressing for Successful Haz-Mat Emergency Response," *Fire Command*, Vol. 56, No. 12, Dec. 1989, p. 36.

Fire, F. L., "1 + 1 = Synergism," *Fire Engineering*, Vol. 140, No. 6, 1987, pp. 19-21.

Fire Protection Guide on Hazardous Materials, 8th ed., National Fire Protection Association, Quincy, MA, 1984.

"Haz-Mats Case Studies for Emergency Responders," (Video), National Fire Protection Association, Quincy, MA., 1986.

Hazardous Materials Emergency Response Plan, Maricopa County Local Emergency Planning Committee, Maricopa County, AZ, 1988.

Hazardous Materials Emergency Response: Training Programs and Response Equipment, Illinois Hazardous Materials Advisory Board, Springfield, IL, 1987.

"Handling Hazardous Materials Transportation Emergencies," (slide/tape), National Fire Protection Association, Quincy, MA, 1983.

"Hazardous Waste and the Fire Service, (slide/tape)," National Fire Protection Association, Quincy, MA, 1984.

Lake, M., "Something in Common," *Fire Engineering*, Vol. 140, No. 6, 1987, pp. 22-25.

Lesak, D. M., "Tactics for HAZ-MAT Incidents," *Fire Engineering*, Vol. 142, No. 10, 1989, p. 89.

McDonald, B. R., "Training for Chemical Emergencies," *Fire Command*, Vol. 56, No. 3, Mar. 1989, pp. 30-35.

Noble, G., *Hazardous Waste and the Public Works Official*, APWA, Chicago, IL, 1984.

Orvos, D. R., and Cairns, J., "Hazmat and Habitat," *Fire Engineering*, Vol. 140, No. 7, 1987, p. 24.

Sudal, F. J., and Staehle, W. J., "Newark's Hazardous Materials Management and Preparedness Programs," *Fire Journal*, Vol. 81, No. 2, 1987, p. 40.

IDENTIFICATION OF THE HAZARDS OF MATERIALS

Revised by Robert P. Benedetti

This chapter describes several systems that are used to identify the hazards of materials. Such identification systems are designed to minimize the danger to emergency personnel who respond to fires and emergencies involving hazardous materials.

Section 2, Chapter 3, "Fire Hazards of Materials," and Chapter 15 of this section, "Handling Hazardous Materials Transportation Emergencies," provide additional information for those concerned with the identification, handling, and transport of hazardous materials.

PRESENTATION OF INFORMATION

Hazards can be identified in the following ways.

1. Large placards, signs, or decals can be posted on storage tanks, on vehicles in storage areas, and on processing equipment. Information is printed in large type for reading at a distance. These placards usually give only a statement of hazard and a simple warning, such as "DO NOT ENTER."
2. Placards can be posted in local areas. These are usually more detailed, and may contain instructions for procedures and safety equipment.
3. Department of Transportation (DOT) hazardous materials placards appear on many, but not all, trucks and rail cars carrying hazardous materials.
4. Containers and shipping packages may be labeled.
5. Materials are listed on the shipping papers in the possession of the vehicle operator.

Organization of Information

Hazard information is organized into recognizable parts. These are listed below in order of importance:

1. A flag to attract attention. This can be a symbol, a color, a shape, a word, or a combination of any of these. Examples include the standardized shapes and colors of roadside traffic signs. On a package label it may be a hazard pictograph or a signal word such as "DANGER," "WARNING," or "CAUTION."
2. A statement describing the type of hazard, such as "FLAMMABLE" or "CAUSES BURNS." There may also be a symbol such as the skull and crossbones that is used on packages of poisons.
3. Precautionary measures telling what to do or what not to do in order to avoid injury. These precautionary measures may be presented by a symbol, such as a sign on a laboratory door showing a pair of safety glasses, meaning that safety glasses are required in the area. On a container label, precautionary measures are part of the text.
4. Instruction for treatment in case of exposure. This may be symbolic, such as the symbol for a safety shower or eyebath, or it may consist of elaborate first-aid instructions on a package label.
5. Special instructions for storage or handling.
6. Instructions for handling fires, leaks, or spills.

Hazard Levels

Hazard information systems commonly recognize four levels of hazard.

1. *Extremely Dangerous*. These materials can cause death or disabling injury on very brief exposure; or they are extremely flammable; or they are subject to detonation or explosive decomposition. Some examples are as follows.
   (a) Explosives and explosively unstable materials;
   (b) High-level radioactive materials;
   (c) Highly flammable gases and materials that give off extremely flammable vapors;
   (d) Extremely toxic materials, such as hydrogen cyanide, which are so poisonous that no bodily exposure should occur;
   (e) Materials that are extremely corrosive to living tissue, such as bromine, which can injure almost instantaneously, or hydrofluoric acid, which can penetrate through the skin to the tissues beneath and cause deep, slow-healing burns. Also included are materials that could cause severe eye injury; and

Mr. Benedetti is flammable liquids engineer on the staff of NFPA.

(f) Materials whose combustion products or products of decomposition fit the descriptions given in (a) through (e) above.

2. *Dangerous Materials*. These are materials that could cause serious injury from brief exposure; or are highly flammable or highly self-reactive materials. Some examples are as follows.

   (a) Flammable liquids and solids;
   (b) Highly toxic materials that are likely to cause some injury or illness, but not death, from a moderate exposure;
   (c) Materials that could cause destruction of tissue, particularly the eyes, if not removed from the body in a very short time; and
   (d) Moderately radioactive materials.

Dangerous materials may, at an extreme, cause some permanent, but not disabling, injury on exposure.

3. *Hazardous Materials*. These include materials that could cause temporary disability or injury that presumably would heal without permanent effects. They also include moderately combustible or self-reactive materials. Some examples include the following.

   (a) Tear gases;
   (b) Severe irritants;
   (c) Toxic (but not highly or extremely toxic) materials; and
   (d) Combustible materials that must be heated before they can be ignited.

4. *Nuisance Hazards*. These could cause temporary irritation or discomfort that would clear up when the exposure is ended, or they could be materials that are only slightly combustible.

Note that the materials classed as "dangerous" could *cause* an emergency. The materials classed as "hazardous" would be less likely to *cause* an emergency, but could *add significantly* to the seriousness of an emergency. Thus, a "combustible" liquid might not catch fire and cause an emergency. In the presence of a fire arising from some other cause, it could ignite and add to the seriousness of the emergency. In present consumer product-labeling practice, materials that could cause an emergency generally use the signal word "DANGER." Materials that could add to the seriousness of an emergency use the signal words "WARNING" and "CAUTION." Note, though, that flammable liquids with flash points between 20 and 100°F (7° to 37.8°C) bear the signal word "WARNING."

A hazard-information system is a compromise between two conflicting requirements: immediacy of information and adequacy of information. A hazard symbol, such as the familiar skull and crossbones, can be read at a glance. It has immediacy. Since it doesn't tell how dangerously poisonous the material is, or whether it enters the body through the skin, the lungs, or the digestive system, it lacks adequacy. A hazard data sheet can give adequate information, but it takes time and good light to read, and it has to be there to be read. A hazard data sheet offers adequacy but lacks immediacy.

DEFINITIONS

The following definitions are used throughout this chapter.

Flammability: The NFPA definitions of flammable and combustible liquids, the methods of determining the flash point, and the classification of these liquids are given in Chapter 6 of Section 2. However, in the regulations of other countries, the classification system may differ from that used by NFPA. For example, in some countries, liquids having flash points up to 141°F (40.8°C) are considered flammable, as opposed to the U.S. where 100°F is considered the top of the range.

Toxicity: In its broadest sense, the term *toxicity* is defined as the ability of a material to cause bodily harm by chemical action. In common usage, the term *toxic* describes a substance that can enter the body through the skin, eyes, lungs, or digestive tract, and produce damage. Toxicity is the measure of the injury produced under test conditions. The damage may occur to organs remote from the point of contact. Where injury occurs at the point of contact, two terms are used: *irritation* for a minor though possibly troublesome injury that heals without leaving a scar, and *corrosiveness* for an injury caused by the destruction of tissue, which leaves a scar when healed.

Several kinds of toxicity are recognized:

Acute toxicity: This is the effect caused by a single, usually large, dose or exposure, and may range from simple headache or nausea to disablement or death. Acute toxicity is the kind that is of most concern to emergency personnel.

Semichronic and chronic toxicity: The effect caused by repeated, usually small, doses of a material.

Sensitization: A person who has been sensitized may suffer an allergic reaction when exposed to the same material again. For example, in photodynamic sensitization, a person who is sensitized by a material will suffer an allergic reaction when exposed to strong sunlight or ultraviolet radiation.

Carcinogens, teratogens, and mutagens: Carcinogens are materials that can cause cancer. Teratogens are materials that can cause pregnant females to bear deformed offspring. Mutagens are materials that can cause exposed persons to bear children with traits differing from those of the parents.

LD_{50}, LC_{50}: Acute toxicity is expressed by the term LD_{50}, which means that a dose of a substance is lethal to 50 percent or more of the animals tested. This term is used for liquids and solids that are swallowed or absorbed through the skin. For inhalation of vapors, mists, fumes, and dusts, the term LC_{50} is used, meaning the concentration in air of a substance that is lethal to half or more than half of the test animals used. The term LD_{50} is usually expressed as milligrams of dose per kilogram of body weight of the test animal, and should include the type of test, thus:

$$\text{Oral } LD_{50} \text{ (rat)} = 30 \text{ mg/k}$$

Note that the smaller the LD_{50}, the more toxic a material is.

Quantitative LD_{50} limits for the levels of toxicity generally increase by a factor of ten for successive classes of toxicity. Thus, for oral toxicity, extremely toxic is applied to materials with an LD_{50} less than or equal to 5 milligrams per kilogram (mg/kg). For a 70- kg (150-lb) human, this figures out to about 7 drops (or less) of a liquid. For a solid, it is somewhat less than the weight of a 5-grain aspirin tablet. This means that a very small amount of an extremely toxic material can cause a noticeable illness or injury—the amount, for instance, that might be ingested by swallowing dust trapped in the upper nose if a respirator is not worn. Container labels carry the signal word "DANGER" and a symbol, such as the familiar skull and crossbones, to indicate the presence of a disabling hazard.

A material highly toxic by oral ingestion is one with an oral LD_{50} of 5 to 50 mg/kg. For a 150-lb (70-kg) human this is two-thirds of a teaspoonful (3.28 mL) of a watery liquid, or 1/10 oz (2.8 g) of a solid (the weight of eight or nine 5-grain aspirin tablets). Container labels use the signal word "DANGER."

A toxic material has an oral LD_{50} of 50 to 500 mg/kg. It is unlikely that an adult will knowingly swallow enough of a material of this hazard level to cause serious injury. Labels bear the signal word "WARNING" to indicate a moderate hazard.

Equivalent doses have been worked out for exposure by inhalation (breathing) and absorption through the skin.

For materials that cause direct injury at the point of contact, there is an animal test that is used to distinguish between an irritant and a corrosive. So far, there are no quantitative degrees of corrosiveness, but industrial practice does make distinctions in label statements based on human experience and the toxicologists' interpretations of animal tests. In inspecting a warehouse, the following graded phrases on package labels may be found:

WARNING: MAY CAUSE BURNS
WARNING: CAUSES BURNS
DANGER: CAUSES BURNS
DANGER: CAUSES SEVERE BURNS
DANGER: RAPIDLY CAUSES SEVERE BURNS
DANGER: CAUSES SEVERE BURNS WHICH HEAL VERY SLOWLY

Wherever possible, levels of hazard should be assigned on the basis of human experience. When human experience is not available, as in the case of a new chemical or because of a good safety program, animal tests are used. Since no animal is exactly equivalent to a human being, most of the value of such animal tests must come from the skilled interpretations of toxicologists.

Instability (Self-Reactivity) and Chemical Reactivity

Two types of chemical reactions are of interest here: those that absorb energy and those that give off energy. When the energy is in the form of heat, reactions that absorb heat are called endothermic, and those that give off heat are called exothermic.

Two kinds of reactivity exist: chemical reactivity and instability or self-reactivity. The term *chemical reactivity* is used when two or more chemicals react with each other, as when sodium and water combine in a violent and dangerous reaction that generates hydrogen gas. *Self-reactivity* comes from internal activity of a material, as when a stick of dynamite explodes. Radioactivity is a specialized type of self-reactivity that is always considered separately. Explosives are generally considered a specialized area with separate hazard-information systems.

Aside from explosives and radioactive materials, there are no agreed-upon standards for defining levels for reactivity. Hazard information is based on experience. NFPA 704, *Standard System for the Identification of the Fire Hazards of Materials*, is the only hazard-information system that attempts to cover the whole span of hazardous self-reactivity, and the latest edition (1990) even attempts to quantify the levels by means of data generated using a device called a differential scanning calorimeter (DSC). The DSC measures the energy released by a small sample of material as the material is slowly heated in an isolated chamber. The NFPA 704 system also includes information on hazardous reactivity with water.

The terms *oxidizer* and *oxidizing action* (or *oxidizing reaction*) mean different things in different systems. In hazard-information systems, the term oxidizer or strong oxidizer defines a chemical that can give off oxygen to increase the burning rate of other materials. Such chemicals are called oxygen donors. Study is being given to use of the term oxidizer for chemicals such as bromine or nitric acid that can ignite other materials on contact. Currently these are recognized in labeling systems by statements of hazard such as "spillage may cause fire." Although organic peroxides may be oxygen donors under some conditions, they are classed separately because of the severe fire and self-reactivity hazards that many of them present.

THE NFPA 704 HAZARD IDENTIFICATION SYSTEM

NFPA 704, *Standard System for the Identification of the Fire Hazards of Materials*, is a symbol- and numeral-based system intended for use on fixed installations, such as chemical processing equipment, storage tanks and bins, storage and warehousing rooms, and laboratory entrances. In its simplest sense, it tells fire fighters what they must do to protect themselves from injury while fighting a fire in the area.

The NFPA 704 Diamond

The system is based on the "704 diamond" (see Fig. 9-13A), which visually presents information on three categories of hazard: health, flammability, and self-reactivity, as well as the degree of severity of each hazard. It also indicates two special hazards: reactivity with water and oxidizing ability. The NFPA 704 diamond symbol is intended to provide immediacy at some sacrifice of adequacy, and there is a tendency to read more into it than it says.

The five degrees of hazard, in descending order, have these general meanings to fire fighters:

4 — Fire is too dangerous to approach with standard fire-fighting equipment and procedures. Withdraw and obtain expert advice on how to handle.

3 — Fire can be fought using methods intended for extremely hazardous situations, such as remote-control monitors or personal protective equipment that prevents all bodily contact.

2 — Fire can be fought with standard procedures, but hazards are present that can be handled safely only with certain special equipment or procedures.

1 — Nuisance hazards are present that require some care, but standard fire-fighting procedures can be used.

0 — No special hazards are present, therefore no special measures are needed.

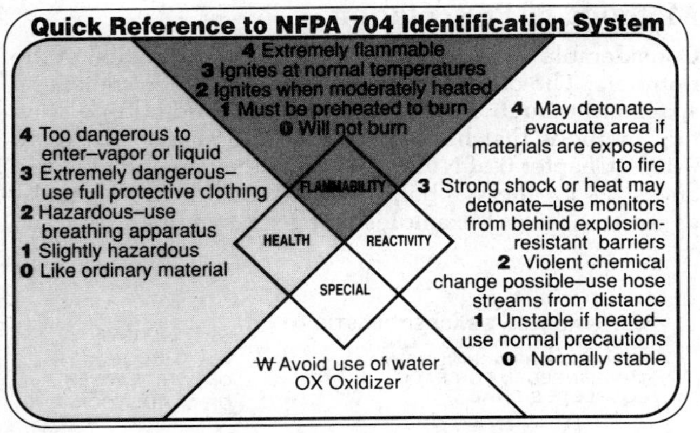

FIG. 9-13A. The NFPA 704 diamond.

NFPA 704 describes the hazard categories and the security levels that the various numbers indicate for the three hazards. The following, adapted from the appendix of the standard, summarizes the hazard information and recommends protective actions.

The numbers from 0 through 4 are placed in the three upper squares of the diamond to show the degree of hazard present for each of the three hazard categories. The 0 indicates the lowest degree of hazard, and 4, the highest. The fourth square, at the bottom, is used for special information. Two symbols for this bottom space are recognized by NFPA 704. (See Fig. 9-13B.) They are:

1. A letter W with a bar through it (W̶) to indicate that a material may have a hazardous reaction with water. This does not mean "do not use water," since some forms of water—fog or fine spray—may be used in many cases. What it does say is: "Water may cause a hazard, so use it very cautiously until you have proper information."
2. The letters *OX* to indicate an oxidizer.

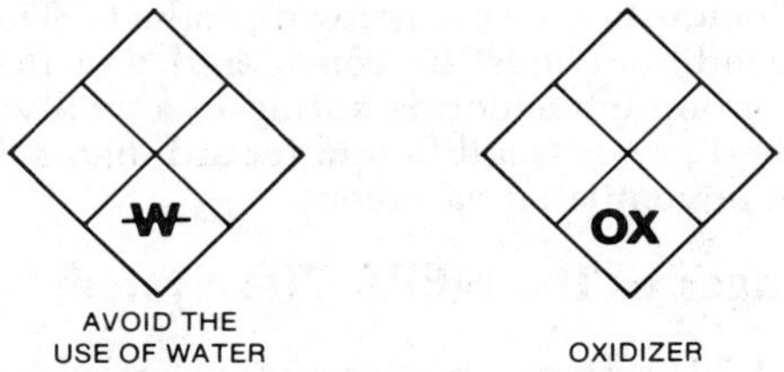

FIG. 9-13B. Special information is presented in the bottom square of the NFPA 704 diamond. This square is color-coded white.

Although not recognized by NFPA 704, some users will insert the letters *ALK* for alkaline materials and *ACID* for acidic materials.

Health Hazards

In general, the health hazard in fire fighting is that of a single exposure which may vary from a few seconds up to an hour. The physical exertion demanded in fire fighting or other emergencies may be expected to intensify the effects of any exposure. In assigning degrees of danger, local conditions must be considered. The following explanation is based upon use of the protective equipment normally worn by fire fighters. (See Fig. 9-13C.)

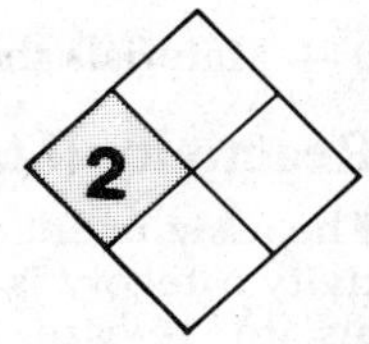

FIG. 9-13C. Hazards to health are presented in the left-hand square of the NFPA 704 diamond. This square is color-coded blue.

4 — Materials that are too dangerous to health for fire fighters to be exposed to. A few whiffs of the vapor could cause death, or the vapor or liquid could be fatal on penetrating the fire fighter's normal protective clothing. The normal full protective clothing and breathing apparatus available to the average fire department will not provide adequate protection against inhalation or skin contact with these materials.

3 — Materials that are extremely hazardous to health, but fire areas may be entered with extreme care. Full protective clothing, self-contained breathing apparatus (SCBA), rubber gloves, boots, and bands around legs, arms, and waist should be provided. No skin surface should be exposed.

2 — Materials that are hazardous to health, but fire areas may be entered freely with self-contained breathing apparatus.

1 — Materials that are only slightly hazardous to health.

0 — Materials that on exposure under fire conditions would offer no health hazard beyond that of ordinary combustible material.

Flammability Hazards

Susceptibility to burning is the basis for assigning degrees within this category. (See Fig. 9-13D.) The method of attacking the fire is influenced by this susceptibility factor.

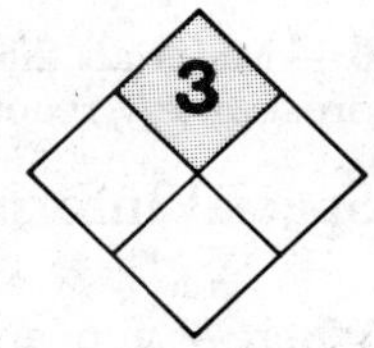

FIG. 9-13D. Flammability hazards are presented in the top square of the NFPA 704 diamond. This square is color-coded red.

4 — Very flammable gases or very volatile flammable liquids. If possible, shut on/off flow and keep cooling water streams on exposed tanks or containers. Withdrawal may be necessary.

3 — Materials that can be ignited under almost all normal temperature conditions. Water may be ineffective because of the low flash point of the materials.

2 — Materials that must be moderately heated before ignition will occur. Water spray may be used to extinguish the fire because the material can be cooled below its flash point.

1 — Materials that must be preheated before ignition can occur. Water may cause frothing if it gets below the surface of the liquid and turns to steam. If this is the case, water fog gently applied to the surface will cause a frothing that will extinguish the fire.

0 — Materials that will not burn.

Reactivity (Stability) Hazards

The assignment of relative degrees of hazard in the reactivity category is based upon the susceptibility of materials to release energy either by themselves or in combination with other materials. (See Fig. 9-13E.) Fire exposure was one of the factors considered along with conditions of shock and pressure.

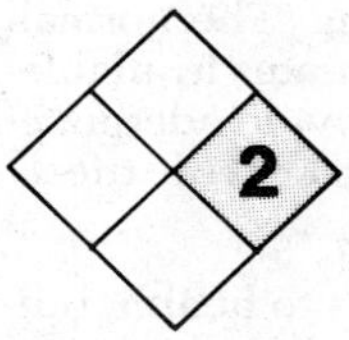

FIG. 9-13E. Reactivity (stability) hazards are presented in the right-hand square of the NFPA diamond. This square is color-coded yellow.

4 — Materials that are readily capable of detonation or explosive decomposition at normal temperatures and pressures. If they are involved in a massive fire, vacate the area.

3 — Materials that when heated and under confinement are capable of detonation or explosive decomposition and that may react violently with water. Fire fighting should be conducted from behind explosion-resistant locations.

2 — Materials that will undergo a violent chemical change at elevated temperatures and pressures but do not detonate. Use portable monitors, hose holders, or straight hose streams from a distance to cool the tanks and the material in them. Use caution.

1 — Materials that are normally stable but may become unstable in combination with other materials or at elevated temperatures and pressures. Use normal precautions as in approaching any fire.

0 — Materials that are normally stable and therefore do not present any reactivity hazard to fire fighters.

Special Information

When W appears at the bottom in the fourth space. (See Fig. 9-13B.)

4 — W is not used with reactivity hazard 4.

3 — In addition to the hazards above, these materials can react explosively with water. Explosion protection is essential if water in any form is used.

2 — In addition to hazards above, these materials may react violently with water or form potentially explosive mixtures with water.

1 — In addition to hazards above, these materials may react vigorously but not violently with water.

0 — W is not used with reactivity hazard 0.

Methods of Presentation

Considerable leeway is allowed in the presentation of the numbers. The only basic requirement is that numbers be spaced as though they were in the diamond outline. Several methods that have been used are shown in Figure 9-13F. Chapter 6 of NFPA 704 gives recommended layout and sizes for the symbol, and a distance-legibility table, as well as several examples using the symbol.

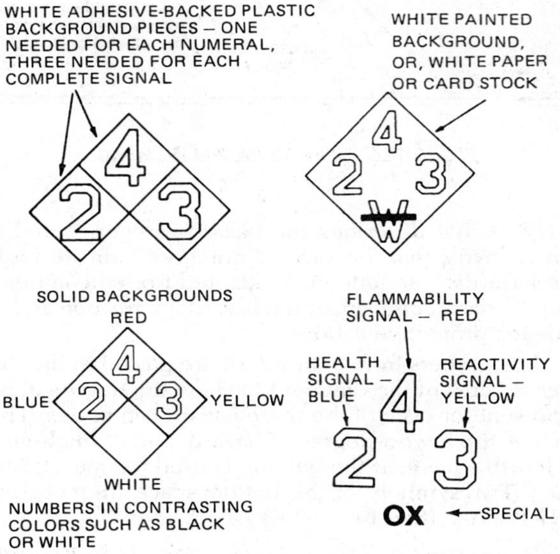

FIG. 9-13F. Methods of presenting the NFPA 704 system hazard information.

Assigning Degrees of Hazard

Numbers (degrees of hazard) for use in the diamond are assigned on the basis of the worst hazard expected in the area, whether it be from hazards of the original material or of its combustion or breakdown products. The effects of local conditions must be considered. For instance, a drum of carbon tetrachloride sitting in a well-ventilated storage shed presents a different hazard than a drum sitting in an unventilated basement.

Advantages of the NFPA 704 System

The NFPA 704 system can warn against hazards under fire conditions of materials that other information systems class as nonhazardous. For example, edible tallow produces toxic and irritating combustion products. It would be given a “2” degree of health hazard, indicating the need for air-supplied respiratory equipment.

NFPA 704 also can warn against overall fire hazards in an area. On the door of a laboratory or storage room, it can warn of the worst hazards likely in a fire situation. Such information is useful both in preplanning and in actual fires.

NFPA 704 can be used without a supplementary manual. Because of its simplicity, the general meanings of the numbers are easily understood and the whole symbol read and interpreted quickly on the spot, in poor light, and at a distance.

Disadvantages of the NFPA 704 System

The NFPA 704 system gives only minimum information on the hazards themselves. Since the system informs on protective measures, the same number may be used for various types of hazards so that, for instance, a health hazard "3" means "no contact" without saying whether the hazard is corrosiveness to the skin or toxicity by absorption through the skin. Thus, the symbol is most useful only to trained or informed persons.

DEPARTMENT OF TRANSPORTATION (DOT) PLACARDS

The Hazardous Materials Regulations of the Department of Transportation (DOT) require placarding of trucks, trailers, railway cars, and bulk intermodal containers carrying dangerous materials. Hazardous materials must be identified on shipping papers regardless of the quantity shipped.

Current DOT Requirements

Over-the-road equipment: Equipment must be marked on front, rear, and both sides with the hazard name at least 4 in. (102 mm) tall. Explosives, extremely toxic materials, and high-strength radioactives in any amount must be marked, along with highly toxic, flammable, and oxidizing materials, corrosive liquids, and both flammable and nonflammable compressed gases, in quantities of 1000 lb (454 kg) or more. A bill of lading indicating mixed hazards totaling more than 1000 lb (454 kg) carries a "DANGEROUS" marking, and is marked as well for explosives, extremely toxic, and high-strength radioactive materials, when they are present. Other than for radioactive materials, a multiple-hazard material is marked only with the name of the most severe hazard present. However, a vehicle or bulk container carrying materials of various hazard classes must be marked with all applicable placards.

Railway equipment: Equipment must be placarded on both sides and ends. Placards for explosives and poison gases are rectangular, the smallest being about 10 by 14 inches (254 by 356 mm). For other hazards, 10¾ in. (273 mm) diamond-shaped placards are used. Radioactives show the name on the placard, while all remaining hazards are identified only by a placard with the word "DANGEROUS" in large red letters. Ladings that have been fumigated in the car and could bear dangerous residues carry a "FUMIGATED" placard on or near the door. Placards may be attached directly to the car or placed in special holders. Tank cars that have been emptied, but contain residues, must carry "DANGEROUS—EMPTY" placards. These are the same size as the originals, but the right half is solid black.

Air shipments: These are generally small quantities since many hazardous materials cannot be shipped by air, particularly in passenger aircraft. Placarding of equipment is not required.

Transportation Emergencies—Identification Problems

Certain deficiencies in current DOT placarding and labeling practices contribute to difficulties in identifying the hazardous nature of some commodities found in transit. For example, placards are not required for the following.

1. Class C explosives. These are principally manufactured articles containing explosives, such as fireworks, squibs, and small-arms ammunition;
2. Moderate and low level radioactives;
3. Tear gases;
4. Corrosive solids, including those that could dissolve in water to produce corrosive liquids; and
5. Over-the-road equipment containing less than 1000 lb (454 kg) of highly toxic, flammable, or oxidizing materials; corrosive liquids, or flammable and nonflammable compressed gases, either singly or as a mixed shipment.

The color-coding of existing placards and package labels is inconsistent for the various modes of transportation, so the use of colors for quick identification is of doubtful value.

DOT Placard and Labeling System

DOT regulations require that each tank vehicle carrying a hazardous material must display a designated four-digit number. The identification number is based on the system adopted for worldwide use by the United Nations Committee of Experts on the Transport of Dangerous Goods.

The numbers are assigned by governmental authorities under the aegis of the Economic and Social Council of the United Nations, and each number has the same meaning throughout worldwide commerce. Each four-digit number identifies a specific hazardous material, and each has no other meaning or use. For example, 1294 will always signify toluene (toluol). (See Figs. 9-13G, H, and I.)

As an adjunct to the identification system, a manual has been prepared to associate the identification number with a brief, concise instruction that is intended to assist emergency personnel during the first few minutes of a hazardous-materials accident. This manual is called the *Emergency Response Guidebook*, and it is carried by all emergency-response vehicles.

To use the *Emergency Response Guidebook*, first identify the material by finding either the four-digit ID number (on a placard or orange panel posted on the vehicle or after the letters UN or NA on the shipping papers) or the name of the material on the shipping papers, placard, label, or package. Next look up either the four-digit number or the material name in the *Guidebook*. The four-digit number will identify the material by name and refer you to a two-digit guide number. (See Fig. 9-13G.) Looking up the material name will refer you to the same two-digit guide number and give you the four digit ID number as a cross-reference. (See Fig. 9-13H.) The two-digit guide number refers you to the proper detailed instruction sheet in the *Guidebook*. (See Fig. 9-13I.)

Tank trucks carrying hazardous materials must have the Hazardous Identification (HI) number on all four sides. It can be displayed in two ways: as an identification number label in addition to the existing placard, with the orange-colored label having a black border and black 4-in-high (102-mm) numbers; or in the existing placard already required by DOT.

ID No.	Guide No.	Name of Material	ID No.	Guide No.	Name of Material
1246	27	METHYLPROPENYL KETONE, inhibited	1266	26	PERFUMERY PRODUCTS, with flammable solvent
1247	27	METHYL METHACRYLATE, monomer, inhibited	1267	27	PETROLEUM CRUDE OIL
1248	26	METHYL PROPIONATE	1268	27	NAPHTHA DISTILLATE
1249	26	METHYL PROPYL KETONE	1268	27	PETROLEUM DISTILLATE, n.o.s.
1250	29	METHYL TRICHLOROSILANE	1268	27	ROAD OIL
1251	28	METHYL VINYL KETONE	1270	27	OIL, petroleum, n.o.s.
1255	27	NAPHTHA, PETROLEUM	1270	27	PETROLEUM OIL
1256	27	NAPHTHA, SOLVENT	1271	26	PETROLEUM ETHER
1257	27	CASINGHEAD GASOLINE	1271	26	PETROLEUM SPIRIT
1257	27	NATURAL GASOLINE	1272	26	PINE OIL
1259	28	NICKEL CARBONYL	1274	26	PROPANOL
1261	26	NITROMETHANE	1274	26	PROPYL ALCOHOL
1262	27	ISOOCTANE	1275	26	PROPIONALDEHYDE
1262	27	OCTANE	1276	26	PROPYL ACETATE
1263	26	COMPOUND, PAINT, etc., removing, reducing, or thinning liquid	1277	68	MONOPROPYLAMINE
1263	26	ENAMEL	1277	68	PROPYLAMINE
1263	26	LACQUER	1278	26	PROPYL CHLORIDE
1263	26	LACQUER BASE, liquid	1279	27	DICHLOROPROPANE
1263	26	PAINT, etc., flammable liquid	1279	27	PROPYLENE DICHLORIDE
1263	26	PAINT RELATED MATERIAL, flammable liquid	1280	26	PROPYLENE OXIDE, inhibited
1263	26	POLISH, liquid	1281	26	PROPYL FORMATE
1263	26	SHELLAC	1282	26	PYRIDINE
1263	26	STAIN	1286	26	RESIN OIL
1263	26	THINNER	1286	26	ROSIN OIL
1263	26	VARNISH	1287	26	RUBBER SOLUTION
1263	26	WOOD FILLER, liquid	1288	27	SHALE OIL
1264	26	PARALDEHYDE	1289	26	SODIUM METHYLATE, solutions in alcohol
1265	27	AMYL HYDRIDE	1292	29	ETHYL SILICATE
1265	27	ISOPENTANE	1292	29	TETRAETHYL SILICATE
1265	27	PENTANE	1293	26	TINCTURE, medicinal
			1294	27	TOLUENE
			1295	30	TRICHLOROSILANE
			1296	68	TRIETHYLAMINE

SEE "HOW TO USE THIS GUIDEBOOK" ON THE FIRST PAGE, IF YOU HAVE NOT YET BECOME FAMILIAR WITH THE DETAILS OF USING THESE INDEXES TO THE GUIDES.

FIG. 9-13G. Sample page from the ID Number Index. *The four-digit ID number 1294 indicates that the cargo is toluene, and that the correct Guide number is 27.*

Name of Material	Guide No.	ID No.	Name of Material	Guide No.	ID No.
TETRAHYDROPHTHALIC ANHYDRIDE	60	2698	THIOUREA	53	2877
TETRAHYDROPYRIDINE	26	2410	THIRAM	55	2771
TETRAHYDROTHIOPHENE	26	2412	THORIUM METAL, pyrophoric	65	2975
TETRALIN HYDROPEROXIDE, technical pure	48	2136	THORIUM METAL, pyrophoric	65	9170
TETRAMETHYL AMMONIUM HYDROXIDE	60	1835	THORIUM NITRATE, solid	64	2976
1,1,3,3-TETRAMETHYLBUTYL HYDROPEROXIDE, technical pure	48	2160	THORIUM NITRATE, solid	64	9171
1,1,3,3-TETRAMETHYLBUTYL-PEROXY-2-ETHYL HEXANOATE, technical pure	52	2161	TIN CHLORIDE, fuming	39	1827
TETRAMETHYL LEAD	56	1649	TINCTURE, medicinal	26	1293
TETRAMETHYLMETHYLENE-DIAMINE	58	9069	TIN TETRACHLORIDE	39	1827
TETRAMETHYL SILANE	29	2749	TITANIUM, metal, powder, dry	37	2546
TETRAPROPYL-ortho-TITANATE	27	2413	TITANIUM, metal, powder, wet with not less than 20% water	32	1352
TETRANITROMETHANE	47	1510	TITANIUM HYDRIDE	32	1871
TEXTILE TREATING COMPOUND	60	1760	TITANIUM SPONGE, granules or powder	32	2878
TEXTILE WASTE, wet, n.o.s.	32	1857	TITANIUM SULFATE SOLUTION	60	1760
THALLIUM CHLORATE	42	2573	**TITANIUM TETRACHLORIDE** •	39	1838
THALLIUM COMPOUND, n.o.s.	53	1707	TITANIUM TRICHLORIDE, pyrophoric	37	2441
THALLIUM NITRATE	42	2727	TITANIUM TRICHLORIDE MIXTURE	60	2869
THALLIUM SALT, n.o.s.	53	1707	TITANIUM TRICHLORIDE MIXTURE, pyrophoric	37	2441
THALLIUM SULFATE, solid	53	1707	TOE PUFFS, nitrocellulose base	32	1353
THIAPENTANAL	55	2785	TOLUENE	27	1294
THINNER	26	1263	TOLUENE DI-ISOCYANATE (T.D.I.)	57	2078
THIOACETIC ACID	26	2436	TOLUENE SULFONIC ACID, liquid	60	2584
THIOGLYCOL	53	2966	TOLUENE SULFONIC ACID, liquid	60	2586
THIOGLYCOLIC ACID	60	1940	TOLUENE SULFONIC ACID, solid	60	2583
THIOLACTIC ACID	59	2936	TOLUENE SULFONIC ACID, solid	60	2585
THIONYL CHLORIDE	39	1836	TOLUIDINES (o-, m-, and p-)	55	1708
THIOPHENE	27	2414			
THIOPHOSGENE	55	2474			
THIOPHOSPHORYL CHLORIDE	60	1837			

• Look for information next to this **NAME** in the TABLE OF EVACUATION DISTANCES in the back of this book. Use this in addition to the Guide Page if there is NO FIRE.

FIG. 13-9H. Sample page from the Materials Name Index. Once again the Guide Number for toluene is 27.

However, a tank vehicle transporting gasoline or fuel oil has a third option because special placarding rules have been established for these products. In order to eliminate the need for changes, a single placard may be used with the HI number associated with the lowest flash point of any distillate fuel ever carried in the tank.

In addition, placards with the words "gasoline" or "fuel oil" on the diamond-shaped placard in place of the HI number are also authorized. If a tank contains only gasoline or fuel oil and has the words "gasoline" or "fuel oil" on each side and rear in 2-in. (50-mm) letters, or uses placards having the words "gasoline" or "fuel oil" in place of the HI number, the HI number will not be required.

PACKAGE AND CONTAINER LABELS

A word of warning: Absence of warning labeling on a package or container does not guarantee that the contents are not hazardous. Also, warnings may be printed on a label separate from the label bearing the product name or the manufacturer's signature, and may be on a separate face of the package.

Two separate but related information systems require labels on shipping packages and on product containers.

Department of Transportation (DOT) Labels

Current DOT hazardous-materials regulations require diamond-shaped labels on shipping containers holding an amount of hazardous material that could cause a hazardous condition in transportation. These color-coded labels bear a hazard symbol, or pictograph, and the name of the hazard. They carry no warning text. Current regulations generally permit only a single label on a multi-hazard exposure, that label showing the most dangerous hazard present. Where a material is extremely toxic, explosive, or highly radioactive, the proper label must be used in addition to any other hazard label. In addition, the package must be marked with the name of contents as it appears on a commodity list in DOT regulations. This may be a chemical name or a class name such as "Corrosive Liquid N.O.S." (not otherwise specified), so it is of secondary usefulness. On compressed-gas cylinders, the label may be attached to a wire-tied tag.

The presence of a DOT label on a package or container indicates a dangerous hazard. Because of exemptions, based mostly on the size of inner containers placed in an outside shipping container, a package without a DOT label may contain significant amounts of fairly dangerous materials, including flammable liquids. (See Figure 9-13J for illustrations of DOT labels.)

Guide 27

POTENTIAL HAZARDS

FIRE OR EXPLOSION

Flammable/combustible material; may be ignited by heat, sparks or flames.
Vapors may travel to a source of ignition and flash back.
Container may explode in heat of fire.
Vapor explosion hazard indoors, outdoors or in sewers.
Runoff to sewer may create fire or explosion hazard.

HEALTH HAZARDS

May be poisonous if inhaled or absorbed through skin.
Vapors may cause dizziness or suffocation.
Contact may irritate or burn skin and eyes.
Fire may produce irritating or poisonous gases.
Runoff from fire control or dilution water may cause pollution.

EMERGENCY ACTION

Keep unnecessary people away; isolate hazard area and deny entry.
Stay upwind; keep out of low areas.
Wear self-contained (positive pressure if available) breathing apparatus and full protective clothing.
Isolate for 1/2 mile in all directions if tank car or truck is involved in fire.
FOR EMERGENCY ASSISTANCE CALL CHEMTREC **(800) 424-9300.**
If water pollution occurs, notify appropriate authorities.

FIRE

Small Fires: Dry chemical, CO_2, water spray or foam.
Large Fires: Water spray, fog or foam.
Move container from fire area if you can do it without risk.
Cool containers that are exposed to flames with water from the side until well after fire is out.
For massive fire in cargo area, use unmanned hose holder or monitor nozzles; if this is impossible, withdraw from area and let fire burn.
Withdraw immediately in case of rising sound from venting safety device or any discoloration of tank due to fire.

SPILL OR LEAK

Shut off ignition sources; no flares, smoking or flames in hazard area.
Stop leak if you can do it without risk.
Use water spray to reduce vapors.
Small Spills: Take up with sand or other noncombustible absorbent material and place into containers for later disposal.
Large Spills: Dike far ahead of spill for later disposal.

FIRST AID

Move victim to fresh air; call emergency medical care.
If not breathing, give artificial respiration.
If breathing is difficult, give oxygen.
In case of contact with material, immediately flush eyes with running water for at least 15 minutes. Wash skin with soap and water.
Remove and isolate contaminated clothing and shoes at the site.

FIG. 9-131. Guide number 27 refers to a set of detailed instructions.

Warning Labels on Immediate Containers

Containers for hazardous materials in interstate commerce usually bear necessary warning labels, but products of small local distributors may not. Warehouses, particularly those of contract packagers, may contain stocks of filled containers intended for labeling to customers' orders. Where the immediate container is also the shipping container, such as a carboy, a drum, or a compressed-gas cylinder, both DOT and warning labels may be present and may be printed on a single label sheet.

Labeling practice is to use the signal word "DANGER" for corrosive liquids, extremely corrosive solids, poisons, flammable gases, and extremely flammable liquids. The signal word "WARNING" is used on flammable liquids, less corrosive solids, toxic materials, and similar levels of hazard. The signal word "CAUTION" is used for the least severe hazards, including combustible liquids and solids, and nonflammable compressed gases. The rest of the warning label is self-explanatory, except to note that warning labels cover only hazards arising from normal use and handling. Hazards under fire conditions are not included in the warning.

Consumer products: Substances or articles intended or suitable for household use are labeled in accordance with the Federal Hazardous Substances Labeling Act, which vests authority in the Consumer Product Safety Commission (CPSC).

SHIPPING PAPERS

Transport regulations require that a truck driver, a train conductor, or an aircraft pilot have a shipping paper for every shipment of hazardous material in his or her transport unit. This lists names and quantities of all hazardous materials, including those exempt packages that bear no labels, and should include hazard and emergency-handling information.

HAZARD EMERGENCY TEAMS

Emergency assistance in identifying hazards of materials and guidance on handling emergencies involving them is available on quick notice from a variety of sources. The assistance ranges from immediate telephone advice to the dispatching of emergency teams to actually assist in field operation. Among those offering services are the following.

CHEMTREC—Phone No. (800)424-9300: CHEMTREC stands for Chemical Transportation Emergency Center, operated by the Chemical Manufacturers Association, 1825 Connecticut Ave. NW, Washington, DC 20009. It handles only transportation emergencies. When called, a CHEMTREC operator provides immediate advice from CHEMTREC files, then notifies the shipper. CHEMTREC maintains close liaison with the Department of Transportation.

NACA Pesticide Safety Team Network: A service sponsored by the National Agricultural Chemicals Association, 1155 15th St. NW, Washington, DC 20005, which covers only pesticides. A network of more than forty teams of specially trained personnel go to the scene of emergencies involving pesticides. Phone-answering service is supplied by CHEMTREC.

TEAP: The Canadian Chemical Producers' Association operates a Transportation Emergency Assistance Program through regional teams prepared to give phone and field response.

CHLOREP: The Chlorine Institute, 342 Madison Ave., New York, NY 10017, operates the Chlorine Emergency Plan in which the nearest chlorine producer responds to a problem.

U.S. Coast Guard's "React Teams": These teams operate on both the East and West Coasts, giving skilled help in spills on water.

Environmental Protection Agency: The EPA sponsors teams that go to emergencies. EPA regions and contact addresses are listed in the "Obtaining Technical Assistance in Hazardous Waste Emergencies" chapter of this handbook.

Many manufacturing companies have organized response capabilities for their own products. In many cases an emergency telephone number is placed on the bill of lading.

OXYGEN placard required for pressurized liquid oxygen.

OXYGEN placard may also be used to identify liquefied oxygen contained in a manner that does not meet the definition of a compressed gas in Sec. 173.300.

CHLORINE placard required only for a packaging having a rated capacity of more than 110 gallons. Use the NON-FLAMMABLE GAS placard for packagings having a rated capacity of 110 gallons or less.

HIGHWAY SHIPMENTS

CARGO TANKS AND PORTABLE TANKS

Above placard may be used in place of FLAMMABLE placard when gasoline is being transported (Sec. 172.542(c)).

Above placard may be used in place of COMBUSTIBLE placard when FUEL OIL that is not classed as a Flammable liquid is being transported (Sec. 172.544(c)).

RAIL SHIPMENTS

EMPTY placard. Each "empty" tank car must be placarded with an EMPTY placard that corresponds to the placard that was required for the material the tank car last contained unless the tank car last contained a Combustible liquid. This placard is required for the following hazardous materials.

Non-Flammable Gas	Flammable Solid
Oxygen	Flammable Solid "W"
Flammable Gas	Oxidizer
Chlorine	Organic Peroxide
Poison Gas	Poison
Flammable	Corrosive

FREIGHT CONTAINERS

FREIGHT CONTAINERS—640 CUBIC FEET OR MORE
(Placard each end and each side)

AIR OR WATER—Placard any quantity

HIGHWAY OR RAIL

1. Placard any quantity of hazardous material classes listed in TABLE 1 (Sec. 172.512(a)).
2. Placard 1,000 pounds or more (aggregate gross weight) of hazardous material classes in TABLE 2 (Sec. 172.512(a)).

NOTE: For placarding options for freight containers of less than 640 cubic feet, see Sec. 172.512(b).

CARGO TANKS AND PORTABLE TANKS

1. Cargo tanks containing any quantity of hazardous material must be placarded.
2. Portable tanks having a rated capacity of 1,000 gallons or more must be placarded.
3. Portable tanks having a rated capacity of less than 1,000 gallons need be placarded on only two opposite sides (Sec. 172.514(a)).
4. Cargo tanks and portable tanks must remain placarded when emptied unless reloaded with a material not subject to CFR, Title 49, Parts 100-199 or sufficiently cleaned and purged to remove any potential hazard. (Sec. 172.514(b)).
5. For Combustible liquids, a FLAMMABLE placard may be used on cargo tanks or portable tanks when transported by highway or water.

USE OF THIS CHART DOES NOT RELIEVE PERSONS INVOLVED FROM COMPLYING WITH THE DOT HAZARDOUS MATERIALS REGULATIONS AS PUBLISHED IN TITLE 49, CODE OF FEDERAL REGULATIONS, PARTS 100-199.

FIG. 9-13J. The "oxygen" label is black on yellow. The "chlorine" label is black on white. The "gasoline" and "fuel oil" labels are white on red. The "empty" sticker is black. (Department of Transportation Chart 5)

PLACARDING ANY QUANTITY—

MOTOR VEHICLES, FREIGHT CONTAINERS AND RAIL CARS

Placard motor vehicles, freight containers, and rail cars containing "any quantity" of hazardous materials listed in TABLE 1.

TABLE 1

HAZARDOUS MATERIAL CLASSED OR DESCRIBED AS	PLACARDS
Class A explosives	EXPLOSIVES A.
Class B explosives	EXPLOSIVES B.
Poison A	POISON GAS.
Flammable solid (DANGEROUS WHEN WET label only)	FLAMMABLE SOLID W.
Radioactive material	RADIOACTIVE.
Radioactive material:	
Uranium hexafluoride, fissile (containing more than 0.7 pct U^{235})	RADIOACTIVE AND CORROSIVE.
Uranium hexafluoride, low specific activity (containing 0.7 pct. or less U^{235})	RADIOACTIVE AND CORROSIVE.

YELLOW III labeled packagings only.

For Uranium Hexafluoride, see Sec. 172.504(a) and TABLE 1.

RAIL PLACARDS

SQUARE BACKGROUND FOR RAIL SHIPMENTS – Each EXPLOSIVE A placard, POISON GAS placard and POISON GAS – EMPTY placard affixed to a rail car must be placed on a square background measuring 14¼ inches on each side with a black border extending to 15½ inches on each side (illustrated in above chart). (See Sec. 172.510(a) and 172.527(a)).

FIG. 9-13J (Continued). DOT Hazardous Materials Warning Placards. The "explosive" labels are black on orange. The "poison gas" labels are black on white. The "flammable solid" label is red, white, blue, and black. The "radioactive" label is yellow, black, and white. (Department of Transportation Chart 5)

OTHER PLACARDING REQUIREMENTS

MOTOR VEHICLES, RAIL CARS AND FREIGHT CONTAINERS

1. Placard motor vehicles and freight containers containing 1,000 pounds or more gross weight of hazardous materials classes listed in TABLE 2.
2. Placard any quantity of hazardous materials classes listed in TABLES 1 and 2 when offered for transportation by air or water.
3. Placard rail cars containing any quantity of hazardous materials classes listed in TABLE 2 except when less than 1,000 pounds gross weight of hazardous materials is transported in TOFC (Trailer on flat car) or COFC (Container on flat car) service.

TABLE 2

HAZARDOUS MATERIAL CLASSED OR DESCRIBED AS	PLACARDS
Class C explosives	FLAMMABLE.
Nonflammable gas	NONFLAMMABLE GAS.
Nonflammable gas (Chlorine)	CHLORINE.
Nonflammable gas (Fluorine)	POISON.
Nonflammable gas (Oxygen, pressurized liquid)	OXYGEN.
Flammable gas	FLAMMABLE GAS.
Combustible liquid	COMBUSTIBLE.
Flammable liquid	FLAMMABLE.
Flammable solid	FLAMMABLE SOLID.
Oxidizer	OXIDIZER.
Organic peroxide	ORGANIC PEROXIDE.
Poison B	POISON.
Corrosive material	CORROSIVE.
Irritating material	DANGEROUS.

Also used for Class C Explosives labeled with an Explosive C label.

Used for materials transported in packaging having a rated capacity of more than 110 gallons.

Other than by water, a FLAMMABLE placard may be displayed in place of a FLAMMABLE SOLID placard except when a DANGEROUS WHEN WET label is specified in Sec. 172.101.

DANGEROUS PLACARD

1. When a freight container, rail car or motor vehicle contains two or more classes of hazardous materials requiring different placards specified in TABLE 2, the DANGEROUS placard may be used in place of the separate placards specified for each class.
2. When 5,000 pounds or more of one class of hazardous material is loaded at one loading facility, the placard for that class in TABLE 2 must be applied.

UNITED NATIONS (UN) HAZARD CLASS NUMBERS

UN hazard class numbers are not required for domestic shipments. The hazard class and division number prescribed for dangerous goods in the United Nations Recommendations entitled "Transport of Dangerous Goods (1970)" may be entered on each placard in the lower corner of the diamond (Sec. 172.519(d)).

FIG. 9-13J (Continued). The "flammable," "flammable gas," and "combustible" labels are white on red. The "poison" and "corrosive" labels are black and white. The "organic peroxide" and "oxidizer" labels are black on yellow. The "nonflammable gas" label is white on green. The "flammable solid" and "dangerous" labels are red, white, and black. (Department of Transportation Chart 5)

BIBLIOGRAPHY

NFPA Codes, Standards, Recommended Practices, and Manuals. (See the latest *NFPA Standards Catalog* for availability of current editions of the following documents.)

NFPA 43A, *Code for the Storage of Liquid and Solid Oxidizing Materials*.

NFPA 49, *Hazardous Chemicals Data*.

NFPA 53M, *Manual on Fire Hazards in Oxygen-Enriched Atmospheres*.

NFPA 325M, *Fire Hazard Properties of Flammable Liquids, Gases, and Volatile Solids*.

NFPA 490, *Code for the Storage of Ammonium Nitrate*.

NFPA 491M, *Manual of Hazardous Chemical Reactions*.

NFPA 495, *Code for the Manufacture, Transportation, Storage, and Use of Explosive Materials*.

NFPA 704, *Standard System for the Identification of the Fire Hazards of Materials*.

Additional Readings

ANSI, 2129.1., *Precautionary Labeling of Hazardous Industrial Chemicals*, American National Standards Institute, New York, NY, 1982.

Bahme, C. W., *Fire Officer's Guide on Dangerous Chemicals*, National Fire Protection Association, Quincy, MA, 1978.

Bahme, C. W., *Fire Officer's Guide to Emergency Action*, National Fire Protection Association, Quincy, MA, 1976.

Bahn, R., *Hazardous Materials*, International Thompson Transport, New York, NY, 1985.

Behrendsen, D. J., *Guidelines to the Handling of Hazardous Materials*, Source of Safety, Inc., Denver, CO, 1977.

Bowen, J. E., "Unforeseen Dangers of Chemical Mixtures," *Fire Engineering*, Vol. 143, No. 2, 1990, p. 33.

Bretherick, A. L., *Handbook of Reactive Chemical Hazards*, Butterworths, Stoneham, MA, 1990.

Burton, B. T., and Marc, J. B., *Hazardous Materials*, Aspen Systems Corp., Gaithersberg, MD., 1985.

Cheremisinoff, P. N., *Hazardous Materials: Managers Desk Book on Regulations*, Pudvan, Northbrook, IL, 1986.

Code of Federal Regulations, Vol. 16, Part 1500, Subchapter C Federal Hazardous Substances Act Regulations, Government Printing Office, Washington, DC.

Coffee, R.,"*Evaluation of Chemical Stability, Fire Technology*," Vol. 7, No. 1, Feb. 1971, pp. 37–45.

Coleman, R. J., *Hazardous Materials Dictionary*, Technomic Publishing, Lancaster, PA, 1988.

Drivers Pocket Guide to Hazardous Materials, 6th ed., J.J. Keller and Associates, Neenah, WI, 1987.

Emergency Guide for Selected Hazardous Materials, DOT Office of Hazardous Materials, Washington, DC, 1978.

Emergency Response Guidebook, DOT P 5800.4, U.S. DOT, distributed by Labelmaster, Chicago, IL 1990.

Fire, F. L., *The Common Sence Approach to Hazardous Materials*, Fire Engineering Books, Tulsa, OK., 1987.

Fire, F. L., "Hazardous Materials," *Fire Engineering*, Vol. 139, No. 6, 1986, Monthly Column.

Fire Protection Guide on Hazardous Materials, 8th ed., National Fire Protection Association, Quincy, MA, 1984.

Guidelines for Hazard Evaluation Procedures, American Institute of Chemical Engineers, New York, NY, 1985.

Handbook of Hazardous Materials, 3rd ed., Alliance of American Insurers, Schaumburg, IL, 1988.

Hazardous Materials, U.S. Postal Service, Washington, DC, 1987.

Hazardous Materials Handbook, 3rd rev. ed., Operations Council of American Trucking Association, Washington, DC, 1982.

Hazardous Materials Identification System, Raw Materials Rating Manual, National Paint and Coatings Association, Washington, DC.

Hazardous Materials: MSDS and Warning Labels, (video), American Hospital Association, Chicago, IL, 1987.

Hazardous Materials: Storage and Handling Handbook, Defense Logistics Agency, Directorate of Supply Operations, Washington, DC, 1987.

"Hazardous Wastes," SW - 138, U.S. Environmental Protection Agency, 1975.

Hazards Communications Guidelines, Alliance of American Insurers, Schaumburg, IL, 1988.

Hilado, C. J., "Screening Materials for Relative Toxicity in Fire Situations," *Modern Plastics*, Vol. 54, No. 7, July 1977, pp. 64-66, 68.

"How to Choose Equipment for Hazardous Locations," *National Safety and Help News*, Vol. 134, No. 3, Sept. 1986, pp. 37-42.

Isman, W. E. and Carlson, G. P., *Hazardous Materials*, Glencoe Publishing Co., Inc., Encino, CA, 1980.

King, P. W. and Magid, J., *Industrial Hazard and Safety Handbook*, 3rd rev. ed., Butterworths, Stoneham, MA, 1982.

Kirk, R. E. and Othmer, D. F., *eds.*, *Encyclopedia of Chemical Technology*, 3rd ed., 24 Vols., Wiley, New York, NY, 1984.

Kmetz, C. J., "An In-Plant Container-Labeling Program," *Chemical Engineering Progress*, Vol. 86, No. 3, March 1990, pp. 33-36.

Lind, C. D. and Whitson, J. C., *Explosion Hazards Associated with Spills of Large Quantities of Hazardous Materials, Phase II*, Department of Transportation, Washington, DC, 1977.

Meidl, J. A., *Explosive and Toxic Hazardous Materials*, Glencoe, Beverly Hills, CA, 1970.

Meidl, J. H., *Flammable Hazardous Materials*, 2nd ed., Glencoe, Encino, CA, 1978.

Meyer, E., *Chemistry of Hazardous Materials*, 2nd ed., Prentice-Hall, Englewood Cliffs, NJ, 1989.

Morton, W. I., "Safety Techniques for Workers Handling Hazardous Materials," *Chemical Engineering*, Vol. 83, No. 22, Oct. 18, 1976, pp. 127-132.

NFPA, *Protective Clothing for Hazardous Material Incidents*, (slide/tape), National Fire Protection Association, Quincy, MA, 1984.

Norback, C. T., *Hazardous Chemicals on File*, Facts on File Publications, New York, NY, 1989.

Pocket Guide to Chemical Hazards, 2nd printing, Pub. No. 85-114, U.S. Department of Health and Human Services, Washington, DC, Sept. 1987.

Sax, N. I., and Lewis, R. J., *Dangerous Properties of Industrial Materials*, 7th ed., Van Nostrand Reinhold, New York, NY, 1989.

Sax, I. and Lewis, R. J., *Hazardous Chemicals Desk Reference*, Van Nostrand Reinhold, New York, NY, 1987.

Turner, C. F., and McCreey, J. W., *The Chemistry of Fire and Hazardous Materials*, Allyn and Bacon, Boston, MA, 1981.

Transport of Dangerous Goods, 5th ed., United Nations Publication, New York, NY, 1988.

Weiss, J., *Hazardous Materials Chemical Data Book*, 2nd ed., Noyes, Park Ridge, NY, 1986.

Williams, L. R., *et al.*, *Hazardous Materials Spill Monitoring; Safety Handbook and Chemical Hazard Guide*, Report No. EPA-600/4-79-008a,—Part A, U.S. Environmental Protection Agency, Las Vegas, NV, 1979.

Young, M. S., "Handling Emergencies Involving Cryogenic Materials," *Fire Command*, Vol. 45, No. 5, May 1978, pp. 20-22.

MANAGING THE RESPONSE TO HAZARDOUS MATERIAL INCIDENTS

Charles J. Wright

Hazardous materials may be an important part of our high standard of living, but when a release occurs, they can harm people, including response personnel, property, and the environment. The effective management of hazardous materials and other chemicals in the community requires a multi-faceted approach including 1) prevention, 2) preparedness, 3) response, and 4) recovery activities. This chapter focuses on the response activity; however, these same concepts are applicable to the other hazardous material management activities.

The purpose of the response activity is "to change the sequence of events constituting the emergency before it has run its course naturally and to minimize harm that would otherwise occur."[1] To accomplish this purpose, four duties must be undertaken. (See Figure 9-14A.)

1. Analyze the problem;
2. Plan a response;
3. Implement the planned response; and
4. Evaluate progress and adjust accordingly.

Each duty involves a series of tasks and steps that must be considered and resolved by decisions and actions. These duties, when supported by the response community, are the framework for an appropriate, survival-oriented response to hazardous material incidents. Reasoned decisions based on this approach will minimize the harm resulting from a hazardous material incident while reducing the risk to responders.

DEFINITIONS

The following terms are used in this chapter.

Bulk Packaging is any containment system, including transport vehicles and freight containers, having a capacity meeting one of the following criteria: liquid—internal volume of more than 119 gal. (450 L); solid—capacity of more than 882 lbs. (400 kg); or compressed gas—water capacity of more than 1001 lbs. (454 kg).

Containment Systems are a combination of a container and its closures which isolate the contents from the surrounding environment. A closure is a device for closing the openings in a container.

Emergency is the term used for a sudden, generally unexpected disruption in a normal sequence of events requiring immediate action.

Hazardous Material, for the purpose of this chapter, is a substance that upon release has the potential of causing harm to people, property, or the environment. This definition includes hazardous materials, hazardous substances, hazardous wastes, and dangerous goods in Canada.

Hazardous Material (DOT) means a substance or material, including a hazardous substance, which has been determined by the Secretary of Transportation to be capable of posing an unreasonable risk to health, safety, and property when transported in commerce, and which has been so designated. Table 9-14A lists the hazard classes and divisions associated with hazardous materials in transportation as identified by the U.S. Department of Transportation (DOT).

Hazardous Substance (DOT) means a material, including its mixtures and solutions, that is in a quantity, in one package, which equals or exceeds the reportable quantity (RQ) listed in 49 CFR Parts 171-172.

Hazardous Waste (DOT) means any material that is subject to the Hazardous Waste Manifest Requirements of the U.S. Environmental Protection Agency (EPA) specified in 40 CFT Part 262.

Hazardous Material Incident is an emergency involving the release or potential release of hazardous materials with or without fire.

Non-bulk Packaging is any containment system having a capacity meeting one of the following criteria: liquid—internal volume of 119 gal. (450 L) or less; solid—capacity of 882 lbs. (400 kg) or less; or compressed gas—water capacity of 101 lbs. (454 kg) or less.

Outcomes are the direct and indirect results or consequences associated with an emergency. Direct outcomes are considered in terms of people, property, and/or the environment. Indirect outcomes are considered in terms

Charles J. Wright is manager of hazardous materials training for the Union Pacific Railroad Company.

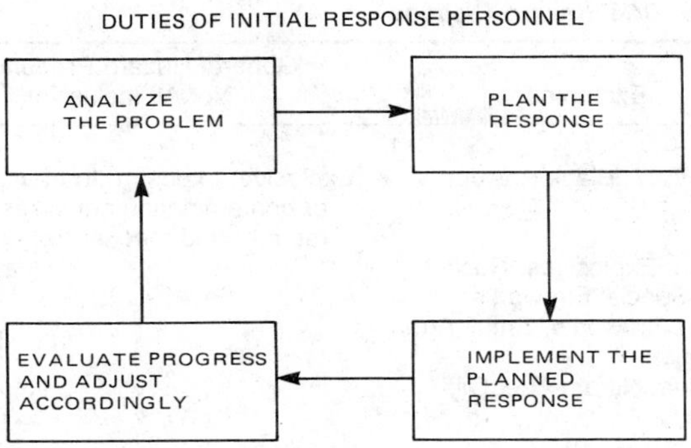

FIG. 9-14A. A flow diagram of the response duties associated with emergencies involving hazardous materials.

of system disruption, damaged reputations, and residual fear of hazardous materials.

Response Community is composed of those individuals, agencies, or companies who have resources that can become involved in handling a hazardous material incident. These may include, but are not limited to, fire-service personnel, law-enforcement personnel, rescue and emergency medical personnel, private-sector response personnel (manufacturers and carriers), and state and federal government response personnel.

Department of Transportation Hazard Classes

The following list presents the general definitions of the various Department of Transportation (DOT) hazard classes as set forth in the cited reference. These definitions should not be used to determine compliance with the DOT hazardous materials regulations, as they do not indicate the exceptions and specificity found in the regulations in all cases.[2]

Class 1 (*Explosives and blasting agents*)

Explosive means any substance or article, including a device, that is designed to function by explosion (i.e., an extremely rapid release of gas and heat) or which, by chemical reaction within itself, is able to function in a similar manner even if not designed to function by explosion. Explosives in Class 1 are divided into six divisions. Each division will have a letter designation.

Division 1.1 consists of explosives that have a mass explosion hazard. A mass explosion is one that affects almost the entire load instantaneously.

Division 1.2 consists of explosives that have a projection hazard but not a mass explosion hazard.

Division 1.3 consists of explosives that have a fire hazard and either a minor blast hazard or a minor projection hazard or both, but not a mass explosion hazard.

Division 1.4 consists of explosive devices that present a minor explosion hazard. No device may contain more than 25 grams (0.9 ounce) of a detonating material.

Division 1.5 consists of very insensitive explosives. These substances have a mass explosion hazard but are so insensitive that there is very little probability of initiation or of transition from burning to detonation under normal conditions of transport.

Division 1.6 consists of extremely insensitive articles which do not have a mass explosion hazard. These articles contain only extremely insensitive detonating substances and demonstrate a negligible probability of accidental initiation or propagation.

Class 2 (*Gases*)

Division 2.1 (flammable gas) means any material that is a gas at 20°C (68°F) or less and 101.3 kPa (14.7 psi) of pressure, or a material that has a boiling point of 20°C (68°F) or less at 101.3 kPa (14.7 psi) that

- is ignitable at 101.3 kPa (14.7 psi) when in a mixture of 13 percent or less by volume with air; or
- has a flammable range of at least 12 percent in air at 101.3 kPa (14.7 psi) regardless of the lower limit.

Division 2.2 (non-flammable, non-poisonous compressed gas, including compressed gas, liquefied gas, pressurized cryogenic gas, and compressed gas in solution). A non-flammable, non-poisonous compressed gas means any material (or mixture) which exerts in the packaging an absolute pressure of 280 kPa (41 psia) at 20°C (68°F).

A *cryogenic liquid* means a refrigerated liquefied gas having a boiling point colder than -90°C (-130°F) at 101.3 kPa (14.7 psi) absolute.

Division 2.3 (poisonous gas) means a material that is a gas at 20°C (68°F) or less and a pressure of 101.3 kPa (14.7 psi or 1 atm), that has a boiling point of 20°C (68°F) or less at 101.3 kPa (14.7 psi), and that

- is known to be so toxic to humans as to pose a hazard to health during transportation; or
- in the absence of adequate data on human toxicity, is presumed to be toxic to humans because, when tested on laboratory animals, it has an LC_{50} value not more than 5000 ppm.

Class 3 (*Flammable liquids*)

Flammable liquid means any liquid having a flash point of not more than 60°C (140°F).

Combustible Liquids

Combustible liquid means any liquid that has a flash point above 60°C (140°F) and below 93°C (200°F).

Class 4 (*Flammable solids and reactive liquids and solids*)

Division 4.1 (flammable solid)—means any of the following three types of materials:

- *wetted explosives*—explosives wetted with sufficient water, alcohol, or plasticizers to suppress explosive properties.
- *self-reactive materials*—materials that are liable to undergo, at normal or elevated temperatures, a strongly exothermal decomposition caused by excessively high transport temperatures or by contamination.
- *readily combustible solids*—solids that may cause a fire through friction and any metal powders that can be ignited.
- *Division 4.2* (spontaneously combustible solid)—means either of the following materials:

TABLE 9-14A. ***Comparison of U.N./U.S. DOT Hazard Classes***

U.N. Classes and Divisions After January 1991	U.S. Classes Pre January 1991	Examples	General Hazard Properties (Not All Inclusive)
Class 1—EXPLOSIVES			
Division 1.1–Mass detonating	Class A Explosives	Dynamite, TNT, Black Powder	Explosive; exposure to heat, shock, or contamination could result in thermal and mechanical hazards.
Division 1.2–Mass detonating w/ fragments	Class A Explosives/ Class B Explosives		
Division 1.3–Fire hazard w/ minor blast or projectile hazard	Class B Explosives	Propellant Explosives, Rocket Motors, Special Fireworks	
Division 1.4–Substances which present no significant hazard	Class C Explosives	Common Fireworks, Small Arms Ammunition	
Division 1.5–Very insensitive explosives	Blasting Agents	Ammonium Nitrate-Fuel Oil Mixtures	
Division 1.6–Extremely insensitive explosives			
Class 2—GASES			
Division 2.1–Flammable Gases	Flammable Gases	Propane, Butadiene (inhibited) Acetylene	Under pressure; container may rupture violently (fire and nonfire); may be a flammable, poisonous, a corrosive, an asphyxiant and/or an oxidizer; may cause frost-bite.
Division 2.2–Nonflammable Gases	Nonflammable Gases	Carbon Dioxide, Methyl Chloride, Anhydrous Ammonia	
Division 2.3–Poisonous Gases	Poison A	Arsine, Phosgene, Hydrogen Fluoride, Chlorine	
Class 3—FLAMMABLE LIQUIDS			
*Division 3.1–flash point $<0^\circ$F	Flammable Liquids	Gasoline	Flammable; container may rupture violently from heat/fire; may be corrosive, toxic, and/or thermally unstable.
*Division 3.2–flash point $\geq 0^\circ$F to $<73^\circ$F	Flammable Liquids	Acetone, Methyl Alcohol, Toluene	
*Division 3.3–flash point $\geq 73^\circ$ to $<141^\circ$F	Flammable/Combustible Liquids	Amyl Acetate	
Combustible Liquids	Combustible Liquids	Fuel Oils	
Class 4—FLAMMABLE SOLIDS OR SUBSTANCES			
Division 4.1–Flammable Solids	Flammable Solids	Pyroxylin Plastics, Magnesium	Flammable, some spontaneously; may be water reactive, toxic, and/or corrosive; may be extremely difficult to extinguish.
Division 4.2–Spontaneously Combustible/ Pyrophoric Liquids	Flammable Solidsand Liquids	Phosphorus	
Division 4.3–Dangerous When Wet	Flammable Solids and Liquids	Metallic Sodium, Potassium, Calcium Carbide	
Class 5—OXIDIZING SUBSTANCES			
Division 5.1–Oxidizing Substances	Oxidizers	Ammonium Nitrate Fertilizer	Supplies oxygen to support combustion; sensitive to heat, shock, friction, and/or contamination.
Division 5.2–Organic Peroxides	Organic Peroxides	Benzoyl Peroxide, Peracetic Acid, Acetal Peroxide Solution	
Class 6—POISONOUS AND INFECTIOUS SUBSTANCES			
Division 6.1–Poisons	Poisons B, Irritants, ORM-A	Aniline, Arsenic Tear Gas, Dry Ice, Carbon Tetrachloride	Toxic by inhalation, ingestion, and skin and eye absorption; may be flammable.
Divison 6.2–Infectious Substances	Etiologic Agents	Anthrax, Botulism, Rabies, Tetanus	
Class 7—RADIOACTIVE SUBSTANCES			
Radioactive Material	Radioactive Materials	Plutonium, Cobalt, Uranium Hexafluoride	May cause burns and biologic effects; energy and matter.
Class 8—CORROSIVES			
Corrosive Material	Corrosive Materials	Hydrochloric Acid, Sulfuric Acid, Sodium Hydroxide, Nitric Acid	Disintegration of contacted tissues; may be fuming, water reactive.
	ORM-B	Unslaked Lime, Metallic Mercury	
Class 9—MISCELLANEOUS HAZARDOUS MATERIALS			
	ORM-C	Bleaching Powder, Molten Sulfur	
	ORM-E	Hazardous substances, (e.g. PCBs)	
ORM- D	ORM-D	Consumer commodities	

*International only.

- *pyrophoric material*—a liquid or solid that, even in small quantities and without an external ignition source, can ignite within 5 minutes after coming in contact with air; or
- *self-heating material*—a material that, when in contact with air and without an energy supply, is liable to self-heat.

Division 4.3 (dangerous-when-wet material)—means a material that, by contact with water, is liable to become spontaneously flammable or to give off flammable or toxic gas at a rate greater than 1 liter per kilogram of the material, per hour.

Class 5 (*Oxidizers and organic peroxides*)

Division 5.1 (oxidizer) means a material that may, generally by yielding oxygen, cause or enhance the combustion of other materials.

Division 5.2 (organic peroxide) means any organic compound containing oxygen (0) in the bivalent -0-0- structure and which may be considered a derivative of hydrogen peroxide, where one or more of the hydrogen atoms have been replaced by organic radicals.

Class 6 (*Poisonous materials and infectious substances*)

Division 6.1 (poisonous material) means a material, other than a gas, which is either known to be so toxic to humans as to afford a hazard to health during transportation, or in the absence of adequate data on human toxicity, is presumed to be toxic to humans.

An *irritating material* causes extreme irritation.

Division 6.2 (infectious substance) means a viable micro-organism, or its toxin, which causes or may cause disease in humans or animals. Infectious substance and etiologic agent are synonymous.

Class 7 (*Radioactive materials*)

Radioactive material means any material having a specific activity greater than 0.002 microcuries per gram (uCi/g).

Class 8 (*Corrosive material*)

Corrosive materials means either a liquid or solid that causes visible destruction or irreversible alterations in human skin tissue at the site of contact, or a liquid that has a severe corrosion rate on steel or aluminum.

Class 9 (*Miscellaneous hazardous materials*)

Miscellaneous hazardous material means a material that presents a hazard during transport, but which is not included in another hazard class, including the following:

- Any material that has an anesthetic, noxious, or other similar property which could cause extreme annoyance or discomfort to a flight-crew member so as to prevent the correct performance of assigned duties.
- Any material that is not included in any other hazard class (a hazardous substance or a hazardous waste).

ORM-D Materials

An *ORM-D material* means a material, such as a consumer commodity, which presents a limited hazard during transportation due to its form, quantity, and packaging.

Other Definitions

Hazard zones are associated with Division 2.3 materials.

- *Hazard zone A*—LC_{50} less than or equal to 200 ppm.
- *Hazard zone B*—LC_{50} greater than 200 ppm and less than or equal to 1000 ppm.
- *Hazard zone C*—LC_{50} greater than 1000 ppm and less than or equal to 3000 ppm.
- *Hazard zone D*—LC_{50} greater than 3000 ppm and less than or equal to 5000 ppm.

Packing Group is an indicaation of the degree of danger presented by hazardous materials.

- *Packing Group I* indicates great danger.
- *Packing Group II* indicates medium danger.
- *Packing Group III* indicates minor danger.

ANALYZING THE HAZARDOUS MATERIAL PROBLEM

Background

Responding to emergencies involving hazardous materials is not easy. Just the shear numbers of these materials present an intimidating list for those who respond to the emergencies they create. Consider these examples.

- A review of the Chemical Abstract Service's (CAS) list indicates that out of 1.5 million chemicals or chemical formulations found outside of the laboratory, 63,000 are considered hazardous.
- The U.S. Department of Transportation (DOT) regulates the transportation of some 3800 hazardous materials.
- The Occupational Safety and Health Administration (OSHA) of the U.S. Department of Labor regulates about 600 hazardous substances on the basis of occupational exposure.

A national U.S. Environmental Protection Agency (EPA) study[3] and subsequent regional studies indicate that the most commonly released chemical is vehicle fuels. Two findings are of interest:

- 49.5 percent of the rest of the releases involved only 10 chemicals in addition to vehicle fuels. (Table 9-14B lists these chemicals.) These additional 10 chemicals are typically produced in the largest volume.
- 74.8 percent of the releases occurred in facilities (production, storage, and use) while the remaining 25.2 percent occurred in transportation.

Regional differences from this national study may change the make-up of the list locally.

Overview

The process of analyzing the hazardous material problem (size-up) provides a way of determining the specific hazards and the potential magnitude of the problem in terms of outcomes. An understanding of the magnitude of the

TABLE 9-14B. ***List of Most Commonly Released Hazardous Materials with the Percentage of Releases and the Percentage of Deaths and Injuries Associated with the Material.***

Chemical Name	Percentage of Releases	Percentage of Deaths and Injuries
PCB (Polychlorinated Biphenyls)	23.0%	2.8%
Sulfuric Acid	6.5%	4.7%
Anhydrous Ammonia	3.7%	6.8%
Chlorine	3.5%	9.6%
Hydrochloric Acid	3.1%	5.6%
Sodium Hydroxide	2.6%	1.9%
Methyl Alcohol	1.7%	0.4%
Nitric Acid	1.7%	1.5%
Toluene	1.4%	2.4%
Methyl Chloride	1.4%	0.0%

problem is the basis for subsequent decisions on the handling of an incident. Failure to consider all the hazards increases the responder's risk.

The analysis process begins when a responder receives notification of a problem and continues throughout the incident, typically at the scene threatened by any hazardous materials involved. Pre-emergency planning, following the same tasks and steps, lessens the time expended to achieve a safe and cost-effective response at a hazardous material incident, and also increases the available response options for that response.

An analysis of the hazardous material problem involves completing the following tasks. (See Figure 9-14B.)

1. Detect the presence of hazardous materials;
2. Survey the hazardous material incident;
3. Collect and interpret hazard and response information;
4. Determine the extent of containment system damage;
5. Predict the likely behavior of the containment system and its contents; and
6. Estimate the potential outcomes within the engulfed area.

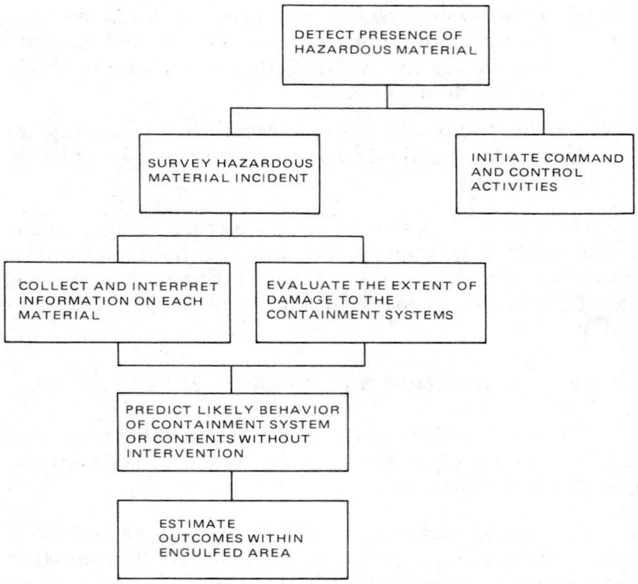

FIG. 9-14B. A flow diagram of the tasks associated with analyzing a hazardous material problem.

Detecting the Presence of Hazardous Materials

The first task in analyzing, and ultimately understanding and solving, hazardous material problems is recognizing those situations where hazardous materials are present. This task begins with the receipt of the initial notification of the emergency and continues throughout the handling of that emergency. Any emergency should be approached from a direction that will provide protection if hazardous materials are present. As with all tasks in the analysis process, detection should be performed from a safe location — upwind, uphill, and upstream, if possible.

The following steps should be taken when responding to any emergency.

Review the initial information received. Clues to the presence of hazardous materials may be provided by the caller or dispatcher.

Review the occupancy, location, or local planning documents for indications of hazardous materials. Planning documents, such as local emergency-response plans, industry site-specific plans, and fire-service pre-emergency response plans, may indicate the presence of hazardous materials. During pre-emergency planning activities, typical occupancies and locations where hazardous materials are manufactured, transported, stored, used, or disposed of in the community, are identified.

Look for containment system characteristics that indicate hazardous materials. The hemispherical ends on the container or the protective housing around the fittings on top of a pressure tank car are indications of hazardous materials. An awareness of the various types of hazardous material containment systems is useful.

Look for facility and transportation markings and color that indicate hazardous materials. The use of color is not consistent nationwide; however, color markings may be consistent in local areas. Various markings indicate the presence of hazardous materials. Some examples are as follows.

DOT identification numbers are four-digit numbers assigned to a specific hazardous material or group of hazardous materials. They are used to cross-reference the name of a material in order to access hazard and response information for that material. In transportation, DOT identification numbers are required on the following:

- non-bulk packages of hazardous materials (except limited quantities) printed adjacent to the required labels on the package; and
- bulk packages of hazardous materials, such as cargo tanks, portable tanks, tank cars, and other bulk shipments. On bulk packages, DOT identification numbers can be displayed on an orange panel, in the center of the appropriate placard, or in the center of a placard-sized, diamond-shaped white display. (See Figure 9-14C.)

On shipping papers, DOT identification numbers are preceded by the prefix "UN" (United Nations) for domestic and international shipments or "NA" (North American) for shipments only within North America.

FIG. 9-14C. Methods of display of Department of Transportation (DOT) identification numbers. The rectangular box has an orange background. The diamonds have white backgrounds.

NFPA 704 markings are diamond-shaped symbols used within facilities to alert people to the type and degree of hazard. They may be found on non-bulk packages; however, they are not used in transportation. The diamond-shaped symbol is divided into four color-coded quadrants. (See Figure 9-14D.) The blue in the left quadrant refers to the health hazard; the red in the top quadrant indicates the flammability hazard; the yellow in the right quadrant refers to the reactivity hazard; and the bottom quadrant carries special information, such as "OX" for oxidizers or "W̶" for water-reactive materials. Each quadrant contains a number from 0 to 4 that represents the relative degree of hazard (0 is low; 4 is high). (See Figure 9-14E.)

Military markings are used to indicate hazardous materials for military shipments.

Special hazard communication markings are used in facility situations to indicate hazardous materials.

Warning labels indicate the presence of hazardous materials using words such as warning, danger, caution, and poison.

Pipeline markers mark the location of pipelines, especially where the pipeline crosses a street.

Container markings, such as the stencilled name of the contents, also may indicate the presence of hazardous materials.

FIG. 9-14D. Sample NFPA 704 marking.

Look for U.S. and Canadian placards and labels. Placards and labels are diamond-shaped symbols that are required by DOT to communicate the presence of hazardous materials in transportation. Placards, $10\frac{3}{4}$-inch square (273 mm), are required on some bulk packages including transport vehicles (*e.g.*, cargo tanks, portable tanks, tank cars, and hopper cars). Labels, four-inch square (102 mm) or smaller for cylinders, are found on some non-bulk packages. Placards and labels convey information by their color, symbol, hazard class and division number, and either the hazard class wording or four-digit identification number. The DOT Chart 9 (see Fig. 9-14F) provides examples of U.S. and Canadian placards and labels.

Transport vehicles and freight containers could contain up to 1000 pounds (4536 kg) of certain hazardous materials without a placard being applied. Limited quantity, infectious substance (etiologic agent), and ORM-D shipments do not require placards. For shipments that last contained a hazardous material, the word "residue" in a black triangle (white triangle for combustible liquids) is added to the lower portion of the placard. Square white backgrounds are used behind Explosives 1.1, Explosives 1.2, Poison Gas, Poison, and Radioactive placards to indicate special handling. The DANGEROUS placard indicates a mixed load of several classes of hazardous materials.

Obtain and review facility documents and shipping papers. Shipping papers accompany each shipment during transportation. They provide detailed information about the contents of the shipment. Shipping papers may indicate the presence of hazardous materials through a variety of required entries (all of which are not always present). The most common entries include the proper shipping name, hazard class or division, identification number, packing group, and the total quantity (by weight, volume, or as otherwise appropriate). Additional entries may include technical and chemical group names, the letters RQ (reportable quantity notation) the "Poison — Inhalation Hazard" "Limited Quantity" notation, "Dangerous When Wet" notation, and shipper-contact information. Shipping papers used in the various modes of transportation (air, highway, rail, and water) are listed in Table 9-14C by mode of transportation, the person responsible, and where the shipping papers are carried.

Facility documents include the Material Safety Data Sheet (MSDS). The MSDS is a document that provides information about the composition, physical and chemical properties, health and safety hazards, emergency response, and waste disposal of materials required by OSHA in 29 CFR 1910.1200.

NFPA 704 Marking System

SCALE	HEALTH HAZARD	FLAMMABILITY HAZARD	REACTIVITY HAZARD
4	Materials which on a very short exposure could cause death or major residual injury. Too dangerous to be approached without specialized personal protective equipment.	Materials which will rapidly or completely vaporize at atmospheric pressure and normal ambient temperature or which is readily dispersed in air and which will burn readily.	Materials which in themselves are readily capable of detonation or of explosive decomposition or reaction at normal temperatures and pressures.
3	Materials which on short exposure could cause serious temporary or residual injury. Requires protection from all contact.	Liquids and solids that can be ignited under almost all ambient temperature conditions.	Materials which in themselves are capable of detonation or explosive reaction but require strong initiating source or which must be heated under confinement before initiation or which react explosively with water.
2	Materials which on intense or continued exposure could cause temporary but not chronic incapacitation or possible residual injury. Requires use of personal protective equipment with independent air supply.	Materials that must be moderately heated or exposed to relatively high ambient temperatures before ignition can occur.	Materials which in themselves are normally unstable and readily undergo violent chemical change but do not detonate. Also materials which may react violently with water or which may form potentially explosive mixtures with water.
1	Materials which on exposure would cause irritation but only minor residual injury. Requires use of approved air purifying respirator.	Materials that must be preheated before ignition can occur.	Materials which in themselves are normally stable, but which can become unstable at elevated temperatures and pressures or which may react with water with some release of energy but not violently.
0	Materials which on exposure under fire conditions would offer no hazard beyond that of ordinary combustible materials.	Materials that will not burn.	Materials which in themselves are normally stable, even under fire exposure conditions and which are not reactive with water.

FIG. 9-14E. A brief explanation of the significance of the numbers found on the NFPA 704 Marking System.[11]

Identify clues (other than occupancy/locations, container shape, markings/color, and placards/labels) that use sight, sound, and odor to indicate hazardous materials. Sensual indications include chemical odors, dead animals and fish, vapor clouds, flames or smoke, irritation of the skin or eyes, the hiss of escaping gas, or the sound of an explosion.

As soon as you detect the presence of hazardous materials, move to the next task in the analysis process.

Initiating Command and Control Activities

Although not part of the analysis process, command and control activities should be initiated upon detecting the presence of hazardous materials and simultaneously with the initial survey of the situation. These command and control action are taken 1) to protect the responder and others during completion of analysis and planning duties, 2) to provide for a command structure at the incident, and 3) to provide for notification of resources required to handle the situation. Specific procedures for initiating command and control activities are found in the local emergency response plan or organization's standard operating procedures.

To initiate command and control activities, take the following steps.

Implement an incident command system. This step provides organization of the incident scene and may begin prior to arrival on the scene.

Locate yourself at a safe distance from the problem. With consideration of the terrain and weather conditions, response personnel should stop at a safe location from the incident - uphill, upwind, and upstream. Suggested minimum "safe" distances should be specified in the local emergency response plan or the organization's standard operating procedures. At this point, the analysis process is not complete, and sufficient information is not available to determine safe distances.

Initiate the notification process. Specific procedures and contacts for notification of required resources should be developed prior to an emergency and listed in the local planning documents.

Control access to the site. Prevent unauthorized persons from entering the area to reduce the negative outcomes in the incident.

The command and control actions taken depend on both the responder's level of training and the resources available. They should be attempted without risk to the responder.

Surveying the Hazardous Materials Incident

After detecting the presence of hazardous materials in an emergency, and while initiating command and control activities, the next task is to survey the hazardous material incident. Completion of this task provides an inventory of the containment systems and materials involved,

U.S. Department of Transportation

Research and Special Programs Administration

DOT CHART 9

Hazardous Materials Marking, Labeling & Placarding Guide

This Marking, Labeling and Placarding Guide will assist shippers, carriers, fire departments, police, emergency response personnel, and others in complying with, and enforcing the regulations governing the safe transport of hazardous materials by highway, rail, water and air.

The information and illustrations presented in this Guide are intended to serve as an introduction to regulations governing hazardous materials transportation. The Guide should be read in conjunction with the Hazardous Materials Regulations (HMR; 49 CFR 100-199). Published annually, and amended periodically, the HMR are the key to compliance and contain the information needed to comply with the requirements for the safe transport of hazardous materials.

Hazardous materials markings, labels, placards, and shipping papers serve to communicate the hazards posed by materials in transportation. Hazard communication is the key to effective emergency response, and is also used to alert transportation workers and the general public of the presence of hazardous materials, insure that noncompatible materials are not loaded together in the same transport vehicle, and provide the necessary information for reporting hazardous materials incidents. The purpose of this Guide is to explain and identify the markings, labels and placards which appear on packages, freight containers and transport vehicles containing hazardous materials.

Marking regulations (Section 172.300) require information, specific to the hazardous material, to be "marked" on the outside of the package. Examples of the information required to be marked on the package are the proper shipping name, identification number and consignor's or consignee's name. For how markings required by the HMR are to be applied to a package, see Section 172.304. For exceptions to the marking requirements and additional marking requirements, see Section 172.300. This chart does not attempt to cover all the marking requirements. In particular this chart does not contain any information related to specification packaging markings addressed in the Parts 178 and 179 of 49 CFR. For further details on required markings, consult the appropriate sections in the HMR.

The Labeling of a package of hazardous material is specific to the hazard class of the material. The Hazardous Material Tables, Section 172.101 and 172.102, identify the proper label(s) for the hazardous material listed. In some cases, a hazardous material will meet the definition of two or more hazard classes. In these instances, the additional labeling requirements of Section 172.402 must be met. Labels, when required, must be placed next to the marked proper shipping name (Section 172.406). The requirements for labels can be found in Section 172.400–172.450.

Placards represent the hazard class(es) of the material(s) contained within the freight container, motor vehicle or rail car. The requirements for placarding are contained in Section 172.500–172.558. **NOTE: This document is for general guidance only and is not a substitute for the requirements of 49 CFR 100-199.**

Response begins with identification.

A transport vehicle carrying 1 package of Radioactive Material labeled Yellow III, 500 pounds of Flammable Liquid and 600 pounds of Corrosive Materials would be placarded with both RADIOACTIVE and DANGEROUS placards.

FIG. 9-14F. Department of Transportation Chart 9 depicting the hazardous materials marking, labeling, and placarding.

Hazardous Materials Warning Labels

DOMESTIC LABELING

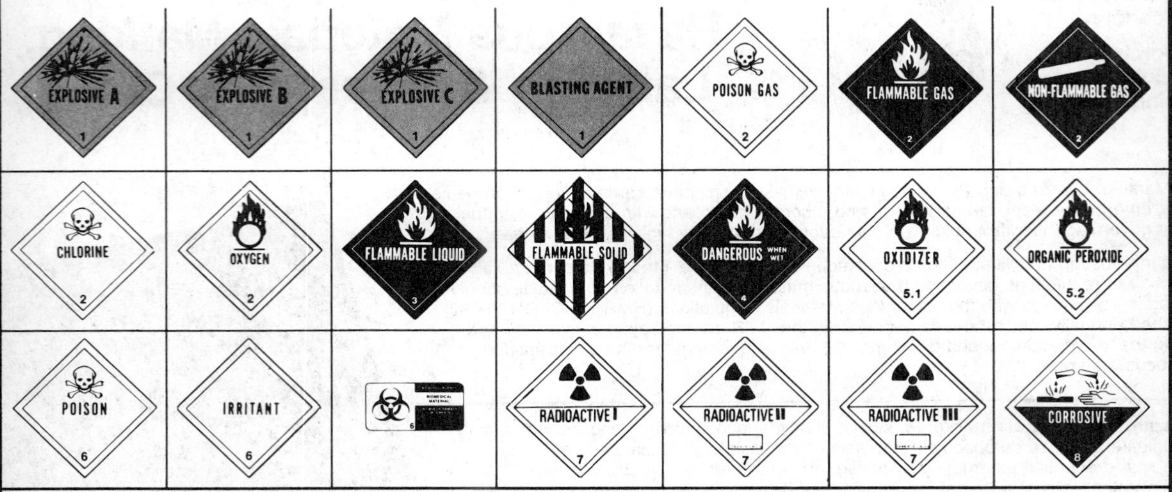

General Guidelines on Use of Labels

(CFR, Title 49, Transportation, Parts 100-177)

- Labels illustrated above are normally for *domestic shipments.* However, some air carriers *may* require the use of International Civil Aviation Organization (ICAO) labels.
- Domestic Warning Labels *may* display UN Class Number, Division Number (and Compatibility Group for Explosives only) [Sec. 172.407(g)].
- Any person who offers a hazardous material for transportation MUST label the package, if required [Sec. 172.400(a)].
- The Hazardous Materials Tables, Sec. 172.101 and 172.102, identify the proper label(s) for the hazardous materials listed.
- Label(s), when required, must be printed on or affixed to the surface of the package near the proper shipping name [Sec. 172.406(a)].
- When two or more different labels are required, display them next to each other [Sec. 172.406(c)].
- Labels may be affixed to packages (even when not required by regulations) provided each label represents a hazard of the material in the package [Sec. 172.401].

Check the Appropriate Regulations
Domestic or International Shipment

Additional Markings and Labels

HANDLING LABELS

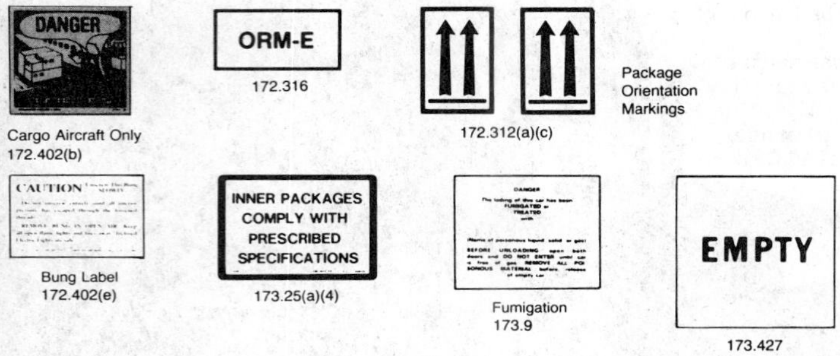

Here are a few additional markings and labels pertaining to the transport of hazardous materials. The section number shown with each item refers to the appropriate section in the HMR. The Hazardous Materials Tables, Section 172.101 and 172.102, identify the proper shipping name, hazard class, identification number, required label(s) and packaging sections.

Poisonous Materials

Materials which meet the inhalation toxicity criteria specified in Section 173.3a(b)(2), have additional "communication standards" prescribed by the HMR. First, the words "Poison-Inhalation Hazard" must be entered on the shipping paper, as required by Section 172.203(k)(4), for any primary capacity units with a capacity greater than one liter. Second, packages of 110 gallons or less capacity must be marked "Inhalation Hazard" in accordance with Section 172.301(a). Lastly, transport vehicles, freight containers and portable tanks subject to the shipping paper requirements contained in Section 172.203(k)(4) must be placarded with POISON placards in addition to the placards required by Section 172.504. For additional information and exceptions to these communication requirements, see the referenced sections in the HMR.

Keep a copy of the DOT Emergency Response Guidebook handy!

FIG. 9-14F. (Continued)

Hazardous Materials Warning Placards

DOMESTIC PLACARDING

Illustration numbers in each square refer to Tables 1 and 2 below.

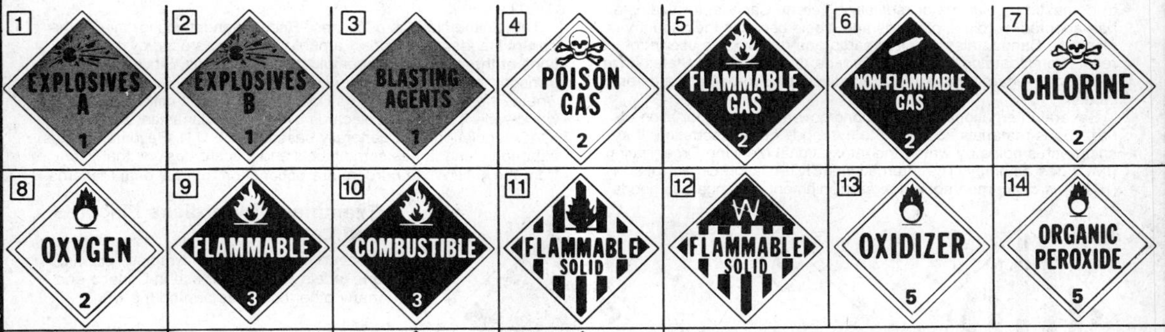

WHITE SQUARE BACKGROUND FOR PLACARD

HIGHWAY

- Used for "HIGHWAY ROUTE CONTROLLED QUANTITY OF RADIOACTIVE MATERIALS." (Sec. 172.507)

RAIL

- Used for RAIL SHIPMENTS "EXPLOSIVE A," "POISON GAS" and "POISON GAS RESIDUE" placards. (Sec. 172.510(a))

Guidelines

(CFR, Title 49, Transportation, Parts 100-177)

- Placard any transport vehicle, freight container, or rail car containing any quantity of material listed in Table 1.
- Materials which are shipped in portable tanks, cargo tanks, or tank cars must be placarded when they contain any quantity of Table 1 and/or Table 2 material.
- Motor vehicles or freight containers containing packages which are subject to the "Poison-Inhalation Hazard" shipping paper description of Section 172.203(k)(4), must be placarded POISON in addition to the placards required by Section 172.504 (see Section 172.505).
- When the gross weight of all hazardous material covered in TABLE 2 is less than 1000 pounds, no placard is required on a transport vehicle or freight container.
- Placard freight containers 640 cubic feet or more containing any quantity of hazardous material classes listed in TABLES 1 and/or 2 when offered for transportation by air or water (see Section 172.512(a)). Under 640 cubic feet see Section 172.512(b).

TABLE 1

Hazard Classes	No.
Class A explosives	1
Class B explosives	2
Poison A	4
Flammable solid (DANGEROUS WHEN WET label only)	12
Radioactive material (YELLOW III label)	16
Radioactive material:	
Uranium hexafluoride fissile (Containing more than 1.0% U^{235})	16 & 17
Uranium hexafluoride, low-specific activity (Containing 1.0% or less U^{235})	16 & 17

Note: For details on the use of Tables 1 and 2, see Sec. 172.504 (see footnotes at bottom of tables.)

TABLE 2

Hazard Classes	No.
Class C explosives	18
Blasting agent	3
Nonflammable gas	6
Nonflammable gas (Chlorine)	7
Nonflammable gas (Fluorine)	15
Nonflammable gas (Oxygen, cryogenic liquid)	8
Flammable gas	5
Combustible liquid	10
Flammable liquid	9
Flammable solid	11
Oxidizer	13
Organic peroxide	14
Poison B	15
Corrosive material	17
Irritating material	18

UN or NA Identification Numbers

MUST BE DISPLAYED ON TANK CARS, CARGO TANKS, PORTABLE TANKS AND BULK PACKAGINGS

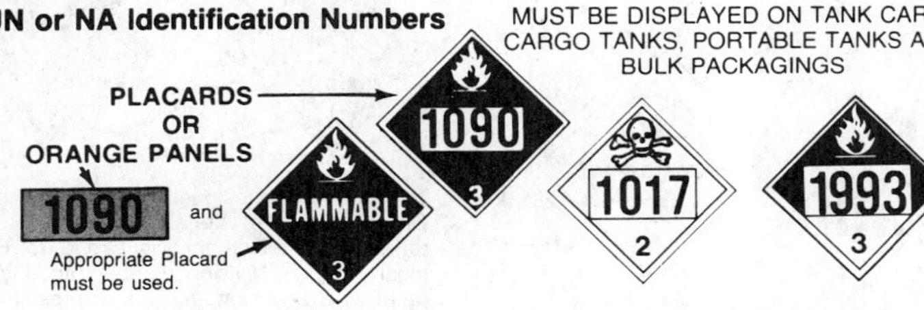

- When hazardous materials are transported in Tank Cars (Section 172.330), Cargo Tanks (Section 172.328), Portable Tanks (Section 172.326) or Bulk Packagings (Section 172.331), UN or NA numbers must be displayed on placards, orange panels or, when authorized, plain white square-on-point configuration.
- UN (United Nations) or NA (North American) numbers are found in the Hazardous Materials Tables, Sections 172.101 and 172.102.
- Identification numbers may not be displayed on "POISON GAS," "RADIOACTIVE," or "EXPLOSIVE A," "EXPLOSIVE B," "BLASTING AGENTS," or "DANGEROUS" placards. (See Section 172.334.)
- In lieu of the orange panel, identification numbers may be placed on plain white square-on-point configuration when there is no placard specified for the hazard class (*e.g.*, ORM-A, B, C, D, or E) or where the identification number may not be displayed on the placard. See Section 172.336(b) for additional provisions and specifications.
- When the identification number is displayed on a placard the UN hazard class number must be displayed in the lower corner of each placard (see Section 172.332 (c)(3)).
- Specifications of size and color of the Orange Panel can be found in Section 172.332(b).
- NA numbers are used only in the USA and Canada.

Additional Placarding Guidelines

A transport vehicle or freight container containing two or more classes of material requiring different placards specified in Table 2 may be placarded DANGEROUS in place of the separate placards specified for each of those classes of material specified in Table 2. However, when 5000 pounds or more of one class of material is loaded therein at one loading facility, the placard specified for that class must be applied. This exception, provided in Section 172.504(b), does not apply to portable tanks, tank cars, or cargo tanks.

CAUTION: Check each shipment for compliance with the appropriate hazardous materials regulations — Proper Classification, Packaging, Marking, Labeling, Placarding, Documentation — prior to offering for shipment.

In an emergency, call Chemtrec, 1-800-424-9300

FIG. 9-14F. (Continued)

Examples of Canadian and International Placards and Labels

The shipment of hazardous materials internationally is governed by one or more regulatory bodies with regulations that may be similar to domestic regulations or radically different. Canada, for example, has adopted wordless placards and labels because their country is bilingual. Canada also requires cargo and rail tanks to use retro-reflective placarding. However, Canada and the United States have reciprocity regarding the use of wordless and worded placards and labels.

Several international organizations govern the transportation of hazardous materials according to the mode of transportation. If a shipment is going by water, the International Maritime Organization (IMO) has authority. The International Civil Aviation Organization (ICAO) is concerned about the safe shipment of dangerous goods (*i.e.*, hazardous materials) by air. Transport Canada (TC) is the Canadian counterpart to the U.S. Department of Transportation (DOT).

The United Nations publishes "Recommendations for the Transport of Dangerous Goods," a publication that is used by many nations of the world when promulgating regulations. Since the safe transport of hazardous materials is of concern to people everywhere, the work done by the United Nations is of critical importance world-wide. Labels and placards used in the Canadian, IMO, and ICAO regulations are generally based on the U.N. Recomendations, although Canada has some labels and placard designs that vary from the U.N. White borders are optional on International Placards.

Examples of Wordless Placards and Labels

Pictured here are typical wordless placards and labels required for use in Canada and many other countries around the world.

Examples of International and Canadian Placards and Labels

Spontaneously Combustible and Keep Away From Food placards and labels are used internationally and in Canada. The Corrosive Gas placard and label are used exclusively in Canada. Most placards and labels used internationally are similar (color and symbols) to those required by DOT regulations.

UN Class Numbers

Class 1: Explosives
Class 2: Gases (compressed, liquified or dissolved under pressure
Class 3: Flammable liquids
Class 4: Flammable solids or substances
Class 5: Oxidizing substances. Division 5.1, Oxidizing substances or agents. Division 5.2, Organic peroxides.
Class 6: Poisonous and infectious substances
Class 7: Radioactive substances
Class 8: Corrosives
Class 9: Misc. dangerous substances

Examples of Explosive Labels

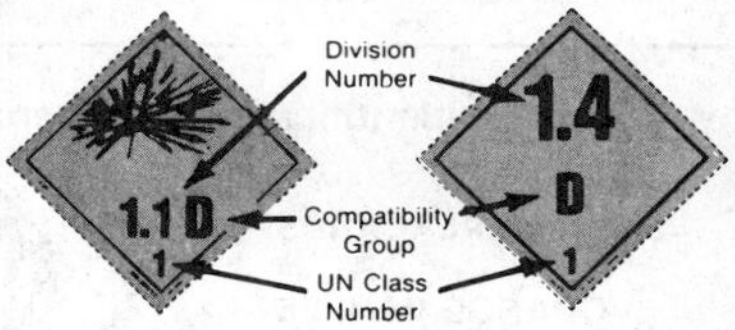

The Numerical Designation represents the Class or Division. Alphabetical Designation represents the Compatibility Group (for Explosives only). Division Numbers and Compatibility Group combinations can result in over 30 different "Explosives" labels (see IMDG Code/ICAO).

For complete details, refer to one or more of the following:

- Code of Federal Regulations, Title 49, Transportation. Parts 100-199. [All modes]
- International Civil Aviation Organization (ICAO) Technical Instructions for the Safe Transport of Dangerous Goods by Air [Air]
- International Maritime Organization (IMO) Dangerous Goods Code [Water]
- "Transportation of Dangerous Goods Regulations" of Transport Canada. [All Modes]

U.S. Department of Transportation
Research and Special Programs Administration

STYLE H-DOT 9

CHART 9
REV. NOVEMBER 1988

FIG. 9-14F. (Continued)

TABLE 9-14C. ***A List of the Shipping Papers by Mode of Transportation, Title of Shipping Paper, Location, and Responsible Person.***

Mode of Transportation	Title of Shipping Paper	Location of Shipping Papers	Responsible Person
Highway	Bill of Lading or Freight Bill	Cab of vehicle	Driver
Rail	Waybill and/or Consist	With member of train crew (conductor or engineer)	Conductor
Water	Dangerous Cargo Manifest	Wheelhouse or pipe-like container or barge	Captain or Master
Air	Air Bill with Shippers Certification for Restricted Articles	Cockpit *(May also be found attached to the outside of packages.)*	Pilot

TABLE 9-14D. ***A Listing of the Various Types of Non-Bulk, Bulk, and Facility Containment Systems.***[12]

Transportation		
Non-Bulk	**Bulk**	**Facility Containment Systems**
Bags	Bulk Bags	Buildings
Bottles	Bulk Boxes	Machinery
Boxes	Cargo Tanks	Open Piles (outdoors and indoors)
Carboys	Covered Hopper Cars	Piping
Cylinders	Freight Containers	Reactors (chemical and nuclear
Drums	Gondolas	Storage Bins, Cabinets, or Shelves
Jerricans	Pneumatic Hopper Trailers	
Multicell	Portable Tanks and Bins	
Tanks and Storage Vessels Packages	Protective Overpacks for Radioactive Materials	
Wooden Barrels	Tank Cars	
	Ton Containers	
	Van Trailers	

materials released, and surrounding conditions. This incident survey should be conducted from a safe distance, without exposure to the released materials.

The following steps should be completed during the survey of a hazardous material incident.

Identify each containment system by type, identifier, and size. Containment systems fit into one of three types: non-bulk, bulk, or facility containment systems. (See Table 9-14D.) The containment system identifier (*e.g.*, facility or carrier name and number) is used to differentiate one containment system from another and to allow tracking of that container throughout the incident. The quantity within or capacity of the containment system can be obtained from markings on the container or entries on the shipping papers or facility documents. The quantity information will help indicate the magnitude of the problem.

Identify the name, DOT identification number, or placard applied to each hazardous material containment system. This information provides a means of accessing various sources of hazard and response information.

For facilities: sources for identifying the material include pre-emergency planning document, markings and color, contact with the facility manager, and review of appropriate MSDS.

In transportation: the identity of the hazardous material can be determined from the DOT identification number, commodity stencil, type of placard or label applied, shipping paper entries, and manufacturer, shipper, or consignee contacts using the 24-hour emergency telephone number on the shipping papers. Pipeline markers provide the name of the commodity or at least the name and telephone number of the pipeline company.

Identify leaking containment systems. Clues indicating leakage include material on the outside of the containment system, taste or smell, presence of vapor clouds, or the operation of a safety relief valve. If possible during the survey, note the form of the released material (solid, liquid, or gas) and the location of the release.

Identify the surrounding conditions. Surrounding conditions should be noted when surveying hazardous material incidents. These conditions include topography, land use, accessibility, weather conditions, bodies of water, public exposure potential, and the nature and extent of injuries. If a facility is involved, look for information about floor drains, ventilation ducts, air returns, etc. as appropriate.

For ease of collection, recording, and interpretation of information obtained during the survey of an incident, a hazardous material incident survey form is used. (See Figure 9-14G.)

Finally, the information collected in the incident survey should be reviewed to verify its accuracy. For example, if the shipping paper identifies the material as a gas and a solid is being released, some of the information obtained may not be correct. An understanding of the characteristics of various containment systems will help to verify information on the contents.

Hazardous Material Incident Survey Form

Location ______________________________

Date ____-____-____ Time: ____ : ____ Weather Conditions ______________________________

Terrain ______________________________

Closest Populated Buildings ______________________________

Closest Bodies of Water ______________________________

Closest Other Buildings ______________________________

No. Deaths* ________ No. Injuries ________ Remedial Actions Taken ______________________________

Containment System			Material Identification			Release		
Container Type	Container ID No.	QTY	DOT ID No.	Placard	Name of Material	Yes	Form	Location
						☑	☐ Solid ☐ Liquid ☐ Gas	
						☑	☐ Solid ☐ Liquid ☐ Gas	
						☑	☐ Solid ☐ Liquid ☐ Gas	
						☑	☐ Solid ☐ Liquid ☐ Gas	
						☑	☐ Solid ☐ Liquid ☐ Gas	
						☑	☐ Solid ☐ Liquid ☐ Gas	

Sketch of scene

N

FIG 9-14G. Hazardous Material Incident Survey Form. This worksheet is used for recording information collected during the task of surveying a hazardous material incident.[4]

Collecting and Interpreting Hazard and Response Information

Once a hazardous material is identified, information about the material's hazards, behavior characteristics, and response should be collected. This information, which may be obtained simultaneously with determining the extent of containment system damage, is used to predict the behavior of that material. The information to be collected is divided into six groups: material identification information, physical properties, chemical properties, physical hazards, health hazards, and response information. The task of obtaining, recording, and interpreting hazardous material information can be lengthy and rigorous. Various forms are being used to record hazard and response information (See Figure 9-14H.)

A number of resources are available for this task, including the following.

Printed Materials. Printed materials include various response guides and MSDS.

Various *response guides* are available for use in obtaining hazard, behavior, and response information. A listing of the sources of the most common response guides is found in Table 9-14E. As you will note from the X's in Table 9-14F, no one printed material source provides all the information. Therefore, more than one resource may have to be consulted to obtain the needed information. An understanding of the type of information available from each resource is important. These references augment personal knowledge and experience.

Material Safety Data Sheets. (MSDS) are available at facilities from the manager or other facility personnel and may be found in transportation. CHEMTREC has more than 250,000 MSDS on file if one is not available locally. MSDS typically provide the following types of information:

- Physical and chemical characteristics;
- Physical hazards of the material;
- Health hazards of the material;
- Signs and symptoms of exposure;
- Routes of entry;
- Permissible exposure limits;
- Responsible party contact;
- Precautions for safe handling (including hygiene practices, protective measures, and procedures for clean-up of spills/leaks);
- Applicable control measures including personal protective equipment; and
- Emergency and first aid procedures.

Technical Resources. A number of technical resources are available including:

CHEMTREC, the Chemical Transportation Emergency Center, is part of the Chemical Manufacturers' Association (CMA). CHEMTREC operates around the clock to receive toll-free calls from the United States and Canada through a wide-area telephone service number (800) 424-9300. If in Washington, D.C., or Alaska, call (202) 483-7617. CHEMTREC can usually provide immediate hazard information from the CHEMTREC files. CHEMTREC will also contact the shipper; therefore, be prepared to provide CHEMTREC with the following information when available:

- Caller's name and phone number where caller can be reached;
- Name of the carrier, shipper, manufacturer, or facility operator;
- Nature, location, and time of the incident;
- Name of the material (or other identifying information); and
- Container type, rail car or truck number, vessel name, or other identifying information such as a rail car's reporting marks (initials) and number.

CHEMTREC can also provide a teleconferencing bridge, connecting technical specialists with those needing technical information.

National Response Center (NRC), operated by the U.S. Coast Guard, receives reports required from spillers of hazardous substances. The NRC also acts as the notification, communications, technical assistance, and coordination center for the National Response Team. After receiving a report, the NRC will immediately relay the information to the responsible, predesignated, Federal On-Scene Coordinator and other resources of the Federal Government. The NRC can be contacted by calling (800) 424-8802.

Local Poison Control Center. For consumer products, comprehensive hazard information is available through the Regional Poison Control Centers. The local planning documents should contain the telephone number.

Manufacturer's Technical Medical Staff. For bulk industrial chemicals, assistance may be available from the technical medical staff of the manufacturer. CHEMTREC will make the contact.

Agency for Toxic Substances and Disease Registry (ATSDR). For chemical mixtures or wastes, when a second opinion is required or when the chemical is unknown, a preferred source of information is the ATSDR, a part of the Center for Disease Control. ATSDR can be reached by calling (404) 639-0615.

Department of Energy. For radioactive materials, contact the Department of Energy by calling (202) 586-8100.

Hazardous Material Emergency Response Teams. Assistance from these sources ranges from immediate telephone advice to the dispatching of emergency teams to actually assist in field operations. Some common examples include the following:

- Pesticide Safety Team Network;
- CHLOREP Teams;
- U.S. Coast Guard Strike Teams;
- Carrier Response Teams;
- U.S. Environmental Protection Agency Regional Response and Technical Assistance Teams; and
- Association of American Railroads, Bureau of Explosives.

On contact with these resources, provide as much information as possible; especially the full name, form, use, and concentration of the chemical, when available. An occupational-health physician may be required to obtain or interpret information from any of these sources.

Assistance in contacting many of these technical resources may be obtained from CHEMTREC or the NRC, if not listed in the local planning documents.

Hazardous Material Data Sheet

Containment System ID.

Material Name ______ DOT ID No ______ STCC No ______

Synonyms ______

Hazard Class ______

NFPA 704 Marking: Health ______ Flammability ______ Reactivity ______ Other ______

Physical Properties

Form	Color	Odor	Chemical Formula	Molecular Wt.
☐ Solid ☐ Liquid ☐ Gas				

Chemical Properties

Actual Temp.	Boiling Point	Melting Point	Vapor Pressure	Expansion Ratio	Specific Gravity	Vapor Density	Soluble?	Degree of Solubility
							☐ YES	

Physical Hazards

Flammable (Heat/Fire) ☐ YES
Cryogenic (cold) ☐ YES
Oxidizer (supports combustion) ☐ YES
Explosive ☐ YES
Reactive ☐ YES
To What? ______

Actual Temperature	Flash Point	Ignition Temperature
Actual Concentration	**Flammable Range**	**Toxic Products of Combustion**

Health Hazards

Acute Health Hazards:
Poisonous ☐ YES
Corrosive ☐ YES
To What? ______
Asphyxiation ☐ YES
Etiologic ☐ YES
Radiation ☐ YES
Type: alpha beta gamma

Actual Concentration	Non-life Threatening Exposure Limits		
	TLV-TWA (PEL)	TLV-C	TLV-STEL
Odor Threshold	**Life Threatening Exposure Limits**		
	IDLH	LC_{50}	LD_{50}

Chronic Health Hazards:
Carcinogen ☐ YES
Mutagen ☐ YES
Teratogen ☐ YES

Aquatic Hazard ☐ YES

Route of Entry ☒ = YES		Toxicity Rating	Notes
Inhalation	☐	1 2 3 4 5 6	
Dermal	☐	1 2 3 4 5 6	
Ingestion	☐	1 2 3 4 5 6	

Response Information

Evacuation Distances ______

First Aid ______

______

Personal Protective Equipment ______

Decontamination ______

Extinguishing Agents ______

Neutralizing Agents ______

FIG. 9-14H. Hazardous material data sheet. This worksheet is used for recording information obtained during the task of collecting and interpreting hazard and response information.[4]

TABLE 9-14E. ***A List of Common Reference Guides for Collecting Hazardous Response Information and Their Sources.*** [4]

Printed Information	Source
Emergency Response Guidebook (DOT)	U.S. Department of Transportation Research and Special Programs Administration Washington, DC 20590
Fire Protection Guide on Hazardous Materials, National Fire Protection Association (NFPA 325, NFPA 49, and NFPA 491)	National Fire Protection Association 1 Batterymarch Park Quincy, MA 02269
Emergency Handling of Hazardous Materials in Surface Transportation (EH) *Emergency Actions Guides* (EAG) (Paper)	Association of American Railroads 50 "F" Street, NW Washington, DC 20001
U.S. Coast Guard Chris Manual Series (CHRIS) *Hazardous Chemical Data* CG-446-2	Superintendent of Documents U.S. Government Printing Office Washington, DC 20402
Farm Chemical Handbook (FCH)	Meister Publishing Company 37841 Euclid Avenue Willoughby, OH 44094
NIOSH/OSHA References (NIOSH) *Pocket Guide to Chemical Hazards*	Superintendent of Documents U.S. Government Printing Office Washington, DC 20402
Threshold Limit Values and Biological Exposure *Indices for 1989–1990*	American Conference of Governmental Industrial Hygienists 6500 Glenway Avenue Building D-7 Cincinnati, OH 45211-4438

Determining the Extent of Containment System Damage

Information on the types and extent of damage to a containment system is used in predicting the likely behavior of the containment system and its contents. This task can be initiated simultaneously with collecting information about the materials involved. Provide appropriate personal protective equipment for the response personnel if they could be exposed to released materials. Contact technical personnel with knowledge of the type of containment systems involved for assistance.

The following steps will help determine the extent of damage to a containment system.

1. **Identify containment systems that are damaged.** Indications of damage include abnormal orientation or position of the containment system, damage to other containment systems in the area, or a change in shape of the containment system.
2. **Determine the construction of the damaged containment system.** Before inspecting the damaged containment system, review the containment system's basic design, construction, and secondary containment features.
3. **Determine the type and location of closures on the containment system.** Review the closures on the containment system by name and purpose. Use of standard terminology will help describe the problem to the technical resources.
4. **Determine the type and location of any damage to the container or its closures.** Cracks, gouges, scores, and punctures should be noted. Using appropriate personal protective equipment when necessary, the containment system must be evaluated for signs of failure or potential failure. If the containment system has not already failed, it may have been weakened and result in failure.
5. **Determine the extent of the damage to the container or its closures.** Information on the extent of damage (*e.g.*, the radius of curvature for dents or the depth of scores and gouges on pressure tank cars) should be determined. It may be necessary to determine the pressure in a bulk packaging or facility containment system using either a pressure gauge or the temperature of the contents.

Figure 9-14I provides an example of a form used for determining the extent of damage to tank cars.

Predicting Likely Behavior

After collecting information on the characteristics of the material and the extent of damage to the containment system, the next task is to predict their likely behavior. This prediction, or "mental movie," is used throughout the response activity as a reference point. A mental movie is made for each containment system and hazardous material involved and is based on the worst possible case. As additional information is obtained, the mental movie is modified. The steps for predicting the behavior of the containment system and its contents include the following.

TABLE 9-14F. ***A Cross-Reference Indicating What Information is Available in the Common Reference Guides.*** An "X" in the intersection of the resource and the required information indicates that the information is typically found in that publication.[4]

Required Information	Primary Resources		Secondary Resources						
	DOT	NIOSH	EAG	EH	NFPA	CHRIS	ACGIH	FCH	MSDS
DOT ID No.	X	X	X	X		X			X
STCC No.			X	X					
Synonyms		X	X		X	X		X	X
Hazard Class			X	X	X	X		X	X
NFPA 704 Marking			X		X	X			
Form		X	X	X	X	X		X	X
Color		X	X	X	X	X		X	X
Odor		X	X	X	X	X		X	X
Chemical Formula		X	X		X	X		X	X
Molecular Weight		X	X			X			X
Boiling Point		X	X		X	X		X	X
Melting Point		X	X			X		X	X
Vapor Pressure		X	X			X			X
Expansion ratio									
Specific gravity			X	X	X	X			X
Vapor density			X	X	X	X			X
Soluble		X	X	X	X	X		X	X
Degree of solubility		X	X	X	X	X		X	X
Flash Point		X	X	X	X	X		X	X
Ignition Temperature			X		X	X			X
Flammable Range		X	X		X	X			X
Toxic Products of Combustion			X			X		X	X
Reactive to what	X	X	X	X		X			X
Odor Threshold			X			X			X
IDLH		X				X			X
LD_{50}						X		X	X
LC_{50}								X	X
TLV-C		X				X	X		X
TLV-STEL			X			X	X		X
TLV-TWA		X	X				X		X
PEL		X							X
Route of Entry	X	X	X	X	X	X		X	X
Toxicity Rating					X	X			
Evacuation Distances	X		X	X		X			X
First Aid	X	X	X	X		X		X	X
Personal Protective Equip.	X	X	X	X	X	X		X	X
Decontamination	X	X	X					X	X
Extinguishing Agents	X		X	X	X	X		X	X
Neutralizing Agents			X	X		X			X

Abbreviations Used for References

Primary Resources

DOT *Emergency Response Guidebook*

NIOSH *Pocket Guide to Chemical Hazards*

Secondary Resources

EAG Association of American Railroads' *Emergency Action Guides*

EH Association of American Railroads' *Emergency Handling of Hazardous Materials in Surface Transportation*

NFPA National Fire Protection Association's *Fire Protection Guide on Hazardous Materials*

CHRIS U.S. Coast Guard's *Hazardous Chemical Data*

ACGIH American Conference ofGovernmental Industrial Hygienists' *Threshold Limit Values and Biological Exposure Indices*

FCH Farm Chemicals Handbook

MSDS Material Safety Data Sheet

1. **Identify the types of stress or potential stress on a containment system and/or its contents.** Stress is the applied force or system of forces that tend to strain or deform a body (either the containment system or the contents). The types of stress include: thermal, mechanical, chemical, irradiation, and etiologic. Thermal, mechanical, and chemical stresses can typically be identified visually, while irradiation and etiologic are more difficult to identify. Considerations include: type and characteristics of the containment system, type of stress, amount of stress applied, intensity of stress, and duration of stress.

Tank Car Damage Assessment

Car Initials & Number

Tank Car Characteristics

Type of Car: ☐ Non-pressure ☐ Pressure ☐ Cryogenic ☐ Other ________

Specification Nº:	Shell Capacity:
Year Constructed:	Tank Test Pressure:

Underframe: ☐ Continuous ☐ Stub sill

†Thermal Protection: ☐ Jacketed ☐ Sprayed-on

Construction Material: Type /Grade ________ Thickness ________

Features	Y	N
Jacketed		
Insulated		
Thermal Protection†		
Linings		
Claddings		
Heater Coils		

Stress: ☐ Thermal ☐ Mechanical ☐ Chemical ☐ None

Jacket, Tank, and Head Damage

Indicate location and severity of damage (punctures, cracks, scores, gouges, wheel burns, dents, rail burns, underframe, and leaks) on the appropriate diagram(s).

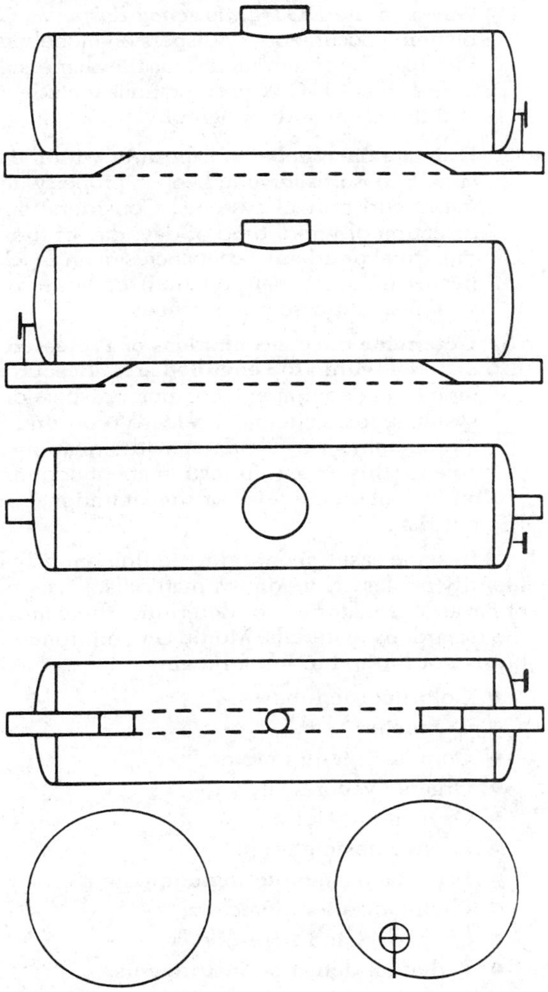

Fitting Damage

Fitting	Damage	Description
☐ Liquid Valve	☐ Yes ☐ Leaking	
☐ Vapor Valve	☐ Yes ☐ Leaking	
☐ Air Valve	☐ Yes ☐ Leaking	
☐ Bottom Outlet Type: ________	☐ Yes ☐ Leaking	
☐ Safety Relief Device Type: ________	☐ Yes ☐ Leaking	
☐ Vacuum Relief	☐ Yes ☐ Leaking	
☐ Gauging Device Type: ________	☐ Yes ☐ Leaking	
☐ Manway Cover	☐ Yes ☐ Leaking	
☐ Fill Hole	☐ Yes ☐ Leaking	
☐ Sample Line	☐ Yes ☐ Leaking	
☐ Thermometer Well	☐ Yes ☐ Leaking	
☐ Washout	☐ Yes ☐ Leaking	
☐ Sump	☐ Yes ☐ Leaking	
☐ Other Type: ________	☐ Yes ☐ Leaking	

FIG. 9-14I. Tank Car Damage Assessment. This worksheet is used for recording results of damage assessment for rail tank cars. (Courtesy of Union Pacific Railroad.)

2. **Predict the way in which the containment system will breach.** A breach is an opening (failure) caused by damage to the containment system through which matter and/or energy can or does escape. The types of breach include: disintegration, runaway linear cracking, closures that open up, punctures, and splits or tears. Considerations include: type and duration of the stress being applied, behavior of the containment system under the stresses applied, behavior of the contents, location of the applied stresses, force of opening of the containment system, size of breach, and speed of the breach event. Even if the containment system has already breached, this prediction step must be considered in light of a further breach.
3. **Predict the way in which the contents will be released.** Release is the escape of the contents through a breach in a containment system. The types of release include: *detonation*—the disintegration of the containment system and/or detonation of the contents; *violent rupture*—the runaway cracking of the containment system or the rapid expansion of the contents that burst the containment system abruptly; *rapid relief*—pressurized flow of the contents through closures, splits or tears, and punctures; and *spill or leak*—gradual flow through closures, splits or tears, and punctures. Considerations include: type of breach, location of breach, quantity of contents, flow characteristics of contents, release rate, length of release, and weather conditions.
4. **Predict the dispersion pattern that will create the engulfed area.** Dispersion is the scattering of the matter and/or energy (from the point of release) to form an engulfed area. The engulfed area is the actual or potential area of exposure from a hazardous material or its containment system. The types of dispersion patterns include: hemisphere, cloud, plume, cone, stream, pool, and irregular. Considerations include: type of release, form of the released contents, weather conditions, topography, release rate, solubility of material, secondary reactions, melting point, freezing point, boiling point, vapor density, specific gravity, secondary containment, vapor pressure, and expansion ratio. For fixed facilities; consider tank spacing, impoundment and diking, tank venting and flaring systems, transfer operations, monitoring and detection systems, and fire protection systems.
5. **Predict the length of contact that exposures will have with the released contents.** Contact means to be exposed to something undesirable or injurious. Type of contact is considered in relationship to time: short term refers to minutes and hours; medium term is associated with days, weeks, and months; and long term is in terms of years and generations. Considerations include: form of the material upon release, dispersion pattern, weather conditions, topography, distance to exposure, barriers or shielding, speed of dispersing materials, and quantity released.
6. **Predict the hazards which will cause harm.** Harm is the injury or damage caused by being exposed to the hazards of the released contents. Types of hazards include: physical hazards including thermal and mechanical effects; and health hazards including chemical (poisonous, corrosive, and asphyxiation), radiation, and etiologic effects. Considerations include: hazards associated with the released contents, concentrations of released materials, duration of contact, and how often the exposures will come into contact with the released materials.

To assist in predicting the behavior of the containment system and its contents, a Behavior Model form is suggested. (See Figure 9-14J.)

If unable to make all the predictions necessary to analyze the incident, seek help from the following resources: manufacturer, shipper and consignee, carrier, and federal, state, and local agencies involved with hazardous materials.

A number of response guides indicate the effects of mixing various chemicals, including NFPA 491M, *Manual of Hazardous Chemical Reactions*.

Estimating Outcomes

This final task in the analysis process results in an indication of the magnitude of the problem in terms of outcomes within the engulfed area. The engulfed area is the actual or potential area of exposure from a hazardous material. The following steps should be taken to estimate outcomes in the engulfed area.

1. **Determine the dimensions of an engulfed area.** Using the Table of Initial Isolation and Protective Action Distances in the DOT *Emergency Response Guidebook*, planning documents, or dispersion modeling programs, identify the potential size of the dispersion pattern. (See Table 9-14G.) Considerations include wind speed and direction and topography.
2. **Estimate the number of exposures within the engulfed area.** Exposures include people, property, the environment, and critical systems. Considerations include: direction of wind, time of day, day of the week, setting (rural or urban), occupancies in area (schools, businesses, industry, transportation), bodies of water, sewer systems, and essential services.
3. **Determine the concentrations of a released hazardous material within the engulfed area.** Resources, such as monitoring equipment, computer dispersion modeling systems, toxic chemical release reporting forms, and a programmable calculator with equations, are available for this step. Information about odor may provide an insight on the level of concentration, but not without risk.

In some cases, monitoring equipment may be used to identify or classify unknown materials, verify the identity of hazardous materials, or determine the concentration of the hazardous materials. Monitoring equipment includes, but is not limited to the following:

- Colorimetric tubes;
- CO meter;
- Combustible-gas meter;
- Organic-vapor analyzer;
- Oxygen meter;
- Passive dosimeter;
- Personal air-monitoring equipment;
- Photoionization detectors;
- pH papers and strips; and
- Radiation-detection instruments.

Where monitoring equipment is available, personnel should be able to select the appropriate monitoring equipment considering its limitations, perform field testing procedures, operate the equipment to collect data, and record

Behavior Model	Containment System ID.

Material: ______________________ Quantity: ______________

Form of Released Material: ☐ Gas ☐ Liquid ☐ Solid

Containment System Type: ______________________

Weather Conditions: Ambient Temperature: ______ ° Wind Speed: ______ m.p.h. Rain ☐ Snow ☐

Terrain: ______________________

Event Sequence

Stress	Breach	Release	Engulf	Contact	Harm

Prediction Steps

Identify the Type of Stress	Predict the Type of Breach	Predict the Type of Release	Predict the Dispersion Pattern	Predict the Length of Exposure	Predict the Hazard causing the Harm

Behavior Options

Stress	Breach	Release	Engulf	Contact	Harm
Thermal	Disintegration	Detonation	Hemisphere	Short term	Physical
Mechanical	Runaway linear cracking	Violent rupture	Cloud	Medium term	*Thermal*
Chemical	Closures open up	Rapid relief	Plume	Long term	*Mechanical*
	Punctures	Spill or leak	Cone		Health
	Splits or tears		Stream		*Poisonous*
			Pool		*Corrosive*
			Irregular		*Asphyxiation*
					Radiation
					Etiologic

(Adapted from Ludwig Benner's Hazardous Materials Emergencies, 1978)

FIG. 9-14J. Behavior Model. This worksheet is used for predicting the behavior of a containment system and its contents in a hazardous material incident.[5]

TABLE 9-14G. ***Sample of the Table of Initial Isolation and Protective Action Distances from the Department of Transportation's 1990 Emergency Response Guidebook.***[8]

USE THIS TABLE WHEN THE MATERIAL IS NOT ON FIRE		SMALL SPILLS (Leak or spill from a small package or small leak from a large package.)		LARGE SPILLS (Leak or spill from a large package or spill from many small packages.)	
ID No.	Name of Material	First ISOLATE in all directions- (Feet)	Then, PROTECT those persons in the DOWNWIND direction (Miles)	First, ISOLATE in all directions- (Feet)	Then, PROTECT those persons in the DOWNWIND direction- (Miles)
1005	Ammonia	150	0.2	300	1
1005	Ammonia, Anhydrous, liquefied	150	0.2	300	1
1005	Ammonia Solution with more than 50% ammonia	150	0.2	300	1
1005	Anhydrous Ammonia	150	0.2	300	1
1008	Boron Trifluoride	1500	5	1500	5
1016	Carbon Monoxide	150	0.4	150	0.8
1017	Chlorine	900	3	1500	5
1023	Coal Gas	300	1	1500	5
1026	Cyanogen	300	1	300	1
1026	Cyanogen, liquefied	300	1	300	1
1026	Cyanogen Gas	300	1	300	1
1040	Ethylene Oxide	150	0.8	600	2
1041	Carbon Dioxide–Ethylene Oxide Mixture, with more than 6% Ethylene Oxide	150	0.8	1200	4
1041	Ethylene Oxide–Carbon Dioxide Mixture, with more than 6% Ethylene Oxide	150	0.8	1200	4
1045	Fluorine, compressed	600	2	600	2
1045	Hydrogen Bromide, anhydrous	1500	5	1500	5
1050	Hydrochloric Acid, anhydrous	600	2	1200	4
1050	Hydrogen Chloride, anhydrous	600	2	1200	4

and interpret the results. If monitoring equipment is not provided, the potential sources of monitoring equipment and personnel to operate the equipment should be identified as part of the pre-emergency planning activities.

Predict the extent of physical, health, and safety hazards within the engulfed area under the current conditions. Predicting health hazards requires an understanding of the various exposure limits, including 1) immediately dangerous to life and health value (IDLH), 2) lethal concentrations (LC_{50}), 3) lethal dose (LD_{50}), 4) permissible exposure limit (PEL), 5) threshold limit value–ceiling (TLV-C), 6) threshold limit value–short-term exposure limit (TLV-STEL), and 7) threshold limit value–time weighted average (TLV-TWA).

Predict the areas of potential harm within the engulfed area. Considerations address likely concentrations, lethal concentrations, length of contact, frequency, and intensity of harm.

Estimate the outcomes within an engulfed area. (See Figure 9-14K.) Considerations include number of exposures in the engulfed area, age and condition of the exposures, anticipated reaction of exposures on contact with material, and weather conditions.

The purpose of analyzing the hazardous material problem is to determine the likely magnitude of the problem in terms of outcomes. While time consuming, this process is an essential part of managing a hazardous material incident. As the incident conditions change, analysis information must be reviewed and updated. When decisions regarding protective actions and control measures are made before completing the analysis process, the risk to the responder is greater.

PLANNING THE RESPONSE

Overview

Based on the magnitude of the problem, appropriate preventive measures and control actions are identified. Control actions include containment, confinement, and extinguishment. The potential impact (benefits and losses) to people, property, equipment, and the environment of each decision is considered.

The result of the planning process is the direction that the response effort will take to influence the sequence of events in the emergency and favorably change the outcome. Response planning is a process for identifying and evaluating response objectives (strategy) and response options (tactics). This process considers the available resources (*e.g.*, personnel, personal protective equipment, and other tools and equipment). The planned response should be consistent with the local emergency response plan and the organization's standard operating procedures.

WORKSHEET FOR LOSS ESTIMATE AND THE AMOUNT THAT COULD BE SAVED

EXPOSURES	ESTIMATED EXPOSED	ESTIMATED TYPE OF HARM	ESTIMATED OUTCOMES	AMOUNT ALREADY LOST	AMOUNT THAT COULD BE SAVED
PEOPLE	#	DEATHS	#		
		INJURIES	#		
PROPERTY	$	DAMAGE	$		
ENVIRONMENT	$	DAMAGE	$		

FIG. 9-14K. Worksheet for loss estimate and determining the amount that could be saved. This worksheet is used for estimating both the outcomes in an emergency and the amount that could be saved.

The planning process begins as part of the pre-emergency response planning efforts prior to the incident and continues on the scene of the incident, again from a safe location. Federal, state, and local agencies, industry, and carrier personnel may be called upon to help.

The process of response planning is based on the following tasks:

1. Determine the response objectives;
2. Determine the available response options that could favorably change the outcomes;
3. Identify the personal protective equipment for the response options;
4. Identify an appropriate decontamination process for each response option;
5. Select the response options within the response community's capabilities that will most favorably change the outcomes; and
6. Develop a plan of action including safety considerations.

Determining the Response Objectives (Strategy)

The first task in planning the response is to determine the response objectives (strategy) based on the estimated outcomes. The response objectives, based on the stage of the incident, are the strategic goals for stopping the event now occurring or keeping future events from occurring. Two basic principles apply to these decisions.

1. You cannot influence events that have already happened or change the outcomes of those events; and
2. The earlier that the event sequence can be interrupted, the more acceptable the loss. (See Figure 9-14L.)

The following steps should be taken when determining response objectives.

Estimate the exposures that could be saved. The level of response and the acceptable risk associated with a response is based on the exposures that can be saved. The number of exposures that could be saved is based on the estimated outcomes minus the exposures already lost. (See Figure 9-14K.)

Determine the response objectives. The response objectives, based on the stage of the incident, are the strategic goals for stopping the event now occurring or keeping future events from occurring. Decisions should focus on changing the actions of the stressors, the containment system, and the hazardous material.

Determining Response Option (Tactics)

Two types of response options are available. Corrective actions are taken to resolve the immediate problem, while preventive actions are taken to prevent the immediate problem from escalating. These actions are intended to keep losses to a minimum.

Determine the potential response options available by response objective. Response options are the tactical activities for stopping the event now occurring or keeping a predicted event from occurring. Response options are associated with the specific events in the emergency. (See Figure 9-14M.) An understanding of the procedures, equipment, and safety precautions for each technique is critical to this decision. Response options include one of the following types: defensive, offensive, and non-intervention. Control options involve either containment or confinement options. The responder must determine which type is appropriate for the incident based on the analysis of the problem.

Estimate how each response option will affect the outcomes. Before a response option is selected, the effect of that response option or combination of response options on the sequence of events and ultimately the outcomes should be reviewed. (See Figure 9-14N.)

Prioritize the response option based on their effect on the outcomes.

Identifying Appropriate Personal Protective Equipment (PPE)

The purpose of identifying appropriate personal protective equipment for each response option is to determine the equipment required to implement the various response options identified. Again, pre-emergency planning cannot be overemphasized in the selection of personal protective equipment.

The following PPE-related definitions are used for the purpose of this chapter.

Personal Protective Equipment is protective clothing and respiratory protection used to shield or isolate a person from the chemical and biological, physical, or thermal hazards that may be encountered at a hazardous material incident. No single combination of personal protective equipment is capable of protecting against all hazards. Personal protective equipment should be used in conjunction with other protective methods, such as medical monitoring and environmental surveillance. For any given situation, personal protective equipment should be selected to

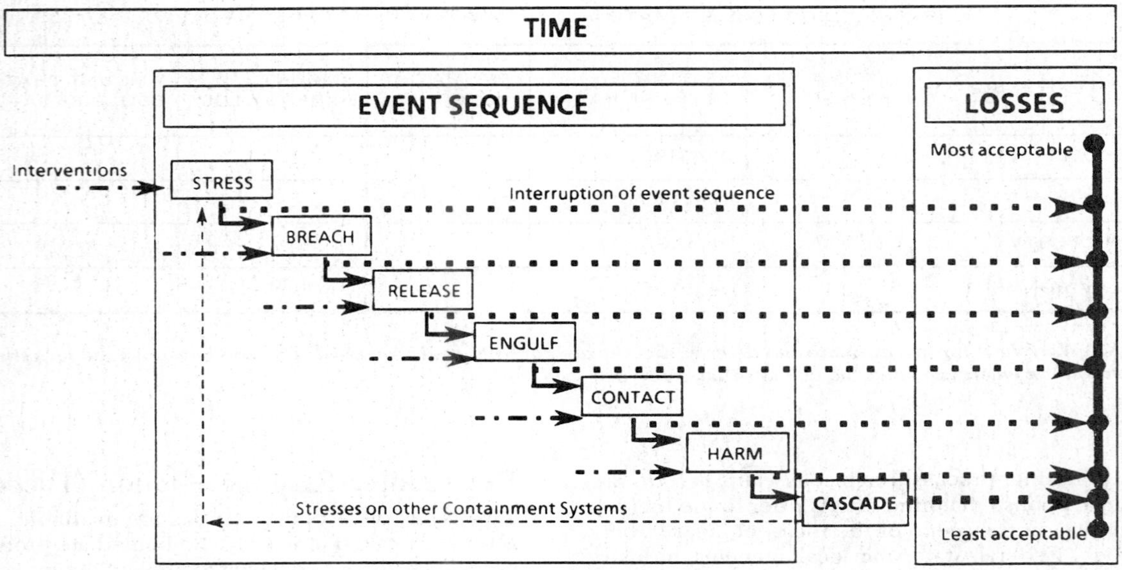

FIG. 9-14L. A chart depicting the relationship of the events sequence and the losses.

provide an adequate level of protection. Both over-protection and under-protection can be hazardous and should be avoided.

Protective Clothing includes those pieces of apparel that are designed to protect the wearer from dermal (skin and eye) contact with the hazardous material. Protective clothing is divided into the following types:

- Structural fire fighting clothing (NFPA 1971);
- Liquid splash protective clothing (NFPA 1992);
- Vapor protective clothing (NFPA 1991); and
- High-temperature clothing.

Respiratory Protection is the equipment designed to protect the wearer from inhaling the hazardous material. Respiratory protection is divided into three types:

- Air-purifying respirators;
- Supplied air respirators (air-line respirators); and
- Positive-pressure self-contained breathing apparatus.

Breakthrough time is the time it takes for the hazardous material to move through the protective material.

Penetration is the movement of a chemical through zippers, stitched seams, or imperfections, such as pinholes, in a protective equipment material.

Permeation is the process by which the chemical dissolves in and moves through a protective clothing material on a molecular level.

Degradation is the physical decomposition of the material due to exposure to chemicals, use, or ambient conditions, such as sunlight.

The identification of appropriate personal protective equipment requires completion of the following steps.

Determine the name, concentration, and hazards of each of the materials involved. This information should have been developed during the process of analyzing the hazardous material problem.

Predict the types of exposure associated with each response option. The types of exposure include:

1. Immersion (*e.g.*, standing in or handling the chemical);
2. Splash (*e.g.*, splash of a liquid from a drum or decontaminating people or equipment coming in direct contact); and
3. Airborne (*e.g.*, exposure to airborne chemicals as a result of sampling).

Determine the level of personal protective equipment required. This step provides a list of the required pieces of personal protective equipment, including suits, gloves, and boots. If the chief threat is through liquid contact, the protective clothing should resist chemical degradation and penetration. For a threat from vapor contact, the protective clothing may have to be airtight and impermeable. The minimum requirement for respiratory protection, set by OSHA in 29 CFR 1910.120, for emergency conditions at hazardous material incidents (until concentrations have been determined) is positive-pressure self-contained breathing apparatus.

The U.S. Environmental Protection Agency identifies four levels of protection.

Level A is the highest level of protection and should be worn when respiratory, skin, eye, and mucous membrane protection is needed.

Level B is the second highest level of protection and should be worn when a lessor level of skin and eye protection is needed. It is the minimum level recommended for initial site entries until the hazards have been determined by monitoring, sampling, or other reliable methods of analysis.

Level C is the third highest level of protection and may be worn only when the type of airborne substance is known, concentration measured, criteria for using air purifying respirators met, and skin and eye exposure is unlikely. Periodic monitoring of the air must be performed while working in level C.

Response Objective Analysis Form	Containment System ID.
	Material

Event Sequence

Stress	Breach	Release	Engulf	Contact	Harm

Response Objectives

Change Applied Stresses	Change Breach Size	Change Quantity Released	Change Size of Danger Zone	Change Exposures Contacted	Change Severity of Harm

Sample Response Options

Move stressor Move stressed system Shield stressed system	Chill contents Limit Stress levels Activate venting devices Mechanical Repair	Change container position Minimize pressure differential Cap off breach Remove contents	Barriers Dikes and Dams Adsorbents Absorbents Diluents Reactants Overpack	Provide Sheltering Begin evacuation Personal Protective Equipment	Rinse off contaminant Increase distance from source Provide shielding Provide Prompt medical attention

(Adapted from Ludwig Benner's Hazardous Materials Emergencies, 1978.)

FIG. 9-14M. Response Objective Analysis Worksheet. This worksheet is used for identifying response options in a hazardous material incident by response objective.[5]

Level D is the lowest level of protection and is primarily a work uniform. It should not be worn on any site where respiratory or skin hazards exist.

Responders must understand the advantages, limitations, and use of each of the levels of protection at hazardous material incidents. If the appropriate level of protection is not available, arrange to obtain it from other resources.

Identify chemically compatible materials for the chemicals involved. Look for breakthrough times of at least two hours. A breakthrough time of two hours represents the normal physical limits of a responder's capacity for effective work in protective equipment. Resources for identifying chemically compatible materials include *Guidelines for the Selection of Chemical Protective Clothing*[6] or the *Quick*

WORKSHEET FOR ESTIMATING THE EFFECT OF EACH RESPONSE OPTION

EXPOSURES/HARM	AMOUNT THAT COULD BE SAVED	AMOUNT THAT COULD BE SAVED WITH OPTION 1	AMOUNT THAT COULD BE SAVED WITH OPTION 2	AMOUNT THAT COULD BE SAVED WITH OPTION 3	AMOUNT THAT COULD BE SAVED WITH OPTION 4	AMOUNT THAT COULD BE SAVED WITH OPTION 5	AMOUNT THAT COULD BE SAVED WITH OPTION 6
PEOPLE DEATHS	#	#	#	#	#	#	#
PEOPLE INJURIES	#	#	#	#	#	#	#
PROPERTY DAMAGE	$	$	$	$	$	$	$
ENVIRON. DAMAGE	$	$	$	$	$	$	$

FIG. 9-14N. Worksheet for estimating the effect of each response option. This worksheet is used for estimating the effect of each response option on the outcomes of the incident.

Selection Guide to Chemical Protective Clothing,[7] various emergency response guides, and chemical compatability charts provided by the manufacturers of chemical protective clothing.

Figure 9-14O provides a worksheet for recording chemically compatible materials identified.

Match the material requirements with personal protective equipment provided or available. Using chemical-compatibility charts provided with the protective equipment available, identify the available equipment that provides the required protection. Multiple materials can be layered to provide the appropriate level of protection.

Identify the appropriate personal protective equipment needed for each response option. Keep in mind the requirement for the buddy system and backup personnel. Considerations include availability of sufficient equipment in the appropriate sizes and the potential of multiple layers providing required protection. The use of personal protective equipment itself can create significant responder hazards, such as heat stress, physical and psychological stress, as well as impaired vision, mobility, and communication.

Identifying Appropriate Decontamination Procedures

With the potential that personnel, personal protective equipment, apparatus, and tools and equipment may become contaminated in a hazardous material incident, a decontamination (contamination reduction) process is established.

CHEMICALLY COMPATIBLE MATERIAL IDENTIFICATION WORKSHEET

CHEMICAL	CHEMICAL CONCENTRATION	CHEMICALLY COMPATIBLE CLOTHING MATERIAL REQUIRED		
		>8 HOURS	>2 HOURS	<1/2 HOUR

FIG. 9-14O. Chemically compatible materials identification worksheet. This worksheet is for recording the chemically compatible protective clothing materials by hazardous material.

Decontamination (contamination reduction) is the act of removing or neutralizing contaminants from equipment or personnel to preclude the occurrence of foreseeable adverse health effects outside the engulfed area. Possible decontamination options include absorption, adsorption, chemical degradation, dilution, neutralization, or solidification.

Decontamination procedures should be tailored to the specific hazards of the incident. They may vary in complexity and number of steps, depending on the level of hazard and the level of exposure to the hazard. The steps to be taken to select an appropriate decontamination (contamination reduction) process include the following.

Identify what needs to be decontaminated ,including injured persons, response personnel, personal protective equipment, other equipment, and emergency-care facilities.

Determine the contaminant and the type and amount of contamination. Considerations include whether the material is organic or inorganic, in the solid, liquid, or gas form, a dermal or inhalation hazard, a local or systemic material, and whether the contaminant is life threatening, injurious, or irritating. Another consideration is whether physical trauma is involved.

Seek appropriate advice. Immediate decontamination guidelines are found in the DOT *Emergency Response Guidebook*[8] (under first aid on the numbered guide pages), the NIOSH *Pocket Guide to Chemical Hazards*,[9] or local planning documents. Follow-up guidance can be obtained from local poison control centers, the shipper or manufacturer through CHEMTREC, or the Agency for Toxic Substances and Disease Registry.

Identify methods for isolating and securing and then disposing of clothing and equipment that cannot be decontaminated.

The local emergency response plan or the organization's standard operating procedures provide guidelines on decontamination (contamination reduction) procedures. Other resources should be identified in pre-emergency planning activities. Follow-up resources include the Agency for Toxic Substances and Disease Registry, poison control centers, and the shipper or manufacturer through CHEMTREC.

Selecting Response Options

The selection of response options to change the outcomes favorably must be consistent with the local emergency response plan and the organization's standard operating procedures and also within the capability of available personnel, personal protective equipment, and control equipment. The steps to be taken in selecting the response options include the following.

Determine the required resources to implement each response option. Required resources include the time to implement the option, availability of sufficient personnel with the appropriate training, and appropriate personal protective equipment, materials for decontamination (contamination reduction) activities, and control equipment.

Inventory the resources available and identify those resources available.

Determine how to obtain the needed resources. A review of the planning documents should provide these answers.

Select the response option(s) consistent with the available resources. Evaluate the potential reaction of the hazardous material to the control action and the ability to contain the side effects of the response option. Surrounding conditions, including topography and weather conditions, and response times can also affect the decision to select the response options.

Developing a Plan of Action

After selecting the response option for a hazardous material incident, a plan of action including safety and health considerations should be developed. This plan of action describes the response objectives and options and the personnel and equipment required to accomplish the objectives. The plan provides a permanent record of the decisions made at the incident. An organization's standard operating procedures provide the basis of this plan of action. Input from all segments of the response community is considered in developing the plan. Based on the specific incident conditions, the standard operating procedures are modified without having to write an entire plan for each incident.

A plan of action also outlines the safety and health procedures to protect responders and the public from the potential hazards at an incident. These procedures should address incident management, communications protocol (both internal and external), control zones for incident security, personal protective equipment use, decontamination procedures, and documentation. They also include designation of a safety sector and a safety officer, emergency medical care procedures, environmental monitoring, emergency procedures, and personnel monitoring.

Components for a typical plan of action include the following:

1. Site description;
2. Entry objectives;
3. On-scene organization and coordination;
4. On-scene control;
5. Hazard evaluation;
6. Personal protective equipment;
7. On-scene work assignments;
8. Communication procedures;
9. Decontamination procedures;
10. On-scene safety and health considerations including designation of the safety officer, emergency medical care procedures, environmental monitoring, emergency procedures, and personnel monitoring.

Response personnel at a hazardous material incident must recognize and understand the potential hazards associated with the incident. They must also be familiar with the procedures contained in the plan of action. Therefore, prior to working on-scene, all personnel must be provided a safety briefing. The safety briefing will describe the assigned tasks and their potential hazards, coordinate activities, identify methods and precautions to prevent injuries, and plan for emergencies. The plan of action can serve as a guide to this safety briefing.

The result of planning a response to a hazardous material incident is a plan of action consistent with the local emergency response plan and the organization's standard operating procedures and within the capability of the resources available. Development of a written plan ensures that all safety aspects of the response are thoroughly examined. Plans should be modified as necessitated by changing conditions on the scene.

IMPLEMENTING THE PLANNED RESPONSE

Overview

Once the plan of action is determined, response personnel must implement the response options in that plan. The following tasks are associated with implementing the planned response to a hazardous material incident:

1. Implement the incident management system (IMS);
2. Implement the selected protective actions;
3. Establish and enforce scene-control procedures; and
4. Implement planned control actions.

Initiating the Incident Management System.

The incident management system (IMS) is an organized approach to control and manage operations effectively at an emergency through a system of roles, responsibilities, and standard operating procedures. The incident management system should be developed as part of pre-emergency planning efforts, including the local emergency-response plan and an organization's standard operating procedures.

One individual is in charge of managing the incident. This individual may delegate responsibility for performing various tasks to others on the scene. All communications are routed through the command post. Delegation of tasks may be by location or by function. Some of the functions include: medical services, evacuation, water supply, resources, media relations, safety, and site control. The incident management system reduces confusion, improves safety, organizes and coordinates actions, and facilitates effective management of the incident.

The National Inter-Agency Incident Management System provides an example of the elements of an incident management system used to coordinate response activities:

1. Common terminology;
2. Modular organizations;
3. Integrated communications;
4. Unified command structure;
5. Consolidated action plans;
6. Manageable span of control;
7. Predesignated incident facilities; and
8. Comprehensive resource management.

Responders should understand the roles and responsibilities of the various positions in the local incident management system as defined in the local emergency response plan or the organization's standard operating procedures.

The incident management system includes the procedures for notification and use of other than local resources (including private, state, and federal government personnel). The incident commander should be familiar with and comply with the requirements of the following plans:

1. Organization's emergency response plan;
2. Organization's standard operating procedures;
3. Local emergency response plan;
4. State emergency response plan;
5. Regional emergency response plan, including the resources available from the regional response team; and
6. Federal emergency response plans.

Response personnel should be aware of the primary local, state, regional, and federal government agencies and understand the scope of their regulatory authority (including the regulations) pertaining to the production, transportation, storage, and use of hazardous materials and the disposal of hazardous wastes. They should also be aware of private-sector resources offering assistance during a hazardous material incident and identify their role and the type of assistance or resources available.

The incident management system should provide a focal point for information transfer to the media and local elected officials. A public-information officer should be designated to provide appropriate information to the media and local, state, and federal officials.

Implementing Selected Protective Actions

Protective measures are those taken to preserve the health and safety of emergency responders and the public during an incident involving the release of hazardous materials. Protective actions include the following.

Isolate the hazard area and deny entry. Keep all persons away from the area if they are not directly involved in emergency response operations. Unprotected emergency responders should not be allowed within the isolation area. Planning documents should include techniques to isolate the hazard area and deny entry to unauthorized persons at hazardous material incidents.

Evacuate persons in the threatened area. Evacuation is defined as a process to "move all people from the threatened area to a safer place."[8] To perform an evacuation, there must be enough time for people to be warned, to get ready, and to leave the area. Even after people are evacuated, they should not be allowed to congregate on the perimeter of the control zones. Evacuees should be sent upwind to a definite place, by a specific route, far enough away so that they will not have to be moved again if the conditions change.

Protect persons who cannot be evacuated in-place. In-place protection is defined as a "means to direct people to quickly go inside a building and remain inside until the danger passes."[8] Certain protective actions must be taken inside the building. In-place protection is used when evacuating the public would cause greater risk than directing them to stay where they are or when an evacuation cannot be performed.

Establishing and Enforcing Scene Control Procedures

Scene-control procedures must be implemented quickly. Control zones (see Figure 9-14P), decontamination (contamination reduction) activities, and communication must be established and maintained throughout the incident. Personnel should move between control zones through access control points.

Scene control is established through the use of control zones based upon safety and the degree of hazard. The hot zone is the area surrounding a hazardous material incident. It extends far enough to prevent adverse effects from hazardous material releases to personnel outside the zone. The warm zone is the area where personnel and equipment decontamination (contamination reduction) takes place. The cold zone is the area containing the command post and other support functions. Access to various zones is determined by need and level of personal protection provided as specified in the plan of action.

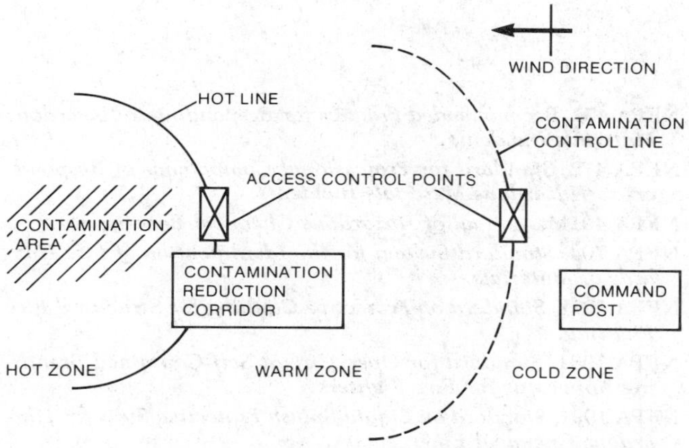

FIG. 9-14P. Diagram of control zones.

Extreme caution is necessary when providing emergency medical care to victims of hazardous material incidents.

Performing Control Functions

Responders are expected to perform control functions identified in the plan of action. They will have to select the tools, equipment, and materials for the tasks assigned. They should also understand the precautions for controlling releases from the containment systems involved.

In conjunction with their ability to use personal protective equipment, response personnel should be able to identify the symptoms of heat and cold stress. Response personnel should be aware of the physical and psychological stresses that can affect users of personal protective equipment. Personnel should be able to identify the signs and symptoms of exposure to any hazardous material involved. Response personnel should be able to record the use, repair, and testing of chemical protective clothing.

EVALUATING PROGRESS AND ADJUSTING ACCORDINGLY

The fourth and final duty in responding to hazardous material incidents is to evaluate the progress of the planned response—whether it stabilizes, intensifies, or otherwise changes. This duty evaluates the effectiveness of the following:

1. Personnel being used;
2. Personal protective equipment;
3. Established control zones;
4. Decontamination process; and
5. Selected action options.

A comparison of the actual behavior to that predicted indicates the effectiveness of the operations. Negative feedback initiates a re-evaluation of the situation, including another analysis of the problem, response objectives and options, and a modified plan of action. Positive feedback indicates successful operations; however, modification of the plan may still be necessary.

Termination

Termination of a hazardous material incident is that portion of incident management in which personnel are involved in documenting safety procedures, site operations, hazards faced, and lessons from the incident. Termination is divided into three phases: debriefing the responders, post-incident analysis, and critiquing the incident.[10]

Debriefing the responders is the process of reviewing a hazardous material incident focusing on the following factors:

1. Informing responders of any potential exposure to hazardous materials and the signs and symptoms associated with that exposure;
2. Identifying equipment damage and unsafe conditions;
3. Assigning information-gathering responsibilities for a critique; and
4. Summarizing the activities performed.

Post-incident Analysis is the reconstruction of the incident to establish a clear picture of the events that took place during the incident. The post-incident analysis focuses on four key topics: command and control, tactical operations, resources, and support services.

Critiquing the incident—emphasizing successful and unsuccessful operations—should be conducted with all response community members. The procedures for conducting a critique of a hazardous material incident should be in the local emergency response plan or the organization's standard operating procedures including written reports to management that suggest ways to improve future operations.

At the termination of the emergency phase, authority may be transferred to those responsible for the recovery activity in the incident. The local emergency response plan or the organization's standard operating procedures outline the steps for terminating the emergency phase of the incident.

Providing Reports and Subsequent Documentation

Responders to hazardous material incidents must comply with the reporting requirements of federal, state, and local agencies. All reports and other incident documents should be consistent with the local, state, and federal requirements.

Training records, exposure records, incident reports, and critique reports should become part of the file for the incident. An activity log and detailed exposure records should be maintained on each hazardous material incident. Typically, requirements for filing documents and maintaining records are found in the local emergency response plan and the organization's standard operating procedures.

SUMMARY

As with any emergency, favorably changing the outcomes requires a logical sequential process involving four duties: analysis, planning, implementation, and evaluation. Each of these duties is made up of tasks that need to be accomplished to complete that duty. Each task requires that certain steps be performed to complete the task. The topics in this chapter describe the duties, tasks, and steps associated with managing the response to hazardous material incidents.

BIBLIOGRAPHY

References

1. Benner, Ludwig, Jr., "D.E.C.I.D.E. In Hazardous Materials Emergencies," *Fire Journal*, Vol. 69, No. 4, p. 13, July 1975.
2. Department of Transportation, Research and Special Programs Administration, "Performance-Oriented Packaging Standards; Changes to Classification, Hazard Communication, Packaging and Handling Requirements Based on UN Standards and Agency Initiative; Final Rule," *Federal Register*, Vol. 55, No. 246, pp. 52402-52729, December 21, 1990.
3. *Acute Hazardous Events*, Data Base, Industrial Economics Inc., Cambridge, MA 02140, Dec. 1985.
4. Ericksen, Nick A., Keffer, William J., and Wright, Charles J., *Introduction to Hazardous Materials Incident Response*, U.S. Environmental Protection Agency and Union Pacific Railroad, Omaha, NE, 1989.
5. Benner, Ludwig, Jr., *Hazardous Materials Emergencies*, 2nd Edition, Lufred Industries, Inc., Oakton, VA, 1978.
6. *Guidelines for the Selection of Chemical Protective Clothing*, Prepared by A. D. Little, Inc., Cambridge, MA 02140, 1987.
7. Forsberg, Krister, and Mansdorf, S. Z., *Quick Selection Guide to Chemical Protective Clothing*, Van Nostrand Reinhold, New York, 1989.
8. *Emergency Response Guidebook*, U.S. Department of Transportation, Research and Special Programs Administration, Washington, DC, 1990.
9. NIOSH, *Pocket Guide to Chemical Hazards*, U.S. Department of Health and Human Services, Government Printing Office, Washington, DC, 1990.
10. Noll, Gregory G., Hildebrand, Michael S., and Yvorra, James G., "Terminating the Incident," *Hazardous Materials: Managing the Incident*, Peake Productions Inc., Annapolis, MD, pp. 183-188, 1988.
11. NFPA, *Fire Protection Guide on Hazardous Materials*, National Fire Protection Association, 1991
12. Chemical Manufacturers Association and Association of American Railroads *Technical Bulletin on Packaging for Hazardous and Non-hazardous Materials*, Chemical Manufacturers Association, Washington, DC, 1989.

NFPA Codes, Standards, Recommended Practices and Manual. (See the latest NFPA Publications *Catalog* for availability of current editions of the following documents.)

NFPA 325M, *Properties of Flammable Liquids, Gases, Solids*.

NFPA 49, *Hazardous Chemicals Data*.

NFPA 471, *Recommended Practice for Responding to Hazardous Materials Incidents*.

NFPA 472, *Standard for Professional Competence of Responders to Hazardous Materials Incidents*.

NFPA 491M, *Manual of Hazardous Chemical Reactions*.

NFPA 704, *Standard System for the Identification of Fire Hazards of Materials*.

NFPA 1971, *Standard on Protective Clothing for Structural Fire Fighting*.

NFPA 1981, *Standard for Open Circuit Self-Contained Breathing Apparatus for Fire Fighters*.

NFPA 1991, *Standard on Liquid Splash Protective Suits for Hazardous Chemical Emergencies*.

NFPA 1992, *Standard on Vapor Protective Suits for Hazardous Chemical Emergencies*.

NFPA 1993, *Standard on Support Function Protective Garments for Hazardous Chemical Emergencies*.

U.S. Government Publications. U.S. Government Printing Office, Superintendent of Documents, Washington, DC 20402

Handbook of Chemical Hazard Analysis Procedures (FEMA, DOT, EPA).

Hazardous Materials Emergency Planning Guide (NRT-1), National Response Team, 1987.

Occupational Safety and Health Standards, Title 29, Code of Federal Regulations, Part 1910.120. "Hazardous Waste Operations and Emergency Response Final Rule," 1989.

Occupational Safety and Health Guidance Manual for Hazardous Waste Site Activities, NIOSH/OSHA/USCG/EPA, U.S. Department of Health and Human Services, NIOSH, 1985.

Standard Operating Safety Guides, Environmental Response Branch, Office of Emergency and Remedial Response, U.S. Environmental Protection Agency, 1988.

Technical Guidance for Hazard Analysis (EPA, FEMA, DOT).

Title 29 CFR Part 1910.1200 (OSHA)—Hazard Communications Standard.

Title 40 CFR Part 261.33 (EPA).

Title 40 CFR Part 302 (EPA).

Title 40 CFR Part 355 (EPA).

Title 49 CFR Parts 170-179 (DOT).

OBTAINING TECHNICAL ASSISTANCE IN HAZARDOUS MATERIALS EMERGENCIES

Revised by Alan S. Cummings

Responding to a hazardous materials incident often requires specialized training, equipment, and materials, and more complex coordination with other agencies than other emergency situations. Local emergency service personnel responding to the scene of a hazardous materials incident are initially responsible for determining what materials are involved and the hazards posed by any resulting fire or spill, for evacuating the surrounding areas, for rescuing trapped persons, for implementing fire- and spill-control measures, and for preventing any further damage to the environment.

When dealing with hazardous materials, technical assistance of one form or another will undoubtedly be required. In order to carry out their responsibilities effectively, local emergency services should first identify and use the equipment, materials, and expertise already available from government agencies and private concerns, as well as emergency guidebooks and other printed matter.

Federal, state, and local governments, as well as private industry, already have many programs in operation for responding to hazardous materials incidents. These programs may be able to fill the gaps in the local emergency response effort. Knowing the capabilities of other agencies and industry also prevents wasteful duplication. This information is best gathered before any potential incident.

Additional information on dealing with hazardous materials emergencies is contained in the other chapters of this section.

FEDERAL GOVERNMENT AGENCIES

The federal government has organized departments and agencies to provide assistance during hazardous materials incidents when state and local resources are exhausted or when technical assistance is needed that is not available locally. Available assistance ranges from determining reasonable public-exposure limits to on-site response activities. Any department or agency can be contacted directly for technical assistance, but all federal resources are part of an organized network that requires a single notification to begin the federal-assistance process during a serious hazardous materials incident.

The National Oil and Hazardous Substance Pollution Contingency Plan (NCP) was developed to provide the organizational structure and procedures for preparing for and responding to discharges of oil and releases of hazardous substances, pollutants, and contaminants (40 CFR 300). The NCP required the development of the National Response Team (NRT) and Regional Response Teams (RRT). The NRT is composed of federal departments and agencies that have been assigned responsibilities during oil or hazardous substances incidents. RRTs are composed of regional personnel from NRT departments and agencies. These teams are "co-chaired" at the national and regional levels by the United States Coast Guard and the U.S. Environmental Protection Agency.

The following is a list of NRT and RRT departments and agencies available for technical assistance during hazardous materials emergencies and plan development. (See Fig. 9-15A.)

U.S. Coast Guard (USCG): The USCG is an agency within the Department of Transportation, except in time of war, when it operates as an agency in the United States Navy. The USCG provides the NRT vice chair, co-chairs for RRTs, and designated on-scene coordinators (OSC) for the coastal zone. The USCG maintains continually manned facilities that can be used for command, control, and surveillance of oil discharges and hazardous substance releases in the coastal zone. (See Fig. 9-15B.)

U.S. Environmental Protection Agency (EPA): The EPA chairs the NRT, co-chairs the RRTs, provides designated OSCs for the inland zone, and provides Remedial Project Managers (RPM) for remedial actions. EPA provides expertise on the environmental effects of oil discharges or releases of hazardous substances, pollutants, or contaminants, as well as environmental pollution control techniques. EPA also provides legal expertise on the interpretation of CERCLA (superfund) and other environmental statutes. (See Fig. 9-15C.)

Mr. Cummings is an environmental specialist on the staff of Ecology and Environment Inc., and past Fire Division Commander of the Gladstone, MO, Public Safety Department.

TABLE 9-15A. ***Summary of Pertinent Federal Laws and Terminology***

CAA:	Clean Air Act (1955, 1977); a federal law which mandates and enforces toxic emissions standards for stationary sources and motor vehicles.
CERCLA:	Comprehensive Environmental Responsibility, Compensation and Liability Act (1976), sometimes referred to as **Superfund**; a federal law which authorizes the identification and remediation of abandoned hazardous waste sites.
CWA:	Clean Water Act (1972); a federal law which regulates the discharge of pollutants into surface waters.
EPA:	Environmental Protection Agency, established under the Reorganizational Plan 3 of 1970 as an independent federal agency to assure the protection of the environment by abating and controlling pollution. It coordinates all governmental action, conducts research, monitors and sets and enforces environmental standards.
FEMA:	Federal Emergency Management Agency; a federal agency which is accountable for all federal emergency preparedness, mitigation and response activities for all natural, man-made, or nuclear emergencies; also responsible for administering certain training funds under **SARA.**
FIFRA:	Federal Insecticide, Fungicide and Rodenticide Act (1972, 1988); a federal law which mandates toxicity testing and registration of pesticides, and establishes tolerance levels for residues of these agents in food.
HCS:	Hazard Communication Standard; is an **OSHA** standard (29 CFR 1910.1200) which requires employers to communicate the risks of hazardous materials to workers in regulated facilities.
HSWA:	Hazardous and Solid Waste Amendments (1984); are amendments to **RCRA** which establish a timetable for **RCRA** land bans and more stringent requirements for underground storge tanks (USTs).
MWTA:	Medical Waste Tracking Act (1988); an amendment to **RCRA** that establishes a demonstration tracking system for medical wastes in ten states.
OSHA:	Occupational Safety and Health Act (1970); a federal law which called for the establishment of the Occupational Safety and Health Administration, which oversees and regulates workplace health and safety.
PEL:	Permissible Exposure Limits; these are specific exposure limits established by **OSHA** for 600 industrial chemicals.
RCRA:	Resource Conservation and Recovery Act (1976); enacted as an amendment to the Solid Waste Disposal Act, **RCRA** protects human health and the environment and encourages the conservation of valuable material and energy sources. It provides assistance to state and local governments for prohibiting open dumping, regulating the management of hazardous wastes, and encouraging recycling, reuse, and treatment of hazardous wastes. **RCRA** provides for "cradle-to-grave" tracking of hazardous wastes, from generator to transporter to treatment, storage, or disposal.
SARA:	Superfund Amendments and Reauthorization Act (1986); a federal law which reauthorizes and expands the jurisdiction of **CERCLA** and designates requirements mandated in Title III of **SARA** for public disclosure of chemical information and the development of emergency response plans.
TSCA:	Toxic Substances Control Act (1976); a federal law which authorizes EPA to gather information on new and existing chemical risks to human health and the environment.
UST:	Underground Storage Tanks; regulated by **RCRA,** these are tanks with 10 or more percent of their volume underground, used to store **CERCLA**-regulated hazardous chemicals or petroleum products.

Federal Emergency Management Agency (FEMA): FEMA provides guidance, policy and program advice, and technical assistance in hazardous materials and radiological emergency-preparedness activities. In a response, FEMA provides advice and assistance to the lead agency on coordinating relocation assistance and mitigation efforts with other federal agencies, state and local governments, and the private sector.

U.S. Department of Defense (DOD): DOD is responsible for taking all action necessary with respect to releases on or from any facility or vessel under the jurisdiction of DOD. Consistent with its operational requirements and upon request of the OSC, DOD may also provide locally deployed U.S. Navy oil-spill equipment and assist other federal agencies on request. Two branches of DOD have particular relevant expertise: the United States Army Corps of Engineers and the United States Navy.

U.S. Department of Energy (DOE): DOE, under the Federal Radiological Emergency Response Plan, provides advice and assistance to OSCs for emergency actions essential for controlling immediate radiological hazards. Assistance is available through the appropriate DOE Radiological Assistance Coordinating Office.

U.S. Department of Agriculture (USDA): USDA can measure, evaluate, and monitor, either on the ground or from aircraft, situations in which hazardous substances and other man-made or natural disasters have had an impact on nat

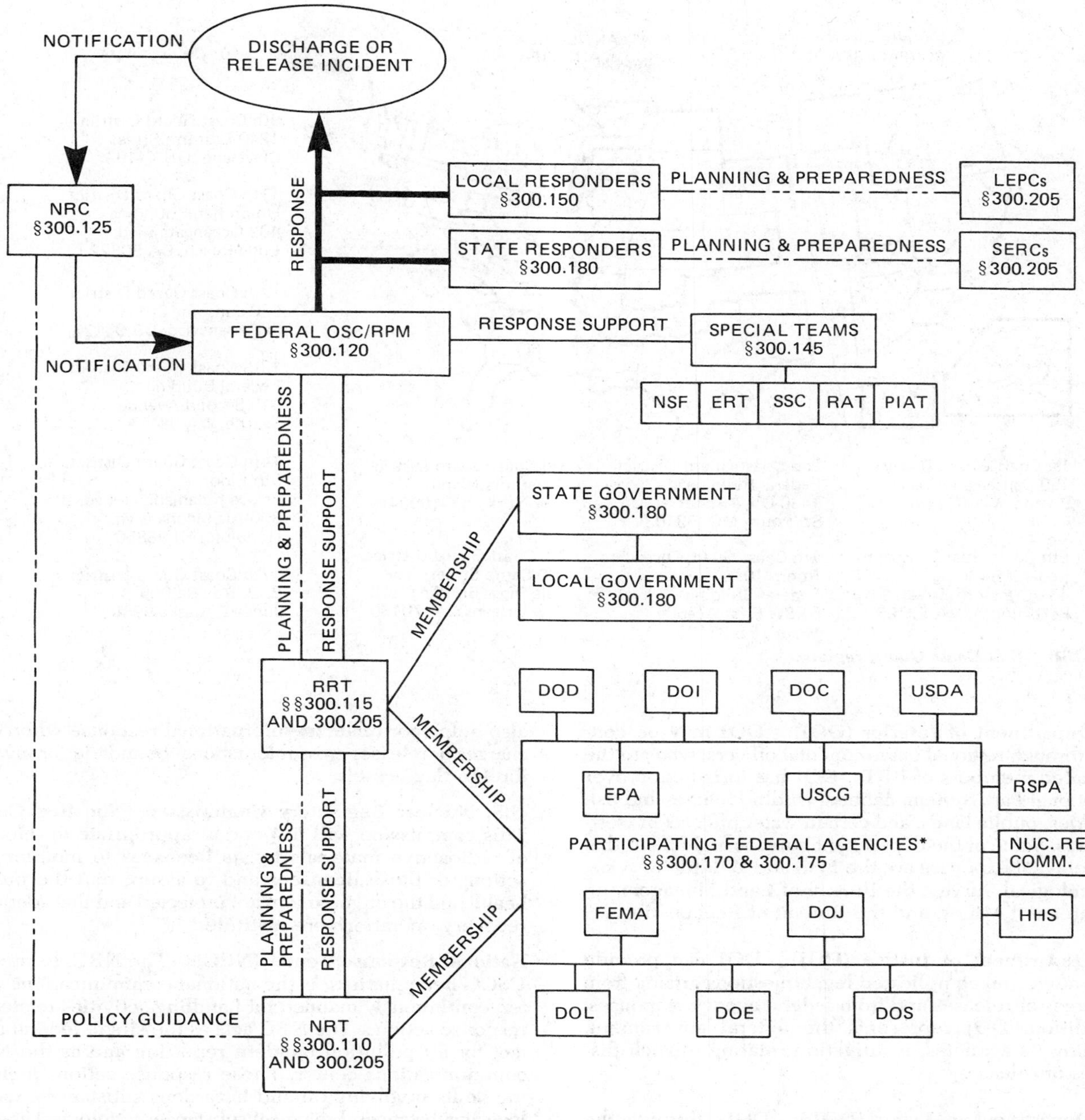

FIG. 9-15A National Response System Concepts. The same federal agencies participate on both the national Response Team (NRT) and the Regional Response Team (RRT). Federal Agencies on the RRT are represented by regional staff.

ural resources, including soil, water, wildlife, and vegetation. The USDA may be contacted through Forest Service emergency staff officers who are the designated members of the RRT. Agencies within USDA that have relevant capabilities and expertise are the Forest Service (FS), the Agriculture Research Service (ARS), the Soil Conservation Service (SCS), the Animal and Plant Health Inspection Service (APHIS), and the Food Safety and Inspection Service (FSIS).

U.S. Department of Commerce (DOC): DOC, through the National Oceanic and Atmospheric Administration (NOAA), provides scientific support for response and contingency planning in coastal and marine areas. This includes predictions of movement and dispersion of oil and hazardous substances through trajectory modeling. NOAA also provides information on actual and predicted meteorological, hydrological, ice, and oceanographic conditions for marine, coastal, and inland waters.

U.S. Department of Health and Human Services (HHS): HHS is responsible for providing assistance on matters related to the assessment of health hazards at a response and to the protection of both response workers and the public's health. The HHS agencies with relevant responsibilities, capabilities, and expertise are the Agency for Toxic Substances and Disease Registry (ATSDR) and the National Institute for Environmental Health Sciences (NIEHS).

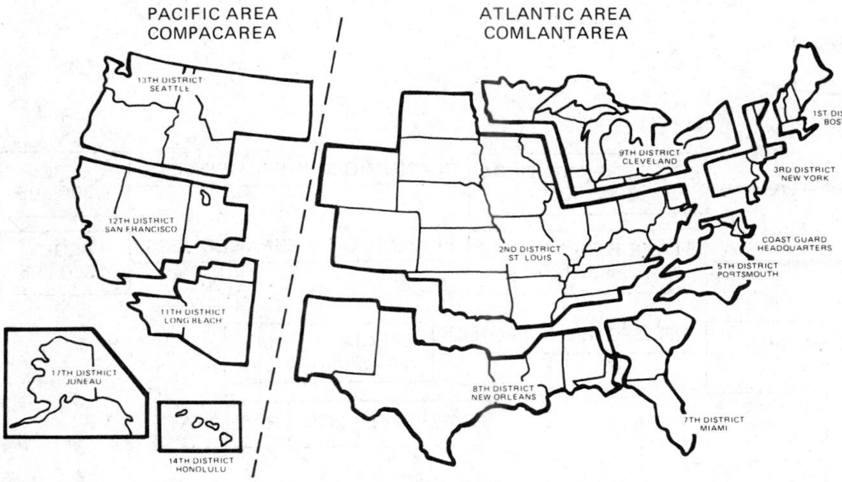

1st Coast Guard District
150 Causeway Street
Boston, MA 02114

2nd Coast Guard District
Federal Building
1430 Olive Street
St. Louis, MO 63103

3rd Coast Guard District
Governors Island
New York, NY 10004

5th Coast Guard District
Federal Building
431 Crawford Street
Portsmouth, VA 23705

7th Coast Guard District
Room 1010
Federal Building
51 SW First Avenue
Miami, FL 33130

8th Coast Guard District
500 Camp Street
Hale Biggs Building
New Orleans, LA 70130

9th Coast Guard District
1240 East 9th Street
Cleveland, OH 44199

11th Coast Guard District
Union Bank Building
402 Oceangate Blvd.
Long Beach, CA 90822

12th Coast Guard District
630 Sansome Street
San Francisco, CA 94126

13th Coast Guard District
Federal Building
915 Second Avenue
Seattle, WA 98174

14th Coast Guard District
9th Floor
Prince Kalanianaole Fed. Bld.
300 Ala Moana Blvd.
Honolulu, HI 96850

17th Coast Guard District
P. O. Box 3-5000
Juneau, Alaska 99802

FIG. 9-15B. U.S. Coast Guard regions.

U.S. Department of Interior (DOI): DOI may be contacted through regional environmental officers, who are the designated members of RRTs. DOI has jurisdiction over the National Park System, national wildlife refuges and fish hatcheries, public lands, and certain water projects in western states. Some of the department bureaus and offices that have relevant expertise are the Fish and Wildlife Service, the Geological Survey, the Bureau of Land Management, the Bureau of Mines, and the Bureau of Reclamation.

U.S. Department of Justice (DOJ): DOJ can provide expert advice on complicated legal questions arising from discharges or releases and from federal agency responses. In addition, DOJ represents the federal government, including its agencies, in litigation relating to such discharges or releases.

U.S. Department of Labor (DOL): DOL, through the Occupational Safety and Health Administration (OSHA), has the authority to conduct safety and health inspections of hazardous waste sites to ensure that employees are being protected and to determine if the site is in compliance with agency standards. On request, OSHA will provide advice and assistance to the OSC regarding hazards to persons engaged in response activities.

U.S. Department of Transportation (DOT): DOT provides response expertise pertaining to the transportation of oil or hazardous substances by all modes of transport. Through the Research and Special Programs Administration, DOT offers expertise in the requirements for packaging, handling, and transporting regulated hazardous materials.

U.S. Department of State (DOS): DOS will lead in the development of international joint-contingency plans. It will also help coordinate an international response when discharges or releases cross international boundaries or involve foreign-flag vessels.

U.S. Nuclear Regulatory Commission (Nuc Reg Com): This commission will respond as appropriate to releases of radioactive materials by its licensees to monitor the actions of those licensees and to assure that the public health and the environment are protected and that adequate recovery operations are instituted.

National Response Center (NRC): The NRC, located at USCG headquarters, is the national communications center, continuously manned for handling activities related to response actions. The NRC acts as the single federal contact for all pollution incident reporting and as the NRT communications center. These response actions include incidents involving oil and hazardous substances, radiological substances, biological substances, etiological agents, surety materials, munitions, and fuels.

The toll-free number for reporting an incident or requesting federal assistance during an incident is (800) 424-8802.

A typical federal response to a hazardous materials incident begins when the NRC receives a report of the incident from the spiller, state or local responders, or witnesses. NRC personnel contact the appropriate regional lead agency—the USCG or EPA—which dispatches a designated OSC. The OSC responds to the incident and evaluates the need for further assistance. The OSC determines the type of technical assistance that is needed and activates the appropriate RRT resources. Responders can also initiate this activity by requesting technical assistance through regional EPA or USCG spill-report lines. In addition to NRT and RRT resources, the OSC also can mobilize the following specialized response teams.

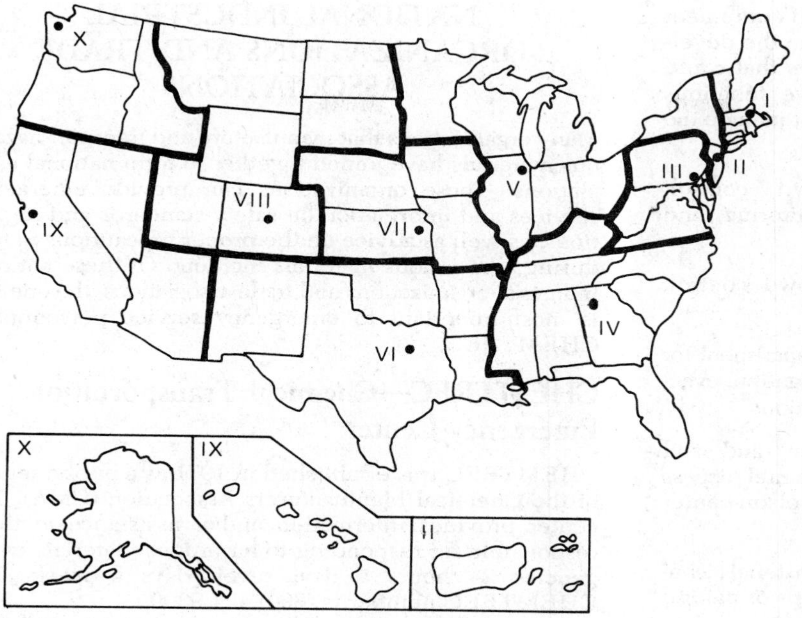

Region I
Chief, Oil & Hazardous Materials Section
Surveillance and Analysis Division
60 Westview Street
Lexington, MA 02173

Region II
Chief, Emergency Response and Hazardous Materials Inspection Branch
Environmental Services Division
Edison, NJ 08837

Region III
Chief, Environmental Emergency Branch
Curtis Building 3ES30
6th and Walnut Streets
Philadelphia, PA 19106

Region IV
Chief, Emergency Remedial & Response Branch
345 Courtland Street, NE
Atlanta, GA 30365

Region V
Chief, Spill Response Section
Environmental Services Division, 5SEES
536 South Clark Street
Chicago, IL 60605

Region VI
Chief, Emergency Response Branch, 6ESE
First International Building
1201 Elm Street
Dallas, TX 75270

Region VII
Chief, Emergency Planning & Response Branch
Environmental Services Division
25 Funston Road
Kansas City, KS 66115

Region VIII
Chief, Emergency Response Branch
Environmental Services Division
1860 Lincoln Street
Denver, CO 80295

Region IX
Chief, Emergency Response Section, T-3-3
Compliance & Response Branch
Toxic & Waste Management Division
215 Fremont Street
San Francisco, CA 94105

Region X
Chief, Environmental Emergency Response Team
Environmental Services Division
1200 6th Avenue
Seattle, WA 98101

FIG. 9-15C. EPA regional emergency response offices.

National Strike Force (NSF): The NSF is composed of two strike teams established by the USCG on the Pacific coast and the Atlantic coast. Strike teams can provide communications support, advice, and assistance for oil and hazardous substances removal. These teams are equipped with specialized containment and removal equipment and have rapid transportation available.

Environmental Response Team (ERT): The ERT is established by EPA in accordance with its disaster and emergency responsibilities. The ERT has expertise in treatment technology, biology, chemistry, hydrology, geology, and engineering. The ERT can provide access to special decontamination equipment for chemical releases and advice to the OSC in hazard evaluation; risk assessment; multimedia sampling and analysis programs; on-site safety; cleanup techniques and priorities; water-supply decontamination and protection; application of dispersants; environmental assessments; and disposal of contaminated material. The ERT offers both introductory and intermediate level training courses for response personnel.

Scientific Support Coordinators (SSC): SSCs are available, at the request of the OSC, to assist with actual or potential responses to discharges of oil or releases of hazardous substances, pollutants, or contaminants. SSCs will provide scientific support for development of OSC contingency plans and response activities.

Radiological Assistance Teams (RATS): Radiological teams have been established by EPA's Office of Radiation Programs to provide response and support for incidents or sites containing radiological hazards. Expertise is available in radiation monitoring, radionuclide analysis, radiation health physics, and risk assessment.

USCG Public Information Assist Team (PIAT): PIAT is available to assist OSCs and regional or district offices to meet the public's demands for information and participation.

For further information about each of the federal departments and agencies listed, contact the agency regional contact or read 40 CFR 300 (NCP). The diverse resources available at the federal level have been coordinated to provide timely and efficient technical assistance for planning and response activities.

STATE GOVERNMENT AGENCIES

Agencies that can provide technical assistance, personnel, materials, and equipment for dealing with a hazardous materials incident vary from state to state. During the planning process, local emergency services are advised to contact their state's information office, Department of Public Safety, Department of Public Health, or Department of Environmental Protection. Ascertaining the emergency telephone numbers of concerned agencies and the types of technical assistance, personnel, materials, and equipment available, as well as their locations, is vital to the development of a sound emergency.State agencies that could provide technical assistance and supportive functions for dealing with a hazardous materials incident include the following:

National Guard: Communications, crowd control, evacuation transportation, radiological monitoring, and helicopters.

Civil Preparedness: Communications, crowd control, evacuation, and radiological monitoring.

Public Safety: State police and/or sheriffs department for crowd control, traffic control, accident investigation, evacuation, property protection, and communications.

Public Health: Monitoring of water, air, and soil for contamination; treatment of injured personnel; access to hospitals and ambulances; and poison-center cooperation.

Public Works: Sand and other containment materials, construction equipment and personnel, and maps of natural watershed areas.

Environmental Protection: Chemists, biologists, and other scientists with specialized knowledge of hazardous materials released into the environment and knowledge of cleanup contractors.

Agriculture: Soil and water testing and knowledge of pesticides and fertilizers.

Fire Marshal, Fire Academy, and Institutions of Higher Education: Training and advice in hazardous materials response and suppression and the use of specialized response equipment.

LOCAL GOVERNMENT AGENCIES

Local government agencies, particularly fire and police departments, are usually the first on the scene of an incident. Federal and state assistance usually is not immediately available. Each segment of local government should know what is expected of it in a hazardous mate-rials emergency. Those who need to be included in the preincident planning process are the following:

Fire Departments: Additional personnel and specialized equipment and materials can be made available through mutual aid programs.

Police Departments: Traffic and crowd control, evacuation, property protection, and accident investigations.

Civil Preparedness: Communications, crowd control, evacuation, and radiological monitoring.

Public Works: Sand and other containment material, as well as construction equipment and personnel, and maps of natural watershed areas.

Public Health: Water, air, and soil monitoring and local poison-center information.

Building Department: Advice on manufacturing locations.

NATIONAL INDUSTRIAL ORGANIZATIONS AND TRADE ASSOCIATIONS

Many organizations that manufacture and transport hazardous materials have joined together to form national associations. These organizations can provide emergency services and information on safety standards and regulations, as well as advice on the proper precautions to take during a hazardous materials incident. Of these national industrial organizations and trade associations, the one that is most important to emergency service personnel is CHEMTREC.

CHEMTREC—Chemical Transportation Emergency Center

CHEMTREC was established in 1971 as a public service of the Chemical Manufacturers Association (CMA). The center provides information and/or assistance to those responsible for responding to hazardous materials emergencies 24 hours a day, seven days a week. The CHEMTREC number is (800) 424-9300.

When an emergency is reported through this number, the person on duty records the appropriate details and offers advice on what to do in case of spills, fire, or exposure. The person on duty then immediately notifies the shipper. The particulars of the emergency are reported to the shipper, who will then offer further assistance to emergency personnel on the scene. CHEMTREC maintains a close working relationship with the Department of Transportation and many other public and private organizations involved in responding to hazardous materials emergencies.

CHEMTREC also maintains a data base containing more than 800,000 MSDSs for emergency information. When a caller provides a chemical or trade name, the CHEMTREC operator can access this data base and, if necessary, ask the caller additional specific information to obtain the specific MSDS for the product involved in the incident. The CHEMTREC operator can then provide the information over the telephone or fax the MSDS to the caller. This is also an emergency service.

CHEMTREC can provide a communications link to private-sector hazardous materials response organizations for chlorine (see below), phosphorus, hydrogen cyanide, and pool chemicals. Industry response organizations are usually activated by the shipper or the manufacturer for serious hazardous materials incidents after CHEMTREC has notified them. CHEMTREC is an important link for hazardous materials emergency resources.

Chlorine Emergency Plan—CHLOREP

CHLOREP, administered and coordinated by the Chlorine Institute, is a voluntary program of aid in chlorine emergencies that occur during transportation or at user locations. It operates on a 24-hr, seven-day-a-week basis. Upon receiving an emergency call, CHEMTREC's dispatcher telephones the designated CHLOREP emergency contact, who notifies the team leader. The CHLOREP team leader, in turn, telephones the emergency caller at the scene and determines what advice and aid are needed. Figure 9-15D charts the flow of communications during an emergency involving chlorine.

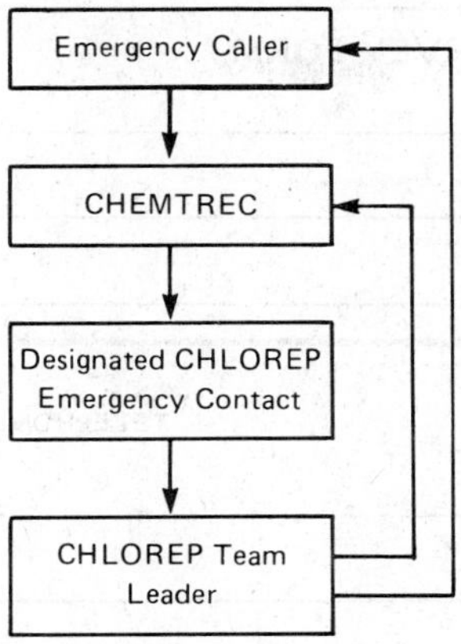

FIG. 9-15D. Flow of communications during an emergency involving chlorine.

Emergency teams, if needed, are dispatched to the site of the incident. Participating chlorine manufacturers sponsor one or more CHLOREP groups consisting of an emergency contact to whom the request for assistance is directed, a CHLOREP team consisting of a team leader and assistants to handle the emergency, and a home coordinator to provide support at the home location. The personnel are employees of the various chemical producers.

Other Private Sources

In addition to CHEMTREC and CHLOREP, there are many other organizations that can provide information, advice, and training materials. They include the following:

American Petroleum Institute
2101 L Street, N.W.
Washington, DC 20037

American Trucking Association
1616 P Street, N.W.
Washington, DC 20006

American Waterways Operator, Inc.
1600 Wilson Boulevard, Suite 1101
Arlington, VA 22209

Association of American Railroads
1920 L Street, N.W.
Washington, DC 20006

Association of Oil Pipelines
1725 K Street N.W., Suite 1208
Washington, DC 20006

Atomic Industrial Forum, Inc.
Public Affairs and Information Program
7101 Wisconsin Ave.
Washington, DC 20014

Chevron Chemical Company
575 Market Street
San Francisco, CA 94105

Dow Chemical U.S.A.
Bennett Building
2030 Dow Center
Midland, MI 48640

E.I. DuPont de Nemours & Company
Hazardous Materials Section
Wilmington, DE 19898

Hazardous Materials Advisory Committee
1100 17th Street, N.W.
Suite 1107
Washington, DC 20036

Interstate Natural Gas Association
1660 P Street, N.W.
Washington, DC 20006

National Tank Truck Carriers, Inc.
1616 P Street, N.W.
Washington, DC 20006

Occupational Health Services, Inc.
400 Plaza Drive
P.O. Box 1505
Seacaucus, NJ 07094

Safety Systems, Inc.
Box 8463
Jacksonville, FL 32239

SCA Chemical Services, Inc.
Corporate Headquarters
60 State Street
Boston, MA 02109

Water Transportation Association
60 East 42nd Street
Suite 2007
New York, NY 10017

LOCAL INDUSTRY

By identifying, through pre-emergency planning, those local industries that manufacture, transport, or use hazardous materials, emergency services can secure prompt information and possible technical assistance at the scene of an incident. Local industries, such as chemical companies, trucking companies, railroads, oil refineries or storage companies, and licensed pollution-spill cleanup contractors, may be able to provide emergency services with equipment and personnel. As with any pre-emergency plan, it is important to keep it continually updated, especially with regard to the names and phone numbers of contact personnel.

Figure 9-15E is a sample hazardous materials pre-emergency survey form. While it is not an official NFPA document, experts believe that a form such as this should be completed for every major site that handles hazardous materials.

HAZARDOUS MATERIALS PREEMERGENCY SURVEY FORM

1. **NAME OF PREMISES**

2. **LOCATION** (ADDRESS IF POSSIBLE)

3. **CONTACT PERSONS** NAME TELEPHONE

OWNER: __________

MANAGER: __________

ENGINEER: __________

SECURITY: __________

NIGHT/WEEK END CONTACT: __________

4. **TYPE OF PROCESS, USE, STORAGE**

5. **HAZARD OF PROCESS, USE, STORAGE**

6. **TYPE(S) OF HAZARDOUS MATERIAL**
(CHEMICAL NAME, TRADE NAME)

1. __________
2. __________
3. __________
4. __________
5. __________

7. **SPECIFIC HAZARD OF MATERIAL**
(MATCH BY NUMBER) (USE DOT TERMINOLOGY)

1. __________
2. __________
3. __________
4. __________
5. __________

FIG. 9-15E. Hazardous materials pre-emergency survey form.

8. SURROUNDING AREA

WEST: OCCUPANCY (MATCH BY NUMBER)

1.
2.
3.

DAY NIGHT
NO. OF OCCUPANTS

1.
2.
3.

TYPE OF HAZARD (LIFE, EXPOSURE)

1.
2.
3.

DEGREE OF HAZARD (SLIGHT, MODERATE, EXTREME)

1.
2.
3.

NORTH: OCCUPANCY (MATCH BY NUMBER)

1.
2.
3.

DAY NIGHT
NO. OF OCCUPANTS

1.
2.
3.

TYPE OF HAZARD (LIFE, EXPOSURE)

1.
2.
3.

DEGREE OF HAZARD (SLIGHT, MODERATE, EXTREME)

1.
2.
3.

SOUTH: OCCUPANCY (MATCH BY NUMBER)

1.
2.
3.

DAY NIGHT
NO. OF OCCUPANTS

1.
2.
3.

TYPE OF HAZARD (LIFE, EXPOSURE)

1.
2.
3.

DEGREE OF HAZARD (SLIGHT, MODERATE, EXTREME)

1.
2.
3.

EAST: OCCUPANCY (MATCH BY NUMBER)

1.
2.
3.

DAY NIGHT
NO. OF OCCUPANTS

1.
2.
3.

TYPE OF HAZARD (LIFE, EXPOSURE)

1.
2.
3.

DEGREE OF HAZARD (SLIGHT, MODERATE, EXTREME)

1.
2.
3.

FIG. 9-15E (cont). Hazardous materials pre-emergency survey form.

9. **FIRE PROTECTION EQUIPMENT**

DETECTION/ALARM SYSTEMS ____

SPRINKLER SYSTEM ____

STANDPIPE SYSTEM ____

SPECIAL EXTINGUISHING SYSTEM (CO_2, HALON 1301) ____

WATER SUPPLY
- PUBLIC ____
- PRIVATE ____

SPECIAL EXTINGUISHING AGENTS (MET-L-X, G1, ETC.) ____

BREATHING APPARATUS (TYPE, LOCATION) ____

ACID SUITS ____

OTHER ____

10. **SPECIAL EQUIPMENT AND MATERIALS**

BULLDOZERS ____ TRUCKS ____

CRANES ____ SAND ____

OTHER ____

11. **POTENTIAL FOR AN INCIDENT**

	YES	NO
IS THERE A CONFLAGRATION POTENTIAL?	___	___
IS THERE AN EARTHQUAKE POTENTIAL?	___	___
IS THERE A WINDSTORM POTENTIAL?	___	___
IS THERE A WINTERSTORM POTENTIAL?	___	___
IS THERE A FLOOD POTENTIAL?	___	___
IS THERE A POTENTIAL FOR WATER CONTAMINATION?	___	___
IS THERE A POTENTIAL FOR STORM AND/OR SANITARY SEWER INVOLVEMENT?	___	___
IS THERE A POTENTIAL FOR AN EXTERNALLY GENERATED ACCIDENT AUTOMOBILE THROUGH FENCE)?	___	___
IS THERE A POTENTIAL FOR SABOTAGE?	___	___

12. **IF THERE WAS A MAJOR INCIDENT AT THIS SITE:**

HOW FAR WOULD EVACUATION HAVE TO BE EXTENDED (INITIALLY)? ____

HOW MANY PEOPLE AT SITE? DAY ____ NIGHT ____

HOW MANY PEOPLE IN EVACUATION ZONE? DAY ____ NIGHT ____

FIG. 9-15E (cont). Hazardous materials pre-emergency survey form.

MAKE DIAGRAM OF THE AREA

INDICATE NORTH

SCALE: ☐ = ________

LEGEND

Fire Dept. Connection . . . .
Sprinkler . . . . (S)
Fire Hydrant . . . . (H)
Tank . . . . (T)
Converter . . . . (C)
Bin . . . . (R)
Railroad . . . .

WALL CONSTRUCTION –
Concrete . . . .
Masonry . . . .
Metal . . . .
Wood . . . .

FENCE –
Wire . . . .
Masonry . . . .
Wood . . . .
Gate . . . .

BUILDING –
Access Door . . . .
Windows . . . .
Fire Door . . . . (FD)

FIG. 9-15E (cont). Hazardous materials pre-emergency survey form.

BIBLIOGRAPHY

Additional Readings

Allan, D. S., "A Cryogenic Line Leak Detector," *Fire Technology*, Vol. 11, No. 4 (Nov. 1975), pp. 270-273.

Bahme, C. W., *Fire Officer's Guide to Dangerous Chemicals*, National Fire Protection Association, Quincy, MA, 1972.

Basic Training Course for Emergency Medical Technicians, 2nd ed. (Course Guide, Instructor Lesson Plans, Student Study Guide), U.S. Government Printing Office, Washington, DC, 1977.

Cashman, J. R., *Hazardous Materials Emergencies*, 2nd ed., Technomic, Lancaster, PA, 1988.

Cheremisinoff, P. N., *Hazardous Materials Emergency Response: Pocket Handbook*, Technomic, Lancaster, PA, 1989.

DePol, D. R. and Cheremisinoff, P. N., *Emergency Response to Hazardous Materials Incidents*, Technomic, Lancaster, PA, 1984.

Emergency Handling of Hazardous Materials in Surface Transportation, Association of Railroads, Washington, DC, 1989.

Emergency Medical Services, National Fire Protection Association, Quincy, MA, 1977.

Emergency Response Guidebook, U.S. Department of Transportation, Washington, DC, 1990.

Emergency Response to Hazardous Materials in Transportation: Self-Study Guide, National Fire Protection Association, Quincy, MA, 1982.

Emergency Services Guide for Selected Hazardous Materials, U.S. Department of Transportation, Washington, DC.

Fire, F. L., "Handling Hazardous Material Incidents," *Fire Engineering*, Vol. 138, No. 2, 1985, pp. 32-34.

Gallagher, G. A. and McCone, S. W., "Lessons in Hazardous Materials Transportation Based on Case Histories," *Plant/Operation Progress*, Vol. 5, No. 3 (July 1986), pp. 186-191.

Garrard, C., "LP — Gas Transport Truck Fire, Aylmer, Ontario," *Fire Journal*, Vol. 59, No. 5. (Sept. 1965), pp. 8-10.

Hazardous Materials Emergency Response Guidebook, U.S. Department of Transportation, Washington, DC, 1990.

Hazardous Materials Handbook, 3rd rev., The Operations Council of American Trucking Association, Washington, DC, 1982.

Hazardous Materials Transportation Accidents, A Compilation of Articles from *Fire Journal* and *Fire Command*, National Fire Protection Association, Quincy, MA, 1978.

Hazardous Materials Transportation: Citations from the NITS Bibliographic Database, National Technical Information Service, Springfield, VA, 1988.

Hazardous Materials Transportation Emergencies, (slide/tape), National Fire Protection Association, Quincy, MA, 1983.

Herman, S. L., *Hazardous Materials Transportation Accidents*, 1st ed., Explosives Research Institute, Scottsdale, AZ, 1982.

Herman, S. L., "Haz-Mat Incidents: Contrasting Scenarios," *Fire Command*, Vol. 57, No. 4 (April 1990), pp. 12-15.

Herman, S. L., "Moving a Haz-Mat Incident," *Fire Engineering*, Vol. 143, No. 2, 1990, p. 42.

Joy, D. S., *Hazardous Materials Transportation and Emergency Response Programs*, (Microform), Oak Ridge National Lab, Oak Ridge, TN, 1983.

Kletz, T. A., "Transportation of Hazardous Substances: The U.K. Scene," *Plant/Operations Progress*, Vol. 5, No. 3 (July 1986), pp. 160-164.

Lesak, D. M., "Tactics for Haz-Mat Incidents," *Fire Engineering*, Vol. 142, No. 10 (Oct. 1989), p. 9.

Lesak, D. M., "Strategic Goals at Haz-Mat Incidents: Part 4," *Fire Engineering*, Vol. 142, No. 9 (Sept. 1989), pp. 60-64.

Lind, C. D. and Whitson, J. C., *Explosion Hazards Associated with Spills of Large Quantities of Hazardous Materials*, Phase II, U.S. Department of Transportation, Washington, DC, 1977.

Reference Handbook on the Transport of Hazardous Materials, Substances and Wastes, Cahners, Boston, MA, 1982.

Terrien, E. J., *Hazardous Materials and Natural Disaster Emergencies: Incident Action Guidebook*, Technomic, Lancaster, PA, 1984.

Transport of Dangerous Goods, 5th ed., United Nations Publications, New York, NY, 1988.

Young, M. S., "Handling Emergencies Involving Cryogenic Materials," *Fire Command*, Vol. 45, No. 5 (May 1978), pp. 20-22.

Zajic, J. E. and Himmelman, W. A., *Highly Hazardous Materials Spills and Emergency Planning*, Marcel Dekker, New York, NY, 1978.

HAZARDOUS WASTE CONTROL

Sami Atallah and Jatin N. Shah

Waste is a natural byproduct of many human activities. The varieties, quantities, and hazards of today's waste appear to be directly proportional to the degree of technological development of a nation. It has been estimated that in the United States, during the course of a year, over 3.5 billion tons (3.3 billion metric tons) of solid waste is produced—roughly 100 lbs (45 kg) per day for every man, woman, and child.[1] Solid waste includes animal, mineral, agricultural, and community waste, of which only a small fraction is collected.

In addition to solid waste, many gaseous products, such as those produced in combustion processes (e.g., CO_2, NO_x, SO_2, soot, and hydrocarbons), and chlorofluorocarbon (CFC) aerosol propellants are released into the atmosphere. The pollution of air with such gaseous-waste products is not only detrimental to human health, it reduces visibility and contributes to the corrosion and deterioration of clothing, art treasures, historical structures, metals, rubber, and paint. Acid rain, the product of further atmospheric oxidation and dissolution of NO_x and SO_x in rain water, adversely affects the growth of forests and agricultural products, and the survival of aquatic life in streams, ponds, and lakes. The accumulation of CO_2 in the atmosphere is expected to have long-range effects on the warming of the planet with dire climatological, agricultural, and ocean-level implications. CFCs destroy the ozone layer in the stratosphere where it protects us against harmful ultraviolet radiation from the sun. Its depletion increases the risk of skin cancer.

Domestic, commercial, and industrial liquid wastes invariably find their way to bodies of water and add to the problem of our dwindling potable water supply. Industrial liquid waste may contain metallic salts that have immediate or long-term effects on humans. High concentrations of these salts may also build up in fishes, crustaceans, and plants with similar effects on people who consume them. Some organic wastes from commercial, household, and industrial sources reduce the concentration of dissolved oxygen in water supplies. This may lead to the extinction of aquatic life, and the growth of disease-carrying bacteria and parasites. Other wastes may contain known or suspected carcinogens, such as chlorinated hydrocarbon solvents, benzene, and polychlorinated biphenyls (PCBs).

Although all waste is a nuisance to society, not all waste is necessarily hazardous. Hazardous waste may be defined as that which poses a threat to human health, the environment, and public property if handled or disposed of improperly. The hazard is created by virtue of the toxicity, flammability, explosivity, reactivity, radioactivity, corrosivity, or etiologic (disease-causing) potential of the waste.

Under Section 313 of the Emergency Planning and Community Right-to-Know Act of 1986, the Environmental Protection Agency (EPA) began collecting annual data on the emission rates of more than 300 hazardous chemicals from qualifying manufacturers. According to the Toxic Release Inventory: National Perspective 1987,[2] 18 billion lbs (8.2 billion kg) of these chemicals were released into the environment, and 4.6 billion lbs (2.1 billion kg) were transferred to off-site facilities, such as public sewage systems or incinerators, for treatment or disposal. Almost half of the total amount of chemical releases and transfers [9.62 billion lbs (4.4 billion kg)] were discharged to surface water. Facilities disposed of an additional 3.2 billion lbs (1.5 billion kg) by injecting the chemicals into underground wells. Our atmosphere received emissions totaling 2.6 billion lbs (1.2 billion kg) and facilities disposed of 2.5 billion lbs (1.1 billion kg) on land. In addition to environmental releases, manufacturers discharged 1.9 billion lbs (0.9 billion kg) of regulated chemicals into public sewage systems, and transported 2.6 billion lbs (1.2 billion kg) to off-site treatment facilities.[3]

Numerous federal, state, and local laws and regulations have been enacted to protect the public and the environment against exposure to hazardous waste. The federal laws attempt to specify and control the quantities, concentrations, and types of chemicals that may be released and the manner in which they may be packaged, stored, transported, and disposed of safely.

Table 9-16A is a summary of pertinent federal laws and related terms used in this chapter. In addition to the federal acts listed in Table 9-16A, parts of other laws and amendments to existing laws regulate specific waste-disposal and handling operations. For example, the Marine

Sami Atallah is president of, and Jatin N. Shah is a Chemical engineer at Risk & Industrial Safety Consultants, Inc., Des Plaines, IL.

TABLE 9-16A. ***Summary of Pertinent Federal Laws and Terminology***

CAA:	Clean Air Act (1955, 1977)—a federal law that mandates and enforces toxic emissions standards for stationary sources and motor vehicles.
CERCLA:	Comprehensive Environmental Responsibility, Compensation and Liability Act (1976), sometimes referred to as **Superfund**—a federal law that authorizes the identification and remediation of abandoned hazardous waste sites.
CWA:	Clean Water Act (1972)—a federal law that regulates the discharge of pollutants into surface waters.
EPA:	Environmental Protection Agency, established under the Reorganizational Plan 3 of 1970 as an independent federal agency to assure the protection of the environment by abating and controlling pollution. It coordinates all governmental action, conducts research, monitors and sets and enforces environmental standards.
FEMA:	Federal Emergency Management Agency—a federal agency that is accountable for all federal emergency preparedness, mitigation and response activities for all natural, manmade or nuclear emergencies; also responsible for administering certain training funds under **SARA.**
FIFRA:	Federal Insecticide, Fungicide and Rodenticide Act (1972, 1988)—a federal law that mandates toxicity testing and registration of pesticides, and establishes tolerance levels for residues of these agents in food.
HCS:	Hazard Communication Standard—an **OSHA** standard (29 CFR 1910.1200) that requires employers to communicate the risks of hazardous materials to workers in regulated facilities.
HSWA:	Hazardous and Solid Waste Amendments (1984)—are amendments to **RCRA** that establish a timetable for **RCRA** land bans and more stringent requirements for underground storge tanks (USTs).
MWTA:	Medical Waste Tracking Act (1988)—an amendment to **RCRA** that establishes a demonstration tracking system for medical wastes in ten states.
OSHA:	Occupational Safety and Health Act (1970)—a federal law which called for the establishment of the Occupational Safety and Health Administration, which oversees and regulates workplace health and safety.
PEL:	Permissible Exposure Limits—these are specific exposure limits established by **OSHA** for 600 industrial chemicals.
RCRA:	Resource Conservation and Recovery Act (1976)—enacted as an amendment to the Solid Waste Disposal Act, **RCRA** protects human health and the environment and encourages the conservation of valuable material and energy sources. It provides assistance to state and local governments for prohibiting open dumping, regulating the management of hazardous wastes, and encouraging recycling, reuse, and treatment of hazardous wastes. **RCRA** provides for "cradle-to-grave" tracking of hazardous waste, from generator to transporter to treatment, storage, or disposal.
SARA:	Superfund Amendments and Reauthorization Act (1986)—a federal law that reauthorizes and expands the jurisdiction of **CERCLA** and designates requirements manadated in Title III of **SARA** for public disclosure of chemical information and the development of emergency response plans.
TSCA:	Toxic Substances Control Act (1976)—a federal law that authorizes EPA to gather information on new and existing chemical risks to human health and the environment.
UST:	Underground Storage Tanks—regulated by **RCRA,** Subtitle I, these are tanks with ten or more percent of their volume underground, used to store **CERCLA**-regulated hazardous chemicals or petroleum products.

Protection, Research, and Sanctuaries Act regulates ocean dumping and incineration on the high seas; the Hazardous Materials Transportation Act regulates the packaging and containerization of hazardous materials, including hazardous wastes; the Hazardous and Solid Waste Amendments to RCRA (Subtitle I) provide for the development and implementation of a comprehensive regulatory program for underground storage tanks; and the Safe Drinking Water Act establishes maximum contaminant levels for drinking water and regulates underground injection of hazardous wastes.

The safe disposal of hazardous waste introduces many problems not only to the industry generating the waste, but also to the waste-transportation and disposal agency, and to fire fighters and other response forces who may be called upon to clean up an accidental release. These problems arise because the contents of waste are usually not well defined—sometimes not even known. Waste is inherently a mixture of many components with differing hazardous properties. One component, for example, may be a flammable solvent while another is a highly toxic pesticide. Disposing of the solvent by burning may release the pesticide (or its toxic combustion products) to the atmosphere. Additional problems arise in handling and storing waste products. Self-heating and ignition, corrosion of pipe and tank-wall materials, and reaction with other noncompatible wastes have been known to cause major catastrophic events. Fire fighters may also be accidentally exposed to a hazardous-waste material released as a result of an unrelated fire or an explosion to which they have responded.

This chapter will discuss the sources and characteristics of waste materials with particular emphasis on hazardous waste, summarize waste handling, disposal, and recovery procedures, and examine the various approaches to fire prevention and protection in cases involving hazardous waste.

SOURCES OF WASTE

There are many sources of waste materials in our society. To a great extent, the source determines what the composition of the waste may be, its bulk, density, quantity, and the type and degree of hazard that it may present. These factors, in turn, determine how the waste should be collected, processed, or disposed of in a practical and safe manner.

Domestic, Commercial, and Industrial Sources

Table 9-16B shows typical breakdowns of the contents of collected solid waste from domestic, commercial, and industrial sources. Obviously, these breakdowns will vary among sources within each category. For example, suburban homes are expected to produce more yard waste than city residences. Restaurants generate more food waste and less paper waste than office buildings. Hospitals dispose of cotton and paper products which may be contaminated with hazardous chemicals and etiologic agents.

TABLE 9-16B. ***Typical Contents of Solid Waste (Percent by Weight)***

	Domestic	Commercial	Industrial
Paper products	51.5	69.0	17.4
Glass	15.0	7.0	3.4
Cans and metals	7.0	10.0	8.0
Plastics	2.0	10.0	
Cloth, leather, rags	4.0		0.4
Food	10.0	4.0	8.4
Wood	2.0		17.9
Yard waste	8.5		
Minerals			36.7
Chemical waste			3.3
Rubber			1.6
Other			3.1

The nature of an industry determines the content of the waste generated. A furniture plant, for example, discards wood scrap, sawdust, and shavings as well as oily rags, stain, varnish, lacquer, glue, etc., in addition to paper, metal, and other commercial items. The waste products of chemical processing plants vary considerably depending on the raw materials used and the end products processed. These plants may discard substantial amounts of off-grade or reject products, byproducts, tars, spent catalyst, precipitates, etc. On the other hand, nuclear power plants produce radioactive waste.

At any processing plant, some materials will be accidentally spilled in storage and handling. Cleanup operations from filling equipment, fabrication operations, and general plant maintenance will generate some waste. Rejected, aged, or damaged packages; off-specification materials; and overruns will also be discarded.

Transportation Sources

The movement of bulk or packaged goods may also generate waste. Broken packages, leaking drums, and overheating or freezing of cargo are contributing sources. Washing tank-cars or tank-trucks produces substantial amounts of waste material that may be emulsified or dissolved in water. A spill of a hazardous liquid or solid-chemical cargo as a result of a railway, truck, ship, or pipeline accident contaminates soil and/or nearby bodies of water and constitutes a public hazard and another waste disposal problem. This is particularly true if the accident occurs in a remote area where experienced personnel are not readily available to assess the potential hazard to the public and the environment and to provide guidance in controlling the hazard.

Storage Sources

Warehouse inventory control necessitates that unmarketable or undesirable materials of all kinds, forms, and hazards be discarded occasionally. Tanks must be cleaned as storage needs change. The washing of transfer lines and tanks results in a waste product.

Materials released as a result of plant accidents, such as when packages are damaged by forklifts, require cleanup and disposal. Water, fire, or explosion damage can also result in substantial amounts of undesired product.

Other Sources

Several other human activities produce waste. Harvesting of agricultural products, mining operations, and demolition of old structures are examples of operations that generate large quantities of waste products with various characteristics.

CHARACTERIZATION OF WASTE

The safe handling, collection, and disposal of hazardous waste can be accomplished only if the physical, chemical, and hazardous properties of its components are known and that information is properly applied. Quite often though, the composition is not known because waste is usually a mixture of many components with differing properties. This section will discuss the physical, chemical, and hazardous properties that may influence the selection of response procedures to accidental releases and the appropriate disposal techniques for wastes.

Physical State

The ease of handling and disposal of waste is highly dependent on its physical state.

Solid waste: This category includes most domestic, commercial, and industrial trash, metal, wood, plastic scrap, chemicals, food, etc. (See Table 9-16B.) It also includes agricultural waste products, demolition waste, and spent ore from mining operations. The bulk density of these wastes differs considerably depending on the source, mix of materials, and the degree of compactness of the waste. For example, uncompacted household waste has a bulk density of 200 to 250 lbs per cu yd (119 to 148 kg/m^3), while waste in a landfill may have a bulk density of 750 to 1,000 lbs per cu yd (445 to 594 kg/m^3). Solid waste also includes combustible metal waste (e.g., magnesium shavings) and semisolids such as waxes, soaps, and elastomers.

Liquid waste: This category includes aqueous and nonaqueous solutions and suspensions generally produced as a result of cleaning operations. Nonaqueous solvents may be flammable (e.g., toluene and xylene) or noncombustible (e.g., tricholorethylene). Viscous liquids, such as pastes and tars, and suspensions, such as acid sludges, require special handling procedures and equipment.

Gaseous waste: Most gaseous waste is generated from industrial operations and is disposed of by venting into the atmosphere. Hazardous gaseous-waste products are regulated by the Environmental Protection Agency (EPA) and must be properly disposed of, such as by flaring or removal of the hazardous components by chemical means. Of particular concern to fire fighting and other response personnel are old unidentifiable gas cylinders with walls that may have become weakened due to age and corrosion. Discarded small butane and LP-Gas cylinders in household trash may also pose a hazard to trash collectors and compactors and to operators of shredding equipment.

Properties of Hazardous Waste

Few discarded materials are so compatible with the environment or so inert as to have no short-term or long-term impact. Hazards that appear minor may have unexpected impacts long after disposal. When two or more hazards pertain to a material, the lesser may not receive the necessary consideration. Mixing of two discarded substances may result in a chemical reaction with severe and unexpected consequences.

Since waste is generally a mixture of many components, its physical and chemical properties cannot be defined with any degree of accuracy. Whenever possible, the approximate composition of a hazardous waste should be ascertained from the originating source or from the manifest accompanying the waste being transported. Generally, when one component predominates, the physical and chemical properties of the waste mixture are nearly those of the major component. This is not true for the hazardous properties of waste mixtures consisting of a relatively harmless major component and small amounts of highly toxic, radioactive, or etiologically active components. The hazard, in this case, is determined by the smaller components.

Hazardous Solid Waste

The Environmental Protection Agency defines hazardous solid waste as that which may: "(i) cause, or significantly contribute to, an increase in mortality or an increase in serious irreversible, or incapacitating reversible, illness; or (ii) pose a substantial present or potential hazard to human health or the environment when it is improperly treated, stored, transported, disposed of, or otherwise managed." The determining characteristic of a hazardous solid waste must be "measurable by an available standardized test method ... or reasonably detectable by generators of solid waste through their knowledge of their waste."[3]

Basically, EPA standards require that a solid waste be listed and treated as hazardous if it meets the ignitability, corrosivity, reactivity, and/or toxicity oharacteristics prescribed by the standard. Highlights of the standard are given below.

Ignitability: A solid waste exhibits this characteristic if a representative sample of the waste has any of the following properties:

1. It is a liquid, other than an aqueous solution containing less than 24 percent alcohol by volume, and has a closed-cup flash point less than 140°F (60°C), as determined by an approved test method.
2. It is not a liquid and is capable under standard temperature and pressure of causing fire through friction, absorption of moisture, or spontaneous chemical changes and, when ignited, burns so vigorously and persistently that it creates a hazard.
3. It is a flammable compressed gas as defined by another federal standard.[4] A flammable compressed gas is defined as one that forms flammable mixtures with air at concentrations less than 13 percent (by volume) or has a flammability range with air which is wider than 12 percent regardless of the lower flammable limit. The standard specifies additional criteria for defining flammable vapors and aerosols.
4. It is an oxidizer, such as a chlorate, permanganate, inorganic peroxide, or a nitrate, that yields oxygen readily to stimulate the combustion of organic matter.[5]

Corrosivity: A solid waste exhibits this characteristic if a representative sample of the waste has either of the following properties:

1. It is aqueous and has a pH of less than or equal to 2 or greater than or equal to 12.5.
2. It is a liquid and corrodes steel at a rate greater than 0.25 in. (6.35 mm) per year at a test temperature of 130°F (55°C).

Reactivity: A solid waste exhibits this characteristic if it behaves in any of the following ways:

1. It is normally unstable and readily undergoes violent change without detonating.
2. It reacts violently with water.
3. It forms potentially explosive mixtures with water.
4. When mixed with water, it generates toxic gases, vapors, or fumes in a quantity sufficient to present a danger to human health or the environment.
5. It is a cyanide-bearing or sulfide-bearing waste which, when exposed to pH conditions between 2 and 12.5, can generate toxic gases, vapors, or fumes in a quantity sufficient to present a danger to human health and the environment.
6. It is capable of detonation or explosive reaction if it is subjected to a strong initiating source or if heated under confinement.
7. It is readily capable of detonation or explosive decomposition or reaction at standard temperature and pressure.
8. It is a known forbidden or a Class A or B explosive.

Toxicity: The EPA defines toxic wastes as those that have been found to be fatal to humans in low doses or, in the absence of data on human toxicity, it has been shown in studies to have an oral LD_{50} toxicity (rat) of less than 50 mg/kg, an inhalation LC_{50} toxicity (rat) of less than 2 mg/L, or a dermal LD_{50} toxicity (rabbit) of less than 200 mg/kg or is otherwise capable of causing or significantly contributing to an increase in serious irreversible, or incapacitating reversible, illness. A toxic waste is also one that contains or degrades into a listed toxic material in large enough concentrations to pose a potential hazard to the public and/or the environment. The standard for toxicity provides descriptions of laboratory tests for extracting and analyzing the potentially toxic components of wastes.

Hazardous Medical Waste

During the summer of 1988, a number of incidents were reported where medical waste, such as blood vials and bags, syringes, pill bottles, and bandages, washed ashore at various public Atlantic coast beaches. The publicity associated with these incidents and others involving the disposal of medical waste in dumpsters, hastened the promulgation of the Medical Waste Tracking Act of 1988. The law required EPA to develop a two-year demonstration cradle-to-grave tracking system for the 10 participating states. Such standards (40 CFR 259) were promulgated on March 24, 1989.[6]

Medical waste is defined as that which is generated during the diagnosis, treatment, or immunization of human beings or animals, in research pertaining thereto, or in the production or testing of regulated biologicals. It is generated at such facilities as hospitals, health-care centers, nursing homes, funeral homes, blood banks, veterinary clinics, and medical-research laboratories.

Medical waste is a likely source of pathogens (infectious agents). Some of the diseases that may be transmitted through improper disposal and handling of infectious medical waste are acquired immune deficiency syndrome (AIDS), typhoid, cholera, dysentery, anthrax, salmonellosis, tuberculosis, and burcellosis. Development of a strict medical-waste management plan would reduce the risk of infection to staff, patients, and the general public.

EPA-regulated medical waste is categorized as follows.

1. Cultures and stocks: cultures and stocks of infectious agents and associated biologicals, including cultures from medical and pathological laboratories; cultures and stocks of infectious agents from research and industrial laboratories; wastes from the production of biologicals; discarded live and attenuated vaccines; and culture dishes and devices used to transfer, inoculate, and mix cultures.
2. Pathological wastes: Human pathological wastes, including tissues, organs, and body parts and body fluids that are removed during surgery or autopsy, or other medical procedures, and specimens of body fluids, and their containers.
3. Human blood and blood products: Liquid-waste human blood, products of blood, items saturated and/or dripping with human blood, items that were saturated and/or dripping with human blood that are now caked with dried human blood; including serum, plasma, and other blood components, and their containers, which were used or intended for use in either patient care, testing, and laboratory analysis, or the development of pharmaceuticals. Intravenous bags are also included in this category.
4. Sharps: These are objects that have been used in animal or human patient care or treatment, or in medical, research, or industrial laboratories. They include hypodermic needles, syringes (with or without the attached needle), pasteur pipettes, scalpel blades, blood vials, needles with attached tubing, and culture dishes (regardless of presence of infectious agents). Also included are other types of broken or unbroken glassware that were in contact with infectious agents, such as used slides and cover slips.
5. Animal waste: Contaminated animal carcasses, body parts, and bedding of animals that were known to have been exposed to infectious agents during research (including research in veterinary hospitals), production of biologicals, or testing of pharmaceuticals.
6. Isolation waste: Biological waste and discarded materials contaminated with blood, excretion, exudates, or secretions from humans who are isolated to protect others from certain highly communicable diseases, or isolated animals known to be infected with highly communicable diseases.
7. Unused sharps: The following unused, discarded sharps: hypodermic needles, suture needles, syringes, and scalpel blades.

COLLECTION, HANDLING, AND DISPOSAL OF WASTE

The disposal of waste may be achieved through a variety of techniques and processes, depending on the physical, chemical, and hazardous properties of the waste. These techniques range from improvements in operations that reduce the total quantity of waste, to the introduction of process changes that reduce the concentration of hazardous components to acceptable levels. Recycling and the recovery of energy from waste streams are other approaches that have become economically acceptable as the cost of energy and raw materials continues to increase.

Treatment of Gaseous Waste

Industrial gaseous waste may be released in the atmosphere provided that the concentrations of the contaminants meet allowable levels set by the Environmental Protection Agency and Clean Air Act. Table 9-16C summarizes the primary ambient air quality standards set by EPA for typical contaminants as compared with their background level in nature.[7]

TABLE 9-16C. ***Ambient Air Quality Standards***

Contaminant	Background Level	EPA Primary Level	Allowable Exposure
SO_2	< .002 ppm	.03 ppm	AAM
		.14 ppm	Max. 24-h conc., N
CO	.03 ppm	9 ppm	8-h AC, N
		35 ppm	1-h AC, N
O_2	.01–.05 ppm	.12 ppm	1-h AC, N
NO_2	4 ppb	52 ppb	AAM
Particulates	10–60 μg/m^3	150 μg/m^3	24-h AC
		50 μg/m^3	AAM

AAM = annual arithmetic mean, AC – average concentration
N = not to be exceeded once per calandar year, h = hour
Sources: Anon., "Pollution Control Technology,"Research and Education Association, New York, NY, 1973, and Code of Federal Regulations, Title 40, Part 50: National Primary and Secondary Ambient Air Quality Standards.

Gaseous waste streams can be purified by removing undesirable components or by reducing their concentrations to acceptable levels. This may be achieved by chemical conversion, absorption, adsorption, or particulate removal.[8]

Chemical conversion: An undersirable component may be allowed to react chemically with other compounds to form a harmless component or one that may be removed easily. Sulfur dioxide, for example, may be removed by reaction with lime or magnesia. Catalytic converters are used to convert nitrogen oxides and hydrocarbons into nitrogen, CO_2, and H_2O.

Absorption: Several gaseous pollutants may be removed by absorption. Ammonia and hydrogen chloride, for example, may be removed by water scrubbing. Sulfur dioxide may be absorbed in an alkaline solution.

Adsorption: Certain solids with a large pore-surface area selectively adsorb small concentrations of specific gases. Activated carbon, silica or alumina gel, fuller's earth and other clays are typical adsorbents. The operator is left with the problem of disposing of the contaminated adsorbent or the concentrated stream of undesirable gas released upon adsorbent regeneration.

Particulate removal: Many industrial gaseous streams contain undesirable dusts, mist, or smoke. These suspensions may be removed by filtration, sedimentation, centrifugal separation, electrostatic precipitation, and wet scrubbing.

Liquid Waste Treatment

The volume and strength of industrial aqueous waste may be reduced by various process modifications. Although the hazard is not completely eliminated, a smaller volume of contaminated water or a stream with a lower concentration of a hazardous component is easier to handle and dispose of. Neutralization of acidic or alkaline waste may be achieved by chemical reaction with the appropriate compounds. Inorganic salts may be removed by precipitation, ion exchange, and adsorption by carbon beds. Holding ponds may be used to retain industrial waste so that it may be disposed of with domestic waste at a constant rate rather than overloading the sewage-disposal system at any one time of the day.

Suspended solids may be separated by such processes as sedimentation (allowing heavy particles to sink to the bottom), flotation (skimming floating materials off the surface), drying followed by incineration, centrifuging, and filtration. Colloidal solids are more difficult to remove because their particle size range falls between that of suspended and dissolved solids. Colloidal solids will not settle down unless chemicals are added that help coagulate the solid into larger masses that would sink. Many toxic pesticides, insecticides, and herbicides may also be removed by adsorption in certain clays.

Many food-processing operations as well as the manufacture of textiles and paper produce a waste that is high in organic matter. Biological degradation is generally achieved by lagooning, treatment with biologically activated sludge, the use of trickling filters, wet combustion, deep-well injection, and other means.

Wastewater from tanneries, slaughterhouses, and canneries may contain etiologic agents. These waters must be sterilized by chlorination, ozonization, or ultraviolet radiation before they are discharged into public water supplies.

Organic liquid waste components may be recovered by fractional distillation. The remaining components may be disposed of by incineration or burial in environmentally acceptable locations.

Disposal and Recovery of Solid Waste

Table 9-16B shows that a large fraction of domestic, commercial, and industrial solid waste is combustible. Thus, the burning of scrap and refuse under controlled conditions is one of the most satisfactory methods of disposal. Municipal incinerators operated primarily for domestic and commercial trash will usually accept industrial refuse as long as it does not introduce additional hazards or operating problems.

In recent years, the recovery of glass and metal from these wastes and the use of the combustible component as a fuel supplement has become economically attractive. The basic steps involved in these recovery operations are waste collection, transportation to the disposal site, storage, shredding, separation and recovery of glass and metal, burning of the combustible component, and ash removal. (See Figure 9-16A.)

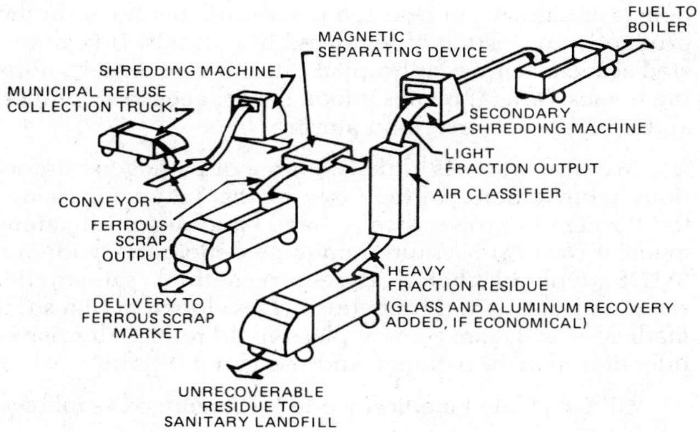

FIG. 9-16A. Typical refuse recovery process.

Air-pollution-control equipment is nearly always needed on industrial incinerators. Environmental-control devices depend upon the composition of the stack effluent. Such devices include the following:

1. Afterburners to ignite combustible particles;
2. Cyclones to remove larger particles;
3. Low-energy scrubbers to remove larger particulates;
4. High-energy venturi scrubbers to remove fine particulates and/or water-soluble acid gases;
5. Electrostatic precipitators to remove fine particulates and mists; and
6. Fabric filters (bag houses) to remove fine particulates.

Principal hazards of operating an incinerator are the following:

1. Overheating due to feeding a large amount of volatiles;
2. Overheating due to an increase in the heat of combustion;
3. Structural failure due to overheating and/or corrosion;
4. Corrosion of scrubber due to acid; and
5. Failure of scrubber system.

Compacted trash on transportation vehicles has been known to result in fires. Ignition sources may be smoldering ashes from fireplaces or unextinguished cigarettes. Shredding operations have also been the scene of occasional explosions and fires; in some cases, as a result of discarded explosive materials. Small butane and LP-Gas cylinders and gasoline containers with some fluid remaining in them are often the source of the flammable vapor. The ignition sources are frictional sparks between the grinding or shredding teeth, the walls of the shredder, and other solid components of the refuse.

Another approach for recovering the heating content of combustible waste is by pyrolysis. When polymers and organic materials are heated, they yield oils and other recoverable compounds. Although pyrolysis has not yet been widely adopted, it has promise as a conservation measure. A retort is charged with selected scrap and then heated to cause decomposition and distillation of the volatiles and oils. The process is somewhat similar to a coke oven, and similar operating hazards should be expected. (See Figure 9-16B.)

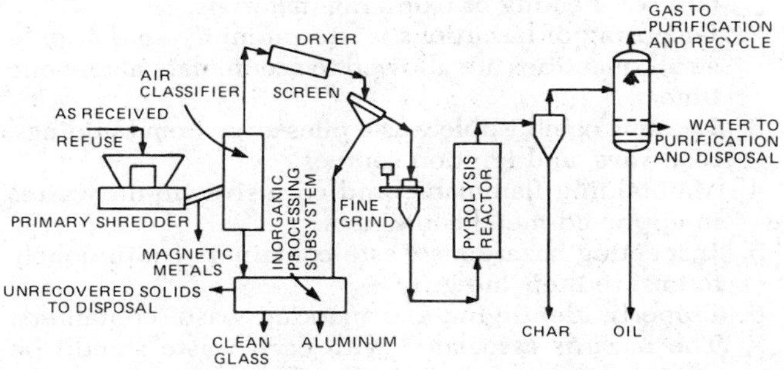

FIG. 9-16B. Flow diagram of a pyrolysis recovery system.

Most nonhazardous domestic, commercial, and industrial waste today is disposed of in sanitary landfills. In a landfill operation, discarded material is mixed with earth and then compacted in a wide trench or other depression. Layer upon layer of mixture is added and then 2 ft (0.6 m) of earth is spread and compacted on top. This process helps control odors, rodents, and scavenger birds.

Successful landfill operation depends heavily upon biological activity within the fill material. There is some tendency for methane gas to be generated during biological activity. There have been some fires and explosions in buildings constructed over old landfills due to the seepage of biologically generated methane into the building and its eventual ignition. The recovery of natural gas from waste landfills is under way in various parts of the United States.

Hazardous wastes cannot be disposed of in a sanitary landfill. They are either chemically treated or incinerated in properly designed furnaces that ensure the complete degradation of the hazardous components of the waste. Otherwise, they may be disposed of in secure landfills. These are properly designed and engineered containment facilities that ensure that no waste can ever seep into the underground water system to pollute natural bodies of water or the public water-supply system. Transporting the hazardous waste from the source to the disposal site usually requires federal, state, and local permits. The waste must be packaged or containerized in approved containers. A manifest describing the contents, their hazards, and emergency-response procedures must accompany the shipment. The operator of the secure landfill generally requires a complete chemical analysis of the hazardous waste so that it may be handled and sited properly.

Treatment of Hazardous Medical Waste

The new federal standard 40 CFR 259 requires proper packaging, segregation, and identification of hazardous medical waste.[9] It also calls for reporting, recordkeeping, and tracking of medical waste. The standard applies to waste generators, transporters, on-site incineration facilities, and off-site treatment, destruction, and disposal facilities.

Noninfectious medical waste generated at any medical facility typically constitutes up to 70 percent of all medical waste. To reduce disposal costs, the noninfectious waste is generally segregated from infectious medical waste at the source. This reduces the potential for cross-contamination and allows disposal at sanitary waste-disposal sites without further treatment. Segregation at the source also reduces the volume of medical waste that needs to be treated before disposal.

A standard operating procedure (SOP) should be developed by all facilities that store, handle, transport, or dispose of infectious waste.[10] Unsightly pathological waste should be placed in opaque plastic bags. All containers and bags should be red, and labeled with the word "infectious" and/or with the international biohazard symbol. (See Figure 9-16C.) Wastes that are to be transported should be double-bagged and placed in a semi-rigid container to prevent leakage. Wastes should be loaded and unloaded manually, and never compacted, to prevent compromising the integrity of the packaging. These wastes should be arranged chronologically to meet state regulations for storage periods. All storage facilities should have limited access with the entrances marked by the international biohazard symbol and the word "infectious."

FIG. 9-16C. The international biohazard symbol.

Infectious medical waste must be treated and rendered harmless prior to disposal at a sanitary waste disposal site. Several treatment methods are available, including the following six methods:

- Steam sterilization
- Incineration
- Thermal inactivation (dry heat sterilization)
- Gas/vapor sterilization
- Sterilization by irradiation
- Chemical disinfection

Steam sterilization is the most commonly used method for destroying pathogens in medical waste. It is preferred for contaminated solid surfaces such as sharps, and low-density waste which may be easily penetrated by steam. Incineration is the preferred method for treating AIDS-contaminated and combustible infectious waste. Proper incineration of waste reduces the volume that needs to be disposed of by up to 95 percent, while rendering the waste totally harmless. Like steam sterilization, thermal inactivation is used for the sterilization of contaminated surgical instruments and equipment. The dry heat has the advantage of not corroding instruments, thereby increasing their life.

Although the remaining three methods may be used to treat medical waste, they tend to be more costly and require special precautions to protect the operator. Gas/vapor sterilization, for example, requires the use of ethylene oxide or formaldehyde, both of which are highly flammable and hazardous to human health. Irradiation with ultraviolet (UV) and gamma radiation is a newly developed technology that is used for pre-sterilization of medical products and may be used to treat waste water. Chemical disinfection is carried out by applying hydrogen peroxide, acids, or alcohols to exposed surfaces, utensils, and medical supplies.

In order to ensure the effectiveness of any treatment, it is important that a SOP be established for each waste stream to be treated. Each SOP should address the type of waste, variations in the waste stream, and the limitations of the treatment apparatus. The SOP must also specify procedures for biologically monitoring and testing of the treated waste to ensure that it is no longer hazardous.

Protection of Hazardous Waste Operators

On March 6, 1989, OSHA issued a final rule concerning the protection of workers involved in hazardous-waste operations, and in responding to accidental releases of hazardous materials and wastes. This law[11] requires the following:

1. The development and implementation of a written safety and health program for employees (and subcontractors' employees) who are involved in hazardous-waste operations. The program must be designed to identify, evaluate, and control safety and health hazards, and provide for emergency response for hazardous-waste operations.
2. Hazardous-waste-site characterization, analysis, and control in order to identify specific site hazards, determine appropriate safety and health control procedures, and to implement these procedures to control employee exposure to the identified hazards.
3. Extensive training and retraining of employees before they are permitted to engage in hazardous-waste operations, and informational programs to ensure that employees and subcontractors are aware of the degree and nature of safety and health hazards specific to the work site.
4. Medical surveillance of employees exposed to (or potentially exposed to) hazardous substances, health hazards, or who wear respirators.
5. The implementation of engineering controls, work practices, and personal protective equipment, and the continuous monitoring of the work area to ensure that employees are not exposed to levels that exceed permissible exposure limits for hazardous substances at the site.
6. The development of a written emergency-response plan to handle anticipated emergencies prior to the commencement of hazardous-waste operations.
7. Additional requirements for the development and implementation of decontamination, and materials-handling procedures, and ensuring the presence of adequate illumination and sanitation facilities at the work site, and that proper excavation procedures are followed.

HAZARD PREVENTION AND CONTROL

Prevention Measures

The probability of exposure to hazardous waste may be reduced through preventive actions achieved through preplanning, proper waste-handling, and storage-handling procedures. Preventive measures include the following:

1. Segregating chemically incompatible wastes, for example, by ensuring that combustible waste does not contain self-heating or oxidizing materials.
2. Disposing of hazardous waste promptly so that only small quantities are allowed to accumulate at any one time.
3. Locating combustible waste piles away from buildings, roadways, and ignition sources.
4. Maintaining flammable and corrosive liquid wastes in approved metal containers.
5. Inspecting hazardous-waste containers continuously to ensure their integrity.
6. Properly identifying and marking waste containers. The hazards associated with each waste should be shown clearly on the exterior of each container, storage tank, transport vehicle, or building.
7. Training personnel in proper waste-handling procedures, use of personal protective equipment, and emergency response measures to an accidental release of hazardous waste. Training should include realistic drills simulating all credible release scenarios.

Emergency Response Planning

A fire department should coordinate and preplan its approach to the handling of hazardous-waste emergencies with all waste-generating industries or disposal facilities within its jurisdiction. The fire department should be aware of the types, quantities, and hazards of all raw materials, products, and wastes stored at each plant site as well as those that are transported to and from the plant. The fire department should then ensure the availability to its personnel of any necessary specialized handling equipment and materials, detection devices, and personal protective equipment.

In preparing fire-response plans, fire fighters should recognize that water used to control or extinguish fires at chemical plants or warehouses where hazardous materials are stored will most likely become contaminated with these materials, and thus constitute a hazardous waste. If the contaminated water is allowed to reach natural bodies of water, such as through the rain-water drainage system, the hazard will spread outside the plant, and endanger the public and the environment. A good example of such an event is the fire that occurred in November, 1986 at a warehouse for agricultural chemicals located along the Rhine River in Basel, Switzerland. The contaminated water resulted in a massive fish kill, and a water-pollution problem that spread all the way to Germany and Holland.

It is very important, therefore, that the fire department, together with plant management, predetermine the locations of storm-water drains and sewers, and the general layout and slope of the land on which the plant is built. Precautions must then be built into the emergency-response plan to ensure that fire-fighting water will not pollute any natural water bodies or drinking-water supplies.

Response Procedures

The potential severity of an accident involving the release of a hazardous waste may be reduced through response measures developed and tested under realistic drill conditions. In the absence of such plans, or when the waste components are not known, it is advisable to assume that an industrial waste is hazardous and to treat it with due care until more information becomes available from reliable sources. In general, response procedures include the following:

1. Wearing full protective clothing and breathing apparatus;
2. Using the appropriate detection devices to check for the flammability, toxicity, or radioactivity of the released waste or its products of combustion;
3. Stemming the flow of the waste at the source;
4. Diking the area around a liquid spill to limit its spread to sewage lines and drains and to reduce the vapor release rate;
5. Staying upwind when fumes are being generated;
6. Controlling ignition sources; and
7. Evacuating people who are downwind.

The decision to extinguish burning waste should be made very carefully after a full assessment of the consequences. Questions to be considered include the following:

1. Is the extinguishing agent to be used compatible with the waste?
2. Are sealed drums or containers of flammable liquids or compressed gases in danger of exposure to the fire?
3. Are there any radioactive, explosive, or oxidizing materials in the burning waste or near the fire?
4. Will extinguishment exacerbate the problem by allowing flammable or toxic vapors to be released once the fire is extinguished?
5. Will the use of water result in a severe pollution problem?

SPECIFIC WASTES

Combustible Refuse

Refuse of a highly combustible nature, such as dry waste paper, excelsior, etc., should be collected in metal containers and not allowed to accumulate. Quantity storage of these materials should be separated from buildings, roadways, and ignition sources by a distance of 50 ft (15 m) or more. Transport to an incinerator or landfill on a frequent schedule will minimize the fire hazard.

Drying Oils

Rags or paper that have absorbed drying-type oils are subject to spontaneous heating. They should be kept in well-covered metal cans and thoroughly dried before collection or transport.

Flammable Liquids and Waste Solvents

Waste solvents have variable flash points, hence varying levels of hazard, depending upon composition. Some may contain solids, tars, waxes, and other materials that impede flow. Chlorinated solvents and water may also be present.

The two most common methods of disposal for such wastes are by incineration or the use of a disposal contractor. In either case, the solvents are collected in 5-gal (19 L) cans or 55-gal (208 L) drums for disposal. If a contractor is used, the approximate composition of the waste must be provided.

Installations having substantial amounts of waste solvent may install their own solvent-recovery system. Alternatively, they may install an incinerator. In that case, an auxiliary gas or oil burner is needed to maintain adequate firebox temperature. Usually a scrubber section is used to remove acid gases and other pollutants. See NFPA 82, *Standard on Incinerators, Waste and Linen Handling Systems and Equipment*, for further information on industrial incinerator installations.

Polychlorinated Biphenyls (PCBs)

PCBs were manufactured and used in a variety of electrical and mechanical applications from the early 1930s until regulated by the Toxic Substances Control Act in 1977. They had been extensively used as a dielectric fluid in capacitors and transformers and as a lubricant in compressors and other machinery. They continue to be used today, but only in enclosed systems.

PCBs have been known to cause temporary skin irritations and nervous-system symptoms in humans and are suspected carcinogens. Improper combustion may produce highly toxic and carcinogenic products.

Extreme care must be taken in handling PCBs and fires involving PCBs. Waste PCBs from old electrical equipment must be disposed of by incineration at an approved site or at sea or buried in approved containers in a secure landfill.

Liquid and Solid Oxidizing Materials

Spilled oxidizing materials and leaking or broken containers should be immediately removed to a safe area to await disposal in conformance with applicable regulations and manufacturers' instructions. (See NFPA 43A, *Code for the Storage of Liquid and Solid Oxidizing Materials*.) Most, if not all, oxidizers can be rendered harmless by dilution with water. However, some solutions cause pollution of streams and rivers, and thus require pretreatment.

Combustible and Reactive Metals

Small scraps of sodium from laboratory use can be dissolved in ethyl alcohol (not isopropyl alcohol) and the resulting alkoxide neutralized with acid. Large quantities can be offered to a vendor for purification and recycling. Oil-contaminated dispersions or other moderate quantities can be burned in dry pans if provision is made to control the oxide fumes, which are highly alkaline. Disposal of sodium by throwing it directly into water is spectacular but extremely hazardous and will contaminate the water with sodium hydroxide. Equipment contaminated with small amounts of sodium may be cleaned by a remotely controlled introduction of water or steam. Potassium, sodium-potassium alloy (NaK) and lithium are handled in the same manner as sodium. Lithium reacts somewhat less violently with water.

It is usually feasible to reclaim magnesium fines and scrap in the form of defective castings, clippings, and coarse chips. If this is to be done, either locally or through a smelting firm, the scrap should be thoroughly dried before remelting. Scrap in the form of fine chips and dust-collector sludge can be disposed of in a specially constructed incinerator or by burning in a safely located outdoor area paved with fire-brick or hard-burned paving brick. By spreading the scrap or sludge in a layer about 4 in. (102 mm) thick, on which ordinary combustible material is placed and ignited, the combustion of magnesium can be safely conducted. Another method of deactivating magnesium sludge is to treat it with a 0.5 percent solution of ferrous chloride. Since hydrogen is generated by this reaction, this method of disposal is conducted in an open container in an outdoor location where the hydrogen can be safely dissipated. (See NFPA 48, *Standard for the Storage, Handling and Processing of Magnesium*.)

Spontaneous combustion of titanium has occurred in fines, chips, and swarf that were coated with water-soluble oil. Disposal containers should be tightly closed and segregated so that spontaneous burning would not involve other exposures. Incineration in the open, as for magnesium scrap, may be feasible. (See NFPA 481, *Standard for the Production, Processing, Handling and Storage of Titanium*.)

While small amounts of zirconium fines can be mixed with sand or other inert material and buried, incineration of this combustible metal is generally preferred for larger quantities. Because of the spontaneous ignition potential, personnel carrying scrap should wear flame-protective clothing and equipment and carry the scrap in buckets on a yoke between them. A layer may be ignited with excelsior. (See NFPA 482, *Standard for the Production, Processing, Handling, and Storage of Zirconium*.)

Lithium hydride and lithium aluminum hydride can ignite upon contact with water or moist air. Alkaline oxides resulting from incineration may be collected and neutralized.

Radioactive Waste

Radioactive waste is generated at nuclear power plants in the form of spent fuel and contaminated instruments, equipment, piping, and other objects such as clothing, gloves, and cleaning rags. Other sources include nuclear-physics research laboratories and tailings from uranium mines.

Recent advances in the use of radioactive materials in medical diagnostics and therapy has led to an increase in the sources of radioactive medical waste. Radioactive isotopes of iodine, cesium, iridium, phosphorus, and gallium are widely used in hospitals and laboratories for diagnostics and patient treatments. Contaminated vials, containers, and capsules are growing in quantity. All radioactively contaminated materials must be properly disposed of.

The packaging of all radioactive waste, including radioactive medical waste, is regulated by the Nuclear Regulatory Commission (NRC) while the Department of Transportation (DOT) regulates its transportation. The EPA has developed standards for protecting the public against exposure to nuclear-reactor wastes in general, and for the proper storage and disposal of such waste. The specific requirements vary greatly, and depend upon the type of radioactive waste that is generated.

For most installations, a contractor licensed to dispose of radioactive materials can be employed. (See NFPA 801, *Recommended Fire Protection Practice for Facilities Handling Radioactive Materials*.) Radioactive materials that are flammable or combustible must be handled with particular care. Combustible radioactive wastes should not be allowed to accumulate. Storage of such wastes near an air intake is particularly undesirable. If the products of combustion of waste materials containing long-lived radioactive materials are dispersed through air-conditioning or compressed-air systems, extensive decontamination may become necessary.

Liquid radioactive waste may be concentrated and retained until the radioactivity has decayed to a safe level. Combustible radioactive waste, such as absorbent paper used to wipe contaminated surfaces, should be placed in approved containers for disposal.

The treatment of radioactive medical wastes is less extensive than that for other medical wastes. For radioactive medical waste with a half-life of less than 65 days, the waste may be stored in a secure area for a minimum period of 10 half-lives and discarded as sanitary wastes. All other radioactive waste must be disposed of at one of three licensed radioactive waste disposal sites located in Beatty, NV; Barnwell, SC; and Richland, WA.[10]

Oil Spills on Water

Booming of spills has been proved effective in containing spills of liquids on relatively calm and current-free waters. Various makeshift designs of booms have been tried with relative ineffectiveness, but commercially available booms which recognize the hydrodynamics and aerodynamics involved in the confinement of spills on water have proved quite effective. Because of ecological considerations, this has become an important means of containing an oil spill, and more effective equipment is now available.

Following the confinement of spills on water, various ways of removing the confined liquid have been used, including skimming devices or absorbents. Absorbents, such as straw, plastics, sawdust, and peat moss, have been spread on the surface of the spill and then collected and burned on shore. Skimming devices operate on several principles, including pumps and separators. Power boats with skimmers on the bow can scoop up oil and water, sending it through an oil separator and rollers to which oil adheres. The oil is then removed by scraping or compression.

Sinking agents to which oil may adhere and sink to the bottom have been used in the past. Several proprietary sinking agents have been developed, but such products as carbonized sand, brick dust, crushed clinkers, and cement also have been used. However, sinking agents are objectionable because they contribute to water pollution and are no longer recommended, except possibly for use in the ocean far from land.

Regardless of whether a spill occurs on land or on water, pre-planning is imperative and should include prompt notification of all local, state, or federal agencies dealing with the problem of water pollution.

Underground Storage Tanks

The EPA estimates that there are more than two million underground-storage-tank (UST) systems in the United States located at more than 700,000 operating facilities nationwide.[12, 13] In addition, there are numerous abandoned tanks. Although most of these tanks are (or were) used for the storage of motor fuels, some are (or were) used for the storage of other hazardous chemicals. Tests on a random sample of more than 10,000 USTs have shown that about 25 percent of these systems are leaking, either because they lack corrosion protection, or because of improper installation, piping failure, and overfilling.

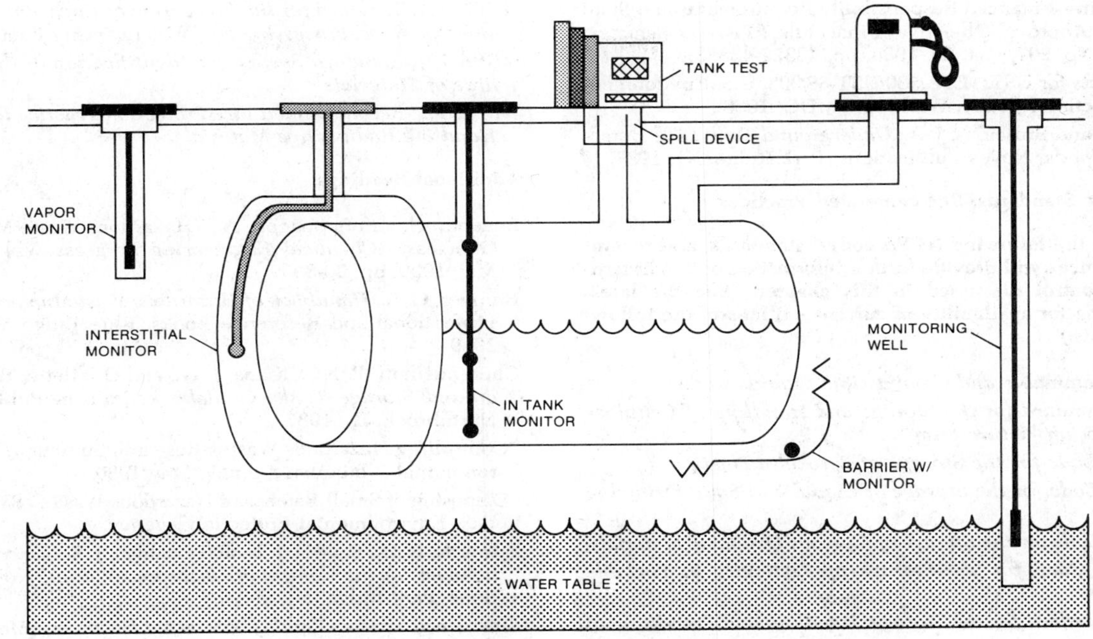

FIG. 9-16D. UST leak detection alternatives.[14]

Underground liquid leaks invariably find their way to groundwater which is the primary source of drinking water for more than 50 percent of the U.S. population. Leaking petroleum products contaminate the soil and the air. Their vapors may accumulate in confined spaces, such as septic tanks, sewers, and building basements. The vapors are hazardous to human health. If ignited, they may result in a fire or an explosion.

To protect the public and the environment against leaks from USTs, the federal government extended and strengthened the provisions of The Solid Waste Disposal Act as amended by RCRA. Subtitle I of RCRA regulates USTs containing "regulated substances" and releases of these substances to the environment.

Subtitle I defined an UST as a tank system, including its piping, that has at least 10 percent of its volume underground. Regulated substances include those defined as hazardous under CERCLA, and petroleum products. This standard requires that USTs installed after 1988 be properly built, certified, equipped with overfill protection and detection systems, and, if made of steel, protected against corrosion. By 1998, all USTs installed before 1988 must have corrosion protection for steel tanks and piping, and devices to prevent overfilling. Existing tanks must also be tested for leaks in accordance with a schedule determined by their age.[14]

Leaks from USTs must be detected by one (or a combination) of the following monitoring methods[15];

1. Automatic tank gaging;
2. Monitoring for vapor in the soil;
3. Interstitial monitoring between the storage tank and an external protective tank; and
4. Monitoring for the presence of contaminants in groundwater.

BIBLIOGRAPHY

References Cited

1. Reindl, J., "Interrelationships Within the Solid Wastes System," *Solid Wastes Management*, Apr. 1977, pp. 22-23, 54-56.
2. EPA, "The Toxic Release Inventory: National Perspective 1987," EPA/560/4-89-005, U.S. Environmental Protection Agency, Washington, DC, 1989.
3. EPA, "Criteria for Identifying the Characteristics of Hazardous Waste and Listing Hazardous Waste," *Federal Register*, Vol. 45, No. 98, Subpart B May 19, 1980, pp. 33121-33122.
4. CFR, "Title 49: Transportation," Subpart G, Section 173.300, *Code of Federal Regulations*, Washington, DC, 1988, p. 584.
5. CFR, *Ibid.*, Subpart E, Section 173.151, pp. 492-493.
6. EPA, "Part II: Environmental Protection Agency, 40 CFR 22 and 259: Standards for the Tracking and Management of Medical Waste; Interim Final Rule and Request for Comments," *Federal Register*, Vol. 54, No. 56, Mar. 24, 1989, pp. 12326-12395.
7. World Bank, *Environmental Considerations for the Industrial Development Sector*, Office of Environmental and Health Affairs, The World Bank, Washington, DC, 1978.
8. Reindl, J., "Examining Disposal and Recycling Techniques for Solid Wastes," *Solid Wastes Management*, May 1977, pp. 60, 68, 70, 92, 94.
9. EPA, "Part II: Environmental Protection Agency, 40 CFR Parts 22 and 259," *Federal Register*, Vol. 54, No. 56, March 24, 1989.
10. Meaney, J. G., and Cheremisinoff, P.N., "Medical Waste Strategy," *Pollution Engineering*, Vol. 21, No. 11, Oct. 1989, pp. 92-106.
11. CFR, "Title 29, Section 1910.120—Final Rule," *Federal Register*, Vol. 54, No. 42, Mar. 6, 1989, pp. 9294-9336.
12. EPA, "Part II: Environmental Protection Agency, 40 CFR Parts 280 and 281: Underground Storage Tanks; Technical Requirements and State Program Approval; Final Rules," Sept. 1988, *Federal Register*, Vol. 53. No. 185, Sept. 23, 1988, pp. 37082-37247.
13. EPA, "Part II: Environmental Protection Agency, 40 CFR Parts 280 and 281: Underground Storage Tanks Containing

Petroleum—Financial Responsibility Requirements and State Program Approval Objective; Final Rule," *Federal Register*, Vol. 53, No. 207, Oct. 26, 1988, pp. 43322-43383.

14. EPA, *Musts for USTs*, EPA/530/UST-88/008, U.S. Environmental Protection Agency, Washington, DC, 1988.
15. Niaki, S., and Broscious, J. A., *Underground Tank Leak Detection Methods*, Noyes Publications, Park Ridge, NJ, 1987.

NFPA Codes, Standards, Recommended Practices

Reference to the following NFPA codes, standards, and recommended practices will provide further information on the hazardous waste control discussed in this chapter. (See the latest *NFPA Catalog* for availability of current editions of the following documents.)

NFPA 30, *Flammable and Combustible Liquids Code*.

NFPA 40, *Standard for the Storage and Handling of Cellulose Nitrate Motion Picture Film*.

NFPA 40E, *Code for the Storage of Pyroxylin Plastic*.

NFPA 43A, *Code for the Storage of Liquid and Solid Oxidizing Materials*.

NFPA 43C, *Code for the Storage of Gaseous Oxidizing Materials*.

NFPA 43D, *Code for the Storage of Pesticides in Portable Containers*.

NFPA 48, *Standard for the Storage, Handling and Processing of Magnesium*.

NFPA 49, *Hazardous Chemicals Data*.

NFPA 61A, *Standard for Prevention of Fire and Dust Explosions in Facilities Manufacturing and Handling Starch*.

NFPA 61B, *Standard for the Prevention of Fires and Explosions in Grain Elevators and Facilities Handling Bulk Raw Agricultural Commodities*.

NFPA 61C, *Standard for the Prevention of Fire and Dust Explosions in Feed Mills*.

NFPA 61D, *Standard for the Prevention of Fire and Dust Explosions in the Milling of Agricultural Commodities for Human Consumption*.

NFPA 82, *Standard on Incinerators, Waste and Linen Handling Systems and Equipment*.

NFPA 85F, *Standard for the Installation and Operation of Pulverized Fuel Systems*.

NFPA 91, *Standard for the Installation of Blower and Exhaust Systems for Dust, Stock and Vapor Removal or Conveying*.

NFPA 325M, *Fire Hazard Properties of Flammable Liquids, Gases and Volatile Solids*.

NFPA 329, *Recommended Practice for Handling Underground Leakage of Flammable and Combustible Liquids*.

NFPA 471, *Recommended Practice for Responding to Hazardous Materials Incidents*

NFPA 472, *Standard for Professional Competence of Responding to Hazardous Materials Incidents*

NFPA 481, *Standard for the Production, Processing, Handling and Storage of Titanium*.

NFPA 482, *Standard for the Production, Processing, Handling, and Storage of Zirconium*.

NFPA 490, *Code for the Storage of Ammonium Nitrate*.

NFPA 491M, *Manual of Hazardous Chemical Reactions*.

NFPA 495, *Code for the Manufacture, Transportation, Storage, and Use of Explosive Materials*.

NFPA 498, *Standard for Explosives Motor Vehicle Terminals*.

NFPA 651, *Standard for the Manufacture of Aluminum and Magnesium Powder*.

NFPA 654, *Standard for the Prevention of Fire and Dust Explosions in the Chemical, Dye, Pharmaceutical, and Plastics Industries*.

NFPA 655, *Standard for Prevention of Sulfur Fires and Explosions*.

NFPA 664, *Standard for the Prevention of Fires and Dust Explosions in Wood Processing and Woodworking Facilities*.

NFPA 704, *Standard System for Identification of the Fire Hazards of Materials*

NFPA 801, *Recommended Fire Protection Practice for Facilities Handling Radioactive Materials*.

Additional Readings

Beecher, N. and Rappaport, A., "Hazardous Waste Management Overseas," *Chemical Engineering Progress*, Vol. 86, No. 5, May 1990, pp. 30-39.

Brunner, C. R., *Handbook of Hazardous Waste Incineration*, TAB Professional and Reference Books, Blue Ridge Summit, PA, 1989.

Cheremisinoff, P. N., Casana, J. G., and Ouellette, R. P., *Underground Storage Tanks Guidebook*, Pudvan Publishing Co., Northbrook, IL, 1987.

"Controlling Hazardous Wastes-Research Summary," U.S. Environmental Protection Agency, May 1980.

"Disposing of Small Batches of Hazardous Waste," SW-562, 1976, U.S. Environmental Protection Agency.

Edwards, B. H., Paullin, J. N. and Coghlan, J. K., *Emergency Technologies for the Control of Hazardous Wastes*, Noyes Publications, Park Ridge, NJ, 1983.

Emergency Services Guide for Selected Hazardous Materials, U.S. Department of Transportation, Washington, DC.

"Engineering Handbook for Hazardous Waste Incineration," SW-889, Sept. 1981, U.S. Environmental Protection Agency.

Evans, D. D., *et al*, "Burning, Smoke Production, and Smoke Dispersion from Oil Spill Combustion," NISTIR 89-4091, May 1989, National Institute for Standards and Technology, Gaithersburg, MD.

Evans, D. D., *et al*, "Combustion of Oil on Water," NBSIR 86-3420, Nov. 1987, National Bureau of Standards, Gaithersburg, MD.

Evans, D. D., *et al*, "Environmental Effects of Oil Spill Combustion," NISTIR 88-3822, Sept. 1988, National Institute for Standards and Technology, Gaithersburg, MD.

Fire Protection Guide to Hazardous Materials, National Fire Protection Association, Quincy, MA 1991.

"Firms Avidly Seeking New Hazardous Waste Treatment Routes," *Chemical Engineering*, Sept. 6, 1982, pp. 53-57.

"Flammable and Combustible Waste Disposal in the Plastics Industry," *Bulletin No. 13*, Society of the Plastics Industry, New York.

Goodier, J. L., Siclari, R. J., and Garrity, P. A., *Spill Prevention and Fail-Safe Engineering for Petroleum and Related Products*, Noyes Publications, Park Ridge, NJ, 1983.

Gronow, J. R., Schofield, A. N., and Jain, R. K., *eds*., Land Disposal of Hazardous Waste, Wiley, New York, 1988.

Guide for Safety in the Chemical Laboratory, 2nd ed., Van Nostrand Co., New York.

"Hazardous Waste Generation and Commercial Hazardous Waste Management," SW-894, 1980, U.S. Environmental Protection Agency.

Hazardous Waste Management Guide, J. J. Keller and Associates, Neenah, WI, 1983.

Hackman, E., *Toxic Organic Chemical Destruction and Waste Treatment*, Noyes Publications, Park Ridge, NY, 1978.

"Hazardous and Industrial Waste," *Proceedings* of the Mid-Atlantic Industrial Waste Conference, Hazardous Materials Control Research Institute, Silver Springs, MD, 1988.

Hazardous Materials: In Site Stabilization, Hazardous Materials Control Research Institute, Silver Spring, MD, 1987.

Hazardous Waste Generation and Shipment Report, U.S. Environmental Protection Agency, Washington, DC, 1987.

Hazardous Waste Management: A Survey of State Legislation, National Conference of State Legislation, Denver, CO, 1982.

Henry, M. F., *Hazardous Materials Response Handbook*, National Fire Protection Association, Quincy, MA 1990.

Henry, M. F., "Update on the Underground Leakage Problem," *Fire Journal*, Vol. 80, No. 1, 1986, p. 26.

Hitchcock, D., "Solid Waste Disposal: Incineration," *Chemical Engineering*, May 21 1979, pp. 185-194.

Johnson, N. P. and Cosmos, M. G., "Thermal Treatment Technologies for Haz Waste Remediation," *Pollution Engineering*, Vol. 21, No. 11, Oct. 1989, pp. 66-85.

La Grega, M. D. and Hendrian, L. K., *eds*., Toxic and Hazardous Waste, Butterworths, Boston, MA, 1983.

Linville, J., *ed*., *Industrial Fire Hazards Handbook*, 2nd ed., National Fire Protection Association, Quincy, MA, 1990.

Melvold, R. W., Gibson, S. C., and Scarberry, R., *Sorbents for Liquid Hazardous Substance Cleanup and Control*, Noyes Publications, Park Ridge, NJ, 1988.

Metry, A. A., *The Handbook of Hazardous Waste Management*, Technomic, Lancaster, PA, 1980.

Perry, B., *ed*., *Handbook of Hazardous Waste Regulation*, 3rd ed., Business and Legal Reports, Madison, CT, 1989.

Pocket Guide to Chemical Hazards, U.S. Department of Health, Education and Welfare, DHEW (NIOSH) Publication No. 85-114, 1987.

Region 5 Hazardous Waste and Toxic Substances, U.S. Environmental Protection Agency, Region 5, Chicago, IL, 1985.

Robinson, J. S., *ed*., *Hazardous Chemical Spill Cleanup*, Noyes Publications, Park Ridge, NJ, 1979.

Shen, T. T., Chen, M., and Lauber, J., "Incineration of Toxic Chemical Wastes," *Pollution Engineering*, Oct. 1978, pp. 45-50.

Sittig, M., *Incineration of Industrial Hazardous Wastes and Sludges*, Noyes Publications, Park Ridge, NJ, 1981.

"Technologies and Management Strategies for Hazardous Waste Control," OTA-M-197, Mar. 1983, Congressional Office of Technology Assessment, Washington, DC.

The Seventh Annual Seminar on Hazardous Wastes and Toxic Torts, Law Journal Seminars-Press, New York, 1989.

Unterberg, W., *et al*, *How to Prevent Spills of Hazardous Substances*, Noyes Publications, Park Ridge, NJ, 1988.

Unterberg, W., *et al*., *How to Respond to Hazardous Chemical Spills*, Noyes Publications, Park Ridge, NJ, 1988.

Vance, M., *Industrial Waste Disposal: A Bibliography*, Vance Bibliographies, Monticello, IL, 1982.

Wilson, D. G., *Handbook of Solid Waste Management*, Van Nostrand Reinhold, NY, 1977.

Worthy, W., "Hazardous Treatment Technology Grows," *C&EN*, Mar. 1982, pp. 10-16.

York, K. G. and Grey, G. L., "Hazardous Materials/Waste Handling for the Emergency Responder," *Fire Engineering*, New York, 1989.

WASTE CONTROL

Lawrence G. Doucet

Although typical solid wastes are rarely a source of ignition, they are a potential source of fuel for fires or ignition from other sources. Therefore, a proper and efficient waste-management system incorporating prompt treatment and disposal is essential for good firesafety. This chapter covers the firesafety aspects of waste management, treatment, and disposal systems and equipment.

Waste management generally comprises the collection, internal transport, interim storage, treatment, and final disposal of wastes. A great variety of alternate processes and equipment are available for providing these functions as part of a total waste management system. Depending upon the specific types, forms, quantities, and hazardous characteristics of the wastes, management systems can range from a few simple processes to a complex combination of many processes.

Waste handling generally refers to those functions associated with the movement of wastes after creation, excluding storage, processing, treatment, and final disposal. It includes collection of wastes at points of generation, transport of the materials, and unloading from the transport system.

Waste handling systems also comprise equipment and devices for loading or charging waste into treatment systems and processes. For example, mechanical loading devices may be part of a system for charging solid waste into an incinerator. Waste handling systems and equipment include conveyors, chutes, carts, and transport vehicles, elevators and lifts. These systems can range in sophistication from fully manual to fully automatic operation.

Waste storage includes the interim containment of accumulated materials prior to subsequent handling, processing, treatment, or disposal. Waste storage, depending on the waste type and form, can be loose, compacted, shredded, or another processed form. It can also be stored in bulk or individual containers, such as drums or cartons.

Waste processing includes those functions that prepare or alter the waste by changing its shape, size uniformity, or consistency. Such processes are usually provided to facilitate handling, storage, treatment , or disposal processes. Waste processing systems and equipment include compactors, shredders, crushers, pulpers, pulverizers, baggers and encapsulators, extruders, and de-watering devices.

Waste treatment and disposal systems include incinerators, steam sterilizers or autoclaves, and various technologies combining shredding with biomedical-waste disinfection or sterilization processes, such as chemical injection, microwaving, infared radiation, and gamma radiation.

WASTE STORAGE ROOMS

Rooms in a building or structure that are used for the storage or handling of waste in any form and in amounts exceeding three cubic yards (2.3 m^3) uncompacted measure are subject to the requirements of NFPA 82, *Standard on Incinerators, Waste and Linen Handling Systems and Equipment*. The walls, ceilings and floors of these rooms are required to have fire resistance ratings, and room openings must be protected by self-closing fire doors suitable for Class B openings. In addition, these rooms require automatic sprinklers, in accordance with NFPA 13, *Standard for Installation of Sprinkler Systems*, and the provision of a hand hose suitable for reaching all portions of the room.

WASTE CHUTES AND HANDLING SYSTEMS

Waste chutes are generally fixed systems for transporting waste from points of generation or interim storage to centralized areas for processing, treatment, or disposal. There are basically five types of chute systems:

1) *General access, gravity type* — This type of chute consists of an enclosed vertical passageway through which waste is transferred by gravity alone. All occupants of the building have unlimited access to the chute.
2) *Limited access, gravity type* — This type of chute is similar to a general access type except that access is restricted. Entry is gained through locked chute doors or locked service opening room doors. These chutes

Mr. Doucet is a principal with the consulting/engineering firm of Doucet & Mainka, P.C., Peekskill, NY.

are used primarily in hospitals and health-care institutions.

3) *Pneumatic system* — This type of system uses air flow to transport waste from chute service openings to a central collection area. Such systems have chutes that may run horizontally, vertically, or inclined, depending upon blower and design characteristics. High-velocity air, which typically transports waste materials at speeds of about 60 mph (79 km/hr), is aspirated through the top of the chute and exhausted at its termination. These systems are usually found in hospitals, but they can be used in any size or type of building. Figure 9-17A shows a diagrammatic view of a pneumatic chute system.

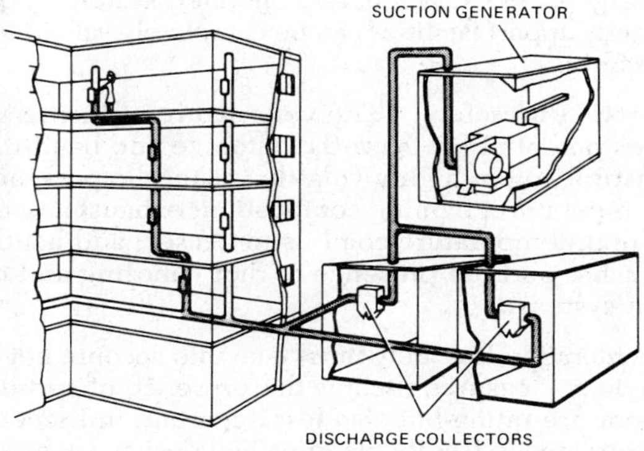

FIG. 9-17A. A diagrammatic representation of a building-wide pneumatic chute system.

4) *Gravity-pneumatic systems* — This type of system uses a conventional gravity chute to feed a collecting chamber which in turn feeds a pneumatic chute system.
5) *Multi-loading pneumatic systems* — This type of system is similar to a pneumatic type except that entry is gained through automatic or self-closing, positive-latching inlet doors which are interlocked so that only one can be opened at a time and not when the material damper is open.

Waste Chute Design and Construction

Waste chute design and construction are critical to firesafety in waste handling systems. Chutes could readily serve as channels capable of carrying smoke and flames throughout a building or facility. They are often considered as waste storage areas since they could become clogged with waste during use and present fire and smoke hazards. Criteria relative to chute construction, chute enclosures, fire dampers, sprinklers, service openings and the like are all directed towards minimizing and controlling potential fire hazards. In this regard, the requirements of NFPA 82 must be strictly adhered to.

Gravity-type chutes may be constructed of unlined steel, refractory-lined steel or masonry, while pneumatic waste handling systems are constructed only of unlined steel. Unlined chutes are fabricated of stainless, galvanized, or aluminized steel for corrosion resistance. Each type of chute construction has separate design and construction criteria, as detailed in NFPA 82, for providing structural integrity combined with adequate firesafety measures.

Chute size: Gravity-type chutes are required to be not less than 22½ by 22½ ins. (570 by 570 mm) or not less than 24 ins. (610 mm) inside diameter. Pneumatic waste handling system chutes are required to be not less than 16 ins. (410 mm) inside diameter but may be smaller if all waste materials are first shredded. However, these sizing criteria are strictly minimum requirements. Waste types and volumes, waste package sizes, user habits and specific applications must be carefully considered before accepting minimum sizing for chutes and service openings. For example, a kitchen compactor may produce a typical package measuring 16 x 16 x 9 ins. (570 x 570 x 230 mm), which would have a recommended chute diameter of about 36 ins. (915 mm).

Chute service openings: Properly sized chute service openings are necessary to prevent chute clogging. Oversized openings increase the probability that overly large or excessive quantities of waste will be loaded into the chute and become clogged. Standards for maximum service opening sizes, developed to prevent such conditions, are as follows:

1) General access gravity chute service openings are limited to one-third of the cross-sectional area of a square chute or 44 percent of the cross-sectional area of a round chute.
2) Limited access gravity-type chutes are limited to two-thirds of the cross-sectional area of the chute.
3) Pneumatic chute service openings may be equivalent to or greater than the cross-sectional area of the chute. However, pneumatic system service entrances, or charging stations, comprise a compartment with electrically interlocked inner and outer doors. The capacity of the charging compartment, with only one door being allowed open at a time, limits the volumes or sizes of waste that can be loaded into the chute.

Chute doors: Chute service openings are required to be equipped with fire-rated door enclosures to prevent or minimize the spread of chute fires. Otherwise, natural air-flows and pressures could cause flames and smoke to be exfiltrated into other building areas. According to NFPA 82, chute doors must also be self-closing and positive latching types. As noted, pneumatic system service openings are required to have two electrically interlocked doors. For structural integrity, door frames must be securely fastened to both the chute and chute enclosure walls.

Chute enclosures and penetrations: In order to insure fire integrity, chute system enclosures, including floor and wall penetrations, require fire-rated protection. Metal chutes, which in themselves offer no fire resistance, must be totally enclosed within walls of masonry or other noncombustible, fire-rated material. However, masonry chutes meeting the fire resistance requirements of NFPA 82 are not required to be enclosed. If a masonry chute penetrates a floor without closing the opening entirely, the space between the floor and chute should be filled with material equivalent to the floor in fire resistance.

Wherever a waste chute penetrates a fire-rated floor-and-ceiling assembly, fire wall or other fire-rated assembly, a fire damper is required. However, a fire damper may not be needed if the chute is enclosed within a fire-rated shaft. Schematic diagrams of typical chute system fire rating requirements are shown in NFPA 82.

Chute discharge and terminal rooms: Waste chutes are required to discharge or terminate in an enclosed room or bin separated from other parts of the building. Since a chute-terminal enclosure area is subject to potential ignition sources, the walls, ceiling, and floor of the room or bin must have a fire-resistance rating equivalent to that required for the chute. Also, such terminal enclosures are required to have automatic fire doors, automatic sprinklers, and hand hose adequate to reach all areas of the room, and a ventilation system designed to exhaust fire and smoke to the outdoors. These requirements are in recognition of the seriousness of fires from waste, which are generally difficult to control and typically generate large quantities of smoke.

In gravity-pneumatic-type chute systems, the collecting chambers, which can be considered interim discharge or terminal points, are vulnerable to potential fires. They should be adequately sprinklered and provided with ready access for fire fighting measures. Also, the valve room of the system should be sprinklered to aid in cooling the space.

Older gravity chute systems typically discharged directly into an incinerator, and in some systems, the waste chute also served as the incinerator chimney. Because of the tremendous potentials for fire and smoke hazards, most of these older installations have been discontinued or abandoned. Today, waste chutes are not permitted to discharge directly into an incinerator. Furthermore, because of the inherent difficulties in maintaining fire integrity, systems for automatically transferring waste materials from chute terminal enclosures directly into an incinerator are not recommended.

Chute sprinklers: According to NFPA 82, chute systems must be either sprinklered or capable of containing a fire and venting products of combustion. Metal chutes require automatic sprinklers at the top and at alternate floor levels. Specific requirements for chute sprinklers are in NFPA 13, *Standard for the Installation of Sprinkler Systems*. A good practice is to locate sprinklers where they can be inspected and maintained and yet be out of reach of vandals and beyond the range of falling waste. Masonry chutes, or chutes constructed in accordance with requirements for factory-built, medium-heat appliance-chimney sections are not required to be sprinklered.

Chute service opening enclosures: For many years it was general practice to put chute service openings in public corridors for convenience sake. However, aside from the problems of unsightliness and poor sanitation, fire hazards were seriously increased and the fire integrity of a building reduced. Fatalities occurred when chute fires spilled into corridors and cut off means of escape. NFPA 82 requires every service opening to be located in a room or compartment separated from other parts of the building by an enclosure or room having fire-rated wall-and-ceiling assemblies and with the opening into the enclosure protected by a self-locking fire door.

INCINERATORS

Incineration is an engineered process using high temperature combustion for the treatment and disposal of waste. Properly designed and operated systems can reduce the weight and volume of most domestic, commercial, institutional and industrial solid waste by as much as 95 percent or more, thereby greatly reducing off-site haulage and disposal costs. Incinerators are often used for the destruction and sterilization of biological and pathological wastes at health care facilities, universities, and the like. Industrial facilities use on-site incineration for the destruction of hazardous and toxic wastes. In addition, incineration with waste heat recovery is often an attractive and cost-effective alternative energy source for many facilities. In terms of firesafety, incineration provides prompt and complete waste destruction which substantially reduces interim, on-site waste storage requirements and associated potential fire hazards.

Many early incinerator designs comprised little more than enclosed, single-chamber fire boxes in which uncontrolled burning took place. Such systems provided poor waste destruction and were notorious sources of smoke and odor problems. However, modern technology offers systems that are readily capable of meeting demanding waste destruction and performance requirements in compliance with stringent environmental regulations. In addition, properly designed, constructed, and operated systems, equipment, and support facilities can be completely safe in terms of firesafety.

Incineration firesafety: The very nature of incineration presents potential fire hazards: storage and handling of combustible, often highly volatile waste; the presence of high-temperature, flaming combustion; exhaust and ducting of high-temperature combustion gases; and handling of hot ashes and the presence of fuel handling and combustion systems.

Incineration firesafety must take into account not only the obvious measures such as the presence of sprinklers and room fire-rating but also less apparent, indirect measures as related to facility planning and design, such as system layout, equipment orientation, waste-flow patterns, system operations, and maintenance practices.

Incinerator Categories

There are many incinerator technologies and designs. There is also a wide variation in the types of waste that can be incinerated, including solids, liquids, sludges, and fumes. This chapter is not intended to cover or include all of the design and construction details for each incinerator technology and application. However, all design, construction, control and other features as needed to reduce or minimize fire hazards are required for all incinerator facilities.

The basic types of solid-waste incinerators that are typically used in institutional, commercial and industrial facilities are as follows:

Multiple-chamber incinerator: Consists of a primary and one or more secondary chambers, and operates with high-excess combustion air— typically 200 to 300 percent. Wastes are loaded into the primary chamber for combustion, and most combustibles entrained in the flue gases are burned in the secondary chambers. These are designed and constructed in accordance with standards developed in the mid 1950s.

Controlled-air incinerator: A two-stage combustion process: wastes in the primary chamber, or first stage, are burned under starved air, or oxygen-deficient conditions; smoke and volatiles from the first stage are combusted in the secondary chamber under excess air conditions— typically 100 to 200 percent.

These systems were first used in the early 1960s and probably more than ninety percent of the incinerators installed since have been of the controlled-air design.

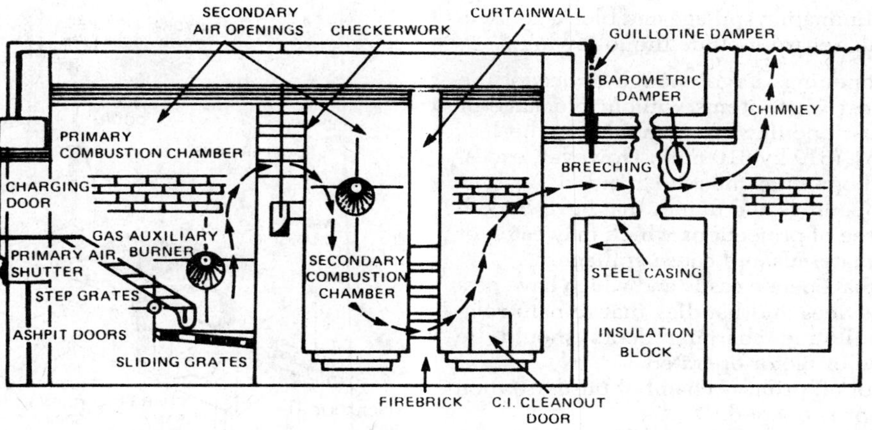

FIG. 9-17B. A typical in-line type multiple-chamber incinerator.

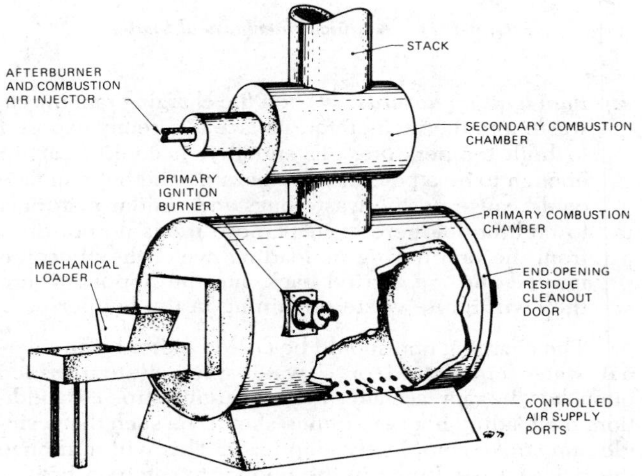

FIG. 9-17C. A schematic of a typical controlled-air incinerator.

Rotary kiln incinerator: Comprises a cylindrical combustion chamber, or kiln, oriented at a slight incline to horizontal, which rotates slowly on its axis. Wastes are loaded at one end, and kiln rotation provides turbulence for thorough waste destruction as well as for the discharge of ash residues from the opposite end. Combustibles entrained in the flue gases from the kiln are burned in a secondary chamber. These are versatile systems widely used for burning virtually all types of industrial waste, and they have recently been used for an increasing number of institutional and commercial waste applications and facilities.

Design and Construction

Incineration systems and equipment, including breechings and stacks, are subject to extremely severe operating conditions. These include very high and widely fluctuating temperatures, thermal shocks from wet material, residues that cause slag, clinkers and spalling of refractory linings, explosions from items such as aerosol cans, corrosive attacks from acids and other chemicals, and mechanical scraping and abrasions from metallic wastes as well as operating and cleanout tools. Incineration systems must be suitably designed, constructed, structurally supported and reinforced to resist cracking, warping, or distortions that may be caused by these severe conditions. Such failures could allow flames and hot gases to escape into building areas and create dangerous fire hazards.

Outside surface, or skin, temperatures must also be limited by proper incinerator design and construction. Incinerator casings accessible to operators must be insulated, shielded, or appropriately shrouded to prevent a temperature rise exceeding 70°F (21°C) over ambient levels, while operating doors and handles must be designed for a maximum 40°F (10°C) rise if metallic and 60°F (15°C) rise if nonmetallic.

Explosion-relief protection is also a requirement. Incinerators must be equipped with a suitable relief door or panel with an effective area of 1 sq ft per 100 cu ft (1 m^2 100 m^3) of primary combustion chamber volume.

Location and Arrangement

Incineration systems should be well planned and implement to assure that 1) waste and residue containers do not block charging and clean out operations or access to work areas, or passageways, 2) waste can be charged in a smooth, efficient manner, 3) all parts of the incinerator, including the ash pit, combustion chambers, and breechings are easily and safely accessible for cleaning, repair, and servicing, and 4) clearances above the charging door and between the incinerator top and sides to combustible materials are in compliance with codes and standards.

Charging Systems

The loading of waste into an incinerator has a particularly high fire-hazard potential in that it provides a direct interface between high-temperature, flaming combustion conditions within the incinerator and surrounding building areas. Inadequate designs and improper operations could permit radiant heat, flames, and combustion products to escape from the incinerator into building areas.

Two methods of incinerator charging are manual loading directly through a charging door and mechanical loading with an automatic-airlock charging system.

Direct manual loading: This charging method is often used on incinerators less than about 500 lb per hr (227 kg/hr) as well as on systems that are batch loaded or that require loading at very infrequent intervals. Fire-prevention measures include minimizing charging-door opening times and eliminating spillage and blockage. Recommendations in this regard include the following:

1) Charging-door openings large enough to accept the largest or bulkiest waste items without blockage or obstruction. Clear opening areas should not be less than 24 by 24 ins. (610 by 610 mm). However, excessively oversized openings must be avoided.
2) Charging-door openings and frames that have smooth edges and are free of projections which may catch or hang up waste materials and cause spillage.
3) Charging doors that operate easily and which have positive latching devices and handles that remain relatively cool. Guillotine charging doors should be counterweighted or motor operated.
4) Interlocks to shut off primary chamber burners when the charging door is opened.
5) Loading trays, where appropriate, in front of charging doors to assist the operators in handling and loading heavy and unwieldy waste materials.

Mechanical loading: Automatic, mechanical charging systems are always used on incinerators greater than about 500 lb per hr (227 kg/hr) and where controlled charging rates are needed. However, they are sometimes employed on smaller-capacity systems where a continuous airlock interface is required. Mechanical loaders are also used to protect against incinerator overcharging conditions.

The latest issue of NFPA 82 requires that waste-charging system and appropriate controls be provided which will prevent the direct discharge of flames, combustion gases, and heat from the incinerator during waste-loading operations. This is to include a hopper/ram-type mechanical loader or other approved system. The standard also stipulates that the only exceptions are those incinerators that are loaded on a batch basis, whereby the charging door is not opened while waste combustion is taking place. Furthermore, it should be noted that many state environmental agencies now legislate mechanical loaders on all incinerators as a means of controlling stack and fugitive emissions.

The most common type of mechanical charging system is the "hopper/ram loader," as shown in Figure 9-17D. Typically, waste is put into the charging hopper and, upon actuation of a system-start switch, the hopper cover closes, the fire door opens, the charging ram injects the waste into the incinerator, the charging ram returns, the fire door closes, and the hopper cover opens for the next loading cycle. Hopper volume and a cycle timer help limit the amount of waste that can be loaded into the incinerator per hour, which helps prevent overcharging. An airlock interface is provided between the incinerator and ambient conditions because the fire door and hopper cover are not both opened simultaneously.

Two potential causes of fire and smoke problems which must be guarded against in hopper/ram loader systems are as follows:

1) *Partial closing of fire door*: Waste can lodge under the door and prevent it from closing tightly. This waste could ignite and spread fire back into the hopper and beyond. The partially closed door could also significantly affect incinerator draft conditions which in turn could result in heavy smoke escaping under the partially closed door. The fire door should be closed by power, not gravity, in order to seal the opening as tightly as possible should any waste become lodged beneath.

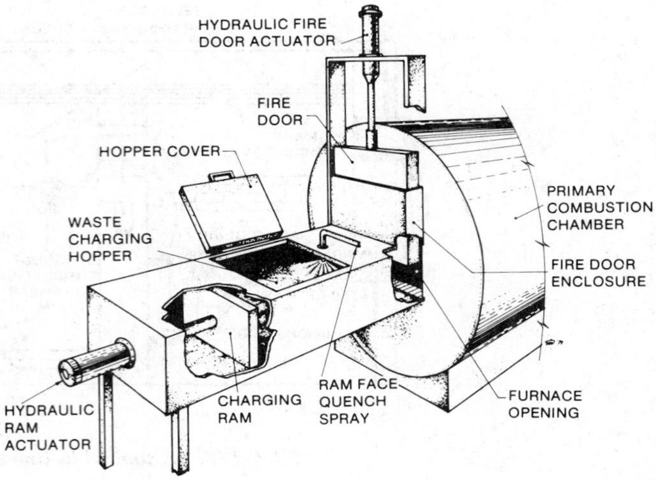

FIG. 9-17D. A typical mechanical loader.

2) *Ram ignition hazards*: When the charging ram injects waste into the incinerator, its face is directly exposed to high temperatures. Eventually, it could heat up enough to be a potential fire hazard. The hot ram face could cause plastic waste bags and similar materials to melt and adhere to it. If these items do not drop from the ram during its loading cycle, they become ignited and are carried back into the hopper where they will ignite waste remaining in the hopper.

The charging ram should be cooled either by an internal water circulation or a water-spray system which quenches the ram face after every charging stroke. In addition, the loading-hopper volume should be such that a single ram stroke completely empties it. This will minimize the risk of waste being in the hopper to catch on fire.

Additional recommended considerations to protect against accidental ignition of wastes in loading hoppers include the following:

1) Provision of a flame scanner for immediate detection of hopper fires. Actuation of the scanner could sound an alarm, activate a hopper water-spray system and/or automatically initiate the loading sequence in order to inject the burning materials into the incinerator.
2) A high-temperature automatic sprinkler directly over the hopper and independent of the room sprinkler system.
3) A manually actuated water spray located above the loading hopper.
4) An emergency switch that would override the normal automatic loading-cycle-control sequence and cause immediate injection of hopper contents into the incinerator.

Residue Handling and Removal

Residue, or ash, handling and removal systems range from fully manual to fully automatic. Because of high costs, space limitations, operational complexities, and technological limitations, most existing older incinerators are cleaned out manually. However, most newer incinerators and almost all incinerators larger than about 1000 lb per hr (464 kg/hr), are equipped with an automatic or semiautomatic ash handling and removal system.

Manual residue removal: This cleanout method involves raking or shoveling ashes into barrels, bins or tubs. Small-capacity incinerators can be cleaned from the outside, but large-capacity units may require the operator to enter the primary chamber for cleanout operations. Manual residue removal is objectionable and potentially hazardous in many respects, including: 1) intensive, difficult labor requirements; 2) dangers to personnel from heat, ash, dust and noxious gases; and 3) fire hazards from the handling and containment of unquenched ash residues. Spraying water into the incinerators to facilitate ash removal by quenching is not recommended because the water will damage the furnace refractory due to thermal shock. Water quenching is limited to ash already removed from the furnace.

Ash cleanout without containment or quenching could be a potential fire hazard if the ashes are hot or contain embers and smoldering materials. Because of this, the latest issue of NFPA 82 requires that a system and appropriate measures be provided to quench adequately and/or fully contain ash residues removed from the incinerator during cleanout operations. This could include such features as water sprays, a wet quench pit or a special containment enclosure to enable ash cleanout with minimal exposure to ambient conditions.

Automatic residue removal: These systems utilize grates, transfer rams, or pulse hearths to transfer and discharge ashes from the primary chamber. In semi-automatic type systems, ashes are collected in residue carts. In fully automatic systems, ashes are discharged into a residue conveyor from which they are continuously transferred to a large container for removal. Residue conveyor systems are equipped with a water trough, or sump, which fully saturates the ashes. With cart-type systems, the ashes are quenched by water sprays surrounding the discharge chute from the incinerator.

For firesafety protection, it is recommended that ash carts used in both manual and semi-automatic systems be handled with care and, prior to off-site disposal, stored in a fire-rated area in a location that is isolated from stored waste materials. Even when quenched by water sprays or hoses, the containers may still be very hot, and residues in the ash carts may tend to ignite spontaneously if disturbed and exposed to room air. It is also recommended that considerations be given for dumping ash carts at a landfill rather than within the facility building areas.

Incinerator Chimneys and Breeching Systems

The design, construction, termination, and clearances of incinerator chimneys, and the flue-gas-ducting, or breeching, systems must be in strict accordance with NFPA 82 and NFPA 211, *Standard for Chimneys, Fireplaces, Vents, and Solid Fuel Burning Appliances* as well as applicable building codes.

Chimneys and breeching systems handling low-temperature, wet, and saturated incinerator-flue gases downstream from a scrubber must be designed and constructed to withstand acidic corrosion conditions. Chimneys and breeching systems handling hot and high-temperature flue gases should be refractory lined. It should be noted that there is no single chimney-refractory lining, or construction material, or family of materials, suitable for insuring chimney integrity and firesafety for all incinerator operating conditions and waste types. Such materials must be carefully evaluated and selected.

NFPA 82 stipulates that chimneys for incinerators serve no other purpose and they shall not be connected to boiler chimneys unless they are of suitable construction and properly designed and controlled for serving both systems.

Auxiliary Fuel Systems

Incinerators require auxiliary, or supplemental, fuel for ignition, warm-up, and maintaining proper combustion temperatures. Most incinerators fire either natural gas or distillate fuel oil. It is imperative that auxiliary fuel systems, including storage and handling systems, burners, and controls, be installed and tested in accordance with all applicable requirements of local codes and NFPA standards. Burners should be of a type specifically designed and constructed for use in incineration systems. Burners must also be equipped with automatic ignition systems, and flame safeguard and management systems.

Combustion and Ventilation Air

Depending on the types and heating values of wastes burned, incinerators typically require on the order of 10 to 20 lb (4.5 to 9 kg) of combustion air per pound (0.45 kg) of waste incinerated. Ventilation air is also required to remove heat that is normally transmitted, or radiated, through incinerator casings in order to maintain comfortable operating conditions and acceptable incinerator-room temperature levels. Insufficient supply of combustion and ventilation air may result in operational problems and unsafe conditions. Incinerators located in confined spaces or areas enclosed by tight-fitting partitions must be provided an air-supply louver or duct in accordance with NFPA 82 requirements. Louvers and ducts providing direct outside air must be sized for one square inch (64.52 mm^2) of free area per 4000 Btu per hr (1172 kW) of total incinerator heat input.

Electrical Service

Power and control wiring, including electrical components and control devices, must be in accordance with applicable local codes and NFPA 70, *National Electrical Code®*. It is recommended that wiring and conduit not be attached directly to incinerator casings. Wiring within about one foot (0.30 m) of incinerator casings should have high-temperature insulation. It is also recommended that incinerator system control panels be located more than 36 in. (0.91 m) from the casing. Wiring, relays, and transformers for auxiliary burners should be either mounted remotely or protected from high-temperature damage by the burner-blower fans.

Incinerator Rooms

Incinerators, including associated waste and residue handling systems, must be located in a separate, fire-rated room or compartment with an automatic fire door suitable for a Class B opening. Such incinerator rooms may also be contained in the same enclosure with the building heating systems and equipment.

Incinerator Operations

To properly manage the severe and complex operating conditions typical of incineration systems well-trained operating personnel are required. Training programs and comprehensive operating and maintenance manuals and instructions are highly recommended. Such instructions should not only assure proper incinerator operations, but also the continued implementation of safe operating conditions.

WASTE COMPACTORS

Waste compactors are devices that use electro-mechanical-hydraulic means to reduce the volume of waste and package it in the reduced condition. The types of compactors regulated by NFPA 82 are domestic and commercial-industrial.

Domestic Compactors

Commonly called kitchen compactors, domestic compactors are designed for use in dwellings and apartment units for compaction of family-developed waste. This appliance reduces the fire hazard of stored waste by retaining it in a metal container under compaction. Units are of the under-counter and moveable types. They must be capable of manual opening such that waste can be easily removed in the event of equipment electrical failure.

Commercial-Industrial Compactors

These compactors are used in multiple-family dwellings and many other classes of occupancies as the prime waste-handling system. They may be located either indoors or outdoors and can be chute or hand fed.

There are four types of compactor systems.

Bulkhead compactor: Waste is compacted in a chamber against a bulkhead. When a compacted block is ready for removal, a bag is installed and filled with the compacted block.

Extruder: Waste is forced through a cylinder that has a restricted area. Driving forces compact the material and extrude it into a "slug" which is broken off and bagged or placed in a container. The operation of this type of compactor is shown in Figure 9-17E.

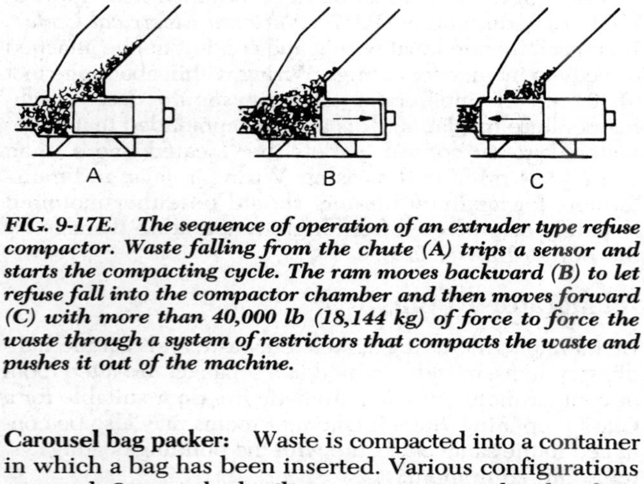

FIG. 9-17E. The sequence of operation of an extruder type refuse compactor. Waste falling from the chute (A) trips a sensor and starts the compacting cycle. The ram moves backward (B) to let refuse fall into the compactor chamber and then moves forward (C) with more than 40,000 lb (18,144 kg) of force to force the waste through a system of restrictors that compacts the waste and pushes it out of the machine.

Carousel bag packer: Waste is compacted into a container in which a bag has been inserted. Various configurations are used. One method utilizes a compaction chamber from which the compacted plug is pushed into the bag. Another uses a cylinder that acts as a compaction chamber that is inserted into the bag. Upon compaction, the cylinder is removed while a compacting head holds the material in place.

Container packers: Waste is compacted directly into a bin, cart or container. When full, the container can be either manually or mechanically removed from the compactor and compaction area.

Compaction containers must be provided with either a $2\frac{1}{2}$-in. (63.5 mm) hose connection suitable for standard fire-fighting equipment (and located near the top of the container) or an access door that can be opened without disconnecting the container from the compactor.

Chute Termination Bin

Most compactor waste chutes do not feed directly into the compactor but into a small storage chamber, chute connector or an impact area that is usually large enough to store small quantities of waste. Potential fire hazards can be minimized by installing sprinklers and providing doors large enough to allow access in the event of fire. If a compactor is charged manually from a large bin with an open top, the bin need not be sprinklered. It is sufficient to rely on the sprinklers protecting the compactor room for protection.

The bottom closure of a storage bin (or area) and its ability to be opened under fire conditions deserves attention. If, for instance, there is equipment failure, waste will not only build up in the chute's termination chamber but also in the chute itself. In the event of a fire and sprinkler discharge, the weight of soggy waste could become excessive and jam simple slide devices. Sufficient strength should be built into these closure devices to allow opening them without breakage under such conditions. The most satisfactory situation is one that allows discharge into other receptacles, bins, or equipment without excessive chute collection.

Chute-fed compactors should be provided with an automatic, special, fine-water-spray sprinkler in the compaction chamber. However, hand-fed compactors do not require such protection.

Compactor Rooms

Compacted waste has a wide range of densities and can burn to produce large amounts of smoke. Therefore, storage of compacted waste in buildings should be minimized.

Compactor systems are required to be enclosed within fire-rated rooms with fire doors suitable for Class B openings. Automatic sprinklers are also required in compactor rooms.

SHREDDERS

Shredders are sometimes used to process waste for volume reduction in order to minimize storage-space requirements and to facilitate systems where waste must be mechanically transferred before storage. They are also used in combination with other processes for disinfecting or sterilizing biomedical waste. It is good practice to sprinkler shredder feed bins. If they are serviced by chutes, arrangements must be made to bypass the shredder, since shredders have frequent periods of repair. All bypass areas and storage areas should also be sprinklered and enclosed within fire-rated rooms with fire doors suitable for Class B openings. The discharge from shredding devices also requires sprinkler protection.

The possibility of explosion is a particular hazard in connection with shredder operations. This can result from ignition of the dust-laden air mixtures which normally surround shredders during operation. A recommended method of protection is to provide an explosion-suppressive system within the shredder room and a vent, preferably above the shredder, to safely relieve the impact of a rapid pressure build-up or explosion.

BIBLIOGRAPHY

Reference to the following codes, standards, and recommended practices will provide further information about waste control. (See the latest NFPA Catalog for availability of the current edition of the following document.)

NFPA 13, *Standard for Installation of Sprinkler Systems*.

NFPA 30, *Flammable and Combustible Liquids Code*.

NFPA 31, *Standard for the Installation of Oil Burning Equipment*.

NFPA 54, *National Fuel Gas Code*.

NFPA 58, *Standard for the Storage and Handling of Liquefied Petroleum Gases*.

NFPA 68, *Guide for Explosion Venting*.

NFPA 69, *Standard on Explosion Prevention Systems*.

NFPA 82, *Standard on Incinerators, Waste and Linen Handling Systems and Equipment*.

NFPA 86, *Ovens and Furnaces: Design, Location and Equipment*.

NFPA 97M, *Standard Glossary of Terms Relating to Chimneys, Vents and Heat Producing Appliances*.

NFPA *101, Code for Safety to Life from Fire in Buildings and Structures*.

NFPA 211, *Standard for Chimneys, Fireplaces, Vents and Solid Fuel Burning Appliances*.

Other Standards

UL 296, *Oil Burners*.

UL 372, *Primary Safety Controls for Gas- and Oil-Fired Appliances*.

UL 795, *Commercial-Industrial Gas-Heating Equipment*.

The above codes and standards are not all-inclusive. Other agencies, such as Industrial Risk Insurers (IRI), American National Standards Institute (ANSI), and American Society for Testing and Materials (ASTM), may have standards applicable to specific waste management and disposal operations. In addition, state and local regulations and requirements may be more stringent than federal regulations or standards.

Additional Readings

American Gas Association Inc., *Guidebook for Industrial and Commercial Gas-Fired Incineration*, New York, 1963.

Conway, R. A. and Ross, R. D., *Handbook of Industrial Waste Disposal*, Van Nostrand Reinhold, New York, 1980.

Doucet, L. G., *State-of-the-Art Hospital and Institutional Waste Incineration: Selection, Procurement, and Operations*, American Society for Hospital Engineering, Technical Document No. 055940, January 1991.

Doucet, L. G. and Knoll, W. G., Jr., "The Craft of Specifying Solid Waste Systems," *Actual Specifying Engineer*, pp. 107-113, May 1974.

Engineering Handbook for Hazardous Waste Incineration, U.S., EPA SW-889, Environmental Protection Agency, Washington, DC, Sept. 1981.

"Fire Protection for Belt Conveyors," *FMRC Loss Prevention Data Sheet 7-11*, Factory Mutual Engineering Corp., Norwood, MA.

"Flammable and Combustible Waste Disposal in the Plastics Industry," *Bulletin No. 13*, Society of the Plastics Industry, New York.

Hitchcock, D., "Solid Waste Disposal: Incineration," *Chemical Engineering*, May 21, 1979, pp. 185-194.

Incinerator Institute of America, *Incinerator Standards*, Falls Church, VA, Nov. 1968.

McColgan, I.J., *Air Pollution Emission and Control Technology: Packaged Incinerators — Economic and Technical Review*, EPS 3-AP-77-3, Canadian Environmental Protection Service, 1977.

Pavoni, J. L., Heer, J.E., Jr., and Hagerty, D.J., *Handbook of Solid Waste Disposal*, Van Nostrand Reinhold, New York, 1975.

Shulz, J. F., "Standards for Refuse-Handling in Apartment Houses," *Fire Journal*, Vol. 68, No. 2, March 1974. pp. 82-86.

Solid Waste Handling and Disposal in Multistory Buildings and Hospitals; Volumes 1 and 11, US EPA, SW-34, Environmental Protection Agency, Washington, DC, 1972.

Vance, M., *Industrial Waste Disposal: A Bibliography*, Vance Bibliographies, Monticello, IL, 1982.

Wilson, D. G., *Handbook of Solid Waste Management*, Van Nostrand Reinhold, New York, 1977.

INFORMATION AND ANALYSIS FOR FIRE PROTECTION

From a conceptual standpoint, fire protection is achieved through a series of coordinated decisions, which is to say, actions based on processed information. There are decisions in design, construction or manufacture, purchase, installation, maintenance, education, response to emergency, and so forth. Every decision is as good as the information it is based on, and so every aspect of fire protection stands to benefit from better sources of information and better methods of analyzing and interpreting the available information. One of the most exciting developments of recent years has been the rapid evolution of analytical tools to provide better information to support decisions and to coordinate them in a systematic approach to firesafety. Section 10 covers these tools.

Chapters 1 and 2 discuss information-gathering in connection with individual fires, either in-depth investigation, in Chapter 1, or routine incident reporting, in Chapter 2. Chapter 3 then discusses the techniques used to analyze this material—to turn raw data into useful statistics, facts into information, observations into knowledge.

Chapters 4 and 5 examine in more detail the use of available data—and not just on fires—to support the myriad decisions required of fire departments, including such central decisions as the level and location of resources. By the middle of Chapter 5, the analytical methods cited have grown sufficiently large and complex to qualify as models and are discussed as such.

Chapters 6 and 7 lay out the essential elements of fire hazard assessment and fire risk analysis, two very general methodologies for combining diverse technical measurements into summary characterizations of the overall fire danger posed by some object of analysis, whether they be products, buildings, or something else. These two analytical methods are at the top end of the hierarchy of fire-related models in terms of scope. Other models, which may be useful in their own right, also will tend to serve as data inputs or components for fire hazard assessment and fire risk analysis models. Much of the work of fire science and fire protection engineering is now explicitly designed to fill gaps or improve accuracy or flexibility in some comprehensive fire hazard or fire risk model.

Chapters 8 through 14 continue the discussion of fire modeling, paying primary attention to physics-based models of fire development, the principal models most people think of when they refer to fire models. Chapter 8 introduces the subject, and Chapter 9 examines at some length the various deterministic models available. Chapter 11 provides practical calculation techniques for everyday use, and Chapters 12 and 13 address real-world applications to fire protection and design, respectively. Chapter 10 addresses probabilistic models, which may be useful in fire development modeling but are even more useful in other aspects of fire risk analysis and on other classes of problems, such as service delivery and resource location problems. Chapter 14 provides a bookend matching the introduction in Chapter 8, as the author looks at foreseeable futures for fire modeling.

Chapters 15 and 16 then examine some special topics—mapping and surveying and the use of microcomputers as especially affordable and convenient platforms for many types of analysis and modeling.

Also look for these: Most of the subjects in this section also are examined in much more detail in *The SFPE Handbook of Fire Protection Engineering*, an indispensable reference for anyone wishing to go further in the use of advanced calculation methods as applied to fire protection. This part of the field is changing so fast that the serious practitioner should also keep abreast of new developments in the technical literature through such publications as the *SFPE Journal of Fire Protection Engineering* and NFPA's *Fire Technology.* By the time material of this kind reaches book form, there often are exciting new developments already in use.

FIRE LOSS INVESTIGATION

Richard L. P. Custer

This chapter discusses fire loss investigation by examining organizations involved in fire loss investigations and the reconstruction and failure analysis process. The remaining two pertinent chapters in this fire loss information section are Chapter 2, "Collecting Fire Data," and Chapter 3, "Use of Fire Loss Information." A discussion of a fault tree for managing fire risk can be found in Section 1, Chapter 3, "Systems Concepts for Building Firesafety," while fire-resistive construction information can be found in Section 6, Chapter 2, "Classification of Building Construction."

Information about the dynamics of fire spread and growth can be found in Section 3, Chapter 1, "Combustion Products and Their Effects on Life Safety, and Chapter 11, "Upholstered Furniture and Mattresses," as well as Section 10, Chapter 11, "Simplified Calculations for Enclosure Fires."

INTRODUCTION

The data gathered during a fire loss investigation has several applications, ranging from filling out the fire department incident report to creating a detailed engineering reconstruction and failure analysis of the incident. Understanding the fire cause and origin can lead to targeted inspection, public education programs, or, perhaps, proposed code changes. A complete failure analysis can reveal factors concerning the fuel, building, and fire suppression that resulted in the ultimate extent of flame and smoke movement. The codes and design standards involved would be included in this analysis, as would construction, operation, and maintenance practices. The results of a failure analysis provide input to insurance loss adjustment and underwriting, improved design practice, and civil and criminal litigation.

In most fires cause and origin are expressed in terms of the heat of ignition, the materials involved, and the area of origin. In the past, only the large-life or property-loss fires received the attention of a complete investigation. In these cases, the reconstruction and failure analysis was often conducted months or years after the fire, when only fragmentary evidence, if any, remained. In these situations, the depth and accuracy of the fire department report can be critical. Recently, insurance claims, subrogation activities, and greatly increased litigation have been concerned with smaller and smaller losses. Thus, more detailed examination is needed of all fires that result in a loss, almost regardless of the extent of the loss.

ORGANIZATIONS INVOLVED IN FIRE LOSS INVESTIGATION

The organizations involved in fire investigation can be separated into two types: public agencies, or those required by law to investigate fires at the local, state, and federal levels; and private-sector organizations.

Local and State

Of the public agencies, the local fire department generally has the primary responsibility to document a fire and to provide an initial determination of the cause and origin. If the department uses NFPA 901, *Uniform Coding for Fire Protection*, as the basis of a reporting system such as the National Fire Incident Reporting System, factors that affected the ultimate course of the fire, such as fire and smoke spread and the performance of fire protection features, may be included.

When a fire department investigation determines that the fire may have been of incendiary or suspicious origin, other organizations may be assigned the legal responsibility to make the final determination of fire cause and to continue the investigation pursuant to possible criminal action. In much of the United States and in all Canadian provinces, the investigation responsibility for incendiary fires is vested in the state or provincial fire marshal's office. In states where this is not the case, the local fire marshal or the local police or fire department may have investigative responsibility, either legally or by delegation from the state.

Mr. Custer is adjunct associate professor of Fire Protection Engineering at the Center for Firesafety Studies, Worcester Polytechnic Institute, Worcester, MA, and principal consultant in the firesafety consulting firm of Richard L. P. Custer and Company of Wrentham, MA.

Federal

Federal agencies are also involved in investigating fires. These agencies are generally charged with investigating incidents to determine compliance with federal regulations and to provide input for the regulatory process to reduce human and property losses.

For example, the National Transportation Safety Board (NTSB), conducts complete reconstruction and failure analysis of accidents, including fire-related incidents, involving air, rail, and highway transportation. Investigations of pipeline incidents and maritime fires are under the authority of the Department of Transportation (DOT). Other federal agencies involved in fire investigations include the Occupational Safety and Health Administration (OSHA), of the Department of Labor; the Bureau of Mines (BoM), of the Department of the Interior; the Federal Bureau of Investigation (FBI); the Bureau of Alcohol, Tobacco, and Firearms (ATF), of the Department of Justice; the Consumer Product Safety Commission (CPSC); the Nuclear Regulatory Commission (NRC); and the National Institute of Standards and Technology (NIST) of the Department of Commerce.

The Federal Emergency Management Agency (FEMA) conducts detailed investigations of fire and hazardous materials incidents and prepares reports that can be obtained through the U.S. fire Administration. Other agency reports are available from the NTIS in Springfield, VA.

In addition to investigating fires under their jurisdiction, these federal agencies may serve as resources for lab analysis and technical information for state and local fire officials.

Committees of the U.S. House of Representatives and the Senate are often very interested in the results of these investigations, particularly when the incidents under investigation deal with timely public policy topics, such as standards for elderly care facilities and prison firesafety.

Private Sector Organizations

Most of the complete reconstruction and failure analyses of fires other then those that fall under government jurisdiction are conducted by private-sector organizations for education, improved design, insurance, and litigation purposes.

The National Fire Protection Association's (NFPA) fire investigations program is a long-standing data collection and engineering analysis activity. The purpose of the program is to collect, analyze, and report detailed fire experience data through on-site investigations. This activity assists NFPA in analyzing and documenting facts about fires for technical or educational value; distributing the information to the fire protection community to help prevent future similar fire losses; publishing of investigation reports in *NFPA Journal*; providing technical assistance to state and local officials as an integral service of the NFPA investigation process; determining important "lessons learned" for input to NFPA technical committees and technical programs; and contributing to an increasing fire incident data base for analysis purposes.

In recent years, NFPA fire investigations have included an analysis of human behavior patterns in selected fires involving large properties, where the discovery of the fire and subsequent evacuation occurred in sufficient time to permit analysis. The human behavior studies have been conducted through on-site interviews with survivors or mailed surveys and have generally been carried out by NFPA staff in combination with leading university authorities on human behavior in fire.

The NFPA has also conducted many fire investigations in cooperation with the U.S. Fire Administration and the National Institute of Standards and Technology (NIST) under a continuing cost-sharing agreement. In 1983, NFPA signed a Memorandum of Understanding for joint, on-scene investigation of selected building fires with representatives of three model building code organizations. In this program, the Council of American Building Officials (CABO) coordinates the activities of the three model building code groups—the Building Officials and Code Administrators International (BOCA), the International Conference of Building Officials (ICBO), and the Southern Building Code Congress International (SBCCI)—with NFPA. The results of most of these special on-site investigations are published as special studies or as reports in various fire protection periodicals.

The insurance industry often reconstructs a fire to evaluate the merits of claims submitted or to identify parties for subrogation action. The reconstruction may be conducted by insurance company personnel, by an adjustment bureau, or by a consultant.

Individual consultants or consulting firms perform reconstruction and failure analysis for a variety of clients, including the insurance industry. Consultants are also retained for litigation purposes by law firms to evaluate fire cause and origin, code compliance, conformance with design standards, and other technical aspects of fire loss.

When major financial consequences are linked to investigators' conclusions, it is not uncommon for two or more parties to retain investigators and for two or more theories of fire origin and development to be presented. The need to resolve such disputes is a major reason for the increasing interest in applying state-of-the-art scientific models, procedures, and test results to fire investigations.

THE RECONSTRUCTION AND FAILURE ANALYSIS PROCESS

The complete reconstruction and failure analysis process involves developing a time history for the incident and establishing the factors that led to ignition and that increased or lessened the severity of the loss. The reconstruction includes the prefire history, as well as the "transfire" events, or those that occur from the point of established burning to extinguishment. Failure analysis is concerned with the design, construction, and performance aspects of the incident. It is also important in the reconstruction to document the successes. Did fire protection features inhibit the spread of fire within a portion of the building, for example?

Time is the framework for reconstruction and failure analysis, and it can be viewed in two scales. These are the macro scale, where time is measured in increments of days, weeks, and years, and the micro scale, where the increments are in seconds, minutes, and hours. Macro time is prefire, while micro time may apply to pre- or transfire events.

The best way to organize the reconstruction and failure analysis information is through the use of timelines or event sequences. In constructing a timeline, it is important to establish benchmark events. A benchmark event can be described as an event that is well-documented in time and space and that serves as a point of reference because it can be assumed to have created a set of specific conditions or initiated a sequence of actions that had a significant impact on the fire. The issuance of a building permit or the time of arrival of the fire department apparatus are good examples of benchmark events. Using time of arrival as a reference event, other events for which the time of occurrence is unknown can be placed approximately in time either before or after arrival of the fire department apparatus. Other examples of typical benchmark events are explosions and the collapse of walls or roofs or calling for multiple alarm response.

A single timeline can be adequate for fires in which only a few events occurred. For more complex situations, separate timelines on the same scale can be used for the history of the building, the evolution of the "model codes," the installation and maintenance history of a suppression system, human activity, or any other time-related aspect of the incident. STEP (sequentially timed events plotting) procedures have been developed to deal with complex accident situations such as major fires.[1]

Prefire timeline information can be obtained from building permits, plans and specifications, inspection reports, fire and building codes, and fire research and engineering literature. Sources of information for use in the development of transfire timelines include the fire department incident report, recordings of fire department radio transmissions during the incident, and interviews with fire fighters and other witnesses.

It should be pointed out that, in many cases, only parts of the reconstruction and failure analysis process are carried out. Many different organizations may be involved in the investigation, often at different times. Since people may have to rely upon information gathered by others, an understanding of the whole process will make it easier to obtain the most complete and accurate data at each step.

The basic steps of overall reconstruction and failure analysis are examination of the scene, collection of background data, testing, incident reconstruction, and specific failure analysis.

Examination of the Scene

Examining the fire scene is critical to the entire reconstruction and analysis process. It is here that the physical and photographic evidence is gathered and the fire damage is documented.

As many photographs as possible should be taken at the scene, and each should be documented on a diagram with a description of the direction of view and contents of the photograph. The techniques of fire-scene photography have been well-reported and can be applied to reconstruction and failure analysis[2,3,4]. Color photography is recommended.

In addition, maps and diagrams should be prepared that include dimensions and interior layout of the building, the location and degree of fire damage, the location and types of fuel materials, and the locations of victims. The location of fire protection features such as fire walls, detectors, and suppression systems should also be noted.

Often, buildings will be modified considerably over their lifetimes, and an individual reviewing the original plans could receive a false impression of the building at the time of the fire. Thus, it is important to record the architectural, construction, and fire protection features of a structure, both as built *and* at the time of the fire.

When fire suppression systems are present, the positions of valves, the locations of discharge nozzles, and the locations and types of detectors used to operate the system should be noted. With special systems, such as those that use halon, CO_2, or dry chemicals, agent storage tanks should be checked to determine whether the system discharged as designed.

A careful study of the damage patterns, combined with on-site interviews and a knowledge of the ignition sources, fuel materials present immediately before the fire, and fire dynamics should be used by an investigator to determine the area of origin. If possible, the source and form of heat of ignition and the type and form of the materials first ignited should be determined. Burn patterns, such as a "V," low burns, and multiple "points of origin," can often be misleading and should only be used to establish cause and origin when they are unambiguous or are supported by other physical evidence.

The investigator should keep in mind that the burn patterns seen after a fire represent the total burning history of the event, including damage that may have occurred during extinguishment and overhaul. As a rule, patterns observed in fires that are extinguished early in their development are more meaningful and useful than those remaining after the near-total destruction of a building or a portion of a building.

Indicators such as depth of char should be used with care. The burning rate of wood traditionally has been calculated as approximately 1.4 inches in 60 minutes (0.6 mm/min). This figure has been used to estimate the time of burning and to detect the presence of flammable liquids. Research has shown that the traditional calculation varies substantially depending on the radiant flux and ventilation. The rate of burning can be as high as 10 in. per hr (4.3 mm/min).[5]

Investigators should also be careful not to assume that certain burn patterns can be used as sole proof of the presence of flammable liquids. Factors such as ventilation, room flashover, floor clutter, room contents, fire duration, and overhaul can affect the patterns seen by investigators. Corroborative evidence, such as pertinent chemical traces or the detected absence of an appropriate prefire fuel load, is needed to establish the presence of flammable liquids. The color of observed smoke is not necessarily evidence of the presence of flammable liquids.

In visualizing conditions in the area of origin, it is often helpful to reconstruct the scene physically by replacing the carpet, furniture, and other items in their original locations. While interviews are conducted at many different times in the reconstruction and failure analysis process, those taken at or close to the time of the incident also can be very useful, particularly in describing the course of the fire. Whenever possible, events described in interviews should be related to benchmark events.

Private sector investigators are often not called in to evaluate a fire scene until well after the incident. Frequently, the scene has been disturbed, or, in some cases, the building has been restored or removed. In these situations, the investigator should review physical evidence collected and photographic evidence. Examination of photographs using 7 to 10 power binocular microscopy can often reveal details, particularly when low-speed film has been used. Fire and police reports, as well as witness statements, should be reviewed.

Although an actual on-scene investigation of a fire is most desirable, careful analysis of a well-documented fire can lead to reliable conclusions regarding the origin and cause of many fires. The effectiveness of a delayed investigation and analysis will depend upon the extent of the fire, as well as the degree of documentation. In some cases where there has been total or near-total destruction, neither an on-scene, well-documented investigation nor subsequent delayed analysis can establish origin or cause.

Collection of Background Data

While some of the background data, such as accounts of activities immediately before the fire, can be gathered at the scene very soon after the fire, most of the information needed for the investigation will be gathered later.

Building plans, permits, and the codes in effect at the time of approval should be obtained, along with the specifications and drawings for the building fire protection features. If any major modifications were made to the building or its fire protection systems or if there was a change of occupancy, the codes, plans, and permits should be obtained again. These materials should be reviewed as part of the reconstruction process, since the changes may have influenced the course of the fire.

Other background data include instruction or training manuals, maintenance records, data on construction and interior finish materials, the previous fire history of the building or equipment involved, the amount of any previous fire damage, the location of contents, and the physical and burning characteristics of the contents. This step also involves obtaining detailed statements from the building occupants to determine the circumstances leading up to ignition and established burning.

Testing

Three types of tests are involved in reconstruction and failure analysis: standard tests of flammability properties, standard analysis of unknown materials, and special tests designed to establish burning behavior under conditions related to a specific fire scenario.

Properties of flammability that may be determined by test include flame spread of materials, fabric flammability, flash point, and rate of heat release, among others.[6,7,8,9,10,11,12,13]

Analysis of unknowns is performed by analytical laboratories using techniques such as gas chromatography and mass spectroscopy to identify unknown materials, particularly possible accelerants. Such analysis should be conducted in accordance with the appropriate ASTM standards. These are ASTM E1385-90, "Standard Practice for Separation and Concentration of Flammable or Combustible Liquid Residues from Fire Debris Samples by Steam Distillation;" ASTM E1386-90, "Standard Practice for Separtion and Concentration of Flammable or Combustible Liquid Residues from Fire Debris Samples by Solvent Extraction;" ASTM E1387-90, "Standard Test Method for Analysis of Flammable or Combustible Liquid Residues in Extracts from Samples of Fire Debris by Gas Chromatography;" ASTM E1388-90, "Standard Practice for Sampling of Headspace Vapors from Fire Debris Samples;" and ASTM E1389-90, "Standard Practice for Cleanup of Fire Debris Sample Extracts by Acid Stripping." Other useful analysis techniques include metallurgical or X-ray analysis.

In collecting samples for testing, it is important to know the sizes and/or amounts of the sample needed for each test, as well as the conditions under which the samples should be transported. This information can be obtained from a testing laboratory or by reviewing a copy of the test method.

Although special tests, sometimes called "demonstrations," can often be extremely revealing in understanding the course of a particular fire, results of these demonstrations can be misleading because the test may not be truly representative of the actual event. Factors such as ventilation, arrangement of the fuel, or even the point of ignition can have a significant effect on the outcome of the test. In other words, a great deal must be known about the specific conditions at the time of the fire, and these conditions must be reasonably reproduced in the demonstration. Special tests or demonstrations should be conducted under laboratory conditions, to permit control of such variables as ambient temperature, relative humidity, and wind effects by personnel familiar with full-scale fire testing.

Reconstruction and Analysis

The fire reconstruction is an organized, step-by-step portrayal of the most likely course of the fire under study, from the ignition sequence through established burning to the limits of flame and smoke movement at the time of extinguishment. It is based upon the facts developed through on-scene investigation, background studies, and testing. The reconstruction should explain the speed and direction of fire growth and smoke spread within the compartment or area of origin and beyond. It also should explain the effects of barriers and automatic suppression systems on fire spread and growth and the effects of manual extinguishment. The reconstruction should also evaluate the performance of the building's life safety features relative to injury or loss of life.

In sorting through the facts to develop the reconstruction, it is often useful to apply the system safety techniques of Failure Modes and Effects Analysis (FMEA) and Fault Tree Analysis.[14] These methods help identify alternative sequences of events that could have led to the observed fire situation, such as the development of room flashover or fire breaching a fire wall. The alternatives can then be evaluated against the evidence to determine the most likely scenario. These techniques are particularly valuable where complex or interrelated machinery, buildings, or human activities are involved.

Computer modeling techniques can also be used to predict the outcome of a series of possible fire causes and growth scenarios. The model results can be compared to actual events to narrow down the likely scenarios for a given event or to evaluate the possible effects that fire protection equipment, such as detectors or sprinklers, might have had on the outcome of a fire. The analyses of the DuPont Plaza and the First Interstate Bank fires, are examples of model applications.[15,16]

Analysis of the ignition sequence is concerned with three specific items: the size, nature, and source of the ignition energy; the physical and chemical fire properties of the materials ignited; and the circumstances, either human or mechanical, that brought the energy in contact with the fuel. In selecting the most likely ignition source, the energy available from a candidate source must be compared with the ignition energy requirements of the fuel in its given form. For example, given the same material and heat source, ignition is more likely if the material is present in finely divided form than if it is in a solid mass. Energy available at the source, such as temperature and thermal radiation; distance from the fuel to the energy source; and time of exposure to the source of energy are also factors that must be considered in ignition sequence analysis.

The circumstances which result in ignition generally involve human factors or equipment failure. Careless welding, poor housekeeping, and improper selection or misuse of materials are examples of human factors. Valve rupture and combustion control failure could be considered equipment failures. Ultimately, most equipment failures can be traced to design, manufacturing, installation, or maintenance problems or to misuse.

If established burning is achieved after ignition, it must be determined why the fire continued to grow to full room involvement—that is, flashover or, in the absence of compartmentation, such as that in a warehouse or industrial building, why it reached a certain extent. In providing answers, a number of factors must be evaluated, including the rates of heat release of the fuels; continuity of the fuels—that is, the proximity of fuel packages to each other—and location of fuels relative to walls; compartment ceiling height; ventilation; and interior finish.

Heat release rate is one of the more important factors in analysis. In many instances, a fire reported to have grown or spread "unusually fast" is characterized as suspicious or incendiary when, in fact, the growth rate may have been due to a combination of the burning properties of the materials and the nature of the compartment in which the fire burned. A number of studies have been carried out to characterize the burning rates of materials and furnishings. Data can be found in NIST reports and in Appendix C of NFPA 72E, *Automatic Fire Detectors*.[12,16,17,18,19,21] The roles of heat release rate, fire location, and ceiling height in fire development also have been reported.[19] Alpert's work includes methods to estimate ceiling temperatures and ceiling gas velocities. Guidance on estimating the likelihood that a given fire size and room ventilation combination can develop flashover also is provided in NIST reports.[22,23]

The performance of automatic suppression systems in controlling the growth and spread of the fire also must be evaluated in the reconstruction process. Here, the factors to be reviewed include the appropriateness of the agent being used; the system response time, as related to the detection devices used, relative to ceiling height and fire growth rate; location of the agent discharge nozzles relative to the source of the fire; agent availability, including rate of discharge, pressure, and adequacy of supply; and conformance of the system design and installation with NFPA standards, industry design, and installation manuals. For example, a sprinkler system may have failed to control a fire due to a very high ceiling that delayed the response time, combined with low water pressure that could not produce the needed water flow rate.

Another component of the reconstruction is barrier performance. Barrier performance evaluation focuses on the nature of the barrier, whether rated or not rated; barrier construction; the thermal stresses to which it was exposed; and the manner in which the barrier failed. Barriers can fail either by passage of flame or hot gases through a small opening, by a hot spot failure, by movement of flame and hot gases through open doors, or by barrier collapse, resulting in a massive failure. Failure of opening protection, poor construction practices, modifications to the barrier after construction, and fire stresses that exceed those assumed in the design can be significant transporters of products of combustion beyond design limits.

Manual suppression activities, whether by a municipal fire department or a plant fire brigade, can have a significant effect on the outcome of a fire. In the absence of fire suppression systems, the response time of the fire department for a given fire will influence the size of the fire at the time of agent application. For ease of analysis, the response time can be broken down into the following segments: detection time, alarm transmission time, dispatch time, travel time, and time from the arrival of fire suppression personnel to agent application. Problems resulting in delays in any of the above time segments will extend the limits of flame and smoke travel. Examples of factors that could cause delays are the absence of automatic detectors, the absence of people in the building, or an improperly designed detection system. Equipment failure or out-of-service fire apparatus can also delay response time. Weather, terrain, traffic, and the condition of apparatus can extend travel time to the incident. Frozen hydrants, blocked access, and shortage of personnel are also examples of factors that could delay application of fire suppression agents.

The reconstruction process also must consider the performance of the building life safety system. This includes the detection and alarm system, the building egress system, and the smoke control system. In addition to the factors discussed above that affect detector response, the audibility of alarms plays a role in life safety. Guidance on this topic can be found in work by Nober[24] and in NFPA 72F, *Installation, Maintenance, and Use of Emergency Voice/Alarm Communication Systems*. Building egress factors include the capabilities of the occupants and the number, capacity, and protection of the egress routes. The movement of smoke in buildings is related to the temperature of the fire gases; differences between inside and outside temperatures, or the stack effect; effects of the building's heating and air conditioning systems; and effects of wind.

Failure Analysis

In a firesafety context, failure can be defined as a fire that results in personal injury, death, or property or monetary losses, or in conditions that prevent buildings or mechanisms from functioning as designed. In fire failure analysis, the objective is to use on-site and background data, testing results, and reconstruction to identify the primary and contributing causes of the failures and their sources. The sources of failures include basic design, material or equipment selection, material or equipment defects, construction or assembly, testing, post-construction modifications, service conditions, and unanticipated conditions or abuse.

The analysis is made by comparing the causes of failures with the codes, standards, design practices, and the state-of-the-art technology present at the time of the fire. In the analysis, it is important to identify noncompliance with the standard practices, but it is even more important to note where compliance with the standards failed to provide the expected or needed degree of firesafety. In either event, the failure analysis should provide recommendations for how the failures could have been prevented or how the knowledge gained can be applied to preventing similar failures in the future.

ORGANIZATION FOR FIRE INVESTIGATION

It is a good idea to be prepared in advance for the investigation of a fire. The preparation may range from identifying an individual or company to hire as needed, to the organization of a permanent fire investigation unit complete with full-time staffing, vehicles, and a laboratory. The level of organization selected is dependent upon the size of the organization, the frequency of need, the resources available, and the legal or statutory requirements. One other factor to be considered is whether or not the organization is in the public sector—the fire department, police department, state and federal government, and so on—or in the private sector—insurance company, product manufacturer, major hotel chain and so on. Frequently, the public-sector needs will include more than just the ability to conduct a fire scene investigation. Should it be determined that the possibility of arson exists, the likelihood of criminal or civil action often requires the involvement of the police or persons trained in the legal aspects of arson and fraud investigation.

Public Sector

In the public sector, most initial investigations are carried out by the fire department personnel responding to the scene. If the cause is easily determined and does not appear to be of a potentially criminal nature, the investigation will end at that level. When the cause cannot be determined or arson is suspected, additional help is generally dispatched. In a small fire department, the local police or the county or state fire marshal's office may be contacted. In some jurisdictions, the assistance may come from the country or state police.

In large cities, a fire investigation unit is usually formed. The unit may be made up of fire department personnel and be wholly within the fire department, or the unit may be within the police department. Regardless of where the unit is placed organizationally, it is generally recommended that both fire investigation and police functions be represented in the background and training of personnel. This objective is often accomplished by selecting individuals from both departments to serve in the fire investigation unit.

In some jurisdictions, an investigations unit is established in the local criminal prosecutor's office. Such a unit will usually have arson detection and prosecution as its major focus where the case load is high. A special prosecutor is often assigned specifically for arson, and that individual frequently is trained in fire investigation techniques.

In many instances, the fire investigation units in both the fire and police departments are called *arson investigation* units. The determination of arson can usually come only after a thorough fire investigation in which other possible causes are ruled out and physical evidence of an incendiary fire is established. This provision should be stressed to investigative personnel so they do not come to believe that their role is to find arson. The term "fire" investigation is more appropriate to the work that is done than *arson investigation*. If arson is a major problem in a community, special arson task forces can be established to identify arson-for-profit groups, associating real estate buying and selling and insurance patterns with arson and arson prevention activities. This work is less concerned with actual fire scene investigation, and deals more with the establishment of motivation, insurance manipulation, and patterns of arson occurrence.

Some federal agencies, such as the General Services Administration or the military services, have personnel who investigate fires involving their facilities. These personnel are generally assigned fire investigation in addition to other functions such as facility safety or fire protection design. In the event of a major fire, an agency may conduct its own investigation or use an outside consultant to assist its own personnel.

Private Sector

In the private sector, large insurance companies may have investigative units that conduct fire scene investigations and perform arson and fraud detection and control functions. Some companies will employ adjustment bureaus or private investigators to make the initial cause determination, and follow up with their own personnel if it appears that arson or fraud is involved or if there is a particularly large loss. Small companies may rely exclusively upon outside investigation services.

A number of large industrial companies also maintain a fire investigative capability, often located in their risk management or loss prevention groups. These groups or individuals may investigate fires in company facilities or fires involving products or systems designed, manufactured, supplied, or installed by the company. These investigations may be for the purpose of future loss prevention or plant safety programs, or they may be carried out in response to actual or potential litigation. An important function of this type of investigation is the identification of the causative factors in the fire that could lead to improved design, manufacturing, installation, or operating practices.

Small companies may not be able to afford their own investigation staffs. In such cases, an appropriate outside capability should be identified in advance for use if the need arises. The individual or firm selected should either have or be given some knowledge of the specific products, facilities, or operations that are likely to be involved.

EDUCATION AND TRAINING OF FIRE INVESTIGATION PERSONNEL

The nature and extent of education, training, and experience needed by investigators obviously varies greatly with the specific goals and objectives for fire investigations set by the organization where they are employed and budget resources. The level of knowledge needed by a fireground officer faced with a residential fire extinguished early in its development, will be less than that needed by an investigator from the department's fire investigation unit. This investigator will have to deal with fires extinguished in more advanced stages, where the evidence of cause is often much less clear. In addition, this investigator will have to deal with fires in the full range of occupancies found in the unit's jurisdiction. This could include residences, office structures, warehousing, manufacturing, and heavy industry.

The private-sector investigator employed by a petrochemical company may need a degree in chemistry or chemical or fire protection engineering in addition to the basic fire scene investigation skills. The specialist in arson investigation will need education and experience in the legal aspects of civil or criminal investigations or possibly both.

Education

In the past decade, a great deal of data regarding the nature of the ignition process and the forces that control fire spread and growth has emerged. Research by university, government, and insurance laboratories has developed information that can explain much of the evidence remaining after a fire has been extinguished, and assist in determining origin and cause.

To determine adequately the cause and origin of a fire, the modern investigator needs a basic knowledge of physics and chemistry, preferably at the post-secondary- school level. He or she should be familiar with the concepts of heat release rate, fire plume and ceiling layer development, and compartment flashover.

All fire investigators should also have some knowledge of the legal aspects of investigations, such as how to gain access to a scene, how to take and handle evidence, and how to question witnesses.

The fire science courses offered at many post-secondary schools today can provide much of the needed background. Where such facilities are not available, basic science courses supplemented by study using the selected readings at the end of this chapter can be employed. In some areas of the country, the U.S. Fire Administration's Open Learning Program is also available through selected local colleges and universities.

In fire investigation units to which both police and fire personnel are assigned, personnel should be cross-trained in basic fire science and law enforcement. Departments that become familiar with each other's technology and terminology benefit from enhanced communication, more complete and thorough investigations, and more successful prosecutions.

Advanced education might include college-level courses in such areas as forensic science, industrial safety, insurance, accident investigation, and fire protection engineering.

Training

All investigators should be trained in the basics of fire scene investigation, which include adequate documentation of the scene, origin determination, and cause determination. Specific emphasis should be placed on techniques for debris removal and scene reconstruction. Although much of this knowledge can be gained by studying text materials, there is no substitute for field experience. Even limited hands-on work can be of great value in relating the text materials to "the real world."

BIBLIOGRAPHY

References Cited

1. Hendrick, K. and Benner, L., *Investigating Accidents with STEP*, Marcel Deckker, New York, NY, 1987.
2. Lyons, P.R., *Techniques of Fire Photography*, National Fire Protection Association, Quincy, MA, 1978.
3. Kodak, *Using Photography to Preserve Evidence*, Pamphlet M-2, Eastman Kodak Company, Rochester, NY, 1976.
4. Kodak, *Fire and Arson Photography*, Pamphlet M-67, Eastman Kodak Company, Rochester, NY, 1977.
5. Drysdale, D., *Introduction to Fire Dynamics*, John Wiley & Sons, New York, NY, 1985.
6. *Test for Flammability of Materials Using a Radiant Heat Energy Source*, ASTM E162-81, American Society for Testing and Materials, Philadelphia, PA, 1990.
7. *Test for Surface Burning Characteristics of Building Materials*, ASTM E84-81, American Society for Testing and Materials, Philadelphia, PA, 1981a.
8. *Standard for the Flammability of Clothing Textiles (CS-191-53)*, 16CFR1610, Code of Federal Regulations, 1953.
9. *Standard for the Flammability of Children's Sleepwear: Sizes 0 through 6X (FF3-71)* 16CFR1615, Code of Federal Regulations, 1981.
10. *Test for Flash and Fire Points by Cleveland Open Cup*, ASTM D92-78, American Society for Testing and Materials, Philadelphia, PA, 1978.
11. *Test for Flash Point by Tag Closed Tester*, ASTM D56-79, American Society for Testing and Materials, Philadelphia, PA, 1979.
12. *Standard Test Method for Heat and Visible Smoke Release Rate for Materials and Products*, ASTM E906-83, American Society for Testing and Materials, Philadelphia, PA, 1990.
13. Babrauskas, V., *et al.*, "Upholstered Furniture Heat Release Rates Measured with a Furniture Calorimeter," *NBSIR 82-2604*, National Bureau of Standards, Gaithersburg, MD, 1982.
14. Henley, E.J. and Kumamoto, H., *Reliability Engineering and Risk Assessment*, Prentice Hall, Englewood Cliffs, NJ, 1981.
15. Nelson, H. E., "Engineering View of the Fire of May 4, 1988 in the First Interstate Bank Building, Los Angeles, California," *NISTR 89-4061*, National Institute of Standards and Technology, Gaithersburg, MD, 1989.
16. Nelson, H. E., "Engineering Analysis of the Early Stages Fire Development—The fire at the DuPont Plaza Hotel and Casino—December 31, 1986," *NBSIR87-3560*, National Institute of Standards and Technology, Gaithersburg, MD, 1987.
17. Babrauskas, V., "Combustion of Mattresses Exposed to Flaming Ignition Sources Part I: Full-Scale Tests and Hazard Analysis," *NBSIR 77-1290*, National Bureau of Standards, Gaithersburg, MD.
18. Babrauskas, V., "Full-Scale Burning Behavior of Upholstered Chairs," *NBSTN 1003*, National Bureau of Standards, Gaithersburg, MD, 1979.
19. Lee, B.T., "Heat Release Rate Characteristics of Some Combustible Fuel Sources in Nuclear Power Plants." *NBSIR 85-3195*, National Bureau of Standards, Gaithersburg, MD, 1985.
20. Walton, W.D. and Twilley, W.H., "Heat Release and Mass Loss Rate for Selected Materials," *NBSIR 84-2960*, National Bureau of Standards, Gaithersburg, MD, 1984.
21. Alpert, R. L. and Ward, E. J., "Evaluation of Unsprinklered Fire Hazards," *Technology Report 83-2*, Society of Fire Protection Engineers, Boston, MA, 1983.
22. Babrauskas, V., "Estimating Room Flashover Potential," *Fire Technology*, Vol. 16, No. 2, 1980, p. 94.
23. Babrauskas, V., "Will the Second Item Ignite?" *Fire Safety Journal*, Vol. 4, 1981-1982, p. 281.
24. Nober, E. H., *et al.* "Waking Effectiveness of Household Smoke and Fire Detection Devices," *NBSGCR-80-284*, National Bureau of Standards, Gaithersburg, MD, 1984.

References

Benner, L., "Accidental Investigations: Multilinear Event Sequencing Methods," *Journal of Safety Research*, Vol. 7, No. 2, 1975, p. 67.

DiNenno, P. J., *et al., eds.*, *SFPE Handbook of Fire Protection Engineering*, National Fire Protection Association, Quincy, MA, 1988.

Ferry, T.S., *Modern Accident Investigation and Analysis*, 2nd ed., John Wiley & Sons, New York, NY, 1990.

NFPA Codes, Standards, and Recommended Practices

Reference to the following NFPA codes, standards, and recommended practices will provide further information about fire loss investigation. (See the latest *NFPA Catalog* for availability of current editions of the following documents.)

NFPA 72E, *Automatic Fire Detectors*.

NFPA 72F, *Standard for the Installation, Maintenance and Use of Emergency Voice/Alarm Communication Systems*.

NFPA 422M, *Aircraft Fire and Explosion Investigations*.

NFPA 901, *Uniform Coding for Fire Protection*.

NFPA 902M, *Fire Reporting Field Incident Manual*.

NFPA 903M, *Fire Reporting Property Survey Manual*.

NFPA 904M, *Incident Follow-Up Report Manual*.

NFPA 907M, *Manual on the Investigation of Fires of Electrical Origin*.

Additional Readings

Berrin, E. R., *Investigative Photography*, 2nd *ed.*, Society of Fire Protection Engineers, Boston, MA, 1982.

Brannigan, F. L., Bright, R. G., and Jason, N. H., *eds.*, *Fire Investigation Handbook 194*, U.S. Government Printing Office, Washington, DC, 1976.

Carper, K. L., *ed.*, *Forensic Engineering*, Elsevier, New York, 1989.

Cole, J. R., *A Survey of Vehicle Fire Causes: A Case Study of Cause and Origin in 233 Vehicle Fire Cases*, Lee Books, 1988.

Cook, R. A. and Ide, R. H., *Principles of Fire Investigation*, Institution of Fire Engineers, Leicester, England, 1985.

Davies, G., *ed.*, *Forensic Science*, 2nd ed., American Chemical Society, Washington, DC, 1986.

deHaan, J. D., *Kirk's Fire Investigation*, 2nd ed., Prentice-Hall, Englewood Cliffs, NJ , 1990.

FIFI-Fire Investigation Field Investigation, National Fire Protection Association, Quincy, MA.

Fire Investigation Handbook, National Bureau of Standards, U.S. Department of Commerce, Washington, DC, 1980.

Fire Investigator's Guide to NFPA 1031, National Fire Protection Association, Quincy, MA, 1983.

Fire Resistance Directory, Underwriters Laboratories, Inc., Northbrook, IL.

Franklin, F. F., "A Survey of Electrical Systems," *Fire Journal*, Vol. 78, No. 2 (Mar. 1984), pp. 41-44.

French, H. M., *The Anatomy of Arson*, ARCO Publishing, Inc., New York, NY, 1979.

Friedman, R., *Fire Protection Chemistry*, 2nd ed., National Fire Protection Association, Quincy, MA, 1989.

Harris, R. J., *Investigation and Control of Gas Explosions in Buildings and Heating Plants*, E & F Spon, Ltd., New York, NY, 1983.

"Investigating the Fireground," *Fire Engineering*, New York, NY, 1986.

Gomberg, A., *Analysis of Electrical Fire Investigations in Ten Cities*, National Bureau of Standards, Washington, D.C., 1983.

Hall, J. R., *U.S. Arson Trends and Patterns*, National Fire Protection Association, Quincy, MA, 1986.

John, H. and McKhene, A. B., "A Fire Investigation Involving Combustion of Carpet Material," *Journal of Forensic Sciences*, Vol. 29, No. 3 (July 1984), pp. 919-922.

Kennedy, P. M., "The Crisis in Fire Investigation Education," *Fire Journal*, Vol. 83, No. 6 (Nov. 1989), p. 13.

Klem, T. J., "Los Angeles High Rise Bank Fire," *Fire Journal*, Vol. 83, No. 3 (May 1989), p. 72.

Klem, T. J., *Investigation Report on the Dupont Plaza Hotel Fire*, National Fire Protection Association, Quincy, MA, 1987.

Kletz, T., *Learning from Accidents in Industry*, Butterworth Co. Ltd., Stoneham, MA, 1988.

Lowe, D., "Fire Investigation: Science or Science Fiction?," *Fire and Arson Investigator*, Sept. 1987.

Mills, J. F., "The Fire Fighter's Role in Fire Investigation," *Fire Command*, Vol. 47, No. 2 (Feb. 1980), p. 25.

Nelson, H. E., "Science in Action: An Engineering View of the Fire at the First Interstate Bank Building," *Fire Journal*, Vol. 83, No. 4 (July/Aug. 1989), p. 28.

Packman, S. C., "Forensic Applications of Combustion Toxicology," *Proceedings* of the Workshop on Toxic Hazards from Fire, Technomic, Lancaster, PA, 1985.

Patton, A. J., *Fire Litigation Sourcebook: Technical, Medical and Legal Aspects*, Garland Law Pub., New York, NY, 1986.

Perroni, C., "Investigating Fires the Scientific Way," *Fire Journal*, Vol. 83, No. 4 (July/Aug. 1989), p. 24.

Rautaheimo, J., "Making of an Arsonist," *Fire Prevention*, No. 223 (Oct. 1989), pp. 30-35.

Skelley, M. J., "An Experimental Investigation of Glass Breakage in Compartment Fires," *NIST-JCR-90-578*, National Institute of Standards and Technology, Gaithersburg, MD, 1990.

Strube, D., "Fire Investigations Involving Motor Loads and Conductor Overcurrent Protection," *Fire Journal*, Vol. 83, No. 5 (Sept. 1989), p. 83.

Tobin, W. A. and Monson, K. L., "Collapsed Springs in Arson Investigations: A Critical Metallurgical Evaluation," *Fire Technology*, Vol. 25, No. 4 (Nov. 1989).

Yereance, R. A., *Electrical Fire Analysis*, Charles C. Thomas, Springfield, IL, 1987.

COLLECTING FIRE DATA

Revised by Carl E. Peterson

Data on individual fires provide a valuable tool for both the fire service and the broader fire protection community in understanding the fires, their growth, and the effect that the community's fire protection efforts had on the fires. Aggregated data on the fire experience of a community, state, or nation is also useful. It permits assessment of the effectiveness of fire prevention and fire suppression methods, allows comparison of the fire problem among communities and regions, and suggests areas for improvement of resource deployment or redirection of programs.

To support this activity, a fire department must produce fire reports that work both as self-standing descriptions of individual incidents and as components in the creation of broad-based fire incident data bases.

The following sections discuss fire reporting and methods for collecting data from fire reports to form broad-based data systems. Use of fire data is discussed in Chapter 3 of this section, "Use of Fire Loss Information."

THE FIRE REPORT

A fire report is the written documentation that a fire occurred. It may be as brief as a basic fact statement or as lengthy as an extensive discussion of the fire, supported by photographs, witness statements, laboratory test results, and physical evidence. The length and complexity of the report will depend upon the size and nature of the fire, the local fire service manager's need for specific data, and the resources available for obtaining information and completing reports.

The fire report should include, at some level of detail, a time-staged description of the circumstances related to the initiation, discovery, growth, and termination of the fire, along with a description of the casualties or the damage resulting from the incident. This report should be in the words of the fire officer and must be complete, so persons who were not at the fire scene can understand what happened.

Purpose of the Fire Report

There are three basic purposes to a fire report at the local level. First, it is the legal record of the fact that the fire occurred and provides official notification to those who may be required legally to know of the incident, such as the state or local fire marshal. It reports facts about the particular property affected, why the fire occurred, how building components and fire protection devices performed, casualties or damage that resulted, and fire department action. Second, it provides information to senior officers and fire department managers so that they are kept informed about what is happening within their areas of responsibility. This allows them to evaluate the performance of their units at the incident and to talk intelligently about the incident. And finally, the report provides data on the fire problem to fire service management so they can track trends, gauge the effectiveness of fire prevention and fire suppression measures presently in practice, evaluate the impact of new methods, and indicate those areas that may require further attention.

The first two purposes can be served by any report that is an accurate description of the incident. The third purpose, however, requires that information be collected in a consistent format that will permit a meaningful aggregation of the data from reports on many incidents.

It is also important that a single report serve the basic data needs of all potential users. The data needed at the state and national levels must be provided from what is collected locally. At the same time, it is important that the locally collected data also have a visible, significant use at the local fire service level. If the data are collected only for the benefit of those outside the local area, the motivation and commitment to quality and completeness may diminish, with a resulting reduction in the usefulness of the data.

Uniformity in Fire Reporting

To maintain uniformity in fire reporting, the NFPA Technical Committee on Fire Reporting has developed NFPA 901, *Uniform Coding for Fire Protection*. This standard establishes basic definitions and terminology for use in fire

Carl Peterson is a senior fire service specialist with the Public Fire Protection Division at NFPA.

reporting and serves as a means of classifying data so that the information can be aggregated either manually or automatically.

NFPA 901 provides the common language used by nearly all large-scale—that is, state and national—data bases in the United States, and many others around the world. A fire department that uses NFPA 901 will find that it is in a position to contribute data most efficiently to larger data bases and, in turn, to use data from these larger data bases in its management of the local fire problem. It also will find that the quality, uniformity, and usefulness of information within the fire department will improve. NFPA 901 contains data elements that provide a classification of property, whether fixed or mobile; a description of a specific structure prior to an incident; a description of the ignition sequence, including the area of origin of the fire; conditions found upon arrival; what action was taken; and why the fire grew or stayed as small as it did. There are also data elements for describing injuries or fatalities to both civilians and fire fighters, the extent of damage, and the investment in personnel and resources to control the incident. NFPA 901 also contains data elements for reporting the handling of hazardous materials spills and for providing emergency medical service data if an agency is involved in providing those services. Useful analysis can be adapted to the particular data elements adopted by the fire department, no matter how few or how many.

FIRE REPORTING SYSTEMS

There is a major difference between a fire report and a fire reporting system. A fire report is only part of a fire reporting system. A complete fire reporting system must address three stages of operation: fact finding, fact processing, and fact use. Each of these is discussed below.

Fact Finding

The traditional functions of a fire report can be satisfied with a minimal written narrative of the basic facts of the incident. To serve as input to a fire reporting system, however, an incident report must be clearly structured and must use uniform definitions and terminology. The collection of such information requires not only the form or other media upon which to record the information desired, but also a set of instructions and related training, so that the information is provided in a uniform manner and a procedure is established for forwarding the information to a central point.

Equally important, however, is ensuring that the persons responsible for reporting the data are trained and capable of investigating a fire to determine the origin, cause, and circumstance of the fire.

Fact Processing

Once data has been recorded, it must be processed into a form useful for legal, statistical, planning, and management purposes. The first step in information processing is to check the incident reports for accuracy, clarity, consistency, and completeness. A procedure of quality-control screening and follow-up corrections is needed for this purpose. For best results, the reports should always be screened manually, even when computerized edit checks are employed. The second step is to combine information about one incident from several individual reports or sources into a composite record. The third step is to create a file of all reported incidents, which then becomes the basic source of information about past incidents. The use to which the file is put will influence the facts that must be recorded on an individual incident report.

Many fire departments now use computers to assist with fact processing. Computer programs can quickly check the consistency and completeness of data about an incident. These same computers build and maintain a data base, which becomes one part of the incident file.

Fact Use

Once an incident file has been created, whether as a paper file, a computerized data base, or some combination of the two, it has many potential uses. At a minimum, the file should meet all the informational needs of the local fire service. Legal and statistical information required to manage the department, spot trends in fire incidence, and provide documentation for program evaluation and fire research will be readily accessible.

Small fire departments have special problems because they may have a low fire incidence level. This means they may be able to analyze their fire problems only by working with several other small departments in a geographic region. Therefore, it is especially important that small fire departments use uniform terminology and uniform coding in collecting information so that data from different fire services can be merged for analysis.

Benefits of a Fire Reporting System

At the local level, a fire department can derive many benefits from a good fire incident reporting system, particularly if it is based on NFPA 901. Some of the following uses involve no more than totaling data from the system. Others require more extensive analysis. Many of these benefits can be derived at the state and national levels when a data base is used that combines the fire experience of many local fire departments.

Describing a community's fire problem: It is possible to pinpoint where fires are occurring, what factors are most responsible for ignitions, and what casualties and damage are occurring as a result of fires. With the problem placed in proper perspective, the most serious and vulnerable aspects of the fire problem can be tackled first.

Supporting budget requests: In this era of increasing concern about taxes, municipal officials are quick to cut budgets and slow to add new programs. Frequently, fire department managers do not have the statistics to support their requests for additional funds. Good statistics will put the fire problem in perspective with other municipal concerns and help community officials realize the consequences of budget cuts or the value of new programs for the fire department. Such new programs may involve the delivery of other emergency services such as emergency medical services and hazardous materials spill mitigation.

Supporting code refinements: A good data base permits fire departments to identify and describe fires that would have developed differently or might not have occurred at all if certain code changes had been in place. Loss statistics from other areas with more stringent codes also can be used for comparison. Estimating the likely impact of a code change can involve complex analysis, however, and no incident data base can address all the subtleties of code impact.

Evaluating code enforcement programs: It is not sufficient to have codes on the books if they are not properly enforced. In evaluating loss experience, it is possible to see whether certain losses are occurring because existing codes are not being properly enforced. The reason for the improper enforcement then can be analyzed and corrected.

Evaluating public fire education programs: Not all problems can be solved by establishing and enforcing codes. There are certain aspects of the fire problem that can best be controlled by public education programs that inform people of the dangers of fire and tell them how to reduce fires, and how to react when hazardous situations arise. Such programs require considerable time and money. It is important to know the exact problem that has to be addressed. Appropriate evaluation criteria must also be in place to measure whether an educational program is in fact helping to solve that aspect of the problem.

Planning future fire protection needs: Many communities and fire departments are becoming very active in planning and are developing master plans. It is essential that the fire service be involved in such planning. A good data base will allow a fire department to compute fire rates relative to population and building inventory. These, with other characteristics of the community fire problem and planning, will support better fire protection in the future based on changing demography and planned community growth. It will also provide input to decisions about the type and level of fire protection a community will provide so that requirements can be established for developers who construct properties that exceed fire department capabilities.

Improving allocation of resources: It is not always possible for a fire department to grow at the rate necessary to protect a changing community. In fact, it may not be necessary for a department to expand. Proper analysis may show where a redeployment of existing resources can provide the same level of protection or even improve the level of protection within a community.

Scheduling nonemergency activities: Training sessions, in-service inspections, and other activities are important aspects of a fire department's function. A fire department that tracks the times fires occur and their severity can schedule these activities when they are least likely to be interrupted by emergency calls or when the normal delay caused by such activities will have the least impact on emergencies.

Regulating product safety: Particularly at the national and state levels, a fire reporting system can be useful in measuring the size and severity of problems associated with various types of consumer products. By identifying the most common ways these products become involved in fire, this reporting system can help manufacturers redesign their products to make them safer, and it can prompt changes in standards and regulations to require safer products. The reported information can be incorporated into public fire education programs to warn consumers of the dangers of using the products, and, if necessary, future sales of products could be prohibited.

Support for major fire engineering analysis: The users of sophisticated engineering models to design or evaluate fire protection will depend upon the output of fire reporting systems on a continuing basis. Each time a method of fire defense works well and fire loss and danger are confined to a small area, the success will increase confidence in that particular method of fire defense. Conversely, each time a method of fire defense fails, as indicated by injuries, deaths, or an expensive loss, it should be recorded so that the method can be reevaluated.

DESIGNING A FIRE REPORTING SYSTEM

When a new fire reporting system is to be designed or an existing system redesigned, the first step should be an analysis of the need for and use of the data that will be collected. Some of the questions that should be answered include:

1. What data are legally required to be collected?
2. What information is this system expected to produce and for what purpose?
3. What data elements are necessary to provide the information needed?
4. How quickly after the incident is the information needed, by whom, and how long after the incident should the information be kept available?
5. Who will be expected to collect the data, assemble it, and screen it for errors?
6. Who will be expected to summarize and analyze the data?
7. What savings or efficiencies could be realized if the data were available?
8. Is any of the needed data already being collected for another use?

The next step is to develop a mechanism and written procedures for collecting the data. This step should include a careful definition of the quality control process and the procedures for filing, storing, and disposing of all related material.

Tools for Data Collection

Data usually are recorded either on a paper form or directly onto some electronic media, typically a computer terminal supported by a large computer system or a stand-alone computer, such as a personal computer. These methods will be discussed separately as there are differences between them that require consideration.

When a paper form is used, data may be keyed from the form to an electronic data base for analysis purposes, but the form is retained as an official record of the incident. When data are collected directly on electronic media, there is no written record in many cases, so more information needs to be captured on the electronic data base.

Paper Forms

If a paper form is to be used, several things should be considered when designing the form. The form should be designed to apply to local needs. However, existing forms should be used where appropriate, because forms designed from scratch may have problems that have already been identified and solved by others.

Enough space to write the answer should be included on the form. Too little space results in illegible handwriting. Never squeeze the space for answers; another page should be added to the form or some of the data elements deleted. If a typewriter is to be used to complete the form, correct spacing between lines is essential. Also consider aligning the answer spaces so tabular settings can be used.

The form should be of standard size. Forms with odd sizes require special file cabinets, which are more expensive, and oversized forms are more difficult to use in the field. If more than one copy of a report will be needed, consider using NCR (no carbon required) paper. Carbon paper is messy and inconvenient. In addition, different colors for different forms help people distinguish the forms at a distance and can facilitate filing.

If electronic data entry is to be done from the form, the form design should be coordinated with the people responsible for the data entry so that the process will proceed smoothly.

Data should be recorded in the order in which it is most likely to be collected, and information on related topics should be kept together. If the whole form need not be completed in all cases, it can be subdivided. Provide brief instructions on the form as to when each section should be used.

Consider providing space at the top or right margin for case identifiers, such as address, file number, date, or whatever other key is used for filing, so that forms can be readily identified by users thumbing through the file. The form should be kept single-sided, if possible.

The written procedures for completing the report should describe the intended use of the data. Procedures should cover, item by item, the kind of information sought, the format in which it should be recorded, and, if it is to be classified, the appropriate classifications. The type of information and extent of detail expected in the remarks section should be defined. Samples of properly completed reports can improve the understanding and use of the reports.

Direct Electronic Data Capture

If the only record is on the electronic media, each data entry screen must be designed to capture groups of related data based on the type of incident. Multiple screens should be used so that a screen does not look jammed.

The system should present screens for completion based on previously entered data. For example, a screen collecting civilian injury data would be presented if the number of civilian injuries was greater than zero.

The data base needs to collect both a narrative description and a classification number as appropriate for each data element, since the narrative description will often be more specific to the incident than the description of the classification number. The system must also be able to capture and store comments or remarks by the fire officer in charge of the incident.

Help screens are useful in selecting appropriate classification numbers for the data element rather than having to refer to printed tables.

Data editing should be done when the data are captured to ensure completeness and accuracy. The system must be able to print a hard-copy report, including the narrative descriptions and remarks, on demand for administrative purposes.

If the data are to be routinely summarized into management reports, the written procedures should define how this is to be done, how often, and which persons should receive copies of the summaries.

Training

Actual use of a new form or a new reporting system must be preceded by training for those individuals who will be responsible for collecting and recording the data. The training should be the responsibility of the training division in the department, which should work closely with whomever developed the reporting system to develop the training materials. Written instructions should be the basis of the training. Questions raised during the training may point to a need for additional written instructions.

Once the initial training has been completed, periodic retraining should be scheduled as part of the normal retraining processes. All persons promoted or assigned to positions where they will be responsible for collecting and recording incident data should receive this special training.

Organizing to Compile Reports

In many fire departments, the data on various aspects of a fire come from different sources. The communications office will be able to provide data on alarm receipt and dispatch. The officer in charge will be responsible for the incident report. The company officers will be in the best position to record the role of their companies and the resources used in an incident. If there were casualties, data on the injuries or fatalities may best be provided by still other personnel. As the fire is investigated, the fire marshal or fire investigation unit may develop details that the officer in charge could not determine at the time of the fire.

All of this data are often recorded separately by the individuals with direct knowledge of a certain part of the fire incident. It is extremely important that all these reports be compiled into a complete fire report and that the data on the various reports be checked for completeness and consistency.

One division within the department, frequently the fire marshal, should be given the responsibility for compiling all fire reports. Clerical personnel should be properly trained in recording fire data. Some of the responsibilities associated with compiling reports include:

1. Ensuring that all required data are recorded and submitted in a timely fashion.
2. Ensuring that all handwritten forms are properly completed and are legible.
3. Screening the reports for obvious errors, omissions, or conflicting data.
4. Following up with the appropriate personnel when necessary to obtain complete or corrected data.
5. Ensuring that any data entry that is to be automated is timely and correct.
6. Filing the complete report, if paper forms are used.
7. Updating the report and the files as new or additional information is received.

Detailed written procedures should be developed for the clerical personnel, outlining how they should perform each step in report compilation. These procedures should address such issues as how the reports are to be edited, processed, and filed, and within what time frame.

It is important that everyone responsible for completing any portion of the report understand the procedure that the clerical staff uses and the schedule they are expected to follow in completing, correcting, and forwarding the data. Delays in submitting data will result in delays in assembling the complete report and in making it available for use.

Quality Control

An important aspect of any record-keeping function is ensuring the quality of the data collected. This starts with proper training of the person responsible for collecting the data. Written instructions should explain how the data is to be recorded, and all data should be edited as part of the process of compiling it into a master record. This editing can be done by a trained clerical person. At least periodically, a supervisor should spot-check a sample of the reports to ensure that they are completed properly. All reports with errors or omissions should be flagged and returned to the originator for correction or completion as appropriate. This procedure reinforces training because the individual will see where the mistakes are and thus may be able to avoid them in the future. If a person continues to make the same mistakes, special training or other action may be necessary to improve the quality of the reports submitted. Incomplete or poor reports waste time and defeat the whole purpose of collecting data.

It is important that supervisory personnel be involved in the quality control process on a regular basis. A computer can do certain editing tasks and force completion of a report, but it cannot check to see that the incident scene was interpreted correctly or that the report accurately reflects the incident. Nor can it determine if files are being updated properly as new information becomes available. Both of these tasks are as important to ensuring a quality data base as any other part of the process.

Record Retention

An important aspect of any record-keeping system is determining how long to keep the records. The answer varies with the purpose of the record and, to some extent, with local and state legal requirements for record retention.

Obviously, paper records require storage space, and storage space costs money. Likewise, the more voluminous the files become, the more likely material will be lost or misfiled.

There should be a written policy that details the length of time a report is to be retained in the active files, the length of time it should be kept in inactive storage, and when it can be discarded. The city attorney's office can help determine legal requirements for retaining records; that office should review the final written policy before its implementation. There may be different requirements for computerized records that require less space and are useful for multiyear analysis.

Setting Standards within the Department

The fire department should have certain standards that apply to all its record-keeping operations. Such standards will help make the data more uniform from report to report and application to application. Standardization aids all users of the data, makes analysis more accurate, and is essential if data is to be automated. Some areas where department standards should be developed include:

1. Methods of entering the names of persons—first name first or last name first—on records.
2. Recording addresses of buildings with multiple or ambiguous addresses, as well as nonstructure locations, such as those on highways or at street intersections.
3. Designating apparatus. Should it be done by company assigned? Serial number? Shop number?
4. Designating employees. Should it be done by name? Badge number? Social security number?
5. The common abbreviations that are acceptable to use.

NFPA 901 can be used as a basis of terminology, definition, and classification if data are to be classified when it is reported.

Data Analysis

In many fire reporting systems, more than 90 percent of the reporting effort is devoted to data collection, and very little effort is devoted to data analysis. Strictly speaking, adding things up is not data analysis.

Data analysis involves determining what the data are really showing relative to the community or the project supported by the data. Data analysis often involves studying the interrelationship between various data elements or various data bases. For example, studying the problem by relating fire data to socioeconomic data for the census tracks will lead to a better understanding of the problem and the population groups who are most affected. Likewise, comparing fire losses over the years to inflation rates and increasing property values may show that fire protection is currently more effective, even though in raw numbers the total loss is greater.

Data analysis is a special skill that should be sought out and used by a fire department. With such analysis, the data are often more meaningful in defining the problem and targeting a solution.

Collecting Data for Special Studies

No one can anticipate all the data that may be needed to understand the fire problem. Once a problem has been identified through an ongoing fire reporting system, a special study may be needed to gather the data required to further define and help solve the problem. The steps in conducting a special study are:

1. Identify the type and sources of data needed to define the problem further. Assess the feasibility and costs of the study, and proceed in the most efficient way. For example, sampling may be appropriate. Previous work to solve this or similar problems should be researched and the results studied.
2. Develop a mechanism or procedure for collecting the needed data. This can be a special form completed by the officer in charge of the incident, additional questions asked on a computer monitor when the data are captured, or a request to include certain data in the remarks section of a report whenever a certain condition is encountered. Alternatively, the procedure may stipulate merely that the officer in charge notify a certain person or agency whenever he or she encounters the particular problem or condition.
3. Collect and analyze the data. Develop a methodology to reduce or solve the problem, based on the results of data analysis and any additional documentation.
4. Terminate the special study. When the methodology is implemented, monitor the progress of the problem-solving methodology using the normal reporting system. Return to Steps 1, 2, or 3 as appropriate if the problem is not being reduced or solved.

BASIC INCIDENT REPORT

902F

Fill In This Report
In Your Own Words

______________________ **Fire Department** ☐ Revised Report

A	FD ID	Incident No.	Index No.	Mo.	Day	Year	Alarm Time	Time on Scene	Time Last Unit Clear
B	Location/Address	City/Town	Zip Code	Property No.					
C	Occupant Name (Last, First, MI)	Telephone No.	Room or Apt.						
D	Owner Name (Last, First, MI)	Address	Telephone No.						
E	Method of Alarm to Fire Department	Type of Incident							
F	Type of Action Taken	District	Shift	No. Alarms	Mutual Aid ☐ Rec'd ☐ Given ☐ N/A				
G	General Property Use	Specific Property Use	County	Census Tract					
H	No. Injuries* Fire Service	Other Emerg.	Civilian	No. Fatalities* Fire Service	Other Emerg.	Civilian			
I	No. Fire Service Personnel Responded	No. Engines Responded	No. Aerial Apparatus Responded	No. Other Vehicles Responded					
J	Condition of Fire upon Arrival of First Unit	Time from Alarm to Agent Application	Area of Fire Origin						
K	Equipment Involved in Ignition	Year	Make	Model	Serial No.				
L	Form of Heat of Ignition	Material First Ignited Form/Use	Type						
M	Ignition Factor	Method of Extinguishment							
N	Property Damage Classification	No. Buildings Damaged	Termination Stage						
O	Construction Type	No. of Stories	Level of Origin						
P	Structure Status	No. of Occupants at Time of Incident							
Q	Material Generating Most Flame Form/Use	Type	Factor Contributing to Flame Travel						
R	Material Generating Most Smoke Form/Use	Type	Avenue of Smoke Travel						
S	Detector Type	Detector Power Supply	Detector Performance						
T	Sprinkler System Performance	No. of Sprinkler Heads Operated							
U	Extent of Flame Damage	Extent of Smoke Damage	Extent of Extinguishing Agent Damage						
V	Mobile Property Type	Year	Make	Model	Serial No.	License No.			
W	No. of Private Acres Burned	No. of Federal Acres Burned	No. of Other Public Acres Burned						
X	Member Making Report	Date	Officer in Charge (Name, Position, Assignment)	Date					
Y	Remarks:								

☐ Remarks continued on reverse side.

Side labels: COMPLETE ON ALL INCIDENTS (A–I); ON ALL FIRES TI 10-19 (J–N); COMPLETE IF FIRE TYPE OF INCIDENT (TI) 10-19 — FOR STRUCTURE FIRE TI 11-13 (O–U); TI 12-14 (V); TI 15 (W); COMPLETE ON ALL INCIDENTS (X–Y).

*A Form 902G must be completed for each Fire Casualty.

This form is for use with NFPA 902M, *Field Incident Manual.* Users should also refer to NFPA 901, *Uniform Coding for Fire Protection,* for information on fire reporting systems and classifications for information entered on this form.

***FIG. 10-2A.** Basic incident report form recommended by NFPA's Technical Committee on Fire Reporting.*

Periodic Review

Over time, information needs within a fire department change, and as they do, it is not uncommon for new reporting requirements to be added. New forms or requirements are introduced or existing systems are expanded. Much less common, however, is a reduction in the amount or type of information collected.

At least yearly and certainly before any form is reprinted, a careful review should be made to determine if the original purpose for collecting the data is still valid and if all the information is still needed in its present format. Do not perpetuate data gathering if the data are not serving a useful purpose. It is easy to fall into the trap of justifying data collection on the basis that "it may be needed someday." This approach generally results in poor-quality data, if and when used, because lack of data use results in lack of accuracy and quality control in collecting the data.

STATUS OF UNIFORM FIRE REPORTING

Fire reporting systems based on NFPA 901 continue to be developed. The NFPA Fire Reporting Committee also has established a basic system, published in NFPA 902M, *Fire Reporting Field Incident Manual*, that provides the necessary instructions for completing an incident report, supplementary reports on civilian or fire fighter casualties suffered at incidents, and EMS reports that can be used by those fire departments providing emergency medical services. Figure 10-2A is an example of a form used in NFPA 902M. Worksheets are provided for summarizing incident data. This system can be used manually or adapted for electronic data processing.

The U.S. Fire Administration (USFA), within the Federal Emergency Management Agency (FEMA), has developed the National Fire Incident Reporting System (NFIRS), which is an automated system based on the work of the NFPA Fire Reporting Committee as published in NFPA 901. The system, which started in 1976, is now operational in 40 states and annually collects data on approximately one million fires from more than 13,400 fire departments.

NFIRS is an incident-based system. Data are reported on an incident-by-incident basis. Computer programs are available to capture and edit the data, maintain a data base, and generate a variety of summary reports. The data collected are similar to the data collected by the basic system published in NFPA 902M.

At the state level, NFIRS provides for the collection of written reports on incidents to which local communities responded. Communities with automated data systems based on NFPA 901 can participate by providing the state with their data on computer tape or other electronic media. Summary reports are then generated on both individual community and statewide fire experience.

At the national level, NFIRS provides for the merging of data bases from individual states to form a national data base. FEMA/USFA analyzes this data base and publishes the analysis. The data base is also available to businesses or individuals who wish to perform their own analyses.

BIBLIOGRAPHY

NFPA Codes, Standards, and Recommended Practices.

Reference to the following NFPA codes, standards, and practices will provide further information on collecting fire data discussed in this chapter. (See the latest *NFPA Codes and Standards Catalog* for availability of current editions of the following documents.)

NFPA 901, *Uniform Coding for Fire Protection.*

NFPA 902M, *Fire Reporting Field Incident Manual.*

NFPA 903M, *Fire Reporting Property Survey Manual.*

NFPA 904M, *Incident Follow-Up Report Manual.*

Additional Readings

DPRA *Capabilities to Prepare Briefings, Data Analysis, and Fire Date Exchange: System Development from the National Fire Incident Reporting System*, Development Planning and Research Associates, Inc., Manhattan, KS, 1985

Fire Incident Data Coding Guide: Based on NFPA 901, 2nd ed., National Fire Protection Association, Quincy, MA, 1985

Jason, N. H., "FIREDOC, A Fire Research Bibliographic Database," *Proceedings* of the Conference on New Technology to Reduce Fire Losses and Costs, Elsevier, 1986, pp. 8-15.

Jenaway, W. F., *Managing Support Systems*, International Association of Fire Service Instructors, Ashland, MA, 1988

National Fire Incident Reporting System Handbook, Version IV, National Fire Information Council, as sponsored by the U.S. Fire Administration, Federal Emergency Management Agency, Washington, DC, 1984. (Computer programs and system documentation available from the U.S. Fire Administration.)

Schaenman, P. S., "Management Information Systems and Data Analysis," *Managing Fire Services, ed.* Ronny Coleman and John A. Granito, International City Management Association, Washington, DC, 1988, pp. 129-166.

Weiner, M. E., *Computers for Fire Departments: Current Technology and Typical Systems*, U.S. Fire Administration, Washington, DC, 1979.

USE OF FIRE LOSS INFORMATION

Dr. John R. Hall, Jr.

The preceding chapter examined techniques for collecting data on fires. This chapter addresses uses of that collected data in fire protection decision-making and planning.

In the past decade, the quantity and quality of fire data available for analysis has grown at an unprecedented rate. In the early 1970s, even the best fire departments typically had fire incident records only in narrative form. Neither the method of storage (in file cabinets, by incident number) nor the method of description (phrases selected by fire officers, without standardized coded descriptions or even a standard list of characteristics to be documented) facilitated analysis of the community's leading fire problems. At the state level, very few states had any fire experience data base. At the national level, the National Fire Protection Association (NFPA) prepared estimates of U.S. incidents, deaths, injuries, and losses from its annual survey, and provided analyses of fire causes and other detailed factors from its Fire Incident Data Organization (FIDO) data base. The Fire Reporting Committee of NFPA had developed NFPA 901, *Uniform Coding for Fire Protection* (hereinafter referred to as NFPA 901),[1] a standard fire incident reporting format, but few fire departments were using it.

In 1977, NFPA modified its survey techniques to take account of modern statistical design principles and, in the process, greatly improved estimates of the size of the national fire problem. At about the same time, the new National Fire Prevention and Control Administration (now the U.S. Fire Administration, a branch of FEMA, the Federal Emergency Management Agency) launched the National Fire Incident Reporting System (NFIRS). Based on NFPA 901, the NFIRS system provided the framework for a large-scale, truly national fire experience data base. Since 1980, NFIRS has had the participation, in whole or in part, of the majority of states and receives standardized reports on roughly one-third of all fire incidents. (As sources of the principal fire data bases, NFPA and FEMA also have helped each other over the years, with FEMA providing financial support and technical suggestions on NFPA data bases and NFPA providing developmental work and analysis services on NFIRS for FEMA.) Other countries, such as Australia, have adopted their own versions of NFIRS, making possible much more valid international comparisons.

A parallel development has enlarged the capacity for analysis of the newly generated fire data. The advent of powerful microcomputers and the increasing affordability and flexibility of computer power in general have made a significant impact upon the fire service and other fire data users. Most readers of the Handbook now have access to valid national and local data bases in forms suitable for analysis, and to the equipment and skills required to analyze that data.

This chapter will first address the techniques of analyzing fire data, including examples demonstrating the amount of information already obtained as a result of the fire community's new data collection and retrieval capabilities. The major data bases now available to analysts then will be reviewed. See Table 10-3A for a sample of the many potential data users and uses.

USING DATA TO CHARACTERIZE THE FIRE PROBLEM

Table 10-3B lists ten major findings on the nature of the fire problem that have emerged from analyses of the past decade. Many of these analyses could not have been conducted without the new and refined data bases that emerged in the late 1970s. This list is not arranged in any order of priority, nor is it necessarily a list of what everyone would consider the ten most important data-based findings. The list does, however, illustrate the ability of data and analysis to identify emerging problems, describe those problems in ways that can help the design of corresponding programs, and track the impact of those programs.

Top-Down and Topic-Driven Analysis

Most characterizations of the fire problem begin with some measures of the problem's size. Why? Implicit in these measurements is the idea that fire is a problem big enough to justify concern and attention. Each year fire kills thou-

Dr. Hall is assistant vice president, Fire Analysis and Research Division, of NFPA.

TABLE 10-3A. ***Typical Users and Uses of Fire Experience Results***

User	Use
1. Fire protection engineers	Defining and quantifying fire scenarios Estimating possibilities of fire incidence and fire protection performance Evaluating fire protection alternatives
2. Fire protection planners at national and state levels	Comparing fire to other problems competing for resources Planning the most effective deployment of resources to make the greatest impact on the fire problem Monitoring fire protection progress
3. Local fire service	Targeting fire prevention and suppression programs Backing up budget requests Enacting and enforcing fire codes Developing community firesafety education program Monitoring progress
4. Technical firesafety standards committees	Identifying needs for standards Keeping standards current Monitoring the performance of standards Analyzing the benefits and costs of standards
5. Communicators/educators	Reporting of fire problems Educating for firesafety
6. Committees developing fire fighter safety standards, individuals, fire departments working to improve fire fighter safety	Identifying reasons for fire fighter deaths and injuries Developing safety and training programs Designing protective equipment
7. Researchers	Establishing firesafety research priorities Designing research programs
8. Insurers	Loss prevention Risk selection and underwriting
9. Industry	Worker safety Loss prevention
10. Product developers	Identifying needed products and markets Modifying products to improve firesafety
11. Building designers, architects, managers	Assuring a firesafe design
12. Legislators, regulators, enforcers, courts	Effective and equitable firesafety laws and regulations

sands of persons, injures tens of thousands more, and destroys billions of dollars worth of property. Many problems causing far less loss of life and property, such as floods and tornadoes, receive much more attention and have much greater resources devoted to the mitigation of their effects. When the fire community wishes to pursue a program that requires the cooperation of others, that community must first attract their attention. The big numbers on fire—incidents, deaths, injuries, and property damage—accomplish this.

Top-down analysis is an approach that begins with the big numbers on fire, then subdivides the totals into their major parts. The top-down approach provides the broadest perspective on the overall fire problem. It differs from *topic-driven analysis*, which begins with interest in certain issues involving only certain types of fires. For example, a top-down analysis of fires in residences might identify smoking materials as the leading factor in civilian fatalities in residences, accounting for nearly three out of every ten cases for which the fire cause was reported. On the other hand, a topic-driven analysis focused on smoking-material fires—for example, a study of the likely impact of a self-extinguishing cigarette or of a public education program aimed at smokers—would involve more than just residences. Although both topic-driven and top-down analyses might be interested in the role of smoking-related fires in residential deaths, the topic-driven analysis also might be interested in the involvement of smoking materials in nonresidential fire fatalities, or in property damage in residential fires. Even though smoking-related fires do not account for the largest shares of the latter two problems (incendiary and suspicious causes lead in both cases), they are still part of the overall smoking-fire problem; any change that affects the smoking-fire problem may affect all smoking-related fires.

In a top-down analysis, the basic rule is to look for the biggest parts of the problem. Why bother subdividing the problem? Why not simply attack the whole problem? The answer is that resources usually are too limited to permit an attack on the whole problem and choices must be made. The use of data to identify the largest manageable parts of the problem is the first step in making those choices.

TABLE 10-3B. ***Ten Major U.S. Data Based Findings of the Last Decade, 1980–1989***

1. *Home smoke detectors are widely used and very effective, but significant gaps in the detector strategy remain.* By the late 1980s, five out of every six U.S. households had at least one smoke detector, but one-third of detectors were not operational (e.g., dead batteries), few homes had rehearsed escape plans to use the extra warning time effectively, many homes did not have as many detectors as they needed for code-compliant coverage, and the one-sixth of homes without detectors had the majority of reported home fires. Despite all this, just having a detector cuts the risk of dying in half if fire occurs, even without specifying complete coverage or operational detectors.

2. *Automatic sprinklers produce large reductions in loss of life and property.* On average, loss of property per fire is cut in half and loss of life per fire is cut by a third to a half, depending on property class, if automatic suppression equipment (typically sprinklers) is present, even without specifying complete systems that are properly installed and maintained. If the latter is specified and the focus is on prevention of life loss in areas away from the point of fire origin, which is the scenario of greatest concern to the public, then automatic sprinklers are nearly perfect, allowing more than two deaths only in rare cases of explosion, flash fire, or major fire fighting operations by on-site personnel, such as fire brigades.

3. *Increased use of portable and area heating equipment, beginning in the late 1970s, drove sharp increases in home fires involving heating equipment.* Increased use of wood stoves led to an increase in home heating fires on the order of tens of thousands of fires a year. Increased use of wood stoves, portable kerosene heaters, and, most recently, gas-fueled space heaters has contributed to a significant shift to home heating by equipment that carries a fatal-fire risk that is much higher than that associated with any type of central heating equipment (i.e., furnace). Three of every ten home fires begin with heating equipment, as do more than one in every six home fire deaths.

4. *Incendiary and suspicious fires continued decline from 1970s peaks, but associated property damage stopped declining.* From 1977 to 1988, the number of reported incendiary and suspicious fires dropped by nearly 40 percent, wiping out most of the huge increase in the previous decade. However, associated property damage adjusted for inflation has been essentially constant since 1983, and associated civilian deaths have increased by 17 percent. Explanations for these divergent trends are elusive, as juvenile firesetting remains the leading component of the arson problem.

5. *Large share of fire fighter fatalities attributed to heart attacks and activities away from the fireground.* NFPA data showed that, since 1977 at least, the more familiar fire fighter fatality scenarios of burns, smoke exposure, falls, and structural collapse have been overshadowed by stress-related heart attacks and accidents away from the fireground. These findings have implications for physical fitness testing and conditioning programs, and training in such areas as operating or riding on fire vehicles. Incidents during vehicle response to and return from a call contributed more than one-fourth of all fire service deaths in 1988, compared to just under one-half that occurred at the fireground.

6. *Rural areas have the highest fire death rates.* Refinements in the NFPA survey techniques in the mid 1970s provided the first hard data on the size of the overall fire problems, hitherto hidden by the large number of small communities among which the fires are scattered. Based on 1984–88 data, the rate of fire deaths per million population in communities of less than 2,500 population is more than double the rate in small cities (25,000 to 50,000 population) and is more than 50 percent higher than the death rate in the largest cities (more than 500,000 population).

7. *Smoking materials igniting upholstered furniture, mattresses or bedding produce the most deadly residential fire scenarios.* In recent years smoking related fire deaths have accounted for nearly three-tenths of all residential fire deaths where the cause of fire was known. Three of every four smoking-related fire deaths where the form of material ignited was known involved upholstered furniture, mattresses or bedding. No other fire scenario of comparable specificity comes close to accounting for this large a share of the residential fire fatality problem.

8. *U.S. and Canadian fire death rates are highest of all developed countries in the free world.* In the late 1970s, a series of reports by Georgia Institute of Technology for FEMA showed that fire fatality rates per million population in the U.S.A. and Canada are at least twice the rates in Japan and western Europe (the only other areas examined). No single cause has been identified to explain this pattern, but analyses have shown that the U.S. does well in holding down the average severity of fires (i.e., quick response and suppression) but very badly in holding down the fire incident rate (i.e., prevention).

9. *The states of the Old South have the highest fire death rates.* The number of civilian fire deaths per million population in the states of the South is one-third percent higher than the national rate. Only Alaska and the District of Columbia outside the South have comparably high rates. Mississippi's fire death rate is double the national average. The leading fire cause in these high rates is the high death rate in fires involving portable and area heating equipment. Poverty and poor education, especially in rural areas, are major factors as well.

10. *Older adults are at particularly high risk of death in fire.* People age 65 and over account for one-fourth of all home fire deaths and have a risk of dying that is twice the national average. Those age 75 and over have three times the average risk, and those age 85 and over have four times the average risk. In the late 1960s and early 1970s, there was a particular problem with nursing home fires. In the late 1970s and early 1980s, the special risks of older adults played a part in the rash of major fires in board and care homes, which killed 300 people in seven years of multiple- death fires (i.e., those killing three or more people). In the late 1980s, these two areas of concern remained and were joined by housing for older adults, which accounted for three major fires in late 1989 alone.

While totals are used to show the overall size of the problem, percentages are used to indicate the largest parts.

Use of percentages to identify the largest parts of the fire problem is not as easy as it sounds. Judgment is involved in selecting the categories for which percentages will be calculated. For example, suppose an analysis showed the biggest subgroup of a particular occupancy group's fire problem consisted of fires involving electrical short circuits. This finding does not fit well into most strategies for attacking the fire problem. If one is going to examine every piece of equipment that could be subject to short circuits, one might as well also check for other electrical faults in that equipment. The available strategy may dictate a broader category, covering fires involving all electrical equipment faults. Or maybe it is easier to design strategies around particular types of electrical equipment—for example, fixed wiring, heating systems, ranges, and ovens—and address all fires involving such equipment, whether the equipment or the user were at fault.

Take another example. Which of the following findings is more useful: (1) 20 percent of all home fires begin in the kitchen; or (2) 15 percent of home fires involve cooking equipment? The latter finding identifies a smaller part of the problem, and uses a completely different categorization (equipment involved in ignition versus area of origin), but it locates the problem much more specifically. In a kitchen, there could be dozens of fire hazards to check out; with cooking equipment, most homes have only a few.

Finally, suppose a categorization includes equipment involvement, material ignited, and the human elements that brought them together. Such a categorization will produce detailed scenarios, but the "leading" category might account for only 2 to 4 percent of all fires. It would be necessary to develop strategies for several dozen scenarios in order to make any noticeable impact upon the total fire problem. If that is so, it may make more sense to select scenarios that fit together logically and can be addressed by variations of the same strategy—that is, use of less specific categories—than to select several dozen distinct scenarios and tackle each one separately. To put it another way, the scenario technique of analyzing several fire characteristics simultaneously is most useful as a second-stage analysis, performed after one characteristic has been used to establish basic clustering.

Therefore, in selecting categories for calculating percentages, it is important to match the structure of the categories to the structure of the strategies available to attack the fire problem. Remember that the size of the problem being attacked is no more or less important than the anticipated leverage on the problem; for example, a 7 percent reduction in a problem that causes 500 deaths a year is worth just as much as a 70 percent reduction in a problem that causes 50 deaths a year. (This is discussed at greater length later in this chapter under the heading "Using Data in Program and Strategy Analysis.") So be sure when you pick out the biggest parts of the problem that they collectively account for a sizable share of the total, but also remember that some parts of the problem may be much more preventable than others.

Figures 10-3A and 10-3B illustrate the effective use of percentages (some implicitly presented through the display of numbers) to describe patterns in the 1988 fire fighter fatality problem. (These figures also illustrate the effective use of graphics to bring potentially dull numbers to life.) In Figure 10-3A, which shows the percentage of fire fighter fatalities by type of duty, the fact that fire fighting is the leading type of duty is not as interesting as the fact that its lead is so small. Response/return, which should involve only controllable dangers and relatively little risk, accounts for more than one-fourth of all fire fighter deaths. Figure 10-3B implicitly demonstrates that as fire fighter age increases, the leading share of deaths dramatically shifts to heart attacks. Such patterns have direct implications for targeting of physical fitness programs.

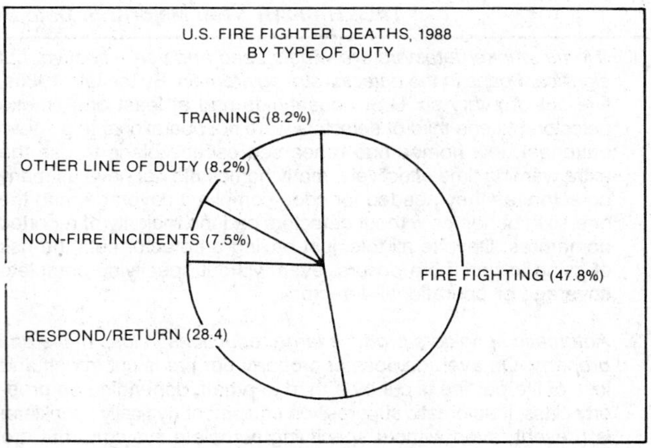

FIG. 10-3A. ***U.S. Fire Fighter Deaths, 1988.***

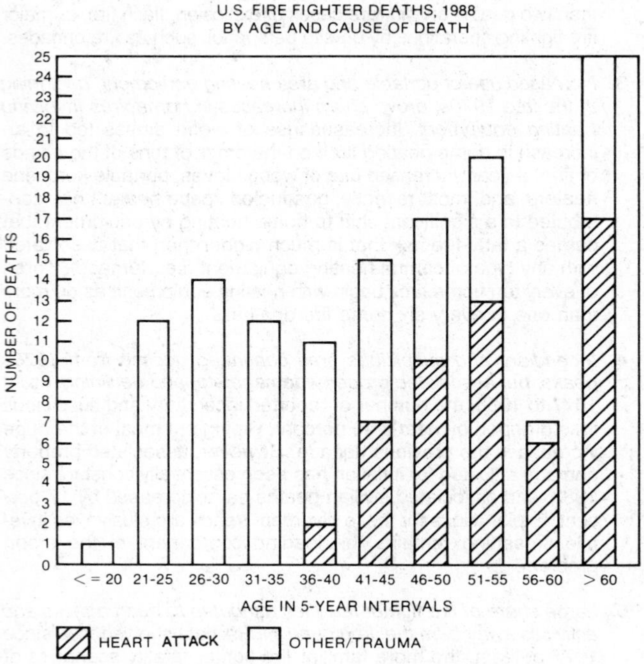

FIG. 10-3B. ***U.S. Fire Fighter Deaths, 1988.***

Analysis by Cause or Property Type

The dimensions most frequently chosen for top-down and topic-driven analyses are fire cause and property type, because most fire prevention strategies are structured along those lines. "Analysis by cause" actually refers to a variety of analyses addressed to different aspects of the ignition factors. The question of how to categorize, already discussed in general terms, becomes especially difficult in analyses of cause-related information.

Even the question of how to refer to cause-based descriptions can be a problem. For example, suppose one observes that nearly three-tenths of all civilian fire fatalities in residential properties with fire cause reported were smoking-related. Does this mean that cigarettes (the principal smoking material involved, by far) were to blame for all those deaths? Not necessarily. If the smokers in question had been careful not to smoke in bed and always to place cigarettes in sturdy ashtrays, few of the deaths would have occurred. Or if the bedding, mattresses, pillows, and upholstered furniture that are the first items ignited in most smoking-related fires had been more ignition-resistant, many or most of the deaths would have been avoided. It is also true that if the cigarettes used had been designed to self-extinguish more quickly, many or most of the deaths would not have occurred. A decision on which dimension to use in categorizing fire causes—the source of heat, items ignited, or the behaviors that brought them together—should be made in a way that supports analyses of workable prevention strategies. Assessments of blame are tasks for lawyers or philosophers; they do not help in the search for ways to reduce fire problems.

Fire incident data coded according to NFPA 901 format, which is used in most major fire data bases, contains five fire-cause-related elements of information: the form of heat producing ignition; equipment involved in ignition, if any; type of material that ignited (e.g., wood, plastic, fabric); the form in which that material appeared (e.g., chair, floor covering, structural beam); and ignition factors—the human or equipment failures that brought together the ignition heat and ignited material. Together, these five dimensions can define billions of distinct fire-cause categories, a clearly unworkable partitioning of the problem. In the face of all this detail, several approaches have been developed to extract major patterns. See Table 10-3C for examples of how different approaches can affect the description of "leading cause."

One approach is to divide fire causes into incendiary causes, suspicious causes, all known causes that are accidental in nature, and unknown causes. For many property types, such a partition sufficiently identifies the major fire causes to justify concentrating on arson problems. If not, a different approach is needed.

A second approach has been to use one of the NFPA 901 cause dimensions to sort the fires. One can use the first digit alone to create ten categories, or both digits to create nearly one hundred categories for each dimension. This approach often proves frustrating, however, because the structure of the coding elements often does not coincide with the issues to be analyzed. For example, suppose the ignition-factor dimension is used. Incendiary and suspicious fires will be easy to identify (codes 10-29). Fires caused by children playing, however, involve two code values (36 and 48) that do not have the same first digit and therefore do not fall into a natural common grouping. An analysis using ignition factors also will produce a large number of entries under "abandoned, discarded material." A novice analyst might not recognize that nearly all of these are smoking-related fires and can best be characterized in this manner.

If the igition-factor dimension has problems when used by itself, what about the other dimensions? Problems arise here because incendiary and suspicious fires are *not* isolated. Under the category of "heat of ignition," arson fires set with matches (the most common type) are indistinguishable from accidental fires involving matches.

A third approach has been to use scenarios based on two or three of the NFPA 901 cause dimensions. This avoids the tendency, in the one-dimensional sort of scenario, for major problems to be mixed together (e.g., arson and accidental match fires) or disguised (e.g., smoking-related fires listed as discarded or abandoned material). The use of even two dimensions of NFPA 901, however—or the use of three dimensions with the first digit only—creates thousands of cause categories, and again one is faced with the likelihood that even the largest parts of the total will not represent a very large share of the total.

The fourth approach has been to use a small number of major, easily recognizable categories based on NFPA 901 data elements, but not necessarily grouped along the lines laid out in the NFPA 901 coding structure. The most widely used scheme based on this approach is a set of thirteen categories developed at the USFA. This scheme uses a hierarchical process to sort fires into categories. For example, one will start with ignition factor and remove all the incendiary, suspicious, and children-playing fires. Then the analyst may switch to heat of ignition and use it to separate fires involving smoking materials.

Criticisms of this or any other hierarchical sorting approach focus on the reasonableness of the sorting priorities and the usefulness of the categories produced. If a fire is caused by a child playing with cigarettes, should that be categorized as a children-playing fire or a smoking-related fire? Is it useful to have a category called "open flame" that combines matches, bonfires, undoused embers, and cutting and welding torches? For most of the categories, the number of fires falling into each category is not greatly dependent upon the sorting order. The most striking exception is match-related fires, which are scattered among the incendiary/suspicious, children-playing, and open-flame categories. As for usefulness, the categories that seem to be most mixed are also categories that account for relatively little of the fire problem in residential properties, the setting for which the categories were designed to be most helpful. For nonresidential properties, particularly manufacturing and industry, the usefulness of the categories may be more questionable.

The last approach, which can be used as a refinement of any of the others, is nesting of cause categories. Start with an initial sorting of fires based on either a single dimension of NFPA 901, a scenario structure, or a hierarchically based structure. Then, for each category of the initial sort that has a sufficient number of fires to be worthy of further analysis, use another dimension of NFPA 901 to provide more detail. Table 10-3D shows this nesting approach applied to an initial scenario sort for large-loss fires in store properties during 1974–1983. Nesting represents the top-down approach at its best—it provides usable levels of detail without sacrificing an overview of the largest parts of the total.

Another matter to consider when analyzing fire data by cause is how to handle incidents for which the cause was unknown or unreported. A sizable share of fires are reported without cause information, particularly severe fires involving deaths or significant loss. Note that several points in this section have been illustrated with the observation that nearly three-tenths of all civilian fire fatalities in residential properties with known cause involved smoking materials. Just under one-fourth of all civilian fire fatalities in residential properties were coded as involving smoking materials. A calculation of percentages based only on cases where cause was reported implicitly assumes (in the absence of contrary evidence) that the cause profile of the fires reported without known cause would look the same (if those causes were known) as the cause profile of the fires reported with known causes. (The two types of percentages are sometimes referred to as causes based on "allocating unknowns over known causes" and causes based on "unallocated unknowns.")

Why is it desirable to allocate unknowns? Suppose two neighboring states have relative cause profiles that look the same, except that fire deaths due to unknown causes appear as 10 percent in one state and 40 percent in the other. Table 10-3E shows the results. State B seems to be doing better than State A with respect to every known cause, but if unknowns are allocated, both states have the same problems to the same degree. If it is necessary or desirable to compare two groups, differences in rates of unknowns need to be taken into consideration.

TABLE 10-3C. ***How "Leading Cause" of Fires Can Depend on How Data is Sorted****

Emphasis on Accidental vs. Intentional	
Incendiary	9%
Suspicious	7%
Accidental	75%
Unknown	9%
Emphasis on Equipment	
No equipment involved	40%
Cooking equipment involved	29%
Heating equipment involved	6%
Electrical distribution equipment involved	5%
Appliances involved	4%
Other known equipment	3%
Unknown equipment	12%
Emphasis on Behavior	
Misuse of heat of ignition (e.g., abandoned material)	29%
Operational deficiency (e.g., something left unattended)	21%
Incendiary or suspicious	15%
Mechanical failure or malfunction (e.g., short circuit)	13%
Misuse of material ignited (e.g., combustible placed too close to heat source)	8%
Design, construction, or installation deficiency	3%
Other known ignition factor	2%
Unknown ignition factor	9%
Emphasis on Heat Source	
Electrically powered equipment involved	27%
Open flame source involved (e.g., match)	18%
Gas-fueled equipment involved	15%
Lighted tobacco product involved (e.g., cigarette)	13%
Other fueled equipment (solid, liquid, unclassified, or unknown fuel) involved	4%
Hot object (excluding electrical equipment) involved	3%
Exposure (to other hostile fire) involved	3%
Other known heat source	3%
Unknown heat source	13%
Emphasis on Item Ignited	
Cooking materials (e.g., spilled food or grease)	24%
Mattress, pillow, or bedding	11%
Trash	9%
Upholstered furniture	6%
Electrical wire or cable insulation	5%
Structural element	4%
Unclassified item	3%
Clothing	3%
Other known item	28%
Unknown form of item	7%
Hierarchial sorting approach	
Cooking equipment	28%
Incendiary or suspicious	15%
Smoking-material related	12%
Other equipment involved	7%
Heating equipment involved	6%
Child playing	6%
Appliance, tool, or air conditioning involved	5%
Electrical distribution system involved	5%
Other known cause	9%
Unknown cause	7%

* Figures in some groupings may not sum to 100 percent because of rounding errors.
Source: 1983–87 national estimates of structure fires in apartments, using NFIRS and NFPA survey.

Why is it difficult to allocate unknowns? Many knowledgeable individuals believe that assessments of probable cause are subject to persistent biases. In fact, no credible evidence, consistent among a variety of fire departments, exists to support the notion that fire officers consistently label fires as suspicious, smoking-related, electrical in origin (all very popular suspicions in certain quarters), or anything else when they really are not sure of the cause.

A more serious argument goes as follows: Probable cause is most difficult to assess in the largest fires because

TABLE 10-3D. ***Ignition Scenarios of U.S. Properties, 1974–1983***

Equipment Involved	Heat of Ignition	Ignition Factor	Percent of Fires	Percent of Dollar Loss
Fixed wiring (37%) Lighting fixtures (28%) Panelboards, etc. (10%) Other electrical (24%) Unknown (1%)	Electrical equipment arcing or overloaded	Mechanical failure or malfunction	36	43.9
	Open flame or incendiary device	Incendiary	28	25.9
Heating (87%) Other equipment (13%)	Fuel-fired or fuel-powered equipment	Mechanical failure or malfunction	5	4.6
	Open flame or incendiary device	Suspicious	5	3.7
	Cigarettes	Carelessly discarded	4	3.5

Based on 280 fires with known ignition scenarios, each resulting in a loss of $500,000 or more reported in the NFPA Fire Incident Data Organization (FIDO) data. All losses have been adjusted to 1974 dollars using the Producer Price Index; total adjusted loss was $229,743,000.

Out of 41 distinct scenarios in this data set, these five scenarios accounted for 78 percent of the fires and 81.6 percent of the dollar loss.

TABLE 10-3E. ***The Problem of Comparisons with Unallocated Unknown Cause Fires***

Cause Category	Percentage of Civilian Fire Fatalities in Residences: State A	State B
Smoking	36%	24%
Heating	18%	12%
Incendiary/Suspicious	18%	12%
Other known	18%	12%
Unknown	10%	40%

more of the evidence of fire origin is destroyed, and the known-cause fires indicate that cause profiles are different for larger versus smaller fires. For example, incendiary/suspicious and electrical-distribution-system fires tend to have greater loss per fire, and incendiary/suspicious and smoking-related fires are more likely than other fires to result in deaths. Therefore, if unknowns are to be allocated, the allocation should take into account the cause profiles for fires of comparable size. This is a fire data analysis issue around which no consensus has yet formed. While the ideal solution would be to find ways to reduce the rate of unknowns, there also may be better ways to arrive at estimates in the face of the unknowns that do exist.

Analyses by property use are much more straightforward. Most analyses are concerned with distinctions covered by the "fixed or specific property use" or "mobile property type" categories of NFPA 901. About the only major property class requiring use of both scales is mobile homes, and there is little difficulty with unknown or unreported property types. However, unknowns are a data problem for many other fire characteristics, not just cause and property type. Many questions analysts would like to have answered on all reported fires are not asked at all, because fire officers cannot be expected to be able to answer them.

A problem can arise in the size of the data base available for analyses aimed at particular property uses. In 1988, according to NFPA, all nonresidential structures combined accounted for 192,500 fires, 215 civilian deaths, 3675 civilian injuries, and $3.168 billion in property damage. Typically, approximately one-third of all fires are represented in the NFIRS, which has individual incident reports and can be used to analyze patterns by specific property use. There are, however, several hundred separate categories of nonresidential properties. A topic-driven analysis focused on one of them might be able to draw upon only a few dozen incidents per year, which is not enough to generate statistical confidence in the results. An analyst who discovers that there is a very small data base available on the property use of interest should do two things. One is to keep the analysis of these fires fairly limited; if each fire represents 2 to 3 percent of the total number of fires being analyzed, there may be no point in conducting fine structure analysis. The other is to reconsider the appropriateness of focusing on this particular property use. If it does not have a large data base it is not suffering many fires. Even the most successful strategy applied to so small a problem can have only minor impact. There may be more appropriate classes of property in which to attack the fire problem.

Rates and Measures of Fire Risk

Having addressed the usefulness of numbers and percentages as measures of the fire problem, attention can now be turned to the third and last type of measure, which is rates. A rate is a ratio consisting of a measure of the size of a fire problem divided by a measure of the size of the group affected by that problem. The U.S. suffers on the order of 20 civilian fire deaths in the home per million persons. That is a rate consisting of the number of home fire deaths divided by the number of persons who live at home. The average fire-related property loss in rural communities is $72 per person per year. That is a ratio consisting of the total property damage in rural communities divided by the number of persons living in those communities.

Rates provide measures of relative fire risk. They can be used, therefore, in any analysis where the size of the group affected by a problem may change. For example, as has been said, the U.S. suffered about 20 civilian fire deaths in the home per million persons in 1988. Because the total population growth adds about 2 million persons to the population each year, the number of civilian fire fatalities will be about 40 deaths higher each year unless increased fire-safety lowers the rate. Along similar lines, the National Safety Council's estimates of fire deaths show total deaths declining by 26 percent from 1971 to 1988, while the fire death rate per million persons declined 39 percent in the same period. Increased firesafety is best measured by the decline in the fire death rate; population growth produced a smaller decline in the death toll.

Risk measures do the best job of bringing the fire problem down to a personal level. Rural communities do not account for a majority of the country's fire deaths, but they have by far the highest fire death rates compared to communities of larger size. Person for person, their citizens are in the most danger from fire. Occupants of manufactured homes suffer a substantially higher rate of fire fatalities per million persons than do occupants of conventional one- and two-family dwellings. Because there are comparatively few manufactured homes, deaths there do not constitute a large share of the total fire fatality problem, but the individuals living in those manufactured homes are more at risk than their counterparts elsewhere and should be concerned. If you as an individual want to know how much and what kind of danger you face from fire, you want to know a measure of risk for people like yourself.

Risk measured by rates is of particular interest if there is the potential for large-scale shifts from one group to another of substantially higher or lower risk. In the early 1980s, analysts determined that solid-fueled heating devices, principally wood-burning stoves, accounted for an unusually high risk; that is, there was a high ratio of fires involving those devices divided by homes using those devices. At the time, it appeared that the generation-long decline in use of these devices was about to be reversed, under the pressure of higher prices for oil and natural gas. This was an ideal opportunity to use data to guide action; at a time when decisions were being made, most people did not know the unusual dangers posed by their choices. As an example of risk moving in the other direction, analysts using fire incident data from the early growth years of smoke-detector usage were able to demonstrate that the rate of deaths per home fire was half as great for homes with detectors as for homes without them. Here again, decisions with substantial impact on risk were being made regarding equipment, so it was possible to get people's attention and encourage the move toward detectors.

For some analyses, it may be difficult or impossible to obtain the information needed to construct the appropriate rate. One example is an analysis comparing the dangers of fire fighting with risks of other professions. The ratio should be number of on-duty fire service deaths to number of hours of exposure by fire fighters. The latter number cannot be easily calculated, however, because no one knows how many hours volunteer fire fighters serve. Also, differences in work week need to be considered for career fire service personnel.

Another example is a comparison of fire fatality risks in homes versus hotels. Numbers of persons cannot be used for both, because length of stay is obviously much shorter for hotels than for homes. Numbers of units might work better if one could obtain that data and if occupancy rates could be ignored. The problems of selecting the right denominator and obtaining data for it usually can be solved to some degree of acceptability, but the process is often complex and challenging.

Another problem in constructing rates can occur if the group of interest is defined too narrowly. A household, for example, might like to be able to calculate a risk index that reflects its smoking and drinking habits, its number of children, the ages of its members, its types of equipment and how they are fueled or powered, and many other characteristics. Today this would pose an insoluble problem. There is not enough data to calculate the numbers of households with all those characteristics (so there can be no denominator), and the list of descriptors defines a class so narrow that the number of fires experienced by households of that precise type would be very small and subject to considerable statistical uncertainty. One could separately measure the effects of some of these characteristics, and then combine the results, but such a calculation would involve modeling assumptions that are already known to be false. Considerable statistical modeling and research will be needed to make progress on questions of this type.

USING DATA TO IDENTIFY TRENDS

While the analyses described above provide a "snapshot" of the fire problem, some questions need a "moving picture." Those questions demand trend analysis. Is a part of the fire problem getting better or worse? Is the character of the fire problem changing? If changes are occurring, do they track with corresponding changes in product use, property use, fire service practices, fire prevention activities, codes and regulations, or other elements of the environment? (For this last question, one may need a full-fledged strategy or program analysis, as described below under "Using Data in Program and Strategy Analysis.")

All trend analyses must address the question of whether or not the past is a consistent guide to the present, let alone the future. It would be nice to be able to say that a trend indicates whether fire risk is going up or coming down. However, a simple trend calculation may not provide this information if the base of comparison has been shifting during the years covered. For example, start with a calculation of the number of fire deaths per year in manufactured homes. If the number dropped over time, that might mean that manufactured homes were becoming safer or it might mean that fewer people were choosing to live in manufactured homes. A trend calculation based on the number of fire deaths per million persons living in manufactured homes would factor out the latter possibility and do a better job of showing whether manufactured homes were becoming safer.

Another problem in trend calculations might be a shift in the sampling technique used to create the data base. Suppose that while analyzing fire deaths per million population, as in the previous paragraph, the state of Alaska was added to the data base in the middle of the trend period. The increase in the number of persons would not by itself bias the results because, all other things being equal, numbers of deaths and persons would rise together. But in this case, all other things are not equal. Alaska has an unusually large percentage of households living in manufactured homes, which exerts a sizable influence on the results, and Alaska presents some additional problems—including a severe climate and above-average rates of alcoholism—that differ from those of other states. There is no way to know how much of any change was due to changes in manufactured home firesafety and how much was due to the addition of Alaska to the data base. In the discussion below of "Available Major Data Bases on Fire," more will be said as to which data bases are better designed for trend analysis.

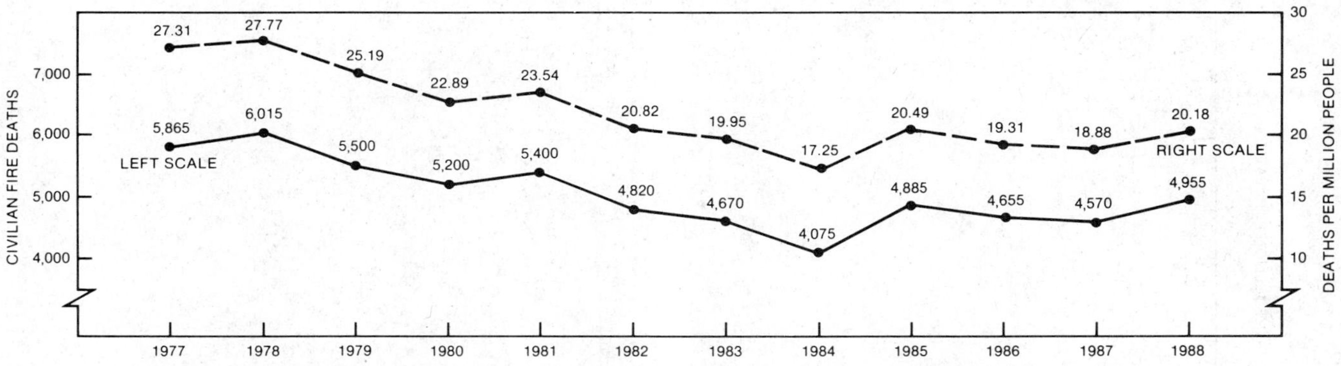

FIG. 10-3C. Civilian fire deaths and rates in the home, 1977–1988. (Note, the full vertical axis is not shown.)

Trends in Fire Fatalities and the Protection of Life

Figure 10-3C shows the 12-year trend in NFPA's estimates of civilian fire deaths in the home, starting with 1977 when the NFPA survey was upgraded. The NSC, which since 1968 has been using a consistent estimating procedure based on state health department records of death certificates, shows a steady decline in the rate of fire deaths per million population. The cumulative drop since 1949 is more than half, and other NSC figures, using slightly different estimating methods, suggest that since 1910 the rates may have dropped by three-fourths to four-fifths. The NSC figures, like NFPA's, indicate that the steady decline in the fire death toll, and to a lesser degree the fire death rate, halted around 1982–1983, to be replaced by a plateau that existed until at least 1988, where fire death rates show no consistent trend up or down. That decline had lasted for two decades, according to the NSC figures. (Note that the NSC method produces a different, lower estimate of fire deaths than the NFPA method.)

The most complete and consistent long-term trends of life loss due to fire are those that focus on fires involving large numbers of fatalities per incident. Figure 10-3D traces the rate of deaths per 10 million persons in building fires killing at least 25 persons each, at five-year intervals from 1900 through 1989. (Chapter 1-1 showed the same figure, annotated to indicate major life-loss fires of the century.) A cutoff of 25 fatalities is used because such fires are the ones most likely to involve factors addressed by fire codes and also because even the poor reporting conditions of the early years are likely to have produced a complete listing of incidents of this magnitude.

Milestones during the century include the formation in 1913 of NFPA's Committee on Safety to Life, which produced several standards addressing exiting provisions and firesafety in factories. The advent of these standards in the first decade of this century was followed by a marked decline in life loss in major incidents in the 1920s.

These gains were wiped out, temporarily, during the years of the Great Depression and World War II. Fires directly related to wartime hazards did not play a major role in this increase in life loss, but there may have been a diversion of resources from fire code enforcement and compliance to wartime production priorities. (Similarly, the loss of resources during the Depression years may have had a disproportionate impact on resources available for code enforcement and compliance.)

Following World War II, the rate of deaths per 10 million persons in building fires killing 25 or more persons dropped to a new low. The rate is so low now that a single fire like the 1977 Beverly Hills Supper Club fire can double or triple the rate for the entire five-year period. In other words, the random effects of a single fire are now sufficient to overshadow any trend, because our progress has been so great. In the period 1985–1989, for the first time since record-keeping began, there were no structure fires that killed 25 or more people.

Table 10-3F provides another view of the same trend. This table shows the three incidents in each of the last nine decades that involved the largest loss of life, plus the number of additional incidents that killed at least 100 persons. This table also includes a number of historical incidents identified since the last edition of the Handbook, particularly coal mine incidents. Note how this table reinforces Figure 10-3D's picture of dramatic reductions in loss of life in major multiple-death fires. The last three decades have seen one fire that killed at least 100 persons—the Beverly Hills Supper Club fire in Kentucky. The previous three decades (1930–1959) had thirteen fires that size. The three prior decades (1900–1929) had thirty-one fires that each killed at least 100 persons. Also, the last three decades have had no fires that killed at least 200 persons, while the preceding six decades averaged three such fires per decade.

Several large historical fires provided the impetus for code changes that reduced the likelihood of further incidents of that size. NFPA's earliest standards included a number with obvious roots in particular turn-of-the-century fires. The 1912 standard on exit drills in factories, schools, department stores, and theaters had its origins in the four building fires listed under the two decades 1900–1919. New York City's Triangle Shirtwaist Company fire in 1911, in particular, even though its 145 deaths did not make it one of the top three of the decade, also spurred the adoption of NFPA's 1918 standard on safeguarding factory workers from fires.

It was the 1944 circus tent fire in Hartford, CT (168 deaths) which focused attention on unconventional structures that were not buildings but still involved major life safety hazards. NFPA 102, *Standard for Assembly Seating, Tents, and Air-Supported Structures*, was developed to address hazards in these structures. In the same decade, further refinements were made to the NFPA code on building exits as a result of fires like the Winecoff Hotel tragedy in Atlanta, GA, in 1946 (119 deaths).

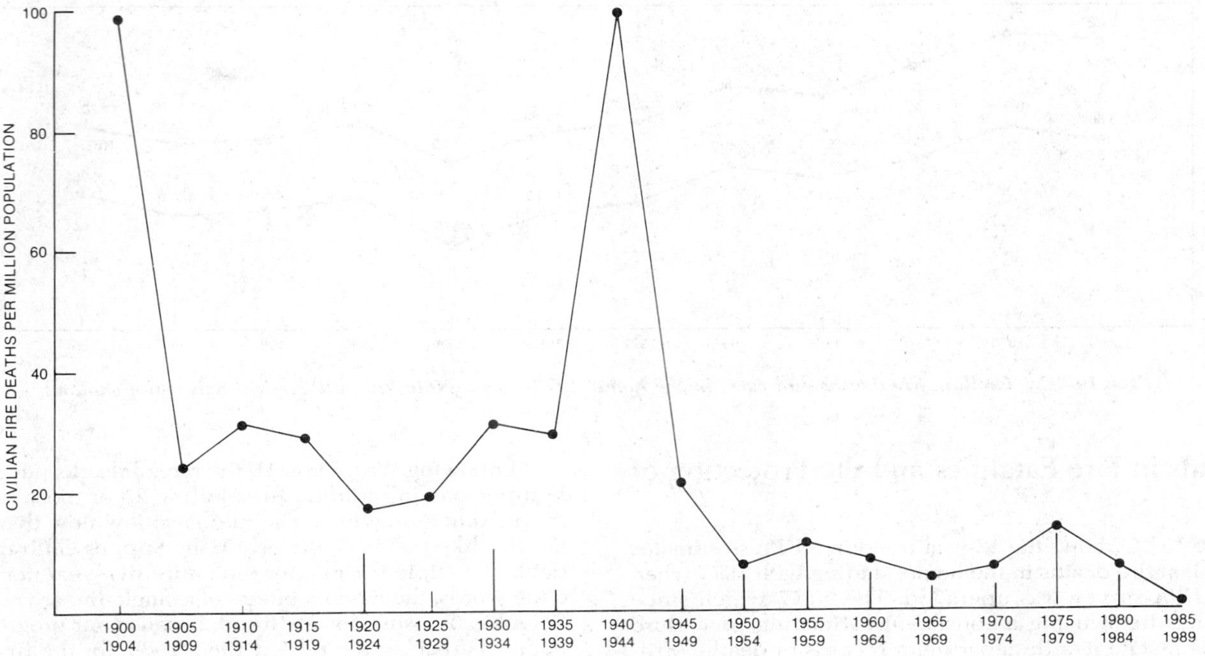

FIG. 10-3D. Major loss of life in Twentieth-century U.S. building fires taking at least 25 lives.

The ability to develop codes that will be translated into law and will receive vigorous enforcement is a key to fire prevention success. The list of major fires points to several instances where this kind of thorough follow-through has occurred. The devastating fire in Chicago's Our Lady of the Angels Grade School in 1958 was the last of four school fires in this century that each killed at least 50 people. The specific impact of that fire was an increase in code requirements, including the addition of requirements on interior finishes in educational occupancies, reflecting the role of combustible ceiling tiles in the Chicago fire, which involved a building that met the less-restrictive codes of its day. Equally important, this fire galvanized the fire service and motivated the educational community and the public to provide the resources necessary to ensure tough standards and close, continuing safety supervision of schools. School fires today kill comparatively few persons. It now takes decades to accumulate a school death toll comparable to that of the Our Lady of the Angels fire.

Just as the 1960s was the decade for a strong attack on the school fire fatality problem, the 1970s was the decade for similar attention to fatal nursing home fires. The 1963 Golden Age Nursing Home fire in Ohio was the third-largest of the decade of 1960–1969. That decade saw most large-life-loss incidents occurring in nonbuilding structures and in vehicles. Requirements of NFPA 101®, *Life Safety Code®* (hereinafter referred to as NFPA 101), were expanded to cover such hazards as carpets, and the federal government provided a major impetus for code compliance by including NFPA 101 in its requirements for Medicare and Medicaid eligibility.

One of the major target occupancies of the 1980s was board and care homes, which changed their character as a result of the widespread deinstitutionalization of chronic mental patients. Persons needing care came in large numbers to facilities not designed for this purpose. These facilities suffered dozens of multiple-death fires, including two that killed at least 25 persons each—one in Farmington, MO, in 1979 (25 deaths) and one in Keansburg, NJ, in 1981 (31 deaths).

A common element of the worst life-loss fires of recent years has been the involvement of properties that are on the fringes of code enforcement. The 1965 Searcy, AR, missile silo fire (53 deaths) and the 1977 Columbia, TN, county jail fire (42 deaths) both involved government properties, which typically are outside the jurisdiction of local fire departments. The 1977 Beverly Hills Supper Club fire, the 1963 Golden Age Nursing Home fire, and the 1972 silver mine fire in Idaho all occurred in small communities where resources for fire code enforcement typically are very limited. These patterns suggest a need to focus attention as much on innovations in the code enforcement process as on modifications to the consensus codes themselves. More generally, note the extent to which fires in mines and vehicles continue to dominate the list of largest life-loss incidents, while most of the attention of the fire community continues to be focused on buildings other than homes.

Event-driven changes in the fire codes primarily involve the fire community. However, getting those changes adopted into law and backing the law with strong enforcement programs require the cooperation of elected officials and the public—who are concerned about many subjects in addition to fire. Recognizing this, some fire chiefs have prepared legal packages targeted at particular problems in advance, holding them in reserve until a major fire provides the visibility and sense of urgency required for adoption.

In view of this strategy, it is worth noting that "newsworthiness" is not always synonymous with incident severity. Two examples will suffice. The third most deadly fire of the decade 1960–1969 was the Golden Age Nursing Home fire, which killed 63 persons; it occurred, however,

TABLE 10-3F. ***Deadliest U.S. Fires and Explosions of the Last Nine Decades, 1900–1989***

	Number Killed
1980–1989	
1. MGM Grand Hotel, Las Vegas, NV (Nov. 21, 1980)	85
2. Galaxy Airlines #203, Reno NV (Jan. 21, 1985)	42
3. United Airlines #232, Sioux City, IA (Jul. 19, 1989)	35*
1970–1979	
1. Beverly Hills Supper Club, Southgate, KY (May 28, 1977)	165
2. Silver mine, Kellogg, ID (May 2, 1972)	91
3. Capital International chartered airliner, Anchorage, AK (Nov. 28, 1970)	47
1960–1969	
1. Coal mine, Farmington, WV (Nov. 20, 1968)	78
2. Indiana State Fairgrounds Coliseum, Indianapolis, IN (Oct. 10, 1963)	75
3. Golden Age Nursing Home, Fitchville Township, OH (Nov. 23, 1963)	63
1950–1959	
1. Coal mine, West Frankfort, IL (Dec. 21, 1951)	119
2. *U.S.S. Bennington* aircraft carrier, off RI coast (May 26, 1954)	103
3. Our Lady of the Angels Grade School, Chicago, IL (Dec. 1, 1958)	95
1940–1949	
1. Cocoanut Grove Night Club, Boston, MA (Nov. 28, 1942)	492
2. *S.S. Grandcamp* and Monsanto Chemical Plant, Texas City, TX (Apr. 16, 1947)	468
3. Munitions ships and depot, Port Chicago, CA (July 17, 1944)	322
Plus 5 other incidents that each killed at least 100 people.	
1930–1939	
1. Ohio State Penitentiary, Columbus, OH (Apr. 21, 1930)	320
2. Consolidated School, New London, TX (Mar. 18, 1937)	294
3. *S.S. Morro Castle*, off NJ coast (Sept. 8, 1934)	135
1920–1929	
1. Coal mine, Mather, PA (May 19, 1928)	273
2. Coal mine, Castle Gate, UT (Mar. 8, 1924)	171
3. Cleveland Clinic, Cleveland, OH (May 15, 1929)	125
Plus 2 other incidents that each killed at least 100 people.	
1910–1919	
1. Forest fire, northern MN (Oct. 12, 1918)	559
2. Coal mine, Dawson, NM (Oct. 22, 1913)	263
3. Aetna Chemical Company, Oakdale, PA (May 18, 1918)	193
Plus 7 other incidents that each killed at least 100 people.	
1900–1909	
1. *S.S. General Slocum* steamship, New York, NY (June 15, 1904)	1,030
2. Iroquois Theater, Chicago, IL (Dec. 30, 1903)	602
3. Coal mine, Monongha, WV (Dec. 6, 1907)	361
Plus 13 other incidents that each killed at least 100 people.	

* Estimate of fire-death portion of total.

on the day after President John F. Kennedy was assassinated. This coincidence of timing sharply reduced the visibility of the fire. By contrast, the 1937 *Hindenburg* zeppelin fire killed "only" 36 persons, a death toll barely a fourth the size of even the third-largest fire of that decade and only one-eighth the size of the New London, TX, school fire in the same year. The zeppelin fire, however, was broadcast "live" and occurred in full view of newsreel cameras, so it was probably the most widely heard and seen fatal U.S. fire until the Challenger space shuttle explosion in 1986. It meant the end of the rigid-airship industry.

These examples also have a lesson for analysis of trends in fire deaths, injuries, or incidents. The more severe the type of incident being tracked, the more random the year-to-year fluctuation. This makes it important to look at trends over an appropriate length of time. For fires as severe as those discussed in the last few paragraphs, only decade-by-decade comparisons suffice to separate real trends from random ups and downs. For total U.S. civilian fire deaths, year-to-year tracking is meaningful. For a single large city, however, year-to-year tracking of fire deaths will be subject to considerable statistical noise; and for town and rural areas, there is no good way to track fatality trends except as part of a larger aggregation, such as the state or the rural portion of the entire region.

Trends in Property Damage Due to Fire

The first fire protection standards promulgated by NFPA were directed principally at property protection, reflecting the association's founding by men in the business of insuring property against loss due to fire. Assessments of the success of strategies for property protection are more difficult than for life protection, however, because data on fire damage is subject to several gaps and quirks that do not affect data on fire deaths. While all indicators of fire—incidents, deaths, injuries, and property damage—are clouded by the absence of information on fires not reported to local fire departments, property damage is the only indicator of severity that is left unreported in a significant minority of reported fires. Estimates of property damage involve more guesswork than estimates of persons killed or injured. Some very-large-loss fires are never reported to local fire departments, because the affected firms are able to handle them with on-site resources. No comparable omissions occur among multiple-death fires.

Trend analysis must take into account the effect of inflation. Table 10-3G shows NFPA's estimates for total national property damage due to fire in the years 1980–1989, both as published and as recalculated in terms of 1980 dollars, using the U.S. Bureau of Labor Statistics' Consumer Price Index to remove the effects of inflation. When inflation is not removed, the loss totals, expressed in what are called "constant dollars," show a 34 percent *increase* in property damage in the nine years from 1980 to 1988. When inflation is removed, the loss totals, now expressed in "real dollars," show a 7 percent *decrease* in property damage for those nine years. Also significant is the effect of changes in the number of fires, because total damage figures involve the total number of fires and the average dollar loss per fire. From 1980 to 1988 the average loss per fire in constant dollars rose 64 percent, but the average loss per fire in real dollars rose only 14 percent.

To put this even more dramatically, suppose an energetic, creative, intelligent, farsighted fire chief had begun a massive ten-year program in 1972 to reduce by half the property damage due to fire in his city. Then suppose he had succeeded. Because of the effects of inflation, his actual reported loss would have shown a 9 percent *increase* in property damage over that decade.

This same effect makes it difficult to compare large-loss experience over several years. In the early 1930s, the NFPA defined a large-loss fire as one involving at least

TABLE 10-3G. ***U.S. Trends in Property Damage Due to Fire, 1980–1988***

Year	Total Estimated Damage	Adjusted to 1980 Dollars
1980	$6.254 billion	$6.254 billion
1981	$6.676 billion	$6.676 billion
1982	$6.432 billion	$5.493 billion
1983	$6.598 billion	$5.457 billion
1984	$6.707 billion	$5.319 billion
1985	$7.324 billion	$5.608 billion
1986	$6.709 billion	$5.044 billion
1987	$7.159 billion	$5.193 billion
1988	$8.352 billion	$5.809 billion

$250,000 in direct property damage. In 1978, a large-loss fire was redefined as one involving at least $500,000, and in the early 1980s the amount became at least $1,000,000 in direct property damage. Each minimum represented the cutoff point for the largest several hundred fires of its time. In the late 1980s, it was further decided to shift the large-loss study to a more detailed treatment of a smaller number of fires, so the threshold was raised to $5,000,000.

Table 10-3H lists the twenty largest-loss fires of 1979–1988, first on the basis of their published losses, then on the basis of real 1988 dollars. Three fires on the second list do not appear on the first list. In those cases, three fires from the beginning of the decade (1980 and 1983) are calculated to have been more costly, in real terms, than several fires from the end of decade (1986–1988) with higher reported losses. The Henderson, NV, fire, which ranked fifth in terms of reported losses, ranked only ninth in terms of 1988 dollars, while a 1979 oil tanker fire rose from eleventh on the reported-loss list to fifth in terms of 1988 dollars.

Difficulties in comparison become more pronounced when points even further back in history are considered. The 1947 chemical plant fire in Texas City, TX, had a reported loss of $67 million. Using the Consumer Price Index, that translates into more than $355 million in 1988. The 1906 earthquake and fire in San Francisco had a reported loss of $350 million. That could mean on the order of $4½ *billion* today—or more than half the loss attributed to all reported fires in the United States in a typical year. At this point, comparisons can become very sensitive to assumptions. Was the property lost in the Texas City fire sufficiently similar to the items covered by the Consumer Price Index? Or should a more industry-specific price index be used? Were the estimates of loss for the San Francisco fire made to the nearest $10 million or even the nearest $50 million? Then the 1980s version of that loss might be accurate to only the nearest $100 million or $500 million, which would mean its range of uncertainty would be higher than the total loss of any recent fire.

The lesson in all this is that trend analysis of loss figures can be very tricky and needs to be done with an eye toward the effects of inflation and population growth (which also affects trends in numbers of fires, deaths, and injuries). Keep in mind that loss trends have a tendency to look bad even if real progress is being made.

Finally, Table 10-3H again illustrates the fact that newsworthiness depends on more than just fire severity. Of the twenty-three fires listed in the top part of Table 10-3H, four fires occurred in a period of just *five days* in May 1988. Each of these fires received extra attention because the others occurred at the same time.

USING DATA IN PROGRAM AND STRATEGY ANALYSIS

Earlier in this chapter, techniques were described for using data to analyze the present (size and characteristics of the fire problem) and the past (trends in the size and nature of the fire problem). Program and strategy analysis is the most decision-relevant use of data because it tries to project the future, and, in particular, the ways in which the future will be different if a particular program or strategy is or is not adopted.

The most fundamental question to be answered in using data for program or strategy analysis is whether past fire experience is a good guide to future fire problems. Sometimes it is; sometimes it is not. However, intelligent use of data with other sources of information is an essential part of the best possible projection of the future. After all, what will we use if not data? Models are tied to reality by validation, which is based on experience of the past. Expert judgment is formed, at least in part, by the experience of the past. The issue is not whether to use the past as a guide; it is how best to characterize the important changes that will occur in the future.

Often the most important aspect of the future will be a different mix of the elements already in place in the present. For example, home smoke-detector usage has grown at a phenomenal rate in the last fifteen years, with most of the growth occurring in or after 1976. Fire incident data from the early years of growth in detector usage showed that smoke detectors reduce by half the risk (measured by the number of deaths per 1000 fires) that a person will die if he or she has a fire. At that point, there were uncertainties about the applicability of this finding to the future. Would the life-saving impact of detectors remain the same when detectors were installed in poorer households with less-educated occupants?

The answer turned out to be yes. But the form of the question shows how data can be used intelligently to try to project the future. Start with the future predicted by a simple projection of recent trends. Using judgment, creativity, and brainstorming, try to identify what aspects of the present environment might be changing in ways that would modify the simple projection. Try to obtain data on the speed of those changes. Try to analyze the fire data in hand to determine the sensitivity of your conclusions to those changes. Combine these results to produce a revised projection.

Most analyses to date have found that environmental changes relevant to fire occur slowly and so produce relatively modest changes in what are called *baseline projections*, that is, projections of the size and character of the fire problem if no new strategies are adopted. For example, the average age of the U.S. population is rising. This means a drop in the percentage of the population in the high-death-rate years of infancy, a rise in the percentage in the high-death-rate elderly years, and other shifts along the age spectrum. By the end of the century the cumulative effect will be large, but on a year-to-year basis it produces only a small predicted change in the national fire death rate.

An analysis of the projected impact of a strategy or program involves these five steps:

1. Identify the part of the fire problem that the strategy can affect and measure the size of that problem. For example, a change in the flame resistance of

TABLE 10-3H. ***Largest Loss U.S. Fires Reported to NFPA, 1979–1988***

Reported Dollars			
1.	Petroleum refinery, Norco, LA	May 5, 1988	$330 million
2.	Chemical manufacturing facility, Pampa, TX	Nov. 14, 1987	$154 million
3.	Jet airplane repair facility, Oklahoma City, OK	Nov. 12, 1984	$138 million
4.	Multi-tenant warehouse complex, Elizabeth, NJ	Feb. 21, 1985	$123 million
5.	Chemical manufacturing facility, Henderson, NV	May 4, 1988	$103 million
6A.	General warehouse, Fallsington, PA	Jun. 21, 1982	$100 million
6B.	Petroleum refinery, Romeoville, IL	Jul. 23, 1984	$100 million
8.	Bank building, Minneapolis, MN	Nov. 25, 1982	$ 92.8 million
9.	Telephone switching station, Hinsdale, IL	May 8, 1988	$ 90 million
10.	General warehouse, Richmond, CA	Jul. 11, 1988	$ 80 million
11.	Petroleum tank ship at refinery, Deer Park, TX	Sept. 1, 1979	$ 77 million
12.	Brush fire, Camarillo, CA	Jul. 1, 1985	$ 75.403 million
13A.	Multi-building group fire, Lynn, MA	Nov. 28, 1981	$ 70 million
13B.	Race track, Arlington Heights, IL	Jul. 31, 1985	$ 70 million
15.	General warehouse, Garland, TX	Oct. 8, 1987	$ 52 million
16A.	Petroleum refinery, Borger, TX	Jan. 20, 1980	$ 50 million
16B.	Hotel, Las Vegas, NV	Nov. 21, 1980	$ 50 million
16C.	Multi-building conflagration, Anaheim, CA	Apr. 21, 1982	$ 50 million
16D.	Electric generating plant, Washburn, ND	Nov. 17, 1986	$ 50 million
16E.	Factory complex, Fall River, MA	Jan. 12, 1987	$ 50 million
16F.	Noncombat military aircraft, Bossier City, LA	Sep. 17, 1987	$ 50 million
16G.	Textile finishing plant, Putnam, CT	Dec. 2, 1987	$ 50 million
16H.	Bank building, Los Angeles, CA	May 4, 1988	$ 50 million
Adjusted to 1988 Dollars			
1.	Petroleum refinery, Norco, LA	May 5, 1988	$330.00 million
2.	Chemical manufacturing facility, Pampa, TX	Nov. 14, 1987	$160.38 million
3.	Jet airplant repair facility, Oklahoma City, OK	Nov. 12, 1984	$156.94 million
4.	Multi-tenant warehouse complex, Elizabeth, NJ	Feb. 21, 1985	$135.08 million
5.	Petroleum tank ship at refinery, Deer Park, TX	Sep. 1, 1979	$125.75 million
6.	General warehouse, Fallsington, PA	Jun. 21, 1982	$122.49 million
7.	Petroleum refinery, Romeoville, IL	Jul. 23, 1984	$113.73 million
8.	Bank building, Minneapolis, MN	Nov. 25, 1982	$113.67 million
9.	Chemical manufacturing facility, Henderson, NV	May 4, 1988	$103.00 million
10.	Multi-building group fire, Lynn, MA	Nov. 28, 1981	$ 90.96 million
11.	Telephone switching station, Hinsdale, IL	May 8, 1988	$ 90.00 million
12.	Brush fire, Camarillo, CA	Jul. 1, 1985	$ 82.81 million
13.	General warehouse, Richmond, CA	Jul. 11, 1988	$ 80.00 million
14.	Race track, Arlington Heights, IL	Jul. 31, 1985	$ 76.88 million
15A.	Petroleum refinery, Borger, TX	Jan. 20, 1980	$ 71.89 million
15B.	Hotel, Las Vegas, NV	Nov. 21, 1980	$ 71.89 million
17.	Plastics manufacturing plant, New Castle, DE	Oct. 21, 1980	$ 65.78 million
18.	Multi-building conflagration, Anaheim, CA	Apr. 21, 1982	$ 61.24 million
19.	Petroleum refinery, Martinez, CA	Apr. 7, 1983	$ 58.10 million
20.	Brush fire, San Bernardino, CA	Nov. 24, 1980	$ 54.68 million

Source: NFPA's Fire Incident Data Organization (FIDO)

upholstered-furniture-covering materials would affect only fires involving those materials. Analysis will show the change would affect primarily those fires that begin with ignition of such materials, inasmuch as the number of severe fires that begin with upholstered furniture appears to be much larger than the number that begin elsewhere and become severe primarily because of spread to upholstered furniture. A change to self-extinguishing cigarettes would affect only fires whose form of heat of ignition was cigarettes, and so on.

2. Estimate the likely percentage reduction in this target fire problem if the strategy or program were adopted, and prepare estimates for each of the measures of fire severity (deaths, injuries, property loss) because the impact probably will be different for each measure. If the strategy or program is already in use (as was true for smoke detectors), then fire incident data analysis may produce these estimates. If the strategy or program is not in use or is in very limited use, as is true for home sprinklers, then some combination of modeling, laboratory tests, and expert judgment will be needed to produce the estimates. In either case, it makes sense to develop a range of estimates, from optimistic to pessimistic.
3. Estimate how much of the target population will adopt the program or strategy, and how quickly. This typically is a marketing question, and the results can be surprising. Most analyses of the growth in smoke detector coverage were too pessimistic on both how much and how fast. At the same time, most analyses were too optimistic about the installation of detectors in homes most likely to have fires. While about five-sixths of U.S. households now have detectors, less than half the home fires are reported to occur in homes with detectors. This discrepancy is not unusual for strategies that work through the marketplace. The first pur-

chasers tend to be more affluent and better educated; these people traditionally have lower fire rates than the rest of the population. Also, speed of adoption will reflect the normal life of a product. Changes in cigarettes can be implemented for all cigarettes in months, while changes in the upholstered furniture ignited by cigarettes may take decades to work their way through the whole population.

4. Estimate how often the strategy will be defeated in practice. For example, what proportion of detector-equipped homes will have their detectors out of service because worn-out batteries were not replaced? Note that if your method in step (2) involved the use of actual fire incident data, your estimate already may include the effects of defeating or attenuation (the latter is a term that does not have the connotation of deliberate sabotage that *defeating* may have for some people).
5. Combine the measures of fire problem size from step (1) and the percentages from steps (2) through (4) to produce estimates of the net percentage reduction in the fire problem and of the new size of the fire problem. With these results, decide how valuable this strategy or program would be and whether to press for its adoption. In some forums, this decision will require a parallel calculation of the cost of the strategy or program, followed by some kind of comparison of the costs and loss reductions.

Analysis can be used not only to make yes or no decisions on adopting a strategy, or to select the strategy with the biggest project impact, but also to fine-tune the design of the strategies themselves. Two examples will illustrate how this can be done.

One city fire department had a small-scale home inspection program, in which fire companies used slack periods to offer home inspections in their first-due areas. Since no one was home at about half the houses visited, this program offered a good opportunity to compare the fire experience of the homes inspected with the fire experience of the similar homes where no one had been home when inspections were offered. Results of the analysis showed no inspection impact, but, more importantly, they showed that the homes chosen for inspection were in areas with some of the lowest fire incident rates in the city. In other words, the program was somehow being targeted at the neighborhoods needing it least. Why? Once the data analysis identified a hitherto unsuspected pattern, the explanation was fairly simple: inspection efforts would be greater in areas with more company slack time, which in turn would tend to be areas requiring fewer company runs, including fewer fires. The analysis pointed to a need to redesign the home inspection program so it would target fire-prone neighborhoods.

Unexpected results of analysis are not the only indicators of the need for design improvements. While designing a public education campaign aimed at heating safety, the Seattle, WA, Fire Department conducted a day-by-day analysis of fire incidence. By comparing that analysis with historical data on Seattle weather, the analysts were able to identify a significant pattern of cold snaps followed three days later by a sharp rise in heating system fires. Vulnerable heating systems, it seemed, would develop fires after sustained heavy use. This analytical discovery had a direct bearing upon the design of the public education campaign, because it suggested that firesafety messages should be released as soon as a cold snap started. People would already be thinking about their heating systems when the messages appeared, so attention would be greater; also, the need to listen and act at once could be underlined by reference to the established pattern. What is more, the three-day lag meant there was time to get out the messages after the cold snap started but before the fires would begin.

The common thread of these two examples is the use of analysis to narrow the target of a program or strategy in order to maximize impact and conserve scarce program resources. In the first case, the geographical targeting was affected; in the second case, the timing benefited from analysis.

Another consideration in analysis is the need to identify clearly which of many important objectives are to be given priority. For example, is it more important to reduce the fire loss actually being suffered, thereby targeting properties where most loss now occurs? Or is it more important to reduce the potential for catastrophic fire loss, thereby targeting properties with sizable numbers of lives or property value at risk, even if their actual loss has been relatively small? Also, is it most important to reduce numbers of fires, numbers of deaths and injuries, or numbers of dollars in direct property loss? In apartment fires, for example, a focus on fires might mean targeting cooking-related fires, a focus on deaths might mean targeting smoking-related fires, and a focus on property loss might mean targeting incendiary and suspicious fires.

Finally, remember that tracking analysis continues to be useful even after a decision has been made and a strategy or program has been implemented. As noted earlier, most of the estimates used in an analysis involve uncertainty; therefore, it may be useful to see whether the future unfolds as projected. If not, some further refinements in the design of a strategy or program may be warranted. Even early termination of a program might be indicated.

AVAILABLE MAJOR DATA BASES ON FIRES

Three major data bases are available to analyze patterns in U.S. fire experience—the annual NFPA survey of fire departments; the FEMA/USFA National Fire Incident Reporting System (NFIRS); and the NFPA Fire Incident Data Organization (FIDO). Together, these three data bases can provide valid, detailed information on national and regional fire problems, overall or by specific property type and cause. The characteristics of the three data bases and the best ways of using each are the subject of this section.

Annual NFPA Survey of Fire Departments

The NFPA survey is based on a stratified random sample of roughly 3000 U.S. fire departments (or roughly one of every ten fire departments in the country). The survey collects the following information: (1) the total number of fire incidents, civilian deaths, and civilian injuries and the total estimated property damage (in dollars) for each of the major property-use classes defined by the NFPA 901 standard for fire incident reporting; (2) similar tallies specifically for incendiary and suspicious fires, separated only into structure versus vehicle; (3) the number of on-duty fire fighter injuries, by type of duty and nature of injury or illness; (4) information on the type of community protected (e.g., county versus township versus city) and the size of the population protected, which is used in the statistical formula for projecting national estimates from sample results; and (5) leads on multiple-death and large-loss fires and fire fighter fatalities, which if cited are then captured under FIDO.

The totals in (1) and the special incendiary and suspicious fire results in (2) are analyzed and reported in NFPA's annual study, "Fire Loss in the United States," which traditionally appears in the September/October issue of *NFPA Journal*. The fire fighter injury information in (3) is analyzed and reported in NFPA's annual report, "U.S. Fire Fighter Injuries," now published in the November/December issue of *NFPA Journal*.

The NFPA survey begins with the NFPA Fire Service Inventory, a computerized file of nearly 30,000 U.S. fire departments, which is the most complete and thoroughly validated such listing in existence. The survey is stratified by size of population protected to reduce the uncertainty of the final estimate. Small, rural communities protect fewer people per department and are less likely to respond to the survey, so a larger number must be surveyed to obtain an adequate sample of those departments. (NFPA also makes follow-up calls to a sample of the smaller fire departments that do not respond, to confirm that those that did respond are truly representative of fire departments their size.) On the other hand, large city departments are so few in number and protect such a large proportion of the population that it makes sense to survey all of them. Most respond, resulting in excellent precision for their part of the final estimate.

These methods have been used in the NFPA survey since 1977 and represent a state-of-the-art approach to sample surveying. Because of the attention paid to representativeness and appropriate weighting formulas for projecting national estimates, the NFPA survey provides a valid basis for measuring national trends in fire incidents, civilian deaths and injuries, and direct property loss, as well as for determining patterns and trends by community size and major region.

FEMA/USFA's National Fire Incident Reporting System (NFIRS)

FEMA/USFA's NFIRS provides annual computerized data bases of fire incidents, with data classified according to a standard format based on NFPA 901. Roughly three-fourths of all states have NFIRS coordinators, who receive fire incident data from participating fire departments and combine the data into a state data base. This data is then transmitted to FEMA/USFA. Participation by the states, and by local fire departments within participating states, is voluntary. NFIRS captures roughly one-third of all U.S. fires each year. More than one-third of all U.S. fire departments are listed as participants in NFIRS, although not all of these departments provide data every year.

One of the strengths of NFIRS is that it provides the most detailed incident information of any national data base not limited to large fires. NFIRS is the only data base capable of addressing national patterns for fires of all sizes by specific property use and specific fire cause. (The NFPA survey separates fewer than twenty of the hundreds of property use categories defined by NFPA 901 and provides no cause-related information except for incendiary and suspicious fires.) NFIRS also captures information on the construction type of the involved building, avenues and extent of flame spread and smoke spread, and performance of detectors and sprinklers.

One weakness of NFIRS is that its voluntary character produces annual samples of shifting composition. Despite the fact that NFIRS draws on three times as many fire departments as the NFPA survey, the NFPA survey is more suitable as a basis for projecting national estimates because its sample is truly random and is systematically stratified to be representative.

Analyses based on NFIRS have been widely calculated only since 1982, the year of publication of the second edition of FEMA/USFA's *Fire in the United States*—the first study based primarily on NFIRS. Because consensus on how best to address the weaknesses of NFIRS does not yet exist, the next few years may see further revisions in the formulas used to calculate statistics from this system. In the meantime, most analysts use NFIRS to calculate percentages (e.g., the percentage of residential fires that occur in apartments, or the percentage of apartment fire deaths that involve discarded cigarettes). Some analysts combine NFIRS-based percentages with NFPA-survey-based totals to produce estimates of numbers of fires, deaths, injuries, and dollar loss for subparts of the fire problem. This is the simplest approach now available to compensate in the area where NFIRS is weak. It has been documented as an analysis method in a 1987 article in *Fire Technology*.[2]

NFPA's Fire Incident Data Organization (FIDO) System

The NFPA FIDO system is a computerized data base that provides the most detailed incident information available, short of a full-scale fire investigation. The fires covered are those deemed to be of high technical interest. The system that identifies fires for inclusion in FIDO is believed to provide virtually complete coverage of incidents reported to fire departments involving three or more civilian deaths, one or more fire fighter deaths, or large dollar loss (redefined periodically to reflect the effects of inflation, and defined since the late 1980s as $5,000,000 or more in direct property damage).

FIDO also captures a selection of smaller incidents as technical interests dictate. These are useful primarily because of the type of property involved (e.g., high-rise buildings), the presence of hazardous materials, or the performance of detectors or sprinklers.

The FIDO system covers these fires from 1971 to date, contains information on more than 66,000 fires, and adds 2500 to 3000 fires per year. NFPA learns of fires that may be candidates for FIDO through a newspaper-clipping service, insurers' reports, state fire marshals, NFIRS, respondents to the NFPA annual survey, and other sources. Once notified of a candidate fire, NFPA seeks standardized incident information from the responsible fire department and solicits copies of other reports prepared by concerned parties, such as the fire department's own incident report and results of any investigations.

The strength of FIDO is its depth of detail on individual incidents. Information captured by FIDO, but not by NFIRS, includes types and performance of all built-in systems for detection, suppression, and control of smoke and flame; detailed information on factors contributing to flame and smoke spread; estimates of time between major events in fire development (e.g., ignition to detection, detection to alarm); reasons for any unusual delay at various points; indirect loss and detailed breakdowns of direct loss; and escapes, rescues, and numbers of occupants. (Building height—necessary to analysis of high-rise building fires—is almost never coded in NFIRS but is available in FIDO.) Additional uncoded information often is available in the hard-copy FIDO files, which are indexed for use in research and analysis.

One weakness of FIDO is that it mostly covers larger incidents. Many questions can best be answered by comparing the characteristics of large and small fires that involved similar types of properties and similar causes of ignition. FIDO does not permit such comparisons.

FIDO supports three annual NFPA reports: "U.S. Fire Fighter Deaths" and "Catastrophic Multiple-Death Fires in the United States," now published in the July/August issue of *NFPA Journal*; and "Large-Loss Fires in the United States," now published in the November/December issue of *NFPA Journal*. FIDO also supports the anecdotal summaries published in the "Firewatch" column of *NFPA Journal* and in the annual study cited earlier on U.S. fire fighter injuries.

Comparing Estimates Using Different Data Bases or Analytic Approaches

Occasionally a situation arises for which two different numbers exist, derived from different sources or different analytical approaches. For nonanalysts who may not know the source of either number, such a situation can prove frustrating and can encourage a cynical attitude about the arbitrariness of all fire statistics. Even analysts familiar with the sources of both numbers may have difficulty pinning down the precise reasons for any discrepancies and deciding how important the differences are and which number is best. It is very important, therefore, for all data users—and others who expect to confront arguments based on fire statistics—to understand how and why estimates can differ. For the most part, variations involve the ways different data sources and estimates deal with the inevitable gaps in coverage that affect all sources of fire incident information.

No fire data base can possibly capture all instances of unwanted fires. Few data bases—and none of the three discussed in this section—cover fires that are not reported to fire departments. (Special studies for some property types do provide one-time estimates of the size and composition of the unreported fire problem.) No fire data base even captures all the fires reported to fire departments, but some data bases, notably the NFPA survey, are built on samples designed to be representative of all fire departments.

By their nature, fire data bases are biased in favor of "failures" rather than "successes." The fire that is controlled so quickly it does not need to be reported to a fire department is not captured by the data bases that cover reported fires. Analyses of the impact of devices and procedures that provide early detection or suppression also need to allow for the phenomenon of missing "success" stories. Moreover, data bases like FIDO that provide the most detail on building features and their performance are limited to the largest of the reported fires.

There is also the issue of quality control for a data base. For data bases with limited depth of detail (like the NFPA survey) or limited breadth of coverage (like FIDO, which is confined to large fires), it is possible to invest considerable effort in ensuring that each report is as complete and accurate as possible. Follow-up calls can be used to fill gaps and check possible odd answers. For a data base with the depth and breadth of NFIRS, however, the same level of quality control effort has not been possible. Consequently, NFIRS is missing more entries and has more that are dubious. The trade-off between data quality and data quantity is never easy; an analyst needs to be aware of the strength and dependability of the sources before conducting an analysis.

Two examples indicate how differences in fire data bases and assumptions can produce different results. The U.S. Department of Justice estimates the size of the nation's arson problem through its Uniform Crime Reports (UCR) based on reports from law-enforcement agencies. NFPA, through its annual survey of fire departments, estimates the size of the nation's fire problem due to incendiary or suspicious causes. For 1983, the UCR estimate of the arson problem in structures was 297 fires per million population. For the same year, NFPA estimates were 524 incendiary or suspicious structure fires per million population and 311 structure fires per million population for incendiary fires alone. The UCR arson estimate and the NFPA incendiary fire estimate differ by about five percent, which is within the range of statistical uncertainty for an estimate based on a survey the size of NFPA's.

Several points are illustrated by this example. First, the UCR estimate is close to the NFPA incendiary-only estimate, because the UCR definition of arson approximates NFPA's definition of incendiary. NFPA and other fire organizations, however, traditionally regard the combination of incendiary and suspicious fires as the best indicator of the nation's problem with intentionally set fires. The UCR and NFPA systems produce roughly the same estimates where they are attempting to measure the same thing. However, because they differ on how to handle the more ambiguous fires, the "arson" numbers they release may appear significantly different to the casual reader or listener.

Second, it makes sense that the UCR estimate would be the lower of the two because fire officers see every reported fire, while police departments see only those fires that might involve crimes. A fire department may conclude that a fire is incendiary, while the corresponding police department either disagrees or is not notified; but the reverse is much less likely to occur. Also, definitions of arson vary from state to state.

Third, if there are differences in the ways that fire departments and police departments define structures, any such differences appear to have negligible impact on these calculations.

The second example of differing estimates involves the 1981 estimates made by FEMA and NFPA of total U.S. civilian fire fatalities. The NFPA estimate, based on the survey, was 6700 deaths. The FEMA estimate, based on a multipart procedure that started with death certificate information reported to the National Center for Health Statistics, was 7600 deaths. At least five significant differences in methods help to account for this discrepancy.

First, NFPA estimates of annual death totals are subject to some uncertainty because they are based upon sample surveys. Using accepted statistical principles, NFPA specified a range for the true value of 6200 to 7200. In other words, if someone else had run the same kind of survey and had produced an estimate that was higher or lower by up to 500 deaths, that would be within the range of precision achievable by a survey of that size. The difference would be the result of random variations in the representativeness of the fire departments selected for the sample.

Second, all fire fatality estimating procedures have difficulty with deaths that could have resulted from multiple causes. The principal examples of this problem are vehicle accidents followed by fire. It must be either determined or estimated whether traumatic injuries in the crash or subsequent fire-related injuries caused death. When FEMA began making estimates, one of its principal objections to NFPA's figures was that they tended to include all crash/fire fatalities. As a result, the two organizations pursued different courses to deal with this problem. NFPA began making follow-up inquiries on vehicle fire deaths, permitting the fatalities of suspect cause to be screened out prior to calculation of national projections. The initiation of this screening reduced estimated total fire deaths by nearly one-third from their previous level. FEMA chose to address this problem by use of a correction formula that assumed vehicle fire deaths would continue to be a constant percentage of structure fire deaths and/or total vehicle deaths. This approach was less satisfactory because it could not detect changes in the relative size of the problem. (FEMA no longer uses this formula.)

Third, the NFPA procedure cannot capture fatalities suffered in fires not reported to fire departments. These deaths principally involve clothing ignitions in which the fire is smothered by a civilian, but not before it has caused fatal injuries. The death certificate approach captures these deaths, which now number about 200 per year. NFPA analyses of clothing-ignition fire deaths suggest that most of these are now reported . It may be that the recent expansion of the fire service into emergency medical service has sharply reduced the number of fire deaths that go unreported. In any event, the principal strength of the death certificate approach is that it collects deaths in unreported fires, which no system based on fire department records can do.

The death certificate data base also does a better job of capturing delayed deaths, in which days or even months pass between fire injury and death. However, such deaths are often recorded in terms of the complications that caused death, so the fire connection may be missed to some degree in both data bases.

Fourth, an approach based on death certificates experienced difficulty in 1981 concerning arson deaths, then classified simply as murder with no indication of the role of fire. Subsequently, the death certificate coding was expanded to increase the number of factors that can be included, so an arson incident coded as murder now can also be coded as involving fire. As of 1981, however, arson deaths were still difficult to identify on death certificates and FEMA had to use other sources to make these estimates. (Suicides by fire could have posed a similar problem, but they are rare in the U.S. In Japan, however, where immolation by fire accounts for about a third of all fire deaths, the decision to include or exclude these victims makes a large difference in the totals.)

The fifth and final difference has to do with timeliness and the methods used to achieve it. As with NFIRS, the death certificate records are assembled on a state-by-state basis with wide variations in speed of delivery. In order to issue an estimated national total in a timely fashion, FEMA was forced to use sources other than death certificates for about one state in four, including some of the largest states. The need to work around late states was a major reason that FEMA abandoned this approach after 1981. Death certificate tracking still has advantages as an after-the-fact check on the accuracy of survey-based estimates, but by itself it cannot provide timely estimates.

SPECIAL DATA BASES ON FIRE

Many special data bases exist. Some concern aspects of the fire problem not well covered by the existing major data bases. Others contain information that may be useful in analysis. The examples cited below are not exhaustive.

Occupational

In addition to NFPA's data bases on fire fighter fatalities and injuries, the International Association of Fire Fighters (IAFF) annually releases totals of on-duty fatalities and injuries among career members of the fire service.

Also, fire injuries suffered on the job in some industries (e.g., the grain storage industry) have been among the occupational injury subjects studied by the National Institute for Occupational Safety and Health (NIOSH). Published reports on these studies are available.

Civilian Injuries

The U.S. Consumer Product Safety Commission (CPSC) maintains a computerized data base drawn from a sample of hospital emergency room cases. The National Electronic Injury Surveillance System (NEISS), dating back to 1972, focuses on product-related injuries in the home. Reports on fire casualties related to consumer products (about five percent of the NEISS total) are published annually. Information collected is similar to that collected for casualties under NFPA 901 but is much more detailed regarding the type of product involved. NEISS is particularly useful for analysis of serious injuries due to electrical shock or burns not caused by fire.

Burn injuries are captured in the National Health Inventory survey done by the U.S. Department of Health and Human Services, but results on burns are rarely tabulated. The small fraction of severely burned patients who pass through burn care units are the subjects of more extensive tracking by the American Burn Association and others.

Transportation

Accidents, including fires, are tabulated by several government agencies. The National Transportation Safety Board (NTSB) publishes accident reports on aircraft and railway accidents and on highway accidents involving hazardous materials. The information collected tends to emphasize the circumstances of the accident with little discussion of the ensuing fire. Some of these reports, however, have unpublished supplements addressing issues (e.g., human factors in escape) and often contain much more fire-related information. The computerized portions of the records have the least information on fires. Human factors studies became routine in the mid-1960s; computerized records date from 1964.

The National Highway Traffic Safety Administration (NHTSA) established a computerized file on fatal highway accidents, beginning in 1975. Statistical summary reports are issued annually.

The U.S. Coast Guard collects reports on accidents involving recreational boats and commercial vessels. As with the other special data bases on vehicle accidents, there is little coded, standardized information on the cause and development of these fires.

International data bases also exist for accidents involving aircraft. Narrative summaries ranging from one sentence to a few paragraphs appear in the *World Airline Accident Summary*, published by the Air Registry Board in England. Standardized narrative reports, usually abstracted from original accident reports prepared by national air safety organizations, are published by the International Civil Aviation Organization, headquartered in Canada, in its *Airline Accident Digest* series.

Forests and Wildlands

The U.S. Forest Service issues annual reports titled *Wildfire Statistics* and *National Forest Fire Report*, and the U.S. Department of the Interior (DOI) Bureau of Land Management issues an annual report of *Public Lands Statistics*. The U.S. Forest Service reports cover fires occurring in national, state, and private forests, including numbers, estimates of the extent of damage (acres burned), and profiles of causes. The DOI reports address fires on the lands it owns and administers. Information addressed includes cause, extent of damage, rate of spread, and method of suppression. These data bases add records on thousands of fires each year.

Military

As with transportation and forest fires, fires on military installations tend to fall outside the jurisdiction of the local fire departments covered by the nation's major data bases (NFIRS and the NFPA survey). The various branches of the military historically have compiled their own fire incident data bases and have produced a number of analyses. Beginning in 1985, the Naval Safety Center at Norfolk, VA, has been the receiving point for fire reporting for all the U.S. military services. Incident records from the center also are submitted to NFIRS.

Electrical

The International Association of Electrical Inspectors (IAEI) and Underwriters Laboratories (UL) maintain data bases generated from clipping files, covering not only electrical fires but also the closely related subject of electrical shocks. The IAEI data is published annually in *IAEI News*. Both organizations discourage the use of this data for statistical analysis because clipping-file records are not representative of incidents of all sizes. By concentrating on large incidents, however, these data bases can be valuable for certain uses.

International

The World Health Organization's *Statistical Annual* includes information on fire death rates by country. It can be difficult, however, to obtain data for many countries for the same year. The World Fire Statistics Centre in England also prepares annual studies with international fire statistic comparisons, covering not only fire fatalities but also property damage and estimates of national expenditures on the various elements of fire protection (e.g., fire departments, insurance, built-in fire protection).

Special Studies

Some special studies have produced one-time data bases or statistics that provide continuing value for fire analysts. In 1985 the CPSC completed its survey of unreported home fires and their characteristics; the resulting data base will be of use for many years. CPSC also has conducted a number of special projects, including in-depth investigations of samples of home fires involving equipment such as electrical systems or alternative heating systems. Reports have been published on all these studies. A similar in-depth study of a sample of mobile home fires was conducted in the late 1970s by the Department of Housing and Urban Development (HUD).

As of 1989, the NFPA fire investigation program, supported by FEMA and the National Bureau of Standards, had generated more than 300 in-depth incident reports. No one property use accounted for enough incidents to form a statistically significant data base. However, some issues, such as those involving patterns in major fires in buildings with large life exposures, might be able to draw on this data base for statistical significance. These incident reports contain unequaled depth of detail on fire development, smoke spread, human factors in escape, and the performance of fire protection systems and features.

BIBLIOGRAPHY

References Cited

[1]NFPA 901, *Uniform Coding for Fire Protection*, 1976 ed. (used in most fire data bases) and 1991 ed.

[2]Hall, J. R., Jr., and Harwood, Beatrice, "The National Estimates Approach to U.S. Fire Statistics," *Fire Technology*, Vol. 25, No. 2, May 1989, pp. 99–113.

Additional Readings

NFPA's "One-Stop Data Shop" program in the Fire Analysis and Research Division produces dozens of reports on fire experience each year, most of them distributed directly through the division and not published in books or periodicals. A listing of reports that may be ordered is available free. The other major source of analyses is the U.S. Fire Administration's *Fire in the United States* series. For additional, detailed material on statistical methods, see *The SFPE Handbook of Fire Protection Engineering*.

EVALUATION AND PLANNING OF PUBLIC FIRE PROTECTION

Revised by John Granito

The purposes of this chapter are to demonstrate that adequate fire protection is an essential component of any community and that both the level and type of services provided should be conscious and carefully considered choices of the community. Further, objective evaluation and planning can ensure that a community's desire for a stipulated level of fire protection is being met in as cost-effective a manner as possible. Several other chapters provide information useful in the self-assessment of a public fire protection system. In addition, certain NFPA publications, including a number of codes, standards, and recommended practices, are applicable. Many of these publications are listed in the bibliography at the end of this chapter.

Public fire protection needs to be carefully planned and requires that certain logical steps be taken to achieve a comprehensive, acceptable, and workable plan. There are two important aspects to any good plan: (1) the plan itself, which must be feasible and directed toward clear goals; and (2) the process by which the plan is developed, which must ensure that all major goals are considered and every constituency to be affected by the plan is reasonably involved in the planning process.

Without adequate involvement of the necessary constituencies, implementation of the plan may likely fail because of a lack of cooperation and commitment. For a satisfactory plan to evolve, the planners must decide the end results they wish to achieve (goals), determine the status of the fire protection system in relation to those goals (evaluation), and calculate how much and what kinds of progress actually can take place over a certain period of time (objectives, tactics, time frame). Each of these three steps—setting goals, evaluation, working out the details—requires the collection and analysis of relevant information. Broad goals are achieved through planned strategies and precise objectives are achieved through implemented tactics. Each must be relevant to the other.

Dr. John Granito is emeritus professor and vice president for Public Service and External Affairs, State University of New York, Binghamton, NY.

Because some degree of public fire protection is almost always in place, it is common for the entire process to begin with an evaluation of the fire protection that is already available. The information obtained from the evaluation, when analyzed in terms of broad, generally recognized public fire protection goals, identifies needs and provides responsible community officials with the approximate parameters of the plan to be developed.

Typical fire department services include fire prevention programs—such as code administration and enforcement through plans review, inspection services, and public education—as well as fire suppression, rescue, emergency medical, hazardous materials response, and disaster response. Various other public services, such as some health screening programs, are sometimes conducted.

As already noted, the plan cannot be developed without the involvement of a wide variety of community groups. Even if the various constituencies seem willing to allow fire protection officials to develop and write the comprehensive plan without their consultation, the fire officials should be cautious; the citizens eventually must be willing to accommodate and pay for the implementation. Since a comprehensive plan envisions a larger group or system of integrated parts, a number of organizations and agencies outside the fire department will need to play important roles in implementation of the plan.

Modern practices make it necessary for fire departments to work cooperatively with a variety of agencies and organizations. These range, for example, from the local building code enforcement staff to the U.S. Coast Guard for hazardous materials spills near navigable waterways. Good planning requires consultation with all operational components.

One basic aspect of a comprehensive public fire protection plan is the concept that it is infinitely better for a community to prevent fires altogether, or to mitigate them automatically through firesafety education and built-in fire protection features, than to depend solely on the fire suppression capabilities of the community's fire department. The goal of reducing the incidence and effects of fire, then, involves all aspects of fire prevention. Historically, much more energy and many more resources have been devoted to evaluating, planning, and implementing fire suppression/fire fighting capabilities than fire prevention capabilities. Simply stated, the United States as a whole has focused more on "fire engines and fire fighters" than on public awareness and built-in mitigation features. That focus is still very necessary and exceedingly important, but effort must be placed also on measures that do not depend solely on fire suppression personnel to reduce the toll of fire. Planning groups have difficulty, however, in evaluating the degree of effectiveness of such multi-faceted fire protection programs.

A reasonably effective method exists for conducting the evaluation, involving two kinds of analysis. The first kind of analysis requires the community to maintain consistent and carefully recorded information each year concerning the number of fires that occur, and the cost of those fires in lives and dollars including wages and tax revenues lost. When those human and physical costs are added to the expense of maintaining fire prevention and suppression systems, plus the cost of fire insurance, a standardized total cost of fire to the community can be compared with that same cost in earlier years, or over an average of three or more years. Necessary adjustments for inflation, community growth or decline, and for other important variables can be made by local officials, thus permitting a community to compare its present to its prior fire performance.

The second kind of analysis most useful in determining cost-effectiveness involves communities identifying other communities that are similar in ways important to fire protection (such as services desired, size, construction, hazards, and geography) and comparing their own total performance to the total performance of the similar communities.

In the first analysis, the community uses an internal data source (itself) as a yardstick, and in the second analysis it uses an external yardstick (other communities). As more data are collected concerning the total cost of fires in various communities operating with various public fire protection plans, any given community will be able to benefit relatively quickly not only from its own experience, but also from the experiences of others.

Important to this planning process is the ability and willingness of the community to finance the total level of fire protection required by the plan's goals. Examples include legislation dealing with the retrofitting of sprinkler systems, or innovative thinking that produces a core group of senior citizen volunteers who conduct firesafety programs for their peers. In some states built-in fire protection requirements are set at the state level, and local government may not increase the level of firesafety provided by building features (automatic fire sprinklers, noncombustible roofing, etc.).

While fire protection officials must always be concerned with reducing the total cost of fire (fire loss, plus costs of insurance, prevention, and suppression), citizens living in tight economic times will ultimately reserve the right to make decisions, or "trade-offs," concerning the level of protection they wish their tax dollars to purchase.

To assist citizens in making decisions concerning budgets, fire protection officials must accurately describe the effect on total cost if additional or fewer resources are applied to particular prevention or suppression efforts. This kind of technical knowledge and analytical ability of officials provides a crucial element to comprehensive planning and evaluation. It is one of the most important responsibilities of the public fire protection officer.

One of the most serious issues faced by public officials and residents is that of adequate fire department staffing. In communities served by volunteer fire fighters there may be very serious volunteer recruitment problems, or problems in providing timely response during working hours when many of the volunteers may not be in the community they protect. In communities served by career, full-time fire fighters, restricted budgets often limit the number of fire fighting vehicles ready to respond, or the crew size for each vehicle. Fire protection officers and municipal officials need to communicate objectively the level of service being provided and how changes in fire department resources will affect that level of service. That is, the type and level of risk should be expressed in terms understandable to the fire protection non-expert and neither over- or understated. Of course, the fire department must bear the responsibility of formulating and operating a cost-effective organization.

EVALUATION

In addition to assessing the capabilities of the fire department and related aspects of fire protection, fire officials evaluating the capability of the existing fire protection system must take a number of factors into account. Examples include known combustibles, the life hazard that exists, fire frequency, climatic conditions, demographic and geographic factors, and a basic consideration of the specific role of a public fire department in providing fire protection to the community. Failure to consider each of these factors adequately can lead to a large-loss fire. A fire department's suppression capabilities can never be expected to compensate totally for the deficiency or lack of built-in fire protection systems.

Rural Fire Protection

One principal difference between rural and urban fire departments is that rural departments must deal with water supply issues with a broader variety of solutions than most urban departments. Rural fire department operations and apparatus emphasize not only fire fighting requirements, but also the provision of water for fire fighting. Rural fire apparatus must have large water tanks to permit effective initial attack on fires while supplementary water supplies are being brought into action. Supplementary water supplies include drafting sources on or adjacent to rural properties, and mobile water tanker vehicles for transporting water from more distant sources. Also in use are portable folding canvas tanks into which tank trucks quickly discharge their water supply. Rural fire departments often use apparatus and hose to relay water from sources several thousand feet (1000 ft equals 304.8 m) from the emergency. Initial response of pumpers, tankers, and auxiliary apparatus should be adequate for a quick attack on the burning property. With adequate highways and well-designed apparatus, it is often possible to bring substantial fire fighting forces to an emergency in rural areas in sufficient time for a properly planned and executed initial fire attack operation to be effective, even though many will arrive in private automobiles. Many rural properties are now located in areas that enjoy some level of fire protection. Some properties, of course, may have to depend entirely upon their own private fire protection and whatever help they may obtain from forestry agencies or distant fire departments.

Minimum protection for a rural area would include a pumper with a large water tank, plus a water tank vehicle responding on an initial alarm. Properly designed tanks should be able to transport water from a source 1 mile (1.6 km) from the scene so a minimum of 100 gpm (378 L/min) can be pumped at the fire scene by the pumper. Since a larger flow often is required to provide adequate fire protection services, additional tankers must be used, or drafting sources within reasonable distance of the fire scene must be identified. Rural apparatus should carry 3½-in. (89-mm) or larger lay-in hose to provide adequate water supply at the fire scene. It is always advisable to lay large-diameter fire hose from the water supply source to as near the fire scene as possible in order to avoid extensive friction loss. At the emergency, large-diameter hose is sometimes connected into smaller handlines, or used more often to supply another pumper from which handlines are extended. Other pieces of equipment, such as rescue and aerial ladder vehicles, should be provided as needed to carry out the mission. Generally, elevated master streams are not needed extensively in rural operations, and normal ladder truck equipment for rescue, forcible entry, ventilation, and salvage operations is carried on the pumper and equipment vehicles.

To be even minimally effective in controlling a fire, the initial responding apparatus should reach the emergency scene before very rapid fire spread. This is termed "initial attack" and is aimed at stopping the fire as close to the point or origin as possible. So-called "sustained attack" attempts to reduce the loss to the exposed adjoining or nearby property. Because of longer response times, rural departments often find themselves in the sustained attack mode upon arrival. Unless sufficient water can be made available within a short time frame, the British thermal units (Btu) generated by the burning material cannot be absorbed so the temperature is not reduced sufficiently to extinguish the fire. The keys to successful rural protection planning usually reduce to response times and water availability.

Of special concern are the sometimes extensive supplies of fertilizer and pesticides located on rural properties. Response crews must be alert also to the possibility of above- and below-ground storage tanks for fuel and other products. The safe operations guidelines for hazardous materials response are applicable in rural as well as urban areas.

To be even minimally effective in controlling a fire, the initial responding apparatus should reach the emergency scene in time to prevent "flashover" (a very rapid spreading of the fire due to the heating of room contents and other combustibles). The time from ignition to flashover is controlled by many variables (i.e., the type of combustibles, the ventilation available, the source of ignition, etc.). The time has been reported from less than four minutes to over ten minutes, but most U.S. fire departments assume flashover will occur in less than ten minutes. Given the unknown component of fire discovery and reporting its existence to the responsible fire suppression agency, it may seem that recommending a "generic" response time may be futile.

However, it is possible to give such counsel if one can make certain assumptions that may be controlled by the community. These assumptions relate primarily to the presence of appropriately placed smoke detectors and other types of fire detection devices and a means to relay that alarm to the fire suppression agency, but they also include the existence of enforced building codes that provide some degree of resistance to fire spread from the room of origin.

When there is no public or private fire protection agency, any fire that is beyond the control of portable extinguishing equipment (extinguishers, garden hose, etc.) may be expected to burn until all fuel in a given fire area has been consumed. Minimum levels of fire protection, while serving to confine fires to isolated properties, leave much to be desired by the property owner who suffers the loss and the fire department whose morale is often affected by its inability to control the average fire successfully. Because of distances, lack of water, and a general resource deficiency, small rural communities frequently suffer heavy fire loss.

Urban Fire Protection

In urban areas, inadequate fire department response to initial alarms can be a major factor in fire losses due to high population and structural densities. The number of simultaneous fire fighting operations that may need to be conducted also dictates the total amount of personnel and equipment needed to provide effective fire fighting operations. In all but the smallest structural fire, several operations must be carried on simultaneously and the fire attack must be made from several points. This cannot be accomplished by the crew of a single fire apparatus. Multiple apparatus must be positioned properly, and adequate waterflow made available to cope with the amount of fuel (fire load) involved or exposed.

In simplest terms, structural fire suppression in an urban setting involves the accomplishment of at least the following tasks, many of which must occur almost simultaneously to ensure effective and safe operations (the proper sequence will vary, depending on circumstances, as will additional tasks):

- Command of the incident (to ensure both effectiveness and safety of the fire fighters)
- Application of water in appropriate quantities (dependent upon the fire environment and other factors)
- Provision of appropriate source of water supply for above
- Ventilation of smoke and other hazardous products of combustion from the fire area to the outside
- Search for and rescue of fire victims
- Forcible entry
- Control of utilities
- Salvage and other property conservation operations

At large-structure fires, additional fire fighting personnel are needed to cover the various points of fire attack. In some cases various functions can be handled more efficiently by specially trained crews such as rescue companies and hazardous material teams operating from specially equipped apparatus.

The number of personnel and equipment necessary to accomplish the above will vary with a number of factors (i.e., the expectations placed on the mobile suppression group, the material burning, the construction of the building, the type of built-in protection provided, separation between buildings, availability of water supply, the number and physical and emotional condition of persons in the fire building, the type of equipment available to fire fighters, the level of proficiency of the fire suppression crew [including the commanders], etc.). Hence, it is impossible to determine a minimum number of fire fighters or equipment required without careful, objective planning.

Some general considerations may, however, be listed:

- The more arduous the expectations placed on the mobile fire suppression crew, the greater the required resources (e.g., the community that expects its fire department to contain fires to the room of origin should expect to provide more fire suppression resources than the community that expects its fire department only to prevent the spread of fire from one building to another; given the same level of protection demands, the community that leaves all fire protection to the mobile fire suppression force will require a more extensive suppression force than the community that requires a high level of built-in protection).
- The more extensive the fire risk, the greater the required fire suppression resources (e.g., given the same expectations of its mobile fire suppression force, a community having high-rise buildings, a high population density, and extensive industrial risks will normally require greater fire suppression resources than a largely residential community).
- The broader the services provided by a fire protection agency, the greater the need for resources (e.g., a fire agency providing emergency medical services will, given the same level of expectations for its mobile suppression forces, require more resources than an agency providing only fire protection services).
- The greater the geographic area protected, the greater the resource requirement of the mobile fire suppression forces (i.e., given the same service level expectations, a community providing service to 20 square miles will require more resources than a community providing protection to only 10 square miles; this is caused by the need for timely arrival at the scene of fire, medical, or environmentally threatening incidents).

In most smaller and medium-size communities, all initial-response (first-alarm) apparatus will not arrive at the fire scene simultaneously. In many departments with on-duty personnel, apparatus has to respond from more than one station, and some apparatus have longer travel times to the fire scene. In volunteer departments, personnel must travel varying distances to get to the fire station or the fire scene, and thus all apparatus cannot go into operation at the same time. Those fire fighters and vehicles that cannot arrive at the fire scene within the first critical time period have limited impact on the initial attack, regardless of the department's response assignment ("running card"). Communities often have a false sense of security in this regard, until actual response times are tested and working initial-attack personnel counted.

The critical numbers for policy makers to use in planning related to staffing of shifts and apparatus crews—sometimes termed "minimum manning"—are those that describe how many trained personnel can arrive within a stipulated initial attack time frame. Ideally, all or most will arrive as composite crews, and not as individuals.

The minimum fire force recommended for any small community is necessarily dependent upon the expectations of the members of the mobile fire force and the environment in which they function. Objective planning and evaluation is necessary to determine the resources required for effective and safe fire suppression operations.

Some fire agencies are addressing the suppression challenge with different arrangements of fire crews within the communities than were heretofore generally accepted (e.g., use of multi-purpose apparatus). In 1991, these new approaches had not yet been in service long enough to determine effect on fire loss or fire fighter safety, but some reports indicated that in certain fire environments multi-purpose apparatus may prove to be as safe for the fire fighter and provide a more flexible level of service. It is important to note that while these different approaches may augment flexibility, they do not appear to reduce the number of suppression personnel required to carry out fire fighting operations safely.

It does seem reasonable to say that not less than two fire suppression vehicles and a command officer should respond to any structure fire and that the number of personnel responding should be sufficient to carry out the tasks indicated above, and whatever else is typically necessary in local operations, in a timely fashion. Normative data are available from some cities. While that number is dependent on numerous factors, it is relevant to note that in the broad spectrum of environments protected by the nineteen fire departments making up the United States portion of the NFPA Urban Fire Forum, no department in 1991 dispatched fewer than eleven fire fighters (including a command officer) to a reported fire in a single-family detached dwelling. The average number dispatched was nineteen.

Critical task analysis indicates that fewer than eleven fire fighters would be most hard pressed to accomplish safe, effective, initial interior fire attack in a timely manner at a detached single-family dwelling.

Where necessitated by fire frequency or response distances, additional pumpers, ladder trucks, and tankers may be needed. Reserve apparatus is desirable not only to permit the repair of first-line equipment without reducing available fireground forces, but to provide additional fire fighting units during major emergencies. Specialized vehicles for hazardous materials response, heavy-duty and specialized rescue—including boats—lighting equipment, breathing apparatus bottles, emergency medical response, etc., also must be planned for. If these cannot be made available locally, then mutual aid arrangements are needed. Different types of vehicles may be necessary for the various levels of emergency medical response: basic life support, advanced life support, and hospital transport.

Commercial, industrial, and mercantile areas generally require an additional apparatus or more in response to the initial alarm. If properties with considerable life hazard are involved (schools, hospitals, nursing homes, etc.) additional resources should be considered for initial alarms. Especially large numbers of personnel are needed for search and rescue operations in these properties, with several fire fighters needed to "sweep and search" each floor.

The required fire fighting units should arrive on scene close enough in time after the initial alarm to operate as an effective fire fighting unit following planned tactical procedures.

In evaluating the adequacy of fire protection in any given area, major consideration must be given to the ability of the fire department to handle efficiently any reasonably anticipated work load. This requires an evaluation of the possibility of simultaneous working fires and other emergencies; weather factors that may contribute to the spread of fire, the delay in response, or the possibility of slow operations at the scene; and other demographic or

TABLE 10-4A. ***Typical Initial Attack Response Capability Assuming Interior Attack and Operations Response Capability***

High-Hazard Occupancies (Schools, hospitals, nursing homes, explosive plants, refineries, high-rise buildings, and other high life hazard or large fire potential occupancies)

At least 4 pumpers, 2 ladder trucks (or combination apparatus with equivalent capabilities), 2 chief officers, and other specialized apparatus as may be needed to cope with the combustible involved; not less than 24 fire fighters and 2 chief officers.

Medium-Hazard Occupancies (Apartments, offices, mercantile and industrial occupancies not normally requiring extensive rescue or fire fighting forces)

At least 3 pumpers, 1 ladder truck (or combination apparatus with equivalent capabilities), 1 chief officer, and other specialized apparatus as may be needed or available; not less than 16 fire fighters and 1 chief officer.

Low-Hazard Occupancies (One-, two- or three-family dwellings and scattered small businesses and industrial occupancies)

At least 2 pumpers, 1 ladder truck (or combination apparatus with equivalent capabilities), 1 chief officer, and other specialized apparatus as may be needed or available; not less than 12 fire fighters and 1 chief officer.

Rural Operations (Scattered dwellings, small businesses, and farm buildings)

At least 1 pumper with a large water tank (500 gal [1.9 m^3] or more), one mobile water supply apparatus (1000 gal [3.78 m^3] or larger), and such other specialized apparatus as may be necessary to perform effective initial fire fighting operations; at least 12 fire fighters and 1 chief officer.

Additional Alarms

At least the equivalent of that required for Rural Operations for second alarms; equipment as may be needed according to the type of emergency and capabilities of the fire department. This may involve the immediate use of mutual aid companies until local forces can be supplemented with additional off-duty personnel. In some communities, single units are "special called" when needed, without always resorting to a multiple alarm. Additional units also may be needed to fill at least some empty fire stations.

geographic conditions that might affect the frequency, severity, and spread of fire occurrence and the response time of initial fire fighting units. Where fire frequency is such that any fire company may expect two or three working fires per day, or where structures to be protected require a heavy initial response, closer geographic spacing of or increased personnel assigned to individual fire companies may be necessary. The number of other fire fighting or related operations such as grass, brush, rubbish, and automobile fires and emergency rescue operations may also require greater-than-normal staffing of equipment and closer spacing of fire companies. Major structural fires may result when the normal first-alarm coverage in a district is depleted through coverage of these other emergencies, making remaining fire fighting forces inadequate. Staffing fire apparatus at a level below minimum requirements will result in less effective fire fighting performance. This factor also has an adverse effect on the number of required fire companies for various alarms, since additional fire companies must be dispatched to the scene of an emergency to provide adequate coverage.

The desirable practice of assigning emergency medical responsibility to the fire department must be calculated into the staffing formula. It is difficult also to obtain effective teamwork and coordination with understrength crews. Some fire departments have attempted to solve this problem by supplementing their crews with part-time or volunteer fire fighters, or by providing off-duty fire fighters with tone-activated radio receivers and paying them for overtime when they respond to a fire. The on-duty personnel make the initial fire attack and holding action while off-duty personnel provide the additional assistance needed for continuing fire fighting operations. Efficiency is lost, and increased fire losses can be expected with this arrangement. Such protection should not be relied upon to replace adequately the required staffing and equipment needed immediately at the scene for initial attack and rescue.

Personnel requirements are not merely a matter of numerical strength, but are also based on the establishment of a well-trained and coordinated team necessary to utilize complicated and specialized equipment under the stress of emergency conditions. Good practice indicates that attempting to operate more fire companies than can be effectively staffed, even if some response distances must be somewhat increased, is less desirable than fewer but appropriately staffed companies. The effectiveness of pumper companies must be measured by their ability to get required hose streams into service quickly and efficiently. NFPA 1410, *Training Standard on Initial Fire Attack*, should be used as a guide in measuring this ability. Seriously understaffed fire companies generally are limited to the use of small hose streams until additional help arrives. Often this action may be totally ineffective in containing even a small fire and in conducting effective rescue operations.

Consideration must be given also to maintaining an adequate concentration of additional forces to handle multiple alarms at the same fire, while still providing minimum fire protection coverage for the other areas under fire department protection. If available personnel prove adequate for routine fires but inadequate for major emergencies, arrangements should be made to supplement the fire protection coverage by calling back the off-shift personnel and by promptly calling nearby fire departments for mutual aid. Off-shift personnel may operate reserve apparatus or relieve or supplement personnel on the fireground. Fire companies not dispatched or utilized on the fire scene should be repositioned throughout the remaining area of the jurisdiction to ensure minimum response times to other alarms.

Reserve apparatus should be properly maintained and equipped, and when placed in service should be staffed to a degree commensurate with standard fire apparatus requirements. Since it may take up to thirty minutes or more to place reserve units in service with personnel recalled in an emergency, these reserve units should not be completely relied upon to provide an adequate level of fire protection services.

Concern must be shown, under legislation, for the health and safety of fire fighters and others, for environmental protection, and for the rights of those being served. Officials must demonstrate reasonable and prudent action with establishment of incident command systems, for example, and the appointment of qualified safety officers.

In cases where several fire departments occupy adjacent or contiguous territories, arrangements should be made for joint response along common boundaries to high-risk hazards and for assistance in covering vacant fire stations at times of major fires. Mutual aid or mutual response should not be relied upon for routine emergencies, since there could be times when local commitments will preclude the anticipated assistance. Mutual-aid agreements do not reduce the responsibility of each jurisdiction to maintain adequate facilities to handle normal fire protection needs. It also must be assumed that teamwork and tactical efficiency at a fire will be somewhat less than that expected of equal units from the same department under a united command. Often, however, specialized units (such as hazardous materials response teams) are organized to protect larger areas encompassing several fire departments.

In the past it was a common practice to relate the number of pumping engines and their pumping capacity, and other apparatus personnel requirements, to the population to be protected. With the industrialization of many areas and the construction of commercial shopping centers, hospitals, schools, and nursing homes in residential areas, it is possible that concentrations of life hazard and property value in areas of small or large populations may require substantial fire fighting forces. Those with the responsibility for providing public fire protection must be prepared to cope with fire potential in any location in the jurisdiction. Fire department response requirements are now based on the water flow in gpm (L/min) that may have to be applied. A rule of thumb often used is to provide one company for each 250 gpm (0.9 m^3/min) that may be needed in an interior attack, plus personnel for rescue and other operations that need to be performed simultaneously with the advancing of hose lines.

Some may argue that it is not the public's responsibility to provide adequate fire protection to high-hazard risks that should have built-in fire protection systems. However, failure to attempt to provide fire protection for large taxable values on which the economy of a community may be based would place the community's fiscal viability at risk. Burned-out businesses often do not rebuild, and thus local people lose employment.

As already described, time is another critical factor in the evaluation of public fire protection. It is generally considered that the first-arriving piece of apparatus should be at the emergency scene within five minutes of the sounding of the alarm, since additional minutes are needed to size up the situation, deploy hose lines, initiate search and rescue, etc. In densely urban settings the desired response time often is shorter. The old adage says, "The first five minutes of most fires is the determining factor as to whether that fire will remain a small fire or become a large fire." While this may not always be true, delays in sounding an alarm obviously must be minimized or eliminated, as well as delays in responding and initiating rescue and attack. Time, however, cannot become the all-important factor at the expense of safety.

There are increasingly numerous instances where highly specialized apparatus and equipment must be available to municipalities. One category of specialization concerns apparatus designed to handle hazardous materials, including spills of petroleum products and other chemicals that require special extinguishing agents such as foams or dry powders, and special equipment to apply these agents. These dangerous substances may be present because of airports, marinas, manufacturing or storage facilities, or transportation routes in the district. Another category of specialization includes apparatus and equipment needed because of particular structures or facilities such as research laboratories, hospitals, high-rise buildings, oil and gas wells, and seaports. In some communities fire departments are expected to conduct specialized functions such as extricating at automobile wrecks and performing water and mountain rescue, as well as providing emergency medical services. These services also require special equipment and possibly special vehicles.

As with standard fire fighting equipment and apparatus, specialized tools cannot be used effectively and safely unless personnel are highly trained in their use under a wide variety of circumstances. Whether personnel are volunteer or career, in rural or urban areas, no plan can be implemented and no reasonable level of fire protection afforded to the community unless well-designed and well-managed training programs are carried out.

Fire Prevention

The term *fire prevention* is used here, as it is generally used, to include both education and equipment meant to reduce the occurrence of fire and to mitigate the effects of that fire prior to the arrival of the mobile suppression force. As an example, the installation of a sprinkler system is not designed to prevent fire but to extinguish it in its very early stages; the "Stop, Drop, and Roll" message of the NFPA Learn Not To Burn® program is clearly a mitigation rather than prevention effort. Other education efforts are directed at stopping the occurrence of fire.

As noted previously, fire prevention activities are somewhat difficult to evaluate. In a real sense, if prevention activities are effective, fires and fire-related tragedies occur with less frequency. There is a reduction or absence of fire activity, and these results are evident statistically although they do not appear in dramatic news clips and photographs. Some departments do report not only dollar amounts of fire loss, but also the value of structures that were threatened by fire and thus "saved." Without careful and systematic long-term record-keeping concerning the incidence of fires and fire losses, the effect of prevention programs cannot be documented. Inability of fire officials to demonstrate the value of committing some additional community resources to the broad range of possible prevention activities may well result in a withdrawal of resources from prevention programs and a subsequent increase in the need for a much larger suppression budget. Rational decisions and sound recommendations concerning evaluation and planning cannot be made unless fire officials learn what changes there can be to total fire cost by reallocating resources applied to the total fire defense system.

Both evaluation and planning require recognition of the component and integrated parts of a fire prevention system. Until recent years prevention was seen as a narrow band of activities, often greatly limited or nonexistent in most smaller communities. In urban areas it was limited frequently to the periodic inspection of certain types of buildings. More modern approaches to fire prevention recognize that a comprehensive program includes all organized activities, other than suppression, that reduce the incidence of fire and fire-related losses. Ideally, these activities would be carried out in communities of every size, whether rural or urban, with appropriate adjustments made for community size, type, location, and fire history.

Prevention activities may be categorized in several ways, but it is usually helpful to group them as follows:

1. Activities that relate to construction, such as building codes, the approval of building and facility plans, and occupancy certification and recertification for new

occupants. Also included may be a sign-off for the presence of smoke detectors when new or old properties are sold.

2. Activities that relate to the enforcement of codes and regulations, such as inspections of certain occupancies, the licensure of certain hazardous facilities, the design of new regulations and codes, and legislation to adopt existing model codes.
3. Activities that relate to the reduction of arson, such as fire investigation and the collection of information and data related to setting fires. Included may be arson investigation and related court proceedings, and programs such as counseling for juvenile fire setters.
4. Activities that relate to the collection of data helpful in improving fire protection, such as standardized fire reporting, case histories, and fire research.
5. Activities that relate to public education and training, including fire prevention safeguards, evacuation and personal safety steps, plant protection training for industrial and other work groups, hazardous materials and devices safeguards, and encouragement to install early warning and other built-in signaling and extinguishing devices. Very popular are programs for school children, such as NFPA's Learn Not To Burn® curriculum and self-help classes such as water safety and similar "Stay Alive 'Til We Arrive" projects.

An analysis of the community's fire history, conducted during the evaluation phase of the fire protection plan, will usually indicate to fire experts and citizen groups which categories need strengthening. Comparing the number of fires and fire-related incidents, plus fire loss (property, life, injury) statistics over several years as more prevention activities are phased in, provides an assessment of program effectiveness. Calculating the total cost of fire to a community (fire loss plus prevention costs plus suppression costs plus fire insurance costs) will enable the fire department and the community to estimate the efficiency or cost-effectiveness of a proposed prevention program.

PUBLIC PROTECTION CLASSIFICATIONS

Fire Department Service-Level Analysis

The public, fire and other government administrators, organized labor, and the fire service in general have for many years sought to find a generally accepted method for the evaluation of services provided to a community by its fire protection agency. The approaches have been as varied as the fire service agencies being evaluated and the parties doing the evaluation. This has resulted in the application of inconsistent methodology and criteria.

For many years material developed by NFPA has been used in the analysis of services provided by fire protection organizations. However, the application of NFPA materials has been inconsistent, and NFPA material existing in 1991 is not entirely adequate for the evaluation of the comprehensive services provided by comprehensive fire/rescue agencies.

In 1990, NFPA determined, therefore, to continue its long history of involvement in the field of fire department evaluation through a program to provide criteria, process, and organization for the analysis of service levels provided by fire departments under the direct oversight of the Association's President. With the Board of Directors' concurrence, the President appointed in 1990 a "Select Committee" to advise in this matter, with representation from the fire service, municipal management, organized labor, and the insurance industry. Appropriate recommendations to the NFPA Standards Council are made as the need is determined.

Initial work of the Select Committee, conducted in 1990 and 1991, determined that the best program for the analysis of services would:

- Consider the total scope of services provided by the fire service agency
- Set forth uniform definitions
- Be primarily performance-based and user-friendly
- Be founded on consensus and other standards to the greatest possible extent
- Include user input
- Be designed for specific community application
- Be capable of self-application
- Include a validation process

While not all states in the United States use the existing Insurance Service Office (ISO) grading schedule, and while it is not used in other nations, it is applied to many departments in most states approximately every ten years. The purpose is to aid in the calculation of fire insurance rates and is not for property loss prevention or life safety purposes.

As will be seen below, the older form of the grading schedule contains more categories and more items than the schedule in current use. However, the older form is still applied in one or more states and is still used by some community officials as a reference tool in self-evaluations.

It should be noted that, typically, the result and classification apply to properties with a needed fire waterflow of 3500 gpm or less. Private and public properties with larger needed flows are individually evaluated.

With improved ratings, fire insurance companies that subscribe to the ISO rating system may lower commercial fire insurance premiums and may lower residential rates in certain instances.

The "Grading Schedule for Municipal Fire Protection," developed originally by the National Board of Fire Underwriters (NBFU) and continued by its successor, the American Insurance Association, and then by the ISO, has provided a guideline for municipalities to classify their fire defenses and physical conditions. The gradings obtained under the schedule were used in establishing base rates for fire insurance purposes. The schedule has been subject to change with the state of the art, and sweeping changes were made in the 1980 edition with the development of a revised "Fire Suppression Rating Schedule."

The Fire Suppression Rating Schedule[1] produces ten different Public Protection Classifications, with Class 1 receiving the most rate recognition and Class 10 receiving no recognition. The Fire Suppression Rating Schedule simply defines different levels of public fire suppression capabilities that are credited in the individual property fire insurance rate relativities.

Starting in 1975, on a state-by-state basis following Insurance Department approval, ISO implemented the Commercial Fire Rating Schedule (CFRS), which was a major revision to the method used to develop individual property rate relativities. The CFRS reviews and correlates the construction, occupancy, exposures, and private and public fire protection (represented by the Public Protection Classification number). This correlation allows development of an equitable rate relativity applicable to the individual property. To this rate relativity, statistical experience adjustments are applied either by ISO or by affiliated companies to produce the applicable fire insurance rate. The Fire Suppression Rating Schedule (FSRS) represents a revision in the method used to derive the Public Protection Classification number used in the CFRS. The Public Protection Classification number is also used as a rate relativity variable for most class-related properties, in addition to construction and occupancy variables.

The *Grading Schedule for Municipal Fire Protection*,[2] although a much-improved system from previous editions, was not developed as an integral part of the individual property rating system. The previous schedules were somewhat independent primarily due to their historical development by the NBFU, which was not an insurance rating organization. The previous schedules were used more to quantify underwriting information, but did define different levels of public fire protection that could be used for a specific rating.

The FSRS is designed to assist in an objective review of those features of available public fire protection that have a significant influence on minimizing damage once a fire has occurred. This revision ties very logically to the review of contributive and causative hazards that can be performed with the CFRS.

Comparison of Details

The following material outlines the specific changes that are incorporated into the FSRS as compared with the 1974 *Grading Schedule for Municipal Fire Protection*.

TABLE 10-4B. ***Comparison of Schedules: Major Items***

1974 Schedule		1980 FSR Schedule	
	Relative Weight (Percent)		Relative Weight (Percent)
Water supply	39	Water supply	40
Fire department	39	Fire department	50
Fire alarm	9	Fire alarm	10
Building laws	1.7		
Electrical laws	.8		100
Fire prevention laws	10.5		
Climate conditions	(variable)		
	100		

Building, electrical, and fire prevention laws, and climatic conditions are not included in the FSRS (Table 10-4B) for the following reasons:

1. Most communities have adopted one of the available model codes; thus differences were not really being measured.
2. Evaluation of codes enforcement and climatic conditions is subjective when trying to review on a citywide basis.
3. Results of the law and its enforcement manifest themselves in the actual conditions found in individual properties when surveyed for application of the CFRS. (See Table 10-4C.)

TABLE 10-4C. ***Comparison of Schedules: Water Supply***

1974 Schedule		1980 FSR Schedule	
	Relative Weight (Percent)		Relative Weight (Percent)
Adequacy of supply works	6	Supply works	
		Fire flow delivery	
Reliability of source of supply	6	Distribution of hydrants	35
Reliability of pumping capacity	3	Hydrants—size, type, and installation	2
Reliability of power supply	4	Hydrants—inspection and condition	3
Condition, arrangement, operation, and reliability of system components	4		40
Adequacy of mains	16		
Reliability of mains	2		
Installation of mains	2		
Arrangement of distribution system	2		
Additional factors and conditions relating to supply and distribution	4		
Distribution of hydrants	5		
Hydrants—size, type, and installation	2		
Hydrants—inspection and condition	2		
Miscellaneous factors and conditions	6		
	64 (Max=39)		

4. The 1974 schedule and its predecessor schedules contained many standards or benchmarks of evaluation that were detailed specifications. If a condition in a community did not meet the specifications, deficiency points were assigned. Specifications decrease a schedule's flexibility in use to evaluate changing conditions and technology properly. Because the FSRS has eliminated essentially all of the specifications that were in the 1974 schedule, it is referred to as a performance schedule. The only criteria in the FSRS that could be considered as specifications are the descriptions of the minimum conditions to be reviewed under the schedule. For example, with the 1974 schedule, it was essentially impossible for a community to receive other than a Class 9 rating if it did not have a water supply with conventional underground water mains. However, the FSRS is based upon delivery performance only, without regard to the delivery method used, and is adaptable to crediting the delivery of water by other means. Specific reference is made to water carried and delivered to the fire location by fire department apparatus.
5. As previously mentioned, the FSRS has been designed to interface directly with individual property insurance rate development. As a result, numerous items that were evaluated both in the individual property review and in the previous public fire protection review have been removed from the FSRS.

The review and enforcement of building, electrical, and fire prevention codes have been deleted from the FSRS because the presence of hazards due to poor codes or lack of enforcement are recognized in an individual property survey and rate review.

Section I of the FSRS can be used to develop a public protection classification that reflects the city's ability to handle fires in small to moderate-size buildings; these are defined as those buildings having a needed fire flow of 3500 gpm (13 m^3/min) or less. Section II of the FSRS can be used to develop public protection classifications for large individual properties having needed fire flows greater than 3500 gpm (13 m^3/min).

Most communities design their fire protection needs around normally expected fires. This design is recognized in the differing concept between these two sections. The Public Protection Classification in Section I is applicable to average buildings, and the influence of the fire protection demands for larger buildings has been removed from that analysis. Section II can be applied individually to each large building to develop an individual public protection classification that reflects the protection available for that specific property.

The 1974 schedule and its predecessors did not provide significant recognition of the decreased need for public fire suppression when large properties are protected by automatic sprinkler systems. The FSRS does recognize this important fact by excluding all properties with standard automatic sprinkler systems from the development of needed fire flow figures.

The water supply items dealing with reliability in the 1974 schedule are not included in the FSRS because recent history has indicated that the dependability and replacement capability of water supply equipment is such that measurement of these features has little bearing on the water supply performance. The remaining items of the 1974 schedule that are not included in the FSRS are omitted because they either require subjective review or are not considered significant enough to measure the performance of the water system for fire insurance rating purposes. The emphasis of the FSRS review regarding a water system is the consideration of the actual water supply that is available for fire suppression at representative locations throughout the city.

As in the water supply feature, items that require subjective review and consider minor features are not included in the FSRS. (See Table 10-4D.) The FSRS places emphasis on the review of the first-alarm response by the fire department because of the importance of initial attack to minimize potential losses. Additionally, the entire fire department item has been given increased weight in the overall review in recognition of the value of fire department operations in early stages of fire suppression and the fact that some operations are possible with less-than-optimum water supplies.

As in the water supply and fire department sections, features that are subjective or are minor items dealing with the fire alarm system are not included in the FSRS. (See Table 10-4E.) The emphasis has been placed on the performance of handling and dispatching fire alarms rather than the method of notification.

Rate-Level Effect

A testing program was conducted by ISO to determine any potential rate-level effect resulting from the introduction of the FSRS. The test results indicate that the introduction of the FSRS will have a negligible rate-level impact.

TABLE 10-4D. ***Comparison of Schedules: Fire Department***

1974 Schedule		1980 FSR Schedule	
	Relative Weight (Percent)		Relative Weight (Percent)
Pumpers	4.8	Engine companies	11
Ladder trucks	3.4	Ladder service companies	6
Distribution of companies and types of apparatus	4	Distribution of dompanies	4
Pumper capacity	4.4	Pumper capacity	5
Design, maintenance, and condition of apparatus	3	Department manning	15
Number of officers	2	Training	9
Department manning	8		50
Engine and ladder company unit manning	6.4		
Master and special stream devices	1		
Equipment for pumpers and ladders	2		
Hose	2.8		
Condition of hose	1.6		
Training	6		
Response to alarms	2		
Fire operations	8		
Special protection	6		
Miscellaneous factors and conditions	6		
	71.4 (Max=39)		

A sample of 500 communities was selected so distribution by protection class and by population group within the protection classes corresponded with the average premium distribution across the U.S. Such a selection process was used so the test results would properly reflect any premium change caused by the introduction of the FSRS.

The communities actually tested were randomly selected from across the country. The FSRS was applied to recent ISO file data. To calculate the expected rate-level impact, the redistribution of protection classes was correlated to the current nationwide average protection-class rate differentials. The test results indicate a 95 percent probability that the rate-level effect will be minus 0.08 percent, plus or minus 1.11 percent.

Not considered in the test was the fact that ISO normally resurveys each community only once every ten years unless requested to do so sooner by the community. Therefore, the actual rate level impact would be somewhat lower than the calculated impact.

Monitoring

The FSRS involves many significant changes in the approach to establishing Public Protection Classifications. As in any comprehensive new rating program, the possibility of unforeseen rating situations cannot be overlooked. Consequently, the results are monitored very carefully to ensure that the program is working as intended. Any

TABLE 10-4E. *Comparison of Schedules: Fire Alarm System*

1974 Schedule	Relative Weight (Percent)	1980 FSR Schedule	Relative Weight (Percent)
Communication center	0.8	Receipt of fire alarms	
Communication center, equipment and current supply	2.8	operators	2
Boxes	1.2	Alarm dispatch	3
Alarm circuits and alarm facilities, including current supply at fire stations	2	Circuit facilities	5
Material, construction, condition and protection of circuit	1		10
Radio	0.8		
Fire department telephone service	1.7		
Fire alarm operators	0.8		
Conditions adversely affecting use	1.3		
Credit for boxes installed in residential districts	−.4		
	12.4 (Max=9)		

required changes to the schedule that are identified through the monitoring program are implemented following thorough evaluation.

Implementation

The revised schedule is applied to communities during the normal resurvey program or when significant changes occur in a community that would require a resurvey. Section II of the FSRS pertaining to individual nonsprinklered properties will not be applied unless Section I has been applied to the community; Section II also will not be applied in cities that are statistically rated.

When application of the schedule results in an improvement in the Public Protection Classification, the new classification is implemented as soon as insurers and producers are notified through ISO's manual page-distribution procedures. Should a community retrogress, the community officials will be notified of the change and the possible effect on insurance rates. If within 90 days the community decides to engage in a program that would improve the classification, the implementation of the poorer classification will be delayed indefinitely as long as an improvement program begins within one year and continues to completion.

Transition Rule

The usual impact of a change in the Public Protection Classification, for those properties that have classifications such as a rating variable, is approximately five percent for each change in class. Even though it is highly unlikely that there would be any significant rate impact for individual property by a change in the Public Protection Classification, the following transition rule is used for any unusual situations that may arise.

When used solely as a result of the application of the FSRS, and when the applicable Public Protection Classification number increases by one or more, the following shall apply to any resulting individual property rate increases:

1. The rate increase shall be limited to 25 percent for the first publication.
2. If the rate increase is between 25 and 50 percent, the balance of the increase shall be included when the rate is next published for the risk, but not sooner than one year after the effective date in Item 1 above.
3. If the rate increase exceeds 50 percent, Items 1 and 2 above shall apply, except that an increase over 50 percent shall not be published sooner than two years from the effective date in Item 1 above.

PLANNING

Whenever a community—rural, suburban, or urban—considers its fire defenses, it must scrutinize the past and present and make predictions or forecasts for the future. Reviewing the past is called *data analysis* and depends upon good record-keeping. *Evaluation*, which is looking at the present, requires the ability to examine a situation objectively. The process of forecasting future conditions and preparing for them requires that a *planning* process be followed. This planning process results in a plan and its implementation, so that future challenges to the community are met. As the plan is implemented, the process must include the establishment of a *feedback loop*, providing a continuing assessment of how well the plan is contributing to successful completion of goals and objectives, and feeding revised data back into the plan so continuing redesign occurs.

Fire protection organizations, and especially fire departments, need to develop several kinds of plans related to fire prevention and fire suppression. These plans should be quite specific, directed at one clearly defined goal, and operational over a relatively brief time period (usually from one to five years). Typically, such plans are internal to the department and do not involve broad-based planning groups from the outside. Examples of these types of plans, which are most often technical in nature, are apparatus replacement plans, training program plans, revised initial-response plans, plans for a special hazardous-materials attack unit, and plans for adapting fireground procedures to incorporate the use of larger-diameter hose. However, once department planning begins to consider aspects of fire protection that will have an impact on external groups, those groups will need to be consulted and incorporated into the planning process. Fire department planning, for example, must consider land-use planning (zoning), water department planning, building code enforcement, etc.

Examples of fire department planning that require the early involvement of other groups are station relocations or closings, building inspection programs, public education programs, and changes in the scheduling of work platoons. These plans, while involving some other groups, are still fairly narrow in scope and usually can be formulated over a relatively short time.

A third type of planning, called comprehensive or master planning, addresses the total community fire protection problem, incorporating both prevention and suppression, and obviously involves many community agencies and organizations, perhaps even county, state, and federal agencies. Comprehensive planning is a necessity for communities and is aimed at integrating all community efforts at prevention and suppression, and improving efficiency and cost-effectiveness of those activities. Improved total community fire protection is the goal of this planning. Its degree of success must be measured by figures relating to the total cost of fire to the community, and not just in gains for one subsystem. Comprehensive plans often consist of a number of subplans from various agencies that are developed at the same time as part of a larger, total process, and that fit together to make a comprehensive and integrated plan.

Comprehensive plans have clearly stated goals with agreed-upon ways of measuring their attainment. These overall goals are reached through overall strategies acceptable to all involved agencies and to the citizens who must pay for the fire protection system. Each goal is composed of some number of subgoals or objectives, and for each objective there is a tactic designed to reach that objective. All objectives lead to the accomplishment of the overall strategies. When the objectives and tactics are laid out on a timeline, the overall time required to implement the comprehensive plan is then known, and the timing for attaining each objective is apparent.

Fire protection has been largely a local responsibility, and for good reasons it seems destined to remain so.*[1] Each community has a set of conditions unique to itself; it cannot be assumed a system of fire protection that works well for one community will work equally well for other communities. To be adequate, the fire protection system must respond to local conditions, especially to changing conditions. Planning is the key: without local-level planning, the fire protection system is apt to be ill-suited to local needs and unadaptable to the changing needs of the community.

Excellent fire protection (for example, in the form of automatic extinguishing systems such as residential sprinklers) is technically available and certainly can be provided with the resources of most communities. Even with considerable public support, however, this protection may require several years to attain. In the meantime, in every fire jurisdiction (whether a municipality, county, or region) fire protection goals must be set and plans made to achieve those goals. The sections below discuss some of the concepts to be defined in setting these standards.

Adequate level of fire protection: The question of "adequacy" is addressed not only in day-to-day needs, but in major contingencies that can be anticipated and for future needs as well. A definition of "optimal" protection is needed—in contrast to "minimal" protection, which fails to meet contingencies and future needs, and "maximal" protection, which is usually more expensive than a community can afford.

Comprehensive planning must include contingencies drawn from an analysis of community hazards. This process of hazard identification and analysis is crucial to fire department planning.

[1] *Some of the information that follows in this chapter has been extracted in whole and in part from *America Burning*[3] *and America Burning Revisited*.[4]

Reasonable community costs: Fire, both as threat and reality, has its costs, including deaths, injuries, property losses, hospital bills, and lost tax revenues, plus the costs of maintaining fire departments, paying fire insurance premiums, and providing built-in fire protection. Each community must decide upon an appropriate level of investment in fire protection. Some costs that are beyond the public's willingness to bear may be transferred to the private sector (as when buildings over a certain size or height or with a certain occupancy are required to have automatic extinguishing systems).

Acceptable risk: A certain level of fire loss must be accepted as tolerable simply because of limited resources of a community. Conditions that endanger the safety of citizens and fire fighters beyond the acceptable risk must be identified as targets for mitigation.

Consideration of these matters helps to determine what functions and emphasis should be assigned to the fire department, other municipal departments, and the private sector both now and in the future. It helps to define new policies, laws, or regulations that may be needed. Most importantly, consideration of these matters makes it clear that firesafety is a responsibility shared by the public and private sectors. Because the fire department cannot prevent all fire losses, formal obligations to have built-in fire protection fall on owners of certain kinds of buildings. For the same reason, private citizens have an obligation to exercise prudence with regard to fire in their daily lives. But prudence also requires education in firesafety, and the obligation to provide that education appropriately falls in the public sector, chiefly the fire department. The public sector (again, chiefly the fire and building code enforcement departments) also has an obligation to see that requirements for built-in protection in the private sector are being met.

A fire department, then, has more than one responsibility—nor are the aforementioned responsibilities exhaustive.

The following are significant functions for which fire protection agencies typically have primary or significant roles.

Fire suppression: Fire fighters need proper training and adequate equipment to save lives, extinguish fires quickly, and also to ensure their own safety.

Specialized emergency and disaster services: These include hazardous-materials incidents, floods, earthquakes, multiple-vehicle accidents, cave-ins, collapsed buildings, volcanic eruptions, searches for lost persons, attempted suicides, a variety of specialized rescue services, etc.

Emergency medical services: Capabilities needed during fires and other emergencies include first aid, resuscitation, and possibly advanced life support (paramedical services). (*Paramedical services* means emergency treatment beyond ordinary first aid, performed by fire service personnel under supervision—through radio communication, for example—of a physician.)

Fire prevention: This includes approval of building plans and actual construction; inspection of buildings, their contents, and their fire protection equipment; and investigation of fire cause and spread to guide future fire prevention priorities and determine when the crime of arson has been committed.

Firesafety and dangerous-situation education: Fire departments have an obligation to bring firesafety and dangerous-situation education not only into schools and private homes but also into occupancies such as restaurants, hotels, hospitals, and nursing homes that have a greater-than-average fire potential or life safety hazard. These programs may include such topics as swimming pool safety and babysitter training.

Deteriorated building hazards: In coordination with other municipal departments, fire departments can work to abate serious hazards to health and safety caused by deteriorated structures or abandoned buildings.

Regional coordination: Major emergencies can exceed the capabilities of a single fire department, and neighboring fire jurisdictions should have detailed plans for coping with such emergencies. But effectiveness may also be improved through sharing of day-to-day operations—such as, for example, an areawide communication and dispatch network.

Data development: Knowledge of fire department performance and how practices should change to improve performance depends upon adequate record-keeping. Microcomputers and minicomputers now play an important role in fire protection and emergency management planning.

Community relations: Fire departments are representative of the local community that supports them. The impression they make on citizens affects how citizens view their government. Volunteer departments dependent upon private donations must, of course, also be concerned with community relations. Moreover, since fire stations are strategically located throughout the community, they can serve as referral or dispensing agencies for a wide range of municipal services.

As communities set out to improve their fire protection, they must not consider the fire department alone. The police have a role in reporting fires and in handling traffic and crowds during fires. The cooperation of the building department is needed to enforce the firesafety provisions of building codes. The work of the water department in maintaining the water system is vital to fire suppression. In firesafety education, the public schools, the department of recreation, and the public library can augment the work of the fire department. Future community development and planning will influence the location of new fire stations and how they will be equipped.

The nine functions above are just the obvious examples of interdependence. Although it may seem trivial, the manner in which house numbers are assigned and posted, for example, can affect the ability of a fire department to respond quickly and effectively to emergencies.

Master Planning

Fire protection is only one of many community services. Not only must it compete for dollars with other municipal needs such as the education system and the police department, but in planning for future growth the fire protection system must account for the changes in progress elsewhere in the community. For example, if a deteriorated area is to be torn down and replaced with high-rise apartment buildings, the fire protection needs of that area will change. Changes in zoning maps will also change the fire protection needs in different parts of the community.

To cope with future growth, local administrators are turning increasingly to the concept of master (comprehensive) planning of municipal functions. Such plans include an examination of existing programs, projection of future needs of the community, and a determination of methods to fill those needs. They seek the most cost-effective allocations of resources to help ensure that the needs will be met.

A major section of a community's general plan of land use should be a master plan for fire protection, which should be written chiefly by fire department managers. This plan should, first of all, be consistent with and reinforce the goals of a city's overall general plan and its time frame. For example, managers should plan the deployment of personnel and equipment according to the kind of growth and the specific areas of growth that the community foresees. It is critical that the comprehensive plan determine and set goals and objectives for the fire protection system and the fire department in terms that are understandable to the citizens being protected.

Having established goals, the department officers should use the plan to establish some form of "management by objectives" (MBO) within the fire department. Management is most effective when each person is aware of how tasks fit into the overall goals and is committed to getting specific jobs done in a specified time.

Because fire departments exist in a real world where a variety of purposes must be served with a limited amount of money, it is important that every dollar be invested for maximum return on investment. The fire protection master plan should not only seek to provide the maximum cost-benefit ratio for fire protection expenditures, but it should also establish a framework for measuring the effectiveness of these expenditures. Lastly, the plan should clarify the fire protection responsibility for other groups, both governmental and private, in the community.

Often, as the result of a comprehensive planning effort, a community will formulate a "developmental plan." This document provides a schedule for implementing those changes in the fire protection system deemed appropriate by the community.

Key questions for developmental plans include:

1. What are the fire protection, rescue, emergency medical, disaster response, and safety education needs?
2. What organizational structure and what resources are currently available to meet those needs?
3. Is there a disparity between what is available and what is needed?
4. What will the community profile be like in five to ten years?
5. What will be needed then to provide adequate protection?
6. What is and what will be the financial resource base?
7. What options are and will be available to enhance protection, or to keep it at an adequate level?
8. How can changes be phased in to gain community goals and cost-effectiveness?

Devising a Fire Protection Plan

Key questions to be asked by those planning for fire protection are:

1. Why is planning necessary for us at this time?
2. What do we need to start the process, and are the necessary groups committed to the process?

3. What are the necessary steps in the planning process?
4. How will the plan be implemented?
5. Are all aspects of the plan legally possible and enforceable?
6. How will the plan be evaluated? Will it be a part of the integrated emergency management plan of the community?
7. How will feedback be gathered and the plan modified and updated?

In its "Introductory Summary: Fire Prevention and Control Master Planning," the U.S. Fire Administration[5] points out the following in providing its overview of the planning process:

"Master planning is a participative process which should result in the establishment of a fire prevention and control system which is goal-oriented, long-term, comprehensive, provides known cost/loss performance, and adapts continually to the changing needs of your community."

"Master planning should consider all community elements...related to fire prevention and control system elements."

"Master planning involves the participation of all parties interested in the development of a defined cost/loss relationship..."

"Master planning allows you...to systematically analyze fire prevention and control through common-sense procedures...master planning has three phases: preplanning, planning, and implementation. The preplanning phase gets necessary commitments, committees, estimates and schedules, and go-ahead approvals. The planning phase gathers and analyzes data, sets goals and objectives, determines an acceptable level of fire protection service, identifies alternatives, and constructs the plan. The implementation phase never ends, because the plan is ongoing and always being revised and updated."

The following can serve as guidelines to fire department administrators for developing and presenting a master fire protection plan as part of the comprehensive master plan outlined earlier.

Phase I

1. Identify the fire protection problems of the jurisdiction.
2. Identify the best combination of public resources and built-in protection required to manage the fire problem, within acceptable limits:
   a. Specify current capabilities of and future needs for public resources;
   b. Specify current capabilities and future requirements for built-in protection.
3. Develop alternative methods that will result in tradeoffs between benefits and risks.
4. Establish a system of goals, programs, and cost estimates to implement the plan:
   a. Develop department goals and programs, including maximum possible participation of fire department personnel of all ranks;
   b. Provide goals and objectives for all divisions, supportive of the overall goals of the department;
   c. Strive to develop management development programs that increase acceptance of authority and responsibility by all fire officers as they strive to accomplish established objectives and programs.

Phase II

1. Develop a definition of the roles of other government agencies in the fire protection process.
2. Present the proposed municipal fire protection system to the city administration for review.
3. Present the proposed system for adoption as the fire protection element of the jurisdiction's general plan. The standard process for development of a general plan provides the fire department administrator an opportunity to inform the community leaders of the fire protection goals and system, and to obtain their support.

Phase III

In considering the fire protection element of the general plan, the governing body of the jurisdiction will have to pay special attention to:

1. Short- and long-range goals.
2. Long-range staffing and capital improvement plans.
3. Code revisions required to provide fire loss management.

Phase IV

The fire loss management system must be reviewed and updated as budget allocations, capital improvement plans, and code revisions occur. Continuing review of results should concentrate on these areas:

1. Did fires remain within estimated limits?
2. Should limits be changed?
3. Did losses prove to be acceptable?
4. Could resources be decreased, or should they be increased?

BIBLIOGRAPHY

References Cited

1. National Commission on Fire Prevention and Control, *America Burning: The Report of the National Commission on Fire Prevention and Control*, U.S. Government Printing Office, Washington, DC, 1974.
2. Insurance Services Office, *Grading Schedule for Municipal Fire Protection*, Insurance Service Office, New York, NY, 1974.
3. NCFPC, *America Burning*, 1974.
4. United States Fire Academy, *America Burning Revisited*, U.S. Fire Administration, Washington, DC, 1987.
5. National Fire Safety and Research Office, "Introductory Summary: Fire Prevention and Control Master Planning," U.S. Department of Commerce, National Fire Safety and Research Office, Washington, DC, no date.

NFPA Codes, Standards, and Recommended Practices

Reference to the following NFPA codes, standards, and recommended practices will provide further information on public fire protection issues discussed in this chapter. (See the latest *NFPA Catalog* for availability of current editions of the following documents.)

NFPA 13E, *Fire Department Operations in Properties Protected by Sprinkler and Standpipe Systems.*

NFPA 295, *Wildfire Control.*

NFPA 297, *Telecommunications Systems—Principles and Practices for Rural and Forestry Services.*

NFPA 402M, *Aircraft Rescue and Fire Fighting Operational Procedures.*

NFPA 403, *Aircraft Rescue and Fire Fighting Services at Airports.*

NFPA 414, *Aircraft Rescue and Fire Fighting Vehicles.*

NFPA 471, *Responding to Hazardous Materials Incidents.*

NFPA 472, *Professional Competence of Responding to Hazardous Materials Incidents.*

NFPA 502, *Limited-Access Highways, Tunnels, Bridges, Elevated Roadways, and Air-Tight Structures.*

NFPA 901, *Uniform Coding for Fire Protection.*

NFPA 902M, *Fire Reporting Field Incident Manual.*

NFPA 903M, *Fire Reporting Property Survey Manual.*

NFPA 904M, *Incident Follow-up Report Manual.*

NFPA 1001, *Fire Fighter Professional Qualifications.*

NFPA 1002, *Fire Apparatus Driver/Operator Professional Qualifications.*

NFPA 1003, *Airport Fire Fighter Professional Qualifications.*

NFPA 1004, *Fire Fighter Medical Technicians Professional Qualifications.*

NFPA 1021, *Fire Officer Professional Qualifications.*

NFPA 1031, *Professional Qualifications for Fire Inspector.*

NFPA 1033, *Professional Qualifications for Fire Investigator.*

NFPA 1035, *Professional Qualifications for Public Fire Educator.*

NFPA 1041, *Professional Qualifications for Fire Service Instructor.*

NFPA 1201, *Developing Fire Protection Services for the Public.*

NFPA 1202, *Organization of a Fire Department.*

NFPA 1221, *Public Fire Service Communication Systems.*

NFPA 1401, *Training Reports and Records.*

NFPA 1402, *Building Fire Service Training Facilities.*

NFPA 1403, *Live Fire Training Evolutions in Structures.*

NFPA 1410, *Initial Fire Attack.*

NFPA 1452, *Dwelling Firesafety Surveys.*

NFPA 1500, *Fire Department Occupational Safety and Health Program.*

NFPA 1501, *Fire Department Safety Officer.*

NFPA 1901, *Pumper Fire Apparatus.*

NFPA 1911, *Service Tests of Pumps on Fire Department Apparatus.*

NFPA 1914, *Testing Fire Department Aerial Devices.*

NFPA 1932, *Fire Department Ground Ladders.*

NFPA 1961, *Fire Hose.*

NFPA 1962, *Care, Use, and Maintenance of Fire Hose, Including Connections and Nozzles.*

NFPA 1964, *Spray Nozzles (Shutoff and Tip).*

NFPA 1971, *Protective Clothing for Structural Fire Fighting.*

NFPA 1972, *Helmets for Structural Fire Fighting.*

NFPA 1973, *Gloves for Structural Fire Fighting.*

NFPA 1974, *Protective Footwear for Structural Fire Fighting.*

NFPA 1975, *Station/Work Uniforms for Fire Fighters.*

NFPA 1981, *Open-Circuit Self-Contained Breathing Apparatus for Fire Fighters.*

NFPA 1982, *Personal Alert Safety Systems (PASS) for Fire Fighters.*

NFPA 1983, *Fire Service Life Safety Rope, Harnesses, and Hardware.*

MFPA 1991, *Vapor-Protective Suits for Hazardous Chemical Emergencies.*

NFPA 1992, *Liquid Splash Protective Suits for Hazardous Chemical Emergencies.*

Additional Readings

A Tale of Two Cities, Institute for Local Self-Government, Berkeley, CA, 1977.

Backoff, Robert W., "Measuring Firefighter Effectiveness: A Preliminary Report," School of Public Administration, Ohio State University, Columbus, OH.

Boswell, C. R., *Standards for Rural Fire Protection,* Department of Extension Forestry, Kansas State University, Manhattan, KA, 1978.

Burns, R. B., "Planning for Community Fire Protection," *Managing Fire Services,* ICMA, Washington, DC, 1986.

Carter, H. R. and Rausch, E., *Management in the Fire Service,* National Fire Protection Association, Quincy, MA, 1989.

Chrissis, James W., "Locating Emergency Service Facilities in a Developing Area," *Fire Technology,* Vol. 16, No. 1, Feb. 1980, pp. 63-69.

"First Responder: An Issue to Be Addressed in Master Planning," Federal Emergency Management Agency, U.S. Fire Administration, Emmitsberg, MD, Oct. 1980.

Federal Emergency Management Agency, *Hazard Identification, Capability Assessments, and Multi-Year Development Plan,* CPG1-34 (Overview); CPG1-35 (Workbook); CPG1-35a (Response Book); Washington, DC, Jan. 1985.

Federal Emergency Management Agency, *The Integrated Emergency Management System: Process Overview,* 1984-445 4/18624, U.S. Government Printing Office, Washington, DC, 1984.

Federal Emergency Management Agency, *Master Planning for Fire Protection,* U.S. Fire Administration, Washington, DC, Mar. 1980.

Federal Emergency Management Agency, *Planning Guide and Checklist for Hazardous Materials Contingency Plans,* FEMH-10, Washington, DC, July 1981.

ISO, *Fire Suppression Rating Schedule,* Insurance Services Organization, New York, NY, 1980.

Granito, J. A., "The Chief's Job, circa 2006," *Fire Command,* Aug. 1981.

Granito, J. A., "Holding the Horses," *Fire Service Today,* Sept. 1983.

Granito, J. A., "Trends in Fire Service Management," *Fire Service Today,* Aug. 1983.

Granito, J. A., *ed., Baseline Data Report* $^{15}/_{2}$, *Fire Personnel Practices,* International City Management Association, Washington, DC, Feb. 1983. Updated periodically by various authors.

Granito, J. A., *ed., Hazardous Materials Incidents: Improving Community Response,* MIS Report 16/I, International City Management Association, Washington, DC, 1984.

Granito, J. A., *ed., Literature Review of Fire Suppression Crew Size and Related Topics,* Project Reference Copy, National Fire Protection Association, Office of Fire Service Relations, Quincy, MA, Feb. 1991.

Granito, J. A. and Dionne, J. M., "Evaluating Community Fire Protection," in *Managing Fire Services,* International City Management Association, Washington, DC, 1986.

Hatry, H. P., *et al., How Effective Are Your Community Services?* The Urban Institute, Washington, DC, 1977.

Henry, M. F., *ed., Hazardous Materials Response Handbook,* National Fire Protection Association, Quincy, MA, 1989.

Hickey, Harry E., "A Comparative Analysis of Resource Allocation Plans for Urban Fire Safety," FPP-B 77-1, Johns Hopkins University, Laurel, MD, Aug. 1977.

Hickey, Harry E., *Public Fire Safety Organization,* National Fire Protection Association, Quincy, MA, 1973.

Hoetmer, G., *ed., Baseline Data Report* $^{16}/_{4}$, *Emergency Management,* International City Management Association, Washington, DC, Apr. 1983.

Huse, Edgar F., *The Modern Manager,* West Publishing Company, St. Paul, MN, 1979.

International City Management Association, *Assessment of the Transferability of the Community Fire Master Planning Program,* ICMA, Washington, DC, 1977.

International City Management Association, *Managing Fire Services,* ICMA, Washington, DC, 1986.

International City Management Association, *Municipal Yearbook,* ICMA, Washington, DC, 1988.

Jacobs, D. T., *Physical Fitness for Public Safety Personnel,* National Fire Protection Association, Quincy, MA, 1990.

"National Association of Counties, Multi-Jurisdictional Fire Protection Planning," prepared for the Federal Emergency Management Agency, U.S. Fire Administration, Washington, DC.

National Fire Prevention and Control Administration (now U. S. Fire Administration), *A Basic Guide for Fire Prevention and Central Master Planning,* U.S. Dept. of Commerce, Washington, DC, 1978.

Niemczewski, C., "Fire Suppression Crew Size," *International Fire Chief,* Jan. 1983.

O'Hagan, J. T., "Staffing Levels," *Fire Command,* Nov. 1984, Dec. 1984, Jan. 1985, Feb. 1985, Mar. 1985, May 1985.

Research Triangle Institute, *et al.*, "Evaluating the Organization of Service Delivery," Research Triangle Institute, Center for Population and Urban-Rural Studies, Durham, NC, no date.

Research Triangle Institute, *et al.*, *Municipal Fire Service Workbook,* Government Printing Office, Washington, DC, no date.

Richman, H. C., *Engine Company Fireground Operations,* National Fire Protection Association, Quincy, MA, 1988.

Richman, H. C., *Truck Company Fireground Operations,* National Fire Protection Association, Quincy, MA, 1988.

Schaenman, Philip S., and Seits, Edward F., *International Concepts in Fire Protection—Practices from Japan, Hong Kong, Australia, and New Zealand,* TriData, Arlington, VA, 1985.

Urban Consortium on Fire Safety and Disaster Preparedness Task Force, *Criteria for Master Planning and Resources Allocation,* Public Technology, Inc., Washington, DC, 1978.

Webber, Ross A., *Management: Basic Elements of Managing Organizations,* Richard D. Irwin, Inc., Homewood, IL, 1979.

Worsham, J. P., *Rural Fire Protection: A Selected Bibliography,* Vance Bibliographies, Monticello, IL, 1978.

ANALYSIS OF FIRE DEPARTMENT DATA AND DECISION-MAKING

Revised by Clifford S. Harvey

Smaller fire departments face many of the same decisions and need much of the same data as large fire departments. With the availability of low-cost computer power, many of the applications discussed in this chapter are achievable in the smaller department by using microcomputers. On the other hand, some of the applications may be adequately handled by a good manual recordkeeping system, with periodic analysis of the data to support the information needs of the department.*

Today, effective management is more critical than ever to the fire service. Economic conditions have reduced local government tax revenues, leading to diminished resources; yet the fire service, like all government units, is being asked to maintain acceptable service levels.

The contradiction of "doing more with less" can be resolved only with improved management practices that result in higher productivity. There are many paths to this goal; one such path is information technology.

While one might argue that the computer is not a panacea, information technology has become a pervasive management tool in many fire departments. Specifically, the computer is being used to help:

1. Strategically position capital resources, such as fire stations.
2. Dispatch and manage fire fighting resources.
3. Manage personnel resources.
4. Control fire department performance.
5. Plan and control budgets.
6. Manage fleet maintenance.
7. Combat arson.
8. Improve organizational communications.
9. Manage energy consumption.
10. Manage fire prevention, inspections, and permits.
11. Manage emergency medical operations.
12. Manage financial resources.

Few fire departments have automated all of these applications. However, almost all fire departments use a computer in one or more of these areas.

For related information, see Section 10, Chapter 2, "Collecting Fire Data"; Section 10, Chapter 3, "Use of Fire Loss Information"; and Section 10, Chapter 16, "Microcomputer Applications in Fire Protection."

MANAGEMENT ISSUES

The successful function of a fire department's information system depends upon how that function is organized and managed. There is, of course, no "single best way" to manage the information resource, since every situation is unique.

There is growing recognition that the information resources of an organization are crucial to that organization's overall effectiveness. Consequently, the information resource is a valuable asset that must be well managed. While there is little controversy over the truth of this statement, there is some confusion over what constitutes the information resource. Mostly, the argument is a matter of emphasis of various professional specialists, whether it's the data administrator, the communications expert, or the records manager.

The broad definition of the information resource would include everything connected with information: data bases, reports, libraries, word processing, computers, etc. The more restrictive view used in this chapter defines the information resource as computers, software, data, and personnel.

A balanced information resource fulfills three needs: (1) strategic planning, (2) management control, and (3) support of daily operations. Each of these is being met by computerized information systems in some fire departments, but it is rare that a department addresses all three needs.

Strategic planning is the process by which management allocates long-range resources, such as fire stations, fire fighting equipment, and fire fighters. Some fire depart-

Clifford S. Harvey is an Assistant Chief with the Boulder, CO, Fire Department, and President of Fire Mark Limited, a fire protection and prevention consulting firm.

*This chapter was condensed from *Fire Department Information Technology in Nine Western Communities,*[1] *prepared for the Federal Emergency Management Agency (FEMA) by the Consortium of Western Fire Agencies on Integrated Information Systems.*

ments have developed sophisticated models for this purpose, while others have contracted for the models and services of outside resource groups. Most fire departments, however, depend upon the statistical information from fire incident and emergency medical reporting systems.

Management control is necessary in several areas: (1) finance, (2) personnel, (3) fire prevention, (4) arson investigation, (5) fire suppression, and (6) energy management. Control information is often provided as a by-product of systems designed to support day-to-day operations. For example, personnel control information may be secondary to the real reason the personnel system was developed—to increase the efficiency of the personnel and the recordkeeping system.

Most fire service information systems are designed to support day-to-day operations. The most common examples of this type of system are computer-aided dispatch (CAD) and "enhanced" 911 (E911). Other systems support financial management, arson investigations, equipment inventory and maintenance, inspections, permits, organizational communications, and personnel management.

While systems may be classified as suggested above, they are rarely developed explicitly in that fashion. Rather, the packaging of information is a function of priorities, systems planning, organizational needs, and other situational factors. There are, however, certain recurring patterns to the way information is packaged into application systems.

COMPUTER-AIDED DISPATCH

Quite literally, the dispatching operation is the nerve center of the fire department. It is here that resource status is maintained, alarms are received, fire stations are alerted, and situations are managed. Because of its importance and high visibility, the dispatching function is usually one of the first fire department operations to be computerized.

Fundamentally, computer-aided dispatch (CAD) is oriented toward operations. Its purpose is to support current activity rather than provide managerial control or strategic planning information. However, the functions of CAD systems often go beyond operational support. In an integrated information systems environment, the CAD system may produce nonoperational information (e.g., incident reporting data) and may use nonreal time inputs (e.g., occupancy data).

CAD systems support several functions of the typical dispatching operation:

1. *Alarm receipt:* Telecommunications management, box decoding, central station communications, etc.
2. *Communications and signaling management:* Alerting (unit/station, two-way exchange of data, audit switching, frequency selection, etc.).
3. *Status maintenance:* Resources, equipment, personnel, system supervisor, etc.
4. *Response assignment:* Dynamic assignment based on current availability and relative location of fire fighting resources to the incident.

Although CAD is usually credited with reducing response time, the payoff is not necessarily in this area. Some departments even report an increase in response time after implementing a CAD system. The real benefits of CAD occur in the management of fire suppression activity. Thus, rapid recall of information, such as apparatus status and occupancy data, is at least as important as response time.

The need for a CAD system must, of course, be balanced against the cost of entry, which can be considerable. San Francisco, CA, for example, paid more than $2 million, while the Phoenix, AZ, CAD cost approximately $5 million.

Choosing a correct approach to implementing a CAD system is a multifaceted problem. The first facet of the problem is related to policy. In some cases, dispatching is a shared police-fire responsibility. In others, dispatch serves multiple jurisdictions. The organizational situation can have an important influence on other aspects of the approach as well as the ultimate usefulness of the system.

A major starting point in CAD development is a decision on the scope of the system. Is the system to be developed only for CAD or will it include other applications? Most departments elect to develop a stand-alone CAD system with the necessary interfaces to other applications (most commonly the sole interface is with the fire incident reporting system).

Closely related to the issue of scope is the degree of modularity built into the system. A highly modular system permits the system to be expanded to include enhanced CAD functions as well as other applications. It also allows new software to be tested in a nonreal time mode and operators to be trained without interfering with operations. Modularity is important in all applications, but it is especially critical in CAD systems because the systems are subject to almost constant change.

Another facet of the approach is the decision on outside *versus* in-house development. Most fire departments choose to have an outside contractor develop, test, and implement the system, but the city of Dallas, TX, successfully developed its system in-house.

Communications is the final aspect of approach. Standard telephone service is typically used for communications between the dispatch center and the fire stations. Increasingly, other ways are being found to transmit data. The 800 mHz radio frequencies have been used successfully, as have microwave links. Digital pagers, with both paper printouts and liquid crystal display (LCD) readouts, are also becoming increasingly popular for dispatching engines and providing updated information to engine company commanders.

ENHANCED 911 SYSTEMS

Enhanced 911, or E911, is an emergency phone system that provides the caller's address, response district, and other important information. When the caller dials 911 to report an emergency, this information automatically appears on the dispatcher's computer screen, along with dispatch information for fire, police, EMS, or other emergency responder. This system is invaluable, especially in those cases where the caller is in an agitated state and may be unable to give information fully or clearly. Such a system, thereby, can have a dramatic effect on reducing response times.

Although some communities have expressed concern for the caller's privacy (regardless of whether or not the call is a true emergency), this system is being widely acclaimed and installed throughout the U.S. Even more sophisticated systems can provide information concerning previous calls to the same address, hazardous materials stored on-site, day care or other life-safety-intensive operations at the address, and other information that is valuable to the responding departments.

PERSONNEL APPLICATIONS

Personnel systems are among the most complex of all fire department applications. Consisting of a number of subapplications, these systems are important in large departments to support the myriad functions of personnel administration, such as basic personnel records management, time and attendance reporting, payroll (sometimes part of financial management), duty schedules, physical fitness and medical records, employee evaluation, training records, position control, badge history and control, and disability/injury analysis.

In the absence of computer support for at least some of the personnel administration functions, large fire departments would find it difficult, if not impossible, to maintain all the necessary paperwork without a large clerical staff. Nevertheless, the complexity of personnel systems has discouraged widespread implementation, although most fire agencies have installed some of the subapplications. Also, personnel systems often are citywide in scope, thus precluding (or at least discouraging) the development of specific fire applications.

The need for personnel information systems exists primarily at the operational level. Although output from these systems is used for both strategic planning and managerial control, the greatest near-term benefit is in making personnel administration more efficient.

The operational benefits are obvious. In a 1,000-person fire department, a large volume of information is needed to carry out standard personnel functions. Fire fighters must be scheduled and personnel balanced daily. Detailed training records are required for each department member. Time and attendance records are necessary for payroll and recordkeeping. Employees must be evaluated and considered for promotion. These functions require an efficient way of storing and retrieving information.

The information that is useful for day-to-day operations also has residual value for strategic planning and managerial control. For example, the roster data may be aggregated in such a way that is useful for position control or personnel resource planning. Time and attendance data may be reviewed by management in an effort to control excessive sick leave or overtime. Much of the information needed for strategic planning and managerial control cannot be defined prior to when it is needed. Therefore, it is useful to have the facility for answering *ad hoc* inquiries using the operational data base.

At the highest level of design, the approach taken will depend upon the relationship of fire department personnel functions to city (or county) personnel functions. For example, the payroll may be prepared by the city from prescribed time and attendance records. In cases like this, it may be difficult for the fire department to develop some of the components of a personnel system.

A second aspect of the design approach is the degree to which the components of the personnel system are integrated. In most cases, the personnel system has been built up over several years, with one component implemented at a time. There has been no overall design that provides for integration of files and input. This piece-meal approach is gradually being replaced by comprehensively planned systems, and although the components may still be implemented separately, the plan provides for eventual integration.

The final aspect of the design approach relates to the extent to which the data base is on-line. Batch systems have been heavily favored but these are losing favor to on-line updating of data bases as well as on-line retrieval. The on-line approach, although more expensive, permits direct involvement of the users and thus increases the benefits of the systems. Data bases are discussed in greater detail later in this chapter.

FLEET MANAGEMENT

After the personnel costs, capital and operational expenditures for vehicles and equipment represent the greatest use of fire department funds. Fleet management systems provide the information needed for budgeting and controlling those expenditures as well as for ensuring that the fleet is maintained in a high state of readiness. The need for information about the fire department fleet exists at all levels: strategic, managerial, and operational.

To accomplish these purposes, fleet management systems may involve several components: fleet inventory, maintenance records, vehicle replacement, fuel consumption, internal billing for vehicle use (e.g., in the case of citywide carpools), tax reporting, and performance analysis. Some or all of these components may be present in any given system.

At the strategic level, information about the existing fleet is needed to plan and budget for vehicle acquisition. To make sound replacement decisions, it is important to have accurate information on maintenance frequency, operating costs, age, etc., for each major piece of equipment. Indeed, those decisions are often so complicated and have such political overtones that decision support software (operations research models) is needed to help analyze the data.

At the managerial control level, fleet managers need computer support to control preventive maintenance intervals, work in progress, gasoline mileage, and staffing of the maintenance facility. Other managers in the department also need control information. For example, administrative services managers need financial data for budgetary control, and line managers need to control the availability of fire fighting apparatus.

Personnel at the operational level also need output from a fleet management system. Most important, of course, is the ability to have instant access to vehicle availability information. While this requirement is not always provided by the fleet management system *per se*, dispatchers need to know what equipment is ready to respond to a given type of emergency. Maintenance personnel also need ready access to certain information (e.g., vehicle performance, previous repair records, interchangeable parts data, and standard repair times for all vehicles).

Few fire departments develop their own fleet management systems. The preferred approaches involve using a commercially available system (either a software package or a time-sharing service) and a citywide fleet management system. Both approaches are viable alternatives to custom-designed software, but both have some problems.

The time-sharing service is a stand-alone service dedicated to fleet management. It is difficult, if not impossible, to interface such systems directly with other department or city systems. Also, added functions, such as vehicle replacement models, cannot be easily integrated with this type of service. Yet, this approach can be implemented easily and is probably cost-effective, especially for fire departments that do not have highly integrated systems.

The citywide approach also suffers from some of the same deficiencies. Since citywide systems are typically designed for standard street vehicles, they may ignore certain features that would be useful to fire departments. For example, the city system may not have a provision for capturing and maintaining elapsed time meters on pumps, or may not provide for helicopter maintenance records. If these deficiencies are to be eliminated, the fire department must take an active part in defining information requirements. When this is done, the citywide approach can be quite worthwhile.

FIRE INCIDENT REPORTING SYSTEMS

Incident reporting systems are used to maintain statistics on fire, medical emergencies, and other emergencies to which a fire department responds. This application is the most common use of information technology.

The methods of capturing data are worthy of mention. The most common is batch data entry, where a form or forms are completed after each incident and the data is keyed in batches at a terminal or other data entry device by someone other than the person completing the form. Departments with a CAD system usually collect at least some of the fire incident reporting system data as a by-product of a CAD operation. This data can then be merged with incident report data.

Departments are now moving in the direction of standalone workstations in the fire station. The process sometimes consists of entering a complete fire report from previously completed forms or field notes. In other cases, the data already captured by a CAD system is displayed on the terminal and this data is supplemented by data from the officer in charge of the fire company or the incident. Allowing the officer in charge to enter the data directly has the advantage of ensuring completeness and correctness because the data can be edited as it is entered and mistakes corrected immediately.

FIRE PREVENTION APPLICATIONS

Fire prevention management information systems are inventory and tracking systems for storing fire-protection-related information on a city's buildings and information on the fire department's contacts with those buildings. The application is useful in planning and managing fire prevention activities, controlling hazardous contents, and prefire planning for fire suppression. The heart of a fire prevention system is a flexible, address-based file of city properties.

Fire prevention records in most cities are in very primitive condition. Long, often handwritten narratives are the rule rather than the exception. This makes it virtually impossible to develop any information on patterns in hazards or violations across the city or for particular property classes. Even within a file on a single property, it can be difficult to ascertain whether the fire department has been providing the kind of frequency of contacts called for by the department's policies. This difficulty exists because such files are often only dumping grounds for any and all papers bearing the property's address. Minor, unofficial correspondence and newsclips may share space with basic inspection reports and detailed, lengthy construction plans. Files on properties not covered by the fire prevention code (such as single-family dwellings), on fire education contacts, and on contacts by other agencies (such as the building and housing departments) are generally nonexistent or wholly separate and incompatible with the fire inspection files. Fire incident records are rarely tied to files on the violation and hazard histories that may have caused the fires. In fact, it would be difficult to identify any aspect of a fire department's recordkeeping that is more in need of refinement and automation than fire prevention.

The first requirement for an adequate fire prevention system is a comprehensive address-based inventory of city properties. This is a very difficult file to create. A 1979 study[2] of fire inspection practices in eleven cities, including two with computerized inspection records, found that every city reported fires in properties that should have been subject to fire inspections but were not shown in the inspection records. These were not new businesses or businesses operating illegally out of homes—they were legitimate businesses of some years' standing that simply had been overlooked.

It may be impossible to guarantee file completeness, but this can be improved. Address files should be linked to the fire incident records, preferably through a link to the city's CAD system, so that emergency runs to corresponding unlisted addresses will lead to the creation of an inspection file.

Sources for both the initial building inventory and periodic updates are the city's tax records, the housing department, the building department, any inspection agency, and city-owned utilities, such as the water, sewer, and light departments. On the other hand, some lists (e.g., the telephone company "Yellow Pages," cross indexes, and mail carrier routes) tend to be unwieldy or poor sources for finding missing addresses.

The fire inspection procedure itself can be a source of effective property list updates. Inspections conducted on a "block by block, always go around the block" basis allow inspectors to see properties they might miss if they were to organize their routes with strict attention to those properties identified only by the computer.

Once the file is created, it can be used as a basis for organizing and scheduling inspections. The system can be set to print inspection reports for properties scheduled for inspection in any given week (thereby helping inspectors plan their work), and for reinspections to check hazard abatement. Inspector workloads can be balanced either by the number of inspections or by the total time spent on inspections if statistics are kept on the typical duration of inspections by type and size of property.

Accuracy is important when computerizing data on buildings in a community. Although the occupants of a building change from time to time, the building itself usually doesn't change much. Some jurisdictions use the Basic Structure Report, Form 903SR, to gather basic information about structures. This form is an excellent way to generate number-based information about buildings that need to be inspected periodically. Furthermore, the information gathered is extremely valuable when training for fire attack on the structure.

For all buildings, especially those that contain more than one occupancy, the Basic Occupancy Report, Form

903TR, provides a way to gather information (e.g., who is using the building) for both inspection and training functions.

Both of these reports are included in NFPA 903, *Fire Reporting Property Survey Guide*, along with an explanation of each entry and how it should be coded. The best asset of such an information-gathering system is that it is number-based: similar property uses are coded in a similar manner; similar fuels are coded in a similar manner. It is also a simple, efficient process and can readily prioritize a fire department's inspection functions based on the severity of the potential fire problem, especially when that department may not have sufficient resources to inspect every building as often as might be desired.

Fire prevention systems can also be used in the control of hazardous materials. In addition to supporting license and permit controls on hazardous materials and processes, a fire prevention file can be expanded to include information on the type, quantity, and location of hazardous materials and the type, frequency, and location of hazardous activities. The prime difficulty in making such a system work is that the situation is so changeable. Types, quantities, and locations of materials may fluctuate widely, according to the demands of the business. Annual or even semiannual updating of a central file may be insufficient to give a picture of the city's true hazard profile.

Ownership information on properties can be among the most difficult to obtain. Current ownership probably is not needed until legal proceedings have to be instituted. It is easier, and more reliable, to check legal ownership in those relatively few cases as they occur than to try to develop and maintain a file on legal ownership for all properties.

EMERGENCY MEDICAL SERVICE

Emergency medical service (EMS) is now provided by many fire departments. EMS activities include rescue operations, first aid, and transportation to a medical facility. Ambulances are sometimes based at fire stations and dispatched by the fire department. Fire equipment and fire fighters may be dispatched for EMS activity if necessary.

In many jurisdictions, the cost of emergency medical service is billed to the patient. Since this represents a substantial revenue source for the city or county, the billing process is the focus of most EMS systems. Two other areas are often also supported: (1) EMS statistics, and (2) computerized radio frequency control.

EMS systems requirements are based on the volume of EMS activity. With several thousand incidents per month, computerized processing of bills is necessary to prevent long billing delays and resulting cash flow problems for a city or town.

The statistics generated from EMS systems are used in both long-range plans and operational planning and control. Response times, locations of incidents, and units responding are required to plan and budget for resources and determine if the resources are being deployed properly.

Billing and statistics subsystems are typically batch-oriented. The ambulance attendants complete a form that is keyed and processed to create the basic incident record. Payment of the bill or other additional data may cause the basic record to be updated either in batches or on-line mode.

In some fire departments, EMS statistics are generated directly from the billing system and the EMS incident record is part of that system. In other departments, data from the billing system is transferred to the fire incident reporting system from which statistics are generated. Having all incident data on the same data base is helpful in studying fire department emergency activity.

Many jurisdictions have chosen to computerize the basic EMS report (Form 902H) to keep track of their EMS activities. This "generic" report is often amended by jurisdictions to reflect their specific EMS functions. An example of this report can be found in NFPA 902M, *Fire Reporting Field Incident Manual*.

Many large jurisdictions are having increasing difficulties in managing the allocation of radio frequencies and eliminating radio interference. Computer control of channel assignments helps ensure that a paramedic can communicate with hospital personnel in life-threatening situations.

The Coordinated Paramedic Communications System (CPCS) in Los Angeles County, CA, was designed to provide improved radio communications between paramedics in the field and paramedic base hospitals. The system serves both public and private providers of paramedic services.

The CPCS system design is based on dynamic channel assignments; that is, biomedical communications channels (MED 1-8) are assigned as needed. With the aid of a computer, a radio telephone operator at the communications coordination center assigns channels to paramedic squads and notifies corresponding paramedic base hospitals of ensuing "radio runs."

The CPCS system has:

1. Significantly reduced radio frequency (RF) interference, which often causes communications problems. Disruptions of communications had hampered the operations of paramedics and hospital personnel during the treatment of patients in the field, sometimes in life-threatening situations.
2. Increased RF coverage and extended it into areas not previously covered.
3. Decreased the average elapsed time between a paramedic squad's decision to talk to a hospital by radio and the corresponding initial response by hospital personnel.
4. Increased the radio communications capability of base hospitals.

CASUALTY REPORTING

Fire fighters experience more casualties from doing their jobs than workers in most other occupations, and tracking those casualties is an important and necessary function for any fire department. Perhaps a certain type of casualty is being caused by a certain type or piece of equipment, or the way it is being used is dangerous. A properly filled-out casualty report, computerized and shared with other departments or the manufacturer of the equipment, could point this out, and cause the equipment to be discontinued or changed in some manner. Such a report is available: the Basic Casualty Report, Form 902G, in NFPA 902M, *Fire Reporting Field Incident Manual*. This report is a number-based data gathering tool, and extremely valuable for tracking casualties in any department.

MATHEMATICAL MODELS

Most management information systems are quite simple conceptually and do not involve any mathematical modeling, not even simple arithmetic operations such as addition and subtraction. Systems in personnel, fire prevention, etc., are fundamentally automated list-making and list-matching programs. As such, they are primarily useful in helping fire service managers track large volumes of information, but not in assessing trade-offs or aiding in resource allocation decisions.

In this context, a mathematical model-based management information system refers to systems that use mathematical formulas in providing management information suitable for comparison of alternative courses of action. The most widely used systems are those that address issues of fire station location and fire company deployment at those stations. The models used in these systems generate statistics that indicate the level of service that would be provided to each part of the city if a certain number of fire stations and companies were in force and deployed at certain locations. Other mathematical models address other deployment-related issues, such as variance of responses by time of day or when and where to move up fire companies for temporary coverage of areas whose assigned companies are already fighting other fires (relocations/move-ups).

Deployment of fire stations, companies, and personnel has traditionally been a matter of intuition and judgment, with few rules to follow except a generalized objective of placing stations on or near main thoroughfares and in areas that are far from existing stations. As fire department budgets have become more constrained, however, fire chiefs have needed more precise tools to address deployment. Fire station configurations that look similar on a map may produce substantially different patterns of fire suppression service. Adding or taking away an additional company or station, or providing units to respond, may make a slight difference in one city and a tremendous difference in another. A fire chief who can produce detailed statistical descriptions of the implications of different decisions is much more likely to be able to obtain the decision that is desired.

The need for modeling help on deployment decisions is particularly great for departments serving rapidly growing or rapidly shrinking cities, including cities that are rapidly growing in some areas and rapidly shrinking in others. In a city where the geographical distribution of fire demand is changing dramatically, it is likely that major changes may be needed in numbers and locations of fire stations and companies or staffing by companies.

Such changes involve millions of dollars in construction costs and more millions each year to staff and equip new companies. Even if a city is shrinking, millions of dollars in potential cost reductions are involved in the decision on how much to shrink, and there are potentially costly implications in the decisions on where to cut back. With millions at stake, the thousands of dollars required to set up and conduct a systematic deployment analysis can be seen as a sound investment, especially when one considers the millions of dollars in fire loss that may be implied in the changing response patterns produced by a deployment change. Once the analytic system is set up, it can be used repeatedly at relatively little additional cost whenever new deployment decisions or questions arise.

There are dozens of published models for use in fire service deployment analysis, but the two widely used approaches are those developed by Public Technology, Inc. (PTI) and the Rand Corporation.* Both approaches generate statistics on travel time from proposed fire station locations to the parts of the city assigned to the stations. The statistics include: (1) average travel time by region of the city, reflecting differences in fire frequency from one block to the next; (2) maximum travel times, as one indication of whether or not all parts of the city will receive adequate services; and (3) percentage of the city reachable in less than some benchmark travel time (for example, two minutes), where the benchmark may be lower for high-priority, high-hazard properties.

At present, the PTI Fire Service Location Package (FSLP) can be run on microcomputers. PTI also offers a resource allocation model: Fire Master. FSLP is being enhanced to integrate with geographic information systems (GIS).

Rand models are now available for microcomputers from FPE Software.

The differences between the two approaches are less in the kind of information they produce than in the ways that information is produced. The Rand Corporation approach, for example, takes advantage of the fact that most cities have streets laid out in a grid network and so uses a mathematical formula, with parameters developed for the particular city, to estimate travel times based on the grid locations of fire stations and fire-involved property. A city that already has geocoding will find this approach especially easy to implement if the geocoding includes the establishment of X-Y coordinates. PTI, on the other hand, calculates travel times over a large number of individual route segments through actual apparatus runs, then calculates station-to-station travel time on a sequence of route segments that form a full route from the station to the fire. This approach requires more time and data collection expense, but can improve accuracy in cases where a city is split by a river, railroad tracks, or other major obstruction that can be crossed in only a few places.

Another difference lies in the organization and documentation of the two systems. PTI is organized to provide technical assistance, and the company has procedures and personnel able to handle all aspects of the analysis process from setting up the study team to presenting and selling the results to all concerned parties. Accordingly, PTI's documentation has a step-by-step, simplified format, designed to be used by an end user assisted by a PTI field person. Rand, on the other hand, is primarily a research organization that supplies reports, programs, and specifications "off the shelf." Rand's documentation provides far more detail on case studies and on the reasoning behind their models, including information on why the models work as they do and how the organizational process of doing a study has operated in a few locations. But as an organization, Rand is not designed to help install systems and shepherd studies in all the cities that want to pursue deployment analysis.

Other differences between the two approaches are really differences in emphasis. Both approaches, for example, permit special attention to target hazards, with travel

* For more information, contact Public Technology, Inc., Decision Support System Group, 1140 Connecticut Ave., NW, Washington, DC 20036; and Rand Corporation, 1700 Main Street, Santa Monica, CA 90406.

time profiles and requirements for only those properties. PTI puts much more emphasis on this aspect of the study, however.

The Seattle, WA, Fire Department has developed an approach to deployment analysis that includes the additional variables of staffing per unit and total response staffing. Seattle undertook a comprehensive analysis of the relationship between fire loss/spread and response time. Based on the parameters of response time experienced, minimal correlation was found. These results agreed very closely with a study done in Great Britain. More recently, the Portland, OR, Fire Bureau conducted a similar analysis, and, again, virtually no correlation was observed. It should be noted that in the case of both Portland and Seattle, mean response times fell between three and four minutes, with a maximum of ten minutes and relatively few times exceeding seven minutes. It may be that studies conducted of areas with significantly larger mean and maximum response times will reveal some correlation between response time and loss/spread. However, the majority of municipalities in the U.S. report mean response time of less than six minutes. Within these parameters, virtually no correlation has yet been observed.

These analyses encouraged Seattle to look more closely at the other major variables of deployment, staffing per unit, and total response staffing. Many departments have constant staffing per unit, but overall response staffing is normally a matter of policy and, therefore, a definable variable. As budgetary pressure increases, per unit staffing necessarily will be considered. The general objective of cost effectiveness necessitates the analysis of staffing deployment at all levels of the fire department.

Seattle developed a deployment model that considers the three variables of response time, staffing per unit, and total response staffing. Seattle's model is intended to provide a comparative index of the level of service (LOS) provided to every intersection in the city. The output of the model can be used to determine optimum station locations as well as staffing deployment. However, the primary purpose of the model is to provide comparative indices of level of service provided at all intersections for any alternative deployment.

A LOS model for emergency medical service has also been developed. Analyses of EMS incidents indicated that, unlike fire, response time is overwhelmingly the most critical variable in EMS LOS. As a result, the EMS and fire LOS models are complementary in utility.

Seattle has also developed a response assignment system that determines the units for all first and second alarm response assignments by type and number for every intersection. A second element of this system generates relocations (move-ups) for all levels of alarms 2 through 5 and all response assignments for alarms 3 through 5. This system is called the vehicle allocation and update system (VAUS) and is designed to be used in either an on-line, real-time environment (CAD) or off-line to produce and maintain assignment files.

ARSON INFORMATION SYSTEMS

The principal advances in the area of arson information systems have been carried out through cooperative neighborhood or community block organizations working with the fire service in their communities. A number of microcomputer data bases have been developed to profile the properties in the neighborhood and assist in identifying arson-prone buildings. The community group or public officials are then able to implement intervention strategies appropriate for the situation.

Much of the early work sponsored by the Federal Emergency Management Agency has led to a developed and tested microcomputer-based Arson Information Management System (AIMS), which is now being supported and distributed to the International Association of Arson Investigators.* The system provides both identification of arson-prone buildings and a case-management system for fire investigators.

NFPA is testing a neighborhood AIMS that allows for the development of a data base with information about neighborhood properties. This data base can then be culled for lists of properties meeting a user-defined profile of those traits that exist in arson fires in that neighborhood. Intervention strategies can then be initiated to prevent future arson fires.

There are many municipal and private data bases or record systems that are typically used to support an arson information management system. These include data bases maintained by data from the fire department incident reporting system and code-enforcement program, the building department, the assessor's office, the police department crime reporting system, the prosecutor's office, the tax collector's office, the registry of deeds, mortgage companies, and the insurance industry.

Many jurisdictions are choosing to computerize the incident follow-up report (Form 904I) found in NFPA 904, *Incident Follow-Up Report Guide 7*, in order to keep track of their fire and arson problem. After the period of time required for data entry, patterns of fire type and/or building ownership will surface, making prosecution an easier task. The forms found in NFPA 906M, *Fire Incident Field Notes*, are also helpful during investigations.

Data collection and verification from all these sources is expensive and time-consuming. However, automatic integration of existing computer data bases has not proved successful, due to the number of data bases and the fact that they were never established with all the data elements needed as keys to ensure a proper matching of records. As such, most communities get listings of the data needed from each data base and manually transfer it to the AIMS data base.

OFFICE AUTOMATION

Office automation is a term used in connection with a group of applications that support clerical and managerial activities. Sometimes called the "office of the future," these applications include word processing, electronic filing, electronic mail, "tickler" systems, teleconferencing and video conferencing, and personal calendar management. Depending upon one's perspective, it may also include more traditional data processing functions, such as data base access.

Boulder, CO, is one example of a community that has completely automated its office functions; that is, all functions are now performed by computer, and account for a large, measurable increase in overall productivity.

*For more information on the FEMA/USFA Arson Information Management System, contact International Association of Arson Investigators, Goodfried Plaza, Suite 281, 184B Broadway, Rte. 1, Saugus, Ma 01906-1029.

The purpose of these applications is to make the executive and the clerical worker more productive. While one might say the same about traditional information systems, the focus here is different. Traditional information system applications are process-oriented; office automation, on the other hand, is more people-oriented. The objective is to make office personnel more productive by allowing them to use computers as a natural extension of their minds and bodies. Hence, one often hears terms like "ergonomics" or "user-friendly" when discussing office automation.

Executives and clerical workers need office automation to cope with the complexities of the modern office. Any fair-sized fire agency must contend with an explosion of information in the form of reports, forms, memoranda, and computer files. The efficient production and effective management of this information resource strains even the most dedicated staff. The computer, through automation applications, extends human intellectual capabilities.

The most common office automation application is word processing. Most fire departments employ word processing to replace typewriters, and thereby obtain more productivity from clerical workers. Reports can be corrected and printed without extensive retyping, form letters can be personalized with the addressee names, and hard-copy output can even be made to look like typeset copy.

Electronic mail extends the capabilities of word processing. Documents prepared on interconnected terminals can be transmitted immediately to any other terminal in the network of terminals. Since documents so prepared can be stored on a disk, electronic filing and retrieval is also possible. An index of key words reduces the possibility of "misfiling" and enhances the ability to retrieve all information relating to a particular point that needs researching.

Executives (or their secretaries) also perform two other tasks that are adaptable to office automation: tracking tasks assigned to subordinates, and arranging meetings. In the first instance, the executive usually maintains some kind of tickler file that shows the date work is due. By maintaining the tickler file on the computer, the executive can review a list of work due today, next week, or anytime in the future. Also, before assigning new work, he or she can identify a staff person who is underloaded or overloaded. In the second instance, executives may maintain their calendars on computer files. If the calendar files are made public, then it is easy to arrange a time for a meeting that will be convenient to a group of executives.

The various approaches to office automation may be classified as to the degree of centralization involved. Historically, office automation has meant the decentralized use of stand-alone word processing machines. Word processors are often brought in on a case-by-case basis to improve clerical productivity in selected instances.

Some organizations use the centralized approach of implementing office automation applications on the central computer. This approach is usually less than satisfactory. The central computer and the data communications network are not designed to cope with the unstructured formats and communications volumes associated with word processing and electronic mail.

To provide the needed integration while retaining the flexibility for stand-alone units, some organizations are turning to so-called "shared logic systems." These are full-fledged computer systems specifically designed (both in terms of hardware and software) to handle office automation, although the more advanced systems also support standard data processing chores. As user needs grow, more systems can be added and networked together. In addition, the office computer can be connected into the central computer network. This allows the user to have a stand-alone workstation on a desktop that can perform all the office automation functions and still have access to the data bases retained on the central computer.

There are several variations on these themes. Depending upon how intelligence is distributed throughout the network, various functions can be performed either by the stand-alone workstation, shared logic system, or the central computer. For example, a local work-station might handle word processing as a stand-alone task, use the shared logic system to transmit electronic mail, and make inquiries into the data bases at the central computer site. The network provides the mechanism to integrate all these activities.

Internal Data Bases

With the advent of desktop and laptop computers, "canned" data bases are becoming the accepted way of gathering information for a fire department. Programs, such as R:Base, Paradox, and dBase, are being widely used at this time. These generic data base packages are known as relational data bases, as opposed to flat data bases. Where flat data bases are acceptable for mailing lists and other mundane data-gathering chores, relational data bases not only accomplish those tasks, but go much further in their usefulness. Relational means information can be compared in relation to other information; for example, "what if" questions are easily and rapidly answered when data is gathered using a relational data base. If a fire chief is asked to cut the budget, and the only way to do so is to close a station for some period of time or send fewer engines, he or she can quickly determine what time period represents the best time to accomplish that reduction in service, simply by asking the computer, "What if I had to close down a station for 12 hours a day to reduce costs? What station runs the least during any 12-hour period?" The computer will quickly be able to analyze run information and report back the best time to close down a station, a time period when it will, statistically, have the smallest impact on the services provided by the department.

Relational data bases, even though created for use on microcomputers, are extremely powerful, highly useful programs. The ease of learning and use of these programs has improved dramatically over the past several years, such that most departments, no matter how large or small, would find them very valuable tools for all types of information management.

External Data Bases

Much of the technical and legal information needed by fire departments exists on commercial data bases. These data bases are created for general use, and users are charged for access on the basis of a flat monthly rate and/or the time actually used. In a very real sense, commercial data bases are a public utility.

The source for the information stored in these data bases is primarily current technical literature and legal materials. In some cases, abstracts of documents and books are stored, while in others, the complete text is stored.

Data bases are provided by numerous firms. Literally hundreds of data bases covering various fields are available today through scores of companies, such as *Reader's*

Digest, *The Source*, and *The New York Times*, and more are being offered daily.

The data bases of greatest utility to the fire service are probably those dealing with hazardous materials and legal information. Chemical and hazardous materials data bases are now available that allow a user to search for a hazardous material by chemical structure, trade name, generic name, CAS registry number, chemical or physical properties, and textual description. These data bases can be powerful tools in handling chemical spills, fires involving hazardous materials, and some emergency medical situations.

Legal information systems are generally of two types: (1) full-text storage, and (2) search and abstracts (headnotes) only. Both types cover case law, statutory law, and some administrative rulings. Mead Data Central's LEXIS* is representative of the full text approach. LEXIS users enter key words, and documents containing the proper sequence, count, and/or combination of those words are displayed. A service of West Publishing Company (WESTLAW)† allows the same type of search, but the object of the search is the West headnotes, rather than the full text.

With the rapid introduction of two-way cable television systems and videotext services, there will likely be more data bases and quick access methods available to fire departments.

Financial Applications

Financial applications include those systems that support budgeting, budget control, general ledger, accounts payable, and billing. Payroll is sometimes included, although more often it is a part of the personnel system. Billing may also be included in specific systems (e.g., emergency medical for patients, and brush clearance for owners needing removal of illegal brush). The implementation of financial systems in fire departments has been slow, partly because the support of staff functions, such as finance, has been secondary to the support of line activities. In addition, municipality-wide financial systems often preempt those in the individual departments.

Perhaps the most critical need for financial information in the fire department occurs during the yearly budget cycle. The arduous and politically risky process of allocating resources requires considerable analysis. Decisions must be supported by the kinds of facts best stored and manipulated by a computerized financial system.

Budget control is also a high priority for fire agencies. Management needs to know if the department is staying within budget. Even if central systems are available for this purpose, they may not provide data in sufficient detail or in a form that is useful to the fire department.

The remaining needs addressed by financial systems are primarily operation-oriented: general ledger, billing, accounts payable, and payroll. The last three requirements more often than not are a part of associated applications (e.g., payroll in the personnel system, billing in the emergency medical system, and accounts payable in the procurement system). Manual or automated "bridges" are then provided to general ledger and budgeting systems.

*For more information on LEXIS, contact Mead Data Central, 200 Park Avenue, New York, NY 10166.

†For more information on WESTLAW, contact West Publishing Company, 50 W. Kellogg Blvd., St. Paul, MN 55165.

The most common design approach to financial systems is a strongly centralized one. This is not surprising in view of the fiduciary responsibility of the chief financial officer in a city or county. Since these systems typically represent the city's or county's first experience with computers, they are usually quite old and, therefore, batch-oriented. While some fire departments have on-line access, that situation is not common.

Energy Management

Energy management systems provide information for control of energy costs. These systems provide information about the consumption of electric power, natural gas, and heating oil. In some cases, the use of motor vehicle fuel may be monitored, although this function is more properly a function of fleet management systems.

Beginning with the oil embargo of 1973, energy costs have represented a major portion of fire department budgets. In addition to this, energy costs in some parts of the nation have been exacerbated by other factors. In the Pacific Northwest, for example, cost overruns on new nuclear power plants have contributed to soaring energy costs. In this kind of environment, the cost of implementing a computerized energy management system can be recovered quickly through lower energy costs.

The typical approach to the design of energy management systems is to capture energy billing data, update master files in batch mode, and print various reports for administrators. This can be done using one of the relational data bases referred to earlier, or a spread sheet. More sophisticated approaches include real-time monitoring systems and even real-time energy control. Computer-based evaluation models are also used to assess the impact of conservation measures.

SYSTEMS INTEGRATION

The typical organization does not have a systematic approach to information systems development. The approach is more often piecemeal without an overall plan for systems integration. By analogy, an airplane designed this way might have three wings, an engine with insufficient power for takeoff, and a fuel tank where there should be cargo or passengers. In short, while each subsystem might fulfill its intended function, the overall system is a failure.

The answer to this problem is information resource planning. Like other organizations, the fire department needs an overall plan for integrating the various component subsystems. This does not mean that all components have to be implemented at one time to have a workable system. But it does require a strategic plan for eventual integration and an action plan indicating how to get there.

Normally there are two levels of integration to be considered. The first of these is integration of fire department systems with citywide systems. Considerable benefits can arise from, say, having a central data base of occupancy data that can be used by the assessor, tax department, and fire department. However, information resource managers in the fire department should be generally wary of data bases over which they have no control. Still, the potential benefits are well worth the necessary effort in working toward a well-developed citywide plan. At a minimum, the fire department should think through potential interfaces with city systems and provide the "hooks" for future connections.

The second level of integration is within the fire department itself. Here, there is significant opportunity for controlling the design of systems and data bases and their interfaces. The remainder of this chapter discusses some techniques for planning such an integrated systems environment.

An organization uses information systems to support strategic planning, managerial control, and operational activities. These activities may be classified into a number of business functions (e.g., scheduling personnel, dispatching, and budgeting). In turn, each function requires a certain subset of the organizational data base. Obviously, different functions may require overlapping data subsets.

This type of analysis suggests two ways to integrate systems. The first approach is related to the way the business functions are "packaged" into application systems. For example, a typical entry-level application in a fire department is computer-aided dispatch (CAD). In most cases, CAD is implemented on a stand-alone microcomputer. However, the boundary of the system could be expanded to include other functions such as inspections and incident reporting. The rationale for this would be based on a broader definition of the dispatch function. In the case of inspections, it could be assumed that the fire fighters need information about hazardous materials, occupancy, guard dogs on premises, etc. In the case of incidence data, CAD collects much of the data needed to report fire incident statistics. Thus, while the focus is still on CAD, the systems boundary would be enlarged to include "subordinate" or supporting functions. The supporting functions would be developed as subsystems with their own data bases (or files) and "hooks" provided to tie them together.

The other approach is based on a "data model" of the organization. The focus here is on the data and their interrelationships. Whereas the data traditionally have been owned by the application, now the application has become almost insignificant, replaced by "transaction sets" that update and query the corporate data base.

In reality, one does not define a single physical data base but rather groups the data bases according to some coherent scheme. (Relational data bases are appropriate.) Such a scheme should ensure that like entities are grouped together. Although other arrangements are possible, this line of thinking suggests the following groupings:

1. *Personnel data base:* Includes data on scheduling of personnel, training, payroll (if not part of the financial system), accidents, assignments, etc.
2. *Financial data base:* Includes data on budgets, flow of funds, etc. This data base is likely to be citywide in scope.
3. *Incidents data base:* Includes historical data on closed incidents, both fire and emergency medical.
4. *Fire prevention data base:* Includes a building inventory and data on occupancy, ownership, hazardous materials, etc. Arson data may also be included in this data base.
5. *Operational data base:* Includes data about incidents in progress. This data is maintained for relatively short durations. At the close of an incident, or periodically, it may be moved to the incidents data base. This prevents overloading the real-time CAD system with non-real-time data.
6. *Supplies and equipment data base:* Includes supplies inventory and equipment inventory and may include fleet maintenance. This is typically a citywide data base.

The data base planning approach has the potential of providing a higher level of integration and a more stable systems environment than the applications planning approach. It is not without problems, however. Users may not want to relinquish control over their data to a central data administration function. Data modeling requires specialized skills often not available to fire departments. Perhaps most importantly, it can lead to "analysis paralysis," the reluctance to implement anything until the last detail has been planned. While this is true of any planning approach, the tightly coupled nature of data base planning increases the danger of overplanning. Yet, the concept of data models is too powerful to be ignored.

There are numerous methodologies for defining both application and data base boundaries, developing data models, and planning the integrated systems environment. Three methodologies are mentioned here, but there are numerous others.

1. The Business Systems Planning (BSP) methodology was developed by IBM and has been used in a variety of organizations. It is extensive in scope and involves users at all levels to define the business functions and data classes. It is especially useful in providing an overview of the systems environment, but is usually not updated on a regular basis because of the resources required.
2. The comprehensive planning methodology uses an approach where one-year and five-year plans are updated annually. The planning process should originate with the central information systems department even if the fire department has its own data processing capability. The fire department can then develop its plan to coordinate with the central information system plan. This will allow for better future integration with citywide systems.
3. Structured methodology is an approach used on a project level.[3] Strictly speaking, this is a project development rather than a strategic planning methodology. The hierarchical nature of the approach permits adaptation for planning purposes, although the level of planning is too detailed for pure long-range planning; however, it can be a useful adjunct to such planning.

These three approaches are just some of the many methodologies that are available to the systems planner. There are many others, some of which are fully automated. Whatever the approach taken, the information systems manager is advised to select one that addresses the problems of systems and/or data base integration. The piecemeal approach is more costly and frustrating in the long run than a carefully planned strategy.

BIBLIOGRAPHY

References Cited

1. *Fire Department Information Technology in Nine Western Communities*, FEMA, Washington, DC, undated.
2. Hall, John R., Jr., *et al.*, *Fire Code Inspections and Fire Prevention: What Methods Lead to Success*, National Fire Protection Association, Quincy, MA, 1979.
3. Game, C., and Sarson, T., *Structured Systems Analysis: Tools and Techniques*, 2nd ed., Prentice-Hall, Englewood Cliffs, NJ, 1979.

NFPA Codes, Standards, and Recommended Practices

Reference to the following NFPA codes, standards, and recommended practices will provide further information on analysis of fire department data and decision making discussed in this chapter. (See the latest *NFPA Catalog* for availability of current editions of the following documents.)

NFPA 901, *Uniform Coding for Fire Protection.*

NFPA 902M, *Fire Reporting Field Incident Manual.*

NFPA 903, *Fire Reporting Property Survey Guide.*

NFPA 904, *Incident Follow-up Report Guide 7.*

NFPA 906M, *Fire Incident Field Notes.*

Additional Readings

Coleman, R. J., and Granito, J. A., eds., *Managing Fire Services*, 2nd ed., International City Management Association, Washington, DC, 1988.

Centaur Associates, Inc., "Fire Suppression Crew Size: Literature Review," prepared for the Federal Emergency Management Agency, U.S. Fire Administration, Washington, DC, 1982.

Doerschler, G. K., "Mapping the Future," *Fire Command*, Vol. 56, No. 8, Aug. 1989, pp. 18-22.

Goliash, B. I., "Ye Cads!" *Fire Command*, Vol. 56, No. 10, Oct. 1989, pp. 16-21.

Hollis, J. B., "Engineering of a Mobil Data System for the London Fire Brigade," *Electronic Technology*, Vol. 22, No. 1, 1988, pp. 13-15.

Ignall, E., et al., "Fire Severity and Response Distance: Initial Findings," *Fire Technology*, Vol. 15, No. 4, Nov. 1979, pp. 245-261.

Jackson, D. P., ed., *Fire Department Information Technologies in Nine Western Communities*, Center for Information Resource Management, California State University, Los Angeles, CA, 1982.

Kolesar, P., and Blum, E. H., "Square Root Laws for Fire Engine Response Distances," *Management Science*, Aug. 1973.

Larson, D. A., and Small, R. D., "Analysis of Large Urban Fire Departments—Part I: Theory. Part II: Parametric Analysis and Model City Simulations," Pacific-Sierra Research Corp., Los Angeles, CA, 1982.

Lewis, R. J., "Fire Station Location Studies Using a Microcomputer," TR 86-1, Society of Fire Protection Engineers, Boston, MA, 1986.

MacGillivray, L., "Decision-Related Research on the Organization of Service Delivery Systems in Metropolitan Areas: Fire Protection," Inter-university Consortium for Political and Social Research, Ann Arbor, MI, 1979.

Nickey, B. B., and Chapman, C. B., "Evaluating Fire Prevention Effectiveness through a Probability Model," *Fire Technology*, Vol. 15, No. 4, Nov. 1979, pp. 291-306.

Pietrzak, L. M., "The Effect of Fire Engine Road Performance on Alarm Response Travel Times," *Fire Technology*, Vol. 15, No. 2, May 1979, pp. 114-121, 129.

Robertson, J. C., "Records, Reports, and Measurement of Results," *Introduction to Fire Prevention*, 3rd ed., Macmillan, New York, NY, 1989, pp. 204-218.

Seamon, R. P., "A County Opts for ICS," *Fire Command*, Vol. 56, No. 10, Oct. 1989, pp. 32-33.

Stringfield, W. H., "Mastering Title III Paper Work," *Fire Command*, Vol. 56, No. 1, Jan. 1989, pp. 24-27.

Uniform Fire Incident Reporting System, National Fire Protection Association, Quincy, MA, 1977.

Walker, W. E., "Changing Fire Company Locations: Fire Implementation Case Studies," U.S. Dept. of Housing and Urban Development, Washington, DC, 1978.

Walker, W. E., *et al.*, *Fire Department Deployment Analysis*, Elsevier, New York, NY, 1979.

FIRE HAZARD ASSESSMENT

Frederic B. Clarke, Ph.D.

Risk and *hazard* are different; they are not interchangeable concepts. *Fire risk* is the expected loss from a fire of given severity. For example, the probability of fire in a given environment may be very high, but, owing to the presence of a sprinkler system, the risk of a *serious* fire may be quite low. Describing a fire risk, or any class of risk, therefore carries with it the need to describe both the likelihood and the severity of the event.

Hazard is less sharply defined. Fire hazard as used in this chapter means the expected level of harm associated with the exposure to a fire or its effluent.[1] The relative fire hazard posed by two materials, therefore, is the relative harm they offer if they were both to burn under the same circumstances. This definition means that it is impossible to discuss fire hazard—or fire risk—without knowing the circumstances in which a product is used and the fire conditions to which it will be exposed. These circumstances together comprise the fire "scenario"[2] for which hazard is to be assessed.

Quantifying Hazard

Fire scenarios may be categorized by increasing complexity. The simplest category of scenario to analyze involves a limited quantity of combustible and occurs in a closed room. The toxic smoke* accumulates and mixes more or less uniformly with the room air. Calculations using the mass of combustible involved, the volume of the room, and the toxic potential of the combustion products, can be performed on the back of an envelope; no computer is needed. The result will show that the maximum survivable quantity of combustible is proportional to the toxic potential of the smoke and inversly proportional to the time of exposure.

The survivable quantity of combustible for most materials in residential-sized rooms is of the order of a pound or two (1 lb = 0.45 kg), so this simple fire scenario is not very realistic. Most dangerous fires involve more material than this, since typical residential fire loads are in excess of 2 or 3 lb per sq ft (10 or 15 kg/m^2). In other words, to survive most potentially lethal fires, it is necessary either to stop the fire or to get away from it. The remaining categories of fire scenarios will deal with escape possibility. (The possibility of suppression is not considered in this chapter.)

Figure 10-6A shows a generalized fire growth curve, where the ordinate is a measure of the intensity, or size, of the fire. For example, the figure could represent the upper room temperature in a room in which the fuel is ignited with a match. Little energy is generated at the outset, but the fire eventually becomes large enough to begin heating the room. The room temperature, which reflects the size of the fire, begins to increase rapidly. This corresponds to the steep middle portion of the curve in Figure 10-6A. Finally, the fire will reach a limit in size either because the entire surface of the item is involved or because air cannot enter the doorway any faster. In either case, the temperature will approach a limiting value, governed by the relative size of the fire, and the rate at which hot gases escape from the doorway. If Figure 10-6A were drawn for a longer period of time, the temperature would eventually decline again as the fuel burned itself out.

Computation of the "time available for escape" (TAE) permits a comparison of the relative hazard posed by products in the same application. A ranking of TAEs is a ranking of hazard for the scenario under consideration. This parameter alone, however, does not determine whether differences in escape time are significant or to what degree a given product is safe. For example, product A may offer two more minutes of available escape time than product B, but if product B already provides 50 minutes of escape time, then the difference would be relatively unimportant. In another case, product A may offer 5 minutes and product B 3 minutes of escape time. If 10 minutes is the time needed, however, then neither product is acceptable.

Determining if a situation is safe requires knowing how much escape time is needed, as well as how much is available. The difference between the time available for

Dr. Clarke is president, Benjamin/Clarke Associates, Inc. in Kensington, MD.

*"Smoke" is used throughout this chapter to mean the *total* airborne effluent from the fire. It includes the gaseous, aerosol, and sootlike products of the fire.

escape (TAE) and the time needed for escape (TNE) is a measure of safety.[3]

$$Escape\ Margin = TAE - TNE$$

A negative escape margin means that the fire is fatal. The larger the positive value of the margin, the better—although, as discussed previously, it is possible to reach a point of diminished significance.

The escape time needed depends upon the nature of the structure, the smoke conditions that are encountered, the capabilities of those exposed to the fire, and the vagaries of human behavior.

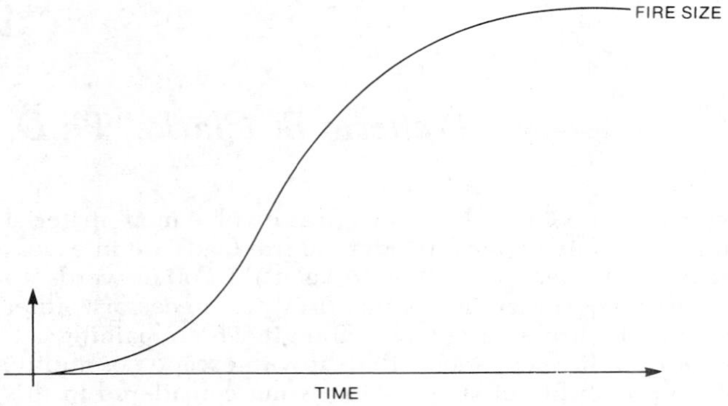

FIG. 10-6A. Typical growth of a room fire.

Time Available for Escape

It is natural to use time as a basis for evaluating the relative hazard of different fires and of the same fire in different locations. This is generally done by identifying some level of temperature and smoke concentration that is unacceptable for life safety and determining how long the fire takes to reach that level.

Figure 10-6B shows the growth of temperature in the upper part of a room in which two different fuel packages, such as sofas, are burned. As the temperature increases, it reaches a point at which escape is no longer possible, shown here somewhat arbitrarily as 302°F (150°C). The sofa represented by Curve 2 reaches this temperature at some time, *T2*, and the slower-growing fire, represented by Curve 1, would reach this temperature after a somewhat greater time, *T1*. The difference between these two times is then a simple measure of the relative hazard posed by these two sofas in this particular room and fire. It is worth noting that if the critical temperature were chosen to be much higher or much lower than 302°F (150°C), the difference in the two times would be different. This illustrates that the relative performance of materials can depend heavily upon how the hazard in a given scenario is characterized.

When hazards associated with smoke are evaluated, the situation is somewhat different. Figure 10-6C shows the same fire growth curve as Figure 10-6A, but a dotted curve showing smoke production has been added. Note that the smoke produced continues to increase steeply even after the temperature has reached a constant value. In effect, the smoke produced is proportional to the area under the fire-size curve so it continues to increase until the fire has gone out.

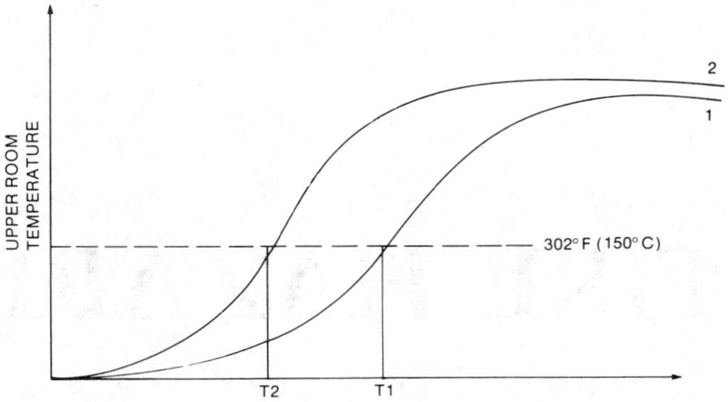

FIG. 10-6B. Comparative growth of two fires burning in a room, showing the time taken in each case to reach 302°F (150°C).

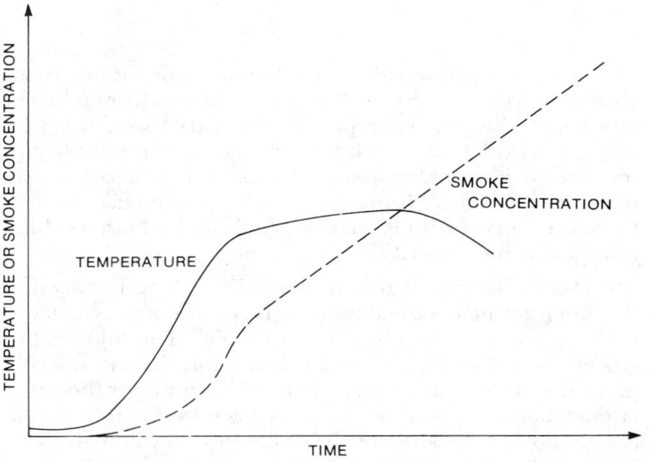

FIG. 10-6C. Growth of temperature and of smoke concentration as a function of time.

The level of smoke that represents unacceptable toxicity is different for each material. The toxicity of the smoke must be measured by some appropriate method and the toxic potency determined. Usually, it is expressed as the dose of smoke required to bring about a given observable biological effect such as incapacitation or death. The dose can generally be related to concentration and time,[4] so it is possible in principle to identify the point on the smoke concentration-time curve that corresponds to the arrival of unacceptably toxic conditions. Then the two materials can be compared. (See Fig. 10-6D.)

As the fire grows, conditions approach those at which human survival is no longer possible. One way of viewing the development of a fire is as a race between an increasingly dangerous fire environment and the efforts of those exposed to escape. The time at which the fire is detected is the starting point of the race.

The human senses are, if unimpaired, good detectors of the signatures of fire, especially smoke. The fact that most fire fatalities occur when the victims are asleep, incapacitated, or physically unable to escape underscores this point.

Except in special circumstances, the fire characteristics that trigger detectors are the same ones that are threats to life—that is, heat and/or smoke. Therefore, the kinds of

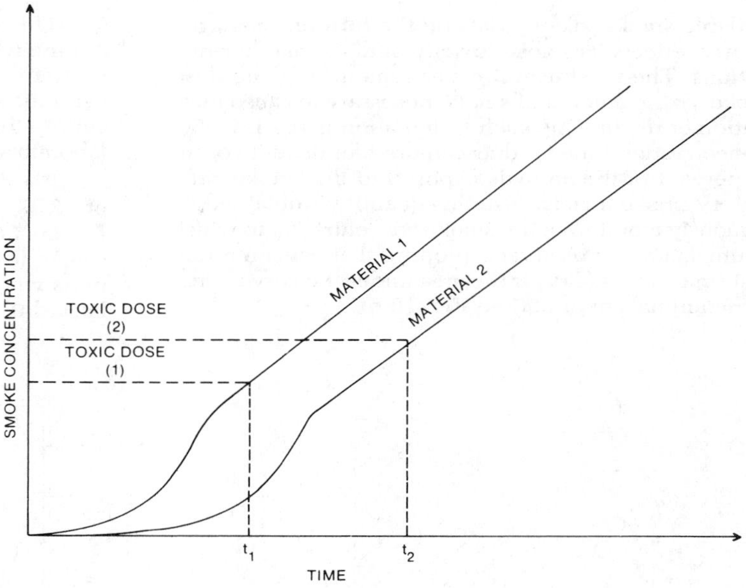

FIG. 10-6D. Comparison of smoke production and development of a toxic smoke dose for two different materials.

calculation needed to predict the development of life-threatening conditions are now relevant to predicting detector response. This means that if temperature and smoke build-up toward untenability can be estimated, detector response can often be estimated, too. In the discussions that follow, the zero point in the fire growth will be assumed to be the time at which detection occurs, rather than the ignition of the fire. It bears repeating, however, that early detection of a fire is the key to survival. In the race between the fire and its victims, the odds increasingly favor the fire as the starting point is delayed.

Two kinds of information must be available before the time difference can be determined:

1. The unacceptable level of temperature or smoke concentration.
2. The fire or smoke growth curve.

The former is directly or indirectly derived from the response of an animal on exposure to hostile heat or smoke conditions. The latter can be obtained either from a full-scale burn experiment or, in many cases, analytically from small-scale laboratory data and knowledge of the fire scenario. Calculations of fire growth using computer-based hazard assessment will be discussed in more detail below.

Estimating Escape Time: Two Simple Examples

The kind of fire growth scenario often determines the nature of the hazard. A rapidly developing flaming fire, whose products accumulate in a relatively confined space, such as a small apartment, produces a well-defined upper layer that descends rapidly from the ceiling. There is little opportunity for the smoke to lose energy to the upper room surfaces, so the layer is quite hot. Once the hot layer has descended to a few feet from the floor, it is difficult for occupants to escape without coming in direct contact with it. Regardless of its chemical composition, this layer poses an immediate threat to life safety because of its temperature.

In a larger space or if the fire is burning more slowly or perhaps smoldering, the layer is cooler. A distinct upper layer may not even be apparent, since it is the elevated temperature that gives the layer its buoyancy and results in stratification. In such cases, the toxic properties of the smoke can become important, since these properties, not the temperature, then determine the tenability of the compartment.

In structures other than one- or two-family residences, it is standard practice to provide barriers to the free passage of smoke or fire into exitways or between floors. Modern apartment buildings, for example, have fire walls between apartments but not as interior partitions. The smoke from a fire may reach areas well removed from the fire, but seldom is it the hot buoyant steam that exists near the fire. In such locations, the primary threat is usually smoke toxicity, not heat.

In a scenario where only one item is burning, it is possible to relate TAE to the fire and smoke toxicity properties of that item. In cases where many items are burning, TAE is influenced by the properties of all the fire's contributors. Scenarios involving multiple items are applicable when considering the hazard attributable to an item that can burn only after exposure to a fairly large ignition source. An example of each kind of scenario is given below.

Burning of a single item in a single room: The first case to consider is a fire ignited in a compartment containing one relatively large item, such as a heavily upholstered chair or loveseat. Because the fire is so restricted, the rest of the room is relatively unimportant, although the thickness and thermal conductivity of the walls and ceiling should be known in order to determine how much of the heat energy is lost to these surfaces. As for the furniture itself, its burning rate—that is, heat release and mass loss rate—must be measured or calculated from small-scale test results.

This exercise assumes that air temperature of 302°F (150°C) represents the upper limit under which humans can escape from the compartment, and supposes that there is available smoke toxicity data on the furniture material that fairly reflects its smoke toxicity under actual burning conditions. The most useful measurement is of the dose of smoke, or the amount of smoke necessary to cause incapacitation or death. One such formulation is the L(Ct)50, the concentration-time product required for death to occur in 50 percent of the animals exposed to the smoke. In a laboratory smoke toxicity test, this quantity is obtained by continuously monitoring the smoke concentration to which the animals are exposed, and plotting that concentration against time. The $L(Ct)_{50}$ is the area under the curve at the time the animals expire. (See Fig. 10-6E.)

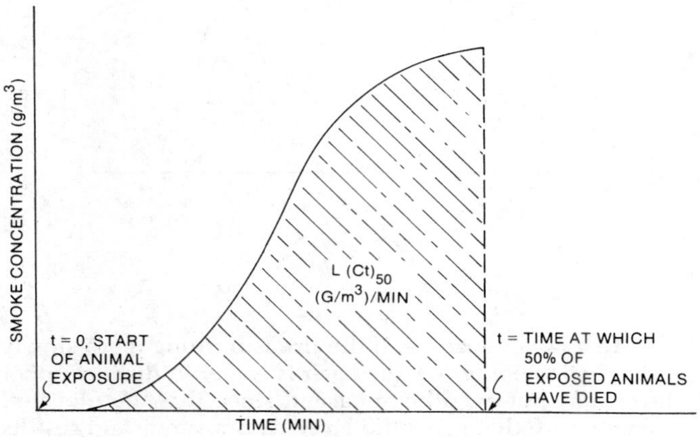

FIG. 10-6E. Plot of smoke concentration against time where test animals are exposed to the smoke. The $L(Ct)_{50}$ is the area under the curve from t=0 to the point at which 50 percent of the animals have expired.

The simplest burning scenario is one in which fire is started on the furniture and does not spread appreciably. If the fire size is 100 kW, or about 2 ft (0.6 m) in diameter, the hot smoke will have filled a normal 1000-sq-ft (93 m^2) room to a depth of 3.28 ft (1 m) from the floor in about 6 minutes; the temperature of the hot layer will have reached 302°F (150°C) after 12 minutes.[5] Hence, by the temperature criterion mentioned above, the environment will become lethal 11 minutes after ignition.

For smoke toxicity to be an important threat in this scenario, the atmosphere must become lethally toxic before it becomes lethally hot:

$$TAE\ (\text{toxicity}) \leq TAE\ (\text{temperature})$$

Knowing the burning rate of the fire and the associated mass loss rate, it is a simple matter to compute the smoke concentration in the hot layer. Assuming that the occupants have been exposed to the smoke from the time the hot layer was at the 5-ft (1.5 m) level, the time to take on a lethal dose of smoke (TAE) is given by the integral over time, *dt*:

$$L(Ct)_{50} = \int_{t5}^{TAE} C_s dt$$

Where $L(Ct)_{50}$ is the lethal dose determined from a laboratory toxicity measurement;

t_5 is the time at which the smoke reaches the 5 ft (1.5 m) level;

C_s is the smoke concentration.

This is simply the mathematical equivalent of determining when the $L(Ct)_{50}$ of the smoke, as measured in the laboratory, is reached in the room. The room's smoke concentration is followed with time, and the area under the curve—the integral is equal to the $L(Ct)_{50}$ observed in the laboratory.

For this scenario, TAE toxicity is plotted as a function of $L(Ct)_{50}$ in Figure 10-6F. It can be seen that, if the smoke has an $L(Ct)_{50}$ below about 200 (g/min)/m^3, death from smoke toxicity could be expected to occur before conditions were thermally untenable. Otherwise, the thermal hazard is more immediate in this scenario.

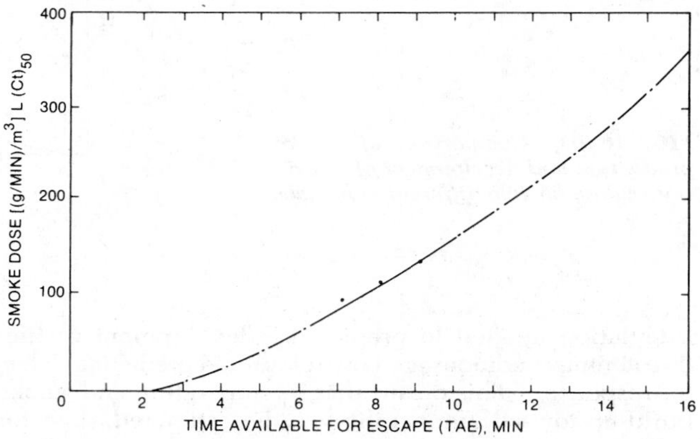

FIG. 10-6F. Time available for escape as a function of lethal dose.

If, instead of flaming, the fire on the furniture is smoldering, there usually is not enough heat generated to maintain a stable upper layer, and the smoke disperses more or less uniformly through the compartment volume.

One would intuitively expect smoke that is twice as toxic or is produced twice as fast to produce untenable conditions in half the time. In fact, the escape time is not actually that sensitive to changes in smoke toxicity or burn rate. Doubling either toxicity or burn rate results in substantially less than a two-fold reduction in escape time.

For a smoldering fire that does not change in size ($\dot{m}$, the mass burning rate, is constant)

$$TAE = [2L(Ct)_{50}\ V/\dot{m}]^{1/2} - t_d$$

where t_d = time at which fire is detected, and V is the compartment volume. For a fire that grows linearly with time ($\dot{m} = kt$),

$$TAE = [6\ L(Ct)_{50}\ V/k]^{1/3} - t_d$$

This trend continues, so that the higher the order of time dependence upon mass loss rate, the less sensitive TAE is to changes in the value of $L(Ct)_{50}$. This is the case for flaming, as well as smoldering fires, although the former are complicated by the hot-layer descent.

Burning of multiple items: Most real fire scenarios involve the thermal exposure of a number of items. In some cases, almost any sequence of ignitions is equally likely: it is as easy to envision drapes igniting from a burning chair as the reverse. In other cases, however, it is far more likely that the sequence will be fixed: combustible materials behind a wall are more likely to be exposed to heat from a room fire than to be ignited directly.

Figure 10-6G shows the buildup of temperature in a room as the result of a known fire, the standard time temperature curve for the ASTM E-119 fire endurance test.[6] It also shows the buildup of temperature behind a wall of ⅝-in. (15 mm) gypsum wallboard.

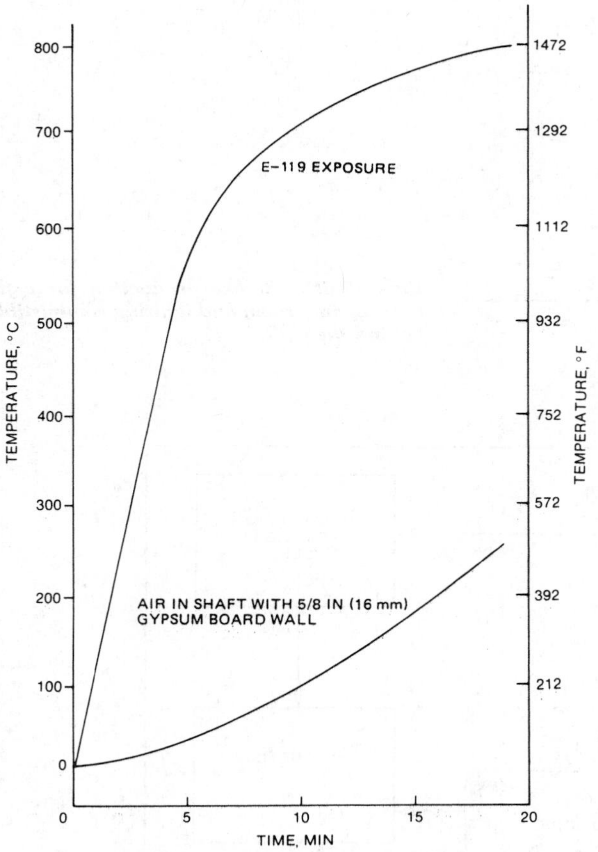

FIG. 10-6G. Time-temperature profile of a fire simulating the ASTM E-119 fire endurance test and of a cavity behind a gypsum board wall.

The temperature in the room becomes intolerable long before the region behind the wall warms appreciably. When the temperature behind the wall is high enough, the combustibles will begin to decompose. Only then do the concealed combustibles begin to contribute to the smoke. To predict when this will happen, one must know the characteristics of mass loss versus temperature.

The curves in Figure 10-6H show the contribution of the in-room and behind-wall fuel packages to the total smoke produced. It is necessary to know the toxicity of the smoke from both fuel sources to predict the effect of the behind-wall material on TAE. It is obvious, however, that its toxicity must be substantially greater than that of the smoke produced in the room before it will have much effect. Formalisms have been proposed to compute the TAE from fires involving multiple components. The TAE is given by the expression:

$$\frac{1}{L(Ct)_{50(1)}} \int_{o}^{TAE} C_{(1)}dt + \frac{1}{L(Ct)_{50(2)}} \int_{o}^{TAE} C_{(2)}dt = 1$$

where the subscripts (1) and (2) denote the in-room and behind-wall concentrations, respectively. The smoke production curves are integrated and normalized with respect to the toxic dose, as determined in advance by a small-scale test. At the time the normalized contributors sum to unity, TAE is deemed to have been reached. This "additive" approach to smoke toxicity is probably sound when the materials produce the same kind of major toxicants, such as carbon monoxide. It also appears to hold for a combination of toxicants such as carbon monoxide and hydrogen cyanide. However, this has not yet been shown to be generally applicable.

The smoke concentration depends both upon the mass loss rate of the fuel and on the point in the building at which fire hazard is being assessed. Hence, knowledge of the building layout may also be needed to make this computation.

In comparing two alternative materials for the same use behind the wall, it is possible to compute a difference in the TAE associated with the change from one material to another. The significance of this difference, however, will be affected by the relative contribution of the in-room fire and by the TNE, which is essentially independent of material composition.

Computer-Based Hazard Assessment

Figure 10-6I illustrates the conceptual framework of fire hazard assessment modeling. The five components at the top of the diagram, labeled N1 to N5, describe the time needed for escape; the seven components labeled A1 to A7 permit computation of the time available. Two inputs, the building layout and protection system models, are used in computing both values.

N1, the occupant location and condition, includes data such as the distance of occupants from exits or refuge areas, whether they can escape unaided, and their estimated age. N2, the behavior/ decision model, describes how the occupants will behave once alerted to the fire. How and when they are alerted is dependent upon N3, the protection system. The evacuation model, N4, predicts how long the building population will take to reach safety in a given layout, N5. The output of N4 is thus the time needed for escape, TNE. The "exposure response evaluation" compares TNE with the time available, TAE, which is computed from the A components. The escape margin differs for occupants in different locations, and the overall effect of a given fire is determined by computing its impact on the entire building population.

The components of this framework labeled "model" quantitatively predict the behavior of the fire, of the smoke movement, or of those evacuating the building—predictions necessary if actual computations of escape margin are to be made.

For some classes of residential occupancies, all the necessary models exist, although in various stages of validation. Together, they underpin an integrated, computer-based assessment method called HAZARD I, which is currently available from NFPA. HAZARD I, which can be applied to a number of, residential fire scenarios

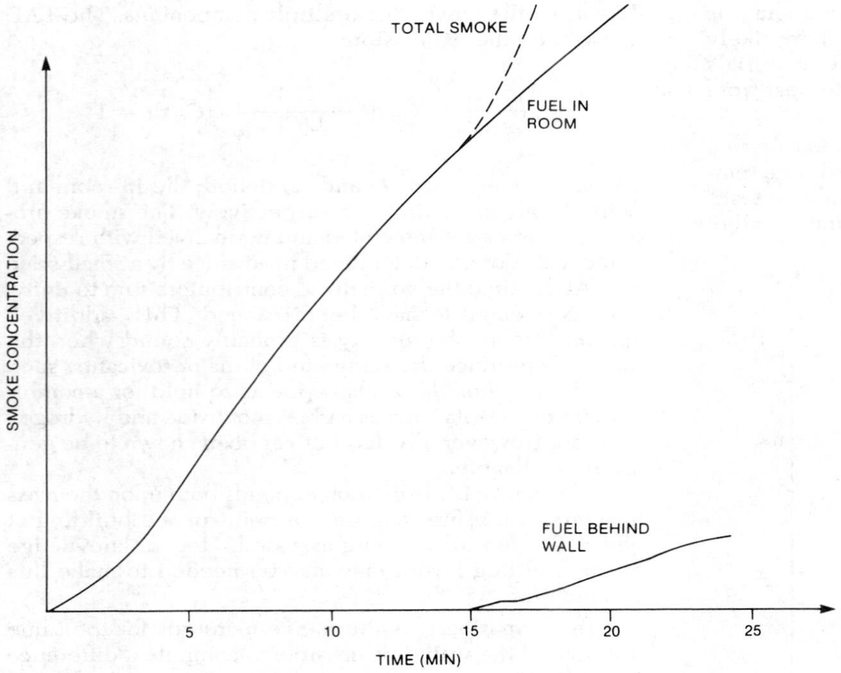

FIG. 10-6H. ***Smoke production for a fire burning in a room and igniting combustibles behind the wall.***

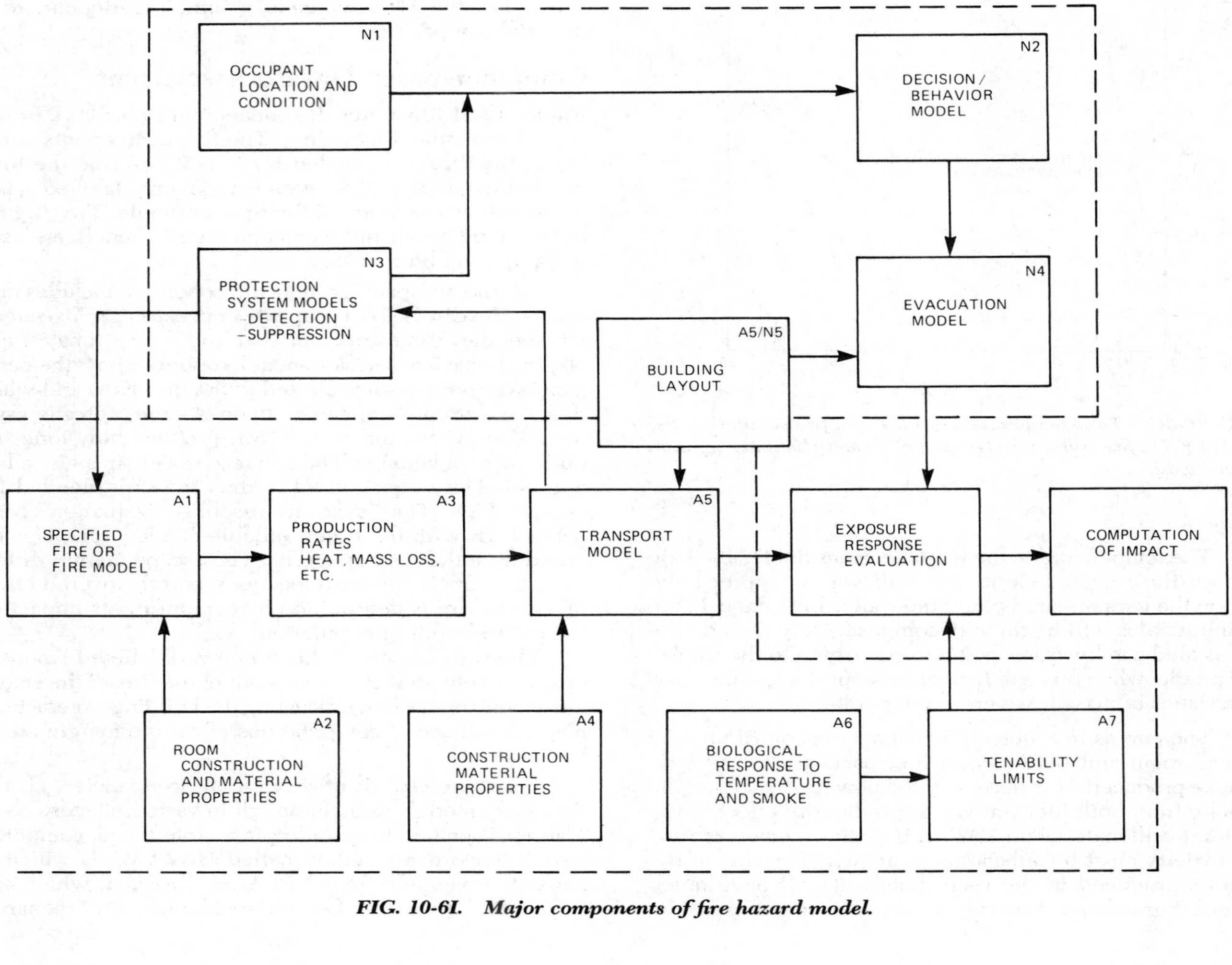

FIG. 10-6I. ***Major components of fire hazard model.***

and will run in a few hours on many modern personal computers, yields results in terms of the expected number of deaths associated with a given fire scenario. For most other occupancies, models of occupant decision-making and evacuation, as well as detailed knowledge of occupant location and condition, are incomplete, so that TNE often cannot be predicted with confidence.

Even when a full hazard assessment according to the framework of Figure 10-6H cannot be carried out, much can be learned by computing escape time. In cases far more complicated than the two examples used in the previous Section, meaningful estimates of escape time can be made. This is because models of the growth and spread of the fire itself are comparatively well advanced.

A number of different computational systems have been developed, all of which are based on modern physics and differ mainly in the aspects of fire that they emphasize. The heart of a fire model is that part that describes the burning process itself. It is here that the flammability properties of the materials and products under study, either measured in a laboratory or taken from the literature, are coupled with the characteristics of the compartment, such as its geometry, the ventilation, and the thermal conductivity of the floors, walls, and ceiling.

The output of the burn calculation can include the fire size, temperature, smoke production rate, and, if sufficient data is available, the concentration of specific toxicants in the smoke. All this information is usually time-dependent, and many models recalculate the data at regular intervals as the fire grows. The rest of the computation is concerned with tracking the spread of fire and the smoke components through whatever kind of compartment, or network of compartments, is under study.

Fire models are discussed elsewhere in this section of the handbook. They are gaining increasing acceptance as practical everyday tools. The more a model is readily adaptable and easy to use, the larger the number of simplifying assumptions and approximations it is likely to contain. All models are thus imperfect: they can simulate real fire experience quite well under the right circumstances, but they fail to do so in other situations. For this reason they will probably remain a tool for the professional, in whose hands they can make hazard assessment an everyday part of fire protection.

SUMMARY

Whether hazard assessment is performed with the aid of a computer or by hand, the essentials of the method are the same. The fire properties and smoke toxicity characteristics of a material or product are related to the development of thermally and toxically hazardous conditions in a given scenario. This allows one to see how changes in these input variables affect the escape time, the TAE. The significance of the TAE depends upon the time needed for escape, TNE, which, in turn, depends upon human behavior and capabilities in a fire.

The most complete hazard assessment can be done for residential fires since the details of human behavior are well-enough known for these occupancies to permit the construction of computer-based models to calculate TNE. For other occupancies, these parts are not available, and one must settle for the often easier job of calculating escape time.

The relative influence of heat release rate, flame spread, smoke toxicity, and escape time depend upon the scenario under study. In general, however, the flammability properties of a material are at least as important as, and often more important than, its smoke toxicity. This is because the flammability properties alone govern thermal hazard, which is often more acute, and they, in concert with smoke toxicity, govern the hazard from smoke.

BIBLIOGRAPHY

References Cited

1. "Standard Terminology of Fire Standards," *ASTM-176-90*, American Society of Testing and Materials, Philadelphia, PA, 1990.
2. Clarke, F. and Ottoson, J., "Fire Scenarios and Fire Safety Planning," *Fire Journal*, Vol 70, No.3 (May 1976).
3. Cooper, L., "Estimating Safe Available Egress Time from Fires," *NBSIR 80-2172*, National Bureau of Standards, Washington, DC, 1981.
4. Alexeeff, G. and Packham, S., "Evaluation of Smoke Toxicity Using Concentration-Time Products," *Journal of Fire Science*, Vol. 2, 1984, p. 362.
5. Cooper, L., "Calculating Available Safe Egress Time (ASET)—A Computer Program and User's Guide," *NBSIR 82-2578*, National Bureau of Standards, Washington, DC, 1985.
6. "Fire Tests of Building Construction and Materials," *ASTM E-119-88*, American Society of Testing and Materials, Philadelphia, PA, 1988.
7. NBS, Adapted from material supplied by H. E. Nelson, National Bureau of Standards, Gaithersburg, MD, undated.

Additional Readings

Alpert, R. L., "Calculation of Response Time of Ceiling-Mounted Fire Detectors," *Fire Technology*, Vol. 18, 1982, pp. 181-195.

Budnick, E. K., "Quantitative Fire Hazards Analysis—An Overview of Needs, Methods, and Limitations," *Fire Safety Journal*, Vol. 11., Nos. 1&2, 1986, pp. 3-14.

Bukowski, R. W., "A Summary of the Assumptions and Limitations in HAZARD I," *9th Joint Panel Meeting* of the UJNR Panel on Fire Research and Safety, NBSIR 88-3753, National Bureau of Standards, Gaithersburg, MD, April 1988, pp. 219-223.

Bukowski, R. W., "Application of Models to the Assessment of Fire Hazard from Consumer Products," NBSIR 85-3219, National Bureau of Standards, Gaithersberg, MD. Aug. 1985.

Bukowski, R. W., "Development of a Method for Assessing Toxic Hazard," *Fire Journal*, Vol. 79, No. 2 (March 1985), p. 24.

Bukowski, R. W., "Evaluation of Furniture-Fire Hazard Using a Hazard-Assessment Computer Model," *Fire and Materials*, Vol. 9, No. 4, 1985, pp. 159-166.

Bukowski, R. W., *et al.*, "HAZARD I Fire Assessment Method," *NIST Handbook 146*, National Institute of Standards and Technology, Gaithersburg, MD.

Dungan, K. W., *ed.*, "Techniques of Quantitative Fire Hazard Analysis," *Fire Safety Journal*, Vol. 11, Nos. 1-2, 1986, p. 139.

Emmons, H. W., "The Prediction of Fire in Buildings," *17th [International] Symposium on Combustion*, The Combustion Institute, Pittsburgh, PA, 1978, pp. 1101-1111.

Gross, D., "Use of Fire Statistics in Assessing the Fire Risk of Products," *INTERFLAM 1985 Conference Workbook*, CIB W14/86/27, International Conference on Flammability, 1985, pp. 11-18.

Heskestad, G., "Physical Modeling of Fire," *Journal of Fire and Flammability*, Vol. 6, 1975, p. 253.

Mudan, K. S. and Croce, P. A., "Fire Hazard Calculations for Large Open Hydrocarbon Flames," *SFPE Handbook for Fire Protection Engineering*, National Fire Protection Association, Quincy, MA., 1988.

Peacock, R. D. and Bukowski, R. W., "A Prototype Methodology for Fire Hazard Analysis," *Fire Technology*, Vol. 26, No. 1 (Feb. 1990), pp. 15-41.

Smith, R. L., "ASKBUDJR: A Primative Expert System for the Evaluation of the Fire Hazard of a Room," *NBSIR 86-3319*, National Bureau of Standards, Gaithersburg, MD, March 1986.

Walton, W. D., "Fire Modeling: A Key Element to Hazard and Risk Assesment," *Proceedings* of the 37th International Wire and Cable Symposium, U.S. Army Communications-Electronics Command, 1988, pp. 517-522.

Watts, J. M., "Dealing with Uncertainty: Some Applications in Fire Protection Engineering," *Fire Safety Journal*, Vol. 11, Nos. 1&2, 1986, pp. 127-134.

FIRE RISK ANALYSIS

John R. Hall Jr., Ph.D.

In the rapidly developing field of scientific research on fire, one of the most useful and unusual branches is fire risk analysis. It is useful because it provides a flexible framework for estimating the impact of any type of firesafety program or strategy in terms of actual reductions in losses—deaths, injuries, property damage—and in terms that can be compared to the costs of those programs and strategies. While fire risk analysis may lack the depth of detail required for complete evaluation of building design alternatives, there is no other method as well suited for the analysis of strategic options affecting large numbers of properties and their occupants. Product development, related research and marketing, and regulatory decisions can benefit from fire risk analysis, as can any program to manage and oversee firesafety from a financial point of view.*

Fire risk analysis is unusual because the framework it uses is taken not from the hard sciences of physics, chemistry, biochemistry, and engineering, which underlie the rest of firesafety research, but from statistical decision theory, which is based upon the fields of economics and operations research. Because fire risk analysis comes from a setting with which much of the fire community may be unfamiliar, this chapter will focus on a discussion of basic concepts, definitions, and approaches.

What Is Fire Risk Analysis?

A measure of fire risk always has two parts: 1) a measure of severity and 2) a probability distribution. The severity measure may also be separated, for the sake of clarity, into two parts. The first part is a specification of the scale that measures severity, such as deaths, injuries, dollars of property damage, area reached by flames, days of business interruption, and so forth. The second part is a specification of the rules for calculating the specific severity measure to be used for a particular fire.

Dr. Hall is NFPA's assistant vice president for Fire Analysis and Research.

* Much of the material in this chapter was first developed for an in-house concept paper at the National Bureau of Standards, Center for Fire Research (NBS/CFR). The author expresses his appreciation for the valuable support accorded this work by NBS/CFR.

For example, suppose the basic scale was dollars of damage. One rule would be to set the severity measure equal to the number of dollars of damage. This would set the stage for a risk analysis on expected loss or average loss, the most common approach. Alternatively, a second rule would be to set the severity measure equal to 1 if damage exceeded $100,000,000 and 0 otherwise. This would set the stage for a risk analysis focusing on large losses, which might be more useful for an insurance company that worries less about ordinary claims than about a single loss so large the company cannot cover it.

The probability distribution gives a probability for each value the severity measure can take. Most often, a probability distribution gives a probability for every type of fire, and then rules for calculating the value of the severity measure for each type of fire provide the translation to a probability distribution for the measure of severity.

In general, the fire risk analyst will specify a scenario structure, which is a set of classification rules for dividing the range of possible fires into a manageable number of relatively homogenous groups. Then probabilities can be calculated or estimated for each scenario (a group of like fires), and a severity measure can be calculated or estimated for the average fire in each scenario, usually by detailed examination of a typical or representative fire from each scenario.

The abstract nature of this explanation so far may lead people to ask a simple question: What good is fire risk analysis? Perhaps the best response is that the practical value of fire risk analysis emerges as these general-purpose measures are calculated under specified real or potential conditions. In any fire risk analysis, there will be a certain set of assumptions about key conditions in the environment of interest: some or all of the buildings have sprinklers or detectors; some or all of the mattresses were built to a certain ignition-resistance standard; some or all of the occupants have been regularly trained in firesafe behavior; and so forth.

Fire risk analysis refers to a systematic examination of how measures of fire risk change as the assumptions change. It may be done in conjunction with a parallel examination of changes in costs. On the one hand, if no detector is present, a household can expect to experience fires with a certain probability, and these fires will have a certain expected severity in terms of deaths, injuries, and property damage. On the other hand, if a detector is present, the household will pay purchase and maintenance costs not paid by the household without detectors, but the detector household can expect on average to achieve lower severities of losses—and in particular, fewer deaths per fire. Risk analysis is used to quantify the expected size of the reductions in deaths, injuries, and damage. One can then determine whether these risk reductions are great enough to justify the cost. This is an analysis of cost versus risk-reduction benefits in which the risk portion is measured explicitly.

The term *risk analysis*, and similar terms such as *hazard analysis*, may be used to describe this kind of analysis, but other kinds of analysis are also labeled with some of these terms. (See Section 10, Chapter 6, "Fire Hazard Assessment.") Three key elements of the fire risk analysis approach are: 1) the explicit estimation of all relevant probabilities; 2) the use of well-defined measures of severity; and 3) the explicit consideration of the uncertainty attached to all estimates developed in the analysis. Some modeling approaches that are called risk assessment omit one or more of these key elements.

For example, the term *fire risk analysis* has sometimes been used to refer to an exercise of listing locations under the jurisdiction of the analyst that present the greatest potential for fire damage or for demand on fire suppression resources. Such an exercise lacks most or all of the key elements of a true fire risk analysis. There is no consideration of probabilities or uncertainty at all, and even the severity measures implicit in the definition of potential damage or demand may not be explicitly defined, let alone measured.

Other commonly used analysis approaches present subtler problems. Fire protection engineers often focus on alternative means for dealing with fires, after fire has begun. It may seem natural to construct a fire risk analysis that takes established burning as given but measures the probability of performance for all building features and systems that operate after the fire. Assuming it makes sense to write off fire prevention, there still will be a need to address explicity different types of initial fires. A fast, accelerant-driven fire or an initial explosion will challenge the built-in fire protection in different ways than an ordinary flaming or smoldering fire. A concealed-space fire will present different problems than a fire in a room, and both will differ from fires started in a means of egress. If each of these fires is analyzed separately, if the analysis leans on physics and chemistry, and if the focus is on preventing major fire extent as an either-or proposition, than the subject is more properly termed a *hazard analysis*. While the terminology is not yet standardized, hazard analysis is best used to describe analyses that do not treat most probabilities explicitly, particularly probabilities of ignition and probabilities of occupant characteristics and behaviors. *Risk analysis* should be reserved for analyses that address all relevant probabilities.

Also, risk analysis usually measures expected deaths, injuries, and property damage rather than stopping with measures of how many rooms or square feet reached a particular temperature or had smoke or gas levels over a particular threshold. In most situations in which risk analysis is used, it is important to address whether people and property are actually damaged, which means implicit or explicit attention to the locations, decisions, movements, and vulnerabilities of occupants—actual, not just potential—and the damageability of property. Risk analysis also requires estimation of the factors that contribute to reliability of systems, such as the probability of features and systems being rendered inoperative or ineffective due to human error or negligence; hazard analysis does not always address field reliability in all its aspects.

Hazard analysis addresses the core concerns of fire development, smoke spread, and sometimes toxicity; it often does so in far greater detail than is possible with risk analysis. Risk analysis includes victim decisions, locations, and characteristics; ignition factors; and reliability of systems and building features. In order to be this broad, fire risk analysis cannot always make use of the full power and sensitivity to detail of the hard-science models of hazard analysis; the only models that can be used are those that can be fitted into the complete risk analysis framework. Thus, hazard analysis has the advantage of being able to examine details of design that fire risk analysis cannot now handle. In the long term, however, work is proceeding on model integration techniques capable of combining the breadth of fire risk analysis with the depth of hazard analysis.

Because real fires reflect all the factors that affect ignition probability and fire severity, fire risk analysis usually begins with calculations from data bases on actual fires. (Over two million fires are reported to the fire service each year.) For most analyses of classes of properties, then, one can identify initial data bases of historical fires that will give statistically meaningful probabilities and severities of fires.

Many situations, however, may dictate going beyond incident data bases in performing a fire risk analysis. First, in analyzing new strategies, products, or systems, there will be no data base of fires reflecting the influence of these innovations. Second, there may be interest in so many product or building characteristics that the data base does not have enough fires to cover all possible combinations. Third, more detail may be needed than is available in the typical data base.

If available fire experience data is insufficient, a fire risk analysis will begin to look more like a hazard analysis, with tree diagrams to capture alternative sequences of events, probabilities for the various possible starting conditions, and probabilities for transitions from one stage to the next in a fire. What is measured and in how much detail may differ from a hazard analysis, in the ways noted earlier.

Already you may have begun to sense how difficult it can be to construct a fire risk analysis that is valid, useful, and of manageable size. Concern over the computational burden is one reason why analysts sometimes conduct fire risk analyses using a very small number of scenarios (e.g., only three alternatives for where and how fire begins). There may also be concern over the shakiness of the available data and a desire to minimize the number of different terms supported by expert judgments.

In a situation like that, it is essential to understand what is being implicitly assumed by the use of a stripped-down scenario structure. One way or another, the scenarios that are modeled explicitly are being treated as representative of the far larger number of scenarios that are not modeled explicitly. If only a few scenarios are modeled explicitly, then each one is implicitly required to be representative of a much larger and more varied collection of other scenarios. There may be no good evidence to support this. Is it better, for example, to examine the different types of flaming fires individually or to assume that they all behave like a burning wood crib ignited by a lighter? The variability and uncertainty are there either way; the only choice is how much to examine explicitly and how much to handle by assumption.

Risk Estimation and Risk Evaluation

Fire risk analysis can sometimes be seperated into (1) *risk estimation*, the estimation and analysis of the measures of severity and probability and their associated uncertainties, and (2) *risk evaluation*, the additional steps required to decide on the importance of a particular value of risk or a change in risk. A fire analysis that includes risk evaluation may be called a *fire risk assessment* to underline the fact that the analysis will support value judgments.

Risk evaluation should be familiar to anyone who has had to make business decisions, because it essentially involves using analysis to determine whether you will get what you pay for. The most common approach to risk evaluation is *cost-benefit analysis*, a technique in which all benefits of risk reduction are translated into monetary equivalents. This technique permits a proposed new product or fire suppression system to be assessed in terms of its net profit or loss, total cost plus loss, or ratio of profit to loss. In such a context, "profit" means saved lives, avoided injuries, and reduced property damage, all combined in one monetary scale, and "loss" means the cost—both initial and ongoing—of the new product or system. A variation is *cost-effectiveness analysis*, in which the benefits of risk reduction are translated into a single nonmonetary scale. For example, it is possible to derive the cost per life saved for a new system or product.

Cost-benefit and cost-effectiveness analyses require the explicit estimation or derivation of some controversial parameters. Examples include the value of reduced risk of death or injury and the discount rate by which future consequences are compared to present consequences (both discussed in more detail later). Because these parameters are controversial, risk evaluation sometimes uses methods that downplay the role of these parameters.

Acceptable risk is a term used when the method of risk evaluation involves treating risk as a constraint. This method may seem attractive because it refuses to consider costs until or unless a sufficient degree of firesafety has been provided. In an acceptable risk approach, a certain level of risk is defined as acceptable; then all alternatives meeting that level are evaluated strictly on the basis of cost.

This approach can produce unsatisfactory results. If risk is greater than the acceptable level by even a small fraction, no cost is too great to reach acceptable risk. If risk already is acceptably low, not a nickel more should be spent, no matter how much more firesafety could be purchased for very little money. This means that the selected level of acceptable risk is often set with an eye toward affordability and may be reset if technology changes. In effect, this makes the acceptable risk approach a kind of backdoor cost-benefit analysis and runs counter to most approaches to decision-making in business.

When acceptable risk is not defined in terms of affordable risk, it is often defined in terms of (a) historically acceptable risk (i.e., anything in use for a long time is all right), which may be overturned if public understanding of the magnitude of the risk changes dramatically, or (b) unavoidable risk, such as the use of background radiation levels as a guide for acceptable exposure to medical X-rays. In fire protection, acceptable risk has sometimes been inferred from provisions of NFPA codes and standards. The most extreme version of an acceptable risk approach is a minimum risk approach, in which cost is not considered unless all feasible safety improvements have been made.

A logical complement to the acceptable risk approach would be an acceptable cost approach, in which the greatest risk reduction available within the fixed cost budget (but no more) would be sought. Although this approach is rarely mentioned in the literature, it almost certainly describes the way some decisions are made.

Note that the acceptable risk and acceptable cost approaches both can be very sensitive to the initial selection of a single key parameter. If these approaches are used, it is necessary to conduct a sensitivity analysis to see how conclusions would be changed if the reference level of acceptable risk or acceptable cost were different. Sensitivity analysis of key parameters is essential to all other forms of risk analysis as well, and is one way in which the uncertainty surrounding estimates can be addressed systematically.

Overview of a Risk Analysis Conceptual Framework

Figure 10-7A provides an overview of the kind of conceptual framework used to identify necessary models and necessary data in risk analysis. The major aspects to be modeled can be grouped into six models, as shown in the ovals: 1) Decision Model, 2) Ignition-Initiation Model, 3) Post-Ignition Model, 4) Loss Evaluation Model, 5) Cost Model, and (6) Cost-Benefit Comparison Model. The rectangles indicate numbers, either inputs or outputs, derived from the models. These numbers may in turn be supplied as inputs to other models later in the modeling sequence. The model refers to a "proposed change," which is a general term for anything that might be modeled—a new sprinkler system, increased compartmentation requirements, no-smoking areas, mandatory self-extinguishing cigarettes, a training program for staff, or any other change that could make fires more or less likely or more or less severe.

A Decision Model is used to describe what the building and its occupants would look like if a proposed change were or were not made. An Ignition-Initiation Model is used to estimate the probabilities of occurrence per year for each type of fire, while a Post-Ignition Model is used in parallel to estimate the expected losses per fire, for each type of fire and each type of loss (i.e., deaths, injuries, property damage). The types of fires are defined by the requirements of the two models. For example, if the Post-Ignition Model uses different parameters for smoldering and flaming fires, then that distinction must be reflected in the separation of fires into types for the Ignition-Initiation Model. When the outputs of these two models are combined, they produce estimates of expected losses per year by type of loss and for all types of fires. Then a Loss Evaluation Model is used to convert all types of loss to a common scale and produce year-by-year projections of overall expected loss, with and without the proposed change.

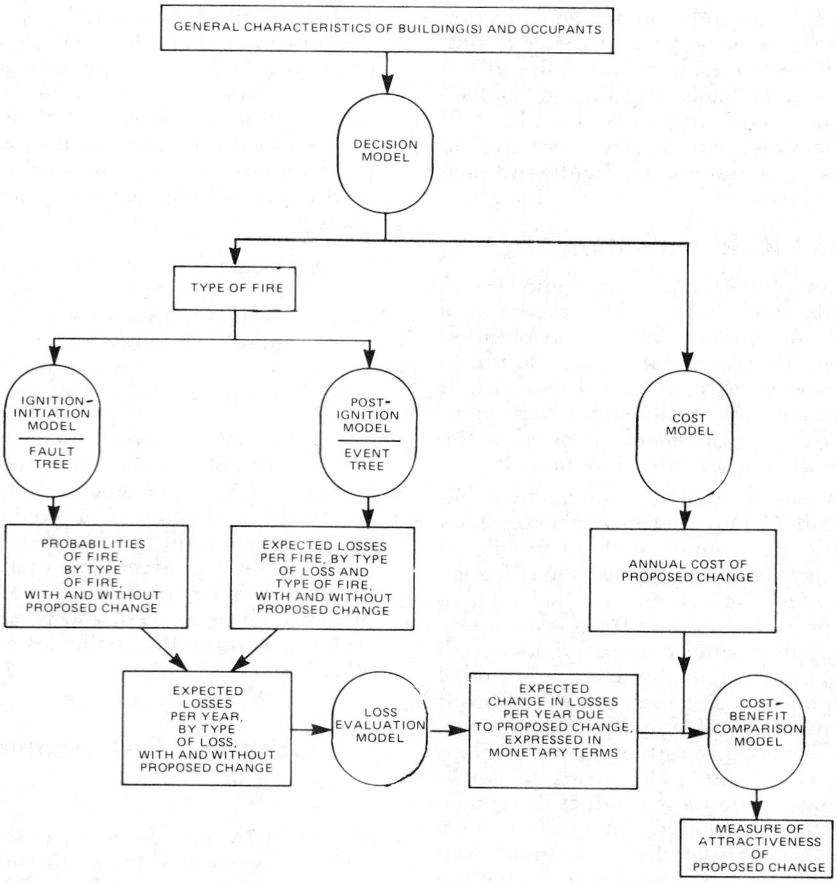

FIG. 10-7A. A risk analysis conceptual framework.

Meanwhile, on the right side of the framework, the purchase, installation, maintenance, inspection, operating, replacement, and other costs of the new system are combined by a Cost Model into year-by-year figures of the cost impact of the proposed change.

Finally, a Cost-Benefit Comparison Model produces a measure of attractiveness for the proposed change. This is simply a comparison of annualized costs and benefits, with the benefits consisting of changes in risk.

The discussion that follows will address the six component models in more detail. With respect to two terms introduced earlier, *risk estimation* involves the Decision Model, the Ignition-Initiation Model, and the Post-Ignition Model, while *risk evaluation* covers the other three models.

General Characteristics and Fire Types

Before the models shown in Figure 10-7A come into play, there must be an initial structure to the problem that describes the type of building, the characteristics of its occupants, and the types of fires to be studied. Probability distributions may be needed for any of these factors. Even if only a single building is being analyzed, that building's behavior with respect to fire may vary as a function of randomly varying conditions such as the positions of doors and windows (open or closed) or of forced air heating and cooling systems (on or off). Occupant locations and conditions also may vary in random or patterned ways. At present, fire risk analysis is able to capture only a fraction of these factors, but useful results are still possible. It is also useful in setting up a problem to be aware of any factors that cannot be explicitly addressed. This helps in interpreting the results.

The most important point to remember in defining types of fires is that all possible fire ignitions must be covered. Fires may have to be grouped into classes that are not entirely homogeneous, but it is not sound practice to exclude certain categories of fires. Suppose that the Post-Ignition Model will require each fire type to be specified in great detail (e.g., location and heat release rate of first material ignited). Then there may be either an unmanageable number of fire types to be modeled or a small number of specific fire types, each used to represent a much larger, less well-defined class.

The classification scheme should distinguish among fire scenarios that are affected differently by the systems or strategies being studied. Suppose fast response sprinklers are being evaluated for possible home use. Then the key properties of fires affecting their response to sprinklers might be identified by answering these questions: Which areas of origin would not be accessible to sprinklers (e.g., the outside of the house, concealed spaces, unsprinklered living areas such as bathrooms)? Could the fire ignition energy best be characterized as smoldering, flaming, or fast-flaming/high energy? The distinction among smoldering, flaming, and fast-flaming fires might be made to recognize the fact that fire growth (which activates the sprinkler) and smoke spread (which is the principal cause of death) do not proceed according to a relationship that is the same for all fires.

Decision Model

In addition to defining types of fires and specifying general building and occupant characteristics, it is necessary to specify all the differences that would occur if the proposed change were made. If the change involves new built-in smoke detection systems, for example, specifications for the systems would be needed. If the systems were available in two or more versions (e.g., ionization and photoelectric smoke detectors), the probability of each version being used should be estimated (e.g., from data on usage patterns or projected shares of market). Probabilities also would be needed for the variations in status of a system (e.g., fully operational, operational but blocked in one room, turned off, or removed). These specifications dictate precisely what fire protection and fire-related features would be in place to influence the course of fire if one occurs.

If the proposed change involves training staff or educating occupants, similar questions would be asked: What are the specifics of the program(s)? What is the likelihood that each version of the program would be used? If fire occurs, what would be the status of the program (e.g., everyone was trained and acted accordingly, some missed the training, some forgot, some panicked, etc.)?

It is sometimes useful to separate the parts of the Decision Model into those characteristics that were selected by a building owner or manager (e.g., a sprinkler was installed) and those that came into play after the selection (e.g., the sprinkler was installed incorrectly). The latter parts are sometimes collectively referred to as the Implementation Model. The Implementation Model isolates those factors that are hardest to control, either because they require continued alertness (e.g., without scheduled testing and maintenance, a sprinkler system's reliability will decrease) or because they are not directly under the control of the building owner or manager (e.g., a manager can order a sprinkler system, but has to work through others to make sure it is installed properly).

Neither the Implementation Model nor the larger Decision Model needs every bit of information on the proposed changes. All the models need are those details that will affect the likelihood of having a fire, the development of that fire, or the reactions of people and property to the fire. For example, some factors will incapacitate the system so that the fire will develop as if no system were present, and that is all the information needed. Some factors will degrade system performance but still permit some impact on fire development; it may be possible to model such reduced impact as simple modifications to the impact expected if the system were fully functional.

Ignition-Initiation Model

The Ignition-Initiation Model is needed to produce estimates of the probability of ignition per year, by type of fire, given a structure of fire scenarios and fire-relevant characteristics of the building and its occupants.

The Ignition-Initiation Model is a device for combining known probabilities in order to infer unknown probabilities. A simple example will illustrate the kinds of calculations that are possible and desirable. Suppose there are n brands of cigarettes. Define p_i as the share of total product usage contributed by product i; in this case p_i *is* the share of all cigarettes smoked that are brand i. Let r_i be the proportion of brand i cigarettes discarded each year in such a way as to make a fire possible. Let q_i be the probability of ignition given such an exposure for brand i; q_i is a measure of the relative self-extinguishing tendencies of brand i, but it can be affected by changes in the ignitability of materials that are typically ignited. Let F be the number of cigarette-related fires per year and let N be the number of cigarettes smoked per year.

$$\text{Then } F = \sum_{i=1}^{n} N_i\, r_i\, q_i$$

Note that there are three ways to cut down on fires from brand i cigarettes: 1) see that almost no one buys them (reduce p_i); 2) see that the people who buy them almost always dispose of used cigarettes properly (reduce r_i) and 3) see that discarded cigarettes usually self-extinguish (reduce q_i).

This model can be used to examine several different types of strategies. A ban on all cigarettes that do not meet a self-extinguishment standard would change the p_i values, because the prohibited brands would have their p_i values cut to zero, and the p_i values of all the other brands would rise to fill the gap in the market. A campaign to educate the public not to discard cigarettes would lower the r_i values; or, a requirement to reduce the flammability of couches would lower all the q_i values, because more cigarettes would self-extinguish if couches were harder to ignite.

To perform the analysis, one must set initial values for the parameters. The purpose of this example is to show how to derive values for the parameters through a combination of direct measurement, reasonable assumptions, and mathematical inference. The values of p_i might be measured through sales records or a survey of product users. The values of q_i might be measured in laboratory tests. The most elusive will be the r_i values, the measures of how often cigarettes are being discarded, whether or not fires result.

If it is assumed or can be proven that all types of cigarettes are equally likely to be discarded, then there is only one common r_i value, and it can be solved for. Or if data can be obtained on numbers of cigarette fires per year by brand of cigarette, then individual r_i values can be solved for.

In a more complex case, suppose the analyst had at least as many years of fire data as there were brands of cigarettes. Also suppose that it can be assumed or shown that year-to-year variations in fire experience were due solely to changes in market share. (This is equivalent to assuming that neither behavior in discarding cigarettes nor the propensity of each brand to start fires if discarded has changed over the years.) Then if p_i values (market shares) could be obtained for each year, it would be possible to solve for the r_i values using the years of fire data as a set of n equations in n unknowns.

These diverse approaches illustrate a general point. To estimate unknown probabilities, it is necessary to a) find direct data sources for the unknowns (e.g., survey of couch usage); b) develop reasonable assumptions as to the values of the unknowns (e.g., why the r_i might all be equal); c) find valid formulas relating the unknowns to other variables on which there is sufficient data to make inferences back to the unknown probabilities; or d) fill the gaps with expert estimates.

A full Ignition-Initiation Model needs to combine far more factors than were used in the simple illustration and to accommodate a multitude of logical and probabilistic interdependencies among the variables. There may be many different factors, none necessary for fire to occur and none sufficient to cause fire except in combination with certain other factors. The standard format for constituting such models is the fault tree or success tree, which is discussed in more detail under the more general name of "Firesafety Concepts Tree" in Section 1, Chapter 3, "Systems Concepts for Building Firesafety."

Post-Ignition Model

The Post-Ignition Model is used for estimating the severity of specified types of fires, given specified building and occupant characteristics and the status of all systems, features, products, and other changes being analyzed. The methodology for tracking the development and final consequences of a specified fire under specified building and occupant conditions may be deterministic, probabilistic, or, more likely, a mix of the two.

Fire protection engineers are aware of the rapid growth in computer-based deterministic models for analyzing the development of a fire and its effects under specified conditions. There are two special requirements for the Post-Ignition Model component of a fire risk analysis that constrain the use of existing deterministic models: 1) it cannot accommodate a more finely divided typology of fires than can be handled by the Ignition-Initiation Model (i.e., for every distinct type of fire whose development and final impact is modeled, it must also be possible to estimate the likelihood of that type of fire); and 2) it must produce not only physical descriptions of flame, gas, and smoke extent but also measures that are useful as end-measures of impact, such as deaths, injuries, and dollar-value property damage.

The Post-Ignition Model—a model of fire development and outcomes—consists of a set of linked time functions of fire characteristics and their effects. For example, the model might need to specify, at each time, the extent of flame, smoke, and gases by type, the status of fire protection systems and other building characteristics, the locations of occupants, the tenability of various locations, etc. No existing model can do all this.

To develop a practical version of the model, one must ask: 1) how many of these characteristics need be known to develop reasonably good estimates of deaths, injuries, and damage from a given fire? and 2) at which points in time will the development of a particular type of fire change as a function of the different input values to be modeled (e.g., different initial statuses of fire protection systems)? In other words, one must identify a limited number of fire descriptors to track and a limited number of points in time at which to check them.

One type of model with which to do this is an "event tree," the standard modeling format of statistical decision theory. In an event tree, each point in time is characterized by a set of events. These events indicate all the states in which the fire might be at given points in time (with the states defined by the limited number of fire descriptors previously cited). Then, for each event, one must specify the probabilities that—starting from that event—the fire will develop into each of the possible states (or events) that could characterize the fire at the next point in time. Event trees work well if all the factors being analyzed operate at relatively well defined points in time or stages of the fire. Experience in using these models indicates that the performance of most fire protection systems and features can be tied to events, which are themselves defined by characteristics of the fire. Figure 10-7B is a simple but still practical and useful example.

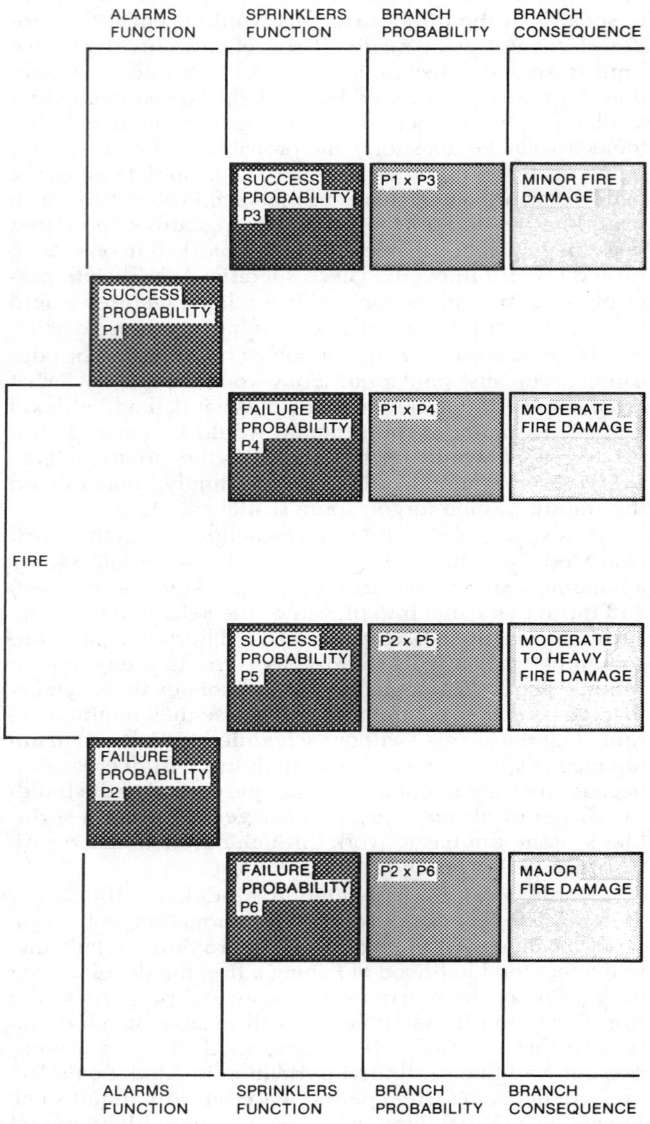

FIG. 10-7B. Event tree. (Source: Factory Mutual's Record.)

Eventually, the event tree approach may be replaced by an integrated system of fire and smoke growth models. Such a system would be based on physics and would thereby model fire development deterministically rather then probabilistically. However, the integrated system would have to be capable of tracking the inherently probabilistic aspects of people movement and of providing outputs measured in deaths, injuries, and property damage. For now, the event tree approach is workable and can produce useful results, albeit much less detailed than might be desirable.

An event tree, like any tree model, consists of nodes and arcs. Each node represents an event or stage in the development of the fire—typically a point where a particular system or feature will activate if it is operational or where the speed of the fire changes dramatically (e.g., flashover). The condition of the fire at extinguishment is captured by the outcome events, which are the various terminal events of the tree. Each outcome event is assigned values of expected losses per fire (i.e., average severity—deaths, injuries, property damage) that are the estimated losses if the fire ends in the way described by the outcome event. However, the only losses covered by these values are those that occur during the final stage of the fire or are otherwise correlated with the ultimate size of the fire. For computational reasons, deaths and some other losses that take place early in the fire may have to be associated with the stage of the fire where they occur. For example, suppose the first event in a fire is ignition and the second is the point where a fast-response sprinkler would activate. Fatal injuries occurring before that second event (e.g., due to clothing ignitions) would be captured in a loss-per-fire figure assigned to that second critical event, and would be understood to occur no matter how the fire does or does not grow after that event. These losses are sometimes referred to as "tolls" because any fire that passes through the event acquires those losses, just as a car pays a toll on an express highway.

At each event (except outcome events), there will be two or more directions in which the fire may subsequently develop, and there will be transitional probabilities associated with each of these directions. All transitional probabilities from an event add up to one. They are conditional probabilities that a fire will reach a particular event, given that it has already reached the immediately preceding event. A path is a possible sequence of events for the fire from the first event (ignition) to one of the outcome events. Each path describes the growth and extinguishment of the fire with as much detail as the model can provide. A path probability is the probability of a complete path, calculated as the product of the transitional probabilities for all the events along the path. Because several outcome events often are identical except for the paths used to reach them, it is sometimes useful to compute an outcome probability. This is the probability of a set of similar outcome events and is equal to the sum of the path probabilities for the paths ending in those outcome events. The expected loss per fire is calculated by multiplying transitional probabilities for branches leading to outcomes by the losses associated with those outcomes, then assigning those losses to the events from which the branches originated and adding any tolls associated with those events. This process is repeated (and is called "rolling back the tree") until an expected loss figure has been computed for the first event (ignition). That value then becomes the expected loss for the event tree.

Loss Evaluation Model

The explicit or implicit assignment of monetary values to lives saved and injuries averted is the key element of this model. It is a difficult step that many people find distasteful or even immoral. The first and most important point to make is that individuals are not being asked to name a price for which they would be willing to die or suffer crippling injury. Instead, they are being asked to name a price they would be willing to accept to allow their current low risk of incurring death or injury in fire to increase or what they would pay to make that risk still smaller. With a resident population of about 230 million and an annual fire death toll in the range of 5000 to 6000, an average U.S. citizen has less than one chance in 40,000 each year of dying in a fire. Even for the highest-risk groups, the risk is probably less than one chance in 5000 each year or less than one chance in 65 over an entire lifetime. A person could rationally attach a price to a 10 or 50 percent change in such a risk and still be consistent in believing life (i.e., the certainty of losing it) is beyond price. A rational person would pay much more to reduce the probability of dying from 1.0 to 0.8 than he or she would pay to cut that risk from 0.3 to 0.1.

If that point is made, the next task is identifying what particular figures should be used for the value of life and the value of injury when considering alternatives that change risks in the range characteristic of fire risk. In the 1960s and earlier, the value of life was generally calculated on the basis of discounted foregone future earnings. This approach implicitly assigned no value to the lives of retired people and full-time housewives, and negligible value to the lives of older workers and young children. Such distinctions were philosophically objectionable. Even for prime wage earners, the methodology did not afford any guarantee that the value obtained would match the price people wanted to pay for risk reduction. In recent years, this approach has been largely abandoned in favor of calculations of willingness to pay to reduce risk of death. Practically speaking, the shift in approach roughly tripled the standard values of life.[1]

For all the philosophical disagreements, the actual values attached to lives saved, however calculated, tend to be concentrated within two orders of magnitude. Most studies estimate the value of life in hundreds of thousands of dollars or millions of dollars. Some of the higher values are taken from jury awards that compensate deaths. No estimates go as high as tens of millions of dollars or as low as the low end of tens of thousands of dollars.

It is difficult to set up fully persuasive methodologies to assess a popular consensus on value of life because people do not like to think about death. If asked about the value of a whole life, they refer to the sanctity of life and say the value is infinite. If asked about the value of a shift in the risk of dying, they find it difficult to relate to such a choice. If presented with forced-choice situations that contain implicit values of life, they give answers that can reflect the way the questions were posed. Nevertheless, a 1988 study of assessments used in evaluating a wide range of proposed federal regulations concluded that "there has recently been some convergence around a figure of $1 to $2 million per statistical life."[2]

Another alternative is to use a value per year of life saved. A large number of regulatory cases were examined and the ranking of alternatives found was not drastically affected by the use of life-year value versus life value.[1] However, use of life-year value tends to give more credit to saving children (by up to double, since their expected life spans are about double those of the population at large) and less credit to saving older adults (by a factor of four or more). Firesafety in schools would be boosted and firesafety in nursing homes might be abandoned if life-year value calculations were used.

Even after deciding to use willingness to pay as the standard for value of life, some difficult technical problems remain. One is the question of whether to calculate separately the willingness to pay for each individual (or each major group) affected by a proposed change. In an analysis aimed at the individual property owner or manager, such differentiation is unavoidable and should be an explicit, or at least implicit, part of any analysis of the market for a new product, system, or approach.

There also have been several studies of factors that affect willingness to pay. Willingness to pay is lower for the poor, older Americans, the seriously ill or handicapped, and the risk takers. For the poor, of course, ability to pay is lower, too. For older Americans and the seriously ill, the lower value given to life seems to reflect the fact that the quantity (for the older American) or the quality (for the sick) of life remaining is well below the national norm. However, all these groups with lower willingness to pay also tend to have relatively high risks of becoming fire fatalities. They are precisely the groups to target if total lives saved were the criterion of choice. Conversely, the people most willing to pay—affluent, healthy, risk-averse, young heads of families—are the ones least likely to benefit because their current risks of dying in fire are already below average.

Another reason for variations in the willingness to pay involves the nature of the risks rather than the characteristics of those who experience these risks. Risks that are voluntary, nonessential, occupational, or results of product misuse are deemed less serious than risks that are involuntary, essential, public, or results of normal product use. A risk of death to someone who lives near a nuclear reactor is valued more highly than an equal risk of death to someone who works in a coal mine. The difference is based on the assumption that occupational risks are more likely to be voluntary and more likely to be financially compensated. (Both of these assumptions are questionable. Workers in hazardous occupations such as mining may have few realistic occupational alternatives, while residents of hazardous areas, like floodplains, may have many alternative places to live and may have received financial compensation in the form of lower housing costs that at least equal any financial benefits received by the workers.) Similarly, risks of death associated with voluntary nonessential activities, such as smoking and hang gliding, are valued less than equal risks associated with voluntary but essential activities, such as driving a car. In fire risk, this argument appears in the debate over the fairness of imposing flame resistance standards (and accompanying costs) on all mattresses to protect people who choose to smoke in bed.

Deaths occurring in major multi-fatality incidents are valued differently—and generally more highly—than deaths occurring in smaller incidents. Major incidents are termed dread hazards in the risk analysis literature; it is the factor of dread—the greater fear of death occurring in a major incident—that inflates the value of risk in such cases. The effect of major incidents on families and communities has been used to argue for both higher and lower weighting of such deaths—higher because familial bloodlines may be extinguished, lower because multiple deaths in one family mean fewer survivors to mourn per fatality.[3]

Dread incidents constitute an especially dramatic example of the phenomenon of risk aversion. For example, most people feel that if loss A is ten times as great as loss B but only one-tenth as likely, losses A and B still are not equally onerous. The general public tends to be more concerned about fire scenarios that may kill, say, 100 people once every three years than they are about fire scenarios that kill one person at a time every week, year after year.

Technical adjustments can be made to incorporate some risk aversion into a benefit calculation. Such adjustments will have less effect on dwelling fire risk calculations, where really large incidents are impossible, than on risk calculations for large residential (e.g., hotel), institutional, or public assembly properties.

Values for injuries avoided can be estimated more directly than values for fatalities avoided because direct costs such as medical expense and lost wages seem more appropriate as indicators of value. A survey was used to estimate direct injury-related costs for residential fires.[4] Based on their figures, after adjusting for inflation and for the fact that their cost-per-injury figures are dominated by very small injuries from unreported fires, an estimate of $5000 might be obtained for actual costs per injury received in a reported fire. Willingness to pay to avoid an injury is greater because of pain and suffering considerations, so a figure of $35,000 was recently derived by economists at the U.S. Consumer Product Safety Commission.[5]

This average is based on a highly skewed distribution. The vast majority of injuries can be valued in the low hundreds of dollars or less, but a small number of serious burn injuries each year—considerably fewer than the corresponding number of fire fatalities—can cost hundreds of thousands or even millions of dollars in medical expenses. These few injuries account for most of the overall cost average. This suggests that analyses of expected impacts of new systems or programs on injuries should, if possible, separate serious and nonserious injuries when average values are used to make sure that the *average* values are not understated as *typical* values.

For property damage, the losses probably will already have emerged from the Post-Ignition Model expressed in monetary terms, but that is not necessarily so, and even if it is, some conversions may still be necessary. If fire growth and smoke spread models have been used, property damage may have been calculated in such terms as rooms exposed to fire or smoke for various lengths of time, or areas where structural integrity has been lost. Converting such descriptions to monetary equivalents would require data and models that do not now exist, despite repeated efforts to develop them.[6]

Even if damage is expressed in dollars, one may wish to take account of the fact that the loss faced by the property owner may be mediated by such things as insurance. In that case, it would be necessary to estimate the likely reduction in out-of-pocket, uninsured damage plus insurance premiums, rather than the likely reduction in total direct damage achievable.

Another consideration in the Loss Evaluation Model is whether to include an adjustment for indirect loss—such items as lost wages, costs of a temporary location, and lost revenue for days that a business is closed. These losses can be very large in individual cases, such as the 1980 MGM Grand Hotel fire, but the most recent studies indicate that in the aggregate they tend to be an order of magnitude smaller than the direct losses.[7]

Cost Model

Costs may be divided into a) initial costs of the proposed changes being studied; b) the ongoing costs of these changes once they have been made; and c) the ripple effects on other costs, such as the need to increase the water supply to support a sprinkler system. The latter could involve cost increases or cost reductions, including calculation of costs for many years into the future. To make this task manageable, the analysis can be set up in terms of the normal periods of maintaining, repairing, and replacing the items being analyzed. This is called life-cycle costing. An overview of major components of each of these three types of costs is shown below.

A. Initial Costs of Changes Being Studied

1. Equipment Costs. For new products, it may be necessary to estimate what costs will be when mass production is under way. In many cases, the mass production cost continues to drop as further development occurs. (Smoke detectors have shown this pattern, for example.)
2. Installation Costs. Estimation of costs of installation may require an analysis of the steps required for installation, because the person-hours and skills required for those steps may be higher or lower than for comparable products already in use. (For example, plastic pipe may be faster to install than iron pipe, and it may require less time-consuming effort to protect carpets and furniture from soiling during installation.)

   Labor costs per hour may vary considerably from one place to another, as may overhead rates; these variations argue in favor of a serious effort to collect representative data.
3. Financing Costs. These will be relevant if the systems are financed through time-payment plans (e.g., as part of what is covered by the building mortgage).
4. Permit/License Costs. There may be some one-time fees required to install the systems.
5. Some Costs Offset in Resale. If the new systems and features add to the resale value of the property, this will partially offset the initial costs.

B. Ongoing Costs of Changes Being Studied

1. Operating Costs. A new system or product may need labor, power, or some other continuing input to operate. These costs need to be included.
2. Inspection and Testing Costs. Many systems require periodic inspection and testing after installation. These costs should be included. Labor usually will be the main cost element, but some tests (such as sprinkler tests) may involve materials costs, and other tests may require destruction of a sample of system components that would need replacement.
3. Repair, Maintenance, and Replacement Costs. Most systems will require repair and maintenance, and—if the study period is long enough—periodic replacement will need to be considered.
4. Costs of Non-Fire Damage Caused by the Systems. An example would be water damage due to accidental discharge of a sprinkler.
5. Permit/License Costs. An example would be the standby water charge levied in some jurisdictions on buildings equipped with sprinklers.
6. Salvage Revenues for Cost Offsets. Equipment that is replaced may be resellable. If so, salvage revenues help reduce net system costs.

C. Ripple Effects on Other Building Costs

1. Costs of Supporting Systems. Many new products may require replacement, modification, or addition of critical supporting systems (e.g., extra water supply for home sprinkler system in a rural area). The equipment and installation costs of these changes in supporting systems need to be identified and included. So do any changes in operating costs, repair and maintenance costs, inspection and testing costs, etc., for the modified supporting systems, and any changes in these ongoing costs for unmodified supporting systems.
2. Special Incentives or Credits. Insurance premium reductions that reflect the expected reduction in direct loss should be counted in the Loss Evaluation Model. Extra reductions offered as inducements to buy systems, as well as incentives or credits in property or income taxes, should be counted here.
3. Property Value and Tax Impacts. Changes in property taxes reflecting changed property value assessments should be considered. There may be tax consequences if the features add value to the property.
4. Changes in Land Costs or Required Building Features. Added safety features may permit trade-offs in the form of increased density or reduced requirements for other building features. These need to be accommodated as costs, and any trade-offs in other safety features need to be addressed in the Loss Evaluation Models as well.
5. Changes in Costs of Public Fire Protection. If buildings in a group receive similar modifications, it may be possible to accept longer response times or reduced sizes of fire suppression teams, resulting in reduced costs of public fire protection.

   These lists are not exhaustive, but they indicate the need to estimate the effects of different decisions and assess their cost impacts.

Cost-Benefit Comparison Model

The Cost Model and Loss Evaluation Model produce time streams of costs and risk-reduction benefits—that is, year-by-year estimates of costs and of reductions in fire deaths, injuries, and property damage, with the latter expressed as total monetized losses. To compare the costs to the benefits, the two time streams need to be combined into a single, manageable, indicator of net benefits.

To compare future and present costs and benefits, it is necessary to decide what the future costs and benefits are worth in the present. This involves the concept of opportunity cost. Suppose $20 was spent now on a fire-safety system and $20 received back 10 years later in the form of reduced property damage in a fire. This would not be a break-even proposition because alternative investments could pay interest over that period.

Assumptions about the attractiveness of such investments are reflected in an assumed discount rate—a proportion between 0 and 1 used to reduce the value of future costs and benefits. Most fire risk reducing strategies involve greater costs than benefits in the near years and greater benefits than costs in the later years; this makes the discount rate a critical factor in overall assessment of whether the benefits justify the costs. Also, even if opportunity costs were not involved, there would be a cost associated with delayed consumption. All other things being equal, people usually prefer to have goods and services now rather than later, and a discount rate reflects that fact.

If a cost is incurred ten years from now, for instance, the discount rate must be applied ten times to translate that cost into a figure comparable with today's costs. This figure is called the present value of a future cost or benefit.

It is calculated as the discount rate raised to a power equal to the number of years in the future when the cost or benefit will occur, then multiplied by the value of that cost or benefit.

A reasonable discount rate can be assumed for the purpose of analysis or can be calculated as the discount rate required just to balance benefits and costs. If the latter is done, the derived discount rate is called the internal rate of return. It can be used to compare alternatives in the same way that a benefit-cost ratio can be used.

The two principal objections to discounting of future safety benefits are 1) the possibility of very large, perhaps even irreversible, effects at a remote point in the future, and 2) the cumulative effects of the short-term biases induced by rigorous application of discounted assessments. The first objection is not a great concern for fire-risk problems because fire does not produce irreversible effects on the scale contemplated by this argument. At most, several small towns could be wiped out by a wildfire (ignoring, for the moment, the possibility of wartime firestorms). Nevertheless, as a technical matter, it is worth considering the possibility that discount rates undervalue the real value people assign to events beyond the next decade or so. For example, most people would regard benefits in 105 years as equal to benefits in 100 years; but under constant discounting of say, 10 percent, the former would be only 59 percent of the latter.[8]

As for the cumulative problems of short-term bias, this has been discussed more in the context of business research, development, and innovation in general, than in regard to safety innovations in particular. In business, investments are expected to balance benefits and costs within three to seven years, but many analysts believe such requirements are too demanding and tend, over time, to choke off truly dramatic breakthroughs. The result, in business, can be eventual loss of competitive edge to a competitor willing to take a longer view. One pertinent article[9] was particularly forceful on this point, arguing that the implied opportunity cost model underlying a short payback period requirement assumes a standard reference alternative investment that, contrary to the model's assumptions, is not itself immune to the cumulative effects of a stream of choices driven by short-term considerations. The fallacy, then, is in assuming that there always is an alternative investment that pays back in three to seven years; the short-term-driven decisions may have the cumulative effect of eroding all such alternatives.

The technical approach to addressing this concern is to check the sensitivity of any conclusions to the use of a lower discount rate. Any innovation that year by year, after the initial cost period, produces more benefits than costs, can be made to look attractive through the selection of a sufficiently low discount rate. It is risky, however, to use too low a discount rate, because that will give a misleading picture of what people will be willing to pay.

Other approaches, such as using a higher discount rate for costs than for benefits, can produce perverse results. For example, such an approach could mean that an attractive safety program would seem even more attractive if its implementation were delayed. In this way, a program can be made to seem attractive but may never be implemented because further delay will always make it seem even more attractive.[10]

Summary of Conclusions

Fire risk analysis is a technique still in its infancy but already capable of pulling together, reducing, and providing perspectives on large quantities of data from many sources. Recent rapid advances in the size and quality of fire-related data bases and in the power and affordability of computers have helped turn fire risk analysis into a practical tool for individual decision-making and especially for large-scale decision-making by governments and companies. The accelerating pace of development of computerized models of fire development and occupant behavior will eventually produce integrated deterministic/probabilistic models, providing even more powerful tools for fire risk analysis.

At present there are only a few abbreviated published examples of fire risk analysis,[11,12] but other more elaborate examples, providing more detailed illustrations and more broadly applicable models, are in progress. The largest single source of developmental studies in general-purpose fire risk analysis in the U.S. has been the National Fire Protection Research Foundation, whose multi-year developmental project was nearly complete at the time this chapter was written. The Nuclear Regulatory Commission has sponsored some of the best work in the field, but it is highly specialized to the problems of nuclear power plants and may need more work to translate to other settings. Individual fire risk analyses have appeared in materials prepared as background for regulatory decisions,[13] but these also tend to be highly specialized.

Until better materials are available to demonstrate the specific analytic techniques of fire risk analysis, it is useful to recognize the essence of fire risk analysis: creation of the simplest possible framework for identifying the available choices and estimating their consequences. Whether the estimates consist of nothing more than a series of guesses or are the result of an elaborate network of sophisticated models, laboratory tests, and fire experience, the framework in principle remains the same. Its purpose is to assemble all the information available, however slight or extensive, and focus that information on how and how much things would change as a result of the choices made. Identifying choices, predicting consequences, evaluating those consequences, and finally making choices—those are the steps of fire risk analysis. However complicated the methods used, the purpose is always to perform these familiar tasks that are the basics of rational decision-making.

BIBLIOGRAPHY

References Cited

1. Graham, J.K., and Vaupel, J. W. 1981. "Value of a Life: What Difference Does It Make?" *Risk Analysis*, March 1981, pp 89–95.
2. Gillette, C. P., and Hopkins, T. D., "Federal Agency Valuations of Human Life," *Report to the Administrative Conference of the United States*, unpublished, April 1988.
3. Starr, C., and Whipple, C., "Risks of Risk Decisions," *Science*, June 6, 1980, pp. 1114ff.
4. Munson, M. J., and Ohls, J. C., *Indirect Costs of Residential Fires*, FA-61, Federal Emergency Management Agency, Washington, DC, April 1980.
5. Hall, J. R., Jr., "Expected Changes in Fire Damage from Reducing Cigarette Ignition Propensity, " *Final Report to Technical Study Group of Cigarette Safety Act of 1984*, National Fire Protection Association, Quincy, MA, July 16, 1987.

6. Hall, J. R., "Reduce Fire Loss Guesstimates," *Fire Service Today*, Nov. 1982, pp. 11–13.
7. Hall, J. R., Jr., *The Total Cost of Fire in the United States through 1988*, NFPA Fire Analysis and Research Division, Quincy, MA, November 1990.
8. Whipple, C., "Energy Production Risks: What Perspective Should We Take?" *Risk Analysis*, March 1981, pp. 29–35.
9. Hayes, R. H., and Garvin, D. A., "Managing As If Tomorrow Mattered," *Harvard Business Review*, May–June 1982, pp. 70ff.
10. Keller, E. B., and Cretin, S., "Discounting of Life-Saving and Other Non-Monetary Effects," *Management Science*, 1983, pp. 300–306.
11. Ruegg, R. T., and Fuller, S. K., "A Benefit-Cost Model of Residential Fire Sprinkler Systems," *NBS Technical Note 1203*, National Bureau of Standards, Gaithersburg, MD, Nov. 1984.
12. Helzer, S. G., *et al.*, "Decision Analysis of Strategies for Reducing Upholstered Furniture Fire Losses," *NBS Technical Note 1101*, National Bureau of Standards, Washington, DC, June 1979.
13. Hall, J. R., Jr., and Stiefel, S. W., "Decision Analysis Model for Passenger-Aircraft Fire Safety With Application to Fire-Blocking of Seats," *NBSIR 84-2817*, National Bureau of Standards, Washington, DC, March 1984.

Additional Readings

Berlin, G. N., "Probability Models in Fire Protection Engineering," *SFPE Handbook of Fire Protection Engineering*, National Fire Protection Association, Quincy, MA, 1988.

Castino, G. T. and Harmathy, T. Z., "Fire Risk Assessment," *ASTM STP 762*, American Society for Testing and Materials, Philadelphia, PA, 1982.

Hall, J. R., Jr., "Progress in Fire Risk Analysis Methods," *9th Joint Panel Meeting* of the UJNR Panel on Fire Research and Safety, NBSIR 88-3753, April 1988, Center for Fire Research, Gaithersberg, MD, Apil 1988, pp. 131–135.

Kazarians, M., Siu, N., and Apostolakis, G., "Risk Management Application of Fire Risk Analysis," *Proceedings* of the First International Symposium on Fire Safety Science, Hemisphere, 1986, pp. 1029-1038.

Kersken-Bradley, M., "Application of Fire Risk Analysis," *SFPE Handbook of Fire Protection Engineering*, National Fire Protection Association, Quincy, MA, 1988.

Lawrence, W. W., *Of Acceptable Risk*, Kaufman Publishing, Los Altos, CA, 1976.

Noonan, F., "Decision Analysis for Risk Management of Firesafety Hazards," *Proceedings* of the First International Symposium on Fire Safety Science, Hemisphere, Washington DC, 1986, pp. 621-625.

Ramachandran, G., "Probabilistic Approach to Fire Risk Evaluation," *Fire Technology*, Vol. 24, No. 3, 1988, p. 204.

Raiter, S., *Risk Analysis and Risk Management: A Selected Bibliography*, Vance Bibliographies, Monticello, IL., 1987.

Rowe, W. D., *An Anatomy of Risk*, reprint, R. E. Krieger, Malabar, FL, 1988.

Sekizawa, A. and Jin, T., "Fire Risk Evaluation Method for Multi-occupancy Building," *9th Joint Panel Meeting* of the UJNR *Panel on* Fire Research and Safety, *NBSIR 88-3753*, National Bureau of Standards, Gaithersburg, MD, pp. 189–202.

Singh, J. and Thomas, P. M., "Calculating the Overall Fire Risk in New Building Designs," *Fire Prevention*, No. 224 (Nov. 1989), pp. 32–36.

Tomes, W. J., "Risk Analysis," *Fire Engineering*, Vol. 138, No. 4, 1985, pp. 20, 22–25.

Vesely, W. E., *et al.*, *Fault Tree Handbook*, National Technical Information Service, Springfield, VA, 1981.

Watts, J. M., "Fire Risk Assessment Schedules," *SFPE Handbook of Fire Protection Engineering*, National Fire Protection Association, Quincy, MA, 1988.

INTRODUCTION TO FIRE MODELING

Dr. Craig Beyler

Modeling is an inherent part of research in science and engineering, and its application to fire is as old as scientific research into fire behavior itself. The first book devoted solely to modeling in fire research was published in 1960.[1] Modern fire research, coupled with the ever-increasing power of computers, has given rise to highly complex models that can only be implemented as computer fire models. While computer fire models have popularized fire modeling, these computer-based models do not differ substantially from earlier fire models; they just are more complex and possess greater capabilities.

Models can be classified into two broad classes: physical models and mathematical models. Physical models attempt to reproduce fire phenomena in a simplified physical situation. Scale models are a very widespread form of modeling, as full-scale experiments are expensive, difficult, and sometimes wholly infeasible. Insights can often be gained by studying fire phenomena at reduced physical scale. Mathematical models are sets of equations that describe the behavior of a physical system. Very often, the goal of physical models is to uncover laws governing the behavior of physical/chemical systems. The resulting mathematical model can then be used to predict the behavior of real physical systems. Thus, physical and mathematical models are interrelated and complementary.

PHYSICAL FIRE MODELS

Physical modeling does not simply mean conducting experiments at reduced physical scale. That is, reducing the linear dimensions of a physical situation and conducting experiments with the reduced-scale model is not sufficient. In addition to geometric scaling, it is necessary to maintain mechanical, thermal, and chemical similarity in the reduced-scale model. The scaling laws required to maintain these similarities can be determined from dimensional analysis or from the fundamental equations describing the physical/chemical phenomena.

The most widespread physical scaling laws in fire are known as "Froude modeling," which is applicable to buoyant flows associated with fires. Froude modeling requires that the ratio of buoyant forces to inertia forces be maintained. The Froude number, Fr, can be expressed as

$$\mathrm{Fr} \sim Q^{2/5}/D \sim V/\sqrt{D}$$

where Q is the fire heat release rate, D is the physical scale of the experiment, and V is a characteristic velocity. Thus, if a half-scale experiment is to be performed, the heat release must be reduced to 18 percent of the full-scale heat release to maintain the same Fr number and thus ensure that the flow velocities scale in geometrically similar locations in the half-scale and full scale models. The velocities themselves scale as the square root of the scale at constant Fr

$$V \sim \sqrt{D}$$

Froude modeling has been used successfully to understand plume flows, ceiling jet flows, and flame heights. Flame-height correlation models based on Froude modeling have been successful over a wide range of physical scales. An example is shown in Figure 10-8A, which was developed by McCaffrey.[2] The flame height to fire source diameter, L/D, is shown as a function of the $\sqrt{\mathrm{Fr}}$. *The correlation is successful over twelve decades of* Fr, *an amazingly wide range of applicability for any correlation or model.*

Because different fire phenomena scale differently, it is not generally possible to study complex fire situations in small scale. This limits the use of scale modeling principles. It is notably difficult to scale convective flows and radiation at the same time. Thus, Froude modeling cannot be applied readily to fire problems where radiation is important, for instance.

Physical modeling does not always involve major reductions in physical scale. Physical models may simply seek to simplify complex phenomena into a manageable and understandable problem. Examples of this type of physical modeling can be found as far back as the ASTM E119 fire-resistance test. The ASTM E119 time-

Dr. Craig Beyler is technical director of Hughes Associates, Inc., editor of the Journal of *Fire Protection Engineering*, section editor of the *SFPE Handbook of Fire Protection Engineering*, and adjunct professor of Fire Protection Engineering at Worcester Polytechnic Institute.

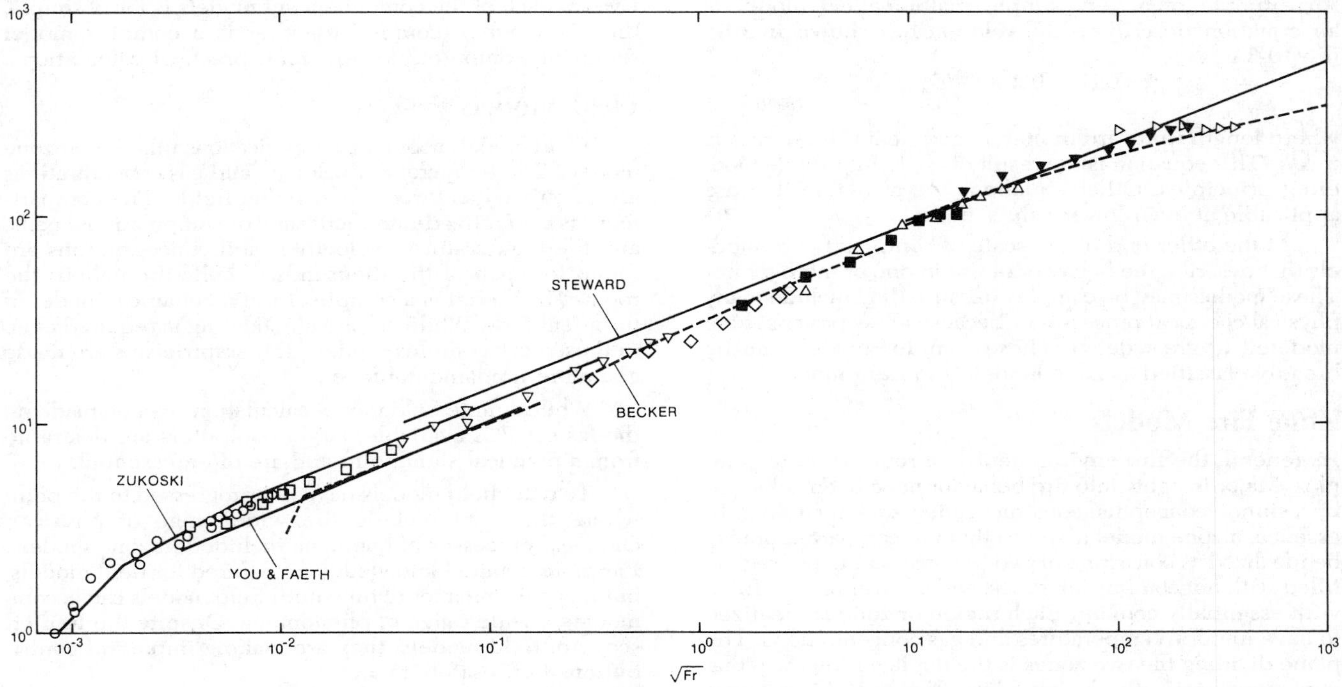

FIG. 10-8A. Flame-height correlation model based on Froude modeling.

temperature curve shown in Figure 10-8B was selected as a representative time-temperature curve for testing structural assemblies. The E119 fire-resistance test is a form of physical modeling. The furnace environment is intended to model the fire environment experienced by structural members in a fire. The portions of the building structure exposed in an E119 furnace are intended to model the fire behavior of the building structure in a fire. No single time-temperature exposure can represent all fires, and testing portions of building structures does not fully represent the behavior of the structure, but the results of the simplified E119 test are useful nonetheless. Over the decades the value and the limitations of this wide-spread physical model have been learned.

All standard fire tests are physical models of fire behavior. The adequacy of these physical models varies widely. There is a trend in the development of modern fire test methods to consider explicitly the adequacy of the test method as a physical model of actual fire behavior and response to fire.

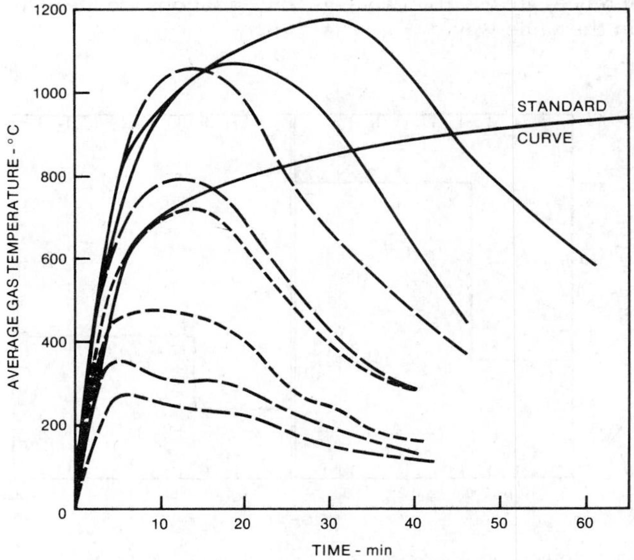

FIG. 10-8B. Representative time-temperature curve.

MATHEMATICAL FIRE MODELS

Mathematical fire models can be classified as either probabilistic or deterministic models. Probabilistic models attempt to deal with the random nature of fire behavior, while deterministic models presume that, given a well-defined physical situation, the fire growth and behavior is entirely determined. Both approaches are valuable in understanding fire.

Deterministic Fire Models

Deterministic fire models can range from simple one-line correlations of data to highly complex models requiring hours of computing time using mainframe computers. The unifying aspect of these models is that the course of a fire is fixed by the variables that establish the environment in which it occurs. The physical conditions that determine the progress and outcome of the fire are called the fire scenario. It includes the fuels involved, the arrangement of the fuels, the characteristics of the building and its fire protection systems, the location of the ignition, the location and capabilities of occupants, and any other variables that affect the fire's outcome. Thus, for all deterministic fire models the formulation of the fire scenario is of critical importance.

An example of a very simple mathematical model is an equation describing the relationship shown in Figure 10-8A.

$$L/D = 0.2\ (Q^{2/5}/D)$$

where length units are in meters and heat release rate is in kW. This equation is the result of applying Froude modeling principles. Other equations are available that are applicable at even lower values of *L/D*.

At the other end of the scale of complexity are models that describe the behavior of fire in one or more rooms. These models may be complex because they include many physical/chemical processes or because a few processes are modeled in great detail. These complex models can be broadly classified as zone models and field models.

Zone Fire Models

In general, the fire environment in a room is quite complex. Major insights into fire behavior have been achieved by a simple conceptual construct called zone modeling. In essence, a zone model assumes that the compartment may be idealized as consisting of two regions: an upper region, filled with hot combustion gases, and a lower region, filled with essentially cool air. Each region or zone is idealized to have uniform temperatures and gas concentrations. The plane dividing the two zones is the hot layer interface that may move vertically during a fire. Figure 10-8C shows a comparison of the temperature profile in a room fire with the idealized zone model equivalent. In one case, the zone model concept matches reality quite well; in the other, differences are clearly seen. Gas concentrations are idealized in the same way.

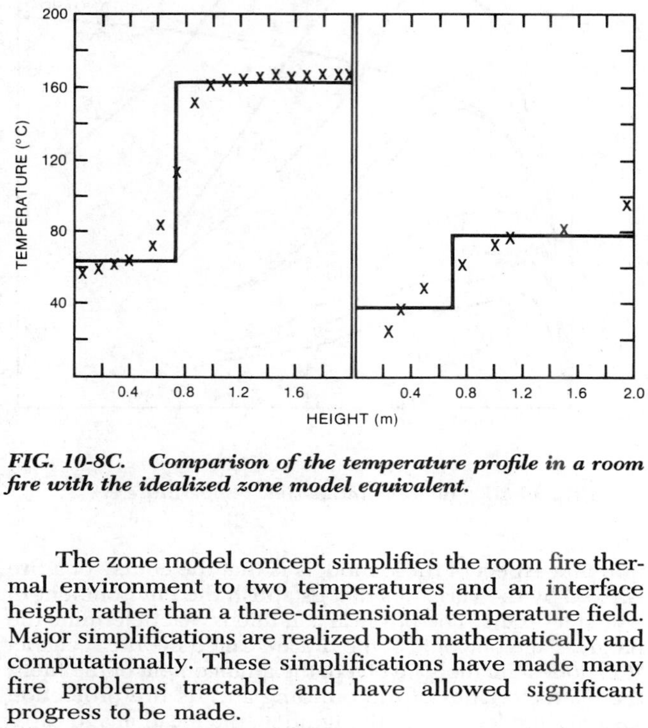

FIG. 10-8C. Comparison of the temperature profile in a room fire with the idealized zone model equivalent.

The zone model concept simplifies the room fire thermal environment to two temperatures and an interface height, rather than a three-dimensional temperature field. Major simplifications are realized both mathematically and computationally. These simplifications have made many fire problems tractable and have allowed significant progress to be made.

Of course, additional components are needed to specify fully the fire environment. Vent flows, plume entrainment, heat transfer, and combustion models are needed. Even if each of the component submodels is fairly simple, the result when coupled together is a complex model requiring computers for efficient, practical calculations.

Field Models

Field models avoid the simplifications inherent in zone models. The temperature, velocity, and gas concentrations are calculated as three-dimensional fields. The compartment is descretized into thousands of computational cells, and the temperatures, velocities, and concentrations are found for each of the thousands of cells throughout the room. The model is a complex fluid mechanical model of turbulent flow. While empirical modeling is required even in these very complex models, the empiricisms are made at a more fundamental level.

While simple field model calculations can be made on the fastest PCs available, larger computers are desirable from a practical standpoint and are often essential.

To date, field models have not progressed to the point where they can include the wide range of physical/chemical processes phenomena included in zone models. Far more detailed knowledge is required for field models, but it is only a matter of time until field models can accommodate a wide range of phenomena. Despite the limited scope of field models, they are making important contributions to firesafety today.

Probabilistic Models

Probabilistic fire models can be categorized into three classes: network, statistical, and simulation. Each of these deals with the uncertainties associated with fire growth processes.

Network models are fire growth models in which the transition from one fire stage to another and the effectiveness of fire suppression systems, manual fire fighting, passive fire protection, and so on are governed by user-assigned probabilities that are based on historical data, or engineering evaluations, or both. In some cases, these probabilities are single values, and in other models, the probabilities are time-dependent.

Statistical models represent the probability of an occurrence as it is determined from historical data. A classic example of a statistical model is the occurrence of fire alarms. Fire alarms are random events that are, within certain constraints, uniform in nature. That is, a fire or fire alarm might occur at any time with equal probability. Clearly, one of the constraints on this behavior is that the time of day must be controlled. It is well known that fires are a function of the time of day, so one must restrict attention to a single time of day. The probability of *k* fire alarms occurring over the period *s* is given by

$$p(k) = \frac{(\lambda s)^k}{k!}\ e^{-\lambda s}$$

where λ is the mean frequency of fire alarms. This statistical model describes the probability of a given number of alarms, *k*, occurring during a specified period of time, *s*. Such a statistical model can be very useful in fire protection resource planning.

Simulation methods are an interesting hybrid of probabilistic and deterministic models. These models regard fires as deterministic once the fire is fully defined. However, the inputs to the models are assumed to follow probabilistic models. Thus, the inputs to the deterministic model are treated as random variables. Such variables might include which furniture item is ignited or how far open the door is when the fire starts. A large series of runs is performed by selecting inputs from the probabilistic models, and the range and frequency of different outcomes are examined. Such modeling combines elements of both probabilistic and deterministic models.[3]

CONCLUSIONS

Fire modeling is an old and well-developed field, though much remains to be done. Physical models and mathematical models have made and are making important contributions to firesafety and fire protection.

These fire models are an important and growing part of fire protection engineering. Computer fire models are simply the most recent and complex engineering models of fire. Their use requires a knowledge of the underlying fire science and fire protection engineering principles. The following chapters in the section of the handbook describe various aspects of fire modeling in more detail.

BIBLIOGRAPHY

References Cited

1. National Academy of Sciences, *The Use of Models in Fire Research*, Conference Proceeding of November 8-10, Washington, DC, 1959.
2. McCaffrey, B., "Some Measurements of the Radiative Power Output of Diffusion Flames," *Paper WSS/CI 81-15*, Western States Section Meeting of the Combustion Institute, 1981.
3. Blasdell, W., *Monte Carlo Simulation of Fire Growth*, Center for Firesafety Studies, Worcester Polytechnic Institute, Worcester, MA, 1987.

DETERMINISTIC COMPUTER FIRE MODELS

William D. Walton, P.E., and Edward K. Budnick, P.E.

Computer models are simply computer programs that model or simulate a process or phenomena. Computer models have been used for some time in the design and analysis of fire protection hardware. The use of computer models, commonly known as design programs, has become the industry's standard method for designing water supply and automatic sprinkler systems. These programs perform large numbers of tedious and lengthy calculations and provide the user with accurate, cost-optimized designs in a fraction of the time required for manual procedures.

In addition to the design of fire protection hardware, computer models may also be used to evaluate the effects of fire on people and property. These computer fire models can provide a faster and more accurate estimate of the impact of a fire and the measures used to prevent or control the fire than many of the methods previously used. While manual calculation methods provide good estimates of specific fire effects (e.g., prediction of time to flashover), they are not well suited for comprehensive analyses involving the time-dependent interactions of multiple physical and chemical processes present in developing fires.

In recent years, increasing attention has been given to the development and use of computer fire models. They have been used by engineers and architects for building design, building officials for plan review, the fire service for pre-fire planning, investigators for post-fire analysis, groups writing fire codes, materials manufacturers, fire researchers, and educators. While these models are not a replacement for building and fire codes, they still can be valuable tools for the fire professional.

The state of the art in computer fire modeling is changing rapidly. Understanding of the processes involved in fire growth is improving, and thus the technical basis for the models is improving. The capabilities, documentation, and support for a given model can change dramatically over a short period of time. In addition, computer technology itself (both software and hardware) is advancing rapidly. A few years ago, a large mainframe computer was required to use most of the computer fire models. Today, almost all of the models can be run on personal computers. Therefore, rather than provide an exhaustive discussion of rapidly changing state-of-the-art available computer models, the following discussion will focus on a representative selection. The reader should refer to the bibliography at the end of this chapter for in-depth reviews of particular models.

In general, computer models for fire hazard prediction can be grouped into two categories: enclosure fire models and special-purpose fire models.

ENCLOSURE FIRE MODELS

Major advancements have occurred in the development of computational models structured to predict the interaction of multiple fire processes involving heat transfer, fluid mechanics, and combustion chemistry occurring at the same time in an enclosure. These models provide estimates of particular elements of hazard development such as fire growth, temperature rise, and smoke generation and transport. Some models are able to address multiple rooms. Others are confined to the room of fire origin. Generally, the large number of mathematical expressions to be solved simultaneously in any of these models necessitates the use of a computer.

There are two general classes of computer models for analyzing enclosure fire development.

Probabilistic Models

Probabilistic models treat fire growth as a series of sequential events or states. These models are sometimes referred to as state transition models. Mathematical rules are established to govern the transfer from one event to another (e.g., from ignition to established burning). Probabilities are assigned to each transfer point based on analysis of relevant experimental data and historical fire incident data. These models do not normally make direct use of the physical and chemical equations describing the fire processes.

Mr. Budnick is a vice president and senior engineer with Hughes Associates, Inc., based in Wheaton, MD. Mr. Walton is a research fire protection engineer in the Fire Suppression Research Group of the U.S. National Institute of Standards and Technology, Building and Fire Research Laboratory, Gaithersburg, MD.

Deterministic Models

In contrast, deterministic models represent the processes encountered in a compartment fire by interrelated mathematical expressions based on physics and chemistry. These models may also be referred to as room fire models, computer fire models, or mathematical fire models. Ideally, such models represent the ultimate capability, which means that discrete changes in any physical parameter could be evaluated in terms of the effect on fire hazard. While the state of the art in understanding fire processes will not yet support the ultimate model, a number of computer models are available that provide reasonable estimates of selected fire effects.

Zone Models: The most common type of physically based fire model is the zone or control volume model, which solves the conservation equations for distinct regions (control volumes). A number of zone models exist, varying to some degree in the detailed treatment of fire phenomena. The dominant characteristic of this class of model is that it divides the room(s) into a hot upper layer and a lower cooler layer. The model calculations provide estimates of key conditions for each of the layers as a function of time.[1,2] Zone models have proven to be a practical method for providing first-order estimates of fire processes in enclosures.

Field Models: The other general type of deterministic model is the field model. This type of model solves the fundamental equations of mass, momentum, and energy at each element in a compartment space that has been divided into a grid of small elements. Imagine an enclosure filled with a 3-D grid of tiny cubes; a field model will calculate the physical conditions in each cube, as a function of time. The calculation will account for physical changes generated within the cube and changes in the cube originating from surrounding cubes. This model will permit the user to determine the conditions at any point in the compartment.

Most field models require expensive commercial software packages to solve the large number of complex equations generated. Furthermore, the computational demands currently required are beyond the capabilities of most desktop computers. Although field models have been successfully used in a number of cases,[3] it will probably be a few years before field models can be used for routine analysis.

Table 10-9A lists a number of zone-type enclosure fire models that are in the public domain. Several of the models from the list are described below. In general these are the models that have been most widely used and are of the greatest interest to the fire community as a whole.

TABLE 10-9A. ***Enclosure Zone Fire Models***

Model Name	Author	Maintaining Organization	Applications and Special Features
ASET	L. Y. Cooper D. W. Stroup	NIST	Single room
ASET-B	W. C. Walton	NIST	Single room
CCFM	L. Y. Cooper G. P. Forney	NIST	Multi-room
COMPBURN	N. Siu	UCLA	Single room, developed for nuclear power facilities
COMPF2	V. Babrauskas	NIST	Single room, post-flashover
FIRST	H. W. Emmons H. E. Milter	NIST	Single room
FAST	W. W. Jones	NIST	Multi-room
OSU	E. E. Smith S. Satija	Ohio State Univ.	Single room, input from ASTM E 906 calorimeter

Overview of Leading Zone Models

ASET: ASET (Available Safe Egress Time) is a program for calculating the temperature and position of the hot smoke layer in a single room with closed doors and windows. ASET can be used to determine the time to the onset of hazardous conditions for both people and property. The required program inputs are the heat loss fractions, the height of the fuel above the floor, criteria for hazard and detection, the room ceiling height, the room floor area, a heat release rate, and a species generation rate of the fire (optional). The program outputs are the temperature, thickness, and (optional) species concentration of the hot smoke layer as a function of time, and the time to hazard and detection. ASET can examine multiple cases in a single run. ASET was written in FORTRAN.[4]

ASET-B: ASET-B is a program for calculating the temperature and position of the hot smoke layer in a single room with closed doors and windows. ASET-B is a compact version of ASET designed to run on personal computers. The required program inputs are a heat loss fraction, the height of the fire, the room ceiling height, the room floor area, the maximum time for the simulation, and the rate of heat release of the fire. The program outputs are the temperature and thickness of the hot smoke layer as a function of time. Species concentrations and time to hazard and detection calculated by ASET are not calculated in the compact ASET-B version. ASET-B was written in BASIC.[5]

COMPF2: COMPF2 is a computer program for calculating the characteristics of a post-flashover fire in a single building compartment, based on fire-induced ventilation through a single door or window. It is intended both for performing design calculations and for the analysis of experimental burn data. Wood, thermoplastic, and liquid fuels can be treated. A comprehensive output format is provided that gives gas temperatures, heat flow terms, and flow variables..The documentation includes input instructions, sample problems, and a listing of the program. The program was written in FORTRAN.[6]

CCFM (version VENTS): CCFM (Consolidated Compartment Fire Model) (version VENTS) is a two-layer zone-type compartment fire model computer code. It simulates conditions caused by user-specified fires in a multi-room, multi-level facility. The required inputs are a description of room geometry and vent characteristics (up to nine rooms and twenty vents), initial state of the inside and outside environments, and fire energy release rates as functions of time (up to twenty fires), and a user-specified heat loss fraction. If simulation of concentrations of products of combustion is desired, then product release rates must also be specified (up to three products). Vents can be simple openings between adjacent spaces (natural vents) or fan/duct forced ventilation systems between arbitrary pairs of spaces (forced vents). For forced vents, flow rates and direction can be user-specified or included in the simulation by accounting for user-specified fan and duct characteristics. Wind and stack effects can be taken into account. The program outputs for each room are pressure at the floor, layer interface height, upper/lower layer temperature, and (optionally) product concentrations. CCFM (version VENTS) is supported by four-part documentation. CCFM (version VENTS) was written in FORTRAN.[7,8,9,10]

FIRST: FIRST (FIRe Simulation Technique) is the direct descendant of the HARVARD V program developed by Howard Emmons and Henri Mitler. The program predicts the development of a fire and the resulting conditions within a room, given a user-specified fire or user-specified ignition. It predicts the heating and possible ignition of up to three targets. The required program inputs are the geometrical data describing the room and openings, and the thermophysical properties of the ceiling, walls, burning fuel, and targets. The generation rate of soot must be specified, and the generation rates of other species may be specified. The fire may be entered either as a user-specified time-dependent mass loss rate or in terms of fundamental properties of the fuel. Among the program outputs are the temperature and thickness of, and species concentrations in, the hot upper layer and also in the cooler, lower layer in the compartment. Also given are surface temperatures, and heat transfer and mass flow rates. The FIRST program was written in FORTRAN.[11]

FAST: FAST (Fire And Smoke Transport) is a multi-room fire model that predicts the conditions within a structure resulting from a user-specified fire. FAST version 17 can accommodate up to ten rooms with multiple openings between the rooms and to the outside. The required program inputs are the geometrical data describing the rooms and connections, the thermophysical properties of the ceiling, walls, and floors, the fire as a rate of mass loss, and the generation rates of the products of combustion. The program outputs are the temperature and thickness of, and species concentrations in, the hot upper layer and the cooler lower layer in each compartment. Also given are surface temperatures and heat transfer and mass flow rates. FAST was written in FORTRAN.[12]

OSU: OSU (Ohio State University) Compartment Fire Model is a program for calculating heat release rate, smoke generation rate, and smoke and heat venting from single compartments. The OSU model takes into account an initiating fire and both horizontal and vertical fire spread, providing a prediction of how combustible materials in the compartment influence the course of a developing fire. The required program inputs are material thermal properties, ignition point, rate of heat and smoke release, and flame propagation parameters. In addition, certain plume properties are required, including dimensions, temperature, and emissivity. Typical model outputs include upper layer air temperature, smoke generation rate, and heat release rate. OSU was written in FORTRAN.[13]

SPECIAL-PURPOSE MODELS

Special-purpose deterministic computer models include computer models designed for special-purpose analyses such as: structural fire resistance, prediction of response time of heat detectors and automatic sprinklers, forest fire development, egress design for building occupants, the design of sprinkler systems, and performance of smoke control or ventilation systems. These models may require or permit coupling with other special-purpose models or with a more general enclosure fire development model.

Table 10-9B lists a number of special-purpose deterministic fire models that are in the public domain. Several of the models from the list are described below. Again, as with the enclosure fire models, these are the models that have been most widely used and are of the greatest interest to the fire community as a whole.

ASCOS: ASCOS (Analysis of Smoke Control Systems) is a program for steady air flow analysis of smoke control systems. This program can analyze any smoke control system that produces pressure differences with the intent of limiting smoke movement in building fire situations. The input consists of the outside and building temperatures, a description of the building flow network, and the flows produced by the ventilation or smoke control system. The output consists of the steady state pressures and flows throughout the building. ASCOS was written in FORTRAN.[14]

DETACT-T2: DETACT-T2 (DETector ACTuation-Time squared) is a program for calculating the actuation time of thermal devices below unconfined ceilings. It can be used to predict the actuation time of fixed-temperature and rate-of-rise heat detectors and of sprinkler heads subject to a user-specified fire that grows as the square of time. DETACT-T2 assumes that the thermal device is located in a relatively large area; that is, only the fire ceiling flow heats the device, and there is no heating from the accumulated hot gases in the room. The required program inputs are the ambient temperature, the response time index (RTI) for the device, the activation and rate-of-rise temperatures of the device, the height of the ceiling above the fuel, the device spacing, and the fire growth rate. The program outputs are the time to device activation and the heat release rate at activation. DETACT-T2 was written in BASIC and FORTRAN.[15]

DETACT-QS: DETACT-QS is a program for calculating the actuation time of thermal devices below unconfined ceilings. It can be used to predict the actuation time of fixed-temperature heat detectors and sprinkler heads subject to a user-specified fire. DETACT-QS assumes that the thermal device is located in a relatively large area; that is, there is no accumulated hot gas layer in the room so only the fire ceiling flow heats the detection device. The required program inputs are the height of the ceiling above the fuel, the distance of the thermal device from the axis of the fire, the actuation temperature of the thermal device, the response time index (RTI) for the device, and the rate of heat release of the fire. The program outputs are the ceiling gas temperature at the device location and the device temperature both as a function of time and the time required for device actuation. DETACT-QS was written in BASIC.[16]

EVACNET+: EVACNET+ (Evacuation Network Computer Model) is an interactive computer program that models emergency building evacuation. It consists of a network of nodes and arcs to represent building locations and connecting paths. Input for this model includes a detailed geometry of the building and contents (multiple rooms and floors can be addressed) and information regarding the initial location of the occupants. Output can be selected from a menu and generally takes the form of optimum evacu-

TABLE 10-9B. *Special-Purpose Deterministic Fire Models*

Model Name	Author	Maintaining Organization	Model Type	Applications and Special Features
ASCOS	J. H. Klote	NIST	Smoke control	Steady-state network flow model for smoke control evaluation, no fire condition
BEHAVE	P. L. Andrews R. E. Burgan R. C. Rothermel	U.S. Forest Service	Forest fire	Forest fire behavior
DETACT-T2	D. W. Stroup	NIST	Thermal device actuation	Calculates action time for heat detectors and sprinklers, unconfined ceilings, time-squared fires
DETACT-QS	D. D. Evans	NIST	Thermal device acuation	Calculates actuation time for heat detectors and sprinklers, unconfined ceilings, user-defined fires
EVACNET+	T. M. Kisko R. L. Francis	U. of Fla.	Building egress	Optimum evacuation routes and times
EXITT	B. M. Levin	NIST	Building egress	Occupant decisions and actions during fire
FIREFORM	H. E. Nelson	NIST	Building fire analysis	Collection of routines to predict impact of fire on buildings and occupants
FIRES-T3	R. H. Idling B. Bresler Z. Nizamuddin	U. of Cal. Berkley	Structural heat transfer	Three-dimensional heat transfer through structural assemblies
FPETOOL	H. E. Nelson	NIST	Building fire analysis	Collecton of routines to predict impact of fire on buildings and occupants (includes FIREFORM)
HAZARD I	R. W. Bukowski R. D. Peacock W. W. Jones C. L. Forney	NIST	Hazard emphasis	Predicts hazards to building occupants from fire (includes FAST, EXITT, and DETACT-QS)
LAVENT	W. D. Davis L. Y. Cooper	NIST	Thermal device actuation	Calculates actuation time for sprinklers and link-actuated ceiling vents with draft curtains
MINE VENT	R. E. Greuer	Michigan Technical University	Shaft vent	Simulation of underground mine ventilation, mine fire interaction

ation times and identification of impediments to smooth, orderly evacuation. Two versions of the program are available, one in FORTRAN and one in BASIC.[17]

EXITT: EXITT is a discrete-event simulation of occupant decisions and actions in a simulated fire. Before the simulation starts, the characteristics of a residence, a fire in that residence, and the occupants of the residence are entered into the computer. Based on a large set of decision rules, the occupants "make" decisions that are a function of the smoke conditions in the building, the characteristics and status of the occupants (including their capabilities), and the available travel routes. The occupants investigate the fire, alert and assist others, and evacuate the building. The simulation ends when all the occupants are either out of the building or are trapped by the smoke. EXITT was written in BASIC.[18]

FIREFORM: FIREFORM (FIRE FORMulas) is a collection of fifteen different fire-related computational procedures based on established formulas. The subjects covered include smoke filling in a room, sprinkler/detector activation, smoke flow through (small) openings, temperatures and pressures developed by fires, flashover and fire severity predictions, fire propagation (in special cases), and simple egress estimation. FIREFORM was written in BASIC.[19]

FIRES-T3: FIRES-T3 (Fire Response of Structures—Thermal Three-Dimensional Version) is a finite-element computer model designed to analyze heat transfer through structural assemblies. A wide variety of structural assemblies can be examined with FIRES-T3, including columns, walls, beams, floor/ceiling assemblies, and roof/ceiling assemblies. The structural assembly may be solid or include air cavities. The input requirements include a description of the structural assembly and the fire exposure. The information necessary to describe the column assembly includes geometric factors (dimensions, shape of assembly) and material property values (thermal conductivity, specific heat, and density) as a function of temperature. The fire exposure is characterized in terms of the temperature of the surrounding media and appropriate heat-transfer coefficients. The output is a tabulation of the temperatures within the structural assembly as a function of time. FIRES-T3 was written in FORTRAN.[20]

FPETOOL: FPETOOL is a computerized package of relatively simple engineering equations and models useful in estimating the potential fire hazard in buildings. The calculations in FPETOOL are based on established engineering relationships. The FPETOOL package addresses problems related to fire development in buildings and the resulting conditions and response of fire protection systems.

In FPETOOL hazardous conditions are expressed in terms of the temperature, location, visual obscuration, latent and potential energy, oxygen content, and carbon monoxide and carbon dioxide concentrations in the smoke and hot gas produced by the fire. FPETOOL also includes means for estimating egress time; ignition of exposed items; smoke flows; fire, wind, and stack pressures on a door; activation of sprinklers and detectors; and other values useful in the evaluation of fire hazard in building spaces. FPETOOL was written in BASIC.[21]

HAZARD I: HAZARD I is a method for predicting the hazards to the occupants of a building from a fire therein. Within prescribed limits, HAZARD I allows one to predict the outcome of a fire in a building populated by a representative set of occupants in terms of which persons successfully escape and which are killed, including the time, location, and likely cause of death for each. HAZARD I is a set of procedures combining expert judgment and calculations to estimate the consequences of a specified fire. These procedures involve four steps: 1) defining the context, 2) defining the scenario, 3) calculating the hazard, and 4) evaluating the consequences. Steps 1, 2, and 4 are largely judgmental and depend on the expertise of the user. Step 3, which involves use of the extensive HAZARD I software, requires considerable the expertise in firesafety practice. The heart of HAZARD I is a sequence of procedures implemented in computer software to calculate the development of hazardous conditions over time, calculate the time needed by building occupants to escape under those conditions, and estimate the resulting loss of life based on assumed occupant behavior and tenability criteria. These calculations are performed for a specified building and set of fire scenarios of concern. HAZARD I consists of a three-volume report and a set of computer disks containing the software necessary to conduct hazard analyses of products used in residential occupancies. The HAZARD I software is used to make detailed predictions of the fire-generated environment within a building; the evacuation process of occupants as they interact with the building, the fire, and each other; and the fate of the occupants as they either successfully escape or are killed. The underlying science—including a detailed presentation of the equations, constants, and assumptions contained in each of the programs—and a set of worked example cases are contained in the Technical Reference Guide. The Software User's Guide includes detailed instructions on use of the software and an extensively illustrated learning section that walks the user through a worked example. Specific applications depend on the user, but some include material/product performance evaluation, fire reconstruction and litigation, evaluation of code changes or variances, fire department preplanning, and extrapolation of fire test data to additional physical configurations.[22,23,24]

LAVENT: LAVENT (Link-Actuated VENT) is a program developed to simulate the environment and the response of sprinkler links in compartment fires with draft curtains and fusible-link-actuated ceiling vents. The model used to calculate the heating of the fusible links includes the effects of the ceiling jet and the upper layer of hot gases beneath the ceiling. The required program inputs are the geometrical data describing the compartment, the thermophysical properties of the ceiling, the fire elevation, the time-dependent energy release rate of the fire, the fire diameter or energy release rate per area of the fire, the ceiling vent area, the fusible-link response time index (RTI) and fuse temperature, the fusible-link positions along the ceiling, the link assignment to each ceiling vent, and the ambient temperature. A maximum of five ceiling vents and ten fusible links are permitted in the compartment. The program outputs are the temperature, mass and height of the hot upper layer, the temperature of each link, the ceiling jet temperature and velocity at each link, the radial temperature distribution along the interior surface of the ceiling, the radial distribution of the heat flux to the interior and exterior surfaces of the ceiling, the fuse time of each link, and the vent area that has been opened. LAVENT was written in FORTRAN.[25]

RELATED ACTIVITIES

As discussed in the introduction, the development of deterministic fire models is a very active area. The above review is intended to offer the reader a perspective on what is currently available. One should also recognize that the information in this chapter is not exhaustive. As an example, little attention has been given to fire modeling efforts and available programs outside the United States. Selected papers listed in the reference section provide some review of such activities.

Most of the computer fire models discussed in this chapter are available only from the authors. The user should be aware that there may be significant differences between computers and between versions of so-called standard computer languages. As a result, programs may not always be transferred directly from one computer to another.

BIBLIOGRAPHY

References Cited

1. Quintiere, J. G., "Fundamentals of Enclosure Fire 'Zone' Models," *Journal of Fire Protection Engineering*, Vol 1, No. 3 (Aug.-Sept. 1989), pp. 99-119.
2. Walton, W. D. and Thomas, P. H., "Estimating Temperatures in Compartment Fires," *SFPE Handbook of Fire Protection Engineering*, National Fire Protection Association, Quincy, MA, 1988, pp. 2-16-2-32.
3. Cox, G., Kumar, S., and Markatos, N. C., "Some Field Model Validation Studies," *Proceedings*, International Association for Fire Safety Science, 1986.
4. Cooper, L. Y. and Stroup, D. W., "ASET—A Computer Program for Calculating Available Safe Egress Time," *Fire Safety Journal*, Vol. 9, 1985, pp. 29-45.
5. Walton, W. D., "ASET-B: A Room Fire Program for Personal Computers," *NBSIR 85-3144*, National Bureau of Standards, Gaithersburg, MD, 1985.
6. Babrauskas, V., "COMPF2—A Program for Calculating Post-Flashover Fire Temperatures," *NBS TN 991*, National Bureau of Standards, Gaithersburg, MD, 1979.
7. Cooper, L. Y. and Forney, G. P., "The Consolidated Compartment Fire Model (CCFM) Computer Code Application CCFM.VENTS—Part I: Physical Basis," *NISTIR 4342*, National Institute of Standards and Technology, Gaithersburg, MD, July 1990.
8. Cooper, L. Y. and Forney, G. P., "The Consolidated Compartment Fire Model (CCFM) Computer Code Application CCFM.VENTS—Part II: Software Reference Guide," *NISTIR 4343*, National Institute of Standards and Technology, Gaithersburg, MD, July 1990.
9. Cooper, L. Y. and Forney, G. P., "The Consolidated Compartment Fire Model (CCFM) Computer Code Application

CCFM.VENTS—Part III: Catalog of Algorithms and Subroutines," *NISTIR 4344*, National Institute of Standards and Technology, Gaithersburg, MD, July 1990.

10. Cooper, L. Y., Forney, G. P., and Moss, W. F., "The Consolidated Compartment Fire Model (CCFM) Computer Code Application CCFM.VENTS—Part IV: User Reference Guide," *NISTIR 4345*, National Institute of Standards and Technology, Gaithersburg, MD, July 1990.
11. Mitler, H. E. and Rockett, J. A., "User's Guide to FIRST, A Comprehensive Single-Room Fire Model," *CIB W14/88/22*, National Bureau of Standards, Gaithersburg, MD, 1987.
12. Jones, W. W., "A Multicompartment Model for the Spread of Fire, Smoke, and Toxic Gases," *Fire Safety Journal*, Vol. 9, 1985, pp. 55-79.
13. Smith, E. E. and Satija, S., "Release Rate Model for Developing Fires," Twentieth Joint ASME/AIChE National Heat Transfer Conference, Milwaukee, WI, Aug. 2-5, 1981.
14. Klote, J. H., "Computer Program for Analysis of Smoke Control Systems," *NBSIR 82-2512*, National Bureau of Standards, Gaithersburg, MD, 1982.
15. Evans, D. D., Stroup, D. W., and Martin, P., "Evaluating Thermal Fire Detection Systems (SI Units)," *NBSSP 713*, National Bureau of Standards, Gaithersburg, MD, April 1986, pp. 549.
16. Evans, D. D. and Stroup, D. W., "Methods to Calculate the Response Time of Heat and Smoke Detectors Installed Below Large Unobstructed Ceilings," *Fire Technology*, Vol. 22, No. 1, 1986, pp. 54-65.
17. Kisko, T. M. and Francis, R. L., "EVACNET+: A Computer Program to Determine Optimal Building Evacuation Plans," *Fire Safety Journal*, Vol. 9, 1985, pp. 211-220.
18. Levin, B. M., "EXITT—A Simulation Model of Occupant Decisions and Actions in Residential Fires," *NBSIR 88-3753*, National Bureau of Standards, Gaithersburg, MD, 1988.
19. Nelson, H. E., "Fireform—A Computerized Collection of Convenient Fire Safety Computations," *NBSIR 86-3308*, National Bureau of Standards, Gaithersburg, MD, 1986.
20. Iding, R. H., Nizamuddin, Z., and Bresler, B., "FIRES T3—A Computer Program for the Fire Response of Structures—Thermal Three-Dimensional Version," *UCB FRG 77-15*, University of California, Berkeley, CA, Oct. 1977.
21. Nelson, H. E., "FPETOOL: Fire Protection Engineering Tools for Hazard Estimation," *NISTIR 4380*, National Institute of Standards and Technology, Gaithersburg, MD, 1990.
22. Bukowski, R. W., Peacock, R. D., Jones, W. W., and Forney, C. L., "Software User's Guide for the HAZARD I Fire Hazard Assessment Method, Volume 1," *NIST HB-146/I*, National Institute of Standards and Technology, Gaithersburg, MD, June 1989, 240 pp.
23. Bukowski, R. W., Peacock, R. D., Jones, W. W., and Forney, C. L., "Technical Reference Guide for the HAZARD I Fire Hazard Assessment Method, Volume 2," *NIST HB-146/II*, National Institute of Standards and Technology, Gaithersburg, MD, June 1989, 323 pp.
24. Bukowski, R. W., Peacock, R. D., Jones, W. W., and Forney, C. L., "Example Cases for the HAZARD I Fire Hazard Assessment Method, Volume 3," *NIST HB-146/III*, National Institute of Standards and Technology, Gaithersburg, MD, June 1989, 314 pp.
25. Cooper, L. Y., "Estimating the Environment and the Response of Sprinkler Links in Compartment Fires with Draft Curtains and Fusible-Link-Actuated Ceiling Vents Theory," *Fire Safety Journal*, Vol. 16, 1990, pp. 137-163.

Additional Readings

Abrahamsson, L., *et al.*, "HSLAB—An Interactive Program for One-Dimensional Heat Flow Problems," *FOA C 20288-D6(A3)*, National Defense Research Institute, Sweden, Jan. 1979.

Alvord, D. M., "Status Report on the Escape and Rescue Model and the Fire Emergency Evacuation Simulation for Multifamily Buildings," *NBS-GCR-85-496*, National Bureau of Standards, Gaithersburg, MD, 1985.

Andrews, P. L., "BEHAVE: Fire Behavior Prediction and Fuel Modeling System—BURN Subsystem, Part 1," *Technical Report INT-194*, U.S. Forest Service, U.S. Department of Agriculture, Washington, DC, 1986, pp. 130.

Barnett, J. R., "Uses and Limitations of Computer Models in Structural Fire Protection Engineering Applications," *Fire Safety Journal*, Vol. 9, No. 2, 1985, pp. 137-146.

Bengtson, S. and Haegglund, B., "Use of a Zone Model in Fire Engineering Application," *Proceedings* of the First International Symposium on Fire Safety Science, Hemisphere, Washington, DC, 1986, pp. 667-675.

Berlin, G. N., "Computer Simulation for Fire Protection Engineering," *SFPE Handbook of Fire Protection Engineering*, National Fire Protection Association, Quincy, MA, 1988.

Bukowski, R. W., "Engineering Applications for Fire-Related Prediction Tools," *NBSIR 86-3360*, National Bureau of Standards, Gaithersburg, MD, Apr. 1986.

Davies, A. D., "Some Tools for Fire Model Validation," *Fire Technology*, Vol. 23, No. 2, 1987, pp. 95-114.

DiNenno, P. J., "Engineering Applications of Computer Fire Models," *Fire Safety Journal*, Vol. 9, No. 1, 1985, pp. 89-102.

Emmons, H. D., "The Prediction of Fires in Buildings," Seventeenth Symposium on Combustion, The Combustion Institute, Pittsburgh, PA, 1979, p. 1101.

Evans, D. D., "Calculating Sprinkler Actuation Time in Compartments," *Fire Safety Journal*, Vol. 9, 1985, pp. 147-155.

Franchuk, D. M., "Its Time We Thought about Using Fire Models to Fight Fires," *Fire Journal*, Vol. 82, No. 6 (Nov.-Dec. 1988), p. 13.

Friedman, R., "Quantification of Threat from a Rapidly Growing Fire in Terms of Relative Material Properties," *Fire and Materials*, Vol. 2, No. 1, 1978.

Greuer, R. E., "Modeling the Movement of Smoke and the Effect of Ventilation Systems in Mine Shaft Fires," *Fire Safety Journal*, Vol. 9, Nos. 1 and 2 (May, June 1985), p. 81.

Hagglund, B., "A Room Fire Simulation Model," *FOA C 20501-D6*, National Defense Research Institute, Sweden, June 1983.

Hagglund, B., "Simulation of Smoke Filling in Single Enclosures," *FOA C 20513-D6*, National Defense Research Institute, Sweden, Oct. 1983.

Haksever, I. A., *A Computer Program HPO 10*, Technical University of Braunschweig, Germany.

Jackson, L., "Modelling the Future by Computer," *Fire Prevention*, No. 215 (Dec. 1988), pp. 34-35.

Jones, W. W., "A Review of Compartment Fire Models," *NBSIR 83-2684*, National Bureau of Standards, Gaithersburg, MD, 1983.

Jones, W. W. and Peacock, R. D., "Guide for FAST, Version 18," *NIST Technical Note 1262*, National Institute of Standards and Technology, Gaithersburg, MD, May 1989.

Jones, W. W. and Quintiere, J. G., "Prediction of Corridor Smoke Filling by Zone Models," *Combustion Science and Technology*, Vol. 11, 1983, p. 111.

Kisko, T. M. and Francis, R. L., "Network Models of Building Evacuation: Development of Software System," *NBS-GCR-84-457*, National Bureau of Standards, Gaithersburg, MD, 1984.

Kisko, T. M. and Francis, R. L., "Network Models of Building Evacuation: Development of Software System," *NBS-GCR-85-489*, National Bureau of Standards, Gaithersburg, MD, 1985.

Klote, J. H., "A Computer Program for Analysis of Pressurized Stairwells and Pressurized Elevator Shafts," *NBSIR 80-2157*, National Bureau of Standards, Gaithersburg, MD, 1981.

Klote, J. H., "Computer Modeling for Smoke Control Design," *Fire Safety Journal*, Vol. 9, 1985, pp. 181-188.

Levine, R. S., "Mathematical Modeling of Fires," *NBSIR 80-2107*, National Bureau of Standards, Gaithersburg, MD, 1980.

Levine, R. S., "User's Needs in Fire Models," *Fire Technology*, Vol. 24, No. 2, 1988, p. 163.

MacArthur, C. D. and Reeves, J. S., "Dayton Aircraft Cabin Fire Model," *FAA-RD-76-120*, University of Dayton, OH, June 1976.

Mitler, H. E., "Comparison of Several Compartment Fire Models: An Interim Report," *NBSIR 85-3233*, National Bureau of Standards, Gaithersburg, MD, Oct. 1985.

Mitler, H. E. and Rocket, J. A., "How Accurate Is Mathematical Fire Modeling?" *NBSIR 86-3459*, National Bureau of Standards, Gaithersburg, MD., Dec. 1986.

Mitler, H. E. and Rocket, J. A., "User's Guide to FIRST, A Comprehensive Single-Room Fire Model," *NBSIR 87-3595*, National Bureau of Standards, Gaithersburg, MD, 1987.

Nakamura, K., "Predicting Capability of a Multiroom Fire Model," *NBSIR 88-3753, 9th Joint Panel Meeting* of the UJNR Panel on Fire Research and Safety, National Bureau of Standards, Gaithersburg, MD, April 1988.

Nelson, H. E., "FIREFORM—A Computerized Collection of Compartment Fire Safety Computations," *NBSIR 86-3308*, National Bureau of Standards, Gaithersburg, MD., 1986.

Parikh, J. S. and Beyreis, J. R., "Survey of the State of the Art of Mathematical Fire Modeling," *SFPE Bulletin*, Mar. 1985.

Pietrzak, L. M. and Johanson, G. A., "Analysis of Fire Suppression Effectiveness Using A Physically Based Computer Simulation," *Proceedings* of the First International Symposium on Fire Safety Science, Hemisphere, Washington DC, 1986, pp. 1207-1216.

Quintiere, J. G., "A Perspective on Compartment Fire Growth," *Combustion Science and Technology*, Vol. 39, 1984, pp. 11-54.

Rasbash, D. J., *Fire Safety Journal*, Vol. 9, Nos. 1 and 2 (May, June 1985).

Rocket, J., Morita, M., and Cooper, L. Y., "Comparisons of NBS/Harvard VI Simulations and Full-Scale, Multi-Room Fire Test Data," *NBSIR 87-3567*, National Bureau of Standards, Gaithersburg, MD, July 1987.

Rothermel, R. C., "How to Predict the Spread and Intensity of Forest and Range Fires," *INT 143*, U.S. Forest Service, U.S. Department of Agriculture, Forest Service, June 1983.

Sander, D. M., "FORTRAN IV Program to Calculate Air Infiltration in Buildings," *DBR Computer Program No. 37*, National Research Council, Ottawa, Canada, May 1974.

Sander, D. M. and Tamura, G. T., "FORTRAN IV Program to Simulate Air Movement in Multistory Buildings," *DBR Computer Program No. 35*, National Research Council, Ottawa, Canada, March 1973.

Siu, N. O., "COMPBRN—A Computer Code for Modeling Compartment Fires," *UCLA-ENG-8257*, University of California, Los Angeles, CA, Aug. 1982.

Stroup, D. W., "A Catalog of Compartment Fire Model Algorithms and Associated Computer Subroutines," *NBSIR 87-3607*, National Bureau of Standards, Gaithersburg, MD, Aug, 1987.

Tanaka, T., *"A Model of Multiroom Fire Spread," NBSIR 83-2718*, National Bureau of Standards, Gaithersburg, MD, 1983.

Todd, N. W. and Ryan, J. D., "Improving Codes by Predicting Product Performance in Real Fires," *Fire Journal*, Vol. 84, No. 2 (Mar. 1990), p. 64.

Underwriters Laboratories, Inc., "Survey of the State of the Art of Mathematical Fire Modeling," *File NC554*, Project 82NK1618, Northbrook, IL, 1983.

Walton, W., "ASET-B, A Room Fire Program for Personal Computers," *NBSIR 83-3144*, National Bureau of Standards, Gaithersburg, MD, 1985.

Walton, W., "User's View of Computer Hardware and Software," *Fire Safety Journal*, Vol. 9, No. 1, 1985, pp. 3-6.

Yoshida, H., Shaw, C. Y., and Tamura, G. T., "A FORTRAN IV Program to Calculate Smoke Concentrations in a Multistory Building," *DBR Computer Program No. 45*, National Research Council, Ottawa, Canada, June 1979.

Zukoski, E. E. and Kubota, T., "Two-Layer Modeling of Smoke Movement in Building Fires," *Fire and Materials*, Vol. 4, No. 1 (Mar. 1980), p. 17.

PROBABILISTIC FIRE MODELS

John M. Watts, Jr.

As indicated in the previous chapter, several excellent deterministic models have been developed to describe fire behavior. So an accurate picture of fire growth seems possible if the needed data are available and if the initial and boundary conditions are given. However, it is unlikely the described result is the most probable fire, which is really required for fire hazard assessments.

This chapter presents information on probabilistic models of fire behavior and other aspects of fire protection. It begins with a brief introduction to probability theory and modeling concepts. It then discusses three basic forms of probabilistic models: event trees, statistical models, and Monte Carlo simulation.

Additional information relating to the material discussed in this chapter can be found in Section 1, Chapter 3, "Systems Concept for Building Firesafety"; Section 10, Chapter 7, "Fire Risk Analysis"; Section 10, Chapter 8, "Introduction to Fire Modeling"; and Section 10, Chapter 14, "The Future of Fire Modeling."

PROBABILITY

Because it plays such a big part in daily life, most people have some idea of what probability is about. They know it involves weighing the chances, or likelihood, that something or other will take place. They often hear, or make statements, such as, "It is likely a fire will start here"; "We have a better chance of controlling the fire if we can ventilate"; "Sprinklers have a very good probability of success." Such statements refer to situations in which the outcome is not certain, but in which one has some degree of confidence that the statement will be correct. The theory of probability provides a mathematical framework for such statements.

The occurrence of fires, aspects of fighting fires, and sprinkler performance are repetitive operations, repeated often under similar circumstances. The percentage of times a certain outcome occurs, under the same conditions, will always remain approximately unchanged, only rarely deviating significantly from some average figure. It can, therefore, be said that this average figure is a characteristic measure of the given repetitive operation, under prescribed conditions. Knowledge of such measures is very important as it enables one not only to describe the outcome of repetitive operations that have already occurred, but also to predict the outcome in the future.

Probability Defined

A repetitive operation is defined as the recurrence of a large number of similar individual operations, such as fires. Of interest is a well-defined result of individual operations, such as fire control, and the number of such results in some repetitive operation, such as how many fires are controlled. The percentage, or fractional part, of "successful" outcomes of a repetitive operation are called the *probability* of this result. It is important to realize that the probability of an event, or result, has meaning only under the precisely defined conditions in which the repetitive operation takes place. Each significant variation of these conditions can cause a change in the probability of the event under consideration.

If the repetitive operation is such that event A, a success, is observed on the average a times in n individual operations, then the probability of event A under the given conditions is a/n. It can then be said that the *probability* of a successful result for any individual operation is the *ratio of the number of "successful" results observed to the total number of individual operations* constituting the prescribed repetitive operation.

$$\text{Probability of Success} = \frac{\text{Number of outcomes with "successful" result}}{\text{Total number of equally likely outcomes}}$$

In reference to fires, it might be more appropriate to talk about "unsuccessful" results. In the theory of probability, however, it is conventional to refer to the event of interest as a success.

Evaluating Probabilities

The probability of an event is always a positive number, ranging from zero to unity. The number cannot be greater

John M. Watts, Jr., Ph. D., is director of the Fire Safety Institute, a not-for-profit information, research, and educational corporation located in Middlebury, Vermont. He also serves as editor of NFPA's quarterly technical journal, *Fire Technology*.

than one because in the fraction, by which it is defined, the numerator cannot be greater than the denominator. The number of successful operations cannot be greater than the number operations undertaken. Neither the numerator nor the denominator can be negative, so probability cannot be less than zero. Thus, when probability is measured, a "scale" that runs from zero to one is used.

If the probability of event *A* is denoted by *P(A)*, then there is the requirement:

$$0 \leq P(A) \leq 1$$

The larger *P(A)* is, the more often event *A* occurs—for example, the greater the probability that a sprinkler system controls the fire, the more fires that are successfully suppressed by sprinklers. If the probability of an event is very small, then it occurs rarely. If $P(A)=0$, then the event either never occurs, or it occurs so rarely that, in practice, it is considered to be impossible—for example, the probability that the item first ignited is a reinforced concrete wall.

In contrast, if *P(A)* is close to one, then the fraction by which the probability is expressed has a numerator close to the denominator, and the overwhelming majority of operations are successful. If $P(A)=1$, then event *A* occurs always or almost always so that, in practice, it can be assumed that its occurrence is certain—for example, in a room containing a functional smoke detector and an alert person, it might be assumed the probability of discovering a fire is one.

If $P(A)=1/2$, then event *A* occurs in approximately half of all cases, or successful operations are observed approximately as often as unsuccessful ones. The classic example is a coin toss. If $P(A)>1/2$, then event *A* occurs more frequently than it does not occur; for $P(A)<1/2$, the reverse is true.

How small the probability of an event must be before it can be assumed to be impossible depends on how important the event is. If 5 percent of smoke detectors manufactured are not sold due to quality control procedures, 0.05 might appear to be a small number. A manufacturer may be able to accept this cost. If 5 percent of smoke detectors sold are defective, however, 0.05 is a very large number. A manufacturer may find it hard to accept this cost knowing that one out of twenty new, installed smoke detectors will not work. In every individual problem, it must be established in advance, based on practical considerations, how small the probability of an event ought to be, so it can be considered to be impossible and of insignificant consequence.

Assigning Probabilities

In applications of probability to fire problems, the assignment of measures and the analysis of logical possibilities may, at times, depend upon masses of data that are best obtained, analyzed, and interpreted by professional statisticians. At other times, the task depends more on qualitative knowledge and judgment of facts with which the fire protection professional is most familiar, and is, therefore, the person best qualified to assign measures and analyze logical possibilities. Very often, a combination of objective fact and subjective judgement is the best source of information in assigning probabilities.

Having a measure for probability is important to be able to deal with situations involving chance or uncertainty. There are many cases when it is useful to find, knowing the probabilities of certain events, the probabilities of more complicated ones. It would be inconvenient to search for a particular method of solution for each new problem of this sort that is encountered. Science tries to form general rules, the knowledge of which would readily permit one to solve mechanically, or almost mechanically, individual problems that are similar to one another. In the area of repetitive phenomena, the science that takes upon itself the formulation of such general rules is called the *theory of probability*. Probability is a branch of mathematics, and, therefore, involves precise reasoning, and uses formulas, tables, diagrams, and so on as its tools.

PROBABILITY MODELS AND MODELING

The word "model" has several different meanings. Even when descriptors are added, such as in the phrase "fire model," it is not always clear what is meant. As the word model appears more frequently in fire protection literature, it becomes more important that its meanings are appreciated.

Analytical Models

Several classifications of models exist that place the models into various groups in an effort to avoid confusion over the term. An important distinction exists between exemplary models and analytical models. An exemplary model is a pattern or design, or otherwise serves as an example for imitation, such as a model code. An analytical model is a tool used to study some aspect of the world so as to make a decision about it. Not all models are easily classified. A scale model may be exemplary, or analytical, or neither.

An analytical model is a description of some part of our environment formulated, in a way, to make it convenient for analysis. It is an efficient way of viewing a problem. The model may not describe every characteristic of a situation, but describe only those features that are deemed important. This may, at times, make it difficult to recognize the "real" world in a model description. For example, the Arabic numerals 1,2,3, and so on are more abstract, or unlike what they represent, than their Roman counterparts I,II,III. However, Arabic numerals are much more efficient to use in mathematics.

Mathematical Models

Another way to classify models is by whether they are physical or symbolic. Model trains are physical models, as they look like the thing being modeled. Most analytical models are symbolic, using symbols to represent the real world. Thus, a pie chart is a symbolic model of how something is divided up. Flow charts and fault trees are also models that use pictures, or graphic symbols. Mathematical models are also symbolic. They use numbers and other mathematical symbols to represent various parameters, or conditions, that influence a situation. Einstein's theory of relativity, $E=mc^2$, is a mathematical model of the relationship between energy and mass in the universe.

Dealing with Uncertainty

Depending upon how mathematical models deal with uncertainty, they may be either deterministic or probabilistic. If, for a specific set of input values, there is a uniquely determined output, the model is deterministic. Such models have fixed values for the input variables, and, therefore, have fixed outputs. On the other hand, a model dealing explicitly with the uncertainty inherent in fire is a probabilistic model.

Fire protection is a discipline in which there is significant uncertainty associated with most decisions. The concept of safety itself is one of uncertainty. As there is no such thing as absolute safety, human activity will always, and unavoidably, involve risks. The concept of fire is also uncertain. Unwanted combustion is the least predictable common physical phenomenon. Reliability of manufactured, or fabricated, systems for suppression and confinement is another source of uncertainty.

With a deterministic model, to get a sense of what might happen under different scenarios, it must be decided which scenarios are important, and then treat each separately. This is not difficult when there are only a few variables and, therefore, scenarios. However, real world systems are complex, and there is no practical way to evaluate enough scenarios with a deterministic model.

Probabilistic models recognize variables as having a degree of randomness. This is usually more accurate than simple deterministic models, and is especially useful when evaluating fire risk, since risk, by definition, is the uncertainty of loss. Probabilistic models can yield a numeric measure of risk.

There are many forms of probabilistic models. Complex models may involve both deterministic and probabilistic components. The remaining sections of this Chapter will introduce three types of probabilistic model which can be used independently or as part of statistical models, and Monte Carlo simulation.

NETWORKS

A network model is a graphic representation of paths, or routes, by which objects, energy, information or logic may flow, or move, from one point to another. Network models are useful for minimizing the time or distance of travel from point to point and have many applications in solving complex problems.

The connected points in a network are called nodes. The connections themselves are called links, arcs, or branches. The simplest network is two nodes connected by a single link. (See Figure 10-10A).

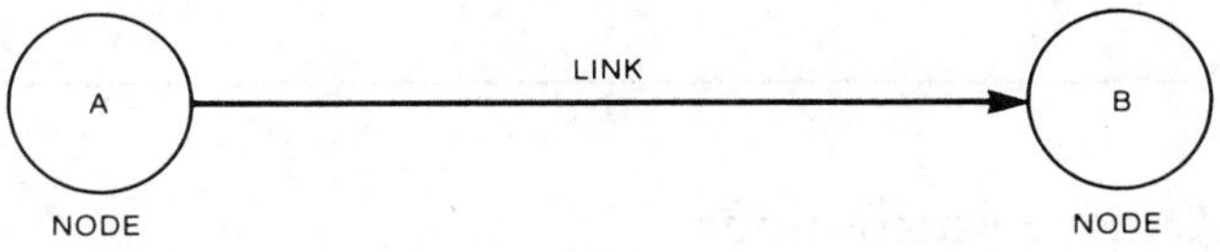

FIG. 10-10A. Network components.

A path is a sequence of links connecting two nodes and usually passing through other nodes. In driving from Los Angeles to New York, for instance, one might go through Denver and St. Louis. The cities could be considered nodes, and the roads between them links. Then one path from Los Angeles to New York would consist of the links connecting the intermediate cities.

A significant advantage of a graphic model, like a network, is the qualitative representation of the structure of the problem, or system. Such a diagram functions as a visual aid to help convey an intuitive understanding of the process for obtaining probabilities.

Event Trees

The term tree is used to describe a special type of network in which there is only one path connecting any two nodes. The simplest probability model, and one of the most powerful, is the event tree.

An event tree is a model of the sequence of possible states of a system and of corresponding events that lead to those states. Nodes represent events, and the links between them show how one event leads to another. Figure 10-10B shows a simple event tree.

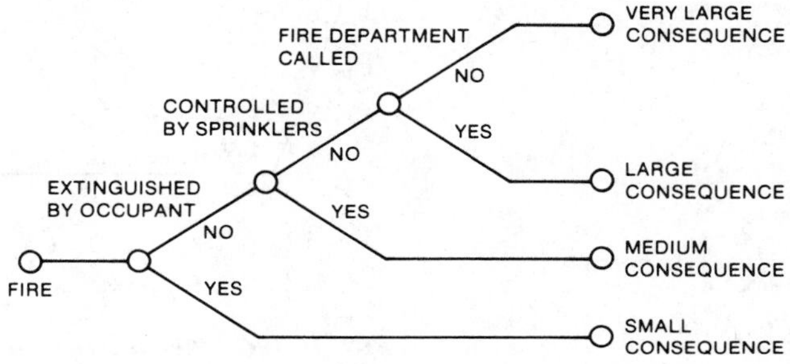

FIG. 10-10B. Event tree.

By assigning probabilities to the outcome of events, an event tree can be used to calculate the probability of the consequences. Figure 10-10C is an event tree that represents the likelihood of discovery of a fire caused by a cigarette in an upholstered chair. Three intermediate events that affect discovery include: (1) someone home, (2) a responsible person awake, and (3) a functional smoke detector. Probabilities of these events are shown on the tree. For each path, a probability of final outcome can be calculated. Assuming the events are independent, the probabilities along each path are multiplied. Thus, looking at the uppermost path, the probability of this path is:

$$(0.95)(0.80)(0.38)(1.00) = 0.038$$

Subsequently, the probabilities for each similar outcome can be summed and results obtained that indicate that the fire will be discovered 82 percent of the time—and that it will not be discovered 18 percent of the time. Using this model, it is relatively easy to see the effect of a smoke detector on the discovery of such a fire.

STATISTICAL MODELS

The fields of probability and statistics are closely linked. Most statistical concepts, such as sampling and hypothesis testing, have their basis in probability theory. Statistical modeling involves the description of random phenomena by an appropriate probability distribution.

Probability Distributions

A probability distribution may be thought of as a mathematical function that defines the probability of an event.

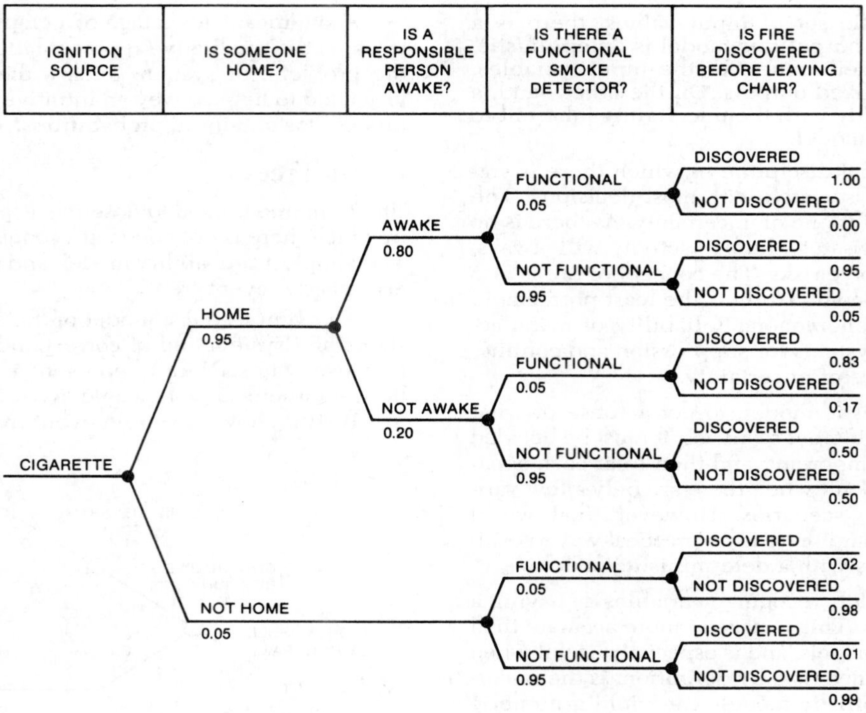

FIG. 10-10C. Event tree for cigarette ignition of upholstered chair.

For example, the probability distribution that describes the roll of a die is:

$$p(x) = 1/6$$

where $x = 1, 2, 3, 4, 5$, or 6.

All the possible outcomes, one through six, have an equal probability of 1/6. This is called the uniform distribution.

Another example of a uniform distribution is the outcome of a spin of a roulette wheel, which can be modeled mathematically as P(n)=.0263158. This equation indicates that the probability of any possible outcome, n (the numbers 1 through 36 plus 0 and 00), is 1/38 or .0263158.

All models have underlying assumptions. In the roulette model, a perfectly fair wheel was assumed. If one chooses not to accept this assumption, then it becomes necessary to collect a lot of statistical information about the roulette wheel to calculate the probability of each outcome.

Poisson Distribution

There are many different probability distributions used to describe many different random events. An example is shown in the data on fire calls in Table 10-10A. The first column shows the number of calls that might be received in any one day, and the second column shows the number of days with that many calls. The data are from a four-month period consisting of a total of 443 calls in 123 days.

Graphing the data, as shown in Figure 10-10D, reveals a trend. The frequency starts out low, increases rapidly, decreases rapidly, and then tails off toward higher numbers of calls. If more data were collected, this trend would be "smoother." The shape of this trend can be mathematically described by a Poisson distribution.

The Poisson distribution is widely used to describe random events having a large opportunity to occur, but a small likelihood that any one of these opportunities will actually result in an occurrence. This very accurately fits the description of fire incidents.

TABLE 10-10A. *Number of Days Having a Specified Number of Calls for Service.*[1]

Number of Calls for Service Per Day (N)	Number of Days Having (N) Public Service Calls
0	6
1	8
2	24
3	22
4	31
5	14
6	7
7	8
8	0
9	0
10	1
11	0

Other Distributions

Other probability distributions used to model aspects of fire protection include the familiar normal distribution and the less familiar lognormal distribution.

The normal distribution (See Figure 10-10E) finds wide application in describing biological phenomena such as human height and IQ. It is also applicable to characteristics such as shoulder width and walking speed to exits.

The lognormal distribution is skewed like the Poisson distribution. (See Figure 10-10F). It has been shown to describe fire load in offices.[2]

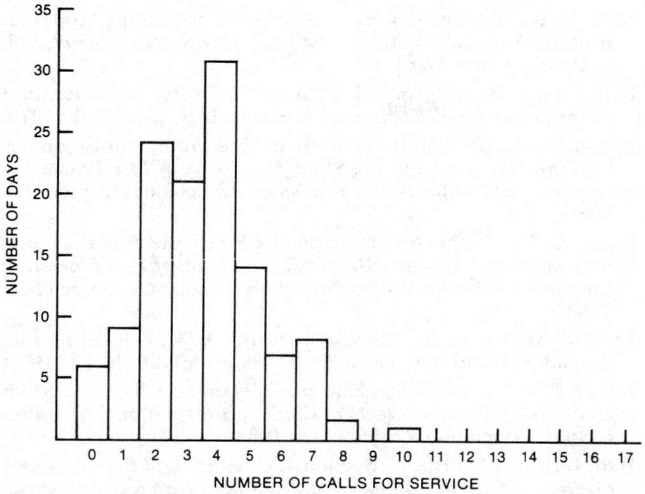

FIG. 10-10D. Distribution of public service calls.[1]

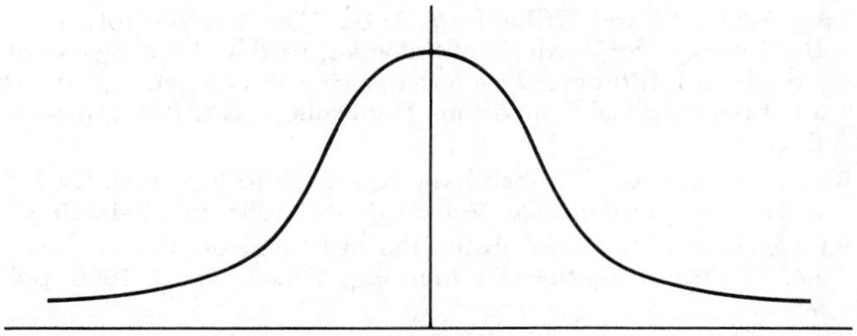

FIG. 10-10E. Normal distribution.

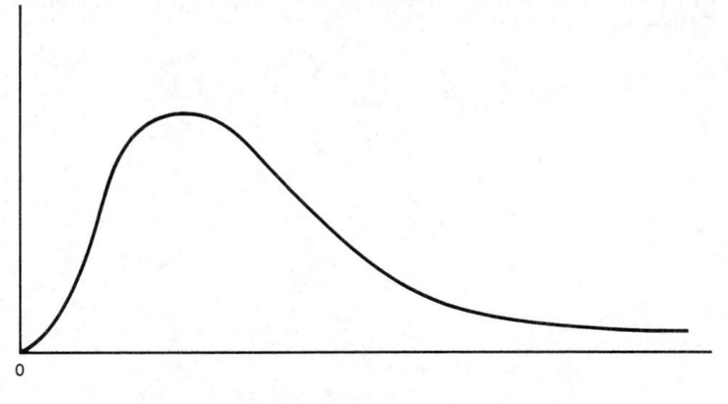

FIG. 10-10F. Lognormal distribution.

The exponential distribution has been suggested as a model of fire growth,[3] and the extreme value distribution is used to characterize fire loss.[4]

More sophisticated probabilistic models use principles of probability theory to combine probability distributions of two or more random variables.[5,6]

SIMULATION

Often, the relevant variables in a decision problem are too numerous, or the interactions too complex, to be handled mathematically. One way to handle such problems is by computer simulation. Simulation models try out different sets of conditions to see how they affect the outcome. This is what happens in a Link Trainer, a physical simulation model, when an airplane pilot tries various maneuvers to see which work and which don't without risking life or the loss of an airplane. The operation of an airplane is "simulated" by the electro-mechanical training device.

Monte Carlo Simulation

A computer simulation uses mathematical models to predict the range of outcomes from probabilistic situations. For the roulette wheel described in the previous section, letting the computer select a random number from 1 to 38 would simulate a spin of the wheel. Using the computer, the wheel can be "spun" thousands of times in 1 sec.

A roulette wheel analogy can be used to describe a computer simulation of fire scenarios. First, the wheel is divided like a pie chart so that a likely ignition source, such as smoking materials, has a big slice covering several numbers and a less likely ignition source, such as spontaneous combustion, has fewer or only one number. Then, spinning the wheel simulates the first part of an ignition sequence, the heat source. Next, a second wheel is divided according to the most common materials first ignited. Spinning the second wheel will complete the ignition simulation. A refinement would be to provide a different second wheel for each heat source, thereby modeling the observed situation that some materials are more likely to be ignited by some heat sources than by others.

Subsequent stages of fire growth can also be included in the simulation. Fire development could be represented by a state transition model, a type of model that describes a progression from one defined state to another. In a fire, these "transitions" are determined by parameters, or variables of the fire area, such as flame spread, fire load, ventilation, and so on. Now, more roulette wheels should be added to represent these varying state transitions and to allow the computer to "spin" all these wheels hundreds of times. This is referred to as a Monte Carlo simulation model.

Applications

Because of the flexibility of simulation modeling, and the complex nature of fire problems, there is a wide range of applications. One area where simulation is used extensively is in the modeling of building evacuation.[7] Computer simulations of emergency egress range from simple travel time models to detailed representations of human decision-making. Other areas of application include fire growth and development,[8,9] and emergency response.[10,11]

An important application of simulation is to confirm that a simpler model may be used safely or even to suggest the form of a simpler model.[12] A simulation model of a complex system is useful, but it also can be time-consuming and costly. Whenever possible, it is preferable to use a simple model relating inputs to outputs. A simulation model can provide insight into what form a simpler model might take. It also can be used to provide a level of confidence that a simpler model is a safe substitute for the more accurate simulation.

BIBLIOGRAPHY

References Cited

1. Nilsson, E. K. and Swartz, J. A., Jr., "Application of Systems Analysis to the Alexandria, Virginia Fire Department," *NBS Report 10 454*, National Bureau of Standards, Washington DC, February 1972.

2. Watts, J. M., Jr., "A Theoretical Rationalization of a Goal-Oriented Systems Approach to Building Fire Safety," *NBS-GCR-79-163*, National Bureau of Standards, Gaithersburg MD, February 1979, pp. 70-92.

3. Ramachandran, G., "Exponential Model of Fire Growth," Fire Safety Science: Proceedings of the First International Symposium, Hemisphere, NY, 1986, pp. 657-666.

4. Ramachandran, G., "Extreme Value Theory," Section 4, Chapter 4, *SFPE Handbook of Fire Protection Engineering*, National Fire Protection Association, Quincy MA, 1988, pp. 29-33.

5. Watts, J. M., Jr., "A Probability Model for Fire Safety Tree Elements," *Hazard Prevention, Journal of the Systems Safety Society*, Vol. 19, No. 6, 1983, pp. 14-15.

6. Gross, D., "Aspects of Stochastic Modeling for Structural Fire Safety", *Fire Technology*, Vol. 19, No. 2 (May 1983), pp. 103-114.

7. Watts, J. M., Jr., "Computer Models for Evacuation Analysis," *Fire Safety Journal*, Vol. 12, 1987, pp. 237-245.

8. Berlin, G. N., "A Simulation Model for Assessing Building Fire Safety," *Fire Technology*, Vol. 18, No. 1, 1982, pp. pp. 66-76.

9. Fahy, R. F., "Building Fire Simulation Model," *Fire Journal*, Vol. 77, No. 4 (July 1983), pp. 93-95, 102-104.

10. Ignall, E. J., "The Fire Operations Simulation Model," Chapter 13, *Rand Fire Project, Fire Department Deployment Analysis*, North Holland, NY, 1979.

11. *Simulation* (special issue on emergency planning), Society for Computer Simulation, San Diego, September 1989.

12. Ignall, Kolesar, and Walker, 1978.

Additional Readings

Arthur, J. L., Frendewey, J. O., Ghandforoush, P., and Rees, L. P., "Microcomputer Simulation System," *Computers and Operations Research*, Vol. 13, No. 2/3, 1986, pp. 167-183.

Banks, J. and Carson, J. S., *Discrete-Event System Simulation*, Prentice-Hall, Englewood Cliffs, NJ, 1984.

Beck, V. R., "Outline of a Stochastic Decision-making Model for Building Fire Safety and Protection," *Fire Safety Journal*, Vol. 6, 1983, pp. 105-120.

Benjamin, J. R. and Cornell, C. A., *Probability, Statistics, and Decision for Civil Engineers*, McGraw-Hill, New York, 1970.

Berlin, G. N., "Probability Models in Fire Protection Engineering," Section 4, Chapter 6, *SFPE Handbook of Fire Protection Engineering*, National Fire Protection Association, Quincy MA, 1988.

Berlin, G. N., "Computer Simulation for Fire Protection Engineering," Section 4, Chapter 10, *SFPE Handbook of Fire Protection Engineering*, National Fire Protection Association, Quincy MA, 1988.

Elms, D. G., Buchanan, A. A., and Dusing, J. W., "Modeling Fire Spread in Buildings," *Fire Technology*, Vol. 20, No. 1, 1984.

Hall, J. R. Jr., "Probability Concepts," Section 4, Chapter 2, *SFPE Handbook of Fire Protection Engineering*, National Fire Protection Association, Quincy MA, 1988.

Hall, J. R. Jr., "Statistics," Section 4, Chapter 3, *SFPE Handbook of Fire Protection Engineering*, National Fire Protection Association, Quincy MA, 1988.

Law, A. M. and Kelton, W. D., *Simulation Modeling and Analysis*, 2nd Ed., McGraw-Hill, New York, 1990.

Ling, W. C. T., and Williamson, R. B., "The Use of Probabilistic Networks for Analysis of Smoke Spread and the Egress of People in Buildings," *Fire Safety Science*, Proceedings of the First International Symposium, Hemisphere, NY, 1986, pp. 953-962.

Ramachandran, G., "Probabilistic Approach to Fire Risk Evaluation," *Fire Technology*, Vol. 24, No. 4, 1988, pp. 204-226.

Ramachandran, G., "Probability-Based Fire Safety Code," *Journal of Fire Protection Engineering*, Vol. 2, No. 3, 1990, pp. 75-91.

Watts, J. M., Jr., "About Models," *Fire Journal*, Vol. 77, No. 4 (July 1983), pp. 104-105.

Watts, J. M., Jr., "Dealing with Uncertainty: Some Applications in Fire Protection Engineering," *Fire Safety Journal*, Vol. 11, 1986, pp. 127-134.

SIMPLIFIED CALCULATIONS FOR ENCLOSURE FIRES

Edward K. Budnick, P.E., David D. Evans, Ph.D., P.E., and Harold E. Nelson, P.E.

As part of a fire protection analysis, it is often desirable to estimate the burning characteristics of selected fuels and their effects in enclosures. Also important for many analyses is the estimation of when fire protection devices such as heat detectors or automatic sprinklers will activate for specific fire conditions. Equations are available, based principally on experimental correlations, which permit the user to estimate these effects.

In this chapter, a brief introduction to enclosure fire effects is presented, along with equations that can be evaluated using hand calculators to provide estimates of particular effects. Generally, the equations presented are well documented and are widely used for such estimates. However, the user is cautioned that most of the equations were developed based on data from experiments that were conducted for very specific, and sometimes idealized, conditions. Therefore, some judgment must be exercised when applying these equations to complex conditions occurring in enclosure fires of general interest.

The equations in this chapter are primarily intended to be used in evaluating fire conditions in enclosures during the pre-flashover fire growth period. Most of the methods presented do not apply to fully developed room fires, such as post-flashover conditions. In addition, these shorthand calculations apply only to the room of fire origin and to a single burning fuel package such as a contiguous grouping of combustibles like an upholstered chair and ottoman or a bookcase full of books. More complicated methods are available for multiroom analysis, but they are beyond the scope of this chapter. Methods to address multiple fuel package involvement are under development but are not yet available.

For some of the effects, more than one equation is presented. In these cases, one equation may be preferred over the other based on the best match of the experimental basis for the equation to the specific case of interest.

Mr. Budnick is a senior engineer and vice president at Hughes Associates, Inc., in Wheaton, MD. Dr. Evans is head of the Fire Suppression Research Group, and Mr. Nelson is a senior scientist at the U.S. National Institute of Standards and Technology, Gaithersburg, MD.

Material properties such as heat of combustion (Δh_c) and stoichiometric air/fuel mass ratio (r_s) are listed in this handbook in Appendix A, "Tables and Charts." For additional information on material properties or the topics introduced in this chapter, refer to Section 2 of the *SFPE Handbook of Fire Protection Engineering.*[1]

ENERGY RELEASE RATE

Calculation procedures for fire effects in enclosures require knowledge of the energy release rate of the burning fuel. The term *energy release rate* is frequently used interchangeably with *heat release rate*, and it is usually expressed in units of kilowatts (kW) and symbolized by $\dot{Q}$.

The energy release rate from burning fuels cannot be predicted from basic measurements of material properties. It depends on the fire environment, the manner in which the fuel is volatilized and the efficiency of the vapor combustion. Therefore, one must rely on available laboratory test data for the specific or similar fuels. In addition, a knowledge of the complete energy release rate history may be required for many situations. This is particularly desirable where the fuel package exhibits unsteady burning. (See Fig. 10-11A.) For those cases where only limiting conditions or worst-case analysis is required, it may be reasonable to assume that the fuel is burning at a constant rate, which simplifies the calculation considerably.

For the equations presented here, the more simplified condition of constant energy release rate is generally assumed. However, techniques are available that represent a growing fire by a series of constant energy release rate fires. This approach can require a great deal of calculation time, depending upon the desired accuracy. Such analysis is generally more suited to computer simulation.

For the complete combustion of a fuel, energy release rate and mass loss rate are related by the equation:

$$\dot{Q} = \Delta h_c \cdot \dot{m} \qquad [1]$$

where:

$\dot{Q}$ = energy release rate (kJ/sec) or (kW)
Δh_c = heat of combustion (kJ/kg)
$\dot{m}$ = mass loss rate (kg/sec)

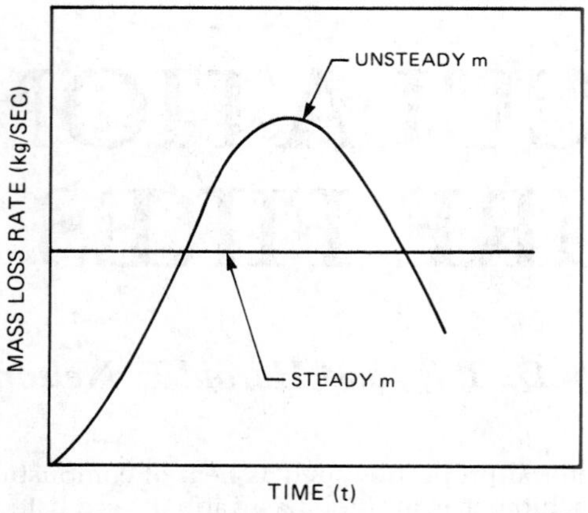

FIG. 10-11A. An illustration of steady and unsteady burning rates.

(The heat of combustion is a material property and is tabulated for selected materials in Appendix A, "Tables and Charts." The mass loss rate is typically found experimentally.)

It should be recognized that most enclosure fires of interest do not exhibit constant energy release rates. Rather, as illustrated in Figure 10-11B for selected items of furniture, the mass loss rate, and therefore the energy release rate, varies over time. Depending upon the detail required, one might select a constant mass loss rate, such as a peak value or an average value as the basis for analysis. Data on mass loss rates for selected fuel packages are available in several publications.[1,2,3,4,5]

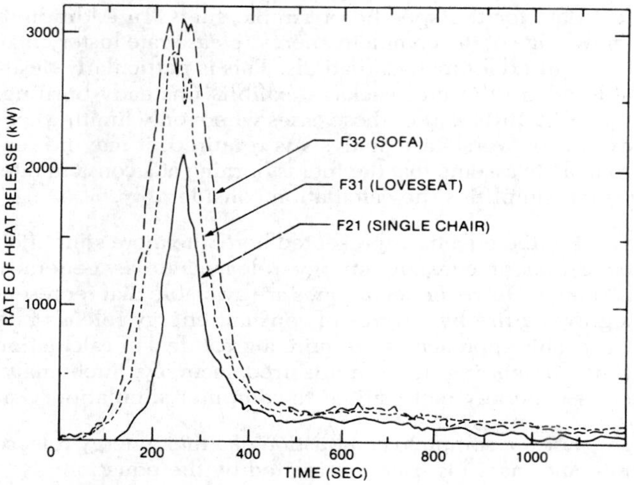

FIG. 10-11B. Free burn heat release rates for selected furniture items.[5]

Most information available on fuel package burning rates is reported for "free burn" conditions—that is, the data are collected for items burning in the open rather than in an enclosure. While enclosure effects are of little importance in evaluating early fire growth, they are important in fully developed room fires. The effects of most importance are those related to radiation feedback to the fuel from the hot smoke and enclosure linings and those related to the ability of the fire to obtain sufficient air for combustion. When fire conditions reach a stage where the smoke and heated room linings approach 932°F (500°C), the radiant feedback normally increases the burning rate above that observed in a free burn situation. The difference between the free burn rate and the radiation-enhanced burning rate increases as the room temperature and resulting radiant impact on the fuel package increase. Once flashover conditions are reached, rates greater than double the free burn rate are not unusual.

The second enclosure effect is the availability of oxygen for combustion. If the air in the space, plus that drawn in through openings, plus that blown into the space by HVAC systems or other means is insufficient to burn all the combustible products driven from the fuel package, only that amount of combustion supportable by the oxygen available in the air will burn the room or other space involved. This situation is referred to as ventilation-limited burning. When ventilation-limited burning occurs, the combustible products driven from the fuel package and not burned in the room often burn when they combine with air outside the room and appear as flame extensions from the room.

The following equation for stoichiometric fuel pyrolysis can be used to estimate the mass loss rate at which these effects begin to dominate:

$$\dot{m}_{st} = \frac{1}{r_s} \cdot 0.5\, A_v \sqrt{h_v} \qquad [2]$$

where:

$\dot{m}_{st}$ = stoichiometric mass loss rate (kg/sec)
r_s = stoichiometric air/fuel mass ratio
A_v = area of ventilation opening (m^2)
h_v = height of ventilation opening (m)

For wood fuel, r_s = 5.7. Values of r_s for other materials can be found in Appendix A, "Tables and Charts."

An estimate of the maximum burning rate possible for an enclosure with a particular opening can be determined from equation 2. If the mass loss rate for a particular fuel package is less than this value, the condition is referred to as fuel-controlled, and results from equation 1 provide a reasonable estimate of the energy release rate. If the free burn mass loss rate is higher than the stoichiometric rate from equation 2, then the rate determined for stoichiometric conditions should be used for combustion within the room.

A more rigorous treatment of energy release rates is available for selected material types such as wood cribs, wood and plastic slabs, and liquid pool fires where experimental correlations have been established. Section 2, Chapter 1, in the *SFPE Handbook of Fire Protection Engineering*[1] provides a detailed discussion of the prediction of burning rates for liquid pool fires. Detailed discussions of energy release rates for specific fuels are available elsewhere.[6,7]

FLAME HEIGHTS

Estimates of flame height L can be important in determining exposure hazards associated with a burning fuel. (See Figure 10-11C.) Experimentally determined "mean" flame heights have been correlated by several researchers. A simple correlation for flame heights for pool or horizontal burning fuels has been developed by Heskested:[8]

$$\frac{L}{D} = -1.02 + 15.6N^{1/5} \qquad [3]$$

where:

L = mean flame height (m)
D = diameter of fire source (m)
and N is a nondimensional parameter:

$$N = \left[\frac{C_pT_\infty}{g\rho_\infty^2\left(\frac{\Delta h_c}{r_s}\right)^3}\right]\frac{\dot{Q}^2}{D^5} \qquad [4]$$

C_p = specific heat of air at constant pressure [(kJ/kg)/K]
T_∞ = ambient temperature (K)
g = acceleration of gravity (9.81 m/s²)
ρ_∞ = ambient air density (kg/m³)
Δh_c = heat of combustion (kJ/kg)
r_s = stoichiometric air/fuel mass ratio
$\dot{Q}$ = total heat release rate (kJ/s) or (kW)

For noncircular fuel packages, an effective D can be estimated by:

$$D = 2\left(\frac{A_f}{\pi}\right)^{1/2} \qquad [5]$$

where:

D = effective diameter (m)
A_f = area of fire (m²)

For a broad range of experimental conditions, $\Delta h_c/r_s$ is nearly constant, representing the heat liberated per unit mass of air entering the combustion reaction. Assuming $\Delta h_c/r_s$ = 3100 kJ/kg and atmospheric conditions such as T_∞ = 293°K, p = 760 mm H_g, equation 3 can be simplified to

$$L = -1.02D + 0.23\dot{Q}^{2/5} \qquad [6]$$

Since flames are unstable, the mean flame height L is generally taken to be the height above the fire source where the flame tip is observed to be at or above this point 50 percent of the time. The above correlation is considered suitable for pool fires or for horizontal surface burning. In addition, the correlation will produce negative values for L at small heat release rates. The available experimental data indicate that the most reliable region of application is where $\dot{Q}^{2/5}/D$ is greater than 16.5. For more detail on flame height calculations, the reader is referred to Beyler[9] and the *SFPE Handbook*.[1]

PLUME CENTERLINE TEMPERATURE AND VELOCITY

The plume centerline excess temperature and velocity at elevations above the mean flame height can be estimated from the following equations:[10] (See Figure 10-11C.)

$$\Delta T_o = 9.1\left[\frac{T_\infty}{gC_p^2\rho_\infty^2}\right]^{1/3}\dot{Q}_c^{2/3}(Z - Z_o)^{-5/3} \qquad [7]$$

$$U_o = 3.4\left[\frac{g}{C_p\rho_\infty T_\infty}\right]^{1/3}\dot{Q}_c^{1/3}(Z - Z_o)^{-1/3} \qquad [8]$$

where:

ΔT_o = excess centerline mean temperature (T_g - T_∞) (K)
T_g = gas temperature (K)
T_∞ = ambient temperature (K)
g = acceleration of gravity (9.81 m/s²)
C_p = specific heat of air at constant pressure [(kJ/kg)/K]
ρ_∞ = ambient air density (kg/m³)
$\dot{Q}_c$ = convective heat release rate (kJ/s) or (kW)
Z = elevation above burning fuel fire source (m)
Z_o = location of virtual fire source (m)
U_o = centerline mean velocity (m/s)

Equations 7 an 8 above are based on extensive experimental data and are known as *strong plume* correlations, which accommodate large density deficiencies present in fire plumes. These equations do not apply to fire plumes with small temperature rises, such as $\Delta T_o/T_\infty$ << 1.

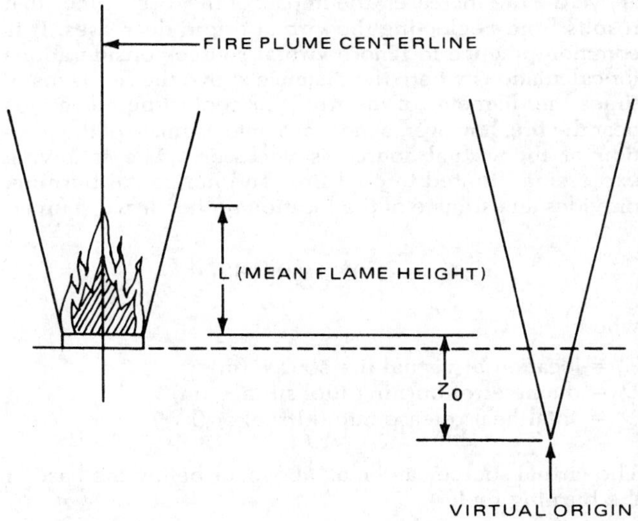

FIG. 10-11C. Flame and fire plume characteristics.

For normal atmospheric conditions, for example:

T_∞ = 293°K
g = 9.81 m/s²
C_p = 1.00 [(kJ/kg)/K]
ρ_∞ = 1.2 kg/m³

equations 7 and 8 can be simplified to

$$\Delta T_o = A\dot{Q}_c^{2/3}(Z - Z_o)^{-5/3} \quad [9]$$

$$U_o = B\dot{Q}_c^{1/3}(Z - Z_o)^{-1/3} \quad [10]$$

where:

A = 25.0 K $m^{5/3}$ $kW^{-2/3}$
B = 1.03 $m^{4/3}$ s^{-1} $kw^{-1/3}$

While methods exist to calculate excess temperature and velocities at locations other than along the plume centerline, the highest confidence is placed on centerline estimates. The reader is referred to DiNenno, Beyler, and Heskestad for a detailed discussion of non-centerline temperature and velocity estimates.[1,9,10]

The use of centerline excess temperature and velocity for evaluating exposure conditions is conservative since the centerline values are the highest values at any elevation. The estimates are sensitive to values for the convective heat release rate—$\dot{Q}_c$—which can vary from 40 to 80 percent of the total heat release rate, depending on the type and arrangement of the burning fuel.

CALCULATING THE HYPOTHETICAL VIRTUAL ORIGIN (Z_o)

In order to estimate the plume centerline mean temperature and velocity, one must first determine the virtual origin. The virtual origin is the hypothetical location or elevation associated with a substitution of a point source fire for the fire in question. (See Fig. 10-11C.) The consideration of virtual origin is most important for evaluating centerline conditions near the fire. As the distance above the fire increases, the impact of the discrepancy that results from neglecting the virtual origin decreases. It is common practice to ignore virtual source considerations for calculations where the distance above the fire is many times the diameter of the fire. For centerline elevations near the fire, however, a more accurate estimate of the position of the virtual source is necessary. The following expression, limited to pool fires and horizontal burning, provides an estimate of the location of the virtual source:[8]

$$Z_o = -1.02D + 0.083\dot{Q}^{2/5} \quad [11]$$

where:

Z_o = location of virtual fire source (m)
D = diameter of burning fuel surface (m)
$\dot{Q}$ = total heat release rate (kJ/sec) or (kW)

The virtual source can be at, above, or below the base of the burning fuel.

RADIANT HEAT FLUX TO A TARGET

For many enclosure fires, it is of interest to estimate the radiation transmitted from a burning fuel array to a target fuel positioned some distance from the fire to determine if secondary ignitions are likely. Figure 10-11D depicts the configuration used in developing the expression:

$$\dot{q}_o'' \approx \frac{P}{4\pi R_o^2} \approx \frac{\chi_r \dot{Q}}{4\pi R_o^2} \quad [12]$$

where:

$\dot{q}_o''$ = incident radiation on the target (kW/m^2)
R_o = distance to target fuel (m)
P = total radiative power of the flame (kW)
χ_r = radiative fraction
$\dot{Q}$ = total heat release rate (kJ/s) or (kW)

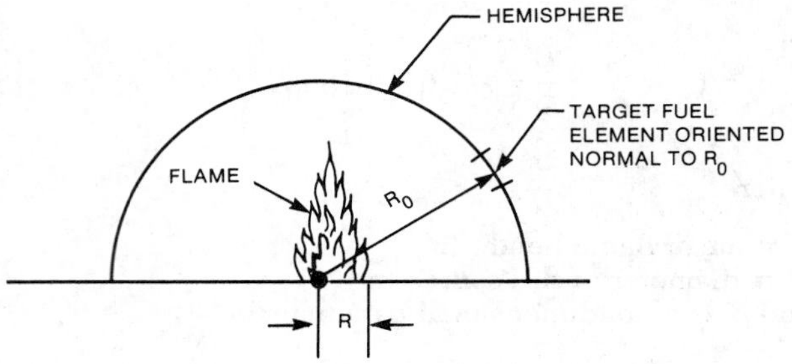

FIG. 10-11D. Illustration of radiant heat transfer to a target fuel.[7]

Usually, χ_r ranges from 20 to 60 percent, depending upon the fuel type. Refer to Appendix A, "Tables and Charts," for values for χ_r for selected liquid pools. Experimental measurements indicate that equation 12 has good accuracy for

$$\frac{R_o}{R} > 4$$

where R (in meters) is the radius of the base of the fire. For radiation at

$$\frac{1}{2} < \frac{R_o}{R} < 4$$

refer to DiNenno for a more exact analysis.[1]

PRE-FLASHOVER TEMPERATURE ESTIMATES

Several researchers have developed correlations for predicting temperature rise in developing enclosure fires before. McCaffrey et al. suggest the following expression for naturally ventilated fires, based on correlation of an extensive number of enclosure experiments:[11]

$$\frac{\Delta T}{T_\infty} = 1.63\left[\frac{\dot{Q}}{C_p \rho_\infty T_\infty A_v \sqrt{g h_v}}\right]^{2/3}\left[\frac{h_k A_s}{C_p \rho_\infty A_v \sqrt{g h_v}}\right]^{-1/3} \quad [13]$$

where:

ΔT = temperature rise of upper gas (K)
T_g = gas temperature (K)
T_∞ = ambient air temperature (K)
$\dot{Q}$ = total heat release rate (kJ/sec) or (kW)
g = acceleration of gravity (m/sec^2)
C_p = specific heat of air at constant pressure [(kJ/kg)/K]
ρ_∞ = density of air (kg/m^3)

A_s = total surface area of enclosure interior excluding vent area (m^2)
A_v = vent area (m^2)
h_v = vent height (m)
h_k = effective enclosure conductance [(kW/m)/K]

The terms $h_k A_s$ and $A_v \sqrt{h_v}$ should be summed in equation 13 for multiple structural materials and openings, respectively. In addition, while it is recognized that the enclosure gas temperature varies within the compartment, this equation is based on the assumption that an average upper-layer temperature and an average lower-layer, or ambient, temperature reasonably approximate temperature conditions in the enclosure. By substituting values for ambient conditions for key variables in equation 13:

C_p = 1.0 (kJ/kg)/K, at one atmosphere
ρ_∞ = 1.18 kg/m^3, density of ambient air
T_∞ = 295 K, ambient air temperature
g = 9.81 m/sec^2, gravitational constant

a simplified expression can be provided of the form:

$$\Delta T = 6.85\left(\frac{\dot{Q}^2}{h_k A_s A_v \sqrt{h_v}}\right)^{1/3} \qquad [14]$$

where:

$$h_k = \left(\frac{k\rho c_p}{t}\right)^{1/2} \quad \text{for } t \le t_p$$

$$h_k = \frac{k}{\delta} \quad \text{for } t > t_p$$

k = thermal conductivity of enclosure surface material [(kW/m)/K]
ρ = density of enclosure materials (kg/m^3)
c_p = specific heat of enclosure material [(kJ/kg)/K]
δ = enclosure material thickness (m)
t = time (sec)

$$t_p = \frac{\rho c_p}{k}\left(\frac{\delta}{2}\right)^2, \quad \text{thermal penetration time (sec)}$$

For an enclosure lined with gypsum board, key variable values are

c_p = 1.1 (kJ/kg)/K
ρ = 960 kg/m^3
K = 0.00017 (kW/m)/K
δ = 0.016 m

Thus,

$$h_K = (0.18/t)^{1/2} \text{ for } t \pm t_p,\ (0.00017/\delta) \text{ for } t > t_p$$

where:

t_p = 400 sec for 16-mm (5/8-in.) thickness of gypsum board.

For the case of completely forced ventilation conditions, a correlation for enclosure temperature rise has been developed by Foote et al.[12]

$$\frac{\Delta T}{T_\infty} = 0.63\left(\frac{\dot{Q}}{\dot{m}_v C_p T_\infty}\right)^{0.72}\left(\frac{h_k A_s}{\dot{m}_v C_p}\right)^{-0.36} \qquad [15]$$

where:

$\dot{m}_v$ = compartment forced mass ventilation rate (kg/sec)

For detailed discussions of methods which address multiple vents as well as forced ventilation, the reader is referred to DiNenno, Foote *et al.*, and Deal and Beyler.[1,12,13]

PREDICTION OF FLASHOVER

A critical point in room fire growth is an event often referred to as "flashover." While a universal definition does not exist, this event is generally associated with rapid transition in fire behavior from localized burning of fuel to involvement of all the combustibles in the enclosure. Experimental work indicates that this transition can occur when upper room temperatures are between 750 and 1112°F (400 and 600°C).[14] Using a value of 932°F (500°C), equation 13 may be solved for the heat release rate necessary to achieve flashover in a naturally ventilated enclosure.[7] The resulting equation is:

$$\dot{Q}_{fo} = 610[h_k A_s A_v \sqrt{h_v}]^{1/2} \qquad [16]$$

where:

$\dot{Q}_{fo}$ = heat release rate at flashover [(kJ/s) or (kW)]
h_k = enclosure conductance [(kW/m^2)/K]
A_s = total enclosure area (m^2), excluding vent area
A_v = area of vent opening (m^2)
h_v = height of vent opening (m)

Assuming that an enclosure has been heated thoroughly before flashover—$t > t_p$, equation 16 can be simplified to*

$$\dot{Q}_{fo(\text{min})} = 610[(k/\delta)A_s A_v \sqrt{h_v}]^{1/2} \qquad [17]$$

where:

k = thermal conductivity of enclosure material [(kW/m)/K]
δs = enclosure material thickness (m)

POST-FLASHOVER TEMPERATURE ESTIMATES

An alternative approach to estimating peak enclosure temperature was originally developed by Thomas[15], and extended by Law[16] to include both natural and forced ventilation. The correlations were based initially on post-flashover enclosure fire data, but they were extended by Law through the evaluation of extensive pre-flashover room fire data. The results indicate that the predictions reasonably, but not exactly, predict the temperatures reported in

*For 1/2- in. (13-mm) thickness of gypsum board enclosure liner, k/δ = 0.014. For 5/8-in. (16-mm) thick gypsum, k/δ = 0.011.

the test fires. The equation does not consider variations in the thermophysical properties of room linings.

Most of the tests used to justify the equation involved rooms lined with gypsum board or concrete block. Caution should be exercised in applying these equations to rooms lined with highly insulating materials, such as fiberglass or foamed materials, or rooms in which major portions of the lining are of thermally thin materials such as steel or glass.

Forced ventilation is considered to occur when significant air is supplied by a ventilation system. The natural ventilation equation assumes that, at the time of peak temperature, all of the air for combustion will be drawn into the room through the vent openings and that these same openings will vent the product gases. This results in a natural sharing of the opening by the incoming air and outflowing gases that obey the laws of conservation of mass. The forced ventilation equation assumes that enough air is supplied to ensure that the fire will be free burning. It should be used only when the rate of air supply is sufficient to ensure such burning. Where forced ventilation is not enough to ensure free burning but is sufficient to cause concern that the assumed conservation in the natural venting equation has not been preserved, the peak temperature is expected to lie between the predictions of the two approaches.

The expression for natural ventilation conditions is

$$\Delta T_{\max} = 6000\left[\frac{(1 - e^{-0.036\eta})}{(\eta)^{1/2}}\right](1 - e^{-0.05\psi}) \quad [18]$$

where:

ΔT_{max} = *peak temperature rise (K)*
η = $(A_s/A_v(h)^{1/2})$
ψ = $L_f/(A_v A_s)^{1/2}$
A_s = total surface area of enclosure interior excluding vent area (m^2)
A_v = vent area (m^2)
h = height of compartment (m)
L_f = total enclosure fire load (equivalent weight of wood) (kg)

The expression for forced ventilation conditions is

$$\Delta T_{\max} = 1200(1 - \theta^{-0.04\psi}) \quad [19]$$

EQUIVALENT FIRE DURATION

Equivalent fire duration or fire severity is an approximation of the potential destructive impact of the burnout of all the available fuel in a room or space with at least one opening. The correlation presented here was developed by Law.[17] The results predict the potential impact of a post-flashover fire in terms of equivalent exposure in a fire-endurance furnace fired to follow the European equivalent exposure of the ASTM E-119 standard time-temperature curve. Law based her correlation on data developed through an international research program carried out under the auspices of the Conseil International du Batiment (CIB). The results of this CIB effort are reported by Thomas and Heselden.[18] All of the tests were conducted with wood crib fuel sources. Law reports about 20 percent variation, depending on the porosity of the fuel. In wood cribs, porosity is based on the ratio of openings between the sticks of the crib and the space filled by those sticks, the greater fire severity being experienced with the more loosely packed cribs.

This correlation is not appropriate for rooms that do not have openings for ventilation. While no precise minimum can be stated, it is suggested that this equation not be used unless the area of the opening is at least greater than that of a typical residential window. The equation also assumes that virtually all of the potential energy in the fuel is released in the involved room. This holds true for the wood cribs used in the CIB tests. This assumption may not hold true where there are large surface areas, such as in rooms having combustible linings or in rooms that contain extensive materials with low thermal inertia, such as foam plastics. In these cases, the generation of pyrolized fuel may significantly exceed the combustion ability of the air drawn through the ventilation openings into the fire room. When this occurs, some of the fuel leaves the room in the vented gases. This often burns in the expelled gases causing the extension of flame from the room. In such cases, this equation should be expected to over-predict the equivalent fire duration by an amount approximately proportional to the portion of the fuel that does not burn in the room being evaluated.

The equation is

$$t = 60\left[\frac{L_f}{\sqrt{A_s A_v}}\right] \quad [20]$$

where:

t = fire severity (sec)
A_s = surface area of enclosure interior surfaces, excluding vent area (m^2)
A_v = vent area (m^2)
L_f = wood fuel mass (kg)

SMOKE PRODUCTION RATE

The rate of smoke-filled gas produced by a fire is nearly equal to the rate of air entrained into the rising fire plume, so the mass production rate of smoke-filled gas can be estimated as equal to the mass flow rate of gas in the fire plume. This mass flow rate into a plume above the visible flame height may be estimated using an expression developed by Zukoski:[19]

$$\dot{m}_s = 0.18\dot{Q}^{1/3}\rho_\infty^{2/3}C_p^{-1/3}T_\infty^{-1/3}g^{1/3}Y^{5/3} \quad [21]$$

where:

$\dot{m}_s$ = rate of smoke-filled gas production (kg/sec)
Q = total heat release rate (kJ/s or kW)
ρ_∞ = density of air (kg/m^3)
C_p = specific heat of air at constant pressure [(kJ/kg)/K]
T_∞ = ambient gas temperature (K)
g = acceleration of gravity (m/sec^2)
Y = distance from the virtual point source for the fire to bottom of smoke layer (m)

Assuming an ambient air temperature of 293 K (20°C), equation 21 can be reduced to

$$\dot{m}_s = 0.065\dot{Q}^{1/3}Y^{5/3} \quad [22]$$

Figure 10-11E provides graphical results based on the calculation of the smoke-filled gas production rate in the above equation for selected values of Q and Y. The mass rate can be changed to a volume rate by dividing by the density of air at the appropriate gas temperature.

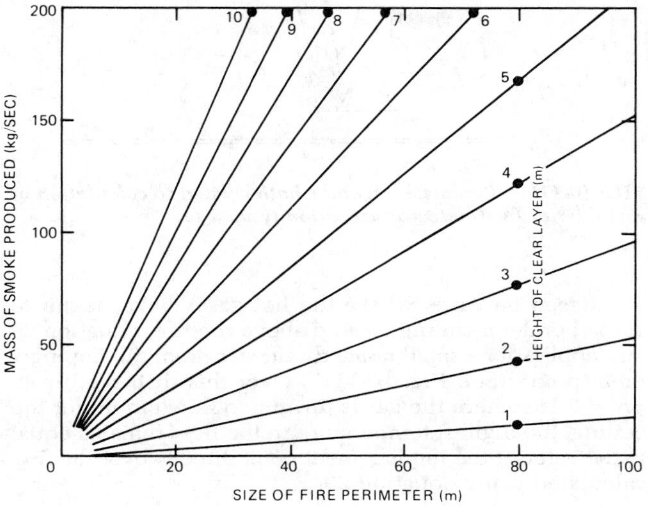

FIG. 10-11E. Smoke production rate for steady fires at various distances (m) from virtual origin to bottom of smoke layer.[19]

Equation 22 does not apply to elevations in the flame region. However, McCaffrey[20] has investigated gas temperatures and velocity distributions within the flame and intermittent flame regions for fire up to 250 kW. Under these conditions, the mass flow rate of combustion products was found to correspond to the expression:

$$\dot{m}_s = 0.055\dot{Q}^{1/2}Y \qquad [23]$$

ENCLOSURE SMOKE FILLING

Smoke from a fire begins to fill an enclosure as it accumulates below the ceiling. The rate of smoke filling depends on the amount of smoke produced and the size and location of vents. The mass rate of smoke flow at any distance above a fire of known heat release rate can be calculated using equation 21. The rate at which a smoke-filled layer descends toward the floor depends on the plan area of the enclosure, the distance of the lower edge of the smoke layer above the fire, and the temperature of the layer.

For an enclosure vented in the lower layer, the upper layer descends with a velocity given by:

$$U_l = \frac{\dot{m}_s}{\rho_l A_p} \qquad [24]$$

U_l = rate of layer descent (m/sec)
$\dot{m}_s$ = mass rate of smoke production (kg/sec)
ρ_l = density of smoke layer (kg/m^3)
A_p = enclosure floor area (m^2)

The lower limit for the velocity of descent is obtained by using the last equation above and the ambient density ρ_∞.

Fires in enclosures in which the upper layer is vented can stabilize at a constant-depth smoke layer. Venting can occur naturally through openings such as doors and windows, or it can be forced by mechanical smoke control systems.

For the case of a known vent flow rate, the height of the bottom of the smoke layer stabilizes above the fire at the position where smoke mass inflow from the fire plume equals vent outflow. This is calculated using a known vent mass flow rate $\dot{m}_{sv}$ and solving equation 22 for position Y_v as

$$Y_v = 1.9\dot{Q}^{-1/5}\dot{m}_{sv}^{3/5} \qquad [25]$$

This shows that the height at which a smoke layer may be stabilized by venting depends mostly on the vent capacity and is relatively insensitive to changes in the fire heat release rate.

BUOYANT GAS HEAD

During a fire, a pressure differential develops between the fire-heated areas and other spaces. Essentially, expressions for pressure differential are derived from the basic hydrostatic equation. The equations below resulted from rearrangement of terms and simplification based on assumed values for selected variables. These expressions are useful in evaluating a range of enclosure effects caused by pressure differentials. Examples include potential for smoke flow to overcome normal air flow, the pressure loading on a door due to the fire, and the uplift pressure on ceiling tiles.

The pressure calculated by these equations results from the difference in density of a heated gas column from the fire and the density of the surrounding environment. A pressure surge can also result from the expansion of heated gases in those situations where the rate of fire development is fast and the space is not vented sufficiently to relieve the resultant increase in gas volume. The equations given below, however, address only the pressure difference caused by the heated gas column condition.

The equations are universal to any heated gas column and can apply to buoyant gas heads caused by building stack effects or other temperature differential effects, including, but not limited to, those caused by fire. The equations, as presented, assume that the entire column of heated gas is at the same temperature. This is a reasonable approximation in many fires but is not exact and would be inappropriate for a fire where the condition consisted of a plume freely entraining cooling air over an extensive portion of its length or any other condition where a significant temperature gradient existed in the heated gas column being appraised.

The general equation can be expressed as

$$\Delta P = (\rho_o - \rho_c)gh \qquad [26]$$

where:

ΔP = pressure difference (Pa)
ρ_o = gas (air) density outside the heated gas column (kg/m^3)
ρ_c = gas (smoke or flame) density of the heated gas column (kg/m^3)
g = gravitational constant (m/sec^2)
h = distance above point where gas column density is same as density outside the heated column. (In a fire, this is normally the base of the hot gas column [m].)

If it is assumed that the outside atmosphere and the gas column are predominantly air at standard atmospheric pressure, the equation can be expressed as

$$\Delta P = 3460\left(\frac{1}{T_\infty} - \frac{1}{T_c}\right)h \qquad [27]$$

where:

ΔP = pressure difference (Pa)
T_∞ = absolute temperature of air outside the heated gas column (K)
T_c = temperature of the heated gas column (K)
h = height of the portion of interest of the hot gas column (m)

For further discussion, see Klote and Fothergill.[21]

THERMAL FIRE DETECTOR RESPONSE

Computer programs have been developed to calculate the response time of heat detectors and sprinklers installed below ceilings in large rooms.[22] These programs can determine the time to operation for a user-specified fire energy release rate history. They are convenient to use because the tedious repetitive calculations needed to analyze a growing fire can be avoided. However, the same calculations can be performed easily with a scientific hand calculator for steady fires that have a constant energy release rate. In cases where a more detailed analysis of a fire that has important changes in energy release rate over time is required, the fire may be represented as a series of steady fires occurring immediately after one another.

A useful calculation directly related to thermal detection is to find the plume temperature at positions directly above the flame produced by burning materials. This can be done using the centerline plume temperature correlation or the simplified correlation:[23]

$$T_{m(\text{plume})} = \left(0.0577\,\frac{\dot{Q}^{2/3}}{h^{5/3}} + 1\right)T_\infty \qquad [28]$$

where:

h = distance above fuel surface (m)
$\dot{Q}$ = fire energy release rate [(kJ/sec) or (kW)]
$T_{m(plume)}$ = plume gas temperature above fire (K)
T_∞ = ambient room temperature (K)

This equation was developed from analysis of experiments with large-scale fires having energy release rates from 670 kW to 100 MW.[24]

As an example, using the last equation, the plume gas temperature ($T_{m(plume)}$) 5 m (h) above the fuel surface of 500 kW ($\dot{Q}$), fire is found to be 366 K (93°C) for an ambient room temperature (T_∞) of 293 K (20°C).

For the case of fixed-temperature detectors, the minimum fire energy release rate Q needed to operate a fixed-temperature detection or suppression device located directly above the fire can be estimated using the last equation, solving for $\dot{Q}$ with $T_{m(plume)}$ set equal to the activation temperature of the thermal device. In this form, equation 28 becomes

$$\dot{Q} = 72.2\left(\frac{T_{m(\text{plume})} - T_\infty}{T_\infty}\right)^{3/2} \times h^{5/2} \qquad [29]$$

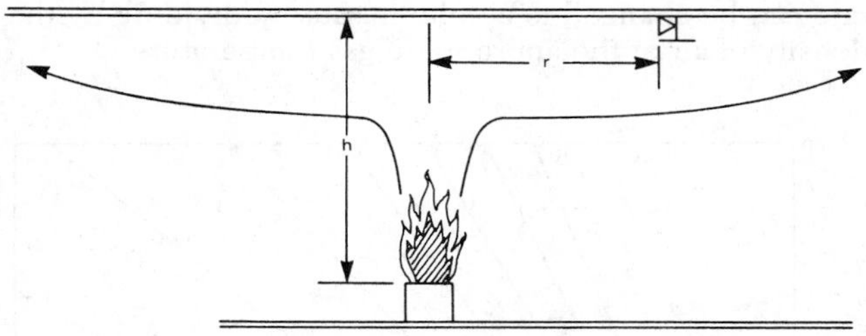

FIG. 10-11F. Parameters h and r both related to calculation of sprinkler or heat-detector actuation time.

Based on cases where the hot gases have begun to spread under a ceiling located above the fire, equation 29 also applies for a small radial distance, r, from the impingement point. (See Fig. 10-11F.) Over this distance, up to $r/h = 0.18$, where the gas is turning to flow out under the ceiling, the highest temperature in the flow remains equal to the value at the impingement point directly over the fire, calculated using equation 29.

At radial distances greater than $r/h = 0.18$, the maximum temperature in the ceiling jet flow depends upon the distance from the impingement point according to

$$T_{m(\text{jet})} = \left(0.0184\,\frac{(\dot{Q}/r)^{2/3}}{h} + 1\right)T_\infty \qquad [30]$$

where:

$T_{m(jet)}$ = temperature of ceiling jet (K)
r = radial distance from plume centerline to device (m)

Correlations are also available for maximum velocities in the ceiling jet flow (U_m) under a ceiling. As with the temperature correlations, there are two regions, one close to the impingement point where velocities are nearly constant and the other farther away where velocities vary with radial position. The two correlations are:

$$U_m = 0.052\left(\frac{\dot{Q}}{h}\right)^{1/3} \quad \text{for } r/h < 0.15, \qquad [31]$$

and

$$U_m = 0.196\left(\frac{\dot{Q}^{1/3}h^{1/2}}{r^{5/8}}\right) \quad \text{for } r/h > 0.15 \qquad [32]$$

where:

U_m = gas velocity (m/sec)

The previous equations can be used to determine whether the temperature of the fire-driven gas flow past a detection device is high enough to operate the device. However, more information is needed to calculate the amount of time needed to heat the detector or sprinkler sensing element to the operating temperature. Often, these elements are made of metal, such as the ordinary solder-type fusible link used in the link and lever sprinklers, or they are liquid-filled glass vials, such as those used in bulb-type sprinklers. Both of these sensing elements require some time to absorb the heat transferred from the hot gas flowing around the device.

For steady fires, the time required to heat the sensing element of a thermal detection or suppression device from room temperature to operation temperature is given by

$$t_{\text{operation}} = \frac{RTI}{\sqrt{U_m}} \log_e \left(\frac{T_m - T_\infty}{T_m - T_{\text{operation}}} \right) \qquad [33]$$

where RTI, the response-time index, is a measure of the ease of heating thermal elements in heat detectors and sprinklers. The larger the RTI value, the greater the lag in heating the sensing element. RTI values for sprinklers have been measured[25] in the range of 15 $m^{1/2}s^{1/2}$ to 400 $m^{1/2}s^{1/2}$.

In the previous example, it was found using an earlier equation that a 500 kW (Q) fire would produce a gas temperature of 93°C ($T_{m(plume)}$) at 5 m (h) above the fuel surface in a room with 20°C (T_∞) ambient temperature. From quation 31, the gas velocity at this position would be 4.4 m/sec (U_m). For a sprinkler with an RTI of 200 $m^{1/2}$ $sec^{1/2}$ and operation temperature of 74°C ($T_{operation}$), the time to operation in response to the steady fire can be calculated from equation 33 as

$$t_{\text{operation}} = \frac{200}{\sqrt{4.4}} \log_e \left(\frac{93 - 20}{93 - 74} \right) = 128 \text{ seconds}$$

The measurement of thermal lag for sprinklers is a topic of current research investigations.[26] Recent progress has included means to account for the effects of heat loss due to conduction.

All calculations in use today for determining times to operation only consider the convective heating of sensing elements by the hot fire gases. They do not account explicitly for any direct heating by radiation from the flames. Research is continuing to improve and generalize these types of calculations.

BIBLIOGRAPHY

References Cited

1. DiNenno, P. J., ed., *SFPE Handbook of Fire Protection Engineering*, National Fire Protection Association, Quincy, MA, 1988.
2. Babrauskas, V. and Krasny, J. F., "Fire Behavior of Upholstered Furniture," *NBS Monograph*, National Bureau of Standards, Gaithersburg, MD, 1985.
3. Lawson, J. R., *et al.*, "Fire Performance of Furnishings as Measured in the NBS Furniture Calorimeter, Part 1," *NBSIR 83-2787*, National Bureau of Standards, Gaithersburg, MD, Jan. 1984.
4. Alpert, R. L. and Ward, E. J., "Evaluating Unsprinklered Fire Hazards," *SFPE TR 83-2*, Society of Fire Protection Engineers, Boston, MA, 1983.
5. Babrauskas, V., *et al.*, "Upholstered Furniture Heat Release Rates Measured with a Furniture Calorimeter," *NBSIR 82-2604*, National Bureau of Standards, Gaithersburg, MD, 1982.
6. Babrauskas, V., "Free-Burning Fires," *Proceedings* SFPE Symposium: Quantitative Methods for Fire Hazard Analysis, University of Maryland, College Park, MD, 1985.
7. Lawson, J. R., and Quintiere, J. G., "Slide-Rule Estimates of Fire Growth," *NBSIR 85-3196*, National Bureau of Standards, Gaithersburg, MD, 1985.
8. Heskestad, G., "Virtual Origins of Fire Plumes," *Fire Safety Journal*, Vol. 5, No. 109, 1983.
9. Beyler, C. L., "Fire Plumes and Ceiling Jets," *Fire Safety Journal*, Vol. 11, No. 53, 1986.
10. Heskestad, G., "Luminous Heights of Turbulent-Diffusion Flames," *Fire Safety Journal*, Vol. 7, No. 25, 1984.
11. McCaffrey, B. J., Quintiere, J. G., and Harkleroad, M. F., "Estimating Room Temperatures and the Likelihood of Flashover Using Fire Test Data Correlations," *Fire Technology*, Vol. 17, No. 2, 1981, p. 98.
12. Foote, K. L., Pagni, P. J., and Alvares, N. J., "Temperature Correlations for Forced-Ventilated Compartment Fires," *Proceedings* of the First International Symposium, International Association for Fire Safety Science, Hemisphere Publishing, 1986, pp. 139-148.
13. Deal, S. D. and Beyler, C. L., "Correlating Preflashover Room Fire Temperatures," *Journal of Fire Protection Engineering*, Vol. 2, No. 2, 1990, pp 33-48.
14. Thomas, P. H., "Testing Products and Materials for Their Contribution to Flashover in Rooms," *Fire and Materials*, Vol. 5, No. 3, 1981, pp. 103-111.
15. Thomas, P. H., *Fire in Model Rooms*, CIB Research Program, Building Research Establishment, Borehamwood, Hertfordshire, England, 1974.
16. Law, M., "Fire Safety of External Building Elements — The Design Approach," *AISC Engineering Journal*, Second Quarter, American Institute of Steel Construction, 1978.
17. Law, M., "Prediction of Fire Resistance," *Proceedings*, Symposium No. 5: Fire-Resistance Requirements for Buildings — A New Approach, Joint Fire Research Organization, H. M. Stationery Office, London, 1973.
18. Thomas, P. H. and Heselden, A. J. M., *Fully Developed Fires in Single Compartments*, A Co-operative Research Programme of the Conseil International du Batiment, Joint Fire Research Organization Research Note No. 923, H. M. Stationery Office, London, 1972.
19. Zukoski, E. E., "Development of a Stratified Ceiling Layer in the Early Stages of a Closed-Room Fire," *Fire and Materials*, Vol. 2, No. 2, 1978.
20. McCaffrey, B. J., "Purely Buoyant Diffusion Flames: Some Experimental Results," *NBSIR 79-1910*, National Bureau of Standards, Gaithersburg, MD, 1979.
21. Klote, J. H. and Fothergill, J. W. Jr., *Design of Smoke Control Systems for Buildings, NBS Handbook 141*, National Bureau of Standards, Gaithersburg, MD, 1983.
22. Evans, D. D. and Stroup, D. W., "Methods to Calculate the Response Time of Heat and Smoke Detectors Installed Below Large Unobstructed Ceilings," *Fire Technology*, Vol. 22, No. 1, 1985, pp. 54-65.
23. Evans, D. D., "Calculating Sprinkler Actuation Time in Compartments," *Fire Safety Journal*, Vol. 9, pp. 1985, 147-155.
24. Alpert, R. L., "Calculation of Response Time of Ceiling-Mounted Fire Detectors," *Fire Technology*, Vol. 8, 1972, pp. 181-195.
25. Heskestad, G. and Smith, H., "Investigation of a New Sprinkler Sensitivity Approval Test: The Plunge Test," *FMRC Serial No. 22485*, Factory Mutual Research Corporation, Norwood, MA, 1976.
26. Heskestad, G. and Bill, R. G., "Quantification of Thermal Responsiveness of Automatic Sprinklers Including Conduction Effects," *Fire Safety Journal*, Vol. 14, No. 1-2, July 1988, pp. 113-125.

Additional Readings

Standard Test Method for Heat and Visible Smoke Release Rates for Materials and Products (E-906-83), American Society for Testing and Materials, Philadelphia, PA, 1983.

Babrauskas, V., "Applications of Predictive Smoke Measurements," *Journal of Fire and Flammability*, Vol. 12, 1981, pp 51.

Babrauskas V., "A Closed-Form Approximation for Post-Flashover Compartment Fire Termperatures," *Fire Safety Journal*, Vol. 4, 1981, pp. 63-73.

Babrauskas, V., "Development of the Cone Calorimeter — A Bench-Scale Heat Release Rate Apparatus Based on Oxygen Consumption," *NBSIR 82-2611*, National Bureau of Standards, Washington, DC, 1982.

Babrauskas, V., "Estimating Room Flashover Potential," *Fire Technology*, Vol. 16 (May 1980), pp. 94-103, 112.

Babrauskas, V., "Free Burning Fires," *Proceedings*, SFPE Symposium: Quantitative Methods for Fire Hazard Analysis, University of Maryland, College Park, MD, 1985.

Babrauskas, V., "Upholstered Furniture Room Fires—Measurements, Comparison with Furniture Calorimeter Data, and Flashover Predictions," *Journal of Fire Sciences*, Vol. 2 (Jan.-Feb. 1984), pp. 5-19.

Babrauskas, V., *et al.*, "Upholstered Furniture Heat Release Rates Measured with a Furniture Calorimeter," *NBSIR 82-2604*, National Bureau of Standards, Washington, DC, 1982.

Babrauskas, V. and Krasny, J. F., "Fire Behavior of Upholstered Furniture," *NBS Monograph*, National Bureau of Standards, Washington, DC, 1985.

Butcher, E. G. and Parnell, A. C., *Smoke Control in Fire Safety Design*, E. and F. N. Spon, Ltd., London, England, 1979.

Curtat, M. R. and Bodart, X. E., "Simple and Not So Simple Models for Compartment Fires," *Proceedings* of the First International Symposium of Fire Safety Science, Hemisphere, 1986, pp. 637-646.

Delichatsios, M. A., "Fire Growth Rates in Wood Cribs," *Combustion and Flame*, Vol., 27, 1976, pp. 267-278.

Drysdale, D., *An Introduction to Fire Dynamics*, John Wiley & Sons, New York, 1985.

Evans, D. D., "Calculation of a Fire Plume in a Two Layer Environment," *Fire Technology*, Vol. 20, No. 3, 1984, p. 39.

Galea, E., "On the Field Modeling Approach to the Simulation of Enclosure Fires," *Journal of Fire Protection Engineering*, Vol.1, No. 1, 1989, pp. 11-22.

Gross, D., "Data Sources for Parameters Used in Predictive Modeling of Fire Growth and Smoke Spread," *NBSIR 85-3223*, National Bureau of Stnadards, 1985, Gaithersberg, MD.

Heskestad, G., *A Fire Products Collector for Calorimetry into the MW Range*, Factory Mutual Research Corp., Norwood, MA, 1981.

Heskestad, G., "Modeling of Enclosure Fires," 14th International Symposium on Combustion, The Combustion Institute, Pittsburgh, PA, pp. 1021, 1973.

Huggett, C., "Estimation of Rate of Heat Release by Means of Oxygen Consumption Measurements," *Fire and Materials*, Vol. 4, 1980, pp. 61-65.

Kawagoe, K. and Sekine, T., *Estimation of Fire Temperature Time Curve for Rooms*, Japanese Ministry of Construction Building Research Institute, June 1963.

Krasner, L. M., *Burning Characteristics of Wooden Pallets as a Test Fuel*, Factory Mutual Engineering, Norwood, MA, 1968.

Law, M., "Radiation from Fires in a Compartment," *Fire Research Tech. Paper No. 20*, British Fire Research Station, 1971.

Law, M., "A Relationship Between Fire Grading and Building Design and Contents," *Fire Research Note 877*, British Fire Research Station, 1971.

Law, M., "Notes on the External Fire Exposure Measured at Lehrte," *Fire Safety Journal*, Vol. 4, 1981-82, pp. 243-246.

Lawson, J. R. and Quintiere, J. G., "Slide Rule Estimates of Fire Growth," *Fire Technology*, Vol. 21, No. 4, 1985, pp. 267-292.

Lawson, J. R. and Quintiere, J. G., "Slide Rule Estimates of Fire Growth," *Fire Technology*, Vol. 22, No. 1, 1986, pp. 45-53.

Lopez, E. L., "Smoke Emission from Burning Cabin Materials and the Effect on Visibility in Wide-Bodied Jet Transports," *Journal of Fire and Flammability*, Vol. 6, 1975.

Modak, A. T., "Thermal Radiation from Pool Fires," *Combustion and Flame*, Vol. 29, 1977, pp. 177-192.

Modak, A. T., and Croce, P. A., "Plastic Pool Fires," *Combustion and Flame*, Vol. 30, 1977, pp. 251-265.

Ove Arup and Partners, *Design Guide for Fire Safety of Bare Exterior Structural Steel*, London, England, Sponsored by American Iron and Steel Institute, Washington, DC, 1977.

Peacock, R. D., Davis, S., and Lee, B. T., "An Experiment Data Set for the Accuracy of Room Fire Models," *NBSIR 88-3752*, National Bureau of Standards, Gaithersburg, MD, April 1988.

Quintiere, J. G., "A Simple Correlation for Predicting Temperature in a Room Fire," *NBSIR 83-2712*, National Bureau of Standards, Washington, DC, 1983.

Quintiere, J., "A Perspective on Compartment Growth," *Combustion Science and Technology*, Vol. 39, 1984, pp. 11-54.

Quintiere, J. G., "Smoke Measurements: An Assessment of Correlations between Laboratory and Full-Scale Experiments," *Fire and Materials*, Vol. 6, Nos. 3 and 4, 1982.

Quintiere, J. G., et al., "An Analysis of Smoldering Fires in Closed Compartments and Their Hazard Due to Carbon Monoxide," *Fire and Materials*, Vol. 16, Nos. 3 and 4, 1982.

Rasbash, D. J., "Smoke and Toxic Products Produced at Fires," *Plastics Institute Transaction and Journal*, Jan 1967, pp. 55-61.

Ramachandran, G., "Exponential Model of Fire Growth," *Proceedings* of the First International Symposium on Fire Safety Science, Hemisphere, 1986, pp. 657-666.

Tewarson, A., "Physico-Chemical and Combustion/Pyrolysis Properties of Polymetric Materials," *NBS-GCR-80-295*, National Bureau of Standards, Washington, DC, 1980.

Than, C. F., "Modeling Fire Behavior in an Enclosure With a Ceiling Vent," *MS Thesis*, Worcester Polytechnic Institute, Worcester, MA, 1989.

Williams, F. A., "Mechanisms of Fire Spread," 16th International Symposium on Combustion, The Combustion Institute, 1976, pp. 1281-1294.

Yamashika, S. and Kurimoto, H., "Burning Rate of Wood Cribs," *Report of the Fire Research Institute of Japan*, Tokyo, No. 41 (Mar. 1976), pp. 8-15.

Zdanowski, M., Teadorczyk, A., and Wojcicki, S., "A Simple Mathematical Model of Flashover in Compartment Fires," *Fire and Materials*, Vol. 10, 1986, p. 145.

APPLICATION OF FIRE GROWTH MODELS TO FIRE PROTECTION PROBLEMS*

Harold E. "Bud" Nelson

During the 1980s, computerized fire growth models were developed and applied to firesafety problems. In general, these models estimate changes to a building or space within a building and its environment as the result of a fire in that structure. For the most part, these models do not model fire but rather the impact of fire. A more extensive discussion of computer fire models and their elements is covered in other chapters in this section. The purpose of this chapter is briefly to advise the user on some of the types of applications where modeling can be of assistance and provide some guidance for the user to establish his or her own criteria for selection of the model chosen.

The reality of accidental fire is more varied and complex than can be exactly described by any existing collection of equations and data. Users should not expect that the model will produce an exact duplication of reality. Rather, the results of models should be considered as engineering estimates, valid to the degree that the physical relationships being calculated are those that actually dominate the situation and that the data entered into the model is accurate. Figures 10-12A through 10-12F demonstrate the type of approximation that should be expected. In Figure 10-12A, four different models and one simple correlation were used in an attempt to reproduce the results from a well-documented test of a fire in a room.† In Figure 10-12A, the curve using the letter x to indicate data points plots the average upper layer temperature computed from thermocouple readings during the test. The other curves graph the predictions by the various models. The complexity of the models varied widely in this exercise. The simplest model was a single correlation equation, while the most complex involved the coordination of almost a hundred variables. In the case of this test, the most sophisticated model was the most accurate, but other much less sophisticated models grouped in the same range. Figure 10-12B is a reproduction of the actual data obtained in the burn test. Figure 10-12B reports the actual measured temperatures detected by a thermocouple tree near the center of the room but away from the fire plume. Every third thermocouple is ploted. Each of the lines depicts the temperature recorded by one of the thermocouples. The thermocouples were mounted with one near the ceiling and the others at 6-in. (0.15-m) intervals, with the bottom thermocouple located about 6 in. (0.15 m) above the floor. Figure 10-12C plots the same information as Figure 10-12B but rearranges the data to show the temperature profile from floor to ceiling as 1-min. intervals through the first 6 min. of the test.

All of the models used to produce the results in Figure 10-12A are classed as zone models; that is, they predicted a single "upper layer" (smoke) temperature. As shown in Figures 10-12B and 10-12C, an upper layer of hot fire gases with an approximately, but not exactly, equal tem-

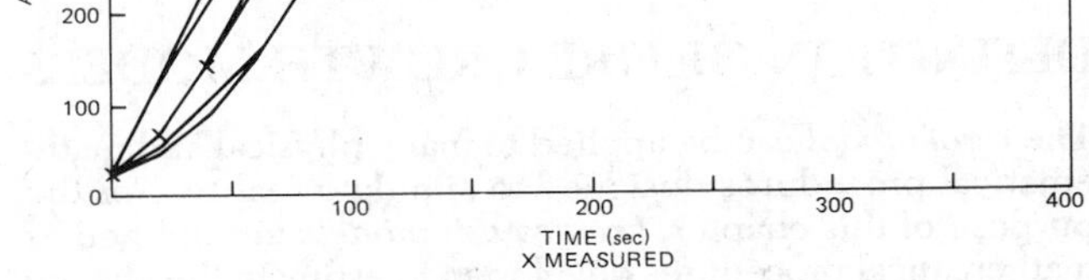

FIG. 10-12A. ***Zone models versus test measurements.***

---

* This chapter is contribution of the National Institute of Standards and Technology and is not subject to copyright.

Mr. Nelson is a senior research engineer at the Building and Fire Research Laboratory, National Institute of Standards and Technology, U.S. Department of Commerce.

† The fire test used for this comparison is test PRC17W4-$^{1}/_{4}$ This was one of a series of compartment fire tests conducted under the sponsorship of the Product Research Committee. Test PRC17W4-$^{1}/_{4}$ was conducted in a room 2.18 m square and 2.41 m high. The room had a single vent opening 0.19 m wide and 2 m high. The fuel for this test consisted of four wood cribs having a total weight of approximately 14 kg located near the center of the room.

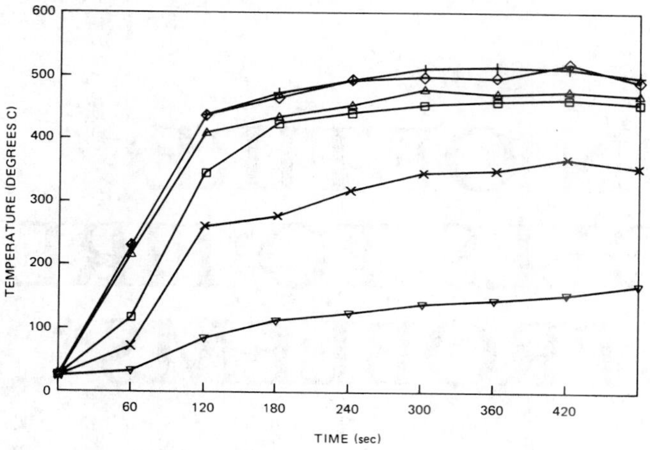

FIG. 10-12B. Temperature plots at various heights.

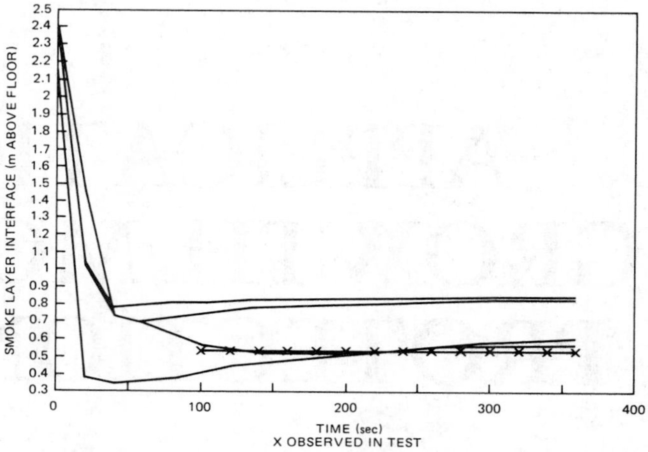

FIG. 10-12D. Zone models versus test measurements.

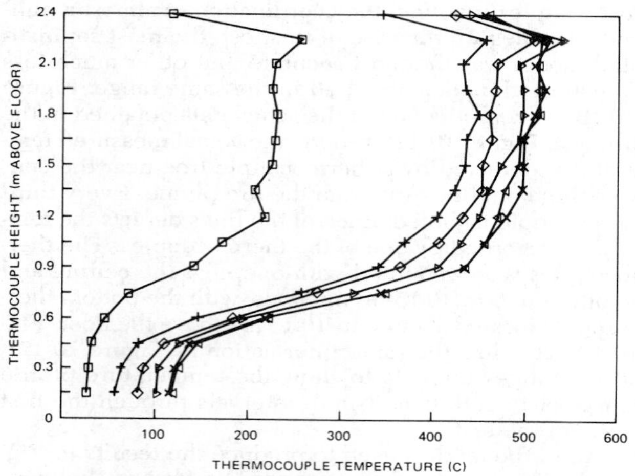

FIG. 10-12C. Temperature profile at 1-min. intervals.

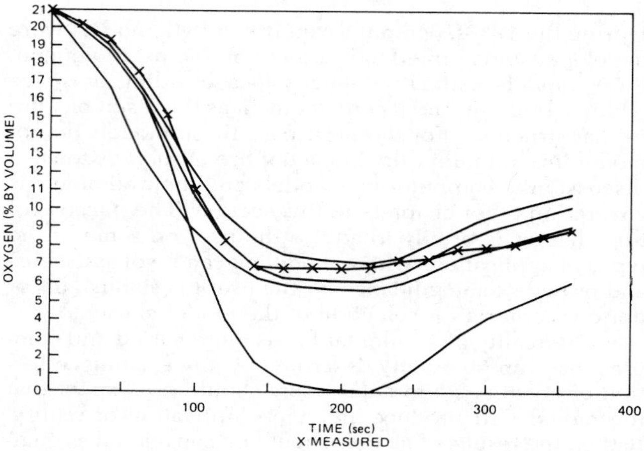

FIG. 10-12E. Zone models versus test measurements.

perature did exist. While the type of approximation produced by these models is often more accurate than previous methods of estimation, the results must still be recognized as an engineering approximation. Figure 10-12D plots the smoke layer interface calculated by the models with that observed by the investigators. Figure 10-12E compares the oxygen concentration measured in the smoke in the test to concentrations calculated by the models. Figure 10-12F compares the measured mass flow through the vent opening with the same flow as calculated by the models. These four measures (temperature, smoke layer interface, oxygen concentration, and mass flow through the vent opening) were chosen to represent the full range of model outputs.

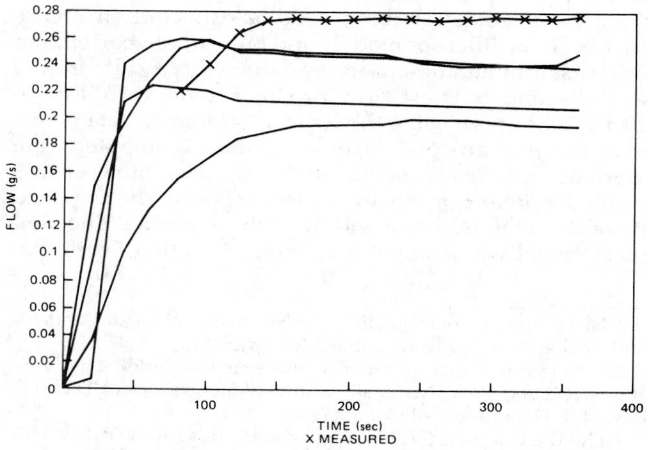

FIG. 10-12F. Zone models versus test measurements.

DEFINITION OF FIRE GROWTH MODELS

The term *model* can be applied to many physical and mathematical procedures designed to simulate reality. For the purpose of this chapter, *fire growth models* are defined as mathematical procedures developed to estimate the change in the environment of a space or building caused by the existence of a fire in that space that varies in intensity and/or area of involvement with time. All of these models predict the temperature of the smoke layer produced by that fire. Most fire growth models also predict the depth of the smoke layer. In addition, many models predict other variables such as the oxygen, carbon monoxide, carbon dioxide, and other gas species concentrations in the smoke; the rate of flow of smoke, gases, and unburned fuel from one space to another; and the temperatures of the walls, ceiling, floor, and air not yet drawn into the fire. Somemodels also predict the time of activation of smoke detectors and heat detectors (including sprinkler heads) and the effects of opening or closing doors, breakage of windows, or other physical events that take place during an accidental fire. Some models are limited to the room of fire involvement, others track the impact of a fire in that room through a series of rooms, and a few can follow the spread of fire outside the room of origin.

Typically, the models involve the simultaneous solution of two or more differential equations. The more sophisticated models involve the simultaneous solution of such equations for many variables and use sophisticated techniques to obtain the results. The range of complexity and sophistication is wide, but all models follow the basic principles of conservation of mass, energy, and momentum. All models also use plume entrainment equations similar to those discussed in "Hand Calculations for Enclosure Fires" (Section 21, Chapter 3).

TYPES OF MODELS

As discussed more thoroughly in Section 10, Chapters 8 and 9, prediction models can generally be classed into the two categories of zone models that solve the basic conservation equation for distinct regions (control volumes) and field models that solve the fundamental equations of mass, momentum, and energy in a space that has been divided into a grid of small-volume cells.

Zone Models

Most of the fire growth models that can be run on modern personal computers are *zone models*. These usually divide each room into two spaces or zones: an upper zone that contains the hot gases produced by the fire and a lower zone that contains a space beneath the upper zone that is the source of the air for combustion. Zone sizes change during the course of the fire. The upper zone can expand to occupy virtually all the space in the room.

Field Models

Conversely, *field models* usually require large-capacity computer work stations or mainframe computers. By dividing the space into many small cells (frequently tens of thousands), field models can examine much greater detail than zone models. Where such detail is needed, it is often necessary to use the sophistication of a field model. In general, however, field models are much more expensive to use, require more time to set up and run, and often require a high level of expertise to make the decisions required in setting up the problem and interpreting the output produced by the model.

Hybrid Models

A *hybrid model* is defined as one that uses elements of both zone models and field models. It is possible that some hybrid models will appear while this Handbook is still in use. However, at the time of this writing, none are available, and the level of sophistication that will be necessary to operate one properly is unknown. It is visualized that hybrid models will be able to use the simplicity of zone models for those spaces or portions of time in the fire where the general average calculations typical of a zone model are sufficient but switch to some type of smaller zones or field model cells when needed.

MODEL APPLICATIONS

In the broadest sense, a fire growth model can be applied as a tool in the solution of any fire protection problem where the fire-produced conditions inside a building or space or the response of fire protection devices in that space are needed as input to the decision. The following are some typical examples of classes of application.

1. *Predicting a hazard.* In this case, *hazard* is defined as the expected fire-produced conditions. To start, a set of circumstances that represents either a specific case of interest or a design case representing the maximum expected fire is postulated. All of the conditions are fixed and the model is run to make a prediction of the rise of smoke (upper layer) temperature, the volume or depth of that smoke, the response of devices, the onset of serious conditions such as flashover, smoke gases or toxicity, or other items of concern. Often, this type of analysis is searching for the most serious case and is used to answer questions such as, "How serious are the fire-produced conditions that can occur in this space?" Frequently, a number of case variations will have to be run to establish the most serious case. For example, consider an analysis of the hazard of a hotel room that contains a bed of a type that fire tests indicate will grow, if ignited, at a moderate rate, eventually reaching a fire size of 2 megawatts (MW); a chair having a very fast fire-growth rate if ignited but a maximum rate of energy of less than 1 MW; and a number of pieces of furniture that would not be expected to be points of ignition but could join a fire at a later state. Discovery of the worse case might require a series of computer runs in which the ignition source was placed first on the bed and then on the chair, runs where the distance between the bed and the chair were varied, runs with the door open and the door closed, and any other possible variations.
2. *Predicting a risk. Risk*, as distinguished from *hazard*, is defined as the likelihood and degree of harm during a given period of exposure. In the example of the hotel room, the period of exposure could be as short as the period of use by a guest or as long as the life of the hotel. The choice depends on the interest of the model user. To determine risk, it is necessary to:

   a. Obtain from statistics or some other source or otherwise estimate the likelihood of each of the variable conditions capable of producing unacceptable results.

   b. Run the model for each of these conditions, estimating the harm caused to the individual material, facility, or investment of concern.

   c. Multiply that harm by the probability of occurrence of the individual case being modeled and add the results of all cases that potentially can reach the unacceptable harm level.

This type of appraisal is most appropriate to resolving the type of questions pertinent to underwriters, risk managers, or public-safety authorities.

3. *Mathematical reconstruction of a fire*. Fire models can be useful in reconstructing incidents that occur during a fire or testing suggested hypotheses or scenarios. In the perfect case, there is enough physical evidence, data on conditions at the time of the fire, and reliable witness statements to produce all of the information necessary to run the model to describe the course of conditions and the phenomena that did occur. In actual practice, only part of the necessary information is usually available, and running the model may in itself involve some rational hypotheses as to what the conditions were most likely to have been. Often, running the model will help demonstrate which hypotheses are plausible and which are not. In the case of the example of the hotel room, the comparison of the known data to the various different scenarios may demonstrate that some would not have run the course known to have occurred. In some cases, a single dominant fire scenario will emerge.
4. *Interpolating between or extrapolating beyond test results*. In many cases, fire tests that simulate a real-world condition have been conducted to obtain data on an arrangement, protection system, product, or other material. In translating that data to real-world applications, the desired use frequently does not match the test array. In many cases, models can be used to appraise the impact of the difference between the test and reality. In such cases, the usual procedure is first to run the model in exactly the arrangement of the test to demonstrate that the model can reasonably approximate the results obtained in the test. In making the comparison between the model and the test result, the user should recognize that there can be a degree of inaccuracy or uncertainty in test results as well as in model predictions. Perfect matches between models and tests seldom occur. Once a reasonable reproduction of the test has been achieved, the model is rerun, changing those variables or parameters that differ between the test and reality. The less change, of course, the more dependable the results.
5. *Evaluation of a parametric variation*. In all of the above examples, it is frequently necessary to answer the question, "What if a change were made?" Models provide excellent tools for such parametric studies. Most frequently, the changes would involve the change of a material (construction, finish, furnishings), a change of an arrangement (door opened or closed, air conditioner on or off, spacing variations between fuel packages), or the presence or absence of a protection system such as smoke detectors or sprinklers. Using the example of the hotel room, typical questions might include the change in hazard or risk that would occur should the mattress be changed from a moderate-burning mattress to one that is fast-burning or one that is treated to burn at a very slow rate. A similar question might relate to the use of a combustible wall material. In the case of a fire analysis, questions might relate to the difference in the situation had there been a sprinkler in the space, had the door been equipped with a smoke-operated door closer, or had some particular material been different. A first-order approximation of the contribution of an item of furnishing or a material can be made by exercising the model with and without that material present and noting the differences.

SOME ADDITIONAL CONSIDERATIONS

Fire models are engineering tools. Like engineering handbooks, they are available to all persons, regardless of competence. Unlike engineering handbooks, however, many models have been made user-friendly and can be executed by persons who may not understand their capabilities, limitations, or the impact of the choices made in setting up the problems. When decisions produced by a model impact on the safety of life and property, one of the two following cases must hold.

1. Users must understand what the model is doing and how it is achieving the results, thereby treating it as an engineering tool. In such cases, the users are as responsible for the results as they would be had they gone to the engineering handbooks and extracted the equations themselves. Engineers are encouraged to use models, understand them, and become fluent with them. They will become an excellent tool under their control. Or,
2. Users must ascertain the limits to which the model has been demonstrated as rational and restrain their use within these bounds. If the occasion necessitates exceeding these bounds, the user should obtain the advice and/or service of individuals competent to examine the model and determine its appropriateness for the use desired.

Many models require that the user provide inputs beyond a simple description of the space and its contents. Some of these inputs can greatly affect the result. The user may or may not have the data available or an understanding of the impact of his or her decision. Some models provide information to assist users; others do not. It is important that users exercise the model, find the variables required, and ensure that they can properly assign these before using the model. An important thing to remember is that many models include default values for the variables. A default value is one that has been included in the model and will be used by the model unless changed by the user. Usually, the values are ones felt to be reasonable by the model developer. However, they may or may not be appropriate for the case involved. The user must examine and responsibly accept or alter the default values as is appropriate for the case at hand.

The sophistication or detail of a model may or may not be related to its accuracy for the case involved. A general principle is to use the simplest model that meets the user's needs for the type and quality of information desired and the information required to run the model. Many of the more sophisticated models provide masses of detail that are not available in the simpler version. Conversely, some of the very simple models omit important fire phenomena. The balance between ensuring that the necessary phenomena are modeled and maintaining the sophistication of the model is best achieved by frequent use and examination of the models of interest.

Finally, many computer fire models undergo regular review and possible adjustments. Users should try to stay abreast of updates, revisions, or other changes to models they use. They should be wary of models that are not being maintained and adjusted as needed by a competent organization.

INTEGRATION OF FIRE MODELS WITH THE DESIGN PROCESS

Frederick W. Mowrer, Ph.D.

The methods of quantitative building fire hazard assessment have been developed and refined during the past decade to the point where they can be used innovatively as part of the building firesafety design process. This chapter addresses a rational design framework for the application of quantitative fire analysis models. Design elements and attributes appropriate for different types of quantitative fire analysis models are developed. Traditional and computer-based design implementations are discussed.

Concurrent with the development of quantitative fire analysis models, the technology of building design has been changing with the development of computers and software suitable for design purposes. This change in design technology, commonly called computer-aided design, or CAD, permits the design process to be implemented in terms of meaningful design elements. This new technology permits unprecedented integration of engineering analyses into the building design and documentation process. Features of CAD systems that allow this integration of design and analysis are discussed in this chapter.

A number of concepts presented here are also discussed in other chapters. The Firesafety Concepts Tree discussed in Section 1, Chapter 3 on "Systems Concepts for Building Firesafety" provides a logical and fairly comprehensive qualitative framework for the analysis and design of building firesafety. Fire modeling provides a mechanism to address quantitatively the topics addressed qualitatively in the Firesafety Concepts Tree. Chapter 10-9, "Deterministic Fire Models," and Chapter 10-11, "Hand Calculations for Enclosure Fires," discuss some of the currently available fire modeling techniques. Chapter 10-6, "Fire Hazard Assessment," also addresses some concepts similar to those presented here.

What Is Design?

Design is decision-making. It is the selection and orientation of basic design elements, which may be materials, products, and assemblies, to serve functional and aesthetic objectives within the constraints imposed by cost, available technology, and safety. The suitability of a product for a particular application is determined by analysis. Different analyses use different properties or attributes of design elements to measure their performance. Design elements selected for use must demonstrate acceptable performance based on these analyses.

Historically, the analysis and design of building firesafety has occurred largely within the context of building code or other regulatory compliance. Within this context, a building is evaluated in terms of the conformance of individual design elements with code requirements. Such compliance should be considered as a necessary but not sufficient condition of adequate firesafety. The selection of design elements for code compliance is necessary from a legal standpoint, but it is not sufficient to demonstrate that adequate firesafety has been provided because current building regulations do not necessarily address the actual fire hazards imposed by products in end use. These hazards may include additive or synergistic effects among design elements that can only be evaluated in the context of use.

The methods available to analyze the actual hazards of products in building fires and the fire mitigation strategies used to counter these fires continue to expand and improve. These analysis tools provide a mechanism to consider the consequences of building fires in quantitative terms with physical meaning. With this ability, a rational design framework similar to ones used in other engineering disciplines can begin to be formalized.

An Engineering Design Framework

A general design framework can be considered in terms of the processes and relationships depicted in Figure 10-13A. A design project begins with problem definition and continues with an iterative design process, composed of analysis, synthesis, and documentation. During this process, the performance of proposed designs is evaluated in terms of design goals and constraints. Ultimately, this process yields a final design.

The first step of the design framework, problem definition, should include the clear specification of design goals and constraints in terms amenable to analysis. These

Frederick Mowrer is assistant professor of fire protection engineering at the University of Maryland.

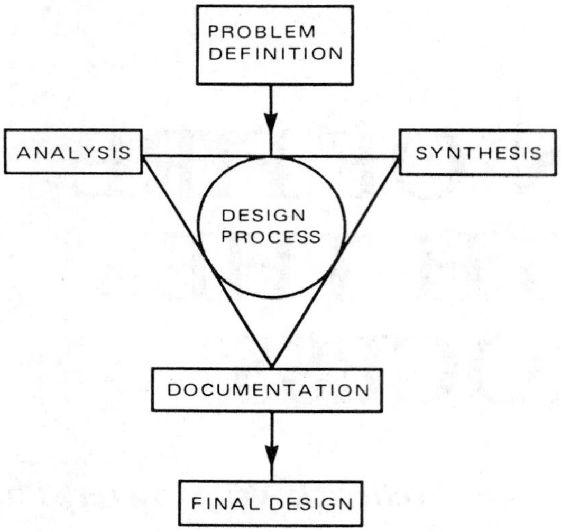

FIG. 10-13A. General design framework.

goals and constraints provide the basis for evaluation of design solutions. The more specifically and operationally a goal or constraint can be defined, the better it can be addressed by quantitative analysis.[1] The topic of problem definition, as applied to firesafety analysis and design, is addressed in more detail below.

Figure 10-13B illustrates the basic concept of analysis in terms of a simple flow diagram. In the analysis segment of the design process, design data are used within an algorithm or model to yield some measurement of performance. The purpose of analysis is to evaluate the suitability of design elements for their anticipated uses. A number of different analyses may be needed to determine this suitability. Foremost, a design element must fulfill its function while maintaining a reasonable level of safety. Other factors, such as cost, will aid in the selection among those design elements meeting the primary criteria.

FIG. 10-13B. The analysis process.

Models with different levels of complexity and sophistication are now available for the analysis of building fire safety. Computer-based models, such as those discussed in Chapter 10-9 on Deterministic Fire Models, support more comprehensive analyses than simple calculation models, such as those described in Chapter 10-11 on Hand Calculations for Enclosure Fires. But the use of the more sophisticated models may not result in changes in design decisions because only a discrete number of suitable design alternatives may exist. From a design standpoint, differences in the capabilities of analytical models are important only insofar as they permit distinctions in the selection of design elements.

Figure 10-13C illustrates the concept of solution synthesis in terms of a basic flow diagram. Solution synthesis is the process of evaluating the results of the various analyses in terms of program requirements and performance criteria to develop acceptable design solutions. The final design should be selected from the subset of solutions that fulfill all the design goals and satisfy all constraints.

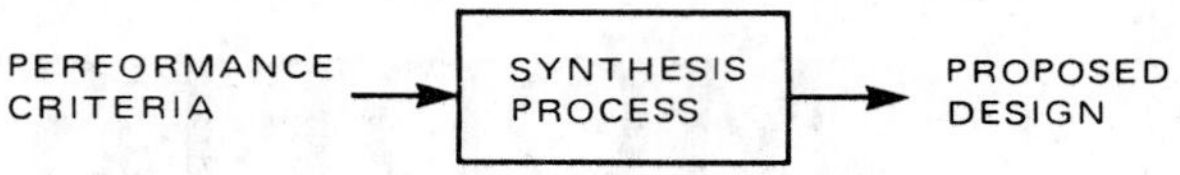

FIG. 10-13C. The synthesis process.

Solution synthesis is an extremely complicated task, requiring all aspects of design to be evaluated before a decision is made. Some formal synthesis techniques to reduce the number of alternative designs to be analyzed do exist for specialized applications, but few synthesis algorithms short of exhaustive search procedures have been developed. Normally, it is the experience of a designer that permits the universe of potential designs to be pared to a manageable list of realistic solution alternatives to be evaluated in detail.

Design documentation completes the design process trilogy. Documentation is essential for the recording of design decisions and for the communication of these decisions to clients, consultants, and contractors. This documentation consists of two types of information: geometric data and physical data. Geometric data is most effectively recorded graphically on drawings to depict the dimensions, shapes, locations, and spatial relationships of design elements. Physical attributes of elements, such as models, weights, material properties, or costs, normally are recorded and conveyed by means of specifications, schedules, and calculations.

Ideally, the design process iterates until a clearly superior final design that meets all program requirements and constraints results. Since many issues are likely to be defined in fuzzy terms and because conflicting goals and constraints may exist, the concept of an optimum design may not be easy to characterize or measure. Typically, the final design is the design deemed most acceptable to be developed within the constraints of a limited design period.

This general design framework operates at various levels in the building design process because one designer's constraints may become another designer's goals. Product manufacturers can use this framework to evaluate and communicate the uses and limitations of the design elements they produce. These limitations then become constraints for building designers, who attempt to coordinate a multitude of design elements.

The goals of the various engineers involved in the design of a building's component subsystems include the assurance that cost, technical, and safety constraints imposed by the architect's functional design are adequately considered. Thus, the architect's constraints frequently become part of the engineering designer's goals. Since both goals and constraints must be satisfied, perhaps the major impact of this distinction is in terms of financing; there seems to be a greater inclination to spend money to fulfill goals than to satisfy constraints, particularly if a constraint is ill-defined or its purpose is not clear.

Definition of Firesafety Goals and Constraints

The implementation of a rational firesafety design framework requires the definition of operationally specific goals and constraints. While a general requirement for adequate firesafety is satisfactory as a universal goal, designers need specific performance criteria to evaluate the acceptability of design solutions. Until standardized firesafety criteria that address actual performance are developed, the use of quantitative fire analysis models will be restricted in practice. Nonetheless, such models remain valuable tools that provide better insight for design decision-making.

Traditional firesafety goals have been defined in terms of pass-fail criteria specified in building and fire regulations. These criteria frequently are specified in terms of various fire indices (e.g., flame spread ratings), which do not describe or appraise the fire hazard or fire risk of a product's performance under actual fire conditions. Pass-fail criteria for fire, such as those used by building codes, have difficulty addressing important factors of firesafety, including:

- The transient characteristics of fires;
- The transitory placements of combustibles in buildings;
- The number of possible ignition and fire scenarios;
- Differences in damage susceptibility or vulnerability;
- The continuous nature of hazard and damage caused by fire.

In other words, it is difficult for such criteria to address the specific context of use of a product, but it is just this context that determines the actual hazard represented by a product. Fire modeling provides a means to evaluate the fire performance of a product in a particular application.

Components of Firesafety Design

A rational framework for firesafety design can be considered in terms of four component parts:

- Fire hazard development;
- Building response;
- Occupant response;
- Fire protection.

The relationships among these components of firesafety design can be considered qualitatively in terms of a "Tetrahedron of Firesafety" as illustrated in Figure 10-13D. Just as the Tetrahedron of Fire has been suggested by Haessler (See Chapter 1-6, "Theory of Fire and Explosion Control") to show the direct linkages between each of the four elements required to sustain flaming combustion, the Firesafety Tetrahedron shown in Figure 10-13D is intended to show that each component of firesafety design is connected to each other component and that all the components and the interrelationships are time-dependent.

Time is the common dimension of fire. Most meaningful fire parameters can be considered as functions of time. The physical hazards of fires are measured in terms such as fire growth rates, flame spread rates, heat release rates, heat fluxes, and burning durations, all functions of time. Similarly, the response of buildings, occupants, and fire protection systems to different fire scenarios can be considered in terms such as fire endurance periods, evacuation times, and fire detection and suppression response times. Consequently, time is an appropriate parameter to use for the quantitative evaluation of alternative fire mitigation strategies.

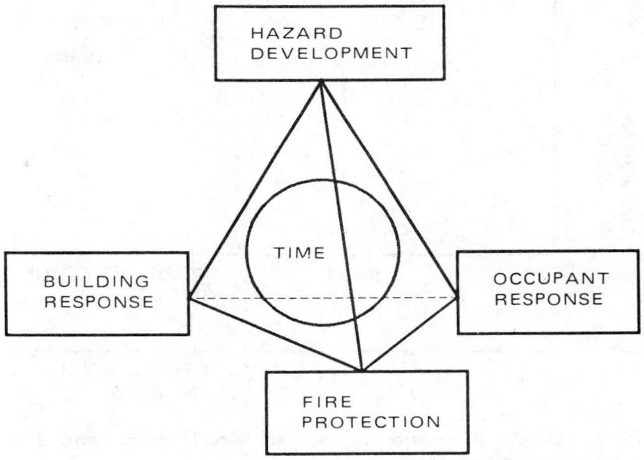

FIG. 10-13D. Components of firesafety design.

Fire mitigation strategies for particular scenarios can be evaluated in terms of two opposing times:

- The time to the onset of unacceptable damage or hazard;
- The time required for fire burnout or control, or for egress.

If the first time exceeds the second for all foreseeable fire scenarios, a fire protection strategy can be considered successful. Cooper[2] applied this concept to the evaluation of available safe egress time. Chapter 10-6 on Fire Hazard Assessment discusses these concepts in more detail.

All unwanted fires cause some damage and present some hazard. To permit quantitative evaluation of fire mitigation strategies, a threshold level of acceptable damage or hazard must be established. The time to the onset of unacceptable damage or hazard for a particular fire scenario depends on two offsetting factors:

- The susceptibility to damage of an object being evaluated;
- The rate of development of a hazardous environment at the location of the object being evaluated.

If these two issues can be assessed quantitatively, they can yield either a time-dependent scale of damage or a time of critical damage onset for a particular fire scenario. The susceptibility to damage of inanimate objects is the subject of the building response component of firesafety design, while the susceptibility of people is part of the occupant response component. The rate of hazard development depends on the fire scenario as well as the fire protection methods employed.

Damage to some objects may be related primarily to the total quantity of a fire signature, such as heat or a smoke component, released during a fire. This is represented as the area under a time-fire signature release rate curve, as illustrated in Figure 10-13E. Other objects may be considered damaged once a critical release rate of a particular fire signature is reached, represented as a single point on a

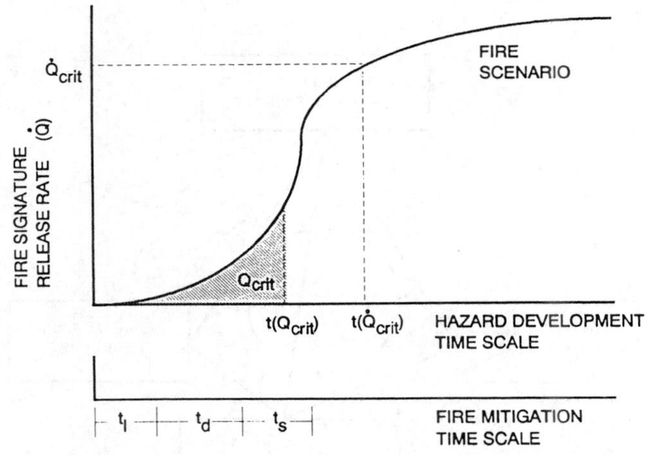

FIG. 10-13E. Concepts of hazard development and fire-mitigation time scales.

time-release rate curve. As indicated in Figure 10-13E, these threshold damage values yield critical times for particular fire hazard scenarios.

Once threshold damage criteria are established, the first question to be addressed by a hazard analysis is whether critical conditions are ever reached for a particular fire scenario. If so, the time at which critical conditions occur provides the maximum acceptable time for fire burnout or control. Once a time scale of damage is established for a particular scenario, the effectiveness of alternative fire mitigation strategies can be considered in terms of their response characteristics.

The total time for control of fires that do not burn out without intervention can be characterized in terms of three distinct intervals.[3]

- A transport time lag, t_l;
- A detection time lag, t_d;
- A suppression time lag, t_s.

These periods are shown qualitatively on the fire mitigation time scale in Figure 10-13E.

The transport time lag represents the interval between the actual generation of heat or another fire signature and the transport of that signature to a fire detection device. The detection time lag represents the period from the first transport of a fire signature to a sprinkler or other fire detector until the device actuates due to detection of a threshold value of that signature. The final time delay, the suppression time lag, represents the period from fire detection until fire suppression commences. For example, wet pipe sprinkler systems will have a nil suppression lag period, while dry-pipe systems designed in accordance with NFPA 13 should have not more than a one-minute delay associated with the time needed for the dry pipe valve to trip and for water to fill the piping. For manual fire fighting, suppression lag periods in excess of ten minutes are common because they include the times associated with signal verification, with fire department notification and response, and with preliminary fire ground operations.

Within a rational firesafety design framework, the primary goal of fire mitigation strategies is to assure that the combined period of these three lag times is less than the time to the onset of unacceptable damage. If not, two general fire mitigation alternatives exist. Either the total time to fire control can be reduced through the selection of appropriate fire protection systems and strategies or the time to the onset of critical damage must be increased. This can be accomplished by decreasing the rate of hazard development or by increasing the damage threshold level of target design elements. Within this context, the duties of the firesafety designer can be characterized as:

- Recognize and characterize potential fire hazard scenarios;
- Establish anticipated damage histories for these scenarios;
- Evaluate alternative fire mitigation strategies;
- Communicate findings and recommendations to the client.

This last duty should include the clear enunciation of expected consequences for each of the alternative fire mitigation strategies evaluated. With this information, more educated assessments of fire risk and decisions regarding appropriate protection strategies can be made.

The Traditional Engineering Design Process

The traditional implementation of the engineering design process can be considered as depicted schematically in Figure 10-13F. A drawing or sketch is normally prepared to represent a preliminary design iteration. This drawing constitutes a physical representation of the proposed design.

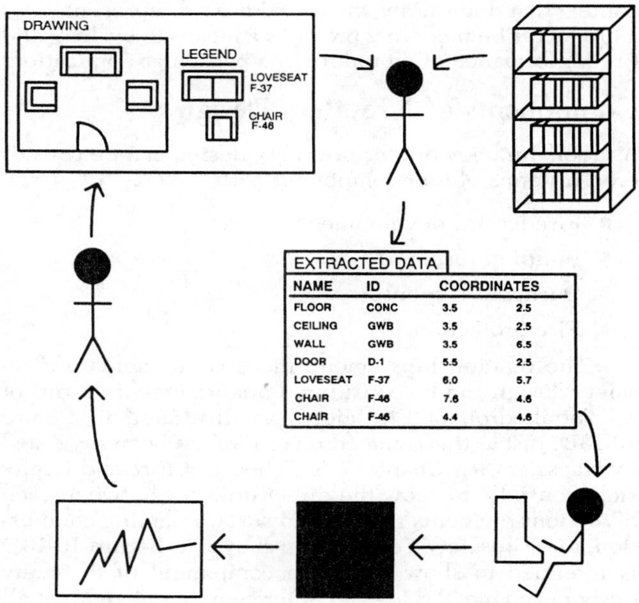

FIG. 10-13F. Traditional implementation of the engineering design process.

The engineering designer, depicted in Figure 10-13F as a stick figure, must interpret the information presented in the drawing and must manually extract pertinent geometric and physical data from the drawing. Typically, the engineer also manually extracts some physical data needed for an analysis from catalogs, handbooks, manuals, or other similar library references.

Geometric and physical data extracted from design drawings and reference materials are compiled for input to an analysis model. Analysis might be performed by hand or with the aid of a calculator, particularly for preliminary design iterations, but for the present discussion it is assumed that the analysis model is computer-based. In this case, the extracted data must be translated into a format appropriate for input to the analysis model and the data must be entered into the computer, typically through a keyboard. This translation process is conceptually simple, but it can be troublesome in practice. For complex analytical models, the data entry process can be tedious and prone to errors in the values of numerical entries and in the format of input data.

Once the data is entered, the analysis model, depicted in Figure 10-13F as a black box to represent its common treatment by designers, is run. Analysis models may be conceptually simple as checks for code compliance or as complex as enclosure fire models. In any case, the model outputs some measure of performance. This output is reviewed and interpreted by the designer, who decides if the performance is acceptable. If not, the engineer may change the solution directly and iterate through the design process until an acceptable solution is found or may report findings and recommendations to the primary building designer for consideration in the next design iteration.This traditional design process has numerous shortcomings. The process is time-consuming and thus limits the number of alternative designs that can be evaluated within a limited design period. The process also has much potential for data extraction and input errors because these procedures are handled manually.

A Computer-Based Approach to Engineering Design

A CAD-based engineering design implementation offers some advantages over the traditional design process. Unlike any previous design medium, computers can be used to represent and process design elements symbolically rather than physically. The capabilities of the computer as a symbolic processor permit the design process to be conceived and implemented in terms of meaningful design elements.[4]

An overview of a computer-based appraisal methodology is illustrated in Figure 10-13G. The CAD system serves as a graphic interface between the designer and a graphics data base maintained in the computer. Design development becomes an act of inserting appropriate design elements into the design-drawing data base, rather than one of drafting on paper physical representations of these elements that require interpretation.

The key distinction of computer-based building descriptions that permits implementation of this design methodology is known as *object orientation*. Physical representations of design, such as manually developed drawings, require human identification and interpretation; symbolic representations permit automatic identification. For example, the seven lines used to represent the chair shown in Figure 10-13G can be defined as a chair within a computer. The symbol representing the chair then may be inserted, deleted, or otherwise manipulated and processed as a distinct unit. It also may be stored in a library of symbols for use in other graphic data bases. The computer recognizes the occurrence of this symbol and thus

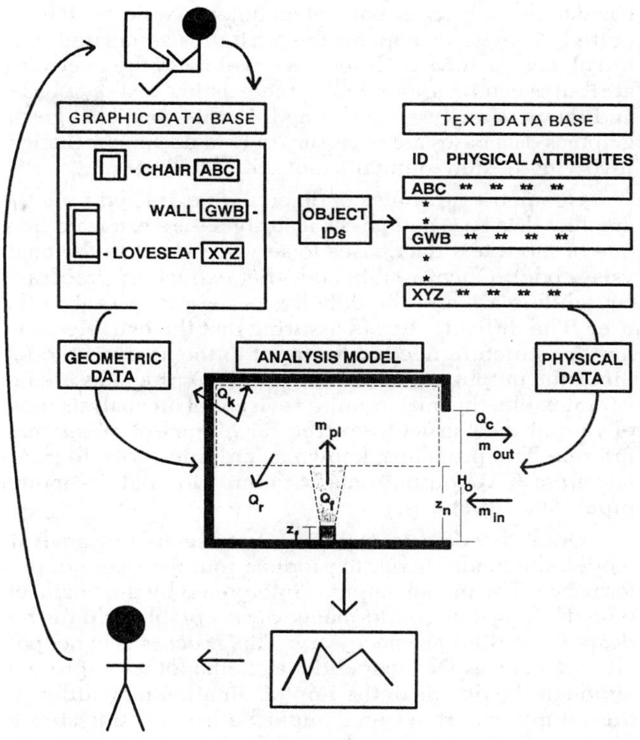

FIG. 10-13G. Computer-based implementation of the engineering design process.

can be used, for example, to extract the number and locations of chairs in a drawing.

The second key feature of CAD programs is the ability to associate attributes with objects. While most current microcomputer-based CAD programs support object orientation, some do not support attribute association and extraction.[5] This feature permits the association of physical or geometric data with objects. This data then may be extracted along with the object for use in an analysis model.

Graphics data bases generated with most current microcomputer-based CAD systems are best suited for storing geometric data regarding objects, such as their locations and dimensions. This geometric data then may be extracted from the graphics data base for use in an analysis model. In general, separate text data bases are more suitable for storing physical attributes of objects. The only non-geometric data other than the object type that must be assigned and stored in a graphics data base is a key attribute used by the CAD system to identify each object uniquely. The key attribute provides cross-reference to text data bases, where physical properties of objects are maintained.

This arrangement minimizes the non-geometric data storage requirements for a graphics data base as well as the data needed at the immediate disposal of the designer. This tends to reduce the potential for user input error, but does not eliminate it entirely because the designer still might enter the wrong ID for an object.

This practice also has the benefit that any changes or additions to the physical attributes or objects only need to be made within the text data base. If these properties were stored with each occurrence of objects in a graphics data base, then each occurrence of an object would have to be edited to revise or append the attributes associated with the object. As new analyses are developed, the necessary attributes can be appended to the existing text data bases and the new analyses performed. In this way, changes to graphics data bases are necessary only to document changes involving design elements, not their attributes.

Geometric attributes of objects are extracted from the graphics data base and physical attributes are extracted from one or more text data bases to serve as input to the analysis model. Once established, this extraction process is straightforward and the details can be transparent to the user. The difficulty lies in assuring that the extracted data has the structure needed for input to the analysis model. Since the output formats of current CAD programs are not very flexible, this may require revision of an analysis model's input data structure or the development of separate intermediate programs, known as preprocessors, to translate from CAD output data structures to analysis model input data structures.

Once the data is extracted for use in the analysis model, the model is run to produce some measure of performance. The model output is interpreted by the engineer, who decides if the performance is acceptable or if further design iterations are necessary. This process is conceptually the same as for the traditional methodology at present, although the details of the implementation may differ. In the future, expert systems might be used at this step to evaluate performance and to help synthesize subsequent design alternatives. The capability of the computer as a symbolic processor would permit this cognitive type of task.

CAD systems that support object orientation and attribute association permit the user to define the desired objects and attributes. The definitions of objects and their attributes depend on the analysis to be performed. For different analyses, it is appropriate to utilize descriptions based on different types of elements.[6] One goal of the design community is to establish an integrated building-description data base that can be used for documentation throughout the life cycle of a building.

Design elements and attributes for the different components of firesafety design are considered next. These same elements and attributes apply for traditional analyses; the object orientation of CAD simply highlights the treatment of design as a process of selecting and orienting suitable design elements based on their attributes.

Elements and Attributes for Firesafety Design

Analysis models have two primary components: data and algorithms. These components cannot be considered independently of one another during model development because the type and structure of the data depends on the algorithm to be used and the structure of an algorithm depends on the type of data available. A model that requires unavailable data serves no current practical design purpose, although it can serve to underscore the need for the acquisition of a particular type of data. This discussion focuses on the design element and attribute data needs of some current fire analysis models. It is intended to provide an overview of what the data needs are for quantitative fire analysis, not to be a comprehensive summary.

Quantitative fire analysis models can be grouped into the categories identified above as the components of firesafety design. Hazard development models calculate expected fire conditions in buildings, while models of building response, occupant response, and fire protection calculate the expected reactions of these components to the imposed conditions. In general, the component models cannot be considered independently because of their influences on each other. For example, the operation of an automatic suppression system will alter the hazard development; ventilation may be changed during the course of a fire due to automatic or occupant-induced changes in the natural or mechanical ventilation of spaces. For the present discussion, these coupled influences are ignored and the models are considered separately to identify the elements and attributes of each component. The general types of design elements for firesafety design are illustrated schematically in Figure 10-13H.

Hazard Development Models

Hazard development models typically calculate physical conditions resulting from fire, such as fire gas temperatures, velocities, and compositions, as functions of time and location. Models, ranging in complexity from fairly simple data correlations through network and zone models to field models, are described in Chapters 10-9 and 10-11. The distinctions among models address differences in the methods and algorithms used to treat the physics more so than differences in the design elements being analyzed. The more sophisticated a model is, the more physical attributes will need to be associated with the design elements. The basic design elements, however, remain the same.

The elements needed to characterize the fire hazard development within a space can be considered in terms of the elements numbered one through four in Figure 10-13H. A burning fuel element, which may be a furnishing or a finish, releases heat and products of combustion. Some of the heat is transferred to solid boundaries, some of it convects through open boundaries via gas flow, and some if it heats other combustible objects within the enclosure. Smoke signatures generated by the combustion reaction are transported by the buoyant plume from the burning object.

Design elements and attributes needed for quantitative enclosure fire hazard analyses are listed in Table 10-13A. These elements include, in general, the fuels, the openings available for natural ventilation, the mechanical ventilation systems, and the solid boundaries enclosing the space.

Fuels that burn in enclosure fires can be distinguished as either furnishings or finishes. Furnishings are discrete objects of fixed initial dimensions and mass. Finishes have dimensions and masses that depend on the geometry of the application; they include wall, ceiling, and floor linings. In residential buildings, combustible furnishings include items such as chairs, sofas, beds, desks, and wardrobes. In industrial buildings, furnishings would include pieces of machinery and equipment, which may use flammable or combustible liquids, as well as pallets or racks of stored products.

The attributes to be associated with these elements are both geometric and physical, as indicated in Table 10-13A. Geometric attributes typically include the dimensions and locations of design elements. The specific physical attributes to be associated with objects depend on the algorithms used for a particular analysis.

The primary physical attributes of furnishings and finishes needed for hazard development models include descriptions of heat and smoke release rate histories. These

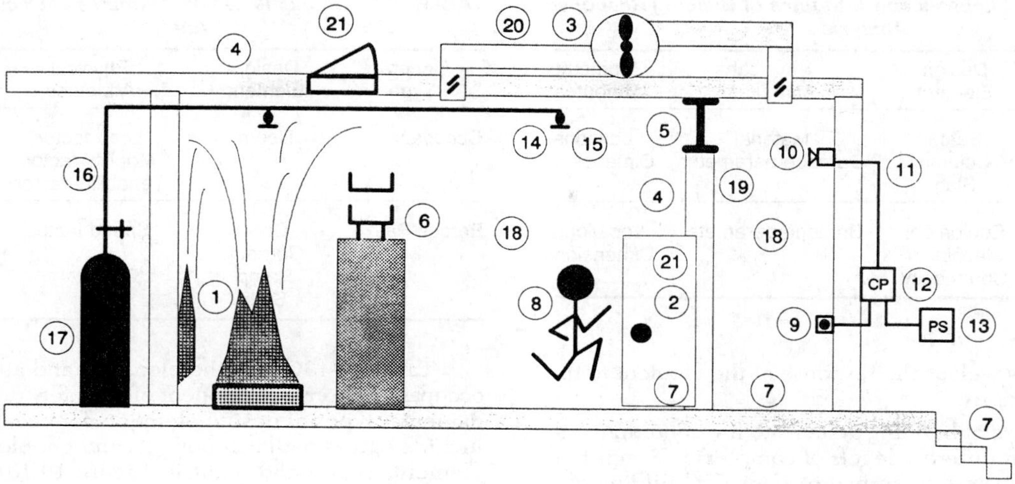

FIG. 10-13H. General types of building firesafety design elements.

TABLE 10-13A. *Elements and Attributes of Fire Hazard Analysis*

General Type	Design Element	Physical Attributes	Geometric Attributes
Fuels	Furnishing finish	Material quanitity release rate	Locations Dimensions
Natural ventilation openings	Door Window Vent	Status Act. parameter	Locations Dimensions
Mechanical ventilation systems	Injection Extraction Recirculation	Flow Rate Status Act. parameter	Locations
Boundaries	Floor Wall Ceiling	Material	Locations Dimensions

may be expressed as characterizations of large-scale fire test data[7] or in terms of fundamental material properties, depending on the algorithms used by a particular model to consider burning rates. For models that calculate the conditions resulting from a prescribed burning history, the first characterization would be appropriate. For models that attempt to predict such burning histories, fundamental data would be needed.

Normally, open natural ventilation openings have only geometric attributes, unless they are designed to close automatically upon detection of a fire signature. These devices, as well as normally closed devices such as roof vents or windows that may open or break during fires, require the association of one or more activation parameters. For these devices, an activation parameter, such as temperature, and a thermal response parameter, such as a time constant or response-time index, could be associated with the device to indicate the conditions under which it will operate. For mechanical ventilation systems, similar actuation parameters would be necessary for systems that are designed to turn on or off automatically under fire conditions.

Material properties are the physical attributes required to model the response of solid boundaries. These properties can be associated with a single parameter that identifies the boundary material. Only this single material attribute needs to be associated with the boundary in the graphics data base; it can then be used to access the thermal properties from a text data base, as illustrated schematically in Figure 10-13G.

Building System Response Models

Design elements and attributes for the analysis of building response to fire are listed in Table 10-13B. The general types of building response design elements are illustrated in Figure 10-13H as elements five and six. Two general types of design element are considered under building response: structural and operational. The design elements for detailed structural response models include slabs, beams, and columns. Operational design elements include equipment, such as electrical cable trays and cabinets, machinery, and stored commodities that may be damaged by fire. If combustible, these same elements may also constitute furnishings with respect to the analysis of hazard development.

Physical attributes of structural and operational elements include their thermal properties, normally represented by a material attribute, and one or more damage parameters, such as a critical temperature or heat flux. The location is needed to evaluate the incident fire conditions imposed on an element for a given scenario, while the dimensions may be needed to evaluate the fire conditions

TABLE 10-13B. *Elements and Attributes of Building Response Analysis*

General Type	Design Element	Physical Attributes	Geometric Attributes
Structural	Beam Column Slab	Material Damage parameter	Locations Dimensions
Operational	Equipment Machinery Commodity	Damage parameter	Locations Dimensions

TABLE 10-13C. *Elements and Attributes of Occupant Response Analysis*

General Type	Design Element	Physical Attributes	Geometric Attributes
Occupant	Room	Load factor Mobility factor Tenability factor	Locations Dimensions
Egress Path	Door Corridor Ramp Stair	Speed factor	Length Width

at an element as well as the response of the element to the imposed conditions.

The response of building systems to fire conditions can be considered at different levels of complexity. Simplified methods to evaluate the thermal response of building elements such as exposed structural steel members have been developed.[8] These models use lumped capacitance formulations to consider the transfer of heat from hot fire gases to heat-sensitive design elements. More sophisticated models employ finite element analysis techniques to calculate in greater detail the thermal and structural response of building elements to fires of specified severity.[9,10] Again, these distinctions relate more to the algorithms used and the attributes needed to analyze the response of building elements than to the definition of the basic design elements.

Occupant Response Models

Of the four components of firesafety design discussed here, occupant response is the most difficult to characterize. Unlike the other design elements described here, occupants are expected to move during a fire scenario. This movement not only influences the fire conditions to which an occupant is exposed, but may also affect the fire ventilation, the movement of smoke, and the operation of fire protection systems. Nonetheless, with respect to occupant safety it is possible to list the design elements and attributes normally considered as part of the firesafety design process.

There are two primary aspects of occupant response to fire: tenability and evacuation. For a given fire scenario, tenability criteria are used to evaluate the time to the onset of untenable conditions, which establishes a maximum time for safe egress. Tenability criteria might include individual toxic combustion product concentrations, smoke obscuration, or a combination of factors.

Evacuation times are a function of the number of people in a space or building and their flow rates. The flow rate of people can be calculated in general as a function of travel speed, egress width, and the density of people.[11,12]

The speed of travel depends on the mobility of the occupants, on their density, and on the type of egress component (e.g., stair, ramp, or corridor). The density of people starts at the normal occupant load of the space, but typically increases as people queue at bottlenecks in the egress path, such as doors leading to exit stairs. Once evacuation begins, the situation becomes dynamic, with varying densities and travel speeds. While the complete analysis of evacuation time problems may require complex computer-based solutions, the basic design elements and attributes can be described simply.

Table 10-13C lists the elements and attributes of the occupant response component of firesafety design. The fundamental types of design elements for occupant response include egress path components and people, identified as elements seven and eight in Figure 10-13H. People are represented for design purposes in terms of rooms or other occupied spaces. Therefore, the specific types of design elements include occupied spaces and egress path components. Occupied spaces are distinguished by their uses, which will have the physical attributes of an occupant load factor, an occupant mobility factor, and tenability criteria. Geometric attributes include the floor-plan dimensions, from which the area and total occupant load can be determined along with the travel distance within the space.

Egress path design elements include doors, corridors, ramps, and stairs. These elements have just a single physical attribute, an evacuation speed parameter, which for stairs is a function of the riser/tread design and whether the egress direction is upward or downward. This speed parameter is also a function of the occupant density. Geometric attributes for egress path elements include an effective width as well as a length, measured along the path of travel.

Fire Protection Models

Building fire protection involves many aspects, including fire detection and alarm, fire suppression, and smoke control. The basic design elements and attributes of these systems are discussed here to demonstrate the treatment of the design of fire protection systems as the selection and orientation of design elements.

The primary design elements of fire detection and alarm systems include alarm initiating devices, alarm indicating devices, control panels, and power supplies. Alarm system circuits can also be considered as distinct design elements. These elements are listed in Table 10-13D and illustrated in Figure 10-13H as elements nine through thirteen.

Alarm initiating devices may be manually or automatically actuated. For automatic alarm initiating devices the physical attributes will include an actuation parameter and a response parameter. The actuation parameter is associated with the threshold concentration of a fire signature required to actuate the device. For heat detectors, this would be the actuation temperature. The response parameter is associated with the inertia of the device. For heat detectors, this would be a time constant or response-time index. Manual initiating devices do not have similar physical attributes; they rely on human intervention for actuation. For sizing power supplies and circuits, the power-demand attributes of the different types of alarm initiating devices are needed.

TABLE 10-13D. ***Elements and Attributes of Fire Alarm Systems***

General Type	Design Element	Physical Attributes	Geometric Attributes
Initiating device	Pull station Fire detector Supervisory	Actuation parameter Response parameter Current demand	Locations
Indicating device	Control panel	Input capacity Output capacity Control logic	Sizes Locations
Circuit	Initiating indicating control power	Current capacity	Locations
Power supply	Primary Secondary	Current capacity duration	Locations sizes

TABLE 10-13E. ***Elements and Attributes of Fire Suppression Systems***

General Type	Design Element	Physical Attributes	Geometric Attributes
Detection device	Sprinkler Heat detector Smoke detector	Actuation parameter Response parameter	Locations
Discharge device	Sprinkler nozzle	K factor	Locations
Distribution system (hydraulic)	Piping Fittings Aux. devices	Friction factors	Lengths Sizes Locations
Suppressant supply	Tank Pump/reservoir	Pressure quantity	Locations Elevations

Indicating devices include audible and visual alarm signaling devices as well as trouble and supervisory signals. For alarm signaling devices, the physical parameters include the intensity and frequency of the device output. With this data, the audibility or visibility of the device can be evaluated for a range of use conditions. The power demand requirements for these devices are also needed to evaluate power supply and circuit size requirements.

The other elements of fire detection and alarm systems are characterized primarily in terms of their electrical attributes. The primary quantitative issues for control panels, circuits, and power supplies are their current capacities. The input and output capacities of control panels establish limitations on their specific applications, both in terms of the number of zones that can be served and the number of devices per circuit. Each alarm initiating device and alarm indication device imposes a current demand on the system. The primary and secondary power supplies must be able to support the power demands imposed by components of the fire alarm signaling system for a specified duration, which is usually established by code.

The control logic of the control panel is an essential component of fire alarm system design. So is system reliability. These components do not fit conveniently into the quantitative design framework presented here. Suffice to say here that control logic and reliability are important design components for fire alarm signaling systems, but they are outside the scope of this discussion.

The general types of design elements for fire suppression systems, the specific design elements, and their physical and geometric attributes are listed in Table 10-13E. Automatic fire suppression systems have four general types of components: detection devices, agent discharge devices, a distribution system, and a supply of extinguishing agent. These are illustrated in Figure 10-13H as elements fourteen through seventeen.

The physical attributes of detection devices required to evaluate their response to a given fire scenario include an actuation parameter and a response parameter. For thermally actuated devices such as sprinklers and heat detectors, the actuation parameter is the temperature rating of the device, while the response characteristic is an appropriate thermal time constant or response-time index.[13] These attributes can be used in conjunction with appropriate models of the environmental fire conditions at the detection device to yield an estimate of the fire detection time for a given fire scenario. These environmental conditions depend on the locations of the detection devices relative to the fire source, so detector locations are the required geometric attributes.

The primary physical attribute to be associated with discharge devices is a flow coefficient that permits calculation of a pressure-flow relationship for a device. The locations of discharge devices are required to calculate head losses and pressure distributions between points. Algorithms used for these friction-loss calculations apply mass and energy conservation principles between nodes to maintain physical consistency.

Another aspect of discharge devices that is currently considered indirectly during normal design practice is the agent distribution characteristics of the discharge device. Currently, this aspect of discharge device attributes is treated in general by the selection of an appropriate type of discharge device for a given application. This selection is based largely on the discharge tests required to list these devices. In the future, if may become possible to evaluate water-spray/fire interactions with greater precision and confidence. At that time, association of one or more characteristic spray attributes with discharge devices would be appropriate.

The primary interests in the distribution system are with its friction-loss characteristics and its support. Elements of the distribution system that influence friction loss include all components of the flow conduit, including pipe, fittings, valves, and any other auxiliary devices. The attributes needed to characterize friction loss include the length, diameter, and friction coefficient of pipe segments and the equivalent lengths of fittings, valves, and auxiliary devices. The types and locations of support components are required to evaluate stresses in the distribution system under static and flow conditions.

The extinguishing agent supply is the last design element for automatic suppression systems. A pressure-flow relationship of the supply is needed along with the total capacity of the supply. For water-based suppression systems, the capacity of the supply may be virtually limitless, but for other types of systems this is not generally the case. For carbon dioxide, Halon, and foam systems, the supply capacity normally will be sized for a specific discharge rate and duration.

The general types of design elements for smoke control systems include smoke zones, smoke barriers, natural ventilation openings, and mechanical ventilation systems. These are illustrated as elements eighteen through twenty-one in Figure 10-13H. Table 10-13F lists the basic elements and attributes of smoke control systems.

TABLE 10-13F. *Elements and Attributes of Smoke Control Systems*

General Type	Design Element	Physical Attributes	Geometric Attributes
Smoke zone	Room Corridor Shaft	Pressure Temperature	Locations Dimensions
Smoke barrier	Floor Wall/Ceiling Door (closed)	Effective flow area	Locations Dimensions
Mechanical ventilation system	Injection Extraction	Pressure/Flow Status Act. parameter	Locations
Vent	Door (open) Window Vent	Flow coeff. status Act. parameter	Locations Dimensions

Smoke zones may be individual rooms or floors, or they may be groups of rooms or floors. They are defined by the smoke barriers that enclose them and by the vents and mechanical air-handling systems used to confine or direct the movement of smoke between zones.

The physical attributes of smoke zones include their initial pressures and temperatures. Subsequent pressures and temperatures may be calculated or may be specified as fixed boundary conditions. The physical attribute required for smoke barriers is an effective leakage area. The attributes of natural ventilation openings and mechanical ventilation systems used for smoke control are virtually the same as described above for hazard analyses.

This concludes the discussion on the basic elements of firesafety design and their attributes. Twenty-one different general types of elements have been identified for the various types of analyses discussed. Many of these elements serve multiple purposes, thus reducing the number of discrete elements that form the basis for firesafety design. For example, the boundary elements for hazard analysis will normally be the same as the smoke barrier elements for smoke control analysis and design, but the physical attributes needed for each type of analysis may be different. It is up to the firesafety designer to select a combination of these design elements that will fulfill all firesafety design goals while satisfying applicable constraints.

The reduction of firesafety design to the selection of a few types of design elements should not be misconstrued as a suggestion that the firesafety design process is simple. The relationships among design components are highly coupled and the number and types of design components in a building can be quite large. Rather, the intent of this discussion is to emphasize two primary points: 1) ultimately, firesafety design must be reduced to the selection and orientation of appropriate design elements to fulfill goals and satisfy constraints; and 2) the purpose of fire analysis models is to aid this selection process, regardless of the sophistication or complexity of the model used.

Limitations

The potential benefits of a rational design framework for building firesafety are substantial, but they are hindered by a number of limitations at present. These limitations include two types of uncertainty:

- Uncertainty regarding physical and chemical relationships;
- Uncertainty regarding the situation of objects in buildings.

The first uncertainty is being reduced through research. Considerable work remains in the prediction of burning and entrainment rates for real objects. The physical interaction between fire and suppression or other mitigation activities is largely undeveloped. Research continues on these topics.

The second uncertainty is likely to remain and must be addressed through appropriate risk-assessment techniques. The importance of this second uncertainty cannot be overemphasized; fire loads in building spaces can change by orders of magnitude simply due to a rearrangement of furniture.

Finally, there is the lack of standardized performance criteria against which a designer can evaluate the acceptability of a design solution. Such criteria should be developed to permit more widespread implementation of a rational firesafety design framework. In the meantime, firesafety designers can establish their own criteria in conjunction with their clients and can apply rational design concepts to the consideration of their current firesafety problems.

Summary

Design is the selection of building elements to achieve functional goals and to satisfy applicable constraints. The selection of design elements is based on the synthesis of appropriate analyses to determine the suitability of a design element to fulfill its anticipated use. Design elements are the basic components chosen by the designer; attributes are the properties of these elements that distinguish their performance and serve as the basis for the selection process.

Appropriate basic design elements and attributes for different types of quantitative fire analysis models have been discussed. Combustible furnishings and finishes are the design elements of major importance for fire hazard development. Their heat and combustion product release rate histories drive the development of hazardous conditions in buildings and consequently the response of building, occupant, and fire protection system design elements.

Computer-aided design programs use the capability of computers as symbolic processors to implement design in terms of relevant design elements. This permits unprecedented integration of engineering analysis with the building design and documentation process. Once established, CAD implementations reduce the potential for user input error and permit more analyses to be performed within a fixed design period. With CAD-based design documentation, new analyses can be applied to existing situations as the analyses become available. Similarly, design changes that occur through the life cycle of a facility can be analyzed more conveniently with a computer-based building description.

Implementation of a rational design framework requires specification of performance-based design criteria. For fire hazard development and fire protection strategies, time is the common parameter for performance evaluation. Successful fire protection strategies mitigate the effects of fire hazards before they reach unacceptable threshold levels.

In view of the limitations discussed above, quantitative fire analyses should be considered at present in terms of their utility to augment and justify, rather than to supersede, many traditional fire protection techniques. Such analyses serve as quantitative tools that can provide insight for the synthesis of rational firesafety design decisions. These tools do not make decisions, however, nor do they determine appropriate situations for their use. These remain duties of the firesafety designer.

BIBLIOGRAPHY

References Cited

1. Dixon, J. R., *Design Engineering: Inventiveness, Analysis, and Decision Making*, McGraw-Hill, New York, 1966, p. 55.
2. Cooper, L. Y., "A Concept For Estimating Available Safe Egress Time in Fires," *Fire Safety Journal*, Vol. 5, 1983, pp. 135-144.
3. Mowrer, F. W., "Lag Times Associated with Fire Detection and Suppression," *Fire Technology*, Vol. 26, No. 3, 1990, pp. 244-265.
4. Radford, A. and Stevens, G., *CAD Made Easy*, McGraw-Hill, New York, 1987, pp. 130-139.
5. Hart, G., "Complex CAD Software for the PC," *PC Magazine*, Vol. 5, No. 5, 1986, pp. 111-148.
6. Mitchell, W. J., *Computer-Aided Architectural Design*, Van Nostrand Reinhold Company, New York, 1977, p. 112.
7. Mowrer, F. W. and Williamson, R. B., "Methods to Characterize Heat Release Rate Data," *Fire Safety Journal*. Vol. 16, (1990) pp. 367-387.
8. Alpert, R. L. and Ward, E. J., "Evaluation of Unsprinklered Fire Hazards," *Fire Safety Journal*, Vol. 7, 1984, pp. 127-143.
9. Bresler, B., "Analytical Prediction of Structural Response to Fire," *Fire Safety Journal*, Vol. 9, 1985, pp. 103-117.
10. Jeanes, D. C., "Application of the Computer in Modeling Fire Endurance of Structural Steel Floor Systems," *Fire Safety Journal*, Vol. 9, 1985, pp. 119-135.
11. Pauls, J., "Movement of People," *SFPE Handbook of Fire Protection Engineering, ed.* P. J. DiNenno *et al.*, National Fire Protection Association, Quincy, MA, 1988, pp. 1-246–1-268.
12. Nelson, H. E. and MacLennan, H. A., "Emergency Movement," *SFPE Handbook of Fire Protection Engineering*, ed. P. J. DiNenno *et al.*, National Fire Protection Association, Quincy, MA, 1988, pp. 2-106–2-115.
13. Heskestad, G. and Smith, H. F., "Investigation of a New Sprinkler Sensitivity Approval Test: The Plunge Test," *Technical Report Serial No. 22485, RC 76-T-50*, Factory Mutual Research Corporation, Norwood, MA, 1976.

THE FUTURE OF FIRE MODELING

Philip J. DiNenno, P.E.

The past ten years have resulted in great progress toward the ability to predict the behavior of fire and its effects. While much of this technical progress has been embodied in the current fire models, a substantial challenge remains in exploiting this capability in the area of fire safety design and practice. The next decade should show continued evolution in three major areas: predictive capability of models, applications, and integration into design practice.

This chapter seeks to identify near-term (less than two-year) and moderate-term (two- to ten-year) trends and likely developments in the area of computer-based fire modeling. The focus of the discussion is on deterministic mathematical fire models, particularly zone models. The chapter begins with a very brief review of the current status of deterministic zone modeling. Field modeling will be treated in the discussion of future trends.

PREDICTIVE CAPABILITY OF ZONE MODELS

Perhaps the single most important attribute of computer fire models is their ability to predict accurately and realistically the relevant fire behavior within their stated limitations. The predictive capability of a model depends on both the underlying scientific understanding of the processes being modeled and the translation of that understanding into some calculation scheme. There remain substantial shortcomings in the scientific understanding of fire and related processes. This knowledge shortfall, however, will not necessarily slow the development of calculations with enhanced predictability. It is not necessary to understand a phenomenon fully in the pure scientific context in order to exploit a lower level of understanding for design and practice purposes. In fact, current models take great advantage of "imperfect" knowledge to yield acceptable results. More general discussions of the state of related fire science can be found in the research of H. W. Emmons, P. J. Pagni and R. Friedman.[1,2,3]

Mr. DiNenno, P.E. is Vice President, Hughes Associates Inc., and Editor-in-Chief of *The SFPE Handbook of Fire Protection Engineering*.

Zone models by definition will always be approximate. The key is whether the predictions are "close enough" to yield significant insight for the situation under study. Zone modeling yields useful insight into many fire problems. The real question is under what conditions these models yield acceptably accurate results. This question has been largely unanswered. There is a reasonable amount of validation test data available for comparison to models with single or with up to six compartments with length scales of ten feet connected via a corridor and modest (less than 1000-kw), well-characterized fire.[4,5,6,7,8,9,10] The extent to which zone models can be effectively applied in large open areas or tall structures is uncertain. The two-zone paradigm does not preclude their use in large or tall structures *per se*, but rather stretches the assumption of uniform properties within a zone. An excellent summary of the underlying assumptions of zone modeling is given by Quintiere.[11] Further discussions of the status and limitations of zone modeling are given by Emmons, and Kawagoe.[12,13]

The status of zone modeling as a predictive tool can be evaluated with acceptable confidence as follows. For a relatively small room (approximately 100 sq. ft.) with a well-described, well-ventilated fire source, the temperature, layer position, and gas concentrations can be estimated with acceptable accuracy. Within the limitations of zone modeling, smoke filling a corridor and then adjacent rooms can also be adequately described. This case does not imply that, for conditions outside this narrow description, modeling is inaccurate or unacceptable but rather that the results must be carefully evaluated in the context of what level of prediction is required as well as independent experimental evidence.

The following discussions attempt to briefly describe the current status and near-term possibilities for modeling some important phenomena. No one model is assumed; rather, the discussion summarizes the integrated capability of the HARVARD/FIRST and FAST zone models.[14,15]

1. *Ignition*. Both piloted and unpiloted ignition due to radiative heating can be approximated, and if the ignition temperature is known, alternative small-scale ignition test data can be used (ASTM E-1354).

2. *Burning behavior*. The burning behavior of a single fuel item cannot currently be predicted. The treatment of this obviously important subphenomenon in models is done through empirical correlations and/or large-scale test data. Approximations using small-scale tests are possible.[16] A more fundamental treatment is unlikely in the near term. Empirical methods, small-scale and large-scale data, and "design basis" fire assumptions will continue to form the basis of zone models.
3. *Flame spread*. This area is currently under active development. In conjunction with LIFT apparatus, opposed-flow flame spread is a candidate for near-term modeling. Upward- or concurrent-flow flame spread predictions using a similar LIFT apparatus are quite promising and could be integrated into models readily in the near term.[17,18,19]
4. *Compartment effects*:
   a. *Energy balance*. Zone-type approximations may be improved with the inclusion of plumes or ceiling jets as subzones. Heating of a ceiling in the vicinity of a flame or plume can be calculated. Enhanced radiation levels can be estimated but it is not possible to predict the general effect on burning behavior.
   b. *Walls and corners*. Current methods used to approximate the impact of walls and corners on plumes, flame heights, and ceiling jets are suspect. Some modest development work is needed before these submodels can be appreciably improved.
   c. *Oxygen starvation*. Currently treated by use of heuristics in conjunction with limited-oxygen index for energy release rate. Smoke and gas yields in underventilated conditions are more challenging but can be grossly approximated.[20]

5. *Multiple room fire and smoke spread*. There are several models that treat smoke spread through multiple compartments using the standard two-zone smoke "filling" approximation. Depending on the problem under analysis, this approach may yield acceptable results. Limited empirical studies on smoke flow in corridors could be integrated near term with uncertain results. Flows in shafts, stairs, and through horizontal vents are more problematic. Some experimental work is required.[21,22] It is expected that useful approximations will be available in the near term.

Fire spread is currently limited to remote ignition of remote objects by heating from flames and the hot layer. Fire spread to multiple compartments is in principle predictable. Unknown effects of multiple compartments burning along a single corridor in close proximity may be important. Fire spread by ignition of a hot layer is currently unresolved.

6. *Forced ventilation*. Several models have attempted to treat forced ventilation under simple vent configurations.[23] There is current active development of a more general model. There appear to be major unresolved technical issues in the full understanding of forced vents and fires that precludes effective modeling for many cases. This area will undergo dramatic improvement in the next decade.
7. *Post-flashover predictions*. The onset of flashover in a compartment poses a difficult prediction problem. Major unresolved technical problems include: prediction of radiation-enhanced burning rate; prediction of CO production in underventilated conditions; ignition of hot layers; burning at vents; and flame spread down corridors.

There is one area where post-flashover fires are very well characterized. The prediction of temperature as a function of time for purposes of calculating the fire resistance of a structure is very well developed. Design approaches using post-flashover models are accepted alternatives to prescriptive fire resistance requirements in several countries.

8. *Detection system activation*. Procedures exist for estimating the response of ceiling-mounted heat detectors via heating by a plume or ceiling jet. These calculations have been relatively well established for small rooms with flat, smooth ceilings, with more limited validation for larger compartments with high ceiling heights or non-smooth, non-flat ceilings.

Methods also exist for estimating smoke-detector response. These have not been generally used due to the unavailability of the necessary detector-specific parameters. Calculation methods exist for detector activation where a layer has formed, although the procedures have not been adequately verified. No procedures currently exist for estimating the activation of detectors in situations where the detector responds before a well-developed plume or ceiling jet forms or where mechanical ventilation appreciably perturbs the flow. Incremental progress is expected in this area in the near and moderate term.

9. *Suppression modeling*. Fire suppression with a total-flooding inert gas system has been successfully modeled. While there is research effort in modeling the suppression of fires by water application, no generally applied design or analysis procedures are expected in the next decade.
10. *Fire effects modeling*.
    a. *Heat damage*. If the temperature threshold of a piece of equipment or material is known, standard heat transfer calculations can be used in conjunction with fire models to estimate the time dependence or degree of damage.
    b. *Smoke damage*. Estimates of smoke damage that reflect the sensitivity of the equipment exposed and type of smoke or fire involved are not generally available. Such calculations involve uncertainties associated with cold smoke transport and deposition, prediction of smoke production and properties, the wide variability of smoke properties, and the sensitivity of equipment to this wide variation of smoke types.
11. *Human interaction*:
    a. *Visibility*. Limited experimental data on visibility combined with small-scale constant-yield smoke concentration and optical property measurements enable rough estimates of human visibility in smoke. Using the results of computer models for smoke, layer depth, and smoke properties, approximate visibility estimates can be made.
    b. *Temperature/radiation*. The effects of heat and radiation can be estimated using empirical human tenability data.

c. *Toxicity*. Although still an area of active research, the ability to estimate human casualties due to smoke remains problematic. It is reasonable to state that, within a factor of two to five, toxic effects can be estimated using bioassay and/or N-gas modeling methods. This very difficult subject area will undergo continued improvement relative to prediction methods.[20]

d. *Human Behavior*. No acceptable prediction scheme for human behavior in fire conditions exists or is likely to be developed in the foreseeable future. Reliance on statistical data, fire experience, and human behavioral studies will continue.

FIELD MODELING

The application of field modeling to fire problems has been dramatically increasing. The ready availability of commercial CFD (computational fluid dynamics) packages with increasing sophistication enables more widespread applications. The vast majority of uses of these programs have nothing to do with fire problems but are concerned with fluid flow in pipes, convective flow in enclosures, cooling of electronic packages, etc.[24] In general, there have not been critical evaluations of these methods relative to their use in fire problems.

Since the basic mass-energy, and momentum-conservation equations are identical for all problems, these codes have potentially dramatic revolutionary impact on fire modeling. The difficulties in field modeling of fires lie in two areas. First, no direct simulation of turbulent diffusion flames—that is, a fire—is currently possible; hence, the fire source itself must be approximated. Other major phenomenon that can only be approximated include turbulence, particularly large eddies associated with strong plumes and flames, and thermal radiation interchange between soot, gases, and solid surfaces. Second, the capability of these codes to handle specific phenomena important in fire modeling varies widely.

The programs require substantial computational effort although most are available in PC versions. More importantly, they require sophisticated users due to the complexity of defining initial and boundary conditions. Field modeling programs have direct and immediate potential application to problems driven largely by fluid mechanics and convective heat transfer. Such problems include far-field smoke flow, details of flow and heat transfer to complex geometries (e.g., sprinkler links), and impact of fixed ventilation flows on buoyancy-driven flows. Applications of field models to fire problems have included aircraft terminals and atria, air-supported structures, electronic generating stations, aircraft cabins, tunnels, hospital wards, and shopping malls.[25,26,27,28,29,30,31] The development of a special-purpose version of one of these codes for fire purposes would be a significant help.

TRENDS

Having briefly discussed the current and near-term capabilities of models to predict fire effects, we will now focus on observable trends and the possibilities for the future of modeling.

Predictive Capability

As indicated in the previous discussion, the predictive capability of computer models is largely uncertain. It is not known with confidence to what limits these models can be applied. It is equally clear that ongoing research and development efforts aimed at resolving some of these uncertainties will result in improved predictive capability. The use of heuristics to aid in simplifying particularly difficult problems will continue. Confidence in the capabilities of models will increase with improved validation and careful use.

Applications

Applications of modeling have included fire litigation and reconstruction, hazard analysis of building materials and contents, and the evaluation of building code exceptions or equivalencies. Computer models and other analytical tools have not, however, been integrated into fire protection engineering design practice.

Several case studies of "reconstructed" fire incidents using computer models have been published.[32,33,34] They generally demonstrate how a computer model used as part of a more general engineering analysis is a powerful tool. One lesson of these case studies is that the state of the art is not such that one sets up a reasonable input file and the computer describes how the fire evolved. Rather, the models are more appropriately used to evaluate in approximate terms the time sequence of the event or to establish in more detail the reasonableness of one or another ignition growth and spread scenarios. These programs are also used to pose "what if" questions related to the contribution of a particular material, furnishing item, etc. versus one of greater or lesser combustibility, energy release rate, and so on. Most modeling applications occur today, as well as in the recent past, in fire litigation circumstances. Most of these applications are never published.

The use of modeling in litigation and fire investigation will expand. The problem of fire reconstruction lends itself readily to modeling tools.

Applications outside of litigation are often associated with the evaluation of the fire hazard posed by a product or material.[19,35,36,37,38,39] Modeling received a major boost in the context of predicting the "toxic hazard" posed by materials. The combination of deterministic models with risk assessment methods into integrated hazard assessment schemes has begun.[40,41] The method enables one to integrate ignition, flammability, and toxicity properties with the end use of the material under varying scenarios to estimate the outcome. As always, the quality of these applications is driven by the methods, data, approximations, and assumptions used. Additional applications that reflect the increasing use of models for a range of applications can be found in work by Bengston and Hagglund, Hagglund and Wickstrom and Bukowski.[32,42,43]

While current applications are somewhat limited in terms of "routine" use, the trend has been for a relatively rapid increase in the application of models across all aspects of fire protection. Clearly, the use of models in fire investigations and litigation will continue, and their application to special facilities and problems not directly dealt with in codes and standards will also increase. Applications of field modeling to unique facilities and problems should dramatically increase.

A major question exists on the application of these models in fire safety design relative to building codes and fire safety standards. The primary determinants in this area will likely be the degree to which relatively prescriptive codes and standards can be harmonized with more performance-based design and engineering methods. This is, of course, more complicated than it sounds, given the legal, social, and political realities under which buildings are approved. An additional prerequisite for the general use of modeling in building design is the need to deal with the inherently probabilistic nature of fire events and the "reliability" of various construction features and fire safety systems. Several generic approaches have been suggested to integrate deterministic modeling with probabilistic problems.[44,45] This challenge also poses the greatest opportunity. The tremendous potential of this significant technological advance for the purpose of improved fire safety will be recognized and exploited.

Hardware

It has become relatively safe to forecast that more powerful, easy-to-use computer hardware will continue to emerge. The past decade has seen a revolution in computing capacity available to individuals. The next decade is more likely to be evolutionary in nature as 386/486 machines become the norm. This will eliminate most computational speed problems with respect to zone models. The computational requirements of field models will continue to be a challenge.

Developments in hardware should also appreciably extend the range and utility of these calculation methods, perhaps into the "real time" world of the fire incident commander. The use of these models in conjunction with interactive video training and simulation will likely result in "fire simulators" becoming widely available to fire departments.

Longer-term hardware developments in the area of intelligent sensors integrated with software derived from fire modeling may revolutionize fire detection. The smart building may well include fire protection.

Acceptance

The trend toward increased acceptance of predicted results in resolving fire safety questions will continue and likely accelerate. A decade of continued progress in modeling, with the increase in the number of published application studies in *NFPA Journal* and other widely read fire literature, has led to a more open approach to the subject by building and fire officials. Progress related to integration of these methods into the design of facilities is more problematic.

Validation

Numerous validation studies of computer fire models have been undertaken. Most have been in relatively small (approximately 100 sq. ft.) compartments with well-defined fire sources (cribs, pool fires, or gas burners). In general the best agreement that can be expected is on the order of ±20 percent in terms of smoke layer temperature and depth.

It is unlikely given funding and prioritization realities that any significant systematic and complete validation will ever be performed on any model. It is arguable that complete validation is an impractical objective. Given this, models will be evaluated and the results accepted in a relatively slowly evolving time frame. The obligation that this lack of independent validation places on users and approving authorities is obvious. Particular attention must be paid to using these programs within their stated limits and, perhaps more importantly, to searching out experimental data for cases similar to the problem being evaluated. The dearth of validation studies should not be taken as rationale for rejecting the use or results of a model in any particular case. The validation picture could improve dramatically if it became clear that the lack thereof was a significant barrier to more widespread use.

Material Flammability Testing

The development of small-scale fire test methods, which in principle enables the extrapolation of the results to "real" fires, was essential to the development of modeling. Some of these test methods have been standardized by ASTM and NFPA. The input data required by models, which describes the burning behavior, energy release rate, smoke properties, and combustion gas yields of materials, comes largely from these small-scale test methods. It is expected that the availability of this data for a wider range of products and materials will increase. This availability will accelerate dramatically if these relevant test methods are referenced in buildings codes and fire standards in lieu of or in conjunction with more traditional methods.

Since models form one basis for extrapolating this flammability data to full-scale performance, increased use of models in this context is expected. In many ways, this particular class of applications may be ideal for the direct integration of modeling into building design standards.

CONCLUSIONS

It is no longer a question of whether modeling will be used in the solution of fire safety problems but rather to what extent. The degree to which scientifically based engineering methods can impact fire safety will be driven largely by their application to design practice. This requires some integration with building codes and fire-safety standards. Without such integration, incremental progress in predictive capability and applications can be expected. If fire safety engineering methods and codes are successfully integrated, the forecast will be one of rapid, revolutionary change in all aspects of modeling as well as building design.

BIBLIOGRAPHY

References Cited

ASTM E-1354, "Standard Test Method for Heat and Visible Smoke Release for Materials and Products Using an Oxygen Consumption Calorimeter," *1990 Annual Book of ASTM Standards*, American Society for Testing and Materials, 1990.

1. Emmons, H. W., "The Needed Fire Science," *Fire Safety Science—Proceedings of the First International Symposium*, Hemisphere Publishing Corp., Washington, DC, 1986, pp. 33-53.
2. Pagni, P. J., "Fire Physics—Promises, Problems, and Progress," *Fire Safety Science—Proceedings of the Second International Symposium*, Hemisphere Publishing Corp., NY, 1989.
3. Friedman, R., "Fire Protection Engineering—Science or Art?" *Journal of Fire Protection Engineering*, Vol. 2, No. 1, 1990, pp. 25-29.
4. Duong, D., "The Accuracy of Computer Fire Models: Some Comparisons with Experimental Data from Australia," *Fire Safety Journal*, Vol. 16, 1990, pp. 415-431.
5. Jones, W. W. and Peacock, R. D., "Refinement and Experimental Verification of a Model for Fire Growth and Smoke

Transport," *Fire Safety Science—Proceedings of the Second International Symposium*, Hemisphere Publishing Corp., NY, 1989, pp. 897-906.

6. Peacock, R. D., Davis, S., and Lee, B. T., "An Experimental Set for Verification of Room Fire Models," NBS 88-3752, National Bureau of Standards, Gaithersburg, M.D., April 1988.
7. Rockett, J. A., "Modeling of NBS Mattress Tests with Harvard Mark V Fire Simulations," *Fire and Materials*, Vol. 6, No. 2, 1982, pp. 80-95.
8. Rockett, J. A., *et al.*, "Comparisons of NBS [National Bureau of Standards]/Harvard III Simulations and Data from All Runs of a Full-Scale Multiroom Fire Test Program," *Fire Safety Journal*, Vol. 15, 1989, pp. 115-116.
9. Rockett, J. A., Marta, M., and Cooper, L. Y., "Comparisons of NBS/Harvard VI Simulations and Full Scale Multiroom Fire Test Data," *NBSIR 87-3567*, National Bureau of Standards, Gaithersburg, MD, 1987.
10. Nakamura, K. and Tanaka, T., "Predicting Capability of a Multiroom Fire Model," *Fire Safety Science—Proceedings of the Second International Symposium*, Hemisphere Publishing Corp., NY, 1989.
11. Quintiere, J. Q., "Fundamentals of Enclosure Fire 'Zone' Models," *Journal of Fire Protection Engineering*, Vol. 1, No. 3, 1989, pp. 99-119.
12. Emmons, H. W., "Experiments with a Fire Math Model," *Fire Safety Science—Proceedings of the Second International Symposium*, Hemisphere Publishing Corp., NY, 1989.
13. Kawagoe, K., "Real Fire and Fire Modeling," *Fire Safety Science—Proceedings of the Second International Symposium*, Hemisphere Publishing Corp., NY, 1989.
14. Mitler, H. E. and Rockett, J. A., *User's Guide to FIRST, Comprehensive Single-Room Fire Model, NBSIR 87-3595*, National Bureau of Standards, Gaithersburg, MD, 1987.
15. Jones, W. W. and Peacock, R. D., *Technical Reference Guide for FAST Version 18*, NIST Technical Note 1262, National Institute of Standards and Technology, Gaithersburg, MD, 1989.
16. Babrauskas, V. and Wickstrom, U., "The Rational Development of Bench-Scale Fire Tests for Full-Scale Fire Prediction," *Fire Safety Science—Proceedings of the Second International Symposium*, Hemisphere Publishing Corp., NY, 1989.
17. Harkleroad, M., Quintiere, J., and Walton, W., "Radiative Ignition and Opposed-Flow Flame Spread Measurements on Materials," DOT/FAA/CT-83/28, U.S. Department of Transportation, Federal Aviation Administration, Technical Center, Atlantic City Airport, NJ, Aug. 1983.
18. Quintiere, J. Q., "Status of Fire Research and Safety," *Fire Safety Science—Proceedings of the Second International Symposium*, Hemisphere Publishing Corp., NY, 1989.
19. DiNenno, P. J. and Beyler, C. L., "Fire Hazard Assessment of Composite Materials, the Use and Limitation of Current Hazard Analysis Methodology," *Proceedings of the ASTM Symposium on Fire Hazards and Fire Risk Assessment, December 3, 1990*, San Antonio, TX, 1990.
20. Babrauskas, V., et al., "The Role of Bench-Scale Test Data in Assessing Real-Scale Fire Toxicity," NIST Technical Note 1284, National Institute of Standards and Technology, Gaithersburg, MD, Jan. 1991.
21. Emmons, H. W., "The Ceiling Jet in Fires," NIST-GCR-90-582, National Institute of Standards and Technology, Gaithersburg, MD, Oct. 1990.
22. Steckler, K., "Fire-Induced Flows in Corridors—A Review of Efforts to Model Key Features," *NISTIR 89-4050*, National Institute of Standards and Technology, Gaithersburg, MD, February 1989.
23. Steele, S. and Rockett, J. A., "Application of the Harvard Multiroom Fire Simulation Where Forced Ventilation Is Important," *Fire Safety Science—Proceedings of the Second International Symposium*, Hemisphere Publishing Corp., NY, 1989.
24. Wolfe, A., "CFD Software: Pushing Analysis to the Limit," *Mechanical Engineering*, Jan. 1991, pp. 48-54.
25. Waters, R. A., "Stansted Terminal Building and Early Atrium Studies," *Journal of Fire Protection Engineering*, Vol. 1, No. 2, 1989, pp. 63-76.
26. Pericleous, K. A., "The Field Modeling of Fire in an Air-Supported Structure," *Fire Safety Science—Proceedings of the Second International Symposium*, Hemisphere Publishing Corp., NY, 1989.
27. Huhaten, R., "Numerical Fire Modeling of a Turbine Hall," *Fire Safety Science—Proceedings of the Second International Symposium*, Hemisphere Publishing Corp., NY, 1989.
28. Galea, E. R. and Markatos, N. C., "Modeling of Aircraft Cabin Fires," *Fire Safety Science—Proceedings of the Second International Symposium*, Hemisphere Publishing Corp., NY, 1989.
29. Kumar, S. and Cox, G., "Mathematical Modeling of Fires in Road Tunnels," Proceedings of Fifth International Conference on Aerodynamics and Ventilation of Vehicle Tunnels, Lille, France, 1985, p. 61.
30. Kumar, S., Hoffman, N., and Cox, G., "Some Validation of Jasmine for Fires in Hospital Wards," *Numerical Simulation of Fluid Flow and Heat/Mass Transfer Processes*, Springer-Verlag, Berlin, 1986, p. 159.
31. Galea, E., "On-the-Field Modeling Approach to the Simulation of Enclosure Fires," *Journal of Fire Protection Engineering*, Vol. 1, No. 1, 1989, pp. 11-22.
32. Bukowski, R., "Fire Models: The Future Is Now," *National Fire Protection Association Journal*, March/April 1991, p. 60.
33. Nelson, H. E., "An Engineering Analysis of Fire Development in the Hospice of Southern Michigan, December 15, 1985," *Fire Safety Science—Proceedings of the Second International Symposium*, Hemisphere Publishing Corp., NY, 1989.
34. Levine, R. S. and Nelson, H. E., *Full-Scale Simulation of a Fatal Fire and Comparison of Results with Two Multiroom Models, NISTIR 90-4268*, National Institute of Standards and Technology, Gaithersburg, MD, 1990.
35. Clarke, F. and DiNenno, P. J., "Computer Based Analysis of the Fire Hazard of Furniture Materials," *Proceedings of SPI 28th Annual Technical Conference*, San Antonio, TX, 1984.
36. Clarke, F. and DiNenno, P. J., "Fire Safety of Wire and Cable Materials, Part III," *Proceedings of International Wire and Cable Symposium*, Reno, NV, Nov. 1984.
37. DiNenno, P. J., "Mathematical Fire Modeling—Toward the Rational Integration of Fire Safety Features," *BVD/SPI Conference on Fire Protection Concepts*, Mar. 1984.
38. Bukowski, R., "Toxic Hazard Evaluations of Plenum Cables," *Fire Technology*, Vol. 21, No. 4, Nov. 1985, pp. 252-266.
39. Peacock, R. D. and Bukowski, R., "A Prototype Methodology for Fire Hazard Analysis," *Fire Technology*, Vol. 26, No. 1, Feb. 1990, p. 15.
40. Clarke, F. B., Bukowski, R. W., Stiefel, S. W., Hall, J. R., and Steele, S. A., "A Method to Predict Fire Risk: The Report of the National Fire Protection Research Foundation Risk Project," *Report to the National Fire Protection Research Foundation (NFPRF)*, Quincy, MA, 1990.
41. Hall, J. R. and Sekizawa, A., "Fire Risk Analysis: General Conceptual Framework for Describing Models," *Fire Technology*, Vol. 27, No. 1, 1991, pp. 33-53.
42. Bengston, S. and Hagglund, B., "The Use of a Zone Model in Fire Engineering Applications," *Fire Safety Science—Proceedings of the First International Symposium*, Hemisphere Publishing Corp., Washington, DC, 1986, pp. 667-675.
43. Hagglund, B. and Wickstrom, U., "Smoke Control in Hospitals—A Numerical Study," *Fire Safety Journal*, Vol. 16, 1990, pp. 53-63.
44. Ling, W. C. and Williamson, R. B., "Using Fire Tests for Quantitative Risk Analysis," *Fire Risk Assessment, ASTM STP 762*, American Society for Testing and Materials, Philadelphia, PA, 1982.
45. Wakamatsu, T., "Development of Design System for Building Fire Safety," *Fire Safety Science—Proceedings of the Second International Symposium*, Hemisphere Publishing Corp., NY, 1989.

INSPECTING, SURVEYING, AND MAPPING

Revised by Lydia A. Butterworth, P.E.

The reasons for inspecting a property are: (1) to evaluate the danger to life from fire, and (2) to evaluate and determine ways for minimizing fire danger to buildings and contents. Inspections are made by fire protection engineers, building and fire officials, insurance representatives, and others similarly qualified.

In order to properly evaluate the protection for a property or specific hazard, a tour or inspection of the premises must be made. Three essential results of the inspection should be:

1. A permanent, precise, and complete narrative report describing the fire protection features and fire hazards of the property.
2. A plan indicating the physical characteristics and layout of the premises.
3. Recommendations for improvement (if necessary).

This chapter provides a list of the key items contained in the written narrative report, a list of the important features to observe when surveying a property, and some guidelines for drawing (mapping) a site plan. Also included are a chart of standard risk analysis diagram symbols and a legend of standard abbreviations.

INSPECTION

Functions performed during an inspection, and the compilation of the narrative report resulting from the inspection, are discussed in detail in the *NFPA Inspection Manual*.[1] The following list forms an outline of the key items that should appear in the written report:

1. Property identification.
   a. Name and address of facility.
   b. Date of report.
   c. Name of inspector.
   d. Building identification.

2. Property use.
   a. General property use; e.g., educational, mercantile, industrial, warehouse.
   b. Specific uses. State each principal use and its location. For storage areas, identify the product(s) stored.
   c. Names of tenants in a building of multiple occupancy, including their location and amount of space occupied.

3. Construction.
   a. Types of construction. For mixed construction, show a table and report percentage of each type construction.
   b. Exterior exposure.
      1. Other buildings.
      2. Outside storage, processes, and parking.
      3. Grass, brush.
   c. Interior exposure.
   d. Fire areas, walls, and partitions.
   e. Protection or lack of protection of horizontal openings.
   f. Protection or lack of protection of vertical openings.

4. Life safety.
   a. Exit facilities.
      1. Adequacy.
      2. Deficiencies.
   b. Exit illumination and emergency lighting.
   c. Interior finish.
   d. Evacuation plan and drills.

5. Common hazards.
   a. Heat, light, power, and air conditioning.
   b. Housekeeping, brush and grass.
   c. Ordinary combustibles.
   d. Electrical appliances.
   e. Smoking.

6. Special hazards.
   a. Finishing processes.
   b. Flammable liquids.
   c. Flammable gases.
   d. Welding and cutting.
   e. Cooking.

Lydia A. Butterworth is a fire protection engineer with the Smithsonian Institution and Chairman of NFPA's Technical Committee on Firesafety Symbols.

   f. Chemicals and plastics, etc.
   g. Electronic equipment.
   h. Others.

7. Water supply.
   a. General description including adequacy, deficiencies, and reliability.
   b. Fire flow requirements, availability determined by tests.
   c. Storage requirements.
   d. Sources of supply.
   e. Storage facilities.
   f. Pumps.
   g. Distribution system and appurtenances.
   h. Maintenance, inspections, and tests.

8. Extinguishing systems and devices.
   a. Automatic sprinkler systems.
      1. Types—wet pipe, dry pipe, deluge, preaction.
      2. Coverage, temperature rating of sprinklers, occupancy classification, spacing of sprinklers.
      3. Adequacy.
      4. Tests and maintenance.
   b. Special hazard systems.
      1. Types (carbon dioxide, foam, dry chemical, wet chemical, Halon).
      2. Hazard protected.
      3. Adequacy.
      4. Tests and maintenance.
   c. Portable extinguishers.
      1. Types and coverage.
      2. Tests and maintenance.
   d. Standpipes and fire hose systems.
      1. Type.
      2. Tests and maintenance.

9. Alarm and detection systems.
   a. Automatic fire detection systems.
      1. Type, coverage, connected to fire alarm.
      2. Power supply.
      3. Tests and maintenance.
   b. Local evacuation alarm systems.
      1. Type, coverage, connected to fire alarm.
      2. Power supply.
      3. Tests and maintenance.

10. Fire prevention.
   a. Building inspection program.
      1. Frequency.
      2. Scope.
      3. Recording forms.
   b. Fire protection system inspection program.
      1. Type.
      2. Frequency.
      3. Scope.
      4. Recording forms.
   c. Employee firesafety training.
      1. Adequacy and frequency of training.
      2. Reference material.
   d. Fire brigade program.
      1. Type of brigade.
      2. Training.
      3. Special equipment provided.

11. Recommendations.

SURVEYING

There are many different routes to choose when touring a property; a particular route is selected according to personal preference and convenience. The inspector should choose a standard touring procedure with which he/she is comfortable, and should adopt that pattern for normal use. It is important for the inspector to pass through the building and the plant yard systematically without leaving any space uncovered.

A thorough understanding of the features depicted on a complete plan is absolutely necessary. The features of any property can be placed in one of four categories: Construction -C-; Occupancy -O-; Protection -P-; and Exposure -E- (COPE). These major classifications of important features are comprised of many components, as shown here.

1. Construction.
   a. Building(s) identification.
   b. Dimensions.
      1. Building area(s).
      2. Distances to exposures, other properties.
      3. Width of streets, natural barriers.
      4. Height of building(s); i.e., number of floors, ceiling heights, concealed spaces, etc.
   c. Date of construction.
   d. Construction material of:
      1. Walls.
      2. Floors.
      3. Roofs.
   e. Location of fire division walls and roof parapets, and type of material.
   f. Location of fire doors and/or other horizontal protected/unprotected opening(s).
   g. Location of stairways, elevators, and other vertical protected/unprotected openings.
   h. Type of windows; i.e., plain glass, wire glass, etc.
   i. Location and type of suspended ceilings.
   j. Chimney location, construction, and height.
   k. Location of fire escapes.

2. Occupancy.
   a. Floor-by-floor listing of major occupancy processes.
   b. Location, size, content, and construction of tanks and/or cylinders.
   c. Ratings for boilers, furnace.
   d. Cooling towers, dust collectors, silos, cranes, conveyors, and other special equipment.
   e. Electrical transformers.
      1. Capacity.
      2. Ownership.
      3. Protection.
      4. Cutoffs.

3. Protection.
   a. Automatic sprinklers.
      1. Type of System—wet pipe, dry pipe with/without accelerator or exhauster, deluge, preaction.
      2. Riser location and diameter.
      3. Areas covered by type.
   b. Control valves for water supplying sprinkler sytem.
      1. Location.
      2. Size.
      3. Type of valve.
      4. Label status of valve, only if it is normally "shut."

c. Fire pumps.
   1. Location of pump and control valves.
   2. Rated capacity—gpm, psi (L/min, kPa).
   3. Type—centrifugal, vertical shaft turbine, rotary, or steam.
   4. Name of manufacturer.
   5. Type of motor drive—diesel, electric, gas, gasoline, or steam.
   6. Suction pressure—head or lift (in feet, or meters).
   7. Starting mechanism—automatic or manual.
d. Water tank, gravity tank, suction tank for fire pumps.
   1. Capacity—gpm, psi (L/min, kPa).
   2. Location and height.
   3. Pipe arrangement to yard main or fire pump.
   4. Percent of capacity for fire protection use.
e. Public water supplies.
   1. Type of system—gravity, direct pumping.
   2. Size of all water mains and locations in relation to plant.
   3. Location, size, and type of control valves.
   4. Type of water service—high and low pressure or fire service only.
f. Yard water mains.
   1. Location.
   2. Size.
   3. Connection arrangement to all supply sources available.
   4. Type of pipe—cement-lined, cast-iron, etc.
g. Fire alarm and detection systems.
   1. Water flow detection on sprinkler risers.
   2. Location of main control valve/panel type detection units.
   3. Products of combustion—rate of heat rise, fixed temperature, photoelectric, and ionization.
   4. Fire department alarm box or type of notification.
h. Location and type of check valves and water meters.
i. Hydrants.
   1. Public.
   2. Private.
   3. Frost-proof.
j. Fire department pumper connections.

4. Exposure.
   a. Indicate proximity, construction, and occupancy of buildings or structures facing the four sides of the building being surveyed.
   b. Location of rivers or other natural exposures (i.e., forests).
   c. Railroad tracks.
   d. Yard storage.

By formulating a short checklist similar to the preceding for each COPE feature, the inspector will be assured of having all the necessary information for preparing a good sketch after the tour. Utilizing such checklists to make rough, hand-drawn sketches of every individual section, floor, or building will reduce the difficulty of preparing the finished plan.

The symbols in Figure 10-15A are used to represent the general location and type of the COPE features of a facility. Occasionally, the use of a symbol alone will not sufficiently describe the situation. In that case, it is also necessary to label that point on the plan. Table 10-15A gives a list of standard abbreviations that can be used. Although brief, the list nevertheless provides all of the abbreviations commonly needed. *Abbreviations for Use on Drawings and in Text*, prepared by the American National Standards Institute,[2] lists additional, less commonly used abbreviations.

MAPPING

Once the necessary information has been collected, a site plan can be drawn readily. A good, practical approach is to split the preparation into three parts:

1. Building sketch.
2. Addition of fire protection equipment.
3. Detailing occupancy and specific processes or hazards.

The initial step is to outline the shape of the building, using an appropriate architect/engineer scale on an adequately sized sheet of paper. Once the shell is complete, the other important construction features referenced in the preceding section on surveying should be added, and various construction material labeled.

The inspector should draw sufficient sectional views to show all vertical areas of the facility or building. Figure 10-15B illustrates what a typical, simple "site sketch" looks like when completed.

The second step is to plot the fire protection facilities and equipment on the finished building sketch. Two important points should be noted. First, water supplies—public or private (yard) mains—are continuous from a point of origin to the individual automatic sprinkler risers. Conversely, the automatic sprinkler systems within the buildings are not entirely shown. (NOTE: Sprinkler occupancy classification and spacing are referred to in the body of the narrative inspection report.) Second, when space limitations prohibit drawing all the equipment on the plan at approximate actual locations (due to size, quantity of symbols, or labeling requirements), a small side sketch (not drawn to scale) can be used effectively.

The last step in completing the plan is to label the internal occupancy or processes of each area of the facility or building, and any yard storage or processes of interest.

The symbols and plans in this HANDBOOK will enable any inspector to develop a building plan in accordance with widespread convention. These symbols are based on NFPA 170, *Standard for Firesafety Symbols*. However, many organizations use their own, slightly different set of symbols and layouts. When trying to take information from a plan developed from another source, it is essential to refer to the legend of symbols used by that organization to interpret the information accurately.

At one time, colors were used to describe the type of construction materials used for walls. Today, color-coded plans are being replaced by black and white drawings to facilitate preparation and for economic reasons, so construction type is being noted narratively.

Table 10-15B identifies colors that should be used if the plan is to be colored. To avoid confusion on complicated plans, construction materials can be labeled in accordance with the abbreviations in Table 10-15A.

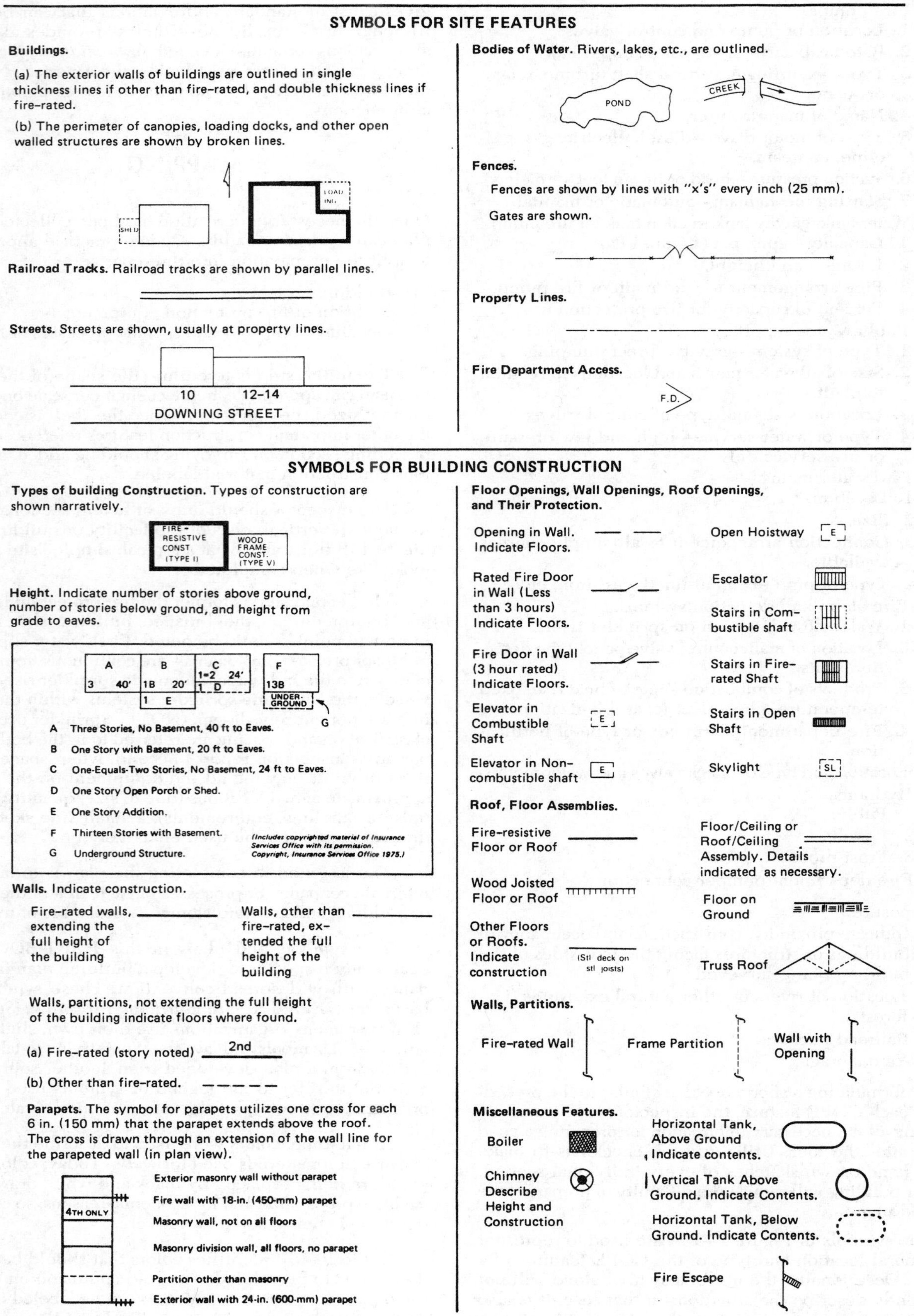

FIG. 10-15A. ***Standard plan symbols used to represent the general location and type of COPE (Construction -C-; Occupancy -O-; Protection -P-; and Exposure -E-) features of a facility.***

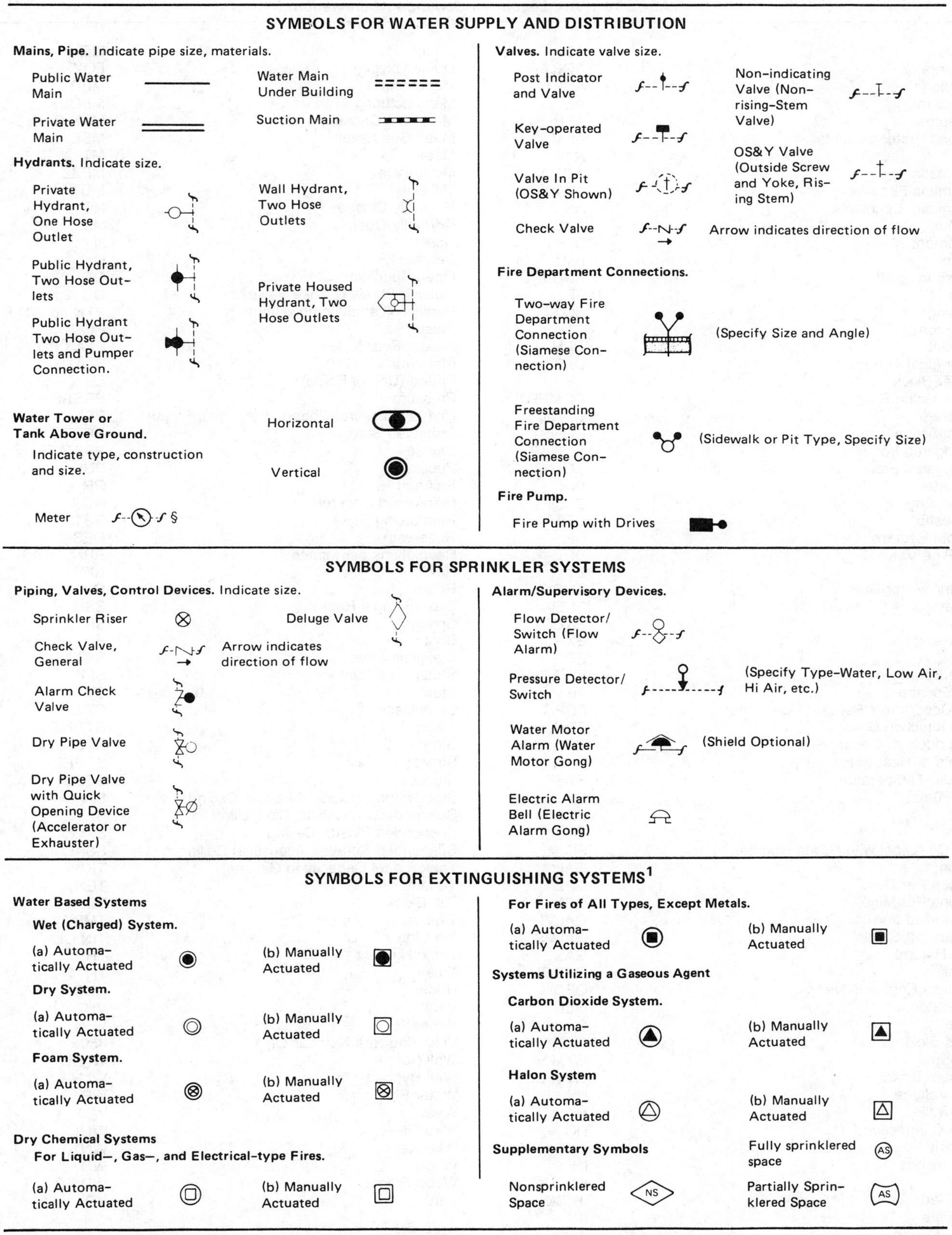

[1]These symbols are intended for use in identifying the type of installed system protecting an area within a building.

FIG. 10-15A. Standard plan symbols used to represent the general location and type of COPE (Construction -C-; Occupancy -O-; Protection -P-; and Exposure -E-) features of a facility.

TABLE 10-15A. ***Legend of Common Abbreviations****

Above	ABV	Liquid	LIQ
Accelerator	ACC	Liquid Oxygen	LOX
Acetylene	ACET	Manufacture	MFR
Aluminum	AL	Manufacturing	MFG
Asbestos	ASB	Maximum Capacity	MAX CAP
Asphalt Protected Metal	APM	Mean Sea Level	MSL
Attic	A	Metal	MT
Automatic	AUTO	Mezzanine	MEZZ
Automatic Fire Alarm	AFA	Mill Use	MU
Automatic, Sprinklers	AS	Normally Closed	NC
Avenue	AVE	Normally Open	NO
Basement	B	North	N
Beam	BM	Number	No
Board on Joist	BDOJ	Open Sprinklers	OS
Brick	BR	Outside Screw & Yoke Valve	OS & Y
Building	BLDG	Partition (Label Composition)	PTN (ie WD PTN)
Cast Iron	CI	Plaster	PLAS
Cement	CEM	Plaster Board	PLAS BD
Centrifugal Fire Pump	CFP	Platform	PLATF
Cinder Block	CB	Pound (Unit of Force)	LB
Composition Roof	COMPR	Pressure	PRESS
Concrete	CONC	Unit of Pressure (Pounds Per Square Inch)	PSI
Construction	CONST	Protected Steel	PROT ST
Corrugated Iron	COR IR	Private	PRIVATE
Corrugated Steel	COR ST	Public	PUB
Diameter	DIA	Railroad	RR
Diesel-Engine	D ENG	Reinforced Concrete	RC
Domestic	DOM	Reinforcing Steel	RST
Double Hydrant	DH	Reservoir	RES
Dry Pipe Valve	DPV	Revolutions per Minute	RPM
East	E	Roof	RF
Electric Motor Driven	EMD	Room	RM
Elevator	ELEV	Slate Shingle Roof	SSR
Engine	ENG	Space	SP
Exhauster	EXH	South	S
Feet	FT	Stainless Steel	SST
Fibre Board	FBR BD	Steam Fire Pump	SFP
Fire Escape	FE	Steel	ST
Fire Department Pumper Connection	FDPC	Steel Deck	ST DK
Fire Detection Units	FDU	Stone	STONE
Products of Combustion	POC	Story	STO
Rate of Heat Rise	RHR	Street	STREET
Fixed Temperature	FTEP	Stucco	STUC
Fire Pump	FP	Suspended Acoustical Plaster Ceiling	SAPL
Floor	FL	Suspended Acoustical Tile Ceiling	SATL
Frame	FR	Suspended Plaster Ceiling	SPC
Fuel Oil (Label with Grade Number)	FO #____	Suspended Sprayed Acoustical Ceiling	SSAL
Gallon	GAL	Tank (Label Capacity in Gallons)	TK
Gallons Per Day	GPD	Tenant	TEN
Gallons Per Minute	GPM	Tile Block	TB
Galvanized Iron	GALVI	Timber	TMBR
Galvanized Steel	GALVS	Tin Clad	TIN CL
Gas, Natural	GAS	Triple Hydrant	TH
Gasoline	GASOLINE	Truss	TR
Gasoline Engine Driven	GED	Under	UND
Generator	GEN	Vault	VLT
Glass	GL	Veneer	VEN
Glass Block	GLB	Volts (Indicate Number Of)	450v
Gypsum	GYM	Wall Board	WLBD
Gypsum Board	GYM BD	Wall Hydrant	WLH
High Voltage	HV	Water Pipe	WP
Hollow tile	HT	West	W
Hose Connection	HC	Wire Glass	WGL
Hydrant	HYD	Wire Net	WN
Inch, Inches	IN	Wood	WD
Iron	IR	Wood Frame	WD FR
Iron Clad	IR CL	Yard	YD
Iron Pipe	IP		
Joist, Joisted	J		

* Some words that have a common abbreviation, e.g. "ST" for "street," are spelled out fully to avoid confusion with similar abbreviations used herein for other terms.1.

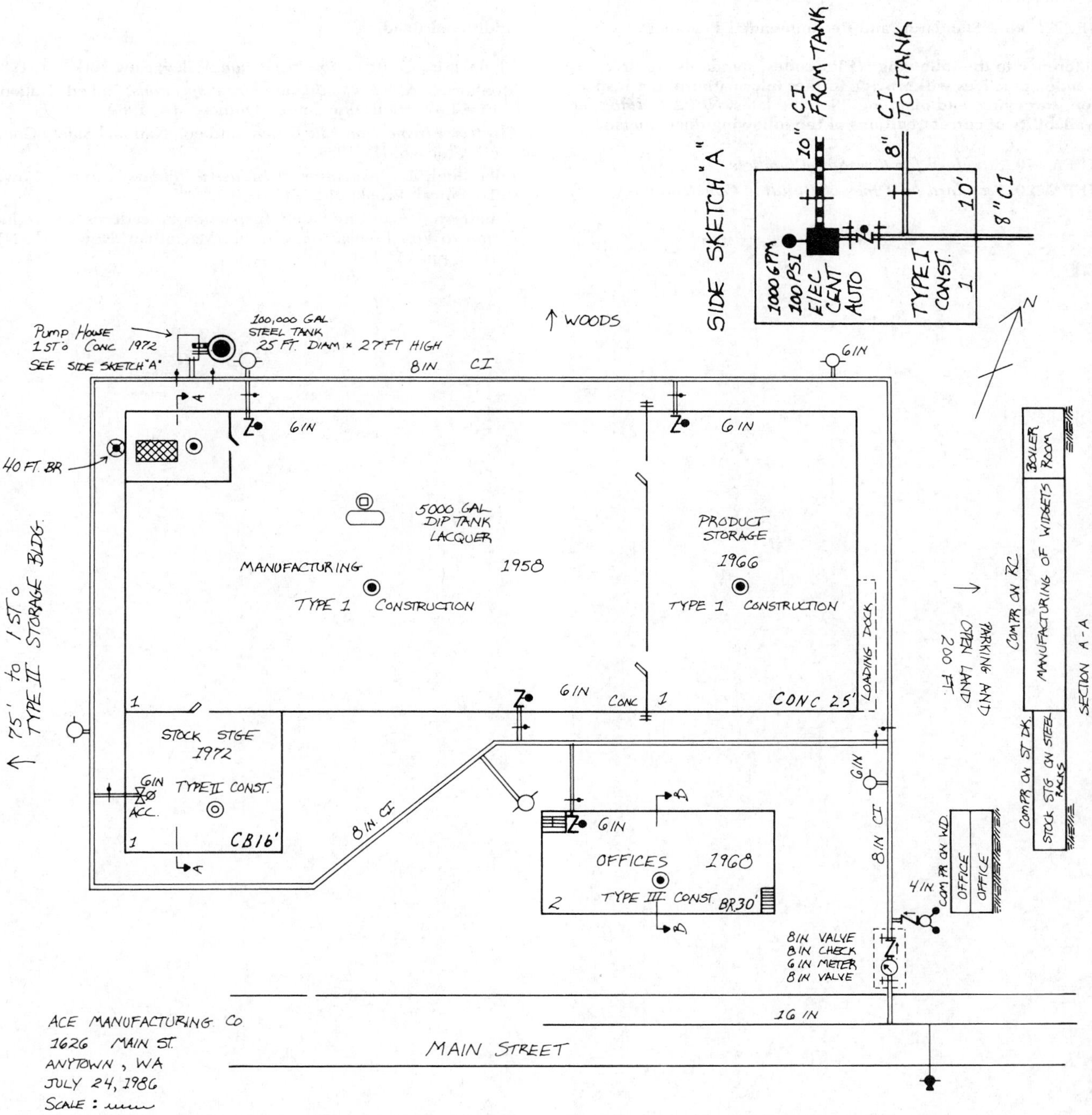

FIG. 10-15B. ***A typical site sketch (top) and small side sketch (bottom) showing fire protection facilities and equipment.***

TABLE 10-15B. ***Color Code for Denoting Construction Materials for Walls***

Color	Interpretation
Brown	Fire resistive protected steel
Red	Brick, hollow tile
Yellow	Frame-wood, stucco
Blue	Concrete, stone, or hollow concrete block
Gray	Noncombustible (sheet metal or metal lath and plaster) unprotected steel

BIBLIOGRAPHY

References Cited

1. Moulton, G. A., *ed.*, *NFPA Inspection Manual*, 6th ed., National Fire Protection Association, Quincy, MA, 1989.

2. ANSI, *Abbreviations for Use on Drawings and in Text*, ANSI Y1.1, American National Standards Institute, New York, NY, 1990.

NFPA Codes, Standards, and Recommended Practices

Reference to the following NFPA codes, standards, and recommended practices will provide further information about inspection, surveying, and mapping. (See the latest *NFPA Catalog* for availability of current editions of the following documents.)

NFPA 170, *Standard for Firesafety Symbols.*

NFPA 220, *Standard on Types of Building Construction.*

Additional Readings

Clyde, J. E., *Construction Inspection*, Wiley, New York, NY, 1983.

Moulton, G. A., *ed.*, *Conducting Fire Inspections*, 2nd ed., National Fire Protection Association, Quincy, MA, 1989.

Electrical Inspection Illustrated, 2nd ed., National Safety Council, Chicago, IL, 1984.

Pilborough, L., *Inspection of Industrial Plants*, 2nd ed., Gower Technical, Brookfield, VT, 1989.

Robertson, J. C., "Fire Safety Inspection Procedures," *Introduction to Fire Prevention*, 3rd ed., Macmillan, New York, NY, 1989, pp. 154-181.

MICROCOMPUTER APPLICATIONS IN FIRE PROTECTION

Revised by John M. Watts, Jr.

In a manner similar to the way the industrial age produced the automatic sprinkler system as a powerful tool to deal with industrial fire problems, the information age has brought the computer to enhance fire protection decision-making. This chapter will present some of the fundamental concepts associated with applications of microcomputers in fire protection. Because this represents an interface with a different technology, a brief glossary is included at the end of the chapter. Terminology not fully explained in the text will be found in the glossary.

Several other chapters in this section deal with specific applications of microcomputers in more detail.

INTRODUCTION

Before the advent of large-scale computers, man had to rely on manual methods and slow mechanical calculators to perform arithmetic operations. No doubt the first devices used as an aid to computation were fingers, sticks, stones, and similar objects. These items served only as reminders or indicators of a particular quantity and could not themselves do any work; the actual computation was carried out in the mind of the individual.

The word *computer* comes from the Latin verb *computare*, which means to reckon or think. Thus a computer is a machine that reckons or thinks. Although it is often asserted that a machine cannot think, this is more a philosophical matter than a technical one. Computers can do whatever humans can do if you can describe to the computer how to do it.

The first significant electronic computer was the electronic numerical integrator and calculator, or ENIAC, built in 1946 at the University of Pennsylvania. The ENIAC used 18,000 vacuum tubes as storage elements. It occupied 4,000 cu ft (113 m^3) of space and cost $480,000. Today's desktop microcomputers are faster, more powerful, and easier to use. (See Fig. 10-16A.)

FIG. 10-16A. Microcomputer.

Vacuum tubes, used in calculating machines, became the "first generation" of electronic computers. When transistors were developed in the 1950s, they became the "second generation." This was followed by the "chip" or IC (integrated circuit), whereby an entire electronic circuit of transistors, resistors, capacitors, and other devices could be etched on a tiny bit of silicon. These educated grains of sand represent the third generation. Now, as a fourth generation, are very-large-scale-integration (VLSI) circuits. (See Fig. 10-16B.) These chips contain logic circuits that have given rise to sophisticated hand calculators and, most recently, microcomputers. All the computing circuitry of ENIAC is now available on a single chip. This is the technology that made the "personal computer" a household word and, for many, a household appliance. In commerce and industry, the microcomputer has become a standard business tool.

Characteristic of these developments is a geometric increase in speed of operation. Today, computer functions take place in a time span of a few nanoseconds. A nanosecond is one-billionth of a second. To understand the significance of a nanosecond, consider that electrical impulses in a computer travel at the speed of light (186,000 mph or

Dr. Watts is Director of the Fire Safety Institute, a not-for-profit information, research, and educational corporation located in Middlebury, VT. He also serves as Editor of NFPA's quarterly technical journal, Fire Technology.

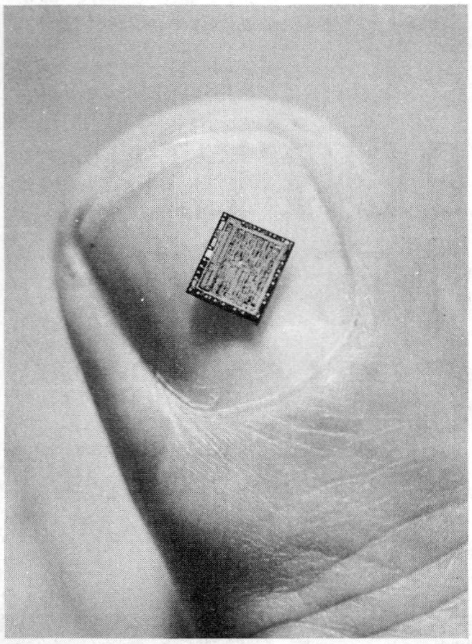

FIG. 10-16B. A microcomputer chip.

300,000 kph). A nanosecond is about how long it takes electricity to travel one foot. Thus, computer components that are several feet apart can double the time of a computer operation. These speeds may increase even more as new materials like gallium arsenide replace silicon in future generations of computer chips.

COMPUTER PRINCIPLES

Modern electronic digital computers use certain basic operating functions. To understand how a computer performs its many tasks, it is necessary to be aware of some fundamental principles of computer operation.

Digital Information

Computers function by reducing all information, no matter how complex, to simple electrical signals grouped together in "bits" and "bytes."

Bit: Computer operations are performed with "bits" (contraction of "binary digits"). A bit holds one of two pieces of information—either a one or a zero. This information is stored as an electric charge on a piece of semiconductor material. If the charge is positive, the bit has a value of one; if the charge is negative, then the value of the bit is zero. A bit may also be thought of as an electronic switch that is either on or off. On indicates a value of one and off indicates zero.

Computers manipulate numbers in the binary system. In a sequence of four bits, each bit represents a value of 2^n where n corresponds to the position of the bit. The first or "rightmost" bit indicates a value of $2^0 = 1$ if it is "on," or a value of 0 if it is "off." The next bit corresponds to $2^1 = 2$ if "on," and 0 if "off." Similarly, the value $2^2 = 4$ is associated with the third bit and $2^3 = 8$ with the "leftmost" of the four bits. Adding these values allows the computer to represent the numbers from zero (0000) to fifteen (1111) using just four bits. For example, the number four is 0100 and the number nine is 1001; adding these together gives 1101 or thirteen. (Fig. 10-16C.) All of the operations in a computer are performed in this manner, by combining values of electronic switches that are either on or off.

BINARY	DECIMAL
0100	4
1001	+9
1101	13

FIG. 10-16C. Binary arithmetic.

Byte: While four bits are adequate to represent decimal digits, more are required to represent all the alphanumeric characters that are convenient to use with a computer. Most often, a string of eight bits is used for this purpose and is referred to as a "byte." Thus each character in the memory of a computer uses eight bits or one byte. Storage capacity of computers is measured in bytes. Since most computers can hold at least thousands of bytes, the common term for expressing memory size is the "kilobyte," indicated by the symbol K. A kilobyte is defined as $2^{10} = 1{,}024$ bytes. For example, a 64K memory has the capacity to hold $64 \times 1{,}024 = 65{,}536$ characters or bytes (524,288 electronic switches). Newer microcomputers have capacities of millions of bytes or megabytes, represented symbolically as MB.

Elements of the Computer

In order for a computer to operate, it requires certain elements for the proper handling of information. A block diagram illustrating the various elements of a computer is shown in Figure 10-16D.

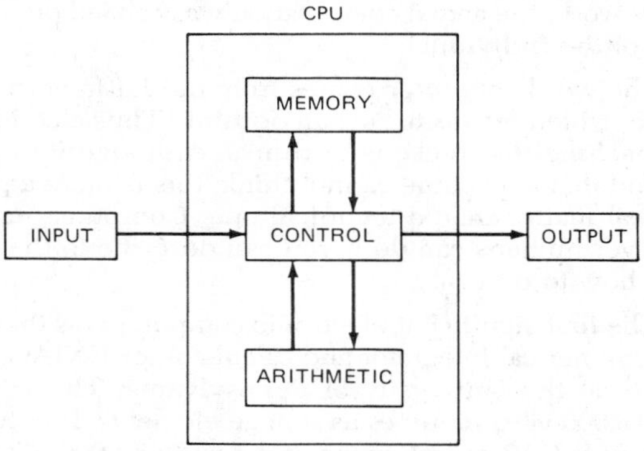

FIG. 10-16D. Elements of a computer.

The input section is capable of accepting information in a variety of forms and converting it to the standard format used by the computing portion of the equipment. The input section obtains information from various input devices in the form of data required to solve a problem or programmed instructions that tell the computer what to do.

The control section serves as the focal point. It directs the input data to an appropriate location in the computer's memory. The control section interprets or decodes instructions stored in the memory section and then sends signals to other parts of the computer to tell it what to do.

The memory section is made up of a large number of storage locations in which information can be kept until it is needed by one of the other sections. The information may be numerical data or program instructions to be executed.

Actual computations specified by input or in a stored program are carried out by the arithmetic section. This section of the computer basically performs addition only. Other arithmetic functions are variations of addition; for example, multiplication is repetitive addition, and subtraction is the addition of a positive and a negative number. Some microcomputers utilize an arithmetic co-processor, which is a separate chip used to speed up the arithmetic operations.

The output section has the function of recording, or writing, the results of computer processing. This section is capable of presenting to the user anything located in memory.

The means by which these different elements of the computer communicate with each other is called a data bus or just "bus." The capacity of the bus determines what size data it can handle and hence the speed at which it operates. A common analogy is to a highway, where bus size in bits is comparable to the number of traffic lanes.

HARDWARE

The actual physical components of a computer that can be touched and felt are the hardware. In some small laptop microcomputers, the hardware may consist of a single piece of equipment. More commonly, a computer has several hardware components. There is usually a central processing unit (CPU) and several input, output, storage, or communications devices, which are collectively referred to as "peripherals."

Central Processing Unit

There are three general sizes of CPUs: mainframes, minicomputers (minis), and microcomputers (micros). The mainframe computer is the largest and most powerful. It has the greatest memory capacity and the fastest speed of computation. At the upper end of the scale are "supercomputers," which continue to increase in processing capacity and computation speed. Advances in computer technology have enabled smaller machines—minicomputers—to perform a great many functions formerly limited to mainframes. While less powerful, minicomputers are more cost-effective for certain applications, and now have a very significant position in the computer world.

The most common size of computer today is the micro or personal computer. A device with many times the computing capacity of the giant ENIAC sits on a desktop or can even be carried around in a briefcase. The personal computer has revolutionized the business and scientific world because it provides ready access to significant computing capability. Many advances in fire protection during the next decade will evolve from the availability of microcomputers.

Computation speed of a CPU is a function of a microscopically vibrating component called a "clock" (not to be confused with the time-of-day clock that may also be present). The CPU clock continuously generates millions of vibrations every second that the computer's power is on. A 20 MHz (megahertz) clock generates 20 million electrical vibrations per second. The faster the clock, the faster the computer instructions get executed and the faster the data gets processed. CPUs can execute from 0.1 to over 100 MIPS (millions of instructions per second).

Memory

Internal memory, also called main memory, is the information storage capacity of a computer that can be accessed without any mechanical interface. It is made up of memory chips directly connected to the microprocessor. Internal memory is generally of two types, ROM and RAM. Read-only memory (ROM), permanently installed in the computer, contains information necessary to the computer's operation and whatever other functions the manufacturer desires. Random-access memory (RAM) is the portion of internal memory available to the user for temporary storage of information being used by the computer for a particular operation. RAM has the characteristic of being "volatile," which means that when the computer is shut off (for whatever reason) the electronic switches are also shut off and all information contained in RAM is lost. Typical microcomputers have RAM capacities of from 1 to 10 MB (megabytes or millions of bytes). The larger the RAM, the easier it is for the computer to work with large amounts of information. However, the volatility of RAM means that other storage media are also necessary.

External or mass memory is information storage that is not electronically directly connected to the microprocessor. It is accessed by the CPU by means of an electromechanical device that can read or write to the storage media. Unlike internal memory, mass memory does not use electronic switches but relies instead on electromagnetic charges. Since magnetic charges are stable without additional power, mass storage is considered nonvolatile; that is, the information is retained on the media when the computer is shut off. This makes the storage of information more permanent and portable. The primary devices for external storage are the floppy disk and the hard disk. These have different characteristics of capacity, speed, cost, reliability, and portability. Mass storage devices have capacities of from 100 kilobytes to over 100 megabytes. Because mechanical devices are typically ten times less reliable than electrical devices and take much longer to access by the computer, mass storage has disadvantages. However, because mass storage is less expensive and nonvolatile, most computer installations use a combination of internal and external storage.

CD-ROM: Compact or optical disk technology using digital information is rapidly developing to become an integral part of information handling and computer operations. Compact disks (CDs) use lasers to read and write data to and from specifically treated disks. While CD audio is maximized for sound reproduction, CD-ROM (Compact Disk—Read-Only Memory) is maximized for data storage and retrieval. CD-ROM disks have data already written to them when they are received by the user. Otherwise, they carry out the functions performed by magnetic disks but have a much greater capacity. A 4.7-inch, 1-ounce CD-ROM disk can hold 650 MB, the equivalent of 250,000 printed pages, 20 filing cabinets, 12 bookcases, or 1650 floppy disks. A limitation of CD-ROM is the relatively slow access time compared to magnetic hard disks.

Peripherals

A peripheral is a device that is external to the CPU and main memory but electrically connected to it, and to some degree is controlled by the computer. In addition to external storage units, the most common peripherals are input/output devices.

The most common form of input device is the keyboard that is similar to a typewriter. Each key or combination of keys sends the computer a coded signal that is interpreted as a particular symbol, command, or alphanumeric character. There are many other forms of input devices. Some of these are listed in Table 10-16A.

TABLE 10-16A. ***Input Devices***

Data tablet	Optical reader
Digitizer	Scanner
Joy stick	Touch screen
Keyboard	Track ball
Light pen	Voice recognition
Mouse	

Almost all microcomputers use a video display as the primary output device. Referred to as monitors, they vary in their resolution and graphics presentation, as well as in their color capability.

Most microcomputer installations also include a printer. Output among the wide variety of printers varies in appearance and speed. Dot matrix printers running at high speed generally yield the squarish characters recognized as computer output. At slower speeds they can form characters with "near-letter quality." Laser printers produce letter-quality hard copy at very high speeds and are also superior at printing graphics. Plotters use one or more ink-filled pens to produce graphic output.

A "modem" (a contraction of "modulator-demodulator") is a peripheral device that functions as both an input and output unit. Modems enable microcomputers to exchange data and information as described under the heading "Telecommunications" in the following section.

Another hardware concept that is increasing in popularity is the local area network (LAN). Several microcomputers can be directly interconnected so they can exchange information and share peripheral devices.

SOFTWARE

Computer hardware, no matter how big, fast, powerful, or expensive, is useless without proper instructions in the form of software. Software is a loosely used term for programs or other forms of instructions that enable a computer to perform its desired functions. There are generally four types of computer software: operating systems, programming languages, applications software, and graphics.

Operating Systems

An operating system is the most basic set of instructions necessary for a computer to function. It controls the transfer of information among the computer's components and translates various input and output signals. A variety of operating systems apply to different types of microcomputers, varying according to the microprocessor chip used and the manufacturer.

Early microcomputer operating systems were similar to mainframe operating systems in their use of a command line interface. The user is presented with a mostly blank screen and must input, character by character, each command. Modern operating systems employ a graphical user interface (GUI). The GUI displays command options for the user graphically in icons and name tags. The user can see all the possible choices and makes a selection by "point and shoot" rather than character-based entries. A GUI also permits different software applications to share the same files and data.

Programming Languages

Programming languages enable a user to give explicit instructions to a computer. These languages have evolved along with other aspects of computer technology. The progressive generations of programming languages are described in Table 10-16B. Originally, most computer users were also programmers since programming was the only way to get the computer to do what you wanted it to. Today, most users are not programmers since applications software has all but eliminated the need to program a computer.

Applications Software

One of the principal causes of the microcomputer revolution is the widespread availability of general-purpose application software. These packages can perform many different jobs within their specific functional areas. Compared to software available on mainframes or minicomputers, they are easy to learn, and hence have given rise to the descriptive phrase "user-friendly." The primary areas of general-purpose applications software are word processing, spreadsheets, data base management, telecommunications, and artificial intelligence.

Word processing: Word processor packages create, revise, edit, and print just about any type of document—correspondence, inspection reports, form letters, mailing labels, permits, and even large handbooks. They speed up processing of paperwork, saving time and money for

TABLE 10-16B. ***Programming Languages***

Generation	Description	Examples
First	Binary notation that gives a location in memory and tells which bits are on or off.	Machine languages 1000 110 0101
Second	Uses English words or other symbols to represent instructions such as add, move, store, branch, etc.	Assembly Languages AUTOCODER EASYCODER
Third	Uses English phrases and mathematical notation. Machine-independent.	High-level Languages BASIC COBOL FORTRAN
Fourth	More easily understood by a larger populaton of users. Uses concepts of artificial intelligence.	High-productivity Languages FOCUS RAMIS

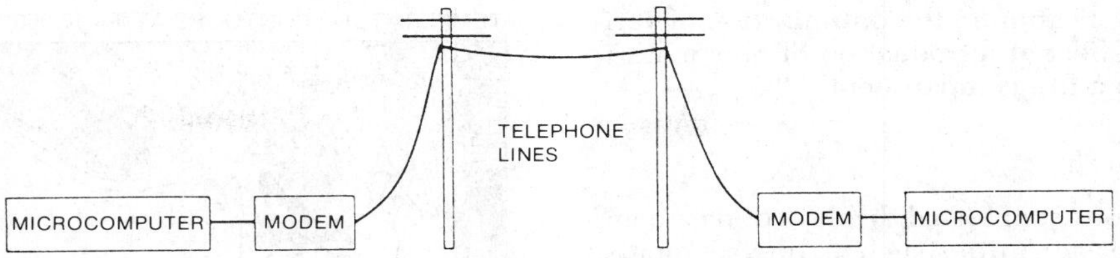

FIG. 10-16E. Ground telecommunications.

clerical effort. These savings result from the ability of word processors to store and edit electronically rather than on paper. Word processing is particularly applicable to updating fire protection inspection surveys. Standard recommendations can be added or deleted with a few keystrokes. Proposals, specifications, and procedures can be similarly updated with ease. Word processing has greatly facilitated the National Fire Protection Association's standard-making procedures.

Desktop publishing (DTP) is a popular extension of word processing. Basically, the term *desktop publishing* is currently used to mean that you can create text and graphics, compose the results in pages with the text flowing around the graphics, and produce camera-ready copy for either a laser printer or phototypesetter. DTP can save up to 50 percent of the time and 90 percent of the cost of traditional printing. It is useful to produce more professional-looking printed materials, to customize printed products, and to publish newsletters.

Spreadsheets: No factor is more responsible for the proliferation of microcomputers among small businesses than the electronic spreadsheet. These programs emulate the columnar page of many rows and columns referred to by accountants as a spreadsheet. The intersection of each row and column, called a cell, can contain written text, numbers, or a formula. The appeal is the almost immediate recalculation of all cell values when any one cell value is altered. While there are many applications for these spreadsheet programs, one of the greatest uses is budget preparation. It is a simple matter to make changes, additions, or deletions of budget items and have all the totals and subtotals recomputed automatically. With an electronic spreadsheet, experiments with reallocations can be done quickly and easily. In project management, spreadsheet analysis is commonly used to estimate costs. Many types of engineering applications, from hydraulic calculations to code requirements, have been adapted to a spreadsheet program. The full range of applications is limited only by the user's imagination.

Data base management: Data base management programs provide a means of storing, retrieving, and rearranging large amounts of similar data. A data base is a collection of information that has been assembled, organized, and presented to serve some specific purpose. Data base management software helps create more orderly, manageable record storage and retrieval systems. Files become instantly accessible and easy to update. Records of inspections, inventory, personnel, customers, training, maintenance, etc., become useful management tools rather than just requirements. Computer data base management provides capability to sort data in any sequence, select specific categories of items, and generate reports with totals, subtotals, and various statistical measures.

"Hypertext" is a type of free-form data base that allows instantaneous cross-referencing. Information in hypertext is organized as a web of separate topics. A topic may consist of an entire document or a small chunk of text. Links express relationships between topics and provide paths for navigating among topics. The essential feature of hypertext is the computer-provided ability to follow links rapidly and automatically within and among documents. Users can navigate the hypertext, skipping from topic to topic by selecting links. Each topic may display icons or text labels that the user selects to display additional topics.

Telecommunications: Telecommunications is a process by which computers transmit data from one computer to another using telephone lines, satellites, or other transmission devices. (See Fig. 10-16E.) Telecommunications requires both special hardware and special software. The hardware required is a "modem," which converts (modulates) a computer's digital signal into analog signals that can be transmitted like a telephone call to another modem, which then demodulates the signal for the receiving computer. Communicating computers may be located in the same room or at opposite sides of the world. Special communications software controls the modem and facilitates the use of telecommunications for many purposes.

Applications of telecommunications include information retrieval, networks, electronic mail, teleconferencing, on-line publishing (electronic newsletters), videotext, and downloading software. The field of telecommunications is one of the fastest-growing, combining computer science with emerging technologies such as fiber optics and direct-broadcast satellites.[1]

Artificial intelligence: One of the most active areas of computer science is artificial intelligence (AI). In recent decades AI has progressed from an area of basic research to commercial applications. Intelligent computer programs are now emerging from the laboratory in the form of robotics, natural languages, expert systems, and neural networks.

Expert systems, also called knowledge-based systems, teach computers to perform tasks with the knowledge and intuition of human experts. Such systems are currently assisting in medical diagnosis, mineral exploration, computer configuration, and structural analysis. By organizing knowledge of established experts into a sophisticated "knowledge base" of patterns and rules, expert systems allow computers to act as intelligent assistants, advising the user with the insight and acumen of experts. Expert systems are most useful when dealing with problems that are too complex to permit precise definition and assessment.

Neural networks are a form of artificial intelligence that processes data in a way that approximates the activity of the neurons of the brain. They can improve the performance of complicated systems through a learning process.

There is potential application in the optimization of variables to control the effect of introduction of new materials and products into a fire compartment.

Graphics

Computer graphics consist of visual displays of data composed of a series of basic entities such as line segments. The graphic is a representation of digital information and is made up of many small parts. (See Fig. 10-16F.)

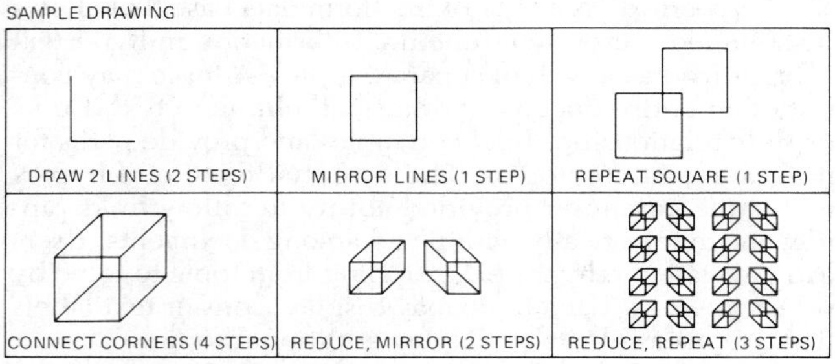

FIG. 10-16F. Typical CADD system commands.

Business graphics: Business graphics refers to presentation quality charts, graphs, and diagrams on video displays, paper, transparencies, or slides. Because images communicate faster and more dramatically than reams of computer printout, using graphics effectively can mean a dynamic increase in productivity and impact. Until recently, it was costly and time-consuming to produce business graphics; now, with microcomputers, they can be produced in the office quickly, easily, and cost-effectively.

Computer-aided drafting and design: Computer-aided drafting and design, or CADD, is the generic term for any system using computer graphics as a replacement for the traditional pen of a designer/drafter. CADD produces plans, detailed layouts, drawings, and visualizations. In the design of structures and mechanical systems, CADD may include interfaces with engineering routines for various load, stress, and sizing calculations. Visualizations may include static views or dynamic simulations in two and three dimensions. Figure 10-16G is a computer graphics illustration in which a field model developed by NIST researchers shows that for a live fire on one side of a room, the hot gases will hit the ceiling and the near wall and then plunge toward the floor while the rest of the hot gas progresses along the ceiling toward the far wall. A number of CADD programs are now available for microcomputers. As memory and speed increase, CADD will become a more common application. CADD has significant potential use in the drawing of fire risk analysis diagrams and the layout of fire protection systems.

Geographic information system: A geographic information system (GIS) is a generic term for a family of computer software packages that store, process, and display geographically referenced information. A GIS has the capability of importing data in a variety of formats and associating the information with geographic coordinates in two or three dimensions. In addition to applications such as computer-aided dispatching and evaluating potential fire station sites,

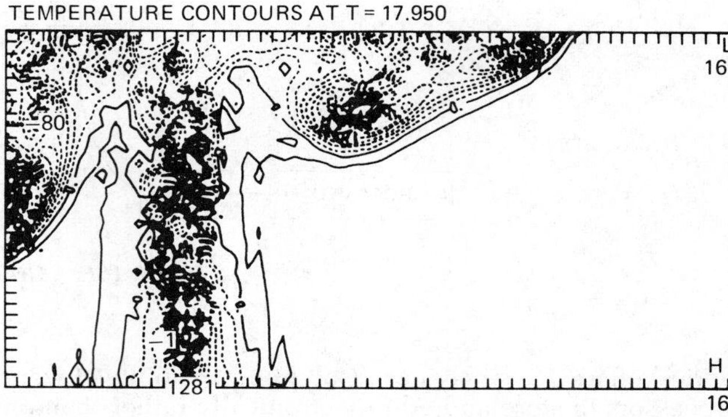

FIG. 10-16G. Computer graphics illustration.

GIS can be used for other disparate functions, such as hazardous material runoff or vapor-cloud dispersion; showing the diameter, flow, material, and age of underground water supply pipes; and tracking incident trends by neighborhood.

Animation: In an animated simulation, key elements of a system (e.g., people, smoke, heat) are represented on a CRT (cathode ray tube) by icons that change shape, color, or position when there is a change in the state of the simulation. Most contemporary animation packages operate in concurrent mode, where the animation is displayed while the simulation is actually running. However, some animation programs function in a playback mode, where the animation is displayed from a disk file after the simulation is completed. The major reason for the popularity of animation is its ability to communicate the essence of a simulation model to executives and juries, greatly increasing the credibility of the model results.

Image processing: Digital image processing is a rapidly expanding computer technology. Images include all the various pictures originating on paper or other media that are so important to our society. Images may appear as charts, diagrams, filled-in forms, signatures, photographs, CAT scans, or fingerprints. Basically, images can be any analog information that is not easily translated into the binary language of the computer. They are important because humans find it easier to deal with images than with text. There are now image management systems that process, store, and retrieve images in a manner similar to text files at a significant saving of time and storage space. Furthermore, processing can modify or improve the appearance of an image, and image analysis can make measurements and collect quantitative data from images.

Multimedia: Computer applications have been greatly enhanced through the integration of digital audio, photographic stills, and animated video images, which collectively is known as "multimedia." Interactive multimedia is the consummate training tool. An example application is an emergency-preparedness system. It creates a simulated experience giving users tools to use, and allows them to actually create a knowledge base by taking notes and storing data in a file. It uses video to model reality, audio to explain information, and input data to guide decision-making and model-building. It allows the user to control and manipulate the environment and provides feedback about correct and incorrect decisions.

FIRE PROTECTION APPLICATIONS

As use of microcomputers becomes more widespread, an increased number of specific fire protection applications have been developed. While a few of these programs are revised from mainframe and minicomputer versions, most are new applications stimulated by the availability of microcomputers. In addition to a great many applications for the fire service, other specialized fire protection software can be categorized by the three areas of application: research, management, and engineering.

Fire Service Applications

Nowhere has the impact of computers on fire protection been more widely felt than in the fire service. The computer has been compared with the internal combustion engine, the centrifugal pump, and the radio as a technological development to improve fire department operations. The low-cost availability of microcomputers enables even the smallest of volunteer fire departments to become "computerized." Some of the most common applications of microcomputers in the fire service are described below.

Preplanning: Computer programs can track building and occupancy information such as basic structural data, building layout, utilities and shutoff details, information on hazardous materials, locations of impaired individuals or children, and other relevant data. Files can be accessed by the dispatcher or fireground commander.

Dispatching: One of the early applications of computers to fire department operations was computer-aided (or assisted) dispatch (CAD).[2] Basically, a CAD system uses the speed and storage capabilities of the computer to monitor fire apparatus location and to dispatch the closest units to the scene of an emergency. Move-up and mutual-aid assignments are also handled. Software can indicate the fastest route to an incident, saving time and guesswork. Map displays using GIS and showing vehicle location and status are a significant component of modern systems. Other information displayed may include hydrant location, cross streets, hazards, telephone numbers, etc. Run-card data can be accessed by business name, box number, street address, telephone number, owner, or other criteria. Interface with preplanning data provides extensive additional information support.

Incident reporting: Data base management systems allow fire departments to enter, update, retrieve, and analyze fire incident reports in accordance with NFPA, NFIRS, and state or other requirements. They prompt the operator for input, print forms, and retain data for future use, as well as provide up-to-the-minute statistics for analysis. Some systems facilitate uploading data directly to the state fire marshal.

Equipment: Inventory systems list equipment, location, age, use, and condition. In addition, they can maintain records of inspections, repairs, and preventive maintenance schedules. There are specific programs for vehicles, hydrants, hoses, and personal protection equipment. Software can also analyze purchase decisions and develop replacement policies.

Training: Fire service training provides one of the most interesting applications of microcomputers. Computer-assisted instruction (CAI) has significant advantages to fire service personnel. Advantages include freeing the instructor to concentrate on field exercises, letting students progress at their own pace, and providing reinforcement. Computer simulations of fire incidents allow officers to test tactics safely and repeatedly. Interactive multimedia packages present realistic situations that can teach and reinforce as well as evaluate and critique.

Personnel: Computerized personnel records contain standard roster information plus details on emergency medical conditions, equipment sign-outs, certification and promotion history, and insurance requirements. Software can handle payroll, scheduling, and performance reviews as well as report on factors such as overtime and absenteeism. Training records track individual drills, hours, courses, and grades, and produce department-wide reports for overall evaluation.

Code enforcement: Inspection management systems record structural and fire hazard abatement data. They track deficiencies, schedule inspections, and issue permits. The status of code violations or complaints can be determined at any time. Follow-up letters can be automatically printed. Information can be exchanged with preplanning software. Inspection schedules can be optimized for workload and effectiveness.[3]

Hazardous materials: Data bases of hazardous materials are widely available. The records include chemical name, family, NFPA 704 codes, and DOT number and emergency response guidelines. Additional features incorporate compliance determination for right-to-know regulations, SARA Title III (Superfund Amendments and Reauthorization Act), and elements of hazard analysis. CAMEO (computer-aided management of emergency operations) is an example of a comprehensive haz-mat software package. It contains information on more than 3300 chemicals, features computerized maps, and provides a plume-dispersion model for tracking material release. Programs like CAMEO are essential to disaster planning for hazardous materials incidents. More information on hazardous materials computer data base systems is available from FEMA's Hazardous Materials Information Exchange.

Deployment analysis: The New York City—Rand Institute research program in the early 1970s made extensive use of computers to analyze and model fire department operations. Computer programs were written to allocate fire companies, locate fire stations, and simulate calls and response. This work is well documented in the book *Fire Department Deployment Analysis.*[4] The programs developed by Rand and other similar software are now available for microcomputers.[5,6].

There are more than twenty commercial companies that produce and distribute computer software for fire service applications. Many of these are turnkey packages that require little or no training to operate. However, many fire departments choose to write their own custom software using modern programming languages or commercial spreadsheet or data base management packages.

Research

Computers have long played an essential part in fire research, both mainframes and minicomputers. Now, significant computing power is more readily available to researchers, and the computational capability to conduct research is extended to any microcomputer user. For example, a microcomputer's capacity to produce sophisticated statistical analysis increases the importance of the collection of meaningful data in areas such as human behavior in fires.

Fire models: Perhaps the most significant area of fire research applications of microcomputers is in fire modeling. Although researchers have long understood many aspects of fire phenomena, attempts at predictive theories were defeated by the complexity of the subject. With the advent of more powerful and more accessible computers, there has been a rapid growth in computer fire modeling technology. Current research is concentrated on fires in compartments and the impact of fire response properties of materials. Through this research, computer fire modeling is evolving as a less expensive and more convenient alternative to experimentation, and many new programs are being developed. However, the results from these models must be validated if they are to be used with any confidence.

Supercomputers: Most models of fire in a compartment in use today are zone models that employ simplifying assumptions of fire dynamics to make the models computationally tractable. Field models avoid these simplifications. In principle, field models can predict unexpected three-dimensional flows, including recirculations, and they also can reveal unexpected physical instabilities in fire growth and development. A relatively new computer architecture is the so-called massively parallel system that can have hundreds or thousands of microprocessors, each performing a single step in a vector operation. Massively parallel systems will be most useful for applications that require repeated calculations over finite matrices of data elements, a characteristic of fluid mechanic field modeling of fire behavior. Fire models are discussed at greater length in other chapters of this section.

Massive data parallelism is also amenable to new developments in specialized structures such as visualization. Scientific visualization is a method for seeing what is not normally visible: heat conduction, fluid flow, molecular motion, etc. Computer graphics, image synthesis, and animation can be used to visualize fire phenomena such as smoke, heat, and toxic gases.

Information technology: Another way that computers are enhancing fire research is through developments in information technology. The Fire Research Information Service (FRIS) at the National Institute of Standards and Technology (NIST) Building and Fire Research Laboratory (BFRL) has a library collection of over 25,000 fire research items consisting of published reports, articles, books, conference proceedings, and audiovisuals.[7] In 1983 FRIS began the development of an on-line computer system to access the literature collection. FIREDOC is the name given to this on-line bibliographic database. It is a computer system that acts as an automated card catalog of the FRIS collection. Each item in the FIREDOC database consists of title, author, accession number, keywords, abstract (if available), and other identifiers. The principal users of the system are the staff of the BFRL, but it is also accessible to other members of the fire community.

Management

Management uses of microcomputers in fire protection are, to a large extent, adaptations of business software. Specific microcomputer application areas with a significant present or future impact on fire protection management include automation, information technology, and expert systems.

Automation: Many facets of fire protection involve recordkeeping and repetitive functions. These are typically the types of activities that are amenable to automation. A particularly apt example is code administration.[8] Commercially available software will record permit applications, check for currency of contractors' licenses, track plan review, issue permits and certificates of occupancy, and allow on-line status inquiry by contractors. Comparable systems are used for insurance inspection and fire protection systems maintenance in industrial complexes.

Information technology: Communication has always been an essential component of management. Microcomputer technology is being used in several ways to enhance communication of ideas among fire protection managers.

FIREfacts is NFPA's on-line electronic gateway to comprehensive sources of fire and public safety information. Subscribers use a microcomputer and modem to send and receive fire-related information anywhere in the world. FIREfacts provides an instantaneous way to ask questions, propose solutions, and communicate viewpoints. It is a cost-effective way to disseminate information, software, and late-breaking news to an increasingly global fire and public safety community. Other FIREfacts components include electronic mail, bulletin boards, and teleconferencing.

ICHIEFS is a private electronic mail communication system dedicated to fire service professionals. ICHIEFS provides access to national and state agencies involved in fire service operations. Fire marshals, chiefs' associations, training academies, fire departments, and individuals can be contacted for information on legislative activities, publications, workshops and conferences, computer applications, and other fire service news.

Another way that computerized information technology is being applied to fire protection is the expanded use of electronic media. Many building and fire codes and standards are now available on-line, on floppy disks, and on CD-ROM. Some systems also include sophisticated search capabilities and cross-referencing. Electronic media reduces the physical storage space occupied by paper volumes and greatly reduces the time required to access information in codes. Specification standards can be readily transferred to word processing programs for inclusion in working documents.

Expert systems: It is hard to imagine a field with a larger, more well-defined body of knowledge than fire protection. Building codes, over two hundred and seventy-five NFPA standards, and many other U.S. and international standards represent an existing knowledge base that is designed to cover every acceptable solution to fire protection problems. The application of this knowledge and the interpretation of its intent is the presently ill-defined activity of the fire protection expert. Using a microcomputer to assist in this practice can reduce much of the routine effort expended in the application of fire codes and standards.

The desirability of expert systems in fire protection stems from two outstanding potential features: (1) they provide an excellent means of transferring research results to the end user, and (2) they provide a superior means of moving toward a more rational knowledge-based code. Some initial approaches to fire protection expert systems have been made. [9, 10, 11] Undoubtedly, the fire protection industry will soon be exploiting the benefits of expert systems more fully.

Engineering

The microcomputer is having a significant impact on how fire protection engineers do things. It has not just replaced the slide rule and hand-held calculator; it has led to new approaches to problem-solving and design.

Automatic sprinklers: One of the most developed areas of microcomputer applications in fire protection is the design and evaluation of automatic sprinkler systems.[12] More than two dozen commercial programs are available and there are an even larger number of privately developed and used programs. These packages come in many forms and capabilities for various hardware configurations; some even come bundled with their own hardware system. There are minimal programs written in relatively slow-running interpretive BASIC, and more complex programs written in standard FORTRAN and newer microcomputer languages. Certain programs will interface with plotters to produce working drawings of sprinkler installations. Some are used merely to check plans, while others have the capacity to optimize pipe sizes to design a minimum-cost system.

There has been a steady succession of improvements in these programs with the addition of looped and gridded system capabilities and CADD systems using state-of-the-art interactive computer graphics. Hydraulic analysis programs are commonplace in engineering offices, and today most hydraulic calculations used in the design of water supply and automatic sprinkler systems are performed on a computer.[13,14]

Computerized design of other types of extinguishing systems is not as widely available for microcomputers. Halon systems, for example, rely on fluid dynamics that vary with each manufacturer's equipment, and design programs are generally proprietary.

Smoke control: Practical implementation of the concept of using mechanical fans to limit smoke movement in fire situations is relatively recent. Hand-calculated analysis of sophisticated smoke-control systems is intractable and, accordingly, computer programs have been written for this purpose. As with many aspects of fire protection engineering, smoke control technology is developing along with computer technology. [15, 16]

Passive protection: In the area of static or passive protection, there are computer programs for the design and evaluation of fire endurance of protected and unprotected steel and reinforced concrete structural assemblies. Like the special-hazard extinguishing systems, they are not widely available for microcomputers.

Emergency evacuation: Microcomputers are just beginning to be used to address issues of emergency evacuation of buildings. While computer simulation is employed extensively to model many aspects of people movement in other disciplines, its use in fire protection has been limited.[17,18]

Hazard and risk analysis: Perhaps the most exciting and potentially effective engineering application of microcomputers is in hazard and risk analysis. Many new aspects of fire protection are being quantified, both objectively and subjectively. Computers offer the capability to handle many of the complex issues of integrating opinion, surveys, statistics, and physics to facilitate fire hazard and risk analysis.[19, 20]

BIBLIOGRAPHY

References Cited

1. Hampton, J. A., "Exploring Tomorrow's Communications Today," *Fire Command*, Oct. 1990, pp. 13-15, 27.
2. Goliash, B. I., "Ye Cads," *Fire Command*, Oct. 1989, pp. 16-21.
3. Miller, D. M., "Computerized Planning System for Bureau Inspectors," *Fire Technology*, Vol. 12, No. 3, (Aug. 1976), pp. 237-246.
4. Walker, W. E., Chaiken, J. M., and Ignall, E. J., *eds.*, Fire Department Deployment Analysis, North Holland, NY, 1979.
5. Reilly, J. and Mirchandani, P. B., "Development and Application of a Fire Station Placement Model," *Fire Technology*, Vol. 21, No. 3, 1985.
6. Pietrzak, L. and Johnson, G., "Directions for Improving Manual Fire Suppression Using a Physically Based Computer Simulation," *Fire Technology*, Vol. 22, No. 3, 1986.
7. Jason, N. H., "FIREDOC Users Manual," 2nd ed., *NISTIR 4526*, National Institute of Standards and Technology, Gaithersburg, MD, March 1991.
8. *Computers in Code Administration*, Building Officials and Code Administrators International, Country Club Hills, IL, 1987.
9. Smith, R. L., "ASKBUDJr: A Precursor of an Expert System for the Evaluation of Fire Hazard," *Fire Technology*, Vol. 25, No. 4, 1987, pp. 5-18.
10. Parsley, R. M., "Computers Cum Laude," *Fire Command*, Oct. 1989, pp. 34-35.
11. Smith, R. L., "EXPOSURE: An Expert System Fire Code," *Fire Technology*, Vol. 27, No. 2 (May 1991), pp. 145-159.
12. Cote, A. E., "The Computer and Fire Protection Engineering—25 Years of Progress," *Fire Technology*, Vol. 26, No. 3 (Aug. 1990), pp. 194-201.
13. Maisch, F. M., Schoenborn, R. M., and Pantumsinchal, P., "Software to Match Distribution System's Needs," *Water Engineering and Management*, Oct. 1987, pp. 20-22.
14. Melly, B. W., "Comparison of Several Computer Hydraulics Programs for the IBM PC and Compatibles," *Fire Technology*, Vol. 25, No. 4 (Feb. 1989), pp. 336-366.
15. Bengston, S. and Hagglund, B. H., "A Smoke-filling Simulation Model and Its Engineering Applications," *Fire Technology*, Vol. 22, No. 2, 1986.
16. Klote, J., "A Computer Model of Smoke Movement by Air Conditioning Systems (SMACS)," *Fire Technology*, Vol. 24, No. 4, 1988.
17. Watts, J. M., Jr., "Computer Models for Evacuation Analysis," *Fire Safety Journal*, Vol. 12, 1987, pp. 237-245.
18. Weinroth, J., "An Adaptable Microcomputer Model for Evacuation Management," *Fire Technology*, Vol. 25, No. 4, 1989, pp. 291-307.
19. Peacock, R. D. and Bukowski, R. W., "A Prototype Methodology for Fire Hazard Analysis," *Fire Technology*, Vol. 26, No. 3, 1990, pp. 15-40.
20. Hall, J. R., Jr. and Sekizawa, A., "Fire Risk Analysis: General Conceptual Framework for Describing Models," *Fire Technology*, Vol. 27, No. 1, 1991, pp. 33-53.

Additional Readings

Bauer, C. J., "Computers Revolutionize Fire Science," *Construction Specifier*, Vol. 41, No. 4, 1988, pp. 48-61.

Levy, S., *Hackers: Heroes of the Computer Revolution*, Anchor Press/Doubleday, Garden City, NY, 1984.

McWilliams, P., *The Personal Computer Book*, Prelude Press, Los Angeles, CA, 1990.

Microcomputer Applications in Occupational Health and Safety, Lewis, Cincinnati, OH, 1987.

On-Line Resources, P.O. Box 140, Emmitsburg, MD 27727. (Monthly newsletter on EMS and fire-service applications of computers.)

Osborne, A., "An Introduction to Microcomputers," in *The Beginner's Book*, Adam Osborne and Associates, Berkeley, CA, 1977.

GLOSSARY

ALPHA NUMERIC—Any letter of the alphabet, numeral, punctuation mark, or other symbolic character.

ANALOG SIGNAL—Electrical signal in the form of a continuously varying physical quantity such as voltage or frequency.

ARTIFICIAL INTELLIGENCE (AI)—A developing field in which computers can be used to solve problems that appear to require imagination, intuition, or intelligence.

ASCII—American Standard Code for Information Interchange. Most common convention for representing alphanumeric data for transmission or storage.

ASSEMBLY LANGUAGE—Machine-specific programming language that uses symbols for fundamental computer instructions.

BACK-UP—Duplicate files on a separate piece of storage media.

BASIC—Beginners' All-purpose Symbolic Instruction Code. Programming language developed at Dartmouth College. Widely available on microcomputers.

BAUD—Unit of speed of data transmission, about equal to bits per second.

BINARY—Number system using only two symbols, one and zero. Inside a computer, the one is represented by an electric charge being on, and the zero by the absence of such a charge (off).

BIT—Short for Binary digIT. Smallest unit of information in a computer. Has a value of one or zero.

BOOT—To start up a microcomputer or a program.

BUFFER—Temporary storage area used during data transmission.

BUG—Any error or malfunction in a program or equipment that causes an undesired outcome.

BULLETIN BOARD—Computer that can be used to send and receive information.

BUS—Group of conductors interconnecting individual circuitry in a computer.

BYTE—A group of 8 bits. Each byte can represent any of 256 different alphanumeric characters. Unit of memory capacity.

CAD—Computer-Aided Dispatch.

CADD—Computer-Aided Drafting and Design.

CAI—Computer-Assisted Instruction.

CARD—Removable internal circuit board in a computer containing electronics to perform a specific function.

CBT—Computer-Based Training.

CD-ROM—Compact Disk-Read-Only Memory.

CELL—Location on a spreadsheet, usually identified by a column letter and a row number.

CHARACTER—One of a set of symbols that may be arranged in ordered groups to express information.

CHIP—Integrated circuit.

CLOCK—Shorthand term for the source of timing signals sequencing electronic events.

COBOL—Common-Business-Oriented Language. High-level computer programming language widely used for business applications.

CODE—Symbols that represent instructions to a computer. A program.

CO-PROCESSOR—Additional microprocessor that handles specific tasks in conjunction with the CPU.

CPS—Characters Per Second. Measure of printing speed.

CPU—Central Processing Unit. The heart of the computer that contains the control, memory, and arithmetic units. A microprocessor.

CRASH—Abnormal termination of a program or loss of data from storage media.

CRT—Cathode Ray Tube. TV-like screen or monitor providing visual display of computer output.

CURSOR—Flashing mark on CRT indicating the position on the screen where the next entry or deletion will be made.

DATA—Basic information elements stored in file, processed, or produced by a computer.

DATA BASE—File of records, each containing comparable information on different items.

DATA BUS—See BUS

DEBUG—To find and remove errors or malfunctions from a program or device.

DEFAULT—Values set by the program when they are not specified by the user.

DENSITY—Compactness of information stored on magnetic media.

DIGITAL SIGNAL—Electrical signal that is either zero (off) or one (on).

DISK—Circular magnetic storage device.

DISKETTE—see FLOPPY DISK.

DOCUMENTATION—Printed matter concerning computer hardware or software, including instruction or operator's manuals and technical specifications.

DOS—Disk Operation System. Widely used microcomputer operating system.

DOT MATRIX—Printer that forms symbols as a pattern of closely positioned dots.

DOWNLOAD—Transferring a file to a computer system from a remote computer via telecommunications.

DRIVE (or DISK DRIVE)—Component to read and write data on disks.

ELECTRONIC MAIL—Transmission of messages between computer users.

EXPERT SYSTEM—An extremely specialized data base and computational computer program that performs like an expert on a particular subject.

FILE—Named collection of data or instructions.

FLOPPY DISK—Flexible plastic disk. Most common form of external storage on microcomputers. Commercial software is typically provided on one or more "floppies."

FONT—A complete assortment of type characters of a given size and style.

FORTRAN—Formula Translator. A high-level computer language originally designed for scientific and mathematical use.

GIS—Geographic Information System. Specialized hardware and software for the manipulation and analysis of maps and geographic data by computers.

GUI—Graphical user interface.

HARD COPY—Computer output printed on paper.

HARD DISK—Inflexible disk storage component with much greater capacity than a floppy disk.

HARDWARE—Physical equipment forming a microcomputer system.

HARD-WIRED—Direct connection of components by wires or cables.

HIGH-LEVEL LANGUAGE—Problem-oriented, human-readable programming language, generally usable on many different types of computers.

HYPERTEXT—Software that allows the user to link information in a nonsequential fashion.

ICON—Graphical representation of an object, data file, or program.

I/O—Input/Output. Communication of information to and from a computer or peripheral device.

IMAGE—A reproduction of an object formed by an optical or electronic device.

INSTRUCTION—Programmed action to be performed by a computer.

INTEGRATED CIRCUIT (or IC)—Small "chip" of silicon on which miniaturized electronic components have been etched.

INTEGRATED SOFTWARE—Programs for different applications that have common features and can exchange data with one another.

INTERFACE—Hardware or software required to connect peripherals to a computer.

KEYBOARD—Typewriter-like component used to enter information into a microcomputer.

KNOWLEDGE BASE—Essential part of an expert system that includes a set of facts applicable to the subject of concern and rules that specify relationships among the facts.

K (or KB)—Kilobyte. 1024 (2 to the 10th power) bytes.

LAN—Local Area Network. Interconnection of geographically close microcomputers.

LANGUAGE—System for writing computer programs that has a highly specific, inflexible vocabulary of commands and syntax.

LASER PRINTER—A nonimpact printer that uses a laser beam to form dot-matrix characters on a photoconductor that are then transferred to paper.

LISTING—Printed copy of a program.

LOAD—Transferring a file into the computer's memory.

MACHINE LANGUAGE—Directly executable binary codes.

MACRO—Sequence of commands executed with a small number of keystrokes.

MAINFRAME—Large-scale, fast-operating computer.

MB (or Mbyte)—Megabyte. 1,048,576 (2 to the 20th power) bytes.

MEMORY—Electronic storage area for data and programs.

MENU—List of programs or options available for selection by a microcomputer user.

MICROCOMPUTER—Smallest-size full-function computer.

MICROPROCESSOR—A CPU on a single chip.

MINICOMPUTER—Midsize computer.

MIPS—Million Instructions Per Second.

MODEL—Representation of an object or system.

MODEM—Modulator-Demodulator. Device to transform signals for transmission of data via telephone lines.

MONITOR—CRT and its housing when not an integral part of the microcomputer.

MOUSE—One type of microcomputer input device.

MULTIMEDIA—Software that incorporates graphics, video, text, and sound into an interactive computer presentation.

MULTITASKING—An operating system feature that allows a CPU to perform several tasks at the same time.

NANOSECOND—One-billionth of a second.

NETWORK—A data communications system wherein multiple computers and peripherals are linked by communication lines and software.

ON-LINE—Connected to a computer system.

OPERATING SYSTEM (also OS)—Program that manages a microcomputer and its peripherals, and controls the operation of a program.

PC—Personal Computer. Microcomputer.

PERIPHERAL—Device connected to a microcomputer.

PIXEL—Picture Element. One of the dots that form the picture on a monitor screen.

PLOTTER—Mechanical device for drawing lines under computer control.

POINT AND SHOOT—Choosing from a list by highlighting as opposed to typing character-based commands.

PORT—A communications connection on a computer.

PROGRAM—Series of instructions to the computer in the form of a step-by-step procedure.

PROTOCOL—Set of parameters defining compatibility for telecommunications.

RAM—Random-Access Memory. Microcomputer internal memory available to the user for storage of data or instructions.

READ—Accept data for processing or transfer.

RECORD—Block of related data stored by data base management programs.

RESOLUTION—Quality of image on a CRT.

ROM—Read-Only Memory. Permanent information stored in the microcomputer.

SCROLL—Move the contents of a screen display up or down.

SOFTWARE—Operating systems and other programs used by computers.

STRING—Group of alphanumeric characters.

TELECOMMUNICATIONS—Use of telephone communications facilities to transmit data and other information between computers.

TERMINAL—Device with a keyboard or other data entry mechanism and a video display or printer to exchange information with a computer system.

TURNKEY—A complete computer system including all the hardware and software required for a specific application.

UPLOAD—Transferring a file from a computer system to some remote computer via telecommunications.

USER-FRIENDLY—A computer system or component that is easy and non-threatening to use and understand.

UTILITY—Program used to assist in operation of a computer.

VALIDATION—Procedure for measuring or evaluating a system to ensure and confirm compliance with the desired requirements.

VOLATILE—Characteristic of memory that loses its contents when the power supply is removed or disrupted.

VSLI—Very-Large-Scale Integration. Technology for putting many electronic circuits (i.e., thousands of them) on a single chip.

WINDOW—Rectangular portion of monitor screen in which an application or document is displayed.

WRITE—Transfer a file from internal to external memory.

WYSIWYG—What You See Is What You Get. Printed output will be the same as what appears on the monitor screen.

APPENDICES

Appendix A

TABLES AND CHARTS

Revised by Dr. Vytenis Babrauskas

TABLE A-1. ***Heats of Combustion and Related Properties For Pure, Simple Substances****

Material	Composition	W Molecular Weight	Δh_c^u Gross (MJ/kg)	Δh_c^l Net (MJ/kg)	$\Delta h_c^l/r_o$ (MJ/kg O_2)	r_o Oxygen-fuel Mass ratio	T_b Boiling temp. (°C)	Δh_v Latent Heat of Vaporization (kJ/kg)	C_{pl} Liquid Heat Capacity (kJ/kg-°C)	C_{pv} Vapor Heat Capacity (kJ/kg-°C)
acetaldehyde	C_2H_4O	44.05	27.07	25.07	13.81	1.816	20.8	—	1.94	1.24
acetic acid	$C_2H_4O_2$	60.05	14.56	13.09	12.28	1.066	118.1	395		1.11
acetone	C_3H_6O	58.08	30.83	28.56	12.96	2.204	56.5	501	2.12	1.29
acetylene	C_2H_2	26.04	49.91	48.22	15.70	3.072	−84.0	—	—	1.69
acrolein	C_3H_4O	56.06	29.08	27.51	13.77	1.998	52.5	505	—	1.17
acrylonitrile	C_3H_3N	53.06	33.16	31.92	14.11	2.262	77.3	615	2.10	1.20
(allene) → propadiene										
ammonium perchlorate†	NH_4ClO_4	117.49	2.35	2.16	3.97	0.545	—	—	—	
iso-amyl alcohol	$C_5H_{12}O$	88.15	37.48	34.49	12.67	2.723	132.0	501	2.90	1.50
aniline	C_6H_7N	93.12	36.44	34.79	13.06	2.663	184.4	478	2.08	1.16
benzaldehyde	C_7H_6O	106.12	33.25	32.01	13.27	2.412	179.2	385	1.61	
benzene	C_6H_6	78.11	41.83	40.14	13.06	3.073	80.1	389	1.72	1.05
benzoic acid†	$C_7H_6O_2$	122.12	26.43	25.35	12.90	1.965	250.8	415	—	0.85
benzyl alcohol	C_7H_8O	108.13	34.56	32.93	13.09	2.515	205.7	467	2.00	1.19
bicyclohexyl	$C_{12}H_{22}$	166.30	45.35	42.44	12.61	3.367	236.	263		
1,2-butadiene	C_4H_6	54.09	47.95	45.51	13.99	3.254	10.8	—	—	1.48
1,3-butadiene	C_4H_6	54.09	46.99	44.55	13.69	3.254	−4.4	—	—	1.47
(1,3-butadiyne) → diacetylene										
n-butane	C_4H_{10}	58.12	49.50	45.72	12.77	3.579	−0.5	—	2.30	1.68
iso-butane	C_4H_{10}	58.12	48.95	45.17	12.62	3.579	−11.8	—	—	1.67
1-butene	C_4H_8	56.10	48.44	45.31	13.24	3.422	−6.2	—	—	1.53
n-butylamine	$C_4H_{11}N$	73.14	41.75	38.45	12.84	2.994	77.8	372	2.57	1.62
d-camphor†	$C_{10}H_{16}O$	152.23	38.75	36.44	12.84	2.838	203.4	—	—	0.82
carbon†	C	12.01	32.80	32.80	12.31	2.664	4200.	—	—	0.71
carbon disulfide	CS_2	76.13	6.34	6.34	5.03	1.261	46.5	351	1.00	0.60
carbon monoxide	CO	28.01	10.10	10.10	17.69	0.571	−191.3	—	—	1.04
cellulose†	$C_6H_{10}O_5$	162.14	17.47	16.12	13.61	1.184	—	—	1.16	—
(chloroethylene) → vinyl chloride										
(chloroform) → trichloromethane										
chlorotrifluoroethylene	C_2F_3Cl	116.47	2.00	2.00	3.64	0.549	−28.3	188	1.34	0.72
m-cresol	C_7H_8O	108.13	34.26	32.64	12.98	2.515	202.2	399	2.00	1.13
cumene	C_9H_{12}	120.19	43.40	41.20	12.90	3.195	152.3	312	1.77	1.26
cyanogen	C_2N_2	52.04	21.06	21.06	17.12	1.230	−21.2	—	—	1.12
cyclobutane	C_4H_8	56.10	48.91	45.77	13.38	3.422	12.9	—	—	1.29
cyclohexane	C_6H_{12}	84.16	46.58	43.45	12.70	3.422	80.7	357	1.84	1.26
cyclohexene	C_6H_{10}	82.14	45.67	42.99	12.99	3.311	82.8	371	1.80	1.28
cyclohexylamine	$C_6H_{13}N$	99.18	41.05	38.17	12.79	2.984	134.5			
cyclopentane	C_5H_{10}	70.13	46.93	43.80	12.80	3.422	49.3	389	2.23	1.18

Dr. Babrauskas is Head, Fire Toxicity Measurement, U.S. National Institute of Standards and Technology, Center for Fire Research, Gaithersburg, MD.

TABLE A-1. ***Heats of Combustion and Related Properties For Pure, Simple Substances* (continued)***

Material	Composition	W Molecular Weight	Δh_c^u Gross (MJ/kg)	Δh_c^l Net (MJ/kg)	$\Delta h_c^l/r_o$ (MJ/kg O_2)	r_o Oxygen-fuel Mass ratio	T_b Boiling temp. (°C)	Δh_v Latent Heat of Vaporization (kJ/kg)	C_{pl} Liquid Heat Capacity (kJ/kg-°C)	C_{pv} Vapor Heat Capacity (kJ/kg-°C)
cyclopropane	C_3H_6	42.08	49.70	46.57	13.61	3.422	−32.9	—	1.92	1.33
(decahydronaphthalene) → *cis*-decalin										
cis-decalin	$C_{10}H_{18}$	138.24	45.49	42.63	12.70	3.356	195.8	309	1.67	1.21
n-decane	$C_{10}H_{22}$	142.28	47.64	44.24	12.69	3.486	174.1	276	2.19	1.65
diacetylene	C_4H_2	50.06	46.60	45.72	15.89	2.877	10.3	—	—	1.47
(diamine) → hydrazine										
diborane	H_6B_2	27.69	79.80	79.80	23.02	3.467	−92.5	—	—	1.75
dichloromethane	CH_2Cl_2	84.94	6.54	6.02	10.65	0.565	39.7	330	1.18	0.60
diethyl cyclohexane	$C_{10}H_{20}$	140.26	46.30	43.17	12.58	3.422	174.		1.87	
diethyl ether	$C_4H_{10}O$	74.12	36.75	33.79	13.04	2.590	34.6	360	2.34	1.52
(2,4 diisocyanotoluene) → toluene diisocyanate										
(diisopropyl ether) → *iso*-propyl ether										
dimethylamine	C_2H_7N	45.08	38.66	35.25	13.24	2.662	6.9	—	—	1.60
(dimethyl aniline) → xylidene										
dimethyldecalin	$C_{12}H_{22}$	166.30	45.70	42.79	13.15	3.254	220.	260		
(dimethyl ether) → methyl ether										
1,1-dimethylhydrazine (UDMH)	$C_2H_8N_2$	60.10	32.95	30.03	14.10	2.130	25.	578	2.73	
dimethyl sulfoxide	C_2H_6SO	78.13	29.88	28.19	15.30	1.843	189.	677	1.89	1.14
1,3 dioxane	$C_4H_8O_2$	88.10	26.57	24.58	9.66	2.543	105.	404		
1,4 dioxane	$C_4H_8O_2$	88.10	26.83	24.84	9.77	2.543	101.1	406	1.74	1.07
ethane	C_2H_6	30.07	51.87	47.49	12.75	3.725	−88.6	—	—	1.75
ethanol	C_2H_6O	46.07	29.67	26.81	12.87	2.084	78.5	837	2.43	1.42
(ethene) → ethylene										
ethyl acetate	$C_4H_8O_2$	88.10	25.41	23.41	12.89	1.816	77.2	367	1.94	1.29
ethyl acrylate	$C_5H_8O_2$	100.12	27.44	25.69	13.39	1.918	100.	290		1.14
ethylamine	C_2H_7N	45.08	38.63	35.22	13.23	2.662	16.5	—	2.89	1.61
ethyl benzene	C_8H_{10}	106.16	43.00	40.93	12.93	3.165	136.1	339	1.75	1.21
ethylene	C_2H_4	28.05	50.30	47.17	13.78	3.422	−103.9	—	2.38	1.56
ethylene glycol	$C_2H_6O_2$	62.07	19.17	17.05	13.22	1.289	197.5	800	2.43	1.56
ethylene oxide	C_2H_4O	44.05	29.65	27.65	15.23	1.816	10.7	—	1.97	1.10
(ethylene trichloride) → trichloroethylene										
(ethyl ether) → diethyl ether										
formaldehyde	CH_2O	30.03	18.76	17.30	16.23	1.066	−19.3	—	—	1.18
formic acid	CH_2O_2	46.03	5.53	4.58	13.15	0.348	100.5	476	2.15	0.98
furan	C_4H_4O	68.07	30.61	29.32	13.86	2.115	31.4	398	1.69	0.96
α-D-glucose†	$C_6H_{12}O_6$	180.16	15.55	14.08	13.21	1.066	—	—	—	—
(glycerine) → glycerol										
glycerol	$C_3H_8O_3$	92.10	17.95	16.04	13.19	1.216	290.0	800	2.42	1.25
(glycerol trinitrate) → nitroglycerin										
n-heptane	C_7H_{16}	100.20	48.07	44.56	12.68	3.513	98.4	316	2.20	1.66
n-heptene	C_7H_{14}	98.18	47.44	44.31	12.95	3.422	93.6	317	2.17	1.58
hexadecane	$C_{16}H_{34}$	226.43	47.25	43.95	12.70	3.462	286.7	226	2.22	1.64
hexamethyldisiloxane	$C_6H_{18}Si_2O$	162.38	38.30	35.80	15.16	2.364	100.1	192	2.01	—
(hexamethylenetetramine) → methenamine										
n-hexane	C_6H_{14}	86.17	48.31	44.74	12.68	3.528	68.7	335	2.24	1.66
n-hexene	C_6H_{12}	84.16	47.57	44.44	12.99	3.422	63.5	333	2.18	1.57
hydrazine	H_4N_2	32.05	52.08	49.34	49.40	0.998	113.5	1180	3.08	1.65
hydrazoic acid	HN_3	43.02	15.28	14.77	79.40	0.186	35.7	690	—	1.02
hydrogen	H_2	2.00	141.79	130.80	16.35	8.000	−252.7	—	—	14.42
(hydrogen azide) → hydrazoic acid										
hydrogen cyanide	HCN	27.03	13.86	13.05	8.82	1.480	25.7	933	2.61	1.33
hydrogen sulfide	H_2S	34.08	48.54	47.25	16.77	2.817	−60.3	548	—	1.00
maleic anhydride†	$C_4H_2O_3$	74.04	18.77	18.17	14.01	1.297	202.0	—	—	—
melamine†	$C_3H_6N_6$	126.13	15.58	14.54	12.73	1.142	—	—	—	—
methane	CH_4	16.04	55.50	50.03	12.51	4.000	−161.5	—	—	2.23
methanol	CH_4O	32.04	22.68	19.94	13.29	1.500	64.8	1101	2.37	1.37
methenamine†	$C_6H_{12}N_4$	140.19	29.97	28.08	13.67	2.054	—	—	—	—
2-methoxyethanol	$C_3H_8O_2$	76.09	24.23	21.92	13.03	1.682	124.4	583	2.23	—
methylamine	CH_5N	31.06	34.16	30.62	13.21	2.318	−6.3	—	—	1.61
(2-methyl 1-butanol) → *iso*-amyl alcohol										
(methyl chloride) → dichloromethane										
methyl ether	C_2H_6O	46.07	31.70	28.84	13.84	2.084	−24.9	—	—	1.43
methyl ethyl ketone	C_4H_8O	72.10	33.90	31.46	12.89	2.441	79.6	434	2.30	1.43
1-methylnaphthalene	$C_{11}H_{10}$	142.19	40.88	39.33	12.95	3.038	244.7	323	1.58	1.12

TABLE A-1. ***Heats of Combustion and Related Properties For Pure, Simple Substances* (continued)***

Material	Composition	W Molecular Weight	Δh_c^u Gross (MJ/kg)	Δh_c^l Net (MJ/kg)	$\Delta h_c^l/r_o$ (MJ/kg O_2)	r_o Oxygen-fuel Mass ratio	T_b Boiling temp. (°C)	Δh_v Latent Heat of Vaporization (kJ/kg)	C_{pl} Liquid Heat Capacity (kJ/kg-°C)	C_{pv} Vapor Heat Capacity (kJ/kg-°C)
methyl methacrylate	$C_5H_8O_2$	100.11	27.37	25.61	12.33	2.078	101.0	360	1.91	—
methyl nitrate	CH_3NO_3	77.04	8.67	7.81	75.10	0.104	64.6	409	2.04	0.99
(2-methyl propane) → *iso*-butane										
naphthalene†	$C_{10}H_8$	128.16	40.21	38.84	12.96	2.996	217.9	—	1.18	1.03
nitrobenzene	$C_6H_5NO_2$	123.11	25.11	24.22	14.90	1.625	210.7	330	1.52	—
nitroglycerin	$C_3H_5N_3O_9$	227.09	6.82	6.34	—	—	unstable	462	1.49	—
nitromethane	CH_3NO_2	61.04	11.62	10.54	15.08	0.699	101.1	567	1.74	0.94
n-nonane	C_9H_{20}	128.25	47.76	44.33	12.69	3.493	150.6	295	2.10	1.65
octamethyl-cyclotetrasiloxane	$C_8H_{24}Si_4O_4$	296.62	26.90	25.10	14.56	1.725	175.0	127	1.88	—
n-octane	C_8H_{18}	114.22	47.90	44.44	12.69	3.502	125.6	301	2.20	1.65
iso-octane	C_8H_{18}	114.22	47.77	44.31	12.65	3.502	117.7	272	2.15	1.65
1-octene	C_8H_{10}	112.21	47.33	44.20	12.92	3.422	121.3	301	2.19	1.59
(1-octylene) → 1-octene										
1,2-pentadiene	C_5H_8	68.11	47.31	44.71	13.60	3.288	44.9	405	2.21	1.55
n-pentane	C_5H_{12}	72.15	48.64	44.98	12.68	3.548	36.0	357	2.33	1.67
1-pentene	C_5H_{10}	70.13	47.77	44.64	13.04	3.422	30.0	359	2.16	1.56
phenol†	C_6H_6O	94.11	32.45	31.05	13.05	2.380	181.8	433	1.43	1.10
phosgene	$COCl_2$	98.92	1.74	1.74	10.74	0.162	8.3	247	1.02	0.58
propadiene	C_3H_4	40.06	48.54	46.35	14.51	3.195	−34.6	—	—	1.44
propane	C_3H_8	44.09	50.35	46.36	12.78	3.629	−42.2	—	2.23	1.67
n-propanol	C_3H_8O	60.09	33.61	30.68	12.81	2.396	97.2	686	2.50	1.45
iso-propanol	C_3H_8O	60.09	33.38	30.45	12.71	2.396	80.3	663	2.42	1.48
propene	C_3H_6	42.08	48.92	45.79	13.38	3.422	−47.7	—	—	1.52
(*iso*-propylbenzene) → cumene										
(propylene) → propene										
iso-propyl ether	$C_6H_{14}O$	102.17	39.26	36.25	12.86	2.819	67.8	286	2.14	1.55
propyne	C_3H_4	40.06	48.36	46.17	14.45	3.195	−23.3	—	—	1.51
styrene	C_8H_8	104.14	42.21	40.52	13.19	3.073	145.2	356	1.76	1.17
sucrose†	$C_{12}H_{22}O_{11}$	342.30	16.49	15.08	13.44	1.122	—	—	1.24	—
(1,2,3,4-tetrahydronaphthalene) → tetralin										
tetralin	$C_{10}H_{12}$	132.20	42.60	40.60	12.90	3.147	207.0	425	1.64	1.19
tetranitromethane	CN_4O_8	196.04	2.20	2.20	—	—	125.7	196—	—	
toluene	C_7H_8	92.13	42.43	40.52	12.97	3.126	110.4	360	1.67	1.12
toluene diisocyanate	$C_9H_6N_2O_2$	174.16	24.32	23.56	13.50	1.746	120.0	—	1.65	—
triethanolamine	$C_6H_{15}NO_3$	149.19	29.29	27.08	15.30	1.770	360.0	—	—	—
triethylamine	$C_6H_{15}N$	101.19	43.19	39.93	12.95	3.083	89.5	303	2.22	1.59
1,1,2-trichloroethane	$C_2H_3Cl_3$	133.42	7.77	7.28	11.02	0.660	114.0	260	1.11	0.67
trichloroethylene	C_2HCl_3	131.40	6.77	6.60	12.05	0.548	86.9	245	1.07	0.61
trichloromethane	$CHCl_3$	119.39	3.39	3.21	9.60	0.335	61.7	249	0.97	0.55
trinitromethane	CHN_3O_6	151.04	3.41	3.25	—	—	unstable	—	—	—
trinitrotoluene†	$C_7H_5N_3O_6$	227.13	15.12	14.64	19.80	0.740	240.0	322	1.40	—
trioxane	$C_3H_6O_3$	90.08	16.57	15.11	14.17	1.066	114.5	450	—	—
urea†	CH_4ON_2	60.06	10.52	9.06	11.34	0.799	—	—	—	1.55
vinyl acetate	$C_4H_6O_2$	86.09	24.18	22.65	13.54	1.673	72.5	167	2.00	1.05
vinyl acetylene	C_4H_4	52.07	47.05	45.36	14.76	3.073	5.1	—	—	1.41
vinyl bromide	C_2H_3Br	106.96	12.10	11.48	13.95	0.823	15.6	—	2.42	0.53
vinyl chloride	C_2H_3Cl	62.50	20.02	16.86	11.97	1.408	−13.8	—	—	0.86
(vinyl trichloride) → 1,1,2-trichlorolthane										
xylenes	C_8H_{10}	106.16	42.89	40.82	12.90	3.165	138–144	343	1.72	1.21
xylidene	$C_8H_{11}N$	121.22	38.28	36.29	12.79	2.838	192.7	366	1.77	—

† Denotes substance in crystalline solid form; otherwise, liquid if $T_b > 25°C$, gaseous if $T_b < 25°C$.
* Sources: 1, 2, 3, 4, 5, 6, 7, 8, 9, 10, 11, 12, 13, 14, 15.

TABLE A-2. ***Heats of Combustion and Related Properties for Plastics****

Material	Unit Composition	W Molecular Weight	Δ_c^u Gross (MJ/kg)	Δ_c^l Net (MJ/kg)	Δ_c^l (MJ/kg O_2)	r_o Oxygen-fuel Mass ratio	C_{ps} Heat Capacity Solid (kJ/kg-°C)
acrylonitrile-butadiene styrene copolymer	—	—	35.25	33.75			1.41–1.59
bisphenol A epoxy	$C_{11.85}H_{20.37}O_{2.83}N_{0.3}$	212.10	33.53	31.42	13.41	2.343	
butadiene-acrylonitrile 37% copolymer	—	—	39.94				
butadiene/styrene 8.58% copolymer	$C_{4.18}H_{6.09}$	56.30	44.84	42.49	13.11	3.241	1.94
butadiene/styrene 25.5% copolymer	$C_{4.60}H_{6.29}$	61.55	44.19	41.95	13.07	3.209	1.82
cellulose acetate (triacetate)	$C_{12}H_{16}O_8$	288.14	18.88	17.66	13.25	1.333	1.34
cellulose acetate-butyrate	$C_{12}H_{18}O_7$	274.27	23.70	22.3	14.67	1.517	1.70
epoxy, unhardened	$C_{31}H_{36}O_{5.5}$	496.63	32.92	31.32	13.05	2.400	
epoxy, hardened	$C_{39}H_{40}O_{8.5}$	644.74	30.27	28.90	13.01	2.221	
melamine formaldehyde (Formica)	$C_6H_6N_6$	162.08	19.33	18.52	12.51	1.481	1.46
nylon 6	$C_6H_{11}NO$	113.08	30.1 –31.7	28.0 –29.6	12.30	2.335	1.52
nylon 6,6	$C_{12}H_{22}N_2O_2$	226.16	31.6 –31.7	29.5 –29.6	12.30	2.405	1.70
nylon 11 (Rilsan)	$C_{11}H_{21}NO$	183.14	36.99	34.47	12.33	2.796	1.70–2.30
phenol formaldehyde	$C_{15}H_{12}O_2$	224.17	27.9 –31.6	26.7 –30.4	11.80	2.427	1.70
-foam			21.6 –27.4	20.2 –26.2			
polyacenaphthalene	$C_{12}H_8$	152.14	39.23	38.14	12.95	2.945	
polyacrylonitrile	C_3H_3N	53.04	32.22	30.98	13.70	2.262	1.50
polyallylphthalate	$C_{14}H_{14}O$	198.17	27.74	26.19	9.54	2.745	
(polyamides) → nylon							
poly-1,4-butadiene	C_4H_6	54.05	45.19	42.75	13.13	3.256	
poly-1-butene	C_4H_8	56.05	46.48	43.35	12.65	3.426	1.88
polycarbonate	$C_{16}H_{14}O_3$	254.19	30.99	29.78	13.14	2.266	1.26
polycarbon suboxide	C_3O_2	68.03	13.78	13.78	14.64	0.941	
polychlorotrifluorethylene	C_2F_3Cl	116.47	1.12	1.12	2.04	0.549	0.92
polydiphenylbutadiene	$C_{16}H_{10}$	202.18	39.30	38.2	13.05	2.928	
polyester, unsaturated	$C_{5.77}H_{6.25}O_{1.63}$	101.60	21.6 –29.8	20.3 –28.5	11.90	2.053	1.20–2.30
polyether, chlorinated	$C_5H_8OCl_2$	154.97	17.84	16.71	12.45	1.342	
polyethylene	C_2H_4	28.03	46.2 –46.5	43.1 –43.4	12.63	3.425	1.83–2.30
polyethylene oxide	C_2H_4O	44.02	26.65	24.66	13.57	1.817	
polyethylene terephthalate	$C_{10}H_8O_4$	192.11	22.18	21.27	12.77	1.666	1.00
polyformaldehyde	CH_2O	30.01	16.93	15.86	14.88	1.066	1.46
poly-1-hexene sulfone	$C_6H_{12}SO_2$	148.13	29.78	28.00	14.40	1.944	
polyhydrocyanic acid	HCN	27.02	23.26	22.45	15.17	1.480	
(polyisobutylene) → poly-1-butene							
polyisocyanurate foam	—		23 –26.3	22.2 –26.2			
polyisoprene	C_5H_8	68.06	44.90	42.30	12.90	3.291	
poly-3-methyl-1-butene	C_5H_{10}	70.06	46.55	43.42	12.67	3.426	
polymethyl methacrylate	$C_5H_8O_2$	100.06	26.64	24.88	12.97	1.919	1.44
poly-4-methyl-1-pentene	C_6H_{12}	84.08	46.52	43.39	12.67	3.425	2.18
poly-α-methylstyrene	C_9H_{10}	118.11	42.31	40.45	13.00	3.116	
polynitroethylene	$C_2H_3O_2N$	73.03	15.96	15.06	19.64	0.767	
polyoxymethylene	CH_2O	30.01	16.93	15.65	14.68	1.066	
polyoxytrimethylene	C_3H_6O	58.04	31.52	29.25	13.27	2.205	
poly-1-pentene	C_5H_{10}	70.06	45.58	42.45	12.39	3.426	
polyphenylacetylene	C_8H_6	102.09	40.00	38.70	13.00	2.978	
polyphenylene oxide	C_8H_8O	120.09	34.59	33.13	13.09	2.531	1.34
polypropene sulfone	$C_3H_6SO_2$	106.10	23.82	22.58	16.64	1.357	
poly-β-propiolactone	$C_3H_4O_2$	72.14	19.35	18.13	13.62	1.331	
polypropylene	C_3H_6	42.04	46.37	43.23	12.62	3.824	2.10
polypropylene oxide	C_3H_6O	58.04	31.17	28.90	13.11	2.205	
polystyrene	C_8H_8	104.10	41.4 –42.5	39.7 –39.8	12.93	3.074	1.40
polystyrene-foam	—		39.7	35.6 –40.8			
polystyrene-foam, FR	—		41.2 –42.9				
polysulfones, butene	$C_4H_8SO_2$	120.11	24.04–26.47	22.25–25.01	14.79	1.598	1.30
polysulfur	S	32.06	9.72	9.72	9.74	0.998	
polytetrafluoroethylene	C_2F_4	100.02	5.00	5.00	7.81	0.640	1.02
polytetrahydrofuran	C_4H_8O	72.05	34.39	31.85	13.04	2.443	
polyurea	$C_{15}H_{18}O_4N_4$	318.20	24.91	23.67	13.45	1.760	

TABLE A-2. ***(continued)***

Material	Unit Composition	W Molecular Weight	Δ_c^u Gross (MJ/kg)	Δ_c^l Net (MJ/kg)	Δ_c^l (MJ/kg O_2)	r_o Oxygen-fuel Mass ratio	C_{ps} Heat Capacity Solid (kJ/kg-°C)
polyurethane	$C_{6.3}H_{7.1}NO_{2.1}$	130.30	23.90	22.70	13.16	1.725	1.75–1.84
polyurethane-foam	—		26.1 –31.6	23.2 –28.0			
polyurethane-foram, FR	—		24.0 –25.0				
polyvinyl acetate	$C_4H_6O_2$	86.05	23.04	21.51	12.86	1.673	
polyvinyl alcohol	C_2H_4O	44.03	25.00	23.01	12.66	1.817	1.70
polyvinyl butyral	$C_8H_{14}O_2$	142.10	32.90	30.70	13.00	2.365	
polyvinyl chloride	C_2H_3Cl	62.48	17.95	16.90	12.00	1.408	0.90–1.20
polyvinyl chloride foam	—		22.83				1.30–2.10
polyvinyl fluoride	C_2H_3F	46.02	21.70	20.27	10.60	1.912	
polyvinylidene chloride	$C_2H_2Cl_2$	96.93	10.52	10.07	12.21	0.825	1.34
polyvinylidene fluoride	$C_2H_2F_2$	64.02	14.77	14.08	11.26	1.250	1.38
urea formaldehyde	$C_3H_6O_2N_2$	102.05	15.90	14.61	13.31	1.098	1.60–2.10
urea formaldehyde-foam	—	—	14.80				

* Sources: 16, 17, 18, 19, 20, 21, 22, 23, 24.

Notes to Tables A-1, A-2, A-3, and A-4

Heats of Combustion: The heat of combustion is, by definition, the enthalpy of reaction when fuel and oxidant at standard conditions are reacted and form products at standard conditions. A unique value for the heat of combustion is possible only if these conditions are fully specified.[2,34] In normal combustion work the standard conditions are taken as:

1. Fuel and oxidant enter at 1 atmosphere pressure and 25°C (298 K) temperature. An amount of heat, which is equal to the heat of combustion, is extracted, so that the products are also at 25°C and 1 atmosphere.
2. The oxidant is gaseous oxygen.
3. The main products consist of liquid H_2O, gaseous CO_2, and gaseous N_2. There is no CO formed.
4. For fuels containing sulfur, the standard products include liquid $H_2SO_4 \cdot 115H_2O$. For chlorine-containing fuels reference states consisting of either liquid HCl in water solution or gaseous Cl_2 have been used.
5. In the combustion of silicones, the silicon goes to amorphous silica, SiO_2.

The state of the fuel — gaseous, liquid or solid — is not standardized and must be specified. The heat of combustion as defined above is termed the gross or upper value and is customarily determined in an oxygen bomb calorimeter.[35] For common materials the value is a negative number; however, customarily a minus sign is included in the definition to make heat of combustion a positive value.[36] Heat of combustion, enthalopy of combustion, calorific value and heating value are synonyms, the latter two being used more commonly in the heating industry.

In many cases the products are not cooled down to 25°C. For modest temperature differences the change in the effective value could be taken as $C_p(T - 25°)$, where C_p is

TABLE A-3. ***Heat of Combustion of Miscellaneous Substances****

Material	Δ_c^u Gross (MJ/kg)	Δ_c^l Net (MJ/kg)
acetate (see cellulose acetate)		
acrylic fiber	30.6–30.8	
blasting powder	2.1–2.4	
butter	38.5	
celluloid (cellulose nitrate and camphor)	17.5–20.6	16.4–19.2
cellulose acetate fiber, $C^8H_{12}O_6$	17.8–18.4	16.4–17.0
cellulose diacetate fiber, $C_{10}H_{14}O_7$	18.7	
cellulose nitrate, $C_6H_9N_1O_7/C_6H_8N_2O_9/C_6H_7N_3O_{11}$	9.11–13.48	
cellulose triacetate fiber, $C_{12}H_{16}O_8$	18.8	17.6
charcoal	33.7–34.7	33.2–34.2
coal-anthracite	30.9–34.6	30.5–34.2
-bituminous	24.7–36.3	23.6–35.2
coke	28.0–31.0	28.0–31.0
cork	26.1	
cotton	16.5–20.4	
dynamite	5.4	
epoxy, $C^{11.9}H_{20.4}O_{2.8}N_{0.3}C_{6.064}H_{7.550}O_{1.222}$	32.8–33.5	31.1–31.4

TABLE A-3. ***Heat of Combustion of Miscellaneous Substances* (continued)***

Material	Δ_c^u Gross (MJ/kg)	Δ_c^l Net (MJ/kg)
fat, animal	39.8	
flint powder	3.0–3.1	
fuel oil-No. 1	46.1	
-No. 6	42.5	
gasketing-chlorosulfonated polyethylene (Hypalon)	28.5	
-vinylidene fluoride/hexafluoropropylene (Fluorel, Viton A)	14.0–15.1	
gasoline	46.8	43.7
jet fuel-JP1		43.0
-JP3		43.5
-JP4	46.6	43.5
-JP5	45.9	43.0
kerosene (jet fuel A)	46.4	43.3
lanolin (wool fat)	40.8	
lard	40.1	
leather	18.2–19.8	
lignin, $C_{2.6}H_3O$	24.7–26.4	23.4–25.1
lignite	22.4–33.3	
modacrylic fiber	24.7	
naphtha	43.0–47.1	40.9–43.9
neoprene, C_5H_5Cl-gum	24.3	
-foam	9.7–26.8	
Nomex (polymethaphenylene isophthalamide) fiber, $C_{14}H_{10}O_2N_2$	27.0–28.7	
oil-castor	37.1	
-linseed	39.2–39.4	
-mineral	45.8–46.0	
-olive	39.6	
-solar	41.8	
paper-brown	16.3–17.9	
-magazine	12.7	
-newsprint	19.7	
-wax	21.5	
paraffin wax	46.2	43.1
peat	16.7–21.6	
petroleum jelly ($C_{7.118}H_{12.957}O_{0.091}$)	45.9	
rayon fiber	13.6–19.5	
rubber-buna N	34.7–35.6	
-butyl	45.8	
-isoprene (natural) C_5H_8	44.9	42.3
-latex foam	33.9–40.6	
-GRS	44.2	
-tire, auto	32.6	
silicone rubber (SiC_2H_6O)	15.5–16.8	
-foam	14.0–19.5	
sisal	15.9	
spandex fiber	31.4	
starch	17.6	16.2
straw	15.6	
sulfur-rhombic		9.28
-monoclinic		9.29
tobacco	15.8	
wheat	15.0	
wood-beech	20.0	18.7
-birch	20.0	18.7
-douglas fir	21.0	19.6
-maple	19.1	17.8
-red oak	20.2	18.7
-spruce	21.8	20.4
-white pine	19.2	17.8
-hardboard	19.9	
woodflour	19.8	
wool	20.7–26.6	

* Sources: 7, 9, 16, 25, 26, 27, 28, 29, 30.

TABLE A-4. ***Heats of Combustion for Metals****

Material	Δh_c (MJ/kg)
Pure elements	
aluminum	31.04
beryllium	66.43
copper	2.45
iron	7.39
magnesium	24.72
manganese	7.01
molybdenum	6.13
nickel	4.10
tantalum	5.66
tin	3.73
titanium	19.71
zinc	5.37
zirconium	12.07
Copper alloys	
bronze (88 Cu/10 Sb/2 Zn)	2.64
red brass (85 Cu/15 Zn)	2.89
cartridge brass (70 Cu/30 Zn)	3.33
yellow brass (60 Cu/40 Zn)	3.62
Iron alloys	
carbon steels	7.4–7.5
stainless steels	7.7–8.4
Nickel alloys	
Inconel 600	5.40
Monel 400	3.60

* Sources: 31, 32, 33.

the constant pressure heat capacity of the products. For this relationship to hold, the enthalpy curve has to be smooth and cannot include condensation. Thus it often becomes convenient to define a lower, or net, heat of combustion where the products are as before except that H_2O stays in gaseous form (and sulfur, if any, goes into gaseous SO_2). The relationship between the values for simple fuels can be expressed as:

$$\Delta h^l_c = \Delta h^u_c - 0.2196\ [\%H]$$

where:

Δh^l_c = lower heat of combustion (MJ/kg)

Δh^u_c = upper heat of combustion (MJ/kg)

[%H] = percent, by mass, of hydrogen in fuel

In practice, combustion is rarely complete. For example, some carbon often goes to CO instead of CO_2. Reactions with fuels containing sulfur, or chlorine or other halogens can go into a variety of products, depending on exact reaction conditions. Incomplete combustion acts to lower the heat of combustion. There are no simple general rules to aid in determining the degree of incomplete combustion. Also explosive and propellant materials rarely exhibit reactions where H_2O and CO_2 are the main products; thus, their heats of explosion or reaction will tend to be substantially different from the heat of combustion.

Even though the state of reactants is not described in the definition, most commonly it is taken as the natural state at ambient pressure and temperature. In some references, however, the gaseous state of fuels such as benzene or methanol is assumed, even though they would be normally considered as liquid fuels. The heat of combustion of fuels from the gaseous state is higher than from the liquid state by an amount equal to the fuel's heat of vaporization at 25°C. For combustion of plastic fuels, the most convenient reference state is the solid phase. In such cases, to compute the heat liberated in a given application, it is *not* necessary to subtract the heat of gasification from the heat of combustion.

Heats of combustion (per kg of fuel) are listed in Tables A-1 through A-3. Also listed in Tables A-1 and A-2 is r_o, the stoichiometric oxygen-fuel mass ratio. The heats can be seen to vary quite a bit for different fuels. Recently, however, increasing engineering use is made of the observation that the heat *of combustion per kg of oxygen consumed* is nearly constant for most organic fuels. It can be shown that a value of $\Delta h^l_c/r_o$ = 13.1 MJ/kg O_2 is near-constant.[37] An assumption of constant heat of combustion per kg of oxygen is useful in heat release rate measurements and for air-limited combustion problems.

For certain fuels it is more convenient to express heats of combustion by use of equations or charts, rather than tables. Two such instances are woods and certain petroleum products. The gross heat of combustion for dry woods is typically in the vicinity of 18-21 MJ/kg. This value varies, however, according to the species and according to the part of the plant. Furthermore, when wood normally burns, pyrolysates are first released and burned, which are lower in calorific value, followed by burning of the remaining char, which has a higher value. The following empirical correlation can be derived, applicable to all species of dry woods, provided the percent carbon, by weight is known.[38]

$$\Delta h^u_c = 0.433\ [\%C] - 1.527$$

where Δh^u_c is the gross heat of combustion for dry wood (MJ/kg) and [%C] is the percent of carbon, by weight. This correlation is equally applicable to charred wood and to wood pyrolysates, provided their ultimate analysis is known. For wet fuels, an additional correction should be made,

$$\Delta h^u_{c,eff} = \Delta h_c\ (1 - M/100) - 0.0257\ M$$

where M is the percent water in the fuel. Lower heats of combustion, if needed, can then be determined as noted above.

For petroleum products a series of empirical rules is available for estimating thermochemical properties, based on specific gravity or on API degrees[39] (See Table A-9.) A determination of the exact heat of combustion by calorimetry is usually not required for typical petroleum products, which include crude oils, fuel oils, kerosenes, and volatile products. These empirical rules are:

Heat of combustion

$$\Delta h^u_c = 52.12 - 8.79\ d^2 - 0.14\ d\ \text{(MJ/kg)}$$

Percent hydrogen

$$[\%H] = 26 - 15\ d$$

Heat of vaporization, at 25°C

$$\Delta h_v = \frac{240}{d} \quad (\text{kJ/kg})$$

Specific heat at 25°C, liquid

$$C_{pl} = \frac{1770}{\sqrt{d}} \quad (\text{J/kg°C})$$

Specific heat at 25°C, vapor

$$C_{pv} = C_{pl} - \frac{380}{d} \quad (\text{J/kg°C})$$

In all the above relationships, d = specific gravity at 15.6°C (60°F). For conversion from degrees API, see Table A-9. The relationship for [%H] can be used to obtain net heat of combustion, according to the general equation given earlier. A more detailed method, requiring additionally the determination of percent aromatics, volatility, and sulfur content, is available as an ASTM method.[40]

In some cases the combustion properties, including heat of combustion, are desired for burning metals. The specified combustion product in each case is a stable metal oxide in crystalline form. Table A-4 lists the heats of combustion for some common metals. For further discussion consult the references.[31,41]

Also listed in the tables, where available, are T_b, the boiling point; the heat capacities C_{pl}, C_{pv}, and C_{ps} of the liquid, vapor, and solid phases respectively, taken at constant pressure at T_b; and Δh_v, the latent heat of vaporization at T_b. For purposes where the total heat of vaporization (i.e., heat to bring a liquid at 25°C up to a gas at T_b) is desired, an estimate can be made by adding to Δh_v the quantity $C_{pl} \cdot (T_b - 25)$. More precise values can be obtained by using enthalpy tables.[5,32]

In some common applications, especially for building materials, a laboratory technique for assessing the possible effect of incomplete combustion is desired. The potential heat test procedure used to be determined by NFPA 259, *Standard Test Method for Potential Heat of Building Materials.* The potential heat test is now rarely specified. Values of "effective heat of combustion," are more commonly determined using ASTM E-1354, *Standard Test for Heat and Visible Smoke Release Rates for Materials and Production Using an Oxygen Consumption Calorimeter.*[51]

Conversion Units: To convert kcal/kg to megajoules/kg multiply by 4.184×10^{-3}
to convert kcal/mol to MJ/kg multiply by 4.184/W where W = molecular weight (g/mol)
to convert kJ/mol to MJ/kg multiply by 1/W
to convert Btu/lb to MJ/kg multiply by 2.322×10^{-3}

TABLE A-5. ***Oxygen Index Values****

Material	Oxygen Index Value†
methanol	11–12
benzene	13–16
sulfur	13.6
polyacetal	14.9
polyoxymethylene	15.7
acetone	16.0
kitchen candle	16.0
cotton	16.0–18.5
mineral oil	16.1
polyurethane foam, typical	16.5
cellulose acetate	16.8
styrene-butadiene-rubber foam	16.9
polybutadiene foam	17.1
natural rubber foam	17.2
polymethylmethacrylate	17.3
polyethylene	17.4
polypropylene	17.4
polystyrene	17.6–18.3
polyacrylonitrile	18.0
paper, cellulose filter	18.2
polybutadiene	18.3
ABS	18.3–18.8
cellulose triacetate	18.4
polyisoprene rubber	18.5
rayon	18.7–18.9
polymethylsiloxane (silicone fluid)	18.9
cellulose	19.0
cellulose acetate-butyrate	19.6
epoxy resin	19.8
polyethylene terephthalate	20.0
nylon	20.1–26.0
birch wood	20.5
polyester fibers	20.6
phenolic resin	21.0
phenolic-paper laminate	21.7
polyvinyl alcohol	22.5
polycarbonate	22.5–28.0
polyvinyl fluoride	22.6
red oak	23.0
wool	23.8
neoprene rubber	26.3–40.0
Nomex fibers	26.7–28.5
modacrylic fibers	26.8
polyphenylene oxide	29.0
silicone rubber	30.0
polysulfone	30–32
leather	34.8
carbon powder	35.0
phenol-formaldehyde resin	35.0
polyimide	36.5
polyvinyl chloride	37.1–49
Kynol fibers	38.0
polybenzimidazole	40.6–41.5
polyvinylidene fluoride	43.7
polyvinyl chloride, chlorinated	45–60
carbon black	56–63
polyvinylidene chloride	60
polychlorotrifluoroethylene	95
polytetrafluoroethylene	95

† The values in the table above were determined using the ASTM Oxygen Test (D2863), and represent typical values for materials without added fire retardants. Adding fire retardants to polymers can increase substantially the measured oxygen index value.

* Sources: 41, 42, 43.

TABLE A-6. ***Miscellaneous Properties or Plastics and Other Combustibles****

Material	Density (kg/m$_3$)	Min. Radiant Flux for Ignition (kW/m$_2$)	Min. Mass Loss Rate for Ignition (g/m$_2$-s)	Energy Required for Ignition (kJ/m$_2$)	Ignition Temperature (K)	Effective Heat of Gasification (MJ/kg)	Smoke Specific Extinction Area (m$_2$/kg)	Soot Yield (kg soot/ kg specimen)
ABS						3.2		
benzene, liquid							830–900	
cellulose						3.5	10–15	
Douglas Fir				650–770		1.8		
fiberglass, FR	—	7	—	3950	740	1.7–2.2	250–370	
nylon 6/6						2.3	410	0.14
paper, corrugated						2.2		
phenolic, foams, rigid	67	45	5.5	390	944	3.7		
polycarbonate						2.1		
polyethylene	920	19	2.5	1500–5100	761	1.5–2.7	290–510	
polyethylene, foams	36–143	19–22	2.5–2.6	1430–1780	761–807	1.5–2.7	360–810	
polyethylene, foam, chlorinated						2.1–3.1	1010–1360	
polyisocyanurate, foams, ridgid	33–36	23	5.5–6.8	850–930	798	4.5		
polymethylmethacrylate	1170	18	4.4	1300–4200	751	1.6	110–260	0.012
polyoxymethylene	1400	17	4.5	2100–6000	740	2.4	0–10	
polypropylene	905	20	2.7	1000–3500	771	1.4–2.0	380–610	0.07–0.09
polystyrene	1050	29	4.0	1300–6400	846	1.7	730–1430	
polystyrene, foams, rigid	16–34	18–27	4.9–6.3	1200–3200	751–831	1.3–3.1	940–1300	
polytetrafluoroethylene		43		9000	933			0.02
polyurethane, foams, flexible	29–47	16–30	5.3–7.2	150–770	729–852	1.2–2.7	100–500	
polyurethane, foams, rigid	36–321	20–28	6.9–8.4	150–1300	771–838	2.0–4.5	100–1000	
polyvinyl chloride	1305	21	—	3320	780	1.7–2.5	1100–1400	0.23
red oak	740	11	2.5	420–920	730	1.7–5.5	80–130	.0002–0.018
styrene, liquid						0.64	780–920	

* Sources: 18, 45, 46, 47, 48, 49, 50.

Notes to Table A-6

In recent years measurement data have started to be tabulated on the engineering performance of plastics. These data are usually measured in heat release rate calorimeters on a bench scale (specimens typically 0.1 m dimension). A number of these data are summarized in Table A-6. In many cases wide variations for a property are shown. These can be attributed to (a) specimen size differences, (b) specimen orientation differences, (c) air flow rate differences, (d) heating flux (irradiance) differences, and (e) specimen composition differences. The data for the plastics listed do not represent pure polymers, but rather engineering plastics, which vary in additives, degree of polymerization, etc. When only a single number is indicated, this should be taken as reflecting a paucity of data, rather than a high precision of measurement.

The minimum flux needed for ignition has sometimes been considered to be a constant. A-6 shows that it varies among materials, but only over a range of about 2:1. Ignition temperatures are seen to vary little for common plastics. The total absorbed energy (kJ/m^2) required for ignition has more recently been considered a measure of ignitability.

The effective heat of gasification is a parameter intended to represent the ease of achieving a given heat release rate. The tabulated values, however, do not show the wide range of heat release rate behaviors seen with commercial products. This is partly because for most materials the heat release progress is highly transient, whereas the definition of the effective heat of gasification (average energy required to gasify a unit mass of material) requires assuming steady-state conditions.

Smoke properties can be measured in two ways: (1) Optically, by determining the obscuration along a light beam. This can be expressed as smoke specific extinction area per unit specimen mass (m^2/kg). The unit system implied here is natural-log (Base-e). (2) Gravimetrically, by determining the soot mass evolved, per unit specimen mass.

TABLE A-7. *Specific Gravity Equivalents for Degrees Baumé*
(Liquids Lighter than Water)

Baumé	Specific Gravity	Lbs per Gallon*	Baumé	Specific Gravity	Lbs per Gallon*	Baumé	Specific Gravity	Lbs per Gallon*
10	1.0000	8.33	45	0.8000	6.66	80	0.6667	5.55
11	0.9929	8.27	46	0.7955	6.63	81	0.6635	5.52
12	0.9859	8.21	47	0.7910	6.59	82	0.6604	5.50
13	0.9790	8.16	48	0.7865	6.55	83	0.6573	5.48
14	0.9722	8.10	49	0.7821	6.52	84	0.6542	5.45
15	0.9655	8.04	50	0.7778	6.48	85	0.6512	5.42
16	0.9589	7.99	51	0.7735	6.44	86	0.6481	5.40
17	0.9524	7.93	52	0.7692	6.41	87	0.6452	5.38
18	0.9459	7.88	53	0.7650	6.37	88	0.6422	5.36
19	0.9396	7.83	54	0.7609	6.34	89	0.6393	5.33
20	0.9333	7.78	55	0.7568	6.30	90	0.6364	5.30
21	0.9272	7.72	56	0.7527	6.27	91	0.6335	5.28
22	0.9211	7.67	57	0.7487	6.24	92	0.6306	5.25
23	0.9150	7.62	58	0.7447	6.20	93	0.6278	5.23
24	0.9091	7.57	59	0.7407	6.17	94	0.6250	5.21
25	0.9032	7.53	60	0.7368	6.14	95	0.6222	5.18
26	0.8974	7.48	61	0.7330	6.11	96	0.6195	5.16
27	0.8917	7.43	62	0.7292	6.07	97	0.6167	5.14
28	0.8861	7.38	63	0.7254	6.04	98	0.6140	5.11
29	0.8805	7.34	64	0.7216	6.01	99	0.6114	5.09
30	0.8750	7.29	65	0.7179	5.98	100	0.6087	5.07
31	0.8696	7.24	66	0.7143	5.95	101	0.6061	5.05
32	0.8642	7.20	67	0.7107	5.92	102	0.6034	5.03
33	0.8589	7.15	68	0.7071	5.89	103	0.6009	5.00
34	0.8537	7.11	69	0.7035	5.86	104	0.5983	4.98
35	0.8485	7.07	70	0.7000	5.83	105	0.5957	4.96
36	0.8434	7.03	71	0.6965	5.80	106	0.5932	4.94
37	0.8383	6.98	72	0.6931	5.78	107	0.5907	4.92
38	0.8333	6.94	73	0.6897	5.75	108	0.5882	4.90
39	0.8284	6.90	74	0.6863	5.72	109	0.5858	4.88
40	0.8235	6.86	75	0.6829	5.69	110	0.5833	4.86
41	0.8187	6.82	76	0.6796	5.66			
42	0.8140	6.78	77	0.6763	5.63			
43	0.8092	6.74	78	0.6731	5.60			
44	0.8046	6.70	79	0.6699	5.58			

* one lb per gallon equals 119.8 kg/m^3

TABLE A-8. *Specific Gravity Equivalents for Degrees Baumé*
(Liquids Heavier than Water)

Baumé	Specific Gravity	Lbs per Gallon*	Baumé	Specific Gravity	Lbs per Gallon*	Baumé	Specific Gravity	Lbs per Gallon*
0	1.0000	8.33	25	1.2083	10.07	50	1.5263	12.72
1	1.0069	8.38	26	1.2185	10.16	51	1.5426	12.85
2	1.0140	8.46	27	1.2288	10.24	52	1.5591	12.99
3	1.0211	8.51	28	1.2393	10.32	53	1.5761	13.13
4	1.0284	8.56	29	1.2500	10.41	54	1.5934	13.27
5	1.0357	8.63	30	1.2609	10.51	55	1.6111	13.42
6	1.0432	8.69	31	1.2719	10.59	56	1.6292	13.57
7	1.0507	8.75	32	1.2832	10.69	57	1.6477	13.72
8	1.0584	8.81	33	1.2946	10.78	58	1.6667	13.87
9	1.0662	8.88	34	1.3063	10.84	59	1.6860	14.04
10	1.0741	8.94	35	1.3182	10.98	60	1.7059	14.21
11	1.0821	9.01	36	1.3303	11.09	61	1.7262	14.38
12	1.0902	9.09	37	1.3426	11.18	62	1.7470	14.55
13	1.0985	9.15	38	1.3551	11.29	63	1.7683	14.72
14	1.1069	9.21	39	1.3679	11.39	64	1.7901	14.91

TABLE A-8. ***Specific Gravity Equivalents for Degrees Baumé (continued)***
(Liquids Heavier than Water)

Baumé	Specific Gravity	Lbs per Gallon*	Baumé	Specific Gravity	Lbs per Gallon*	Baumé	Specific Gravity	Lbs per Gallon*
15	1.1154	9.29	40	1.3810	11.51	65	1.8125	15.10
16	1.1240	9.36	41	1.3942	11.61	66	1.8354	15.29
17	1.1328	9.43	42	1.4078	11.72	67	1.8590	15.48
18	1.1417	9.51	43	1.4216	11.84	68	1.8831	15.68
19	1.1508	9.59	44	1.4356	11.96	69	1.9079	15.89
20	1.1600	9.67	45	1.4500	12.08	70	1.9333	16.10
21	1.1694	9.74	46	1.4646	12.21	71	1.9595	16.32
22	1.1789	9.81	47	1.4796	12.33	72	1.9864	16.55
23	1.1885	9.90	48	1.4948	12.46	73	2.0139	16.78
24	1.1983	9.99	49	1.5104	12.58	74	2.0423	17.01
						75	2.0714	17.25

This table and Table 5-11G have been adopted by the U.S. National Bureau of Standards from the formula:

Liquids heavier than water, degrees Baumé $= 145 - \frac{145}{R}$

Liquids lighter than water, degrees Baumé $= \frac{140}{R} - 130$

Where R is the ratio of the density of a liquid to that of distilled water, both densities being taken at 60°F (15.5°C).

NOTE: Degrees API, used to measure the density of petroleum oils, differ slightly from the Baumé scale for liquids lighter than water. API specific gravity is determined by a similar formula, using the figures 141.5 and 131.5 instead of 140 and 130.

* One lb per gallon equals 119.8 kg/m^3.

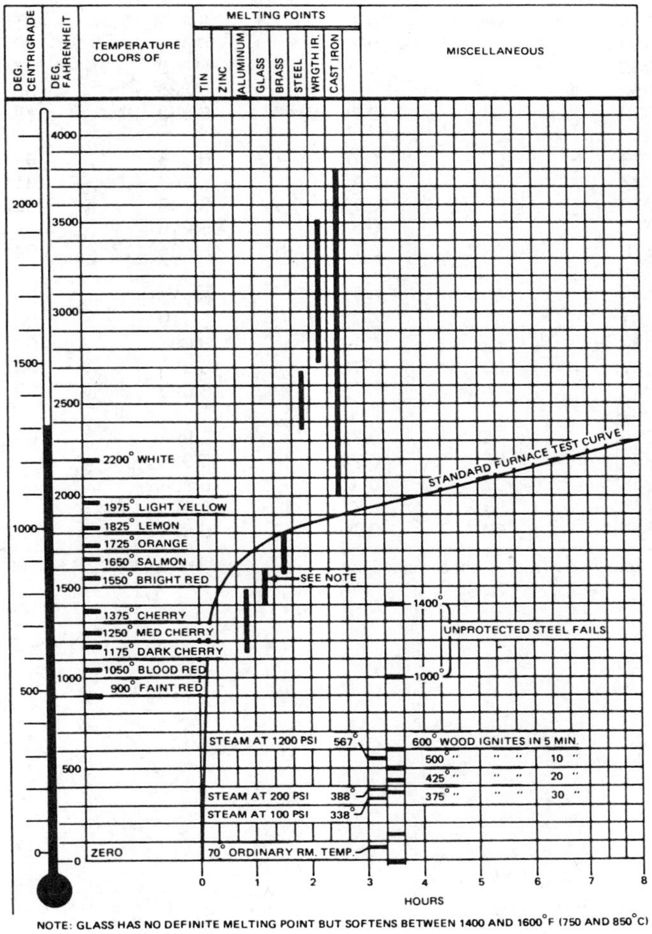

NOTE: GLASS HAS NO DEFINITE MELTING POINT BUT SOFTENS BETWEEN 1400 AND 1600°F (750 AND 850°C)

FIG.A-1A. Temperature colors, melting points of various substances, and data on the behavior of some materials at elevated temperatures and pressures.

TABLE A-9. ***Specific Gravity Equivalents, Degrees API***

The specific gravity of gasoline and other petroleum products is commonly given in Degrees API (American Petroleum Institute). The API degree is based on the following formula:

$$\text{Degrees API} = \frac{141.5}{\text{specific gravity}} - 131.5.$$

The standard method of test for gravity of petroleum and petroleum products by means of a hydrometer specifies 60°F as the test temperature, and the formula is based on the specific gravity of the liquid tested at 60°F as compared with water at 60°F.

Degrees API	Specific Gravity at 60/60°F	Pounds per Gallon at 60°F	Degrees API	Specific Gravity at 60/60°F	Pounds per Gallon* at 60°F	Degrees API	Specific Gravity at 60/60°F	Pounds per Gallon* at 60°F
0	1.076	8.962	35	0.8498	7.076	70	0.7022	5.845
1	1.066	8.895	36	0.8448	7.034	71	0.6988	5.817
2	1.060	8.828	37	0.8398	6.993	72	0.6953	5.788
3	1.052	8.762	38	0.8348	6.951	73	0.6919	5.759
4	1.044	8.698	39	0.8299	6.910	74	0.6886	5.731
5	1.037	8.634	40	0.8251	6.870	75	0.6852	5.703
6	1.029	8.571	41	0.8203	6.830	76	0.6819	5.676
7	1.022	8.509	42	0.8155	6.790	77	0.6787	5.649
8	1.014	8.448	43	0.8109	6.752	78	0.6754	5.622
9	1.007	8.388	44	0.8063	6.713	79	0.6722	5.595
10	1.0000	8.328	45	0.8017	6.675	80	0.6690	5.568
11	0.9930	8.270	46	0.7972	6.637	81	0.6659	5.542
12	0.9861	8.212	47	0.7927	6.600	82	0.6628	5.516
13	0.9792	8.155	48	0.7883	6.563	83	0.6597	5.491
14	0.9725	8.099	49	0.7839	6.526	84	0.6566	5.465
15	0.9659	8.044	50	0.7796	6.490	85	0.6536	5.440
16	0.9593	7.989	51	0.7753	6.455	86	0.6506	5.415
17	0.9529	7.935	52	0.7711	6.420	87	0.6476	5.390
18	0.9465	7.882	53	0.7669	6.385	88	0.6446	5.365
19	0.9402	7.830	54	0.7628	6.350	89	0.6417	5.341
20	0.9340	7.778	55	0.7587	6.316	90	0.6388	5.316
21	0.9279	7.727	56	0.7547	6.283	91	0.6360	5.293
22	0.9218	7.676	57	0.7507	6.249	92	0.6331	5.269
23	0.9159	7.627	58	0.7467	6.216	93	0.6303	5.246
24	0.9100	7.578	59	0.7428	6.184	94	0.6275	5.222
25	0.9042	7.529	60	0.7389	6.151	95	0.6247	5.199
26	0.8984	7.481	61	0.7351	6.119	96	0.6220	5.176
27	0.8927	7.434	62	0.7313	6.087	97	0.6193	5.154
28	0.8871	7.387	63	0.7275	6.056	98	0.6166	5.131
29	0.8816	7.341	64	0.7238	6.025	99	0.6139	5.109
30	0.8762	7.296	65	0.7201	5.994	100	0.6112	5.086
31	0.8708	7.251	66	0.7165	5.964			
32	0.8654	7.206	67	0.7128	5.934			
33	0.8602	7.163	68	0.7093	5.904			
34	0.8550	7.119	69	0.7057	5.874			

* "Apparent weight," or weight when weighed in air. True weight corrected for weight of air, differs by less than 1/10 of 1 percent. One lb per gallon equals 119.8 kg/m^3. 60°F equals 15.55°C.

TABLE A-10. ***Materials Subject to Spontaneous Heating***

(Originally prepared by the NFPA Committee on Spontaneous Heating and Ignition which has been discontinued. Omission of any material does not necessarily indicate that it is not subject to spontaneous heating.)

Name	Tendency to Spontaneous Heating	Usual Shipping Container or Storage Method	Precautions Against Spontaneous Heating	Remarks
Alfalfa Meal	High	Bags, Bulk	Avoid moisture extremes. Tight cars for transportation are essential.	Many fires attributed to spontaneous heating probably caused by sparks, burning embers, or particles of hot metal picked up by the meal during processing. Test fires caused in this manner have smoldered for 72 hours before becoming noticeable.
Burlap Bags "Used"	Possible	Bales	Keep cool and dry.	Tendency to heat dependent on previous use of bags. If oily would be dangerous.
Castor Oil	Very slight	Metal Barrels, Metal Cans in Wooden Boxes	Avoid contact of leakage from containers with rags, cotton, or other fibrous combustible materials.	Possible heating of saturated fabrics in badly ventilated piles.
Charcoal	High	Bulk, Bags	Keep dry. Supply ventilation.	Hardwood charcoal must be carefully prepared and aged. Avoid wetting and subsequent drying.
Coal, Bituminous	Moderate	Bulk	Store in small piles. Avoid high temperatures.	Tendency to heat depends upon origin and nature of coals. High volatile coals are particularly liable to heat.
Cocoa Bean Shell Tankage	Moderate	Burlap Bags, Bulk	Extreme caution must be observed to maintain safe moisture limits.	This material is very hygroscopic and is liable to heating if moisture content is excessive. Precaution should be observed to maintain dry storage, etc.
Cocoanut Oil	Very slight	Drums, Cans, Glass	Avoid contact of leakage from containers with rags, cotton, or other fibrous combustible materials.	Only dangerous if fabrics, etc., are impregnated.
Cod Liver Oil	High	Drums, Cans, Glass	Avoid contact of leakage from containers with rags, cotton, or other fibrous combustible materials.	Impregnated organic materials are extremely dangerous.
Colors in Oil	High	Drums, Cans, Glass	Avoid contact of leakage from containers with rags, cotton, or other fibrous combustible materials.	May be very dangerous if fabrics, etc., are impregnated.
Copra	Slight	Bulk	Keep cool and dry.	Heating possible if wet and hot.
Corn-Meal Feeds	High	Burlap Bags, Paper Bags, Bulk	Material should be processed carefully to maintain safe moisture content and to cure before storage.	Usually contains an appreciable quantity of oil which has rather severe tendency to heat.
Corn Oil	Moderate	Barrels, Tank Cars	Avoid contact of leakage from containers with rags, cotton, or other fibrous combustible materials.	Dangerous heating of meals, etc., unlikely unless stored in large piles while hot.
Cottonseed	Low	Bags, Bulk	Keep cool and dry.	Heating possible if piled wet and hot.
Cottonseed Oil	Moderate	Barrels, Tank Cars	Avoid contact of leakage from containers with rags, cotton, or other fibrous combustible materials.	May cause heating of saturated material in badly ventilated piles.
Distillers' Dried Grains with oil content (Brewers' grains)	Moderate	Bulk	Maintain moisture 7 percent to 10 percent. Cool below 100°F (38°C) before storage.	Very dangerous if moisture content is 5 percent or lower.
No oil content	Moderate	Bulk	Maintain moisture 7 percent to 10 percent. Cool below 100°F (38°C) before storage.	Very dangerous if moisture content is 5 percent or lower.
Feeds, various	Moderate	Bulk, Bags	Avoid extremely low or high moisture content.	Ground feeds must be carefully processed. Avoid loading or storing unless cooled.
Fertilizers				
Organic, Inorganic, Combination of both	Moderate	Bulk, Bags	Avoid extremely low or high moisture content.	Organic fertilizers containing nitrates must be carefully prepared to avoid combinations that might initiate heating.
Mixed, Synthetic, containing nitrates and organic matter	Moderate	Bulk, Bags	Avoid free acid in preparation.	Insure ventilation in curing process by small piles or artificial drafts. If stored or loaded in bags, provide ventilation space between bags.

TABLE A-10. ***Materials Subject to Spontaneous Heating (Continued)***

Name	Tendency to Spontaneous Heating	Usual Shipping Container or Storage Method	Precautions Against Spontaneous Heating	Remarks
Fish meal	High	Bags, Bulk	Keep moisture 6 percent to 12 percent. Avoid exposure to heat.	Dangerous if overdried or packaged over 100°F (38°C).
Fish Oil	High	Barrels, Drums, Tank Cars	Avoid contact of leakage from containers with rags, cotton, or other fibrous combustible materials.	Impregnated porous or fibrous materials are extremely dangerous. Tendency of various fish oils to heat varies with origin.
Fish Scrap	High	Bulk, Bags	Avoid moisture extremes.	Scrap loaded or stored before cooling is extremely liable to heat.
Foam Rubber in Consumer Products	Moderate		Where possible remove foam rubber pads, etc., from garments to be dried in dryers or over heaters. If garments containing foam rubber parts have been artificially dried, they should be thoroughly cooled before being piled, bundled, or put away. Keep heating pads, hair dryers, other heat sources from contact with foam rubber pillows, etc.	Foam rubber may continue to heat spontaneously after being subjected to forced drying as in home or commercial dryers, and after contact with heating pads and other heat sources. Natural drying does not cause spontaneous heating.
Grain (various kinds)	Very slight	Bulk, Bags	Avoid moisture extremes.	Ground grains may heat if wet and warm.
Hay	Moderate	Bulk, Bales	Keep dry and cool.	Wet or improperly cured hay is almost certain to heat in hot weather. Baled hay seldom heats dangerously.
Hides	Very slight	Bales	Keep dry and cool.	Bacteria in untreated hides may initiate heating.
Iron Pyrites	Moderate	Bulk	Avoid large piles. Keep dry and cool.	Moisture accelerates oxidation of finely divided pyrites.
Istle	Very slight	Bulk, Bales	Keep cool and dry.	Heating possible in wet material. Unlikely under ordinary conditions. Partially burned or charred fiber is dangerous.
Jute	Very slight	Bulk	Keep cool and dry.	Avoid storing or loading in hot wet piles. Partially burned or charred material is dangerous.
Lamp Black	Very slight	Wooden Cases	Keep cool and dry.	Fires most likely to result from sparks or included embers, etc., rather than spontaneous heating.
Lanolin	Negligible	Glass, Cans, Metal Drums, Barrels	Avoid contact of leakage from containers with rags, cotton, or other fibrous combustible materials.	Heating possible on contaminated fibrous matter.
Lard Oil	Slight	Wooden Barrels	Avoid contact of leakage from containers with rags, cotton, or other fibrous combustible materials.	Dangerous on fibrous combustible substances.
Lime, unslaked (Calcium Oxide, Pebble Lime, Quicklime)	Moderate	Paper Bags, Wooden Barrels, Bulk	Keep dry. Avoid hot loading.	Wetted lime may heat sufficiently to ignite wood containers, etc.
Linseed	Very slight	Bulk	Keep cool and dry.	Tendency to heat dependent on moisture and oil content.
Linseed Oil	High	Tank Cars, Drums, Cans, Glass	Avoid contact of leakage from containers with rags, cotton, or other fibrous combustible materials.	Rags or fabrics impregnated with this oil are extremely dangerous. Avoid piles, etc. Store in closed containers, preferably metal.
Manure	Moderate	Bulk	Avoid extremes of low or high moisture contents. Ventilate the piles.	Avoid storing or loading uncooled manures.
Menhaden Oil	Moderate to high	Barrels, Drums, Tank Cars	Avoid contact of leakage from containers with rags, cotton, or other fibrous combustible materials.	Dangerous on fibrous product.
Metal Powders*	Moderate	Drums, etc.	Keep in closed containers.	Moisture accelerates oxidation of most metal powders.
Metal Turnings*	Practically none	Bulk	Not likely to heat spontaneously.	Avoid exposure to sparks.
Mineral Wool	None	Pasteboard Boxes, Paper Bags	Noncombustible. If loaded hot may ignite containers and other combustible surroundings.	This material is mentioned in this table only because of general impression that it heats spontaneously.

TABLE A-10. ***Materials Subject to Spontaneous Heating (Continued)***

Name	Tendency to Spontaneous Heating	Usual Shipping Container or Storage Method	Precautions Against Spontaneous Heating	Remarks
Mustard Oil, Black	Low	Barrels	Avoid contact of leakage with rags, cotton or other fibrous combustible materials.	Avoid contamination of fibrous combustible materials.
Oiled Clothing	High	Fiber Boxes	Dry thoroughly before packaging.	Dangerous if wet material is stored in piles without ventilation.
Oiled Fabrics	High	Rolls	Keep ventilated. Dry thoroughly before packing.	Improperly dried fabrics extremely dangerous. Tight rolls are comparatively safe.
Oiled Rags	High	Bales	Avoid storing in bulk in open.	Dangerous if wet with drying oil.
Oiled Silk	High	Fiber Boxes, Rolls	Supply sufficient ventilation.	Improperly dried material is dangerous in form of piece goods. Rolls relatively safe.
Oleic Acid	Very slight	Glass Bottles, Wooden Barrels	Avoid contact of leakage from containers with rags, cotton, or other fibrous combustible materials.	Impregnated fibrous materials may heat unless ventilated.
Oleo Oil	Very slight	Wooden Barrels	Avoid contact of leakage from containers with rags, cotton, or other fibrous combustible materials.	May heat on impregnated fibrous combustible matter.
Olive Oil	Moderate to Low	Tank Cars, Drums, Cans, Glass	Avoid contact of leakage from containers with rags, cotton, or other fibrous combustible materials.	Impregnated fibrous materials may heat unless ventilated. Tendency varies with origin of oil.
Paint containing drying oil	Moderate	Drums, Cans, Glass	Avoid contact of leakage from containers with rags, cotton, or other fibrous combustible materials.	Fabrics, rags, etc., impregnated with paints that contain drying oils and driers are extremely dangerous. Store in closed containers, preferably metal.
Paint Scrapings	Moderate	Barrels, Drums	Avoid large unventilated piles.	Tendency to heat depends on state of dryness of the scrapings.
Palm Oil	Low	Wooden Barrels	Avoid contact of leakage from containers with rags, cotton, or other fibrous combustible materials.	Impregnated fibrous materials may heat unless ventilated. Tendency varies with origin of oil.
Peanut Oil	Low	Wooden Barrels, Tin Cans	Avoid contact of leakage from containers with rags, cotton, or other fibrous combustible materials.	Impregnated fibrous materials may heat unless ventilated. Tendency varies with origin of oil.
Peanuts, "Red Skin"	High	Paper Bags, Cans, Fiber Board Boxes, Burlap Bags	Avoid badly ventilated storage.	This is the part of peanut between outer shell and peanut itself. Provide well ventilated storage.
Peanuts, shelled	Very slight or Negligible	Paper Bags, Cans, Fiber Board Boxes, Burlap Bags	Keep cool and dry.	Avoid contamination of rags, etc., with oil.
Perilla Oil	Moderate to High	Tin Cans, Barrels	Avoid contact of leakage from containers with rags, cotton, or other fibrous combustible materials.	Impregnated fibrous materials may heat unless ventilated. Tendency varies with origin of oil.
Pine Oil	Moderate	Glass, Drums	Avoid contact of leakage from containers with rags, cotton, or other fibrous combustible materials.	Impregnated fibrous materials may heat unless ventilated. Tendency varies with origin of oil.
Powdered Eggs	Very slight	Wooden Barrels	Avoid conditions that promote bacterial growth. Inhibit against decay. Keep cool.	Possible heating of decaying powder in storage.
Powdered Milk	Very slight	Wooden and Fiber Boxes, Metal Cans	Avoid conditions that promote bacterial growth. Inhibit against decay. Keep cool.	Possible heating by decay or fermentation.
Rags	Variable	Bales	Avoid contamination with drying oils. Avoid charring. Keep cool and dry.	Tendency depends on previous use of rags. Partially burned or charred rags are dangerous.
Red Oil	Moderate	Glass Bottles, Wooden Barrels	Avoid contact of leakage from containers with rags, cotton, or other fibrous combustible materials.	Impregnated porous or fibrous materials are extremely dangerous. Tendency varies with origin of oil.

TABLE A-10. ***Materials Subject to Spontaneous Heating (Continued)***

Name	Tendency to Spontaneous Heating	Usual Shipping Container or Storage Method	Precautions Against Spontaneous Heating	Remarks
Roofing Felts and Papers	Moderate	Rolls, Bales, Crates	Avoid over-drying the material. Supply ventilation.	Felts, etc., should have controlled moisture content. Packaging or rolling uncooled felts is dangerous.
Sawdust	Possible	Bulk	Avoid contact with drying oils. Avoid hot, humid storage.	Partially burned or charred sawdust may be dangerous.
Scrap Film (Nitrate)	Very slight	Drums and Lined Boxes	Film must be properly stabilized against decomposition.	Nitrocellulose film ignites at low temperature. External ignition more likely than spontaneous heating. Avoid exposure to sparks, etc.
Scrap Leather	Very slight	Bales, Bulk	Avoid contamination with drying oils.	Oil-treated leather scraps may heat.
Scrap Rubber or Buffings	Moderate	Bulk, Drums	Buffings of high rubber content should be shipped and stored in tight containers.	Sheets, slabs, etc., are comparatively safe unless loaded or stored before cooling thoroughly.
Sisal	Very slight	Bulk, Bales	Keep cool and dry.	Partially burned or charred material is particularly liable to ignite spontaneously.
Soybean Oil	Moderate	Tin Cans, Barrels, Tank Cars	Avoid contact with rags, cotton, or fibrous materials.	Impregnated fibrous materials may heat unless well ventilated.
Sperm Oil—See Whale Oil				
Tankage	Variable	Bulk	Avoid extremes of moisture contents. Avoid loading or storing while hot.	Very dry or moist tankages often heat. Tendency more pronounced if loaded or stored before cooling.
Tung Nut Meals	High	Paper Bags, Bulk	Material must be very carefully processed and cooled thoroughly before storage.	These meals contain residual oil which has high tendency to heat. Material also susceptible to heating if over-dried.
Tung Oil	Moderate	Tin Cans, Barrels, Tank Cars	Avoid contact of leakage from containers with rags, cotton, or other fibrous combustible materials.	Impregnated fibrous materials may heat unless ventilated. Tendency varies with origin of oil.
Turpentine	Low	Tin, Glass, Barrels	Avoid contact of leakage from containers with rags, cotton, or other fibrous combustible materials.	Has some tendency to heat but less so than the drying oils. Chemically active with chlorine compounds and may cause fire.
Varnished Fabrics	High	Boxes	Process carefully. Keep cool and ventilated.	Thoroughly dried varnished fabrics are comparatively safe.
Wallboard	Slight	Wrapped Bundles, Pasteboard Boxes	Maintain safe moisture content. Cool thoroughly before storage.	This material is entirely safe from spontaneous heating if properly processed.
Waste Paper	Moderate	Bales	Keep dry and ventilated.	Wet paper occasionally heats in storage in warm locations.
Whale Oil	Moderate	Barrels and Tank Cars	Avoid contact of leakage from containers with rags, cotton, or other fibrous combustible materials.	Impregnated fibrous materials may heat unless ventilated. Tendency varies with origin of oil.
Wool Wastes	Moderate	Bulk, Bales, etc.	Keep cool and ventilated or store in closed containers. Avoid high moisture.	Most wool wastes contain oil, etc., from the weaving and spinning and are liable to heat in storage. Wet wool wastes are very liable to spontaneous heating and possible ignition.

*Refers to iron, steel, brass, aluminum, and other common metals, for information on magnesium, sodium, zirconium, etc.

BIBLIOGRAPHY

References Cited

1. Domalski, E. S. Selected Values of Heats of Combustion and Heats of Formation of Organic Compounds Containing The Elements C, H, N, O, P, and S. *Journal of Physical and Chemical Reference Data*. Vol 1. pp 221-227, 1972.

2. Gray, D. E., ed. *American Institute of Physics Handbook*. Section 41. McGraw-Hill. New York, 1972.

3. Rossini, F. D. *Selected Values of Physical and Thermodynamic Properties of Hydrocarbons and Related Compounds*. American Petroleum Institute/Carnegie Press. Pittsburgh, PA, 1953.

4. Tinnermans, J. *Physio-Chemical Constants of Pure Organic Compounds*. 2 Vols. Elsevier. New York, 1950-65.

5. Thermodynamics Research Center. *Selected Values of Properties of Chemical Compounds; and Selected Values of Properties of Hydrocarbons and Related Compounds*. Texas A & M University, College Station, TX, undated.

6. Stull, D. R., Westrom, Jr., E. F. and Sinke, G. C. *Thermodynamics of Organic Compounds*. Wiley. New York, 1969.

7. *Landolt-Bornstein Physikalisch-Chemische Tabellen*. Fifth series: main work (vol 2, 1923); first supplement (vol 2, 1927); second supplement (vol 2, 1931); third supplement (vol 3, 1936). Sixth series: Part 2 (vol 4, 1961). Springer-Verlag. Berlin, Republic of Germany, 1927-61.

8. Reid, R. C., Prausnitz, J. M., and Sherwood, T. K. *The Properties of Gases and Liquids*. McGraw-Hill. New York, 1977.

9. NACA. *Basic Considerations in the Combustion of Hydrocarbon Fuels in Air* (NACA Report 1300). National Advisory Committee on Aeronautics, 1957.

10. Belenyessy, L. I. et al. Heats of Combustion of Complex Saturated Hydrocarbons, *J. Chem. and Engrg. Data*. Vol 7, 1962, pp 66-68.

11. Rand Corp. *Physical Properties and Thermodynamic Functions of Fuels, Oxidizers, and Products of Combustion, I. Fuels*. NTIS No AD 605 967. Battelle Memorial Institute, Columbus, OH, 1949.

12. Dreisbach, R. R. *Physical Properties of Chemical Compounds*. v. 1 (1955), v. 2 (1959), v. 3 (1961). American Chemical Society. Washington, DC, 1955-61.

13. Cox, J. D., and Pilcher, G. *Thermochemistry of Organic and Organometallic Compounds*. Academic Press. London, England, 1970.

14. Kharasch, M. S. Heats of Combustion of Organic Compounds. *Bur. of Standards J. of Research*. Vol 2, 1929, pp 359-430.

15. Lipowitz, J. Flammability of Poly(dimethylsiloxanes). *J. Fire Flamm*. Vol 7, 1976, pp 482-503 and 504-529.

16. Throne, J. L., and Griskey, R. G. Heating Values and Thermochemical Properties of Plastics, *Modern Plastics*. Vol 49. pp 96-200. November 1972.

17. Hognon, B. Contribution possible des principaux isolants synthetiques a l'aggravation des dangers en cas d'incendie. *Cahiers du Centre Scientifique et Technique du Batiment*. p 1392 Sept. 1976.

18. NBS. Unpublished tests. U.S. National Bureau of Standards, undated.

19. Roff, W. J., and Scott, J. R. *Handbook of Common Polymers*. Butterworth, London, England, 1971.

20. Joshi, R. M. A New Generalized Bond Energy/Group Contribution Scheme for Calculating the Standard Heat of Formation of Monomers and Polymers. Part V. Oxygen Compounds. *J. Macromol. Sci. Chem.* A9, pp 1309-1383, 1975.

21. Van Krevelen, D. W. *Properties of Polymers*. Elsevier. Amsterdam, Holland, 1976.

22. Berlin, A. A. et al. Intermolecular Interaction in Polyconjugated Systems. *Acad. of Sciences (USSR) Bulletin. Div. of Chemical Science*. pp 1392-1395. July 1969.

23. Franz, J., Mische, W., and Kuzay, P. Zur Bestimmung Von Verbrennungswarmen Von Plasten. *Plaste Und Kautschuk*. Vol 14, pp 472-476, 1967.

24. Janssens, M., "Some Experience with the Cone Calorimeter, and Instrument to Measure the Rate of Smoke and Heat Release," in *Fundamental Aspects of Polymer Flammability*, G. Cox and G Stevens, eds. Institute of Physics, London, pp 111-125, 1987.

25. Moore, L. D. Full-Scale Burning Behavior of Curtains and Draperies (NBSIR 78-1448). U.S. National Bureau of Standards, 1978.

26. Domalski, E. S., Evans, W. H., and Jobe, T. L., Jr. Thermodynamic Data for Waste Incineration (NBSIR 78-1479). U.S. National Bureau of Standards, 1978.

27. Bostic, J. E., Jr., Yeh, K-N., and Barker, R. H. Pyrolysis and Combustion of Polyester. *Journal of Applied Polymer Science*. Vol 17, pp 471 - 482, 1973.

28. Lobanov, G. A., and Martynovskaya, L. I. Estimation of the Enthalpies of Combustion of Resin and Rubber Type Compounds. *Izv. Vyssh. Ucheb. Zaved., Khim. Tekhnol*. Vol 15, pp 1747-1748, 1972.30.

29. Ohe, H., Mastsuura, K., and Sakai, N. The Heat of Combustion and Oxygen Index of Fibrous Materials. *Textile Research J*. Vol 47, 1977, pp 212-216.

30. Lowrie, R. Heat of Combustion and Oxygen Compatibility. *Flammability and Sensitivity of Materials in Oxygen-Enriched Atmospheres* (ASTM STP 812). pp 84-96. Amer. Soc. for Testing and Materials. Philadelphia, PA, 1983.

31. Hust, J. G., and Clark, A. F. "A Survey of Compatibility of Materials with High Pressure Oxygen Service." *Cryogenics*. Vol 13, pp 325-336, 1973.

32. Stull, D. R., and Prophet, H. *JANAF Thermochemical Tables* (NSRDS-NBS 37). U.S. National Bureau of Standards, 1971.

33. Brandes, E. A. *Smithells Metals Reference Book*. Butterworths, London, England, 1983.

34. Rossini, F. D., ed. *Experimental Thermochemistry*. Vol 1. Interscience, New York, 1956.

35. ASTM, *Standard Method of Test for Gross Calorific Value of Solid Fuel by the Isothermal-Jacket Bomb Calorimeter* (D3286). American Society for Testing and Materials, undated.

36. ASTM, *Standards Definitions of Terms Relating to Coal and Coke* (ANSI/ASTM D 121). American Society for Testing and Materials, undated.

37. Huggett, C. "Estimation of Rate of Heat Release by Means of Oxygen Consumption Measurements." *Fire and Materials*, Vol 4, 1980.

38. Susott, R. A., DeGroot, W. F., and Shafizadeth, F. Heat Content of Natural Fuels. *J. of Fire and Flammability*. Vol 6, 1975, pp 311-325.

39. ASTM, *Standard Method for Estimation of Heat of Combustion of Aviation Fuels* (ANSI/ASTM D3338). American Society for Testing and Materials, undated.

40. Cragoe, C. S. *Thermal Properties of Petroleum Products* (Miscellaneous Publication 97). National Bureau of Standards, 1929.

41. Skinner, H. A., ed. *Experimental Thermochemistry*, Vol 2. Interscience, New York, 1962.

42. Cullis, C.F. and Hirschler, M.M. *The Combustion of Organic Polymers*. Clarendon Press. Oxford, England, 1981.

43. Factory Mutual Research Corp. "unpublished data," Factory Mutual Research Corp., Norwood, MA.

44. Hilado, C.J. *Flammability Handbook for Plastics*. Technomic. Westport, CT, 1982.

45. Tewarson, A. *Flame-Retardant Polymeric Materials*, Chapter 3, Plenum. New York, NY, 1982.

46. Tewarson, A. *Particulate Formation in Fires*. Paper presented at Conference on Large Scale Fire Phenomenology. Washington, DC. 1984.

47. Tewarson, A. *Physico-Chemical and Combustion/Pyrolysis Properties of Polymeric Materials* (NBS-GCR-80-295). U.S. National Bureau of Standards, 1980.

48. Tewarson, A., Khan, M. M., and Steciak, J. *A Study of Combustibility of Electrical Wires and Cables Used in Rail Rapid Transit Systems*. Transportation Systems Center. U.S. Dept. of Transportation, 1982.

49. Tewarson, A., Lee, J. L., and Pion, R. F. *Categorization of Cable Flammability*. Part I (EPRI NP-1200, Part 1). Electric Power Research Inst. Palo Alto, CA. 1979.

50. Tewarson, A., Lee, J. L., and Pion, R. F. *Fuel Parameters for Evaluation of the Fire Hazard of Red Oak* (FMRC J.I.OC6N2.RC). Factory Mutual Research Corp. Norwood, MA.1981.

51. *Standard Test Method for Heat and Visible Smoke Release Rates for Materials and Products Using an Oxygen Consumption Calorimeter,* (ASTM E 1354), American Society for Testing and Materials, Philadelphia, PA, 1990.

SI UNITS AND CONVERSION TABLES

Peter F. Johnson

Introduction to SI

This HANDBOOK serves as a major fire protection reference not only in the United States but throughout many other parts of the world. Almost all other countries use metric units for measurement and calculation, and the U. S. is expected to make the transition to metric units in the future. It is therefore appropriate and timely that this HANDBOOK be metricated as far as possible, while still retaining the customary units with which most people in the U.S. are familiar.

There are several versions of the metric system, but the one used by NFPA for this HANDBOOK is Le Systeme International d'Unites, commonly known as the International System of Units or simply "SI." The SI system constitutes a logical set of units based on powers of 10 that permits ease of manipulation and avoids the use of confusing numerical factors such as 1,760 yards (or 5,280 feet) in a mile.

The extent to which SI units have been incorporated varies throughout the HANDBOOK. Generally, a quantity expressed in customary units has been followed by the appropriate SI value and unit in parentheses, e.g., 14.7 psi (101 kPa). In many chapters, however, there are formulas that are unit dependent; they only give the correct answer when customary units are used. These formulas have been supplemented (where possible) with new formulas for use with SI units and the inclusion of relevant SI examples illustrating the use of these formulas. In many cases, supplemental columns and curves representing metric units have been added to existing tables and graphs. In some chapters, however, supplemental SI graphs or tables are either not warranted or have not yet been generated. In these cases, appropriate conversion factors have been included in the captions (or as footnotes) to existing graphs and tables.

Mr. Johnson is principal materials scientist (Fire Systems) at the Scientific Services Laboratory of Australian Construction Services, Melbourne.

Base units for SI

The use of SI units has generally followed the approach outlined in ASTM E-380—89, *Standard for Metric Practice*.[1] The seven base units defined in E-380—82 are:

Quantity	Unit	Symbol
length	meter	m
mass	kilogram	kg
time	second	s
electric current	ampere	A
thermodynamic temperature	kelvin	K
amount of substance	mole	mol
luminous intensity	candela	cd

Temperature Scales

One base unit worthy of further mention is the degree kelvin (K). This is the SI unit for thermodynamic (or absolute) temperature, and it has been properly used throughout the HANDBOOK for expressing thermodynamic and heat transfer quantities. For example, heat capacity is expressed as J/(kg • K), and radiant power is proportional to the fourth power of the absolute temperature T_k.

The degree Celsius (°C) also has been used extensively. Degree Celsius is the SI unit for expressing measured temperature or temperature intervals. Thus, the flashpoint of a flammable liquid is expressed in degrees Celsius. Similarly, a sprinkler head set to operate at 60°C (rather than 343 K) is appropriate.

The relationship between the measured temperature T (°C) and the thermodynamic temperature T_k is:

$$T_k = T\ (°C) + 273.15$$

A similar relationship exists between the measured temperature (°F) and the thermodynamic degree Rankine (R):

$$T_R = T\ (°F) + 459.7$$

Prefixes

To get multiples or submultiples of any SI unit, a range of standard prefixes is used, and the usual practice of choosing a prefix to limit the numerical value of a quantity to four or less digits has been followed, e.g., 28 000 m is better written as 2.8 km; 0.0017 g should be 1.7 mg.

tera	T	10^{12}
giga	G	10^{9}
mega	M	10^{5}
kilo	k	10^{3}
milli	m	10^{-3}
micro	μ	10^{-6}
nano	n	10^{-9}
pico	p	10^{-12}
femto	f	10^{-15}
atto	a	10^{-18}

Special Comments

Meter versus Metre: One departure from the SI system has been to use the spelling "meter" and "liter" throughout the HANDBOOK instead of the more international "metre" and "litre." This was done because the former terms are more commonly used in the U.S. and to maintain consistency with other NFPA publications.

Minute versus Second: A second difference is the choice of liter per minute and cubic meter per minute (L/min and m^3/min) for fluid flow instead of the more international L/s or m^3/s, particularly for hydraulics and water supplies. The minute was chosen in preference to the second because m^3/min or L/min more nearly equate to gallons per minute (gpm), and fire protection practitioners in many countries find gallons per minute an easier quantity to conceptualize and use in calculations. In addition, L/min and m^3/min are used in other NFPA publications, so consistency is again maintained.

Force and Mass: One area of confusion for those new to SI units is the conversion of force and mass terms. In the customary system a body may have a mass (amount of material) of 20 lb and a gravitational force of 20 lb wt on it (sometimes 20 lbf). The unit of pound (lb) appears in both terms. In SI totally different units are used for mass and force. The SI unit for mass is the kilogram (kg) and the unit for force is the newton (N). The appropriate conversion factors are:

Mass 1 lb = 0.453 25 kg

Force 1 lb wt (1 bf) = 4.448 N

The newton (N) and not the kilogram (kg) consequently appear in force-related terms like pressure (N/m^2 = Pa), energy (N · m = J), and power (N · m/s = W).

ROUNDING OFF

The approach to conversion from customary units to SI has been to retain both the number and its precision. For example, "It is about 8 miles" translates properly to "It is about 13 kilometers." Conversion to "It is about 12.88245 kilometers" would be totally inappropriate.

Conversions have been chosen to reflect the precision with which the quantity can be measured within the context of the chapter where the unit is used. As an illustration, a 125-ft length of sprinkler pipe measured to the nearest foot would convert to 38.1 m. However, if measured to the nearest 5 ft, 38 m would be the appropriate conversion. This consistent approach to rounding off has been taken throughout the HANDBOOK.

The SI units into which quantities have been converted have, for the most part, followed the SI practice of expressing a quantity so that its numerical value falls between 0.1 and 1000. An example found widely is the conversion of atmospheric pressure of 14.7 psi into 101 kPa, not 101 000 Pa. Under certain circumstances, however, permitted deviations from this practice are used. In particular, this applies where a range of values of the same quantity is being compared or presented in tabular form, e.g., if four samples had masses of 500 kg, 800 kg, 900 kg, and 1200 kg, it would not be appropriate to express the last mass as 1.2 Mg.

Conversion Factors

Conversion factors used throughout this HANDBOOK are detailed in Tables 22-2A and 22-2B. They include conversions within customary units as well as into SI units.

BIBLIOGRAPHY

References Cited

1. "Standard for Metric Practice," *ASTM E-380-89*. American Society for Testing and Materials, Philadelphia, PA.

Additional Readings

Metric Practice Guide—SI Units and Conversion Factors for the Steel Industry, 3rd ed., American Iron & Steel Institute, Washington, DC, 1978.

SI Units in Fire Protection Engineering, SFPE-MFP Report—1980, Society Of Fire Protection Engineers, Boston, MA, 1980.

TABLE 22-2A. ***Conversion Factors***

Length

1 inch = 0.08333 foot, 1,000 mils, 25.40 millimeters.
1 foot = 0.3333 yard, 12 inches, 0.3048 meter, 304.8 millimeters.
1 yard = 3 feet, 36 inches, 0.9144 meter.
1 rod = 16.5 feet, 5.5 yards, 5.029 meters.
1 mile (U.S. and British) = 5,280 feet, 1.609 kilometers, 0.8684 nautical mile.
1 millimeter = 0.03937 inch, 39.37 mils, 0.001 meter, 0.1 centimeter, 100 microns.
1 meter = 1.094 yards, 3.281 feet, 39.37 inches, 1,000 millimeters.
1 kilometer = 0.6214 mile, 1.094 yards, 3,281 feet, 1,000 meters.
1 nautical mile = 1.152 miles (statute), 1.853 kilometers.
1 micron = 0.03937 mil, 0.00003937 inch.
1 mil = 0.001 inch, 0.0254 millimeters, 25.40 microns.
1 degree = 1/360 circumference of a circle, 60 minutes, 3,600 seconds.
1 minute = 1/60 degree, 60 seconds.
1 second = 1/60 minute, 1/3600 degree.

Area

1 square inch = 0.006944 square foot, 1,273,000 circular mils, 645.2 square millimeters.
1 square foot = 0.1111 square yard, 144 square inches, 0.09290 square meter, 92,900 square millimeters.
1 square yard = 9 square feet, 1,296 square inches, 0.8361 square meter.
1 acre = 43,560 square feet, 4,840 square yards, 0.001563 square mile, 4,047 square meters, 160 square rods.
1 square mile = 640 acres, 102,400 square rods, 3,097,600 square yards, 2.590 square kilometers.
1 square millimeter = 0.001550 square inch, 1,974 circular mils.
1 square meter = 1.196 square yards, 10.76 square feet, 1,550 square inches. 1,000,000 square millimeters.
1 square kilometer = 0.3861 square mile, 247.1 acres, 1,196,000 square yards, 1,000,000 square meters.
1 circular mil = 0.7854 square mil, 0.0005067 square millimeter, 0.0000007854 square inch.

Volume (Capacity)

1 fluid ounce = 1.805 cubic inches, 29.57 milliliters, 0.03125 quarts (U.S.) liquid measure.
1 cubic inch = 0.5541 fluid ounce, 16.39 milliliters.
1 cubic foot = 7.481 gallons (U.S.) 6.229 gallons (British), 1,728 cubic inches, 0.02832 cubic meter, 28.32 liters.
1 cubic yard = 27 cubic feet, 46,656 cubic inches, 0.7646 cubic meter, 746.6 liters, 202.2 gallons (U.S.), 168.4 gallons (British).
1 gill = 0.03125 gallon, 0.125 quart, 4 ounces, 7.219 cubic inches, 118.3 milliliters.
1 pint = 0.01671 cubic foot, 28.88 cubic inches, 0.125 gallon, 4 gills, 16 fluid ounces, 473.2 milliliters.
1 quart = 2 pints, 32 fluid ounces, 0.9464 liter, 946.4 milliliters, 8 gills, 57.75 cubic inches.
1 U.S. gallon = 4 quarts, 128 fluid ounces, 231.0 cubic inches, 0.1337 cubic foot, 3.785 liters (cubic decimeters), 3,785 milliliters, 0.8327 Imperial gallon.
1 Imperial (British and Canadian) gallon = 1.201 U.S. gallons, 0.1605 cubic foot, 277.3 cubic inches, 4.546 liters (cubic decimeters), 4,546 milliliters.
1 U.S. bushel = 2,150 cubic inches, 0.9694 British bushel, 35.24 liters.
1 barrel (U.S. liquid) = 31.5 gallons (various industries have special definitions of a barrel.)
1 barrel (petroleum) = 42.0 gallons.
1 millimeter = 0.03381 fluid ounce, 0.06102 cubic inch, 0.001 liter.
1 liter (cubic decimeter) = 0.2642 gallon, 0.03532 cubic foot, 1.057 quarts, 33.81 fluid ounces, 61.03 cubic inches, 1,000 milliliters.
1 cubic meter (kiloliter) = 1.308 cubic yards, 35.32 cubic feet, 264.2 gallons, 1,000 liters.
1 cord = 128 cubic feet, 8 feet × 4 feet × 4 feet, 3.625 cubic meters.

Weight

1 grain = 0.0001428 pound.
1 ounce (avoirdupois) = 0.06250 pound (avoirdupois) = 0.06250 pound (avoirdupois), 28.35 grams, 437.5 grains.
1 pound (avoirdupois) = the mass of 27.69 cubic inches of water weighed in air at 4°C (39.2°F) and 760 millimeters of mercury (atmospheric pressure), 16 ounces (avoirdupois), 0.4536 kilogram, 453.6 grams, 7,000 grains.
1 long ton (U.S. and British) = 1.120 short tons, 2,240 pounds, 1.016 metric tons, 1016 kilograms.
1 short ton (U.S. and British) = 0.8929 long ton, 2,000 pounds, 0.9072 metric ton, 907.2 kilograms.
1 milligram = 0.001 gram, 0.000002205 pound (avoirdupois).
1 gram = 0.002205 pound (avoirdupois), 0.03527 ounce, 0.001 kilogram, 15.43 grains.
1 kilogram = the mass of 1 liter of water in air at 4°C and 760 millimeters of mercury (atmospheric pressure), 2.205 pounds (avoirdupois), 35.27 ounces (avoirdupois), 1,000 grams.
1 metric ton = 0.9842 long ton, 1.1023 short tons, 2,205 pounds, 1,000 kilograms.

Velocity

1 foot per second = 0.6818 mile per hour, 18.29 meters per minute, 0.3048 meters per second.
1 mile per hour = 1.467 feet per second, 1.609 kilometers per hour, 26.82 meters per minute, 0.4470 meters per second.
1 kilometer per hour = 0.2778 meter per second, 0.5396 knot per hour, 0.6214 mile per hour, 54.68 feet per minute.
1 meter per minute = 0.03728 mile per hour, 0.05468 foot per second, 0.06 kilometer per hour, 16.67 millimeters per second, 3.281 feet per minute.
1 knot per hour = 1.152 miles per hour, 1.689 feet per second, 1.853 kilometers per hour.
1 revolution per minute = 0.01667 revolution per second, 6 degrees per second.
1 revolution per second = 60 revolutions per minute, 360 degrees per second.

Acceleration

Standard gravity = 32.17 feet per second per second, 9.807 meters per second per second.

Density

1 gram per millimeter = 0.03613 pound per cubic inch, 8.345 pounds per gallon, 62.43 pounds per cubic foot, 998.9 ounces per cubic foot.
Mercury at 0°C = 0.1360 grams per millimeter, basic value used in expressing pressures in terms of columns of mercury.
1 pound per cubic foot = 16.02 kilograms per cubic meter.
1 pound per gallon = 0.1198 grams per milliter.

Flow

1 cubic foot per minute = 0.1247 gallon per second, 0.4720 liter per second, 472.0 milliliters per second.
1 gallon per minute = 0.06308 liter per second, 1,440 gallons per day, 0.002228 cubic foot per second.
1 liter per second = 2.119 cubic feet per minute, 15.85 gallons (U.S.) per minute.
1 liter per minute = 0.0005885 cubic foot per second, 0.004403 gallon per second.
1 gallon per minute per square foot = 40.746 liters per minute per square meter.

TABLE 22-2A. ***(Con't)***

Pressure

Absolute pressure = the sum of the gage pressure and the barometric pressure.

1 atmosphere = pressure exerted by 760 millimeters of mercury of standard density at 0°C, 14.70 pounds per square inch, 29.92 inches of mercury at 32°F, 33.90 feet of water at 39.2°F, 101.3 kilopascal.

1 millimeter of mercury (at 0°C) = 0.001316 atmosphere, 0.01934 pound per square inch, 0.04460 foot of water (4°C or 39.2°F), 0.0193 pound per square inch, 0.1333 kilopascal.

1 inch of water (at 39.2°F) = 0.00246 atmosphere, 0.0361 pound per square inch, 0.0736 inch of mercury (at 32°F). 0.2491 kilopascal.

1 foot of water (at 39.2°F) = 0.02950 atmosphere, 0.4335 pound per square inch, 0.8827 inch of mercury (at 32°F), 22.42 millimeters of mercury, 2.989 kilopascal.

1 inch of mercury (at 32°F) = 0.03342 atmosphere, 0.4912 pound per square inch, 1.133 feet of water, 13.60 inches of water (at 39.2°F), 3.386 kilopascal.

1 millibar (1/1000 bar) = 0.02953 inch of mercury. A bar is the pressure exerted by a force of one million dynes on a square centimeter of surface.

1 pound per square inch = 0.06805 atmosphere, 2.036 inches of mercury, 2.307 feet of water, 51.72 millimeters of mercury, 27.67 inches of water (at 39.2°F), 144 pounds per square foot, 2,304 ounces per square foot, 6.895 kilopascal.

1 pound per square foot = 0.00047 atmosphere, 0.00694 pound per square inch, 0.0160 foot of water, 0.391 millimeter of mercury, 0.04788 kilopascal.

1 ton (short) per square foot = 0.9451 atmosphere, 13.89 pounds per square inch, 9.765 kilograms per square meter.

1 Torr = 0.013 Pascal.

Power

1 British thermal unit per hour = 0.293 watts.

1 British chemical unit per minute = 1.054 kW.

1 British chemical unit per second per square foot = 11.33 kilowatts per square meter.

1 horsepower = 746 watts, 1.014 metric horsepower, 10.69 kilograms-calories per minute, 42.42 British thermal units per minute, 550 pound-feet per second, 33,000 pound-feet per minute.

1 kilowatt = 1.341 horsepower, 1.360 metric horsepower, 14.33 kilogram-calories per minute, 56.90 British thermal units per minute, 1,000 watts.

Heat (Mean Values)

1 British thermal unit = 0.2520 kilogram-calorie, 1,055 joules (absolute).

1 kilogram-calorie = 3.969 British thermal units, 4,187 joules.

1 British thermal unit per pound = 0.5556 kilogram-calorie per kilogram, 2.325 joules per gram.

1 gram-calorie per gram = 1.8 British thermal units per pound, 4.187 joules per gram.

Electrical

1 volt = potential required to produce current flow of 1 ampere through a resistance or impedance of 1 ohm, or current flow of 2 amperes through resistance of ½ ohm, etc.

1 ampere = current flow through a resistance or impedance of 1 ohm produced by a potential of 1 volt, or current flow through a resistance of 100 ohms produced by a potential of 100 volts, etc.

1 milliampere = 0.001 ampere.

1 ohm = resistance or impedance through which current of 1 ampere will flow under a potential of 1 volt.

1 microhm = 0.000001 ohm.

mho = Unit of conductance. In a direct current, circuit conductance in mhos is the reciprocal of number of ohms resistance.

1 watt = power developed by current flow of 1 ampere under potential of 1 volt. (DC, or AC with power factor unity.) See also Power.

1 joule = 1 watt second. A flow of 1 ampere through a resistance of 1 ohm for 1 second (see also Heat).

1 millijoule = 0.001 joule.

Radiation

1 curie = the emission of 3.70 × 1010 beta particles per second (the particles emitted per second from 1 gram of radium).

1 roentgen = the quantity of X-rays which will produce 2.08×10^9 ion pairs in 1 cubic centimeter of dry air at 0°C and standard atmospheric pressure.

TABLE 22-2B. ***Temperature Conversion, Celsius—Fahrenheit***

Temp. Celsius = 5/9 (Temp. F − 32 deg.)
Temp. Fahrenheit = 9/5 × Temp. C + 32 deg.
Rankine (Fahrenheit Absolute) = Temp. F + 459.67 deg.
kelvin (Celsius Absolute) = Temp. C + 273.15 deg.
Freezing point of water: Celsius = 0 deg.; Fahr. = 32 deg.
Boiling point of water: Celsius = 100 deg.; Fahr. = 212 deg.
Absolute zero: Celsius = −273.15 deg.; Fahr. = −459.67 deg.

Celsius	Fahrenheit	Celsius	Fahrenheit	Celsius	Fahrenheit	Celsius	Fahrenheit
−273.15	−459.67	21	69.8	48.9	120	98	208.4
−200	−328	21.1	70	49	120.2	98.9	210
−100	−148	21.7	71	50	122	99	210.2
0	32	22	71.6	51	123.8	100	212
0.56	33	22.2	72	52	125.6	120	248
1	33.8	22.8	73	53	127.4	121.1	250
1.11	34	23	73.4	54	129.2	140	284
1.67	35	23.3	74	54.4	130	148.9	300
2	35.6	23.9	75	55	131	160	320
2.22	36	24	75.2	56	132.8	176.7	350
2.78	37	24.4	76	57	134.6	180	356
3	37.4	25	77	58	136.4	200	392
3.33	38	25.6	78	59	138.2	204.4	400
3.89	39	26	78.8	60	140	250	482
4	39.2	26.1	79	61	141.8	260	500
4.44	40	26.7	80	62	143.6	300	572
5	41	27	80.6	63	145.4	315.8	600
5.56	42	27.2	81	64	147.2	350	662
6	42.8	27.8	82	65	149	371.1	700
6.11	43	28	82.4	65.6	150	400	752
6.67	44	28.3	83	66	150.8	426.7	800
7	44.6	28.9	84	67	152.6	450	842
7.22	45	29	84.2	68	154.4	482.2	900
7.78	46	29.4	85	69	156.2	500	932
8	46.4	30	86	70	158	537.8	1000
8.33	47	30.6	87	71	159.8	600	1112
8.89	48	31	87.8	71.1	160	648.9	1200
9	48.2	31.1	88	72	161.6	700	1292
9.44	49	31.7	89	73	163.4	760	1400
10	50	32	89.6	74	165.2	800	1472
10.6	51	32.2	90	75	167	871.1	1600
11	51.8	32.8	91	76	168.8	900	1652
11.1	52	33	91.4	76.7	170	982.2	1800
11.7	53	33.3	92	77	171.6	1000	1832
12	53.6	33.9	93	78	172.4	1093.3	2000
12.2	54	34	93.2	79	174.2	1100	2012
12.8	55	34.4	94	80	176	1200	2192
13	55.4	35	95	81	177.8	1204.4	2200
13.3	56	35.6	96	82	179.6	1300	2372
13.9	57	36	96.8	82.2	180	1315.6	2400
14	57.2	36.1	97	83	181.4	1400	2552
14.4	58	36.7	98	84	183.2	1428	2600
15	59	37	98.6	85	185	1500	2732
15.6	60	37.2	99	86	186.8	1537.8	2800
16	60.8	37.8	100	87	188.6	1600	2912
16.1	61	38	100.4	87.8	190	1648.9	3000
16.7	62	39	102.2	88	190.4	1700	3092
17	62.6	40	104	89	192.2	1760	3200
17.2	63	41	105.8	90	194	1800	3272
17.8	64	42	107.6	91	195.8	1871.1	3400
18	64.4	43	109.4	92	197.6	1900	3452
18.3	65	43.3	110	93	199.4	1982	3600
18.9	66	44	111.2	93.3	200	2000	3632
19	66.2	45	113	94	201.2	2204.4	4000
19.4	67	46	114.8	95	203	2500	4532
20	68	47	116.6	96	204.8	2760	5000
20.6	69	48	118.4	97	206.6	3000	5432

ORGANIZATIONS WITH FIRE PROTECTION INTERESTS IN THE UNITED STATES

Since fire is a universal threat, it is natural that a large number of organizations take an active interest in fire prevention and control. The degree of interest and activity varies widely. This appendix provides information on some representative organizations that have demonstrated interest in fire prevention and control. It is not a complete listing but may serve to indicate the breadth of the interest and the availability of resources. This appendix is presented as follows:

A. National Fire Protection Association.
B. Insurance Organizations in the United States with Fire Protection Interests.
C. National Fire Service Organizations in the United States.
D. Fire Research Laboratories.
E. Fire Testing Laboratories.
F. Society of Fire Protection Engineers.
G. Federal Involvement in Fire Protection.

A. NATIONAL FIRE PROTECTION ASSOCIATION

The National Fire Protection Association (NFPA), organized in 1896, has as its mission the safeguarding of people, their property, and the environment from destructive fire, using scientific and engineering techniques and education. The Association was incorporated in 1930 under laws of the Commonwealth of Massachusetts and has its headquarters in Quincy, MA.

NFPA is an independent, voluntary membership, nonprofit (tax-exempt) organization. A 30-member Board of Directors has general charge of the affairs of the Association, which has a staff of some 150 professional men and women, plus more than 178 support personnel.

NFPA is financed principally by sales of its publications and audiovisual materials, membership dues, income from seminars, research grants, and contributions. It operates on an annual budget of $35 million.

Membership in NFPA totals more than 60,000 individuals and 115 national trade and professional organizations. The vast majority of the members are residents of the United States, but, due to our international status, we have many members from Canada and 85 other nations. Members are drawn from fire departments (24%); health care facilities (11%); business and industry (20%); insurance (6%); federal, state and local government (7%); architects and engineers (8%); fire equipment manufacturers and distributors (6%); trade and professional associations (2%); and other fields (16%).

Voting Members are in six categories: Regular, Life, Senior, Organization, Sustaining, and Honorary. Nonvoting Memberships are in two categories: Affiliate and Student.

Within the Voting Membership are 13 Sections. Oldest is the Fire Marshals Association of North America, founded in 1906 and reorganized in 1927 as the Fire Marshals Section of NFPA. Other Sections, in order of their founding, are Electrical (1948), Rail Transportation Systems (1963), Industrial Fire Protection (1963), Fire Service (1973), Health Care (1976), Fire Science and Technology Educators (1976), Architects, Engineers and Building Code Officials (1979), Aviation (1980), Education (1981), Research (1987), Wildland Fire Management (1988), and Lodging Industry (1988).

To facilitate communication between Association members and management, the Member Advisory Council was established in 1975. Its members are well distributed geographically as well as representative of the diversified interests in the Association membership. It is administered to on a local level by eight Regional Vice Chairmen, each, themselves, Council members. The Council serves voluntarily to communicate to NFPA management the thoughts and suggestions of members of the Association. It meets once a year, during the Fall Meeting in November.

The four-day NFPA Annual Meeting and Firesafety Exhibit takes place each May, with an average attendance of 5,000 persons and the largest firesafety exhibit of its kind in North America. The Fall Meeting, which lasts three or four days and attracts some 1,200 persons, occurs each November. To reach a larger segment of members, meetings are held in various locations throughout the United States; some take place in Canada; and one, thus far, has been in Europe. Technical presentations on new developments and concepts, discussions, voting on Technical Committee standards actions, NFPA Section meetings, conduct of other Association business, and special events make up the Meeting programs. Registration is open to all who are interested, although only Voting Members may vote.

Since 1982, Regional Membership Meetings have taken place in various cities throughout the U.S. and Canada each year. These one-day events enable NFPA members in a region to meet each other; to meet and hear from NFPA Board of Directors, administration and staff members; to discuss openly any problem of concern; and to learn first-hand about new developments in firesafety.

Activities of NFPA generally fall into two broad, interrelated areas: technical and educational.

The basic technical activity involves development, publication, and dissemination of timely consensus standards intended to minimize the possibility and effects of fire in all aspects of contemporary activity.

In addition, efforts directed at people of all ages and regions continue to educate with regard to preventing the loss of life and property from fire. Key to this educational effort are the teaching of standards and the importance of firesafety as a way of life.

Standards and codes are developed by more than 225 NFPA Committees, each of which represents a balance of affected interests. More than 4,500 individuals serve on the Association's Committees, all on a voluntary, unpaid basis. Committees operate according to the detailed official Regulations Governing Committee Projects, and are administered by the Standards Council which reports to the Association's Board of Directors.

Built into the standards development and adoption process is the publication of calls for proposals to amend existing documents, or to shape the content of new documents. These public proposals, together with the committee action on each proposal, as well as committee-generated proposals, are published in the Technical Committee Reports (TCR) for public review and comment. Public comments, together with the committee action on each comment, are then published in the Technical Committee Documentation (TCD). Only after this public review and comment cycle has been completed is the final committee report brought before the membership for action. This democratic legislative procedure allows proponents and opponents to be freely heard. Once adopted by the NFPA membership at either an Annual Meeting or a Fall Meeting, and issued by the Standards Council, standards are published and made available for voluntary adoption.

Tentative Interim Amendments and Formal Interpretations are issued from time to time. Notices of the issuance of Amendments and Interpretations are published in *Fire News* and other media.

Each official NFPA document is published in a pamphlet edition. All documents appear in the multi-volume set of *National Fire Codes®*. Among the most widely used documents are the *National Electrical Code®* (NFPA 70); the *Life Safety Code®* (NFPA 101®); the *Flammable and Combustible Liquids Code* (NFPA 30); the *Automatic Sprinkler Standard* (NFPA 13); the *Liquefied Petroleum Gases Standard* (NFPA 58); and the *Health Care Facilities Standard* (NFPA 99).

NFPA standards and codes, which currently number about 275, have great influence because they are widely used as the basis of legislation and regulation at all levels of government, from local to national. Many are referenced by agencies of the federal government, such as the Occupational Safety and Health Administration (OSHA) in their own regulations. The documents also are used by insurance authorities for risk evaluation and premium rating.

A National Fire Codes Subscription Service is offered, through which over 20,000 subscribers automatically receive the *Fire Codes* in loose-leaf format, along with all other standards-related information, such as Tentative Interim Amendments, Formal Interpretations, TCDs, and TCRs.

The Engineering Services Division is responsible for providing advisory services and liaison to Technical Committees relative to fire protection standards dealing with fire protection equipment, occupancies, and equipment hazards. Technical advisory services are provided on both a formal and an informal basis, regarding questions on and interpretations of NFPA Codes and Standards. Five special Field Service groups were established to provide guidance in the application of pertinent standards in specialized areas. The Field Services include Electrical, Life Safety, Gases, Flammable Liquids, and Marine. Through the Marine Chemist Qualification Board, the Association administers the NFPA Certificated Marine Chemist Program. Engineering staff perform the Executive Secretarial function for six NFPA Membership Sections: Architects', Engineers' and Building Officials' Section; Aviation Section; Electrical Section; Health Care Section; Industrial Fire Protection Section; and Rail Transportation Systems Section. Engineering Division technical staff also serve as instructors, lecturers, and panelists in a variety of Association and non-Association fire protection-related programs throughout the world.

The Public Fire Protection Division responds to all inquiries related to the public fire service. Division staff—all with fire service experience—provide liaison for all fire service-related Technical Committees and serve as Executive Secretaries for three NFPA Membership Sections: Fire Service, Fire Science and Technology Educators, and Wildfire Management. The National Fire Service Certification Program is administered by the Division. Division staff also are involved in the development and marketing of NFPA products for the fire service, and participate in training seminars and conferences throughout North America and abroad.

The Association's technical and general interest publications program ranges across the fire protection spectrum. In addition to codes and standards, it includes handbooks, reference books, fire service publications, textbooks, field guides, and training manuals.

The Association is also a major distributor of film and videotape programs covering a wide range of fire protection and fire prevention topics.

The newly redesigned *NFPA Journal* is the official journal of the NFPA, reaching all its various firesafety professionals. Covering major topics in fire protection and suppression, the *Journal* carries investigation reports authored by NFPA specialists, special NFPA statistical studies on large-loss fires, multiple deaths, fire fighter deaths and injuries and others annually, as well as articles on fire protection advances, public education, and information of interest to NFPA members. Timely articles on fire fighting techniques, and fire department management are covered. *Fire Technology*, a quarterly technical journal, reaches some 5,000 international subscribers interested in receiving information about the scientific and technical aspects of fire, including reports on fire modeling, sprinklering, fire fighter safety, and tests results from laboratory experimentation. *Fire News* is the bi-monthly member newsletter. Issues go to every NFPA member, providing Standards information and Association reports on events of interest to the entire membership. The *NFPA Buyer's Guide* is an annual NFPA member publication that provides a guide to the names, offices, and products or services of all leading fire protection and fire service manufacturers. *Noticiero Tecnico sobre Incendios* is the NFPA's Spanish-language bulletin containing reports, articles, and meeting notices of interest to the international Spanish-speaking community. In addition, many NFPA Sections publish their own informational newsletters.

The *NFPA Journal* and the *NFPA Buyers'Guide* are supported, in part, through the sale of product and service advertisements. The Association solicits paid ads through traditional avenues, such as direct selling by representatives, promotional materials, and attendance at several trade shows. The Association has formulated an advertising standards policy which is widely known throughout the industries served by the publications. The Association also maintains a standing Advertising Review Board which checks every ad submitted for compliance with the published standards policy.

The Association maintains one of the world's most extensive fire experience data bases. NFPA's annual survey of fire departments and the Fire Incident Data Organization (FIDO) file on large fires and other fires of major technical interest are used along with special studies and other major data bases, most notably the Federal Emergency Management Agency's (FEMA) National Fire Incident Reporting System (NFIRS). The Fire Analysis and Research Division produces more than a dozen annual reports and many special studies on aspects of the nation's fire problem; responds to thousands of individual data requests; supports the information needs of NFPA's committees, membership sections, and technical programs; and provides analysis and data services for government agencies and private sector organizations. The Division also provides the Executive Secretary for the NFPA Research Section and maintains liaisons and activities in several areas of research, notably fire risk assessment.

Reports and packages on a wide range of topics are available through the Division's One-Stop Data Shop program. Special analyses and summaries of sample incidents relating to specific interests can be obtained, with great flexibility in meeting the needs of requesters. Members receive discounts on fees assessed for special data base research and analyses.

The Fire Investigations Division conducts investigations of major fires of technical or educational interest. Important lessons learned from the fires provide input to NFPA Technical Committees and technical programs and are distributed to various NFPA networks and to the fire community. In addition, the Fire Investigations Division issues special firesafety alert bulletins, regularly coordinates with fire marshals, metropolitan fire chiefs, building code groups, and allied organizations on fire investigations and fire hazard studies.

NFPA also maintains the Charles S. Morgan Technical Library which was founded in 1945. The library, which covers all facets of the fire problem, comprises the largest fire protection collection in the United States, and is one of the world's finest English-language resources in its field. The technical and reference data contained in this continually expanding collection numbers approximately 5,000 books, 250 periodical titles, 12,500 technical reports, 13,000 pieces of microform, 275 film reels, 350 audiocassette tapes, 45 shelf-feet of voluntary industrial standards, and 200 shelf-feet of NFPA-published archives dating back to 1896.

The NFPA's Research Foundation was established in 1982 to provide a catalyst for conducting independent research on fire risk and new technologies and strategies. Broad-based technical advisory committees guide each project, and the Foundation collaborates with laboratories throughout the world.

The Association frequently is called upon to present expert testimony before Congressional committees and at other federal hearings. Consequently, NFPA maintains offices in Washington, DC, for close liaison with Congress as well as with departments and independent agencies of the federal government. In addition, the NFPA Washington office has the responsibility of working with the Association's Washington-based members, and with members who may be visiting in the area.

The Association's international operations also are based in the NFPA Washington office. NFPA provides liaison and a wide variety of supporting services to its overseas members located in more than 85 countries.

NFPA has established regional representation through a western office and a southern and central states representative to better serve members in these areas. The Western Regional Office is located in Ontario, CA, and the southern and central states representative operates out of Gainesville, FL. The northeastern U.S. and Canada are served by representatives based at the headquarters office in Quincy, MA.

Learn Not to Burn® is the theme and focus of NFPA's comprehensive firesafety education initiatives, reorganized in 1988 within the new Public Education Division. Assisted by a regional team of Firesafety Education Representatives located throughout the U.S. and Canada, NFPA helps fire departments and communities promote awareness of the fire/burn problem and implements effective educational programs to address it. Through the Education Section, NFPA supports an expanding national network of individuals committed to applying innovative educational methods to reduce the loss of life and property from fire.

One of NFPA's most important commitments is to developing future generations of firesafe adults. Children in kindergarten through eighth grade receive critical life-safety skills through the comprehensive *Learn Not to Burn Curriculum*. Since its release in 1979, the Curriculum, now in its third edition, has been credited with saving well over 175 people from fire injury or death. Material in the Curriculum is structured around 22 key firesafety behaviors and is organized in three learning levels. The program provides lesson plans and suggested activities to allow the teacher to integrate firesafety lessons into regular classroom subject areas. More than 50,000 units of the *Learn Not to Burn Curriculum* have been distributed throughout the United States and Canada.

Since 1922, NFPA has served as the national sponsor of Fire Prevention Week each October. The Association produces posters, booklets, flyers, and children's items that teach personal, home, and on-the-job firesafety. The NFPA produces over 30 brochures covering a broad range of firesafety topics such as match and lighter firesafety, exit drills, school fire drills, cooking firesafety, health care facilities, high rise firesafety, hotel/motel firesafety, etc. Sparky's®

Firesafety Coloring Book, Little Folks Firesafety Fun, *Sparky's Team* comic book, and Sparky's Membership Kit are some of the educational and fun products designed to teach children important firesafety lessons. The National Firesafety Poster contest, conducted each year in conjunction with Fire Prevention Week, attracts more than 5,000 entries from school children learning important firesafety behaviors in their classrooms.

NFPA established the Learn Not to Burn Foundation in 1986 to secure funding for targeted educational programs which address special problems and audiences. The mission of the Foundation is "to reduce deaths, injuries, and loss of property from fires and burns among people shown to be at highest risk to fires." The Foundation is particularly interested in reaching young children, older adults, and low-income populations in urban and rural areas. Some projects for 1991 include the development of an animated television public service announcement addressed to young children on the subject of matches and lighters. The PSA, aimed at children ages 3 to 6, will teach preschoolers to "tell a grown-up when you find matches and lighters." This project was funded by the Lighter Association which also funded a television public service announcement in 1988 starring "Sesame Street's" Alaina Reed, urging parents to keep matches and lighters away from young children. Under a generous grant from the Continental Corporation Foundation, the Learn Not to Burn Foundation has developed a preschool module of the *Learn Not to Burn Curriculum*® which includes a musical tape featuring songs and words specifically written for preschoolers by a nationally recognized folk singer. *Learn Not to Burn: The Preschool Program* focuses on seven key firesafety behaviors adapted for the very vulnerable age group of 3- to 5-year-old children. In addition, the Foundation is beginning to formulate fundraising ideas to support projects which will address the firesafety needs of the rural and urban poor.

The Learn Not to Burn Foundation also supports the work of the Technical Advisory Council (TAC), a group of leading scientific and educational experts who meet regularly to apply the findings of new research to firesafety messages. Since 1987, the TAC has reviewed and made recommendations on important issues such as the proper placement of hands during the Stop, Drop and Roll technique; where and how to feel a door before exiting a room during a fire; firesafety needs of the hearing-impaired; and fabric flammability standards for adult sleepwear.

In other educational activities, NFPA disseminates knowledge and methodology on fire-related problems and solutions through NFPA-sponsored and contracted seminars and workshops. These programs involve discussion and application of codes and standards, plus application of state-of-the-art fire protection technology. Current programs support the various NFPA codes and standards, such as the *Life Safety Code* (NFPA 101), the *National Electrical Code* (NFPA 70), the Fire Alarms and Signaling Seminars (NFPA 72 series), and *Automatic Sprinklers* (NFPA 13). Other programs are directed toward special audiences such as health care and correctional officials. All the Division's programs are available for on-site, contracted training.

Yet another form of educational activity is carried on by NFPA through its public information program. The Association is recognized by the electronic and print media as the nation's authoritative source of technical background, data, and consumer advice on the fire problem and firesafety. Staff specialists frequently are interviewed by international, national, and local media. The Association continues to supply timely material on a regular basis to specialized periodicals in virtually every field.

The Marketing and Sales Division serves the broad needs of members and customers, providing NFPA products and membership services on an efficient and timely basis. To make the nationwide ordering of products easier, an 800 number (1-800-344-3555) operates from 8:30 AM to 8 PM Eastern Time. Division staff market products through direct response marketing methods. The Director of Sales markets products like the *National Electrical Code* through a small group of distributors.

In the Spring of 1981, the Association moved from downtown Boston, where it rented office space for some 80 years, to Quincy, about 10 miles to the south. There, at Batterymarch Park, NFPA occupies its first permanent headquarters, situated on a 52-acre hilltop site.

B. INSURANCE ORGANIZATIONS IN THE UNITED STATES WITH FIRE PROTECTION INTERESTS

American Insurance Service Group, 85 John St., New York, NY 10038

Incorporated in 1984 as a not-for-profit organization, the American Insurance Services Group, Inc. (AISG) provides specialized services to the property-casualty insurance industry as a subsidiary of the American Insurance Association, the nation's oldest and largest insurance trade association. The American Insurance Association was created in 1964 by merging the National Board of Fire Underwriters (organized 1866), the Association of Casualty and Surety Companies (organized 1926), and the former American Insurance Association (founded 1953).

Among the important services provided by AISG is its Engineering and Safety Service, a direct successor to the National Board of Fire Underwriters. As of 1987, the Engineering and Safety Service had over 250 subscriber insurance companies, representing nearly 90 percent of the property-casualty insurance business. The Service is dedicated to providing information, education, and consultation to the technical and loss control personnel of its subscribing companies. It accomplishes this through a series of technical reports and bulletins, training programs, and conferences, dealing with a variety of technical categories and supporting a total loss control concept, including boilers and machinery, building technology, commercial vehicles, construction hazards, crime prevention, environmental science, fire protection, industrial hygiene, occupational safety and health, pollution control, product safety, and special and chemical hazards. The Service also publishes a wide variety of accident prevention publications, fire prevention education materials, a specialized publication on fire resistance of construction assemblies, and numerous other related items, many of which are available to the public.

Alliance of American Insurers, 20 North Wacker Dr., Chicago, IL 60606

The Alliance, organized in 1922, is a national organization of 150 property loss control and casualty insurance companies providing engineering, legal, legislative, educational, and public relations services for its member companies. Its staff is oriented, in part, to fire loss prevention studies, and this work is carried out through the Alliance's Accident and Fire Prevention Department with advice from a Loss Control Committee and its Fire Safety Subcommittee composed of engineers and other technically qualified persons in its member companies.

The Loss Control Department offers technical seminars in fire protection, safety, and industrial hygiene, and publishes a wide array of training materials for company loss control personnel. Firesafety materials include the series "Judging the Fire Risk" and "Simplified Water Supply Testing." In addition, the Alliance's *Journal of American Insurance* and other public information programs disseminate firesafety and anti-arson materials to the insurance industry, government, and the general public.

Factory Mutual System, 1151 Boston-Providence Turnpike, Norwood, MA 02062

The Factory Mutual (FM) System is composed of three large mutual property insurance companies (Allendale Insurance; Arkwright-Protection Mutual Insurance), two System associates (Factory Mutual International, Factory Mutual Engineering and Research), and the Factory Mutual Research Corporation. It was founded in 1835 to provide mutual fire insurance coverage for large industrial and commercial properties in the United States and Canada, but is now multi-international in scope. Its objective is to minimize losses to property and associated interruption to production from such perils as fire, explosion, wind, collapse, and conventional boiler and machinery accidents. It also seeks to provide insurance at minimum cost through loss prevention inspections of plants, research, and consultation services to its insureds. It is also known for its testing and approval services.

Since 1973, Factory Mutual System has published the multi-volume, loose-leaf *Loss Prevention Data* books (with an updating service) which are available to companies insured by the FMRC system. They contain information and recommendations for the prevention of fire, explosions, wind damage, electrical breakdowns, and boiler and machinery accidents. FMRC also produces training films on fire and explosion hazards. It publishes numerous loss prevention materials, among them *The Handbook of Property Conservation*, a 264-page, pocket-size manual directed to property conservation directors to help them maintain active plant emergency organizations. The *Factory Mutual Record*, which covers property conservation engineering and management, is published bimonthly and sent free to Factory Mutual members, and is also available on a subscription basis.

Industrial Risk Insurers, 85 Woodland St., Hartford CT 06102

This underwriting and loss prevention organization was founded in 1890 as the Factory Insurance Association, which merged in 1975 with the Oil Insurance Association to form Industrial Risk Insurers (IRI).

IRI provides property insurance for well-protected risks in numerous industries, e.g. metalworking, chemicals, oil, gas petrochemicals, paper, textiles, food, wood, leather, rubber, synthetic fuels, and others, including service risks such as hospitals, universities, and shopping centers.

IRI issues policies covering property damage (including builders risk), business interruption, extra expense, contingent business interruption, and boiler and machinery on both a named peril and all-risk basis. The all-risk program may include earthquake, flood, and transit.

In addition to IRI's home office in Hartford, CT, and regional offices in Chicago, San Francisco, and Hartford, some 26 district offices are located in major industrial concentrations throughout the country, other offices are situated in Europe and the Far East. These offices, plus a large staff of resident technical representatives here and overseas, provide the inspection, loss prevention, research, and underwriting facilities that are available to IRI insureds and member company agents and brokers.

Loss prevention surveys of insured property are conducted on a scheduled basis. Visits are made as necessary for consultation with insureds regarding changes in construction, occupancy, or protection, and IRI representatives recommend special protective measures during repairs or modifications to the fire protective equipment. The organization advises insureds on the conduct of periodic operating tests of fire pumps and other water supplies, sprinkler systems, and other protection equipment. Particular emphasis is placed upon management's responsibilities in loss prevention by means of a formalized program, known as OVERVIEW.

A Loss Prevention Training Center, maintained in Hartford, enhances the training of IRI loss prevention staff and familiarizes representatives of its policyholders and others with fire protection equipment. In addition to this training, research is conducted on a year-round basis at various testing facilities. For example, the burning properties of many classes of merchandise and the capabilities of protective devices to cope with such conditions are thoroughly analyzed in real-life situations. Research findings provide input for recommendations to maintain state-of-the-art practices. Periodicals and pamphlets are published on various loss control subjects.

In addition to IRI's domestic and overseas activities, it cooperates in the operations of a Canadian pool, known as Canadian Industrial Risk Insurers, which writes Canadian accounts under terms and conditions similar to those in the United States.

Insurance Services Office Inc., 160 Water St., New York, NY 10038

The Insurance Services Office (ISO) is a national, not-for-profit corporation providing a wide range of advisory services to property-casualty insurance companies. ISO functions, as provided by law, as an insurance rating organization; as an insurance actuarial service or advisory organization; and as a statistical agent. In 1987, it served approximately 1300 affiliated insurance companies, and had a countrywide staff of 4000.

It was formed in 1971 through the consolidation of several national insurance industry service organizations, including the Fire Insurance Research and Actuarial Association, the Inland Marine Insurance Bureau, the Insurance Rating Board, the Multi-Line Insurance Rating Bureau, and the National Insurance Actuarial and Statistical Association. Most of the former state and regional fire rating organizations in the United States are now a part of ISO.

ISO serves 15 kinds of personal and commercial lines of insurance, including commercial general liability, and dwelling fire and allied lines. The other thirteen are: boiler and machinery, commercial auto, commercial multiple line, commercial crime, homeowners, commercial glass, commercial inland marine, nuclear energy liability and property, private passenger auto, personal inland marine, professional liability, farm, and personal insurance coverages (PIC). CRS, ISO's property services subsidiary, provides services for Commercial Fire and Allied Lines Insurance, and field services in many personal lines areas.

The municipal grading and classification function for the larger cities was transferred to ISO from the American Insurance Association (formerly the National Board of Fire Underwriters) in 1971. In 1983 the responsibility for evaluation and classification of cities, both large and small, in ISO states was transferred to CRS. The "Commercial Fire Rating Schedule" and the "Fire Suppression Rating Schedule" are important publications available from CRS.

Other Insurance Organizations

There are many other important groups performing varied fire protection and inspection services on behalf of the insurance industry and their insureds. Among these are:

American Hull Insurance Syndicate, 14 Wall St., New York, NY 10005: An insurance syndicate created to insure vessels of high value.

American Institute of Marine Underwriters, 99 John St., New York, NY 10038: Organized to serve American marine underwriters and to promote, advance, and protect their interests.

American Nuclear Insurers (ANI), 270 Farmington Avenue, Suite 245, Farmington, CT 06032: American Nuclear Insurers is a voluntary, unincorporated association of insurance companies formed for the purpose of providing property and liability insurance protection at a fair price to the nuclear energy industry and at a reasonable profit to its participating companies.

Formerly known as NEL-PIA, it was formed in 1974 through the merger of two organizations—the Nuclear Energy Liability Insurance Association (NELIA) and the Nuclear Energy Property Insurance Association (NEPIA)—both of which began writing nuclear insurance in 1957. Its new name, American Nuclear Insurers, was adopted early in 1978.

Association of Mill and Elevator Mutual Insurance Companies, 2 North Riverside Plaza, Chicago, IL 60606: A group of mutual insurance companies serving the mill and elevator industry's insurance needs.

Assurex International, 6500 Busch Blvd., Columbus, OH 43229: A corporation owned by independent agents and brokers throughout the North American continent to provide education, marketing, engineering, and selling support services for its agency owners.

Cotton Fire and Marine Underwriters (A Division of Marine Office—Appleton & Cox Corp.), 1810 Commerce St., P. O. Box 1849, Dallas, TX 75221: A group of the cotton departments of insurance carriers which underwrites insurance against fire, marine, and other risks on cotton warehouses, gins, compresses, and other buildings and facilities for the storage, processing, and handling of cotton.

GAB Business Services, Inc., 123 William St., New York, NY 10038 (a Division of UAL, Inc.): A loss and claims adjusting organization with over 700 offices in the 50 states, the Caribbean, and London (England).

Improved Risk Mutuals (IRM), 15 North Broadway, White Plains, NY 10601: Improved Risk Mutual is a property insurance underwriting organization, established in 1921, comprised of 18 member companies that reinsure jointly large industrial, commercial, and institutional properties. Its engineering department provides fire protection engineering inspections and risk improvement programs.

Independent Insurance Agents of America, 85 John St., New York, NY, 10038: A large insurance producer association dedicated to the interests of the insurance consumer through upholding the principles of the American Agency System.

Insurance Information Institute, 110 William St., New York, NY 10038: An educational, fact- finding, and communications organization for the property and liability insurance business. It has more than 200 company members and also provides public relations services to other organizations in the fields of property, liability, fidelity, surety, and marine insurance.

Insurance Institute for Highway Safety (IIHS) (The), Watergate 600, Washington, DC 20037: The IIHS is an independent, nonprofit, scientific, and educational organization. It is dedicated to reducing losses/deaths, injuries, and property damage resulting from crashes on the nation's highways. The Institute is supported by the American Insurance Highway Safety Association, the American Insurers Highway Safety Alliance, the National Association of Independent Insurers Safety Association, and several individual insurance companies.

Mill Mutual Fire Prevention Bureau, 2 North Riverside Plaza, Chicago, IL 60606: A group of insurance companies established the Bureau to investigate loss/cause of mill and elevator fires and explosions and to provide engineering technology in the interest of prevention of such fires and explosions for the benefit of their members.

Mutual Atomic Energy Reinsurance Pool (administered by the American Mutual Reinsurance Company), One East Wacker Dr., Chicago, IL 60601: A pool that has the capacity to insure in excess of $55 million per occurrence on any one nuclear reactor installation or any other operation involving radiation hazards.

Mutual Reinsurance Bureau, 1550 Pearl St., P. O. Box 188, Belvidere, IL 61008: An organization to provide property and casualty reinsurance for a large segment of the mutual insurance industry, plus statistical services to member companies.

National Association of Insurance Brokers, Inc. (The), 1511 K St., N.W., Suite 316, Washington, D.C. 20005: An association to keep track of proposed and current state and national legislation supporting what is in the best interests of brokers and the insurance-buying public.

National Association of Insurance Commissioners, 633 W. Wisconsin Ave., Suite 1015, Milwaukee, WI 53203: A voluntary association of the chief insurance regulatory officials of the 50 states, the District of Columbia, Guam, Puerto

Rico, and the Virgin Islands to promote legislative uniformity and provide a means for protecting the insurance-consuming public.

National Association of Mutual Insurance Companies, 7931 Castleway Drive, Indianapolis, IN 46250: An association of over 1,100 mutual fire and casualty insurance companies, about 75 percent of which are farm, county, or township mutuals, and 25 percent are large and small advance-premium automobile, casualty, and general-writing fire mutuals.

National Association of Professional Insurance Agents (PIA), 400 N. Washington St., Alexandria, VA 22314: This association represents 36,000 independent insurance agents who primarily sell and service property and casualty insurance.

National Automobile Theft Bureau (NATB), 30 E. 42nd St., New York, NY 10017: The NATB is a crime-prevention organization supported by more than 500 property-casualty insurance companies to provide assistance to law enforcement, insurers, and the public. It is an agency for the location and identification of stolen vehicles and for the promotion of vehicle theft prevention activities.

National Cargo Bureau, Inc., Suite 2757, One World Trade Center, New York, NY 10048: A nonprofit membership organization to formulate recommendations to government on regulations for the safe stowage of dangerous goods and other cargos and ancillary cargo-handling techniques for water transportation. Offers cargo-loading inspection services to promote security of life and property on the seas.

Property Loss Research Bureau (PLRB), 20 N. Wacker Drive, Chicago, IL 60606: The Property Loss Research Bureau (PLRB) is a nonprofit corporation working to better the insurance climate on behalf of property and casualty insurers, their policyholders, and insurance companies. More than 100 property and casualty insurance companies nationally are PLRB members. PLRB's efforts are directed toward property loss adjustment services in five general categories: (1) educational development programs, (2) legal research and consulting services, (3) publications services, (4) catastrophe services, and (5) anti-fraud activities.

The latter objective is accomplished by PLRB personnel, expert in detection and investigation of arson fraud, who conduct arson seminars, and participate in arson educational forums sponsored by various fire marshals and educational institutions nationwide.

Transportation Insurance Rating Bureau, 175 W. Jackson Blvd., Chicago, IL 60604: A rating and statistical organization licensed in all states, the District of Columbia, and Puerto Rico for inland marine, aircraft, and multiple-line insurance, including fire and allied lines. Includes mutual fire and casualty insurance companies and some stock and reciprocal companies.

C. NATIONAL FIRE SERVICE ORGANIZATIONS IN THE UNITED STATES.

The following national and international associations are the most prominent groups serving the needs of the fire service in the United States.

Fire Marshals Association of North America, (FMANA), One Batterymarch Park, Quincy, MA 02269.

The Fire Marshals Association of North America, organized in 1906 and reorganized in 1927 as a section of the National Fire Protection Association, is a body of fire marshals, heads of fire prevention bureaus, fire investigators and their staffs. Members are those officials holding the positions named above who work for a state, a province, a county, a town, a city, a municipality or a fire protection district, and to whom the responsibility for fire prevention or investigation has been assigned by law or delegated by the chief of the fire department.

Associate members are nonsalaried or part-time legally designated officials who enjoy all the privileges of membership except that of elective office. The Fire Marshals Association of North America publishes a Bulletin and Yearbook and holds two meetings annually at the time and place of the national meetings of the National Fire Protection Association. Its objectives and purposes are: (1) to unite for mutual benefit those public officials engaged primarily in the control of arson or the prevention of fire, or both; (2) to act as a central agency for exchange of professional information among its members; (3) to assist Fire Marshals in the conduct of their professional activities; and (4) to correlate the activities of Fire Marshals toward the reduction of fire waste.

Fire Service Section of the National Fire Protection Association, One Batterymarch Park, Quincy, MA 02269

Organized in 1973, this organization is open to any member of the National Fire Protection Association who: (1) is a member of a fire department providing public fire prevention and fire suppression services to a state, county, municipality, or organized fire district; (2) is a member of a fire department providing fire prevention and fire suppression services to airfields or military bases; and (3) is principally engaged in the training and education of fire department members. Its objectives are: (1) to unite for mutual professional benefit those members of NFPA who are members of the fire service; (2) to act as a vehicle for the exchange of information among its members; (3) to advance the interests of the profession in the fields of fire protection, prevention, and suppression; (4) to stimulate awareness of the need for continually improving programs in management, training, and education; (5) to encourage and assist its members in conducting meetings, conferences, seminars, and such other forums as may be practicable for the exchange of information and the encouragement of professionalism; (6) to encourage participation of its members on the Technical Committees of the NFPA; (7) to advance and encourage the development of improved fire suppression equipment, apparatus, and all related facilities together with methods and practices used by the fire service by pooling experience and correlating the recommendations of its members; (8) to encourage public authorities to specify and purchase fire protection equipment on the basis of performance standards; (9) to bring to the attention of its members such matters of legislation and regulations as would be of interest; (10) to promote cooperation within the fire service and between the fire service and other fire protection practitioners; (11) to help the fire service achieve its primary goal of protection of life and property; and (12) to provide for the establishment, within the Section, of a fire service professional society.

International Association of Arson Investigators (IAAI), P. O. Box 600, 25 Newton St., Marlboro, MA 01752

The International Association of Arson Investigators was formed at Purdue University, West Lafayette, IN, in 1949, when insurance industry, fire service, and law enforcement personnel from the United States and Canada met to discuss the growing arson problem, and the need for training and education in fire investigation. The Association has the following objectives:

- To unite for mutual benefit those public officials and private persons engaged in the control of arson and kindred crime;
- To provide for exchange of technical information and developments;
- To cooperate with other law enforcement agencies and associations to further fire prevention and the suppression of crime;
- To encourage high professional standards of conduct among arson investigators; and
- To continually strive to eliminate all factors that interfere with administration of crime suppression.

Active membership in the IAAI is open to any representative (21 years of age or over) of government or of a governmental agency, and any representative of a business or industrial concern who is actively engaged in some phase of the suppression of arson and whose qualifications meet the requirements of the Membership Committee of the Association. Associate Membership is open to persons not qualified for Active Membership after determination of their qualification by the Membership Committee. The IAAI publishes a quarterly bulletin, *The Fire and Arson Investigator*, and conducts an annual meeting in conjunction with a conference on arson, normally in conjunction with a State Arson Seminar. Various Committees are organized to assist the Association in its attack on the arson problem, such as the Fire Marshal Advisory Committee, the Fraud Fires and Organized Crime Committee, the Insurance Advisory Committee, the Legislative Committee, the Photography Committee, the Police Advisory Committee, the Riots and Civil Disorders Committee, and the Technical Advisory and Training Committee.

International Association of Black Professional Fire Fighters (IABPFF), 5332 Kershaw St., Philadelphia, PA 19131

The IABPFF was organized in 1970 to: (1) create a liaison between black fire fighters across the nation; (2) compile information concerning injustices that exist in the working conditions in the fire service, and to implement action to correct them; (3) collect and evaluate data on all deleterious conditions where minorities exist; (4) see that competent blacks are recruited and employed as fire fighters where they reside; (5) promote interracial progress throughout the fire service; and (6) aid in motivating African Americans to seek advancement to elevated ranks. The organization is a Life Member of the National Association for the Advancement of Colored People.

International Association of Fire Chiefs (IAFC), 1329 18th St., N.W., Washington, DC 20036

The IAFC was organized in 1873 to further the professional advancement of the fire service, and to insure and maintain greater protection of life and property from fire. Its purposes are fulfilled by: (1) conducting research and studies of major problems affecting the fire service at community, state, provincial, regional, national, and international levels; (2) developing and implementing an active program vital to the continued well-being of the fire service; (3) serving as the recognized organization for the exchange of ideas, information, knowledge, and experience in areas affecting the safety of life and property from fire; (4) encouraging and developing public education in fire prevention to preserve human life and material resources; and (5) promoting educational programs in the best interests of the fire service. Active Members include: the Chief of Department and all Chief Officers of regularly organized public, governmental, or industrial fire departments; State and Provincial Fire Marshals; Fire Commissioners and/or Fire Directors who devote full time to administration and fire fighting operations. Associate Members include Fire Commissioners and/or Fire Directors not responsible for administration or for fire fighting operations; Directors of Public Safety, public officials, officers and members of fire departments; individuals interested in the protection of life and property from fire; and officers of recognized fire prevention organizations. Sustaining Members include: individuals and/or concerns engaged in the manufacture or sale of emergency apparatus or equipment, and/or individuals or concerns otherwise interested in the field of fire protection. Other membership categories are: Active Life Members, Associate Life Members, and Honorary Life Members.

The IAFC also has over twenty committees, or interest groups, that function for the organization including the Metropolitan Committee (chiefs of the major cities) who serve the Association in the special areas of their concern. These committees include: Arson, Building Code, Automatic Detection and Warning, Education and Training, Fire Prevention, Volunteer, Urban, Research, Emergency Preparedness, Employee Relations, Fire Department Equipment and Safety, Hazardous Materials, Industrial and Federal Fire Departments, and Physical Fitness. The IAFC holds an annual conference with a major technical and educational exhibition each year, and offers a series of publications on fire service matters to all interested persons. It has a membership in the range of 7,500 to 8,000 and a headquarters staff of 11 to 15.

International Association of Fire Fighters (IAFF), 1750 New York Ave., NW, Washington, DC 20006

Organized in 1918, the IAFF has approximately 175,000 members in the United States and Canada. The IAFF is affiliated with the American Federation of Labor and Congress of Industrial Organizations in the United States and the Canadian Labour Congress (AFL-CIO/CLC). Any person, who is engaged as a permanent and paid employee of a fire department, is eligible for active membership through the chartered locals, state or provincial associations, and joint councils. Conventions of the Association are biennial. The IAFF headquarters provides a variety of services to the membership, to include: technical assistance in the occupational safety and health area; labor relations expertise through in-house personnel and field representatives; an extensive educational seminar program; legislative representation at the national level; and public relations guidance. The Association's official publication, *The International Fire Fighter*, is published monthly under the direction of the International president. Among other publications are the annual *Death and Injury Survey*, a *Public Relations Manual*, and *Salary and Working Conditions Surveys*.

The International Fire Service Accreditation Congress, Oklahoma State University, Stillwater, Ok 74078

The Congress is an accreditation system operated by member organizations.

Its purpose is to accredit entities that provide certification of Fire Service personnel, utilizing professional qualification standards at the state, province or territory level.

International Fire Service Training Association (IFSTA), Oklahoma State University, Stillwater, OK 74078

IFSTA is an educational alliance formed in 1934 to develop training materials for the fire service. Committees meet each July in Stillwater to review existing or proposed manuals. All validated manuals are published by the Fire Protection Publications division of Oklahoma State University. IFSTA's objectives are: (1) to develop training materials and visual aids for publication; (2) to add new techniques and developments; (3) to delete obsolete and outmoded methods; (4) to validate training material for publication; (5) to provide materials for students and instructors to assist in certification; and (6) to upgrade the fire service through training. IFSTA publications are used in all of the United States and Canadian Provinces, and are adopted by most. Also, a number of federal government agencies and several foreign countries have adopted the IFSTA publications as their official training manuals.

International Municipal Signal Association (IMSA), P. O. Box 8249, Fort Worth, TX 76112

IMSA was organized in 1896 and currently has 3,000 to 3,500 members. It is an educational, nonprofit organization dedicated to conveying knowledge, technical information, and guidance to its membership, which consists of municipal signal and communication department heads and their first assistants. The range of communications covered includes traffic control, fire alarm, and police alarm. There are sixteen Sections of IMSA (based on geographical areas in the United States and Canada) and a Sustaining Section. The former serve the regional needs of its members. The *IMSA Signal Magazine* is the Association's bimonthly publication.

International Society of Fire Service Instructors (ISFSI), 20 Main St., Ashland, MA 01721

The International Society of Fire Service Instructors was organized in 1960. The Society is comprised of those persons who are responsible for the training of fire officers, fire fighters, and rescue and emergency medical personnel. The goal is to develop uniform professional standards for fire service instructors, to assist in the development of fire service instructors through better training and educational opportunities, to provide the means for continuous upgrading of such instructors through in-service training, and to actively promote the role of the fire service instructor in the total fire service organization. It has membership in all fifty states and ten foreign countries.

National Board on Fire Service Professional Qualifications (NBFSPQ), P. O. Box 492, Quincy, MA 02269

The National Board on Fire Service Professional Qualifications (NBFSPQ) is designed to improve life safety and fire protection through a national system of fire service professional qualifications certification and accreditation. The NBFSPQ supports the development of an NFPA Standard (NFPA 1000) on certification and accreditation, the utilization of such an Standard, a National Registry of Fire Service Professional Qualifications Certification, and the NFPA Fire Service Professional Qualification Standards. Accreditation of certifying organizations will continue to be carried out by the National Professional Qualifications Board (NPQB) under the direction of the Board of the Directors of the NBFSPQ. The Board of Directors will receive advice from an "Advisory Council" made up of representatives of those organizations utilizing the system. The Board of Directors represent the organizations appointed August 2, 1989, by the former Joint Council of National Fire Service Organizations to a select committee for determining the future for a national fire service certification accreditation program. The work of the select committee in establishing the NBFSPQ constituted the last activity of the former Joint Council.

Metropolitan Committee of the International Association of Fire Chiefs, 1329 18th Street, NW, Washington, DC 20036

The Metropolitan Committee of the International Association of Fire Chiefs was organized in 1965. The membership of the Metropolitan Committee is limited to active fire chiefs of cities or jurisdictions having a population of more than 200,000, or a minimum of 400 career members, and who are current members of the International Association of Fire Chiefs. The mission of the Metropolitan Committee is to assist the International Association of Fire Chiefs in developing and propagating policy concerning major fire departments.

National Volunteer Fire Council (NVFC), 45 Sussex Drive, Lewes, DE 19958

The NVFC was organized in 1976 and is an organization of various state fire fighters associations and of individual volunteer fire fighters. Its purpose is to represent and pursue the interests of volunteer fire fighters and volunteer fire departments throughout the United States. Among its objectives is to provide a forum for the formulation of unified positions concerning developments nationally affecting volunteers, and to support fire prevention education in the lower grades of school systems.

D. FIRE RESEARCH LABORATORIES

There are many laboratories in the United States capable of performing, to varying degrees, fire-related research. Broadly speaking, these laboratories can be classified into three general categories: (1) private and industrial laboratories, (2) university laboratories, and (3) government laboratories.

Representative of laboratories in the private sector are Underwriters Laboratories, Inc., Factory Mutual Research Corporation, and Southwest Research Institute; in the academic sector—Ohio State University; and in government sector—the National Institute of Standards and Technology. Fire research is by no means limited to the representative laboratories mentioned above. In fact, there has been a marked increase in research activity in recent years as a result of a heightened interest nationally in firesafety and health related issues.

A good source of information on the extent of fire research and the laboratories involved in it is the *Directory of Fire Research in the United States* which is published periodically by the Committee on Fire Research of the Division of Engineering, National Research Council, National Academy of Sciences, 2101 Constitution Avenue, Washington, DC 20418.

The following descriptions of the activities of the representative laboratories mentioned earlier in this text are given as an indication of the type of activities fire research oriented laboratories are engaged in. Inclusion in the listing is in no way an endorsement of the laboratories by the NFPA.

Underwriters Laboratories Inc.

Underwriters Laboratories Inc. (UL), with headquarters at 333 Pfingsten Road, Northbrook, IL 60062, is a not-for-profit corporation having as its sole objective the promotion of public safety through conduct of "scientific investigation, study, experiments, and tests, to determine the relation of various materials, devices, products, equipment, constructions, methods, and systems to hazards appurtenant thereto or to the use thereof affecting life and property and to ascertain, define, and publish standards, classifications, and specifications for materials, devices, products, equipment, constructions, methods, and systems affecting such hazards, and other information tending to reduce or prevent bodily injury, loss of life, and property damage from such hazards."

The organization was founded in 1894 by the fire insurance industry under whose sponsorship it operated until 1968 when it became an independent, public service type corporation. It has no capital stock, nor shareholders, and exists solely for the service it renders in the fields of fire, crime, and casualty prevention.

Factory Mutual Research Corporation

The research function of Factory Mutual Research Corporation (FMRC), with headquarters at 1151 Boston-Providence Turnpike, Norwood, MA 02062, is to conduct research and development in the field of property loss control. This activity serves the needs of the Factory Mutual System and is available to other entities, such as government agencies, trade associations, and individual businesses, through contracts.

The scope of the research ranges from basic research into the nature of fire to the development of standards for direct use by industry in establishing practices designed to minimize loss. Although such standards are intended primarily for Factory Mutual System members, they are recognized and widely used by others. Between the extremes of basic research and standards, major effort is made in the area of applied research. This activity includes: studies, surveys, operations research, experimentation, laboratory-scale testing, and full-scale testing to evaluate hazards and protection of storage, manufacturing operations, and construction arrangements.

Southwest Research Institute

The Southwest Research Institute (SwRI), located at 6220 Culebra Road, San Antonio, TX 78284, is a nonprofit organization devoted to government and industrial research. SwRI's Department of Fire Technology has a staff of professional personnel encompassing disciplines of organic, physical, analytical, and polymer chemistry, chemical engineering, mechanical engineering, fire services technology, and inhalation toxicology. The Department is organized into four sections, each focusing on a different aspect of the technology of fire.

The Standard Testing Services Section offers thirty five tests, including ignition, flame-spread, smoke-development, and fire-endurance. The Fire Performance Evaluations Section conducts a wide variety of large-scale fire evaluations of materials and assemblies, often on a custom-designed basis. The section also performs many specialized large-scale tests, including those for smoke detectors and fire penetration through seal installations at openings in fire barriers.

The Fire Chemistry Section offers services in combustion and fire gas analysis, along with the development of specialized analytical procedures as may be required. Heat-release calorimetry, including the use of a room-sized calorimeter for the study of assemblies, is also offered.

The Applied Environmental Toxicology Section conducts a variety of smoke toxicity tests using both standard and custom-designed methodology. Included in these studies are both lethality and incapacitation determinations, generally utilizing rodents as the animal model.

Building and Fire Research Laboratory, National Institute of Standards and Technology

Formerly the National Bureau of Standards' Center for Fire Research, the Building and Fire Research Laboratory (BFRL) of the National Institute of Standards and Technology (NIST) is located in the NIST complex at Gaithersburg, MD. The laboratory conducts research designed to improve codes and standards. This work is done by developing improved or new test methods and by using large-scale tests to validate the test method developments. Work is also conducted on developing knowledge of the properties of materials and their performance in fire conditions. The laboratories also develop mathematical models to predict performance of materials under fire conditions.

Ohio State University

Fire research at Ohio State University, Columbus, OH, includes a wide range of activities. The Building Research Lab in the College of Engineering, which includes the School of Architecture, maintains facilities for evaluating the performance characteristics of building materials and building construction systems. The fundamental combustion characteristics of structure designs, materials, and contents are also studied. Such data permit computer modeling of simulated fire scenarios, which can then be verified experimentally in full-scale compartment tests. These experiments can also include measurement and identification of the thermal and chemical products of combustion.

The bioeffects of fire exposure on both man and animals are studied in cooperation with the Colleges of Medicine and Veterinary Medicine. Studies of the human response to a fire emergency are examined by the College of Behavioral Sciences. Methods of improved audio and visual communications are developed by communications specialists and the Vision Research Institute. Problems in fire risk management are explored by The College of Administrative Sciences, with the campus community of the university serving as a testing ground for the fire prevention and control systems involved.

E. FIRE TESTING LABORATORIES

Many fire research laboratories are also testing laboratories that act as third-party certifiers of products and materials. Both Underwriters Laboratories and Factory Mutual Research Corporation function as testing laboratories, as well as research laboratories.

For many years, the phrase "a nationally recognized testing laboratory" was used somewhat indiscriminantly to call attention to the sources for testing of products and assemblies to determine if they meet the performance (and sometimes specification) requirements of fire protection standards. Thus, a standard user would be directed to use only products and assemblies that had been "listed" or "approved" by a nationally recognized testing laboratory if compliance with certain provisions of the standard in question was the goal. Unfortunately, there was always a doubt about what exactly was a "nationally recognized testing laboratory," thus, the phrase has been dropped from NFPA published documents.

An effort to bring order to the question of identifying technically competent testing laboratories in a consistent and uniform fashion has been established within the framework of the U.S. Department of Commerce (DOC). The National Voluntary Laboratory Accreditation Program (NVLAP), established in 1976, has as its goal "to serve on a timely basis the needs of industry, consumers, the government, and others by accrediting the nation's testing laboratories." To date, however, the NVLAP program only covers a few of the many products, materials, and devices that are tested and "listed" or "approved" by testing laboratories.

F. SOCIETY OF FIRE PROTECTION ENGINEERS

Organized in 1950, the Society of Fire Protection Engineers (SFPE), with headquarters at 60 Batterymarch St., Boston, MA 02210, is the professional society for engineers involved in the multi-faceted field of fire protection engineering. The purposes of the Society are to advance the art and science of fire protection engineering and its allied fields, to maintain a high ethical standing among its members, and to foster fire protection engineering education. Its worldwide members include engineers in private practice, in industry, and in local, regional, and national government, as well as technical members of the insurance industry. Forty chapters of the Society are located in the United States, Canada, Europe, and Australia.

Membership in the Society is open to those possessing engineering or physical science qualifications, coupled with experience in the field, and to those in associated professional fields.

The Society serves as an international clearinghouse for fire protection engineering state-of-the-art advances and information. It publishes the *SFPE Bulletin*, a newsletter with regular features, the *Journal of Fire Protection Engineering*, and a series of "Technology Reports" covering technical developments of interest to the engineering community. It also publishes occasional special reports.

G. FEDERAL INVOLVEMENT IN FIRE PROTECTION

The Federal Government has been involved in fire protection for many decades. Prior to the 1970's the federal role was minimal and decisively non-regulatory so far as the general public was concerned; it provided for the protection of federal property, and employees and the public while on federal property. Developments in various fields of technology and in communications, a growing awareness of public safety in general, and an increasingly responsive social conscience manifested by Congress intensitifed federal activities in fire protection beginning in the 1970's. As a result, the related federal concerns became multi-faceted, complex, and regulatory in nature. These concerns are administered within the jurisdiction of 12 Executive Branch departments and 10 independent agencies. These departments and agencies are headquartered in the Washington, DC area, and many oversee regional and field offices in other parts of the country. Their functions encompass fire research, fire training, actual fire prevention, detection and suppression, technical and financial assistance, intra-agency self-regulatory programs, the promulgation and enforcement of both prescriptive and conditioning rules and regulations, fire investigations, criminal investigation and enforcement, and the development and administration of safety policy. The NFPA enjoys a cooperative relationship with these agencies. A number of agencies rely upon NFPA standards and participate in the NFPA standards-making process.

Lead Agencies

In 1974, Congress established the first major federal program to enhance the firesafety of the general public. While recognizing that state and local governments have primary concern for firesafety, the Federal Fire Prevention and Control Act of 1974 (15 U.S.C. 2201) provides training, assistance and coordination in the field of fire protection. Pursuant to the findings and recommendations of the underlying report "America Burning," the Act authorized the establishment of an Administration to oversee these activities, and assigned specific responsibilities regarding fire protection to the National Bureau of Standards (NBS) within the U.S. Department of Commerce (DOC).

United States Fire Administration (USFA)

Headquartered in Emmitsburg, MD, the USFA administers an extensive fire data and analysis program, provides overall fire policy and coordination, and acts as the lead agency in federal fire prevention and arson control programs in coordination with state and local fire service and law enforcement agencies. In conjunction with the National Institute of Occupational Safety and Health, the USFA administers a program concerned with fire fighter health and safety. The USFA Administrator reports to the Director of the Federal Emergency Management Agency (FEMA). As originally established the agency functioned under the name National Fire Prevention and Control Administration (NFPCA) within the DOC and was transferred in 1978 to the then recently created FEMA.

National Fire Academy (NFA)

The NFA is part of FEMA's Office of Training, and its National Emergency Training Center (NETC), located in Emmitsburg, MD. The NFA provides training programs ranging from fire service management to the hazard mitigation of various materials, and from arson investigation techniques to fire code application and enforcement by architects and local officials. Some fire-related training is also provided by the NETC's Emergency Management Institute (EMI). The EMI's main focus, however, is on the training of civil defense forces which include the fire services. The NFPA and the EMI are headed by superintendents reporting to the FEMA Associate Director for Training.

PROGRAMS AFFECTING PUBLIC FIRE SAFETY

Department of Agriculture (DOA)

The Department's fire protection programs are aimed at fire prevention and education in rural areas, and are carried out by the U.S. Forest Service and the Farmers' Home Administration.

U.S. Forest Service (USFS)

Known to millions through its familiar symbol Smokey the Bear, the USFS provides fire protection to more than 200 million acres of forests, grasslands, and nearby private lands (National Forest System), conducts research and develops improved methods in forest fire management (Forest Fire and Atmospheric Research), and provides technical and financial assistance to state forestry organizations to improve fire protection efficiency on non-federal wildlands (Cooperative Fire Protection). Research is also conducted on wood and wood-based products.

The Farmers' Home Administration (FMHA) makes loans to public bodies and nonprofit corporations in rural areas for the construction of fire stations, the provision of water supply, and for the purchase of fire suppression apparatus and equipment.

Department of Housing and Urban Development (HUD)

The Manufactured Housing and Construction Standards Division promulgates and enforces rules regarding the safety and durability of manufactured housing, including firesafety standards for consumer protection to determine eligibility for HUD loans and mortgage insurance policies.

Department of Interior (DOI)

The Bureau of Land Management (BLM) provides protection against wildfires on 545 million acres of public land, natural resources, and other values, and services and supports the Interagency Fire Center in Boise, ID. The Center provides logistic support for the DOA's Forest Service, the DOC's National Oceanic and Atmospheric Administration (NOAA), and the DOI's BLM, Bureau of Indian Affairs, National Park Service (NPS), and Fish and Wildlife Service. The NPS also provides presuppression and suppression services, and administers a Fire Safety Program to protect visitors, national park employees, resources and facilities.

Department of Labor (DOL)

Congress, in 1970, established the Occupational Safety and Health Administration (OSHA) within the DOL to develop and promulgate mandatory occupational safety and health standards—rules and regulations applicable at the workplace. As part of the enforcement of its rules, OSHA conducts investigations and inspections, and cites and penalizes workplaces for violations.

The Mine Safety and Health Administration was established in 1977 with a functional scope similar to that of OSHA, but with a focus on the mining industry.

Department of Transportation (DOT)

Ten major operational units within the DOT investigate, research, analyze, and provide for the safety of vehicles, avenues, environment, passengers, and cargoes in all modes of transportation. All of these functions heavily involve firesafety. The organizational units are: five divisions of the U.S. Coast Guard (ports, marine environment, merchant marine, marine firesafety, safety programs), three divisions within the Federal Aviation Administration (airports, special programs, aircraft safety and airport technology), the Federal Highway Administration (interstate highways), the Federal Railroad Administration, the National Highway Traffic Safety Administration (on-road vehicle safety hazards, accidents), the Maritime Administration (merchant marine), the Urban Mass Transportation Administration (buses, subways), the Materials Transportation Bureau (hazardous materials), the Transportation Safety Institute (safety and security management, training), and the Transportation Systems Center (applied research). Related to, but independent from the DOT, the National Transportation Safety Board investigates and makes recommendations with respect to traffic accidents, including vehicular fire incidents.

Department of Treasury

Through its network of agents throughout the United States, the Bureau of Alcohol, Tobacco and Firearms (BATF) conducts a vigorous arson investigation program, including training and technical assistance to state and local law enforcement and fire authorities. The BATF's Firearms and Explosives programs protects interstate and foreign commerce from interference and disruption by reducing hazards to persons and property stemming from the insecure storage of explosives.

Consumer Product Safety Commission (CPSC)

The CPSC's Fire and Thermal Burn Program encompasses the investigation of injury patterns, data collection, research, and the promulgation and enforcement of mandatory standards, with respect to consumer products.

OTHER FEDERAL AGENCIES

Within the NIST, the Center for Building Technology conducts laboratory, field, and analytical research, and develops technologies to predict, measure, and test the performance—including under conditions of fire—of building materials, components, systems, and practices. In the Department of Defense, the Office of Safety Policy at the Secretary's level provides guidelines for all military departments. Each branch of the Armed Forces deals with its firesafety concerns individually. The Directorate of Engineering and Services in the Air Force, the Corps of Engineers in the Army, the Naval Material Command, and the Marine Installations and Logistics staff address fire prevention and protection concerns.

The Department of Energy's (DOE) Safety and Engineering Analysis Division, located in Germantown, MD, provides for the fire protection of all DOE facilities, including those that manufacture the Nation's nuclear weapons stockpile. The DOE's authority—and thus, its fire protection concerns—is extremely broad, ranging from nuclear research reactors to petroleum reserves—assests valued at more than $75 billion. The Department of Health and Human Services (HHS), and in particular the National Institute of Health (NIH), administers its own fire protection program; and the Department of Justice (DOJ) Bureau of Prisons provides fire protection to all federal correctional institutions. The U.S. Department of State also has an extensive and unique fire protection program, one that involves the safeguarding of U.S. Government property abroad.

Among the independent agencies, the General Services Administration (GSA) acts as the "housekeeper" within the government, providing supplies, services, and facilities for government agencies. Larger than many blue-chip corporations, the GSA manages some 325 million square feet of existing space in about 8000 buildings, and oversees major construction projects. The GSA's Public Building Services (PBS) provides for the fire protection of these buildings. As part of the GSA, the National Archives and Records Service presents a special risk because of the priceless historic documents and government records stored by that service.

Beside its large-scale fire protection program, the National Aeronautics and Space Administration (NASA) has an active technology transfer program by which concepts, materials, and products used in the Nation's space program are being applied in earth-bound, civilian programs. A number of fire fighter safety devices and materials have their origins at NASA.

The Environmental Protection Agency's (EPA) Solid Waste Management underground storage tank, and hazardous materials storage programs have firesafety implications, and the Nuclear Regulatory Commission's function by which it inspects, investigates, and certifies privately owned and operated nuclear reactors contains a rather significant and unique fire protection program. In addition to the above, the Smithsonian Institution, the U.S. Postal Service, and the Veterans Administration have their own, unique firesafety and fire protection programs.

By virtue of the Occupational Safety and Health Act of 1970, administered by the DOL, each federal department and agency, and frequently some subordinate units of these departments and agencies, has its own OSHA program.

Finally, a number of federal programs affect or are of interest to the fire services. Federal Fire Fighters' Retirement funds are administered by the Office of Personnel Management (OPM). Public Safety Officers' Death Benefits are provided by the DOL. Overtime exemptions for federal fire fighters are administered by the Wage and Hour Division of the DOL, and Surplus Military Equipment is made available to state and local fire fighting agencies by the DOD, Bidder Control Office in Battle Creek, MI. The provision of Public Safety Awards was authorized by the Federal Fire Prevention and Control Act of 1974, and so were Reimbursements for Fire Fighting on Federal Property. Fire Suppression Disaster Assistance was authorized by the Disaster Relief Act of 1974. These programs are administered by FEMA.

CAREER OPPORTUNITIES IN FIRE PROTECTION

Fire can be one of the most dangerous and costly of all destructive forces. Because of the hazard that fire presents to both life and property, the scientific study of fire protection and the methods of fire prevention have grown since the early 19th century. From this growth and from recent technological advances in building design and the increasing use of hazardous materials, the fire protection profession has become highly specialized and challenging.

It is beyond the scope of this appendix to detail each and every career that a student of the fire sciences may enter. Many types of persons with fire science backgrounds are hired by insurance companies, building departments, and divisions of the state government, whose responsibility it is to provide bases for evaluating danger to life from fire and for evaluating and determining ways for minimizing fire danger to buildings and their contents. Architectural firms often hire or consult fire science professionals to examine the firesafety of proposed building designs, and a great many industries have their own fire protection staffs and private fire brigades.

The increase in fire science specialty fields has brought about a greater need for education and training. During the early 1960s, there was an increase in the number of two-year community college fire science programs in the United States. Community college fire science programs are usually designed to supplement, but not replace, fire training provided by fire departments and state training agencies. Four-year fire science programs offered by universities, however, expand upon the traditional career of fire fighter by offering degrees in fire protection engineering and technology and fire protection administration, which can help qualify individuals for work in fire protection fields other than fire departments.

Oklahoma State University at Stillwater provides a Bachelor of Science degree in Fire Protection and Safety Engineering Technology. During the first two years of study, emphasis is placed on fire protection engineering. Junior and senior years of study concentrate on safety engineering, industrial hygiene, and security, as well as other advanced subjects that are intended to ensure the competence of the graduate in the professional world.

Bachelor of Science and Masters degrees in Fire Protection Engineering are offered by the University of Maryland upon completion of curricula that provide the student with knowledge of engineering, physics, mathematics, and the major aspects of fire protection engineering. Among the various fields in which fire protection engineers can work after graduation are industry, fire protection consulting firms, insurance companies, automatic sprinkler companies, the military, the federal government, and the fire service.

Eastern Kentucky University in Richmond KY, offers a four year degree in Fire and Safety Engineering Technology as part of their College of Law Enforcement.

Worcester Polytechnic Institute in Worcester, MA, offers a Masters degree in Fire Protection Engineering. Admission to the program requires an undergraduate degree in engineering or one of the sciences.

Many universities offer a degree in Fire Protection Administration which is designed to provide expertise in the management of fire service organizations. Generally, this course of study will prepare persons for upper level management positions at the chief officer level.

Fire Protection Careers

Safeguarding people and property from the ravages of fire offers rewarding career opportunities to large numbers of people with many and varied skills. Thus, for today's fire science student, many types of careers in fire protection are available.

Fire fighters are needed to fight fires in homes, industrial and mercantile properties, farms and forests, planes and ships and tank trucks, hospitals and nursing homes, and all other places where people live, work, and play.

They are needed to prevent fires from starting by making fire inspections and by enforcing the laws and codes enacted at all levels of government.

People are needed for the fire prevention education of adults and school children. They are needed to investigate fires, to control arson, and to train others in fire fighting procedures and fire prevention measures.

People are needed to conduct the fire insurance business, to make rates, to write policies, and to remove hazards.

Still others are needed to design, manufacture, and sell fire apparatus, automatic sprinklers and other extinguishing systems, alarm systems, fire doors, first-aid fire appliances, fire-retardant materials.

Fire protection engineers are needed in ever-increasing numbers to cope with ever-greater fire protection problems, such as those involving high-rise buildings, new chemical hazards, rapid increase in the use of plastics with accompanying smoke and toxic fume hazards, automated warehouses.

Among the many professionals who play a major role in solving the growing number of fire protection problems is the fire protection engineer. Most fire protection engineers receive their undergraduate educations from accredited colleges or universities. The principal areas in which a fire protection engineer may work are industrial engineering, research and product design, sales, and insurance.

For the fire protection engineer, industrial engineering usually involves direct problem-solving. The engineer evaluates information to establish the extent of fire and explosion potential and may also design systems such as automatic sprinklers, water supplies, fire alarm and control systems, and municipal fire defenses for large cities. In the areas of research and product design, the fire protection engineer is concerned with such diverse problems as fabric flammability, firesafety in high-rise buildings, and protection of automated storage warehouses. Fire protection engineers are also utilized by the fire insurance industry, where they are involved with evaluating fire risks, studying fire losses, underwriting analysis, and management concerns. Some fire protection engineers become involved in selling fire protection and extinguishing equipment systems. Fire protection engineers may also provide specialized expertise working in state fire marshals offices or fire prevention bureaus of local fire departments.

Careers in a Fire Department

In addition to the various levels of fire fighters and the various ranks of officers, today's fire departments have a need for individuals trained to perform specialized functions that require mechanical, automotive, and communications skills. Such positions include motor pump operator, chief dispatcher, fire alarm dispatcher, automotive mechanical supervisor, fire equipment mechanic, and emergency medical technician (EMT). Depending upon the geographical location of the fire department and the specific fire hazards of a community, there may be a need for fireboat pilots, marine engineers, fire investigators, and airport fire fighters.

As different communities have specific fire protection needs, qualifications for the preceding positions are determined at the local level. National standardized qualifications do exist, however, for the fire fighter and the apparatus driver/operator. These are published in NFPA 1001, *Fire Fighter Professional Qualifications*, NFPA 1002, *Fire Apparatus Driver/Operator Professional Qualifications*, NFPA 1003, *Airport Fire Fighter Professional Qualifications*, and NFPA 1004, *Fire Fighter Medical Technicians Professional Qualifications*, details of which are given in the remaining paragraphs of this appendix. The qualifications are intended to ensure that any individual measured by them truly possesses the skills needed to perform the tasks required by each position. Because nationally recognized qualifications exist for fire fighter and apparatus driver/operator, these two careers will be examined in detail in the following paragraphs, as will be the position of fire department paramedic.

Fire fighter: A fire fighter's main responsibility is to protect the public from the dangers of fire, to prevent loss of life from fire, and to minimize the property damage that fire can cause. This is accomplished through highly organized teamwork under the supervision of a fire officer. Thus, the career of the fire fighter involves a group work activity. Some fire fighters are assigned to forcible entry tasks, others to pumping apparatus, and others to the operation and placement of ladders. After the extinguishment of a fire, fire fighters remain on the scene to ensure that no further danger exists from rekindling. Therefore, while fire fighters may have specialized tasks on the fire scene, it is through the work of each individual that the entire unit accomplishes its task.

Between fires, fire fighters may be assigned to inspect buildings for compliance with fire codes and safety regulations. During these inspections, fire fighters may apply their knowledge of firesafe buildings to ensure that exits, passageways, and hallways are not blocked, that combustibles are stored safely, and that any hazards or inoperable firesafety devices are corrected.

Fire fighter applicants must be at least eighteen years old and have a high school diploma or recognized equivalent. Because of the physical demands of the job, candidates must posses strength, endurance, dexterity, and the ability to transport heavy equipment under adverse conditions. They must also be able to deal with injured and panic-stricken individuals and guide such persons to safety. The physical and mental demands of the job mandate a physical examination and an evaluation of the candidate's character before an applicant may be accepted into the fire department. NFPA 1001, *Fire Fighter Professional Qualifications*, details the medical requirements that should be met by fire department candidates.

Fire apparatus driver operator: NFPA 1002, *Fire Apparatus Driver/Operator Professional Qualifications*, outlines the minimum requirements of professional competence that the individual seeking this position must possess. Before being certified as a driver/operator, the individual must already be a member of a fire department or fire brigade and must have fulfilled the requirements of Fire Fighter II, defined in NFPA 1001, *Fire Fighter Professional Qualifications*, as follows:

> ....at the second level of progression in the fire department, (one) who has demonstrated the knowledge of, and the ability to perform the objectives specified in this Standard for that level, and who works under minimum supervision.

The driver/operator must be able to demonstrate the performance of routine tests, inspections, and servicing functions of fire department vehicles to ensure that they are in good working order. This preventive maintenance includes such component parts as the battery, the braking, coolant, and electrical systems, engine and hydraulic oil levels, and tire care for all department vehicles. A knowledge is also needed of conditions that may result in pump damage or unsafe operation, as is the ability identify measure for the correction of such conditions.

The driver/operator must be legally licensed for the particular class of vehicle and must have a thorough knowledge of the state and local laws governing the safe operation of the vehicle. A driving test must be passed in which the candidate displays the ability maneuver the vehicle as prescribed in NFPA 1002, *Fire Apparatus Driver/Operator Professional Qualifications*. The vehicles that the driver/operator must be familiar with include all fire department apparatus equipped with fire pumps, aerial ladders, tillers, and elevating platforms.

Fire fighter emergency medical technician (EMT)/fire fighter paramedic: Most fire departments today provide emergency medical services. These services extend from the role of "first responds" to that of operating ambulance services involving the transport of accident victims.

The fire fighter EMT must be able to determine the type and severity of the injuries present in order to establish proprieties for the required emergency care. Certain medical knowledge is needed, as it may be necessary to open and maintain an airway, control hemorrhaging, assist at childbirth, perform initial care for burn victims, and treat shock.

In the case of paramedics, they are allowed under the auspices of a physician, to administer drugs, including intravenous fluids.

SUMMARY

The basic goal of fire protection organization is to help solve the country's fire problems. This can be accomplished in many ways, as reflected in the vast number of such organizations and in the various roles they play. While some groups primarily sponsor educational activities, both for members of the fire service and for the public-at-large, other associations provide insurance for property damages that may result from fires or explosions. Within the fire service itself are several national and international organizations that seek to unite fire officers and fire fighters; to provide special training for them; and to establish a forum for the exchange of ideas relating to fire protection, fire prevention, and fire suppression.

Under many departments of the federal government are agencies with fire protection interests. These agencies perform a variety of services, from developing and enforcing standards and codes to regulating the transportation of hazardous materials. The federal government also sponsors fire testing and research laboratories, as do private industries, colleges, and universities throughout the country.

The diversity and specialization of careers available to those interested in the fire sciences is a reflection of the need for a thorough knowledge of fire and its properties. Additionally, the types of careers available in the fire service have expanded considerably in scope in order to keep pace with the staggering losses in life and property from fire.

Complete Titles of All Official NFPA Documents

As of April 29, 1991

Compiled by Leona Attenasio Nisbet

NFPA 1, *Fire Prevention Code*
NFPA 10, *Standard for Portable Fire Extinguishers*
NFPA 10L, *Model Enabling Act for the Sale or Leasing & Servicing of Portable Fire Extinguishers*
NFPA 11, *Standard for Low Expansion Foam and Combined Agent Systems*
NFPA 11A, *Standard for Medium- and High-Expansion Foam Systems*
NFPA 11C, *Standard for Mobile Foam Apparatus*
NFPA 12, *Standard on Carbon Dioxide Extinguishing Systems*
NFPA 12A, *Standard on Halon 1301 Fire Extinguishing Agent Systems*
NFPA 12B, *Standard on Halon 1211 Fire Extinguishing Systems*
NFPA 13, *Standard for the Installation of Sprinkler Systems*
NFPA 13A, *Recommended Practice for the Inspection, Testing and Maintenance of Sprinkler Systems*
NFPA 13D, *Standard for the Installation of Sprinkler Systems in One- and Two-Family Dwellings and Mobile Homes*
NFPA 13E, *Recommendations for Fire Department Operations in Fire Department Operations in Properties Protected by Sprinkler and Standpipe Systems*
NFPA 13R, *Standard for the Installation of Sprinkler Systems in Residential Occupancies Up to & Including Four Stories in Height*
NFPA 14, *Standard for the Installation of Standpipe & Hose Systems*
NFPA 14A, *Recommended Practice for Testing, Inspection and Maintenance of Standpipe and Hose Systems*
NFPA 15, *Standard for Water-Spray Fixed Systems for Fire Protection*
NFPA 16, *Standard on Deluge Foam-Water Sprinkler and Foam-Water Spray Systems*
NFPA 16A, *Recommended Practice for the Installation of Closed-Head Foam-Water Sprinkler Systems*
NFPA 17, *Standard for Dry Chemical Extinguishing Systems*
NFPA 17A, *Standard on Wet Chemical Extinguishing Systems*
NFPA 18, *Standard on Wetting Agents*
NFPA 20, *Standard for the Installation of Centrifugal Fire Pumps*
NFPA 22, *Standard for Water Tanks for Private Fire Protection*
NFPA 24, *Standard for the Installation of Private Fire Service Mains and Their Appurtenances*
NFPA 26, *Recommended Practice for the Supervision of Valves Controlling Water Supplies for Fire Protection*
NFPA 30, *Flammable and Combustible Liquids Code*
NFPA 30A, *Automotive and Marine Service Station Code*
NFPA 30B, *Code for the Manufacture and Storage of Aerosol Products*
NFPA 31, *Standard for the Installation of Oil Burning Equipment*
NFPA 32, *Standard for Drycleaning Plants*
NFPA 33, *Standard for Spray Application Using Flammable and Combustible Materials*
NFPA 34, *Standard for Dipping and Coating Processes Using Flammable or Combustible Liquids*
NFPA 35, *Standard for the Manufacture of Organic Coatings*
NFPA 36, *Standard for Solvent Extraction Plants*
NFPA 37, *Standard for the Installation & Use of Stationary Combustion Engines and Gas Turbines*
NFPA 40, *Standard for the Storage and Handling of Cellulose Nitrate Motion Picture Film*
NFPA 40E, *Code for the Storage of Pyroxylin Plastic*
NFPA 43A, *Code for the Storage of Liquid and Solid Oxidizing Materials*
NFPA 43B, *Code for the Storage of Organic Peroxide Formulations*
NFPA 43C, *Code for the Storage of Gaseous Oxidizing Materials*
NFPA 43D, *Code for the Storage of Pesticides in Portable Containers*
NFPA 45, *Standard on Fire Protection for Laboratories Using Chemicals*
NFPA 46, *Recommended Safe Practices for the Storage of Forest Products*
NFPA 49, *Hazardous Chemicals Data*

Ms. Nisbet is the Standards Administrator for NFPA and Recording Secretary for the NFPA Standards Council.

NFPA 50, *Standard for Bulk Oxygen Systems at Consumer Sites*
NFPA 50A, *Standard for Gaseous Hydrogen Systems at Consumer Sites*
NFPA 50B, *Standard for Liquefied Hydrogen Systems at Consumer Sites*
NFPA 51, *Standard for the Design and Installation of Oxygen-Fuel Gas Systems for Welding, Cutting and Allied Processes*
NFPA 51A, *Standard for Acetylene Cylinder Charging Plants*
NFPA 51B, *Standard for Fire Prevention in Use of Cutting and Welding Processes*
NFPA 52, *Standard for Compressed Natural Gas (CNG) Vehicular Fuel Systems*
NFPA 53M, *Manual on Fire Hazards in Oxygen-Enriched Atmospheres*
NFPA 54, *National Fuel Gas Code*
NFPA 58, *Standard for the Storage & Handling of Liquefied Petroleum Gases*
NFPA 59, *Standard for the Storage and Handling of Liquefied Petroleum Gases at Utility Gas Plants*
NFPA 59A, *Standard for the Production, Storage & Handling of Liquefied Natural Gas (LNG)*
NFPA 61A, *Standard for Prevention of Fire & Dust Explosions in Facilities Manufacturing and Handling Starch*
NFPA 61B, *Standard for the Prevention of Fires and Explosions in Grain Elevators and Facilities Handling Bulk Raw Agricultural Commodities*
NFPA 61C, *Standard for the Prevention of Fire and Dust Explosions in Feed Mills*
NFPA 61D, *Standard for the Prevention of Fire and Dust Explosions in the Milling of Agricultural Commodities for Human Consumption*
NFPA 65, *Standard for the Processing and Finishing of Aluminum*
NFPA 68, *Guide for Venting of Deflagrations*
NFPA 69, *Standard on Explosion Prevention Systems*
NFPA 70, *National Electrical Code*
NFPA 70A, *Electrical Code for One- & Two-Family Dwellings*
NFPA 70B, *Recommended Practice for Electrical Equipment Maintenance*
NFPA 70E, *Standard for Electrical Safety Requirements for Employee Workplaces*
NFPA 71, *Standard for the Installation, Maintenance, and Use of Signaling Systems for Central Station Service*
NFPA 72, *Installation, Maintenance, and Use of Protective Signaling Systems*
NFPA 72E, *Standard on Automatic Fire Detectors*
NFPA 72G, *Guide for the Installation, Maintenance and Use of Notification Appliances for Protective Signaling Systems*
NFPA 72H, *Guide for Testing Procedures for Local, Auxiliary, Remote Station, and Proprietary Protective Signaling Systems*
NFPA 74, *Standard for the Installation, Maintenance & Use of Household Fire Warning Equipment*
NFPA 75, *Standard for the Protection of Electronic Computer/Data Processing Equipment*
NFPA 77, *Recommended Practice on Static Electricity*
NFPA 78, *Lightning Protection Code*
NFPA 79, *Electrical Standard for Industrial Machinery*
NFPA 80, *Standard for Fire Doors and Windows*
NFPA 80A, *Recommended Practice for Protection of Buildings from Exterior Fire Exposures*
NFPA 81, *Standard for Fur Storage, Fumigation and Cleaning*
NFPA 82, *Standard on Incinerators, Waste and Linen Handling Systems and Equipment*
NFPA 85A, *Standard for the Prevention of Furnace Explosions in Fuel Oil- and Natural Gas-Fired Single Burner Boiler-Furnaces*
NFPA 85F, *Standard for the Installation and Operation of Pulverized Fuel Systems*
NFPA 85H, *Standard for the Prevention of Combustion Hazards in Atmospheric Fluidized Bed Combustion System Boilers*
NFPA 85I, *Recommended Practices for Stoker Operations*
NFPA 86, *Standard for Ovens and Furnaces*
NFPA 86C, *Standard for Industrial Furnaces Using Special Processing Atmosphere*
NFPA 86D, *Standard for Industrial Furnaces Using Vacuum as an Atmosphere*
NFPA 88A, *Standard for Parking Structures*
NFPA 88B, *Standard for Repair Garages*
NFPA 90A, *Standard for the Installation of Air Conditioning and Ventilating Systems*
NFPA 90B, *Standard for the Installation of Warm Air Heating and Air Conditioning Systems*
NFPA 91, *Standard for Exhaust Systems for Air Conveying of Materials*
NFPA 92A, *Recommended Practices on Smoke Control Systems*
NFPA 92B, *Guide for Smoke Management Systems in Malls, Artria, and Large Areas*
NFPA 96, *Standard for the Installation of Equipment for Removal of Smoke and Grease-Laden Vapors from Commercial Cooking Equipment*
NFPA 97M, *Standard Glossary of Terms Relating to Chimneys, Vents, and Heat-Producing Appliances*
NFPA 99, *Standard for Health Care Facilities*
NFPA 99B, *Standard on Hypobaric Facilities*
NFPA 101, *Code for Safety to Life from Fire In Buildings and Structures*
NFPA 101M, *Manual on Alternative Approaches to Life Safety*
NFPA 102, *Standard for Assembly Seating, Tents and Air-Supported Structures*
NFPA 105, *Recommended Practice for the Installation of Smoke Control Door Assemblies*
NFPA 110, *Standard for Emergency and Standby Power Systems*
NFPA 110A, *Standard on Stored Electrical Energy Emergency and Standby Power Systems*
NFPA 120, *Standard for Coal Preparation Plants*
NFPA 121, *Standard on Fire Protection for Self-Propelled and Mobile Surface Mining Equipment*
NFPA 122, *Standard for the Storage of Flammable and Combustible Liquids Within Underground Metal and Nonmetal Mines (Other than Coal)*
NFPA 123, *Standard for Fire Prevention and Control in Underground Bituminous Coal Mines*
NFPA 124, *Standard for Fire Protection of Diesel Fuel and Diesel Equipment in Underground Mines*
NFPA 130, *Standard for Fixed Guideway Transit Systems*
NFPA 150, *Standard on Firesafety in Racetrack Stables*
NFPA 170, *Firesafety Symbols*
NFPA 203M, *Manual on Roof Coverings and Roof Deck Construction*
NFPA 204M, *Guide for Smoke and Heat Venting*
NFPA 211, *Standard for Chimneys, Fireplaces, Vents and Solid Fuel Burning Appliances*

NFPA 214, *Standard on Water-Cooling Towers*
NFPA 220, *Standard on Types of Building Construction*
NFPA 224, *Standard for Homes and Camps in Forest Areas*
NFPA 231, *Standard for General Storage*
NFPA 231C, *Standard for Rack Storage of Materials*
NFPA 231D, *Standard for Storage of Rubber Tires*
NFPA 231E, *Recommended Practice for Storage of Baled Cotton*
NFPA 231F, *Standard for the Storage of Roll Paper*
NFPA 232, *Standard for Protection of Records*
NFPA 232AM, *Manual for Fire Protection for Archives and Record Centers*
NFPA 241, *Standard for Safeguarding Construction, Alteration, and Demolition Operations*
NFPA 251, *Standard Methods of Fire Tests of Building Construction and Materials*
NFPA 252, *Standard Methods of Fire Tests of Door Assemblies*
NFPA 253, *Standard Method of Test for Critical Radiant Flux of Floor Covering Systems Using Radiant Heat Energy Source*
NFPA 255, *Standard Method of Test of Surface Burning Characteristics of Building Materials*
NFPA 256, *Standard Methods of Fire Tests of Roof Coverings*
NFPA 257, *Standard for Fire Tests of Window Assemblies*
NFPA 258, *Standard Research Test Method for Determining Smoke Generation of Solid Materials*
NFPA 259, *Standard Test Method for Potential Heat of Building Materials*
NFPA 260, *Standard Methods of Tests and Classification System for Cigarette Ignition Resistance of Components of Upholstered Furniture*
NFPA 261, *Standard Method of Test for Determining Resistance of Mock-Up Upholstered Furniture Material Assemblies to Ignition by Smoldering Cigarettes*
NFPA 262, *Standard Method of Test for Fire and Smoke Characteristics of Electrical Wires and Cables*
NFPA 263, *Standard Method of Test for Heat and Visible Smoke Release Rates for Materials and Products*
NFPA 264A, *Standard Method of Test for Heat Release Rates of Upholstered Furniture*
NFPA 291, *Recommended Practice for Fire Flow Testing and Marking of Hydrants*
NFPA 295, *Standard for Wildfire Control*
NFPA 296, *Guide for Air Operations for Forest, Brush and Grass Fires*
NFPA 297, *Guide on Telecommunications Systems - Principles and Practices for Rural and Forestry Services*
NFPA 298, *Standard on Foam Chemicals and Wildland Fire Control*
NFPA 302, *Fire Protection Standard for Pleasure and Commercial Motor Craft*
NFPA 303, *Fire Protection Standard for Marinas and Boatyards*
NFPA 306, *Standard for the Control of Gas Hazards on Vessels*
NFPA 307, *Standard for Construction & Fire Protection of Marine Terminals, Piers & Wharves*
NFPA 312, *Standard for Fire Protection of Vessels During Construction, Repair & Lay-Up*
NFPA 321, *Standard on Basic Classification of Flammable and Combustible Liquids*
NFPA 325M, *Manual on Fire Hazard Properties of Flammable Liquids, Gases, and Volatile Solids*
NFPA 327, *Standard Procedures for Cleaning or Safeguarding Small Tanks and Containers*
NFPA 328, *Recommended Practices on the Control of Flammable and Combustible Liquids and Gases in Manholes, Sewers, and Similar Underground Structures*
NFPA 329, *Recommended Practice for Handling Underground Leakage of Flammable and Combustible Liquids*
NFPA 385, *Standard for Tank Vehicles for Flammable and Combustible Liquids*
NFPA 386, *Standard for Portable Shipping Tanks for Flammable & Combustible Liquids*
NFPA 395, *Standard for the Storage of Flammable and Combustible Liquids on Farms and Isolated Construction Projects*
NFPA 402M, *Manual for Aircraft Rescue and Fire Fighting Operational Procedures*
NFPA 403, *Standard for Aircraft Rescue & Fire Fighting Services at Airports*
NFPA 407, *Standard for Aircraft Fuel Servicing*
NFPA 408, *Standard for Aircraft Hand Fire Extinguishers*
NFPA 409, *Standard on Aircraft Hangars*
NFPA 410, *Standard on Aircraft Maintenance*
NFPA 412, *Standard for Evaluating Aircraft Rescue and Fire Fighting Foam Equipment*
NFPA 414, *Standard for Aircraft Rescue and Fire Fighting Vehicles*
NFPA 415, *Standard on Aircraft Fueling Ramp Drainage*
NFPA 416, *Standard on Construction & Protection of Airport Terminal Buildings*
NFPA 417, *Standard on Construction & Protection of Aircraft Loading Walkways*
NFPA 418, *Standard on Roof Top Heliport Construction and Protection*
NFPA 419, *Guide for Master Planning Airport Water Supply Systems for Fire Protection*
NFPA 422M, *Manual for Aircraft Fire and Explosion Investigators*
NFPA 423, *Standard for Construction & Protection of Aircraft Engine Test Facilities*
NFPA 424M, *Manual for Airport/Community Emergency Planning*
NFPA 471, *Recommended Practice for Responding to Hazardous Materials Incidents*
NFPA 472, *Standard for Professional Competence of Responding to Hazardous Materials Incidents*
NFPA 480, *Standard for the Storage, Handling & Processing of Magnesium*
NFPA 481, *Standard for the Production, Processing, Handling & Storage Titanium*
NFPA 482, *Standard for Production, Processing, Handling & Storage of Zirconium*
NFPA 490, *Code for the Storage of Ammonium Nitrate*
NFPA 491M, *Manual of Hazardous Chemical Reactions*
NFPA 495, *Code for the Manufacture, Transportation, Storage, and Use of Explosive Materials Code*
NFPA 496, *Standard for Purged and Pressurized Enclosures for Electrical Equipment*
NFPA 497A, *Recommended Practice for Classification of Class I Hazardous (Classified) Locations for Electrical Installations in Chemical Process Areas*
NFPA 497B, *Recommended Practice for Classification of Class II Hazardous (Classified) Locations for Electrical Installations in Chemical Processing Plants*

NFPA 497M, *Manual for Classification of Gases, Vapors, and Dusts for Electrical Equipment in Hazardous (Classified) Locations*

NFPA 498, *Standard for Explosives Motor Vehicle Terminals*

NFPA 501A, *Standard for Firesafety Criteria for Manufactured Home Installations, Sites, and Communities*

NFPA 501C, *Standard on Firesafety Criteria for Recreational Vehicles*

NFPA 501D, *Standard for Firesafety Criteria for Recreational Vehicle Parks and Campgrounds*

NFPA 502, *Recommended Practice on Fire Protection for Limited Access Highways, Tunnels, Bridges, Elevated Roadways, and Air Right Structures*

NFPA 505, *Firesafety Standard for Type Designations, Areas of Use, Maintenance, and Operation of Powered Industrial Trucks*

NFPA 512, *Standard for Truck Fire Protection*

NFPA 513, *Standard for Motor Freight Terminals*

NFPA 550, *Guide for Firesafety Concepts Tree*

NFPA 600, *Standard on Industrial Fire Brigades*

NFPA 601, *Standard for Guard Service in Fire Loss Prevention*

NFPA 602, *Standard for Guard Operations in Fire Loss Prevention*

NFPA 650, *Standard for Pneumatic Conveying Systems for Handling Combustible Materials*

NFPA 651, *Standard for the Manufacture of Aluminum and Magnesium Powder*

NFPA 654, *Standard for Prevention of Fire and Dust Explosion in Chemical, Dye, Pharmaceutical, and Plastics Industries*

NFPA 655, *Standard for the Prevention of Sulfur Fires and Explosions*

NFPA 664, *Standard for the Prevention of Fires and Explosions in Wood Processing and Woodworking Facilities*

NFPA 701, *Standard Methods of Fire Tests for Flame-Resistant Textiles and Films*

NFPA 703, *Standard for Fire Retardant Impregnated Wood and Flame Retardant Coatings for Building Materials*

NFPA 704, *Standard System for Identification of the Fire Hazards of Materials*

NFPA 801, *Recommended Fire Protection Practice for Facilities Handling Radioactive Materials*

NFPA 802, *Recommended Fire Protection Practice for Nuclear Research Reactors*

NFPA 803, *Standard for Fire Protection for Light Water Nuclear Power Plants*

NFPA 820, *Recommended Practice for Wastewater Treatment Plants*

NFPA 850, *Recommended Practice for Fire Protection for Fossil Fueled Steam and Combustion Turbine Electric Generating Plants*

NFPA 851, *Recommended Practice for Fire Protection for Hydroelectric Generating Plants*

NFPA 901, *Uniform Coding for Fire Protection*

NFPA 902M, *Fire Reporting Field Incident Manual*

NFPA 903, *Fire Reporting Property Survey Guide*

NFPA 904, *Incident Follow-Up Report Guide 7*

NFPA 906M, *Guide for Fire Incident Field Notes*

NFPA 907M, *Manual for the Determination of Electrical Fire Causes*

NFPA 910, *Recommended Practice for Protection of Libraries and Library Collections*

NFPA 911, *Recommended Practice for Protection of Museums and Museum Collections*

NFPA 912, *Recommended Practices for Fire Protection in Places of Worship*

NFPA 913, *Recommended Practice for Protection of Historic Structures and Sites*

NFPA 914, *Recommended Practice for the Fire Protection in Rehabilitation and Adaptive Reuse of Historic Structures*

NFPA 1001, *Standard for Fire Fighter Professional Qualifications*

NFPA 1002, *Standard for Fire Apparatus Driver/Operator Professional Qualifications*

NFPA 1003, *Standard for Airport Fire Fighter Professional Qualifications*

NFPA 1021, *Standard for Fire Officer Professional Qualifications*

NFPA 1031, *Standard for Professional Qualifications for Fire Inspector*

NFPA 1033, *Standard for Professional Qualifications for Fire Investigator*

NFPA 1035, *Standard for Professional Qualifications for Public Fire Educator*

NFPA 1041, *Standard for Professional Qualifications For Fire Service Instructor*

NFPA 1122, *Code for Unmanned Rockets*

NFPA 1123, *Standard for Outdoor Display of Fireworks*

NFPA 1124, *Code for the Manufacture, Transportation, and Storage of Fireworks*

NFPA 1125, *Code for the Manufacture of Model Rocket Motors*

NFPA 1141, *Standard for Fire Protection in Planned Building Groups*

NFPA 1201, *Recommendations for Developing Fire Protection Services for the Public*

NFPA 1221, *Standard for the Installation, Maintenance, and Use of Public Fire Service Communication Systems*

NFPA 1231, *Standard on Water Supplies for Suburban & Rural Fire Fighting*

NFPA 1401, *Recommended Practice for Fire Protection Training Reports and Records*

NFPA 1402, *Standard on Building Fire Service Training Centers*

NFPA 1403, *Standard on Live Fire Training Evolutions in Structures*

NFPA 1404, *Standard for a Fire Department Self-Contained Breathing Apparatus Program*

NFPA 1405, *Guide for Land-Based Fire Fighters Who Respond to Marine Vessel Fires*

NFPA 1410, *Standard on Initial Fire Attack*

NFPA 1410, *Standard on Initial Fire Attack*

NFPA 1452, *Guide for Training Fire Department Personnel to Make Dwelling Firesafety Surveys*

NFPA 1500, *Standard on Fire Department Occupational Safety & Health Program*

NFPA 1501, *Standard for Fire Department Safety Officer*

NFPA 1561, *Standard for Fire Department Incident Management System*

NFPA 1901, *Standard for Pumper Fire Apparatus*

NFPA 1902, *Standard for Initial Attack Fire Apparatus*

NFPA 1903, *Standard for Mobile Water Supplies*

NFPA 1904, *Standard for Aerial Ladder & Elevating Platforms Fire Apparatus*

NFPA 1911, *Standard on Service Tests of Pumps on Fire Department Apparatus*

NFPA 1914, *Standard for Testing Fire Department Aerial Devices*

NFPA 1921, *Standard for Fire Department Portable Pumping Units*
NFPA 1931, *Standard on Design, and Design Verification Tests for Fire Department Ground Ladders*
NFPA 1932, *Standard on the Use, Maintenance & Service Testing of Fire Department Ground Ladders*
NFPA 1961, *Standard for Fire Hose*
NFPA 1962, *Standard for the Care, Use and Maintenance of Fire Hose, Including Connections and Nozzles*
NFPA 1963, *Standard for Screw Threads and Gaskets for Fire Hose Connections*
NFPA 1964, *Standard on Spray Nozzles (Shutoff and Tip)*
NFPA 1971, *Standard on Protective Clothing for Structural Fire Fighting*
NFPA 1972, *Standard on Helmets for Structural Fire Fighting*
NFPA 1973, *Standard on Gloves for Structural Fire Fighting*
NFPA 1974, *Standard on Protective Footwear for Structural Fire Fighting*
NFPA 1975, *Standard on Station/Work Uniforms for Fire Fighters*
NFPA 1981, *Standard on Open-Circuit Self-Contained Breathing Apparatus for Fire Fighters*
NFPA 1982, *Standard on Personal Alert Safety Systems (PASS) for Fire Fighters*
NFPA 1983, *Standard on Fire Service Life Safety Rope, Harness, and Hardware*
NFPA 1991, *Standard on Vapor-Protective Suits for Hazardous Chemical Emergencies*
NFPA 1992, *Standard on Liquid Splash Protective Suits for Hazardous Chemical Emergencies*
NFPA 1993, *Standard on Support Function Protective Garments for Hazardous Chemical Operations*

INDEX

B

C

D

G

H

M

N

O

Q

S

T

U

V

W